SAN FRANCISCO PUBLIC LIBRARY
3 1223 03239 6732

S0-BUX-533

Directory of Special Libraries and Information Centers

Highlights

The 16th edition of the *Directory of Special Libraries and Information Centers (DSL)* is a current and comprehensive guide to more than 20,800 subject-specific resource collections maintained by:

- government agencies
- businesses of all types
- newspaper and book publishers
- educational institutions
- nonprofit organizations
- associations and societies

As varied as the types of collections identified by *DSL* is the subject matter of these collections. The libraries and information centers described in *DSL* maintain collections focusing on topics spanning a wide range of disciplines and interests, including:

- Africa
- AIDS
- Alcoholism
- Biotechnology
- Business
- Child welfare
- Eastern Europe
- Ecology
- Fashion
- Geriatrics
- Investments
- Japan
- Law
- Middle East
- Mysticism
- Space Sciences
- Technology
- Women

16th Edition Expands and Updates European Coverage

The ongoing political, social, economic, and structural changes in Europe have created a demand for a more global information base. The 16th edition of *DSL* reflects an increase in the number of listings from outside the U.S. and Canada of more than 45%, including:

- 570 profiles of newly identified special libraries located in countries other than the United States and Canada.
- New Appendix of European Community Depository Libraries located throughout the United States.

Increased cross-referencing of foreign-language library names enhances access to such entries.

Companion Volume Provides Additional Access Points

Available separately, Volume 2 of *DSL, Geographic and Personnel Indexes,* provides a geographic rearrangement of the basic contact information for the profiled libraries, as well as an alphabetical listing by surname of professional staff mentioned in the descriptive listings.

***DSL* Information Available in Other Formats**

The information contained in *DSL* is also available on diskette or magnetic tape in a fielded format. Customized mailing labels can be generated from the *DSL* database as well.

ISSN 0731-633X

Directory of Special Libraries and Information Centers

16th Edition

A Guide to More Than 20,800 Special Libraries, Research Libraries, Information Centers, Archives, and Data Centers Maintained by Government Agencies, Business, Industry, Newspapers, Educational Institutions, Nonprofit Organizations, and Societies in the Fields of Science and Engineering, Medicine, Law, Art, Religion, the Social Sciences, and Humanities.

1993

DEBRA M. KIRBY
Editor

JOANNA M. ZAKALIK
Associate Editor

VOLUME 1
PART 1
A-M

(Entries 1-10,948)

• DETROIT • LONDON

Amy Lucas, *Senior Editor*

Debra M. Kirby, *Editor*

Eric G. Carlson and Joanna M. Zakalik, *Associate Editors*
Sandra Doran and Christine Mathews, *Assistant Editors*

Research Staff

Victoria B. Cariappa, *Research Manager*
Gary J. Oudersluys, *Research Supervisor*
Lisa Lantz, *Editorial Associate*
Melissa E. Brown, Daniel L. Day, Charles A. Jewell, Richard A. Lawson,
L. Philip Naud, Phyllis Shepherd, Patricia A. Taraskiewicz, and Tracie A. Wade,
Editorial Assistants

Production Staff

Mary Beth Trimper, *Production Director*
Shanna Heilveil, *Production Assistant*

Arthur Chartow, *Art Director*
Cynthia Baldwin, *Graphic Designer*
C.J. Jonik, *Keyliner*

Benita L. Spight, *Data Entry Supervisor*
Gwendolyn S. Tucker, *Data Entry Group Leader*
Marjorita Onyekuru and Constance J. Wells, *Data Entry Associates*

Theresa A. Rocklin, *Supervisor of Editorial Programming Services*
Donald G. Dillaman, *Programming Consultant*

The paper used in this publication meets the minimum requirements of American National Standard for Information Sciences—Permanence Paper for Printed Library Materials, ANSI Z39.48-1984.

Library of Congress Catalog Number 84-640165
ISBN 0-8103-7661-X (set)
ISBN 0-103-7742-X (Part 1)
ISSN 0731-633X

Printed in the United States of America

Published simultaneously in the United Kingdom
by Gale Research International Limited
(An affiliated company of Gale Research Inc.)

Contents

Volume 1, Part 1

Highlights ii
Introduction vii
User's Guide x
Abbreviations xiv
Descriptive Listings, A-M 1

Volume 1, Part 2

User's Guide vi
Abbreviations x
Descriptive Listings, N-Z 1163
Appendix A—Networks and Consortia 2221
Cumulative Index to Appendix A 2243
Appendix B—Regional and Subregional Libraries for the Blind and Physically Handicapped 2249
Appendix C—Patent and Trademark Depository Libraries 2257
Appendix D—Regional Government Depository Libraries 2261
Appendix E—United Nations Depository Libraries 2265
Appendix F—World Bank Depository Libraries 2277
Appendix G—European Community Depository Libraries (in the U.S.) 2285
Geographic Abbreviations 2287
(U.S. state codes, Canadian province codes, and international country codes)
Subject Index 2291

Introduction

Thirty years ago, the first edition of the *Directory of Special Libraries and Information Centers (DSL),* covering approximately 10,000 libraries, was published by Gale Research Inc. Now in its 16th edition, the *Directory* provides comprehensive and completely updated and revised information on 20,851 special resource collections in the United States, Canada, and worldwide.

In contrast to public and academic libraries, which provide access to resources on a variety of general topics, special libraries maintain more detailed collections focused on a specific subject or a group of closely related topics. *DSL* furnishes full contact and descriptive information on libraries and information centers that contain resources on topics spanning a wide range of disciplines and interests, including:

- Africa
- AIDS
- Alcoholism
- Biotechnology
- Business
- Child welfare
- Eastern Europe
- Ecology
- Fashion
- Forestry
- Geriatrics
- Investments
- Law
- Middle East
- Mysticism
- Space Sciences
- Technology
- Women

Increased Focus on International Coverage

The disintegration of the Soviet Union and resulting formation of the Commonwealth of Independent States, the continuing ethnic unrest in Yugoslavia, the ongoing unification of European Community countries, the Middle East peace conferences, and other recent world events are creating greater demand for the unique resources offered through special libraries to scholars, the media, government, and the public. In recognition of the ever increasing global reach of information, *DSL* continues to widen its international coverage of special libraries and resource centers. In this edition users will find:

- Nearly 1,750 collections located outside the United States and Canada, including 570 new to this edition

- New Appendix listing European Community Depository Libraries located throughout the United States

- Increased cross-referencing of foreign-language library names

Scope

As defined for purposes of this directory, special libraries are libraries built around a collection limited by subject matter or form. Functionally, these libraries (which may also have collections of a general nature) operate in support of a special mission or activity chosen by their sponsoring organizations.

The libraries and information centers in this directory fall within five major categories:

1) Subject divisions, departmental collections, and professional libraries maintained by colleges and universities.

2) Branches, divisions, departments, and special collections in large public library systems that concentrate exclusively upon one particular subject or group of subjects.

3) Company libraries that operate within the framework of a business or industry producing goods, services, or information for profit.

4) Governmental libraries, including:
   - –those serving city departments, bureaus, and boards;
   - –state legislative reference libraries as well as those in departments, divisions, and ministries of state or provincial government;
   - –libraries within federal departments, agencies, and military establishments; and
   - –divisions of national libraries.

5) Libraries supported by nonprofit organizations, associations, and institutions, including those of:
   - –scientific, technical, and learned societies;
   - –civic, social, and religious organizations;
   - –historical societies, bar associations, museums, and hospitals;
   - –business and trade associations; and
   - –significant private collections available for research use.

Certain categories of libraries, occasionally found in other listings of special libraries, were omitted. Among these are collections of purely recreational reading material found in hospitals and prisons. Inclusion in this directory should not be construed as recognition of any organization, nor does omission imply lack of importance.

Content and Arrangement

Volume 1 of the *Directory of Special Libraries and Information Centers* consists of descriptive listings, appendixes, and a Subject Index. It is published in two parts:

- Part 1 contains descriptive listings A-M (entries 1-10,948).
- Part 2 contains descriptive listings N-Z (entries 10,949-20,851), appendixes, and the subject index.

The **descriptive listings** are arranged alphabetically by the name of the sponsoring organization of each library or information center. More than 7,750 cross-references are interfiled throughout the listings to direct users to organization and library names.

Seven **appendixes** follow the descriptive listings:

- Networks and Consortia (includes a cumulative index)
- Regional and Subregional Libraries for the Blind and Physically Handicapped
- Patent and Trademark Depository Libraries
- Regional Government Depository Libraries
- United Nations Depository Libraries
- World Bank Depository Libraries
- European Community Depository Libraries (in the U.S.)

The **Subject Index,** appearing at the end of Part 2, classifies the libraries and information centers described in the main section of the book by the principal topics covered by their holdings.

For additional information on the content of the descriptive listings, appendixes, and index, consult the "User's Guide" following this introduction.

Preparation of This Edition

The editorial objective for each edition of *DSL* is complete verification/revision/updating of existing entries and an intensive effort to identify new or previously unlisted facilities. This effort includes not only special mail surveys, carried out in two phases, but also direct contact by telephone and personal correspondence with nonresponding organizations. This policy—in addition to giving *DSL* users the most current and accurate information—affords each listed facility an opportunity to update its description and make changes. As a result, this edition incorporates thousands of changes in library names, addresses, contact numbers, personal names, and other details.

Supplement Monitors Library Activity

An annual supplement to the main edition of *DSL, New Special Libraries,* provides the user with details on newly established libraries and information centers, significant changes to corporate or institutional affiliations since the last edition, and libraries newly identified by the editorial staff.

Companion Volume Provides Additional Access Points

Available separately, Volume 2 of *DSL, Geographic and Personnel Indexes,* provides a geographic rearrangement of the basic contact information for the libraries profiled in the descriptive listings portion of Volume 1, as well as an alphabetical listing by surname of all librarians mentioned within those listings. The volume enables users to:

- identify libraries located within a particular geographic region;
- determine the number of libraries located in a specific city;
- locate the place of employment of a particular librarian when only her/his name is known.

DSL Information Offered in Other Formats

The information contained in the *Directory of Special Libraries* is available for licensing on magnetic tape or diskette in a fielded format, either as the complete database or as a custom selection of entries. The database is available for internal data processing and nonpublishing purposes only. Mailing labels can also be generated from the *DSL* database. For more information or ordering, contact Customer Services at 800-877-GALE.

Acknowledgments

The editors are obliged to the large number of conscientious librarians and information specialists, in the United States and abroad, who responded to our questionnaires, provided additional information in response to our many telephone requests, and helped in the shaping of this edition with comments and suggestions throughout the year.

Suggestions Welcome

Users of this directory are invited to send information on new facilities or those not yet listed. Comments and suggestions regarding contents and format are always welcome. Please contact:

Directory of Special Libraries
and Information Centers
Gale Research Inc.
835 Penobscot Bldg.
Detroit, MI 48226-4094

Phone: (313)961-2242
Toll-Free: 800-347-GALE
Telex: 810 221 7086
FAX: (313)961-6815

Debra M. Kirby

User's Guide

Volume 1 of the *Directory of Special Libraries and Information Centers* consists of descriptive listings, appendixes, and the Subject Index. It is published in two parts:

- Part 1 contains entries A through M
- Part 2 contains entries N through Z, seven appendixes, and the Subject Index.

Descriptive Listings

Entries within the main section of *DSL* are arranged in alphabetical order; libraries associated with a company, institution, agency, or association are grouped under the official name of the parent organization. Several exceptions to the alphabetical arrangement exist:

–The libraries of the U.S. Department of Veterans Affairs (formerly the U.S. Veterans Administration) are subarranged geographically.

–The information units of the Environmental Protection Agency as well as some other U.S. government agencies and departments are listed numerically by region.

–Some United States state supreme courts are arranged numerically by judicial district.

–Libraries within a university system with more than one campus are grouped alphabetically by campus. For instance, the University of Wisconsin, Madison libraries appear together as a group before libraries situated at the University of Wisconsin, Milwaukee.

–Federal governmental units are listed under the country of origin; for example, entries for the National Library of Canada are found in the Cs as Canada—National Library of Canada.

More than 7,750 cross-references are interfiled throughout the listings to direct the user to main entries. Cross-references are supplied for libraries well known by an acronym, libraries with multiple sponsors, facilities with memorial or bilingual names, libraries of subsidiaries of large corporations, and many governmental agencies.

The fictitious entry shown below is followed by a brief description of the individual components of the listing. Each numbered item is explained in the descriptive paragraph bearing the same number.

[1] ★562★ [2] **Agricultural Research Center, Inc.— [3] Library [4]** (Agri; Biol Sci)
[5] 789 Minnesota Ave. [6] Phone: (913)237-8884
Kansas City, KS 66101 [7] Margaret Miller-Holmes, Dir.
[8] **Founded:** 1972. [9] **Staff:** Prof 6; Other 12. [10] **Subjects:** Agronomy, plant breeding, soil fertility, entomology, dairy science, animal health. [11] **Special Collections:** Biotechnology Research Collection (24 VF drawers of technical reports).
[12] **Holdings:** 75,000 books; 150 bound periodical volumes; 85 microfiche; 100 reels of microfilm; 250 AV programs; 6500 internal and technical reports; 4689 government documents. [13] **Subscriptions:** 75 journals and other seials; 12 newspapers.
[14] **Services:** interlibrary loan; copying; SDI; library open to the public for reference use only. [15] **Automated Operations:** Computerized cataloging, acquisitions, serials, and circulation. [16] **Computerized Information Services:** OCLC, DIALOG Information Services; Ag-viser (internal database; BITNET (electronic mail service). Performs searches on fee basis. Contact Person: Winston C. Darnay, Online Serv.Libn., 237-8871. [17] **Networks/Consortia:** Member of Bibliographical Center for Research, Rocky Mountain Region, Inc. (BCR). [18] **Publications:** Library Newsletter, quarterly—to selected agricultural libraries; New Acquisitions List, monthly—for internl distribution only. [19] **Special Catalogs:** Catalog of Biotechnology Research Collection (loose-leaf). [20] **Special Indexes:** Indexes to AV programs and internal and technicl reports (card). [21] **Remarks:** FAX (913) 237-8888. Telex: 924421. Electronic mail address(es): HOLMES@ARC (BITNET). Maintains a branch library in Lawrence, KS. [22] **Formerly:** Farming Resources Corporation. [23] **Formed by the merger of:** Technical Information Center and Corporte Library. [24] **Also Known As:** ARC. [25] **Staff:** Martin Lessner, Chf., Tech.Serv.; Don H. Bunny, Chf., Pub.Serv.; Kathleen O'Brien, Libn.; Derek Morrison, Libn.; Miranda Kern, Libn.

1 **Entry Number.** The entries in *DSL* are numbered sequentially. The sequential entry number (rather than the page number) is used in the Subject Index to refer to an entry, and also follows the entry title in Volume 2, Geographic and Personnel Indexes. To facilitate location of an entry, the first entry number on each left-hand page and the last entry number on each right-hand page are provided at the top outer corners of the pages.

2 **Name of Organization.** Name of parent organization, society, or agency that sponsors or is served by the library or information center. Independent libraries and centers and those commonly known by a distinctive name are entered directly under the library's name. Cross-references are included in the body of the work for those libraries which may be known by two or more distinct names.

3 **Name of Library or Information Center.** Descriptive and memorial names are given as reported. Otherwise, the appropriate generic term is used, e.g., library, archives, collection, information center. In many cases, the generic term has been supplied by the editors and the inclusion of the term library may not indicate the existence of a formal library.

4 **Principal Subject Keyword.** The major subject or type of material represented by the collection as a whole. When there are two areas of equal importance, both are indicated. If a collection has more than four major subjects or is general in scope, no keyword is used. The keywords offer a classification by broad subject category only; each library's more specialized interests are mentioned in the body of each listing. Both the general keywords and specialized interests are used as headings in the Subject Index. The following keywords are employed:

Agri	–Agriculture
Area-Ethnic	–Area-Ethnic
Art	–Art
Aud-Vis	–Audiovisual
Biol Sci	–Biological sciences
Bus-Fin	–Business and finance
Comp Sci	–Computer science
Educ	–Education
Energy	–Energy
Env-Cons	–Environment and conservation
Food-Bev	–Food and beverages
Geog-Map	–Geography and maps
Hist	–History
Info Sci	–Information science
Law	–Law
Med	–Medicine
Mil	–Military
Mus	–Music
Plan	–Planning
Publ	–Publishing
Rare Book	–Rare Book
Rec	–Recreation
Rel-Phil	–Religion and philosophy
Sci-Engr	–Science and engineering
Soc-Sci	–Social science
Theater	–Theater
Trans	–Transportation

5 **Mailing Address.** The permanent mailing address of the library or center. In some instances this will differ from the headquarters address of the parent organization and the physical location of the library. When there is a separate location address, it is given under "Remarks" (see item 21).

6 **Phone Number.** Area code and telephone number. Alternate phone numbers are listed under "Remarks" (see item 21). Extensions are not provided, since they are subject to frequent change.

7 **Head of Library or Information Center.** Name and title of the person directly in charge of the library or information center. Where no librarian has been identified or where there is no position as such, the name of the administrative officer may be given. When the directorship is shared by two persons, the names of both individuals are provided in the "Staff Names" section (see item 25).

8 **Founding Date.** Year when library or information center was established, either formally or informally.

9 **Number of Staff.** Number of individuals directly engaged in the operation of the library or center on a regular basis. Part-time employees are included but student assistants and other occasional help generally are not. Professional staff includes librarians, bibliographers, subject specialists, information specialists, and other related specialists. Semiprofessionals and clerical assistants are grouped in the second category. Distinction between professional and nonprofessional staff is made by the respondents. Where the differentiation is not made, the total number of staff is listed.

10 **Subjects.** Terms specifically designating the most important subjects represented in the collection as a whole. Citations in the Subject Index generally correspond to this section of the entry, as provided by the listee.

11 **Special Collections.** Separately grouped collections of unusual or notable interest that are identifiable by subject, form, name of donor, or distinctive name.

12 **Holdings.** Quantitative data concerning collections. Numbers of books, bound periodical volumes, pamphlets, and technical reports are given separately when supplied by respondents. When the term "volumes" is used, it generally indicates bound units or collections of bound and unbound items which have been accessioned and cataloged. Unbound material is indicated either by unit count, number of vertical file (VF) drawers, linear shelf feet, or cubic storage space. Estimates rather than the exact statistics have frequently been given. Holdings of nonbook materials are also indicated whenever of significant size and importance.

13 **Subscriptions.** Figures generally represent the number of journal and serial titles, not separate copies, received by paid subscription, gift, and exchange. Newspaper subscriptions are given separately.

14 **Services.** Most special libraries provide bibliographic or reference services primarily for their own organizations. For these, an appropriate statement of service limitations is given. When the library or center provides some form of access to outside clientele, it is so indicated. When services offered are of an unusual nature they are noted and indication is given whether such services are for internal or external use. Entries for libraries which honor interlibrary loan requests include the appropriate information, as do those for libraries with copying or reproducing facilities. Normally, copying services to outside users are on a fee basis. Some libraries now charge for interlibrary loans and this information is included when supplied by respondent.

15 **Automated Operations.** Computerized library management functions such as public access catalog, cataloging, circulation, acquisitions, and serials, are identified here.

16 **Computerized Information Services.** Indicates a special library's access to online information systems, such as MEDLINE, DIALOG Information Services, LEXIS, etc. CD-ROMs, internally produced databases, and electronic mail services are also listed. Also included here are fee policies for online searches the library may perform for the public, and name and telephone number of contact person.

17 **Networks/Consortia.** Lists the special library's memberships in formal or informal groups involved in cooperative sharing of library resources on the local, regional, or national level. Acronyms are used for networks and consortia which are familiar to the library profession (e.g., CLASS, ILLINET). Appendix A lists geographically the names and addresses of the networks and consortia reported by the special libraries in this directory. An alphabetical index follows.

18 **Publications.** Periodical, serial, and other publications issued or prepared by the library or information center are included. Title, frequency, and basis of distribution are indicated when known.

19 **Special Catalogs.** Unique and unusual catalogs which are locally prepared and maintained, including card, book, computer printout, and other formats.

20 **Special Indexes.** Unique and unusual indexes which are locally prepared and maintained.

21 **Remarks.** Additional information not adaptable to the standard entry format, including historical data, explanatory notes, and descriptions of unusual activities. Corporate affiliations are often noted here. Also included is the address of a special library's location when it differs from the mailing address in item 5, and any toll-free telephone numbers, alternate telephone numbers, telex numbers, telefacsimile numbers, and electronic mail addresses. Facsimile correspondence should be addressed to the attention of the special library or information center because in some cases the number listed is that of the overall organization or general library.

22 **Formerly.** Former name and/or location of a special library or its parent organization when there is a recent change of name and/or location under which they were formerly listed. Cross-references are generally supplied from the former names.

23 **Formed by the merger of.** When the special library has been created by the merger of two or more units previously listed as separate entries, the names of the components are identified here. Mergers of parent organizations which affect the special library are also noted.

24 **Also Known As.** Variant names of a special library or its parent organization, including translations of non-English names if provided by the respondent. Cross-references from these are provided when needed.

25 **Staff Names.** Names and titles of professional and supervisory personnel in the special library or information center. Only principal members of the professional staff are listed for operations with large staffs.

Appendixes

The descriptive listings are followed by seven appendixes that group specific types of special libraries. Listings typically include library name, address, and telephone number. Entries within each appendix are arranged geographically. The appendixes are:

Appendix A - Networks and Consortia lists organizations involved in cooperative efforts to share resources. Listings also may include contact person and notes covering former and alternate names, the names of member organizations, references to other listings in *DSL,* and address rotation schedules. The appendix is followed by a cumulative index to all cited networks and consortia and their alternate names.

Appendix B - Regional and Subregional Libraries for the Blind and Physically Handicapped identifies libraries that cooperate with the Library of Congress in providing free library services to persons who are unable to read or use standard printed material because of visual or physical impairment. Listings may also include contact name, notes covering services offered or geographic area served, alternate, toll-free, TTY, and TDD numbers.

Appendix C - Patent and Trademark Depository Libraries lists libraries that are designated as patent depository libraries by the U.S. Patent and Trademark Office and are open to the public.

Appendix D - Regional Government Depository Libraries identifies libraries that make federal government information available to the public through participation in the U.S. Government Printing Office's Depository Library Program.

Appendix E - United Nations Depository Libraries lists libraries throughout the world that house documents and publications issued by the United Nations.

Appendix F - World Bank Depository Libraries identifies libraries providing free and public access to materials produced by or for the World Bank. Telephone, facsimile, telex, and contact names are given for selected entries.

Appendix G - European Community Depository Libraries lists libraries throughout the United States that maintain European Community document collections.

Subject Index

The Subject Index employs more than 4,000 terms and cross-references to classify the major fields of interest of each library described in the listing portion of *DSL.*

While the index is based on terms provided by librarians describing the subject interests of their collections, the editors exercised considerable selection and interpretation to arrive at standard headings. Cross-references link synonyms and related terms. *Library of Congress Subject Headings* was used as a professional guide but was not followed in all cases.

The Subject Index refers users to entry numbers, not page numbers. Entry numbers following a subject term are arranged geographically as follows: United States entries are arranged by state code; Canadian entries are arranged by province or territory code; and International entries are arranged by country code. A key to the state, province, and country codes precedes the index.

Abbreviations

Acq. -Acquisitions
Act. -Acting
Actv. -Activities, Activity
Adm. -Administration, Administrative, Administrator
Adv. -Advisor
AFB -Air Force Base
Aff. -Affairs
Agri. -Agricultural, Agriculture
AHEC -Area Health Education Center
Amer. -American
ANGB -Air National Guard Base
Anl. -Analysis, Analyst, Analytical
APO -Army Post Office
Arch. -Architect, Architectural, Architecture
Archeo. -Archeological, Archeologist, Archeology
Archv. -Archival, Archives, Archivist
ART -Accredited Record Technician
Assn. -Association
Assoc. -Associate
Asst. -Assistant
Att. -Attorney
Aud. -Audio
AV -Audiovisual
Ave. -Avenue
B.P. -Boite Postale
Bd. -Board
Biblio. -Bibliotechnicien(ne), Bibliothecaire
Bibliog. -Bibliographer, Bibliographic, Bibliographical, Bibliography
Biol. -Biological, Biologist, Biology
Biomed. -Biomedical, Biomedicine
Bk.,Bks. -Book, Books
Bldg. -Building
Blvd. -Boulevard
Br. -Branch
Bro. -Brother
Bur. -Bureau
Bus. -Business
C.P. -Caixa Postal, Caja Postale, Case Postale, Casetta Postale
Capt. -Captain
Cart. -Cartographer, Cartographic, Cartography
Cat. -Catalog, Cataloger, Cataloging
CD-ROM -Compact Disk Read-Only Memory
Cedex -Courrier d'Entreprise a Distribution Exceptionnelle
Ch. -Chair, Child, Children, Children's
Chem. -Chemical, Chemist, Chemistry
Chf. -Chief
Chm. -Chairman
Circ. -Circulation
Ck. -Clerk
Class. -Classical, Classification, Classified
Clghse. -Clearinghouse
Clin. -Clinical
Co. -Company
Col. -Colonel
Coll. -Collection(s), College
COM -Computer Output Microfilm/Microfiche
Comm. -Committee
Commn. -Commission
Commnr. -Commissioner
Commun. -Communication(s), Community
Comp. -Computer, Computerized, Computing
Cons. -Conservation, Conservator, Consultant, Consulting
Cont. -Continuing, Control
Coop. -Cooperating, Cooperation, Cooperative
Coord. -Coordinating, Coordination, Coordinator
Corp. -Corporate, Corporation
Coun. -Council
Couns. -Counsel, Counseling, Counselor
Ct. -Court
Ctr. -Center, Centre
Ctrl. -Central
Cur. -Curator, Curatorial
Curric. -Curricular, Curriculum
Cust. -Custodian
Dept., Depts. -Department, Departmental, Departments
Des. -Design, Designer
Dev. -Development, Developmental
Dir. -Director
Dissem. -Dissemination
Dist. -District
Distr. -Distribution, Distributor
Div. -Division, Divisional
Doc., Docs. -Document, Documentalist(e), Documentation, Documents
DOD -U.S. Department of Defense
DOE -U.S. Department of Energy
Dp. -Deputy
Dr. -Doctor,Drive
E. -East
Econ. -Economic(s)
Ed. -Editor, Editorial
Educ. -Education, Educational, Educator
Engr. -Engineer, Engineering
Env. -Environment, Environmental
Exch. -Exchange
Exec. -Executive
Expy. -Expressway
Ext. -Extended, Extension, External
Fac. -Facilitator, Facility, Faculty
Fed. -Federal, Federation
Fin. -Finance, Financial
Fl. -Floor
Fld. -Field
Found. -Foundation
FPO -Fleet Post Office
Fr. -Father
Ft. -Fort
FTS -Federal Telephone System
Fwy. -Freeway
G.P.O. -General Post Office
Gen. -General
Geneal. -Genealogical, Genealogist, Genealogy
Geog. -Geographer, Geographic, Geographical, Geography
Geol. -Geological, Geologist, Geology
Govt. -Government, Governmental
Hd. -Head
Hea. -Health
Hist. -Historian, Historic, Historical, History
Hndcp. -Handicap, Handicapped
Hon. -Honorable, Honorary
Hosp. -Hospital
HQ -Headquarters
Hum. -Humanities
Hwy. -Highway
ILL -Interlibrary Loan
Illus. -Illustrated, Illustration, Illustrative, Illustrator
Indiv. -Individual

Indus.	-Industrial, Industry
Info.	-Information, Informational
Inst.	-Institute, Institution, Institutional
Instr.	-Instruction, Instructional, Instructor
Int.	-Internal
Interp.	-Interpretation, Interpreter, Interpretive
Intl.	-International
Jnl.	-Journal
Jr.	-Junior
Kpr.	-Keeper
KWIC	-Keyword in Context
KWOC	-Keyword out of Context
Lab., Labs.	-Laboratory, Laboratories
Lang.	-Language(s)
LATCH	-Literature Attached to the Chart (Medical)
LCDR	-Lieutenant Commander
Ldr.	-Leader
Leg.	-Legal, Legislation, Legislative, Legislator, Legislature
Lib., Libs.	-Library, Libraries
Libn.	-Librarian
Lit.	-Literary, Literature
Ln.	-Lane
LRC	-Learning Resource(s) Center
Lrng.	-Learning
Lt.	-Lieutenant
LTC	-Lieutenant Colonel
Maint.	-Maintenance
Maj.	-Major
Math.	-Mathematical, Mathematics
Med.	-Medical, Medicine
Mfg.	-Manufacturing
Mgr.	-Manager
Mgt.	-Management
Mil.	-Military
Mktg.	-Marketing
Mng.	-Managing
Ms., Mss.	-Manuscript, Manuscripts
Mt.	-Mount
Mtls.	-Materials
Mus.	-Music, Musical
Musm.	-Museum
Myth.	-Mythology
N.	-North
Natl.	-National
NCME	-Network for Continuing Medical Education
No.	-Number, Numero
Nurs.	-Nursing
Off.	-Office, Officer
Oper.	-Operations, Operator
Org.	-Organization, Organizational
P.O.	-Post Office
P.R.	-Public Relations
Per.	-Periodical(s)
Perf.	-Perform, Performing
Pers.	-Personnel
Pharm.	-Pharmaceutical, Pharmacy
Photo.	-Photograph(s), Photographer, Photographic
Photodup.	-Photoduplication
Pict.	-Pictorial, Picture(s)
Pk.	-Park
Pkwy.	-Parkway
Pl.	-Place
Plan.	-Planner, Planning
Pres.	-President
Presrv.	-Preservation
Prin.	-Principal
Proc.	-Process, Processing, Processor
Prod.	-Product, Production
Prof.	-Professional, Professor
Prog.	-Program(s), Programmer, Programming
Proj.	-Project(s)
Prov.	-Province, Provincial
Psych.	-Psychiatric, Psychiatry, Psychological, Psychology
Pub.	-Public
Publ.	-Published, Publisher, Publishing
Pubn., Pubns.	-Publication, Publications
R&D	-Research and Development
Rd.	-Reader(s), Road
Rec.	-Record(s), Recreation
Ref.	-Reference
Reg.	-Region, Regional, Registrar
Rel.	-Relations, Religion, Religious
Rep.	-Representative
Repro.	-Reproduction
Res.	-Research, Researcher
Resp.	-Responsible
Ret.	-Retired, Retrieval
Rev.	-Reverend
Rm., Rms.	-Room, Rooms
Rpt.	-Report(s)
Rsrc., Rsrcs.	-Resource, Resources
Rte.	-Route
S.	-South
S/N	-Sin Numero
Sch.	-School
Sci.	-Science(s), Scientific, Scientist
SDI	-Selective Dissemination of Information
Sec.	-Secretary
Sect.	-Section
Sel.	-Selection
Ser.	-Serial(s)
Serv.	-Service(s)
Sgt.	-Sergeant
SLA	-Special Libraries Association
Soc.	-Social, Society
Spec.	-Special, Specialist, Specialized
Sq.	-Square
Sr.	-Senior, Sister
St.	-Saint, Street
Sta.	-Station
Stat.	-Statistical, Statistics
Ste.	-Sainte, Societe
Sts.	-Saints, Streets
Stud.	-Student(s), Studies, Study
Succ.	-Succursale
Sup.	-Support, Supporting
Supt.	-Superintendent
Supv.	-Supervising, Supervisor, Supervisory
Sys.	-System(s)
Tchg.	-Teaching
TDD	-Telecommunications/Telephone Device for the Deaf
Tech.	-Technical, Technological, Technology
Techn.	-Technician
Theol.	-Theological, Theology
Tpke.	-Turnpike
Trans.	-Transportation
Transl.	-Translation, Translator
Treas.	-Treasurer
Trng.	-Training
TTY	-Teletypewriter
U.N.	-United Nations
U.S.	-United States
UNESCO	-United Nations Educational, Scientific, and Cultural Organization
Univ.	-University
Unpubl.	-Unpublished
V.P.	-Vice President
Vet.	-Veteran(s), Veterinary
VF	-Vertical File(s)
Vis.	-Vision, Visual
Vol., Vols.	-Volume, Volumes
W.	-West

Directory of Special Libraries and Information Centers

VOLUME 1, PART 1

A-M

Directory of Special Libraries and Information Centers

A

★1★
A.W. Research Laboratories - Library (Sci-Engr)
711 Laurel St. Phone: (218)829-7974
Brainerd, MN 56401 Alan Cibuzar
Staff: 5. **Subjects:** Remote Sensing and analytical chemistry with applications to environmental issues. **Holdings:** 500 volumes. **Subscriptions:** 25 journals and other serials; 10 newspapers. **Services:** Library not open to the public. **Computerized Information Services:** Teltech, Inc. **Special Catalogs:** Fire Protection Film Catalogue, 1988; Supplement 1988. **Remarks:** FAX: (218)829-1316. Telex: 650-506-8951.

AAA
See: **American Automobile Association** (491)

★2★
AAI Corporation - Technical Library (Sci-Engr)
Box 126 Phone: (301)628-3193
Hunt Valley, MD 21030-0126 Barbara A. Nasim, Libn.
Founded: 1957. **Staff:** Prof 1. **Subjects:** Electronics, training, and simulation; automatic test equipment; weapons and munitions; ordnance vehicles; industrial, aviation, and marine materials handling equipment; hydraulic systems; solar energy systems; unmanned systems and robotics. **Holdings:** 3248 books; 40 bound periodical volumes; 4 VF drawers; NASA microfiche; 10,000 reports. **Subscriptions:** 111 journals and other serials. **Services:** Interlibrary loan; copying; library open to industrial research and development librarians. **Remarks:** Library located at Industry Lane, Cockeysville, MD 21030. FAX: (301)683-6432. Telex: Coye 8-7849; 710-232-1800.

A.H. Aaron Health Sciences Library
See: **Buffalo General Hospital, Inc.** (2337)

★3★
AB Bookman Publications, Inc. - Library (Publ)
Box AB Phone: (201)772-0020
Clifton, NJ 07015 Ellen Chernofsky, Libn.
Founded: 1948. **Staff:** Prof 1. **Subjects:** Bibliography, book trade history, printing history, book production arts, literary biography, censorship. **Holdings:** 5500 books; 1200 bound periodical volumes. **Subscriptions:** 45 journals and other serials. **Services:** Library open to qualified researchers by written request only. **Remarks:** Publishes AB Bookman's Weekly. FAX: (201)772-9281.

ABAM Engineers Inc.
See: **Berger/ABAM Engineers, Inc. - Technical Library** (1737)

★4★
ABB - Process Automation Inc. - Engineering Information Operations - Library (Bus-Fin, Sci-Engr)
650 Ackerman Rd. Phone: (614)261-2000
Columbus, OH 43202 Carol J. Staudenheimer, Libn.
Founded: 1981. **Staff:** 1. **Subjects:** Sensor/actuator technology, computer science. **Special Collections:** Pulp and paper technology (100 volumes). **Holdings:** 1500 books; 20 bound periodical volumes; 1093 technical reports. **Subscriptions:** 60 journals and other serials. **Services:** Interlibrary loan; library not open to the public. **Automated Operations:** Computerized cataloging. **Computerized Information Services:** DIALOG Information Services, OCLC, NEXIS; MULTICS (internal database). **Publications:** Ex Libris, quarterly - for internal distribution only. **Remarks:** FAX: (614)261-2172. Telex: 246675. Parent company is Asea Brown Boveri.

★5★
ABB Combustion Engineering, Inc. - Windsor Support Services - Library (Energy)
Dept. 2570 Phone: (203)285-4329
Windsor, CT 06095 Frank Richters, Mgr.
Founded: 1956. **Staff:** Prof 2; Other 1. **Subjects:** Energy systems, fossil fuels technology and engineering, nuclear technology and engineering, environmental science and technology, management, marketing, business and finance, government regulations, physics, metallurgy, chemistry, computer science, engineering, mathematics. **Special Collections:** Government R&D reports; U.S. Nuclear Regulatory Commission Power Reactors Docket Materials; standards (association, military, federal). **Holdings:** 20,000 books; 15,000 bound periodical volumes; 2000 conference proceedings; 2000 reprints; 250,000 government documents on microfiche; 10,000 bound government documents. **Subscriptions:** 500 journals and other serials. **Services:** Interlibrary loan; center not open to the public. **Computerized Information Services:** DIALOG Information Services, BRS Information Technologies, NEXIS, Mead Data Central, PFDS Online, Integrated Technical Information System (ITIS), Reuters **Publications:** The Digest. **Remarks:** FAX: (203)285-5605. Parent company is Asea Brown Boveri. **Staff:** Barbara Dembek, Libn.; Cathy Fischer, Info.Spec.

★6★
ABB Environmental Services Inc. - Library (Sci-Engr)
Box 7050 Phone: (207)775-5401
Portland, ME 04112 James R. Lawson, Libn.
Founded: 1969. **Staff:** Prof 1; Other 1. **Subjects:** Engineering - environmental, design, civil; geotechnical/earth resources; solid and hazardous waste; environmental regulations. **Holdings:** 4000 books; 48

bound periodical volumes. **Subscriptions:** 150 journals and other serials; 6 newspapers. **Services:** Interlibrary loan; copying; library open to the public by appointment by referral. **Automated Operations:** Computerized cataloging and serials routing. **Computerized Information Services:** DIALOG Information Services, OCLC EPIC. **Remarks:** FAX: (207)772-4762.

★7★

ABB Lummus Crest, Inc. - Lummus Technology Division - Library (Sci-Engr)
1515 Broad St. Phone: (201)893-2251
Bloomfield, NJ 07003 Mary A. Ciaramella, Chf.Libn.
Founded: 1939. **Staff:** Prof 1; Other 1. **Subjects:** Chemical engineering, petroleum refining, petrochemicals. **Special Collections:** Crude oil manuals (8 VF drawers). **Holdings:** 8900 books; 2600 bound periodical volumes; 40,000 microfiche. **Subscriptions:** 270 journals and other serials. **Services:** Interlibrary loan; copying; SDI; library open to the public by appointment. **Automated Operations:** Computerized serials. **Computerized Information Services:** DIALOG Information Services. **Publications:** New Acquisitions List, monthly - for internal distribution only. **Special Indexes:** Index of company manuals and confidential documents; index of Lummus-authored papers and articles. **Remarks:** FAX: (201)893-2412. Parent company is Asea Brown Bovari.

★8★

ABB Lummus Crest, Inc. - Technical Library (Sci-Engr)
12141 Wickchester Phone: (713)531-2301
Houston, TX 77079 Rosie R. Alcala, Tech.Libn.
Staff: Prof 1. **Subjects:** Chemical engineering; petrochemicals; petroleum refining; oil and gas engineering - production systems, field processing facilities, onshore and offshore pipeline systems. **Holdings:** 1200 books; 325 bound periodical volumes; standards and technical publications; government reports. **Subscriptions:** 80 journals and other serials. **Services:** Library not open to the public. **Remarks:** FAX: (713)531-2720. Telex: 166492. Parent company is Asea Brown Bovari.

★9★

ABB Vetco Gray, Inc. - Technical Library (Sci-Engr)
10777 Northwest Fwy.
Suite 700 Phone: (713)681-4685
Houston, TX 77092 Gloria Pena, Tech.Libn.
Founded: 1982. **Staff:** Prof 1. **Subjects:** Engineering - offshore, mechanical, petroleum; metallurgy; welding; nondestructive examination. **Special Collections:** National Standards Association vendor catalogs (9000 on microfiche). **Holdings:** 500 books; 8 VF drawers of industrial and governmental engineering standards; 10 VF drawers of U.S. mechanical and design patents; 8 VF drawers of engineering periodical reprints (arranged by subject); 78 VF drawers of internal engineering reports and project files. **Subscriptions:** 150 journals and other serials. **Services:** Interlibrary loan; copying; library open to the public by appointment with restrictions. **Automated Operations:** Computerized cataloging, acquisitions, and serials. **Computerized Information Services:** DIALOG Information Services, BRS Information Technologies, PFDS Online, RLIN, LEXIS, NEXIS. **Networks/Consortia:** Member of CLASS. **Special Catalogs:** Government and Industry Codes, Regulations, Standards and Specifications Held in the Technical Library (computer printout). **Remarks:** FAX: (713)683-2471. Pa;rent company is Asea Brown Bovari. **Formerly:** Vetco Gray, Inc.

★10★

Robert Abbe Museum of Stone Age Antiquities - Library (Hist)
P.O. Box 286 Phone: (207)288-3519
Bar Harbor, ME 04609 Rebecca Cole-Will, Cur.
Founded: 1928. **Staff:** 4.**Subjects:** Maine - archeology, Indians; general archeology; Indians of North America - arts, crafts, material culture. **Special Collections:** The Jesuit Relations and allied documents collection. **Holdings:** 800 volumes. **Subscriptions:** 10 journals and other serials. **Services:** Library open to the public with restrictions. **Computerized Information Services:** Internal database. **Staff:** Rebecca Cole-Will, Cur.

Maxwell Abbell Library
See: **North Suburban Synagogue Beth El - Joseph and Mae Gray Cultural Learning Center** (11954)

★11★

Abbey of Regina Laudis, Order of St. Benedict - Library (Rel-Phil)
Bethlehem, CT 06751 Phone: (203)266-7727
Sr. Lucia Kuppens, O.S.B.
Founded: 1947. **Staff:** Prof 1; Other 1. **Subjects:** Patrology, scripture, theology, ecclesiastical history, social sciences, art, musicology, New England history, natural sciences, literature. **Special Collections:** Patristic writings through the Middle Ages; Newman's writings; medieval mystics. **Holdings:** 22,700 books; 100 bound periodical volumes; 100 manuscripts on monasticism; 1600 pamphlets; 50 reels of microfilm of medieval and monastic history; 500 reels of magnetic tape; 3000 slides of New England themes. **Subscriptions:** 34 journals and other serials; 8 newspapers. **Services:** Interlibrary loan; copying; collection available to serious researchers with prior permission. **Networks/Consortia:** Member of Region One Cooperating Library Service Unit, Inc.

★12★

Abbey of Regina Laudis, Order of St. Benedict - Our Lady of the Rock - Priory Library (Rel-Phil)
Box 425 Phone: (206)468-2321
Shaw Island, WA 98286 Mother Dilecta Planansky, O.S.B., Libn.
Founded: 1977. **Staff:** 3. **Subjects:** Scripture, theology, patristics, musicology, ecclesiastical history, art, Japanese history and literature, oriental studies. **Special Collections:** Herbs and spices (58 items); musical scores (90). **Holdings:** 2900 books. **Subscriptions:** 12 journals and other serials. **Services:** Library not open to the public.

★13★

Abbott Laboratories - Abbott Information Services (Biol Sci, Med)
PPRD-0441, AP6B
One Abbott Park Rd. Phone: (708)937-6012
Abbott Park, IL 60064-3500 John D. Opem, Mgr.
Founded: 1888. **Staff:** Prof 19; Other 14. **Subjects:** Chemistry, pharmacology, medicine, pharmacy, microbiology. **Special Collections:** Abbott archives. **Holdings:** 18,000 volumes. **Subscriptions:** 1200 journals and other serials. **Services:** Interlibrary loan; copying; SDI; services open to the public by appointment. **Automated Operations:** Computerized cataloging, acquisitions, serials, and circulation. **Computerized Information Services:** DIALOG Information Services, PFDS Online, BRS Information Technologies, STN International, IMSBASE, Questel, NEXIS, LEXIS, Dow Jones News/Retrieval, Data-Star, DataTimes, Finsbury Data Services, Inc., VU/TEXT Information Services, Dialcom, Inc. **Networks/Consortia:** Member of Northeastern Illinois Library Consortium. **Publications:** Gateway, quarterly; Abbott Authors, annual; New Books, monthly; New Publications, monthly; Patent Alert, weekly. **Special Indexes:** Information Index, bimonthly. **Remarks:** Also maintains Business, Legal, Patent, and Trademark collections and Information Services. FAX: (708)937-2013.

★14★

Abbott Laboratories, Ltd. - Company Library (Med)
Sta. A, P.O. Box 6150 Phone: (514)340-7100
Montreal, PQ, Canada H3C 3K6 Genevieve Heroux, Libn.
Founded: 1944. **Staff:** Prof 1. **Subjects:** Medicine, nutrition, pharmacology. **Holdings:** 1000 volumes. **Subscriptions:** 90 journals. **Services:** Interlibrary loan; library not open to the public. **Computerized Information Services:** MEDLARS, CAN/OLE, DIALOG Information Services, Data-Star; Envoy 100 (electronic mail service). **Remarks:** FAX: (514)342-3544. Electronic mail address(es): HEROUX.GENEVIEVE (Envoy 100).

★15★

Abbott-Northwestern Hospital Corporation - Library/Media Services (Med)
800 E. 28th St. Phone: (612)863-4312
Minneapolis, MN 55407 Donna Johnson, Dir.
Founded: 1970. **Staff:** Prof 5; Other 5. **Subjects:** Medicine, nursing, health care administration, psychology. **Holdings:** 7000 books; 25,000 bound periodical volumes; 2 VF drawers of clippings and pamphlets; 140 filmstrip/record sets; 250 videotapes. **Subscriptions:** 625 journals and other serials. **Services:** Interlibrary loan; copying; SDI; center open to the public for reference use only with librarian's permission. **Automated Operations:** Computerized public access catalog, cataloging, and serials. **Computerized Information Services:** BRS Information Technologies, BRS/COLLEAGUE, DIALOG Information Services, NLM, DataTimes, WILSONLINE; OnTyme Electronic Message Network Service (electronic mail service). Performs searches on fee basis. Contact Person: Marianne Kelley, Mgr., Lib.Serv., 863-5470. **Networks/Consortia:** Member of Twin Cities Biomedical Consortium (TCBC). **Remarks:** Includes some of the holdings of the Sister Kenny Institute. FAX: (612)863-5695. **Staff:** Elaine Trzebiatowski, Supv., Pub.Serv.; Mary Ellinghuysen, Supv., Outreach Serv.

★16★
ABC-CLIO, Inc. - The Inge P. Boehm Library (Hist)
P.O. Box 1911 Phone: (805)968-1911
Santa Barbara, CA 93116-1911 Euzetta E. Williams, Lib.Dir.
Founded: 1967. **Staff:** 6. **Subjects:** History, political science, social sciences, humanities. **Holdings:** 1100 books. **Subscriptions:** 2200 journals and other serials. **Services:** Library open to the public with special permission. **Computerized Information Services:** DIALOG Information Services. **Remarks:** FAX: (805)685-9685.

★17★
ABC News - Research Center (Info Sci)
47 W. 66th St. Phone: (212)887-3796
New York, NY 10023-6290 Madeline Cohen, Mgr., Res.Lib. & Info.Ctr.
Founded: 1945. **Staff:** Prof 6; Other 6. **Subjects:** General reference, current events, broadcast journalism. **Holdings:** 8000 volumes; 50 VF drawers of current and background news clippings; 10 cabinets of microfilm. **Subscriptions:** 400 journals and other serials; 20 newspapers. **Services:** Center not open to the public. **Automated Operations:** Computerized public access catalog, acquisitions, and serials. **Computerized Information Services:** DIALOG Information Services, NEXIS, LEXIS, WILSONLINE, BRS Information Technologies, VU/TEXT Information Services, DataTimes, Reuters. **Remarks:** FAX: (212)887-2450. **Staff:** C.B. Hayden, Supv., Online Serv.

Abell Library
See: **Austin College** (1311)

Lelia Abercrombie Historical Library
See: **Pensacola Historical Society** (12919)

Lady Aberdeen Library of the History of Women
See: **University of Waterloo - Dana Porter Library** (19543)

Abernathy Salmon Culture Technology Center
See: **U.S. Fish & Wildlife Service** (17496)

★18★
(Abidjan) Centre Culturel Americain - USIS Library (Educ)
Blvd. de la Rocade, Angle
Ave. de l'Entente, Cocody
B.P. 1866
Abidjan 01, Cote d'Ivoire
Remarks: Maintained or supported by the U.S. Information Agency. Focus is on materials that will assist peoples outside the United States to learn about the United States, its people, history, culture, political processes, and social milieux.

★19★
Abilene Reporter-News - Library (Publ)
Box 30 Phone: (915)673-4271
Abilene, TX 79604 Anne Holland, Libn.
Founded: 1940. **Staff:** Prof 2. **Subjects:** Newspaper reference topics. **Holdings:** Microfilm. **Subscriptions:** 35 newspapers. **Services:** Library open to the public by appointment. **Remarks:** FAX: (915)673-1901. **Staff:** Anne Pilgrim, Adm.Asst.

★20★
Abilene State School - Special Library
Box 451
Abilene, TX 79604
Defunct.

Abington Library Society - Jenkintown Library
See: **Jenkintown Library** (8363)

★21★
Abington Memorial Hospital - School of Nursing Library (Med)
1942 Horace Ave. Phone: (215)576-2598
Abington, PA 19001 Carol Paskowsky, Libn.
Founded: 1914. **Staff:** Prof 1; Other 1. **Subjects:** Nursing. **Holdings:** 2000 books; 125 bound periodical volumes. **Subscriptions:** 75 journals and other serials. **Services:** Interlibrary loan; copying; library open to the public by appointment. **Computerized Information Services:** MEDLINE. **Networks/Consortia:** Member of Delaware Valley Information Consortium (DEVIC), National Network of Libraries of Medicine - Middle Atlantic Region. **Remarks:** FAX: (215)576-8127.

★22★
Abington Memorial Hospital - Wilmer Memorial Medical Library (Med)
1200 York Rd. Phone: (215)576-2096
Abington, PA 19001 Marion C. Chayes, Dir.
Founded: 1916. **Staff:** Prof 1; Other 3. **Subjects:** Surgery, internal medicine, obstetrics/gynecology, nursing. **Special Collections:** Consumer health collection. **Holdings:** 1800 books; 10,000 bound periodical volumes. **Subscriptions:** 300 journals and other serials. **Services:** Interlibrary loan; copying; SDI; library open to the public. **Computerized Information Services:** NLM, BRS Information Technologies; DIALOG Information Services; CD-ROM (Silver-Platter). **Networks/Consortia:** Member of Delaware Valley Information Consortium (DEVIC), National Network of Libraries of Medicine - Middle Atlantic Region, BHSL.

★23★
Abitibi-Price Inc. - Research Centre Library (Sci-Engr)
Sheridan Park Phone: (416)822-4770
Mississauga, ON, Canada L5K 1A9 G. Gressi, Act.Libn.
Founded: 1947. **Staff:** Prof 1. **Subjects:** Pulp, paper, board, graphic arts. **Holdings:** 4000 books; 2000 bound periodical volumes; 48 VF drawers. **Subscriptions:** 150 journals and other serials. **Services:** Interlibrary loan; copying; library open to other libraries only. **Computerized Information Services:** PFDS Online, DIALOG Information Services. **Remarks:** FAX: (416)823-9651.

James Madison Abney Library
See: **D.A. Tompkins Memorial Library & Archives** (16402)

Henry and Grete Abrahams Library of Life Sciences and Medicine
See: **Tel Aviv University - Henry and Grete Abrahams Library of Life Sciences and Medicine** (16062)

★24★
ABT Associates Inc. - Library & Information (Soc Sci)
55 Wheeler St. Phone: (617)492-7100
Cambridge, MA 02138-1168 Anish Bania, Libn.
Founded: 1974. **Staff:** Prof 1; Other 1. **Subjects:** Social sciences. **Special Collections:** Company reports. **Holdings:** 6000 books. **Subscriptions:** 153 journals and other serials. **Services:** Interlibrary loan; copying; library open to the public with restrictions. **Computerized Information Services:** DIALOG Information Services, NEXIS, LEXIS, BRS Information Technologies, Dow Jones News/Retrieval. Performs searches on fee basis. **Special Catalogs:** Catalog of Company Reports. **Remarks:** FAX: (617)492-5219.

AC Rochester Division
See: **General Motors Corporation** (6331)

Academia de Ciencias de Cuba
See: **Cuban Academy of Sciences** (4466)

Academia Colombiana de Ciencias Exactas, Fisicas y Naturales
See: **Colombian Academy of Exact, Physical and Natural Sciences** (3925)

★25★
Academia Sinica - Institute of Atomic Energy - Library (Energy, Sci-Engr)
No. 23
P.O. Box 275
Beijing, People's Republic of China Xu Fanggui, Libn.
Founded: 1956. **Staff:** 31. **Subjects:** Nuclear science and engineering, mathematics, physical sciences, chemistry, electronics, electrical and mechanical engineering, metallurgy, environmental protection, biology, medicine. **Holdings:** 103,069 volumes; 2017 periodicals; 44,057 technical reports; 40,682 AV programs and microforms. **Subscriptions:** 2000 journals and other serials; 12 newspapers. **Services:** Interlibrary loan. **Computerized Information Services:** Internal databases. **Publications:** New Book Reports, irregular; Library Newsletter, semiannual.

★26★
Academia Sinica - Institute of Coal Chemistry - Library (Energy)
5 Taoyuan, Nan Lu Phone: 440491
Taiyuan, Shanxi Province, People's Republic of China Fan Fubi, Libn.
Founded: 1961. **Staff:** 11. **Subjects:** Coal - chemistry, combustion, gasification, liquefaction; fuel chemistry; catalysis; carbon materials; fluidization; chemical reaction engineering; separation; analysis; testing; electronics. **Special Collections:** Coal chemistry; coal energy transformation; comprehensive utilization of coal and allied materials; academic reports on fuel chemistry, 1958 to present (in Chinese). **Holdings:** 40,761 volumes; 32,000 technical reports; 300,000 microforms and AV programs. **Subscriptions:** 1829 journals and other serials. **Services:** Copying. **Publications:** Journal of Fuel Chemistry and Technology.

★27★
Academia Sinica - Institute of Genetics - Library (Biol Sci, Soc Sci)
De Wai Bei Sha Tan 917 Da Lu Phone: 1 4021551
Beijing, People's Republic of China Ms. Zhou Xia-Xian, Libn.
Subjects: Biological genetics, Marx, Engels, Lenin, Stalin, Chairman Mao, politics, economics, history, languages. **Holdings:** 21,235 books; 400 periodicals; 24 AV programs and microforms; threadbound ancient Chinese books. **Services:** Interlibrary loan.

★28★
Academia Sinica - Institute of Mathematics - Library (Sci-Engr)
128 Yenchiu Yuan Rd
Sec 2 Phone: 2 7851211
Taipei 115, Taiwan Ko-Wei Lih
Founded: 1947. **Staff:** Prof 3; Other 1. **Subjects:** Mathematics, statistics. **Holdings:** 26,000 books; 15,400 bound periodical volumes. **Subscriptions:** 1000 journals and other serials. **Services:** Interlibrary loan; copying; library open to the public. **Computerized Information Services:** CD-ROM (Math/Sci Disc) ; BITNET (electronic mail service). Contact Person: Ms. Shu-Fen Kuo. **Remarks:** FAX: 2 7827432. Electronic mail address(es): MATH@TWNAS886 (BITNET).

★29★
Academia Sinica - Institute of Semiconductors - Library (Sci-Engr)
P.O. Box 912 Phone: 288131-330
Beijing 100083, People's Republic of China Liang Xinxi, Libn.
Founded: 1960. **Staff:** 15. **Subjects:** Semiconductors - physics, materials, devices; integrated circuits, microwave devices, microelectronics, surface and interface, optoelectronics, superlattices. **Holdings:** 43,780 volumes; 930 periodicals; 3000 technical reports. **Subscriptions:** 584 journals and other serials; 52 newspapers. **Services:** Interlibrary loan; copying. **Computerized Information Services:** INSPEC-SDI (internal database). **Publications:** Chinese Journal of Semiconductors; Research Progress Report. **Remarks:** FAX: 86-01-2562389.

★30★
Academia Sinica - Library (Sci-Engr, Area-Ethnic)
8 Kexueyuan Nanlu, Zhongguancun Phone: 2566846
Beijing, People's Republic of China Shi Jian, Lib.Hd.
Founded: 1950. **Staff:** 418. **Subjects:** Natural sciences, social sciences, philosophy, new technology. **Special Collections:** District histories; collected works of the Ming and Qing dynasties; stone tablet rubbings (30,000). **Holdings:** 1.6 million volumes; 35,269 periodicals; 1.04 million scientific and technical reports; 462,019 volumes of threadbound Chinese ancient books; international abstract and index journals; proceedings and publications of worldwide scientific research organizations. **Subscriptions:** 3676 journals and other serials. **Services:** Interlibrary loan; copying; library open to certified individuals. **Computerized Information Services:** STN International, Data-Star; internal database. **Publications:** Chinese Physics Abstracts; Chinese Mathematics Abstracts; hi-tech reports. **Remarks:** Telex: 2566846. **Also Known As:** Chinese Academy of Sciences-Documentation and Information Center.

★31★
Academia Sinica - Shanghai Library (Biol Sci, Med, Sci-Engr, Agri)
319 Yue Yang Rd. Phone: 21 4336650
Shanghai, People's Republic of China Yitai Gong
Founded: 1953. **Staff:** Prof 112; Other 38. **Subjects:** Biology, medicine, chemistry, environment, agriculture, science and technology. **Holdings:** 662,429 books; 288,097 bound periodical volumes; 8400 reports; 120 microfiche; 100 reels of microfilm. **Subscriptions:** 3832 journals and other serials; 28 newspapers. **Services:** Interlibrary loan; copying; SDI; library open to the public. **Computerized Information Services:** DIALOG Information Services; The Chinese Biological Database (internal database). Contact Person: Mr. Chen Chenzai, Hd. of Database Res.Dept. **Publications:** The Chinese Biological Abstracts, monthly; Life Sciences, bimonthly. **Remarks:** FAX: 21 4718906.

★32★
Academia Sinica - Wuhan Institute of Virology - Documentation and Information Division (Sci-Engr)
Xiao Hong Shan Phone: 811641
Wuhan, Hubei, People's Republic of China Liu Hong, Dir.
Founded: 1956. **Staff:** 10. **Subjects:** Microbiology, virology, biochemistry, agricultural science, environmental science, medicine. **Special Collections:** Microbiology collection (1643 books; 711 periodicals; 2642 other documents). **Holdings:** 22,829 books; 93,724 bound periodical volumes; 2592 documents; 273 nonbook items. **Subscriptions:** 256 journals and other serials; 24 newspapers. **Services:** Interlibrary loan; copying; library open to the public with restrictions. **Publications:** Virologica Sinica, quarterly. **Remarks:** Alternate telephone number(s): 813712. Telex: 7114. **Staff:** Chen Min-bin, Dp.Dir.; Liu Jun, Libn.

★33★
Academy of Art College - Library (Art)
2300 Stockton St. Phone: (415)765-4202
San Francisco, CA 94133 Lillian Hetherington, Dir.
Founded: 1977. **Staff:** Prof 1; Other 12. **Subjects:** Commercial arts, photography, fine arts, art history, interior design, fashion. **Holdings:** 15,000 books; 300 bound periodical volumes; 60,000 slides; VF drawers of art-related ephemera; American and foreign college catalogs on microfiche; picture file. **Subscriptions:** 213 journals and other serials. **Services:** Copying; library open to the public for reference use only. **Automated Operations:** Computerized cataloging. **Computerized Information Services:** RLIN; RLG (electronic mail service). **Publications:** ACADEMY GAZETTE (newsletter), biweekly during academic year - for internal distribution only.

Academy of Athens - Hellenic Folklore Research Center
See: **Hellenic Folklore Research Center** (7117)

Academy of Food Marketing
See: **St. Joseph's University - Academy of Food Marketing** (14421)

Academy Hall Museum
See: **Rocky Hill Historical Society** (14023)

Academy of Independent Scholars
See: **Vanderbilt Family Foundation** (19764)

★34★
Academy of Medicine, Toronto - William Boyd Library (Med)
288 Bloor St., W. Phone: (416)964-7088
Toronto, ON, Canada M5S 1V8 Sheila Swanson, Libn.
Founded: 1888. **Staff:** Prof 2; Other 2. **Subjects:** Clinical medicine, history of medicine. **Special Collections:** T.G.H. Drake Collection (history of pediatrics); Klotz Collection (pathology); W.S. Stanbury Collection (hematology); J.W. Graham Collection (rheumatology). **Holdings:** 40,000 books; 40,000 bound periodical volumes; 10,000 pamphlets, reports, and reprints. **Subscriptions:** 600 journals and other serials. **Services:** Interlibrary loan; copying; special services to hospitals; library open to the public for reference use only. **Computerized Information Services:** MEDLINE. **Remarks:** FAX: (416)964-9668. **Staff:** Dianne Garami.

★35★
Academy of Motion Picture Arts and Sciences - Margaret Herrick Library (Theater)
333 S. La Cienega Blvd. Phone: (213)247-3000
Beverly Hills, CA 90211 Linda Harris Mehr, Dir.
Founded: 1927. **Staff:** Prof 12; Other 25. **Subjects:** Motion picture history, biography, and production. **Special Collections:** George Stevens; John Huston; Fred Zinnemann; George Cukor; Mack Sennett; Alfred Hitchcock; Sam Peckinpah; William Selig; Paul Mazursky; Martin Ritt; William Friedkin; Cary Grant; Mary Pickford; Pete Smith; Jules White; U.S. and British patents; Scrapbook Collection (Richard Barthelmess, Jean Hersholt, Louella Parsons, Hedda Hopper, Irene, Henry Grace); Lux Radio Theatre scripts; Paramount Collection (scripts; production stills); RKO Collection (production stills); MGM Collection (production stills); Cecil B. DeMille Collection (production stills); Thomas Ince Collection (production stills); Motion Picture Association of America Production Code Files. **Holdings:** 19,000 books; 2500 bound periodical volumes; 1250 VF drawers of clippings and production stills; 8000 scripts; 5.5 million photographs. **Subscriptions:** 225 journals and other serials; 12 newspapers. **Services:** Copying; photographic reproduction; library open to the public for reference use only; special collections open to the public by appointment. **Publications:** Union list of screenplays in the Los Angeles area. **Special Indexes:** Annual Index to Motion Picture Credits; Periodical Index (card). **Remarks:** Alternate telephone number(s): (213)247-3020; 247-3220 (reference). **Staff:** Susan Oka, Asst.Libn.; Robert Cushman, Photographic Serv.; Sam Gill, Archv. Emeritus; Sandra Archer, Asst.Libn.; Lucia Schultz, Asst.Libn.; Alison Pinsler, Asst.Libn.; Eve Sullivan, Asst.Libn.; Don Lee, Asst.Libn.; Howard Prouty, Acq.Archv.; Val Almendarez, Coll.Archv.; Barbara Hall, Oral Hist.; Doug Bell, Oral Hist.

★36★
Academy of Natural Sciences - Library (Sci-Engr, Env-Cons, Biol Sci)
1900 Benjamin Franklin Pkwy. Phone: (215)299-1040
Philadelphia, PA 19103-1195 Carol M. Spawn, Libn.
Founded: 1812. **Staff:** Prof 4; Other 5. **Subjects:** Ecology, biosystematics, marine biology, geology-paleontology, history of science, museology. **Special Collections:** Library of the American Entomological Society; Pre-Linnean collection (pre-1750 imprints; 900 volumes); manuscript collection (250,000); photograph collection (25,000 images). **Holdings:** 160,000 volumes; 5000 maps. **Subscriptions:** 3317 journals and other serials. **Services:** Interlibrary loan; copying; library open to the public. **Automated Operations:** Computerized cataloging. **Computerized Information Services:** DIALOG Information Services, OCLC; internal database. Performs searches on fee basis. **Networks/Consortia:** Member of Philadelphia Area Consortium of Special Collections Libraries (PACSCL), PALINET. **Publications:** Serial Titles Held by the Academy of Natural Sciences (1987); newsletter - to Friends of the Library; **Special Catalogs:** Guide to the Manuscript Collection of the Academy of Natural Sciences (1963; book). **Special Catalogs:** Catalog of the Wolf Room Collection (book); Catalog of the Library of the Academy of Natural Sciences of Philadelphia (1972; book). **Remarks:** FAX: (215)299-1028. **Staff:** Karen D. Stevens, Ms./Archv.Libn.; Linda Rossi, Pub.Serv.Libn.

★37★
Academy of the New Church - Swedenborg Library (Rel-Phil)
2815 Huntingdon Pike
Box 278-68 Phone: (215)938-2524
Bryn Athyn, PA 19009 Carroll C. Odhner, Dir.
Founded: 1876. **Staff:** Prof 2.5; Other 2. **Subjects:** Religion, literature, history, arts, sciences, philosophy, education, language, biography and travel. **Special Collections:** Swedenborgiana (Emanuel Swedenborg's works in original translations and 16th-18th century works studied and referred to by Swedenborg; 5220 volumes). **Holdings:** 85,000 volumes; 65 VF drawers of pamphlets, pictures, recordings; 609 reels of microfilm. **Subscriptions:** 352 journals and other serials; 11 newspapers. **Services:** Interlibrary loan; copying; library open to the public with borrowing through interlibrary loan. **Computerized Information Services:** BRS Information Technologies; New Search (full text of E. Swedenbourg's Theological Works; internal database); CD-ROMs (ERIC, Academic Index, Grolier Electronic Encyclopedia). **Networks/Consortia:** Member of PALINET, Tri-State College Library Cooperative (TCLC). **Remarks:** FAX: (215)938-2637. **Staff:** Patricia Hay.

Academy of Religion and Psychical Research
See: **Spiritual Frontiers Fellowship International** (15588)

★38★
Academy of Science of Guangdong Province - Guangdong Entomological Institute - Library (Biol Sci)
105 Xingang Rd., W., 510260
Guangzhou, Guangdong Province, Phone: 448651
People's Republic of China Zhiqing Zhang, Assoc.Prof.
Founded: 1958. **Subjects:** Insects - natural enemies, systematics; termites; pest control; protection of rare animals; wildlife utilization; integrated pests management. **Holdings:** 22,078 books; 8320 bound periodical volumes. **Subscriptions:** 186 journals and other serials; 13 newspapers. **Services:** Interlibrary loan; copying; SDI; library open to the public.

Academy of Sciences of the U.S.S.R. - Astronomical Council
See: **U.S.S.R. Academy of Sciences - Astronomical Council** (17957)

Academy of Security Educators and Trainers
See: **Nine Lives Associates** (11812)

★39★
Academy of Social and Political Sciences - Art History Institute - Library (Area-Ethnic, Art)
Calea Victoriei 196 Phone: 90 50 56 80
Bucharest 1, Romania Alexandra Revenco, Libn.
Subjects: Romania - art and artists, fine arts, music, theater, cinema. **Holdings:** 49,500 volumes. **Also Known As:** Institutul de Istoria Artei.

★40★
Academy of Traditional Chinese Medicine - Library (Med)
Haiyuncang
Dongzhimennei Phone: 1 446661
Beijing, People's Republic of China Geng Jianting, Dp.Libn.
Founded: 1955. **Staff:** 23. **Subjects:** Traditional Chinese medicine, medicine, science, applied technology, medical and pharmaceutical research. **Special Collections:** Traditional Chinese medicine (70,000 volumes; manuscripts from different dynasties, 13th-19th century). **Holdings:** 200,000 volumes; 1890 periodicals. **Services:** Copying. **Publications:** Journal of Traditional Chinese Medicine; Traditional Chinese Medicine Abstracts; Traditional Chinese Medicine Bulletin; Foreign Medical Sciences, Traditional Chinese Medical Science and Medicine Series. **Special Catalogs:** Union Catalog of Books on Traditional Chinese Medicine.

Acadia National Park
See: **U.S. Natl. Park Service - Acadia Natl. Park** (17662)

★41★
Acadia University - Center for Estuarine Research - Library (Sci-Engr)
ACER Phone: (902)542-2201
Wolfville, NS, Canada B0P 1X0 Dr. Graham R. Daborn
Founded: 1985. **Staff:** Prof 2; Other 2. **Subjects:** Marine biology, marine ecology, estuarine and coastal studies, alternative energy, environmental impacts, sedimentology, aquaculture. **Special Collections:** Miramichi River, New Brunswick collection; Annapolis River, Nova Scotia collection. **Holdings:** 400 books; 10 unbound periodical volumes; 4 reports; 21 microfiche; 8 reels of microfilm. **Services:** Library open to the public for reference use only. **Computerized Information Services:** BITNET (electronic mail service). **Remarks:** FAX: (902)542-1454. Electronic mail address(es): UACER1N@ACADIAU (BITNET).

★42★
Acadia University - Vaughan Library - Special Collections (Hum, Rare Book)
Acadia St. Phone: (902)542-2201
Wolfville, NS, Canada B0P 1X0 Iain J. Bates, Univ.Libn.
Founded: 1838. **Special Collections:** Canadiana Collection; J.D. Logan Collection of Canadian Literature; Eric R. Dennis Collection of Canadiana; Thomas Chandler Haliburton Collection; William Inglis Morse Collection; rare book collection; Kirkconnell Collection; Swiss Studies Collection; Atlantic Baptist Historical Collection; military and strategic studies. **Services:** Interlibrary loan; SDI; collections open to the public with restrictions. **Automated Operations:** Computerized public access catalog, cataloging, acquisitions, and circulation. **Computerized Information Services:** DIALOG Information Services, PFDS Online, CAN/OLE, CAN/LAW, Info Globe, WILSONLINE, MEDLINE, STN International; Envoy 100, BITNET (electronic mail services). Performs searches free of charge for area residents. Contact Person: Jacqueline MacDonald, Sci.Libn. or Betty Jeffery, Mgt./Educ.Libn. **Remarks:** FAX: (902)542-4727. **Staff:** Patricia Gallant; Andre Quay; Nirnival Jain; Ruthmary Marpherson; Edith Haliburton ; Joan Mercer; Mary MacLeod.

★43★
Accademia Britannica - British School at Rome - Library (Hist)
Piazzale W. Churchill 5 Phone: 6 3222155
I-00197 Rome, Italy Valerie Scott
Founded: 1912. **Staff:** Prof 2. **Subjects:** Archeology, classical studies, medieval history, history of art, Italian topography. **Holdings:** 35,000 books; 15,000 bound periodical volumes. **Subscriptions:** 530 journals and other serials. **Services:** SDI; library open to the public with restrictions. **Publications:** Papers of the British School at Rome, annual. **Remarks:** FAX: 6 3221201.

★44★
ACCESS: A Security Information Service (Soc Sci)
1730 M St., N.W., Suite 605 Phone: (202)785-6630
Washington, DC 20036 Bruce Seymore, II, Info.Spec.
Founded: 1985. **Staff:** Prof 8. **Subjects:** International security and peace, foreign and military affairs, regional conflicts, arms control. **Special Collections:** Collection of organizational directories concerning international security and peace (5 linear feet). **Holdings:** 150 books; 48 VF drawers on organizations and related issues; 2000 sources from U.S. and abroad. **Subscriptions:** 22 journals and other serials. **Services:** Service open to the public. **Computerized Information Services:** Internal database. Performs searches on fee basis. **Publications:** ACCESS Resource Brief, 6-8/year; ACCESS Security Spectrum, 2-3/year; The ACCESS Resource Guide: An International Directory on War, Peace, and Security (1988); Rating the Resources: Congressional Staff Evaluate Information on National Security (1988); Search for Security: The ACCESS Guide to Foundations in Peace, Security, and International Relations (1989); Peace and International Security Internships in the Washington, D.C. Area (1991). **Remarks:** FAX: (202)223-2737.

★45★
Access Information Associates, Inc. - Houston Engineering Library Project (Sci-Engr)
4710 Bellaire Blvd., Suite 140 Phone: (713)664-4357
Bellaire, TX 77401 Janice C. Anderson, Pres.
Founded: 1985. **Staff:** Prof 6; Other 1. **Subjects:** Engineering, petroleum industry and trade. **Holdings:** 500 books; 400 bound periodical volumes. **Subscriptions:** 6 journals and other serials. **Services:** Interlibrary loan; copying; SDI; library open to clients. **Computerized Information Services:** DIALOG Information Services, ORBIT Search Service, NEXIS, VU/TEXT Information Services, DataTimes, National Planning Data Corporation, WILSONLINE, NewsNet, Inc., STN International, Reuters Information Services; DIALMAIL (electronic mail service). Performs searches. **Publications:** Access Newsletter, bimonthly - available on request. **Remarks:** FAX: (713)664-4825. Electronic mail address(es): 11319 (DIALMAIL). **Staff:** Ann M. Robertson, V.P. & Mgr., Cons.Serv.; Michael J. Benedict, Mgr., Staffing & Sup.Serv.; Dayna F. Smith, Info.Assoc.; Winnie Isaacs, Info.Assoc.; Sidney L. Blumenthal, Mgr., Res.Serv. & Mktg.

★46★
Access Innovations, Inc. - National Information Center for Educational Media (NICEM) (Aud-Vis)
Box 40130 Phone: (505)265-3591
Albuquerque, NM 87196 Marjorie M.K. Hlava, Pres.
Founded: 1978. **Staff:** Prof 20; Other 10. **Subjects:** Nonprint educational materials in various media (16mm films, 35mm filmstrips, motion picture cartridges, videotapes, software, multimedia items, overhead transparencies, phonograph records, audiotapes, and slides). **Holdings:** Catalogs from 23,000 distributors. **Services:** Center open to the public. **Automated Operations:** Computerized cataloging. **Computerized Information Services:** DIALOG Information Services, PFDS Online, BRS Information Technologies, Control Data Corporation (CDC), National Technical Information Service (NTIS); internal databases; CD-ROM (AV-Online). **Special Indexes:** NICEM Indexes. **Remarks:** All information is contained in bibliographic-citation databases. Library located at 4314 Mesa Grande, S.E., Albuquerque, NM 87108. Toll-free telephone number(s): (800)468-3453. FAX: (505)256-1080. **Staff:** Patrick J. Sauer, Mng.Ed.; Karen Backman, Sr.Ed.; Judith Bateman, Ed.; Mark Strong, Verifier; Leland Yates, Prog.

★47★
Access Network - Media Resource Centre (Info Sci)
295 Midpark Way, S.E. Phone: (403)256-1100
Calgary, AB, Canada T2X 2A8 Bev Waud, Dir.
Staff: Prof 1; Other 2. **Subjects:** Communications, microcomputers, broadcasting, business, education. **Holdings:** 1920 books; 5000 bound periodical volumes; 4000 videotapes; 200 computer courseware programs; 713 archival materials; laserdiscs. **Subscriptions:** 135 journals and other serials; 25 newspapers. **Services:** Interlibrary loan; copying; center open to the public for reference use only. **Automated Operations:** Computerized cataloging, acquisitions, serials, statistical records, and inventory control. **Computerized Information Services:** DIALOG Information Services, Info Globe, FORMAT, UTLAS, SPIRES; internal databases. **Publications:** MRC Update (newsletter), monthly - for internal distribution only; Courseware Directory (printout). **Special Catalogs:** Serials (printout); A/V Catalogue (book). **Remarks:** FAX: (403)256-6837. Telex: 03 824867. **Staff:** Darnell Waldner, Lib.Techn.

★48★
Accokeek Foundation - National Colonial Farm - Library (Agri)
3400 Bryan Point Rd. Phone: (301)283-2113
Accokeek, MD 20607 Clara Moran, Libn.
Founded: 1958. **Staff:** 1. **Subjects:** Agriculture, history, land use. **Holdings:** 1070 books; 30 reports of research projects. **Subscriptions:** 32 journals and other serials. **Services:** Copying; library open to the public by appointment. **Publications:** National Colonial Farm Research Reports, irregular. **Remarks:** FAX: (301)283-2049.

(Accra) USIS Collection
See: **Martin Luther King, Jr. Library** (8715)

Achenbach Foundation for Graphic Arts Reference Library
See: **Fine Arts Museums of San Francisco - Library** (5703)

★49★
Acheson Industries, Inc. - Corporate Information Center (Sci-Engr)
511 Fort St., Suite 315
Box 610489 Phone: (313)984-5583
Port Huron, MI 48061 C. Grant Taylor, Patent & Trademark Adm.
Founded: 1957. **Staff:** Prof 1; Other 1. **Subjects:** Colloid chemistry, lubrication, graphite, carbon chemistry, engineering. **Special Collections:** Archives of Dr. E.G. Acheson. **Holdings:** Figures not available. **Services:** Interlibrary loan. **Computerized Information Services:** Internal databases. **Publications:** Library and Patent Acquisitions Lists - for internal distribution only. **Remarks:** FAX: (313)984-5980. Telex: 810 231 6771. Library also serves Acheson Colloids Company and Acheson Industries Ltd. (Europe) divisions.

★50★
The Acid Rain Foundation, Inc. - Library (Env-Cons)
1410 Varsity Dr. Phone: (919)828-9443
Raleigh, NC 27606-2010 Dr. Harriett S. Stubbs, Exec.Dir.
Founded: 1981. **Staff:** 1. **Subjects:** Acid deposition, air pollution, global climate change, recycling. **Special Collections:** Gray literature (acid rain; international). **Holdings:** 500 books; 3000 scientific papers; 1000 uncataloged items. **Subscriptions:** 20 journals and other serials. **Services:** Library open to the public by appointment for reference use. **Publications:** List of publications - available on request. **Remarks:** FAX: (919)515-3593.

★51★
Ackerman Institute for Family Therapy, Inc. - Library
149 E. 78th St.
New York, NY 10021
Founded: 1960. **Subjects:** Psychiatry, family psychotherapy, family studies, couples therapy. **Holdings:** 750 books; journals; monographs. **Remarks:** Library is currently inactive. Institute is dedicated to the treatment and study of families and to the training of family therapists.

Louise S. Ackerman Fine Arts Library
See: **San Francisco Museum of Modern Art** (14736)

Justice Henry Ackerson Law Library
See: **Rutgers University - Justice Henry Ackerson Law Library** (14168)

★52★
Acne Research Institute, Inc. - Library (Med)
1236 Somerset Ln. Phone: (714)722-1805
Newport Beach, CA 92660 Dr. James E. Fulton, Jr.
Founded: 1974. **Staff:** 1. **Subjects:** Acne - pathogenesis, aggravating factors, available treatments; cosmetic surgery. **Holdings:** Figures not available. **Services:** Interlibrary loan; library open to the public. **Remarks:** FAX: (714)722-6826.

★53★
Acoustical Engineers, Inc. - Library (Sci-Engr)
1864 S. State St., Suite 270
Salt Lake City, UT 84115 Phone: (801)467-4206
Subjects: Acoustical engineering, noise control, vibration, electronics. **Holdings:** 500 items. **Subscriptions:** 3 journals and other serials. **Services:** Copying; library open to the public by appointment. **Remarks:** FAX: (801)484-5408.

★54★
Acphanutics Corporation - Library (Bus-Fin)
111 Presidential Blvd., Suite 239 Phone: (215)664-6480
Bala Cynwyd, PA 19004 Charles Renfro, Pres.
Founded: 1978. **Staff:** Prof 2. **Subjects:** Econometric software, statistical software, economic analysis and forecasts, economic data banks, econometric models and modeling. **Holdings:** 2000 volumes. **Subscriptions:** 7 journals and other serials; 2 newspapers. **Services:** Library not open to the public. **Computerized Information Services:** CITIBASE, International Economic Appraisal Service, The Economist Work Station, POWERSTATION; EasyLink (electronic mail service). Performs searches on fee basis. **Remarks:** FAX: (215)667-8390. **Formerly:** C.G. Renfro and Associates.

★55★
Acres International - Library (Sci-Engr)
500, 10201 Southport Rd., S.W. Phone: (403)253-9161
Calgary, AB, Canada T2W 4X9 Evelyn Ross, Libn.
Founded: 1981. **Staff:** Prof 1. **Subjects:** Civil engineering, hydrology, geotechnology. **Holdings:** 2000 books; 1700 reports; 200 texts. **Subscriptions:** 35 journals and other serials. **Services:** Interlibrary loan; copying; library open to the public. **Automated Operations:** Computerized cataloging. **Computerized Information Services:** Internal database. **Remarks:** FAX: (403)255-2444.

★56★
Acres International - Library (Sci-Engr)
5259 Dorchester Rd.
Box 1001 Phone: (416)374-5200
Niagara Falls, ON, Canada L2E 6W1 Marion D'Amboise, Libn.
Founded: 1959. **Staff:** Prof 2. **Subjects:** Engineering - civil, mechanical, hydraulic, environmental, electrical, geotechnical. **Holdings:** 10,000 books. **Subscriptions:** 300 journals and other serials. **Services:** Interlibrary loan; library open to the public with restrictions. **Computerized Information Services:** ORBIT Search Service, Info Globe, DIALOG Information Services, CAN/OLE. **Remarks:** FAX: (416)374-1157.

★57★
Acres International - Toronto Library (Sci-Engr)
480 University Ave., 13th Fl.
Toronto, ON, Canada M5G 1V2 Phone: (416)595-2002
Founded: 1967. **Subjects:** Engineering, economics, transportation, urban and regional planning, natural resources. **Holdings:** 3000 books; 700 standards; 150 maps; 500 catalogs. **Subscriptions:** 273 journals and other serials. **Services:** Interlibrary loan; copying; library open to the public by appointment for reference use. **Automated Operations:** Computerized serials. **Computerized Information Services:** DIALOG Information Services. **Publications:** Library - Whats New. **Remarks:** FAX: (416)595-2004. Telex: 06-217815.

★58★
Acres International Inc. - Library (Env-Cons)
140 John James Audubon Pkwy. Phone: (716)689-3737
Amherst, NY 14228-1180 Marion D'Amboise
Staff: Prof 1; Other 1. **Subjects:** Wastewater treatment, hydropower, geotechnology, air and water pollution, environment, hazardous substances. **Holdings:** 4200 volumes; internal reports; product catalogs; topographic maps. **Subscriptions:** 60 journals and other serials. **Services:** Interlibrary loan; copying. **Computerized Information Services:** DIALOG Information Services, PFDS Online. **Networks/Consortia:** Member of Western New York Library Resources Council (WNYLRC).

Acton Library
See: **University of Cambridge - Library** (18441)

ACTS Library
See: **Northwest/ACTS Library** (12036)

Acurex Corporation - Aerotherm Library
See: **Aerotherm Corporation** (111)

★59★
Adams Advertising Agency, Inc. - Library (Bus-Fin)
111 N. Canal St. Phone: (312)930-9446
Chicago, IL 60606 A.C. Hibbs, Libn.
Staff: Prof 3; Other 1. **Subjects:** Advertising, sales promotion, psychology. **Holdings:** 75,000 books. **Subscriptions:** 400 journals and other serials; 75 newspapers. **Services:** Copying; library open to the public with restrictions. **Staff:** Lori Solomon.

★60★
Adams County Historical Society - Archives (Hist)
1330 N. Burlington Ave.
Box 102 Phone: (402)463-5838
Hastings, NE 68901 Catherine Renschler, Dir.
Founded: 1965. **Staff:** Prof 2. **Subjects:** Local history, the Great Plains. **Holdings:** 300 books; 250 bound periodical volumes; 500 reels of microfilm of newspapers; 500 cassette tapes; 25 AV programs; 62 document cases of church records; 30 linear feet of school records; 150 maps; 100 document cases of other archival materials; inventory of county and city records, 1873 to present. **Subscriptions:** 10 journals and other serials. **Services:** Copying; archives open to the public. **Publications:** Historical News, bimonthly. **Special Indexes:** Index to Burton and Lewis, Past and Present of Adams County, Nebraska, published 1916; index to Goodspeed's Biographical and Historical Memoirs of Adams, Clay, Hall, and Hamilton Counties, 1890-Adams County portion; area tombstone index; Adams County naturalizations index; Adams County marriages index.

★61★
Adams County Historical Society - Library (Hist)
Schmucker Hall
Seminary Campus, Box 4325 Phone: (717)334-4723
Gettysburg, PA 17325 Dr. Charles H. Glatfelter, Dir.
Founded: 1943. **Subjects:** Adams County history. **Holdings:** 1000 volumes; 172 VF drawers of records, manuscripts, clippings, newspapers, genealogical files. **Subscriptions:** 13 journals and other serials. **Services:** Library and museum open to the public.

★62★
Adams County Law Library (Law)
Courthouse, Rm. 207 Phone: (513)544-2921
West Union, OH 45693 Donna Dillo, Jr., Libn.
Staff: 1. **Subjects:** Law. **Holdings:** 5130 books; 50 bound periodicals. **Services:** Library open to the public. **Remarks:** Maintained by Adams County Law Library Association.

★63★
Adams County Law Library (Law)
Court House Phone: (717)334-6781
Gettysburg, PA 17325 Julian Forrest, Law Libn.
Subjects: Law. **Holdings:** 26,000 volumes. **Services:** Interlibrary loan; copying; library open to the public.

★64★
Adams, Duque & Hazeltine - Library (Law)
777 S. Figueroa Phone: (213)620-1240
Los Angeles, CA 90017 Barbara Gabor, Libn.
Staff: Prof 2; Other 3. **Subjects:** Law - California, federal, civil, insurance, corporate, real estate, tax, environmental. **Holdings:** 35,000 volumes. **Subscriptions:** 150 journals and other serials. **Services:** Interlibrary loan; library not open to the public. **Computerized Information Services:** LEXIS, Dow Jones News/Retrieval, DIALOG Information Services, Information America, WESTLAW, Legi-Tech, LEGI-SLATE, VU/TEXT Information Services, Dun & Bradstreet Business Credit Services. Performs searches on fee basis. **Remarks:** FAX: (213)896-5500. Telex: 68-6135.

★65★
Adams Express Company - Library (Bus-Fin)
7 St. Paul St., Suite 1140 Phone: (301)752-5900
Baltimore, MD 21202 Dorothy Marvel, Libn.
Founded: 1930. **Staff:** Prof 1; Other 1. **Subjects:** Business, finance, economics. **Holdings:** 1100 books; 140 bound periodical volumes; 135 VF drawers of corporate and industrial files; 46 investment services and statistical releases; 10K, 10Q, SEC reports for 150 corporations on microfiche; 30 Investment Titles/Services. **Subscriptions:** 77 journals and other serials; 20 newspapers. **Services:** Library not open to the public.

Hunter M. Adams Architecture Library
See: **University of Kentucky** (18750)

Adams National Historic Site - Stone Library
See: **U.S. Dept. of the Interior - Adams National Historic Site** (17245)

★66★
Adams & Reese - Law Library (Law)
4500 One Shell Sq. Phone: (504)581-3234
New Orleans, LA 70139 Ronald G. Aucoin, Libn.
Founded: 1960. **Staff:** Prof 1; Other 1. **Subjects:** United States law. **Special Collections:** Louisiana law (3000 volumes); health and medicine (2000 volumes); maritime law (1600 volumes); environmental law (1500 volumes); business law (1000 volumes); international law (600 volumes). **Holdings:** 12,000 books; 1000 bound periodical volumes; 1000 reports; 350 archival items; 5000 microfiche; 200 reels of microfilm. **Subscriptions:** 550 journals and other serials; 50 newspapers. **Services:** Library open to the public at librarian's discretion. **Automated Operations:** Computerized public access catalog (Data Trek). **Computerized Information Services:** WESTLAW, LEXIS, MEDLARS. **Remarks:** FAX: (504)566-0210. Telex: 584426.

Adams & Rinehart Inc.
See: **Ogilvy Adams & Rinehart** (12254)

★67★
Adams State College - Library - Special Collections (Hist)
Alamosa, CO 81102 Phone: (719)589-7781
James B. Hemesath, Dir.
Founded: 1925. **Special Collections:** San Luis Valley history. **Services:** Interlibrary loan; copying; library open to the public. **Computerized Information Services:** DIALOG Information Services, OCLC, MARMOT. **Networks/Consortia:** Member of Southwest Regional Library Service System (SWRLSS), Bibliographical Center for Research, Rocky Mountain Region, Inc. (BCR). **Staff:** Christine Moeny, Spec.Coll.

★68★
Adath Jeshurun Congregation - Jenny Gross Memorial Library (Rel-Phil)
3400 Dupont Ave., S.
Minneapolis, MN 55408 Phone: (612)824-2685
Founded: 1931. **Staff:** Prof 1. **Subjects:** Zionism, Bible, theology, Jewish history, liturgy, law and literature, modern Israel. **Special Collections:** Children's Book Collection. **Holdings:** 5000 books. **Subscriptions:** 10 journals and other serials. **Services:** Library open to the public.

★69★
Addiction Research Foundation - Library (Med)
33 Russell St.
Toronto, ON, Canada M5S 2S1 Phone: (416)595-6144
Founded: 1958. **Staff:** Prof 4; Other 7. **Subjects:** Alcoholism and drug abuse. **Special Collections:** Staff publications; Temperance collection; Drug Education Resources. **Holdings:** 14,500 books; 12,500 reprints; 250 films. **Subscriptions:** 450 journals. **Services:** Interlibrary loan (in Canada only); copying; SDI; library open to the public. **Automated Operations:** Integrated library system. **Computerized Information Services:** BRS Information Technologies, QL Systems, DIALOG Information Services, CAN/OLE, Infomart Online. **Networks/Consortia:** Member of Substance Abuse Librarians and Information Specialists (SALIS). **Publications:** Acquisitions List, monthly; Serials List; Film List - all free upon request. **Remarks:** FAX: (416)595-6036. **Staff:** Christopher Stanley, Mgr., Info. Response Serv.; Louise Hamel, Mgr., Lib. & Stat.Rsrcs.; Debbie Monkman, Ref.Libn.

Addison Gallery of American Art
See: **Phillips Academy** (13004)

★70★
Addison-Wesley Publishing Company - Library (Publ)
2725 Sand Hill Rd. Phone: (415)854-0300
Menlo Park, CA 94025 Elede Toppy Hall, Info.Serv.Spec.
Staff: Prof 1; Other 1. **Subjects:** Reference. **Special Collections:** Company archives (articles about company; complete set of School Division and Trade Division publications). **Holdings:** 2500 volumes. **Subscriptions:** 200 journals and other serials. **Services:** Interlibrary loan; copying; library not open to the public. **Computerized Information Services:** DIALOG Information Services, WILSONLINE; internal databases. **Publications:** Acquisition list and periodical holding list - to staff. **Remarks:** FAX: (415)853-2505. Library also serves Benjamin/Cummings Publishing Co., a subsidiary of Addison-Wesley Publishing Company.

★71★
Addison-Wesley Publishing Company - Library (Publ)
Jacob Way Phone: (617)944-3700
Reading, MA 01867 Dorothy Abbott, Libn.
Founded: 1967. **Staff:** Prof 1; Other 1. **Subjects:** Physics, mathematics, engineering science, business and economics, biological sciences, sociology, health and physical education, psychology, anthropology. **Special Collections:** Company archives (copies of all company publications). **Holdings:** 25,000 books; reports; pamphlets. **Subscriptions:** 500 journals and other serials; 10 newspapers. **Services:** Library not open to the public. **Remarks:** FAX: (617)942-1117. Telex: 989572 ADWES UD.

Adelaide Circulating Library
See: **State Library of South Australia - Special Collections** (15695)

★72★
Adelaide Festival Centre Trust - Performing Arts Collection of South Australia (Theater)
Adelaide Festival Centre
G.P.O. Box 1269 Phone: 8 216-8769
Adelaide, SA 5001, Australia Jo Peoples, Cur.
Founded: 1979. **Staff:** 2. **Subjects:** Drama, music theater, dance, music, opera, magicians, circus. **Special Collections:** Colin Ballantyne Collection (photographs); Agnes Dobson Collection (photographs, programs); Daisy Kennedy Collection; Joanne Priest Collection (memorabilia); Carl Fredrich Oberle Collection (complete set of costume sketches for "A Dream Play"); Luciana Arrighi Collection (complete set of costume designs for "Death in Venice"). **Holdings:** 600 books; documents; ephemera. **Subscriptions:** 10 journals and other serials; 5 newspapers. **Services:** Interlibrary loan; copying; collection open to the public for reference use only. **Remarks:** Alternate telephone number(s): 08 216-8767. FAX: 08 212-7849. Telex: 08 88724. **Staff:** Jo Landsberg.

★73★
Adelphi University - Fine/Performing Arts Library - Special Collections - Archives (Art, Hist)
Swirbul Library
Box 701 Phone: (516)877-3563
Garden City, NY 11530 Dr. Erica Doctorow, Coord.
Founded: 1896. **Staff:** Prof 2; Other 2. **Subjects:** Fine and performing arts. **Special Collections:** William Cobbett; Americana; William Blake; Gerhart Hauptmann; Small Presses; Expatriate Writers; Spanish Civil War; Richard Stoelzer; university archives. **Holdings:** 35,000 books; 3240 folders; 11,000 slides; 9000 sound recordings; 165 slide kits. **Subscriptions:** 150 journals and other serials. **Services:** Interlibrary loan; copying; special collections and archives open to the public for reference use only. **Computerized Information Services:** DIALOG Information Services, Mead Data Central, MEDLARS, BRS Information Technologies, OCLC. **Networks/Consortia:** Member of Long Island Library Resources Council. **Publications:** Handbook, annual - for internal distribution only. **Special Catalogs:** William Cobbett Collection at Adelphi University (1982); The Stoelzer Collection at Adelphi University (1985); exhibition catalogs. **Remarks:** FAX: (516)877-3592. Alternate telephone number(s): (516)877-3560; 877-3561; 877-3562; 877-3564. **Staff:** Gary E. Cantrell, Perf. Arts Libn.

★74★
Adelphi University - Science Library (Sci-Engr)
Garden City, NY 11530 Phone: (516)877-4166
Arthur Lifshin, Hd./Sci.Libn.
Founded: 1959. **Staff:** Prof 1; Other 3. **Subjects:** Physics, chemistry, biology. **Special Collections:** Henry Drysdale Dakin Memorial Collection (organic chemistry). **Holdings:** 22,000 books; 29,000 bound periodical volumes; 19,500 microforms. **Subscriptions:** 500 journals and other serials. **Services:** Interlibrary loan; copying; library open to the public for reference use only. **Automated Operations:** Computerized cataloging, acquisitions, and circulation. **Computerized Information Services:** DIALOG Information Services, STN International, NLM. **Networks/Consortia:** Member of Long Island Library Resources Council.

★75★
Adirondack Historical Association - Library (Hist)
Adirondack Museum
Box 99 Phone: (518)352-7311
Blue Mountain Lake, NY 12812 Jerold Pepper, Libn.
Founded: 1957. **Staff:** Prof 1; Other 1. **Subjects:** Adirondack Mountains - history, geography, natural history, economic history, recreation, art. **Special Collections:** E.Z.C. Judson (Ned Buntline) writings and memorabilia; Association for the Protection of the Adirondacks papers; McIntyre Iron Mine papers; Northern New York newspapers (700 reels of microfilm). **Holdings:** 8186 volumes; 60,000 photographs and postcards; 1310 maps; 615 linear feet of manuscripts; 1812 reels of microfilm; 46 VF drawers. **Subscriptions:** 390 journals and other serials. **Services:** Interlibrary loan; copying; library open to outside users by appointment. **Networks/Consortia:** Member of North Country Reference and Research Resources Council (NCRRRC).

★76★
Adis International - Library (Med)
Private Bag, Mairangi Bay Phone: 9 4038100
Auckland 10, New Zealand Adrian Beasley, Chf.Libn.
Staff: 20. **Subjects:** Clinical pharmacology, therapeutics. **Holdings:** 1000 volumes; 40,000 journal reprints. **Subscriptions:** 600 journals and other serials. **Services:** Interlibrary loan; library open to the public by appointment. **Computerized Information Services:** Produces AdiSearch database (available online through BRS Information Technologies). Performs searches. **Remarks:** FAX: 9 4781418. Telex: 21334 NZ. **Formerly:** ADIS Press Ltd. **Staff:** Sue Shoolbread, Chf. Indexer; Joanna van Dam, Asst.Libn.

★77★
Adistra Corporation - R & D Library
101 Union St.
Plymouth, MI 48170-1692
Defunct.

Alfred Adler Institute
See: **Adler School of Professional Psychology** (81)

★78★
Alfred Adler Institute - Library (Med)
250 W. 57th St. Phone: (212)974-0431
New York, NY 10023 Leo Rattner, Ph.D., Exec.Dir.
Founded: 1950. **Subjects:** Psychotherapy, psychology, psychiatry, counseling. **Holdings:** 500 volumes.

★79★
Adler Planetarium - Library (Sci-Engr)
1300 S. Lake Shore Dr. Phone: (312)322-0593
Chicago, IL 60605 Dr. Evelyn D. Natividad, Lib.Adm.
Founded: 1973. **Staff:** Prof 1. **Subjects:** Astronomy, astrophysics, science, mathematics, space technology, archeoastronomy. **Special Collections:** Rare books on astronomy, 1480-1800 (800); atlases, 1482 to present (50); Juvenile Collection. **Holdings:** 6600 books; 1500 bound periodical volumes; 100 early prints of antique instruments; 50 celestial charts and maps; VF drawers on astronomy topics and allied subjects. **Subscriptions:** 35 journals and other serials. **Services:** Copying; astronomical information service by telephone and letter; library open to the public by appointment. **Computerized Information Services:** OCLC. **Networks/Consortia:** Member of ILLINET, Chicago Library System, Consortium of Museum Libraries in the Chicago Area. **Special Indexes:** Index to NASA Materials. **Remarks:** FAX: (312)322-2257.

★80★
Adler Pollock & Sheehan, Inc. - Law Library (Law)
2300 Hospital Trust Tower Phone: (401)274-7200
Providence, RI 02903 Paul R. Dumaine, Law Libn.
Staff: Prof 2; Other 1. **Subjects:** Law - business, corporate, commercial, labor, tax, securities; estate planning; litigation. **Holdings:** 7000 books; 1000 bound periodical volumes; 500 legal memoranda. **Subscriptions:** 70 journals and other serials. **Services:** Interlibrary loan (limited); library not open to the public. **Computerized Information Services:** VU/TEXT Information Services, DIALOG Information Services, Dow Jones News/Retrieval, Legal Resource Index, LEXIS, NEXIS, WESTLAW, State Net, Dun & Bradstreet Credit Services; J/TEXT (internal database). **Remarks:** FAX: (401)751-0604. **Staff:** Eileen F. Paolino, Asst. Law Libn.

★81★
Adler School of Professional Psychology - Sol and Elaine Mosak Library (Soc Sci)
65 E. Wacker Pl., 20th Fl. Phone: (312)294-7109
Chicago, IL 60601 Karen Drescher, Hd.Libn.
Founded: 1964. **Staff:** 4. **Subjects:** Psychology, psychotherapy, substance abuse, psychiatry, education, counseling, guidance. **Special Collections:** Adlerian Psychology (350 books). **Holdings:** 8000 volumes; 1500 articles and reprints; 2600 journals and periodicals; 500 films and videotapes; 1500 cassettes and audiotapes. **Subscriptions:** 110 journals and other serials. **Services:** Interlibrary loan; library open to the public by appointment. **Computerized Information Services:** DIALOG Information Services, BRS Information Technologies. **Special Indexes:** Author, Subject Title Index to Individual Psychology. **Remarks:** FAX: (312)201-5900. **Formerly:** Alfred Adler Institute. **Staff:** Beverly Martin; Bob Lamielle; Miriam Tabachnik.

Adler-Shinensky Library
See: **Central Agency for Jewish Education** (3321)

★82★
Admedia - Library (Bus-Fin)
Postbus 2216 Phone: 20 5455555
NL-1180 EE Amstelveen, Netherlands Mrs. A.G. Cox
Founded: 1970. **Staff:** 1. **Subjects:** Netherlands consumer markets and products. **Holdings:** 2500 bound volumes. **Subscriptions:** 150 journals and other serials. **Services:** Library not open to the public. **Remarks:** FAX: 20 5455550. Telex: 16671.

★83★
Administrative Conference of the United States (ACUS) - Library (Law)
2120 L St., N.W., Suite 500 Phone: (202)254-7065
Washington, DC 20037 Cari L. Votava, Libn./Info.Off.
Staff: Prof 1; Other 1. **Subjects:** Administrative law and procedure, government regulation. **Special Collections:** Administrative Procedure Act materials; agency archives and work product, 1968 to present. **Holdings:** 7000 books; government documents. **Subscriptions:** 60 journals and other serials; 10 newspapers. **Services:** Interlibrary loan; copying; library open to the public with restrictions. **Computerized Information Services:** LEXIS, NEXIS.

★84★
Adoptee-Birthparent Support Network - Library (Soc Sci)
3421 M St., N.W., Suite No. 328 Phone: (202)686-4611
Washington, DC 20007 Robyn S. Quinter, Lib./Res.Dir.
Founded: 1986. **Staff:** 1. **Subjects:** Adoption. **Holdings:** 400 books, journals, audio- and videotapes.

★85★
Adoption Awareness Press - Library (Soc Sci)
Box 1860 Phone: (813)542-1342
Cape Coral, FL 33910 Pat Lamarco
Founded: 1980. **Subjects:** Adoption reform, genealogy. **Special Collections:** U.S. adoption reform newsletters. **Holdings:** 200 books. **Services:** Library open to the public. **Publications:** Freedom Rider. **Remarks:** FAX: (813)549-9393. Maintained by the Musser Foundation. **Formerly:** Adoption Triangle Ministries.

★86★
Adria Laboratories, Inc. - Library
Box 16529 Phone: (614)764-8356
Columbus, OH 43216 Larry Hagerman, Libn.
Founded: 1974. **Staff:** 4. **Subjects:** Medicine - oncology, AIDS. **Holdings:** Figures not available. **Services:** Interlibrary loan; Library not open to the public. **Computerized Information Services:** DIALOG Information Services, STN International, InvesText, OCLC. **Remarks:** FAX: (614)761-4040.

★87★
Adult Migrant Education Service - Learning Resource Centre (Educ)
127 Rundle Mall
Renaissance Ctr. Phone: 8 2240922
Adelaide, SA 5000, Australia Liz Crawford, Sr.Libn.
Founded: 1976. **Staff:** Prof 1.5; Other 4. **Subjects:** English language, education, immigration. **Holdings:** 46,000 books; 12,000 audiocassettes and videocassettes. **Subscriptions:** 85 journals and other serials; 3 newspapers. **Services:** Interlibrary loan; copying; SDI; library open to the public for reference use only. **Computerized Information Services:** DELTAA (internal database). Contact Person: Annette Langham, State Libn. **Remarks:** FAX: 8 2321826.

★88★
Adult Migrant English Service - Library (Educ)
175 Collins St. Phone: 02 307121
Hobart, TAS 7001, Australia Mrs. F. Millar, Lib.Hd.
Founded: 1980. **Staff:** Prof 1; Other 1. **Subjects:** English as a second language; language acquisition. **Holdings:** 25,000 books. **Subscriptions:** 60 journals and other serials; 2 newspapers. **Services:** Interlibrary loan; library open to the public with restrictions. **Computerized Information Services:** Internal databases. **Remarks:** FAX: 02 313049.

★89★
Advanced Biotechnologies, Inc. - Library (Biol Sci)
9108 Guilford Rd.
Rivers Park II Phone: (301)470-3220
Columbia, MD 21046 Louise Lane
Founded: 1982. **Subjects:** Molecular biology - lymphokine and growth factor purification, characterization, monoclonal antibody yield optimization analysis, development of acquired immune deficiency syndrome (AIDS) reagents, virus purification, viral genetics, electron microscopy, cell culture, media, sera, research and development services. **Holdings:** 1500 volumes; 31 periodicals. **Subscriptions:** 15 journals and other serials; 3 newspapers. **Services:** Library not open to the public.

★90★
Advanced Information Consultants - Library (Info Sci)
45912 Geddes Rd. Phone: (313)397-3660
Canton, MI 48188 Barton B. Bryant, Hd.
Staff: Prof 1. **Subjects:** Information science, religion. **Holdings:** 3000 books. **Subscriptions:** 18 journals and other serials. **Computerized Information Services:** DIALOG Information Services, BRS Information Technologies, PFDS Online, Questel, VU/TEXT Information Services, STN International. Performs searches on fee basis.

★91★
Advanced Micro Devices, Inc. - Technical Library (Sci-Engr)
901 Thompson Place
Mail Stop 169
Box 3453 Phone: (408)749-2260
Sunnyvale, CA 94088 John Owen, Mgr., Lib.Serv.
Founded: 1971. **Staff:** Prof 1; Other 1. **Subjects:** Semiconductor technology. **Holdings:** 3000 books; 500 bound periodical volumes; 10 VF drawers of military specifications and standards; patents. **Subscriptions:** 200 journals and other serials. **Services:** Interlibrary loan; library not open to the public. **Computerized Information Services:** DIALOG Information Services. **Networks/Consortia:** Member of CLASS, South Bay Cooperative Library System (SBCLS).

★92★
Advanced Nuclear Fuels Corporation - Library (Energy)
2101 Horn Rapids Rd.
Box 130 Phone: (509)375-8659
Richland, WA 99352 Joan Okrent, Libn.
Subjects: Nuclear energy. **Holdings:** Figures not available.

★93★
Advanstar Communications, Inc. - Business Information Services (Publ)
7500 Old Oak Blvd. Phone: (216)826-2839
Cleveland, OH 44130 Lori Fraser, Mgr.
Founded: 1988. **Staff:** Prof 1; Other 2. **Subjects:** Professional and business publications. **Holdings:** 200 books; 133 titles of bound periodical volumes; photograph file; prints; transparencies; slides. **Subscriptions:** 63 journals and other serials. **Services:** Copying; services open to the public. **Computerized Information Services:** Internal database. Performs searches on fee basis. **Publications:** Newsletter, quarterly - for internal distribution only. **Special Indexes:** Magazine index of company publications; photofile index of company artwork (both online). **Remarks:** Toll-free telephone number(s): is (800)225-4569. FAX: (216)891-2726. **Formerly:** Edgell Communications, Inc.

★94★
Advanswers Media/Programming, Inc. - Information Center (Bus-Fin)
10 Broadway Ave., 21st Fl. Phone: (314)444-2216
St. Louis, MO 63102 Angie Odem, Sec.
Founded: 1902. **Staff:** Prof 1; Other 1. **Subjects:** Marketing, advertising, media, creative writing. **Holdings:** 500 books; 100 periodicals. **Subscriptions:** 15 journals and other serials. **Services:** Interlibrary loan; center not open to the public. **Computerized Information Services:** DIALOG Information Services. **Remarks:** Alternate telephone number(s): (314)444-2357. FAX: (314)444-2216.

★95★
Adventist Health Systems Sunbelt - Walker Memorial Hospital - S.C. Pardee Medical Library (Med)
Hwy. 27, N. Phone: (813)453-7511
Avon Park, FL 33825-1200 Monica Lescay, Dir., Med.Rec. & Lib.
Staff: 1. **Subjects:** Medicine and allied health sciences. **Holdings:** Figures not available. **Services:** Interlibrary loan; library open to the public with restrictions. **Computerized Information Services:** MEDLINE. **Remarks:** FAX: (813)453-5673.

★96★
Advertising Research Foundation - Library (Bus-Fin)
3 E. 54th St. Phone: (212)751-5656
New York, NY 10022 Roslyn Arnstein, Mgr., Info.Ctr.
Founded: 1952. **Staff:** Prof 2. **Subjects:** Market research, advertising, research methods, media research. **Special Collections:** Foundation publications. **Holdings:** 3000 volumes; 2000 vertical files of clippings, reports, surveys. **Subscriptions:** 110 journals and other serials. **Services:** Library open to members and qualified graduate students for reference use only. **Publications:** List of publications - available on request. **Remarks:** FAX: (212)319-5265. **Staff:** Delritta Hornbuckle, Asst.Libn.

★97★
Advisory Commission on Intergovernmental Relations - Library (Soc Sci)
800 K St., N.W., South, Suite 450 Phone: (202)653-5540
Washington, DC 20575 Joan A. Casey, Info.Off.
Founded: 1960. **Staff:** Prof 1; Other 1. **Subjects:** Intergovernmental relations, state and local government, metropolitan problems, taxation, federal and state aid, public administration. **Holdings:** 7000 books. **Subscriptions:** 75 journals and other serials; 3 newspapers. **Services:** Interlibrary loan; copying; library open to the public. **Remarks:** FAX: (202)653-5429.

★98★
Advisory Group on Electron Devices - Library (Sci-Engr)
Palisades Institute
2011 Crystal Dr.
Crystal Park 1, Suite 307 Phone: (703)486-3850
Arlington, VA 22202 Denise Thomas, Tech.Libn.
Subjects: Electron devices. **Holdings:** 9000 technical reports. **Subscriptions:** 15 journals and other serials. **Services:** Library not open to the public. **Remarks:** Library provides specialized informational services to government agencies and government contractors on research and development in the field of electron devices. FAX: (703)979-7416.

The Advocate Library
See: **Southern Connecticut Newspapers Inc.** (15481)

★99★
AECL CANDU - Information Resources Centre (Sci-Engr, Energy)
2251 Speakman Dr. Phone: (416)823-9040
Mississauga, ON, Canada L5K 1B2 Laurie J. Scott, Hd.
Founded: 1957. **Staff:** Prof 1; Other 4. **Subjects:** Nuclear power, engineering, energy, business and economics, management, computer science. **Holdings:** 10,000 books; 770 bound periodical volumes; 30,000 hardcopy reports; 70,000 reports on microfiche; 100,000 standards; 1000 pamphlets. **Subscriptions:** 530 journals and other serials. **Services:** Interlibrary loan; library open to the public by appointment. **Automated Operations:** Computerized cataloging, serials, and circulation. **Computerized Information Services:** DIALOG Information Services, CAN/OLE, Infomart Online, Info Globe, UTLAS, Reuters; CD-ROMs (COMPENDEX PLUS, International Nuclear Information System); Envoy 100 (electronic mail service). **Networks/Consortia:** Member of Sheridan Park Association. **Publications:** IRC brochure, irregular; New Arrivals, bimonthly - both for internal distribution only. **Remarks:** FAX: (416)823-6120. Telex: 06 982372. Electronic mail address(es): LIBRARY.SP (Envoy 100). **Formerly:** AECL Research - CANDU Operations Library.

★100★
AECL CANDU - Library (Energy)
1155 Metcalfe St., 8th Fl. Phone: (514)871-1116
Montreal, PQ, Canada H3B 2V6 Susan J. Nish, Libn.
Founded: 1977. **Staff:** 1. **Subjects:** Nuclear power, nuclear reactors, design engineering. **Holdings:** 2000 books; 1000 standards; 1000 reports. **Subscriptions:** 80 journals and other serials. **Services:** Interlibrary loan; library not open to the public. **Computerized Information Services:** DIALOG Information Services, CAN/OLE, UTLAS, Infomart Online; BASIS (internal database). **Remarks:** FAX: (514)934-1322. **Formerly:** AECL Research - CANDU Operations Library.

★101★
AECL Research - Chalk River Laboratories - Library (Sci-Engr)
Chalk River Nuclear Laboratories Phone: (613)584-3311
Chalk River, ON, Canada K0J 1J0 O.S. Tatone, Search Spec.
Founded: 1944. **Staff:** Prof 4; Other 14. **Subjects:** Nuclear science, engineering, physics, chemistry, metallurgy, electronics, materials, mathematics, biology. **Holdings:** 76,000 books and pamphlets; 53,000 bound periodical volumes; 7600 hardcopy translations; 25,600 translations in microform; 167,000 hardcopy reports; 500,000 external reports in microform; 2700 microfilm cartridges of periodicals and abstracts. **Subscriptions:** 600 journals and other serials. **Services:** Interlibrary loan (inquiries by mail preferred); copying; SDI. **Automated Operations:** Computerized acquisitions, serials, circulation, and reports catalog. **Computerized Information Services:** CAN/SDI, CAN/OLE, PFDS Online, DIALOG Information Services, Info Globe, BRS Information Technologies. **Publications:** AECL List of Publications, annual; Serial Holdings; AECL Technical Reports, annual. **Special Indexes:** Computer generated indexes for technical reports in nuclear and related subjects. **Remarks:** FAX: (613)584-4024. **Formerly:** Atomic Energy of Canada, Ltd. **Staff:** T.P. Alburger, Acq. & Cat. Libn.

★102★
AECL Research - Whiteshell Laboratories - Library (Sci-Engr)
Pinawa, MB, Canada R0E 1L0 Phone: (204)753-2311
Sharon Taylor, Act.Libn.
Founded: 1963. **Staff:** Prof 3; Other 7. **Subjects:** Nuclear science, nuclear waste management, chemistry, geology, environmental science, materials science, metallurgy, computing, mathematics, engineering. **Holdings:** 60,000 books; 300,000 microfiche. **Subscriptions:** 800 journals and other serials. **Services:** Interlibrary loan; copying; library open to the public with permission. **Automated Operations:** Computerized cataloging, acquisitions, and circulation. **Computerized Information Services:** DIALOG Information Services, International Nuclear Information System (INIS), STN International, Info Globe, DOBIS Canadian Online Library System, QL Systems, CAN/OLE; Envoy 100 (electronic mail service). **Remarks:** FAX: (204)753-2455; 753-8404. Telex: 063671345. Electronic mail address(es): WNRE.LIBRARY (Envoy 100).

AECOM Technology Corporation
See: **Consoer Townsend & Associates** (4223)

★103★
Aero Vironment Inc. - Library (Energy)
222 E. Huntington Dr. Phone: (818)357-9983
Monrovia, CA 91016 Heidi Nikpur
Subjects: Alternative energy, aerodynamics, environmental science, air pollution, hazardous waste. **Holdings:** 300 books; 100 journals; 5000 technical reports. **Remarks:** FAX: (818)359-9628. Telex: 467121 (AEROVIR-CI).

★104★
Aerodyne Research, Inc. - Technical Information Center (Sci-Engr)
45 Manning Rd. Phone: (508)663-9500
Billerica, MA 01821 Susan Mast, Info.Spec.
Founded: 1976. **Staff:** Prof 1. **Subjects:** Chemistry, molecular and laser physics, optics, materials science, infrared imaging. **Holdings:** 2000 books; 130 bound periodical volumes; unclassified reports. **Subscriptions:** 115 journals and other serials; 5 newspapers. **Services:** Interlibrary loan; center not open to the public. **Computerized Information Services:** DIALOG Information Services; UNCLASS (internal database); BITNET, DIALMAIL (electronic mail services). **Publications:** Technical Information Center Bytes, irregular - for internal distribution only. **Remarks:** FAX: (508)663-4918.

★105★
Aerojet Propulsion Division - Library (Sci-Engr)
Box 13222 Phone: (916)355-2201
Sacramento, CA 95813 Richard E. Shallenberger, Supv.Tech.Libn.
Founded: 1954. **Staff:** Prof 2. **Subjects:** Engineering, rocket propulsion, materials, chemistry. **Holdings:** 9000 books; 5500 bound periodical volumes; 30,000 government and company reports; 250,000 NASA reports, 1963 to present, on microfiche. **Subscriptions:** 90 journals and other serials. **Services:** Interlibrary loan; center not open to the public. **Automated Operations:** Computerized cataloging and serials. **Computerized Information Services:** DIALOG Information Services, NASA/RECON, DTIC, Dow Jones News/Retrieval. **Publications:** Library Newsletter, monthly - for internal distribution only. **Remarks:** FAX: (916)355-2104. Affiliated with GenCorp Aerojet. **Staff:** Cary O'Keeffe, Assoc.Tech.Libn.

★106★
Aerojet Solid Propulsion Co. - Technical Information Center (Sci-Engr)
Box 13222 Phone: (916)355-4076
Sacramento, CA 95813 Rimma Mironenko, Res.Libn.
Staff: Prof 1. **Subjects:** Chemistry, aerospace. **Holdings:** 10,000 books; 10,000 bound periodical volumes. **Subscriptions:** 125 journals and other serials. **Services:** Center not open to the public. **Remarks:** Affiliated with GenCorp Aerojet.

★107★
Aeronautical Research Laboratory - Library (Sci-Engr)
506 Lorimer St. Phone: 3 6477433
Fishermen's Bend, VIC 3207, Australia Paula Carr
Founded: 1941. **Staff:** Prof 3; Other 4. **Subjects:** Aeronautical engineering, mechanics, materials, aerodynamics, propulsion, simulation. **Holdings:** 15,000 books; 10,000 bound periodical volumes; 125,000 reports. **Subscriptions:** 450 journals and other serials; 4 newspapers. **Services:** Interlibrary loan; library not open to the public but phone or written inquiries accepted. **Automated Operations:** Computerized public access catalog. **Computerized Information Services:** DIALOG Information Services, STN International, ESA/IRS, ORBIT Search Service, AUSINET, OZLINE; ILANET (electronic mail service). Contact Person: Roger Cooper, Mgr. **Remarks:** FAX: 3 6465584. Electronic mail address(es): MLN 300450 (ILANET).

★108★
Aerophilatelic Federation of the Americas - Earl H. Wellman, Sr., Memorial Library of the AFA (Rec)
Tower Bldg.
100 E. Chicago St., Lower Lobby, Suite D
Box 1239 Phone: (708)468-0840
Elgin, IL 60120 Walter Rose, Assoc.Libn.
Founded: 1943. **Staff:** 3. **Subjects:** Aero-philatelic history, astro-philatelic history, philatelic history of the Americas, aviation records, aviation philatelic publications. **Special Collections:** Schedules of airlines, 1929 to present. **Holdings:** 3000 books; 200 bound periodical volumes; contemporary material issued on long-gone air services; manuscripts; clippings; data on early pilots. **Subscriptions:** 50 journals and other serials. **Services:** Copying; library open to researchers by request. **Publications:** Jack Knight Air Log, quarterly - by subscription. **Special Catalogs:** Air Transport Label Catalog of the World (5 volumes); rocket mail catalog; American air mail catalog.

Aerospace Audiovisual Service
See: **U.S. Air Force - Aerospace Audiovisual Service** (16786)

★109★
Aerospace Corporation - Charles C. Lauritsen Library (Sci-Engr)
Box 80966, Sta. M1-199 Phone: (213)336-6738
Los Angeles, CA 90080-0966 Susan B. Crowe, Mgr., Lib.Serv.
Founded: 1960. **Staff:** Prof 15; Other 26. **Subjects:** Aerospace management and technology, systems engineering, satellite systems, weapon systems, re-entry vehicles, space physics, computer science. **Special Collections:** Aerospace Corporation Authors Collection. **Holdings:** 103,000 books; 33,000 bound periodical volumes; 210,000 technical reports; 636 pamphlets; 25,000 microforms; 500 maps and charts; 12,000 specifications and standards; 150 AV programs. **Subscriptions:** 1200 journals and other serials; 10 newspapers. **Services:** Interlibrary loan; library open by appointment only. **Automated Operations:** Computerized public access catalog, circulation, and file maintenance. **Computerized Information Services:** DIALOG Information Services, BRS Information Technologies, NASA/RECON, DTIC, CompuServe Information Service, Aerospace Online, NEXIS, ORION, RLIN, STN International, WILSONLINE, OCLC EPIC, UnCover, ORBIT Search Service; OnTyme Electronic Message Network Service (electronic mail service). **Networks/Consortia:** Member of CLASS. **Publications:** Library Services Announcements; Professional Papers. **Remarks:** Library located at 2350 E. El Segundo Blvd., El Segundo, CA 90245-4691. FAX: (213)336-1467. Telex: 66-4460. Electronic mail address(es): AERO (OnTyme Electronic Message Network Service). **Staff:** Virginia Ford, Lit.Res.Anl.; Patricia Green, Supv., Tech.Serv.; Benita Campbell, Ref.Libn.; Shirley McElroy, Lit.Res.Anl.; Karen Olds, Lit.Res.Anl.; Ruby Oshiro, Supv., User Serv.; Theodore Podgorski, Rec.Mgmt.Asst.; Michael Toman, Ref.Libn.; Joan Tseng, Ref.Libn.; Edward Galvin, Supv., Archv./Rec.Mgt.; Kay Wade, Supv., Rpt.Distr.; Nancy Olmstead, Subject Anl.

★110★
Aerospace Industries Association of America - Library (Sci-Engr)
1250 Eye St., N.W. Phone: (202)371-8565
Washington, DC 20005 Mrs. Billie Ann Perry, Libn.
Founded: 1962. **Staff:** Prof 1. **Subjects:** Aeronautics, astronautics, aircraft industries, spacecraft, business economics, procurement, exports and imports. **Holdings:** 2300 books; directories; government documents; newspapers. **Subscriptions:** 150 journals and other serials; 5 newspapers. **Services:** Interlibrary loan; library open to the public by appointment. **Remarks:** FAX: (202)371-8470. Telex: 710-822-0134-A1A BC T/L U.

Aerospace Medical Association Archives
See: **Wright State University - School of Medicine - Fordham Health Sciences Library** (20645)

Aerospace Structures Information & Analysis Center
See: **U.S. Air Force - Air Force Materiel Command - Wright Aeronautical Laboratories** (16805)

★111★
Aerotherm Corporation - Technical Library (Energy, Sci-Engr)
580 Clyde Ave.
P.O. Box 7040 Phone: (415)961-6100
Mountain View, CA 94039 Karen Milos, Lib.Serv.Mgr.
Founded: 1972. **Staff:** 2. **Subjects:** Aerospace, materials, science. **Holdings:** 1500 books; 50 bound periodical volumes; 20,000 technical reports; 1500 internal reports. **Subscriptions:** 100 journals and other serials; 5 newspapers. **Services:** Interlibrary loan; copying. **Automated Operations:** Computerized cataloging, acquisitions, serials, and circulation. **Computerized Information Services:** DIALOG Information Services, NASA/RECON, DTIC, Dun & Bradstreet Business Credit Services. Performs searches on fee basis. **Networks/Consortia:** Member of CLASS. **Remarks:** FAX: (415)964-8349. **Formerly:** Acurex Corporation - Aerotherm Library.

★112★
Aesthetic Realism Foundation - Library (Hum)
141 Greene St. Phone: (212)777-4490
New York, NY 10012 Richita Anderson, Libn.
Founded: 1973. **Staff:** Prof 1. **Subjects:** Literature, drama, poetry, the physical and social sciences, art and aesthetics. **Special Collections:** Published poems and philosophic essays, published and unpublished lectures by Eli Siegel. **Holdings:** 4800 volumes. **Services:** Library open by appointment to persons seriously studying the Aesthetic Realism of Eli Siegel. **Special Indexes:** Index to lectures by Eli Siegel (card); Index to The Right of Aesthetic Realism to Be Known. **Remarks:** FAX: (212)777-4426. The Aesthetic Realism Foundation is a not-for-profit educational foundation. Its teaching is based on the principle: "The world, art, and self explain each other: each is the aesthetic oneness of opposites," as stated by Eli Siegel (1902-1978), American poet, critic, and founder of Aesthetic Realism. The Foundation publishes The Right of Aesthetic Realism to Be Known, a weekly international periodical edited by Ellen Reiss, Class Chm. of Aesthetic Realism.

★113★
Aestheticians International Association - Library (Sci-Engr)
4447 Mc Kinney Ave. Phone: (214)526-0752
Dallas, TX 75205 Ron Renee, Pres.
Founded: 1978. **Staff:** 2. **Subjects:** Skin care, makeup, body therapy, spa treatments, permanent cosmetics, paramedical cosmetics. **Holdings:** 250 volumes; 50 AV programs. **Services:** Library not open to the public. **Remarks:** FAX: (214)526-2925.

★114★
Aetna Life & Casualty - Corporate Information Center (Bus-Fin)
151 Farmington Ave. - S112 Phone: (203)727-4311
Hartford, CT 06156 Beth Dominianni, Mgr.
Founded: 1931. **Staff:** Prof 11; Other 7. **Subjects:** Business, insurance, management, communications, health, information technology. **Holdings:** 10,000 books. **Subscriptions:** 550 journals and other serials. **Services:** Interlibrary loan; copying; current awareness; center open to public for reference use on request. **Automated Operations:** Computerized cataloging, acquisitions, and circulation. **Computerized Information Services:** DIALOG Information Services, NEXIS, BRS Information Technologies, Dow Jones News/Retrieval, OCLC, TEXTLINE, TRAINET, Dun & Bradstreet Credit Services. **Networks/Consortia:** Member of Capital Region Library Council (CRLC), NELINET, Inc. **Publications:** On-line Info; Preview. **Remarks:** FAX: (203)727-4429. Aetna Life & Casualty - Financial Information Center was previously listed as a separate entry. **Staff:** Celeste Dougherty, Tech.Serv.Hd.; Adreana Scussel, Info.Serv.Cons.; Marianne Cirrito, Site Hd.Cons.; Linda Green, Site Hd.Cons.; Jane Zande; Laurice Klemarczyk, Info.Serv.Cons.; Marcia Thomas, Info.Serv.Cons.; Christine Floramo, Info.Serv.Cons.; Paul Lasewicz, Archv.; Dan Weinstein, Info.Cons.; Karen Rich, Info.Cons.

★115★
Aetna Life & Casualty - Corporate Information Center (Bus-Fin)
1000 Middle St., MC11 Phone: (203)636-6063
Middletown, CT 06457 Marianne Cirrito, Info.Serv. Liaison/Cons.
Founded: 1984. **Staff:** Prof 2; Other 2. **Subjects:** Employee benefits, managed health care, group insurance, pensions and financial services, management, data processing. **Holdings:** 1500 books; self-paced educational programs. **Subscriptions:** 180 journals and other serials. **Services:** Interlibrary loan; copying; SDI; center open to the public by appointment for reference use only. **Automated Operations:** Computerized cataloging, acquisitions, and circulation. **Computerized Information Services:** DIALOG Information Services, NEXIS, Dow Jones News/Retrieval, VU/TEXT Information Services, NewsNet, Inc., DataTimes. **Remarks:** FAX: (203)636-2044. **Staff:** Christine Floramo, Pat Mote.

★116★
Aetna Life & Casualty - Engineering Library (Sci-Engr)
151 Farmington Ave. Phone: (203)683-3648
Hartford, CT 06156 Nadine Clegern, Tech.Libn.
Staff: Prof 2; Other .5. **Subjects:** Engineering - safety, chemical, construction, electrical, transportation; products liability; industrial hygiene. **Holdings:** 3000 volumes; 150 National Institute for Occupational Saftey and Health documents; 180 VF drawers. **Subscriptions:** 125 journals and other serials. **Services:** Interlibrary loan; copying; library open to the public by appointment. **Computerized Information Services:** DIALOG Information Services, MEDLARS, Occupational Health Services, Inc. (OHS), Chemical Information Systems, Inc. (CIS), WESTLAW, LEXIS, NEXIS. **Remarks:** FAX: (203)683-3746.

Aetna Life & Casualty - Financial Information Center
See: **Aetna Life & Casualty - Corporate Information Center** (114)

★117★
Aetna Life & Casualty - Law Library (Law)
151 Farmington Ave. No. RC4A Phone: (203)273-8183
Hartford, CT 06156-3124 Patricia Sechrist, Law Libn.
Staff: Prof 3. **Subjects:** Law. **Holdings:** 25,000 books. **Subscriptions:** 1200 journals and other serials; 11 newspapers. **Services:** Interlibrary loan; library not open to the public. **Computerized Information Services:** WESTLAW, LEXIS. **Staff:** Frances Bertelli, Tech.Serv.Libn.; Janet H. Axman.

★118★
Aetna Life & Casualty - MP&P Medical Library MCA3 - Library (Med)
151 Farmington Ave. Phone: (203)636-1087
Hartford, CT 06156 Deborah Beauvais
Founded: 1988. **Staff:** Prof 1; Other 2. **Subjects:** Medical reference. **Holdings:** 150 books. **Subscriptions:** 71 journals and other serials. **Services:** Interlibrary loan; library not open to the public. **Computerized Information Services:** DIALOG Information Services, MEDLARS. **Remarks:** FAX: (203)636-2180.

Affaires des Anciens Combattants Canada
See: **Canada - Veterans Affairs Canada** (2882)

Affaires Exterieures et Commerce International Canada
See: **Canada - External Affairs and International Trade Canada** (2724)

AFL-CIO
See: **American Federation of Labor and Congress of Industrial Organizations - Library** (578)

AFL-CIO - AFSCME
See: **American Federation of State, County and Municipal Employees** (581)

AFL-CIO - Amalgamated Clothing & Textile Workers Union
See: **Amalgamated Clothing & Textile Workers Union, AFL-CIO** (439)

Africa - Institut Africain pour le Developpement Economique et Social
See: **Institut Africain pour le Developpement Economique et Social** (7862)

Africa Bureau Information Center
See: **U.S. Agency for International Development - Research and Reference Services - Africa Bureau Information Center** (16784)

★119★
Africa Institute of South Africa - Library (Area-Ethnic, Soc Sci)
P.O. Box 630 Phone: 12 286970
Pretoria 0001, Republic of South Africa Elizabeth Wessels, Libn.
Founded: 1960. **Staff:** 2. **Subjects:** Africa - political stability, international relations, intra-regional cooperation, socioeconomic change, education in multicultural societies. **Special Collections:** Greenfield Collection. **Holdings:** 55,000 volumes. **Subscriptions:** 530 journals and other serials; 20 newspapers. **Services:** Library open to the public. **Computerized Information Services:** Internal database. **Publications:** List of new titles, monthly - by subscription. **Remarks:** FAX: 12 3238153. Maintained by South Africa - Department of National Education. **Staff:** Amanda Wortmann.

★120★
Africa News Service, Inc. - Library (Area-Ethnic)
P.O. Box 3851 Phone: (919)286-0747
Durham, NC 27702 Betsy Hankin
Subjects: African news - politics, economics, foreign affairs, culture, media, women, sports. **Holdings:** 2000 books; 136 VF drawers of news clippings, documents, radio transcriptions, and other materials. **Subscriptions:** 300 journals and other serials. **Computerized Information Services:** Internal database. **Remarks:** Telex: 3772229.

★121★
African American Historical and Cultural Society - Library of San Francisco (Hist)
Fort Mason Center Bldg C
No 165 Phone: (415)928-8546
San Francisco, CA 94123 Juliana Haile
Staff: Prof 3. **Subjects:** African Americans - history, biography, autobiography, fiction. **Holdings:** Figures not available.

★122★
African-American Institute - Africa Policy Information Center (Area-Ethnic)
833 United Nations Plaza Phone: (212)949-5666
New York, NY 10017 Russell Geekie, Asst.Ed.
Founded: 1974. **Staff:** Prof 1. **Subjects:** Africa - commodities, oil, U.S. foreign policy, United Nations, development. **Special Collections:** News clippings from American, European, and African publications, 1974 to present. **Holdings:** Magazines; conference reports; Africa Report (a complete set of the institute's publication). **Subscriptions:** 200 journals and other serials; 50 newspapers. **Services:** Copying; center open to the public. **Remarks:** FAX: (212)682-6421. Telex: 666 565.

★123★
African American Museum - Library (Area-Ethnic)
1765 Crawford Rd. Phone: (216)791-1700
Cleveland, OH 44106 Dr. Joan Baker, Dir./Cur.
Founded: 1953. **Staff:** Prof 3. **Subjects:** African and African-American history and culture. **Special Collections:** African-American music; blacks in aviation; black theology; black church in Cleveland. **Holdings:** 200 books; 200 bound periodical volumes; 10,000 negatives; 100 paintings; 100,000 news clippings; 500 slides; 100 audiotapes; 50 pieces of art; 15 proclamations; 3 Reconstruction maps. **Services:** Library open to the public with restrictions. **Staff:** Julia Haynes, Libn.

★124★
African Heritage Research Library (Area-Ethnic, Soc Sci)
P.O. Box 121
Ila-Orangun, Osur State, Nigeria Bayo Adebowale, Dir./Founder
Founded: 1988. **Staff:** 4. **Subjects:** Africa - history, culture, science, agriculture, law, technology, social sciences, religion, literature, sports, education; Africans in the Diaspora. **Special Collections:** African Literature (2505 volumes); Marcus Garvey Collection (525 volumes and manuscripts); Agriculture Collection (5678 volumes); Children's Collection (3027 volumes); African Oral History Collection (207 cassettes); textbooks (1270 volumes). **Holdings:** 17,375 books; 90 bound periodical volumes; 9091 unbound periodicals; 561 documents; 71 microforms; 76 manuscripts. **Subscriptions:** 491 journals and other serials; 26 newspapers. **Services:** Interlibrary loan; copying; SDI; library open to the public. **Publications:** African Heritage Magazine; Library Bulletin, quarterly. **Special Indexes:** Special Subjects Index. **Remarks:** Is said to be the first rural-based African studies library on the continent of Africa, covering all disciplines as well as Africans located throughout the world. It is a depository, and will serve as a clearinghouse, for all publications on Africa and Africans worldwide. **Staff:** Mrs. YeYe Akilimali F. Olade, Chf.Libn.

★125★
African Institute for Economic Development and Planning - Library (Soc Sci)
Rue du 18 Juin
Boite Postale 3186
Dakar, Senegal Phone: 221020
Subjects: Africa - economic development and planning, industrialization, energy and development, human resources development, agriculture and rural development. **Holdings:** 20,000 books, periodicals, and documents. **Computerized Information Services:** Internal database. **Remarks:** Telex: 579 SG.

★126★
African Literature Association - Library (Area-Ethnic)
Africana Studies and Research Center
Cornell University
310 Triphammer Rd. Phone: (607)255-2000
Ithaca, NY 14853 Prof. Anne Adams
Staff: Prof 1. **Subjects:** African literature. **Holdings:** 5 VF drawers of business and editorial archives. **Publications:** Directory, annual; Annual Selected Conference Papers. **Remarks:** Alternate telephone number(s): 255-4625; 255-5229. Archival materials 5 years and older are on deposit in Northwestern University - Melville J. Herskovits Library of African Studies.

★127★
African Regional Centre for Technology - Library (Sci-Engr)
Boite Postale 2435 Phone: 257712
Dakar, Senegal Michael William Nageri
Founded: 1977. **Staff:** Prof 4. **Subjects:** Technology in Africa - development, planning, research, human resources, indigenous capabilities, rural development, socioeconomic growth. **Holdings:** 7000 volumes. **Subscriptions:** 300 journals and other serials; 10 newspapers. **Services:** Interlibrary loan; copying; SDI; library open to the public. **Computerized Information Services:** Internal databases. **Publications:** African Technodevelopment Bulletin; Infonet Bulletin; Alert Africa Newsletter. **Remarks:** FAX: 257713. Telex: 61282 SG. **Staff:** Christiana Cole; Renu Rattan; Assane Gueue.

★128★
African Regional Organization for Standardization - Library (Sci-Engr)
P.O. Box 57363 Phone: 2 24561
Nairobi, Kenya Edward Chonelwa
Staff: 3. **Subjects:** Industrial and socioeconomic development through scientific and technological applications. **Holdings:** 50,000 volumes of standards and documentation. **Computerized Information Services:** Internal database. **Remarks:** Serves as a clearinghouse for standards and technical regulations from the African Region; maintains training, promotional activities, and advisory services for, and coordinates the activities of, the ARSO Network of Documentation and Information Systems on standards and technical regulations (ARSO-DISNET). Alternate telephone number(s): 330882. FAX: 2 218792. Telex: 22097 ARSO. **Also Known As:** Organisation Regionale Africaine de Normalisation (ORAN).

★129★
African Training and Research Centre in Administration for Development - Division of Documentation and Information (Soc Sci)
B.P. 310 Phone: 9 36430
Tangier, Morocco M.N. Lelo, Chf.
Founded: 1964. **Staff:** 6. **Subjects:** Africa - local government, rural and urban development, organizational development, human resources, personnel management, training, and financial, project, public enterprises management, administrative reform, women in development. **Special Collections:** African government publications. **Holdings:** 20,000 volumes. **Subscriptions:** 350 journals and other serials. **Services:** Microform copying; library open to African libraries and government agencies. **Computerized Information Services:** Produces African Network of Administrative Information; internal databases. **Publications:** Subject bibliographies. **Remarks:** FAX: 9 941415. Telex: 33664 M. **Also Known As:** Centre Africain de Formation et de Recherche Administratives pour le Developpement.

★130★
Africare - Library (Soc Sci)
440 R St., N.W.
Washington, DC 20001 Phone: (202)462-3614
Subjects: Rural Africa - health, environmental protection, water and agricultural resources, development. **Holdings:** 3300 volumes. **Remarks:** FAX: (202)387-1034.

★131★
Afrika Studiecentrum - Bibliotheek (Hum, Soc Sci)
Wassenaarseweg 52
POB 9555 Phone: 71 273354
NL-2300 RB Leiden, Netherlands J. van der Meulen
Founded: 1946. **Staff:** 8. **Subjects:** Africa political development, cultural anthropology, literature, socio-economic development, history, and law. **Special Collections:** Development plans of African countries (5000 microfiche). **Holdings:** 30,000 books; 35,000 bound periodical volumes; 2000 reports; 23,000 microfiche; 40 reels of microfilm. **Subscriptions:** 6000 journals and other serials. **Services:** Interlibrary loan; copying; library open to the public. **Automated Operations:** Computerized cataloging and indexing. **Publications:** List of aqcuisitions; Documentatieblod: the abstracts journal of the African Studies Centre Leider. **Remarks:** FAX: 71 273344.

Afro-Asian Institute for Cooperative and Labour Studies
See: **International Institute for Development, Cooperation and Labour Studies - Library** (8126)

AFSCME
See: **American Federation of State, County and Municipal Employees** (581)

★132★
AG Communication Systems - Library (Comp Sci)
2500 W. Utopia Rd.
P.O. Box 52179 Phone: (602)582-7268
Phoenix, AZ 85072-2179 Suzanne Lennon, Libn.
Founded: 1981. **Staff:** Prof 1; Other 1. **Subjects:** Computer science, software development, telephony, electronic engineering, engineering management. **Holdings:** 2000 books; 275 bound periodical volumes; 1200 reports; 11,000 microfiche; 102 VF drawers of locally produced research reports. **Subscriptions:** 51 journals and other serials. **Services:** Interlibrary loan; library not open to the public. **Computerized Information Services:** DIALOG Information Services; SprintMail (electronic mail service). **Publications:** List of new acquisitions. **Remarks:** FAX: (602)582-7111. Electronic mail address(es): S.Lennon (SprintMail).

Agape Library
See: **Star Throwers** (15668)

★133★
JFT Agapito & Associates, Inc. - Library (Sci-Engr)
715 Horizon Dr., Suite 340 Phone: (303)242-4220
Grand Junction, CO 81506 Kimberly Greathouse, Libn.
Subjects: Geology, rock mechanics, mining engineering, nuclear waste. **Holdings:** 200 books; 500 bound periodical volumes; 1000 reports. **Services:** Library open to the public. **Remarks:** FAX: (303)245-9234.

★134★
Agbabian Associates - Library (Sci-Engr)
1111 S. Arroyo Pkwy., No. 405 Phone: (818)441-1060
Pasadena, CA 91105 Charisse Smith, Info.Dir.
Staff: Prof 1. **Subjects:** Structural analysis, applied mathematics, physics, engineering, geology, computer sciences. **Holdings:** 1080 books; 30 bound periodical volumes; 25,000 technical documents; 2000 microfiche. **Subscriptions:** 55 journals and other serials. **Services:** Interlibrary loan; library not open to the public. **Remarks:** FAX: (818)441-0757.

Age of Steam Museum
See: **Southwest Railroad Historical Society** (15533)

★135★
Age Wave, Inc. - Library (Med)
1900 Powell St., Suite 800 Phone: (510)652-9099
Emeryville, CA 94608 Judith Peck, Res.Dir.
Founded: 1984. **Staff:** 1. **Subjects:** Aging, health, stress management, communications, marketing to older adults. **Holdings:** 1300 books; 20 VF drawers; periodicals; pamphlets. **Subscriptions:** 60 journals and other serials. **Computerized Information Services:** DIALOG Information Services, BRS Information Technologies; Revelation (internal database). **Remarks:** FAX: (415)652-8245.

Rucker Agee Cartographical Collection
See: **Birmingham Public and Jefferson County Free Library - Linn-Henley Library for Southern Historical Research** (1858)

Agence Canadienne de Developpement International
See: **Canada - Canadian International Development Agency** (2670)

Agency for International Development
See: **U.S. Agency for International Development** (16783)

Agoos Medical Library
See: **Beth Israel Hospital** (1769)

★136★
Agracetus - Library (Biol Sci)
8520 University Green Phone: (608)836-7300
Middleton, WI 53562 Carolyn De Luna, Info.Spec.
Founded: 1982. **Staff:** Prof 1.5. **Subjects:** Biotechnology, agronomy, biobusiness. **Holdings:** 700 books; 110 bound periodical volumes; patents; government documents. **Subscriptions:** 119 journals and other serials. **Services:** Interlibrary loan; copying; SDI; library open to the public with director's permission. **Automated Operations:** Computerized cataloging. **Computerized Information Services:** DIALOG Information Services. **Networks/Consortia:** Member of South Central Library System. **Remarks:** FAX: (608)836-9710. **Staff:** Elizabeth Bauer.

Agri-Source Software Library
See: **Small Business Computer Systems, Inc.** (15227)

Agricultural Cooperative Development International
See: **National Council of Farmer Cooperatives - Library** (11138)

Agricultural Research Institute of Senegal - Dakar-Thiaroye Center for Oceanographic Research
See: **Dakar-Thiaroye Center for Oceanographic Research** (4526)

Agriculture Canada
See: **Canada - Agriculture Canada** (2631)

★137★
Agudas Achim Congregation - Stein Memorial Library (Rel-Phil)
2767 E. Broad St. Phone: (614)237-2747
Columbus, OH 43209 Virginia Gold, Libn.
Founded: 1962. **Staff:** 1. **Subjects:** Judaica. **Holdings:** 3238 volumes. **Services:** Library not open to the public.

★138★
Agudath Achim Synagogue - Abe and Esther Tenenbaum Library (Rel-Phil)
9 Lee Blvd. Phone: (912)352-4737
Savannah, GA 31405 Arlene Coleman, Libn.
Founded: 1971. **Staff:** Prof 1; Other 1. **Subjects:** Jewish literature, authors, biographies, and children's books. **Holdings:** 2000 books. **Services:** Library open to the public for research purposes.

★139★
Agudath Israel Congregation - Malca Pass Library (Rel-Phil)
1400 Coldrey Ave. Phone: (613)722-3501
Ottawa, ON, Canada K1Z 7P9 Frieda Lauterman, Libn.
Founded: 1960. **Staff:** Prof 1. **Subjects:** Judaism - religion, art, philosophy, biography; holocaust literature; children's Judaica. **Special Collections:** Judaic and general art; Canadian Judaica. **Holdings:** 6300 books; 85 video cassettes; 30 audio cassettes. **Subscriptions:** 3 journals and other serials. **Services:** Library open to the public with restrictions.

★140★
AHEC Rural Health Office - Library (Med)
2501 E. Elm St. Phone: (602)606-7946
Tucson, AZ 85716 Patricia A. Auflick, LRS Coord.
Founded: 1976. **Staff:** Prof 1. **Subjects:** Rural health, health policy, health statistics, consumer health information. **Holdings:** 600 books. **Subscriptions:** 20 journals and other serials. **Services:** Interlibrary loan; copying; SDI; library open to the public. **Computerized Information Services:** MEDLARS; BITNET, InterNet (electronic mail services). **Publications:** Arizona Rural Health Needs Assessment; Arizona Urban Health Needs Assessment. **Remarks:** FAX: (602)326-6429. Electronic mail address(es): PAUFLICK@ARIZRVAX (BITNET); PAUFLICK@RVAX.CCIT.ARIZONA.EDU (InterNet).

★141★
Ahmadiyya Movement in Islam - Muslim Library (Rel-Phil)
2141 Leroy Place, N.W. Phone: (202)232-3737
Washington, DC 20008 Zafar A. Sarwar, Libn.
Staff: Prof 2; Other 1. **Subjects:** Islamic theology, history of different countries and religions, politics. **Special Collections:** Work of Hazrat Ahmad the Promised Messiah on Islam and other religions. **Holdings:** 2040 books; 500 bound periodical volumes; 5000 other cataloged items; 10 drawers of newspapers and periodicals. **Subscriptions:** 16 journals and other serials; 5 newspapers. **Services:** Copying; library open to the public for reference use only. **Publications:** Muslim Sunrise, quarterly; Ahmadiyya Gazette, monthly; Annoor, monthly.

Ahmadu Bello University - Institute for Agricultural Research
See: **Institute for Agricultural Research** (7898)

★142★
Ahmedabad Textile Industry's Research Association - National Information Centre for Textile and Allied Subjects - ATIRA Library (Sci-Engr, Bus-Fin)
3rd Fl. Phone: 442671
Ahmedabad 380 015, Gujarat, India P.C. Shah, Asst.Dir./Hd., Lib.Info.Serv.
Founded: 1945. **Staff:** 12. **Subjects:** Textile industry - technology, management, new products and processes; increasing industry productivity, quality, economy. **Holdings:** 35,000 volumes. **Subscriptions:** 350 journals and other serials; 10 newspapers. **Services:** Interlibrary loan; copying; SDI; translation service; document procurement; referral; library open to staff of member companies. **Computerized Information Services:** ISTAS, ALIRS, Periodical Management Systems, TEXINCON (internal databases). **Publications:** TEXINCON, quarterly; Recent Additions. **Remarks:** Telex: 121-6571 ATRA IN. **Also Known As:** NICTAS. **Staff:** Mrs. J.J. Parikh; Mrs. Hina Shah; Miss Nistha Budhinaja.

★143★
Aid Association for Lutherans - Corporate Library (Bus-Fin)
4321 N. Ballard Rd. Phone: (414)734-5721
Appleton, WI 54919 Kathleen Brandel, Mgr., Lib./Archv.Serv.
Founded: 1968. **Staff:** Prof 3; Other 2. **Subjects:** Life and health insurance, actuarial science, business management, fraternal benefit societies, corporate history. **Special Collections:** Ziegler Collection (history of fraternal benefit societies; 250 volumes); corporate oral histories (60). **Holdings:** 4,000 books; 25 VF drawers of subject files; 450 cubic feet of archival materials and artifacts. **Subscriptions:** 400 journals and other serials; 6 newspapers. **Services:** Interlibrary loan; copying; SDI; library open to the public for reference use only by permission. **Automated Operations:** Computerized public access catalog and serials. **Computerized Information Services:** DIALOG Information Services, NewsNet, Inc., LEXIS, NEXIS, DataTimes. **Networks/Consortia:** Member of Fox Valley Library Council. **Publications:** Acquisition list, bimonthly - for internal distribution only; periodical holdings list, annual. **Remarks:** FAX: (414)730-4757. **Staff:** Yvonne Rohm, Libn.; Janice Krahn, Archv.

★144★
AIDS Library of Philadelphia (Med)
32 N. 3rd St. Phone: (215)922-5120
Philadelphia, PA 19106 Jean Hofacket
Founded: 1987. **Staff:** Prof 2; Other 5. **Subjects:** AIDS. **Holdings:** 2200 books; 60,000 clippings. **Subscriptions:** 100 periodicals. **Services:** Copying; library open to the public. **Computerized Information Services:** CD-ROM (AIDS Compact Disc Library). **Remarks:** FAX: (215)922-6762.

★145★
Aikins, MacAulay & Thorvaldson - Library (Law)
360 Main St., 30th Fl. Phone: (204)957-0050
Winnipeg, MB, Canada R3C 4G1 Virginia Scott, Libn.
Subjects: Law. **Holdings:** Figures not available. **Services:** Library not open to the public. **Computerized Information Services:** QL Systems, CAN/LAW, WESTLAW, CBANET. **Remarks:** FAX: (204)957-0840. Telex: 07-587612.

★146★
AIL Systems Inc. - Research Library (Sci-Engr)
M.S. D1, Commack Rd. Phone: (516)595-5000
Deer Park, NY 11729 Roberta Elliott, Libn.
Founded: 1945. **Staff:** Prof 1; Other 3. **Subjects:** Electronics, navigation, space science, antennas, aircraft landing systems. **Holdings:** 28,000 books; 8000 bound periodical volumes. **Subscriptions:** 200 journals and other serials. **Services:** Interlibrary loan; copying; library not open to the public. **Computerized Information Services:** DIALOG Information Services, DTIC. **Networks/Consortia:** Member of Long Island Library Resources Council. **Publications:** Library Bulletin, semimonthly. **Remarks:** Subsidiary of Eaton Corporation. **Formerly:** Located in Melville, NY.

Fred C. Ainsworth Endowment Library
See: **U.S. Army Hospitals - Walter Reed Army Medical Center - WRAMC Medical Library** (17054)

★147★
Air Canada - Library
Place Air Canada
Montreal, PQ, Canada H2Z 1X5
Defunct.

Air Force
See: **U.S. Air Force**

★148★
Air Force Association - Research Library (Mil)
1501 Lee Hwy. Phone: (703)247-5800
Arlington, VA 22209-1198 Pearlie M. Draughn, Res.Libn.
Founded: 1956. **Staff:** Prof 1. **Subjects:** Military aviation, history, budget. **Holdings:** 2000 books. **Services:** Library open to the public for reference use only on request.

★149★
Air Line Pilots Association - Engineering and Air Safety Resource Center (Trans)
535 Herndon Pkwy. Phone: (703)689-4204
Herndon, VA 22070 John O'Brien, Dir.
Founded: 1981. **Staff:** Prof 2; Other 1. **Subjects:** Aviation regulations, air safety, aircraft performance, human factors in aviation. **Holdings:** 650 books; 30 bound periodical volumes; 16,000 reports; Jeppesen worldwide flight charts; federal aviation regulations. **Subscriptions:** 10 journals and other serials; 5 newspapers. **Services:** Interlibrary loan; center open to the public at director's discretion. **Automated Operations:** Computerized cataloging and serials. **Computerized Information Services:** LIB1 (internal database). **Remarks:** FAX: (703)689-4370. **Staff:** Pablo Santamaria, Tech.Libn.

★150★
Air Products and Chemicals, Inc. - Corporate Business Information Center (Bus-Fin)
7201 Hamilton Blvd. Phone: (215)481-7442
Allentown, PA 18195 Michelle A. Burylo, Supv.
Founded: 1975. **Staff:** Prof 2; Other 1. **Subjects:** Business, chemical industry, business statistics. **Holdings:** 2800 books; 285 linear feet of vertical files; 700 reels of microfilm. **Subscriptions:** 300 journals and other serials; 7 newspapers. **Services:** Interlibrary loan; center not open to the public. **Automated Operations:** Computerized cataloging and circulation. **Computerized Information Services:** DIALOG Information Services, ORBIT Search Service, BRS Information Technologies, Dow Jones News/Retrieval, Mead Data Central, VU/TEXT Information Services, WILSONLINE, NewsNet, Inc., CDA Investment Technologies, Inc., Reuters Information Services, Inc., U.S. National Technical Information Service, Questel, Data-Star, Nihon Keizai Shimbun, Inc. (NIKKEI). **Networks/Consortia:** Member of PALINET. **Publications:** Infolink News, bimonthly - for internal distribution only. **Remarks:** FAX: (215)481-3575. **Staff:** Leslie A. Mortimer, Info.Spec.

★151★
Air Products and Chemicals, Inc. - Information Services (Sci-Engr)
7201 Hamilton Blvd. Phone: (215)481-7292
Allentown, PA 18195-1501 Valerie K. Tucci, Mgr., Info.Serv./Tech.Comm.
Founded: 1953. **Staff:** Prof 13; Other 13. **Subjects:** Chemistry, gas technology, catalysis, cryogenics, polymers and polymerization, chemical engineering. **Holdings:** 34,000 books. **Subscriptions:** 465 journals and other serials. **Services:** Interlibrary loan (limited). **Automated Operations:** Computerized public access catalog, cataloging, acquisitions, circulation, and journal routing. **Computerized Information Services:** DIALOG Information Services, PFDS Online, BRS Information Technologies, NLM, VU/TEXT Information Services, OCLC, STN International, NewsNet, Inc., Chemical Information Systems, Inc. (CIS), WILSONLINE, DTIC/DROLS, NASA/RECON, Dow Jones News/Retrieval, NEXIS, LEXIS, Data-Star, Integrated Technical Information System (ITIS), Questel, TRAINET, Human Resource Information Network (HRIN), PIERS (Port Import/Export Reporting Service), TRADSTAT; Research Report Retrieval System (internal database); CD-ROMs (Business Periodicals Ondisc, Sigma-Aldrich Material Safety Data Sheets, PatentImages). **Networks/Consortia:** Member of PALINET. **Publications:** Infolink News - for internal distribution only. **Remarks:** FAX: (215)481-6517. Telex: 847416. **Staff:** R.B. Smith, Supv., Tech.Info. & Database Serv.; L. Dragotta, Supv., IS Oper. & Plan.; D. Wilson, Supv., Quality & Tech.Comm.; K. Musselman, Info.Spec.; D. Einhorn, Ref.Libn.

Air Resources Information Clearinghouse
See: **Center for Environmental Information, Inc.** (3238)

Air Traffic Safety Information Center
See: **U.S. Federal Aviation Administration - Technical Center Library (ACM-651)** (17487)

★152★
Air Transport Association of America - Library (Trans)
1709 New York Ave., N.W. Phone: (202)626-4184
Washington, DC 20006 Mrs. Marion Mistrik, Libn.
Founded: 1936. **Staff:** Prof 1; Other 1. **Subjects:** Scheduled air carrier financial and traffic statistics, air transportation, public utility regulation, law, aviation law, aeronautics. **Special Collections:** Official Airline Guide, 1929 to present; legislative histories of Air Commerce Act, 1926, and Civil Aeronautics Act, 1938. **Holdings:** 12,000 volumes; 11 VF drawers of pamphlets and annual reports; 350 reels of microfilm; 3 drawers of microfiche; 1800 report files. **Subscriptions:** 150 journals and other serials; 10 newspapers. **Services:** Interlibrary loan; copying; library open to the public by appointment. **Automated Operations:** Computerized cataloging. **Computerized Information Services:** DIALOG Information Services, WESTLAW. **Remarks:** Alternate telephone number(s): 626-4185. FAX: (202)626-4181.

Air University Library
See: **U.S. Air Force - Air University Library** (16812)

★153★
Air & Waste Management Association - Library (Env-Cons)
Box 2861 Phone: (412)232-3444
Pittsburgh, PA 15230 H.M. Englund, Ed.
Founded: 1950. **Subjects:** Air pollution, hazardous waste management. **Holdings:** 1000 books. **Services:** Copying; library open to members of the association and students. **Remarks:** FAX: (412)232-3450.

★154★
AIRCHIVE - Historair File (Rec)
1215 Interlacken Phone: (217)546-6646
Springfield, IL 62704 Job C. Conger, IV, Exec.Dir.
Staff: 3. **Subjects:** Aviation history, aircraft, model aircraft history, biography. **Holdings:** 1000 books; 40 bound periodical volumes; 10,000 photographs; file cabinets of clippings; oral history tapes; slides; unbound periodicals. **Services:** Copying; files open to the public. **Automated Operations:** Computerized public access catalog. **Special Indexes:** Magazine Index File; Aircraft Data Index File (ADIF); Aircraft Name File; Point In Time File (all on cards). **Remarks:** AIRCHIVE stands for Aviation's International Repository Combining Historical Indexes Very Effectively.

★155★
Aircraft Technical Publishers - Resource Center (Publ)
101 South Hill Dr. Phone: (415)468-1705
Brisbane, CA 94005 Susan Gorter, Act.Dir., Rsrc.Ctr.
Founded: 1973. **Staff:** Prof 1; Other 18. **Subjects:** Aviation maintenance, avionics, air transportation. **Special Collections:** Manufacturers' maintenance documents; government regulations and specifications; aviation industry publications. **Holdings:** 650 books; 14,000 microfiche; 5400 hardcopy service information documents and manuals. **Subscriptions:** 30 journals and other serials. **Services:** Center not open to the public. **Automated Operations:** Computerized cataloging and acquisitions. **Computerized Information Services:** AVCOM (internal database). **Publications:** Aviation maintenance library service (on microfiche), biweekly - to maintenance facilities, regulatory agencies, and mechanics schools. **Special Indexes:** Service information and government publications indexes (microfiche). **Remarks:** FAX: (415)468-1596.

★156★
Aird & Berlis - Law Library (Law)
181 Bay St.
BCE Pl., N. Tower, Ste. 1800
PO Box 754 Phone: (416)364-1241
Toronto, ON, Canada M5J 2T9 Joan Rataic-Lang, Libn.
Staff: Prof 1; Other 1. **Subjects:** Corporate and tax law, municipal law, real estate, litigation. **Holdings:** 2000 books; 200 bound periodical volumes. **Subscriptions:** 70 journals and other serials. **Services:** Interlibrary loan; library open to other special libraries. **Computerized Information Services:** QL Systems, LEXIS, NEXIS, Info Globe, Infomart Online, WESTLAW, The Financial Post Information Service, DIALOG Information Services, STM Systems Corporation. **Publications:** What's New (current awareness newsletter), monthly. **Special Indexes:** Index to current federal and provincial legislation. **Remarks:** FAX: (416)364-4916.

Airesearch, Los Angeles Division
See: **Allied-Signal Aerospace Company** (399)

Airport Operators Council International
See: **Airports Association Council International** (157)

★157★
Airports Association Council International - Library (Trans)
1220 19th St., N.W., Suite 200 Phone: (202)293-8500
Washington, DC 20036 George P. Howard, Exec.Dir.
Founded: 1948. **Staff:** Prof 16. **Subjects:** Airport security, economics, environment, law, government and international affairs, marketing, public and community relations. **Holdings:** Figures not available. **Subscriptions:** 7 journals and other serials; 5 newspapers. **Services:** Library open to the public. **Publications:** List of publications - available on request. **Remarks:** FAX: (202)331-1362. **Formed by the merger of:** Airport Operators Council International and International Civil Airports Association.

★158★
Airpower Museum - Library (Trans)
Antique Airfield
Rte. 2, Box 172 Phone: (515)938-2773
Ottumwa, IA 52501-9802 Robert L. Taylor, Bd.Chm.
Founded: 1965. **Subjects:** Historical and current aviation. **Special Collections:** Early airframe drawings, 1920-1945 (750). **Holdings:** 750 books; 20,000 periodical volumes; scrapbooks; brochures; lithographs; logbooks. **Services:** Library open to the public with restrictions. **Publications:** Airpower Museum Bulletin. **Special Indexes:** Index to back issues of Antique Airplane Association publications. **Remarks:** Affiliated with the Antique Airplane Association.

Aiso Library
See: **U.S. Dept. of Defense - Language Institute - Aiso Library** (17224)

★159★
Ajax Magnethermic Corporation - Research & Development Library (Bus-Fin)
1745 Overland, N.E. Phone: (216)372-8781
Warren, OH 44482 Rosemary Cleary, Libn.
Founded: 1942. **Staff:** Prof 1. **Subjects:** Induction melting and heating, solid state power supplies, steelmaking, foundries. **Special Collections:** Papers of Dr. Edwin Northrup; U.S. patent collection. **Holdings:** 870 books; 40 bound periodical volumes. **Subscriptions:** 251 journals and other serials. **Services:** Library not open to the public. **Computerized Information Services:** Internal database. **Publications:** Digest of Literature (abstracts of journal articles and patents), weekly; DIRECT-LINE (newsletter), irregular - for internal distribution only. **Remarks:** FAX: (216)372-8644. Telex: 0982482.

★160★
Akademia Rolnicza w Lublinie - Biblioteka Glowna (Agri)
ul. Radziszewskiego 11
PL-20-036 Lublin, Poland Phone: 81 375892
Founded: 1956. **Staff:** Prof 40; Other 1. **Subjects:** Agriculture, veterinary science, horticulture, zootechnics, mechanization of agriculture, food processing technology. **Holdings:** 195,000 books; 117,000 bound periodical volumes; 12,000 archival items; 800 microfiche; 450 cartographic items. **Subscriptions:** 1660 journals and other serials; 85 newspapers. **Services:** Interlibrary loan; copying; SDI; library open to the public. **Publications:** Bibliography of Publications of Workers at the Agricultural University; List of Foreign Acquisitions.

★161★
Akademia Rolnicza w Poznaniu - Biblioteka Glowna Centrum Informacji Naukowej (Agri)
ul. Witosa 45 Phone: 61 417288
PL-60-625 Poznan, Poland Wlodzimierz Golab
Founded: 1953. **Subjects:** Agriculture, forestry, wood technology, horticulture, food technology, drainage. **Holdings:** 450,000 books; 350,000 bound periodical volumes; 30,000 microfiche; 3200 maps. **Subscriptions:** 1600 journals and other serials; 25 newspapers. **Services:** Interlibrary loan; copying; SDI; library open to the public. **Computerized Information Services:** AGRIS. **Publications:** Guidebook for the Main Library and Center of Scientific Information; bibliography of Taxus Baccate in Poland. **Special Catalogs:** Central catalog of natural periodicals of Poznan.

★162★
Akademia Rolnicza w Szczecinie - Biblioteka (Agri)
ul. Janosika 8 Phone: 91 220851
PL-71-424 Szczecin, Poland Tadeusz Cieslak
Founded: 1954. **Subjects:** Agriculture, animal husbandry, agricultural engineering, food storage and preservation, agricultural economics, food economy. **Holdings:** 182,000 books; 43,000 bound periodical volumes; 150 microfiche titles. **Subscriptions:** 1300 journals and other serials. **Services:** Interlibrary loan; library open to the public for reference use only. **Computerized Information Services:** CD-ROMs (Agris, AGRICOLA, Food Science and Technology Abstracts, CAB Abstracts). **Publications:** Bibliography of publications by Akademia Rolnicza staff 1954-1964, 1965-1969, 1970-1974, 1975-1977, 1978-1980, 1981-1983, 1984-1986. **Remarks:** FAX: 91 232417. Telex: 0425494.

Akademio Internacia de la Sciencoj
See: **International Academy of Sciences** (8050)

Mary Lee Jobe Akeley Collection
See: **Mystic River Historical Society - William A. Downes Archives** (10947)

★163★
Akerman, Senterfitt, & Eidson - Law Library (Law)
255 S. Orange Ave., 10th Fl.
P.O. Box 231 Phone: (407)843-7861
Orlando, FL 32802 Mary Smith Forman, Dir., Lib.Serv.
Founded: 1920. **Staff:** Prof 1; Other 1. **Subjects:** Law. **Holdings:** 20,000 books; 6000 ultrafiche; 1500 microfiche. **Subscriptions:** 102 journals and other serials. **Services:** Interlibrary loan; library not open to the public. **Automated Operations:** Computerized cataloging and serials. **Computerized Information Services:** WESTLAW, DIALOG Information Services, VU/TEXT Information Services, DataTimes, WILSONLINE, LEXIS, Dow Jones News/Retrieval, Dun & Bradstreet Business Credit Services, OCLC, LEGI-SLATE, BASELINE, State Net, Information America, CCH (Commerce Clearing House, Inc.). **Networks/Consortia:** Member of Central Florida Library Consortium (CFLC), SOLINET. **Remarks:** FAX: (407)843-6610. Telex: 56 4335.

★164★
Akiba Hebrew Academy - Joseph M. First Library (Educ)
223 N. Highland Ave. Phone: (215)839-3540
Merion, PA 19066 Jane E. Schofer, Libn.
Staff: Prof 2. **Subjects:** History, Hebraica and Judaica. **Holdings:** 12,000 volumes. **Subscriptions:** 71 journals and other serials. **Services:** Interlibrary loan; copying; library open to the public for reference use only. **Automated Operations:** Computerized cataloging and overdue notices. **Computerized Information Services:** DIALOG Information Services, BRS Information Technologies. **Remarks:** FAX: (215)667-1046. **Staff:** Norma Perilstein.

★165★
Akin, Gump, Hauer & Feld - Law Library (Law)
4100 First City Ctr.
1700 Pacific Ave. Phone: (214)969-4628
Dallas, TX 75201 Joan Hass, Hd.Libn.
Founded: 1973. **Staff:** Prof 2; Other 1. **Subjects:** Law - civil procedure, corporate, securities, tax, real estate, labor. **Holdings:** 40,000 volumes. **Subscriptions:** 50 journals and other serials. **Services:** Interlibrary loan; library not open to the public. **Computerized Information Services:** LEXIS, WESTLAW, DIALOG Information Services, Dow Jones News/Retrieval, Information America. **Remarks:** FAX: (214)922-8043. **Formerly:** Akin, Gump, Strauss, Hauer & Feld. **Staff:** Sandi Troyer, Asst.Libn.

★166★
Akin Hall Association - Akin Free Library (Hist)
Quaker Hill Phone: (914)855-5099
Pawling, NY 12564 James Mandracchia, Libn.
Staff: Prof 1. **Subjects:** Quakers, local authors, genealogy. **Special Collections:** Quaker Hill Historical Series. **Holdings:** 10,000 volumes; ledgers, 1769-1825. **Services:** Library open to the public on a limited schedule. **Remarks:** Alternate telephone number(s): (203)354-2822.

Akins Library
See: **(Nova Scotia) Public Archives of Nova Scotia** (12152)

★167★
Akron Art Museum - Library (Art)
70 E. Market St. Phone: (216)376-9185
Akron, OH 44308 Marcianne Herr, Dir., Educ.
Founded: 1922. **Staff:** Prof 1; Other 6. **Subjects:** Art history and criticism, museology. **Special Collections:** Edwin Shaw Archives. **Holdings:** 5000 books; exhibition catalogs; art periodicals; artist monographs; 5000 slides. **Subscriptions:** 50 journals and other serials. **Services:** Library and slide collection open to members and area students only. **Publications:** Annual reports. **Special Catalogs:** Exhibition catalogs.

★168★
Akron Beacon Journal - Editorial Reference Library (Publ)
44 E. Exchange St. Phone: (216)996-3898
Akron, OH 44328 Catherine M. Tierney, Chf.Libn.
Founded: 1939. **Staff:** Prof 2. **Subjects:** Newspaper reference topics. **Special Collections:** Clippings on the Kent State University student shootings, May, 1970-April, 1971 (microfilm); Akron-built dirigibles; rubber industry. **Holdings:** 2000 books; newspapers, 1839 to present, on microfilm; clipping and picture files. **Services:** Library not open to the public. **Computerized Information Services:** VU/TEXT Information Services, DIALOG Information Services, DataTimes. **Special Indexes:** Typed topic index (for marking paper). **Remarks:** FAX: (216)996-3075. Published by Knight-Ridder, Inc. **Staff:** Norma J. Stuhldreher-Hill, Asst.Libn.

★169★
Akron City Health Department - Public Health Library (Med)
177 S. Broadway Phone: (216)375-2180
Akron, OH 44308 John Jenning
Subjects: Public health, medicine, nursing. **Holdings:** 675 books; 80 boxes of reference files; 33 films and filmstrips; pamphlets.

★170★
Akron City Hospital - Medical Library (Med)
55 Arch St., Ste. G-3 Phone: (216)375-3260
Akron, OH 44304 Marilee S. Creelan, Dir., Hosp.Libs.
Founded: 1946. **Staff:** Prof 4; Other 4. **Subjects:** Medicine, nursing, allied health sciences, social sciences, hospital administration. **Holdings:** 8200 books; 20,000 bound periodical volumes; 100 AV programs; 750 Audio-Digest tapes. **Subscriptions:** 370 journals and other serials. **Services:** Interlibrary loan; copying; SDI; library open to the public with director's approval. **Automated Operations:** Computerized cataloging, acquisitions, serials, and circulation. **Computerized Information Services:** BRS Information Technologies; CD-ROMs (MEDLINE, CINAHL, HLTH). Performs searches on fee basis. **Networks/Consortia:** Member of NEOUCOM Council Associated Hospital Librarians. **Publications:** Library brochure, annual; newsletter - for internal distribution only. **Remarks:** FAX: (216)375-3978. **Staff:** Evangeline Chekouras, Ref.Libn.; Bani Bose, Circuit Libn.; Linda Geary, Ref.Libn.

★171★
Akron Department of Planning and Urban Development - Library (Plan)
403 Municipal Bldg. Phone: (216)375-2084
Akron, OH 44308 Louise A. Morris, Libn.
Founded: 1960. **Staff:** Prof 2. **Subjects:** Planning, transportation, economics, recreation, urban renewal, housing, census, federal aid programs, economic development, historic preservation. **Special Collections:** Ohio & Erie Canal; Akron, Ohio history. **Holdings:** 2000 books; maps; aerial photographs. **Subscriptions:** 150 journals and other serials; 10 newspapers. **Services:** Interlibrary loan; copying; SDI; map reproduction; library open to the public for reference use only. **Remarks:** FAX: (216)375-2041. **Staff:** Beatrice Lasher, Asst.Libn.

★172★
Akron General Medical Center - J.D. Smith Memorial Library (Med)
400 Wabash Ave. Phone: (216)384-6242
Akron, OH 44307 Christine J. Williams, Dir., Lib.Serv.
Founded: 1947. **Staff:** Prof 2; Other 1. **Subjects:** Medicine. **Holdings:** 3200 books; 7000 bound periodical volumes; audiotapes. **Subscriptions:** 287 journals and other serials. **Services:** Interlibrary loan; library not open to the public. **Computerized Information Services:** BRS Information Technologies; CD-ROM (MEDLINE). **Networks/Consortia:** Member of NEOUCOM Council Associated Hospital Librarians. **Publications:** Bookmark (newsletter), irregular - for internal distribution and to the public. **Remarks:** FAX: (216)384-1834. **Staff:** Ann Carlson.

★173★
Akron Law Library (Law)
Summit County Court House, 4th Fl. Phone: (216)379-2804
Akron, OH 44308-1675 Rosemarie Chrisant, Lib.Dir.
Founded: 1888. **Staff:** Prof 2; Other 4. **Subjects:** Law. **Holdings:** 72,000 volumes. **Subscriptions:** 3 newspapers. **Services:** Interlibrary loan; library not open to the public. **Automated Operations:** Data Trek. **Computerized Information Services:** WESTLAW. **Remarks:** FAX: (216)535-0077. **Staff:** Corliss Davis, Asst.Libn.

★174★
Akron-Summit County Public Library - Business, Labor and Government Division (Bus-Fin, Law, Trans)
55 S. Main St. Phone: (216)762-7621
Akron, OH 44326-0001 Dana Kwasnicka, Div.Hd.
Staff: Prof 9; Other 2. **Subjects:** Investments, business, law, transportation, economics, government. **Special Collections:** Trucking history; mail order catalogs; telephone directories (3000). **Holdings:** 27,801 books; government contracts information collection. **Subscriptions:** 972 journals and other serials; 44 newspapers. **Services:** Interlibrary loan; division open to the public. **Automated Operations:** Computerized cataloging. **Computerized Information Services:** OCLC, DIALOG Information Services, VU/TEXT Information Services. Performs searches free of charge. **Networks/Consortia:** Member of Cleveland Area Metropolitan Library System (CAMLS). **Publications:** Business Insight, quarterly - to area businesses. **Special Indexes:** Index to telephone directories (card). **Staff:** Kay Clark; Richelle Ethington; Jon Hershey; Beth Hollis; Mary Ann Hoyt; Amy Price; Elizabeth Reed; Denise Lee.

★175★
Akron-Summit County Public Library - Science and Technology Division (Sci-Engr)
55 S. Main St. Phone: (216)762-7621
Akron, OH 44326 Joyce A. McKnight, Div.Hd.
Staff: Prof 6; Other 1. **Subjects:** Science and technology. **Special Collections:** Rubber and plastics; lighter-than-air; radio and television schematics. **Holdings:** 49,000 volumes; 50,000 pamphlets and clippings; depository for government documents; government and industry specifications and standards. **Subscriptions:** 575 journals and other serials. **Services:** Interlibrary loan; division open to the public. **Automated Operations:** Computerized cataloging. **Computerized Information Services:** OCLC, DIALOG Information Services, VU/TEXT Information Services; CD-ROMs. **Networks/Consortia:** Member of Cleveland Area Metropolitan Library System (CAMLS). **Special Catalogs:** Lighter-Than-Air Collection catalog (pamphlet). **Special Indexes:** Science Fair Project Index. **Remarks:** FAX: (216)762-6623.

★176★
Akusticeskij Institut AN SSR - Biblioteka (Sci-Engr)
Svernika 4 Phone: 95 1269027
117036 Moscow, Russia N.E. Shmakova
Founded: 1954. **Staff:** Prof 4. **Subjects:** Acoustics, oceanology, oceanography, applied physics. **Holdings:** 35,000 books; 55,000 bound periodical volumes; 2000 reports; 3000 microfiche. **Services:** Interlibrary loan; library open to the public with restrictions. **Computerized Information Services:** Bibliographic data base of general and applied acoustics (internal database). Contact Person: E.V. Udina. **Publications:** References to contemporary papers on acoustics, monthly. **Remarks:** FAX: 95 1268411.

★177★
Akwesasne Library Cultural Center (Area-Ethnic)
RR 1, Box 14C Phone: (518)358-2240
Hogansburg, NY 13655 Carol White, Dir.
Founded: 1971. **Staff:** 4. **Special Collections:** American Indian collection (1900 items). **Holdings:** AV programs; pamphlets; framed pictures. **Subscriptions:** 71 journals and other serials. **Services:** Interlibrary loan; copying; library open to the public. **Networks/Consortia:** Member of Clinton-Essex-Franklin Library System, North Country Reference and Research Resources Council (NCRRRC). **Publications:** Ka-Ri-Wen-Ha-Wi Newsletter, bimonthly - free upon request. **Staff:** Beatrice Cole, Libn.; Corinne White, Libn.

★178★
AKZO Chemicals Inc. - Dr. Harold S. Mickley Research Library (Food-Bev, Sci-Engr)
Dobbs Ferry, NY 10522-3401 Phone: (914)674-5000
Ramona C.T. Crosby, Mgr., Tech.Info.Serv.
Founded: 1965. **Subjects:** Phosphorous chemistry, polymers and plastics, lubricants, specialty chemicals, biochemistry, electronic chemicals, organic synthesis, organometallics, materials science, ceramics, homogenous and heterogeneous catalysis. **Holdings:** 14,422 books; 6500 reels of microfilm of periodicals and U.S. patent files; 3 VF drawers of pamphlets. **Subscriptions:** 619 journals and other serials. **Services:** Interlibrary loan; library open to the public with restrictions. **Automated Operations:** Computerized cataloging. **Computerized Information Services:** DIALOG Information Services, PFDS Online, OCLC, Chemical Information Systems, Inc. (CIS), STN International; INQUIRE (internal database). **Networks/Consortia:** Member of SUNY/OCLC Library Network. **Publications:** Library Bulletin, monthly; Information Services Bulletin, 2/year - for internal distribution only. **Special Catalogs:** Book Catalog (microfiche and hardcopy); AKZO Chemie America Union List. **Special Indexes:** Terminal Report Index. **Remarks:** FAX: (914)693-1758.

ALA
See: **American Library Association** (665)

★179★
ALA Gay & Lesbian Task Force - Clearinghouse (Soc Sci)
c/o American Library Association
Office of Library Outreach Services
50 E. Huron Phone: (312)944-6780
Chicago, IL 60611 JoAnn Segal, Assoc.Dir. for Prog.
Founded: 1970. **Subjects:** Homosexuality, lesbianism/feminism, gay rights. **Holdings:** 2000 books, pamphlets, periodical titles. **Publications:** Gay Bibliography - for sale; list of additional publications - available on request. **Remarks:** Affiliated with the American Library Association, Social Responsibilities Round Table. For further information, write to GLTF c/o Roland Hansen, Sec./Treas., 3824 N. Fremont, Chicago, IL 60613. **Formerly:** Gay Task Force of ALA - Information Center, located in Philadelphia, PA.

★180★
Alabama A & M University - J.F. Drake Memorial Learning Resources Center (Educ)
Box 489 Phone: (205)851-5760
Normal, AL 35762 Dr. Birdie O. Weir, Dir.
Founded: 1904. **Staff:** Prof 8; Other 14. **Subjects:** Education, business and economics, agriculture, the sciences, computer science, literature. **Special Collections:** Black Collection (3285 items); Archival Collection (2965 items); Curriculum Collection (5323 items); Children's Collection (5565 items); Schomburg Collection; Carnegie-Mydral Collection; J.F. Kennedy Memorial Collection; International Studies Collection (1525 items). **Holdings:** 275,564 books; 20,350 bound periodical volumes; 4542 AV programs; 15,469 periodicals on microfilm; 737 college catalogs; 661 telephone directories; 10,876 vertical files; 93,746 ERIC microfiche; 122,504 government documents; Wall Street Journal on microfiche (10,352); NewsBank on microfiche (18,084); Business NewsBank on microfiche (1726). **Subscriptions:** 1567 journals and other serials; 92 newspapers; 652 microfilm subscriptions. **Services:** Interlibrary loan; copying; videotaping; center open to the public; courtesy card must be purchased for check out of materials by persons not enrolled at the university or at one of the cooperating institutions. **Automated Operations:** Computerized public access catalog, cataloging, and ILL. **Computerized Information Services:** DIALOG Information Services. Performs searches on fee basis. Contact Person: Prudence W. Bryant, Supv., Ref. & Info.Serv. **Networks/Consortia:** Member of Network of Alabama Academic Libraries (NAAL), Alabama Library Exchange, Inc. (ALEX), SOLINET. **Publications:** Mixed Media (newsletter), annual; In the News (newsletter) - for internal distribution only; LRC Fast Facts; LRC Handbook of Programs and Services; brochures. **Remarks:** FAX: (205)851-5768 (Dir.'s Off.); (205)851-5901 (ILL). **Also Known As:** Alabama Agricultural and Mechanical University. **Staff:** Gloria B. Evans, Supv., Tech.Serv.; Barbara P. Rooks, Acq.Libn.; Sebastine O. Nwaneri, ILL Libn.; Terrell Barkley, Spec.Coll.Libn.; Rhonda Willams-Henry, Media Cat.; Regina Massey-Hick, Asst.Tech.Serv.Libn.

★181★
Alabama Aviation & Technical College - Learning Resources Center (Trans)
Hwy. 231, S.
Box 1209 Phone: (205)774-5113
Ozark, AL 36361 Megan Johnson, Libn.
Founded: 1984. **Staff:** 2.5.**Subjects:** Aviation, automobiles. **Special Collections:** Private and commerical aviation. **Holdings:** 6000 books; 10,000 microfiche. **Subscriptions:** 140 journals and other serials; 5 newspapers. **Services:** Interlibrary loan; copying; center open to the public for reference use only. **Remarks:** FAX: (205)774-5113. Toll-free telephone number(s): (800)624-3468.

Alabama Baptist State Convention Archives
See: **Samford University - Harwell Goodwin Davis Library - Baptist Historical Collection** (14662)

Alabama Gay Archives
See: **Lambda, Inc. - Barnes Library** (8914)

Alabama Geological Survery
See: **Geological Survey of Alabama** (6363)

★182★
Alabama Institute for the Deaf and Blind - Library and Resource Center for the Blind and Physically Handicapped (Aud-Vis)
Box 698 Phone: (205)761-3288
Talladega, AL 35160 Teresa Lacy, Libn.
Founded: 1965. **Staff:** Prof 3; Other 6. **Subjects:** General collection. **Special Collections:** Reference Collection on Blindness. **Holdings:** 28,000 books. **Subscriptions:** 35 journals and other serials. **Services:** Interlibrary loan; copying; large print copying; Summer Reading Program; library open to the blind, physically handicapped, and professionals in the field of blindness. **Networks/Consortia:** Member of National Library Service for the Blind & Physically Handicapped (NLS). **Publications:** Newsletter, quarterly. **Remarks:** FAX: (205)761-3337. Institute serves Talladega, Coosa and St. Clair Counties as a subregional of the National Library Service (NLS) for the Blind and Physically Handicapped, and provides education and rehabilitation programs throughout the state of Alabama. Library also produces braille materials. **Staff:** Marta Thompson, Rd.Adv.; Jim Stoval, Coord.

Alabama Journal
See: **Montgomery Advertiser and Alabama Journal** (10675)

Alabama Law Review
See: **University of Alabama - School of Law** (18166)

★183★
Alabama League of Municipalities - Library (Soc Sci)
Box 1270 Phone: (205)262-2566
Montgomery, AL 36102 Perry C. Roquemore, Jr., Exec.Dir.
Subjects: Municipal law and ordinances, intergovernmental relations, census data. **Holdings:** 1200 books; 250 bound periodical volumes; Alabama newspaper clippings; municipal subject files; state and federal agency publications. **Subscriptions:** 85 journals and other serials; 20 newspapers. **Services:** Copying; library open to the public with restrictions. **Special Indexes:** Index to Alabama Municipal Journal.

Alabama Museum of the Health Sciences
See: **University of Alabama at Birmingham - Lister Hill Library of the Health Sciences** (18171)

★184★
Alabama Power Company - Library (Energy)
600 N. 18th St.
Box 2641 Phone: (205)250-2876
Birmingham, AL 35291-0251 Sherie A. Mattox, Supv.
Founded: 1925. **Staff:** Prof 2; Other 3. **Subjects:** Electric utilities, engineering, management. **Special Collections:** Company archives. **Holdings:** 10,000 books; 1500 bound periodical and microfiche volumes; 2000 AV programs. **Subscriptions:** 600 journals and other serials. **Services:** Interlibrary loan; library not open to the public. **Automated Operations:** Computerized public access catalog, cataloging, acquisitions, serials, and circulation. **Computerized Information Services:** DIALOG Information Services, WILSONLINE, Knight-Ridder Unicom News, Dow Jones News/Retrieval. **Remarks:** FAX: (205)250-2100. **Staff:** Dawn Peavey, Res./Info.Anl.

★185★
Alabama Public Library Service - Information Service (Soc Sci)
6030 Monticello Dr. Phone: (205)277-7330
Montgomery, AL 36130 Patricia L. Harris, Dir.
Founded: 1959. **Staff:** Prof 23; Other 26. **Subjects:** Public administration and planning, social problems and welfare, library science. **Special Collections:** Alabamiana. **Holdings:** 138,773 books; 1496 bound periodical volumes; 752,781 microfiche; 12,008 reels of microfilm; 5038 16mm films; 349 video cassettes. **Subscriptions:** 1026 journals and other serials; 14 newspapers. **Services:** Interlibrary loan; copying; back-up reference for Alabama libraries; film and video booking; service open to the public for reference use only. **Automated Operations:** Computerized cataloging, acquisitions, circulation, and ILL. **Computerized Information Services:** DIALOG Information Services, OCLC. **Networks/Consortia:** Member of Alabama Library Information Network (ALIN), SOLINET, Network of Alabama Academic Libraries (NAAL). **Publications:** Cottonboll, quarterly; APLSauce, biweekly. **Special Catalogs:** ALICAT (Ondisc); MICROCAT (both on microfiche). **Remarks:** FAX: (205)272-9419. **Staff:** Alice Stephens, Hd., Lib.Oper.; Janet Hamilton, Hd., Tech.Serv.; Judy Shepard, Hd., Info.Serv.; Robyn Long, Hd., AV.

★186★
Alabama Public Library Service - Regional Library for the Blind and Physically Handicapped (Aud-Vis)
6030 Monticello Dr. Phone: (205)277-7330
Montgomery, AL 36130 Fara L. Zaleski, Hd.
Founded: 1978. **Staff:** Prof 3; Other 4. **Subjects:** Recorded and braille fiction and nonfiction. **Special Collections:** Locally recorded materials (297 titles). **Holdings:** 230,828 books. **Subscriptions:** 8 journals and other serials. **Services:** Interlibrary loan; library open to the public with restrictions. **Automated Operations:** Computerized circulation. **Networks/Consortia:** Member of National Library Service for the Blind & Physically Handicapped (NLS). **Publications:** WHAT'S LINE, quarterly - to mailing list. **Special Catalogs:** Regional Bookshelf (large print). **Remarks:** FAX: (205)272-6514. **Staff:** Michael Coleman, Rd.Adv.; Susan Clements, Rd.Adv.; James Gibson, Braille Libn.

★187★
Alabama Space and Rocket Center - Library/Archives (Sci-Engr)
One Tranquility Base Phone: (205)837-3400
Huntsville, AL 35807 James Hagler, Dir., Lib./Archv. & Cur.
Founded: 1977. **Staff:** Prof 2; Other 2. **Subjects:** U.S. and foreign space programs, history of space travel, space exploration, rockets and guided missiles. **Special Collections:** Dr. Werner von Braun Collection (professional and personal papers of Dr. von Braun and 41 of his colleagues and associates). **Holdings:** 60,000 books, manuscripts, journals, and other documents; 50 oral history audiotapes; 14 oral history videotapes; 100 space flights, space history, and other space program magnetic tapes and videotapes. **Subscriptions:** 34 journals and other serials. **Services:** Copying; library open to the public by appointment. **Networks/Consortia:** Member of Alabama Library Exchange, Inc. (ALEX). **Remarks:** FAX: (205)837-6137.

★188★
Alabama (State) Department of Archives and History - Reference Room (Hist)
624 Washington Ave. Phone: (205)242-4435
Montgomery, AL 36130 Jeff Jakeman, Hd., Pub.Serv.Div.
Founded: 1901. **Staff:** Prof 11; Other 7. **Subjects:** Alabama - history, politics and government, economic conditions, family history, social life and customs. **Holdings:** State and local government records; state publications; private records; maps; photographs; newspapers. **Subscriptions:** 90 journals and other serials. **Services:** Interlibrary loan (limited); copying; room open to the public with restrictions (registration required). **Computerized Information Services:** OCLC, RLIN; RLG (electronic mail service). **Networks/Consortia:** Member of SOLINET. **Staff:** Edwin C. Bridges, Dir. of Dept.; Alden N. Monroe, Hd., Coll.Mgt.Div.; Alice Knierim, Hd., Spec.Proj.; Deborah Skaggs, Hd., Rec.Mgt.Div.; Norwood A. Kerr, Hd., Archv.Ref.Sect.; Frazine Taylor, Hd., Ready Ref.Sect.

★189★
Alabama (State) Department of Economic & Community Affairs - Library Reference Service (Plan)
State Capitol Phone: (205)284-8910
Montgomery, AL 36130 Rochelle C. Anderson, Adm.
Founded: 1935. **Staff:** 1. **Subjects:** Alabama development and planning. **Holdings:** 500 books and documents; 200 state and local documents on Alabama. **Subscriptions:** 50 journals and other serials. **Services:** Interlibrary loan; copying; SDI; current awareness; service open to the public for reference use only. **Publications:** List of publications - available on request. **Remarks:** FAX: (205)284-8670.

★190★
Alabama (State) Department of Public Health - Health Resource Center (Med)
434 Monroe St. Phone: (205)242-5095
Montgomery, AL 36130 Fran Edwards, Lib.Techn.
Founded: 1915. **Staff:** 2.5. **Subjects:** Preventable diseases, smoking, injury prevention, health education. **Special Collections:** Transactions and annual reports, 1852 to present; Alabama legislation. **Holdings:** 250 books; 500 bound periodical volumes; 807 films. **Subscriptions:** 22 journals. **Services:** Interlibrary loan; copying; center open to the public. **Computerized Information Services:** NLM, MEDLINE. **Networks/Consortia:** Member of Montgomery Area Health Information Consortium (MAHIC). **Publications:** Annual Reports of the Health Department, 1900 to present - free upon request to libraries; Alabama's Health, monthly. **Remarks:** FAX: (205)240-3097. **Staff:** Carol Bigger, Film Libn.

★191★
Alabama (State) Supreme Court - Supreme Court and State Law Library (Law)
Judicial Bldg.
445 Dexter Ave. Phone: (205)242-4347
Montgomery, AL 36130 William C. Younger, Dir. & State Law Libn.
Founded: 1828. **Staff:** Prof 6; Other 8. **Subjects:** Law. **Holdings:** 179,000 volumes. **Subscriptions:** 975 legal periodicals. **Services:** Interlibrary loan; copying; library open to the public. **Computerized Information Services:** WESTLAW, OCLC, LEXIS. **Networks/Consortia:** Member of SOLINET. **Remarks:** FAX: (205)242-4484. **Staff:** Tim Lewis, Rd.Serv.Libn.; Sarah L. Frins, Tech.Serv.Libn.; Lynn D. Boyd, Govt.Doc.Libn.; Lynne B. Kitchens, Res.Att.; Alma Surles, Asst.Rd.Serv.Libn.

★192★
Alabama State University - University Library & Learning Resources - Archives & Special Collections (Area-Ethnic)
Levi Watkins Learning Center
915 S. Jackson St. Phone: (205)293-4106
Montgomery, AL 36195-0301 Rubye J. Sullivan, Spec.Coll.Libn.
Staff: Prof 1; Other 6. **Subjects:** Afro-Americans. **Special Collections:** Atlanta University's Black Culture Collection (181 reels of microfilm); George W. Carver Correspondence Collection (67 reels of microfilm); Bibliography of Doctoral Research on the Negro, 1933-1966; E.D. Nixon Collection; Alabama Statewide Oral History Project (10 volumes of transcribed interviews); Montgomery, Alabama Bus Boycott, 1955-1957 (4 volumes). **Holdings:** 11,980 books; 600 bound periodical volumes; 384 reels of microfilm; 435 microfiche; 305 16mm films, cassettes, filmstrip/cassette sets; 2 vertical files of clippings; 200 phonograph records, slides, audiotapes; 1690 theses. **Subscriptions:** 50 journals and other serials; 30 newspapers. **Services:** Copying; collections open to the public. **Special Indexes:** Index to Periodicals by and about Negroes (book); Indexes to Vertical Files (card); Index to Black Cultural Collection (book); Index to Doctoral Research on the Negro (card).

AlaBenton Genealogical Society
See: **Public Library of Anniston & Calhoun County - Alabama Room** (13476)

★193★
Alamance Community College - Learning Resources Center (Sci-Engr)
Box 623 Phone: (919)578-2002
Haw River, NC 27258 Laura S. Gorham, Coord.
Founded: 1959. **Staff:** Prof 3; Other 1. **Subjects:** Applied arts, business and engineering technology, health and mechanical occupations. **Holdings:** 20,000 books; 2918 microforms. **Subscriptions:** 160 journals and other serials. **Services:** Interlibrary loan; copying; center open to the public. **Computerized Information Services:** DIALOG Information Services; EasyLink (electronic mail service). **Remarks:** FAX: (919)578-5561. Electronic mail address(es): 62792985 (EasyLink).

★194★
Alamance County Historic Properties Commission - Historic Restoration Resources Library (Hist)
124 W. Elm St. Phone: (919)228-1312
Graham, NC 27253 M.M. Way, Adm.Off.
Founded: 1978. **Subjects:** Local historic sites, restoration of historic properties. **Holdings:** 150 books; 600 local historic site files; 300 cemetery listings; slide programs. **Subscriptions:** 2 journals and other serials. **Services:** Copying; library open to the public with restrictions.

★195★
Alamance Health Services, Inc. - Medical Library (Med)
P.O. Box 202 Phone: (919)570-5027
Burlington, NC 27216-0202 Virginia Marshall, Educ.Dir.
Founded: 1982. **Subjects:** Medicine, nursing, pharmacology, hospital administration, biomedical engineering. **Holdings:** 350 books; 85 audio cassettes; 50 videotapes. **Subscriptions:** 72 journals and other serials. **Services:** Interlibrary loan; copying; library open to the public. **Computerized Information Services:** BRS Information Technologies. Performs searches on fee basis. **Remarks:** FAX: (919)570-5033.

★196★
Alameda-Contra Costa Medical Association & Highland Hospital - Library (Med)
1411 E. 31st St. Phone: (510)536-3331
Oakland, CA 94602 Linda M. Morgan, Med.Libn.
Founded: 1915. **Staff:** Prof 1; Other 2. **Subjects:** Medicine, surgery, orthopedics. **Holdings:** 2000 books; 16,500 bound periodical volumes; 700 cassettes. **Subscriptions:** 248 journals and other serials. **Services:** Interlibrary loan; copying; library open to medical and paramedical personnel. **Automated Operations:** Computerized circulation, serials, and record keeping. **Computerized Information Services:** MEDLINE, BRS Information Technologies, MEDLARS. **Networks/Consortia:** Member of Northern California and Nevada Medical Library Group (NCNMLG), National Network of Libraries of Medicine - Pacific Southwest Region. **Remarks:** Alternate telephone number(s): 437-4701.

★197★
Alameda County Law Library (Law)
1225 Fallon St. Phone: (510)272-6481
Oakland, CA 94612 Cossette T. Sun, Dir.
Founded: 1891. **Staff:** Prof 7; Other 8. **Subjects:** Law. **Special Collections:** California briefs. **Holdings:** 161,640 volumes; 188,640 microfiche. **Subscriptions:** 3000 journals and other serials; 6 newspapers. **Services:** Interlibrary loan; library open to the public. **Automated Operations:** Integrated library system (Sydney). **Computerized Information Services:** WESTLAW, RLIN, DIALOG Information Services, LEXIS. Performs searches on fee basis. Contact Person: Robert Podlech, Pub.Serv.Libn., 272-6486. **Networks/Consortia:** Member of LAWNET. **Publications:** Acquisitions list; Alameda County Law Library Newsletter. **Remarks:** FAX: (510)763-3753. One branch library is maintained within the County. **Staff:** Susanne Pierce Dyer, Ref.Libn.; Colleen Kensinger, Tech.Serv.Libn.; Greg Fite, Br.Ref.Libn.; Evelyn Lord, Ref.Libn.

★198★
Alameda County Law Library - South County Branch (Law)
224 W. Winton Ave., Rm. 162 Phone: (510)670-5230
Hayward, CA 94544 Cossette T. Sun, Law Lib.Dir.
Founded: 1967. **Staff:** Prof 1; Other 3. **Subjects:** Law. **Holdings:** 22,952 volumes. **Subscriptions:** 694 journals and other serials. **Services:** Library open to the public. **Computerized Information Services:** RLIN, LEXIS, WESTLAW. **Networks/Consortia:** Member of Bay Area Library and Information Network, LAWNET. **Publications:** Acquisitions list; ACLL Newsletter. **Staff:** Gregory Fite, Br.Ref.Libn.

★199★
Alameda County Library - Business Library (Bus-Fin, Soc Sci)
2201 Broadway Phone: (510)271-4292
Oakland, CA 94612-3044 Joan Galvez, Mgr.
Founded: 1968. **Staff:** Prof 6; Other 6. **Subjects:** How to start and manage a business, investments, real estate, international business, management and personnel, career planning, San Francisco Bay area. **Special Collections:** Alameda County employment information. **Holdings:** 12,000 books; 150 audiocassettes; 30 videocassettes; 1500 annual reports; clippings on local companies. **Subscriptions:** 450 journals and other serials; 30 newspapers. **Services:** Interlibrary loan; copying; library open to the public. **Automated Operations:** Computerized circulation. **Computerized Information Services:** DIALOG Information Services, Dow Jones News/Retrieval. **Networks/Consortia:** Member of Bay Area Library and Information System (BALIS). **Publications:** News and New Books, irregular - free upon request; subject bibliographies, irregular. **Special Indexes:** Analytical index to representative subject material in books, documents, clippings, and reports (cards); directory holdings by subject (multimate files). **Remarks:** FAX: (510)272-0873. **Staff:** Devon McLaughlin, Libn.; Kathy Greenstein, Libn.; Karman Reta, Libn.; Mary-Ellen Mort, Libn.; David Weber, Libn.; Ann Nally, Supv.Ck.

★200★
Alameda County Office of Education - Teachers' Professional and Curriculum Library (Educ)
313 W. Winton Ave. Phone: (510)887-0152
Hayward, CA 94544-1198 Dr. Loretta M. Chin, Coord., Lib.Rsrc.Serv.
Founded: 1961. **Staff:** Prof 1; Other 2. **Subjects:** Education. **Special Collections:** State Instructional Materials - Print/Non-Print Display Center. **Holdings:** 9500 volumes; 450 curriculum materials. **Subscriptions:** 75 journals and other serials. **Services:** Library open to the public for reference use only. **Remarks:** FAX: (510)783-5304.

Domingo Toledo Alamo Law Library
See: **Inter American University of Puerto Rico - School of Law** (8031)

★201★
Alaska Air National Guard - 176th USAF Clinic Medical Library (Med)
Kulis Air Natl. Guard Base
6000 Air Guard Rd. Phone: (907)249-1416
Anchorage, AK 99502-1998 Rosa Williams, Med.Libn.
Staff: 1. **Subjects:** Emergency medicine, dentistry, pharmacy, bioenvironmental and environmental health, nursing, optometry. **Holdings:** 80 books. **Services:** Library not open to the public. **Remarks:** FAX: (907)249-1145. Alternate telephone number(s): (907)249-1276.

★202★
Alaska Bible College - Library Center - Captain Vincent J. Joy, Jr. Memorial Library (Rel-Phil)
Box 289 Phone: (907)822-3202
Glennallen, AK 99688 Annette Ball, Libn.
Founded: 1966. **Staff:** 1.6. **Subjects:** Theology, Bible. **Special Collections:** Alaskana. **Services:** Interlibrary loan; copying; library open to the public.

Alaska Climate Center
See: **University of Alaska, Anchorage - Arctic Environmental Information and Data Center** (18175)

★203★
Alaska Council on Prevention of Alcohol and Drug Abuse - Library (Med)
3333 Denali St., Suite 201 Phone: (907)258-6021
Anchorage, AK 99503 Joyce Paulus
Founded: 1979. **Staff:** Prof 1; Other 2. **Subjects:** Alcohol and other drugs. **Special Collections:** Sample curricula. **Holdings:** 1000 books; 120 videotapes. **Subscriptions:** 180 journals and other serials. **Services:** Library not open to the public. **Computerized Information Services:** AskSam (internal database). **Publications:** Alaska Native Populations. **Remarks:** FAX: (907)258-6052.

★204★
Alaska Energy Authority - Library (Energy)
P.O. Box 190869 Phone: (907)561-7877
Anchorage, AK 99519-0869 Suzi Bailey, Rec.Coord.
Staff: 2. **Subjects:** Energy, hydroelectric power, state of Alaska. **Holdings:** 3000 volumes. **Services:** Interlibrary loan. **Remarks:** FAX: (907)561-8584.

Alaska Native Language Center
See: **University of Alaska, Fairbanks** (18180)

★205★
Alaska Oil and Gas Conservation Commission - Library (Env-Cons)
3001 Porcupine Dr. Phone: (907)279-1433
Anchorage, AK 99501-3192 Larry J. Grant
Founded: 1955. **Staff:** Prof 2. **Subjects:** Drilling histories, electric logs, mud logs. **Holdings:** 1600 books; 1000 bound periodical volumes; 4000 reports; 10,000 microfiche. **Subscriptions:** 350 journals and other serials. **Services:** Interlibrary loan; library open to the public in state only. **Publications:** AOGCC Statistical Reports (bulletin), monthly. **Remarks:** FAX: (907)276-7542.

★206★
Alaska Public Utilities Commission - Library (Energy)
1016 W. 6th, Suite 400 Phone: (907)276-6222
Anchorage, AK 99501 Tammy Alexander, Doc.Proc.IV
Founded: 1974. **Staff:** 42. **Subjects:** Public utilities, oil and gas pipelines, law. **Holdings:** 750 books. **Subscriptions:** 75 journals and other serials; 10 newspapers. **Services:** Interlibrary loan; library open to the public. **Publications:** Annual Reports. **Remarks:** FAX: (907)276-0160.

★207★
Alaska (State) Court System - Alaska Court Libraries (Law)
303 K St. Phone: (907)264-0585
Anchorage, AK 99501 Cynthia S. Petumenos, State Law Libn.
Founded: 1960. **Staff:** Prof 4; Other 10. **Subjects:** Law. **Special Collections:** Alaska Supreme Court and Court of Appeals briefs, 1960 to present. **Holdings:** 20,000 books; 115,000 serial volumes. **Subscriptions:** 3000 journals and other serials. **Services:** Interlibrary loan; library open to the public for reference use only. **Automated Operations:** Computerized public access catalog, cataloging, serials, and circulation. **Computerized Information Services:** WESTLAW, LEXIS, DIALOG Information Services, ALECSYS; internal database; WLN IMAIL, MCI Mail (electronic mail services). **Networks/Consortia:** Member of Western Library Network (WLN). **Remarks:** FAX: (907)264-0733. Electronic mail address(es): CPETUMENOS (MCI Mail). Totals above include the holdings of the 16 branch libraries located in Barrow, Bethel, Dillingham, Fairbanks, Homer, Juneau, Kenai, Ketchikan, Kodiak, Kotzebue, Nome, Palmer, Petersburg, Sitka, Valdez, and Wrangell. **Staff:** Michael Catoggio, Ref.Libn.; Beth Odsen, Tech.Serv.Libn.; Peggy Michielsen, Ref.Libn.

★208★
Alaska (State) Court System - Ketchikan Law Library (Law)
State Office Bldg.
415 Main St., Rm. 208 Phone: (907)225-0500
Ketchikan, AK 99901 Berniece Cleveland, Libn.
Staff: 1. **Subjects:** Law. **Holdings:** 15,000 volumes. **Subscriptions:** 20 journals and other serials. **Services:** Library open to the public for reference use only.

Alaska State Data Center
See: **Alaska (State) Department of Labor - Research and Analysis Section** (215)

★209★
Alaska (State) Department of Education - Division of Libraries, Archives and Museums (Info Sci)
State Office Bldg.
Box G Phone: (907)465-2910
Juneau, AK 99811 Karen R. Crane, Dir., Lib.Div.
Founded: 1957. **Staff:** Prof 26; Other 42. **Subjects:** Alaska, Arctic, government and legislative reference, planning. **Holdings:** 90,000 volumes; 600,000 microfiche; 85,000 reels of microfilm; manuscripts; clippings; archives; pamphlets; documents. **Subscriptions:** 600 journals and other serials; 48 newspapers. **Services:** Interlibrary loan; copying; library open to the public. **Automated Operations:** Computerized cataloging and circulation. **Computerized Information Services:** DIALOG Information Services, OCLC, OCLC EPIC, LEGI-SLATE, LC Direct. **Networks/ Consortia:** Member of Western Library Network (WLN), Alaska Library Network (ALN). **Publications:** Alaska Blue Book. **Special Catalogs:** Film, record, and cassette catalogs. **Special Indexes:** Alaska Directory Index. **Remarks:** Includes regional offices in Anchorage and Fairbanks, film library in Anchorage, and Blind and Physically Handicapped Services in Anchorage. FAX: (907)465-2665. **Staff:** George V. Smith, Dp.Dir.; Nina Malyshev, Hd., Lib.Serv.; Kay Shelton, Hd., Alaska Hist.Lib.Sect.; Mary Jennings, Film/Hndcp.Serv.; Audrey Kolb, Northern Reg.Coord.; Judy Monroe, South Central Reg.Coord.; Aja Razumny, Southeastern Reg.Coord.; B. Jo Morse, Sch./Media Coord.; Mike Mitchell, Hd. of Info.Serv.; Lynne Williams, Hd. of Coll.Sup.Serv.; Patience Frederiksen, Hd. of Docs.

★210★
Alaska (State) Department of Education - Division of Libraries, Archives and Museums - Archives & Records Management Services (ARMS) (Hist)
141 Willoughby Ave. Phone: (907)465-2275
Juneau, AK 99801-1720 Virginia A. Newton, Ph.D., State Archv.
Founded: 1971. **Staff:** Prof 6; Other 7. **Subjects:** Alaska territorial and state government. **Holdings:** 10,000 cubic feet of territorial and state government records. **Services:** Copying; archives open to the public. **Computerized Information Services:** WLN; internal database. **Publications:** Alaska State Archives: A Guide. **Special Catalogs:** Finding aids to records. **Special Indexes:** Microfilm index (card); index to noncurrent foreign and domestic corporation records (online); Alaska State Government Records Management Manual; Alaska Local Government General Records Retention Schedules; Alaska School District General Retention Schedules; Records Management Resources for Local Governments in Alaska. **Remarks:** FAX: (907)465-2465. The archives are the official repository for all permanently valuable records of the executive, legislative, and judicial branches of Alaska's state government. **Staff:** Larry Hibpshman, Archv.; Al Minick, Archv.; Mike Ryan, Archv.; Charlie Childress, Rec.Anl.; Patrick O'Brien, Micgraphs Serv.Mgr.

★211★
Alaska (State) Department of Education - Division of Libraries, Archives and Museums - Historical Library Section (Hist)
Box G Phone: (907)465-2925
Juneau, AK 99811-0571 Kathryn H. Shelton, Hd., Hist.Lib.
Founded: 1900. **Staff:** Prof 2; Other 4. **Subjects:** Alaska, Yukon, Arctic; Russian, especially Siberian, culture. **Special Collections:** Alaska government publications; James Wickersham Collection; Dolgopolov Russian History and Culture Collection; Vinokouroff Russian Collection; records of the Alaska Packers Association; publications of Alaska Native Corporations; L.H. Bayers Maritime Collection; Winter and Pond photograph collection; John Granger Alaska postcard collection. **Holdings:** 34,000 volumes, manuscripts, tapes, video cassettes, maps; 110,000 photographs; microfilm. **Services:** Mail or telephone reference and copying services; noncirculating collection open to the public for research. **Automated Operations:** Computerized public access catalog, cataloging, and circulation. **Computerized Information Services:** DIALOG Information Services, OCLC. **Networks/Consortia:** Member of Western Library Network (WLN), Alaska Library Network (ALN). **Publications:** Some Books About Alaska Received, annual; Polar Libraries Bulletin, biannual; historical monograph series, guides, and bibliographies. **Remarks:** FAX: (907)465-2665. **Staff:** India Spartz, Ref. & Photo.Libn.; Rose Schreier, Cat. & Ref.Libn.

★212★
Alaska (State) Department of Environmental Conservation - Library (Env-Cons)
Box O Phone: (907)465-2692
Juneau, AK 99811-1800 Katie Sloan, Libn.
Founded: 1982. **Staff:** 1. **Subjects:** Air and water quality, environmental health, wastewater treatment, hazardous and solid waste, oil and hazardous substance spill response, mining, facilities inspection and operation. **Holdings:** 12,000 items. **Subscriptions:** 85 journals and other serials. **Services:** Interlibrary loan; copying; library open to the public. **Automated Operations:** Computerized public access catalog. **Computerized Information Services:** DIALOG Information Services, WLN, EPA (U.S. Environmental Protection Agency). **Networks/Consortia:** Member of Alaska Library Network (ALN), Western Library Network (WLN). **Publications:** New acquisitions list, weekly - available on request. **Remarks:** FAX: (907)465-2617. Library located at 410 Willoughby Ave., Juneau, AK.

★213★
Alaska (State) Department of Fish and Game - Habitat Library (Env-Cons, Biol Sci)
333 Raspberry Rd. Phone: (907)267-2312
Anchorage, AK 99518-1599 Celia Rozen, Libn.
Founded: 1982. **Staff:** Prof 1. **Subjects:** Fish and wildlife habitat, Arctic exploration, oil and gas impacts, coastal zone management, ecology, human usage. **Holdings:** 11,000 books; 12,000 maps; 10,000 reprints. **Subscriptions:** 30 journals and other serials. **Services:** Interlibrary loan; copying; library open to the public for reference use only. **Automated Operations:** Computerized public access catalog, cataloging, and circulation. **Computerized Information Services:** DIALOG Information Services; LEXIS; Environmental Library System (internal database). **Networks/ Consortia:** Member of Alaska Library Network (ALN), Western Library Network (WLN).

★214★
Alaska (State) Department of Fish and Game - Library (Biol Sci)
Box 240020 Phone: (907)465-4119
Douglas, AK 99824-0020 Paul DeSloover, Libn.
Founded: 1954. **Staff:** Prof 1; Other 1. **Subjects:** Fisheries management, aquaculture, aquatic life, oceanography. **Holdings:** 450 volumes; 2100 microfiche; 175 dissertations; 50 reels of microfilm; 10,500 unbound reports. **Subscriptions:** 50 journals and other serials; 5 newspapers. **Services:** Interlibrary loan; copying; SDI; library open to the public. **Automated Operations:** Computerized cataloging. **Computerized Information Services:** DIALOG Information Services. Performs searches on fee basis. **Networks/ Consortia:** Member of Alaska Library Network (ALN). **Remarks:** FAX: (907)586-9522.

★215★
Alaska (State) Department of Labor - Research and Analysis Section - Alaska State Data Center (Soc Sci)
Box 25504 Phone: (907)465-4500
Juneau, AK 99802-5504 Kathryn Lizik, Labor Economist II
Founded: 1980. **Staff:** 3. **Subjects:** U.S. census and demographics, population trends. **Holdings:** 1500 publications and periodicals. **Subscriptions:** 2 journals and other serials. **Services:** Interlibrary loan; center open to the public. **Publications:** Newsletter. **Remarks:** FAX: (907)465-2101.

★216★
Alaska (State) Department of Law - Attorney General's Library (Law)
State Capitol Bldg.
Box K Phone: (907)465-3600
Juneau, AK 99811 Beverly Haywood, Legal Adm.
Staff: 1. **Subjects:** Law. **Special Collections:** Alaska Session Laws and Alaska Senate and House Journals; Alaska Constitutional Convention Minutes; informal and formal Attorney General Opinions, 1959 to present. **Holdings:** 3025 volumes. **Subscriptions:** 10 journals and other serials; 20 newspapers. **Services:** Copying; library open to the public for reference use only. **Remarks:** FAX: (907)463-5295.

★217★
Alaska (State) Department of Natural Resources - Division of Land - Robert F. Goddard Memorial Library (Plan)
Box 107005 Phone: (907)561-5807
Anchorage, AK 99510-7005 Odin Brudie, Natural Rsrc.Off.
Founded: 1980. **Subjects:** Land use planning, resource and socio-economic analysis. **Special Collections:** Alaska Land Use Planning. **Holdings:** 500 volumes. **Subscriptions:** 2 journals and other serials. **Services:** Library open to the public by appointment. **Remarks:** FAX: (907)561-5807.

★218★
Alaska (State) Energy Extension Service - Energy Resource and Information Center (Energy)
333 W. 4th Ave., Suite 220 Phone: (907)269-4642
Anchorage, AK 99501 Ginny Moore, Libn.
Founded: 1984. **Staff:** Prof 1. **Subjects:** Energy - conservation, renewable sources and applications, building construction, management, education, housing, electricity sources efficiency, conservation; indoor air quality. **Holdings:** 2000 books; 100 films and videotapes; reports and studies. **Subscriptions:** 50 journals and other serials. **Services:** Interlibrary loan; copying; library open to the public. **Automated Operations:** Computerized cataloging and acquisitions. **Remarks:** Toll-free telephone number(s): (800)478-4636 (in Alaska). **Formerly:** University of Alaska, Anchorage - Energy Extension Service - Energy Resource and Information Center.

★219★
Alaska (State) Legislature/Legislative Affairs Agency - Reference Library (Law)
State Capitol
P.O. Box Y Phone: (907)465-3808
Juneau, AK 99811 Mary Van Nimwegen, Libn.
Staff: Prof 1; Other 1. **Subjects:** State law. **Special Collections:** Alaska law; audiotapes and files of Alaska legislative committees; publications of legislature and Legislative Affairs Agency. **Holdings:** 1500 books; all states' current statutes and session laws; bills introduced to Alaska legislature on microfilm. **Subscriptions:** 100 journals and other serials. **Services:** Copying; library open to the public for reference use only. **Computerized Information Services:** Alaska Legislative Computer Systems (ALECSYS; internal database).

★220★
Alaska State Library - Alaska Health Sciences Library (Med)
3211 Providence Dr. Phone: (907)786-1870
Anchorage, AK 99508 Jeraldine Jo van den Top, Libn.
Staff: Prof 2; Other 3. **Subjects:** Medicine, dentistry, nursing. **Holdings:** Figures not available. **Services:** Interlibrary loan; copying; SDI; library open to the public (fee). **Computerized Information Services:** MEDLARS, BRS Information Technologies; OnTyme Electronic Message Network Service (electronic mail service). Contact Person: Loretta Andress, Libn. **Remarks:** FAX: (907)786-1608. Electronic mail address(es): CLASS.AHSL (OnTyme Electronic Message Network Service). Library affiliated with the University of Alaska, Anchorage - Library - Archives & Manuscripts.

★221★
Alaska State Library - Northern Region Coordinator (Info Sci)
1215 Cowles St. Phone: (907)452-2999
Fairbanks, AK 99701 Karen Crane, Div. of State Libs.
Staff: Prof 1. **Subjects:** Library science. **Holdings:** 100 books. **Subscriptions:** 16 journals and other serials; 2 newspapers. **Services:** Interlibrary loan; copying. **Publications:** Training materials; Manual for Small Libraries in Alaska; Tracings, the Village Library Newsletter. **Remarks:** Field office of the Alaska State Library. Library located at the Fairbanks N. Star Borough Library. **Remarks:** FAX: (907)459-1024.

Alaska (State) Resources Library
See: **U.S. Bureau of Land Management - Alaska State Office - Alaska Resources Library** (17100)

★222★
Alaska Yukon Library (Area-Ethnic)
327 E. 13th Ave., No. 1 Phone: (907)272-6647
Anchorage, AK 99501 Jean Anderson Graves, Lib.Cons.
Founded: 1988. **Staff:** Prof 1. **Subjects:** Alaska Natives, Circumpolar indigenous peoples, Native Americans, Pacific Island indigenous peoples. **Holdings:** Books; reports; archives; microfiche; vertical files of clippings; monographs; original documents. **Services:** Copying; library open to the public on a fee basis.

★223★
Albany College of Pharmacy - Library (Med)
106 New Scotland Ave. Phone: (518)445-7217
Albany, NY 12208 Irene Petzinger Kaplan, Libn.
Founded: 1927. **Staff:** Prof 2; Other 4. **Subjects:** Pharmacy, medicine, chemistry, biology, technology. **Holdings:** 6000 books; 2000 bound periodical volumes; 155 periodicals; Iowa Drug Information Service; 25 linear feet of archival material. **Subscriptions:** 155 journals and other serials. **Services:** Interlibrary loan; copying; SDI; library open to the public with restrictions. **Automated Operations:** Computerized public access catalog and cataloging. **Computerized Information Services:** BRS Information Technologies, DIALOG Information Services, STN International, NLM; MESSAGES (electronic mail service). Performs searches free of charge and on fee basis. **Networks/Consortia:** Member of Capital District Library Council for Reference & Research Resources (CDLC). **Publications:** Newsletter, irregular. **Staff:** Debra Locascio.

★224★
Albany County Historical Association - Library
9 Ten Broeck Pl.
Albany, NY 12210
Subjects: Local and county history. **Holdings:** Figures not available. **Remarks:** Currently inactive.

★225★
Albany General Hospital - Stanley K. Davis Library (Med)
1046 W. 6th Phone: (503)926-9449
Albany, OR 97321 Roger Davis, Libn.
Staff: Prof 1. **Subjects:** Clinical medicine, nursing, hospital administration, radiology. **Holdings:** 800 books; 300 bound periodical volumes. **Subscriptions:** 180 journals and other serials. **Services:** Interlibrary loan; copying; SDI; library open to the public by appointment. **Computerized Information Services:** NLM, BRS Information Technologies; OnTyme Electronic Message Network Service (electronic mail service). Performs searches on fee basis. **Networks/Consortia:** Member of Oregon Health Information Online (ORHION). **Remarks:** FAX: (503)926-9449.

★226★
Albany Herald - Library (Publ)
132 Pine Ave. Phone: (912)888-9371
Albany, GA 31703 Claudia Starr Strese
Founded: 1973. **Staff:** Prof 1. **Subjects:** Newspaper reference topics. **Holdings:** Clippings (1836 to present); reels of microfilm (1836 to 1991). **Services:** Library not open to the public. **Remarks:** FAX: (912)888-9357.

★227★
Albany Institute of History and Art - McKinney Library (Art, Hist)
125 Washington Ave. Phone: (518)463-4478
Albany, NY 12210 Prudence Backman, Chf.Libn.
Staff: Prof 2. **Subjects:** Albany and Upper Hudson region history, American painting and decorative art, Hudson River School of Art. **Special Collections:** Papers of Thomas Cole, 1801-1848 (395 items); Erastus Corning, 1794-1872 (40,000 items); Erastus Dow Palmer, 1817-1904 (361 items); John Q.A. Ward, 1830-1910 (700 items); Albany imprints, directories, almanacs; broadsides, including the DeWitt Clinton Collection; manuscripts, including papers of the Dutch in the Upper Hudson Valley, 17th and 18th centuries; Albany social, political, and business history, 18th and 19th centuries; American painters and sculptors. **Holdings:** 14,000 books; 800 bound periodical volumes; 2200 exhibition catalogs; 500,000 manuscripts; 12,000 photographs; 6 VF drawers; maps; 2000 deeds and indentures. **Subscriptions:** 55 journals and other serials. **Services:** Copying; library open to the public.

★228★
Albany International Corp. - Albany International Research Co. - Research Library (Sci-Engr)
777 West St.
Box 9114 Phone: (508)339-7300
Mansfield, MA 02048-9114 Jeanette H. Davis
Founded: 1942. **Staff:** Prof 1; Other 1. **Subjects:** Textiles, composites, polymers, paper, papermaking, materials related to textiles. **Special Collections:** Textiles (750); polymers/polymer chemistry and physics (600). **Holdings:** 5000 books; 50 bound periodical volumes; 20,000 reports. **Subscriptions:** 200 journals and other serials; 50 newspapers. **Services:** Library open to the public by appointment. **Computerized Information Services:** DIALOG Information Services, STN International, PFDS Online; internal database; DIALMAIL (electronic mail service). **Remarks:** FAX: (508)339-4996.

Albany Law School
See: **Union University - Albany Law School** (16669)

Albany Medical College - Capital District Psychiatric Center
See: **Capital District Psychiatric Center** (3031)

★229★
Albany Medical College - Schaffer Library of Health Sciences (Med)
47 New Scotland Ave. Phone: (518)445-5586
Albany, NY 12208 Sherry A. Hartman, Dir./Libn.
Founded: 1928. **Staff:** Prof 8; Other 35. **Subjects:** Medicine, pre-clinical sciences, nursing, psychiatry. **Holdings:** 40,847 books; 115,187 bound periodical volumes; 2380 AV programs. **Subscriptions:** 928 journals and other serials. **Services:** Interlibrary loan; copying; SDI; library open to allied health personnel. **Automated Operations:** Computerized public access catalog, cataloging, and serials. **Computerized Information Services:** BRS Information Technologies, NLM, OCLC, DIALOG Information Services; CD-ROM. Performs searches on fee basis. Contact Person: Melanie Mundy, Online Serv.Coord., 445-5532. **Networks/Consortia:** Member of Capital District Library Council for Reference & Research Resources (CDLC), National Network of Libraries of Medicine - Middle Atlantic Region. **Publications:** Library Newsletter, irregular - to users and interested libraries. **Staff:** Rene Molineaux, Mgr., Multi Media Ctr.; Gail Botta, CDPC Br.; Judy Doyle, Coll.Dev.; Enid Geyer, Hd., Tech.Serv.; Charlene La Grange, Hd., Pub.Serv.

★230★
Albany Memorial Hospital - Education Resource Center (Med)
Northern Blvd. Phone: (518)471-3264
Albany, NY 12204 Barbara Ost, Hosp.Libn.
Founded: 1960. **Staff:** Prof 1. **Subjects:** Medicine, nursing. **Holdings:** 4000 books; 300 bound periodical volumes; tapes; films. **Subscriptions:** 100 journals and other serials. **Services:** Interlibrary loan; copying; SDI; library open to the public by appointment. **Computerized Information Services:** MEDLINE, BRS/COLLEAGUE. **Networks/Consortia:** Member of Capital District Library Council for Reference & Research Resources (CDLC), National Network of Libraries of Medicine - Middle Atlantic Region. **Remarks:** FAX: (618)471-3051. **Formerly:** Memorial Hospital - Health Sciences Library.

Carl Albert Center Congressional Archives
See: **University of Oklahoma** (19123)

★231★
Alberta Advanced Education - Alberta Vocational College - ESL Learning Resources Centre (Educ)
Winnifred Stewart Campus
11140 131st St. Phone: (403)422-9063
Edmonton, AB, Canada T5M 1C1 Sabine Sintenis, Asst.Libn.
Founded: 1986. **Staff:** Prof 1; Other 2. **Subjects:** English as a second language. **Holdings:** 7043 books; 1028 AV items. **Subscriptions:** 20 journals and other serials. **Services:** Center open to the public with restrictions. **Publications:** AVC Echo, weekly during school year. **Staff:** Helen Gordon, Lib.Techn.

★232★
Alberta Advanced Education - Alberta Vocational College - Learning Resources Centre Library (Educ)
10215 108th St. Phone: (403)427-5488
Edmonton, AB, Canada T5A 2N2 Vickii Williams, Mgr., LRC
Staff: Prof 2; Other 8. **Subjects:** Education. **Holdings:** 25,000 books. **Subscriptions:** 200 journals and other serials; 5 newspapers. **Services:** Interlibrary loan; copying; SDI; library open to the public for reference use only. **Computerized Information Services:** DIALOG Information Services. **Publications:** Spotlight (newsletter), 5/year - for internal distribution only. **Remarks:** FAX: (403)427-5465.

★233★
Alberta Advanced Education - Alberta Vocational College, Calgary - Learning Resource Centre (Educ)
332 6th Ave., S.E. Phone: (403)297-4978
Calgary, AB, Canada T2G 4S6 Nora Robinson, Libn.
Founded: 1973. **Staff:** 4. **Holdings:** 28,000 books. **Subscriptions:** 160 journals and other serials; 3 newspapers. **Services:** Interlibrary loan; center open to the public for reference use only. **Remarks:** FAX: (403)297-4081. **Formerly:** Its Alberta Vocational Centre, Calgalry.

★234★
Alberta Advanced Education - Alberta Vocational College, Lac La Biche - Library (Educ)
Box 417 Phone: (403)623-5650
Lac La Biche, AB, Canada T0A 2C0 Lucy M. Chang, Libn.
Founded: 1968. **Staff:** Prof 2; Other 3. **Subjects:** Canadian native culture and history; automotives; engineering; community social services; business careers; carpentry; community health and welfare; commercial cooking; early childhood development. **Holdings:** 16,348 books; 164 filmstrips; 127 audio cassettes; 538 software programs; 886 16mm films; 22 laser discs; 1661 video recordings; 406 kits. **Subscriptions:** 162 journals and other serials; 25 newspapers. **Services:** Interlibrary loan; library open to community and local agency members. **Computerized Information Services:** DOBIS Canadian Online Library System. **Publications:** Subject bibliographies (family violence, suicide, coping with loss, etc.) **Special Catalogs:** AV Catalogue. **Remarks:** FAX: (403)623-5639. **Formerly:** Its Learning Resource Centre. **Staff:** P. Kennedy, Lib.Techn.

★235★
Alberta Advanced Education - Alberta Vocational College, Lesser Slave Lake - Library (Educ)
Grouard, AB, Canada T0G 1C0 Phone: (403)751-3915
Robert Bruce, Libn.
Founded: 1975. **Staff:** 7. **Subjects:** Vocational education. **Holdings:** 23,215 books; 2946 AV materials. **Subscriptions:** 310 journals and other serials. **Services:** Interlibrary loan; library open to the public. **Computerized Information Services:** MULTILIS (internal database). **Staff:** Dev Yadav, Asst.Libn.

★236★
Alberta Advanced Education - Library (Soc Sci)
Devonian Bldg., East Wing, 9th Fl.
11160 Jasper Ave. Phone: (403)427-5590
Edmonton, AB, Canada T5K 0L3 Linda Harris, Dept.Libn.
Founded: 1971. **Staff:** Prof 1; Other 1. **Subjects:** Higher education, adult education. **Holdings:** 6000 books; Statistics Canada publications;

microforms; Alberta legislative materials. **Subscriptions:** 200 journals and other serials. **Services:** Interlibrary loan; copying; library open to the public with restrictions on borrowing. **Automated Operations:** Computerized cataloging. **Computerized Information Services:** DIALOG Information Services; Envoy 100 (electronic mail service). **Publications:** Library Acquisitions, monthly - for internal distribution only; Table of Contents, monthly - for internal distribution only. **Remarks:** FAX: (403)427-4185. Electronic mail address(es): AEAE (Envoy 100).

★237★
Alberta Agriculture - Airdrie Regional Office - Library (Agri)
Bag Service 1
Airdrie, AB, Canada T4B 2C1 Phone: (403)948-8511
Remarks: No further information was supplied by respondent.

★238★
Alberta Agriculture - Barrhead Regional Office - Branch Library (Agri)
Box 1540 Phone: (403)674-8264
Barrhead, AB, Canada T0G 0E0 Eileen Hannah, Libn.
Subjects: Agriculture. **Holdings:** 250 volumes. **Services:** Library not open to the public.

★239★
Alberta Agriculture - Fairview Regional Office - Library (Agri)
Box 7777 Phone: (403)835-2291
Fairview, AB, Canada T0H 1L0 Linda Brazel, Libn.
Subjects: Agriculture. **Holdings:** Figures not available. **Remarks:** FAX: (403)835-5834.

★240★
Alberta Agriculture - Film Library (Agri)
J.G. O'Donahue Bldg.
7000 113th St. Phone: (403)427-2127
Edmonton, AB, Canada T6H 5T6 Ken Blackley, Film Libn.
Staff: 1.5. **Subjects:** Agriculture, home economics, communications, human resources. **Holdings:** 1000 films, videotapes, slide kits, and audiocassettes. **Services:** Library open to the public. **Special Catalogs:** Audio Visual Catalogue, every 1.5 years; What's New (catalog update), biannual. **Remarks:** FAX: (403)427-2861.

★241★
Alberta Agriculture - Food Processing Development Centre (Agri)
6309 45th St.
Box 3476 Phone: (403)986-4793
Leduc, AB, Canada T9E 6M2 Lorea Ladner, Libn.
Founded: 1984. **Staff:** Prof 1. **Subjects:** Food science and technology, product and process development. **Holdings:** 250 books. **Subscriptions:** 45 journals and other serials. **Services:** Interlibrary loan; copying; center open to persons in the food industry. **Computerized Information Services:** DIALOG Information Services. Performs searches on fee basis. Contact Person: Susan Lutz. **Publications:** Innovation Technologies: Your Competitive Edge (brochure). **Remarks:** FAX: (403)986-5138.

★242★
Alberta Agriculture - Irrigation & Resources Management Division - Branch Library (Agri)
Agriculture Centre Phone: (403)381-5140
Lethbridge, AB, Canada T1J 4C7 Erica Wentz, Libn.
Remarks: No further information was supplied by respondent.

★243★
Alberta Agriculture - Lethbridge Regional Office - Library (Agri)
Agriculture Centre Phone: (403)381-5118
Lethbridge, AB, Canada TlJ 4C7 Cheryl Koyata, Libn.
Holdings: 100 books; 200 reports. **Subscriptions:** 35 journals and other serials; 6 newspapers. **Services:** library not open to the public. **Remarks:** FAX: (403)382-4526.

★244★
Alberta Agriculture - Library (Agri)
7000 113th St. Phone: (403)427-2104
Edmonton, AB, Canada T6H 5T6 Robert A. Bateman, Hd.Libn.
Founded: 1972. **Staff:** Prof 4; Other 4. **Subjects:** Agriculture, agricultural economics, veterinary sciences, plant and animal sciences, home economics. **Special Collections:** American Society of Agricultural Engineers papers, 1976 to present (on microfiche); NTIS Selected Research in Microfiche Agriculture Collection, 1981 to 1991. **Holdings:** 32,000 books; 4000 bound periodical volumes; 12,000 pamphlets; 50,000 microfiche. **Subscriptions:** 1250 journals and newsletters. **Services:** Interlibrary loan; copying; SDI; library open to the public with restrictions. **Automated Operations:** Computerized cataloging. **Computerized Information Services:** DIALOG Information Services, CAN/OLE, UTLAS, WILSONLINE, Info Globe, OCLC EPIC, Infomart Online; Envoy 100 (electronic mail service). **Publications:** Library Recent Additions, monthly. **Special Indexes:** Agricultural Conference Proceedings Index - free upon request. **Remarks:** FAX: (403)427-2861. Electronic mail address(es): ILL.AEAG (Envoy 100). **Staff:** Jane Starr, Tech.Serv.Libn.; Connie Hruday, Ref.Libn.; Jennifer Fullen, Ref.Libn.

★245★
Alberta Alcohol and Drug Abuse Commission - Library (Soc Sci)
10909 Jasper Ave., 7th Fl. Phone: (403)427-7303
Edmonton, AB, Canada T5J 3M9 Bette Reimer, Hd.Libn.
Founded: 1974. **Staff:** Prof 2; Other 4. **Subjects:** Alcoholism, drug dependence, counseling. **Holdings:** 7000 books; 6000 reprints; 6 linear feet of news clippings. **Subscriptions:** 200 journals and other serials. **Services:** Interlibrary loan; copying; SDI; library open to the public. **Automated Operations:** Computerized public access catalog and cataloging (Inmagic). **Computerized Information Services:** DIALOG Information Services, Info Globe, QL Systems, BRS Information Technologies; AADAC Library Online Database (internal database). **Networks/Consortia:** Member of Alberta Government Libraries' Council (AGLC), Substance Abuse Librarians and Information Specialists (SALIS). **Publications:** Newsletter, monthly; acquisitions list, monthly; Current Awareness, weekly. **Special Indexes:** KWOC index to reprints held by library; KWOC index to addiction articles contained in library serials collection (both online). **Remarks:** FAX: (403)427-2352.

★246★
Alberta Association of Registered Nurses - Library (Med)
11620 168th St. Phone: (403)451-0043
Edmonton, AB, Canada T5M 4A6 Carol Morgan, Libn.
Founded: 1958. **Staff:** Prof 2. **Subjects:** Nursing. **Holdings:** 5000 books. **Subscriptions:** 110 journals and other serials. **Services:** Interlibrary loan; copying; library open to registered nurses and nursing students. **Publications:** AARN Documents. **Remarks:** FAX: (403)452-3276.

★247★
Alberta Attorney General - Court of Appeal - Law Library (Law)
611-4th St. Phone: (403)297-7475
Calgary, AB, Canada T2P 1T5 Robert W.E. Leigh, Libn.
Founded: 1986. **Staff:** Prof 2; Other 4. **Subjects:** Law. **Holdings:** 6362 books. **Subscriptions:** 115 journals and other serials. **Services:** Library not open to the public. **Automated Operations:** Computerized cataloging. **Computerized Information Services:** QL Systems.

★248★
Alberta Attorney General - Court of Queen's Bench - Law Library (Law)
611 4th St., S.W. Phone: (403)297-7475
Calgary, AB, Canada T2P 1T5 Robert W.E. Leigh, Libn.
Staff: Prof 1; Other 4. **Subjects:** Law. **Special Collections:** Biographical information for all federal judges in Alberta. **Holdings:** 8720 volumes; 2 drawers of unreported decisions of Alberta and federal supreme courts. **Subscriptions:** 186 journals and other serials. **Services:** Interlibrary loan; library not open to the public. **Remarks:** Housed with Law Society of Alberta - Calgary Library. Alternate telephone number(s): 297-2209.

★249★
Alberta Attorney General - Law Library (Law)
403 Bowker Bldg., 4th Fl.
9833 109th St. Phone: (403)498-3412
Edmonton, AB, Canada T5K 2E8 Andrew Balazs, Libn.
Founded: 1912. **Staff:** Prof 1; Other 2. **Subjects:** Canadian constitutional, criminal, civil, and international law. **Special Collections:** 16th to 19th century English, Canadian, and American classical legal texts (44 volumes). **Holdings:** 5650 books; 12,748 bound law reports; 1150 government documents; 168 Criminal Law Audio Series audiotapes; 36 research digest titles. **Subscriptions:** 356 journals and other serials. **Services:** Interlibrary loan (limited); library not open to the public. **Publications:** Recent Acquisitions in the Alberta Attorney General Law Library, monthly - to all solicitors. **Remarks:** FAX: (403)427-6821. Telex: 610-831-1167 TWX. Alternate telephone number(s): (403)498-3415.

Alberta Attorney General - Law Society of Alberta
See: **Law Society of Alberta** (8989)

★250★
Alberta Attorney General - Provincial Court Libraries (Law)
Law Courts, 5th Fl.
1A Sir Winston Churchill Sq. Phone: (403)427-5579
Edmonton, AB, Canada T5J 0R2 Heather Schneider, Prov.Ct.Libn.
Founded: 1976. **Staff:** Prof 5; Other 32. **Subjects:** Law. **Holdings:** 160,000 books. **Subscriptions:** 294 journals and other serials. **Services:** Interlibrary loan (limited); rural libraries open to the public by appointment. **Automated Operations:** Computerized cataloging. **Computerized Information Services:** WESTLAW, UTLAS, QL Systems, CAN/LAW, Info Globe. **Publications:** Alberta Provincial Court Decisions, annual - for internal distribution only. **Remarks:** FAX (403)427-0481. Regional library maintained at 323 6th Ave., S.E., Calgary, AB T2G 4V1. **Staff:** Peter Curtis, Crown/Pub.Serv.Libn.; E. Tooby, Crown Libn. (South); L. Ball, Cat.Libn.; J. Dennis, Supv. of Orders & Accounts; S. Powelson, Reg.Libn. (South).

★251★
Alberta Attorney General - Provincial Court Library, Calgary (Law)
323 6th Ave., S.E. Phone: (403)297-3126
Calgary, AB, Canada T2G 5V1 Susan Powelson, Reg.Libn.
Subjects: Law. **Services:** Library not open to the public. **Computerized Information Services:** QL Systems, CAN/LAW, Info Globe.

★252★
Alberta Attorney General - Provincial Court Library, Fort Saskatchewan (Law)
10504 100th Ave. Phone: (403)998-1200
Fort Saskatchewan, AB, Canada T8L 3S9 Harriet W. Schultz, Lib.Ck.
Founded: 1980. **Staff:** 1. **Subjects:** Law. **Holdings:** 5860 volumes; 3 VF drawers. **Subscriptions:** 71 journals and other serials. **Services:** Interlibrary loan; copying; library open to the public for reference use only.

★253★
Alberta Attorney General - Provincial Court Library, Leduc (Law)
4612 50th St. Phone: (403)986-6911
Leduc, AB, Canada T9E 6L1 Barbara Johnson, Libn.
Subjects: Law. **Remarks:** No further information was supplied by respondent.

★254★
Alberta Bureau of Statistics - Information Centre (Bus-Fin)
Park Plaza
10611 98th Ave., Suite 600 Phone: (403)427-3058
Edmonton, AB, Canada T5K 2R7 Harvey Ford, Dir.
Founded: 1955. **Staff:** 1. **Subjects:** Statistics, economics, census of Canada. **Special Collections:** Statistics Canada publications (1500). **Holdings:** 4600 volumes; maps; microforms. **Services:** Library open to the public for reference use only. **Automated Operations:** Computerized serials. **Special Catalogs:** Statistics catalog. **Special Indexes:** Index to microforms. **Remarks:** FAX: (403)427-0409.

★255★
Alberta Career Development & Employment - Library (Bus-Fin)
CityCentre, 9th Fl.
10155-102 St. Phone: (403)422-4752
Edmonton, AB, Canada T5J 4L5 Judy E. Sponholz, Libn.
Founded: 1982. **Staff:** Prof 3; Other 1. **Subjects:** Manpower/labor market, career planning, demography, economics, statistics, industry. **Special Collections:** Statistics Canada documents; government and corporation annual reports; Canadian university and college calendars. **Holdings:** 9000 books. **Subscriptions:** 450 journals and other serials; 5 newspapers. **Services:** Interlibrary loan; copying; library open to the public with restrictions. **Automated Operations:** Computerized cataloging. **Computerized Information Services:** DIALOG Information Services, Info Globe, Infomart Online. **Publications:** Off the Shelf, monthly - for internal distribution only. **Remarks:** FAX: (403)422-5126. **Staff:** Colleen Good, Lib.Techn.; Christine Adams, Lib.Techn.

★256★
Alberta Children's Hospital - Library (Med)
1820 Richmond Rd., S.W. Phone: (403)229-7077
Calgary, AB, Canada T2T 5C7 Barbara Hatt, Libn.
Founded: 1982. **Staff:** Prof 1. **Subjects:** Children's health care. **Holdings:** 2700 books. **Subscriptions:** 250 journals and other serials. **Services:** Interlibrary loan; library not open to the public. **Computerized Information Services:** DIALOG Information Services, MEDLARS; Envoy 100 (electronic mail service). **Remarks:** FAX: (403)229-7221. Electronic mail address(es): ILL.ACACH (Envoy 100).

★257★
Alberta College of Art - Luke Lindoe Library (Art)
1407 14th Ave., N.W. Phone: (403)284-7631
Calgary, AB, Canada T2N 4R3 Christine E. Sammon, Dir., Lrng.Rsrcs.
Staff: Prof 1; Other 5. **Subjects:** Art history, painting, sculpture, graphic arts, textiles, photography, glass, ceramics, advertising art, jewelry. **Holdings:** 14,970 books; 250 bound periodical volumes; 88,700 slides; 3000 mounted prints; 1000 picture clippings. **Subscriptions:** 85 journals and other serials. **Services:** Interlibrary loan; copying; center open to the public. **Automated Operations:** Computerized public access catalog, acquisitions, cataloging, and circulation. **Publications:** Periodical holdings list. **Special Catalogs:** Film catalog. **Special Indexes:** Index to slide collection (card). **Remarks:** FAX: (403)284-3355.

★258★
Alberta Consumer and Corporate Affairs - Resource Centre (Bus-Fin)
10025 Jasper Ave., 22nd Fl. Phone: (403)422-2010
Edmonton, AB, Canada T5J 3Z5 Carole Dawson, Hd., Res.Ctr.
Staff: Prof 1; Other 2. **Subjects:** Consumer education, corporation information, insurance, real estate, cooperatives. **Holdings:** 12,000 volumes; 7000 pamphlets. **Subscriptions:** 246 journals and other serials; 6 newspapers. **Services:** Interlibrary loan; copying; center open to the public. **Automated Operations:** Computerized cataloging and serials. **Computerized Information Services:** DIALOG Information Services, Info Globe, Infomart Online, INSIGHT, QL Systems, SPIRES. **Networks/Consortia:** Member of Alberta Government Libraries' Council (AGLC). **Publications:** Library Consumer Resources (bibliography), annual - distributed to public libraries in Alberta. **Special Indexes:** KWOC index to magazine collection; KWOC index to pamphlet collection. **Remarks:** FAX: (403)422-3579.

Alberta Culture and Multiculturalism
See: **Royal Tyrrell Museum of Palaeontology** (14138)

★259★
Alberta Culture and Multiculturalism - Provincial Archives of Alberta - Library (Area-Ethnic, Hist)
12845 102nd Ave. Phone: (403)427-1750
Edmonton, AB, Canada T5N 0M6 M.K. Aubrey, Hd.Libn.
Founded: 1963. **Staff:** Prof 11; Other 5. **Subjects:** Alberta - history, government departments, photographers, political parties, churches, trade unions; archive administration; historic preservation. **Special Collections:** Papers of Alberta Premier's office, Oblates of Mary Immaculate, United Church of Canada, Alberta and Northwest Conference, and Anglican Church of Canada, Dioceses of Athabasca, Mackenzie River, and Edmonton; Alberta local history; history of Western Canada. **Holdings:**

7,000 books; 11,799 linear meters of government documents; 3587 linear meters of private manuscript records; 250,000 photographs; 34,000 reels of microfilm; 8500 hours of sound recordings; 3500 hours of film; maps. **Subscriptions:** 50 journals and other serials. **Services:** Copying; archives open to the public. **Automated Operations:** Computerized cataloging. **Publications:** Sources of Women's History; Writing Local History; Government Records Collections; Alberta's Local Histories; Native Peoples of Alberta: A Bibliographic Guide. **Special Catalogs:** Periodical holdings (book). **Special Indexes:** Collection inventories. **Remarks:** FAX: (403)454-6629. **Staff:** W. Brian Speirs, Prov.Archv.; David Leonard, Chf.Archv., Govt.Rec.; Keith Stotyn, Chf.Archv., Mss.; Brock Silversides, Chf.Archv., AV & Tech.Serv.

★260★

Alberta Culture and Multiculturalism - Reynolds-Alberta Museum - Resource Centre (Hist)
Hwy. 13 W.
PO Box 6360 Phone: (403)361-1351
Wetaskiwin, AB, Canada T9A 2G1 Judy-Lynn Downey, Libn.
Founded: 1982. **Staff:** 1. **Subjects:** Transportation, agriculture, industry. **Special Collections:** Original catalogs, manuals, parts lists (for vehicles, machinery, and equipment; 6000). **Holdings:** 1500 books; 650 subject files; 900 advertisement files. **Subscriptions:** 60 magazines and newsletters. **Services:** Interlibrary loan; copying; library open to the public for reference use only. **Automated Operations:** Computerized public access catalog. **Remarks:** FAX: (403)361-1239. **Formerly:** Reynolds Museum - Library.

★261★

Alberta Department of the Solicitor General - Calgary Correctional Centre - Staff Library (Law)
P.O. Box 3250, Sta. B
Calgary, AB, Canada T2M 4L9 Phone: (403)239-0010
Founded: 1982. **Staff:** 2. **Subjects:** Corrections, management, law, psychology. **Holdings:** 125 books; 50 reports. **Subscriptions:** 17 journals and other serials. **Services:** Interlibrary loan; library not open to the public. **Remarks:** FAX: (403)297-4577.

★262★

Alberta Department of the Solicitor General - Reference Centre (Law)
John E. Brownlee Bldg., 10th Fl.
10365 97th St. Phone: (403)427-3421
Edmonton, AB, Canada T5J 3W7 Eunice Cutting, Ref.Libn.
Staff: Prof 2; Other 1. **Subjects:** Criminal justice and corrections, law enforcement, crime prevention, impaired driving. **Holdings:** 2000 documents; 850 microfiche. **Subscriptions:** 175 journals and other serials. **Services:** Interlibrary loan; copying; library open to the public for reference use only at discretion of librarian. **Computerized Information Services:** DIALOG Information Services, QL Systems, Info Globe, CAN/OLE, DOBIS, Infomart Online, ESA/IRS; Envoy 100 (electronic mail service). **Networks/Consortia:** Member of Alberta Government Libraries' Council (AGLC), Criminal Justice Information Exchange Group. **Publications:** Current Journal Contents, monthly. **Remarks:** FAX: (403)427-1903. Electronic mail address(es): ILL.ASGLS (Envoy 100). **Staff:** Mary Leung.

★263★

Alberta Distance Learning Centre - Library (Educ)
4801 63rd Ave.
Box 4000 Phone: (403)674-5333
Barrhead, AB, Canada T0G 2P0 Dawn I. Hagan, Info.Mgr.
Founded: 1983. **Staff:** Prof 1; Other 1. **Subjects:** Education, elementary and secondary curriculum, professional reference. **Special Collections:** Distance education. **Holdings:** 25,000 books. **Subscriptions:** 137 journals and other serials. **Services:** Center not open to the public. **Remarks:** FAX: (403)674-6561. **Formerly:** Alberta Correspondence School - Distance Education Resource Center.

★264★

Alberta Economic Development and Trade - Library (Bus-Fin)
Sterling Place
9940 106th St., 8th Fl. Phone: (403)427-4957
Edmonton, AB, Canada T5K 2P6 Donna M. Gordon, Libn.
Founded: 1979. **Staff:** Prof 2; Other 2. **Subjects:** International trade, industry promotion, small business, strategic planning, transportation, economics. **Special Collections:** Annual reports from 700 companies (8 drawers). **Holdings:** 5500 books. **Subscriptions:** 500 journals and other serials; 15 newspapers. **Services:** Interlibrary loan; copying; library open to the public for reference use only. **Automated Operations:** Computerized cataloging. **Computerized Information Services:** DIALOG Information Services, Info Globe, CAN/OLE, Infomart Online; Envoy 100 (electronic mail service). **Remarks:** FAX: (403)427-0610. Electronic mail address(es): ILL.AEED (Envoy 100).

★265★

Alberta Education - Lethbridge Regional Office - Resource Centre (Educ)
Provincial Bldg.
200 5th Ave., S.
Bag No. 3014 Phone: (403)381-5243
Lethbridge, AB, Canada T1J 4C7 Candice St. Clair, Libn.
Subjects: Education. **Holdings:** Figures not available. **Services:** Centre open to the public for reference use only.

★266★

Alberta Education - Library Services (Educ)
Devonian Bldg., West Tower
11160 Jasper Ave. Phone: (403)427-2985
Edmonton, AB, Canada T5K 0L2 Shirley Wolodko, Mgr., Lib.Serv.
Founded: 1971. **Staff:** Prof 5; Other 2. **Subjects:** Education - reference and research, policy analysis and development, administration, evaluation, supervision, preschool-secondary, special, gifted. **Special Collections:** Alberta Education Documents Collection (3000); Canadian and U.S. curriculum guides (20,000); Curriculum Lab Collection (basic and recommended resources for Alberta schools); Microlog Education Fiche. **Holdings:** 20,000 monographs; 1000 bound periodical volumes; ERIC microfiche; pamphlets. **Subscriptions:** 900 journals and other serials; 7 newspapers. **Services:** Interlibrary loan; copying; library open to the public. **Automated Operations:** Computerized cataloging, acquisitions, and serials. **Computerized Information Services:** DIALOG Information Services, BRS Information Technologies, CAN/OLE, UTLAS, ESA/IRS, Infomart Online, Info Globe, QL Systems, SPIRES, WILSONLINE, PFDS Online, Industrielle-Services Techniques Inc. (IST), Mead Data Central, DOBIS Canadian Online Library System, iNET 2000, GTE Education Network, York Online; CD-ROMs (ERIC); Curriculum Resources Evaluation Database (internal database); Envoy 100 (electronic mail service). **Publications:** Library Acquisitions List; Content Pages. **Special Catalogs:** Union Lists of Professional and Curriculum Collections (microfiche). **Remarks:** FAX: (403)427-5927. Electronic mail address(es): ILL.AEE (Envoy 100). **Staff:** Charlotte Landry, Ref.; Christine Andrews, Ref.

★267★

Alberta Education - Materials Resource Centre for the Visually Impaired North (Educ, Aud-Vis)
Edwards Bldg., 1st Fl.
10053 111th St. Phone: (403)427-4681
Edmonton, AB, Canada T5K 2H8 Kathryn Ribeiro, Mgr.
Founded: 1970. **Staff:** Prof 2; Other 11. **Special Collections:** Educational materials from preschool to grade 12 for the visually impaired. **Holdings:** 1391 books; 2770 braille titles; 2510 audiotape titles; 2790 large print titles; 345 kit titles. **Subscriptions:** 20 journals and other serials. **Services:** Interlibrary loan (to other provincial resource centers for the visually impaired); center open to the public for reference use only. **Computerized Information Services:** UTLAS, DOBIS Canadian Online Library System; Dataease (internal database); Envoy 100 (electronic mail service). **Remarks:** FAX: (403)427-6683. Electronic mail address(es): ILL.AEEM (Envoy 100). Holdings are combined figures for both the North and South Centres. **Staff:** Lorie McArthur.

★268★

Alberta Education Materials Resource Centre for the Visually Impaired - South (Educ)
575 28th St., S.E., Bay 15 Phone: (403)297-4378
Calgary, AB, Canada T2A 6X1 Colleen Tobman, Mgr.
Founded: 1982. **Staff:** 10. **Special Collections:** Educational materials from preschool to grade 12 in special formats for the visually impaired. **Holdings:** 1557 books; 2835 braille titles; 2583 audiotape titles; 2839 large print titles; 361 kit titles. **Subscriptions:** 10 journals and other serials. **Services:** Interlibrary loan (restricted to Canadian provincial resource centers for the visually impaired); library open to the public for reference use only.

Computerized Information Services: UTLAS, DOBIS Canadian Online Library System, Canadian Union Catalogue of Library Materials for the Print Handicapped (CANUC:H); internal database; Envoy 100 (electronic mail service). **Special Catalogs:** Titles and subjects catalogs, semiannual; series, authors, and shelflist catalogs, for internal distribution only; accessions list, 9/year. **Remarks:** FAX: (403)297-4365. Electronic mail address(es): ILL.ACEM (Envoy 100). Holdings are combined figures for both the North and South Centres. **Staff:** Lucinda Yaworski, Lib.Techn.

★269★
Alberta Education Response Centre - Reference Centre (Med, Educ)
6240 113th St. Phone: (403)422-6326
Edmonton, AB, Canada T6H 3L2 Connie L. Hall, Mgr., Ref.Ctr.
Founded: 1982. **Staff:** 1. **Subjects:** Deaf - teaching, psychology, special education, research, educational technology. **Special Collections:** Alberta Education documents. **Holdings:** 2000 books; 50 videotapes; 170 periodical volumes. **Subscriptions:** 80 journals and other serials; 3 newspapers. **Services:** Interlibrary loan; copying; SDI; library open to the public by appointment to researchers, parents, and teachers. **Automated Operations:** Computerized public access catalog. **Computerized Information Services:** CompuServe Information Service, DIALOG Information Services, CAN/OLE, UTLAS. **Publications:** Parent Resources Inventory, Alberta. **Remarks:** FAX: (403)422-2039.

★270★
Alberta Energy/Forestry, Lands and Wildlife - Library (Energy, Biol Sci)
Petroleum Plaza, South Tower, 9th Fl.
9915 108th St. Phone: (403)427-7425
Edmonton, AB, Canada T5K 2C9 Susan Carlisle, Hd.
Founded: 1977. **Staff:** Prof 1; Other 6. **Subjects:** Energy economics and resources, forestry, forest industry, mineral resources, public lands, energy conservation, fish and wildlife. **Holdings:** 12,000 books; 200 bound periodical volumes; 250 folders in VF drawers; 200 microfiche; 18,000 reports. **Subscriptions:** 265 journals and other serials; 5 newspapers. **Services:** Interlibrary loan; copying; library open to the public for reference use only. **Automated Operations:** Computerized cataloging. **Computerized Information Services:** DIALOG Information Services, QL Systems, Info Globe, PFDS Online, Infomart Online, STM Systems Corporation, WILSONLINE, CAN/OLE, UTLAS; Envoy 100 (electronic mail service). Performs searches on fee basis (partial charge-back). **Networks/Consortia:** Member of Alberta Government Libraries' Council (AGLC). **Publications:** New Books, bimonthly; Current Magazine Articles, weekly - both for internal distribution only. **Special Indexes:** Speeches and news releases indexes; natural resources KWOC index. **Remarks:** FAX: (403)422-3578. Electronic mail address(es): AENR (Envoy 100). **Staff:** C. Ingram, Tech.Serv.Supv.; M. Wickramasekara, ILL.

★271★
Alberta Energy Resources Conservation Board - Library (Energy)
640 5th Ave., S.W. Phone: (403)297-8242
Calgary, AB, Canada T2P 3G4 Ms. E.A. Johnson, Libn.
Founded: 1964. **Staff:** Prof 1; Other 3. **Subjects:** Oil, gas, coal, hydro and electric power, pipelines, geology, energy economics. **Holdings:** 6000 books; 7000 government documents. **Subscriptions:** 450 journals and other serials; 12 newspapers. **Services:** Interlibrary loan; copying; library open to the public. **Automated Operations:** Computerized cataloging. **Computerized Information Services:** DIALOG Information Services, ORBIT Search Service, CAN/OLE, Info Globe, QL Systems, SPIRES, Infomart Online; DIALMAIL, Envoy 100 (electronic mail services). **Publications:** Library Bulletin - available upon request. **Remarks:** FAX: (403)297-7040. Electronic mail address(es): ERCB.LIB (Envoy 100).

★272★
Alberta Environment - Library (Env-Cons)
Oxbridge Place, 14th Fl.
9820 106th St. Phone: (403)427-6132
Edmonton, AB, Canada T5K 2J6 Deb Fralick, Hd., Lib.Serv.
Founded: 1971. **Staff:** Prof 2; Other 7. **Subjects:** Water resources; land use planning; environmental conservation; pollution - air, water, odor, noise. **Holdings:** 35,000 books; 6 drawers of maps; 4 cabinets of microfiche; NTIS publications. **Subscriptions:** 700 journals and other serials; 25 newspapers. **Services:** Interlibrary loan; copying; library open to the public. **Automated Operations:** Computerized cataloging. **Computerized Information Services:** DIALOG Information Services, MEDLINE, QL Systems, CAN/OLE, Infomart Online Info Globe; SCITECH database (internal database). **Publications:** Acquisition list, monthly; periodical list, semimonthly. **Special Indexes:** Index to periodical articles held by library. **Staff:** Ann Schiebelbein.

★273★
(Alberta) Environment Council of Alberta - Information Centre (Env-Cons)
Weber Centre, 8th Fl.
5555 Calgary Trail Southbound, N.W.
Edmonton, AB, Canada T6H 5P9 Phone: (403)427-5792
Founded: 1971. **Staff:** Prof 1. **Subjects:** Conservation, energy, land use, renewable and nonrenewable resources, pollution, urbanization. **Special Collections:** Mackenzie Valley Pipeline Inquiry Transcripts (281 volumes); World Conservation Strategy (238 documents). **Holdings:** 6000 books and government reports; ECA reports, recommendations, proceedings, summaries of public hearings; 2 VF drawers of pamphlets; 8 VF drawers of clippings. **Subscriptions:** 69 journals and other serials. **Services:** Interlibrary loan; library open to the public with restrictions on borrowing. **Automated Operations:** Computerized cataloging. **Computerized Information Services:** DIALOG Information Services. **Publications:** List of ECA publications - available upon request. **Remarks:** FAX: (403)427-0388.

★274★
Alberta Environmental Centre - Library (Env-Cons, Biol Sci)
Bag 4000 Phone: (403)632-8415
Vegreville, AB, Canada T0B 4L0 Sherry van Roodselaar, Libn.
Founded: 1978. **Staff:** Prof 1; Other 5. **Subjects:** Science - environmental, animal, plant; chemical analysis; toxicology; ecology. **Holdings:** 11,500 books; 3500 technical reports. **Subscriptions:** 300 journals and other serials; 7 newspapers. **Services:** Interlibrary loan; SDI. **Automated Operations:** Computerized cataloging and circulation. **Computerized Information Services:** DIALOG Information Services, PFDS Online, CAN/OLE II, MEDLARS, STN International; CD-ROMs (MEDLINE, AGRICOLA, TOXLINE, CRIS/ICAR, Selected Water Resources Abstracts, CCINFOdisc); Envoy 100, UTLAS REFCATTS (electronic mail services). Performs searches. **Remarks:** FAX: (403)632-8379. Electronic mail address(es): ILL.AVEE; INFO.SERVICES; COMMON SERVICES; AEC.LIBRARY (Envoy 100).

★275★
Alberta Family and Social Services - Library (Soc Sci)
Seventh Street Plaza, 6th Fl.
10035 108th St. Phone: (403)427-7272
Edmonton, AB, Canada T5J 3E1 Teresa Bendall, Lib.Adm.
Founded: 1972. **Staff:** Prof 1; Other 3. **Subjects:** Family and social services, handicapped. **Holdings:** 10,000 volumes; 8 VF drawers; 20 shelves of Statistics Canada publications. **Subscriptions:** 200 journals and other serials; 7 newspapers. **Services:** Interlibrary loan; copying; library open to the public with restrictions. **Computerized Information Services:** DIALOG Information Services, MEDLINE, BRS Information Technologies, iNET 2000; Envoy 100 (electronic mail service). **Networks/Consortia:** Member of Alberta Government Libraries' Council (AGLC). **Publications:** New Books, bimonthly; Current Journal Articles, semimonthly - both for internal distribution only. **Remarks:** FAX: (403)422-0031. Electronic mail address(es): ILL.AEHSD (Envoy 100).

★276★
Alberta Federal and Intergovernmental Affairs - Library (Soc Sci)
10025 Jasper Ave., Suite 2200 Phone: (403)427-2614
Edmonton, AB, Canada T5J 1S6 Anita E. Duncan, Libn.
Founded: 1972. **Staff:** 2. **Subjects:** Intergovernmental affairs, political science. **Holdings:** 4500 books; 2347 federal and provincial government publications and documents; 800 Alberta, federal, provincial, and business annual reports; 9 VF drawers of newspaper clippings; federal and provincial statutes. **Subscriptions:** 350 journals and other serials; 22 newspapers. **Services:** Interlibrary loan; library open to the public with restrictions on borrowing. **Remarks:** FAX: (403)423-6654.

★277★
Alberta Federation of Labour - Resource Centre (Bus-Fin)
10451 170th St., Suite 350
Edmonton, AB, Canada T5P 4T2 Phone: (403)483-3021
Remarks: FAX: (403)484-5928. No further information was supplied by respondent.

★278★
Alberta Forestry, Lands and Wildlife - Maps Alberta - Reference Library (Geog-Map)
North Petroleum Plaza, 2nd Fl. W.
9945 108th St. Phone: (403)427-7417
Edmonton, AB, Canada T5K 2G6 Alice S. Chen, Supv.
Founded: 1967. **Staff:** Prof 1; Other 2. **Subjects:** Aerial photographs and maps of Alberta. **Holdings:** 275 books; 950,000 aerial photographs; 6000 maps; 950 microfilm cassettes. **Services:** Library open to the public for reference use only. **Publications:** Maps Alberta Newsletter, semiannual - to the public. **Special Catalogs:** Maps Alberta Catalogue, annual. **Remarks:** FAX: (403)422-9683.

Alberta Health - Alberta Mental Health Services
See: **Alberta Mental Health Services** (289)

Alberta Health - Hospitals and Medical Care - Library
See: **Alberta Health - Library and Inquiry Services Branch - Hospitals and Medical Care Section** (280)

★279★
Alberta Health - Library and Inquiry Services Branch (Med)
10709 Jasper Ave., 6th Fl. Phone: (403)427-3530
Edmonton, AB, Canada T5J 3N3 Joanne Lavkulich, Act.Dir.
Founded: 1988. **Staff:** Prof 3; Other 6. **Subjects:** Health - public, mental, environmental; hospitals and medical care. **Special Collections:** AIDS collection; departmental publications. **Holdings:** 14,000 books; 1100 films and videos. **Subscriptions:** 600 journals and other serials; 15 newspapers. **Services:** Interlibrary loan; SDI; library open to the public with restrictions. **Automated Operations:** Computerized public access catalog, cataloging, acquisitions, circulation. **Computerized Information Services:** DIALOG Information Services, MEDLARS, CAN/OLE, SIEC (Suicide Information and Education Centre), OCLC, DOBIS Canadian Online Library System; Envoy 100 (electronic mail service). **Networks/Consortia:** Member of OCLC Pacific Network. **Publications:** Recent Acquisitions, monthly; current awareness bulletins; AIDS bibliographies. **Special Catalogs:** Film Catalog - on request; report reference file of departmental publications. **Remarks:** Alternate telephone number(s): 427-8720. FAX: (403)427-5698; (403)422-3658. Electronic mail address(es): AECOH.ILL; PK.YEH (both Envoy 100). **Staff:** Peggy Yeh, Libn.; Linda Bumstead, Pub.Serv.Libn.; Judith McKettrick, Info.Spec.; Anna Duerr, Info./Database Spec.; Kathy Lema, Info.Spec.

★280★
Alberta Health - Library and Inquiry Services Branch - Hospitals and Medical Care Section (Med)
10025 Jasper Ave., 24th Fl.
Box 2222 Phone: (403)427-8720
Edmonton, AB, Canada T5J 2P4 Peggy Yeh, Libn.
Staff: Prof 1; Other 2. **Subjects:** Health care, hospital administration, hospitals and nursing homes, health and medical legislation, management, records management, hospital architecture, health manpower, long-term care, physical and occupational therapy, drug information, nursing management. **Holdings:** 7000 books; 1000 microfiche; 30 videotapes; 100 audio cassettes. **Subscriptions:** 275 journals and other serials. **Services:** Interlibrary loan; copying; SDI; library open to the public with restrictions on borrowing. **Automated Operations:** Computerized circulation and cataloging. **Computerized Information Services:** DIALOG Information Services, CAN/OLE, BRS Information Technologies, Info Globe, DOBIS, MEDLARS; internal database; Envoy 100 (electronic mail service). **Networks/Consortia:** Member of Northern Alberta Health Libraries Association, Alberta Government Libraries' Council (AGLC). **Publications:** Recent Journals, biweekly; New Book Additions, quarterly - both for internal distribution only. **Special Indexes:** Index to Alberta Health Departmental Reports. **Remarks:** FAX: (403)427-2511. **Formerly:** Alberta Health - Hospitals and Medical Care - Library. **Staff:** Kathy Lema, Lib.Techn.

★281★
Alberta Healthcare Association - Resource Library (Med)
10009 108th St. Phone: (403)498-8400
Edmonton, AB, Canada T5J 3C5 Patricia Baxter, Libn.
Staff: 1. **Subjects:** Health care management and research. **Holdings:** 4000 books; 400 bound periodical volumes; 400 briefs and studies. **Subscriptions:** 80 journals and other serials. **Services:** Interlibrary loan; copying; SDI; library open to the public at librarian's discretion. **Automated Operations:** Computerized public access catalog. **Computerized Information Services:** DIALOG Information Services. **Remarks:** FAX: (403)498-8465. **Formerly:** Alberta Hospital Association.

★282★
Alberta Historical Resources Foundation - Library
102 8th Ave., S.E.
Calgary, AB, Canada T2G 0K6
Defunct.

Alberta Hospital Association
See: **Alberta Healthcare Association** (281)

★283★
Alberta Hospital Edmonton - Library (Med)
Box 307 Phone: (403)472-5555
Edmonton, AB, Canada T5J 2J7 Margaret Pierre, Med.Lib.Techn.
Founded: 1968. **Subjects:** Psychiatry, psychiatric nursing, psychology, neuropsychology, social service, occupational and recreational therapy, gerontology, forensic psychiatry, hospital administration, rehabilitation. **Holdings:** 5000 books; 134 periodicals; 109 videotapes; 121 audio cassettes. **Services:** Interlibrary loan; library not open to the public. **Networks/Consortia:** Member of Northern Alberta Health Libraries Association.

★284★
Alberta Hospital Ponoka - Library Resources Centre (Med)
P.O. Box 1000 Phone: (403)783-7691
Ponoka, AB, Canada T0C 2H0 Peter Managhan, Staff Libn.
Founded: 1972. **Staff:** Prof 1; Other 1. **Subjects:** Psychiatry, psychology, nursing, social work, gerontology. **Special Collections:** Brain injury rehabilitation. **Holdings:** 3000 books; VF material; cassette tapes. **Subscriptions:** 163 journals and other serials. **Services:** Interlibrary loan; copying; SDI; library open to the public with restrictions. **Computerized Information Services:** CD-ROM (CINAHL). **Networks/Consortia:** Member of Northern Alberta Health Libraries Association. **Remarks:** FAX: (403)783-7730.

★285★
Alberta Labour - Information Services (Bus-Fin)
10808 99th Ave., Rm. 300 Phone: (403)427-8533
Edmonton, AB, Canada T5K 0G5 Heather Gordon, Dir.
Founded: 1975. **Staff:** Prof 2; Other 5. **Subjects:** Labor law, human rights, building standards, inspection services, industrial relations, personnel management, career planning. **Holdings:** 15,000 books; 450 bound periodical volumes; 1000 microforms; 5000 pamphlets. **Subscriptions:** 500 journals and other serials; 5 newspapers. **Services:** Interlibrary loan; copying; SDI; branch open to the public. **Automated Operations:** Computerized public access catalog, cataloging, acquisitions, serials, and periodical routing. **Computerized Information Services:** DIALOG Information Services, Info Globe, WILSONLINE, CAN/OLE, QL Systems, Infomart Online; internal databases; Envoy 100 (electronic mail service). **Publications:** Current Contents, biweekly; New Books, monthly. **Special Indexes:** Alberta Labour Relations Precedents Index Series: Alberta Labour Relations Board Decisions Index (online), Alberta Employment Standards Umpire Awards Index, Alberta Grievance Arbitration Awards Index (online), Alberta Interest Arbitration Awards Index. **Remarks:** FAX: (403)422-5070. Electronic mail address(es): ALTA.LABOUR.INFO (Envoy 100). **Staff:** Debbie Hunter, Pub.Serv.Libn.

★286★
Alberta Labour - Information Services - Audio-Visual Services (Aud-Vis)
10808 99th Ave., 3rd Fl. Phone: (403)427-8533
Edmonton, AB, Canada T5K 0G5 Heather Gordon, Dir.
Founded: 1982. **Staff:** 1. **Subjects:** Fire safety, labor relations, career planning and development, human resource management. **Holdings:** 600 films, slide/tape sets, and video cassettes. **Services:** Services open to the public. **Special Catalogs:** Fire Protection Film Catalogue, 1991. **Remarks:** FAX: (403)422-5070. **Staff:** Halina Mzyk, Lib.Techn.

★287★
Alberta Law Reform Institute - Library (Law)
402 Law Centre
University of Alberta Phone: (403)492-5291
Edmonton, AB, Canada T6G 2H5 Tanya Filanovsky, Inst.Libn.
Founded: 1968. **Staff:** Prof 1; Other 1. **Subjects:** Law, law reform. **Special Collections:** Commonwealth Law Reform Publications (2600). **Holdings:** 1070 books; 3550 bound periodical volumes; 9 boxes of pamphlets. **Subscriptions:** 100 journals and other serials. **Services:** Copying; library open to the public for reference use only. **Computerized Information Services:** QL Systems, DIALOG Information Services. **Publications:** List of publications - available upon request. **Remarks:** FAX: (403)492-1790.

★288★
(Alberta) Legislative Assembly of Alberta - Legislature Library (Law)
902 Legislature Annex Phone: (403)422-5085
9718 107 St. D.B. McDougall, Asst.Dep.
Edmonton, AB, Canada T5K 1E4 Minister/Leg.Libn.
Founded: 1906. **Staff:** Prof 6; Other 10. **Subjects:** Political science, public administration, law, economics, sociology, Canadian history. **Special Collections:** Most provincial weekly newspapers, 1907 to present. **Holdings:** 203,538 volumes; Alberta and federal government documents. **Subscriptions:** 450 journals and other serials; 163 newspapers. **Services:** Interlibrary loan; copying; library open to the public with restrictions. **Automated Operations:** Computerized cataloging and serials. **Computerized Information Services:** CAN/OLE, Canadian Business and Current Affairs (CBCA), DIALOG Information Services, Info Globe, PFDS Online, QL Systems, SPIRES; QuickLaw (electronic mail service). **Networks/Consortia:** Member of Alberta Government Libraries' Council (AGLC). **Publications:** New Books in the Library, 12/year; Selected Periodical Articles List, 11/year; Alberta Government Libraries' Newsletter, 11/year; Directory of Alberta Government Libraries, semiannual; Library Handbook, biennial. **Special Catalogs:** Alberta Government Libraries' Union Catalog; Union List of Serials in Alberta Government Libraries. **Remarks:** FAX: (403)427-6016. Electronic mail address(es): 270 ALTALL (QuickLaw). **Staff:** L.R. Buhr, Mgr., Info. & Ref.Serv.; K.L. Powell, Mgr., Coop.Govt.Lib.Serv.

★289★
Alberta Mental Health Services - Clinic Library (Med)
9942 108th St., 5th Fl. Phone: (403)427-4444
Edmonton, AB, Canada T5K 2J5 Nirmala Koganty
Founded: 1948. **Staff:** 1. **Subjects:** Psychiatry, psychology, nursing, occupational therapy, social work, domestic science. **Holdings:** 1594 books. **Subscriptions:** 38 journals and other serials. **Services:** Library not open to the public. **Remarks:** FAX: (403)427-0424. Maintained by Alberta Health.

★290★
Alberta Mental Health Services - Regional Library
206-301 14th St., N.W.
Calgary, AB, Canada T2P 2A4
Defunct.

★291★
Alberta Municipal Affairs - Library (Plan)
CityCentre, 17th Fl.
10155 - 102 St. Phone: (403)427-4829
Edmonton, AB, Canada T5J 4L4 Dolores Ogilvie, Dept.Libn.
Founded: 1975. **Staff:** Prof 1; Other 3. **Subjects:** Urban and regional planning, municipal government, housing, native affairs. **Holdings:** 15,000 books; 150 AV materials. **Subscriptions:** 425 journals and other serials. **Services:** Interlibrary loan; copying; library open to the public for reference use only. **Automated Operations:** Computerized cataloging and circulation. **Computerized Information Services:** DIALOG Information Services. **Publications:** Urban & Regional Studies in Alberta, annual; Alberta Municipal Affairs Publications, annual; Journal Contents, monthly; New Book List, bimonthly. **Special Indexes:** Acts Administered by Alberta Municipal Affairs; Alberta General Plans; Alberta Municipal Affairs Orders-In-Council, 1912 to present; subject index to periodicals. **Remarks:** FAX: (403)422-9105.

★292★
Alberta Natural Gas Company Ltd. - Information Centre (Energy)
2900, 240 4th Ave. S.W. Phone: (403)691-7632
Calgary, AB, Canada T2P 4L7 Susan Tyrrell, Supv., Info.Serv.
Founded: 1961. **Staff:** Prof 1; Other 3. **Subjects:** Petroleum and gas industries, management, law, government regulation, engineering, computer science. **Holdings:** 5000 books; 7000 regulatory documents; 12 feet of clippings and pamphlet files; 500 annual reports, videotapes, computer programs; microfiche. **Subscriptions:** 500 journals and other serials; 10 newspapers. **Services:** Interlibrary loan; copying; SDI; library open to the public with restrictions. **Automated Operations:** Computerized cataloging, circulation, serials, and acquisitions. **Computerized Information Services:** PFDS Online, DIALOG Information Services, Info Globe, STM Systems Corporation, BRS Information Technologies, Infomart Online, WILSONLINE, CAN/OLE, FP OnLine, QL Systems; internal database; Envoy 100, DIALMAIL (electronic mail services). **Publications:** InfoBulletin (newsletter), monthly. **Remarks:** FAX: (403)691-7629. Electronic mail address(es): ACAS.ILL (Envoy 100). **Formerly:** Alberta and Southern Gas Company Ltd.

★293★
Alberta Occupational Health and Safety - Library (Med)
1021 10th Ave., S.W., 3rd Fl. Phone: (403)297-7860
Calgary, AB, Canada T2R 0B7 Carol Perry, Info.Spec.
Subjects: Occupational health and safety. **Holdings:** 1000 books. **Subscriptions:** 30 journals and other serials. **Services:** Interlibrary loan; library open to the public. **Automated Operations:** Computerized public access catalog. **Computerized Information Services:** CD-ROM (Canadian Centre for Occupational Health and Safety Information Disc). **Remarks:** FAX: (403)297-7854.

★294★
Alberta Occupational Health and Safety - Library Services (Med)
10709 Jasper Ave., 6th Fl. Phone: (403)427-3530
Edmonton, AB, Canada T5J 3N3 Joanne Lavkulich, Act.Mgr.
Founded: 1977. **Staff:** Prof 1; Other 4. **Subjects:** Occupational health and safety. **Special Collections:** U.S. National Institute for Occupational Safety and Health (NIOSH) Standards; Workplace Hazardous Materials Information System (WHMIS). **Holdings:** 8000 books; 600 films and videos. **Subscriptions:** 350 journals and other serials. **Services:** Interlibrary loan; SDI; library open to the public with restrictions. **Automated Operations:** Computerized public access catalog, cataloging, acquisitions, and circulation. **Computerized Information Services:** DIALOG Information Services, MEDLARS Online, CAN/OLE, CCOHS (Canadian Centre for Occupational Health and Safety Online); SIEC (Suicide Information and Education Centre); Envoy 100 (electronic mail service). **Networks/Consortia:** Member of OCLC Pacific Network. **Publications:** Brochures; bibliographies; current awareness bulletins. **Special Catalogs:** AV catalog. **Remarks:** Alberta Occupational Health and Safety is one of two agencies that formerly comprised Alberta Community & Occupational Health. FAX: (403)427-5698. Electronic mail address(es): AECOH.ILL (Envoy 100). **Staff:** Meredith Day, Media/Info.Spec.

★295★
Alberta Office of the Ombudsman - Ombudsman's Library (Soc Sci)
1630 Phipps-McKinnon Bldg.
10020 101A Ave. Phone: (403)427-2756
Edmonton, AB, Canada T5J 3G2 Lynn Scott, Admin./Asst.
Subjects: Government information, law. **Holdings:** 300 books; 80 bound periodical volumes; 70 pamphlets; 14 maps; government reports and statutes; Ombudsman annual reports from around the world; special reports of the Ombudsman, Province of Alberta. **Subscriptions:** 20 journals and other serials; 8 newspapers. **Services:** Interlibrary loan (limited); library not open to the public. **Remarks:** FAX: (403)427-2759.

★296★
Alberta Oil Sands Technology and Research Authority - Library and Information Centre (Sci-Engr)
Highfield Place, 6th Fl.
10010 106th St.
Edmonton, AB, Canada T5J 3L8 Helga Petri, Mgr.
Founded: 1975. **Staff:** Prof 5; Other 9. **Subjects:** Oil sands, heavy oil, enhanced recovery. **Holdings:** 30,000 volumes. **Subscriptions:** 65 journals and other serials. **Services:** Copying; center open to the public. **Automated Operations:** Computerized acquisitions and circulation. **Computerized Information Services:** SPIRES, CAN/OLE, QL Systems; BITNET (electronic mail service). Performs searches on fee basis. Contact Person: Information Officers or Technicians. **Publications:** TAR Paper (newsletter), quarterly. **Special Indexes:** Alberta Oil Sands Index; Heavy Oil/Enhanced Recovery Index (hardcopy, online, microfiche). **Remarks:** FAX: (403)422-9112. Telex: 037 3519.

★297★
Alberta Petroleum Marketing Commission - Library (Energy)
250 6th Ave., S.W., Suite 1900 Phone: (403)297-5482
Calgary, AB, Canada T2P 3H7 Roberta M. Keith, Libn.
Staff: Prof 1; Other 1. **Subjects:** Energy economics. **Holdings:** 4000 books; periodicals. **Subscriptions:** 275 journals and other serials. **Services:** Interlibrary loan; library open to the public by appointment. **Automated Operations:** Computerized public access catalog, cataloging, and serials. **Computerized Information Services:** DIALOG Information Services, Info Globe. **Publications:** New books list, irregular - for internal distribution only. **Remarks:** FAX: (403)263-8144.

★ 298 ★
Alberta Public Affairs Bureau - Provincial Film Library (Aud-Vis)
11510 Kingsway Ave. Phone: (403)427-4381
Edmonton, AB, Canada T5G 2Y5 Mr. Ashley Daniel, Mgr.
Founded: 1948. **Staff:** Prof 2. **Subjects:** Health, hunter training, recreational activities, parenting of children, consumer affairs, driver training, native issues, Alberta, teens and adolescents. **Holdings:** 3300 16mm films; video cassettes; slide/tape sets; filmstrips. **Services:** Interlibrary loan; library open to Alberta residents. **Automated Operations:** Computerized cataloging and circulation. **Computerized Information Services:** GMT media booking system (internal database). **Special Catalogs:** Provincial Film Library Resource Catalogue, biennial. **Remarks:** FAX: (403)452-0668. **Staff:** Gisele Pomerleau, Film Coord.

★ 299 ★
Alberta Public Utilities Board - Library (Energy)
10055 106th St., 11th Fl. Phone: (403)427-4901
Edmonton, AB, Canada T5J 2Y2 James E. McKee, Lib.Techn.
Founded: 1915. **Staff:** 2. **Subjects:** Public utilities, law, accounting, engineering, business, statistics. **Holdings:** 2100 books; 200 reports and government documents. **Subscriptions:** 60 journals and other serials. **Services:** Library not open to the public. **Computerized Information Services:** Micro OnLine Library Information (MOLLI, internal database). **Remarks:** A branch library is maintained in Calgary. FAX: (403)427-6970.

★ 300 ★
Alberta Public Works, Supply & Services - Departmental Library (Comp Sci)
6950 113th St., Main Fl. Phone: (403)427-2353
Edmonton, AB, Canada T6H 5V7 Robin Brown, Coord., Lib.Serv.
Founded: 1977. **Staff:** Prof 2; Other 2. **Subjects:** Computer science, data processing, management, architecture, engineering. **Holdings:** 5000 books; 200 reports. **Subscriptions:** 440 journals and other serials; 15 newspapers. **Services:** Interlibrary loan; library not open to the public. **Automated Operations:** Computerized cataloging and acquisitions. **Computerized Information Services:** DIALOG Information Services; internal database. Performs searches free of charge. **Publications:** Library Bulletin, monthly - available upon request. **Remarks:** FAX: (403)422-9754. **Staff:** Harry Schuld, Ref.Libn.; Genevieve Sveinson, Lib.Techn.

★ 301 ★
Alberta Recreation & Parks - Alberta Sports & Recreation for the Blind - Percy Page Resource Centre (Rec)
11759 Groat Rd. Phone: (403)453-8663
Edmonton, AB, Canada T5M 3K6 Lynn Hauck, Lib.Techn.
Subjects: Recreation, natural history, administration, specific sports. **Holdings:** 7000 titles; 100 cassettes; 40 microforms; 500 microfiche. **Subscriptions:** 50 journals and other serials. **Services:** Interlibrary loan; copying; SDI; center open to the public for reference use only. **Automated Operations:** Computerized cataloging and circulation. **Remarks:** FAX: (403)453-8553.

★ 302 ★
Alberta Research Council - Industrial Information
P.O. Box 8330, Sta. F
Edmonton, AB, Canada T6H 5X2
Defunct.

★ 303 ★
Alberta Research Council - Library Services (Sci-Engr)
P.O. Box 8330, Sta. F Phone: (403)450-5055
Edmonton, AB, Canada T6H 5X2 Barbara M. Storms, Coord., Lib.Serv.
Founded: 1921. **Staff:** Prof 3; Other 6. **Subjects:** Geology, groundwater, soils, forest products, engineering, chemistry, biotechnology, computing, chemical processing, oil sands, coal, advanced technologies, robotics, energy, management. **Holdings:** 15,000 books; 5000 maps; 10,000 government documents. **Subscriptions:** 600 journals and other serials; 20 newspapers. **Services:** Interlibrary loan; SDI; library open to the public. **Automated Operations:** Computerized cataloging and serials. **Computerized Information Services:** DIALOG Information Services, PFDS Online, CAN/OLE, SPIRES, ESA/IRS, STN International, STM Systems Corporation, SCITECH; SERIALS (internal databases); Envoy 100 (electronic mail service). **Networks/Consortia:** Member of SCITECH. **Remarks:** Maintains 4 branch libraries. **Remarks:** FAX: (403)461-2651. Electronic mail address(es): AER.MW (Envoy 100).

★ 304 ★
Alberta Research Council - Library Services - Calgary Branch Library (Comp Sci)
6815 8th St., N.E., 3rd Fl. Phone: (403)297-2620
Calgary, AB, Canada T2E 7H7 Gail Grout, Br.Libn.
Founded: 1985. **Staff:** 1. **Subjects:** Artificial intelligence, robotics, expert systems, CAD/CAM, industrial engineering, interactive learning environments, advanced manufacturing technologies. **Holdings:** 2000 books. **Subscriptions:** 150 journals and other serials; 5 newspapers. **Services:** Interlibrary loan; SDI; library open to the public. **Automated Operations:** Computerized cataloging and serials. **Computerized Information Services:** PFDS Online, DIALOG Information Services, CAN/OLE, QL Systems, SCITECH; Envoy 100 (electronic mail service). **Networks/Consortia:** Member of SCITECH. **Remarks:** FAX: (403)275-3005. Electronic mail address(es): GROUT@NOAH.ARC.CA (Envoy 100).

★ 305 ★
Alberta School for the Deaf - L.A. Broughton Library (Med, Educ)
6240 113th St. Phone: (403)422-0244
Edmonton, AB, Canada T6H 3L2 Connie L. Hall, Libn.
Founded: 1967. **Staff:** 1. **Subjects:** Deaf - teaching, psychology, research, educational technology. **Holdings:** 1500 books; tapes; 80 periodicals. **Subscriptions:** 71 journals and other serials. **Services:** library open to the public for reference use only to students, teachers, and parents. **Remarks:** FAX: (403)422-2036.

★ 306 ★
Alberta Securities Commission - Library
10025 Jasper Ave., 21st Fl.
Edmonton, AB, Canada T5J 3Z5
Defunct.

Alberta and Southern Gas Company Ltd.
See: **Alberta Natural Gas Company Ltd.** (292)

Alberta Sports & Recreation for the Blind
See: **Alberta Recreation & Parks** (301)

★ 307 ★
Alberta Teachers' Association - Library (Educ)
Barnett House
11010 142nd St. Phone: (403)453-2411
Edmonton, AB, Canada T5N 2R1 Elaine Atwood, Libn.
Founded: 1935. **Staff:** Prof 1; Other 1.5. **Subjects:** Instructional methods, philosophy, psychology, educational research, sociology, history of education, administration, wellness. **Special Collections:** ATA publications; publications from other provincial teacher associations. **Holdings:** 10,000 volumes. **Subscriptions:** 400 journals and other serials. **Services:** Library open to the public with restrictions. **Publications:** The Book Book, biennial. **Remarks:** FAX: (403)455-6481.

★ 308 ★
Alberta Tourism - Library (Bus-Fin)
10155 - 102 St., 5th Fl. Phone: (403)427-3299
Edmonton, AB, Canada T5J 4L6 Susan McConkey, Libn.
Founded: 1986. **Staff:** Prof 1. **Subjects:** Tourist trade, tourism, recreation. **Holdings:** 8000 books; Statistics Canada publications. **Subscriptions:** 400 journals and other serials; 10 newspapers. **Services:** Interlibrary loan; copying; library open to the public for reference use only. **Computerized Information Services:** Infomart Online, DIALOG Information Services, DOBIS, Tourism Canada. **Publications:** New Acquisition List; Table of Contents. **Remarks:** FAX: (403)422-1180 (Tourism Conferences).

★ 309 ★
Alberta Transportation & Utilities - Library (Trans)
Twin Atria Bldg., Main Fl.
4999 98th Ave. Phone: (403)427-8802
Edmonton, AB, Canada T6B 2X3 Diane L. Smith, Dept.Libn.
Founded: 1975. **Staff:** Prof 2; Other 4. **Subjects:** Highway planning, design, construction, maintenance; urban transportation; transportation economics,

safety, and policy; electric and natural gas utilities. **Special Collections:** Transportation Research Board reports; Transport and Road Research Laboratory reports. **Holdings:** 15,000 books and cataloged reports; 6000 technical reports; 8 VF drawers of pamphlets and reports; 15 films; 150 audiocassettes; 8000 microfiche. **Services:** Interlibrary loan; copying; SDI; library open to the public for reference use only. **Automated Operations:** Computerized public access catalog, cataloging, acquisitions, serials, and circulation. **Computerized Information Services:** DIALOG Information Services, CAN/OLE, Info Globe, ESA/IRS, Infomart Online, WILSONLINE. **Networks/Consortia:** Member of Alberta Government Libraries' Council (AGLC). **Publications:** Library Bulletin. **Remarks:** FAX: (403)468-3134.

Alberta Treasury - Bureau of Statistics Library
See: **Alberta Bureau of Statistics - Information Centre** (254)

★310★
Alberta Treasury - Library Services (Bus-Fin)
304 Terrace Bldg.
9515 107th St. Phone: (403)427-7595
Edmonton, AB, Canada T5K 2C3 Joy Fulton, Supv., Lib.Serv.
Founded: 1974. **Staff:** Prof 3. **Subjects:** Economics, banking, taxation, statistics. **Holdings:** 8000 books. **Subscriptions:** 450 journals and other serials; 10 newspapers. **Services:** Interlibrary loan; copying; library open to the public with special permission. **Automated Operations:** Computerized public access catalog, cataloging, acquisitions, and circulation. **Computerized Information Services:** QL Systems, Infomart Online. **Remarks:** FAX: (403)427-0178.

★311★
Alberta Treasury - Tax Resource Centre (Bus-Fin)
Sir Fredrick Haultain Bldg., 2nd Fl. N.E.
9811 109th St. Phone: (403)427-8790
Edmonton, AB, Canada T5K 2L5 Johanna H. Breijer, Br.Libn.
Founded: 1981. **Staff:** Prof 1; Other 1. **Subjects:** Taxation, business, law, computer auditing and accounting. **Special Collections:** Taxation reference materials (250 loose-leaf volumes); Dominion Tax cases, 1920 to present; Alberta statutes. **Holdings:** 2000 books; 42 bound periodical volumes; 120 boxes of government documents; 3 file cabinets of current awareness clippings. **Subscriptions:** 120 journals and other serials; 6 newspapers. **Services:** Interlibrary loan; copying; library open to the public with restrictions. **Automated Operations:** Computerized acquisitions. **Remarks:** FAX: (403)422-5284.

Alberta Vocational College
See: **Alberta Advanced Education** (232)

★312★
Alberta Wheat Pool - Reference Library (Agri)
505 2nd St., S.W.
P.O. Box 2700 Phone: (403)290-5581
Calgary, AB, Canada T2P 2P5 Jane Fournier, Libn.
Founded: 1925. **Staff:** 1. **Subjects:** Agriculture, grain transportation, statistics. **Holdings:** 13,000 books. **Subscriptions:** 350 journals and other serials; 100 newspapers. **Services:** Interlibrary loan; library open to the public. **Computerized Information Services:** Internal database. **Remarks:** FAX: (403)290-5550. Electronic mail address(es): AWP.MAILBOX ATTENTION: JFOURNIER (Envoy 100).

★313★
Alberto-Culver Company - Research Library (Sci-Engr)
2525 Armitage Ave. Phone: (708)450-3155
Melrose Park, IL 60160 Jo Rathgeber, Res.Libn.
Staff: 1. **Subjects:** Toiletries, household and grocery products. **Holdings:** 2000 books; 500 bound periodical volumes; 12 VF drawers of pamphlets. **Subscriptions:** 126 journals and other serials; 5 newspapers. **Services:** Interlibrary loan; library not open to the public. **Computerized Information Services:** DIALOG Information Services, STN International. **Remarks:** FAX: (708)450-3067.

★314★
Albertson College of Idaho - Regional Studies Center - Library (Area-Ethnic)
2112 Cleveland Blvd. Phone: (208)459-5214
Caldwell, ID 83605 Dale Corning, Libn.
Staff: Prof 1; Other 1. **Subjects:** Snake River Basin and Idaho, folklore, water quality, groundwater irrigation, natural resources, land use planning, environmental education. **Holdings:** 1500 books; 1000 35mm slides; 30 videotapes. **Services:** Interlibrary loan; library open to the public.

★315★
Albright-Knox Art Gallery - Art Reference Library & Archives (Art)
1285 Elmwood Ave. Phone: (716)882-8700
Buffalo, NY 14222 Kari Horowicz, Libn.
Founded: 1905. **Staff:** Prof 3; Other 1. **Subjects:** Art - contemporary, modern, history. **Special Collections:** Artist's books (300); illustrated books. **Holdings:** 31,000 books; 1000 bound periodical volumes; 20,000 other cataloged items; 10,000 vertical files, including folders on artists, dealers, and museums throughout the world; archival materials; microfiche; videotapes. **Subscriptions:** 353 journals and other serials. **Services:** Interlibrary loan; copying; library open to the public. **Automated Operations:** Computerized cataloging. **Networks/Consortia:** Member of Western New York Library Resources Council (WNYLRC). **Remarks:** FAX: (716)882-1958. **Staff:** Janice Lurie, Asst.Libn.; Estelle Diamond, Cat.

★316★
W.F. Albright Institute of Archaeological Research - Library (Area-Ethnic, Geog-Map)
26 Salahadin St.
P.O. Box 19096
91190 Jerusalem, Israel Phone: 2 282131
Staff: 1. **Subjects:** Archaeology - Israel, Middle East; Biblical research. **Special Collections:** Gordon, Saltz. **Holdings:** 20,000 books; reports; manuscripts; archival materials; microfiche; microfilm. **Subscriptions:** 200 journals and other serials. **Services:** Library not open to the public. **Remarks:** FAX: 2 894424. Telex: 25330 NAWASIL. **Staff:** Hanna Caine

★317★
Albright & Wilson Americas - Central Library (Sci-Engr)
2 Gibbs Rd. Phone: (416)239-7111
Islington, ON, Canada M9B 1R1 Nancy L. Logan, Corp.Libn.
Founded: 1898. **Staff:** Prof 1. **Subjects:** Phosphorus and phosphates, pulp and paper bleaching chemicals, electrochemistry, business, water treatment. **Holdings:** 5000 books. **Subscriptions:** 150 journals. **Services:** Interlibrary loan; copying; SDI; library open to the public by appointment. **Automated Operations:** Computerized cataloging and serials. **Computerized Information Services:** DIALOG Information Services, STN International, CAN/OLE, Info Globe, Infomart Online. **Networks/Consortia:** Member of Sheridan Park Association. **Publications:** Acquisitions list, bimonthly. **Remarks:** FAX: (416)232-2146. Telex: 06-9676630. A subsidiary of Tenneco Canada, Inc.

★318★
Albuquerque Public Library - Special Collections Branch (Area-Ethnic)
423 Central, N.E. Phone: (505)848-1376
Albuquerque, NM 87102 Laurel E. Drew, Libn.
Founded: 1977. **Staff:** Prof 2; Other 1. **Subjects:** Genealogy, local and state history. **Holdings:** 19,000 books; 475 bound periodical volumes; 7000 reels of microfilm and microfiche. **Subscriptions:** 150 journals and other serials. **Services:** Copying; collections open to the public.

★319★
Albuquerque Publishing Company - Library (Publ)
Drawer J-T Phone: (505)823-3493
Albuquerque, NM 87103 Judy C. Pence, Dir.
Founded: 1985. **Staff:** Prof 1; Other 6. **Subjects:** Newspaper reference topics; Albuquerque and New Mexico. **Holdings:** 700 books; 1306 linear feet of clipping files; 275 linear feet of photographs; 1640 reels of microfilm. **Subscriptions:** 43 journals and other serials; 68 newspapers. **Services:** Copying; library open to the public with restrictions. **Computerized Information Services:** NEXIS, DIALOG Information Services, DataTimes, VU/TEXT Information Services. Performs searches on fee basis. **Remarks:** Library located at 7777 Jefferson St., N.E., Albuquerque, NM 87109.

★320★
Albuquerque Technical-Vocational Institute - Montoya Campus - Library Services
4700 Morris, N.E.
Albuquerque, NM 87111
Defunct.

★321★
Alcan Aluminum, Ltd. - Information Centre (Sci-Engr, Bus-Fin)
1188 Sherbrooke St., W. Phone: (514)848-8319
Montreal, PQ, Canada H3A 3G2 Lucie Dion, Chf.Libn.
Founded: 1945. **Staff:** Prof 3; Other 6. **Subjects:** Aluminum, business management, commerce, finance, industrial medicine, metallurgy, energy. **Special Collections:** Company Archives. **Holdings:** 8000 books; 500 videotapes; 500 annual reports. **Subscriptions:** 1000 journals and other serials. **Services:** Interlibrary loan; center open to the public on request. **Automated Operations:** Computerized cataloging, serials, and circulation. **Computerized Information Services:** DIALOG Information Services, QL Systems, Infomart Online, LEXIS, NEXIS, Info Globe, Reuter TEXTLINE; BASIS (internal database); DIALMAIL (electronic mail service). **Remarks:** FAX: (514)848-1469.

★322★
Alcan International, Ltd. - Kingston Research & Development Centre - Technical Information Centre (Sci-Engr)
P.O. Box 8400 Phone: (613)541-2065
Kingston, ON, Canada K7L 5L9 Mr. B. Chenoweth, Mgr.
Founded: 1941. **Staff:** Prof 2; Other 3. **Subjects:** Metallurgy of light metals; aluminum smelting, fabrication, production; materials science; engineering. **Holdings:** 10,000 volumes; 25,000 reports; 6000 patents; 150,000 pamphlets; 450 reels of microfilm; 49 VF drawers of correspondence; 5000 slides. **Subscriptions:** 500 journals and other serials. **Services:** Interlibrary loan; copying; library open to the public on request. **Automated Operations:** Computerized public access catalog, cataloging, and serials. **Computerized Information Services:** DIALOG Information Services, PFDS Online, LEXIS, NEXIS, STN International, CAN/OLE, DOBIS Canadian Online Library System; BASIS (internal database); Envoy 100 (electronic mail service). **Publications:** Accessions List, monthly - for internal distribution only. **Remarks:** FAX: (613)547-6401. Electronic mail address(es): OKA.ILL (Envoy 100). **Staff:** Jenifer Wartman, Info.Spec.

★323★
Alcan International, Ltd. - Technical Information Centre (Sci-Engr)
C.P. 1250 Phone: (418)699-2844
Jonquiere, PQ, Canada G7S 4K8 Ms. P. Leclerc, Chf.Libn.
Founded: 1950. **Staff:** Prof 4; Other 6. **Subjects:** Aluminum technology, chemistry, metallurgy, engineering. **Holdings:** 17,000 books; 3000 bound periodical volumes; technical reports; patents; correspondence; microfilm. **Subscriptions:** 550 journals and other serials. **Services:** Interlibrary loan; library not open to the public. **Automated Operations:** Computerized cataloging, acquisitions, and serials. **Computerized Information Services:** DIALOG Information Services, Infomart Online, CAN/OLE, QL Systems; BASIS (internal database). **Remarks:** FAX: (418)699-3996. **Staff:** Jean Bell, Ref.Spec.; Louis Brisson, Ref.Spec.

★324★
Alcan Smelters and Chemicals, Ltd. - Technical Library
Box 1800 Phone: (604)639-8560
Kitimat, BC, Canada V8C 2H2 Nora Brown, Tech.Libn.
Holdings: Figures not available. **Computerized Information Services:** DIALOG Information Services, CAN/OLE; BASIS (internal database); Envoy 100 (electronic mail service). **Remarks:** FAX: (604)639-8644.

★325★
Alcatel Canada Wire Inc. - Technical Library (Sci-Engr)
22 Commercial Rd. Phone: (416)467-4079
Toronto, ON, Canada M4G 3W1 Dianne Crompton, Lib.Techn.
Founded: 1965. **Staff:** Prof 1; Other 1. **Subjects:** Electrical engineering, mathematics, chemistry, management, marketing, mechanical engineering, industrial engineering. **Holdings:** 694 books and bound periodical volumes; 2000 patents; 1900 standards and specifications; 2 VF drawers of technical information; 1 VF drawer of archives. **Subscriptions:** 200 journals and other serials. **Services:** Interlibrary loan; copying; library open to the public with restrictions. **Computerized Information Services:** DIALOG Information Services, Info Globe. **Remarks:** FAX: (416)421-4779. **Formerly:** Canada Wire and Cable, Ltd.

★326★
Alcatel Network Systems, Inc. - Information Center (Sci-Engr)
1225 N. Alma Rd. Phone: (214)996-6022
Richardson, TX 75081 Wanda J. Fox, Mgr.
Founded: 1960. **Staff:** Prof 1; Other 1. **Subjects:** Electronics, communications. **Special Collections:** International Business Collection; commercial and international specifications and standards. **Holdings:** 12,000 books; 2000 bound periodical volumes; 500 financial and marketing files. **Subscriptions:** 200 journals and other serials. **Services:** Interlibrary loan; center not open to the public. **Computerized Information Services:** DIALOG Information Services, NEXIS, Dow Jones News/Retrieval, Dun & Bradstreet Business Credit Services. **Publications:** Business Information Update. **Remarks:** FAX: (214)996-7063; (214)996-7624. **Formerly:** Rockwell International - Electronics Operations - Dallas Information Center. **Staff:** Sharon Bulls, Sr.Dept.Sup.Coord.

★327★
Alcatel Network Systems, Inc. - Library (Sci-Engr)
2912 Wake Forest Rd. Phone: (919)850-6414
Raleigh, NC 27609 Joan Viscounty, Libn.
Founded: 1958. **Staff:** Prof 1. **Subjects:** Telecommunications, electronics, computers, business management. **Special Collections:** Standards and other company publications. **Holdings:** 3000 books; 120 bound periodical volumes; 175 proceedings of conferences and symposia; 200 engineering reports. **Subscriptions:** 225 journals and other serials. **Services:** Interlibrary loan; copying; library open to the public by appointment. **Automated Operations:** Computerized cataloging and circulation. **Computerized Information Services:** DIALOG Information Services; internal database. Performs searches free of charge. **Remarks:** FAX: (919)850-6171. Telex: 919-850-5444.

Alcoa Technical Center
See: **Aluminum Company of America** (432)

★328★
Alcohol Research Group - Library (Med)
2000 Hearst Phone: (510)642-5208
Berkeley, CA 94709-2176 Andrea L. Mitchell, Dir.
Founded: 1959. **Staff:** Prof 2; Other 1. **Subjects:** Alcohol use and abuse, epidemiology of alcohol use and allied problems, drug use and abuse. **Special Collections:** History of Alcohol Use and Policy. **Holdings:** 6000 books; 50,000 reprints, reports, dissertations. **Subscriptions:** 180 journals and other serials. **Services:** Copying; SDI; library open to the public. **Automated Operations:** Computerized cataloging and acquisitions. **Computerized Information Services:** DIALOG Information Services, BRS Information Technologies. **Networks/Consortia:** Member of Substance Abuse Librarians and Information Specialists (SALIS). **Remarks:** FAX: (510)642-7175. Jointly maintained by Medical Research Institute of San Francisco and University of California, Berkeley. **Staff:** Marilyn Plotkin.

Alcoholism and Drug Addiction Research Foundation - Library
See: **Addiction Research Foundation** (69)

★329★
Alcoholism Foundation of Manitoba - William Potoroka Memorial Library (Med)
1031 Portage Ave. Phone: (204)944-6233
Winnipeg, MB, Canada R3G 0R8 Rita Shreiber, Mgr., Lib.Serv.
Staff: Prof 2; Other 1. **Subjects:** Alcohol and drug use and abuse, psychology, education, treatment, counseling, values clarification. **Holdings:** 3200 books; 19 pamphlet titles; 100 16mm films; 80 filmstrips; 200 videotapes. **Subscriptions:** 45 journals and other serials. **Services:** Interlibrary loan; copying; library open to the public. **Automated Operations:** Sydney Integrated library system. **Special Catalogs:** AV catalog. **Remarks:** FAX: (204)786-7768.

★330★
Alcon Laboratories, Inc. - Research & Development Library (Rl-30) (Med)
6201 S. Freeway Phone: (817)551-8319
Fort Worth, TX 76134-2099 Sharon L. McAllister, Sci.Libn.
Founded: 1959. **Staff:** Prof 1; Other 2. **Subjects:** Ophthalmology, lens care, pharmaceutics. **Holdings:** 6500 books; 10,000 bound periodical volumes;

4000 patents; 2000 reels of microfilm. **Subscriptions:** 375 journals and other serials. **Services:** Interlibrary loan; will answer brief inquiries and make referrals; library open to the public by appointment. **Computerized Information Services:** DIALOG Information Services, MEDLARS, Data-Star, Dow Jones News/Retrieval. **Networks/Consortia:** Member of Health Libraries Information Network (HealthLINE). **Publications:** Serials holdings list. **Remarks:** FAX: (817)568-6254. **Staff:** Melissa White, ILL Libn.; Karen Fuller, Asst.Libn.

Rosita C. Alcorn Library
See: **McAllen International Museum** (9867)

★331★
Alcorn State University - John Dewey Boyd Library - Special Collections (Hist, Info Sci)
Box 539 Phone: (601)877-6350
Lorman, MS 39096 Dr. Epsy Y. Hendricks, Lib.Dir.
Holdings: Government documents (228,362); university archives (1,500 linear feet; 37,452 volumes in microform). **Subscriptions:** 764 journals and other serials; 13 newspapers. **Services:** Interlibrary loan; copying; collections open to the public for reference use only. **Automated Operations:** Computerized public access catalog, cataloging, acquisitions, serials, and circulation. **Computerized Information Services:** BRS Information Technologies. Performs searches on fee basis. Contact Person: Mary Harris, Ref.Libn., 877-6357. **Networks/Consortia:** Member of SOLINET. **Remarks:** FAX: (601)877-3885. **Staff:** Ms. Jessie Arnold, Govt.Docs.Libn.

★332★
Louisa May Alcott Memorial Association - Library (Hist)
Box 343 Phone: (617)369-4118
Concord, MA 01742 Carol Burns, Staff Libn. & Rsrc.Mgr.
Founded: 1911. **Subjects:** The Alcott family, especially 1857-1877, the years spent at Orchard House. **Holdings:** 500 photographs, letters, manuscripts. **Services:** Collection open to the public by appointment. **Remarks:** Collection located at Orchard House, 399 Lexington Rd., Concord, MA. House open for tours April through October, and by appointment the rest of the year.

★333★
Alden Research Laboratory, Inc. (ARL) - Library (Sci-Engr)
30 Shrewsbury St. Phone: (508)829-4323
Holden, MA 01520 George E. Hecker, Pres.
Founded: 1894. **Subjects:** Fluid mechanics. **Holdings:** 650 volumes; laboratory reports. **Subscriptions:** 27 journals and other serials. **Services:** Library not open to the public. **Remarks:** FAX: (508)829-5939.

★334★
Aldersgate College - Wilson Memorial Library (Rel-Phil)
Box 460 Phone: (306)693-7773
Moose Jaw, SK, Canada S6H 4P1 Lorraine Tanner, Dir., Lib.Serv.
Staff: Prof 1; Other 15. **Subjects:** Theology, Biblical literature, pastoral care, Christian education, literature, humanities. **Special Collections:** Wesleyana (200 volumes). **Holdings:** 14,000 books; 350 bound periodical volumes; 350 volumes in microform; 200 tapes and cassettes. **Subscriptions:** 154 journals and other serials. **Services:** Interlibrary loan; library open to the public for reference use only. **Computerized Information Services:** Internal databases. **Remarks:** FAX: (306)692-8821

★335★
Aldersgate United Methodist Church - Library (Rel-Phil)
4115 Dewey Ave. Phone: (716)663-3665
Rochester, NY 14616 Carol Poole, Libn.
Founded: 1975. **Staff:** Prof 1; Other 3. **Subjects:** Bible study, Christian living, Christian education. **Holdings:** 2636 books; 260 AV programs. **Subscriptions:** 12 journals and other serials. **Services:** Interlibrary loan; library open to the public with restrictions.

★336★
Alderson-Broaddus College - Pickett Library - Special Collections (Hist)
Philippi, WV 26416 Phone: (304)457-1700
David Hoxie, Lib.Dir.
Subjects: History of Alderson-Broaddus College and the Baptist church, 1870 to present. **Special Collections:** Civil War Collection. **Holdings:** 4000 photographs and slides; minutes from meetings of national and local Baptist associations; local church records; college archives: annual reports, trustee minutes, college bulletins. **Services:** Copying; collections open to the public. **Automated Operations:** Computerized cataloging. **Computerized Information Services:** OCLC.

★337★
Aldrich Chemical Company, Inc. - Library (Sci-Engr)
940 W. St. Paul Ave. Phone: (414)273-3850
Milwaukee, WI 53233 Connie Harder
Subjects: Organic chemistry. **Holdings:** Figures not available. **Services:** Library not open to the public. **Remarks:** FAX: (414)273-4979.

★338★
Mariska Aldrich Memorial School of Music and Archive (Mus)
8451-8491 Swarthout Canyon Rd.
Box 369 Phone: (619)249-6751
Wrightwood, CA 92397-0369 Ric Anderson, Chm./Chf.Exec.Off.
Founded: 1965. **Staff:** Prof 3; Other 1. **Subjects:** Music, musicians. **Holdings:** 6000 books; 45,000 33rpm phonograph records; 450,000 historical 78rpm phonograph records; 450 compact discs; 4100 audiotapes; 4000 piano rolls (Reproducing Ampico, Duo Art, and Welte); 2100 videotapes; scores and sheet music; music and recording periodicals; antique instruments; historical audio equipment; antique phonographs. **Subscriptions:** 16 journals and other serials. **Services:** Copying; library open to the public by appointment. **Automated Operations:** Computerized cataloging. **Remarks:** FAX: (619)249-6751. **Formerly:** Mariska Aldrich Memorial Foundation, Inc. - Aldrich Library of Music. **Staff:** Meeka Anderson, Pres./Cur.

Robert Aldrich Collection
See: **American Film Institute** (584)

★339★
Alexander Consulting Group - Research & Training Services Library (Bus-Fin)
44 Merrimac St.
Box 926 Phone: (508)465-5374
Newburyport, MA 01950 Marian C. Schwaller-Carney, Libn.
Founded: 1987. **Staff:** Prof 2; Other 1. **Subjects:** Employee benefits, human resources management, insurance law. **Holdings:** 300 books; 150 bound periodical volumes; 200 vertical files; 200 model documents; 300 surveys; legislative histories. **Subscriptions:** 163 journals and other serials. **Services:** Interlibrary loan; library not open to the public. **Automated Operations:** Computerized cataloging and serials. **Computerized Information Services:** DIALOG Information Services, LEXIS, CCH Access, CQ Washington Alert Service; internal database. **Publications:** Friends of the RTS Library Bulletin. **Remarks:** FAX: (508)465-4011.

Franz Alexander Library
See: **Southern California Psychoanalytic Institute** (15474)

★340★
Hezekiah Alexander Foundation - Lassiter Library (Hist)
3500 Shamrock Dr. Phone: (704)568-1774
Charlotte, NC 28215 G. Wade Carmichael
Founded: 1980. **Staff:** Prof 1. **Subjects:** American history, decorative arts, local and state history, local genealogy. **Holdings:** 600 books; 100 bound periodical volumes. **Subscriptions:** 11 journals and other serials. **Services:** Copying; library open to the public on a limited schedule. **Remarks:** Affiliated with Charlotte Museum of History - Hezekiah Alexander Homesite.

★341★
(Alexandria) American Cultural Center - USIS Library (Educ)
3 Pharana St. Phone: 3 4824009
Alexandria, Egypt Layla A. Hady, Lib.Dir.
Founded: 1979. **Holdings:** 8000 books; bound periodical volumes. **Subscriptions:** 200 journals and other serials. **Services:** SDI; library open to the public with restrictions. **Computerized Information Services:** DIALOG Information Services. **Remarks:** FAX: 3 4833811. Maintained or supported by the U.S. Information Agency. Focus is on materials that will assist peoples outside the United States to learn about the United States, its people, history, culture, political processes, and social milieux. **Staff:** Mona Issawi; Omneya Serry; Yvonne A. Kader.

★342★
Alexandria City Public Schools - Educational Media Center - Nichols Professional Library (Educ)
3801 W. Braddock Rd. Phone: (703)824-6674
Alexandria, VA 22302 Virginia S. Turner, Dir., Lib. & Instr.Rsrcs.
Founded: 1968. **Staff:** Prof 1; Other 1. **Subjects:** Education. **Holdings:** 9,000 books; 300,000 ERIC microfiche. **Subscriptions:** 215 journals and other serials; 3 newspapers. **Services:** Interlibrary loan; copying; SDI; library open to the public for reference use with limited circulation. **Computerized Information Services:** DIALOG Information Services, ED-LINE. Performs searches on fee basis. **Remarks:** FAX: (703)998-8299. **Staff:** Sarah C. Slough.

★343★
Alexandria Hospital - Medical Library (Med)
4320 Seminary Rd. Phone: (703)379-3126
Alexandria, VA 22304 Nina S. McCleskey, Med.Lib.Dir.
Staff: Prof 1; Other 1. **Subjects:** Medicine, nursing, health care administration. **Holdings:** 2000 books; 1500 bound periodical volumes. **Subscriptions:** 250 journal titles. **Services:** Interlibrary loan; copying; SDI; library open to the public. **Computerized Information Services:** MEDLINE, BRS Information Technologies. **Remarks:** FAX: (703)379-3176. **Formerly:** Its Health Sciences Library.

★344★
Alexandria Library - Lloyd House (Hist)
220 Washington St. Phone: (703)838-4577
Alexandria, VA 22314-2420 Yvonne Carignan, Br.Libn.
Founded: 1794. **Staff:** Prof 3. **Subjects:** History - Virginia, America, Alexandria; genealogy; Alexandria manuscripts. **Special Collections:** Virginia Collection; Manuscript Collection; Sweeney Papers (social history of Alexandria City; 3000 items); McKnight Papers (35 items); Alexandria Library Company Collection (19th century subscription library; 2500 volumes); photograph collection (8000). **Holdings:** 15,550 books; 1862 bound periodical volumes; 14,000 pamphlets; 539 boxes of manuscripts; 9750 reels of microfilm; personal recollections; 4 boxes of early city records. **Subscriptions:** 108 journals and other serials. **Services:** Copying; library open to the public with restrictions on circulation. **Automated Operations:** Computerized acquisitions and circulation. **Computerized Information Services:** OCLC. **Networks/Consortia:** Member of SOLINET. **Special Indexes:** Indexes to manuscript collections, vertical files, map collection, microfilm collection, and photograph collection. **Staff:** Sandra O'Keefe; T. Michael Miller.

★345★
Alexian Brothers Medical Center - Medical Library (Med)
800 W. Biesterfield Rd. Phone: (708)981-3657
Elk Grove Village, IL 60007 Elizabeth Clausen, Med.Libn.
Founded: 1967. **Staff:** Prof 1; Other 1. **Subjects:** Medicine, nursing, allied health sciences. **Holdings:** 2700 books; 5500 bound periodical volumes; 6 VF drawers of pamphlets; 300 videotapes; 470 audiotapes; 47 slide/tape sets. **Subscriptions:** 132 journals and other serials. **Services:** Library not open to the public. **Computerized Information Services:** MEDLARS, MEDLINE, BRS Information Technologies. **Networks/Consortia:** Member of Fox Valley Health Science Library Consortium (FVHSL), National Network of Libraries of Medicine - Greater Midwest Region, North Suburban Library System (NSLS). **Publications:** Monthly New Books List. **Remarks:** Alternate telephone number(s): (708)437-5500. FAX: (708)981-5922.

Ahmed Al-Farsi Library
See: **(Bahrain) College of Health Sciences** (1409)

★346★
Alfred University - Geology Documents Library (Sci-Engr)
Dept. of Geology Phone: (607)871-2203
Alfred, NY 14802 Dr. Michele M. Hluchy, Asst.Prof.
Founded: 1980. **Staff:** 1. **Subjects:** Geology, hydrology. **Special Collections:** Depository for U.S. Geological Survey maps and documents; holdings of State Geological Surveys; geology field guides (700). **Holdings:** 100 books; 6000 bound periodical volumes; 5000 maps. **Services:** Copying; library open to the public with restrictions.

★347★
Alfred University - Herrick Memorial Library - Special Collections (Hist, Rel-Phil)
Alfred, NY 14802 Phone: (607)871-2184
Toni P. Olshan
Staff: Prof 1. **Special Collections:** Alfred Collection (university history, faculty publications, Seventh Day Baptist history, biography; 625 volumes; 69 linear feet of manuscripts; 1013 linear feet of archival material); Waid Collection (German and Nazi history, 1914-1950; U.S. and Allied occupation serials and monographs; 1035 volumes); Rare and Special Book Collection (including 19th century American social history and 17th century philosophy and literature; 1586 volumes); Howells/Frechette Collection (William Dean Howells and Achille Frechette families; 66 linear feet, including 228 volumes and 7000 letters); Openhym Collection of Modern British Literature and Social History (Bloomsbury core; rare and limited editions; 7000 volumes; 500 letters representing Virginia Woolf, David Garnett, Carrington, H.E. Bates, T.F. Powys, and 91 other major British authors). **Services:** Copying; collections open to the public with restrictions on circulation. **Automated Operations:** Computerized cataloging. **Computerized Information Services:** OCLC. **Networks/Consortia:** Member of South Central Research Library Council (SCRLC). **Publications:** Openhym Collection Bibliography; Guide to Special Collections. **Special Catalogs:** Special Collections catalog (card); catalog to Openhym Collection. **Special Indexes:** Name index to Alfred Sun, weekly; faculty publications index; student and faculty name index; index to student and university publications. **Remarks:** FAX: (607)871-2992.

Alfred University - New York State College of Ceramics
See: **New York State College of Ceramics at Alfred University** (11645)

Algemeen Rijksarchief's - Gravenhage
See: **Netherlands - Bibliotheek van het Algemeen Rijksarchief** (11399)

Alger - Organisme National sur la Recherche Scientifique - Centre d'Etudes et de Recherches en Economie Apliquee
See: **Algeria - National Organization of Scientific Research - Applied Economics Studies and Research Center for Development** (350)

★348★
Algeria - Archives Nationales de l'Algerie - Direction des Archives de la Wilaya de Constantine (Hist, Rel-Phil, Soc Sci)
1 rue du Docteur Moussa Phone: 2946706
Constantine, Algeria Belkacem Karim Boughida
Founded: 1874. **Staff:** Prof 3; Other 15. **Subjects:** History, religion, humanities, administration, art, social sciences. **Special Collections:** Archives from the 16th century. **Holdings:** 50,000 books; 800 bound periodical volumes; 8000 linear meters of archives; 1000 microfiche; 400 reels of microfilm; maps. **Subscriptions:** 13 journals and other serials; 8 newspapers. **Services:** Interlibrary loan; library open to the public. **Publications:** Publications de la DAWC; Repertoires. **Special Catalogs:** Catalogue d' Expositions. **Remarks:** Alternate telephone number(s): 2942901. Telex: 91200 CONST DZ.

★349★
Algeria - Bibliotheque Nationale (Soc Sci)
1 ave. Frantz Fanon Phone: 630632
Algiers, Algeria Abdelkrim Badjadja, Dir.
Founded: 1835. **Staff:** Prof 28; Other 107. **Subjects:** North Africa, Arabic studies, social sciences, Islamic studies, classical literature. **Special**

Collections: Manuscripts collection (3100 items); Brazza Collection; Gsell Collection. **Holdings:** 350,000 books; 4377 periodical titles; 1700 microfiche; 2300 reels of microfilm; 4650 records. **Subscriptions:** 350 journals and other serials; 97 newspapers. **Services:** Interlibrary loan; copying; library open to the public. **Publications:** Bibliographie de l'Algerie; Annuaire Bibliographique sur l'Algerie; Bibliographies et Catalogues; Etudes et Documents; Relations de voyages; Histoire et Civilisation. **Also Known As:** The National Library of Algeria. **Staff:** Mohamed Aissamoussa, Chf., Dept.Tech.; Zahia Fellah, Chf., Dept. of Pubns. & Res.; Zahira Bouzaher, Chf., Serv.Intl.; Rose-Marie Chait, Chf., Serv.Exch.; Aicha Khammar, Chf., Serv.Leg.; Nouar Djedouani; Abdelkader Ouk aci; Tidjani Mecheri; Koula Nait-Djoudi; Hacina Medjahed; Habiba Douida; Me Bouayed; Bouzid Khelili.

Algeria - Ministry of Public Health - Pasteur Institute of Algeria
See: **Pasteur Institute of Algeria** (12785)

★350★
Algeria - National Organization of Scientific Research - Applied Economics Studies and Research Center for Development - Library (Bus-Fin)
20, rue Chahid Khalef Mustapha-Ben Aknoun Phone: 78 12 72
Algiers, Algeria Mrs. Touahar Nabila, Libn.
Subjects: Applied economics; energy studies; politics of agricultural trade; development of industry and agriculture in the private sector; sociology of work. **Holdings:** 3350 volumes. **Also Known As:** Alger - Organisme National sur la Recherche Scientifique - Centre d'Etudes et de Recherches en Economie Apliquee (CREAA).

★351★
(Algiers) American Cultural Center - USIS Library (Educ)
8 rue Ali Messaoud
Hydra
Algiers, Algeria
Remarks: Maintained or supported by the U.S. Information Agency. Focus is on materials that will assist peoples outside the United States to learn about the United States, its people, history, culture, political processes, and social milieux.

★352★
Algoma Steel Corporation Ltd. - Research Library (Sci-Engr)
Administration Bldg.
Queen St., W. Phone: (705)945-3874
Sault Ste. Marie, ON, Canada P6A 5P2 Mary Guzzo, Supv., Info.Serv.
Founded: 1975. **Staff:** Prof 1. **Subjects:** Ferrous metallurgy. **Holdings:** 5000 books; 1500 bound periodical volumes. **Subscriptions:** 150 journals and other serials; 5 newspapers. **Services:** Interlibrary loan; copying; library open to the public with restrictions. **Automated Operations:** Computerized cataloging, serials, and circulation. **Computerized Information Services:** DIALOG Information Services, PFDS Online, Info Globe, QL Systems, CAN/OLE, EBSCONET; internal databases; DIALMAIL, Envoy 100 (electronic mail services). **Publications:** Research Library Bulletin, monthly - for internal distribution only. **Special Indexes:** Translations index; patents index; internal reports KWIC index; shelf list (all online). **Remarks:** FAX: (705)945-2332.

★353★
Algonquin College of Applied Arts & Technology - Resource Centres (Educ)
1385 Woodroffe Ave. Phone: (613)727-7713
Nepean, ON, Canada K2G 1V8 Jocelyne Chaperon-Beck, Dir.
Founded: 1967. **Staff:** Prof 5; Other 42. **Subjects:** Business, trades and technology, social sciences, nursing and allied health sciences, applied arts. **Special Collections:** Fine Arts Slide Collection (19,603). **Holdings:** 111,607 books; 3037 bound periodical volumes; 2231 reels of microfilm; 3330 microfiche; 1366 films; 595 filmstrips; 28,831 slides; 5727 phonograph records; 1863 video records. **Subscriptions:** 1501 journals and other serials; 41 newspapers. **Services:** Interlibrary loan; centers open to the public. **Automated Operations:** Computerized cataloging, acquisitions, and circulation. **Computerized Information Services:** DIALOG Information Services, CAN/OLE, Info Globe, SDM Inc., Infomart Online; Envoy 100 (electronic mail service). **Networks/Consortia:** Member of The Bibliocentre. **Remarks:** FAX: (613)727-7684. **Staff:** Danuta Hauck, Dept.Hd.; Joan Daly, Dept.Hd.

★354★
Algonquin Park Museum - Library & Archives (Env-Cons)
Box 219 Phone: (705)633-5592
Whitney, ON, Canada K0J 2M0 Ronald G. Tozer, Park Naturalist
Founded: 1953. **Subjects:** Algonquin Park ecology and history. **Special Collections:** Historical Photograph Archives (early logging; 7000 photographs). **Holdings:** 350 books; 5000 unbound reprints, reports, manuscripts; 2000 newspaper clippings; 100 oral history tapes. **Services:** Library open to the public with prior notification and approval. **Remarks:** FAX: (613)637-2864. Maintained by Ontario Ministry of Natural Resources.

★355★
Alko Ltd. - Information Services (Food-Bev, Biol Sci)
Porkkalankatu 52
POB 350 Phone: 0 13311
SF-00101 Helsinki, Finland Ritva Linko
Founded: 1947. **Staff:** 11. **Subjects:** Alcohol policy, biotechnology, biomedicine, beverage industry, alcoholism and treatment. **Holdings:** 20,000 books; 30,000 bound periodical volumes. **Subscriptions:** 900 journals and other serials; 20 newspapers. **Services:** Interlibrary loan; copying; SDI; library open to the public. **Computerized Information Services:** DIALOG Information Services, BRS Information Technologies, Data-Star, ESA/IRS, Reuters, ESMERK, Helecon; ALKINFO Alcohol Literature 1978- (internal database). Contact Person: Pirkko Romakkaniemi, Info.Spec. **Publications:** Alcohol Studies in Finland (annual bibliography). **Remarks:** FAX: 0 1333314. Telex: 57 123992.

All India Institute of Hygiene and Public Health
See: **India - Ministry of Health and Family Welfare** (7743)

★356★
All Saints Catholic Church - Parish Resource Library (Rel-Phil)
5231 Meadowcreek Phone: (214)661-8814
Dallas, TX 75248 Maria I. Bellavance, Libn.
Founded: 1979. **Staff:** Prof 1. **Subjects:** Catholic literature, religious education, self-help, psychology, philosophy. **Special Collections:** Parish archives. **Holdings:** 9078 books; 35 bound periodical volumes; 1888 audio cassettes; 60 filmstrip kits; 395 video recordings; vertical files. **Subscriptions:** 93 journals and other serials; 6 newspapers. **Services:** Interlibrary loan; copying; library open to the public when sponsored by a registered parishioner. **Automated Operations:** Computerized cataloging, serials, and circulation. **Computerized Information Services:** Internal database. **Publications:** New acquisitions list, monthly; newsletter, monthly.

★357★
All Saints Church - Library (Rel-Phil)
338 E. Lyman Ave. Phone: (407)647-3413
Winter Park, FL 32789 Evelyn M. Runyon
Subjects: Religion, family life, healing. **Holdings:** 4000 books. **Subscriptions:** 3 journals and other serials. **Services:** Library open to the public.

★358★
All Souls Unitarian Church - E. Burdette Backus Memorial Library (Rel-Phil)
5805 E. 56th St. Phone: (317)545-6005
Indianapolis, IN 46226 Mrs. Victor Amand, Chm., Lib.Comm.
Subjects: General nonfiction. **Special Collections:** Unitarian-Universalist publications. **Holdings:** 1500 books; 200 tapes. **Services:** Library open to friends and members of the church.

★359★
Allaire Village, Inc. - Allaire Research Library (Hist)
Allaire, NJ 07727 Phone: (908)938-2253
Patrick Clarke, Exec.Dir.
Founded: 1957. **Subjects:** James P. Allaire; Howell Works (iron industry); history - Monmouth and Ocean Counties, and Allaire Village, New Jersey; social history (early to mid-1800s). **Holdings:** 300 books; 70 bound periodical volumes; 7 nonbook items; 60 manuscripts; deeds; letters; account books. **Subscriptions:** 2 journals and other serials. **Services:** Copying; library open to the public by appointment. **Remarks:** FAX: (908)938-3302.

Allan Memorial Institute
See: **Royal Victoria Hospital - Allan Memorial Institute** (14140)

★360★
Allegany County Circuit Court - Library (Law)
Court House
Washington St.
Cumberland, MD 21502 Phone: (301)777-5921
Staff: Prof 1. **Subjects:** Law. **Holdings:** 15,000 volumes. **Services:** Library open to the public with restrictions.

★361★
Allegany County Museum - Library (Hist)
Court St. Phone: (716)268-9293
Belmont, NY 14813 Craig R. Braack, Hist.
Staff: Prof 1; Other 1. **Subjects:** Local history and genealogy. **Special Collections:** John Barker Church Land Tract Records. **Holdings:** 1000 books; 150 volumes of local newspaper on microfilm. **Services:** Copying; library open to the public. **Special Catalogs:** Cemetery listings (card). **Special Indexes:** Indexes to 1810-1855 county census. **Remarks:** FAX: (716)268-9446.

★362★
Allegheny College - Walter M. Small Geology Library (Sci-Engr)
Alden Hall
555 N. Main St. Phone: (814)332-3768
Meadville, PA 16335 Margaret L. Moser, Libn.
Staff: Prof 1; Other 1. **Subjects:** Geology, marine geology. **Special Collections:** Catalog of fossil spores and pollen. **Holdings:** 700 books; 400 bound periodical volumes; 200 quadrangle maps; 3225 Geological Society of America bulletins and professional papers; 725 State Geological Survey publications; 6 VF drawers of student projects. **Subscriptions:** 30 journals and other serials. **Services:** Interlibrary loan; library open to the public with restrictions.

★363★
Allegheny County Court of Common Pleas - Law Library (Law)
921 City County Bldg. Phone: (412)355-5353
Pittsburgh, PA 15219 Joel Fishman, Dir.
Staff: Prof 1; Other 1. **Subjects:** Pennsylvania law. **Holdings:** 25,000 books; encyclopedias; reporters; statutes; loose-leaf services. **Services:** Interlibrary loan; library not open to the public. **Computerized Information Services:** DIALOG Information Services.

★364★
Allegheny County Department of Planning - Archives (Plan)
441 Smithfield St., 2nd Fl. Phone: (412)355-4691
Pittsburgh, PA 15222-2219 Dhyam Saikia
Founded: 1960. **Subjects:** Physical planning, local government documents. **Special Collections:** Zoning and subdivision ordinances of Allegheny County municipalities. **Holdings:** 1000 books. **Subscriptions:** 12 journals and other serials. **Services:** Library open to planning professionals. **Remarks:** FAX: (412)355-4330.

★365★
Allegheny County Health Department - Library (Med)
301 39th St., Bldg. 7 Phone: (412)578-8028
Pittsburgh, PA 15201 Lois Jackson, Dir.
Founded: 1972. **Staff:** Prof 1; Other 1. **Subjects:** Public health. **Holdings:** 13,568 books. **Subscriptions:** 135 journals and other serials. **Services:** Interlibrary loan; copying; library open to the public for reference use only. **Computerized Information Services:** DIALOG Information Services, MEDLINE, TOXNET. **Publications:** Timely Topics, monthly - for internal distribution only.

★366★
Allegheny County Law Library (Law)
921 City-County Bldg. Phone: (412)355-5353
Pittsburgh, PA 15219 Joel H. Fishman, Law Libn.
Founded: 1867. **Staff:** Prof 4; Other 5. **Subjects:** Law. **Special Collections:** Original papers and briefs of the Alaskan Boundary Dispute with Great Britain; original records and briefs of U.S. Supreme Court, 1912 to present; U.S. Government Depository Library. **Holdings:** 130,000 books; 30,000 bound periodical volumes; 2000 reels of microfilm; 350,000 microfiche. **Subscriptions:** 1200 journals and other serials. **Services:** Interlibrary loan; copying; library open to the public. **Automated Operations:** Computerized cataloging. **Computerized Information Services:** DIALOG Information Services, LEXIS. **Networks/Consortia:** Member of Pittsburgh Regional Library Center (PRLC), Mid-Atlantic Law Library Cooperative (MALLCO). **Publications:** Allegheny County Law Library Law, History and Genealogy Series. **Remarks:** FAX: (412)355-5889.

★367★
Allegheny General Hospital - Health Sciences Library (Med)
320 E. North Ave. Phone: (412)359-3040
Pittsburgh, PA 15212-9986 Susan B. Hoehl, Dir.
Founded: 1936. **Staff:** Prof 5; Other 7. **Subjects:** Medicine, surgery, oral surgery, obstetrics, gynecology, neurosciences, musculoskeletal disorders, cardiology, nursing, oncology, health administration. **Holdings:** 7000 books; 13,000 bound periodical volumes; 450 audiotapes; 900 videotapes. **Subscriptions:** 640 journals and other serials; 20 microfilm subscriptions. **Services:** Interlibrary loan; copying; SDI; library open to the public. **Automated Operations:** Computerized cataloging, acquisitions, serials, circulation, and ILL. **Computerized Information Services:** DIALOG Information Services, MEDLARS, BRS Information Technologies; internal databases. **Networks/Consortia:** Member of Southeast Pittsburgh Library Consortium, BHSL. **Publications:** Health Sciences Library Acquisitions List, bimonthly; subject specific current contents, monthly. **Remarks:** FAX: (412)359-4420. **Staff:** Susan S. Walko, Hea.Info.Spec.; Diane M. Faust, Hea.Info.Spec.; Linda L. Hogan, Hea.Info.Spec.; Kathleen M. Yasenosky, Hea.Info.Spec.

★368★
Allegheny Ludlum Steel - Technical Center Library (Sci-Engr)
Alabama & Pacific Aves. Phone: (412)226-6367
Brackenridge, PA 15014 Eileen W. Gallagher, Libn.
Founded: 1952. **Staff:** 2. **Subjects:** Metallurgy, chemistry, physics. **Special Collections:** Brutcher Translations (microfiche). **Holdings:** 4950 books; 1500 bound periodical volumes; 12 VF drawers of United States patents; 6 VF drawers of foreign patents; 2500 slides; 4000 technical translations. **Subscriptions:** 300 journals and other serials. **Services:** Interlibrary loan; library not open to the public. **Remarks:** FAX: (412)226-5067. Telex: 199141 ALUDSTLA BCKG. A subsidiary of Allegheny Ludlum Corporation. **Staff:** Leona Sikorski, Supv., Tech.Info.

Allegheny Observatory
See: **University of Pittsburgh** (19201)

Allegheny Portage Railroad National Historic Site
See: **U.S. Natl. Park Service** (17664)

★369★
Allelix Biopharmaceuticals Inc. - Information Centre (Sci-Engr)
6850 Goreway Dr. Phone: (416)677-0831
Mississauga, ON, Canada L4V 1P1 Beth Barnes, Hd., Info.Serv.
Founded: 1983. **Staff:** Prof 2. **Subjects:** Biotechnology, biochemistry, microbiology, biopharmaceuticals, genetic engineering, molecular biology, protein engineering. **Holdings:** 3000 books; 11,000 patents; 1600 annual reports. **Subscriptions:** 150 journals and other serials. **Services:** Interlibrary loan; copying; SDI; center open to the public by appointment. **Automated Operations:** Computerized cataloging and acquisitions. **Computerized Information Services:** DIALOG Information Services, CAN/OLE, Info Globe, STN International; Envoy 100 (electronic mail service). **Networks/Consortia:** Member of Sheridan Park Association. **Remarks:** FAX: (416)677-9595. Telex: 06-968036. Electronic mail address(es): BE.BARNES (Envoy 100). **Staff:** Betty Hagen.

★370★
Allen-Bradley Company - Library (Sci-Engr)
1201 S. 2nd St.
Box 2983 Phone: (414)382-2342
Milwaukee, WI 53201 Linda L. LeVeille, Hd.Libn.
Founded: 1942. **Staff:** Prof 1; Other 3. **Subjects:** Electrical engineering, electronic engineering, metallurgy, physics, chemistry, mathematics,

management, computers. **Holdings:** 12,000 books; 9000 bound periodical volumes. **Subscriptions:** 400 journals and other serials. **Services:** Interlibrary loan; library not open to the public. **Automated Operations:** Computerized public access catalog, cataloging, and circulation. **Computerized Information Services:** DIALOG Information Services, RTIS; CD-ROMs (Moody's Company Data, Computer Select, Business Periodicals Index, Applied Science & Technology Index); OnTyme Electronic Message Network Service (electronic mail service). **Networks/Consortia:** Member of Library Council of Metropolitan Milwaukee, Inc. (LCOMM). **Publications:** Book lists; Strategic Information Update, weekly - both for internal distribution only. **Remarks:** FAX: (414)382-4444. A subsidiary of Rockwell International.

Charlotte Whitney Allen Library
See: **University of Rochester** (19276)

★371★
Allen County-Fort Wayne Historical Society - Library and Manuscript Collections (Hist)
302 E. Berry St. Phone: (219)426-2882
Fort Wayne, IN 46802 Walter Font, Cur.
Founded: 1950. **Staff:** Prof 1. **Subjects:** Allen County and Fort Wayne history, local politics, architecture, business. **Special Collections:** Reports of county commissioners; Nickle Plate Railroad (13 manuscript boxes); Allen Hamilton Papers, 1831-1875; Wing and Mahurin architectural drawings; Brentwood Tolan architectural renderings; Samuel Hanna business papers, 1840-1880; Ivan Lebamoff mayoral papers, 1971-1975; Ruth Budd Vaudeville Collection. **Holdings:** 2000 books; 8 VF drawers of architectural drawings; 19 VF drawers of maps and prints; 200 reels of microfilm of letters to the Secretary of War. **Subscriptions:** 5 journals and other serials. **Services:** Copying; library open to the public for reference use only. **Publications:** Old Fort News, semiannual - to members; Inside Old Fort Wayne, quarterly. **Special Indexes:** Index to Wing and Mahurin drawings.

★372★
Allen County Historical Society - Elizabeth M. MacDonell Memorial Library (Hist)
620 W. Market St. Phone: (419)222-9426
Lima, OH 45801-4604 Anna B. Selfridge, Cur., Archv. & Mss.
Founded: 1908. **Staff:** Prof 1. **Subjects:** Local history and genealogy, Ohio history, railroading, American Indian. **Special Collections:** John H. Keller Railroad Collection; Interurban and Street Railway Collection; Lima Locomotive Works Collection; Railroad Labor History Collection (30 cubic feet). **Holdings:** 8271 books; 585 bound periodical volumes; Lima, Ohio newspapers, 1840s to present; Lima directories, 1876 to present; 1938 reels of microfilm of newspapers and census records. **Subscriptions:** 40 journals and other serials. **Services:** Copying; library open to the public. **Publications:** Allen County Reporter, 3/year; newsletter, bimonthly - both to members. **Remarks:** Library is part of Allen County Museum.

★373★
Allen County Law Library (Law)
3rd District Court of Appeals Bldg.
204 N. Main St., 102 Phone: (419)223-1426
Lima, OH 45801 Gretchen Hooks, Ck./Libn.
Staff: 3. **Subjects:** Law. **Holdings:** 30,000 volumes. **Services:** Copying; library open to the public for reference use only. **Remarks:** Maintained by Allen County Law Library Association. **Staff:** Robert Whitlatch, Attorney/Libn.

★374★
Allen County Law Library Association, Inc. (Law)
Courthouse, Rm. 105 Phone: (219)428-7638
Fort Wayne, IN 46802 Virginia B. Howell, Law Libn.
Founded: 1900. **Staff:** Prof 1. **Subjects:** Law. **Holdings:** 17,000 books; 15,000 bound periodical volumes. **Subscriptions:** 20 journals and other serials. **Services:** Library not open to the public. **Automated Operations:** Computerized acquisitions. **Computerized Information Services:** WESTLAW. Performs searches on fee basis.

★375★
Allen County Public Library - Business and Technology Department (Bus-Fin, Sci-Engr)
900 Webster St.
Box 2270 Phone: (219)424-0497
Fort Wayne, IN 46801 Susan M. Riehm, Dept.Mgr.
Founded: 1900. **Staff:** Prof 9; Other 6. **Subjects:** Business, economics, investments, sciences, medicine, agriculture, automobiles, home economics, management, manufacturing, engineering, law. **Special Collections:** State and federal government documents; topographic maps; foreign trade; U.S. city directories; auto service manuals; U.S. Federal Reporter; supplement and regional reporters. **Holdings:** 80,000 books; 22,000 bound periodical volumes. **Subscriptions:** 1500 journals and other serials; 45 newspapers. **Services:** Interlibrary loan; copying. **Computerized Information Services:** BRS Information Technologies, DIALOG Information Services, EPIC, EDIN, VU/TEXT Information Services, WILSONLINE, OCLC FirstSearch Catalog. **Remarks:** FAX: (219)422-9688.

★376★
Allen County Public Library - Fred J. Reynolds Historical Genealogy Collection (Hist)
900 Webster St.
P.O. Box 2270 Phone: (219)424-7241
Fort Wayne, IN 46802 Curt B. Witcher, Mgr.
Founded: 1961. **Staff:** Prof 5; Other 11. **Subjects:** North American genealogy and family history, Indiana history, heraldry. **Special Collections:** Collection of passenger and immigration records, including thousands of rolls of ships' passenger lists for major U.S. ports; collection of North American historical and genealogical society serial publications; U.S. Census population schedules, 1790-1910; Soundexes, 1880-1910 (microfilm); North Carolina Core Collection (county records through 1868; 4500 reels of microfilm); Canadian census schedules, 1825-1891; ships passenger lists, 1820-1945; Black American family history; Native American family history. **Holdings:** 159,000 books; 8500 bound periodical volumes; 500 vertical file materials and clippings; 194,000 microforms; 9 AV programs; 273,000 clippings and pamphlets. **Subscriptions:** 2232 journals and other serials. **Services:** Interlibrary loan; copying; collection open to the public. **Computerized Information Services:** DIALOG Information Services, BRS Information Technologies, CompuServe Information Service, WILSONLINE, OCLC, OCLC FirstSearch Catalog; internal database. Performs searches on fee basis. Contact Person: Susan M. Riehm, Online Serv.Coord. **Publications:** Bibliographies; pathfinders; Periodical Source Index. **Special Indexes:** Subject index to genealogical periodical literature. **Remarks:** Is said to house the largest group of genealogical materials in a North American public library. FAX: (219)422-9688. **Staff:** Steven W. Myers; John D. Beatty; Delia C. Bourne; Dawne Slater-Putt.

David F. Allen Memorial Learning Resources Center
See: **Indiana Law Enforcement Academy** (7759)

★377★
Fanny Allen Hospital - Health Science Library (Med)
101 College Pkwy. Phone: (802)654-1270
Colchester, VT 05446 Ann M. Bousquet, Med.Libn.
Founded: 1971. **Staff:** 2. **Subjects:** Medicine, nursing, hospital administration, patient education. **Holdings:** 600 books; patient education pamphlets and AV programs. **Subscriptions:** 85 journals and other serials. **Services:** Interlibrary loan; copying; SDI; LATCH; library open to the public. **Computerized Information Services:** MEDLARS, MEDLINE; DOCLINE (electronic mail service). Performs searches on fee basis. **Networks/Consortia:** Member of North Country Consortium (NCC), Health Science Libraries of New Hampshire & Vermont (HSL-NH/VT). **Publications:** Quarterly Briefs - to physicians on staff. **Remarks:** FAX: (802)654-1109

★378★
Allen House Museum - Reference Collection (Hist)
303 N. Pt. Crescent St.
Bad Axe, MI 48413 Phone: (517)269-6479
Subjects: Bad Axe area history. **Special Collections:** 1881 Fire collection; Huron City Centennial history, 1859-1959; Bad Axe Golden Jubilee 1885-1935; 1890 county platbook; 1904 platbook with biographies; Indian Dave Collection. **Holdings:** 50 books. **Services:** Collection open to the public for reference use only. **Formerly:** Bad Axe Museum of Local History.

Ivan Allen, Jr. Department of Science, Industry and Government
See: **Atlanta-Fulton Public Library** (1241)

★379★
J.C. Allen and Son, Inc. - Photo Library (Agri, Aud-Vis)
1341 Northwestern Ave.
Box 2061
West Lafayette, IN 47906 Phone: (317)463-9614
Founded: 1912. **Staff:** 2. **Subjects:** Agriculture, farms, livestock, flowers. **Holdings:** 77,000 black/white negatives and 30,000 color transparencies showing agricultural activities in the Corn Belt states. **Services:** library open to the public.

★380★
Allen, John E. Inc. - Motion Picture Archives (Aud-Vis)
116 North Ave. Phone: (201)391-3299
Park Ridge, NJ 07656 John E. Allen, Archv.
Staff: Prof 3; Other 1. **Subjects:** Motion pictures, 1896-1955. **Special Collections:** Kinogram Newsreel Company, 1915-1931; Telenews Company, 1947-1953; industry, 1910-1950s; transportation, 1900-1965; World Wars I and II newsreels and miscellanea; feature pictures, 1905-1965. **Holdings:** 30 million feet of 35mm and 16mm film, 1900-1970; 1 million still photographs and lobby cards pertaining to motion picture industry. **Services:** Copying; archives open to the public by appointment on fee basis. **Special Catalogs:** Subject catalog. **Remarks:** FAX: (201)391-6335. **Staff:** Martha Allen, Archv., Still Photo.

Allen Library
See: **First United Methodist Church** (5808)

★381★
Allen Memorial Hospital - Libraries (Med)
1825 Logan Ave. Phone: (319)235-3681
Waterloo, IA 50703 Risa Lumley, Libn.
Staff: Prof 2. **Subjects:** Nursing, medicine, hospital administration. **Holdings:** 3500 books; 600 bound periodical volumes. **Subscriptions:** 153 journals and other serials. **Services:** Interlibrary loan; copying; library open to the public. **Computerized Information Services:** BRS Information Technologies. Performs searches on fee basis. **Networks/Consortia:** Member of National Network of Libraries of Medicine - Greater Midwest Region. **Staff:** Robin Nicholson, Media Spec.

Allen Memorial Library
See: **Cleveland Health Sciences Library** (3805)

Allen Memorial Library
See: **University of Hartford - Hartt School of Music** (18614)

Allen Research Center Library
See: **Quantum Chemical Corporation** (13568)

Warren D. Allen Music Library
See: **Florida State University** (5920)

★382★
Allendale Mutual Insurance Company - Library (Bus-Fin)
Allendale Park
Box 7500 Phone: (401)275-3000
Johnston, RI 02919 Carol Emby, Libn./Rec.Ctr.Mgr.
Founded: 1973. **Staff:** Prof 2. **Subjects:** Insurance, fire and fire protection, engineering, business, management. **Holdings:** 2000 books; 250 audio cassette programs; 10 films. **Subscriptions:** 200 journals and other serials. **Services:** Interlibrary loan; library not open to the public. **Publications:** Acquisitions list, monthly - to employees. **Remarks:** FAX: (401)275-3029. Telex: 92 7500.

★383★
Allentown Art Museum - Art Reference Library (Art)
5th & Court Sts.
P.O. Box 388
Allentown, PA 18105-0388 Phone: (215)432-4333
Founded: 1959. **Staff:** Prof 1. **Subjects:** Art history. **Holdings:** 10,000 books; 421 bound periodical volumes; 48 VF drawers; auction catalogs; museum bulletins. **Subscriptions:** 78 journals and other serials. **Services:** Copying; Library open to researchers by appointment. **Computerized Information Services:** Access to OCLC. **Remarks:** FAX: (215)434-7409.

★384★
The Allentown Hospital - Lehigh Valley Hospital Center - Health Sciences Library (Med)
17th & Chew Sts. Phone: (215)778-2263
Allentown, PA 18102 Barbara J. Iobst, Dir., Lib.Serv.
Founded: 1940. **Staff:** Prof 2.5; Other 4. **Subjects:** Medicine, surgery, basic sciences, obstetrics, gynecology, nursing, psychiatry, trauma, critical care. **Holdings:** 7000 books; 15,000 bound periodical volumes; 300 AV programs. **Subscriptions:** 504 journals and other serials. **Services:** Interlibrary loan; copying; SDI; library open to the public for reference use only. **Automated Operations:** Computerized cataloging and acquisitions. **Computerized Information Services:** DIALOG Information Services, MEDLINE, BRS Information Technologies; DOCLINE (electronic mail service). Performs searches on fee basis. **Remarks:** A HealthEast Hospital. FAX: (215)778-2548. Alternate telephone number(s): (215)778-2269 (ILL). **Staff:** Chad Carver, ILL.

★385★
(Allentown) Morning Call - Newspaper Library (Publ)
Box 1260 Phone: (215)820-6693
Allentown, PA 18105 Lois A. Doncevic, Dir. of Lib.Serv.
Founded: 1932. **Staff:** Prof 5; Other 5. **Subjects:** Newspaper reference topics. **Holdings:** 1000 books; pamphlets; VF drawers; microfiche. **Subscriptions:** 30 journals and other serials; 25 newspapers. **Services:** Interlibrary loan; copying; library open to the public with restrictions. **Computerized Information Services:** NEXIS, VU/TEXT Information Services, DataTimes; internal databases. Performs searches on fee basis (Morning Call stories only). **Remarks:** FAX: (215)820-6693. Published by Times-Mirror Company. **Staff:** Diane Knauss; Ruth Burns; Patrice Swartz; Gene Tauber.

★386★
Allentown Osteopathic Medical Center - Learning Resource Center (Med)
1736 Hamilton St. Phone: (215)770-8355
Allentown, PA 18104 Linda Schwartz, Med.Libn.
Staff: 1. **Subjects:** Medicine, nursing, osteopathic medicine. **Holdings:** 1700 books; 300 AV programs. **Subscriptions:** 118 journals and other serials; 2 newspapers. **Services:** Interlibrary loan; copying; SDI; center open to the public at librarian's discretion. **Computerized Information Services:** BRS Information Technologies, MEDLARS. **Networks/Consortia:** Member of BHSL.

★387★
Allentown State Hospital - Heim Memorial Library (Med)
1600 Hanover Ave.
Allentown, PA 18103-2498 Phone: (215)740-3412
Founded: 1959. **Staff:** Prof 1. **Subjects:** Psychiatry, psychology, social work, religion. **Special Collections:** Archives. **Holdings:** 2000 books. **Subscriptions:** 82 journals and other serials. **Services:** Interlibrary loan; copying; library open to the public by recommendation of staff member. **Networks/Consortia:** Member of Cooperating Hospital Libraries of the Lehigh Valley Area. **Special Catalogs:** Union journal list, annual - to area libraries; union catalog of books in consortium (card); union media catalog. **Remarks:** FAX: (215)740-3413.

★388★
Allergan, Inc. - Corporate Information Center (Med)
2525 Dupont Dr. Phone: (714)752-4314
Irvine, CA 92715-1599 Heidemarie von Tilsit, Mgr.
Founded: 1964. **Staff:** Prof 14. **Subjects:** Ophthalmology, dermatology, contact lenses, pharmacology, chemistry, business and management, general

medicine and science. **Holdings:** 6000 books; 3800 bound periodical volumes; 300 technical reports. **Subscriptions:** 717 journals and other serials. **Services:** Interlibrary loan; copying; SDI; center not open to the public. **Automated Operations:** Computerized cataloging, acquisitions, serials, and circulation. **Computerized Information Services:** NLM, DIALOG Information Services, STN International, PFDS Online, BRS Information Technologies, Mead Data Central, Data-Star, Dow Jones News/Retrieval, CompuServe Information Service, NewsNet, Inc., Questel, VU/TEXT Information Services, Reuters, QL Systems, Reuters; Allergan Literature File Index, Laboratory Notebook Index (internal databases). **Networks/Consortia:** Member of National Network of Libraries of Medicine - Pacific Southwest Region, CLASS. **Publications:** Current awareness bulletins, semimonthly; Current Patents Bulletin, monthly; Federal Register Excerpts, weekly; News Update, daily. **Special Indexes:** Index to Allergan Lecture Series; Index to Product Bibliographies. **Remarks:** FAX: (714)955-6756. **Staff:** K. DuBrin, Sr.Info.Spec.; F. Kleist, Sr.Info.Spec.; S. Lee, Sect.Mgr.Corp.Lib.; V. Hartinger, Sr.Info.Spec.; M. Hoch, Sr.Info.Spec.; A. Schultz, Info.Spec.; B. Murphy, Tech.Serv.Spec.; A. Nardiello, Tech.Serv.Spec.; T. Merritt, Sr.Info.Assoc. B. Nadler, Supv., Rec.Mgt.; L. Cermak, Rec.Coord.; S. Kaliel, Rec.Assoc.; M. Winslow, Dp.Sec.

Robert Allerton Library
See: **Honolulu Academy of Arts** (7377)

James L. Allhands Memorial Library
See: **Associated General Contractors of America** (1137)

Alliance Francaise
See: **French Institute/Alliance Francaise** (6145)

★389★
Alliance of Resident Theatres/New York - Library
131 Varic St., Rm. 904
New York, NY 10013
Defunct.

★390★
Alliance Technologies Corporation - Library (Env-Cons)
Boott Mills S.
Foot of John St. Phone: (508)970-5600
Lowell, MA 01852 Linda A. Callahan, Libn.
Founded: 1960. **Staff:** Prof 1; Other 1. **Subjects:** Air and water pollution, solid and hazardous waste. **Special Collections:** Archive collection of internal reports and papers appearing in the open literature. **Holdings:** 7000 books; 3500 bound periodical volumes; 8500 unbound reports; 6000 microfiche. **Subscriptions:** 200 journals and other serials. **Services:** Interlibrary loan; copying; library open to the public by arrangement. **Computerized Information Services:** NLM, DIALOG Information Services. **Remarks:** FAX: (508)452-6033.

Alliance Theological Seminary
See: **Nyack College and Alliance Theological Seminary** (12171)

★391★
Alliant Health System - Library/Media Services (Med)
Box 35070 Phone: (502)629-8125
Louisville, KY 40232 Wenda Webster Fischer, Dir.
Founded: 1958. **Staff:** Prof 3; Other 5. **Subjects:** Medicine, nursing, hospital administration, psychiatry, pediatrics, women's health, orthopedics. **Special Collections:** Flexner Historical Collection. **Holdings:** 5000 books; pamphlets; audio and video cassettes. **Subscriptions:** 300 journals and other serials. **Services:** Interlibrary loan; library not open to the public. **Automated Operations:** Computerized cataloging, acquisitions, serials, and circulation. **Computerized Information Services:** OCLC, MEDLINE, BRS Information Technologies, DataTimes. **Networks/Consortia:** Member of Kentucky Health Sciences Library Consortium, Kentucky Library Network, Inc. (KLN). **Remarks:** FAX: (502)629-8138. **Staff:** Rucell Cobb, Mgr., Media Serv.; Ann Schaap, Info.Spec.3

Alliant Techsystems - Metrum Information Storage
See: **Metrum Information Storage** (10236)

★392★
Alliant Techsystems Inc. - Technical Information Center (Sci-Engr)
6500 Harbour Heights Pkwy. Phone: (206)356-3645
Mukilteo, WA 98275-4844 Christine Mackey, Tech.Libn.
Founded: 1956. **Staff:** 2. **Subjects:** Electronics, acoustics, communication systems, data processing, sonics, ocean engineering. **Holdings:** 2500 books; 50 bound periodical volumes; 25,000 technical documents; 3000 microfiche of technical reports; visual search microfilm of all military and federal specifications and standards. **Subscriptions:** 120 journals and other serials. **Services:** Center not open to the public. **Computerized Information Services:** DIALOG Information Services. **Publications:** Monthly Acquisitions Report - for internal distribution only. **Formerly:** Located in Everett, WA.

★393★
Alliant Techsystems Inc. - Technical Library (Sci-Engr, Mil)
MN 50-4050
5901 Lincoln Dr. Phone: (612)939-2372
Edina, MN 55436 Margaret A. Garske, Libn.
Founded: 1957. **Staff:** Prof 1; Other 3. **Subjects:** Military ordnance, design engineering, electronics, controls, aerospace technology, explosives. **Holdings:** 5000 books; 950 bound periodical volumes; 125,000 military, government, and engineering reports. **Subscriptions:** 175 journals and other serials. **Services:** Interlibrary loan; library not open to the public. **Computerized Information Services:** DIALOG Information Services, DTIC. **Networks/Consortia:** Member of MINITEX Library Information Network. **Publications:** Recent Acquisitions Bulletin, semimonthly - for internal distribution only. **Remarks:** FAX: (612)939-2480.

★394★
Allied/Amphenol Corporation - Bendix Connector Operations - Engineering Library (Sci-Engr)
40-60 Delaware St. Phone: (607)563-5729
Sidney, NY 13838 Brenda Palmatier, Libn.
Founded: 1942. **Staff:** Prof 1. **Subjects:** Electrical engineering, physics, ignition systems and devices, materials engineering, microelectronics, fuel injection. **Holdings:** 2300 books; 10 VF drawers of internal reports; 750 microfiche; 1000 government reports; 1100 pamphlets; 65 shelves of unbound periodicals. **Subscriptions:** 80 journals and other serials. **Services:** Interlibrary loan (limited); library not open to the public. **Automated Operations:** Computerized cataloging and serials.

★395★
Allied Corporation - Bendix Engine Controls Division - Engineering Library (Sci-Engr)
717 N. Bendix Dr. Phone: (219)231-2000
South Bend, IN 46620 Patricia Rulli, Libn.
Founded: 1935. **Staff:** 1. **Subjects:** Aeronautical engineering, strength of materials and structures, propulsion, energy absorption, fuel controls. **Holdings:** 2300 books; 1800 bound periodical volumes; 10,000 technical reports. **Subscriptions:** 300 journals and other serials. **Services:** Interlibrary loan.

★396★
Allied Laboratories, Inc. - Library (Sci-Engr)
716 N. Iowa Phone: (708)279-0390
Villa Park, IL 60181 Dr. Irving Domsky, Dir.
Subjects: Analytical chemistry, environmental sciences. **Holdings:** 50 books; 25 bound periodical volumes; 15,200 reports. **Services:** Library open to the public.**Remarks:** FAX: (708)279-3114.

★397★
Allied-Signal Aerospace Canada - Garrett Canada - Engineering Library (Sci-Engr)
255 Attwell Dr. Phone: (416)675-1411
Rexdale, ON, Canada M9W 6L7 Judith Bain, Eng.Libn.
Founded: 1967. **Staff:** Prof 1; Other 2. **Subjects:** Electronics, circuit design, aeronautics, properties of materials, metal fabrication, mechanical engineering. **Special Collections:** Standards and specifications (15,000; microfilm and CD-ROMs). **Holdings:** 1000 books; 2000 technical papers. **Subscriptions:** 150 journals and other serials. **Services:** Interlibrary loan; library not open to the public. **Automated Operations:** Computerized cataloging, acquisitions, serials, and circulation. **Computerized Information Services:** CAN/OLE, DIALOG Information Services. **Remarks:** FAX: (416)674-8276.

★398★
Allied-Signal Aerospace Company - Aerospace Technology Center - Library (Sci-Engr)
9140 Old Annapolis Rd., Rte. 108 Phone: (301)964-4189
Columbia, MD 21045-1998 Sam Dove, Mgr., Lib.Servs.
Founded: 1981. **Staff:** Prof 1. **Subjects:** Microelectronics, fault-tolerant design, microwave integrated circuits, smart power devices, signal processing, neural networks. **Holdings:** 5000 books; 2000 bound periodical volumes. **Subscriptions:** 125 journals and other serials. **Services:** Interlibrary loan; copying; library open to the public by appointment. **Automated Operations:** Computerized public access catalog, cataloging, acquisitions, serials, and circulation. **Computerized Information Services:** DIALOG Information Services, OCLC. Performs searches on fee basis. **Networks/Consortia:** Member of PALINET. **Publications:** Centerline, monthly. **Remarks:** Alternate telephone number(s): 964-4190. FAX: (301)992-5813.

★399★
Allied-Signal Aerospace Company - Airesearch, Los Angeles Division - Technical Library (Sci-Engr)
Dept. 93295/T-40
2525 W. 190th St. Phone: (213)512-3666
Torrance, CA 90509-2960 Yanghoon Rhee, Sr.Tech.Libn.
Founded: 1941. **Staff:** Prof 2. **Subjects:** Aeronautical, material, mechanical engineering; heat transfer; energy; turbomachinery. **Special Collections:** NACA Technical Reports. **Holdings:** 14,000 volumes; 130,000 technical reports. **Subscriptions:** 150 journals and other serials. **Services:** Interlibrary loan; library not open to the public. **Computerized Information Services:** DIALOG Information Services, OCLC, NASA/RECON, DTIC. **Special Indexes:** Index of Airesearch Reports. **Staff:** Louise Sakamoto.

★400★
Allied-Signal Aerospace Company - Bendix Communications Division - Engineering Library (Sci-Engr)
1300 E. Joppa Rd. Phone: (301)583-4382
Baltimore, MD 21204 Phyllis A. Farmer, Libn.
Founded: 1950. **Staff:** Prof 1; Other 1. **Subjects:** Electrical and electronic technology, physics, mathematics, business. **Holdings:** 2935 books; 900 bound periodical volumes; 53 VF drawers of transactions; 35 shelf feet of conference proceedings; 35 VF drawers. **Subscriptions:** 105 journals and other serials. **Services:** Interlibrary loan; copying; library open to the public with restrictions. **Computerized Information Services:** DIALOG Information Services, OCLC. **Publications:** Bulletin - for internal distribution only. **Remarks:** FAX: (301)337-7485.

★401★
Allied Signal Aerospace Company - Garrett Fluid Systems Division - Technical Library 1207-3M (Sci-Engr)
1300 W. Warner Rd.
Box 22200 Phone: (602)893-7162
Tempe, AZ 85285-2200 Mitzi M. Rinehart, Sr.Tech.Libn.
Founded: 1986. **Staff:** Prof 1; Other 2. **Subjects:** Aerospace. **Holdings:** Books; reports; microfiche; microfilm. **Subscriptions:** 84 journals and other serials. **Services:** Interlibrary loan; library not open to the public. **Automated Operations:** Computerized cataloging and serials. **Computerized Information Services:** DIALOG Information Services, ORBIT Search Service. **Publications:** Technical Library News - monthly. **Remarks:** FAX: (602)893-5123.

★402★
Allied-Signal Aerospace Company - Guidance Systems Division - Engineering Library (Sci-Engr)
Rt. 46 Phone: (201)393-3190
Teterboro, NJ 07608-1171 Dale Carpenter, Mgr.
Founded: 1940. **Staff:** Prof 2; Other 2. **Subjects:** Aerospace sciences, mathematics, computer sciences, electronic engineering, physics, mechanical engineering. **Special Collections:** Bendix Teterboro historical and photograph collection. **Holdings:** 4000 books; government reports; military and NASA specifications and standards. **Subscriptions:** 215 journals and other serials; 15 newspapers. **Services:** Interlibrary loan; library not open to the public. **Automated Operations:** Computerized cataloging, acquisitions, serials, and circulation. **Computerized Information Services:** DIALOG Information Services; internal database. **Publications:** Engineering Library Bulletin, monthly - for internal distribution only. **Remarks:** FAX: (201)393-6610; (201)393-6611.

★403★
Allied-Signal Aerospace Company - Kansas City Division - Technical Information Center (Sci-Engr)
Box 419159 Phone: (816)997-2694
Kansas City, MO 64141-6159 Martha Conley, Libn.
Founded: 1970. **Staff:** Prof 1; Other 2. **Subjects:** Materials, processing, computers, manufacturing. **Holdings:** 6000 books; military and federal specifications and standards; technical reports; vendor catalogs. **Subscriptions:** 300 journals and other serials. **Services:** Interlibrary loan; center not open to the public. **Computerized Information Services:** Online system.

★404★
Allied-Signal Aerospatiale - Engineering Library (Sci-Engr)
200 Laurentian Blvd. Phone: (514)744-2811
Montreal, PQ, Canada H4M 2L5 Louise Murphy, Libn.
Founded: 1959. **Staff:** 1. **Subjects:** Aerospace; engineering - mechanical, electron. **Holdings:** 1650 books; 550 reels of microfilm. **Subscriptions:** 100 journals and other serials. **Services:** Interlibrary loan; library not open to the public. **Automated Operations:** Computerized cataloging and circulation. **Computerized Information Services:** CAN/OLE. **Remarks:** FAX: (514)342-3795. **Staff:** J. Butlin, Mgr.

★405★
Allied-Signal, Inc. - Allied-Signal Aerospace Sector - Garrett Engine Division - Engineering Library 503-1L (Sci-Engr)
111 S. 34th St.
Box 5217 Phone: (602)231-2062
Phoenix, AZ 85010 Denise Birnbaum, Supv.
Founded: 1956. **Staff:** Prof 1; Other 2. **Subjects:** Engineering, automotive engineering, aeronautics, mathematics, management, metallurgy, solar energy. **Holdings:** 18,000 books; 2200 bound periodical volumes; 25,000 hardcopy government reports; 300,000 government reports on microfiche. **Subscriptions:** 300 journals and other serials. **Services:** Library not open to the public. **Computerized Information Services:** Internal database. **Publications:** What's New in the Engineering Library, quarterly.

★406★
Allied-Signal, Inc. - Automotive Library (Bus-Fin)
20650 Civic Center Dr. Phone: (313)827-5618
Southfield, MI 48086-5029 Mary M. Blaschak, Res.Libn.
Founded: 1983. **Staff:** Prof 1. **Subjects:** Mergers and acquisitions, automotive suppliers, business. **Holdings:** 500 books. **Subscriptions:** 50 journals and other serials. **Services:** Library not open to the public. **Computerized Information Services:** DIALOG Information Services, Dun & Bradstreet Business Credit Services, VU/TEXT Information Services, Reuter TEXTLINE, WILSONLINE, Dow Jones News/Retrieval. **Remarks:** FAX: (313)827-5427.

★407★
Allied-Signal, Inc. - Buffalo Research Laboratory - Library (Sci-Engr)
20 Peabody St. Phone: (716)827-6229
Buffalo, NY 14210-1599 Janice Hood, Libn.
Founded: 1879. **Staff:** Prof 1. **Subjects:** Organic chemicals, organofluoro chemicals, inorganic chemicals, polymers. **Holdings:** 5500 books; 2000 bound periodical volumes; 6000 internal reports; 400,000 U.S. chemical patents; 100 dissertations. **Subscriptions:** 225 journals and other serials. **Services:** Interlibrary loan; copying; library open to the public by appointment. **Automated Operations:** Computerized cataloging, acquisitions, serials, circulation, internal reports, and laboratory notebooks. **Computerized Information Services:** DIALOG Information Services, STN International; Datatrieve (internal database). **Networks/Consortia:** Member of Western New York Library Resources Council (WNYLRC). **Remarks:** FAX: (716)827-6221.

★408★
Allied-Signal, Inc. - Fibers Division - Technical Center Library (Sci-Engr)
Box 31 Phone: (804)520-3617
Petersburg, VA 23804 Mrs. R.P. Murphy, Libn.
Founded: 1955. **Staff:** Prof 1; Other 1. **Subjects:** Polymer science, textile chemistry, organic chemistry. **Holdings:** 4500 books; 300 bound periodical volumes. **Subscriptions:** 150 journals and other serials. **Services:** Interlibrary loan; copying (limited); library open to the public by appointment. **Computerized Information Services:** DIALOG Information Services, ORBIT Search Service, STN International. Occupational Health Services, Inc. **Remarks:** FAX: (804)520-3568.

★409★
Allied-Signal, Inc. - Library & Information Services (Sci-Engr)
Box 1021 Phone: (201)455-3014
Morristown, NJ 07962-1021 Linnea Ditchey, Mgr.
Staff: Prof 5; Other 2. **Subjects:** Polymers, chemistry, materials science. **Special Collections:** Toxicology; regulations; business; health sciences. **Holdings:** 20,000 books; 25,000 bound periodical volumes; U.S. patents, 1960 to present, on microfilm. **Subscriptions:** 850 journals and other serials. **Services:** Interlibrary loan; copying; library open to the public with restrictions. **Computerized Information Services:** PFDS Online, DIALOG Information Services, NLM; STN International; TECHLIB (internal database). **Publications:** New Book List - for internal distribution only. **Remarks:** FAX: (201)455-5295. **Staff:** Mary Ann Bury, Bus.Info.Spec.; Emma Gergely, Health Sci.Info.Spec.; Anne McKay, Tech.Info.Spec.; Erszebet Szollosi, Acq./Abstracting Spec.

Hector Alliot Memorial Library of Archaeology
See: **Southwest Museum - Braun Research Library** (15532)

Allnutt Health Sciences Library
See: **St. Elizabeth Medical Center** (14282)

Alloy Phase Diagram Data Center
See: **U.S. Natl. Institute of Standards and Technology** (17612)

Allport Library and Museum of Fine Arts
See: **State Library of Tasmania** (15696)

★410★
Allstate Insurance Company - Corporate Library (Law, Bus-Fin)
Allstate Plaza, Bldg. C02 Phone: (708)402-3413
Northbrook, IL 60062 Alice Bruemner, Div.Mgr.
Founded: 1974. **Staff:** Prof 2; Other 3. **Subjects:** Business, insurance. **Holdings:** 5000 books; 300 microfiche. **Subscriptions:** 300 journals and other serials; 7 newspapers. **Services:** Interlibrary loan; copying; library open to the public with restrictions. **Computerized Information Services:** DIALOG Information Services, VU/TEXT Information Services, NEXIS, OCLC. **Networks/Consortia:** Member of ILLINET. **Publications:** New Book List, monthly - for internal distribution only. **Remarks:** Alternate telephone number(s): 402-6014; 402-5407. FAX: (708)402-3192. **Staff:** Judith A. Carlson.

Edna Allyn Room
See: **Hawaii State Public Library System - Hawaii State Library** (7040)

★411★
Lyman Allyn Art Museum - Library (Art)
625 Williams St.
New London, CT 06320 Phone: (203)443-2545
Staff: Prof 1; Other 2. **Subjects:** Furniture and decorative arts, American art, fine arts. **Holdings:** 7700 books; exhibition catalogs; museum reports; drawings. **Services:** Copying; library open to the public for reference use only.

★412★
Alpena County Law Library (Law)
Courthouse Phone: (517)356-0395
Alpena, MI 49707 Joyce D. McLain, Law Libn.
Staff: Prof 1. **Subjects:** Law. **Holdings:** Figures not available. **Services:** Library open to the public for reference use only.

★413★
Alphatech, Inc. - Library (Comp Sci)
50 Mall Rd. Phone: (617)273-3388
Burlington, MA 01803 Julie Cohen, Libn.
Founded: 1980. **Staff:** 1. **Subjects:** Systems engineering, artificial intelligence, cybernetics. **Holdings:** 300 books; 800 bound periodical volumes; 500 reports. **Subscriptions:** 80 journals and other serials; 5 newspapers. **Services:** Library open to the public at librarian's discretion. **Remarks:** FAX: (617)273-9345.

Albert Alphin Music Library
See: **Boston Conservatory of Music** (1983)

★414★
Alpine Club of Canada - Library (Rec)
Box 160 Phone: (403)762-2291
Banff, AB, Canada T0L 0C0 Mary Andrews, Libn.
Founded: 1906. **Staff:** Prof 2; Other 2. **Subjects:** Mountaineering, mountains, rock climbing, glaciology, mountain sports. **Holdings:** 2593 books and pamphlets; 2108 bound periodical volumes; **Subscriptions:** 158 journals and other serials. **Services:** Copying; library open to the public for reference use only. **Remarks:** Maintained by Whyte Museum of the Canadian Rockies - Archives. **Staff:** Don Bourdon, Hd.Archv.; Beverly Bendell, Hon.Libn.

★415★
Alpine County Law Library (Law)
Box 276 Phone: (916)694-2281
Markleeville, CA 96120 Karen Keebaugh, Alpine County Ck.
Staff: 2. **Subjects:** Law. **Holdings:** 4000 books. **Services:** Library open to the public by appointment. **Remarks:** FAX: (916)694-2491.

Alpine County Museum
See: **Historical Society of Alpine County** (7262)

★416★
ALS and Neuromuscular Research Foundation - Brian Polsley Memorial Audio/Video Library (Med)
2351 Clay St., No. 416 Phone: (415)923-3604
San Francisco, CA 94115 Linda Elias, Patient Care Coord.
Founded: 1981. **Staff:** 9. **Subjects:** ALS (amyotrophic lateral sclerosis). **Holdings:** AV programs. **Services:** Library open to the public. **Publications:** Patient support group newsletter, monthly. **Remarks:** FAX: (415)923-3197.

Jacob Alson Memorial Library
See: **Anti-Defamation League of B'nai B'rith** (897)

★417★
Alston & Bird - Library (Law)
One Atlantic Center
1201 W. Peachtree St. Phone: (404)881-7100
Atlanta, GA 30309-3424 Frances D. Pughsley, Lib.Dir.
Founded: 1911. **Staff:** Prof 6; Other 2. **Subjects:** Law - corporate/securities, tax, antitrust, labor, health; litigation. **Holdings:** 40,000 volumes; 10 VF drawers of pamphlets; 4000 volumes in microform. **Subscriptions:** 1000 journals and other serials; 10 newspapers. **Services:** Interlibrary loan; library not open to the public. **Computerized Information Services:** DataTimes, Dun & Bradstreet Business Credit Services, Dow Jones News/Retrieval, DIALOG Information Services, LEGI-SLATE, LEXIS, WESTLAW, OCLC, VU/TEXT Information Services, Information America, NewsNet, Inc., RLIN. **Publications:** Pocket Part (newsletter), monthly; Information Store (orientation booklet) - both for internal distribution only. **Special Catalogs:** Memoranda of Law. **Remarks:** FAX: (404)881-7777. Telex: 54-2996 AMG-ATL. **Staff:** Terri Holsten, Ref.Libn.; Susan Pinckard, Cat.; Shirley McDonald, Ref.Libn.; Shirley Wise, Ref.Libn.; Mary Tucker, Ref.Libn.

★418★
Alta Bates-Herrick Hospitals - Alta Bates Hospital - Stuart Memorial Library (Med)
3001 Colby at Ashby Phone: (510)540-1696
Berkeley, CA 94705 Kay Kammerer, Hea.Sci.Libn.
Founded: 1975. **Staff:** Prof 1. **Subjects:** Medicine. **Holdings:** 1800 books; 2500 bound periodical volumes. **Subscriptions:** 260 journals and other serials. **Services:** Interlibrary loan; copying; library open to health science professionals for reference use. **Computerized Information Services:** MEDLINE.

★419★
Alta Bates-Herrick Hospitals - Herrick Health Sciences Library (Med)
2001 Dwight Way Phone: (510)540-4517
Berkeley, CA 94704 Dorrie Slutsker, Libn.
Founded: 1957. **Staff:** Prof 1. **Subjects:** Psychoanalysis, psychiatry, psychology, neurology, psychosomatic medicine, rehabilitation. **Holdings:** 7000 volumes. **Subscriptions:** 150 journals and other serials. **Services:** Interlibrary loan; library open to individuals in the area working in the mental health field. **Computerized Information Services:** DIALOG Information Services, MEDLARS. Performs searches on fee basis. **Networks/Consortia:** Member of National Network of Libraries of Medicine - Pacific Southwest Region, Northern California and Nevada Medical Library Group (NCNMLG), Northern California Consortium of Psychology Libraries (NCCPL).

★420★
Alta Bates-Herrick Hospitals - Vintage Health Library and Resource Center (Med)
2001 Dwight Way Phone: (510)540-4475
Berkeley, CA 94704 Maureen Rafferty, Mgr.
Founded: 1987. **Staff:** 1. **Subjects:** Aging and health, gerontology, geriatrics. **Holdings:** 950 books; 60 AV programs. **Subscriptions:** 22 journals and other serials. **Services:** Library open to the public. **Publications:** Just for You (newsletter), quarterly; Berkeley & Albany Resources for Older Adults, irregular. **Staff:** Mary Jo Brazil.

★421★
Alternative Energy Resources Organization (AERO) - Library (Energy)
44 N. Last Chance Gulch Phone: (406)443-7272
Helena, MT 59601-4122 Al Kurki, Dir.
Founded: 1974. **Staff:** 3. **Subjects:** Sustainable agriculture, renewable energy, local economic development, pesticide toxicology. **Holdings:** 250 books; 200 bound periodical volumes; 2 VF drawers of renewable resource material. **Subscriptions:** 15 journals and other serials. **Services:** Copying; library open to the public for reference use only. **Computerized Information Services:** HandsNet, EcoNet (electronic mail services). **Publications:** List of publications - available on request. **Remarks:** FAX: (406)442-9120.

★422★
Alternative Press Center - Library (Soc Sci)
Box 33109 Phone: (301)243-2471
Baltimore, MD 21218 Bill Wilson, Coord.
Founded: 1969. **Staff:** Prof 3. **Subjects:** Liberation - women's, gay, black; Third World movement; ecology; alternative life styles. **Holdings:** 420 volumes. **Subscriptions:** 120 journals and other serials; 180 newspapers. **Services:** Library open to the public. **Publications:** Alternative Press Index, quarterly. **Staff:** Les Wade; Dave Schubert.

★423★
Altobello Children and Youth Center - Library (Soc Sci)
Undercliff Rd. Phone: (203)238-6097
Meriden, CT 06450 Michael Lustick, M.D.
Founded: 1982. **Subjects:** Adolescence; violence and adolescence. **Holdings:** 100 books. **Subscriptions:** 6 journals and other serials. **Services:** Library not open to the public.

★424★
Alton Mental Health and Developmental Center - Professional Library (Med)
4500 College Ave. Phone: (618)465-5593
Alton, IL 62002 Thomas H. Johnson, Act.Dir. of Training
Founded: 1941. **Subjects:** Psychiatry, psychology, nursing, activity therapy, social work, mental retardation, medicine. **Holdings:** 2127 books; 495 bound periodical volumes. **Subscriptions:** 42 journals and other serials. **Services:** Interlibrary loan; copying; library open to students and consortium members. **Networks/Consortia:** Member of Areawide Hospital Library Consortium of Southwestern Illinois (AHLC). **Remarks:** FAX: (618)465-4800. **Formerly:** Alton Mental Health Center. **Staff:** Sarah Ringhausen.

★425★
Alton Telegraph Printing Company - Library (Publ)
111 E. Broadway Phone: (618)463-2573
Alton, IL 62002 Sue Johnson, Libn.
Staff: Prof 1. **Subjects:** Newspaper reference topics. **Holdings:** 9 file cabinets and 60 archive boxes of clippings; 550 reels of microfilm of early Alton newspapers and Alton Telegraph. **Services:** Library not open to the public. **Special Indexes:** Newspaper index, 1836-1936. **Remarks:** Toll-free telephone number(s): (800)642-2118, ext. 2573. FAX: (618)463-9829.

★426★
Altoona Area Public Library & District Center - Pennsylvania Room (Hist)
1600 5th Ave. Phone: (814)946-0417
Altoona, PA 16602 Sonia L. Keiper, Ref.Libn.
Founded: 1927. **Staff:** Prof 2; Other 1. **Subjects:** State and local history, genealogy, biography, fiction by Pennsylvania authors, railroads, travel, folklore. **Special Collections:** Negatives and glass plates from the test plant of the Pennsylvania Railroad (13,000 items). **Holdings:** Books; 17 drawers of clippings and unbound reports. **Subscriptions:** 5 journals and other serials. **Services:** Copying; room open to the public. **Automated Operations:** Computerized public access catalog, cataloging, and circulation. **Computerized Information Services:** OCLC, WILSONLINE, BRS Information Technologies; Pennsylvania State Library Electronic Mail System (electronic mail service). Performs searches on fee basis. Contact Person: Matthew J. Kane. **Networks/Consortia:** Member of Pittsburgh Regional Library Center (PRLC). **Remarks:** FAX: (814)946-3230. **Staff:** Georgia Kuhn.

★427★
Altoona Hospital - Glover Memorial Library (Med)
620 Howard Ave. Phone: (814)946-2318
Altoona, PA 16601-4899 Tracie L. Kahler, Chf., Lib.Serv.
Founded: 1940. **Staff:** Prof 1; Other 2. **Subjects:** Medicine, nursing, oncology. **Special Collections:** History of medicine. **Holdings:** 7480 books; 1746 bound periodical volumes; 2 VF drawers; 33 films; 1785 slides; 138 filmstrips; 23 film loops; 55 sound film loops; 32 models; 500 audiotapes; 56 videocassettes. **Subscriptions:** 300 journals and other serials. **Services:** Interlibrary loan; copying; SDI; library open to the public for reference use only. **Automated Operations:** Computerized cataloging. **Computerized Information Services:** MEDLARS, DIALOG Information Services, Physician Data Query (PDQ); CD-ROMs (CORE MEDLINE, CINAHL). Performs searches on fee basis. **Networks/Consortia:** Member of Central Pennsylvania Health Sciences Library Association (CPHSLA), National Network of Libraries of Medicine - Middle Atlantic Region. **Publications:** New Book List and Film List, monthly - for internal distribution only. **Special Indexes:** Index to Nursing Service Manuals (book). **Remarks:** FAX: (814)946-2074.

★428★
Altoona Mirror - Library (Publ)
1000 Green Ave.
Box 2008 Phone: (814)946-7458
Altoona, PA 16603 John T. Doyle, Libn.
Founded: 1929. **Staff:** Prof 1. **Subjects:** Newspaper reference topics. **Holdings:** Altoona Mirror, 1874-1878 and 1888-1989, on microfilm. **Services:** Library open to the public by permission. **Remarks:** Published by Thomson Company.

★429★
Altrurian Public Library - Southwest Collection (Hist)
201 W. Chaco Phone: (505)334-9456
Aztec, NM 87410 Kathi Browning, Libn.
Staff: 2. **Subjects:** U.S. Southwest - history and culture. **Holdings:** 450 books; large print book collection. **Subscriptions:** 29 journals and other serials; 3 newspapers. **Services:** Interlibrary loan; copying; children's and adult programming; collection open to the public. **Remarks:** FAX: (505)334-3586.

Altschul Medical Library
See: **Monmouth Medical Center** (10615)

★430★
Alumax Inc. - Market Research Library (Sci-Engr)
5655 Peachtree Pkwy. Phone: (404)246-6673
Norcross, GA 30092-2812 Ms. Quita Crump, Mktg.Res. & Info.Spec.
Staff: Prof 2; Other 1. **Subjects:** Aluminum and aluminum products, markets. **Holdings:** Books; annual reports; newspapers; government documents; periodicals. **Subscriptions:** 300 journals and other serials; 12 newspapers. **Services:** Interlibrary loan; copying; library open to the public by appointment and with approval. **Computerized Information Services:** DIALOG Information Services; MCI Mail (electronic mail service). **Remarks:** FAX: (404)246-6668. Electronic mail address(es): QUITA CRUMP (MCI Mail).

★431★
Aluminum Association - Information Center (Sci-Engr)
900 19th St., N.W., Suite 300
Washington, DC 20006 Phone: (202)862-5100
Founded: 1980. **Subjects:** Aluminum and aluminum products. **Holdings:** 2000 books and reports. **Services:** Center open to the public with restrictions. **Remarks:** FAX: (202)862-5164.

★432★
Aluminum Company of America - Alcoa Technical Center - Information Center (Sci-Engr)
100 Technical Dr. Phone: (412)337-2438
Alcoa Center, PA 15069 C.A. Hodgson, Supv., Tech.Info.Rsrcs.
Founded: 1919. **Staff:** Prof 4; Other 5. **Subjects:** Aluminum, nonferrous metals, polymers, ceramics, materials science, composites, surface science, geology, separation science. **Special Collections:** Alcoa Technical Center Historical Collection; Aluminum Association publications. **Holdings:** 22,000 volumes; 5000 bound periodical volumes; 17,000 monographs; 60,000 microforms; 8000 translations of journal articles; geological maps. **Subscriptions:** 400 journals and other serials. **Services:** Interlibrary loan; center open to the public by appointment. **Automated Operations:** Computerized cataloging, acquisitions, serials, and circulation. **Computerized Information Services:** DIALOG Information Services, Chemical Information Systems, Inc. (CIS), PFDS Online, ORBIT Search Service, NERAC, Inc., BRS Information Technologies, STN International, LEXIS, NEXIS, DTIC, NewsNet, Inc., OCLC; internal databases of internal reports, correspondence, and Alcoa Laboratories authored publications. **Networks/Consortia:** Member of Pittsburgh Regional Library Center (PRLC). **Publications:** Research Report, semiannual; Guide to Information Center Services. **Remarks:** FAX: (412)337-5436. **Formerly:** Aluminum Company of America - Alcoa Laboratories. **Staff:** C.M. Hennrich, Tech.Info.Sci.; Earl Mounts, Ref.Info.Sci.; N.C. Kotow, Ref.Info.Sci.

★433★
Aluminum Company of America - Corporate Library (Sci-Engr)
1725 Alcoa Bldg. Phone: (412)553-4482
Pittsburgh, PA 15219 Barbara R. Stewart, Info.Serv.Adm.
Founded: 1949. **Staff:** Prof 2; Other 1. **Subjects:** Management, finance, nonferrous metals industry. **Special Collections:** Aluminum industry history. **Holdings:** 5000 volumes; 35 VF drawers. **Subscriptions:** 150 journals and other serials; 7 newspapers. **Services:** Interlibrary loan; library open to the public with manager's permission. **Automated Operations:** Computerized acquisitions and serials. **Computerized Information Services:** NEXIS, LEXIS, NewsNet, Inc., InvesText, DIALOG Information Services, Dow Jones News/Retrieval, Data-Star, WILSONLINE, Reuter TEXTLINE, VU/TEXT Information Services, DataTimes. **Publications:** Library Brochure. **Remarks:** FAX: (412)553-4820. **Staff:** Lori L. Ransom, Info.Anl.; Marge Burke, Info.Techn.

★434★
Alures S.C.p.A. - Istituto Sperimentale Mefalli Leggeri - Biblioteca (Sci-Engr)
Via Bovio 6 Phone: 321 3811
I-28100 Novara, Italy Gianni Martinetti
Founded: 1937. **Staff:** Prof 1; Other 1. **Subjects:** Aluminum and other metals. **Holdings:** 13,000 books; 30,000 reports; 1000 microfiche; 9000 copies of internal publications. **Subscriptions:** 151 journals and other serials. **Services:** Library open to the public. **Computerized Information Services:** ESA/IRS. **Publications:** Rassegna Stampatechica. **Remarks:** FAX: 321 691955.

★435★
Lisandro Alvarado Foundation - Biblioteca Dr. Antonio Requena (Soc Sci, Area-Ethnic)
Apartado de Correos, No. 4518
Frente Plaza Girardot Phone: 43 457308
Maracay 2101-A, Venezuela Mercedes G. de Garrido, Libn.
Founded: 1970. **Subjects:** Lake Valencia region of Venezuela - archeology, anthropology, ethnology, history, economy, native culture, ecology. **Holdings:** 5500 books; 12,000 bound periodical volumes. **Subscriptions:** 46 journals and other serials. **Services:** Library open to the public for reference use only.

★436★
Alverno College - Research Center on Women (Soc Sci)
3401 S. 39th St.
P.O. Box 343922 Phone: (414)382-6061
Milwaukee, WI 53234-3922 Lola Stuller, Libn.
Staff: Prof 1; Other 1. **Subjects:** Women - careers/professions, education, religion, life styles, employment; women's movement. **Holdings:** 3000 books; 110 bound periodical volumes; 100 AV program/microform titles. **Subscriptions:** 250 journals and other serials. **Services:** Interlibrary loan; center open to the public. **Computerized Information Services:** OCLC, DIALOG Information Services.

★437★
Alza Corporation - Research Library (Sci-Engr, Med)
950 Page Mill Rd. Phone: (415)494-5548
Palo Alto, CA 94304 Helen T. Rolen, Mgr., Lib.Serv.
Founded: 1968. **Staff:** Prof 2; Other 3. **Subjects:** Pharmacology, biochemistry, medicine, dermatology, veterinary medicine, pharmaceuticals, obstetrics, gynecology, physiology, polymer science, analytical chemistry, chemical engineering. **Holdings:** 20,000 books; 20,000 bound periodical volumes; 5000 reels of microfilm; 500 microfiche; 20 VF drawers. **Subscriptions:** 550 journals and other serials; 6 newspapers. **Services:** Interlibrary loan; copying; library open to the public by appointment. **Remarks:** FAX: (415)494-8811. **Staff:** Olga Kallos, Libn./Info.Anl.

AMA
See: **American Medical Association** (678)

★438★
Amador County Law Library (Law)
108 Court St. Phone: (209)223-6477
Jackson, CA 95642 Rhonda Wike, Law Lib.Ck.
Staff: Prof 1. **Subjects:** Law. **Holdings:** Figures not available. **Services:** Library open to the public.

★439★
Amalgamated Clothing & Textile Workers Union, AFL-CIO - Research Department Library (Bus-Fin)
15 Union Sq.
New York, NY 10003 Phone: (212)242-0700
Founded: 1954. **Subjects:** Labor economics; industry data on male apparel, textiles, headwear, and shoes in the U.S. and Canada; collective bargaining; minimum wages; trade unions; labor statistics; wages and hours. **Holdings:** 4500 books; 33 VF drawers of government reports, documents, and hearings. **Subscriptions:** 363 journals and other serials. **Services:** Interlibrary loan; library open to graduate students and others doing special work by permission. **Automated Operations:** Computerized cataloging, acquisitions, and serials. **Computerized Information Services:** DIALOG Information Services, BRS Information Technologies. **Remarks:** FAX: (212)255-7230.

★440★
Amana Heritage Society - Library (Hist)
Amana, IA 52203 Phone: (319)622-3567
Lanny Haldy, Dir.
Founded: 1977. **Staff:** 1. **Subjects:** Immigration, travel, and settlement of the Amana people, 1714 to present. **Holdings:** 1000 books; 5000 photographs; diaries; letters; deeds; records; oral history tapes; videocassettes; local newspapers on microfilm. **Services:** Archives open to the public by appointment. **Special Indexes:** Index to newspapers on microfilm. **Remarks:** The majority of the documents are in old German script. **Staff:** Barbara S. Hoehnle.

Amarillo Bar Association
See: **Potter County Law Library** (13275)

★441★
Amarillo Genealogical Library (Hist)
Amarillo Public Library
Box 2171 Phone: (806)378-3054
Amarillo, TX 79189 Mary Kay Snell, Dir., Lib.Serv.
Subjects: Family histories. **Holdings:** 5740 books; 1250 bound periodical volumes; 5750 reels of microfilm; county resource material. **Subscriptions:** 1320 journals and other serials. **Services:** Interlibrary loan; copying; library open to the public. **Special Catalogs:** Catalog of genealogical material in the Amarillo Public Library (book).

★442★
Amarillo Globe-News - Library (Publ)
907 Van Buren Bldg., 3rd Fl.
Box 2091 Phone: (806)376-4488
Amarillo, TX 79166 Lois Baker, Hd.Libn.
Founded: 1950. **Staff:** Prof 1; Other 2. **Subjects:** Newspaper reference topics. **Special Collections:** History of the Texas Panhandle (material published in the Globe-News papers). **Holdings:** 1800 bound volumes of newspapers; clipping files. **Services:** Library open to the public with restrictions. **Remarks:** FAX: (806)373-0810. Toll-free telephone number(s): (800)692-4052. Published by Morris Communications.

★443★
Amarillo Public Library - Local History Collection (Hist)
413 E. 4th
Box 2171 Phone: (806)378-3054
Amarillo, TX 79189-2171 Mary Kay Snell, Dir., Lib.Serv.
Staff: 1. **Subjects:** Southwestern history, Indian tribes and customs, religion. **Special Collections:** Bush/FitzSimon Collection of Books on the Southwest; John L. McCarty Papers (4030). **Holdings:** 5078 books; 765 unbound periodicals; 219 maps. **Services:** Interlibrary loan; copying; collection open to the public with restrictions. **Automated Operations:** Computerized public access catalog, cataloging, and circulation. **Computerized Information Services:** OCLC. **Networks/Consortia:** Member of Harrington Library Consortium (HLC). **Publications:** Bibliography of the Bush/FitzSimon/McCarty Southwestern Collections. **Remarks:** FAX: (806)378-4245. **Staff:** Greg Thomas, Asst.Dir., Lib.Serv.

★444★
Amateur Astronomers Association - Jane H. Douglas Memorial Library (Sci-Engr)
Edwin P. Hubble Planetarium
Edward Murrow High School
1600 Ave. L Phone: (718)258-9283
Brooklyn, NY 11230 Samuel Storch, Libn.
Founded: 1930. **Staff:** Prof 2. **Subjects:** Amateur astronomy, general astronomy, history of astronomy, observational astronomy. **Special Collections:** Historical archives of New York area astronomy. **Holdings:** 1600 books; 3 VF drawers of clippings, articles, and papers relating to amateur and career astronomy in New York City. **Services:** Library not open to the public. **Staff:** John Pazmino, Asst.Libn.

★445★
Amateur Athletic Foundation of Los Angeles - Library (Rec)
2141 W. Adams Blvd. Phone: (213)730-9696
Los Angeles, CA 90018 Wayne Wilson, Lib.Dir.
Founded: 1936. **Staff:** Prof 3; Other 1. **Subjects:** Sports - history and instruction. **Special Collections:** Olympic Games Official Reports, 1896-1988; athletic and sports guides. **Holdings:** 15,000 books; 10,000 bound periodical volumes; 4000 video volumes; 50,000 photographs; bound newspaper sport pages; sports record files; historical documents; scrap books; souvenir programs. **Subscriptions:** 275 journals and other serials. **Services:** Interlibrary loan; copying; library open to the public by appointment. **Automated Operations:** Computerized public access catalog, cataloging, acquisitions, circulation, and serials. **Computerized Information Services:** DIALOG Information Services, BRS Information Technologies, DataTimes, VU/TEXT Information Services, NEXIS, DataTimes, Burrelle's Broadcast Database, OCLC. Performs searches on fee basis. **Networks/Consortia:** Member of Metropolitan Cooperative Library System (MCLS). **Publications:** Sportsletter, bimonthly. **Remarks:** Library holdings of sports materials are said to be among the most comprehensive in the United States. FAX: (213)730-9637. Telex: 9102409846. **Staff:** Shirley Ito, Libn.; Michael Salmon, Libn.

★446★
Amateur Softball Association - ASA Research Center and Library (Rec)
2801 N.E. 50th St. Phone: (405)424-5266
Oklahoma City, OK 73111 Bill Plummer, Dir. of PR/Media
Founded: 1979. **Staff:** 2. **Subjects:** Softball - history, skills analysis/tests, teaching methods, biomechanics, kinesiology, psychology. **Holdings:** 122 books; 67 bound periodical volumes; 95 dissertations and theses; 82 video cassettes; 33 softball guides; 150 souvenir programs; 162 magazine articles; newspaper clippings. **Subscriptions:** 24 journals and other serials. **Services:** Copying; library open to the public for reference use only. **Remarks:** FAX: (405)424-3855.

★447★
Amateur Video News Network - Archive (Aud-Vis)
PO Box 4625 Phone: (303)721-6397
Englewood, CO 80155 Ron G. Brown
Founded: 1987. **Staff:** Prof 1; Other 1. **Subjects:** News, sports, poparazzi, weather, entertainment. **Holdings:** Amateur video news footage (1987 to present). **Services:** Copying; archive open to broadcast and cable television professionals. **Computerized Information Services:** AVNN (electronic bulletin board). **Publications:** Newsmaker (newsletter), monthly. **Remarks:** FAX: (303)290-6179. Toll-free telephone number(s): (800)221-6397. Archive provides permission and clearances for use and broadcast of archival footage and breaking news stories.

AMAX Gold Inc.
See: **AMAX Resource Conservation - Science Library** (450)

★448★
AMAX, Inc. - Law Library (Law)
200 Park Ave.
New York, NY 10166 Phone: (212)856-4200
Subjects: Law. **Holdings:** 3000 volumes; 500 other items. **Services:** Library not open to the public. **Remarks:** FAX: (212)856-5934.

★449★
AMAX Research & Development Center - Technical Library (Sci-Engr)
5950 McIntyre St. Phone: (303)273-7200
Golden, CO 80403 Jane Riggs, Tech.Info.Spec.
Founded: 1974. **Staff:** Prof 1. **Subjects:** Coal, composite materials, metallurgy, chemistry, hazardous waste. **Holdings:** 2200 books; 2000 bound periodical volumes; 7500 patents; 18,000 internal reports. **Subscriptions:** 125 journals and other serials. **Services:** Interlibrary loan; library not open to the public. **Automated Operations:** Computerized cataloging, serials, and circulation. **Computerized Information Services:** DIALOG Information Services, STN International. Performs searches on fee basis. **Remarks:** FAX: (303)273-7204.

★450★
AMAX Resource Conservation - Science Library (Sci-Engr)
1626 Cole Blvd. Phone: (303)231-0284
Golden, CO 80401-3293 Kathy R. Seprino, Mgr., Info.Serv.
Staff: Prof 1. **Subjects:** Minerals and metals, mining engineering, geology, geophysics, geochemistry, environmental science. **Special Collections:** U.S. Bureau of Mines and U.S. Geological Survey Bulletins; professional papers and monographs. **Holdings:** 2000 books; 100 bound periodical volumes; 7000 government documents; 3000 maps. **Subscriptions:** 100 journals and other serials; 6 newspapers. **Services:** Interlibrary loan; copying; SDI; library open to the public with management approval. **Computerized Information Services:** BRS Information Technologies, DIALOG Information Services, PFDS Online, Dow Jones News/Retrieval, TOXNET, CIS. **Remarks:** FAX: (303)231-0404. **Formerly:** AMAX Gold Inc.

★451★
Ambassador College - Roy Hammer Library - Special Collections (Rare Book)
Box 111 Phone: (903)636-2080
Big Sandy, TX 75755 John D. Crissinger, Dir.
Founded: 1957. **Staff:** Prof 5; Other 1. **Subjects:** Religion, Worldwide Church of God. **Special Collections:** Rare book collection (religion and history; 750 volumes). **Services:** Interlibrary loan; copying; SDI; collections open to the public by appointment. **Automated Operations:** Computerized cataloging and acquisitions. **Computerized Information Services:** OCLC. **Remarks:** Maintained by the Worldwide Church of God. FAX: (215)438-7110.

★452★
Ambric Testing & Engineering Associates, Inc. - Library (Sci-Engr)
3502 Scotts Ln. Phone: (215)438-1800
Philadelphia, PA 19129 J. Washington, Hd.
Subjects: Materials analysis. **Holdings:** 500 books; 3000 reports. **Services:** Library open to the public with permission. **Remarks:** FAX: (215)438-7110.

★453★
AMC Cancer Research Center - Medical Library (Med)
1600 Pierce St. Phone: (303)239-3368
Denver, CO 80214 Eleanor Krakauer, Libn.
Founded: 1970. **Staff:** Prof 1. **Subjects:** Cancer - research, prevention, control. **Holdings:** 4000 books; 5500 bound periodical volumes; 8 VF drawers of pamphlets. **Subscriptions:** 180 journals and other serials. **Services:** Interlibrary loan; copying; library open to those with valid reason for use. **Computerized Information Services:** NLM, DIALOG Information Services, OCLC, BRS Information Technologies. **Networks/Consortia:** Member of Colorado Council of Medical Librarians. **Remarks:** FAX: (303)233-9562. Alternate telephone number(s): 233-6501.

★454★
AMC Rambler Club - Library (Rec)
2645 Ashton Rd. Phone: (216)371-5946
Cleveland Heights, OH 44118 Elaine V. Wrenick, Libn.
Founded: 1980. **Staff:** Prof 1; Other 1. **Subjects:** American Motors Corporation automobiles, 1958-1969. **Holdings:** 500 items. **Subscriptions:** 1200 journals and other serials. **Services:** Copying; library open to the public by appointment.

★455★
Amdahl Corporation - Corporate Library (Comp Sci)
1250 E. Arques Ave, MIS247 Phone: (408)746-6376
Sunnyvale, CA 94088-3470 Lourdes (Ludy) Dorilag, Mgr.
Founded: 1978. **Staff:** Prof 3; Other 3. **Subjects:** Computers, electronics, engineering, data processing, science and technology. **Holdings:** 4500 books; 2500 bound periodical volumes. **Subscriptions:** 200 journals and other serials. **Services:** Interlibrary loan; library not open to the public. **Automated Operations:** Computerized cataloging, acquisitions, serials, and circulation. **Computerized Information Services:** DIALOG Information Services, OCLC, RLIN; electronic mail service. **Networks/Consortia:** Member of CLASS **Staff:** Jessie Shangkuan, Sr.Info.Spec.; Gloria Curtis, Info.Spec.

★456★
Amelia Historical Society - Amelia Historical Library (Hist)
Jackson Bldg., Box 113 Phone: (804)561-3180
Amelia, VA 23002 Elva F. Warren, Chm.
Founded: 1957. **Staff:** 2. **Subjects:** Genealogy, local artifacts and history. **Special Collections:** Gemstones historical collection; Indian artifacts. **Holdings:** 950 books. **Subscriptions:** 5 journals and other serials. **Services:** Copying; library open to the public on a limited schedule. **Publications:** Newsletters. **Staff:** Inez West; Rachel Bowlin.

★457★
Amerada Hess Corporation - U.S. Exploration - Technical Library (Energy)
1201 Louisiana, 7th Fl. Phone: (713)658-9770
Houston, TX 77002 Steve DeClue, Supv.
Founded: 1985. **Staff:** Prof 1; Other 7. **Subjects:** Domestic on and offshore petroleum exploration; petroleum exploration in Alaska. **Holdings:** 1000 books; well, prospect, lease, and log files; U.S. Geological Survey (U.S.G.S.) publications. **Subscriptions:** 20 journals and other serials. **Services:** Interlibrary loan; library not open to the public. **Computerized Information Services:** DIALOG Information Services. **Remarks:** FAX: (713)951-5581. Telex: 790 244.

★458★
American Academy of Dramatic Arts - Library (Theater)
120 Madison Ave. Phone: (212)686-9244
New York, NY 10016 Lynne-Marie Jackson, Libn.
Founded: 1980. **Staff:** Prof 1; Other 2. **Subjects:** Theater, acting as a profession. **Holdings:** 7000 books; 250 audiotapes; 450 videotapes. **Subscriptions:** 18 journals and other serials. **Services:** Interlibrary loan; copying; library open to the public with referral from another library. **Networks/Consortia:** Member of New York Metropolitan Reference and Research Library Agency. **Remarks:** FAX: (212)545-7934.

★459★
American Academy of Family Physicians - Huffington Library (Med)
8880 Ward Pkwy.
P.O. Box 8418 Phone: (816)333-9700
Kansas City, MO 64114-0418 Patricia A. Gibson, Ph.D.
Founded: 1982. **Staff:** Prof 3; Other 4. **Subjects:** Current clinical medicine, family practice. **Holdings:** 1415 books; 50 archival items; 1250 microfiche. **Subscriptions:** 507 journals and other serials. **Services:** Interlibrary loan; copying; library open to the public by appointment. **Computerized Information Services:** NLM, DIALOG Information Services, BRS Information Technologies; Health Education and Speakers' Bureau internal databases. Contact Person: David Wright, Ref.Libn. **Remarks:** FAX: (816)822-0907. **Staff:** Carolyn Ruby, Med.Libn.

★460★
American Academy and Institute of Arts and Letters - Library (Hum)
633 W. 155th St. Phone: (212)368-6361
New York, NY 10032 Nancy Johnson, Libn.
Founded: 1898. **Staff:** Prof 2. **Subjects:** Works by and about members of the American Academy and Institute of Arts and Letters; literature; art; music. **Special Collections:** Archives (correspondence, manuscripts, memorabilia, photographs, clippings). **Holdings:** 22,000 books; 500 phonograph records. **Services:** Library open to the public by appointment. **Remarks:** FAX: (212)491-4615. **Staff:** Kathryn Talalay.

★461★
American Academy of Ophthalmology - Library (Med)
P.O. Box 7424 Phone: (415)561-8500
San Francisco, CA 94120-7424 Beverly Taugher, Info.Coord.
Staff: 1. **Subjects:** Ophthalmology. **Holdings:** 2000 books; 1000 bound periodical volumes; 5000 artifacts (instruments, visual aids, memorabilia, art, photography). **Subscriptions:** 60 journals and other serials; 2 newspapers. **Services:** Library not open to the public. **Computerized Information Services:** DIALOG Information Services. **Remarks:** FAX: (415)561-8533.

★462★
American Academy of Optometry - Library (Med)
4330 East West Hwy., No. 1117 Phone: (301)718-6500
Bethesda, MD 20814 David Lewis, Exec.Dir.
Subjects: Optometry, physiological optics, ocular pathology. **Holdings:** Optometry & Vision Science (formerly the American Journal of Optometry & Physiological Optics). **Subscriptions:** 12 journals and other serials. **Services:** Library not open to the public. **Remarks:** FAX: (301)656-0989. All requests referred to International Library, Archives, & Museum of Optometry in St. Louis, MO, tel. at (314)991-4100. **Formerly:** Located in Chevy Chase, MD.

★463★
American Academy of Pediatrics - Bakwin Library (Med)
141 Northwest Point Blvd. Phone: (708)981-4722
Elk Grove Village, IL 60009-0927 Virginia S. King, Academy Libn.
Founded: 1983. **Staff:** Prof 2; Other 1. **Subjects:** Academy policy, health care advocacy for children. **Special Collections:** Archival collection of academy publications. **Holdings:** 2000 books; 800 bound periodical volumes. **Subscriptions:** 225 journals and other serials. **Services:** Interlibrary loan; library open to the public by appointment. **Computerized Information Services:** BRS Information Technologies, DIALOG Information Services. **Networks/Consortia:** Member of Metropolitan Consortium of Chicago, North Suburban Library System (NSLS). **Remarks:** FAX: (312)228-5097. **Staff:** Chris D. Kwiat, Asst.Libn.

★464★
American Academy of Physician Assistants - Information Center (Med)
950 N. Washington St. Phone: (703)836-2272
Alexandria, VA 22314 F. Lynn May, Exec. V.P.
Staff: Prof 1. **Subjects:** Physician assistants, health manpower. **Holdings:** 200 books; 1000 journal articles and bibliographic research materials. **Subscriptions:** 45 journals and other serials. **Services:** Copying; center open to the public by appointment. **Remarks:** FAX: (703)684-1924. Includes holdings of the Association of Physician Assistant Programs.

★465★
American Academy of Political & Social Science - Reference Library (Soc Sci)
3937 Chestnut St. Phone: (215)386-4594
Philadelphia, PA 19104 Richard D. Lambert, Lib.Dir.
Subjects: Political and social science. **Holdings:** Figures not available. **Services:** Library not open to the public. **Remarks:** FAX: (215)386-4630.

★466★
American Academy of Reflexology - Library (Med)
4070 W. 3rd St.
Los Angeles, CA 90020 Phone: (213)389-4424
Founded: 1982. **Subjects:** Reflexology. **Holdings:** 200 volumes.

★467★
American Advertising Museum - Library (Bus-Fin)
9 N.W. Second Ave. Phone: (503)226-0000
Portland, OR 97209 Kimberly Barta, Cur.
Founded: 1986. **Staff:** 4. **Subjects:** Advertising, media, marketing and public relations, advertising history. **Special Collections:** Printers Ink (complete set). **Holdings:** 2000 books. **Subscriptions:** 2 journals and other serials. **Services:** Copying; library open to the public. **Publications:** Update, quarterly.

American Aerospace Exploration Archives
See: **Virginia Polytechnic Institute and State University - University Libraries** (19875)

★468★
American Air Filter - Technical Library
215 Central Ave.
P.O. Box 35690
Louisville, KY 40232
Defunct.

★469★
American Airlines, Inc. - Corporate Library (Trans)
MD 5190 HDQ
P.O. Box 619616 Phone: (817)967-1464
DFW Airport, TX 75261 Kevin Park, Corp.Libn.
Founded: 1940. **Staff:** Prof 1. **Subjects:** Airline and transportation statistics, aviation history, economics, finance, business statistics. **Special Collections:** Official Airline Guide, 1930 to present. **Holdings:** 1500 books; 40 VF drawers of pamphlets and reports. **Subscriptions:** 120 journals and other serials; 5 newspapers. **Services:** Interlibrary loan. **Automated Operations:** Computerized cataloging, serials, and circulation. **Computerized Information Services:** DIALOG Information Services, DataTimes, NEXIS, LEXIS, Aviation Online, Congressional Quarterly Washington Alert Service, InvesText. **Remarks:** Alternate telephone number(s): 967-1464. FAX: (817)967-9631. American Airlines, Inc. is a division of AMR Corporation.

★470★
American Airlines, Inc. - Engineering Library (Sci-Engr)
3800 N. Mingo Rd. Phone: (918)292-2931
Tulsa, OK 74158-2809 O. Fern McCoy, Supv., Engr.Lib.
Staff: 6. **Subjects:** Active fleet support, general aviation, aerospace. **Holdings:** 5000 books; 1000 standards and specifications; 1000 catalogs and vendor data; 6000 vendor catalogs on microfiche; technical reports; 15,000 approved component maintenance manuals; 1 million Boeing and Douglas aircraft drawings on microfilm. **Services:** Interlibrary loan; library not open to the public. **Computerized Information Services:** Vendor Data Tracking (internal database). **Remarks:** FAX: (918)292-3168.

American Alliance for Health, Physical Education, Recreation and Dance
See: **National Association for Sport & Physical Education** (11077)

★471★
American Alpine Club - Library (Rec)
113 E. 90th St. Phone: (212)722-1628
New York, NY 10128 P.A. Fletcher, Libn.
Founded: 1913. **Staff:** Prof 1. **Subjects:** Mountaineering. **Holdings:** 12,000 volumes; maps; photographs; slides. **Services:** Copying; library open to the public by appointment. **Remarks:** FAX: (212)534-2648.

★472★
American Ambulance Association - Resource Library (Med)
3814 Auburn Blvd., Suite 70 Phone: (916)483-3827
Sacramento, CA 95821 Brenda Staffan, Dir. of Pubns.
Founded: 1975. **Staff:** Prof 2; Other 1. **Subjects:** Emergency medical services - personnel training, regulatory control, state information and public education; legislation; Medicare. **Holdings:** 220 books; 10 VF drawers of unbound reports; 3 VF drawers of manuscripts; 28 boxes of archival material. **Subscriptions:** 30 journals and other serials. **Services:** Interlibrary loan; copying; library open to the public on fee basis. **Publications:** Directory of EMS Services, annual - to members; Ambulance Industry Journal, bimonthly - to members and by subscription; Resource Library Index, annual - to officers and staff. **Remarks:** FAX: (916)482-5473.

★473★
American Antiquarian Society - Library (Hist)
185 Salisbury St. Phone: (508)755-5221
Worcester, MA 01609 Marcus A. McCorison, Pres.
Founded: 1812. **Staff:** Prof 31; Other 18. **Subjects:** American history, literature, and culture through 1876. **Special Collections:** Early American newspapers, imprints, almanacs, directories, children's books, broadsides, prints, maps, manuscripts, genealogies, music, state and local histories, and periodicals. **Holdings:** 662,000 books; 150,000 bound periodical volumes and newspaper volumes; 1900 linear feet of manuscripts. **Subscriptions:** 674 journals and other serials. **Services:** Copying; library open to qualified adult researchers. **Automated Operations:** Computerized cataloging. **Computerized Information Services:** RLG (electronic mail service). **Networks/Consortia:** Member of Worcester Area Cooperating Libraries (WACL), Research Libraries Information Network (RLIN). **Publications:** Monographs; Proceedings, 2/year; newsletters. **Remarks:** FAX: (508)754-9069. **Staff:** Nancy Burkett, Libn.

American Apicultural Lending Library
See: **Santa Cruz Apiaries** (14812)

★474★
American Arbitration Association - Eastman Arbitration Library (Bus-Fin)
140 W. 51st St. Phone: (212)484-4127
New York, NY 10020 Laura Ferris Brown, Chf.Libn.
Founded: 1954. **Staff:** Prof 2; Other 2. **Subjects:** Arbitration, mediation, and other forms of alternative dispute resolution - general, commercial, international, labor, environmental, compulsory, maritime, insurance, medical and health, public employment. **Special Collections:** Archival collection of early history and development of arbitration in the U.S.; arbitration rules of trade associations, chambers of commerce, and arbitral institutions throughout the world; arbitration statutes. **Holdings:** 16,000 volumes; arbitration awards; 19,500 microfiche. **Subscriptions:** 240 journals and other serials. **Services:** Interlibrary loan; copying; library open to the public. **Automated Operations:** Computerized cataloging, circulation, and acquisitions. **Computerized Information Services:** DIALOG Information Services. **Publications:** List of publications - available on request. **Remarks:** FAX: (212)765-4874. Telex: 12463. **Staff:** Robert Schernwetter, Ref.Libn.

American Archive of Encyclopaedia Cinematographica
See: **Pennsylvania State University - Audiovisual Services** (12895)

American Archives of the Factual Film
See: **Iowa State University - Library - Department of Special Collections** (8239)

American Armenian International College
See: **University of La Verne - American Armenian International College** (18761)

American Arriaga Archive
See: **University of Wisconsin--Milwaukee - Golda Meir Library - Music Collection** (19635)

★475★
American Association for the Advancement of Science - Library (Sci-Engr)
1333 H St., N.W. Phone: (202)326-6610
Washington, DC 20005 Janet Kegg, Libn.
Staff: 1. **Special Collections:** Publications of the association. **Holdings:** 3000 volumes. **Subscriptions:** 55 journals and other serials. **Services:** Interlibrary loan; library open to the public by appointment. **Computerized Information Services:** DIALOG Information Services, NLM, WILSONLINE, EPIC, BRS Information Technologies, DataTimes.

★476★
American Association of Advertising Agencies - Member Information Service (Bus-Fin)
666 3rd Ave. Phone: (212)682-2500
New York, NY 10017 Marsha C. Appel, V.P.
Founded: 1938. **Staff:** Prof 10; Other 7. **Subjects:** Advertising, marketing. **Holdings:** 2000 books; 400 VF drawers of clippings, reports, pamphlets. **Subscriptions:** 350 journals and other serials. **Services:** Interlibrary loan; copying; primarily serves association members. **Automated Operations:** Computerized circulation, cataloging, acquisitions, and serials. **Computerized Information Services:** NEXIS, DIALOG Information Services, DataTimes. **Staff:** Marge Morris, Asst.Mgr.; Julie-Ann Zilavy, Sr.Info.Spec.; Edith Ziffer, Mgr., Tech.Serv.; Susan Hubbard, Info.Spec.; Harvey Wiener, Info.Spec.; Rhonda Kleiman, Info.Spec.; Lynda Bronaugh, Info.Spec.; Carol David, Info.Spec.; Kelli Erickson, Info.Spec.

★477★
American Association of Botanical Gardens & Arboreta - Resource Center (Biol Sci)
786 Church Road Phone: (215)688-1120
Wayne, PA 19087 Elizabeth Sullivan, Asst. to the Dir.
Subjects: Public horticulture, botanic gardens, conservation, collections management, finances in public horticulture, native plants. **Holdings:** Books; manuscripts; samples of botanical garden policies, reports, and published materials. **Services:** Center not open to the public - requests for information can be made by telephone or mail.

★478★
American Association of Cost Engineers - Library (Bus-Fin)
P.O. Box 1557 Phone: (304)296-8444
Morgantown, WV 26507-1557 Kenneth K. Humphreys, Exec.Dir.
Founded: 1956. **Staff:** Prof 6; Other 8. **Subjects:** Cost engineering, cost estimation, project management, business planning, management science, construction costs, engineering economy. **Holdings:** 8600 volumes. **Subscriptions:** 30 journals and other serials. **Services:** Interlibrary loan (limited); library not open to the public. **Remarks:** FAX: (304)291-5728.

★479★
American Association for Counseling and Development - Professional Information Service (Educ)
5999 Stevenson Ave. Phone: (703)823-9800
Alexandria, VA 22304 Sylvia Nisenoff, Prof.Info.Spec.
Founded: 1952. **Staff:** Prof 1; Other 1. **Subjects:** Counseling in all settings, student development work, rehabilitation counseling, career counseling, school counseling, exceptional children, tests and testing, mental health counseling. **Holdings:** 5017 volumes; 100 journals, 10,000 pamphlets, reports, articles, booklets, newsletters; 60 VF drawers of archival materials. **Subscriptions:** 86 journals; 32 newspapers and newsletters. **Services:** Interlibrary loan (limited); copying; service open to the public for research purposes only. **Computerized Information Services:** Published Information Index (internal database). **Remarks:** FAX: (703)823-0252.

★480★
American Association of Crimean Turks - Ismail Gaspirali Library (Area-Ethnic)
c/o Halim Saylik
4509 Utrecht Ave. Phone: (718)672-1708
Brooklyn, NY 11219 Izet Kara, Mgr.
Founded: 1965. **Staff:** 3. **Subjects:** Crimean Turks - history, culture, literature. **Holdings:** 200 books. **Services:** Library open to the public.

American Association of Law Libraries Archives
See: **University of Illinois - Law Library** (18681)

★481★
American Association of Medico-Legal Consultants - Library (Law)
The Barclay
Rittenhouse Square Phone: (215)545-6363
Philadelphia, PA 19103-6164 Arlene Goldman, Adm.Asst.
Founded: 1972. **Staff:** Prof 2. **Subjects:** Medicine, law, pharmacology, malpractice, medicolegal subjects. **Holdings:** 350 books. **Services:** Interlibrary loan; copying; library open to the public by request. **Remarks:** FAX: (215)545-2163. **Staff:** Evelyn M. Goldstein, Dir.

★482★
American Association of Museums - Technical Information Service (Hum)
1225 Eye St., N.W.
Washington, DC 20005 Phone: (202)298-1818
Founded: 1906. **Staff:** 2. **Subjects:** Museology, museum related topics. **Holdings:** Books, VF drawers; technical resource reports. **Services:** Service not open to the public. **Publications:** List of publications - available on request. **Remarks:** FAX: (202)289-6578. **Formerly:** Its Museum Resources and Information Service.

★483★
American Association of Occupational Health Nurses - Library (Med)
50 Lenox Pointe
Atlanta, GA 30324-3176 Phone: (404)262-1162
Founded: 1965. **Staff:** 1. **Subjects:** Occupational health nursing, occupational medicine. **Holdings:** 1200 books; 24 bound periodical volumes; 1050 pamphlets. **Subscriptions:** 54 journals and other serials; 6 newspapers. **Services:** Interlibrary loan; copying; library open to the public with restrictions.

★484★
American Association of Orthodontists - Charles R. Baker Memorial Library (Med)
460 Lindbergh Rd. Phone: (314)993-1700
St. Louis, MO 63141 Celia Giltinan, Ref.Libn.
Subjects: Orthodontics. **Holdings:** 800 books; 10,000 bound and unbound periodical volumes. **Services:** Interlibrary loan; library not open to the public. **Computerized Information Services:** MEDLINE.

★485★
American Association of Petroleum Geologists - Library (Sci-Engr)
1444 S. Boulder
Box 979 Phone: (918)584-2555
Tulsa, OK 74101 Katherine N. Shanks, Libn.
Founded: 1965. **Staff:** Prof 2. **Subjects:** Petroleum geology, geology. **Special Collections:** Publications of the AAPG and its affiliated societies. **Holdings:** 2000 books; 64 bound periodical volumes. **Subscriptions:** 100 journals and other serials. **Services:** Copying; library open to the public with restrictions. **Computerized Information Services:** DIALOG Information Services, ORBIT Search Service. **Remarks:** FAX: (918)584-0469. **Staff:** Karen Piqune.

American Association for Protecting Children
See: **American Humane Association - American Association for Protecting Children** (620)

★486★
American Association of Retired Persons - Research Information Center (Soc Sci)
601 E St., N.W., A-Z Phone: (202)434-6240
Washington, DC 20049 Paula M. Lovas, Dir.
Founded: 1965. **Staff:** Prof 11; Other 7. **Subjects:** Social gerontology, retirement, pre-retirement planning, voluntarism, association management. **Special Collections:** White House Conference on Aging, 1961, 1971, 1981; Congressional Committees on Aging publications. **Holdings:** 30,000 books; 500 bound periodical volumes; 500 pamphlet files. **Subscriptions:** 380 journals; 9 newspapers. **Services:** Interlibrary loan; copying; SDI; center open to the public. **Automated Operations:** Computerized cataloging, acquisitions, serials, and mailing lists. **Computerized Information Services:** DIALOG Information Services, NEXIS, BRS Information Technologies, OCLC, WESTLAW, LEGI-SLATE; produces AgeLine (database on middle age and aging). **Networks/Consortia:** Member of CAPCON Library Network. **Publications:** Accessions List, monthly; Acronyms in Aging; Thesaurus of Aging Terminology - all free upon request. **Remarks:** FAX: (202)434-6451. **Formerly:** Its National Gerontology Resource Center. **Staff:** Jo-Ellen Vernali-Knoerl, Mgr., Ref.Serv.; Margaret Eccles, Mgr., AgeLine Database; Eve Rafferty, Mgr., Tech.Serv.; Robin Duggar, Sys.Mgr.

★487★
American Association of Textile Chemists and Colorists - Library (Sci-Engr)
Box 12215 Phone: (919)549-8141
Research Triangle Park, NC 27709 Jerry G. Tew, Tech.Dir.
Subjects: Textile test methods for wet processing. **Holdings:** Figures not available. **Services:** Library open to members only. **Remarks:** FAX: (919)549-8933.

★488★
American Association of University Women - Educational Foundation Library and Archives (Educ)
111 16th St., N.W.
Washington, DC 20036 Phone: (202)785-7763
Founded: 1960. **Staff:** Prof 1. **Subjects:** Education and higher education; women's activities and achievements; status of women. **Special Collections:** Graduate Woman (formerly AAUW Journal), complete bound collection since its beginning in 1898 as ACA Journal (also on microfilm). **Holdings:** 400 archival and records boxes relating to history and formation of the association; work done on research education projects; study topics and issues; bound volumes of board meetings for both association and foundation; biennial reports for association, 1933 to present, and foundation, 1958 to present; 158 reels of microfilm of archival materials, 1881-1976. **Subscriptions:** 150 journals and other serials; 5 newspapers. **Services:** Copying (limited); SDI; library open to graduate students in education, women's studies, or related fields and to others by prior appointment. **Automated Operations:** INMAGIC.

American Association of University Women (Maryland Division) Archives
See: **University of Maryland, College Park Libraries - McKeldin Library - Historical Manuscripts and Archives Department** (18818)

★489★
American Association of Variable Star Observers - McAteer Library (Sci-Engr)
25 Birch St. Phone: (617)354-0484
Cambridge, MA 02138-1205 Dr. Janet A. Mattei, Dir.
Subjects: Astronomy, mathematics. **Holdings:** 1500 books; 10 bound periodical volumes; reports; archives. **Subscriptions:** 75 journals and other serials. **Services:** Library open to members. **Remarks:** FAX: (617)354-0665. **Also Known As:** AAVSO.

★490★
American Audio Prose Library, Inc. (Hum)
910 E. Broadway, Suite C
Box 842 Phone: (314)443-0361
Columbia, MO 65205 Kay Bonetti, Dir.
Founded: 1980. **Staff:** Prof 3; Other 1. **Subjects:** Contemporary American fiction writers. **Holdings:** Readings and interviews of 121 writers. **Services:** Library open to the public with permission. **Publications:** American Audio Prose Catalog, Fall, 1991-Summer, 1992. **Remarks:** Toll-free telephone number(s): (800)447-2275. Audio cassette tapes are available for purchase from the Library. Archives of the tapes, which are available for reference use, are housed at the Western Historical Manuscript Collection/State Historical Society of Missouri Manuscript Joint Collection (described in a separate entry). **Staff:** Shelda Eggers, Bus.Mgr.

★491★
American Automobile Association - Library (Trans)
1000 AAA Dr. Phone: (407)444-7965
Heathrow, FL 32746-5063 Stephanie Haimes, Libn.
Founded: 1955. **Staff:** Prof 2; Other 1. **Subjects:** Travel guide books; market studies; highway and traffic safety; driver education; automobiles - history, statistics, insurance; business management. **Special Collections:** AAA Tour Books and road maps; official Automobile Blue Books, 1910 to present; rare guide books. **Holdings:** 14,000 books; 120 bound periodical volumes; 20 VF drawers of pamphlets, reports, articles. **Subscriptions:** 600 journals and other serials. **Services:** Interlibrary loan; library open to researchers with permission. **Automated Operations:** Computerized serials. **Computerized Information Services:** DIALOG Information Services, NEXIS, LEXIS, Dun's Direct Access. **Networks/Consortia:** Member of Central Florida Library Consortium (CFLC). **Remarks:** FAX: (407)444-7380. **Also Known As:** AAA. **Staff:** Carlyn Ewald, Tech.Serv.Libn.

★492★
American Aviation Historical Society - AAHS Reference Library (Hist)
2333 Otis St. Phone: (714)549-4818
Santa Ana, CA 92704 Norbert S. Gurell, Off.Mgr.
Founded: 1955. **Staff:** 1. **Subjects:** Aviation - history, personalities, manufacture; military aviation. **Holdings:** 5500 books; 1000 unbound periodical volumes; 15,000 negatives and aircraft photos; 2000 slides; 25 VF drawers of clippings, drawings, reference data. **Services:** Interlibrary loan; copying; library open for validated research projects. **Special Catalogs:** Negatives Lending Library Catalog. **Special Indexes:** Yearly index of journal and newsletter with cumulative index published every ten years.

American Ballet Theatre Archives
See: **New York Public Library for the Performing Arts - Dance Collection** (11636)

American Bandmasters Association Research Center
See: **University of Maryland, College Park Libraries - Music Library** (18821)

★493★
American Banker, Inc. - Editorial Library (Publ)
1 State St. Plaza Phone: (212)943-4844
New York, NY 10004 Mary Callinan, Hd.Libn.
Founded: 1968. **Staff:** Prof 2; Other 2. **Subjects:** Banking and banks. **Special Collections:** Archives; American Banker, original volumes to present (incomplete). **Holdings:** 2000 books; 400,000 clippings, 1964 to present; 24 VF drawers of pamphlets; 28 VF drawers of annual reports; microfilm. **Subscriptions:** 100 journals and other serials. **Services:** Library not open to the public. **Computerized Information Services:** NEXIS, Data-Star, DIALOG Information Services. **Publications:** Reprints of special features. **Special Indexes:** American Banker Index (book).

American Banker, Inc. - Trans Data Corporation
See: **Trans Data Corporation** (16452)

★494★
American Bankers Association - Center for Banking Information (Bus-Fin, Law)
1120 Connecticut Ave., N.W. Phone: (202)663-5221
Washington, DC 20036 Joan Gervino, Dir.
Founded: 1907. **Staff:** Prof 9; Other 9. **Subjects:** Law, banking and finance, legislative documents, economics. **Special Collections:** Stonier Graduate School of Banking and National Graduate Trust School theses. **Holdings:** 75,000 volumes; serials and legislative documents on microfilm and microfiche; 10 VF drawers. **Subscriptions:** 1000 journals and other serials. **Services:** Interlibrary loan; copying; center open to nonmembers on a fee basis. **Automated Operations:** Computerized public access catalog, cataloging, acquisitions, serials, and circulation. **Computerized Information Services:** DIALOG Information Services, Dow Jones News/Retrieval, VU/TEXT Information Services, NEXIS, LEXIS; Banking Literature Index (internal database). Performs searches on fee basis. **Networks/Consortia:** Member of CAPCON Library Network. **Special Indexes:** Banking Literature Index, monthly with annual cumulation - by subscription. **Remarks:** FAX: (202)828-4535. Make available information kits on key banking issues. **Staff:** Linda Wengel, Assoc.Dir.; Sommers Pierce, Mgr., Tech.Serv.; Bianca Johnson, Ref.Libn.; Audrey Thompson, Ref.Libn.; Ann Kessler, Ref.Libn.; Elinor Dumont, Index Spec./Ref.Libn.; Carole Dempsey, Mgr, Info.Serv.; Mioling Lin, Cat.

★495★
American Baptist Churches in the U.S.A. - Board of Educational Ministries - Editorial Library (Rel-Phil, Publ)
Valley Forge, PA 19481 Phone: (215)768-2378
Founded: 1923. **Subjects:** Theology, Christian education, Bible, church history. **Special Collections:** Judson Press Historical Collection (all the books and material printed and published by the American Baptist Publication Society, including curriculum and Sunday School materials; 2300 volumes); current books of Judson Press. **Holdings:** 3000 books; 500 bound periodical volumes; 100 minutes of American Baptist Publication Society and American Baptist Board of Educational Publications; 200 pamphlets; 200 archival materials. **Subscriptions:** 30 journals and other serials. **Services:** Copying; library open to the public for reference use in consultation with librarian.

★496★
American Baptist Churches in the U.S.A. - Board of International Ministries - Library and Central Files (Rel-Phil)
Box 851 Phone: (215)768-2365
Valley Forge, PA 19482-0851 Priscilla B. Shaw, Libn.
Staff: 2. **Subjects:** Mission material - historical, biographical, ethnological. **Special Collections:** Biographical material on Adoniram Judson and his wives. **Holdings:** 4333 books; 720 bound periodical volumes; 1727 other cataloged items; 571 reels of microfilm; 4 VF drawers of maps; 288 VF drawers of reports, clippings, pamphlets; 41 VF drawers of biographical files; 30 VF drawers of property files; 34 VF drawers of candidate files. **Subscriptions:** 115 journals and other serials. **Services:** Copying; library open to public with permission of Overseas Secretary. **Remarks:** FAX: (215)768-2088.

★497★
American Baptist Churches in the U.S.A. - Board of National Ministries - Records Management & Central Files (Rel-Phil)
Box 851 Phone: (215)768-2383
Valley Forge, PA 19482-0851 Dorothy Carew, Dir., Word Mgt.
Founded: 1832. **Staff:** Prof 1. **Subjects:** Missions. **Special Collections:** Historical and current records of Board of National Ministries. **Holdings:** 54 volumes of minutes of the American Baptist Home Mission Societies, 1832-1989; 35 file cabinets of unbound material; 985 reels of microfilm of records. **Services:** Files open to the public for reference use only with clearance from the Board of National Ministries. **Remarks:** FAX: (215)768-2470.

★498★
American Baptist Historical Society - American Baptist-Samuel Colgate Historical Library (Rel-Phil, Hist)
1106 S. Goodman St. Phone: (716)473-1740
Rochester, NY 14620 James R. Lynch, Dir.
Founded: 1853. **Staff:** Prof 1; Other 2. **Subjects:** Baptist history, theology, and authors. **Special Collections:** Walter Rauschenbusch papers; Danish Baptist General Conference of America Archives. **Holdings:** 85,000 volumes; 225,000 annual reports and pamphlets; 450 manuscript collections; clippings; photographs; microfilm; oral history cassette tapes. **Subscriptions:** 300 journals and other serials. **Services:** Interlibrary loan (limited); library open to the public by appointment. **Publications:** Baptist Bibliography, volumes 1-25 published; Guide to Manuscript Collections. **Remarks:** Maintains Danish Baptist General Conference of America - Archives and American Bible Union - Archives. Is an official depository library of the American Baptist Churches of the U.S.A.

★499★
American Baptist Theological Seminary - T.L. Holcomb Library (Rel-Phil)
1800 Baptist World Center Dr. Phone: (615)228-7877
Nashville, TN 37207 Dorothy B. Lucas, Libn.
Founded: 1924. **Staff:** Prof 1; Other 4. **Subjects:** Bible, religion, theology, black studies. **Holdings:** 36,214 books; 715 bound periodical volumes; 2576 vertical file materials; 1078 AV programs. **Subscriptions:** 220 journals and other serials. **Services:** Interlibrary loan; copying; library open to the public for reference use only.

★500★
American Bar Association - Center on Children and the Law (Law)
1800 M. St., N.W. Phone: (202)331-2250
Washington, DC 20036 Sally Inada, Dir. of Pubns.
Founded: 1978. **Subjects:** Child abuse and neglect, foster care, adoption, parental kidnapping of children, child support, grandparents' rights, developmentally disabled children's rights, child exploitation. **Holdings:** 5000 books, periodicals, reports, and training and conference materials. **Subscriptions:** 12 journals and other serials. **Services:** Center open to child welfare professionals.

★501★
American Bar Association - Washington Office - Information Services (Law)
1800 M St., N.W., 2nd Fl. South Phone: (202)331-2207
Washington, DC 20036 M. Sharon Greene, Staff Dir., Info.Serv.
Staff: Prof 2; Other 4. **Subjects:** Legal profession, ethics, and education. **Special Collections:** State and local bar journal collection (82 titles); American Bar Association Reports to the House of Delegates, 1881 to present. **Holdings:** 2800 books; 1100 bound periodical volumes; American Bar Association publications. **Subscriptions:** 182 journals and other serials. **Services:** Interlibrary loan; copying; services open to the public by appointment. **Computerized Information Services:** WESTLAW, LEXIS, LEGI-SLATE. **Publications:** Washington Summary, weekly when Congress is in session; Washington Letter, monthly - both by subscription.

American Bar Association Committee on Continuing Professional Education - Library
See: **American Law Institute - Library** (661)

★502★
American Bible Society - Library (Rel-Phil)
1865 Broadway Phone: (212)408-1204
New York, NY 10023 Dr. Peter J. Wosh, Dir. of Archv./Lib.Serv.
Founded: 1816. **Staff:** 12. **Subjects:** A collection of 50,000 copies of the Bible or its parts in more than 1900 languages and dialects; related information about science of linguistics and language location, translations of the Bible, Bible printing, use and influence of the Bible. **Special Collections:** Reference works about the Bible, translation, linguistics, and missions (7463 volumes); holdings of the Chicago Bible Society (605 volumes); American Bible Society and United Bible Societies Archives. **Holdings:** 50,000 books; 700 linear feet of archival documents; 10,000 reels of microfilm. **Subscriptions:** 400 journals and other serials. **Services:** Interlibrary loan (limited); copying; microfilming; library open to the public for special research. **Computerized Information Services:** OCLC; internal databases. **Publications:** Historical Catalog of Printed Bibles, English 1525-1961 (with British & Foreign Bible Society, London); The English Bible in America, 1777-1957 (with New York Public Library); The Book of a Thousand Tongues (2nd revision, 1972; 3rd revision in process); A Concise History of the English Bible; Scriptures of the World, 1990. **Remarks:** FAX: (212)408-1512. **Staff:** Mary Ellen Gleason, S.C., Archv./Musm.Educ.Coord.; Dr. Mary Cordato, Asst.Archv./Hist.Res.; Virginia Carew, Ref.Libn.; Liana Lupas, Cat.; Alexander Plaza, Acq.Libn.; Dorothea Colligan, Cons.; Denise Stuempfle, Ref.Libn.

American Bible Union - Archives
See: **American Baptist Historical Society - American Baptist-Samuel Colgate Historical Library** (498)

★503★
American Blake Foundation - Research Library (Hum)
c/o Kay Parkhurst Easson
Dept. of English
Memphis State University Phone: (901)678-2651
Memphis, TN 38152 Dr. Roger R. Easson, Exec.Dir.
Founded: 1970. **Staff:** Prof 2; Other 1. **Subjects:** William Blake - his art, editions of his works, biography, bibliography, original engravings, his followers, auction catalogs, poetry criticism. **Holdings:** 1800 books; 1500 pages of unpublished essays and catalogs; 2000 prints and slides. **Subscriptions:** 15 journals and other serials. **Services:** Copying; library open to the public with written permission. **Remarks:** Alternate telephone number(s): (901)678-4510.

★504★
American Booksellers Association (ABA) - Information Center (Publ)
560 White Plains Rd. Phone: (914)631-7800
Tarrytown, NY 10591 John Cinalli, Res.Coord.
Founded: 1989. **Staff:** Prof 1. **Subjects:** Book selling and publishing. **Special Collections:** Stephen Greene Memorial Library of the Association of American Publishers (575 volumes; 1000 periodicals; 10 VF drawers). **Holdings:** 3000 books; 700 bound periodical volumes; 5000 publishers catalogs. **Subscriptions:** 96 journals and other serials. **Services:** Copying; library open to the public by appointment. **Remarks:** FAX: (212)463-9353.

★505★
American Brahman Breeders Association - Library (Agri)
1313 La Concha Ln. Phone: (713)795-4444
Houston, TX 77054 Wendell Schronk, Exec. V.P.
Staff: Prof 4; Other 8. **Subjects:** Registered Brahman cattle, other cattle, crossbreeding, animal science. **Holdings:** 5000 volumes. **Subscriptions:** 125 journals and other serials. **Services:** Copying; library open to the public for reference use only. **Remarks:** FAX: (713)795-4450.

★506★
American Buddhist Movement - Archives (Rel-Phil)
301 W. 45th St. Phone: (212)489-1075
New York, NY 10036 Rev.Dr. Kevin R. O'Neil, Dir.
Founded: 1983. **Staff:** Prof 1; Other 2. **Subjects:** Buddhism, Asian meditation, Zen, Tibetan Buddhism, Buddhist art and culture. **Special Collections:** O'Neil Collection (Buddhism and Buddhist studies; 5000 volumes). **Holdings:** 8000 volumes; dissertations; Buddhist lectures on cassette. **Subscriptions:** 15 journals and other serials; 5 newspapers. **Services:** Interlibrary loan; copying; archives open to the public. **Automated Operations:** Computerized cataloging and acquisitions. **Staff:** Marian C. Valchar, Libn.

★507★
American Bugatti Club, Inc. - Archives (Rec)
400 Buckboard Ln.
Persimmon Hill Phone: (818)640-1155
Ojai, CA 93023 Leo A. Keoshian, Chf.Archv.
Founded: 1989. **Staff:** Prof 1. **Subjects:** Bugatti automobiles. **Holdings:** Bound periodicals; photographs. **Services:** Archives open by appointment to qualified scholars only. **Publications:** Pur Sang; The Bugatti Register - to members only.

★508★
American Bureau for Medical Advancement in China - Archives
2 E. 103rd St.
New York, NY 10029
Defunct. Holdings absorbed by Columbia University - Butler Library.

★509★
American Camellia Society - Library (Biol Sci)
Massee Lane Garden
1 Massee Lane Phone: (912)967-2358
Fort Valley, GA 31030 Ann Blair Brown, Exec.Dir.
Staff: 5. **Subjects:** Camellias. **Holdings:** 2000 books; 150 bound periodical volumes; color slides of camellias. **Subscriptions:** 15 journals and other serials. **Services:** Library open to the public for reference use only.

★510★
American Camping Association - Library (Rec)
5000 State Rd., 67 N. Phone: (317)342-8456
Martinsville, IN 46151 John Miller, Exec.V.P.
Founded: 1910. **Subjects:** Organized camping, recreation, education, nature, camp administration. **Holdings:** 5500 volumes; 1000 pamphlets and reprints. **Services:** Copying; library open to qualified students for reference.

★511★
American-Canadian Genealogical Society, Inc. - Library (Hist)
Holy Angels School, St. Marie's Parish
P.O. Box 668 Phone: (603)622-1554
Manchester, NH 03105 Connie Hamel, Lib.Bd.Chm.
Founded: 1973. **Staff:** 50. **Subjects:** French-Canadian American materials, genealogy, history. **Special Collections:** Loiselle Index of Quebec Marriages (microfilm/microfiche); Diocese of Moncton, New Brunswick (microfilm). **Holdings:** 3500 books; 3000 bound periodical volumes; family histories, town histories; marriage repertoires, Quebec; archival resources; maps. **Subscriptions:** 41 journals and other serials. **Services:** Research on payment of fee; library open to the public on fee basis. **Computerized Information Services:** Internal database. **Publications:** The Genealogist, 4/year - to members. **Special Indexes:** Surname research index; Marriage Index of Franklin, NH; index of genealogical resources in France from the Church of Jesus Christ of Latter-Day Saints; 500 Hard to Find Marraiges and their lineages; Index to the Genealogist I & II; Taftville, Connecticut marriages. **Staff:** Pauline Cusson, Pres.; Robert Paquette, V.P.

★512★
American Cancer Society - Audio Visual Libraries (Med, Aud-Vis)
1599 Clifton Rd. Phone: (404)329-5781
Atlanta, GA 30329 Brenda L. McNeal, Adm.Spec.
Staff: Prof 2; Other 1. **Subjects:** Cancer - diagnosis, treatment, rehabilitation, prevention, protection. **Holdings:** 16mm films; video cassettes; filmstrips; slide sets; audio cassettes. **Services:** Library open to the public with restrictions. **Special Catalogs:** Audiovisual catalog, annual. **Remarks:** All AV programs are available for distribution through local chapters of the American Cancer Society. FAX: (404)325-2217.

American Cancer Society - Lending Video Library
See: **Whedon Cancer Foundation - Library** (20374)

★513★
American Cancer Society - Medical Library (Med)
1599 Clifton Rd. Phone: (404)320-3333
Atlanta, GA 30329 Betsy Hintze, Libn.
Founded: 1947. **Staff:** Prof 4; Other 4. **Subjects:** Oncology, biochemistry, cytology, public health, rehabilitation of the cancer patient, smoking, radiobiology, general medicine. **Holdings:** 18,000 books; 7000 bound periodical volumes; 30 file holders of reports from foundations, institutes, and laboratories. **Subscriptions:** 620 journals and other serials. **Services:** Interlibrary loan; library serves all state and local divisions of the society in the United States; library open to the public by appointment. **Publications:** Bibliographies on specific subjects - available on request to researchers, doctors, and investigators. **Staff:** Julia Chai, Asst.Dir., Med.Lib.; Alice Wou, Online Serv.; Flora Seruya, Cat.

★514★
American Capital Asset Management, Inc. - Research Library (Bus-Fin)
2800 Post Oak Blvd. Phone: (713)993-4283
Houston, TX 77056-6198 Amy Mollberg, Mgr.
Founded: 1928. **Staff:** Prof 1; Other 2. **Subjects:** Business, finance. **Special Collections:** Moody's, 1928 to present; Weisenberger Investment Company, 1947 to present. **Holdings:** 600 books; financial files on 3000 corporations; corporate 10K and 10Q reports on microfiche, 1979 to present; 200 industry files. **Subscriptions:** 116 journals and other serials. **Services:** Interlibrary loan; library open to researchers. **Computerized Information Services:** DIALOG Information Services. **Remarks:** FAX: (713)993-4362. A subsidiary of Primerica Corp. - American Capital Co.

★515★
American Cast Iron Pipe Company - Technical Library (Sci-Engr)
2930 N. 16th St. Phone: (205)325-8978
Birmingham, AL 35207-4806 Lela Turner, Tech.Libn.
Staff: Prof 1. **Subjects:** Foundry practices, engineering, corrosion, hydraulics, metallurgy. **Holdings:** Figures not available. **Subscriptions:** 78 journals and other serials. **Services:** Interlibrary loan; library not open to the public. **Remarks:** FAX: (205)325-8095.

★516★
American Catholic Philosophical Association - Resource Library (Rel-Phil)
Adm.Bldg., Rm. 403
Catholic University of America Phone: (202)319-5518
Washington, DC 20064 Therese-Anne Druart, Natl.Sec.
Staff: Prof 2. **Subjects:** Philosophy, theology, epistemology, ethics, religion, Aquinas, Aristotle. **Holdings:** 64 bound periodical volumes.

★517★
American Catholic Union - Library (Rel-Phil)
P.O. Box 2622 Phone: (510)232-3323
Richmond, CA 94801 Right Reverend G.D.V Wiebe, Rector
Founded: 1984. **Staff:** 3. **Subjects:** Theology, catechetics, ecclesiology, history, liturgics, canon law. **Special Collections:** Old Catholic history and liturgics. **Holdings:** 5000 books; manuscripts; monographs. **Services:** Interlibrary loan; copying; library open to the public by appointment. **Remarks:** Library is part of Regina Coeli Seminary.

★518★
American Center for the Quality of Work Life - Library (Bus-Fin)
37 Tip Top Way
Berkeley Heights, NJ 07922 Phone: (201)464-4609
Subjects: Labor/management cooperation, organization development, occupational safety, improvement of work life. **Holdings:** 9000 books, research articles, and reports.

★519★
American Ceramic Society - James I. Mueller Ceramic Library (Sci-Engr)
757 Brooksedge Plaza Dr. Phone: (614)890-4700
Westerville, OH 43081-6136 Thomas Shreves, Libn.
Founded: 1954. **Staff:** Prof 1. **Subjects:** Ceramics, glass, materials science. **Special Collections:** Ross Coffin Purdy Museum of Ceramics. **Holdings:** 8600 books; 16,560 bound periodical volumes; 350 patents and unbound reports. **Subscriptions:** 371 journals and other serials. **Services:** Interlibrary loan; SDI; document delivery; library open to the public. **Computerized Information Services:** PFDS Online, DIALOG Information Services, STN International; Ceramic Abstracts Online (internal database). Performs searches on fee basis. **Remarks:** FAX: (614)899-6109.

American Ceramic Society - Phase Diagrams for Ceramists
See: **U.S. Natl. Institute of Standards and Technology - Phase Diagrams for Ceramists** (17622)

★520★
American Cetacean Society - National Library (Biol Sci)
Box 2639 Phone: (310)548-6279
San Pedro, CA 90731 Virginia C. Callahan, Libn.
Founded: 1980. **Staff:** Prof 1. **Subjects:** Whales, marine mammals. **Special Collections:** International Whaling Commission reports; Ray Gilmore Collection; Outer Continental Shelf Environmental Assessment Program (OCSEAP) reports. **Holdings:** 800 books; 1386 periodicals; 800 reports and reprints; 5 films; 6 records; 60 videocassettes; 10 audio cassettes; sheet music. **Subscriptions:** 10 journals and other serials. **Services:** Copying; library open to the public for reference use only, by appointment. **Automated Operations:** Computerized cataloging. **Computerized Information Services:** Computer Effects (internal database). **Publications:** Whalewatcher, quarterly. **Remarks:** FAX: (310)548-6950.

★521★
American Chamber of Commerce in Austria - Reference Library (Bus-Fin)
Porzellangasse 35
A-1090 Vienna, Austria Phone: 222 3195751
Founded: 1960. **Staff:** Prof 1. **Subjects:** Business in Austria and the United States. **Holdings:** Figures not available. **Subscriptions:** 22 journals and other serials. **Services:** Copying; library open to the public on a limited schedule. **Computerized Information Services:** Internal databases. **Publications:** List of U.S. Subsidiaries in Austria; list of Austrian companies in the United States; U.S. Representations in Austria; selected list of Austrian companies active in East West trade; newsletter, monthly. **Remarks:** FAX: 222 3195151.

★522★
American Chamber of Commerce for Brazil - Rio de Janeiro - Library (Bus-Fin)
Praca Pio X, 15, Andar 5
20040 Rio de Janeiro, RJ, Brazil Phone: 21 2032477
Subjects: Brazil - economy, free enterprise, bilateral trade, legislation. **Holdings:** 2000 items including general economic data, statistics, other cataloged items. **Remarks:** FAX: 21 2634477. Telex: 2134084 AMCH BR.

American Chemical Society - Chemical Abstracts Service
See: **Chemical Abstracts Service** (3469)

★523★
American Chemical Society - Library (Sci-Engr)
1155 16th St., N.W. Phone: (202)872-4509
Washington, DC 20036 Dr. Maureen W. Matkovich, Lib.Mgr.
Founded: 1962. **Staff:** Prof 5; Other 2. **Subjects:** Chemistry, chemical engineering, chemical industry. **Holdings:** 10,000 books; 7000 bound ACS periodical volumes; 100,000 photographs; 1000 other cataloged items; 300 bound volumes of non-ACS publications; American Chemical Society publications and other periodicals on microfilm. **Subscriptions:** 1000 journals and other serials; 10 newspapers. **Services:** Interlibrary loan; library open to the public. **Automated Operations:** Computerized cataloging, circulation, and serials. **Computerized Information Services:** DIALOG Information Services, PFDS Online, WILSONLINE, LEXIS, NEXIS, STN International; BITNET (electronic mail service). **Networks/Consortia:** Member of CAPCON Library Network. **Publications:** ACS Library Acquisitions List, monthly. **Special Indexes:** Chemical and Engineering News Index. **Remarks:** FAX: (202)872-6257. **Staff:** Ruby G. Alvarado, Cat.

American Chemical Society - National Foundation for History of Chemistry
See: **University of Pennsylvania - National Foundation for History of Chemistry - Library** (19190)

★524★
American Chemical Society - Rubber Division - John H. Gifford Memorial Library & Information Center (Sci-Engr)
University of Akron Phone: (216)972-7197
Akron, OH 44325-3907 Ruth Murray, Libn.
Staff: Prof 1; Other 1. **Subjects:** Rubber, polymers, rubber history. **Special Collections:** Rubber Reserve Reports; reprints of the Rubber Division, ACS meeting papers and symposia. **Holdings:** Books; periodicals; symposia; catalogs. **Services:** Interlibrary loan (limited); copying; library open to the public with borrowing limited to members. **Publications:** List of Bibliographies - available on request. **Remarks:** FAX: (216)972-5574. The Library and Information Center shares the holdings held by the Science and Technology Library of the University of Akron and it draws upon resources of the rubber companies' research libraries. This combined listing makes available practically all literature in the rubber and polymer fields. Services are available to all of the rubber industry and to those outside the industry who need information about rubber. Special rates and privileges are available to members and affiliates of the Rubber Division and subscribers to Rubber Chemistry and Technology.

American Choral Foundation Library
See: **Free Library of Philadelphia - Music Department - Drinker Library of Choral Music** (6120)

★525★
American Civil Liberties Union - ACLU/CNSS Library (Soc Sci)
122 Maryland Ave., N.E. Phone: (202)544-1681
Washington, DC 20002 Tamara Silver, Libn.
Founded: 1979. **Staff:** Prof 1; Other 2. **Subjects:** Civil rights, religious freedom, reproductive freedom, alien rights and immigration, national security, criminal justice, freedom of speech. **Holdings:** 2500 books; 100 reports. **Subscriptions:** 2000 journals and other serials. **Services:** Interlibrary loan; copying; library open to the public. **Publications:** First Principles: National Security and Civil Liberties. **Remarks:** FAX: (202)546-0738. **Also Known As:** ACLU Center for National Security Studies.

★526★
American Civil Liberties Union - Library/Archives (Law, Soc Sci)
132 W. 43rd St. Phone: (212)944-9800
New York, NY 10036 Thomas Hilbink, Libn.
Founded: 1920. **Staff:** Prof 1. **Subjects:** Civil liberties, law. **Holdings:** 3000 books; 50 files of ACLU board and committee minutes and reports, affiliate mailings, press releases; annual reports; ACLU pamphlets and newsletters, 1920 to present. **Services:** Copying; library open to the public for research only. **Remarks:** Archives housed at Princeton University.

American Civil Liberties Union Transsexual Rights Committee
See: **J2CP Information Services** (8299)

★527★
American Classical College - Library (Hum)
Box 4526 Phone: (505)296-2320
Albuquerque, NM 87196-4526 Dr. C.M. Flumiani, Dir.
Founded: 1960. **Staff:** Prof 1. **Subjects:** Art, psychology, business, Italian. **Special Collections:** Art. **Holdings:** 11,256 volumes; art items. **Subscriptions:** 25 journals and other serials. **Services:** Copying; library open to members. **Publications:** The American Idea. **Remarks:** Library is located at 11501 McNaul St., Albuquerque, NM 87158.

★528★
American Classical College - Stock Market Library (Bus-Fin)
Box 4526 Phone: (505)296-2320
Albuquerque, NM 87196-4526 Dr. C.M. Flumiani, Dir.
Staff: Prof 1. **Subjects:** Stock market, Wall Street. **Holdings:** 3000 books; papers; reports. **Services:** Library not open to the public. **Publications:** Reports, biweekly. **Remarks:** Library is located at 614 Indian School Rd., Albuquerque, NM 87102.

★529★
American Clock and Watch Museum - Edward Ingraham Library (Rec)
100 Maple St. Phone: (203)583-6070
Bristol, CT 06010 Joyce Stoffers, Mng.Dir.
Founded: 1952. **Staff:** 2. **Subjects:** Horology - history, mechanics. **Special Collections:** Largest known collection of American Clock trade catalogs (1200). **Holdings:** 1500 books; 600 bound periodical volumes; 5000 horological photographs; 25 original patents; copies of 10,000 patents; 32 VF drawers of horological pamphlets; 50 volumes of account books and materials. **Subscriptions:** 3 journals and other serials. **Services:** Library open to serious horological researchers, preferably members. **Publications:** Annual reproduction trade catalogs; newsletter, quarterly; Timepiece Journal, semiannual.

★530★
American Collectors Association, Inc. - Ralph Smith Memorial Library (Bus-Fin)
4040 W. 70th St. Phone: (612)926-6547
Minneapolis, MN 55435 John W. Johnson, Exec. V.P.
Staff: 1. **Subjects:** Debt collection. **Special Collections:** State collection agency laws (50 volumes); state assignment laws (50 volumes); ACA State Units bylaws and constitutions (50 volumes). **Holdings:** 365 books; 22 bound periodical volumes; 130 notebooks. **Subscriptions:** 50 journals and other serials. **Services:** Library open to members of ACA only. **Remarks:** FAX: (612)926-1624.

★531★
American College - Vane B. Lucas Memorial Library (Bus-Fin)
270 S. Bryn Mawr Ave. Phone: (215)526-1305
Bryn Mawr, PA 19010-2196 Judith L. Hill, Libn.
Founded: 1931. **Staff:** Prof 2; Other 2. **Subjects:** Life and health insurance, insurance history, estate planning, pensions, taxation, finance, adult learning, management, testing. **Holdings:** 8000 books; 350 bound periodical volumes; 100 microforms; 50 AV programs; 22 VF drawers; 1000 microfiche. **Subscriptions:** 500 journals and other serials; 20 newspapers. **Services:** Interlibrary loan; copying; SDI; library open to the public for reference use only. **Automated Operations:** Computerized cataloging and serials. **Computerized Information Services:** DIALOG Information Services, BRS Information Technologies, OCLC, VU/TEXT Information Services, LEXIS, NEXIS, Dow Jones News/Retrieval. **Networks/ Consortia:** Member of PALINET. **Publications:** Library Bulletin, monthly. **Remarks:** FAX: (215)526-1310. **Staff:** Jane M. Dawson, Asst.Libn.

★532★
American College - Vane B. Lucas Memorial Library - Oral History Center & Archives (Hist)
270 Bryn Mawr Ave. Phone: (215)526-1452
Bryn Mawr, PA 19010 Marjorie Amos Fletcher, Archv.
Founded: 1977. **Staff:** Prof 1; Other 1. **Subjects:** History - American College, life insurance business and education, women in life insurance as a profession, professional education. **Special Collections:** Solomon S. Huebner Archives (1800 cubic feet); Solomon S. Huebner writings translated into Japanese and Chinese; Edward A. Woods Ivory Collection; Class of 1951 Oral History Interviews (150); photographs (200 cubic feet). **Holdings:** 200 books; 70 cubic feet of records; museum display cases. **Services:** Copying; center open to the public (limited hours). **Special Indexes:** Index for each oral history interview. **Remarks:** FAX: (215)526-1310.

★533★
American College of Cardiology - Griffith Resource Library (Med)
9111 Old Georgetown Rd. Phone: (301)897-5400
Bethesda, MD 20814 Helene Goldstein, Dir.
Founded: 1977. **Staff:** Prof 2; Other 1. **Subjects:** Cardiovascular disease and surgery. **Holdings:** 1500 books; 350 bound periodical volumes; 250 AV programs. **Subscriptions:** 160 journals and other serials. **Services:** Copying; SDI; library open to the public. **Automated Operations:** Computerized cataloging. **Computerized Information Services:** BRS Information Technologies, NLM, DIALOG Information Services. Performs searches on fee basis. **Publications:** Cardiovascular Software Directory; Seminar on Computer Applications for the Cardiologist. **Special Catalogs:** Audiovisual Catalog. **Remarks:** FAX: (301)897-9745.

★534★
American College of Health Care Administrators - ACHCA Library (Med)
325 S. Patrick St. Phone: (703)549-5822
Alexandria, VA 22314 Laura R. Ellis, Info.Spec.
Staff: Prof 2. **Subjects:** Long-term care, gerontology. **Holdings:** 1000 books. **Subscriptions:** 80 journals and other serials. **Services:** Copying; center open to the public by appointment. **Automated Operations:** Computerized public access catalog. **Computerized Information Services:** HEALTH; CD-ROM. **Networks/Consortia:** Member of National Network of Libraries of Medicine - Southeastern/Atlantic Region. **Remarks:** FAX: (703)739-7901. **Formerly:** Its Information Central. **Staff:** Juanita C. Smith, Libn.

★535★
American College of Healthcare Executives - Richard J. Stull Memorial Learning Resources Center (Bus-Fin)
840 N. Lake Shore Dr. Phone: (312)943-0544
Chicago, IL 60611 Arthur Strobeck, Lrng.Rsrcs.Coord./Libn.
Founded: 1983. **Staff:** Prof 1; Other 1. **Subjects:** Health services administration, management. **Holdings:** 1000 books; 8 drawers of AV cassettes. **Subscriptions:** 100 journals and other serials; 6 newspapers. **Services:** Interlibrary loan; copying; SDI; center open to the public by appointment. **Automated Operations:** Computerized cataloging and serials. **Computerized Information Services:** DIALOG Information Services. Performs searches on fee basis. **Publications:** Access to Information for Management. **Remarks:** Supports the Ray E. Brown Management Collection which is housed in American Hospital Association - Resource Center.

★536★
American College of Heraldry - Library (Hist)
Drawer CG
Tuscaloosa, AL 35486-2870 Dr. David P. Johnson, Pres.
Founded: 1972. **Subjects:** Heraldry, chivalry, genealogy, names, flags. **Holdings:** 561 books; 251 bound periodical volumes. **Services:** Library not open to the public.

★537★
American College of Obstetricians and Gynecologists - Resource Center (Med)
409 12th St., S.W. Phone: (202)638-5577
Washington, DC 20024 Pamela Van Hine, Assoc.Dir.
Founded: 1970. **Staff:** Prof 5; Other 3. **Subjects:** Obstetrics, gynecology, medical socioeconomics, medical education, women's health care, abortion,

contraception, venereal disease, sex education, patient education. **Special Collections:** Archives; history of obstetrics-gynecology. **Holdings:** 8000 books; reprints. **Subscriptions:** 300 journals and other serials. **Services:** Interlibrary loan; copying; center open to the public by appointment. **Computerized Information Services:** BRS Information Technologies, DIALOG Information Services, NLM, ACOGNET (internal database). **Networks/Consortia:** Member of District of Columbia Health Sciences Information Network (DOCHSIN). **Special Indexes:** Educational Materials for Obstetrics and Gynecology. **Staff:** Lisa Weisshaar, Libn.; Susan Rishworth, Libn.

★538★
American College Testing Program - Library (Educ)
2201 N. Dodge, Box 168 Phone: (319)337-1165
Iowa City, IA 52243 Joyce Giaquinta
Founded: 1968. **Staff:** Prof 1; Other 2. **Subjects:** Education, psychology, psychometrics, educational sociology. **Holdings:** 26,000 books; 12 VF drawers of documents; 10 VF drawers of archival materials; 350 reels of microfilm; ERIC microfiche. **Subscriptions:** 500 journals and other serials. **Services:** Interlibrary loan; copying; library open to qualified researchers in education. **Computerized Information Services:** DIALOG Information Services. **Networks/Consortia:** Member of National Network of Libraries of Medicine - Greater Midwest Region. **Publications:** Selected New Book List, quarterly - to staff members.

★539★
American Concrete Institute - Library (Sci-Engr)
Box 19150
Detroit, MI 48219 Phone: (313)532-2600
Subjects: Concrete materials and structural design, concrete construction. **Holdings:** 1550 books; 450 bound periodical volumes; 3000 technical reports. **Subscriptions:** 238 journals and other serials. **Services:** Interlibrary loan; copying; library open to the public for reference use only. **Remarks:** FAX: (313)538-0655. Telex: 810 2211454. **Staff:** Julie Marshall, Info.Spec.

★540★
American Congregational Association - Congregational Library (Rel-Phil)
14 Beacon St. Phone: (617)523-0470
Boston, MA 02108 Rev.Dr. Harold F. Worthley, Libn.
Founded: 1853. **Staff:** Prof 2; Other 4. **Subjects:** Congregationalism; 16th, 17th, and 18th century religion and theology; modern writings in the field of religion and theology. **Special Collections:** Congregational Councils; church records; hymnals; town histories; local church histories; works of Richard, Increase, Cotton, and the Minor Mathers. **Holdings:** 125,000 books; 100,000 pamphlets and periodicals. **Subscriptions:** 80 journals and other serials. **Services:** Interlibrary loan; copying; direct mail service available to individuals in the U.S.; library open to the public. **Publications:** Bulletin of the Congregational Library, 3/year - for sale. **Staff:** Ms. Sandra Sudak.

★541★
American Congress on Surveying and Mapping - Library (Geog-Map)
5410 Grosvenor Ln. Phone: (301)493-0200
Bethesda, MD 20814 Marshall W. Davies, Dp.Exec.Dir.
Founded: 1941. **Subjects:** Surveying, cartography, geodesy, GIS/LIS. **Holdings:** 1100 books and papers; atlases. **Subscriptions:** 3 journals and other serials. **Services:** Library not open to the public. **Remarks:** FAX: (301)493-8245.

★542★
American Connection - Library (Bus-Fin)
56 Ocean Dr., E. Phone: (203)359-9359
Stamford, CT 06902 Nathalie B. Berliet, Pres.
Founded: 1982. **Staff:** Prof 3. **Subjects:** Business, computers, biotechnology, high technology, medicine, industrial products. **Holdings:** Figures not available. **Subscriptions:** 50 journals and other serials. **Services:** Library not open to the public. **Computerized Information Services:** DIALOG Information Services, BRS Information Technologies, VU/TEXT Information Services, PFDS Online, Reuters, Questel, Dow Jones News/Retrieval, Data-Star, Global Scan, PROFILE Information; MCI Mail (electronic mail service). Performs searches on fee basis. **Remarks:** FAX: (203)359-4591. **Staff:** Yves Berliet, MIS Mgr.; Catherine Scherr.

★543★
American Conservatory of Music - Robert R. McCormick Memorial Library (Mus)
17 N. State St., 19th Fl. Phone: (312)263-4161
Chicago, IL 60602 Teresa O. Kane, Libn.
Founded: 1962. **Staff:** Prof 1; Other 4. **Subjects:** Music - piano, strings, woodwinds, brass, opera, lieder, classical guitar, jazz. **Special Collections:** Complete works; J.S. Bach Gesellschaft (40 volumes); Bach Neue Ausgabe Samtlicher Werke (67 volumes); Beethoven Werke (24 volumes); Chopin Works (18 volumes); Haydn Werke (44 volumes); Mozart Neue Ausgabe (107 volumes); Archives des Maitres de l'Orgue des XVI, XVII et XVIII Siecles (10 volumes; microfiche); L'Arte musicale in Italia from XVI to XVIII Centuries (7 volumes; microfiche); Denkmaler der Tonkunst in Osterreich (83 volumes; microfiche); Denkmaler deutscher Tonkunst (65 volumes; microfiche); Les Maitres Musiciens de la Renaissance Francaise (23 volumes; microfiche); Publikation alterer praktischer und theoretischer Musikwerke (29 volumes; microfiche); International Library of Piano Music (17 volumes); Die Musik in Geschichte und Gegenwart (16 volumes); New Oxford History of Music (11 volumes); New Grove's Dictionary of Music and Musicians (20 volumes); New Grove's Dictionary of American Music (4 volumes); New Grove's Dictionary of Jazz (2 volumes). **Holdings:** 15,628 books and music scores; 563 bound periodical volumes; 276 dissertations; 2784 discs; 584 audio and video tapes. **Subscriptions:** 61 journals and other serials. **Services:** Copying; library open to the public for reference use only. **Networks/Consortia:** Member of ILLINET. **Remarks:** FAX: (312)263-8419.

★544★
American Contract Bridge League - Albert H. Morehead Memorial Library (Rec)
2990 Airways Blvd.
Box 161192 Phone: (901)332-5586
Memphis, TN 38116-3847 Sue Emery
Founded: 1927. **Subjects:** Bridge. **Special Collections:** Publications about bridge from all over the world. **Holdings:** 1450 books; 250 bound periodical volumes; pamphlet material. **Subscriptions:** 50 journals and other serials. **Services:** Interlibrary loan (limited); library open to the public for research. **Publications:** Contract Bridge Bulletin, monthly; Official Encyclopedia of Bridge. **Remarks:** FAX: (901)398-7754.

★545★
American Correctional Association - Anthony P. Travisono Library (Law)
8025 Laurel Lakes Ct. Phone: (301)206-5100
Laurel, MD 20707 Diana Travisono, Libn.
Founded: 1973. **Subjects:** Corrections, correctional institutions, offenders, criminal justice. **Special Collections:** Corrections photograph collection (2000 prints); American Correctional Association Congresses (proceedings, 1870 to present). **Holdings:** 5000 books; 4 VF drawers of photographs and clippings. **Subscriptions:** 50 journals and other serials. **Services:** Copying (limited); SDI; library open to the public for reference use only. **Special Indexes:** Index to Corrections Today, bimonthly. **Remarks:** FAX: (301)206-5061.

★546★
American Council on Alcoholism, Inc. - Walker Library (Med)
5024 Campbell Blvd., No. H Phone: (410)931-9393
Baltimore, MD 21236-5974 Robert G. Kirk, Exec.Dir.
Founded: 1985. **Staff:** Prof 4; Other 1. **Subjects:** Alcoholism. **Special Collections:** State alcoholism treatment directories (50). **Holdings:** 1,500 books; 200 bound periodical volumes. **Subscriptions:** 10 journals and other serials; 2 newspapers. **Services:** Interlibrary loan; copying; library open to the public for reference use only. **Publications:** Journal; Research Review; Newsletter. **Remarks:** FAX: (410)931-4585. Toll-free telephone number(s): (800)527-5344 (help-line).

★547★
American Council for the Arts - Library (Art)
1 E. 53rd St. Phone: (212)245-4510
New York, NY 10022 David Bosca, Dir. of Lib.
Staff: Prof 1. **Subjects:** Arts - education, policy, management, agencies. **Holdings:** 1500 books; 30 VF drawers of reports, clippings, pamphlets, archival materials. **Subscriptions:** 85 journals and other serials. **Services:** Copying; library open to the public by appointment. **Automated Operations:** Computerized cataloging.

★548★
American Council of Christian Churches - Religious Research Library (Rel-Phil)
P.O. Box 816 Phone: (215)566-8154
Valley Forge, PA 19482 Dr. Donald McKnight
Founded: 1941. **Remarks:** No further information was supplied by respondent.

★549★
American Council on Education - Library and Information Service (Educ)
One Dupont Circle, Suite 640 Phone: (202)939-9405
Washington, DC 20036 Jill Bogard, Dir.
Founded: 1952. **Staff:** 1. **Subjects:** Higher education policy and administration. **Special Collections:** Complete holdings of the publications of the American Council on Education including special newsletters and research reports; reports of the Carnegie Commission on Higher Education, Carnegie Council on Policy Studies, Carnegie Foundation for the Advancement of Teaching, Jossey-Bass Higher Education Series, Sloan Commission on Government and Higher Education, and National Commission on Student Financial Assistance. **Holdings:** 7000 books; college catalogs on microfiche. **Subscriptions:** 100 journals and other serials. **Services:** Interlibrary loan; copying; library open to the public with restrictions. **Computerized Information Services:** CD-ROM (ERIC). **Publications:** New acquisitions list, monthly. **Remarks:** FAX: (202)833-4760.

★550★
American Council of the International Institute of Welding - Library (Sci-Engr)
550 N.W. LeJeune Rd.
Box 351040 Phone: (305)443-9353
Miami, FL 33135 H. Glenn Ziegenfuss, Sec.-Treas.
Founded: 1948. **Staff:** Prof 2. **Subjects:** Welding, international welding problems and standards. **Holdings:** 5000 technical papers. **Services:** Copying; library open to the public. **Remarks:** FAX: (305)443-7559. Telex: 51-9245 AMWELD SOC. Jointly maintained by American Welding Society and Welding Research Council.

★551★
American Council of Life Insurance - Information Resource Center (Bus-Fin)
1001 Pennsylvania Ave., N.W. Phone: (202)624-2475
Washington, DC 20004-2502 Karen Mark, Mgr.
Founded: 1976. **Staff:** Prof 4. **Subjects:** Life insurance, financial services, economics, vital statistics, retirement, pensions. **Holdings:** 3000 volumes; 50,000 volume law collection; 1200 volumes of proceedings; 75 VF drawers of pamphlets and clippings; 35 VF drawers of archival materials. **Subscriptions:** 300 journals and other serials. **Services:** Interlibrary loan. **Automated Operations:** Computerized cataloging. **Computerized Information Services:** DIALOG Information Services, BRS Information Technologies, NEXIS, OCLC, VU/TEXT Information Services, Dow Jones News/Retrieval; Life Insurance Today (internal database). **Publications:** Acquisitions list, quarterly; newsletter - both for internal distribution only. **Remarks:** FAX: (202)624-2319. **Staff:** Karen Sherwood, Info.Spec.; Elinor Miller, Law Libn.

American Council for Nationalities Service - United States Committee for Refugees
See: **United States Committee for Refugees** (17134)

★552★
American Council for University Planning & Academic Excellence - Library (Educ)
Box 9751 Phone: (301)948-5876
Washington, DC 20016 Dr. John H. Chen, Hd.Libn.
Founded: 1981. **Staff:** 17. **Subjects:** Higher education, university planning and administration, curriculum, general education. **Holdings:** 27,610 volumes. **Subscriptions:** 21 journals and other serials, 16 newspapers. **Services:** Interlibrary loan; copying; library open to the public. **Publications:** Directory of United States Traditional and Alternative Colleges and Universities; Comprehensive Guide to the Best Colleges and Universities in the United States; National Register of Social Prestige and Academic Ratings of American Colleges and Universities; list of additional publications - available on request.

★553★
American Council for University Planning & Academic Excellence - National Association of State Approved Colleges & Universities - Data & Information Center-Library (Educ)
Box 9751 Phone: (301)330-0558
Washington, DC 20016 Dr. John Chen, Hd.Libn.
Founded: 1981. **Staff:** Prof 10; Other 7. **Subjects:** Academia, curriculum evaluation, academic statistics and ratings. **Special Collections:** Traditional and alternative academic programs in the United States. **Holdings:** 9600 books; 123 bound periodical volumes; complete statistics on academic offerings and accredited programs/schools in the U.S.; reports. **Subscriptions:** 120 journals and other serials; 10 newspapers. **Services:** Copying; SDI; library open to the public with restrictions. **Publications:** Directory of United States Traditional and Alternative Colleges and Universities; Comprehensive Guide to the Best Colleges and Universities in the United States; National Register of Academic Programs and College Ratings; list of additional publications - available upon request. **Staff:** Sandra Reading, Data & Info.Off.; Carole Copeland, Coord.-Ref.

American Craft Council - Library
See: **American Craft Information Center** (554)

★554★
American Craft Information Center (Art)
72 Spring St. Phone: (212)274-0630
New York, NY 10012 Mary Hujsak, Libn.
Founded: 1956. **Staff:** Prof 1; Other 1. **Subjects:** Contemporary crafts - fiber, clay, metal, wood, glass, enamel, plastics. **Special Collections:** Slide registry of biographical and visual data on contemporary American craftspeople (over 3000); Photo and Print Archives of the American Craft Museum; Your Portable Museum (35mm slide kits, filmstrips, and 16mm film available for purchase or study); Archives of the American Craft Council. **Holdings:** 5000 books; 350 bound periodical volumes; 6000 exhibition catalogs; craft organizations' newsletters; 12 VF drawers of clippings; 55 VF drawers of archival materials; 300 slide study sets. **Subscriptions:** 150 journals and other serials. **Services:** Library open to the public with restrictions. **Automated Operations:** Computerized public access catalog and cataloging. **Computerized Information Services:** OCLC; American Craft Council Artist Registry, Craft and Craft-Related Organizations (internal databases). **Publications:** Information Sources. **Remarks:** FAX: (212)274-0650. **Formerly:** American Craft Council - Library.

★555★
American Cyanamid Company - Agricultural Research Division - Technical Information Services (Biol Sci, Agri)
Box 400 Phone: (609)799-0400
Princeton, NJ 08543-0400 David S. Saari, Mgr.
Founded: 1947. **Staff:** Prof 8; Other 11. **Subjects:** Agronomy, entomology, veterinary medicine, agricultural chemicals. **Special Collections:** U.S.D.A. and Agricultural Experiment Stations publications. **Holdings:** 9000 books; 45,500 bound periodical volumes; 20 VF drawers of patents; 400 dissertations; 16 VF drawers of pamphlets. **Subscriptions:** 550 journals and other serials. **Services:** Interlibrary loan; services not open to the public. **Automated Operations:** Computerized serials and cataloging. **Computerized Information Services:** DIALOG Information Services, PFDS Online, NLM, OCLC. **Publications:** Library Accessions Bulletin, monthly; patent bulletins - both limited distribution. **Remarks:** FAX: (609)275-3576. Telex: 851267487. **Staff:** Lila Apgar, Libn.; Karen Ferguson, Info.Sci.; Andrew Granett, Info.Sci.; Patricia Evanylo, Info.Sci.; Adrienne Shanler, Info.Sci.; David L. Sharkey, Info.Sci.; Carol Singer, Info.Sci.

★556★
American Cyanamid Company - Business Information Center (Bus-Fin)
1 Cyanamid Plaza Phone: (201)831-4076
Wayne, NJ 07470-2012 Marie C. Sparks, Mgr.
Founded: 1951. **Staff:** Prof 4; Other 2. **Subjects:** Business, finance, management, marketing, economics. **Holdings:** 3000 books; 1000 special reports; 2500 company annual reports; foreign annual reports on microfiche. **Subscriptions:** 400 journals and other serials; 15 newspapers. **Services:** Interlibrary loan; center not open to the public. **Automated Operations:** Computerized cataloging and serials. **Computerized Information Services:** DIALOG Information Services, Reuter TEXTLINE, ORBIT Search Service, BRS Information Technologies, WILSONLINE, VU/TEXT Information Services, Info Globe, Data-Star, DataTimes, Reuters, IMSBASE, NewsNet, Inc., Mead Data Central, Dun & Bradstreet Business

Credit Services, Dow Jones News/Retrieval, TRADSTAT, PIERS (Port Import Export Reporting Services), STN International. **Networks/ Consortia:** Member of New Jersey Library Network. **Publications:** Serials holdings list, annual; industry newsletters, weekly; bulletin, quarterly. **Remarks:** FAX: (201)831-3551. **Staff:** Julia David, Bus.Info.Spec.; Jim Garrison, Bus.Info.Spec.; Sandy Kramer, Bus.Info.Spec.

★557★
American Cyanamid Company - Environmental Health Information Center (Med)
1 Cyanamid Plaza Phone: (201)831-3027
Wayne, NJ 07470 Anita M. Jones, Supv./Info.Sci.
Founded: 1952. **Staff:** Prof 1; Other 1. **Subjects:** Toxicology, occupational medicine, industrial hygiene and safety, clinical medicine, environmental protection, loss prevention. **Holdings:** 5000 books; 350 bound periodical volumes; 2000 pamphlets; 12 VF drawers of reprints. **Subscriptions:** 150 journals and other serials. **Services:** Interlibrary loan; center open to the public with restrictions. **Computerized Information Services:** DIALOG Information Services, LEXIS, NEXIS, NLM, Chemical Information Systems, Inc. (CIS), Occupational Health Services, Inc. (OHS), STN International, Chemical Abstracts Service (CAS), National Emissions Data System (NEDS); Toxic Release Inventory (TRI), LAN (internal databases). **Publications:** Items of current interest and acquisitions, bimonthly - to physicians and technical personnel of the plants. **Remarks:** FAX: (201)831-4456. **Formerly:** Its Environmental Health Library.

★558★
American Cyanamid Company - Fiber Division Library (Sci-Engr)
1801 Cyanamid Rd.
Milton, FL 32570-2799 Phone: (904)994-5311
Founded: 1958. **Staff:** Prof 1. **Subjects:** Organic and inorganic chemistry; textiles; management; statistics; computers; safety. **Holdings:** 2500 books; 1000 bound periodical volumes; 4 VF drawers of patents; 36 VF drawers of technical project reports and memos. **Subscriptions:** 72 journals and other serials. **Services:** Library not open to the public.

★559★
American Cyanamid Company - Lederle Laboratories Division - Subbarow Memorial Library (Med)
401 N. Middletown Rd. Phone: (914)732-5000
Pearl River, NY 10965 Dr. M. Gert Howell, Hd., Tech.Info.Serv.
Founded: 1930. **Staff:** Prof 12; Other 6. **Subjects:** Biomedical sciences, pharmacology, organic chemistry, management. **Holdings:** 80,000 volumes; 10,000 reels of microfilm; 150 AV programs. **Subscriptions:** 1100 journals and other serials. **Services:** Interlibrary loan; SDI; library open to the public with restrictions. **Automated Operations:** Computerized cataloging, circulation, acquisitions, and serials. **Computerized Information Services:** DIALOG Information Services, PFDS Online, BRS Information Technologies, NLM, Chemical Information Systems, Inc. (CIS), STN International, Questel, Data-Star, OCLC. **Networks/Consortia:** Member of Health Information Libraries of Westchester (HILOW), Medical Library Center of New York (MLCNY), Southeastern New York Library Resources Council (SENYLRC), SUNY/OCLC Library Network. **Staff:** Tom A. Wainwright, Libn.; Anne T. O'Brien, Group Ldr., Ref.Gp.; Stanley E. DeVoe, Mgr., Lit.Serv.

★560★
American Cyanamid Company - Technical Information Services (Sci-Engr)
1937 W. Main St.
Box 60 Phone: (203)321-2200
Stamford, CT 06904-0060 Martha Reiter, Mgr.
Founded: 1936. **Staff:** Prof 4; Other 3. **Subjects:** Chemistry, physics, physical chemistry, polymer chemistry. **Holdings:** 10,000 books; 20,000 bound periodical volumes. **Subscriptions:** 350 journals and other serials. **Services:** Services not open to the public. **Computerized Information Services:** STN International, DIALOG Information Services, PFDS Online, NewsNet, Inc., Mead Data Central, BRS Information Technologies, NLM. **Remarks:** FAX: (203)321-2298.

★561★
American Dairy Products Institute - Library (Food-Bev)
130 N. Franklin St. Phone: (312)782-5455
Chicago, IL 60606 Warren S. Clark, Jr., Exec.Dir.
Subjects: Evaporated and dry milk, whey products. **Holdings:** Figures not available. **Remarks:** Alternate telephone number(s): 782-4888. FAX: (312)782-5299.

★562★
American Defense Institute - Library (Mil)
1055 N. Fairfax St., 2nd Fl.
Alexandria, VA 22314 Phone: (703)519-7000
Founded: 1983. **Staff:** Prof 7; Other 4. **Subjects:** Central America, Soviet military and foreign policy, Strategic Defense Initiative (SDI), U.S. foreign policy and defense strategy. **Holdings:** Figures not available. **Services:** Library will answer mail or telephone inquiries. **Publications:** List of publications - available on request; ADI Newsletter, quarterly; ADI Briefing, monthly; ADI Security Review, quarterly. **Remarks:** FAX: (703)519-8627. **Formerly:** American Defense Institute - Information Clearinghouse and Audio-Visual Library located in Washington, DC.

★563★
American Dehydrated Onion and Garlic Association - Library (Food-Bev)
1 Maritime Plaza, 23rd Fl. Phone: (415)392-7077
San Francisco, CA 94111 J. Dennis McQuaid, Sec./Treas.
Founded: 1956. **Staff:** Prof 2. **Subjects:** Dehydrated onions and garlic - microbiological methods, industrial standards and methods. **Holdings:** Figures not available. **Automated Operations:** Computerized cataloging. **Publications:** Newsletter - for internal distribution only. **Remarks:** FAX (415)392-3969. **Staff:** Madeleine E. Sloane, Asst.Sec./Treas.

★564★
American Dental Association - Bureau of Library Services (Med)
211 E. Chicago Ave. Phone: (312)440-2642
Chicago, IL 60611 Aletha A. Kowitz, Dir.
Founded: 1927. **Staff:** Prof 7; Other 8. **Subjects:** Dentistry. **Special Collections:** Association archives; portraits. **Holdings:** 20,000 books; 35,000 bound periodical volumes; 3500 package libraries on 2200 topics. **Subscriptions:** 1050 journals and other serials. **Services:** Interlibrary loan; copying; library use is a privilege of membership but is generally open to all dental auxiliary personnel, physicians, nurses, and graduate students; all others on an individual basis. **Computerized Information Services:** OCLC, MEDLINE. **Networks/Consortia:** Member of Chicago Library System. **Publications:** Books and Package Libraries for Dentists, annual; Rare Books in BLS Collection; Basic Dental Reference Works - both free upon request. **Special Indexes:** Index to Dental Literature (cumulative indexing service), quarterly - by subscription or in annual volume. **Remarks:** FAX: (312)440-2774. **Staff:** Ruth Schultz, Asst.Dir.

American Dental Society of Anesthesiology Archives
See: **Loma Linda University** (9256)

★565★
American Donkey and Mule Society - Information Office (Rec)
2901 N. Elm St. Phone: (817)382-6845
Denton, TX 76201 Betsy Hutchins, Info.Off.
Staff: 2. **Subjects:** Donkeys, mules. **Holdings:** 300 books; 900 unbound periodicals. **Subscriptions:** 14 newsletters. **Services:** Copying; office open to the public by appointment. **Publications:** List of publications - available on request. **Remarks:** This is a private collection in a private home. Visitors and researchers are welcome.

★566★
American Electric Power Service Corporation - Corporate Library (Energy, Sci-Engr)
1 Riverside Plaza Phone: (614)223-1826
Columbus, OH 43215 Marjorie L. Popovich, Supv., Corp.Lib.
Staff: Prof 1; Other 4. **Subjects:** Engineering - civil, electrical, environmental, mechanical; electric utilities; occupational safety and health;

energy; business management. **Special Collections:** Institute of Electrical and Electronics Engineers (IEEE) Transactions, 1900 to present; American Electric Power Author Paper File; Sporn Collection (company archives). **Holdings:** 7000 books; 200 bound periodical volumes; 80 VF drawers of corporate and technical reports and pamphlets; 10,000 reports and documents; 600 reels of microfilm. **Subscriptions:** 1300 journals and other serials; 5 newspapers. **Services:** Interlibrary loan; SDI; library open to the public by appointment only. **Automated Operations:** Computerized cataloging, acquisitions, and circulation. **Computerized Information Services:** PFDS Online, DIALOG Information Services, OCLC, EPIC, The Source Information Network; SRL (internal database); Knight-Ridder Unicom (electronic mail service). **Networks/Consortia:** Member of Columbus Area Libraries Information Council of Ohio (CALICO), OHIONET. **Publications:** Corporate Library Bulletin, bimonthly. **Special Indexes:** Key Word Index (online, hardcopy). **Remarks:** FAX: (614)223-1823.

★567★
American Electric Power Service Corporation - Law Library (Law)
1 Riverside Plaza, 29th Fl.
Columbus, OH 43215 Phone: (614)223-1690
Staff: Prof 1. **Subjects:** Law - environmental, securities, real estate, tax, corporate. **Holdings:** 3000 books. **Subscriptions:** 118 journals and other serials. **Services:** Library not open to the public. **Computerized Information Services:** LEXIS, NEXIS, CCH (Commerce Clearing House, Inc.). **Remarks:** FAX: (614)223-1687.

★568★
American Embassy in Lisbon - American Library - USIS Library (Educ)
Ave. Das Forcas Armadas
Apdo. 4258
P-1507 Lisbon, Portugal Phone: 1 570102
Staff: 3. **Subjects:** United States - social sciences, humanities. **Holdings:** 7000 books; 50 reports; 10 microfiche; 1 reel of microfilm. **Subscriptions:** 100 journals and other serials; 5 newspapers. **Services:** Interlibrary loan; copying; SDI; library open to the public. **Computerized Information Services:** DIALOG Information Services, LEGI-SLATE; CD-ROM. **Publications:** Resources of the U.S. Bibliography. **Special Catalogs:** Periodica - Video Catalog. **Remarks:** FAX: 1 3520038. Maintained or supported by the U.S. Information Agency. Focus is on materials that will assist peoples outside the United States to learn about the United States, its people, history, culture, political processes, and social milieux.

★569★
American Embassy in Stockholm - Documentation Center - Reference Collection (Soc Sci)
Strandvagen 101 Phone: 8 7835300
S-115 89 Stockholm, Sweden Jan O. Nyman, Lib.Dir.
Founded: 1986. **Staff:** 2. **Special Collections:** Reference collection; document collection. **Holdings:** Vertical files; reports; microfiche; microfilm. **Subscriptions:** 60 journals and other serials; 2 newspapers. **Services:** Interlibrary loan; copying; SDI; library not open to the public. **Computerized Information Services:** DIALOG Information Services, LEGI-SLATE, PDQ, DataArkiv AB; CD-ROMs; Lan-net (internal database). **Publications:** Information Alert; Documents List. **Remarks:** FAX: 8 6653303. **Staff:** Leif G. Zalle, Lib.Asst.

★570★
American Enterprise Institute for Public Policy Research - Library (Soc Sci)
1150 17th St., N.W. Phone: (202)862-5831
Washington, DC 20036 Evelyn B. Caldwell, Libn.
Founded: 1972. **Staff:** Prof 1. **Subjects:** Economics, political science, international relations. **Holdings:** 8000 books; pamphlet files. **Subscriptions:** 175 journals and other serials; 5 newspapers. **Services:** Interlibrary loan; copying; library open to the public with librarian's permission. **Computerized Information Services:** DIALOG Information Services. **Remarks:** FAX: (202)862-7178.

American Entomological Society - Library
See: **Academy of Natural Sciences - Library** (36)

★571★
American Express Company - Card Division - Systems Library (Comp Sci)
1725 N. Commerce Pkwy. Phone: (305)384-3365
Fort Lauderdale, FL 33326 Diane Carignan, Exec.Sec.
Founded: 1975. **Staff:** Prof 1. **Subjects:** Data processing industry, management, credit cards. **Special Collections:** IBM System 370 Manuals (200); American Express Internal Standards Manuals (20); Center for Human Potential (management; 50 volumes). **Holdings:** 500 books; 2000 technical reports on microfiche; 16 VF drawers of internal documents. **Subscriptions:** 28 journals and other serials. **Services:** Library not open to the public. **Computerized Information Services:** TSO (internal database). **Networks/Consortia:** Member of Associated Colleges of the St. Lawrence Valley, Inc. (ACSLV). **Special Indexes:** AMEXCO Internal Document Identifier Index; IBM Manuals Inventory (both online and hardcopy). **Remarks:** FAX: (305)474-6302.

★572★
American Express Company - Travelers Cheque Operating Center - Systems Library (Comp Sci)
4315 S. 2700 W. Phone: (801)965-5559
Salt Lake City, UT 84184-4600 Louise Pollard, Sys.Libn.
Founded: 1982. **Staff:** Prof 2. **Subjects:** Computer systems design and development, data processing, personal computers, management. **Holdings:** 350 books; 800 IBM manuals; internal computer programs on 17,500 microfiche; 200 binders of systems documentation; 90 presentation materials on file; PC software and manuals. **Subscriptions:** 49 journals and other serials. **Services:** Library not open to the public. **Automated Operations:** Computerized cataloging, serials, and circulation. **Computerized Information Services:** DIALOG Information Services; CD-ROM (Computer Library); internal database. **Publications:** Recent Acquisitions, monthly - for internal distribution only. **Remarks:** FAX: (801)965-5310. **Staff:** Nancy Hill.

★573★
American Family Foundation - Resource Center (Soc Sci)
P.O. Box 336 Phone: (617)893-0930
Weston, MA 02193 Dr. Michael Langone, Dir. of Res. & Educ.
Subjects: Cults and cultic groups, manipulative techniques of persuasion and control. **Holdings:** Books; reports; articles; files on more than 300 groups. **Services:** Copying. **Publications:** Catalog.

★574★
American Family Mutual Insurance Group - Corporate Library (Bus-Fin)
3099 E. Washington Ave. Phone: (608)249-2111
Madison, WI 53783-0000 Lee A. Weinberger, Corp.Libn.
Staff: Prof 1; Other 1. **Subjects:** Insurance, human resources, employee development, management, supervision. **Holdings:** Figures not available. **Services:** Library not open to the public. **Automated Operations:** Computerized cataloging and serials. **Computerized Information Services:** DIALOG Information Services, BRS Information Technologies, VU/TEXT Information Services, DataTimes, Human Resource Information Network (HRIN). **Networks/Consortia:** Member of South Central Library System.

★575★
American Family Records Association - Library (Hist)
P.O. Box 15505
Kansas City, MO 64106 Phone: (816)373-6570
Subjects: Genealogy, history, adoptive relationships. **Holdings:** 1800 volumes. **Remarks:** Association promotes preservation of and access to public and private genealogical records.

★576★
American Farm Bureau Federation - Library (Agri)
225 Touhy Ave. Phone: (312)399-5781
Park Ridge, IL 60068 Susan J. Schultz, Res.Libn.
Founded: 1980. **Staff:** Prof 1; Other 2. **Subjects:** Agricultural economics, agribusiness. **Holdings:** 300 books; 8000 reports. **Subscriptions:** 300 journals and other serials. **Services:** Interlibrary loan; library not open to the public. **Automated Operations:** Computerized cataloging. **Computerized Information Services:** DIALOG Information Services, WILSONLINE, VU/TEXT Information Services, DataTimes, State Net 50. **Remarks:** FAX: (312)399-5896.

★577★
American Federation of Astrologers, Inc. - Library (Rel-Phil)
Box 22040 Phone: (602)838-1751
Tempe, AZ 85285-2040 Robert W. Cooper, Exec.Sec.
Founded: 1938. **Staff:** Prof 3; Other 7. **Subjects:** Astrology. **Holdings:** 2500 titles; 7500 bound periodical volumes; 50,000 data cards. **Services:** Library not open to the public. **Staff:** Sara E. Cooper, Chf.Libn.

American Federation of Jews from Central Europe, Inc. - Research Foundation for Jewish Immigration, Inc.
See: **Research Foundation for Jewish Immigration, Inc. - Archives** (13836)

American Federation of Labor and Congress of Industrial Organizations - Amalgamated Clothing & Textile Workers Union
See: **Amalgamated Clothing & Textile Workers Union, AFL-CIO** (439)

★578★
American Federation of Labor and Congress of Industrial Organizations - Library (Bus-Fin)
815 16th St., N.W. Phone: (202)637-5297
Washington, DC 20006 Ruby U. Tyson, Libn.
Founded: 1916. **Staff:** Prof 1; Other 2. **Subjects:** Labor, labor economics, trade unions, industrial relations. **Special Collections:** International union proceedings. **Holdings:** 20,000 volumes; 75 VF drawers of pamphlets and clippings. **Subscriptions:** 325 journals and other serials. **Services:** Interlibrary loan; library open to the public. **Computerized Information Services:** DIALOG Information Services, LEXIS, NEXIS, OCLC, DataTimes, VU/TEXT Information Services. **Networks/Consortia:** Member of CAPCON Library Network. **Publications:** Acquisitions List, bimonthly. **Remarks:** FAX: (202)637-5058. **Also Known As:** AFL-CIO.

★579★
American Federation of Police Research Center and Library (Law)
3801 Biscayne Blvd. Phone: (305)573-0070
Miami, FL 33137 Gerald Arenberg, Exec.Dir.
Founded: 1960. **Staff:** Prof 1; Other 2. **Subjects:** Law enforcement, crime and crime prevention. **Holdings:** 2000 books; 100 police films; 100 videocassettes. **Subscriptions:** 200 journals and other serials. **Services:** Library not open to the public. **Remarks:** FAX: (305)573-9819.

★580★
American Federation of Small Business - Information Center (Bus-Fin)
407 S. Dearborn St., Suite 500 Phone: (312)427-0207
Chicago, IL 60605 Thomas Hugh Latimer, Exec. V.P.
Founded: 1954. **Staff:** Prof 1. **Subjects:** Small business, economic education, congressional and state legislation, labor law. **Special Collections:** Soviet Imperialism; Communist subversion in the U.S.; Union Power vs. The Right to Work; Criminal Justice. **Holdings:** 3000 volumes; 500 pamphlets; 100 current position papers. **Subscriptions:** 50 journals and other serials. **Services:** Copying; center open to the public with restrictions.

★581★
American Federation of State, County and Municipal Employees - AFSCME Information Center (Bus-Fin)
1625 L St., N.W. Phone: (202)429-1060
Washington, DC 20036 William R. Wilkinson, Labor Economist/Info.Spec.
Founded: 1974. **Staff:** Prof 1; Other 2. **Subjects:** Labor relations, civil service, state and local government employment and finance, pay equity, occupational safety and health. **Special Collections:** AFSCME constitutions and proceedings; AFL-CIO proceedings. **Holdings:** 8750 books; 35 VF drawers of subject files; 9000 microfiche. **Subscriptions:** 650 journals and other serials; 25 newspapers. **Services:** Interlibrary loan; center open to the public by appointment. **Automated Operations:** Computerized public access catalog, cataloging, and serials. **Computerized Information Services:** DIALOG Information Services, BRS Information Technologies, NEXIS, LEXIS, VU/TEXT Information Services, DataTimes, WILSONLINE, NewsNet, Inc., State Net 50, Human Resource Information Network (HRIN), OCLC EPIC. **Publications:** Serials Listing, annual; Current Acquisitions, bimonthly. **Remarks:** FAX: (202)429-1293. Affiliated with the AFL-CIO. **Also Known As:** AFSCME.

★582★
American Federation of State, County and Municipal Employees - DC37 Research Library (Bus-Fin)
125 Barclay St. Phone: (212)815-1470
New York, NY 10007 Evelyn Seinfeld, Assoc.Dir.
Founded: 1974. **Staff:** Prof 1; Other 3. **Subjects:** Labor-management relations, collective bargaining in New York City, labor unions, U.S. economy, urban crisis. **Special Collections:** Contracts between New York City and District Council 37; New York City fiscal crisis; Public Sector Productivity; New York City Civil Service. **Holdings:** 10,000 government documents; unbound periodicals; contracts; local documents; newspaper clipping file. **Subscriptions:** 150 journals and other serials; 20 newspapers. **Services:** Library open to the public by appointment. **Publications:** Acquisitions list. **Remarks:** Affiliated with the AFL-CIO. **Also Known As:** AFSCME.

★583★
American Federation of Teachers - Library (Educ)
555 New Jersey Ave., N.W. Phone: (202)879-4481
Washington, DC 20001 Paula O'Connor, Dir., Info.Serv.
Founded: 1916. **Staff:** Prof 1; Other 2. **Subjects:** Labor, childcare, education, women's rights. **Holdings:** 20,000 books. **Subscriptions:** 450 journals and other serials; 7 newspapers. **Services:** Interlibrary loan; copying; library open to the public. **Computerized Information Services:** DIALOG Information Services, NEXIS, Human Resource Information Network (HRIN). **Publications:** Convention Report. **Remarks:** FAX: (202)879-4545.

★584★
American Film Institute - Louis B. Mayer Library (Aud-Vis)
2021 N. Western Ave.
Box 27999
Los Angeles, CA 90027 Phone: (213)856-7654
Founded: 1969. **Staff:** 2. **Subjects:** Moving pictures, television, video, cable, satellite. **Special Collections:** Mitchell Leisen Collection; George B. Seitz Collection; Buster Keaton Scrapbook (1902-1909); Henry Hathaway Script Collection; Darryl F. Zanuck Script Collection; Robert Aldrich Collection; George Byron Sage Story Analyst Collection; Martin Scorsese Collection; Levinson/Link Collection. **Holdings:** 10,000 books; 1400 bound periodical volumes; 10,000 motion picture and television scripts; 44 oral history transcripts; 535 seminar transcripts; 600 seminar audiotapes; 2 file drawers of Film Festival information; 70,000 files of clippings; 75 reels of microfilm. **Subscriptions:** 207 journals and other serials; 5 newspapers. **Services:** Copying; library open to the public. **Special Indexes:** Writer, director, and subject index to Script Collections (card); FIAF Periodical Indexing Service (microfiche); Film Production Index, 1930-1969 (card). **Remarks:** FAX: (213)467-4578.

★585★
American Film and Video Association - Library and Information Center (Aud-Vis)
PO Box 48659
Niles, IL 60648 Phone: (708)698-6440
Founded: 1943. **Staff:** Prof 1. **Subjects:** Educational and nontheatrical film and video; library and school media. **Holdings:** 500 books; 144 linear feet of clippings; educational film card file containing 200,000 entries. **Subscriptions:** 75 journals and newsletters. **Services:** Copying; telephone reference services. **Computerized Information Services:** American Film and Video Festival (internal database). **Publications:** Sightlines, quarterly; AFVA, bimonthly; American Film and Video Association Evaluations, biannual. **Special Catalogs:** American Film & Video Festival Catalog, annual. **Special Indexes:** Filmographies. **Remarks:** FAX: (708)823-1561. **Formerly:** Located in La Grange Park, IL.

★586★
American Fire Sprinkler Association - Library (Sci-Engr)
11325 Pegasus, Suite S-220 Phone: (214)349-5965
Dallas, TX 75238 Melissa Parks, Exec.Dir.
Founded: 1981. **Staff:** 11. **Subjects:** Automatic sprinklers, fire sprinkler industry, apprenticeship training. **Holdings:** 150 volumes. **Services:** Library open to the public. **Remarks:** FAX: (214)343-8898.

American First Day Cover Society Archives
See: **American Philatelic Research Library** (711)

★587★
American Fitness Association - Library (Rec)
6285 E. Spring St. Phone: (310)596-8660
Long Beach, CA 90808 Ms. Brooks, Libn./Media Dir.
Founded: 1986. **Staff:** Prof 1. **Subjects:** Fitness, sports medicine. **Holdings:** 2500 books; tapes. **Services:** Library not open to the public. **Remarks:** FAX: (310)596-2486.

★588★
American Floral Art School - Floral Library (Art)
539 S. Wabash Ave. Phone: (312)922-9328
Chicago, IL 60605 James Moretz, Dir.
Staff: 1. **Subjects:** Flower arrangement and symbolism, floral design, language of flowers. **Holdings:** 4000 books; 500 uncataloged items. **Subscriptions:** 55 journals and other serials. **Services:** Library open to the public by appointment.

American Folklife Center
See: **Library of Congress - American Folklife Center** (9108)

American Forest Institute - Archives
See: **Forest History Society, Inc. - Library and Archives** (5979)

American Forestry Association - Archives
See: **Forest History Society, Inc. - Library and Archives** (5979)

★589★
American Forestry Association - McArdle Memorial Library (Env-Cons)
1516 P St., N.W. Phone: (202)667-3300
Washington, DC 20005 Deborah Gangloff
Subjects: Forestry and allied subjects of soil, water, wildlife, and recreation. **Holdings:** 6000 books. **Services:** Library open to the public for reference use only. **Automated Operations:** Computerized cataloging. **Computerized Information Services:** Internal database. **Remarks:** FAX: (202)667-7751.

★590★
American Foundation for the Blind - Helen Keller Archives (Soc Sci, Aud-Vis)
15 W. 16th St. Phone: (212)620-2157
New York, NY 10011 Alberta J. Lonergan, Archv.
Subjects: Helen Keller; Anne Sullivan Macy; John Albert Macy; Polly Thomson; work on behalf of the blind, deaf-blind, and deaf; children and women in factories; planned parenthood; labor movements; peace; suffrage. **Holdings:** 65,000 manuscripts, sound recordings, photographs, films, slides, letters, speeches, literary manuscripts, legal and genealogical material. **Services:** Copying; archives open to the public by appointment only.

★591★
American Foundation for the Blind - M.C. Migel Memorial Library (Aud-Vis)
15 W. 16th St. Phone: (212)620-2162
New York, NY 10011 Leslie Rosen, Hd.Libn.
Founded: 1926. **Staff:** Prof 4; Other 3. **Subjects:** Blindness - education, psychology, rehabilitation. **Special Collections:** AFB Photograph Collection. **Holdings:** 40,000 volumes. **Subscriptions:** 150 journals and other serials. **Services:** Interlibrary loan; copying; library open to the public on a limited schedule. **Automated Operations:** Computerized cataloging, acquisitions, and circulation. **Computerized Information Services:** DIALOG Information Services; BRS Information Technologies; SpecialNet (electronic mail service); Performs searches on fee basis. Telephone 620-2160. **Networks/Consortia:** Member of New York Metropolitan Reference and Research Library Agency. **Remarks:** FAX: (212)620-2105. **Staff:** Gilbert Hennessey, Tech.Serv.Libn., Alberta Lonergan, Archv.

★592★
American Foundrymen's Society, Inc. - Technical Information Center (Sci-Engr)
505 State St. Phone: (708)824-0181
Des Plaines, IL 60016 Elizabeth Klein, Libn.
Staff: Prof 1; Other 1. **Subjects:** Cast metals, safety, foundry practice, hygiene, air pollution control. **Holdings:** 3500 volumes. **Subscriptions:** 50 journals and other serials. **Services:** Copying; center open to the public. **Computerized Information Services:** CAST. Performs searches on fee basis. **Networks/Consortia:** Member of North Suburban Library System (NSLS). **Publications:** Metal Casting Abstract Service, monthly - by subscription. **Remarks:** FAX: (708)824-7848. Toll-free telephone number(s): (800)537-4237. **Staff:** Virginia Kahtib, Asst.Libn.

★593★
American-French Genealogical Society - Library (Hist)
Box 2113 Phone: (401)726-0254
Pawtucket, RI 02861-2113 Janice Burkhart, Pres. & Libn.
Founded: 1978. **Staff:** 5. **Subjects:** American-French genealogy. **Special Collections:** Forget File (pre-1900 Rhode Island marriages); pre-1900 Massachusetts marriages; Loiselle-Rivest-Fabien files. **Holdings:** 3000 books; 100 bound periodical volumes; French obituary and marriage records; indexes of marriages, births, and deaths; family histories; parish and school histories; VT records (pre-1878). **Subscriptions:** 84 journals and other serials. **Services:** Copying; library open to the public with restrictions and on a limited schedule. **Computerized Information Services:** Internal database. Performs searches on fee basis. Contact Person: Theresa Poliquin. **Publications:** Je Me Souviens, semiannual - to members. **Staff:** Henri Leblond; Roger Beaudry.

★594★
American Gas Association - Laboratories Library (Energy)
8501 E. Pleasant Valley Rd. Phone: (216)524-4990
Cleveland, OH 44131 Cathy Rake, Libn.
Staff: 1. **Subjects:** Gas, natural. **Holdings:** 1150 books; 1200 reports. **Subscriptions:** 90 journals and other serials. **Services:** Interlibrary loan; library not open to the public. **Computerized Information Services:** DIALOG Information Services. **Remarks:** FAX: (216)642-3463.

★595★
American Gas Association - Library (Energy)
1515 Wilson Blvd. Phone: (703)841-8400
Arlington, VA 22209 Steven J. Dorner, Dir. Industry Info.Serv.
Founded: 1919. **Staff:** Prof 3; Other 2. **Subjects:** Natural gas, gas utility industry, gas pipeline industry, gas research and technology, utility regulation, gas appliances, synthetic natural gas, liquified natural gas. **Special Collections:** History of the Gas Industry in the U.S., 19th century to present (proceedings of predecessor associations); gas company annual reports. **Holdings:** 26,255 books; 600 reels of microfilm; 200 VF drawers of clippings, pamphlets, archival materials. **Subscriptions:** 630 journals and other serials; 8 newspapers. **Services:** Interlibrary loan; copying; library open to the public by appointment only. **Computerized Information Services:** DIALOG Information Services, Integrated Technical Information System (ITIS), A.G.A. GasNet; A.G.A. GasNet (electronic mail service). **Publications:** New in the Library, monthly - to association staff and member company libraries. **Remarks:** FAX: (703)841-8406. Telex: (710)955-9848. Electronic mail address(es): II2002 (A.G.A. GasNet). **Staff:** L. Cate, Asst.Libn

★596★
American Gear Manufacturers Association - Memorial Library (Sci-Engr)
1500 King St., Suite 201 Phone: (703)684-0211
Alexandria, VA 22314 John R. Schultheis, Mgr., Adm.Serv.
Founded: 1916. **Subjects:** Gear data. **Holdings:** Figures not available. **Special Indexes:** AGMA Standards and Technical Publications Index - free upon request. **Remarks:** FAX: (703)684-0242. **Staff:** Lenell Hyman, Libn.

★597★
American Genealogical Lending Library (Hist)
Box 244 Phone: (801)298-5358
Bountiful, UT 84010 Bradley W. Steuart, Pres./Hd.Libn.
Founded: 1983. **Staff:** Prof 10; Other 12. **Subjects:** Genealogy. **Special Collections:** Southwest Library Collection; Milton Rubincam Collection;

Draper Manuscripts, Ohio Pioneer Project Collection; Indiana Works Progress Administration (WPA) Index Collection; federal population census and other National Archives records of genealogical interest (microfilm); local history collections. **Holdings:** 100,000 reels of microfilm including census records, mortality schedules, ship passenger lists, military records, vital records, deeds, wills, tax lists, county and family histories. **Subscriptions:** 10 journals and other serials. **Services:** Interlibrary loan; microfilming; library open to the public. **Automated Operations:** Computerized public access catalog, cataloging, and circulation. **Publications:** Research guides; U.S. census map guides. **Remarks:** FAX: (801)298-5468. **Staff:** Raeone C. Steuart, Sr. Staff Libn.; Juanita Price, Staff Libn.

★598★
American Geographical Society Collection of the University of Wisconsin--Milwaukee - Golda Meir Library (Geog-Map)
Box 399 Phone: (414)229-6282
Milwaukee, WI 53201 Roman Drazniowsky, Cur.
Founded: 1852. **Staff:** Prof 5; Other 8. **Subjects:** Geography, exploration, cartography, earth sciences, social sciences, history. **Holdings:** 209,016 books and bound periodical volumes; 439,674 maps; 7841 atlases; 138,823 photographs; 32,655 pamphlets; 70 globes; 98,000 Landsat Images. **Subscriptions:** 2000 journals and other serials. **Services:** Interlibrary loan. **Publications:** Current Geographical Publications, monthly (except July and August) - by subscription. **Special Catalogs:** Research Catalog (book), 1962; First Supplement, 1972-73; Regional Section, 1974; Second Supplement, Regional and Topical, 1978. **Special Indexes:** Index to Maps in Books and Periodicals, 1968; First Supplement, 1971; Second Supplement, 1975; Third Supplement, 1986. **Remarks:** Alternate telephone number(s): (414)229-3984. Toll-free telephone number(s): (800)558-8993. **Staff:** Susan Ewart Peschel, Cat./Ref.Libn.; Christopher M. Baruth, Map & Imagery Libn.; Howard A. Deller, Lit.Anl.; Jovanka Ristic, Map Cat./Ref.Libn.

★599★
American Geological Institute - GeoRef Information System (Sci-Engr)
4220 King St. Phone: (703)379-2480
Alexandria, VA 22302 John Mulvihill, Dir.
Staff: Prof 13; Other 12. **Subjects:** Earth sciences, geology, geophysics, hydrology, paleontology, environmental geology. **Services:** Document Delivery Service; SDI; open to the public. **Computerized Information Services:** DIALOG Information Services, OCLC. **Publications:** Bibliography and Index of Geology, monthly with annual cumulation - for sale. **Special Catalogs:** List of serials in GeoRef (microfiche); GeoRef Thesaurus and Guide to Indexing. **Remarks:** Institute produces GeoRef, a worldwide bibliographic database of 1.4 million citations in earth science, 1785 to present. **Remarks:** FAX: (703)379-7563. **Staff:** Sharon Tahirkheli, Chf.Ed.; Linda Radcliffe Libn.

★600★
American Graduate School of International Management - Barton Kyle Yount Memorial Library (Bus-Fin)
Thunderbird Campus Phone: (602)978-7232
Glendale, AZ 85306 Susan Bledsoe, Lib.Dir.
Founded: 1946. **Staff:** Prof 5; Other 6. **Subjects:** International commerce, international affairs, country studies, management, finance, languages. **Holdings:** 70,000 books; 1500 bound periodical volumes; 6600 reels of microfilm; 68,000 microfiche; 85 dissertations. **Subscriptions:** 1100 journals and other serials; 58 newspapers. **Services:** Interlibrary loan; copying; library open to the public for reference use only. **Automated Operations:** Computerized cataloging. **Computerized Information Services:** DIALOG Information Services, Data-Star; CD-ROMs (ABI/INFORM, Business Dateline, Business Periodicals Ondisc, Newspaper Abstracts, Disclosure Incorporated, National Trade Data Bank). **Networks/Consortia:** Member of AMIGOS Bibliographic Council, Inc. **Publications:** Thunderword. **Remarks:** FAX: (602)978-0362. **Staff:** Dixie Klatt; Lisa Miller; Kris Swank; Charlotte Cohen.

★601★
American Graduate University - Library (Soc Sci)
733 N. Dodsworth Ave. Phone: (818)966-4576
Covina, CA 91724 Marie Sirney, V.P., Res.
Founded: 1975. **Staff:** Prof 1; Other 1. **Subjects:** Government contracts, project management. **Holdings:** 5000 books; 6000 reports; 800 microfiche. **Subscriptions:** 63 journals and other serials. **Services:** Interlibrary loan; library open to the public. **Publications:** Government Contracts Service.

American Hall of Aviation History
See: **Northrop University - Alumni Library** (12030)

★602★
American Hardware Insurance Group - Library
5995 Opus Pkwy.
Minnetonka, MN 55343
Defunct.

★603★
American Harp Society Repository (Mus)
123 1/2 Weatherstone Dr. Phone: (704)245-7052
Forest City, NC 28043 Helen Rifas
Founded: 1980. **Staff:** 1. **Subjects:** All aspects of the harp. **Holdings:** Manuscripts; letters; autograph scores; historic sound recordings; microfilm; scrapbooks. **Services:** Copying (limited); repository open to serious scholars, harpists, and composers. **Remarks:** Society is affiliated with the World Association of Harpists, Paris, France. **Formerly:** Located in Hollywood, CA.

★604★
American Health Foundation - Naylor Dana Institute for Disease Prevention - Library (Med)
Dana Rd. Phone: (914)592-2600
Valhalla, NY 10595 Noreen T. Sweeney, Libn.
Staff: Prof 1; Other 1. **Subjects:** Medicine, science, social science. **Special Collections:** Smoking and health; nutrition; biology and chemistry. **Holdings:** 2000 books; 3000 bound periodical volumes. **Subscriptions:** 211 journals and other serials. **Services:** Interlibrary loan; copying; SDI; library open to the public by appointment. **Automated Operations:** Computerized cataloging. **Computerized Information Services:** NLM, DIALOG Information Services, BRS Information Technologies. **Networks/Consortia:** Member of Medical Library Center of New York (MLCNY), Health Information Libraries of Westchester (HILOW). **Publications:** AHF Health Letter; Preventive Medicine. **Remarks:** FAX: (914)592-6317.

★605★
American Health Information Management Association - FORE Resource Center (Med)
919 N. Michigan Ave., Suite 1400 Phone: (312)787-2672
Chicago, IL 60611 Robin Lee Jones, Libn.
Founded: 1965. **Staff:** Prof 1; Other 1. **Subjects:** Medical records. **Holdings:** 2500 books. **Subscriptions:** 185 journals and other serials. **Services:** Copying; library open to the public. **Computerized Information Services:** DIALOG Information Services. Performs searches on fee basis. **Publications:** Keep Current With FORE, monthly. **Remarks:** FORE is an acronym for Foundation of Record Education. **Formerly:** American Medical Record Association.

★606★
American Health Research Institute - Library (Med)
4111 Gallows Rd. Phone: (703)642-3138
Annandale, VA 22003 Karen Kelly
Founded: 1982. **Staff:** 1. **Subjects:** Biomedicine, biology, anatomical sciences, injuries, malpractice, biotechnology, psychology and allied subjects. **Holdings:** 2200 books; 21,000 reports. **Subscriptions:** 15 journals and other serials; 4 newspapers. **Services:** Library not open to the public. **Publications:** List of publications - available on request.

★607★
American Heart Association - Corporate Reference Center (Med)
7320 Greenville Ave. Phone: (214)706-1408
Dallas, TX 75231 Vanessa S. Perez, Mgr.
Founded: 1954. **Staff:** Prof 1; Other 2. **Subjects:** Cardiovascular and cerebrovascular diseases. **Holdings:** 2900 books; 1000 bound periodical volumes; microforms. **Subscriptions:** 274 journals and other serials. **Services:** Interlibrary loan; library not open to the public. **Computerized Information Services:** DIALOG Information Services, BRS Information Technologies, MEDLARS. **Networks/Consortia:** Member of Health Libraries Information Network (HealthLINE). **Remarks:** FAX: (214)706-1341.

★608★
American Helicopter Society - Technical Information Library (Trans)
217 N. Washington St.
Alexandria, VA 22314 Phone: (703)684-6777
Founded: 1943. **Staff:** Prof 6. **Subjects:** Helicopter operations, aerodynamics, history of the helicopter. **Holdings:** 400 books; 4000 articles and papers; government documents. **Subscriptions:** 30 journals and other serials; 12 newspapers. **Services:** Interlibrary loan (limited to members); copying; SDI; library open to members only. **Computerized Information Services:** On-Line Bibliographic Retrieval System (OBRS; internal database). Performs searches for members. **Special Catalogs:** Publications catalog, 1943-1974 - for sale; Supplemental Publications Catalog, 1985-1986. **Remarks:** FAX: (703)739-9279.

★609★
American Hemerocallis Society - Archives (Agri)
Minnesota Landscape Arboretum
P.O. Box 39 Phone: (612)443-2440
Chanhassen, MN 55317 Nancy Allison, Libn.
Founded: 1946. **Subjects:** Gardening, daylilies. **Holdings:** 16 books; 75 bound periodical volumes; 30 reports; 130 archival items. **Services:** Library open to members only. **Remarks:** FAX: (612)443-2521.

★610★
American Herb Association - Library (Biol Sci)
PO Box 1673 Phone: (916)626-5046
Nevada City, CA 95959-1673 Robert Brucia, Dir.
Founded: 1981. **Subjects:** Herbs, herbal products. **Special Collections:** Medical botany. **Holdings:** 1000 volumes. **Subscriptions:** 600 journals and other serials. **Services:** Library not open to the public.

★611★
American Heritage Publishing Company, Inc. - Library (Publ)
Forbes Bldg.
60 5th Ave. Phone: (212)206-5107
New York, NY 10011 Laura Allen
Founded: 1956. **Staff:** Prof 1. **Subjects:** American history and art. **Holdings:** 3000 books; 150 bound periodical volumes; 250,000 pictures. **Subscriptions:** 50 journals and other serials. **Services:** Library open to the public by appointment. **Remarks:** FAX: (212)620-2332.

★612★
American Historical Society of Germans from Russia - Library (Area-Ethnic)
631 D St. Phone: (402)474-3363
Lincoln, NE 68502-1199 Michael Ronn, Libn.
Founded: 1968. **Staff:** 1. **Subjects:** Germans from Russia - culture, history, genealogy. **Holdings:** 3100 books; 175 yearbook and periodical titles; 16 AV programs; 120 nonbook items. **Subscriptions:** 18 journals and other serials. **Services:** Interlibrary loan; copying; library open to the public. **Publications:** AHSGR Library-Family History List. **Remarks:** FAX: (402)474-7229.

★613★
American Holistic Nurses Association - Library (Med)
4101 Lake Boome Trail, No. 201 Phone: (919)787-5181
Raleigh, NC 27607-6518 Cathy Young, Exec.Dir.
Founded: 1981. **Staff:** 3. **Subjects:** Holistic health, nursing, communication. **Holdings:** 150 books; videotapes. **Subscriptions:** 15 journals and other serials. **Services:** Interlibrary loan; library not open to the public. **Remarks:** FAX: (919)787-4916.

★614★
American Home Economics Association - Library (Agri)
1555 King St. Phone: (703)706-4600
Alexandria, VA 22314 Dr. Gladys Vaughn
Founded: 1970. **Subjects:** Home economics. **Special Collections:** American Home Economics Association publications; early home economics books (historical collection); Ellen H. Richards Collection. **Holdings:** 1000 books. **Services:** Interlibrary loan (limited); library open to the public with restrictions. **Remarks:** FAX: (703)706-4663.

★615★
American Home Food Products, Inc. - CRL Library (Food-Bev)
100 Marr St. Phone: (717)742-9614
Milton, PA 17847-1598 Elaine Parker, Info.Spec.
Founded: 1984. **Staff:** Prof 1. **Subjects:** Food science and technology, chemistry. **Holdings:** 600 books; U.S. patents. **Subscriptions:** 50 journals and other serials. **Services:** Interlibrary loan; library not open to the public. **Automated Operations:** Computerized cataloging, serials, and circulation. **Computerized Information Services:** DIALOG Information Services. **Remarks:** FAX: (717)742-1718.

★616★
American Home Food Products, Inc. - Information Services (Agri)
685 3rd Ave. Phone: (212)878-6300
New York, NY 10017 Laura Schneck, Dir., Market Res.
Subjects: Food industry.

★617★
American Home Products Corporation - Wyeth-Ayerst Laboratories Division - Library (Med)
Box 8299 Phone: (215)341-2491
Philadelphia, PA 19101-8299 Beverly L. Cantor, Supv., Lib.Serv.
Founded: 1945. **Staff:** Prof 2; Other 3. **Subjects:** Pharmacy, medicine, marketing. **Holdings:** 5000 books; 20,000 bound periodical volumes; 12,350 microforms; pharmaceutical patents. **Subscriptions:** 600 journals and other serials. **Services:** Interlibrary loan; copying; library open to the public by appointment. **Computerized Information Services:** DIALOG Information Services, MEDLINE, PFDS Online, BRS Information Technologies. **Networks/Consortia:** Member of PALINET. **Remarks:** Library located at King of Prussia Rd. & Lancaster Pike, Radnor, PA 19087. FAX: (215)975-0268. **Staff:** Judith Bryant, Asst.Libn.

★618★
American Horticultural Society - Library (Biol Sci)
7931 East Boulevard Dr. Phone: (703)768-5700
Alexandria, VA 22308 Frank L. Robinson, Exec.Dir.
Subjects: Horticulture. **Special Collections:** Harold B. Tukey Collection; George L. Slate Collection. **Holdings:** 5000 books. **Subscriptions:** 25 journals and other serials. **Services:** Library open to the public by appointment. **Publications:** American Horticulturist and News Edition. **Remarks:** Toll-free telephone number(s): (800)777-7931. FAX: (703)765-6032.

★619★
American Hospital Association - AHA Resource Center (Med, Bus-Fin)
840 N. Lake Shore Dr. Phone: (312)280-6263
Chicago, IL 60611 Eloise C. Foster, Dir.
Founded: 1920. **Staff:** Prof 12; Other 14. **Subjects:** Administration, planning, and financing of health care facilities; administrative aspects of medical, nursing, paramedical, and prepayment fields. **Special Collections:** Center for Hospital and Healthcare Administration History; Ray E. Brown Management Collection. **Holdings:** 55,000 volumes; 36,000 microfiche; 2 VF drawers of hospital annual reports; 500 cassettes. **Subscriptions:** 1000 journals and other serials. **Services:** Interlibrary loan (fee); copying; center open for reference use to anyone with legitimate interest. **Automated Operations:** Computerized cataloging, acquisitions, and serials. **Computerized Information Services:** BRS Information Technologies, OCLC, DIALOG Information Services, Maxwell Online, Inc., NLM; CLASS OnTyme, DOCLINE (electronic mail services). **Networks/Consortia:** Member of National Network of Libraries of Medicine - Greater Midwest Region. **Publications:** Hospital Literature Index, quarterly with annual cumulation - by subscription; Cumulative Index of Hospital Literature, multiannual cumulations of Hospital Literature Index from 1945-1977. **Remarks:** FAX: (312)280-3061. Electronic mail address(es): AMERHOSP (CLASS OnTyme); 60611A (DOCLINE). The Ray E. Brown Management Collection and the Center for Hospital and Healthcare Administration History are sponsored jointly with the American College of Healthcare Executives. **Staff:** Patricia J. Wakeley, Mgr.; Elizabeth Crabtree, Staff Spec.; Diana Culbertson, Staff Spec.; Ann Carbery Fox, Staff Spec.; Jeanette Harlow, Staff Spec.; Robin Swanson, Staff Spec.; Sara A. Beazley, Staff Assoc.; Michael P. McCue, Staff Assoc.

★620★
American Humane Association - American Association for Protecting Children - National Resource Center on Child Abuse and Neglect (Soc Sci)
63 Inverness Dr., E. Phone: (303)792-9900
Englewood, CO 80112-5117 Robyn Alsop, Coord.Info.Serv.
Founded: 1986. **Staff:** Prof 1. **Subjects:** Children - abuse, neglect, sexual abuse; risk assessment; case decisionmaking; staffing; caseload management; community resource integration; reasonable efforts. **Special Collections:** Child protective services policies and procedures manuals for all states; People of color leadership institute collection. **Holdings:** 1000 books; 5 VF drawers of subject files; 5 VF drawers of organizations; 50 state child protective service newsletters. **Subscriptions:** 100 journals and other serials. **Services:** Interlibrary loan; copying; SDI; center open to the public for reference use only. **Computerized Information Services:** POCLI (People of Color Leadership Institute), bibliographic research database (internal databases). Performs searches on fee basis. **Networks/Consortia:** Member of Central Colorado Library System (CCLS). **Publications:** Protecting Children, quarterly - available by subscription or membership; Child Sexual Abuse Curriculum; Framework for Advocacy; Research Issues in Risk Assessment; Understanding Medical Diagnosis of Child Maltreatment; list o f publications - available on request. **Remarks:** Toll-free telephone number(s): (800)227-5242. FAX: (303)792-5333. Member of National Child Welfare Resource and Research Centers and National Child Abuse Coalition. Affiliated with the Clearinghouse on Child Abuse and Neglect (Federal).

★621★
American Hungarian Educators' Association - Library (Area-Ethnic)
707 Snider Ln. Phone: (301)384-4657
Silver Spring, MD 20905 Eniko Molnar Basa, Pres.
Founded: 1976. **Subjects:** Hungarian history, folk art, and literature; German literature. **Holdings:** 200 volumes. **Services:** Copying; library open to the public with restrictions.

★622★
American Hungarian Library and Historical Society (Area-Ethnic)
213 E. 82nd St. Phone: (212)744-5298
New York, NY 10028 Paul E. Vesenyi, Contact
Founded: 1955. **Subjects:** Hungaricana. **Holdings:** 4000 volumes. **Publications:** Studies on Hungarian culture, irregular. **Remarks:** Society promotes research and study on the contribution of Hungarian culture to that of the United States.

★623★
American Hypnotists' Association - Hypnosis Technical Center (Med)
Glanworth Bldg., Suite 6
1159 Green St. Phone: (415)775-6130
San Francisco, CA 94109 Dr. Angela Bertuccelli, Libn.
Founded: 1959. **Staff:** Prof 1. **Subjects:** Hypnosis - medical, psychological, surgical; methods of hypnotism; history and practice of hypnosis. **Special Collections:** Historical publications (worldwide). **Holdings:** 3800 books; 304 bound periodical volumes; International Association of Hypnotists' reports. **Services:** Interlibrary loan; center open to members only.

★624★
American Indian Archaeological Institute - Library (Area-Ethnic)
38 Curtis Rd.
Box 1260 Phone: (203)868-0518
Washington, CT 06793-0260 Dr. Russell G. Handsman, Dir. of Res.
Founded: 1975. **Staff:** 9. **Subjects:** Prehistoric and historic American archeology; American Indian literature, history, crafts; ethnobotany. **Holdings:** 2000 books. **Services:** Copying; library open to the public by appointment for reference use. **Publications:** List of publications - available on request. **Remarks:** FAX: (203)868-1649.

★625★
American Indian Bible College - Dorothy Cummings Memorial Library (Rel-Phil, Area-Ethnic)
10020 N. 15th Ave. Phone: (602)944-3335
Phoenix, AZ 85021-2199 John S. Rose, Dir.
Staff: Prof 1; Other 1. **Subjects:** Biblical studies, Native Americans. **Special Collections:** Native American collection. **Holdings:** 14,000 books; 625 microfiche; 780 audio cassettes. **Subscriptions:** 115 journals and other serials; 5 newspapers. **Services:** Interlibrary loan; copying; library open to ministers for reference use only. **Automated Operations:** Computerized public access catalog, cataloging, and acquisitions.

★626★
American Indian Center of Santa Clara Valley, Inc. - Indian Center Library (Area-Ethnic)
919 The Alameda
San Jose, CA 95126-3135 Phone: (408)971-0772
Founded: 1972. **Staff:** 1.5. **Subjects:** American Indian. **Special Collections:** American Indian newspapers and language tapes. **Holdings:** 3000 books; 60 bound periodical volumes; phonograph records; films; book and audiovisual teaching materials for and about Native Americans; pamphlets; government documents; maps; charts; pictures; publications from Indian reservations. **Subscriptions:** 29 journals and other serials; 36 newspapers. **Services:** Library open to the public.

★627★
American Indian Research Project - Library (Hist, Area-Ethnic)
17 Dakota Hall
University of South Dakota Phone: (605)677-5208
Vermillion, SD 57069 leonard Bruguier, Dir.
Founded: 1966. **Staff:** Prof 1; Other 1. **Subjects:** South Dakota and Indian history. **Special Collections:** Jurrens Collection of Native American music (36 tapes); South Dakota Folk Music (22 tapes). **Holdings:** 5000 audiotapes. **Services:** Copying; SDI; library open for scholarly research. **Publications:** The South Dakota Experience (5 volumes, continuing); list of additional publications - both available upon request. **Special Catalogs:** Oyate Iyechinka Woglakapi (Indian collection catalog, 4 volumes). **Special Indexes:** Subject index to American Indian collection; American Indian Research Project Index - available on request. **Remarks:** Alternate telephone number(s): (605)677-5011.

American Industrial Arts Association Archives
See: **Millersville University** (10403)

★628★
American Institute of Aeronautics and Astronautics - Technical Information Service - AIAA Library (Sci-Engr)
555 W. 57th St. Phone: (212)247-6500
New York, NY 10019 David Purdy, Mgr., Lib.
Founded: 1936. **Staff:** Prof 2; Other 10. **Subjects:** Aeronautics, aerospace, astronautics, space sciences, physics, chemistry and materials, engineering, geosciences, life sciences, mathematics, computer sciences, social sciences. **Holdings:** 35,000 books; 1000 bound periodical volumes; 50,000 conference papers; 750,000 microfiche. **Subscriptions:** 1600 journals and other serials. **Services:** Interlibrary loan; copying; SDI; library open to the public. **Computerized Information Services:** DIALOG Information Services, NASA/RECON; DIALMAIL (electronic mail service). Performs searches on fee basis. **Networks/Consortia:** Member of NASA Aerospace Research Information Network (ARIN). **Publications:** Selected bibliographies; Finding Guide to AIAA Meeting Papers (annual and cumulative editions). **Remarks:** FAX: (212)765-4782. Electronic mail address(es): Aerospace Database ID no. 9176 (DIALMAIL). **Staff:** Danny Luce, Asst.Libn., Circ.; George Cholewczynski, Asst.Libn., Acq.

★629★
American Institute of Architects - AIA Library (Plan)
1735 New York Ave., N.W. Phone: (202)626-7492
Washington, DC 20006 Judy Marks Cohen, Sr.Mgr.
Founded: 1857. **Staff:** Prof 6; Other 6. **Subjects:** American architecture and architectural practice, building technology, urban planning. **Special Collections:** AIA Archives; Richard Morris Hunt Collection; rare book collection. **Holdings:** 30,000 volumes; 20 VF drawers of pamphlets and clippings; 50,000 slides; 3500 linear feet of archival material; 130,000 photographs; films; videotapes. **Subscriptions:** 400 journals and other serials. **Services:** Interlibrary loan (limited); copying; library open to the public for reference use only. **Computerized Information Services:** DIALOG Information Services, WILSONLINE, RLIN, Avery Index to Architectural Periodicals; Design for Aging, Building Security Design (internal databases). Performs searches on fee basis. **Networks/Consortia:** Member of Research Libraries Information Network (RLIN). **Publications:** Acquisitions List, quarterly; bibliographies (520). **Remarks:** FAX: (202)626-7420. **Staff:** Ben Silverstein, Tech.Serv.; Sheryl Romeo, Slide Libn.; Tony Wrenn, Archv.; Carole Twombly, Ref.Libn.; Michelle Jones, AV; Wayne Kemp, Tech.Serv.

★630★
American Institute of Baking - Ruth Emerson Library (Food-Bev)
1213 Bakers Way Phone: (913)537-4750
Manhattan, KS 66502 Ronald Wirtz, Libn.
Founded: 1925. **Staff:** Prof 1; Other 2. **Subjects:** Baking science and technology, food chemistry, nutrition. **Holdings:** 5000 books; 3500 bound periodical volumes; 64 VF drawers of unbound material on baking and nutrition. **Subscriptions:** 240 journals and other serials. **Services:** Interlibrary loan; copying; library open to the public for reference use only. **Automated Operations:** Computerized cataloging and circulation. **Computerized Information Services:** DIALOG Information Services; Ruth (internal database). Performs searches on fee basis. **Remarks:** FAX: (913)537-1493. Telex: 881039 AIB MAN UD. **Staff:** Cam Ingelin, Asst.Libn.

★631★
American Institute for Biosocial Research, Inc. - Library (Soc Sci)
PO Box 1174 Phone: (206)922-0448
Tacoma, WA 98401-1174 Rebecca Paulson, Libn.
Founded: 1978. **Staff:** 2. **Subjects:** Behavioral science - eating disorders, abnormal behavior, learning disabilities, behavior disorders; mental illness; biochemistry; environmental health; nutrition; psychology; sociology; criminology; medicine; organic chemistry; botanical pharmacognosy; photobiology; neurology; toxicology. **Holdings:** 6724 books; 117 periodicals. **Subscriptions:** 113 journals and other serials; 2 newspapers. **Services:** Library not open to the public. **Computerized Information Services:** DIALOG Information Services; Endnote, Endlink (internal databases). **Remarks:** FAX: (206)922-0479. **Staff:** Laura Babin; Alexander Schauss.

★632★
American Institute of Business - Library (Educ)
2500 Fleur Dr. Phone: (515)244-4221
Des Moines, IA 50321 Kathryn A. Griffin, Dir.
Founded: 1929. **Staff:** 3. **Subjects:** Court reporting, travel, tourism, secretary training, business management, general economics, computer programming. **Special Collections:** Dictation tapes for court reporting and shorthand students (4800 audiocassettes). **Holdings:** 5000 books; 9500 periodical volumes; 115 AV programs; 4800 nonbook items. **Subscriptions:** 212 journals and other serials; 7 newspapers. **Services:** Interlibrary loan; copying; library open to the public. **Remarks:** FAX: (515)244-6773.

★633★
American Institute of Certified Public Accountants - Library Services Division (Bus-Fin)
1211 Ave. of the Americas
New York, NY 10036-8775 Karen Hegge Neloms, Dir.
Founded: 1918. **Staff:** Prof 11; Other 11. **Subjects:** Accounting, auditing, taxation, finance, management. **Special Collections:** Old accounting texts. **Holdings:** 28,000 books; 3700 bound periodical volumes; 76,000 pamphlets; all New York and American Stock Exchange and Over-The-Counter annual reports, 1977-1990, on microfiche; Laser Disclosure annual and 10K reports, 1990 to present; 140 tax and business loose-leaf services. **Subscriptions:** 800 journals and other serials. **Services:** Interlibrary loan; copying; library open to the public but only AICPA members may borrow. **Automated Operations:** Computerized cataloging, acquisitions, and serials. **Computerized Information Services:** DIALOG Information Services, BRS Information Technologies, Mead Data Central, ORBIT Search Service. **Publications:** Accountants' Index, quarterly with annual cumulation - by subscription; AICPA Library Acquisitions List, monthly - on request to AICPA and SLA members; AICPA Library Classification Schedule, 1990; Accountants' Index Master List of Subject Headings, 1989; Accountants Database (online), updated quarterly; journals list for Accountants' Index/ Accountants Database - free upon request. **Remarks:** Toll-free telephone number(s): (800)223-4155 (outside New York); (800)522-5434 (in New York). FAX: (212)575-3846. Telex: 703396. **Staff:** Lillian Rosenfeld, Ref.Libn.; Linda C. Pierce, Index Ed.; Ileane Silver, Asst.Libn.; Cynthia Hiris, Asst.Libn.; J. Patricia Meyer, Asst.Libn.; Susan Lynn Bolmer, Asst.Libn.; Peter L. Durham, Asst.Libn.; Lauraine C. Arp, Asst.Libn.; Boris Musich, Asst.Libn.; Andrea L. Leal, Asst.Libn.

★634★
American Institute for Chartered Property Casualty Underwriters - Insurance Institute of America - Library (Bus-Fin)
720 Providence Rd. Phone: (215)644-2100
Malvern, PA 19355 Kim Holston, Libn.
Founded: 1978. **Staff:** Prof 1. **Subjects:** Insurance, risk management, economics, management, accounting, continuing education. **Special Collections:** O.D. Dickerson Memorial Library (insurance, mathematics; 500 volumes). **Holdings:** 8000 books. **Subscriptions:** 100 journals and other serials. **Services:** Copying; library open to the public. **Computerized Information Services:** DIALOG Information Services. **Publications:** CPCU/IIA Library Reports. **Remarks:** FAX: (215)251-9995. **Formerly:** American Institute for Property & Liability Underwriters.

American Institute of Chemical Engineers - National Foundation for History of Chemistry
See: **University of Pennsylvania - National Foundation for History of Chemistry - Library** (19190)

★635★
American Institute of Commerce - Library (Bus-Fin)
1801 E. Kimberly Rd. Phone: (319)355-3500
Davenport, IA 52807 Jon Grate
Staff: 3.5. **Subjects:** Business, travel, industrial technology, hospitality, radio broadcasting. **Holdings:** 1200 books; audiocassettes; videocassettes. **Subscriptions:** 78 journals and other serials; 2 newspapers. **Services:** Interlibrary loan; copying. **Networks/Consortia:** Member of Quad Cities Libraries in Cooperation (Quad-LINC). **Remarks:** FAX: (319)355-1320.

★636★
American Institute for Economic Research - E.C. Harwood Library (Bus-Fin)
P.O. Box 1000 Phone: (413)528-1216
Great Barrington, MA 01230 Amy Halberstadter, Libn.
Founded: 1933. **Staff:** Prof 10; Other 25. **Subjects:** Economics - general, history, international; money and banking; business cycles; public finance. **Holdings:** 10,000 volumes. **Subscriptions:** 70 journals and other serials; 7 newspapers. **Services:** Interlibrary loan; copying; library open to the public for reference use only. **Publications:** Research Reports, semimonthly; Economic Education Bulletins, monthly. **Remarks:** FAX: (413)528-0103.

★637★
American Institute of Food Distribution, Inc. - Information and Research Center (Food-Bev)
28-12 Broadway Phone: (201)791-5570
Fair Lawn, NJ 07410 Frank Panyko
Founded: 1928. **Staff:** 2. **Subjects:** Food industry. **Holdings:** 1800 books. **Subscriptions:** 400 journals and other serials. **Services:** Center open to the public on fee basis. **Publications:** Merger & Acquisitions; Grocery Wholesaling. **Special Indexes:** Food Institute Report Index. **Remarks:** FAX: (201)791-5222.

★638★
American Institute of Islamic Studies - Muslim Bibliographic Center (Rel-Phil, Area-Ethnic)
Box 10398 Phone: (303)936-0108
Denver, CO 80210 C.L. Geddes, Dir.
Founded: 1965. **Staff:** Prof 1; Other 2. **Subjects:** Islamic and Muslim culture; North African, Southeast Asian, and Near Eastern bibliography. **Holdings:** 7500 books and bound periodical volumes; 150 reels of microfilm. **Subscriptions:** 32 journals and other serials. **Services:** Interlibrary loan; copying; center open to the public by appointment. **Publications:** Bibliographic series, irregular - for sale.

★639★
American Institute of Management - Library (Bus-Fin)
P.O. Box 7039 Phone: (617)472-0277
Quincy, MA 02269 D. Ellis, Libn.
Subjects: Business management and allied subjects. **Holdings:** Figures not available. **Services:** Library not open to the public. **Publications:** List of publications - available on request. **Remarks:** Library located at 270 Beacon St., Boston, MA.

★640★
American Institute of Parliamentarians - Library (Soc Sci)
203 W. Wayne, Suite 312 Phone: (219)422-3680
Fort Wayne, IN 46802 Cleon C. Babcock, CPP, Pres.
Founded: 1958. **Staff:** Prof 2. **Subjects:** Parliamentary procedure. **Holdings:** 300 volumes; 10 volumes of bound sets of journals. **Subscriptions:** 1400 journals and other serials. **Services:** Library not open to the public. **Publications:** Parliamentary Directory, annual; Parliamentary Bibliography (about every 5 years); Parliamentary Journal, quarterly; Parliamentary Opinions, 1982; Parliamentary Law and Procedure (instructors manual and student workbook), 1987. **Special Indexes:** Update on Parliamentarian Journal Index, 1960-1986.

★641★
American Institute of Physics - Center for History of Physics - Niels Bohr Library (Sci-Engr)
335 E. 45th St. Phone: (212)661-9404
New York, NY 10017-3483 Bridget Sisk, Archv./Libn.
Founded: 1962. **Staff:** Prof 5; Other 2. **Subjects:** History and philosophy of physics and allied sciences, especially 19th and 20th century; physics; history and philosophy of science. **Holdings:** 18,000 books; 3500 bound periodical volumes; manuscripts; notebooks; photographs; autobiographies; oral history materials; dissertations; microfilm; archival materials. **Subscriptions:** 60 journals and other serials. **Services:** Copying; access to archival materials only upon application. **Publications:** Newsletter, biennial. **Special Catalogs:** Catalog of Sources for History of Physics (online). **Remarks:** FAX: (212)949-0473. **Staff:** Spencer Weart, Mgr.; Joan Warnow, Asst.Mgr.

American Institute for Property & Liability Underwriters
See: **American Institute for Chartered Property Casualty Underwriters - Insurance Institute of America - Library** (634)

American Institute for Psychoanalysis - Muriel Ivimey Library
See: **Muriel Ivimey Library** (8293)

★642★
The American Institute of Wine & Food - Simon-Lowenstein Collection (Food-Bev)
1550 Bryant St., Suite 700 Phone: (415)255-3000
San Francisco, CA 94103 Bill Huggins, Exec. Dir.
Founded: 1981. **Subjects:** Gastronomy, food, wine. **Holdings:** 858 books. **Services:** Collection not open to the public. **Publications:** Bibliography of Simon-Lowenstein Collection. **Remarks:** Collection is housed at the University of California, Santa Barbara, Department of Special Collections and is administered by AIWF, San Francisco office.

★643★
American Institutes for Research - Library (Educ)
1791 Arastradero Rd.
Box 1113 Phone: (415)493-3550
Palo Alto, CA 94302 Nancy K. Hull, Libn.
Founded: 1967. **Staff:** Prof 2. **Subjects:** Education, psychology. **Special Collections:** AIR technical reports (2500 titles). **Holdings:** 3000 books; 1200 bound periodical volumes; 7000 internal and external reports; 10 VF drawers of pamphlets; 10 VF drawers of tests (internal use only). **Subscriptions:** 140 journals and other serials. **Services:** Interlibrary loan; copying; library open to the public for reference use only by advance arrangement. **Computerized Information Services:** InterNet (electronic mail service). **Remarks:** FAX: (415)858-0958. Electronic mail address(es): XT.NKH@FORSYTHE.STANFORD.EDU (InterNet).

★644★
American Institutes for Research - Library (Soc Sci)
3333 K St., N.W. Phone: (202)342-5047
Washington, DC 20007 Ruth Papis, Libn.
Staff: Prof 1. **Subjects:** Psychology, education, human factors, human computer interaction, health, criminal justice, document design, usability testing. **Holdings:** 3000 books; 6 VF drawers; 200 technical reports. **Subscriptions:** 30 journals and other serials. **Services:** Interlibrary loan; copying; library open to the public by appointment. **Computerized Information Services:** DIALOG Information Services. **Publications:** Serialized Bibliography of Project Reports. **Special Catalogs:** AIR reports. **Remarks:** The AIR library supports the research staff in proposal and report preparation. A branch library is maintained in Palo Alto, CA.

★645★
American Institutes for Research - Project TALENT Data Bank (Educ)
Box 1113 Phone: (415)493-3550
Palo Alto, CA 94302 Lauri Steel, Dir., Data Bank
Founded: 1960. **Staff:** Prof 1. **Subjects:** Education, psychology, testing, measurement, statistics, students, schools. **Holdings:** Longitudinal data spanning 15 years (ages 14-29) on 400,000 students and their (circa 1000) high schools; 150 final reports, dissertations, journal articles based on Project TALENT Data Bank studies; 4000 case Public Use File. **Services:** Data analysis and worktape preparation for outside users (fee). **Publications:** Research reports; Project TALENT Data Bank Handbook; annotated bibliography.

★646★
American Insurance Association - Law Library (Law, Bus-Fin)
1130 Connecticut Ave., N.W., Suite 1000 Phone: (202)828-7183
Washington, DC 20036 Allen K. Haddox, Libn.
Staff: Prof 1; Other 1. **Subjects:** Insurance, law. **Holdings:** 50,000 volumes; 215 VF drawers. **Subscriptions:** 120 journals and other serials; 5 newspapers. **Services:** Library open to the public by appointment. **Computerized Information Services:** LEXIS, NEXIS. **Publications:** Summary of Suggested State Laws and Regulations for Auto Insurance; Compilation of Workers' Compensation Laws; Agent's Digest; Termination and Renewal of Property/Casualty Insurance Policies; Summary of State Regulations and Laws Affecting General Contractors; Environmental Liability Laws. **Remarks:** FAX: (202)293-1219.

★647★
American Insurance Services Group, Inc. - Engineering & Safety Service Information Center (Sci-Engr)
85 John St. Phone: (212)669-0478
New York, NY 10038 Cendrella Abdallah, Libn.
Founded: 1975. **Staff:** Prof 1; Other 1. **Subjects:** Fire protection, loss control, safety engineering. **Holdings:** 1600 books; 125 VF drawers. **Subscriptions:** 105 journals and other serials. **Services:** Interlibrary loan; copying; library open to subscribers. **Automated Operations:** Computerized cataloging. **Computerized Information Services:** DIALOG Information Services, MEDLARS, FIREDOC, STN International; LOSSPAC (internal database). Performs searches free of charge. **Remarks:** FAX: (212)669-0535.

★648★
American International College - James J. Shea Memorial Library - Oral History Center (Hist)
1000 State St. Phone: (413)747-6225
Springfield, MA 01109-3189 Dr. F. Knowlton Utley, Dir. of Lib.
Founded: 1885. **Staff:** Prof 3; Other 4. **Subjects:** Business, education, history, psychology, nursing. **Special Collections:** Western Massachusetts and Connecticut Valley oral history. **Holdings:** 600 oral history tapes. **Subscriptions:** 489 journals and other serials; 8 newspapers. **Services:** Interlibrary loan; copying; center open to the public with restrictions. **Automated Operations:** Computerized cataloging. **Computerized Information Services:** DIALOG Information Services; CD-ROMS (ACADEMIC INDEX, NewsBank). **Networks/Consortia:** Member of C/W MARS, Inc., Cooperating Libraries of Greater Springfield, A CCGS Agency (CLGS). **Remarks:** FAX: (413)737-2803. **Staff:** Matthew N. Pappathan, Ref.Libn.; Ira Glonts, Tech.Serv.Libn.

★649★
American International Group - Corporate Information Center (Bus-Fin)
70 Pine St., 8th Fl. Phone: (212)770-7911
New York, NY 10270 Lucy Lettis, Mgr.
Founded: 1980. **Staff:** Prof 5; Other 1. **Subjects:** Insurance, business. **Holdings:** 1500 books; 43 microfiche; 3 reels of microfilm; 700 subject files. **Subscriptions:** 200 journals and other serials. **Services:** Center not open to the public. **Computerized Information Services:** DIALOG Information Services, Dow Jones News/Retrieval, NEXIS, TEXTLINE, DataTimes, NewsNet, Inc., VU/TEXT Information Services, Disclosure Incorporated, CORIS - Thomson Financial Networks Inc. **Publications:** Insurance Daily - for internal distribution only. **Remarks:** FAX: (212)742-0949. **Staff:** Julia Dorn, Info.Spec.; Dennis DiRaffaele, Info.Spec.; Beverly Rosignolo, Info.Spec.; Janet Stoller, Info.Spec.

★650★
American Irish Historical Society - Library (Area-Ethnic)
991 5th Ave.
New York, NY 10028 Phone: (212)288-2263
Subjects: Irish in the American colonies and the United States. **Holdings:** 25,000 books; 200 linear feet of archives and manuscripts. **Subscriptions:** 500 journals and other serials. **Services:** Library open to the public by appointment. **Remarks:** FAX: (212)628-7927.

American Iron and Steel Institute - National Corrugated Steel Pipe Association
See: **National Corrugated Steel Pipe Association** (11134)

★651★
American Ivy Society - Library (Biol Sci)
Box 520 Phone: (513)434-7069
West Carrollton, OH 45449-0520 Dr. Sabina Mueller Sulgrove, Dir. of Res.
Founded: 1973. **Staff:** Prof 1. **Subjects:** Ivy (Hedera) - nomenclature, description, culture, history, use, topiary, hardiness. **Special Collections:** Bess Shippy Collection. **Holdings:** Books; pamphlets. **Subscriptions:** 350 journals and other serials. **Services:** Copying; library open to the public with restrictions. **Special Indexes:** Index to Ivy Journal Photo 1980-1984. **Remarks:** Society maintains an information clearinghouse on using and growing ivies in the home and garden.

American Jewish Archive
See: **Congregation Shearith Israel - Sophie and Ivan Salomon Library Collection** (4168)

American Jewish Archives
See: **Hebrew Union College - Jewish Institute of Religion** (7095)

★652★
American Jewish Committee - Blaustein Library (Area-Ethnic, Soc Sci)
165 E. 56th St. Phone: (212)751-4000
New York, NY 10022 Cyma M. Horowitz, Lib.Dir.
Founded: 1939. **Staff:** Prof 2. **Subjects:** Intergroup relations, Jewish community organization, contemporary Jewish problems, civil rights and liberties, ethnic groups, interreligious relations. **Holdings:** 30,000 books and pamphlets; 60 VF drawers; 1450 reels of microfilm. **Subscriptions:** 575 journals and other serials; 50 newspapers. **Services:** Library open to qualified scholars for reference use only. **Staff:** Michele Anish, Asst.Libn.

★653★
American Jewish Committee - Oral History Library (Area-Ethnic)
165 E. 56th St. Phone: (212)751-4000
New York, NY 10022 Suki Sandler, Dir.
Founded: 1969. **Staff:** Prof 2. **Subjects:** All aspects of the "American Jewish Experience in the 20th Century." **Special Collections:** Oral memoirs, including the Jacob Blaustein Oral History Collection; Irving M. Engel Oral History Collection on Civil Rights; Lautenberg Collection on East European Jewish Communities; The Politics of American Jews: The Election of 1972; A Study in American Pluralism Through Oral Histories of Holocaust Survivors; Oral Histories of Recent Soviet Emigres in America; American Jewish Women of Achievement; The Twentieth Century American Jewish Family: An Oral History Across Three Generations; American Jews in Sports; Louis G. Cowan Broadcasting Collection; History of the Lower East Side of New York & The Hebrew Orphan Asylum; Soviet Jewry Movement in America Collection; Israeli Women of Achievement Collection; American Jews of Sephardic Origin; Jewish Veterans of the Gulf War. **Holdings:** 2000 taped interviews and transcripts. **Services:** Library open to accredited researchers. **Special Catalogs:** Catalogue of Memoirs (Volumes I & II). **Remarks:** FAX: (212)751-4017. Collection is housed at the New York Public Library - Jewish Division. **Staff:** Hilary Bosch, Lib.Coord.

★654★
American Jewish Congress - Commission on Law and Social Action - Shad Polier Memorial Library (Soc Sci, Law)
15 E. 84th St. Phone: (212)879-4500
New York, NY 10028-0407 Sarah Witt, Libn.
Founded: 1978. **Staff:** Prof 1. **Subjects:** Constitutional law, church-state relations, civil rights, history of discrimination, civil liberties, social and economic affairs. **Special Collections:** Commission archives (130 VF drawers); U.S. Supreme Court briefs; American Jewish Congress historical material; commission reports. **Holdings:** 3000 books; 600 pamphlets. **Subscriptions:** 49 journals and other serials. **Services:** Copying; library open to the public by appointment only. **Computerized Information Services:** WESTLAW. **Special Indexes:** Index to Commission Archives. **Remarks:** Alternate telephone number(s): (212)360-1549. FAX: (212)249-3672.

★655★
American Jewish Historical Society - Library (Area-Ethnic, Hist)
2 Thornton Rd. Phone: (617)891-8110
Waltham, MA 02154 Nathan M. Kaganoff, Libn.
Founded: 1892. **Staff:** Prof 4; Other 2. **Subjects:** American Jewish history. **Special Collections:** Sang Collection of American Judaica. **Holdings:** 90,000 books; 500,000 unbound periodicals; 12 million manuscript pieces; 500 Yiddish theater posters; 2000 pieces of Yiddish sheet music; 75,000 synagogue and other Jewish institutional items. **Subscriptions:** 250 journals and other serials; 300 newspapers. **Services:** Interlibrary loan; copying; library open to the public with restrictions. **Special Catalogs:** Catalogs of manuscript collections; catalog of theater posters; catalog of art treasures and daguerreotypes; catalog of Sang Collection. **Remarks:** FAX: (612)899-9208. **Staff:** Gina Hsin, Asst.Libn.

★656★
American Jewish Joint Distribution Committee - Archives (Area-Ethnic)
711 3rd Ave. Phone: (212)687-6200
New York, NY 10017 Denise Bernard Gluck, Dir. of Arch. & Rec.
Founded: 1914. **Staff:** Prof 1; Other 1. **Subjects:** 20th century Jewish history. **Holdings:** 1500 linear feet of archival material. **Services:** Copying; archives open to accredited scholars. **Special Catalogs:** Annotated catalog, 1914-1964. **Remarks:** FAX: (212)370-5467. Telex: 62873.

★657★
American Jewish Joint Distribution Committee - Library (Area-Ethnic)
711 3rd Ave. Phone: (212)687-6200
New York, NY 10017 Micha F. Oppenheim, Libn.
Founded: 1979. **Staff:** Prof 1; Other 1. **Subjects:** Refugees, Holocaust, Israel/Palestine, Jews in other countries, JDC history. **Holdings:** 3000 books; JDC publications. **Services:** Library open to the public by appointment. **Publications:** Acquisitions list. **Remarks:** FAX: (212)370-5467. Telex: 62873. **Also Known As:** Joint Distribution Committee.

American Jewish Periodical Center
See: **Hebrew Union College - Jewish Institute of Religion** (7096)

★658★
American Journal of Nursing Company - Sophia F. Palmer Library (Med, Publ)
555 W. 57th St. Phone: (212)582-8820
New York, NY 10019 Frederick W. Pattison, Libn.
Founded: 1951. **Staff:** Prof 1. **Subjects:** Nursing and allied fields. **Special Collections:** Early nursing books and history of nursing. **Holdings:** 9000 books and bound periodical volumes. **Subscriptions:** 300 journals and other serials. **Services:** Library open to graduate students and researchers by appointment only. **Computerized Information Services:** MEDLINE; DOCLINE (electronic mail service). **Networks/Consortia:** Member of National Network of Libraries of Medicine - Middle Atlantic Region. **Special Indexes:** International Nursing Index, quarterly - by subscription; annual indexes to company journals; index to American Journal of Nursing, annual.

★659★
American Judicature Society - Research Library (Law)
25 E. Washington St., 16th Fl. Phone: (312)558-6900
Chicago, IL 60602 Kathleen M. Sampson, Libn.
Founded: 1913. **Staff:** 1. **Subjects:** Judicial administration. **Special Collections:** Court studies (300); judicial conduct and ethics material (18 file drawers). **Holdings:** 5000 books. **Subscriptions:** 75 journals and other serials. **Services:** Interlibrary loan; copying; library open to the public by appointment.

★660★
American Kennel Club - Library (Rec, Biol Sci)
51 Madison Ave. Phone: (212)696-8245
New York, NY 10010 Roberta A. Vesley, Lib.Dir.
Founded: 1934. **Staff:** Prof 1; Other 3. **Subjects:** Dogs - breeding, training, health, literature, art, sports. **Special Collections:** Domestic and foreign stud books; collections of prominent past and present dog-fanciers, including John W. Cross, Shearer, and Rosenberg. **Holdings:** 15,000 volumes; VF drawers of clippings; VF drawers of pictures and photographs of dogs; VF drawers of uncataloged pamphlets; videocassettes; fine art collection. **Subscriptions:** 400 journals and other serials. **Services:** Copying; library open to the public. **Computerized Information Services:** NEXIS, LEXIS. **Remarks:** FAX: (212)696-8299. **Staff:** Susan Lesser, Libn.

★661★
American Law Institute - Library (Law)
4025 Chestnut St. Phone: (215)243-1654
Philadelphia, PA 19104 Pearl Nei-Chien Li, Libn.
Founded: 1965. **Staff:** Prof 2. **Subjects:** Law, legal education. **Special Collections:** American Law Institute publications (Restatement of the Law, Uniform Commercial Code, Model Penal Code, and other special projects); American Law Institute-American Bar Association Committee on Continuing Professional Education publications; continuing legal education publications of various bar associations. **Holdings:** 14,000 books; 1000 pamphlets; 33 volumes of clippings; 8 drawers of microfiche. **Subscriptions:** 200 journals and other serials; 9 newspapers. **Services:** Interlibrary loan (limited); library open to the public with permission of librarian. **Computerized Information Services:** DIALOG Information Services, WESTLAW; LEXIS; ABANet (electronic mail service). **Remarks:** FAX: (215)243-1664. Library also serves the American Law Institute-American Bar Association Committee on Continuing Professional Education. **Staff:** Harry Kyriakodis, Asst.Libn.

★662★
American Lawn Bowls Association - Library (Rec)
P.O. Box 46065 Phone: (213)876-7563
Los Angeles, CA 90046 Michael Ashton-Phillips, ALBA, Mktg.
Staff: 1. **Subjects:** Lawn bowling. **Holdings:** 500 volumes; magazines; club histories; organizational records; minutes; yearbooks; photographs; drawings. **Services:** Library not open to the public. **Remarks:** FAX: (213)876-6883. Historical files are maintained by Harold L. Esch, Hist., Box 1231, Mount Dora, FL 32757, telephone: (904)383-6769.

★663★
American Legion - National Headquarters - Library (Mil)
700 N. Pennsylvania St.
Box 1055 Phone: (317)635-8411
Indianapolis, IN 46206 Joseph J. Hovish, Dir.
Founded: 1923. **Staff:** Prof 2; Other 4. **Subjects:** Veterans' affairs, children and youth, national defense, patriotism, American Legion. **Special Collections:** Founding Fathers Exhibit; Archives of the American Legion, including national and state organizations and posts; World War posters. **Holdings:** 8500 volumes; 300 periodicals; 1140 VF drawers of pamphlets, reports, manuscripts, correspondence, other archival material. **Subscriptions:** 200 journals and other serials. **Services:** Interlibrary loan; copying; library open to the public for reference use only by appointment. **Remarks:** FAX: (317)635-8411, ext. 401. **Staff:** John Kristelli, Asst.Dir.

★664★
American Leprosy Missions, Inc. - Library (Med)
1 Alm Way Phone: (803)271-7040
Greenville, SC 29601 Jim Gittings, Dir. of Com.
Founded: 1906. **Staff:** Prof 1. **Subjects:** Leprosy treatment, medical missionary efforts to overcome the disease, ALM history, reconstructive surgery, rehabilitation, village health care. **Special Collections:** History of leprosy care facilities, 1930s to present (3000 photographs). **Holdings:** 1200 books; films; videotapes; ALM records; slides. **Subscriptions:** 20 journals and other serials. **Services:** Library open to the public. **Remarks:** FAX: (803)271-7062. Toll-free telephone number(s): (800)543-3131.

★665★
American Library Association - Headquarters Library and Information Center (Info Sci)
50 E. Huron St. Phone: (312)280-2153
Chicago, IL 60611 Charles Harmon, HQ Libn.
Founded: 1924. **Staff:** Prof 2; Other 3. **Subjects:** Library science, library associations, library architecture, association management. **Special Collections:** Materials selection policy statements; library building programs, plans, pictures, and slides; public relations materials; IFLA Conference Papers; library staff personnel and procedure manuals; library surveys; materials produced, published, or sponsored by ALA. **Holdings:** 7500 books; 3000 bound periodical volumes; 220 reels of microfilm; 8 drawers of microforms. **Subscriptions:** 615 journals and other serials. **Services:** Interlibrary loan; copying; library open to ALA members and other researchers. **Automated Operations:** Computerized cataloging and serials. **Computerized Information Services:** DIALOG Information Services, OCLC, ALANET; CD-ROMs; ALANET (electronic mail service). **Networks/Consortia:** Member of Chicago Library System, ILLINET. **Remarks:** FAX: (312)440-9374. Electronic mail address(es): ALA. Library (ALANET). **Also Known As:** ALA.

American Library Association - Social Responsibilities Round Table
See: **ALA Gay & Lesbian Task Force** (179)

★666★
American Library in Hong Kong - USIS Library (Educ)
United Centre
Shopping Arcade, 1st Fl.
95 Queensway, Central Phone: 5299661
Hong Kong, Hong Kong Catherine Priest
Founded: 1950. **Staff:** 6. **Subjects:** United States. **Holdings:** 12,000 books; 72,000 microfiche; 1240 reels of microfilm; 473 videocassettes. **Subscriptions:** 187 journals and other serials; 6 newspapers. **Services:** Interlibrary loan; SDI; library open to the public with restrictions. **Computerized Information Services:** DIALOG Information Services, LEGI-SLATE, Economic Bulletin Board, PDQ. **Publications:** DATA; Table of Contents Service (TOC); Selective Dissemination of Information (SDI); Subject Bibliographies. **Remarks:** FAX: 8656114. Maintained or supported by the U.S. Information Agency. Focus is on materials that will assist peoples outside the United States to learn about the United States, its people, history, culture, political processes, and social milieux. **Staff:** Constance Yeung.

★667★
American Library in Paris (Hum, Hist)
10 rue du Genera Camou Phone: 1 45514682
F-75007 Paris, France Robert Grattan, III
Founded: 1920. **Staff:** Prof 5; Other 6. **Subjects:** American literature, American history. **Holdings:** 70,000 books; 9000 bound periodical volumes; 1200 reels of microfilm. **Subscriptions:** 350 journals and other serials; 3 newspapers. **Services:** Interlibrary loan; library open to the public on a fee basis. **Computerized Information Services:** UTLS Library System (internal database); ALANET (electronic mail service). **Remarks:** FAX: 1 45502583. Electronic mail address(es): ALA1903 AM.LIB.PARIS (ALANET).

★668★
American Library of Railway and Traction History (Trans)
449 1/2 Riverside Dr. Phone: (818)846-6098
Burbank, CA 91506 Brian C. Smith, Dir.
Founded: 1963. **Staff:** Prof 1. **Subjects:** Interurban electric railways, railroads, rapid transit, street railways, subways, urban transit. **Holdings:** 2054 books; 82 reels of microfilm; 17 films; 32 videocassettes; 11 VF drawers of railroad information. **Subscriptions:** 15 journals and other serials. **Services:** Interlibrary loan; copying; library open to the public with restrictions. **Remarks:** FAX: (818)841-3002.

★669★
American Life Foundation - Prang-Mark Society - Library (Art)
Box 349 Phone: (607)535-4737
Watkins Glen, NY 14891-0349 John Crosby Freeman, Coord.
Staff: Prof 1; Other 3. **Subjects:** Printing, early greeting cards, tradecards. **Special Collections:** Original Prang Prints. **Holdings:** 7000 books. **Services:** Library open to the public by appointment only, June 1 through September 1.

★670★
American Life Foundation and Study Institute - Americana Research Library (Art)
Box 349 Phone: (215)539-3010
Watkins Glen, NY 14891-0349 John Crosby Freeman, Dir.
Staff: Prof 1. **Subjects:** Decorative arts, architecture, art, history, agriculture, landscape architecture. **Special Collections:** Ruth S. Freeman Collection of Children's Picture Books; Victorian Periodical Library; Larry Freeman Decorative Arts Library. **Holdings:** 5000 books; 1500 bound periodical volumes; 5000 art and architecture slides; 20 drawers of posters and broadsides; 3000 pamphlets. **Subscriptions:** 15 journals and other serials. **Services:** Library open for special research only. **Remarks:** Alternate telephone number(s): (215)539-3010.

★671★
American Life Lobby - Library (Soc Sci)
P.O. Box 490 Phone: (703)659-4171
Stafford, VA 22554 Robert Marshall
Founded: 1979. **Staff:** 2. **Subjects:** Abortion; euthanasia; infanticide; opposition to tax-subsidized birth control organizations, population control in foreign countries; opposition to sex, violence, and profanity on television and radio; opposition to school and television sex education programs. **Holdings:** 17,000 flyers, leaflets, booklets, books, audiovisual materials, and other items. **Services:** Interlibrary loan; copying; library open to the public by appointment. **Remarks:** FAX: (703)659-2586.

American Lifesaving Emergency Response Team (A.L.E.R.T.)
See: **United States Lifesaving Association** (17597)

★672★
American Lung Association of Hawaii - Learning Center for Lung Health (Med)
245 N. Kukui St. Phone: (808)537-5966
Honolulu, HI 96817 Rosemary Respicio, Dir.
Founded: 1981. **Staff:** Prof 3; Other 1. **Subjects:** Lung health, asthma education, smoking prevention, air pollution, adult patient health care. **Holdings:** 100 books; 40 bound periodical volumes; 100 air pollution materials; 50 smoking prevention educational items; 25 marijuana and health education materials. **Services:** Interlibrary loan; center open to the public.

★673★
American Lung Association of Kansas - Information Center (Med)
4300 Drury Ln.
Box 4426 Phone: (913)272-9290
Topeka, KS 66604-2419 Mavis Glenn, Prog.Sec.
Founded: 1908. **Staff:** 12. **Subjects:** Lung diseases - emphysema, tuberculosis, asthma; air pollution; smoking and health. **Special Collections:** Public/workplace smoking cessation clinics; family asthma programs; Better Breathing Clubs. **Holdings:** Books; pamphlets; filmstrips; films; videotapes. **Services:** Films, filmstrips, and videotapes loaned on request. **Remarks:** FAX: (913)272-9297. Toll-free telephone number(s): (800)432-3957 (in Kansas). **Staff:** Steve Berndsen, Exec.Dir.

★674★
American Lutheran Church - South Dakota Synod - Archives
Center for Western Studies
Augustana College
Box 727
Sioux Falls, SD 57197
Defunct. Holdings absorbed by Evangelical Lutheran Church in America - ELCA Region III Archives.

★675★
American Management Association - Information Resource Center (Bus-Fin)
135 W. 50th St. Phone: (212)903-8182
New York, NY 10020 Anne Jones, Mgr.
Founded: 1923. **Staff:** Prof 5; Other 3. **Subjects:** Management, personnel, marketing, finance, production, international operations. **Holdings:** 10,000 books; 175 file drawers of clippings, pamphlets, company documents. **Subscriptions:** 267 journals and other serials. **Services:** Library open to members only. **Automated Operations:** Computerized cataloging. **Computerized Information Services:** DIALOG Information Services, NEXIS; internal database. **Remarks:** FAX: (212)903-8163. **Staff:** Elizabeth A. Keegan, Sr.Info.Couns.; Gordon H. Evans, Info.Couns.; Carol Blagman, Info.Couns.; Richard Waller, Libn.

★676★
American Marketing Association - Marguerite Kent Library/Information Center (Bus-Fin)
250 S. Wacker Dr. Phone: (312)648-0536
Chicago, IL 60606 Lorraine V. Caliendo, Dir.
Founded: 1977. **Staff:** Prof 3; Other 2. **Subjects:** Marketing. **Special Collections:** Complete collection of all association publications, including Journal of Marketing, Journal of Health Care Marketing, Journal of Marketing Research, Marketing News, and conference proceedings; software demonstration discs (210 titles; loaned to AMA members only). **Holdings:** 5000 books; 140 bound periodical volumes; 124 VF drawers of pamphlets. **Subscriptions:** 75 journals and other serials. **Services:** Interlibrary loan; copying; center open to the public by appointment ($10 student fee; $25 professional fee). **Computerized Information Services:** DIALOG Information Services. Performs searches on fee basis for members only. Contact Person: Amy Wenshe. **Publications:** Bibliographies. **Special Indexes:** Index for Software Review Center Collection. **Remarks:** FAX: (312)993-7542. **Staff:** Jacquelyn Van Gorp.

★677★
American Mathematical Society - Mathematical Reviews - Library (Sci-Engr)
416 4th St.
Box 8604 Phone: (313)996-5267
Ann Arbor, MI 48107 Ella Ponomarenko, Hd.Libn.
Staff: Prof 2; Other 11. **Subjects:** Mathematics. **Special Collections:** Russian mathematical publications (200 journals; 130 serials). **Holdings:** 1200 reference volumes; 60,000 unbound periodicals; 1000 reels of microfilm. **Subscriptions:** 3400 journals and other serials. **Services:** Document delivery; library not open to the public. **Automated Operations:** Computerized cataloging and acquisitions. **Computerized Information Services:** DIALOG Information Services; produces MathSci (Mathematics and Statistical Information Online); CD-ROM (MathSci, Mathematical Reviews, Current Mathematical Publications); Internet (electronic mail service). Performs searches on fee basis. **Publications:** Mathematical Reviews, monthly; Current Mathematical Publications, triweekly - both by subscription. **Remarks:** FAX: (313)996-2916. Electronic mail address(es): Math Doc@Math.AMS.COM; EIP@MATH.AMS.COM (Internet). **Staff:** Bert TePaske-King, Acq. Libn.

★678★
American Medical Association - Division of Library and Information Management (Med)
515 N. State St. Phone: (312)464-4818
Chicago, IL 60610 Arthur W. Hafner, Ph.D., Dir.
Founded: 1911. **Staff:** Prof 13; Other 27. **Subjects:** Clinical medicine, medical socioeconomics, U.S. medical history, international health. **Special Collections:** Archive of American Medical Association and of Organized Medicine; sociology and economics of medicine, 1962 to present; Historical Health Fraud Collection; Deceased Physician Masterfile, 1803-1969. **Holdings:** 21,575 volumes; 62,790 items in medical socioeconomics file; 165,290 documents and artifacts; 170 linear feet of general medical and pamphlet material; 350 linear feet of biographical data in Physician File; 145,575 volumes on microfilm. **Subscriptions:** 1970 journals and other serials. **Services:** Interlibrary loan; document delivery; current awareness service; SDI; library open to AMA members, researchers and allied health organizations by appointment. **Computerized Information Services:** NLM, BRS Information Technologies, DIALOG Information Services, DataTimes, OCLC; AMA Policy Database and Deceased Physician Masterfile Database (internal database). **Networks/Consortia:** Member of Chicago Library System, National Network of Libraries of Medicine - Greater Midwest Region, ILLINET. **Publications:** Proceedings of the AMA House of Delegates, semiannual; AMA Directory of Officials and Staff, annual; Professional Liability Clearinghouse, monthly; AMA Referral Directory, quarterly; serials holdings list, quarterly; Guide to the Historical Health Fraud Collection of the AMA; monthly list of AMA councils, committees, and sponsored national meetings; Books Received by AMA Division of Library and Information Management. **Special Indexes:** Index to Proceedings of AMA House of Delegates, semiannual; Index to AMA Policy Compendium; Index to Medical Socioeconomic Literature, 1962-1970; Index to AM News, annual; Index to Journal of the American Medical Association, semiannual; indexes to nine AMA specialty journals, annual. **Remarks:** FAX: (312)464-4184. Telex: 28-0248. **Also Known As:** AMA. **Staff:** Norman Frankel, AMA Sci.-Soc.Econ. Indexing; Anne White-Michalski, Online Search Anl.; Marguerite Fallucco, Archv.; Ashish Bajaj, Off.Mgr.; Sandra R. Schefris, Dir., Ser. & Tech.Serv.

★679★
American Medical Association - Washington Office Library (Med)
1101 Vermont Ave., N.W.
Washington, DC 20005 Phone: (202)789-7448
Staff: Prof 1. **Subjects:** Medical socioeconomics, health statistics, health policy. **Special Collections:** AMA House of Delegates proceedings and

selected other AMA publications and statements. **Holdings:** 350 titles. **Subscriptions:** 175 journals and other serials; 5 newspapers. **Services:** Interlibrary loan; library open to postgraduate reseachers by appointment only. **Computerized Information Services:** Dow Jones News/Retrieval, DIALOG Information Services, OCLC, WILSONLINE, LEGI-SLATE, NLM, NEXIS; Dialmail (electronic mail service). **Remarks:** FAX: (202)789-7479.

★680★
American Medical Laboratories, Inc. - Library (Med)
14225 Newbrook Dr. Phone: (703)691-9100
Chantilly, VA 22021 Cecilia Durkin, Libn.
Founded: 1980. **Staff:** Prof 1. **Subjects:** Laboratory medicine, pathology, toxicology, immunology, industrial medicine, cytogenetics. **Holdings:** 1600 books; 2000 bound periodical volumes. **Subscriptions:** 150 journals and other serials; 5 newspapers. **Services:** Interlibrary loan; copying; SDI; library not open to the public. **Automated Operations:** Computerized public access catalog. **Computerized Information Services:** NLM, MEDLARS, DIALOG Information Services, ELSS (Electronic Legislative Search System). **Remarks:** FAX: (703)385-4858.

American Medical Record Association
See: **American Health Information Management Association** (605)

American Medical Women's Association Archives
See: **New York Hospital-Cornell Medical Center - Medical Archives** (11579)

American Merchant Marine Library Association
See: **United Seaman's Service - American Merchant Marine Library Association** (16780)

★681★
American Meteorological Society - Abstracts Project - Library (Sci-Engr)
45 Beacon St. Phone: (617)227-2425
Boston, MA 02108 Richard E. Hallgren, Exec.Dir.
Founded: 1949. **Staff:** Prof 11; Other 2. **Subjects:** Meteorology, geophysics, astrophysics, hydrology, oceanography, atmospheric sciences, environmental sciences. **Special Collections:** Russian language serials and monographs in atmospheric sciences. **Holdings:** 2600 books; 300 bound periodical volumes; 25,000 unbound periodical issues. **Subscriptions:** 100 journals and other serials. **Services:** Library not open to the public. **Computerized Information Services:** Online systems. **Publications:** Journal of Meteorological & Geoastrophysical Abstracts, monthly. **Special Indexes:** Annual indexes in card and book form.

★682★
American Meteorological Society - Brooks Library (Sci-Engr)
45 Beacon St.
Boston, MA 02108 Phone: (617)227-2425
Founded: 1965. **Subjects:** Meteorology, history of meteorology. **Special Collections:** Papers and letters of Charles F. Brooks and A. Lawrence Rotch. **Holdings:** 6000 books; 350 bound periodical volumes. **Services:** Library not open to the public. **Computerized Information Services:** SCIENCEnet (electronic mail service). **Remarks:** FAX: (617)742-8718. Electronic mail address(es): R.HALLGREN (SCIENCEnet). Historical library for headquarters use only.

★683★
American Mime, Inc. - Library (Theater)
61 4th Ave. Phone: (212)777-1710
New York, NY 10003 Paul J. Curtis, Dir.
Founded: 1970. **Subjects:** History of the American Mime Theatre. **Holdings:** Course syllabi; picture files; scrapbooks; clippings; American Mime scripts; bibliography of mime works. **Services:** Library open to the public for reference use only with permission of the director. **Staff:** Jean Barbour, Adm.

★684★
American Museum of Fly Fishing, Inc. - Library (Rec)
Box 42 Phone: (802)362-3300
Manchester, VT 05254 Alanna Fisher, Cur.
Founded: 1968. **Staff:** 4. **Subjects:** Fly fishing; history, lore, and literature of angling; entomology; geography. **Special Collections:** File of patent applications relating to fly fishing, mid-19th century to present. **Holdings:** 2500 volumes; periodicals, 1820 to present; articles; memorabilia; original manuscripts. **Subscriptions:** 20 journals and other serials. **Services:** Library open to the public on request. **Publications:** A Bibliography of American Sporting Periodicals (book); American Fly Fishing: A History (book); A Treasury of Reels.

★685★
American Museum of Magic - Library (Rec)
107 E. Michigan
Box 5 Phone: (616)781-7666
Marshall, MI 49068 Robert Lund, Owner
Staff: 1. **Subjects:** Conjuring, confidence games, superstition. **Special Collections:** Irving Desfor collection of photographs of magicians (40,000). **Holdings:** 10,000 books; 25,000 magazines; 150,000 letters, newspaper clippings, programs, photographs, films, posters, manuscripts. **Subscriptions:** 25 journals and other serials. **Services:** Library open to the public with restrictions. **Remarks:** Alternate telephone number(s): (616)781-7674.

★686★
American Museum of Natural History - Department of Ichthyology - Dean Memorial Library (Biol Sci)
Central Park W. at 79th St. Phone: (212)769-5798
New York, NY 10024 Dr. Gareth Nelson, Cur.
Staff: Prof 3; Other 3. **Subjects:** Fish - anatomy, physiology, classification, ecology, distribution. **Holdings:** 3000 books and bound periodical volumes; 5000 pamphlets. **Subscriptions:** 5 journals and other serials. **Services:** Copying; library open to qualified users by appointment. **Remarks:** FAX: (212)769-5233 (Museum).

★687★
American Museum of Natural History - Department of Library Services (Sci-Engr, Biol Sci)
Central Park W. at 79th St. Phone: (212)769-5400
New York, NY 10024-5192 Nina J. Root, Dir.
Founded: 1869. **Staff:** Prof 12; Other 15. **Subjects:** Anthropology, archeology, paleontology, entomology, mammalogy, ornithology, ichthyology, malacology, herpetology, mineralogy, geology, museology, zoology, travels and voyages, natural history. **Special Collections:** Rare books, manuscripts, museum archives, art and memorabilia, rare films, photographic collection (750,000 items). **Holdings:** 136,000 books; 260,000 bound periodical volumes. **Subscriptions:** 6000 journals and other serials. **Services:** Interlibrary loan; copying; photo and film rights and reproduction; department open to the public. **Computerized Information Services:** DIALOG Information Services, OCLC. **Networks/Consortia:** Member of New York Metropolitan Reference and Research Library Agency, SUNY/OCLC Library Network. **Publications:** Recent Publications in Natural History, quarterly - by subscription. **Special Catalogs:** Research Catalogs of the AMNH Library; slide catalogs; Catalog of AMNH Film Archives, 1987. **Special Indexes:** Index to Natural History (card). **Staff:** Miriam Tam, Asst.Dir., Tech.Serv.; Donald Jacobsen, Asst.Dir., Ref.Serv.

★688★
American Museum of Natural History - Hayden Planetarium - Richard S. Perkin Library (Sci-Engr)
Central Park W. at 81st St. Phone: (212)769-5909
New York, NY 10024 Sandra Kitt, Libn.
Founded: 1958. **Staff:** Prof 1. **Subjects:** Astronomy, astronautics, radio astronomy, planetariums, space flight, meteorology, navigation. **Special Collections:** Bliss Collection of Antique Astronomical Instruments; Palomar Sky Survey. **Holdings:** 30,000 books; 500 bound periodical volumes; 25,000 photographs; 300 pamphlets; 150 astronomical films; 100 maps and charts; 35,000 reprints from observatories and planetariums; Hayden Planetarium archives. **Subscriptions:** 92 journals and other serials. **Services:** Interlibrary loan (with restrictions); copying; library open to the public for reference use only by appointment. **Computerized Information Services:** OCLC.

★689★
American Museum of Natural History - Osborn Library of Vertebrate Paleontology (Biol Sci)
Central Park W. at 79th St. Phone: (212)796-5000
New York, NY 10024 Charlotte Holton, Libn.
Founded: 1908. **Staff:** 1. **Subjects:** Vertebrate paleontology. **Holdings:** 10,000 books and pamphlets; 15,000 reprints. **Services:** Library not open to the public.

★690★
American Music Center - Library (Mus)
30 W. 26th St., Suite 1001 Phone: (212)366-5260
New York, NY 10010 Eero Richmond, Dir., Info.Serv.
Founded: 1940. **Staff:** Prof 2; Other 1. **Subjects:** Works of contemporary American composers. **Holdings:** 35,000 published and unpublished scores; 2000 phonograph records; 8000 tapes; 7000 files of composers' biographies. **Subscriptions:** 75 journals and other serials. **Services:** Interlibrary loan; library open to the public. **Automated Operations:** Computerized cataloging. **Networks/Consortia:** Member of Research Libraries Information Network (RLIN). **Special Catalogs:** AMC Library catalogs (book): Volume 3, Orchestra and band music; Volume 4, Opera and theater music. **Remarks:** FAX: (212)366-5265. Telex: 6503685633. **Staff:** Daniel Cherubin, Mus.Cat.; Jerome Kitzke, Info.Spec.

American Music Research Collection
See: **University of Colorado--Boulder - Music Library** (18504)

★691★
American Mustang and Burro Association, Inc. - Library (Rec)
P.O. Box 7 Phone: (509)588-6336
Benton City, WA 99320-0007 Barbara J. Rehfield, C.E.O.
Founded: 1983. **Subjects:** Wild horses and burros - history, care, general information, fiction. **Special Collections:** Video library (roundups, breaking and training, care). **Holdings:** Books; newspaper and magazine article files; artwork; sculpture. **Services:** Copying; library open to the public.

★692★
American Name Society - Library (Geog-Map)
James Gilliam Gee Library
East Texas State University Phone: (903)886-5737
Commerce, TX 75428 Dr. Fred Tarpley, Natl.Dir.
Founded: 1889. **Subjects:** U.S. geographical names. **Special Collections:** Texas-U.S. Geological Survey Map Collection. **Holdings:** 391 books; 300 bound periodical volumes; 75,000 Texas place names on cards; 35 theses and dissertations on place names. **Subscriptions:** 2 journals and other serials. **Services:** Interlibrary loan; copying; library open to the public for reference use only. **Computerized Information Services:** OCLC, DIALOG Information Services, ERIC. **Remarks:** For further information, contact Dr. Randal Detro, Nicholls State University Library, Thibodaux, LA 70310.

★693★
American National Can Co. - Technical Information Center (Sci-Engr)
433 N. Northwest Hwy. Phone: (708)304-3662
Barrington, IL 60010 M.T. Gormley, Mgr.
Staff: Prof 2. **Subjects:** Basic sciences, materials science, engineering, metallurgy, plastics, packaging, canning and preserving, food technology. **Holdings:** 1500 books; 3000 bound periodical volumes; pamphlets; reprints; patents; microfilm. **Subscriptions:** 450 journals and other serials. **Services:** Interlibrary loan; library not open to the public. **Automated Operations:** Computerized cataloging. **Computerized Information Services:** DIALOG Information Services, PFDS Online, OCLC, NLM. **Networks/Consortia:** Member of North Suburban Library System (NSLS). **Remarks:** FAX: (708)304-2914.

★694★
American National Metric Council - Library
1735 N. Lynn St., Suite 950
Arlington, VA 22209
Subjects: Metric system. **Holdings:** Figures not available. **Remarks:** Currently inactive. **Formerly:** Located in Washington, DC.

★695★
American Natural Hygiene Society, Inc. - Herbert Shelton Library (Med)
Box 30630
Tampa, FL 33630 Phone: (813)855-6607
Founded: 1984. **Staff:** Prof 1; Other 1. **Subjects:** Natural hygiene, health, fasting, diet and nutrition, physical culture. **Special Collections:** Herbert Shelton Manuscript Collection (10 cubic feet). **Holdings:** 2000 books; 500 bound periodical volumes. **Services:** Copying; library open to the public by appointment. **Remarks:** Library located at 11816 Race Track Rd., Tampa, FL 33626.

★696★
American Nepal Education Foundation - Wood Nepal Library (Area-Ethnic)
2790 Cape Meares Loop Phone: (503)842-4024
Tillamook, OR 97141 Hugh B. Wood, Exec.Dir.
Founded: 1959. **Staff:** Prof 1. **Subjects:** Nepal, education, social sciences. **Special Collections:** Archives of the University of Oregon/Nepal/USAID Contract Project, 1954-1959; documents of the American Nepal Education Foundation. **Holdings:** 900 books; 30 bound periodical volumes; 400 photocopies of periodical materials; 22 dissertations; 60 reports; 2000 slides; 2 16mm films; files of Nepal English-language newspapers. **Services:** Interlibrary loan; copying; library open to researchers by appointment only. **Special Catalogs:** Catalog of 152 out-of-print publications distributed by the American Nepal Education Foundation. **Remarks:** FAX: (503)842-4654.

American Newspaper Publishers Association
See: **ANPA** (883)

★697★
American Nuclear Insurers - Library/Research Center (Sci-Engr, Energy)
The Exchange, Suite 245
270 Farmington Ave. Phone: (203)677-7305
Farmington, CT 06032 Dottie Sherman, Dir.
Founded: 1974. **Staff:** Prof 3; Other 2. **Subjects:** Nuclear power plants, nuclear engineering, health physics, nuclear law, management, engineering, accounting, nuclear insurance. **Special Collections:** Nuclear power plant facility information (1 million microfiche; 500 hardcopy reports); nuclear standards; nuclear insurance. **Holdings:** 2000 books; 8000 technical reports. **Subscriptions:** 300 journals and newsletters. **Services:** Copying; center open to the public with restrictions. **Computerized Information Services:** DIALOG Information Services, U.S. Nuclear Regulatory Commission Bibliographic Retrieval Service, VU/TEXT Information Services, Mead Data Central, LEXIS, NEXIS. **Networks/Consortia:** Member of Capital Region Library Council (CRLC). **Publications:** Acquisitions List, quarterly; library bulletin, irregular; New Nuclear Publications, irregular. **Remarks:** FAX: (203)678-9083. **Staff:** Therese Baylock, Ref.Libn., Lisa Pearson, Tech.Proc.Libn.; Nellie Rodriguez, Lib.Tech.Asst.; Steve Moyer, Lib.Tech.Asst.

★698★
American Nuclear Society - Library (Energy, Sci-Engr)
555 N. Kensington Ave. Phone: (708)352-6611
La Grange Park, IL 60525 Lois S. Webster, Exec.Asst.
Founded: 1973. **Staff:** Prof 1; Other 1. **Subjects:** Nuclear science and engineering, business management, science biographies. **Holdings:** 2800 books. **Subscriptions:** 169 journals and other serials. **Services:** Interlibrary loan; copying; SDI; library open to the public with restrictions. **Computerized Information Services:** DIALOG Information Services, NEXIS. **Networks/Consortia:** Member of Suburban Library System (SLS). **Remarks:** FAX: (708)352-6464. Telex: 4972673.

American NUKEM - ENSR Consulting & Engineering
See: **ENSR Consulting & Engineering** (5366)

★699★
American Numismatic Association - Library (Rec)
818 N. Cascade Ave. Phone: (719)632-2646
Colorado Springs, CO 80903-3279 Lynn Chen, Libn.
Founded: 1891. **Staff:** Prof 1; Other 1. **Subjects:** Coins, medals, currency, tokens, check collecting, banks and banking. **Special Collections:** Arthur

Braddan Coole Library on Oriental Numismatics (250 titles in Chinese; 100 titles in Japanese; 150 titles in western languages). **Holdings:** 10,000 books; 5000 bound periodical volumes; 20,000 auction catalogs; 4 VF drawers of pamphlets and articles; 35mm slide programs. **Subscriptions:** 140 journals and other serials. **Services:** Interlibrary loan; copying; library open to the public for reference use only. **Automated Operations:** Computerized cataloging and circulation. **Special Indexes:** Index to The Numismatist. **Remarks:** FAX: (719)634-4085.

★700★
American Numismatic Society - Library (Rec)
Broadway at 155th St. Phone: (212)234-3130
New York, NY 10032 Francis D. Campbell, Libn.
Founded: 1858. **Staff:** Prof 2. **Subjects:** Numismatics. **Special Collections:** David M. Bullowa Collection; George C. Miles Collection; Virgil M. Brand Archives; New Netherlands Coin Company Archives; Norweb Collection Ledgers; auction catalogs. **Holdings:** 70,000 books; 10,000 bound periodical volumes; 10,000 other cataloged items; 350 reels of microfilm. **Subscriptions:** 260 journals and other serials. **Services:** Copying (limited); library open to the public with restrictions. **Automated Operations:** Computerized subject authority file. **Remarks:** FAX: (212)234-3381. **Staff:** Kay Brooks, Assoc.Libn.

★701★
American Nurses Association - Library Information Center (Med)
600 Maryland Ave., S.W., Suite 100 W. Phone: (202)554-4444
Washington, DC 20024-2571 Richard J. Barry, M.L.S.
Founded: 1952. **Staff:** Prof 1; Other 1. **Subjects:** Nurses, nursing, health care. **Special Collections:** ANA publications, 1900 to present; state nurses journals. **Holdings:** 2280 books; 420 bound periodical volumes; 1275 reports. **Subscriptions:** 70 journals and other serials; 4 newspapers. **Services:** Library not open to the public. **Remarks:** FAX: (202)554-2262.

American Nurses Association Archives
See: **University of Missouri--Kansas City - Health Sciences Library** (18974)

★702★
American Occupational Therapy Foundation and Association - Wilma L. West Library (Med)
1383 Piccard Dr.
Box 1725 Phone: (301)948-9626
Rockville, MD 20849-1725 Mary S. Binderman, Libn.
Founded: 1980. **Staff:** Prof 1.5. **Subjects:** Occupational therapy - physical, developmental, and psychosocial disabilities, human occupation, perceptual motor disabilities, child development, geriatrics, leisure time, work and rehabilitation. **Special Collections:** A. Jean Ayres Collection (sensory integration, neuropsychology; 63 books); Mary Reilly Collection (work, play, and the psychology of occupation; 500 books); journals, 1916 to present; dissertations; theses. **Holdings:** 4000 books; 200 bound periodical volumes; 3 VF drawers of pamphlets. **Subscriptions:** 63 journals and other serials; 14 newsletters. **Services:** Interlibrary loan; copying; library open to health professionals and self-help group participants. **Automated Operations:** Computerized public access catalog and cataloging. **Computerized Information Services:** NLM, BRS Information Technologies. Performs searches on fee basis. **Networks/Consortia:** Member of Maryland Association of Health Science Librarians (MAHSL), Maryland and D.C. Consortium of Resource Sharing (MADCORS), Maryland Interlibrary Organization (MILO), District of Columbia Health Sciences Information Network (DOCHSIN), National Network of Libraries of Medicine - Southeastern/Atlantic Region. **Publications:** Library brochure, annual; Thesaurus of Occupational Therapy Subject Headings. **Special Indexes:** Index to occupational therapy special interest newsletters (card); key-word index to theses and dissertations held in the library; cumulative index to American Journal of Occupational Therapy. **Remarks:** FAX: (301)948-5512. AOTA archives are housed at Moody Medical Library, University of Texas, Galveston, TX. **Staff:** Nancy Zaharko, Cecille Jech.

★703★
American Optical Corporation - Research Center Library (Sci-Engr)
14 Mechanic St. Phone: (508)765-9711
Southbridge, MA 01550 Dr. Nori Chu
Founded: 1954. **Staff:** 2. **Subjects:** Optics; physics; chemistry - physical, polymer, organic. **Holdings:** 3800 books; 2450 bound periodical volumes. **Subscriptions:** 30 journals and other serials. **Services:** Interlibrary loan; library not open to the public. **Remarks:** FAX: (508)764-8506.

American Optometric Association Archives
See: **International Library, Archives & Museum of Optometry** (8146)

★704★
American Orchid Society - Library (Biol Sci)
6000 S. Olive Ave. Phone: (407)585-8666
West Palm Beach, FL 33405 Lee S. Cooke, Exec. Dir.
Founded: 1921. **Staff:** 1. **Subjects:** Orchid - culture, floras/monographs, science, history. **Special Collections:** Rare books. **Holdings:** 850 books; 400 bound periodical volumes. **Subscriptions:** 20 journals and other serials. **Services:** Library open to AOS staff members and to members by appointment and reference use only. **Remarks:** FAX: (407)585-0654.

American Oriental Society Library
See: **Yale University** (20697)

★705★
American Osteopathic Association - A.T. Still Osteopathic Library and Research Center (Med)
142 E. Ontario St.
Chicago, IL 60611 Phone: (312)280-5800
Founded: 1930. **Subjects:** Medicine, osteopathic medicine. **Holdings:** 1700 books; 540 bound periodical volumes. **Subscriptions:** 250 journals and other serials. **Services:** Library not open to the public. **Computerized Information Services:** MEDLINE. Contact Person: Sandra Williamson, telephone (312)280-5863.

★706★
American Otological Society, Inc. - Library (Med)
Duke University Medical Center
Box 3805 Phone: (919)684-6357
Durham, NC 27710 Dr. Joseph C. Farmer, Jr., M.D., Ed.-Libn.
Subjects: Otology. **Holdings:** 114 books; transactions of the American Otological Society. **Services:** Library not open to the public. **Remarks:** FAX: (408)971-3277. **Formerly:** Located in San Jose, CA.

American Painting Research Library
See: **Cahoon Museum of American Art** (2442)

★707★
American Paper Institute - Library (Sci-Engr)
260 Madison Ave.
New York, NY 10016 Phone: (212)340-0612
Staff: Prof 1. **Subjects:** Paper - manufacturing, history, products; management; business; finance. **Holdings:** 500 books; 10 VF drawers. **Subscriptions:** 250 journals and other serials. **Services:** Interlibrary loan; library open to the public by appointment. **Remarks:** FAX: (212)689-2628. **Staff:** Doreen McCoy, Lib.Asst.

★708★
American Pedestrian Association - APA Library
P.O. Box 624
Forest Hills, NY 11375
Defunct.

★709★
American Petroleum Institute - Library (Energy)
1220 L St., N.W. Phone: (202)682-8042
Washington, DC 20005 Edna W. Paulson, Libn.
Founded: 1932. **Staff:** Prof 3; Other 2. **Subjects:** Petroleum, natural gas, energy, environmental affairs, economics and statistics, legislative development, historical development. **Holdings:** 3500 books; 1300 periodical volumes on microfilm; 16,000 reports and papers; API publications and proceedings. **Subscriptions:** 300 journals and other serials. **Services:** Interlibrary loan; copying; library open to the public. **Automated Operations:** Computerized cataloging and acquisitions. **Computerized Information Services:** DIALOG Information Services, NLM, PFDS Online, LEXIS, NEXIS, OCLC, Chemical Information Systems, Inc. (CIS), BRS Information Technologies, Washington Alert Service, VU/TEXT Information Services, DataTimes, WILSONLINE, STN International, Oil and Gas Journal Energy Database. **Networks/Consortia:** Member of CAPCON Library Network. **Remarks:** FAX: (202)682-8232. Telex: 62771747. **Staff:** Lois J. Schuermann, Asst.Libn.; Kevin Holloway, Tech.Serv.Spec. Telex: 62771747.

★710★
American Pharmaceutical Association - Foundation Library (Med)
2215 Constitution Ave., N.W.
Washington, DC 20037 Phone: (202)429-7524
Founded: 1934. **Staff:** 1. **Subjects:** Pharmacy, pharmacology, medicine. **Special Collections:** APhA policies and publications; history of pharmacy. **Holdings:** 6000 books; 2000 bound periodical volumes; 45 VF drawers of pharmacy and association materials. **Subscriptions:** 225 journals and other serials. **Services:** Copying; library open to the public. **Computerized Information Services:** DIALOG Information Services. **Special Catalogs:** Drug compendiums. **Remarks:** FAX: (202)783-2351.

★711★
American Philatelic Research Library (Rec)
Box 8338 Phone: (814)237-3803
State College, PA 16803 Gini Horn, Libn.
Founded: 1968. **Staff:** Prof 3; Other 2. **Subjects:** Stamp collecting, postal history, U.S. postal records, stamp production. **Special Collections:** American First Day Cover Society Archives; Postal History Society Library. **Holdings:** 12,000 books; 4000 bound periodical volumes. **Subscriptions:** 450 journals and other serials; 6 newspapers. **Services:** Interlibrary loan; copying; library open to the public for reference use only. **Automated Operations:** Computerized cataloging. **Computerized Information Services:** DayFlo (internal database). Performs searches on fee basis. **Networks/Consortia:** Member of Pittsburgh Regional Library Center (PRLC). **Publications:** Philatelic Literature Review, quarterly - to members. **Special Catalogs:** Manual of Philatelic Headings, American Philatelic Periodicals. **Remarks:** FAX: (814)237-6128. **Staff:** Gladys C. Hoffman, Cat.; Martha Micuda, Asst.Libn.

★712★
American Philosophical Society - Library (Sci-Engr, Hist)
105 S. Fifth St. Phone: (215)440-3400
Philadelphia, PA 19106-3386 Dr. Edward C. Carter, II, Libn.
Founded: 1743. **Staff:** Prof 11; Other 4. **Subjects:** History of American science including important European background material; Americana (early imprints, travels). **Special Collections:** Papers of Benjamin Franklin, Charles Darwin, Charles Willson Peale; Lewis and Clark Journals; American Indian linguistics; Thomas Paine; Simon Flexner; genetics; Stephen Girard papers; Franz Boas Collection; Society's archives (history of American science through 1908); history of quantum physics. **Holdings:** 173,500 volumes; 6 million manuscripts; microfilm; maps; prints, especially of Philadelphia and Frankliniana. **Subscriptions:** 950 journals and other serials. **Services:** Interlibrary loan; copying; library open to the public for research. **Computerized Information Services:** RLIN. **Publications:** Annual Report of the Committee on Library - free to libraries. **Special Catalogs:** Guide to Archives and Manuscript Collection; Guide to Manuscripts relating to the American Indian; Sources for the Histo ry of Quantum Physics; Calendar of the Papers of Benjamin Franklin; Calendar of the Correspondence of George Weedon, Richard Henry Lee, Hon. Arthur Lee, and Nathanael Green relating to the American Revolution; The Thomas Paine Collection of Richard Gimbel in the Library; Electricity, Magnetism and Animal Magnetism: a Checklist; An Annotated Calendar of the Letters of Charles Darwin in the Library. Catalog of Portraits; Catalog of Instruments and Models. **Remarks:** FAX: (215)440-3423. **Staff:** Hildegard Stephans, Assoc.Libn., Adm.; Roy E. Goodman, Reading Rm.Libn.; Elizabeth Carroll-Horrocks, Mss.Libn.

★713★
American Photographic Historical Society - Library (Hist)
1150 Avenue of the Americas
New York, NY 10036 Phone: (212)575-0483
Founded: 1972. **Subjects:** Photography, history. **Holdings:** 300 volumes; biographical and early photo archives. **Subscriptions:** 500 journals and other serials. **Services:** Library open to the public by appointment.

★714★
American Physical Therapy Association - Library (Med)
1111 N. Fairfax St. Phone: (703)684-2782
Alexandria, VA 22314 Phyllis Quinn
Staff: 2. **Subjects:** Physical therapy. **Holdings:** 500 books; 70 bound periodical volumes; 200 archival items. **Services:** Interlibrary loan; copying; library open to the public by appointment. **Remarks:** FAX: (703)684-7343.

American Planning Association
See: **Merriam Center Library** (10161)

★715★
American Planning Association - Library (Plan)
1776 Massachusetts Ave., N.W., Suite 704
Washington, DC 20036 Phone: (202)872-0611
Subjects: Urban and rural development, urban renewal, zoning. **Holdings:** Books; pamphlets; comprehensive plans; zoning ordinances; decisions.

★716★
American Plywood Association - Records Center (Sci-Engr)
Box 11700 Phone: (206)565-6600
Tacoma, WA 98411 Patricia M. Nino, Supv.
Founded: 1968. **Staff:** Prof 1; Other 2. **Subjects:** Forestry products, structural wood panels, wood statistics, business. **Special Collections:** Plywood Historical Monographs; American Plywood Association publications, 1938 to present; photograph collection (industry products used in building construction). **Holdings:** 500 books and bound periodical volumes; internal records and reports. **Subscriptions:** 88 journals and other serials. **Services:** Interlibrary loan; center not open to the public. **Publications:** New Acquisitions, irregular.

★717★
American Polar Society - Polar Information Center (Sci-Engr)
125 S. Oval Mall Phone: (614)292-6531
Columbus, OH 43210 Peter J. Anderson, Exec.Dir.
Founded: 1934. **Subjects:** History and exploration of Arctic and Antarctic regions. **Holdings:** 375 books, maps, photographs. **Services:** Center not open to the public. **Computerized Information Services:** BITNET, SCIENCEnet (via Byrd Polar Research Center; electronic mail services). **Remarks:** FAX: (614)292-4697. **Formerly:** Located in Rego Park, NY. **Staff:** Lynn Lay, Hd., Info.Ctr.

American Political Science Association Archives
See: **Georgetown University - Special Collections Division - Lauinger Memorial Library** (6379)

★718★
American Postal Workers Union - APWU Library Information Center (Bus-Fin)
1300 L St., N.W., Suite 407 Phone: (202)842-4278
Washington, DC 20005 Evelyn E. Johnson, Lib.Info.Dir.
Founded: 1987. **Staff:** 2. **Subjects:** Collective bargaining. **Special Collections:** American Postal Workers Union negotiation history. **Holdings:** 5000 books; 80 bound periodical volumes. **Subscriptions:** 102 journals and other serials; 6 newspapers. **Services:** Library not open to the public. **Computerized Information Services:** DIALOG Information Services, LEXIS, NEXIS, VU/TEXT Information Services, DataTimes; Alertline (internal database). **Networks/Consortia:** Member of CAPCON Library Network. **Remarks:** FAX: (202)842-4297. **Staff:** Valerie Foster, Asst.Libn.

★719★
American Power Jet Company - Library (Trans)
705 Grand Ave. Phone: (201)945-8203
Ridgefield, NJ 07657 Jacqueline Stopsky, Libn.
Founded: 1947. **Staff:** Prof 2. **Subjects:** Logistics, transportation, operations research, systems analysis, defense, aviation. **Holdings:** 5000 books; 200 bound periodical volumes; 5000 reports; 18,000 microfiche; 3000 reels of microfilm. **Subscriptions:** 21 journals and other serials. **Remarks:** FAX: (201)945-0589.

★720★
American Printing House for the Blind - Library (Aud-Vis, Educ)
1839 Frankfort Ave.
P.O. Box 6085 Phone: (502)895-2405
Louisville, KY 40206-0085 Bill Duckworth, Res.Sci./Libn.
FO 1969. **Subjects:** Publishing for the blind and visually impaired - braille, large print, recorded; educational aids for visually impaired; research oriented print materials. **Holdings:** 3500 volumes. **Subscriptions:** 95 journals and other serials. **Services:** Copying; library open to the public by appointment for reference use only. **Computerized Information Services:** Produces American Printing House for the Blind Central Automated Resource List (APH-CARL). **Remarks:** FAX: (502)895-2405.

★721★
American Private Press Association - Library (Publ)
112 E. Burnett St. Phone: (503)769-6088
Stayton, OR 97383 Martin M. Horvat, Libn.
Founded: 1904. **Staff:** 1. **Subjects:** Amateur journalism, science fiction/fantasy, printing, typography. **Holdings:** 2000 books; 200 bound periodical volumes; 20 manuscripts; 60,000 printing samples; 450,000 privately printed journals; 200,000 science fiction/fantasy materials; 2000 photographs. **Subscriptions:** 160 journals and other serials. **Services:** Copying; library open to the public with restrictions. **Publications:** Journal of the Library, annual. **Remarks:** Contains the holdings of The Fossils, Inc. FAX: (503)769-4520.

★722★
American Productivity & Quality Center - Information Services (Bus-Fin)
123 N. Post Oak Ln. Phone: (713)681-4020
Houston, TX 77024 Charlotte Scroggins, V.P., Commun. & Info.Serv.
Staff: Prof 2; Other 1. **Subjects:** Productivity, quality, quality of work life, industrial economics. **Holdings:** 4000 books; 10,000 special articles; 2500 reports and documents. **Subscriptions:** 100 journals and other serials. **Services:** Copying; services open to the public by appointment. **Remarks:** FAX: (713)681-8578.

★723★
American Psychiatric Association - Library and Archives (Med)
1400 K St., N.W. Phone: (202)682-6080
Washington, DC 20005 William E. Baxter, Dir.
Founded: 1961. **Staff:** Prof 3; Other 2. **Subjects:** Psychiatry - community and social, child and adolescent, forensic, history in America; psychoanalysis; psychosomatic medicine. **Special Collections:** Rare Book Collection; APA Archives. **Holdings:** 17,000 volumes. **Subscriptions:** 302 journals and other serials. **Services:** Interlibrary loan; copying; current awareness; library open to the public by appointment. **Computerized Information Services:** BRS Information Technologies, MEDLARS, DIALOG Information Services; APA Official Position Statements, Psychiatric News Index (internal databases); DOCLINE (electronic mail service). Telephone 682-6057.

★724★
American Psychological Association - Arthur W. Melton Library (Soc Sci)
750 First St., N.E., Rm. 3012 Phone: (202)336-5640
Washington, DC 20002-4242 Rick A. Sample, Hd.Libn.
Founded: 1971. **Staff:** Prof 2. **Subjects:** Psychology, mental health, and allied disciplines. **Special Collections:** APA central office, division, and state association journals, newsletters, and publications, 1894 to present. **Holdings:** 1400 books and journals. **Subscriptions:** 35 journals and other serials; 4 newspapers. **Services:** Interlibrary loan; copying; library open to qualified researchers by appointment. **Automated Operations:** Computerized cataloging, serials, budgeting, and archives. **Computerized Information Services:** CD-ROMs. **Publications:** APA Award List. **Special Indexes:** Index to Psychological Abstracts. **Remarks:** FAX: (202)336-5643. The library is the records manager for the American Psychological Association Archives. **Staff:** Laura E. Dworken, Assoc.Libn.

American Psychological Association Archives
See: **American Psychological Association** (724)

★725★
American Public Health Association - International Health Programs - Resource Center (Med)
1015 15th St., N.W., Suite 300 Phone: (202)789-5600
Washington, DC 20005 Gayle Gibbons, Info.Spec.
Staff: Prof 1; Other 1. **Subjects:** Developing countries - health delivery systems, nutrition, development, water and sanitation, family planning, maternal and child health. **Special Collections:** Association reports (400); primary health care collection. **Holdings:** 1000 books; 130 newsletters; 120 pamphlet boxes; reports; monographs. **Subscriptions:** 110 journals and other serials. **Services:** Interlibrary loan; copying; center open to the public with restrictions. **Computerized Information Services:** DIALOG Information Services, NTIS. **Publications:** Information packets, bimonthly. **Remarks:** Center is clearinghouse for publications regarding infant feeding and maternal nutrition.

★726★
American Public Power Association - Library (Energy)
2301 M St., N.W. Phone: (202)467-2957
Washington, DC 20037 Deborah J. Nuttall, Mgr., Info.Rsrcs.
Staff: Prof 2; Other 2. **Subjects:** Electric utilities, energy, environment. **Holdings:** 4000 books; 60 bound periodical volumes; 2183 volumes of technical reports; 1000 congressional documents. **Subscriptions:** 243 journals and other serials. **Services:** Interlibrary loan; copying; library open to the public by appointment only. **Computerized Information Services:** DIALOG Information Services. **Special Catalogs:** Audiovisual catalog, biennial. **Special Indexes:** Public Power; Public Power Weekly Newsletter; APPA Conference and Workshop papers. **Remarks:** FAX: (202)467-2910. **Staff:** Mary Rufe, Libn.

★727★
American Public Transit Association - APTA Information Center (Trans)
1201 New York Ave., N.W. Suite 400 Phone: (202)898-4089
Washington, DC 20005 Rose M. Gandee, Mgr., Info.Ctr.
Staff: Prof 1; Other 1. **Subjects:** Public transit, rail rapid transit, transit systems, transit operations and equipment, policy and regulations. **Holdings:** 250 books; 120 periodicals; 3000 federal, state, and local reports; 2000 slides; Passenger Transport, 1943 to present; annual operating report, 1929 to present; Transit Fact Book, 1943 to present; association publications; Urban Mass Transportation Administration documents depository; training programs; AV programs. **Subscriptions:** 140 journals and other serials. **Services:** Interlibrary loan, copying, center open to the public by appointment. **Computerized Information Services:** DIALOG Information Services; internal databases. Performs searches on fee basis. **Special Catalogs:** Catalog of Member Products and Services (COMPS). **Special Indexes:** Passenger Transport Index, biennial; publication list, annual. **Remarks:** Alternate telephone number(s): (202)898-4000. FAX: (202)898-4070; (202)898-4049.

★728★
American Public Welfare Association - Resource Center
810 First St., Suite 500
Washington, DC 20002
Subjects: Public welfare, income maintenance, public health, homelessness, immigration, child welfare. **Special Collections:** Association archives (2000 documents); history of welfare and welfare reform (50 volumes). **Holdings:** 1000 books; 40 bound periodical volumes; 2000 reports, public laws, bills, hearings. **Remarks:** Currently inactive.

★729★
American Public Works Association - Information Services (Sci-Engr, Plan)
1313 E. 60th St. Phone: (312)667-2200
Chicago, IL 60637 Hilary Green, Dir. of Info.
Founded: 1894. **Staff:** Prof 2; Other 5. **Subjects:** Public works, buildings and grounds management, transportation, solid waste, equipment services, utilities, emergency management, water resources. **Special Collections:** Public Works Historical Society Collection. **Holdings:** 36,000 volumes. **Subscriptions:** 350 journals and other serials; 15 newspapers. **Services:** Copying; services open to the public with restrictions. **Automated Operations:** Computerized cataloging, acquisitions, serials, and circulation. **Computerized Information Services:** DIALOG Information Services; CAIRS (internal database). **Publications:** Public Works History Archives. **Staff:** Larry Barr, Info.Spec.

★730★
American Railway Car Institute - Library (Trans)
Governors Office Park Bldg. V
19900 Governors Dr., Suite 10 Phone: (708)747-0511
Olympia Fields, IL 60461 Elwyn T. Ahnquist, Pres.
Subjects: Transportation, railroad cars. **Holdings:** Figures not available. **Remarks:** FAX: (708)747-0793.

★731★
American Resources Group - Library (Env-Cons)
374 Maple Ave., E., Suite 204 Phone: (703)255-2700
Vienna, VA 22180 Keith A. Argow, Pres.
Founded: 1981. **Staff:** 4. **Subjects:** Forestry, non-industrial private forestry, watershed, land management. **Holdings:** 2300 volumes. **Subscriptions:** 53 journals and other serials; 2 newspapers. **Services:** Library not open to the public. **Computerized Information Services:** Internal database.

American River Hospital
See: **Mercy American River Hospital** (10125)

American Road and Transportation Archives
See: **Virginia Transportation Research Council - Library** (19898)

★732★
American Rose Society - Library (Biol Sci)
Box 30000 Phone: (318)938-5402
Shreveport, LA 71130-0030 Kris McKnight, Exec.Dir.
Founded: 1892. **Subjects:** Roses and rose culture, horticulture, landscape design. **Special Collections:** Old and rare volumes on roses. **Holdings:** 7200 books and bound periodical volumes; 100 boxes of manuscripts, articles, research data; 1200 slides. **Services:** Library open to the public for special reference or research; mail rental of some materials for members only. **Remarks:** FAX: (318)938-5405.

American Saddle Horse Museum - Library
See: **Audrain County Historical Society** (1289)

★733★
American Saddle Horse Museum - Library (Biol Sci)
4093 Iron Works Pike Phone: (606)259-2746
Lexington, KY 40511 Keith D. Bartz, Dir.
Subjects: Saddlebred history, Saddlebred bloodlines, training, riding, driving, art. **Special Collections:** American Saddle Horse Registers (complete set; 65); George Ford Morris Portraitures of Horses. **Holdings:** 830 books; 200 bound periodical volumes. **Services:** Library open to the public at librarian's discretion.

★734★
American Schizophrenia Association - Huxley Institute for Biosocial Research - Library and Resource Center (Med)
900 N. Federal Hwy., Suite 330 Phone: (407)393-6167
Boca Raton, FL 33432 Mary Roddy Haggerty, Dir.
Founded: 1971. **Subjects:** Orthomolecular medicine. **Holdings:** Figures not available.

★735★
American School of Classical Studies at Athens - Gennadius Library (Area-Ethnic, Hist)
Odos Souidias 61 Phone: 1 7210536
GR-106 76 Athens, Greece Sophie Papageorgiou, Libn.
Founded: 1926. **Staff:** Prof 2. **Subjects:** Greece; Byzantium; Turkish rule of Greece; Greek War of Independence. **Special Collections:** Greece, Balkans, and Near East Geography and Travel section. **Holdings:** 85,000 books; archival materials; microfilm; art works. **Subscriptions:** 358 journals and other serials. **Services:** Copying; library open to scholars only. **Publications:** The New Griffon (newsletter). **Special Catalogs:** Gennadius Library Catalogue, 9 vols.

★736★
American Scottish Foundation, Inc. - Scottish Research Library (Area-Ethnic)
575 Madison Ave., 10th Fl. Phone: (212)682-1070
New York, NY 10021 Elizabeth Maysilles, Ph.D.
Founded: 1976. **Subjects:** Scotland - clans, history, traditions, literature, genealogy, travel. **Holdings:** Figures not available. **Subscriptions:** 5 journals and other serials. **Services:** Library not open to the public.

American Sculpture Archives
See: **Brookgreen Gardens - Library** (2216)

★737★
American Seafood Retailers Association - Seafood Information Center (Food-Bev)
c/o Seafood Management Corp.
Salt Water Farm Phone: (207)781-2997
Falmouth, ME 04105-6157 Judith Hill, Exec. V.P.
Founded: 1981. **Subjects:** Seafood, food processing, packaging, finance, planning. **Holdings:** 200 books; 1000 bound periodical volumes. **Subscriptions:** 54 journals and other serials. **Services:** Interlibrary loan; copying; center open to the public by appointment on fee basis. **Automated Operations:** Computerized cataloging. **Computerized Information Services:** Dow Jones News/Retrieval, DIALOG Information Services, Dun & Bradstreet Business Credit Services. Performs searches on fee basis. Contact Person: Judith Hill. **Remarks:** FAX: (207)781-7112. Parent company is Seafood Management Corporation.

★738★
American Security Council Foundation - Sol Feinstone Library (Mil, Soc Sci)
Washington Communication Center Phone: (703)547-1776
Boston, VA 22713 JoAnn Swan, Libn.
Founded: 1973. **Staff:** Prof 1; Other 2. **Subjects:** National defense, international affairs. **Holdings:** 19,000 books; 3000 government hearings; 4000 vertical files. **Subscriptions:** 390 journals and other serials; 30 newspapers. **Services:** Library not open to the public. **Automated Operations:** Computerized acquisitions. **Computerized Information Services:** NEXIS, Washington Alert Service. **Remarks:** Library receives almost every English language defense publication from around the world. It receives all relevant Congressional hearings, nonclassified U.S. Department of Defense and CIA reports on national defense, and many foreign radio broadcast summaries.

★739★
American Seed Trade Association, Inc. - Library (Agri)
601 13th St., N.W., Suite 570, S.
Washington, DC 20005-1593 Phone: (202)638-3128
Founded: 1883. **Staff:** Prof 5; Other 5. **Subjects:** Seed raising, development, conditioning, and marketing. **Special Collections:** Proceedings of the Corn & Sorghum Industry Research Conferences, the Soybean Seed Research Conferences, and the Farm Seed Research Conferences. **Holdings:** 20 bound periodical volumes. **Services:** Library not open to the public. **Special Catalogs:** Variety name listing program. **Remarks:** FAX: (202)638-3171. Telex: 710-822-9257 ASTA WASH. **Staff:** Dolores Wilkinson.

American Self-Help Clearinghouse
See: **St. Clares-Riverside Medical Center** (14267)

★740★
American Short Line Railroad Association - Library
2000 Massachusetts Ave., N.W.
Washington, DC 20036
Founded: 1913. **Subjects:** Transportation and railroads. **Special Collections:** Legislative histories and legal records relating to railroads and railway labor organizations. **Remarks:** Currently inactive.

★741★
American Society of Abdominal Surgeons - Donald Collins Memorial Library (Med)
675 Main St. Phone: (617)665-6102
Melrose, MA 02176 Dr. Blaise F. Alfano, Hd.Libn.
Founded: 1959. **Staff:** Prof 2. **Subjects:** Surgery, medicine. **Holdings:** 900 books; 45 bound periodical volumes. **Subscriptions:** 52 journals and other serials; 10 newspapers. **Services:** Interlibrary loan; library open to the public on request. **Staff:** Priscilla Maher, Asst.Libn.

★742★
American Society of Agronomy - Library (Agri)
677 S. Segoe Rd. Phone: (608)273-8080
Madison, WI 53711 Jay Poster
Subjects: Agronomy, crops, soils. **Holdings:** Figures not available. **Services:** Library not open to the public. **Publications:** List of publications - available upon request. **Remarks:** Affiliated with Soil Science Society of America and Crop Science Society of America.

★743★
American Society of Anesthesiologists - Wood Library-Museum of Anesthesiology (Med)
520 N. Northwest Hwy. Phone: (708)825-5586
Park Ridge, IL 60068-3189 Patrick Sim, Libn.
Founded: 1929. **Staff:** Prof 2. **Subjects:** Anesthesiology, resuscitation, shock, medical applications for hypnotism, inhalation therapy, history of anesthesiology. **Special Collections:** Museum of anesthesiological equipment and apparatus; Living History of Anesthesiology (videocassette). **Holdings:** 8000 books; 1000 bound periodical volumes; 40 VF drawers of pamphlets, photographs, clippings; 20 shelf feet of manuscripts. **Subscriptions:** 100 journals and other serials. **Services:** Interlibrary loan; copying; library open to the public. **Computerized Information Services:** MEDLARS. Performs searches on fee basis. **Networks/Consortia:** Member of National Network of Libraries of Medicine - Greater Midwest Region. **Publications:** Anesthesiology Bibliography, quarterly; History of Anesthesiology Reprint Series, annual; Resuscitation: An Historical Perspective; Classical Anesthesia Files. **Staff:** Sally S. Graham, Asst.Libn.

★744★
American Society of Appraisers - International Valuation Sciences Centre Library (Bus-Fin)
535 Herndon Pkwy, Suite 150 Phone: (703)478-2228
Herndon, VA 22070-5226 Shirley A. Belz, Pub.Rel.Dir.
Founded: 1977. **Staff:** 1. **Subjects:** Appraisal of real estate, personal property, natural resources, machinery, equipment, business valuation. **Holdings:** 1100 books and bound periodical volumes; 100 papers and pamphlets. **Subscriptions:** 31 journals and other serials. **Services:** Copying; library open to the public with restrictions. **Publications:** ASA Valuation, biannual; ASA Monographs, irregular. **Remarks:** FAX: (703)742-8471.

★745★
American Society of Artists, Inc. - Resource Center (Art)
Box 1326 Phone: (312)751-2500
Palatine, IL 60078 Donald Metcoff, Libn.
Founded: 1978. **Staff:** Prof 1. **Subjects:** Art, crafts, supplies. **Special Collections:** Foreign art catalogs and journals; slide and photo files of arts and crafts by members of the society. **Holdings:** 25 volumes; 43 VF drawers. **Subscriptions:** 11 journals and other serials. **Services:** Lectures, demonstrations, seminars, and workshops are available. **Publications:** Lecture and Demonstration Service Guide; Art Lovers Bulletin, quarterly; ASA Artisan, quarterly - to members. **Special Catalogs:** Arts and crafts supply catalogs. **Remarks:** The society has a national membership of professional artists and craftspeople; associate and patron memberships are available to the public.

★746★
American Society of Association Executives - Information Central Resource Center (Bus-Fin)
1575 Eye St., N.W. Phone: (202)626-2723
Washington, DC 20005 Eve Shepard, Mgr., Res. & Info.
Founded: 1954. **Staff:** Prof 3; Other 3. **Subjects:** Association - management and law, communications, personnel, conventions, education, voluntarism, finance, membership promotion, government relations. **Special Collections:** Bound volumes of Association Management, the official ASAE monthly publication. **Holdings:** 2000 books and research publications; 20 VF drawers containing samples of association management materials. **Services:** Loan material available to members; center open to the public on a limited schedule. **Computerized Information Services:** ASAE ASSIST, Information Central Database (internal databases). Performs searches free of charge. Contact Person: Chris Condeelis, Mgr. Res. & Info., 626-2746. **Special Catalogs:** ASAE Publications Catalog, annual. **Remarks:** FAX: (202)371-8825. **Staff:** Tracy Hulin, Res. & Info.Adm.; Lauael Viguera, Data Base Adm.; Deborah Smith-Cohen, Res.Assoc.

★747★
American Society of Bakery Engineers - Information Service and Library (Food-Bev)
Two N. Riverside Plaza, Rm. 1733 Phone: (312)332-2246
Chicago, IL 60606 Robert A. Fischer, Pres.
Staff: 4. **Subjects:** Baking and allied subjects. **Holdings:** 10,000 references.

American Society for Biochemistry and Molecular Biology - National Foundation for History of Chemistry
See: **University of Pennsylvania - National Foundation for History of Chemistry - Library** (19190)

★748★
American Society of Dowsers - Library (Rec)
Danville, VT 05828 Phone: (802)684-3417
Donna Robinson, Dir.
Staff: 3. **Subjects:** Dowsing - history, theory, practice. **Holdings:** 300 books; bound periodical volumes; scrapbooks. **Services:** Library open to the public by appointment.

American Society for Engineering Education - Engineering Technnology Divisions - Archives
See: **Wentworth Institute of Technology - Alumni Library** (20167)

★749★
American Society of International Law - Library (Law)
2223 Massachusetts Ave., N.W. Phone: (202)265-4313
Washington, DC 20008 Jill McC. Watson, Libn.
Founded: 1961. **Staff:** Prof 1. **Subjects:** International law and allied subjects. **Holdings:** 8000 books; 3000 bound periodical volumes; 6500 pamphlets, documents, reprints. **Subscriptions:** 250 journals and other serials. **Services:** Interlibrary loan; copying; library open to the public. **Computerized Information Services:** Index to International Law articles (internal database). **Remarks:** FAX: (202)797-7133.

★750★
American Society of Landscape Architects - Information Resource Center (Plan)
4401 Connecticut Ave., N.W. Phone: (202)686-2752
Washington, DC 20008-2302 Aline Martinez, Info.Rsrc.Ctr.Mgr.
Founded: 1989. **Staff:** Prof 1. **Subjects:** Landscape architecture, landscape design, urban planning and development, land use and design, environment, gardens. **Holdings:** 1500 books; 1000 nonbook items. **Subscriptions:** 93 journals and other serials. **Services:** Interlibrary loan; library open to the public by appointment. **Computerized Information Services:** Landscape Architects Database (internal database). Performs searches on fee basis. **Remarks:** FAX: (202)686-1001.

American Society of Landscape Architects - Michigan Chapter Archives
See: **Michigan State University - C.W. Barr Planning and Design Library** (10317)

★751★
American Society of Law & Medicine - Elliot L. and Annette Y. Sagall Library
765 Commonwealth Ave., 16th Fl.
Boston, MA 02215
Founded: 1979. **Subjects:** Medicolegal relations, health law, biomedical ethics, medical malpractice, regulation of health professions, forensic medicine. **Holdings:** 5000 books; 4000 VF items, including journal articles and court cases. **Remarks:** Currently inactive.

American Society for Mass Spectrometry - National Foundation for History of Chemistry
See: **University of Pennsylvania - National Foundation for History of Chemistry - Library** (19190)

★752★
American Society for Medical Technology - Information Center (Med)
2021 L St., N.W., Suite 400 Phone: (202)785-3311
Washington, DC 20036 Morris Bailey, Coord., Member Oper.
Founded: 1932. **Staff:** 15. **Subjects:** Cytology, histology, microbiology, hematology, biochemistry. **Holdings:** Figures not available. **Subscriptions:** 2 journals and other serials. **Services:** Center not open to the public. **Publications:** List of publications - available on request. **Remarks:** The Society seeks to promote and maintain high standards in clinical laboratory methods and research, and to advance standards of education and training of personnel. FAX: (202)466-2254.

★753★
American Society of Military History - Library (Mil, Hist)
1816 S. Figueroa St. Phone: (213)746-1776
Los Angeles, CA 90015 Donald Michelson, Exec.Dir.
Staff: Prof 1; Other 3. **Subjects:** Military history. **Holdings:** 10,000 books; 7000 bound periodical volumes; 5000 defense department papers. **Services:** Library open to the public under supervision.

★754★
American Society for Nondestructive Testing - Memorial Library (Sci-Engr)
1711 Arlingate Ln.
Columbus, OH 43228 Phone: (614)274-6003
Founded: 1990. **Subjects:** Nondestructive testing - radiography, eddy currents, magnetic particles, penetrants, ultrasonics, infrared. **Holdings:** 800 volumes; 500 technical reports; manuscripts; microfilm; slides; films; tapes. **Subscriptions:** 25 journals and other serials. **Services:** Copying; library open for members by appointment only. **Remarks:** FAX: (614)274-6899. Telex: 245347. **Staff:** Jody Van Cooney, Pubns.Mgr.; Terry Fogle, Libn.

★755★
American Society of Notaries - Library (Law)
918 16th St., N.W. Phone: (202)955-6162
Washington, DC 20006 Eugene E. Hines, Exec.Dir.
Founded: 1965. **Staff:** Prof 1. **Subjects:** Law of notary public, commercial law, trade associations. **Holdings:** 400 books; 500 ancient notarized documents, deeds, memorabilia of the office of notary public. **Services:** Interlibrary loan; copying; library open to the public with restrictions. **Remarks:** FAX: (202)955-6163.

★756★
American Society for Photogrammetry and Remote Sensing - Heinz Gruner Library (Sci-Engr)
5410 Grosvenor Ln., Suite 210 Phone: (301)493-0290
Bethesda, MD 20814 William D. French, Exec.Dir.
Founded: 1979. **Subjects:** Photogrammetry, remote sensing, mapping, photography, geographic information systems. **Holdings:** 2500 books; 54 bound periodical volumes; proceedings of technical meetings; 12 shelves of technical reports. **Subscriptions:** 57 journals and other serials. **Services:** Library open to the public for reference use only. **Publications:** Photogrammetric Engineering and Remote Sensing, monthly - to members and by subscription. **Special Indexes:** Complete Index to Photogrammetric Engineering and Remote Sensing, 1934-1979 (book). **Remarks:** FAX: (301)493-0208. **Remarks:** FAX: (301)493-0208.

★757★
American Society for Psychical Research, Inc. - A.S.P.R. Library (Rel-Phil)
5 W. 73rd St. Phone: (212)799-5050
New York, NY 10023 John LaMartine, Libn.
Founded: 1918. **Staff:** 1. **Subjects:** Psychical research, parapsychology, spiritualism, philosophy, psychology, religion. **Special Collections:** Shaker Collection (books; periodicals; manuscripts). **Holdings:** 8000 books; 300 bound periodical volumes; 1000 unbound periodicals; 50 unbound reports; 50 unbound theses and dissertations; 100 sound recordings; 2000 items in article file; 200 linear feet of archives and manuscripts. **Subscriptions:** 110 journals and other serials. **Services:** Copying; library open to members. **Computerized Information Services:** DIALOG Information Services, RLIN; INPSITE (internal database). **Special Indexes:** Index for Journal of the American Society for Psychical Research, 1885-1960 (card). **Remarks:** FAX: (212)496-2497.

★758★
American Society for Quality Control - Library (Sci-Engr)
611 E. Wisconsin Ave.
P.O. Box 3005 Phone: (414)272-8575
Milwaukee, WI 53201-3005 Ann Lorenz, Libn., Tech.Serv.
Staff: 1. **Subjects:** Quality assurance, quality control, statistical quality control, and quality management in consumer products, fabrication industries, health and process industries, standards activities, quality methodologies and technologies. **Special Collections:** ASQC publications. **Holdings:** 1000 texts and manuals; foreign language materials. **Services:** Copying; library open to public for reference use only with prior appointment. **Remarks:** FAX: (414)272-1734.

★759★
American Society of Sugar Beet Technologists - Library (Agri)
90 Madison St., No. 208 Phone: (303)321-1520
Denver, CO 80206 Thomas K. Schwartz, Exec.V.P.
Subjects: Agronomy, entomology, plant pathology, agricultural engineering, sugar beet chemistry and production. **Holdings:** Journals, reports, foreign literature, and data exchange from European countries. **Remarks:** FAX: (303)321-1558. **Also Known As:** Beet Sugar Development Foundation.

★760★
American Society for Surgery of the Hand - Museum and Library (Med)
3025 S. Parker Rd., Suite 65
Aurora, CO 80014-2911 Phone: (303)755-4597
Staff: Prof 1. **Subjects:** Hand surgery. **Holdings:** 282 books; 453 bound periodical volumes; 62 audiovisual tapes. **Subscriptions:** 19 journals and other serials. **Services:** Interlibrary loan; copying; library open to the public with restrictions. **Computerized Information Services:** MEDLARS, DIALOG Information Services. **Formerly:** Located in San Francisco, CA.

★761★
American Society for Testing and Materials - Information Center (Sci-Engr)
1916 Race St. Phone: (215)299-5475
Philadelphia, PA 19103 Dolores G. Collyer, Mgr.
Founded: 1960. **Staff:** 1. **Subjects:** Standards, materials science. **Holdings:** 3400 books; 13,000 unbound standards. **Subscriptions:** 270 journals and other serials. **Services:** Center open to the public for reference use only. **Remarks:** FAX: (215)977-9679. Telex: 710 670 1037.

★762★
American Society for Training and Development - Information Center (Bus-Fin)
1640 King St. Phone: (703)683-8183
Alexandria, VA 22313-2043 Edith Allen, Mgr.
Founded: 1984. **Staff:** Prof 3. **Subjects:** Human resource development - general, management, training, career development, organization development, consulting skills. **Holdings:** 3000 bound volumes. **Subscriptions:** 70 journals and other serials. **Services:** Library open to national members of the Society. **Computerized Information Services:** Produces TRAINET; Member Information Exchange (internal database). **Special Indexes:** Training and Development Literature Index, quarterly. **Remarks:** FAX: (703)683-8103.

★763★
American Sokol Education and Physical Culture Organization - Library-Archives (Rec)
6424 W. Cermak Rd. Phone: (708)795-6671
Berwyn, IL 60402 Annette B. Schabowski
Founded: 1976. **Staff:** Prof 3; Other 2. **Subjects:** Athletics, gymnastics, physical fitness, Czechoslovak and Sokol history. **Holdings:** 3145 books; 313 bound periodical volumes; 1360 pamphlets; 572 gymnastic and drill materials; 430 folk dance and musical items; 3083 pictures; 17 photograph albums; 1869 archival materials; 40 films; 14 videotapes; 926 program books. **Services:** Copying; library open to members for reference use only.

★764★
American Soybean Association - Technical Information Center (Agri)
540 Maryville Centre Dr., Suite 400
P.O. Box 419200 Phone: (314)576-1770
St. Louis, MO 63141 Marianne Gibson, Libn.
Founded: 1977. **Staff:** Prof 1; Other 1. **Subjects:** Agriculture, economics, nutrition, food processing. **Special Collections:** William H. Morse Collection (25 volumes). **Holdings:** 3000 books. **Subscriptions:** 502 journals and other serials. **Services:** Interlibrary loan; copying; library open to the public with restrictions. **Automated Operations:** Computerized circulation. **Computerized Information Services:** DIALOG Information Services; ASA Database (internal database). Performs searches on fee basis. **Publications:** Animal Nutrition Highlights; soybean bibliography; Soybean Digest. **Remarks:** FAX: (314)576-2786.

★765★
American Speech-Language-Hearing Association - ASHA Library (Med)
10801 Rockville Pike
Rockville, MD 20852 Phone: (301)897-5700
Founded: 1986. **Staff:** Prof 1. **Subjects:** Speech, hearing, language, management, government affairs. **Special Collections:** Journal of Speech & Hearing Research (complete set); Speech and Hearing Disorders (complete set). **Holdings:** 1630 books; 60 bound periodical volumes; workshop and conference reports. **Services:** Interlibrary loan; library open to staff and ASHA members. **Automated Operations:** Computerized cataloging, serials, and circulation. **Computerized Information Services:** Internal database. **Networks/Consortia:** Member of District of Columbia Health Sciences Information Network (DOCHSIN). **Publications:** Current Awareness Service, every 3 weeks; Recent Additions to the ASHA Library, monthly - both for internal distribution only. **Special Indexes:** Author index for archival collection. **Remarks:** FAX: (301)571-0457.

★766★
American Standards Testing Bureau, Inc. - Sam Tour Library (Sci-Engr)
40 Water St. Phone: (212)943-3160
New York, NY 10004 Mr. C. Chavis, Hd.Libn.
Founded: 1947. **Staff:** Prof 3; Other 1. **Subjects:** Standards and specifications - chemistry, physics, engineering, arson and fire, mathematics. **Holdings:** 16,000 books. **Subscriptions:** 100 journals and other serials; 10 newspapers. **Services:** Interlibrary loan; library not open to the public. **Remarks:** FAX: (212)825-2250.

★767★
American States Insurance Company - Library (Bus-Fin, Law)
500 N. Meridian St.
Box 1636 Phone: (317)262-6560
Indianapolis, IN 46207 Susan A. Jones, Libn.
Founded: 1973. **Staff:** Prof 1. **Subjects:** Law, insurance, management, psychology, accounting. **Holdings:** 9000 books; 20 bound periodical volumes; 300 cassette tapes; 200 videotapes. **Subscriptions:** 150 journals and other serials. **Services:** Interlibrary loan; SDI; library open to the public. **Automated Operations:** Computerized cataloging and acquisitions. **Computerized Information Services:** DIALOG Information Services, WESTLAW, Insurance Information Institute Data Base, VU/TEXT Information Services; Aclinet (internal database). **Special Catalogs:** Library and video services catalog. **Remarks:** FAX: (317)262-6290.

★768★
American Sterilizer Company - Library (Biol Sci, Med)
2424 W. 23rd St. Phone: (814)870-8453
Erie, PA 16514 Janis M. Ruben, Info.Spec.
Founded: 1959. **Staff:** Prof 1; Other 1. **Subjects:** Bacteriology, medicine, microbiology, engineering, industrial design, marketing, management. **Holdings:** 3500 books; 300 bound periodical volumes; 13 drawers of reprints; 8 drawers of patents; microforms. **Subscriptions:** 350 journals and other serials. **Services:** Interlibrary loan; library open to the public with identification. **Computerized Information Services:** DIALOG Information Services, NERAC, Inc., Teltech, Inc.; internal database. **Networks/Consortia:** Member of Erie Area Health Information Library Cooperative (EAHILC), Northwest Interlibrary Cooperative of Pennsylvania (NICOP). **Remarks:** FAX: (814)870-8233.

★769★
American Stock Exchange - Martin J. Keena Memorial Library (Bus-Fin)
86 Trinity Pl. Phone: (212)306-1290
New York, NY 10006-1881 Sue H. Trowbridge, Mgr.
Founded: 1966. **Staff:** 5. **Subjects:** Corporation records, government regulations. **Special Collections:** Prices of all equities and options listed on AMEX, 1980 to present. **Holdings:** Corporate reports of 900 listed companies; 70 drawers of microfiche; annual reports; prospectuses; proxies. **Subscriptions:** 60 journals and other serials. **Services:** Copying; library open to the public. **Publications:** Reports of American Stock Exchange, quarterly & annual; technical reports; information booklets - all available on request through publications department. **Remarks:** FAX: (212)306-1372. **Also Known As:** AMEX. **Staff:** Neville Hutchinson, Microfilm Supv.; Myrrah Sestoso, Info.Coord.

★770★
American Studies Research Centre - Library (Hum)
Osmania University Campus Phone: 842 71182
Hyderabad 500 007, Andhra Pradesh, India Dr. Mohamed Taher
Founded: 1964. **Staff:** Prof 10; Other 60. **Subjects:** American studies. **Special Collections:** Indian contributions to American studies; Indian reprints of American books; American studies in Indian languages. **Holdings:** 108,108 books; 17,415 bound periodical volumes; 17,868 microfiche; 7393 reels of microfilm. **Subscriptions:** 691 journals and other serials; 8 newspapers. **Services:** Interlibrary loan; copying; library open on membership basis. **Computerized Information Services:** CDS/ISIS. Contact Person: Dr. N.G. Satis, Dp.Libn. **Publications:** Acquisition list.

★771★
American Suffolk Horse Association (ASHA) - Library (Rec)
Rte. 1, Box 212
Ledbetter, TX 78946 Mary Margaret M. Read, Sec.-Treas.
Staff: 1. **Subjects:** Suffolk horses. **Holdings:** Figures not available. **Publications:** Information brochure (includes list of breeders). **Remarks:** Said to be most complete collection of Suffolk horse material in North America.

★772★
American Swedish Historical Museum - Nord Library (Area-Ethnic, Hist)
1900 Pattison Ave. Phone: (215)389-1776
Philadelphia, PA 19145 Ann Barton Brown, Musm.Dir.
Founded: 1926. **Subjects:** Books by and about Swedish Americans; Swedish colonization of the Delaware Valley; Swedish contributions to religious life in the U.S.; reference works pertaining to Sweden, Swedish culture, literature, handcrafts. **Special Collections:** John Ericsson, Jenny Lind, and Fredrika Bremer collections; diaries, letters, other memoirs of Swedish immigrants. **Holdings:** 10,000 books and bound periodical volumes; manuscripts; clippings; pamphlets; dissertations; documents; slides; maps; prints; pictures. **Subscriptions:** 19 journals and other serials. **Services:** Copying; inquiries answered; library open to students and scholars for research. **Publications:** Newsletter, quarterly - to members and consulates. **Remarks:** FAX: (215)389-7701.

★773★
American Swedish Institute - Library and Archives (Area-Ethnic)
2600 Park Ave., S. Phone: (612)871-4907
Minneapolis, MN 55407 Marita Karlisch, Archv./Libn.
Founded: 1929. **Staff:** Prof 1. **Subjects:** Swedish - culture, history, immigration history; Swedish-American life. **Special Collections:** Swan Turnblad Collection; C.J. Johnson Collection; Vega Library. **Holdings:** 13,000 books; 212 reels of microfilm; 800 microfiche of Swedish emigration records. **Subscriptions:** 10 journals and other serials; 7 newspapers. **Services:** Copying; library open to the public. **Remarks:** FAX: (612)871-8682.

American Technical Education Association - National Library
See: **North Dakota State College of Science** (11920)

★774★
American Tekdyne, Inc. - Library (Med)
P.O. Box 7059
Princeton, NJ 08540 Phone: (609)683-1990
Subjects: Hospital and biomedical engineering, electromechanical techniques in medicine. **Holdings:** 160 volumes. **Computerized Information Services:** Internal database. **Remarks:** FAX: (609)921-0389. **Formerly:** Hospital Engineering Logistics & Planning, Inc.

★775★
American Textile Manufacturers Institute (ATMI) - Library (Sci-Engr)
1801 K St., N.W., Suite 900 Phone: (202)862-0500
Washington, DC 20006 Mabry R. McCloud, Libn.
Staff: Prof 1. **Subjects:** U.S. textile industry; textiles - fibers, fabrics, history; international trade; chemicals; safety and health. **Holdings:** 1200 books; 600 ATMI historical records. **Subscriptions:** 110 journals and other serials; 10 newspapers. **Services:** Interlibrary loan; copying (limited). **Remarks:** FAX: (202)862-0570.

★776★
American Theatre Organ Society - Archives/Library (Mus)
785 Palomino Ct. Phone: (619)471-6194
San Marcos, CA 92069-2102 Vernon P. Bickel, Cur.
Founded: 1976. **Staff:** Prof 1. **Subjects:** The theater pipe organ - history, current installations, technical information, music, artists, theater organ builders. **Special Collections:** Wurlitzer pipe organ rolls; sets of glass song slides. **Holdings:** Books; pamphlets; periodicals; 12,000 music titles; audiotapes; videotapes; motion pictures; phonograph records; silent motion picture cue sheets and scores. **Services:** Copying; library open to the public by appointment only. **Special Catalogs:** Catalog of archival material - for sale. **Formerly:** Located in Chula Vista, CA.

★777★
American Tobacco Company - Department of Research & Quality Assurance Library (Sci-Engr, Agri)
Box 899 Phone: (804)751-7517
Hopewell, VA 23860 Dorothy D. Robben, Mgr., Lib. & Rec.
Founded: 1936. **Staff:** Prof 3; Other 2. **Subjects:** Tobacco, engineering, mathematics, physics, plant physiology, quality control, ecology. **Holdings:** 4545 books; 5520 bound periodical volumes; 25,400 patents, technical articles, translations; 10,900 microforms. **Subscriptions:** 189 journals and other serials; 4 newspapers. **Services:** Interlibrary loan; copying; library open to the public by request. **Computerized Information Services:** DIALOG Information Services, STN International. **Publications:** Library Accessions, monthly - for internal distribution only. **Special Catalogs:** Annual Tobacco Titles (computer-generated). **Remarks:** Library located at 13101 N. Enon Church Rd., Chester, VA 23831. **Staff:** Laurel B. Lonnes; Dana S. Barefoot.

★778★
American Truck Historical Society - Library (Trans)
PO Box 531168 Phone: (205)870-0566
Birmingham, AL 35253 Larry L. Scheef, Mng.Dir.
Founded: 1971. **Staff:** 5. **Subjects:** Trucks, truck companies, people in trucking. **Holdings:** 300 books; 180 bound periodical volumes; 250 biographies; 500 company histories; 8000 unbound periodicals; 75 films; 500 slides; 60 videotapes; 50,000 photographs. **Subscriptions:** 15 journals and other serials. **Services:** Copying; library open to the public. **Publications:** Wheels of Time, bimonthly. **Remarks:** FAX: (205)870-3069.

★779★
American Trucking Associations, Inc. - Information Center (Trans)
2200 Mill Rd. Phone: (703)838-1880
Alexandria, VA 22314 Linda S. Rothbart, Dir., Info.Serv.Dept.
Founded: 1933. **Staff:** Prof 4; Other 2. **Subjects:** Economic and financial analysis of trucking industry, trucking regulation, highway legislation, truck engineering and safety, freight transportation. **Special Collections:** Motor carrier and railroad stockholders reports. **Holdings:** 20,000 volumes. **Subscriptions:** 384 journals and other serials. **Services:** Interlibrary loan; copying; center open to the public by appointment. **Automated Operations:** Computerized cataloging, acquisitions, and serials. **Computerized Information Services:** DIALOG Information Services, NEXIS, WESTLAW, LEGI-SLATE, Dun & Bradstreet Business Credit Services. **Publications:** Trucksource: Sources of Truck Industry Information, annual; Motor Carrier Professional Services Directory, annual; ATA Staff Specialists. **Remarks:** FAX: (703)519-5272. **Staff:** Cathy Mallet; Janice Dluzynski; John Farrant; Mona Heath; Suzanne Hess.

★780★
American Type Culture Collection - Donovick Library (Biol Sci)
12301 Parklawn Dr. Phone: (301)881-2600
Rockville, MD 20852 Mary Jane Edwards, Sr.Ed.Info.Spec.
Founded: 1965. **Staff:** Prof 1; Other 1. **Subjects:** Microbiology, bacteriology, protistology, virology, tissue culture, mycology, molecular biology, plasmids, biotechnology. **Holdings:** 3600 books; 2600 bound periodical volumes. **Subscriptions:** 300 journals and other serials. **Services:** Interlibrary loan; copying; library open to the public with restrictions.

★781★
American United Life Insurance Company - Library (Bus-Fin)
1 American Square Phone: (317)263-1709
Indianapolis, IN 46204 Nancy A. Piercy, Libn.
Staff: 1. **Subjects:** Insurance - life and health; pensions. **Holdings:** Books; archives; microfiche; microfilm. **Services:** Interlibrary loan; copying; library open to the public. **Remarks:** FAX: (317)263-1979.

★782★
American University - Washington College of Law - Library (Law)
Myers II Bldg.
4400 Massachusetts Ave., N.W. Phone: (202)885-2627
Washington, DC 20016-8087 Patrick E. Kehoe, Dir.
Founded: 1896. **Staff:** Prof 8; Other 10. **Subjects:** Law, international law. **Special Collections:** CERDEC (European Economic Community Research Center and Collection). **Holdings:** 310,000 volumes. **Subscriptions:** 4622 journals and other serials. **Services:** Interlibrary loan; copying; library open to students, alumni, and other qualified users. **Automated Operations:** Computerized public access catalog, acquisitions, cataloging, circulation, and serials. **Computerized Information Services:** LEXIS, NEXIS, VU/TEXT Information Services, WESTLAW, DIALOG Information Services, Veralex 2, OCLC; MCI Mail (electronic mail service). Performs searches on fee basis. **Networks/Consortia:** Member of CAPCON Library Network. **Publications:** Users guide, annual; New Acquisitions, monthly. **Remarks:** Public access catalog is electronically linked to catalogs at Georgetown University Law Library and George Washington University Law Library. FAX: (202)885-2703. Telex: 650 234 4870 MCI. Electronic mail address(es): 234 4870 (MCI Mail). **Staff:** Margaret M. Milam, Assoc.Dir, Tech.Serv.; Gary McCann, Assoc.Dir., Rd.Serv.; Amelia Sandique-Owens, Cat.; Joanne Zich, Govt.Docs. & Media Libn.; John Heywood, Ref. & Intl. Law Libn.; Marla Schwartz, Ser.; William Ryan, Circ. & Ref.

★783★
American University Alumni - Language Center Library - USIS Collection (Educ)
179 Rajdamri Rd.
Bangkok 10500, Thailand
Remarks: Maintained or supported by the U.S. Information Agency. Focus is on materials that will assist peoples outside the United States to learn about the United States, its people, history, culture, political processes, and social milieux.

★784★
American Veterinary Medical Association - Library (Med)
1931 N. Meacham Rd., Suite 100 Phone: (708)925-8070
Schaumburg, IL 60173-4360 Liane Lenski, Libn.
Founded: 1945. **Staff:** Prof 1. **Subjects:** Veterinary medicine and allied fields. **Holdings:** 5000 books; 300 bound periodical volumes. **Subscriptions:** 35 journals and other serials; 185 exchanges. **Services:** Copying (limited); library open to the public for reference use only. **Remarks:** FAX: (708)925-1329.

★785★
American Watchmakers Institute - ELM Trust - Henry B. Fried Library (Sci-Engr)
3700 Harrison Ave. Phone: (513)661-3838
Cincinnati, OH 45211 Nancy Danner, Libn.
Founded: 1960. **Staff:** Prof 2; Other 2. **Subjects:** Horology. **Holdings:** Figures not available. **Services:** Interlibrary loan; copying; library open to the public with permission. **Remarks:** FAX: (513)661-3131. **Staff:** Milton C. Stevens, Dir./AWI Elm Trust.

★786★
American Water Works Association - Information Services Department (Env-Cons, Sci-Engr)
6666 W. Quincy Ave. Phone: (303)794-7711
Denver, CO 80235 Kurt M. Keeley, Dir., Info.Serv.
Founded: 1977. **Staff:** Prof 3; Other 1. **Subjects:** Water - treatment, conservation, utility management, quality; wastewater treatment; reuse; water rates. **Holdings:** 2500 books; 200 bound periodical volumes; 150 AV programs; 2000 technical reports. **Subscriptions:** 175 journals and other serials. **Services:** Copying; department open to the public by appointment. **Computerized Information Services:** DIALOG Information Services, PFDS Online; WATERNET (internal database); DIALMAIL (electronic mail service). Performs searches on fee basis. **Networks/Consortia:** Member of Bibliographical Center for Research, Rocky Mountain Region, Inc. (BCR). **Publications:** Topical bibliographies, monthly; Waternet Thesaurus. **Special Catalogs:** AV Catalog, annual. **Special Indexes:** Annual book index. **Remarks:** FAX: (303)795-1440. **Staff:** Cathy Beatty, Tech.Info.Spec.; Susan Sept, Tech.Info.Spec.; Connie Hardesty, Tech.Info.Spec.

American Welding Society - American Council of the International Institute of Welding
See: **American Council of the International Institute of Welding** (550)

★787★
American Work Horse Museum - Library
Box 88
Paeonian Springs, VA 22129
Defunct. Holdings absorbed by Virginia Polytechnic Institute and State University - Libraries.

★788★
American Youth Work Center (Soc Sci)
1751 N St., N.W., Suite 302 Phone: (202)785-0764
Washington, DC 20036 William Treanor, Exec.Dir.
Staff: Prof 3; Other 2. **Subjects:** Youth programs and problems, juvenile justice, youth alcohol and drug abuse, youth employment, missing children, exchange programs. **Holdings:** Figures not available. **Publications:** List of publications - available on request. **Remarks:** FAX: (202)782-0657. Telex: 89 2320. **Staff:** Toni Smith, Int'l.Prog.Asst.

Americana Research Library
See: **American Life Foundation and Study Institute - Americana Research Library** (670)

★789★
Americans Combatting Terrorism - Library (Soc Sci)
P.O. Box 370
Telluride, CO 81435-0370 Thomas P. O'Connor, Dir.
Remarks: No further information was supplied by respondent.

★790★
Americans United for Life - Library (Soc Sci)
343 S. Dearborn St., Suite 1804 Phone: (312)786-9494
Chicago, IL 60604 Rhonda Best
Subjects: Abortion, euthanasia, infanticide. **Holdings:** Books, articles, government publications. **Automated Operations:** Computerized cataloging.

★791★
Americans United for Separation of Church and State - Archives (Soc Sci)
8120 Fenton St. Phone: (301)589-3707
Silver Spring, MD 20910 Catherine Shelley
Founded: 1947. **Subjects:** Religious liberty and church-state separation. **Special Collections:** Documents on religion in the public schools, public funds for parochial schools, constitutional convention, and Vatican ambassadorship question. **Holdings:** 1200 books; 50 bound periodical volumes; 125 boxes of papers and documents; minutes of AUSCS staff and board meetings. **Subscriptions:** 4 journals and other serials. **Services:** Library not open to the public. **Remarks:** FAX: (301)495-9173.

★792★
Amerika Haus Berlin - USIS Library (Educ)
22-24 Hardenbergstrasse
W-1000 Berlin 12, Germany
Remarks: Maintained or supported by the U.S. Information Agency. Focus is on materials that will assist peoples outside the United States to learn about the United States, its people, history, culture, political processes, and social milieux.

★793★
Amerika Haus Frankfurt - USIS Library (Educ)
1 Staufenstrasse
W-6001 Frankfurt am Main 1, Germany
Remarks: Maintained or supported by the U.S. Information Agency. Focus is on materials that will assist peoples outside the United States to learn about the United States, its people, history, culture, political processes, and social milieux.

★794★
Amerika Haus Hamburg - USIS Library (Educ)
Tesdorpfstrasse 1
W-2000 Hamburg 13, Germany
Remarks: Maintained or supported by the U.S. Information Agency. Focus is on materials that will assist peoples outside the United States to learn about the United States, its people, history, culture, political processes, and social milieux.

★795★
Amerika Haus Hannover - USIS Library (Educ)
Prinzenstrasse 4
Postfach 440 Phone: 511 327286
W-3000 Hannover 1, Germany Thea Bohse-Ziganke, Lib.Dir.
Founded: 1950. **Staff:** 2.5. **Subjects:** American studies - general politics, social and economic issues, fiction, international relations, security issues. **Holdings:** 8500 books; microfiche; 220 audiotapes. **Subscriptions:** 179 journals and other serials; 3 newspapers. **Services:** Interlibrary loan; copying; library open to the public on a limited schedule. **Computerized Information Services:** DIALOG Information Services; Public Diplomacy Query System (internal database). **Remarks:** FAX: 511 321634. Maintained or supported by the U.S. Information Agency. Focus is on materials that will assist peoples outside the United States to learn about the United States, its people, history, culture, political processes, and social milieux. **Staff:** Ursula Truman, Ref.Libn.; Barbel Rebe, Exch.Spec.

★796★
Amerika Haus Koln - USIS Library (Educ)
Apostelnkloster 13/15 Phone: 221 2090147
W-5000 Cologne 1, Germany Brigitta A. Tabertshofer
Founded: 1955. **Staff:** 3. **Subjects:** American studies. **Holdings:** 12,000 books; reports; microfiche; microfilm. **Subscriptions:** 300 journals and other serials; 5 newspapers. **Services:** Interlibrary loan; copying; SDI; library open to the public. **Computerized Information Services:** DIALOG Information Services, LEGI-SLATE; PDQ (internal database); DIALMAIL (electronic mail service). **Remarks:** FAX: 221 244543. Electronic mail address(es): 27537 (DIALMAIL). Maintained or supported by the U.S. Information Agency. Focus is on materials that will assist peoples outside the United States to learn about the United States, its people, history, culture, political processes, and social milieux. **Staff:** Mechthild Hoelker; Renate Heckel.

★797★
Amerika Haus Munchen - USIS Library (Educ)
Karolinenplatz 3
W-8000 Munich 2, Germany
Remarks: Maintained or supported by the U.S. Information Agency. Focus is on materials that will assist peoples outside the United States to learn about the United States, its people, history, culture, political processes, and social milieux.

★798★
Amerika Haus Stuttgart - USIS Library (Educ)
Friedrichstrasse 23A
W-7000 Stuttgart 1, Germany Phone: 711 2298317
Founded: 1946. **Staff:** 3. **Holdings:** 9000 books. **Subscriptions:** 250 journals and other serials; 6 newspapers. **Services:** Interlibrary loan; copying; library open to the public. **Remarks:** FAX: (711)229-8339

★799★
Amerika Haus Vienna - USIS Library (Educ)
Friedrich Schmidt-Platz 2 Phone: 1 315511
A-1010 Vienna, Austria Dr. Roswitha Haller
Founded: 1946. **Staff:** Prof 3. **Subjects:** American studies. **Holdings:** 13,000 books; reports; microfiche; microfilm; videotapes. **Subscriptions:** 180 journals and other serials. **Services:** Interlibrary loan; copying; SDI; library open to the public on a limited schedule. **Computerized Information Services:** LEXIS, NEXIS, DIALOG Information Services, LEGI-SLATE; internal databases. **Publications:** List of periodicals, videotapes, and new books. **Remarks:** FAX: 1 435260. Maintained or supported by the U.S. Information Agency. Focus is on materials that will assist peoples outside the United States to learn about the United States, its people, history, culture, political processes, and social milieux.

★800★
Amerind Foundation, Inc. - Fulton-Hayden Memorial Library (Soc Sci)
Dragoon, AZ 85609 Phone: (602)586-3666
Anne I. Woosley, Dir.
Founded: 1937. **Staff:** Prof 1; Other 1. **Subjects:** Archeology, anthropology, Greater American Southwest, ethnology and history. **Special Collections:** Parral Archives (complete on microfilm); facsimile editions of major American codices. **Holdings:** 18,000 books; 1000 bound periodical volumes; 2260 pamphlets and reprints; 415 manuscripts; 250 maps; 1300 slides and photographs; 2 VF drawers of clippings and translations. **Subscriptions:** 150 journals and other serials. **Services:** Copying; library open to serious researchers by appointment only and with written statement of intent.

Ameritech Corp. - Ohio Bell
See: **Ohio Bell** (12262)

★801★
Ameritech Publishing, Inc. - Information Research Center (Publ, Bus-Fin)
100 E. Big Beaver Rd., 200W Phone: (313)524-7514
Troy, MI 48083 Timothy D. Sharnas, Venture Anl./IRC Mgr.
Founded: 1986. **Staff:** 4.5 **Subjects:** Publishing industry, printing industry, telecommunications industry, Yellow Pages industry, strategic planning, marketing, advertising, general business. **Holdings:** 2000 books; 800 documents; 5000 nonbook items. **Subscriptions:** 275 journals and other serials. **Services:** Interlibrary loan; information brokering; center open to the public by appointment. **Computerized Information Services:** DIALOG Information Services, DRI/McGraw-Hill, NewsNet, Inc., VU/TEXT Information Services, Dun & Bradstreet Business Credit Services, Dow Jones News/Retrieval, Online Information Network, Human Resource Information Network (HRIN), Global Scan; Yellow Pages Publishing Industry Database (internal database). **Networks/Consortia:** Member of Michigan Library Consortium (MLC). **Publications:** Industry Update (Yellow Pages Publishing). **Remarks:** FAX: (313)524-7315. **Staff:** Mario Angelo, Venture Asst./IRC Asst.Mgr.; Eleanor Plec, Venture Asst./IRC Res.Asst.; Ruth Stockler, Venture Asst./IRC Res.Asst.

★802★
Amersham Corporation - Library
2636 S. Clearbrook Dr.
Arlington Heights, IL 60005 Phone: (708)539-6300
Founded: 1976. **Remarks:** FAX: (708)593-1044. No further information was supplied by respondent.

Ames Library of South Asia
See: **University of Minnesota** (18891)

★803★
Ames Public Library - Ames and Iowa History Collection (Hist)
515 Douglas Ave. Phone: (515)233-4500
Ames, IA 50010-6215 George T. Lawson, Dir.
Founded: 1903. **Staff:** 25.5. **Subjects:** State and local history, genealogy. **Holdings:** Books; pamphlets; clippings; state and federal census data on microfilm; photographs; scrapbooks; telephone directories; city and county documents; publications of local organizations; yearbooks; atlases; genealogical materials. **Subscriptions:** 480 journals and other serials; 31 newspapers. **Services:** Interlibrary loan; copying; collection open to the public. **Automated Operations:** Computerized cataloging and circulation. **Computerized Information Services:** DIALOG Information Services, OCLC. Performs searches on fee basis. Contact Person: Michael G. Quinn, Info.Serv.Coord., 233-2115. **Networks/Consortia:** Member of Bibliographical Center for Research, Rocky Mountain Region, Inc. (BCR). **Publications:** Calendar of Events, monthly. **Remarks:** FAX: (515)232-4571.

Ames Research Center
See: **NASA - Ames Research Center** (10979)

★804★
Ametek, Inc. - Operations Headquarters - Marketing Information Center (Sci-Engr)
Station Square
Paoli, PA 19301 Phone: (215)647-2121
Founded: 1982. **Staff:** Prof 1; Other 1. **Subjects:** Electronics, control instrumentation, mechanical engineering, management, business. **Holdings:** 500 books. **Subscriptions:** 412 journals and other serials. **Services:** Interlibrary loan; center not open to the public. **Computerized Information Services:** DIALOG Information Services, Mead Data Central, Dow Jones News/Retrieval, DunsPrint. **Remarks:** FAX: (215)296-3412. Telex: 83-4637.

★805★
Amgen, Inc. - Information Service Group (Biol Sci)
Amgen Center Phone: (805)499-5725
Thousand Oaks, CA 91320-1789 Susan Sprague
Founded: 1981. **Staff:** Prof 6; Other 7. **Subjects:** Biotechnology, molecular biology, pharmaceutical industry. **Holdings:** 5000 books; 50 reports; patents on microfilm. **Subscriptions:** 350 journals and other serials; 8 newspapers. **Services:** Interlibrary loan; SDI; group open to the public by appointment. **Computerized Information Services:** DIALOG Information Services, BRS Information Technologies, Data-Star, Dow Jones News/Retrieval, ORBIT Search Service, LEXIS, STN International, Questel, VU/TEXT Information Services, MEDLARS, TOXNET; Amgen Author Publications, Patents, Product Literature (internal databases). **Networks/Consortia:** Member of CLASS. **Publications:** A.I.S. Newsletter, monthly; Patent Alert, weekly; Meetings Update, quarterly; subject bibliographies. **Remarks:** FAX: (805)498-1425. Telex: 4994440. **Staff:** Susan Stearns, Tech.Serv.Libn.; Susan Willcox, Clin.Info.Spec.; Carla Moore, Patent Info.Spec.; Elisa Bass, Bus.Info.Spec.

★806★
Amherst College - Science Library (Sci-Engr)
Amherst, MA 01002 Phone: (413)542-2076
Founded: 1968. **Subjects:** Astronomy, chemistry, physics. **Holdings:** 7600 books; 9000 bound periodical volumes. **Subscriptions:** 150 journals and other serials. **Services:** Interlibrary loan; library open to the public for reference use only. **Computerized Information Services:** DIALOG Information Services, OCLC. **Networks/Consortia:** Member of SUNY/OCLC Library Network. **Remarks:** The collection of books on astronomy has existed since the 19th century.

★807★
Amherst College - Special Collections and Archives Department (Hum)
Robert Frost Library
Amherst, MA 01002 Phone: (413)542-2068
Founded: 1821. **Staff:** Prof 2; Other 3. **Subjects:** American poetry and theater, English literature and theater, Amherst College history. **Special Collections:** Samuel Goodrich and Peter Parley (600 volumes); Louise Bogan papers (15 linear feet); Richard Wilbur papers (18 linear feet); Dwight Morrow papers (120 linear feet); Clyde Fitch collection (1000 volumes; 5 linear feet); Emily Dickinson papers (15 linear feet; limited access; photocopies available); Robert Frost Collection (5 linear feet and 750 volumes); Joseph Eastman papers (40 linear feet); Rolfe Humphries papers (10 linear feet); George Bellows papers (3 linear feet); Charles Morgan papers on George Bellows (7 linear feet); Marshall Bloom/LNS underground newspapers (400 linear feet); Amherst College Buildings and Grounds collection (50 linear feet); Amherst College Weather Station records (2 linear feet); Snell Family papers (15 linear feet); President Edward Hitchcock papers (11 linear feet); Dr. Edward Hitchcock papers (4.5 linear feet); Julius Hawley Seelye papers (8 linear feet); Bliss Family papers (3 linear feet); John J. McCloy papers (54 linear feet); college history collection (1000 linear feet of historical manuscripts; 400 linear feet of honors and masters' theses; 1500 linear feet of other bound manuscripts and printed college history sources); Porter-Phelps-Huntington papers (90 linear feet); Hills Family papers (16 linear feet). **Holdings:** 30,000 books; 50,000 acting editions of English and American plays. **Services:** Copying; department open to the public. **Automated Operations:** Computerized cataloging. **Computerized Information Services:** OCLC. **Networks/Consortia:** Member of NELINET, Inc., HILC, Inc., SUNY/OCLC Library Network. **Remarks:** Alternate telephone number(s): 542-2299; FAX: (413)542-2662. **Staff:** John Lancaster, Cur. of Spec.Coll.; Daria D'Arienzo, Archv.

★808★
Amherst College - Vincent Morgan Music Library (Mus)
Amherst, MA 01002 Phone: (413)542-2387
Sally Evans, Mus.Libn.
Staff: Prof 1; Other 2. **Subjects:** Music. **Holdings:** 9300 books; 12,200 scores; 17,200 sound recordings. **Subscriptions:** 63 journals and other serials. **Services:** Interlibrary loan (limited); library open to the public. **Computerized Information Services:** BITNET (electronic mail service). **Remarks:** FAX:(413)542-2662. Electronic mail address(es): SREVANS@AMHERST (BITNET).

★809★
Amherst Town Records Center (Hist)
500 Smith Rd. Phone: (716)636-7045
East Amherst, NY 14051 Susan J. Grelick, Rec.Mgr.
Founded: 1981. **Staff:** Prof 1. **Subjects:** Municipal government, local history. **Special Collections:** Residential and commercial structures, 1956-1957 (5000 photographs). **Holdings:** 2800 cubic feet of records; 500,000 documents on microfilm. **Services:** Copying; center open to the public. **Publications:** Guide to the Archives of the Town of Amherst. **Special Catalogs:** A Photographic Collection of the Town of Amherst. **Special Indexes:** Key word index to Town Board Resolutions, 1953 to present. **Remarks:** Maintained by Town of Amherst. Alternate telephone number(s): 631-7046. FAX: (716)631-7012.

★810★
Amistad Research Center - Library/Archives (Area-Ethnic)
Tulane University
6823 St. Charles Ave. Phone: (504)865-5535
New Orleans, LA 70118 Dr. Clifton H. Johnson, Exec.Dir.
Founded: 1966. **Staff:** Prof 6; Other 14. **Subjects:** Ethnic minorities of America, Afro-American history and culture, civil rights, Africa, abolitionism, United Church of Christ. **Special Collections:** Manuscript collections (8 million items); Aaron Douglas Art Collection (200 items); Victor DuBois Art Collection (81 items); Amistad Collection of African and American Art (65 items). **Holdings:** 19,000 books; 1600 bound periodical volumes; 15,000 pamphlets; 210 dissertations on microfilm; 2310 reels of microfilm; 500,000 clippings. **Subscriptions:** 650 journals and other serials; 31 newspapers. **Services:** Interlibrary loan; copying; library open to the public. **Computerized Information Services:** OCLC. **Networks/Consortia:** Member of SOLINET. **Publications:** Amistad Reports (newsletter), quarterly; Amistad Log (magazine), annual; Historical Source Research Materials on microfilm, irregular - all free upon request; Amistad Research Center manuscipt holdings, irregular - for sale. **Special Catalogs:** Catalog of the American Missionary Association Archives. **Staff:** Ulysses Ricard, Ref.Archv.; Andrew Simon, Asst.Archv.; Emanuella Spencer, Asst.Archv.; Wayne Coleman, Asst.Archv.; Robert M. Peck, Archv./Cat.; Venola Jones, Cat.; Grant Spradling, Adm. Aaron Douglas Coll.

★811★
(Amman) American Center - USIS Library (Educ)
Jebel Amman, Third Circle
Post Box 676
Amman, Jordan
Remarks: Maintained or supported by the U.S. Information Agency. Focus is on materials that will assist peoples outside the United States to learn about the United States, its people, history, culture, political processes, and social milieux.

★812★
Amoco Canada Petroleum Company, Ltd. - Library/Information Center (Energy, Sci-Engr)
P.O. Box 200, Sta. M
Calgary, AB, Canada T2P 2H8 Phone: (403)233-5606
Founded: 1965. **Staff:** 3. **Subjects:** Geology, petroleum engineering, petroleum economics, management, geophysics. **Holdings:** 25,052 books; 15,000 government documents; 4000 confidential reports; 2500 pamphlets. **Subscriptions:** 500 journals and other serials; 8 newspapers. **Services:** Interlibrary loan; copying; library open to the public with restrictions. **Automated Operations:** Computerized acquisitions, serials, and circulation. **Computerized Information Services:** PFDS Online, Info Globe, Dow Jones News/Retrieval, CAN/OLE. **Remarks:** Library located at 240 4th Ave., S.W.

★813★
Amoco Corporation - Central Research Library (Energy, Sci-Engr)
Amoco Research Center, Box 3083 Phone: (708)420-5545
Naperville, IL 60566-7083 B. Camille Stryck, Res.Supv.
Founded: 1920. **Staff:** Prof 4; Other 5. **Subjects:** Petroleum chemistry, physics, engineering, chemistry, chemical engineering, polymers. **Holdings:** 35,000 books; 40,000 bound periodical volumes; 15,000 reports; 15,000 cartridges of microfilm of journals; U.S. chemical patents, 1970 to present, on microfilm. **Subscriptions:** 2500 journals and other serials. **Services:** Interlibrary loan; copying; SDI; library open to the public with restrictions. **Automated Operations:** Computerized cataloging, serials, and journal routing. **Computerized Information Services:** DIALOG Information Services, ORBIT Search Service, OCLC, STN International; OnTyme Electronic Message Network Service, DIALMAIL (electronic mail services). **Networks/Consortia:** Member of ILLINET. **Publications:** Library Bulletin, monthly; Reports Alert, monthly; Current Awareness Bulletins - for internal distribution only. **Remarks:** FAX: (708)961-7992. Electronic mail address(es): AMOCO (OnTyme Electronic Message Network Service); 12844 (DIALMAIL). **Staff:** Beverly S. Tucker, Info.Spec.; Joy C. Greene, Info.Spec.; Bobbye D. Galloway, Info.Spec.

★814★
Amoco Corporation - Library/Information Center (Bus-Fin, Energy)
200 E. Randolph St. Phone: (312)856-5961
Chicago, IL 60601 Vicky A. Perlman, Mgr.
Founded: 1973. **Staff:** Prof 8; Other 9. **Subjects:** Petroleum technology, business, law, chemistry, engineering. **Holdings:** 65,000 volumes; technical reports; patents; business and technical information files; microforms. **Subscriptions:** 1000 journals and other serials; 20 newspapers. **Services:** Interlibrary loan; library open to researchers by appointment. **Automated Operations:** Computerized cataloging, serials, and circulation. **Computerized Information Services:** DIALOG Information Services, PFDS Online, Dow Jones News/Retrieval, Mead Data Central. **Publications:** Current Acquisitions List, biweekly - for internal distribution only. **Staff:** M. Evans, Supv.; M. Dorigan, Sys.Spec.; L. Matera, Info.Spec.; M. Vacula, Info.Spec.; N. Kelly, Info.Spec.; T. Pardo, Supv.

★815★
Amoco Production Company - Law Department Library
Box 591
Tulsa, OK 74102
Defunct.

★816★
Amoco Production Company - Library Information Center (Sci-Engr, Energy)
501 WestLake Park Blvd. Phone: (713)556-4217
Houston, TX 77079 Eloise F. Martinez, Lib.Supv.
Founded: 1980. **Staff:** Prof 5. **Subjects:** Geology, petroleum, geophysics, engineering, geoscience, business. **Special Collections:** Foreign scouting service documents; oceanography collection. **Holdings:** 38,000 books; 42,000 maps; 3700 reports; 800 dissertations; 60,000 microfiche. **Subscriptions:** 900 journals and other serials; 5 newspapers. **Services:** Interlibrary loan; copying; SDI; library open to the public with restrictions. **Automated Operations:** Computerized cataloging, acquisitions, serials, and circulation. **Computerized Information Services:** DIALOG Information Services, PFDS Online, Data-Star, RLIN, VU/TEXT Information Services; Corporate Libraries Network (internal database). **Networks/Consortia:** Member of Research Libraries Information Network (RLIN). **Publications:** New Acquisitions List; Petroconsultant's Daily News Telex. **Remarks:** FAX: (713)556-2139. Telex: 791226. **Staff:** Linda Delaney, Info. & Res.Libn.; Priscilla Johansen, Map Libn.; James Hooper, ILL Libn.; Verna M. Beal, Ref.Libn.; Mary Stein, Acq.Libn.; Yvette Crawford, Proc.; Lori Daskam, Circ.

★817★
Amoco Production Company - Research Center Library (Energy, Sci-Engr)
Box 3385 Phone: (918)660-3238
Tulsa, OK 74102 David Sollars, Tech.Serv.
Founded: 1943. **Staff:** 5. **Subjects:** Petroleum exploration and production, mathematics, physics, geology, chemistry, electronics, computer science. **Special Collections:** State and U.S. Geological Survey publications. **Holdings:** 40,000 volumes; 1600 maps; 800 reels of microfilm. **Subscriptions:** 500 journals and other serials. **Services:** Interlibrary loan; copying; library open by appointment. **Automated Operations:** Computerized cataloging and serials. **Computerized Information Services:** OCLC. **Remarks:** FAX: (918)660-4163. **Staff:** Paula Eggert; Paula Higgins; John Westervelt.

David A. Amos Health Sciences Library
See: **Mercy Hospital** (10132)

★818★
Amos Press - Library (Publ, Rec)
911 Vandemark Rd. Phone: (513)498-2111
Sidney, OH 45367 Karli Spiers, Libn.
Founded: 1966. **Staff:** Prof 1. **Subjects:** Coin and stamp collecting, collectible classic and antique cars. **Special Collections:** Numismatic collection; philatelic collection. **Holdings:** 18,500 volumes; 650 reels of microfilm. **Subscriptions:** 900 journals and other serials. **Services:** Copying (limited); library open to the public for research by appointment only. **Computerized Information Services:** CompuServe Information Service. **Remarks:** Publishes Coin World, Linn's Stamp News, and Cars & Parts. **Staff:** Kaeli Spiers, Libn.

★819★
AMP, Inc. - Technology Information Center (Sci-Engr)
Mail Stop 21-02
Box 3608 Phone: (717)541-3050
Harrisburg, PA 17105-3608 Bob Kuhn, Mgr.
Founded: 1956. **Staff:** Prof 3; Other 3. **Subjects:** Engineering - electrical, electronic, mechanical; plastics technology; electroplating; business. **Holdings:** 10,000 books; 500 journals; 10,000 volumes of back files. **Services:** Interlibrary loan; center not open to the public. **Automated Operations:** Computerized serials. **Computerized Information Services:** DIALOG Information Services; SCAN (internal database). **Remarks:** FAX: (717)541-3028. **Formerly:** Its Technical Library.

★820★
Ampex Corporation - Technical Information Services (Sci-Engr)
401 Broadway Phone: (415)367-3368
Redwood City, CA 94063 Marjorie Pettit Wilbur, Mgr.
Founded: 1959. **Staff:** Prof 1; Other 3. **Subjects:** Magnetics, magnetic recording, television, electronics, physics, chemistry, mathematics, optics, business, management. **Holdings:** 9000 books; 8000 bound periodical volumes; 2200 literature searches. **Subscriptions:** 380 journals and other serials; 11 newspapers. **Services:** Interlibrary loan; services not open to the public. **Automated Operations:** Computerized cataloging. **Computerized Information Services:** DIALOG Information Services, PFDS Online, LEXIS, NEXIS, Dow Jones News/Retrieval. **Publications:** Current literature bulletin, monthly; Magnetic Recording Bibliography. **Remarks:** FAX: (415)367-2810.

AMR Corporation - American Airlines, Inc.
See: **American Airlines, Inc.** (469)

AMS Information Clearinghouse
See: **National Arthritis and Musculoskeletal and Skin Diseases Information Clearinghouse** (11047)

Amstar Corporation
See: **Domino Sugar Corporation** (4950)

★821★
Amt der Burgenlandischen Landesregierung - Musiksammlung der Bibliothek des Burgenlandischen Landesmuseums (Mus)
Haydngasse 21 Phone: 2682 265229
A-7000 Eisenstadt, Austria Dr. Hanns Schmid, Hd. of Musm.
Subjects: Joseph Haydn, Johann Nepomuk Hummel, Franz Liszt. **Special Collections:** Bucherei der Rudolf Otte-Stiftung Raiding. **Holdings:** 620 books; 5 bound periodical volumes. **Services:** Library open to the public with restrictions. **Staff:** Dr. Gerhard Winkler, Mus.Ref.

★822★
Amundson Associates - Planning Reference Library
200 S. Mill
Springfield, OR 97477
Founded: 1955. **Subjects:** Building design, technical planning, Construction Specification Institute (CSI). **Holdings:** 600 books; 10,000 articles, papers; 5000 reports; 3000 slides. **Remarks:** Currently inactive.

★823★
Amway Corporation - Corporate Library (Bus-Fin)
7575 E. Fulton St. Phone: (616)676-6308
Ada, MI 49355 Leslie Burke, Corp.Libn.
Founded: 1970. **Staff:** Prof 1; Other 1.5. **Subjects:** Chemistry, direct selling, business. **Holdings:** 10,000 books; 10,000 archival items. **Subscriptions:** 1400 journals and other serials; 7 newspapers. **Services:** Interlibrary loan; copying; SDI; library open to the public by appointment for reference use only. **Computerized Information Services:** DIALOG Information Services, InvesText, Dow Jones News/Retrieval; produces internal database (Amway literature and publicity). **Networks/Consortia:** Member of Michigan Library Consortium (MLC), Lakeland Area Library Network (LAKENET). **Remarks:** FAX: (616)676-7142.

AMX Library
See: **Classic AMX Club, International** (3781)

★824★
ANACOMP - Engineering Technical Library (Sci-Engr)
5940 Fairmount Ave. Phone: (619)291-9960
San Diego, CA 92120 Fay Christman
Subjects: Computer output microfilm, optics, photographic science and engineering, electronics, electronic data processing, software development. **Holdings:** 3000 volumes. **Subscriptions:** 83 journals and other serials; 6 newspapers. **Services:** Interlibrary loan; copying; library open to the public by application.

★825★
Anaheim Memorial Hospital - Medical Library (Med)
1111 W. LaPalma Ave.
P.O. Box 3005 Phone: (714)999-6020
Anaheim, CA 92803 Veena N. Vyas, Dir., Med.Libn.
Staff: Prof 1; Other 1. **Subjects:** Medicine. **Holdings:** 1200 books. **Subscriptions:** 136 journals and other serials. **Services:** Interlibrary loan; library not open to the public. **Computerized Information Services:** MEDLINE, DIALOG Information Services. **Networks/Consortia:** Member of National Network of Libraries of Medicine - Pacific Southwest Region. **Remarks:** FAX: (714)999-6099.

★826★
Analytic & Biological Laboratories, Inc. - Library (Biol Sci)
24350 Indoplex Circle Phone: (313)477-6666
Farmington Hills, MI 48331 Maureen Menequzzo, Libn.
Subjects: Chemistry, microbiology, minerals, toxicology. **Holdings:** 600 books; 2400 reports. **Subscriptions:** 24 journals and other serials. **Services:** Library not open to the public. **Remarks:** FAX: (313)477-4604.

★827★
The Analytic Sciences Corporation - Corporate Library (Sci-Engr)
55 Walkers Brook Dr. Phone: (617)942-2000
Reading, MA 01867 Martha E. Dionne, Dir.
Staff: Prof 2; Other 2. **Subjects:** Control systems, navigation, math and mathematical modeling, electrical engineering, waste management, computer programming, physics, meteorology, artificial intelligence, image processing, medical imaging. **Holdings:** 15,000 books; 16,000 technical reports. **Subscriptions:** 627 journals and other serials. **Services:** Library not open to the public. **Automated Operations:** Computerized circulation. **Computerized Information Services:** DIALOG Information Services, Remote Sensing On-Line Retrieval System (RESORS), DunsPrint. **Publications:** Library Bulletin, monthly. **Remarks:** FAX: (617)942-7100. **Also Known As:** TASC.

★828★
The Analytic Sciences Corporation - TASC Technical Library (Bus-Fin)
1101 Wilson Blvd., Suite 1500 Phone: (703)351-6551
Arlington, VA 22209 Katherine M. LaVallee, Libn.
Subjects: Economic and cost analysis, systems engineering, operations research, communications, navigation, computer sciences. **Holdings:** 2000 books; 100 documents. **Subscriptions:** 135 journals and other serials; 2 newspapers. **Services:** Interlibrary loan; library not open to the public. **Computerized Information Services:** DIALOG Information Services, U.S. National Technical Information Service (NTIS), DTIC. **Remarks:** Alternate telephone number(s): 558-7400. FAX: (703)524-6666.

★829★
Analytical Psychology Club of New York - Kristine Mann Library (Soc Sci)
C.G. Jung Center, 4th Fl.
28 E. 39th St.
New York, NY 10016 Phone: (212)697-7877
Founded: 1945. **Staff:** 2. **Subjects:** Carl Gustav Jung, analytical psychology. **Special Collections:** Jung Press Archive (C.G. Jung and/or analytical psychology; 2500 clippings from newspapers and periodicals in the United States and abroad, 1905 to present). **Holdings:** 10,325 books; 400 bound periodical volumes; 3099 clipped articles; 645 cassettes and tapes. **Subscriptions:** 40 journals and other serials. **Services:** Copying; library open to the public. **Computerized Information Services:** DIALOG Information Services. **Remarks:** The collection includes everything published by Jung in German and English editions; all the works of other specialists in the field of analytical psychology; books and articles by others about analytical psychology; allied materials in mythology, folklore, religions, alchemy, art, anthropology, and symbolism. **Staff:** Doris B. Albrecht, Libn. and Co-Ch.; Peggy Brooks, Co-Ch.

★830★
Analytical Systems Engineering Corporation - Library (Sci-Engr)
5 Burlington Woods, No.100 Phone: (617)272-7910
Burlington, MA 01803-4939 Rayna Lee Caplan, Libn.
Staff: Prof 1. **Subjects:** Communication, marine and urban transportation, navigation systems, environmental engineering. **Holdings:** 500 books; 3000 technical reports. **Subscriptions:** 50 journals and other serials. **Services:** Interlibrary loan; copying; library open to the public with restrictions. **Publications:** Library Accessions List, monthly - for internal distribution only. **Remarks:** FAX: (617)272-1341.

★831★
Anchor Foundation - Library of Social History
410 West St.
New York, NY 10014
Founded: 1972. **Subjects:** U.S. socialist movements and labor history. **Holdings:** 5000 books; 265 bound periodical volumes; 160 reels of microfilm. **Remarks:** Currently inactive.

★832★
Anchorage Daily News - Library (Publ)
1001 Northway
P.O. Box 149001 Phone: (907)257-4593
Anchorage, AK 99514 Sharon Palmisano
Founded: 1985. **Staff:** Prof 2. **Subjects:** Newspaper reference topics. **Special Collections:** Anchorage Daily News, 1972 to present (microfilm). **Holdings:** 2000 books. **Subscriptions:** 30 journals and other serials; 50 newspapers. **Services:** Library open to the public on a limited schedule. **Computerized Information Services:** VU/TEXT Information Services, DIALOG Information Services, DataTimes. **Remarks:** FAX: (907)258-2157.

★833★
Anchorage Museum of History and Art - Archives (Hist, Art)
121 W. 7th Ave. Phone: (907)343-6189
Anchorage, AK 99501 M. Diane Brenner, Musm.Archv.
Founded: 1968. **Staff:** Prof 1. **Subjects:** Alaskana - prehistoric, native, Russian, Gold Rush, current; fine arts. **Special Collections:** Valdez photographs, 1900-1910 (12 albums); Alaska Railroad historical photographs (10,000); Ward Wells photograph collection (100,000); FAA Collection (10,000); Stephen D. McCutcheon photograph collection (50,000). **Holdings:** 6000 books; 200,000 photographs; 16 boxes of Alaskana archives; 10,000 slides of contemporary Alaskan art; 8 VF drawers; 8 drawers of biographies of Alaska artists; 200 maps. **Subscriptions:** 15 journals and other serials. **Services:** Interlibrary loan (limited); copying; archives open to the public. **Special Indexes:** Index to Alaska Railroad Microfiche Project; Ward Wells Stock Series Indexing Project (Alaska Historical Commission Studies in History, No. 186). **Remarks:** FAX: (907)343-6149.

★834★
Anchorage School District - Bilingual Educational Program - Library (Educ, Hum)
4600 Debarr (Adm. Annex) Phone: (907)269-2256
Anchorage, AK 99504 Vicki Lee Ross, Quality Assurance Spec.
Founded: 1978. **Staff:** 1. **Subjects:** English as a second language, Spanish, Korean, Japanese, multicultural literature, Pacific Rim social studies. **Holdings:** 5000 books; records; audiocassettes; software programs; language master cards. **Services:** Interlibrary loan; library open to the public with restrictions. **Networks/Consortia:** Member of Western Library Network (WLN). **Remarks:** FAX: (907)269-2222.

★835★
Ancient and Honorable Artillery Company of Massachusetts - Library (Hist)
427 Commercial St.
Coast Guard Base Phone: (617)227-1638
Boston, MA 02109 John F. McCauley, Cur.
Founded: 1638. **Staff:** Prof 1. **Subjects:** History - military, colonial, 19th century military. **Holdings:** 2000 books; company records. **Services:** Copying; library open to researchers for reference use only.

★836★
Ancora Psychiatric Hospital - Health Sciences Library (Med)
Hammonton, NJ 08037 Phone: (609)561-1700
Lorraine L. Chudomelka, Libn.
Founded: 1955. **Staff:** Prof 1. **Subjects:** Psychiatry, psychology, medicine, occupational therapy. **Holdings:** 3500 books; 600 bound periodical volumes; 289 audio cassettes; 24 video cassettes; 16 films. **Subscriptions:** 72 journals and other serials. **Services:** Interlibrary loan; copying; library open to the public for reference use only.

★837★
Andean Group - Cartagena Agreement Board - Documentation Center (Soc Sci)
Avenida Paseo de la Republica 3895
Casilla de Correo 18-1177 Phone: 14 414212
Lima 27, Peru Marina Schreiber Duarte, Libn.
Founded: 1970. **Staff:** 9. **Subjects:** Andean countries - economic development, economic integration, industry; technology; agriculture; international and Andean economics. **Special Collections:** Documents of international organizations (ALADI, CEPAL, UNCTAD, GATT, SIECA, CEE, UNESCO, OEA, OMPI, SELA). **Holdings:** 35,000 books, serials, documents, maps, microfiche, reels of microfilm, and vertical files. **Subscriptions:** 200 journals and other serials. **Services:** Center open to qualified investigators and on demand to the private and public sectors. **Computerized Information Services:** BIBLIOGRAPHIC, LEGAL, DOCUMENTAL (internal databases). **Publications:** Microtesauro de Terminos de Integracion, 3rd edition; Bibliografia de Integracion, annual; Revistas CENDOC (periodicals table of contents), bimonthly; Alerta CENDOC (recent acquisitions), bimonthly - for internal distribution only; Leyes Economicas (Andean countries legislation abstracts), monthly - for internal distribution only. **Remarks:** FAX: 14-420911. Telex: JUNAC 20104 PE; JUNAC 21107 PE. **Staff:** Carmen Caparo, Libn.; Maria Luisa Thornberry, Libn.; Araceli Rivas De Ramos, Econ.; Cecilia Davila De Subauste, Libn.

★838★
Arthur Andersen - Business Information Center (Bus-Fin)
33 W. Monroe St. Phone: (312)507-6029
Chicago, IL 60603 Lynn D. Rendall, Dir., Lib.Serv.
Founded: 1959. **Staff:** Prof 5; Other 5. **Subjects:** Accounting, business, finance. **Holdings:** 16,000 books; 1000 bound periodical volumes; 50 VF drawers; 100,000 items on microfilm; U.S. Securities and Exchange Commission (SEC) filings, 1969 to present, on microfiche or compact disc; Wall Street Journal market sections, 1969 to present, on microfiche. **Subscriptions:** 400 journals and other serials; 25 newspapers. **Services:** Interlibrary loan; SDI; library open to the public by appointment. **Computerized Information Services:** DIALOG Information Services, LEXIS, NEXIS, VU/TEXT Information Services, Dow Jones News/Retrieval, DataTimes; CD-ROMs (Lotus One Source, Compact Disclosure, Business Periodicals Ondisc, Dun's Million Dollar Disc, Laser D/SEC). **Networks/Consortia:** Member of Chicago Library System. **Remarks:** FAX: (312)507-6748. **Formerly:** Arthur Andersen & Co.

★839★
Arthur Andersen/Andersen Consulting - Library (Bus-Fin)
45 S. 7th St. Phone: (612)334-4436
Minneapolis, MN 55402 Doris A. Dingley, Hd.Libn.
Founded: 1940. **Staff:** Prof 2; Other 3. **Subjects:** Taxation, accounting, auditing, systems integration, change management. **Holdings:** 1000 books; loose-leaf tax, accounting, and computer services. **Subscriptions:** 200 journals and other serials; 2 newspapers. **Services:** Library not open to the public. **Automated Operations:** Computerized cataloging, serials, and acquisitions (Datatrek). **Computerized Information Services:** DIALOG Information Services, NAARS, LEXIS, NEXIS, Dow Jones News/Retrieval, DataTimes, WESTLAW. **Publications:** Library News (newsletter), 4/year - for internal distribution only. **Remarks:** FAX: (612)334-4700. A branch library is maintained in St. Paul, MN., FAX: (612)290-6959. **Staff:** David Lane, Ref.Libn., (334-4422).

★840★
Arthur Andersen & Co. - Andersen Consulting Library (Bus-Fin)
1717 E. 9th St. Phone: (216)781-2140
Cleveland, OH 44114 Karen Perman, Libn.
Subjects: Taxation, auditing, industry research, computer software and applications. **Holdings:** 2000 books; 20 nonbook items. **Subscriptions:** 204 journals and other serials. **Services:** Library not open to the public. **Computerized Information Services:** DIALOG Information Services, Dow Jones News/Retrieval, Dun & Bradstreet Business Credit Services, LEXIS, DataTimes, ORBIT Search Service. **Remarks:** FAX: (216)781-3683.

★841★
Arthur Andersen & Co. - Audit, Tax, and Consulting Library (Bus-Fin)
1 Renaissance Square
2 N. Central Ave., Suite 1000 Phone: (602)257-9234
Phoenix, AZ 85004 Linda Barzilai, Head
Staff: 1. **Subjects:** Taxation - federal and state; auditing; management information systems. **Holdings:** Figures not available. **Subscriptions:** 60 journals and other serials; 5 newspapers. **Services:** Copying; library open to clients, former employees, and referrals. **Computerized Information Services:** Mead Data Central, Inc., NEXIS, LEXIS, National Automated Accounting Research System. **Publications:** List of publications - available on request. **Remarks:** FAX: (602)495-8765. Telex: 668430.

★842★
Arthur Andersen & Co. - Central Library (Bus-Fin)
711 Louisiana, Suite 700 Phone: (713)237-2754
Houston, TX 77002 Linda S. Dodson, Libn.
Founded: 1941. **Staff:** Prof 1; Other 4. **Subjects:** Taxation, accounting, auditing, computer hardware and software. **Holdings:** 5000 books; 400 bound periodical volumes; 800 reels of microfilm; 500 ultrafiche. **Subscriptions:** 303 journals and other serials. **Services:** Library open to the public with restrictions. **Computerized Information Services:** Maxwell Macmillan Taxes Online, DIALOG Information Services, Dow Jones News/Retrieval, DataTimes, WESTLAW, CCH (Commerce Clearing House, Inc.), Mead Data Central; CD-ROMs (CD/Corporate, CD/Private Plus, Compustat PC Plus). **Remarks:** FAX: (713)237-2786. Telex: 775-431. **Staff:** Penny Knox; Ann Lujan; Elise McCutchen; Mary Jo Pena.

★843★
Arthur Andersen & Co. - Information Centre (Bus-Fin)
Toronto Dominion Centre
Box 29 Phone: (416)863-1540
Toronto, ON, Canada M5K 1B9 Susan C. Lipsey, Hd.Libn.
Founded: 1960. **Staff:** Prof 1; Other 2. **Subjects:** Accounting, auditing, taxation, management consulting, information technology, industry. **Holdings:** 2000 books; 20 bound periodical volumes; 100,000 subject files on microfilm; 500 company publications. **Subscriptions:** 150 journals and other serials; 6 newspapers. **Services:** Interlibrary loan; library not open to the public. **Automated Operations:** Computerized cataloging and serials. **Computerized Information Services:** Info Globe, QL Systems, LEXIS, NEXIS, Infomart Online, Reuters, DIALOG Information Services, Computer Intelligence, Canadian Tax Online, CCH Access, Business Opportunities Sourcing System; internal databases. **Publications:** Canadian Tax and Trade Brief, irregular - to clients and interested parties. **Remarks:** FAX: (416)947-7878. **Formerly:** Its Library.

★844★
Arthur Andersen & Co. - Learning Resource Center - Center for Professional Education (Bus-Fin)
1405 N. 5th Ave. Phone: (708)444-4514
St. Charles, IL 60174 Marilyn G. Taillon, Libn.
Founded: 1980. **Staff:** Prof 2; Other 2.5. **Subjects:** Training, management development, organizational development, adult education, evaluation. **Holdings:** 2400 books; 1200 reports; 25 microfiche; 200 reels of microfilm. **Subscriptions:** 4 newspapers. **Services:** Interlibrary loan; center not open to the public. **Computerized Information Services:** DIALOG Information Services, T.R.A.I.N. (Education and Training Courses), NEXIS. Contact Person: Vicky Michalik. **Networks/Consortia:** Member of DuPage Library System. **Remarks:** FAX: (708)377-3794.

★845★
Arthur Andersen & Co. - Library (Bus-Fin)
Box 193938 Phone: (415)546-8466
San Francisco, CA 94119 Martha Ruske Kassin, Dir., Lib.Serv.
Staff: Prof 2; Other 2. **Subjects:** Tax law, accounting, management consulting, auditing, business. **Holdings:** 2900 books; releases of the Financial Accounting Standards Board and the American Institute of Certified Public Accountants; 190 loose-leaf services. **Subscriptions:** 390 journals and other serials; 20 newspapers. **Services:** Interlibrary loan; library open to the public only with approval of company partner. **Automated Operations:** Computerized cataloging. **Computerized Information Services:** DIALOG Information Services, LEXIS, NEXIS, Dow Jones News/Retrieval, NewsNet, Inc., RLIN, National Automated Accounting Research System (NAARS), DataTimes, Legi-Tech, InvesText. **Networks/Consortia:** Member of CLASS, Bay Area Library and Information Network. **Remarks:** Library located at One Market Plaza, Spear St. Tower, Suite 3400, San Francisco, CA 94105. FAX: (415)543-1827.

★846★
Arthur Andersen & Co. - Library (Bus-Fin)
One Financial Plaza
Hartford, CT 06103 Phone: (203)280-0526
Founded: 1962. **Staff:** Prof 1; Other 1. **Subjects:** General accounting - taxation, auditing and consulting; tax law. **Holdings:** 500 books; reports; microfilm. **Subscriptions:** 250 journals and other serials; 4 newspapers. **Services:** Interlibrary loan; answers telephone queries; library open to the public by special arrangement. **Computerized Information Services:** LEXIS, Dun & Bradstreet Business Credit Services, DIALOG Information Services. **Remarks:** FAX: (203)280-0894. **Staff:** Cynthia A. Goldman, Libn.

★847★
Arthur Andersen & Co. - Library (Bus-Fin)
International Place
Fort Hill Sq. Phone: (617)330-4596
Boston, MA 02110 Paula Ingraham, Libn.
Staff: Prof 1; Other 1. **Subjects:** Tax law and legislation, accounting and auditing, management consulting, business, computer applications, statistics. **Holdings:** 3700 books; 30 titles on microfilm; 500 annual reports; 600 reels of microfilm; 32 VF drawers of company reports; 500 pamphlets. **Subscriptions:** 500 journals, newsletters, and other serials; 20 newspapers. **Services:** Interlibrary loan; copying; library open to clients and students with restrictions. **Automated Operations:** Computerized acquisitions, cataloging, and circulation. **Computerized Information Services:** LEXIS, InvesText, DIALOG Information Services, Dow Jones News/Retrieval, Dun & Bradstreet Business Credit Services, CI (Computer Intelligence), WESTLAW ;internal database; CD-ROM. **Remarks:** FAX: (617)439-9731. For telex information, call (617)443-0107.

★848★
Arthur Andersen & Co. - Library (Bus-Fin)
1010 Market St.
St. Louis, MO 63101 Phone: (314)621-6767
Founded: 1982. **Staff:** Prof 1; Other 1. **Subjects:** Accounting, taxation, consulting, software. **Holdings:** 7000 books; company publications. **Subscriptions:** 200 journals and other serials; 6 newspapers. **Services:** Library not open to the public. **Computerized Information Services:** DIALOG Information Services, Dow Jones News/Retrieval, Mead Data Central, InvesText; CD-ROM (COMPACT DISCLOSURE). **Remarks:** FAX: (314)621-1956. **Staff:** Marsha Fulton.

★849★
Arthur Andersen & Co. - Library (Bus-Fin)
1345 Avenue of the Americas Phone: (212)708-4000
New York, NY 10105 Louise Wagner, Libn.
Founded: 1921. **Staff:** Prof 1; Other 7. **Subjects:** Accounting, management information consulting, general business. **Special Collections:** Management consulting. **Holdings:** 8000 volumes; 250 VF drawers; disclosure file of annual and 10K reports and proxies for 15,000 companies on microfiche. **Subscriptions:** 460 journals and other serials; 20 newspapers. **Services:** Interlibrary loan; copying; library open to the public by appointment. **Automated Operations:** Computerized cataloging, acquisitions, serials, and circulation. **Computerized Information Services:** DIALOG Information Services, Mead Data Central, Dow Jones News/Retrieval, Disclosure Information Group, Dun & Bradstreet Business Credit Services, INVESTEXT; internal database.

★850★
Arthur Andersen & Co. - Tax Library (Law)
10 S. LaSalle St., Rm. 3033 Phone: (312)507-7126
Chicago, IL 60603 Maria B. Smyk, Tax Libn.
Staff: Prof 2; Other 1. **Subjects:** United States and international tax law. **Holdings:** 5500 books; 40 bound periodical volumes; 6 VF drawers; pamphlets. **Subscriptions:** 250 journals and other serials. **Services:** Interlibrary loan; library not open to the public. **Computerized Information Services:** DIALOG Information Services, LEXIS, NEXIS. **Remarks:** FAX: (312)507-7210. **Staff:** Joshua Ben Avraham.

C.W. Andersen Library
See: **Australian Society of CPAs** (1347)

★851★
Andersen Consulting - Consulting Library (Comp Sci)
33 W. Monroe St. Phone: (312)507-7976
Chicago, IL 60603 Judith Keeley, Ref.Libn.
Founded: 1978. **Staff:** Prof 2; Other 2. **Subjects:** Computers, management consulting. **Holdings:** 1500 books; 500 reports; 15 microfiche. **Subscriptions:** 175 journals and other serials; 4 newspapers. **Services:** Interlibrary loan; SDI; library open to the public through ILL only. **Automated Operations:** Computerized cataloging. **Computerized Information Services:** DIALOG Information Services, DataTimes, NEXIS, OCLC EPIC. **Networks/Consortia:** Member of Chicago Library System. **Remarks:** FAX: (312)507-0123.

Elmer L. & Eleanor J. Andersen Horticultural Library
See: **University of Minnesota - Landscape Arboretum** (18917)

★852★
Andersen Laboratories, Inc. - Library (Sci-Engr)
45 Old Iron Ore Rd. Phone: (203)286-9090
Bloomfield, CT 06002 Fran Feldman, Libn.
Founded: 1964. **Staff:** 2. **Subjects:** Electronics, microwave, television. **Holdings:** 632 books. **Subscriptions:** 23 journals and other serials. **Services:** Library not open to the public. **Remarks:** FAX: (203)242-4472.

★853★
Andersen Window Corporation - Information Center (Sci-Engr)
100 4th Ave., N. Phone: (612)430-7370
Bayport, MN 55003-1096 Catherine Lange, Info.Ctr.Adm.
Staff: Prof 1. **Subjects:** Windows, plastics, wood. **Special Collections:** Sweets Catalog Collection. **Holdings:** 500 books; 25 bound periodical volumes. **Subscriptions:** 542 journals and other serials; 5 newspapers. **Services:** Interlibrary loan; center not open to the public. **Computerized Information Services:** DIALOG Information Services, NERAC, Inc.

Allen C. Anderson Memorial Law Library
See: **Pinellas County Law Library - St. Petersburg Branch** (13068)

★854★
Anderson and Associates, Inc. - Library (Sci-Engr)
919 F.M. Rd. 1959 Phone: (713)481-5840
Houston, TX 77034 Jerry Garwood, Libn.
Subjects: Metallurgy, analytical chemistry. **Holdings:** 500 books; 2000 bound periodical volumes; 4000 reports. **Services:** Library open to the public on fee basis.

Betty M. Anderson Library
See: **Intercollegiate Center for Nursing Education** (8033)

Dwight Anderson Memorial Music Library
See: **University of Louisville - Dwight Anderson Memorial Music Library** (18769)

★855★
Anderson Fine Arts Center - Research Library (Art)
226 W. 8th St. Phone: (317)649-1248
Anderson, IN 46016 Deborah McBratney-Stapleton, Dir.
Founded: 1967. **Staff:** Prof 1. **Subjects:** Art. **Holdings:** 750 books; 1900 unbound periodicals; 500 exhibition catalogs. **Subscriptions:** 20 journals and other serials. **Services:** Interlibrary loan; copying; library open to the public for reference use only. **Publications:** Newsletter, quarterly - to members, media, and other cultural institutions. **Special Catalogs:** Special exhibition catalogs.

Anderson House Museum
See: **Society of the Cincinnati Library - Anderson House Museum** (15314)

I.C. Anderson Memorial Library & Media Center
See: **First Baptist Church** (5728)

John E. Anderson Graduate School of Management
See: **University of California, Los Angeles - John E. Anderson Graduate School of Management - Library** (18387)

★856★
Anderson, Kill, Olick & Oshinsky - Library (Law)
666 3rd Ave. Phone: (212)850-0768
New York, NY 10017 Nina Cerny, Libn.
Staff: Prof 1; Other 4. **Subjects:** Bankruptcy, securities, products liability, insurance, corporate and antitrust law. **Holdings:** 15,000 books. **Subscriptions:** 138 journals and other serials; 5 newspapers. **Services:** Interlibrary loan; library not open to the public. **Computerized Information Services:** LEXIS, DIALOG Information Services, WESTLAW. **Publications:** From the Law Library (newsletter), monthly - for internal distribution only. **Remarks:** FAX: (212)850-0733.

L.W. Anderson Genealogical Library
See: **Vassar Priscilla Anderson Memorial Foundation** (19790)

★857★
Anderson Laboratories, Inc. - Library (Sci-Engr)
6330 Industrial Loop Phone: (414)421-7600
Greendale, WI 53129 Ralph Meyer, Hd.
Subjects: Metallurgy. **Holdings:** 500 books; 1500 reports. **Services:** Library open to the public on fee basis. **Remarks:** FAX: (414)421-6540.

Anderson Library
See: **Georgia (State) Department of Natural Resources - Coastal Resources Division** (6402)

M.D. Anderson Cancer Center
See: **University of Texas - M.D. Anderson Cancer Center** (19374)

★858★
R.V. Anderson Associates Limited - Library (Env-Cons)
1210 Sheppard Ave., E., Suite 401 Phone: (416)497-8600
Willowdale, ON, Canada M2K 1E3 Linda Diener, Libn.
Founded: 1975. **Staff:** Prof 1. **Subjects:** Pollution control, water supply and resources, tunnels and shafts, environmental planning, transportation, urban development. **Holdings:** 2004 volumes; company reports and proposals; provincial, federal, U.S. government documents. **Subscriptions:** 60 journals and other serials; 20 newspapers. **Services:** Interlibrary loan; copying; library open to the public by appointment. **Computerized Information Services:** CAN/OLE, DIALOG Information Services. **Remarks:** FAX: (416)497-0342.

Anderson Resource Centre
See: **Loyalist College of Applied Arts & Technology** (9417)

★859★
Andover College - Library (Educ)
901 Washington Ave. Phone: (207)774-6126
Portland, ME 04103 Janet Harmon, Libn.
Staff: Prof 1; Other 1. **Subjects:** Business, accounting, management, secretarial science, computer science, medical assistance, paralegal. **Holdings:** 6372 books. **Subscriptions:** 48 journals and other serials. **Services:** Interlibrary loan; copying; library open to the public by appointment. **Computerized Information Services:** InfoTrac.

Andover-Harvard Theological Library
See: **Harvard University - Divinity School** (6958)

★860★
Andover Historical Society - Caroline M. Underhill Research Library (Hist)
97 Main St. Phone: (508)475-2236
Andover, MA 01810 Charlotte E. Smith, Dir./Cur.
Founded: 1911. **Staff:** 3. **Subjects:** Local history, genealogy, architecture, decorative arts. **Special Collections:** Andover imprints (270 volumes). **Holdings:** 2000 books; 16 VF drawers; 17,500 historical and contemporary photographs and negatives; 100 linear feet of manuscript materials; prints; drawings; maps; architectural plans. **Services:** Copying; library open to the public. **Staff:** Charlotte E. Smith, Dir./Cur.; Barbara Thibault, Dir. of Educ.; Peg Hughes, Asst. to Dir./Cur.

★861★
Andover Newton Theological School - Trask Library (Rel-Phil)
169 Herrick Rd. Phone: (617)964-1100
Newton Centre, MA 02159 Sharon Taylor, Dir.
Founded: 1807. **Staff:** Prof 3; Other 4. **Subjects:** Religion, theology. **Special Collections:** Papers of Isaac Backus (7 feet; 4 reels of microfilm); papers of Jonathan Edwards (4 feet; 10 reels of microfilm); records of New England Baptist Library Association (21 feet). **Holdings:** 212,955 volumes; 5000 pamphlets; 890 microforms. **Subscriptions:** 581 journals and other serials. **Services:** Interlibrary loan; copying; library open to graduate students only upon request. **Automated Operations:** Computerized cataloging. **Computerized Information Services:** OCLC. **Networks/Consortia:** Member of Boston Theological Institute Libraries, NELINET, Inc. **Remarks:** FAX: (617)965-9756. **Staff:** Louise Pippin, Hd., Circ.; Diana Yount, Assoc.Dir. & Spec.Coll.; Jeffrey Brigham, Tech.Serv.Libn.

Andrews Air Force Base
See: **U.S. Air Force Base - Andrews Base Library** (16825)

Arthur Andrews Memorial Library
See: **Grand Rapids Junior College** (6634)

★862★
Andrews University - James White Library - Special Collections (Rel-Phil, Educ)
Berrien Springs, MI 49104 Phone: (616)471-3264
Marley H. Soper, Dir.
Founded: 1962. **Staff:** 26. **Holdings:** Adventist Heritage Center: history and development of the Adventist Movement and of the Seventh-day Adventist Church before and since 1844 (475 linear feet of personal papers, letters, manuscripts, photographs); books, special collections, and theses (27,002); S.D.A. denominational and Millerite periodicals (6112); pamphlets (10,611). Teaching Materials Center: pamphlets and curriculum guides (20,014); textbooks (11,331); recordings (12,532); filmstrips, film loops, slide sets (12,993); complete ERIC microfiche collection. Music Materials Center: sound recordings (5257); scores (6549); reference books (941). Architecture Resource Center: volumes (9000); Environmental Design Research Association collection. **Subscriptions:** 2977 journals and other serials; 43 newspapers. **Services:** Interlibrary loan; copying; collections open to the public with restrictions. **Automated Operations:** Computerized cataloging, acquisitions, and serials. **Computerized Information Services:** BRS Information Technologies, DIALOG Information Services, OCLC; CD-ROMs. Performs searches on fee basis. Contact Person: Harvey Brenneise, Hd.Ref.Libn., 471-3275. **Networks/Consortia:** Member of Berrien Library Consortium, Southwest Michigan Library Cooperative (SMLC). **Publications:** SDA Obituary Bibliography (on microfiche). **Remarks:** FAX: (616)471-9895. Houses E.G. White Research Center. **Staff:** Jess Oliver, Dir., Tchg.Mtls.Ctr.; Elaine Waller, Dir., Mus.Mtls.Ctr.; Louise Dederen, Cur., Adventist Heritage Ctr.

★863★
Androscoggin Historical Society - Clarence E. March Library (Hist)
County Bldg.
2 Turner St.
Auburn, ME 04210 Phone: (207)784-0586
Founded: 1923. **Staff:** 3. **Subjects:** History of Androscoggin County and Maine. **Special Collections:** Early photographs of local people and places (500). **Holdings:** 5000 books; 50 bound periodical volumes; 2000 historical papers; 1000 records; 70 maps; 400 documents; 5000 pages on microfilm. **Services:** Copying; library open to the public for reference use only. **Staff:** Robert C. Beliveau, Cur.; Robert Taylor, Dir./Exec.Sec.

★864★
Androscoggin Valley Hospital - Medical Library (Med)
59 Page Hill Rd. Phone: (603)752-2200
Berlin, NH 03570 Linda Laperle
Subjects: Medicine. **Holdings:** 450 volumes. **Subscriptions:** 18 journals and other serials. **Services:** Interlibrary loan; copying; library open to the public. **Networks/Consortia:** Member of North Country Consortium (NCC). **Remarks:** FAX: (603)752-2376.

Harvey A. Andruss Library
See: **Bloomsburg University** (1904)

Ang Pambansang Aklatan
See: **Philippines - National Library - Special Collections** (13002)

★865★
Angel Mounds State Historic Site - Library (Soc Sci)
8215 Pollack Ave. Phone: (812)853-3956
Evansville, IN 47715 Rebecca Harris, Cur.
Staff: 5. **Subjects:** Native Americans, Mississippian Indians, nature, Indiana history. **Holdings:** 100. **Subscriptions:** 4 journals and other serials. **Services:** Copying; library open to the public for reference use only. **Staff:** Peggy Brooks, Asst.Cur.

Katharine Angell Library
See: **Culinary Institute of America** (4470)

Angell Memorial Animal Hospital Library
See: **Massachusetts Society for the Prevention of Cruelty to Animals (MSPCA)** (9827)

★866★
Anglican Church Army in Canada - Cowan Memorial Library (Rel-Phil)
397 Brunswick Ave.
Toronto, ON, Canada M5R 2Z2 Phone: (416)924-9279
Founded: 1975. **Staff:** Prof 1. **Subjects:** Christology, Old and New Testament, Christian ethics, Christian doctrine, church history, evangelism, sermons. **Special Collections:** Catalog and index of the W.W. and R.F. Judd Collection; early Church Army photographs; Canada and United Kingdom, early to mid-20th century. **Holdings:** 12,020 books; 120 tapes; 2 drawers of photographs and slides. **Subscriptions:** 12 journals and other serials, 12 newspapers. **Services:** Interlibrary loan; copying; library open to the public.

★867★
Anglican Church of Canada - Church House Library (Rel-Phil)
600 Jarvis St. Phone: (416)924-9192
Toronto, ON, Canada M4Y 2J6 Karen Evans, Libn.
Founded: 1965. **Staff:** Prof 2; Other 1. **Subjects:** Anglican Communion, social conditions, missions, Christian education. **Holdings:** 2000 books; 70 unbound periodicals; 27 VF drawers; 16 drawers of photographs. **Subscriptions:** 200 journals and other serials. **Services:** Interlibrary loan; copying; SDI (limited); library open to the public with priority to internal clientele. **Automated Operations:** INMAGIC. **Computerized Information Services:** Envoy 100 (electronic mail service). **Special Catalogs:** Resource Centre catalog of AV materials and print items, annual. **Remarks:** FAX: (416)968-7983. Electronic mail address(es): Marturia (Envoy 100). **Also Known As:** Chancellor R.V. Harris Memorial Library.

★868★
Anglican Church of Canada - Diocese of Calgary - Anglican Archives (Rel-Phil)
Special Collections - Humanities/Arts/Social Sciences Area
Mackimmie Library
University of Calgary
2500 University Dr., N.W. Phone: (403)220-5972
Calgary, AB, Canada T2N 1N4 Apollonia Lang Steele, Spec.Coll.Libn.
Founded: 1945. **Subjects:** History of the Anglican Church in Calgary. **Holdings:** Correspondence and records, 1883 to present. **Services:** Archives open to the public only with permission of the Diocese. **Computerized Information Services:** Electronic mail. **Remarks:** FAX: (403)282-6837.

★869★
Anglican Church of Canada - Diocese of Montreal - Archives (Rel-Phil)
1444 Union Ave. Phone: (514)843-6577
Montreal, PQ, Canada H3A 2B8 Dr. Richard Virr, Archv.
Founded: 1950. **Staff:** Prof 1; Other 6. **Subjects:** History of the Diocese of Montreal, Ecclesiastical Province of Canada, and General Synod of the Anglican Church of Canada. **Holdings:** Registers of marriages, births, and deaths; old parish and other records; Episcopal and other letters; Anglican journals and newspapers. **Services:** Archives open to accredited researchers. **Remarks:** FAX: (514)843-6344. **Also Known As:** Montreal Diocesan Archives.

★870★
Anglican Church of Canada - Ecclesiastical Province of British Columbia & Diocese of New Westminster - Archives (Rel-Phil)
6000 Iona Dr. Phone: (604)228-9031
Vancouver, BC, Canada V6T 1L4 Doreen Stephens, Archv.
Founded: 1956. **Staff:** Prof 1. **Subjects:** History and official records of the Anglican Church in British Columbia and the Yukon. **Special Collections:** Diary of Bishop George Hills, 1838-1895 (39 volumes); British Columbia and Yukon Church Aid Society Collection; Alan Greene Collection (Columbia Coast Mission). **Holdings:** 1100 books; 121 bound periodical volumes; 70 meters of diocesan documents; 111 reels of microfilm; 100 maps; 64 manuscripts; 2000 photographs. **Subscriptions:** 13 journals and other serials. **Services:** Copying; archives open to the public. **Remarks:** FAX: (604)228-0189. Archives located at Vancouver School of Theology.

Anglican Church of Canada - Ecclesiastical Province of Rupert's Land Archives
See: **(Manitoba) Provincial Archives of Manitoba** (9625)

★871★
Anglican Church of Canada - General Synod Archives (Rel-Phil)
600 Jarvis St. Phone: (416)924-9192
Toronto, ON, Canada M4Y 2J6 Mrs. Terry Thompson, Archv.
Founded: 1955. **Staff:** Prof 2; Other 1. **Subjects:** General Synod of the Anglican Church of Canada and its departments, Canadian Anglican history. **Special Collections:** Archival collections of the Canadian Anglican Dioceses of the Arctic and Moosonee; church newspapers (hardcopy and microfilm). **Holdings:** Synod journals; reports of English Missionary Societies about Canada; parish histories; sermons; Episcopal charges; religious literature printed in native languages; biographies. **Subscriptions:** 26 Canadian Anglican newspapers and periodicals. **Services:** Archives open to serious researchers. **Automated Operations:** Computerized indexing. **Remarks:** FAX: (416)968-7983. **Staff:** Dorothy Kealey, Archv./Rec.Mgt.

Anglo-American Art Museum
See: **Louisiana State University - Anglo-American Art Museum** (9375)

★872★
Anglo-European Chiropractic College - Library (Med)
Anglo-European Chiropractic College
13/15 Parkwood Rd. Phone: 202 431021
Bournemouth, Dorset BH5 2DF, England D. O'Neill, Libn.
Subjects: Chiropractic and life sciences. **Holdings:** 8000 books. **Subscriptions:** 164 journals and other serials. **Services:** Interlibrary loan; copying; SDI; library open to the public for reference use only. **Computerized Information Services:** MEDLINE, AMED. **Remarks:** FAX: 202 417352.

★873★
Anheuser-Busch Companies, Inc. - Corporate Library (Food-Bev)
1 Busch Place Phone: (314)577-2669
St. Louis, MO 63118 Ann Lauenstein, Corp.Libn.
Founded: 1933. **Staff:** Prof 2; Other 1. **Subjects:** Brewing chemistry, fermentation technology, food and beverage industries, alcohol and alcoholism, yeast, business and industrial management. **Special Collections:** History of beer and brewing industry. **Holdings:** 20,000 books; 30,000 bound periodical volumes; 100 pamphlet boxes of annual reports; 25 VF drawers of U.S. and foreign patents; 70 pamphlet boxes of clippings. **Subscriptions:** 800 journals and other serials. **Services:** Interlibrary loan; copying; library open to the public by appointment. **Automated Operations:** Computerized cataloging, acquisitions, serials, circulation, and ILL. **Computerized Information Services:** DIALOG Information Services, BRS Information Technologies, NEXIS, Dow Jones News/Retrieval, Info Globe, PFDS Online, Chemical Abstracts Service (CAS), WILSONLINE; BREWINFO (internal database). **Networks/Consortia:** Member of St. Louis Regional Library Network. **Publications:** New acquisitions list, bimonthly - to department heads and assistants and by request; Annual Periodical Holdings List. **Remarks:** FAX: (314)577-2006. **Staff:** Elizabeth Landgraf, Asst.Libn.

Anheuser-Busch Entertainment Corp. - Sea World
See: **Sea World, Inc.** (14978)

★874★
Animal Medical Center - Library (Med)
510 E. 62nd St. Phone: (212)838-8100
New York, NY 10021 A. Christine MacMurray, Ed.
Staff: Prof 2. **Subjects:** Veterinary medicine, medicine. **Holdings:** 1000 books; 1000 bound periodical volumes; 500 periodical volumes on microfiche. **Subscriptions:** 75 journals and other serials. **Services:** Interlibrary loan; medical editing; library open to the public by appointment. **Computerized Information Services:** BRS Information Technologies, MEDLARS; DOCLINE (electronic mail service). **Networks/Consortia:** Member of Manhattan-Bronx Health Sciences Library Consortia, New York Metropolitan Reference and Research Library Agency. **Staff:** James Kannengieser, Asst.Ed./Libn.

★875★
Animal Protection Institute of America - Technical Library (Env-Cons)
Box 22505 Phone: (916)731-5521
Sacramento, CA 95822 Emily R. Baker, Libn.
Founded: 1984. **Subjects:** Animal protection, endangered species, humane education, pet overpopulation, wilderness, world future. **Holdings:** 700 books; 185 government documents. **Subscriptions:** 110 journals and other serials. **Services:** Library open to the public. **Remarks:** FAX: (916)731-4467.

Ankara - British Institute of Archaeology
See: **British Institute of Archaeology - Library** (2188)

★876★
(Ankara) Amerikan Kutuphanesi - USIS Library (Educ)
Cinnah Caddesi No. 20
Kavaklidere Phone: 4 1263720
Ankara, Turkey Esin Solakoglu, Lib. Dir.
Founded: 1945. **Staff:** 7. **Subjects:** United States - political processes, international relations, economics, arts, humanities. **Special Collections:** U.S. National Archives on U.S.-Turkish relations. **Holdings:** 12,300 books; unbound periodical volumes; microfilm; archives. **Subscriptions:** 194 journals and other serials; 5 newspapers. **Services:** Interlibrary loan; copying; SDI; library open to the public. **Computerized Information Services:** DIALOG Information Services, LEGI-SLATE, PDQ. **Publications:** What's New (recent acquisitions listing). **Remarks:** FAX: 4 1276432. Maintained or supported by the U.S. Information Agency. Focus is on materials that will assist peoples outside the United States to learn about the United States, its people, history, culture, political processes, and social milieux. **Staff:** Gediz Berktin; Gulsan Bekem; Gulseven Dura; Selda Tirpanci; Aylin Torgul; Figen Sahin.

★877★
Ann Arbor News - Library (Publ)
340 E. Huron St. Phone: (313)994-6953
Ann Arbor, MI 48106 Grace Puravs, Libn.
Founded: 1938. **Staff:** Prof 1; Other 1. **Subjects:** Newspaper reference topics. **Special Collections:** Notebooks on specific events or activities; Washtenaw County newspapers, 1829 to present, on microfilm. **Holdings:** Reference books; clippings; photographs. **Subscriptions:** 20 newspapers. **Services:** Library not open to the public.

★878★
Annenberg Research Institute - Library (Rel-Phil)
420 Walnut St. Phone: (215)238-1290
Philadelphia, PA 19106 Aviva Astrinsky, Lib.Dir.
Founded: 1907. **Staff:** Prof 5; Other 5. **Subjects:** Biblical and post-Biblical learning, Semitic languages, Jewish studies, Assyriology, Egyptology, Rabbinic literature, patristics, Islamica, Ancient Near East. **Special Collections:** Genizah fragments (450); Oriental manuscripts (405 volumes); correspondence relating to American Jewish history; Leeser Collection of American Judaica (800); Shulman Archives; B.Z. Goldberg Archives; Dropsie Archives. **Holdings:** 170,000 books; 8049 bound periodical volumes; 7000 rare books; 10,000 microfiche; 600 reels of microfilm; Abraham I. Katsh microfilm collection of Hebraica manuscripts and documents from the U.S.S.R., Poland, and Hungary; Vatican Hebrew manuscript collection on microfilm. **Subscriptions:** 450 journals and other serials. **Services:** Interlibrary loan; copying; library open to the public for reference use only and at librarian's discretion. **Automated Operations:** Computerized public access catalog (ALEPH), cataloging, and acquisitions. **Computerized Information Services:** OCLC, DIALOG Information Services, RLIN; CD-ROMs; BITNET (electronic mail service). **Networks/Consortia:** Member of PALINET, Southeastern Pennsylvania Theological Library Association (SEPTLA), Council of Archives and Research Libraries in Jewish Studies (CARLJS), Research Libraries Information Network (RLIN), Philadelphia Area Consortium of Special Collections Libraries (PACSCL). **Publications:** Jewish Quartely Review. **Remarks:** FAX: (215)238-1540. Electronic mail address(es): ANNERS (BITNET). **Staff:** Ruth Ronen, Cat.; Dr. Sol Cohen, Coll.Dev.; Samuel Cardillo, Acq.; Jonathan Kraus, Ser.; Judith Leifer, ILL.

Annenberg School for Communication
See: **University of Pennsylvania - Annenberg School for Communication - Library** (19174)

Annenberg Washington Program in Communications Policy Studies
See: **Northwestern University - Annenberg Washington Program in Communications Policy Studies** (12078)

★879★
Anniston Museum of Natural History - Kathryn Hamilton Library (Biol Sci)
4301 McClellan Blvd.
Box 1587 Phone: (205)237-6766
Anniston, AL 36202 Christopher J. Reich, Dir.
Founded: 1930. **Staff:** 20. **Subjects:** Natural history, environmental education, museum studies. **Holdings:** 1600 books. **Subscriptions:** 26 journals and other serials. **Services:** Library not open to the public. **Staff:** W. Peter Conroy, Cur. of Natural Hist.

★880★
Anoka County Historical Society - Library (Hist)
1900 3rd Ave., S. Phone: (612)421-0600
Anoka, MN 55303 Pat Schwappach, Musm.Dir./Res.
Founded: 1934. **Staff:** 3. **Subjects:** Anoka County and Minnesota history; geneaology. **Holdings:** 3 VF drawers of manuscripts; 18 drawers of county birth, death, and marriage records, 1863-1920; 60 reels of microfilm; 25 oral history tapes and maps; newspapers; clippings; research reference books; family history books. **Services:** Interlibrary loan (microfilm only); copying; library open to the public for reference use only. **Remarks:** Library will conduct research for non-residents of Minnesota (fee required).

★881★
Anoka-Metro Regional Treatment Center - Library (Med)
3300 4th Ave., N. Phone: (612)422-4330
Anoka, MN 55303-1119 Betty Palfalvi, Libn.
Founded: 1951. **Staff:** Prof 1. **Subjects:** Medicine, psychiatry, psychology, social science, nursing. **Holdings:** 3300 books. **Subscriptions:** 46 journals and other serials. **Services:** Interlibrary loan; copying; library open to the public. **Networks/Consortia:** Member of Minnesota Department of Human Services Library Consortium.

★882★
Anoka Technical College - Media Center (Educ)
1355 W. Hwy. 10 Phone: (612)427-1880
Anoka, MN 55303 Deborah J. Brude, Media Serv.Coord.
Founded: 1971. **Staff:** Prof 3; Other 3. **Subjects:** Nursing and allied health fields; electronics; business; technology; horticulture. **Holdings:** 25,000 books; 1355 bound periodical volumes; 1816 AV programs. **Subscriptions:** 366 journals and other serials; 10 newspapers. **Services:** Center open to the public for reference use only. **Automated Operations:** Computerized cataloging. **Computerized Information Services:** DIALOG Information Services, OCLC. **Networks/Consortia:** Member of MINITEX Library Information Network, Metronet. **Publications:** Media Highlights - for internal distribution only; Scanning Scene (newsletter). **Remarks:** FAX: (612)323-0447. **Staff:** Irene Joyce, Cat.; Bruce Anderson, AV Prod.

★883★
ANPA - Library (Publ)
The Newspaper Center
11600 Sunrise Valley Dr. Phone: (703)648-1090
Reston, VA 22091 Pat Bennett, Dir.
Founded: 1952. **Staff:** Prof 1; Other 2. **Subjects:** Newspaper publishing and history, freedom of the press, journalism, advertising, telecommunication. **Special Collections:** Special editions of newspapers, including anniversary editions, progress editions, final editions, bicentennial editions, and new plant editions; reports and papers on newspaper librarianship. **Holdings:** 5000 books; 700 bound periodical volumes; Editor & Publisher and other journals on microfilm. **Subscriptions:** 498 journals and other serials; 6 newspapers. **Services:** Interlibrary loan; copying (limited); library open to the public by appointment. **Computerized Information Services:** LEXIS, NEXIS, WESTLAW. **Remarks:** Library located at the Newspaper Center, 11600 Sunrise Valley Dr., Reston, VA 22091. FAX: (703)620-4557. **Also Known As:** American Newspaper Publishers Association. **Staff:** Yvonne Egertson, Libn.

★884★
ANPA - Technical Research Department - Library
The Newspaper Center
Box 17407
Dulles International Airport
Washington, DC 20041
Subjects: Printing, paper, ink, graphic arts. **Holdings:** 3000 books. **Remarks:** Currently inactive. **Also Known As:** American Newspaper Publishers Association.

★885★
Anresco - Library (Food-Bev)
1370 Van Dyke Ave.
San Francisco, CA 94124 Phone: (415)822-1100
Subjects: Food technology, science. **Holdings:** 400 books; 100 bound periodical volumes; 3500 reports. **Services:** Library not open to the public.

Marian and Fred Anschutz Science Library
See: **University of Kansas - Marian and Fred Anschutz Science Library** (18731)

★886★
ANSER - Technical Library (Mil)
1215 Jefferson Davis Hwy., Suite 800 Phone: (703)685-3111
Arlington, VA 22202 Deborah Bradley, Mgr.
Founded: 1960. **Staff:** Prof 3. **Subjects:** Military science, operations research, mathematics, physics. **Holdings:** 3000 books; 17,000 government and contractor documents. **Subscriptions:** 200 journals and other serials. **Services:** Interlibrary loan; copying. **Automated Operations:** Computerized cataloging, acquisitions, serials, and circulation. **Computerized Information Services:** DIALOG Information Services, DTIC, BiblioTech. **Networks/ Consortia:** Member of Interlibrary Users Association (IUA). **Publications:** ANSER Library Accession List, monthly - to ANSER clients. **Remarks:** FAX: (703)685-3225. **Staff:** Karren Waddy, Libn.; Lin Rose, Libn.

★887★
Anshe Hesed Temple - Library (Rel-Phil)
10th and Liberty Sts.
Erie, PA 16502 Phone: (814)454-2427
Founded: 1945. **Staff:** 4. **Subjects:** Jewish fiction, literature, biography, history; Bible and Talmud; religion; art. **Holdings:** 3000 books. **Services:** Library open to the public by appointment. **Staff:** Kathy Berlin; Cathy Zacks.

★888★
Anshen & Allen, Architects - Library
901 Market St., 6th Fl.
San Francisco, CA 94103 Phone: (415)882-9500
Subjects: Practice and history of architecture, interior design, hospital design and construction. **Special Collections:** Photograph and rendering archive; Healthcare Facilities Research Center. **Holdings:** 2000 books; 800 product catalogs; 4 VF drawers. **Remarks:** Currently inactive.

★889★
(Antananarivo) Centre Culturel Americain - USIS Library (Educ)
4, Lalana Dr. Razafindratandra
B.P. 620
Antananarivo, Madagascar
Remarks: Maintained or supported by the U.S. Information Agency. Focus is on materials that will assist peoples outside the United States to learn about the United States, its people, history, culture, political processes, and social milieux.

★890★
Anterra Company - Resource Center
5520 LBJ Fwy., Suite 300
Dallas, TX 75240 Phone: (214)404-7100
Subjects: Real estate. **Holdings:** 65 books; 75 prospectuses; 25 reports. **Remarks:** Currently inactive. **Formerly:** Murray Properties Company.

★891★
Anthology Film Archives - Library (Aud-Vis)
32-34 2nd Ave. Phone: (212)505-5181
New York, NY 10003-8631 Robert Haller, Libn.
Founded: 1970. **Staff:** Prof 1; Other 5. **Subjects:** History of cinema, avant-garde film, video, performance art. **Special Collections:** Biographical files on individual film makers, video makers, and critics (1642); original manuscripts; Joseph Cornell Collection (52 folders). **Holdings:** 4500 books; 225 bound periodical volumes; 650 magnetic tapes; 525 stills files (arranged by director); 450 film and video organization files; audiotapes of lectures; international publications and periodicals. **Subscriptions:** 300 journals and other serials. **Services:** Copying; library open to the public by appointment. **Publications:** Film Culture Magazine. **Special Catalogs:** Catalog of books and articles on avant-garde film (card). **Remarks:** Includes the holdings of Film Culture Non-Profit Corporation. **Also Known As:** Film Art Fund Inc.

Harold S. Anthon Memorial Library
See: **Chicago Transit Authority** (3549)

★892★
Anthro Research Inc. - Library (Soc Sci)
Box 1218 Phone: (406)222-3168
Livingston, MT 59047 Larry Lahren, Libn.
Subjects: Anthropology, archeology. **Holdings:** 500 books; 100 bound periodical volumes; 300 reports. **Services:** Library open to the public.

★893★
Anthropology Film Center Foundation - Library (Aud-Vis)
1626 Canyon Rd. Phone: (505)983-4127
Santa Fe, NM 87501 Carroll W. Williams, Exec.Dir.
Founded: 1965. **Subjects:** Visual anthropology and communication, culture and human perception, visual/aural arts and media. **Holdings:** Journals; unpublished papers and documents; films. **Services:** Copying; library open to the public on a limited schedule. library open to the public. **Computerized Information Services:** Internal database. **Publications:** Filmography for American Indian Education; Directory of Anthropology Film Center Graduates.

★894★
Anthroposophical Society in America - Rudolf Steiner Library (Rel-Phil)
RD 2
Box 215 Phone: (518)672-7690
Ghent, NY 12075 Fred Paddock, Libn.
Founded: 1928. **Subjects:** Anthroposophy, Western spirituality, goetheanism. **Special Collections:** Rudolf Steiner - complete collected works (in German; 355 volumes), published works (in English translation; 250 volumes), and complete unpublished works (in English; 500 titles). **Holdings:** 15,000 books; 650 bound periodical volumes; 500 manuscripts. **Subscriptions:** 20 journals and other serials. **Services:** Interlibrary loan; copying; library open to the public on a fee basis.

★895★
Anthroposophical Society of Canada - Rudolph Steiner Library (Rel-Phil)
81 Lawton Blvd. Phone: (416)488-2886
Toronto, ON, Canada M4V 1Z6 Helen Cass, Libn.
Founded: 1953. **Staff:** Prof 2; Other 2. **Subjects:** Anthroposophy; spiritual science in religion, art, philosophy. **Special Collections:** Rudolph Steiner's writings and printed lectures on spiritual research on the history and evolution of man. **Holdings:** 5500 books (half in German); 200 bound periodical volumes. **Subscriptions:** 10 journals and other serials. **Services:** Interlibrary loan; library open to the public; mail service to Canadian patrons. **Special Catalogs:** Lists of holdings in English and in German. **Staff:** Helen Marr, Libn.

★896★
Anti-Catholic League - Library
18620 McCracken Rd.
Maple Heights, OH 44137
Defunct.

★897★
Anti-Defamation League of B'nai B'rith - Jacob Alson Memorial Library (Soc Sci)
823 United Nations Plaza Phone: (212)490-2525
New York, NY 10017 Helen Schneider, Libn.
Founded: 1939. **Staff:** Prof 1; Other 4. **Subjects:** Human relations, discrimination, civil rights, intergroup relations, anti-Semitism, political extremism. **Special Collections:** Anti-Semitic periodicals. **Holdings:** 5000 books; 10,000 pamphlets; 8 VF drawers of pamphlets (uncataloged); 300 reels of microfilm. **Subscriptions:** 300 journals and other serials; 30 newspapers. **Services:** Interlibrary loan; copying; library open to scholars. **Computerized Information Services:** DIALOG Information Services. **Remarks:** library is one section of Anti-Defamation League's Department of Research and Evaluation. FAX: (212)867-0779.

Anti-Defamation League of Minnesota-Dakotas
See: **Jewish Community Relations Council - Anti-Defamation League of Minnesota-Dakotas - Library** (8386)

Anti-fascistim We'Kurbanot Ha'Nazism in Israel
See: **Association of Anti-Fascists and Victims of Nazism in Israel** (1145)

Antietam National Battlefield
See: **U.S. Natl. Park Service** (17666)

★898★
Antioch/New England Graduate School - Professional Resource Center (Soc Sci)
103 Roxbury St. Phone: (603)357-3122
Keene, NH 03431 Deborah Swartout, Libn./Dir., Academic Sup.Serv.
Founded: 1982. **Staff:** Prof 2; Other 3. **Subjects:** Psychology, environmental studies, dance movement therapy, resource management, elementary education, organization and management, Psychology Doctoral Program. **Holdings:** 5000 books. **Subscriptions:** 216 journals and other serials. **Services:** Interlibrary loan; copying; center open to the public with restrictions. **Automated Operations:** Computerized serials and indexing. **Computerized Information Services:** DIALOG Information Services; CD-ROMs (ERIC, PsycLIT, Environment Abstracts, Books in Print Plus). **Remarks:** FAX: (603)357-0718. Affiliated with Antioch College - Olive Kettering Library. **Staff:** Penelope A. Eggleston, Asst.Dir., Academic Sup.Serv.

Antioch University - Glen Helen Association
See: **Glen Helen Association** (6495)

Antiquarian & Numismatic Society of Montreal
See: **Societe d'Archeologie et de Numismatique de Montreal** (15299)

Antique Airplane Association - Airpower Museum
See: **Airpower Museum** (158)

★899★
Antique Automobile Club of America - AACA Library & Research Center, Inc. (Rec)
501 W. Governor Rd.
Box 417 Phone: (717)534-2082
Hershey, PA 17033 Kim M. Miller, Libn.
Founded: 1972. **Staff:** Prof 1; Other 1. **Subjects:** Automobiles, automotive history, automobile restoration, commercial vehicles, trucks, motorcycles. **Special Collections:** Russell E. Stadt Marmon Literature and Blueprint Collection. **Holdings:** 5200 books; 300 bound periodical volumes; 18,000 pieces of sales literature, owners and shop manuals; 70 reels of microfilm; 3000 microfiche; 15 drawers of blueprints; paint chips; photographs; sheet music; memorabilia; maps; postcards. **Subscriptions:** 215 journals and other serials. **Services:** Copying; library open to the public. **Publications:** Newsletter - to members. **Remarks:** Library will research by mail on a fee basis.

★900★
Antique Boat Museum, Inc. - Gilbart B. Mercier Memorial Library (Hist)
750 Mary St. Phone: (315)686-4104
Clayton, NY 13624 Phoebe B. Tritton, Vol.Libn.
Founded: 1983. **Staff:** 1. **Subjects:** Freshwater nautical history, St. Lawrence River and Seaway history, boat building and restoration. **Special Collections:** Sparkman and Stephens boat brokerage files (9331); Paul Malo Collection (Thousand Islands history; 3 linear feet); Homer Dodge Collection (canoeing; 3 boxes); permanently registered boat files (260); Evinrude-Elto Collection (9500 photographs, manuals, related correspondence, scrapbooks; 1909-1947). **Holdings:** 500 books; 2000 periodicals (1900 to present); 4000 photographs; 100 charts and maps; 20 oral history tapes; 6 VF drawers of boat plans, parts and equipment information, engine manuals, and boat manufacturers catalogs; 4 VF drawers of clippings; historic postcard files. **Subscriptions:** 25 journals and other serials; 17 newsletters. **Services:** Copying; library open to the public with restrictions on a limited schedule. **Networks/Consortia:** Member of North Country Reference and Research Resources Council (NCRRRC). **Publications:** Gazette, quarterly - to members. **Special Catalogs:** Catalog of OMC-Evinrude-Elto Collection. **Special Indexes:** Index to Sparkman and Stephens brokerage files; index to photographs; index to periodicals (all on cards). **Remarks:** Alternate telephone number(s): 686-4127. **Formerly:** Thousand Islands Shipyard Museum, Inc.

★901★
Antique and Classic Car Club of Canada - Library (Rec)
7013 Cadiz Crescent
Mississauga, ON, Canada L5N 1Y3
Founded: 1955. **Staff:** 1. **Subjects:** Automobiles - antique, classic, veteran, vintage, postwar thoroughbred.

★902★
Antique Doorknob Collectors of America - Emil Miller Memorial Library (Rec)
Box 126 Phone: (708)357-2381
Eola, IL 60519 Barbara Menchhofer, Archv.
Founded: 1983. **Staff:** 2. **Subjects:** Door knobs. **Holdings:** 55 hardware catalogs. **Services:** Library not open to the public. **Staff:** Steve Menchhofer.

★903★
Antique & Historic Glass Foundation - Library (Art)
4962 Macklyn Dr. Phone: (419)531-5679
Toledo, OH 43615 Carl U. Fauster, Dir.
Subjects: American glass, New England Glass Company, Libbey Glass Company. **Special Collections:** Libbey Glass (200 pieces). **Holdings:** 200 books; Libbey catalogs, booklets, advertisments, documents, photographs. **Publications:** Amberina Glass, New England Glass Works, 1884; Libbey Cut Glass, 1896 (both reprints); Libbey Glass since 1818.

★904★
Antique Phonograph Monthly Archives - APM Library of Recorded Sound (Aud-Vis)
502 E. 17th St. Phone: (718)941-6835
Brooklyn, NY 11226 Allen Koenigsberg, Dir.
Founded: 1968. **Staff:** Prof 2; Other 1. **Subjects:** History of recorded sound, discography, antique phonograph repair. **Special Collections:** Early history of sound recording on cylinder records, 1892-1929 (5000 cylinders). **Holdings:** 500 books; 12 bound periodical volumes; 2000 phonograph patents; 200 trade catalogs; 75 antique phonographs, 1878-1913. **Subscriptions:** 15 journals and other serials. **Services:** Copying; library open to the public by appointment. **Automated Operations:** Computerized cataloging. **Computerized Information Services:** Internal database. Performs searches on fee basis. **Publications:** List of publications - available on request. **Special Catalogs:** Edison Cylinder Records, 1889-1912; A Patent History of the Phonograph; Edison Blue Amberol Recordings, 1912-1929; Columbia Cylinder Records, 1890-1909 (cards). **Special Indexes:** Victor Record Index, 1900-1909 (book).

★905★
Antique Stove Association - Library (Rec)
417 N. Main St. Phone: (219)583-6465
Monticello, IN 47960 Clifford Boram, Libn.
Founded: 1984. **Staff:** 1. **Subjects:** Antique stoves. **Holdings:** Stove Trade Journal, 1890; stove trade histories; manufacturers' catalogs, 1860-1939. **Services:** Copying; answers mail inquiries; library open to the public with restrictions.

Antique Telephone Collectors Association
See: **Museum of Independent Telephony** (10904)

★906★
Antique Wireless Association, Inc. - Library (Info Sci)
Main St. (East Bloomfield) Phone: (716)657-7489
Holcomb, NY 14469 Bruce Kelley, Dir./Cur.
Staff: 2. **Subjects:** History of radio, television, telegraph; electricity; communication. **Holdings:** 2000 books; 5000 radio/electronic magazines. **Subscriptions:** 10 journals and other serials. **Services:** Library open to the public by appointment.

The Antiques Magazine
See: **Brant Publications, Inc.** (2083)

★907★
(Antwerp) Museum voor Kunstambachten - Bibliotheek (Art)
Waalse Kaai 47 Phone: 3 2162211
B-2000 Antwerp, Belgium Luc Salu
Subjects: Photography. **Holdings:** 17,000 books. **Subscriptions:** 100 journals and other serials. **Services:** Interlibrary loan; copying; library open to the public. **Remarks:** FAX: 3 3262544. **Formerly:** Museum Sterckshof. **Staff:** Luk Wellens, Lib.Asst.

(Antwerp) Museum Sterckshof
See: **(Antwerp) Museum voor Kunstambachten - Bibliotheek** (907)

★908★
Aomori Agricultural Experiment Station - Library (Agri)
1-1 Sakaimatsu Phone: 172 524311
Kuroishi 036-03, Aomori, Japan Sadao Wasio
Founded: 1900. **Staff:** Prof 1. **Subjects:** Agriculture, biotechnology. **Holdings:** 2600 books; 450 bound periodical volumes; 48,000 archival items. **Services:** Library open to the public. **Publications:** Bulletin of the Aomori Agricultural Experiment Station. **Remarks:** FAX: 172 524399. **Also Known As:** Aomoriken Nogyo Shikenjo - Library.

★909★
Apache Nitrogen Products, Inc. - Library (Sci-Engr)
Box 700
Benson, AZ 85602 Phone: (602)720-2217
Founded: 1925. **Subjects:** Explosives, chemical engineering, chemistry, blasting techniques, safety, personnel, government publications. **Holdings:** 400 books; 100 bound periodical volumes; 75 reports. **Subscriptions:** 15 journals and other serials. **Services:** Interlibrary loan; library not open to the public. **Remarks:** FAX: (602)720-4158.

Apostle Islands National Lakeshore
See: **U.S. Natl. Park Service** (17667)

★910★
Appalachia Educational Laboratory - Resource Center (Educ)
1031 Quarrier St.
Box 1348 Phone: (304)347-0428
Charleston, WV 25325 Marilyn Slack, Coord.
Staff: Prof 1. **Subjects:** Education, psychology, language, sociology, applied technology. **Holdings:** 8000 books; 100 periodical titles, unbound and on microfilm; complete set of ERIC microfiche. **Subscriptions:** 105 journals and other serials. **Services:** Interlibrary loan; copying; center open to the public for reference use only.

★911★
Appalachian Bible College - John Van Puffelen Library (Rel-Phil)
Bradley, WV 25818 Phone: (304)877-6428
Ed A. Chesley, Act.Libn.
Founded: 1950. **Staff:** Prof 1; Other 1. **Subjects:** Religion, theology, Bible. **Special Collections:** Patterson Collection of Judaica (500 items). **Holdings:** 34,000 books. **Subscriptions:** 200 journals and other serials. **Services:** Interlibrary loan; copying; library open to the public.

★912★
Appalachian Mountain Club - Library (Rec)
5 Joy St. Phone: (617)523-0636
Boston, MA 02108 Jessica Gill, Staff Libn.
Founded: 1876. **Subjects:** Mountains, mountaineering, exploration, history of mountain areas. **Special Collections:** Journals of mountain clubs around the world; White Mountains. **Holdings:** 8000 books, periodicals, pamphlets, photographs, maps, lantern slides. **Services:** Copying; library open to the public with restrictions. **Computerized Information Services:** Internal databases. **Remarks:** FAX: (617)523-0722.

Appalachian Oral History Project
See: **Alice Lloyd College** (9236)

★913★
Appalachian Regional Healthcare - Beckley Appalachian Regional Hospital - Medical Library (Med)
306 Stanaford Rd. Phone: (304)255-3420
Beckley, WV 25801 Barbara Frame-Cook, Coord., Educ.
Founded: 1956. **Subjects:** Internal medicine, surgery, pediatrics, nursing, psychiatry and behavioral science, allied health sciences. **Holdings:** 1228 books; 425 bound periodical volumes. **Subscriptions:** 90 journals and other serials. **Services:** Library open to the public with restrictions.

★914★
Appalachian State University - Belk Library - Justice-Query Instructional Materials Center (Educ)
Boone, NC 28608 Phone: (704)262-2186
Pat Farthing, Libn.
Staff: Prof 3; Other 2. **Subjects:** Education, educational planning, young people's literature. **Holdings:** 28,000 books; 7200 AV programs; 3500 16mm film and videotape titles; 900,000 microforms; 460 standardized tests; 800 curriculum guides. **Services:** Interlibrary loan; copying; center open to the public. **Automated Operations:** Computerized cataloging, acquisitions, circulation, serials. **Computerized Information Services:** DIALOG Information Services, BRS Information Technologies; CD-ROMs (ERIC, GPO, PsycLit). Performs searches free of charge. **Remarks:** FAX: (704)262-3001. **Staff:** Susan Golden, Libn./Ch.Lit.Spec.; Gaye Golds, Film Libn.

★915★
Appalachian State University - Music Library (Mus)
Broyhill Music Center Phone: (704)262-2388
Boone, NC 28608 Karl Van Ausdal, Music Libn.
Founded: 1952. **Staff:** Prof 1; Other 1. **Subjects:** Music and music education. **Holdings:** 7000 books; 13,000 music scores; 8700 phonograph records and tapes. **Services:** Library open to the public for reference use only. **Automated Operations:** Computerized cataloging, acquisitions, and circulation. **Publications:** Bibliography of new materials, irregular. **Remarks:** FAX: (704)262-3001.

★916★
Appalachian State University - William L. Eury Appalachian Collection (Hist, Area-Ethnic)
University Hall Phone: (704)262-4041
Boone, NC 28608 Eric Olson, Libn.
Founded: 1965. **Staff:** Prof 1; Other 1. **Subjects:** Appalachian region, folk culture, local history. **Holdings:** 17,000 books; 1600 reels of microfilm; 1000 microfiche; 500 audiotapes; 900 phonograph records; 100 linear feet of manuscripts; 1500 slides; 500 photographs. **Subscriptions:** 50 journals and other serials. **Services:** Interlibrary loan; copying; collection open to the public for reference use only. **Automated Operations:** Computerized cataloging, circulation, and acquisitions. **Computerized Information Services:** DIALOG Information Services, BRS Information Technologies, ERIC. Performs searches on fee basis. **Remarks:** FAX: (704)262-3001.

★917★
Appaloosa Museum - Library (Hist)
Pullman Hwy.
Box 8403 Phone: (208)882-5578
Moscow, ID 83843 Claudia McGehee, Musm.Cur.
Subjects: Appaloosa, Nez Perce Indians, Chief Joseph, horses, Northwest Indians, history. **Special Collections:** Appaloosa News & Journal magazines (complete set). **Holdings:** 105 volumes; 3 documents; 1 AV program. **Services:** Copying; library open to the public with restrictions.

★918★
Apple Computer Inc. - Library and Information Resources (Comp Sci)
10381 Bandley Dr., 8C Phone: (408)974-2400
Cupertino, CA 95014 Monica Ertel, Mgr., Info.Rsrcs.
Founded: 1981. **Staff:** Prof 14; Other 6. **Subjects:** Microcomputers, computer programming and software, education, business. **Special Collections:** Apple archives; HyperCard stacks. **Holdings:** 10,000 books; 3000 other cataloged items; software library. **Subscriptions:** 700 journals and other serials; 25 newspapers. **Services:** Interlibrary loan; library not open to the public. **Automated Operations:** Computerized cataloging, acquisitions, serials, circulation, and statistics. **Computerized Information Services:** DIALOG Information Services, The Source, NEXIS, BRS Information

Technologies, RLIN, Dow Jones News/Retrieval, VU/TEXT Information Services, NewsNet, Inc., DataTimes; internal databases. **Networks/ Consortia:** Member of CLASS, SOUTHNET. **Publications:** Current Awareness Bulletin - for internal distribution only; Apple Library Users Group Newsletter. **Remarks:** FAX: (408)725-8502. **Staff:** Rosanne Macek, Mgr., Lib.Oper.; Janet Vratny-Watts, Info.Sci.; Lynne Bidwell, Supv., Tech.Serv.; Mary Ellen Bercik, Supv., Ref.; Marcia Singer, Info.Spec.; Jane Oros, Info.Spec.; Kevin Broun, Info.Spec.; Steve Cisler, Sr.Sci.; Dale Mead, Info.Spec.; Lorin Hawley, Assoc.Info.Spec.; Pedro Echeandia, Assoc.Info.Spec.; Greg Gilman, Assoc.Info.Spec.; Joanne McKinney, Info.Spec.

★919★
Apple Creek Developmental Center - Professional Library/Information Center (Med)
2532 S. Apple Creek Rd. Phone: (216)698-2411
Apple Creek, OH 44606 Frank Columbo
Staff: Prof 1. **Subjects:** Mental retardation, behavior modification, psychology, medicine. **Holdings:** 1150 books. **Subscriptions:** 20 journals and other serials. **Services:** Library open to the public.

★920★
Appleton Museum of Art - Library (Art)
4333 E. Silver Springs Blvd. Phone: (904)236-5050
Ocala, FL 32666 Rosalie Cauthen, Educ.Coord.
Founded: 1986. **Subjects:** Fine arts, decorative arts, architecture, Oriental art, African art; Pre-Columbian art. **Holdings:** 500 titles; museum and auction catalogs. **Subscriptions:** 15 journals and other serials; 3 newspapers. **Services:** Library open to museum members and students. **Remarks:** FAX: (904)236-5056.

★921★
Applied Geologic Studies, Inc. - Library (Sci-Engr, Info Sci)
2875 W. Oxford, Suite 3 Phone: (303)761-5624
Englewood, CO 80110 Bob Wilson, Sr.Geol.
Founded: 1982. **Staff:** 1. **Subjects:** Economic geology, mining, geochemicals. **Special Collections:** Anaconda Mining Company exploration databases, 1982 to present. **Holdings:** Maps; reports; documents; assay reports. **Services:** Library not open to the public. **Computerized Information Services:** Internal databases.

★922★
Applied Information Science and Technology - Information Analysis Center (Comp Sci)
314 Oakland St. Phone: (617)237-0890
Wellesley, MA 02181 Richard D. Ferguson, Jr., Ph.D, Pres.
Founded: 1975. **Staff:** 6. **Subjects:** Software development, management information systems, software conversion, artificial intelligence. **Holdings:** 1000 reports; 500 NTIS microfiche. **Subscriptions:** 30 journals and other serials. **Services:** Center not open to the public. **Computerized Information Services:** Internal databases. **Publications:** Citation Analysis; indexes; abstracts. **Remarks:** Develops and provides MIS and other decision support software.

★923★
Applied Research Associates - Library
51 Bellevue St.
Dorchester, MA 02125
Defunct.

Appomattox Court House National Historical Park
See: **U.S. Natl. Park Service** (17668)

★924★
Appraisal Institute - Y.T. and Louise Lee Lum Library (Plan)
875 N. Michigan Ave., Suite 2400 Phone: (312)335-4467
Chicago, IL 60611-1980 Eric B. Goodman, Dir.
Founded: 1992. **Staff:** 1. **Subjects:** Real estate appraisal, real estate market analysis, real estate finance. **Holdings:** 1000 books; 37 bound periodical volumes. **Subscriptions:** 50 journals and other serials. **Services:** Library open to members, affiliates, nonmember appraisers, and allied real estate professionals. **Computerized Information Services:** LEXIS, NEXIS. **Remarks:** FAX: (312)335-4486.

★925★
Appraisal Institute of Canada - Library
93 Lombard Ave., Suite 101 Phone: (204)942-0751
Winnipeg, MB, Canada R3B 3B1 E. Foulkes
Remarks: No further information was supplied by respondent.

★926★
Appropriate Health Resources and Technologies Action Group - Library (Med)
1 London Bridge St. Phone: 71 3781403
London SE1 9SG, England Suzanne Fustukian
Founded: 1977. **Staff:** 3. **Subjects:** Health care in developing countries - disease, disability, high infant mortality. **Holdings:** 10,000 volumes. **Subscriptions:** 200 journals and other serials. **Services:** Library open to the public by appointment. **Remarks:** FAX: 71 4036003.

★927★
Aquatic Hall of Fame and Museum of Canada, Inc. - Library (Rec)
25 Poseidon Bay Phone: (204)284-4031
Winnipeg, MB, Canada R3M 3E4 Vaughan L. Baird, Pres.
Founded: 1967. **Staff:** 1. **Subjects:** Aquatics - swimming, synchronized swimming, diving, water polo. **Holdings:** Figures not available. **Services:** Library open to the public.

★928★
Aquatic Research Institute - Aquatic Sciences & Technology Archive (Biol Sci)
2242 Davis Court Phone: (510)784-0945
Hayward, CA 94545 V. Parker, Archv.
Founded: 1962. **Subjects:** Aquatic sciences; limnology; oceanology; marine, freshwater, and estuarine biology; water quality; aquaculture and mariculture; fisheries; ocean engineering and mining; submersibles; undersea military; aquarium technology. **Special Collections:** Rare books on fish and fisheries. **Holdings:** 40,000 biological specimens; 45,000 volumes; 1000 journals; 5000 photographs; 3000 slides; 1000 maps and charts; 1100 abstracts and indexes; 1500 technical reports; 150,000 pamphlets; 1000 microforms. **Services:** Interlibrary loan; copying (limited); identifies aquatic organisms; archive open to the public when archivist is present. A fee may be charged for services depending on the nature and extent of the service requested.

★929★
Aquidneck Data Company - Library (Comp Sci)
170 Enterprise Ctr.
Middletown, RI 02840 Phone: (401)847-7260
Subjects: Software systems engineering. **Special Collections:** Naval instructions/directories; U.S. government specifications; military handbooks (all microfiche). **Holdings:** 500 books; 2000 reports. **Subscriptions:** 100 journals and other serials. **Services:** Library not open to the public. **Computerized Information Services:** Mineral Industry Location System (MILS), Federal Information Processing Standards (FIPS), Qualified Products Lists and Sources (QPL & S). **Remarks:** FAX: (401)849-3629.

Aquinas Medical Library
See: **St. Michael Medical Center** (14545)

★930★
Aquinas Newman Center - Library (Rel-Phil)
1815 Las Lomas Rd., N.E. Phone: (505)247-1094
Albuquerque, NM 87106 Betty Innerst, Libn.
Founded: 1954. **Staff:** Prof 3; Other 3. **Subjects:** Religion, theology, philosophy and logic, literature, fine arts, Biblical references, biography. **Holdings:** 7000 volumes; 8 VF drawers of clippings and pamphlets; 30 AV programs. **Subscriptions:** 35 journals and other serials. **Services:** Library open to students, faculty, and parishioners. **Staff:** Mercedes Gugisberg, Libn.; Fr. C. Thomas Moore, O.P., Dir.

★931★
Arab Administrative Development Organization - Library (Bus-Fin)
P.O. Box 17159 Phone: 6 811394
Amman, Jordan Ms. Azza Hammad, Hd., Lib. & Doc.
Founded: 1979. **Staff:** 3. **Subjects:** Public administration and policy, business administration, finance, accounting, management. **Holdings:** 22,000 books; 1500 bound periodical volumes. **Subscriptions:** 350 journals and other serials. **Services:** Copying; library open to the public. **Publications:** Bibliography, semiannual. **Remarks:** Telex: 21594 ARADO JO. FAX: 6 816972. **Formerly:** Arab Organization of Administrative Development.

★932★
Arab Center for the Study of Arid Zones and Dry Lands - ACSAD Library (Agri)
P.O. Box 2440 Phone: 755713
Damascus, Syrian Arab Republic Ouni Jalahej, Libn.
Subjects: Arid zones agriculture and development. **Holdings:** 42,000 volumes. **Services:** Library open to experts and students only. **Computerized Information Services:** CDS/ISIS (internal database). **Remarks:** Telex: 412697. Affiliated with League of Arab Countries; represents 16 Arab nations.

★933★
Arab Gulf States Information Documentation Center (Info Sci)
P.O. Box 5063 Phone: 5564171
Baghdad, Iraq Nazar M. Ali, Dir.Gen.
Founded: 1981. **Staff:** Prof 23; Other 7. **Subjects:** Affairs of the Arab Gulf States, mass media, information science, journalism, documentation, computation, library science. **Holdings:** 10,000 books in Arabic; 7000 books in English; 3708 microfiche; 492 reels of microfilm; 118 clipping files on microfiche; dissertations; videocassettes; audio cassettes; slides; photographs; maps. **Subscriptions:** 718 journals and other serials; 50 newspapers. **Services:** Interlibrary loan; copying; SDI; microfilming; center open to member institutions, students, scholars, researchers. **Computerized Information Services:** DIALOG Information Services; Events of Years in Islamic and Christian Calendars (1-1409H, 622-1989 A.D.), Events and Occasions (1986-1989), Arab Gulf Periodicals, Arab Gulf Personalities, The Center's Library Acquisitions, Arab Gulf Publishers, The Iraq-Iran War in Arabic and Foreign Sources (1980-1986), Conferences and Symposiums on Arab Gulf States, Information Thesaurus, Arab Gulf Information Institutions, Guide to Arab Gulf States, and the Speeches of President Saddam Hussein (Pres. of Iran), King Fahd Bin Abdul Aziz (the Custodian of the two holy cities), Shaikh Hamad Bin Khaleefa Al Thani (Amir of Qatar), Shaikh Issa Bin Salman Al Khaleefa (Amir of Bahrain), Shaikh Zaed Bin Sultan Al Nihayan (Pres. of UAE), Shaikh Jabir Al Ahmed Al Sabah (Amir of Kuwait), and Sultan Qaboos Bin Saeed (Sultan of Oman) (internal databases). Performs searches free of charge. Contact Person: Miss Hayla A. Jajawi, Hd., Comp.Dept. **Publications:** Information Documentation Journal, biennial; The Center Guide, biennial; Indexes (online); Arab Women Bibliography (dissertations, books, research; online); list of publications available. **Special Indexes:** Index Arabicus (index to Arabic Periodicals, 1876-1984; online); Araq Arabia Index (an Iraqi Journal; online). **Remarks:** Center is composed of the following member states: United Arab Emirates, Bahrain, Saudi Arabia, Iraq, Oman, Qatar, Kuwait. Alternate telephone number(s): 5555962. FAX: 5567629. Telex: 213267. **Staff:** Mrs. Najeeba Nafi' AlRawi, Chf.Libn.; Miss Samera Abbas, Info.Spec.

Arab Organization of Administrative Development
See: **Arab Administrative Development Organization** (931)

★934★
Arabian Horse Owners Foundation - W.R. Brown Memorial Library (Rec)
Box 31391 Phone: (602)749-9009
Tucson, AZ 85751 Howard F. Shenk, Exec.Dir.
Founded: 1957. **Staff:** Prof 1. **Subjects:** Arabian horses - history, breeding, use; horses in general - use, care, training, literature, history. **Special Collections:** Correspondence and farm records for Maynesboro Stud, owned by W.R. Brown. **Holdings:** 1200 books; 20 bound periodical volumes; films; photographs; Arabian show and sale programs. **Services:** Copying; library open to the public by appointment. **Publications:** Reprints of historical books and pamphlets, irregular.

★935★
Arabian Horse Trust - Library (Rec)
12000 Zuni St. Phone: (303)450-4710
Westminster, CO 80234 Leslie F. Holley, Libn./Archv.
Founded: 1974. **Staff:** Prof 1. **Subjects:** Arabian horses - breeding, history, bloodlines; horsemanship. **Special Collections:** James Lewis Collection; Preston Dyer Collection; The Smyth Collection (20,000 pictures of Arabian horses); Randolph Huntington Collection; John Rogers Collection; Anna Best Joder Collection (photographs and research notes); rare books (460); Arabian Heritage Video Library (McCoy's, Santa Catalina Island, San Simeon, Calarabia, J. & T. Dean, W.K. Kellogg Arabians, 2nd Gleannloch Farms). **Holdings:** 1500 books; 150 bound periodical volumes; 18,000 horse photographs; Arabian Horse Registry of America, Inc. horse application papers. **Subscriptions:** 43 journals and other serials. **Services:** Copying; library open to the public. **Publications:** The Arabian Horse Bibliography; 30 Year Breeder Scrapbook Program; And Miles to Go (reprint); The Arabian Horse Through History. **Special Catalogs:** A Catalog of Travelers Rest Arabian Horses (reprint). **Remarks:** FAX: (303)450-5127.

Arbejderbevaegelsens Bibliotek og Arkiv
See: **The Labour Movement** (8862)

The Arboretum at Flagstaff
See: **Transition Zone Horticultural Institute** (16459)

★936★
Arbuckle Research Foundation - Arbuckle Exchange (Hist)
1844 S. 1700 E. Phone: (801)485-5162
Salt Lake City, UT 84108 W.L. Arbuckle, Pres.
Subjects: Arbuckle family genealogy and history. **Holdings:** 10,000 family manuscripts.

ARC Professional Services Group - Information Systems Division - ERIC Processing and Reference Facility
See: **ERIC Processing and Reference Facility** (5411)

★937★
Arcane Order - Library (Rel-Phil)
Studio of Contemplation
2904 Rosemary Ln.
Falls Church, VA 22042 Jennifer E. O'Neill, Cur.
Founded: 1950. **Staff:** 4. **Subjects:** Psychology, parapsychology, mysticism, biography, art, history. **Special Collections:** Archive of publications of the Arcane Order. **Holdings:** 1500 books; 25 bound periodical volumes; 30 art works; 2 cases of correspondence with members; 30 other cataloged items. **Subscriptions:** 25 journals and other serials; 5 newspapers. **Services:** Library not open to the public. **Publications:** Academic Research Cenotaph (serial publication) - to members; Second Intellectual List of Leaders Yearbook, irregular. **Special Catalogs:** Catalog of membership (1010 cards).

★938★
Archaeological Society of New Jersey - Library (Soc Sci)
Humanities Bldg., Rm. 106
Seton Hall University Phone: (201)761-9543
South Orange, NJ 07079 Joan E. Kraft, Chm., Lib.Comm.
Founded: 1931. **Staff:** 1. **Subjects:** Prehistoric and historic archeology, American Indian ethnology. **Special Collections:** Reports and references dealing with New Jersey prehistory. **Holdings:** 300 books; 200 periodicals. **Subscriptions:** 20 journals and other serials. **Services:** Interlibrary loan; copying; library open to the public with restrictions and by appointment. **Publications:** Bulletin of the Archaeological Society of New Jersey, 1-2/year; Newsletter of the Archaeological Society of New Jersey, quarterly. **Special Indexes:** Index of Bulletins of the A.S.N.J., 1-40.

★939★
Archbold Biological Station - Library (Biol Sci)
P.O. Box 2057 Phone: (813)465-2571
Lake Placid, FL 33852 Fred E. Lohrer, Libn.
Founded: 1941. **Staff:** Prof 1. **Subjects:** Entomology, ichthyology, herpetology, ornithology, mammalogy, animal ecology, plant ecology,

limnology, general biology, Florida natural history. **Special Collections:** Results of the Archbold Expeditions - Numbers 1-86 (Zoology, 9 bound volumes; Botany, 4 bound volumes); Physiological Ecology of Vertebrates (3 VF drawers of reprints). **Holdings:** 4200 books; 4300 bound periodical volumes; 13,500 color transparencies of Florida natural history; 2000 U.S. Geological Survey quadrangle maps of Florida; 1940, 1944, 1958, 1966, 1971, 1981, and 1986 series of U.S. Department of Agriculture aerial photographs of the station and surrounding areas; 17,000 reprints on vertebrate ecology; 12 VF drawers of archives of Archbold Biological Station and Expeditions. **Subscriptions:** 300 journals and other serials. **Services:** Interlibrary loan; copying; library open to the public by appointment. **Automated Operations:** Computerized cataloging and serials. **Computerized Information Services:** Internal database. **Publications:** List of Recent Publications of the Archbold Biological Station, irregular - by exchange; Bibliography of the Archbold Biological Station (online). **Special Catalogs:** Catalog of the Florida Natural History Slide Collection (online). **Remarks:** FAX: (813)699-1927.

★940★
John D. Archbold Memorial Hospital - Ralph Perkins Memorial Library (Med)
PO Box 1018 Phone: (912)228-2795
Thomasville, GA 31799-1018 Susan Statom, Med.Libn.
Staff: Prof 1. **Subjects:** Medicine, nursing, allied health sciences. **Holdings:** 120 books; 2000 bound periodical volumes; 40 video cassettes. **Subscriptions:** 10 journals and other serials. **Services:** Interlibrary loan; copying; SDI; current awareness services; library open to the public for reference use only. **Computerized Information Services:** NLM; GaIN (electronic mail service). Performs searches on fee basis. **Networks/Consortia:** Member of South Georgia Associated Libraries (SGAL), Southwest Georgia Health Sciences Library Consortium, Georgia Interactive Network for Medical Information (GaIN). **Remarks:** FAX: (912)228-2777. Electronic mail address(es): Statom (GaIN).

★941★
Archdiocese of Boston - Archives (Rel-Phil, Hist)
2121 Commonwealth Ave. Phone: (617)254-0100
Brighton, MA 02135 Ronald D. Patkus, Archv.
Subjects: Archdiocesan and parish history, Catholic Church in New England, social and cultural history. **Holdings:** 1500 linear feet of records of bishops and archbishops of Boston, 1808 to present; records of parishes, institutions, organizations, individuals associated with the archdiocese, 1789 to present; photographs; motion pictures; tapes. **Services:** Copying; archives open to the public. **Automated Operations:** Computerized cataloging. **Computerized Information Services:** Internal database. **Publications:** Guide to the Archives of the Archdiocese of Boston, 1981. **Remarks:** FAX: (617)787-8144.

Archdiocese of Boston - Pope John XXIII National Seminary
See: **Pope John XXIII National Seminary** (13218)

★942★
Archdiocese of Cincinnati - Archives (Rel-Phil)
6616 Beechmont Ave. Phone: (513)231-0810
Cincinnati, OH 45230 Don H. Buske, Archv.
Staff: Prof 1; Other 2. **Special Collections:** History of the Archdiocese of Cincinnati (manuscripts); Cincinnati Archdiocesan Records, 1813-1928 (50 linear feet); Mt. St. Mary of the West Seminary, Cincinnati, Ohio, 1850-1948 (25 linear feet); Catholic Student Mission Crusade, 1918-1978 (50 linear feet); papers and correspondence of: Archbishop John Baptist Purcell, 1818-1883 (15 linear feet); Archbishop William Henry Elder, 1824-1904 (41 linear feet); Archbishop Henry Moeller, 1875-1924 (50 linear feet); Archbishop John Timothy McNicholas, 1900-1950 (14 linear feet); Archbishop Karl J. Altar, 1950-1969 (100 linear feet); Archbishop Paul F. Leibold, 1969-1972 (15 linear feet). The Catholic Telegraph, 1831 to present. **Services:** Copying; archives open to researchers.

Archdiocese of Cincinnati - Athenaeum of Ohio - Mount St. Mary's Seminary of the West
See: **Athenaeum of Ohio - Mount St. Mary's Seminary of the West** (1226)

★943★
Archdiocese of Hartford - Catholic Library & Information Center (Rel-Phil)
125 Market St. Phone: (203)522-0602
Hartford, CT 06103 Rev. Edward J. McLean, Exec.Dir.
Founded: 1935. **Staff:** Prof 1; Other 6. **Subjects:** Theology, church history, scripture, biography. **Special Collections:** Georges Rouault Art Collection. **Holdings:** 10,000 books. **Subscriptions:** 8 newspapers. **Services:** Interlibrary loan; library open to the public with restrictions.

Archdiocese of Newark - Archives
See: **Seton Hall University - University Archives - Special Collections Center** (15050)

★944★
Archdiocese of Philadelphia - Catholic Information Center (Rel-Phil)
936 Market St. Phone: (215)587-3520
Philadelphia, PA 19107 Rev. Francis J. Renz, SJ, Dir.
Founded: 1953. **Staff:** Prof 1; Other 3. **Subjects:** Catechetics, Biblical exegesis, biography, prayer and meditation, moral theology, religion and the arts. **Holdings:** 1800 books; 10 racks of pamphlets and educational materials. **Subscriptions:** 25 journals and other serials; 7 newspapers. **Services:** Interlibrary loan; copying; SDI; center open to the public.

★945★
Archdiocese of San Antonio - Catholic Archives (Rel-Phil, Hist)
Box 28410 Phone: (512)734-2620
San Antonio, TX 78228 Bro. Edward J. Loch, S.M., Archv.
Founded: 1974. **Staff:** Prof 1. **Subjects:** History of the Roman Catholic Church in Texas, 1703 to present. **Special Collections:** Administrative records of the chancery and papers of the bishops of the Archdiocese; pastoral letters of Bishop Belaunzaran; San Fernando Cathedral Historical Collection; Mutual Aid Societies; Blueprints Collection; Victoria and San Antonio Archdioceses' sacramental records (all parishes); Papal Visit Collection (papers; 170 hours of videotape; memorabilia); New Orleans Morning Star, 1868-1879; Southern Messenger, 1892-1942; Alamo Register, 1942-1957; Alamo Messenger, 1958-1971; Today's Catholic, 1971 to present. **Holdings:** 500 books; 43 audiotapes; 10 videocassettes; 10 films; 944 reels of microfilm; 310 linear feet of documents. **Subscriptions:** 5 journals and other serials. **Services:** Copying; archives open to the public with restrictions. **Publications:** A Guide to Catholic Archives of San Antonio, 1976.

★946★
Archdiocese of San Francisco - Chancery Archives (Rel-Phil)
320 Middlefield Rd. Phone: (415)328-6502
Menlo Park, CA 94025 Dr. Jeffrey M. Burns, Archv.
Founded: 1978. **Staff:** Prof 1. **Subjects:** Catholic Church in Northern California, California missions and history, charitable organizations. **Special Collections:** Alexander S. Taylor collection of manuscripts relating to California missions, 1772-1849 (2550). **Holdings:** 800 books; 154 VF drawers of correspondence and miscellaneous reports, 1850-1952; San Francisco Catholic newspapers, 1867-1981, hardcopy and on microfilm. **Services:** Copying; archives open to the public with restrictions. **Formerly:** Located in Colma, CA. **Staff:** Fr. John Reilly.

★947★
Archer Daniels Midland Company - Library (Food-Bev)
4666 Faries Pkwy. Phone: (217)424-5397
Decatur, IL 62526 Teresa A. Moore, Libn.
Founded: 1969. **Staff:** Prof 2; Other 1. **Subjects:** Foods, fats and oils, grains, agricultural economics, agribusiness, finance, nutrition. **Holdings:** 8300 books; 500 bound periodical volumes; 9000 U.S. and foreign patents; 6500 reports, reprints; 1500 reels of microfilm of serials; 7000 microfiche; 1300 slides; 19 VF drawers. **Subscriptions:** 600 journals and other serials. **Services:** Interlibrary loan; copying; library open to the public by appointment. **Computerized Information Services:** DIALOG Information Services, PFDS Online, Dow Jones News/Retrieval, NEXIS, BRS Information Technologies, STN International, VU/TEXT Information Services. **Networks/Consortia:** Member of Rolling Prairie Library System (RPLS). **Staff:** Linda Mills, Lib.Asst.

★948★
Archer & Greiner - Library (Law)
1 Centennial Square Phone: (609)795-2121
Haddonfield, NJ 08033 Elizabeth Olson, Libn.
Staff: Prof 1; Other 3. **Subjects:** Law. **Holdings:** 12,000 books. **Subscriptions:** 140 journals and other serials. **Services:** Interlibrary loan; library open to the public for reference use only by appointment. **Computerized Information Services:** DIALOG Information Services, LEXIS, Dow Jones News/Retrieval, WESTLAW, VU/TEXT Information Services. **Networks/Consortia:** Member of South Jersey Regional Library Cooperative. **Remarks:** FAX: (609)795-0574.

Archibald Foundation Library
See: **Canadian Bible College/Canadian Theological Seminary** (2896)

Archibald Library
See: **Briercrest Bible College** (2123)

★949★
Architects Collaborative - Library (Plan)
46 Brattle St.
Cambridge, MA 02138 Phone: (617)868-4200
Founded: 1956. **Staff:** Prof 1. **Subjects:** Architecture, interiors, building, planning, landscape architecture. **Special Collections:** Manufacturer's catalogs (1500). **Holdings:** 2600 books; 270 bound periodical volumes; 400 internal reports; 80,000 slides of firm's work; 78,000 construction drawings, 1946 to present; 850 reels of microfilm of working drawings, job files, specifications. **Subscriptions:** 190 journals and other serials. **Services:** Library not open to the public. **Automated Operations:** Computerized circulation. **Publications:** Guide to the Library. **Remarks:** FAX: (617)868-4226.

★950★
Architectural Association - Library (Plan)
34/36 Bedford Sq. Phone: 71 6360974
London WC1B 3ES, England Elizabeth A. Underwood, Tech.Libn.
Founded: 1861. **Staff:** 3. **Subjects:** Architecture. **Special Collections:** Slide library. **Holdings:** 25,000 volumes, including rare books; 50,000 classified periodical articles; technical reference materials. **Subscriptions:** 300 journals and other serials. **Services:** Library open to Architectural Association students and members only. **Publications:** Guide to the Library; theses; subject bibliographies. **Remarks:** FAX: 71 436 8740. **Staff:** Elizabeth A. Underwood; Aileen E. Smith; Michael J. Smith.

★951★
Architectural Dimensions - Business Library (Plan)
1600 S. Main St., No. 195 Phone: (510)932-8651
Walnut Creek, CA 94596-5341 Tim Dell'Ara, Libn.
Founded: 1982. **Staff:** Prof 1. **Subjects:** Architecture, engineering. **Holdings:** 54 volumes; 1000 manufacturers catalogs. **Services:** Library not open to the public. **Automated Operations:** Computerized cataloging. **Computerized Information Services:** Internal database.

★952★
Architectural Energy Corporation - Library (Plan, Energy)
2540 Frontier Ave., Suite 201 Phone: (303)444-4149
Boulder, CO 80301 Laurel Van Driest
Subjects: Building science, architecture, energy and the built environment, energy conservation, energy systems design, space planning. **Holdings:** 7000 volumes. **Subscriptions:** 50 journals and other serials. **Services:** Library open to the public at librarian's discretion. **Remarks:** FAX: (303)444-4304. Telex: 3720504 (AEC). **Staff:** Nancy Rhoades.

★953★
Architectural and Transportation Barriers Compliance Board (ATBCB) - Technical Services Library (Plan)
1331 F St., N.W., Suite 1000
Washington, DC 20004-1111 Phone: (202)653-7834
Staff: 6. **Subjects:** Accessibility; barrier-free and accessible design; federal requirements for accessible design; transportation, communication, and attitudinal barriers removal; recreation accessibility. **Holdings:** 3000 books; 500 documents. **Subscriptions:** 25 journals and other serials. **Services:** Library open to the public by appointment. **Automated Operations:** Computerized cataloging. **Remarks:** FAX: (202)653-7863. **Staff:** Marsha Mazz, Accessibility Spec.

★954★
Architectural Woodwork Institute - Library (Art)
P.O. Box 1550
Centreville, VA 22020 Phone: (703)222-1100
Founded: 1954. **Staff:** 13. **Subjects:** Architectural woodwork and woodwork practice. **Holdings:** Books; reports; photographs; data. **Subscriptions:** 30,000 journals and other serials. **Services:** Library open to qualified users. **Remarks:** FAX: (703)222-2499.

Archive of American Ceramics
See: **Everson Museum of Art** (5514)

★955★
ARChive of Contemporary Music (Mus)
132 Crosby St. Phone: (212)226-6967
New York, NY 10012 Robert George, Dir.
Founded: 1985. **Staff:** 5. **Subjects:** Popular music. **Holdings:** 600 books; 275,000 sound recordings; 2 million photographs and press clippings. **Subscriptions:** 60 journals and other serials; 12 newspapers. **Services:** Copying (limited); archive open to the public with restrictions. **Computerized Information Services:** Internal database. **Publications:** Newsletter, quarterly. **Remarks:** FAX: (212)226-6540. **Staff:** Jon Hafter, Archv.

★956★
Archive Films - Stock Footage Library (Aud-Vis)
530 W. 25th St. Phone: (212)620-3955
New York, NY 10001 William McCahey, Hd.Libn.
Staff: 35. **Subjects:** Historical film footage. **Remarks:** FAX: (212)645-2137.

Archive of Folk Culture
See: **Library of Congress - American Folklife Center** (9108)

Archive for the History of Quantum Physics
See: **University of Minnesota - Science and Engineering Library** (18928)

Archive for New Poetry
See: **University of California, San Diego - University Libraries** (18420)

★957★
Archive Photos - Library (Aud-Vis)
530 W. 25th St. Phone: (212)675-0115
New York, NY 10001 Eric Rachlis, Mgr.
Founded: 1938. **Staff:** Prof 9; Other 8. **Subjects:** Historical and current photographs of many subjects including people in different situations, industry, sports, architecture, landscapes, railroads, U.S.A., farming, interiors. **Special Collections:** Historical aviation, ships, and sports; World War I; Americana; historical New York City. **Holdings:** 5 million photographs, color transparencies, black/white prints, engravings. **Services:** Library open by appointment. **Special Indexes:** Frederick Lewis Picture Index - free to publishers. **Remarks:** Toll-free telephone number(s): (800)688-5656. FAX: (212)675-0379. **Formed by the merger of:** Frederic Lewis Stock Photos - Photographic Library and Pictorial Parade.

Archive of Popular American Music
See: **University of California, Los Angeles** (18367)

Archive for Research in Archetypal Symbolism
See: **C.G. Jung Institute of Los Angeles, Inc. - Max and Lore Zeller Library** (8495)

Archives Acadiennes
See: **Association Culturelle et Historique du Mont-Carmel** (1154)

★958★
Archives of the Airwaves (Hist)
Box 4
Needham, MA 02192 Roger C. Paulson, Owner
Founded: 1967. **Subjects:** Radio programming history, biographical data on radio performers. **Special Collections:** Radio Programs on tape (25,000). **Holdings:** 700 books; 30 VF drawers of other cataloged items. **Services:** Mail requests for information accepted.

Archives of American Aerospace Exploration
See: **Virginia Polytechnic Institute and State University - Libraries - Special Collections Department** (19874)

★959★
Archives of American Art/Smithsonian Institution - National Headquarters (Art)
8th & F Sts., N.W. Phone: (202)357-2781
Washington, DC 20560 Dr. Richard J. Wattenmaker, Dir.
Founded: 1954. **Staff:** Prof 31; Other 8. **Subjects:** American art, history of American visual arts, general American history. **Holdings:** 8 million manuscripts in over 3000 collections; 2500 oral history interviews; 15,000 art auction catalogs; 2000 exhibition catalogs; official records of galleries and art institutions, some on microfilm. **Services:** Interlibrary loan; archives open to scholars. **Computerized Information Services:** Produces catalog of archival and manuscript holdings (available online through RLIN). **Publications:** Archives of American Art Journal, quarterly; Arts in America: A Bibliography (4 volumes). **Special Catalogs:** Card Catalog of the Manuscript Collection of the Archives of American Art (10 volumes); Card Catalog of the Oral History Collections of the Archives of American Art (1 volume). **Remarks:** The archives maintains 5 research centers and the microfilm holdings are available in all centers. The centers are located as follows: New York Area - 1285 6th Ave., New York, NY 10019 (for research purposes); New England Area - 87 Mount Vernon St., Boston, MA 02108; Washington Area - Fine Arts & Portrait Gallery Bldg., 8th & F Sts., N.W., Washington, DC 20560; Midwest Area - Detroit Institute of Arts, 5200 Woodward Ave., Detroit, MI 48202; West Coast Area - Henry E. Huntington Library and Art Gallery, 1151 Oxford Rd., San Marino, CA 91108.

★960★
Archives of the American Musical Theatre (Theater)
Box 201 Phone: (616)943-8260
Grawn, MI 49637 David Hummel, Cur.
Founded: 1970. **Staff:** Prof 1. **Subjects:** Musical theater. **Holdings:** 120 books; 6000 phonograph records; 2500 reel-to-reel tapes; 3000 cassette tapes; 1000 compact discs; 900 theater programs; 4 VF drawers of program copies and reviews. **Services:** Archives open to qualified researchers by appointment only. **Publications:** The Collector's Guide To The American Musical Theatre.

Archives of Appalachia
See: **East Tennessee State University** (5127)

Archives de la Bastille
See: **France - Bibliotheque de l'Arsenal** (6061)

★961★
Archives of California Art (Art)
Oakland Museum
1000 Oak St. Phone: (510)273-3005
Oakland, CA 94607 Christine Droll, Libn.
Subjects: Historical and contemporary California art, Gold Rush Period, Mission Days. **Holdings:** 2500 books; 3000 catalogs, including those of Western museums; archival material on 15,000 artists, craftsmen, photographers. **Subscriptions:** 20 journals and other serials. **Services:** Archives open to the public by appointment. **Remarks:** FAX: (510)273-2258.

Archives Canadiennes du Mouvement des Femmes
See: **Canadian Women's Movement Archives** (3004)

Archives of Cooperative Lutheranism
See: **Evangelical Lutheran Church in America - ELCA Archives** (5495)

★962★
Archives Departementales de la Loire Atlantique - Bibliotheque (Hist)
6 rue de Bouille
F-44000 Nantes, France Phone: 40200232
Founded: 1880. **Staff:** Prof 2; Other 4. **Subjects:** History - Loire Atlantique, Anjou, Brittany, Vendee. **Special Collections:** St. Stanislau School's Library; Marcel Potisou's Library. **Holdings:** 15,000 books; 450 bound periodical volumes; archives; microfiche; microfilm. **Subscriptions:** 16 newspapers. **Services:** Library open to the public for reference use only.

Archives of the General Federation of Women's Clubs
See: **General Federation of Women's Clubs - Women's History and Resource Center** (6323)

Archives of the History of American Psychology
See: **University of Akron** (18151)

Archives of the Livingston Family
See: **U.S. Presidential Libraries - Franklin D. Roosevelt Library** (17922)

Archives Nationales du Canada
See: **Canada - National Archives of Canada** (2770)

Archives of the Order of St. John of Jerusalem
See: **Malta - National Library of Malta** (9576)

Archives du Seminaire de Trois-Rivieres
See: **Corporation du Seminaire St-Joseph de Trois-Rivieres - Archives du Seminaire de Trois-Rivieres** (4339)

Archives of the South Georgia Conference United Methodist Church
See: **United Methodist Church - South Georgia Conference - Commission on Archives and History - Arthur J. Moore Methodist Museum - Library** (16739)

Archives and Special Collections on Women in Medicine
See: **Medical College of Pennsylvania** (9997)

Archives des Ursulines de Quebec
See: **Monastere des Ursulines** (10602)

Archives of the XV Olympic Winter Games
See: **Calgary City Archives** (2454)

Archivo General de Puerto Rico
See: **(Puerto Rico) Institute of Puerto Rican Culture** (13519)

Archivo Nacional de Honduras
See: **Honduras - National Archives** (7364)

ARCO Exploration and Production Technology - Technical Information Center
See: **Atlantic-Richfield Company** (1260)

ARCO Oil & Gas Company
See: **Atlantic-Richfield Company** (1260)

★963★
Arctic Alaska Testing Laboratories - Library (Sci-Engr)
Box 70843
Fairbanks, AK 99707 Phone: (907)479-0600
Subjects: Materials analysis, permafrost, arctic soils. **Holdings:** 800 books; 1500 reports. **Services:** Library open to the public on fee basis.

★964★
Arctic Bible Institute - Library
HCO 4
Box 9100
Palmer, AK 99645
Founded: 1970. **Subjects:** Bible, theology. **Holdings:** 1500 books. **Remarks:** Currently inactive.

★965★
Arctic Institute of North America - Library (Sci-Engr)
University of Calgary Library
2500 University Dr., N.W. Phone: (403)220-5650
Calgary, AB, Canada T2N 1N4 C. Eric Tull, Northern Stud.Libn.
Founded: 1945. **Subjects:** Arctic and Antarctic regions - geology, geography, meteorology, oceanography, glaciology, zoology, botany; snow, ice, and permafrost studies; history of exploration; native studies; economic and social development; energy resources. **Special Collections:** Pipelines Collection (600 documents). **Holdings:** 20,000 volumes; 25,000 reprints and pamphlets; 600 archival materials; 15,000 government documents; 500 microforms. **Subscriptions:** 275 journals and other serials; 12 newspapers. **Services:** Interlibrary loan; copying; library open to the public. **Automated Operations:** Computerized cataloging, acquisitions, and circulation. **Computerized Information Services:** DIALOG Information Services, QL Systems, PFDS Online, CAN/OLE (through University of Calgary Library); Envoy 100, BITNET (electronic mail services). Performs searches on fee basis. **Remarks:** FAX: (403)282-6837. TULL@UNCAMULT (BITNET).

Arctic Institute of North America Collection
See: **University of Calgary - University Libraries - Sciences/Professions Area** (18295)

★966★
ARE, Inc. - Library (Sci-Engr)
2600 Dellana Ln.
Austin, TX 78746 Phone: (512)327-3520
Subjects: Civil engineering. **Holdings:** 1000 books; 5000 reports. **Services:** Library open to the public with restrictions. **Remarks:** FAX: (512)327-0822.

★967★
Area Agency on Aging - Region IB - Library (Med)
400 Franklin Ctr.
29100 Northwestern Hwy. Phone: (313)948-1640
Southfield, MI 48034 Colleen Blaesing, Dir. of Commun.
Founded: 1980. **Subjects:** Older adult issues. **Special Collections:** Older Adult Audio-Visual Collection (29 slides; 3 filmstrips; 9 16mm films; 3 6.35mm films; 2 videotapes; 29 videocassettes). **Holdings:** 1310 books. **Subscriptions:** 18 journals and other serials; 9 newspapers. **Services:** Interlibrary loan; library open to the public by appointment. **Computerized Information Services:** Information and Referral (internal database). Contact Person: Camille Evans, Info. and Referral Spec.

Arecibo Observatory
See: **Cornell University - Arecibo Observatory** (4303)

Arensberg Archives
See: **Francis Bacon Foundation, Inc. - Francis Bacon Library** (1401)

★968★
Arent, Fox, Kintner, Plotkin & Kahn - Library (Law)
1050 Connecticut Ave., N.W. Phone: (202)857-6296
Washington, DC 20036 Mark P. Shaw, Libn.
Staff: Prof 4; Other 4. **Subjects:** Law. **Special Collections:** Federal and District of Columbia legislative histories. **Holdings:** 40,000 books. **Subscriptions:** 16 newspapers. **Services:** Interlibrary loan; library not open to the public. **Automated Operations:** Computerized cataloging, serials, acquisitions, and ILL. **Computerized Information Services:** DIALOG Information Services, LEXIS, Dow Jones News/Retrieval, WESTLAW, VU/TEXT Information Services, Bureau of National Affairs (BNA), Prentice-Hall, Inc., DunsPrint, DataTimes, Information America, CCH, ELSS (Electronic Legislative Search System), LEGI-SLATE, C.Q. Alert, Reuters, OCLC EPIC, Exportnet. **Remarks:** FAX: (202)857-6395. Telex: 892672 Western Union. **Staff:** Robert Dickey, Asst.Libn.; Debra Atkins, Fed.Leg.Libn.; Stephanie Paup, D.C. Leg.Libn.

Arents Collection of Books in Parts
See: **New York Public Library - Arents Collection of Books in Parts** (11595)

George Arents Research Library for Special Collections
See: **Syracuse University - George Arents Research Library for Special Collections** (15961)

Arents Tobacco Collection
See: **New York Public Library - Arents Tobacco Collection** (11596)

★969★
Argentina - Biblioteca Nacional de Aeronautica (Trans)
Paraguay 748
Casilla de Correo 3389
1000 Buenos Aires, Bs. As., Phone: 1 3938061
Argentina Angelica Amalia Llorca, Chf.Libn.
Founded: 1927. **Staff:** Prof 3; Other 2. **Subjects:** Aviation. **Holdings:** 25,000 books; 20,000 bound periodical volumes; 10,000 reports. **Services:** Interlibrary loan; copying; library open to the public. **Publications:** Conoce Usted la Biblioteca Nacional de Aeronautica; catalogo de la biblioteca circulante; catalogo de la biblioteca estudiantil; abstracts of new books (published in Revista Nacional de Aeronautica).

★970★
Argentina - Comision Nacional de Energia Atomica - Div. Centro de Informacion (Energy)
Av. del Libertador 8250 Phone: 1 707711
1429 Buenos Aires, Argentina Alejandra M. Nardi
Founded: 1950. **Staff:** 24. **Subjects:** Atomic energy, nuclear sciences, medicine, engineering sciences, biological sciences, earth sciences, physical sciences, chemical sciences, information sciences, social sciences, environmental sciences, technology, materials. **Holdings:** 36,000 volumes; 322,000 microfiche; 81,400 reports. **Subscriptions:** 400 journals and other serials. **Services:** Interlibrary loan; copying; SDI; consulting; data collection and analysis; referrals; library open to the public. **Computerized Information Services:** STN International; CD-ROMs; DOCSIS, PERSIS, PRESTA (internal databases). **Publications:** CNEA Reports, irregular; Technical Notes, irregular; Courses, irregular - all available on exchange. **Remarks:** FAX: 1 5449252. Telex: 23458 CNEA SC AR. Alternate telephone number(s): 1 5442582. **Also Known As:** Argentina - National Atomic Energy Commission - Department of Technical Information. **Staff:** Gloria Rollan, Hd., Tech.Proc.Sect.; Maria Nunez Casal, Hd., Info. Networks Sect.; Alejandra Chavez-Flores, Hd., Diffusion of Info.Sect.; Alicia Cassanello, Libn.; Ada I. Vogt, Libn.; Nancy Gomez, Libn.

Argentina - Ministry of Defense - National Directorate of the Antarctic - Argentine Antarctic Institute
See: **Argentine Antarctic Institute** (972)

Argentina - Ministry of the Economy - Obispo Colombres Agro-Industrial Experiment Station
See: **Obispo Colombres Agro-Industrial Experiment Station** (12226)

Argentina - Ministry of Education and Justice - Miguel Lillo Foundation
See: **Fundacion Miguel Lillo - Centro de Informacion Geo-Biologica, NOA** (6215)

Argentina - National Atomic Energy Commission - Department of Technical Information
See: **Argentina - Comision Nacional de Energia Atomica** (970)

Argentina - National Institute for the Study of the Theater
See: **National Institute for the Study of the Theater** (11216)

★971★
Argentina - Office of the Secretary-General of the Navy - Department of Naval Historical Studies - Library (Mil)
Jefatura del Estado Mayor General de la Armada
Avenida Almirante Brown 401 Phone: 01 362-1130
1155 Buenos Aires, Argentina Dora Martinez, Libn.
Subjects: World and Argentine naval history. **Holdings:** 7500 volumes. **Services:** Copying; library open to the public for reference use only. **Remarks:** Alternate telephone number(s): 1 3621248.

Argentina - Secretariat of Culture - National Institute for the Study of the Theater
See: **National Institute for the Study of the Theater** (11216)

★972★
Argentine Antarctic Institute - Library (Sci-Engr)
Cerrito 1248
1010 Buenos Aires, Bs. As., Argentina Phone: 1 8120071
Founded: 1951. **Staff:** 1. **Subjects:** Geology, geophysics, seismology, glaciology, physical and chemical oceanography, radiation, human and comparative physiology, animal biology, limnology, geomagnetism, ionospheric physics, auroras. **Holdings:** 8000 volumes. **Services:** Interlibrary loan; copying; library open to the public. **Remarks:** FAX: 1 5412039. Maintained by Argentina - Ministry of Defense - National Directorate of the Antarctic. **Also Known As:** Instituto Antartico Argentino. **Staff:** Marta Cardinali, Libn./Asst.Mgr.

★973★
Argentinian Association of Dermatology - Library (Med)
Mexico 1720 Phone: 1 3812737
1100 Buenos Aires, Argentina Pablo M. Rusca, Libn.
Founded: 1907. **Staff:** 2. **Subjects:** Dermatology. **Holdings:** 2100 volumes. **Subscriptions:** 45 journals and other serials. **Services:** Interlibrary loan; copying; SDI; library open to the public. **Computerized Information Services:** CD-ROMs (MEDLINE). **Publications:** Revista Argentina de Dermatologia. **Remarks:** Alternate telephone number(s): 1 3812737. **Also Known As:** Asociacion Argentina de Dermatologia. **Staff:** Pedro H. Magnin, M.D.

★974★
Argo-Tech Corporation - Library (Sci-Engr)
23555 Euclid Ave. Phone: (216)692-5287
Cleveland, OH 44117 Sharon K. DeLong, Libn.
Founded: 1954. **Staff:** Prof 1; Other 1. **Subjects:** Metallurgy, nonmetallic materials, aerospace technology, mechanical engineering. **Holdings:** 5000 books; 4300 bound periodical volumes; 15,000 company reports; 40,000 contractor and government reports; 25,000 military specifications and standards. **Subscriptions:** 150 journals and other serials. **Services:** Interlibrary loan; library open to the public by appointment. **Computerized Information Services:** DIALOG Information Services. **Remarks:** FAX: (216)692-5584.

★975★
Argonne National Laboratory - Argonne-West Technical Library (Energy)
Box 2528 Phone: (208)533-7237
Idaho Falls, ID 83403-2528 Judy Krieger, Libn.
Staff: Prof 1; Other 1.5. **Subjects:** Chemistry, physics, mathematics, nuclear and mechanical engineering, computers. **Special Collections:** Liquid metal fast breeder reactor and sodium technology materials. **Holdings:** 10,000 books; 110,000 microfiche; 14,000 unbound reports. **Subscriptions:** 300 journals and other serials. **Services:** Interlibrary loan; copying; library open to holders of U.S. security clearances. **Computerized Information Services:** DIALOG Information Services, OCLC. **Networks/Consortia:** Member of FEDLINK. **Remarks:** FAX: (801)533-7656. Argonne National Laboratory is operated by the University of Chicago under contract to the U.S. Department of Energy.

★976★
Argonne National Laboratory - National Energy Software Center (Comp Sci)
9700 S. Cass Ave. Phone: (708)972-7250
Argonne, IL 60439 Margaret K. Butler, Dir.
Founded: 1960. **Staff:** Prof 5; Other 1. **Subjects:** Computer software in energy research and development areas, mathematical software. **Holdings:** 1700 computer software packages. **Services:** Library open to the public with restrictions. **Automated Operations:** Computerized cataloging, acquisitions, and circulation. **Computerized Information Services:** ACCESS, Software Referral System (internal databases); BITNET (electronic mail service). Contact Person: Jan Buckley. **Publications:** ANL-7411 Revised, ANL-7416; frequent notes, bulletins, and newsletters. **Remarks:** The Argonne National Laboratory is operated by the University of Chicago under contract to the U.S. Department of Energy. FAX: (708)972-2206. Telex: 687 1701 DOE ANL. Electronic mail address(es): NESCINFO@ANLNESC (BITNET).

★977★
Argonne National Laboratory - Technical Information Services Department - Information and Publishing Division (Energy, Sci-Engr)
9700 S. Cass Ave., Bldg. 203-D140 Phone: (708)252-4215
Argonne, IL 60439 Yvette N. Woell, Mgr., Lib.Info.Serv.Sect.
Founded: 1946. **Staff:** Prof 16; Other 17. **Subjects:** Nuclear science and engineering, physics, mathematics, chemistry, chemical engineering, biological sciences, medicine, materials science, energy and environmental sciences. **Special Collections:** DOE and foreign reports on topics of programmatic interest. **Holdings:** 60,000 books; 150,000 bound periodical volumes; 1 million unclassified reports; 3200 journal titles. **Subscriptions:** 2300 journals. **Services:** Interlibrary loan; SDI; libraries open to the public upon application. **Automated Operations:** Argonne Information Management System. **Computerized Information Services:** DTIC, NASA/RECON, STN International, PFDS Online, DIALOG Information Services, BRS Information Technologies, Integrated Technical Information System (ITIS), MEDLINE, RLIN, OCLC; ALANET, BITNET (electronic mail services). **Networks/Consortia:** Member of Suburban Library System (SLS), ILLINET. **Publications:** ANL Technical Publications Guide; ANL List of Publications. **Remarks:** The Argonne National Laboratory is operated by the University of Chicago under contract to the U.S. Department of Energy. Holdings of the Technical Information Services Department are distributed among ten technical libraries: Biomedical, Chemistry, Chemical Engineering, Engineering/Reactor Science, Environmental Assessment, High Energy Physics/Energy Sciences, Materials Science, Mathematics/Physics/Computer Science, Solid State Physics, and Synchrotron . FAX: (708)972-3609. **Staff:** Shannon D. Savage, Dir.; Jane F. Biewer, Bio.Med.; Jean A. Castle, High Engery Physics/Energy Sci.; Sharon M. Clark, Chem.Engr.; Gary N. Davidoff, Math/Physics/Comp.Sci.; Susan E. Hilchey, Env. Assessment; Veronica E. Johnson, Synchrotron; Joan I. Tuss, Mtls.Sci.; Melissa Gregory, Mgr., Lib.Sup.Serv.Sect.; Gail Hoef, Bibliog. Control; David Hamrin, Mgr., Tech.Pubns.Serv.Sect.

★978★
Argosystems Inc. - Technical Library (Sci-Engr)
430 N. Mary Ave., MS 10-1B Phone: (408)737-2000
Sunnyvale, CA 94086 Sylvia Rathbun, Info.Rsrcs.Mgr.
Staff: Prof 1.5. **Subjects:** Radar, signal processing, telecommunications, computers, mathematics, systems analysis. **Holdings:** 3600 books; 1150 other cataloged items. **Subscriptions:** 220 journals and other serials. **Services:** Interlibrary loan; library not open to the public. **Automated Operations:** Computerized cataloging, acquisitions, circulation, and ILL. **Computerized Information Services:** DIALOG Information Services, Dow Jones News/Retrieval, Dun & Bradstreet Business Credit Services; OnTyme Electronic Message Network Service (electronic mail service). **Publications:** Monthly bulletin. **Special Indexes:** Periodical holdings index; map index. **Remarks:** FAX: (408)737-2726. Electronic mail address(es): CLASS.ARGO (OnTyme Electronic Message Network Service).

★979★
Argus Archives (Soc Sci)
228 E. 49th St. Phone: (212)355-6140
New York, NY 10017 Julie Van Ness
Founded: 1969. **Staff:** 2. **Subjects:** Animal welfare, animal rights, humane education. **Holdings:** 350 books; 18 lateral file drawers of reports, clippings, other materials. **Subscriptions:** 100 journals and other serials. **Services:** Copying; archives open to the public by appointment. **Publications:** Animal Films for Humane Education.

★980★
Argus Research Corporation - Library (Bus-Fin)
17 Battery Pl. Phone: (212)425-7500
New York, NY 10004 Richard Cuneo, Libn.
Staff: 1. **Subjects:** Business and industry. **Holdings:** Company and industry files; government publications. **Subscriptions:** 50 journals and other serials; 12 newspapers. **Services:** Interlibrary loan (clients only); library open to clients only. **Computerized Information Services:** Argus On-line, Vickers On-Line Service. **Remarks:** FAX: (212)509-5408.

ARIC
See: **Center for Environmental Information, Inc.** (3238)

★981★
Arica Institute, Inc. - Library and Archives (Soc Sci)
150 5th Ave., No. 912 Phone: (212)807-9600
New York, NY 10013-4311 David J. Johnson, Libn./Archv.
Founded: 1975. **Subjects:** Psychology, medicine, creativity, organization, metaphysics, enlightenment. **Holdings:** Figures not available. **Services:** Library not open to the public. **Remarks:** FAX: (212)727-0521.

Arid Lands Information Center
See: **University of Arizona** (18208)

★982★
ARINC Inc. - Technical Library (Mil)
4055 Hancock St. Phone: (619)222-7447
San Diego, CA 92110 Elenia H. Hofler, Libn.
Founded: 1979. **Staff:** Prof 1. **Subjects:** Aircraft, missiles, ship systems, ordnance, communications, database management. **Special Collections:** ARINC technical reports (4000); ARINC documents. **Holdings:** 300 books. **Subscriptions:** 100 journals and other serials. **Services:** Interlibrary loan; library not open to the public. **Computerized Information Services:** DIALOG Information Services, Government-Industry Data Exchange Program (GIDEP). **Publications:** Acquisitions list, monthly; Aeroline; Plane Talk - all for internal distribution only. **Special Catalogs:** Directory of ARINC reports and publications. **Formerly:** ARINC Research Corporation.

★983★
ARINC Inc. - Technical Library (Comp Sci, Mil)
2551 Riva Rd. Phone: (301)266-4000
Annapolis, MD 21401-7465 William O. Lively, Libn.
Staff: Prof 1; Other 1. **Subjects:** Reliability, maintainability, cost analysis, systems architecture, systems analysis. **Holdings:** 3000 books; 5000 Defense Documentation Center reports; 450 NASA reports; 20,000 specifications, standards, handbooks; 8000 DDC and NASA reports on microfiche. **Subscriptions:** 105 journals and other serials. **Services:** Interlibrary loan; library not open to the public. **Remarks:** FAX: (301)266-2047.

Arizona AFL-CIO Labor Union Archives
See: **Northern Arizona University - Cline Library - Special Collections and Archives Department** (11992)

Arizona Business Gazette
See: **Phoenix Newspapers, Inc.** (13022)

★984★
Arizona Cactus and Succulent Research, Inc. - Library (Biol Sci)
8 Mulberry Ln. Phone: (602)432-7040
Bisbee, AZ 85603 Janet Boccino
Founded: 1983. **Staff:** Prof 1. **Subjects:** Arid land plants, cactus plants, arid land botany, ethnobotany, Southwestern Indians. **Holdings:** 1550 books; 35 bound periodical volumes; 1000 reports. **Subscriptions:** 8 journals and other serials; 26 newspapers. **Services:** Copying; library open to the public for reference use only. **Computerized Information Services:** Internal database. Contact Person: David L. Eppele, Pres. **Special Indexes:** Index of Cactus Illustrations, 1900-1989.

Arizona Costume Institute Library
See: **Phoenix Art Museum - Library** (13015)

★985★
Arizona Daily Star - Library (Publ)
4850 S. Park Ave.
Box 26807 Phone: (602)573-4160
Tucson, AZ 85726 Elaine Y. Raines, Chf.Libn.
Founded: 1950. **Staff:** Prof 1; Other 8. **Subjects:** Newspaper reference topics; Tucson subjects, 1939 to present. **Special Collections:** Tucson telephone directories, 1937 to present; Tucson city directories, 1918 to present. **Holdings:** 1200 books; Daily Star, 1877 to present, on microfilm; newspaper clippings with emphasis on Tucson, 1939 to present; 200,000 photographs; 9000 pamphlets. **Subscriptions:** 40 journals and other serials; 17 newspapers. **Services:** Copying. **Computerized Information Services:** DIALOG Information Services, VU/TEXT Information Services, DataTimes.

★986★
Arizona Geological Survey - Library (Sci-Engr, Energy)
845 N. Park Ave. Phone: (602)882-4795
Tucson, AZ 85719 Thomas G. McGarvin, Geol.
Founded: 1915. **Staff:** 1. **Subjects:** Geology, mineral resources, applied geology, geologic framework, mining geology. **Special Collections:** Mining Company and Mine Collection (20 VF drawers of newspaper clippings); geology of Arizona (20 VF drawers of newspaper clippings and other materials); Arizona Bureau of Geology and Mineral Technology (5 VF drawers of open file reports). **Holdings:** 300 books; 500 bound periodical volumes; 400 open file reports of the U.S. Geological Survey and the U.S. Bureau of Mines; 125 dissertations and theses; 8000 government documents; 15 VF drawers and 4 map cases of maps. **Subscriptions:** 10 journals and other serials. **Services:** Library open to the public for reference use only.

Arizona Health Sciences Center Library
See: **University of Arizona** (18209)

★987★
Arizona Historical Foundation - Library (Hist)
Hayden Library
Arizona State University Phone: (602)966-8331
Tempe, AZ 85287-1006 Dr. Paul G. Hubbard, Exec. V.P.
Founded: 1959. **Staff:** Prof 1; Other 2. **Subjects:** Arizona and American Southwestern history. **Special Collections:** Papers of Senator Barry Goldwater and Senator Paul Fannin; collections of Goldwater family, Dr. Benjamin Sacks, Thomas Maddock, Roscoe Willson, Orme Lewis, Grace Sparkes, and Richard Schaus; Arizona Bankers Association Collection; Arizona Cattle Growers Association Collection (135 cubic feet of books, biographies, photographs, negatives); Arizona Cotton Growers Association Collection; Arizona Society of Certified Public Accountants Collection; Phoenix YMCA Collection; Mecham Recall Collection; Planned Parenthood of Central and Northern Arizona Collection; Allen A. Dutton Photograph Collection (2 linear feet); Ruth Reinhold Aviation Collection (15 linear feet of manuscripts, photographs, research notes); Dane Coolidge Photograph Collection. **Holdings:** 5000 books; 4000 periodical titles; 2500 linear feet of manuscript materials; 50,000 photographic images; 35 map case drawers; 30 linear feet of AV materials; 30 drawers of microfilm; 30 linear feet of ephemera. **Subscriptions:** 30 journals and other serials. **Services:** Copying; historical consulting; library open to the public. **Automated Operations:** Computerized cataloging. **Networks/Consortia:** Member of Colorado Alliance of Research Libraries (CARL). **Publications:** Manuscript guides and calendars. **Special Indexes:** Index to Benjamin Sacks Collection (card); map index; index to photographs (card); Arizona and Southwest index of photographs, biographical material, ephemera, and manuscript collections (online). **Remarks:** Alternate telephone number(s): (602)965-3283. **Staff:** Dennis D. Madden, Cur.; Marlene Ware, Archv.

★988★
Arizona Historical Society - Library (Hist)
949 E. 2nd St. Phone: (602)628-5774
Tucson, AZ 85719 Margaret S. Bret-Harte, Hd.Libn.
Founded: 1884. **Staff:** Prof 7. **Subjects:** Southwestern Americana - Arizona territorial and state government, mining, Mexican history, Spanish North American colonial history, military history, ranching, Southwestern Indians. **Special Collections:** W.J. Holliday books and manuscripts (6113

items); Charles B. Gatewood military collection; Byron Cummings ethnological and archaeological collection; Frederick S. Dellenbaugh Colorado River collection; Aguiar Collection of early 19th century Mexican documents; Carl Hayden biographical files of 1854-1864 Arizonans; Will C. Barnes ranching and forestry papers; manuscript collections (1120). **Holdings:** 50,000 books; 5000 bound periodical volumes; 10,000 pamphlets; 5000 maps; 250,000 photographs; 1000 manuscripts; 750 linear feet of documents. **Subscriptions:** 39 journals and other serials; 33 newspapers. **Services:** Copying; library open to the public for reference use only; copies from the photograph collection are available for a fee. **Computerized Information Services:** Internal databases. **Publications:** Journal of Arizona Histo ry, quarterly. **Staff:** Lori Davisson, Res.Spec.; Barbara Bush, Photo.Libn.; Deborah Shelton, Photo.Archv.; Heather Hatch, Photo.Archv.; Susan Peters, Bk.Cat. & Ethnic Spec.; Riva Dean, Gen.Ref.; Mark Sawyer, Photo.; Stephen Eiswierth, Photo.

★989★
Arizona Historical Society Museum - Library (Hist)
1242 N. Central Ave. Phone: (602)255-4479
Phoenix, AZ 85004 Janet Michaelieu, Libn.
Staff: Prof 2; Other 12. **Subjects:** Arizona and western history, antiques and preservation. **Holdings:** 2000 volumes; 62 boxes of historical photographs; 120 boxes of manuscript collections; 1500 films and videotape programs; 750 oral history tapes; 500 architectural drawings. **Subscriptions:** 25 journals and other serials. **Services:** Copying; library open to the public on a limited schedule. **Remarks:** FAX: (602)255-5289. **Staff:** James Reynolds.

★990★
Arizona Hospital Association - Library (Med)
Park Bridge at Fountainhead
1501 W. Fountainhead Pkwy., Suite 650 Phone: (602)968-1083
Tempe, AZ 85282 Thomas D. Misch
Founded: 1987. **Staff:** 1. **Subjects:** Health care, hospitals, nursing. **Holdings:** 30 books; 400 bound periodical volumes; 500 newsletters and newspapers. **Subscriptions:** 7 newspapers. **Services:** Library open to the public by appointment. **Remarks:** FAX: (602)967-2029.

Arizona Instructional Resource Center
See: **Foundation for Blind Children** (6035)

Arizona Lumber and Timber Company Archives
See: **Northern Arizona University - Cline Library - Special Collections and Archives Department** (11992)

★991★
Arizona Public Service Company - Corporate Library (Energy)
P.O. Box 53999, Sta. 1118 Phone: (602)250-4140
Phoenix, AZ 85072 Nadine Feldman
Founded: 1986. **Staff:** 1. **Subjects:** Electric utilities, business, management, electric power industry, personal development. **Holdings:** 2000 books. **Subscriptions:** 80 journals and other serials. **Services:** Interlibrary loan; publication routing. **Automated Operations:** Computerized indexing. **Remarks:** FAX: (602)250-4411.

Arizona Republic
See: **Phoenix Newspapers, Inc.** (13022)

★992★
Arizona-Sonora Desert Museum - Library (Env-Cons, Biol Sci)
2021 N. Kinney Rd. Phone: (602)883-1380
Tucson, AZ 85743 Georgia Eddy, Educ.Spec.
Founded: 1952. **Staff:** Prof 1; Other 1. **Subjects:** Deserts, conservation, earth sciences, Sonoran Desert region, mammals, Southwestern plants, insects, reptiles, amphibians, birds. **Holdings:** 6500 books; 400 bound periodical volumes; 500 unbound sets; 450 unbound monographs and bulletins; 4000 slides; 200 photographs; 3000 separates and pamphlets. **Subscriptions:** 82 journals and other serials. **Services:** Copying; library open to museum members, staff, and docents. **Remarks:** FAX: (602)883-2500.

★993★
Arizona (State) Attorney General - Water Rights Adjudication Team (WRAT) Research Room (Sci-Engr)
1275 W. Washington Phone: (602)542-1401
Phoenix, AZ 85007 Mary Lu Moore
Founded: 1988. **Staff:** Prof 1. **Subjects:** Hydrology, water law, geology, local history, ethnology, agriculture. **Holdings:** 600 books. **Subscriptions:** 75 journals and other serials. **Services:** Research Room not open to the public. **Computerized Information Services:** Internal database. **Remarks:** FAX: (602)542-4385.

Arizona (State) Commission of Agriculture and Horticulture - Agricultural Laboratories Division - Biological Laboratories Section - Library
See: **Arizona (State) Department of Agriculture - State Agricultural Laboratory - Biological Section - Library** (994)

★994★
Arizona (State) Department of Agriculture - State Agricultural Laboratory - Biological Section - Library (Biol Sci)
2422 W. Holly Phone: (602)253-1920
Phoenix, AZ 85009 Ron Ykema, Lab.Mgr.
Staff: Prof 5; Other 3. **Subjects:** Entomology, plant pathology, horticulture, cacti and native plants, agronomy. **Holdings:** 3000 books; 20 VF drawers of technical papers and bulletins. **Subscriptions:** 12 journals and other serials. **Services:** Library not open to the public. **Computerized Information Services:** Electronic mail service. **Remarks:** FAX: (602)253-2247. **Formerly:** Arizona (State) Commission of Agriculture and Horticulture - Agricultural Laboratories Division - Biological Laboratories Section - Library.

★995★
Arizona (State) Department of Economic Security - Arizona Training Program at Coolidge - Administration Library (Med)
Box 1467
Coolidge, AZ 85228-1467 Phone: (602)723-4151
Staff: 4. **Subjects:** Developmental disabilities, psychology, behavioral management, medicine, teaching, social work. **Holdings:** 1200 books; 300 other cataloged items. **Subscriptions:** 10 journals and other serials. **Services:** Library open to the public for reference use only by appointment.

★996★
Arizona (State) Department of Economic Security - Authority Library (Soc Sci)
1789 W. Jefferson Phone: (602)542-4777
Phoenix, AZ 85007 Wesley M. Rader, Supv.
Staff: Prof 1; Other 1. **Subjects:** Public welfare, labor, management, child welfare, census. **Special Collections:** Departmental documents. **Holdings:** 2000 books; 10,000 other cataloged items. **Subscriptions:** 130 journals and other serials; 11 newspapers. **Services:** Interlibrary loan; copying; library open to the public. **Publications:** New Editions, monthly.

★997★
Arizona (State) Department of Education - Educational Information Center (Educ)
1535 W. Jefferson Phone: (602)542-5416
Phoenix, AZ 85007 Linda Edgington, Dir.
Staff: Prof 1; Other 2. **Subjects:** Education. **Holdings:** 10,000 books; ERIC microfiche, 1968 to present; 19 microfiche cabinets. **Subscriptions:** 195 journals and other serials. **Services:** Center open to the public for reference use only. **Computerized Information Services:** DIALOG Information Services. **Remarks:** FAX: (602)542-5283.

★998★
Arizona (State) Department of Environmental Quality - Library (Env-Cons)
2005 N. Central Ave. Phone: (602)257-6959
Phoenix, AZ 85004 Maryalice Waldrip
Founded: 1988. **Staff:** Prof 1. **Subjects:** Water quality, hazardous waste, wastewater, water pollution, air quality, solid waste. **Special Collections:** Department of Environmental Quality documents (complete set); Environmental Protection Agency documents (1000 documents). **Holdings:** 2000 reports. **Services:** Library open to the public for reference use only.

★999★
Arizona (State) Department of Health Services - Public Health Library (Med)
1740 W. Adams Phone: (602)542-1013
Phoenix, AZ 85007 Patricia L. Aiken, Lib.Mgr.
Founded: 1975. **Staff:** Prof 1; Other 3. **Subjects:** Public health, environmental health, medical statistics, epidemiology, nursing, medicine. **Special Collections:** Film and video collection (public health issues including sexually transmitted diseases, teenage pregnancy, suicide, substance abuse, driver education; 500 16mm films; 250 videocassettes). **Holdings:** 5000 books; 600 state documents. **Subscriptions:** 225 journals. **Services:** Interlibrary loan; copying; films and videocassettes for loan to schools and community groups; library open to the public for reference use only. **Computerized Information Services:** MEDLARS, BRS Information Technologies, DIALOG Information Services. **Networks/Consortia:** Member of Central Arizona Biomedical Libraries (CABL), National Network of Libraries of Medicine - Pacific Southwest Region. **Special Catalogs:** Media catalog. **Remarks:** FAX: (602)542-1235.

★1000★
Arizona (State) Department of Library, Archives & Public Records (Info Sci)
State Capitol, Rm. 200
1700 W. Washington Phone: (602)542-4035
Phoenix, AZ 85007 Sharon G. Womack, Dir.
Founded: 1864. **Staff:** Prof 44; Other 72. **Subjects:** Arizona and southwestern history, law, genealogy. **Special Collections:** State Archives. **Holdings:** 1.1 million volumes; federal document depository; state document center; state reference center (Arizona public libraries only). **Subscriptions:** 1700 journals and other serials; 130 newspapers. **Services:** Interlibrary loan; library open to the public for reference use only. **Automated Operations:** Computerized cataloging. **Computerized Information Services:** DIALOG Information Services, WESTLAW, VU/TEXT Information Services, LEGI-SLATE, WILSONLINE, ELSS (Electronic Legislative Search System); Readers Advisory (computerized circulation system for blind and physically handicapped; internal database). Performs searches on fee basis. **Networks/Consortia:** Member of AMIGOS Bibliographic Council, Inc. **Remarks:** FAX: (602)542-4400 (Res.Div.); 542-4500 (ILL); 256-6372 (Lib. Extension Div.); 255-4312 (AV Sect.) **Staff:** Arlene Bansal, Dp.Dir.; Ray Tevis, Res.Div.Dir.; David Hoober, State Archv., Tony Miele, Lib. Extension Div.Dir.; Michael Carman, Musm.Div.Dir.; Martin Richelsoph, Rec.Mgmt.Div.Dir.; Richard Peel, Div.Dir., Lib. for the Blind and Physically Handicapped.

★1001★
Arizona (State) Department of Mines & Mineral Resources - Library (Sci-Engr)
1502 W. Washington Phone: (602)255-3791
Phoenix, AZ 85007-3210 Leroy E. Kissinger, Dir.
Founded: 1939. **Staff:** 8. **Subjects:** Mining and geology in Arizona. **Holdings:** Figures not available. **Services:** Library open to the public for research. **Publications:** Directories; mineral reports; information circulars. **Remarks:** FAX: (602)255-3777.

★1002★
Arizona State Energy Office - Information Center (Energy)
3800 N. Central, Suite 1200 Phone: (602)280-1402
Phoenix, AZ 85012 Pam Paschal, Mgt.Asst.
Staff: Prof 1. **Subjects:** Community energy consciousness, energy conservation, energy planning and policy, solar/alternate energy. **Special Collections:** Arizona Energy Flow Studies; 1981 Arizona Energy Inventory; 1979 final report of Governor's Conference on Energy Policy. **Holdings:** Figures not available. **Subscriptions:** 171 journals and other serials. **Services:** Energy hotline for Arizona residents. **Automated Operations:** Computerized cataloging, acquisitions, and circulation. **Computerized Information Services:** Integrated Technical Information System (ITIS), Mead Data Central, DIALOG Information Services, The Source Information Network; Arizona Energy Data System (internal database); Dialcom, Inc. (electronic mail service). Performs searches free of charge. Contact Person: Lee Connelly, Energy Data Adm., 280-1420. **Publications:** Brochures and fact sheets on energy-related subjects - free upon request. **Special Indexes:** Indexes to energy publications and AV programs. **Remarks:** Toll-free telephone number(s): (800)352-5499 (in Arizona).

★1003★
Arizona (State) Governor's Office of Tourism - Library (Bus-Fin)
1100 W. Washington
Phoenix, AZ 85007 Phone: (602)542-8687
Founded: 1975. **Subjects:** Tourism, travel-related studies. **Holdings:** 50 volumes. **Services:** Library open to the public. **Remarks:** FAX: (602)542-4068.

★1004★
Arizona State Hospital - Medical Library (Med)
2500 E. Van Buren Phone: (602)220-6045
Phoenix, AZ 85008 Walter K. Wrobel, Med.Libn.
Founded: 1954. **Staff:** Prof 1. **Subjects:** Psychiatry, psychiatric nursing, psychology, psychotherapy and psychoanalysis, social case work, child psychiatry, addictive behaviors. **Holdings:** 7850 books; 3700 bound periodical volumes; 730 cassettes and tapes. **Subscriptions:** 142 journals and other serials. **Services:** Interlibrary loan; copying; library open to the public for reference use only. **Computerized Information Services:** BRS Information Technologies. **Networks/Consortia:** Member of Central Arizona Biomedical Libraries (CABL), National Network of Libraries of Medicine - Pacific Southwest Region.

★1005★
Arizona State Library for the Blind & Physically Handicapped (Aud-Vis)
1030 N. 32nd St. Phone: (602)225-5578
Phoenix, AZ 85008 Richard C. Peel, Adm.Libn.
Staff: Prof 10; Other 11. **Subjects:** Fiction, nonfiction, blindness, physical handicaps. **Special Collections:** Arizona and Southwest U.S. recorded books; Spanish recorded books. **Holdings:** 275,000 talking books. **Subscriptions:** 90 journals and other serials. **Services:** Interlibrary loan; library open to eligible public. **Automated Operations:** Computerized cataloging, acquisitions, serials, and circulation. **Computerized Information Services:** BRS Information Technologies; DRANET (electronic mail service). Performs searches free of charge. Contact Person: Karen Odean, Asst.Dir. **Networks/Consortia:** Member of National Library Service for the Blind & Physically Handicapped (NLS). **Publications:** Newsletter, bimonthly; Volunteer Newsletter, quarterly. **Remarks:** Toll-free telephone number(s): (800)255-5578 (in Arizona). FAX: (602)255-4312. **Staff:** Glenore Cole, Tech.Serv.; Linda Montgomery, Spec.Serv.

Arizona State Museum Library
See: **University of Arizona** (18210)

★1006★
Arizona (State) Oil and Gas Conservation Commission - Well Sample/ Well File Library (Energy)
845 N. Park Ave., Suite 100 Phone: (602)882-4795
Tucson, AZ 85719 Steven L. Rauzi, Prog.Adm.
Founded: 1959. **Staff:** Prof 1; Other 1. **Subjects:** Petroleum geology of Arizona. **Holdings:** 110 books; 120 bound periodical volumes; 130 reports; 95 maps; 29 reels of microfilm; 2000 microfiche; 1000 well files; 1700 boxes of well samples; 295 other cataloged items. **Subscriptions:** 2 journals and other serials; 5 newspapers. **Services:** Copying; library open to the public. **Computerized Information Services:** Internal database. **Remarks:** FAX: (602)628-5106. **Formerly:** Located in Phoenix, AZ.

★1007★
Arizona State Parks - Homolovi Ruins State Park Library (Area-Ethnic)
523 W. 2nd St. Phone: (602)289-4106
Winslow, AZ 86047 Karen Berggren, Pk.Mgr.
Founded: 1987. **Staff:** Prof 1. **Subjects:** Anasazi culture; prehistory of Southwestern United States; Hopi, Navajo, and other Northern Arizona Indian cultures; history of Northern Arizona. **Special Collections:** Development documents of Homolovi Ruins State Park. **Holdings:** 200 books; 50 other cataloged items. **Services:** Interlibrary loan; copying; library open to the public for reference use only. **Remarks:** TDD: (602)289-4421.

★1008★
Arizona State School for the Deaf & Blind - Library (Educ)
1200 W. Speedway Phone: (602)628-5723
Tucson, AZ 85703 Janet Miller, Libn.
Staff: 3. **Subjects:** Education, professional development. **Special Collections:** Parent Lending Library for Visually Handicapped & Hearing Handicapped. **Holdings:** 15,000 volumes; other cataloged items. **Subscriptions:** 14 journals and other serials. **Services:** Library open to the public with restrictions. **Remarks:** FAX: (602)628-5723.

★1009★
Arizona State University - Architecture and Environmental Design Library (Plan)
College of Architecture Phone: (602)965-6400
Tempe, AZ 85287-1705 Berna E. Neal, Head
Founded: 1960. **Staff:** Prof 1; Other 2. **Subjects:** Architecture, city planning, landscape architecture, industrial design, interior design, solar energy. **Special Collections:** Paolo Soleri Archives; Frank Lloyd Wright Special Research Collection; Paul Schweiker Archives; Victor Olgyay Archives. **Holdings:** 28,000 volumes; 150 cassette and tape recordings; 563 titles on microfilm; 25 films and video cassettes. **Subscriptions:** 200 journals and other serials. **Services:** Interlibrary loan; copying; library open to the public; special collections open to the public by appointment. **Automated Operations:** Computerized public access catalog and circulation. **Computerized Information Services:** BITNET (electronic mail service). **Special Indexes:** Index to Paolo Soleri Archives. **Remarks:** FAX: (602)965-1594. Electronic mail address(es): IACBXN@ASUACA (BITNET).

★1010★
Arizona State University - Center for Meteorite Studies - Library (Sci-Engr)
Tempe, AZ 85287 Phone: (602)965-6511
Carleton B. Moore, Dir.
Founded: 1961. **Staff:** 4. **Subjects:** Meteorites. **Special Collections:** Meteorite articles. **Holdings:** 3000 items on microfilm. **Services:** Interlibrary loan; copying; center open to the public. **Publications:** Publications of the Center for Meteorite Studies, irregular.

★1011★
Arizona State University - Chicano Research Collection (Area-Ethnic)
Department of Archives and Manuscripts
Hayden Library Phone: (602)965-3145
Tempe, AZ 85287-1006 Christine N. Marin, Archv./Cur.
Founded: 1970. **Staff:** 16. **Subjects:** Mexican-American literature, history; chicanas; activism; bilingual education; political science; Chicano movement leaders. **Special Collections:** Chicano newspapers and manuscripts; Mexican-American biographies (50); Chicano Movement literature; student activism reports; family histories. **Holdings:** 1500 books; 25 bound periodical volumes; 500 unbound reports; 2000 newspaper clippings; 2,000 pieces of ephemera; photographs; videotapes. **Subscriptions:** 20 journals and other serials. **Services:** Interlibrary loan; copying (both limited); collection open to the public. **Automated Operations:** Computerized public access catalog, cataloging, acquisitions, serials, and circulation. **Computerized Information Services:** OCLC; BITNET (electronic mail service). **Networks/Consortia:** Member of AMIGOS Bibliographic Council, Inc., Center for Research Libraries (CRL), Colorado Alliance of Research Libraries (CARL). **Remarks:** FAX: (602)965-9169. Electronic mail address(es): iaccnm@ASUACAD (BITNET).

★1012★
Arizona State University - College of Law - Library (Law)
Armstrong Hall Phone: (602)965-6141
Tempe, AZ 85287 Richard L. Brown, Dir.
Founded: 1967. **Staff:** Prof 7; Other 9. **Subjects:** Law - American, English, foreign. **Holdings:** 212,662 volumes; 4341 reels of microfilm; 330,403 microfiche. **Subscriptions:** 4650 journals and other serials; 8 newspapers. **Services:** Interlibrary loan; copying; library open to the public for legal research. **Automated Operations:** Computerized cataloging. **Computerized Information Services:** LEXIS, WESTLAW. **Publications:** Weekly Acquisitions - for internal distribution only. **Remarks:** FAX: (602)965-2427. **Staff:** Richard M. Nash, Assoc. Law Libn.; Jeannette Chin Chun Au, Hd., Tech.Serv.; Sharon Firestone, Acq. & Ser.Libn.; Marianne Alcorn, Ref.Libn.; Marcelle Chase, Foreign Law & Ref.Libn.; Donna Larson, Govt.Doc.Libn.

★1013★
Arizona State University - Daniel E. Noble Science and Engineering Library (Sci-Engr)
Tempe, AZ 85287 Phone: (602)965-7607
Vladimir T. Borovansky, Ph.D., Hd.
Founded: 1983. **Staff:** Prof 10; Other 30. **Subjects:** Engineering; physical, life, health sciences; mathematics; agriculture; geography. **Special Collections:** Solar energy (50,000 archival materials including DOE reports, pamphlets); patent depository library (complete collection; in microform). **Holdings:** 250,000 books; 115,000 bound periodical volumes; 155,000 maps; 292,000 microforms. **Subscriptions:** 3860 journals and other serials. **Services:** Interlibrary loan; copying; SDI; library open to the public. **Automated Operations:** Computerized public access catalog and circulation. **Computerized Information Services:** DIALOG Information Services, PFDS Online, BRS Information Technologies, U.S. Patent Classification System, OCLC, STN International; CD-ROMs; BITNET, InterNet (electronic mail services). Performs searches on fee basis. **Networks/Consortia:** Member of AMIGOS Bibliographic Council, Inc., Colorado Alliance of Research Libraries (CARL). **Special Indexes:** Solar Energy Index (online); Map Index (online). **Remarks:** FAX: (602)965-0883. Electronic mail address(es): IACVTB@ASUACAD (BITNET, InterNet). **Staff:** Mara Pinckard, Hd., Sci.Ref.; Helen Seaton, Health Sci.Libn.; Frances New, Engr.Ref.Libn.; Sheila Curl, Engr. & Comp.Sci.Ref.Libn.; Linda Shackle, Chem. & Geol. Libn.; Diane Rhodes, Biol. & Agri.Libn.; George Bell, Pysics, Astronomy, Math Libn.; Christine Kolczynski, Supv., Per./Microforms; Betty Dong, Supv., Circ.; Rosanna Miller, Hd., Map Coll.

★1014★
Arizona State University - Daniel E. Noble Science and Engineering Library - Map Collection (Geog-Map)
Tempe, AZ 85287-1006 Phone: (602)965-3582
Rosanna Miller, Hd., Map Coll.
Founded: 1970. **Staff:** Prof 1; Other 3. **Subjects:** Geology, transportation, mines and mineral resources, hydrography, economics, history. **Special Collections:** Sanborn Fire Insurance Maps for Arizona, Utah, Nevada, and New Mexico (13 reels of microfilm). **Holdings:** 2495 books; 175 bound periodical volumes; 158,148 sheet maps; 9893 aerial photographs; 50 satellite images; 80 raised relief models. **Subscriptions:** 12 journals and other serials. **Services:** Interlibrary loan; copying; library open to the public. **Computerized Information Services:** BRS Information Technologies, DIALOG Information Services; BITNET (electronic mail service). Performs searches on fee basis. **Special Indexes:** Map catalog index (online). **Remarks:** FAX: (602)965-0883. Electronic mail address(es): IACRXM@ASUACAD (BITNET).

★1015★
Arizona State University - Department of Archives and Manuscripts (Hist)
Hayden Library Phone: (602)965-4932
Tempe, AZ 85287-1006 Edward C. Oetting, Hd., Archv.& Mss.
Founded: 1943. **Staff:** Prof 5; Other 9. **Subjects:** Arizona and Southwestern United States - history, politics, water, land use, peoples, Mexican-Americans; Arizona State University; visual literacy. **Special Collections:** Senator Carl T. Hayden papers; Congressman John J. Rhodes papers; Governor George W.P. Hunt papers; William J. Murphy Collection; Hayden Pioneer Biographical Files; The Collection of Arizona Photography; Southwest Autobiographies; oral histories; George H.N. Luhrs papers; Arizona tribal publications; Arizona State University Archives; The Visual Literacy Collection; Chicano Research Collection. **Holdings:** 20,000 books; 1120 bound periodical volumes; 7000 linear feet of manuscripts; 300,000 photographic images; 28 drawers of microfilm; 60 map case drawers; biographical and general information files on Arizona history; 180 linear feet of ephemera; 311 cubic feet of color separates. **Subscriptions:** 140 journals and other serials. **Services:** Copying (limited); collections open to the public. **Automated Operations:** Computerized public access catalog. **Computerized Information Services:** VU/TEXT Information Services; BITNET (electronic mail service). **Networks/Consortia:** Member of AMIGOS Bibliographic Council, Inc., Colorado Alliance of Research Libraries (CARL). **Publications:** Manuscript guide and calendars. **Special Indexes:** The Arizona and Southwest Collection Index (Online index to ephemera, photographs, biographies, oral histories, manuscripts); KWOC index to Hayden papers; ASU Newspaper Index (online); Arizona Newspaper Index (online). **Remarks:** FAX: (602)965-9169. Electronic mail address(es): IACECO@ASUACAD (BITNET). **Staff:** Christine Marin, Cur., Chicano Res.Coll.; Robert Spindler, Cur., Mss.; Richard Pearce-Moses, Cur., Photo.; Patricia Etter, Asst.Archv. for Info.Serv.

★1016★
Arizona State University - East Asian Language Collection (Area-Ethnic)
University Library
Tempe, AZ 85287-1006 Phone: (602)965-7240
Founded: 1973. **Staff:** Prof 2; Other 2. **Subjects:** East Asia - language, literature, history, political science, art, religion (mainly Buddhism), philosophy. **Holdings:** 53,257 volumes and other cataloged items. **Subscriptions:** 150 journals and other serials. **Services:** Interlibrary loan; copying; collection open to the public. **Automated Operations:** Computerized cataloging, acquisitions, serials, and circulation. **Computerized Information Services:** RLIN; InterNet, BITNET (electronic mail services). **Networks/Consortia:** Member of Research Libraries Information Network (RLIN). **Special Catalogs:** East Asian Language Catalog (card). **Remarks:** Alternate telephone number(s): (602)965-7199. FAX: (602)965-9169. Electronic mail address(es): BM.AZO@RLG (BITNET); ICAHW@ASUACAD (BITNET); ICKHL@ASUACAD (BITNET). **Staff:** Ai-Hwa Wu, Area Spec./Cat.Libn. for Chinese Stud.; Katsuko Hotelling, Area Spec./Cat.Libn. for Japanese Stud.

★1017★
Arizona State University - Music Library (Mus)
Tempe, AZ 85287 Phone: (602)965-3513
Arlys L. McDonald, Hd.
Founded: 1965. **Staff:** Prof 3; Other 10. **Subjects:** Music. **Special Collections:** International Percussion Reference Library (3500 items); Pablo Casals International Cello Library; Wayne King Collection of Popular Music (5300 items, including television films); sheet music collection (9000 pieces). **Holdings:** 56,000 books and scores; 1600 microforms; 25,000 sound recordings. **Subscriptions:** 200 journals and other serials. **Services:** Interlibrary loan (through Hayden Library, 965-3282); copying; library open to the public for reference use only. **Automated Operations:** Computerized public access catalog, cataloging, circulation, and indexing. **Computerized Information Services:** DIALOG Information Services, BRS Information Technologies, PFDS Online, OCLC; BITNET, InterNet (electronic mail services). **Networks/Consortia:** Member of AMIGOS Bibliographic Council, Inc. **Special Indexes:** Song Index (online). **Remarks:** FAX: (602)965-7690; (602)965-2659. Electronic mail address(es): IACALM@ASUACAD (BITNET); IACALM@ASUVM.INRE.ASU.EDU (InterNet). **Staff:** Shelley Mc Gehee; Annette Voth; Linda Elsasser; D'Lynne Stone.

★1018★
Arizona State University - Space Photography Laboratory (Sci-Engr)
Department of Geology Phone: (602)965-7029
Tempe, AZ 85287-1404 Ronald Greeley, Professor
Founded: 1978. **Staff:** 1. **Subjects:** Space images. **Holdings:** 500,000 images. **Services:** Library not open to the public. **Computerized Information Services:** SPACEL BIRP (internal database); NASAMAIL, SPAN (electronic mail services). **Networks/Consortia:** Member of National Planetary Image Libraries. **Remarks:** FAX: (602)965-8102. Telex: 1561058 ASU UT. Electronic mail address(es): RGreeley (NASAMAIL); ASUIPF::Greeley (SPAN).

★1019★
Arizona State University - Special Collections (Hum)
University Library Phone: (602)965-6519
Tempe, AZ 85287 Marilyn Wurzburger, Hd., Spec.Coll.
Founded: 1969. **Staff:** Prof 1; Other 2. **Subjects:** Pre-Raphaelite Brotherhood, Victorian literature and illustrators, children's literature, book arts, nineteenth and twentieth century first editions. **Special Collections:** Kelmscott Press; Mosher Press; George Moore; Rubaiyat of Omar Khayyam; papers of Glendon and Kathryn Swarthout, Elleston Trevor, William S. Burroughs, Edwin Bliss Hill, Marian T. Place, Ted Schwarz, Paul Cook, Alan Dean Foster, and Philo T. Farnsworth; Performing Arts Collection including the personal papers of Steve Allen, Gene Blakely, Peter Lawford, Jimmy Starr (film history) and the Child Drama and Everyman Players Collections; Newsweek Video Archive. **Holdings:** 35,000 books. **Services:** Copying; collections open to the public. **Automated Operations:** Computerized cataloging. **Computerized Information Services:** OCLC; BITNET (electronic mail service). **Networks/Consortia:** Member of AMIGOS Bibliographic Council, Inc. **Publications:** Brochure. **Special Catalogs:** Chronological, binder, and printer files of rare book s (card). **Remarks:** Electronic mail address(es): IACMJW@ASUACAD (BITNET).

★1020★
Arizona State University - University Archives (Hist)
University Archives Bldg. Phone: (602)965-7645
Tempe, AZ 85287-1006 Edward C. Oetting, Univ.Archv.
Founded: 1972. **Staff:** Prof 2; Other 3. **Subjects:** Arizona State University. **Special Collections:** University records; faculty and student publications, 1885-1991; board of regents and faculty senate minutes; presidential correspondence; theses and dissertations, 1885-1991; Samuel Burkhard Collection (188 articles, books, monographs); James John Jelinek Collection (184 articles, books, monographs); Agnes Smedley Collection (56 bound volumes, 1900-1980); Jeannette Veatch Collection (109 cassettes); Paula Kloster Wasser Collection (14 bound volumes); C. Gilbert Wrenn Collection (208 articles, books, monographs). **Holdings:** 15,000 volumes; 300 cassettes; 30,000 photographic prints; 85,000 negatives; 4200 slides; 105 VF drawers; 1000 linear feet of university records and manuscript collections; 7508 theses and dissertations. **Subscriptions:** 371 journals and other serials. **Services:** Interlibrary loan (limited); copying; archives open to the public with restrictions. **Computerized Information Services:** Manuscripts and Archives Database, ASU Newspaper Index, Arizona and Southwest Collections Index (internal databases). **Remarks:** FAX: (602)965-9169. **Staff:** Robert Spindler, Cur. of Mss.

Arizona Woolgrowers Association Archives
See: **Northern Arizona University - Cline Library - Special Collections and Archives Department** (11992)

★1021★
Arjuna Library (Art, Sci-Engr)
1025 Garner St., D, Space 18
Colorado Springs, CO 80905-1774 Joseph A. Uphoff, Jr., Dir.
Founded: 1963. **Staff:** 1. **Subjects:** Surrealism; visual art; visual poetry; prose poetry; dynamic forms - theater, martial arts; artistic/literary criticism - biography, philosophy, art theory; metamathematics - logic and symbolism. **Special Collections:** Local historical material; artwork and print portfolios (250); manuscripts, letters, and publications on the Mathematical Theory in the Fine Arts. **Holdings:** 2100 books; 1000 bound periodical volumes; 900 fine art slides of local displays. **Services:** Library open to the public with written request for appointment. **Publications:** Journal of Regional Criticism, irregular; Arjuna Library Press Limited Edition Pamphlets, 6-12/year; Arjuna Library Press Pamphlets. **Remarks:** A portion of the collection is currently in storage. The present emphasis of proceedings of the library is to investigate the plexus between Conceptual and Performance Art in terms of convergence versus metaphor and rehearsal versus interpretation.

★1022★
Arkansas Arts Center - Elizabeth Prewitt Taylor Memorial Library (Art, Mus)
MacArthur Park, Box 2137
Little Rock, AR 72203 Phone: (501)372-4000
Founded: 1963. **Staff:** Prof 1; Other 2. **Subjects:** Art, drama, early American jazz. **Special Collections:** John D. Reid Collection of Early American Jazz (4000 phonograph records; 70 books; pamphlet files of unbound catalogs, photographs, and other memorabilia); George Fisher Cartoons Collection. **Holdings:** 7000 books; 900 bound periodical volumes; 16 VF drawers of pamphlets; 1940 AV programs; 300 pamphlet boxes of exhibition catalogs. **Subscriptions:** 89 journals and other serials; 5 newspapers. **Services:** Interlibrary loan; copying; library open to the public with limited circulation. **Computerized Information Services:** OCLC. **Networks/Consortia:** Member of AMIGOS Bibliographic Council, Inc. **Special Catalogs:** Catalog of John Reid Jazz Collection (book, card); George Fisher Cartoons Catalog.

★1023★
Arkansas College - Mabee Library - Regional Studies Center (Hist)
Batesville, AR 72501 Phone: (501)698-4330
Nancy S. Griffith, Dir., Reg.Stud.Ctr.
Subjects: Arkansas history, Arkansas folklore, Ozark folk music, local genealogy, Civil War. **Special Collections:** John Quincy Wolf Collection (Ozark folk singers and folk music; 480 field recordings); Presbyterian Collection. **Holdings:** Figures not available. **Services:** Center open to the public with restrictions on borrowing.

★1024★
Arkansas Gazette - News Library
P.O. Box 1821
Little Rock, AR 72203
Defunct.

Arkansas Institute for Economic Advancement
See: **University of Arkansas, Little Rock - Arkansas Institute for Economic Advancement - Research Library** (18237)

★1025★
Arkansas Power and Light Company - Library (Sci-Engr, Energy)
425 W. Capital, 26th Fl.
Box 551 Phone: (501)377-5848
Little Rock, AR 72203 Mary Mobley, Libn.
Staff: Prof 1. **Subjects:** Engineering; energy - fossil, hydro; technical analysis; quality assurance. **Special Collections:** Equipment manuals (1750). **Holdings:** 3000 books; 700 government documents; 375 technical reports; 100 codes and standards; Electric Power Research Institute (EPRI) documents and microfiche. **Subscriptions:** 102 journals and other serials. **Services:** Interlibrary loan; library not open to the public. **Computerized Information Services:** DIALOG Information Services. **Remarks:** FAX: (501)377-5857.

Arkansas State Data Center
See: **University of Arkansas, Little Rock - Arkansas Institute for Economic Advancement - Research Library** (18237)

Arkansas (State) Department of Human Services - Benton Services Center
See: **Benton Services Center** (1726)

★1026★
Arkansas (State) Energy Office Library (Energy)
One Capitol Mall, Suite 4B-215
Little Rock, AR 72201 Phone: (501)682-1370
Founded: 1977. **Subjects:** Energy - policy and legislation, conservation and management, resources, data. **Holdings:** 3500 books and reports; maps; slides. **Services:** Reference service available by telephone.

★1027★
Arkansas (State) Geological Commission - Library (Sci-Engr)
3815 W. Roosevelt Rd. Phone: (501)324-9165
Little Rock, AR 72204 Oleta Sproul, Libn.
Founded: 1963. **Staff:** 1. **Subjects:** Arkansas geology. **Special Collections:** M.S. and Ph.D. Theses on Arkansen Geology. **Holdings:** 40,000 volumes; state surveys; U.S. Geological Survey publications. **Subscriptions:** 23 journals and other serials. **Services:** Interlibrary loan; copying; library open to the public. **Computerized Information Services:** Internal database. **Remarks:** FAX: (501)663-7360.

★1028★
Arkansas (State) Highway and Transportation Department - Public Transportation Section - Library
P.O. Box 2261
Little Rock, AR 72203
Founded: 1974. **Subjects:** Public transportation. **Holdings:** 250 volumes. **Remarks:** Currently inactive.

★1029★
Arkansas (State) History Commission - Archives (Hist)
One Capitol Mall Phone: (501)682-6900
Little Rock, AR 72201 Dr. John L. Ferguson, State Hist.
Founded: 1905. **Staff:** Prof 7; Other 12. **Subjects:** Arkansas history, Civil War, genealogy, family history, the South, Ozarks, Arkansas folklore. **Holdings:** 20,000 books; 1000 bound periodical volumes; 100,000 reels of microfilm; 600 maps; 4000 photographs and paintings; 500 cubic feet of manuscript materials; 5000 pamphlets; 100 VF drawers of clippings; Arkansas newspaper files; county records; cemetery records; church records; Civil War records. **Subscriptions:** 30 journals and other serials; 200 newspapers. **Services:** Copying; archives open to the public. **Staff:** Russell P. Baker, Dp.Dir.

★1030★
Arkansas State Hospital - Medical Library (Med)
4313 W. Markham St. Phone: (501)686-9040
Little Rock, AR 72205 Bernadine F. Zerr, Libn.
Founded: 1883. **Staff:** Prof 1. **Subjects:** Psychiatry, psychology, social work, mental health. **Holdings:** 5100 books; 100 bound periodical volumes; 113 other cataloged items; 19 drawers of cassette tapes. **Subscriptions:** 113 journals and other serials. **Services:** Interlibrary loan; library not open to the public. **Publications:** Bibliographies - for internal distribution only.

★1031★
Arkansas State Library (Info Sci)
One Capitol Mall Phone: (501)682-1527
Little Rock, AR 72201 Jack C. Mulkey, Assoc.Dir.
Founded: 1935. **Staff:** Prof 12; Other 35. **Special Collections:** Arkansas. **Holdings:** 144,278 volumes; 24 VF drawers. **Subscriptions:** 285 journals and other serials. **Services:** Library open to the public. **Computerized Information Services:** OCLC. **Networks/Consortia:** Member of AMIGOS Bibliographic Council, Inc. **Remarks:** FAX: (501)682-1529. Electronic mail address(es): ALA 0967 (ALANET).

★1032★
Arkansas (State) Supreme Court - Library (Law)
625 Marshall St.
Justice Bldg. Phone: (501)682-2147
Little Rock, AR 72201 Jacqueline S. Wright, Libn.
Founded: 1851. **Staff:** Prof 2; Other 1. **Subjects:** Law. **Special Collections:** State statutes. **Holdings:** 80,195 volumes. **Subscriptions:** 1200 journals and other serials. **Services:** Library open to the public.**Automated Operations:** Computerized cataloging. **Computerized Information Services:** LEXIS, WESTLAW; BITNET, InterNet (electronic mail services). **Remarks:** FAX: (501)682-6877. Electronic mail address(es): SCLIBRARY@UALR (BITNET); SCLIBRARY@UALR.EDU (InterNet). **Staff:** Timothy N. Holthoff, Asst.Libn.

★1033★
Arkansas State University - Dean B. Ellis Library - Special Collections (Hum, Sci-Engr)
Box 2040 Phone: (501)972-5706
State University, AR 72467-2040 James Hansard
Founded: 1909. **Staff:** Prof 1. **Special Collections:** Lois Lenski Collection; Arkansas Authors of Children's Books; Cass S. Hough Aeronautical Collection; Steve Clark Creation Science Papers. **Services:** Interlibrary loan; copying; collections open to the public. **Automated Operations:** Computerized public access catalog, cataloging, acquisitions, serials, and circulation. **Computerized Information Services:** BRS Information Technologies, OCLC, DIALOG Information Services. Performs searches on fee basis. Contact Person: Terry Sypolt, Hd.Ref.Libn., 972-3077. **Networks/Consortia:** Member of AMIGOS Bibliographic Council, Inc. **Publications:** Lois Lenski Collection in Dean B. Ellis Library: A Bibliography, Arkansas State University, 1972. **Special Indexes:** Index to Graighead County Historical Quarterly, vol. 9, 1971-vol. 26, 1989. **Remarks:** FAX: (501)972-5706. **Staff:** Willis Brenner, Docs.Libn.

★1034★
Arkansas State University - Museum - Library/Archives (Hist)
Box 490 Phone: (501)972-2074
State University, AR 72467 Joanna Davis, Cur.
Founded: 1936. **Staff:** 4. **Subjects:** History - Indian, American military, Arkansas, United States, European; old textbooks; religion; children's rare books; minerals and fossils. **Special Collections:** Rare newspapers, 1750-1960 (1500); sheet music, 1840-1950 (1050 pieces); Sharp County, Arkansas Courthouse Ledgers. **Holdings:** 5000 books; 6500 other cataloged items. **Subscriptions:** 3 journals and other serials. **Services:** Interlibrary loan; library open to the public. **Remarks:** FAX: (501)972-5706. **Staff:** Margaret Denny.

★1035★
Arkansas State Workers' Compensation Commission - Library (Law)
Justice Bldg.
State Capitol Grounds Phone: (501)682-3930
Little Rock, AR 72201 Pat Capps, Libn.
Founded: 1940. **Staff:** Prof 1. **Subjects:** Arkansas law, workers' compensation law, medicine, rehabilitation. **Special Collections:** Workers'

Compensation Opinions; Streepey's Digest of Workers' Compensation Opinions. **Holdings:** 3200 books. **Subscriptions:** 16 journals and other serials. **Services:** Copying; library open to the public for reference use only. **Publications:** Opinions of the Arkansas Workers' Compensation Commission, monthly - state authorized distribution; Streepey's Digest of Workers' Compensation Opinions, annual. **Special Indexes:** Index to Arkansas workers' compensation decisions in Appellate Court cases. **Remarks:** FAX: (501)682-2777.

★1036★
Arkansas Tech University - Tomlinson Library - Special Collections (Info Sci, Rec)
Russellville, AR 72801 Phone: (501)968-0289
Bill Parton, Lib.Dir.
Founded: 1926. **Staff:** 10. **Special Collections:** Nuclear energy collection (13,500 items); recreation and parks collection (6000 items). **Holdings:** 61,000 government documents. **Subscriptions:** 1210 journals and other serials. **Services:** Interlibrary loan; copying; library open to the public. **Automated Operations:** Computerized public access catalog and cataloging. **Computerized Information Services:** DIALOG Information Services, BRS Information Technologies, OCLC, ERIC, Nursing & Allied Health Database; InfoTrac. **Networks/Consortia:** Member of AMIGOS Bibliographic Council, Inc. **Special Indexes:** Arkansas Gazette Index. **Remarks:** FAX: (501)968-2185.

★1037★
Arkansas Territorial Restoration - Library (Hist)
Third & Scott Phone: (501)324-9351
Little Rock, AR 72201 Starr Mitchell, Musm.Prog.Spec.
Founded: 1941. **Staff:** Prof 7. **Subjects:** Arkansas history, decorative arts, conservation, historic preservation, gardens. **Special Collections:** Territorial and early statehood documents. **Holdings:** 500 books; 100 archival materials; 200 documents; 25 maps. **Subscriptions:** 10 journals and other serials. **Services:** Library open to the public. **Remarks:** FAX: (501)324-9345. **Staff:** Georgann McKinney, Libn.; Swannee Bennett, Cur.; W.B. Worthen, Dir.

Arkitekthogskolen - Biblioteket
See: **Oslo School of Architecture - Library** (12592)

★1038★
Arlington Baptist College - Earl K. Oldham Library (Rel-Phil)
3001 W. Division
Arlington, TX 76012 Phone: (817)461-8741
Founded: 1939. **Staff:** Prof 2; Other 1. **Subjects:** Religion. **Special Collections:** Learning resources center (teacher's curriculum materials). **Holdings:** 22,000 volumes; 1000 theses and tracts. **Subscriptions:** 132 journals and other serials. **Services:** Interlibrary loan; copying; library open to the public with restrictions. **Remarks:** Maintained by World Baptist Fellowship. FAX: (817)274-1138.

Arlington County Bar Association - Walter T. McCarthy Law Library
See: **Walter T. McCarthy Law Library** (9875)

★1039★
Arlington County Central Library - Virginia Room (Hist)
1015 N. Quincy St. Phone: (703)358-5700
Arlington, VA 22201 Sara Collins, Virginiana Libn.
Founded: 1961. **Staff:** Prof 2.5. **Subjects:** Arlington County, Virginia - history, current information; northern Virginia and metropolitan Washington area. **Special Collections:** Library-Zonta Oral History Collection (300 transcribed interviews); community archives (200 linear feet); periodicals, newspapers, county court records, 1801-1865 (309 reels of microfilm). **Holdings:** 10,000 volumes; 800 unbound reports and documents; 32 VF drawers of clippings and ephemera; 100 linear feet of manuscripts; 6000 photographs; 400 maps; 300 videotapes. **Subscriptions:** 67 journals and other serials. **Services:** Copying; room open to the public for reference use only. **Automated Operations:** Computerized public access catalog, cataloging, acquisitions, and circulation. **Computerized Information Services:** DIALOG Information Services; internal database. Performs searches on fee basis. **Publications:** A Guide to the Community Archives. **Special Indexes:** Index to articles in local newspapers, 1980 to present (card); Index to Arlington Historical Magazine, 1957-1980. **Remarks:** FAX: (703)892-3468. **Staff:** Maggie Kalil, Arc hv.; Phyllis Lyons, Libn.

★1040★
Arlington Historical Society - Smith Museum Archives (Hist)
7 Jason St. Phone: (617)648-4300
Arlington, MA 02174 Vivian Wood, Reg.
Founded: 1897. **Staff:** 1. **Subjects:** History, religion, fashion, Arlington. **Special Collections:** Document collection (letters, diaries, deeds, wills, town records, and other items). **Holdings:** 200 books; 75 bound periodical volumes; 500 documents. **Subscriptions:** 5 journals and other serials. **Services:** Copying; library open to the public under staff supervision. **Staff:** Susana Forster-Castillo, Dir.

★1041★
Arlington Hospital - Doctors' Library (Med)
1701 N. George Mason Dr. Phone: (703)558-6524
Arlington, VA 22205 Donna Giampa, Libn.
Founded: 1954. **Staff:** Prof 1; Other 1. **Subjects:** Medicine. **Holdings:** 650 books; 2725 bound periodical volumes; 960 audiotapes; 130 videocassettes; 386 unbound volumes of journals. **Subscriptions:** 115 journals and other serials. **Services:** Interlibrary loan (fee); copying; AV programs in continuing medical education; library open to the public by special permission only. **Computerized Information Services:** MEDLINE, DIALOG Information Services, BRS Information Technologies. **Networks/Consortia:** Member of Northern Virginia Health Sciences Libraries. **Publications:** Bibliographies.

Arlington House, the Robert E. Lee Memorial
See: **U.S. Natl. Park Service - Arlington House, the Robert E. Lee Memorial** (17669)

★1042★
Arlington Public Schools - Professional Library (Educ)
1426 N. Quincy St. Phone: (703)358-6085
Arlington, VA 22207 Dale W. Brown, Supv., Lib. Media Serv.
Staff: Prof 1; Other 1. **Subjects:** Education. **Holdings:** 7000 books; microfiche. **Subscriptions:** 160 journals and other serials. **Services:** Interlibrary loan; copying; library open to teachers and residents of Arlington. **Computerized Information Services:** DIALOG Information Services, NOTIS. **Remarks:** FAX: (703)358-6089.

★1043★
Armbruster Associates - Library (Sci-Engr)
43 Stockton Rd. Phone: (908)277-1614
Summit, NJ 07901 David Armbruster, Pres.
Founded: 1982. **Subjects:** Chemical marketing and technologies. **Holdings:** 500 books; 200 reports. **Subscriptions:** 25 journals and other serials. **Services:** Library not open to the public. **Remarks:** FAX: (908)277-1573.

★1044★
Armco, Inc. - Technical Information Center (Sci-Engr)
705 Curtis St. Phone: (513)425-2504
Middletown, OH 45043 David Britton, Supv.
Staff: Prof 1; Other 3. **Subjects:** Ferrous metallurgy, physical and analytical chemistry, instrumentation, composite materials, business management. **Holdings:** 7500 volumes; 10,000 government reports; 2500 translations; 3000 corporate annual reports; 1500 volumes of journals on microfilm. **Subscriptions:** 500 journals and other serials. **Services:** Interlibrary loan; copying; center open to the public by appointment. **Computerized Information Services:** DIALOG Information Services, LEXIS, NEXIS, STN International, Dow Jones News/Retrieval, ORBIT Search Service. **Publications:** Alerting Bulletin, monthly - for internal distribution only. **Remarks:** FAX: (513)425-2587.

Armed Forces
See: **U.S. Armed Forces**

★1045★
Armed Forces Communications and Electronics Association - C3I Library (Mil)
4400 Fair Lakes Ct. Phone: (703)631-6188
Fairfax, VA 22033-3899 Judith H. Shreve
Subjects: Command, control communications, computers and intelligence (C4I), electronics, imagery, computer sciences, information systems. **Holdings:** Periodicals. **Services:** Library open to association members only. **Computerized Information Services:** Internal database. **Remarks:** FAX: (703)631-6188.

★1046★
Armenian Agricultural Institute - Biblioteka (Agri)
ul. Terjana 74 Phone: 8852 521451
SU-375009 Yerevan 9, Armenia Sirvard Zakarian
Founded: 1931. **Subjects:** Plant growing, fruit and vegetable growing, agricultural machinery, engineering, hydraulics, politics. **Special Collections:** Unique literature on agriculture (1883 to present; 316 books). **Holdings:** 275,950 books; 832,253 bound periodical volumes; 1749 reports. **Subscriptions:** 306 journals and other serials; 101 newspapers. **Services:** Interlibrary loan; library open to the public for reference use only. **Publications:** Bibliography of the theses maintained in the institute; bibliography of new books on agriculture.

★1047★
Armenian Apostolic Church of America - St. Nerses Shnorhali Library (Area-Ethnic)
138 E. 39th St. Phone: (212)689-7810
New York, NY 10016 Mrs. Houri Ghougassian
Founded: 1975. **Staff:** Prof 1. **Subjects:** Armenian studies - religious, cultural, and political history; Christian studies. **Special Collections:** Classical and Modern Armenian Literature collection. **Holdings:** 8000 books; 500 bound periodical volumes. **Subscriptions:** 25 journals and other serials; 20 newspapers. **Services:** Library open to the public by appointment. **Remarks:** FAX: (212)689-7168.

★1048★
Armenian Assembly Charitable Trust - Library and Information Center (Area-Ethnic)
122 C St., N.W., Suite 350 Phone: (202)393-3434
Washington, DC 20001 Ross Vartian, Exec.Dir.
Founded: 1972. **Staff:** 12. **Subjects:** Armenian history, culture, genocide, political evolution. **Holdings:** 400 volumes; 100 pamphlets; 1 VF drawer of clippings; AV programs. **Subscriptions:** 50 journals and other serials. **Services:** Copying; library open to the public with permission of director. **Publications:** Directory of Armenian Scholars; Participation in the Democratic Process; Newsletter, monthly; Armenian Information Service Bulletin, weekly. **Remarks:** FAX: (202)638-4904.

★1049★
Armenian Cultural Foundation - Library (Area-Ethnic)
441 Mystic St. Phone: (617)646-3090
Arlington, MA 02174 Mr. Hagop Atamian, Cur.
Founded: 1945. **Staff:** 1. **Subjects:** Armenia - literature, history, art. **Holdings:** 10,000 books; 200 bound periodical volumes. **Subscriptions:** 8 newspapers. **Services:** Library open to the public by appointment. **Remarks:** Holdings are primarily in English, as well as in French, German, Italian, and Russian.

★1050★
Armenian General Benevolent Union - Library (Area-Ethnic)
585 Saddle River Rd. Phone: (201)797-7600
Saddle Brook, NJ 07662 Diana Adjamian
Staff: Prof 2. **Subjects:** Armenia - literature, culture, history, genocide, art. **Holdings:** 4000 books. **Subscriptions:** 5 journals and other serials; 10 newspapers. **Services:** Library open to the public. **Remarks:** Holdings are in English and French.

★1051★
Armenian Library and Museum of America (Area-Ethnic)
65 Main St. Phone: (617)926-2562
Watertown, MA 02172 Gary Lind-Sinanian, Cur.
Founded: 1971. **Staff:** Prof 1. **Subjects:** Armenia - history, art, culture. **Special Collections:** Armenian Rug Society Data Bank; ALMA Oral History collections (Genocide survivors, 500 audiotapes). **Holdings:** 10,000 volumes; 60 bound periodical volumes; archival materials; oral history tapes. **Subscriptions:** 10 journals and other serials. **Services:** Copying; library open to the public for reference use only.

★1052★
Armenian Numismatic Society - Library (Rec)
8511 Beverly Park Pl. Phone: (310)695-0380
Pico Rivera, CA 90660-1920 Mr. W. Gewenian, Libn.
Founded: 1971. **Staff:** 1. **Subjects:** Armenian numismatics. **Holdings:** 2500 books; 200 bound periodical volumes; 250 reports; 2250 other cataloged items. **Subscriptions:** 10 journals and other serials; 10 newspapers. **Services:** Copying; library not open to the public but will respond to mail inquiries. **Publications:** Armenian Numismatic Journal.

★1053★
Armenian Society of Los Angeles - Armenak and Nunia Harutunian Library (Hum)
221 S. Brand Blvd. Phone: (818)240-0619
Glendale, CA 91204 Tadevos Ter Sarkissian
Founded: 1981. **Staff:** 1. **Subjects:** Armenian literature - general, translations; English literature; Persian literature. **Holdings:** 5000 books. **Subscriptions:** All Armenian newspapers published in United States and overseas. **Services:** Interlibrary loan; library open to the public.

★1054★
Armm Group, Inc. - Library (Sci-Engr)
N. King & Warren Sts.
Box 229 Phone: (609)456-8788
Gloucester City, NJ 08030 Patricia Smith, Controller
Founded: 1957. **Subjects:** Engineering, materials strength, waterproofing, roofing. **Holdings:** 300 books; 1200 reports. **Subscriptions:** 20 journals and other serials. **Services:** Library open to the public. **Remarks:** FAX: (609)456-6920.

Armour Pharmaceutical Company
See: **Rhone-Poulenc Rorer - Armour Pharmaceutical Company** (13889)

★1055★
Armour Swift-Eckrich - Research Library (Food-Bev)
3131 Woodcreek Dr. Phone: (708)512-1084
Downers Grove, IL 60515 Dolores Dlesk, Libn.
Founded: 1905. **Staff:** Prof 1. **Subjects:** Meat science, chemistry, microbiology, food, nutrition, fats and oils. **Holdings:** 5300 books; 3000 bound periodical volumes; 100 microfiche; 500 reels of microfilm. **Subscriptions:** 65 journals and other serials. **Services:** Interlibrary loan; library not open to the public. **Computerized Information Services:** DIALOG Information Services, NERAC, Inc., USDA ONLINE, U.S. Environmental Protection Agency (EPA) Newsletter. **Remarks:** FAX: (708)512-1125. Parent company is Conagra, Inc. **Formed by the merger of:** Swift-Eckrich, Inc. and Armour.

Arms Control and Disarmament Agency
See: **U.S. Arms Control and Disarmament Agency** (16917)

Armstrong Browning Library
See: **Baylor University** (1602)

★1056★
Armstrong County Law Library (Law)
Court House Phone: (412)543-1120
Kittanning, PA 16201 Janet Shuster, Libn.
Subjects: Law. **Holdings:** Books. **Services:** Library open to the public. **Remarks:** No further information was supplied by respondent.

Armstrong Memorial Medical Library
See: **Butler Memorial Hospital** (2415)

★1057★
Armstrong State College - Lane Library - Special Collections (Hum)
11935 Abercorn St. Phone: (912)927-5332
Savannah, GA 31419-1997 Byung Lee, Dir., Lib.Serv.
Founded: 1935. **Subjects:** Savannah authors and history, costal Georgia, college archives. **Special Collections:** Florence Powell Minis Collection. **Holdings:** 1029 books; 269 bound periodical volumes. **Services:** Interlibrary loan; copying; collection open to the public. **Automated Operations:** Computerized cataloging. **Computerized Information Services:** DIALOG Information Services, OCLC. Performs searches on fee basis. Contact Person: Caroline Hopkinson. **Networks/Consortia:** Member of SOLINET, South Georgia Associated Libraries (SGAL). **Publications:** Conrad Aiken Collection: A Bibliography. **Special Indexes:** Minis Collection holdings list (online). **Remarks:** FAX: (912)927-5387.

★1058★
Armstrong University - Library (Bus-Fin)
2222 Harold Way Phone: (510)848-2500
Berkeley, CA 94704 Joseph Liebman, Libn.
Founded: 1918. **Staff:** Prof 1; Other 3. **Subjects:** Management, economics, finance, marketing, accounting. **Special Collections:** Annual reports of top thousand companies in Fortune Magazine; biographies (500 volumes). **Holdings:** 15,000 books; 165 reels of microfilm; 11 boxes of archival material; 52 student theses and papers. **Subscriptions:** 154 journals and other serials. **Services:** Library open to the public for reference use only.

★1059★
Armstrong World Industries, Inc. - Innovation Center - Technical Information Services (Sci-Engr)
2500 Columbia Ave.
Box 3511 Phone: (717)396-5766
Lancaster, PA 17604 Mary Ann Filler, Mgr.
Founded: 1926. **Staff:** Prof 3; Other 3. **Subjects:** Chemistry, polymer science, chemical engineering, physics, mathematics. **Holdings:** 10,000 volumes; 9500 research reports; U.S. patents on microfilm; microforms. **Subscriptions:** 350 journals and other serials. **Services:** Interlibrary loan; copying; SDI; library open to the public for reference use on request. **Automated Operations:** Computerized journal circulation. **Computerized Information Services:** DIALOG Information Services, PFDS Online, Chemical Abstracts Service (CAS), BRS Information Technologies, PLASTISERV Information Systems; internal databases. **Publications:** Current Awareness Bulletin, monthly - for internal distribution only. **Special Catalogs:** Catalog of corporate holdings (book). **Remarks:** FAX: (717)396-5234. **Staff:** T.G. Stauffer, Info.Ret.; Susan I. Wood, Tech.Libn.; Cynthia E. Hornberger, Lib.Asst.

★1060★
Armstrong World Industries, Inc. - Management Reference Services (Bus-Fin)
Liberty & Charlotte Sts.
Box 3001 Phone: (717)396-3420
Lancaster, PA 17604 Rose M. Fronczak, Supv.
Founded: 1926. **Staff:** 2; Other 1. **Subjects:** Management - factory, business, personnel; personnel training; manufacturing methods and processes; economics; statistics; accounting; finance. **Holdings:** 3000 books; 130 VF drawers of archival materials; 25 VF drawers of pamphlets; 75 audio cassette sets; 50 videotapes; 12 IBM compatible computer programs. **Subscriptions:** 400 journals and other serials; 6 newspapers. **Services:** Interlibrary loan; copying; library open to the public with restrictions. **Computerized Information Services:** DIALOG Information Services. **Publications:** Resource Readings, monthly - for internal distribution only. **Remarks:** FAX: (717)396-2093.

★1061★
Armstrong World Industries, Inc. - New Ideas - Interior Design Center Library (Art)
1861 Colonial Village Ln.
P.O. Box 10247 Phone: (717)293-4028
Lancaster, PA 17601 Rebecca Gordon, Libn.
Remarks: No further information was supplied by respondent.

★1062★
Armstrong World Industries, Inc. - Product Styling & Design Library
2500 Columbia Ave.
Box 3511 Phone: (717)397-0611
Lancaster, PA 17604 Linda Gantz, Libn.
Services: Library not open to the public. **Remarks:** No further information was supplied by respondent.

Army
See: **U.S. Army**

Army Field Law Library
See: **U.S. Army - Corps of Engineers - Seattle District - Library** (16960)

★1063★
Army and Navy Club - Library (Mil)
Farragut Square
901 17th St., N.W. Phone: (202)628-8400
Washington, DC 20006 Barbara S. Cassedy, Libn.
Founded: 1885. **Staff:** Prof 1. **Subjects:** Military history. **Special Collections:** Reginald Oakie Collection (Civil War stereographs). **Holdings:** 15,000 volumes. **Subscriptions:** 42 journals and other serials; 15 newspapers. **Services:** library open to the public for reference use only. **Automated Operations:** Computerized public access catalog, cataloging, and ILL (Inmagic). **Computerized Information Services:** Internal database. **Remarks:** FAX: (202)296-8787.

★1064★
Army Times Publishing Co. - Library (Mil, Publ)
6883 Commercial Dr. Phone: (703)750-8696
Springfield, VA 22159 Patricia White-Williams
Founded: 1940. **Staff:** Prof 2; Other 1. **Subjects:** Military history, military hardware, international defense, world affairs, journalism. **Special Collections:** World War II unit histories; Civil Conservation Corps collection. **Holdings:** 6000 books; 50 bound periodical volumes; 100 archival volumes; 2000 microfiche; 500 reels of microfilm. **Subscriptions:** 50 journals and other serials; 10 newspapers. **Services:** Interlibrary loan; library not open to the public. **Computerized Information Services:** NEXIS; DIALOG Information Services; VU/TEXT Information Services; AP Newsfinders; internal database. Contact Person: Andrew Kersey, Res. **Publications:** At Your Service Reports. **Remarks:** FAX: (703)750-8622.

Arneson Library
See: **Park-Nicollet Medical Foundation** (12747)

Trevor Arnett Library of Black Culture
See: **University of the District of Columbia - Georgia/Harvard Campus - Harvard Street Library** (18553)

★1065★
Arnhold and S. Bleichroeder, Inc. - Library (Bus-Fin)
45 Broadway Phone: (212)943-9200
New York, NY 10006 Joseph Keenan, Libn.
Founded: 1937. **Staff:** Prof 2; Other 2. **Subjects:** Investment banking, international securities, corporate financing. **Holdings:** 32 bound periodical volumes; 100 VF drawers of corporate and industry reports; vertical files. **Subscriptions:** 15 journals and other serials; 10 newspapers. **Services:** Interlibrary loan; library not open to the public. **Automated Operations:** Computerized cataloging and circulation. **Staff:** David Genna, Libn.

Arnold Aboretum
See: **Harvard University - Botany Libraries** (6950)

Arnold Engineering Development Center
See: **U.S. Air Force - Air Force Materiel Command - Arnold Engineering Development Center** (16796)

Arnold Library
See: **Straub Clinic & Hospital, Inc.** (15824)

Arnold Library of Agricultural Credit
See: **Ohio State University - Agriculture Library** (12293)

★1066★
Arnold and Porter - Library (Law)
1200 New Hampshire Ave., N.W., 8th Fl. Phone: (202)872-3994
Washington, DC 20036 James W. Shelar, Libn.
Staff: Prof 10; Other 11. **Subjects:** Law. **Special Collections:** Congressional documents: hearings, reports, committee prints (10,000). **Holdings:** 50,000 books; 2000 bound periodical volumes. **Subscriptions:** 900 journals and other serials; 20 newspapers. **Services:** Interlibrary loan (with special permission of librarian); library not open to the public. **Automated Operations:** Computerized cataloging, serials, acquisitions. **Computerized Information Services:** LEXIS, DataTimes, DIALOG Information Services, Dow Jones News/Retrieval, WESTLAW, NewsNet, Inc., BRS Information Technologies, VU/TEXT Information Services, CompuServe Information Service, OCLC; internal database. **Networks/Consortia:** Member of CAPCON Library Network.

★1067★
Arnold, White & Durkee - Library (Law)
Box 4433 Phone: (713)787-1400
Houston, TX 77210 Genel F. Moran, Libn.
Staff: Prof 2; Other 1. **Subjects:** Law - patent, trademark, copyright, antitrust, franchise. **Special Collections:** Official Gazette of Patents; Official Gazette of Trademarks. **Holdings:** 7900 books; 360 bound periodical volumes. **Subscriptions:** 123 journals and other serials; 6 newspapers. **Services:** Interlibrary loan; copying; library open to the public by appointment. **Computerized Information Services:** DIALOG Information Services, LEXIS, WESTLAW, PFDS Online, Dun & Bradstreet Business Credit Services, TRW Business Profiles, Information America, VU/TEXT Information Services, DataTimes. **Remarks:** FAX: (713)789-2679. **Staff:** Sue Lollis, Libn.

★1068★
Arnold's Archives (Aud-Vis)
1106 Eastwood, S.E. Phone: (616)949-1398
East Grand Rapids, MI 49506 Arnold Jacobsen, Archv.
Staff: Prof 1. **Subjects:** Recordings and tapes, 1898-1950, especially Broadway shows and musical comedy. **Special Collections:** Songs pertaining to presidential and political campaign issues through the years. **Holdings:** 200,000 phonograph records; books; sheet music; record catalogs; discographies. **Services:** Copying; archives open to the public by appointment. **Publications:** Catalog of holdings - for sale. **Special Indexes:** Title and subject indexes. **Remarks:** Archives include out-of-print phonograph records of popular personalities, jazz, blues, dance bands, country western and folk music, spoken word, instrumental music, and opera. Archives have been reserved by The Chicago Public Library for acquisition over the next three years. Research and taping services will continue to be available.

★1069★
Arnot-Ogden Medical Center - Wey Memorial Library (Med)
600 Roe Ave. Phone: (607)737-4101
Elmira, NY 14905-1676 Peggy Sleeth, Dir., Lib.Serv.
Founded: 1934. **Staff:** Prof 1; Other 1. **Subjects:** Medicine, nursing, and allied health sciences. **Holdings:** 4200 books; 3300 bound periodical volumes; 28 VF drawers; 300 cataloged items in historical collection; 600 AV programs. **Subscriptions:** 300 journals and other serials. **Services:** Interlibrary loan; copying. **Computerized Information Services:** DIALOG Information Services, NLM. **Networks/Consortia:** Member of South Central Research Library Council (SCRLC).

★1070★
Arnstein & Lehr - Library (Law)
120 S. Riverside Plaza, Suite 1200 Phone: (312)876-7170
Chicago, IL 60606-3913 Frank Drake, Dir., Lib.Serv.
Founded: 1893. **Staff:** Prof 1. **Subjects:** Law, trade regulation, labor, taxation, accounting. **Holdings:** 10,000 books; 700 bound periodical volumes; 1000 microfiche; 400 reels of microfilm. **Subscriptions:** 100 journals and other serials. **Services:** Interlibrary loan; copying; library open to the public by appointment. **Computerized Information Services:** DIALOG Information Services, LEXIS, WESTLAW, Dow Jones News/ Retrieval, Information America; trial bank (internal database). **Remarks:** FAX: (312)876-0288. Telex: 9102211142.

★1071★
Aroostook Medical Center - A.R. Gould Division - Health Sciences Library (Med)
P.O. Box 151 Phone: (207)768-4173
Presque Isle, ME 04769-0151 Marilyn W. Dean, Lib.Supv.
Staff: Prof 1. **Subjects:** Medicine, surgery, nursing. **Holdings:** 300 books; 94 periodicals. **Services:** Interlibrary loan; copying; library open to the public with restrictions. **Computerized Information Services:** MEDLINE; DOCLINE (electronic mail service). **Networks/Consortia:** Member of Health Science Library and Information Cooperative of Maine (HSLIC).

Rex Arragon Library
See: **Portland Art Museum** (13236)

★1072★
Art Association of Richmond - Library (Art)
350 Whitewater Blvd. Phone: (317)966-0256
Richmond, IN 47374 Ruth B. Mills-Varnell, Dir.
Staff: 1. **Subjects:** Art. **Holdings:** 1000 books. **Services:** Library open to the public.

★1073★
Art Center College of Design - James Lemont Fogg Memorial Library (Art)
1700 N. Lida St. Phone: (818)584-5013
Pasadena, CA 91103 Elizabeth Galloway, V.P., Lib.Dir.
Founded: 1930. **Staff:** Prof 4; Other 4. **Subjects:** Fine arts, communications design, graphics/packaging, advertising design, industrial design, illustration, photography and film. **Holdings:** 45,000 books; 4200 bound periodical volumes; 2086 exhibition catalogs; 16 VF drawers; 1900 annual reports; 60,000 slides; 133 films; 1061 videotapes. **Subscriptions:** 550 journals and other serials; 10 newspapers. **Services:** Copying; library open to the public by appointment. **Automated Operations:** Computerized public access catalog, cataloging, circulation and serials. **Networks/Consortia:** Member of OCLC Pacific Network. **Publications:** New books list, monthly - for internal distribution only. **Special Indexes:** Index to visual file and slides. **Remarks:** FAX: (818)405-9104. Telex: 6711486ARTCE UW. **Staff:** Alison Holt, Asst.Libn./Cat.; Theresa Pendelbury, Media Cur.; George Porcari, Acq.Libn.

Art Colony at Old Lyme Archives
See: **Lyme Historical Society, Inc. - Archives** (9473)

★1074★
Art Complex Museum - Carl A. Weyerhaeuser Library (Art)
189 Alden St.
P.O. Box 2814 Phone: (617)934-6634
Duxbury, MA 02332 Nancy Grinnell, Libn.
Subjects: Asian and American art, Shaker furniture. **Holdings:** 4000 books. **Services:** Copying; library open to the public for reference use only.

★1075★
Art Gallery of Greater Victoria - Library (Art)
1040 Moss St.
Victoria, BC, Canada V8V 4P1 Phone: (604)384-4101
Founded: 1951. **Subjects:** Art - Canadian, Oriental, European. **Holdings:** 5370 books; 4225 exhibition catalogs; 4400 artist files; 141 reels of microfilm. **Subscriptions:** 36 journals and other serials. **Services:** Library open to the public for reference use only by written request. **Remarks:** FAX: (604)361-3995.

★1076★
Art Gallery of Hamilton - Muriel Isabel Bostwick Library (Art)
123 King St., W. Phone: (416)527-6610
Hamilton, ON, Canada L8P 4S8 Jennifer Watson, Cur.
Founded: 1966. **Staff:** Prof 2; Other 2. **Subjects:** Art - Canadian, American, British, international; local history; art history. **Special Collections:** Early Canadian art book collection; Canadian art catalogs and research material. **Holdings:** 3000 books; 4000 files on artists; 2000 exhibition catalogs; 3 VF drawers of gallery archives; 6 VF drawers of annual reports. **Subscriptions:** 55 journals and other serials. **Services:** Interlibrary loan; copying; library open to the public for reference use only. **Computerized Information Services:** Pictorial and Artifact Retrieval and Information System (PARIS). **Staff:** Agnes Richard, Registrar; Jane Bradley, Asst. Registrar.

★1077★
Art Gallery of Ontario - E. P. Taylor Research Library and Archives (Art)
317 Dundas St., W. Phone: (416)979-6642
Toronto, ON, Canada M5T 1G4 Karen McKenzie, Chf.Libn.
Founded: 1933. **Staff:** Prof 4; Other 5. **Subjects:** Art history - Renaissance to present; Canadian art. **Special Collections:** Allan Garrow Collection (English book illustration, 1855-1875); Canadian artists (manuscripts; memorabilia); Canadian book illustration. **Holdings:** 100,000 volumes; 40,000 auction catalogs; 40,000 artist files of clippings, reproductions, photographs; 3000 microforms; exhibition catalogs; museum publications; institutional archives. **Subscriptions:** 450 journals and other serials. **Services:** Interlibrary loan (limited); copying; library open to the public with restrictions. **Automated Operations:** Computerized cataloging. **Computerized Information Services:** DIALOG Information Services. **Special Indexes:** The Art Gallery of Ontario: 60 years of exhibitions, 1906-1966; Exhibitors Finding Aid (card). **Remarks:** FAX: (416)979-6646. Gallery maintained by Ontario Ministry of Citizenship and Culture. **Staff:** Larry Pfaff, Dp.Libn.; Jane Rhodes, Cat.Libn.; Elizabeth Hulse, Archv.

★1078★
Art Gallery of Ontario - Edward P. Taylor Audio-Visual Centre (Art, Aud-Vis)
317 Dundas St., W. Phone: (416)977-0414
Toronto, ON, Canada M5T 1G4 Margaret Brennan, Hd.
Founded: 1927. **Staff:** Prof 3; Other 1. **Subjects:** Art - Canadian, European, American, Far Eastern. **Special Collections:** Henry Moore Archives (slides and films). **Holdings:** 95,456 circulating slides; 36,956 archival slides; 227 films; 621 videotapes; 805 audiotapes; 97 media kits. **Subscriptions:** 2 journals and other serials. **Services:** Library open to Canadian residents. **Automated Operations:** Computerized cataloging. **Computerized Information Services:** DataEase (internal database). Performs searches free of charge. Contact Person: Sandra Vilimas, Loans Cons. **Remarks:** FAX: (416)979-6674. **Staff:** Barbara Isherwood, Res.-Cat.

★1079★
Art Gallery of Western Australia - Administration Centre - Library (Art)
Perth Cultural Centre Phone: 9 3287233
Perth, WA 6000, Australia Joyce Carter, Libn.
Founded: 1976. **Staff:** 1.5. **Subjects:** Western Australian art, Australian art, aboriginal art, American Art from 1960s. **Special Collections:** Artists' Files (1117 clippings, exhibition information materials, curriculum vitae). **Holdings:** 11,500 books. **Subscriptions:** 71 journals and other serials; 33 auction house catalogues. **Services:** Interlibrary loan; copying; SDI; library open to the public by appointment. **Computerized Information Services:** DIALOG Information Services; National Library of Australia - Australian Bibliographic Network. Performs searches.

★1080★
Art Information Center, Inc. (Art)
280 Broadway, Suite 412 Phone: (212)227-0282
New York, NY 10007 Dan R. Concholar, Dir.
Founded: 1959. **Staff:** Prof 3. **Subjects:** Contemporary art by living visual artists. **Holdings:** Information regarding 65,000 living artists and where they exhibit. **Services:** Center open to the public by appointment. Helps artists to find New York outlets for their work. Supplies information by telephone or mail (if return postage is supplied). **Remarks:** Center is a free clearinghouse of information on contemporary fine arts.

★1081★
Art Institute of Boston - Library (Art)
700 Beacon St. Phone: (617)262-1223
Boston, MA 02215-2598 Valda Bolis
Founded: 1969. **Staff:** Prof 1; Other 6. **Subjects:** Art history, photography, graphics, design, humanities. **Holdings:** 7000 volumes; 25,000 slides; 7 VF drawers of picture reference files; 4 VF drawers of exhibition catalogs; 1 VF drawer of pamphlets. **Subscriptions:** 48 journals and other serials. **Services:** Copying; library open to the public for reference use only. **Special Catalogs:** Card cross reference catalog for picture collection. **Remarks:** FAX: (617)437-1226. **Staff:** Leslie Goldstein, Slide Libn.

★1082★
Art Institute of Chicago - Ryerson and Burnham Libraries (Art)
Michigan Ave. at Adams St. Phone: (312)443-3666
Chicago, IL 60603 Jack Perry Brown, Dir.
Founded: 1879. **Staff:** Prof 10; Other 14. **Subjects:** Fine arts, architecture. **Special Collections:** Mary Reynolds Collection on Surrealism and its affinities; Percier and Fontaine Collection (architecture and decorative arts); Collins Archive of Catalan Art and Architecture; Burnham Library Archives (letters and manuscripts of Chicago architects); AIC Archival records, 1879 to present. **Holdings:** 250,000 books; 75,000 pamphlets and exhibition catalogs; 380,000 slides; 10,000 photographs; 1448 reels of microfilm; 8873 microfiche. **Subscriptions:** 1500 journals and other serials. **Services:** Interlibrary loan (limited); copying; library open to museum staff, School of Art Institute faculty and students, members, and visiting curators. **Automated Operations:** Computerized public access catalog, acquisitions, serials, and cataloging. **Computerized Information Services:** RLIN, Avery Index to Architectural Periodicals, Sales Catalog Index Project Input On-line (SCIPIO), Eighteenth Century Short Title Catalog (ESTC), DIALOG Information Services, WILSONLINE, Telesystems Questel, VU/TEXT Information Services, ArtQuest; RLIN (electronic mail service). Performs searches on fee basis. **Networks/Consortia:** Member of Research Libraries Information Network (RLIN). **Publications:** Architectural Records in Chicago, 1981. **Special Indexes:** Ryerson Index to Art Periodicals, volumes 1-11, First Supplement, 1975; Burnham Index to Architectural Periodicals, 1919 to 1963; Chicago Art and Artists Scrapbook, 1890 to present (Chicago newspaper clippings on microfilm). **Remarks:** FAX: (312)443-0849. **Staff:** Susan Glover Godlewski, Assoc.Dir.; Louis Hammack, Hd., Tech.Serv.; Leigh Gates, Hd., Slide Dept.; Maureen Lasko, Ref. & ILL Libn.; Mary Woolever, Arch.Libn.; Ann Jones, Ser.Libn.

★1083★
Art Institute of Chicago - School of the Art Institute of Chicago - John M. Flaxman Library (Art)
37 S. Wabash Phone: (312)899-5097
Chicago, IL 60603 Nadene Byrne, Dir.
Founded: 1972. **Staff:** Prof 3; Other 4. **Subjects:** Art, photography, film, humanities, education, music, art therapy. **Special Collections:** Joan Flasch Artists' Book Collection (1813); Film Study Collection (452). **Holdings:** 34,000 books; 1599 bound periodical volumes; 16 VF drawers of pictures; 1000 pamphlets; 2300 audiotapes; 30 reels of microfilm; 182 videotapes. **Subscriptions:** 521 journals and other serials; 5 newspapers. **Services:** Interlibrary loan; copying; library open to the public for reference use only. **Automated Operations:** Computerized public access catalog, cataloging, acquisitions, serials, circulation, and ILL. **Computerized Information Services:** OCLC. **Networks/Consortia:** Member of Chicago Library System, ILLINET. **Publications:** Ferret guides to the collections. **Remarks:** FAX: (312)263-0141. **Staff:** Fred Hillbruner, Hd., Tech.Serv.; Roland Hansen, Hd., Rd.Serv.; Sally Alatalo, Joan Flasch Artists' Bk.Coll. Cur.

★1084★
The Art Institute of Dallas - Learning Resource Center (Art)
Two Northpark
8080 Park Ln. Phone: (214)692-8080
Dallas, TX 75321 Bobbie G. Long
Staff: 1. **Subjects:** Photography, video-music business, visual communications, fashion merchandising, interior design, computer aided drafting, fashion design, media telecommunications. **Holdings:** 4097 books; 96 bound periodical volumes; art and fashion slides; 150 audio- and videotapes; 4000 visual reference files; computer tutorials. **Subscriptions:** 102 journals and other serials; 5 newspapers. **Services:** Interlibrary loan; copying; center open to the public (borrowing privileges limited to students). **Remarks:** FAX: (214)692-6541.

Art Institute of Philadelphia
See: **Educational Management Corporation** (5259)

★1085★
Art Metropole - Library (Art)
788 King St., W. Phone: (416)367-2304
Toronto, ON, Canada M5V 1N6 Amy Maggiacomo, Coll.Coord.
Founded: 1974. **Staff:** 3. **Subjects:** Art; avant-garde practice. **Holdings:** Artist books and videotapes; multiple-format and media-related works. **Services:** Library open to the public. **Remarks:** FAX: (416)365-9208. **Staff:** Annette Hurtig, Dir.

★1086★
Art Museum of South Texas - Library (Art)
1902 N. Shoreline Phone: (512)884-3844
Corpus Christi, TX 78401 Michelle W. Locke
Founded: 1960. **Staff:** Prof 1. **Subjects:** Art - general, contemporary, American. **Holdings:** 2500 books; 196 bound periodical volumes; 8 VF drawers of clippings; 4 VF drawers of exhibition catalogs. **Subscriptions:** 33 journals and other serials. **Services:** Interlibrary loan; copying (limited); library open to the public for reference use only. **Remarks:** Maintained by the Corpus Christi Art Foundation.

★1087★
Art Museum of Southeast Texas - Library (Art)
500 Main St.
Beaumont, TX 77704-3703 Phone: (409)832-3432
Staff: Prof 1; Other 4. **Subjects:** Art history, artists, architecture. **Holdings:** 3000 volumes; 1575 exhibition catalogs; 8700 art color slides; videotapes. **Subscriptions:** 11 journals and other serials. **Services:** Library open to the public with restrictions.

★1088★
Art Students League of New York - Library (Art)
215 W. 57th St. Phone: (212)247-4510
New York, NY 10019 R.A. Florio, Exec.Dir.
Founded: 1875. **Subjects:** Art. **Holdings:** 2000 books; 17 VF drawers. **Services:** Library open to the public with permission of director.

★1089★
Artcher, Haeden, Lawler, Felix & Hall - Law Library (Law)
700 S. Flower St., Suite 3000 Phone: (213)629-9411
Los Angeles, CA 90017 Anna Delgado, Libn.
Staff: Prof 2; Other 1. **Subjects:** Law. **Holdings:** 35,000 books. **Subscriptions:** 50 journals and other serials. **Services:** Interlibrary loan; copying; library not open to the public. **Computerized Information Services:** LEXIS, NEXIS, WESTLAW, BRS Information Technologies, Dow Jones News/Retrieval, DIALOG Information Services, Information America, VU/TEXT Information Services, DataTimes, OCLC. **Remarks:** FAX: (213)627-7156. Alternate telephone number(s): (213)629-9300. **Formerly:** Lawler, Felix & Hall.

★1090★
Artesia Historical Museum and Art Center - Research Facility (Hist)
505 W. Richardson Phone: (505)748-2390
Artesia, NM 88210 Nancy Klawans, Musm.Dir.
Founded: 1970. **Staff:** Prof 2; Other 1. **Subjects:** Area history, farming, ranching, geneology. **Holdings:** 284 books; 378 bound periodical volumes; newspapers, 1903-1974; 28 oral history tapes of pioneer life; 56 school annuals; pamphlets; photographs; genealogies. **Subscriptions:** 4 journals and other serials. **Services:** Copying (limited); library open to the public for reference use only. **Staff:** Merle Rich, Reg.

★1091★
Artists Space - Artists File (Art)
223 W. Broadway Phone: (212)226-3970
New York, NY 10013 Hendrika ter Elst, Slide File Coord.
Founded: 1973. **Staff:** 8. **Subjects:** Artists. **Holdings:** Slide files of 3000 New York State and New Jersey artists, including resumes, photos, slide sheets, and descriptive material. **Services:** File open to the public by appointment. **Automated Operations:** Computerized cataloging. **Special Catalogs:** Exhibition catalogs for Artists Space. **Remarks:** FAX: (212)966-1434. **Staff:** Hendrika ter Elst, Coord.

★1092★
Arts Consortium Library (Bus-Fin)
1 E. 53rd St. Phone: (212)245-4510
New York, NY 10022 David Bosca, Lib.Mgr.
Founded: 1988. **Staff:** Prof 5. **Subjects:** Arts - administration, policy, financing and fundraising, grants and awards, education, careers, law. **Holdings:** 6000 books; 600 files on arts service organizations; 250 subject files on arts management. **Subscriptions:** 300 journals and other serials. **Services:** Copying; center open to the public by appointment and for reference use only. **Publications:** List of publications - available upon request. **Remarks:** FAX: (212)245-4514. The library is a program of the American Council for the Arts, and Volunteer Lawyers for the Arts.

★1093★
Arts and Letters Club - Library (Hum)
14 Elm St. Phone: (416)597-0223
Toronto, ON, Canada M5G 1G7 David Skene-Melvin, Libn.
Founded: 1908. **Subjects:** Canadian arts and letters. **Holdings:** 5000 books; 200 bound periodical volumes. **Subscriptions:** 30 journals and other serials. **Services:** Library not open to the public.

★1094★
Anne Arundel County Circuit Court - Law Library (Law)
Court House
7 Church Circle
Box 2395 Phone: (301)222-1387
Annapolis, MD 21404-2395 Joan B. Simison, Libn.
Staff: Prof 1. **Subjects:** Law. **Holdings:** 16,301 books; 181 bound periodical volumes. **Subscriptions:** 87 journals and other serials. **Services:** Copying; library open to the public. **Computerized Information Services:** WESTLAW, Dow Jones News/Retrieval, OCLC EPIC, VU/TEXT Information Services. **Remarks:** FAX: (301)268-9762.

★1095★
Anne Arundel County Office of Planning and Zoning - Library (Plan)
2664 Riva Rd: MS-6403
P.O. Box 2700 Phone: (301)222-7434
Annapolis, MD 21404-2700 Alexander D. Speer, Planner III
Staff: Prof 2. **Subjects:** Planning, zoning, budgets, demographics, water quality, law. **Holdings:** 500 books; 10 bound periodical volumes; 2000 unbound reports; 3 files of microfiche. **Subscriptions:** 10 journals and other serials. **Services:** Interlibrary loan; copying; library open to the public by appointment. **Automated Operations:** Computerized public access catalog, cataloging, acquisitions, and circulation. **Computerized Information Services:** Internal databases. **Publications:** Holdings List, annual; office memorandum - to state and regional planning libraries. **Remarks:** FAX: (301)222-7255. **Staff:** Sharon Huffman, Planner I.

★1096★
Anne Arundel Medical Center - Memorial Library (Med)
Franklin & Cathedral Sts. Phone: (301)267-1562
Annapolis, MD 21401 Joyce Richmond, Libn.
Staff: Prof 1; Other 1. **Subjects:** Medicine, nursing. **Holdings:** 1200 books; 600 bound periodical volumes; 80 AV programs. **Subscriptions:** 248 journals and other serials. **Services:** Interlibrary loan; copying; library open to the public for reference use only. **Computerized Information Services:** MEDLINE, DIALOG Information Services; DOCLINE (electronic mail service). **Networks/Consortia:** Member of National Network of Libraries of Medicine - Southeastern/Atlantic Region, Maryland Association of Health Science Librarians (MAHSL).

★1097★
ARUSHA Centre - International Development Resource Centre (Soc Sci)
233 10th St., N.W. Phone: (403)270-3200
Calgary, AB, Canada T2N 1V5 Janet Pyrch, Libn.
Subjects: International development, third world, development education, social justice, immigrant and refugee issues, race relations, cross-cultural understanding, environment, peace. **Special Collections:** Third world fiction (children and adult); One Stop to Overseas section; files on organizations involved in third world development. **Holdings:** 4000 books; 15 bound periodical volumes; 18,000 documents; 160 AV programs; 50 nonbook items; 1200 manuscripts. **Subscriptions:** 140 journals and other serials. **Services:** Interlibrary loan; copying; center open to the public. **Automated Operations:** Computerized cataloging. **Computerized Information Services:** Global Alternative Information Network, International Development Research Centre Database (internal databases). Performs searches on fee basis. **Publications:** Bibliographies. **Special Catalogs:** AV guide.

★1098★
As-You-Like-It Library (Rel-Phil)
915 E. Pine St., Rm. 401 Phone: (206)329-1794
Seattle, WA 98122 Philip Lipson, Libn.
Founded: 1961. **Staff:** Prof 1; Other 4. **Subjects:** New age resources, spirituality, metaphysics, astrology, psychology, religion, unidentified flying objects, consciousness expansion channelled material, future science. **Special Collections:** Astrology (500 volumes); occult and parapsychology (rare books; 500 volumes). **Holdings:** 12,000 books; 200 cassette tapes. **Services:** Library open to the public. **Publications:** Library newsletter, 6/year. **Remarks:** Library offers mail order services.

Asaf Ha-Rofe Medical Center
See: **Israel - Ministry of Health** (8263)

Asami Library of Yi Dynasty
See: **University of California, Berkeley - East Asian Library** (18316)

★1099★
Asbestos Information Association/North America - Technical and Medical Files (Sci-Engr)
1745 Jefferson Davis Hwy.
Crystal Square 4, Suite 509 Phone: (703)979-1150
Arlington, VA 22202 Bob Pigg
Staff: 2. **Subjects:** Health and asbestos, asbestos regulation. **Special Collections:** Asbestos information (technical, medical, regulatory). **Holdings:** 300 books; 10 VF drawers of clippings and medical files. **Subscriptions:** 18 journals and other serials. **Services:** Library open to the public by appointment. **Publications:** News and Notes, monthly; educational and scientific information on asbestos fiber. **Remarks:** FAX: (703)979-1152. Telex: 1 440730 ITS UT.

★1100★
The Asbestos Institute - Archives (Med)
1130 Sherbrooke St., W., Suite 410 Phone: (514)844-3956
Montreal, PQ, Canada H3A 2M8 Claude deLery, Dir./Adm.
Founded: 1966. **Subjects:** Biological effects of asbestos. **Holdings:** 775 books; 7000 documents. **Subscriptions:** 53 journals and other serials. **Services:** Library open to persons concerned with the problems of asbestos and health. **Remarks:** FAX: (514)844-1381. Telex: 055-60565 INSTAM MTL. **Staff:** Francine Marcoux.

★1101★
Asbury Park Press - Library (Publ)
3601 Hwy. 66
P.O. Box 1550 Phone: (201)922-6000
Neptune, NJ 07754-1551 Mollie F. Graham
Staff: Prof 1; Other 3. **Subjects:** Newspaper reference topics. **Holdings:** Microfilm (1879 to present). **Services:** Library not open to the public. **Computerized Information Services:** DataTimes, VU/TEXT Information Services; Front-End (internal database). **Remarks:** FAX: (908)922-4818.

★1102★
Asbury Theological Seminary - B.L. Fisher Library (Rel-Phil)
Seminary Post Office Phone: (606)858-3581
Wilmore, KY 40390 D. William Faupel, Dir., Lib.Serv.
Founded: 1939. **Staff:** Prof 6; Other 8. **Subjects:** Bible, theology, Methodism, missiology, pastoral ministries. **Special Collections:** Holiness Movement. **Holdings:** 166,000 books; 13,000 bound periodical volumes; 4500 microforms; 1500 linear feet of archival material; 12,000 other cataloged items. **Subscriptions:** 725 journals and other serials; 15 newspapers. **Services:** Interlibrary loan; copying; library open to the public with approval. **Automated Operations:** Computerized public access catalog, cataloging, acquisitions, and circulation. **Computerized Information Services:** OCLC. **Networks/Consortia:** Member of SOLINET, Team-A Librarians. **Remarks:** FAX: (606)858-4509. **Staff:** John A. Seery, Pub.Serv.; Kenneth A. Boyd, Media Serv.; Donald A. Butterworth, Asst.Dir.; Michele Hillard, Circ.Supv.; John Walters, Coll.Dev.Libn.; Bill Kostlevy, Spec.Coll.Libn.

★1103★
Asbury United Methodist Church - Library (Rel-Phil)
P.O. Box 9187 Phone: (206)472-4239
Tacoma, WA 98409-0187 Crystal M. Parks, Act.Libn.
Staff: 2. **Subjects:** Religious education, hymns, missionary biographies. **Special Collections:** Dr. H.W. Michener Collection - Puget Sound Conference, 1884-1981 (Methodist Annual Conference Journals). **Holdings:** 1800 books; 50 bound periodical volumes; maps. **Services:** Interlibrary loan; library open to the public with restrictions.

★1104★
Ascension Lutheran Church - Library (Rel-Phil)
28081 Lorain Rd. Phone: (216)777-6365
North Olmsted, OH 44070 Kaethe Karabinus, Libn.
Staff: Prof 1; Other 2. **Subjects:** Christian life, Bible studies, inspirational biographies. **Special Collections:** Martin Luther Collection (translations; 25 volumes); Anchor Bible Series (23 volumes). **Holdings:** 4000 books. **Services:** Interlibrary loan; library open to the public.

★1105★
Ascension Lutheran Church - Library (Rel-Phil)
1236 S. Layton Blvd. Phone: (414)671-5066
Milwaukee, WI 53215 Lorraine H. Pike, Libn.
Founded: 1954. **Staff:** Prof 2; Other 3. **Subjects:** Religion and allied subjects. **Special Collections:** Memorial Organ Music Collection (4 file drawers); movies and motion picture production (85 volumes); movies and movie related subjects (40 books). **Holdings:** 12,450 volumes; 125 books in Spanish; 4 VF drawers; 2 drawers of teaching pictures; 1 drawer of flannelgraphs; 56 religious pictures; 600 phonograph records; 80 audio cassettes; 120 filmstrips. **Subscriptions:** 20 journals and other serials. **Services:** Interlibrary loan (limited); library open to the public. **Staff:** Grace Fiedler, Asst.Libn.

Asea Brown Bovari - ABB Vetco Gray, Inc.
See: **ABB Vetco Gray, Inc. - Technical Library** (9)

Asea Brown Boveri - ABB Combustion Engineering, Inc. - Windsor Support Services Library
See: **ABB Combustion Engineering, Inc.** (5)

Asea Brown Boveri - ABB Lummus Crest, Inc.
See: **ABB Lummus Crest, Inc.** (7)

Asea Brown Boveri - ABB Process Automation Inc.
See: **ABB - Process Automation Inc.** (4)

Ash Library
See: **U.S. Armed Forces Institute of Pathology** (16913)

★1106★
Ash Stevens, Inc. - Library (Med)
5861 John C. Lodge Fwy. Phone: (313)872-6400
Detroit, MI 48202 Dr. Arthur B. Ash, Chf.Exec.Off.
Subjects: Experimental and clinical drug research and development. **Holdings:** 800 books; 600 bound periodical volumes; 500 reports. **Services:** Library not open to the public.

Norman and Helen Asher Library
See: **Spertus College of Judaica - Norman and Helen Asher Library** (15584)

★1107★
Asheville Citizen-Times - Library (Publ)
14 O'Henry Ave.
P.O. Box 2090 Phone: (704)252-5610
Asheville, NC 28802 Holly MacKenzie
Founded: 1930. **Staff:** Prof 2. **Subjects:** Newspaper reference topics. **Holdings:** 800 books; 200 bound periodical volumes; 1510 reels of microfilm; 560,000 clippings; 250,000 photographs. **Services:** Copying; library open for research upon permission from executive editor. **Remarks:** FAX: (704)251-0585.

★1108★
Ashland Avenue Baptist Church - Library (Rel-Phil)
2001 Ashland Ave. Phone: (419)243-3171
Toledo, OH 43620 Vivian J. Sollman
Founded: 1987. **Subjects:** Religion, biblical topics, social issues, youth, current events, biographies. **Holdings:** Archives. **Subscriptions:** 8 journals and other serials. **Services:** Library not open to the public.

★1109★
Ashland Chemical, Inc. - Library and Information Services (Sci-Engr)
P.O. Box 2219 Phone: (614)889-3281
Columbus, OH 43216 Priscilla Ratliff, Supv.
Founded: 1970. **Staff:** Prof 3; Other 2. **Subjects:** Chemistry - organic, polymer, analytical; chemical industry. **Special Collections:** Chemical Abstracts, 1907 to present (complete). **Holdings:** 8000 books; 12,000 bound periodical volumes; 33,500 U.S. patents; 20,700 foreign patents; 1750 U.S. and foreign annual reports; U.S. chemical patents, 1960 to present, on microfilm. **Subscriptions:** 450 journals and other serials; 10 newspapers. **Services:** Interlibrary loan; copying; SDI; library open to the public on fee basis. **Computerized Information Services:** DIALOG Information Services, PFDS Online, NLM, Chemical Information Systems, Inc. (CIS), OCLC, STN International, Questel, VU/TEXT Information Services, LEXIS, NEXIS; internal database. **Networks/Consortia:** Member of OHIONET. **Publications:** Library and Information Services Bulletin, monthly - for internal distribution only; Journal Holdings; Current Subscriptions. **Remarks:** Center located at 5200 Blazer Pkwy., Dublin, OH 43017. FAX: (614)889-4269. **Formerly:** Ashland Chemical Company. **Staff:** Michael E. Pettiford, Res.Chem.

★1110★
Ashland Exploration, Inc. - Information Center (Sci-Engr)
Box 218330 Phone: (713)531-2930
Houston, TX 77218-8330 Teresa A. Matlock, Info.Ctr.Supv.
Staff: Prof 1; Other 3.5. **Subjects:** Geology, petroleum engineering. **Holdings:** 4600 volumes; 150 other cataloged items. **Subscriptions:** 220 journals and other serials. **Services:** Interlibrary loan; copying; center open to the public by appointment only. **Computerized Information Services:** DIALOG Information Services, ORBIT Search Service, LEXIS, NEXIS, Dow Jones News/Retrieval, DataTimes, VU/TEXT Information Services, Petroleum Information Corporation, Dwight's Energydata, Inc. **Publications:** Ashland Ampersand, quarterly - for internal distribution only. **Remarks:** Center located at 14701 St. Mary's Lane, Suite 200, Houston, TX, 77079. FAX: (713)531-2902. Telex: 3712778.

★1111★
Ashland Historical Society - Library (Hist)
2 Myrlte St.
Box 145 Phone: (508)881-8183
Ashland, MA 01721 Cynthia C. Winterhalter, Cur.
Founded: 1909. **Staff:** 1. **Subjects:** Local history and genealogy. **Holdings:** 300 books and pamphlets; manuscripts; clippings; ephemera; local newspapers, 1869-1915, on microfilm; photographs and portraits of town officials, 1850-1900; 400 slides. **Services:** Library open to the public by appointment.

★1112★
Ashland Petroleum Co. - Technical Information Center (Sci-Engr, Energy)
Box 391 Phone: (606)327-6989
Ashland, KY 41101 Ruby Yang, Lit.Chem.
Staff: Prof 1. **Subjects:** Petroleum technology, organic chemistry, mathematics, engineering, analytical chemistry. **Holdings:** 5600 books; 3000 bound periodical volumes; 8000 U.S. and foreign patents; U.S. chemical patents, 1975 to present. **Subscriptions:** 150 journals and other serials. **Services:** Center not open to the public. **Staff:** Sherry Connor, Libn.

★1113★
Ashland Theological Seminary - Roger Darling Memorial Library (Rel-Phil)
910 Center St. Phone: (419)289-5169
Ashland, OH 44805 Rev. Bradley E. Weidenhamer, Libn.
Founded: 1963. **Staff:** Prof 1; Other 2. **Subjects:** Biblical and textual commentaries, Anabaptist and pietistic works, Biblical archeology. **Special Collections:** J. Allen Miller Collection; Sauer Bibles; Darling Debate Collection; Mary Queen of Scots Collection; Robert H. Smith Archaeological Collection; Charles F. Pfeiffer Collection. **Holdings:** 71,500 volumes; 4677 bound periodical volumes; 10 cartons and 43 unbound volumes of Brethren Church Archives. **Subscriptions:** 365 journals and other serials. **Services:** Interlibrary loan; copying; library open to qualified persons.

Ashton Library
See: **Trinity Episcopal Church** (16506)

★1114★
Asia Pacific Foundation of Canada - Information Centre (Bus-Fin)
666-999 Canada Place Phone: (604)684-5986
Vancouver, BC, Canada V6C 3E1 Anne Cayouette, Info.Asst.
Subjects: Business, trade, cross-cultural communication, telecommunications, information technology. **Holdings:** 550 books; VF drawers. **Subscriptions:** 75 journals and other serials; 5 newspapers. **Services:** Interlibrary loan (limited); center not open to the public. **Computerized Information Services:** DIALOG Information Services, Dow Jones News/Retrieval, Info Globe, Infomart Online, Reuters Information Services (Canada) Ltd., The Financial Post DataGroup, Nikkei Telecom Japan News & Retrieval, NewsNet, Inc., QL Systems; Pacific Information Exchange (PIE; internal database); Envoy 100 (electronic mail service). **Publications:** Backgrounders; Cross Cultural Business Skills Bibliographies. **Remarks:** The Foundation's Information Programme provides a referral service to the public regarding Canada's relationship with Asia. FAX: (604)681-1370. Telex: 04-53332.

★1115★
Asia-Pacific Institute for Broadcasting Development - Library (Info Sci)
Jalan Pantai Bahru
P.O. Box 1137
59700 Kuala Lumpur, Malaysia Phone: 3 2744618
Subjects: Broadcasting development, broadcasting problems related to the social and economic development of member countries, communications. **Holdings:** 5000 volumes; 350 audiovisual cassettes. **Remarks:** Telex: APBRO MA30083. Cable: UNESBROAD.

★1116★
Asia Resource Center (Area-Ethnic)
Box 15275 Phone: (202)547-1114
Washington, DC 20003 Roger Rumpy, Exec.Dir.
Staff: Prof 4. **Subjects:** Vietnam, Laos, Kampuchea, Thailand, Philippines, Taiwan, Korea, Indonesia, Pacific Basin. **Holdings:** 500 volumes; 13 drawers of Indochina clipping files, 1971 to present; 15 drawers of other East and Southeast Asia clipping files, 1976 to present; photograph files; films and video cassettes; slide programs. **Subscriptions:** 34 journals and other serials. **Services:** Center open to the public with restrictions. **Remarks:** FAX: (202)543-7891. **Staff:** Kumar Ramanathan, Assoc.Dir., Asia.

Asian Art Institute Library
See: **Museum of Classical Chinese Furniture** (10893)

★1117★
Asian Art Museum of San Francisco - Library (Art)
Golden Gate Park Phone: (415)668-6502
San Francisco, CA 94118-4598 Fred A. Cline, Jr., Libn.
Founded: 1967. **Staff:** Prof 1. **Subjects:** Asian art. **Special Collections:** Khmer photo archives. **Holdings:** 22,000 books; 1000 bound periodical volumes; 960 microfiche; 40 reels of microfilm; 1000 items in pamphlet file. **Subscriptions:** 140 journals and other serials. **Services:** Copying; library open to the public on a limited schedule. **Special Indexes:** Index to Chinese and Japanese artists in books. **Remarks:** Museum is responsible for all Oriental art owned by the City of San Francisco. FAX: (415)668-8928.

★1118★
Asian Development Bank - Library (Bus-Fin)
2330 Roxas Boulevard Phone: 2 7113851
Manila 1300, Philippines Ms. Gerda Ruehl
Founded: 1967. **Staff:** 19. **Subjects:** Economic development in Asian countries. **Special Collections:** ADB publications; Indian and British standards. **Holdings:** 40,000 volumes. **Subscriptions:** 702 journals and other serials; 301 newspapers. **Services:** Interlibrary loan; copying; library open to the public with restrictions. **Computerized Information Services:** DIALOG Information Services; internal database. **Publications:** Bibliography of recent acquisitions, monthly. **Special Indexes:** Periodicals index. **Remarks:** FAX: 2 7417961. Telex: 29066 ADB PH RCA; 42205 ADB PM ITT; 63587 ADB PN ETPI. **Staff:** Rosario Angustia; Dionisia Boro; Frema Esquejo; Cecilia Guioguio; Sandra Gonzales; Nilda Ocampo; Lucila Rogel; Maria Theresa Perez.

Asian Geotechnical Engineering Information Center (AGE)
See: **Asian Institute of Technology - Library and Regional Documentation Center - Asian Geotechnical Engineering Information Center (AGE)** (1119)

★1119★
Asian Institute of Technology - Library and Regional Documentation Center - Asian Geotechnical Engineering Information Center (AGE) (Sci-Engr)
P.O. Box 2754 Phone: 2 5245862
Bangkok 10501, Thailand Mr. H.A. Vespry, Dir.
Founded: 1973. **Staff:** 6. **Subjects:** Engineering - geotechnical, foundation, earthquake; soil and rock mechanics; engineering geology. **Holdings:** 200,000 volumes. **Subscriptions:** 1400 journals and other serials. **Services:** Center open to the public. **Publications:** Bibliographies. **Remarks:** Center provides geotechnical information to developing and developed countries. FAX: 2 5162126; 2 5245870. Telex: 84276 TH.

★1120★
Asian Mass Communication Research and Information Centre (AMIC) - Library (Info Sci, Publ)
39 Newton Rd Phone: 2515106
Singapore 1130, Singapore Elsie Bong, Prog.Spec.
Founded: 1971. **Staff:** Prof 1; Other 1. **Subjects:** Broadcasting, journalism, film, advertising, publishing, media technology. **Special Collections:** Conference papers. **Holdings:** 8000 books; 3000 reports; 300 AV materials. **Subscriptions:** 250 journals and other serials; 3 newspapers. **Services:** Interlibrary loan; copying; library open to the public with restrictions on borrowing. **Computerized Information Services:** AMICDU (internal database). **Publications:** Subject bibliographies. **Special Indexes:** Mass Comm Periodical Index. **Remarks:** Alternate telephone number(s): 2515107. FAX: 2534535. Telex: AMICSI RS 55524.

Asian Pacific American Photographic Archives
See: **Visual Communications** (19905)

★1121★
Asian and Pacific Development Centre - Library and Documentation Centre (Soc Sci)
Pesiaran Duta
P.O. Box 12224 Phone: 3 2548088
50770 Kuala Lumpur, Malaysia Ms. Siti Rafeah Shamsudin, Libn.
Founded: 1980. **Staff:** 5. **Subjects:** Socioeconomic development of Asian and Pacific countries - development policies, strategies, programs; agricultural development; international trade and regional cooperation; new technologies; public management; energy planning; women and development. **Holdings:** 37,600 volumes. **Subscriptions:** 96 journals and other serials; 7 newspapers. **Services:** Interlibrary loan; copying; SDI; library open to staff of Malaysian government ministries, diplomatic missions, and research institutions. **Computerized Information Services:** Internal database. **Publications:** Recent additions; bibliographies, irregular; current contents lists. **Remarks:** FAX: 3 2550316. Telex: 30676 APDEC MA. **Staff:** Ms. Wan Kamaliah Wan Dagang.

★1122★
Asian Studies Newsletter Archives (Area-Ethnic)
9225 Limestone Pl. Phone: (301)935-5614
College Park, MD 20740-3943 Frank Joseph Shulman, Cur.
Founded: 1976. **Staff:** Prof 1. **Subjects:** Asian studies, China, Southeast Asia, Japan, Korea, South Asia. **Holdings:** 200 linear feet of newsletters and bulletins. **Subscriptions:** 1000 newsletters. **Services:** Copying; archives open to the public by appointment. **Remarks:** The collection of newsletters is undertaken by Frank Joseph Shulman on a private basis as a service to individuals interested in Asian studies. He will answer mail requests for xerox copies (at cost) whenever possible.

★1123★
Asian Vegetable Research and Development Center - Library (Agri)
P.O. Box 42
Shanhua Phone: 6 5837801
Tainan 74199, Taiwan Mr. Teng-Hui Hwang, Sr.Libn.
Founded: 1972. **Staff:** 5. **Subjects:** Vegetables - tomato, chinese cabbage, garlic, onion, shallot, soybean, mungbean, pepper; nutrition; appropriate technology; horticultural research; plant breeding. **Holdings:** 14,070 books; 12,117 bound periodical volumes; 30,397 documents. **Subscriptions:** 1140 journals and other serials. **Services:** Copying; SDI; current awareness service; document delivery; library open to the public. **Computerized Information Services:** Produces Tropical Vegetable Information Services database; AVLIB, CHINESE, INSM, HOLD, THESMAST (internal databases); CD-ROMs (AGRICOLA, AGRIS, CAB Abstracts). **Publications:** Hot Peppers and Sweet Peppers (citations); Radishes (citations); Bibliography of Tropical and Subtropical Soybeans, 1970-1982; Bibliography of Soybean Rust, 1895-1986; Diseases and Insect Pest of Mungbean nd Blackgram: a Bibliography; Annotated Bibliography of Diamondback Moth; new acquisition list; Tropical Vegetable Information SDI Bulletin. **Remarks:** FAX: 6 5830009. Telex: 73560 AVRDC. Cable Asveg Shanhua. Sponsored by U.S. Agency for International Development, the Republic of China, the Federal Republic of Germany, Korea, Japan, Thailand, and the Philippines.

★1124★
Asiatic Research Center - Library (Area-Ethnic, Soc Sci)
Korea Univ.
1 Anam-dong
Sungbuk-ku Phone: 2 922-4117
Seoul 136-701, Republic of Korea Bok-Ho Shin, Libn.
Subjects: Contemporary problems in Asia, Korean studies, pre-1949 China, Southeast Asia studies, Japanese studies, communist societies, international relations and security problems. **Holdings:** 100,000 volumes. **Remarks:** FAX: 2 923-2289. Center is a component of Korea University.

Sarah Byrd Askew Library
See: **William Paterson College of New Jersey** (12787)

★1125★
ASM International - Materials Information (Sci-Engr)
Materials Park, OH 44073 Phone: (216)338-5151
Eleanor M. Baldwin, Lib.Mgr.
Founded: 1960. **Staff:** Prof 1; Other 3. **Subjects:** Technical information on all aspects of metals and other engineered materials: extraction and refining, fabrication, properties, applications, including areas of mechanical and electrical engineering, electronics, solid state physics, inorganic chemistry. **Special Collections:** Eisenman Rare Book Collection (59 titles, 1534-1893); Henry Brutcher Technical Translations. **Holdings:** 14,000 books; reports; reprints; pamphlets; microfilm. **Subscriptions:** 1200 journals and other serials. **Services:** Interlibrary loan; copying; SDI; translation distribution service; open to the public. **Automated Operations:** Computerized cataloging and serials. **Computerized Information Services:** DIALOG Information Services, PFDS Online, STN International. Performs searches on fee basis. Contact Person: Leslie Chom, Mgr., Info. Retrieval. **Publications:** Metals Abstracts; digest series; Engineered Materials Abstracts, monthly; Materials Business Alerts: Ferrous, Non-Ferrous and Polymers/Ceramics/Composites, monthly - by subscription; World Aluminum Abstracts, monthly - by subscription; ASM Translations Index, quarterly; Source Journals in Metallurgy, irregular; bibliographies; Industry Report Series, irregular. **Remarks:** FAX: (216)338-8091. Telex: 980619.

Asociacao Portuguesa de Fundicao
See: **Portuguese Foundry Association** (13265)

★1126★
Asociacion Argentina de Cultura Inglesa - Biblioteca (Hum)
Suipacha 1333 Phone: 1 3934864
1011 Buenos Aires, Bs. As., Argentina Beatriz E. De Lome, Libn.
Subjects: English culture - literature, history, philosophy, art, music, architecture, theater, law. **Holdings:** 36,345 books. **Subscriptions:** 9 journals and other serials. **Services:** Interlibrary loan; library not open to the public. **Remarks:** FAX: 1 3932003.

Asociacion Argentina de Dermatologia
See: **Argentinian Association of Dermatology** (973)

Asociacion de Biologos y Ecologos de Nicaragua
See: **Association of Biologists and Ecologists of Nicaragua** (1149)

Asociacion Colombiano por Derechos Humanos (ACDHUM)
See: **Colombian Association for Human Rights** (3926)

Asociacion Cristiana de Jovenes
See: **Young Men's Christian Association** (20815)

Asociacion Nacional de Mineros Medianos
See: **National Medium Miners Association** (11235)

★1127★
Asociacion Nacional Por Personas Mayores - Library (Soc Sci)
3325 Wilshire Blvd., Suite 800 Phone: (213)487-1922
Los Angeles, CA 90010 Carmela G. Lacayo, Natl.Exec.Dir.
Founded: 1975. **Staff:** Prof 2; Other 1. **Subjects:** Minority aging, Hispanic aging and elderly, Hispanic affairs. **Holdings:** 3500 volumes; 6 VF drawers. **Services:** Training seminars and conferences; library open to the public. **Publications:** Legislative bulletin and newsletter, quarterly. **Remarks:** FAX: (213)385-3014. **Also Known As:** National Association for Hispanic Elderly. **Staff:** Peggy Smith, Exec.Asst.

★1128★
Aspen Historical Society - Library (Hist)
620 W. Bleeker St. Phone: (303)925-3721
Aspen, CO 81611 Lisa Hancock, Archv.Cur.
Founded: 1963. **Staff:** 1. **Subjects:** Aspen area history, Colorado state. **Holdings:** 800 books; 120 bound periodical volumes; 16,000 photographs; 200 tapes; 2000 glass plates; 16 VF drawers of clippings; 40 16mm films; Aspen Times Newspaper, 1880 to present; 200 videotapes. **Subscriptions:** 12 journals and other serials. **Services:** Copying; library open to members.

Aspen Systems Corporation - HUD Library
See: **U.S. Dept. of Housing and Urban Development - Library** (17241)

★1129★
Aspen Systems Corporation - Information Center (Info Sci)
1600 Research Blvd. Phone: (301)251-5000
Rockville, MD 20850 Shu-Shun Chiang, V.P., Prog.Plan
Founded: 1982. **Staff:** Prof 2; Other 4. **Subjects:** Information and computer science, business, government, law. **Holdings:** 1000 books. **Subscriptions:** 27 journals and other serials. **Services:** Center not open to the public. **Computerized Information Services:** DIALOG Information Services, BRS Information Technologies, NewsNet, Inc., VU/TEXT Information Services, MEDLINE.

★1130★
Asphalt Institute - Research Library (Sci-Engr)
P.O. Box 14052 Phone: (606)288-4960
Lexington, KY 40512-4052 Ross Bentsen, Dir.of Pubns.
Founded: 1919. **Subjects:** Asphalt - technology, history, industry. **Holdings:** 1000 volumes; 288 boxes of fugitive literature. **Subscriptions:** 20 journals and other serials. **Services:** Library open to serious students by advance application. **Computerized Information Services:** Pro-Cite. **Remarks:** FAX: (606)288-4999.

★1131★
Aspira Association - Library (Area-Ethnic)
1112 16th St., N.W., Suite 340
Washington, DC 20036 Phone: (202)835-3600
Subjects: Educational counseling, leadership development for Hispanic youth. **Holdings:** 5000 volumes. **Remarks:** FAX:(202)223-1253.

Assad National Library
See: **Syria - Assad National Library** (15969)

★1132★
Assam Agricultural University - Khanpara Campus - Library (Agri)
Guwahati 781 022, India Phone: 8 7908
M.N. Borah, Dp.Libn.
Founded: 1979. **Staff:** Prof 7; Other 20. **Subjects:** Animal husbandry, veterinary science, wildlife, biological sciences, poultry science, extension education. **Holdings:** 32,000 books; 33,000 bound periodical volumes; 127 reports; 197 theses and dissertations. **Subscriptions:** 197 journals and other serials; 11 newspapers. **Services:** Interlibrary loan; copying; library open to research scholars.

★1133★
Assassination Archives and Research Center (Soc Sci)
918 F St., N.W., Suite 510 Phone: (202)393-1917
Washington, DC 20004 Jim Lesar
Founded: 1984. **Staff:** Prof 1; Other 3. **Subjects:** Assassinations, including John F. Kennedy, Robert F. Kennedy, and Martin Luther King, Jr.; intelligence operations; organized crime. **Special Collections:** Assassinations scholars and authors research files (20 file cabinets); President Kennedy Assassination Collection (audiotapes; photographs). **Holdings:** 1500 books; 20 bound periodical volumes; 15 file cabinets of government documents; 1000 audiotapes; 25 films; photographs. **Subscriptions:** 12 journals and other serials. **Services:** Interlibrary loan; copying; center open to the public. **Computerized Information Services:** Internal database. Performs searches free of charge. **Publications:** Bibliographies on assassinations.

Assateague Island National Seashore
See: **U.S. Natl. Park Service** (17670)

Assemblies of God Northwest College
See: **Northwest College of the Assemblies of God** (12044)

★1134★
Assemblies of God Theological Seminary - Cordas C. Burnett Library (Rel-Phil)
1445 Boonville Ave. Phone: (417)862-3344
Springfield, MO 65802 Joseph F. Marics, Jr., Libn.
Founded: 1973. **Staff:** Prof 1; Other 11. **Subjects:** Bible, theology, Holy Spirit, missions, anthropology, communications, philosophy and psychology, sociology, Assemblies of God. **Holdings:** 64,929 volumes; 55,055 microforms; 3351 audio-visuals; 300 dissertations and theses. **Subscriptions:** 485 journals and other serials. **Services:** Interlibrary loan; copying; library open to the public with restrictions. **Automated Operations:** Computerized cataloging. **Computerized Information Services:** BRS Information Technologies, OCLC. **Networks/Consortia:** Member of Assemblies of God Library Consortium, Missouri Library Network Corp. (MLNC), Southwest Michigan Library Network (SMLN). **Staff:** Doug Loftis, Acq.Coord.; Dan Latham, Tech.Serv.Coord.; Stephen M. Kersting, Circ.Coord.; Rick Vickery, Ref.Coord.

Assmann Health Sciences Library
See: **Mountainside Hospital** (10831)

Associated Colleges of Upper New York Archives
See: **State University of New York at Binghamton - Special Collections** (15731)

★1135★
Associated Collegiate Press/National Scholastic Press Association - Information Center (Publ)
University of Minnesota
620 Rarig Ctr.
330 21st Ave., S. Phone: (612)625-8335
Minneapolis, MN 55455-0478 Tom Rolnicki, Exec.Dir.
Founded: 1921. **Staff:** Prof 5. **Subjects:** Educational services concerning publishing and production of student publications. **Special Collections:** American college and high school yearbooks, magazines, newspapers. **Holdings:** Figures not available. **Services:** Interlibrary loan (fee); center open to the public with restrictions. **Publications:** Scholastic Editor's Trends in College Media, 4/academic year; Scholastic Editor's Trends in High School Media, 4/academic year - both by subscription.

★1136★
Associated General Contractors of America - Information Center (Bus-Fin)
23999 Northwestern Hwy., Suite 150 Phone: (313)948-7000
Southfield, MI 48075 Joseph F. Neussendorfer, Dir., Member Serv.
Founded: 1981. **Staff:** Prof 1. **Subjects:** Construction labor relations, history of Detroit construction industry, construction literature, construction site safety. **Holdings:** 500 books; slide shows on construction safety. **Subscriptions:** 25 journals and other serials; 5 newspapers. **Services:** Interlibrary loan; copying; center open to the public by appointment.

★1137★
Associated General Contractors of America - James L. Allhands Memorial Library (Bus-Fin)
1957 E St., N.W. Phone: (202)393-2040
Washington, DC 20006 Donald Scott
Founded: 1963. **Staff:** 2. **Subjects:** History of construction industry. **Holdings:** 250 books. **Services:** Interlibrary loan; library open to the public by appointment only.

★1138★
Associated Grantmakers of Massachusetts, Inc. - Resource Center for Philanthropy (Bus-Fin)
294 Washington St., Suite 840 Phone: (617)426-2606
Boston, MA 02108 Philip Conley, Libn.
Founded: 1971. **Staff:** Prof 1; Other 1. **Subjects:** Foundations, corporate philanthropy, fund raising, nonprofit management. **Special Collections:** Tax return forms filed with Internal Revenue Service (IRS) by Massachusetts private foundations (microfilm). **Holdings:** 750 volumes; 500 annual reports of national foundations; 8 VF drawers of pamphlets. **Subscriptions:** 20 journals and other serials. **Services:** Copying; center open to the public. **Networks/Consortia:** Member of Consortium of Foundation Libraries (CFL). **Publications:** Massachusetts Grantmakers (1990); Resources for Nonprofits: An Annotated Bibliography, annual - both for sale.

★1139★
Associated Mennonite Biblical Seminaries - Library (Rel-Phil)
3003 Benham Ave. Phone: (219)295-3726
Elkhart, IN 46514 Eileen K. Saner, Hd.Libn.
Founded: 1945. **Staff:** Prof 2; Other 4. **Subjects:** Biblical studies, theology, missions, church history, Christian education, psychology, ethics. **Special Collections:** Studer Bible Collection; Mennonitica. **Holdings:** 100,000 volumes. **Subscriptions:** 500 journals and other serials. **Services:** Interlibrary loan; copying; library open to the public. **Automated Operations:** Computerized cataloging and ILL. **Computerized Information Services:** OCLC. **Networks/Consortia:** Member of INCOLSA. **Remarks:** FAX: (219)295-0092. **Staff:** Lois Longenecker, Asst.Libn.

★1140★
Associated Press - News Library (Publ)
50 Rockefeller Plaza Phone: (212)621-1580
New York, NY 10020 Barbara Shapiro, Chf. News Libn.
Founded: 1900. **Staff:** Prof 4; Other 4. **Subjects:** Newspaper reference topics. **Special Collections:** Associated Press annual reports, 1892 to present; Associated Press log, 1936 to present; Associated Press World (magazine), 1942 to present; New York Times film, 1948 to present; Associated Press stories, 1937 to present (1000 reels of microfilm). **Holdings:** 1000 books; 36 VF drawers of newspaper and magazine clippings. **Subscriptions:** 18 journals and other serials; 6 newspapers. **Services:** Library open to members only. **Computerized Information Services:** VU/TEXT Information Services, NEXIS, DIALOG Information Services, DataTimes, NewsNet, Inc., POLL; CompuServe Information Service (electronic mail service). **Special Indexes:** Name and subject index to abstracts of all Associated Press stories (card). **Remarks:** FAX: (212)621-1527. Electronic mail address(es): 76166,3637 (CompuServe Information Service). **Staff:** Randy Herschaft, Libn.; Arnold Wilkinson, Libn.; Susan James, Libn.

★1141★
Associated Press - Newsphoto Library (Aud-Vis)
50 Rockefeller Plaza Phone: (212)621-1500
New York, NY 10020 Kevin Kushel, Dir.
Founded: 1927. **Staff:** Prof 20. **Subjects:** General. **Holdings:** 50 million images (negatives, slides, prints). **Services:** Library open to the public through application to Wide World Photos, Inc. **Remarks:** FAX: (212)621-7546.

Associated Public-Safety Communications Officers Historical Collection
See: **Bradley University** (2058)

★1142★
Associated Risk Managers International - Library (Bus-Fin)
702 Colorado St., Suite 200 Phone: (512)479-6886
Austin, TX 78701 John M. Atkinson, Pres.
Founded: 1970. **Subjects:** Insurance and risk management, business management, marketing, insurance agency automation, microcomputers. **Holdings:** 500 volumes. **Services:** Library not open to the public. **Computerized Information Services:** EasyLink (electronic mail service). **Remarks:** FAX: (512)479-0577. Telex: 333314. Electronic mail address(es): 62863117 (EasyLink).

★1143★
Associated Technical Services, Inc. - Research Library (Sci-Engr)
855 Bloomfield Ave. Phone: (201)748-5673
Glen Ridge, NJ 07028 Leon Jacolev, Lib.Dir.
Founded: 1949. **Staff:** Prof 1; Other 1. **Subjects:** Chemistry, chemical engineering, petroleum production and refining, earth sciences, palynology, linguistics, biosciences, bibliography. **Special Collections:** Dictionaries and glossaries in 60 languages covering the entire spectrum of science and technology (5500); translations in science and technology (21,000); collection of Russian technical journals. **Holdings:** 800 books; 1300 pamphlets; 15 filing cabinets of clippings, catalogs, tear sheets, and translations. **Services:** Library not open to the public. **Special Catalogs:** Comprehensive dictionary catalog (1500 titles), irregular - for sale; descriptive flyers - free upon request. **Remarks:** FAX: (201)748-5560. The library is said to have one of the most extensive technical dictionary and glossary collections in existence; inquires from scholars and lexicographers are welcome. **Staff:** Ruth E. Leffler, Tech.Lib.

Association for the Advancement of Psychoanalysis - Muriel Ivimey Library
See: **Muriel Ivimey Library** (8293)

Association of American Publishers - International Copyright Information Center
See: **International Copyright Information Center** (8089)

★1144★
Association of American Railroads - Library (Trans)
50 F St., N.W., Rm. 5800 Phone: (202)639-2334
Washington, DC 20001 Joyce W. Koeneman, Supv.
Founded: 1910. **Staff:** Prof 1; Other 1. **Subjects:** American railroads - economics, law, history, research, engineering. **Special Collections:** Source material on railroads, 1808 to present; annual statistical and corporate reports of railroad companies; engineers' surveys and reports; congressional materials; proceedings of railroad associations; technical reports. **Holdings:** 34,000 volumes; 2400 bound periodical volumes. **Subscriptions:** 240 journals and other serials; 4 newspapers. **Services:** Interlibrary loan; copying; library open to the public by appointment. **Automated Operations:** Computerized public access catalog, cataloging, and serials. **Computerized Information Services:** DIALOG Information Services, Dow Jones News/Retrieval, BRS Information Technologies; internal databases; DIALMAIL (electronic mail service). Performs searches on fee basis. **Remarks:** FAX: (202)639-2986.

★1145★
Association of Anti-Fascists and Victims of Nazism in Israel - Library (Soc Sci)
P.O. Box 29891 Phone: 3 440827
61297 Tel Aviv, Israel Batia Neumann
Founded: 1970. **Subjects:** Anti-fascism, peace, Nazism. **Holdings:** 600 volumes. **Services:** Library open to members and friends of the Association. **Also Known As:** Anti-fascistim We'Kurbanot Ha'Nazism in Israel.

★1146★
Association of Arab-American University Graduates - Library (Area-Ethnic)
556 Trapelo Rd.
Belmont, MA 02178 Phone: (617)484-5483
Staff: 1. **Subjects:** Arab World, Third World countries. **Holdings:** 1010 volumes; 75 volumes of clipping services; 6 boxes of U.N. documents; 3 boxes of newsletters; 6 boxes of research reports; 1 box of unpublished reports and papers. **Subscriptions:** 70 periodicals and journals; 5 newspapers. **Services:** Copying; library not open to the public.

★1147★
Association of Balloon & Airship Constructors - Technical Library (Trans)
P.O. Box 90864 Phone: (619)270-4049
San Diego, CA 92169 F. Marc de Piolenc, Archv.
Founded: 1974. **Staff:** Prof 1; Other 4. **Subjects:** Airship design, balloon technology, hot-air balloon construction. **Holdings:** 200 books; 2000 reports; article and clippings file. **Services:** Copying; library open to the public with restrictions. **Publications:** Bibliographic papers on selected Lighter Than Air technology subjects for technical society meetings; new acquisitions list, semiannual. **Remarks:** FAX: (619)270-4049.

★1148★
Association of the Bar of the City of New York - Library (Law)
42 W. 44th St. Phone: (212)382-6744
New York, NY 10036 Fredrick Baum, Dir.
Founded: 1870. **Staff:** Prof 13; Other 45. **Subjects:** Law - Anglo-American, foreign, international. **Special Collections:** Appellate Court briefs and records. **Holdings:** 600,000 volumes. **Services:** Copying; library not open to the public. **Automated Operations:** Computerized serials. **Computerized Information Services:** DIALOG Information Services, WESTLAW, RLIN, Legislative Retrieval System. **Remarks:** FAX: (202)543-7891. **Staff:** Anthony Grech, Cur.; Daniel Jacobs, Ref.Libn.; Anthony Burgalassi, Rd.Serv.Libn.; Geoffrey Swindells, Rd.Serv.Libn.; Phoebe Ruiz Valera, Hd.Tech.Serv.; Richard Tuske, Copy Serv.; Mary Matuszak, Rdr.Serv.Libn.; Robert Richlan, Rdr.Serv.Libn.

Association of Bay Area Governments (ABAG)
See: **Metropolitan Transportation Commission** (10233)

★1149★
Association of Biologists and Ecologists of Nicaragua - Library (Env-Cons)
Casa Ricardo Morales Aviles 1-C
Abajo 3 1/2-C al Sur
Managua, Nicaragua Phone: 2 22732
Subjects: Natural resources - protection, conservation; biology; ecology. **Holdings:** 1000 volumes. **Also Known As:** Asociacion de Biologos y Ecologos de Nicaragua.

★1150★
Association of Book Publishers of British Columbia - Library (Publ)
1622 W. 7th Ave. Phone: (604)734-1611
Vancouver, BC, Canada V6J 1S5 Margaret Reynolds, Exec.Dir.
Staff: 2. **Subjects:** Books published in British Columbia. **Special Collections:** Members' books. **Holdings:** 700 books; 40 catalogs. **Services:** Library open to the public for reference use only. **Special Catalogs:** Directory of British Columbia publishers. **Remarks:** FAX: (604)734-4041.

Association Canadienne d'Education
See: **Canadian Education Association** (2924)

Association Canadienne d'Etudes Fiscales
See: **Canadian Tax Foundation** (2992)

Association Canadienne de Normalisation
See: **Canadian Standards Association** (2991)

★1151★
Association Canado-Americaine - Institut Canado-Americain (Area-Ethnic)
52 Concord St.
P.O. Box 989 Phone: (603)625-8577
Manchester, NH 03101 Robert A. Beaudoin, M.D., Libn.
Founded: 1943. **Staff:** Prof 1. **Subjects:** French in North America - history, literature, genealogy, religion, language, life. **Special Collections:** Sculptures by Alfred Laliberte of Montreal (54); paintings by Lorenzo de Nevers (15); manuscripts of Henri D'Arles (14); role of the French in the exploration and settlement of Canada and the U.S. **Holdings:** 30,000 volumes; 280 reels of microfilm of old French newspapers published in the United States; 200 VF drawers of miscellanea; 55,000 index cards; 17th-19th century rare books; photographs; archival materials; theses. **Subscriptions:** 15 journals and other serials. **Services:** Copying; library open to the public for reference use only. **Computerized Information Services:** Internal database. Performs searches free of charge. **Special Catalogs:** Musee de l'Association Canado-Americaine (photos and descriptions of art in collection). **Remarks:** The library of L'Association Canado-Americaine, called L'Institut Canado-Americain, is supported and housed by the ACA, a Franco-American fraternal life insurance society. FAX: (603)625-1214. **Staff:** Sr. Alice A. Aubo.

Association for Childhood Education International Archives
See: **University of Maryland, College Park Libraries - McKeldin Library - Historical Manuscripts and Archives Department** (18818)

★1152★
Association for Children with Down Syndrome - Library (Med)
2616 Martin Ave. Phone: (516)221-4700
Bellmore, NY 11710 Dolores Seelig
Founded: 1978. **Subjects:** Down syndrome, mental retardation, early childhood education, special education, advocacy, families with special needs. **Holdings:** 1000 books; periodicals; audiotapes; videotapes; toys. **Subscriptions:** 10 journals and other serials. **Services:** Library open to Association members. **Publications:** Special Kids Make Special Friends (book); Self Help manual (available in English and Spanish); ACDS Publication List; ACDS newsletter, bimonthly. **Remarks:** FAX: (516)221-4311.

Association for Commercial Real Estate
See: **NAIOP, The Association for Commercial Real Estate** (10955)

★1153★
Association of Community Travel Clubs - Library (Rec)
2330 S. Brentwood Blvd., Suite 666 Phone: (314)961-2300
St. Louis, MO 63144-2096 Maven A. Goniff, Sr.
Founded: 1966. **Staff:** 13. **Subjects:** Group air and cruise ship travel, incentive travel, meetings and convention management, site selection. **Holdings:** 1123 travel guides; travel information materials. **Subscriptions:** 43 journals and other serials; 27 newspapers. **Services:** Library open to the public on a limited schedule by appointment only. **Computerized Information Services:** DIALOG Information Services. **Remarks:** FAX: (314)961-9828.

★1154★
Association Culturelle et Historique du Mont-Carmel - Archives Acadiennes (de la Vallee St-Jean) (Hist)
P.O. Box 150 Phone: (207)895-3339
Lille-sur-St-Jean, ME 04746-0150 Joseph D. Cyr, Dir.
Founded: 1985. **Staff:** 1. **Subjects:** History of the Acadians, Micmacs, Malecites; local history. **Special Collections:** History of the Madawaska Territory. **Holdings:** 150 books. **Services:** Archives open to the public for reference use only.

Association pour le Developpement de la Riziculture en Afrique de l'Ouest
See: **West Africa Rice Development Association** (20181)

★1155★
Association des Ecrivains Belges de Langue Francaise - Bibliotheque (Area-Ethnic, Hum)
150, chausee de Wavre
B-1050 Brussels, Belgium Phone: 2 5122968
Founded: 1902. **Staff:** 1. **Subjects:** Belgian writers. **Holdings:** 12,000 volumes; biographical archives. **Services:** Library open to members and students for reference use only.

★1156★
Association for Experiential Education (AEE) - Library (Educ)
Box 249-CU Phone: (303)492-1547
Boulder, CO 80309 Dr. Daniel Garvey, Exec.Off.
Subjects: Experiential education. **Holdings:** 200 books; 4 VF drawers of program reports; 1000 copies of newsletters and journals published by the AEE; 6 tapes of speeches. **Services:** Copying; library open to the public. **Remarks:** FAX: (303)492-7090. AEE places its materials into circulation through the ERIC Clearinghouse.

★1157★
Association Francaise de Normalisation - Centre de Documentation (Sci-Engr)
Tour Europe Phone: 1 42915555
F-92080 Paris la Defense Cedex 07, France Karine Ambjerg, Resp.
Subjects: Technology, food and agriculture, safety, standardization. **Holdings:** 3000 books; 600 bound periodical volumes; 5000 microforms; 450,000 standards and specifications. **Services:** SDI; center open to the public. **Computerized Information Services:** Telesystemes Questel, DIALOG Information Services, Bank Group for Automation in Management (G.CAM), PFDS Online. Performs searches on fee basis. **Remarks:** FAX: 1 42 91 5656. Telex: 611 974 AFNOR F.

Association Francaise de Normalisation - French National Standards Institute - Norex U.S.A. Information Center
See: **Norex U.S.A. Inc. - Library** (11843)

★1158★
Association for Gerontology in Higher Education - Resource Library (Soc Sci)
1001 Connecticut Ave., N.W., Ste. 410 Phone: (202)429-9277
Washington, DC 20036 Elizabeth Douglass, Exec.Dir.
Staff: 2. **Subjects:** Aging - education, training programs, courses. **Holdings:** Brochures and information for 300 schools offering programs and courses in aging. **Services:** Library open to the public with restrictions. **Computerized Information Services:** National Database of Gerontology in Higher Education (internal database); MCI Mail (electronic mail service). Performs searches on fee basis. **Publications:** National Directory of Educational Programs in Gerontology, 5th edition (1991). **Staff:** Joy Lobenstine, Assoc.Dir., Membership/Info.

★1159★
Association of Governing Boards of Universities and Colleges - Trustee Information Center (Soc Sci)
One Dupont Circle, Suite 400 Phone: (202)296-8400
Washington, DC 20036 Peter A. Hartman, Coord., Trustee Info.Ctr.
Founded: 1974. **Staff:** Prof 1. **Subjects:** Higher education issues - governance, trusteeship, trustee role and responsibility, board organization. **Holdings:** 2000 books; 1000 clippings. **Subscriptions:** 30 journals and other serials. **Services:** Copying; center open to the public by appointment. **Computerized Information Services:** Internal database. **Publications:** Bibliographies; briefing papers; informational kits. **Remarks:** FAX: (202)775-8790.

Association for Humanistic Psychology
See: **University of California, Santa Barbara - Library - Humanistic Psychology Archive** (18432)

★1160★
Association for Information and Image Management - Resource Center (Comp Sci)
1100 Wayne Ave., Suite 1100 Phone: (301)587-8202
Silver Spring, MD 20910 Marilyn Courtot, Dir.
Founded: 1974. **Staff:** Prof 1; Other 1. **Subjects:** Micrographics, optical disks, records management, electronic imaging, computer-aided design and manufacturing, imaging industry. **Special Collections:** Market materials, proceedings, industry standards. **Holdings:** AIIM publications; microfiche collection. **Subscriptions:** 200 journals and other serials. **Services:** Center open to the public. **Automated Operations:** Computerized acquisitions, serials, and circulation. **Computerized Information Services:** NEXIS; internal database. Performs searches on fee basis. Contact Person: Jacqueline A. Virando, Mgr. **Publications:** Special Interest Packages; Resource Reports. **Special Indexes:** Resource Center Index; Monthly Monitor (updates to index) - by subscription. **Remarks:** FAX: (301)587-2711. **Also Known As:** AIIM. **Staff:** Cleoo Calderon, Res.

Association for Intercollegiate Athletics for Women Archives
See: **University of Maryland, College Park Libraries - McKeldin Library - Historical Manuscripts and Archives Department** (18818)

★1161★
Association of International Colleges & Universities - AICU International Education Library (Educ)
1301 S. Noland Rd. Phone: (816)461-3633
Independence, MO 64055 Dr. John W. Johnston, Dir.
Founded: 1973. **Staff:** Prof 1; Other 4. **Subjects:** Education - comparative, international, transcultural. **Holdings:** 1225 books; 125 bound periodical volumes; 95 manuscripts; 51 dissertations; 54 unbound reports; 300,000 clippings. **Subscriptions:** 30 journals and other serials. **Services:** Copying; library open to selected researchers. **Publications:** AICU Report, quarterly - by subscription. **Remarks:** FAX: (816)461-3634.

Association Internationale Futuribles
See: **Futuribles International** (6222)

Association Internationale de Recherche Apicole
See: **International Bee Research Association - Library** (8064)

Association for Investment Management and Research - New York Society of Security Analysts
See: **New York Society of Security Analysts** (11642)

★1162★
Association of Junior Leagues International, Inc. - Resource Center (Soc Sci)
660 1st Ave.
New York, NY 10016-3241
Founded: 1971. **Subjects:** Voluntarism, women, children, advocacy, management. **Services:** Center not open to the public.

★1163★
Association of Minicomputer Users - Library (Comp Sci)
363 E. Central St. Phone: (508)520-1555
Franklin, MA 02038 Naomi Wehring
Founded: 1978. **Staff:** 1 Prof. **Subjects:** Minicomputers, distributed systems, microcomputers, information systems, CASE (Computer Aided Software Engineering). **Special Collections:** Minicomputer vendor materials. **Holdings:** 3000 volumes. **Subscriptions:** 70 journals and other serials. **Services:** Interlibrary loan and copying. **Computerized Information Services:** Minicomputer Software Directory (internal database). **Remarks:** FAX: (508)520-1558.

Association de Montreal pour la Deficience Intellectuelle
See: **Montreal Association for the Intellectually Handicapped** (10692)

★1164★
Association of Operating Room Nurses - Library (Med)
10170 E. Mississippi Ave. Phone: (303)755-6300
Denver, CO 80231 Sara Katsh, Hd.Libn.
Founded: 1972. **Staff:** Prof 2; Other 1. **Subjects:** Nursing, surgery. **Special Collections:** Thesis collection; AORN publications. **Holdings:** 3300 books; 1500 bound periodical volumes. **Subscriptions:** 300 journals and other serials. **Services:** Interlibrary loan; SDI; library open to the public with restrictions. **Automated Operations:** Computerized cataloging. **Computerized Information Services:** NLM, BRS Information Technologies, WILSONLINE, OCLC EPIC; DOCLINE, OCLC, TenTime (electronic mail services). Performs searches on fee basis. **Networks/Consortia:** Member of Colorado Council of Medical Librarians, Bibliographical Center for Research, Rocky Mountain Region, Inc. (BCR). **Remarks:** FAX: (303)368-4460. **Staff:** Margaret Illes, Libn., Susan Osborn, Lib.Tech.

★1165★
Association de Paralysie Cerebrale du Quebec, Inc. - Centre de Documentation
525, boul. Hamel est, Sous-Sol/Aile A-50
Quebec, PQ, Canada G1M 2S8
Defunct.

Association of Physician Assistant Programs
See: **American Academy of Physician Assistants - Information Center** (464)

★1166★
Association for the Preservation of Virginia Antiquities - Library (Art)
2300 E. Grace St. Phone: (804)648-1889
Richmond, VA 23223 Elizabeth Stanton Kostelny, Cur.
Founded: 1970. **Staff:** 1. **Subjects:** Art, architecture, decorative arts, Virginia history, museum operations. **Holdings:** 3200 books; 100 research reports. **Subscriptions:** 27 journals and other serials. **Services:** Library not open to the public. **Remarks:** FAX: (804)775-0802.

★1167★
Association Quebecoise pour Enfants avec Problemes Auditifs - Centre de Documentation en Deficience Auditive (Med)
3700 rue Berri, 4th Fl.
Montreal, PQ, Canada H2L 4G9 Phone: (514)842-8706
Founded: 1977. **Staff:** 1. **Subjects:** Deafness, information for parents. **Special Collections:** Vivre avec son enfant sourd (7 volumes). **Holdings:** 150 books; 300 bound periodical volumes; 150 other cataloged items; 20 videotapes; 35 films. **Services:** Library open to the public. **Publications:** Entendre. **Also Known As:** Quebec Association for Hearing-Impaired Children - Information Center for Deafness.

★1168★
Association for Research and Enlightenment - Edgar Cayce Foundation - Library (Rel-Phil)
Box 595 Phone: (804)428-3588
Virginia Beach, VA 23451 Stephen Jordan, Lib.Mgr.
Founded: 1931. **Staff:** Prof 4; Other 7. **Subjects:** Psychic phenomena; religious thought; holistic health; reincarnation; Bible and allied subjects; psychology; metaphysical thought; dreams. **Special Collections:** Psychic Readings of Edgar Cayce (typescripts of 14,145 discourses and answers given by Edgar Cayce in response to questions while in a trance state, 643 volumes); Andrew Jackson Davis Collection; Egerton Sykes Collection on Atlantis (3000 volumes); San Francisco Metaphysical Library (4000 volumes). **Holdings:** 52,000 books; 1000 bound periodical volumes; 2500 other cataloged items; 2000 cassettes; 15 VF drawers. **Subscriptions:** 178 journals and other serials; 10 newspapers. **Services:** Interlibrary loan; copying; library open to the public for reference use only. **Publications:** Booklets, 3/year; Perspective, bimonthly - both to members; acquisitions list, monthly; Venture Inward, bimonthly - to members and by subscription. **Special Indexes:** Index to the Cayce "readings" by subject (card); special supplemental indexes. **Remarks:** FAX: (804)422-4631. **Staff:** Ruth White, Tech.Serv.Libn.; Mary Lawsine, Circ.Libn.; Grace Fogg, Ref. & Per.Libn.

★1169★
Association for the Study of Afro-American Life and History - Carter G. Woodson Library
1407 14th St., N.W.
Washington, DC 20005
Founded: 1915. **Subjects:** Afro-American history. **Special Collections:** Rare books on black involvement in America prior to 1865 (200 books). **Holdings:** 4200 books; 88 bound periodical volumes. **Remarks:** Currently inactive.

★1170★
Association for Systems Management - Library (Bus-Fin)
P.O. Box 38370 Phone: (216)243-6900
Cleveland, OH 44138-0370 Bernie Thiel, Dir. of Pub.Commun.
Founded: 1947. **Staff:** 2. **Subjects:** Information systems, business management, computers. **Holdings:** 2000 volumes. **Subscriptions:** 30 journals and other serials. **Services:** Interlibrary loan; copying; library open to the public. **Remarks:** Library located at 1433 W. Bagley Rd., Berea, OH 44017. FAX: (216)234-2930.

★1171★
Association of Tongue Depressors - Library (Med)
c/o Matthew Schorr
100 E. Maple St. Phone: (201)387-6969
Teaneck, NJ 07666 Matthew Schorr, Sec.
Founded: 1978. **Subjects:** Health care, medical products, marketing. **Holdings:** 280 volumes.

Association of Universities for Research in Astronomy, Inc. - Cerro Tololo Inter-American Observatory
See: **Cerro Tololo Inter-American Observatory** (3396)

★1172★
Association of University Programs in Health Administration - Resource Center for Health Services Administration Education (Med)
1911 N. Fort Myer Dr., Suite 503 Phone: (703)524-5500
Arlington, VA 22209 Donna Royston
Founded: 1948. **Staff:** Prof 1. **Subjects:** Health services administration, health services administration education, long-term care administration, international health, hospital administration, higher education, medical care, medical economics and public health. **Special Collections:** U.S. and Canadian accreditation surveys of graduate health administration programs (55); International Health Administration Education materials. **Holdings:** 2000 books; 150 program information files; 55 accreditation self-survey reports; 75 geographic files; 200 files for allied organizations. **Subscriptions:** 100 journals and other serials. **Services:** Copying; center open to the public by appointment. **Computerized Information Services:** Internal databases. **Publications:** Descriptive flyer. **Remarks:** FAX: (703)525-4791. **Also Known As:** The Michael M. Davis Reading Room.

★1173★
Association of University Related Research Parks - Reference Library (Sci-Engr)
4500 S. Lakeshore Dr., Suite 475 Phone: (602)752-2002
Tempe, AZ 85282 Debbie Muse, Adm.Asst.
Founded: 1986. **Staff:** Prof 3. **Subjects:** Research parks, technology transfer, planning issues, high technology, university/industrial relations, real estate, incubators. **Special Collections:** United Kingdom Science Parks Collection. **Holdings:** 45 books; 1,000 periodical articles and reports; 300 vertical files. **Services:** Library not open to the public. **Computerized Information Services:** Internal database. **Publications:** The Research Park Forum (newsletter), quarterly - for members only. **Remarks:** FAX: (602)752-2003.

★1174★
Association for Voluntary Surgical Contraception - Library (Med)
79 Madison Ave. Phone: (212)561-8040
New York, NY 10016 William J. Record, Libn.
Staff: Prof 1; Other 1. **Subjects:** Sexual sterilization. **Holdings:** 3010 books; 80 feet of vertical files. **Subscriptions:** 118 journals and other serials. **Services:** Interlibrary loan; copying; library open to the public by appointment. **Computerized Information Services:** BRS Information Technologies, DIALOG Information Services, MEDLARS. Performs searches on fee basis. **Networks/Consortia:** Member of New York Metropolitan Reference and Research Library Agency, Manhattan-Bronx Health Sciences Library Consortia, APLIC International Census Network. **Remarks:** FAX: (212)779-9439.

Associazione Italiana Biblioteche
See: **Italian Library Association** (8279)

Associazione Italiana Donne per la Sviluppo
See: **Italian Association for Women in Development** (8276)

Associazione Italiana Santa Cecelia
See: **Italian Association of Saint Cecilia** (8275)

★1175★
Assumption - St. John Seminary - Library (Rel-Phil)
2600 W. Woodlawn
Box 28240
San Antonio, TX 78828 Phone: (512)734-5137
Founded: 1952. **Staff:** 2. **Subjects:** Theology, Mexican-American literature, psychology, family relationships. **Holdings:** 20,000 books; 500 bound periodical volumes; 1000 pamphlets. **Subscriptions:** 200 journals and other serials; 20 newspapers. **Services:** Interlibrary loan; library open to the public with special permission.

★1176★
Assumption Abbey, Inc. - Library (Rel-Phil)
Box A Phone: (701)974-3315
Richardton, ND 58652 Bro. Aaron Jensen, Libn.
Founded: 1893. **Staff:** 1. **Subjects:** Theology, scripture, Benedictines, monasteries, religion, history (especially North Dakota). **Holdings:** 85,000 books; 2500 bound periodical volumes. **Subscriptions:** 80 journals and other serials; 8 newspapers. **Services:** Interlibrary loan; copying; library open to the public with restrictions.

★1177★
Assumption University - Archives (Hist)
105 Rolling Acres Dr. Phone: (519)973-7033
Welland, ON, Canada L3C GK5 Michael Power, Act.Archv.
Founded: 1975. **Staff:** Prof 1. **Special Collections:** Administrative history of Assumption College/University. **Holdings:** College records. **Services:** Copying; archives open to the public by appointment. **Publications:** A Documentary History of Assumption College: Years of Uncertainty, 1855-1870, Volume I (1987); The O'Connor Years, 1870-1890, Volume II (1986); List of Graduates of Assumption College, 1920-1953, Volume IV; The Making of a Modern School, 1890-1919, Volume III (1989). **Remarks:** Library located at 400 Huron Church Rd., Windsor, ON, Canada.

Birdie Goldsmith Ast Resource Collection
See: **Barnard College - Barnard Center for Research on Women** (1532)

★1178★
ASTB Analytically Services - Library (Sci-Engr)
4027 New Castle Ave. Phone: (302)571-8882
New Castle, DE 19720 Olga S. Mahaney, Libn.
Subjects: Biochemistry, industrial chemistry. **Holdings:** 500 books; 1000 reports. **Subscriptions:** 30 journals and other serials. **Services:** Library not open to the public. **Formerly:** ASTB/Crippen Laboratories, Inc.

ASTB/Crippen Laboratories, Inc.
See: **ASTB Analytically Services** (1178)

★1179★
Astor Home for Children - Professional Library (Soc Sci)
36 Mill St., P.O. Box 5005 Phone: (914)876-4081
Rhinebeck, NY 12572 Theresa Brettschneider, Libn.
Staff: Prof 1. **Subjects:** Child psychology and allied sciences; residential treatment centers; foster child care; adoption. **Special Collections:** Bibliotherapy collection. **Holdings:** 3000 books; 872 bound periodical volumes. **Subscriptions:** 40 journals and other serials. **Services:** Interlibrary loan; copying; library open to the public with restrictions. **Networks/Consortia:** Member of Southeastern New York Library Resources Council (SENYLRC). **Remarks:** FAX: (914)876-2020.

Samuel & Rebecca Astor Judaica Library
See: **East County Jewish Community Center** (5117)

★1180★
Astoria Public Library - Children's Literature Special Collection (Hum)
450 10th St. Phone: (503)325-7323
Astoria, OR 97103 Bruce Bernoy, Lib. Dir.
Founded: 1892. **Staff:** Prof 4. **Subjects:** Children's literature. **Holdings:** 150 books. **Services:** Interlibrary loan.

★1181★
Astre Corporate Group - Library (Med)
809 Princess St. Phone: (703)739-0397
Alexandria, VA 22314 Roy A. Ackerman, Tech.Dir.
Founded: 1969. **Staff:** Prof 2; Other 1. **Subjects:** Medicine, pharmaceuticals, biomedical and biochemical engineering, water pollution, hazardous wastes, chemical engineering, fermentation, strategic planning. **Holdings:** 600 books; 11,210 reports. **Subscriptions:** 320 journals and other serials; 5 newspapers. **Services:** Library not open to the public. **Automated Operations:** Computerized cataloging. **Computerized Information Services:** DIALOG Information Services; WPF, BME (internal databases); MCI Mail (electronic mail service). Performs searches on fee basis. **Remarks:** FAX: (703)684-3767.

★1182★
Astronomical Society of the Pacific - Library (Sci-Engr)
390 Ashton Ave. Phone: (415)337-1100
San Francisco, CA 94112 Andrew Fraknoi, Lib.Coord.
Founded: 1889. **Staff:** Prof 1. **Subjects:** Astronomy and astronomy history, space science. **Holdings:** 2500 books; 300 bound periodical volumes; 2000 photographs. **Subscriptions:** 50 journals and other serials. **Services:** Copying; library open to members and to visiting scholars by appointment. **Computerized Information Services:** Portraits of Astronomers (internal database). **Remarks:** FAX: (415)337-5205. Produces information packets, bibliographies, and slide sets on astronomy. Free catalogs are available by mail.

★1183★
Astronomisches Rechen-Institut - Library (Sci-Engr)
Moenchhofstrasse 12-14 Phone: 6221 4050
W-6900 Heidelberg 1, Germany Dr. H. Hefele, Libn.
Staff: Prof 1. **Subjects:** Astronomy, astrophysics, celestial mechanics, dynamics of the galaxy. **Holdings:** 50,000 volumes. **Subscriptions:** 80 journals and other serials. **Services:** Library not open to the public. **Remarks:** FAX: 6221 4050. Telex: 461336 arihd d. Affiliated with Baden-Wurtemberg State Ministry of Science and Art. **Also Known As:** Institute for Astronomical Computations.

★1184★
Astrophysical Institute Potsdam - Library (Sci-Engr)
Rosa-Luxemburg-Str 17a Phone: 33 762216
W-1502 Potsdam, Germany Regina Berlepsch, Dipl. Physiker
Founded: 1700. **Staff:** Prof 2. **Subjects:** Astrophysics, general relativity. **Special Collections:** Publications of astronomical observatories. **Holdings:** 20,000 books; 30,000 bound periodical volumes; reprints. **Subscriptions:** 80 journals and other serials. **Services:** Library open to the public with restrictions. **Remarks:** FAX: 33 762309. Telex: 15471 adwrzb. **Also Known As:** Astrophysikalisches Institut Potsdam.

Astrophysikalisches Institut Potsdam
See: **Astrophysical Institute Potsdam** (1184)

★1185★
(Asuncion) Centro Cultural Paraguayo-Americano - USIS Collection (Educ)
Ave. Espana 532
Asuncion, Paraguay
Remarks: Maintained or supported by the U.S. Information Agency. Focus is on materials that will assist peoples outside the United States to learn about the United States, its people, history, culture, political processes, and social milieux.

★1186★
AT & T Bell Laboratories - Atlanta Technical Library (Sci-Engr)
2000 Northeast Expy.
Rm. AK 2N-02 Phone: (404)447-2803
Norcross, GA 30071 Patricia J. Zang, Lib.Mgr.
Founded: 1972. **Staff:** Prof 1; Other 2. **Subjects:** Electronics, telecommunications, polymer science, fiber optics, plastics, metals and metallurgy, materials science. **Holdings:** 8000 books. **Subscriptions:** 350 journals and other serials; 2 newspapers. **Services:** Interlibrary loan (limited); library not open to the public. **Computerized Information Services:** DIALOG Information Services, STN International, NewsNet, Inc. **Special Catalogs:** Visual Search Microfile. **Remarks:** FAX: (404)441-7157.

★1187★
AT & T Bell Laboratories - Crawford Hill Library (Sci-Engr)
Holmdel-Keyport Rd. Phone: (201)888-7001
Holmdel, NJ 07733 John T. Shaw, Mgr., Tech.Lib.
Staff: 1. **Subjects:** Physics, astronomy, electronics, electrical engineering. **Holdings:** 200 books. **Subscriptions:** 100 journals and other serials. **Services:** Interlibrary loan; library not open to the public.

★1188★
AT & T Bell Laboratories - Dallas Technical Library (Bus-Fin)
3000 Skyline Dr. Phone: (214)288-2319
Mesquite, TX 75149 Robert Farlong, Mgr.
Founded: 1989. **Staff:** Prof 1. **Subjects:** Business management, chemistry, materials science, computer science, medicine, engineering, metallurgy, environmental safety, industrial security, telecommunications. **Holdings:** 250 books. **Subscriptions:** 50 journals and other serials; 5 newspapers. **Services:** Library not open to the public. **Automated Operations:** Computerized cataloging, acquisitions, and serials. **Computerized Information Services:** DIALOG Information Services; internal databases. **Remarks:** FAX: (214)288-2042. **Staff:** Stacy Weissman.

★1189★
AT & T Bell Laboratories - Holmdel Library (Sci-Engr, Info Sci)
Rm. 6F-202 Phone: (201)949-5236
Holmdel, NJ 07733 John T. Shaw, Lib.Mgr.
Founded: 1962. **Staff:** Prof 1; Other 8. **Subjects:** Electronics, statistics, systems and electrical engineering, mathematics, physics, computer technology, telecommunications. **Special Collections:** BTL-authored book collection. **Holdings:** Figures not available. **Subscriptions:** 700 journals and other serials. **Services:** Interlibrary loan (limited); library not open to the public. **Remarks:** FAX: (201)834-8013. **Staff:** Mary McVicar, Ref.Libn.; Karen Rihacek, Ref.Libn.

★1190★
AT & T Bell Laboratories - Indian Hill Library (Comp Sci)
200 N. Naperville Rd. Phone: (708)979-2550
Naperville, IL 60566 Robert E. Furlong, Lib.Mgr.
Founded: 1966. **Staff:** Prof 1; Other 4. **Subjects:** Electrical engineering, computer sciences, artificial intelligence, electronics, telecommunications, mathematics. **Holdings:** 26,000 books. **Subscriptions:** 600 journals and other serials. **Services:** Interlibrary loan (limited); library not open to the public. **Publications:** Read Out. **Remarks:** FAX: (312)979-3152. **Staff:** Ruby Chapman, Ref.Libn.

★1191★
AT & T Bell Laboratories - Libraries and Information Systems Center (Sci-Engr, Info Sci)
600 Mountain Ave.
PO Box 636
Murray Hill, NJ 07974 Phone: (908)582-4840
Staff: Prof 50; Other 95. **Services:** Library not open to the public. **Automated Operations:** Computerized cataloging, acquisitions, serials, and circulation. **Computerized Information Services:** DIALOG Information Services, NLM, BRS Information Technologies, NEXIS, Chemical Abstracts Service (CAS), Electronic Materials Information Service (EMIS), Dow Jones News/Retrieval, NewsNet, Inc., TEXTLINE, VU/TEXT Information Services, OCLC; numeric information retrieval systems, MERCURY (internal database). **Networks/Consortia:** Member of PALINET. **Publications:** Current Telecommunications Information, monthly; Current Management Information, monthly; Current Technical Papers, semimonthly; New Books, monthly; Marketplace Newsletters, weekly; Current Computing Information, monthly; bibliographies - for internal distribution only. **Special Catalogs:** Serial catalog - for internal distribution only. **Remarks:** The AT & T Information Services Network operated by AT & T Bell Laboratories comprises the principal libraries whose listings follow. A number of these are jointly managed by AT & T Bell Laboratories and AT & T Technologies. Network holdings include: 300,000 books; 165,000 journal volumes; 41,000 external technical reports; 753,000 internal technical reports; 10,883 journal subscriptions. Centralized system activities not shown in the unit library listings are: Systems Design and Programming, Business Development, Library Network Support, Electronic Database Services, Internal Technical Document Services, Central Information Service, Information Alerting Service, Archives and Records Management, Document Supply Service, and Publication Clearance Service. Total staff figures above include supervisory personnel in all units listed. FAX: (201)582-3146. **Staff:** Nancy Miller; Ina Brown.

★1192★
AT & T Bell Laboratories - Library (Sci-Engr)
1600 Osgood St. Phone: (508)960-6750
North Andover, MA 01845 Dale E. Lewis, Lib.Mgr.
Founded: 1957. **Staff:** Prof 2; Other 2. **Subjects:** Electronics, electrical engineering, telecommunications, computer sciences, business, finance. **Holdings:** 12,000 books; 2000 bound periodical volumes. **Subscriptions:** 450 journals and other serials, 8 newspapers. **Services:** Interlibrary loan (limited); library not open to the public. **Computerized Information Services:** DIALOG Information Services, Dun & Bradstreet Business Credit Services, NEXIS. **Publications:** Transmission Topics. **Remarks:** FAX: (508)960-1211. **Staff:** Diane M. Heer.

★1193★
AT & T Bell Laboratories - Murray Hill Library (Sci-Engr, Info Sci)
600 Mountain Ave., Rm. 6A200
P.O. Box 636 Phone: (201)582-4612
Murray Hill, NJ 07974 Suzanne Gordon, Lib.Mgr.
Founded: 1925. **Staff:** Prof 1; Other 7. **Subjects:** Telecommunications, physics, mathematics, electronic engineering, chemistry, computers, psychology, management, metallurgy, materials. **Holdings:** 52,000 books. **Subscriptions:** 1100 journals and other serials. **Services:** Interlibrary loan (limited); library not open to the public. **Remarks:** FAX: (201)582-7591. **Staff:** Karen Parry, Ref.Libn.

★1194★
AT & T Bell Laboratories - Richmond Information Access Station - Technical Library (Sci-Engr)
4500 Laburnum Ave., S. Phone: (804)226-5712
Richmond, VA 23231 Paula M. Greenwood, Tech.Libn.
Founded: 1985. **Staff:** Prof 1. **Subjects:** Engineering, chemistry, computers, manufacturing process. **Holdings:** 1200 books; 60 unbound periodical titles; 500 microforms and nonbook items; 100 patents and documents. **Subscriptions:** 50 journals and other serials. **Services:** Interlibrary loan; library not open to the public. **Computerized Information Services:** DIALOG Information Services, OCLC. **Remarks:** FAX: (804)221-5545.

★1195★
AT & T Bell Laboratories - Short Hills Library Network Access Station
101 J.F. Kennedy Pkwy.
Short Hills, NJ 07078
Defunct.

★1196★
AT & T Bell Laboratories - Whippany Library (Sci-Engr, Info Sci)
Whippany Rd. Phone: (201)386-2604
Whippany, NJ 07981 Carolyn C. Mims, Mgr.
Founded: 1940. **Staff:** Prof 1; Other 5. **Subjects:** Mathematics, systems engineering, statistics, electronics, physics, solar energy, underwater technology, telecommunications. **Holdings:** 23,000 books. **Services:** Interlibrary loan (limited); library not open to the public. **Special Catalogs:** Visual Search Microfile. **Remarks:** FAX: (201)952-3647. **Staff:** Sherry Markowitz, Ref.Spec.

★1197★
AT & T Bell Laboratories & Technologies - Library (Sci-Engr)
6200 E. Broad St. Phone: (614)860-3696
Columbus, OH 43213 Beverly A. Fox, Lib.Mgr.
Founded: 1959. **Staff:** Prof 1; Other 4. **Subjects:** Electronics, engineering, physics, chemistry, switching theory, computer science, mathematics, telecommunications, photonics. **Holdings:** 9500 books. **Subscriptions:** 400 journals and other serials. **Services:** Interlibrary loan (limited); library not open to the public. **Publications:** Library Bulletin. **Special Catalogs:** Visual Search Microfile. **Remarks:** FAX: (614)860-4322. **Staff:** Deborah Barrett, Ref.Libn.

★1198★
AT & T Bell Laboratories & Technologies - Library (Sci-Engr)
555 Union Blvd., Rm. AL1B-122 Phone: (215)439-7648
Allentown, PA 18103 Audrey Harvey, Lib.Mgr.
Founded: 1957. **Staff:** Prof 1; Other 4. **Subjects:** Materials, electronics, chemistry, telecommunications, solid state physics. **Holdings:** 9400 books; 10,590 internal technical documents; Visual Search Microfile manufacturers catalog service; standards. **Subscriptions:** 319 journals and other serials. **Services:** Interlibrary loan (limited); library not open to the public. **Computerized Information Services:** DIALOG Information Services, STN International, VU/TEXT Information Services. **Publications:** Hot Off the Press; New Books and Journals Newsletter. **Remarks:** Maintains satellite library at Cedar Crest, PA. **Remarks:** FAX: (215)439-5514. **Staff:** Darla L. Wagner, Ref.Libn.

★1199★
AT & T Bell Laboratories & Technologies - Library (Sci-Engr)
2525 N. 12th St.
P.O. Box 13566 Phone: (215)939-6392
Reading, PA 19612-3566 A. Harvey, Lib.Mgr.
Founded: 1961. **Staff:** Prof 1; Other 1. **Subjects:** Physics, chemistry, mathematics, electronics, telecommunications. **Holdings:** 8000 books; Visual Search Microfile manufacturers catalog service; standards. **Subscriptions:** 250 journals and other serials. **Services:** Interlibrary loan (limited); library not open to the public. **Computerized Information Services:** DIALOG Information Services, NewsNet, Inc., NEXIS. **Publications:** New Books and Journals. **Remarks:** FAX: (215)939-3284. **Staff:** Catherine R. Boyer, Ref.Libn.

★1200★
AT & T Communications and Computer Products - Teletype Library (Sci-Engr)
7600 Interstate 30
P.O. Box 8912 Phone: (501)569-4260
Little Rock, AR 72219 Donna Mattingly, Hd.Libn.
Founded: 1983. **Subjects:** Computing, telecommunications, systems engineering. **Holdings:** Figures not available.

★1201★
AT & T Consumer Products - Heritage Park Technical Library (Sci-Engr, Info Sci)
6612 E. 75th St., Rm. 1C-114
Box 1008 Phone: (317)845-3682
Indianapolis, IN 46206 Christopher K. Miller, Supv., Lib.Serv.
Founded: 1962. **Staff:** Prof 2; Other 2. **Subjects:** Consumer electronics, computer science, telecommunications, voice recognition, acoustics, electrical and mechanical engineering, plastics and coatings, materials. **Holdings:** 6100 books; 1500 bound periodical volumes; 300 standards; Visual Search Microfile manufacturers' catalog service for 5000 vendors. **Subscriptions:** 275 journals and other serials. **Services:** Interlibrary loan (limited); library not open to the public. **Automated Operations:** Computerized acquisitions and circulation. **Computerized Information Services:** DIALOG Information Services, BRS Information Technologies, PFDS Online, OCLC, NewsNet, Inc., WILSONLINE; CD-ROMs. **Networks/Consortia:** Member of AT & T Library Network. **Publications:** New Directions in Research; Library Bulletin, semimonthly - for internal distribution only. **Special Catalogs:** Visual Search Microfile. **Remarks:** FAX: (317)845-3711. **Staff:** Suzanne B. Whaley, Ref.Info.Spec.

★1202★
AT & T Federal Systems - Information Research Center (Bus-Fin, Info Sci)
8403 Colesville Rd. Phone: (301)608-4720
Silver Spring, MD 20910 Lydia S. Clary, Staff Supv.-Lib.
Founded: 1973. **Staff:** Prof 1; Other 1. **Subjects:** Telecommunications, government, business. **Holdings:** 500 books; 15 VF drawers; 175 audio cassettes; 100 video cassettes. **Subscriptions:** 100 journals and other serials. **Services:** Interlibrary loan; library not open to the public. **Computerized Information Services:** DIALOG Information Services, NEXIS, NewsNet, Inc., OCLC, Dun & Bradstreet Business Credit Services. **Networks/Consortia:** Member of AT & T Library Network. **Remarks:** FAX: (301)608-5809. **Formerly:** Located in Washington, DC.

★1203★
AT & T Information Research Center
227 W. Monroe, 14th Fl.
Chicago, IL 60606
Defunct.

★1204★
AT & T Information Research Center (Bus-Fin, Info Sci)
295 N. Maple Ave., Rm. 4430C1 Phone: (908)221-4141
Basking Ridge, NJ 07920 Alice Swenson, Res.Spec.
Founded: 1975. **Staff:** Prof 4; Other 3. **Subjects:** Business, management and administration, human resources, quality. **Holdings:** 9960 books; 50 tapes. **Subscriptions:** 1200 journals and other serials; 10 newspapers. **Services:** Center not open to the public. **Automated Operations:** Computerized cataloging, acquisitions, and circulation. **Computerized Information Services:** DIALOG Information Services, Dun & Bradstreet Business Credit Services, NEXIS, Dow Jones News/Retrieval; internal databases. **Remarks:** This is one of 5 branch facilities of the AT & T Information Research Center, headquartered in Bernardsville, NJ. **Staff:** Dena Leiter, Res.Spec.; Althea Johnson, Res.Spec.; Al Giradi, Res.Spec.

★1205★
AT & T Information Research Center (Info Sci)
Rm. 2B100 Phone: (908)234-3343
Bedminster, NJ 07921 Dawn Swallick, Fac.Mgr.
Founded: 1984. **Staff:** Prof 1; Other 4. **Subjects:** Communications, telecommunications products, network engineering. **Holdings:** 1519 books. **Subscriptions:** 225 journals and other serials; 10 newspapers. **Services:** Interlibrary loan; center not open to the public. **Automated Operations:** Computerized cataloging, acquisitions, and circulation. **Computerized Information Services:** DIALOG, Dun & Bradstreet Business Credit Services, NEXIS. **Remarks:** This is one of 5 branch facilities of the AT & T Information Research Center, headquartered in Bernardsville, NJ.

★1206★
AT & T Information Research Center
1 Oak Way, Rm. 3EA104
Berkeley Heights, NJ 07922
Defunct.

★1207★
AT & T Information Research Center (Info Sci, Bus-Fin)
150 Morristown Rd. Phone: (908)204-1100
Bernardsville, NJ 07924 H. Dean Allison, Dist.Mgr.
Founded: 1976. **Staff:** Prof 73; Other 41. **Subjects:** Communications, information technology and applications, business management and administration, U.S. industries, international affairs, economics, marketing. **Holdings:** 5110 books; 100 tapes. **Subscriptions:** 4000 journals and other serials; 50 newspapers. **Services:** Interlibrary loan; center not open to the public. **Automated Operations:** Computerized cataloging and acquisitions. **Computerized Information Services:** DIALOG Information Services, Dow Jones News/Retrieval, NewsNet, Inc., NEXIS, Computer Library, FT PROFILE, TEXTLINE, VU/TEXT Information Services, Chemical Information Systems, Inc. (CIS), OCLC, Nihon Keizai Shimbun, Inc. (NIKKEI), Human Resource Information Network (HRIN), DataTimes, Disclosure Incorporated, Standard & Poor's COMPUSTAT Services, Inc., MIC, TimePlace; CD-ROM (ABI/INFORM); internal databases. **Networks/Consortia:** Member of PALINET. **Publications:** TeleScope, weekly; Product Lines, biweekly; International Monitor, biweekly; IIM & M (Industry Information Movement and Management), monthly; Fiber Optic Update, monthly; Skyview, monthly; Telemarketing Update, monthly; CITE, biweekly; Airline Research Summary, quarterly; Management Bulletin, monthly; Quality, monthly; Wireless, biweekly; Regulatory, biweekly; New Acquisitions, monthly - all for internal distribution only. **Remarks:** This is the headquarters research facility of the AT & T Information Research Center (IRC). There are also 5 IRC branch locations. **Staff:** Liza Strub, Res.Mgr.; Janice Schrimpe, Res.Mgr.; Tony Spina, Sys.Mgr.; Melanie Strub, Prod./Mktg.Mgr.; Betty Kauffman, Res./Tech.Serv.Mgr.; Diane Klaiber, Pub.Mgr.

★1208★
AT & T Information Research Center
55 Corporate Dr., Rm. 21B05
Bridgewater, NJ 08807
Defunct.

★1209★
AT & T Information Research Center (Sci-Engr)
99 Jefferson Rd., Rm. 3F4D Phone: (201)581-6358
Parsippany, NJ 07054 Susan Niewenhous, Res.Spec.
Founded: 1984. **Staff:** Prof 1; Other 1. **Subjects:** Communications, telecommunications products. **Holdings:** 132 books. **Subscriptions:** 100 journals and other serials. **Services:** Interlibrary loan; center not open to the public. **Automated Operations:** Computerized cataloging, acquisitions, and circulation. **Computerized Information Services:** DIALOG Information Services, Dun & Bradstreet Business Credit Services, NEXIS, NewsNet, Inc.; internal databases. **Remarks:** This is one of 5 branch facilities of the AT & T Information Research Center, headquartered in Bernardsville, NJ.

★1210★
AT & T Information Research Center (Comp Sci)
30 Knightsbridge Rd., Rm. 31A186
Piscataway, NJ 08854
Defunct.

★1211★
AT & T Information Research Center (Info Sci)
650 Liberty Ave., Rm. 5V Phone: (908)851-3356
Union, NJ 07083 June Eddleton, Fac.Spec.
Staff: 1. **Subjects:** Engineering, electronics, telecommunications products, military standards. **Holdings:** 1185 books. **Subscriptions:** 170 journals and other serials. **Services:** Center not open to the public. **Automated Operations:** Computerized cataloging, acquisitions, and circulation. **Computerized Information Services:** DIALOG Information Services, NEXIS, NewsNet, Inc., Dow Jones News/Retrieval; internal databases. **Remarks:** This is one of 5 branch facilities of the AT & T Information Research Center, headquartered in Bernardsville, NJ.

★1212★
AT & T Information Research Center (Bus-Fin, Info Sci)
550 Madison Ave., 5th Fl. Phone: (212)605-7732
New York, NY 10022 Randi Fishbein, Res.Spec.
Founded: 1910. **Staff:** Prof 1. **Subjects:** Professional services, telecommunications, business. **Holdings:** 2829 books. **Subscriptions:** 250 journals and other serials. **Services:** Interlibrary loan; center not open to the public. **Automated Operations:** Computerized cataloging, acquisitions, and circulation. **Computerized Information Services:** NEXIS, DIALOG Information Services, Dun & Bradstreet Business Credit Services, Dow Jones News/Retrieval, NewsNet, Inc.; internal databases. **Remarks:** This is one of 5 branch facilities of the AT & T Information Research Center, headquartered in Bernardsville, NJ.

★1213★
AT & T Information Research Center
15 W. Sixth St., 5th Fl.
Cincinnati, OH 45202
Defunct.

★1214★
AT & T Information Resource Center (Comp Sci)
2600 Warrenville Rd. Phone: (708)510-4342
Lisle, IL 60532 Ruby K. Chu, Libn.
Founded: 1983. **Staff:** Prof 1; Other 2. **Subjects:** Telecommunications, computing, systems engineering, management. **Holdings:** 2000 books; 420 bound periodical volumes; internal technical documents; videotapes; audiotapes. **Subscriptions:** 235 journals and other serials. **Services:** Interlibrary loan; center not open to the public. **Automated Operations:** Computerized public access catalog, cataloging, acquisitions, and circulation. **Computerized Information Services:** DIALOG Information Services, OCLC, NewsNet, Inc.; internal databases; ALANET (electronic mail service). **Networks/Consortia:** Member of AT & T Library Network, Suburban Library System (SLS). **Publications:** New in the IRC, weekly; IRC Searchlight - both for internal distribution only; subject bibliographies. **Special Catalogs:** Video catalogs; journal catalogs. **Remarks:** FAX: (708)510-6234.

★1215★
AT & T Laboratories - Engineering Research Center - Technical Library (Sci-Engr, Info Sci)
Carter Rd., Rm. 5-2120
Box 900 Phone: (609)639-2385
Princeton, NJ 08540 Kim M. Rotter
Founded: 1965. **Staff:** Prof 1; Other 2. **Subjects:** Electronics, telephone communications, computer science, chemical and physical sciences, fiber optics, lightwave technology, quality in manufacturing. **Holdings:** 9950 books; 13,000 internal technical documents; Visual Search Microfile manufacturers catalog service; standards. **Subscriptions:** 450 journals and other serials. **Services:** Interlibrary loan; library not open to the public. **Automated Operations:** Computerized circulation. **Computerized Information Services:** DIALOG Information Services, STN International, NewsNet, Inc. **Networks/Consortia:** Member of AT & T Library Network. **Publications:** New Books and Journals Newsletter; Current Periodicals Table of Contents; Information Montage. **Remarks:** FAX: (609)639-3065.

★1216★
AT & T Lincroft Technical Library (Sci-Engr)
307 Middletown-Lincroft Rd., Rm. 1R-129 Phone: (908)576-3116
Lincroft, NJ 07738 John Shaw, Mgr.
Staff: Prof 1; Other 1. **Subjects:** Electronics, statistics, competitive analysis, marketing, computer technology, software engineering, data communications, telecommunications. **Special Collections:** Foreign national standards (500 issues). **Holdings:** 1000 books; 50 bound periodical volumes. **Subscriptions:** 90 journals and other serials. **Services:** Interlibrary loan; library not open to the public. **Automated Operations:** Computerized cataloging, acquisitions, serials, and circulation. **Computerized Information Services:** DIALOG Information Services, OCLC; internal database. **Networks/Consortia:** Member of AT & T Library Network. **Remarks:** FAX: (201)576-3030. **Staff:** Jeanette Walker, Info.Ref.Spec.

★1217★
AT & T Middletown Technical Library (Comp Sci, Info Sci)
200 Laurel Ave., Rm. 2C-131 Phone: (908)957-2049
Middletown, NJ 07748 John T. Shaw, Mgr.
Founded: 1986. **Staff:** Prof 2; Other 4. **Subjects:** Computer science, data communications, telecommunications, mathematics. **Holdings:** 5000 books; 2000 bound periodical volumes; 200 U.S. and foreign standards. **Subscriptions:** 303 journals and other serials. **Services:** Interlibrary loan; library not open to the public. **Automated Operations:** Computerized cataloging, acquisitions, serials, and circulation. **Computerized Information Services:** DIALOG Information Services, OCLC. **Networks/Consortia:** Member of AT & T Library Network. **Remarks:** FAX: (908)957-7112. **Staff:** Jane M. Bogdan, Info.Ref.Spec.

★1218★
AT & T Summit Technical Library (Comp Sci, Info Sci)
190 River Rd., Rm. 3-229 Phone: (908)522-6469
Summit, NJ 07901 Carolyn Mimms, Mgr.
Founded: 1982. **Staff:** Prof 1; Other 1. **Subjects:** Computer programming, data communications, telecommunications, management. **Holdings:** 3500 books; 1500 bound periodical volumes. **Subscriptions:** 183 journals and other serials. **Services:** Interlibrary loan; library not open to the public. **Automated Operations:** Computerized cataloging, acquisitions, serials, and circulation. **Computerized Information Services:** DIALOG Information Services, OCLC. **Networks/Consortia:** Member of AT & T Library Network. **Staff:** Sylvia Hsieh, Ref.Libn.

★1219★
AT & T Technical Library (Sci-Engr, Comp Sci)
11900 N. Pecos St., Rm. 2H60
Denver, CO 80234 Phone: (303)538-1580
Founded: 1969. **Staff:** 3. **Subjects:** Computer science, electrical and mechanical engineering, competitive intelligence, management, marketing. **Special Collections:** Affirmative action (200 volumes). **Holdings:** 10,000 books; 96 bound periodical titles; AT & T product brochures. **Subscriptions:** 175 journals and other serials; 3 newspapers. **Services:** Interlibrary loan (limited); library not open to the public. **Automated Operations:** Computerized cataloging, acquisitions, serials, and circulation. **Computerized Information Services:** DIALOG Information Services. **Networks/Consortia:** Member of Central Colorado Library System (CCLS). **Remarks:** FAX: (303)538-1949. **Staff:** Paula Burt, Lib.Coord.

★1220★
AT & T Technologies, Inc. - Guilford Center Library (Sci-Engr, Info Sci)
I-85 & Mt. Hope Church Rd.
Box 25000 Phone: (919)279-5012
Greensboro, NC 27420 Edward H. Uhler, Libn.
Founded: 1967. **Staff:** Prof 1; Other 1. **Subjects:** Management, telecommunications, economics, industrial engineering, electronics, computers, mathematics, technical writing. **Holdings:** 4850 books; 250 bound periodical volumes. **Subscriptions:** 170 journals and other serials. **Services:** Interlibrary loan; library not open to the public. **Automated Operations:** Computerized circulation. **Remarks:** FAX: (919)279-6512.

★1221★
AT & T Technologies, Inc. - Library (Sci-Engr)
505 N. 51st Ave. Phone: (602)233-5771
Phoenix, AZ 85002-2700 J.T. Gentry, Libn.
Founded: 1972. **Staff:** 1. **Subjects:** Engineering, mathematics, human anatomy, AT & T history, electronics, management, computers, communications. **Holdings:** 3485 books; 9 VF drawers of Bell System technical reports; 60 volumes of company instructions and manuals; 1 VF drawer of Western Electric literature searches; microfiche. **Subscriptions:** 56 journals and other serials; 8 newspapers. **Services:** Interlibrary loan; library not open to the public.

★1222★
Atascadero Historical Society - Museum (Hist)
6500 Palma Ave.
Box 1047 Phone: (805)466-8341
Atascadero, CA 93423 Marjorie R. Mackey, Cur.
Founded: 1965. **Subjects:** Atascadero history, primarily of its colony days (1913-1923). **Special Collections:** Photographs and other records of early colony development and enterprises of its founder, E.G. Lewis. **Holdings:** 300 volumes; 25 oral history tapes; ledgers; deeds; Atascadero newspapers; high school yearbooks. **Services:** Museum open to the public. **Publications:** Atascadero History: Colony Days; Birth of Atascadero; Recalling Atascadero.

★1223★
Atascadero State Hospital - Professional Library (Med)
Box 7001 Phone: (805)461-2491
Atascadero, CA 93423-7001 Beverly J. Clayman, Sr.Libn.
Founded: 1957. **Staff:** Prof 1; Other 1. **Subjects:** Sex pathology, forensic psychiatry, criminal insanity, psychotherapy, nursing and nursing education, medicine. **Holdings:** 11,266 books; 4500 bound periodical volumes; 984 AV programs; 5 VF drawers. **Subscriptions:** 155 journals and other serials. **Services:** Interlibrary loan; copying; library open to the public for reference use only upon request. **Computerized Information Services:** DIALOG Information Services, MEDLINE. Performs searches on fee basis. Contact Person: Jane Haggard, Off.Tech. **Networks/Consortia:** Member of Total Interlibrary Exchange (TIE), Costal Health Library Information Consortium (CHLIC). **Publications:** What's New in the Professional Library, monthly; current journal holdings. **Remarks:** FAX: (805)466-6011.

Atcherley Medical Library
See: **Northridge Hospital Medical Center** (12024)

★1224★
Atchison County Historical Society - Amelia Earhart Library (Hist)
10th Utah St. Phone: (913)367-6238
Atchison, KS 66002 Connie Scholz, Cur.
Founded: 1966. **Staff:** Prof 1; Other 2. **Subjects:** Amelia Earhart, Edgar Watson Howe, Santa Fe Railroad, Corn Carnivals, Indian artifacts. **Special Collections:** Guns; Amelia Earhart Collection - letters, photos, books, scrapbooks. **Holdings:** 1124 books; 224 bound periodical volumes; county scrapbooks; newsletters. **Subscriptions:** 16 journals and other serials. **Services:** Library open to the public for reference use only. **Automated Operations:** Computerized public access catalog and acquisitions. **Publications:** Newsletter, monthly. **Remarks:** FAX: (913)316-0731. **Staff:** Rev. Angelus Lingenfelser, Pres.

AT&E Laboratories, Inc.
See: **Seiko Telecommunication Systems Inc.** (15016)

★1225★
ATE Management and Service Company, Inc. - Resource Center (Trans)
49 E. 4th St., Suite 700 Phone: (513)381-7424
Cincinnati, OH 45202 Eleanor Horton, Libn.
Staff: Prof 1. **Subjects:** Mass transit, motor buses, transit marketing, business, paratransit/ridesharing. **Special Collections:** U.S. Department of Transportation - Urban Mass Transportation Administration depository. **Holdings:** 400 books; 2500 government technical reports; 1000 internal reports; 17 VF drawers of catalogs, specifications, marketing samples and forms. **Subscriptions:** 180 journals and other serials. **Services:** Interlibrary loan; copying; center open to the public by appointment. **Automated Operations:** Computerized cataloging. **Computerized Information Services:** OCLC, DIALOG Information Services, Dun & Bradstreet Business Credit Services; internal databases. Performs searches on fee basis. **Networks/Consortia:** Member of OHIONET.

★1226★
Athenaeum of Ohio - Mount St. Mary's Seminary of the West - Eugene H. Maly Memorial Library (Rel-Phil)
6616 Beechmont Ave. Phone: (513)231-2223
Cincinnati, OH 45230 Sr. Deborah Harmeling, Hd.Libn.
Founded: 1829. **Staff:** Prof 1; Other 3. **Subjects:** Biblical studies, sacred theology, pastoral theology, ecclesiastical history, dogmatic theology, ethics. **Special Collections:** Bibles and rare books pertaining to history of the Archdiocese of Cincinnati (archdiocesan archives); American Church History. **Holdings:** 49,865 books; 11,889 bound periodical volumes; 564 rare books; 3313 cassettes and tapes; 59 theses; 31 manuscripts; 1121 microforms. **Subscriptions:** 385 journals and other serials; 20 newspapers. **Services:** Interlibrary loan; copying; library open to priests and religious of the archdiocese and members of consortia institutions with restrictions. **Automated Operations:** Computerized cataloging. **Computerized Information Services:** OCLC; CD-ROM (Religion Index). **Networks/Consortia:** Member of Greater Cincinnati Library Consortium (GCLC). **Remarks:** FAX: (513)231-3254. Maintained by Archdiocese of Cincinnati. **Staff:** Sr. Marguerite Wolf, Per.Libn./Cat.; Mary Alfieri, Pub.Serv.Libn.; Sr. Mary Ruth Leandres, Off.Mgr.

★1227★
Athenaeum of Philadelphia (Hum, Hist)
219 S. Sixth St. Phone: (215)925-2688
Philadelphia, PA 19106 Dr. Roger W. Moss, Jr., Exec.Dir.
Founded: 1814. **Staff:** Prof 5; Other 5. **Subjects:** 19th century America - architecture, decorative arts, interior decoration, biographies, periodicals; early travel and exploration; western Americana; early 19th century French culture in America. **Holdings:** 75,000 volumes; 120,000 architectural drawings; 25,000 architectural photographs; architectural manuscripts representing work of 500 American architects, 1794-1945; microfilm; literary and historical manuscript collections; trade catalogs; Philadelphia French Language Imprints. **Subscriptions:** 40 journals and other serials. **Services:** Interlibrary loan (restrictions on all books printed prior to 1900); copying; library open to the public for reference use only. **Computerized Information Services:** OCLC, RLIN. **Networks/Consortia:** Member of PALINET. **Publications:** Athenaeum Library of the Nineteenth Century (reprint series); Athenaeum Annotations, quarterly; Biographical Dictionary of Philadelphia Architects, 1700-1930. **Special Catalogs:** Catalog of A rchitectural Drawings, 1986. **Staff:** Keith A. Kamm, Bibliog.; Ellen Batty, Circ.Libn.; Eileen Magee, Prog.Coord.; Bruce Laverty, Archv.

★1228★
(Athens) American Library - USIS Library (Educ)
22 Massalias St. Phone: 1 3638114
GR-10680 Athens, Greece Mary Tseroni
Founded: 1945. **Staff:** Prof 5. **Subjects:** United States - literature, economics, international affairs, government, politics, and allied subjects. **Holdings:** 12,000 books; 1200 reports; 2000 reels of microfilm. **Subscriptions:** 170 journals and other serials; 3 newspapers. **Services:** Copying; SDI; library open to the public. **Computerized Information Services:** DIALOG Information Services; CD-ROMs (ERIC, International Drug Library, Federal Register, LEGI-SLATE). **Publications:** Subject bibliographies. **Special Catalogs:** Periodicals catalog. **Remarks:** Alternate telephone number(s): 1 3637740. FAX: 1 3642986. Maintained or supported by the U.S. Information Agency. Focus is on materials that will assist peoples outside the United States to learn about the United States, its people, history, culture, political processes, and social milieux. **Staff:** Markella Karagiorga; Vassilis Tsiboukis; Marianna Lippi; Era Kouyiomtzian.

★1229★
Athens County Law Library (Law)
Courthouse, 3rd Fl. Phone: (614)593-8893
Athens, OH 45701 Mickey Prisley, Law Libn.
Founded: 1898. **Staff:** Prof 1. **Subjects:** Law. **Holdings:** 10,000 volumes; law reporters; form books; treatises; tax services; microfiche. **Services:** Copying; library open to the public with permission of trustees. **Computerized Information Services:** LEXIS. **Remarks:** FAX: (614)593-8893. Maintained by Athens County Law Library Association.

★1230★
Athens Mental Health Center - Staff Library (Med)
Richland Ave. Phone: (614)592-3031
Athens, OH 45701 Judy McGinn, Staff Libn.
Staff: Prof 1. **Subjects:** Psychology, psychiatry, medicine, nursing, sociology. **Holdings:** 3200 books; 675 bound periodical volumes; 150 indexes, directories, reference tools; 9 VF drawers of pamphlets and clippings; 150 audio cassette tapes. **Subscriptions:** 40 journals and other serials. **Services:** Copying; library open to the public with restrictions.

★1231★
Athens Technological Organization - Athens Center of Ekistics - Library (Soc Sci)
24 Strat. Syndesmou St. Phone: 1 3623-216
GR-10673 Athens, Greece Rodney J. Rooke, Hd.Libn.
Subjects: Development of human settlements. **Holdings:** 35,000 volumes. **Remarks:** Telex: 215227.

★1232★
Athletics Congress of the U.S.A. - National Track & Field Hall of Fame - Historical Research Library (Rec)
Irwin Library
Butler University
4600 Sunset Ave. Phone: (317)283-9265
Indianapolis, IN 46208 Gisela S. Terrell, Libn.
Founded: 1986. **Staff:** Prof 1; Other 1. **Subjects:** History and development of track and field events, Olympic games, and other competitive events; sports medicine; coaching; training; statistics; autobiographies and biographies of athletes and coaches. **Holdings:** 4100 books; 41 bound periodical volumes; 9950 single periodical issues; 1900 photographs; track and field archives; clippings; programs; textbooks; videocassettes. **Subscriptions:** 21 journals and other serials. **Services:** Interlibrary loan (through copying); copying; library open to the public upon registration. **Automated Operations:** Computerized cataloging. **Computerized Information Services:** OCLC. **Networks/Consortia:** Member of INCOLSA. **Publications:** Descriptive, annotated, indexed catalog of current holdings - by subscription; information brochures; flyers. **Remarks:** FAX: (317)283-9515.

Athlone Court & Historiographer Royal Research Library
See: **The Jacobite Association** (8316)

★1233★
Gordon Atkins and Associates Architects Ltd. - Library (Plan)
1909 17th Ave., S.W. Phone: (403)245-4545
Calgary, AB, Canada T2T 0E9 Robert Weston, Libn.
Founded: 1961. **Subjects:** Design - architectural, graphic, industrial, interior, landscape; photography; community and urban planning; art. **Holdings:** 350 books; 2000 bound periodical volumes; 600 product specification manuals; drawings for 70 architectural projects; 10,000 photograph negatives. **Subscriptions:** 11 journals and other serials. **Services:** Library open to the public on request. **Remarks:** FAX: (403)244-2667.

★1234★
ATL Testing Laboratories - Library (Sci-Engr)
2922 W. Clarenden Ave. Phone: (602)241-1097
Phoenix, AZ 85017 Roland Boyer
Subjects: Geology, geotechnical engineering, materials testing. **Holdings:** 300 books; 100 bound periodical volumes; 2000 reports. **Services:** Library open to the public by appointment. **Remarks:** FAX: (602)234-0699.

★1235★
Atlanta Botanical Garden - Sheffield Botanical Library (Biol Sci)
P.O. Box 77246
Piedmont Park at The Prado Phone: (404)876-5859
Atlanta, GA 30357 Lu Anne Schwarz, Libn.
Founded: 1986. **Subjects:** Botany, horticulture, gardening. **Holdings:** 2000 books; 100 unbound periodical titles; society newsletters. **Subscriptions:** 60 journals and other serials. **Services:** Library open to the public for reference use only. **Staff:** Miriam Boland, Libn.

★1236★
Atlanta College of Art - Library (Art)
1280 Peachtree St., N.E. Phone: (404)898-1166
Atlanta, GA 30309 Barbara Hutsell, Hd.Libn.
Founded: 1928. **Staff:** Prof 3; Other 5. **Subjects:** Visual arts - studio arts, computer graphics, video and film, photography, design; art history. **Special Collections:** Artists' books (1200); Georgia Artist Registry (1575 files). **Holdings:** 20,450 books; 2012 bound periodical volumes; 2259 art and exhibition catalogs; 2167 microforms; 60,000 slides; 193 videotapes; 954 reproductions; 411 albums; 36 cassettes. **Subscriptions:** 216 journals and other serials. **Services:** Interlibrary loan; copying; library open to the public for reference use only. **Networks/Consortia:** Member of University Center in Georgia, Inc., CCLC. **Staff:** Kevin Fitzgerald, Visual Coll.Cur.; Janet Dodd, Asst.Libn.

Atlanta Constitution
See: **Atlanta Journal/Atlanta Constitution** (1247)

★1237★
Atlanta-Fulton Public Library - Arts/Humanities Department (Art, Hum)
1 Margaret Mitchell Square Phone: (404)730-1700
Atlanta, GA 30303 Julie Compton, Mgr.
Staff: 17. **Subjects:** Fine arts, history and biography, literature and language, religion and philosophy, psychology. **Holdings:** 211,000 books (3000 foreign-language titles); 10,000 bound periodical volumes; 9600 cassettes; 1500 compact discs; 10,000 scores; microform biographical collection. **Services:** Interlibrary loan; copying; department open to the public. **Automated Operations:** Computerized acquisitions, cataloging, serials, and circulation. **Publications:** Annual Atlanta Symphony Orchestra Discography; annotated booklists, irregular. **Remarks:** FAX: (404)730-1757. Staff available for book talks and reviews. **Staff:** Mavis Jackson, Libn. III; Anthony Miller, Libn. II; James Taylor, Libn. II; Myron Casteel, Libn. II; Sandra Anderson, Libn. II; Marianna Kaufman, Libn. II; Margaret Bradford, Libn. I; Wen-Yuan Chao, Libn. I; Jacob Crouch, Libn. I; George Dowman Wilson, Libn. I.

★1238★
Atlanta-Fulton Public Library - Children's Department - High Collection (Hum)
1 Margaret Mitchell Square Phone: (404)730-1845
Atlanta, GA 30303 Lynne R. Pickens, Mgr.
Founded: 1938. **Subjects:** Children's literature - classic, historically important, award winners, and outstanding current books. **Holdings:** 2000 books; 122 bound periodical volumes. **Services:** Copying; collection open to the public. **Remarks:** FAX: (404)730-1851.

★1239★
Atlanta-Fulton Public Library - Film Department (Art, Theater)
1 Margaret Mitchell Square Phone: (404)730-1726
Atlanta, GA 30303 Karen J. Harris, Mgr.
Founded: 1971. **Staff:** Prof 3, Other 9. **Subjects:** Literature, history, global issues, live performances, musicals, children's films, black studies, foreign films, educational films and videos, business and management films and videos. **Holdings:** 8000 video cassettes; 3000 films. **Subscriptions:** 7 journals and other serials. **Services:** Department provides free service to city and county residents; outside residents pay fee. **Automated Operations:** Computerized cataloging and circulation. **Special Catalogs:** General Film Catalog, Children's Filmography, Black Experience Filmography, Religious/Philosophy Catalog, Feature Film Catalog. **Staff:** Diana M. Aleman, Asst.Mgr., Film Dept.; Carolyn L. Clark, Libn.

★1240★
Atlanta-Fulton Public Library - Information Line (Bus-Fin)
1 Margaret Mitchell Square Phone: (404)730-1700
Atlanta, GA 30303 Katharine Suttell, Mgr.
Founded: 1973. **Staff:** Prof 6; Other 6. **Subjects:** General reference, business. **Holdings:** 1100 books; 552 reels of microfilm; 1 box of microfiche; 2 VF drawers; 900 telephone directories. **Subscriptions:** 453 journals and other serials. **Services:** Copying (limited). **Computerized Information Services:** DIALOG Information Services, OCLC. **Remarks:** FAX: (404)730-1989.

★1241★
Atlanta-Fulton Public Library - Ivan Allen, Jr. Department of Science, Industry and Government (Bus-Fin, Sci-Engr)
1 Margaret Mitchell Square Phone: (404)730-1700
Atlanta, GA 30303 William Munro, Mgr.
Founded: 1950. **Staff:** Prof 12; Other 10. **Subjects:** Industry and finance, business and management, social science, law, government, pure and applied science. **Special Collections:** Atlanta city documents and plat maps; federal document depository (partial). **Holdings:** 80,000 volumes; annual and 10K reports for 11,000 corporations for past five years, on microfiche; Georgia Laws, 1787 to present; Georgia House and Senate Journals, 1820-1950; 1500 VF folders; subject directories. **Subscriptions:** 80 investment advisory services. **Services:** Interlibrary loan; copying; department open to the public. **Automated Operations:** Computerized cataloging, acquisitions, serials, and circulation. **Computerized Information Services:** DIALOG Information Services, OCLC, LOGIN, WESTLAW, VU/TEXT Information Services. **Networks/Consortia:** Member of SOLINET. **Publications:** I.A.D. Annotated Research Guides - free upon request. **Remarks:** FAX: (404)730-1986.

★1242★
Atlanta-Fulton Public Library - Ivan Allen, Jr. Department of Science, Industry and Government - Foundation Collection (Bus-Fin)
1 Margaret Mitchell Square Phone: (404)730-1700
Atlanta, GA 30303 William Munro, Mgr.
Founded: 1962. **Staff:** 1. **Subjects:** Grantsmanship, philanthropy, proposal writing, foundations in the Southeast, fund raising. **Special Collections:** Internal revenue forms (990-AR and 990-PF) for all private foundations in Georgia, South Carolina, Florida, Tennessee, Alabama. **Holdings:** 120 books; 13 bound periodical volumes; 18 file boxes of annual reports; 13 boxes of microforms; 3 loose-leaf notebooks of foundation newsletters. **Subscriptions:** 38 journals and other serials. **Services:** Copying; collection open to the public; orientation available by appointment. **Networks/Consortia:** Member of Consortium of Foundation Libraries (CFL). **Remarks:** FAX: (404)730-1986. The Foundation Collection is a regional cooperating collection of the Foundation Center in New York City. **Staff:** Nancy Powers.

★1243★
Atlanta-Fulton Public Library - Learning Center Library (Educ)
1 Margaret Mitchell Sq., N.W. Phone: (404)730-1960
Atlanta, GA 30303 Ronald Dubberly
Staff: Prof 3; Other 1. **Subjects:** Literacy program, visually impaired assistance, hearing impaired assistance, test preparation materials. **Special Collections:** Large Print Collection; Visually/Hearing Impaired Periodicals; Literacy Instructional and Leisure Reading Materials. **Holdings:** Figures not available. **Subscriptions:** 10 journals and other serials. **Services:** Interlibrary loan; copying; library open to the public. **Computerized Information Services:** CD-ROMs.

★1244★
Atlanta-Fulton Public Library - Newspapers/Periodicals Department (Bus-Fin)
1 Margaret Mitchell Square Phone: (404)730-1700
Atlanta, GA 30303 Isaac Washington, Mgr.
Staff: Prof 3; Other 9. **Subjects:** Newspaper reference topics, business, government, law; local, national, and international news. **Holdings:** 40,000 bound periodical volumes; 100,000 nonbook items. **Subscriptions:** 2400 journals and other serials; 2500 newspapers. **Services:** Copying; department open to the public. **Computerized Information Services:** DIALOG Information Services, InfoTrac, VU/TEXT Information Services, NewsBank. **Special Catalogs:** Atlanta-Fulton Public Library System's Periodicals Holdings. **Remarks:** FAX: (404)730-1985. **Staff:** Lonnie L. Lee, Libn.

★1245★
Atlanta-Fulton Public Library - Special Collections Department (Area-Ethnic, Hist)
1 Margaret Mitchell Square Phone: (404)730-1700
Atlanta, GA 30303 Janice White Sikes, Mgr.
Founded: 1925. **Staff:** Prof 5; Other 3. **Subjects:** African-American studies, genealogy, Georgia history and literature, oral history, Margaret Mitchell. **Special Collections:** Hattie Wilson High Memorial Genealogical Collection (6800 books, 372 bound periodical volumes, 129 unbound periodicals, 214 city directories, 1200 maps, 160 reels of microfilm); Samuel Williams Collection of materials by and about Afro-Americans (40,000 books, 1600 bound periodical volumes, 2100 reels of microfilm, 1000 microfiche); Margaret Mitchell Collection (1766 items); Atlanta-Fulton Public Library Archives; rare books. **Holdings:** 54,300 books; 3930 bound periodical volumes; 4396 reels of microfilm; 11,000 microfiche; 300 audiocassettes; 790 other cataloged items. **Subscriptions:** 350 journals and newsletters; 15 newspapers. **Services:** Copying; department open to the public for reference use only. **Publications:** Bibliographies and guides. **Remarks:** FAX: (404)730-1989. **Staff:** Gloria Mims, Asst.Dept.Mgr.; Henrietta Payne Graham; Herman Mason; Sharon Robinson.

★1246★
Atlanta Historical Society - Archives/Library (Hist)
3101 Andrews Dr., N.W. Phone: (404)261-1837
Atlanta, GA 30305 Anne A. Salter, Dir., Lib. & Archv.
Founded: 1926. **Staff:** Prof 7. **Subjects:** History of Atlanta and its environs, personalities, organizations, businesses; Civil War history. **Special Collections:** Official City and County Records (1143 cubic feet); Atlanta maps and plats (500); 1200 cataloged private collections (5000 cubic feet); architectural drawings (80,000); ephemera (90 cubic feet); Official Records of the Union and Confederate Armies - War of the Rebellion (complete set); Coca-Cola Company Cook Book Collection (471 volumes); Cherokee Garden Club Library (1800 volumes; periodicals; archives). **Holdings:** 19,000 books; 545 bound periodical volumes; 152 newspaper titles; 203 periodical titles; 85,000 indexed photographs; 20,000 slides; 172 cubic feet of vertical files. **Subscriptions:** 150 journals and other serials. **Services:** Copying; library open to the public. **Computerized Information Services:** OCLC. **Networks/Consortia:** Member of SOLINET. **Publications:** Newsletter, bimonthly; Quarterly Journal. **Special Indexes:** Descriptive inventories (card); Guide to Manuscript Collections, 1976. **Remarks:** FAX: (404)238-0669.

★1247★
Atlanta Journal/Atlanta Constitution - Reference Library (Publ)
72 Marietta St., N.W. Phone: (404)526-5420
Atlanta, GA 30303 Diane C. Hunter, Mgr., Lib.Serv.
Founded: 1950. **Staff:** Prof 6; Other 13. **Subjects:** Newspaper reference topics, Atlanta and Georgia history. **Holdings:** 2200 books; 100 bound periodical volumes; 11 million newspaper clippings; 2.5 million photographs, maps, and graphics. **Subscriptions:** 50 journals and other serials; 45 newspapers. **Services:** Interlibrary loan; library open to professional researchers and journalists with approval of head librarian. **Computerized Information Services:** DIALOG Information Services, Dow Jones News/Retrieval, NEXIS, Information America, DataTimes, VU/TEXT Information Services; internal database. **Remarks:** FAX: (404)526-5840. **Staff:** Richard Hallman, Ref.Libn.; Mary Civille, Text Libn.; Valerie Lyons, Photo Libn; Katherine Walker, Libn.; Vivian Flagg, Sys.Libn.; Larry Andrews, Libn.; Kay Pinckney, Pub.Info.

★1248★
Atlanta Law School - Library (Law)
880 W. Peachtree, No. B Phone: (404)872-0990
Atlanta, GA 30309 Jeannie Ashley, Libn.
Founded: 1890. **Staff:** Prof 2; Other 2. **Subjects:** Law. **Holdings:** 20,000 books; other cataloged items. **Subscriptions:** 22 journals and other serials. **Services:** Library not open to the public.

★1249★
Atlanta Lesbian Feminist Alliance - Southeastern Lesbian Archives (Soc Sci)
Box 5502
Atlanta, GA 30307 Phone: (404)378-9769
Staff: Prof 2; Other 2. **Subjects:** Lesbian feminism, women's theory, lesbianism, feminism. **Holdings:** 800 books; 435 periodical titles; 10 linear feet of archives. **Subscriptions:** 192 journals and other serials. **Services:** Copying; archives open to women. **Networks/Consortia:** Member of Lesbian Circle of Indexers. **Publications:** Atalanta, monthly - by subscription or membership.

★1250★
Atlantic Baptist College - Library (Rel-Phil)
Box 6004 Phone: (506)858-8970
Moncton, NB, Canada E1C 9L7 Ivan Douthwright, Libn.
Founded: 1949. **Staff:** Prof 1. **Subjects:** Theology, business, music, literature, history, philosophy. **Special Collections:** Baptist history. **Holdings:** 29,800 books. **Subscriptions:** 134 journals and other serials. **Services:** Interlibrary loan; copying; library open to the public. **Automated Operations:** Computerized cataloging. **Computerized Information Services:** DIALOG Information Services, CAN/OLE; Envoy 100 (electronic mail service). **Remarks:** FAX: (506)858-9694.

★1251★
Atlantic City Free Public Library - Special Collections (Hist)
1 N. Tennessee Ave. Phone: (609)345-2269
Atlantic City, NJ 08401 Maureen Sherr Frank, Dir.
Founded: 1901. **Staff:** Prof 1; Other 1. **Subjects:** State and local history, genealogy. **Special Collections:** Heston Collection on Atlantic City history (3000 postcards; 10,000 photographic negatives; 100 oral history tapes; 2500 35mm slides; 1000 reels of microfilm; 150 manuscripts; 500 VF folders of clippings and pamphlets); gambling collection (300 books); manuscripts and records of the Atlantic City Woman's Research Club. **Holdings:** 3500 books; 150 bound periodical volumes. **Subscriptions:** 15 journals and other serials; 5 newspapers. **Services:** Copying; collections open to the public with valid

identification. **Automated Operations:** Computerized cataloging and ILL. **Computerized Information Services:** DIALOG Information Services, WILSONLINE, OCLC; internal databases. Contact Person: Robert Rynkiewicz, Asst.Dir./Tech.Serv. **Networks/Consortia:** Member of PALINET, South Jersey Regional Library Cooperative. **Publications:** Atlantic City fact sheets, irregular; bibliographies of specialized holdings. **Special Indexes:** Local newspaper index (online). **Staff:** Christine King Asst.Dir./Pub.Serv.

★1252★
Atlantic City Medical Center - Atlantic City Division - Health Science Library (Med)
1925 Pacific Ave. Phone: (609)652-1000
Atlantic City, NJ 08401 John P. Doesburgh, Dir., Hea.Sci.Libs.
Founded: 1940. **Staff:** Prof 1. **Subjects:** Medicine, nursing, and allied health sciences. **Holdings:** 875 books; 2750 bound periodical volumes; Audio-Digest tapes in surgery, family practice, and internal medicine. **Subscriptions:** 254 journals and other serials. **Services:** Interlibrary loan; copying; library open to the public with restrictions. **Automated Operations:** Computerized ILL (DOCLINE). **Computerized Information Services:** MEDLINE. **Networks/Consortia:** Member of Southwest New Jersey Consortium for Health Information Services, BHSL, Health Sciences Library Association of New Jersey (HSLANJ). **Remarks:** FAX: (609)441-2137.

★1253★
Atlantic City Medical Center - Mainland Division - Health Science Library (Med)
Jim Leeds Rd. Phone: (609)652-1000
Pomona, NJ 08240 John P. Doesburgh, Dir., Hea.Sci.Libs.
Founded: 1983. **Staff:** Prof 1. **Subjects:** Medicine, nursing, and allied health sciences. **Holdings:** 273 books; 383 bound periodical volumes. **Subscriptions:** 51 journals and other serials. **Services:** Interlibrary loan; copying; library open to the public with restrictions. **Automated Operations:** Computerized ILL (DOCLINE). **Computerized Information Services:** MEDLINE. **Networks/Consortia:** Member of Southwest New Jersey Consortium for Health Information Services. **Remarks:** FAX: (609)652-3504.

★1254★
Atlantic Council of the United States - Library (Soc Sci)
1616 H St., N.W., Suite 300 Phone: (202)347-9353
Washington, DC 20006 Ambassador Razanne Ridgway, Pres.
Staff: Prof 1; Other 1. **Subjects:** Atlantic alliance, NATO, Atlantic-international relations, world politics, intergovernmental organizations, international communism, international law, economics, energy, defense strategy. **Special Collections:** International organization publications: Organization for Economic Cooperation and Development (OECD), International Monetary Fund (IMF), European Economic Community (EEC), European Free Trade Association (EFTA), General Agreement on Tariffs and Trade (GATT), the U.N. **Holdings:** 2500 books; 50 bound periodical volumes; 250 special studies; 2 VF drawers of North Atlantic Council documents; 1 VF drawer of Atlantic Treaty Association documents; 4 VF drawers of newsletters and publications from NATO countries. **Subscriptions:** 60 journals and other serials. **Services:** Library open to the public for reference use only.

★1255★
Atlantic County Historical Society - Library (Hist)
907 Shore Rd.
Box 301 Phone: (609)927-5218
Somers Point, NJ 08244 Elizabeth Ehrhardt, Lib.Dir.
Founded: 1913. **Subjects:** History, genealogy, and maritime history of Atlantic County and Southern New Jersey; Civil War. **Special Collections:** 400 Directories covering cities in the Middle Atlantic states, New England, Delaware, Maryland, Ohio, North Carolina, Colorado, and Louisiana - 1891 to 1970. **Holdings:** 6000 books and bound periodical volumes; 15 VF drawers; 35 manuscript books; 100 family Bibles; 132 maps; Atlantic County census data on microfilm; photographs; lantern slides; postcards; deeds; letters; diaries; shiplogs; oral history tapes. **Subscriptions:** 14 journals and other serials. **Services:** Copying; library open to the public. **Computerized Information Services:** Internal database. **Publications:** Journal of local history and genealogy, annual; Atlantic Heritage (newsletter), quarterly; Absegami Yesteryear (book); Railroading in Atlantic County, New Jersey; pamphlets on Atlantic County history; Guide to the Genealogical History Library. **Special Indexes:** Indexes of manuscript and image collections; marriages; obituaries.

★1256★
Atlantic Electric Co. - Corporate Library (Energy)
1199 Black Horse Pike
P.O. Box 1500-MLC Phone: (609)625-5878
Pleasantville, NJ 08232 Riesa E. Levine, Corp.Libn.
Founded: 1986. **Staff:** 2. **Subjects:** Energy, management, electric generation, engineering. **Holdings:** 2500 books; 450 patents and documents; 350 AV programs; 1000 nonbook materials. **Subscriptions:** 80 journals and other serials; 5 newspapers. **Services:** Interlibrary loan; copying; SDI; library open to the public with restrictions. **Computerized Information Services:** DIALOG Information Services, LEXIS, NEXIS, VU/TEXT Information Services, ORBIT Search Service; Knight-Ridder Unicom News, UIDC, URAP (electronic mail services). **Remarks:** FAX: (609)625-5853.

★1257★
Atlantic Provinces Economic Council - Library (Bus-Fin)
5121 Sackville St., Suite 500
Halifax, NS, Canada B3J 1K1 Phone: (902)422-6516
Founded: 1957. **Subjects:** Economy of the Atlantic Provinces, statistics. **Holdings:** Books; government reports; pamphlets; clippings. **Subscriptions:** 30 journals and other serials; 10 newspapers. **Services:** Interlibrary loan; copying; library open to the public by special permission. **Computerized Information Services:** Internal database. **Remarks:** FAX: (902)429-6803.

★1258★
Atlantic Research Corporation - Propulsion Division - Technical Information Center (Sci-Engr)
5945 Wellington Rd. Phone: (703)754-5590
Gainesville, VA 22065-1699 Patti Kerns, Asst.Libn.
Founded: 1983. **Staff:** Prof 1; Other 1. **Subjects:** Propulsion, chemistry, aerospace, engineering. **Holdings:** 2200 books; 16,000 technical reports. **Subscriptions:** 300 journals and other serials. **Services:** Interlibrary loan; center not open to the public. **Computerized Information Services:** DIALOG Information Services, DTIC, NASA/RECON; internal database. **Networks/Consortia:** Member of Interlibrary Users Association (IUA). **Publications:** Technical Information Center (TIC) Newsletter, monthly; Library Bulletin, quarterly. **Special Catalogs:** Technical Reports Catalog (online). **Remarks:** FAX: (703)754-5638. Telex: 710 833 0720.

★1259★
Atlantic-Richfield Company - ARCO Chemical Company - Business and Technical Information Center (Energy)
3801 West Chester Pike Phone: (215)359-2905
Newton Square, PA 19073 Francis Hilbert, Supv.
Founded: 1924. **Staff:** Prof 3; Other 3. **Subjects:** Chemistry, chemical engineering and economics, petroleum and petroleum technology, mathematics, physics, polymers. **Special Collections:** Technical Oil Mission Reels; American Petroleum Institute materials. **Holdings:** 20,000 books; 9000 bound periodical volumes; technical reports and memoranda; reprints; audio cassettes; microforms. **Subscriptions:** 700 journals and other serials. **Services:** Interlibrary loan; copying; SDI; library open to the public by appointment. **Automated Operations:** Computerized cataloging, circulation, and ILL. **Computerized Information Services:** DIALOG Information Services, PFDS Online, MEDLARS, OCLC, BRS Information Technologies, Chemical Abstracts Service (CAS), WILSONLINE, NEXIS, World Petrochemicals, VU/TEXT Information Services. Performs searches on fee basis. **Networks/Consortia:** Member of PALINET. **Publications:** R&D Library Bulletin, bimonthly. **Remarks:** Alternate telephone number(s): 359-2908; FAX: (215)359-6025. **Staff:** Barbara Gaffney, Lib.Sys./Info.Spec.; Diane Ladner, Info.Spec.

★1260★
Atlantic-Richfield Company - ARCO Exploration and Production Technology - Technical Information Center (Energy)
PRC-F1100
2300 W. Plano Pkwy. Phone: (214)754-6102
Plano, TX 75075 Katherine Godby, Supv.
Founded: 1942. **Staff:** Prof 5. **Subjects:** Chemistry, economics and planning, electrical engineering, electronics, civil and mechanical engineering, geology, geophysics, mathematics, petroleum exploration and production, paleontology, oceanography, remote sensing in earth sciences, synthetic fuels. **Holdings:** 12,000 books; 10,000 bound periodical volumes; 22,000 publications. **Subscriptions:** 450 journals and other serials. **Services:** Center not open to the public. **Automated Operations:** Computerized cataloging, acquisitions, circulation, and serials. **Computerized Information Services:** DIALOG Information Services, PFDS Online, NLM, STN International, OCLC, RLIN, NEXIS, LEXIS. **Remarks:** FAX: (214)754-6502. **Formerly:** Atlantic-Richfield Company - ARCO Oil & Gas Company - Research & Technical Services. **Staff:** Janis Turner; Kevin Weissman; Rosalyn Wilhelm; Polly Carper.

Atlantic-Richfield Company - ARCO Oil & Gas Company
See: **Atlantic-Richfield Company** (1260)

★1261★
Atlantic-Richfield Company - Information Resource Center (Bus-Fin, Energy)
515 S. Flower St.
Box 2679, Terminal Annex — Phone: (213)486-2400
Los Angeles, CA 90051 — Felicia Bagby
Founded: 1972. **Staff:** Prof 5. **Subjects:** Economics, petroleum and petroleum refining, management, foreign affairs. **Holdings:** 7700 books; 1500 bound periodical volumes; 500 unbound periodicals; 760 annual reports; 200 reels of microfilm of newspapers and journals; microfiche; databases of API Refining literature and patents and Tulsa University Petroleum Abstracts. **Subscriptions:** 300 journals and other serials; 20 newspapers. **Services:** Interlibrary loan; copying (both limited); library open to the public by appointment. **Automated Operations:** Computerized cataloging and acquisitions. **Computerized Information Services:** DIALOG Information Services, Dow Jones News/Retrieval, Mead Data Central, Reuters; internal database. **Networks/Consortia:** Member of CLASS. **Publications:** Special bibliographies. **Special Catalogs:** Library Administrative System (COM catalog), monthly; joint journal holdings list. **Remarks:** FAX: (213)486-1472. **Staff:** F.A. Bowman, Cons.; L.A. Cainglet, Info.Spec.; S.C. Satin, Sr.Info.Spec.; Marilyn Ayala, Info.Res.Spec.

★1262★
Atlantic-Richfield Company - Photography Collection (Aud-Vis, Energy)
515 S. Flower St.
C Level — Phone: (213)486-3386
Los Angeles, CA 90071 — Stephen Szymanski
Founded: 1953. **Staff:** 1. **Subjects:** Oil and gas-petroleum industry, coal mining. **Special Collections:** ARCO Video Production. **Holdings:** Original negatives and transparencies. **Services:** Contents of collection available to publications, the government, and qualifying individuals; use is subject to ARCO approval; lab fees must be paid by requestor. **Automated Operations:** Computerized cataloging. **Computerized Information Services:** PMIS (Photographic Management Information System; internal database). **Remarks:** FAX: (213)486-1986. **Staff:** David Allen Moss.

Atlantic and St. Lawrence Railroad Archives
See: **Bowdoin College - Library - Special Collections** (2033)

★1263★
Atlantic Salmon Federation - J. Kenneth Stallman Memorial Library (Biol Sci)
P.O. Box 429 — Phone: (506)529-4581
St. Andrews, NB, Canada E0G 2X0 — Carol A. James
Founded: 1976. **Staff:** 1. **Subjects:** Atlantic salmon - general information, genetic and aquacultural research, restoration, education, international programs; angling; conservation. **Special Collections:** Rare fishing books and gear; Atlantic Salmon Federation Special Publications Series; Atlantic Salmon Federation (ASF) and Salmon Genetics Research Program (SGRP) technical reports series; International Council for the Exploration of the Sea/International Commission for the Northwest Atlantic Fisheries (ICES/ICNAF) Anadromous/Catadromous Fish Committee Reports. **Holdings:** Books; periodical volumes; reprints; technical, research, statistical, and government reports; films; slides. **Subscriptions:** 15 journals and other serials. **Services:** Copying; library open to the public with restrictions. **Publications:** ASF Research Reports, annual. **Remarks:** FAX: (506)529-4438.

★1264★
Atlantic School of Theology - Library (Rel-Phil)
640 Francklyn St. — Phone: (902)423-7986
Halifax, NS, Canada B3H 3B5 — Alice W. Harrison, Hd.Libn.
Founded: 1971. **Staff:** Prof 3; Other 3. **Subjects:** Theology and allied subjects. **Special Collections:** Rare books; church history; missions; hymnody. **Holdings:** 68,620 books; 3015 bound periodical volumes; 396 dissertations in theology; 537 phonograph records; 622 cassettes; 291 audiotapes; 101 videotapes; 144 reels of microfilm; 14 microfiche. **Subscriptions:** 384 journals and other serials. **Services:** Interlibrary loan; library open to students and faculty of local universities and clergy of the Atlantic provinces. **Computerized Information Services:** Envoy 100 (electronic mail service). **Publications:** Bibliographies (pamphlet form). **Remarks:** FAX: (902)492-4048. Electronic mail address(es): NSHPH.ILL (Envoy 100). **Staff:** Lloyd J. Melanson, Tech.Serv.Libn.; Norma Gilchrist-Dobson, Ref.Libn.

AtlantiCare Medical Center
See: **Union Hospital** (16654)

Atlas Library
See: **ICI Americas Inc.** (7641)

★1265★
Atlas Powder Company - Research & Development Laboratory - Library (Sci-Engr)
P.O. Box 577 — Phone: (717)386-4121
Tamaqua, PA 18252-0577 — Sylvia A. Harker, Adm.Asst.
Staff: 1. **Subjects:** Explosives, mining, chemistry, chemical engineering, pharmaceuticals, computers, self-improvement. **Holdings:** 2500 books; 12 file drawers of U.S. and foreign patents; 20 file drawers of Bureau of Mines reports; 3 file drawers of Department of Defense - Index of Federal Specifications and Standards. **Subscriptions:** 66 journals and other serials. **Services:** Interlibrary loan; library not open to the public. **Computerized Information Services:** DIALOG Information Services; TelTech (internal database). **Publications:** Library Information News. **Remarks:** FAX: (717)386-5751.

★1266★
Atlas Traffic Consultants - Tariff Department Library (Trans, Bus-Fin)
18-42 College Point Blvd. — Phone: (718)461-0556
Flushing, NY 11356 — Diana Lee, Tariff Libn.
Staff: Prof 1. **Subjects:** Freight tariffs. **Special Collections:** Interstate Commerce Commission reports. **Holdings:** 10,000 books. **Services:** Library not open to the public. **Remarks:** FAX: (718)461-0657.

★1267★
Atlas Travel, Inc. - Library (Rec)
3411 Montrose — Phone: (713)527-4555
Houston, TX 77006 — Tracy Gutch, Libn.
Staff: Prof 1. **Subjects:** Travel, tourism, geography. **Special Collections:** Travel and tour publications. **Holdings:** 294 books; maps; brochures. **Subscriptions:** 54 journals and other serials. **Services:** Copying; SDI; library not open to the public. **Publications:** Atlas Travel Notes. **Special Indexes:** Special Events Index.

★1268★
Atmaniketan Ashram - Library (Rel-Phil)
1291 Weber St. — Phone: (714)629-8255
Pomona, CA 91768-2215 — Michael Zucker, Libn.
Founded: 1973. **Staff:** Prof 1; Other 3. **Subjects:** Sri Aurobindo, Indian spirituality, Vedanta, Sanskrit studies, Vedic-Upanishadic texts, education. **Special Collections:** Sri Aurobindo Birth Centenary Library (30 volumes); Collected Works of the Mother (15 volumes); Mahabharata (12 volume English translation); Cultural Heritage of India (5 volume set); Sacred Books of the East (50 volume set); Rigveda Samhita (6 volume set). **Holdings:** 2000 books; 60 bound periodical volumes; 100 papers and reprints; complete back issue sets of annual, monthly, and quarterly journals of Sri Aurobindo Ashram. **Services:** Library open to the public by appointment. **Publications:** Purna Yoga, biennial. **Remarks:** FAX: (714)623-9877. **Also Known As:** Auromere.

Atmospheric Sciences Model Division Library
See: **U.S. Environmental Protection Agency** (17457)

★1269★
ATOCHEM North America - Organic Peroxides Division - Research Library (Sci-Engr)
1740 Military Rd.
P.O. Box 1048 — Phone: (716)877-1740
Buffalo, NY 14240 — L. Yvonne Curry, Tech.Libn.
Founded: 1932. **Staff:** Prof 1; Other 1. **Subjects:** Peroxides, organic chemistry, free radicals, chemical safety, polymerization, toxicology. **Holdings:** 6000 monographs; 2500 bound periodical volumes; 15 VF drawers of peroxide literature. **Subscriptions:** 180 journals and other serials. **Services:** Interlibrary loan (fee); copying; library open to the public with restrictions. **Computerized Information Services:** DIALOG Information Services, STN International, Technical Database Services, Inc. **Networks/Consortia:** Member of Western New York Library Resources Council (WNYLRC). **Special Catalogs:** Peroxides, polymerization, azo compounds catalog (card). **Remarks:** FAX: (716)877-3959. **Staff:** Sue Gimbarski, Asst.Tech.Libn.

★1270★
ATOCHEM North America - Research Library (Sci-Engr)
5101 W. 21st St. Phone: (918)583-0851
Tulsa, OK 74107 Dr. Charles Lindahl, Gen.Mgr.
Staff: 1. **Subjects:** Chemistry - general, fluorine, inorganic; chemicals for dental application. **Holdings:** 500 books; 300 bound periodical volumes; 50 volumes of unbound journals. **Subscriptions:** 24 journals and other serials. **Services:** Library not open to the public.

★1271★
ATOCHEM North America - Technical & Business Information Center (Sci-Engr)
900 1st Ave.
P.O. Box 1536 Phone: (215)337-6500
King of Prussia, PA 19406 Louis P. Torre, Ph.D., Dir.
Founded: 1916. **Staff:** Prof 5; Other 6. **Subjects:** Chemistry, ceramics, plastics, organometallic chemistry, glass coatings, tin chemistry, electroplating, electronic chemicals, pesticides, marine anti-fouling paints, fine chemicals, reagents. **Special Collections:** Organotin Literature. **Holdings:** 12,000 books; 11,500 bound periodical volumes; 7000 technical reports and pamphlets; 145,000 patents; 16,000 photocopies; 150 theses; microfilm. **Subscriptions:** 450 journals and other serials. **Services:** Interlibrary loan; center not open to the public. **Computerized Information Services:** DIALOG Information Services, STN International, ORBIT Search Service, BRS Information Technologies, PFDS Online, Questel, Mead Data Central, Dow Jones News/Retrieval, Chemical Information Systems, Inc. (CIS), Molecular Design Ltd. MACCS. **Networks/Consortia:** Member of Research Libraries Information Network (RLIN). **Publications:** Monthly Accessions List; Monthly List of Online Searches. **Special Indexes:** Organotin Index. **Remarks:** FAX: (201)707-4928. **Formerly:** Located in Somerville, NJ. **Staff:** Dorothy I. Eska, Tech. Indexing Supv.; John Hack, Sr.Lit.Chem.; Juliette O. Arnheim, Sr.Lit.Chem.; Barbara Cavallo, Lib.Supv.; John Wallmark, Tech.Info.Sys.Spec.; Cathy Ryan, Lit.Chem.

ATOCHEM North America Inc.
See: **ELF ATOCHEM North America Inc.** (5296)

Atomic Collision Cross Section Data Center
See: **University of Colorado--Boulder - Joint Institute for Laboratory Astrophysics (JILA) - Atomic Collision Cross Section Data Center** (18500)

Atomic Energy Authority - AEA Technology - Culham/Harwell Library
See: **Great Britain - Atomic Energy Authority - AEA Technology - Culham/Harwell Library** (6663)

Atomic Energy Commission (of France)
See: **France - Atomic Energy Commission - Saclay Research Center - MIST** (6060)

★1272★
Atomic Energy Control Board - Library (Sci-Engr, Energy)
PO Box 1046, Sta. B Phone: (613)995-1359
Ottawa, ON, Canada K1P 5S9 Jane Naisbitt
Founded: 1976. **Staff:** Prof 2; Other 3. **Subjects:** Nuclear science, radiation dosimetry, reactors, safeguards, regulatory bodies. **Special Collections:** Proprietary collection. **Holdings:** 35,000 books; 500 NTIS microfiche; complete set of Atomic Energy of Canada, Ltd. reports; complete INIS ATOMINDEX. **Subscriptions:** 220 journals and other serials; 7 newspapers. **Services:** Interlibrary loan; copying; SDI; library open to the public with restrictions. **Automated Operations:** Computerized cataloging and circulation. **Computerized Information Services:** MINISIS, CAN/OLE, DIALOG Information Services, DOBIS; CD-ROMs; Envoy 100 (electronic mail service). **Publications:** Accessions List, biweekly - available upon request; AECB Library Serials List, annual. **Remarks:** FAX: (613)995-5086. Telex: 053-3771. **Staff:** Frank Rautenkranz, Sys./Coll.Dev.; Mary Didyk, Proprietary Coll.

★1273★
Atomic Energy Corporation of South Africa Limited - AEC Library and Information Services (Energy)
P.O. Box 582 Phone: 12 3165211
Pretoria 0001, Republic of South Africa Mr. C.N. van der Merwe, Mgr.
Founded: 1960. **Staff:** Prof 11; Other 14. **Subjects:** Nuclear-related physical sciences - general, chemistry, materials sciences, earth sciences, life sciences, isotopes, isotope and radiation applications, engineering and technology; nuclear energy - general, economics, law, documentation, safeguards, waste disposal, inspection. **Holdings:** 71,228 books; 529,760 reports; 40,982 bound periodical volumes. **Subscriptions:** 1100 journals and other serials. **Services:** Interlibrary loan; SDI; current awareness; services available to the South African nuclear community. **Computerized Information Services:** International Nuclear Information System (INIS), DIALOG Information Services, STN International. **Remarks:** FAX: 12 3165709. Telex: 3 22948 SA. **Staff:** Ms. M.J.S. Scheepers; Mr. J.A. Kok; Ms. A.J. Pretorius; Mrs. M. van der Merwe; Mrs. I. Bartmann; Ms. H. Finger; Mrs. A. Foster; Mrs. F. van Zyl; Mrs. A. Wortmann; Mr. N.J. de Jong.

Atomic Energy Levels Data Center
See: **U.S. Natl. Institute of Standards and Technology** (17613)

Atonement Seminary Library
See: **Franciscan Friars of the Atonement** (6073)

★1274★
Jozsef Attila Tudomanygeyetem Angol Tanszek - Konyvtara (Hum)
Egyetem u 2 Phone: 62 21111
H-6701 Szeged, Hungary Eva Gazdag
Subjects: Linguistics, history, theory and criticism, teaching, stylistics. **Holdings:** Figures not available. **Subscriptions:** 9 journals and other serials. **Services:** Interlibrary loan. **Computerized Information Services:** Internal database; BITNET (electronic mail service). **Remarks:** FAX: 62 21843. Electronic mail address(es): H822ROZ@ELLA.HU (BITNET).

Atwater Library
See: **Mechanics' Institute of Montreal** (9975)

Margaret Atwood Collection
See: **University of Western Ontario** (19555)

Will Aubrey Memorial Library
See: **San Francisco Press Club** (14738)

Auburn Automotive Heritage, Inc. - Auburn-Cord-Duesenberg Museum
See: **Auburn-Cord-Duesenberg Museum** (1276)

★1275★
Auburn-Cord-Duesenberg Club - Library (Rec)
1600 S. Wayne St.
P.O. Box 271 Phone: (219)925-1444
Auburn, IN 46706 Sandy Kern, Libn.
Founded: 1982. **Subjects:** Automotive manufacturing and history. **Special Collections:** Auburn Automobile Company; Lycoming Manufacturing Company; Duesenberg, Inc.; Cord Corporation. **Holdings:** Periodicals; photographs; catalogs. **Services:** Copying; library open to the public by appointment. **Computerized Information Services:** Paradox (internal database).

★1276★
Auburn-Cord-Duesenberg Museum - Automotive Archives (Trans)
1600 S. Wayne St.
P.O. Box 271 Phone: (219)925-1444
Auburn, IN 46706 Gregg Buttermore, Archv.
Founded: 1971. **Staff:** Prof 1; Other 1. **Subjects:** Automotive literature, transportation. **Special Collections:** Auburn, Cord, and Duesenberg automobiles; Auburn, Indiana automobile manufacturers. **Holdings:** 500 books; 10,000 pamphlets; 3400 photographs; 3900 magazines; 450 blueprints; 10 films. **Subscriptions:** 35 journals and other serials. **Services:** Copying; collection open to the public by appointment or by mail request. **Computerized Information Services:** Paradox (internal database). **Remarks:** FAX: (219)925-6266. Maintained by Auburn Automotive Heritage, Inc.

★1277★
Auburn Memorial Hospital - Library/Resource Center (Med)
5-19 Lansing St. Phone: (315)255-7231
Auburn, NY 13021 Anne Costello Tomlin, Libn.
Founded: 1951. **Staff:** 1. **Subjects:** Medicine, nursing, and allied health sciences. **Special Collections:** Hospital archives (15 drawers). **Holdings:** 1850 books; 3500 bound periodical volumes. **Subscriptions:** 167 journals and other serials. **Services:** Interlibrary loan; copying; reference service; media management; library open to the public by appointment or referral. **Computerized Information Services:** MEDLARS. **Networks/Consortia:** Member of South Central Research Library Council (SCRLC). **Special Catalogs:** Printed list of journals currently received. **Remarks:** FAX: (315)255-7012.

★1278★
Auburn University - Architecture Library (Plan, Art)
Dudley Hall Phone: (205)844-1752
Auburn University, AL 36849-5606 Vinson E. McKenzie, Hd.
Founded: 1952. **Staff:** Prof 1; Other 4. **Subjects:** Architecture, landscape architecture, community planning, building science, industrial design, interior design. **Special Collections:** African-American Architects. **Holdings:** 30,285 bound volumes; 35,331 slides. **Subscriptions:** 191 journals and other serials. **Services:** Interlibrary loan; copying; library open to the public for reference use only. **Automated Operations:** Computerized cataloging, acquisitions, serials, and circulation. **Computerized Information Services:** OCLC, DIALOG Information Services, PFDS Online, BRS Information Technologies, U.S. Patent Classification System, NASA/RECON, WILSONLINE, RLIN, National Ground Water Information Center Data Base. **Networks/Consortia:** Member of SOLINET, Network of Alabama Academic Libraries (NAAL). **Publications:** African-American Architects and Builders: A Historical Overview.

★1279★
Auburn University - Archives (Soc Sci)
Ralph B. Draughon Library Phone: (205)844-1705
Auburn University, AL 36849-5606 Dr. Dwayne Cox, Univ.Archv.
Founded: 1964. **Staff:** Prof 3; Other 4. **Subjects:** Politics, agriculture, religion, Civil War, southern history, architecture, Auburn University history. **Special Collections:** Congressman George Andrews papers (100 linear feet); Dr. George Petrie papers (36 linear feet); Congressman Bill Nichols papers (459 linear feet); Alabama League of Women Voters records (79 linear feet); Fred Allison papers (15 linear feet); James H. Lane papers (4 linear feet); Alabama Farm Bureau Federation records (71 linear feet); Alabama Republican Party records (54 linear feet); Senator Jeremiah Denton papers (285 linear feet). **Holdings:** 2000 pamphlets; 900 manuscript and record groups; 6900 tape recordings; 112 reels of microfilm; 152,445 photographs; 3151 films and videotapes. **Services:** Copying; archives open to the public. **Computerized Information Services:** OCLC. **Publications:** Descriptive brochure; selected subject guides to holdings. **Staff:** David J. Rosenblatt, Asst.Archv.; Kayla Barrett, Asst.Archv.; Beveley S. Powers, Ref.Asst.

★1280★
Auburn University - Center for Governmental Services - Resource Center (Soc Sci, Bus-Fin)
2232 Haley Center Phone: (205)844-4782
Auburn University, AL 36849-5225 Sharon Sharp, Adm.Asst.
Staff: 3. **Subjects:** Public administration and finance; government - local, state, federal; personnel management; legislation. **Holdings:** 2613 books. **Subscriptions:** 145 journals and other serials. **Services:** Copying; center open to public officials. **Publications:** Public Sector (newsletter), quarterly - free upon request; list of additional publications - free upon request. **Remarks:** Alternate telephone number(s): 844-1919. FAX: (205)844-1919.

★1281★
Auburn University - Department of Special Collections (Hist)
Ralph B. Draughon Library Phone: (205)844-1700
Auburn University, AL 36849-5606 Gene Geiger, Spec.Coll.Libn.
Founded: 1963. **Staff:** Prof 1; Other 3. **Subjects:** Alabama, history, genealogy. **Special Collections:** Treasure Collection (rare books); Petrie Memorial Collection (history and religion); genealogy; Streit Collection (sports); Alabama Collection; Dobbins Collections (Alabamiana); Oxmoor House Collection; Special Collection of semi-rare and fragile books; theses and dissertations; maps (128,134). **Holdings:** 90,468 volumes. **Subscriptions:** 697 journals and other serials. **Services:** Interlibrary loan; copying; department open to the public. **Automated Operations:** Computerized cataloging, acquisitions, and serials. **Computerized Information Services:** DIALOG Information Services, PFDS Online, BRS Information Technologies, OCLC, WILSONLINE. **Networks/Consortia:** Member of SOLINET, Network of Alabama Academic Libraries (NAAL). **Remarks:** FAX: (205)844-1753.

★1282★
Auburn University - International Center for Aquaculture - Library (Biol Sci)
Swingle Hall Phone: (205)844-4786
Auburn University, AL 36849 Dr. B.L. Duncan, Dir.
Staff: Prof 1; Other 1. **Subjects:** Aquaculture in fresh, brackish, and marine water; aquatic plants management; nutrition and feeds; parasites and disease; limnology; water quality and management for aquaculture; international development for fisheries and aquaculture. **Holdings:** 2500 books; annual reports of the Fisheries Resources Unit, 1936 to present; 10,000 slides and pictures; 250 dissertations; 550 theses. **Services:** Copying; library open to the public with supervision of librarian. **Publications:** Abstracts, Articles and Reprints from the International Center for Aquacultures; newsletter, quarterly; list of other publications - available upon request. **Remarks:** FAX: (205)844-9208. Telex: 5106 002392.

★1283★
Auburn University - Learning Resources Center (Aud-Vis, Educ)
3402 Haley Center Phone: (205)844-4306
Auburn University, AL 36830 Dr. C.D. Wright, Dir.
Staff: Prof 7; Other 10. **Subjects:** Education. **Holdings:** 19,500 books; 875 dissertations; 783 phonograph records; 3675 filmstrips; 602 sound filmstrips; 210 kits; 96 games; 42 maps; 2 models; 187 pictures; 2020 motion pictures; 323 audiotapes; 136 audio cassettes; 130 video recordings; 226 slides; 227 transparencies; 319 computer software programs. **Subscriptions:** 80 journals and other serials. **Services:** Copying; center open to the public for reference use only. **Automated Operations:** Computerized circulation. **Computerized Information Services:** Internal database. **Special Catalogs:** Title and subject lists of films (book). **Staff:** Rowena Boland, Coord. LRC Serv. & Mgr., Micro-Ctr.

★1284★
Auburn University - Veterinary Medical Library (Med)
Veterinary Medical Complex
Greene Hall Phone: (205)844-1749
Auburn University, AL 36849 Tamera P. Lee, Hd.
Founded: 1971. **Staff:** Prof 1; Other 3. **Subjects:** Veterinary medicine. **Holdings:** 33,000 volumes. **Subscriptions:** 600 journals and other serials. **Services:** Interlibrary loan; copying; library open to the public for reference use only. **Automated Operations:** Computerized cataloging, acquisitions, serials, and circulation. **Computerized Information Services:** DIALOG Information Services, PFDS Online, BRS Information Technologies, MEDLINE, STN International; internal database; CD-ROM (MEDLINE); electronic mail service. Performs searches on fee basis. **Networks/Consortia:** Member of SOLINET, Network of Alabama Academic Libraries (NAAL). **Publications:** Reference database guides. **Remarks:** FAX: (205)844-1753. Telex: ATTNET 221-1750.

★1285★
Auburn University - Water Resources Research Institute (WRRI) - Information Center (Env-Cons)
202 Hargis Hall Phone: (205)844-5075
Auburn University, AL 36849-5124 Prof. Joseph F. Judkins, Dir.
Founded: 1965. **Staff:** 3. **Subjects:** All aspects of water resources. **Holdings:** Figures not available. **Services:** Center open to the public on limited basis. **Publications:** Technical bulletins; Proceedings (newsletter), quarterly; annual report. **Remarks:** FAX: (205)844-6414.

★1286★
(Auckland) American Center - USIS Library (Educ)
29 Shortland St. Phone: 9 779735
Auckland, New Zealand Elspeth A. Barclay, Supv.Libn.
Founded: 1970. **Staff:** 2. **Subjects:** American political system, American foreign policy, business, labor, media. **Special Collections:** Student advising materials. **Holdings:** 1000 books; videotapes. **Subscriptions:** 90 journals and other serials; 6 newspapers. **Services:** Interlibrary loan; copying; SDI; library open to the public. **Computerized Information Services:** Internal database. **Remarks:** Maintained or supported by the U.S. Information Agency. Focus is on materials that will assist peoples outside the United States to learn about the United States, its people, history, culture, political processes, and social milieux. FAX: 9 3660870.

★ 1287 ★
Auckland City Council - Auckland Public Library - Commerce, Science, and Technology Library (Bus-Fin)
P.O. Box 4138 Phone: 9 770 209
Auckland, New Zealand Jan Thompson, City Libn.
Subjects: New Zealand - business, statistics, genealogy. **Special Collections:** New Zealand company reports; Sir George Grey Rare Books Collection; Maori manuscripts; documents (UN, EC, FAO). **Holdings:** Figures not available. **Services:** Interlibrary loan; copying; library open to the public. **Computerized Information Services:** DIALOG Information Services, Reuters, Kiwinet, Baycorp, NZBN. Performs searches on fee basis. Contact Person: Marion Saunders, Commerce, Sci. & Tech.Libn. **Remarks:** FAX: 9 3077741.

★ 1288 ★
Audio-Visual Resource Library (Aud-Vis)
The Gateson House
3725 Chestnut St. Phone: (215)387-6335
Philadelphia, PA 19104 Ann R. Snyder, Mgr.
Founded: 1965. **Staff:** Prof 1; Other 5. **Subjects:** Christian education, ethics, social concerns. **Holdings:** 3000 filmstrips; 500 videotapes; 500 sound recordings; 1000 audio cassettes. **Subscriptions:** 5 journals and other serials. **Services:** Copying; library open to the public on fee basis. **Publications:** More Than Enough (newsletter). **Special Catalogs:** Catalog of Video Resources. **Remarks:** Library is maintained by the Episcopal Diocese of Pennsylvania, the Episcopal Diocese of New Jersey, the United Church of Christ Southeast Conference, and the Philadelphia Baptists. **Formerly:** St. Faith Episcopal Church - Audio-Visual Resource Library.

★ 1289 ★
Audrain County Historical Society - Graceland Library/American Saddle Horse Museum - Library (Hist)
501 South Muldrow Phone: (314)581-3910
Mexico, MO 65265 Clara Kaiser, Libn./Geneal.
Subjects: County history, saddle horses. **Holdings:** 500 books; magazines; newspapers; breeder manuals; genealogical records; cemetery records. **Services:** Copying; library open to the public for reference use only on a limited schedule.

★ 1290 ★
Audubon Naturalist Society - Library (Biol Sci)
8940 Jones Mill Rd. Phone: (301)652-9188
Chevy Chase, MD 20815 Ken Nicholls, Dir.
Subjects: Ornithology, natural history, environmental conservation, ecology. **Holdings:** 3000 books; 50 bound periodical volumes; 200 monographs, 4 VF drawers of pamphlets. **Formerly:** Audubon Naturalist Society of the Central Atlantic States.

★ 1291 ★
Audubon Society of Rhode Island - Harry S. Hathaway Library of Natural History and Conservation (Env-Cons)
12 Sanderson Rd. Phone: (401)231-6444
Smithfield, RI 02917-2606 Eugenia Marks, Dir., Issues/Pubns.
Founded: 1950. **Subjects:** Animals, plants, geology of the region and state; environmental problems and management; ecology. **Special Collections:** Complete Elephant Folio (Audubon's Mammals and other old books on birds and animals); Elizabeth Dicken's Journals. **Holdings:** 1000 books; 200 unbound periodical volumes; 300 pamphlets. **Subscriptions:** 25 journals and other serials. **Services:** Interlibrary loan; library open to the public.

Edward Daniel Auer Library
See: **Fort Wayne Museum of Art** (6018)

Auerbach Art Library
See: **Wadsworth Atheneum** (19931)

★ 1292 ★
Auglaize County Law Library (Law)
Court House
203 Perry St. Phone: (419)738-3124
Wapakoneta, OH 45895 Bridget Weller, Libn.
Founded: 1895. **Staff:** Prof 2. **Subjects:** Law. **Holdings:** 22,000 volumes; 1700 volumes on microfiche. **Services:** Copying; library open to the public at librarian's discretion. **Computerized Information Services:** LEXIS.

★ 1293 ★
Augsburg College - George Sverdrup Library and Media Center (Rel-Phil, Hum)
731 21st Ave., S. Phone: (612)330-1017
Minneapolis, MN 55454 Elaine R. Cline, Dir.
Founded: 1869. **Staff:** Prof 6.5; Other 12. **Subjects:** Theology, education, American and English literature, urban studies. **Special Collections:** Manuscript collection of George Sverdrup and Sven Oftedal; Meridel LeSueur Collection; Scandinavian music. **Holdings:** 156,325 books; 15,500 bound periodical volumes; 9581 phonograph records, scores, tapes, films, slide sets, filmstrips; college archives; theses in theology. **Subscriptions:** 833 journals and other serials; 21 newspapers. **Services:** Interlibrary loan; copying; library open to the public with deposit. **Automated Operations:** Computerized public access catalog and cataloging. **Computerized Information Services:** DataTimes, DIALOG Information Services, OCLC; InterNet (electronic mail service). **Networks/Consortia:** Member of Cooperating Libraries in Consortium (CLIC), MINITEX Library Information Network. **Remarks:** FAX: (612)330-1649. Electronic mail address(es): library@augsburg.edu (InterNet). **Staff:** Boyd Koehler, Circ. & B.I. Libn.; Karen Mateer, Cat. & Automation Libn.; Grace K. Sulerud, Acq. & Ref.Libn.; Brian Hackney, AV Dir.; Maria Woroby, Ref. & Info.Serv.; Kathy Enger, Ref.Libn.; Della Shupe, Ref.Libn .

★ 1294 ★
Augusta Chronicle-Herald News - Library (Publ)
725 Broad St.
Box 1928 Phone: (404)724-0851
Augusta, GA 30913-1928 Rhoda Cato, Chf.Libn.
Staff: 3. **Subjects:** Newspaper reference topics. **Holdings:** 573 drawers of news clippings; 22 drawers of microfilm of newspapers, 1786 to present; 217 drawers of pictures. **Services:** Copying (limited); library open to the public with restrictions. **Remarks:** Published by Southeastern Newspapers Corporation.

★ 1295 ★
Augusta Technical Institute - Library (Sci-Engr, Info Sci)
3116 Deans Bridge Rd. Phone: (404)796-6900
Augusta, GA 30906 Dr. Robert W. Duttweiler, Lib.Dir.
Founded: 1971. **Staff:** Prof 2; Other 3. **Subjects:** Telecommunications, electronics, engineering, business. **Special Collections:** Women's Studies Collection. **Holdings:** 50,000 books; 5000 bound periodical volumes; government documents depository; industry standards. **Subscriptions:** 300 journals and other serials; 25 newspapers. **Services:** Interlibrary loan; copying; library open to the public. **Automated Operations:** Computerized serials. **Computerized Information Services:** DIALOG Information Services, WILSONLINE. **Networks/Consortia:** Member of Georgia Online Database (GOLD), SOLINET. **Special Indexes:** Index to serials; index to AV materials (both online). **Remarks:** FAX: (404)796-8810.

★ 1296 ★
Augustana College - Center for Western Studies (Hist, Rel-Phil)
P.O. Box 727 Phone: (605)336-4007
Sioux Falls, SD 57197 Arthur R. Huseboe, Exec.Dir.
Founded: 1970. **Staff:** 4. **Subjects:** Upper Great Plains history and literature, American literature, Plains Indians history, South Dakota history, Sioux Falls history. **Special Collections:** Episcopal Diocese of South Dakota Archives; United Church of Christ, South Dakota Conference Archives (including Stephen Riggs papers); Augustana College Archives; Goertz Germans from Russia Collection. **Holdings:** 30,000 books and bound periodical volumes; 1500 linear feet of manuscript, photograph, and artifact collections. **Subscriptions:** 10 journals. **Services:** Copying; Norwegian translation; center open to the public. **Automated Operations:** PALS. **Networks/Consortia:** Member of South Dakota Library Network (SDLN). **Publications:** Guide to Collections Relating to South Dakota Norwegian-Americans. **Special Catalogs:** Publications catalog; collections catalog - both available on request. **Staff:** Harry Thompson, Cur./Mng.Ed.; Dean Schueler, Dev.Dir.

★1297★
Augustana College - Library - Special Collections (Hum)
639 38th St. Phone: (309)794-7317
Rock Island, IL 61201 Judy Belan, Spec.Coll.Libn.
Founded: 1860. **Staff:** Prof 1; Other 1. **Special Collections:** Upper Mississippiana; English literature, 17th-19th centuries. **Holdings:** Figures not available. **Services:** Copying; collections open to the public for reference use only.

★1298★
Augustana Lutheran Church - Library (Rel-Phil)
5000 E. Alameda Ave. Phone: (303)388-4678
Denver, CO 80222 Ellen Swanson, Chm., Lib.Comm.
Founded: 1963. **Staff:** 4. **Subjects:** Religion. **Holdings:** 7500 books; phonograph records; 3 drawers of pamphlets, maps, charts; 20 cassettes. **Services:** Library open to members of Denver Lutheran churches.

★1299★
Augustana University College - Library - Scandinavian Collection (Area-Ethnic)
4901 46th Ave. Phone: (403)679-1144
Camrose, AB, Canada T4V 2R3 Asgeir Ingibergsson, Hd.Libn.
Special Collections: Scandinavian immigration history collection (books, letters, and memorabilia). **Services:** Interlibrary loan; copying; library open to the public with restrictions. **Publications:** List of periodicals. **Remarks:** FAX: (403)679-1129. **Formerly:** Camrose Lutheran University. **Staff:** Nancy Goebel, Rd.Serv.Libn.; Pat Day, Cat.; Berniece Sogge, Per.; Carol Wilcox, Acq.

Augustine Library
See: **St. Norbert Abbey** (14551)

Augustinerkloster - Bibliothek
See: **Augustinian Monastery - Library** (1302)

★1300★
Augustinian Historical Institute - Library (Rel-Phil)
Augustinian Room
301 Old Falvey
Villanova University Phone: (215)645-7590
Villanova, PA 19085 Rev. Joseph C. Schnaubelt, O.S.A. Dir.
Founded: 1972. **Staff:** Prof 2. **Subjects:** Theology, philosophy, missiology, biography. **Special Collections:** History of the Augustinian Order. **Holdings:** 4300 books; 1050 bound periodical volumes; 8 VF drawers of pamphlets, pictures, clippings; 255 reels of microfilm; 250 manuscripts; journals. **Subscriptions:** 31 journals and other serials. **Services:** Copying; library open to the public with approval of director.

★1301★
Augustinian Historical Institute - Library (Rel-Phil)
Pakenstraat 109
B-3030 Leuven, Belgium Phone: 16 22319
Founded: 1954. **Staff:** Prof 2. **Subjects:** Augustinus, Augustiniana (history of order). **Holdings:** 40,000 books; 160 bound periodical volumes; 400 microfiche. **Services:** Copying; library open to the public. **Automated Operations:** DOBIS-LIBIS. **Publications:** Augustiniana Review. **Remarks:** FAX: 16 292733. **Also Known As:** Orde der Augustijnen - Bibliotheek.

★1302★
Augustinian Monastery - Library (Rel-Phil)
Klostergasse 10
Postfach 1165 Phone: 7933 690
W-8732 Munnerstadt, Germany Rev. Leonard A. Lochner, Libn.
Founded: 1279. **Staff:** 2. **Subjects:** Theology, classical studies. **Holdings:** 80,000 books. **Services:** Library open to the public for reference use only. **Also Known As:** Augustinerkloster - Bibliothek.

Augustinian Philippines Library
See: **Estudio Teologico Agustiniano - Padres Agustinos - Biblioteca** (5465)

John Augustus Foundation - J2CP Information Services
See: **J2CP Information Services** (8299)

Aullwood Audubon Center and Farm
See: **National Audubon Society** (11084)

★1303★
Ault Foods Ltd. - Research & Development Library (Food-Bev)
P.O. Box 2185 Phone: (519)667-7709
London, ON, Canada N6A 4E5 Terry J. Maurice, V.P., R & D
Founded: 1968. **Staff:** 26. **Subjects:** Dairy science, food science, nutrition, microbiology, chemistry. **Holdings:** Figures not available. **Subscriptions:** 31 journals and other serials. **Services:** Interlibrary loan. **Remarks:** FAX: (519)667-7725.

★1304★
Aultman Hospital - Library (Med)
2600 6th St., S.W.
Canton, OH 44710 Phone: (216)452-9911
Founded: 1954. **Staff:** 4. **Subjects:** Medicine, nursing, education. **Special Collections:** History of medicine and nursing. **Holdings:** 8000 books; 7000 bound periodical volumes; 600 AV programs; 8 VF drawers of pamphlets and clippings. **Subscriptions:** 299 journals and other serials. **Services:** Interlibrary loan; library not open to the public. **Automated Operations:** Computerized cataloging and indexing. **Computerized Information Services:** BRS Information Technologies; CD-ROM (MEDLINE); DOCLINE (electronic mail service). **Networks/Consortia:** Member of NEOUCOM Council Associated Hospital Librarians, National Network of Libraries of Medicine - Greater Midwest Region. **Publications:** Journal Review for Nursing, monthly; Door to Knowledge, monthly - to school and hospital personnel. **Special Catalogs:** Medical Periodicals in Northeast Ohio (notebook). **Remarks:** FAX: (216)438-6356. **Formed by the merger of:** Aultman Hospital - Medical Library and Aultman Hospital - School of Nursing Library. **Staff:** Leah R. Lloyd, Libn.; Fay Rue.

Aultman Hospital - Medical Library
See: **Aultman Hospital - Library** (1304)

Aultman Hospital - School of Nursing Library
See: **Aultman Hospital - Library** (1304)

Auraria Higher Education Center Archives
See: **University of Colorado--Denver - Auraria Library - Archives and Special Collections** (18510)

Sri Aurobindo Birth Centenary Library
See: **Atmaniketan Ashram - Library** (1268)

Auromere
See: **Atmaniketan Ashram - Library** (1268)

Aurora Health Care Libraries - St. Luke's Medical Center
See: **St. Luke's Medical Center** (14487)

Aurora Health Care Libraries - Sinai Samaritan Medical Center - Hurwitz Memorial Library
See: **Sinai Samaritan Medical Center** (15187)

Aurora Health Care Libraries - Sinai Samaritan Medical Center - Jamron Health Science Library
See: **Sinai Samaritan Medical Center - Jamron Health Science Library** (15188)

★1305★
Aurora Historical Society - ScheideMantel House - Elbert Hubbard Home - Library and Museum (Hist)
5 S. Grove St. Phone: (716)652-3280
East Aurora, NY 14052 Genevieve M. Steffen, Cur.
Founded: 1962. **Staff:** 4. **Subjects:** Books authored by Elbert and Alice Hubbard, biographies of Elbert Hubbard, books by other authors printed and bound by Roycrofters. **Special Collections:** Furniture, copper, silver, and leather items manufactured by Roycrofters. **Holdings:** 1000 books; 100 bound periodical volumes; 2 VF drawers of clippings; 6 VF drawers of pictures; manuscripts; Hubbard magazines. **Services:** Copying; library open to the public by appointment.

★1306★
Aurora History Museum - Library (Hist)
15001 E. Alameda Dr. Phone: (303)340-2220
Aurora, CO 80012 Virginia Steele, Musm.Adm.
Founded: 1979. **Staff:** 6. **Subjects:** Aurora and Colorado history. **Special Collections:** Paul Beck Collection (local politics; 6 cubic feet); Hilbert Meyer (local politics; 18 cubic feet). **Holdings:** 1000 books; 10 AV programs; 10,000 photographs; 200 cubic feet of documents and manuscripts. **Subscriptions:** 20 journals and other serials; 4 newspapers. **Services:** Copying; library open to the public for reference use only. **Remarks:** FAX: (303)340-2214.

★1307★
Aurora Public Schools - Professional Library (Educ)
Highline Bldg. A
15751 E. 1st. Ave. Phone: (303)340-0854
Aurora, CO 80011 Bill Murray, Dir.
Founded: 1960. **Staff:** Prof 1; Other 2. **Subjects:** Education, psychology, management, communications. **Holdings:** 3500 books; 314 kits; 525 computer disks. **Subscriptions:** 302 journals and other serials. **Services:** Interlibrary loan; copying; disk duplication; library open to the public. **Automated Operations:** Computerized cataloging. **Computerized Information Services:** Online systems. **Networks/Consortia:** Member of Central Colorado Library System (CCLS). **Special Catalogs:** Aurora Public School, Film/Video Catalog, 1991-1995. **Remarks:** FAX: (303)340-0857.

★1308★
Aurora University - Jenks Memorial Collection of Adventual Materials (Rel-Phil)
347 S. Gladstone
Aurora, IL 60507 Phone: (708)844-5445
Founded: 1920. **Staff:** 1. **Subjects:** History and thought of the Millerite movement; development of early Adventist Churches; history and thought of the Advent Christian Church, 1860 to present; the Life and Advent Union, 1863-1964; Evangelical Adventists, 1855-1920; missionary development, 1800s to present. **Special Collections:** Papers of William Miller; correspondence of missionaries from various fields; Millerite periodicals and tracts; hymnody of the Millerite/Advent Christian people. **Holdings:** 1600 books; 600 bound periodical volumes; 4000 pamphlets and tracts; manuscript sermons; 300 research papers; 25 theses and dissertations; 140 reels of microfilm; 60 audiotapes; 7 linear feet of diaries and scrapbooks; 21 prophetic charts; manuscripts and correspondence of leaders and institutions of the Advent Christian Church; 22 linear feet of materials of the American Advent Mission Society and Woman's Home; Foreign Mission Society; 12 linear feet of records of defunct churches, conferences, and societies; 5 linear feet of records of Western Advent Christian Publication Association; 10 linear feet of photographs. **Subscriptions:** 17 journals and other serials. **Services:** Interlibrary loan; copying (both limited); library open to the public upon application and advance notice. **Automated Operations:** Computerized cataloging and circulation. **Computerized Information Services:** OCLC. **Networks/Consortia:** Member of LIBRAS Inc., DuPage Library System, ILLINET. **Remarks:** FAX: (708)892-9286.

Aussenpolitische Bibliothek
See: **Austria - Ministry of Foreign Affairs - Library** (1353)

★1309★
Jane Austen Society of North America - Archives (Hum)
4169 Lions Ave. Phone: (604)988-0479
North Vancouver, BC, Canada V7R 3S2 Eileen Sutherland, Pres.
Founded: 1979. **Subjects:** Jane Austen criticism and biography, Austeniana. **Special Collections:** Periodicals; rare critical information. **Holdings:** 1000 books; periodical articles; recordings; tapes; slides; postcards; memorabilia; dramatizations. **Services:** Archives open to the public through correspondence.

★1310★
Austin American-Statesman - Library (Publ)
Box 670 Phone: (512)445-3676
Austin, TX 78767 Peggy Itzen, Dir., Info.Serv.
Founded: 1975. **Staff:** Prof 2; Other 6. **Subjects:** Newspaper reference topics. **Holdings:** 700 books; 2174 reels of microfilm; 49,000 clipping files; 75,000 photographs; 34,000 sports and byline files. **Subscriptions:** 13 journals and other serials. **Services:** Library not open to the public; will provide assistance to media libraries on a fee basis. **Computerized Information Services:** DataTimes; DataTimes (electronic mail service). **Special Indexes:** Index to Austin American-Statesman (card). **Remarks:** FAX: (512)445-3679. Electronic mail address(es): AUSPI (DataTimes). **Staff:** Karen Anderson, Libn.; Betty Hudman, Night Supv.; Tracy Duncan, Photo.Libn.

Austin City Parks and Recreation Department - Elisabet Ney Museum and Archives
See: **Elisabet Ney Museum and Archives** (11791)

★1311★
Austin College - Abell Library - Special Collections (Hist)
900 N. Grand Phone: (903)813-2556
Sherman, TX 75091 Susan Myers, Dir.
Founded: 1849. **Staff:** 10. **Holdings:** Berzunza Collection (Alexander the Great; 825 volumes). **Subscriptions:** 913 journals and other serials; 21 newspapers. **Services:** Collection open to the public for reference use only. **Automated Operations:** Computerized cataloging, acquisitions, serials, and ILL. **Computerized Information Services:** DIALOG Information Services, WILSONLINE, OCLC. **Networks/Consortia:** Member of AMIGOS Bibliographic Council, Inc., Association for Higher Education of North Texas (AHE). **Remarks:** Alternate telephone number(s): 813-2236 (circulation). FAX: (903)813-3199. **Staff:** Cathy Hartman; Dayna Williams-Capone; John West.

★1312★
Austin Community College - Health Sciences Collection (Med)
1020 Grove Blvd. Phone: (512)389-4003
Austin, TX 78741 Margaret Peloquin, Hd.Libn.
Staff: Prof 5; Other 7. **Subjects:** Medicine, surgery, nursing, public health, hospitals. **Special Collections:** History of nursing and nursing education (220 volumes). **Holdings:** 8000 books; 1100 AV programs; 8 VF drawers of reprints, pamphlets, medical care materials. **Subscriptions:** 350 journals and other serials. **Services:** Copying; collection open to the public with restrictions. **Computerized Information Services:** NLM, DIALOG Information Services, BRS Information Technologies. **Remarks:** FAX: (512)389-4002.

★1313★
The Austin Company - Library (Plan)
3650 Mayfield Rd. Phone: (216)291-6636
Cleveland, OH 44121 Helen M. Makela, Info.Rsrcs.Coord.
Founded: 1942. **Staff:** Prof 1. **Subjects:** Architecture, engineering, building materials, construction, business. **Holdings:** 2000 books; 500 bound periodical volumes. **Subscriptions:** 153 journals and other serials. **Services:** Interlibrary loan; library not open to the public. **Automated Operations:** Computerized cataloging. **Computerized Information Services:** DIALOG Information Services; STN International. **Networks/Consortia:** Member of Cleveland Area Metropolitan Library System (CAMLS). **Publications:** Annotated acquisitions list, quarterly; in-house exchange of technical information and ideas, quarterly. **Remarks:** FAX: (216)291-6684 (Attn: H. Makela).

Ethel L. Austin Library
See: **South Congregational Church** (15414)

★1314★
Austin Presbyterian Theological Seminary - Stitt Library (Rel-Phil)
106 W. 27th St. Phone: (512)472-6736
Austin, TX 78705 Dr. Valerie R. Hotchkiss, Dir.
Founded: 1902. **Staff:** Prof 2; Other 2. **Subjects:** Bible, theology, Christianity, Presbyterianism, biblical archeology, patristics. **Special Collections:** O.K. Rumble Communion Token Collection. **Holdings:** 136,801 books; 9300 bound periodical volumes; microfilm. **Subscriptions:** 489 journals and other serials. **Services:** Interlibrary loan; copying; library open to the public with restrictions. **Automated Operations:** Computerized public access catalog, acquisitions, circulation, and cataloging. **Computerized Information Services:** BRS Information Technologies, OCLC; CD-ROM (Religion Index). **Remarks:** FAX: (512)479-0738. **Staff:** Helen Kennedy.

★1315★
Austin Public Library - Austin History Center (Hist)
P.O. Box 2287 Phone: (512)499-7480
Austin, TX 78768 Biruta Celmins Kearl, Archv.
Founded: 1955. **Staff:** Prof 10; Other 17. **Subjects:** Local and county history and demographics, city and county government, Austin architecture, Austin music. **Special Collections:** O. Henry Collection; Pease Papers (Texas Governor, 1853-1857); Jane McCallum Papers; architecural drawings collection. **Holdings:** 13,000 books; 2000 linear feet of manuscripts and archives; 1000 maps; 90,000 printed items; 100,000 photographic images; 100,000 clippings; 11,000 slides; 800 tape recordings; 1000 videotapes; 1000 inactive periodical titles; county and municipal documents. **Subscriptions:** 150 journals and other serials; 30 newspapers. **Services:** Copying; center open to the public for reference use only. **Automated Operations:** Computerized cataloging and acquisitions. **Computerized Information Services:** DOBIS Canadian Online Library System; internal databases. **Special Indexes:** Index to Austin American-Statesman (online); photography index (online); index of archival papers; index to file of Austin organizations. **Remarks:** FAX: (512)499-7516. Center manages the City of Austin Records Management program. **Staff:** Jan Berry, Asst.Archv.; Linda Zezulka, Cur., Mss.; Karen Warren, Supv., Pub.Serv.; Claire Maxwell, Cur., Photo.; Tom Myers, Rec.Mgt.Supv.

★1316★
Austin State Hospital - Staff Library (Med)
4110 Guadalupe St. Phone: (512)371-6740
Austin, TX 78751 Nancy H. Dobson, Libn.
Founded: 1980. **Staff:** Prof 1. **Subjects:** Psychiatry, psychology, nursing, neurology, community mental health. **Holdings:** 4000 books; 1000 bound periodical volumes; 150 tape recordings. **Subscriptions:** 90 journals and other serials. **Services:** Interlibrary loan; copying; SDI; library open to the public with restrictions. **Computerized Information Services:** DIALOG Information Services, MEDLARS. **Networks/Consortia:** Member of National Network of Libraries of Medicine - South Central Region.

★1317★
Stephen F. Austin State University - Steen Library - Special Collections Department (Hist)
SFA Sta., Box 13055 Phone: (409)568-4100
Nacogdoches, TX 75962 Linda Cheves Nicklas, Spec.Coll.Libn.
Founded: 1924. **Staff:** Prof 1; Other 2. **Subjects:** Local and East Texas history and literature; social, economic, and religious life of East Texas; works by and about East Texans; forest history. **Special Collections:** Forest History Collection (1755 linear feet); university archives (305 linear feet); R.B. Blake Collection (93 volumes). **Holdings:** 16,750 books; 930 bound periodical volumes; 2080 linear feet of manuscripts; 530 maps; 4000 photographs; 2400 microforms. **Subscriptions:** 83 journals and other serials. **Services:** Copying; department open to the public. **Automated Operations:** Computerized cataloging. **Publications:** A Guide to Special Collections; guides, inventories, calendars for manuscript collections. **Special Indexes:** Map, photograph, and vertical file indexes (all on cards); name index to R.B. Blake Collection (card). **Remarks:** FAX: (409)568-4117.

★1318★
Austine School - Library (Educ)
120 Maple St. Phone: (802)254-4571
Brattleboro, VT 05301 Joan Naturale, Libn.
Founded: 1912. **Staff:** 1. **Subjects:** Education of the deaf. **Special Collections:** Deaf culture; sign language. **Holdings:** 10,000 books; 350 bound periodical volumes. **Subscriptions:** 40 journals and other serials. **Services:** Library open to students interested in education of the deaf. **Staff:** John Enola, Captioned Films Coord.

★1319★
Australia - Australian Nuclear Science and Technology Organisation - Lucas Heights Research Laboratories - Library (Energy)
Private Mail Bag No. 1 Phone: 2 5433111
Menai, NSW 2234, Australia Wendy M. Bartlett, Mgr., Lib.Serv.
Staff: 10. **Subjects:** Atomic energy research, radioisotopes, radioactive waste disposal, nuclear medicine, radiation protection, oil shales. **Holdings:** 45,000 books; 15,000 bound periodical volumes; 250,000 patents and documents; 500,000 microforms. **Subscriptions:** 626 journals and other serials. **Services:** Interlibrary loan; copying; SDI; library open to the public with restrictions. **Computerized Information Services:** DIALOG Information Services, STN International, ORBIT Search Service, ESA/IRS, MEDLINE, AUSTRALIS, Australian Bibliographic Network (ABN), AUSINET, Dun & Bradstreet Business Credit Services, INIS (International Nuclear Information System); ILANET, CSIRONET (electronic mail services). Performs searches on fee basis. Contact Person: Sandra Gorringe, Ref.Libn., 543-3679. **Remarks:** Library located at New Illawarra Rd., Lucas Heights, NSW 2234. FAX: 2 543 5097. Telex: AA24562. Library is the Australian input center for International Nuclear Information System (INIS). **Staff:** Judy Engall, Cat.Libn.; Mary Huxlin, INIS Off.

★1320★
Australia - Bread Research Institute of Australia - Library (Agri)
P.O. Box 7 Phone: 612 888-9600
North Ryde, NSW 2113, Australia Jill Chambers, Libn.
Founded: 1949. **Subjects:** Quality, processing, and marketability of wheat and wheat products; cereals - triticale, barley, rice, oats. **Holdings:** 1500 volumes. **Subscriptions:** 110 journals and other serials. **Services:** Interlibrary loan; copying; library open to the public. **Computerized Information Services:** DIALOG Information Services. **Remarks:** FAX: (612)888-5821. Telex: 120033. Also serves Australia - Commonwealth Scientific and Industrial Research Organization (CSIRO) - Division of Plant Industry - CSIRO Wheat Research Unit.

★1321★
Australia - Bureau of Meteorology - Library (Sci-Engr)
GPO Box 1289 K Phone: 3 6694471
Melbourne, VIC 3001, Australia Pamela Tonkin, Sr.Libn.
Founded: 1908. **Staff:** Prof 4. **Subjects:** Meteorology. **Special Collections:** Climate data. **Holdings:** 70,000 volumes. **Subscriptions:** 750 journals and other serials. **Services:** Interlibrary loan; copying; library open to the public by appointment. **Computerized Information Services:** DIALOG Information Services. **Publications:** Periodical Alert; Monthly Accessions List. **Remarks:** Library located at 150 Lonsdale St., 12th Floor, Melbourne, VIC 3000, Australia. FAX: 3 6694611. Telex: 30664 AA. Electronic mail address(es): MLN 302500 (ILANET). **Formerly:** Australian Capital Territory Department of Science - Bureau of Meteorology. **Staff:** Trevor Wakely, Tech.Serv.; Judith Dawson, Ref.Libn.; Patricia Pace, Loans Ck.; Jill Nicholls, Cat.; Laurie Long, Cat.; Ira Udawella, Acq.Off.

★1322★
Australia - Commonwealth Scientific and Industrial Research Organization (CSIRO) - Black Mountain Laboratory - Library (Biol Sci, Agri)
Clunies Ross St
GPOB 109 Phone: 6 2464911
Canberra, ACT 2600, Australia Peter Russell
Founded: 1928. **Staff:** Prof 5; Other 6. **Subjects:** Biological science, agriculture, entomology. **Holdings:** 35,000 books; 100,000 bound periodical volumes. **Subscriptions:** 3000 journals and other serials. **Services:** Interlibrary loan; copying; SDI; library open to the public. **Computerized Information Services:** DIALOG Information Services; CLINES (internal database). Contact Person: Mrs. C. Murray. **Remarks:** FAX: 6 2465684.

★1323★
Australia - Commonwealth Scientific and Industrial Research Organization (CSIRO) - Division of Applied Physics - Library (Sci-Engr)
Bradfield Rd.
P.O. Box 218 Phone: 2 4137097
Lindfield, NSW 2070, Australia Miss Robin Shelley-Jones, Libn.
Founded: 1942. **Staff:** 4. **Subjects:** Physics measurement and science, industrial physics, manufacturing technology, chemistry, engineering. **Special Collections:** Standards published by Standards Association of Australia. **Holdings:** 21,000 books; 600 serial titles; 21,000 monographs. **Subscriptions:** 460 journals and other serials. **Services:** Interlibrary loan; copying; SDI; library open to the public with lending through ILL. **Computerized Information Services:** DIALOG Information Services, CSIRO Australis, Australian Bibliographic Network; InterNet (electronic mail service). **Remarks:** FAX: 2 4137636. Telex: NMLAB AA26296. Electronic mail address(es): LIBRARY@DAP.CSIRO.au (InterNet). **Also Known As:** CSIRO. **Staff:** Virginia Carter, Cat.; Curtis Simmonds, Ref.Libn.

★1324★
Australia - Commonwealth Scientific and Industrial Research Organization (CSIRO) - Division of Building Construction and Engineering - National Building Technology Centre - Library (Plan)
87-101 Delhi Rd. Phone: 888-8888
North Ryde, NSW 2113, Australia Kaye Nolan, Libn.
Subjects: Building research, fire technology. **Holdings:** 27,000 volumes. **Subscriptions:** 227 journals and other serials. **Services:** Interlibrary loan; copying; SDI; library open to the public. **Computerized Information Services:** OZLINE, AUSTRALIS, CLINES, DIALOG Information Services, ESA/IRS, ORBIT Search Service, BRANZINFO; PcSTATUS (internal database); electronic mail service. **Remarks:** FAX: 888-9335. Telex: 123400 AA. **Formed by the merger of:** Australia - Department of Housing and Construction and Australia - Commonwealth Scientific and Industrial Rsearch Organization (CSIRO) - Division of Building Research.

Australia - Commonwealth Scientific and Industrial Research Organization (CSIRO) - Division of Plant Industry - CSIRO Wheat Research Unit - Library
See: **Australia - Bread Research Institute of Australia - Library** (1320)

★1325★
Australia - Commonwealth Scientific and Industrial Research Organization (CSIRO) - Division of Wool Technology - Sydney Laboratory - Library (Sci-Engr)
P.O. Box 7 Phone: 2 8099421
Ryde, NSW 2112, Australia Pauline Quan, Libn.
Staff: Prof 2; Other 1. **Subjects:** Wool, textiles, robotics, computer systems. **Holdings:** 15,500 volumes. **Subscriptions:** 302 journals and other serials. **Services:** Interlibrary loan; copying; library open to the public by appointment. **Automated Operations:** Computerized public access catalog, cataloging, and circulation. **Computerized Information Services:** DIALOG Information Services, CSIRO Australis; CSIRONET (electronic mail service). **Remarks:** FAX: 2 8099378. Telex: 70827. **Staff:** Sue Gallard, Asst.Libn.

★1326★
Australia - Commonwealth Scientific and Industrial Research Organization (CSIRO) - Information Services Branch - Library Network Services (Sci-Engr, Info Sci)
314 Albert St. Phone: 3 4187333
East Melbourne, VIC 3002, Australia John Thawley, Mgr., Lib. Network Serv.
Founded: 1916. **Staff:** 20.5. **Subjects:** Science, science policy, librarianship, information science, communications, computers. **Holdings:** 10,000 books; 2500 serial titles. **Subscriptions:** 600 journals and other serials. **Services:** Interlibrary loan; copying; unit open to the public. **Computerized Information Services:** CSIRO Australis, DIALOG Information Services, ESA/IRS, AUSINET, Australian Bibliographic Network (ABN), ORBIT Search Service, PFDS Online, Ozline, Australian MEDLINE. Performs searches on fee basis. Contact Person: Penny Braybrook, Online Search Spec., tel. 3 4187250. **Publications:** Directory of CSIRO research programs; research in progress databases; CSIRO Index Database; scientific and technical research centres in Australia. **Remarks:** FAX: 3 4190459. Telex: AA 30236.

★1327★
Australia - Commonwealth Scientific and Industrial Research Organization (CSIRO) - Western Australian Laboratories - Library (Sci-Engr)
Private Bag
P.O. Wembley Phone: 9 3870200
Floreat Park, WA 6014, Australia Bernadette Waugh
Staff: Prof 2; Other 1. **Subjects:** Earth sciences, water resources, mineral chemistry, animal production, plants, forestry. **Holdings:** 25,000 books; 14,000 bound periodical volumes. **Subscriptions:** 1200 journals and other serials. **Services:** Interlibrary loan; library open to the public for reference use only. **Computerized Information Services:** DIALOG Information Services, STN International, AUSTRALIS, OZLINE, ORBIT Search Service; CSIRO Library Network Catalogue (CLINES; internal database); ILANET, AARNET (electronic mail services). **Remarks:** FAX: 9 3876046. Telex: AA92178. Electronic mail address(es): MLN900250 (ILANET); WAUGHB@PER.DWR.CSIRO.AU (AARNET).

Australia - Defence Science and Technology Organisation
See: **Defence Science and Technology Organisation** (4701)

★1328★
Australia - Department of Agriculture - Library (Agri)
GPO Box 1671 Phone: 8 2260362
Adelaide, SA 5001, Australia Carla Mellor
Founded: 1907. **Subjects:** Agriculture, veterinary medicine, animal nutrition, horticulture, soils, irrigation, agricultural economics. **Holdings:** 11,000 books; 13,000 bound periodical volumes; 20 microfiche; 5 reels of microfilm; 120 videotapes. **Subscriptions:** 1300 journals and other serials; 30 newspapers. **Services:** Interlibrary loan; copying; library open to the public for reference use only. **Computerized Information Services:** DIALOG Information Services, AUSTRALIS. **Remarks:** Library located at 25 Grenfell St., Adelaide, SA 5000, Australia. FAX: 8 2260260.

Australia - Department of the Attorney General and Justice
See: **Australia - Department of Courts Administration** (1329)

★1329★
Australia - Department of Courts Administration - Law Courts Library (Law)
Law Courts Bldg., 15th Level Phone: 2 230 8232
Sydney, NSW 2000, Australia Lynn Pollack, Libn.
Staff: 19. **Subjects:** Law. **Special Collections:** Judges' papers. **Holdings:** 24,072 books; 116,752 bound periodical volumes; 39,596 microforms. **Subscriptions:** 2702 journals and other serials; 8 newspapers. **Services:** Interlibrary loan; copying; library open to the public with restrictions. **Computerized Information Services:** Info-One International Pty. Ltd., SCALE, LEXIS, DIALOG Information Services, QL Systems, CAN/LAW, LINK, AUSINET, Reuters Information Services (Canada), Kiwinet. **Publications:** List of publications - available on request. **Remarks:** FAX: 2 2337952. **Formerly:** Australia - Department of the Attorney General & Justice. **Staff:** Josie Taylor, Dp.; Brana Rejulie, Sys.Libn.; Ela Hav, Tech.Serv.

★1330★
Australia - Department of Defence - Defence Regional Library Victoria/Tasmania (Mil, Sci-Engr)
Defence Centre
350 St. Kilda Rd. Phone: 3 2825383
Melbourne, VIC 3004, Australia Ms. E. Alexander, Reg.Libn.
Founded: 1977. **Staff:** 8.5. **Subjects:** Engineering, military history, electronics, computers, military art and science, management. **Special Collections:** Australian military history. **Holdings:** 20,000 books; 3000 historical materials; 150 microforms. **Subscriptions:** 654 journals and other serials. **Services:** Interlibrary loan; copying; SDI; library open to the public with restrictions. **Computerized Information Services:** DIALOG Information Services, PFDS Online, ESA/IRS, AUSINET, Australian Bibliographic Network (ABN), AUSTRALIS. **Remarks:** FAX: 3 2825230. Library is part of the Defence Information Services (DIS) Network whose headquarters is in Canberra, Australia. It encompasses more than 85 member libraries. **Staff:** Mrs. M. Turnbull, Mgr., Reg.Lib.; Ms. D. Murphy; Miss C. Knaggs.

★1331★
Australia - Department of Education - Library (Educ)
31 Flinders St. Phone: 8 2263416
Adelaide, SA 5001, Australia Penelope Curtin, Libn.
Subjects: Curriculum development, higher education, vocational education. **Special Collections:** National TATE Information Network collection. **Holdings:** 4500 books; 3000 microfiche. **Subscriptions:** 90 journals and other serials; 5 newspapers. **Services:** Interlibrary loan; library not open to the public. **Computerized Information Services:** DIALOG Information Services, BRS Information Technologies, AUSINET, OZLINE, Australian Bibliographic Network; VOCED, ILRAD (internal databases). **Remarks:** FAX: 8 2263350. Library serves both the Department of Education and the Department of Technical and Further Education.

★1332★
Australia - Department of Primary Industries and Energy - Library (Agri, Env-Cons)
John Curtin House
Brisbane Ave. Phone: 6 2724548
Barton, ACT 2600, Australia Charles Ironside
Founded: 1940. **Staff:** Prof 7; Other 5. **Subjects:** Agriculture, energy, environment, mining, climate, science. **Subjects:** National Energy Research Demonstration and Development collection; End of Grant Report Collection (900). **Holdings:** 16,000 books; 1000 bound periodical volumes; 3000 reports; 7000 archival items; 5000 microfiche. **Subscriptions:** 900 journals and other serials; 25 newspapers. **Services:** Interlibrary loan; copying; SDI; library open to the public. **Computerized Information Services:** DIALOG Information Services, ORBIT Search Service, AUSINET; CD-ROM. Contact Person: Tori May. **Remarks:** FAX: 6 2724709.

Australia - Department of Technical and Further Education - Library
See: **Australia - Department of Education - Library** (1331)

Australia - National Building Technology Centre
See: **Australia - Commonwealth Scientific and Industrial Research Organization (CSIRO) - Division of Building Construction and Engineering - National Building Technology Centre** (1324)

★1333★
Australia - National Library of Australia (Area-Ethnic, Hum, Info Sci)
Parkes Pl. Phone: 6 2621111
Canberra, ACT 2600, Australia Mr. W.M. Horton, Dir.-Gen.
Founded: 1961. **Staff:** 589. **Subjects:** Australiana, Pacificana, representative literature in English and European languages. **Special Collections:** Ferguson, Petherick, and Rex Nan Kivell collections of Australiana. **Holdings:** 2.7 million books; 23,966 AV programs; 1.9 million microforms; 563,843 aerial photographs; 408,375 maps; 513,649 photographs; 40,490 paintings, drawings, and prints; 153,817 music scores; 57,625 oral histories and tapes; 8560 meters of manuscripts. **Subscriptions:** 200,503 journals, newspapers, and other serial titles. **Services:** Interlibrary loan; copying; SDI; library open to the public. **Computerized Information Services:** AUSINET, DIALOG Information Services, PFDS Online, ESA/IRS, Australian Bibliographic Network (ABN), BLAISE Online Services, QL Systems, International Nuclear Information System (INIS); OTC Minerva (electronic mail service). Performs searches on fee basis. Contact: Chief Librarian, Computer Search Services. **Publications:** Australian National Bibliography. **Special Catalogs:** National Union Catalogue of Serials (NUCOS). **Special Indexes:** Australian Public Affairs Information Index (APAIS). **Remarks:** FAX: 6 2571703. Telex: 62100 LIBAUST. Electronic mail address(es): MLN600000 (ILL, including films); MLN600001 (Reference and Computer Search Services); MLN 600002 (ABN Office); MLN600003 (Selection, Acquisition & Serials Section) - all addresses via OTC Minerva.

Australia - Royal Botanic Gardens & National Herbarium
See: **Royal Botanic Gardens & National Herbarium** (14104)

Australia - State Library of the Northern Territory
See: **State Library of the Northern Territory - Northern Australia Collection** (15690)

★1334★
Australian Archives - Library (Info Sci)
PO Box 34 Phone: 6 2093645
Dickson, ACT 2602, Australia Veronica Keraitis
Founded: 1974. **Staff:** Prof 1; Other 3. **Subjects:** Archival science, preservation of archival materials, records management, public administration. **Holdings:** 8000 books; annual reports of archival institutions. **Subscriptions:** 314 journals and other serials; 4 newspapers. **Services:** Interlibrary loan; copying; SDI; library open to the public. **Computerized Information Services:** SCALE (Statutes Cases Automated Legal Enquiry; internal database). Performs searches. **Remarks:** FAX: 6 2093693. **Staff:** Eileen Iannachiow, Current Awareness Off.; Lorelle Arkley, Cat. & ILL Off.

★1335★
Australian Book Publishers' Association - Library (Publ)
161 Clarence St.
Sydney, NSW 2000, Australia Phone: 2 295422
Subjects: Publishing - Australian, international; book design and production. **Holdings:** 800 volumes.

★1336★
Australian Broadcasting Tribunal - Library (Info Sci)
76 Berry St
P.O. Box 1308 Phone: 2 9597811
North Sydney, NSW 2059, Australia Lurline Caffery, Lib.Hd.
Founded: 1973. **Staff:** Prof 2; Other 1. **Subjects:** Radio broadcasting, television broadcasting, telecommunications, mass media, law, advertising. **Holdings:** 7000 books. **Subscriptions:** 300 journals and other serials. **Services:** Interlibrary loan; SDI; library open to the public by appointment for reference use only. **Automated Operations:** Computerized public access catalog (INMAGIC). **Computerized Information Services:** DIALOG Information Services, AUSINET, ABN (Australian Bibliographic Network), Info-One International, Telecom Discovery; CD-ROMs. **Publications:** Library bulletin, quarterly; Contents pages, monthly; Information Handbook - for internal distribution only. **Remarks:** FAX: 2 9544328.

Australian Capital Territory Department of Science - Bureau of Meteorology
See: **Australia - Bureau of Meteorology - Library** (1321)

★1337★
Australian Council for Educational Research - Library and Information Services Unit (Educ)
9 Frederick St. Phone: 3 8191400
Hawthorn, VIC 3122, Australia Peter Mathews, Hd.
Staff: Prof 4; Other 20. **Subjects:** Australia - education. **Holdings:** 26,000 bound volumes. **Subscriptions:** 2400 journals and other serials. **Services:** Interlibrary loan (limited). **Computerized Information Services:** Produces AEI Data Base (available through AUSINET and AUSTROM CD-ROM); KEYLINK, InterNet (electronic mail services). **Publications:** Australian Education Index, quarterly with annual cumulation; Bibliography of Education Theses in Australia, annual; Australian Thesaurus of Education Descriptors; Australian Education Directory, annual. **Remarks:** Alternate telephone number(s): 3 8906089. FAX: 3 8195502. Telex: 10722065 AA. Electronic mail address(es): MLN 301 450 (KEYLINK); MATHEWS@ACER.ED.AU (InterNet). **Staff:** Elspeth Miller, AEI Ed.; Rachel Salmond, Ser.Libn.; Denise Balint, Tech.Serv.Libn.; Julie Badger, Indexer.

★1338★
Australian Embassy in Washington - Library (Area-Ethnic)
1601 Massachusetts Ave., N.W. Phone: (202)797-3126
Washington, DC 20036 Patricia Kay, Libn.
Founded: 1975. **Staff:** Prof 1; Other 1. **Subjects:** Australia. **Holdings:** 10,000 books; 950 bound periodical volumes; annual reports of 27 Australian government departments and statutory corporations; Parliamentary papers; Australian state statutes; 10 VF drawers of Australian press clippings. **Subscriptions:** 504 journals and other serials; 6 newspapers. **Services:** Interlibrary loan; copying; library open to the public. **Computerized Information Services:** LEGI-SLATE, DIALOG Information Services, NEXIS, OCLC; Data Trek, Remo, Ross (internal databases). **Networks/Consortia:** Member of CAPCON Library Network. **Remarks:** FAX: (202)797-3362.

★1339★
Australian Heritage Commission - Library (Area-Ethnic)
GPO Box 1567 Phone: 6 2732042
Canberra, ACT 2601, Australia Elizabeth Thompson, Libn.
Founded: 1980. **Staff:** Prof 2. **Subjects:** Australia - natural environment, cultural environment. **Special Collections:** National Estate Grants Program (1500 reports). **Holdings:** 10,000 monographs. **Subscriptions:** 250 journals and other serials; 6 newspapers. **Services:** Interlibrary loan; copying; SDI; library open to the public. **Computerized Information Services:** Produces Heritage Australia Information System (available online through AUSTRALIS). Performs searches on fee basis. **Publications:** HERA Update, quarterly. **Remarks:** FAX: 6 2732395. **Staff:** Dianne Calvert.

★1340★
Australian Institute of Archaeology - Library (Hist)
174 Collins St. Phone: 03 650-3477
Melbourne, VIC 3000, Australia Mr. Piers Crocker, Dir.
Subjects: Archeology - biblical, Egyptian, Mesopotamian; theology; ancient languages. **Holdings:** 8000 books; 2000 bound periodical volumes. **Subscriptions:** 44 journals and other serials. **Services:** Library open to the public for reference use only. **Staff:** Jenny Blake.

Australian International Development Assistance Bureau - Centre for Pacific Development and Training
See: **Centre for Pacific Development and Training** (3277)

★1341★
Australian Maritime College - Library (Trans)
Newnham Hall
POB 986 Phone: 03 260773
Launceston, TAS 7250, Australia Coralie Mallitt
Founded: 1979. **Staff:** Prof 6; Other 1. **Subjects:** Navigation, shipping, marine engineering, fishing technology, electronic communications, maritime commerce. **Holdings:** 30,000 books; 1600 bound periodical volumes; 200 archival items; 500 microfiche; 600 AV items. **Subscriptions:** 170 journals and other serials; 5 newspapers. **Services:** Interlibrary loan; copying, library open to the public for reference use only. **Automated Operations:** Computerized cataloging. **Computerized Information Services:** DIALOG Information Services, AUSINET, BMT Abstracts Online (BOATS), AUSTRALIS. Contact Person: Robyn Conway. **Publications:** Accessions list, monthly; Audio visual serials list. **Remarks:** FAX: 3 260821.

Australian Medical Association Library
See: **Western Sydney Area Health Services - Westmead Hospital - AMA Library** (20302)

★1342★
Australian National Gallery - Research Library (Art)
GPO Box 1150 Phone: 6 2712532
Canberra, ACT 2601, Australia J. Margaret Shaw, Chf.Libn.
Founded: 1975. **Staff:** Prof 6; Other 6. **Subjects:** Art - Australian, Aboriginal, pre-Columbian, contemporary; photography; prints; Ballets Russes; Indonesian textiles. **Holdings:** 70,000 books; 30,000 bound periodical volumes; 45,000 microforms; manuscripts; extensive documentation collection. **Subscriptions:** 1200 journals and other serials. **Services:** Interlibrary loan; copying; library open to the public with restrictions. **Automated Operations:** Computerized public access catalog, cataloging, acquisitions, and circulation. **Computerized Information Services:** DIALOG Information Services, RLIN. Performs searches on fee basis. Contact Person: Gillian Currie, Bibl.Serv.Libn., 712534. **Special Indexes:** Australian National Gallery Library List of Periodicals (ANGALLOP). **Remarks:** Telex: AA 61500. FAX: 6 2712529. **Staff:** John Thomson, Dp. & Ser.Libn.

★1343★
Australian National Kennel Council - Library (Rec)
Royal Show Grounds
Ascot Vale, VIC, Australia Phone: 3 3763733
Subjects: Dogs - breeding and showing. **Holdings:** 3000 volumes. **Remarks:** FAX: 3 3762973. Provides research for educational institutions.

★1344★
Australian National University - University Library - John Curtin School of Medical Research Library (Med, Biol Sci)
P.O. Box 334 Phone: 492597
Canberra, ACT 2601, Australia Miss J. Nicholson, Libn.
Subjects: Immunology, microbiology, biochemistry, cancer research, vision, neurology. **Holdings:** 45,000 volumes. **Remarks:** Library is a branch of the University Library of the Australian National University.

Australian Nuclear Science and Technology Organisation
See: **Australia - Australian Nuclear Science and Technology Organisation** (1319)

★1345★
Australian Overseas Information Service - Reference Library/ Information Service (Area-Ethnic)
636 5th Ave. Phone: (212)245-4000
New York, NY 10111 W. O'Reilly, Libn.
Founded: 1945. **Staff:** 2. **Subjects:** Australia - economics, Aboriginals, law, history, geography, arts, industry and resources, literature, sport, transport, flora and fauna, education, politics and government, science. **Special Collections:** Australian photographs and slides; extensive holdings on the Australian Aboriginals. **Holdings:** 10,000 books and pamphlets; 3 drawers of biographical files; 25 drawers of statistical publications; 1000 vertical files of newspaper and magazine clippings (by subject); parliamentary papers and ministerial press releases. **Subscriptions:** 120 journals and other serials; 10 newspapers. **Services:** Interlibrary loan; library open to the public by appointment. **Publications:** Business News from Australia, bimonthly; Australia Now, irregular; Australia Handbook, annual; fact sheets and reference papers, irregular - all free upon request; Australian Environment; Churinga. **Special Indexes:** Index of news items in daily Radio Australia broadcast (online). **Remarks:** FAX: (212)265-4917. Telex: 12328 AUSTCON NYK. Library located in the Australian Consulate-General. **Staff:** A. Malone, Tech.Serv.

★1346★
Australian Road Research Board Ltd. - Library (Trans)
500 Burwood Hwy. Phone: 3 8811555
Vermont South, VIC 3133, Australia Judy Tickner, Mgr., Info.Serv.
Staff: Prof 4; Other 2.5. **Subjects:** Australia - roads and transport. **Holdings:** 28,000 bound volumes. **Subscriptions:** 500 journals and other serials. **Services:** SDI; current awareness. **Computerized Information Services:** Produces INROADS (available online through AUSTRALIS); ILANET (electronic mail service). Performs searches on fee basis. **Publications:** Roadlit, biweekly - available by subscription. **Special Indexes:** Australian Road Index (ceased publication with 1985 volume). **Remarks:** FAX: 3 8878104. Telex: 33113 AA. Electronic mail address(es): MLN 305700 (ILANET). **Staff:** Lynne Beaumont, Info.Off.

★1347★
Australian Society of CPAs - C.W. Andersen Library (Bus-Fin)
170 Queen St. Phone: 3 6069606
Melbourne, VIC 3000, Australia Joyce Korn, Ctrl.Libn.
Founded: 1887. **Staff:** Prof 3; Other 4. **Subjects:** Accounting, company law, taxation, auditing. **Special Collections:** ASCPA archival materials. **Holdings:** 30,000 books; 5000 bound periodical volumes; 1000 microforms; 5000 ASCPA seminar papers. **Subscriptions:** 500 journals and other serials; 6 newspapers. **Services:** Interlibrary loan; copying; SDI; library open to the public with restrictions. **Automated Operations:** Computerized cataloging. **Computerized Information Services:** LEXIS, NEXIS, DIALOG Information Services, AUSINET, Maxwell Online, Inc., Info-One International Pty. Ltd.; CD-ROM (ABI/INFORM); internal database. **Publications:** Library accessions list, quarterly; periodical and serials list. **Special Indexes:** Index to The Australian Accountant. **Remarks:** FAX: 3 6705328. Telex: 32283 ASAML. **Formerly:** Australian Society of Accountants. **Staff:** Jill Bright, Ref.Libn.; Pat McGregor, Sys.Libn.

Australian Tourism Index
See: **Victoria University of Technology - Library** (19831)

★1348★
Australian Tourist Commission - Library (Bus-Fin)
80 William St., Level 3
Woolloomooloo, NSW 2011, Australia Phone: 2 360 1111
Staff: 1. **Subjects:** Tourism in Australia. **Special Collections:** ATC publications archives. **Holdings:** 3500 volumes. **Subscriptions:** 600 journals and other serials; 3 newspapers. **Services:** Interlibrary loan; library open to members of travel industry or by annual subscription. **Computerized Information Services:** DIALOG Information Services, Australian Bibliographic Network, OZLINE, AUSTRALIS. **Remarks:** FAX: 2 3314809.

★1349★
Australian Trade Union Training Authority - TUTA Information Service (Bus-Fin)
Nordsvan Dr.
POB 510 Phone: 60 553293
Wodonga, VIC 3689, Australia Kay Hathway
Founded: 1975. **Staff:** Prof 2; Other 2. **Subjects:** Industrial relations, conditions of employment, industrial law, labor history. **Holdings:** Figures not available. **Services:** Interlibrary loan; service not open to the public. **Computerized Information Services:** ORBIT Search Service, AUSINET, ABN; TUTA Information Service (internal database). Contact Person: Chris Adams, Res.Off.

★1350★
Australian War Memorial - Research Centre (Mil)
G.P.O. Box 345 Phone: 6 2434211
Canberra, ACT 2601, Australia Dr. Michael McKernan, Dp.Dir., Natl.Coll.
Founded: 1917. **Staff:** 35. **Subjects:** Australian military history, Australian Defence Force history. **Holdings:** 50,000 books; 4000 serial titles; 850,000 photographs; 4000 film titles; 5000 sound recordings; 4000 meters of official and personal papers and archival materials. **Subscriptions:** 299 journals and other serials. **Services:** Interlibrary loan; copying; center open to the public. **Computerized Information Services:** Internal database (photographs, film, private records, books, serials). **Publications:** A General Guide to the Library Collections and Archives; Roll Call: A Guide to Genealogical Sources in the Australian War Memorial; Bibliographies of Military History; A Guide to the Personal, Family and Official Papers of C.E.W. Bean; A Guide to the Australian War Memorial. **Remarks:** FAX: 6 2475184. Telex: AA 61986.

Austria - Bundesministerium fur Unterricht und Kunst
See: **Austria - Ministry of Education and Arts** (1352)

Austria - Bundesministerium fuer Wissenschaft und Forschung
See: **Austria - Oesterreichisches Theatermuseum** (1355)

★1351★
Austria - Federal Ministry of Agriculture and Forestry - Library (Agri, Biol Sci)
Stubenring 1 Phone: 222 7500
A-1011 Vienna, Austria Ingrid Saberi
Subjects: Agriculture, forestry, plant and animal production, environmental contaminants, agrarian policies, wildlife, hunting, vegetation and watershed management, farm mechanization, standardization. **Special Collections:** Torrent control (avalanches); Royal and Imperial Ministry of Agriculture collection (10,000 books). **Holdings:** 708,000 books; 554 bound periodical volumes. **Services:** Interlibrary loan; library open to the public with restrictions. **Also Known As:** Bundesministerium fur Land- und Forstwirtschaft.

Austria - Geological Survey of Austria
See: **Geological Survey of Austria** (6364)

★1352★
Austria - Ministry of Education and Arts - Ministry of Science and Research - Library (Sci-Engr)
Minoritenpl 5 Phone: 1 531204295
A-1014 Vienna, Austria Gerhard Silvestri, Dir.
Founded: 1848. **Staff:** Prof 11. **Subjects:** History of Austrian science (1848 to present). **Special Collections:** Collection of all State-approved school books and annual secondary school programmes (1848 to present); documentation on research policy. **Holdings:** 377,446 books; microfiche; audiovisual materials. **Subscriptions:** 845 journals and other serials. **Services:** Interlibrary loan; copying; library open to scientists, students, and teachers. **Computerized Information Services:** BIBOS (internal database). **Publications:** Verzeichnis des Bucherzuwachles, monthly; Forschungspolitische Dokumentation, quarterly. **Remarks:** FAX: 222 531204499. Telex: 115532; 111157. Serves as an administrative library of the Austrian Ministry of Science and Research. **Also Known As:** Austria - Bundesministerium fur Unterricht und Kunst.

★1353★
Austria - Ministry of Foreign Affairs - Library (Soc Sci)
Favoritenstrasse 15 Phone: 222 5052868
A-1040 Vienna, Austria Dr. Gottfried Loibl
Founded: 1983. **Staff:** Prof 7. **Subjects:** Foreign affairs, international relations, diplomacy, international culture. **Holdings:** 35,722 books; 17,200 bound periodical volumes; 2000 microfiche; 86 reels of microfilm. **Subscriptions:** 658 journals and other serials; 27 newspapers. **Services:** Interlibrary loan; library open to the public. **Remarks:** 222 5042265. **Also Known As:** Aussenpolitische Bibliothek.

Austria - Ministry of Science and Research
See: **Austria - Ministry of Education and Arts** (1352)

Austria - Ministry of Science and Research - Geological Survey of Austria
See: **Geological Survey of Austria** (6364)

Austria - Oberoesterreichisches Landesarchiv
See: **Oberoesterreichisches Landesarchiv** (12223)

★1354★
Austria - Oesterreichische Nationalbibliothek - Special Collections (Publ)
Josefplatz 1 Phone: 222 53410
A-1015 Vienna, Austria Dr. Magda Strebl, Dir.
Founded: 1300s.**Staff:** 291. **Special Collections:** Print collection; manuscript collection (101,237); incunabula; letter collection; map collection (55,645); globe museum; music collection; papyrus collection (94,129 items); portrait collection and archives of documentary photo-negatives; Internationales Esperanto Museum Sammlung fuer Plansprachen (language design; 19,070 items). **Holdings:** 2.7 million books; 11,374 periodicals; 31,394 microfilm. **Subscriptions:** 11,394 journals and other serials; 123 newspapers. **Services:** Interlibrary loan; copying; library open to the public. **Computerized Information Services:** DIALOG Information Services, Questel, ECHO, STN International, Data-Star, Zeitschriftendatenbank (ZDB), INKDATA, Bertelsmann InformationService, EDV GmbH. Performs searches on fee basis. Contact Person: Dr. Karl Megner, Adv. **Publications:** Corpus Papyrorum Raineri; Mitteilungen aus der Papyrussammlung der Oesterreichischen Nationalbibliothek (1920-1929); Oesterreichische Nationalbibliothek (1975); Oesterrichs Zeitungen au f Mikrofilm; Palatina Nachrichten; Zentrale Redaktion des Oesterreichischen Bibliothekverbundes. **Remarks:** FAX: 222 53410280. Telex: 112624. **Staff:** Dr. Victoria Lunzer, Adv.; Dr. Fritz Dollmanits, Adv.

★1355★
Austria - Oesterreichisches Theatermuseum (Theater)
Lobkowitzpl. 2 Phone: 222 5128800
A-1010 Vienna, Austria Dr. Oskar Pausch, Lib.Hd.
Founded: 1923. **Staff:** 20. **Subjects:** Performing arts. **Special Collections:** Theater designs and prints; photograph collection; memorabilia collection; costume collection; Herman Bahr and Anna Bahr Mildenburg Memorial Room; Emmerich Kalman Memorial Room; Carl M. Ziehrer Memorial Room; Josef Kainz Memorial Room; Caspar Neher Memorial Room; Max Reinhardt Memorial Room; Hugo Thimig Memorial Room; Richard Teschner Memorial Room; Fritz Wotruba Centre. **Holdings:** 1.5 million items; 70,000 books; 71,000 manuscripts. **Services:** Interlibrary loan; copying; library open to the public. **Computerized Information Services:** Online systems. **Special Catalogs:** Kataloge des Oesterreichischen Theatermuseums. **Remarks:** FAX: 222 512880045. Maintained by the Bundesministerium fuer Wissenschaft und Forschung.

★1356★
Austria - Post and Telegraph Administration - Library (Info Sci)
Postgasse 8 Phone: 222 515515301
A-1011 Vienna, Austria Dr. Christine Kainz
Founded: 1839. **Staff:** Prof 6. **Subjects:** Post, telecommunication. **Holdings:** 44,000 books; 25,000 bound periodical volumes; 2000 reports; 24,000 microfiche. **Subscriptions:** 802 journals and other serials; 21 newspapers. **Services:** Copying; library open to the public for reference use only. **Computerized Information Services:** Eurobases, FIZ-Technik; BIS/DABIS (internal databases). Contact Person: Eva Wiesinger. **Remarks:** FAX: 222 5125252.

★1357★
Austrian Cultural Institute - Library (Area-Ethnic)
11 E. 52nd St. Phone: (212)759-5165
New York, NY 10022 Friederike Zeitlhofer, Libn.
Founded: 1962. **Staff:** Prof 1. **Subjects:** Austria - history, literature, art, geography, philosophy, and allied subjects. **Holdings:** 7500 books; 25 unbound periodicals. **Subscriptions:** 25 journals and other serials; 5 newspapers. **Services:** Interlibrary loan; copying; library open to the public. **Remarks:** FAX: (212)319-9639.

★1358★
Austrian Federal Railways - Library (Trans)
Praterstern 3 Phone: 222 580035210
A-1020 Vienna, Austria Manfred Schuh
Founded: 1896. **Staff:** Prof 8. **Subjects:** Railway, traffic, technology, administration, law. **Holdings:** 128,144 books; timetables. **Subscriptions:** 205 journals and other serials. **Services:** Interlibrary loan; copying; library open to railway employees only. **Remarks:** Telex: 1377. **Also Known As:** Osterreichische Bundesbahnen - Bibliothek.

★1359★
Austrian Institute of East and Southeast European Studies - Library (Area-Ethnic)
Augustinerstrasse 12 Phone: 222 512 43 28
A-1010 Vienna, Austria Ilona Slawinski, Libn.
Founded: 1959. **Special Collections:** East Europe - history, geography, economics, education and cultural relations, law, political science, nationalities and national minorities. **Holdings:** 30,500 books. **Subscriptions:** 840 journals and other serials. **Services:** Copying; library open to the public. **Remarks:** Alternate telephone number(s): 222 512 18 95. FAX: 222 512 18 95 53. **Also Known As:** Oesterreichisches Ost- und Sudosteuropa-Institut.

★1360★
Austrian Patent Office - Library (Law)
Kohlmarkt 8-10 Phone: 1 53424152
A-1014 Vienna, Austria Ingrid Weidinger, Dir.
Founded: 1899. **Staff:** Prof 2; Other 9. **Subjects:** Patent documents, technical literature, legal literature; patent, trademark and design gazettes. **Special Collections:** Austrian privileges. **Holdings:** 30,620 books; 53,083 bound periodical volumes; 26 reports; 984,674 microfiche; 24,236 reels of microfilm. **Subscriptions:** 537 journals and other serials. **Services:** Interlibrary loan; copying; library open to the public. **Computerized Information Services:** Internal databases; CD-ROMs. Contact Person: Dr. Dietmar Trattner. **Publications:** Austrian Patent Gazette; Austrian Trademark Gazette; Austrian Design Gazette; Annual Report. **Remarks:** FAX: 1 53424110. Telex: 136 847. **Also Known As:** Osterreichisches Patentamt - Bibliothek.

★1361★
Austrian Press and Information Service (Area-Ethnic)
31 E. 69th St. Phone: (212)288-1727
New York, NY 10021 Dagmar Baldwin, Press Attache
Founded: 1948. **Staff:** 6. **Subjects:** Austrian affairs. **Holdings:** 300 volumes; current Austrian newspapers and periodicals; photographs; slides; films. **Subscriptions:** 20 journals and other serials; 10 newspapers. **Services:** General political, economic, educational, and cultural information supplied; service open to the public with restrictions. **Publications:** Austrian Information, monthly; Economic News from Austria, quarterly. **Remarks:** FAX: (212)772-8926. Telex: 147 285. **Staff:** Sylvia Gardner-Wittgenstein.

★1362★
Authenticated News International - Photo Library (Aud-Vis)
34 High St. Phone: (914)232-7726
Katonah, NY 10536-1117 Sidney Polinsky, Mng.Ed.
Founded: 1948. **Staff:** Prof 4. **Subjects:** All subjects, including personality file, photojournalism, news, and politics. **Special Collections:** Color photograph collection. **Holdings:** 1.5 million photographs. **Services:** Library not open to the public. **Staff:** Helga Brink Polinsky, Exec.Ed.

★1363★
Autism Research Institute - Library and Information Referral (Med)
4182 Adams Ave. Phone: (619)281-7165
San Diego, CA 92113 Mollie Odle
Founded: 1967. **Staff:** Prof 2; Other 4. **Subjects:** Autism, nutrition. **Holdings:** 1000 books; archival materials. **Services:** Library open to the public for reference use only. **Publications:** Newsletter, quarterly; publication list.**Remarks:** FAX: (619)563-6840.

★1364★
Autism Society of America - Information & Referral Service
8601 Georgia Ave., Suite 503
Silver Spring, MD 20910
Founded: 1965. **Subjects:** Autism and allied subjects. **Holdings:** 200 books; 500 bound periodical volumes; 40 VF drawers of articles, lists, pamphlets, reports, bibliographies. **Remarks:** Currently inactive. **Formerly:** Located in Washington, DC.

★1365★
Automated Logistic Management Systems Agency - Library (Comp Sci)
Federal Bldg.
12th and Spruce Phone: (314)331-4128
St. Louis, MO 63103 Oneta M. Welch, Lib.Techn.
Staff: 1. **Subjects:** Automatic data processing. **Holdings:** 500 books; 100 periodical volumes; 1000 regulations. **Subscriptions:** 75 journals and other serials. **Services:** Interlibrary loan; library open to government employees only. **Remarks:** Administered by the U.S. Army - Materiel Command.

★1366★
Automated Sciences Group, Inc. - Library (Sci-Engr)
Marketing Support
1010 Wayne Ave. Phone: (301)587-8750
Silver Spring, MD 20910-5600 Marvin L. Doxie, Sr.
Founded: 1980. **Staff:** 2. **Subjects:** Telecommunications, systems and software engineering, system integration, hardware, software, peripherals. **Special Collections:** Energy Analyst collection (CD-ROMs). **Holdings:** 800 books; 700 reports; hardware and software specifications; government directories; ADP forecast/industry profiles. **Subscriptions:** 215 journals and other serials. **Services:** Library not open to the public. **Computerized Information Services:** Internal databases. **Remarks:** FAX: (301)565-9412. **Staff:** Pamela Prue; Fitz-Roy Peaut.

★1367★
Automatic Switch Company - ASCO Library (Sci-Engr)
50 Hanover Rd. Phone: (201)966-2479
Florham Park, NJ 07932 Patrice R. Tobin, Libn.
Founded: 1956. **Staff:** Prof 1. **Subjects:** Engineering - electrical, electronic, hydraulic; business. **Holdings:** 2000 books; 55 VF drawers; 10 VF drawers of standards; complete set of military specifications and standards on microfilm; vendor catalogs. **Subscriptions:** 325 journals and other serials. **Services:** Interlibrary loan; copying; library open to the public with restrictions. **Computerized Information Services:** DIALOG Information Services. **Networks/Consortia:** Member of Northwest Regional Library Cooperative. **Publications:** Abstract Bulletin - for internal distribution only. **Remarks:** FAX: (201)966-2628.

★1368★
Automobile Club of Southern California - Technical Information Center (Trans)
Terminal Annex, Box 2890 Phone: (213)741-4336
Los Angeles, CA 90051 Rashel Esfandi, Mgr.
Founded: 1974. **Staff:** Prof 3; Other 3. **Subjects:** Highway engineering, transportation planning, traffic safety, automotive engineering. **Holdings:** 16,000 books; 170 bound periodical volumes; 8000 reports; 3500 VF folders. **Subscriptions:** 120 journals and other serials. **Services:** Center open to the public with restrictions. **Computerized Information Services:** DIALOG Information Services. **Publications:** Recent Acquisitions, monthly. **Remarks:** FAX: (213)741-4670. Center located at 2601 S. Figueroa St., Los Angeles, CA 90007. **Staff:** Mohammed Khan, Info.Spec.

★1369★
Automotive Hall of Fame, Inc. - Library (Trans)
3225 Cook Rd.
Box 1727 Phone: (517)631-5760
Midland, MI 48641-1727 Donald N. Richetti, Pres.
Subjects: History of automobiles, biography. **Holdings:** Figures not available. **Services:** Library open to the public. **Remarks:** FAX: (517)631-5761.

★1370★
Automotive Information Council - Library (Trans)
13505 Dulles Technology Dr. Phone: (703)713-0700
Herndon, VA 22071-3415 Christine Rudolf, Mgr., Ref.Ctr.
Founded: 1972. **Staff:** Prof 1. **Subjects:** Motor vehicles - manufacture, maintenance, repair; environment; consumerism; safety. **Special Collections:** Periodicals dealing with all facets of the automotive industry. **Holdings:** 100 books; 4000 newspaper clippings indexed under 215 subject headings. **Subscriptions:** 60 journals and other serials. **Services:** Copying; library open to the public by appointment. **Computerized Information Services:** Internal database. **Publications:** NewsFocus, 12/year. **Special Indexes:** Index of information in automotive journals not indexed elsewhere (online). **Remarks:** FAX: (703)713-0727. Affiliated with the National Institute of Automotive Service Excellence.

★1371★
Autoresearch Laboratories, Inc. - Library (Trans)
6735 S. Old Harlem Ave.
Chicago, IL 60638 Phone: (312)563-0900
Subjects: Automotive research and testing. **Holdings:** 300 books; 1000 reports. **Services:** Library not open to the public.

★1372★
Autovative Computer Extensions, Inc. - Library
9734 S. Roberts Rd.
Palos Hills, IL 60465
Founded: 1981. **Subjects:** Data processing, computer intelligence. **Holdings:** 2000 books; vendor information. **Remarks:** Currently inactive.

★1373★
Avantek, Inc. - Technical Information Service (Sci-Engr)
3175 Bowers Ave. Phone: (408)970-2490
Santa Clara, CA 95054-3292 Florence A. Haas, Corp.Libn.
Founded: 1970. **Staff:** Prof 1. **Subjects:** Microwave technology, semiconductors, systems engineering. **Holdings:** 2000 books; 500 government/industry technical reports; 800 patents; military specifications. **Subscriptions:** 210 journals and other serials; 30 newspapers. **Services:** Interlibrary loan; service not open to the public. **Automated Operations:** Computerized cataloging. **Computerized Information Services:** DIALOG Information Services, NASA/RECON, SRI International; OnTyme Electronic Message Network Service (electronic mail service). **Networks/Consortia:** Member of SOUTHNET. **Special Catalogs:** Union List, annual.

Avco Research Laboratory, Inc. - Textron Division
See: **Textron Defense Systems - Everett Library** (16286)

Avery Architectural and Fine Arts Library
See: **Columbia University - Avery Architectural and Fine Arts Library** (4002)

★1374★
Avery Dennison Company - Avery Research Center - Information Services (Sci-Engr)
2900 Bradley St. Phone: (818)398-2555
Pasadena, CA 91107-1599 Dale Stanley, Group Ldr.Info.Sci.
Founded: 1968. **Staff:** Prof 2; Other 1. **Subjects:** Adhesives, polymer chemistry, process and control engineering. **Holdings:** 5000 books; 110 bound periodical volumes; 15,000 patents. **Subscriptions:** 200 journals and other serials. **Services:** Interlibrary loan (limited); center not open to the public. **Automated Operations:** Computerized cataloging, acquisitions, serials, and circulation. **Computerized Information Services:** DIALOG Information Services, Dow Jones News/Retrieval, LEXIS, PFDS Online, DataTimes; internal databases; CD-ROMs; DIALMAIL (electronic mail service). **Publications:** Current Literature; New Acquisitions - for internal distribution only. **Remarks:** FAX: (818)398-2553. **Staff:** Karen Wright, Info.Technologist; Louanne Kalvinskas, Res.Assoc. Patent Spec.

★1375★
Avery Dennison Company - Information Resources (Sci-Engr)
300 Howard St. Phone: (617)879-0511
Framingham, MA 01701 Eva M. Bonis, Mgr.
Founded: 1935. **Staff:** Prof 1; Other 2. **Subjects:** Chemistry, chemical engineering, physics, mechanical engineering, business, marketing. **Holdings:** 4000 books; 4 VF drawers of reprints. **Subscriptions:** 158 journals and other serials. **Services:** Interlibrary loan; resources not open to the public. **Automated Operations:** Computerized circulation. **Computerized Information Services:** DIALOG Information Services, Dow Jones News/Retrieval, ORBIT Search Service. **Publications:** CIR Newsletter, 3-4/month - for internal distribution only. **Remarks:** FAX: (508)879-0525. Contains the holdings of Carter's Ink Company - Technical Library. **Formed by the merger of:** Avery International and Dennison Manufacturing Company. **Staff:** Maryellen White, Asst.Libn.

★1376★
Avery, Hodes, Costello & Burman - Library (Law)
180 N. LaSalle St., Suite 3800 Phone: (312)855-7929
Chicago, IL 60601 Susan Strauch, Libn.
Staff: 2. **Subjects:** Litigation, bankruptcy, corporate and trade law, securities, taxation, real property. **Holdings:** 15,000 books; 50 bound periodical volumes; 6 boxes of microfiche. **Subscriptions:** 280 journals and other serials; 10 newspapers. **Services:** Interlibrary loan; library not open to the public. **Computerized Information Services:** LEXIS, DIALOG Information Services, Hannah Information Systems, Dun & Bradstreet Legal Search. **Networks/Consortia:** Member of Chicago Library System. **Remarks:** Alternate telephone number(s): 855-7928. FAX: (312)855-5190.

★1377★
Aviation Consulting Enterprises Co. - Library (Trans)
P.O. Box 9241 Phone: (515)282-4600
Des Moines, IA 50306-9241 John R. DeWitt, Pres.
Founded: 1971. **Staff:** 2. **Subjects:** Aviation crash analysis, operational efficiency and safety; aircraft and aviation product design and certification. **Holdings:** 2500 FAA and DOD reports and investigatory files; technical data and manuals from a variety of trade and professional entities, governmental agencies, and manufacturers. **Subscriptions:** 25 journals and other serials. **Services:** Copying; library open to the public with restrictions. **Computerized Information Services:** Online systems. **Remarks:** FAX: (515)243-2700. **Staff:** Mark H. Goodrich, Gen.Couns. & Sr.Cons.

Aviation Foundation
See: **EAA** (5089)

★1378★
Aviation Information Services Ltd. - Library (Trans)
Cardinal Point, Newall Rd.
Heathrow Airport (London)
Hounslow, Greater London TW6 2AS, England Phone: 81 897 1066
Subjects: Aviation; airliner, commuter, and business aircraft accidents; airline and commuter airline fleets; airliner production; aircraft disposition. **Holdings:** 1500 bound volumes. **Subscriptions:** 100 journals and other serials. **Computerized Information Services:** Produces Aircraft Accident Data Base. Performs searches on fee basis. **Publications:** Index of Aviation Articles, monthly. **Remarks:** FAX: 81 897 0300. Telex: 934679 AIRCLM G. **Staff:** M.J. Stanley, Tech.Libn.

★1379★
Aviation Safety Consultants - Library (Sci-Engr)
HC-30, Box 813 Phone: (602)445-1555
Prescott, AZ 86301 Virginia Hasbrook
Founded: 1950. **Staff:** 1. **Subjects:** Aviation and air safety. **Special Collections:** Crash safety; crash injury; human factors; in-flight research. **Holdings:** 500 books; 1000 reports. **Subscriptions:** 5 journals and other serials. **Services:** Library open to the public on fee basis. **Staff:** Mary Ann Hoffman.

★1380★
Aviation Safety Institute - Library (Trans)
6797 N. High St., Suite 316
Box 304 Phone: (614)885-4242
Worthington, OH 43085 Judith R. Lowe, V.P., Dev.
Founded: 1973. **Staff:** 8. **Subjects:** Aviation accidents, incidents, and hazards; flight attendant and pilot fatigue and stress studies. **Holdings:** 53 books and bound periodical volumes; reports; microfiche; periodicals; flight recorder archives. **Subscriptions:** 23 journals and other serials. **Services:** Copying; library open to the public by prior arrangement. **Computerized Information Services:** CompuServe Information Service, Aviation Forum (AVSIG). **Remarks:** FAX: (614)885-5891. **Staff:** Leona Drake

Aviation's International Repository Combining Historical Indexes Very Effectively
See: **AIRCHIVE** (154)

Andrey Avinoff Library
See: **Carnegie Museum of Natural History - Library** (3085)

★1381★
Aviodome National Aerospace Museum - Nederlandse Bibliotheek voor Luchtvaart en Ruimtevaart (Sci-Engr)
NL-1118 AA Schiphol, Netherlands Phone: 20 6041521
B. Van Splunter
Founded: 1907. **Staff:** 12. **Subjects:** Aeronautics. **Holdings:** 10,000 books; 6000 bound periodical volumes; 16,000 archival items. **Subscriptions:** 10 journals and other serials. **Services:** Copying; library open to members of aviation societies only. **Computerized Information Services:** Internal database.

★1382★
AVKO Educational Research Foundation - Library (Educ)
3084 W. Willard Rd.
Birch Run, MI 48415 Phone: (313)686-9283
Founded: 1974. **Subjects:** Special education, reading, spelling, dyslexia. **Holdings:** 4000 volumes. **Services:** Copying; library open to the public. **Remarks:** FAX: (313)686-1101.

★1383★
Avon Products, Inc. - Research Library (Sci-Engr, Med)
Division St. Phone: (914)357-2000
Suffern, NY 10901 Sarah Boroson, Prog.Ldr.
Founded: 1934. **Staff:** Prof 1; Other 1. **Subjects:** Cosmetics, packaging, toxicology, dermatology, pharmacology, chemistry, engineering, microbiology. **Holdings:** 6500 books; 5000 bound periodical volumes; 6000 U.S. and foreign patents. **Subscriptions:** 300 journals and other serials. **Services:** Interlibrary loan; SDI; library open to the public for reference use only on request. **Automated Operations:** Computerized serials. **Computerized Information Services:** DIALOG Information Services, ORBIT Search Service, STN International, Chemical Information Systems, Inc. (CIS), Data-Star, MEDLINE; DIALMAIL (electronic mail service). **Networks/Consortia:** Member of Southeastern New York Library Resources Council (SENYLRC). **Special Catalogs:** List of serials received by library. **Remarks:** FAX: (914)357-6094.

★1384★
The Awareness Research Foundation, Inc. - Metaphysical Library (Rel-Phil)
PO Box 134 Phone: (704)389-8744
Brasstown, NC 28902 Jewell Palland Bowles, Exec.Dir.
Subjects: Metaphysics, astrology, spaceships, space people, Bible prophecy, philosophy. **Holdings:** 1000 books. **Services:** Library open to the public. **Publications:** List of publications - available on request. **Formerly:** Located in Hayesville, NC.

Leonard H. Axe Library
See: **Pittsburg State University** (13082)

★1385★
Axon Group - Library
747 Dresher Rd.
Horsham, PA 19044
Founded: 1978. **Subjects:** Labor relations, insurance, business, human resources. **Holdings:** 5000 books; 1000 bound periodical volumes; microfilm; microfiche. **Remarks:** Currently inactive. **Formerly:** Located in Fort Washington, PA.

★1386★
NW Ayer Incorporated - Ayer Information Center (AIC) (Publ)
Worldwide Plaza
825 8th Ave. Phone: (212)474-5181
New York, NY 10019-7498 Holly J. Bussey, V.P., Mgr.
Founded: 1969. **Staff:** Prof 2. **Subjects:** Advertising, general business, merchandising, sales, statistics, trade directories. **Holdings:** 2000 volumes; 300 VF drawers. **Subscriptions:** 300 journals and other serials; 5 newspapers. **Services:** Center not open to the public. **Computerized Information Services:** DIALOG Information Services, NewsNet, Inc., NEXIS, DataTimes, VU/TEXT Information Services, CompuServe Information Service, InvesText. **Remarks:** FAX: (212)474-5038; 474-5178. **Staff:** Maxine Brennan, Comp.Info.Spec.

Ayer Ornithology Library
See: **Field Museum of Natural History - Library** (5684)

★1387★
Ayerst, McKenna & Harrison, Inc. - Library (Sci-Engr)
1025 Blvd. Laurentien Phone: (514)744-6771
St. Laurent, PQ, Canada H4R 1J6 Nicole Barrette-Pilon, Libn.
Founded: 1940. **Staff:** Prof 1; Other 1. **Subjects:** Chemistry, medicine, pharmaceuticals, veterinary medicine. **Holdings:** 1000 books; 5000 bound periodical volumes; 400 reels of microfilm. **Subscriptions:** 290 journals and other serials. **Services:** Interlibrary loan; copying; library open to the public by appointment. **Computerized Information Services:** CAN/OLE, DIALOG Information Services, Questel, STN International, MEDLINE, Data-Star, Infomart Online, ORBIT Search Service; Envoy 100 (electronic mail service). **Publications:** Library Bulletin, monthly. **Remarks:** FAX: (514)744-0550. Electronic mail address(es): 2MAX.PEB (Envoy 100).

★1388★
Azerbaijan Composers' Union - Library (Mus)
Ulitsa Khagani 27
Baku, Azerbaijan Phone: 93 2258
Subjects: Music. **Holdings:** 6000 books, notes, records, and composers' monographs.

★1389★
King Abdul Aziz Research Center - Library (Area-Ethnic)
P.O. Box 2945
King Faisal Hospital Rd. Phone: 1 4412316
Riyadh 11461, Saudi Arabia Abdul Aziz Abu-Butain, Lib.Hd.
Subjects: Saudi Arabia - history, geography, literature, cultural and intellectual heritage; history of Arabian peninsula; Arab Islamic countries. **Holdings:** 29,000 volumes. **Services:** Library open to the public.

Aztec Ruins National Monument
See: **U.S. Natl. Park Service** (17671)

★1390★
Azusa Pacific University - Special Collections (Hist, Rel-Phil)
901 E. Alosta Ave.
PO Box APU Phone: (818)969-3434
Azusa, CA 91702 Paul Gray
Subjects: American West, history of religion in America, Southern California history. **Special Collections:** George Fullerton Collection of Western Americana (9000 volumes); Azusa Foothill Citrus Collection on the Southern California Citrus Industry (6000 documents); John Hess Memorial Holiness Collection (1000 volumes); Alfred H. Wilcox Papers (500 pieces); Macneil Family Collection (500 pieces); Roger P. Dalton Collection (1000 pieces); Monsignor Francis Weber Collection on American Catholic Church (3 drawers); Irving Stone Collection on Abraham Lincoln and John Adams (450 volumes). **Holdings:** 20,000 books; 200 bound periodical volumes; document collections on Southern California history. **Services:** Collections open to the public with restrictions. **Remarks:** FAX: (818)969-6611.

B

★1391★
B.C. Hydro - Information Services (Energy)
970 Burrard St. Phone: (604)663-2416
Vancouver, BC, Canada V6Z 1Y3 Elizabeth McLaren, Mgr.
Founded: 1957. **Staff:** Prof 3; Other 5. **Subjects:** Public utilities, electrical engineering, industrial development, statistics, civil and mechanical engineering, structural engineering, management. **Holdings:** 11,000 books; 750 bound periodical volumes; 2000 pamphlets; 28 VF drawers of annual reports; 26 VF drawers of government documents; 17 VF drawers of standards. **Subscriptions:** 530 journals and other serials. **Services:** Interlibrary loan; copying; center open to the public for reference use only on request. **Automated Operations:** Computerized serials. **Computerized Information Services:** DIALOG Information Services, CAN/OLE, QL Systems, Info Globe, WESTLAW, Mead Data Central, PFDS Online, Reuters; internal database. **Remarks:** FAX: (604)663-3515. Electronic mail address(es): BCH (Envoy 100).

B.C. Hydro - Powertech Labs Inc.
See: **Powertech Labs Inc.** (13282)

★1392★
B.C. Rail - Library
P.O. Box 8770 Phone: (604)984-5248
Vancouver, BC, Canada V6B 4X6 Kathryn Boegel, Libn.
Remarks: No further information was supplied by respondent.

★1393★
B & W Nuclear Technologies - Library (Sci-Engr)
Box 10935 Phone: (804)385-2476
Lynchburg, VA 24506-0935 Karen A. Wolfe, Hd.Libn.
Founded: 1956. **Staff:** Prof 1; Other 1. **Subjects:** Nuclear technology, physics, materials, computer technology, chemistry. **Holdings:** 10,000 books; 700 bound periodical volumes; 40,000 technical reports; 500,000 technical reports on microfiche; 17 VF drawers of standards and conference papers. **Subscriptions:** 100 journals and other serials. **Services:** Interlibrary loan; copying; library open to the public by appointment. **Automated Operations:** Computerized public access catalog, cataloging, and circulation. **Computerized Information Services:** DIALOG Information Services, OCLC. **Publications:** Information Services Digest, monthly - to company engineers. **Remarks:** FAX: (804)385-3663. Telex: 19 7899 BW LYN.

Charles Babbage Institute Collection
See: **University of Minnesota** (18899)

Homer Babbidge Library
See: **University of Connecticut - Homer Babbidge Library - Special Collections** (18519)

Babcock Graduate School of Management
See: **Wake Forest University** (19938)

★1394★
Babcock and Wilcox Company - Corporate Information Center (Energy, Sci-Engr)
Box 835 Phone: (216)821-9110
Alliance, OH 44601 Mary Sue Michael, Supv.
Founded: 1947. **Staff:** Prof 1; Other 4. **Subjects:** Mechanics, chemical engineering, fuels engineering, heat transfer, chemistry, metallurgy, welding, electronics, nuclear science and technology. **Holdings:** 18,000 books; 1500 reels of microfilm of periodical back files; 29,000 government and company reports on microfiche. **Subscriptions:** 375 journals and other serials. **Services:** Interlibrary loan; copying; library open to the public. **Automated Operations:** Computerized public access catalog and circulation. **Computerized Information Services:** DIALOG Information Services, PFDS Online, BRS Information Technologies, STN International, NEXIS, Dow Jones News/Retrieval; DataTimes; internal database. **Remarks:** FAX: (216)823-0639. Babcock and Wilcox is a subsidiary of McDermott Inc.

★1395★
Babson College - Babson College Archives (Hum)
Horn Library Phone: (617)239-4570
Wellesley, MA 02157-0901 Elizabeth Tate, Archv. & Recs.Mgt.Coord.
Founded: 1980. **Subjects:** Roger W. Babson and Babson College. **Holdings:** College records (founding years to present); books; manuscripts; visual materials. **Services:** Archives open to Babson College community and qualified researchers.

★1396★
Babson College - Horn Library - Sir Isaac Newton Collection (Sci-Engr)
Wellesley, MA 02157-0901 Phone: (617)239-4570
Elizabeth Tate, Archv. & Recs.Mgt.Coord.
Founded: 1980. **Holdings:** 1000 volumes of Newton's work (English and foreign); biographies; autograph manuscripts; portraits; maps; medals; memorabilia. **Services:** Collection is open to Babson College community and qualified researchers. **Special Catalogs:** Catalog of Newton Collection. **Remarks:** Several volumes in the collection are from Newton's library and contain annotations and corrections in Newton's hand.

Babson Library
See: **Springfield College** (15601)

Paul Talbot Babson Memorial Library
See: **Newton-Wellesley Hospital** (11789)

Roger W. Babson Collection
See: **Babson College** (1395)

★1397★
Francois Baby House: Windsor's Community Museum - Reference Library (Hist)
254 Pitt St., W. Phone: (519)253-1812
Windsor, ON, Canada N9A 5L5 Laurence Grant, Cur.
Founded: 1958. **Staff:** 4. **Subjects:** Local history. **Holdings:** 985 books; 29 bound periodical volumes; 327 archival materials; 506 maps; 3221 photographs; 184 reels of microfilm; 1800 microfiche. **Subscriptions:** 26 journals and other serials. **Services:** Copying; library open to the public. **Remarks:** Maintained by the Windsor Public Library Board. **Remarks:** Alternate telephone number(s): (519)253-0919. **Formerly:** Hiram Walker Historical Museum.

Bacchus Works Library
See: **Hercules Aerospace Company - Bacchus Works Library** (7146)

Bach Library
See: **Baldwin-Wallace College - Riemenschneider Bach Institute** (1432)

★1398★
Betty Bacharach Medical/Clinical Staff Library (Med)
Jim Leeds Rd. Phone: (609)748-5391
Pomona, NJ 08240 Susan B. Kidd, Med./Clin.Staff Libn.
Staff: Prof 1. **Subjects:** Physical therapy, audiology, respiratory therapy, physical medicine, clinical psychology, rehabilitative nursing. **Holdings:** 218 books; 50 documents. **Subscriptions:** 38 journals and other serials. **Services:** Interlibrary loan; library not open to the public. **Networks/Consortia:** Member of Pinelands Consortium for Health Information, South Jersey Regional Library Cooperative. **Publications:** Listing of new acquisitions, irregular - for internal distribution only.

★1399★
Backer Spielvogel Bates - Information Center (Bus-Fin)
405 Lexington Ave. Phone: (212)297-8709
New York, NY 10174 Ms. Bert Schachter, Dir./V.P.
Founded: 1940. **Staff:** Prof 2; Other 2; **Subjects:** Advertising, marketing. **Special Collections:** Photographs. **Holdings:** 3500 volumes; 75 VF drawers. **Subscriptions:** 250 journals and other serials. **Services:** Copying; center open to SLA members by appointment. **Computerized Information Services:** DIALOG Information Services, NEXIS, Dow Jones News/Retrieval. **Remarks:** FAX: (212)697-1443.

E. Burdette Backus Memorial Library
See: **All Souls Unitarian Church** (358)

★1400★
William W. Backus Hospital - Medical/Nursing Library (Med)
326 Washington St. Phone: (203)823-6327
Norwich, CT 06360 Elaine Spalding, Med.Libn.
Staff: Prof 1. **Subjects:** Anesthesiology, surgery, obstetrics, gynecology, internal medicine, pediatrics. **Holdings:** 500 books; 1700 bound periodical volumes. **Subscriptions:** 100 journals and other serials. **Services:** Interlibrary loan; library open to the public by appointment. **Computerized Information Services:** MEDLINE.

Bacon Collection
See: **Dalhousie University** (4539)

★1401★
Francis Bacon Foundation, Inc. - Francis Bacon Library (Hum)
655 N. Dartmouth Ave. Phone: (714)624-6305
Claremont, CA 91711 Elizabeth S. Wrigley, Dir.
Founded: 1938. **Staff:** Prof 3; Other 2. **Subjects:** Francis Bacon, 16th-18th century English literature and history, Dante, anti-Shakespeareana. **Special Collections:** Lee-Bernard Collection (18th century American political theory); 16th and 17th century Emblem literature; Arensberg Archives (20th century art, Dada period; 650 manuscripts and letters); cryptography; Rosicrucians. **Holdings:** 12,500 volumes; 105 bound periodical volumes; 20 unbound reports; 130 Princeton files of pamphlets; 25 maps; 2 VF drawers of clippings; 4 VF drawers of photographs and photostats; 22 boxes of archival materials; 45 manuscripts; 84 reels of microfilm. **Subscriptions:** 42 journals and other serials. **Services:** Interlibrary loan (limited); copying; library open to the public for reference use only. **Networks/Consortia:** Member of Cooperating Librarians in Claremont (CLIC). **Special Catalogs:** Catalog to STC numbers (1475-1640) in the Bacon Library; catalog to Wing numbers (1641-1700) in the Bacon Library - both free to libraries; Supplement to STC and Wing holdings in the Library - for sale; Lee-Bernard Collection (long-title) - for sale; Cryptography (book); Shakespeare (book); Bacon (book); Rosicrucian and Occult (book); Emblems (book); Brown Collection of Elizabethan and Jacobean Literature (book). **Remarks:** Foundation is affiliated with The Claremont Colleges. **Staff:** Naomi S. Gorse, Archv.; Elizabeth Earle, Asst.Libn.

★1402★
Bacon Industries, Inc. - Library (Sci-Engr)
192 Pleasant St. Phone: (617)926-2550
Watertown, MA 02172 Richard Cass, Pres.
Founded: 1952. **Subjects:** Materials. **Holdings:** 200 books; 800 reports. **Subscriptions:** 20 journals and other serials. **Services:** Library not open to the public. **Remarks:** FAX: (617)926-2022. Telex: 710 327 6518.

★1403★
Bacone College - Library - Special Collections (Area-Ethnic)
East Shawnee Phone: (918)683-4581
Muskogee, OK 74403 Frances A. Donelson, Libn.
Founded: 1880. **Staff:** Prof 1; Other 1. **Subjects:** North American Indians, nursing, radiologic technology, religion. **Holdings:** 31,000 books; 4746 bound periodical volumes; 10 drawers of microfiche; 2 cabinets of microfilm; 20 video cassettes. **Subscriptions:** 150 journals and other serials; 17 newspapers. **Services:** Interlibrary loan; copying; collections open to the public. **Staff:** Lois Webb, Asst.Libn.

Bad Axe Museum of Local History
See: **Allen House Museum** (378)

Baden-Wurtemberg State Ministry of Science and Art - Institute for Astronomical Computations
See: **Astronomisches Rechen-Institut** (1183)

Badger Engineers, Inc.
See: **Raytheon Company** (13726)

Badlands National Park
See: **U.S. Natl. Park Service** (17672)

★1404★
Leo Baeck Institute - Library (Area-Ethnic)
129 E. 73rd St. Phone: (212)744-6400
New York, NY 10021 Robert A. Jacobs, Exec.Dir.
Founded: 1955. **Staff:** Prof 7; Other 7. **Subjects:** History and literature of German-speaking Jewry in Central Europe. **Holdings:** 60,000 books; 10,000 bound periodical volumes; 2000 linear feet of archival materials; 2000 reels of microfilm; 1200 unpublished memoirs, manuscripts, typescripts; 385 manuscripts. **Subscriptions:** 96 journals and other serials. **Services:** Interlibrary loan; copying; library open to the public. **Automated Operations:** Computerized cataloging. **Computerized Information Services:** RLIN. **Networks/Consortia:** Member of Research Libraries Information Network (RLIN). **Publications:** Leo Baeck Institute Library & Archives News, 2/year - to libraries, scholars, and institutions. **Special Catalogs:** Katalog: LBI New York "Bibliothek und Archiv," Volume I, 1970; Catalog of Archival Collections, Volume III, 1990. **Remarks:** FAX: (212)988-1305. **Staff:** Evelyn Ehrlich, Libn.; Nusi Sznaider, Archv.; Frank Mecklenburg, Archv.; Diane Spielmann, Archv.; Yitzhak Kertesz, Dp.Libn.

Baetjer Memorial Library
See: **Johns Hopkins University - School of Medicine - Department of Pediatrics** (8430)

★1405★
Bagaduce Music Lending Library (Mus)
Greene's Hill
P.O. Box 829 Phone: (207)374-5454
Blue Hill, ME 04614 Marcia W. Chapman, Exec.Dir.
Founded: 1983. **Staff:** Prof 4; Other 30. **Subjects:** Music - choral, keyboard, instrumental, vocal. **Special Collections:** Maine state collection (2000 titles). **Holdings:** 3000 books; 500,000 pieces of music. **Subscriptions:** 4 journals and other serials. **Services:** Copying; library open to the public; borrowing privileges limited to members. **Automated Operations:** Computerized cataloging. **Networks/Consortia:** Member of Maine Regional Library System. **Publications:** Upbeat, semiannual - available on request. **Special Catalogs:** Music catalogs (printouts). **Staff:** Mary Cheyney Gould, Mus.Dir.; Sue K. Loomis, Assoc.Dir.; Gigi Leonard, Circ.Mgr.; Karen Dickes, Coll.Mgr.

Marguerite G. Bagshaw Collection
See: **Toronto Public Library** (16416)

★1406★
Baha'i Faith Library & Archives (Rel-Phil)
5209 N. University Phone: (309)691-9311
Peoria, IL 61614 Juliette Whittaker, Libn.
Founded: 1928. **Staff:** Prof 1. **Subjects:** Bahai, comparative religions, world order administration, philosophy, sociology, spirituality of man, education. **Special Collections:** Star of the West (30 volumes); Bahai News (complete); Bahai World (complete set). **Holdings:** 2233 books; 50 bound periodical volumes; 1400 pamphlets; music; 132 tapes; 25 filmstrips and slides; 55 videotapes. **Subscriptions:** 7 journals and other serials; 3 newspapers. **Services:** Library open to the public on request. **Remarks:** Maintained by Peoria Bahai Assembly.

★1407★
Baha'i World Centre - Library (Rel-Phil)
16 Golomb Ave.
P.O. Box 155 Phone: 4 358358
31001 Haifa, Israel Louise Mould, Act.Hd.
Founded: 1977. **Staff:** 12. **Subjects:** Baha'i and Babi religions, Iran and the Middle East, Islam, comparative religion. **Special Collections:** A.L.M. Nicolas Collection (Shaykhi, Babi, and Baha'i manuscripts); Mirza Abu'l-Fadl Gulpaygani Library; A.H. Ishraq-Khvari Collection; Library of Shoghi

Effendi (Guardian of the Baha'i Faith); Baha'i faith, 1977 to present (27,000 clippings). **Holdings:** 26,678 books; 1040 bound periodical volumes; 61,850 pamphlets; 4600 AV programs; 2000 microforms; 300 nonbook items. **Subscriptions:** 400 journals and other serials; 10 newspapers. **Services:** Copying (limited); library open to accepted researchers only. **Computerized Information Services:** Computerized cataloging. **Computerized Information Services:** DIALOG Information Services, Dow Jones News/Retrieval, LEXIS, NEXIS, OCLC, Conservation Information Network, Easynet. **Remarks:** Alternate telephone number(s): 4 372426. FAX: 4 358280. Telex: 46626 BAYT IL. **Staff:** J. Beavers, Ref.Libn.; M. Rowshan, Acq.Libn., Monographs; B. Deamer, Acq.Libn., Per.

★1408★
Baham Corporation - Library (Sci-Engr)
9135 Guilford Rd., Suite 200 Phone: (301)498-4100
Columbia, MD 21046 Gary Baham, Pres.
Founded: 1976. **Subjects:** Engineering - naval, marine, mechanical; computer science. **Holdings:** 5000 books; 20 bound periodical volumes; 1000 reports. **Subscriptions:** 20 journals and other serials; 4 newspapers. **Services:** Library not open to the public. **Computerized Information Services:** DIALOG Information Services, Dow Jones News/Retrieval, The Source. **Publications:** U.S. Navy Computerized Ship Design Abstracts. **Remarks:** FAX: (301)498-8876.

Tom and Mae Bahan Library
See: **Sherman College of Straight Chiropractic** (15126)

★1409★
(Bahrain) College of Health Sciences - Ahmed Al-Farsi Library (Med)
POB 12 Phone: 252761
Manama, Bahrain Dr. Bruce M. Manzer, Chf.Med.Libn.
Founded: 1976. **Staff:** Prof 3; Other 3. **Subjects:** Medicine, health education, nursing. **Special Collections:** Bahrain Collection. **Holdings:** 25,000 books; 8000 bound periodical volumes; 1000 AV materials. **Subscriptions:** 556 journals and other serials; 3 newspapers. **Services:** Copying; library open to the public for reference use only. **Computerized Information Services:** CD-ROM (MEDLINE). **Publications:** List of serials, annual. **Remarks:** FAX: (973) 252569. Telex: 8511 HEALTH BN.

Bailey Hortorium Library
See: **Cornell University - Bailey Hortorium Library** (4304)

Jean Bailey Memorial Library
See: **Burnaby School Board - Teachers' Professional Library** (2380)

John Reid Bain Library
See: **Queen's University at Kingston** (13651)

★1410★
Baird, Holm, McEachen, Pedersen, Hamann, Strasheim - Library (Law)
1500 Woodmen Tower Phone: (402)344-0500
Omaha, NE 68102 Anne Lomax Baumgartner, Libn.
Staff: Prof 1; Other 1. **Subjects:** Law - taxation, bankruptcy, school, labor, hospital, securities, banking, insurance, litigation, education. **Holdings:** 15,000 books; 600 bound periodical volumes. **Subscriptions:** 200 journals and other serials; 15 newspapers. **Services:** Library not open to the public. **Computerized Information Services:** DIALOG Information Services, WESTLAW, Nebraska Health Network, LEXIS, Nebraska Legislative Shared Information System, internal database. **Remarks:** FAX: (402)344-0588.

Eugenie Silverman Baizerman Archive
See: **University of North Carolina at Greensboro** (19081)

Saul Baizerman Archive
See: **University of North Carolina at Greensboro** (19089)

Blanche M. Baker Memorial Library
See: **ONE, Inc.** (12419)

★1411★
Baker & Botts - Law Library (Law)
3000 One Shell Plaza Phone: (713)229-1643
Houston, TX 77002 Robert K. Downie, Libn.
Staff: Prof 6; Other 10. **Subjects:** Law - tax, intellectual property, public utilities, labor, bankruptcy, corporate, energy, real estate, oil and gas, probate, international, trial, banking, environmental, admiralty, antitrust. **Holdings:** 75,000 books. **Subscriptions:** 1500 journals and other serials. **Services:** Interlibrary loan; copying; library open to attorneys. **Computerized Information Services:** DIALOG Information Services, WESTLAW, LEXIS, Dow Jones News/Retrieval, ORBIT Search Service, VU/TEXT Information Services, DataTimes, Information America, LEGI-SLATE, Prentice Hall Online. **Publications:** Library Notes, monthly - to all attorneys. **Special Indexes:** Automated index to firm memos. **Staff:** Donna Joity, Assoc. & Acq.Libn.; Emily Clement, Ref.Libn.; Suzanne Estep, Cat.; Cynthia Montalvo, Ref. & ILL Libn.; Donna Dixon, Ref.Libn.; Cathy LoPiccolo, Ref.Libn.

Charles R. Baker Memorial Library
See: **American Association of Orthodontists** (484)

★1412★
Baker College of Muskegon - Library (Bus-Fin)
141 Hartford Phone: (616)726-4904
Muskegon, MI 49442 Margaret Moon, Libn.
Founded: 1885. **Staff:** 3. **Subjects:** Business management, economics, accounting. **Holdings:** 24,000 books. **Subscriptions:** 180 journals and other serials. **Services:** Library not open to the public.

★1413★
Baker & Daniels - Law Library (Law)
300 N. Meridian St., Suite 2700 Phone: (317)237-0300
Indianapolis, IN 46204 Angela G. Doll, Lib.Dir.
Staff: Prof 2; Other 3. **Subjects:** Law. **Holdings:** 50,000 books; 3000 bound periodical volumes; 4300 microfiche; 15 drawers of pamphlets. **Subscriptions:** 250 journals and other serials; 7 newspapers. **Services:** Interlibrary loan; library not open to the public. **Computerized Information Services:** LEXIS, DIALOG Information Services, WESTLAW, Information America, Human Resource Information Network (HRIN), VU/TEXT Information Services, DataTimes. **Networks/Consortia:** Member of Indianapolis Law Cataloging Consortium, Central Indiana Area Library Services Authority (CIALSA). **Publications:** Newsletter, monthly. **Remarks:** FAX: (317)237-1000. **Staff:** Paula O. Schmidt.

★1414★
H.M. Baker Associates - Research Collection (Hist)
Box 363 Phone: (908)233-5514
Westfield, NJ 07090 Helen Baker Cushman, Mng.Assoc.
Founded: 1958. **Staff:** Prof 1. **Subjects:** Business history. **Holdings:** Books, archives, and photos. **Services:** Collection not open to the public. **Publications:** Business histories.

Herman M. Baker, M.D. Memorial Library
See: **St. Mary's Medical Center** (14531)

★1415★
Baker and Hostetler - Library (Law)
3200 National City Ctr. Phone: (216)621-0200
Cleveland, OH 44114 Alvin M. Podboy, Dir. of Libs.
Staff: Prof 2; Other 4. **Subjects:** Law. **Holdings:** 50,000 volumes. **Services:** Interlibrary loan; library open to the public by invitation. **Computerized Information Services:** LEXIS, NEXIS, DIALOG Information Services, WESTLAW, VU/TEXT Information Services, Hannah Information Systems, LEGI-SLATE, DataTimes, Maxwell Macmillan Taxes Online. **Remarks:** FAX: (216)696-0740. **Staff:** Susan Miljenovic, Libn.

★1416★
Baker and Hostetler - Library (Law)
65 E. State St., Suite 2100 Phone: (614)462-2608
Columbus, OH 43215 Judith P. Rodgers, Libn.
Staff: Prof 1; Other 2. **Subjects:** Ohio law. **Holdings:** 20,000 books. **Subscriptions:** 112 journals and other serials; 7 newspapers. **Services:** Library not open to the public. **Automated Operations:** Computerized cataloging. **Computerized Information Services:** DIALOG Information Services, LEXIS, WESTLAW. **Remarks:** FAX: (614)462-2616.

★1417★
Baker & Hostetler, McCutchen Black - Law Library (Law)
600 Wilshire Blvd. Phone: (213)624-2400
Los Angeles, CA 90017 Stewart Annand, Libn.
Staff: 2. **Subjects:** Law. **Holdings:** 30,000 volumes. **Subscriptions:** 200 journals and other serials. **Services:** Library not open to the public. **Computerized Information Services:** DIALOG Information Services, LEXIS, WESTLAW, Information America, LEGI-SLATE, Legi-Tech. **Remarks:** FAX: (213)975-1740; (213)975-1741.

★1418★
J.E. Baker Company - Library (Sci-Engr)
Box 1189 Phone: (717)792-4615
York, PA 17405 Nancy Stough, Libn.
Subjects: Ceramics, refractories. **Holdings:** 500 books; 5000 reports. **Subscriptions:** 15 journals and other serials. **Services:** Library not open to the public. **Computerized Information Services:** DIALOG Information Services. **Remarks:** FAX: (717)792-5103.

★1419★
J.T. Baker Inc. - The Library Center (Sci-Engr)
Phillipsburg, NJ 08865 Phone: (201)859-2151
Janie E. Welty, Lib./Info.Mgr.
Founded: 1945. **Staff:** Prof 1; Other 1. **Subjects:** Chemistry - analytical, organic. **Holdings:** 10,000 monographs; 10,000 bound periodical volumes; 15 drawers of microfilm cartridges. **Subscriptions:** 180 journals and other serials. **Services:** Interlibrary loan; library not open to the public. **Computerized Information Services:** PFDS Online, DIALOG Information Services, STN International, NLM. **Networks/Consortia:** Member of Northwest Regional Library Cooperative. **Remarks:** FAX: (201)859-9454. **Formerly:** Its A.J. Barnard Jr. Library.

James A. Baker, III Political Archive
See: **Rice University - Woodson Research Center** (13897)

K.M. Baker Memorial Library
See: **Lansing General Hospital, Osteopathic** (8947)

Baker Library
See: **Harvard University - Harvard Business School - Baker Library** (6969)

Baker Library
See: **U.S. Air Force Base - Castle Base** (16833)

Marjorie Montgomery Ward Baker Library
See: **Visiting Nurse Association of Chicago** (19901)

★1420★
Baker & McKenzie - Law Library (Law)
805 3rd Ave. Phone: (212)891-3968
New York, NY 10022 Janet S. Zagorin, Lib.Dir.
Founded: 1971. **Staff:** Prof 2; Other 2. **Subjects:** Law, foreign law, international law, captive insurance. **Holdings:** 10,000 volumes. **Subscriptions:** 100 journals and other serials. **Services:** Interlibrary loan; library open to the public by appointment. **Computerized Information Services:** WESTLAW, LEXIS, DIALOG Information Services, Dow Jones News/Retrieval, VU/TEXT Information Services, LEGI-SLATE, DataTimes, RLIN, Financial Post Information Service; internal database. **Staff:** Joann Doria, Ref.Libn.; Pat Stern, Asst.Libn.

★1421★
Baker & McKenzie - Library (Law)
2 Embarcadero Center, Suite 2400 Phone: (415)576-3066
San Francisco, CA 94111-3909 Donna Purvis, Libn.
Founded: 1970. **Staff:** Prof 2; Other 2. **Subjects:** Law. **Holdings:** 2000 books; 100 bound periodical volumes. **Subscriptions:** 250 journals and other serials; 15 newspapers. **Services:** Interlibrary loan; library not open to the public. **Automated Operations:** Computerized public access catalog (Data Trek). **Computerized Information Services:** LEXIS, DIALOG Information Services, WESTLAW, Dow Jones News/Retrieval, RLIN, LEGI-TECH, Dun & Bradstreet Business Credit Services, DataTimes, Information America. **Remarks:** FAX: (415)576-3099. Telex: 278588 ABOG UR. **Staff:** Caren Doyle, Ref.Libn.

★1422★
Baker & McKenzie - Library (Law, Bus-Fin)
One Prudential Plaza, Suite 2800
130 E. Randolph Dr. Phone: (312)861-2915
Chicago, IL 60601 Lorraine A. Kulpa, Lib.Dir.
Founded: 1950. **Staff:** 10. **Subjects:** U.S. taxation; corporations; foreign trade and investment; Illinois law; foreign and international material on company law, civil law and civil procedure, investment laws, securities, and taxation. **Special Collections:** Foreign law; Baker & McKenzie copyrighted publications. **Holdings:** 42,000 volumes. **Subscriptions:** 600 journals and other serials. **Services:** Interlibrary loan. **Automated Operations:** Computerized cataloging, acquisitions, and serials. **Computerized Information Services:** LEXIS, WESTLAW, OCLC, DIALOG Information Services; internal databases. **Networks/Consortia:** Member of ILLINET. **Remarks:** FAX: (312)861-2898; (312)861-2899. Telex: 254425; 206010.

★1423★
Michael Baker, Jr., Inc. - Library (Sci-Engr)
4301 Dutch Ridge Rd.
P.O. Box 280 Phone: (412)495-4357
Beaver, PA 15009 Ruth J. Williams, Libn.
Founded: 1972. **Staff:** Prof 1. **Subjects:** Civil engineering, hazardous waste, environmental planning, business, structural and highway engineering, geographic digital mapping information. **Special Collections:** Company planning reports (300 bound volumes); Federal Register, 1976 to present (microfiche); American Society of Civil Engineers Journal, 1966 to present; Transportation Research Board publications. **Holdings:** 5000 books; 12 VF drawers of pamphlets; 351 reels of microfilm. **Subscriptions:** 100 journals and other serials; 4 newspapers. **Services:** Interlibrary loan; copying; library at librarian's discretion. **Computerized Information Services:** DIALOG Information Services, Institute for Scientific Information (ISI), National Ground Water Information Center Data Base, Occupational Health Services, Inc. (OHS). **Remarks:** FAX: (412)495-4001.

Solomon R. Baker Library
See: **Bentley College** (1724)

★1424★
Tom Baker Cancer Centre - Library (Med)
1331 29th St., N.W. Phone: (403)670-1765
Calgary, AB, Canada T2N 4N2 Judy Flax, Libn.
Founded: 1982. **Staff:** Prof 1. **Subjects:** Oncology. **Holdings:** 1300 books; 900 bound periodical volumes; 60 audio cassettes; 105 videocassettes; 6 slide/tape programs. **Subscriptions:** 87 journals and other serials. **Services:** Interlibrary loan; copying; library open to area health professionals, patients, and their families. **Computerized Information Services:** MEDLARS, DIALOG Information Services; Envoy 100 (electronic mail service). **Remarks:** FAX: (403)670-1765. Electronic mail address(es): ILL.TBCC (Envoy 100).

★1425★
Baker University - Archives and Historical Library (Rel-Phil, Hist)
Collins Library Phone: (913)594-6451
Baldwin City, KS 66006 Maxine Kreutziger, Adm.Sec.
Staff: 1. **Subjects:** United Methodism, Kansas. **Special Collections:** Baker Archives. **Holdings:** 10,000 books and bound periodical volumes; 50 file drawers of manuscripts and photographs; church histories and records; clippings; missionary artifacts; Baker University memorabilia. **Services:** Copying (limited); library open to the public. **Automated Operations:** Computerized cataloging. **Remarks:** Jointly maintained with Commission on Archives and History of the Kansas East Conference of the United Methodist Church.

★1426★
Baker University - Quayle Rare Bible Collection (Rel-Phil)
Library
8th St. Phone: (913)594-6451
Baldwin City, KS 66006 Dr. John M. Forbes, Dir. of Libs.
Founded: 1925. **Staff:** Prof 1; Other 1. **Subjects:** Rare Bibles and religious works. **Special Collections:** Bishop William Alfred Quayle Collection of Rare Bibles (275). **Holdings:** 450 books; 4 clay tablets and papyrus fragment. **Services:** Copying (limited); collection open to the public by appointment.

Bakhmeteff Archive of Russian and East European History and
See: **Columbia University - Rare Book and Manuscript Library** (4023)

★1427★
The Bakken: A Library and Museum of Electricity in Life (Sci-Engr, Hist)
3537 Zenith Ave., S. Phone: (612)927-6508
Minneapolis, MN 55416 Dorina Morawetz, Interim Dir.
Founded: 1976. **Staff:** 6. **Subjects:** History of electricity, electrophysiology, electrotherapeutics, and magnetism; mesmerism; animal magnetism; alternative medicine. **Special Collections:** Instrument collection (2000 electrical and electrotherapeutic instruments, 18th-20th centuries); Mesmerism manuscript collection (56 items); Albert Abrams papers (7 boxes). **Holdings:** 9000 books; 2000 bound periodical volumes; 300 trade catalogs; 200 pieces of ephemera; 30 manuscripts. **Subscriptions:** 24 journals and other serials. **Services:** Copying; library open to the public for reference use by appointment. **Publications:** The Electric Quarterly. **Special Catalogs:** Catalog of books and manuscripts (card). **Special Indexes:** Index to ephemera; index to instruments. **Remarks:** FAX: (612)927-7265. **Staff:** Elizabeth Ihrig, Cur., Bks. & Mss.; Albert Kuhfeld, Cur., Instruments; Naum Kipnis, Sci. Educator.

Lavola Bakken Memorial Library
See: **Douglas County Museum** (4973)

Bakwin Library
See: **American Academy of Pediatrics** (463)

Jack Balaban Memorial Library
See: **Temple Sinai** (16125)

Balai Besar Penelitian dan Pengembangan Industri Kerajinan dan Batik
See: **Institute for Research and Development of Handicraft and Batik Industries** (7971)

★1428★
Balalaika and Domra Association of America - Library (Mus)
2225 Madison Square Phone: (215)985-4678
Philadelphia, PA 19146 Stephen M. Wolownik, Exec.Dir.
Founded: 1978. **Subjects:** Music written for the balalaika, domra, and allied instruments; musical and cultural heritage of Eastern Europe. **Holdings:** 5000 volumes. **Services:** Library not open to the public. **Remarks:** FAX: (301)564-2594. Telex: 6504073138 MCI UW.

★1429★
Balch & Bingham - Library (Law, Bus-Fin)
1710 N. 6th Ave. Phone: (205)251-8100
Birmingham, AL 35203 Patricia M. Levine
Founded: 1920. **Staff:** Prof 1; Other 3. **Subjects:** Law, business. **Holdings:** 29,000 volumes; legislative and government documents. **Subscriptions:** 266 journals and other serials. **Services:** Interlibrary loan; library not open to the public. **Computerized Information Services:** LEXIS, NEXIS, WESTLAW, DIALOG Information Services. **Remarks:** FAX: (205)252-0420.

★1430★
Balch Institute for Ethnic Studies - Library (Hist, Area-Ethnic)
18 S. 7th St. Phone: (215)925-8090
Philadelphia, PA 19106 R. Joseph Anderson, Lib.Dir.
Founded: 1971. **Staff:** Prof 6; Other 2. **Subjects:** North American immigration and ethnic history, labor movement, radicalism. **Special Collections:** Ethnic Heritage Curriculum Collection; Scotch-Irish Foundation Library and Archives. **Holdings:** 60,000 books and other printed items; 2700 linear feet of manuscripts; 200 sound recordings; 12,000 photographs; 500 broadsides; 5000 reels of microfilm. **Subscriptions:** 300 journals and other serials. **Services:** Interlibrary loan; copying; library open to the public with restrictions. **Automated Operations:** Computerized cataloging. **Computerized Information Services:** OCLC. **Networks/Consortia:** Member of PALINET. **Publications:** New Dimensions, 2/year; A Selected List of Newspaper and Manuscript Holdings, 1980; Forgotten Doors: The Other Ports of Entry to the United States, 1988; ethnic reading lists; list of publications is available upon request. **Remarks:** FAX: (215)922-3201. **Staff:** Patricia Proscino, Ref./Acq.; Sheila Walker, Cat.; Monique Borque, Archv.; Margo Szabunia, Fld.Archv.; Sandy Van Doren, Asst.Fld.Archv.

★1431★
Abraham Baldwin Agricultural College - Baldwin Library (Agri)
ABAC Station Phone: (912)386-3223
Tifton, GA 31794-2693 Harriett E. Mayo, Hd.Libn.
Founded: 1908. **Staff:** Prof 3; Other 5. **Subjects:** Agriculture, forestry, home economics, business, computer science, liberal arts, nursing. **Special Collections:** Georgiana collection. **Holdings:** 60,500 books; 3300 bound periodical volumes. **Subscriptions:** 470 journals and other serials; 10 newspapers. **Services:** Interlibrary loan; copying; library open to the public. **Automated Operations:** Computerized cataloging and ILL. **Computerized Information Services:** OCLC. **Networks/Consortia:** Member of SOLINET, South Georgia Associated Libraries (SGAL). **Remarks:** FAX: (912)386-7006. **Staff:** Brenda A. Sellers, Asst.Libn.; Bettie E. Frye, Asst.Libn.

Baldwin Library
See: **University of Florida - Special Collections** (18583)

★1432★
Baldwin-Wallace College - Riemenschneider Bach Institute - Bach Library (Mus)
275 Eastland Rd. Phone: (216)826-2207
Berea, OH 44017-2088 Dr. Elinore Barber, Dir.
Founded: 1969. **Staff:** Prof 5; Other 3. **Subjects:** Johann Sebastian Bach, Baroque and other periods of music and literature. **Special Collections:** J.S. Bach works, 1731-1850 (1100 items including 380 rare prints, autograph manuscripts, and Bach Circle manuscripts); other rare music prints and first editions, 1568-1900 (90 vault items); Hans David papers and publications; Albert Riemenschneider papers and publications; Villella Opera Collection (400 books; 9660 sound recordings; 2 file drawers of opera memorabilia); Baroque musical treatises. **Holdings:** 9840 books and scores; 589 bound periodical volumes; 1073 unbound periodical volumes; 9251 phonograph records; 80 archival boxes and 2 cabinets of archival materials; 34 reels of microfilm; 156 reel-to-reel tapes; 13 videotapes; 68 sets of microfiche. **Subscriptions:** 29 journals and other serials. **Services:** Copying (limited); library open to the public for reference use only. **Publications:** BACH (journal), semiannual - to members and subscribers. **Special Catalogs:** Catalog of the Riemenschneider Bach Collection (book); addenda catalog volumes of the Martin, David, and Villella Collections; acquisitions of Riemenschneider Collection from 1970 to present. **Remarks:** FAX: (216)826-2329. **Staff:** Carol Walker, Assoc.Mus.Libn.; Sandra Eichenberg, Assoc.Mus.Libn.; Mary Gay, Pubn.Asst. to Dir.; Susan Monseau, Pubn.Asst. to Dir.

Balian Library
See: **St. Mary's Armenian Apostolic Church** (14508)

★1433★
Ball Corporation - Business Research & Information Center (Sci-Engr)
1600 Commerce St. Phone: (303)939-5755
Boulder, CO 80301-2734 Vicky Schneller, Supv.
Founded: 1961. **Staff:** 3. **Subjects:** Aerospace, astronomy, electronics, engineering, optics, physics, cryogenics. **Holdings:** 6400 books. **Subscriptions:** 300 journals and other serials. **Services:** Interlibrary loan; collection not open to the public. **Computerized Information Services:** Aerospace Online, BRS Information Technologies, DIALOG Information Services, DTIC, NASA/RECON, NewsNet, Inc. **Networks/Consortia:** Member of Bibliographical Center for Research, Rocky Mountain Region, Inc. (BCR), INCOLSA. **Remarks:** FAX: (303)939-4142. Telex: 301 7486. **Staff:** Fran Brown; Teresa Harris; Brenda Klundt.

★1434★
Ball Corporation - Library Services (Bus-Fin)
345 S. High St.
P.O. Box 2407 Phone: (317)747-6421
Muncie, IN 47307-0407 Rebecca Shipley Ziga, Mgr., Lib.Serv.
Founded: 1974. **Staff:** 3. **Subjects:** Business, management, law. **Holdings:** 3500 books. **Subscriptions:** 150 journals and other serials; 6 newspapers. **Services:** Interlibrary loan; collection open to the public by appointment. **Computerized Information Services:** DIALOG Information Services, BRS Information Technologies, Dow Jones News/Retrieval, NewsNet, Inc., LEXIS, NEXIS; NAMNET (internal database). **Networks/Consortia:** Member of Eastern Indiana Area Library Services Authority (EIALSA). **Remarks:** FAX: (317)747-6813. Telex: 305 0483. **Staff:** Linda Putman, ILL.

★1435★
Ball Corporation - Library Services (Sci-Engr)
1509 S. Macedonia Phone: (317)747-6707
Muncie, IN 47302 Elaine Mathews, Libn.
Founded: 1970. **Staff:** 3. **Subjects:** Ceramics, glass, metallurgy, plastics, chemistry, packaging. **Holdings:** 2500 books. **Subscriptions:** 203 journals and other serials. **Services:** Interlibrary loan; collection open to the public by appointment. **Computerized Information Services:** BRS Information Technologies, DIALOG Information Services, Dow Jones News/Retrieval, NewsNet, Inc., LEXIS, NEXIS. **Remarks:** FAX: (317)747-6553. Telex: 305-0483. **Formerly:** Its Technical Collection.

May Ball Library
See: **Queen's University at Kingston - May Ball Library** (13655)

★1436★
Ball Memorial Hospital - Health Science Library (Med)
2401 University Ave. Phone: (317)747-3204
Muncie, IN 47303-0137 Jane A. Potee, Dir. of Lib.Serv.
Founded: 1961. **Staff:** Prof 3; Other 2. **Subjects:** Clinical medicine, nursing, allied health sciences, health administration, medical education, business management. **Holdings:** 3500 books; 12,000 bound periodical volumes; 15 files of subject headings; VF drawers. **Subscriptions:** 900 journals and other serials. **Services:** Interlibrary loan; copying; consulting services available; library open to students in health sciences. **Automated Operations:** Computerized cataloging, acquisitions, serials, and circulation. **Computerized Information Services:** DIALOG Information Services, MEDLARS, BRS Information Technologies; McDonald Douglas Hospital Information System for internal distribution only; CD-ROMs (MEDLINE, CINAHL, Health Planning and Administrative Data Base, International Pharmaceutical Abstracts); DOCLINE (electronic mail service). Performs searches on fee basis. **Remarks:** Alternate telephone number(s): 747-4471. FAX: (317)747-0137. Maintains "The Library of Life, Love & Laughter," a humor library for patients. **Staff:** Melinda Guffey Orebaugh, Info.Spec.; Dana Fine, Lib.Techn.

★1437★
Ball State University - Architecture Library (Art, Plan)
College of Architecture & Planning Bldg., Rm. 116 Phone: (317)285-5858
Muncie, IN 47306 Wayne Meyer, Arch.Libn.
Founded: 1966. **Staff:** Prof 1; Other 2. **Subjects:** Architecture, landscape architecture, historic preservation, urban planning. **Special Collections:** Mary Jeglum Historic Preservation Collection (781 items). **Holdings:** 25,302 books; 4995 bound periodical volumes; 25 VF drawers; 60,000 35mm slides; 597 product catalogs; 147 office brochures; 718 U.S. Geological Survey (U.S.G.S.) maps; 7050 microfiche; 332 reels of microfilm. **Subscriptions:** 94 journals. **Services:** Interlibrary loan; copying; library open to the public. **Automated Operations:** Computerized public access catalog, cataloging, circulation, and acquisitions. **Computerized Information Services:** DIALOG Information Services, OCLC; CD-ROM (WILSONDISC). **Publications:** Monthly acquisitions list - for internal distribution only. **Special Catalogs:** Student theses; product catalogs (both on cards); architectural office brochures; Mary Jeglum Collection; U.S.G.S. maps; vertical files. **Remarks:** FAX: (317)285-5351.

★1438★
Ball State University - Bracken Library - Archives & Special Collections (Hum, Hist)
Bracken Library, Rm. 210 Phone: (317)285-5078
Muncie, IN 47306 Nancy K. Turner, Hd., Archv. and Spec.Coll.
Founded: 1972. **Staff:** Prof 2; Other 1. **Subjects:** Local, university, and Indiana history; American and European literature; music; 20th century poetry; Middletown studies. **Special Collections:** Sir Norman Angell Papers; John Steinbeck Collection (including Steinbeck Society materials); Aldous Huxley Collection; Ku Klux Klan Collection; Nazi Collection; International Horn Society Archives; Contemporary Poetry Collection; United States Volleyball Association Archives; University Archives; Stoeckel Archives (local history); Middletown Studies Collections. **Holdings:** 12,144 books; 6664 dissertations, theses, research papers; 3500 linear feet of manuscripts and records; 500,000 feet of film and videotape; 15,000 photographic prints and negatives; 300 hours of oral history interviews; 900 maps. **Services:** Copying; collections open to the public. **Automated Operations:** Computerized cataloging. **Computerized Information Services:** OCLC; BITNET (electronic mail service). **Networks/Consortia:** Member of INCOLSA. **Special Catalogs:** Registers for archival collections. **Remarks:** FAX: (317)285-5351. Electronic mail address(es): OONKTURNER@BSUvax1 (BITNET).

★1439★
Ball State University - Center for Energy Research/Education/Service (CERES) (Energy)
2000 University Ave., AB G18 Phone: (317)285-1135
Muncie, IN 47306 Robert J. Koester, Dir.
Founded: 1982. **Staff:** Prof 4; Other 2. **Subjects:** Energy, solar energy, community planning, design, building performance analysis, computer simulation. **Holdings:** 200 books; 200 technical reports. **Subscriptions:** 20 journals and other serials. **Services:** Copying; center open to the public with restrictions. **Remarks:** FAX: (317)285-3726.

★1440★
Ball State University - Department of Library Service - Government Publications (Info Sci)
Bracken Library, Rm. 224 Phone: (317)285-1110
Muncie, IN 47306 Diane Calvin, Govt.Pubns.Libn.
Founded: 1960. **Staff:** Prof 1; Other 2. **Subjects:** Education, health and human services, U.S. Congress. **Holdings:** 87,294 federal government documents; 2550 Indiana state documents; 24,536 microfiche. **Services:** Copying; library open to the public. **Remarks:** FAX: (317)285-5351.

★1441★
Ball State University - Department of Library Service - Map Collection (Geog-Map)
Bracken Library, Rm. 218 Phone: (317)285-1097
Muncie, IN 47306 Paul W. Stout, Map Libn.
Founded: 1976. **Staff:** Prof 1; Other 1. **Subjects:** Indiana and worldwide maps - topographic, thematic, city, aeronautical, nautical, road. **Special Collections:** Bicycle route maps; university campus maps, urban bird's-eye views. **Holdings:** 131,380 maps. **Services:** Interlibrary loan; copying; collection open to the public. **Computerized Information Services:** BITNET (electronic mail service). **Remarks:** FAX: (317)285-5351. Electronic mail address(es): OOPWSTOUT@BSUVAX1 (BITNET).

★1442★
Ball State University - Music Library (Mus)
Muncie, IN 47306 Phone: (317)285-5065
Dr. Nyal Z. Williams, Mus.Libn.
Founded: 1975. **Staff:** Prof 1; Other 1. **Subjects:** Music. **Special Collections:** Tubists Universal Brotherhood Association (TUBA) Resource Library (400 scores for tuba); Cecil Leeson Archival Saxophone Collection (17 historical instruments; 10 boxes of manuscripts); archives of Buescher and Conn instrument makers; International Horn Society materials. **Services:** Interlibrary loan; copying; library open to the public for reference use only. **Automated Operations:** Computerized cataloging. **Computerized Information Services:** OCLC. **Networks/Consortia:** Member of INCOLSA. **Remarks:** FAX: (317)285-5351.

Frances Hall Ballard Library
See: **Manhattan School of Music** (9594)

★1443★
Ballard, Spahr, Andrews and Ingersoll - Law Library (Law)
1735 Market St. Phone: (215)864-8150
Philadelphia, PA 19103-7599 David Proctor, Lib.Dir.
Subjects: Law. **Holdings:** 20,000 volumes. **Services:** Library not open to the public. **Computerized Information Services:** DIALOG Information Services, WESTLAW, LEXIS, VU/TEXT Information Services, Dow Jones News/Retrieval, Information America, Dun & Bradstreet Business Credit Services. **Networks/Consortia:** Member of PALINET. **Remarks:** FAX: (215)864-8199. Telex: 83 4532. **Staff:** Kathy Caron.

Hosea Ballou Collection
See: **Tufts University - Nils Yngve Wessell Library** (16552)

L.E. & E.L. Ballou Library
See: **Buena Vista College** (2323)

★1444★
Baltimore City Department of Legislative Reference - Library (Soc Sci)
626 City Hall
100 N. Holliday St. Phone: (301)396-4730
Baltimore, MD 21202 Karen Dull, Libn.
Founded: 1907. **Staff:** Prof 4; Other 6. **Subjects:** Baltimore ordinances, ordinances of other cities, state and municipal codes, municipal planning, welfare, social services, housing, community development. **Special Collections:** Baltimore City Directories, 1796-1964. **Holdings:** 54,000 books; 1000 bound periodical volumes; 20 drawers of clippings on local items, elections, referenda; 7 drawers of biographies; 25 drawers of municipal documents and reports; 20 drawers of proceedings, ordinances, resolutions. **Subscriptions:** 59 journals and other serials; 7 newspapers. **Services:** Copying; library open to the public. **Computerized Information Services:** DIALOG Information Services, DataTimes. Performs searches on fee basis. **Publications:** City Code; Municipal Handbook; Building and Fire Code Supplements; City Charter, City Council Rules; Baltimore City Public Local Laws.

★1445★
Baltimore City Life Museums - Peale Museum - Reference Center (Hist, Aud-Vis)
225 Holliday St. Phone: (301)396-1164
Baltimore, MD 21202 Mary Markey, Ref.Ctr.Supv.
Founded: 1931. **Staff:** Prof 1. **Subjects:** History of Baltimore, especially architectural, maritime, and social history. **Special Collections:** Hambleton Collection of Baltimore Views (450 historical prints); A. Aubrey Bodine Photographic Collection (12,000 images); Baltimore Gas & Electric Photographic Collection, 1906-1955 (25,000 images). **Holdings:** 1400 books; 75,000 prints and photographs; 225 printed maps; architectural drawings; 9 VF drawers of mixed media subject files. **Subscriptions:** 35 journals and other serials. **Services:** Copying; center materials available for reference use only. **Remarks:** FAX: (301)962-8757.

★1446★
Baltimore City Public Schools - Professional Library (Educ)
200 E. North Ave. Phone: (301)396-8977
Baltimore, MD 21202 Elsie H. Lawson, Libn.
Founded: 1925. **Staff:** Prof 1. **Subjects:** Education. **Holdings:** 7000 books; 14 VF drawers. **Subscriptions:** 150 journals and other serials; 70 microfilm subscriptions. **Services:** Interlibrary loan; copying; SDI; center open to the public for reference use only.

★1447★
Baltimore County Circuit Court - Law Library (Law)
401 Bosley Ave. Phone: (301)887-3086
Towson, MD 21204 Cynthia N. Catterton, Lib.Dir.
Staff: Prof 3; Other 3. **Subjects:** Law. **Special Collections:** Old English cases. **Holdings:** 100,000 volumes. **Subscriptions:** 120 journals and other serials. **Services:** Interlibrary loan; library open to the public. **Remarks:** FAX: (301)887-4807. **Staff:** Marielle Marne, Assoc.Libn.; Stephanie Papa, Assoc.Libn.

★1448★
Baltimore County General Hospital - Health Sciences Library (Med)
5401 Old Court Rd. Phone: (301)521-2200
Randallstown, MD 21133 Betty Myers, Hea.Sci.Libn.
Founded: 1969. **Staff:** Prof 1. **Subjects:** Medicine, surgery, cardiology, orthopedics, management, nursing process. **Holdings:** 1475 books; college catalogs; Audio-Digest tapes (5 years of internal medicine and surgery, 5 years of opthalmology). **Subscriptions:** 72 journals and other serials. **Services:** Interlibrary loan; copying; library open to the public with restrictions. **Computerized Information Services:** MEDLARS, MEDLINE; DOCLINE (electronic mail service). **Networks/Consortia:** Member of National Network of Libraries of Medicine (NN/LM). **Remarks:** FAX: (301)922-7549.

★1449★
Baltimore County Historical Society - Library (Hist)
9811 Van Buren Ln. Phone: (410)666-1876
Cockeysville, MD 21030 Elmer, R. Haile, Jr., Libn.
Founded: 1959. **Staff:** 2. **Subjects:** Baltimore County, Maryland - history, genealogy, cemeteries, roadside markers. **Special Collections:** Transcriptions of grave markers. **Holdings:** 1200 books; 10 manuscripts; 20 nonbook items; 60 VF drawers of clippings, pamphlets, circulars, letters, pictures, family charts, group sheets, Bible records, and family histories. **Services:** Copying; library open to the public for reference use only. **Publications:** History Trails, quarterly.

★1450★
Baltimore Gas and Electric Company - Library/Resource Center (Energy)
Gas & Electric Bldg., Rm. 1101
Box 1475 Phone: (301)234-6291
Baltimore, MD 21203 Kathleen A. Lynch, Rsrc.Spec.
Founded: 1912. **Staff:** Prof 1. **Subjects:** Public utilities - electric, nuclear, gas. **Special Collections:** Baltimore and Maryland history collections. **Holdings:** 260 books; 25 bound periodical volumes. **Subscriptions:** 70 journals and other serials. **Services:** Interlibrary loan; library not open to the public. **Automated Operations:** Computerized acquisitions. **Computerized Information Services:** DIALOG Information Services, EBSCONET, NewsNet, Inc., Knight-Ridder Unicom. **Remarks:** FAX: (301)685-0667.

★1451★
Baltimore Hebrew University - Joseph Meyerhoff Library (Rel-Phil)
5800 Park Heights Ave. Phone: (410)578-6936
Baltimore, MD 21215 Dr. Arthur M. Lesley, Dir.
Founded: 1919. **Staff:** Prof 5. **Subjects:** Jewish studies, modern Middle East, religion. **Special Collections:** Rare book collection (650 volumes). **Holdings:** 53,000 books; 5900 bound periodical volumes; 4000 microforms; 25 VF drawers. **Subscriptions:** 240 journals and other serials. **Services:** Interlibrary loan; copying; library open to the public. **Automated Operations:** Computerized cataloging and acquisitions. **Computerized Information Services:** Internal database; BITNET (electronic mail service). **Publications:** A Guide to Research in the Joseph Meyerhoff Library. **Remarks:** FAX: (410)578-6940. Electronic mail address(es): GURFEL (BITNET). **Staff:** Andrew Johnson, Libn.; Elaine Mael, Judaica Libn.; Dr. Rosy Bodenheimer, Ref.Libn.; Devora Finkelstein, Acq.Libn.; Jeanette Katcoff, Per.Libn.

★1452★
The Baltimore Museum of Art - E. Kirkbride Miller Art Research Library (Art)
Art Museum Dr. Phone: (410)396-6317
Baltimore, MD 21218 Cynthia Tripoulas, Libn.
Founded: 1930. **Staff:** Prof 1. **Subjects:** History of art; 19th and 20th century painting and sculpture; photography; arts of Africa, Oceania, and the Americas; American decorative arts; graphic arts. **Special Collections:** Cone Collection of Books; archives. **Holdings:** 39,822 books; 3000 bound periodical volumes; 11,800 auction catalogs; 144 drawers of artist vertical files, exhibition catalogs, annual reports, bulletins. **Subscriptions:** 150 journals and other serials. **Services:** Interlibrary loan; copying; library open to the public by appointment. **Automated Operations:** Computerized cataloging. **Networks/Consortia:** Member of PALINET. **Remarks:** FAX: (410)396-6562.

★1453★
Baltimore Museum of Industry - Library and Archives (Hist)
1415 Key Hwy. Phone: (301)727-4808
Baltimore, MD 21230 Nancy Perlman, Archv.
Founded: 1978. **Staff:** 1.5. **Subjects:** Baltimore industrial and technological history. **Special Collections:** Baltimore companies' archives; Bethlehem Steel Company's Key Highway Shipyard records; industrial photograph collections; trade literature; history of technology (books; monographs). **Holdings:** 2160 books; 700 linear feet of archival and manuscript material; 300 linear feet of nonbooks items; VF drawers. **Subscriptions:** 15 journals and other serials. **Services:** Copying; library open to the public. **Staff:** Matthew White, Asst.Archv.

★1454★
Baltimore Police Department - Education and Training Division - Library (Law, Soc Sci)
601 E. Fayette St. Phone: (301)396-2518
Baltimore, MD 21202 Faye Redding, Libn.
Founded: 1978. **Staff:** Prof 1. **Subjects:** Law and law enforcement, police administration, sociology, management, psychology, physical training. **Holdings:** 10,000 books; 275 bound periodical volumes; 200 microfiche; 5 VF drawers of newspaper clippings and pamphlets. **Subscriptions:** 10 journals and other serials. **Services:** Interlibrary loan; library not open to the public. **Networks/Consortia:** Member of Maryland Interlibrary Organization (MILO).

★1455★
Baltimore Regional Council of Governments - Regional Information Center (Plan)
601 N. Howard St. Phone: (301)333-4881
Baltimore, MD 21201-4585 Mary Logan, Mgr.
Founded: 1963. **Staff:** Prof 2; Other 1. **Subjects:** Planning, economic development, urban affairs, environment, transportation, demography. **Special Collections:** Maryland and Baltimore region government publications; Regional Council publications. **Holdings:** 13,000 books; 60 bound periodical volumes; 500 technical reports on microfiche. **Subscriptions:** 320 journals and other serials; 15 newspapers. **Services:** Interlibrary loan; copying; library open to the public for reference use only. **Networks/Consortia:** Member of Maryland Interlibrary Organization (MILO). **Publications:** Information Update, bimonthly; List of Current Publications of the Baltimore Regional Council of Governments, annual - both free upon request. **Remarks:** FAX: (301)659-1260. **Staff:** Elinore Krell

★1456★
The Baltimore Sun - Library (Publ)
501 N. Calvert St. Phone: (301)332-6250
Baltimore, MD 21278-0001 Carolyn J. Hardnett, Dir.Lib.Serv.
Founded: 1906. **Staff:** Prof 2; Other 18. **Subjects:** Newspaper reference topics, Marylandia, Baltimoriana. **Special Collections:** Reports and studies dealing with Maryland and city of Baltimore. **Holdings:** 3000 books; 110 telephone books; 20 million newspaper clippings (18 million in 350,000 microfilm jackets); 4 million photographs; 4000 reels of microfilm of newspapers; 3 lateral file cabinets; pamphlets; maps; charts. **Subscriptions:** 80 journals and other serials. **Services:** Interlibrary loan; library not open to the public. **Computerized Information Services:** NEXIS, VU/TEXT Information Services, DataTimes, DIALOG Information Services, Dow Jones News/Retrieval; library available online through DataTimes, DIALOG Information Services, Dow Jones News/Retrieval, VU/TEXT Information Services. **Special Indexes:** Sunpapers card index, 1891-1951 (174 reels of microfilm). **Remarks:** FAX: (301)752-6049. Library serves staff of The Sun, The Evening Sun, The Sunday Sun, The Hartford Sun, The Howard Sun, The Arundel Sun, The Carroll Sun. **Staff:** Mary Agnes Schultz, Asst.Dir.Lib.Serv.; Jean Packard, Asst.Chf.Libn.

★1457★
Baltimore Zoo - Arthur R. Watson Library (Biol Sci)
Druid Hill Park Phone: (410)396-6013
Baltimore, MD 21217 Ethel R. Hardee, Libn.
Founded: 1980. **Staff:** Prof 1; Other 3. **Subjects:** General zoology, ornithology, herpetology, mammalogy, ecology, natural history, veterinary medicine. **Holdings:** 2800 volumes; 4 VF drawers of journal reprints, dissertations, clippings, pamphlets; 2 VF drawers of photographs, clippings, graphic materials. **Subscriptions:** 120 journals and other serials. **Services:** Copying; library open to the public for reference use only. **Publications:** Serials holding list - free upon request.

★1458★
Balzekas Museum of Lithuanian Culture - Research Library (Area-Ethnic)
6500 S. Pulaski Rd. Phone: (312)582-6500
Chicago, IL 60629-5136 David Fainhauz, Ph.D., Hd.Libn./Res.Cons.
Founded: 1966. **Staff:** 4. **Subjects:** History of Lithuania and other Eastern European countries, Lithuanian culture, numismatics, philately, fiction. **Special Collections:** Eastern European genealogy and heraldry; rare books on Eastern European history dating back to the 16th century (500); rare maps of Eastern Europe (550); photo archives; art archives. **Holdings:** 30,000 books; 1600 periodical volumes; 1500 manuscripts; 1700 files of pamphlets and records. **Subscriptions:** 30 journals and other serials; 10 newspapers. **Services:** Library not open to the general public. **Publications:** Lithuanian Museum Review, quarterly - to members and donors. **Special Catalogs:** Lithuanian Artists. **Remarks:** Museum includes a children's museum, main exhibit, art gallery, numismatics and philately departments, and rare maps gallery.

★1459★
(Bamako) Bibliotheque de l'Ambassade des Etats-Unis de l'Amerique (Educ)
Ave. Mohd. V et Rue Testard
Post Box 34
Bamako, Mali
Remarks: Maintained or supported by the U.S. Information Agency. Focus is on materials that will assist peoples outside the United States to learn about the United States, its people, history, culture, political processes, and social milieux.

★1460★
Banco Totta & Acores - Centro de Documentacao - Biblioteca (Bus-Fin)
Rua de Centro Cultural, 45-10
P-1700 Lisbon, Portugal Phone: 1 8484839
Founded: 1970. **Staff:** Prof 4. **Subjects:** Economics, law, sectorial activity, accounting. **Holdings:** 14,000 books; 1200 bound periodical volumes; 3000 reports. **Subscriptions:** 300 journals and other serials; 80 newspapers. **Services:** Interlibrary loan; copying; SDI; library open to the public. **Remarks:** FAX: 8484853.

★1461★
Bancroft, Avery and McAlister - Law Library (Law)
601 Montgomery St., Suite 900 Phone: (415)788-8855
San Francisco, CA 94111 Mark E. Mackler, Libn.
Founded: 1955. **Staff:** Prof 1; Other 2. **Subjects:** Law - U.S., California, estate planning, tax, business. **Holdings:** 30,000 books; 720 bound periodical volumes; 600 tapes. **Subscriptions:** 530 journals and other serials; 5 newspapers. **Services:** Interlibrary loan; library open to the public with special permission. **Computerized Information Services:** DIALOG Information Services, WESTLAW, RLIN. **Remarks:** FAX: (415)397-1925.

Bancroft Library
See: **University of California, Berkeley** (18303)

Bancroft Pre-Raphaelite Library
See: **Delaware Art Museum - Helen Farr Sloan Library** (4715)

★1462★
Bancroft-Whitney Company - B.E. Witkin Editorial Library (Publ, Law)
3250 Van Ness Ave. Phone: (415)929-3500
San Francisco, CA 94109-1099 Sandye Taylor, Lib.Hd.
Founded: 1855. **Staff:** 7. **Subjects:** Law, state laws, jurisprudence, medicolegal material. **Holdings:** 250,000 books; 3000 bound periodical volumes. **Subscriptions:** 100 journals and other serials; 10 newspapers. **Services:** Library not open to the public. **Remarks:** FAX: (415)441-5513.

★1463★
Band, Lavis & Associates, Inc. - Company Technical Library (Mil)
900 Ritchie Hwy. Phone: (301)544-2800
Severna Park, MD 21146 Linda Peters
Founded: 1977. **Staff:** 1. **Subjects:** Advanced marine vehicles, air cushion vehicles, surface effect ships, navy ships, navy and army programs. **Holdings:** 500 books; 500 bound periodical volumes; 12,000 reports, papers, and drawings. **Subscriptions:** 15 journals and other serials. **Services:** Library not open to the public. **Automated Operations:** Computerized cataloging. **Remarks:** FAX: (301)647-3411.

Bandelier National Monument
See: **U.S. Natl. Park Service** (17673)

W.T. Bandy Center for Baudelaire Studies
See: **Vanderbilt University - Jean and Alexander Heard Library - Special Collections Department** (19773)

★1464★
Banff Centre for Continuing Education - Library (Art)
Box 1020 Phone: (403)762-6265
Banff, AB, Canada T0L 0C0 Bob Foley, Hd.Libn.
Founded: 1980. **Staff:** Prof 3; Other 4. **Subjects:** Music, visual arts, performing arts, management. **Special Collections:** Art video (500 items). **Holdings:** 20,000 books; 9000 scores; 26,000 slides; 1000 audiotapes; 2000 art catalogs; 7000 phonograph records. **Subscriptions:** 200 journals and other serials. **Services:** Interlibrary loan; copying; SDI; library open to the public for reference use only. **Computerized Information Services:** DIALOG Information Services, The Financial Post DataGroup, Info Globe, Infomart Online; CD-ROMs; Envoy 100, BITNET (electronic mail services). **Remarks:** FAX: (403)762-6266. Telex: ARTSBANFF. Electronic mail address(es): LIBRARY.BNFFCNTR (Envoy 100); FOLEY@CPSC.VCALGARY.CA (BITNET). **Staff:** Deborah Rosen, Mus.Libn.; Elizabeth Kundert, Archv.

Bangladesh - Ministry of Agriculture - Agriculture and Forestry Division - Bangladesh Jute Research Institute
See: **Bangladesh Jute Research Institute** (1467)

★1465★
Bangladesh - National Archives of Bangladesh (Hist)
National Library Bldg.
Sher-e-Bangla Nagar
Agargaon Phone: 2 326572
Dacca 1207, Bangladesh Shah Muhammad Nazmul Alam, Dir.
Founded: 1983. **Staff:** Prof 10; Other 11. **Subjects:** Bangladesh - history, politics, government. **Special Collections:** Speeches of Sher-e-Bangla A.K. Fozlul Hoque (political leader of Bangladesh). **Holdings:** 3500 books; 50 volumes of microfilm; annual reports; government historical records and other archival items. **Services:** Interlibrary loan; copying; library open to members. **Staff:** Md. Shahabuddin Khan, Act Dp.Dir.

★1466★
Bangladesh Agricultural University - Library (Agri)
Mymensingh 2202, Bangladesh Phone: 91 569597
Abdul Gafur Dewan, Libn.
Founded: 1961. **Staff:** 79. **Subjects:** Agriculture - general, economics, and engineering; fisheries; veterinary science; animal husbandry. **Holdings:** 148,739 volumes; monographs; theses; pamphlets; 16mm filmstrips; microfilm; microfiche; video recordings. **Subscriptions:** 325 journals and other serials; 14 newspapers. **Services:** Interlibrary loan; copying; SDI (all on request); library open to institutions by permission. **Computerized Information Services:** NAIS, Ucat Databases of AIC, List of Periodical holdings of BAU Library (internal databases). Performs searches. **Publications:** Library Bulletin, quarterly. **Staff:** A.K.M. Abdun Nur, Libn; A.K.M. Badrudduza, Dp.Libn.; Nurul Amin, Dp.Libn.; Salima Banu, Asst.Libn.; Prabir Kumar Mitra Biswas, Asst.Libn.; Md. Fazlul Hoque, Asst.Libn.; Reazul Hannan Md. Yusuf, Asst.Libn.; A.K.M. Shams Uddin, Sr.Cat.; Shahida Akhter, Sr.Cat.; Md. Abdul Wahab, Sr.Cat.; Bijoy Bhushan Bhowmick, Sec.Off.

★1467★
Bangladesh Jute Research Institute - Library (Agri)
Manik Miah Ave.
Dacca 7, Bangladesh Abdur Rouf Mian, Libn.
Subjects: Jute, kenaf, and mesta fibers - production, development, technology. **Holdings:** 3800 volumes. **Subscriptions:** 1500 journals and other serials. **Remarks:** Maintained by Bangladesh - Ministry of Agriculture - Agriculture and Forestry Division.

★1468★
Bangor Daily News - Library (Publ)
491 Main St. Phone: (207)990-8100
Bangor, ME 04401 Charles A. Campo, Chf.Libn.
Founded: 1960. **Staff:** Prof 1; Other 2. **Subjects:** Newspaper reference topics. **Holdings:** Newspaper clippings, 1960 to present. **Services:** Copying; library open to the public. **Automated Operations:** Computerized indexing. **Computerized Information Services:** NEXIS; internal database. **Remarks:** FAX: (207)941-9476.

★1469★
Bangor Historical Society - Library (Hist)
159 Union St. Phone: (207)942-5766
Bangor, ME 04401 Diane Vatne, Exec.Dir.
Founded: 1911. **Staff:** 3. **Subjects:** Bangor area history. **Holdings:** 900 books; 400 ledgers, scrapbooks, and recordbooks; 3 videotapes; 500 receipts, letters, ephemera; 650,000 linear feet of television film transferred to video (1953-1974). **Services:** Library open to the public for reference use only. **Staff:** Abigail Ewing Zelz, Cur.

★1470★
Bangor Mental Health Institute - Health Sciences Media Center (Med)
P.O. Box 926 Phone: (207)941-4226
Bangor, ME 04401 Daphne Crocker, Libn. II
Founded: 1971. **Staff:** Prof 1; Other 1. **Subjects:** Psychiatry, psychology, mental health services, medicine, psychiatric nursing, geriatrics, social work. **Holdings:** 2500 books; 12 drawers of pamphlets; 170 AV programs. **Subscriptions:** 150 journals and other serials. **Services:** Interlibrary loan; copying; SDI; center open to the public. **Computerized Information Services:** DIALOG Information Services. Performs searches on fee basis. **Networks/Consortia:** Member of Health Science Library and Information Cooperative of Maine (HSLIC), North Atlantic Health Science Libraries (NAHSL). **Publications:** The Right to Refuse Treatment and the Obligation to Treat: a selected bibliography. **Remarks:** Bangor Mental Health Institute is a state psychiatric hospital.

★1471★
Bangor Theological Seminary - General Theological Library (Rel-Phil)
159 State St. Phone: (207)874-2214
Portland, ME 04101 Clifton G. Davis, Libn.
Founded: 1860. **Staff:** Prof 1. **Subjects:** Theology, philosophy, psychology, the Bible, world religions, archeology. **Holdings:** 35,000 books. **Services:** Mail service to U.S.; center open to the public with restrictions. **Publications:** Bulletin of the General Theological Library, quarterly. **Formerly:** General Theological Center of Maine.

★1472★
Bangor Theological Seminary - Moulton Library (Rel-Phil)
300 Union St. Phone: (207)942-6781
Bangor, ME 04401 Clifton G. Davis, Libn.
Founded: 1814. **Staff:** 2. **Subjects:** Maine church history, church history, Biblical literature, theology, philosophy. **Special Collections:** Rare theological volumes (350). **Holdings:** 75,000 books; 12,000 bound periodical volumes; 3000 archival materials and pamphlets. **Subscriptions:** 425 journals and other serials. **Services:** Interlibrary loan; copying; library open to the public. **Computerized Information Services:** Mainecat (internal database). **Staff:** Paul Schroeder, Asst.Libn.

★1473★
Banister Inc. - Library
9910 39th Ave.
P.O. Box 2408
Edmonton, AB, Canada T5J 2R4
Defunct.

★1474★
Bank Administration Institute - Research Service Center (Bus-Fin)
1 N. Franklin Phone: (312)553-4600
Chicago, IL 60606 Irena Case, Asst.Libn.
Subjects: Banking, finance. **Holdings:** 1000 books; 60 VF drawers of clippings and annual reports; 4 periodical titles on microfilm. **Services:** Center not open to the public. **Formerly:** Located in Rolling Meadows, IL.

★1475★
Bank of America - Southern California Headquarters - Law Library, Legal No. 4017 (Law)
555 S. Flower St., 7th Fl. Phone: (213)228-3148
Los Angeles, CA 90071-2399 Christina Leiva
Staff: 1. **Subjects:** Banking law, California law. **Holdings:** 20,000 books; 1000 bound periodical volumes; 50 audio and video cassettes. **Subscriptions:** 100 journals and other serials; 6 newspapers. **Services:** Interlibrary loan; copying; SDI. **Automated Operations:** Computerized cataloging and serials. **Computerized Information Services:** LEXIS, DIALOG Information Services, RLIN, WESTLAW. **Remarks:** FAX: (213)228-2530.

★1476★
Bank of America - Technical Library (Comp Sci)
Bldg. C
1755 Grant St., Dept.3099 Phone: (510)675-1361
Concord, CA 94520 Jeannette E. Glynn, Mgr.
Staff: Prof 2. **Subjects:** Data processing, software engineering, artificial intelligence, telecommunications, programming, systems analysis. **Holdings:** 3500 books; 4000 vendor manuals. **Subscriptions:** 380 journals and other serials. **Services:** Interlibrary loan; library open to the public by appointment. **Computerized Information Services:** DIALOG Information Services, Knowledge Index, NewsNet, Inc., LEXIS, NEXIS. **Networks/Consortia:** Member of Bay Area Library and Information Network. **Remarks:** FAX: (510)675-1402. **Staff:** Emma Higgs, Coll.Dev.Libn.

★1477★
Bank of America, NT & SA - Law Library (Law)
Bank of America Center
Box 37000 Phone: (415)622-6040
San Francisco, CA 94137 Lauri Flynn, Dir. of Info.Res.
Staff: Prof 2; Other 2. **Subjects:** Law. **Holdings:** 24,000 volumes. **Subscriptions:** 230 journals and other serials. **Services:** Interlibrary loan; library not open to the public. **Computerized Information Services:** Mead Data Central, RLIN, WESTLAW, DataTimes, LEGI-SLATE. **Publications:** Daily Notes; CLE Calendar; Acquisitions Memo and Information Services Bulletin - for internal distribution only. **Remarks:** (415)622-9238. **Staff:** Trish McCurdy, Law Libn.

★1478★
Bank of America, NT & SA - Research Library & Information Center (Bus-Fin)
555 California St.
Box 37000 Phone: (415)622-2068
San Francisco, CA 94137 Ruth Girill, Mgr., Lib. & Info.Serv.
Founded: 1921. **Staff:** Prof 4; Other 3. **Subjects:** Banking, economics, foreign trade, international business, agriculture. **Special Collections:** Foreign government and bank reports. **Holdings:** 10,000 books; 19,000 pamphlets; 4600 files. **Subscriptions:** 1500 journals and other serials; 24 newspapers. **Services:** Interlibrary loan; library not open to the public. **Computerized Information Services:** DIALOG Information Services, PFDS Online, NEXIS, Dow Jones News/Retrieval, TEXTLINE, WILSONLINE; OnTyme Electronic Message Network Service, DIALNET (electronic mail services). **Networks/Consortia:** Member of CLASS. **Publications:** Selected Additions to the Research Library, quarterly - available to libraries on request. **Remarks:** FAX: (415)622-3018. **Staff:** Janet Baker, Libn.; Jane Pratt, Libn.; Patricia Wong, Mgr., Lib.Serv.

★1479★
Bank of Canada - Library (Bus-Fin)
245 Sparks St. Phone: (613)782-8466
Ottawa, ON, Canada K1A 0G9 Sheila Bradley, Chf.Libn.
Founded: 1935. **Staff:** Prof 7; Other 16. **Subjects:** Banking, finance, economic conditions, international finance. **Holdings:** 40,000 monograph titles. **Subscriptions:** 6000 journals and other serials; 50 newspapers. **Services:** Interlibrary loan; library open to the public for reference use only. **Automated Operations:** Computerized serials and ILL. **Computerized Information Services:** DIALOG Information Services, BRS Information Technologies, Info Globe, QL Systems, CAN/OLE, TEXTLINE, INSIGHT, WILSONLINE, Infomart Online, PROFILE Information, Reuter Country Reports, LEXIS, NEXIS; Envoy 100 (electronic mail service). **Remarks:** FAX: (613)782-8655. Telex: 053-4241; 053-4515. Electronic mail address(es): ILL.OOB (Envoy 100). **Also Known As:** Banque du Canada. **Staff:** Leslie Firth, Hd., Tech.Serv.; Louise Gibson, Hd., Ref.Serv.; Carly Hunt, Hd. Current Awareness Serv.

★1480★
Bank of Hawaii - Information and Reference Center (Bus-Fin)
Bancorp Tower Bldg., 11th Fl.
Box 2900 Phone: (808)537-8375
Honolulu, HI 96846 Elaine Schultz, Info.Mgr.
Founded: 1968. **Staff:** Prof 2; Other 1. **Subjects:** Economics, business statistics, finance and banking, visitor industry, construction, demography, domestic and foreign trade. **Special Collections:** Business and economic development surveys of Hawaii, Pacific Islands. **Holdings:** 1500 books and pamphlets; 24 VF drawers of newspaper clippings. **Subscriptions:** 550 journals and other serials. **Services:** Interlibrary loan; copying; center open to the public for reference use only. **Automated Operations:** Computerized serials. **Computerized Information Services:** DIALOG Information Services. Performs searches on fee basis. **Publications:** What's New in the Information Center, bimonthly - for internal distribution only. **Remarks:** FAX: (808)536-9433. **Staff:** Martha Laxson, Info.Spec.

★1481★
Bank Marketing Association - Information Center (Bus-Fin)
309 W. Washington St. Phone: (312)782-1442
Chicago, IL 60606 Johanne Sognnaes, Mgr., Info.Serv.
Staff: Prof 5; Other 5. **Subjects:** Banking, financial services, marketing, sales, training, advertising. **Special Collections:** Golden Coin Competition Entries (750); School of Bank Marketing project reports (1200). **Holdings:** 2000 books; 1300 theses; 100 vertical files. **Subscriptions:** 400 journals and other serials. **Services:** Interlibrary loan; center not open to the public. **Computerized Information Services:** DIALOG Information Services, Mead Data Central; produces FINIS: Financial Industry Information Service. Performs searches on fee basis. **Networks/Consortia:** Member of Chicago Library System. **Special Indexes:** FINIS: Financial Industry Information Service Index (online). **Remarks:** Toll-free telephone number(s): (800)433-9013. FAX: (312)782-0321. **Staff:** Ann Wakefield, Info.Spec.; Stacy Hedrick, Info.Spec.; Lorie Mynda, Tech.Serv.; Lisa Nadziejka, Database Coord.; Sylvester Flood, Database Ed.; Tanya Wallace, FINIS Doc. Delivery.

★1482★
Bank of Montreal - Business Information Centre (Bus-Fin)
P.O. Box 7000
Scarborough, ON, Canada M1S 4M5 Phone: (416)498-8800
Founded: 1978. **Staff:** Prof 3. **Subjects:** Data processing, banking, office automation, economics, management, communication. **Holdings:** 1500 books; 250 reports; IBM and vendor manuals; technical reports. **Subscriptions:** 324 journals and other serials. **Services:** Interlibrary loan; center not open to the public. **Automated Operations:** Computerized cataloging, acquisitions, serials, and circulation. **Computerized Information Services:** DIALOG Information Services, Info Globe. **Publications:** BIC Bulletin, monthly. **Remarks:** FAX: (416)498-8800, ext. 4618.

★1483★
Bank of Montreal - Business Information Centre (Bus-Fin)
First Canadian Place
P.O. Box 1 Phone: (416)867-4880
Toronto, ON, Canada M5X 1A1 M. Nelson
Founded: 1982. **Staff:** 15. **Subjects:** Banking, business, management, economics. **Holdings:** 8000 books; 1500 company annual reports. **Subscriptions:** 600 journals and other serials; 20 newspapers. **Services:** Interlibrary loan; center not open to the public. **Automated Operations:** Computerized cataloging. **Computerized Information Services:** DIALOG Information Services, Info Globe, LEXIS, NEXIS, Canada Systems Group (CSG), The Financial Post DataGroup, Infomart Online, Data-Star, VU/TEXT Information Services; CD-ROMs. **Publications:** BIC Bulletin. **Remarks:** FAX: (416)867-6951.

★1484★
Bank of Montreal - Business Information Centre (Comp Sci)
129 St. Jacques, 2nd Fl.
P.O. Box 6002, Place d'Armes Phone: (514)877-9383
Montreal, PQ, Canada H2Y 3S8 Sylvia E.A. Piggott, Mgr.
O$**Founded:** 1973. **Staff:** Prof 5; Other 5. **Subjects:** Data processing, banking, economics, office automation, communication, management. **Holdings:** 2000 books; 250 unbound reports; 800 brokerage and annual reports; systems documentation and journals; bank project documents. **Subscriptions:** 310 journals and other serials; 10 newspapers. **Services:** Interlibrary loan; copying; SDI; center open to the public by appointment.

Automated Operations: Computerized cataloging, acquisitions, serials, and circulation. **Computerized Information Services:** DIALOG Information Services, Info Globe, PFDS Online, Dow Jones News/Retrieval, NewsNet, Inc., Mead Data Central, TEXTLINE, CAN/OLE, DOBIS Canadian Online Library System, CompuServe Information Service, InvesText/Plus; CD-ROMs; electronic mail service. **Publications:** BIC Bulletin, monthly; Interpreter, monthly - both for internal distribution only. **Special Catalogs:** Union List of Serials - for internal distribution only. **Remarks:** FAX: (514)877-8189. **Staff:** Phong Kieu, Sr.Info.Anl.; Richard Orlando, Sr.Info.Anl.

★1485★
Bank of New England - Information Services
28 State St.
Boston, MA 02109-1784
Defunct.

★1486★
Bank of Nova Scotia - Library and Business Research (Bus-Fin)
P.O. Box 7007
Adelaide Postal Station — Phone: (416)866-6257
Toronto, ON, Canada M5C 2K7 — Marion Miwa, Mgr./Chf.Libn.
Founded: 1951. **Staff:** Prof 4; Other 4. **Subjects:** Banking, finance, economics, business, industry. **Special Collections:** OSC filings; CCA filings; foreign bank publications; Statistics Canada publications. **Holdings:** 15,000 books. **Subscriptions:** 2500 journals and other serials; 40 newspapers. **Services:** Library not open to the public. **Automated Operations:** Computerized public access catalog, cataloging, acquisitions, serials, and circulation. **Computerized Information Services:** DIALOG Information Services, Info Globe, Dow Jones News/Retrieval, TEXTLINE, QL Systems, PROFILE Information, VU/TEXT Information Services, CAN/OLE, Mead Data Central, Infomart Online, InvesText/Plus, NewsNet, Inc., Business Opportunities Sourcing System (BOSS), Reuters Country Reports; CD-ROMs (Compact Disclosure, Canadian Business and Current Affairs (CBCA), Computer Library, CD/Corporate, Business Dateline). **Publications:** Library bulletin, monthly - for internal distribution only. **Remarks:** FAX: (416)866-2829. **Staff:** Susan Keith, Asst.Mgr., Ref.Serv.; Leslie Peel, Ref.Serv.

★1487★
Bank of Nova Scotia - Technical Resource Centre (Comp Sci)
2201 Eglinton Ave. E. — Phone: (416)288-3571
Scarborough, ON, Canada M1L 4S2 — Lynda Cavanagh, Libn.
Founded: 1972. **Staff:** Prof 3. **Subjects:** Data processing, management, banking. **Holdings:** 1500 books; 3500 IBM manuals. **Subscriptions:** 300 journals and other serials; 5 newspapers. **Services:** Interlibrary loan; library not open to the public. **Automated Operations:** Computerized cataloging, serials, and circulation. **Computerized Information Services:** CD-ROM; internal database. **Publications:** Library newsletter, monthly - for internal distribution only. **Remarks:** FAX: (416)288-4445. **Staff:** Anna Grabowski; Christine Wood.

★1488★
Bank Street College of Education - Library (Educ)
610 W. 112th St., 5th Fl. — Phone: (212)222-6700
New York, NY 10025 — Eleanor R. Kulleseid, Dir.
Founded: 1915. **Staff:** Prof 6; Other 5. **Subjects:** Child development, early childhood education, elementary education, psychology, sociology, children's literature, elementary curriculum materials. **Holdings:** 112,382 books; 224,430 research reports on microfiche. **Subscriptions:** 357 journals and other serials. **Services:** Interlibrary loan; copying; library open to the public with restrictions. **Computerized Information Services:** DIALOG Information Services. **Networks/Consortia:** Member of New York Metropolitan Reference and Research Library Agency. **Remarks:** FAX: (212)932-1594. **Staff:** Lelita P. Jaspal, Asst.Dir. & Ref.; Linda Greengrass, Coord.Sch.Serv.; Sharon Cohen, Ref.

★1489★
Bankers Life & Casualty Company - Marketing Library (Bus-Fin)
1000 Sunset Ridge Rd. — Phone: (708)498-1500
Northbrook, IL 60062 — Anthony Witt, Libn.
Staff: Prof 1. **Subjects:** Health insurance. **Special Collections:** Internal reports (microfiche). **Holdings:** 600 books; 2600 marketing surveys and projects; 200 competitive company comparisons. **Subscriptions:** 41 journals and other serials. **Services:** Library open to the public. **Automated Operations:** Computerized cataloging. **Computerized Information Services:** Internal database. **Special Indexes:** Health Insurance Research Data Bank; Competitive Companies Information File.

★1490★
Bankers Research Institute - Ezra Pound Institute of Civilization - Library (Hum, Soc Sci)
Box 1105
Staunton, VA 24401 — Eustace Mullins, Pres./Dir.
Founded: 1972. **Staff:** Prof 1; Other 2. **Subjects:** Economics, politics. **Special Collections:** Ezra Pound personal letters and memorabilia; rare books and pamphlets on Federal Reserve System. **Holdings:** 30,000 books; 100 bound periodical volumes; manuscripts of Ezra Pound, e.e. cummings, George S. Viereck, and other writers. **Subscriptions:** 28 journals and other serials; 7 newspapers. **Services:** Interlibrary loan; library not open to the public.

★1491★
Bankers Research Institute - Library (Bus-Fin)
Box 1105 — Phone: (703)886-5580
Staunton, VA 24401 — Eustace Mullins, Pres./Dir.
Founded: 1982. **Staff:** 1. **Subjects:** Banking, political affairs. **Holdings:** 3000 volumes. **Services:** Library not open to the public. **Remarks:** Affiliated with the National Council for Medical Research and the National Commission for Judicial Reform.

★1492★
Bankers Trust Company - Information Center (Bus-Fin)
280 Park Ave., 9th Fl. West — Phone: (212)454-3282
New York, NY 10017 — Carol L. Ginsburg, V.P./Info.Off.
Founded: 1982. **Staff:** Prof 8; Other 8. **Subjects:** Business, economics, finance. **Holdings:** 700 books; annual, 10K, 10Q, and 8K reports of New York Stock Exchange, American Stock Exchange, and Over-The-Counter (1976 to present) on microfiche and CD-ROM. **Subscriptions:** 400 journals and other serials; 25 newspapers. **Services:** Interlibrary loan; copying; SDI; center open to SLA members. **Automated Operations:** Computerized cataloging, acquisitions, and serials. **Computerized Information Services:** DIALOG Information Services, Mead Data Central, VU/TEXT Information Services, Info Globe, DataTimes, Dow Jones News/Retrieval, TEXTLINE, Spectrum Ownership Profiles Online, Securities Data Co., Inc., IDD Information Services, Inc.; internal database; CD-ROMs (Compact Disclosure Canada, Compact Disclosure Worldscope, Compact Disclosure SEC, Lotus One Source, Business Dateline Ondisc, BP Ondisc, Grolier Encyclopedia, Moody's OnDisc). **Publications:** IB Information Center Newsletter, irregular. **Special Indexes:** Lists of central files, subject files, and periodical collection. **Remarks:** FAX: (212)454-1486. Branch library maintained at Broadgate St., 6th Fl., London, England. **Staff:** Carole Ottenheimer, Asst.V.P.; Linda Bovo, Asst.V.P. Louise Masarof, Libn.; Sharon Young, Libn.; Richard Lemberg, Asst.V.P.

Daniel T. Banks Health Science Library
See: **St. Vincent's Medical Center** (14622)

★1493★
R.L. Banks & Associates, Inc. - Library (Trans)
1717 K St., N.W., Suite 1010 — Phone: (202)296-6700
Washington, DC 20006-1515 — Delores Dola, Libn.
Subjects: Transportation, economics, engineering. **Holdings:** 1000 books; 1000 bound periodical volumes; 4000 reports. **Services:** Library open to the public by appointment. **Remarks:** FAX: (202)296-3700.

William and Evelyn Banks Library
See: **La Grange College** (8844)

★1494★
General Phineas Banning Residence Museum - Library (Hist)
401 E. M St. — Phone: (213)548-7777
Wilmington, CA 90748 — Margery Hughes, Chm.
Founded: 1974. **Staff:** 1. **Subjects:** California history, Victoriana, decorative arts. **Holdings:** 300 books; 50 tapes. **Subscriptions:** 25 journals and other serials; 3 newspapers. **Services:** Library open to the public by appointment. **Remarks:** FAX: (213)548-2644.

★1495★
Bannisters International Banana Club - International Banana Club Museum & Library (Rec)
2524 N. El Molino Ave. Phone: (818)798-2272
Altadena, CA 91001 Mr. Bannister, Pres.
Founded: 1976. **Subjects:** Bananas. **Holdings:** "Everything anyone has ever seen to do with bananas" (15,000 items). **Services:** Library open by appointment only. **Publications:** Newsletter, semiannual.

Bannon Health Science Library
See: **St. Elizabeth Hospital Medical Center** (14279)

Banque du Canada
See: **Bank of Canada** (1479)

Banque Nationale du Canada
See: **National Bank of Canada** (11087)

Banque Royale du Canada - Informatheque
See: **Royal Bank of Canada** (14100)

Banting & Best Department of Medical Research
See: **University of Toronto** (19430)

★1496★
Baptist Bible College - Vick Memorial Library (Rel-Phil)
628 E. Kearney St. Phone: (417)869-9811
Springfield, MO 65803 Jack Burr, Dir.
Founded: 1956. **Staff:** Prof 1; Other 14. **Subjects:** Bible, theology, elementary education, business. **Special Collections:** Baptist History. **Holdings:** 42,700 books; 920 bound periodical volumes; 1827 theses; 17,000 nonbook materials. **Subscriptions:** 390 journals and other serials. **Services:** Interlibrary loan; copying; computer laboratory. **Automated Operations:** Computerized cataloging. **Networks/Consortia:** Member of Missouri Library Network Corp. (MLNC).

★1497★
Baptist Bible College of Pennsylvania - Richard J. Murphy Memorial Library (Rel-Phil)
538 Venard Rd. Phone: (717)587-1172
Clarks Summit, PA 18411 David C. McClain, Hd.Libn.
Founded: 1932. **Staff:** Prof 2; Other 12. **Subjects:** Bible and theology, Christian education, church history, church ministries, music. **Holdings:** 82,264 books; 3340 bound periodical volumes; 39 VF drawers of pamphlets and Clippings; 8017 microforms; 10,439 phonograph records and cassette tapes; 1444 filmstrips; 727 scores; 7277 pictures; 3553 transparencies. **Subscriptions:** 475 journals and other serials. **Services:** Interlibrary loan; copying; library open to the public with special permission. **Staff:** Richard Erickson, Dir., IMC.

★1498★
Baptist Convention of Ontario and Quebec - Canadian Baptist Archives (Rel-Phil)
McMaster Divinity College Phone: (416)525-9140
Hamilton, ON, Canada L8S 4K1 Judith Colwell, Archv.
Founded: 1865. **Staff:** Prof 1. **Subjects:** English and French Canadian Baptists in Ontario, Quebec, and Western Canada. **Special Collections:** Plymouth Brethren; biographical material for prominent Canadian Baptists (29 shelves); McMaster University Archives (to 1957); C.H. Spurgeon Collection; John Milton Society For the Blind in Canada Archives. **Holdings:** 208 shelves of books and bound periodical volumes; 835 shelves of church and denominational records; 125 shelves of Canadian Baptist educational records; 20 shelves of pamphlets; 58 VF drawers of clippings, photographs, historical sketches. **Subscriptions:** 20 journals and other serials. **Services:** Archives open to the public with restrictions. **Automated Operations:** Computerized cataloging and serials. **Computerized Information Services:** Internal database.

★1499★
Baptist General Conference - Archives (Rel-Phil)
3949 Bethel Dr. Phone: (612)638-6282
St. Paul, MN 55112 Norris Magnuson, Archv.
Founded: 1890. **Staff:** Prof 1. **Subjects:** Archives of Baptist General Conference and its antecedent, Swedish Baptist General Conference; Bethel College and Seminary Archives. **Holdings:** 1010 books; 430 bound periodical volumes; 202 linear feet of correspondence; 153 linear feet of biography and history; 1020 audiotapes; 200 reels of microfilm; pictures; slides. **Services:** Copying; archives open to the public. **Remarks:** Alternate telephone number(s): 638-6183. Housed in the Bethel Theological Seminary Library.

★1500★
Baptist Hospital - Medical Library (Med)
1000 W. Moreno Phone: (904)434-4877
Pensacola, FL 32501 Ellen Richbourg, Libn.
Founded: 1959. **Staff:** Prof 1. **Subjects:** Medicine. **Holdings:** 600 books; 5000 bound periodical volumes. **Subscriptions:** 150 journals and other serials. **Services:** Interlibrary loan; library not open to the public. **Computerized Information Services:** MEDLARS, MEDLINE.

★1501★
Baptist Hospital - Medical Library (Med)
E. 8th St.
Box 745 Phone: (605)842-2110
Winner, SD 57580 Kris Hauf, Dir., Med.Rec.
Founded: 1981. **Staff:** 1. **Subjects:** Medicine. **Holdings:** 200 books. **Subscriptions:** 15 journals and other serials. **Services:** Interlibrary loan; library not open to the public. **Networks/Consortia:** Member of Central South Dakota Health Science Library Consortium. **Remarks:** FAX: (605)842-0433.

★1502★
Baptist Hospital - Medical Library (Med)
2000 Church St. Phone: (615)329-5373
Nashville, TN 37236 Lynne A. Wood, Chf.Med.Libn.
Founded: 1978. **Staff:** Prof 1. **Subjects:** Medicine, nursing, and allied health sciences. **Holdings:** 2928 books; 1690 bound periodical volumes; 980 pamphlets and clippings; 12 AV items. **Subscriptions:** 140 journals and other serials. **Services:** Interlibrary loan (fee); copying; library open to health care professionals for reference use only. **Automated Operations:** Data Trek. **Computerized Information Services:** MEDLARS, MEDLINE, EBSCO; CD-ROM (MEDLINE). **Publications:** Newsletter, quarterly - for internal distribution only. **Remarks:** FAX: (615)340-4610.

★1503★
Baptist Hospital East - Hagan-Pedigo Library (Med)
4000 Kresge Way Phone: (502)897-8183
Louisville, KY 40207 Kay Goldberg, Dir., Lib.Serv.
Founded: 1978. **Staff:** Prof 2. **Subjects:** Medicine, nursing, hospital administration. **Holdings:** 1200 books. **Subscriptions:** 250 journals and other serials. **Services:** Interlibrary loan; current awareness service; library not open to the public. **Automated Operations:** Computerized cataloging and ILL (OCLC). **Computerized Information Services:** NLM, BRS Information Technologies; MESSAGES (electronic mail service). **Networks/Consortia:** Member of Kentucky Health Sciences Library Consortium, Bluegrass Medical Libraries Consortium. **Remarks:** FAX: (502)897-8020. Electronic mail address(es): TUOA (MESSAGES). **Staff:** Nancy Porter, Libn.

★1504★
Baptist Hospital of Miami - Health Sciences Library (Med)
8900 N. Kendall Dr. Phone: (305)596-6506
Miami, FL 33176 Diane F. Ream, Dir.
Founded: 1965. **Staff:** Prof 1; Other 2. **Subjects:** Medicine, nursing, allied health sciences, hospital administration, consumer health. **Holdings:** 550 books; 1800 bound periodical volumes; 4 VF drawers of pamphlets, reprints, clippings; 5500 slides; 500 audio cassettes. **Subscriptions:** 200 journals and other serials. **Services:** Interlibrary loan; copying; library open to nursing students. **Automated Operations:** Computerized cataloging and circulation. **Computerized Information Services:** PaperChase, DIALOG Information Services, NLM, BRS Information Technologies; internal database; CD-ROM (MEDLINE); DOCLINE (electronic mail service). Performs searches. **Networks/Consortia:** Member of Miami Health Sciences Library Consortium (MHSLC). **Publications:** Library Letter, semiannual. **Remarks:** FAX: (305)598-5910.

★1505★
Baptist Hospital of Southeast Texas - Medical Library
College & 11th
Box 1591
Beaumont, TX 77704
Founded: 1962. **Subjects:** Nursing, health administration, medicine, surgery, obstetrics, pediatrics. **Holdings:** 5539 books; 1296 bound periodical volumes; 2 VF drawers of pamphlets; 569 Audio-Digest tapes; 13 films; 101 files of clippings. **Remarks:** Currently inactive.

★1506★
Baptist Medical Center - Library (Med)
6601 Rockhill Rd. Phone: (816)276-7863
Kansas City, MO 64131 Richard Dalton, Dir.
Staff: Prof 1; Other 1. **Subjects:** Health sciences. **Holdings:** 5500 books; 3500 bound periodical volumes; 10 VF drawers of pamphlets. **Subscriptions:** 283 journals and other serials. **Services:** Interlibrary loan; copying; library open to the public with restrictions. **Computerized Information Services:** DIALOG Information Services, NLM. **Networks/Consortia:** Member of Kansas City Library Network, Inc. (KCLN). **Remarks:** FAX: (816)926-2265.

★1507★
Baptist Medical Center - Margaret Clark Gilbreath Memorial Library (Med)
9601 Interstate 630 Phone: (501)227-2671
Little Rock, AR 72205 Auburn Steward, Libn.
Founded: 1974. **Staff:** Prof 1; Other 1. **Subjects:** Nursing, medicine. **Holdings:** 1900 books; 2400 bound periodical volumes. **Subscriptions:** 197 journals and other serials. **Services:** Interlibrary loan; copying; SDI; library open to nursing students of the University of Central Arkansas, Harding College, and Henderson State College and medical students from the University of Arkansas Medical Sciences Campus. **Computerized Information Services:** NLM. Performs searches on fee basis for students. **Publications:** Keeping Up (newsletter), quarterly - for internal distribution only. **Remarks:** FAX: (501)227-1740. Contains the holdings of the former Baptist Medical System - Sheppard Professional Library.

★1508★
Baptist Medical Center - Medical Library (Med)
2105 E. South Blvd.
Box 11010 Phone: (205)286-2952
Montgomery, AL 36198 Jerrie Burton, Libn.
Staff: Prof 1. **Subjects:** Medicine, nursing, allied health sciences. **Holdings:** 1029 books; 1060 bound periodical volumes. **Subscriptions:** 99 journals and other serials. **Services:** Interlibrary loan; copying; library open to the public for reference use only. **Computerized Information Services:** MEDLINE, NLM. **Networks/Consortia:** Member of Montgomery Area Health Information Consortium (MAHIC). **Remarks:** Alternate telephone number(s): 286-2910.

★1509★
Baptist Medical Center - Pitts Memorial Library (Med)
Taylor at Marion St. Phone: (803)771-5281
Columbia, SC 29220 Pat Pavlick, Libn.
Founded: 1954. **Staff:** Prof 1; Other 1. **Subjects:** Nursing, medicine, pharmacology, pastoral care, respiratory therapy, hospital administration. **Holdings:** 800 books; 105 bound periodical volumes; 12 VF drawers of clippings and pamphlets; masters' theses. **Subscriptions:** 100 journals and other serials. **Services:** Interlibrary loan; copying; library open to the public with restrictions; reference assistance and orientation to nursing and allied health students. **Automated Operations:** Computerized ILL (DOCLINE). **Computerized Information Services:** MEDLINE. **Networks/Consortia:** Member of Columbia Area Medical Librarians' Association (CAMLA), South Carolina Health Information Network (SCHIN).

★1510★
Baptist Medical Center - Wann Langston Memorial Library (Med)
3300 Northwest Expy. Phone: (405)949-3766
Oklahoma City, OK 73112 Cheryl Suttles, Dir., Med.Lib.
Founded: 1968. **Staff:** Prof 1; Other 1. **Subjects:** Geriatrics, medicine, nursing, hospital management. **Holdings:** 2186 books; 3654 bound periodical volumes. **Subscriptions:** 270 journals and other serials. **Services:** Interlibrary loan; copying; SDI; library open to the public with permission of librarian. **Computerized Information Services:** MEDLINE, DIALOG Information Services, BRS Information Technologies. **Networks/Consortia:** Member of Greater Oklahoma City Area Health Sciences Library Consortium (GOAL), Metronet. **Remarks:** FAX: (405)945-3883.

★1511★
Baptist Medical Center, Princeton - Medical Library (Med)
701 Princeton Ave., S.W. Phone: (205)783-3078
Birmingham, AL 35211 Maureen S. Battistella, Med.Libn.
Founded: 1942. **Staff:** Prof 1; Other 1.5. **Subjects:** Medicine, surgery, nursing. **Holdings:** 2058 books; 6200 bound periodical volumes. **Subscriptions:** 195 journals. **Services:** Interlibrary loan; copying; SDI; library open to the public with administrative approval. **Computerized Information Services:** NLM, KNOWLEDGE INDEX, MEDLINE/EBSCO, DIALOG Information Services, Human Resource Information Network (HRIN), CompuServe Information Service; CD-ROM. Performs searches free of charge for Alabama residents. **Networks/Consortia:** Member of Alabama Health Libraries Association (ALHELA), Jefferson County Hospital Librarians' Association, National Network of Libraries of Medicine - Southeastern/Atlantic Region. **Publications:** Patient Education Resource Manual; Princeton Authors (1985-1990).

★1512★
Baptist Medical Centers-Samford University - Ida V. Moffett School of Nursing - L.R. Jordan Library (Med)
820 Montclair Rd. Phone: (205)592-5103
Birmingham, AL 35213 Jewell Alexander Carter, Lib.Dir.
Founded: 1922. **Staff:** Prof 1; Other 5. **Subjects:** Nursing, allied health sciences. **Special Collections:** Nursing Historical Collection. **Holdings:** 8951 books; 2169 bound periodical volumes; 420 VF folders; 1718 AV programs. **Subscriptions:** 139 journals and other serials. **Services:** Interlibrary loan; copying; library open to the public for reference use only.

★1513★
Baptist Memorial Hospital - John L. McGehee Library (Med)
899 Madison Ave. Phone: (901)227-5140
Memphis, TN 38146 Nancy N. Smith, Med.Libn.
Staff: Prof 1; Other 1. **Subjects:** Medicine. **Holdings:** 1000 books; 3000 bound periodical volumes. **Subscriptions:** 131 journals and other serials. **Services:** Interlibrary loan; library open to residents and medical staff only. **Automated Operations:** Computerized ILL (DOCLINE). **Computerized Information Services:** MEDLARS. **Networks/Consortia:** Member of Association of Memphis Area Health Science Libraries (AMAHSL).

★1514★
Baptist Memorial Hospital - Medical Library (Med)
1007 Goodyear Ave. Phone: (205)494-4128
Gadsden, AL 35999 Paula G. Davis, Med.Libn.
Founded: 1970. **Staff:** Prof 1. **Subjects:** Medicine, nursing, surgery, obstetrics, gynecology, management. **Holdings:** 1800 books; 1000 bound periodical volumes. **Subscriptions:** 131 journals and other serials. **Services:** Interlibrary loan; library not open to the public. **Automated Operations:** Computerized ILL (DOCLINE). **Computerized Information Services:** MEDLINE, DIALOG Information Services, BRS Information Technologies. Performs searches on fee basis. **Networks/Consortia:** Member of Alabama Health Libraries Association (ALHELA). **Remarks:** FAX: (205)494-4498.

★1515★
Baptist Memorial Hospital - School of Nursing - Library (Med)
999 Monroe Phone: (901)227-4307
Memphis, TN 38104 Sherry Young, Libn.
Founded: 1920. **Staff:** Prof 1; Other 1. **Subjects:** Nursing, health care. **Special Collections:** First editions. **Holdings:** 6864 books; 245 bound periodical volumes; 1 VF drawer of clippings and pamphlets; 45 anatomical maps and charts; 225 slides. **Subscriptions:** 51 journals and other serials. **Services:** Interlibrary loan; copying; library open to the public for reference use only. **Networks/Consortia:** Member of Association of Memphis Area Health Science Libraries (AMAHSL). **Remarks:** Alternate telephone number(s): (901)522-4301.

★1516★
Baptist Memorial Hospital System - Bruce A. Garrett Memorial Library & Media Center (Med)
111 Dallas St. Phone: (512)554-2507
San Antonio, TX 78286 Ruth R. Libby, Lib.Dir.
Founded: 1968. **Staff:** Prof 1; Other 5. **Subjects:** Medicine, nursing, hospital administration, counseling, religion. **Holdings:** 3120 books; 376 bound periodical volumes. **Subscriptions:** 144 journals and other serials. **Services:** Interlibrary loan; copying; library open to the public for reference use only. **Computerized Information Services:** MEDLINE. **Networks/Consortia:** Member of Health Oriented Libraries of San Antonio (HOLSA), National Network of Libraries of Medicine - South Central Region. **Remarks:** FAX: (512)554-2839.

★1517★
Baptist Missionary Association Theological Seminary - Kellar Library (Rel-Phil)
1410 E. Pine St. Phone: (903)586-2501
Jacksonville, TX 75766-5414 James C. Blaylock, Dir.
Founded: 1957. **Staff:** 4. **Subjects:** Religion, Bible, theology. **Special Collections:** Association and convention minutes (8462); Baptist history. **Holdings:** 49,920 books; 6000 bound periodical volumes; 279 reels of microfilm; 525 titles on microfiche; 4045 cassette tapes. **Subscriptions:** 653 journals and other serials. **Services:** Interlibrary loan; copying; library open to the public.

★1518★
Baptist Union of Denmark - Library (Rel-Phil)
Laerdalsgade 5
DK-2300 Copenhagen S, Denmark Phone: 31 590708
SSubjects: Baptists. **Holdings:** 10,000 volumes. **Remarks:** FAX: 31 590133. **Also Known As:** Det Danske Baptistsamfund.

★1519★
Baptist Union of Romania - Library (Rel-Phil)
Blvd. N. Titulescu 56 A
78152 Bucharest, Romania Phone: 0 173705
Subjects: Baptists. **Holdings:** 3000 volumes.

★1520★
Baptist Union of Western Canada - Baptist Leadership Training School Library (Rel-Phil)
4330 16th St., S.W. Phone: (403)243-3770
Calgary, AB, Canada T2T 4H9 Myrna Sears, Libn.
Staff: Prof 3; Other 21. **Subjects:** Theology, devotional life, Christian education and biography, church history and music. **Holdings:** 5000 books; school yearbooks. **Subscriptions:** 15 journals and other serials. **Services:** Interlibrary loan; library open to the public with restrictions. **Remarks:** FAX: (403)287-1930.

Bar of Montreal
See: **Barreau de Montreal** (1540)

★1521★
Bar llan University - English Department - Seminar Library (Hum)
Bar llan Campus Phone: 3 5318797
52900 Ramat Gan, Israel Gloria Cohen
Founded: 1967. **Staff:** Prof 2; Other 4. **Subjects:** English literature, American literature, linguistics, art, world literature. **Holdings:** 40,000 books; 20 bound periodical volumes; 45 videocassettes. **Subscriptions:** 133 journals and other serials; 10 newspapers. **Services:** Interlibrary loan; library open to the public with restrictions. **Staff:** Dina Goldsmidt, Libn.

★1522★
Bishop Baraga Association - Archives (Hist)
444 S. 4th St.
Box 550 Phone: (906)225-1141
Marquette, MI 49855 Regis Walling, Archv.
Founded: 1930. **Staff:** Prof 1. **Subjects:** Bishop Frederic Baraga, native Americans, Catholic Church, United States history. **Special Collections:** Baraga Collection (books, diaries, letters, 1830-1868); microfilm of the Office of Indian Affairs, early 1800s. **Holdings:** 1003 books; microfilm. **Services:** Copying; archives open to the public by appointment. **Publications:** Baraga Bulletin, quarterly. **Remarks:** FAX: (906)225-0437.

★1523★
Barbados Museum & Historical Society - Shilstone Library (Hist)
St. Ann's Garrison Phone: (809)427-0201
St. Michael, Barbados Betty Carrillo-Shannon, Libn.
Founded: 1933. **Staff:** 2. **Subjects:** West Indian history, house architecture, sugar plantations, furniture, artists' works. **Special Collections:** Plantation records (18th and 19th century); Parish Vestry minutes (19th century); genealogical family history collection. **Holdings:** 4000 books; 10 manuscripts; historic photographs and postcards. **Services:** Copying, library open to the public for reference use only. **Publications:** BMHS Journal, annual; Journal index. **Remarks:** Alternate telephone number(s): (809)436 1956. FAX: (809)429 5946.

Barbeau, Sutherland, Falk - Library
See: **Sutherland, Johnston, MacLean - Library** (15895)

★1524★
Grosvenor Barber and Associates - Library (Info Sci)
724 Miller Ave. Phone: (703)759-6587
Great Falls, VA 22066 Grosvenor Barber, Pres.
Subjects: Business, technology, information sources. **Holdings:** 600 bound volumes. **Subscriptions:** 20 journals and other serials. **Services:** Library not open to the public. **Computerized Information Services:** BRS Information Technologies, DIALOG Information Services, NLM; internal databases; CompuServe Information Service (electronic mail service). Performs searches on fee basis. **Publications:** The Price Sheet, weekly. **Remarks:** FAX: (703)759-9233. Electronic mail address(es): 71460,1506 (CompuServe Information Service).

★1525★
Richard J. Barber Associates, Inc. - Library (Trans)
1828 L St., N.W., Suite 406 Phone: (202)785-0597
Washington, DC 20036 Verna Wolfe, Chf.Libn.
Founded: 1972. **Staff:** Prof 1; Other 1. **Subjects:** Rail and other transportation, antitrust economics, energy, corporate finance. **Holdings:** 3000 books; 75 bound periodical volumes; 60 other cataloged items. **Subscriptions:** 60 journals and other serials; 6 newspapers. **Services:** Interlibrary loan; library not open to the public. **Remarks:** Provides consultative services to business and the legal profession.

★1526★
Barberton Citizens Hospital - Medical Library (Med)
155 Fifth St., N.E. Phone: (216)745-1611
Barberton, OH 44203 Karen Swiatek
Staff: Prof 1; Other 1. **Subjects:** Clinical medicine and nursing. **Holdings:** 962 books; 2487 bound periodical volumes. **Subscriptions:** 112 journals and other serials. **Services:** Interlibrary loan; library not open to the public. **Automated Operations:** Computerized cataloging. **Computerized Information Services:** NLM. **Networks/Consortia:** Member of NEOUCOM Council Associated Hospital Librarians. **Remarks:** FAX: (216)848-9902.

★1527★
Barberton Public Library - Special Collections (Hist)
602 W. Park Ave. Phone: (216)745-1194
Barberton, OH 44203-2458 Phyllis Taylor, Barberton Hist.Spec.
Founded: 1903. **Staff:** Prof 6. **Subjects:** Local and state history. **Special Collections:** Barberton Sports Hall of Fame. **Holdings:** Papers of William Johnston, first Barberton surveyor; 20 VF drawers of Barberton and Ohio vertical file materials; 56 reels of microfilm of Barberton Herald; 6 reels of microfilm of the Barberton News; 5 reels of microfilm of the Barberton Leader; 6 reels of microfilm of the Barberton Post; 300 linear feet of books about Barberton and Ohio; 70 framed and mounted pictures and wall maps; Barberton and Ohio memorabilia; 4 display cases of Barberton memorabilia. **Subscriptions:** 7 journals and other serials. **Services:** Interlibrary loan; copying; collections open to the public. **Automated Operations:** Computerized cataloging and indexing. **Networks/Consortia:** Member of North Central Library Cooperative (NCLC). **Publications:** Keylines, bimonthly. **Special Indexes:** Barberton Herald index, 1986 to present (online). **Remarks:** FAX: (216)745-8261. Library has 7 stained glass windows from O.C. Barber mansion. **Staff:** Barbara Kirbawy, Dir.; Kathleen Jones, Asst.Dir.; Barbara Gercken, Children's Libn.; Martha Thrall, Libn.; Jean Swinehart, Libn.; Steven Steigerwald, Libn.

Clifford E. Barbour Library
See: **Pittsburgh Theological Seminary** (13088)

★1528★
(Barcelona) Institute of North American Studies - Library (Educ)
Via Augusta 123 Phone: 3 2007551
E-08006 Barcelona, Spain Jane Ishibashi, Chf.Libn.
Staff: 3. **Subjects:** United States. **Holdings:** 9500 books. **Subscriptions:** 105 journals and other serials; 3 newspapers. **Services:** Copying; library open to the public. **Remarks:** FAX: 3 2020690. Library is a part of non-profit cultural institution with some financial support from the U.S. Information Agency. Focus is on materials that will assist peoples outside the United States to learn about the United States, its people, history, culture, political processes, and social milieux. **Staff:** Daina Grinbergs.

H. Douglas Barclay Law Library
See: **Syracuse University** (15962)

Barco Law Library
See: **University of Pittsburgh - Barco Law Library** (19204)

★1529★
Barium and Chemicals, Inc. - Research Library (Sci-Engr)
County Rd. 44
P.O. Box 218 Phone: (614)282-9776
Steubenville, OH 43952 Eleanor R. Naylor, Libn.
Founded: 1947. **Staff:** 1. **Subjects:** Inorganic and organic chemicals, ores and mining, chemical engineering. **Holdings:** 1000 books; 3000 bound periodical volumes; 16 VF drawers of research reports, pamphlets, patents concerning alkaline earth compounds. **Services:** Library open to the public with permission of management. **Remarks:** FAX: (614)282-9161.

Barker Engineering Library
See: **Massachusetts Institute of Technology** (9796)

Barker Texas History Center
See: **University of Texas at Austin - Barker Texas History Center** (19379)

★1530★
Barkerville Historic Town - Resource Information Centre (Hist)
P.O. Box 19 Phone: (604)994-3332
Barkerville, BC, Canada V0K 1B0 W.G. Quackenbush, Cur.
Founded: 1985. **Staff:** Prof 1. **Subjects:** Barkerville and provincial history, Cariboo regional history, mining history, Victorian era culture, artifact identification. **Special Collections:** Mining records, 1858-1900; Chinese in Barkerville, 1858-1900 (8 meters); Victorian Trades and Technology; Preservation and Museum Techniques; Cariboo Sentinel Newspaper on microfilm; personal papers (6.67 meters); Barkerville Survey Collection (2 meters); Barkerville Commercial Papers Collection (8.4 meters); Land Lot Files (NewWestminster to the Cariboo). **Holdings:** Books; 4.9 meters of photographs; 4000 maps, plans, and drawings; 200 record groups. **Subscriptions:** 11 journals and other serials. **Services:** Center open to the public with restrictions. **Automated Operations:** Computerized cataloging. **Computerized Information Services:** Museum Artifact Registration System (M.A.R.S., internal database). **Special Indexes:** Indexes to archives, maps, prints, posters (online). **Remarks:** FAX: (604)994-3435. Maintained by British Columbia Ministry of Tourism.

Barksdale Medical Library
See: **Virginia Baptist Hospital** (19858)

★1531★
Barlow Respiratory Hospital - Elks Library (Med)
2000 Stadium Way Phone: (213)250-4200
Los Angeles, CA 90026-2696 Rose Thompson, Libn.
Founded: 1946. **Staff:** Prof 1. **Subjects:** Tuberculosis and diseases of the chest. **Holdings:** 3500 volumes; 12,000 medical reprints. **Subscriptions:** 70 journals and other serials. **Services:** Interlibrary loan; copying; library open to health professionals and students. **Formerly:** Barlow Hospital.

Ralph S. Barnaby Archives
See: **National Soaring Museum** (11288)

E.T. Barnad Library
See: **Otter Tail County Historical Society - E.T. Barnad Library** (12605)

A.J. Barnard, Jr. Library
See: **J.T. Baker Inc.** (1419)

Barnard Center for Research on Women
See: **Barnard College - Barnard Center for Research on Women** (1532)

★1532★
Barnard College - Barnard Center for Research on Women - Birdie Goldsmith Ast Resource Collection (Soc Sci)
101 Barnard Hall
3009 Broadway Phone: (212)854-2067
New York, NY 10027 Leslie Caleman, Dir., Women's Ctr.
Founded: 1971. **Staff:** Prof 2. **Subjects:** Feminist theory; sex roles and sex differences; women's movement; education; employment; legal status; health; violence and sexual exploitation; women in other countries, history, and the arts; women and development. **Special Collections:** Bobbye Ortiz Collection on Women in Developing Nations; Helen Marieskind health files; Working Women's Institute files on sexual harassment; Professor Ruth Milkman's Materials on Comparable Worth & Pay Equity; Norma Wikler files on reproductive technology. **Holdings:** 1800 volumes; 5700 journal articles, reports, clippings, fact sheets, pamphlets, conference proceedings, unpublished papers, government documents; bibliographies; handbooks; directories; special issues of journals. **Subscriptions:** 160 periodicals, newspapers, and newsletters. **Services:** Collection open to the public for reference use only. **Computerized Information Services:** Winnebago (internal database). **Publications:** List of publications - available on request. **Remarks:** FAX: (212)854-7491. Maintains current information on internships and job opportunities in fields related to women's issues, as well as information on graduate and undergraduate programs in women's studies. **Staff:** Valerie Green.

George Grey Barnard Archive
See: **Metropolitan Museum of Art - Cloisters Library** (10209)

Joseph F. Barnard Memorial Law Library Association
See: **New York State Supreme Court - 9th Judicial District** (11705)

★1533★
Barnes College - Nursing Library & Instructional Resource Laboratory (Med)
416 S. Kingshighway Blvd. Phone: (314)362-1566
St. Louis, MO 63110 Beth G. Carlin, Libn.
Founded: 1955. **Staff:** Prof 1; Other 2. **Subjects:** Nursing. **Holdings:** 4000 books; 300 bound periodical volumes; AV programs; computer software; 12 VF drawers. **Subscriptions:** 90 journals and other serials. **Services:** Interlibrary loan; copying; library open to the public for reference use only. **Automated Operations:** Computerized cataloging. **Computerized Information Services:** BRS Information Technologies, NLM, MEDLINE; CD-ROM (SilverPlatter). **Networks/Consortia:** Member of National Network of Libraries of Medicine - Midcontinental Region. **Remarks:** Alternate telephone number(s): 362-1567. FAX: (314)362-1880.

Barnes Library
See: **Lambda, Inc. - Barnes Library** (8914)

★1534★
Barnes & Thornburg - Library (Law)
1313 Merchant Bank Bldg.
11 S. Meridian St. Phone: (317)638-1313
Indianapolis, IN 46204-3599 Mary Ann Roman, Libn.
Staff: Prof 2; Other 3. **Subjects:** Law. **Holdings:** 30,000 books; 400 bound periodical volumes; 500 other cataloged items. **Subscriptions:** 300 journals and other serials; 9 newspapers. **Services:** Interlibrary loan; copying; library open to the public with restrictions. **Computerized Information Services:** LEXIS, WESTLAW, DIALOG Information Services. Performs searches on fee basis. Contact Person: Steven Ries, Ref.Libn., 231-7272. **Networks/Consortia:** Member of Central Indiana Area Library Services Authority (CIALSA), INCOLSA. **Publications:** Library Bulletin, monthly - for internal distribution only.

Ward E. Barnes Education Library
See: **University of Missouri--St. Louis - Ward E. Barnes Education Library** (18983)

Barnett-Briggs Library
See: **San Francisco General Hospital Medical Center** (14733)

Barnett-Hall Library
See: **Palo Alto Medical Foundation** (12710)

Richard W. Barnett Memorial Library
See: **Hudson River Environmental Society - Richard W. Barnett Memorial Library** (7497)

Maginel Wright Barney Archives
See: **Frank Lloyd Wright Home and Studio Foundation - Research Center** (20641)

★1535★
Barnstable Law Library (Law)
First District Court House
Main St. Phone: (508)362-2511
Barnstable, MA 02630 Martha W. Elkins, Law Libn.
Founded: 1889. **Staff:** Prof 1; Other 3. **Subjects:** State and federal law. **Holdings:** 16,000 books; 2500 reports on microfiche; 24 reels of microfilm; National Reporters; loose-leaf legal services. **Subscriptions:** 30 journals and other serials. **Services:** Interlibrary loan; copying; library open to the public. **Automated Operations:** Computerized cataloging. **Computerized Information Services:** WESTLAW, LEXIS, Veralex 2, Inc.; Bulletin Board (electronic mail service). **Publications:** Trial Court Law Library Newsletter - for internal distribution only. **Remarks:** Alternate telephone number(s): 362-8539. Part of the Massachusetts State Trial Court; Marnie Warner, Law Lib.Coord.

P.T. Barnum Collection
See: **Tufts University - Nils Yngve Wessell Library** (16552)

Baron-Forness Library
See: **Edinboro University of Pennsylvania** (5232)

★1536★
Baroque Strings of Vancouver - Library
104-1425 Esquimalt Ave.
West Vancouver, BC, Canada V7T 1L1
Defunct.

C.W. Barr Planning and Design Library
See: **Michigan State University - C.W. Barr Planning and Design Library** (10317)

★1537★
Barr Engineering Company - Library (Sci-Engr)
8300 Norman Center Dr., No. 300 Phone: (612)832-2855
Minneapolis, MN 55437 Karen Oakes, Tech.Libn.
Founded: 1962. **Staff:** Prof 1. **Subjects:** Water resources, hydrology, hydraulics, soil mechanics, solid waste, environmental engineering. **Special Collections:** Company reports. **Holdings:** 2000 books; 115 bound periodical volumes; 400 government reports. **Subscriptions:** 85 journals and other serials. **Services:** Interlibrary loan; library not open to the public. **Computerized Information Services:** DIALOG Information Services. **Publications:** Library Bulletin, monthly.

Barr Library
See: **Mary Holmes College** (7338)

Barr Memorial Library
See: **St. Thomas Catholic Church** (14594)

Robert N. Barr Public Health Library
See: **Minnesota (State) Department of Health** (10480)

★1538★
W.W. Barr Law Library (Law)
Court House Phone: (814)226-9351
Clarion, PA 16214 Tammy Slike, Libn.
Subjects: Law. **Services:** Library open to the public.

★1539★
(Barranquilla) Biblioteca Centro Colombo-Americano - USIS Collection (Educ, Hum)
Carrera 43, No. 51-95 Phone: 58 318084
Barranquilla, Colombia Maria Eugenia Guevara
Founded: 1956. **Staff:** 2. **Subjects:** American literature, linguistics, economics. **Holdings:** 4000 books. **Subscriptions:** 50 journals and other serials; 2 newspapers. **Services:** Center open to the public. **Remarks:** FAX: 58 324724. Library assisted by the U.S. Information Agency. Focus is on materials that will assist peoples outside the United States to learn about the United States, its people, history, culture, political processes, and social milieux. **Staff:** Roxana Jaime.

Barratt's Chapel Museum Library
See: **United Methodist Church - Peninsula Annual Conference** (16737)

★1540★
Barreau de Montreal - Bibliotheque (Law)
Palais de Justice Phone: (514)393-2057
Montreal, PQ, Canada H2Y 1B6 Arthur Perrault, Libn.
Founded: 1828. **Staff:** Prof 2; Other 5. **Subjects:** Law. **Special Collections:** Canadiana. **Holdings:** 100,144 volumes. **Subscriptions:** 550 journals and other serials. **Services:** Interlibrary loan; copying; library open to members of the bar and judges. **Also Known As:** Bar of Montreal. **Staff:** Richard Dubuc, Assoc.Libn.

Barrett-Byam Homestead Library
See: **Chelmsford Historical Society** (3464)

Dr. C.R. Barrett Library
See: **Marine Institute - Dr. C.R. Barrett Library** (9671)

Kim Barrett Memorial Library
See: **Hospital for Special Surgery** (7423)

Barrier Free Environments, Inc.
See: **BFE/Barrier Free Environments, Inc. - Library** (1807)

★1541★
Edward F. Barrins Memorial Library (Med)
2023 E. Adams St. Phone: (602)327-7956
Tucson, AZ 85719 Christine L. Taylor-Parsil, Libn.
Founded: 1979. **Staff:** 1. **Subjects:** Hypnosis, alternate methods of healing, religion, reincarnation, 20th century fiction. **Special Collections:** Catherine M. Willy Commemorative Collection (200 volumes); Phyllis C. Barrins Collection (complete works); children's books. **Holdings:** 8000 books; 24 linear feet of pamphlets; 15 VF drawers of research manuscripts and transcripts; 15 cases of audiotapes; 18 linear feet of clippings. **Subscriptions:** 54 journals and other serials. **Services:** Library open to St. Johns University (Louisiana) and Eastern Nebraska Christian College affiliates only.

★1542★
Barrons Ltd. - C & O Canal Museum - Library (Hist)
P.O. Box 356 Phone: (301)432-8726
Sharpsburg, MD 21782 Lee D. Barron
Subjects: C & O Canal, Western Maryland and Maryland history. **Special Collections:** C & O Canal Company records. **Holdings:** 3000 books; 50 documents; 12 AV programs; 300 nonbook items; 6 manuscripts. **Services:** Library open to the public with restrictions.

Edith Cleaves Barry Library
See: **Brick Store Museum** (2113)

Barsky Memorial Library
See: **Kennedy Memorial Hospitals/University Medical Center - Washington Township Division** (8633)

Richard Barthelmess Collection
See: **Museum of Modern Art - Film Stills Archive** (10908)

★1543★
Bartholomew County Historical Society - Cline-Keller Library (Hist)
524 3rd St. Phone: (812)372-3541
Columbus, IN 47201 Helen Rowell, Libn.
Staff: 3. **Subjects:** Local and state history, antiques, genealogy. **Special Collections:** George Pence Manuscript Collection (12 cubic feet); Grace Hull family research (1 VF drawer); The Republic's card file of World War II county men; antique identification and collecting (250 volumes); Passenger & Immigration Lists Index (12 volumes). **Holdings:** 500 books; 500 bound periodical volumes; 12 cubic feet of clippings and ephemera; 300 volumes of City of Columbus records; 57 volumes of city county directories; 90 volumes of high school year books; 700 family history files; cemetery records; naturalization records. **Services:** Copying; library open to the public on a limited schedule. **Computerized Information Services:** Internal database. **Publications:** Newsletter, quarterly; Pence papers; World War II cardfile. **Special Indexes:** Probate index; tax index; marriage index; index to wills; scrapbook indexes; index to County Commissioner records, 1821-1850; photograph index.

★1544★
Bartlesville Public Library - Bartlesville Area History Museum & Archives (Hist)
6th & Johnstone Phone: (918)333-8897
Bartlesville, OK 74003 Joan Singleton, Pub.Serv.Libn.
Founded: 1964. **Staff:** Prof 1. **Subjects:** State and local history and genealogy, Delaware Indians. **Special Collections:** Frank Griggs Collection (70 year photographic history of Bartlesville); Isaac McCoy papers; Pratt papers. **Holdings:** 1900 books; 1900 and 1910 Oklahoma census records; tribal rolls and censuses; mortuary records; newspapers. **Services:** Interlibrary loan; copying; archives open to the public. **Special Indexes:** Obituary index; wedding index of Washington County. **Remarks:** FAX: (918)333-9037. **Staff:** Jan Sanders, Dir.; Elsie Green, Tech.Serv.Libn.; Kathleen Mulligan, Ref.Libn.; Katherine Hanson, Ref.Libn.

Bartlett Arboretum
See: **University of Connecticut** (18514)

★1545★
Barton-Aschman Associates, Inc. - Library (Plan)
111 3rd Ave., S., Suite 350 Phone: (612)332-0421
Minneapolis, MN 55401 Eve Sather, Libn.
Founded: 1975. **Staff:** 1. **Subjects:** Transportation, urban planning, environment. **Holdings:** 300 books; 3000 reports and documents. **Subscriptions:** 100 journals and other serials; 10 newspapers. **Services:** Library not open to the public. **Automated Operations:** Computerized cataloging. **Remarks:** FAX: (612)332-6180.

Bruce Barton Memorial Library
See: **International Center for the Disabled (ICD)** (8070)

Clara Barton National Historic Site
See: **U.S. Natl. Park Service** (17691)

Edwin M. Barton Library
See: **Columbia County Historical Society** (3982)

★1546★
Barton Myers Associates - Library (Plan)
6834 Hollywood Blvd. Phone: (213)466-4051
Los Angeles, CA 90028 Terri Hartman, Hist.
Staff: 1. **Subjects:** Architecture, planning, geography. **Special Collections:** Rare architectural volumes. **Holdings:** 4000 books; slides. **Subscriptions:** 12 journals and other serials. **Services:** Library not open to the public. **Remarks:** FAX: (213)466-5068. **Formerly:** Located in Toronto, Canada.

Celeste Bartos International Film Study Center
See: **Museum of Modern Art** (10906)

Joseph W. Bartunek III Law Library
See: **Cleveland State University** (3832)

★1547★
Belle W. Baruch Institute for Marine Biology and Coastal Research - Library (Biol Sci)
University of South Carolina Phone: (803)777-5288
Columbia, SC 29208 Ms. V. Smith, Adm.Asst.
Subjects: Marine biology, marine geology, physical and chemical oceanography, ecosystem studies. **Holdings:** Figures not available. **Also Known As:** Belle W. Baruch Library in Marine Science.

★1548★
Bernard Baruch College of City University of New York - Library (Bus-Fin)
155 E. 24th St. Phone: (212)447-3870
New York, NY 10010 Kristin McDonough, Chf.Libn.
Founded: 1929. **Staff:** Prof 22; Other 20. **Subjects:** Business, economics and finance, social studies, history. **Holdings:** 410,000 volumes; 12,000 reels of microfilm; 20 VF drawers of pamphlets; SEC 10K reports; 80 business, labor, tax services. **Subscriptions:** 4645 journals and other serials; 28 newspapers. **Services:** Interlibrary loan; library open to the public for reference use only. **Automated Operations:** Computerized cataloging, acquisitions, circulation, and serials. **Computerized Information Services:** DIALOG Information Services, BRS Information Technologies, PFDS Online, Mead Data Central, Dow Jones News/Retrieval, OCLC; CD-ROMs. **Networks/Consortia:** Member of New York Metropolitan Reference and Research Library Agency. **Remarks:** FAX: (212)447-3705. **Staff:** Ida Lowe, Tech.Serv.Libn.; Sara Sluss, Coord., Rd.Serv.

Bernard Baruch College of the City University of New York - National Center for the Collective Bargaining in Higher Education and the Professions
See: **National Center for the Study of Collective Bargaining in Higher Education and the Professions** (11109)

Bascom Palmer Eye Institute
See: **University of Miami - School of Medicine - Bascom Palmer Eye Institute** (18848)

★1549★
BASF Corporation - Business Information Center (Sci-Engr)
8 Campus Dr. Phone: (201)397-2700
Parsippany, NJ 07054 Ingrid Friedenson, Bus.Info.Anl./Mgr.
Staff: Prof 1; Other 1. **Subjects:** Chemical and polymer industries, dyes and pigments, agricultural chemicals, magnetic recording media. **Holdings:** 1500 books; 678 reports; 28 VF drawers of company, industry, product information; 3 VF drawers of economic forecasting services documents. **Subscriptions:** 164 journals and other serials. **Services:** Interlibrary loan; center not open to the public. **Computerized Information Services:** DIALOG Information Services, PFDS Online, NEXIS, SAGE DATA, Inc., INVESTEXT, Dow Jones News/Retrieval, VU/TEXT Information Services. Performs searches on fee basis. **Publications:** Daily News Bulletin; Business Information Topics, quarterly - both for internal distribution only. **Special Catalogs:** Card file on marketing/industry reports.

★1550★
BASF Corporation - Coatings and Inks Division - Corporate Library
1255 Broad St.
Clifton, NJ 07015
Defunct.

★1551★
BASF Corporation - Colorants Library (Sci-Engr)
491 Columbia Ave. Phone: (616)392-2391
Holland, MI 49423-4899 Pam Nienhuis, Mgr., Off.Serv.
Staff: Prof 1; Other 1. **Subjects:** Pigments, inks, paint, coatings, chemistry, physics, printing, resins, lacquers, emulsions. **Holdings:** 2000 books; 3500 bound periodical volumes; 10,000 patents. **Subscriptions:** 250 journals and other serials. **Services:** Interlibrary loan; library not open to the public. **Automated Operations:** Computerized cataloging. **Computerized Information Services:** DIALOG Information Services, STN International, Dow Jones News/Retrieval; internal database. **Networks/Consortia:** Member of Lakeland Area Library Network (LAKENET), Michigan Library Consortium (MLC). **Publications:** Acquisitions Bulletin - for internal distribution only. **Remarks:** FAX: (616)392-1340.

★1552★
BASF Corporation - Corporate Research Library (Sci-Engr)
1419 Biddle Ave. Phone: (313)246-6200
Wyandotte, MI 48192-3736 Janice B. Spector, Mgr.
Founded: 1939. **Staff:** Prof 2; Other 2. **Subjects:** Organic and inorganic chemistry, agricultural chemicals, dyes, alkalies, cleaning compounds, surfactants, urethanes, thermoplastics, polymers, structural materials, coatings, engineering plastics. **Holdings:** 25,000 books; bound periodical volumes. **Subscriptions:** 700 journals and other serials. **Services:** Library not open to the public. **Automated Operations:** Computerized cataloging, acquisitions, serials, and circulation. **Computerized Information Services:** DIALOG Information Services, PFDS Online, STN International, NLM, INKA, Questel, WILSONLINE, LEXIS, NEXIS, Dow Jones News/Retrieval, PLASTEC Data Base, Syracuse Research Corporation (SRC), Data-Star, Chemical Information Systems, Inc. (CIS), PFDS Online, DataTimes. **Remarks:** FAX: (313)246-5248. **Staff:** Marie Fraties, Libn.

★1553★
BASF Corporation - Fibers Division - Technical Library/Information Systems (Sci-Engr)
Sand Hill Rd. Phone: (704)667-6936
Enka, NC 28728-9999 Karen Powell, Libn.
Founded: 1951. **Staff:** Prof 1. **Subjects:** Textiles, polymer chemistry, chemistry, engineering, business management, physics. **Holdings:** 5000 books; 1500 bound periodical volumes; 8 VF drawers of pamphlets; 28 VF drawers of reports; 1450 boxes of microfilm; 400 company annual reports. **Subscriptions:** 303 journals and other serials. **Services:** Interlibrary loan; copying; library open to the public by appointment. **Computerized Information Services:** DIALOG Information Services. **Publications:** Weekly Reading List; Annual Report - all for internal distribution only. **Remarks:** FAX: (704)667-6903.

★1554★
BASF Corporation - Wyandotte Division - Development Laboratory - Library
36 Riverside Ave.
Rensselaer, NY 12144-2900
Defunct.

BASF K & F Corporation - Knoll Pharmaceuticals
See: **Knoll Pharmaceuticals** (8767)

Basileiad Library
See: **Manor Junior College** (9638)

Rose Basloe Library
See: **Temple Beth Joseph** (16090)

★1555★
Basque Cultural Center - Library (Area-Ethnic)
Box 640037 Phone: (415)583-4035
San Francisco, CA 94164 Franxoa Bidaurreta, Pres.
Founded: 1985. **Staff:** 5. **Subjects:** Basque language, history, anthropology, customs, folklore, literature. **Special Collections:** University of Nevada Press Basque Series (50 volumes); Illustrated Encyclopedia of the Basque Country (50 volumes); simplified Basque language books (Euskara Batua "Euskalduntzen"; 10); Acts of 2nd Basque World Congress (1989; 30 volumes). **Holdings:** 650 books; videotapes. **Subscriptions:** 18 journals and other serials. **Services:** Copying; library open to the public with restrictions. **Automated Operations:** Computerized cataloging. **Remarks:** FAX: (415)753-0298. **Staff:** Martin Minaberry, Coord.

Harry W. Bass Collection in Business History
See: **University of Oklahoma** (19129)

★1556★
Bass Research Foundation - Library (Biol Sci)
1001 Market St. Phone: (615)756-2514
Chattanooga, TN 37402 Susan Joyner, Off.Mgr.
Founded: 1973. **Subjects:** Black bass, fishing, fish management. **Holdings:** Research papers concerning bass. **Publications:** Indexed bibliography on the largemouth bass; "Live Release of Bass" (booklet).

Sophie Frye Bass Library of Northwest Americana
See: **Historical Society of Seattle & King County - Sophie Frye Bass Library of Northwest Americana** (7288)

Bassett Army Community Hospital
See: **U.S. Army Hospitals** (17031)

★1557★
Mary Imogene Bassett Hospital - Medical Library (Med)
Atwell Rd. Phone: (607)547-3115
Cooperstown, NY 13326 Linda F. Muehl, Med.Libn.
Staff: Prof 1; Other 1. **Subjects:** Clinical medicine, surgery. **Holdings:** 5000 books; 25,000 bound periodical volumes. **Subscriptions:** 524 journals and other serials. **Services:** Interlibrary loan; copying; SDI; library open to the public for reference use only. **Computerized Information Services:** MEDLARS, DIALOG Information Services, BRS Information Technologies. **Networks/Consortia:** Member of South Central Research Library Council (SCRLC). **Publications:** Medical Library Bulletin, monthly - for internal distribution only; bibliographies of staff's published materials, annual. **Remarks:** FAX: (607)547-3006.

★1558★
Bassett Public Library (Hist)
Rte. 7, PO Box 250 Phone: (703)629-2426
Bassett, VA 24055 Beth Lawrey
Founded: 1939. **Staff:** Prof 4. **Special Collections:** Genealogy and local history (2700 volumes; vertical files). **Services:** Interlibrary loan; copying; library open to the public. **Remarks:** FAX: (703)629-9840.

★1559★
Bassist College - Library (Art)
2000 S.W. Fifth Ave. Phone: (503)228-6528
Portland, OR 97201 Norma H. Bassist, Exec.Libn.
Founded: 1963. **Staff:** Prof 3; Other 2. **Subjects:** Fashion and costume history, interior decoration, furniture history, world history, textiles, clothing and fashion industry, retailing and marketing. **Special Collections:** Peterson's magazine; Godey's magazine; fashion history, including rare volumes. **Holdings:** 13,305 books; 110 bound periodical volumes; 150 carousel slide trays; 245 VF boxes; 52 video cassettes. **Subscriptions:** 115 journals and other serials; 10 newspapers. **Services:** Copying; library open to professionals in the field with permission of college president. **Automated Operations:** Computerized acquisitions. **Staff:** Joseph A. Schiwek, Jr., Libn.; Nancy W. Thurston, Libn.

Henry Bast Preaching Resources Center
See: **Western Theological Seminary - Beardslee Library** (20304)

Bruce Everett Bates Memorial Library
See: **Museum of Arts and Sciences** (10888)

★1560★
Bates College - George and Helen Ladd Library - Special Collections (Hum)
Lewiston, ME 04240 Phone: (207)786-6272
Mary Riley, Spec.Coll.Libn.
Founded: 1863. **Special Collections:** Free Will Baptists (425 volumes); Batesiana (3892 volumes); Stanton Natural History (605 volumes); William Lyon Phelps collection of signed first editions (420 volumes); Marsden Hartley (185 volumes); Maine Small Press Publications (390 volumes); library of Rabbi David Berent (Hebrew and Yiddish titles; 565 volumes); library of Dr. Isaac L. Rice (French history and biography, German political economy; 1545 volumes). **Services:** Interlibrary loan; copying; collections open to the public for reference use only. **Automated Operations:** Computerized cataloging. **Computerized Information Services:** OCLC. **Networks/Consortia:** Member of NELINET, Inc.

Congressmen George and William Bates Archives
See: **Salem State College - Library - Special Collections** (14634)

Bates Library
See: **Northeast Baptist Hospital** (11967)

★1561★
Bath Memorial Hospital - Health Science Library (Med)
1356 Washington St. at Davenport Circle Phone: (207)443-5524
Bath, ME 04530 Joan M. Barnes, Libn.
Staff: Prof 1. **Subjects:** Medicine, allied health sciences. **Holdings:** 260 books. **Subscriptions:** 75 journals and other serials. **Services:** Interlibrary loan; copying; SDI; library open to the public with restrictions. **Computerized Information Services:** MEDLINE; DOCLINE (electronic mail service). Performs searches on fee basis. **Networks/Consortia:** Member of Health Science Library and Information Cooperative of Maine (HSLIC), North Atlantic Health Science Libraries (NAHSL).

★1562★
Baton Rouge State-Times & Morning Advocate Newspapers - Library (Publ)
525 Lafayette St. Phone: (504)383-1111
Baton Rouge, LA 70821 Mona Hatfield, Lib.Dir.
Founded: 1950. **Staff:** Prof 6; Other 1. **Subjects:** Newspaper reference topics. **Holdings:** 1200 books; photograph files; clipping files. **Services:** Library open to other media sources on approval. **Computerized Information Services:** NEXIS, DataTimes, CompuServe Information Service, MEDLARS, VU/TEXT Information Services. **Remarks:** FAX: (504)388-0371.

★1563★
Battelle - Northwest - Pacific Northwest Laboratory - Reference Center (Sci-Engr, Energy)
370 L'Enfant Promenade, S.W., Suite 900 Phone: (202)646-5230
Washington, DC 20024-2115 Betty Fimiani, Mgr., Info.Serv.
Founded: 1964. **Staff:** Prof 2; Other 1.5. **Subjects:** Energy, environment, science and technology, education, transportation and space, biotechnology. **Holdings:** 6000 government documents; congressional reports; unbound periodicals. **Subscriptions:** 70 journals and other serials; 7 newspapers. **Services:** Center not open to the public. **Computerized Information Services:** Washington Alert Service, DataTimes; internal databases. **Publications:** Internal Acquisitions List, 12/year. **Remarks:** FAX: (202)646-5233.

★1564★
Battelle Institute e.V. - Library (Sci-Engr, Soc Sci)
Am Romerhof 35
Postfach 900160 Phone: 69 79082210
W-6000 Frankfurt am Main 90, Germany R. Skoutajan, Libn.
Staff: Prof 3. **Subjects:** Physics, chemistry, biology, information processing, materials technology, economics, social sciences, energy and transportation systems. **Holdings:** 60,000 books; 50,000 bound periodical volumes. **Subscriptions:** 330 journals and other serials. **Services:** Copying; library open to the public by prior application. **Remarks:** FAX: 69 790880. Telex: 411966.

★1565★
Battelle Memorial Institute - Battelle Edgewood Operations - Chemical Warfare/Chemical and Biological Defense Information Analysis Center (CBIAC) - Library (Mil)
2113 Emmorton Park Rd., Suite 200
Edgewood, MD 21040 Phone: (410)676-9030
Founded: 1986. **Staff:** Prof 3. **Subjects:** Chemical warfare, chemical and biological defense, chemical warfare treaties, NBC materials survivability. **Holdings:** 1500 bound volumes. **Subscriptions:** 15 journals and other serials. **Services:** Library open to Department of Defense and Department of Defense contractors. **Computerized Information Services:** BRS Information Technologies, DIALOG Information Services, ORBIT Search Service, STN International; produces CBIAC User Database. **Remarks:** FAX: (410)676-9703. CBIAC is a U.S. Department of Defense Information Analysis Center, sponsored by the U.S. Defense Technical Information Center and monitored by the U.S. Army Chemical Research, Development and Engineering Center. **Staff:** Francis T. Crimmons, Dir.; James J. McNeely, Dp.Dir.; Nancy R. Brletich, Res.Sci.; Jeanne M. Rosser, Info.Anl.

★1566★
Battelle Memorial Institute - Copper Data Center (Sci-Engr)
505 King Ave. Phone: (614)424-7715
Columbus, OH 43201 Ross A. Gubiotti, Proj.Mgr.
Founded: 1965. **Staff:** Prof 3; Other 1. **Subjects:** Copper and copper-base alloy technology. **Holdings:** 50,000 reports, articles, patents. **Subscriptions:** 40 journals and other serials. **Services:** Center open to the public. **Computerized Information Services:** TYMNET, BASIS. **Publications:** Extracts of documents on copper technology (97 volumes). **Special Indexes:** Thesaurus (book), biennial. **Remarks:** FAX: (614)424-3288. **Staff:** Carolyn A. Green; Helen C. Pestel; Dorothea M. Johnson.

★1567★
Battelle Memorial Institute - Human Affairs Research Center - Library/Information Center (Energy)
4000 N.E. 41st St.
P.O. Box 5395 Phone: (206)528-3370
Seattle, WA 98105-5428 Karen Marshall Aoyama, Lib.Mgr.
Founded: 1968. **Staff:** Prof 2; Other 3. **Subjects:** Nuclear power plants, human factors, nuclear waste management, emergency preparedness, population studies, environmental health and policy. **Holdings:** 200 books; 1000 reports. **Subscriptions:** 139 journals and other serials. **Services:** Interlibrary loan; copying; SDI; library open to the public by appointment. **Computerized Information Services:** DIALOG Information Services, WLN, POPLINE, OCLC. **Networks/Consortia:** Member of Western Library Network (WLN). **Special Indexes:** Index to reports and active projects (online). **Remarks:** FAX: (206)528-3553. **Staff:** Janette Schueller.

★1568★
Battelle Memorial Institute - Library (Sci-Engr, Biol Sci)
505 King Ave. Phone: (614)424-6302
Columbus, OH 43201-2693 Kemberly A. Meiners, Mgr., Lib.Serv.
Founded: 1929. **Staff:** Prof 6; Other 8. **Subjects:** Engineering, chemistry, physics, biosciences. **Holdings:** 150,000 volumes; 220,000 technical reports; 100 drawers of microfilm and microcards. **Subscriptions:** 1100 journals and other serials; 7 newspapers. **Services:** Interlibrary loan (fee); copying; library open to the public. **Automated Operations:** Computerized cataloging, acquisitions, and ILL. **Computerized Information Services:** OCLC, DIALOG Information Services, BRS Information Technologies, ORBIT Search Service, DTIC, PFDS Online, Data-Star; InterNet (electronic mail service). Performs searches on fee basis. Contact Person: David Blum, Libn., 424-5138. **Publications:** Newbooks List. **Remarks:** Alternate telephone number(s): 424-6302. FAX: (614)424-3607. Electronic mail address(es): Library@BCLCL1.IM.BATTELLE.ORG (InterNet). **Staff:** Michelle Brown, ILL Libn.; William Buckel, Ref.Libn.; Bobbie Jean Powell, Circ.Libn.

★1569★
Battelle Memorial Institute - Stack Gas Emission Control Coordination Center - Library (Env-Cons)
505 King Ave. Phone: (614)424-7885
Columbus, OH 43201-2693 Dr. Joseph H. Oxley, Mgr.
Founded: 1973. **Subjects:** Sulfur dioxite, scrubbers, fuel gas desulfurization, clean fuels, coal utilization techniques, waste-to-energy systems. **Holdings:** Figures not available. **Services:** Information available on a quick response basis for an annual fee. **Publications:** Bimonthly and quarterly reports. **Remarks:** FAX: (614)424-5263. Telex: 24-5454.

★1570★
Battelle Memorial Institute - Tactical Technology Center (Mil)
505 King Ave. Phone: (614)424-5047
Columbus, OH 43201 Dr. Larry W. Williams, Mgr.
Founded: 1963. **Staff:** Prof 5; Other 4. **Subjects:** Tactical warfare. **Holdings:** 3000 books; 65,000 reports. **Subscriptions:** 50 journals and other serials. **Services:** Interlibrary loan; center open to U.S. Department of Defense agencies or others by permission of Defense Advanced Research Projects Agency. **Computerized Information Services:** DIALOG Information Services, PFDS Online; internal database. **Publications:** Reports and responses to users, irregular. **Remarks:** FAX: (614)424-5059. The Tactical Technology Center is sponsored by the Defense Advanced Research Projects Agency. **Staff:** Edwin Westbrook; Josephene Huggins.

★1571★
Battelle-Northwest - Legal Library (Law)
Federal Bldg., Rm. 431, A4-78 Phone: (509)376-6807
Richland, WA 99352 Margaret K. Dagle, Legal Libn.
Staff: Prof 1. **Subjects:** State and federal law. **Holdings:** 8000 books; 8 bound periodical volumes. **Subscriptions:** 62 journals and other serials. **Services:** Library not open to the public. **Computerized Information Services:** LEXIS.

★1572★
Battelle-Northwest - Pacific Northwest Laboratory - Hanford Technical Library (Sci-Engr, Energy)
Box 999
Mail Stop P8-55 Phone: (509)376-5451
Richland, WA 99352 J.R. Judy, Mgr.
Founded: 1952. **Staff:** Prof 9; Other 21. **Subjects:** Energy technology, nuclear science, engineering, physics, chemistry, mathematics, metallurgy, radiological sciences, environment. **Holdings:** 60,000 books; 60,000 bound periodical volumes; 100,000 technical reports; 850,000 technical reports in microform. **Subscriptions:** 1200 journals and other serials. **Services:** Interlibrary loan; library open to the public with restrictions. **Automated Operations:** Computerized cataloging, acquisitions, serials, and circulation. **Computerized Information Services:** DIALOG Information Services, EasyNet, U.S. Patents Files, Integrated Technical Information System (ITIS), NASA/RECON, MEDLARS, DTIC, STN International, RLIN, OCLC, NewsNet, Inc. **Networks/Consortia:** Member of Western Library Network (WLN). **Remarks:** FAX: (509)376-1422. Battelle-Northwest operates the Pacific Northwest Laboratory under contract to the U.S. Department of Energy. **Staff:** J.L. Hare, Spec.Asst.; E.L. Daniel, Supv., Lib.Oper.; N.G. Carter, Sr. Automation Spec.; S.P. Gydesen, Sr.Info.Spec.; R.A. Bush, Sr.Info.Spec.; P.M. Cleavenger, Info.Spec.; C.A. Bauman, Class.Off.; Jackie Madison, Info.Spec.; Nancy Doran, Info.Spec.; Edee Edwards, Info.Spec.

★1573★
Battelle Ocean Sciences Library (Biol Sci)
397 Washington St.
Box AH Phone: (617)934-0571
Duxbury, MA 02332 Ellen S. Rosen, Libn.
Founded: 1934. **Staff:** Prof 1. **Subjects:** Marine biology, oceanography, environmental research. **Holdings:** 3000 books; 100 bound periodical volumes. **Subscriptions:** 75 journals and other serials. **Services:** Interlibrary loan; copying; SDI; library open to the public by appointment. **Computerized Information Services:** DIALOG Information Services, OCLC. **Publications:** Battelle Ocean Sciences Serials List. **Formerly:** Battelle New England Marion Research Laboratories.

★1574★
Batten, Barton, Durstine, Osborn - Chicago Information Center (Bus-Fin)
410 N. Michigan Ave. Phone: (312)337-7860
Chicago, IL 60611 Jerry Delaney, Info.Ctr.Dir.
Staff: Prof 1; Other 1. **Subjects:** Advertising, marketing, graphic arts, confectionery, chewing gum. **Holdings:** 1260 books; 16 VF drawers; 4 drawers of pictures; 106 research reports. **Subscriptions:** 250 journals and other serials; 5 newspapers. **Services:** Interlibrary loan; center not open to the public. **Automated Operations:** Computerized serials. **Computerized Information Services:** DIALOG Information Services, NEXIS, VU/TEXT Information Services, MAID Systems Ltd. **Publications:** It's New at the BBDO Chicago Information Center, quarterly - for internal distribution only; Wrigley Update, monthly - to client and account personnel. **Remarks:** FAX: (312)337-6871.

★1575★
Batten, Barton, Durstine, Osborn - Information Resource Center (Bus-Fin)
1285 Avenue of the Americas Phone: (212)459-6311
New York, NY 10019 Mary Muenkel, V.P. & Dir. of Info.Serv.
Founded: 1964. **Staff:** Prof 13; Other 5. **Subjects:** Advertising, marketing, general business. **Special Collections:** Competitive advertising; collection of print advertising; photo files. **Holdings:** 4000 books; 2000 corporate, product, subject files. **Subscriptions:** 500 journals and other serials. **Services:** Interlibrary loan; center not open to the public. **Automated Operations:** Computerized cataloging and serials. **Computerized Information Services:** DIALOG Information Services, NEXIS, MAID Systems Ltd., The Financial Post DataGroup, InvesText, PRODUCTSCAN, Dow Jones News/Retrieval, Dun & Bradstreet Business Credit Services, Global Scan, Reuters; Dialcom, Inc. (electronic mail service). **Publications:** Cross Border Business: summary of worldwide news, weekly; Changes: summary of client activity, monthly. **Remarks:** FAX: (212)459-6417. Telex: 175423 BBDO UT. **Staff:** Sylvia Wachtel; Judy Cyr; Maria Patorti; Robert Dudley; Mary Beth Corey; Wendy Scott-Williams; James Linderman; Robert Kopka; Svetlana Druker; Kathleen Brady; Delia Congram; Jacqueline Santos.

★1576★
The O.A. Battista Research Institute - Library (Sci-Engr)
3863 Southwest Loop - 820, Suite 100 Phone: (817)292-4272
Fort Worth, TX 76133-2076 David M. Whitely, Libn.
Founded: 1971. **Staff:** Prof 3; Other 7. **Subjects:** Polymer science and technology, chemistry, medicine. **Holdings:** 3000 books. **Subscriptions:** 102 journals and other serials. **Services:** Library not open to the public. **Automated Operations:** Computerized cataloging, acquisitions, serials, and circulation. **Publications:** Knowledge Magazine. **Remarks:** Alternate telephone number(s): 292-4270. FAX: (817)294-2893. **Staff:** S. Scott Lee, Inst.Mgr.

★1577★
Battle Creek Adventist Hospital - Professional Library (Med)
165 N. Washington Ave. Phone: (616)964-7121
Battle Creek, MI 49016 Lanette J. Penrod, Libn.
Founded: 1914. **Staff:** Prof 1. **Subjects:** Psychiatry, psychology, social work, substance abuse. **Holdings:** 540 books; 253 AV programs. **Subscriptions:** 55 journals and other serials. **Services:** Interlibrary loan; library not open to the public. **Networks/Consortia:** Member of Michigan Health Sciences Libraries Association (MHSLA).

★1578★
Battle Creek Art Center - Michigan Art Archives (Art)
265 E. Emmett Phone: (616)962-9511
Battle Creek, MI 49017 Ben Mitchell, Cur.
Founded: 1978. **Staff:** Prof 1. **Subjects:** Michigan art. **Special Collections:** Bibliographies and information on Michigan art and artists. **Holdings:** 300 books; 600 files of clippings and archival materials. **Services:** Copying; archives open to the public with restrictions. **Computerized Information Services:** Detroit Art Registration Information System (DARIS).

★1579★
Battle Creek Enquirer - Editorial Reference Library (Publ)
155 W. Van Buren St. Phone: (616)964-7161
Battle Creek, MI 49016 Linda F. Willison, Libn.
Staff: Prof 1. **Subjects:** Newspaper reference topics, area history. **Special Collections:** Battle Creek newspapers, 1846 to present, on microfilm. **Holdings:** 1100 books; 900 reels of microfilm; maps; newspaper clippings; photographs. **Services:** Library open to the public for reference use only with permission. **Remarks:** The Enquirer is published by Gannett Newspapers. FAX: (616)964-0299.

★1580★
Battle Creek Health System - Professional Library (Med)
300 North Ave. Phone: (616)966-8331
Battle Creek, MI 49016 Robin Alanen Mosher, Libn.
Founded: 1929. **Staff:** Prof 1. **Subjects:** Medicine, nursing, and allied health sciences. **Holdings:** 2758 volumes; 400 audio cassettes; 25 video cassettes. **Subscriptions:** 500 journals and other serials. **Services:** Interlibrary loan; SDI; library open to the public. **Automated Operations:** Computerized cataloging and ILL. **Computerized Information Services:** MEDLINE, BRS Information Technologies. Performs searches on fee basis. **Networks/Consortia:** Member of Woodlands Library Cooperative, Michigan Health Sciences Libraries Association (MHSLA), National Network of Libraries of Medicine - Greater Midwest Region. **Publications:** Information Explosion, irregular - for internal distribution only. **Remarks:** FAX: (616)966-8332.

★1581★
Battleford's Union Hospital - Memorial Library (Med)
1092 107th St. Phone: (306)446-7381
North Battleford, SK, Canada S9A 1Z1 Debbie Iwanchuk, Hosp.Libn.
Founded: 1987. **Staff:** 1. **Subjects:** Medicine, nursing, emergency medicine, surgery, pediatrics, pharmacy. **Holdings:** 1100 books; AV programs. **Subscriptions:** 90 journals. **Services:** Interlibrary loan; copying; library open to the public for reference use only.

★1582★
Bauder Fashion College - Library (Art)
508 S. Center St. Phone: (817)277-6666
Arlington, TX 76010 John MacAyeal, Libn.
Founded: 1967. **Staff:** 1. **Subjects:** Fashion design and merchandising, interior design, history of costume and art. **Special Collections:** Designer files; merchandizer/merchant files. **Holdings:** 4500 books; 200 videotapes; 6500 slide sets; 100 filmstrips. **Subscriptions:** 100 journals and other serials; 6 newspapers. **Services:** Interlibrary loan; library not open to the public. **Automated Operations:** Computerized cataloging. **Computerized Information Services:** DataTimes. **Special Indexes:** Fashion Bibliography; Index of Designers; Bibliography for Self-Assessment & Evaluation for Post-Secondary Institutions.

★1583★
Bausch & Lomb - Information Resource Center (Sci-Engr)
Optics Center
1400 N. Goodman St. Phone: (716)338-6053
Rochester, NY 14692 Adwoa Boateng, Mgr.
Founded: 1916. **Staff:** Prof 2. **Subjects:** Ophthalmology, optics, chemistry, pharmacology, business, management. **Holdings:** 4000 books. **Subscriptions:** 300 journals and other serials. **Services:** Interlibrary loan; center not open to the public. **Computerized Information Services:** DIALOG Information Services, TEXTLINE, STN International, NEXIS, LEXIS; internal database. **Networks/Consortia:** Member of Rochester Regional Library Council (RRLC). **Remarks:** Alternate telephone number(s): 338-5523. FAX: (716)338-6896. Telex: 361237 BAUSCHLOMBROC.

Bavarian State Library
See: **Bayerische Staatsbibliothek** (1597)

Bavarian State Ministry for Science - East European Institute, Munich
See: **East European Institute, Munich** (5119)

Bavarian State Ministry for Science and Culture - Institute of Contemporary History
See: **Institute of Contemporary History** (7920)

Baver Memorial Library
See: **Pennsylvania Dutch Folk Culture Society, Inc.** (12841)

★1584★
Governor Baxter School for the Deaf - Library (Educ)
Box 799 Phone: (207)781-3165
Portland, ME 04104-0799 Barbara Fertig, Dir., Lib./Media Serv.
Staff: Prof 3. **Subjects:** Deafness, sign language, special education, professional education. **Holdings:** 7000 books; 100 bound periodical volumes; 300 unbound reports; 500 nonprint materials; American Annals of the Deaf, 1878-1984 (incomplete); 1100 Captioned Films for the Deaf (depository library). **Subscriptions:** 74 journals and other serials; 6 newspapers. **Services:** Copying; library open to the public. **Computerized Information Services:** Deafnet, SpecialNet, CAN/OLE.

★1585★
Baxter Healthcare Corporation - Baxter Dade Division - Research Library (Med)
1851 Delaware Pkwy.
Box 520672 Phone: (305)633-6461
Miami, FL 33152 Bernadene A. Chang, Res.Lib.Supv.
Staff: Prof 1; Other 2. **Subjects:** Clinical chemistry, biochemistry, immunology, medicine, pathology. **Holdings:** 2560 books; 1200 bound periodical volumes; 2000 unbound journals; 20 directories; 10,000 patents; 75 journal titles on microfilm. **Subscriptions:** 200 journals and other serials. **Services:** Interlibrary loan; library open to the public by appointment. **Computerized Information Services:** BRS Information Technologies, DIALOG Information Services, STN International, OCLC EPIC, NewsNet, Inc., DataTimes; DOCLINE, (electronic mail service). **Networks/Consortia:** Member of Miami Health Sciences Library Consortium (MHSLC). **Remarks:** FAX: (305)637-6913.

★1586★
Baxter Healthcare Corporation - Information Resource Center (Med, Sci-Engr)
Rte. 120 & Wilson Rd., RLT-22 Phone: (708)270-5361
Round Lake, IL 60073 David Anderson, Mgr., Info.Rsrc.Ctr.
Founded: 1950. **Staff:** Prof 12. **Subjects:** Medicine, parenteral nutrition, hematology, pharmaceuticals, plastics, biomedical engineering, engineering, business and management, sales and management, corporate and patent law, international business and law, health care administration, human resources. **Holdings:** 30,000 titles. **Subscriptions:** 600 journals and other serials. **Services:** Interlibrary loan; copying; SDI; literature searching and analysis; center open to the public. **Automated Operations:** Computerized cataloging, acquisitions, serials, and ILL. **Computerized Information Services:** DIALOG Information Services, BRS Information Technologies, NLM, OCLC, INVESTEXT, TEXTLINE, Chemical Abstracts Service (CAS), Dow Jones News/Retrieval, Questel, PFDS Online, LEXIS, NEXIS, VU/TEXT Information Services, WILSONLINE, U.S. Patents Files, Data-Star, DataTimes. **Networks/Consortia:** Member of North Suburban Library System (NSLS), Northeastern Illinois Library Consortium. **Publications:** IRC Newsletter - for internal distribution only. **Formed by the merger of:** Its William B. Graham Research Center, Round Lake Technology Building, and Deerfield Information Resource Centers.

★1587★
Baxter Healthcare Corporation - Pharmaseal Division - Information Center (Med)
27200 N. Tourney Rd.
Box 5900
Santa Clarita, CA 91355 Phone: (805)253-1300
Founded: 1983. **Staff:** 2. **Subjects:** Medicine, applied technology, business, basic sciences. **Holdings:** 2300 books; 1100 reports and pamphlets; 27 periodicals in microform. **Subscriptions:** 240 journals and other serials. **Services:** Interlibrary loan; library not open to the public. **Automated Operations:** Computerized circulation, cataloging, and internal records. **Computerized Information Services:** DIALOG Information Services, WILSONLINE, Dow Jones News/Retrieval, NewsNet, Inc., STN International, Data-Star, DataTimes, VU/TEXT Information Services, ORBIT Search Service; PIC Abstracts (internal database). Contact Person: Evette Datin. **Publications:** The Advantage (newsletter). **Remarks:** FAX: (805)286-4258. **Staff:** Evette Ross Datin, Info.Spec.; Marilou Balkam, Lib.Coord.

★1588★
Baxter Hyland Division - Research Library (Med, Biol Sci)
1710 Flower Ave. Phone: (818)305-6042
Duarte, CA 91010 Joy A. Johnsen, Libn.
Founded: 1955. **Staff:** Prof 1; Other 2. **Subjects:** Immunology, biochemistry, hematology, virology, microbiology. **Holdings:** 2000 books; 5000 bound

periodical volumes. **Subscriptions:** 250 journals and other serials. **Services:** Interlibrary loan; library open to the public by appointment. **Computerized Information Services:** MEDLARS, DIALOG Information Services. **Networks/Consortia:** Member of National Network of Libraries of Medicine - Pacific Southwest Region. **Remarks:** FAX: (818)359-0006.

L.C. Baxter Medical Library
See: **Tulsa Regional Medical Center** (16574)

★1589★
Bay Area Council on Soviet Jewry - Archives (Area-Ethnic)
106 Baden Phone: (415)585-1400
San Francisco, CA 94131 Natasha Kats, Res.Dir.
Founded: 1967. **Staff:** Prof 1. **Subjects:** Refuseniks; USSR - prisoners of conscience, emigration, religious persecution, psychiatric abuse. **Holdings:** 40 VF drawers of articles, reports, manuscripts, documents, newsletters. **Subscriptions:** 20 journals and other serials; 5 newspapers. **Services:** Archives open to the public by telephone request. **Computerized Information Services:** Refusenik Database (internal database); MCI Mail (electronic mail service). **Publications:** Outcry (newsletter), monthly - to members and by subscription. **Remarks:** FAX: (415)585-3290.

Bay Area Electric Railroad Association - Western Railway Museum
See: **Western Railway Museum** (20290)

★1590★
Bay County Historical Society - Library (Hist)
321 Washington Ave.
Bay City, MI 48708 Phone: (517)893-5733
Founded: 1919. **Staff:** Prof 2. **Subjects:** History - Bay County, Michigan, U.S.; Great Lakes shipping, especially Lake Huron; lumbering. **Special Collections:** Bay City directories, 1866-1990; Michigan Pioneer & Historical Collection, volumes 1-40; Michigan Manual, 1899-1962; Public Acts of Michigan, 1872-1954; Archives of Monitor Sugar Company. **Holdings:** 2000 books; periodicals; 35 diaries; 90 scrapbooks; 50 albums containing 3000 photographs; 100 linear feet of archival materials; 12 file drawers of pamphlets and clippings; 12 map drawers of maps; blueprints and publications of Aladdin, Sterling, Lewis, and Liberty Homes. **Subscriptions:** 15 journals and other serials. **Services:** Copying; research; library open to the public on a limited schedule but staff member must be present. **Staff:** Dr. Steven Berg, Res.; Michael Breza, Cur.

★1591★
Bay De Noc Community College - Learning Resource Center - Special Collections (Hist)
2001 N. Lincoln Rd. Phone: (906)786-5802
Escanaba, MI 49829 Chris Holmes, Libn.
Founded: 1965. **Staff:** Prof 1; Other 5. **Special Collections:** Oral History of Delta County, Michigan; fire-fighting (AV materials); American Welding Society publications; genealogy. **Services:** Interlibrary loan; copying; center open to the public. **Computerized Information Services:** DIALOG Information Services; OCLC. Performs searches. Contact Person: Ann Bissell. **Special Catalogs:** Audiovisual catalog.

★1592★
Bay Harbor Hospital - Medical Library (Med)
1437 W. Lomita Blvd. Phone: (213)325-1221
Harbor City, CA 90710 James H. Harlan, Libn.
Founded: 1970. **Staff:** 1. **Subjects:** Medicine, allied health sciences, nursing, hospital administration. **Holdings:** 931 books; Audio-Digest tapes. **Subscriptions:** 42 journals. **Services:** Interlibrary loan; library not open to the public. **Automated Operations:** Computerized ILL (DOCLINE). **Computerized Information Services:** MEDLINE, Nursing & Allied Health Database, DIALOG Information Services. **Remarks:** FAX: (213)534-3286.

★1593★
Bay Meadows Racetrack - William P. Kyne Memorial Thoroughbred Racing Library (Rec)
Box 5050 Phone: (415)574-7223
San Mateo, CA 94402 Rusty Mathieson, Asst.Libn.
Founded: 1973. **Staff:** Prof 1; Other 1. **Subjects:** Thoroughbred horses - racing, breeding, training, diseases, history; personalities in racing. **Special Collections:** Complete Racing Records Horses Foaled, 1960-1989 (microfiche); The Racing Calendar, 1727-1958. **Holdings:** 1681 books; 157 bound periodical volumes; photographs; national and international racing programs. **Services:** Copying; library open to the public for reference use only. **Remarks:** (415)573-4670.

★1594★
Bay Medical Center - Health Sciences Library (Med)
1900 Columbus Ave. Phone: (517)894-3782
Bay City, MI 48708-6880 Barbara Kormelink, Hea.Sci.Libn.
Founded: 1958. **Staff:** Prof 1; Other 1. **Subjects:** Medicine, nursing, hospital administration, allied health sciences. **Holdings:** 2500 books; 5210 bound periodical volumes; 200 slide sets; 110 titles on microfilm; 355 AV programs; 12 VF drawers of pamphlets. **Subscriptions:** 285 journals and other serials. **Services:** Interlibrary loan; copying; library open to the public. **Automated Operations:** DOCLINE. **Computerized Information Services:** MEDLINE, BRS Information Technologies; CD-ROM. Performs searches on fee basis. **Networks/Consortia:** Member of Michigan Library Consortium (MLC), National Network of Libraries of Medicine (NN/LM), National Network of Libraries of Medicine - Greater Midwest Region. **Remarks:** FAX: (517)894-4862.

★1595★
Baybank Systems Inc. - Technical Data Library (Comp Sci)
1025 Main St. Phone: (617)788-1172
Waltham, MA 02154-7408 Marian Stewart, Libn.
Founded: 1981. **Staff:** Prof 1. **Subjects:** Computer science, banking, management. **Holdings:** 700 books; 900 IBM manuals. **Subscriptions:** 100 journals and other serials. **Services:** Interlibrary loan; research; library not open to the public. **Computerized Information Services:** DIALOG Information Services. Performs searches on fee basis. **Publications:** Data Library News, quarterly - for internal distribution only.

★1596★
Baycrest Centre for Geriatric Care - Staff Library (Med)
3560 Bathurst Ave. Phone: (416)789-5131
Toronto, ON, Canada M6A 2E1 Madeline Grant, Dir., Lib.Serv.
Founded: 1981. **Staff:** Prof 2; Other 2. **Subjects:** Geriatrics, geriatric psychiatry and nursing, gerontology, medical sciences, hospital administration. **Holdings:** 2000 books; 1000 bound periodical volumes; article files; 80 videocassettes; 300 audiocassettes; VF materials; Baycrest publications; government documents. **Subscriptions:** 220 journals and other serials. **Services:** Interlibrary loan; copying; library open to the public for reference use only. **Automated Operations:** Computerized cataloging and circulation. **Computerized Information Services:** MEDLARS, DIALOG Information Services. **Networks/Consortia:** Member of Ontario Hospital Libraries Association (OHLA), Canadian Health Libraries Association. **Publications:** Contents Update; acquisitions lists; directory of Baycrest publications. **Remarks:** FAX: (416)785-2378. **Staff:** Inez Rost, Lib.Techn.

★1597★
Bayerische Staatsbibliothek (Hist, Hum)
Ludwigstrasse 16
Postfach 340150 Phone: 89 286380
W-8000 Munich 34, Germany Dr. Franz Kaltwasser, Dir.
Founded: 1558. **Staff:** 510. **Special Collections:** Prehistory and early history; classical antiquity, including ancient history; medieval Latin and Neo-Latin studies; Byzantine studies; modern Greece; cultural and language strata - Albania, Baltic countries, Bulgaria, Czechoslovakia, Poland, Romania, Soviet Union, Yugoslavia; general history; history of German-speaking countries; history of France; history of Italy; musicology; Bavarian studies; Germanic and Romance languages; belles lettres; theology; art history; Oriental studies (Middle East and Far East); Judaic studies; maps and travel literature (298,000 maps); music collection (280,000 printed music items, 45,000 sound recordings); manuscripts and rare print section (68,500 manuscripts, 850 bequests, 35,000 autographs, 76,000 rare books, 18,500 incunabula); biomedical and scientific periodicals. **Holdings:** 6.1 million books; 500,000 microforms; 150,000 book covers **Subscriptions:** 37,000 journals and other serials. **Services:** Interlibrary loan; copying; SDI; library open to the public. **Computerized Information Services:** DIALOG Information Services, Questel, STN International, Deutsches Bibliotheksinstitut (DBI), Deutsches Institut fuer Medizinische Dokumentation und Information (DIMDI). Performs searches on fee basis. Contact Person: Dr. Rainer Schoeller, Lib.Dir., 89 28638396. **Special Catalogs:** Catalogus codicum manuscriptorum Bibliothecae Regiae Monacensis, 1858 ff.; Bayerische Staatsbibliothek Fahresbericht, 1973 ff.; New Contents Slavistics (contents of current periodicals in the field of Slavic linguistics, literature, and folklore), 1980 ff. **Remarks:** Alternate telephone number(s): 89 28638205. FAX: 89 28638293. Depository library for official publications of the Federal Republic or the states of Germany, and publications of the United Nations, United Nations Educational, Scientific and Cultural Organization (UNESCO), Food and Agricultural Organization (FAO), and the European Common Market. **Also Known As:** Bavarian State Library.

★1598★
Bayfront Medical Center, Inc. - Health Sciences Library (Med)
701 6th St., S. Phone: (813)893-6136
St. Petersburg, FL 33701 Sylvia Cesanek, Hea.Sci.Libn.
Founded: 1945. **Staff:** Prof 1; Other 2. **Subjects:** Medicine, family practice, geriatrics, nursing, obstetrics, gynecology, oncology, physical rehabilitation. **Holdings:** 1500 books; 3000 bound periodical volumes; 25,000 microfiche cards; 200 Audio-Digest tapes; 310 video cassettes. **Subscriptions:** 200 journals. **Services:** Interlibrary loan; library not open to the public. **Computerized Information Services:** DIALOG Information Services, MEDLARS, MEDLINE, CINAHL; DOCLINE (electronic mail service). **Networks/Consortia:** Member of Tampa Bay Medical Library Network, Florida Health Sciences Library Association (FHSLA). **Remarks:** FAX: (813)893-6797.

★1599★
Bayley Seton Hospital - Charles Ferguson Medical Library (Med)
Bay St. & Vanderbilt Ave. Phone: (718)390-5525
Staten Island, NY 10304 Marie A. Sheldon, Libn.
Founded: 1950. **Staff:** 1. **Subjects:** Medicine, surgery, radiology, urology, dermatology, pediatrics, nursing. **Holdings:** 4100 books; 7950 bound periodical volumes; 408 audiotapes; 126 cassette tapes; 110 video cassettes; 107 slide and cassette programs. **Subscriptions:** 243 journals and other serials. **Services:** Interlibrary loan; copying; library open to college students and individuals in the health care field. **Computerized Information Services:** MEDLARS. **Networks/Consortia:** Member of Brooklyn-Queens-Staten Island Health Sciences Librarians (BQSI), New York Metropolitan Reference and Research Library Agency, BHSL.

★1600★
Baylor College of Medicine - Department of Ophthalmology - Cullen Eye Institute Library (Med)
6501 Fannin Phone: (713)798-3035
Houston, TX 77030 Gylene Wilcox, Libn.
Founded: 1958. **Staff:** Prof 1. **Subjects:** Ophthalmology. **Holdings:** 1924 books; 2632 bound periodical volumes; 477 AV programs. **Subscriptions:** 55 journals and other serials. **Services:** Interlibrary loan; copying; library open to the public with restrictions. **Computerized Information Services:** BRS Information Technologies.

★1601★
Baylor Health Sciences Library (Med)
3500 Gaston Ave. Phone: (214)820-2372
Dallas, TX 75246 Barbara A. Downey, Dir.
Founded: 1954. **Staff:** Prof 3; Other 5. **Subjects:** Medicine, dentistry, nursing. **Special Collections:** Lyle Sellers Medical Collection (early medicine). **Holdings:** 8928 books; 27,436 bound periodical volumes; 1303 reels of microfilm; 1 drawer of microfiche; 4 VF drawers. **Subscriptions:** 614 journals and other serials. **Services:** Interlibrary loan; copying; SDI; library open to the public for reference use only. **Automated Operations:** Computerized cataloging. **Computerized Information Services:** MEDLARS, DIALOG Information Services, OCLC EPIC, WILSONLINE; CD-ROM (CD Plus/MEDLINE). **Networks/Consortia:** Member of Health Libraries Information Network (HealthLINE). **Remarks:** FAX: (214)821-5606. Library serves Baylor College of Dentistry and Baylor University Medical Center. **Staff:** Betty L. Freeman, Info.Serv.Libn.; Steven R. Mehal, Info. Access Libn.

★1602★
Baylor University - Armstrong Browning Library (Hum)
P. O. Box 97152 Phone: (817)755-3566
Waco, TX 76798-7152 Roger L. Brooks, Dir.
Founded: 1912. **Staff:** Prof 2; Other 2. **Special Collections:** Robert Browning; Elizabeth Barrett Browning; Browning Family; Browning contemporaries; Edward Dowden; Browning-Milsand; Edward Robert Bulwer Lytton; A. Joseph Armstrong; Meynell; Hagedorn; Shields; Gibbs; John Forster; 19th century American and British literature; Religion and Science Collection. **Holdings:** 12,945 books; 2675 periodicals; 21 volumes of clippings; 673 reels of microfilm; 4872 manuscripts and letters; 5850 slides and taped lectures; 58 phonograph records. **Subscriptions:** 28 journals and other serials. **Services:** Interlibrary loan; copying; consultation and research; library open to the public for reference use only. **Publications:** Studies in Browning and His Circle, annual; Baylor Browning Interests, irregular; Armstrong Browning Library Newsletter, semiannual. **Special Catalogs:** Music catalog (book); catalog of literary manuscripts. **Staff:** Betty A. Coley, Libn.

★1603★
Baylor University - Baylor Collections of Political Materials (Soc Sci)
P.O. Box 97153 Phone: (817)755-3540
Waco, TX 76798-7153 Kent Keeth, Dir.
Founded: 1979. **Staff:** 2. **Subjects:** Federal, state, and local government. **Special Collections:** Congressional papers of former congressmen W.R. Poage, E.L. Gossett, Thomas A. Pickett, Marvin Leath, O.C. Fisher, John Dowdy, Alan Steelman, Jack Hightower, Sam Hall, and former state legislators Chet Edwards and Donald Adams. **Holdings:** 3757 books; 2285 linear feet of personal and legislative papers and other documents. **Services:** Copying; collection open to the public with restrictions. **Remarks:** FAX: (817)755-1468.

★1604★
Baylor University - Crouch Music Library (Mus)
Moody Memorial Library
P.O. Box 97148
Waco, TX 76798-7148 Phone: (817)755-6731
Founded: 1929. **Staff:** Prof 3; Other 2.5. **Subjects:** Musicology, music theory, church music, instrumental and orchestral music, historical sets (collected), music education, vocal music, editions and monuments of music. **Special Collections:** Mrs. J.W. Jennings Collection (medieval music manuscripts and early printed music); Mr. and Mrs. Travis Johnson Collection (early American songbooks); Francis G. Spencer Collection of American Printed Music; David W. Guion Collection (manuscripts); eighteenth century editions of ensemble music; eighteenth and nineteenth century American hardbacks. **Holdings:** 10,000 books; 3400 bound periodical volumes; 700 microforms; 56,666 musical items; 25,847 phonograph records; 3000 compact disc recordings; 300 videocassettes; 5500 tapes; 810 orchestrations. **Subscriptions:** 200 journals and other serials. **Services:** Library open to the public. **Automated Operations:** Computerized public access catalog (BayLis). **Computerized Information Services:** OCLC, DIALOG Information Services; BITNET (electronic mail service). **Publications:** Ex Bibliotheca Musicae - The Music Library Newsletter. **Remarks:** FAX: (817)752-5332. **Staff:** Miriam Griffis, Audio Supv.; Gregg S. Geary, Pub.Serv.Supv.; Beth Tice, Tech.Serv.Asst.; Tammy Waldrop, Night Supv.

★1605★
Baylor University - Ferdinand Roemer Geological Library (Sci-Engr)
Moody Memorial Library
P.O. Box 97148
Waco, TX 76798-7148 Phone: (817)755-2673
Founded: 1952. **Staff:** 1. **Subjects:** Geology, earth sciences. **Special Collections:** Student papers and theses (2000). **Holdings:** 5063 books; 9000 bound periodical volumes; 3500 maps; 100,000 well logs; 3200 aerial photographs. **Subscriptions:** 60 journals and other serials. **Services:** Interlibrary loan; library open to the public for reference use only. **Publications:** Baylor Geological Studies, semiannual. **Remarks:** FAX: (817)755-2673.

★1606★
Baylor University - J.M. Dawson Church-State Research Center - Library (Rel-Phil)
P.o. Box 97308 Phone: (817)755-1510
Waco, TX 76798-7308 James E. Wood, Jr.
Founded: 1957. **Staff:** 5. **Subjects:** Church-state relations. **Holdings:** 7919 books; 895 bound periodical volumes; 21 VF drawers of pamphlets, archives, reports, clippings; 54 bound volumes of theses and dissertations; 166 reels of microfilm; 229 tapes. **Subscriptions:** 232 journals and other serials. **Services:** Copying; library open to the public for reference use only. **Publications:** Journal of Church and State, 4/year - by subscription. **Remarks:** FAX: (817)755-3740. **Staff:** Derek Davis, Assoc.Dir.

★1607★
Baylor University - M.C. & Mattie Caston Law Library (Law)
P.O. Box 97128 Phone: (817)755-2168
Waco, TX 76706-7128 David G. Cowan, Dir.
Founded: 1920. **Staff:** Prof 4; Other 2. **Subjects:** Law. **Special Collections:** Frank M. Wilson Rare Book Collection. **Holdings:** 172,197 volumes. **Subscriptions:** 2643 journals and other serials. **Services:** Interlibrary loan; copying; computer lab; library open to the public for reference use only. **Automated Operations:** Computerized public access catalog (BayLis). **Computerized Information Services:** LEXIS, NEXIS, WESTLAW, DIALOG Information Services; InterNet, BITNET (electronic mail services). **Publications:** A Guide to the Law Library; The Frank W. Wilson Rare Book Room. **Remarks:** FAX: (817)755-2294. Electronic mail address(es): Cowand@baylor.edu (InterNet); Corand@baylor (BITNET). **Staff:** Della M. Geyer; Susan Kendrick; Denyse Seaman.

★ 1608 ★
Baylor University - Strecker Museum Library (Biol Sci)
Sid Richardson Bldg.
P.O. Box 97154 Phone: (817)755-1110
Waco, TX 76798-7154 Calvin B. Smith, Musm.Dir.
Founded: 1893. **Subjects:** Natural history, anthropology, archeology. **Special Collections:** Ottys Sanders Herpetological Library. **Holdings:** 1000 books; 83 bound periodical volumes; 6000 natural history reprints. **Subscriptions:** 55 journals and other serials. **Services:** Interlibrary loan; library open to the public by request with limited circulation. **Remarks:** FAX: (817)755-1321.

★ 1609 ★
Baylor University - Texas Collection (Hist)
Carroll Library Bldg.
P.O. Box 97142 Phone: (817)755-1268
Waco, TX 76798-7142 Kent Keeth, Dir.
Founded: 1923. **Staff:** Prof 3; Other 2. **Subjects:** Texana, Baylor University. **Holdings:** 87,306 books; 6517 bound periodical volumes; 559 transcribed oral history memoirs with tapes; 267 linear feet of subject files; 9650 maps; 2910 collections of historical manuscripts; Baylor University archives; 52,700 photographs; microfilm; Texas newspapers; depository for records of 11 central Texas counties of Texas State Library's Regional Historical Resource Depository program. **Subscriptions:** 900 journals and other serials; 15 newspapers. **Services:** Interlibrary loan; copying; collection open to the public with restrictions. **Computerized Information Services:** DataTimes; InterNet (electronic mail service). **Publications:** A Treasure of Maps, 1975; The Connally-Dobie Gift, 1974; occasional publications. **Special Indexes:** Biographical reference file (punched card and printed); index to census reports published in quarterlies (book); printed guide to oral history memoirs, picture file (card); registers and calendars of selected manuscript and archival holdings (book); indexes to selected nonself-indexed periodicals (book). **Remarks:** FAX: (817)755-1368. Electronic mail address(es): TXCOLL@Baylor. Edn (InterNet). **Staff:** Ellen K. Brown, Archv.; Michael Toon, Hd.Libn.; Richard Veit, Lib.Mgr.

Bayne-Jones Army Community Hospital
See: **U.S. Army Hospitals** (17032)

★ 1610 ★
Baystate Medical Center - Health Sciences Library (Med)
759 Chestnut St. Phone: (413)784-5442
Springfield, MA 01199 Isabel Hunter, Dir.
Staff: Prof 3; Other 8. **Subjects:** Medicine, nursing, allied health sciences, health care administration. **Holdings:** 22,000 volumes. **Subscriptions:** 500 journals and other serials. **Services:** Interlibrary loan; copying; library open to the public. **Computerized Information Services:** MEDLINE, BRS Information Technologies; DOCLINE (electronic mail service). **Networks/Consortia:** Member of Cooperating Libraries of Greater Springfield, A CCGS Agency (CLGS), Western Massachusetts Health Information Consortium, C/W MARS, Inc., Massachusetts Health Sciences Libraries Network (MaHSLiN). **Publications:** What's New (newsletter), bimonthly. **Remarks:** FAX: (413)784-4197. **Staff:** Lily Peng, Info./Circ.Libn.; Diane Mazur, Cat.; Shirley Kolby, Coord./Acq.; Louise Roberts, Coord./Ser.

Dr. Massimo Bazzini Memorial Library
See: **Cabrini Medical Center** (2435)

★ 1611 ★
BC Transit - Library (Trans)
520 Gorge Rd., E.
Victoria, BC, Canada V8W 2P3 Phone: (604)385-2551
Services: Library not open to the public. **Remarks:** FAX: (604)384-5412. No further information was supplied by respondent.

BCI Geonetics, Inc. - Library
See: **Hydrosource Associates/ - Library** (7605)

BCR
See: **Bibliographical Center for Research - Rocky Mountain Region, Inc.** (1816)

★ 1612 ★
BCR National Laboratory - Library
500 William Pitt Way
Pittsburgh, PA 15238
Founded: 1936. **Subjects:** Coal - combustion, carbonization, gasification, mining, preparation; environmental improvement. **Holdings:** 1800 books; 325 bound periodical volumes; 5000 technical publications; 15,000 technical abstracts on cards. **Remarks:** Currently inactive.

★ 1613 ★
BDM International - Information Services Center (Sci-Engr)
1801 Randolph, S.E. Phone: (505)848-5637
Albuquerque, NM 87106 Steve Wade, Assoc. Staff Member/Ldr.
Staff: 2. **Subjects:** Engineering. **Holdings:** 1000 books; 50 AV programs; 10,000 nonbook items. **Subscriptions:** 30 journals and other serials; 8 newspapers. **Services:** Interlibrary loan; center not open to the public. **Computerized Information Services:** DIALOG Information Services, NEXIS, OCLC. **Remarks:** FAX: (505)848-5531.

★ 1614 ★
BDM International - Technical Reference Center (Mil)
7915 Jones Branch Dr. Phone: (703)848-5007
McLean, VA 22102 James S. Milichich, Mgr.
Founded: 1976. **Staff:** Prof 1; Other 1. **Subjects:** Defense, transportation, communications, environment, energy, advanced technology. **Holdings:** 4000 books; 15,000 reports. **Subscriptions:** 120 periodical titles. **Services:** Interlibrary loan; library not open to the public. **Automated Operations:** Computerized cataloging, acquisitions, and circulation. **Computerized Information Services:** DTIC, NASA/RECON, DIALOG Information Services, BRS Information Technologies, OCLC; internal databases. **Networks/Consortia:** Member of Interlibrary Users Association (IUA). **Special Catalogs:** Technical Reports Catalog (printout). **Remarks:** FAX: (703)848-7324.

★ 1615 ★
BEA Associates, Inc. - Library/Information Center (Bus-Fin)
1 Citicorp Center, 58th Fl.
153 E. 53rd St. Phone: (212)310-0230
New York, NY 10022 Betsy A. Heffron, Res.Libn.
Staff: Prof 2. **Subjects:** Finance, investments, portfolio management, corporations. **Special Collections:** Broker research; Standard & Poor's and Moody's credit ratings; foreign broker research; foreign company files; bond files. **Holdings:** 500 books; 219 periodicals volumes; annual reports. **Subscriptions:** 20 journals and other serials; 6 newspapers. **Services:** Interlibrary loan; copying; SDI; center open to the public. **Automated Operations:** Computerized cataloging, acquisitions, serials, and circulation. **Computerized Information Services:** Dow Jones News/Retrieval, InvesText, Trading System, CompuServe Information Service, NEXIS; CD-ROMs (Lotus One Source); internal databases. Performs searches on fee basis. **Remarks:** FAX: (212)355-1662. Telex: 220879. **Staff:** Hyacinth Davis, Asst.Libn.

★ 1616 ★
Beal College - Library (Educ)
629 Main St.
P.O. Box 450 Phone: (207)947-4591
Bangor, ME 04401 Ann W. Rea, Libn.
Founded: 1965. **Staff:** Prof 1. **Subjects:** Business management, hotel management, tax accounting, data processing, medical assisting, paralegal training, travel careers. **Holdings:** 4000 volumes; 28 file drawers of pamphlets. **Subscriptions:** 100 journals and other serials. **Services:** Interlibrary loan; copying; library open to the public. **Automated Operations:** Computerized cataloging (MaineCat). **Computerized Information Services:** DIALOG Information Services. **Remarks:** FAX: (207)947-0208.

Dr. R.S. Beal, Sr. Library
See: **Southwestern Conservative Baptist Bible College** (15539)

Beal Library
See: **Macomb Intermediate School District** (9508)

Beale Memorial Library
See: **Kern County Library System** (8682)

Eva Bean Research Room
See: **Bethel Historical Society** (1785)

Bean Museum
See: **Brigham Young University** (20800)

★1617★
Bear Mountain Trailside Museums - Library
Bear Mountain State Park
Bear Mountain, NY 10911
Subjects: History, natural history. **Special Collections:** Daniel Carter Beard material. **Holdings:** 5000 books. **Remarks:** Currently inactive.

★1618★
Bear, Stearns & Co. Inc. - Library (Bus-Fin)
245 Park Ave. Phone: (212)272-2607
New York, NY 10167 Tim McThue, Lib.Mgr.
Staff: Prof 4; Other 13. **Subjects:** Investment and securities, finance, business conditions. **Holdings:** 2700 books; 16,000 microfiche of periodicals; 350,000 microfiche of corporate annual reports, 10K reports, proxies, prospectuses; corporate files on 6000 companies. **Subscriptions:** 250 journals and other serials; 20 newspapers. **Services:** Interlibrary loan; library not open to the public. **Computerized Information Services:** DIALOG Information Services, Disclosure Information Group, Dow Jones News/Retrieval, LEXIS, NEXIS, DunsPRINT, Interactive Data, INVESTEXT, NewsNet, Inc., Spectrum Ownership Profiles Online, DataTimes, Info Globe, TEXTLINE, Vickers Institutional Stock System, Warner Computer Systems, Inc., ADP Financial Information Services Inc., WILSONLINE. **Remarks:** FAX: (212)272-3083. **Staff:** Peter S. Pirog, Asst.Libn.; Brigitte Anderson-Crumb, Ref.Libn.; Carman Lopez, Ref.Libn.

★1619★
James Beard Foundation, Inc. - Archive and Library (Food-Bev)
167 W. 12th St. Phone: (212)675-4984
New York, NY 10011 Ruth Diebold, Libn.
Founded: 1986. **Staff:** Prof 1. **Subjects:** Cookery, food, and wine, with emphasis on James Beard and American cookery. **Special Collections:** Beardiana Collection. **Holdings:** 2200 books; 50 bound periodical volumes; 120 videotapes; clipping files. **Services:** Library open to the public by appointment.

James Beard of St. Helena Archive
See: **University of San Francisco - Special Collections Department/ Donohue Rare Book Room** (19290)

Beardslee Library
See: **Western Theological Seminary - Beardslee Library** (20304)

★1620★
Beasley, Casey, Colleran - Library (Law)
1125 Walnut St. Phone: (215)592-1000
Philadelphia, PA 19107 Amy Foy
Founded: 1978. **Staff:** Prof 1. **Subjects:** Law, medicine. **Subscriptions:** 30 journals and other serials; 5 newspapers. **Services:** Library open to the public by appointment. **Computerized Information Services:** DIALOG Information Services. **Remarks:** FAX: (215)592-8360.

Beaton Institute
See: **University College of Cape Breton - Beaton Institute** (18484)

Beatrice/Hunt-Wesson - Technical Library
See: **Hunt-Wesson - Technical Library** (7560)

★1621★
Beatrice State Developmental Center - Library/Media Center (Med)
3000 Lincoln Blvd. Phone: (402)223-2302
Beatrice, NE 68310 Donald G. Robertson, Libn./Media Spec.
Founded: 1981. **Staff:** Prof 1. **Subjects:** Mental retardation, behavior modification, psychiatry, psychology. **Holdings:** 1500 books; 110 periodical titles; 350 other cataloged items. **Subscriptions:** 40 journals and other serials. **Services:** Interlibrary loan; copying; center open to the public for reference use only. **Automated Operations:** Computerized cataloging. **Computerized Information Services:** OCLC, Nebraska Libraries Communication System (NELCMS). **Remarks:** FAX: (402)223-6043.

Beattie Library
See: **Ottawa Regional Cancer Centre** (12602)

★1622★
Beauchemin-Beaton-Lapointe, Inc. - BBL Library (Plan)
1134 W. Ste-Catherine St., 12th Fl. Phone: (514)871-9555
Montreal, PQ, Canada H3B 1H4 Linda Jeremia
Staff: 1. **Subjects:** Architecture; city planning; construction - buildings, roads, municipal facilities, airports; environment and pollution control; projects management. **Holdings:** 2000 books. **Subscriptions:** 90 journals and other serials. **Services:** Interlibrary loan; library not open to the public.

★1623★
Beaumont Enterprise Co. - Library (Publ)
380 Main St. Phone: (409)833-3311
Beaumont, TX 77701-2359 Jeanne E. Houston, Libn.
Founded: 1953. **Staff:** Prof 1; Other 1. **Subjects:** Newspaper reference topics. **Holdings:** Clippings; photographs; microfilm. **Subscriptions:** 15 newspapers. **Services:** Library not open to the public.

★1624★
Beaumont Public Library System - Tyrrell Historical Library (Hist)
695 Pearl St.
P.O. 3827 Phone: (409)833-2759
Beaumont, TX 77704 Maurine Gray, Dir. of Lib.
Founded: 1975. **Staff:** Prof 2; Other 2. **Subjects:** Texas history, genealogy, art. **Special Collections:** Texana, Beaumont, and genealogy file collections (120 linear feet of vertical files); City of Beaumont Archival Records (200 cubic feet); Beaumont Manuscript (100 cubic feet). **Holdings:** 16,000 books; 1200 bound periodical volumes; 200 cubic feet of archives; 6000 reels of microfilm; 11,000 microfiche; 100 linear feet of Texas documents; 2000 photographs; 5000 stereoscopes. **Subscriptions:** 125 journals and other serials. **Services:** Copying; library open to the public. **Publications:** Tyrrell Historical Library Association Newsletter; Tyrrell Historical Library Association Journal. **Remarks:** FAX: (409)833-5828. **Staff:** David Montgomery, Mgr.; Marcus Robbins.

William Beaumont Army Medical Center
See: **U.S. Army Hospitals** (17055)

★1625★
William Beaumont Hospital - Medical Library (Med)
3601 W. 13 Mile Rd. Phone: (313)551-1750
Royal Oak, MI 48073 Joan M.B. Smith, Dir.
Founded: 1956. **Staff:** Prof 3; Other 9. **Subjects:** Medicine, nursing. **Holdings:** 9500 books; 17,000 bound periodical volumes. **Subscriptions:** 740 journals and other serials. **Services:** Interlibrary loan; copying; SDI. **Computerized Information Services:** MEDLINE, TOXLINE, DIALOG Information Services, BRS Information Technologies, Northwestern Online Total Integrated System (NOTIS). **Networks/Consortia:** Member of Detroit Associated Libraries. **Publications:** Books and journal lists. **Staff:** Joan A. Emahiser, Assoc.Med.Libn.; Jean S. Gilbert, Assoc.Med.Libn.

★1626★
Beaver County Law Library (Law)
Court House Phone: (412)728-5700
Beaver, PA 15009 Bette Sue Dengel, Law Libn.
Founded: 1960. **Staff:** 1. **Subjects:** Law. **Holdings:** 23,250 books. **Subscriptions:** 70 journals and other serials. **Services:** Copying; library open to the public for reference use only. **Computerized Information Services:** WESTLAW, PaperChase; internal database (local court opinions and ordinances) **Publications:** Newsletter, bimonthly. **Special Indexes:** Index to local court opinions and ordinances (card and online). **Remarks:** FAX: (412)728-4133.

★1627★
Beaver County Times - Library (Publ)
400 Fair Ave.
Box 400 Phone: (412)775-3200
Beaver, PA 15009 Linda B. DiSante, Hd.Libn.
Founded: 1957. **Staff:** Prof 1; Other 2. **Subjects:** Newspaper reference topics. **Holdings:** 1 million newspaper clippings in 80,000 envelopes; Beaver County Times and its predecessors, 1900 to present, on microfilm; Beaver Falls News Tribune, 1903-1979, on microfilm. **Subscriptions:** 16 journals and other serials. **Services:** Library not open to the public. **Remarks:** FAX: (412)775-7212. Maintained by Beaver Newspapers, Inc.

The Beaver Defenders
See: **Unexpected Wildlife Refuge** (16628)

R. Pierce Beaver Missions Library
See: **Memphis Theological Seminary - Library** (10078)

★1628★
Bechtel - Audio-Visual Library (Bus-Fin)
Box 3965 Phone: (415)768-1413
San Francisco, CA 94119 Tom Gable
Subjects: Bechtel Power Corporation. **Holdings:** 500,000 photographs, slides, transparencies.

★1629★
Bechtel - Finance Library (Bus-Fin)
Box 3965 Phone: (415)768-5100
San Francisco, CA 94119 Kathleen A. McLaughlin, Res.Anl.
Founded: 1978. **Staff:** Prof 1. **Subjects:** Business and finance, project financing, economic and statistical information, domestic and foreign banking, country and regional information. **Holdings:** Figures not available. **Subscriptions:** 179 journals and other serials. **Services:** Interlibrary loan; research. **Computerized Information Services:** DIALOG Information Services, Reuters, Reuter TEXTLINE, NEXIS. **Remarks:** FAX: (415)768-2154.

★1630★
Bechtel Canada Engineers Limited - Library
10 Gateway, Suite 200
Don Mills, ON, Canada M3C 3N8
Founded: 1960. **Subjects:** Engineering - mining, civil, mechanical, electrical; metallurgy; instrumentation. **Holdings:** 1000 books; 700 engineering standards; 4 VF drawers; 75 Canadian Government documents; 500 vendor catalogs. **Remarks:** Currently inactive.

★1631★
Bechtel Corporation - Central Library (Sci-Engr, Bus-Fin)
50 Beale St. Phone: (415)768-5306
San Francisco, CA 94105 Jeffery Mah, Chf.Libn.
Founded: 1951. **Staff:** Prof 5; Other 1. **Subjects:** Engineering, construction, business, power industry. **Special Collections:** U.S. Nuclear Regulatory Commission Dochet Information (400,000 microfiche). **Holdings:** 35,000 books; 6750 unbound periodical titles; 5000 government documents; 2000 miscellaneous reports and pamphlets; 5000 codes and standards. **Subscriptions:** 550 journals and other serials. **Services:** Interlibrary loan; library not open to the public. **Automated Operations:** Computerized public access catalog, cataloging, acquisitions, serials, and circulation. **Computerized Information Services:** DIALOG Information Services, NEXIS, DataTimes, VU/TEXT Information Services, ORBIT Search Service, RLIN, NewsNet, Inc. **Networks/Consortia:** Member of CLASS. **Publications:** Periodicals List, annual; Newsletter. **Remarks:** FAX: (415)768-6997. Contains the holdings of the former Bechtel Corporation - San Francisco Regional Office - Library. **Staff:** Erica Rosen-Malozsak, Libn.Tech.Sup.; Joan Epstein, Libn.; Bok Ng, Libn.; Elisa Deang, Libn.

★1632★
Bechtel Corporation - Legal Department Library (Law)
Box 193965 Phone: (415)768-7635
San Francisco, CA 94119 Yoshiko Jitosho
Staff: 1. **Subjects:** Law - labor, environmental, government contracts, construction contracts, foreign, nuclear regulation. **Holdings:** Books; periodicals; legal forms. **Subscriptions:** 113 journals and other serials. **Services:** Interlibrary loan; library not open to the public. **Computerized Information Services:** LEXIS, NEXIS. **Remarks:** FAX: (415)768-2563. Telex: 34783. **Formerly:** Its San Francisco Regional Office - Legal Department Library.

★1633★
Bechtel Corporation - Library (Sci-Engr)
9801 Washingtonian Blvd. Phone: (301)417-3000
Gaithersburg, MD 20878-5356 Carol A. Bell, Hd.Libn.
Founded: 1962. **Staff:** Prof 1. **Subjects:** Engineering, nuclear engineering. **Holdings:** 3500 books; documents; codes and standards. **Subscriptions:** 50 journals and other serials. **Services:** Interlibrary loan; copying; library open to the public by appointment.

★1634★
Bechtel Corporation - San Francisco Regional Office - Computer Services Library (Comp Sci)
Box 193965 Phone: (415)768-9015
San Francisco, CA 94119-3965 Mercedes Dumlao, Libn.
Staff: Prof 1; Other 1. **Subjects:** Data processing. **Holdings:** Documentation, listings, files of Bechtel's production engineering and business programs; bibliographic guides to computer programs; vendor software manuals. **Services:** Library not open to the public. **Automated Operations:** Computerized cataloging, reports, and distribution lists. **Computerized Information Services:** CSL (internal database). **Publications:** Bechtel Standards for Production Computer Applications; Computer Services Procedures Quality Program Related - both for internal distribution only. **Special Catalogs:** Bechtel Catalog of Computer Programs. **Remarks:** FAX: (415)768-4710.

★1635★
Bechtel Corporation - San Francisco Regional Office - Library
Box 193965
San Francisco, CA 94119
Defunct. Holdings absorbed by Bechtel Corporation - Central Library.

★1636★
Bechtel Corporation - Southern California Regional Office - Library (Sci-Engr)
12440 E. Imperial Hwy. Phone: (310)807-2000
Norwalk, CA 90004 Dee Morris, Chf.Libn.
Staff: Prof 1. **Subjects:** Technology - engineering, nuclear, environmental; management. **Holdings:** Foreign standards and codes (microform); foreign language textbooks; government documents. **Services:** Interlibrary loan. **Remarks:** An alternate telephone number is 807-2000. FAX: (310)807-3434.

★1637★
Bechtel Geotechnical Library (Sci-Engr)
Box 193965 Phone: (415)786-5353
San Francisco, CA 94119 Betty Jo Hardison, Chf.Libn.
Staff: 2. **Subjects:** Geology, geotechnical engineering, hydrology. **Holdings:** 18,000 books, technical reports, documents, maps, and other cataloged items. **Services:** Interlibrary loan; library not open to the public. **Computerized Information Services:** DIALOG Information Services, OCLC, EPIC, Ground Water Network - National Ground Water Information Center. Performs searches on fee basis. **Remarks:** FAX: (415)768-4955.

★1638★
Bechtel Inc. - Houston Central Library (Sci-Engr)
3000 Post Oak Blvd. Phone: (713)235-5350
Houston, TX 77056-6580 Carylen W. Terry, Libn.
Founded: 1966. **Staff:** Prof 1. **Subjects:** Power plant engineering and construction, environment, offshore technology. **Special Collections:** Video Magazine; pictorials. **Holdings:** 5000 books; 125 bound periodical volumes; industry standards; microfilm; Nuclear Regulatory Commission and NTIS documents. **Subscriptions:** 129 journals and other serials. **Services:** Interlibrary loan; copying; library open to the public for reference use only by request. **Automated Operations:** Computerized cataloging, acquisitions, and circulation. **Computerized Information Services:** DIALOG Information Services, Dun & Bradstreet Business Credit Services, DataTimes. Performs searches on fee basis.

Ira M. Beck Memorial Archives
See: **Rocky Mountain Jewish Historical Society** (14025)

★1639★
R.W. Beck & Associates - Information Center (Energy)
4th & Blanchard Bldg.
2101 4th Ave., Suite 600 Phone: (206)441-7500
Seattle, WA 98121-2375 Enid Miller Slivka, Libn.
Founded: 1972. **Staff:** Prof 1; Other 1. **Subjects:** Public utilities, engineering, economics. **Holdings:** 4000 books; 7500 technical reports. **Subscriptions:** 1000 journals and other serials; 15 newspapers. **Services:** Interlibrary loan; copying; SDI; center open to the public with restrictions. **Computerized Information Services:** DIALOG Information Services, BRS Information Technologies, Integrated Technical Information System (ITIS), Dow Jones News/Retrieval, PFDS Online, WESTLAW, VU/TEXT Information Services, DataTimes, NewsNet, Inc., OCLC, Data-Star; OnTyme Electronic Message Network Service, DIALMAIL (electronic mail services). Performs searches on fee basis. **Remarks:** FAX: (206)441-4962. Electronic mail address(es): CLASS.RWBA (OnTyme Electronic Message Network Service).

William C. Beck Health Science Library and Resource Center
See: **Guthrie Medical Center** (6816)

★1640★
Becker County Historical Society - Walter D. Bird Memorial Historical Library (Hist)
P.O. Box 622 Phone: (218)847-2938
Detroit Lakes, MN 56501 Harriet Davis, Dir.
Staff: Prof 2. **Subjects:** History - Northwest Area, Minnesota, Becker County. **Special Collections:** P.F. Schroeder's law books. **Holdings:** 2500 volumes; 15 VF drawers of letters, manuscripts, clippings; 25 linear feet of township and school records; 8 VF drawers of photographs; 125,500 cards of county vital statistics records; Chippewa Indian artifacts. **Subscriptions:** 3 newspapers. **Services:** Copying; library open to the public with restrictions. **Networks/Consortia:** Member of Northern Lights Library Network (NLLN). **Staff:** Otto F. Zeck, Cur.; Becky Olerud, Asst.Dir.

★1641★
Becker & Hayes, Inc. - Library (Info Sci)
13585 Romany Dr.
Pacific Palisades, CA 90272 Phone: (213)829-6866
Subjects: Information systems, library automation, networks. **Holdings:** 500 books; 2000 reports. **Services:** Library not open to the public. **Remarks:** FAX: (213)453-6607. **Formerly:** Located in Santa Monica, CA.

Becker Library
See: **Springfield College in Illinois** (15602)

Beckley Appalachian Regional Hospital
See: **Appalachian Regional Healthcare** (913)

★1642★
Beckman Instruments, Inc. - Research Library (Sci-Engr)
2500 Harbor Blvd. Phone: (714)773-8906
Fullerton, CA 92634 Jean R. Miller, Mgr., Info. & Lib.Serv.
Founded: 1954. **Staff:** Prof 2; Other 5. **Subjects:** Electrochemistry, scientific instrumentation, spectroscopy, chemistry, chromatography, medical electronics, clinical chemistry. **Holdings:** 8100 books; 8320 bound periodical volumes; 1200 reports, papers, pamphlets; 10 VF drawers of cataloged pamphlets; 2550 reels of microfilm; 4050 microfiche. **Subscriptions:** 425 journals and other serials. **Services:** Interlibrary loan; copying; library open to the public with referral from outside library. **Automated Operations:** Computerized serials. **Computerized Information Services:** DIALOG Information Services, PFDS Online, MEDLINE; OnTyme Electronic Message Network Service, DOCLINE (electronic mail services). **Networks/Consortia:** Member of CLASS. **Publications:** Monthly accessions list; Periodical Holdings list, annual. **Remarks:** FAX: (714)773-8969. Telex: 678413.

★1643★
Beckman Instruments, Inc. - Spinco Division - Technical Library (Biol Sci)
1050 Page Mill Rd.
Box 10200 Phone: (415)859-1734
Palo Alto, CA 94303-0803 Margaret Omar Fischer, Libn.
Founded: 1958. **Staff:** Prof 3. **Subjects:** Biochemistry, molecular biology, engineering. **Holdings:** 7500 books; 6000 bound periodical volumes; 36 VF drawers of reprints, reports, and theses. **Subscriptions:** 160 journals and other serials. **Services:** Interlibrary loan; copying; library open to the public by appointment. **Computerized Information Services:** DIALOG Information Services, RLIN. **Networks/Consortia:** Member of Northern California and Nevada Medical Library Group (NCNMLG). **Publications:** Accession List, monthly - for internal distribution only. **Special Indexes:** Extensive index to ultracentrifuge and amino acid analyzer applications published in the periodical literature since 1958 (online). **Remarks:** FAX: (415)859-1550. Electronic mail address(es): CLASS.Beckman (OnTyme Electronic Message Network Service). **Staff:** Phyllis M. Browning, Sci.Info.Mgr.

★1644★
Becton, Dickinson & Company - Corporate Information Center (Med)
1 Becton Dr. Phone: (201)847-7230
Franklin Lakes, NJ 07417-1880 Faina Menzul, Mgr.
Staff: Prof 3; Other 2. **Subjects:** Medicine, science and technology, law, business, marketing. **Holdings:** 2000 books; 220 periodicals. **Subscriptions:** 133 journals and other serials. **Services:** Interlibrary loan; SDI; center open to the public by telephone or written appointment. **Automated Operations:** Computerized cataloging. **Computerized Information Services:** DIALOG Information Services, MEDLINE, OCLC, LEXIS, NEXIS, Data-Star, Dow Jones News/Retrieval, STN International. **Remarks:** FAX: (201)847-6475. **Staff:** Karen M. Little, Ref.Libn.; Barbara G. Inglese, Mktg.Info.Spec.

★1645★
Becton Dickinson Research Center - Information Center (Med)
Box 12016 Phone: (919)549-8641
Research Triangle Park, NC 27709 Barbara K. Post, Hd., Info.Ctr.
Founded: 1973. **Staff:** Prof 2; Other 1. **Subjects:** Biomedicine, organic chemistry, polymer chemistry, microbiology and immunology, materials science, business. **Holdings:** 1800 books; 150 bound periodical volumes; 350 microfiche; pamphlets. **Subscriptions:** 300 journals and other serials. **Services:** Interlibrary loan; center open to the public with restrictions. **Automated Operations:** public access catalog. **Computerized Information Services:** MEDLARS, DIALOG Information Services, STN International, BRS Information Technologies, Data-Star. **Publications:** Acquisitions List, monthly - for internal distribution only. **Staff:** Denise N. Boldt, Info.Spec.

★1646★
BEDCO - Library (Bus-Fin)
36 S. Charles St., Suite 1600 Phone: (301)837-9305
Baltimore, MD 21201 Susan Eliasberg
Staff: 1. **Subjects:** Industrial and economic development, demographics. **Holdings:** 500 books. **Subscriptions:** 65 journals and other serials; 7 newspapers. **Services:** Copying; library open to the public by appointment. **Remarks:** FAX: (301)547-7211.

Arthur J. Bedell Memorial Library
See: **Wills Eye Hospital and Research Institute** (20457)

Evan Bedford Library of Cardiology
See: **Royal College of Physicians of London** (14113)

★1647★
Bedford Historical Society - Library (Hist)
15 The Great Rd.
Bedford, MA 01730 Mary S. Hafer, Cur.
Founded: 1893. **Staff:** Prof 1; Other 1. **Subjects:** Local history, Bedford flag, battles of Lexington and Concord, Rufus Porter. **Special Collections:** Lane Family papers, 17th-19th centuries; Davis Family papers. **Holdings:** 2000 deeds, wills, legal documents, receipts, school and church records, photographs; town annual reports, 1892 to present; newspaper columns, 1910-1929. **Services:** Library open to the public by appointment. **Remarks:** Maintains Museum of Bedford History.

★1648★
Bedford Historical Society - Library (Hist)
30 S. Park St.
Box 46282 Phone: (216)232-0796
Bedford, OH 44146 Richard J. Squire, Dir.
Founded: 1955. **Staff:** Prof 1. **Subjects:** Ohio and local history, local government, 1876 centennial, Lincoln and Civil War, railroads and electric traction. **Special Collections:** Jacka 1876 Centennial Collection (320 books, medals, other cataloged items); Leonard Seigel railroad collection (280 volumes; 900 slides). **Holdings:** 6500 books; 150 bound periodical volumes; 190 ledgers, record books, scrapbooks, albums; 160 file boxes and drawers of manuscripts, archival materials, maps, other cataloged items. **Subscriptions:** 11 journals and other serials. **Services:** Library open to the public. **Publications:** Newsletter, bimonthly - to members.

Bedford Institute of Oceanography
See: **Nova Scotia Department of Fisheries and Oceans - Scotia Fundy Regional Library** (12138)

★1649★
Bedford Research Consultants - Information Center (Bus-Fin)
210 Little Falls St., Suite 103 Phone: (703)532-2990
Falls Church, VA 22046-4303 Lorna M. Dailey, V.P., Intl.Serv.
Founded: 1986. **Staff:** Prof 1. **Subjects:** Foreign social security and pensions, institutional investments. **Holdings:** 200 books. **Subscriptions:** 50 journals and other serials. **Services:** Interlibrary loan; SDI; center open to the public with restrictions. **Computerized Information Services:** Bedford Marketing Support System, Bedford Report Management System (internal databases). **Special Indexes:** Bedford Index (bibliography of foreign pension and social security books and articles); subject heading list of foreign pension terms. **Remarks:** Center also supports the publications and research projects of the parent firm. FAX: (703)532-2992.

★1650★
Bee Biology and Systematics Laboratory - Library (Agri, Biol Sci)
Utah State University
UMC 5310
Logan, UT 84322 Phone: (801)750-2524
Founded: 1946. **Staff:** 8. **Subjects:** Bees, pollination, crops, systematics, biology, management and control. **Holdings:** 15,000 volumes. **Services:** Library not open to the public. **Remarks:** FAX: (801)750-3075. Affiliated with U.S. Department of Agriculture - Agriculture Research Service. **Staff:** Dr. Terry Griswold.

George H. Beebe Communication Reference Library
See: **Boston University - George H. Beebe Communication Reference Library** (2010)

★1651★
Beech-Nut Nutrition Corporation - Library (Biol Sci)
2 Church St. Phone: (518)673-3251
Canajoharie, NY 13317 Virginia A. San Fanandre-Russo, Libn.
Staff: 1. **Subjects:** Nutrition, pediatrics, food chemistry. **Holdings:** 1000 books. **Subscriptions:** 31 journals and other serials. **Services:** Library not open to the public. **Remarks:** FAX: (518)673-3259.

Henry Ward Beecher Collection
See: **Brooklyn Historical Society - Library** (2235)

Clifford Beers Memorial Library
See: **National Mental Health Association** (11236)

Beeson Library
See: **Blackford County Historical Society - Museum and Beeson Library** (1881)

Beet Sugar Development Foundation
See: **American Society of Sugar Beet Technologists** (759)

Behan Health Science Library
See: **South Hills Health System** (15429)

★1652★
Behringer-Crawford Museum - Lawrence Duba Research Library (Soc Sci)
P.O. Box 67 Phone: (606)491-4003
Covington, KY 41012-0067 Greg Harper, Dir.
Founded: 1950. **Subjects:** Northern Kentucky archeology and history. **Special Collections:** Frye Steamboat Collection. **Holdings:** 1186 books; 296 bound periodical volumes; 400 documents; 555 photographs. **Services:** Copying; library open to the public by appointment.

★1653★
BEI Golembe, Inc. - Library (Bus-Fin)
1025 Thomas Jefferson St., N.W., No. 301 Phone: (202)337-5550
Washington, DC 20007 Kim Lowry, Dir., Info.Serv.
Staff: Prof 2. **Subjects:** Banking, finance. **Special Collections:** Annual and quarterly reports of 300 bank holding companies and banks, 1986 to present; 150 stock thrifts, 1986 to present; annual reports of 60 international banks, 1986 to present. **Holdings:** 500 books; 60 VF drawers of subject files. **Subscriptions:** 125 journals and other serials; 7 newspapers. **Services:** Interlibrary loan; copying; library open to the public by appointment on a limited basis. **Computerized Information Services:** DIALOG Information Services, NEXIS, LEXIS, Dow Jones News/Retrieval; CD-ROM (Lotus One-Source). **Remarks:** FAX: (202)965-3403.

★1654★
Beihoff Music Corporation - Sheet Music Department (Mus)
5040 W. North Ave. Phone: (414)442-3100
Milwaukee, WI 53208 Brian McLinden, Mgr.
Staff: Prof 2; Other 4. **Subjects:** Music - band, orchestra, choral. **Holdings:** Music for instrumental and vocal solos and ensembles; popular instrumental and vocal collections and sheets. **Subscriptions:** 15 journals and other serials. **Services:** Department open to the public.

★1655★
Beijing Agricultural University - Library (Agri, Biol Sci)
2 West Yuanmingyuan Lu
Beijing 100094, People's Republic of China Phone: 1 2582244
Yang Zhi-Min, Prof., Chf.Libn.
Founded: 1949. **Staff:** 63. **Subjects:** Agriculture; genetic crop breeding; plant physiology, biochemistry, pathology; entomology; agricultural microbiology; animal husbandry; veterinary medicine; agricultural economics; soil science; land resources; laboratory animal science; agricultural meteorology; food science; horticulture; agricultural chemistry; plant nutrition; allied sciences and technology. **Special Collections:** Chinese and foreign publications on plant pathology, entomology, veterinary parasitology, pesticides, plant physiology and biochemistry, genetic breeding, fertilizers; ancient Chinese agricultural works (300 titles). **Holdings:** 998,372 volumes; 78,067 periodicals. **Subscriptions:** 1866 journals and other serials; 60 newspapers. **Services:** Interlibrary loan; copying. **Computerized Information Services:** CD-ROMs (AGROCOLA, CRIS, Cambridge Life Sciences, Dissertation Abstracts Ondisc). **Publications:** Bulletin of Beijing Agricultural University; Journal of Plant Protection; Journal of Animal Breeding and Veterinary Medicine. **Remarks:** Includes the holdings of the former Tsin Hwa University, Peking University, North China University, and the Catholic University Agricultural Faculty. FAX: 1 2582332. Telex: 222487 BAU CN. **Staff:** Bing-Fang Yang, Assoc.Prof.; Xiu-Han Yang, Assoc.Prof.; He-Ping We, Assoc.Prof.; Chun-Ya Lin, Assoc.Prof.; Li-Ye Qiu, Assoc.Prof.; Ke-Qin Yang, Assoc.Prof.; Mei Zhu, Assoc.Prof.; Bing-Hui Lui, Assoc.Prof.

★1656★
Beijing College of Linguistics - Library (Hum)
Dongsheng Lu
Haidian District Phone: 1 277531
Beijing, People's Republic of China Li Xinmin, Dp.Libn.
Founded: 1961. **Staff:** 26. **Subjects:** Chinese, English, French, Japanese, Spanish, German, and Arabian languages; philology; literature. **Holdings:** 303,675 volumes; 1097 periodicals; 1100 AV programs and microforms; threadbound ancient Chinese books. **Services:** Copying.

★1657★
Beijing Film Academy - Library (Theater)
4, XiTuCheng Rd. Phone: 2012126
Beijing 100088, People's Republic of China Shiping Lu
Founded: 1956. **Staff:** 16. **Subjects:** Literature, art, cinema. **Special Collections:** Playscripts (Chinese and translations of foreign movies; 10,300 volumes). **Holdings:** 87,200 volumes; 291 periodicals; bound volumes of pre-Liberation movie magazines; 143,749 slides; 861 photographs. **Subscriptions:** 350 journals and other serials; 35 newspapers. **Services:** Copying.

★1658★
Beijing Petroleum Design Institute - Library (Energy)
P.O. Box 10053 Phone: 1 445261
Beijing, People's Republic of China Qian Peiliang, Libn.
Staff: 8. **Subjects:** Petroleum processing; petrochemical technology, devices, equipment, machinery; oil product storage and transportation; water supply and drainage; heat; electricity; building structure; earthquake engineering; waste treatment; computers. **Holdings:** 160,000 volumes; 1000 periodicals; 5000 technical reports; 100 AV programs and microforms.

★1659★
Beijing University - Library (Soc Sci, Rel-Phil, Hum)
Haidian District Phone: 1 282471
Beijing, People's Republic of China Xie Daoyuan, Libn.
Founded: 1902. **Subjects:** Philosophy, politics, economics, language, literature, history, history of philosophy, history of literature. **Special Collections:** Chinese ancient books (1.6 million volumes); books in English, French, German, Spanish (500,000); Japanese books (200,000); Complete Works of Shakespeare, 1623; Dante; Schiller. **Holdings:** 3.3 million volumes; 15,000 back issues of periodicals. **Subscriptions:** 7000 journals and other serials. **Special Catalogs:** Catalog of Remarkable Edition Books Held by the Library; Catalog of Chinese History Books Held by the Library. **Special Indexes:** Subject index to Lu Xun's Articles.

Beinecke Rare Book and Manuscript Library
See: **Yale University** (20703)

Richard S. Beinecke Medical Library
See: **Good Samaritan Medical Center** (6556)

★1660★
(Beirut) USIS Library (Educ)
American Embassy
Beirut, Lebanon
Remarks: Maintained or supported by the U.S. Information Agency. Focus is on materials that will assist peoples outside the United States to learn about the United States, its people, history, culture, political processes, and social milieux.

★1661★
Leo Beiser Inc. - Library (Sci-Engr)
151-77 28th Ave. Phone: (718)353-7298
Flushing, NY 11354 Leo Beiser, Res.Dir.
Founded: 1952. **Staff:** Prof 1; Other 1. **Subjects:** Technology - laser scanning, laser/optics, CRT & E-beam; information science. **Special Collections:** Image and data scanning and recording technology, 1952 to present (12 VF drawers); holography collection; Dennis Gabor papers and private communications. **Holdings:** 215 books; 1075 bound periodical volumes; 100 technical reports; 115 catalogs; 35 directories and guides; 990 patents; 20 VF drawers of reports, manuscripts, technical papers, and clippings. **Subscriptions:** 6 journals and other serials; 6 newspapers. **Services:** Library open to the public at librarian's discretion. **Remarks:** FAX: (718)353-7098.

Belarus - Agricultural Research Library
See: **Belorusskaja Respublikanskaja Naucnaja Selskochozjajstvennaja Biblioteka im. I.S. Lupinovica** (1707)

★1662★
(Belem) Centro Cultural Brasil-Estados Unidos - USIS Collection (Educ)
Travessa Padre Eutiquio, 1309
66000 Belem, Para, Brazil
Remarks: Maintained or supported by the U.S. Information Agency. Focus is on materials that will assist peoples outside the United States to learn about the United States, its people, history, culture, political processes, and social milieux.

★1663★
Belgian Consulate General - Library (Area-Ethnic)
50 Rockefeller Plaza Phone: (212)586-5110
New York, NY 10020 Lorette Moureau
Staff: 1. **Subjects:** Belgian history, art, culture, life; Belgian literature in French, Dutch, and English translation. **Holdings:** 6000 volumes; reports; documents; pamphlets; photographs. **Services:** Library open to the public for reference use only. **Remarks:** FAX: (212)582-9657.

★1664★
Belgian Royal Museum of Fine Arts - Library (Art, Hist)
Museum St. 9 Phone: 2 5139630
B-1000 Brussels, Belgium Mrs. C. Heesterbeek, Art Hist./Sci.Libn.
Founded: 1803. **Staff:** 5. **Subjects:** Fine arts - Middle Ages to present; theoretical studies in art history. **Special Collections:** Exhibition and auction catalogs. **Holdings:** 250,000 books; 1500 periodicals. **Subscriptions:** 450 journals and other serials. **Services:** Copying; library open to the public with restrictions. **Computerized Information Services:** Online systems. **Publications:** Bulletin des Musees Royaux des Beaux-Arts de Belgique; Bulletin van de Koninklijke Musea voor Schone Kunsten van Belgie; exhibition catalogs. **Remarks:** FAX: 2 5118339. Is said to be the most important library of fine arts in Belgium.

★1665★
Belgische Boerenbond - Bibliotheek (Agri)
Postbus 101 Phone: 16 242078
B-3000 Leuven, Belgium Marc F. Demeyer
Founded: 1912. **Subjects:** Agriculture, ecology. **Holdings:** 40,000 books; 10,000 bound periodical volumes. **Subscriptions:** 500 journals and other serials; 15 newspapers. **Services:** Interlibrary loan; copying; library open to the public. **Automated Operations:** Computerized public access catalog (LIBIS). **Remarks:** FAX: 16 242175.

★1666★
Belgium - Flemish Ministry of Education - Library (Educ)
150 Koningstraat Phone: 2 2105376
B-1000 Brussels, Belgium Fred Deprez, Hd.Libn.
Founded: 1879. **Staff:** Prof 11; Other 1. **Subjects:** Education, administration. **Holdings:** 250,000 books; 50,000 bound periodical volumes. **Subscriptions:** 500 journals and other serials. **Services:** Interlibrary loan; copying; library open to teachers and other education professionals. **Computerized Information Services:** ADIOV (internal database). Contact Person: Wilfried Boomgaert, Doc. **Special Catalogs:** CAO - Subject Catalog. **Remarks:** FAX: 2 2105409.

★1667★
Belgium - Ministere des Affaires Etrangeres du Commerce Exterieur et de la Cooperation au Developpement - Bibliotheque Africaine (Area-Ethnic)
rue Belliard 65 Phone: 2 5115870
B-1040 Brussels, Belgium Wilfried Van Hemelrijck, Chf.Libn.
Founded: 1884. **Staff:** 10 Prof. **Subjects:** Sub-Sahara Africa - politics, anthropology, social problems, economics, ethnology, arts. **Holdings:** 350,000 books; 150,000 bound periodical volumes. **Subscriptions:** 675 journals and other serials. **Services:** Interlibrary loan; copying; library open to the public. **Computerized Information Services:** BELINDIS, AFLI. **Publications:** Acquisitions list, monthly.

Belgium - Ministry of Culture
See: **Koninklijk Museum voor Schone Kunsten - Bibliotheek** (8785)

★1668★
Belgium - Ministry of Economic Affairs - Fonds Quetelet Library (Soc Sci)
6, rue de l'Industrie Phone: 2 5065111
B-1040 Brussels, Belgium G. De Saedeleer, Hd.Libn.
Founded: 1841. **Staff:** 30. **Subjects:** Economics, social sciences, statistics. **Holdings:** 700,000 volumes. **Subscriptions:** 3000 journals and other serials. **Services:** Library open to the public. **Computerized Information Services:** Internal database. Performs searches on fee basis. **Remarks:** FAX: 2 5134657.

★1669★
Belgium - Ministry of Education - Gembloux Faculty of Agricultural Sciences - Library (Agri)
B-5030 Gembloux, Belgium Phone: 32 81610100
Micheline Populer, Cons.
Founded: 1860. **Staff:** 6. **Subjects:** Agronomy, biology, soil and environmental sciences, animal and plant products, engineering, economics. **Special Collections:** Ancient agricultural books. **Holdings:** 100,000 volumes. **Subscriptions:** 800 journals and other serials; 10 newspapers. **Services:** Interlibrary loan; library not open to the public. **Computerized Information Services:** DIALOG Information Services, ESA/IRS, DIMDI, ECHO; MIDAS, Belgian Bibliografy, Antilope (internal databases); EARN (electronic mail service). **Remarks:** Alternate telephone number(s): 2 81622103. FAX: 2 81614544. Telex: 58482 FSAGX. Electronic mail address(es): BIBLIO@BGXFSA51 (EARN). **Also Known As:** Faculte des Sciences Agronomiques de Gembloux. **Staff:** Bernard Pochet; Apolena Roubinkova, Agri.Engr.

Belgium - Ministry of the Interior - Royal Observatory of Belgium
See: **Royal Observatory of Belgium** (14127)

★1670★
Belgium - Ministry of Labour and Employment - Central Library (Law, Soc Sci)
Belliardstraat 51 Phone: 2 2334459
B-1040 Brussels, Belgium Jef Cassimons, Lib.Hd.
Founded: 1896. **Staff:** Prof 5; Other 12. **Subjects:** Labor law, social sciences, industrial relations, health and safety. **Holdings:** 68,000 books; 9000 bound periodical volumes. **Subscriptions:** 450 journals and other serials. **Services:** Copying; library open to the public. **Computerized Information Services:** Internal database. **Remarks:** FAX: 2 2334455.

★1671★
Belgium - Ministry of National Education - Bibliotheque Royale de Belgique (Info Sci)
4, Boulevard de l'Empereur Phone: 2 519 53 11
B-1000 Brussels, Belgium Martin Wittek, Chf.
Subjects: Library science, bibliography. **Special Collections:** Incunabula and early imprints; manuscripts (37,000); maps; Belgian music; engravings; coins and medals. **Holdings:** 3.5 million volumes. **Services:** Interlibrary loan; copying; SDI; library open to the public. **Computerized Information Services:** BELINDIS, O.R.I., DIMDI, STN International, GENIOS, Data-Star, ESA/IRS, Questel, Juridial, GCAM, BNDO, Electronic Data Systems Ltd. (EDS), BLAISE Online Services, Reuters, Datasolve Ltd., I/S Datacentralen (DC), ECHO, CELEX, DIALOG Information Services, PFDS Online, Chemical Abstracts Service (CAS), INFORDOC. Performs searches free of charge. Contact Person: Catherina Pletinckx-Oukhow. **Publications:** Bibliographie de Belgique, monthly; bulletin, quarterly; additional publications available. **Special Catalogs:** Catalogue des manuscrits de la Bibliotheque royale de Belgique, 8/year; additional catalogs available. **Also Known As:** Bibliotheque Royale Albert 1er; Koninklijke Bibliotheek Albert I.

★1672★
Belgium - Nationaal Scheepvaartmuseum - Historische Musea - Bibliotheek (Trans)
Steenplein 1 Phone: 3 2320850
B-2000 Antwerp, Belgium W. Johnson
Founded: 1952. **Staff:** Prof 1; Other 2. **Subjects:** Belgian maritime history, maritime history. **Special Collections:** Belgian South Pole expedition collection (de Gerlache); Bureau Veritas and Lloyd's complete registers; seventeenth century atlases; Belgian Shipping Archives, 1830-1930. **Holdings:** 42,000 books; 120 bound periodical volumes; archival items; microfiche. **Subscriptions:** 65 journals and other serials; 5 newspapers. **Services:** Interlibrary loan; copying; library open to the public. **Remarks:** FAX: 3 2208657.

★1673★
Belgium - Provinciaal Archief - en Documentatiecentrum (Hist)
Begijnhof
Zuivelmarkt 33 Phone: 11 210266
B-3500 Hasselt, Belgium R. Van Laere, Bibl.
Founded: 1982. **Staff:** Prof 10. **Subjects:** Limburg, French Revolution. **Holdings:** 40,000 books; 5000 bound periodical volumes; 1.5 million archives. **Subscriptions:** 1500 journals and other serials; 2 newspapers. **Services:** Interlibrary loan; library open to the public. **Automated Operations:** DOBIS-LIBIS. **Publications:** Bibliograpie Limburg; Bibliografische Analyses. **Remarks:** Alternate telephone number(s): 11 211229.

Belgium - Royal Meteorological Institute of Belgium
See: **Royal Observatory of Belgium** (14127)

Belgium - Royal Observatory of Belgium
See: **Royal Observatory of Belgium** (14127)

★1674★
(Belgrade) Americki Centar - USIS Library (Educ)
Cika Ljubina 19 Phone: 11 630011
YU-11000 Belgrade, Yugoslavia Olga Jovanovic, Chf.Libn.
Founded: 1945. **Staff:** 8. **Subjects:** U.S. social and political issues; international relations and economics; humanities; social sciences; literature. **Holdings:** 12,000 books; microfiche; microfilm. **Subscriptions:** 163 journals and other serials; 3 newspapers. **Services:** Interlibrary loan; copying; SDI; library open to the public. **Computerized Information Services:** LEGI-SLATE; CD-ROMs. **Publications:** Annotated list of periodicals; NewBooks. **Remarks:** FAX: 11 620691. Telex: 12988. Maintained or supported by the U.S. Information Agency. Focus is on materials that will assist peoples outside the United States to learn about the United States, its people, history, culture, political processes, and social milieux. **Staff:** Nevena Osojnik, Ref.Libn.; Jasminka Kunic, Tech.Serv.Libn.; Bojana Popovic, Circ.Libn.; Natasa Petkovic, Cat.; Damir Strbic, Lib.Asst.; Dusan Carnic, Exhibits; Jovanka Nikolic, Video Libn.

★1675★
Belize - National Library Service - Central Library - National Collection (Hist)
P.O. Box 287 Phone: 2 77267
Belize City, Belize Lawrence Vernon, Chf.Libn.
Founded: 1935. **Staff:** Prof 2; Other 39. **Subjects:** History, archeology, sociology, geography, literature. **Special Collections:** West Indian Collection (450 items); Central American Collection (325 items). **Holdings:** 1750 books; 250 bound periodical volumes; 80 reports. **Subscriptions:** 6 journals and other serials; 5 newspapers. **Services:** Interlibrary loan; copying; library open to the public. **Publications:** Bibliography of Collection.

Belk Library
See: **Appalachian State University - Belk Library** (914)

Belknap Collection for the Performing Arts
See: **University of Florida - Special Collections** (18584)

Waldron P. Belknap Research Library of American Painting
See: **Winterthur Library** (20503)

★1676★
Bell Aerospace Textron - Technical Information Services
Box 1
Buffalo, NY 14240
Defunct. Holdings absorbed by Textron Defense Systems.

★1677★
Alexander Graham Bell Association for the Deaf - Volta Bureau Library (Med)
3417 Volta Place, N.W. Phone: (202)337-5220
Washington, DC 20007 Judith A. Anderson, Libn.
Founded: 1893. **Staff:** 1. **Subjects:** Deafness, hearing, speech. **Special Collections:** Rare and out-of-print books on hearing and deafness; letters and books of Alexander Graham Bell, Alexander Melville Bell, John Hitz, and Helen Keller. **Holdings:** 28,000 books; 2500 bound periodical volumes; photographs; 640 shelf feet of pamphlets, reports of schools for the deaf; 30 VF drawers of clippings and reprints. **Subscriptions:** 190 journals and other serials. **Services:** Copying; SDI; library open to the public by appointment.

★1678★
Bell Canada - Historical Services (Hist, Aud-Vis)
1050 Beaver Hall Hill, Rm. 820 Phone: (514)870-5214
Montreal, PQ, Canada H2Z 1S4 Stephanie L. Sykes, Dir.
Founded: 1936. **Staff:** 16. **Subjects:** History of Bell Canada, history of telephone in Canada, Alexander Graham Bell, telecommunications, Canadian telephone companies. **Special Collections:** Telephone equipment, photographs, maps, directories, documents, letters, 1870s to present. **Holdings:** 100,000 pictures; documents; photographs on videodisc. **Services:** Center open to the public with restrictions. **Computerized Information Services:** Envoy 100 (electronic mail service). **Remarks:** FAX (514)875-2537. Electronic mail address(es): S.Sykes (Envoy 100).

★1679★
Bell Canada - Information Resource Centre (Bus-Fin)
1050 Beaver Hall Hill, 1st Fl. Phone: (514)870-8500
Montreal, PQ, Canada H2Z 1S4 Stephanie Boyd, Dir.
Founded: 1926. **Staff:** Prof 4; Other 8. **Subjects:** Telecommunications, business and management, technology, economics, labor relations, telephony, data processing, personnel management, finance. **Holdings:** 10,000 books; 1500 bound periodical volumes; 2000 other cataloged items. **Subscriptions:** 850 journals and other serials; 10 newspapers. **Services:** Interlibrary loan; center not open to the public. **Automated Operations:** Computerized cataloging and periodicals routing. **Computerized Information Services:** DIALOG Information Services, Infomart Online, QL Systems, CAN/OLE, Info Globe, NewsNet, Inc., Infomart Online, Questel; Envoy 100 (electronic mail service). **Publications:** Information Resource Centre Bulletin, bimonthly - for internal distribution only. **Remarks:** FAX: (514)876-8826. Electronic mail address(es): IRC.MTL.GENERAL (Envoy 100). **Staff:** Paloma Gonzalez, Ref.Libn.; Colette Nishizaki, SDI Libn.; Edmund Toombs, Cat.Libn.

★1680★
Bell Canada - Law Library (Law)
1050 Beaver Hall Hill, Suite 1500 Phone: (514)870-6550
Montreal, PQ, Canada H2Z 1S4 Judith Bird, Law Libn.
Founded: 1924. **Staff:** Prof 1; Other 2. **Subjects:** Telephony; law - civil, communications, common. **Holdings:** 6200 books; 4200 bound periodical volumes. **Subscriptions:** 200 journals and other serials. **Services:** Interlibrary loan; library not open to the public. **Computerized Information Services:** QL Systems, WESTLAW, Quebec Society for Legal Information (SOQUIJ), CAN/LAW, CBA/NET, LEXIS, NEXIS; iNET 2000, Envoy 100 (electronic mail services). **Remarks:** FAX: (514)876-4497.

★1681★
Bell Canada - O.R. Information Resource Centre (Bus-Fin, Info Sci)
Bell Trinity Square
North Tower, 1st Fl. Phone: (416)581-4258
Toronto, ON, Canada M5G 2E1 Vivian Lung, Libn.
Founded: 1954. **Staff:** Prof 2; Other 5. **Subjects:** Business, telecommunications, engineering, management. **Special Collections:** Telephony. **Holdings:** 6000 books; 50 bound periodical volumes; 40 VF drawers of pamphlets and clippings. **Subscriptions:** 550 journals and other serials. **Services:** Interlibrary loan; copying; center open to the public upon special request. **Automated Operations:** Computerized serials. **Computerized Information Services:** Info Globe, Dow Jones News/Retrieval, NewsNet, Inc., Canadian Financial Database (C.F.D.), Canada Systems Group (CSG), DIALOG Information Services, PFDS Online; Envoy 100 (electronic mail service). **Publications:** Periodical checklist; periodical holdings list; IRC Bulletin. **Special Indexes:** Subject index to vertical file material. **Remarks:** FAX: (416)340-0324. Electronic mail address(es): IRC.TOR (Envoy 100).

David Winton Bell Memorial Library
See: **Delta Waterfowl and Wetlands Research Station** (4759)

★1682★
Bell Helicopter Textron - Engineering Library (Sci-Engr)
Box 482 Phone: (817)280-3608
Fort Worth, TX 76101 Donald A. Welch, Libn.
Founded: 1952. **Staff:** Prof 1. **Subjects:** Aerospace, aeronautics, engineering, mathematics, computer science, management. **Special Collections:** Aerospace technology/helicopters; reference data on BHT helicopters; Bell Helicopter files/archives; engineering reports. **Holdings:** 3000 books; 200 bound periodical volumes; 20,000 technical reports; visual search microfilm files of military specifications; 100 AV programs. **Subscriptions:** 102 journals and other serials. **Services:** Interlibrary loan (limited); library not open to the public. **Automated Operations:** Computerized cataloging, acquisitions, serials, and circulation. **Computerized Information Services:** DIALOG Information Services, DTIC DROLS. **Remarks:** FAX: (817)280-8688.

★1683★
Bell Helicopter Textron - Logistic Technical Publications Library (Trans)
3000 S. Norwood Dr. & Trinity Blvd. Phone: (817)280-6726
Hurst, TX 76053 Irene E. Cordova, Libn.
Founded: 1981. **Staff:** Prof 1. **Subjects:** Commercial and military helicopters - operation, maintenance, parts. **Special Collections:** Bell Helicopter historical files (800 microfilm cartridges); reference data on BHC model helicopters. **Holdings:** 2000 manuals; 5000 technical data reports; military specifications and standards on microfilm; Air Force, Army, and Navy publications; Bell publications, 1950 to present. **Services:** Library not open to the public. **Remarks:** FAX: (817)280-6473. **Formerly:** Its Logistics Operations Library located in Fort Worth, TX.

James Ford Bell Library
See: **University of Minnesota** (18915)

James Ford Bell Technical Center
See: **General Mills, Inc.** (6329)

Bell-Marsh Memorial Library
See: **Medical Center Hospital** (9992)

Bell Museum of Natural History
See: **University of Minnesota** (18893)

★1684★
Bell-Northern Research Ltd. - Information Resource Center (Info Sci, Comp Sci)
P.O. Box 3511, Sta. C Phone: (613)763-2469
Ottawa, ON, Canada K1Y 4H7 Grant Birks, Mgr., Info.Rsrc.Ctr.
Founded: 1971. **Staff:** Prof 12; Other 18. **Subjects:** Telecommunications, computer science, electronics, systems engineering, business. **Special Collections:** Standards and marketing information. **Holdings:** 12,000 books; 3000 bound periodical volumes; reports; vertical files containing annual reports, pamphlets, and documents; internal confidential reports; technical and engineering letters. **Subscriptions:** 800 journals and other serials; 15 newspapers. **Services:** Interlibrary loan; center not open to the public. **Automated Operations:** Computerized cataloging and serials. **Computerized Information Services:** DIALOG Information Services, Info Globe, CAN/OLE, NewsNet, Inc., Infomart Online; internal databases; Envoy 100 (electronic mail service). **Publications:** Electronic Current Awareness. **Special Catalogs:** TRICAT Union Catalogue (online); Union List of Serials, semiannual. **Remarks:** FAX: (613)763-4282. **Staff:** B. Patel, Ref.Serv.; K. Dokken, ILL; P. Cross, Network Serv.

★1685★
Bell-Northern Research Ltd. - Information Resource Centre (Info Sci)
3, place du Commerce Phone: (514)765-7731
Verdun, PQ, Canada H3E 1H6 Pierre Dion, Mgr.
Founded: 1975. **Staff:** 4. **Subjects:** Telecommunications, computer communications, fiber optic communications, telephony. **Holdings:** 2800 books; 550 bound periodical volumes; 500 other cataloged items. **Subscriptions:** 225 journals and other serials; 12 newspapers. **Services:** Interlibrary loan; copying; center open to the public with permission. **Computerized Information Services:** Online systems; Envoy 100 (electronic mail service). **Remarks:** FAX: (514)765-7900. Electronic mail address(es): ILL.QMBNR (Envoy 100). This is a branch of the Bell-Northern Information Resource Centre in Ottawa.

Winthrop P. Bell Collection of Acadiana
See: **Mount Allison University** (10797)

★1686★
Bella Vista Historical Society - Museum/Library (Hist)
1885 Bella Vista Way
Bella Vista, AR 72714 Phone: (501)855-2335
Founded: 1976. **Staff:** 1. **Subjects:** History, genealogy, archaeology. **Special Collections:** C.A. Linebarger Collection (900 items). **Holdings:** 500 books; 700 bound periodical volumes; 4200 documents; 12 AV programs; 6 manuscripts; 9000 nonbook items. **Subscriptions:** 4 journals and other serials; 2 newspapers. **Services:** Copying; library open to the public for reference use only. **Publications:** Bella Vista Story; newsletter, bimonthly.

★1687★
Bellarmine College - Thomas Merton Studies Center (Rel-Phil)
Newburg Rd. Phone: (502)452-8187
Louisville, KY 40205 Robert E. Daggy, Dir.
Staff: Prof 1. **Subjects:** Thomas Merton, monasticism, spirituality, peace and peace movements, literary criticism, civil rights, creation spirituality. **Holdings:** 1708 books; 16,104 journals and pieces of correspondence; 1122 typescripts and other manuscripts; 3469 photographs and drawings; 518 tapes. **Services:** Copying; center open to the public with restrictions. **Automated Operations:** Computerized public access catalog and cataloging. **Publications:** The Merton SEASONAL: A Quarterly Review; The Merton Annual - both for sale.

★1688★
Bellcore - Library (Info Sci)
290 W. Mount Pleasant Ave., Rm. 3CG07 Phone: (201)740-4030
Livingston, NJ 07039-0486 Marianne Beddes, Staff Mgr.
Founded: 1985. **Staff:** Prof 2; Other 2. **Subjects:** Telecommunications, tariffs, regulations, finance, management, economics, statistics, marketing. **Holdings:** 11,250 books; 1500 bound periodical volumes; 1500 reels of microfilm. **Subscriptions:** 350 journals and other serials. **Services:** Interlibrary loan; copying (both limited); limited access by written request. **Computerized Information Services:** DIALOG Information Services, NewsNet, Inc., Dow Jones News/Retrieval, NEXIS. **Networks/Consortia:** Member of Essex Hudson Regional Library Cooperative. **Remarks:** FAX: (201)740-6886. **Staff:** Martha Broad, Ref.Libn.

★1689★
Bellcore - Library (Info Sci, Sci-Engr)
445 South St.
Box 1910 Phone: (201)829-4601
Morristown, NJ 07960-1910 Donald E. Sunday, Staff Mgr.
Founded: 1985. **Staff:** Prof 2; Other 5. **Subjects:** Telecommunications, mathematics, information science, electrical engineering, computer technology, artificial intelligence. **Holdings:** 12,000 books; 5000 bound periodical volumes; 3000 reels of microfilm; Bellcore internal documents. **Subscriptions:** 630 journals and other serials. **Services:** Interlibrary loan; copying (both limited); limited access by written request. **Computerized Information Services:** DIALOG Information Services. **Remarks:** FAX: (201)829-5891. **Staff:** Daniel T. Patricia, Ref.Libn.

★1690★
Bellcore - Library (Info Sci, Comp Sci)
6 Corporate Pl.
Box 1320 Phone: (908)699-5189
Piscataway, NJ 08855-1320 Susan J. Kaplan, Staff Mgr.
Founded: 1972. **Staff:** Prof 2; Other 2. **Subjects:** Computers, data processing, telecommunications, management, training, education. **Holdings:** 14,600 books; 10,000 bound periodical volumes; 4000 reels of microfilm; 250 AV items. **Subscriptions:** 350 journals and other serials. **Services:** Interlibrary loan; copying (both limited); limited access by written request. **Computerized Information Services:** DIALOG Information Services, DunsPrint, MEDLARS. **Networks/Consortia:** Member of Union Middlesex Regional Library Cooperative. **Remarks:** FAX: (908)336-2217. **Staff:** Jean Carrigan, Ref.Libn.

★1691★
Bellcore - Library (Info Sci, Comp Sci)
444 Hoes Ln. Phone: (908)336-2940
Piscataway, NJ 08854-4182 Virginia Lee Miller, Staff Mgr.
Founded: 1986. **Staff:** Prof 3; Other 4. **Subjects:** Computers, business information systems, software engineering, telecommunications, data processing, management. **Holdings:** 10,000 books; 3000 bound periodical volumes; 2000 reels of microfilm; 1000 computing documents. **Subscriptions:** 360 journals and other serials. **Services:** Interlibrary loan; copying (both limited); limited access by written request. **Computerized Information Services:** DIALOG Information Services. **Networks/Consortia:** Member of Union Middlesex Regional Library Cooperative. **Remarks:** FAX: (908)336-2940. **Staff:** Donna Lowich, Ref.Libn.; Yvonne Yeh, Ref.Libn.

★1692★
Bellcore - Library (Info Sci, Sci-Engr)
331 Newman Springs Rd., Box 7030 Phone: (908)758-2407
Red Bank, NJ 07701-7030 Miranda D. Scott, Staff Mgr.
Founded: 1984. **Staff:** Prof 2; Other 5. **Subjects:** Telecommunications, electronic and systems engineering, computer technology, physics, mathematics, chemistry, metallurgy, standards, statistics, human factors. **Holdings:** 15,000 books; 2000 bound periodical volumes; 2000 reels of microfilm. **Subscriptions:** 590 journals and other serials. **Services:** Interlibrary loan; copying (both limited); limited access by written request. **Computerized Information Services:** DIALOG Information Services, Chemical Abstracts Service (CAS). **Networks/Consortia:** Member of Central Jersey Regional Library Cooperative. **Remarks:** FAX: (908)758-4333. **Staff:** Cecilia J. Fiscus, Ref.Libn.

★1693★
Bellcore - Library and Information Services Network (Sci-Engr, Info Sci, Bus-Fin)
331 Newman Springs Rd.
Box 7020 Phone: (908)758-2277
Red Bank, NJ 07701-7020 E.H. Brodfuhrer, Dir.
Staff: Prof 28; Other 24. **Services:** Interlibrary loan; copying; limited access by written request only. **Automated Operations:** Computerized cataloging, acquisitions, serials, and circulation. **Computerized Information Services:** DIALOG Information Services, Dow Jones News/Retrieval, NewsNet, Inc., OCLC, Dun & Bradstreet Business Credit Services, MEDLARS, Chemical Abstracts Service (CAS), NEXIS; internal databases. **Networks/Consortia:** Member of PALINET, (New Jersey) Regional Library Cooperatives. **Publications:** Bellcore Mercury Bulletin - for internal distribution only. **Remarks:** Bellcore Library and Information Services Network includes the five Bellcore Libraries whose listings precede this entry. Centralized network activities not shown in the library listings are network support services, which include technical processing, automated systems support, clearance of internal documents, publication of information products, and forms and records management. Total staff figures above include supervisory personnel in all units listed. **Staff:** Anne N. Kneller, Mgr., Lib. Network Oper.; Amy L. Howard, Mgr., Lib. Network Sup.Serv.

★1694★
Bellcore TEC - Information Resources Center (Info Sci)
6200 Rte. 53 Phone: (708)960-6392
Lisle, IL 60532 Carol D. Todd, Assoc.Mgr.
Founded: 1977. **Staff:** Prof 1; Other 2. **Subjects:** Telecommunications, management, education and training. **Special Collections:** Complete collection of Bellcore and AT & T practices. **Holdings:** 1600 books; 135 bound periodical volumes; 20 drawers of microforms; 100 cassettes; 900 videotapes; 30 AV programs. **Subscriptions:** 124 journals and other serials. **Services:** Interlibrary loan; center not open to the public. **Computerized Information Services:** Bi-Line, Telaris (internal databases). **Networks/Consortia:** Member of Suburban Library System (SLS). **Remarks:** FAX: (708)960-6360. Bellcore TEC provides technical training primarily to telecommunications managers of the Bell Operating Companies.

★1695★
The Belleville Intelligencer (Publ)
45 Bridge St., E. Phone: (613)962-9171
Belleville, ON, Canada K8N 1L5 Nick Palmer, Ed.
Subjects: Newspaper reference topics. **Remarks:** No further information was supplied by respondent.

★1696★
Bellevue Hospital - Clarence De La Chapelle Medical Library (Med)
1st Ave. at 27th St. Phone: (212)561-6535
New York, NY 10016 Martha Lynch, Dir.
Staff: Prof 2. **Subjects:** Clinical medicine. **Holdings:** 3000 books; 20,000 bound periodical volumes. **Subscriptions:** 301 journals and other serials. **Services:** Interlibrary loan; copying; library open to the public by appointment. **Computerized Information Services:** NLM. **Networks/Consortia:** Member of Manhattan-Bronx Health Sciences Library Consortia, New York Metropolitan Reference and Research Library Agency, BHSL.

★1697★
Bellin Memorial Hospital - Health Sciences Library (Med)
744 S. Webster Ave.
Box 1700 Phone: (414)433-3693
Green Bay, WI 54305 Cynthia M. Reinl, Hea.Sci.Libn.
Founded: 1909. **Staff:** Prof 1; Other 7. **Subjects:** Nursing, medicine, quality. **Holdings:** 2700 books; 1055 bound periodical volumes; 500 video cassettes; 400 filmstrip programs; 20 motion pictures; 3 VF drawers of pamphlets and clippings. **Subscriptions:** 210 journals and other serials. **Services:** Interlibrary loan; copying; library open to the public for reference use only. **Computerized Information Services:** DIALOG Information Services, MEDLINE, WILSONLINE. **Networks/Consortia:** Member of National Network of Libraries of Medicine - Greater Midwest Region, Fox River Valley Area Library Consortium (FRVALC), Northeast Wisconsin Intertype Libraries (NEWIL). **Remarks:** FAX: (414)433-7498.

★1698★
Bellingham Herald - Library (Publ)
1155 N. State St.
P.O. Box 1277 Phone: (206)676-2620
Bellingham, WA 98227 Carole Teshima Morris
Founded: 1978. **Staff:** Prof 1. **Subjects:** Newspaper reference topics. **Holdings:** Newspaper clippings; photographs. **Services:** Library not open to the public; open to reference calls from other libraries. **Remarks:** FAX: (206)647-9260.

Bellis Medical Library
See: **St. Mary Medical Center** (14505)

Russell Bellman Medical Library
See: **St. Joseph's Hospital of Atlanta** (14409)

★1699★
Belmont Abbey College - Abbot Vincent Taylor Library - Special Collections (Rel-Phil)
Belmont, NC 28012 Phone: (704)825-6740
Marjorie McDermott, Dir., Lrng.Rsrcs.
Founded: 1876. **Staff:** 9. **Subjects:** Theology, literature, history. **Special Collections:** Benedictine Monasticism (3000 volumes); Caroliniana (950 volumes); rare books (13,000 volumes). **Holdings:** 92,693 books; 12,929 bound periodical volumes; 45,365 microfiche; 4274 reels of microfilm. **Subscriptions:** 540 journals and other serials; 21 newspapers. **Services:** Interlibrary loan; copying; collections open to the public with restrictions. **Automated Operations:** Computerized circulation and serials. **Computerized Information Services:** OCLC, DIALOG Information Services, BRS Information Technologies. **Networks/Consortia:** Member of Charlotte Area Educational Consortium. **Remarks:** FAX: (704)825-6743. **Staff:** Susan Mayes, Cat.; Jane Stubblefield, Ref.

★1700★
Belmont County Law Library (Law)
Court House
Main St. Phone: (614)695-2121
St. Clairsville, OH 43950 John W. Greenlee, Libn.
Staff: 1. **Subjects:** Law. **Holdings:** 22,000 volumes. **Services:** Library open to the public. **Computerized Information Services:** WESTLAW. **Remarks:** FAX: (614)695-4968.

Belmont Regional Library
See: **New York Public Library - Belmont Regional Library** (11597)

★1701★
(Belo Horizonte) Instituto Cultural Brasil-Estados Unidos - USIS Collection (Educ)
Rua da Bahlia, 1723
30000 Belo Horizonte, Minas Gerais, Brazil
Remarks: Maintained or supported by the U.S. Information Agency. Focus is on materials that will assist peoples outside the United States to learn about the United States, its people, history, culture, political processes, and social milieux.

★1702★
Beloit College - Anthropology Department Library (Soc Sci)
700 College St. Phone: (608)363-2769
Beloit, WI 53511 Dr. Lawrence Breitborde,
Assoc.Prof./Chm., Anthropology
Staff: Prof 5; Other 2. **Subjects:** Ethnography, archeology, biological anthropology, linguistics. **Holdings:** 600 books; 100 bound periodical volumes; 50 reports. **Subscriptions:** 10 journals and other serials. **Services:** Interlibrary loan; copying. **Publications:** Bulletin series; occasional papers, both irregular.

★1703★
Beloit College - Colonel Robert H. Morse Library - Richard & Marieluise Black Information Center (Soc Sci, Hum)
731 College St. Phone: (608)363-2481
Beloit, WI 53511 Dennis W. Dickinson, Coll.Libn.
Founded: 1847. **Staff:** Prof 5; Other 7.5. **Subjects:** Anthropology, economics, Shakespeare, international relations, geology, sociology. **Special Collections:** Joseph Rheingold Roosevelt Collection; Irving S. Kull Wilson Collection; Beloit Poetry Journal Collection; Martin Luther King, Jr. Collection. **Holdings:** 222,501 books; 40,587 bound periodical volumes; 4826 reels of microfilm. **Subscriptions:** 847 journals and other serials; 19 newspapers. **Services:** Interlibrary loan; library open to the public for reference use only. **Computerized Information Services:** DIALOG Information Services, Chemical Abstracts Service (CAS), Knowledge Index. Performs searches. Contact Person: Christine Nelson, Pub.Serv.Libn. **Remarks:** FAX: (608)363-2487. **Staff:** Holly Lovejoy-Nesvold, Tech.Serv.Libn.; Richard Burtt, Assoc.Libn., Info.Serv.; Fred Burwell, Archv.

★1704★
Beloit Corp. - Research Center - Technical Library (Bus-Fin)
1165 Prairie Hill Rd. Phone: (608)364-8522
Rockton, IL 61072-1595 Lawrence Dawson, Tech.Libn.
Founded: 1960. **Staff:** Prof 1; Other 1. **Subjects:** Pulp and paper industry, mechanical engineering, graphic arts. **Holdings:** 3000 books; 1500 bound periodical volumes; 2000 reports. **Subscriptions:** 126 journals and other serials. **Services:** Interlibrary loan; copying; library open to the public by referral only. **Automated Operations:** Computerized cataloging. **Computerized Information Services:** DIALOG Information Services, PFDS Online, Data-Star; central engineering file (internal database). **Networks/Consortia:** Member of Northern Illinois Library System (NILS), ILLINET, Wisconsin Interlibrary Services (WILS). **Remarks:** FAX: (608)364-8600. Telex: 6878014; 6878031. A branch library, Beloit Corp. - Engineering Department - Standards Library, is maintained at 1 St. Lawrence Ave., Beloit, WI, 53511. Telephone: (608)365-3311.

★1705★
Beloit Historical Society - Arthur L. Luebke Memorial Library (Hist)
Lincoln Center
845 Hackett St. Phone: (608)365-7835
Beloit, WI 53511 Paul K. Kerr, Dir.
Founded: 1910. **Staff:** Prof 2; Other 4. **Subjects:** Local history, politics, education, religion, industry, home and family. **Holdings:** 1000 books, diaries, journals; scrapbooks. **Subscriptions:** 12 journals and other serials. **Services:** Library open to the public for reference use only. **Publications:** Pioneer Beloit, 1976; Lincoln in Beloit, 1982.

★1706★
Belorussian Institute of Arts and Sciences, Inc. - Library (Area-Ethnic)
230 Springfield Ave. Phone: (201)933-6807
Rutherford, NJ 07070 Zora Kipel, Libn.
Founded: 1951. **Staff:** Prof 1. **Subjects:** Byelorussia - literature, history, culture. **Special Collections:** Development of Byelorussian printing (5000 items); history of Byelorussians in the United States; Byelorussian Democratic Republic, 1918-1920. **Holdings:** 5000 books; 500 bound periodical volumes. **Subscriptions:** 10 journals and other serials; 10 newspapers. **Services:** Library open to the public by appointment. **Special Catalogs:** Byelorussian publications outside of Soviet Byelorussia. **Remarks:** FAX: (201)438-4565.

★1707★
Belorusskaja Respublikanskaja Naucnaja Selskochozjajstvennaja Biblioteka im. I.S. Lupinovica (Agri, Biol Sci)
Kazinca 88 Phone: 252266
220108 Minsk, Belarus V.A. Golubev
Founded: 1960. **Staff:** Prof 40; Other 15. **Subjects:** Agriculture, forestry, food technology, agricultural biology. **Holdings:** 330,000 books; 5000 bound periodical volumes; 2000 microfiche. **Subscriptions:** 500 journals and other serials; 40 newspapers. **Services:** Interlibrary loan; copying; SDI; library open to the public. **Computerized Information Services:** Flax, Agricultural Bibliography of Byelorussia (internal databases). Contact Person: A.A. Gan, Engr. **Also Known As:** Byelorussia - Agricultural Research Library.

★1708★
Belt Collins & Associates (Hawaii) Ltd. - Information Center (Plan)
680 Ala Moana Blvd., Suite 200 Phone: (808)521-5361
Honolulu, HI 96813 Cheryl Goody, Info.Spec.
Staff: 1. **Subjects:** Land use and planning, engineering, landscape architecture. **Special Collections:** Belt Collins & Associates technical reports. **Holdings:** 3000 books; 2000 nonbook items. **Subscriptions:** 125 journals and other serials. **Services:** Center not open to the public. **Publications:** Bibliographies of all in-house collectios (online). **Special Indexes:** Index of drawings and maps. **Remarks:** FAX: (808)538-7819.

Elmer Belt Library of Vinciana
See: **University of California, Los Angeles - Arts, Architecture and Urban Planning Library** (18370)

★1709★
Beltrami County Historical Society - Archives (Hist)
300 Bemidji Ave.
P.O. Box 683 Phone: (218)751-7824
Bemidji, MN 56601 Carol Eberhardt, Exec.Dir.
Subjects: Beltrami County, lumber industry. **Special Collections:** Jens J. Opsahl papers (50 volumes and 12 square feet); Euclid Bourgeois Collection (surveyor; 400 maps). **Holdings:** 500 books; 500 maps; 2000 photographs; 36 linear feet and 100 volumes of manuscripts. **Services:** Copying; archives open to the public.

Belvoir Research, Development & Engineering Center
See: **U.S. Army - Belvoir Research, Development & Engineering Center** (16924)

Bemidji State University - North Central Minnesota Historical Center
See: **North Central Minnesota Historical Center** (11913)

★1710★
Ben Gurion University of the Negev - Institutes for Applied Research - Library (Agri, Biol Sci)
P.O. Box 1025 Phone: 57 461913
84110 Beer Sheva, Israel Ms. Tzvie Wolf, Lib.Hd.
Founded: 1959. **Staff:** Prof 2. **Subjects:** Agriculture, biotechnology, applied biology, chemical technology. **Holdings:** 14,000 books; 9500 bound periodical volumes; 1350 reports. **Subscriptions:** 101 journals and other serials. **Services:** Interlibrary loan; copying; SDI; library open to the public. **Computerized Information Services:** DIALOG Information Services. **Remarks:** FAX: 57 71612. Telex: 5379 BGUCC IL (Attn. DBA 5100).

★1711★
Bend Research - Library (Sci-Engr)
64550 Research Rd. Phone: (503)382-4100
Bend, OR 97701 Kim Plumber, Libn.
Staff: 1. **Subjects:** Membrane science. **Holdings:** 1600 books; 300 bound periodical volumes; 4000 reports. **Subscriptions:** 130 journals and other serials. **Services:** Interlibrary loan; copying; library open to local users. **Computerized Information Services:** DIALOG Information Services, OCLC. **Remarks:** FAX: (503)382-2713. Telex: 517787.

John H. Bender Library of Prints & Drawings
See: **Nelson-Atkins Museum of Art - Spencer Art Reference Library** (11388)

Lauretta Bender Staff Library
See: **Queens Children's Psychiatric Center** (13635)

★1712★
Matthew Bender and Company, Inc. - Editorial Library (Law)
11 Penn Plaza, 12th Fl. Phone: (212)216-8680
New York, NY 10001 Marie H. Rothman, Sr.Mng.Libn.
Founded: 1887. **Staff:** Prof 1; Other 2. **Subjects:** Law. **Holdings:** 60,000 books. **Subscriptions:** 215 journals and other serials; 25 newspapers. **Services:** Interlibrary loan (limited); library not open to the public. **Automated Operations:** Computerized serials. **Computerized Information Services:** LEXIS, NEXIS, EPIC, WESTLAW, DIALOG Information Services, RLIN, LEGI-SLATE, LRS (Legislative Retrieval System). **Remarks:** Alternate telephone number(s): (212)216-8681. FAX: (212)564-9579; (212)244-3188.

★1713★
Bendix Environmental Research, Inc. (BERI) - Library (Env-Cons)
1390 Market St., Suite 418 Phone: (415)861-8484
San Francisco, CA 94102 Selina Bendix, Ph.D., Pres.
Founded: 1980. **Subjects:** Environment, toxicology, hazardous materials. **Holdings:** Articles and offprints on 400 subjects. **Subscriptions:** 100 journals and other serials. **Services:** Copying; library open to the public by appointment. **Computerized Information Services:** DIALOG Information Services; CANSIT (internal database). Performs searches on fee basis.

★1714★
Bendix Oceanics, Inc. - Library (Sci-Engr)
15825 Roxford St. Phone: (818)367-0111
Sylmar, CA 91342-3597 Buddy Flick, Sr.Libn.
Staff: Prof 1. **Subjects:** Underwater acoustics, electrical engineering. **Holdings:** 5000 books. **Subscriptions:** 140 journals and other serials; 3 newspapers. **Services:** Interlibrary loan; library not open to the public. **Automated Operations:** Computerized cataloging, acquisitions, serials, and circulation. **Computerized Information Services:** Internal database. **Publications:** Newsletter - for internal distribution only. **Remarks:** FAX: (818)367-0403.

★1715★
Benedict Estuarine Research Laboratory - Library (Biol Sci, Env-Cons)
Academy of Natural Sciences
Benedict Ave. Phone: (301)274-3134
Benedict, MD 20612 Lori Baldwin
Staff: 1. **Subjects:** Marine biology, estuarine ecology, biogeochemistry, toxic marine pollutants. **Holdings:** 300 books; 500 reports. **Subscriptions:** 13 journals and other serials. **Services:** Library not open to the public. **Computerized Information Services:** OMNET (electronic mail service). **Remarks:** FAX: (301)274-3137. Electronic mail address(es): BENEDICT.LAB (OMNET).

★1716★
Benedictine Monastery Melk - Stiftsbibliothek (Rel-Phil, Hist)
Abt. Berthold Dietmayrstrasse 1 Phone: 02752 2312/342
A-3390 Melk, Austria P. Gottfried Glassner, Lib.Hd.
Subjects: Theology, history of Austria. **Holdings:** 80,000 books; 5000 bound periodical volumes; 1130 microfilms; 1800 manuscripts. **Services:** Copying; library open to the public by appointment. **Remarks:** FAX: 02752 2312/52.

★1717★
Beneficial Management Corporation - Information Services-Corporate Community Affairs (Bus-Fin)
200 Beneficial Ctr. Phone: (201)781-3744
Peapack, NJ 07977 Patricia A. Moffat, Mgr.
Founded: 1955. **Staff:** 1. **Subjects:** Consumer finance. **Holdings:** 900 books. **Subscriptions:** 100 journals and other serials. **Services:** Library not open to the public. **Computerized Information Services:** NEXIS, Dow Jones News/Retrieval; internal database. **Formerly:** Its Public Affairs Department.

★1718★
Benefit Capital Co. Inc. - Library (Bus-Fin)
721 Bonhill Rd. Phone: (213)440-2296
Los Angeles, CA 90049 M.T. Smiley, Libn.
Founded: 1970. **Staff:** 3. **Subjects:** Employee stock ownership plans. **Holdings:** 350 books; 1000 reports. **Subscriptions:** 123 journals and other serials; 7 newspapers. **Services:** Library open to clients only. **Remarks:** FAX: (213)471-4072.

Benet Laboratories
See: **U.S. Army - Armament, Munitions & Chemical Command - Benet Laboratories** (16919)

Benet Library
See: **St. Benedict's Abbey** (14248)

Benger Laboratory
See: **E.I. Du Pont de Nemours & Company, Inc.** (5019)

★1719★
Benham Group - Information Resource Center (Plan, Sci-Engr)
9400 N. Broadway
Box 20400 Phone: (405)478-5353
Oklahoma City, OK 73156 Kim Kirkpatrick, Mgr.
Founded: 1980. **Staff:** 5. **Subjects:** Architecture; engineering - mechanical, civil, structural, electrical; power; environmental services; planning. **Special Collections:** Webster L. Benham Engineering Collection. **Holdings:** 3000 books; 175 bound periodical volumes; 50,000 slides; 60 reels of microfilm; 300 microfiche. **Subscriptions:** 257 journals and other serials; 9 newspapers. **Services:** Center not open to the public. **Automated Operations:** Computerized cataloging, serials, and circulation. **Computerized Information Services:** DIALOG Information Services. **Remarks:** FAX: (405)478-5660.

★1720★
Benin - Bibliotheque Nationale (Soc Sci)
Boite Postale 401 Phone: 212585
Porto Novo, Benin Julien C. Djosse
Founded: 1975. **Staff:** Prof 11; Other 27. **Subjects:** Social sciences, history, literature, applied sciences, pure sciences, religion. **Special Collections:** Rare book collection on the history of Benin (1000 books). **Holdings:** 8500 books; 300 bound periodical volumes; 300 microfiche; 10 reels of microfilm; 100 records. **Subscriptions:** 30 journals and other serials; 10 newspapers. **Services:** Library open to the public. **Publications:** National Bibliography.

Benjamin/Cummings Publishing Co.
See: **Addison-Wesley Publishing Company** (70)

Benner Library and Resource Center
See: **Olivet Nazarene University** (12403)

Benner Spring Fish Research Station
See: **Pennsylvania State Fish Commission Library** (12872)

Charles A. Bennett Collection
See: **Bradley University - Virginius H. Chase Special Collections Center - Charles A. Bennett Collection** (2059)

★1721★
Bennett College - Thomas F. Holgate Library - Special Collections (Area-Ethnic, Hist)
900 E. Washington
Campus Box M Phone: (919)273-4431
Greensboro, NC 27401 Dr. Haith
Special Collections: Afro-American Women's Collection (480 books; 2 VF drawers); Norris Wright Cuney Papers (personal and business correspondence, diaries, and newspaper clippings); College Archives (51 boxes; 3 file cabinets; 28 shelves; 1 bookcase). **Services:** Copying; collections open to the public by appointment. **Networks/Consortia:** Member of CCLC.

★1722★
Bennett Jones Verchere - Library (Law)
4500 Bankers Hall, E.
855 2nd St., S.W. Phone: (403)298-3165
Calgary, AB, Canada T2P 4K7 Susan L. Ross, Libn.
Staff: Prof 2; Other 2. **Subjects:** Law. **Holdings:** 27,000 books. **Subscriptions:** 200 journal titles. **Services:** Interlibrary loan; copying; SDI; library open to clients. **Computerized Information Services:** Info Globe, DIALOG Information Services, CAN/LAW, Infomart Online, QL Systems, WESTLAW, LEXIS; internal database. Performs searches on fee basis. **Special Indexes:** Index to legal memoranda (database). **Remarks:** FAX: (403)265-7219.

W.A.C. Bennett Library
See: **Simon Fraser University** (6105)

★1723★
Bennington Museum - Genealogy Library (Hist)
W. Main St. Phone: (802)447-1571
Bennington, VT 05201 Hugh Thomas
Staff: Prof 1. **Subjects:** Genealogy, regional and state history. **Holdings:** 4500 books; manuscripts; bound newspaper files; Vermont atlases. **Services:** Interlibrary loan; copying; library open to the public on fee basis.

Alexander Benois Library
See: **Boston Public Library - Fine Arts Department** (1992)

Agnes & Clarence Benschoter Memorial Library
See: **Sheridan County Historical Society, Inc.** (15125)

Benson Judaica Collection
See: **St. Deiniol's Residential - Library** (14272)

Benson Latin American Collection
See: **University of Texas at Austin - Benson Latin American Collection** (19380)

★1724★
Bentley College - Solomon R. Baker Library (Bus-Fin)
175 Forest Phone: (617)891-2231
Waltham, MA 02154-4705 Sherman Hayes, Dir.
Founded: 1959. **Staff:** Prof 14; Other 15. **Subjects:** Accounting, auditing, taxation, finance, economic and business conditions. **Special Collections:** Historical Accounting Collection; business histories collection. **Holdings:** 169,179 volumes; 10,000 slides; 600 cassettes; 301 filmstrips; 198,811 microfiche; 300 videotapes; 100 films. **Subscriptions:** 2540 journals and other serials; 8 newspapers. **Services:** Interlibrary loan; copying; library open to the public. **Automated Operations:** Computerized public access catalog, cataloging, serials, circulation, and acquisitions. **Computerized Information Services:** DIALOG Information Services, Dow Jones News/Retrieval, VU/TEXT Information Services, LEXIS, NEXIS, OCLC, NAARS; InfoTrac; CD-ROMs (ERIC, ABI/INFORM, BIP, PC-SIG Inc.). **Networks/Consortia:** Member of WELEXACOL, NELINET, Inc. **Publications:** Media holdings; journal listing; Research Guides. **Remarks:** FAX: (617)891-2830. **Staff:** Tjalda Belastock, Assoc.Dir./Info.Serv.; Sheila Ekman, Hd., Ref.; Colleen Murphy, Assoc.Dir., Media Serv.; Lindsey Carpenter, ILL; Linda Roscoe, Hd., Circ.; Amy Lewortin, Bibliog.Instr.; Rob Favini, Database Serv.; Stephanie Griffin, Cat.; Ruth Horowitz, Video; Don Brown, Graphics; John Cathcart, Archv.

Bentley Historical Library
See: **University of Michigan - Michigan Historical Collections** (18875)

★1725★
Benton County Historical Society - Library/Archives (Hist)
Box 1034 Phone: (501)273-3890
Bentonville, AR 72712-1034 Raymond E. Jefferies, Pres.
Founded: 1954. **Subjects:** Local history and genealogy. **Holdings:** 116 books and bound periodical volumes. **Subscriptions:** 5 journals and other serials. **Services:** Library open to the public on a limited schedule. **Publications:** The Pioneer, quarterly. **Special Indexes:** Indexes to all issues of the Pioneer. **Remarks:** Library located at 304 N.E. 2nd St., Bentonville, AR.

★1726★
Benton Services Center - Medical Library (Med)
Hwy. 67 Phone: (501)778-1111
Benton, AR 72015 Susan Carson
Founded: 1964. **Staff:** 1. **Subjects:** Psychiatry, geriatrics, psychology, medicine, nursing, social work. **Holdings:** 4259 books; 604 bound periodical volumes; 86 article files on mental health; 200 pamphlets and documents (uncataloged). **Subscriptions:** 55 journals and other serials. **Services:** Interlibrary loan; copying; library open to the public for reference use only. **Networks/Consortia:** Member of National Network of Libraries of Medicine - South Central Region. **Remarks:** Maintained by Arkansas State Department of Human Services.

Bent's Old Fort National Historic Site
See: **U.S. Natl. Park Service** (17674)

Cardinal Beran Library
See: **St. Mary's Seminary** (14538)

★1727★
Berea College - Hutchins Library - Special Collections (Hum, Hist)
Berea, KY 40404 Phone: (606)986-9341
Gerald F. Roberts, Spec.Coll.Libn.
Founded: 1914. **Staff:** Prof 2; Other 2. **Subjects:** Appalachia, Berea, Lincoln, rare books. **Special Collections:** Weatherford-Hammond Appalachian Collection (14,220 volumes); Berea Collection (1950 volumes); Lincoln Collection (1690 volumes); rare books (10,000 volumes); Southern Appalachian Archives (750 linear feet); college archives (1000 linear feet). **Holdings:** 27,860 books; 1000 bound periodical volumes. **Subscriptions:** 50 journals and other serials; 11 newspapers. **Services:** Interlibrary loan; copying; collections open to the public with restrictions. **Automated Operations:** Computerized cataloging. **Computerized Information Services:** OCLC. **Networks/Consortia:** Member of SOLINET. **Publications:** Guides to Collections in Berea College and the Southern Appalachian Archives (booklets). **Staff:** Shannon Wilson, Coll.Archv.

★1728★
Berean Institute - Library (Educ)
1901 W. Girard Ave. Phone: (215)763-4833
Philadelphia, PA 19130 Anthony Thoai Nguyen, Act.Lib.Dir.
Founded: 1920. **Staff:** Prof 1. **Subjects:** Business administration, secretarial science, electronics, cosmetology, data processing, paralegal. **Special Collections:** Edyth Ingraham (black history and education; 600 volumes). **Holdings:** 5000 books; 2000 unbound periodicals; 500 cassette tapes; 100 filmstrips; 125 transparencies; 700 slides; 450 microfiche. **Subscriptions:** 34 journals and other serials. **Services:** Interlibrary loan; copying; library open to the public for reference use only. **Computerized Information Services:** CD-ROM; internal database. **Publications:** Acquisitions list, bimonthly; bibliographies, irregular - for internal distribution only. **Remarks:** FAX: (215)236-6011. **Staff:** Jayne Downing.

Conrad Berens Library
See: **National Society to Prevent Blindness** (11295)

Berenson Archive
See: **Cleveland Museum of Art - Ingalls Library** (3813)

Berenson I-Tatti Archive
See: **Columbia University - Department of Art History & Archaeology** (4013)

Berg Collection
See: **New York Public Library - Berg Collection** (11598)

Eric Richard Berg Memorial Library
See: **University of Alberta - Department of Rural Economy** (18189)

★1729★
Bergan Mercy Hospital - Medical Library (Med)
7500 Mercy Rd. Phone: (402)398-6092
Omaha, NE 68124 Ken Oyer, Libn.
Staff: Prof 1. **Subjects:** Medicine, nursing, management, health care administration. **Holdings:** 2000 books; 25,000 microfiche. **Subscriptions:** 194 journals and other serials. **Services:** Interlibrary loan. **Computerized Information Services:** MEDLARS; EasyNet (electronic mail service). **Networks/Consortia:** Member of National Network of Libraries of Medicine - Midcontinental Region, ICON. **Publications:** Journal Holdings List; Educational Highlights (newsletter); Recent Acquisitions List; Management Bibliographies.

★1730★
Bergen Brunswig Corporation - Library (Bus-Fin)
4000 Metropolitan Dr. Phone: (714)385-4454
Orange, CA 92668 Charlotte LaBorde, Dir.
Founded: 1983. **Staff:** 3. **Subjects:** Distribution - pharmaceuticals, consumer electronics, prerecorded videocassettes. **Holdings:** 1000 books; 500 nonbook items; 75 AV programs; trade literature. **Subscriptions:** 160 journals and other serials; 7 newspapers. **Computerized Information Services:** DIALOG Information Services, Dow Jones News/Retrieval, DataTimes, DunsPrint, InvesText, NEXIS. **Special Indexes:** Index to trade journal articles (online). **Staff:** Judith Wood.

★1731★
Bergen Community College - Library & Learning Resources Center - Special Collections (Med)
400 Paramus Rd. Phone: (201)447-7131
Paramus, NJ 07652 Barbara Alper
Founded: 1965. **Staff:** Prof 12; Other 25. **Subjects:** Nursing. **Services:** Interlibrary loan; copying; library open to the public. **Automated Operations:** NOTIS. **Computerized Information Services:** DIALOG Information Services, BRS Information Technologies, WILSONLINE, NLM. Contact Person: Dr. Sarah K. Thomson. **Remarks:** FAX: (201)444-7036.

★1732★
Bergen County Division on Aging - Library
Court Plaza S.
21 Main St., Rm. 109 W. Wing
Hackensack, NJ 07601-7000
Defunct.

★1733★
Bergen County Historical Society - Johnson Library (Hist)
Box 55 Phone: (201)343-9492
River Edge, NJ 07661 Maureen Taffe, Lib.Dir.
Founded: 1902. **Staff:** Prof 1. **Subjects:** State and local history, genealogy. **Special Collections:** Colonial and early American manuscripts of local importance; historical atlases and maps (original editions and facsimiles). **Holdings:** 2900 books; 30 VF drawers of pamphlets; 5 VF drawers of maps; 49 reels of microfilm of manuscripts; 68 reels of microfilm of newspapers. **Subscriptions:** 43 journals and other serials. **Services:** Copying; library open to the public. **Remarks:** Library located at 274 Main St., Hackensack, NJ 07601.

★1734★
Bergen County Law Library (Law)
Justice Bldg.
Main & Hudson St. Phone: (201)646-2056
Hackensack, NJ 07601 Edna M. Oakley, Libn.
Subjects: Law. **Holdings:** 11,000 volumes. **Services:** Copying.

★1735★
Bergen Pines County Hospital - Medical Library (Med)
E. Ridgewood Ave. Phone: (201)967-4000
Paramus, NJ 07652 Victoria E. Gonzalez, Med.Libn.
Staff: Prof 1. **Subjects:** Medicine. **Holdings:** 1400 books; 1824 bound periodical volumes. **Subscriptions:** 180 journals and other serials. **Services:** Library not open to the public. **Computerized Information Services:** MEDLINE. **Networks/Consortia:** Member of Bergen Passaic Regional Library Cooperative.

★1736★
Bergen Sjofartsmuseums - Bibliotek (Trans)
Postboks 2736 Mohlenpris Phone: 5 327980
N-5026 Bergen, Norway Mrs. Marit Kolltveit
Founded: 1921. **Staff:** Prof 1. **Subjects:** Maritime history. **Special Collections:** Bergen shipping history collection; companies' archives. **Holdings:** 20,000 books. **Subscriptions:** 160 journals and other serials. **Services:** Library open to the public for reference use only. **Remarks:** Library located at HaaKon Shefeligs plass 2, Bergen, Norway. **Also Known As:** Bergen Maritime Museum - Library.

★1737★
Berger/ABAM Engineers, Inc. - Technical Library (Sci-Engr)
33301 9th S., Suite 300 Phone: (206)952-6100
Federal Way, WA 98003-6395 Ann Kennedy, Tech.Libn.
Founded: 1965. **Staff:** Prof 1. **Subjects:** Engineering, concrete. **Holdings:** 2500 books; 2000 other cataloged items. **Subscriptions:** 50 journals and other serials. **Services:** Library not open to the public. **Computerized Information Services:** DIALOG Information Services. **Remarks:** FAX: (206)952-4686.

Berger Band Library
See: **University of Minnesota - Music Library** (18925)

★1738★
C. Berger and Company - Library (Info Sci)
327 E. Gundersen Dr. Phone: (708)653-1115
Carol Stream, IL 60188-2421 Linnea Anderson, Libn.
Founded: 1982. **Staff:** Prof 1. **Subjects:** Library science, information management, business administration, computers, personnel management. **Holdings:** 900 books; 10 serials in microform; 50 other cataloged items. **Subscriptions:** 115 journals and other serials. **Services:** Interlibrary loan; library not open to the public. **Automated Operations:** Computerized cataloging. **Computerized Information Services:** DIALOG Information Services, OCLC, MEDLINE, WILSONLINE; ALANET (electronic mail service). Performs searches on fee basis. **Networks/Consortia:** Member of DuPage Library System, ILLINET. **Publications:** CBC Guide for the Substitute Librarian (1987); Library Lingo, a Glossary of Terms for Nonlibrarians, 2nd edition (1990). **Remarks:** FAX: (708)653-1691. Electronic mail address(es): 2642 (ALANET).

Clyde C. Berger Resource Center
See: **Institute of Logopedics** (7953)

★1739★
Berger & Montague - Library (Law)
1622 Locust St. Phone: (215)875-3035
Philadelphia, PA 19103 Ellen Bodenheimer, Lib.Dir.
Subjects: Law. **Remarks:** No further information was supplied by respondent.

Ehrling Bergquist Strategic Hospital
See: **U.S. Air Force Hospital** (16900)

Dr. Richard V. Bergren Library
See: **Alfred University - Herrick Memorial Library** (347)

★1740★
Berkeley Planning Associates - Library (Soc Sci)
440 Grand Ave., Suite 500 Phone: (510)465-7884
Oakland, CA 94610 Linda Tom Barker, V.Pres.
Founded: 1972. **Subjects:** Housing, disability, child welfare, labor, social services, health care financing. **Holdings:** 500 books; 1000 reports. **Subscriptions:** 12 journals and other serials. **Services:** Library open to the public on fee basis. **Remarks:** FAX: (510)465-7885.

★1741★
Berkeley Public Library - Art and Music Department (Art, Mus)
2090 Kittredge St. Phone: (510)649-3928
Berkeley, CA 94704 Patricia Mullan, Supv.Libn.
Founded: 1960. **Staff:** Prof 4; Other 7. **Subjects:** Art, music. **Special Collections:** The Greenwood Press Collection (historic jazz periodicals). **Holdings:** 22,000 books; 3000 scores; 15,000 phonograph records; 20,000 art slides; 350 miniature scores; 3000 audiocassettes; 2000 compact discs. **Subscriptions:** 60 journals and other serials. **Services:** Interlibrary loan; copying; department open to the public. **Networks/Consortia:** Member of Bay Area Library and Information System (BALIS). **Remarks:** FAX: (510)845-7598. **Staff:** Lynn Murdock Wold, Sr.Libn.; Martha Morec, Libn.; Andrea Segall, Libn.

★1742★
Berkeley Public Library - Children's Literature Special Collection (Hum)
2090 Kittredge Phone: (510)649-3943
Berkeley, CA 94704 Linda Perkins
Staff: Prof 3.5; Other 6. **Subjects:** Children's literature. **Special Collections:** Historical children's books (1500 books); story collection (folktales, 300 books); multilingual collection. **Holdings:** 35,000 books. **Subscriptions:** 57 journals and other serials. **Services:** Interlibrary loan; copying; library open to the public. **Publications:** Subject-specific bibliographies (peace, multicultural topics, graded reading lists, books for preschoolers). **Remarks:** FAX: (510)845-7598.

Wilhelm C. Berkenmeyer Colonial Parish Library
See: **Wittenberg University - Thomas Library** (20546)

★1743★
Berklee College of Music - Library (Mus)
150 Massachusetts Ave. Phone: (617)266-1400
Boston, MA 02115 John F. Voigt, Dir. of Libs.
Founded: 1945. **Staff:** Prof 4; Other 22. **Subjects:** Core music, jazz, core humanities, commercial music. **Special Collections:** Jazz. **Holdings:** 18,957 books; 619 bound periodical volumes; 8721 sound recordings; 10,611 standard repertoire scores; 9554 jazz and popular music scores. **Subscriptions:** 44 journals and other serials. **Services:** Library open to the public by appointment. **Automated Operations:** Computerized acquisitions and cataloging. **Special Catalogs:** Sheet music catalog. **Staff:** Gary Haggerty, Asst.Dir.; Molly Porterfield, Cat.; Ralph Rosen, Ref.Libn.

Berkowitz Library
See: **Des Moines Botanical Center** (4791)

★1744★
Berks County Law Library (Law)
Court House
633 Court St. Phone: (215)378-8189
Reading, PA 19601-3566 Linda Fuerle Fisk, Law Libn.
Founded: 1859. **Staff:** Prof 1. **Subjects:** Law. **Holdings:** 28,000 books and bound periodical volumes. **Subscriptions:** 185 journals and other serials. **Services:** Interlibrary loan; library open to the public. **Computerized Information Services:** WESTLAW. **Networks/Consortia:** Member of Berks County Library Association (BCLA). **Remarks:** FAX: (215)378-8913.

★1745★
Berkshire Athenaeum - Music and Arts Department
1 Wendell Ave.
Pittsfield, MA 01201
Defunct.

★1746★
Berkshire Botanical Garden - Library (Biol Sci)
P.O. Box 826 Phone: (413)298-3926
Stockbridge, MA 01262 Dr. J.G. Strauch, Jr., Exec.Dir.
Subjects: Horticulture. **Holdings:** 1000 books. **Subscriptions:** 20 journals and other serials. **Services:** Library not open to the public.

★1747★
Berkshire Christian College - Dr. Linden J. Carter Library (Rel-Phil)
Box 826 Phone: (508)468-7111
Haverhill, MA 01831 David A. Dean, Dir.
Founded: 1897. **Subjects:** Bible, theology, religion, history. **Special Collections:** History and doctrine of 19th century Adventist movement; archives of Advent Christian Church. **Holdings:** 5000 books and bound periodical volumes. **Subscriptions:** 10 journals and other serials. **Services:** Interlibrary loan; library not open to the public. **Remarks:** Substantial part of collection absorbed by Gordon-Conwell Theological Seminary - Goddard Library.

★1748★
Berkshire Eagle - Library (Publ)
75 S. Church St. Phone: (413)447-7311
Pittsfield, MA 01202 Grace McMahon, Libn.
Founded: 1891. **Staff:** 1. **Subjects:** Newspaper reference topics. **Holdings:** 500,000 clippings (through 1990); current and historical pictures. **Services:** Library open to the public on a limited schedule. **Computerized Information Services:** NEXIS. **Remarks:** Published by Eagle Publishing Company.

★1749★
Berkshire Law Library (Law)
Court House
76 East St. Phone: (413)442-5059
Pittsfield, MA 01201 Janice Shotwell, Law Libn.
Founded: 1842. **Staff:** Prof 1; Other 1. **Subjects:** Massachusetts and federal law. **Holdings:** 26,500 books; 150 bound periodical volumes; 175 documents; 1400 microfiche. **Subscriptions:** 27 journals and other serials. **Services:** Interlibrary loan; copying; library open to the public. **Networks/Consortia:** Member of NELINET, Inc. **Remarks:** Part of the Massachusetts State Trial Court; Marnie Warner, Law Library Coordinator.

★1750★
Berkshire Medical Center - Medical Library (Med)
725 North St. Phone: (413)447-2000
Pittsfield, MA 01201 Eleanor M. McNutt, Dir.
Founded: 1964. **Staff:** Prof 1; Other 2. **Subjects:** Medicine, nursing, allied health sciences. **Holdings:** 8500 books; 6000 bound periodical volumes; 2 VF drawers. **Subscriptions:** 167 journals and other serials. **Services:** Library open to the public when staff member is present. **Computerized Information Services:** MEDLINE. **Networks/Consortia:** Member of Western Massachusetts Health Information Consortium, Massachusetts Health Sciences Libraries Network (MaHSLiN).

Berkshire Sanctuaries
See: **Massachusetts Audubon Society** (9787)

★1751★
Berlack, Israels and Liberman - Law Library (Law)
120 W. 45th St., 29th Fl. Phone: (212)704-0100
New York, NY 10036 Lynne Baxter Cruz, Libn.
Staff: Prof 1. **Subjects:** United States and New York law, public utilities, U.S. Securities and Exchange Commission rules and regulations, corporations, litigation, bankruptcy, taxation. **Holdings:** 8339 books; 100 bound periodical volumes. **Subscriptions:** 39 journals and other serials; 6 newspapers. **Services:** Interlibrary loan; library not open to the public. **Computerized Information Services:** LEXIS, NEXIS, WESTLAW, Dun & Bradstreet Business Credit Services. **Remarks:** FAX: (212)704-0196.

★1752★
Berlex Biosciences Inc. - Library (Biol Sci)
1501 Harbor Bay Pkwy. Phone: (510)769-5216
Alameda, CA 94501 Margaret N. Burnett, Libn.
Founded: 1984. **Staff:** Prof 1. **Subjects:** Molecular biology, immunology, biochemistry, virology, genetics. **Holdings:** 2500 books; 150 bound periodical volumes. **Subscriptions:** 234 journals and other serials. **Services:** Interlibrary loan; copying; SDI; library open to the public by appointment. **Computerized Information Services:** DIALOG Information Services, NLM, Mead Data Central, Data-Star, STN International, PFDS Online, OCLC; DIALMAIL (electronic mail service). **Remarks:** FAX: (510)769-5237. Telex: 171816. Electronic mail address(es): 15972. **Formerly:** Triton Biosciences Inc.

★1753★
Berlex Laboratories, Inc. - Research and Development Division Library (Med)
110 E. Hanover Ave. Phone: (201)292-8075
Cedar Knolls, NJ 07927 Lorene Connolly, Mgr., Lib.Serv.
Staff: Prof 2; Other 3. **Subjects:** Pharmacology and the pharmaceutical industry, chemistry, internal medicine. **Holdings:** 7500 books; 7500 bound periodical volumes; 17,000 reels of microfilm of periodicals; 3000 reels of microfilm of patents. **Subscriptions:** 600 journals and other serials. **Services:** Interlibrary loan; library not open to the public. **Automated Operations:** Computerized cataloging, serials, and circulation. **Computerized Information Services:** DIALOG Information Services, BRS Information Technologies, PFDS Online, NLM, Chemical Abstracts Service (CAS); Berlex Private File of Marketed Compounds (internal database). **Publications:** Berlex Library News, quarterly; Berlex Library Serials, annual; BERLEX Database Previews, weekly. **Remarks:** FAX: (201)540-9046. Telex: 136 354. **Staff:** Elizabeth Keith, Tech.Serv.Libn.

Muriel and Philip Berman National Medical Library
See: **Hebrew University of Jerusalem** (7103)

★1754★
Bermuda Biological Station for Research, Inc. - Edward Laurens Mark Memorial Library (Biol Sci)
17 Biological Station Lane Phone: (809)297-1880
Ferry Reach GE 01, Bermuda F.J. Chatterjee, Libn.
Founded: 1947. **Staff:** Prof 1. **Subjects:** Marine biology and ecology, oceanography, geology. **Special Collections:** Bermuda Biological Station Special Publications (set of 29); Bermuda Biological Station Contributions (numbers 1 to 1400). **Holdings:** 16,000 volumes. **Subscriptions:** 154 journals and other serials. **Services:** Interlibrary loan; copying; library open to the public for reference use only. **Computerized Information Services:** DIALOG Information Services, SprintMail, SCIENCEnet (electronic mail service). **Publications:** List of publications - available on request.**Remarks:** FAX: (809)297 8143. Electronic mail address(es): BDA.BIOSTATION (SCIENCEnet).

★1755★
Bernalillo County District Court - Law Library (Law)
415 Tijeras, N.W.
Box 488
Albuquerque, NM 87103 Phone: (505)841-7408
Staff: Prof 1. **Subjects:** Law. **Special Collections:** New Mexico reports, 1852 to present. **Holdings:** 16,000 volumes. **Services:** Library open to judges, staff, and members of the bar.

David Bernard Memorial Aviation Law Library
See: **University of California, Los Angeles - Law Library** (18389)

Dorothy L. Bernhard Library
See: **Child Welfare League of America - Information Service** (3560)

Bernhard-Nocht-Institut fuer Tropenmedizin
See: **Bernhard Nocht Institute for Tropical Medicine** (11825)

Albion O. Bernstein Library
See: **Medical Society of the State of New York** (10013)

★1756★
Sanford C. Bernstein & Company, Inc. - Business Library
767 5th Ave., 22nd Fl. Phone: (212)756-4609
New York, NY 10153 Nancy E. Anderson, Corp.Libn.
Founded: 1967. **Staff:** Prof 1. **Subjects:** Investments - finance and corporation. **Holdings:** 100 bound periodical volumes; Wall Street Journal, 1971 to present; Stock Guides and Bond Guides, 1970 to present. **Subscriptions:** 350 journals and other serials; 10 newspapers. **Services:** Interlibrary loan; copying; library open to SLA members only. **Automated Operations:** Computerized acquisitions and circulation. **Remarks:** FAX: (212)486-8772.

★1757★
Bernstein, Shur, Sawyer & Nelson - Library (Law)
100 Middle St.
Box 9729 Phone: (207)774-1200
Portland, ME 04104-5029 Linda Stanton, Libn.
Founded: 1981. **Staff:** Prof 1. **Subjects:** Law - federal, state, tax, commercial, banking, environmental. **Holdings:** 5000 books; 50 bound periodical volumes; 800 brief and memo documents; 30 loose-leaf services; 100 audiotapes; 25 videotapes; 3 cases of microfiche. **Subscriptions:** 45 journals and other serials. **Services:** Interlibrary loan; library not open to the public. **Computerized Information Services:** LEXIS, NEXIS, WESTLAW, DIALOG Information Services. **Special Indexes:** Index of Maine Public Utilities Commission Orders; index of internal briefs and memoranda (both online). **Remarks:** FAX: (207)774-1127.

★1758★
Berrien County Historical Association - Library (Hist)
1839 Courthouse Square
P.O. Box 261 Phone: (616)471-1202
Berrien Springs, MI 49103 Robert C. Myers, Cur.
Founded: 1967. **Subjects:** Berrien County history. **Special Collections:** County Probate Court records, 1831-1930 (microfilm); photographic collection (1600 images). **Holdings:** 200 books; 1000 manuscripts. **Services:** Copying; library open to the public by appointment. **Special Indexes:** Index of 1871 Berrien County directory; index of 1873 Berrien County atlas; index of Berrien County naturalization applications, 1840-1894. **Remarks:** Library located at corner of Cass & Union streets. **Formerly:** 1839 Courthouse Museum - Library.

E.Y. Berry Library-Learning Center
See: **Black Hills State University** (1875)

★1759★
Bertha Historical Society - Museum Library (Hist)
Box 307 Phone: (218)924-4095
Bertha, MN 56437 Laura Foster, Pres.
Founded: 1970. **Subjects:** Local history. **Holdings:** Local newspapers (1901-1906, 1917-1926, 1928-1936, 1938 to present; all bound); list of all Bertha graduates, 1921-1990. **Services:** Library open to the public for reference use only on a limited schedule.

Ellen Clarke Bertrand Library - Special Collections
See: **Bucknell University** (2315)

★1760★
Bessemer Trust Company, N.A. - Investment Library/Information Center (Bus-Fin)
630 5th Ave. Phone: (212)708-9184
New York, NY 10111 Louise Stoops, Mgr.
Staff: Prof 1; Other 2. **Subjects:** Corporate records, finance, banking. **Special Collections:** International financial and corporate information. **Holdings:** 300 books; 120 bound periodical volumes; 52 VF drawers of corporate records and subject files; 200 microfiche. **Subscriptions:** 200 journals and other serials. **Services:** Interlibrary loan; library not open to the public. **Computerized Information Services:** DIALOG Information Services, NEXIS, Dow Jones News/Retrieval.

★1761★
Jesse Besser Museum - Philip M. Park Memorial Library (Hist)
491 Johnson St.
Alpena, MI 49707 Phone: (517)356-2202
Staff: Prof 2. **Subjects:** 19th and 20th century American art, American antiques and collectibles, local and regional history, Great Lakes Indian history, museum administration, local genealogy. **Holdings:** 2650 books; 2400 archival materials; 3500 photographs. **Subscriptions:** 50 journals and other serials. **Services:** Copying; library open to the public for reference use only. **Staff:** Sandra Mitchell, Asst.Libn.

Colonel Tharratt Gilbert Best Library
See: **Oneida County Historical Society - Colonel Tharratt Gilbert Best Library** (12421)

Best Foods Research Center
See: **CPC International** (4400)

★1762★
Betac Corporation - Library (Mil)
2001 N. Beauregard St., Suite 1100 Phone: (703)824-3100
Alexandria, VA 22311 Deidra Dicks, Libn.
Founded: 1982. **Staff:** 2. **Subjects:** Security, nuclear weapons, data processing, command, control, communications, intelligence systems, engineering. **Holdings:** 3000 books. **Subscriptions:** 25 journals and other serials. **Services:** Library not open to the public. **Remarks:** Alternate telephone number(s): 824-3285. FAX: (703)824-0333. **Formerly:** Located in Arlington, VA.

Ramon E. Betances Library
See: **Puerto Rico Department of Health** (13513)

★1763★
Beth David Congregation - Harry Simons Library (Rel-Phil)
2625 S.W. Third Ave. Phone: (305)854-3911
Miami, FL 33129 Lillian S. Beer, Lib.Chm.
Founded: 1962. **Staff:** Prof 1; Other 3. **Subjects:** Judaica. **Holdings:** 7000 books; videotapes. **Subscriptions:** 4 journals and other serials; 2 newspapers. **Services:** Library not open to the public. **Staff:** Gloria Waldenberg.

★1764★
Beth David Reform Congregation - Jewel K. Markowitz Library (Rel-Phil)
1130 Vaughans Ln.
Box 287 Phone: (215)896-7485
Gladwyne, PA 19035 Jennifer Hoffman, Act.Libn.
Founded: 1947. **Staff:** Prof 1; Other 7. **Subjects:** Judaica, Jewish literature. **Holdings:** 4500 books; synagogue archives. **Services:** library not open to the public.

★1765★
Beth El Synagogue - Max Shapiro Library (Rel-Phil)
5224 W. 26th St. Phone: (612)920-3512
St. Louis Park, MN 55416 Marcia Oleisky, Libn.
Staff: 1. **Subjects:** Judaica, Jewish literature, religion, philosophy. **Holdings:** 3000 books. **Subscriptions:** 35 journals and other serials. **Services:** Library open to the public.

★1766★
Beth El Temple Center - Carl Kales Memorial Library (Rel-Phil)
2 Concord Ave. Phone: (617)484-6668
Belmont, MA 02178 Leslie S. Lundberg, Libn.
Staff: 2. **Subjects:** Israel, Judaism, religion, philosophy, Bible, history, theology, customs. **Holdings:** 2370 books; 500 bound periodical volumes. **Services:** Interlibrary loan; library open to the public for reference use only.

★1767★
Beth Emet, The Free Synagogue - Bruce Gordon Memorial Library (Rel-Phil)
1224 Dempster
Evanston, IL 60202 Phone: (708)869-4230
Founded: 1950. **Staff:** Prof 1; Other 2. **Subjects:** Judaica and religion. **Holdings:** 8000 volumes. **Subscriptions:** 18 journals and other serials. **Services:** Interlibrary loan; copying; library open to the public. **Staff:** Rosalind Shlaes, Libn.; Myrtle Gordon Libn.

★1768★
Beth Israel Congregation - Beth Israel Library (Rel-Phil)
1015 E. Park Ave. Phone: (609)691-0852
Vineland, NJ 08360 Ruth Greenblatt, Dir.
Founded: 1926. **Staff:** 1. **Subjects:** Judaism - customs, ceremonies, biography, literature, fiction; Hebrew - language, music, art; history - biblical times to modern Israel; the Bible. **Special Collections:** Holocaust Collection (313 books); Israel Collection (266 books). **Holdings:** 7480 books; 4 VF drawers of pamphlets and other items; 165 audiotapes; 146 phonograph records; 138 video cassettes. **Subscriptions:** 39 journals and other serials. **Services:** Interlibrary loan (limited); copying; library open to the public at librarian's discretion. **Networks/Consortia:** Member of South Jersey Regional Library Cooperative. **Publications:** SCROLL (newsletter), monthly; Chronicle, quarterly. **Staff:** Phyllis Zislin, Cat.

★1769★
Beth Israel Hospital - Agoos Medical Library (Med)
330 Brookline Ave.
Boston, MA 02215 Phone: (617)735-4225
Founded: 1928. **Staff:** Prof 2; Other 2. **Subjects:** Medicine and allied health sciences. **Holdings:** 3200 books; 3800 bound periodical volumes. **Subscriptions:** 221 journals and other serials. **Services:** Interlibrary loan; copying; library open to the public with restrictions. **Computerized Information Services:** PaperChase. **Networks/Consortia:** Member of Boston Biomedical Library Consortium. **Staff:** J.A. Daly, Med.Libn.; M. Coletti, Med.Libn.

★1770★
Beth Israel Hospital North - Eckman Medical Library (Med)
170 East End Ave. at 87th St. Phone: (212)870-9470
New York, NY 10128 Antoinette Drago, Libn.
Founded: 1982. **Staff:** Prof 1. **Subjects:** Medicine, surgery. **Holdings:** 3000 books; 300 bound periodical volumes. **Subscriptions:** 100 journals. **Services:** Interlibrary loan. **Computerized Information Services:** MEDLARS. **Networks/Consortia:** Member of Manhattan-Bronx Health Sciences Library Consortia, New York Metropolitan Reference and Research Library Agency. **Remarks:** FAX: (212)870-9404. A member of the Beth Israel Health Care System. **Formerly:** Doctors Hospital.

★1771★
Beth Israel Medical Center - Hospital for Joint Diseases Orthopaedic Institute - Seymour J. Phillips Health Sciences Library (Med)
1st Ave. at 16th St. Phone: (212)420-2855
New York, NY 10003 Ellen H. Poisson, Dir., Lib.Serv.
Founded: 1952. **Staff:** Prof 3; Other 7. **Subjects:** Medicine, nursing, allied health sciences, social work, orthopedics, substance abuse. **Holdings:** 14,000 books; 16,000 bound periodical volumes. **Subscriptions:** 670 journals and other serials. **Services:** Interlibrary loan; library not open to the public. **Automated Operations:** Computerized public access catalog, cataloging, serials, and circulation. **Computerized Information Services:** MEDLARS, BRS Information Technologies, OCLC, DIALOG Information Services, WILSONLINE. **Networks/Consortia:** Member of National Network of Libraries of Medicine - Middle Atlantic Region, Medical Library Center of New York (MLCNY), New York Metropolitan Reference and Research Library Agency. **Remarks:** FAX: (212)420-4640. **Staff:** Dorothy D. Schwartz, Sr.Med.Libn., User Serv.; Patricia Gallagher, Med.Libn., Tech.Serv.

★1772★
Beth Jacob Synagogue - Library (Rel-Phil)
400 New London Tpke. Phone: (203)886-2459
Norwich, CT 06360 Bella Shedroff, Libn.
Founded: 1950. **Staff:** 1. **Subjects:** Jewish history, theology, and allied topics. **Holdings:** 1150 books; magazines; newspapers. **Services:** Library open to the public with restrictions.

★1773★
Beth Shalom Congregation - Blanche and Ira Rosenblum Memorial Library (Rel-Phil)
9400 Wornall Rd. Phone: (816)363-3331
Kansas City, MO 64114 Frances Wolf, Libn.
Staff: 1. **Subjects:** Judaica. **Holdings:** 10,000 books; 300 phonograph records; 150 filmstrips; 50 videotapes. **Subscriptions:** 25 journals and other serials. **Services:** Library open to the public with restrictions.

★1774★
Beth Shalom Congregation - Joseph & Elizabeth Schwartz Library (Rel-Phil)
Foxcroft & Old York Rd. Phone: (215)887-1342
Elkins Park, PA 19117 Maxine Chiger, Libn.
Founded: 1959. **Staff:** Prof 1; Other 1. **Subjects:** Jewish music and Judaica. **Special Collections:** Jewish music and art. **Holdings:** 7500 volumes; 500 phonograph recordings. **Subscriptions:** 18 journals and other serials. **Services:** Library open to the public at librarian's discretion.

★1775★
Beth Tzedec Congregation - Max & Beatrice Wolfe Library (Rel-Phil)
1700 Bathurst St. Phone: (416)781-3511
Toronto, ON, Canada M5P 3K3 Zina Glassman, Libn.
Founded: 1956. **Staff:** Prof 2. **Subjects:** Judaism - history, religion, philosophy, art, literature; Israel; holocaust. **Special Collections:** Abraham Nahum Memorial Collection of Hebraica. **Holdings:** 18,000 books; VF drawers of pamphlets and documents. **Subscriptions:** 22 journals and other serials; 10 newspapers. **Services:** Interlibrary loan; copying; library open to the public for reference use only. **Remarks:** FAX: (416)781-0150. **Staff:** Fagi Goldfarb.

★1776★
Bethania Mennonite Personal Care Home - Library (Med)
1045 Concordia Ave. Phone: (204)667-0795
Winnipeg, MB, Canada R2K 3S7 Esther Fransen
Founded: 1970. **Staff:** Prof 1. **Subjects:** Gerontology, nursing, medicine, psychology. **Holdings:** 500 books; 40 bound periodical volumes. **Subscriptions:** 35 journals and other serials. **Services:** Interlibrary loan; copying; library open to family members of residents, staff and students. **Networks/Consortia:** Member of Manitoba Library Consortium, Inc. **Remarks:** FAX: (204)667-7078.

★1777★
Bethany Bible College - Library (Rel-Phil)
800 Bethany Dr. Phone: (408)438-3800
Scotts Valley, CA 95066 Arnold McLellan, Hd.Libn.
Founded: 1919. **Staff:** Prof 2; Other 5. **Subjects:** Religion, liberal arts, Bible, theology. **Special Collections:** Pentecostalism (500 books). **Holdings:** 57,550 books; 981 bound periodical volumes; 995 reels of microfilm. **Subscriptions:** 425 journals and other serials; 8 newspapers. **Services:** Interlibrary loan; copying; library open to the public. **Staff:** Edward A. Koetitz, Ref.Libn.

★1778★
Bethany-Calvary United Methodist Church - Library (Rel-Phil)
7265 W. Center St. Phone: (414)258-2868
Wauwatosa, WI 53210 Leslie Karabon, Libn.
Staff: Prof 1. **Subjects:** Philosophy, religion. **Holdings:** 425 books. **Services:** Library not open to the public.

★1779★
Bethany College - Chemistry Library (Sci-Engr)
Richardson Hall of Science Phone: (304)829-7711
Bethany, WV 26032 Tony Krug, Hd.Libn.
Founded: 1956. **Staff:** Prof 1; Other 1. **Subjects:** All branches of chemistry. **Holdings:** 2133 books; 2268 bound periodical volumes; 6 VF drawers of pamphlets, technical literature, clippings, and reprints; 1 journal, 1949-1956, on microcard. **Subscriptions:** 31 journals and other serials. **Services:** Interlibrary loan; copying; library open to the public at librarian's discretion. **Networks/Consortia:** Member of Pittsburgh Regional Library Center (PRLC).

★1780★
Bethany Lutheran Theological Seminary - Library (Rel-Phil)
447 N. Division St. Phone: (507)625-2977
Mankato, MN 56001 Prof. Glenn E. Reichwald, Act.Libn.
Founded: 1946. **Staff:** Prof 2; Other 1. **Subjects:** Bible, theology, religions, history, hymnody, catechisms. **Special Collections:** English, German, Norwegian, and Danish Hymnals (705); English, German, Norwegian, and French catechisms (604); rare theological books (1000). **Holdings:** 10,239 books; 1052 bound periodical volumes; 1825 monographs and booklets; 12 VF drawers of pamphlets. **Subscriptions:** 127 journals and other serials. **Services:** Interlibrary loan; copying; library open to the public at librarian's discretion. **Automated Operations:** Computerized cataloging, acquisitions, serials, and circulation. **Computerized Information Services:** OCLC. Performs searches free of charge. **Networks/Consortia:** Member of MINITEX Library Information Network, Southcentral Minnesota Inter-Library Exchange (SMILE). **Special Catalogs:** Rare books catalog (microfiche). **Remarks:** FAX: (507)625-1849. **Staff:** Melvina Aaberg, Asst.Libn.

★1781★
Bethany Medical Center - W.W. Summerville Medical Library (Med)
51 N. 12th St. Phone: (913)281-8770
Kansas City, KS 66102 Kathleen McClure, Med.Libn.
Staff: Prof 1; Other 1. **Subjects:** Medicine, nursing, and allied health sciences. **Holdings:** 1750 books; 3000 bound periodical volumes. **Subscriptions:** 300 journals and other serials; 5 newspapers. **Services:** Interlibrary loan; copying; library open to medical staff only. **Computerized Information Services:** MEDLINE, BRS Information Technologies. **Networks/Consortia:** Member of Kansas City Library Network, Inc. (KCLN).

★1782★
Bethany & Northern Baptist Seminary - Library (Rel-Phil)
Butterfield & Meyers Rds. Phone: (708)620-2214
Oak Brook, IL 60521 Dr. Helen Kenik Mainelli, Lib.Dir.
Founded: 1913. **Staff:** Prof 3.5; Other 5. **Subjects:** Baptist history, Church of the Brethren history, history of Christianity, biblical studies, missions, pacifism, intentional and Utopian communities. **Special Collections:** Cassel Collection (religion and history of the 16th-19th centuries); Huston Bible Collection (300 English language Bibles). **Holdings:** 150,000 volumes; 4389 microforms. **Subscriptions:** 606 journals and other serials; 5 newspapers. **Services:** Interlibrary loan; copying; library open to the public for reference use only. **Automated Operations:** Computerized cataloging and ILL. **Computerized Information Services:** CD-ROM (Religion Index). **Networks/Consortia:** Member of Association of Chicago Theological Schools Library Council, DuPage Library System. **Formerly:** Bethany/ Northern Baptist Theological Seminaries - Seminary Library. **Staff:** Brent A. Koehn, Tech.Serv.; Jana Fast, Pub.Serv.; Dolores Keck, Ser.

★1783★
Bethel Baptist Church - Bethel Media Library (Rel-Phil)
2420 N. Garden Phone: (505)622-8182
Roswell, NM 88201 Cheryl McCleskey, Chm., Lib.Comm.
Subjects: Religion, biography, fiction. **Holdings:** 1600 books. **Subscriptions:** 4 journals and other serials. **Services:** Library open to the public.

★1784★
Bethel College - Mennonite Library and Archives (Rel-Phil)
300 E. 27th Phone: (316)283-2500
North Newton, KS 67117-9989 Dale R. Schrag, Dir. of Libs.
Founded: 1935. **Staff:** Prof 2; Other 2. **Subjects:** Anabaptists; Mennonites in Europe, America, Latin America, and Asia; peace; Kansas. **Special Collections:** Manuscript collection (1500 shelf feet); General Conference Church Archives (2000 shelf feet); oral history of World War I and II conscientious objectors; rare Anabaptist books; H.R. Voth Manuscript and Photograph Collection on Hopi Indians; Rodolphe Petter manuscript collection on Cheyenne Indians; H.P. Krehbiel manuscript collection on peace; Mennonite hymnbooks (2000); Mennonite art collection (including 17th century Dutch art). **Holdings:** 25,300 books; 3200 bound periodical volumes; 1000 reels of microfilm; 1000 audiotapes; 150 maps. **Subscriptions:** 300 journals and other serials; 80 newspapers. **Services:** Interlibrary loan; copying; library open to the public. **Automated Operations:** Computerized cataloging. **Computerized Information Services:** OCLC; internal database. **Networks/Consortia:** Member of Associated Colleges of Central Kansas Libraries Committee (ACCK). **Publications:** Mennonite Life, quarterly; Gleanings from the Threshing Floor (newsletter), irregular - free subscription; Guide to Mennonite Library and Archives, 1981; A Guide to the Art Collection of the Mennonite Library and Archives, 1983. **Remarks:** FAX: (316)284-5286. **Staff:** Barbara A. Thiesen, Libn.; John D. Thiesen, Archv.

★1785★
Bethel Historical Society - Eva Bean Research Room (Hist)
Dr. Moses Mason House
15 Broad St.
P.O. Box 12 Phone: (207)824-2908
Bethel, ME 04217 Stanley Russell Howe, Dir.
Founded: 1976. **Staff:** 2. **Subjects:** History - western Maine, White Mountain region of New Hampshire and Maine; western Maine genealogy. **Special Collections:** Eva Bean papers; Oxford County newspapers (microfilm); Bethel town records (microfilm); area vital records and cemetery inscriptions. **Holdings:** 3000 books; 100 bound periodical volumes; 100 AV programs; 400 nonbook items; 1000 manuscripts; maps; photographs; pamphlets. **Subscriptions:** 30 journals and other serials; 2 newspapers. **Services:** Copying; genealogical research by mail; room open to the public. **Publications:** Guide to genealogical research; cemetery inventory; census inventory. **Special Indexes:** Series of town history indexes; newspaper vital records indexes. **Staff:** Randall H. Bennett, Cur. of Coll.; Jane W. Hosterman, Reg.

Bethel Theological Seminary - Baptist General Conference - Archives
See: **Baptist General Conference - Archives** (1499)

★1786★
Bethel Theological Seminary - Resource Center (Rel-Phil)
3949 Bethel Dr. Phone: (612)638-6184
St. Paul, MN 55112 Norris Magnuson, Dir.
Founded: 1871. **Staff:** Prof 2; Other 4. **Subjects:** Biblical studies, missions, theology, church history, practical theology. **Special Collections:** Skarstedt Collection of Pietistic Literature; Lundquist-Nelson Collection of Literature of Spirituality; Klingberg Collection of Puritan Literature. **Holdings:** 138,000 books; 12,096 bound periodical volumes. **Subscriptions:** 799 journals and other serials. **Services:** Interlibrary loan; copying; center open to the public. **Automated Operations:** Computerized public access catalog, cataloging, and serials. **Networks/Consortia:** Member of Minnesota Theological Libraries Association (MTLA). **Special Indexes:** Scripture index to books of sermons; index to The Standard (Baptist General Conference publication). **Staff:** Pam Jervis, Cat.Libn.; Betty Kleinschmidt, Asst.Libn.; Sandra Oslund, Circ.Libn.

Bethesda Hospital
See: **Bethesda PsycHealth System - Professional Library** (1792)

★1787★
Bethesda Hospital - CME/Library Services (Med)
2951 Maple Ave. Phone: (614)454-4624
Zanesville, OH 43701 Lea Craig, Mgr.
Founded: 1952. **Staff:** Prof 1; Other 1. **Subjects:** Internal medicine, cardiology, surgery, pediatrics, oncology, psychiatry. **Special Collections:** Rare medical books (65). **Holdings:** 800 volumes; 133 bound periodical volumes; pamphlets. **Subscriptions:** 121 journals and other serials. **Services:** Interlibrary loan; copying; library open to the public with recommendation by a physician. **Computerized Information Services:** MEDLINE. **Networks/Consortia:** Member of National Network of Libraries of Medicine - Greater Midwest Region, Central Ohio Hospital Library Consortium. **Publications:** Periodical List, annual. **Remarks:** FAX: (614)454-4779.

★1788★
Bethesda Lutheran Home - National Christian Resource Center (Med, Rel-Phil)
700 Hoffmann Dr. Phone: (414)261-3050
Watertown, WI 53094 Linda A. Sires, Dir.
Founded: 1985. **Staff:** Prof 2; Other 3. **Subjects:** Mental retardation, religious special education, long term healthcare management, special education. **Holdings:** 3000 books. **Subscriptions:** 53 journals and other serials. **Services:** Interlibrary loan; copying; center open to the public with restrictions. **Computerized Information Services:** Service Providers for Mental Retardation (internal database). Performs searches free of charge. **Networks/Consortia:** Member of South Central Wisconsin Health Science Libraries Consortium. **Publications:** Staff Development Videotape Modules; Workshops. **Remarks:** Toll-free telephone number(s): (800)369-4636.

★1789★
Bethesda Lutheran Hospital - Library
559 Capitol Blvd.
St. Paul, MN 55103
Subjects: Nursing, medicine, hospital administration, allied health sciences. **Holdings:** Figures not available. **Remarks:** A HealthEast hospital. Currently inactive. **Also Known As:** Sister Esther Porter Medical-Nursing Library.

★1790★
Bethesda Memorial Hospital - Medical Library (Med)
2815 S. Seacrest Blvd. Phone: (407)737-7733
Boynton Beach, FL 33435 Catherine J. Greene, Med.Libn.
Founded: 1967. **Staff:** Prof 1; Other 2. **Subjects:** Medicine, nursing, hospital administration, allied health sciences. **Holdings:** 2100 books; 3218 bound periodical volumes; 253 unbound volumes; 6 VF drawers of clippings and pamphlets; 600 videocassettes. **Subscriptions:** 178 journals and other serials. **Services:** Interlibrary loan. **Computerized Information Services:** MEDLINE. **Networks/Consortia:** Member of Palm Beach Health Sciences Library Consortium (PBHSLC), National Network of Libraries of Medicine (NN/LM), Miami Health Sciences Library Consortium (MHSLC), National Network of Libraries of Medicine - Southeastern/Atlantic Region. **Publications:** Bibliographies. **Remarks:** FAX: (407)737-7733.

★1791★
Bethesda Oak Hospital - Medical Library (Med)
619 Oak St. Phone: (513)569-6176
Cincinnati, OH 45206 Beth White, Med.Libn.
Staff: Prof 1; Other 3. **Subjects:** Medicine, nursing, allied health sciences, health administration. **Holdings:** 1500 books. **Subscriptions:** 350 journals and other serials. **Services:** Interlibrary loan; copying; SDI; library open to the public for reference use only. **Automated Operations:** Computerized cataloging. **Computerized Information Services:** BRS Information Technologies, NLM, DIALOG Information Services.

★1792★
Bethesda PsycHealth System - Professional Library (Med)
4400 E. Iliff Ave. Phone: (303)758-1514
Denver, CO 80222 Nancy L. Jones, Staff Dev.Coord.
Founded: 1960. **Staff:** 1. **Subjects:** Medicine, psychiatry, psychology, nursing, management. **Holdings:** 800 books. **Subscriptions:** 18 journals and other serials. **Services:** Interlibrary loan (fee); library open to professionals and students. **Networks/Consortia:** Member of National Network of Libraries of Medicine - Midcontinental Region. **Formerly:** Bethesda Hospital - Professional Library.

★1793★
Bethesda United Methodist Church - S. Carroll Coale Library (Rel-Phil)
8300 Old Georgetown Rd.
Bethesda, MD 20814 Phone: (301)652-2990
Staff: Prof 2; Other 5. **Subjects:** Christian education, Bible studies, church history, missions, children's literature. **Holdings:** 4000 books; 700 nonbook items. **Subscriptions:** 12 journals and other serials. **Services:** Interlibrary loan; library open to the public. **Publications:** The Messenger (newsletter), monthly; Library News, quarterly - both available upon request.

★1794★
Bethlehem Lutheran Church - Library (Rel-Phil)
215 4th Ave., S.E. Phone: (605)225-9740
Aberdeen, SD 57401 Bernice Theeler, Libn.
Founded: 1964. **Staff:** 2. **Subjects:** Lutheran Church, inspirational works, theology. **Holdings:** 4000 books. **Subscriptions:** 3 journals and other serials. **Services:** Interlibrary loan; library open to church members. **Staff:** Ardis Mottle, Libn.

Bethlehem Steel/Charles Schwab Library
See: **Hugh Moore Historical Park and Museums - Canal Museum - Research Library/Archives** (10711)

★1795★
Bethlehem Steel Corporation - Bernard D. Broeker Law Library (Law)
Martin Tower Bldg., Rm. 2027 Phone: (215)694-5002
Bethlehem, PA 18016 David D. Hendley, Law Libn.
Founded: 1954. **Staff:** Prof 1. **Subjects:** Law - corporate, antitrust, labor. **Holdings:** 30,000 volumes. **Subscriptions:** 200 journals and other serials. **Services:** Library open to attorneys only. **Computerized Information Services:** LEXIS, NEXIS. **Remarks:** FAX: (215)694-1447.

★1796★
Bethlehem Steel Corporation - Corporate Information Center (Bus-Fin, Sci-Engr)
701 E. Third St., Rm. 320A Phone: (215)694-3325
Bethlehem, PA 18016 Marie F. Sterlein, Sr.Info.Spec.
Founded: 1949. **Staff:** Prof 2. **Subjects:** Steelmaking economics and technology, metallurgy, business and economics, engineering. **Holdings:** 20,000 volumes; annual reports; specifications; 15 drawers of newspapers on microfilm. **Subscriptions:** 300 journals; 6 newspapers. **Services:** Interlibrary loan; SDI; center open to the public by arrangement. **Computerized Information Services:** DIALOG Information Services, Dow Jones News/Retrieval, VU/TEXT Information Services, LEXIS, NEXIS; BASIS (internal database). **Publications:** Acquisitions List, semimonthly - for internal distribution only. **Remarks:** FAX: (215)694-3290. **Staff:** Lillian M. Austen, Sr.Info.Spec.

★1797★
Bethlehem Steel Corporation - Research Library (Sci-Engr)
Homer Research Laboratories - G61 Phone: (215)694-6443
Bethlehem, PA 18016 Sally R. Moyer, Libn.
Founded: 1938. **Staff:** 1. **Subjects:** Metallurgy, ceramics, engineering, chemistry, physics, mechanics. **Holdings:** 7000 books; 2500 bound periodical volumes. **Subscriptions:** 240 journals and other serials. **Services:** Library not open to the public. **Computerized Information Services:** NERAC; BASIS (internal database).

Ade Bethune Collection
See: **College of St. Catherine - Library** (3907)

Bettis Atomic Power Laboratory
See: **Westinghouse Electric Corporation - Bettis Atomic Power Laboratory** (20311)

★1798★
Bettmann - Bettmann Archive/Bettmann Newsphotos (Aud-Vis)
902 Broadway Phone: (212)777-6200
New York, NY 10010 David Greenstein, Dir.
Founded: 1936. **Staff:** Prof 65; Other 12; **Subjects:** History, culture, daily life, science, sport. **Special Collections:** Movie stills, 1920 to present; historical and current exclusive news coverage, 1900 to present; United Press International and Reuters Photograph Libraries (13.5 million black/white and color photographs of significant events and personalities of the 20th century); Underwood and Underwood News Photos, Inc., 1890-1940 (several million photographs); North American agents for B.B.C. Hulton Picture Library (9 million pictures); ACME News Photos; Springer Film Stills; International News Photos. **Holdings:** 16 million black/white photographs, color photographs, engravings, woodcuts. **Services:** Photographs available for loan; archive open to communications professionals only. **Publications:** Bettmann Portable Archive - for sale. **Remarks:** FAX: (212)533-4034.

★1799★
Betz Laboratories, Inc. - Research Library (Sci-Engr)
4636 Somerton Rd. Phone: (215)355-3300
Trevose, PA 19053 Joan E. Goldberg, Sr.Libn.
Founded: 1925. **Staff:** Prof 2; Other 1. **Subjects:** Industrial and municipal water treatment, pollution control. **Holdings:** 2500 books; 3000 bound periodical volumes; 12 VF drawers of patents. **Subscriptions:** 200 journals and other serials. **Services:** Interlibrary loan; SDI; library open to the public by appointment. **Computerized Information Services:** DIALOG Information Services, ORBIT Search Service, NLM, STN International, WILSONLINE. **Networks/Consortia:** Member of PALINET, Delaware Library Consortium (DLC). **Special Indexes:** Internal Reports Index (online). **Remarks:** FAX: (215)953-2494. **Staff:** Melissa Dicker, Tech.Libn.

★1800★
Beverly Hills Public Library - Fine Arts Division (Art)
444 N. Rexford Dr. Phone: (213)288-2233
Beverly Hills, CA 90210 Nicholas Cellini, Hd., Fine Arts Serv.
Founded: 1970. **Staff:** Prof 8; Other 6. **Subjects:** Art, film, theater, photography. **Special Collections:** Dorathi Bock Pierre Dance Collection (500 items); American and European auction catalogs; Zeta Zech Collection of Interior Design (organized by American Society of Interior Decorators; 800 books); naive collection. **Holdings:** 5000 books; 5000 exhibition catalogs; 20,000 slides. **Subscriptions:** 90 journals and other serials. **Services:** Interlibrary loan; copying; division open to the public for reference use only. **Remarks:** FAX: (213)278-3387. **Staff:** Dr. Stefan Klima, Asst.Hd., Fine Arts Serv.; Cal Davis, Fine Arts Libn.; Jeri Byrne, Fine Arts Libn.

★1801★
Beverly Historical Society & Museum - Library and Archives (Hist)
Cabot House
117 Cabot St. Phone: (508)922-1186
Beverly, MA 01915 Fred Hammond, Chm.
Founded: 1891. **Staff:** 2. **Subjects:** Americana; history - local, general, maritime; genealogy. **Special Collections:** Charles William Galloupe Library; Robert Rantoul family and business papers; Roger Hanners Collection; Essex Institute Historical Collection. **Holdings:** 5000 books; 500 bound periodical volumes; 20,000 manuscripts; maps; broadsides. **Services:** Copying; library open to the public with restrictions.

★1802★
Beverly Hospital - Breitman Memorial Library (Med)
309 W. Beverly Blvd. Phone: (213)726-1222
Montebello, CA 90640 Margot D. Jensen, Libn.
Founded: 1978. **Subjects:** Medicine. **Holdings:** 750 books; 718 bound periodical volumes. **Subscriptions:** 123 journals and other serials; 2 newspapers. **Services:** Interlibrary loan; library not open to the public. **Computerized Information Services:** MEDLINE. **Remarks:** FAX: (213)889-2424.

★1803★
Beverly Hospital - Library (Med)
Herrick St. Phone: (508)922-3000
Beverly, MA 01915 Ann M. Tomes, Libn.
Staff: Prof 1. **Subjects:** Medicine. **Holdings:** 6000 volumes. **Subscriptions:** 125 journals and other serials. **Services:** Interlibrary loan; SDI; library open to the public with restrictions. **Computerized Information Services:** MEDLINE. Performs searches on fee basis. **Networks/Consortia:** Member of Northeastern Consortium for Health Information (NECHI).

Bevier Engineering Library
See: **University of Pittsburgh** (19205)

Bexar Archives
See: **University of Texas at Austin - Barker Texas History Center** (19379)

★1804★
Bexar County Law Library (Law)
Court House, 5th Fl. Phone: (512)227-8822
San Antonio, TX 78205 Jimmy Allison, Exec.Dir.
Subjects: Law. **Holdings:** 60,000 volumes. **Services:** Library open to the public. **Remarks:** FAX: (512)271-9614.

★1805★
Bexar County Medical Library Association (Med)
202 W. French Pl.
Box 12678 Phone: (512)734-6691
San Antonio, TX 78212 Laura Ibara, Libn.
Founded: 1912. **Staff:** Prof 1. **Subjects:** Medicine. **Holdings:** 7000 books; 150 bound periodical volumes; 10 VF drawers of clippings. **Subscriptions:** 17 journals and other serials. **Services:** Copying; library open to the public.

★1806★
Beyond Baroque Foundation - Small Press Library (Publ)
Box 2727 Phone: (213)822-3006
Venice, CA 90291 William Slattery, Hd.Libn.
Founded: 1977. **Staff:** 2. **Subjects:** Modern poetry, fiction, arts. **Special Collections:** Small press literary publications; readings by visiting poets (100 cassettes). **Holdings:** 27,000 volumes. **Subscriptions:** 11 newspapers. **Services:** Interlibrary loan; library open to nonmembers on payment of refundable fee. **Publications:** FOREHEAD (literary/arts magazine), annual.

★1807★
BFE/Barrier Free Environments, Inc. - Library (Plan)
Box 30634 Phone: (919)782-7823
Raleigh, NC 27622 Rex Pace, Info.Spec.
Founded: 1974. **Staff:** 2. **Subjects:** Design for the aging, disability access, architecture, product design, legislation for access, housing. **Holdings:** 650 books; 600 bound periodical volumes; 650 reports; 15,000 slide files. **Subscriptions:** 25 journals and other serials. **Services:** Copying; library open to the public for reference use only. **Computerized Information Services:** BRS Information Technologies, ABLEDATA; GENIE (electronic mail service). **Remarks:** FAX: (919)787-1984.

★1808★
Bhandarkar Oriental Research Institute - Library (Area-Ethnic)
Poone 411 004, Maharashtra, India Phone: 336932
Mr. V.L. Manjul, Libn.
Founded: 1917. **Staff:** 3. **Subjects:** Sanskrit, Indology, Oriental studies. **Special Collections:** Manuscripts on paper, birch bark, and palm leaf; rare and illustrated manuscripts; copper plates and clay tablet (500 B.C.). **Holdings:** 75,500 books; 27,000 manuscripts. **Subscriptions:** 160 journals. **Services:** Interlibrary loan; copying; microfilming; library open to the public for reference use only. **Publications:** Personal Bibliographies of Indological Scholars. **Staff:** Mr. Satish G. Sangle, Asst.; Mrs. M.M. Deshpande, Asst.

★1809★
BHP-Utah Minerals International - Information Services/Library (Sci-Engr)
550 California St. Phone: (415)774-2454
San Francisco, CA 94104 Tim DeWolf, Mgr.
Founded: 1973. **Staff:** Prof 2. **Subjects:** Mining, geology, business. **Special Collections:** Early history of construction in the West (photographs). **Holdings:** 15,000 books. **Subscriptions:** 500 journals and other serials. **Services:** Interlibrary loan; library open to the public by appointment. **Automated Operations:** Computerized cataloging. **Computerized Information Services:** DIALOG Information Services, RLIN. **Networks/Consortia:** Member of CLASS. **Remarks:** FAX: (415)774-2213. **Staff:** Julianna Hueter, Info.Spec.

Bhubaneshwar Archive on Modern Orissa
See: **University of Chicago - Southern Asia Collection** (18460)

★1810★
Bhutan - National Museum of Bhutan - Reference Library (Area-Ethnic)
Paro, Bhutan Phone: 00975 57
Mynak R. Tulku, Musm.Dir.
Subjects: Museology, conservation, Mahayana Buddhism, Central Asia, Bhutan, Tibet. **Special Collections:** Books on Buddhist iconography. **Holdings:** 3000 books.

★1811★
Bi-County Community Hospital - Library (Med)
13355 E. 10 Mile Rd. Phone: (313)759-7345
Warren, MI 48089 Gayle A. Williams, Dir.
Founded: 1966. **Staff:** Prof 1; Other 2. **Subjects:** Medicine, nursing, health care management, allied health sciences. **Holdings:** 2200 books; 3500 bound periodical volumes. **Subscriptions:** 200 journals and other serials. **Services:** Interlibrary loan; copying; SDI; computer learning lab; library open to the public with restrictions. **Computerized Information Services:** DIALOG Information Services, BRS Information Technologies, NLM, WILSONLINE, OCLC. **Networks/Consortia:** Member of Michigan Library Consortium (MLC), Michigan Health Sciences Libraries Association (MHSLA), National Network of Libraries of Medicine - Greater Midwest Region. **Remarks:** FAX: (313)759-1490.

Angelo H. Bianchi Library
See: **Eastchester Historical Society** (5137)

★1812★
Bibb County Law Library (Law)
661 Mulberry St. Phone: (912)749-6341
Macon, GA 31201 Roycine G. Roberson, Law Libn.
Founded: 1960. **Staff:** Prof 1. **Subjects:** Law. **Holdings:** 12,000 volumes. **Services:** Library not open to the public.

Basil G. Bibby Library
See: **Eastman Dental Center** (5176)

★1813★
Bible-Science Association - Research Center (Rel-Phil)
P.O. Box 32457 Phone: (612)755-8606
Minneapolis, MN 55432 Gregory A. Hull, Exec.Dir.
Staff: 1. **Subjects:** Creation, model of origins, Bible and science relationships. **Holdings:** Figures not available. **Subscriptions:** 10 periodicals. **Services:** Library not open to the public.

★1814★
Biblical Theological Seminary - Library (Rel-Phil)
200 N. Main St. Phone: (215)368-5000
Hatfield, PA 19440 John D. Evans, Libn.
Founded: 1971. **Staff:** Prof 2; Other 2. **Subjects:** Bible, theology, Christian education, church history. **Special Collections:** Biblical Seminary in New York thesis collection; Interdisciplinary Biblical Research Institute papers and tapes. **Holdings:** 45,887 books; 3026 bound periodical volumes; 520 titles in microform; 1154 cassettes; 28 phonograph records; 23 videotapes. **Subscriptions:** 280 journals and other serials. **Services:** Interlibrary loan; copying; library open to the public. **Automated Operations:** Computerized cataloging and acquisitions. **Computerized Information Services:** BRS Information Technologies; Ecunet (internal database). **Networks/Consortia:** Member of Delaware Valley Information Consortium (DEVIC), Southeastern Pennsylvania Theological Library Association (SEPTLA), Tri-State College Library Cooperative (TCLC). **Remarks:** FAX: (215)368-7002. **Staff:** Joanna Hause, Tech.Serv.Libn.

★1815★
Bibliographic Research Services Library (Info Sci)
964 Chapel Hill Way Phone: (408)297-2810
San Jose, CA 95122 Robert B. Harmon, Res.Bibliog.
Founded: 1970. **Staff:** 1. **Subjects:** Bibliography. **Special Collections:** John Steinbeck collection. **Holdings:** 350 books; 40 bound periodical volumes. **Services:** Copying; library not open to the public.

★1816★
Bibliographical Center for Research - Rocky Mountain Region, Inc. (Info Sci)
4500 Cherry Creek Dr. S., No. 206 Phone: (303)691-0550
Denver, CO 80222 David H. Brunell, Exec.Dir.
Founded: 1935. **Staff:** Prof 12; Other 11. **Special Collections:** Professional collection of library and networking materials (1000 volumes). **Holdings:** 200 software packages. **Subscriptions:** 135 journals and other serials. **Services:** Center not open to the public. **Automated Operations:** Computerized public access catalog, cataloging, and acquisitions. **Computerized Information Services:** DIALOG Information Services, BRS Information Technologies, BiblioFile, OCLC, Books in Print (BIP) Data Base, Bowker's International Serials Database, VU/TEXT Information Services; CD-ROM. **Publications:** Action for Libraries, monthly; The Third Indicator, bimonthly. **Remarks:** Bibliographical Center for Research (BCR) is a library network. FAX: (303)691-0112. **Staff:** Gretchen Redfield, Mgr., Bibliog.Sys. & Serv.; Connee Chandler, Mgr., Ref.Sys. & Serv.; James Hensinger, Mgr., Microsystems & Serv.; Arleta Gutierrez, Mgr., Bus.Off.; Joyce Hillshafer, Mgr., Adm.Serv.

Biblioteca Agropecuaria de Colombia
See: **Colombia - Instituto Colombiano Agropecuario** (3923)

★1817★
Biblioteca Amador-Washington - (Panama City) USIS Library (Educ)
Edif. Gusromares
Ave. Balboa y Federico Boyd
Apdo. 6959
Panama 5, Panama
Remarks: Maintained or supported by the U.S. Information Agency. Focus is on materials that will assist peoples outside the United States to learn about the United States, its people, history, culture, political processes, and social milieux.

★1818★
Biblioteca Artigas-Washington - (Montevideo) USIS Library (Educ)
Paraguay 1217
Montevideo, Uruguay
Remarks: Maintained or supported by the U.S. Information Agency. Focus is on materials that will assist peoples outside the United States to learn about the United States, its people, history, culture, political processes, and social milieux.

★1819★
Biblioteca Benjamin Franklin - (Guadalajara) USIS Library (Educ)
Paseo del Hospicio 65-3er Piso
Plaza Tapatia Phone: 36 176711
44100 Guadalajara, Jalisco, Mexico Maria Elena Saucedo Lugo, Dir.
Founded: 1949. **Staff:** 2. **Subjects:** United States - foreign policy, economics, environment. **Holdings:** 7396 books; bound periodical volumes; 50 reports. **Subscriptions:** 113 journals and other serials; 6 newspapers. **Services:** Interlibrary loan; copying; library open to the public. **Computerized Information Services:** CD-ROMs; internal databases. **Publications:** Special bibliographies; new acquisitions list, monthly. **Remarks:** FAX: 36 176893. Maintained or supported by the U.S. Information Agency. Focus is on materials that will assist peoples outside the United States to learn about the United States, its people, history, culture, political processes, and social milieux. **Staff:** Sergio Lopez Ruelas.

★1820★
Biblioteca Benjamin Franklin - (Mexico City) USIS Library (Soc Sci, Hum)
Londres 16, Col. Juarez Phone: 5 2110042
06600 Mexico City, DF, Mexico Bo Gilliam, Dir.
Founded: 1942. **Staff:** 17. **Subjects:** Political and social science, humanities, American studies. **Holdings:** 21,431 books; 5000 VF drawers of reports; 12,998 microforms; 730 videotapes. **Subscriptions:** 350 journals and other serials; 7 newspapers. **Services:** Interlibrary loan; copying; SDI; library open to the public. **Automated Operations:** Computerized cataloging, circulation, and reference. **Computerized Information Services:** DIALOG Information Services, LEGI-SLATE; CD-ROMs (Books in Print, Dissertation Abstracts Ondisc, Chicano Database, Ulrich's Plus); DIALMAIL (electronic mail service). **Publications:** Selected list of new acquisitions; RECURSOS, A directory of Mexican-American institutions. **Remarks:** FAX: 5 5350909. Maintained or supported by the U.S. Information Agency. Focus is on materials that will assist peoples outside the United States to learn about the United States, its people, history, culture, political processes, and social milieux. **Staff:** Irma C. de Perez Monroy, Asst.Dir.; Mabel Cabrera, Ref.Libn.; Juan Villicana, Cat.

Biblioteca Carlos Monge Alfaro
See: **Universidad de Costa Rica - Sistema de Bibliotecas, Documentacion e Informacion** (17989)

Biblioteca del Centro de Investigaciones Biologicas
See: **Spain - Biological Research Center** (15558)

Biblioteca Dr. Antonio Requena
See: **Lisandro Alvarado Foundation - Biblioteca Dr. Antonio Requena** (435)

Biblioteca Estanislao S. Zeballos
See: **Facultad de Ciencias Economicas** (5548)

★1821★
Biblioteca Guarnacci (Rel-Phil, Hist)
Palazzo Vigilanti
Via Don Minzoni 3 Phone: 588 85449
I-56048 Volterra, Italy M. Ballani
Founded: 1779. **Staff:** 4. **Subjects:** Religion, local history, medicine, geography, art, literature. **Special Collections:** Fondo Funaioli; Fondo Pacciani; Fond Aulo Persio Flacco. **Holdings:** 50,000 books; 131 bound periodical volumes; 40 reels of microfilm. **Subscriptions:** 10 journals and other serials; 5 newspapers. **Services:** Copying; library open to the public. **Remarks:** FAX: 588 85214. **Staff:** Dr. Angelo Marrucci.

★1822★
Biblioteca John F. Kennedy - (Manizales) Centro Colombo-Americano - USIS Collection (Educ)
Calle 26, No. 21-37 Phone: 68 845984
Manizales, Colombia Adriana Ramirez Vinasco, Libn.
Founded: 1961. **Holdings:** 3200 books; 800 bound periodical volumes; reports; archival items; videotapes. **Subscriptions:** 27 journals and other serials; 3 newspapers. **Services:** Interlibrary loan; copying; library open to the public. **Remarks:** FAX: 68 845582. Maintained or supported by the U.S. Information Agency. Focus is on materials that will assist peoples outside the United States to learn about the United States, its people, history, culture, political processes, and social milieux.

★1823★
Biblioteca Lincoln - (Santo Domingo) USIS Library (Educ)
Ave. Abraham Lincoln, No. 21
Santo Domingo, Dominican Republic
Remarks: Maintained or supported by the U.S. Information Agency. Focus is on materials that will assist peoples outside the United States to learn about the United States, its people, history, culture, political processes, and social milieux.

Biblioteca Lucchesi Palli
See: **Italy - Ministero beni Cultrali - Biblioteca Nazionale Vittorio Emanuele III** (8280)

Biblioteca Luis Demetrio Tinoco
See: **Universidad de Costa Rica - Sistema de Bibliotecas, Documentacion e Informacion** (17989)

Biblioteca Luis Lopez de Mesa
See: **Colombian Academy of Exact, Physical and Natural Sciences** (3925)

Biblioteca Nacional Jose Marti
See: **Cuba - Ministerio de Cultura** (4464)

Biblioteca Nacional del Paraguay
See: **Paraguay - Biblioteca Nacional del Paraguay** (12736)

Biblioteca Nazionale Vittorio Emanuele III
See: **Italy - Ministero beni Cultrali - Biblioteca Nazionale Vittorio Emanuele III** (8280)

Biblioteca Rafael Garcia Granados
See: **Universidad Nacional Autonoma de Mexico - Instituto de Investigaciones Historicas** (17993)

★1824★
Biblioteca Washington Irving - (Madrid) Centro Cultural de los Estados Unidos - USIS Library (Educ)
Marques de Villamagna 8
E-28001 Madrid, Spain
Remarks: Maintained or supported by the U.S. Information Agency. Focus is on materials that will assist peoples outside the United States to learn about the United States, its people, history, culture, political processes, and social milieux.

Biblioteko Hector Hodler
See: **Universala Esperanto-Asocio** (17977)

Bibliotheca Crawfordiana
See: **F. Marion Crawford Memorial Society** (4417)

Bibliotheca Hertziana
See: **Max Planck Institute - Bibliotheca Hertziana** (13098)

Bibliotheek van het Algemeen Rijksarchief
See: **Netherlands - Bibliotheek van het Algemeen Rijksarchief** (11399)

Bibliotheek Koninklijke Nederlandse Akademie van Wetenschappen
See: **Royal Netherlands Academy of Arts and Sciences** (14126)

Bibliotheek van het Ruusbroecgenootschap
See: **Universiteit Antwerpen - Universitaire Faculteiten Sint-Ignatius Antwerpen** (18131)

Bibliothek der Friedrich-Ebert-Stiftung
See: **Friedrich Ebert Foundation** (5198)

Bibliotheque Albert-Prevost
See: **Hopital du Sacre Coeur de Montreal** (7398)

Bibliotheque Alfred-Monnin
See: **College Universitaire de St. Boniface** (3917)

Bibliotheque de l'Arsenal
See: **France - Bibliotheque de l'Arsenal** (6061)

★1825★
Bibliotheque des Arts et Metiers (Art)
Derriere les Remparts 5
CH-1700 Fribourg, Switzerland Phone: 37 252509
Founded: 1890. **Staff:** Prof 1. **Subjects:** Art, handicraft. **Holdings:** 12,000 books. **Subscriptions:** 200 journals and other serials; 10 newspapers. **Services:** Interlibrary loan; copying; library open to the public.

★1826★
Bibliotheque Historique de la Ville de Paris (Hist)
24, rue Pavee Phone: 1 42744444
F-75004 Paris, France M. Jean Derens, Chf.Cons.
Staff: 50. **Subjects:** History of Paris, French Revolution, theater. **Special Collections:** Feminism; Dreyfus Affair; Jules Michelet; George Sand. **Holdings:** 700,000 books; 6000 bound periodical volumes; 200 microforms; 6000 volumes of manuscripts. **Subscriptions:** 800 journals and other serials; 8 newspapers. **Services:** Copying; library open to the public. **Publications:** Publications de la Commission des Travaux historiques; Bulletin de la Bibliotheque et des Travaux Historiques. **Remarks:** FAX: 1 42740316. Maintained by the city of Paris. **Staff:** Maria Deurbergue, Cons.; Maryse Goldemberg, Cons.; Alfred Fiero, Cons.; Marie de Thezy, Cons.; Claude Billaud, Cons.; Veronique Laisne, Cons.; Luc Panian, Cons.; Marie-Odile Gigou, Cons.; Geneveve Madore, Cons.; Francoise Courbage, Cons.

Bibliotheque Litteraire Jacques Doucet
See: **Universites de Paris** (18133)

Bibliotheque Mallet
See: **Union Saint-Jean-Baptiste and Catholic Family Life Insurance - Mallet Library** (16665)

★1827★
Bibliotheque Martin Luther King, Jr. - (Bujumbura) USIS Library (Educ)
20-22 Chaussee Prince Louis
Rwagasore
B.P. 810
Bujumbura, Burundi
Remarks: Maintained or supported by the U.S. Information Agency. Focus is on materials that will assist peoples outside the United States to learn about the United States, its people, history, culture, political processes, and social milieux.

★1828★
Bibliotheque Martin Luther King, Jr. - (Port-au-Prince) Institut Haitiano-Americain - USIS Collection (Educ)
Angle Rue Capois & Rue St. Cyr
Port-au-Prince, Haiti
Remarks: Maintained or supported by the U.S. Information Agency. Focus is on materials that will assist peoples outside the United States to learn about the United States, its people, history, culture, political processes, and social milieux.

★1829★
Bibliotheque Municipale de Montreal - Cinematheque (Aud-Vis)
880 Roy st. E., Suite 200 Phone: (514)872-3680
Montreal, PQ, Canada H2L 1E6 Lise Depatie-Bourassa, Chf., AV Serv.
Founded: 1947. **Staff:** Prof 2; Other 9. **Subjects:** Arts, children's films, geography, social sciences. **Holdings:** 7000 16mm films; 32,000 slides; 8000 video cassettes. **Subscriptions:** 18 journals and other serials. **Services:** Interlibrary loan; copying; library open to the public. **Special Catalogs:** Film, slide, and video catalogs (each in book form). **Remarks:** Alternate telephone number(s): 872-1535. FAX: (514)872-7735. **Also Known As:** Montreal City Library. **Staff:** Sylvie Burelle, Libn.

★1830★
Bibliotheque Municipale de Montreal - Collection Gagnon (Hist, Hum)
1210 Sherbrooke St., E. Phone: (514)872-1631
Montreal, PQ, Canada H2L 1L9 Daniel Olivier, Dept.Hd.
Founded: 1902. **Staff:** Prof 2; Other 4. **Subjects:** Canadian history, French Canadian genealogy, French and English Canadian literature, Canadian geography, French Canadian heritage, Americana. **Special Collections:** Manuscripts and maps of Old Canada; original editions. **Holdings:** 51,383 books; 3000 bound periodical volumes; 20,459 pamphlets; 43,934 photographs and portraits; 70,834 microcards; 12,995 reels of microfilm; 1546 maps, plans, and surveys; 1200 engravings and illustrations; 874 cartons of archives; 1200 slides; 1618 rare books. **Subscriptions:** 201 journals and other serials. **Services:** Interlibrary loan; copying; reference by telephone and mail; bibliographic and information retrieval; collection open to the public. **Computerized Information Services:** DIALOG Information Services, Info Globe, Questel, WILSONLINE, Infomart Online, STM Systems Corporation (INSIGHT), Services Documentaires Multimedia Inc. (SDM), Banque de Terminologie du Quebec (BTQ), CAN/OLE; electronic mail. Performs searches on fee basis. **Remarks:** Alternate telephone number(s): 872-2900. FAX: (514)872-4911. **Also Known As:** Montreal City Library. **Staff:** Marie Baboyant, Libn.; Louise Hotte, Lib.Techn.; Yvette Pouliot, Lib.Techn.

★1831★
Bibliotheque Municipale de Montreal - Phonotheque (Aud-Vis)
880 Roy St. E., Suite 300 Phone: (514)872-2860
Montreal, PQ, Canada H2L 1E6 Gerald Forget, Libn.
Founded: 1982. **Staff:** Prof 1; Other 14. **Subjects:** Music - classical, jazz, rock, pop, blues, international; spoken word recordings. **Holdings:** 28,000 titles. **Subscriptions:** 24 journals and other serials. **Services:** Collection open to the public. **Remarks:** FAX: (514)872-7735. **Staff:** Lise Depatie-Bourassa, Chf., AV Serv.

★1832★
Bibliotheque Musicale Gustav Mahler (Mus)
11 bis rue Vezelay Phone: 1 42562017
F-75008 Paris, France Marie-Gabrielle Soret
Founded: 1986. **Staff:** Prof 4. **Subjects:** Music. **Holdings:** 20,000 books; 40,000 LP records; 5000 compact discs; 6000 autographed letters and music manuscripts; 10,000 scores. **Services:** Library open to the public by appointment. **Remarks:** FAX: 1 43597022.

Bibliotheque Nationale (of Algeria)
See: **Algeria - Bibliotheque Nationale** (349)

Bibliotheque Nationale (of Benin)
See: **Benin - Bibliotheque Nationale** (1720)

Bibliotheque Nationale du Canada
See: **Canada - National Library of Canada** (2803)

Bibliotheque Nationale (of Cote d'Ivoire)
See: **Cote d'Ivoire - Bibliotheque Nationale** (4350)

Bibliotheque Nationale (de France)
See: **France - Bibliotheque Nationale** (6062)

Bibliotheque Nationale du Quebec
See: **(Quebec Province) Bibliotheque Nationale du Quebec** (13576)

Bibliotheque Nationale Suisse
See: **Switzerland - Swiss National Library** (15943)

★1833★
Bibliotheque Nationale et Universitaire de Strasbourg (Hum, Sci-Engr, Law, Med)
5, rue du Marechal Joffre
B.P. 1029/F Phone: 88252800
F-67070 Strasbourg Cedex, France Michel Boisset, Cons. en chef/Adm.
Subjects: Humanities, science and technology, medicine, law, France. **Special Collections:** Regional collections; manuscripts; incunabula; papyrii; cuneiform tablets; ostraca; coins and medals. **Holdings:** 3 million books; maps; plans; seals; photographs. **Subscriptions:** 6076 journals and other serials. **Services:** Interlibrary loan; copying; library open to the public. **Computerized Information Services:** Online systems. Performs searches on fee basis. **Publications:** Bibliographie alsacienne; Papyrus grecs de la B.N.U.S. **Special Catalogs:** Catalogues collectifs de periodiques. **Remarks:** FAX: 88252803. Library is part of France - Ministere de l'Education Nationale - Direction de la Programmation et du Developpement Universitaire - Soua Direction des Bibliotheques.

Bibliotheque Patrick Allen
See: **Ecole des Hautes Etudes Commerciales de Montreal** (5205)

Bibliotheque Royale Albert 1er
See: **Belgium - Ministry of National Education - Bibliotheque Royale de Belgique** (1671)

Bibliotheque Royale de Belgique
See: **Belgium - Ministry of National Education - Bibliotheque Royale de Belgique** (1671)

Bibliotheque Scientifique Charles-Auguste Gauthier
See: **Hopital de l'Enfant-Jesus - Bibliotheque Scientifique Charles-Auguste Gauthier** (7387)

Bibliotheque de la Sorbonne
See: **Universites de Paris I, III, IV, V, VII** (18134)

★1834★
The Bickelhaupt Arboretum - Education Center (Biol Sci)
340 S. 14th St. Phone: (319)242-4771
Clinton, IA 52732 F.K. Bickelhaupt, Libn.
Founded: 1970. **Staff:** Prof 1; Other 1. **Subjects:** Trees and shrubs, planting and pruning, indoor plants, vegetable gardening, ecology, urban forestry. **Special Collections:** Tree identification book collection; urban forestry files; Education Center Slide Collection. **Holdings:** 910 books; 50 other cataloged items; 247 files on arboreta and botanical gardens around the world; 1200 microfiche containing information on landscape and woody plants native and hardy to the Midwest. **Subscriptions:** 28 journals and other serials. **Services:** Copying; center open to the public. **Publications:** List of publications - available on request.

Alice J. Bickers Library
See: **Nutley Historical Society Museum** (12168)

Biddle Law Library
See: **University of Pennsylvania** (19177)

Bernice Bienenstock Furniture Library
See: **Furniture Library Association** (6219)

★1835★
Bienville Historical Society - Center for Gulf Studies (Hist)
4559 Old Citronelle Hwy. Phone: (205)457-5242
Prichard, AL 36613 Johnnie Andrews, Jr., Dir.
Founded: 1955. **Staff:** Prof 3; Other 2. **Subjects:** City of Mobile and Alabama; genealogy; history of Louisiana, Florida, Mississippi, Georgia, and South Carolina; French, Spanish, and English colonial history; black history. **Special Collections:** Manuscripts; early church records dating from 1594 from numerous colonial towns; art collection, 1717 to present (1000 prints, etchings, and paintings); Blakeley, Alabama ghost town papers (6000 pages); Pensacola, Florida papers, 1559-1763 (7000 pages); Africa Town, Alabama papers (1000 pages); descriptive catalog of library collection from 1978-1988. **Holdings:** 29,000 books; 1500 colonial manuscripts; 2700 Andry-Chastang Family Papers, 1805-1989; 200 Overby photo manuscripts; 300 railroad manuscripts; 300 early maps; 5000 pamphlets; 60,000 clippings in vertical files; 5000 photographs, 1855 to present; 20,000 copies of colonial archives . **Subscriptions:** 137 journals and other serials; 20 newspapers. **Services:** Copying; translation of holdings; library open to the public by appointment only. **Publications:** 60 publications on Gulf South history and genealogy. **Special Indexes:** Card indexes to library holdings of local history collections in 170 Southern libraries; Index of 150,000 Gulf Coast area residents from 1559-1876 (card). **Formerly:** Cleveland Prichard Memorial Library. **Staff:** Michael G. Mc Donald, Asst.Dir.; Charles Ray Parris, Asst.Dir.

Big Hole National Battlefield
See: **U.S. Natl. Park Service** (17675)

Big Spring State Hospital - Professional Library
See: **Texas (State) Department of Mental Health & Mental Retardation** (16244)

Big Timbers Museum
See: **Prowers County Historical Society** (13456)

Bigelow Laboratory for Ocean Sciences
See: **Maine State Department of Marine Resources - Fisheries Research Station - Library** (9561)

★1836★
Bigham, Englar, Jones and Houston - Library (Law)
14 Wall St. Phone: (212)732-4646
New York, NY 10005 Maria Cucarese
Staff: Prof 1; Other 1. **Subjects:** Law. **Special Collections:** Admiralty law. **Holdings:** 10,000 volumes. **Subscriptions:** 4 newspapers. **Services:** Interlibrary loan (limited); library not open to the public.

★1837★
Bigham & Raffensperger - Library
16 Lincoln Square Phone: (717)334-2159
Gettysburg, PA 17325 Robert Bigham, Lib.Dir.
Remarks: No further information was supplied by respondent.

Bighorn Canyon National Recreation Area
See: **U.S. Natl. Park Service** (17676)

A.C. Bilbrew Library
See: **County of Los Angeles Public Library - Black Resource Center** (4380)

★1838★
Billings Gazette - News Library (Publ)
P.O. Box 36300 Phone: (406)657-1289
Billings, MT 59107 Connie Lar, Libn.
Founded: 1970. **Staff:** Prof 1. **Subjects:** Newspaper reference topics. **Holdings:** Newspaper, 1882 to present, on microfilm. **Services:** Library open to other journalists. **Remarks:** The Gazette is published by Lee Enterprises, Inc.

★1839★
Billington, Fox & Ellis - Research Department - Library (Bus-Fin)
20 N. Wacker Dr.
Chicago, IL 60606 Mary Ann Bock, Res.Dir.
Staff: 4. **Subjects:** Business. **Holdings:** 500 books; 1500 linear feet of vertical files. **Subscriptions:** 10 journals and other serials. **Services:** Interlibrary loan; library not open to the public.

Rowell A. Billups Memorial Library
See: **Cottonlandia Educational and Recreational Foundation, Inc. - Rowell A. Billups Memorial Library** (4353)

Biloxi Sun Herald
See: **Gulf Publishing Co., Inc.** (6809)

★1840★
Bingham Dana and Gould - Law Library (Law)
150 Federal St. Phone: (617)951-8000
Boston, MA 02110-1726 Christine Matz, Dir.
Staff: Prof 2; Other 4. **Subjects:** Law - banking, corporate, admiralty, tax, labor, litigation, family, environment. **Holdings:** 32,000 books. **Subscriptions:** 500 journals and other serials; 12 newspapers. **Services:** Interlibrary loan; library not open to the public. **Computerized Information Services:** LEXIS, DIALOG Information Services, NEXIS, Dow Jones News/Retrieval, VU/TEXT Information Services, WESTLAW, Dun & Bradstreet Business Credit Services, NewsNet, Inc., RLIN, Veralex 2, Information America, LEGI-SLATE, State Net. **Remarks:** FAX: (617)951-8736. Telex: 275147. **Staff:** Alfreda B. Russell.

★1841★
Bingham Memorial Hospital - Medical Library (Med)
98 Poplar St. Phone: (208)785-4100
Blackfoot, ID 83221 Margaret Davis, Med.Libn.
Staff: Prof 1. **Subjects:** Medicine, nursing, hospital management, allied health sciences. **Holdings:** 400 books; 20 bound periodical volumes; 22 boxes of audiotapes; 80 videotapes. **Subscriptions:** 25 journals and other serials. **Services:** Interlibrary loan; copying; library open to the public with restrictions. **Automated Operations:** Computerized cataloging. **Networks/Consortia:** Member of Southeast Idaho Health Information Consortium. **Special Catalogs:** Periodical file.

Binghamton General Hospital
See: **United Health Services/Binghamton General Hospital** (16714)

★1842★
(Binghamton) Press and Sun-Bulletin - Library (Publ)
Vestal Pkwy., E.
P.O. Box 1270 Phone: (607)798-1159
Binghamton, NY 13902 Nancy L. George, Lib.Coord.
Founded: 1942. **Staff:** Prof 1; Other 2. **Subjects:** Newspaper reference topics. **Holdings:** 400 books; 6 cabinets of microfilm; 50 cabinets of clippings; 30 cabinets of pictures; maps. **Subscriptions:** 22 journals and other serials. **Services:** Library not open to the public. **Special Indexes:** Subject index to clippings files (online). **Remarks:** Published by Gannett Newspapers.

Binghamton Psychiatric Center
See: **New York (State) Office of Mental Health** (11673)

★1843★
Bio-Rad Laboratories - Sadtler Division - Library (Sci-Engr)
3316 Spring Garden St. Phone: (215)382-7800
Philadelphia, PA 19104 Bernadette Steiner, Libn.
Founded: 1966. **Staff:** 1. **Subjects:** Spectroscopy - infrared, ultraviolet, nuclear magnetic resonance; gas chromatography; analytical chemistry. **Special Collections:** Spectra consisting of infrared, ultraviolet, nuclear magnetic resonance, attenuated total reflectance, and differential thermal analysis for 100,000 compounds. **Holdings:** 2500 books; 2500 bound periodical volumes. **Subscriptions:** 50 journals and other serials. **Services:** Interlibrary loan; copying; library open to the public for reference use only with appointment. **Remarks:** FAX: (215)662-0585.

★1844★
Bio-Technical Resources - Library (Biol Sci)
1035 S. 7th St.
Manitowoc, WI 54220 Phone: (414)684-5518
Founded: 1962. **Subjects:** Bioengineering, microbiology, and chemistry as applied to fermentation, brewing and malting, distilling, food and flavor, seed germination, hydrocarbon bioconversion, grain processing, microbial leaching of ore, and water/wastewater analyis and control. **Holdings:** 4000 volumes. **Subscriptions:** 50 journals and other serials; 2 newspapers. **Services:** Library not open to the public. **Remarks:** FAX: (414)684-5519.

★1845★
Biola University - Rose Memorial Library (Rel-Phil)
13800 Biola Ave. Phone: (310)903-4834
La Mirada, CA 90639-0001 Rodney M. Vliet, Ph.D., Lib.Dir.
Founded: 1907. **Staff:** Prof 4.5; Other 7.5. **Subjects:** Bible and theology, psychology, evangelical Christianity, intercultural studies, U.S. history. **Special Collections:** Bible versions; U.S. Evangelical Christianity; music of Raynor Brown (complete). **Holdings:** 208,412 books; 31,000 bound periodical volumes; 3254 reels of microfilm; 321,878 microfiche; 10 drawers of maps and charts; 28 VF drawers; 40 drawers of microforms. **Subscriptions:** 1174 journals and other serials; 7 newspapers. **Services:** Interlibrary loan; copying; library open to the public with payment of annual fee. **Automated Operations:** INLEX. **Computerized Information Services:** DIALOG Information Services; CD-ROM (Business Periodicals Index, Religion Index, ERIC, PsycLIT). **Networks/Consortia:** Member of CLASS. **Special Indexes:** Sermon files; Subject Index (sermons and speech illustrative material); Hymn Index (all three on cards). **Remarks:** FAX: (310)903-4840. Includes the holdings of Rosemead Graduate School of Professional Psychology - Library. **Staff:** Charles K. Church, Per. & Sys.Libn.; Dr. William Hunter, Coll.Dev.Libn.; Susan Johnson, Tech.Serv.Libn.; Beth Patton, Ref./Circ.Libn.

Biologische Bundesanstalt fur Land- und Forstwirtschaft - Dokumentationsstelle fur Phytomedizin
See: **Germany - Federal Research Center for Agriculture and Forestry - Documentation Center for Phytomedicine** (6446)

★1846★
Biomass Energy Institute - Library (Energy, Biol Sci)
1329 Niakwa Rd. E. Phone: (204)257-3891
Winnipeg, MB, Canada R2J 3T4 Beth Candlish, Ph.D., Exec.Dir.
Founded: 1971. **Staff:** Prof 2. **Subjects:** Bio-energy, bioconversion, energy policy, solar energy, wind energy. **Special Collections:** Biomass Abstracts (25,000 references and abstracts). **Holdings:** 20,000 books and government reports. **Subscriptions:** 100 journals and other serials. **Services:** Interlibrary loan (limited); copying; library open to the public. **Publications:** Bio-Joule, quarterly.

★1847★
Biotechnology Research Institute - Library (Biol Sci)
1330-A Piccard Dr. Phone: (301)258-5200
Rockville, MD 20850-4373 Exie M. Henderson, Libn.
Founded: 1963. **Staff:** Prof 1. **Subjects:** Biotechnology, cancer research, immunology, virology. **Holdings:** 3700 books; 150 bound periodical volumes. **Subscriptions:** 165 journals and other serials. **Services:** Interlibrary loan; library not open to the public. **Computerized Information Services:** MEDLINE. **Publications:** Library Acquisitions List, quarterly - for internal distribution only. **Remarks:** FAX: (301)840-2161.

★1848★
BIPE Conseil - Library (Bus-Fin)
12, rue Rouget de Lisle
Axe Seine 21
F-92442 Issy-les-Moulineaux Cedex, Phone: 1 46623300
France Herve Passeron, Chm. & Mng.Dir.
Founded: 1961. **Staff:** Prof 2. **Subjects:** Economic and technological forecasting - industry, agriculture, building construction, electronics, consumer goods, new technologies, services, trade, and transportation; social research; environmental studies. **Holdings:** 3000 bound volumes; reports. **Subscriptions:** 700 journals and other serials. **Services:** Library not open to the public. **Computerized Information Services:** Europeenne de Donnees, Data-Star, FT PROFILE, O.R. Telematique. **Remarks:** FAX: 1 46626220. Telex: 631586 F. **Formerly:** Office of Economic Information and Forecasting. **Staff:** Renee Saveant, Hd., Info.Dept.; Jacqueline Hautin.

★1849★
Biphase Energy Systems - Library (Sci-Engr)
2800 Airport Ave.
Santa Monica, CA 90405 Phone: (213)391-0691
Subjects: Two-phase fluid flow, thermodynamics, rotor-dynamics, heat transfer. **Holdings:** 4500 volumes. **Remarks:** FAX: (213)397-6801. Telex: 4720221. Subsidiary of Transamerica Delaval Inc.

E.S. Bird Library
See: **Syracuse University - E.S. Bird Library** (15959)

Gustavus C. Bird, III, M.D. Library of Diagnostic Imaging
See: **Temple University Hospital - Diagnostic Imaging Department** (16150)

Robert M. Bird Health Sciences Library
See: **University of Oklahoma - Health Sciences Center** (19132)

Walter D. Bird Memorial Historical Library
See: **Becker County Historical Society** (1640)

George David Birkhoff Library
See: **Harvard University - Mathematical Library** (6983)

Birlesnris Milletler Turk Dernegi
See: **United Nations Association of Turkey** (16755)

★1850★
Birmingham Botanical Gardens - Horace Hammond Memorial Library (Biol Sci)
2612 Lane Park Rd. Phone: (205)879-1227
Birmingham, AL 35223 Gary G. Gerlach, Dir.
Founded: 1971. **Staff:** Prof 1; Other 19. **Subjects:** Horticulture, botany, floriculture, gardens and gardening, landscaping, flower arranging. **Special Collections:** Complete set of Richenbachia (4 volumes); rare books (68); set of 1st edition Luther Burbank (12 volumes). **Holdings:** 4000 books; 50 bound periodical volumes; 500 pamphlets; 8 lateral file drawers of newspaper clippings, magazine articles, and garden club program materials. **Subscriptions:** 125 journals and other serials. **Services:** Copying (limited); library open to the public. **Staff:** Mrs. D.J. Burns, Libn.

★1851★
Birmingham Museum of Art - Clarence B. Hanson, Jr. Library (Art)
2000 8th Ave., N. Phone: (205)254-2982
Birmingham, AL 35203-2278 Jane Mcrae, Libn.
Founded: 1966. **Staff:** Prof 1; Other 1. **Subjects:** Oriental art, decorative arts, American West, American painting, European painting, traditional art, art history, photography, modern art. **Special Collections:** Wedgewood Collection. **Holdings:** 12,000 books. **Subscriptions:** 106 journals and other serials. **Services:** Copying; library open to the public by appointment only. **Remarks:** FAX: (202)254-2714.

★1852★
Birmingham News - Reference Library (Publ)
2200 N. 4th Ave.
Box 2553 Phone: (205)325-2466
Birmingham, AL 35202 Laurie Orr Dean, Hd., Ref.Lib.
Founded: 1950. **Staff:** Prof 1; Other 2. **Subjects:** Newspaper reference topics. **Special Collections:** Historical pictures. **Holdings:** 1500 books; clipping files; photographs; microfilm. **Services:** Library not open to the public. **Computerized Information Services:** NEXIS.

★1853★
Birmingham Public and Jefferson County Free Library - Arts, Music and Recreation (Art, Mus)
2100 Park Place Phone: (205)226-3670
Birmingham, AL 35203 Linda M. Classen, Dept.Hd.
Staff: Prof 3; Other 5. **Subjects:** Music, art, architecture, arts and crafts, photography, costume, landscape architecture, performing arts, recreation, sports. **Special Collections:** Circulating art collection (190 reproductions). **Holdings:** 32,500 books; 7135 bound periodical volumes; 18,950 phonograph records; 6025 cassettes; 3200 compact discs; 250 reels of microfilm and 13,000 sheets of microfiche of periodicals; 22 VF drawers of clippings; 27 VF drawers of mounted pictures. **Subscriptions:** 150 journals and other serials. **Services:** Listening facilities for records, cassettes, and compact discs (for members only); circulating mounted picture file; public typewriters; department open to the public. **Automated Operations:** Computerized cataloging, acquisitions, and serials. **Computerized Information Services:** DIALOG Information Services, OCLC; internal database. **Networks/ Consortia:** Member of SOLINET. **Remarks:** FAX: (205)226-3743. **Staff:** Linda M. Cohen; Deborah Loftis.

★1854★
Birmingham Public and Jefferson County Free Library - Collins Collection of the Dance (Theater)
2100 Park Place Phone: (205)226-3670
Birmingham, AL 35203 Linda M. Classen, Dept.Hd.
Founded: 1967. **Staff:** 1. **Subjects:** Dance. **Holdings:** 2500 books; 1441 bound periodical volumes. **Subscriptions:** 2 journals and other serials. **Services:** Copying; collection open to the public. **Remarks:** FAX: (205)226-3743. **Staff:** Linda M. Cohen; Deborah Loftis.

★1855★
Birmingham Public and Jefferson County Free Library - Government Documents Department (Info Sci)
2100 Park Place Phone: (205)226-3680
Birmingham, AL 35203 Rebecca Scarborough, Hd., Govt.Doc.Dept.
Founded: 1895. **Staff:** Prof 2; Other 3. **Subjects:** Census, patents, statistics, federal legislation, laws and regulations. **Special Collections:** ASI microfiche collection (complete, 1974 to present); U.S. Patent Depository (mechanical, electrical, and chemical patents, 1962 to present; design patents, 1923 to present); CIS full microfiche collection (1970 to present; pre-1970 reports, prints, serial set); SRI microfiche collection (January 1981 to present); Foundation Center. **Holdings:** 250,000 documents; 2500 shelves of federal documents; 6000 reels of microfilm; 670,500 microfiche. **Services:** Interlibrary loan; copying; SDI; department open to the public. **Computerized Information Services:** DIALOG Information Services, Classification and Search Support Information Sustem (CASSIS). **Publications:** List of new documents and subject bibliographies, irregular - for library departments, branches, and patrons; Alabama Foundation Directory. **Remarks:** FAX: (205)226-3743.

★1856★
Birmingham Public and Jefferson County Free Library - Linn-Henley Library for Southern Historical Research - Department of Archives and Manuscripts (Hist)
2100 Park Place Phone: (205)226-3645
Birmingham, AL 35203 Marvin Y. Whiting, Archv./Cur., Mss.
Founded: 1976. **Staff:** Prof 2; Other 1. **Subjects:** Birmingham, Alabama - history, civil rights, real estate development, politics and government, private utilities, industry, civic organizations, photographic history, women's history. **Special Collections:** Birmingham Municipal Records (510 linear feet); Jefferson County Public Records (1550 linear feet); Civil Rights in Alabama (90 linear feet and microforms); Robert Jemison, Jr. papers (250 linear feet); Birmingham Water Works Company records (180 linear feet); Southern Women's Archives (500 linear feet). **Holdings:** 1055 books; 405 bound periodical volumes; 9000 linear feet of archives and manuscripts; 923 reels of microfilm of archives and manuscripts; 2106 microfiche; 600 oral history cassette tapes; 215,000 photographic prints and negatives. **Subscriptions:** 9 journals and other serials; 21 newspapers. **Services:** Interlibrary loan; copying; department open to the public for reference use only. **Computerized Information Services:** OCLC; internal databases. **Publications:** A Guide to the Collecti ons of the Department of Archives and Manuscripts, Linn-Henley Research Library - for sale. **Special Catalogs:** Preliminary and Descriptive Inventories for Manuscript Collections and Archival Records Groups, Sub-groups, & Series. **Special Indexes:** Subject file index to photographic collections (card). **Remarks:** FAX: (205)226-3743. **Staff:** James B. Murray, Asst.Archv.; Don M. Veasey, Cur., Photo.

★1857★
Birmingham Public and Jefferson County Free Library - Linn-Henley Library for Southern Historical Research - Grace Hardie Collection of Children's Books (Hum)
2100 Park Place Phone: (205)226-3665
Birmingham, AL 35203 Anne F. Knight, Cur.
Founded: 1948. **Staff:** Prof 1. **Subjects:** 19th century children's books. **Holdings:** 427 books; 80 bound periodical volumes. **Services:** Collection open to the public for reference use only. **Automated Operations:** Computerized cataloging and acquisitions. **Remarks:** FAX: (205)226-3743.

★1858★
Birmingham Public and Jefferson County Free Library - Linn-Henley Library for Southern Historical Research - Rucker Agee Cartographical Collection (Geog-Map)
2100 Park Place Phone: (205)226-3665
Birmingham, AL 35203 Yvonne Crumpler, Cur.
Founded: 1964. **Subjects:** Alabama, Southeast, historical cartography, discovery and exploration, Civil War. **Special Collections:** Rucker Agee Collection; Joseph H. Woodward, II Collection. **Holdings:** 2533 volumes; 3675 maps; 700 atlases. **Subscriptions:** 13 journals and other serials. **Services:** Copying; collection open to the public by appointment. **Automated Operations:** Computerized cataloging, acquisitions, and serials. **Computerized Information Services:** DIALOG Information Services, OCLC. **Networks/Consortia:** Member of SOLINET. **Publications:** A List of Nineteenth Century Maps of the State of Alabama (1973); List of Maps of Birmingham (1978); A List of 16th, 17th, and 18th Century Material in the Rucker Agee Map Collection (1978); The Rucker Agee Map Collection: Issued on the Occasion of the Twenty-Fifth Anniversary Exhibition (1989). **Remarks:** FAX: (205)226-3743.

★1859★
Birmingham Public and Jefferson County Free Library - Linn-Henley Library for Southern Historical Research - Tutwiler Collection of Southern History and Literature (Hist)
2100 Park Place Phone: (205)226-3665
Birmingham, AL 35203 Anne F. Knight, Dept.Hd.
Founded: 1927. **Staff:** Prof 4; Other 8. **Subjects:** Birmingham and Alabama history and literature; Southeastern genealogy; Civil War and Reconstruction history; slave history. **Special Collections:** State, county, and municipal documents. **Holdings:** 62,500 books; 7200 bound periodical volumes; 11,500 reels of microfilm; 1800 pamphlets; 6100 microforms; 154 VF drawers. **Subscriptions:** 358 journals and other serials. **Services:** Collection open to the public for reference use only. **Automated Operations:** Computerized cataloging, acquisitions, and serials. **Computerized Information Services:** DIALOG Information Services, OCLC. **Networks/ Consortia:** Member of SOLINET. **Publications:** George B. Ward: Birmingham's Urban Statesman; Research in Black History; Genealogical Research in the Tutwiler Collection; Bibliography of Birmingham, Alabama, 1872-1972 (book); Contemporary Literature in Birmingham; Eyewitness Accounts of the Civil War series - Battle of the Crater, Raid of the Confederate Cavalry, Service in the Cavalry of the Army of the Potomac, and Synopsis of the Military Career of General Joseph Wheeler; The Secret Proceedings and Debates of the Convention to Form the U.S. Constitution; Creek Indian History. **Special Indexes:** Index to the Birmingham News-Birmingham Post Herald, 1978 to present (microfiche). **Remarks:** FAX: (205)226-3743. **Staff:** Yvonne Crumpler, Libn.; Diane Stewart, Libn.; Carol Hunter, Libn.

★1860★
Birmingham Public and Jefferson County Free Library - Media Services (Aud-Vis)
2100 Park Place Phone: (205)226-3655
Birmingham, AL 35203 Linda M. Classen, Dept.Hd.
Staff: Prof 1; Other 5. **Holdings:** 1692 films; 3700 video cassettes; 3000 slides; 3964 compact discs; 2100 audiocassettes. **Subscriptions:** 4 journals and other serials. **Special Catalogs:** Film and video catalog - free to libraries, for sale to others; spoken audio catalog - for reference use only. **Remarks:** FAX: (205)226-3743.

★1861★
Birmingham Public and Jefferson County Free Library - Science, Technology - Special Collections (Rec)
2100 Park Place
Birmingham, AL 35203 Phone: (205)226-3630
Founded: 1895. **Staff:** Prof 3; Other 2. **Subjects:** Guns and gun collecting. **Holdings:** Materials of Alabama Gun Collectors Association, including books on gun collecting and identification; history of guns; uniforms and memorabilia; other weapons. **Subscriptions:** 2 journals and other serials. **Services:** Interlibrary loan; copying; SDI; collections open to the public. **Automated Operations:** Computerized cataloging, acquisitions, and circulation. **Publications:** Subject and title bibliographies. **Remarks:** FAX: (205)226-3743. **Staff:** Haruyo Miyagawa; Shannon Williams.

★1862★
Birmingham Southern College - Charles Andrew Rush Learning Center/ Library - Special Collections (Rel-Phil, Hist)
800 8th Ave., W.
Box A-20 Phone: (205)226-4744
Birmingham, AL 35254-9990 Billy Pennington, Dir.
Founded: 1859. **Staff:** 12. **Special Collections:** Methodism (880 volumes); Alabama History and Authors (4013 volumes); Branscomb Collection For, By, About Women (510 volumes); BSC Archives (636 items). **Services:** Interlibrary loan (fee); copying; collections open to the public. **Automated Operations:** Computerized public access catalog, acquisitions, serials, and circulation. **Networks/Consortia:** Member of SOLINET, Network of Alabama Academic Libraries (NAAL). **Staff:** Janice Poplau; Caroline Smith; Charlotte Ford.

★1863★
Birmingham Temple - Library (Rel-Phil)
28611 W. 12 Mile Rd. Phone: (313)477-1410
Farmington Hills, MI 48334 Pera Kane, Libn.
Founded: 1971. **Staff:** Prof 1. **Subjects:** Humanism, Judaism, philosophy. **Holdings:** 2000 books. **Subscriptions:** 20 journals and other serials. **Services:** Interlibrary loan; library open to the public by special request. **Publications:** High Holy Days for Humânists; Meditation Services for Humanistic Judaism; What is Humanist Judaism - for sale.

Henry Birnbaum Library
See: **Pace University - Henry Birnbaum Library** (12655)

★1864★
Bisbee Mining and Historical Museum - Shattuck Memorial Library (Hist)
Box 14 Phone: (602)432-7071
Bisbee, AZ 85603-0014 Tom Vaughan, Cur., Archv.Coll.
Founded: 1970. **Staff:** Prof 1; Other 8. **Subjects:** Copper mining, genealogy, Bisbee and Tombstone history, Mexican Revolution. **Special Collections:** Mining company records; Bisbee city directories, 1898-1942; Bisbee records and newspapers, 1898-1942; Tombstone newspapers, 1880-1900; oral history tapes (300); hospital records. **Holdings:** 850 books; 150 bound periodical volumes; 100 manuscript collections; 12,000 photographic prints and negatives. **Subscriptions:** 3 journals and other serials. **Services:** Copying; library open to the public.

★1865★
Bernice P. Bishop Museum - Library (Biol Sci, Hist)
1525 Bernice St.
Box 19000-A Phone: (808)848-4147
Honolulu, HI 96817-0916 Duane E. Wenzel, Lib.Chm.
Founded: 1889. **Staff:** Prof 4; Other 3. **Subjects:** Anthropology, archaeology, entomology, botany, malacology, marine biology, vertebrate and invertebrate zoology, Hawaiiana, exploration, history, linguistics, geology. **Special Collections:** Fuller Collection of Pacific Books (anthropology; 2500 volumes); 19th century Hawaiian language newspapers; Carter Collection of Hawaiiana (1500 volumes); early Pacific voyages; Pacific island language texts. **Holdings:** 90,000 volumes; 1500 microfiche; 1000 reels of microfilm; 25,000 pamphlets. **Subscriptions:** 1700 journals and other serials. **Services:** Copying; library open to the public. **Computerized Information Services:** OCLC. **Publications:** Additions to the Catalog, quarterly - to staff, the University of Hawaii, and other Pacific libraries; directories and guides to place names. **Remarks:** Alternate telephone number(s): 848-4148. FAX: (808)841-8968. **Staff:** Janet Short, Cat.Libn.; Patrice Belcher, Ref.Libn.

★1866★
Bishop & McKenzie, Barristers & Solicitors - Library (Law)
2500, 10104 103rd Ave. Phone: (403)426-5550
Edmonton, AB, Canada T5J 1V3 Katherine McKenney, Libn.
Staff: Prof 1. **Subjects:** Law. **Holdings:** 5000 volumes. **Subscriptions:** 115 journals and other serials. **Services:** Library not open to the public. **Computerized Information Services:** QL Systems, WESTLAW, CAN/ LAW. **Remarks:** FAX: (403)426-1305.

Bishop Memorial Library
See: **Wyoming Historical and Geological Society** (20661)

★1867★
Bishop's Mill Historical Institute - Sol Feinstone Library (Hist)
Ridley Creek State Park Phone: (215)566-1725
Media, PA 19063 Patricia Theodore, Sec.
Founded: 1974. **Staff:** 1. **Subjects:** Pennsylvania colonial history. **Holdings:** 1500 books; 500 bound periodical volumes; 125 reels of microfilm of county records; 25 local maps; 25 local architectural drawings. **Services:** Library open to the public with restrictions.

★1868★
Bismarck Tribune - News Library (Publ)
707 E. Front Ave.
Box 1498 Phone: (701)223-2500
Bismarck, ND 58502 Barbara J. Herzberg-Bender, Libn.
Staff: Prof 1; Other 4. **Subjects:** Newspaper reference topics. **Holdings:** 125 books; 40 binders of Tribune special sections; cuts; mats; clippings; pictures; graphics. **Subscriptions:** 28 newspapers. **Services:** Library open to the public. **Special Indexes:** Index to subject files (binder); graphics index; legislative indexes; index to negatives and contact sheets. **Remarks:** FAX: (701)224-1412.

★1869★
Emily P. Bissell Hospital - Medical Library (Med)
3000 Newport Gap Pike Phone: (302)995-8435
Wilmington, DE 19808 Margaret A. Lacy, Med.Serv.Sec.
Subjects: Pulmonary tuberculosis, medicine, geriatrics. **Holdings:** 250 books. **Services:** Library not open to the public.

★1870★
Bitter Root Valley Historical Society - Ravalli County Museum - Miles Romney Memorial Library (Hist)
Old Court House
205 Bedford Ave. Phone: (406)363-3338
Hamilton, MT 59840 Helen Ann Bibler, Dir.
Founded: 1979. **Staff:** Prof 1. **Subjects:** Pioneer and Indian history. **Special Collections:** Indian Collection; Granville Stuart Collection; Western News Files, 1890-1977; Ravalli Republican Files, 1899 to present; Northwest Tribune Files, 1906-1950; Stevensville Register Files, 1906-1914; western history (two private libraries). **Holdings:** 500 books. **Subscriptions:** 219 newspapers. **Services:** Copying; library open to the public for reference use only. **Staff:** Lucille Gordon, Archv.

Billy Bitzer Collection
See: **Museum of Modern Art - Film Stills Archive** (10908)

★1871★
Emma L. Bixby Hospital - Patmos/Jones Memorial Library (Med)
818 Riverside Ave. Phone: (517)263-0711
Adrian, MI 49221 Cinda Walton, Dir. of Med.Rec.
Staff: 1. **Subjects:** Medicine, surgery, obstetrics-gynecology, pediatrics. **Holdings:** 500 books; 150 bound periodical volumes. **Subscriptions:** 25 journals and other serials. **Services:** Interlibrary loan (limited); library not open to the public. **Formerly:** Its Patmos Memorial Library.

★1872★
Bjorksten Research Laboratories - Library (Sci-Engr)
Box 9444
Madison, WI 53715 Phone: (608)271-6900
Subjects: Inorganic and organic chemistry, biochemistry, chemical engineering, materials, chemicals, processes. **Holdings:** 400 books. **Subscriptions:** 60 journals and other serials. **Services:** Library not open to the public. **Remarks:** FAX: (608)271-6930.

★1873★
BK Associates - Technical Library (Trans)
1295 Northern Blvd.
Manhasset, NY 11030 Phone: (516)365-6272
Staff: 1. **Subjects:** Commercial aeronautics, aeroplanes, aeronautics, air traffic control, airlines marketing, electronic data processing. **Special Collections:** R. Dixon Speas Associates Client Project Collection. **Holdings:** 1700 volumes; 1600 volume project collection; 200 VF drawers of aviation reference files. **Subscriptions:** 400 journals and other serials. **Services:** Interlibrary loan; copying; library open to the public by advance request. **Publications:** Recent Acquisitions, irregular - for internal distribution only.

★1874★
Black Hawk College - Learning Resources Center - Belgian Collection (Area-Ethnic)
6600 34th Ave. Phone: (309)796-1311
Moline, IL 61265 Charlet Key, Lib.Dir.
Founded: 1946. **Staff:** Prof 3; Other 3. **Special Collections:** Belgian history and culture. **Holdings:** 800 books; 250 music tapes. **Services:** Interlibrary loan; copying; collections open to the public by appointment. **Networks/Consortia:** Member of Quad Cities Libraries in Cooperation (Quad-LINC). **Remarks:** FAX: (309)796-0393.

★1875★
Black Hills State University - E.Y. Berry Library-Learning Center - Curriculum Library (Educ)
University St. Phone: (605)642-6833
Spearfish, SD 57799-9573 Pamela M. Blome, Lib.Assoc.
Founded: 1968. **Staff:** Prof 1; Other 10. **Subjects:** Instructional materials for preschool through 12th grade; special education. **Special Collections:** Indian studies; early education. **Holdings:** 12,019 books; 624 AV programs; 1081 multimedia items; 938 curriculum guides and enrichment manuals; filmstrips; phonograph records; teachers' guides; textbooks; tests; workbooks; publishers' catalogs. **Services:** Copying; library open to the public with restrictions. **Computerized Information Services:** Internal database.

★1876★
Black Hills State University - E.Y. Berry Library-Learning Center - Special Collections (Hist)
1200 University Phone: (605)642-6361
Spearfish, SD 57799-9511 Dora Ann Jones, Spec.Coll.Libn.
Founded: 1925. **Staff:** Prof 1. **Subjects:** Local and regional history, biography, Dakota Indians, western industry, transportation, North American Indians. **Special Collections:** E.Y. Berry Collection (manuscripts, photographs, color slides, tape recordings, and films, all dealing with his 20 years of service in the U.S. House of Representatives, 1951-1971); Black Hills State University Archives; Leland D. Case Library for Western Historical Studies; Library of American Civilization (microfiche); Wagner-Camp Collection (microcard); Cox Library (microfilm). **Holdings:** 12,392 volumes; 918 manuscript boxes; 54 VF drawers; 85 drawers of maps and photographs; 12,888 titles on 14,548 microforms. **Subscriptions:** 60 journals and other serials; 7 newspapers. **Services:** Copying; collections open to the public with restrictions. **Automated Operations:** Computerized cataloging, acquisitions, serials, and circulation. **Computerized Information Services:** OCLC. **Networks/Consortia:** Member of MINITEX Library Information Network, South Dakota Library Network (SDLN). **Remarks:** FAX: (605)642-6298.

Richard & Marieluise Black Information Center
See: **Beloit College - Colonel Robert H. Morse Library** (1703)

★1877★
Black Rock Forest Library (Biol Sci)
Continental Rd.
Box 483 Phone: (914)534-4517
Cornwall, NY 12518 Jack J. Karnig, Director
Subjects: Forestry. **Holdings:** 11,156 books and bound periodical volumes. **Subscriptions:** 36 journals and other serials. **Services:** Library not open to the public. **Computerized Information Services:** OCLC. **Networks/Consortia:** Member of NELINET, Inc., Center for Research Libraries (CRL).

Black Sparrow Press Archives
See: **University of Alberta - Humanities and Social Sciences Library - Bruce Peel Special Collections Library** (18196)

Black Sparrow Press Archives
See: **University of Arizona - Special Collections Department** (18231)

★1878★
Black & Veatch - B & V Central Library (Sci-Engr)
8400 Ward Pkwy.
Box 8405 Phone: (913)339-2216
Kansas City, MO 64114-0405 Leo M. Hack, Libn.
Staff: Prof 1; Other 4. **Subjects:** Engineering. **Holdings:** 3000 books; 100 bound periodical volumes. **Subscriptions:** 150 journals and other serials. **Services:** Interlibrary loan. **Computerized Information Services:** DIALOG Information Services. **Remarks:** FAX: (913)339-2934.

★1879★
Black & Veatch Engineers-Architects - Library (Sci-Engr)
Box 728 Phone: (919)672-3600
Asheboro, NC 27204-0728 Pat Garner
Founded: 1975. **Staff:** Prof 1. **Subjects:** Architecture; sanitary, electrical, and civil engineering. **Holdings:** 600 books; 650 technical reports. **Subscriptions:** 100 journals and other serials. **Services:** Interlibrary loan; library open to the public with restrictions. **Special Indexes:** KWIC index to technical reports.

★1880★
Black Women in Church and Society - Research/Resource Center (Soc Sci)
Inter Denominational Theological Center
671 Beckwith St., S.W. Phone: (404)527-7740
Atlanta, GA 30314 Jacqueline Grant
Subjects: Liberation theology, feminism, women's movements, women in ministry. **Holdings:** 250 volumes.

Blackader Library of Architecture
See: **McGill University - Blackader Library of Architecture/Lauterman Library of Art** (9892)

George C. Blackburn Memorial Library
See: **Reformed Theological Seminary - Library** (13781)

Blackburn Library
See: **Covenant Theological Seminary - J. Oliver Buswell, Jr. Library** (4391)

Blacker/Wood Library of Biology
See: **McGill University - Blacker/Wood Library of Biology** (9893)

★1881★
Blackford County Historical Society - Museum and Beeson Library (Hist)
Box 264 Phone: (317)348-1905
Hartford City, IN 47348 Catherine Sparks, Pres.
Founded: 1956. **Staff:** 1. **Subjects:** Local history, genealogy. **Special Collections:** Local newspapers, 1890-1963 (100 bound volumes). **Holdings:** 200 books; 100 bound periodical volumes; 100 Quaker records and 40 county records on microfilm; 20 genealogies. **Services:** Copying; library open May-September with restrictions.

★1882★
Blackhawk Genealogical Society - Library (Hist)
Box 3912 Phone: (309)786-5927
Rock Island, IL 61204-3912 Pamela Langston
Founded: 1972. **Subjects:** Genealogy, history. **Holdings:** 250 books; 950 unbound periodicals; pamphlets; 51 reels of microfilm of U.S. Locality Microfilm Collection of Church of Jesus Christ of Latter-Day Saints Family History Center. **Subscriptions:** 28 journals and other serials. **Services:** Copying; library open to the public. **Remarks:** Library located at Rock Island Public Library, 401 19th St., Rock Island, IL 61201.

★1883★
Blackhawk Technical College - Library (Educ)
6004 Prairie Rd.
Box 5009 Phone: (608)757-7705
Janesville, WI 53547 Janet L. White, Libn.
Founded: 1965. **Staff:** Prof 2; Other 2. **Subjects:** Health, electronics, avionics, marketing, agriculture, business occupations. **Special Collections:** Child care. **Holdings:** 25,000 books; 3500 AV programs; 1500 computer software packages; 200 periodical titles on microfiche. **Subscriptions:** 440 journals and other serials; 9 newspapers. **Services:** Interlibrary loan; copying; SDI; center open to the public. **Automated Operations:** Computerized circulation. **Computerized Information Services:** Internal database. **Networks/Consortia:** Member of National Network of Libraries of Medicine - Greater Midwest Region, South Central Wisconsin Health Science Libraries Consortium. **Special Catalogs:** AV Software & Computer Software Catalog, annual. **Staff:** William R. Curtis, Media Rsrcs.Dir.

★1884★
Samuel H. Blackmer Memorial Library (Law)
County Court House
207 South St.
Box 157
Bennington, VT 05201 Phone: (802)447-2700
Founded: 1952. **Subjects:** Law. **Special Collections:** Old Vermont statutes. **Holdings:** 2000 volumes. **Services:** Library open to the public by appointment for reference use.

Blackwell Library
See: **Salisbury State University** (14640)

★1885★
Blackwell & Walker, P.A. - Law Library (Law)
2400 Amerifirst Bldg.
One S.E. Third Ave. Phone: (305)995-5717
Miami, FL 33131 Ray Richards, Law Libn.
Staff: Prof 1. **Subjects:** Law - business, insurance, medical, litigation. **Holdings:** 25,000 volumes. **Subscriptions:** 20 journals and other serials. **Services:** Library not open to the public. **Computerized Information Services:** LEXIS, WESTLAW. **Remarks:** FAX: (305)372-1468.

Blagg-Huey Library
See: **Texas Woman's University** (16279)

Allan Blair Memorial Clinic
See: **Saskatchewan Cancer Foundation** (14840)

★1886★
Blair County Law Library (Law)
County Court House
423 Allegheny St. Phone: (814)695-5541
Hollidaysburg, PA 16648 June C. Ringdal, Law Libn.
Subjects: Law, tax. **Holdings:** Figures not available. **Services:** Library not open to the public.

Blair-Lippincott Library/LRC
See: **Eye and Ear Institute Pavilion** (5537)

★1887★
William Blair & Co. - Information Services (Bus-Fin)
135 S. LaSalle St. Phone: (312)853-8334
Chicago, IL 60603 Janice Skidmore Keeler, Mgr., Info.Serv.
Founded: 1988. **Staff:** 5. **Subjects:** Corporate information, finance, business. **Special Collections:** Corporate annual reports. **Holdings:** 250 books; corporate documents. **Subscriptions:** 250 journals and other serials. **Services:** Services not open to the public. **Automated Operations:** Computerized acquisitions, circulation, and serials. **Computerized Information Services:** DIALOG Information Services, Dow Jones News/Retrieval, NEXIS, VU/TEXT Information Services, NewsNet, Inc., CDA Investment Technologies, Inc, DataTimes, Data-Star, Securities Data, IRI Online, InvesText. **Networks/Consortia:** Member of Chicago Library System. **Remarks:** FAX: (312)236-1673.

★1888★
Blake, Cassels & Graydon - Library (Law)
Commerce Court West
P.O. Box 25 Phone: (416)863-2650
Toronto, ON, Canada M5L 1A9 Sandra M. Morris, Libn.
Founded: 1858. **Staff:** Prof 3; Other 5.5. **Subjects:** Law - corporate, commercial, securities, litigation, banking, tax. **Holdings:** 12,000 books; 3000 bound periodical volumes; 6000 bound reports; 5000 bound statutes; 10 drawers of microfiche. **Subscriptions:** 127 journals and other serials; 8 newspapers. **Services:** Interlibrary loan; copying; SDI; library open by appointment. **Computerized Information Services:** Info Globe, DIALOG Information Services, Dow Jones News/Retrieval, STM Systems Corporation, Infomart Online, Marketscan, LEXIS, WESTLAW, QL Systems, Canadian Tax Online, Reuters, Data-Star, CAN/LAW, Library of Legal Memoranda, Library of Legal Precedents (internal databases). Performs searches on fee basis. **Publications:** Blake's Current Law Newsletter, weekly. **Special Indexes:** Indexes to federal and provincial legislation, federal legislative histories, vertical files, and unreported decisions. **Remarks:** FAX: (416)863-4261. Telex: 06-219687. **Staff:** Dawn M. Urquhart, Dept.Hd., Tech.Serv.; Wray W. Roulston, Res.Libn.

Martha A. Blake Memorial Library
See: **U.S. Army - Corps of Engineers - Construction Engineering Research Laboratory** (16936)

Rosanna A. Blake Library of Confederate History
See: **Marshall University - James E. Morrow Library** (9724)

Stuart B. Blakely Memorial Library
See: **United Health Services/Binghamton General Hospital** (16714)

Blanchfield Army Community Hospital
See: **U.S. Army Hospitals** (17033)

Schuyler Otis Bland Memorial Library
See: **U.S. Merchant Marine Academy** (17607)

★1889★
Blanden Memorial Art Museum - Art Library (Art)
920 3rd Ave., S. Phone: (515)573-2316
Fort Dodge, IA 50501 Philip A. LaDouceur, Dir.
Subjects: Art history, artists, architecture. **Holdings:** 4000 volumes. **Subscriptions:** 20 journals and other serials. **Services:** Library open to the public by appointment. **Remarks:** FAX: (515)573-2317.

Blandy Experimental Farm Library
See: **University of Virginia** (19499)

★1890★
Blaney, McMurtry, Stapells - Law Library (Law)
Cadillac Fairview Tower
20 Queen St., W., Suite 1400 Phone: (416)593-1221
Toronto, ON, Canada M5H 2V3 Linda Zardo, Libn.
Staff: Prof 1; Other 1. **Subjects:** Law. **Holdings:** 10,000 books and law reports. **Subscriptions:** 100 journals and other serials. **Services:** Interlibrary loan; library not open to the public. **Computerized Information Services:** CAN/LAW, QL Systems, WESTLAW, The Financial Post DataGroup, Infomart Online, VU/TEXT Information Services. **Publications:** Library Information Bulletin, weekly. **Remarks:** FAX: (416)593-5437.

★1891★
Blank Park Zoo of Des Moines - Library (Biol Sci)
7401 S.W. 9th St. Phone: (515)285-4722
Des Moines, IA 50315 Monica Watson, Educ.Cur.
Founded: 1982. **Staff:** Prof 1; Other 1. **Subjects:** Zoology, biology, natural history. **Holdings:** 500 books; animal records. **Subscriptions:** 5 journals and other serials. **Services:** Library not open to the public.

★1892★
Blank, Rome, Comisky & McCauley - Library (Law)
Woodland Falls Corp. Park
210 Lake Dr., E., Suite 200
Cherry Hill, NJ 08002 Phone: (609)779-3600
Staff: 1.5. **Subjects:** Law. **Holdings:** Figures not available. **Services:** Library not open to the public. **Computerized Information Services:** LEXIS, Westlaw, VU/TEXT Information Services, Information America. **Remarks:** FAX: (609)779-7647.

★1893★
Blank, Rome, Comisky & McCauley - Library (Law)
4 Penn Center Plaza Phone: (215)569-5490
Philadelphia, PA 19103-2599 Kit Boyle
Staff: Prof 2; Other 2. **Subjects:** Law. **Holdings:** 25,000 books; 1000 bound periodical volumes. **Subscriptions:** 400 journals and other serials; 25 newspapers. **Services:** Interlibrary loan; copying; library open to the public by appointment. **Remarks:** FAX: (215)569-5555. **Staff:** Edmund Sonnenberg.

John H. Blankenbuehler Memorial Library
See: **Hobart Institute of Welding Technology** (7299)

Helen Blau Memorial Library
See: **Central Synagogue of Nassau County** (3371)

Jacob and Bessye Blaufarb Videotape Library
See: **New York University - Tamiment Library** (11733)

Blaustein Library
See: **American Jewish Committee** (652)

Blaxter Memorial Library
See: **Children's Hospital of Pittsburgh** (3583)

★1894★
Blessed Sacrament Seminary - Library (Rel-Phil)
5384 Wilson Mills Rd. Phone: (216)442-3411
Cleveland, OH 44143 William Young, Act.Libn.
Founded: 1931. **Staff:** 1. **Subjects:** Theology, philosophy, humanities, religion, biblical studies. **Special Collections:** Migne's Patrologia Graeca, Latina (386 volumes). **Holdings:** 25,000 books; 3500 bound periodical volumes; 16 VF drawers of pamphlets and documents. **Subscriptions:** 40 journals and other serials; 4 newspapers. **Services:** Library open to the public with restrictions at librarian's discretion. **Remarks:** FAX: (216)449-3862. Maintained by the Blessed Sacrament Fathers.

Blessing Hospital
See: **Blessing-Rieman College of Nursing - Library** (1895)

★1895★
Blessing-Rieman College of Nursing - Library (Med)
Broadway at 11th St.
P.O. Box C3 Phone: (217)223-8400
Quincy, IL 62305-3117 Arlis Dittmer, Libn.
Founded: 1892. **Staff:** Prof 1; Other 1. **Subjects:** Nursing, medicine. **Holdings:** 3500 books; 720 bound periodical volumes; 230 reports; 520 AV programs. **Subscriptions:** 83 journals and other serials. **Services:** Interlibrary loan; copying; SDI; library open to the public for reference use only. **Computerized Information Services:** DIALOG Information Services. **Networks/Consortia:** Member of West Central Consortium (WCC), ILLINET. **Remarks:** FAX: (217)223-6400.

★1896★
Blind Children's Fund - Parent Resource Center - Library (Med)
230 Central St. Phone: (617)332-4014
Auburndale, MA 02166-2399 Sherry Raynor, Dir.
Subjects: Blind infants and toddlers - pre-braille skills, assessment tools, home teaching, preschool curriculums, special toys and equipment; premature infants; multihandicapped children. **Holdings:** Figures not available. **Services:** Library open to parents and professionals. **Staff:** Jocelyn Chemel, Parent Coord.

Bliss Army Hospital
See: **U.S. Army Hospitals** (17034)

Bliss Memorial Library
See: **First Methodist Church** (5782)

Blitman Reading Room
See: **Temple University - Department of Journalism** (16145)

John Blizard Research Center
See: **Foster Wheeler Development Corporation** (6033)

★1897★
Ernest Bloch Society - Archives (Mus)
34844 Old Stage Rd. Phone: (503)639-3734
Gualala, CA 95445 Lucienne Bloch Dimitroff, Supv.
Founded: 1969. **Staff:** 1. **Subjects:** Ernest Bloch - biography, music, bibliography. **Special Collections:** Ernest Bloch letters (300); notes on Bloch's pedagogy; complete list of The E.B. Bulletin, 1938 to present. **Holdings:** 60 scores; 150 Ernest Bloch recordings; 20 concert tapes; 50 books on science and philosophy annotated by Ernest Bloch; 100 photographs; 200 programs and clippings; 30 articles on or by Bloch; compact discs. **Services:** Archives open to members by appointment. **Publications:** Ernest Bloch Society Bulletin (newsletter), annual - to members and libraries. **Remarks:** The Sibley Library of the Eastman School of Music maintains a collection of Bloch's work. In addition, the music departments of the Library of Congress and of the University of California in Berkeley have music and letters by Ernest Bloch. The Center for Creative Photography, University of Arizona at Tucson has E. Bloch's photograph collection in its archives.

Isidore Bloch Memorial Library
See: **Congregation B'nai Israel** (4155)

★1898★
Block Drug Company - Research and Development Library (Med)
257 Cornelison Ave. Phone: (201)424-3000
Jersey City, NJ 07302 Karen Berryman, Tech.Libn.
Founded: 1960. **Staff:** Prof 1; Other 2. **Subjects:** Dentistry, medicine, pharmacology, dermatology. **Holdings:** 2000 books. **Services:** SDI; library not open to the public. **Computerized Information Services:** DIALOG Information Services, STN International, Data-Star, ORBIT Search Service, NLM. **Remarks:** FAX: (201)434-0842.

Charles L. Blockson Afro-American Historical Collection
See: **Temple University - Charles L. Blockson Afro-American Historical Collection** (16144)

★1899★
Blodgett Memorial Medical Center - Richard Root Smith Library (Med)
1840 Wealthy St., S.E. Phone: (616)774-7624
Grand Rapids, MI 49506 Brian Simmons, Med.Libn.
Staff: Prof 2. **Subjects:** Medicine, surgery, allied health sciences. **Holdings:** 1800 books; 7100 bound periodical volumes; 500 audiotape cassettes; 3000 anatomical slides; 3000 unbound periodicals. **Subscriptions:** 250 journals and other serials. **Services:** Interlibrary loan; copying; SDI; library open to the public. **Computerized Information Services:** MEDLINE, DIALOG Information Services; electronic mail service. Performs searches on fee basis. **Networks/Consortia:** Member of Michigan Health Sciences Libraries Association (MHSLA), Lakeland Area Library Network (LAKENET). **Staff:** Lois K. Huisman, Asst.Libn.

★1900★
Blommel Historic Automotive Data Collection - Library and Information Center (Hist)
Rte. 5 Phone: (317)825-9259
Connersville, IN 47331 Henry H. Blommel, Collector-Dir.
Founded: 1928. **Subjects:** History - Connersville, Fayette County, Indiana, U.S. and Indiana automotive industry, U.S. Army and its vehicles. **Special Collections:** Connersville industrial history and "Little Detroit" era of Indiana and U.S. automotive makers; Cord Corporation automobiles. **Holdings:** 650 books; 1500 bound periodical volumes; 500 other cataloged items; collections of former craftsmen. **Subscriptions:** 25 journals and other serials; 10 newspapers. **Services:** Library open to the public with restrictions.

Blommer Science Library
See: **Georgetown University** (6375)

★1901★
Bloodstock Research Information Services, Inc. - Library (Rec)
801 Corporate Dr., 3rd Fl.
P.O. Box 4097
Lexington, KY 40544 Phone: (606)223-4444
Subjects: Thoroughbred horses, horse breeding, horse racing, horse and farm management. **Holdings:** 1000 bound volumes. **Subscriptions:** 20 journals and other serials. **Computerized Information Services:** Produces databank on thoroughbred horses. Performs searches on fee basis. **Remarks:** Toll-free telephone number(s): (800)354-9206. FAX: (606)223-7024.

★1902★
Bloomfield College - George Talbott Hall Library (Bus-Fin, Hum, Soc Sci)
467 Franklin St. Phone: (201)748-9000
Bloomfield, NJ 07003 Danilo Figueredo, Dir.
Founded: 1957. **Staff:** Prof 5; Other 10. **Subjects:** Business administration, nursing, social and behavioral sciences, humanities, physical science, fine arts. **Special Collections:** Presbyterian Church history; Bloomfield College history. **Holdings:** 59,000 books; 2361 bound periodical volumes; 4500 reels of microfilm. **Subscriptions:** 350 journals and other serials. **Services:** Interlibrary loan; copying; collections open to the public for reference use only. **Automated Operations:** Computerized cataloging. **Computerized Information Services:** DIALOG Information Services, BRS Information Technologies, OCLC. **Networks/Consortia:** Member of Essex Hudson Regional Library Cooperative, PALINET. **Publications:** Library Notes, 3/year. **Remarks:** FAX: (201)743-3998. **Staff:** Jamileh Amirzafari, Ref.Libn.; Barbara Isacson, AV Coord.; Rita Willis, Acq. & Per. Coord.; Allison Capel, Circ.Hd.

★1903★
Bloomington-Normal Pantagraph - Newspaper Library (Publ)
301 W. Washington St.
Box 2907 Phone: (309)829-9411
Bloomington, IL 61701 Diane Sponsler, Lib.Dir.
Founded: 1930. **Staff:** Prof 2; Other 1. **Subjects:** Newspaper reference topics. **Special Collections:** Adlai Stevenson II (news articles and pictures). **Holdings:** 500 books; clippings; 6000 photographs; 80,000 microfiche. **Subscriptions:** 10 journals and other serials; 15 newspapers. **Services:** Library not open to the public. **Computerized Information Services:** DataTimes. **Remarks:** FAX: (309)829-7000. **Staff:** Carlene Mathias-Kull, Libn.

★1904★
Bloomsburg University - Harvey A. Andruss Library - Special Collections (Educ)
Bloomsburg, PA 17815 Phone: (717)389-4204
J. Daniel Vann, III, Dean, Lib.Serv.
Founded: 1839. **Staff:** 23.5. **Subjects:** Education, history, children's literature. **Holdings:** Juvenile literature (12,691 volumes); Elinor R. Keefer Collection of Newbery and Caldecott Award winners; art exhibition catalogs; university archives. **Subscriptions:** 1689 journals and other serials; 32 newspapers. **Services:** Interlibrary loan; copying; collections open to the public. **Automated Operations:** Computerized public access catalog and circulation (PALS). **Computerized Information Services:** DIALOG Information Services, OCLC, UMI Article Clearinghouse; PALINET, CALL (electronic mail services). Performs searches on fee basis. Contact Person: Loanne Snavely Ref.Libn. **Networks/Consortia:** Member of Susquehanna Library Cooperative, State System of Higher Education Libraries Council (SSHELCO), PALINET. **Remarks:** FAX: (717)389-3895.

Glenn O. Blough Library
See: **National Science Teachers Association** (11283)

★1905★
Blount Memorial Hospital - Leslie R. Lingeman Memorial Medical Library (Med)
907 E. Lamar Alexander Hwy. Phone: (615)977-5520
Maryville, TN 37801-5193 Barbara H. Payne, Med.Libn.
Founded: 1947. **Staff:** Prof 1. **Subjects:** Internal medicine, pediatrics, nursing, psychiatry, surgery, dermatology, obstetrics, gynecology, urology, orthopedics, cardiology, and allied health subjects. **Holdings:** 773 books; 1511 bound periodical volumes; 6 VF drawers of pamphlets. **Subscriptions:** 85 journals and other serials. **Services:** Interlibrary loan; copying; library open to the public. **Computerized Information Services:** MEDLINE. **Networks/Consortia:** Member of Knoxville Area Health Sciences Library Consortium (KAHSLC), Tennessee Health Science Library Association (THeSLA). **Remarks:** FAX: (615)981-2473.

★1906★
Blue Cloud Abbey - Library (Rel-Phil, Area-Ethnic)
Box 98 Phone: (605)432-5528
Marvin, SD 57251 Rev. John David McMullen, O.S.B., Hd.Libn., MSLS
Founded: 1954. **Staff:** Prof 1; Other 2. **Subjects:** Scripture, monastic theology, patristics, church history, general theology, Indian history. **Special Collections:** Bureau of American Ethnology publications (complete set). **Holdings:** 50,000 books; 600 bound periodical volumes. **Subscriptions:** 150 journals and other serials; 20 newspapers. **Services:** Interlibrary loan; copying; library open to the public with librarian's permission. **Automated Operations:** Computerized cataloging and circulation. **Remarks:** FAX: (605)432-4754.

★1907★
Blue Cross and Blue Shield Association - Library (Bus-Fin)
676 N. St. Clair Phone: (312)440-5510
Chicago, IL 60611 Shirley Cunningham, Hd.Libn.
Founded: 1956. **Staff:** Prof 2. **Subjects:** Health - insurance, economics, services; business. **Holdings:** 15,000 books; 3000 congressional documents; Federal Register, 1965 to present, on microfilm. **Subscriptions:** 180 journals and other serials. **Services:** Interlibrary loan; copying; library open to the public by request. **Computerized Information Services:** DIALOG Information Services, NEXIS. **Networks/Consortia:** Member of National Network of Libraries of Medicine - Greater Midwest Region, Chicago Library System. **Staff:** Mary T. Drazba, Libn.

★1908★
Blue Cross and Blue Shield of Florida - Corporate Research Library (Bus-Fin)
532 Riverside Ave.
Box 1798 Phone: (904)791-6937
Jacksonville, FL 32231 William J. Condon, Lib.Mgr.
Staff: Prof 2. **Subjects:** Health insurance, health care, insurance, demographics, management, employee benefits. **Holdings:** 4000 books. **Subscriptions:** 220 journals and other serials. **Services:** Interlibrary loan; copying; library open to college students or others doing serious research. **Computerized Information Services:** DIALOG Information Services, NEXIS, Dow Jones News/Retrieval, VU/TEXT Information Services. **Remarks:** FAX: (904)791-6181. **Staff:** Marjorie Pace, Libn.

★1909★
Blue Cross and Blue Shield of Missouri - Library (Bus-Fin)
4444 Forest Park Blvd. Phone: (314)658-4774
St. Louis, MO 63108 Howard E. Miller, Act.Libn.
Founded: 1970. **Staff:** Prof 1. **Subjects:** Health care, insurance, economics, business. **Holdings:** 6000 books; 210 bound periodical volumes; 9 VF drawers of pamphlets and clippings; 2 VF drawer of speeches and reports. **Subscriptions:** 228 journals and other serials. **Services:** Interlibrary loan; SDI; library open to the public by appointment. **Networks/Consortia:** Member of St. Louis Regional Library Network. **Publications:** Library Bulletin, monthly - for internal distribution only. **Remarks:** FAX: (314)658-4809. **Staff:** Marilyn Love, Lib.Asst.

★1910★
Blue Cross and Blue Shield of North Carolina - Information Center (Bus-Fin)
Box 2291 Phone: (919)490-4176
Durham, NC 27702 Elizabeth J. Turner, Mgr., Corp.Info.Ctr.
Founded: 1970. **Staff:** Prof 2; Other 1. **Subjects:** Health insurance, health economics, management, North Carolina population and economy. **Holdings:** 2000 books; 130 bound periodical volumes; 50,500 reports; 10,000 microfiche. **Subscriptions:** 175 journals and other serials; 7 newspapers. **Services:** Interlibrary loan; copying; center open to the public by appointment. **Automated Operations:** Computerized cataloging. **Computerized Information Services:** DIALOG Information Services, LEXIS, NEXIS, OCLC. **Networks/Consortia:** Member of North Carolina Information Network (NCIN). **Publications:** For Your Information, monthly - to management. **Special Indexes:** Index to BCBSNC's filings with North Carolina Department of Insurance; current index to insurance literature. **Remarks:** Alternate telephone number(s): 489-7431. FAX: (919)419-1082. **Staff:** Michael West, Libn.

★1911★
Blue Cross of Western Pennsylvania - Corporate Library (Bus-Fin)
Fifth Avenue Place, Suite 1718 Phone: (412)255-8220
Pittsburgh, PA 15222 William R. Harrison, Corp.Libn.
Founded: 1945. **Staff:** Prof 1; Other 1. **Subjects:** Employee benefits, health care financing. **Holdings:** 3000 books; 1000 pamphlets. **Subscriptions:** 88 journals and other serials. **Services:** Interlibrary loan; library not open to the public. **Automated Operations:** Computerized cataloging, acquisitions, and circulation. **Computerized Information Services:** DIALOG Information Services, OCLC, Mead Data Central, Risk and Insurance Management Society (RIMS), Human Resource Information Network (HRIN). **Remarks:** FAX: (412)255-8159.

★1912★
Blue Cross of Western Pennsylvania - Health Education Center Library (Med)
Fifth Avenue Place, Suite 313 Phone: (412)255-7390
Pittsburgh, PA 15222 Tina Palaggo-Toy, Mgr.
Founded: 1976. **Staff:** Prof 1. **Subjects:** Health education and promotion, prevention, wellness, health care delivery, disease, patient education. **Special Collections:** Consumer health education (3500 pamphlets). **Holdings:** 700 books; 10,000 newsletters, pamphlets, reports, preprints. **Subscriptions:** 52 journals and newsletters. **Services:** Copying; library open to the public. **Networks/Consortia:** Member of Pittsburgh Regional Library Center (PRLC). **Publications:** Update (newsletter), bimonthly.

★1913★
Blue Earth County Historical Society - Archives (Hist)
Heritage Center
415 Cherry St. Phone: (507)345-5566
Mankato, MN 56001 Jeffrey A. Kroke, Archv.
Founded: 1916. **Staff:** Prof 1; Other 1. **Subjects:** Blue Earth County history - agriculture, Indians, industries, genealogy, organizations. **Special Collections:** Papers of Thomas Hughes, R. Dean Hubbard, J. A. Willard family, Franklin H. Waite, and Anna Wiecking. **Holdings:** 500 books; 250 daybooks, diaries, manuscript collections; 2500 other cataloged items; scrapbooks; atlases; maps; 1000 photographs; bound newspaper volumes; newspapers, church and cemetery records on microfilm. **Subscriptions:** 15 journals and other serials. **Services:** Copying; archives open to the public. **Special Indexes:** Index to county newspapers; index to obituaries; index to photographs; index to subject file (all on cards); index of county tombstone transcriptions (online); cemetery transcription index (online).

Blue Hill Meteorological Observatory Library
See: **Harvard University - Division of Applied Sciences** (6959)

★1914★
Blue Mountain College - Music Library (Mus)
Blue Mountain, MS 38610 Phone: (601)685-4771
Carolyn Mounce, Libn.
Subjects: Music. **Holdings:** 1970 books and scores; 2713 recordings; 196 unbound periodical volumes; 92 computer discs. **Services:** Interlibrary loan; copying; library open to the public with permission.

Blue Ridge Heritage Archive
See: **Ferrum College** (5673)

★1915★
Blue Springs Historical Society - Library (Hist)
3929 Milton Dr. Phone: (816)373-5309
Independence, MO 64055 Larry Wiebusch, Musm.Chm.
Founded: 1976. **Subjects:** Local history. **Holdings:** 50 books; 5 oral histories. **Services:** Library not open to the public. **Publications:** Newsletters, irregular; Cook Book; Blue Springs History. **Staff:** Robert L. Grover, Chm.

★1916★
Bluefield Daily Telegraph - Library (Publ)
928 Bluefield Ave. Phone: (304)327-6171
Bluefield, WV 24701-2744 Sue Richmond, Info.Dir.
Staff: Prof 1. **Subjects:** Newspaper reference topics, coal, railroads, state education, state politics. **Holdings:** Bluefield Daily Telegraph, 1893 to present. **Subscriptions:** 10 journals and other serials. **Services:** Copying; library open to the public with restrictions. **Remarks:** FAX: (304)327-6179.

★1917★
Bluffton College - Mennonite Historical Library (Rel-Phil)
280 W. College Ave. Phone: (419)358-3365
Bluffton, OH 45817 Ann Hilty, Act.Libn.
Founded: 1937. **Staff:** 1. **Subjects:** History - Mennonite, Amish, Anabaptist, Hutterian Brethren, Apostolic Christian Church; Mennonite family genealogy; peace. **Holdings:** 17,000 books; 500 bound periodical volumes; 30 boxes of letters and manuscripts; 200 reels of microfilm; 1000 theses, dissertations, pictures, maps, miscellaneous papers. **Subscriptions:** 300 journals and other serials; 10 newspapers. **Services:** Interlibrary loan; library open to the public. **Automated Operations:** Computerized cataloging and ILL. **Computerized Information Services:** OCLC.

F.D. Bluford Library
See: **North Carolina A&T State University** (11876)

★1918★
Blume, Vazquez, Goldfaden, Berkowitz, et al. - Library (Law)
5 Commerce St. Phone: (201)622-1881
Newark, NJ 07102 June Beckford-Smith, Libn.
Founded: 1976. **Staff:** Prof 1. **Subjects:** Law, medical malpractice, products liability. **Special Collections:** Obstetrics and gynecology collection. **Holdings:** 3000 books; 100 standards; 600 pamphlets; 1500 internal documents. **Subscriptions:** 40 journals and other serials. **Services:** Library not open to the public. **Computerized Information Services:** DIALOG Information Services, Dun & Bradstreet Business Credit Services, WESTLAW. **Remarks:** FAX: (201)622-1643; (201)622-3526.

Blumenthal Rare Book and Manuscript Library
See: **Judah L. Magnes Memorial Museum - Blumenthal Rare Book and Manuscript Library** (9537)

Erle M. Blunden, M.D. Memorial Library
See: **Mercy American River Hospital** (10125)

Joseph E. Bluth Memorial Library
See: **Columbia College-Hollywood** (3980)

★1919★
BMT CORTEC Limited - Library (Trans, Sci-Engr)
Wallsend Research Station
Wallsend, Tyne and Wear NE28 6UY, England
Phone: 91 2625242
G. Smith, Hd. of Info.Serv.
Founded: 1945. **Staff:** Prof 2; Other 1. **Subjects:** Ship operation, offshore engineering, ship/offshore design, ocean engineering, fluid mechanics, maritime technology. **Holdings:** 5000 books; 500 bound periodical volumes; 30,000 other cataloged items. **Subscriptions:** 403 journals and other serials. **Services:** Interlibrary loan; copying; SDI; library not open to the public. **Automated Operations:** Computerized cataloging. **Computerized Information Services:** Internal database. Performs searches on fee basis. **Publications:** BMT Abstracts, monthly - by subscription. **Remarks:** FAX: 91 2638754. Telex: 53476. **Formerly:** British Maritime Technology Ltd.

★1920★
B'nai Brith Hillel Foundation at McGill University - Library (Area-Ethnic, Rel-Phil)
3460 Stanley St.
Montreal, PQ, Canada H3A 1R8
Phone: (514)845-9171
Founded: 1950. **Subjects:** Philosophy and religion of Judaism; Jewish law; contemporary Jewish problems; Jewish art, music, drama; Jewish history; Israel; Zionism. **Holdings:** 6000 books; 400 bound periodical volumes; 700 pamphlets. **Subscriptions:** 100 journals and other serials; 15 newspapers. **Services:** Library open to the public for reference use only. **Remarks:** FAX: (514)842-6405.

★1921★
B'nai Jeshurun Temple on the Heights - Jacobson Library (Rel-Phil)
27501 Fairmount Blvd.
Pepper Pike, OH 44124
Phone: (216)831-6555
Andrea Davidson, Libn.
Founded: 1928. **Staff:** Prof 1. **Subjects:** Judaica, Holocaust, juvenile Judaica, Israel. **Holdings:** 9000 volumes. **Subscriptions:** 25 journals and other serials. **Services:** Library open to members only.

★1922★
B'nai Zion Temple - Memorial Library (Rel-Phil)
245 Southfield Dr.
Shreveport, LA 71105
Phone: (318)861-2122
Judy Grunes, Libn.
Staff: Prof 1; Other 3. **Subjects:** Judaica - reference and teaching, history, philosophy, literature, language, arts, music. **Holdings:** 4016 books; 102 bound periodical volumes. **Subscriptions:** 14 journals and other serials. **Services:** Library not open to the public.

★1923★
Board of Cooperative Educational Services of Nassau County (BOCES) - REP Information Center (Educ)
Carle Place Concourse
234 Glen Cove Rd.
Carle Place, NY 11514
Phone: (516)294-4160
Founded: 1971. **Staff:** Prof 1; Other 2.5. **Subjects:** Education. **Special Collections:** Resources for education professionals in special education, English as a second language, occupational education, curriculum development, administration and supervision, gifted and talented students, and education law. **Holdings:** 20,000 books; 550 unbound periodical volumes; 3000 curriculum guides; complete set of ERIC microfiche; 2000 AV programs; 500 16mm films, kits, filmstrips, video cassettes. **Subscriptions:** 200 journals and other serials. **Services:** Interlibrary loan (limited); center not open to the public. **Computerized Information Services:** BRS Information Technologies, WILSONLINE, DataTimes, DIALOG Information Services. **Networks/Consortia:** Member of Long Island Library Resources Council. **Publications:** Bibliographies on current educational topics; acquisitions lists. **Remarks:** FAX: (516)747-0418. **Formerly:** Its Nassau Educational Resource and Planning Center (NERPC). **Staff:** Elinor Haber, Lib./Media Spec.

★1924★
Board of Jewish Education of Greater New York - Educational Resource Library (Rel-Phil)
426 W. 58th St.
New York, NY 10019
Phone: (212)245-8200
Rabbi Harry Cohenson, Assoc., Judaic Rsrcs.
Staff: 1. **Subjects:** Jewish education, Judaica, general education. **Special Collections:** Resources on the Holocaust, Israel, Biblical and Talmudic studies, Jewish history and Hebrew literature. **Holdings:** 10,000 books; 10 bound periodical volumes; professional journals. **Subscriptions:** 12 journals and other serials. **Services:** Copying; library open to the public by appointment. **Remarks:** FAX: (212)586-9579. Also maintains a Media Department.

★1925★
Board of Trade of Metropolitan Toronto - Resource Centre (Bus-Fin)
1 First Canadian Place
Box 60
Toronto, ON, Canada M5X 1C1
Phone: (416)366-6811
M.J. de Reus, Libn.
Founded: 1977. **Staff:** Prof 1; Other 1. **Subjects:** Urban planning, international trade, business and finance. **Special Collections:** Board of Trade Council Minutes and Metropolitan Toronto Business Journal (both on microfilm). **Holdings:** 2500 books; 50 bound periodical volumes; 50 reels of microfilm. **Subscriptions:** 200 journals and other serials; 22 newspapers. **Services:** Interlibrary loan; copying; center open to the public by appointment. **Publications:** The Metropolitan Toronto Business & Market Guide, annual; Metropolitan Toronto Business Journal, 10/year; Directory of Trade and Professional Associations in the Toronto Region; Chambers of Commerce & Boards of Trade in Ontario; Executive Compensation Survey, annual; Middle Management & Professional Compensation Survey, annual; Data Processing Salary Survey, annual; Clerical Salary Survey, annual; Guide to the Toronto Region's Top Employers, annual. **Special Indexes:** Board of Trade Submissions Index. **Remarks:** FAX: (416)366-5620.

★1926★
Boardman United Methodist Church - Library (Rel-Phil)
6809 Market St.
Youngstown, OH 44512
Mary Lou Henneman, Libn.
Staff: Prof 1; Other 1. **Subjects:** Theology, Bible, devotions, counseling, parenting. **Holdings:** 600 books. **Services:** Library open to other churches. **Publications:** The Carillon (newsletter) - for internal distribution only.

★1927★
The BOC Group Inc. - Technical Center - Information Center (Sci-Engr, Med)
100 Mountain Ave.
Murray Hill, NJ 07974
Phone: (908)665-2400
Robert N. Yeager, Mgr.
Founded: 1947. **Staff:** Prof 3; Other 6. **Subjects:** Chemical engineering, cryogenics, metallurgy, ceramics, engineering, anesthesiology, health care, industrial gases. **Holdings:** 25,000 volumes; 4000 volumes on microfilm; AV programs. **Subscriptions:** 550 journals and other serials. **Services:** Interlibrary loan; copying; SDI; center open to the public for reference use only by special arrangement. **Automated Operations:** Computerized cataloging, acquisitions, serials, and circulation. **Computerized Information Services:** DIALOG Information Services, STN International, MEDLARS, Data-Star, Occupational Health Services, Inc. (OHS), WILSONLINE, BEST North America; CD-ROM. **Publications:** Tech News, monthly; Translations, semiannual. **Special Indexes:** Technical Reports. **Remarks:** FAX: (908)771-6182. **Staff:** Doris Yeager, Info.Sci.; Rosann Kaladas, Chem.Info.Spec.

★1928★
Boca Raton Community Hospital - Health Sciences Library (Med)
800 Meadows Rd.
Boca Raton, FL 33486
Phone: (407)393-4070
Carolyn F. Hill, Med.Libn.
Staff: Prof 1; Other 1. **Subjects:** Medicine, nursing. **Holdings:** 1325 books; 2500 bound periodical volumes; 1 VF drawer of medical material. **Subscriptions:** 210 journals and other serials. **Services:** Interlibrary loan; copying; library open to students for reference use only with permission. **Computerized Information Services:** MEDLARS. **Networks/Consortia:** Member of Palm Beach Health Sciences Library Consortium (PBHSLC).

★1929★
BOCES - Orleans-Niagara Educational Communications Center (Educ, Aud-Vis)
195 Beattie Ave. Phone: (716)439-4333
Lockport, NY 14094-5618 Douglas David, Supv., Instr.Serv.
Founded: 1968. **Staff:** 13. **Holdings:** 10,703 AV programs. **Remarks:** Maintained by the Orleans-Niagara BOCES (Orleans-Niagara Board of Cooperative Educational Services).

★1930★
BOCES - Putnam/Northern Westchester - BOCES Professional Library (Educ)
Yorktown, NY 10598 Phone: (914)245-2700
Susan Rubin, Media Spec.
Subjects: Education, child psychology. **Holdings:** 9500 books; 16,000 bound periodical volumes; 300,000 nonbook items. **Services:** Interlibrary loan; copying; library open to the public with restrictions (reference use only for those not residing or working in the 18 school districts). **Computerized Information Services:** BRS Information Technologies, ERIC, Bibliofile, Mandarin. **Special Catalogs:** Union list of serials for secondary schools. **Remarks:** Maintained by the Putnum/Northern Westchester BOCES (Board of Cooperative Educational Services).

★1931★
Bockus Research Institute - Library (Med)
415 S. 19th St.
Philadelphia, PA 19146 Diane Farney
Founded: 1962. **Subjects:** Cardiovascular research, cardiology, physiology, cancer research, neurology, emphysema. **Holdings:** 1000 volumes. **Subscriptions:** 25 journals and other serials. **Services:** Library open to graduate hospital staff. **Computerized Information Services:** BRS Information Technologies. **Remarks:** FAX: (215)893-2385.

Bodega Marine Laboratory - Library
See: **University of California** (18296)

★1932★
Bodine Electric Company - Library (Sci-Engr)
2500 W. Bradley Place Phone: (312)478-3515
Chicago, IL 60618 Kristine A. Hack, Sec.
Staff: 1. **Subjects:** Microprocessors, electrical engineering, mechanical engineering, business administration. **Holdings:** 1610 volumes; 551 manufacturers' catalogs; 238 engineering project reports; 27 VF drawers. **Subscriptions:** 119 journals and other serials. **Services:** Interlibrary loan; library not open to the public.

Martin Bodmer Foundation
See: **Fondation Martin Bodmer - Bibliotheca Bodmeriana** (5946)

★1933★
Seymour S. Bodner Collection (Sci-Engr)
27 Shadowlawn Dr. Phone: (201)994-3472
Livingston, NJ 07039 Seymour S. Bodner, Prin.
Founded: 1971. **Subjects:** Forensic and mechanical engineering, history of industrial and product safety standards. **Special Collections:** Plastics molding machinery. **Holdings:** Figures not available. **Services:** Collection open to attorneys and insurance companies.

Boeckmann Center for Iberian and Latin American Studies
See: **University of Southern California - Library - Boeckmann Center for Iberian and Latin American Studies** (19335)

Boeckmann Library
See: **Ramsey County Medical Society - Boeckmann Library** (13702)

The Inge P. Boehm Library
See: **ABC-CLIO, Inc.** (16)

★1934★
Boehringer Ingelheim Animal Health, Inc. - Library (Med, Biol Sci)
2621 N. Belt Hwy. Phone: (816)233-2571
St. Joseph, MO 64506 Judy Heinje, Libn.
Staff: Prof 1; Other 1. **Subjects:** Veterinary medicine, bacteriology, virology, pharmaceuticals, immunology, parasitology. **Holdings:** 5000 books; 15,000 bound periodical volumes; 750 documents and dissertations. **Subscriptions:** 165 journals and other serials. **Services:** Interlibrary loan; copying; library open to researchers for reference use only. **Networks/Consortia:** Member of National Network of Libraries of Medicine - Midcontinental Region. **Remarks:** FAX: (816)233-0251.

★1935★
Boehringer Ingelheim Ltd. - Scientific Information Services (Sci-Engr, Med)
900 Old Ridge Berry Rd. Phone: (203)798-5156
Ridgefield, CT 06877 Margaret Norman, Mgr.
Founded: 1975. **Staff:** Prof 6; Other 5. **Subjects:** Pharmacology, chemistry, biochemistry, clinical medicine, pharmaceutical trade and industry, business. **Holdings:** 7,500 books; 16,000 bound periodical volumes; 35,000 items in product files. **Subscriptions:** 1400 journals and other serials. **Automated Operations:** Computerized cataloging, acquisitions, serials, and circulation (TECHLIBplus; Faxon LINX). **Computerized Information Services:** BRS Information Technologies, PFDS Online, NLM, WILSONLINE, Chemical Abstracts Service (CAS), Occupational Health Services, Inc. (OHS), DIALOG Information Services, STN International, Dow Jones News/Retrieval, Data-Star, LEXIS, NEXIS; internal databases; DOCLINE (electronic mail service). **Networks/Consortia:** Member of Southwestern Connecticut Library Council (SWLC). **Publications:** Notes and Acquisitions, monthly; Product Bibliography, monthly - both to corporate staff; SISzling News, daily; Library Guide, annual. **Remarks:** FAX: (203)790-6815. Telex: 179153 BICUT. **Staff:** Tari McTague, Info.Sci.; Margaret Drenowatz, Info.Sci.; Margaret Hentz, Info.Sci.; Rita Goetz, Info.Sci.; Frances Ruppell, ILL; Peggy Anthony Acq.; Nancy Cunniff, Ser.

★1936★
Boeing Aerospace Operations, Inc. - Technical Library
16840 Buccaneer Phone: (713)280-2000
Houston, TX 77058 Sue York, Data Mgt.Mgr.
Services: Library not open to the public. **Remarks:** No further information was supplied by respondent.

Boeing of Canada Ltd. - De Havilland Aircraft Company of Canada
See: **Boeing of Canada Ltd. - De Havilland Division** (1937)

★1937★
Boeing of Canada Ltd. - De Havilland Division - Library Services (Sci-Engr)
Garratt Blvd.
MS: N17-09 Phone: (416)375-3365
Downsview, ON, Canada M3K 1V5 Catherine Parsons, Libn.
Founded: 1955. **Staff:** 1. **Subjects:** Aeronautics. **Special Collections:** Canadian and international reports, papers, regulations, standards. **Holdings:** 2000 books; 500 bound periodical volumes; 259,000 technical reports; 10,000 microfiche; abstracts and indexes. **Subscriptions:** 115 journals and other serials. **Services:** Interlibrary loan; copying (both limited); library open to the public for research with restrictions on borrowing. **Remarks:** FAX: (416)375-4533. Telex: 06-22128 DE HAV TOR.

★1938★
Boeing Company - Boeing Support Services - Technical Libraries (Sci-Engr)
Box 3707, MS 6H-LC Phone: (206)237-8314
Seattle, WA 98124-2207 Corinne A. Campbell, Mgr.
Founded: 1929. **Staff:** Prof 28; Other 27. **Subjects:** Aeronautics, astronautics, engineering, electronics, computing, transportation, industrial medicine, business, management. **Special Collections:** International Data Bank. **Holdings:** 73,000 books; 18,000 bound periodical volumes; 150,000 reports; one million reports on microfiche; 175,000 company documents; 5000 maps; 8000 films and videos. **Subscriptions:** 5000 journals and other serials. **Services:** Interlibrary loan; library not open to the public. **Automated Operations:** Computerized cataloging, acquisitions, serials, and circulation.

Computerized Information Services: DIALOG Information Services, PFDS Online, BRS Information Technologies, Dow Jones News/Retrieval, NEXIS, LEXIS, NASA/RECON, Integrated Technical Information System (ITIS), DTIC, Congressional Quarterly, Reuter TEXTLINE, Reuter Country Reports, NewsNet, Inc., Gartner Group, Inc., Dun & Bradstreet Business Credit Services, Data Resources (DRI), MEDLINE, DataTimes, STN International, VU/TEXT Information Services, WLN, WILSONLINE, OCLC; internal databases for access to trade newsletters. **Networks/Consortia:** Member of Western Library Network (WLN), Seattle Area Hospital Library Consortium (SAHLC). **Publications:** Technical Libraries Accession Bulletin, monthly; Boeing Documents Announcement Bulletin, monthly; custom literature searches and information surveys. **Special Catalogs:** Catalog of holdings and Boeing documents (online); Union List of Serials (hardcopy). **Remarks:** FAX: (206)237-3491. Collections include the holdings of the Bellevue, Kent, and Renton Technical Libraries, the Safety, Health and Environmental Affairs (SHEA) Library, and the company Film Library. FAX: (206)237-3491. **Staff:** Katherine R. Harkness, Info. & Res.Serv.Mgr.; Cheryl C. Morton, Tech.Proc.Mgr.; Jennifer M. Choate, Renton Lib.Res. Lead; Sarah R. Cannon, Renton Info.Serv. Lead; Richard A. Curtis, Kent Lib.Res. Lead; T. Patrick Dwyer, Kent Info.Serv. Lead; Julia Phillips, Bellevue Lib. Lead; Brenda H. Sharp, Film Lib.Lead; Christine M. Kramer, SHEA Libn.; Geneva St. Clair, Acq. Lead; Roseann Nystrom, Ser. Lead; Kathryn A. Trump, Doc.Cat. Lead; Gail S. Shurgot, Cat. Lead; Michael A. Crandall, Ext.Sys. Requirements Libn. .

★1939★
Boeing Helicopters - Lydia Rankin Technical Library (Sci-Engr)
P.O. Box 16858
Philadelphia, PA 19142 Phone: (215)591-2536
Founded: 1945. **Staff:** Prof 1; Other 1. **Subjects:** Helicopters, rotorcraft, aircraft, aerospace, composite materials, military specifications and standards. **Special Collections:** Peterson Memorial Collection (transportation); Boeing Management Collection (business). **Holdings:** 1500 books; 50 bound periodical volumes; 5000 reports; 32,000 technical reports; 250 VF drawers of military specifications; 200 reels of microfilm; 40 drawers of microfiche. **Subscriptions:** 200 journals and other serials. **Services:** Interlibrary loan; library not open to the public. **Automated Operations:** Computerized cataloging. **Computerized Information Services:** DIALOG Information Services; DOBIS Canadian Online Library System. **Formerly:** Boeing Helicopter Co.

★1940★
Boeing Hunstville Technical Library (Sci-Engr)
PO Box 240002
499 Boeing Blvd., M/S JC-73 Phone: (205)461-2549
Huntsville, AL 35824-6402 Harriet B. McKay, Tech.Libn.
Founded: 1985. **Staff:** Prof 1; Other 1. **Subjects:** Space Station Freedom, space, defense. **Holdings:** Space Station Freedom documents. **Subscriptions:** 51 journals and other serials. **Services:** Interlibrary loan; SDI; library open to the public upon registration at visitor center. **Computerized Information Services:** NERAC, Inc.; DOBIS (internal database). **Publications:** Recent Acquisitions. **Remarks:** FAX: (205)461-5666.

★1941★
Boeing Wichita Technical Library (Sci-Engr)
P.O. Box 7730, K78-38 Phone: (316)526-3801
Wichita, KS 67277-7730 Roger Zwenke, Lib.Mgr.
Founded: 1948. **Staff:** Prof 2; Other 1. **Subjects:** Engineering - aeronautical, electrical, mechanical; aerospace; physics; mathematics; computer science, manufacturing, materials handling, management, metallurgy, plastics. **Holdings:** 8,000 volumes; 6,500 technical reports; 3 drawers of microfilm. **Subscriptions:** 325 journals and other serials. **Services:** Interlibrary loan; library not open to the public. **Computerized Information Services:** DOBIS Canadian Online Library System; PROFS (internal database). Performs searches. **Remarks:** Library located at 3801 S. Oliver, Wichita, KS 67210-2196. Alternate telephone number(s): 526-3802. FAX: (316)526-8535. **Staff:** Mary K. Yeager, Acq.; Darline Shaw, Circ.Libn.; Jack B. Robertson, Hd.Libn./Cat., Online.

★1942★
(Bogota) Centro Colombo-Americano - USIS Collection (Educ)
Ave. 19, No. 3-05
Apdo. 3815 Phone: 1 3421758
Bogota, Colombia Cecilia Granados, Lib.Dir.
Founded: 1942. **Staff:** 8. **Subjects:** Social science, history, linguistics. **Holdings:** 10,500 books; 855 microfiche. **Subscriptions:** 157 journals and other serials; 5 newspapers. **Services:** Copying; SDI; library open to the public. **Computerized Information Services:** CD-ROMs; internal database. **Publications:** Subject bibliographies. **Remarks:** Alternate telephone number(s): 1 2851300, ext. 315. FAX: 1 2823372. A Branch library is located at Calle 109A, No. 17-10. Maintained or supported by the U.S. Information Agency. Focus is on materials that will assist peoples outside the United States to learn about the United States, its people, history, culture, political processes, and social milieux. **Staff:** Piedad de Ortiz; Ivan Gonzalez; Luz Mary Suarez.

★1943★
Bogue Banks Library (Biol Sci)
320 Salter Path Rd.
Pine Knoll Village Phone: (919)247-4660
Pine Knoll Shores, NC 28512 Joyce Knight, Libn.
Founded: 1981. **Staff:** 1.5. **Subjects:** Marine sciences. **Holdings:** 6000 volumes. **Subscriptions:** 13 journals and other serials; 6 newspapers. **Services:** Interlibrary loan; copying; library open to the public with restrictions. **Remarks:** Affiliated with Craven-Pamlico-Carteret Regional Library. **Formerly:** NC Aquarium/Pine Knoll Shores. **Staff:** Elinor Hawkins, Dir., Lib.Sys.; Ann Johnston, Dir., Adult Serv.

Niels Bohr Library
See: **American Institute of Physics - Center for History of Physics** (641)

★1944★
Boiron Research Foundation, Inc. - Library (Med)
1208 Amosland Rd. Phone: (215)532-8288
Norwood, PA 19074 Thierry R. Montfort
Founded: 1982. **Subjects:** Homeopathy, autohemic therapy. **Holdings:** 100 volumes. **Publications:** International Journal of Immunotherapy.

★1945★
Boise Art Museum - Library (Art)
670 S. Julia Davis Dr.
Boise, ID 83702 Phone: (208)345-8330
Founded: 1971. **Subjects:** Art. **Holdings:** 1200 books; 2000 national and international exhibition catalogs. **Subscriptions:** 10 journals and other serials. **Services:** Library open to the public by appointment. **Remarks:** FAX: (208)345-8333.

★1946★
Boise Bible College - Library (Rel-Phil)
8695 Marigold Phone: (208)376-7731
Boise, ID 83714 Carl A. Douthit, Libn.
Founded: 1946. **Staff:** Prof 1; Other 2. **Subjects:** Bible, missions, Greek, speech, psychology, archeology, Hebrew history. **Special Collections:** U.S. Restoration history (300 volumes). **Holdings:** 27,800 books; 178 bound periodical volumes; 10 VF drawers of reports, pamphlets, and documents; 407 cassettes; 924 volumes on microfiche. **Subscriptions:** 126 journals and other serials. **Services:** Interlibrary loan; copying.

★1947★
Boise Cascade Corporation - Corporate Library Services (Sci-Engr, Agri)
One Jefferson Square Phone: (208)384-6694
Boise, ID 83728 Marlene P. Klein, Libn.
Founded: 1969. **Staff:** 1. **Subjects:** Law, business, forest products, pulp and paper. **Holdings:** 10,000 volumes. **Subscriptions:** 200 journals and other serials. **Services:** Center open to the public at librarian's discretion. **Automated Operations:** Computerized cataloging and serials. **Computerized Information Services:** DIALOG Information Services, LEXIS, NEXIS; CD-ROM (WLN LaserCat). **Remarks:** Telex: 170 362VIATRT. FAX: (208)384-7945.

★1948★
Boise Cascade Corporation - Technical Resource Center (Sci-Engr)
4435 N. Channel Ave. Phone: (503)286-7415
Portland, OR 97217-7652 Andrea Nelin-Roth, Mgr.
Founded: 1947. **Staff:** Prof 1. **Subjects:** Pulp and paper technology, chemistry, chemical engineering. **Holdings:** 1200 books; 3500 bound periodical volumes; 72 VF drawers of special reports, reprints, proceedings, patents. **Subscriptions:** 85 journals and other serials. **Services:** Interlibrary copying; library open to the public. **Computerized Information Services:** DIALOG Information Services; internal database. **Publications:** Current Awareness Bulletin, biweekly. **Special Catalogs:** Unbound special reports and translations; bibliographies and literature searches by subject. **Special Indexes:** Subject index of current literature. **Remarks:** FAX: (503)286-7467. **Formerly:** Its Pulp & Paper Research Library.

Anton Boisen Professional Library
See: **Elgin Mental Health Center** (5298)

Priscilla Fairfield Bok Library
See: **Monterey Institute for Research in Astronomy** (10671)

Paul L. Boley Law Library
See: **Lewis and Clark Law School - Northwestern School of Law** (9076)

Bolivia - Ministry of Agriculture and Campesino Affairs - Bolivian Institute of Agricultural Technology
See: **Instituto Boliviano de Tecnologia Agropecuaria - Centro de Documentacion e Informacion** (7997)

★1949★
Bolivia - National Scientific and Technological Documentation Center (Sci-Engr)
P.O. Box 9357 Phone: 2 359586
La Paz, Bolivia Arzil Aramayo, Dir.
Staff: Prof 1. **Subjects:** Science and technology, health sciences, education. **Special Collections:** Depository library for publications of several international organizations. **Holdings:** 1500 bound volumes; 1700 bibliographies. **Subscriptions:** 100 journals and other serials. **Services:** Current awareness; copying; microfilm reproduction; center open to the public. **Publications:** Actualidades, irregular; Serie Bibliografica. **Remarks:** Alternate telephone number(s): 2 359593. Telex: 3438-BV-UMSA. Center is administered by the University Mayor of San Andres. **Also Known As:** Centro Nacional de Documentacion Cientifica y Tecnologica.

(Bolivia) Camara de Industria y Comercio
See: **Chamber of Commerce and Industry (Bolivia)** (3415)

(Bolivia) National Medium Miners Association
See: **National Medium Miners Association** (11235)

Bolivian Institute of Agricultural Technology - Information and Documentation Center
See: **Instituto Boliviano de Tecnologia Agropecuaria - Centro de Documentacion e Informacion** (7997)

Richard Walker Bolling Memorial Medical Library
See: **St. Luke's Hospital Center** (14484)

★1950★
Bolt Beranek and Newman Inc. - Library (Sci-Engr)
70 Fawcett St. Phone: (617)873-3279
Cambridge, MA 02138 Marian Bremer, Libn.
Founded: 1960. **Staff:** Prof 3; Other 4. **Subjects:** Technology - architectural, acoustics, environmental, noise control, underwater; data communications; information sciences; computer systems; artificial intelligence; statistical analysis. **Holdings:** 9000 books; 1600 bound periodical volumes; 1000 government reports; 6000 internal reports. **Subscriptions:** 500 journals and other serials. **Services:** Interlibrary loan; library not open to the public. **Computerized Information Services:** DIALOG Information Services, USNI Military Database, NewsNet, Inc., DTIC; InterNet (electronic mail service). **Remarks:** FAX: (617)576-0695. Electronic mail address(es): library@bbn.com (InterNet). **Staff:** Robert T. Menk; Bridget Mooney.

★1951★
Bombardier - Canadair Group - Technical Information Center (Sci-Engr)
P.O. Box 6087, Sta. A Phone: (514)744-1511
Montreal, PQ, Canada H3C 3G9 Margaret I. Levesque, Supv., Lib.Serv/Rec.
Founded: 1946. **Staff:** 9. **Subjects:** Aeronautics, electronics, space research, transportation, management. **Holdings:** 8000 books; 2500 bound periodical volumes; 100,000 reports and pamphlets; 20,000 specifications. **Subscriptions:** 250 journals and other serials. **Services:** Interlibrary loan; library not open to the public. **Computerized Information Services:** DIALOG Information Services, Government-Industry Data Exchange Program (GIDEP). **Publications:** Library Accession List - for internal distribution only. **Remarks:** FAX: (514)748-2544.

★1952★
(Bombay) American Center - USIS Library (Educ)
4 New Marine Lines
Bombay 400 020, Maharashtra, India
Remarks: Maintained or supported by the U.S. Information Agency. Focus is on materials that will assist peoples outside the United States to learn about the United States, its people, history, culture, political processes, and social milieux.

★1953★
Bon Secours Hospital - Health Science Library (Med)
2000 W. Baltimore St. Phone: (301)362-3000
Baltimore, MD 21223 Sheila Oliveira, R.N.
Founded: 1970. **Staff:** 1. **Subjects:** Medicine, surgery, obstetrics and gynecology, cardiovascular diseases, pathology, nursing. **Holdings:** 1908 books; 1876 bound periodical volumes; 2985 Audio-Digest tapes. **Subscriptions:** 81 journals and other serials; 7 newspapers. **Services:** Interlibrary loan; library open to the public with restrictions. **Networks/Consortia:** Member of Maryland Association of Health Science Librarians (MAHSL).

★1954★
Bon Secours Hospital - Health Science Library (Med)
468 Cadieux Rd. Phone: (313)343-1619
Grosse Pointe, MI 48230 Beth S. Navalta, Lib.Supv.
Founded: 1971. **Staff:** Prof 1; Other 2. **Subjects:** Medicine, nursing, hospital administration, pharmacology. **Holdings:** 4500 books; 3300 bound periodical volumes; 170 slide/tape sets; 220 videotapes; 628 AV programs; 200 government documents; 8 VF drawers of clippings, pamphlets, and newspaper articles. **Subscriptions:** 470 journals and other serials; 5 newspapers. **Services:** Interlibrary loan; copying; SDI; library open to the public with sponsorship. **Automated Operations:** Computerized serials, circulation, and inventory. **Computerized Information Services:** MEDLINE, BRS Information Technologies, DIALOG Information Services. **Networks/Consortia:** Member of Michigan Library Consortium (MLC), Michigan Health Sciences Libraries Association (MHSLA), Wayne Oakland Library Federation (WOLF), DGP Consortium (Detroit, Grosse Pointe). **Remarks:** FAX: (313)343-1947.

Baldassare Boncompagni Archives
See: **Cornell University - History of Science Collections** (4313)

★1955★
(Bonn) USIS Library (Educ)
American Embassy
Deichmanns Aue 29 Phone: 228 3392339
W-05300 Bonn 2, Germany Susan B. Aramayo, Country Lib.Dir.
Founded: 1974. **Staff:** 8. **Subjects:** United States politics and government. **Special Collections:** Goverment publications. **Holdings:** 3200 books; reports; microfiche; microfilm. **Subscriptions:** 195 journals and other serials; 5 newspapers. **Services:** Interlibrary loan; copying; SDI; mail and phone reference service; library open to the public. **Services:** DIALOG Information Services, NEXIS, LEXIS, LEGI-SLATE; internal databases. **Publications:** Bibliographies on several subjects. **Remarks:** FAX: 228 334102. Maintained or supported by the U.S. Information Agency. Focus is on materials that will assist peoples outside the United States to learn about the United States, its people, history, culture, political processes, and social milieux. **Staff:** Aurelia Tigler, Lib.Dir.; Brigitte James, Chf.Ref.Libn.; Petra Spitz, Ref.Libn.

★1956★
Bonner County Historical Society, Inc. - Research Library (Hist)
Lakeview Park
609 S. Ella St.
P.O. Box 1063
Sandpoint, ID 83864 Phone: (208)263-2344
Founded: 1980. **Staff:** 1. **Subjects:** Local history, biography. **Holdings:** 350 books; 3500 photographs; 50 maps; 5000 clippings; 85 oral history tapes; 3000 pieces of memorabilia; newspaper file (print and microfilm); obituary file. **Subscriptions:** 3 newspapers. **Services:** Copying; library open to the public for reference use only on request. **Special Catalogs:** Photographs and books (card); oral history tapes (book); newspapers by subject (card).

★1957★
Bonner & Moore Associates, Inc. - Library (Energy)
2727 Allen Pkwy. Phone: (713)831-9784
Houston, TX 77019 Judy G. Lawton, Corp.Libn.
Founded: 1977. **Staff:** Prof 1; Other 1. **Subjects:** Energy, market analyses, petroleum, petrochemicals, oil, gas, economics, software. **Holdings:** 4000 volumes; 20 VF drawers of government documents; 7 VF drawers of unbound reports, clippings, documents; 10 VF drawers of company annual reports; 1 file drawer of company archives. **Subscriptions:** 400 journals and other serials. **Services:** Interlibrary loan; copying; library open to the public by appointment. **Automated Operations:** Computerized cataloging, circulation, and acquisitions. **Special Catalogs:** Listing of all company documents (online). **Remarks:** FAX: (713)522-1134. Telex: 910 881 2542.

Bonneville Power Administration
See: **U.S. Dept. of Energy** (17230)

★1958★
Book Club of California - Library (Publ)
312 Sutter St., Suite 510 Phone: (415)781-7532
San Francisco, CA 94108 Albert Sperisen, Libn.
Founded: 1912. **Staff:** Prof 1. **Subjects:** Printing, bookbinding, typography, books, papermaking, private presses, history of printing and printing methods. **Holdings:** 2000 books; ephemera from private presses. **Subscriptions:** 13 journals and other serials. **Services:** Library open to the public. **Computerized Information Services:** RBASE (internal database). **Publications:** Quarterly News-Letter; Keepsakes (fine press books). **Remarks:** FAX: (415)391-9603. **Staff:** Karl A. Vollmayer.

Books Across the Sea Library
See: **English-Speaking Union of the U.S.A.** (5360)

★1959★
Boone County Genealogical Society - Library (Hist)
Boone Madison Public Library
375 Main St.
Box 306 Phone: (304)369-4675
Madison, WV 25310 Sue Roberts, Sec.
Founded: 1974. **Subjects:** Genealogy. **Special Collections:** Boone County records, 1853 to present; family genealogies (200). **Holdings:** 250 books; microfilm. **Subscriptions:** 30 journals and other serials. **Services:** Copying; library open to the public. **Publications:** Kith and Kin of Boone County West Virginia, annual.

Boone and Crockett Club Library
See: **Carnegie Museum of Natural History - Library** (3085)

Boone Memorial Library
See: **De Paul Medical Center** (4671)

★1960★
Boot Hill Museum - Research Library/Archives (Hist)
Front St. Phone: (316)227-8188
Dodge City, KS 67801 Darleen Clifton Smith, Cur.
Staff: 2. **Subjects:** Dodge City history, 19th century social history, material culture, decorative arts. **Special Collections:** Repository for Ford County court records; historic photograph collection; archives. **Holdings:** 957 books; 50 bound periodical volumes; 40,000 nonbook items; 20 manuscripts. **Subscriptions:** 71 journals and other serials. **Services:** Copying; library open to the public by appointment.

★1961★
Catherine Booth Bible College - Library (Rel-Phil)
447 Webb Place Phone: (204)947-6701
Winnipeg, MB, Canada R3R 2P2 Adrian B. Dalwood, Libn.
Founded: 1982. **Staff:** Prof 4; Other 15. **Subjects:** Theology, religion, Biblical studies, Christian education, social service, philosophy, ethics. **Holdings:** 19,000 books; 248 videotapes; 302 audio cassettes; 102 reels of microfilm. **Subscriptions:** 262 journals and other serials. **Services:** Interlibrary loan; library open to the public. **Computerized Information Services:** DIALOG Information Services, UTLAS, OCLC, ACCESS, BallenNet, BT Link; internal databases. **Special Indexes:** Index to Salvation Army Periodical Literature. **Remarks:** FAX: (204)942-3856. Maintained by the Salvation Army. **Staff:** Cheryl-Anne North, Libn.; Nora Lubossiere, Techn.; Gerry Dueck, Techn.

★1962★
Booth Memorial Medical Center - Health Education Library (Med)
Main St. at Booth Memorial Ave. Phone: (718)670-1118
Flushing, NY 11355 Rita S. Maier, Lib.Dir.
Founded: 1961. **Staff:** Prof 2; Other 3. **Subjects:** Medicine, surgery, pediatrics, obstetrics and gynecology, nursing, dentistry. **Holdings:** 3200 books; 7800 bound periodical volumes; 350 AV programs. **Subscriptions:** 400 journals and other serials. **Services:** Interlibrary loan; copying; library open to the public with director's approval. **Computerized Information Services:** MEDLARS, BRS Information Technologies; CD-ROM; DOCLINE (electronic mail service). **Networks/Consortia:** Member of Medical Library Center of New York (MLCNY), National Network of Libraries of Medicine - Middle Atlantic Region, Brooklyn-Queens-Staten Island Health Sciences Librarians (BQSI), New York Metropolitan Reference and Research Library Agency. **Publications:** Library Acquisitions, 6/year; bibliographies. **Remarks:** FAX: (718)358-4216.

Mrs. Arthur W. Booth Library
See: **Chemung County Historical Society, Inc.** (3475)

★1963★
Booz, Allen & Hamilton, Inc. - Information Center (Bus-Fin)
225 W. Walker Dr., 17th Fl. Phone: (312)346-1900
Chicago, IL 60606 Rebecca Chekouras, Mgr.
Staff: Prof 3; Other 2. **Subjects:** Management, agribusiness, finance, marketing, manufacturing, retailing, information management, consumer products, health care, telecommunications. **Holdings:** 1000 books; client reports; company annual reports. **Subscriptions:** 500 serials. **Services:** Interlibrary loan; center not open to the public. **Computerized Information Services:** DIALOG Information Services, Mead Data Central, Dun & Bradstreet Business Credit Services, VU/TEXT Information Services, ADP Network Service, Inc., CompuServe Information Service. **Remarks:** FAX: (312)578-4695. **Staff:** CHarles Jordan, Res.Libn.; Robert Depke, Res.Libn.; Patricia Skaja, Tech.Serv.Libn.

★1964★
Booz, Allen & Hamilton, Inc. - Library (Sci-Engr)
4330 East-West Hwy. Phone: (301)951-2727
Bethesda, MD 20814 Linda Dodson, Libn.
Founded: 1955. **Staff:** Prof 1; Other 2. **Subjects:** Computers, telecommunications, defense electronics and industry, mathematics. **Holdings:** 3700 volumes. **Subscriptions:** 300 journals and other serials. **Services:** Interlibrary loan; copying; library open to the public at librarian's discretion. **Computerized Information Services:** DIALOG Information Services, NEXIS, COMPUSTAT Services, Inc. (C/S), Computer Intelligence (CI), DTIC, Dow Jones News/Retrieval, Data-Star, OCLC; DIALMAIL (electronic mail service).

★1965★
Booz, Allen & Hamilton, Inc. - Research Service (Bus-Fin)
101 Park Ave. Phone: (212)697-1900
New York, NY 10178 Sandra Manning, Rsrc.Coord.
Founded: 1945. **Staff:** Prof 5; Other 3. **Subjects:** Business organization, industrial and consumer marketing, production, finance, mergers and acquisitions. **Holdings:** 3000 books; 300 VF drawers; 1135 reels of microfilm of periodicals. **Subscriptions:** 350 journals and other serials; 10 newspapers. **Services:** Interlibrary loan; service not open to the public. **Automated Operations:** Computerized cataloging, acquisitions, and serials. **Computerized Information Services:** DIALOG Information Services, PFDS Online, Standard & Poor's COMPUSTAT Services, Inc., BRS Information Technologies, NEXIS, Info Globe, Dun's Marketing Services (DMS), Reuter TEXTLINE, BestLink Market Advisor, ADP Network Services, Inc., WILSONLINE, NewsNet, Inc., DRI/McGraw-Hill, Dun & Bradstreet Business Credit Services, Information Intelligence, Inc., Securities Data Company, Inc., CI, InvesText, Dow Jones News/Retrieval, Data-Star, IDD Information Services, Inc. (IDDIS), Newport Associates, Ltd., NewsNet, Inc.; internal databases. **Remarks:** FAX: (212)880-9732. **Staff:** Catherine Ruggieri, Res.; Alder Ellis, Res.; Raphael Lasar, Res.

John R. Borchert Map Library
See: **University of Minnesota** (18916)

★1966★
Borden Inc. - Gail Borden Research Centre - Library (Food-Bev)
1 Gail Borden Dr. Phone: (315)477-0218
Syracuse, NY 13204 Cara Jane Burton, Info.Spec.
Staff: Prof 1; Other 2. **Subjects:** Food science and technology. **Holdings:** 1700 books; 1600 bound periodical volumes; 14 VF drawers of pamphlets and reprints; 7500 patents. **Subscriptions:** 130 journals and other serials. **Services:** Interlibrary loan; copying; SDI; library open to the public by appointment. **Automated Operations:** Computerized cataloging. **Computerized Information Services:** DIALOG Information Services, Teltech Inc, OCLC EPIC. **Remarks:** FAX: (315)477-0203.

★1967★
Borden Inc. - Tape Library (Aud-Vis)
180 E. Broad St., 33rd Fl. Phone: (614)225-4352
Columbus, OH 43215-7508 JoAnn Sorenson, Libn.
Remarks: No further information was supplied by respondent.

★1968★
Borderland Sciences Research Foundation - B.S.R.F. (Rel-Phil)
Box 429 Phone: (707)986-7211
Garberville, CA 95440 Thomas J. Brown, Dir.
Founded: 1945. **Staff:** 3. **Subjects:** Radionics, ether physics, Tesla, color, dowsing, health, spiritual science. **Holdings:** 1000 volumes. **Subscriptions:** 30 journals and other serials; 5 newspapers. **Services:** Copying; archives open to members only.

★1969★
Jules Bordet Institute - Library (Med)
Bd de Waterloo, 121 Phone: 2 5354673
B-1000 Brussels, Belgium A. Bormans, Libn.
Staff: 1. **Subjects:** Hematology, cancer, infectious diseases, endocrinology, pharmacology, experimental chemotherapy. **Holdings:** 75,000 volumes. **Subscriptions:** 137 newspapers. **Services:** Library open to the public with restrictions. **Computerized Information Services:** DIMDI; CD-ROM (Compact Cambridge). **Remarks:** FAX: 2 5371868. Institute is the tumor center of Brussels University Medical School. **Also Known As:** Institut Jules Bordet.

★1970★
Borgess Medical Center - Health Information Library (Med)
1521 Gull Rd. Phone: (616)383-7360
Kalamazoo, MI 49001 Sr. Norma Harvey, Lib.Mgr.
Founded: 1946. **Staff:** Prof 1; Other 2. **Subjects:** Medicine, nursing, pharmacology, allied health sciences. **Special Collections:** Consumer Health Information Service. **Holdings:** 4500 books; 6500 periodical volumes, hardcopy or microform; AV programs; models; 12 drawers of pamphlets and information files. **Subscriptions:** 400 journals and other serials. **Services:** Interlibrary loan; SDI; LATCH; current awareness; library open to the public with restrictions. **Automated Operations:** Computerized acquisitions and serials. **Computerized Information Services:** DIALOG Information Services, BRS Information Technologies, NLM; CD-ROM (MEDLINE, Health Planning and Administrative Data Base). Performs searches on fee basis. Contact Person: T. Ezell, 388-6877. **Networks/Consortia:** Member of Michigan Library Consortium (MLC), Southwest Michigan Library Cooperative (SMLC). **Publications:** Newsletter; Acquisition List, bimonthly. **Remarks:** FAX: (616)388-6881.

★1971★
Boricua College - Library - Special Collections (Area-Ethnic)
3755 Broadway Phone: (212)694-1000
New York, NY 10032 Dulce Maria Ivarbe, Libn.
Founded: 1973. **Staff:** 6. **Subjects:** Puerto Rican history and culture, Puerto Ricans in the United States. **Special Collections:** Puerto Rican Collection; Honorable Hernan Badillo papers; Repository of Puerto Rican Records/ Archivo de Documentation Puertorriquena; map collection. **Holdings:** Books; bound periodical volumes; VF drawers; filmstrips; slides. **Subscriptions:** 88 journals and other serials; 3 newspapers. **Services:** Interlibrary loan; copying; bibliographic services; collections open to the public for reference use only. **Networks/Consortia:** Member of New York Metropolitan Reference and Research Library Agency. **Publications:** Library brochure. **Special Indexes:** Indexes to periodical holdings, Badillo papers, map collection, and North American Congress on Latin America (NACIA) books on Latin America. **Remarks:** FAX: (212)694-1015. **Staff:** Dr. Mercedes Alicea, Dir. of Lrng.Rsrcs.; Juan Cintron, Sr.Prog.Off.; Eulogio Villanueva, Sr.Prog.Off.; Jose Camacho, Prog.Off.; Ismael Ramos, Prog.Off.

Borland Health Sciences Library
See: **University of Florida - Borland Health Sciences Library** (18560)

★1972★
Borland International - Reference Center (Comp Sci)
1800 Green Hills Rd.
Scotts Valley, CA 95066 Phone: (408)438-8400
Founded: 1985. **Staff:** Prof 1. **Subjects:** Computer software, computer industry, business skills, self-improvement. **Holdings:** 50 books; 800 periodicals. **Subscriptions:** 50 journals and other serials; 5 newspapers. **Services:** Center open to the public with restrictions. **Computerized Information Services:** DIALOG Information Services; internal database; MCI Mail (electronic mail service). **Remarks:** FAX: (408)439-9344.

Max Born Collection
See: **University of Maryland, College Park Libraries - Engineering & Physical Sciences Library** (18813)

★1973★
Borough of Collingswood - Free Public Library - New Jersey History Room (Hist)
Haddon & Frazer Aves. Phone: (609)858-0649
Collingswood, NJ 08108 Peter P. Childs, Dir.
Special Collections: New Jersey History Room (2750 books; 1000 periodicals); Dromgoole-Patterson Collection of Architectural Drawings (400 local drawings); maps of Collingswood and South Jersey, 1699 to present (30); photographs of Early Camden County and Collingswood (1000). **Services:** Interlibrary loan; copying; room open to the public for reference use only.

G.L. Borrowman Astronautics Library
See: **United States Space Education Association** (17943)

★1974★
Don Bosco Technical Institute - Lee Library (Educ)
1151 N. San Gabriel Blvd.
Rosemead, CA 91770 Phyllis Swistock, Hd.Libn.
Founded: 1957. **Staff:** Prof 1; Other 1. **Subjects:** Metallurgy, electronics, drafting, mathematics, religion, history, English, chemistry, physics, general science. **Holdings:** 15,000 volumes. **Subscriptions:** 110 journals and other serials. **Services:** Copying.

★1975★
Boston Architectural Center - Alfred Shaw and Edward Durell Stone Library (Plan)
320 Newbury St. Phone: (617)536-9018
Boston, MA 02115 Susan Lewis, Hd.Libn.
Founded: 1966. **Staff:** Prof 3; Other 3. **Subjects:** Architectural design and history, building technology, urban planning, urban design, landscape architecture, photography, interior design, energy conservation, solar energy. **Special Collections:** 19th and early 20th century architectural books and journals (1500 volumes, housed separately). **Holdings:** 22,000 books; 500 bound periodical volumes; 800 student theses; 40,000 slides; 500 other cataloged items. **Subscriptions:** 163 journals and other serials. **Services:** Library open to the public. **Automated Operations:** Computerized circulation. **Publications:** Recent Acquisitions, bimonthly - free on request to libraries, students, and faculty. **Staff:** Sarah Dickinson, Asst.Libn.; Matt Woolman, Media Dir.

Boston Art Festival Archives
See: **Boston Public Library - Fine Arts Department** (1992)

★1976★
Boston Athenaeum Library (Hist, Hum)
10 1/2 Beacon St. Phone: (617)227-0270
Boston, MA 02108-3777 Rodney Armstrong, Dir. & Libn.
Founded: 1807. **Staff:** Prof 32; Other 8. **Subjects:** History, fine and decorative arts, belles lettres, biography. **Special Collections:** Confederate

States imprints; books owned by George Washington, General Henry Knox, and the Adams family; King's Chapel Library, 1698; early U.S. documents; 18th-19th century tracts; gypsy literature; Charles E. Mason Print Collection; early photographs and daguerreotypes. **Holdings:** 700,000 volumes; 15,000 pamphlets; maps; manuscripts; 3700 broadsides; 2200 reels of microfilm; archives. **Subscriptions:** 450 journals and other serials; 20 newspapers. **Services:** Interlibrary loan; copying; library open to scholars and persons seeking information that is unique to the Boston Athenaeum. **Automated Operations:** Computerized cataloging and ILL. **Computerized Information Services:** OCLC. **Networks/Consortia:** Member of NELINET, Inc. **Publications:** Readers Guide to the Boston Athenaeum; Athenaeum Items; monographs, irregular. **Special Catalogs:** Exhibition catalogs. **Special Indexes:** Print and Photograph Collection Index; Portrait File; Views of Boston houses; Provenance and Bookplate file; Obituary Index to Boston Transcript, 1830-1874. **Remarks:** FAX: (617)227-5266. **Staff:** Norman P. Tucker, Assoc.Dir.; John P. Harrison, Hd.Cat.; Jill Erickson, Hd.Ref.Libn.; Jan Malcheski, ILL Libn.; John Lannon, Hd., Acq./Spec.Coll.; Sally Pierce, Cur., Prints/Photos.; Stanley E. Cushing, Consrv.; Donald Kelley, Art Gallery; Michael Wentworth, Cur., Painting/Sculpture.

Boston Biomedical Research Institute - Library
See: **Eye Research Institute/Boston Biomedical Research Institute - Library** (5539)

★1977★
Boston City Hospital - Medical Library (Med)
818 Harrison Ave. Phone: (617)534-4198
Boston, MA 02118 Margi Dempsey, Dir. of Med.Lib.
Founded: 1864. **Staff:** Prof 1; Other 3. **Subjects:** Medicine, health sciences, Boston medical history. **Special Collections:** Anthony Michelidakis Memorial Collection (a history of medicine collection as well as a history of Boston City Hospital and Boston medicine; 131 volumes). **Holdings:** 3239 books; 11,614 bound periodical volumes; 504 pictures; 123 microforms; 592 audiotapes; 16 slide sets. **Subscriptions:** 259 journals and other serials. **Services:** Interlibrary loan; copying; library open to students and researchers. **Networks/Consortia:** Member of National Network of Libraries of Medicine - New England Region, Boston Biomedical Library Consortium. **Remarks:** Alternate telephone number(s): 534-5000.

★1978★
Boston City Hospital - Nursing - Morse-Slanger Library (Med)
818 Harrison Ave. Phone: (617)424-4926
Boston, MA 02118 Margi Dempsey, Dir.
Founded: 1878. **Staff:** Prof 1; Other 2. **Subjects:** Nursing - medical, surgical, maternal, infant; pediatrics; paramedical sciences; psychology; sociology. **Holdings:** 1892 books; 723 bound periodical volumes. **Subscriptions:** 82 journals and other serials. **Services:** Interlibrary loan; copying; SDI; library open to the public for reference use only. **Computerized Information Services:** MEDLARS; DOCLINE (electronic mail service). **Networks/Consortia:** Member of Massachusetts Health Sciences Libraries Network (MaHSLiN), Libraries and Information for Nursing Consortium (LINC).

★1979★
Boston College - Catherine B. O'Connor Library (Sci-Engr)
Weston Observatory Phone: (617)899-0950
Weston, MA 02193 Patricia Donovan, Lib.Supv.
Founded: 1961. **Staff:** 1. **Subjects:** Geology, geophysics, seismology. **Holdings:** 7513 volumes; 10,000 maps; 188 other cataloged items. **Subscriptions:** 31 journals and other serials. **Services:** Interlibrary loan; copying; library open to the public for reference use only. **Networks/Consortia:** Member of Boston Library Consortium (BLC).

★1980★
Boston College - Graduate School of Social Work Library (Soc Sci)
McGuinn Hall Phone: (617)552-3233
Chestnut Hill, MA 02167 Kathleen Boyd, Hd.Libn.
Founded: 1936. **Staff:** Prof 2; Other 4. **Subjects:** Clinical social work; child welfare and families, individuals, and groups; ethnic studies and special populations; gerontology; human behavior; mental health; social policy; administration and research; social planning. **Holdings:** 30,333 books; 5733 bound periodical volumes; 840 masters' theses; 800 doctoral dissertations in social work on microfiche; government documents. **Subscriptions:** 300 journals and other serials. **Services:** Interlibrary loan; copying; library open to the public. **Automated Operations:** Computerized public access catalog, cataloging, acquisitions, serials, and circulation. **Computerized Information Services:** BRS Information Technologies, DIALOG Information Services, CD-ROM. Performs searches on fee basis. Contact Person: Donna L. Ferullo, Ref.Libn. **Networks/Consortia:** Member of Boston Library Consortium (BLC), Northeast Consortium of Colleges and Universities in Massachusetts (NECCUM), NELINET, Inc. **Publications:** Periodic acquisitions list; subject bibliographies. **Remarks:** FAX: (617)552-3199.

★1981★
Boston College - John J. Burns Library - Special Collections and Archives (Hum, Rel-Phil)
Chestnut Hill, MA 02167 Phone: (617)552-3282
Robert K. O'Neill, Ph.D., Burns Libn.
Staff: Prof 6; Other 4. **Special Collections:** Hilaire Belloc Collection and Archives, 1870-1953; Banking Archives (includes Hibernia Savings Bank, Union Warren, The Provident Institution for Savings, Yankee Bank for Finance and Savings, and Savings Banks Association of Massachusetts); British Catholic Authors (Maurice Baring, George Barker, Robert Hugh Benson, Pamela Frankau, Graham Greene, Ronald Knox, Peter Levi, Cardinal Newman, James Spencer Northcote, Elizabeth Jennings, Coventry Patmore, and Evelyn Waugh); Gilbert Keith Chesterton Collection, 1874-1936; Citywide Coordinating Council Archives, 1975-1978; Dolmen Press Collection; The Rev. Robert F. Drinan, S.J. papers; fine print collection (small presses - Foulis Press, Golden Cockerel, Nonesuch (London), Oriole Press, Peppercannister, St. Dominic's, Stanbrook Abbey); Irish Collection (includes Canon Rogers Collection of 20th century Religious and Political Pamphlets and Broadsides; Irish political, social, religious, and music archives, 1590-1773; agriculture; literary renaissance poets and playwrights; Seamus Heaney; writers; private presses); Jesuitana Collection, 1540-1773; Rita Kelleher Collection (nursing); Liturgy and Life, 1925-1975; Meynell Family Collection; Thomas P. O'Neill, Jr., papers; Rex Stout Collection and Archives, 1886-1975; Francis Thompson Collection, 1859-1907; typography and design collection (books, woodblocks, and prints from Eric Gill, David Jones, Bruce Rogers, and George F. Trenholm); Nicholas M. Williams Collection (Jamaica, Judaica, West Africa, South America; includes Anansi Folktale Archives); Maurice Baring Collection, 1847-1945; Bookbuilders of Boston Archives, 1938 to present; Burns, Oates, and Washbourne Collection, 1847-1954; Annie Christitch (Christic) papers, 1885-1977; Charlotte Louisa Hawkins Dempster Collection, 1835 -1913; Eleanor Early papers, 1895-1969; Eire Society of Boston Archives; Fatherless Children of France Memorial Volume Records, 1915-1921; Eric Gill Collection; David Goldstein papers, 1870-1958; Graham Greene Collection, 1904 to present; Peter Levi Collection and papers, 1931 to present; Joseph McCarthy papers, 1915-1980; Thomas Merton Collection, 1915-1968; Morrisey Collection of Japanese Prints, 18th-19th centuries; Music Manuscripts of American Popular Songs, 1900-1940; Nonesuch Press Collection; James Spencer Northcote Collection, 1821-1907; Bruce Rogers Collection; Salem, Massachusetts, First Church of Christ Library (including the library of John Prince, 1751-1836); Joseph Coolidge Shaw Collection, 1821-1851; Edith Sitwell Collection, 1887-1964; McNiff Collection of the Stanbrook Abbey Press; Playbill collection; George Francis Trenholm papers, 1886-1958; Evelyn Waugh Collection, 1903-1966; Leeming - W.B. Yeats Collection; Samuel Beckett Collection (books, periodicals, manuscripts); Rep. Boland Archive; Gerard Manley Hopkins and Family (books and memorabilia belonging to family, letter from Gerard Manley Hopkins, Hopkins' Bible with notes in his own hand). **Holdings:** 95,000 books; 4 million manuscripts. **Services:** Copying; collections open to qualified researchers with restrictions. **Computerized Information Services:** OCLC. **Networks/Consortia:** Member of Boston Library Consortium (BLC), Boston Theological Institute Libraries. **Publications:** List of publications - available on request. **Remarks:** FAX: (617)552-2465. **Staff:** H. Lawrence Durant, Cat.; John Atteberry, Ref.Libn.; William J. Leonard, S.J., Cur., Liturgy and Life Coll.; Aimee Felker, Asst.Univ.Archv.; Marilyn Heskett, Cons.; Philip Bantin, Hd., Archv. & Mss.

★1982★
Boston College - Law School Library (Law)
885 Centre St. Phone: (617)552-4405
Newton, MA 02159 Sharon Hamby, Dir.
Founded: 1929. **Staff:** Prof 10; Other 9. **Subjects:** Anglo-American law, international law and relations, comparative law, Common Market materials. **Special Collections:** Moreana (St. Thomas More collection); Massachusetts Supreme Judicial Court papers and briefs, 1935 to present; U.S. Supreme Court Papers and Briefs, 1946 to present (microform). **Holdings:** 200,000 books; 79,000 volumes in microform. **Subscriptions:** 2000 journals and other serials. **Services:** Interlibrary loan; copying; library open to the public with restrictions. **Automated Operations:** Computerized

cataloging and serials. **Computerized Information Services:** LEXIS, WESTLAW, DIALOG Information Services, NEXIS. **Networks/ Consortia:** Member of Boston Library Consortium (BLC), New England Law Library Consortium (NELLCO). **Publications:** Library Guide, annual - to entering students. **Remarks:** FAX: (617)552-2889. **Staff:** Gyorgy Lang, Ref.Libn.; Joan Shear, Ref.Libn.; Mark Sullivan, Ref.Libn.; Deena Frazier, Cat.; Michael Chiorazzi, Dp.Dir.; Diane Knights, Coll.Serv.; Susan Sullivan, Pub.Serv.; Margaret Soo, Cat.; Jonathon Thomas, Coll.Dev.

★1983★
Boston Conservatory of Music - Albert Alphin Music Library (Mus, Theater)
8 The Fenway Phone: (617)536-6340
Boston, MA 02215 Reginald Didham, Hd.Libn.
Founded: 1867. **Staff:** Prof 2; Other 2. **Subjects:** Music, music education, drama, musical theater, dance, opera, humanities. **Special Collections:** Jan Veen-Katrine Amory Hooper Memorial Dance and Art Collection; Joan Katherine Rossi Memorial Music Education Collection. **Holdings:** 12,000 books; 800 tapes; 6000 phonograph records; 16,000 scores. **Subscriptions:** 80 journals and other serials. **Services:** Interlibrary loan; library open to the public for reference use only. **Computerized Information Services:** OCLC. **Staff:** Beverly Sweetman, Asst.Libn.

★1984★
Boston Consulting Group - Research Library (Bus-Fin)
200 S. Wacker Dr. Phone: (312)993-3300
Chicago, IL 60606 S. Norris Palmore, Hd., Info.Serv.
Founded: 1979. **Staff:** Prof 4; Other 1.5. **Subjects:** Statistics, finance, industry. **Holdings:** 4000 books; 3000 annual reports; 21 linear feet of microfiche; 84 reels of microfilm. **Subscriptions:** 400 journals and other serials; 8 newspapers. **Services:** Interlibrary loan; library not open to the public. **Automated Operations:** Computerized cataloging. **Computerized Information Services:** DIALOG Information Services, BRS Information Technologies, Dow Jones News/Retrieval, Data-Star, GBI, Info Globe, InvesText, NEXIS, DataTimes, OCLC, The Financial Post DataGroup, PRODUCTSCAN, VU/TEXT Information Services, WILSONLINE, DunsPrint, Reuters. **Networks/Consortia:** Member of Chicago Library System. **Remarks:** FAX: (312)715-2250. **Staff:** Cindy Yi, Res.Libn.; Pat Heidkamp, Ref.Libn.

★1985★
Boston Consulting Group - West Coast Information Center (Bus-Fin)
333 S. Grand Ave., Suite 4262 Phone: (213)621-2772
Los Angeles, CA 90071 Ruth E. Corn, Mgr., Info.Serv.
Founded: 1984. **Staff:** Prof 1; Other 1. **Subjects:** Business management and consulting, corporations. **Holdings:** 1100 books; annual reports; current industrial reports. **Subscriptions:** 75 journals and other serials; 5 newspapers. **Services:** Interlibrary loan; center not open to the public. **Automated Operations:** Computerized cataloging. **Computerized Information Services:** DIALOG Information Services, Dun & Bradstreet Business Credit Services, NEXIS, Dow Jones News/Retrieval, PFDS Online, VU/TEXT Information Services, MAX, DataTimes, INVESTEXT, NewsNet, Inc. **Networks/Consortia:** Member of CLASS, BCG Systemwide Information Resource Network. **Remarks:** FAX: (213)687-4175. A branch library is maintained at 100 Spear St., San Francisco, CA 94105.

★1986★
Boston Edison Company - Corporate Library (Energy)
800 Boylston St.
Boston, MA 02199 Phone: (617)424-3127
Founded: 1961. **Staff:** Prof 1. **Subjects:** Electric utilities. **Special Collections:** Electric Power Research Institute reports (hardcopy and microfiche). **Holdings:** 3000 books and reports. **Subscriptions:** 100 journals and other serials. **Services:** Interlibrary loan; copying; library open to the public by appointment. **Computerized Information Services:** DIALOG Information Services. **Publications:** Acquisitions list, quarterly. **Staff:** Lisa McDonough.

★1987★
Boston Globe Newspaper Company - Library (Publ)
135 Morrissey Blvd. Phone: (617)929-2541
Boston, MA 02107 Shirley A. Jobe, Lib.Dir.
Founded: 1872. **Staff:** Prof 5; Other 9. **Subjects:** Newspaper reference topics. **Special Collections:** News clippings (10 million); photographs (1 million). **Holdings:** 4000 books; 372 bound periodical volumes; 800 pamphlets; 9 VF drawers of statistical reports; 30 VF drawers of pamphlets; 500 maps; 5400 reels of microfilm. **Subscriptions:** 65 journals and other serials; 30 newspapers. **Services:** Interlibrary loan; library not open to the public. **Computerized Information Services:** NEXIS, VU/TEXT Information Services, Dow Jones News/Retrieval, DIALOG Information Services, DataTimes. Performs searches on fee basis. **Publications:** Library News. **Special Catalogs:** Guide to the Library. **Remarks:** FAX: (617)929-3314.

Boston Herald Library
See: **News Group Boston, Inc.** (11779)

Boston Medical Library
See: **Harvard University - Schools of Medicine, Dental Medicine & Public Health - Boston Medical Library** (6996)

★1988★
Boston Municipal Research Bureau, Inc. - Library (Soc Sci)
24 Province St., Unit 854 Phone: (617)227-1900
Boston, MA 02108 Samuel R. Tyler, Exec.Dir.
Founded: 1932. **Staff:** 3. **Subjects:** Municipal government organization, law, personnel, education, public finance, economic conditions. **Special Collections:** Boston and Massachusetts material. **Holdings:** 5000 books; 500 reports and pamphlets. **Subscriptions:** 20 journals and other serials. **Services:** Library open to the public by request. **Publications:** Special Report, monthly - to members and City of Boston officials; Boston Facts & Figures, annual; A Statistical Perspective on Boston's Government.

★1989★
Boston Organ Club - Library (Mus)
P.O. Box 104 Phone: (603)827-3055
Harrisville, NH 03450-0104 Alan M. Laufman, Treas.
Subjects: Pipe organs in New England, in the U.S., and worldwide; 19th and 20th century American organ building; church architecture and histories; organ dedication programs. **Special Collections:** Opus lists of 19th and 20th century organ builders. **Holdings:** Books; 24 bound periodical volumes; patents; documents; AV programs; manuscripts. **Services:** Copying; library open to the public by appointment. **Remarks:** Club is a chapter of the Organ Historical Society. Part of the club's collection is housed in Claremont, New Hampshire.

★1990★
Boston Psychoanalytic Society & Institute, Inc. - Library (Med)
15 Commonwealth Ave. Phone: (617)266-0953
Boston, MA 02116 Sanford Gifford, Dir. of Lib.
Staff: Prof 1. **Subjects:** Psychoanalysis. **Special Collections:** Archives; oral histories; photographs. **Holdings:** 5000 books; 2000 bound periodical volumes; reports; reprints. **Subscriptions:** 85 journals and other serials. **Services:** Interlibrary loan; copying; library open to the public with restrictions. **Networks/Consortia:** Member of Consortium of Psychoanalytic Libraries. **Special Catalogs:** Catalog of the Edward and Grete L. Bibring Collection (booklet). **Remarks:** FAX: (617)266-3466. **Staff:** Ann Menashi, MLS, Libn.

★1991★
Boston Public Library - Alice M. Jordan Collection (Hum)
Copley Square
P.O. Box 286 Phone: (617)536-5400
Boston, MA 02117 Linda Murphy, Cur.
Subjects: Children's literature, folklore, fairy tales. **Special Collections:** Children's literature research collection, 1860 to present; American tract books (200); contemporary juvenile foreign imprints (50,000); New England Round Table of Children's Librarians Archives (28 boxes, 6 videotapes, 52 cassettes). **Holdings:** 150,000 books. **Subscriptions:** 39 journals and other serials. **Services:** Interlibrary loan; copying (both limited); collection open to the public with courtesy card.

★1992★
Boston Public Library - Fine Arts Department (Art)
Copley Square
P.O. Box 286 Phone: (617)536-5400
Boston, MA 02117 Janice Chadbourne, Cur., Fine Arts
Founded: 1854. **Staff:** Prof 4; Other 3. **Subjects:** Art history, art techniques, architecture and design, sculpture, painting, graphic and decorative arts. **Special Collections:** Society of Arts and Crafts, Boston Archives; Shore Galleries and Holman Print Shop Archives; ephemera on New England artists and art galleries; Ball Collection of ephemera on American artists; photographs, illustrations, and postcards of Boston architecture; Charles J. Connick Stained Glass Archives; Peabody & Stearns architectural drawings; William G. Preston architectural drawings; auction and exhibition catalogs; Boston Art Festival Archives; Clarence Blackall scrapbooks and sketchbooks; vertical files on Boston architects. **Holdings:** 156,000 titles. **Subscriptions:** 320 journals and other serials. **Services:** Interlibrary loan; copying; department open to the public with borrower's or visitor's card. **Computerized Information Services:** DIALOG Information Services, WILSONLINE. **Networks/Consortia:** Member of Boston Library Consortium (BLC). **Special Catalogs:** Afro-American Artists (book); Department Description (pamphlets); Society of Arts & Crafts, Boston; Exhibition Record and History (book); Childs Gallery, Boston: Exhibition Chronology and Publications (book). **Special Indexes:** Index to Boston Building Inspector's Reports, 1879-1900; Boston Architects and Architecture; Boston/New England Art Information File; Art in the BPL - all on cards. **Staff:** Evelyn Lannon, Sr.Ref.Libn.; Kim Tenney, Ref.Libn.; Jane Duggan, Ref.Libn.

★1993★
Boston Public Library - Government Documents (Info Sci)
Copley Square
P.O. Box 286 Phone: (617)536-5400
Boston, MA 02117 V. Lloyd Jameson, Coord.
Staff: Prof 5; Other 5. **Subjects:** The Government Documents Section serves as a depository for United Nations, Danube Commission, and U.S. Government Printing Office (1859 to present; regional, 1971 to present). Special strengths include U.S. congressional publications, censuses, publications of many international organizations, Current Urban Documents, 19th and early 20th century foreign and state publications, federal and Massachusetts laws and regulations, court decisions, Massachusetts and Boston documents, 18th-20th century British documents, and indexing services; member of Documents Expediting Project. **Special Collections:** Canadian Provincial journals & reports (circa 1790-1950). **Holdings:** Figures not available. **Services:** Interlibrary loan; copying; section open to the public. **Computerized Information Services:** DIALOG Information Services. **Publications:** Government Publications on Microform in the Boston Public Library. **Special Catalogs:** Boston Public Library Government Documents Department State & Local Catalog (microfiche). **Special Indexes:** Boston and Massachusetts documents (online). **Staff:** John Hooper, Ref.Libn.; Gail Fithian, Ref.Libn.; Betsey Anderson, Ref.Libn.; Linda MacIver, Ref.Libn.

★1994★
Boston Public Library - Humanities Reference (Hum)
Copley Square
P.O. Box 286
Boston, MA 02117 Phone: (617)536-5400
Staff: Prof 4; Other 1. **Subjects:** Philosophy, psychology, religion, language, literature, bibliography, library science. **Holdings:** Figures not available. **Services:** Interlibrary loan; copying; open to the public with courtesy card. **Computerized Information Services:** DIALOG Information Services, WILSONLINE. **Networks/Consortia:** Member of Boston Library Consortium (BLC). **Staff:** Joseph Fullum, Sr.Ref.Libn.; Katherine Phillips, Ref.Libn.; Irena Balgalvis, Ref.Libn.; Sandra Sidoti, Ref.Libn.

★1995★
Boston Public Library - Kirstein Business Branch (Bus-Fin)
20 City Hall Ave. Phone: (617)523-0860
Boston, MA 02108 Dolores Schueler, Bus.Br.Libn.
Founded: 1930. **Staff:** Prof 5; Other 3. **Subjects:** Business administration, retailing, advertising, finance, marketing, real estate, insurance, banking, taxation, accounting, investments, economics, business law, small business. **Holdings:** Moody's Manuals (latest 50 years); Commercial and Financial Chronicle, 1957-1987; Bank and Quotation Record, 1928-1987; Standard and Poor's Daily Stock Price Record: New York and American Stock Exchanges, 1962 to present; over-the-counter stocks, 1968 to present; domestic and foreign trade directories; city directories for major cities in the U.S. and Canada; telephone directories for New England and U.S. cities with populations over 50,000 and major foreign cities; New York and American Stock Exchange companies annual and 10K reports on microfiche (latest 10 years); Wall Street Journal on microfilm (latest 10 years); Wall Street Transcript on microfilm (latest 5 years); D-U-N-S Business Identification Service (latest 5 years). **Subscriptions:** 414 journals and other serials; 13 newspapers. **Services:** Copying is available through the library's interlibrary loan department. **Computerized Information Services:** CD-ROMs (Standard & Poor's, Moody's Company Data, Compact Disclosure, ABI/INFORM). **Staff:** Richard Sullivan, Sr.Ref.Libn.; Helen Bender, Ref.Libn.; Margaret Phillibert, Ref.Libn.; Karol Bartlett, Ref.Libn.

★1996★
Boston Public Library - Microtext/Newspaper Department (Hist)
666 Boylston St. Phone: (617)536-5400
Boston, MA 02117 Charles Longley, Cur.
Staff: Prof 2; Other 8. **Subjects:** Newspapers, history, genealogy, literature. **Special Collections:** Boston and Massachusetts newspapers; primary and secondary sources in American, British, and international government documents; biographical, city, telephone, manufacturers', trade, and sales catalogs and directories; genealogical resources for the New England States including federal censuses, passenger arrival manifests and indexes, family genealogies and community histories; Massachuetts town, city, and vital records; early American and British periodicals and monographs; collections of American and British drama and American literature; music scores and librettos; art exhibit and sales catalogs, and national art surveys; first and princeps editions of scientific works and papers; runs of university and national scientific society journals; presidential, personal, business, and administrative correspondence; records pertaining to private, commercial, governmental, and religious affairs; photographic collections documenting social life and conditions; resources in black history, American Indian history, labor history, and women's history. **Holdings:** 35,000 bound periodical volumes; 152,600 reels of microfilm; 2.2 million microfiche; 1.6 million other cataloged items. **Subscriptions:** 300 newspapers. **Services:** Copying; library open to the public. **Special Indexes:** Index to obituaries in Boston newspapers (card); limited subject indexing to some Boston and suburban newspapers (microfiche). **Remarks:** The Department was formerly part of the Government Documents, Microtext, Newspapers department of the Boston Public Library (see entry number 1743). **Staff:** Henry Scannell, Ref.Libn.II.

★1997★
Boston Public Library - Music Department (Mus)
Copley Square
P.O. Box 286 Phone: (617)536-5400
Boston, MA 02117 Diane Ota, Cur., Mus.
Founded: 1852. **Staff:** Prof 4. **Subjects:** Music - scores, theory, literature; dance. **Special Collections:** Allen A. Brown Music Collection of music scores and reference works (40,000); Koudelka Collection of early theoretical works; Koussevitzky Collection (scores, scrapbooks, and memorabilia; 2000 items); Walter Piston Collection; Handel and Haydn Society Collection; Victor Young Collection; Laning Humphrey Journalistic Archives. **Holdings:** 124,000 books, scores, and bound periodical volumes; 10,000 scrapbooks, letters, and unbound sheet music. **Subscriptions:** 400 journals and other serials. **Services:** Interlibrary loan; copying (both limited); department open to the public for reference use only. **Computerized Information Services:** DIALOG Information Services, WILSONLINE. **Networks/Consortia:** Member of Boston Library Consortium (BLC). **Special Catalogs:** Catalog of the Allen A. Brown Music Collection; Dictionary Catalog of the Music Collection (24 volumes, 1972-1976). **Special Indexes:** Song index; first performances; obituary file; vertical file; organ builder index. **Staff:** Charlotte Kolczynski, Ref.Libn.; Elisa Birdseye-Clark, Ref.Libn.

★1998★
Boston Public Library - Print Department (Art)
Copley Square
P.O. Box 286 Phone: (617)536-5400
Boston, MA 02117 Sinclair H. Hitchings, Kpr. of Prints
Founded: 1941. **Staff:** Prof 3; Other 1. **Subjects:** Old Master prints and drawings; 19th Century French, British, and American prints and drawings; Boston pictorial archive of prints, drawings, and photographs; American 19th Century photographs by Bell, O'Sullivan, and W.H. Jackson. **Special Collections:** Rowlandson; Goya; Daumier; Toulouse-Lautrec; Fantin-Latour; Forain; George Bellows; Charlet; Gavarni; Meryon; Jacques Villon;

Charles Shannon; John Copley; Prints after Homer and Nast; Whistler; Pennell; Hassam. **Holdings:** 75,500 prints and drawings; 650,400 photographs. **Services:** Copying (limited, by special arrangement); department open to the public. **Special Indexes:** Card index of Boston pictorial collection. **Staff:** Wendy Gogel, Ref.Libn.; Karen Smith-Shafts, Kpr., Prints.

★1999★
Boston Public Library - Rare Books and Manuscripts (Rare Book)
Copley Square
P.O. Box 286 Phone: (617)536-5400
Boston, MA 02117 Dr. Laura V. Monti, Kpr.
Founded: 1934. **Staff:** Prof 4; Other 2. **Subjects:** American history; literature - American, English, French, Italian; Spanish and Portuguese civilization; landscape architecture; early astronomy; mathematics and navigation; graphic arts; theater history; antislavery movement; the Caribbean; French-American culture; juvenile literature. **Special Collections:** Prince Collection of Americana; Barton Collection of English Literature; Ticknor Collection of Spanish Literature; Benton Collection of Book of Common Prayer; Allen A. Brown Dramatic Collection; Chamberlain Collection of Manuscripts; 20th Regiment Collection of Civil War Material; Bowditch Collection of Astronomy and Mathematics; Sabatier Collection of Franciscana; Bentley Collection of early books on accounting; Feer Collection of World Fairs of North America; William A. Dwiggin s Collection; Library of the Browning Society; Library of the Boston Authors Club; Trent Collection of Defoe and Defoeniana; Chamberlain Collection of autographs; Felicani Collection of Sacco-Vanzetti Papers; Fred Allen Collection; Wilfrid Beaulieu Papers on Franco-American Subjects; Codman Collection of Gardening and Landscape Architecture; Galatea Collection of History of Women (5200 volumes); Alexander Benois costume designs and painting sketches collection; collection of costume designs for operas and ballets performed in Italian theaters, 1850-1937. **Holdings:** 270,000 books; bound periodical volumes; 1.04 million manuscript items; 575 reels of microfilm. **Subscriptions:** 4 journals and other serials. **Services:** Copying (limited, by special arangement); open to qualified researchers. **Computerized Information Services:** OCLC. **Special Catalogs:** Catalogs to most of the collections; BPL Cooperative Catalog (online). **Remarks:** FAX: (617)267-8273. **Staff:** Roberta Zonghi, Cur., Rare Bks.; Guiseppe Bisaccia, Ph.D., Cur., Mss.; Eugene Zepp, Ref.Libn.

★2000★
Boston Public Library - Science Reference Department (Sci-Engr)
Copley Square
P.O. Box 286 Phone: (617)536-5400
Boston, MA 02117 Marilyn T. McLean, Cur., Sci.Ref.
Staff: Prof 4; Other 2. **Subjects:** Science and technology; patents - U.S., British; European Patent Office, Patent Cooperation Treaty. **Special Collections:** Patent Depository Library. **Holdings:** Figures not available. **Services:** Interlibrary loan; copying; department open to the public. **Computerized Information Services:** BRS Information Technologies, DIALOG Information Services, PFDS Online, Chemical Abstracts Service (CAS), VU/TEXT Information Services, U.S. Patent Classification System, MEDLARS, WILSONLINE. **Staff:** George M.A. Cumming, Jr., Ref.Libn. II; H. James Merrick, Ref.Libn.; Sandra Sidoti, Ref.Libn.

★2001★
Boston Public Library - Social Sciences (Soc Sci, Bus-Fin, Rec)
Copley Square
P.O. Box 286 Phone: (617)536-5400
Boston, MA 02117 Edwin G. Sanford, Coord.
Staff: Prof 5; Other 1. **Subjects:** History, business and economics, education, financial reporting services, geography and maps, genealogy and heraldry, political science, sports and games, travel. **Holdings:** College catalogs (hardcopy and microfiche); U.S., Canada, and major foreign city street maps; International Genealogical Index (IGI); annual reports for major U.S. corporations. **Services:** Interlibrary loan; copying; open to the public with courtesy card. **Computerized Information Services:** DIALOG Information Services; CD-ROMs. **Special Catalogs:** American families' coat-of-arms and family histories. **Staff:** Dolores E. Schueler, Ref.Libn. II; Joseph G.V. Maciora, Ref.Libn.; Mary Frances O'Brien, Ref.Libn.; Patricia E. Feeley, Ref.Libn.

★2002★
Boston Redevelopment Authority - Library (Plan)
City Hall, 9th Fl.
1 City Hall Square Phone: (617)722-4300
Boston, MA 02201 Maxine Strickland, Mgr., Lib.Serv.
Founded: 1966. **Staff:** Prof 1; Other 1. **Subjects:** Urban renewal, city planning, housing, zoning, urban economics. **Special Collections:** City of Boston planning and urban renewal plans and reports; developers' proposals (4 VF drawers). **Holdings:** 20,000 volumes; 8 VF drawers of newspaper clippings. **Subscriptions:** 130 journals and other serials; 17 newspapers. **Services:** Library open for research use only. **Automated Operations:** Computerized cataloging and serials. **Computerized Information Services:** DIALOG Information Services, VU/TEXT Information Services, WESTLAW. **Publications:** BRA Library brochure; Table of Contents pages; BRA Library Acquisitions, quarterly.

★2003★
(Boston) School Committee of the City of Boston - Administration Library (Educ)
26 Court St. Phone: (617)726-6200
Boston, MA 02108 R. Patricia Anderson, Dir., Lib.Info.Serv.
Founded: 1923. **Staff:** Prof 1; Other 2. **Subjects:** Education. **Special Collections:** Documents of the Boston School Committee. **Holdings:** 12,911 books and pamphlets. **Subscriptions:** 120 journals and other serials. **Services:** Interlibrary loan; library serves public occasionally when need is established. **Remarks:** FAX: (617)726-6200, ext. 5220.

Boston Society of Natural History
See: **Museum of Science - Library** (10919)

★2004★
Boston State Hospital - Medical Library (Med)
591 Morton St. Phone: (617)436-6000
Boston, MA 02124 John B. Picott, Libn.
Founded: 1874. **Staff:** Prof 1. **Subjects:** Psychiatry, neurology, community mental health, psychiatric nursing, social service. **Holdings:** 2300 books; 1000 unbound and bound periodical volumes. **Subscriptions:** 199 journals and other serials. **Services:** Interlibrary loan; copying; library open to the public at librarian's discretion. **Networks/Consortia:** Member of Massachusetts Health Sciences Libraries Network (MaHSLiN), National Network of Libraries of Medicine - New England Region. **Publications:** Acquisition lists, irregular.

Boston Symphony Orchestra Archive
See: **Boston University - Music Library** (2015)

Boston Transportation Planning Review - Archives
See: **Massachusetts State Transportation Library** (9834)

★2005★
Boston University - African Studies Library (Area-Ethnic)
771 Commonwealth Ave. Phone: (617)353-3726
Boston, MA 02215 Gretchen Walsh, Hd.
Founded: 1953. **Staff:** Prof 2; Other 2. **Subjects:** Africa - political science, history, economics, anthropology, languages, linguistics, literature. **Special Collections:** African government documents (65,000 volumes). **Holdings:** 65,000 books; 500 maps; 5000 pamphlets and pieces of political ephemera; 4500 microforms. **Subscriptions:** 600 journals and other serials; 30 newspapers. **Services:** Interlibrary loan; library open to the public. **Automated Operations:** Computerized public access catalog. **Networks/Consortia:** Member of Boston Library Consortium (BLC). **Special Catalogs:** Catalog of African Government Documents and Area Index (3rd edition; 1976); Censuses, Development Plans and Statistical Abstracts: A Working List of Holdings in the Boston University Documents Collection; Union List of African Censuses, Development Plans and Statistical Abstracts (1985); African Language Materials in the Boston University Libraries (1988). **Remarks:** FAX: (617)353-2084. **Staff:** David Westley, Libn.

★2006★
Boston University - College of Liberal Arts - Stone Science Center - Library (Soc Sci)
675 Commonwealth Ave., Rm. 440 Phone: (617)353-5679
Boston, MA 02215 David A. Sauer, Hd.Libn.
Founded: 1988. **Staff:** Prof 2. **Subjects:** Archeology, energy, environmental studies, geography, geology, remote sensing. **Special Collections:** Archives of the Archaeological Institute of America; photographic archives from NASA's Apollo missions; newsletters and special publications from constituent departments and centers. **Holdings:** 6700 books; 120 bound periodical volumes; 1800 technical reports; 20,000 topographic and geological maps; 200 magnetic tapes; 3500 reprints, pamplets, and clippings; 32,500 aerial and space photographs. **Subscriptions:** 150 journals and other serials. **Services:** Copying; library open to the public. **Automated Operations:** Computerized public access catalog, cataloging, and serials. **Computerized Information Services:** BRS Information Technologies, DIALOG Information Services, WILSONLINE, RESORS, OCLC; BITNET, DIALMAIL (electronic mail services). **Networks/Consortia:** Member of NELINET, Inc. **Publications:** Newsletter, irregular. **Special Indexes:** Ephemera (reprints, pamphlets, and clippings); Tech Reports; Union List of Serials. **Remarks:** FAX: (617)353-5986. Electronic mail address(es): sauer@bu-geo.bu.edu (BITNET). **Staff:** Nasim Momen, Map Libn.

★2007★
Boston University - Corporate Education Center - Computer Technology Research Library (Sci-Engr, Comp Sci)
72 Tyng Rd. Phone: (508)649-9731
Tyngsboro, MA 01879-2099 Sherry Bailey, Libn.
Founded: 1980. **Staff:** Prof 2; Other 1. **Subjects:** Software engineering, business administration and management, computer programming languages, program methodology, project management, artificial intelligence, computer science, social work. **Special Collections:** Technical reports; standards. **Holdings:** 5000 books; 4000 technical reports. **Subscriptions:** 264 journals and other serials; 10 newspapers. **Services:** Interlibrary loan; copying; SDI; library open to the public by appointment. **Automated Operations:** Computerized public access catalog, cataloging, acquisitions, and circulation. **Computerized Information Services:** DIALOG Information Services; internal databases; BITNET (electronic mail service). Performs searches on fee basis. **Networks/Consortia:** Member of NELINET, Inc. **Remarks:** FAX: (508)649-6926. Electronic mail address(es): library@butyng.bu.edu (BITNET). **Staff:** Martha Dionne, Asst.Libn.; Donna Gouldson, Lib.Coord.

★2008★
Boston University - Department of Special Collections (Hist, Hum)
771 Commonwealth Ave. Phone: (617)353-3696
Boston, MA 02215 Dr. Howard B. Gotlieb, Dir.
Founded: 1963. **Staff:** Prof 3; Other 8. **Subjects:** Literature - English, American, Afro-American; military history; private presses; Spanish history and literature. **Special Collections:** Twentieth century archives: papers of over 1200 individuals, including Dr. Martin Luther King, Jr. (180 boxes); Bette Davis (18 boxes; 50 scrapbooks); Isaac Asimov (400 boxes); John W. McCormack (200 boxes); Dan Rather (63 boxes); Endowment for Biblical Research: Bibles and Books of Common Prayer (2000 volumes); Robert Frost (6 manuscript boxes; 820 books); Theodore Roosevelt (100 manuscripts; 800 letters; 400 books); Richards Collection of historical and literary manuscripts, 1495-1970 (4000 items); Bortman Collection of Colonial Americana (2000 printed and manuscript items); Abraham Lincoln Collection (4582 books; 100 letters and documents; memorabilia); medieval manuscripts (20 volumes; 80 leaves). **Holdings:** 89,000 books; 30,000 boxes of manuscripts. **Subscriptions:** 35 journals and other serials. **Services:** Copying (limited); department open to the public by appointment. **Automated Operations:** Computerized cataloging and serials. **Networks/Consortia:** Member of Boston Library Consortium (BLC). **Publications:** Special Collections at Boston University (1981); Some Notable Recent Gifts to the Twentieth Century Archives (1984; brochure); Manuscripts Sacred and Secular (1985). **Special Catalogs:** Catalogs to manuscript collections (card); catalogs of printers, presses, illustrators, association copies, and provenance (card). **Special Indexes:** Index to individual collections. **Remarks:** FAX: (617)353-2838. **Staff:** Margaret R. Goostray, Asst.Dir.; Katherine Kominis, Book Selector/Archv.

★2009★
Boston University - Department of Special Collections - Nursing Archives (Med)
771 Commonwealth Ave. Phone: (617)353-3696
Boston, MA 02215 Margaret R. Goostray, Asst.Dir., Spec.Coll.
Founded: 1966. **Subjects:** History - nursing education, nursing organizations and institutions, individual nurses. **Special Collections:** Collections of 120 individuals and 40 organizations or institutions including records of the American Nurses' Association (450 manuscript boxes) and the American Journal of Nursing Company, Inc. (65 manuscript boxes); Florence Nightingale letters (200). **Holdings:** 1835 volumes; 3050 manuscript boxes; 30 oral histories. **Services:** Copying (limited); archives open to the public by appointment. **Automated Operations:** Computerized cataloging and serials. **Publications:** Brochures and books describing the Nursing Archives and documenting the contributions of nursing leaders; Nursing Archives Newsletter, irregular - to donors and members of Nursing Archives Associates; Journal of Nursing History, Vol. 1-3 (back issues available on request). **Special Indexes:** Each collection has its own index. **Remarks:** FAX: (617)353-2838. **Staff:** Helen Sherwin, Archv.

★2010★
Boston University - George H. Beebe Communication Reference Library (Info Sci)
College of Communication
640 Commonwealth Ave. - B31 Phone: (617)353-7649
Boston, MA 02215 Anne K. Ilacqua, Hd.
Founded: 1972. **Staff:** Prof 1; Other 1. **Subjects:** Journalism, broadcasting, mass communication, film, advertising, public relations. **Special Collections:** Boston Herald newspaper morgue, late 1800s to mid-1970s; local newspaper clippings, through 1985; Boston Herald-Traveler newspaper clippings (late 1800s to early 1970s). **Holdings:** 40 books. **Subscriptions:** 63 journals and other serials; 20 newspapers. **Services:** Copying; library open to the public. **Automated Operations:** Computerized public access catalog. **Computerized Information Services:** NEXIS; BITNET (electronic mail service). Contact Person: James H. Gallagher, Lib.Coord. **Networks/Consortia:** Member of Boston Library Consortium (BLC). **Remarks:** FAX: (617)353-3405. Electronic mail address(es): SEDNAQN@BUACCA.BU.EDU (BITNET).

★2011★
Boston University - Gerontology Center - Louis Lowy Library (Soc Sci)
67 Bay State Rd. Phone: (617)353-5045
Boston, MA 02215 Nan Genger, Act.Lib.Chf.
Founded: 1974. **Staff:** 2. **Subjects:** Aging - health, housing, training, education, policy, House and Senate hearings, international aspects. **Holdings:** 1000 books; 2000 published and unpublished reports, papers, directories, articles, newsletters, and national conference notices. **Subscriptions:** 54 journals and other serials. **Services:** Copying; center open to the public for reference use only. **Publications:** Boston University Series in Gerontology, irregular. **Remarks:** FAX: (617)353-5047. **Staff:** Elizabeth Markson, Assoc.Ctr.Dir.

★2012★
Boston University - Krasker Memorial Film/Video Library (Aud-Vis)
565 Commonwealth Ave. Phone: (617)353-3227
Boston, MA 02215 Gloria Thompson, Act.Dir.
Staff: Prof 1; Other 8. **Holdings:** 9500 16mm films and videotapes. **Services:** Library open to the public on fee basis. **Special Catalogs:** Catalogue of 16mm Films - free upon request.

★2013★
Boston University - Laboratory of Neuropsychology - Library (Med)
Dept. of Behavioral Neuroscience
M-9, 85 E. Newton St.
Boston, MA 02118 Phone: (617)638-4803
Founded: 1981. **Subjects:** Neuropsychology. **Holdings:** 300 books; 50 reports. **Subscriptions:** 10 journals and other serials. **Services:** Library not open to the public. **Computerized Information Services:** BITNET (electronic mail service). **Remarks:** FAX: (617)638-4806. Electronic mail address(es): MED9DMN@BUACCA(BITNET).

★2014★
Boston University - Mugar Memorial Library - Educational Resources Library (Educ)
605 Commonwealth Ave. Phone: (617)353-3734
Boston, MA 02215 Anne K. Ilacqua, Hd.
Staff: Prof 1; Other 3. **Subjects:** Juvenile and young adult literature, K-12 textbooks, instructional aids, curriculum-oriented periodicals, curriculum guides, standardized education & psychology tests. **Holdings:** 20,000 books; EdD dissertations (latest 5 years). **Subscriptions:** 81 journals and other serials. **Services:** Interlibrary loan; copying; library open to the public for reference use only. **Automated Operations:** Computerized public access catalog, cataloging, acquisitions, and circulation. **Computerized Information Services:** DIALOG Information Services, BRS Information Technologies, OCLC; BITNET, CompuServe Information Service (electronic mail services). Performs searches on fee basis. Telephone 353-3735. **Networks/Consortia:** Member of Boston Library Consortium (BLC), NELINET, Inc. **Publications:** Research Guides, various topics. **Remarks:** FAX: (617)353-3924. Electronic mail address(es): SED94LN@BUACCA.BU.EDU (BITNET); 76012,2254 (CompuServe Information Service).

★2015★
Boston University - Music Library (Mus)
771 Commonwealth Ave. Phone: (617)353-3705
Boston, MA 02215 Holly E. Mockovak, Hd.
Staff: Prof 2; Other 4. **Subjects:** Music theory, musicology, Byzantine and medieval music, British Renaissance music, musical historiography. **Special Collections:** Arthur Fiedler Collection; Byzantine Research Collection of Egon Wellesz; Boston Symphony Orchestra tape and opera score archive; Conservatoire de Paris Archives, 1796-early 20th century; Franz Liszt Collection. **Holdings:** 62,000 book titles; 5100 bound periodical volumes; 47,000 sound recordings; 3700 reels of microfilm. **Subscriptions:** 425 journals and other serials. **Services:** Interlibrary loan; library open to the public with restrictions. **Computerized Information Services:** DIALOG Information Services, BRS Information Technologies, PFDS Online, OCLC, NEXIS; CD-ROMs; InterNet (electronic mail service). **Networks/Consortia:** Member of Boston Library Consortium (BLC), Boston Area Music Libraries (BAML). **Special Catalogs:** Sound Recording Label File; Lieder File; Renaissance File; Voisin Brass Collection; Foreign-language spoken word recordings; Music Theater Pam; Choral Pam. **Remarks:** FAX: (617)353-2084. Electronic mail address(es): Mockovak@bu-pub.bu.edu (InterNet). **Staff:** Richard S. Seymour, Asst.Hd.

★2016★
Boston University - Pappas Law Library (Law)
765 Commonwealth Ave. Phone: (617)353-3151
Boston, MA 02215 Dan J. Freehling, Dir./Assoc.Prof.
Staff: Prof 10; Other 16. **Subjects:** Law. **Special Collections:** Taxation; banking law; law and medicine; international law. **Holdings:** 248,000 books; 176,100 volumes in microform. **Subscriptions:** 5700 journals and other serials. **Services:** Interlibrary loan. **Automated Operations:** Computerized public access catalog, acquisitions, circulation, and serials. **Computerized Information Services:** LEXIS, NEXIS, WESTLAW, DIALOG Information Services, RLIN; BITNET (electronic mail service). **Networks/Consortia:** Member of Research Libraries Information Network (RLIN), Boston Library Consortium (BLC), New England Law Library Consortium (NELLCO). **Publications:** Pappas Papers (newsletter), quarterly - for internal distribution only. **Remarks:** FAX: (617)353-5995. Electronic mail address(es): lawi2hn@buacca (BITNET). **Staff:** Marlene H. Alderman, Assoc.Dir./Hd., Pub.Serv.; Anne Myers, Hd., Tech.Serv.

★2017★
Boston University - School of Medicine - Alumni Medical Library (Med)
80 E. Concord St. Phone: (617)638-4230
Boston, MA 02118-2394 Irene Christopher, Chf.Libn.
Founded: 1873. **Staff:** Prof 9; Other 9. **Subjects:** Medicine, dentistry, public health. **Holdings:** 107,240 volumes. **Subscriptions:** 1413 journals and other serials. **Services:** Interlibrary loan; library not open to the public. **Automated Operations:** Computerized cataloging and serials. **Computerized Information Services:** DIALOG Information Services, BRS Information Technologies, NLM, OCLC. **Networks/Consortia:** Member of Boston Library Consortium (BLC), National Network of Libraries of Medicine - New England Region. **Remarks:** FAX: (617)638-4233. **Staff:** Emily L. Beattie, Hd., Tech.Serv.; Nancy J. Golden, Hd., Bibliog.Serv.; Joseph J. Harzbecker, Jr., Ref.Libn.; Brenda L. Ecsedy, Sys.Libn.

★2018★
Boston University - School of Theology Library (Rel-Phil)
745 Commonwealth Ave. Phone: (617)353-3034
Boston, MA 02215 Myra Siegenthaler, Hd.Libn.
Founded: 1839. **Staff:** Prof 4; Other 3. **Subjects:** Bible, theology, church history, social ethics, psychology of religion, pastoral care. **Special Collections:** Metcalf-Nutter Hymnal Collection; Massachusetts Bible Society Library; Kimball Bible Collection. **Holdings:** 119,251 volumes; 30 VF drawers of New England Methodist history packets. **Subscriptions:** 1033 journals and other serials; 6 newspapers. **Services:** Interlibrary loan; copying; library open to the public with proper credentials. **Automated Operations:** Computerized cataloging. **Networks/Consortia:** Member of Boston Theological Institute Libraries.

★2019★
Boston University - Science and Engineering Library (Sci-Engr, Comp Sci, Biol Sci)
38 Cummington St. Phone: (617)353-3733
Boston, MA 02215 Ardelle F. Legg, Hd.
Founded: 1983. **Staff:** Prof 3; Other 9. **Subjects:** Biology, chemistry, computer science, engineering, mathematics, physics. **Holdings:** 50,000 books; 50,000 bound periodical volumes. **Subscriptions:** 1500 journals and other serials. **Services:** Interlibrary loan; copying; library open to the public. **Automated Operations:** Computerized public access catalog, cataloging, acquisitions, and serials. **Computerized Information Services:** BRS Information Technologies, DIALOG Information Services, PFDS Online. Performs searches on fee basis. **Networks/Consortia:** Member of Boston Library Consortium (BLC). **Remarks:** FAX: (617)353-3470. **Staff:** Sue Vazakas, Bibliog.; Michael Wilson, Bibliog.; Marcia Fishman, Circ.Supv.

★2020★
Boston University - Women's Center - Library (Soc Sci)
GSU Student Center
775 Commonwealth Ave., Suite 9 Phone: (617)353-2000
Boston, MA 02215 Maureen Hurley, Adv.
Founded: 1976. **Staff:** 15. **Subjects:** Women's studies, lesbianism, sociology, psychology, fiction, health, poetry. **Holdings:** 300 books; 40 reports; 100 back issues of MS. magazine; 3 drawers of clippings and archival materials. **Services:** Library open to the public for reference use only.

★2021★
Bostonian Society - Library (Hist)
Old State House
206 Washington St. Phone: (617)720-3285
Boston, MA 02109 Philip Bergen, Libn.
Founded: 1881. **Staff:** Prof 1. **Subjects:** Boston history, antiquities, marine history. **Special Collections:** Colburn collection of autographs; Boston directories. **Holdings:** 6500 books; 300 bound periodical volumes; 80 volumes of clippings; 20 boxes of documents and manuscripts; 10 drawers of maps of Boston; 9500 photographs and negatives; 1100 prints and lithographs; 100 broadsides; scrapbooks on microfilm. **Subscriptions:** 10 journals and other serials. **Services:** Copying; photograph reproduction; library open to the public with restrictions. **Publications:** Proceedings, irregular; Newsletter, quarterly. **Remarks:** FAX: (617)720-3289. Library located at 15 State Street, 3rd Fl., Boston, MA 02109.

Muriel Isabel Bostwick Library
See: **Art Gallery of Hamilton** (1076)

★2022★
Boswell Memorial Medical Center - Library (Med)
10401 Thunderbird Blvd. Phone: (602)977-7211
Sun City, AZ 85351 Thelma Wheeler, Libn.
Founded: 1975. **Staff:** Prof 1. **Subjects:** Geriatrics. **Subjects:** 550 books; 20 bound periodical volumes titles. **Subscriptions:** 101 journals and other serials. **Services:** Interlibrary loan; copying; library open to the public with restrictions. **Computerized Information Services:** MEDLARS.

Roy V. Boswell Collection for the History of Cartography
See: **California State University, Fullerton - University Archives and Special Collections** (2566)

Thomas E. Boswell Memorial Library
See: **First Presbyterian Church** (5798)

Bosworth Memorial Library
See: **Lexington Theological Seminary** (9094)

★2023★
Botanic Gardens of Adelaide and State Herbarium - Library (Biol Sci)
North Terrace Phone: 8 2282325
Adelaide, SA, Australia Miss Gaye Denny, Libn.
Founded: 1855. **Staff:** 1.5. **Subjects:** Taxonomic botany, ornamental horticulture, plant pathology. **Special Collections:** Microfiche collection (older and out-of-print monographs and periodical back-runs; 500 titles); archival/historical collection (botanic gardens history); rare books collection. **Holdings:** 19,370 volumes. **Subscriptions:** 400 journals and other serials. **Services:** Interlibrary loan; library open to bona fide research workers from affiliated institutions by appointment only; post-graduate students may be admitted by written application. **Remarks:** FAX: 8 2231809. Maintained by Government of South Australia. Also serves the staff at the following South Australian locations: Wittunga Botanic Garden, Blackwood, Mt. Lofty Botanic Garden, Black Hill Flora Centre, and Beechwood Heritage Garden at Marbury School, Aldgate. **Also Known As:** Library of the Botanic Gardens of Adelaide and State Herbarium.

★2024★
Botanica, The Wichita Gardens - Frank Good Library (Biol Sci)
701 N. Amidon Phone: (316)264-0448
Wichita, KS 67203 Amy Kaspar Woolf, Libn.
Founded: 1987. **Staff:** 1. **Subjects:** Horticulture, xeriscape, botany, wildflowers, insects, birds. **Special Collections:** Xeriscape. **Holdings:** 2700 books; 100 videotapes; 200 current garden catalogs. **Subscriptions:** 20 journals and other serials. **Services:** Copying; library open to the public for reference use only with borrowing privileges reserved for members. **Remarks:** FAX: (316)264-0587.

Botanisches Institut der Universitat Wien
See: **University of Vienna - Botany Library** (19490)

★2025★
Botsford General Hospital - Hospital Library and Media Center (Med)
28050 Grand River Ave. Phone: (313)471-8515
Farmington Hills, MI 48336-5933 Deborah L. Adams, Dir.
Founded: 1971. **Staff:** Prof 2; Other 3.5. **Subjects:** Medicine, nursing, health administration. **Special Collections:** Osteopathy. **Holdings:** 2700 books; 270 journal titles on microfilm; AV programs. **Subscriptions:** 270 journals and other serials. **Services:** Interlibrary loan; copying; SDI; library open to the public with restrictions. **Automated Operations:** Computerized public access catalog, cataloging, circulation, and ILL. **Computerized Information Services:** MEDLARS, DIALOG Information Services, BRS Information Technologies; CD-ROM (MEDLINE). Performs searches on fee basis. **Networks/Consortia:** Member of Michigan Health Sciences Libraries Association (MHSLA), Detroit Associated Libraries, Michigan Library Consortium (MLC). **Remarks:** Library provides AV equipment and produces computerized slides. FAX: (313)471-8505. **Staff:** Karen Zinterhofer, Libn.

Botswana - Ministry of Finance and Development - Planning - Botswana Technology Center
See: **Botswana Technology Center** (2027)

★2026★
Botswana - National Archives and Records Services (Info Sci)
Government Enclave
P.O. Box 239 Phone: 31 3601000
Gaborone, Botswana Mrs. T.M. Lekaukau
Founded: 1967. **Staff:** Prof 6; Other 10. **Subjects:** Government records and publications, archival reference materials, record management, Botswana, Southern Africa. **Special Collections:** Botswana Collection (books, journals, reports). **Holdings:** 14,000 titles; 460 linear meters of archives; 1364 microfilm titles; 75 audiocassettes. **Services:** Copying; library open to the public with a permit from the office of the president. **Publications:** Annual report. **Remarks:** FAX: 313584. Telex: 2994BD.

★2027★
Botswana Technology Center - Library (Sci-Engr)
Private Bag 0082 Phone: 31 4161
Gaborone, Botswana Ms. Oonayang Dilebanye, Libn.
Founded: 1979. **Staff:** 2. **Subjects:** Renewable energy sources, small-scale production, electronics, food processing, information collection and dissemination. **Holdings:** 7500 books. **Subscriptions:** 127 journals and other serials. **Services:** Interlibrary loan; copying; SDI; library open to the public. **Computerized Information Services:** Internal databases. **Remarks:** FAX: 31 4161. Telex: 374677. Center is sponsored by the Botswana Ministry of Finance and Development Planning. **Staff:** Mrs. L. Philip, Info.Off.; Mrs. Piro Ngidi, Asst.Info.Off.; Ms. Boan Lucky Raboma, Act.Libn.

★2028★
Boulder Community Hospital - Medical Library (Med)
P.O. Box 9019 Phone: (303)440-2273
Boulder, CO 80301 Teri Manzanares, Med.Libn.
Founded: 1922. **Staff:** Prof 1. **Subjects:** Clinical medicine. **Holdings:** 400 books; 1200 bound periodical volumes. **Subscriptions:** 98 journals and other serials. **Services:** Interlibrary loan; library not open to the public. **Computerized Information Services:** MEDLARS. **Formed by the merger of:** Boulder Valley Medical Library and Boulder Memorial Hospital.

★2029★
Boulder Daily Camera/Sunday Camera - Library (Publ)
1048 Pearl St. Phone: (303)442-1202
Boulder, CO 80302 Charlotte Smokler
Founded: 1940. **Staff:** Prof 1. **Subjects:** Newspaper reference topics. **Holdings:** 100 years of microfilm; clippings; photographs; other cataloged items. **Services:** Library open to the public. **Remarks:** FAX: (303)449-9358.

★2030★
Boulder Public Library - Carnegie Branch Library for Local History (Hist)
1125 Pine St.
P.O. Drawer H Phone: (303)441-3100
Boulder, CO 80306 Lois Anderton, Libn./Archv.
Founded: 1983. **Staff:** Prof 3; Other 2. **Subjects:** History - Colorado, Boulder, Boulder County. **Special Collections:** Oral history tapes (567 interviews); Photographs of Boulder and Boulder County Mining and Agricultural Towns, 1866-1970 (200,000). **Holdings:** 5000 books; 40 bound periodical volumes; 10 VF drawers of clippings; 2000 linear feet of manuscripts; 300 linear feet of genealogical materials; 20 boxes of unbound reports; 4 drawers of microfilm of archival materials; 240 historic maps; 60 videocassettes. **Services:** Copying; library open to the public. **Automated Operations:** Computerized cataloging. **Computerized Information Services:** Internal database. **Networks/Consortia:** Member of Colorado Alliance of Research Libraries (CARL). **Publications:** Archival Procedure Manual, 1990. **Remarks:** FAX: (303)442-1808. Digitized images of historic photographs may be viewed on Public Access Computers. **Staff:** Jody Corruccini, Ref.Libn.; Jane Perlmutter, Ref.Libn.

Boulder Valley Medical Library
See: **Boulder Community Hospital - Medical Library** (2028)

Paul-Emile Boulet Bibliotheque
See: **Universite du Quebec a Chicoutimi** (18107)

★2031★
Boundary Layer Wind Tunnel Laboratory - Information Centre (Sci-Engr, Energy)
Faculty of Engineering Science
University of Western Ontario
London, ON, Canada N6A 5B9 Phone: (519)661-3338
Founded: 1965. **Staff:** Prof 1; Other 1. **Subjects:** Wind and wave engineering, allied sciences. **Holdings:** 500 books; 22,000 reports; 16,000 slides. **Subscriptions:** 40 journals and other serials. **Services:** Library open to the public with permission of director. **Automated Operations:** Computerized cataloging. **Computerized Information Services:** Internal database. **Remarks:** FAX: (519)661-3339.

Henry Bouquet Room
See: **Fort Ligonier Association** (6007)

★2032★
Bow Valley Industries Ltd. - Records & Library Services (Energy)
321 6th Ave., S.W., Suite 1300
Box 6610, Sta. D. Phone: (403)261-6115
Calgary, AB, Canada T2P 3R2 Audrey Hawthorne, Supv./Libr.Serv.
Founded: 1984. **Staff:** 2. **Subjects:** Petroleum. **Holdings:** 2000 books; periodicals; papers. **Subscriptions:** 250 journals and other serials; 6 newspapers. **Services:** Interlibrary loan; copying; library open to consultants only. **Remarks:** FAX: (403)261-6105.

Ingersoll Bowditch Library
See: **Faulkner Hospital** (5614)

★2033★
Bowdoin College - Library - Special Collections (Hist, Hum)
Brunswick, ME 04011 Phone: (207)725-3288
Dianne M. Gutscher, Cur.
Founded: 1794. **Staff:** 2. **Subjects:** Bowdoin College history, Maine authors and history, graphic arts, Brunswick history. **Special Collections:** Abbott Memorial Collection - ca. 800 books and 26 linear feet of manuscripts by and concerning Jacob (1803-1879), Gorham (1807-1874), John S.C. (1805-1877), Edward (1841-1908), and Lyman (1835-1922); American Imprints (2500 books and pamphlets printed in the United States and the English colonies before 1821); Anthoensen Press Collection (1200 books and pamphlets; 200 brochures and bookplates); Atlantic and St. Lawrence Railroad Archives, 1844-1889 (800 items); Robert A. Bartlett Papers (Arctic exploration; 9 linear feet of correspondence, manuscripts, photographs, and clippings); Beston Collection - 150 volumes, 14.5 linear feet of correspondence and manuscripts by and concerning Henry Beston (1888-1968) and his wife Elizabeth Coatsworth (1893-1986); Susan Dwight Bliss Fine Bindings Collection (1200 volumes); Vance Bourjaily Papers (11 linear feet of manuscripts and correspondence); Bowdoin Collection (2700 volumes; 1000 pamphlets; 70 manuscript items of Gov. James Bowdoin (1726-1790) and his son, James (1752-1811)); Horatio Bridge Papers (100 items); Charles Brockden Brown Papers (159 letters and manuscripts); Thomas Carlyle Collection (1500 volumes; 24 pieces of correspondence); Joshua L. Chamberlain Papers (2.5 linear feet of correspondence and addresses); Chase-Johnson Papers (history of Brunswick and Bowdoin College; 8000 items); Parker Cleaveland Papers (1600 items); Robert P.T. Coffin Collection (125 volumes, 42 linear feet of manuscripts and correspondence); Cuala Press Collection (73 volumes); Fessenden Papers - 4000 items, primarily by or concerning William Pitt Fessenden (1806-1869); Nathaniel Hawthorne Collection (759 volumes; 170 letters); Oliver Otis Howard Papers (150,000 items); Hubbard Family Papers - 12,000 items, primarily by or concerning John (1794-1869) and Thomas H. (1838-1915); Elijah Kellogg Collection (80 volumes; 1500 other items); Henry Wadsworth Longfellow Collection (1200 volumes; 160 manuscripts; 665 pieces of sheet music); McArthur Family Papers (8000 items); Donald B. MacMillan Collection (arctic exploration; clippings; scrapbooks; journals; photographs; maps; other records); Maine Collection (books and pamphlets printed in Maine before 1836); Mellen Papers (New England history; 5000 items); Mosher Press Collection (500 volumes); Pickard Limited Editions Club Collection (500 volumes); Franklin Pierce Collection (29 manuscripts and letters); Thomas Brackett Reed Papers (200 items); Charles Asbury Stephens Collection (40 volumes; 2350 manuscripts); Tucker Papers (Wiscasset, Maine shipping, 1813-1873; 8000 letters and documents); Thomas C. Upham Collection (65 volumes); Kate Douglas Wiggin Collection (450 volumes; scrapbooks; correspondence); William Willis Papers (355 items); Marguerite Yourcenar Collection (100 volumes); Jesse Appleton Papers (900 manuscripts); Huguenot Collection (800 volumes); Joseph Priestley Collection (95 volumes); Samuel Vaughan Collection (1200 volumes); Thomas Wallcut Collection (550 volumes); Charles S. Daveis papers (400 items); Charles H. Livingston French Autograph Collection (includes letters of Balzac, Diderot, Rousseau, and Voltaire; 800 letters); Magoun & Clapp papers (Bath, Maine shipping; 10,000 items); Charles Vaughan Family Papers (1774-1875; 1300 letters and documents); Alfred Otto Gross Collection (ornithology; 5000 books, pamphlets, and articles; 11 linear feet of correspondence, journals, and notes, 1900-1968; 7000 photographic negatives, 1915-1960); Cyrus Hamlin Papers (700 letters and documents, 1828-1902); Shepley Family Papers (1200 letters, 1802-1972; includes Sergeant Family and Katharine Sergeant White (1892-1977) letters). **Holdings:** 50,000 books; 600 bound periodical volumes; 1353 linear feet of manuscripts; 1452 linear feet of archival materials; 1800 honors theses. **Services:** Copying; collections open to the public. **Automated Operations:** Computerized public access catalog, cataloging, acquisitions, serials, and circulation. **Computerized Information Services:** BRS Information Technologies, DIALOG Information Services, OCLC; CD-ROMs (PAIS, PsycLIT, Books in Print, MaineCat); InterNet (electronic mail service). **Networks/Consortia:** Member of NELINET, Inc. **Special Catalogs:** Chronological and alphabetical lists of manuscript collections (binders). **Remarks:** FAX: (207)725-3083. Electronic mail address(es): DGUTSCHER@JAMES.BOWDOIN.EDU (InterNet). **Staff:** Susan B. Ravdin, Asst. to Cur.

Charles W. Bowers Memorial Museum - Library and Archives
See: **Bowers Museum of Cultural Art** (2034)

★2034★
Bowers Museum of Cultural Art - Library and Archives (Area-Ethnic, Hist)
2002 N. Main St. Phone: (714)972-1900
Santa Ana, CA 92706 Jacqueline Bryant, Cur.Res.
Founded: 1936. **Staff:** 1. **Subjects:** California and the Southwest; Orange County history; Southwestern Indians; Pre-Columbian art; African, Oceanian, and Asian studies. **Holdings:** 1600 books. **Services:** Library open to the public by appointment to researchers. **Computerized Information Services:** Internal database. **Special Catalogs:** Exhibit catalogs. **Remarks:** FAX: (714)835-5937. **Formerly:** Charles W. Bowers Memorial Museum - Library and Archives. **Staff:** Teresa Ridgeway, Reg.

R.R. Bowker Co. - Frederic G. Melcher Library
See: **Cahners Publishing Company/R.R. Bowker Co.** (2441)

★2035★
Bowling Green State University - Center for Archival Collections (Hist)
Library, 5th Fl. Phone: (419)372-2411
Bowling Green, OH 43403-0175 Paul D. Yon, Dir.
Founded: 1968. **Staff:** Prof 9; Other 2. **Subjects:** State and local history, rare books, university archives, historic preservation. **Special Collections:** State and local government records; manuscripts (4000 cubic feet); newspapers (1000 cubic feet); published materials; archives (1000 cubic feet); Ohio Labor History (400 cubic feet); Sam Pollock Collection (150 cubic feet); Women's History (300 cubic feet); National Student Affairs Archives (400 cubic feet); Ray Bradbury Collection (1500 volumes); Franklin D. Roosevelt Collection (1000 volumes; 1000 pieces of ephemera). **Holdings:** 10,000 volumes; 1500 volumes of newspapers from 19 counties of northwest Ohio; 3000 volumes of local government records; 20,000 microforms; 200,000 photographs; 3800 other cataloged items. **Subscriptions:** 77 journals and other serials; 55 newspapers. **Services:** Photocopying; photography; microphotography; document conservation; center open to the public. **Networks/Consortia:** Member of Ohio Network of American History Research Centers (ONARCH). **Publications:** Archival Chronicle, 3/year - free upon request. **Special Catalogs:** Wood County Historical Church Records Survey; Guide to Newspaper Holdings at the Center for Archival Collections; Guide to Local Government Records at the Center for Archival Collections. **Remarks:** FAX: (419)372-7996. Contains the holdings of the former Wood County Historical Society - Historical Museum Library. **Staff:** Ann M. Bowers, Asst.Dir., Univ.Archv.; Lee McLaird, Cur. of Rare Bks.; Susan Hughes, Microfilm Spec.; Marilyn I. Levinson, Cat. & Cur. of Mss.; Steve Charter, Ref.Archv.; Monica Manny, Mss.Proc.; Eric Honneffer, Cons. & Rec.Mgr.; Glenn A. Harper, Reg.Coord., Hist.Presrv.

★2036★
Bowling Green State University - Curriculum Resource Center (Educ)
Jerome Library Phone: (419)372-2956
Bowling Green, OH 43403 Virginia Nordstrom, Hd.Libn.
Founded: 1967. **Staff:** Prof 1; Other 3. **Subjects:** Education - preschool through grade 12, all subjects. **Special Collections:** Late 19th and early 20th century textbooks (600); children's and young adults' literature (fiction and nonfiction; 20,920 volumes). **Holdings:** 149 bound periodical volumes; 13,936 reference books, curriculum resource materials, and school textbooks; 3993 curriculum guides; 2003 multimedia sets/teaching aids/videotapes/computer software; 8732 pictures; 4658 pamphlets; 2332 publishers' catalogs; 104 tests. **Subscriptions:** 11 children's journals and other serials. **Services:** Interlibrary loan (through university library services); multimedia materials available to the university community only; center open to the public. **Automated Operations:** Computerized cataloging, acquisitions, serials, and circulation (OhioLINK). **Computerized Information Services:** BITNET (electronic mail service). **Publications:** Acquisitions, monthly; bibliographies. **Remarks:** FAX: (419)372-7996. Electronic mail address(es): VNORDST@OPIE.BGSU.EDU (BITNET).

★2037★
Bowling Green State University - Institute for Great Lakes Research (Trans)
12764 Levis Pkwy. Phone: (419)874-3907
Perrysburg, OH 43551 Robert W. Graham, Archv.
Founded: 1983. **Staff:** Prof 2; Other 2. **Subjects:** Great Lakes history, maritime history. **Special Collections:** Naval architecture (drawings and photographs). **Holdings:** 8000 books; 510 periodical titles; 250,000 marine engineering drawings and tracings; 2000 linear feet of manuscripts; 538 linear feet of newspaper clippings; 40 linear feet of pamphlets; 874 reels of microfilm; 250,000 photographs; 1500 navigational charts; 3500 slides. **Subscriptions:** 70 journals and other serials; 8 newspapers. **Services:** Copying; Institute open to the public. **Remarks:** FAX: (419)372-7996.

★2038★
Bowling Green State University - Map Collection (Geog-Map)
Jerome Library Phone: (419)372-7905
Bowling Green, OH 43403 Miss Evron Collins, Hd.
Founded: 1981. **Staff:** 1.5. **Subjects:** Cartographic materials; maps - Ohio, Michigan, Indiana, Great Lakes, United States, world. **Holdings:** 50 bound periodical volumes; 600 atlases; 55,000 maps. **Subscriptions:** 11 journals and other serials. **Services:** Interlibrary loan; collection open to the public. **Automated Operations:** Computerized public access catalog, serials, and circulation. **Computerized Information Services:** BRS Information Technologies, OCLC, DIALOG Information Services. Performs searches on fee basis. **Networks/Consortia:** Member of OHIONET.

★2039★
Bowling Green State University - Music Library (Mus)
Jerome Library Phone: (419)372-2307
Bowling Green, OH 43403-0179 Suzanne Eggleston, Hd., Mus.Lib.
Founded: 1967. **Staff:** Prof 3. **Subjects:** Popular music, recording industry, classical music. **Special Collections:** Sound Recordings Archives (515,000 sound recordings of popular music, 1890 to present); popular music journals; portrait and biographical items (24 VF drawers); release notices and other discographic tools; old-time radio show tapes; film music shorts (900); New Music Festival Archives (600 unpublished contemporary scores; videotaped interviews with composers; recordings of New Music Festival concerts, 1980 to present; master tapes of New Music Festival radio programs (PBS); correspondence; programs; posters). **Holdings:** 35,000 books and scores; 1700 bound periodical volumes; 13,000 pieces of popular sheet music; 6 drawers of popular music posters. **Subscriptions:** 115 journals and other serials. **Services:** Library open to the public with restrictions; researchers should contact library prior to making extended visit. **Automated Operations:** Computerized cataloging, acquisitions, and circulation. **Computerized Information Services:** OCLC. **Special Indexes:** Index to Old-Time Radio Shows (loose-leaf notebook); index to popular sheet music collection (online). **Remarks:** FAX: (419)372-7996. **Staff:** William L. Schurk, Sound Recording Archv.; Martin Rosen, Asst.Mus.Libn./Cat.

★2040★
Bowling Green State University - Popular Culture Library (Hum)
Bowling Green, OH 43403-0600 Phone: (419)372-2450
Brenda McCallum, Hd.Libn.
Founded: 1969. **Staff:** Prof 4; Other 24. **Subjects:** 19th and 20th century American culture - popular literature, performing arts and entertainment industry, comic and poster art, recreation and leisure, allied nonfiction (including social history, popular science and religion, self-help). **Special Collections:** Ray and Pat Browne Popular Culture Research Collections; Guymon Detective Fiction Collection (200 linear feet); Saunders Comic Strip Collection (60 linear feet); Horvitz Science Fiction Collection (90 linear feet); performing arts collection (5000 items). **Holdings:** 90,000 books; 6000 bound periodical volumes; 100,000 nontraditional serials including 8500 pulp magazines, 2000 dime and serial novels, 3500 fanzines, and 40,000 comic books; 3500 linear feet of scripts and manuscripts; 5000 vintage fiction paperbacks; movie, World War I, and World War II posters; Big Little Books; trading cards; sales catalogs; alternative press publications; 50,000 postcards; greeting cards. **Subscriptions:** 100 journals and other serials. **Services:** Copying; SDI; library open to the public for reference use only. **Automated Operations:** Computerized public access catalog, cataloging, acquisitions, and serials. **Computerized Information Services:** DIALOG Information Services, OCLC; internal databases; BITNET, InterNet (electronic mail services). Performs searches on fee basis. **Publications:** Acquisitions, monthly; guides to manuscript holdings, pulp magazines, and television scripts - free upon request. **Special Indexes:** Indexes to special subject periodicals and to nontraditional holdings (card); inventories of manuscript holdings (online). **Remarks:** FAX: (419)372-7996. Electronic mail address(es): BMCCALL@OPIE.BGSU.EDU (InterNet); BMCCALL@BGSUOPIE (BITNET). **Staff:** Jean Geist, Lib.Assoc. II; Nancy White Lee, Lib.Assoc. II; Sharon L. Book, Lib. Media Tech.Asst. II.

★2041★
Bowling Green State University - Science Library (Sci-Engr)
Mathematical Sciences Bldg. Phone: (419)372-2591
Bowling Green, OH 43403 Chris Miko, Hd.
Founded: 1962. **Staff:** Prof 3; Other 5. **Subjects:** Biological sciences, mathematics, chemistry, health sciences, technology, geology. **Holdings:** 130,000 books; 69,000 bound periodical volumes. **Subscriptions:** 1665 journals and other serials. **Services:** Interlibrary loan; copying; library open to the public. **Automated Operations:** Computerized cataloging and circulation. **Computerized Information Services:** BRS Information Technologies, DIALOG Information Services. Performs searches on fee basis. Contact Person: Ed Weilant, Ref.Libn., 372-2528. **Remarks:** FAX: (419)372-6817. **Staff:** Jennine Catau, Hd., Tech.Serv.; Floris Wood, Data Archv.; Barb Garay, Hd., Pub.Serv.

★2042★
Box Butte County Law Library (Law)
Clerk of the Dist. Court
Courthouse
Alliance, NE 69301 Phone: (308)762-6493
Subjects: Law. **Holdings:** 100 books; 2000 reports.

★2043★
Boy Scouts of America - Library (Rec, Soc Sci)
1325 W. Walnut Hill Ln.
Box 152079 Phone: (214)580-2292
Irving, TX 75015-2079 Dorothy Edwards, Libn.
Founded: 1950. **Staff:** Prof 1; Other 2. **Subjects:** Youth, psychology, leadership training, camping, recreation, nature and conservation, education, handicrafts, health and safety, American Indians. **Special Collections:** Early and current books on the History of Scouting: books by Baden-Powell, Ernest T. Seton, and William D. Boyce. **Holdings:** 8000 books; 300 bound periodical volumes; 3000 other cataloged items. **Subscriptions:** 125 journals and other serials. **Services:** Interlibrary loan; copying; library open to the public by appointment. **Remarks:** FAX: (214)580-2502.

Boy Scouts of America-Philmont Scout Ranch - Seton Memorial Library
See: **Seton Memorial Library** (15052)

★2044★
Boy Scouts of Canada - Museum & Archives of Canadian Scouting (Hist, Rec)
1345 Base Line Rd.
Sta. F, Box 5151 Phone: (613)224-5131
Ottawa, ON, Canada K2C 3G7 Gertrude Butlin, Libn.
Founded: 1951. **Staff:** Prof 1. **Subjects:** Lord Baden-Powell; early days in the Canadian scouting movement; national and world Boy Scout Jamborees and other scouting events. **Special Collections:** Siege of Mafeking, South African War, where Baden-Powell was commanding officer; South African Constabulary, founded by Baden-Powell. **Holdings:** Historical records; photographs; memorabilia; documents. **Services:** Museum open to the public. **Remarks:** Alternate telephone number(s): 224-5151. FAX: (613)224-3571. **Staff:** Robert Milks, Musm.Coord.

James P. Boyce Centennial Library
See: **Southern Baptist Theological Seminary** (15463)

William T. Boyce Library
See: **Fullerton College** (6203)

★2045★
Boyd County Public Library - Boyd County Historical Society Collection (Hist)
1740 Central Ave. Phone: (606)329-0090
Ashland, KY 41101 Lawrence J. Frank, Dir.
Founded: 1954. **Staff:** 1. **Subjects:** Local and corporate history; history of Ashland and Boyd County, Kentucky; Big Sandy River region of eastern Kentucky. **Special Collections:** Photograph archives. **Holdings:** Personal, corporate, and business records; photographs; newsclippings; scrapbooks. **Services:** Copying; library open to the public. **Remarks:** FAX: (606)329-0578. **Staff:** James C. Powers, Resident Hist.

James Boyd Memorial Library
See: **U.S. Bureau of Mines - Branch of Library Services - James Boyd Memorial Library** (17111)

John Dewey Boyd Library
See: **Alcorn State University** (331)

Philip L. Boyd Deep Canyon Desert Research Center
See: **University of California, Riverside** (18405)

William Boyd Library
See: **Academy of Medicine, Toronto** (34)

Beryl L. Boyer Library
See: **National Foundation of Funeral Service** (11173)

Esther Boyer College of Music
See: **Temple University - Esther Boyer College of Music - New School Institute** (16146)

★2046★
George F. Boyer Museum - Library (Hist)
3907 Pacific Ave. Phone: (609)523-0277
Wildwood, NJ 08260 Al Brannen, Ch.
Founded: 1962. **Subjects:** State and local history, American history. **Holdings:** 1200 books; 2300 bound periodical volumes; 1400 school records; newspapers, 1899 to present; city records; clippings; photographs. **Services:** Library open to the public on limited schedule.

★2047★
Boys' Club of New York - Library
321 E. 111th St. Phone: (212)534-2662
New York, NY 10029 Richard Griffin, Libn.
Remarks: No further information was supplied by respondent.

★2048★
Bozell Inc. - Corporate Information Center (Bus-Fin)
625 N. Michigan Ave. Phone: (312)988-2153
Chicago, IL 60611 Debra L. Hammond, V.P./Dir., Corp.Info.Ctr.
Founded: 1977. **Staff:** Prof 2; Other 1. **Subjects:** Advertising, marketing. **Holdings:** 1000 books; 25 VF drawers of reports, clippings, and pamphlets. **Subscriptions:** 130 journals and other serials; 5 newspapers. **Services:** Interlibrary loan; copying; center open to the public by appointment. **Computerized Information Services:** DIALOG Information Services, DataTimes, VU/TEXT Information Services, InvesText, NEXIS, LEXIS, PRODUCTSCAN, MAID, Telmar. **Networks/Consortia:** Member of ILLINET. **Remarks:** FAX: (312)988-2194. **Staff:** Mary A. Bartolucci, Info.Spec.; Anna M. Rentmeesters, Asst.

★2049★
BP America, Inc. - Reference Center
30-A BP America Bldg.
200 Public Square
Cleveland, OH 44114-2375
Defunct.

BP Canada Inc. - BP Resources Canada Ltd.
See: **BP Resources Canada Ltd. - Library** (2053)

★2050★
BP Chemicals (Hitco) Inc. - Technical Library (Sci-Engr)
1600 W. 135th St. Phone: (310)527-0700
Gardena, CA 90249 Jamee Howell, Act.Libn.
Founded: 1940. **Staff:** Prof 1; Other 1. **Subjects:** Carbon fibers, composites, advanced materials and structures. **Holdings:** 4500 volumes; 5100 technical reports; 14,500 patents. **Subscriptions:** 98 journals and other serials. **Services:** Interlibrary loan; limited public access upon approval. **Automated Operations:** Computerized cataloging. **Computerized Information Services:** DIALOG Information Services. **Remarks:** A division of BP America. FAX: (213)532-7451.

★2051★
BP Exploration (Alaska), Inc. - Information Resource Center (Energy, Sci-Engr)
900 E. Benson Blvd.
Box 196612 Phone: (907)564-4975
Anchorage, AK 99519-6612 Kitty J. Farnham, Supv., Info.Serv.
Staff: Prof 2; Other 2. **Subjects:** Oil and gas exploration, petroleum production, geology, reservoir engineering, arctic environment, business management. **Holdings:** 9000 books; 15,000 technical and well reports; 1000 reels of microfilm of industry standards and vendor catalogs; 500 reels of microfilm of journals. **Subscriptions:** 125 journals and other serials. **Services:** Interlibrary loan; copying; SDI. **Automated Operations:** Computerized cataloging, acquisitions, and serials. **Computerized Information Services:** DIALOG Information Services, ORBIT Search Service, Dow Jones News/Retrieval, LEXIS, NEXIS; CD-ROMs. **Networks/Consortia:** Member of Alaska Library Network (ALN). **Publications:** Acquisitions List, quarterly - for internal distribution only; subscription list, annual; special bibliographies and handouts, irregular. **Remarks:** FAX: (907)564-4995. **Staff:** Stephanie A. Zurinski, Info.Spec.; Diann Boreta, Sr.Lib.Tech.Asst.

★2052★
BP Research, Inc. - Technical Information Center (Sci-Engr)
4440 Warrensville Center Rd. Phone: (216)581-5600
Cleveland, OH 44128 Ron I. Beach, Mgr.
Founded: 1958. **Staff:** Prof 9; Other 5. **Subjects:** Chemistry. **Holdings:** 20,000 books; 2000 reports; 20,000 internal technical reports; patents, 1948 to present. **Subscriptions:** 900 journals and other serials. **Services:** Copying; SDI; center open to the public with permission of manager. **Automated Operations:** Computerized cataloging, acquisitions, serials, and circulation; electronic document imaging system. **Computerized Information Services:** DIALOG Information Services, ORBIT Search Service, STN International, OCLC; internal database. **Networks/Consortia:** Member of OHIONET. **Remarks:** FAX: (216)581-5621. **Formerly:** BP America, Inc. - Technical Information Center. **Staff:** Laurence D. Fogel, Patents & Lit.Hd.; Sally B. Fell, Tech.Proc.Supv.

★2053★
BP Resources Canada Ltd. - Library (Energy)
855 2nd St., S.W., Suite 2100 Phone: (403)231-6458
Calgary, AB, Canada T2P 4J9 Susan Boulette, Libn.
Staff: 3. **Subjects:** Oil and gas, energy, economics. **Holdings:** 5000 books. **Subscriptions:** 400 journals and other serials. **Computerized Information Services:** ORBIT Search Service, DIALOG Information Services; Bibliotech (internal database). **Remarks:** Affiliated with BP Canada Inc. Telex: 038-24782. FAX: (403)237-1902.

Brace Research Institute Library
See: **McGill University - Macdonald Campus** (9904)

★2054★
Bracewell & Patterson - Law Library (Law)
2900 South Tower, Pennzoil Place Phone: (713)221-1240
Houston, TX 77002 Robert S. Grundy
Staff: Prof 2; Other 4. **Subjects:** Law. **Holdings:** 25,000 books; 2000 bound periodical volumes. **Subscriptions:** 350 journals and other serials; 8 newspapers. **Services:** Interlibrary loan; copying; SDI; library open to the public with restrictions. **Computerized Information Services:** DIALOG Information Services, LEXIS, WESTLAW, DataTimes, VU/TEXT Information Services, Dow Jones News/Retrieval, Information America, LEGI-SLATE, Dun & Bradstreet Business Credit Services. **Publications:** Law Library Bulletin, monthly. **Remarks:** FAX: (713)221-1212. Telex: 89-2573. **Staff:** Connie Pine, Assoc.Libn.

Bracken Library
See: **Ball State University - Bracken Library - Archives & Special Collections** (1438)

Bracken Library
See: **Queen's University at Kingston** (13644)

★2055★
Bradenton Herald - Library (Publ)
102 Manatee Ave., W.
P.O. Box 921 Phone: (813)745-7097
Bradenton, FL 34206 Mary K. Shealy, Libn.
Staff: Prof 1; Other 1. **Subjects:** Newspaper reference topics. **Special Collections:** Historical photographs (250). **Holdings:** 600 books; 200 reports; 75 years of microfilm. **Subscriptions:** 40 journals and other serials; 5 newspapers. **Services:** Copying; library open to the public on a fee basis. **Computerized Information Services:** VU/TEXT Information Services, CompuServe Information Service; SAVE Electronic Library (internal database). **Remarks:** FAX: (813)745-7097.

★2056★
Bradford Hospital - Huff Memorial Library (Med)
116-156 Interstate Pkwy. Phone: (814)362-8254
Bradford, PA 16701 Janet Stanek, RRA
Staff: 1. **Subjects:** Medicine. **Holdings:** 460 books; 760 bound periodical volumes. **Subscriptions:** 37 journals and other serials. **Services:** Interlibrary loan; copying; library open to the public with restrictions. **Remarks:** FAX: (814)368-5722.

William Bradford Library
See: **Plimoth Plantation, Inc.** (13144)

William L. Bradford, M.D. Library of the History of Pediatrics
See: **Children's Mercy Hospital - Medical Library** (3589)

★2057★
Emma Pendleton Bradley Hospital - Austin T. and June Rockwell Levy Library (Med)
1011 Veterans Memorial Pkwy. Phone: (401)434-3400
East Providence, RI 02915 Deborah Shea Porrazzo, Dir., Lib. & Info.Serv.
Founded: 1932. **Staff:** Prof 1; Other 1. **Subjects:** Child psychiatry, child psychology, social work, special education, child neurology, pediatrics. **Holdings:** 3250 books; 1500 bound periodical volumes; 300 archival materials; 200 pamphlets; 400 audiotape cassettes. **Subscriptions:** 200 journals and other serials. **Services:** Interlibrary loan; library not open to the public. **Computerized Information Services:** MEDLINE; internal database. **Networks/Consortia:** Member of Association of Rhode Island Health Sciences Librarians (ARIHSL), North Atlantic Health Science Libraries (NAHSL).

Justice Bradley Law Library
See: **Rutgers University - Justice Henry Ackerson Law Library** (14168)

Sydney Wood Bradley Memorial Library
See: **Canadian Dental Association** (2922)

★2058★
Bradley University - Virginius H. Chase Special Collections Center - APCO Historical Collection (Hist)
Cullom-Davis Library Phone: (309)677-2823
Peoria, IL 61625 Charles J. Frey, Spec.Coll.Libn.
Founded: 1982. **Staff:** 3.5. **Subjects:** History of the national and state chapters of the Associated Public-Safety Communications Officers (APCO); public safety telecommunications. **Holdings:** 42 linear feet of APCO Bulletin and proceedings of annual conferences. **Services:** Copying (limited); collection open to the public for reference use only. **Remarks:** FAX: (309)677-2827.

★2059★
Bradley University - Virginius H. Chase Special Collections Center - Charles A. Bennett Collection (Sci-Engr)
Cullom-Davis Library Phone: (309)677-2823
Peoria, IL 61625 Charles J. Frey, Spec.Coll.Libn.
Founded: 1939. **Staff:** 3.5. **Subjects:** Industrial education and industrial arts. **Special Collections:** Wahlstrom Collection; Manual Arts Press Collection (2250 books). **Holdings:** 1140 books; 6692 pamphlets. **Services:** Copying; collection open to the public for reference use only. **Remarks:** FAX: (309)677-2827.

★2060★
Bradley University - Virginius H. Chase Special Collections Center - Chase Collection (Hist, Rel-Phil)
Cullom-Davis Library Phone: (309)677-2823
Peoria, IL 61625 Charles J. Frey, Spec.Coll.Libn.
Founded: 1979. **Staff:** 3.5. **Subjects:** Bishop Philander Chase, Jubilee College, Kenyon College, Protestant Episcopal Church, history of Illinois. **Special Collections:** J. Chase Scully Collection; Robert Herschel Collection; Library of the Citizens to Preserve Jubilee College. **Holdings:** 290 books and pamphlets; 2400 manuscript letters. **Services:** Copying (limited); collection open to the public for reference use only. **Computerized Information Services:** DIALOG Information Services, OCLC EPIC. **Special Indexes:** Name, place, and date index to letters. **Remarks:** FAX: (309)677-2827.

★2061★
Bradley University - Virginius H. Chase Special Collections Center - Lincoln Collections (Hist)
Cullom-Davis Library Phone: (309)677-2823
Peoria, IL 61625 Charles J. Frey, Spec.Coll.Libn.
Founded: 1949. **Staff:** 3.5. **Subjects:** Abraham Lincoln, Civil War. **Special Collections:** Houser Collection; Sours Collection; Stone Collection; microfilm collection. **Holdings:** 1900 items. **Services:** Copying; collections open to the public for reference use only. **Computerized Information Services:** DIALOG Information Services, OCLC EPIC. **Publications:** The Lincoln Collections of Bradley University (an inventory with subject index). **Remarks:** FAX: (309)677-2827.

★2062★
David Bradwell & Associates, Inc. - Library
880 Las Gallinas Ave.
San Rafael, CA 94903
Subjects: Planning, Bay Area and California economy, U.S. labor force, small business development. **Holdings:** 1000 books; 1200 bound periodical volumes; 1980 California census data on microfiche; 80 diskettes of survey data; planning reports. **Remarks:** Currently inactive.

Fred C. Brady, M.D. Memorial Library
See: **Mercy Hospital of Pittsburgh** (10151)

Brady/Green Library
See: **University of Texas Health Science Center at San Antonio - Briscoe Library - Brady/Green Library** (19417)

★2063★
Braille Circulating Library, Inc. (Rel-Phil, Aud-Vis)
2700 Stuart Ave. Phone: (804)359-3743
Richmond, VA 23220 Robert N. Gordon, Exec.Dir.
Founded: 1925. **Staff:** Prof 12. **Subjects:** Bible, Christian biographies, fiction, Bible studies, missionary messages, sermons. **Special Collections:** Writings of James H. McConkey (43 books and booklets). **Holdings:** 5500 braille books; large print books; talking book records, cassettes, reel tapes. **Services:** Interlibrary loan; copying; library open to the public by appointment. **Publications:** Thermo-form copies of library's braille books. **Special Catalogs:** Ink-print catalog of all departments; catalog of braille and talking books and cassette tapes (braille).

★2064★
Braille Institute of America - Library Services (Aud-Vis)
741 N. Vermont Ave. Phone: (213)660-3880
Los Angeles, CA 90029 Dr. Henry Chang, Lib.Dir.
Founded: 1934. **Staff:** Prof 5; Other 36. **Subjects:** General collection of books for the blind and physically handicapped. **Special Collections:** Southern California Collection; blindness and other handicapped reference material. **Holdings:** 22,634 braille volumes; 126,723 talking books; 568,900 cassette tapes. **Subscriptions:** 54 talking book periodicals; 36 braille periodicals. **Services:** Library open to the public. **Computerized Information Services:** Library for the Blind & Physically Handicapped, Braille Institute of America, Inc. Data Base. **Remarks:** FAX: (213)663-0867. **Staff:** Sherry Brent, Ref.Libn.; Mary E. Gabalawi, Foreign Lang.Libn.; Sigrun Hauksdottier, Sys.Libn.; Eric Ichon, Rd.Serv.Mgr.

George B. Brain Education Library
See: **Washington State University** (20044)

Brain Information Service
See: **University of California, Los Angeles** (18372)

★2065★
Brainerd State Regional Human Services Center - Library (Med)
177 E. Oak St., Hwy. 18 Phone: (218)828-2357
Brainerd, MN 56401 Rod Brixius, Libn.
Founded: 1961. **Staff:** Prof 1. **Subjects:** Mental retardation, psychiatry and psychotherapy, alcoholism. **Holdings:** 2560 volumes. **Subscriptions:** 52 journals and other serials. **Services:** Interlibrary loan; library not open to the public. **Computerized Information Services:** Online systems. **Networks/Consortia:** Member of National Network of Libraries of Medicine - Greater Midwest Region.

★2066★
Braintree Historical Society - Library (Hist)
31 Tenney Rd. Phone: (617)848-1640
Braintree, MA 02184-6512 Marjorie Maxham, Lib.Archv.
Founded: 1930. **Subjects:** Local history and genealogy. **Special Collections:** Rev. Dr. George Penniman Genealogical Library (300 volumes). **Holdings:** 1000 volumes. **Services:** Copying; library open to the public by appointment. **Publications:** Thayer genealogy of 1874 (reprints); The Penniman Family, 1631-1900; Braintree Massachusetts, Its History (1985); Early Braintree Gravestone Art, 1728-1850 (1986); Hunt and Allen Fans (1988). **Remarks:** Society also maintains the General Sylvanus Thayer Birthplace (National Register), a barn/library/museum, and a school program featuring historic living for all 5th grades in Braintree.

★2067★
Brakeley, John Price Jones Inc. - Library (Bus-Fin)
2777 Summer St. Phone: (203)348-8100
Stamford, CT 06905 Rose M. Price, Libn.
Founded: 1919. **Staff:** 1. **Subjects:** Fundraising, philanthropy, public relations. **Holdings:** 3000 books; 150 VF drawers of clippings, pamphlets, foundation annual reports. **Subscriptions:** 28 journals and other serials. **Services:** Library open to the public with special permission. **Remarks:** FAX: (203)978-0114.

★2068★
Bramson ORT Technical Institute - Library and Learning Resource Center (Educ)
69-30 Austin St. Phone: (718)261-5800
Forrest Hills, NY 11375 Lydia Lerman, Libn.
Staff: Prof 1; Other 2. **Subjects:** Electrical engineering, computers, mathematics, business. **Special Collections:** Judaica. **Holdings:** 9500 volumes. **Subscriptions:** 50 journals. **Services:** Interlibrary loan; SDI; library open to the public with restrictions. **Networks/Consortia:** Member of New York Metropolitan Reference and Research Library Agency. **Publications:** Library guides. **Remarks:** Maintained by Women's American ORT Federation.

Brand Library
See: **Glendale Public Library** (6500)

★2069★
Brandeis-Bardin Institute - House of the Book (Rel-Phil)
Brandeis, CA 93064 Phone: (818)348-7201
Hannah R. Kuhn, Spec.Libn.
Founded: 1973. **Staff:** Prof 1. **Subjects:** Judaica, Bible, Talmud, Jewish history and literature, Israel and Zionism. **Special Collections:** Hebrew collection (3000 items). **Holdings:** 10,000 books; 3000 audiotapes of lectures. **Subscriptions:** 25 journals and other serials. **Services:** Library not open to the public. **Publications:** Torah at Brandeis Institute. **Remarks:** FAX: (805)526-1398. Alternate telephone number(s): (805)582-4450.

★2070★
Brandeis University - Center for Human Resources - Library (Bus-Fin)
The Heller School
60 Turner St.
Box 9110 Phone: (617)736-3770
Waltham, MA 02254-9110 Alan Melchior, Sr.Res.Assoc.
Subjects: Employment and income research, youth employment and education, employee benefits, welfare reform, public/private partnership, networking in social programs. **Holdings:** 3000 volumes. **Services:** Library open to the public by appointment. **Publications:** Youth Programs, quarterly. **Remarks:** Toll-free telephone number(s): (800)343-4705. FAX: (617)736-3773.

★2071★
Brandeis University - Gerstenzang Science Library (Sci-Engr, Biol Sci)
415 South St. Phone: (617)736-4728
Waltham, MA 02254 Ann Schaffner, Asst.Dir., Sci.Lib.
Founded: 1965. **Staff:** Prof 3; Other 3. **Subjects:** Biochemistry, chemistry, biology, physics, mathematics, computer science. **Holdings:** 143,000 volumes. **Subscriptions:** 1000 serials. **Services:** Interlibrary loan; copying; SDI; contact librarian for information about use of library; membership program for business and research organizations. **Automated Operations:** Computerized public access catalog, cataloging, acquisitions, serials, and circulation. **Computerized Information Services:** DIALOG Information Services, NLM, BRS Information Technologies, Chemical Abstracts Service (CAS); internal database; CD-ROMs (MEDLINE, Science Citation Index, MathSci, Applied Science & Technology Index); BITNET (electronic mail service). Performs searches on fee basis. **Networks/Consortia:** Member of Boston Library Consortium (BLC). **Remarks:** FAX: (617)736-4723. Electronic mail address(es): SCILIB@BRANDLOG (BITNET). **Staff:** Sally Wyman, Sr.Rd.Serv.Libn.; Kathy Button, Sr.Rd.Serv.Libn.

★2072★
Brandeis University - Libraries - Special Collections Department (Hist)
Waltham, MA 02254-9110 Phone: (617)736-4682
Charles Cutter, Hd., Spec.Coll.
Staff: Prof 1. **Subjects:** Spanish Civil War, exploration, Leonardo da Vinci, history of science, political extremism, Sacco and Vanzetti case. **Special Collections:** Spanish Civil War; McKew-Parr Collection on Magellan and Age of Discovery; Vito Volterra Collection on History of Science and Mathematics; Bern Dibner Leonardo da Vinci Collection; Edward G. Levy Dime Novel Collection (20,000). **Holdings:** 60,000 books; 2000 bound periodical volumes; 400 linear feet of archival materials; 357 linear feet of manuscripts; 6 films; 5000 photographs. **Subscriptions:** 25 journals and other serials. **Services:** Copying (limited); collections open to the public by appointment. **Automated Operations:** Computerized cataloging and serials. **Computerized Information Services:** BRS Information Technologies, OCLC. **Networks/Consortia:** Member of Boston Library Consortium (BLC). **Remarks:** FAX: (617)736-4675.

Brandes Memorial Library
See: **Willmar Regional Treatment Center - Library** (20456)

★2073★
Brandon General Hospital - Library Services (Med)
150 McTavish Ave., E. Phone: (204)726-2257
Brandon, MB, Canada R7A 2B3 Kathy Eagleton, Dir.
Founded: 1955. **Staff:** Prof 1; Other 3. **Subjects:** Medicine, nursing, allied health sciences, hospital administration. **Holdings:** 7000 books; AV programs. **Subscriptions:** 250 journals and other serials. **Services:** Interlibrary loan; copying; library open to the public for reference use only on request. **Computerized Information Services:** MEDLARS, DIALOG Information Services, Canadian Centre for Occupational Health and Safety; Envoy 100 (electronic mail service). **Networks/Consortia:** Member of Manitoba Library Consortium, Inc. **Remarks:** FAX: (708)981-5561. Electronic mail address(es): ILL.MBGH (Envoy 100).

★2074★
Brandon Mental Health Centre - Reference and Lending Library (Med)
Box 420 Phone: (204)726-2587
Brandon, MB, Canada R7A 5Z5 Marjorie G. McKinnon, Lib.Techn.
Founded: 1963. **Staff:** Prof 1; Other 2. **Subjects:** Psychiatry, psychiatric treatment services, psychology, social work, hospital administration. **Special Collections:** Early psychiatric texts. **Holdings:** 7980 books; 217 bound periodical volumes; 1487 cassette tapes; 7 drawers of pamphlets; 45,692 journals; 28 reel-to-reel tapes; 50 VF drawers; 226 videotapes, films, and filmstrips. **Subscriptions:** 144 journals and other serials. **Services:** Interlibrary loan; copying; library open to the public with restrictions. **Networks/Consortia:** Member of Manitoba Library Consortium, Inc. **Special Indexes:** Indexes of AV programs and VF files (card and book).

★2075★
Brandon Sun - Library (Publ)
501 Rosser Ave. Phone: (204)727-2451
Brandon, MB, Canada R7A 5Z6 Brenda Kurtenbach, Libn.
Founded: 1883. **Staff:** Prof 1. **Subjects:** Newspaper reference topics. **Holdings:** Bound newspapers, 1883 to present. **Subscriptions:** 10 journals and other serials; 10 newspapers. **Services:** Copying; library open to the public. **Automated Operations:** Computerized circulation. **Remarks:** FAX: (204)727-0385.

★2076★
Brandon Training School - Library (Med)
Brandon, VT 05733 Phone: (802)247-5711
Sandi Sanderson, Lib.Ck.
Founded: 1968. **Subjects:** Mental retardation, education, psychology. **Holdings:** 1600 books; 60 bound periodical volumes; 80 AV programs. **Subscriptions:** 65 journals and other serials. **Services:** Interlibrary loan; copying; library open to the public.

★2077★
Brandon University - Christie Education Library (Educ)
270 18th St. Phone: (204)727-9688
Brandon, MB, Canada R7A 6A9 Linda Burridge, Libn.
Founded: 1967. **Staff:** Prof 1; Other 3. **Subjects:** Education development, curriculum. **Holdings:** 35,000 books; 250,000 ERIC microfiche; 2000 AV programs. **Subscriptions:** 600 journals and other serials. **Services:** Interlibrary loan; copying; library open to the public with restrictions. **Automated Operations:** Computerized public access catalog, cataloging, acquisitions, and serials. **Computerized Information Services:** ERIC; Envoy 100 (electronic mail service). **Remarks:** Alternate telephone number(s): (204)728-9520.

★2078★
Brandon University - John E. Robbins Library - Music Library (Mus)
270 18th St. Phone: (204)727-9630
Brandon, MB, Canada R7A 6A9 June D. Jones, Music Libn.
Founded: 1963. **Staff:** Prof 1; Other 3. **Subjects:** Music history, theory, and criticism; musical theater, applied music. **Holdings:** 5400 books; 1150 bound periodical volumes; 9435 scores; 7500 sound recordings; 700 compact discs; 150 video cassettes; 600 dissertations in microform; 5000 tapes. **Subscriptions:** 150 journals and other serials. **Services:** Interlibrary loan; library open to the public with restrictions on borrowing. **Automated Operations:** Computerized cataloging and acquisitions. **Computerized Information Services:** DIALOG Information Services, CAN/OLE, QL Systems; internal database; Envoy 100 (electronic mail service). Performs searches on fee basis. Contact Person: Linda Burridge, 727-9645.

★2079★
Brandywine Hospital and Trauma Center - Health Sciences Library (Med)
201 Reeceville Rd. Phone: (215)383-8147
Coatesville, PA 19320 Rosemary Conway, Dir.
Founded: 1981. **Staff:** Prof 2; Other 1. **Subjects:** Nursing, nursing research and education, medicine, allied health sciences, radiology education. **Special Collections:** Medical history collection; history of hospital and school of nursing. **Holdings:** 3000 books; 1500 bound periodical volumes; 500 AV programs; 15 VF drawers. **Subscriptions:** 298 journals and other serials. **Services:** Interlibrary loan; copying; library open to the public by appointment. **Computerized Information Services:** MEDLARS, DIALOG Information Services; DOCLINE (electronic mail service). **Networks/Consortia:** Member of Consortium for Health Information & Library Services (CHI), BHSL. **Remarks:** Alternate telephone number(s): 383-8585. FAX: (215)384-6330. **Staff:** Annie E. Law, Asst.

★2080★
Brandywine River Museum Library (Art)
Box 141 Phone: (215)388-7601
Chadds Ford, PA 19317 Ruth Bassett, Libn.
Founded: 1971. **Staff:** Prof 1; Other 2. **Subjects:** American art, Brandywine Valley artists, Howard Pyle, N.C. Wyeth, Andrew Wyeth, James Wyeth, Pyle students, American illustrators. **Special Collections:** N.C. Wyeth Collection (includes proofs and photographs); Thornton Oakley Collection (letters; exhibition catalogs; scrapbooks; artists' research file). **Holdings:** 6000 books; 400 bound periodical volumes; microfilm periodicals; prints; posters; calendars; exhibition catalogs. **Subscriptions:** 33 journals and other serials. **Services:** Copying; SDI; library open to the public by appointment. **Special Indexes:** Index of titles and locations of illustrations by the Wyeth family, Pyle students, and othe American illustrators. **Remarks:** FAX: (215)388-1197.

Branner Earth Sciences Library
See: **Stanford University** (15644)

★2081★
Brant County Museum - Library (Hist)
57 Charlotte St. Phone: (519)752-2483
Brantford, ON, Canada N3T 2W6 Susan Twist, Dir.
Staff: Prof 2. **Subjects:** Local history. **Special Collections:** Alexander Graham Bell; Joseph Brant; Pauline Johnson; Thomas B. Costain. **Holdings:** 500 books; 200 pamphlets; 200 documents; 2000 pictures; 400 files of clippings; 17 binders of historical articles. **Services:** Copying (limited); library open to the public. **Remarks:** Maintained by Brant Historical Society.

★2082★
Joseph Brant Memorial Hospital - Hospital Library (Med)
1230 Northshore Blvd. Phone: (416)632-3730
Burlington, ON, Canada L7R 4C4 Catherine Newman, Libn.
Staff: 1. **Subjects:** Medicine, nursing, administration, paramedical sciences. **Holdings:** 500 books; videotapes. **Subscriptions:** 150 journals and other serials. **Services:** Library not open to the public. **Computerized Information Services:** DIALOG Information Services. **Networks/Consortia:** Member of Hamilton/Wentworth District Health Library Network. **Remarks:** FAX: (416)336-4146.

★2083★
Brant Publications, Inc. - The Antiques Magazine - Library (Publ, Art)
575 Broadway Phone: (212)941-2800
New York, NY 10012 Allison Eckardt Ledes, Ed.
Staff: 1. **Subjects:** Decorative and fine arts, architecture, history. **Holdings:** 3500 books; 250 bound periodical volumes; 500 other cataloged items. **Subscriptions:** 18 journals and other serials. **Services:** Library not open to the public. **Special Indexes:** Annual index to The Antiques Magazine. **Remarks:** FAX: (212)941-2819.

Otto C. Brantigan, M.D. Medical Library
See: **St. Joseph Hospital** (14378)

★2084★
Brasil - Secretaria de Estado da Saude - Coordenacao dos Institutos de Pesquisa - Centro de Documentacao de Hansenologia e Dermatologia Sanitaria Luiza Keffer (Med)
Avenida Dr. Eneas Carvalho Aguiar, 188-10 Andar
C.P. 22180 - CEP 01499 Phone: 11 282-0962
Sao Paulo, SP, Brazil Carmen Campos Arias Paulenas, Libn.
Staff: 8. **Subjects:** Dermatology, leprosy. **Holdings:** 8000 volumes. **Services:** Library open to the public. **Also Known As:** Brazil - Ministry of Health - Institute of Health - Library. **Staff:** Maria Aparecida Esteues; Hilda Souza Constantino; Maria Lucia F. Tallarico; Arlene Pereira; Lenita Castanho; Maria Lazara C. Santos; Gilmar Da Silva.

★2085★
(Brasilia) USIS Reference Library (Educ)
Casa Thomas Jefferson
SHIS OI 9 conj. 17, lote L Phone: 61 2487363
71600 Brasilia, DF, Brazil Maria E.F. Motta, Hd.Libn.
Staff: 3. **Subjects:** Economics, politics, foreign relations, U.S. Constitutional Law, U.S. Government, energy, environment. **Holdings:** 6623 books; 495 Reports; 132 bound periodical titles; 23 periodical titles on microfilm. **Subscriptions:** 129 journals and other serials; 3 newspapers. **Services:** Interlibrary loan; copying; SDI; library open to the public with restrictions. **Computerized Information Services:** LEGI-SLATE; CD-ROM (Readers' Guide to Periodical Literature); internal database. **Publications:** Library Alert; Special Bibliographies. **Remarks:** FAX: 61 2487359. Telex: 61 2108. Maintained or supported by the U.S. Information Agency. Focus is on materials that will assist peoples outside the United States to learn about the United States, its people, history, culture, political processes, and social milieux. **Staff:** Vanny de Mattos Pereira, Ref.Libn.

★2086★
Bratislava - City Museum - Library (Art)
Primaciane nam 2 Phone: 7 334742
CS-815 18 Bratislava, Czechoslovakia Monika Surdova
Founded: 1902. **Staff:** 1. **Subjects:** History of the city, art history, museology, applied art, archeology, numismatics. **Holdings:** 18,000 books; 2000 bound periodical volumes. **Subscriptions:** 15 journals and other serials. **Services:** Library open to the public for reference use only.

★2087★
Brattleboro Memorial Hospital - Medical Library (Med)
9 Belmont Ave. Phone: (802)257-8357
Brattleboro, VT 05301 Martha J. Fenn, Libn.
Founded: 1970. **Staff:** Prof 1. **Subjects:** Medicine, nursing, hospitals, health. **Holdings:** 1700 books; 100 pamphlets and clippings. **Subscriptions:** 80 journals and other serials. **Services:** Interlibrary loan; copying; library open to the public by permission. **Computerized Information Services:** MEDLARS; DOCLINE (electronic mail service). **Networks/Consortia:** Member of Health Science Libraries of New Hampshire & Vermont (HSL-NH/VT).

★2088★
Brattleboro Retreat - Asa Keyes Medical Library (Med)
75 Linden St.
Box 803 Phone: (802)257-7785
Brattleboro, VT 05301 Jane Rand, Dir. of Lib.Serv.
Staff: 2. **Subjects:** Psychiatry, behavioral sciences. **Holdings:** 2500 books; 643 bound periodical volumes. **Subscriptions:** 66 journals and other serials. **Services:** Interlibrary loan; copying; library open to professionals. **Computerized Information Services:** MEDLARS; DOCLINE (electronic mail service). **Networks/Consortia:** Member of Health Science Libraries of New Hampshire & Vermont (HSL-NH/VT).

William G. Braude Library
See: **Temple Beth-El** (16085)

Alfred T. Brauer Library
See: **University of North Carolina at Chapel Hill** (19056)

★2089★
Braun Center for Holocaust Studies - Library (Hist)
823 United Nations Plaza Phone: (212)490-2525
New York, NY 10017 Dr. Dennis B. Klein, Dir.
Founded: 1978. **Subjects:** The Holocaust; non-Jewish rescuers of Jews. **Holdings:** 3000 volumes; biographical archives; documents; films; newspaper clippings. **Services:** Library open to the public by appointment. **Remarks:** Serves as a central resource for information on the Holocaust. FAX: (212)867-0779. Telex: 649278. **Formerly:** International Center for Holocaust Studies.

Braun Research Library
See: **Southwest Museum - Braun Research Library** (15532)

Jack Brause Library
See: **New York University - Real Estate Institute** (11729)

Dr. Bray Associates Libraries
See: **University of King's College** (18760)

L.G. Brayley Health Sciences Library
See: **Mississauga Hospital** (10510)

★2090★
Brazil - Camara dos Deputados - Biblioteca (Law, Soc Sci)
Palacio do Congresso
Nacional Praca dos Tres Poderes Phone: 61 2245669
70160 Brasilia, Brazil Marli Elizabeth Schreiber, Directora
Founded: 1866. **Staff:** Prof 27; Other 33. **Subjects:** Law, political science, economy, public administration, social sciences, reference materials. **Special Collections:** Special collections of international organizations; rare books. **Holdings:** 350,000 books; 450 reports. **Subscriptions:** 1500 journals and other serials; 38 newspapers. **Services:** Interlibrary loan; copying; SDI; library open to the public with restrictions. **Computerized Information Services:** PRODASEN (internal database). **Publications:** Sumario de Periodicos, monthly; Lista de Novas Aquisicoes, monthly. **Remarks:** Telex: 0611657; 0611773.

★2091★
Brazil - Centro de Pequisa Agropecuaria dos Cerrados (EMBRAPA) - Biblioteca (Agri)
Estrada Brasilia Fortaleze km 18
CP 08223 Phone: 61 3891171
73301 Planaltina, DF, Brazil Maria Alice Bianchi
Founded: 1976. **Staff:** Prof 4; Other 3. **Subjects:** Cerrados region, agriculture, animal production. **Special Collections:** Agriculture in Cerrados, Brazil (3500 items); rare book collection (130). **Holdings:** 8000 books; 5567 slides. **Subscriptions:** 340 journals and other serials. **Services:** Interlibrary loan; copying; library open to the public. **Publications:** Cerrados: Resumos Informativos, v.1 to 4, v.5 in print. **Remarks:** FAX: 61 3892953.

★2092★
Brazil - Ministerio da Cultura - Fundacao Biblioteca Nacional (Info Sci, Area-Ethnic)
Fundacao Nacional Pro-Leitura
Ave. Rio Branco, 219-39 Phone: 21 2409229
20042 Rio de Janeiro, RJ, Brazil Affonso Romano de Sant'Anna, Dir.
Founded: 1810. **Staff:** 463. **Special Collections:** Colecao Barbosa Machado (Brazilian and Portuguese history; 5764 volumes); Colecao Conde da Barca; Colecao de Angelis (Paraguayan and Brazilian history; 2747 volumes, 1295 manuscripts); Colecao Teresa Cristina Maria (48,236 volumes); Colecao Salvador de Mendonca; Colecao Jose Antonio Marques; Colecao Wallenstein; Colecao Benedito Otoni. **Holdings:** 1,183,201 books; 4,000,000 periodicals; 672,358 manuscripts and other documents; phonograph records; iconographic material. **Services:** Library open to the public. **Publications:** Bibliografia Brasileira 3/year; Anais da Biblioteca Nacional, annual. **Remarks:** Alternate telephone number(s): 2408929. FAX: 21 2204173. Telex: 21 22941. Maintained by the Secretaria de Cultura de Presidencia da Republica. **Staff:** Suely Dias; Marcio Souza; Esther Bertoletti; Thomas de Aquino Chaves de Melo.

★2093★
Brazil - Ministry of Agriculture - National Center for Agricultural Documentary Information - Library (Agri)
C.P. 10.2432
Anexo I, Bloco B
70043 Brasilia, DF, Brazil Phone: 61 2251101
Subjects: Agriculture, allied areas of natural science, technology, history, legislation. **Holdings:** 56,000 volumes; 250,000 documents on microfiche; 69,000 computer records. **Subscriptions:** 7342 serials. **Computerized Information Services:** AGROBASE (internal database). Performs searches on fee basis. **Publications:** Bibliografia Brasileira de Agricultura; Levantamentos Bibliograficos; additional publications available. **Also Known As:** Centro Nacional de Informacao Documental Agricola.

Brazil - Ministry of Health - Institute of Health
See: **Brasil - Secretaria de Estado da Saude - Coordenacao dos Institutos de Pesquisa** (2084)

★2094★
Brazil - National Center for Information Management Development - Library
Rua Haddock Lobo, 585, 5th Fl.
01414 Sao Paulo, Brazil
Defunct.

★2095★
Brazil - National Council of Scientific and Technological Development - Brazilian Institute for Information in Science and Technology - Department of Dissemination of Scientific Technological Information (Info Sci)
SAS, Quadra 5, Lote 6, Bloco H Phone: 61 2252367
70070 Brasilia, DF, Brazil Maria Angelica Quemel
Founded: 1954. **Staff:** 195. **Subjects:** Library and information science, documentation, scientific and technological information policy. **Holdings:** 200,000 volumes; dissertations; pamphlets; microfiche. **Subscriptions:** 195 journals and other serials. **Services:** Interlibrary loan; copying; library open to the public. **Computerized Information Services:** EVENTOS, BEN, BPS, TESES, FILMES, CLIP, EMPRESAS, CIENTE, ACERVO; CD-ROMs (LISA, NTIS, CHEMBANK, OSHROM, MEDLINE, LILACS, Ulrich's, ABI/INFORM, Periodical Abstracts Ondisc, Science Citation Index, The Serials Directory); electronic mail. **Publications:** Ciencia da Informacao, semimonthly; Qualidade & Produtividade: Eventos e Cursos, quarterly; Calendario de Eventos em Ciencia e Tecnologia, quarterly - all available by subscription; Informativo IBICT (newsletter), bimonthly; Guia de Publicacoes Seriadas Brasileiras, irregular. **Special Catalogs:** Catalogo Coletivo de Publicacoes Periodicas/National Union Catalog of Periodical Publications. **Remarks:** FAX: 61 2262677. Telex: 61 2481 CICT BR. **Also Known As:** Conselho Nacional de Desenvolvimento Cientifico e Tecnologico - Instituto Brasileiro de Informacao em Ciecia e Tecnologia. **Staff:** Matie Nogi; Nadia Tiemi Hamamoto; Marcela Zampronha Moraes; Sabrina Falluh; Helia de Sousa Chaves Ramos.

Brazil - Secretary of State for Health - Butantan Institute
See: **Butantan Institute** (2406)

Brazil-U.S. Cultural Union - Library
See: **Uniao Cultural Brasil** (16630)

★2096★
Brazilian Agricultural Research Corporation - Agricultural Research Center for the Humid Tropics - Library (Biol Sci)
C.P. 48 Phone: 2261941
66000 Belem, Para, Brazil Isanira Coutinho Vaz Pereira, Libn.
Subjects: Animal pathology, climatology, entomology, botany, phytopathology. **Holdings:** 150,000 volumes. **Services:** Interlibrary loan; library open to the public. **Also Known As:** Empresa Brasileira de Pesquisa Agropecuria - Centro de Pesquisa Agropecuaria do Tropico Umido.

★2097★
Brazilian Agricultural Research Corporation - National Center for Agricultural and Agro-Industrial Food Technology - Information and Documentation Section (Food-Bev)
Avenida das Americas, 29501
Guaratiba Phone: 21 410 1353
23020 Rio de Janeiro, RJ, Brazil Maria Ruth Martins Leao, Libn.
Subjects: Food technology and science, chemistry, fats and oils, natural products, essential oils. **Holdings:** 5500 books; 22,000 bound periodical volumes; 800 patents; 250 dissertations; Chemical Abstracts, 1907 to present; Food Science & Technology Abstracts, 1969 to present; Food Science Abstracts, 1950 to present; Nutrition Abstracts, 1970 to present; Microbiology Abstracts, 1970 to present; Nucleic Acid Abstracts, 1971 to present. **Subscriptions:** 400 journals and other serials; 10 newspapers. **Services:** Interlibrary loan; copying; SDI. **Publications:** List of publications available. **Remarks:** Telex: 21 33267 EBPA BR. **Also Known As:** Empresa Brasileira de Pesquisa Agropecuaria - Centro Nacional de Pesquisa de Tecnologia Agroindustrial de Alimentos. **Staff:** Rejane G. Maron, Libn.

★2098★
Brazilian-American Cultural Institute, Inc. - Harold E. Wibberley, Jr. Library (Area-Ethnic)
4103 Connecticut Ave., N.W.
Washington, DC 20008 Phone: (202)362-8334
Staff: Prof 2. **Subjects:** Brazilian history, literature and arts, anthropology, cultural history. **Special Collections:** 19th and 20th century Brasiliana. **Holdings:** 6000 books; 1050 bound periodical volumes; 1500 slides, cassettes, and films. **Services:** Interlibrary loan; library open to the public with restrictions. **Remarks:** FAX: (202)362-8337. **Staff:** Dr. Jose Neistein, Exec.Dir.

★2099★
Brazilian Chamber of Publishing - Library (Publ)
Ave. Ipiranga 1267, Andar 10
01039 Sao Paulo, SP, Brazil Phone: 11 2297855
Subjects: Publishing, bookselling, libraries. **Holdings:** 5000 volumes. **Remarks:** FAX: 11 2297463. Telex: 11 24 788 VRLI. **Also Known As:** Camara Brasileira do Livro.

Brazilian Institute for Information in Science and Technology
See: **Brazil - National Council of Scientific and Technological Development - Brazilian Institute for Information in Science and Technology** (2095)

★2100★
Brazoria County Historical Museum - Museum Research Center (Hist)
100 E. Cedar Phone: (409)849-5711
Angleton, TX 77515 Linda Wood, Res.Ctr.Info.Coord.
Founded: 1983. **Staff:** 1. **Subjects:** Brazoria County and Texas history. **Special Collections:** Historical photographs of Brazoria County (2063 photographs); Families of Brazoria County (175 oral history tapes); early Texas history; Southwestern Historical Quarterly (complete set). **Holdings:** 623 books; 9 VF drawers of pamphlets, manuscripts, and clippings; 4 slide/tape sets; videotapes. **Services:** Copying; center open to the public. **Special Catalogs:** Catalogs of photographs and tapes (card). **Special Indexes:** Indexes to family biographies and cemeteries in Brazoria County.

★2101★
Brazosport Facts - Library (Publ)
720 S. Main
Box 549 Phone: (409)265-7411
Clute, TX 77531-0549 Margaret Rice, Libn.
Founded: 1980. **Staff:** Prof 1; Other 1. **Subjects:** Newspaper reference topics, Brazosport and Brazoria County history. **Special Collections:** Photographs of southern Brazoria County, Texas (180,000 negatives). **Holdings:** 460 books; 328 bound periodical volumes; 294 reels of microfilm; 88 VF drawers of indexed clippings; 40 VF drawers of photographs. **Subscriptions:** 30 journals and other serials. **Services:** Interlibrary loan; interlibrary copying; library open to the public with restrictions. **Computerized Information Services:** Internal database. **Remarks:** FAX: (409)265-2213.

★2102★
Brazosport Museum of Natural Science - Library (Biol Sci)
400 College Dr. Phone: (409)265-7831
Lake Jackson, TX 77566 Margaret Rice, Libn.
Founded: 1964. **Staff:** 1. **Subjects:** Malacology, marine science, mineralogy, birds and other wildlife, archaeology, paleontology. **Special Collections:** National Geographic magazine (1927-1987); monographs of the marine mollusks of the North Atlantic; The Veliger (vol. 1-20); Nautilus (88-98); Johnsonia (vol.1) **Holdings:** 654 books; 34 bound periodical volumes. **Services:** Copying; library open to the public for reference use only. **Remarks:** Library located in the Brazosport Center for the Arts & Sciences.

★2103★
(Brazzaville) Centre Culturel Americain - USIS Library (Educ)
Ave. Foch et Malamine
B.P. 1015
Brazzaville, Congo
Remarks: Maintained or supported by the U.S. Information Agency. Focus is on materials that will assist peoples outside the United States to learn about the United States, its people, history, culture, political processes, and social milieux.

★2104★
Bread for the World Institute on Hunger & Development - Resource Room (Soc Sci)
802 Rhode Island Ave., N.E. Phone: (202)269-0200
Washington, DC 20018 Christine Matthews, Libn.
Founded: 1982. **Staff:** Prof 1; Other 1. **Subjects:** Hunger, poverty, international relief and development, public policies, food and agriculture, Christian perspectives. **Holdings:** 2000 books; 5 VF drawers; 200 government documents; 2000 documents and serial monographs; internal publications; vertical files. **Subscriptions:** 84 journals and other serials. **Services:** Interlibrary loan; copying; center open to the public by appointment. **Publications:** Bread for the World Newsletter, 8/year - to members. **Remarks:** FAX: (202)529-8546.

James Carson Breckinridge Library
See: **U.S. Marine Corps University** (17605)

★2105★
Breed, Abbott & Morgan - Library (Law)
153 E. 53rd St. Phone: (212)888-0800
New York, NY 10022 Carol H. Barra, Hd.Libn.
Founded: 1898. **Staff:** Prof 3; Other 3. **Subjects:** Law. **Holdings:** 40,000 volumes. **Subscriptions:** 195 journals and other serials. **Services:** Interlibrary loan; library not open to the public. **Computerized Information Services:** LEXIS, DIALOG Information Services, Dow Jones News/Retrieval, WESTLAW. **Remarks:** FAX: (212)888-0258. **Staff:** Elaine Egan, Asst.Libn.; Elizabeth Grunwald, Tech.Serv.Libn.

Andrew W. Breidenbach Environmental Research Library
See: **U.S. Environmental Protection Agency** (17456)

Breitman Memorial Library
See: **Beverly Hospital** (1802)

Anne Bremer Memorial Library
See: **San Francisco Art Institute** (14726)

Brenau College
See: **Northeast Georgia Medical Center & Hall School of Nursing/ Brenau College** (11968)

Thomas R. Brendle Memorial Library & Museum
See: **Historic Schaefferstown, Inc.** (7254)

Brenham State School - Staff Library
See: **Texas (State) Department of Mental Health & Mental Retardation** (16245)

Breniman Nautical-Wireless Library & Museum of Communications
See: **Society of Wireless Pioneers, Inc.** (15343)

Joseph Brennemann Library
See: **Children's Memorial Hospital** (3588)

Brenner Library
See: **Quincy College** (13667)

★2106★
Brentwood Hospital - Library (Med)
4110 Warrensville Center Rd. Phone: (216)283-3458
Cleveland, OH 44122 Jean Dreifort, Dir., Educ.Info.Serv.
Founded: 1978. **Staff:** Prof 1; Other 2. **Subjects:** Medicine, osteopathic medicine. **Holdings:** 5000 books; 1300 bound periodical volumes; 550 AV programs; 30 shelves of video cassettes; 28 drawers of audio cassettes. **Subscriptions:** 452 journals and other serials. **Services:** Interlibrary loan; copying; SDI; library open to the public at librarian's discretion. **Automated Operations:** Computerized cataloging, acquisitions, serials, and circulation. **Computerized Information Services:** BRS Information Technologies, DIALOG Information Services, MEDLARS; internal database. **Networks/ Consortia:** Member of National Network of Libraries of Medicine - Greater Midwest Region, Cleveland Area Metropolitan Library System (CAMLS). **Publications:** Acquisitions list, monthly - to staff and selected libraries; newsletter, irregular - for internal distribution only. **Remarks:** FAX: (216)283-3451.

★2107★
Brest Van Kempen & Associates, Inc. - Library (Sci-Engr)
4920 Emigration Canyon
Salt Lake City, UT 84108 Phone: (801)582-8769
Subjects: Engineering, materials, mining, ground control, drilling, economics, finance. **Holdings:** 1000 books; 300 reports. **Subscriptions:** 10 journals and other serials. **Services:** Library not open to the public.

★2108★
Brethren in Christ Church and Messiah College - Archives (Rel-Phil)
Messiah College Phone: (717)691-6048
Grantham, PA 17027 Dr. E. Morris Sider, Archv.
Founded: 1952. **Staff:** Prof 1; Other 1. **Subjects:** History and life of the Brethren in Christ Church and allied subjects. **Holdings:** 120 books; 240 bound periodical volumes; 600 boxes of historical manuscripts; council records; tapes; films; pamphlets; photographs; 150 museum items. **Services:** Copying; archives open to the public with restrictions on use of some material. **Publications:** Brethren in Christ History and Life, 3/year - by subscription. **Special Indexes:** Index to minutes of the General Conference of the Brethren in Christ (1871-1960); Index to Brethren in Christ History and Life; Index to Evangelical Visitor (1887 to present). **Remarks:** FAX: (717)691-6042.

★2109★
Brevard County - A. Max Brewer Memorial Law Library (Law)
County Courthouse
506 S. Palm Ave. Phone: (407)264-5303
Titusville, FL 32796 Mrs. George McFarland, Law Libn.
Staff: Prof 1; Other 1. **Subjects:** Law. **Holdings:** 20,000 volumes. **Services:** Copying; library open to the public for reference use only. **Computerized Information Services:** WESTLAW, VU/TEXT Information Services. Performs searches on fee basis. Contact Person: George McFarland, Law Lib.Dir. **Remarks:** FAX: (407)264-5305.

★2110★
Brevard County - A. Max Brewer Memorial Law Library - Melbourne Branch Law Library (Law)
50 S. Nieman Ave. Phone: (407)952-4609
Melbourne, FL 32901 Annette Melnicove, Law Libn.
Founded: 1985. **Staff:** Prof 1. **Subjects:** Law. **Holdings:** 6100 books; 47 bound periodical volumes. **Subscriptions:** 11 journals and other serials. **Services:** Copying; library open to the public with restrictions. **Computerized Information Services:** WESTLAW. Performs searches on fee basis. **Remarks:** FAX: (407)952-4610.

A. Max Brewer Memorial Law Library
See: **Brevard County - A. Max Brewer Memorial Law Library** (2109)

★2111★
Brewers Association of Canada - Library (Food-Bev)
Heritage Place, Suite 1200
155 Queen St. Phone: (613)232-9601
Ottawa, ON, Canada K1P 6L1 Edwin Gregory, Libn.
Founded: 1970. **Staff:** Prof 1. **Subjects:** Alcoholic beverages and their abuse, history of the brewing industry, taverns and inns. **Holdings:** 500 books; 500 papers on use and abuse of alcohol. **Subscriptions:** 60 journals and other serials; 19 newspapers. **Services:** Interlibrary loan; library open to the public by appointment only. **Computerized Information Services:** CAN/OLE, DIALOG Information Services, DOBIS, Info Globe. **Publications:** Press Clipping Survey, weekly - for internal distribution only; About Beer and the Brewing Industry; International Survey, 7th edition (1989); On Tap (newsletter), 4/year. **Remarks:** FAX: (613)232-2283.

Brewster Library
See: **Essex County Historical Society - Brewster Library** (5445)

Brewster Memorial Library
See: **The Hoyt Library** (7484)

★2112★
Brick Institute of America - Library (Sci-Engr)
11490 Commerce Park Dr. Phone: (703)620-0010
Reston, VA 22091 Brian Trimble, Staff Engr.
Founded: 1934. **Subjects:** Engineering and research pertinent to masonry construction. **Holdings:** 3000 volumes. **Services:** Library open to the public with approval from Engineering Dept. **Remarks:** FAX: (703)620-3928.

★2113★
Brick Store Museum - Edith Cleaves Barry Library (Hist)
117 Main St.
Box 177 Phone: (207)985-4802
Kennebunk, ME 04043 Joyce Butler, Libn.
Founded: 1936. **Staff:** Prof 1. **Subjects:** Maine and local history, antiques, maritime history, genealogy. **Special Collections:** Local documents (5000); William Lord papers (450). **Holdings:** 2200 books; 100 bound periodical volumes; 500 pamphlets; 2 file drawers of handwritten genealogical information; 13,500 photographs; 3000 glass plate negatives. **Subscriptions:** 10 journals and other serials. **Services:** Library open to the public by appointment.

★2114★
Bridgeport (City) Department of Archives, Records, and Information Services (Soc Sci)
City Hall, Rm. 13
45 Lyon Terr. Phone: (203)576-8192
Bridgeport, CT 06604 Mollie Keller, City Rec.Mgr.
Founded: 1983. **Staff:** Prof 1. **Subjects:** City government. **Special Collections:** Bridgeport city records, documents, and archives (1428 linear feet of archives). **Holdings:** 250 books; 50 maps; 5000 prints and drawings; 5000 linear feet of inactive records. **Services:** Copying; department open to the public. **Automated Operations:** Computerized records management. **Computerized Information Services:** Internal database. **Remarks:** FAX: (203)576-8330.

★2115★
Bridgeport Hospital - Reeves Memorial Library (Med)
267 Grant St.
Box 5000 Phone: (203)384-3254
Bridgeport, CT 06610 Katherine Stemmer, Dir.
Founded: 1948. **Staff:** Prof 1; Other 1. **Subjects:** Medicine, allied health sciences. **Holdings:** 3675 books; 4513 bound periodical volumes; 872 AV programs. **Subscriptions:** 300 journals and other serials; 5 newspapers. **Services:** Interlibrary loan; copying; SDI; library open to the public for reference use only. **Computerized Information Services:** MEDLARS, BRS Information Technologies. Performs searches on fee basis. **Networks/Consortia:** Member of Connecticut Association of Health Science Libraries (CAHSL), Southwestern Connecticut Library Council (SWLC), North Atlantic Health Science Libraries (NAHSL). **Remarks:** FAX: (203)384-3318.

★2116★
Bridgeport Public Library - Historical Collections (Hist)
925 Broad St. Phone: (203)576-7417
Bridgeport, CT 06604 Mary K. Witkowski, Dept.Hd.
Founded: 1936. **Staff:** Prof 1; Other 4. **Subjects:** Local history, genealogy, circus, P.T. Barnum, labor and business history. **Special Collections:** Circus and P.T. Barnum Collection (1160 items); Calliopean Society Library, pre-1855 (1225 volumes). **Holdings:** 13,500 books; 670 bound periodical volumes; 750 linear feet of manuscripts and archival materials; 420 linear feet of newspaper clipping files; 2800 photographs; 100 bound volumes of newspapers; 5260 reels of microfilm; 250 maps. **Subscriptions:** 250 journals and other serials. **Services:** Copying; collections open to the public. **Automated Operations:** Computerized cataloging and circulation. **Computerized Information Services:** DIALOG Information Services. **Networks/Consortia:** Member of NELINET, Inc., Southwestern Connecticut Library Council (SWLC). **Publications:** Brief Guide, 1987 - free upon request. **Special Catalogs:** Manuscript and archival registers. **Remarks:** FAX: (203)576-8255.

★2117★
Bridgeport Public Library - Technology and Business Department (Bus-Fin, Sci-Engr)
925 Broad St. Phone: (203)576-7406
Bridgeport, CT 06604 Barbara Bennorth, Hd.
Staff: Prof 4; Other 8. **Subjects:** Technology, business, physical sciences. **Holdings:** 75,374 books; vocational pamphlets; topographic maps; government documents. **Subscriptions:** 400 journals and other serials. **Services:** Interlibrary loan; copying (limited); department open to the public. **Automated Operations:** Computerized cataloging and circulation. **Computerized Information Services:** DIALOG Information Services, Dow Jones News/Retrieval, WILSONLINE, OCLC, EPIC. Performs searches on fee basis. **Networks/Consortia:** Member of Southwestern Connecticut Library Council (SWLC). **Remarks:** FAX: (203)576-8255. **Staff:** Nancy Johmann, Asst.Dir.; Louise Minervino, Hd.Libn.

★2118★
Bridgestone/Firestone Inc. - Central Research Library (Sci-Engr)
1200 Firestone Pkwy. Phone: (216)379-7430
Akron, OH 44317-0001 S. Koo, Sr.Res.Libn.
Founded: 1945. **Staff:** Prof 1. **Subjects:** Rubber, plastics, textiles, chemical and mechanical engineering, polymer chemistry. **Holdings:** 7500 books; 11,000 bound periodical volumes; 54 VF drawers of patents; 12 VF drawers of pamphlets; 2000 government documents; 3750 reels of microfilm; 3000 microfiche; 10,000 internal research reports. **Subscriptions:** 250 journals and other serials. **Services:** Interlibrary loan; library not open to the public. **Automated Operations:** Computerized circulation. **Computerized Information Services:** DIALOG Information Services, PFDS Online. **Publications:** U.S. Patents Bulletin, weekly; Table of Contents Bulletin, biweekly; Translation Bulletin, irregular; Foreign Patent Bulletin, weekly. **Remarks:** Alternate telephone number(s): (216)379-7000. FAX: (216)379-6144.

★2119★
Bridgeton Free Public Library - Special Collections (Area-Ethnic)
150 E. Commerce St. Phone: (609)451-2620
Bridgeton, NJ 08302-2684 Patricia W. McCulley, Lib.Dir.
Staff: Prof 3; Other 8. **Subjects:** Cumberland County history, local genealogy, Woodland Indians. **Holdings:** 2000 volumes, including newspapers, 1881 to present, bound and on microfilm; 20,000 Indian artifacts, 10,000 B.C. to circa 1700 A.D., collected within a 30-mile radius of the library. **Services:** Interlibrary loan; copying; collections open to the public. **Staff:** Grace Stirneman.

★2120★
Bridgewater College - Alexander Mack Memorial Library - Special Collections (Rel-Phil)
Bridgewater, VA 22812 Phone: (703)828-2501
Ruth Greenawalt, Dir.
Founded: 1880. **Staff:** Prof 4.5; Other 3. **Special Collections:** Church of the Brethren (1550); Virginia history (1500); genealogy (650). **Holdings:** 37,000 U.S. government documents. **Services:** Interlibrary loan; copying; collections open to the public with restrictions. **Automated Operations:** Computerized cataloging. **Computerized Information Services:** DIALOG Information Services, Knowledge Index; CD-ROMs (Periodical Abstracts Ondisc, ABI/INFORM). Contact Person: Thelma Hall, Pub.Serv.Libn. **Networks/Consortia:** Member of Shenandoah Valley Independent College Library Cooperative, SOLINET. **Remarks:** FAX: (703)828-4856. **Staff:** Dr. Buu Duong, Acq.; Carin Teets, Cat.; Brenda Yocum, Pub.Serv.Libn.

★2121★
Bridgewater Courier-News - Library (Publ)
1201 U.S. Hwy. 22, W.
Box 6600 Phone: (908)722-8800
Bridgewater, NJ 08807 Susan Hofmann, Libn.
Staff: Prof 1. **Subjects:** Local history, newspaper reference topics. **Holdings:** 200 volumes; 240 VF drawers of clippings; 22 VF drawers of microfilm; 9 VF drawers of photographs; 2 VF drawers of maps. **Subscriptions:** 7 newspapers. **Services:** Copying; library open to the public. **Remarks:** Published by Gannett Newspapers.

★2122★
Bridgewater State College - The Clement C. Maxwell Library (Educ)
Shaw Rd. Phone: (508)697-1256
Bridgewater, MA 02325 Ratna Chandrasekhar, Lib.Dir.
Founded: 1840. **Staff:** Prof 14; Other 16. **Subjects:** Education. **Special Collections:** Theodore Roosevelt Collection; Charles Dickens; early American textbooks; Lincoln Collection. **Holdings:** 267,209 volumes; 461,863 ERIC microfiche; 41,108 pieces of microfiche; 7566 reels of microfilm; 17,963 ultrafiche. **Subscriptions:** 1380 journals and other serials; 44 newspapers. **Services:** Interlibrary loan; copying; library open to the public with restrictions. **Automated Operations:** Computerized public access catalog and cataloging. **Computerized Information Services:** OCLC EPIC, DIALOG Information Services. **Networks/Consortia:** Member of Southeastern Massachusetts Cooperating Libraries (SMCL), NELINET, Inc. **Remarks:** FAX: (508)697-1705. **Staff:** S. Mabell Bates, Spec.Coll.Libn.; Sheau-Hwang Chang, Spec.Coll./Sys.Libn.; Alan G. Howell, Acq.Libn.; Mary H. Myers, Per.Libn.; Carol B. Neubauer, Circ.Libn.; Susan C. Pfister, Cat.Libn.; Robert M. Simmons, Curric.Libn.; Shu-Chen H. Tu, Ref.Libn.; Cynthia Webber, Ref.Libn.; Adeline Ziino, Cat.Libn.

The Bridwell Library
See: **Southern Methodist University - Perkins School of Theology - The Bridwell Library** (15503)

Margaret M. Bridwell Art Library
See: **University of Louisville - Allen R. Hite Art Institute** (18767)

★2123★
Briercrest Bible College - Archibald Library (Rel-Phil)
Caronport, SK, Canada S0H 0S0 Phone: (306)756-3252
Laura Klassen, Act.Dir.
Founded: 1935. **Staff:** 5. **Subjects:** Christian education. **Holdings:** 42,000 books; 3600 bound periodical volumes; 500 archival files; 259,454 microforms; 2500 slides and cassettes. **Subscriptions:** 419 journals and other serials. **Services:** Interlibrary loan; copying; library open to the public with restrictions. **Remarks:** FAX: (306)756-3366. **Staff:** John Plantz, Pub.Serv.Libn.; Corinne Ronald, Acq./Sec.

★2124★
Briger & Associates - Library (Law)
300 Park Ave., 24th Fl. Phone: (212)758-4000
New York, NY 10022-7402 Erika Soldano, Libn.
Staff: Prof 1. **Subjects:** Tax law, international law. **Holdings:** 4000 books. **Services:** Interlibrary loan; copying. **Remarks:** FAX: (212)888-7587.

Hilton M. Briggs Library
See: **South Dakota State University** (15424)

Carl Campbell Brigham Library and Test Collection
See: **Educational Testing Service** (5262)

★2125★
Briley, Wild and Associates, Inc. - Library (Sci-Engr)
1042 U.S. Highway 1 North
Box 607 Phone: (904)672-5660
Ormond Beach, FL 32175 John W. Casey, Libn.
Staff: Prof 1. **Subjects:** Water, wastewater treatment, facilities planning, water resources. **Holdings:** 5300 volumes; 7500 documents; 1 VF drawer of clippings. **Subscriptions:** 200 journals and other serials. **Services:** Copying; library open to the public with restrictions. **Computerized Information Services:** ACER (internal database).

Abraham A. Brill Library
See: **New York Psychoanalytic Institute** (11591)

Brill Science Library
See: **Miami University** (10265)

Ira F. Brilliant Center for Beethoven Studies
See: **San Jose State University** (14759)

H.H. Brimley Memorial Library
See: **North Carolina State Museum of Natural Sciences** (11895)

★2126★
Brion Research Institute of Taiwan - Library (Med)
116 Chung-ching South Rd., Section 3 Phone: 2 303 4828
Taipei 10743, Taiwan Hsiu-tzu Wang, Libn.
Subjects: Pharmaceuticals, Chinese medicine, herbs. **Holdings:** 30,000 volumes. **Remarks:** Affiliated with the Oriental Healing Arts Institute of Palo Alto, CA, USA.

Briscoe Library
See: **University of Texas Health Science Center at San Antonio** (19416)

★2127★
Bristol Historical Preservation Society - Library (Hist)
48 Court St. Phone: (401)253-6948
Bristol, RI 02809 Helene L. Tessler, Cur.-Libn.
Founded: 1936. **Staff:** 1. **Subjects:** Genealogy and local history. **Special Collections:** Ships logs, journals, crew lists. **Holdings:** 1500 volumes; 4 VF drawers of shipping papers; 12 VF drawers of local area clippings, obituaries, deeds, correspondence. **Services:** Copying; library open to the public with fee for nonmembers.

★2128★
Bristol Law Library (Law)
Superior Court House
9 Court St. Phone: (508)824-7632
Taunton, MA 02780 Margaret M. Hayden, Libn.
Founded: 1858. **Staff:** Prof 1. **Subjects:** Law. **Holdings:** 16,469 volumes; 10,448 volumes in microform. **Subscriptions:** 20 journals and other serials. **Services:** Copying; library. **Services:** Copying; library open to the public. **Computerized Information Services:** OCLC, WESTLAW, LEXIS, DIALOG Information Services. **Remarks:** Part of the Massachusetts State Trial Court; Marnie Warner, Law Library Coordinator.

★2129★
Bristol-Myers Products - Technical Information Center (Biol Sci, Med)
1350 Liberty Ave.
Hillside, NJ 07205 Phone: (201)851-6244
Founded: 1946. **Staff:** Prof 2; Other 3. **Subjects:** Biology, pharmacology, chemistry, pharmaceutical science, toiletries. **Holdings:** 12,000 books; 11,000 bound periodical volumes; 7500 reels of microfilm of periodicals; 5 drawers of patents, microfiche and hardcopy; 40 drawers of documents and reports, microfiche and hardcopy. **Subscriptions:** 225 journals and other serials; 3 newspapers. **Services:** Interlibrary loan; copying; SDI. **Automated Operations:** Computerized cataloging and serials. **Computerized Information Services:** Chemical Abstracts Service (CAS), DIALOG Information Services, NLM, LEXIS, Dow Jones News/Retrieval. **Networks/Consortia:** Member of PALINET. **Publications:** Recent Acquisitions Bulletin, monthly; Subject Profiles, weekly; Industry Briefs, biweekly; Patent Briefs, monthly - all for internal distribution only. **Remarks:** FAX: (201)851-6073. **Staff:** Ann M. Swist, Mgr.; Joanne Freeman, Libn.

Bristol-Myers Squibb Company - Drackett Company
See: **Drackett Company** (4995)

★2130★
Bristol-Myers Squibb Company - Medical Library (Med)
2365 Cote de Liesse Rd. Phone: (514)333-2057
Montreal, PQ, Canada H4N 2M7 Donna Gibson, Med.Libn.
Founded: 1985. **Staff:** 1.5. **Subjects:** Medicine, pharmacology, chemistry, pharmaceuticals. **Holdings:** 5000 unbound periodical volumes; 600 monographs. **Subscriptions:** 167 journals; 8 newsletters. **Services:** Interlibrary loan; copying; library open to the public by appointment. **Computerized Information Services:** MEDLARS, DIALOG Information Services. **Remarks:** FAX: (514)335-4102.

★2131★
Bristol-Myers Squibb Company - New Brunswick Library (Med, Sci-Engr)
Rte. 1 & College Farm Rd., Bldg. 100 Phone: (908)519-2268
New Brunswick, NJ 08903 Phyllis J. Minicuci, Supv., Lib.Oper.
Founded: 1971. **Staff:** Prof 2; Other 2. **Subjects:** Analytical chemistry, pharmaceutics, pharmacology, quality control, biochemistry. **Holdings:** 4000 books; 6600 bound periodical volumes. **Subscriptions:** 400 journals and other serials. **Services:** Interlibrary loan; copying; SDI; library open to other librarians and researchers with authorization. **Computerized Information Services:** DIALOG Information Services, PFDS Online, STN International, OCLC; DIALMAIL, STN Mail (electronic mail services). **Networks/Consortia:** Member of MEDCORE. **Publications:** Taxol bibliography. **Remarks:** FAX: (908)249-6729. **Staff:** Michael Rogers.

★2132★
Bristol-Myers Squibb Company - Pharmaceutical Research Institute - Research Library (Med)
100 Forest Ave. Phone: (716)887-3637
Buffalo, NY 14213 Rose Ann Gubbins, Asst.Mgr., Lib.Oper.
Founded: 1983. **Staff:** Prof 2; Other 1. **Subjects:** Dermatology, chemistry, pharmacology, pharmacy and pharmaceuticals, medicine. **Holdings:** 4200 books; 8000 bound periodical volumes; 2000 microfilm cartridges; 150 audio cassettes. **Subscriptions:** 500 journals and other serials. **Services:** Interlibrary loan; library not open to the public. **Automated Operations:** Computerized public access catalog, acquisitions, and serials. **Computerized Information Services:** DIALOG Information Services, Dow Jones News/Retrieval, STN International, VU/TEXT Information Services, Data-Star, DataTimes, OCLC EPIC; CD-ROMs (MEDLINE, Physicians Desk Reference); internal database; DOCLINE (electronic mail service). Contact Person: Karen Kreizman, Res.Libn. **Networks/Consortia:** Member of Western New York Library Resources Council (WNYLRC). **Publications:** Bulletins; Bibliographies, irregular - both for internal distribution only. **Remarks:** FAX: (716)887-7662.

★2133★
Bristol-Myers Squibb Company - Pharmaceutical Research Institute - Science Information Department (Sci-Engr, Med)
Box 4000 Phone: (609)921-4844
Princeton, NJ 08543 Helen Kosowski, Mgr. of Lib.Oper.
Founded: 1925. **Staff:** Prof 10; Other 16. **Subjects:** Pharmacology, chemistry, medicine, pharmacy. **Holdings:** 30,000 books; 60,000 bound periodical volumes; 30,000 volumes on microfilm; 100 VF drawers. **Subscriptions:** 1600 journals and other serials. **Services:** Interlibrary loan; copying; department open to the public by appointment. **Automated Operations:** Computerized public access catalog, cataloging, acquisitions, serials, and circulation. **Computerized Information Services:** DIALOG Information Services, Maxwell Online, Inc., OCLC, MEDLINE, U.S. Patents Files, NEXIS, STN International, Dow Jones News/Retrieval, Data-Star, BRS Information Technologies. **Networks/Consortia:** Member of MEDCORE, New Jersey Library Network. **Publications:** Index Squibbicus, bimonthly; PharmNews; Intercom Management Digest - all for internal distribution only; Monthly Acquisitions Bulletin. **Remarks:** FAX: (609)683-6226. **Formerly:** Its Squibb Institute for Medical Research. **Staff:** Steve Highcock, Mgr., Lit. Search

★2134★
Bristol-Myers Squibb Company - Scientific Information Department (Sci-Engr, Med)
Box 4755 Phone: (315)432-2231
Syracuse, NY 13221-4755 John Silvin, Mgr.
Founded: 1946. **Staff:** Prof 2; Other 1. **Subjects:** Pharmacology, pharmacy, organic chemistry, engineering, biotechnology, toxicology. **Holdings:** 4000 books; 15,000 bound periodical volumes; 4 VF drawers; 75 VF drawers of reprints; 3200 microfilm cartridges. **Subscriptions:** 275 journals and other serials; 5 newspapers. **Services:** Interlibrary loan; copying; SDI; department open to the public by appointment. **Computerized Information Services:** DIALOG Information Services, STN International, MEDLINE, NLM. **Networks/Consortia:** Member of Central New York Library Resources Council (CENTRO). **Remarks:** FAX: (315)432-2235. Telex: 4442011. **Staff:** Esther Comereski, Coord., Sci.Info.; Sharon Elmy, Interloan Ser. Control.

★2135★
Bristol-Myers Squibb Company - Scientific Information Department - Research Library/809 (Med)
5 Research Pkwy.
Box 5103 Phone: (203)284-6221
Wallingford, CT 06492-7663 John E. MacNintch, Dir.
Founded: 1986. **Staff:** Prof 7; Other 6. **Subjects:** Pharmacology, organic chemistry, microbiology, medicine, oncology, cardiovascular/central nervous system. **Holdings:** 20,000 books; 26,000 bound periodical volumes; 6600 reels of microfilm. **Subscriptions:** 650 journals and other serials. **Services:** Interlibrary loan; copying; translating; library open to the public by appointment. **Computerized Information Services:** DIALOG Information Services, STN International; OASYS (internal database). **Networks/Consortia:** Member of Southern Connecticut Library Council (SCLC), Southwestern Connecticut Library Council (SWLC). **Remarks:** Alternate telephone number(s): 284-6228. **Staff:** Theodora J. Myllymaki, Mgr., Lib.Oper.

★2136★
Bristol-Myers Squibb Company - U.S. Pharmaceutical & Nutrition Group - Library and Information Services (Med)
2400 Lloyd Expy. Phone: (812)426-8679
Evansville, IN 47721-0001 Alice M. Weisling, Libn.
Founded: 1951. **Staff:** Prof 4; Other 3. **Subjects:** Chemistry, pharmaceuticals, marketing, nutrition, medicine, pediatrics, sales, human resources, management, finance, economics, psychology, law. **Holdings:** 50,000 books; 10,000 bound periodical volumes; 8 VF drawers of patents; 10,000 reels of microfilm of journals and patents. **Subscriptions:** 700 journals and other serials. **Services:** Translating; services open to the public at librarian's discretion. **Automated Operations:** Computerized public access catalog, cataloging, serials, and circulation. **Computerized Information Services:** MEDLINE, DIALOG Information Services, PFDS Online, STN International, Data-Star, InvesText, NewsNet, Inc., Mead Data Central, Dow Jones News/Retrieval, Dun & Bradstreet Business Credit Services, VU/TEXT Information Services, Questel, WILSONLINE, BRS Information Technologies, Faxon Data Bases, OCLC, Chemical Abstracts Service (CAS), LEXIS, NEXIS, CompuServe Information Service, PFDS Online, Interactive Market Systems (IMS), BT Tymnet, Burrelle's, EPIC. **Networks/Consortia:** Member of INCOLSA, Evansville Area Libraries Consortium. **Publications:** Bibliographies. **Remarks:** FAX: (812)421-0358. Contains the holdings of the former Brystol-Myers U.S.P.N.G. Institute - Library. **Staff:** Karen Kelley, Supv., Lib.Oper.; Janet Marunyez, Supv.Lit.Serv.

★2137★
Bristol Public Library (Hist)
701 Goode St. Phone: (703)669-9444
Bristol, VA 24201 William A. Muller, III
Founded: 1930. **Subjects:** East Tennessee, Virginia. **Special Collections:** Genealogy and local history collection. **Holdings:** 1782 books; 48 bound periodical volumes; 177 reels of microfilm. **Subscriptions:** 227 journals and other serials; 22 newspapers. **Services:** Interlibrary loan; copying; library open to the public. **Remarks:** FAX: (703)669-5593.

Brite Divinity School Collection
See: **Texas Christian University - Mary Couts Burnett Library** (16208)

British Architectural Library
See: **Royal Institute of British Architects** (14120)

★2138★
British Cement Association - Concrete Information Service (Plan)
Wexham Springs Phone: 753 662727
Slough, Berkshire SL3 6PL, England Mrs. E. Lee, Hd. of Dept.
Staff: Prof 4. **Subjects:** Portland cement concretes, concrete technology and design. **Holdings:** 8000 bound volumes; reports; pamphlets; and other cataloged items. **Subscriptions:** 500 journals and other serials. **Computerized Information Services:** Produces the Library Information On-Line System (LIONS) Data Base. Performs searches on fee basis. **Remarks:** FAX: 753 660499. Telex: 848352.

★2139★
British Columbia Alcohol and Drug Programs - Library
1019 Wharf St., 5th Fl.
Victoria, BC, Canada V8V 1X4
Defunct.

British Columbia Archives of Medicine
See: **College of Physicians and Surgeons of British Columbia - Medical Library Service** (3903)

★2140★
British Columbia Archives and Records Service - Library (Hist)
655 Belleville St. Phone: (604)387-6504
Victoria, BC, Canada V8V 1X4 Linda Webster, Act.Hd., Lib. Unit
Founded: 1983. **Staff:** Prof 2; Other 1. **Subjects:** History of the Pacific Northwest and British Columbia. **Holdings:** 65,000 volumes. **Subscriptions:** 300 journals and other serials. **Services:** Copying; archives open to the public. **Computerized Information Services:** Internal databases. **Remarks:** FAX: (604)387-2072. **Formerly:** British Columbia Ministry of Provincial Secretary & Government Services - Provincial Archives. **Staff:** David Mattison.

★2141★
British Columbia Archives and Records Service - Map Collection (Geog-Map, Plan)
655 Belleville St. Phone: (604)387-2985
Victoria, BC, Canada V8V 1X4 Glen Isaac, Archv., Mss. & Maps
Staff: Prof 1; Other 1. **Special Collections:** Cartographic and architectural archives of British Columbia; published maps and atlases of British Columbia and northwestern North America; F.M. Rattenbury architectural plans. **Holdings:** 200 atlases; 35,000 maps and plans. **Services:** Copying; collection open to the public. **Computerized Information Services:** DIALOG Information Services. **Remarks:** FAX: (604)387-2072. Affiliated with British Columbia Ministry of Provincial Secretary.

★2142★
British Columbia Cancer Agency - Library (Med)
600 W. 10th Ave. Phone: (604)877-6000
Vancouver, BC, Canada V5Z 4E6 David Noble, Hd.Libn.
Staff: Prof 2; Other 3. **Subjects:** Radiotherapy, medical oncology, cancer nursing, immunology. **Holdings:** 3500 books; 3500 bound periodical volumes; 100 annual reports. **Subscriptions:** 213 journals and other serials. **Services:** Interlibrary loan; SDI; library open to the public. **Automated Operations:** Computerized cataloging. **Computerized Information Services:** MEDLARS, BRS Information Technologies. Performs searches free of charge to British Columbians. **Publications:** Accession lists. **Remarks:** FAX: (604)872-4596. **Staff:** Beth Morrison, Libn.

★2143★
British Columbia Capital Regional District - Community Health Services Library (Med)
524 Yates St.
P.O. Box 1000 Phone: (604)388-4421
Victoria, BC, Canada V8W 2S6 Patrick Lindsay, Mgr.
Holdings: 200 volumes. **Remarks:** No further information was supplied by respondent.

★2144★
British Columbia Capital Regional District - Regional Information Service
524 Yates St.
Victoria, BC, Canada V8W 2S6
Subjects: Land use, economic development. **Holdings:** 1000 volumes. **Remarks:** Currently inactive.

★2145★
British Columbia Central Credit Union - Corporate Information Centre (Bus-Fin)
1441 Creekside Dr. Phone: (604)737-5057
Vancouver, BC, Canada V6J 4S7 Georgia Whiten, Libn.
Founded: 1977. **Staff:** Prof 1; Other 2. **Subjects:** Banking, credit unions, finance, marketing, economics, business. **Special Collections:** Credit Unions, Canada (1200 books; 1000 subject files). **Holdings:** 2000 books; 6000 annual reports; 125 cubic feet of credit union records; 35 oral history tapes; 2000 photographs; video cassettes; clippings. **Subscriptions:** 343 journals and other serials. **Services:** Interlibrary loan; center not open to the public. **Automated Operations:** Computerized cataloging, serials, and circulation. **Computerized Information Services:** DIALOG Information Services, Info Globe, Dow Jones News/Retrieval. Performs searches on fee basis. **Publications:** Central Notes; Fact Finder, biweekly - to credit union managers, staff, and directors. **Remarks:** FAX: (604)737-5055.

★2146★
British Columbia Council of Forestry Inc. - Library (Agri)
555 Burrard St., Suite 1200 Phone: (604)684-0211
Vancouver, BC, Canada V7X 1S7 Sheila M. Foley, Libn.
Founded: 1974. **Staff:** 1. **Subjects:** Forest industry economics and trade; environmental issues; transportation. **Holdings:** 4000 books; 70 Statistics Canada titles; Canadian, U.S., foreign government documents. **Subscriptions:** 155 journals and other serials. **Services:** Interlibrary loan; copying; library open to the public with restrictions.

★2147★
British Columbia Ferry Corporation - Library (Trans)
1112 Fort St. Phone: (604)381-1401
Victoria, BC, Canada V8V 4V2 Marilyn Grant, Libn.
Founded: 1981. **Staff:** Prof 1. **Subjects:** Ferry transportation, shipbuilding, management, finance, government regulations. **Holdings:** 6000 books. **Subscriptions:** 140 journals and other serials; 10 newspapers. **Services:** Interlibrary loan; copying. **Automated Operations:** Computerized cataloging, acquisitions, and circulation. **Computerized Information Services:** DIALOG Information Services, CAN/OLE, Info Globe, DOBIS Canadian Online Library System, MARNA; Envoy 100 (electronic mail service). **Publications:** Maps; serials; acquisitions; library services. **Remarks:** FAX: (604)381-5452. Electronic mail address(es): FERRY (Envoy 100).

★2148★
British Columbia Genealogical Society - Reference Library (Hist)
P.O. Box 94371
Richmond, BC, Canada V6Y 2A8 Ruth Blue
Founded: 1971. **Staff:** 30. **Subjects:** Genealogy, history. **Special Collections:** British Columbia Research File (100,000 3x5 cards of vital statistics from church records and newspapers); Humphrey Toms Collection (Cornwall and Devon reference books); Scottish Peerage Collection; Walter Draycott Collection (emphasis on Leicestershire, Staffordshire, and Derbyshire); Ian Scheidel Collection (Mennonites). **Holdings:** 6500 books; 550 bound periodical volumes; 200 reels of microfilm; 5000 microfiche; Canadian census films; maps. **Subscriptions:** 200 journals and other serials. **Services:** Interlibrary loan; copying; library open to the public by appointment. **Automated Operations:** Computerized cataloging. **Computerized Information Services:** Internal database.

★2149★
British Columbia Health Association - Library (Med)
1985 W. Broadway, Suite 500 Phone: (604)734-2423
Vancouver, BC, Canada V6J 4Y3 Carolyn Hall, Lib.Coord.
Founded: 1974. **Staff:** 1. **Subjects:** Hospital and health care administration. **Holdings:** 2000 books; 4000 unbound periodicals; hospital annual reports; 60 films and videotapes; 200 pamphlets. **Subscriptions:** 75 journals and other serials. **Services:** Interlibrary loan; library not open to the public. **Automated Operations:** Computerized public access catalog. **Computerized Information Services:** MEDLINE. **Publications:** BCHA Reports, semimonthly - to members; bibliography of materials published by the association. **Remarks:** FAX: (604)734-7202.

★2150★
British Columbia Institute of Technology - Library Services Division (Bus-Fin, Sci-Engr)
3700 Willingdon Ave. Phone: (604)432-8360
Burnaby, BC, Canada V5G 3H2 Paula Piek, Inst.Libn.
Founded: 1964. **Staff:** Prof 9; Other 27. **Subjects:** Business; management - administrative, operations, financial; computer systems; tourism; engineering - mechanical, civil, structural; forest resources; electricity and electronics; building; natural resources; chemistry and metallurgy; natural gas and petroleum; health technologies; nursing; trades training. **Holdings:**

400,000 books, government publications, and technical reports; 1637 films; 3364 videotapes; 10,000 reels of microfilm; 2000 audiotapes; 32,400 pamphlets; 229,500 microfiche; standards; 1100 microcomputer software. **Subscriptions:** 3250 journals and other serials. **Services:** Interlibrary loan (fee); copying; library open to the public with restrictions. **Automated Operations:** Computerized public access catalog, cataloging, acquisitions, serials, and circulation. **Computerized Information Services:** BRS Information Technologies, DIALOG Information Services, CAN/LAW, CAN/OLE, UTLAS, DOBIS Canadian Online Library System; PROFS (internal database); Envoy 100 (electronic mail service). Performs searches. **Remarks:** FAX: (604)430-5443. **Staff:** Margot Allingham; Yu-Mei Choi; Ana Ferrinho; Tony Kelly; Frank Knor; Gerry Weeks; Merilee MacKinnon, DOBIS Sys.Libn.; Robert Roy.

★2151★
British Columbia Judges' Library - Superior & County Courts (Law)
Law Courts, 800 Smithe St. Phone: (604)660-2799
Vancouver, BC, Canada V6Z 2E1 A. Rector, Libn.
Founded: 1945. **Staff:** 2. **Subjects:** Law, allied subjects. **Holdings:** 9000 books. **Services:** Interlibrary loan; library not open to the public. **Computerized Information Services:** QL Systems; internal database. **Publications:** Digests of Judgments of the Courts.

★2152★
British Columbia Justices' Library - The Law Courts (Law)
850 Burdett Ave.
Victoria, BC, Canada V8W 1B4 Phone: (604)356-1018
Subjects: Law, allied subjects. **Holdings:** 5500 books. **Services:** Library not open to the public. **Remarks:** Administered by the Vancouver Judges' Library staff.

★2153★
British Columbia Legislative Library (Law, Soc Sci)
Parliament Bldgs. Phone: (604)387-6510
Victoria, BC, Canada V8V 1X4 Joan Barton, Dir.
Founded: 1863. **Staff:** Prof 16; Other 17. **Subjects:** Government, political science, constitutional law. **Special Collections:** British Columbia government publications; sessional clipping books. **Holdings:** 145,000 books; 60,000 bound periodical volumes; 1 million government publications; 270,000 microforms. **Subscriptions:** 1500 journals and other serials; 260 newspapers. **Services:** Interlibrary loan; copying; library open to referrals from other libraries only. **Computerized Information Services:** DIALOG Information Services, QL Systems, BRS Information Technologies, CAN/OLE, ORBIT Search Service, WESTLAW, Info Globe, CAN/LAW, Insight, Infomart Online, VU/TEXT Information Services, WILSONLINE; Envoy 100 (electronic mail service). **Special Indexes:** British Columbia newspaper index; government publications index. **Remarks:** FAX: (604)356-1373. Electronic mail address(es): LEGLIB (Envoy 100). **Staff:** John MacEachern, Mgr., Govt.Pubns.; Maureen Lawson, Mgr., Ref.Serv.; Sheila Gann, Mgr., Tech.Serv.

★2154★
British Columbia Medical Association - Archives (Med)
1665 W. Broadway, Suite 115
Vancouver, BC, Canada V6J 5A4 Phone: (604)736-5551
Founded: 1965. **Subjects:** Medicine in British Columbia. **Holdings:** 80 boxes of documents. **Services:** Copying; archives open to the public with restrictions. **Publications:** Guide to the Medical Archives of British Columbia, 1989. **Remarks:** FAX: (604)736-4566.

British Columbia Medical Library Service
See: **College of Physicians and Surgeons of British Columbia - Medical Library Service** (3903)

★2155★
British Columbia Ministry of the Attorney General - Victoria Law Library (Law)
609 Broughton St., 4th Fl. Phone: (604)356-8400
Victoria, BC, Canada V8V 1X4 Jane Taylor, Dir., Lib.Serv.
Subjects: Law. **Remarks:** No further information was supplied by respondent.

British Columbia Ministry of Crown Lands
See: **British Columbia Ministry of Environment, Lands and Parks** (2161)

★2156★
British Columbia Ministry of Development, Trade, and Tourism - Library (Bus-Fin)
712 Yates St. Phone: (604)387-0340
Victoria, BC, Canada V8W 1X5 Margaret Palmer, Libn.
Founded: 1910. **Staff:** Prof 1; Other 2. **Subjects:** Economics, industry, business, foreign trade, tourism, communications, technology, statistics. **Special Collections:** Federal and provincial government news releases; federal and provincial agreements. **Holdings:** 25,000 books; corporate annual reports; newspaper clipping files; pamphlets. **Subscriptions:** 400 journals and other serials; 5 newspapers. **Services:** Interlibrary loan; copying; library open to the public for reference use only. **Computerized Information Services:** DIALOG Information Services, Info Globe, Infomart Online, The Financial Post DataGroup; BC Business Network (internal database); Envoy 100 (electronic mail service). **Publications:** Periodicals List, irregular. **Remarks:** FAX: (604)356-8035. Electronic mail address(es): ECONDEV.LIB (Envoy 100). **Formerly:** British Columbia Ministry of Regional and Economic Development - Library.

★2157★
British Columbia Ministry of Education - Library
Parliament Bldgs.
Victoria, BC, Canada V8V 2M4
Defunct. Holdings absorbed by University of Victoria - McPherson Library.

★2158★
British Columbia Ministry of Energy, Mines and Petroleum - Library (Energy)
Douglas Bldg., Rm. 430
617 Government St. Phone: (604)387-6407
Victoria, BC, Canada V8V 1X4 S.E. Ferris, Libn.
Founded: 1896. **Staff:** Prof 1. **Subjects:** Geology, chemistry, mining, economic geology, mining engineering, petroleum engineering, energy. **Holdings:** 9000 books; 3000 bound periodical volumes; 18,000 papers. **Subscriptions:** 160 journals and other serials. **Services:** Library open to the public for reference use only. **Automated Operations:** Computerized cataloging and serials. **Computerized Information Services:** DIALOG Information Services; Envoy 100 (electronic mail service). **Publications:** Annual Reports: Geology, Exploration and Mining in British Columbia; bulletins. **Special Indexes:** Index of annual reports and bulletins; index to Bedrock geological mapping. **Remarks:** FAX: (604)356-6767.

★2159★
British Columbia Ministry of Environment, Lands and Parks - B.C. Environment Library (Env-Cons)
810 Blanshard St., 1st Fl. Phone: (604)387-9745
Victoria, BC, Canada V8V 1X4 Kathleen M. Neer, Ministry Libn.
Staff: Prof 1; Other 2. **Subjects:** Pollution management, fish and wildlife management, water management. **Special Collections:** Wildlife original reports; Water Treaty documents. **Holdings:** 30,000 books; 250 bound periodical volumes; water treaty theses; archival materials. **Subscriptions:** 800 journals and other serials; 10 newspapers. **Services:** Interlibrary loan; library open to the public with restrictions. **Automated Operations:** Computerized cataloging, acquisitions, and circulation. **Computerized Information Services:** DIALOG Information Services, CAN/OLE, MEDLARS, Infomart Online, QL Systems; Envoy 100 (electronic mail service). **Publications:** New Acquisitions List - for internal distribution only. **Remarks:** FAX: (604)356-9145. Electronic mail address(es): ENVLIB.BC (Envoy 100).

★2160★
British Columbia Ministry of Environment, Lands and Parks - Parks Library (Env-Cons, Rec)
800 Johnson St., 2nd Fl. Phone: (604)387-3974
Victoria, BC, Canada V8V 1X4 Shirley Desrosiers, Libn.
Founded: 1971. **Staff:** 2. **Subjects:** Park and wilderness management, outdoor recreation, tourism and travel research, conservation, administration. **Holdings:** 10,000 books; 3800 vertical file materials; AV programs. **Subscriptions:** 175 journals and other serials. **Services:** Interlibrary loan; copying; library open to the public. **Computerized Information Services:** Envoy 100 (electronic mail service). **Publications:** Accessions List, irregular; Journals: Tables of Contents, monthly - both for internal distribution only. **Special Catalogs:** Catalog of AV programs (online). **Special Indexes:** Index to reprint and journal literature in parks and outdoor recreation. **Remarks:** Alternate telephone number(s): 387-3966. FAX: (604)387-5757. Electronic mail address(es): PARKSLIB (Envoy 100). **Formerly:** British Columbia Ministry of Parks - Library.

★2161★
British Columbia Ministry of Environment, Lands and Parks - Surveys and Resource Mapping Branch - MAPS-B.C. (Geog-Map)
1802 Douglas St., 3rd Fl. Phone: (604)387-1441
Victoria, BC, Canada V8V 1X5 Mark Poire, Hd.
Staff: 6. **Special Collections:** Published provincial maps; provincial thematic maps; large-scale topographic, planimetric, cadastral, and orthophoto maps of selected areas of British Columbia; British Columbia government air photographs of British Columbia and air photo indices, 1936 to present; federal government airphotos and indices on microfilm; technical reports; Landsat 5 Satellite imagery of British Columbia (microfiche); 1:20000 scale Terrain Resource Information Management (TRIM) Program; digital positional and representational files. **Holdings:** 20,000 manuscripts; 400 reports. **Services:** MAPS-B.C. open to the public. **Computerized Information Services:** PROFS (electronic mail service). **Special Catalogs:** Map and Air Photo Catalogue; Resource Mapping Inventory; Base Mapping Inventory; Reference Mapping Inventory; Photo Indexing Inventory. **Remarks:** MAPS is an acronym for Map and Air Photo Sales. FAX: (604)387-3022. Telex: 049-7135. Electronic mail address(es): BCL01(MPOIRE) (PROFS). **Formerly:** British Columbia Ministry of Crown Lands.

★2162★
British Columbia Ministry of Forests - Library (Biol Sci)
1450 Government St. Phone: (604)387-3628
Victoria, BC, Canada V8W 3E7 Susanne Barker, Mgr.
Founded: 1911. **Staff:** 1; Other 2. **Subjects:** Forest management, forest protection, range management, wildlife management, logging and logging equipment, multiple land use. **Special Collections:** Ministry internal and external reports. **Holdings:** 50,000 books, serials, and government documents; 5000 bound periodical volumes. **Subscriptions:** 320 journals and other serials. **Services:** Interlibrary loan; SDI; library open to the public for reference use only. **Automated Operations:** Computerized cataloging, acquisitions, serials, and circulation. **Computerized Information Services:** DIALOG Information Services, CAN/OLE, DOBIS Canadian Online Library System, Infomart Online; Envoy 100 (electronic mail service). **Publications:** Bibliographies. **Remarks:** Alternate telephone number(s): (604)387-8610. FAX: (604)387-0046. Electronic mail address(es): FORLIB (Envoy 100). **Staff:** Roxanne Smith, Lib.Tech.

★2163★
British Columbia Ministry of Forests - Nelson Forest Region Library (Biol Sci)
518 Lake St. Phone: (604)354-6285
Nelson, BC, Canada V1L 4C6 Chris Thompson
Founded: 1956. **Staff:** 1. **Subjects:** Forestry, natural resources. **Holdings:** 2000 books; 400 bound periodical volumes; 2500 research papers; 300 government documents. **Subscriptions:** 50 journals and other serials. **Services:** Interlibrary loan; copying; library open to the public with restrictions. **Automated Operations:** Computerized cataloging, acquisitions, and serials. **Publications:** Accession List, monthly - for internal distribution only; Selected Bibliography of Canadian Forest Literature, 1917-1946. **Remarks:** FAX: (606)354-6250.

★2164★
British Columbia Ministry of Health - Dr. Ken Kaye Memorial Library (Med)
3405 Willingdon Ave. Phone: (604)660-5886
Burnaby, BC, Canada V5G 3H4 Joy Fourchalk, Lib.Techn.
Founded: 1957. **Staff:** 1. **Subjects:** Forensic psychiatry, psychiatry, psychology, nursing, social sciences. **Holdings:** 3045 books; 1200 bound periodical volumes; 336 Audio-Digest tapes. **Subscriptions:** 53 journals. **Services:** Interlibrary loan; library not open to the public.

★2165★
British Columbia Ministry of Health - Library and A-V Library (Med)
1515 Blanshard St., Main Fl. Phone: (604)387-2337
Victoria, BC, Canada V8W 3C8 Elizabeth M. Woodworth, Dir., Lib.Serv.
Founded: 1946. **Staff:** Prof 2; Other 5. **Subjects:** Public health, medicine, hospital administration, nursing, mental health, nutrition, geriatrics, health education. **Holdings:** 14,000 books; 22,000 bound periodical volumes; 12 VF drawers of pamphlets; 2600 AV filmstrips and cassettes. **Subscriptions:** 400 journals and other serials. **Services:** Interlibrary loan; copying; library open to registered borrowers. **Automated Operations:** Computerized cataloging and circulation. **Computerized Information Services:** MEDLINE, PFDS Online, BRS Information Technologies; internal database; electronic mail service. **Publications:** Accessions list, semimonthly; serials list, annual; AV Library Catalogue, irregular. **Remarks:** FAX: (604)356-9937. Telex: 049-7462. **Staff:** Andy Buhler; Jim Maclock, AV Ck.

British Columbia Ministry of Municipal Affairs, Recreation & Culture
See: **British Columbia Ministry of Tourism & Culture** (2170)

★2166★
British Columbia Ministry of Municipal Affairs, Recreation & Culture - Ministry Library (Plan)
Parliament Bldg.
800 Johnson St., Rm. 101 Phone: (604)356-1440
Victoria, BC, Canada V8V 1X4 Anne Morgan, Mgr., Ministry Lib.
Founded: 1978. **Staff:** Prof 1; Other 1. **Subjects:** Historic preservation, architecture, archeology, history, zoning, land use planning, recreation, sports and cultural industries, regulatory codes. **Special Collections:** Archeological permit reports (investigations, site surveys, and excavations carried out under the auspices of the Heritage Conservation Act; 500); Canadian Inventory of Historic Buildings - British Columbia (microfiche; 25 lateral file drawers). **Holdings:** 15,000 reports and books; 100 films & videotapes; 15 slide/tape kits; newspaper clippings. **Subscriptions:** 300 journals and other serials. **Services:** Interlibrary loan; copying; center open to the public. **Automated Operations:** Computerized public access catalog, cataloging, acquisitions, and circulation. **Computerized Information Services:** DIALOG Information Services, CAN/OLE; Envoy 100 (electronic mail service). **Publications:** Audiovisual List, irregular - free upon request. **Remarks:** FAX: (604)387-4048. Electronic mail address(es): BVIHCR (Envoy 100).

British Columbia Ministry of Parks
See: **British Columbia Ministry of Environment, Lands and Parks** (2160)

British Columbia Ministry of Regional and Economic Development
See: **British Columbia Ministry of Development, Trade, and Tourism** (2156)

★2167★
British Columbia Ministry of Social Services & Housing - Library (Soc Sci)
800 Cassiar St. Phone: (604)660-7666
Vancouver, BC, Canada V5K 4N6 Robert D. Harvey, Libn.
Founded: 1974. **Staff:** 4. **Subjects:** Social welfare, social work, sociology, psychology, child welfare, management. **Holdings:** 10,000 books; 1000 AV programs; archival materials. **Subscriptions:** 100 journals and other serials. **Services:** Interlibrary loan; library not open to the public. **Automated Operations:** Computerized cataloging. **Publications:** Accessions List. **Special Catalogs:** Media Catalog. **Remarks:** FAX (604)660-5210.

★2168★
British Columbia Ministry of Solicitor General - Vancouver Pretrial Services Centre - Library (Law)
275 E. Cordova St. Phone: (604)683-0381
Vancouver, BC, Canada V6A 3W3 Barbara Artinian, Libn.
Founded: 1983. **Staff:** Prof 1. **Subjects:** Criminal law, corrections. **Holdings:** 4000 books; 180 bound periodical volumes; reports. **Subscriptions:** 60 journals and other serials. **Services:** Interlibrary loan; library not open to the public. **Remarks:** FAX: (604)683-8825.

British Columbia Ministry of Tourism - Barkerville Historic Town
See: **Barkerville Historic Town** (1530)

★2169★
British Columbia Ministry of Tourism - Image Bank (Aud-Vis)
865 Hornby St., Suite 802
Vancouver, BC, Canada V6Z 2G3 Phone: (604)660-2861
Founded: 1950. **Staff:** 1. **Subjects:** Travel and recreation; films, videos, still photography. **Holdings:** 150 motion picture prints; 20,000 negatives and transparencies. **Services:** Library open to travel industry. **Remarks:** FAX: (604)660-3383. **Staff:** Larry Leonard.

★2170★
British Columbia Ministry of Tourism & Culture - Fort Steele Heritage Town - Research Library (Hist)
Fort Steele, BC, Canada V0B 1N0 Phone: (604)489-3351
Ken Zurosky, Cur.
Founded: 1965. **Staff:** 2. **Subjects:** East Kootenay and British Columbia history, 19th century material culture, Kootenay Indians, mining. **Special Collections:** Archives of personal papers, business papers, and diaries (800 feet). **Holdings:** 8000 books; 20,000 photographs; 130 audiotapes (interviews and historical readings); 500 microforms; 650 manuscripts. **Subscriptions:** 6 journals and other serials. **Services:** Copying; library open to the public for research only. **Computerized Information Services:** PROSPECT (internal database). **Special Indexes:** Index to the Fort Steele Prospector newspaper. **Remarks:** Library's main focus is on Southeastern British Columbia, 1860-1930. FAX: (604)489-2624. Telex: 489-2624. **Formerly:** British Columbia Ministry of Municipal Affairs, Recreation & Culture. **Staff:** Derryll White, Heritage Rsrcs.Spec.

★2171★
British Columbia Ministry of Transportation & Highways - Library Resource Center (Trans)
940 Blanshard St., Rm. 3C Phone: (604)387-5512
Victoria, BC, Canada V8W 3E6 A.A. Del Rosario, Ministry Libn.
Staff: 2. **Subjects:** Construction, bridge, and road engineering. **Holdings:** Figures not available. **Subscriptions:** 850 journals and other serials. **Services:** Library not open to the public. **Computerized Information Services:** DIALOG Information Services, QL Systems. **Remarks:** FAX: (604)387-5012. Collection and services are presently under review.

★2172★
British Columbia Rehabilitation Society - G.F. Strong Centre - Staff Medical Library (Med)
4255 Laurel St. Phone: (604)734-1313
Vancouver, BC, Canada V5Z 2G9 Patricia Boileau, Lib.Tech.
Founded: 1978. **Staff:** Prof 1.5. **Subjects:** Physical medicine, rehabilitation, long term care, chronic disease. **Holdings:** 1200 books. **Subscriptions:** 110 journals and other serials. **Services:** Interlibrary loan; library not open to the public. **Automated Operations:** Computerized cataloging, acquisitions, and serials. **Computerized Information Services:** DIALOG Information Services, MEDLARS, BRS Information Technologies, internal databases; Envoy 100 (electronic mail service). Performs searches on fee basis. **Publications:** Library Bulletin - for internal distribution only. **Remarks:** FAX: (604)737-6359. Society encompasses the G.F. Strong Centre and the George Pearson Centre. It is affiliated with the University of British Columbia.

★2173★
British Columbia Rehabilitation Society - George Pearson Centre - Information Resource Dept. (Med)
700 W. 57th Ave. Phone: (604)321-3231
Vancouver, BC, Canada V6A 1S1 Patricia Boileau, Lib.Tech.
Founded: 1985. **Staff:** 1.6. **Subjects:** Physical medicine, rehabilitation, long term care, chronic disease. **Holdings:** 1200 books. **Subscriptions:** 110 journals and other serials. **Services:** Interlibrary loan; department not open to the public. **Automated Operations:** Computerized cataloging, acquisitions, and serials. **Computerized Information Services:** MEDLARS, DIALOG Information Services, BRS Information Technologies, internal databases; Envoy 100 (electronic mail service). Performs searches on fee basis. **Publications:** Library bulletin. **Remarks:** FAX: (604)321-7833. Affiliated with the G.F. Strong Rehabilitation Centre.

★2174★
British Columbia Research Corporation - Library (Sci-Engr, Comp Sci)
3650 Wesbrook Mall Phone: (604)224-4331
Vancouver, BC, Canada V6S 2L2 Viona Esen, Hd.Libn.
Founded: 1946. **Staff:** Prof 1; Other 3. **Subjects:** Waste treatment, water and air pollution, ocean engineering, corrosion, mineral studies, applied chemistry, wood preservation, offshore technology, electro-luminescence, management services, marine biology, applied engineering, biotechnology. **Special Collections:** Computer-aided design/computer-aided manufacturing. **Holdings:** 22,500 books; 10,000 bound periodical volumes; 17,500 separates. **Subscriptions:** 400 journals and other serials; 5 newspapers. **Services:** Interlibrary loan; copying; SDI; library open to outside users in a professional capacity. **Computerized Information Services:** DIALOG Information Services, PFDS Online, BRS Information Technologies, QL Systems, CAN/OLE, CAN/SND, Info Globe, Questel, CANSIM, Chemical Information Systems, Inc. (CIS), Canada Systems Group (CSG), RESORS, CAN/DOC, NVG, STN International. Performs searches on fee basis. **Networks/Consortia:** Member of Western Library Network (WLN). **Publications:** Accessions list, bimonthly. **Remarks:** FAX: (604)224-0540. **Staff:** Heather Anderson, Lib.Techn.; Angela Wong, Lib.Techn.; Birgit Kajat, Lib.Tech.

★2175★
British Columbia Research Corporation - Uranium Information Centre (Sci-Engr)
3650 Wesbrook Mall Phone: (604)224-4331
Vancouver, BC, Canada V6S 2L2 Viona Esen, Libn.
Founded: 1980. **Staff:** 1. **Subjects:** Uranium - environmental impact, exploration, waste disposal, mining and milling, occupational health and safety. **Special Collections:** Royal Commission of Inquiry into Health and Environmental Protection in Uranium Mining. **Holdings:** 3000 books; 49 bound periodical volumes; 533 exhibits; 15 video cassettes; 74 transcripts; 300 microfiche. **Services:** Copying; center open to the public for reference use only. **Computerized Information Services:** DIALOG Information Services, Infomart Online, ESA/IRS, CAN/OLE, Canadian Centre for Occupational Health & Safety, Info Globe, BRS Information Technologies, Chemical Information Systems, Inc. (CIS), QL Systems, INFOLINE. **Remarks:** FAX: (604)224-0540. **Staff:** Heather Anderson.

★2176★
British Columbia School Trustees Association - Library (Educ)
1155 W. 8th Ave.
Vancouver, BC, Canada V6H 1C5 Phone: (604)734-2721
Staff: Prof 2. **Subjects:** Education. **Holdings:** 2400 books. **Subscriptions:** 85 journals and other serials. **Services:** Library open to the public for reference use only. **Automated Operations:** Computerized cataloging. **Computerized Information Services:** PFDS Online, The Source Information Network. **Remarks:** FAX: (604)732-4559. **Staff:** Susan Job, Coord., Res./Anl.Serv.; Nancy Singbeil, Libn.

★2177★
British Columbia Securities Commission - Library (Bus-Fin)
865 Hornby St., 10th Fl. Phone: (604)660-9692
Vancouver, BC, Canada V6Z 2H4 Carol Williams, Libn.
Staff: Prof 1. **Subjects:** Securities. **Holdings:** 2000 books. **Subscriptions:** 100 journals and other serials; 5 newspapers. **Services:** Interlibrary loan; copying; library open to the public for reference use only. **Automated Operations:** Computerized public access catalog, cataloging, and acquisitions. **Computerized Information Services:** DIALOG Information Services, Info Globe, QL Systems, CAN/OLE, Infomart Online; Envoy 100 (electronic mail service). **Remarks:** FAX: (604)660-5473. Telex: 04-54599. Electronic mail address(es): BVASEC (Envoy 100).

★2178★
British Columbia Systems Corporation - Library (Comp Sci)
4000 Seymour Place Phone: (604)389-3941
Victoria, BC, Canada V8X 4S8 Karol Sinats, Coord., Lib.Serv.
Founded: 1979. **Staff:** Prof 2; Other 2. **Subjects:** Data processing, telecommunications, information management, business management. **Special Collections:** IBM technical manuals (5000). **Holdings:** 5500 books; 3 VF drawers of computer-related material. **Subscriptions:** 250 journals and other serials; 5 newspapers. **Services:** Interlibrary loan; library open to provincial government employees. **Automated Operations:** Computerized public access catalog, acquisitions, and circulation. **Computerized Information Services:** DIALOG Information Services, Info Globe, Infomart Online, CompuServe Information Service; CD-ROM; Envoy 100 (electronic mail service). **Publications:** Introduction to the B.C. System Library; bibliographies on employment equity, management, customer service, career development. **Special Indexes:** Index of internal IBM technical manuals (online, printout). **Remarks:** FAX: (604)389-3916. **Staff:** Christine Webb; Dauna Neveaux; Pamela Pearse-Greaves.

★2179★
British Columbia Teachers' Federation - Resources Centre (Educ)
2235 Burrard St. Phone: (604)731-8121
Vancouver, BC, Canada V6J 3H9 Diana Broome, Coord., Info.Rsrcs.
Founded: 1966. **Staff:** Prof 2; Other 3. **Subjects:** Education, labor, law. **Special Collections:** British Columbia Teachers' Strike Archive. **Holdings:** 9000 books; 250 unbound periodicals; films; tapes; kits. **Subscriptions:** 350 journals and other serials. **Services:** Interlibrary loan; copying. **Automated Operations:** Computerized cataloging and acquisitions. **Computerized Information Services:** DIALOG Information Services, QL Systems, Info Globe, CAN/LAW, Infomart Online. **Special Catalogs:** AV catalogs, annual. **Remarks:** FAX: (604)731-4891. **Staff:** Alice Wong, Cat.

★2180★
British Columbia Telephone Company - Business Library (Sci-Engr)
3777 Kingsway, 5th Fl.
Burnaby, BC, Canada V5H 3Z7 Phone: (604)432-2671
Founded: 1948. **Staff:** 2. **Subjects:** Telephone, telecommunications, electronics, public relations, business, management. **Holdings:** 2000 volumes; 20 VF drawers of clippings; 1800 pamphlets. **Subscriptions:** 200 journals and other serials; 20 newspapers. **Services:** Interlibrary loan; library not open to the public. **Automated Operations:** Computerized cataloging. **Computerized Information Services:** DIALOG Information Services, Info Globe, The Financial Post DataGroup, CAN/OLE, NewsNet, Inc., Infomart Online; Envoy 100 (electronic mail service). **Special Indexes:** COM Pamphlet Index; British Columbia Telephone News Index. **Remarks:** Alternate telephone number(s): (604)432-2151. FAX: (604)433-1241. Electronic mail address(es): BCT.ILL (Envoy 100).

★2181★
British Columbia Utilities Commission - Library (Law)
6th Floor
900 Howe St. Phone: (604)660-4700
Vancouver, BC, Canada V6Z 2N3 A. Cormack, Lib.Asst.
Founded: 1973. **Staff:** Prof 1. **Subjects:** Utility regulation. **Holdings:** 1000 books; hearing documents. **Subscriptions:** 30 journals and other serials. **Services:** Interlibrary loan; copying; library open to the public for reference use only. **Special Indexes:** Index to selected hearing transcripts. **Remarks:** FAX: (604)660-1102.

★2182★
British Columbia Worker's Compensation Board - Library (Med, Law)
6951 Westminster Hwy. Phone: (604)273-2266
Richmond, BC, Canada V7C 1C6 Lance Nordstrom, Libn.
Founded: 1971. **Staff:** Prof 1; Other 3. **Subjects:** Industrial hygiene and medicine, worker's compensation law, accident prevention, first aid and safety training, rehabilitation of the industrially injured. **Holdings:** 15,000 books; 5000 bound periodical volumes; 1500 government publications. **Subscriptions:** 850 journals and other serials. **Services:** Interlibrary loan; copying; library open to the public for reference use only. **Automated Operations:** Computerized cataloging and acquisitions. **Computerized Information Services:** UTLAS, CAN/OLE, BRS Information Technologies, DIALOG Information Services, MEDLARS; Envoy 100 (electronic mail service). **Publications:** Monthly list of acquisitions; subject bibliographies, irregular. **Remarks:** FAX: (604)276-3097. Electronic mail address(es): W.C.B.LIBRARY (Envoy 100).

★2183★
British Columbia and Yukon Chamber of Mines - Library (Sci-Engr, Bus-Fin)
840 W. Hastings St. Phone: (604)681-5328
Vancouver, BC, Canada V6C 1C8 Jack M. Patterson, Mng.Dir.
Staff: 1. **Subjects:** Geology and mineral deposits of British Columbia and Yukon Territory; minerals and markets. **Special Collections:** Mineral and rock collection. **Holdings:** 3000 volumes of bound and unbound periodicals, journals, and government publications; company, mineral, and map files. **Subscriptions:** 19 journals and other serials. **Services:** Copying; library open to the public. **Remarks:** Library maintained primarily for prospectors and interested public. FAX: (604)681-2363. **Staff:** Dan Pegg, Geol.

★2184★
British Council (in Belgium) - Resources Centre - Library (Area-Ethnic, Hum)
Britannia House
Rue Joseph 11 30 Phone: 2 2193600
B-1040 Brussels, Belgium Linda Bull, Hd. of Rsrcs.Ctr.
Staff: Prof 2; Other 1. **Subjects:** English language, English literature, contemporary Britain, British arts, teaching. **Holdings:** 10,000 books; art catalogs; AV materials. **Subscriptions:** 40 journals and other serials; 3 newspapers. **Services:** Interlibrary loan; copying; library open to the public with restrictions. **Remarks:** FAX: 2 2175811. Telex: 24743 BCBEL B.

★2185★
British Council (in Cologne) - Library (Hum)
Hahnenstrasse 6 Phone: 221 206440
W-5000 Cologne 1, Germany Monika Segbert, Info.Mgr.
Founded: 1952. **Staff:** Prof 7; Other 2. **Subjects:** British studies and institutions, English language and literature. **Holdings:** 35,000 books; videotapes; audiocassettes; slides. **Subscriptions:** 200 journals and other serials. **Services:** Library open to the public. **Computerized Information Services:** DIALOG Information Services, BLAISE, ESA/IRS; CD-ROMs (BOOKBANK, Book Data, ECCTIS, BEST, NPI, BNTS). **Publications:** British Studies Current Awareness Files. **Remarks:** FAX: 221 2064455.

★2186★
British Council in Kuala Lumpur - Library (Law, Hum)
Jalan Bukit Aman
POB 10539
50916 Kuala Lumpur, Malaysia Phone: 3 2987555
Founded: 1952. **Staff:** Prof 3; Other 8. **Subjects:** English language, English literature, English law, science, technology. **Holdings:** 33,000 books. **Subscriptions:** 126 journals and other serials. **Services:** Interlibrary loan; copying; SDI; library open to the public. **Computerized Information Services:** CD-ROMs. **Remarks:** FAX: 3 2937214. Telex: 9312130704 BC.

British Food Manufacturing Industries Research Association
See: **Leatherhead Food Research Association** (9033)

British and Foreign Bible Society Library
See: **University of Cambridge - Library** (18441)

★2187★
British Information Services - Library (Area-Ethnic)
845 3rd Ave. Phone: (212)745-0200
New York, NY 10022 Margaret J. Gale, Hd., Ref. & Lib.Div.
Founded: 1942. **Staff:** 8. **Subjects:** British affairs - government, politics, economics, education, foreign affairs, trade and industry, social services. **Holdings:** 5000 books; 12,000 British Government documents; 2000 clipping files. **Services:** Interlibrary loan; library not open to the public. **Computerized Information Services:** LEXIS, NEXIS. **Remarks:** FAX: (212)758-5395. **Staff:** Peter McInally, Asst.Libn.

★2188★
British Institute of Archaeology - Library (Soc Sci)
24 Tahran Caddesi Phone: 4 4275487
TR-06700 Ankara, Turkey Dr. David H. French, Dir.
Founded: 1947. **Staff:** 3. **Subjects:** Archeology in Turkey, epigraphy. **Holdings:** 30,000 volumes. **Services:** Library open to the public. **Computerized Information Services:** Internal database. **Remarks:** FAX: 4 4280159.

★2189★
British Institute of Management - Management Information Centre (Bus-Fin)
Management House
Cottingham Rd.
Corby, Northamptonshire NN17 1TT, England Phone: 536 204222
Bob Norton, Hd., Info.Serv.
Founded: 1947. **Staff:** Prof 9; Other 5. **Subjects:** Management, personnel management, education and training, industrial relations. **Special Collections:** Institute archives. **Holdings:** 50,000 books. **Subscriptions:** 250 journals and other serials. **Services:** Interlibrary loan; copying; SDI (all limited); center open to the public for reference use only. **Computerized Information Services:** DIALOG Information Services, Pergamon Financial Data Services, KOMPASS Online, INFOCHECK, Reuter TEXTLINE; produces HELPLINE gateway information service for managers; ASSASSIN (internal database). Performs searches on fee basis. **Publications:** Bibliographies; journals bulletin; acquisitions bulletin; factsheets; general publications in information management. **Remarks:** FAX: 536 201651. **Staff:** Nick Parker, Info.Res.; Kate Runciman, Info.Res.; Cathy Smith, Info.Res.; Debbie Ellis, Info.Res.; Gill Tivey, Info.Res.; Ruth Wheatley, Info.Res.; Catherine Baker, Info.Res.; Geoff d'Vaz, Info.Res.

British Library
See: **Great Britain - British Library** (6664)

British Library of Political and Economic Science
See: **London School of Economics** (9271)

British Maritime Technology Ltd.
See: **BMT CORTEC Limited** (1919)

British School at Rome
See: **Accademia Britannica - British School at Rome - Library** (43)

★2190★
British Shingon Buddhist Association - Library (Rel-Phil)
Kongoryuji
London Rd. Phone: 362 693962
East Dereham, Norfolk NR19 1AS, England Dr. T. Dukes, Dir.
Founded: 1950. **Staff:** 2. **Subjects:** Buddhism, Buddhist cultural arts and healing. **Holdings:** 15,000 Buddhist texts in Chinese, English, Japanese, Sanskrit. **Services:** Library open to the public by appointment. **Computerized Information Services:** Internal database.

★2191★
British Standards Institution - Library and Information Department (Sci-Engr)
Linford Wood Phone: 908 220022
Milton Keynes, Buckinghamshire Mrs. P.A. Heffernan, Mgr.
MK14 6LE, England Database/Lib.Serv.
Staff: Prof 11; Other 8. **Subjects:** Standards, codes of practice, laws, regulations, and other technical requirements affecting the design, operation, or performance of a piece of equipment or a service; systems for certification, approval, or compliance. **Holdings:** 2000 volumes; 500,000 British, international, and foreign standards, technical regulations, specifications. **Subscriptions:** 400 journals and other serials. **Services:** Interlibrary loan; inquiry service; SDI; translations; library open to the public for reference use only. **Computerized Information Services:** DIALOG Information Services, Data-Star, FIZ Technik, EUROBASES, PFDS Online, BLAISE, Questel, ECHO, BELINDAS; produces Standardline database of British standards; CD-ROMs (PERINORM, United Kingdom Official Publications, DODISS Plus and Qualified Products List). Performs searches on fee basis. Contact Person: Mrs. Mary Yates, Serv.Libn., 220022, ext. 2034. **Publications:** Worldwide Standards Information (SDI service of new British and overseas standards added to the BSI Library, arranged by subject and country), monthly - by subscription; Overseas Standards Updating Service (members' lists of standards documents monitored for revisions, changes, etc.), monthly - by subscription; Biblio-tech (newsletter), quarterly; bibliographies of standards covering specific subject areas; a brief guide to standards databases. **Remarks:** FAX: 908 320856. Telex: 825777 BSIMK G. **Staff:** Miss Helen Ward, Sys.Libn.

British Telecommunications PLC - North America - Technical Library
See: **BT North America Inc. - Technical Library** (2307)

★2192★
British Universities Film & Video Council - Information Service (Aud-Vis)
55 Greek St. Phone: 71 734 3687
London W1V 5LR, England James Ballantyne, Hd. of Info.
Staff: Prof 3. **Subjects:** Audiovisual media, materials and techniques for degree-level teaching and research in higher-education institutions. **Holdings:** 1770 bound volumes; 700 British and 230 foreign audiovisual-distributor catalogs; 740 pamphlets. **Subscriptions:** 62 journals and other serials. **Computerized Information Services:** Produces ADVANCE. Performs searches on fee basis. **Publications:** Viewfinder (magazine), 3/year; The BUFVC Handbook for Film and Television in Education. **Remarks:** FAX: 71 2873914. **Staff:** Marilyn Sarmiento, Asst.Info.Off.

Brittain Library
See: **First United Presbyterian Church of the Covenant** (5823)

Harold H. Brittingham Memorial Library
See: **MetroHealth Medical Center** (10193)

Robert Broad Medical Library
See: **Tompkins Community Hospital** (16401)

★2193★
Broadcast Music, Inc. - BMI Archives (Mus)
320 W. 57th St.
New York, NY 10019 Phone: (212)586-2000
Founded: 1949. **Staff:** Prof 1; Other 1. **Subjects:** Music, music history, musicians, composers. **Special Collections:** Frances Preston Collection of 20th century American music (300 autograph items of musical interest); Edward M. Cramer Collection of Civil War and Confederate Music (300 pieces of sheet music); Contemporary American Composers Collection (1200 items); Carl Haverlin Collection (first editions, great composers, and American sheet music, 1790-1920). **Holdings:** 300 volumes; 4000 musical items, 16th century to present; 1500 pieces of American sheet music; composers' biographies; manuscripts; first editions. **Subscriptions:** 29 journals and other serials. **Services:** Interlibrary loan; archives open to the public by appointment. **Remarks:** FAX: (212)586-2000.

★2194★
Broadcast Pioneers Library (Info Sci)
1771 N St., N.W. Phone: (202)223-0088
Washington, DC 20036 Catharine Heinz, Dir.
Founded: 1971. **Staff:** Prof 1; Other 2. **Subjects:** Radio and television broadcasting history. **Special Collections:** William S. Hedges Collection (12,000 items); Elmo Neale Pickerill Collection (1610 items); Mrs. Alois Havrilla Photo Collection; St. Louis Post-Dispatch Photo Collection; Phillips Carlin scrapbooks; John D. Fitzgerald scrapbooks; Joseph E. Baudino Collection (933 items); Rod Phillips Children's Books Collection (193 volumes); Group W Collection (Washington News Bureau Sound Archive; 2300 items); Philip James Collection. **Holdings:** 8700 books; 1350 bound periodical volumes; 320 VF drawers and boxes of archives, clippings, research studies, scripts, scrapbooks, documents, and correspondence; 900 oral histories, including interviews with prominent broadcasters; 5445 audiotapes; 22,000 photographs; 1500 subject files. **Subscriptions:** 24 journals and other serials. **Services:** Copying; library open to the public by appointment. **Publications:** Newsletter, quarterly.

Broadhurst Library
See: **First United Methodist Church** (5809)

William Broadhurst Library
See: **Nazarene Theological Seminary** (11356)

★2195★
Broadlawns Medical Center - Health Sciences Library (Med)
18th & Hickman Rd. Phone: (515)282-2394
Des Moines, IA 50314 Phyllis A. Anderson, Libn.
Staff: Prof 1. **Subjects:** Medicine, nursing, psychiatry. **Holdings:** 800 books. **Subscriptions:** 110 journals and other serials. **Services:** Interlibrary loan; library open to the public at the discretion of the librarian or doctor. **Networks/Consortia:** Member of Polk County Biomedical Consortium (PCBC), National Network of Libraries of Medicine - Greater Midwest Region.

★2196★
Brobeck, Phleger & Harrison - Library (Law)
444 S. Flower St., Suite 4300 Phone: (213)745-3406
Los Angeles, CA 90017 Jaane M. McMahon, Libn.
Staff: Prof 1; Other 1. **Subjects:** Law - corporate, bankruptcy, tax. **Holdings:** 10,000 volumes; AV programs. **Subscriptions:** 100 journals and other serials; 7 newspapers. **Services:** Interlibrary loan; library open to other law firm librarians. **Computerized Information Services:** DIALOG Information Services, RLIN, LEXIS, NEXIS, WESTLAW, Information America, Prentice Hall Online, DataTimes. **Remarks:** FAX: (213)745-3345. Telex: 181164 BPH LSA.

★2197★
Brobeck, Phleger & Harrison - Library (Bus-Fin, Law)
1 Market Plaza
Spear St. Tower Phone: (415)979-2619
San Francisco, CA 94105 Alice McKenzie, Libn.
Staff: Prof 4; Other 9. **Subjects:** Law, business. **Special Collections:** Asbestos documents. **Holdings:** 40,000 books; 2000 bound periodical volumes.

Subscriptions: 200 journals and other serials; 20 newspapers. **Services:** Interlibrary loan (limited); library not open to the public. **Automated Operations:** Computerized cataloging. **Computerized Information Services:** WESTLAW, Dow Jones News/Retrieval, NewsNet, Inc., Washington Alert Service, LEGI-TECH, DIALOG Information Services, LEXIS, NEXIS, RLIN, OCLC; OnTyme Electronic Message Network Service, MCI Mail (electronic mail services). **Networks/Consortia:** Member of Research Libraries Information Network (RLIN), CLASS. **Remarks:** FAX: (415)979-2966. **Staff:** Alan R. MacDougall, Ref.Libn.; Marie Scheidner, Tech.Serv.; Vicki Oppenheim, Prod. Liability.

Benjamin L. Brock Medical Library
See: **A.G. Holley State Hospital** (7330)

★2198★
Brock University - Instructional Resource Centre (Educ)
College of Education Phone: (416)688-5550
St. Catharines, ON, Canada L2S 3A1 Joanne E. Smith, Mgr.
Founded: 1974. **Staff:** Prof 1; Other 8. **Subjects:** Educational curriculum. **Special Collections:** Master of Education theses and projects. **Holdings:** 28,000 books; 2000 unbound periodical volumes; 3000 nonprint materials. **Subscriptions:** 84 journals and other serials. **Services:** Center open to practicing educators. **Automated Operations:** Computerized cataloging, acquisitions, serials, and circulation. **Computerized Information Services:** Brock Master of Education Project/Thesis Database (internal database). **Remarks:** FAX: (416)685-4131.

★2199★
Brock University - Map Library (Geog-Map)
Mackenzie Chown Complex, Rm. C306 Phone: (416)688-5550
St. Catharines, ON, Canada L2S 3A1 Colleen Beard, Supv.
Founded: 1975. **Staff:** 2. **Subjects:** Topography, cartography, aerial photography, geology. **Special Collections:** Historical map collection of the Welland Canals; historical map collection of the Niagara Region. **Holdings:** 1500 books & government documents; 60,000 maps; 15,000 aerial photographs; 600 atlases; cartography documents. **Subscriptions:** 14 journals and other serials. **Services:** Interlibrary loan; copying; library open to the public with loan restrictions. **Automated Operations:** Computerized public access catalog, cataloging, and acquisitions. **Publications:** Monthly acquisitions list; subject guides. **Special Indexes:** Computerized graphical indexes. **Remarks:** FAX: (416)682-9020.

Eleanor S. Brockenbrough Library
See: **Confederate Memorial Literary Society - Museum of the Confederacy** (4134)

★2200★
Brockton Daily Enterprise and Brockton Times-Enterprise - Library (Publ)
60 Main St.
Box 1450 Phone: (508)586-6200
Brockton, MA 02403 Stephen D. Sharp, Libn.
Founded: 1880. **Subjects:** Newspaper reference topics, history of Brockton and southeastern Massachusetts. **Holdings:** 316 VF drawers of clippings; microfilm. **Services:** Library not open to the public.

★2201★
Brockton Hospital - Library (Med)
680 Centre St. Phone: (508)586-2600
Brockton, MA 02402 Lovisa Kamenoff, Mgr., Lib.Serv.
Staff: Prof 1; Other 5. **Subjects:** Medicine, nursing, hospital administration. **Holdings:** 2575 books; 6000 bound periodical volumes; 28 VF drawers of health sciences bibliographies. **Subscriptions:** 260 journals and other serials. **Services:** Interlibrary loan; copying; library open to the public for reference use only. **Computerized Information Services:** BRS Information Technologies, MEDLINE. **Networks/Consortia:** Member of Massachusetts Health Sciences Libraries Network (MaHSLiN), Southeastern Massachusetts Consortium of Health Science Libraries (SEMCO).

★2202★
Brockton Law Library (Law)
Superior Court House
72 Belmont St. Phone: (508)586-7110
Brockton, MA 02401 Jean C. Medeiros, Libn.
Staff: Prof 1. **Subjects:** Law. **Holdings:** 15,000 volumes. **Services:** Interlibrary loan; copying; library open to the public. **Computerized Information Services:** OCLC; Union listing of all Massachusetts trial court law libraries holdings (internal database). **Remarks:** FAX: (508)588-8483. Part of the Massachusetts State Trial Court. **Staff:** Marnie Warner, Law Lib.Coord.

★2203★
Brockville Psychiatric Hospital - Library Resources and Information Centre (Med)
Box 1050 Phone: (613)345-1461
Brockville, ON, Canada K6V 5W7 Michelle R. Lamarche, Staff Libn.
Founded: 1975. **Staff:** Prof 1. **Subjects:** Psychiatry, psychology, geriatrics, nursing, hospital administration, social work. **Special Collections:** Bulletin of the Ontario Hospital for the Insane, 1894-1911 (on microfiche). **Holdings:** 2800 books; 3 VF drawers; 15,000 periodicals; Audio-Digest tapes. **Subscriptions:** 90 journals and other serials. **Services:** Interlibrary loan; copying; SDI; library open to the public for reference use only. **Automated Operations:** Computerized cataloging. **Computerized Information Services:** DIALOG Information Services, MEDLARS, CAN/OLE, CCINFO; Envoy 100 (electronic mail service). **Publications:** Research and Education Newsletter, monthly - available on request; What's New - New Additions to the Staff Library. **Special Catalogs:** Recent additions to the library; serials list. **Special Indexes:** KWOC index to tape collection (card). **Remarks:** FAX: (613)342-6194. Electronic mail address(es): BROCKVILLE.PSYCH (Envoy 100).

★2204★
Broco, Inc. - Technical Information Center (Sci-Engr)
2824 N. Locust Ave. Phone: (714)350-4701
Rialto, CA 92376 J.S. Brower, Libn.
Founded: 1960. **Staff:** Prof 1; Other 1. **Subjects:** Explosives, pyrotechnics. **Special Collections:** Dupont's Eastern Library. **Holdings:** 3000 books; 1000 other cataloged items. **Subscriptions:** 30 journals and other serials. **Services:** Center not open to the public. **Remarks:** FAX: (714)356-1426.

★2205★
Saul Brodsky Jewish Community Library (Area-Ethnic)
12 Millstone Campus Phone: (314)432-0020
St. Louis, MO 63146 Barbara Raznick, Hd.Libn.
Founded: 1983. **Staff:** Prof 2. **Subjects:** Jewish history, philosophy, religion, art, literature, fiction, Hebrew, Yiddish, Russian. **Special Collections:** Holocaust; Children's Judaica Collection. **Holdings:** 17,000 books. **Subscriptions:** 75 journals and other serials; 13 newspapers. **Services:** Interlibrary loan; copying; library open to the public. **Publications:** The Sagarin Review; St. Louis Jewish Literary Journal, annual. **Remarks:** FAX: (314)432-1277.

Bernard D. Broeker Law Library
See: **Bethlehem Steel Corporation** (1795)

★2206★
Brome County Historical Society - Archives (Hist)
130 Lakeside
P.O. Box 690 Phone: (514)243-6782
Knowlton, PQ, Canada J0E 1V0 Marion L. Phelps, Archv.
Founded: 1897. **Staff:** Prof 2. **Subjects:** Eastern Townships history; World War I. **Special Collections:** McCorkill-Allsopp journals and papers; pioneer papers; Hon. Christopher Dunkin file; Hon. Sydney Fisher file. **Holdings:** 2012 volumes; 12 drawers of subject, personage, and genealogical files; census records to 1891; Protestant and Catholic church records for District of Bedford; directories; documents; local newspapers. **Services:** Interlibrary loan; copying; archives open to the public by appointment. **Publications:** Yesterdays of Brome County (8-volume series, 1967-1991). **Special Catalogs:** Preliminary Inventory 1954 (pioneer papers); finding aids for documents and papers. **Special Indexes:** Index for Eastern Township books (card). **Staff:** Arlene Royea, Off.Coord.

★2207★
BroMenn Healthcare - A.E. Livingston Health Sciences Library (Med)
Virginia and Franklin Ave. Phone: (309)454-1400
Normal, IL 61761 Toni Tucker, Dir.
Founded: 1947. **Staff:** Prof 2; Other 2.5. **Subjects:** Health sciences, nursing. **Special Collections:** Historical Nursing Collection (105 books). **Holdings:** 9000 books; 232 bound periodical volumes. **Subscriptions:** 491 journals and other serials. **Services:** Interlibrary loan; copying; library open to healthcare students. **Computerized Information Services:** DIALOG Information Services. Performs searches on fee basis. **Networks/Consortia:** Member of Corn Belt Library System, ILLINET, Heart of Illinois Library Consortium (HILC). **Remarks:** FAX: (309)829-0707. **Staff:** Sally Vance; Diane Mather.

★2208★
Bromfield Street Educational Foundation - Gay Community News - Library (Soc Sci, Publ)
62 Berkeley St.
Boston, MA 02116-6215 Phone: (617)426-4469
Subjects: Homosexuality. **Holdings:** News and features of interest to lesbians and gays, 1973 to present. **Services:** Library open to the public with restrictions. **Special Indexes:** Alternative Press Index (online).

Bronck Museum Library
See: **Greene County Historical Society - Vedder Memorial Library** (6726)

★2209★
Bronson Methodist Hospital - Health Sciences Library (Med)
252 Lovell St., E. Phone: (616)341-6318
Kalamazoo, MI 49007 Marge Kars, Dir., Lib.Serv.
Founded: 1947. **Staff:** Prof 3; Other 3. **Subjects:** Medicine, nursing, and allied health sciences. **Special Collections:** Consumer Health Information Library. **Holdings:** 11,000 volumes. **Subscriptions:** 500 journals and other serials. **Services:** Interlibrary loan; copying; SDI; library open to the public. **Computerized Information Services:** NLM, DIALOG Information Services, WILSONLINE, BRS Information Technologies; DOCLINE. (electronic mail service). Performs searches on fee basis. **Networks/Consortia:** Member of Southwest Michigan Library Cooperative (SMLC), Michigan Health Sciences Libraries Association (MHSLA). **Remarks:** FAX: (616)341-8828. **Staff:** Mary Griswold, Libn.; Glenda Evans, Libn.

★2210★
Silas Bronson Library - Business, Industry, and Technology Department (Bus-Fin, Sci-Engr)
267 Grand St. Phone: (203)574-8233
Waterbury, CT 06702 Blanche T. Clark, Dept.Hd.
Founded: 1917. **Staff:** Prof 3. **Subjects:** Business, industry, technology. **Holdings:** Figures not available. **Subscriptions:** 321 journals; 23 newspapers. **Services:** Interlibrary loan; copying; library open to the public. **Automated Operations:** Computerized cataloging and circulation. **Computerized Information Services:** GEAC Library Information System. **Remarks:** Alternate telephone number(s): (203)574-8225. This is a U.S. and Connecticut State Depository Library. Maintained by the city of Waterbury. **Staff:** Michael De Leo; Elizabeth Schofield; Algio Stankis-Saulitis.

★2211★
Bronx County Bar Association - Bar Library (Law)
851 Grand Concourse, Rm. 124 Phone: (212)293-5600
New York, NY 10451 Irving Rosen, Chr., Lib.Comm.
Founded: 1902. **Staff:** 2. **Subjects:** Law. **Holdings:** 10,000 volumes. **Services:** Library not open to the public.

★2212★
Bronx County Historical Society - Theodore Kazimiroff Research Library (Hist)
3309 Bainbridge Ave. Phone: (212)881-8900
Bronx, NY 10467 Dr. Gary Hermalyn, Exec.Dir.
Founded: 1955. **Staff:** Prof 2; Other 3. **Subjects:** Bronx and New York City history. **Special Collections:** The Bronx Home News, 1907-1948 (microfilm); County Archives; Bronx business records. **Holdings:** 7000 books; 30,000 photographs; current Bronx newspapers; atlases; pamphlets; audio and video cassettes; clipping files; postcards; maps; manuscripts; slides; microfilm. **Subscriptions:** 20 journals and other serials; 8 newspapers. **Services:** Copying; photo and slide duplication; library open to the public. **Publications:** Genealogy in the Bronx: An Annotated Guide to Sources of Information; Landmarks of the Bronx. **Special Catalogs:** The Bronx in Print: An Annotated Catalogue of Books and Pamphlets About the Bronx. **Special Indexes:** 25 Year Index to Bronx County Historical Journal (in progress); two W.P.A. indexes to archives. **Staff:** Mary Ilario, Coll.Asst.

Bronx Criminal-Family Courts
See: **New York State Bronx Criminal-Family Courts - Library** (11644)

★2213★
Bronx-Lebanon Hospital Center - Concourse Division Medical Library (Med)
1650 Grand Concourse Phone: (212)518-5707
Bronx, NY 10457 Gerardo Gomez, Libn.
Founded: 1910. **Staff:** 2. **Subjects:** Medicine, allied health sciences. **Holdings:** 1200 books; 6497 bound periodical volumes. **Subscriptions:** 156 journals and other serials. **Services:** Interlibrary loan; library not open to the public. **Computerized Information Services:** BRS Information Technologies; DOCLINE (electronic mail service). **Networks/Consortia:** Member of Medical Library Center of New York (MLCNY), New York Metropolitan Reference and Research Library Agency. **Remarks:** FAX: (212)518-5707.

★2214★
Brook Lane Psychiatric Center - Medical Library (Med)
Box 1945 Phone: (301)733-0330
Hagerstown, MD 21740 Curtis E. Miller, Libn.
Staff: 1. **Subjects:** Psychiatry, child psychiatry, social work, psychiatric nursing. **Holdings:** 700 books; 5 other cataloged items. **Subscriptions:** 48 journals and other serials. **Services:** Interlibrary loan; library open to the public with restrictions.

Brook Run - Professional Library
See: **Georgia (State) Department of Human Resources** (6398)

★2215★
Brookdale Hospital Medical Center - Marie Smith Schwartz Medical Library (Med)
Linden Blvd. & Rockaway Pkwy. Phone: (718)240-5312
Brooklyn, NY 11212 Sophie Winston, Chf.Med.Libn.
Founded: 1970. **Staff:** Prof 2; Other 2. **Subjects:** Medicine, health sciences, nursing. **Holdings:** 3500 books; 17,000 bound periodical volumes; 50 audiotapes; 40 slide programs; 80 videotapes; 10 CAI programs. **Subscriptions:** 400 journals and other serials. **Services:** Interlibrary loan; library not open to the public. **Automated Operations:** Computerized ILL (DOCLINE). **Computerized Information Services:** MEDLARS, BRS Information Technologies, DIALOG Information Services; CD-ROM (MEDLINE). **Networks/Consortia:** Member of Medical Library Center of New York (MLCNY). **Remarks:** FAX: (718)240-5030.

Brooke Army Medical Center
See: **U.S. Army Hospitals** (17035)

Dr. H.H.W. Brooke Memorial Library
See: **Burnaby Hospital** (2379)

Brookens Library
See: **Sangamon State University** (14792)

★2216★
Brookgreen Gardens - Library (Biol Sci)
Murrells Inlet, SC 29576 Phone: (803)237-4218
Robin Salmon, V.P., Academic Affairs
Founded: 1931. **Staff:** Prof 2. **Subjects:** Plant taxonomy, horticulture, sculpture, zoology, South Carolina history. **Special Collections:** American Sculpture Archives (clippings; photographs; correspondence; interviews; exhibit catalogs). **Holdings:** 2500 books; 100 bound periodical volumes; 2000 newspaper clippings; 15,000 slides; 2000 photographs. **Subscriptions:** 72 journals and other serials. **Services:** Library not open to the public. **Publications:** Brookgreen Journal, quarterly. **Remarks:** FAX: (803)237-1014.

★2217★
Brookhaven Memorial Hospital Medical Center - Dr. Joseph D'Agrosa Medical Library (Med)
101 Hospital Rd. Phone: (516)654-7774
Patchogue, NY 11772 Mrs. Freddie Borock, Med.Libn.
Founded: 1975. **Staff:** Prof 1; Other 2. **Subjects:** Medicine, nursing, and allied health sciences. **Holdings:** 3500 books. **Subscriptions:** 350 journals and other serials. **Services:** Interlibrary loan; copying; SDI; library open to the public by appointment. **Computerized Information Services:** MEDLARS, DIALOG Information Services. **Networks/Consortia:** Member of Medical & Scientific Libraries of Long Island (MEDLI), BHSL, Long Island Library Resources Council. **Remarks:** FAX: (516)654-5721.

★2218★
Brookhaven National Laboratory - AGS Alternate Gradient Synchrotron Library
Bldg. 911C
Upton, NY 11973
Defunct.

★2219★
Brookhaven National Laboratory - Department of Nuclear Energy - Nuclear Safety Library (Energy)
Bldg. 130 Phone: (516)282-2398
Upton, NY 11973 Helen K. Todosow, Supv.Libn.
Founded: 1977. **Staff:** Prof 1; Other 2. **Subjects:** Nuclear reactor safety, nuclear engineering, quantitative risk assessment, probability studies, mechanical and structural engineering, metallurgy and corrosion sciences. **Special Collections:** Nuclear reactor safety and engineering; safety analysis reports on all operating nuclear power plants. **Holdings:** 10,000 volumes; 1200 bound periodical volumes; 10,000 microfiche of reports; 50,000 reports. **Subscriptions:** 150 journals and other serials. **Services:** Interlibrary loan; copying; SDI; library open to the public by appointment. **Automated Operations:** Computerized cataloging and acquisitions. **Computerized Information Services:** DIALOG Information Services, Integrated Technical Information System (ITIS), DOE Energy Data Base (EDB), STN International; Nuclear Regulatory Commission Public Document Room Database. **Publications:** Federal Register Current Awareness, weekly; Current Contents of NSL Core Journals, weekly - both for internal distribution only; NSL Select Acquisitions, monthly. **Special Catalogs:** Final Safety Analysis Reports Collection; Special Collection on Nuclear Power (online); standards. **Remarks:** Alternate telephone number(s): 282-2063. FAX: (516)282-3957. Brookhaven National Laboratory operates under contract to the U.S. Department of Energy.

★2220★
Brookhaven National Laboratory - National Nuclear Data Center
Bldg. 197 D
Upton, NY 11973 Charles L. Dunford
Subjects: Neutron data, charged particle data, nuclear structure data, reactor physics data. **Special Collections:** Bibliographies and libraries of experimental and evaluated nuclear data (online). **Holdings:** Figures not available. **Remarks:** Currently inactive.

★2221★
Brookhaven National Laboratory - Nuclear Safeguards Library (Sci-Engr)
Bldg. 197C Phone: (516)282-7537
Upton, NY 11973 Kathryn J. Lancaster, Libn.
Staff: Prof 1. **Subjects:** Nuclear safeguards, arms control, nuclear nonproliferation, physical security systems. **Special Collections:** Publications of the International Atomic Energy Agency (IAEA). **Holdings:** 2500 books; 7500 reports. **Subscriptions:** 30 journals and other serials. **Services:** Interlibrary loan; copying; SDI; library open to the public by appointment. **Automated Operations:** Computerized cataloging. **Computerized Information Services:** DIALOG Information Services, DTIC, DOE/ITIS, LEXIS, NEXIS; internal database. **Publications:** The Nuclear Safeguards Library Database - User's Manual and Guide to Searching, updated periodically - to selected recipients; library acquisitions newsletter, monthly - to selected recipients; The Nuclear Safeguards Library Directory - A Guide to Information Sources and Services, annual. **Special Indexes:** Keyword index for the field of nuclear safeguards (book). **Remarks:** FAX: (516)282-7533. The Brookhaven National Laboratory operates under contract to the U.S. Department of Energy.

★2222★
Brookhaven National Laboratory - Nuclear Waste Management Library (Sci-Engr)
Bldg. 830 Phone: (516)282-7159
Upton, NY 11973 Sandra G. Lane, Sr.Libn.
Founded: 1980. **Staff:** Prof 1; Other 1. **Subjects:** Nuclear waste management, metals, corrosion, polymers and plastics, chelates, chemistry. **Special Collections:** Nuclear waste management. **Holdings:** 3600 books; 13,000 bound reports; 500 unbound reports; 600 microfiche; 150 patents. **Subscriptions:** 80 journals and other serials. **Services:** Interlibrary loan; copying; library open to the public by appointment. **Automated Operations:** Computerized cataloging and acquisitions. **Computerized Information Services:** DIALOG Information Services, Integrated Technical Information System (ITIS); NWM (internal database). **Publications:** Nuclear Waste Management Library Acquisitions Memo, biweekly - for internal distribution only. **Remarks:** The Brookhaven National Laboratory operates under contract to the U.S. Department of Energy.

★2223★
Brookhaven National Laboratory - Technical Information Division - Research Library (Energy, Sci-Engr)
Bldg. 477 Phone: (516)282-3489
Upton, NY 11973 Diane C. Mirvis, Mgr.
Founded: 1947. **Staff:** Prof 10; Other 11. **Subjects:** Physics, chemistry, mathematics, biology, medicine, environment, energy, instrumentation, nuclear science and engineering. **Special Collections:** U.S. Department of Energy contractor reports; Environmental R&D administrative reports; Atomic Energy Commission reports; European technical reports in nuclear science. **Holdings:** 60,000 books; 40,000 bound periodical volumes; 200,000 reports; 6000 reels of periodical volumes; 522,000 reports on microfiche. **Subscriptions:** 818 journals and other serials. **Services:** Interlibrary loan; division open to the public by permission. **Automated Operations:** TECHLIBplus. **Computerized Information Services:** DIALOG Information Services, ORBIT Search Service, NLM, Integrated Technical Information System (ITIS), OCLC, STN International, NEXIS, LEXIS, Data-Star, LEGI-SLATE, BASISplus, Current Contents; CD-ROMs; InterNet (electronic mail service). **Networks/Consortia:** Member of Long Island Library Resources Council. **Remarks:** FAX: (516)282-2090. Electronic mail address(es): MIRVIS@BNLCL6.BNL.GOV (InterNet). Brookhaven National Laboratory operates under contract to the U.S. Department of Energy. **Staff:** Marilynn Harned, Dp.Mgr.; Betsy Schwartz, Sys.Spec.; Louise Heusinkveld, Database Spec.

★2224★
Brookings Hospital - Brookview Manor - Library (Med)
300 22nd Ave. Phone: (605)692-6351
Brookings, SD 57006 Judy Costar, Dept.Hd., Med.Rec.
Staff: 1. **Subjects:** Medicine. **Holdings:** 302 volumes. **Subscriptions:** 15 journals and other serials. **Services:** Library open to the public. **Computerized Information Services:** MEDLARS. **Remarks:** FAX: (605)697-7380.

★2225★
Brookings Institution - Library (Soc Sci, Bus-Fin)
1775 Massachusetts Ave., N.W. Phone: (202)797-6240
Washington, DC 20036 Laura Walker, Lib.Dir.
Founded: 1927. **Staff:** Prof 4; Other 4. **Subjects:** Economics, political science, governmental studies, international relations. **Holdings:** 80,000 volumes. **Subscriptions:** 700 journals and other serials. **Services:** Interlibrary loan; library not open to the public. **Automated Operations:** Computerized public access catalog, circulation, acquisitions, and serials. **Computerized Information Services:** DIALOG Information Services, OCLC, VU/TEXT Information Services; BITNET (electronic mail service). **Publications:** Books Added to Library and Selected Titles of Articles in Periodicals, biweekly - for internal distribution only. **Remarks:** FAX: (202)797-6004. Electronic mail address(es): IN%LWALKER@BROOK (BITNET). **Staff:** Susan McGrath, Ref.Libn.; Mary Fry, Acq./Per.Libn.; David Bair, Cat.

★2226★
Brooklyn Bar Association Foundation, Inc. - Library (Law)
123 Remsen St.
Brooklyn, NY 11201 Phone: (718)624-0675
Staff: Prof 1. **Subjects:** Law. **Holdings:** 15,000 volumes. **Subscriptions:** 13 journals and other serials. **Services:** Copying; library open to the public by appointment. **Remarks:** FAX: (718)797-1713.

★2227★
Brooklyn Botanic Garden - Library (Biol Sci)
1000 Washington Ave. Phone: (718)941-4044
Brooklyn, NY 11225 Brenda Weisman, Dir., Info.Serv.
Founded: 1911. **Staff:** Prof 1; Other 3. **Subjects:** Horticulture, botany. **Holdings:** 15,552 volumes; 22,000 bound periodical volumes; 5120 pamphlets. **Subscriptions:** 500 journals and other serials. **Services:** Interlibrary loan; copying; telephone ready reference. **Networks/Consortia:** Member of New York Metropolitan Reference and Research Library Agency, Council on Botanical Horticultural Libraries. **Staff:** Victoria Jahn, Assoc.Dir., Info.Serv.; Joseph Masny, Info.Asst.

★2228★
Brooklyn Children's Museum - Children's Resource Library (Hist)
145 Brooklyn Ave.
Brooklyn, NY 11213-9001 Phone: (718)735-4400
Founded: 1899. **Staff:** Prof 1. **Subjects:** Cultural and natural history, sciences, arts and crafts, folktales and legends. **Holdings:** 2000 books. **Subscriptions:** 20 journals and other serials. **Services:** Interlibrary loan; library open to the public. **Networks/Consortia:** Member of New York Metropolitan Reference and Research Library Agency.

★2229★
Brooklyn Children's Museum - Staff Research Library (Hist)
145 Brooklyn Ave. Phone: (718)735-4400
Brooklyn, NY 11213 Nancy Paine
Founded: 1899. **Staff:** Prof 1. **Subjects:** Anthropology, history, arts and crafts, sciences, natural history. **Special Collections:** The Kofod Slide Collection (ethnography; 25,000); the Brooklyn Children's Museum Archives, 1899 to present. **Holdings:** 7000 books; 260 bound periodical volumes; uncataloged pamphlets; maps; atlases; photographs. **Subscriptions:** 30 journals and other serials. **Services:** Library open to the public by appointment. **Remarks:** FAX: (718)604-7442.

★2230★
Brooklyn College of City University of New York - Center for Latino Studies - Library (Area-Ethnic)
1205 Boylan Hall
Bedford Ave. & Ave. H Phone: (718)780-5561
Brooklyn, NY 11210 Prof. H. Carrasquillo
Founded: 1969. **Staff:** Prof 1. **Subjects:** Puerto Rican literature, bilingual education, Puerto Rican history. **Holdings:** 400 books. **Services:** library not open to the public.

★2231★
Brooklyn College of City University of New York - Center for Responsive Psychology - Library (Law)
Rm. 5111, James Hall Phone: (718)780-5960
Brooklyn, NY 11210 Robert Buckhout, Ph.D., Prof. of Psychology
Staff: Prof 2; Other 1. **Subjects:** Eyewitness testimony, jury selection, psychology and law. **Holdings:** 515 volumes; 4000 other cataloged items. **Subscriptions:** 15 journals and other serials. **Services:** Interlibrary loan; library open to the public by appointment. **Automated Operations:** Computerized cataloging. **Computerized Information Services:** Internal databases; MCI Mail (electronic mail service). Performs searches on fee basis. **Publications:** Social Action and the Law, quarterly; Center Monograph Series, 8-10/year.

★2232★
Brooklyn College of City University of New York - Harry D. Gideonse Library - Special Collections (Hist)
403 LaGuardia Hall
Bedford Ave. & Ave. H Phone: (718)780-5485
Brooklyn, NY 11210 Prof. Anthony M. Cucchiara, Archv.
Staff: Prof 1. **Subjects:** Brooklyniana. **Holdings:** College archives; historical manuscripts; alumni manuscripts; masters' theses; miscellaneous collections. **Services:** Collections open to the public with restrictions. **Automated Operations:** Computerized cataloging, acquisitions, and circulation.

★2233★
Brooklyn College of City University of New York - Institute for Studies in American Music - Library (Mus)
415 Whitehead Hall Phone: (718)780-5655
Brooklyn, NY 11210 H. Wiley Hitchcock, Dir.
Founded: 1971. **Staff:** Prof 2; Other 4. **Subjects:** American music. **Holdings:** 2000 books; 1750 recordings. **Services:** Library open to the public with restrictions. **Publications:** ISAM Monographs; ISAM Newsletter. **Remarks:** FAX: (718)951-6140. **Staff:** K. Robert Schwarz, Res.Asst.

★2234★
Brooklyn College of City University of New York - Walter W. Gerboth Music Library (Mus)
LaGuardia Hall
Bedford Ave. & Ave. H Phone: (718)780-5844
Brooklyn, NY 11210 Honora Raphael, Music Libn.
Founded: 1954. **Staff:** Prof 1; Other 6. **Subjects:** Music, dance. **Special Collections:** American music; Brooklyn College music theses; theoretical treatises. **Holdings:** 18,500 volumes; 4700 bound periodical volumes; 36,500 scores; 17,500 phonograph records; 700 compact discs; 93 videocassettes; 12 VF drawers of clippings, pamphlets, libretti, and program notes; 1000 reels of microfilm; octavo scores. **Subscriptions:** 140 journals and other serials. **Services:** Interlibrary loan; library not open to the public. **Automated Operations:** Computerized cataloging, acquisitions, serials, and circulation. **Computerized Information Services:** DIALOG Information Services, BRS Information Technologies. **Networks/Consortia:** Member of New York Metropolitan Reference and Research Library Agency. **Special Catalogs:** Union List of City University music periodicals (online). **Remarks:** An alternate telephone number is 780-5564.

★2235★
Brooklyn Historical Society - Library (Hist)
128 Pierrepont St. Phone: (718)624-0890
Brooklyn, NY 11201 Irene Tichenor, Hd.Libn.
Founded: 1863. **Staff:** Prof 3; Other 1. **Subjects:** Brooklyn, Long Island, New York City, history, genealogy, biography. **Special Collections:** Henry Ward Beecher Collection; bookplate collection; scrapbook collection (local history; 165 indexed volumes). **Holdings:** 155,000 volumes; 1000 bound periodical volumes; 1700 linear feet of manuscripts; 90,000 photographs; 700 periodical titles; 350 local and regional newspapers; 750 maps and atlases; newspapers in microform. **Subscriptions:** 167 journals and other serials; 25 newspapers. **Services:** Copying; library open to the public. **Computerized Information Services:** OCLC. **Publications:** Newsletter - to members. **Special Catalogs:** Catalogue of American Genealogies in the Library of the Long Island Historical Society (book); Catalogue of American Revolutionary Manuscripts (1980); Checklist of Long Island Printing (1977); A Guide to Brooklyn Manuscripts in the Long Island Historical Society (1980); Brooklyn Before the Bridge: American Paintings from the Long Island Historical Society (1982). **Special Indexes:** Index to Brooklyn Archives. **Staff:** Roger Mohovich, Cat.; Clara Lamers, Asst.Hd.Libn.

★2236★
Brooklyn Hospital - Medical Library (Med)
121 DeKalb Ave. Phone: (718)403-6943
Brooklyn, NY 11201 Narciso Rodriguez, Libn.
Founded: 1926. **Staff:** Prof 1. **Subjects:** Medicine, medical specialties. **Holdings:** 1200 books; 6000 bound periodical volumes; 250 AV programs. **Subscriptions:** 130 journals and other serials. **Services:** Interlibrary loan; library not open to the public. **Computerized Information Services:** BRS Information Technologies.

★2237★
Brooklyn Law School - Law Library (Law)
250 Joralemon St. Phone: (718)780-7973
Brooklyn, NY 11201 Sara Robbins, Law Libn./Assoc.Prof.
Founded: 1902. **Staff:** Prof 11; Other 10. **Subjects:** Law. **Holdings:** 196,000 volumes; 11,445 reels of microfilm; 779,856 microfiche. **Subscriptions:** 4023 serials. **Services:** Interlibrary loan; library open to the public with restrictions. **Automated Operations:** Computerized public access catalog, cataloging, acquisitions, and serials. **Computerized Information Services:** DIALOG Information Services, BRS Information Technologies, LEXIS, NEXIS, WESTLAW, WILSONLINE, VU/TEXT Information Services, Dow Jones News/Retrieval. **Networks/Consortia:** Member of SUNY/OCLC Library Network, New York Metropolitan Reference and Research Library Agency. **Publications:** Brooklyn School Library Guide, annual; Inform (newsletter), irregular. **Remarks:** FAX: (718)625-2925. **Staff:** Linda Holmes, Assoc.Libn.; Dorothy Li, Assoc.Libn.; George Prayer, Hd.Cat; James Gordon, Ref.Libn.; Mary Morrison, Cat.; Rosemary H. Campagna, Govt.Docs.Libn.; Howard Brenner, Ref.Libn.; H.C. Singh, Acq./Ser.Libn.; Jindi Zhang, Libn.

★2238★
Brooklyn Museum - Art Reference Library (Art)
200 Eastern Pkwy. Phone: (718)638-5000
Brooklyn, NY 11238 Deirdre E. Lawrence, Prin.Libn.
Founded: 1823. **Staff:** Prof 4; Other 4. **Subjects:** American and European painting and sculpture; decorative arts; art - African, Oceanic, American Indian; prints and drawings; Asian art; costumes and textiles. **Special Collections:** American fashion sketches, 1900-1950; museum archives. **Holdings:** 140,000 books and exhibition catalogs; 25,000 bound periodical volumes; 100 VF drawers of ephemeral materials; museum archival materials. **Subscriptions:** 400 journals and other serials. **Services:** Interlibrary loan; copying; library open to the public by appointment. **Automated Operations:** Computerized cataloging. **Computerized Information Services:** RLIN; RLIN (electronic mail service). **Networks/Consortia:** Member of New York Metropolitan Reference and Research Library Agency. **Remarks:** FAX: (718)638-3731. Electronic mail address(es): BM.BML (RLIN). **Staff:** Nina Kurilof, Coord. of Tech.Serv.; Deborah Wythe, Archv.

★2239★
Brooklyn Museum - Wilbour Library of Egyptology (Art)
200 Eastern Pkwy. Phone: (718)638-5000
Brooklyn, NY 11238 Diane Guzman, Libn.
Founded: 1934. **Staff:** Prof 2; Other 1. **Subjects:** Ancient Egyptian art, archeology, philology, travel in Egypt from antiquity to modern times. **Special Collections:** Egyptological collections of Charles Edwin Wilbour, Carl Richard Lepsius, and Georg Steindorff. **Holdings:** 30,000 books; 11,000 bound periodical volumes; 7000 pamphlets. **Subscriptions:** 200 journals and other serials. **Services:** Copying; library open to the public by appointment. **Computerized Information Services:** RLIN; RLIN (electronic mail service). **Networks/Consortia:** Member of New York Metropolitan Reference and Research Library Agency. **Publications:** Egyptology Titles published at Heidelberg University (acquisitions of the institution). **Remarks:** FAX: (718)638-3731. Electronic mail address(es): BM.BML (RLIN).

★2240★
Brooklyn Public Library - Art and Music Division (Art, Mus)
Grand Army Plaza Phone: (718)780-7784
Brooklyn, NY 11238 Sue Sharma, Div.Chf.
Founded: 1941. **Staff:** Prof 5; Other 2. **Subjects:** Art history, architecture, design, film, photography, music, theater and dance, recreation and sport. **Holdings:** 123,000 books; 3250 bound periodical volumes; 56,000 scores; 90,000 mounted pictures; 4000 sheets of music; 6 VF drawers of pamphlets; 10 VF drawers of artists' exhibition catalogs; orchestra parts; microcards. **Subscriptions:** 420 journals and other serials. **Services:** Interlibrary loan; copying; division open to the public. **Special Catalogs:** Catalog of orchestra parts (791 works). **Staff:** Sharon Vairamides, Asst.Div.Chf.

★2241★
Brooklyn Public Library - Audio Visual/Media Room Division (Aud-Vis)
Grand Army Plaza Phone: (718)780-7793
Brooklyn, NY 11238 Gaetano Verdini, Div.Chf.
Staff: Prof 2; Other 8. **Holdings:** 250 books; 3548 16mm sound films; 1425 filmstrips; 39,351 phonograph records; 178 8mm films; 14,332 tape cassettes; 4072 compact discs; 7023 videotapes. **Subscriptions:** 17 journals and other serials. **Services:** Internal production of training and promotional videotapes and slides; films may be borrowed by New York City residents only. **Special Catalogs:** Film Catalog; Video Catalog. **Staff:** Uldis A. Skrodelis, Asst.Chf.

★2242★
Brooklyn Public Library - Business Library (Bus-Fin)
280 Cadman Plaza, W. Phone: (718)780-7800
Brooklyn, NY 11201 Joan Canning, Bus.Libn.
Founded: 1943. **Staff:** Prof 8; Other 5. **Subjects:** Accounting, advertising, business management, business procedure, finance, insurance, investment, public relations, small business, real estate, taxation. **Special Collections:** Trade and professional directories; foreign corporation annual reports; domestic 10K reports; U.S. and foreign telephone directories; financial and investment services. **Holdings:** 120,000 books; 30,000 microcards; 500,000 microfiche; 16,450 reels of microfilm; 32,000 microprints; 2900 directories; selective U.S. Government documents depository; Business Index; Newspaper Index; Government Publications Index. **Subscriptions:** 4500 journals and other serials; 20 newspapers. **Services:** Copying; library open to the public. **Computerized Information Services:** ABI/INFORM; CD-ROM (ABI/INFORM). **Networks/Consortia:** Member of New York Metropolitan Reference and Research Library Agency, New York State Interlibrary Loan Network (NYSILL). **Publications:** Business Rankings Annual. **Remarks:** FAX: (718)260-9773. **Staff:** Elizabeth Lukacs, Asst.Bus.Libn.

★2243★
Brooklyn Public Library - History, Travel, Religion and Biography Division (Hist, Rel-Phil)
Grand Army Plaza Phone: (718)780-7794
Brooklyn, NY 11238 Vernon Jordan, Div.Chf.
Founded: 1941. **Staff:** Prof 5; Other 2. **Subjects:** History, travel, biography, religion. **Special Collections:** Local (Brooklyn) history; Brooklyn Eagle Morgue (210 VF cases); Brooklyn pictures (10,000 negatives and prints in 28 VF drawers); current Brooklyn materials (60 VF drawers); Civil War Collection-Map Collection (71,342 maps). **Holdings:** 282,731 books; 7650 bound periodical volumes; 11 VF cases of pamphlets. **Subscriptions:** 376 journals and other serials; 71 newspapers. **Services:** Interlibrary loan (except Brooklyn Collection materials); copying (except most Brooklyn Collection materials). **Staff:** Elizabeth White, Asst.Div.Chf.; Andrew Stevenson, Map Libn.; Judy Walsh, Brooklyn Libn.

★2244★
Brooklyn Public Library - Languages and Literature Division (Hum)
Grand Army Plaza Phone: (718)780-7733
Brooklyn, NY 11238 Monte Olenick, Div.Chf.
Founded: 1941. **Staff:** Prof 5; Other 5. **Subjects:** Fiction, literary criticism, foreign languages, poetry, drama, essays, language learning, linguistics, books and libraries, computer science. **Special Collections:** Walt Whitman Collection (various editions plus biography and criticism; 481 items); Benjamin De Casseres letters (274); H.L. Mencken letters (138); Puerto Rican Collection (1462 items in Spanish); Haitian Collection (270 items in French); large print books (11,300 titles); Henry Miller Collection (100 volumes). **Holdings:** 470,880 books; 25,692 bound periodical volumes; 20,586 reels of microfilm; 109,870 microcards; 4130 microfiche. **Subscriptions:** 1205 journals and other serials; 12 newspapers. **Services:** Interlibrary loan; copying. **Staff:** Bob Shatkin, Asst.Div.Chf.; Anna Boychuk, Foreign Lang.Spec.; Joan Eskenazi, Fiction Libn.

★2245★
Brooklyn Public Library - Science and Industry Division (Sci-Engr)
Grand Army Plaza Phone: (718)780-7745
Brooklyn, NY 11238 Walter Wolff, Div.Chf.
Staff: Prof 5; Other 3. **Subjects:** Anthropology, automobiles, biology, birds, chemistry, cookery, engineering, geology, mathematics, product technology, radio, standards, television, health, nursing, patents and trademarks. **Special Collections:** Fire Protection Collection; Hotel and Restaurant Industry Collection. **Holdings:** 115,000 books; 3000 bound periodical volumes; 40 VF drawers of pamphlets. **Subscriptions:** 900 journals and other serials. **Services:** Interlibrary loan; copying. **Computerized Information Services:** Internal database. **Publications:** Service to Business and Industry (published jointly with the Business Library), 10/year - free on request to local libraries, on exchange to others. **Staff:** Martin Leibowitz, Asst.Chf.

★2246★
Brooklyn Public Library - Social Science/Philosophy Division (Soc Sci)
Grand Army Plaza Phone: (718)780-7746
Brooklyn, NY 11238 Madeline Kiner, Div.Chf.
Founded: 1941. **Staff:** Prof 6; Other 5. **Subjects:** Economics, education, demography, philosophy, psychology, sociology, womens' history, politics and government, labor, law. **Special Collections:** College histories; comparative folklore (in English); railroads. **Holdings:** 200,000 books; 7000 periodicals, bound and on microfilm; ERIC on microfiche, 1980 to present; U.S. government documents; New York State documents (partial depository); 4 VF drawers of pamphlets. **Subscriptions:** 850 journals and other serials. **Services:** Interlibrary loan; copying; division open to the public. **Networks/Consortia:** Member of New York Metropolitan Reference and Research Library Agency. **Staff:** Opal B. Lindsay, Asst.Div.Chf.; Lana Buu-Sao, Doc.Libn.; Robert Carlson, Per.Libn.; Nancy Quade, VF Libn.

★2247★
Brooks Institute of Photography - Library (Art)
1321 Alameda Padre Serra Phone: (805)966-3888
Santa Barbara, CA 93103 Isabelle Higgins, Libn.
Founded: 1973. **Staff:** Prof 2; Other 5. **Subjects:** Photography. **Holdings:** 6000 books; 25,000 unbound periodicals; 2500 pamphlets. **Subscriptions:** 128 journals and other serials. **Services:** Copying; library open to the public for reference use only. **Special Indexes:** Index to technical photography magazines (card). **Remarks:** FAX: (805)564-1475. **Staff:** Gail Miller, Asst.Libn.

Brooks Library
See: **American Meteorological Society** (682)

Lyman Beecher Brooks Library
See: **Norfolk State University** (11849)

Walter Brooks Library
See: **New York Institute for Special Education** (11582)

★2248★
Brookside Congregational Church - Library (Rel-Phil)
2013 Elm St. Phone: (603)669-2807
Manchester, NH 03104 Suzanne Webster
Founded: 1987. **Subjects:** Religion, social science. **Special Collections:** Children's Library. **Holdings:** 450 books; 10 reports. **Services:** Library open to the public.

★2249★
Brookside Hospital - Medical Staff Library (Med)
2000 Vale Rd. Phone: (415)235-7000
San Pablo, CA 94806 Barbara T. Dorham, Libn.
Founded: 1972. **Staff:** Prof 1. **Subjects:** Medicine. **Holdings:** 500 books; 100 bound periodical volumes. **Subscriptions:** 152 journals and other serials. **Services:** Interlibrary loan; copying; library open to the public by appointment. **Computerized Information Services:** MEDLINE, DIALOG Information Services.

★2250★
Brookside Hospital - Professional Library (Med)
11 Northwest Blvd. Phone: (603)886-5000
Nashua, NH 03063 Laurie Smith, Libn.
Founded: 1985. **Subjects:** Psychiatry, mental health, chemical dependency. **Holdings:** 400 books. **Subscriptions:** 50 journals and other serials. **Services:** Interlibrary loan; copying; library open to the public on a limited schedule. **Computerized Information Services:** DIALOG Information Services, NLM. **Remarks:** FAX: (603)886-5127.

Brookside Saratoga County History Center
See: **Saratoga County Historical Society** (14831)

Brookview Manor
See: **Brookings Hospital** (2224)

★2251★
Broome County Historical Society - Josiah T. Newcomb Library (Hist)
30 Front St. Phone: (607)772-0660
Binghamton, NY 13905 Marjory B. Hinman, Libn.
Founded: 1919. **Staff:** 1. **Subjects:** History of Broome County and New York State, genealogy. **Special Collections:** William Bingham papers (100 pieces); Whitney Family papers (1800 pieces); Broome County photographic archive; trade catalogs collection of Broome County firms; The Lacey Architecture Archives (1200 photographs, blueprints, correspondences); Daniel S. Dickinson papers, 1830s-1860s (Lieutenant Governor and Senator; 150 pieces); Ben F. Sisson Collection (84 pieces); Locy Halsted Collection (245 pieces); William L. Ford Collection (1500 pieces); Uriah Gregory Collection (865 pieces); Dr. A.E. Stillson Collection (461 pieces); David Hotchkiss Family Collection (100 pieces); Richard Juliand land grant papers (125 pieces); Robert Harpur land account books, 1788-1818; Mersereau account book, 1765-1803; almanacs, 1799-1907 (100); 19th century American humor (100 volumes). **Holdings:** 2500 books; 5000 documents; 18 VF drawers; personal letters; furnishings. **Services:** Copying; library open to the public. **Remarks:** The Broome County Historical Society is a constituent member of Roberson Center for the Arts and Sciences and is housed there.

★2252★
Broome Developmental Services - Staff Library (Med)
241 Glenwood Rd. Phone: (607)770-0410
Binghamton, NY 13905-1695 Mary Jeanne Perlmutter, Sr.Libn.
Staff: Prof 1; Other 2. **Subjects:** Mental retardation, developmental disabilities. **Holdings:** 9650 books. **Subscriptions:** 131 journals and other serials. **Services:** Interlibrary loan; copying; SDI; library open to the public for reference use only. **Networks/Consortia:** Member of South Central Research Library Council (SCRLC). **Remarks:** Maintains 2588 volume library for residents. FAX: (607)770-0392.

★2253★
Brothers Three of Moriarty - Library (Rec)
1917 Fort Union Dr. Phone: (505)982-2947
Santa Fe, NM 87501 John Bennett Shaw, Owner
Subjects: Sherlock Holmes. **Holdings:** 10,000 books; 300 bound periodical volumes; 19,000 clippings; 200 games, puzzles, and toys; 250 posters and prints; 5000 other cataloged items. **Services:** Library open to the public by appointment. **Remarks:** This private library is said to be the largest such collection relating to all aspects of Sherlock Holmes.

★2254★
Broughton Hospital - John S. McKee, Jr., M.D. Memorial Library (Med)
1000 S. Sterling St. Phone: (704)433-2303
Morganton, NC 28655 Mary E. Bush, Libn.
Staff: Prof 1. **Subjects:** Psychiatry, psychiatric social work, psychology, child psychiatry, geriatric psychiatry, medicine. **Special Collections:** Hospital archives. **Holdings:** 3100 books; 2000 bound periodical volumes; clippings; archives; publications. **Subscriptions:** 27 journals and other serials. **Services:** Interlibrary loan; copying (limited); library open to the public. **Computerized Information Services:** MEDLINE, BRS Information Technologies. **Networks/Consortia:** Member of Northwest AHEC Library Information Network. **Remarks:** FAX: (704)433-2097.

L.A. Broughton Library
See: **Alberta School for the Deaf** (305)

Heywood Broun Library
See: **Newspaper Guild** (11784)

★2255★
Broward County Historical Commission - Historical Research Facilities (Hist)
100 S. New River Dr., E. Phone: (305)765-4670
Fort Lauderdale, FL 33301 F.K. Walker, Chm.
Founded: 1972. **Staff:** Prof 3; Other 7. **Subjects:** South Florida, Broward County, South Florida Indians, Florida. **Special Collections:** L. Clayton Nance Rare Book Collection. **Holdings:** 850 volumes; 500 maps; 375 reels of microfilm of newspapers, 1891-1962; Seminole War manuscripts on microfilm; 200 oral history tapes; photograph collection. **Subscriptions:** 19 journals and other serials. **Services:** Copying; open to the public for reference use only. **Publications:** Broward Legacy, semiannual - by subscription. **Staff:** Rodney Dillon, Coord.; Helen Landers, Hist.

★2256★
Broward County Law Library (Law)
444 County Courthouse
201 S.E. 6th St. Phone: (305)357-6226
Fort Lauderdale, FL 33301 Jeanne Underhill, Dir.
Staff: Prof 2; Other 3. **Subjects:** Law. **Holdings:** 65,000 volumes. **Services:** Library open to the public. **Computerized Information Services:** DIALOG Information Services, WESTLAW. **Staff:** Dorothy Brening, Asst.Libn.

★2257★
Broward County Public Schools - Learning Resources - Professional Library (Educ)
6650 Griffin Rd. Phone: (305)765-6153
Davie, FL 33314 Barbara J. Correll, Educ.Spec., Media
Staff: Prof 1; Other 1. **Subjects:** Education. **Holdings:** 8589 books; 330,773 ERIC microfiche; 1385 reels of microfilm; 8 VF drawers of clippings. **Subscriptions:** 193 journals and other serials. **Services:** Interlibrary loan; copying; library open to the public. **Computerized Information Services:** BRS Information Technologies; CD-ROM (ERIC). **Special Catalogs:** Professional Library Catalog. **Remarks:** FAX: (305)765-6773.

Broward County School Board - Florida Diagnostic & Learning Resources System
See: **Florida Diagnostic & Learning Resources System** (5872)

Alice Pratt Brown Library
See: **Rice University - Alice Pratt Brown Library** (13893)

Annmary Brown Memorial Collections
See: **Brown University - Special Collections** (2283)

★2258★
Brown & Bain, P.A. - Library (Law)
2901 N. Central Phone: (602)351-8039
Phoenix, AZ 85012-2788 Ellen Hepner, Libn.
Staff: Prof 1; Other 4. **Subjects:** Law. **Special Collections:** Antitrust law; American Indian law; computer/technology law; trade secrets. **Holdings:** 30,000 volumes. **Subscriptions:** 350 journals and other serials. **Services:** Interlibrary loan; library not open to the public. **Computerized Information Services:** DIALOG Information Services, LEXIS, NEXIS, WESTLAW, VU/TEXT Information Services, Information America, Dun & Bradstreet Business Credit Services, DataTimes. **Remarks:** FAX: (602)351-8516. Telex: 910 951 0646.

★2259★
Brown Brothers - Photograph Collection (Aud-Vis)
Sterling, PA 18463 Phone: (717)689-9688
Raymond A. Collins, Pres.
Subjects: Stock photograph collection - news, history, geography. **Holdings:** 12 million photographs; old illustrations; movie stills; color transparencies. **Services:** Photographs available for reproduction on fee basis. **Computerized Information Services:** CompuServe Information Service, MCI Mail (electronic mail services). **Remarks:** FAX: (717)689-7873.

★2260★
Brown Brothers Harriman & Co. - Research Library (Bus-Fin)
59 Wall St. Phone: (212)493-8306
New York, NY 10005 Agnes Kelly Mattis, Libn.
Staff: Prof 2; Other 3. **Subjects:** Banking, economic and business conditions, finance, investments, corporation records. **Holdings:** 1000 books; 125 bound periodical volumes; 4000 microfiche files. **Subscriptions:** 400 journals and other serials. **Services:** Interlibrary loan (to members of Special Libraries Association). **Remarks:** FAX: (212)493-7997. **Staff:** Andrew M. Gazzale.

★2261★
Brown & Caldwell - Consultants - Seattle Branch Office Library (Sci-Engr)
100 W. Harrison Phone: (206)281-4000
Seattle, WA 98119 Marilyn Burwell, Libn.
Founded: 1979. **Staff:** .5. **Subjects:** Wastewater, water resources, stormwater and drainage, groundwater, industrial wastes, Puget Sound. **Holdings:** 700 books; 1763 technical reports; 12 shelves of unbound periodicals; 12 shelves of reference materials; 10 shelves of specifications and cost indexes; 26 shelves of uncataloged technical reports. **Subscriptions:** 36 journals and other serials. **Services:** Interlibrary loan; SDI; library open to the public with restrictions. **Computerized Information Services:** DIALOG Information Services, Toxicology Data Network (TOXNET); CAN/OLE. **Remarks:** FAX: (206)286-3510.

★2262★
Brown & Caldwell - Library (Sci-Engr)
2300 Oakmont Way, Suite. 100 Phone: (503)686-9915
Eugene, OR 97401 Linda Coad, Libn.
Founded: 1972. **Staff:** Prof 1. **Subjects:** Engineering - general, sanitary, civil, mechanical, electrical, energy. **Holdings:** 3000 books; 1000 government documents; 500 standards; company reports; Environmental Protection Agency (EPA) documents. **Subscriptions:** 60 journals and other serials. **Services:** Interlibrary loan; library not open to the public. **Computerized Information Services:** DIALOG Information Services. **Remarks:** FAX: (503)686-1417.

★2263★
Brown & Caldwell Consultants - Library (Sci-Engr)
Box 8045 Phone: (510)210-2364
Walnut Creek, CA 94596-1220 Paula Spurlock, Libn.
Staff: Prof 1; Other 2. **Subjects:** Environmental engineering, water resources, water and wastewater treatment, hazardous waste, energy conservation. **Holdings:** 5000 books; 400 bound periodical volumes; 500 maps; 2000 vendors catalogs; 4000 reports; 2000 microfiche; 800 reels of microfilm. **Subscriptions:** 200 journals and other serials. **Services:** Interlibrary loan; copying; SDI; library open to the public by appointment. **Automated Operations:** Computerized cataloging and serials. **Computerized Information Services:** DIALOG Information Services; MELVYL (internal database). **Networks/Consortia:** Member of Bay Area Library and Information System (BALIS), CLASS. **Publications:** Library Acquisition List. **Remarks:** Library located at 3480 Buskirk Ave., Pleasant Hill, CA 94523. FAX: (510)937-9026.

★2264★
Brown County Historical Society - Archives (Hist)
2 N. Broadway
Box 116 Phone: (507)354-2016
New Ulm, MN 56073 Darla Cordes Gebhard, Res.Libn.
Founded: 1930. **Staff:** Prof 1. **Subjects:** Local and regional history. **Special Collections:** Autographed portraits and letters (3000 figures in art, literature, and science, 1890-1925); Dakota War of 1862. **Holdings:** 2000 books; Family Record Files for 4240 families; 7 journals; 340 reels of microfilm. **Subscriptions:** 5 newspapers. **Services:** Copying; archives open to the public for reference use only. **Publications:** News Notes, 4/year - for internal distribution only. **Special Indexes:** Index to obituaries in New Ulm Review and New Ulm Post, 1854-1935 (card and online), 1936-1960 (card only).

★2265★
Brown County Historical Society - Genealogy Collection (Hist)
P.O. Box 668 Phone: (812)988-4297
Nashville, IN 47448 Helen H. Reeve, Geneal.
Founded: 1972. **Staff:** 2. **Subjects:** Genealogy of Brown County. **Special Collections:** Local family lineages collection (400 items, 2000 in progress). **Holdings:** 50 books, 15 reels of microfilm, microfiche. **Subscriptions:** 4 journals and other serials. **Services:** Copying; library open to the public. **Special Indexes:** Brown County Marriages; Cemeteries; Obituaries; Federal Census Index, 1840-1910; Funeral Home Records.

★2266★
Brown County Mental Health Center - H.H. Humphrey Memorial Staff Library (Med)
2900 St. Anthony Dr. Phone: (414)468-1136
Green Bay, WI 54311 Cindy M. Ducat, Lib.Mgr.
Staff: Prof 2. **Subjects:** Psychiatry, psychology, social work, nursing, growth and development, geriatrics, mental retardation, developmental disability, alcohol and drug abuse. **Holdings:** 2000 books; 100 bound periodical volumes; 100 AV programs. **Subscriptions:** 45 journals and other serials. **Services:** Interlibrary loan; copying; library open to the public by appointment. **Computerized Information Services:** Internal database. **Remarks:** FAX: (414)468-4213.

Dr. W. Gordon Brown Memorial Library
See: **Central Baptist Seminary** (3328)

★2267★
Earle Palmer Brown - Information Center (Bus-Fin)
6935 Arlington Rd. Phone: (301)657-6023
Bethesda, MD 20814 Stefan Powers, Info.Dir.
Staff: Prof 2. **Subjects:** Advertising, marketing, business. **Holdings:** 250 books. **Subscriptions:** 20 journals and other serials; 5 newspapers. **Computerized Information Services:** DIALOG Information Services, NEXIS, DataTimes, Telmar Group, Inc. **Remarks:** FAX: (301)657-2590. Alternate telephone number(s): (301)986-0510.

★2268★
George Brown College of Applied Arts & Technology - Archives (Hist)
Box 1015, Sta. B Phone: (416)867-2000
Toronto, ON, Canada M5T 2T9 John L. Hardy, Assoc.Dir., Educ.Rsrcs.
Founded: 1975. **Staff:** Prof 1. **Subjects:** College history, labor relations, fashion industry. **Special Collections:** Dr. Louis Fine papers (Labour Relations Consultant's File); records of the Men's Clothing Manufacturer's Association of Ontario (2 meters); history project collection of the Association of Colleges of Applied Arts and Technology of Ontario (8 meters); records of the Nightingale School of Nursing (7 meters); records of the Committee of Registrars and Admissions Officers of the Colleges of Applied Arts and Technology of Ontario (38 cm.); records of the Committee of Librarians of the Colleges of Applied Arts and Technology of Ontario (1.3 meters); records of the Association of Colleges of Applied Arts and Technology of Ontario (31.6 meters). **Holdings:** 85 cubic meters of records and manuscripts. **Services:** Archives open to the public with restrictions.

★2269★
George Brown College of Applied Arts & Technology - Library (Educ)
Box 1015, Sta. B Phone: (416)944-4632
Toronto, ON, Canada M5T 2T9 John L. Hardy, Assoc.Dir., Educ.Rsrcs.
Founded: 1968. **Staff:** Prof 18. **Subjects:** Engineering and architectural technology, nursing, business and commerce, food technology, fashion technology, child care, addiction counselling. **Holdings:** 105,172 books; 1600 bound periodical volumes; 900 films; 180 meters of archival materials. **Subscriptions:** 651 journals and other serials; 6 newspapers. **Services:** Library open to the public with fee for borrowing. **Automated Operations:** Computerized cataloging and circulation. **Computerized Information Services:** DOBIS Canadian Online Library System. **Special Catalogs:** Film catalog. **Remarks:** (416)944-4438. The library's holdings are dispersed among the college's four campuses. **Staff:** V. Eccles, Group Ldr.; B. Reed, Group Ldr.; L. Pena, Group Ldr.; I. Grant, Libn.; M. Pulleyblank, Libn.; N. Love, Libn.

George Warren Brown School of Social Work
See: **Washington University** (20063)

Herbert C. Brown Archives
See: **Purdue University - Chemistry Library** (13533)

★2270★
John Carter Brown Library (Hist)
Box 1894 Phone: (401)863-2725
Providence, RI 02912 Norman Fiering, Dir./Libn.
Founded: 1846. **Staff:** Prof 8; Other 12. **Subjects:** Discovery and exploration of North and South America to 1820; comparative colonization of the Americas, including Spain, Portugal, England, France, and Holland; impact of the new world on the old world, 1493-1800; history - maritime, science, printing. **Special Collections:** Braziliana; Caribbeana; maritime history; American Indian linguistics (books; manuscripts); history of cartography (2000 books); American Revolution (15,000 items); Arnold-Green papers (132 linear feet); Bartlett papers (15 linear feet); Brown papers (681 linear feet); History of printing in the Americas (through 1820). **Holdings:** 55,000 volumes; 3000 bound periodical volumes; 1200 maps; 350 bound volumes of codices; 36 linear feet of manuscripts. **Subscriptions:** 35 journals and other serials. **Services:** Microfilming; library open to the public with restrictions. **Automated Operations:** Computerized cataloging. **Computerized Information Services:** RLIN. **Networks/Consortia:** Member of Research Libraries Information Network (RLIN). **Publications:** Bibliographies; newsletter, irregular. **Special Catalogs:** Exhibition catalogs, 2/year; chronological files; imprint file; provenance file; engravers file; dedicatee file (all on cards). **Remarks:** FAX: (401)863-3700. **Staff:** Susan Danforth, Asst.Libn./Cur.; Richard N. Hurley, Photo.; Susan Newbury, Chf.Cat.; Maria Cassiet, Cat.Libn.; Dennis Landis, Ed.; Ann Barry, Asst.Ed.; A.F. Gunther Buchheim, Cat.Libn.; Daniel J. Slive, Ref.Libn.

John Young Brown Memorial Library
See: **St. John's Mercy Medical Center** (14342)

★2271★
Brown Maroney & Oaks Hartline - Law Library (Law)
111 Congress Ave., Suite 1400 Phone: (512)472-5456
Austin, TX 78701 Evan Quenon, Libn.
Founded: 1981. **Staff:** Prof 2; Other 1.25. **Subjects:** Law - environmental, business, utilities, banking, public; litigation. **Holdings:** 17,000 books; 400 bound periodical volumes; 15 drawers of microfiche; 300 audio cassettes; 50 video cassettes. **Subscriptions:** 400 journals and other serials; 10 newspapers. **Services:** Interlibrary loan; copying; SDI; library not open to the public. **Automated Operations:** Computerized cataloging and circulation. **Computerized Information Services:** DIALOG Information Services, WESTLAW, LEXIS, NEXIS, DataTimes, Information America, VU/TEXT Information Services; internal databases. **Publications:** Newsletter, monthly - for internal distribution only. **Special Indexes:** Expert witness index; work product index. **Remarks:** FAX: (512)479-1101. **Staff:** Anna C. Stavinoha.

Brown Memorial Library
See: **Protestant Episcopal Church - Episcopal Diocese of Southwest Florida** (13430)

Moses and Obadiah Brown Libraries
See: **Society of Friends - New England Yearly Meeting of Friends - Archives** (15322)

★2272★
Brown & Root Braun - Library (Sci-Engr, Energy)
1000 S. Fremont Ave.
Box 4000 Phone: (818)300-2330
Alhambra, CA 91802 Beverly Muller, Lib.Mgr.
Founded: 1935. **Staff:** Prof 2; Other 1. **Subjects:** Petrochemicals; petroleum; energy; engineering - civil, chemical, electrical, mechanical, hydraulic, ocean; naval architecture; offshore construction; pipelines; business and management. **Holdings:** 34,000 books; 6000 bound periodical volumes; 6000 microfiche; language tapes; standards and codes; maps; reports. **Subscriptions:** 400 journals and other serials. **Services:** Interlibrary loan; library not open to the public. **Automated Operations:** Computerized cataloging. **Computerized Information Services:** DIALOG Information Services, NEXIS, PFDS Online. **Publications:** Periodicals list; New Acquisitions List - for internal distribution only. **Remarks:** FAX: (818)300-3291. Telex: 674888. **Staff:** Helen A. Kramer, Asst.Libn.

★2273★
Brown & Root, Inc. - Information Resource Center (Sci-Engr, Plan)
Box 3 Phone: (713)676-3373
Houston, TX 77001-0003 Kathy Hubbard, Mgr.
Founded: 1960. **Staff:** Prof 9; Other 10. **Subjects:** Engineering, construction, environmental science, technology. **Holdings:** 21,000 books; 6200 bound periodical volumes; 48 VF drawers of reports, dissertations, documents. **Subscriptions:** 300 journals and other serials. **Services:** Interlibrary loan; copying; library open to the public by appointment. **Automated Operations:** Computerized public access catalog, cataloging, acquisitions, serials, and circulation. **Computerized Information Services:** DIALOG Information Services, BRS Information Technologies, PFDS Online, NEXIS, LEXIS, NewsNet, Inc., DataTimes, VU/TEXT Information Services, OCLC. **Publications:** Interface. **Remarks:** FAX: (713)676-5715.

★2274★
Brown University - Art Slide Library (Art)
Box 1855, List Art Bldg.
64 College St. Phone: (401)863-3218
Providence, RI 02912 Norine Duncan Cashman, Cur.
Staff: Prof 3. **Subjects:** Architecture - modern, medieval, Renaissance, Baroque; painting and sculpture - modern, Renaissance, Baroque; Roman and Greek art and architecture. **Holdings:** 175,000 slides; 37,000 photographs; 9000 microfiche. **Services:** Collections not open to the public. **Computerized Information Services:** BITNET (electronic mail service). **Remarks:** Electronic mail address(es): AP201030@BROWNVM (BITNET). **Staff:** Karen Bouchard, Assoc.Cur.

★2275★
Brown University - Center for Environmental Studies - Library (Env-Cons)
Box 1943
Providence, RI 02912 Phone: (401)863-2715
Staff: 1. **Subjects:** Environmental issues. **Special Collections:** Environmental equity collection; theses and dissertations collection; solid waste management collection. **Holdings:** 500 books; 200 reports. **Subscriptions:** 18 journals and other serials. **Services:** Library open to the public for reference use only. **Remarks:** FAX: (401)863-3503.

★2276★
Brown University - Center for Neural Sciences (Med)
P.O. Box 1953 Phone: (401)863-3548
Providence, RI 02912 Mary Ellen Flinn-Butera, Adm.Asst.
Subjects: Brain and cerebral cortex - models and mechanisms of learning, memory, plasticity. **Holdings:** Journals. **Services:** Center not open to the public.

★2277★
Brown University - Christine Dunlap Farnham Archives (Soc Sci)
John Hay Library
Box A
Providence, RI 02912 Phone: (401)863-2148
Subjects: History of women at Brown University and Pembroke College; history of Brown alumnae; women in Rhode Island; women's higher education, literature, and social history. **Holdings:** Manuscripts; organizational records; photographs; ephemera; Pembroke College records; student papers, correspondence, diaries, lecture notes, photographs, memorabilia, films, and scrapbooks. **Services:** Copying. **Computerized Information Services:** Online systems. **Publications:** Research Guide to the Christine Dunlap Farnham Archives.

★2278★
Brown University - East Asian Collection (Area-Ethnic)
Providence, RI 02912 Phone: (401)863-2171
John Stanley, Spec.Coll.Dir.
Founded: 1961. **Staff:** Prof 1; Other 1. **Subjects:** East Asia - language, politics and government, sociology, art, geography, literature, religion, philosophy, history, economics. **Special Collections:** C.S. Gardner Collection. **Holdings:** 90,100 books; 608 reels of microfilm; 2746 slides. **Subscriptions:** 185 journals and other serials; 14 newspapers. **Services:** Interlibrary loan; copying; collection open to the public with restrictions. **Automated Operations:** Computerized cataloging, acquisitions, serials, and circulation. **Computerized Information Services:** DIALOG Information Services, BRS Information Technologies, RLIN; internal database. **Networks/Consortia:** Member of Research Libraries Information Network (RLIN). **Publications:** BiblioFile (newsletter), irregular - for internal distribution only.

★2279★
Brown University - Orwig Music Library (Mus)
Box A Phone: (401)863-3759
Providence, RI 02912 Carol Tatian, Hd.Mus.Libn.
Founded: 1988. **Staff:** Prof 1; Other 1. **Subjects:** Music. **Holdings:** 15,000 volumes; 10,000 scores; 10,000 sound recordings. **Services:** Interlibrary loan; library open to persons affiliated with Brown University. **Automated Operations:** Computerized cataloging and circulation. **Networks/Consortia:** Member of Research Libraries Information Network (RLIN). **Special Catalogs:** Catalog for sound recordings.

★2280★
Brown University - Population Studies and Training Center - Demography Library (Soc Sci)
Box 1916 Phone: (401)863-2668
Providence, RI 02912 Dr. Frances Goldscheider, Dir.
Founded: 1965. **Staff:** Prof 1; Other 2. **Subjects:** Population, human ecology, urbanization, migration. **Holdings:** 9400 books; 1600 publications; 6500 reprints; World Fertility Survey depository; recoded 1/1000 1960 U.S. Census tapes; Survey of Economic Opportunity tape; 1980 U.S. Census tapes for Rhode Island; 1970 U.S. Census tapes; National Longitudinal Survey (Parnes); various KAP and Demographic Survey tapes; census tapes for selected developing countries; 200 foreign census reports; 1970 Canadian Census tapes; WFS tapes for over 30 countries. **Subscriptions:** 80 journals and other serials. **Services:** Library not open to the public. **Computerized Information Services:** BITNET (electronic mail service). **Networks/Consortia:** Member of APLIC International Census Network. **Publications:** Accessions List - for internal distribution only. **Remarks:** FAX: (401)863-3213. Electronic mail address(es): SO430000@BROWNVM (BITNET). **Staff:** Carol L. Knopf, Libn.

★2281★
Brown University - Sciences Library (Sci-Engr)
Brown Univ. Library, Box I Phone: (401)863-2405
Providence, RI 02912 Florence Kell Doksansky, Asst.Univ.Libn.
Founded: 1971. **Staff:** Prof 8; Other 15. **Subjects:** Health sciences, life sciences, physical sciences, engineering. **Special Collections:** Mathematics. **Holdings:** 513,529 volumes. **Subscriptions:** 5432 journals and other serials. **Services:** Interlibrary loan (fee); copying; library open to the public for bona fide scholarly use only. **Automated Operations:** Computerized circulation and cataloging. **Computerized Information Services:** DIALOG Information Services, BRS Information Technologies, MEDLARS, OCLC; CD-ROMs (MEDLINE, PsycLIT, AGRICOLA, Institute for Scientific Information Science Citation Index, AMA Freida, MathSci, Bio Abstracts); BITNET (electronic mail service). **Networks/Consortia:** Member of Consortium of Rhode Island Academic and Research Libraries, Inc. (CRIARL), National Network of Libraries of Medicine - New England Region, NELINET, Inc., Research Libraries Information Network (RLIN). **Special Catalogs:** Serials Holdings List (microfiche). **Remarks:** FAX: (401)863-2753. Electronic mail address(es): AP010038@BROWNVM (BITNET). **Staff:** Ronald Fark, Hd., Ref.; Janet Crager, Biomed.Ref.Libn.; Patricia Galkowski, Phys.Sci.Ref.Libn.; Caroline Helie, Phys.Sci.Ref.Libn.; Frank Kellerman, Biology & Psych.Ref.Libn.; Tovah Reis, Med.Lib.Coord.

★2282★
Brown University - Special Collections (Hist, Hum)
John Hay Library, Box A
20 Prospect St. Phone: (401)863-2146
Providence, RI 02912 Samuel A. Streit, Asst.Univ.Libn.
Founded: 1939. **Staff:** Prof 12; Other 11. **Special Collections:** American poetry and plays (500,000 items); military history (100,000 items); Lincoln and John Hay (40,000); American pamphlets (30,000); incunabula (800); Rhode Island history (13,500); Legend of Wandering Jew (1500); Thoreau (450); Whaling (1100); history of science (30,000); magic (5000 volumes); Rhode Island Medical Society (7500 volumes); university archives. **Holdings:** 300,000 volumes; 500,000 historical and literary manuscripts; 40,000 broadsides (chiefly American verse and Lincoln); 60,000 prints, slides, drawings, photographs; 500,000 pieces of American sheet music. **Subscriptions:** 450 journals and other serials. **Services:** Copying; collections open to the public. **Automated Operations:** Computerized public access catalog, cataloging, acquisitions, and serials. **Computerized Information Services:** BITNET (electronic mail service). **Networks/Consortia:** Member of Research Libraries Information Network (RLIN). **Publications:** Books at Brown, annual; Special Collections at Brown University: A History and Guide, 1988; Research Guide to the Christine Dunlap Farnum Archives, 1989. **Special Catalogs:** Dictionary Catalog of the Harris Collection of American Poetry and Plays, 1972, First Supplement, 1977; American Poetry 1609-1900 (microfilm). **Remarks:** FAX: (401)863-1272. Electronic mail address(es): BROWNVM (BITNET). **Staff:** Martha L. Mitchell, Univ.Archv.; Rita Warnock Cur., Broadsides; John H. Stanley, Hd.Spec.Coll.Libn.; Rosemary L. Cullen, Cur., Amer. Poetry/Plays; Jennifer B. Lee, Cur., Printed Bks.; Mark N. Brown, Cur., Mss.; Catherine Denning, Cur., Incunabula; Peter Harrington, Cur., Mil.Coll.; Jean Rainwater, Rd.Serv.; Richard Noble, Cat.; Ann Morgan Dodge, Paper Cons.

★2283★
Brown University - Special Collections - Annmary Brown Memorial Collections (Rare Book)
John Hay Library, Box A
20 Prospect St. Phone: (401)863-2429
Providence, RI 02912 Catherine Denning, Cur.
Founded: 1907. **Staff:** Prof 1. **Subjects:** Invention and dissemination of printing in the 15th century. **Special Collections:** Papers of the Ninth New York Volunteer Regiment (Hawkins Zouaves), 1860-1863; Colonial Connecticut court records (witchcraft trials); personal papers of General Rush Hawkins and the Brown family. **Holdings:** 1500 books. **Services:** Library open to the public. **Computerized Information Services:** BITNET (electronic mail service). **Formerly:** Brown University - Annmary Brown Memorial Library.

W.R. Brown Memorial Library
See: **Arabian Horse Owners Foundation** (934)

★2284★
Brown and Williamson Tobacco Corporation - Research Library (Sci-Engr)
1600 W. Hill St. Phone: (502)568-7683
Louisville, KY 40210 Carol S. Lincoln, Info.Spec.
Founded: 1958. **Staff:** Prof 1; Other 1. **Subjects:** Chemistry, tobacco, agriculture, chemical engineering, physics, statistics. **Holdings:** 6000 books; 5000 bound periodical volumes; 35,000 patents; 6000 company reports; 15 VF drawers of pamphlets and miscellanea. **Subscriptions:** 285 journals and other serials. **Services:** Interlibrary loan; library not open to the public. **Computerized Information Services:** DIALOG Information Services, PFDS Online, NLM, Chemical Abstracts Service (CAS); internal database. **Publications:** Periodic Accessions List - . **Remarks:** FAX: (502)568-8226; (502)568-8225.

★2285★
Brown & Wood - Library (Law)
1 World Trade Center Phone: (212)839-5444
New York, NY 10048 Connie L. Kluever, Libn.
Staff: Prof 1; Other 1. **Subjects:** Law. **Holdings:** 15,000 books. **Subscriptions:** 40 journals and other serials. **Services:** Library not open to the public.

Benjamin P. Browne Library
See: **Judson College** (8490)

Lois Brownell Research Library
See: **College of the Ozarks - Ralph Foster Museum** (3901)

★2286★
Browning-Ferris Industries, Inc. - Corporate Office - Library (Law, Bus-Fin)
P.O. Box 3151 Phone: (713)870-7011
Houston, TX 77253 Mary F. Magner, Hd.Libn.
Founded: 1970. **Staff:** 4. **Subjects:** Law, business. **Special Collections:** Environmental recycling. **Holdings:** Figures not available. **Subscriptions:** 150 journals and other serials; 5 newspapers. **Services:** Interlibrary loan; library not open to the public. **Computerized Information Services:** DIALOG Information Services, NEXIS, LEXIS, DataTimes, VU/TEXT Information Services, Dun & Bradstreet. **Remarks:** FAX: (713)870-7825. **Staff:** Deneen Martin; Janet Fagan; Pat Roche.

★2287★
Brownstein, Zeidman & Schomer - Law Library (Law)
1401 New York Ave., N.W., Suite 900 Phone: (202)879-5854
Washington, DC 20005 William T. Owens-Smith, Libn.
Founded: 1972. **Staff:** Prof 1; Other 1. **Subjects:** Law - housing, franchising, trademark, securities, real estate, taxation, international trade. **Holdings:** 12,000 books. **Subscriptions:** 120 journals and other serials; 8 newspapers. **Services:** Interlibrary loan; library not open to the public. **Computerized Information Services:** LEXIS, DIALOG Information Services, WESTLAW, Dow Jones News/Retrieval. **Networks/Consortia:** Member of CAPCON Library Network. **Remarks:** FAX: (202)879-5773.

★2288★
The Grey Bruce Regional Health Centre - Health Sciences Library (Med)
1400 8th St., E.
P.O. Box 1400 Phone: (519)376-2121
Owen Sound, ON, Canada N4K 6M9 Vicky Duncan, Hea.Sci.Libn.
Staff: Prof 1; Other 2. **Subjects:** Medicine, nursing, psychiatry, psychology, allied health sciences, patient education. **Holdings:** 2100 books; 77 government documents. **Subscriptions:** 210 journals and other serials. **Services:** Interlibrary loan; copying (limited); SDI; library open to practicing health care professionals. **Computerized Information Services:** CATLINE, MEDLARS, DIALOG Information Services; Envoy 100 (electronic mail service). Performs searches free of charge for health care professionals. **Networks/Consortia:** Member of Central Ontario Health Libraries Association (COHLA). **Publications:** INQUIRY (newsletter), quarterly; General Information, Interlibrary Loans (brochures). **Remarks:** FAX: (516)376-1846. Electronic mail address(es): ILL.OOWGM (Envoy 100). **Staff:** Nancy Beer, Lib.Techn.

★2289★
Bruce Mines Museum and Archives (Hist)
Taylor St. Phone: (705)785-3426
Bruce Mines, ON, Canada P0R 1C0 Arthur Henderson, Cur.
Staff: 1. **Subjects:** History, genealogy. **Holdings:** 5000 books; mining manuscripts; pioneer artifacts; newspapers, 1901-1943, on microfilm. **Services:** Archives open to the public.

The Bruening-Marotta Library
See: **St. Mary Seminary** (14507)

★2290★
Brugler & Levin - Library
10 S. Wayne St. Phone: (717)248-4971
Lewistown, PA 17044 Wendy Levin, Lib.Dir.
Remarks: No further information was supplied by respondent.

Henry J. Bruman Map Library
See: **University of California, Los Angeles - Henry J. Bruman Map Library** (18385)

★2291★
Brundage, Story & Rose, Investment Counsel - Library & Information Center (Bus-Fin)
1 Broadway Phone: (212)269-3050
New York, NY 10004 Kathleen M. Halston, Info.Mgr.
Staff: Prof 1; Other 1. **Subjects:** Investments, business, economics, investment counseling, petroleum, mining. **Special Collections:** Moody's Manuals, 1915 to present; Poor's Manual of Railroads; Wall Street Journal, 1942 to present (microfilm); corporate annual reports; historical collection. **Holdings:** 1120 books; 300 bound periodical volumes; 5100 company files, including annual and quarterly reports, proxies, and prospectuses, 10K reports in hardcopy; economic and company charts. **Subscriptions:** 195 journals and other serials; 22 newspapers. **Services:** Interlibrary loan; copying; library open to clients or persons known to the staff. **Computerized Information Services:** DIALOG Information Services. **Remarks:** FAX: (212)425-4286.

★2292★
Brush Wellman, Inc. - Technical Library (Sci-Engr)
17876 St. Clair Ave. Phone: (216)486-4200
Cleveland, OH 44110 Sophie Patterson, Libn.
Staff: Prof 1; Other 1. **Subjects:** Beryllium metallurgy, metallurgy, ceramics. **Holdings:** 3000 books; uncataloged technical reports. **Subscriptions:** 250 journals and other serials. **Services:** Interlibrary loan; library open to the public by appointment for reference use. **Computerized Information Services:** DIALOG Information Services, Copper Development Association, PFDS Online; internal database. **Publications:** Newsletter, quarterly.

★2293★
(Brussels) American Library - USIS Library (Educ)
Square du Bastion 1c Phone: 2 5133830
B-1050 Brussels, Belgium Eddy M. Olislaeger, Lib.Dir.
Founded: 1945. **Staff:** 4. **Subjects:** United States studies - institutions, history, foreign relations, literature, economic conditions. **Holdings:** 10,000 books; 220 bound periodical volumes; 3000 reports; 600 documentary program videotapes. **Subscriptions:** 220 journals and other serials; 5 newspapers. **Services:** Interlibrary loan; copying; SDI; library open to the public. **Automated Operations:** Computerized public access catalog. **Computerized Information Services:** DIALOG Information Services, LEGI-SLATE, Congressional Quarterly's Washington Alert; internal databases; DIALMAIL (electronic mail service). **Remarks:** FAX: 2 5119652. Electronic mail address(es): 13684 (DIALMAIL). Maintained or supported by the U.S. Information Agency. Focus is on materials that will assist peoples outside the United States to learn about the United States, its people, history, culture, political processes, and social milieux.

Brussels University - Medical School - Jules Bordet Institute
See: **Jules Bordet Institute** (1969)

Brute Library
See: **Old Cathedral Parish Church** (12380)

★2294★
Bryan, Cave, McPheeters & McRoberts - Law Library (Law)
333 S. Grand Ave., 31st Fl. Phone: (213)628-8000
Los Angeles, CA 90071 Karen Lasnick, Libn.
Staff: Prof 1. **Subjects:** Law, labor, government contracts law. **Holdings:** 5000 books; microfiche. **Subscriptions:** 100 journals and other serials; 5 newspapers. **Services:** Interlibrary loan; library not open to the public. **Computerized Information Services:** DIALOG Information Services, LEXIS, WESTLAW, Information America; internal databases (litigation support). **Remarks:** FAX: (213)628-3642. Telex: 4720314 BCMM LSA.

★2295★
Bryan, Cave, McPheeters & McRoberts - Law Library (Law)
One Metro Square
211 N. Broadway, Ste. 3600 Phone: (314)259-2000
St. Louis, MO 63102 Judith L. Gutglass, Hd.Libn.
Staff: Prof 1; Other 5. **Subjects:** American law. **Holdings:** 22,000 books. **Subscriptions:** 200 journals and other serials; 5 newspapers. **Services:** Interlibrary loan (limited); library open to clients. **Automated Operations:** Computerized cataloging, acquisitions, and circulation. **Computerized Information Services:** DIALOG Information Services, Dow Jones News/Retrieval, Information America, VU/TEXT Information Services, LEXIS, WESTLAW. **Networks/Consortia:** Member of Missouri Library Network Corp. (MLNC). **Publications:** Annual report. **Special Indexes:** Subject index to loose-leaf services. **Remarks:** FAX: (314)231-8600, ext. 434.

★2296★
G. Werber Bryan Psychiatric Hospital - Professional Library (Med)
220 Faison Dr. Phone: (803)935-7851
Columbia, SC 29203 Steven T. Leap, Libn.
Founded: 1978. **Staff:** Prof 1. **Subjects:** Psychiatry, social work, psychology, recreation therapy. **Holdings:** 600 books. **Subscriptions:** 21 journals and other serials. **Services:** Interlibrary loan; copying; library open to Department of Mental Health employees. **Networks/Consortia:** Member of Columbia Area Medical Librarians' Association (CAMLA), South Carolina Health Information Network (SCHIN).

Bryan-Lang Historical Library
See: **Guale Historical Society** (6785)

★2297★
Bryan Memorial Hospital - Medical Library (Med)
1600 S. 48th Phone: (402)483-3030
Lincoln, NE 68506 Brian Tuttle, Med.Lib.Spec.
Staff: Prof 1. **Subjects:** Clinical medicine, cardiovascular medicine. **Special Collections:** Management/supervisory coping (textbooks; tapes). **Holdings:** 300 books. **Subscriptions:** 62 journals and other serials. **Services:** Interlibrary loan; copying; literature searches; library open to the public with physician's referral and to students. **Computerized Information Services:** MEDLARS, BRS Information Technologies. **Networks/Consortia:** Member of Lincoln Health Science Library Group (LHSLG). **Special Indexes:** Index to patient education materials (card). **Remarks:** FAX: (402)483-8392.

★2298★
Bryan Memorial Hospital - School of Nursing - Helene Fuld Memorial Learning Resource Center (Med)
5000 Sumner St. Phone: (402)483-3908
Lincoln, NE 68506 Susan P. Echols, Libn.
Founded: 1926. **Staff:** 2. **Subjects:** Nursing, nursing education. **Holdings:** 4500 books; 100 bound periodical volumes; journals on microfiche. **Subscriptions:** 75 journals and other serials. **Services:** Copying; center open to the public for reference use only. **Networks/Consortia:** Member of Lincoln Health Science Library Group (LHSLG).

William Jennings Bryan-Dorn Veterans Hospital
See: **U.S. Dept. of Veterans Affairs (SC-Columbia)** (17412)

Herbert L. Bryans Memorial Library
See: **University Hospital and Clinic** (18637)

★2299★
Bryant College of Business Administration - Edith M. Hodgson Memorial Library (Bus-Fin)
1150 Douglas Pike Phone: (401)232-6125
Smithfield, RI 02917-1284 Dr. John P. Hannon, Dir.
Founded: 1955. **Staff:** Prof 5; Other 8. **Subjects:** Accounting, marketing, management, finance, economics, taxation. **Holdings:** 122,000 books; 5000 bound periodical volumes; 6746 reels of microfilm; 9846 microfiche. **Subscriptions:** 1250 journals and other serials; 23 newspapers. **Services:** Interlibrary loan; copying; library open to the business community. **Automated Operations:** Computerized public access catalog, cataloging, acquisitions, serials, and circulation. **Computerized Information Services:** DIALOG Information Services, LEXIS, NEXIS, OCLC; University Microfilms International (UMI); LINX Courier (electronic mail service). Performs searches on fee basis. Contact Person: Constance Cameron, Assoc.Libn. **Networks/Consortia:** Member of Consortium of Rhode Island Academic and Research Libraries, Inc. (CRIARL), NELINET, Inc., Rhode Island Library Network (RHILINET). **Remarks:** FAX: (401)232-6319. **Staff:** Tom Magill, Asst.Libn.; Mary Moroney, Assoc.Libn., Tech.Serv.

★2300★
Bryant Library - Local History Collection (Hist)
Paper Mill Rd. Phone: (516)621-2240
Roslyn, NY 11576-2193 Myrna L. Sloam, Archv.
Staff: Prof 1; Other 1. **Subjects:** Local history, literature. **Special Collections:** Christopher Morley Collection (manuscripts and correspondence; 338 items); William Cullen Bryant Collection; Long Island Collection; Roslyn Collection; Mackay Collection; early 19th century business account books; Architecture Preservation Collection. **Holdings:** 5000 books; 100 bound periodical volumes; 350 local maps; 10,000 manuscripts, photographs, and archival materials; 70 oral history tapes. **Subscriptions:** 46 journals and other serials. **Services:** Copying; collection open to the public.

★2301★
Bryant & Stratton Business Institute (Educ)
1259 Central Ave. Phone: (518)437-1802
Albany, NY 12205 Betty Koska
Founded: 1961. **Staff:** Prof 1. **Subjects:** Economics, secretarial practice, accounting, data processing, marketing, business management. **Holdings:** 4900 books; 350 bound periodical volumes. **Subscriptions:** 49 journals and other serials. **Services:** Library not open to the public. **Networks/Consortia:** Member of Capital District Library Council for Reference & Research Resources (CDLC).

★2302★
Bryant & Stratton Business Institute - Resource Center (Educ)
1028 Main St. Phone: (716)884-9120
Buffalo, NY 14202 Philip Mure, Rsrc.Ctr.Supv.
Founded: 1854. **Staff:** Prof 1; Other 1. **Subjects:** Business, economics, electronics, medical and dental assisting, commercial art, computers, secretarial training, travel, and interior design. **Holdings:** 3412 books; pamphlets; audiotapes; video programs; slides; filmstrips; **Subscriptions:** 192 journals and other serials. **Services:** Library open to sudents and faculty. **Publications:** Student Resource Handbook, annual.

★2303★
Bryn Mawr College - Geology Library (Sci-Engr)
Bryn Mawr, PA 19010 Phone: (215)526-5118
Carol Bartholomew, Lib.Asst.
Founded: 1890. **Staff:** Prof 1; Other 1. **Subjects:** General geology, mineralogy, petrology, structural geology, geochemistry, stratigraphic geology, paleontology. **Special Collections:** U.S. Geological Survey publications and maps; Pennsylvania geologic and topographic publications; Geological Survey of Canada publications; guidebooks of geological societies. **Holdings:** 6200 books; 6850 bound periodical volumes; 14,200 surveys and reports; 1000 microfiche. **Subscriptions:** 110 journals and other serials. **Services:** Interlibrary loan; copying; library open to the public with introduction from faculty member. **Automated Operations:** Computerized cataloging. **Computerized Information Services:** OCLC, DIALOG Information Services, BRS Information Technologies. **Networks/Consortia:** Member of PALINET. **Remarks:** FAX: (215)526-5086. **Staff:** Anne Pringle.

★2304★
Bryn Mawr College - Mariam Coffin Canaday Library - Special Collections (Rare Book, Hum)
Bryn Mawr, PA 19110 Phone: (215)526-5272
James Tanis
Founded: 1886. **Staff:** 6. **Subjects:** Incunabula, literature, voyages and travel, botany, illustration of books, private presses. **Special Collections:** The Goodhart Medieval Collection (1040 incunabula); Dillingham & Monegal Collection of Latin American History and Literature; Adelman Collection (materials on John Keats and his Circle, A.E. Housman, R. Hodgson, Claud Lovat Fraser, Thomas and Susan Macdowell Eakins, and Americana); Castle Collection (works on botany and ornithology); Manuscripts Collection (women's studies, British and American literary history); graphics collection (15th century to present). **Holdings:** 33,000 books; 286 linear feet of manuscripts. **Subscriptions:** 12 journals and other serials. **Services:** Library open to scholars with proper identification for reference use only. **Computerized Information Services:** BRS Information Technologies, DIALOG Information Services; internal database. **Networks/Consortia:** Member of Philadelphia Area Consortium of Special Collections Libraries (PACSCL). **Remarks:** FAX: (215)526-7480. **Staff:** Mary S. Leahy, Hd., Rare Bk.Coll.; Seymour Adelman, Rare Bk.Libn.; Leo Dolenski, Mss.Libn.; M. Winslow Lundy, Rare Bk.Cat.; Kimberly Pelkey, Rare Bk.Cat.; Carol W. Campbell, Cur., Coll.; John Dooley, Bibliog.

★2305★
Bryn Mawr Hospital - Clothier Nursing Library (Med)
130 S. Bryn Mawr Ave. Phone: (215)526-3084
Bryn Mawr, PA 19010 L.D. Gundry, Chf.Med.Libn.
Founded: 1953. **Staff:** Prof 2; Other 1. **Subjects:** Nursing, medicine. **Special Collections:** Nursing history. **Holdings:** 3500 books; 1000 bound periodical volumes. **Subscriptions:** 90 journals and other serials. **Services:** Interlibrary loan; copying; library open to the public. **Computerized Information Services:** BRS Information Technologies. **Networks/Consortia:** Member of Delaware Valley Information Consortium (DEVIC). **Remarks:** FAX (215)525-5931. **Staff:** Alexander Kulchar, Med.Libn.; Lunetta Headley, Asst.Med.Libn.

★2306★
Bryn Mawr Hospital - Joseph N. Pew, Jr. Medical Library (Med)
Bryn Mawr, PA 19010 Phone: (215)526-3160
L.D. Gundry, Chf.Med.Libn.
Founded: 1893. **Staff:** Prof 4; Other 3. **Subjects:** Medicine, surgery, allied health sciences. **Holdings:** 3000 books; 5000 bound periodical volumes. **Subscriptions:** 200 journals and other serials. **Services:** Interlibrary loan; copying; library open to the public. **Computerized Information Services:** BRS Information Technologies. **Networks/Consortia:** Member of Delaware Valley Information Consortium (DEVIC). **Remarks:** FAX: (215)525-5931. **Staff:** Alexander Kulchar, Med.Libn.; Doris Mohn, Cat.

★2307★
BT North America Inc. - Technical Library (Info Sci)
2560 N. 1st St.
P.O. Box 49019 Phone: (408)922-6720
San Jose, CA 95161-9019 Janis Patellaro, Libn./Supv.
Founded: 1974. **Staff:** Prof 1; Other 1. **Subjects:** Data communications, satellites, telecommunications, software systems. **Holdings:** 1200 books; 2000 technical reports; 17 cases of manuals and archives; 1000 microfiche; 60 video cassettes of technology seminars. **Subscriptions:** 160 journals and other serials; 12 newspapers. **Services:** Interlibrary loan; library not open to the public. **Automated Operations:** Computerized cataloging. **Computerized Information Services:** DIALOG Information Services; Dialcom, Inc. TYMNET (electronic mail services). **Networks/Consortia:** Member of CLASS, South Bay Cooperative Library System (SBCLS). **Publications:** Technical Library Newsletter, quarterly. **Remarks:** FAX: (408)922-6170. Electronic mail address(es): Janis.Patellaro@Dialcom.Tymnet.Com (Dialcom, Inc.); JanisP@Tymnet.Com (Tymnet). BT North America, Inc. is a subsidiary of British Telecommunications PLC. **Formerly:** BT Tymnet Inc. **Staff:** Mary Proffitt.

★2308★
(Bucaramanga) El Biblioteca Centro Colombo-Americano - USIS Collection (Educ)
Carrera 22, No.37-74
Bucaramanga, Colombia Phone: 976 457816
Staff: 2. **Holdings:** 8000 books; 35 bound periodical volumes. **Subscriptions:** 25 journals and other serials; 4 newspapers. **Services:** Interlibrary loan; copying; library open to the public. **Remarks:** FAX: 976 453374. Maintained or supported by the U.S. Information Agency. Focus is on materials that will assist peoples outside the United States to learn about the United States, its people, history, culture, political processes, and social milieux.

Joseph F. Bucci Health Sciences Library
See: **Frick Community Health Center** (6166)

★2309★
Buchanan County Public School - Special Collections (Hist)
Rte. 2, Box 3 Phone: (703)935-6581
Grundy, VA 24614 Patricia Hatfield, Libn.
Founded: 1961. **Staff:** Prof 1; Other 8. **Subjects:** Local history, genealogy. **Special Collections:** Edgar Rice Burroughs Collection (First editions of Tarzan series and other titles). **Holdings:** 65,000 books; 150 bound periodical volumes; 5 microfiche; 10 reels of microfilm. **Subscriptions:** 130 journals and other serials; 10 newspapers. **Services:** Interlibrary loan; copying; library open to the public. **Computerized Information Services:** WILSONDISC. **Remarks:** FAX: (703)935-6292.

★2310★
Buchanan, Ingersoll P.C. - Library (Law)
600 Grant St., 57th Fl. Phone: (412)562-1693
Pittsburgh, PA 15219 Betsey Laffey, Info.Mgr.
Staff: Prof 2; Other 2. **Subjects:** Law - corporate, taxation, pensions, labor, general, banking, health care. **Holdings:** 24,000 books. **Services:** Library not open to the public. **Computerized Information Services:** LEXIS, WESTLAW, DIALOG Information Services. **Staff:** Lori Zilla, Asst.Libn.

★2311★
James Buchanan Foundation for the Preservation of Wheatland - Library (Hist)
1120 Marietta Ave. Phone: (717)392-8721
Lancaster, PA 17603 Sally Smith Cahalan, Dir.
Founded: 1936. **Staff:** 2. **Subjects:** 19th century American history. **Holdings:** Figures not available. **Publications:** Newsletter, biennial. **Remarks:** Wheatland is the restored Federal mansion residence of President James Buchanan (1857-1861). In addition to other period rooms, it contains a small, period library of books owned by President Buchanan.

★2312★
(Bucharest) Biblioteca Americana - USIS Library (Educ)
Str. Alexandru Sahia, No. 7-9
70201 Bucharest, Romania
Remarks: Maintained or supported by the U.S. Information Agency. Focus is on materials that will assist peoples outside the United States to learn about the United States, its people, history, culture, political processes, and social milieux.

Bucharest University - Institute for Southeast European Studies
See: **Institute for Southeast European Studies** (7980)

★2313★
Pearl S. Buck Birthplace Foundation - Historic House Museum (Hum)
Box 126 Phone: (304)456-4430
Hillsboro, WV 24946 Mrs. E.W. Rexrode, Pres.
Staff: 5. **Special Collections:** Works by and about Pearl S. Buck in English and foreign languages; original manuscripts of Pearl S. Buck (323 cataloged). **Holdings:** 500 books; tapes of seminars and various speeches involving Pearl S. Buck. **Services:** Museum open to the public. **Publications:** Periodical information letters to members of the foundation. **Remarks:** Manuscripts remain stored at West Virginia Wesleyan College, Buckhannon, WV, until suitable storage can be made available at Hillsboro. Manuscripts accessible to researchers with specific requirements for care and usage.

Christopher Buckley, Jr. Library
See: **U.S. Navy - Naval Postgraduate School - Dudley Knox Library** (17868)

★2314★
Buckman Laboratories International - Technical Information Center (Sci-Engr)
1256 N. McLean Blvd. Phone: (901)278-0330
Memphis, TN 38108 W. Ellen McDonell, Mgr.
Staff: Prof 3; Other 3. **Subjects:** Chemistry, microbiology, corrosion, pulp and paper, water treatment, agriculture. **Special Collections:** National Technical Information Service (NTIS) Collection in Environmental Sciences. **Holdings:** 11,000 books; 300 bound periodical volumes; U.S. and foreign patents; microfilm; reports. **Subscriptions:** 737 journals and other serials. **Services:** Interlibrary loan; center not open to the public. **Automated Operations:** Computerized cataloging, acquisitions, serials, and circulation. **Computerized Information Services:** DIALOG Information Services, STN International, PFDS Online, MEDLARS, Toxicology Data Network (TOXNET), National Pesticide Information Retrieval System (NPIRS), Dow Jones News/Retrieval, Dun & Bradstreet Business Credit Services. **Networks/Consortia:** Member of Association of Memphis Area Health Science Libraries (AMAHSL), SOLINET. **Remarks:** FAX: (901)276-5343. Telex: 6828020.

★2315★
Bucknell University - Ellen Clarke Bertrand Library - Special Collections (Hum)
Lewisburg, PA 17837 Phone: (717)524-1557
Ann de Klerk, Dir.
Founded: 1846. **Staff:** Prof 20.75; Other 25. **Subjects:** Irish authors; fine presses. **Special Collections:** Oliver S. Gogarty (letters and manuscripts; 5 linear feet); D.H. Lawrence (5 items); William Butler Yeats (letters); George Bernard Shaw (letters and pamphlets; 5 boxes). **Holdings:** 5500 volumes; 197 literary manuscripts and family papers; 1800 archival items. **Services:** Interlibrary loan; copying; library open to the public for reference use only. **Automated Operations:** Computerized public access catalog, cataloging, acquisitions, and circulation. **Computerized Information Services:** OCLC; BITNET (electronic mail service). Contact Person: Jane Burchfield. **Networks/Consortia:** Member of Associated College Libraries of Central Pennsylvania (ACLCP), PALINET, Susquehanna Library Cooperative. **Publications:** Ellen Clarke Bertrand Library Limited Edition Series (The Man Who Loved Islands, Nine Answers, Ballylee, The Tower Poem); The Wood Engravings of John DePol; Hand Bookbinding: Art and Craft; My Dear Gogarty. **Remarks:** FAX: (717)524-1237.

★2316★
Bucknell University - Ellen Clarke Bertrand Library - University Archives (Hist)
Lewisburg, PA 17837 Phone: (717)524-3101
Ann DeKlerk, Lib.Dir.
Staff: Prof 1; Other 1. **Subjects:** Bucknell University and local history. **Special Collections:** David Jayne Hill Collection, U.S. Diplomatic Corps; university records and publications; N.F. Davis photographs (covered bridges, early transportation, nature studies); 51st Regiment of the Pennsylvania Volunteers (military documents; personal papers). **Holdings:** 2500 books; 160 bound periodical volumes; 4050 other cataloged items. **Services:** Interlibrary loan; copying (limited); archives open to the public for reference use only. **Remarks:** Alternate telephone number(s): (717)524-1557.

Buckner News Alliance - Minot Daily News
See: **Minot Daily News** (10495)

★2317★
Bucks County Courier Times - Library (Publ)
8400 Rte. 13 Phone: (215)949-4169
Levittown, PA 19057-5198 Susan Y. Ditterline, Libn./Supv.
Founded: 1965. **Staff:** Prof 1; Other 4. **Subjects:** Newspaper reference topics. **Holdings:** 29,600. Newspaper clippings; photographs; directories; pamphlets; reference books; microfilm. **Subscriptions:** 15 journals and other serials. **Services:** Interlibrary loan; library not open to the public. **Remarks:** FAX: (215)949-4122.

★2318★
Bucks County Historical Society - Spruance Library (Hist)
84 S. Pine St. Phone: (215)345-0210
Doylestown, PA 18901 Terry A. McNealy, Libn.
Founded: 1880. **Staff:** Prof 1. **Subjects:** Bucks County history and genealogy, history of crafts and technology. **Special Collections:** Manuscript collections concerned largely with Bucks County and its people; Durham Furnace account books; craftsmen's account books; turnpike records; handwritten school books. **Holdings:** 18,000 volumes; 1000 cubic feet of Bucks County Archives. **Subscriptions:** 30 journals and other serials. **Services:** Copying; library open to the public. **Remarks:** FAX: (215)230-0823.

★2319★
Bucks County Law Library (Law)
Court House Phone: (215)348-6023
Doylestown, PA 18901 Katharine P. Lehnig, Lib.Dir.
Staff: Prof 2; Other 1. **Subjects:** Law. **Holdings:** 30,500 volumes. **Subscriptions:** 124 journals and other serials. **Services:** Interlibrary loan; copying; library open to Bucks County residents for reference use. **Automated Operations:** Computerized circulation. **Computerized Information Services:** WESTLAW. Performs searches on fee basis. **Publications:** Newsletter, semiannual. **Remarks:** FAX: (215)348-6827.

★2320★
Bucks County Planning Commission - BCPC Staff Library (Plan)
The Almshouse
Neshaminy Manor Center Phone: (215)345-3431
Doylestown, PA 18901 Cheryl Zabinski, Libn.
Founded: 1951. **Staff:** Prof 1. **Subjects:** Bucks County demographics, housing, land use planning, water resources and solid waste management, community development, agricultural preservation, transportation, open space and recreation. **Special Collections:** Bucks County Municipal Documents (300); Bucks County Demographics (25 volumes). **Holdings:** 8000 books; 50 bound periodical volumes; 200 pamphlets; 100 microfiche; 100 maps. **Subscriptions:** 100 journals and other serials; 3 newspapers. **Services:** Copying; library open to the public for reference use only. **Publications:** Publications List; newsletter. **Remarks:** FAX: (215)345-3886.

★2321★
Budapest - Museum of Applied Arts - Library (Art)
Ulloi u 33-37 Phone: 1 175222
H-1091 Budapest, Hungary Esther Tiszavari, Lib.Hd.
Founded: 1874. **Staff:** Prof 2; Other 3. **Subjects:** Applied and decorative arts, crafts, art history, museology, modern art, art nouveau, Hungarian and world history. **Special Collections:** Hungarian Applied Arts periodicals (1885 to present); Exhibition catalogs of the museum (1890 to present); literature of World Exhibitions. **Holdings:** 30,000 books; 10,000 bound periodical volumes; archives. **Subscriptions:** 460 journals and other serials. **Services:** Interlibrary loan; copying; library open to the public for reference use only. **Remarks:** FAX: 1 1175838. **Also Known As:** Iparmuveszeti Muzeum - Konyvtar.

W.A. Budden Memorial Library
See: **Western States Chiropractic College** (20301)

★2322★
Buddhist Information Bureau - Library (Rel-Phil)
5 Muzeum St. Phone: 1 189258
H-1088 Budapest, Hungary Dr. Ernest Hetenyi, Ed.
Founded: 1991. **Subjects:** Buddhism. **Special Collections:** Photograph archive; Oriental lexicon collection; Tibetan block-prints collection. **Holdings:** 4000 volumes. **Computerized Information Services:** Internal databases. **Remarks:** FAX: 1 189258. **Formerly:** Buddhist Mission - Library. **Also Known As:** Buddhista Tajekoztato Iroda.

Buddhista Tajekoztato Iroda
See: **Buddhist Information Bureau - Library** (2322)

William P. Budner Library
See: **Temple Emanu-El** (16102)

★2323★
Buena Vista College - L.E. & E.L. Ballou Library - Special Collections (Educ)
Storm Lake, IA 50588 Phone: (712)749-2127
James R. Kennedy, Lib.Dir.
Founded: 1891. **Staff:** 6. **Holdings:** Iowa authors' books; curriculum collection; state, local, and college history; textbooks; juvenile books. **Services:** Interlibrary loan; copying; collections open to the public. **Automated Operations:** Computerized cataloging. **Computerized Information Services:** DIALOG Information Services, ABI/INFORM; CD-ROMs (Business Periodicals Ondisc, Newspaper Abstracts, Compact Disclosure, PsycLIT, ERIC); InterNet (electronic mail service). Performs searches on fee basis. Contact Person: Jodie Morin, Ref.Libn. **Networks/Consortia:** Member of Bibliographical Center for Research, Rocky Mountain Region, Inc. (BCR). **Remarks:** FAX: (712)749-2059. Electronic mail address(es): JIMK@BVC.EDU (InterNet).

Buenger Memorial Library
See: **Concordia College** (4113)

★2324★
(Buenos Aires) Museo de Arte Moderno - Biblioteca (Art)
Corrientes 1530, 7th Fl.
1042 Buenos Aires, Bs. As., Argentina
Phone: 46 9426
Monica E. Bergman, Dir., Info.Div.
Subjects: Art, Argentinian artists, foreign artists. **Special Collections:** Archivo Jose Leon Pagano (Argentine art; aboriginal times to 1937). **Holdings:** 385 books; 35 bound periodical volumes; 16 AV programs; 2000 catalogs; 2500 artists' portfolios. **Services:** Library open to the public. **Remarks:** Alternate telephone number(s): 49 4796.

(Buenos Aires) USIS Library
See: **Lincoln Center - (Buenos Aires) USIS Library** (9172)

★2325★
Buffalo Bill Historical Center - McCracken Research Library (Hist)
Box 1000
Cody, WY 82414
Phone: (307)587-4771
Christina K. Stopka, Libn./Archv.
Founded: 1980. **Staff:** Prof 1; Other 1. **Subjects:** Western American history and art, Indians of North America, firearms. **Special Collections:** William F. Cody Collection; Valley Ranch manuscript collection; Charles Belden Photo Collection; Mercaldo Photo Archives of Western subjects; photographs of noted Indians, military leaders, Indian campaigns; Winchester Repeating Arms Company archives; Yellowstone National Park (100 volumes; maps, stereoviews, and other nonbook items); Frederic Remington Illustrations (200 books; clippings; ephemera; reference photographs); Frank Tenney Johnson Archives; Joseph H. Sharp Archives; W.H.D. Koerner Studio Archives. **Holdings:** 15,000 volumes; 30 volumes of press clippings; motion picture films; 616 reels of microfilm and 7000 books in the Yale Western Americana microfilm collection; 4000 slides; vertical files of gallery, museum, artist files, subject files. **Subscriptions:** 40 journals and other serials. **Services:** Interlibrary loan; copying; library open to qualified researchers by appointment; will answer walk-in reference questions, and telephone and mail inquiries. **Computerized Information Services:** DIALOG Information Services; ARGUS, Frederic Remington Catalog Raissone (internal databases). **Publications:** Finding guides for the Vincent Mercaldo Photograph Collection; The Charles Belden Photograph Collection; William F. Cody Collection; Yellowstone Park Collection; BBHC publications; finding guides for Johnson & Sharp collections. **Remarks:** FAX: (307)587-5714.

★2326★
Buffalo Bill Memorial Museum - Information Center (Hist)
987 1/2 Lookout Mountain Rd.
Golden, CO 80401
Phone: (303)526-0744
Lynn M. Slouka, Cur.
Founded: 1921. **Staff:** 1. **Subjects:** William F. Cody, Old American West. **Holdings:** 300 books; 220 pamphlets; 450 periodicals; 800 documents; 1500 photographs. **Services:** Copying; center open to the public on request. **Remarks:** Affiliated with the city and county of Denver.

★2327★
Buffalo Color Corporation - Technical Library (Sci-Engr)
Box 7027
Buffalo, NY 14240
Phone: (716)827-4549
Carol Laschinger, Libn.
Subjects: Chemistry - dyes, organic, analytical; industrial hygiene. **Holdings:** 1200 books. **Subscriptions:** 35 journals and other serials. **Services:** Interlibrary loan, library not open to the public.

★2328★
Buffalo & Erie County Historical Society - Library (Hist)
25 Nottingham Ct.
Buffalo, NY 14216
Phone: (716)873-9644
Mary F. Bell, Dir., Lib. & Archv.
Founded: 1862. **Staff:** Prof 2; Other 1. **Subjects:** City of Buffalo, Erie County, Western New York, Niagara Frontier, military history. **Special Collections:** Manuscript collections of Millard Fillmore; manuscript collections of Peter B. Porter; War of 1812 materials; Niagara Falls; Erie Canal; Wilbur Porterfield photographic collection. **Holdings:** 40,000 bound volumes; 50,000 periodicals and ephemera; manuscript collections of over 500,000 separate items; iconographic collections of over 130,000 separate items; large clipping file; large scrapbook collection; local newspapers on microfilm. **Subscriptions:** 27 journals and other serials. **Services:** Interlibrary loan; copying (both limited); limited staff research for appropriate inquiries; library open to the public for reference use only. **Special Indexes:** All society publications and newspapers received are indexed. **Staff:** Patricia Virgil, Asst.Libn.

★2329★
Buffalo & Erie County Public Library - Business and Labor Department (Bus-Fin)
Lafayette Square
Buffalo, NY 14203
Phone: (716)858-7096
Joyce M. Davoli, Hd.
Founded: 1952. **Staff:** Prof 8; Other 3. **Subjects:** Economics, banking, finance, investments, accounting, statistics, real estate, advertising, insurance, transportation, small business, labor. **Special Collections:** Federal Census Depository; New York State Data Affiliate (unpublished federal census data); Western New York Mortgage Disclosure Data Depository; Small Business Collection; Export-Import Collection. **Holdings:** 70,459 books; 11,353 bound periodical volumes; state industrial, trade, and foreign directories; 27 VF cabinets; newspapers and periodicals on microfilm; annual reports of companies on the New York and American Stock Exchanges; local company information file. **Subscriptions:** 1058 journals and other serials. **Services:** Interlibrary loan; copying; department open to the public. **Automated Operations:** Computerized cataloging, acquisitions, serials, and circulation. **Computerized Information Services:** Western New York Newspaper Index, Dow Jones News/Retrieval, DIALOG Information Services; CD-ROMs (Business Periodicals Index, InfoTrac, COMPACT D/SEC, Compact Disclosure Canada, American Business Disk, Dun's Million Dollar Disc, National Trade Data Base, PTS F&S Indexes); internal database. Performs searches on fee basis. Contact Person: Ron Padwater, telephone 858-7097. **Remarks:** FAX: (716)858-7237.

★2330★
Buffalo & Erie County Public Library - Education, Sociology, Philosophy & Religion Department (Educ)
Lafayette Square
Buffalo, NY 14203
Phone: (716)858-7111
Mary Jane Smith, Hd.
Staff: Prof 4; Other 2. **Subjects:** Education, sociology, social welfare, philosophy, psychology, religion, history of religions. **Special Collections:** CASA (alcohol and substance abuse collection; 1736 volumes). **Holdings:** 133,768 books; 12,000 bound periodical volumes; 8 VF drawers. **Subscriptions:** 368 journals and other serials. **Services:** Interlibrary loan; copying. **Computerized Information Services:** DIALOG Information Services; InfoTrac; CD-ROM (Books in Print Plus). Performs searches on fee basis. **Remarks:** FAX: (716)858-6211. **Staff:** Tom Morrissey; Suzanne O'Shea; Bruce Weymouth.

★2331★
Buffalo & Erie County Public Library - Film and Video Department (Aud-Vis)
Lafayette Square
Buffalo, NY 14203
Phone: (716)858-7188
Robert M. Gurn, Hd.
Staff: Prof 1; Other 6. **Holdings:** 3000 films; 3500 video cassettes. **Services:** Department open to the public. **Special Catalogs:** Video catalog. **Remarks:** FAX: (716)858-6211.

★2332★
Buffalo & Erie County Public Library - History, Travel and Government Department (Hist)
Lafayette Square
Buffalo, NY 14203
Phone: (716)858-7102
Ruth Willet, Dept.Hd.
Founded: 1836. **Staff:** Prof 4; Other 3. **Subjects:** History, travel, government, sports, archeology, geography, numismatics. **Special Collections:** Local history (94 VF drawers); county, state, town histories; genealogy and heraldry. **Holdings:** 373,500 books; 12,750 bound periodical volumes; 80,000 maps. **Subscriptions:** 800 journals and other serials; 16 newspapers. **Services:** Interlibrary loan; copying. **Computerized Information Services:** DIALOG Information Services; InfoTrac, Social Sciences Index; Readers Guide Abstracts (internal database) **Special Indexes:** Local history newspaper index (online). **Remarks:** FAX: (716)858-6211.

★2333★
Buffalo & Erie County Public Library - Language, Literature and Arts Department (Hum)
Lafayette Square
Buffalo, NY 14203
Phone: (716)858-7111
Mary Jane Smith, Hd.
Staff: Prof 3; Other 2. **Subjects:** Fine arts and architecture, language, linguistics, journalism, literature, literary texts, history and criticism. **Holdings:** 246,949 books; 8062 bound periodical volumes; 6461 volumes of foreign fiction; 2 VF drawers. **Subscriptions:** 145 journals and other serials. **Services:** Interlibrary loan; copying. **Computerized Information Services:** DIALOG Information Services; InfoTrac; CD-ROMs. **Remarks:** FAX: (716)858-6211. **Staff:** Peter T. Brand; Marie M. Brewster; Karen P. Miller.

★2334★
Buffalo & Erie County Public Library - Music Department (Mus)
Lafayette Square Phone: (716)858-7121
Buffalo, NY 14203 Norma Jean Lamb, Hd.
Founded: 1922. **Staff:** Prof 3; Other 2. **Subjects:** Music and dance. **Special Collections:** 19th century American music (sheet music; bound volumes; songsters; tunebooks; broadsides). **Holdings:** 92,000 books and scores; 2200 bound periodical volumes; 117,300 song sheets; 2600 orchestral scores and parts; manuscripts of 8 contemporary composers; 106,200 phonograph records, tapes, audio cassettes, compact discs. **Subscriptions:** 250 journals and other serials. **Services:** Interlibrary loan; copying. **Special Indexes:** Title index to song sheets and folios (card). **Remarks:** FAX: (716)858-6211.

★2335★
Buffalo & Erie County Public Library - Rare Book Room (Rare Book)
Lafayette Square Phone: (716)858-7118
Buffalo, NY 14203 William H. Loos, Cur.
Founded: 1944. **Staff:** Prof 1; Other 1. **Subjects:** American history and literature, English literature, private press books, American almanacs, early Bibles, bibliography, costume and colorplate books, early medicine and science, music, minstrel song books, Shakers, antislavery movement, Western New York imprints and history. **Special Collections:** James Fenimore Cooper; Henry James; Dard Hunter; Julius J. Lankes; Elbert Hubbard and the Roycroft Press; Mark Twain; editions, translations, and manuscript of Huckleberry Finn; history of printing (43 incunabula); books illustrated with original photographs (210 titles); Thomas D. Mahoney Collection of Niagara Falls Guidebooks (310 titles); Edward F. Ellis Collections of Rip Van Winkle (210 titles) and ABC Books (440 titles); George Nathan Newman Collection of English Coaching Prints (26) ; American broadside ballads (2150). **Holdings:** 40,000 books; 4500 literary and historic manuscripts and letters; 234 Niagara Falls prints; 3820 posters, mostly World Wars I and II. **Services:** Copying (limited); room open to the public. **Special Catalogs:** Checklists of Short Title Catalog, Wing, Evans, and Shaker holdings available. **Remarks:** FAX: (716)858-6211.

★2336★
Buffalo & Erie County Public Library - Science and Technology Department (Sci-Engr)
Lafayette Square Phone: (716)858-7101
Buffalo, NY 14203 Sharon L. Edward, Hd.Libn.
Staff: Prof 7; Other 3. **Subjects:** Engineering, mathematics, life sciences, earth sciences, agriculture, astronomy, military science, naval science, computer science and technology. **Holdings:** 225,000 books; 48,000 bound periodical volumes; U.S. patents, 1871 to present. **Subscriptions:** 1850 standards, journals, and other serials. **Services:** Interlibrary loan; copying. **Computerized Information Services:** DIALOG Information Services, U.S. Patent Classification System, Chemical Information Systems, Inc. (CIS); CD-ROMs (U.S. Patent Classification System, OCLC GPO Monthly Catalog, InfoTrac, Toxic Chemical Release Inventory, Health Index). Performs searches on fee basis. **Special Indexes:** Western New York Geology Index; scientific biography index. **Remarks:** FAX: (716)858-7237.

★2337★
Buffalo General Hospital, Inc. - A.H. Aaron Health Sciences Library (Med)
100 High St. Phone: (716)845-2878
Buffalo, NY 14203 Wentsing Liu, Lib.Dir.
Founded: 1920. **Staff:** Prof 2; Other 2. **Subjects:** Medicine, surgery, dentistry, nursing, pharmacology. **Special Collections:** Maisel Collection (gastroenterology); Norcross Collection (rheumatology); orthopedics. **Holdings:** 3200 books; 10,000 bound periodical volumes; Audio-Digest tapes on internal medicine and surgery; 950 AV programs. **Subscriptions:** 400 journals and other serials. **Services:** Interlibrary loan; copying; library open to the public for reference use only. **Automated Operations:** Computerized cataloging and acquisitions. **Computerized Information Services:** MEDLARS, BRS Information Technologies, DIALOG Information Services; CD-ROM (MEDLINE). **Networks/Consortia:** Member of Library Consortium of Health Institutions in Buffalo (LCHIB), Western New York Library Resources Council (WNYLRC). **Remarks:** FAX: (716)845-1527. **Staff:** Barbara Ciambor, Med.Libn.

★2338★
The Buffalo News - Library (Publ)
1 News Plaza
Box 100 Phone: (716)849-4401
Buffalo, NY 14240 Elliot Shapiro, Electronic Sys.Dir.
Founded: 1920. **Staff:** Prof 2; Other 3. **Subjects:** Newspaper reference topics. **Special Collections:** Buffalo and Western New York history. **Holdings:** 500 volumes; pictures; clippings; maps; microfilm. **Services:** Library open to qualified researchers only with permission from editor. **Computerized Information Services:** VU/TEXT Information Services. **Remarks:** (716)856-5150.

★2339★
Buffalo Psychiatric Center - BPC Library (Med)
400 Forest Ave. Phone: (716)885-2261
Buffalo, NY 14213 Mark Wudyka
Staff: Prof 1; Other 1. **Subjects:** Psychiatry, psychology, psychiatric nursing. **Holdings:** 6000 books; clippings. **Services:** Interlibrary loan; copying; library open to the public at librarian's discretion.

★2340★
Buffalo Society of Natural Sciences - Research Library (Sci-Engr, Biol Sci)
Buffalo Museum of Science
Humboldt Pkwy. Phone: (716)896-5200
Buffalo, NY 14211 Lisa A. Seivert, Libn.
Founded: 1861. **Staff:** Prof 1; Other 1. **Subjects:** Anthropology, astronomy, geology, botany, zoology. **Special Collections:** Milestones of Science (200 items); Elizabeth W. Hamlin Oriental Library of Art and Archaeology (900 books). **Holdings:** 14,000 books; 28,000 bound periodical volumes; archival material; manuscripts; 7500 maps; 1750 microforms. **Subscriptions:** 600 journals and other serials. **Services:** Interlibrary loan; copying (limited); library open to the public by appointment. **Automated Operations:** Computerized cataloging. **Computerized Information Services:** OCLC. **Networks/Consortia:** Member of Western New York Library Resources Council (WNYLRC), SUNY/OCLC Library Network. **Special Catalogs:** Milestones of Science Catalog.

Buhl Library
See: **University of Pittsburgh - School of Social Work** (19224)

★2341★
Building Owners and Managers Association International - Library (Bus-Fin)
1201 New York Ave., N.W., Suite 300 Phone: (202)408-2662
Washington, DC 20005 Mark W. Hurwitz, CAE, Exec. V.P.
Founded: 1908. **Staff:** 35. **Subjects:** Owning, managing, developing, and investing in commercial office buildings. **Holdings:** 1500 volumes. **Services:** Library not open to the public. **Publications:** Skylines magazine. **Remarks:** FAX: (202)371-0181. **Also Known As:** BOMA. **Staff:** Henry Chamberlain, V.P., Commun.; Jeanie Markel, Ed.

★2342★
Building Service Contractors Association International - Information Central (Bus-Fin)
10201 Lee Hwy., Suite 225 Phone: (703)359-7090
Fairfax, VA 22030-2202 Sharon A. Ferraro, Dir., Membership Serv.
Staff: Prof 13; Other 5. **Subjects:** Janitorial companies, bidding, carpet and floor care, marketing. **Holdings:** Figures not available. **Services:** Service not open to the public. **Publications:** List of publications - available on request. **Remarks:** FAX: (703)352-0493. Toll-free telephone number(s): (800)368-3414. **Staff:** Leslie Fillebrown, Membership Serv.Asst.

★2343★
Building Services Research and Information Association - BSRIA Information Centre (Plan)
Old Bracknell Ln., W. Phone: 344 426511
Bracknell, Berkshire RG12 4AH, England S.R. Loyd, Info.Off.
Staff: Prof 5. **Subjects:** Mechanical and electrical services associated with buildings; heating; air conditioning; ventilation; plumbing and sanitation; lighting and power; controls and instrumentation; corrosion; heat transfer

and fluid control; energy management and sources; alternative energy; indoor environment; noise and vibration; thermal and sound insulation; site and office organization; fire protection. **Holdings:** 6000 bound volumes; 90,000 reports, standards, and other pamphlets. **Subscriptions:** 300 journals and other serials. **Services:** Copying; document delivery; center open to the public with restrictions. **Computerized Information Services:** ESA/IRS; produces IBSEDEX database, ASHRAE database, and Health and Buildings Database. Performs searches on fee basis. **Publications:** International Building Services Abstracts, bimonthly with annual cumulative author/subject indexes; Engineering Services Management, bimonthly; Library Bulletin, quarterly - free to members and other libraries. **Remarks:** FAX: 344 487575.

(Bujumbura) USIS Library
See: **Bibliotheque Martin Luther King, Jr.** (1827)

Charles Bukowski Archives
See: **University of Southern California - Library - Department of Special Collections - American Literature Collection** (19338)

H.C. Buley Library
See: **Southern Connecticut State University** (15482)

★ 2344 ★
Bulgaria - Academy of Agriculture - Fruit Growing Institute - Library (Agri)
12 Ostromila — Phone: 32 778081
BG-4004 Plovdiv, Bulgaria — Lidia Petrova, Libn.
Founded: 1964. **Staff:** 2. **Subjects:** Mechanization of fruit-growing processes; agro-technology; field management; plant protection; breeding, propagation, physiology, economics of fruit-growing. **Holdings:** 27,000 volumes. **Subscriptions:** 41 journals and other serials; 17 newspapers. **Services:** Interlibrary loan; copying; library open to the public. **Publications:** Information Bulletin. **Special Indexes:** Index of scientific publications, annual. **Remarks:** FAX: 32 265747. Telex: 44609. **Formerly:** Bulgaria - National Agro-Industrial Union - Research Institute on Fruit Growing - Library. **Staff:** Sophia Manolova, Libn.

★ 2345 ★
Bulgaria - Committee of Culture - St. Cyril and St. Methodius National Library (Area-Ethnic, Info Sci)
Blvd. Tolbuhin 11 — Phone: 2 88-28-11
BG-1504 Sofia, Bulgaria — Dr. Elena Janakieva, Hd., Info.Ctr.
Founded: 1878. **Staff:** 450. **Subjects:** General collection. **Special Collections:** Music collection (66,715 items); graphic arts collection (151,313 items); archival collection (3.03 million archival materials); official publications (390,000). **Holdings:** 1,469,667 books; 690,095 bound periodical volumes; 290,597 patents; 24,000 tapes and phonograph records; 381,469 microforms; 10,262 cartographic materials; 18,699 unpublished materials; 5475 manuscripts. **Subscriptions:** 10,638 journals and other serials. **Services:** Interlibrary loan; copying; library open to the public with restrictions. **Publications:** National Bibliography of Bulgaria; Proceedings of the Cyril and Methodius National Library, annual; Bibliotekar, monthly. **Special Indexes:** Index of Bulgarian books; index of Bulgarian periodicals. **Remarks:** FAX: 2 881600. Telex: 22432 NATLIB. Serves as the National Library of Bulgaria.

★ 2346 ★
Bulgaria - Medical Academy - Center for Scientific Information in Medicine and Public Health - Central Medical Library (Med)
1 Georgi Sofijski St.
BG-1431 Sofia, Bulgaria — Phone: 2 522342
Subjects: Medicine, public health. **Holdings:** 706,356 bound volumes. **Subscriptions:** 3845 journals and other serials. **Services:** SDI; library open to the public. **Computerized Information Services:** MEDIK, Chorisont, Sirena, INIS (International Nuclear Information System), BIOSIS, INSPEC, COMPENDEX, CIS, EMBASE, VINITI, MEDLINE. Performs searches on fee basis. **Publications:** Bibliographies. **Also Known As:** Tsentar za Nauchna Informacija po Meditsina i Zdraveopazvane.

★ 2347 ★
Bulgaria - Medical Faculty - Department of Dermatology and Venereology - Library (Med)
1 Georgi Sofijski St. — Phone: 51-73-42
BG-1431 Sofia, Bulgaria — Rene Todorova, Libn.
Founded: 1920. **Staff:** 1. **Subjects:** Dermatology, allergies, occupational and oncological dermatoses, venereology, physiotherapy. **Holdings:** 10,000 volumes. **Services:** Library open to the public with restrictions. **Computerized Information Services:** MEDLARS, BIOSIS, Inis, Excerpta Medica, and others. **Formerly:** Bulgaria - Medical Academy - Institute of Dermatology and Venereology. **Staff:** V. Trenkova; R. Menkadgieva; S. Nedkova.

Bulgaria - Ministry of National Education - National Sports Academy
See: **Bulgaria - National Sports Academy** (2350)

Bulgaria - Ministry of National Education - Technical University - Library
See: **Technical University** (16032)

★ 2348 ★
Bulgaria - National Agro-Industrial Union - Agricultural Academy - Center for Scientific, Technical and Economic Information - Central Agricultural Library (Agri)
125 Lenin Blvd., Block No. 1
BG-1113 Sofia, Bulgaria — Phone: 74371
Subjects: Agriculture, animal husbandry, veterinary medicine, agronomy, food industry. **Holdings:** 288,000 volumes; reports; dissertations; translations; microfilm; miscellanea. **Subscriptions:** 3000 journals and other serials. **Services:** Interlibrary loan; SDI; library open to government agencies. **Computerized Information Services:** BIOSIS, INIS (International Nuclear Information System), COMPENDEX, AGRIS. Performs searches on fee basis. **Publications:** Bibliographies. **Remarks:** Telex: 23083. **Also Known As:** Natsionalen Agrarno-Promishlen Suyuz - Selskostopanska Akademiya - Tsentur za Naouchno-Technicheska i Ikonomicheska Infomatsiya.

★ 2349 ★
Bulgaria - National Agro-Industrial Union - Institute of Mechanization & Electrification of Agriculture - Library (Agri)
3 Chaussee Bankja St. — Phone: 2-52-41
BG-1331 Sofia, Bulgaria — Antoaneta Andonova, Libn.
Founded: 1965. **Staff:** 1. **Subjects:** Agricultural machinery. **Holdings:** 22,132 volumes. **Subscriptions:** 27 journals and other serials; 18 newspapers. **Services:** Interlibrary loan; library open to the public. **Remarks:** FAX: 247842. Telex: 22805; 22520.

Bulgaria - National Agro-Industrial Union - Research Institute on Fruit Growing - Library
See: **Bulgaria - Academy of Agriculture** (2344)

★ 2350 ★
Bulgaria - National Sports Academy - Library (Rec, Educ)
1 Tina Kirkova St. — Phone: 2 879620
Sofia, Bulgaria — M. Karparova, Libn.
Founded: 1942. **Staff:** 7. **Subjects:** Physical culture and sports - medicine, physiology, psychology, history, organization and managment. **Holdings:** 119,000 volumes. **Subscriptions:** 501 journals and other serials. **Services:** Interlibrary loan; library open to the public. **Remarks:** FAX: 2 883064. Maintained by Bulgaria - Ministry of National Education. **Formerly:** Georgi Dimitrov Higher Institute of Physical Culture. **Also Known As:** Natsionalna Sportna Academia. **Staff:** Emilia Simova; Silvia Sapunarova; Tsenka Kancheva; Blaga Beljakova; Gabriela Nikolova; Radoslava Stoimenova.

Bulgaria - Natsionalna Sportna Academia
See: **Bulgaria - National Sports Academy** (2350)

★2351★
Bulgarian Academy of Sciences - Center for Research in Linguistics and Literature - Library (Area-Ethnic, Hum)
52 Capaev St.
BG-1113 Sofia, Bulgaria Phone: 2 72-20-58
Subjects: History of Bulgarian language and literature, Bulgarian dialects, Slavic literature, Balkan linguistics, comparative linguistics and literature. **Holdings:** 100,000 volumes. **Staff:** Marietta Cukova, Libn.; Ivanka Manova, Libn.

★2352★
Bulimia Anorexia Nervosa Association - Library (Med)
c/o Psychological Services
University of Windsor
401 Sunset Ave. Phone: (519)253-7545
Windsor, ON, Canada N9B 3P4 Mary Kaye Lucier, M.S.W.
Founded: 1983. **Staff:** 1. **Subjects:** Eating disorders, stress management, assertiveness. **Holdings:** 100 books; 50 AV programs. **Subscriptions:** 2 journals and other serials; 46 newsletters. **Services:** Library open to the public. **Publications:** BANA Newsletter, quarterly - for members only; Preventive Curriculum for Anorexia Nervosa and Bulimia - for sale.

★2353★
Bull H N Information Systems - Computer House - Technical Library
Great West Rd.
Brentford, S. Yorks. TW8 9DH, England
Defunct.

★2354★
Bull H N Information Systems, Inc. - Information and Library Services (Comp Sci)
300 Concord Rd., MS 813 Phone: (508)294-3748
Billerica, MA 01821 Margaret Cardello, Mgr.
Staff: Prof 2; Other 2. **Subjects:** Computer science, data processing, computer marketing, electronics, engineering, business, management science. **Holdings:** 3000 books; 1000 technical manuals; technical reports; proceedings; market studies; annual reports. **Subscriptions:** 350 journals and other serials; 5 newspapers. **Services:** Interlibrary loan. **Automated Operations:** Computerized cataloging. **Computerized Information Services:** DIALOG Information Services, NEXIS, Dow Jones News/Retrieval, NewsNet, Inc., VU/TEXT Information Services, OCLC; InterNet (electronic mail service). **Networks/Consortia:** Member of NELINET, Inc. **Special Catalogs:** List of Serials. **Remarks:** Maintains 2 libraries in Billerica, MA. FAX: (508)294-3635. Electronic mail address(es): Cardello@cass.MA02.bull.com (Internet). **Staff:** Naka Ishii, Ref.Libn.; Lee Bracken, Acq.

★2355★
Bull H N Information Systems, Inc. - Minkel Information Center Z-12 (Sci-Engr, Comp Sci)
P.O. Box 8000 Phone: (602)862-4115
Phoenix, AZ 85066 Jackie Whitford, Mgr., Lib.Serv.
Founded: 1958. **Staff:** Prof 2; Other 1. **Subjects:** Computer technology, software development, engineering, computer programming, business, management. **Special Collections:** Computer Technology. **Holdings:** 20,000 books; 2000 bound periodical volumes; 10,000 reports; 2500 company internal reports and customer software manuals; 1200 Institute of Electrical and Electronics Engineers (IEEE) publications on microfiche; library collection (online). **Subscriptions:** 300 journals and other serials; 15 newspapers. **Services:** Interlibrary loan; center not open to the public. **Automated Operations:** Computerized cataloging, acquisitions, and circulation. **Computerized Information Services:** DIALOG Information Services, Dow Jones News/Retrieval, VU/TEXT Information Services, NewsNet, Inc., BRS Information Technologies; MULTICS, GECOS (internal databases); Honeywell E-Mail (electronic mail service). **Networks/Consortia:** Member of Honeywell Information Network (HIN). **Publications:** Newsletter, monthly. **Special Indexes:** Index of acquisitions, annual. **Remarks:** FAX: (602)862-6973. Telex: 910-957-4580.

★2356★
Bull, Housser and Tupper - Library (Law)
3000 Royal Centre
1055 W. Georgia
P.O. Box 11130 Phone: (604)687-6575
Vancouver, BC, Canada V6E 3R3 Catherine J.G. Ryan, Chf.Libn.
Staff: Prof 2; Other 1. **Subjects:** Law. **Holdings:** 18,000 books. **Subscriptions:** 100 journals and other serials; 15 newspapers. **Services:** Library not open to the public. **Automated Operations:** Computerized cataloging. **Computerized Information Services:** QL Systems, CAN/LAW, Infomart Online, Info Globe, LEXIS, WESTLAW. **Remarks:** Alternate telephone number(s): (604)641-4878. FAX: (604)641-4949. **Staff:** Lois Burkell.

Buller Memorial Library
See: **Canada - Agriculture Canada - Research Station, Winnipeg - Library** (2666)

★2357★
Bullhead Community Hospital - Medical Library (Med)
2735 Silver Creek Rd. Phone: (602)763-2273
Bullhead City, AZ 86442 Kathleen Stanley, Med.Libn.
Founded: 1986. **Staff:** Prof 1. **Subjects:** Medicine, nursing, and allied health sciences. **Holdings:** 500 books. **Subscriptions:** 25 journals and other serials. **Services:** Interlibrary loan; copying; SDI; library open to the public for reference use only. **Computerized Information Services:** MEDLARS. **Remarks:** FAX: (602)763-0235.

Dorothy Stimson Bullitt Library
See: **Seattle Art Museum** (14991)

★2358★
Joseph Bulova School - Library (Sci-Engr)
40-24 62nd St.
Box 465 Phone: (718)424-2929
Woodside, NY 11377 Richard Switzer, Exec.Dir.
Founded: 1945. **Subjects:** Clock and watchmaking, machine-shop practice, jewelry repair, lapidary, digital electronics, computer repair. **Holdings:** 200 books. **Subscriptions:** 38 journals and other serials. **Services:** Interlibrary loan; library open to persons working in the jewelry and watch fields. **Remarks:** FAX: (718)335-0545.

Bultema Memorial Library
See: **Grace Bible College** (6595)

★2359★
Buma Library (Hum)
Boterhoek 1
NL-8911 BG Leeuwarden, Netherlands Phone: 58 133245
Founded: 1876. **Staff:** Prof 1. **Subjects:** Classical studies. **Holdings:** 40,000 books; 5000 bound periodical volumes. **Subscriptions:** 200 journals and other serials. **Services:** Library open to the public. **Remarks:** FAX: 58 130884.

Bund Archives of the Jewish Labor Movement
See: **Jewish Labor Bund** (8399)

★2360★
Bundesamt fur Seeschiffahrt und Hydrographie - Library (Sci-Engr, Agri)
Postfach 30 12 20 Phone: 40 31902493
W-2000 Hamburg 36, Germany Gunter Heise
Founded: 1875. **Staff:** Prof 5; Other 4. **Subjects:** Hydrography, oceanography, navigation safety, geodesy, marine sciences, geophysics, nautical engineering, agricultural meteorology, marine meteorology, worldwide climatological and meteorological observations. **Special Collections:** Nautical charts and books (in German). **Holdings:** 130,000 volumes. **Subscriptions:** 1500 journals and other serials. **Services:** Library open to the public. **Computerized Information Services:** STN International, DIMDI; internal database (hydrographic documentation). **Publications:** List of Periodicals (Zeitschriften-Liste). **Remarks:** Maintained by Federal Republic of Germany - Ministry of Transport. Library located at Bernhard-Nocht-Strasse 78, W-2000 Hamburg 36, Germany. FAX: 40 31905150. Telex: 02 11 138 bsh hh d. **Formerly:** German Hydrographic Institute; Deutsches Hydrographisches Institut.

★2361★
Bundesanstalt fur Agrarwirtschaft - Bibliothek und Dokumentationsstelle (Agri)
Schweizertalstr 36 Phone: 222 82365147
A-1133 Vienna, Austria Werner Pevetz, Dipl.Ing.
Founded: 1960. **Staff:** 1.5. **Subjects:** Agricultural economics, rural planning, rural sociology, environmental economics. **Holdings:** 34,000 books; 3500 bound periodical volumes; 6000 reports; maps. **Subscriptions:** 250 journals and other serials. **Services:** Interlibrary loan; copying; SDI; library open to the public. **Automated Operations:** Computerized cataloging. **Computerized Information Services:** Internal database. **Publications:** Das Schrifttum der Agrarwirtschaft, 6/year; Zugangsverzeichnis der Bibliothek, semiannual.

Bundesanstalt fur Arbeit - Institut fur Arbeitsmarkt- und Berufsforschung - Informations- und Dokumentationsstelle
See: **Germany - Federal Employment Institute - Institute of Employment Research - Information and Documentation Department** (6442)

Bundesanstalt fur Arbeitsschutz - Informations- und Dokumentationzentrum fur Arbeitsschutz
See: **Germany - Federal Institute for Occupational Safety - Information and Documentation Center for Occupational Safety** (6445)

★2362★
Bundesanstalt fur Fleischforschung - Bibliothek (Sci-Engr)
E. C. Baumann Str 20 Phone: 9221 803246
W-8650 Kulmbach, Germany Brigitta Lewerenz
Founded: 1938. **Staff:** Prof 2. **Subjects:** Meat science. **Holdings:** 24,000 books; 19,000 photocopies. **Subscriptions:** 150 journals and other serials. **Services:** Interlibrary loan; library open to the public. **Computerized Information Services:** DIMDI, STN International. Contact Person: Dr. Hubertus Wagner. **Remarks:** FAX: 9221 803244.

Bundesanstalt fur Strassenwesen
See: **Germany - Federal Highway Research Institute - Documentation and Information Systems** (6444)

Bundesforschungsanstalt fur Fischerei - Informations- und Dokumentationsstelle
See: **Germany - Federal Research Center for Fisheries - Information and Documentation Center** (6447)

Bundesinstitut fuer Ostwissenschaftliche und Internationale Studien
See: **Federal Institute for East European and International Studies** (5630)

Bundesinstitut fur Sportwissenschaft - Fachbereich Dokumentation und Information
See: **Federal Institute for Sports Science - Documentation and Information Division** (5631)

Bundesministerium fur Land- und Forstwirtschaft
See: **Austria - Federal Ministry of Agriculture and Forestry** (1351)

Bundesministerium fur Wirshaft - Bundesstelle fur Aussenhandelsinformation
See: **Germany - Ministry of Economics - Federal Office of Foreign Trade Information - Library** (6450)

Bundesministerium fur Wissenschaft und Forschung - Bibliothek der Geologischen Bundesanstalt
See: **Geological Survey of Austria** (6364)

Dr. Paul G. Bunker Memorial Medical Library
See: **St. Lukes Midland Regional Medical Center - Dr. Paul G. Bunker Memorial Medical Library** (14489)

Bainbridge Bunting Memorial Slide Library
See: **University of New Mexico** (19039)

Burbank Community Hospital
See: **Thompson Memorial Medical Center** (16323)

★2363★
Burbank Public Library - Warner Research Collection (Art)
110 N. Glenoaks Blvd. Phone: (818)953-9743
Burbank, CA 91502 Helen Wang, Ref.Coord.
Staff: 3. **Subjects:** Architecture, police and military, travel, transportation, history, costume. **Holdings:** 40,000 books; 5000 bound periodical volumes; 2 million clipping files; 500 research compilations; 14 VF drawers of license plates. **Subscriptions:** 78 journals and other serials. **Services:** Copying; collection open to the public by appointment on fee basis. **Computerized Information Services:** DIALOG Information Services. **Networks/Consortia:** Member of Metropolitan Cooperative Library System (MCLS). **Remarks:** Collection is designed to aid in the creative preparation of motion picture, television, and theatrical productions. FAX: (818)953-8639.

John T. Burch, M.D. Memorial Library
See: **San Pedro Peninsula Hospital** (14774)

Burchfield Art Center
See: **State University College at Buffalo - Burchfield Art Center - Research Library** (15703)

Charles E. Burchfield Archive
See: **State University College at Buffalo - Burchfield Art Center - Research Library** (15703)

★2364★
Burdick International Ancestry Library (Hist)
2317 Riverbluff Pkwy., No. 249 Phone: (813)922-7931
Sarasota, FL 34231-5032 Frank P. Mueller, Exec.Dir.
Subjects: Burdick family. **Special Collections:** Written material authored by Burdicks. **Holdings:** Historical records. **Services:** Library not open to the public. **Publications:** The Burdick Family Chronology (560 pp.).

Bureau of Applied Social Science Research Archives
See: **Columbia University - Herbert H. Lehman Library** (4015)

★2365★
Bureau County Historical Society - Museum & Library (Hist)
209 Park Ave., W. Phone: (815)875-2184
Princeton, IL 61356 Mary W. Williams, Cur.
Founded: 1937. **Staff:** Prof 2; Other 4. **Subjects:** Bureau County history, Civil War histories, local genealogies. **Holdings:** 1500 books; 100 bound periodical volumes; 400 other cataloged items; 20 VF drawers of manuscripts and clippings; local newspapers. **Services:** Library not open to the public. **Publications:** New Brochure. **Remarks:** Reprints of 1867 and 1885 histories of Bureau County, Illinois are available. **Staff:** Marguerite Dart, Geneal.

★2366★
Bureau pour l'Enseignement de la Langue et de la Civilisation Francaises a l'Etranger - Centre de Documentation et d'Information (Hum, Educ)
9, rue Lhomond Phone: 1 47074273
F-75007 Paris, France C. De Quatrebarbes
Founded: 1960. **Subjects:** Teaching French as a foreign language, language teaching, French linguistics, teaching aids, linguistics, French culture. **Special Collections:** French textbooks for French as a foreign language, 1960 to present; foreign books (800). **Holdings:** 18,800 books; 4000 brochures. **Subscriptions:** 180 journals and other serials. **Services:** Center open to teachers of French and researchers on language teaching. **Publications:** Accession list, 9/year; bibliographies. **Remarks:** FAX: 1 43379961.

★2367★
Bureau of Governmental Research - Library (Soc Sci)
837 Gravier, Suite 1308 Phone: (504)525-4152
New Orleans, LA 70112 James C. Brandt, Exec.Dir.
Founded: 1932. **Staff:** 2. **Subjects:** Public administration, city finances, personnel administration, police and fire departments, public works, recreation, intergovernmental relations. **Holdings:** 450 books; 450 bound periodical volumes; 7500 pamphlets; 8 VF drawers of clippings; maps. **Subscriptions:** 200 journals and other serials. **Services:** Library open to BGR members and students. **Publications:** Reports on city finance, and research reports on urban public policy issues.

Bureau International de l'Union Postale Universelle
See: **Universal Postal Union** (17975)

★2368★
Bureau of Jewish Ecucation of Greater Los Angeles - Jewish Community Library - Peter M. Kahn Memorial Library (Area-Ethnic)
6505 Wilshire Blvd. Phone: (213)852-1234
Los Angeles, CA 90048 Mrs. Hava Ben-Zvi, Hd.Libn.
Founded: 1947. **Staff:** Prof 1; Other 3. **Subjects:** Jewish culture - education, sociology, history, life in America; Israel and Zionism; Yiddish and Hebrew literature. **Special Collections:** Historical documents and pictures pertaining to the history of the Jewish community in Los Angeles and vicinity. **Holdings:** 30,000 books; 4000 bound periodical volumes; 20 cases of pamphlets; 69 reels of microfilm; archives of the parent organization. **Subscriptions:** 80 journals and other serials; 20 newspapers. **Services:** Copying; library open to the public with deposit required for borrowing. **Publications:** Acquisitions lists; bibliographies - by request; compilations of literature and teaching aids. **Remarks:** FAX: (213)852-1494. **Formerly:** Its Peter M. Kahn Jewish Community Library.

Bureau of Jewish Education - Community Library
See: **Milton Plesur Memorial Library** (13143)

★2369★
Bureau of Jewish Education - Jewish Community Library (Rel-Phil, Area-Ethnic)
601 14th Ave. Phone: (415)751-6983
San Francisco, CA 94118 Frederick Isaac, Hd.Libn.
Founded: 1950. **Staff:** Prof 3; Other 1. **Subjects:** Judaica, Bible, Jewish history, Hebrew and Yiddish literature, Israel, Jewish music. **Special Collections:** Havas Children's Library. **Holdings:** 26,000 books; 600 phonograph records and tapes; sheet music; vertical files. **Subscriptions:** 52 journals and other serials; 6 newspapers. **Services:** Copying; library open to the public. **Publications:** Bibliographies on special holdings. **Special Catalogs:** Catalog to Children's Collection (card). **Staff:** Jonathan Schwartz, Libn.; Joyce Ahern, Children's Libn.

Bureau of Maternal and Child Health and Resources Development - National Center for Education in Maternal and Child Health
See: **National Center for Education in Maternal and Child Health - Library** (11102)

★2370★
Bureau of National Affairs, Inc. - Library (Law, Bus-Fin)
1231 25th St., N.W. Phone: (202)452-4466
Washington, DC 20037 Kamla King Hedges, Lib.Mgr.
Staff: Prof 8; Other 8. **Subjects:** Law, labor-management relations, economics, government regulation, business, environment, industrial safety and health. **Holdings:** 20,000 volumes. **Subscriptions:** 850 journals and other serials; 30 newspapers. **Services:** Interlibrary loan; library open to subscribers by special arrangement only. **Computerized Information Services:** DIALOG Information Services, ORBIT Search Service, BRS Information Technologies, Dow Jones News/Retrieval, OCLC, DataTimes, VU/TEXT Information Services, WESTLAW, MEDLARS, NEXIS, LEXIS, LEGI-SLATE, Info Globe, Human Resource Information Network (HRIN), Reuters Reuter TEXTLINE; DIALMAIL (electronic mail service). Performs searches on fee basis. **Publications:** BNA's Directory of State Courts, Judges and Clerks - for sale. **Remarks:** Toll-free telephone number(s): (800)452-7773. FAX: (202)822-8092. Electronic mail address(es): 10344 (DIALMAIL). Telex: 285656 BNAI WSH. **Staff:** Rhonda Oziel, Ref.Libn.; Marilyn Bromley, Online Libn.; Catherine Kitchell, Online Libn.; Le-Chi Gallagher, Cat.Libn.; Le Pham, ILL; John R. Jones, Archv.Spec.; Thomas E. Vanderloo, State Info.Spec.; Judy Springberg, Database Mgr. ; Ophelia Thomas, Tech.Serv.Supv.

Thomas Burford Ltd.
See: **Celebrity Access - Film/TV Information Center** (3196)

Warren E. Burger Library
See: **William Mitchell College of Law** (10555)

Burgess-Carpenter Library
See: **Columbia University - Burgess-Carpenter Library** (4004)

★2371★
Thornton W. Burgess Society, Inc. - Museum and Nature Center (Sci-Engr)
6 Discovery Hill Rd. Phone: (508)888-6870
East Sandwich, MA 02537 Jeanne Johnson, Dir.
Founded: 1984.**Subjects:** Thornton W. Burgess, author and naturalist; natural history of the northeastern U.S. **Holdings:** 1900 volumes. **Services:** Center open to the public. **Remarks:** Includes holdings of the Robert S. Swain Natural History Library.

Carleton F. Burke Memorial Library
See: **California Thoroughbred Breeders Association** (2579)

Burke Library
See: **Union Theological Seminary** (16667)

(Burkina Faso) Chambre de Commerce, d'Industrie et d'Artisanat du Burkina
See: **Chamber of Commerce, Industry and Trades of Burkina** (3416)

Burlew Medical Library
See: **St. Joseph Hospital** (14367)

Merrill G. Burlingame Special Collections/Archives
See: **Montana State University - Libraries** (10654)

★2372★
Burlington County College - Library - Special Collections (Hist)
Pemberton/Browns Mills Rd. Phone: (609)894-9311
Pemberton, NJ 08068 Dr. Frank L. Nappo
Founded: 1970. **Staff:** Prof 5; Other 8. **Special Collections:** Genealogy collection (Pinelands, New Jersey). **Services:** Interlibrary loan; copying; library open to the public with restrictions. **Computerized Information Services:** MLA; CD-ROMs (WILSONLINE, Silverplatter).

★2373★
Burlington County Historical Society - Delia Biddle Pugh Library (Hist)
457 High St. Phone: (609)386-4773
Burlington, NJ 08016 Kathryn Heuer, Libn.
Founded: 1915. **Staff:** 1. **Subjects:** History of Burlington County and New Jersey; antiques; colonial arts and crafts; genealogy. **Special Collections:** James Fenimore Cooper works and critiques; imprints from presses of Stephen Ustick and Isaac Collins. **Holdings:** 1900 books; periodicals; deeds; photographs; slides; clippings; maps; prints; postcards; manuscripts; microfilm. **Subscriptions:** 10 journals and other serials. **Services:** Copying; library open to the public on a limited schedule.

★2374★
Burlington County Lyceum of History and Natural Science (Hist)
307 High St. Phone: (609)267-7111
Mt. Holly, NJ 08060 C. Jackson Caldwell, Lib.Dir.
Founded: 1866. **Staff:** Prof 3; Other 6. **Subjects:** Local history, American Indians. **Special Collections:** Bridgetown Library Collection; Nathan Dunn Collection; Henry Shinn Collection; Levis Collection; Judge William Slaughter Collection of the American Indian; Robert Mills' original plans for Mount Holly's landmark jail; Robert Mills' narrative on penal system revision. **Holdings:** 445 books; 1500 pamphlets, pictures, genealogical records, manuscripts, photographs, 1765 Library Charter. **Services:** Interlibrary loan; copying; lyceum open to the public for reference use only by appointment. **Computerized Information Services:** Internal database. **Networks/Consortia:** Member of South Jersey Regional Library Cooperative. **Remarks:** Holdings listed are for the historical collection only. FAX: (609)267-7495. Maintained by Mount Holly Public Library and Langstaff Foundation.

★2375★
Burlington County Times - Library (Publ)
Rte. 130 Phone: (609)871-8000
Willingboro, NJ 08046 Annette Parker, Libn.
Staff: Prof 1; Other 1. **Subjects:** Newspaper reference topics. **Holdings:** 160 books; newspapers, 1955 to present, on microfilm. **Subscriptions:** 16 journals and other serials. **Services:** Library not open to the public.

★2376★
Burlington Industries, Inc. - Library Information Services (Sci-Engr)
Box 20288 Phone: (919)379-2773
Greensboro, NC 27420 Connie Childers, Libn.
Founded: 1963. **Staff:** Prof 1. **Subjects:** Textiles, chemistry, management. **Holdings:** 6000 books; 5000 bound periodical volumes. **Subscriptions:** 150 journals and other serials; 10 newspapers. **Services:** Library not open to the public. **Automated Operations:** Computerized cataloging. **Computerized Information Services:** DIALOG Information Services, PFDS Online, Reuter TEXTLINE, NEXIS, LEXIS, Journal of Commerce, PIERS.

★2377★
Burlington Medical Center - Library (Med)
602 N. 3rd Phone: (319)753-3631
Burlington, IA 52601 Judy Watson, Libn.
Staff: 1. **Subjects:** Nursing, medicine. **Holdings:** 1000 books. **Subscriptions:** 250 journals and other serials. **Services:** Interlibrary loan; copying; SDI; library open to the public. **Computerized Information Services:** MEDLINE. Performs searches on fee basis. **Networks/Consortia:** Member of Quad City Area Biomedical Consortium. **Remarks:** FAX: (319)753-3221.

Burlington Textiles Library
See: **North Carolina State University** (11898)

★2378★
Burlington Times-News - Library (Publ)
707 S. Main Phone: (919)227-0131
Burlington, NC 27215 Annette L. Crespo
Founded: 1972. **Staff:** Prof 1. **Subjects:** Newspaper reference topics. **Holdings:** 300 books; reels of microfilm (1917 to present). **Subscriptions:** 15 newspapers. **Services:** Library not open to the public. **Computerized Information Services:** Stauffer Gold (internal database). **Remarks:** FAX: (919)229-2463.

★2379★
Burnaby Hospital - Dr. H.H.W. Brooke Memorial Library (Med)
3935 Kincaid St. Phone: (604)434-4211
Burnaby, BC, Canada V5G 2X6 Mr. Hoong Lim, Libn.
Founded: 1977. **Staff:** Prof 1. **Subjects:** Medicine, nursing, health care administration. **Holdings:** 800 books; 500 bound periodical volumes; 4000 pamphlets and clippings. **Subscriptions:** 85 journals and other serials. **Services:** Interlibrary loan; copying; SDI; library open to the public if cleared by administration. **Computerized Information Services:** MEDLINE. **Publications:** Library Update, monthly - for internal distribution only. **Remarks:** FAX: (604)434-5294.

★2380★
Burnaby School Board - Teachers' Professional Library (Educ)
Schou Education Centre
4041 Canada Way
Burnaby, BC, Canada V5G 1G6 Phone: (604)437-4511
Subjects: Teacher education, curriculum, philosophy, psychology, child study. **Holdings:** 400 books. **Subscriptions:** 60 journals and other serials; 2 newspapers. **Services:** Library not open to the public. **Also Known As:** Jean Bailey Memorial Library.

★2381★
Burnaby School District 41 - Media Loans (Aud-Vis)
Schou Education Centre
4041 Canada Way Phone: (604)437-4511
Burnaby, BC, Canada V5G 1G6 R. Donald Lyon, Coord.
Founded: 1971. **Staff:** Prof 2; Other 4. **Subjects:** Instructional material for public schools. **Holdings:** 14,000 videotapes, films, filmstrips, slides, multimedia kits, computer software, biological models. **Services:** Library not open to the public. **Automated Operations:** Computerized cataloging and circulation. **Computerized Information Services:** MEDIAMATE (internal database). **Publications:** Inside Schou, monthly - to Burnaby teachers. **Special Catalogs:** Book catalog of loan materials. **Remarks:** FAX: (604)299-8593.

John Miller Burnam Classical Library
See: **University of Cincinnati** (18473)

★2382★
Burndy Library (Sci-Engr)
Electra Square Phone: (203)838-0260
Norwalk, CT 06856 Dorothea Nelhybel, Libn.
Founded: 1936. **Staff:** Prof 1; Other 1. **Subjects:** History of science and technology to 1900. **Special Collections:** Electricity and magnetism; Galileo; Newton; Einstein; Darwin; Pasteur; Volta; Leonardo da Vinci; John Tyndall. **Holdings:** 30,000 books; 2000 portraits of scientists; 100 medals; 325 scientific instruments. **Subscriptions:** 25 journals and other serials. **Services:** Copying; library open to the public. **Publications:** Monographs on the history of science. **Remarks:** FAX: (203)838-2502.

★2383★
Burnet, Duckworth & Palmer, Barristers & Solicitors - Library (Law)
1400,350 7th Ave., S.W. Phone: (403)260-0179
Calgary, AB, Canada T2P 3N9 Anne Helgason, Libn.
Staff: Prof 1; Other 1. **Subjects:** Law - Canada, Great Britain, United States. **Holdings:** 10,000 volumes. **Subscriptions:** 190 journals and other serials. **Services:** Interlibrary loan; library not open to the public. **Computerized Information Services:** QL Systems, WESTLAW, Info Globe, DIALOG Information Services, CAN/LAW, The Financial Post DataGroup, LEXIS, NEXIS, Infomart Online, INSIGHT. **Remarks:** FAX: (403)260-0332.

Cordas C. Burnett Library
See: **Assemblies of God Theological Seminary** (1134)

★2384★
Leo Burnett Company, Inc. - Library (Bus-Fin)
35 W. Wacker Dr., 14th Fl. Phone: (312)220-5959
Chicago, IL 60601 Deborah Morrow Vaughan, Dir.
Founded: 1950. **Staff:** Prof 4; Other 2. **Subjects:** Advertising, marketing, food and beverages. **Special Collections:** Picture file (500,000 pictures, 2000 subject headings); subject files (25 VF drawers, 900 subject headings). **Holdings:** 3000 books; 200 bound periodical volumes; 200 reports; 300 reels of microfilm. **Subscriptions:** 700 journals and other serials; 5 newspapers. **Services:** Interlibrary loan; copying; library not open to the public but answers requests from other libraries. **Automated Operations:** Computerized cataloging and serials. **Computerized Information Services:** DIALOG Information Services, NEXIS, VU/TEXT Information Services, DataTimes. **Networks/Consortia:** Member of ILLINET. **Publications:** Food News, monthly - for internal distribution only. **Remarks:** FAX: (312)220-6534. **Staff:** Astrida Robeznieks, Assoc.Dir.; Rae Kalin, Info.Spec.; Kathleen Munson, Info.Spec.

Mary Couts Burnett Library
See: **Texas Christian University - Mary Couts Burnett Library** (16208)

Guy H. Burnham Map and Aerial Photograph Library
See: **Clark University** (3776)

Burnham Library
See: **Art Institute of Chicago - Ryerson and Burnham Libraries** (1082)

Burnham Tavern Museum
See: **National Society, Daughters of the American Revolution - Hannah Weston Chapter** (11290)

Burns Clinic Medical Center
See: **The Dean C. Burns Health Sciences Library** (2385)

★2385★
The Dean C. Burns Health Sciences Library (Med)
560 W. Mitchell Phone: (616)348-4500
Petoskey, MI 49770 Kay Kelly, Dir.
Founded: 1971. **Staff:** Prof 1; Other 1. **Subjects:** Health sciences. **Holdings:** 2240 books; 4500 bound periodical volumes; slides; audio- and videotapes. **Subscriptions:** 400 journals and other serials. **Services:** Interlibrary loan; copying; library open to the public with restrictions. **Automated Operations:** Computerized serials. **Computerized Information Services:** MEDLINE. **Networks/Consortia:** Member of Northland Interlibrary System (NILS). **Remarks:** Maintained by Northern Michigan Hospitals, Inc. and Burns Clinic Medical Center, P.C. FAX: (616)348-4284.

Edward L. Burns Health Sciences Library
See: **Mercy Hospital** (10133)

Jacob Burns Law Library
See: **George Washington University - National Law Center** (20009)

John A. Burns School of Medicine
See: **University of Hawaii - John A. Burns School of Medicine** (18619)

John J. Burns Library
See: **Boston College** (1981)

Landon Burns Memorial Library
See: **Carroll County Farm Museum** (3101)

★2386★
Burns and McDonnell Engineering Company - Information Center (Sci-Engr)
Box 419173 Phone: (816)333-4375
Kansas City, MO 64141 Kimberly K. Mosshart, Info.Spec.
Founded: 1959. **Staff:** Prof 1; Other 1. **Subjects:** Engineering - civil, environmental, mechanical, electrical; architecture. **Holdings:** 2700 books; 500 bound periodical volumes; 3100 government documents; standards from 90 organizations (incomplete set); 20 VF drawers drawers of technical information; 2000 manufacturers' catalogs; 2 VF drawers of archival materials; technical reports. **Subscriptions:** 200 journals and other serials. **Services:** Interlibrary loan. **Computerized Information Services:** DIALOG Information Services, Veralex 2, MEDLARS, PASS (Procurement Automated Source System), LEXIS, Chemical Information Systems, Inc. (CIS), Dow Jones News/Retrieval; DIALMAIL (electronic mail service). **Publications:** Burns and McDonnell Info Line (newsletter), monthly - for internal distribution only. **Remarks:** FAX: (816)822-3414.

★2387★
Burns and Roe Enterprises Inc. - James B. MacLean Technical Library (Sci-Engr)
800 Kinderkamack Rd.
Oradell, NJ 07649 Phone: (201)265-2000
Staff: Prof 1. **Subjects:** Engineering - electrical, mechanical, civil; industry standards; government regulations; energy; nuclear energy. **Holdings:** 1500 books; 15 VF drawers of industry standards; vendor catalogs on microfilm (VSMF); preliminary and final safety analysis reports for 40 nuclear power plants; 100 boxes of technical reports. **Subscriptions:** 60 journals and other serials. **Services:** Interlibrary loan; library not open to the public. **Computerized Information Services:** DIALOG Information Services.

W. Atlee Burpee Seed and Nursery Company Archives
See: **Smithsonian Institution Libraries - Office of Horticulture - Branch Library** (15283)

★2388★
Aaron Burr Association - Library
c/o Dr. F. Burr Anderson
4520 King Edward Ct.
Annandale, VA 22003
Defunct.

★2389★
Burr-Brown Corporation - Library (Sci-Engr)
Box 11400 Phone: (602)746-7186
Tucson, AZ 85734 Rao Aluri, Mgr., Lib.Serv.
Founded: 1979. **Staff:** Prof 3. **Subjects:** Semiconductors, microelectronics, business, management. **Holdings:** 3000 books; 500 slides and video cassettes; 2000 federal specifications and standards; 1500 archival materials. **Subscriptions:** 300 journals and other serials. **Services:** Interlibrary loan; library not open to the public. **Automated Operations:** Computerized cataloging and SDI. **Computerized Information Services:** DIALOG Information Services, Dun & Bradstreet Business Credit Services, RLIN, NERAC, Inc. **Networks/Consortia:** Member of CLASS. **Remarks:** FAX: (602)746-7211. **Staff:** Marc Finkelstein, Libn.; Steve Malone, Commun.Spec.

Elihu Burritt Library
See: **Central Connecticut State University** (3337)

★2390★
Burroughs-Audobon Society - Burroughs-Audobon Center and Library (Env-Cons)
R.R. 3, Box 120 Phone: (816)795-8177
Blue Springs, MO 64015 Anne Duffer, Mgr.
Founded: 1971. **Staff:** 1. **Subjects:** Ornithology, natural history, conservation. **Holdings:** 4000 books. **Subscriptions:** 56 journals and other serials. **Services:** Interlibrary loan; library open to the public (borrowing privileges limited to members). **Staff:** Ruth S. Scott, Libn.

Edgar Rice Burroughs Collection
See: **University of Wisconsin--Madison - Cooperative Children's Book Center (CCBC)** (19590)

★2391★
Burroughs Wellcome Company - Library (Sci-Engr, Med)
3030 Cornwallis Rd. Phone: (919)248-4908
Research Triangle Park, NC 27709 Ildiko Trombitas, Mgr., Tech.Info.Dept.
Founded: 1929. **Staff:** Prof 19; Other 13. **Subjects:** Organic chemistry, medicine, biochemistry, pharmacology, microbiology, toxicology, business. **Holdings:** 13,896 books; 30,381 bound periodical volumes; product literature files; 3 bookcases of archival materials. **Subscriptions:** 1576 journals and other serials; 5 newspapers. **Services:** Interlibrary loan; copying; SDI; library open to the public by appointment. **Automated Operations:** Integrated library system (NOTIS). **Computerized Information Services:** NLM, DIALOG Information Services, ORBIT Search Service, BRS Information Technologies, Chemical Abstracts Service (CAS), STN International, Data-Star, OCLC. **Networks/Consortia:** Member of SOLINET. **Publications:** TID News. **Remarks:** An alternate telephone number is 248-4869. FAX: (919)248-3052. Telex: 510 9270915. **Staff:** Gina Jones, Hd., Lib.Tech.Serv.; Rolly L. Simpson, Biomed.Info.; Robert B. Kilgore, Bus.Info.Spec.; Margaret Day, Hd., Chemistry, Patent Serv.; David Price, Biomed.Info.Spec.; C. Walton, Biomed.Info.Spec.; S. McKee, Chemical Info.Spec.; Mary-Jane Pugh, Chemical Info.Spec.; K. Webb, Biomed.Info.Spec.; M. Parker, Biomed.Info.Spec.; David Wilson, Chemical Info.Spec.; M. Pratt, Doc. Delivery/Circ.Coord.; Robert K. Larson, Sys./Strategic Plan.Coord.; Judy McConnell, Acq. & Cat.Coord.; Allen Jones, Hd., Info.Tech. & Pubns.; Susan Wood, Tech.Sys.Libn.; Andrea Rohrbacher, Biomed.Info.Spec.; Elaine Teague, Ser.Coll.Coord.

★2392★
Burroughs Wellcome Company - Medical Library (Med)
16751 Trans Canada Rd.
Kirkland, PQ, Canada H9H 4J4 Phone: (514)694-8220
Staff: 1. **Subjects:** Medicine, basic sciences, pharmacy. **Holdings:** 250 books; 2500 unbound periodicals; 15,000 microfiche. **Subscriptions:** 100 journals and other serials; 6 newspapers. **Computerized Information Services:** DIALOG Information Services, MEDLARS, Questel, Info Globe, CAN/OLE, Infomart Online; electronic mail serivce. **Remarks:** FAX: (514)694-8201. Telex: 05-821860. **Formerly:** Its Medical Information Center. **Staff:** Georgette Puscer.

★2393★
Burroughs Wellcome Company - Technical Information Department (Sci-Engr, Med)
Box 1887 Phone: (919)758-3436
Greenville, NC 27834 Hyder A. Zahed, Hd., Tech.Info./Lib.Serv.
Founded: 1977. **Staff:** Prof 2; Other 2. **Subjects:** Pharmaceutical sciences and technology, chemistry, engineering, medicine. **Holdings:** 7000 books; 1650 bound periodical volumes. **Subscriptions:** 250 journals and other serials. **Services:** Interlibrary loan; copying; SDI; department open to the public with restrictions. **Computerized Information Services:** DIALOG Information Services, BRS Information Technologies, NLM, Occupational Health Services, Inc., STN International. **Remarks:** FAX: (919)830-0095. The Technical Library is a satellite of the main library of the Burroughs Wellcome Company facility in Research Triangle Park, North Carolina.

Edward F. Burrow Memorial Library
See: **Grand View Hospital** (6646)

★2394★
Burson-Marsteller - Information Services (Bus-Fin)
One E. Wacker Dr. Phone: (312)329-9292
Chicago, IL 60601 Ellen S. Kuner, Mgr., Info.Serv.
Founded: 1967. **Staff:** Prof 2; Other 3. **Subjects:** Advertising, public relations. **Holdings:** 2000 books; 1000 internal reports; 20 VF drawers of clippings; 20,000 pictures. **Subscriptions:** 1000 journals and other serials; 11 newspapers. **Services:** Interlibrary loan; copying; services open to the public by appointment. **Computerized Information Services:** DIALOG Information Services, Dow Jones News/Retrieval, Mead Data Central, VU/TEXT Information Services, CDA Investment Technologies, Inc., Roper Center for Public Opinion Research, DataTimes, WILSONLINE, BRS Information Technologies, Vickers Stock Research Corporation, Information Resources, Inc. (IRI). **Networks/Consortia:** Member of ILLINET. **Publications:** News Summary, biweekly - for internal distribution only. **Remarks:** FAX: (312)329-7583; (312)329-7595. Telex: 824-633 BMA UF. **Staff:** Janet Farral, Sr.Info.Spec.

★2395★
Burson-Marsteller - Information Services (Bus-Fin)
230 Park Ave., S. Phone: (212)614-4255
New York, NY 10003 Philip Smith, V.P., Info.Serv.
Founded: 1955. **Staff:** Prof 2; Other 2. **Subjects:** Advertising, public relations, marketing research. **Holdings:** 750 books. **Subscriptions:** 100 journals and other serials. **Services:** Interlibrary loan; library open to clients and librarians. **Computerized Information Services:** DIALOG Information Services, DataTimes, NEXIS, Dow Jones News/Retrieval, POLL, WILSONLINE, NewsNet, Inc., VU/TEXT Information Services, Reuters. **Staff:** Nancy Marino.

★2396★
Burt County Museum, Inc. - Library (Hist)
319 N. 13th St. Phone: (402)374-1505
Tekamah, NE 68061 Bonnie Newell, Cur.
Founded: 1967. **Subjects:** Burt County history, genealogy. **Special Collections:** Centennial books; Nebraska authors; town books; local newspapers from 1896. **Holdings:** Books; reports. **Services:** Copying; library open to the public on a limited schedule. **Publications:** Tekamah Cemetery Book (1984).

★2397★
Burt Hill Kosar Rittelmann Associates - Library (Plan, Energy)
400 Morgan Center Phone: (412)285-4761
Butler, PA 16001 Stacy Fetterman, Libn.
Subjects: Energy use in buildings, solar energy, building products and design, architecture, engineering, interior design. **Holdings:** 10,000 volumes. **Services:** Library not open to the public. **Computerized Information Services:** Internal database.

Burton Historical Collection
See: **Detroit Public Library** (4816)

★2398★
Burwell Enterprises - Library (Bus-Fin)
5106 F M 1960 Rd., W., Suite 349 Phone: (713)537-9051
Houston, TX 77069 Helen P. Burwell, Pres.
Founded: 1987. **Staff:** Prof 2; Other 2. **Subjects:** Business, law, information brokering. **Holdings:** 500 books. **Subscriptions:** 10 journals and other serials, 2 newspapers. **Services:** Library open to Burwell Enterprises clients. **Automated Operations:** Computerized cataloging. **Computerized Information Services:** DIALOG Information Services, WESTLAW, BRS Information Technologies, EasyNet, CompuServe Information Service, VU/TEXT Information Services, Data-Star, DataTimes; Information Brokers (internal database); DIALMAIL (electronic mail service). **Publications:** Burwell Directory of Information Brokers; Bibliography on Information Brokering; Information Broker (newsletter). **Remarks:** FAX: (713)537-8332; Electronic mail address(es): Burwell (DIALMAIL).

Bush Center
See: **St. John's Abbey and University - Hill Monastic Manuscript Library** (14334)

Bush-Holley House
See: **The Historical Society of the Town of Greenwich, Inc.** (7290)

Bush Memorial Library
See: **Hamline University - Bush Memorial Library - Special Collections** (6870)

★2399★
Bushnell Congregational Church - Library (Rel-Phil)
15000 Southfield Rd. Phone: (313)420-0528
Detroit, MI 48223 Mrs. George Unterburger, Lib.Cons.
Subjects: Bible and theology. **Holdings:** 1800 books; 19 bound periodical volumes; 310 filmstrips; 70 phonograph records; 50 slides. **Subscriptions:** 16 journals and other serials. **Services:** Library open to qualified persons by appointment.

★2400★
Business Communications Co., Inc. - Library (Sci-Engr)
25 Van Zant St. Phone: (203)853-4266
Norwalk, CT 06855 Robert Butler, Dir. of Oper.
Founded: 1971. **Staff:** Prof 12; Other 10. **Subjects:** Materials, energy, transportation, plastics, polymers, chemicals, biotechnology, communications, electronics, foods, beverages, health care. **Holdings:** 200 books; 10 VF drawers of clippings; 12 unbound manuscripts; research studies. **Services:** Library not open to the public. **Publications:** List of publications - available on request. **Remarks:** FAX: (203)853-0348.

★2401★
Business and Industrial Market Research Corporation - Factfinders (Bus-Fin)
245 E. 6th St., 4th Fl. Phone: (612)292-8513
St. Paul, MN 55101-1927 V.B. Colaiuta, Gen.Mgr.
Founded: 1979. **Staff:** 5. **Subjects:** Manufacturing and high technology industries and markets including computers, electronics, telecommunications, plastics, adhesives, sealants, coatings. **Holdings:** Figures not available. **Services:** Provides primary and secondary market research and business research including competitive analyses, market potential studies, industry overviews, market overviews, image surveys, and customer satisfaction surveys to businesses and the public on a fee basis. **Computerized Information Services:** DIALOG Information Services, BRS Information Technologies, CDC, PFDS Online, Mead Data Central; internal databases. **Remarks:** FAX: (612)291-9179.

★2402★
Business International - Information Center (Bus-Fin)
215 Park Ave. S. Phone: (212)460-0600
New York, NY 10003 Beth Kilmer, Mgr., Info.Ctr.
Founded: 1957. **Staff:** Prof 1. **Subjects:** Foreign investment, international trade, economics, finance, forecasting, critical issues monitoring. **Holdings:** Business International and Economist Intelligence Unit publications (complete set); corporate directories; annual reports on 1500 U.S. and foreign companies; databases for the United Nations, the World Bank, and major regional economic organizations. **Subscriptions:** 300 journals and other serials; 7 newspapers. **Services:** Interlibrary loan; copying; center open to clients, graduate students, and other business librarians by appointment. **Computerized Information Services:** DIALOG Information Services, LEXIS, Global Report; MARK*NET Service (electronic mail service). **Special Indexes:** Index to Business International weekly newsletters. **Remarks:** FAX: (212)995-8837.

Business Library for Job Seekers
See: **Haven Scott Associates** (7014)

★2403★
Business and Professional Women's Foundation - Marguerite Rawalt Resource Center (Soc Sci)
2012 Massachusetts Ave., N.W. Phone: (202)293-1200
Washington, DC 20036 Linda C. Hauck, Cons.Libn.
Founded: 1956. **Staff:** Prof 1. **Subjects:** Women, with special emphasis on economic issues of importance to working women: jobs, careers, occupational segregation, comparable worth, sexual harassment, displaced homemakers, women's legal status. **Holdings:** 5000 books; 650 dissertations on microfilm; 12,000 VF materials; archival materials. **Subscriptions:** 113 journals and other serials. **Services:** Center open to staff only. **Computerized Information Services:** BRS Information Technologies. **Publications:** Selected Acquisitions, bimonthly.

★2404★
Business and Professional Women's Foundation - Rawalt Resource Center (Bus-Fin)
2012 Massachusetts Ave., N.W. Phone: (202)293-1100
Washington, DC 20036 Irma Burks, Dir. of Educ.
Subjects: Working women - participation in business and professions, equal opportunities, economic self-sufficiency. **Holdings:** 20,000 volumes. **Subscriptions:** 125 journals and other serials. **Services:** Center not open to the public. **Formerly:** National Federation of Business and Professional Women's Clubs, Inc. of the U.S.A.

★2405★
Business Trend Analysis - Library (Bus-Fin)
2171 Jericho Tpke. Phone: (516)462-5454
Commack, NY 11725 J. Marquart, Libn.
Founded: 1979. **Staff:** 1. **Subjects:** Marketing, business, economics. **Special Collections:** 400 industry reports; 315 subject and company article files. **Holdings:** 200 reports. **Subscriptions:** 400 journals and other serials; 8 newspapers. **Services:** Library not open to the public. **Computerized Information Services:** DIALOG Information Services. **Remarks:** FAX: (516)462-1842. Telex: 4973973 (BTA UI). **Staff:** Carol Cornell, Dir. of Res.

Business Week Magazine Library
See: **McGraw-Hill, Inc.** (9915)

J. Oliver Buswell, Jr. Library
See: **Covenant Theological Seminary - J. Oliver Buswell, Jr. Library** (4391)

Buswell Memorial Library
See: **Wheaton College** (20369)

★2406★
Butantan Institute - Library (Biol Sci, Med)
Avenida Vital Brazil, 1500
C.P. 65 Phone: 11 8137222
01051 Sao Paulo, SP, Brazil Renata Lara Paes de Barros, Chf.Libn.
Founded: 1899. **Staff:** 10. **Subjects:** Biology, immunology, bacteriology, chemistry, pharmacology, herpetology, biotechnology, production of serums and vaccines. **Holdings:** 71,000 volumes. **Subscriptions:** 109 journals and other serials; 3 newspapers. **Services:** Interlibrary loan; copying; SDI; library open to the public. **Publications:** Memorias Instituto Butantan; Coletanea Resumos Trab. Publ. Pesq. I. Butantan; Monografias I. Butantan; Bol. Biotecnologia. **Remarks:** FAX: 11 8151505. Telex: 11 83325 BUTA BR. Maintained by Brazil - Secretary of State for Health. **Also Known As:** Instituto Butantan. **Staff:** Ana Cristina Pavan Medeiros.

Butcher Toy Lending Library
See: **Emporia State University** (5345)

★2407★
Butler & Binion - Law Library (Law)
1600 First Interstate Plaza Phone: (713)237-3655
Houston, TX 77002-0000 Margarita Bull, Lib.Dir.
Staff: Prof 1; Other 3. **Subjects:** Law - oil and gas, securities, tax, labor, patent, corporate, banking. **Special Collections:** Early Laws of Texas (complete set). **Holdings:** 32,000 books. **Subscriptions:** 100 journals and other serials. **Services:** Interlibrary loan; copying; library open to librarians and local attorneys by appointment. **Computerized Information Services:** LEXIS, WESTLAW, DIALOG Information Services. **Publications:** Library Bulletin; Tax Bulletin, both monthly - both for internal distribution only. **Remarks:** FAX: (713)237-3202 and (713)237-3201.

Butler Center Library
See: **Mansfield University** (9643)

★2408★
Butler County Historical and Genealogical Society - Library (Hist)
P.O. Box 435 Phone: (502)526-4722
Morgantown, KY 42261 Syble Givens, Hd.Libn.
Subjects: History - local, family, surrounding counties and families. **Holdings:** 300 books; 25 nonbook items. **Services:** Copying; library open to the public. **Remarks:** Library located at Butler County Library, 125 W. Ohio St., Morgantown, KY 42261.

★2409★
Butler County Historical Society - Greenville-Butler County Library (Hist)
101 Adams St. Phone: (205)382-3216
Greenville, AL 36037 Judy Taylor
Subjects: History - family, Butler County, Alabama; photograph history. **Special Collections:** Cemetery, family, church, county, and courthouse records. **Holdings:** Figures not available. **Services:** Copying; library open to the public for reference use only.

★2410★
Butler County Historical Society - Olive Clifford Stone Library (Hist)
381 E. Central
Box 696 Phone: (316)321-9333
El Dorado, KS 67042 Anna Louise Borger, Libn.
Staff: Prof 1. **Subjects:** Local history, genealogy, oil history. **Special Collections:** William Allen White Collection (313 volumes); composer Robert Graham (manuscripts of musical scores). **Holdings:** 3037 books. **Subscriptions:** 7 journals and other serials. **Services:** Copying; library open to the public. **Publications:** Newsletter, bimonthly.

★2411★
Butler County Law Library (Law)
Court House
P.O. Box 1208 Phone: (412)284-5206
Butler, PA 16003-1208 Marcia S. Rettig, Law Libn.
Staff: Prof 1. **Subjects:** Law. **Holdings:** 21,000 volumes; 131 volumes of Federal Regulation Codes; Federal Register (daily); 145 Advance Sheets; 35 binders of CCH Tax Service. **Subscriptions:** 15 journals and other serials. **Services:** Interlibrary loan; copying; library open to the public. **Computerized Information Services:** WESTLAW. **Publications:** Genealogical Abstracts from the Statutes at Large and the Laws of Pennsylvania, 1683-1820. **Remarks:** FAX: (412)284-5210.

★2412★
Butler County Law Library Association (Law)
141 Court St. Phone: (513)887-3456
Hamilton, OH 45011 Anita K. Shew, Lib.Dir.
Founded: 1889. **Staff:** Prof 1; Other 3. **Subjects:** Law. **Holdings:** 45,000 volumes. **Subscriptions:** 150 journals. **Services:** Library open to the public. **Computerized Information Services:** WESTLAW, Hannah Ohio Legislative Service, LEXIS. **Networks/Consortia:** Member of OHIONET. **Remarks:** FAX: (513)887-3696.

Edward H. Butler Library
See: **State University College at Buffalo** (15704)

Eva Butler Library
See: **Indian and Colonial Research Center, Inc.** (7748)

★2413★
Butler Hospital - Isaac Ray Medical Library (Med)
345 Blackstone Blvd. Phone: (401)455-6248
Providence, RI 02906 Ruthann Gildea, Libn.
Founded: 1952. **Staff:** 1.5. **Subjects:** Psychiatry, psychology. **Special Collections:** Butler Hospital Archives; Isaac Ray Collection (medical and psychiatric books published before the 20th century). **Holdings:** 3000 books; 5000 bound periodical volumes. **Subscriptions:** 100 journals and other serials. **Services:** Interlibrary loan; copying; library open to the public by appointment. **Computerized Information Services:** BRS Information Technologies, DOCLINE; CD-ROM (MEDLINE). Performs searches. **Networks/Consortia:** Member of Association of Rhode Island Health Sciences Librarians (ARIHSL), BHSL, National Network of Libraries of Medicine - New England Region, Rhode Island Library Network (RHILINET). **Publications:** New book list 4/year; journal holdings list.

★2414★
Butler Institute of American Art - Hopper Resource Library (Art)
524 Wick Ave. Phone: (216)743-1107
Youngstown, OH 44502 Peggy (Margarat S.) Kaulback, Dir. of Res./Archv.
Founded: 1919. **Staff:** Prof 1; Other 1. **Subjects:** Artists, American art, graphic arts, Indians, art schools and periods, European art. **Holdings:** 2000 books; 1600 slides; files and catalogs on American artists; archival materials. **Services:** Library open to the public for reference use only. **Remarks:** FAX: (216)743-9567. **Staff:** Dr. Louis A. Zona, Dir.

John A. Butler Learning Center
See: **Dunwoody Institute** (5062)

Butler Library
See: **Columbia University - Butler Library** (4005)

★2415★
Butler Memorial Hospital - Armstrong Memorial Medical Library (Med)
911 E. Brady St. Phone: (412)284-4240
Butler, PA 16001 Rita V. Liebler, Med.Libn.
Staff: Prof 1. **Subjects:** Medicine, nursing, and allied health sciences. **Holdings:** 1100 books; 300 bound periodical volumes; 275 videotapes; 575 audiotapes. **Subscriptions:** 117 journals and other serials. **Services:** Interlibrary loan; copying; library open to the public for reference use only when librarian is present. **Computerized Information Services:** BRS Information Technologies. **Networks/Consortia:** Member of National Network of Libraries of Medicine - Middle Atlantic Region. **Remarks:** FAX: (412)284-4645.

★2416★
Butler University - Irwin Library - Hugh Thomas Miller Rare Book Room (Area-Ethnic, Hum)
46th & Sunset Phone: (317)283-9265
Indianapolis, IN 46208 Gisela S. Terrell, Rare Bks. & Spec.Coll.Libn.
Staff: Prof 1; Other 1. **Subjects:** Liberal arts and sciences, pharmacy, education, fine and performing arts, athletics. **Special Collections:** William F. Charters South Sea Islands Collection, 18th-20th centuries (2700 titles); Harold E. Johnson Sibelius Collection (scores; books; recordings, including little-known compositions never performed in the U.S.); Lincoln Collection (including the library of Charles W. Moores; books; pamphlets; manuscripts; newspapers; memorabilia); Kate Greenaway Collection; Kin Hubbard-Gaar Williams Collection (original cartoons; sketchbooks; books; manuscripts; memorabilia); Jeanette Siron Pelton Botanical Print Collection, 15th-19th centuries; zoological print collection, 15th-19th centuries; 19th century American sheet music; Alice Bidwell Wesenberg Collection of 20th Century American Poetry; Dellinger Collection of Early Educational Materials; Butler University Archives (485 linear feet); National Track and Field Hall of Fame Historical Research Library (25,000 books, periodical issues, films, photographs, programs, archives). **Holdings:** 36,500 book titles; 327 serial titles; 2060 pieces of sheet and bound music; 500 manuscripts; 225 phonograph records; 250 prints; 2445 photographs; 172 pieces of original art. **Subscriptions:** 36 journals and other serials. **Services:** Interlibrary loan; copying; collections open to the public upon registration. **Automated Operations:** Computerized cataloging. **Computerized Information Services:** OCLC, Eighteenth Century Short Title Catalogue (ESTC). **Publications:** Newsletter, irregular; special bibliographies. **Special Catalogs:** Lincolniana (catalog of Charles W. Moore's Lincoln Collection); checklist of Gaar Williams Materials; checklist of American popular music before 1901; checklist of Dellinger Collection; Sibelius checklist of scores; National Track & Field Hall of Fame Library Catalogue of Current Holdings; Treasures at Butler University (illustrated catalog of print and manuscript specimen collections); Lincoln Portraits (Durman Collection Catalogue); special archives checklists. **Special Indexes:** Special archives indexes. **Remarks:** FAX: (317)283-9519.

★2417★
Butler University - Jordan College of Fine Arts Music Library (Mus, Art)
46th & Sunset Phone: (317)283-9243
Indianapolis, IN 46208 Phyllis J. Schoonover, Music Libn.
Founded: 1951. **Staff:** Prof 2. **Subjects:** Art, arts administration, music, music literature, dance, radio and television, theater arts. **Special Collections:** Music education; American popular music, 1900-1960 (6000 items). **Holdings:** 12,633 books; 1295 bound periodical volumes; 17,819 scores; 10,195 sound recordings; 205 cassettes; 128 compact discs; 271 video cassettes; 234 masters and honors theses. **Subscriptions:** 93 journals and other serials. **Services:** Interlibrary loan; copying; library open to the public for reference use only. **Remarks:** (317)283-9519. **Staff:** Mark Crayton, Assoc. Music Libn.

★2418★
Butler University - Science Library (Sci-Engr, Biol Sci)
46th & Sunset Phone: (317)283-9401
Indianapolis, IN 46208 Barbara Howes, Sci.Libn.
Founded: 1973. **Staff:** Prof 1.5; Other 1. **Subjects:** Botany, chemistry, environmental sciences, mathematics, pharmacy, physics, zoology. **Holdings:** 21,000 books; 26,500 bound periodical volumes; 12 VF drawers; 750 AV programs. **Subscriptions:** 600 journals and other serials. **Services:** Interlibrary loan; copying; library open to the public. **Computerized Information Services:** DIALOG Information Services. **Networks/Consortia:** Member of INCOLSA. **Remarks:** FAX: (317)283-9519.

Marshall W. Butt Library
See: **Portsmouth Naval Shipyard Museum** (13255)

★2419★
Butte County Law Library (Law)
Superior Court
One Court St. Phone: (916)538-7611
Oroville, CA 95965 Rose-Ellen Leonard, Law Libn.
Founded: 1907. **Staff:** 2. **Subjects:** Law. **Holdings:** 17,700 volumes. **Subscriptions:** 81 journals and other serials. **Services:** Copying; library open to the public. **Computerized Information Services:** DIALOG Information Services, WESTLAW. **Remarks:** Alternate telephone number(s): (916)538-7122.

Buttenwieser Library
See: **92nd Street Young Men's and Young Women's Hebrew Association - Buttenwieser Library** (11815)

★2420★
Butterick Company, Inc. - Archives (Art)
161 Avenue of the Americas Phone: (212)620-2500
New York, NY 10013-1252 Lillian Esposito, Promotion Mgr.
Founded: 1863. **Staff:** 1. **Subjects:** Vogue/Butterick costume and marketing history. **Special Collections:** Archives of Butterick and Vogue Patterns; Butterick Fashion Marketing Company. **Holdings:** 200 books; 1500 bound periodical volumes; 1300 cubic feet of archival materials; 100 cubic feet of pictures, clippings, posters. **Subscriptions:** 10 journals and other serials. **Services:** Archives open to students for research. **Staff:** Sherry Onna Handlin, Proj.Archv.

★2421★
Butterworth Hospital - Butterworth Nursing Library (Med)
100 Michigan, N.E. Phone: (616)774-1779
Grand Rapids, MI 49503 Diane Hummel, Nurs.Libn.
Founded: 1957. **Staff:** Prof 2. **Subjects:** Nursing and nursing education, psychology. **Special Collections:** National League for Nursing (NLN) publications; American Nurses' Association publications (12 VF drawers for both collections). **Holdings:** 2564 books; 1702 bound periodical volumes; 580 AV programs. **Subscriptions:** 106 journals and other serials. **Services:** Interlibrary loan; copying; library open to the public for reference use only. **Automated Operations:** Computerized cataloging. **Computerized Information Services:** MEDLINE. **Remarks:** FAX: (616)732-3527. **Staff:** Marie Deyman, Asst.Libn.

★2422★
Butterworth Hospital - Health Sciences Library (Med)
100 Michigan, N.E. Phone: (616)774-1655
Grand Rapids, MI 49503-9979 Eileen M. Dechow, Dir.
Founded: 1948. **Staff:** Prof 2; Other 1.5. **Subjects:** Medicine, surgery, medical/surgical specialties. **Special Collections:** Butterworth Management Institute Library (general management; 260 titles, including AV programs). **Holdings:** 3400 books; 6700 bound periodical volumes; pamphlets; 1650 audio and videocassettes. **Subscriptions:** 230 periodicals. **Services:** Interlibrary loan; copying; SDI; library open to the public by appointment. **Computerized Information Services:** MEDLARS, DIALOG Information Services. Performs searches on fee basis. **Networks/Consortia:** Member of National Network of Libraries of Medicine - Greater Midwest Region, Lakeland Area Library Network (LAKENET). **Publications:** Medical Library News, monthly - for internal distribution only. **Remarks:** FAX: (616)732-3527. **Staff:** Sandra K. Swanson, Libn.

Edith Buxbaum Library
See: **Seattle Institute for Psychoanalysis - Edith Buxbaum Library** (14994)

★2423★
BYGGDOK/The Swedish Institute of Building Documentation - Information Center (Plan)
Haelsingegatan 47 Phone: 8 34 01 70
S-113 31 Stockholm, Sweden Bengt Eresund, Mng.Dir.
Founded: 1966. **Staff:** 24. **Subjects:** Construction, building, architecture, planning, building services, environment, environmental technology. **Special Collections:** Swedish Council for Building Research reports (complete set). **Holdings:** 1000 linear meters of books. **Subscriptions:** 650 journals and other serials. **Services:** Interlibrary loan; copying; center open to the public with restrictions. **Computerized Information Services:** DIALOG Information Services, PFDS Online, STN International; produces the BYGGDOK system with the following databases: BODIL, BYGGFO, VA NYTT, REGLER. Performs searches on fee basis. Contact Person: Monica Stroemberg. **Publications:** Byggreferat abstract journal; VA NYTT abstract journal. **Remarks:** FAX: 8 324859. Telex: 12563. **Also Known As:** Institutet for Byggdokumentation. **Staff:** Borje Hoglander; Gerard Lingre; Barbro Widell, Libn.; Monica Stromberg, Libn.; Inger Hellden, Libn.

Byrd Polar Research Center
See: **Ohio State University - Byrd Polar Research Center** (12298)

John Byrne Memorial Library
See: **Des Plaines Historical Society** (4793)

Byzantine Library
See: **Harvard University - Dumbarton Oaks Research Library and Collection** (6963)

C

C.A.B. International
See: **Great Britain - C.A.B. International - Library Services Centre** (6670)

★2424★
C.K. Geoenergy Corporation - Library
1569 Santa Anita
Las Vegas, NV 89119
Subjects: Geology, petroleum engineering. **Holdings:** 500 books; 350 reports. **Remarks:** Currently inactive.

★2425★
C.N.R. Istituto Sperimentale Talassografico A Cerruti - Biblioteca (Biol Sci)
Via Roma 3 Phone: 99 494957
I-74100 Taranto, Italy Dr. S. Geraci
Founded: 1920. **Staff:** Prof 1; Other 1. **Subjects:** Marine biology, oceanography, analytical chemistry, marine microbiology. **Special Collections:** Rare "Infolio" editions. **Holdings:** 2500 books; 700 bound periodical volumes; 14,000 reports; 10 blocks of microfiche. **Services:** Library open to the public with special permission. **Computerized Information Services:** Internal Database. Performs searches. Contact Person: Ms. M. Filippi, Libn. **Publications:** Oebalia; Technical Report; Journal of Marine Biology and Oceanography. **Special Indexes:** Key-Words Index. **Remarks:** FAX: 99 494811.

C & O Canal Museum
See: **Barrons Ltd.** (1542)

C & O Canal NHP Resource Center
See: **U.S. Natl. Park Service - Chesapeake & Ohio Canal National Historical Park** (17688)

★2426★
C & S/Sovran - Corporate Library (Bus-Fin)
2 Commercial Pl.
Box 600 Phone: (804)441-4419
Norfolk, VA 23510 Lois Reeves, Corp.Libn.
Founded: 1968. **Staff:** Prof 1; Other 1. **Subjects:** Banking, finance, management, personnel administration, accounting. **Holdings:** 2600 volumes; 15 VF drawers; 337 cassettes; 16 directories; 45 theses; microfiche. **Subscriptions:** 200 journals and other serials. **Services:** Interlibrary loan; copying; library open to the public for reference use only. **Computerized Information Services:** DIALOG Information Services. **Publications:** Recent Acquisitions, irregular; Periodical Holdings List, quarterly; Audio Cassette List, quarterly - all for internal distribution only; Guide to the Corporate Library, irregular. **Remarks:** Alternate telephone number(s): 441-4489.

★2427★
Cabell Huntington Hospital - Health Science Library (Med)
1340 Hal Greer Blvd. Phone: (304)526-2022
Huntington, WV 25701 Deborah L. Woodburn, Hea.Sci.Libn.
Staff: Prof 1. **Subjects:** Medicine, surgery, neonatal care, pediatric intensive care, burns, kidney dialysis, allied health sciences. **Holdings:** 1466 books; 207 bound periodical volumes. **Subscriptions:** 102 journals and other serials. **Services:** Interlibrary loan; library not open to the public. **Networks/Consortia:** Member of Huntington Health Science Library Consortium.

James Branch Cabell Library
See: **Virginia Commonwealth University - James Branch Cabell Library** (19861)

★2428★
Cable News Network, Inc. - Library (Aud-Vis, Info Sci)
One CNN Center
Box 105366 Phone: (404)827-1125
Atlanta, GA 30348 Kathy D. Christensen, Dir.
Founded: 1980. **Staff:** Prof 10; Other 13. **Subjects:** International, national, and regional news. **Special Collections:** News Video Archive, 1980 to present. **Holdings:** 8500 reels of videotape; 35,000 videocassettes. **Subscriptions:** 45 journals and other serials; 10 newspapers. **Services:** Library not open to the public. **Automated Operations:** Computerized video cataloging and circulation. **Computerized Information Services:** DIALOG Information Services, NEXIS, DataTimes, Washington Alert Service, VU/TEXT Information Services; internal video database. Performs searches on fee basis on video database only. Contact Person: CNN Library Tape Sales, 827-1335. **Remarks:** FAX: (404)827-1840. **Staff:** Claudia Burton, Libn.; William Allen, Libn.; Lesley DiPlacido, Lib.Mgr.; Sally Griffin, Sys.Libn.; Fran Pici, Libn.; Debra Bade, Libn. Michelle Hall, Libn.; Becky Cline, Libn.

★2429★
Cable Television Information Center (Info Sci)
1700 Skaker Church Rd., N.W. Phone: (206)866-2080
Olympia, WA 98502 Harold E. Horn, Pres.
Founded: 1972. **Subjects:** Cable television. **Holdings:** Figures not available. **Subscriptions:** 45 journals and other serials. **Remarks:** The center is a nonprofit, nonpartisan organization designed to help local government officials make informed decisions about cable television by providing background information, valuable contacts, and suggestions.

★2430★
Cabot Corporation - Boyertown Technical Library (Sci-Engr)
County Line Rd. Phone: (215)369-8300
Boyertown, PA 19512 Catherine Yoder, Libn.
Founded: 1960. **Subjects:** Columbium, tantalum, chemical and metallurgical processing. **Holdings:** 1500 books; 200 bound periodical volumes; 1 VF drawer of patents; 1 drawer of microfiche; 18 shelves of documents. **Subscriptions:** 52 journals and other serials; 11 newspapers. **Services:** Interlibrary loan. **Computerized Information Services:** DIALOG Information Services, Teltech Inc. **Remarks:** FAX: (215)367-2068. **Staff:** Anthony J. Hickl, Ph.D., Mgr., Tech.

★2431★
Cabot Corporation - Research & Development Library (Sci-Engr)
Box 5001 Phone: (806)665-0961
Pampa, TX 79065 Barry Hedrick, Supv.
Subjects: Thermodynamics, fluid flow, combustion, flame theory. **Holdings:** 650 books. **Subscriptions:** 22 journals and other serials. **Services:** Library not open to the public.

★2432★
Cabot Corporation - Technical Information Center (Sci-Engr)
157 Concord Rd. Phone: (508)663-3455
Billerica, MA 01821 Angea S. Reid, Mgr.
Founded: 1947. **Staff:** Prof 2; Other 2. **Subjects:** Chemistry, chemical engineering, polymers and plastics, paints, carbon black and white pigments, physics, inks, petroleum, rubber. **Holdings:** 7000 books; 8000 bound periodical volumes; 12 VF drawers of patents; 33 VF drawers of reprints and pamphlets; 15 VF drawers of trade literature; 40 VF drawers and 12,000 microfiche of company reports and correspondence; 40,000 cards of technical abstracts. **Subscriptions:** 250 journals and other serials. **Services:** Interlibrary loan; center open to the public on request. **Automated Operations:** Computerized cataloging, acquisitions, and serials. **Computerized Information Services:** DIALOG Information Services, PFDS Online, STN International; internal database. **Special Catalogs:** Patent Catalog; Research Reports Catalog. **Special Indexes:** Keyword index to company research reports (online). **Remarks:** FAX: (508)663-5471.

Godfrey Lowell Cabot Science Library
See: **Harvard University** (6966)

★2433★
Cabot Institute of Applied Arts and Technology - Library (Educ)
Prince Philip Dr.
P.O. Box 1693 Phone: (709)778-2547
St. John's, NF, Canada A1C 5P7 Beverley Neable, Libn.
Founded: 1963. **Staff:** Prof 2; Other 3. **Subjects:** Business, engineering technology, electronics technology, medical technology. **Holdings:** 25,000 books; 800 bound periodical volumes; 750 volumes of serials on microfilm. **Subscriptions:** 400 journals and other serials; 14 newspapers. **Services:** Interlibrary loan; copying; library open to the public. **Publications:** Books added to the library, monthly - for internal distribution only. **Remarks:** FAX: (709)737-2182. **Staff:** Joan Roberts.

★2434★
Cabot Institute of Applied Arts and Technology - Topsail Campus Resource Center (Educ)
P.O. Box 1693
St. John's, NF, Canada A1C 5P7 Phone: (709)778-2320
Founded: 1975. **Staff:** Prof 1. **Subjects:** Medical laboratory and x-ray technology, nursing, food management, commercial art, respiratory therapy, ultrasonography, biomedical technology. **Holdings:** 7000; 600 BPV; 300 AV programs; 300 volumes of periodicals on microfiche. **Subscriptions:** 175 journals and other serials. **Services:** Interlibrary loan; copying; library open to the public with restrictions. **Automated Operations:** Computerized cataloging and serials. **Remarks:** FAX: (709)778-2349. **Staff:** Joan E. Roberts, Libn.

Cabots Old Indian Pueblo Museum
See: **Landmark Conservators** (8931)

Cabrillo Marine Museum
See: **Los Angeles Department of Recreation and Parks** (9340)

Cabrillo National Monument
See: **U.S. Natl. Park Service** (17678)

★2435★
Cabrini Medical Center - Dr. Massimo Bazzini Memorial Library (Med)
227 E. 19th St.
New York, NY 10003 Phone: (212)995-6630
Founded: 1930. **Staff:** Prof 3; Other 3. **Subjects:** Medicine, surgery, nursing. **Holdings:** 2950 books; 2700 bound periodical volumes; 470 AV programs. **Subscriptions:** 290 journals and other serials. **Services:** Interlibrary loan; library open to the public by appointment. **Computerized Information Services:** NLM, BRS Information Technologies, DIALOG Information Services. **Networks/Consortia:** Member of Medical Library Center of New York (MLCNY). **Publications:** Newsletter and accessions list, quarterly. **Special Catalogs:** Audiovisual holdings; publications on religion and related subjects. **Remarks:** FAX: (212)995-6639. **Staff:** Rustico Paras, Asst.Libn.; Trevor St. Hill, Media Spec.

G.H. Cachiaras Memorial Library
See: **Minnesota Bible College - Library** (10461)

★2436★
Cadmium Council, Inc. - Library (Sci-Engr)
P.O. Box 2664 Phone: (203)625-0911
Greenwich, CT 06836 Hugh Morrow, Exec.Dir.
Founded: 1980. **Staff:** Prof 1. **Subjects:** Cadmium - metal, compounds, industry, markets and applications, health effects, recycling and recovery, regulations. **Special Collections:** Proceedings of International Cadmium Conference. **Holdings:** Figures not available. **Services:** Interlibrary loan, copying. **Remarks:** FAX: (203)625-0918.

★2437★
CAE Electronics, Ltd. - Engineering Reference Library (Sci-Engr)
P.O. Box 1800 Phone: (514)341-6780
St. Laurent, PQ, Canada H4L 4X4 Ms. Barbara Clement
Founded: 1955. **Staff:** 2. **Subjects:** Component engineering, electrical engineering, computer systems, aeronautics, space technology, communications, simulation, mechanical engineering. **Holdings:** 3200 books; 10,000 commercial specifications and standards; military specifications and federal standards (complete set). **Subscriptions:** 250 journals and other serials; 5 newspapers. **Services:** Interlibrary loan; library not open to the public. **Computerized Information Services:** CAN/OLE. **Remarks:** FAX: (514)341-7699. Telex: 05-824856. Library located at 8585 Cote de Liesse Rd., Montreal, PQ H4T 1G6.

★2438★
CAE Link Corporation - Link Flight Simulation Division - Information Center (Sci-Engr)
Colesville Rd., MS659 Phone: (607)721-4953
Binghamton, NY 13902 Carol Weissman, Mgr.Adm.Serv.
Founded: 1951. **Staff:** Prof 1; Other 1. **Subjects:** Electrical and electronic engineering; aeronautics; economics; mathematics; computers. **Holdings:** 7000 books; internal and technical reports; manuals; reprints; handbooks; microforms. **Subscriptions:** 150 journals and other serials. **Services:** Interlibrary loan; copying; center open to the public by appointment. **Computerized Information Services:** DIALOG Information Services, BRS Information Technologies, DTIC, OCLC, NASA/RECON, NEXIS. **Networks/Consortia:** Member of South Central Research Library Council (SCRLC). **Remarks:** FAX: (607)721-4952. Telex: 607-771-8477. **Staff:** Robin Petrus, Info.Couns.; Sue Beckwith, Info.Assoc.

Jefferson Caffery Louisiana Room
See: **University of Southwestern Louisiana - Jefferson Caffery Louisiana Room** (19356)

John Cage Archive
See: **Northwestern University - Music Library** (12086)

★2439★
Cahill Gordon & Reindel - Law Library (Law)
80 Pine St. Phone: (212)701-3542
New York, NY 10005 Margaret J. Davenport, Libn.
Founded: 1920. **Staff:** Prof 3; Other 11. **Subjects:** Law - antitrust, corporation, securities, tax. **Holdings:** 6750 texts; 3100 bound periodical volumes; 21,000 other volumes; 40 VF drawers; 650 reels of microfilm. **Subscriptions:** 275 journals and other serials. **Services:** Interlibrary loan; copying; library open to the public by permission only. **Computerized Information Services:** DIALOG Information Services, LEXIS, Dow Jones News/Retrieval, WESTLAW, NewsNet, Inc., LEGI-SLATE, VU/TEXT Information Services, DataTimes, Information America, Financial Times Profile Business Information (FTBI), Maxwell Online, Inc., ORBIT Search Service, Securities Data Company. **Remarks:** FAX: (212)269-5420. **Staff:** Chan-Shen Lung, Asst.Libn.; Mary Cahn, Ref.Libn.

★2440★
Cahill Gordon & Reindel - Library (Law)
1990 K St., N.W., Suite 950 Phone: (202)862-8960
Washington, DC 20006 Denise Gorham Brown, Law Libn.
Staff: Prof 1. **Subjects:** Law - corporate, antitrust, international, government contracts, communications, taxation, immigration. **Holdings:** 6000 books. **Subscriptions:** 51 journals and other serials; 7 newspapers. **Services:** Interlibrary loan; copying; library open to the public by appointment. **Computerized Information Services:** LEXIS, NEXIS, WESTLAW.

★2441★
Cahners Publishing Company/R.R. Bowker Co. - Frederic G. Melcher Library (Publ)
245 W. 17th St. Phone: (212)463-6850
New York, NY 10011 Jean Peters, Libn.
Founded: 1963. **Staff:** Prof 2. **Subjects:** Book industries and trade, library science. **Special Collections:** Adolf Growoll scrapbooks on book trade history. **Holdings:** 8000 books; 700 bound periodical volumes; 85 VF drawers. **Subscriptions:** 400 journals and other serials. **Services:** Interlibrary loan; library open to the public for reference use only on request. **Computerized Information Services:** DIALOG Information Services. **Remarks:** The library serves both Cahners Publishing Company and R.R. Bowker Co. **Formerly:** R.R. Bowker Company - Frederic G. Melcher Library.

★2442★
Cahoon Museum of American Art - American Painting Research Library (Art)
4676 Falmouth Rd.
P.O. Box 1853 Phone: (508)428-7581
Cotuit, MA 02635 Maureen A.V. Twohig, Asst. to Dir./Assoc.Cur.
Founded: 1984. **Staff:** 3. **Subjects:** American painting - revolutionary times to 1940. **Holdings:** 2000 books; periodicals; auction sale records; exhibition catalogs. **Subscriptions:** 3 journals and other serials. **Services:** Copying; library open to members by appointment only. **Special Catalogs:** American Paintings From Nature: Flowers, Fruits and Leaf (exhibition catalog).

★2443★
CAI - Technical Library (Sci-Engr)
550 W. Northwest Hwy.
Barrington, IL 60010 Phone: (708)381-2400
Staff: 1. **Subjects:** Mathematics, optics, electronics, photography. **Holdings:** 650 volumes; 4 VF drawers of patents; 8 VF drawers of pamphlets. **Subscriptions:** 110 journals and other serials. **Services:** Library not open to the public. **Remarks:** A division of Recon/Optical, Inc. **Also Known As:** Chicago Aerial Industries.

J.B. Cain Archives of Mississippi Methodism and Millsaps College
See: **Millsaps College - Millsaps-Wilson Library - J.B. Cain Archives of Mississippi Methodism and Millsaps College** (10412)

★2444★
(Cairo) American Center - American Cultural Center Library (Educ)
4, Ahmed Ragheb St.
Garden City Phone: 3558927
Cairo, Egypt Akhnoukh L. Fanous, Lib.Dir.
Founded: 1974. **Staff:** 10. **Special Collections:** U.S. Congressional Hearings collection. **Holdings:** 15,700 books; 800 reports; 132 reels of microfilm; 692 videotapes. **Subscriptions:** 205 journals and other serials; 4 newspapers. **Services:** Interlibrary loan; copying; SDI; library open to the public with restrictions. **Computerized Information Services:** DIALOG Information Services; internal database. **Publications:** Current Awareness Service (FOCUS). **Remarks:** FAX: 3573591. Telex: 23227 AMEMB UN. Maintained or supported by the U.S. Information Agency. Focus is on materials that will assist peoples outside the United States to learn about the United States, its people, history, culture, political processes, and social milieux. **Formerly:** Its USIS Library. **Staff:** Magda S. Kamel; Atef Hamdy; Suzan Metry; Mervat Habashi.

★2445★
Cal Recovery Systems, Inc. - Library (Env-Cons)
725C Alfred Nobel Dr. Phone: (510)724-0220
Hercules, CA 94547 Lisa Reece, Libn.
Subjects: Wastes, alternative energy sources. **Holdings:** 500 books; 1500 reports. **Subscriptions:** 30 journals and other serials. **Services:** Library not open to the public. **Formerly:** Located in Richmond, CA.

★2446★
Calais Free Library (Hist)
Calais, ME 04619 Phone: (207)454-2758
E. Marilyn Diffin, Libn.
Founded: 1892. **Staff:** Prof 3; Other 1. **Special Collections:** James Shepherd Pike Papers; Vroom Papers (35 newspaper articles); Hayden Diaries (60 notebooks); Ned Lamb Scrapbook (148 pages); Calais cemetery records; Calais Advertisers, 1836 to present (newspaper on microfilm). **Holdings:** 24,723 volumes. **Subscriptions:** 39 journals and other serials. **Services:** Interlibrary loan; copying; library open to the public with restrictions. **Staff:** Karen Herrick, Asst.Libn.; Dona Stover, Children's Libn.

★2447★
Calais Regional Hospital - Health Science Library (Med)
50 Franklin St. Phone: (207)454-7521
Calais, ME 04619 Janet Barnes, Ck.
Founded: 1976. **Staff:** 1. **Subjects:** Internal medicine, pediatrics, surgery, gynecology, nursing, anesthesia. **Holdings:** 1000 books. **Subscriptions:** 43 journals and other serials. **Services:** Library open to the public by appointment. **Remarks:** FAX: (207)454-3616.

★2448★
Calaveras County Law Library (Law)
Government Center Phone: (209)754-6314
San Andreas, CA 95249 Mike Ibold, Libn.
Subjects: California and federal law. **Holdings:** 7000 books; periodicals. **Services:** Copying; library open to the public for reference use only.

★2449★
Calaveras County Museum and Archives (Hist)
30 N. Main St.
P.O. Box 1281 Phone: (209)754-6513
San Andreas, CA 95249 Lorrayne Kennedy, Archv.
Founded: 1977.**Staff:** 1. **Subjects:** Local and state history, mother lode region, mining, Indians. **Special Collections:** Calaveras County Archives (407 linear feet of inquests, probates, great registers, court records, assessments, tax records, mining claims, hardcopy and microfilm); U.S. Census, 1850-1910; birth records; marriage records; cemetery records. **Holdings:** 350 books; 50 bound periodical volumes; diaries; manuscripts; documents; clippings; 120 oral history tapes; local maps. **Services:** Copying; archives open to the public on a limited schedule. **Publications:** Trips to the Mines. **Special Catalogs:** County Archives, newspapers, photographs.

★2450★
Calbiochem Corporation - Library (Biol Sci)
10933 N. Torrey Pines Rd. Phone: (619)450-5701
La Jolla, CA 92037 Susan Wright, Libn.
Founded: 1971. **Staff:** Prof 1. **Subjects:** Biochemistry, microbiology, enzymology, fermentation technology, organic and bio-organic chemistry, immunochemistry. **Holdings:** 500 books; 1000 bound periodical volumes. **Subscriptions:** 30 journals and other serials; 5 newspapers. **Services:** Library not open to the public. **Computerized Information Services:** DIALOG Information Services. **Remarks:** Company manufactures specialty research products in the above subject areas. FAX: (619)453-3552. Telex: 697934.

★2451★
(Calcutta) American Center - USIS Library (Educ)
7 Jawaharlal Nehru Rd.
Calcutta 700 013, India
Remarks: Maintained or supported by the U.S. Information Agency. Focus is on materials that will assist peoples outside the United States to learn about the United States, its people, history, culture, political processes, and social milieux.

★2452★
(Calcutta) American University - USIS Library (Educ)
1 Bidhan Sarani
Calcutta 700 073, India
Remarks: Maintained or supported by the U.S. Information Agency. Focus is on materials that will assist peoples outside the United States to learn about the United States, its people, history, culture, political processes, and social milieux.

Louis Calder Memorial Library
See: **University of Miami - School of Medicine** (18849)

Mary S. Calderone Library
See: **Sex Information & Education Council of the U.S. (SIECUS)** (15060)

★2453★
Calgary Board of Education - Professional Resource Centre (Educ, Info Sci)
2519 Richmond Rd., S.W. Phone: (403)294-6331
Calgary, AB, Canada T3E 4M2 M. Jane Webb, Lib.Hd.
Founded: 1973. **Staff:** Prof 3; Other 4. **Subjects:** Education. **Holdings:** 30,000 books; ERIC microfiche, 1969 to present. **Subscriptions:** 600 journals and other serials. **Services:** Copying; center open to the public for reference use only. **Computerized Information Services:** DIALOG Information Services; CD-ROM (ERIC). **Staff:** Katy Morrison, Teacher-Libn.; Carole Metcalfe, Libn.

★2454★
Calgary City Archives (Hist)
Box 2100, Sta. M
Calgary, AB, Canada T2G 2E3 Phone: (403)268-8180
Founded: 1981. **Staff:** Prof 4; Other 3. **Subjects:** City of Calgary. **Special Collections:** Archives generated by the City of Calgary, 1884-1980; Archives of the XV Olympic Winter Games, 1980-1988. **Holdings:** 1700 meters of records. **Services:** Copying; archives open to the public with restrictions. **Computerized Information Services:** Internal database. **Special Indexes:** Archival inventories. **Remarks:** FAX: (403)268-2362. **Staff:** Elizabeth Eso, City Archv.

★2455★
Calgary City Electric System - Resource Centre 1961 (Sci-Engr)
2808 Spiller Rd., S.E.
P.O. Box 2100, Sta. M Phone: (403)268-1100
Calgary, AB, Canada T2P 2M5 Shannon Christoffersen, Supv.
Founded: 1981. **Staff:** Prof 3. **Subjects:** Electrical engineering, transmission, distribution, customer relations, safety and training. **Holdings:** 6000 books; 150 videotapes, slide sets, films; 3000 other cataloged items. **Subscriptions:** 320 journals and other serials; 8 newspapers. **Services:** Interlibrary loan; SDI; AV services. **Automated Operations:** Computerized cataloging, acquisitions, and serials. **Computerized Information Services:** DIALOG Information Services, CAN/OLE; internal database. **Publications:** Library News, monthly - for internal distribution only. **Special Catalogs:** Standards list. **Remarks:** FAX: (403)269-1833.

★2456★
Calgary City Law Department - Library 8053 (Law)
Municipal Bldg.
800 McLeod Trail, S.E. Phone: (403)268-2429
Calgary, AB, Canada T2G 2M5 Leanne Culshaw-Ewert, Libn.
Staff: 1. **Subjects:** Law. **Services:** Library not open to the public. **Remarks:** FAX: (403)268-4634.

Calgary Correctional Centre
See: **Alberta Department of the Solicitor General** (261)

★2457★
Calgary Engineering & Environmental Library 8026 (Sci-Engr)
P.O. Box 2100, Sta. M Phone: (403)268-2793
Calgary, AB, Canada T2P 2M5 Allisen Stubbs, Lib.Spec.
Founded: 1985. **Staff:** 1. **Subjects:** Water treatment and distribution, soil science, sewerage, street design and maintenance. **Holdings:** 4500 books. **Subscriptions:** 210 journals and other serials. **Services:** Interlibrary loan; copying; library open to the public. **Automated Operations:** Computerized cataloging. **Computerized Information Services:** Internal database. **Remarks:** FAX: (403)268-8260.

★2458★
Calgary General Hospital - Library Services (Med)
841 Centre Ave., E. Phone: (403)268-9234
Calgary, AB, Canada T2E 0A1 Elizabeth Kirchner, Chf.Med.Libn.
Founded: 1940. **Staff:** Prof 2; Other 6. **Subjects:** Medicine, dentistry, hospital administration, nursing, paramedical sciences, allied health sciences. **Holdings:** 9000 books; 9000 bound periodical volumes; 1400 tapes and slides. **Subscriptions:** 450 journals and other serials. **Services:** Interlibrary loan; copying; LATCH; library open to the public with permission from the chief medical librarian. **Automated Operations:** Computerized public access catalog, cataloging, and circulation. **Computerized Information Services:** MEDLARS, DIALOG Information Services, MEDLINE, CAN/OLE, access to DOBIS Canadian Online Library System; CD-ROMs (MEDLINE, CINAHL); Envoy 100 (electronic mail service). **Special Catalogs:** AV catalog by title and by subject; union list of serials (both typed lists). **Remarks:** FAX: (403)268-9222.

★2459★
Calgary Herald - Library (Publ)
215 16th St., S.E. Phone: (403)235-7361
Calgary, AB, Canada T2P 0WB Karen Liddiard, Chf.Libn.
Founded: 1929. **Staff:** Prof 1; Other 8. **Subjects:** Newspaper reference topics. **Holdings:** 700 books; 1440 reels of microfilm of Calgary Herald; clippings; pictures. **Subscriptions:** 60 journals and other serials; 8 newspapers. **Services:** Library not open to the public. **Computerized Information Services:** QL Systems, Info Globe, Infomart Online, NEXIS. **Remarks:** FAX: (403)235-7379.

Calgary Institute of Religion
See: **Church of Jesus Christ of Latter-Day Saints** (3654)

★2460★
Calgary Planning & Building Department - Information Centre 8108 (Plan)
Box 2100, Postal Sta. M Phone: (403)268-5438
Calgary, AB, Canada T2P 2M5 Linda D. Read, Info.Off.
Founded: 1965. **Staff:** Prof 1; Other 2. **Subjects:** City planning; land use and controls; transportation; environment; parks and recreation; citizen participation; urban affairs; records management. **Special Collections:** City of Calgary publications (500 documents). **Holdings:** 10,000 books. **Subscriptions:** 270 journals and other serials; 5 newspapers. **Services:** Interlibrary loan; copying; center open to the public with prior arrangement. **Computerized Information Services:** Internal database. **Publications:** List of Publications, annual; What's New, bimonthly; Annual Report; In the News, daily - for internal distribution only. **Remarks:** FAX: (403)268-1528.

★2461★
Calgary Police Service - Library (Law)
316 7th Ave., S.E. Phone: (403)265-9870
Calgary, AB, Canada T2G 0J2 Lanette Morden, Lib.Techn.
Founded: 1980. **Staff:** Prof 1. **Subjects:** Law enforcement, training, management. **Holdings:** 5000 books; reports; microfiche. **Subscriptions:** 150 journals and other serials. **Services:** Interlibrary loan; copying; library open to the public for reference use only. **Automated Operations:** Computerized cataloging. **Publications:** Library news. **Remarks:** FAX: (403)265-9870.

★2462★
Calgary Social Services Department - Library (Soc Sci)
Box 2100, Sta. M (8116) Phone: (403)268-5111
Calgary, AB, Canada T2P 2M5 Judith Rempel, Libn.
Staff: Prof 2. **Subjects:** Social sciences, policy, and welfare; child development; juveniles; social services in other Canadian provinces; government publications. **Holdings:** 1200 books; 150 bound periodical volumes; 200 other cataloged items. **Subscriptions:** 60 journals and other serials. **Services:** Copying; library open to the public for reference use only. **Remarks:** FAX: (403)268-5765. Library located at Calgary Municipal Bldg., 7th Fl., 800 MacLeod Trail, S.E., Calgary, AB. **Staff:** Dilshad Jina, Info.Ck.

★2463★
Calgary Society for Students with Learning Difficulties - The Learning Centre - Learning Difficulties Library & Resource Centre (Educ)
3930 20 St., S.W. Phone: (403)686-9322
Calgary, AB, Canada T2T 4Z9 Thelma M. Wager, Libn.
Founded: 1984. **Staff:** Prof 1. **Subjects:** Learning disabilities in children, adolescents, and adults. **Special Collections:** Children's Library (800 titles); test library. **Holdings:** 100 taped books; 1500 professional, teaching, and learning resources; 6 VF drawers of articles; 180 assessment tools; 2 VF drawers of transparencies and internal reports. **Subscriptions:** 10 journals and other serials. **Services:** Interlibrary loan; copying; SDI; center open to the public. **Computerized Information Services:** DIALOG Information Services; internal database. **Publications:** Learning Centre News (newsletter), monthly - to the public. **Remarks:** FAX: (403)686-0627.

★2464★
Calgary Sun - Library (Publ)
2615 12th St., N.E. Phone: (403)250-4135
Calgary, AB, Canada T2E 7W9 Valerie Law, Chf.Libn.
Founded: 1955. **Staff:** Prof 2; Other 1. **Subjects:** Newspaper reference topics. **Holdings:** Newspaper clippings; Albertan, 1898-1980, and Calgary Sun, 1980 to present, on microfilm; photographs; pamphlets. **Services:** Library not open to the public. **Remarks:** FAX: (403)291-4116.

★2465★
Calgary Zoological Society - Technical Services Department (Biol Sci)
P.O. Box 3036, Sta. B Phone: (403)232-9300
Calgary, AB, Canada T2M 4R8 Karen Almadi, Libn.
Staff: Prof 1. **Subjects:** Animals, zoology, captive animal management, veterinary medicine. **Holdings:** 1504 volumes. **Subscriptions:** 88 journals and other serials. **Services:** Department open to the public for reference use only. **Computerized Information Services:** ISIS (International Species Identification System); AARS (Automated Animal Records System), ARKS (Animal Records Keeping System), MedARKS (internal databases). **Remarks:** FAX: (403)237-7582.

★2466★
Calgene, Inc. - Corporate Information Center (Biol Sci)
1920 5th St. Phone: (916)753-6313
Davis, CA 95616 Deanna L. Johnson, Libn.
Founded: 1982. **Staff:** Prof 1; Other 1. **Subjects:** Plant biochemistry, molecular biology, plant cell culture, plant propagation. **Holdings:** 1400 books; 700 bound periodical volumes; 25 microfiche. **Subscriptions:** 155 journals and other serials; 15 newspapers. **Services:** Interlibrary loan; copying; library not open to the public. **Automated Operations:** Computerized cataloging. **Computerized Information Services:** DIALOG Information Services, BIOSIS Connection, ORBIT Search Service, Dow Jones News/Retrieval, EPIC; DIALMAIL (electronic mail service). **Remarks:** FAX: (916)753-1510. Telex: 350370 CGENE.

Calgon Corporation
See: **Merck & Company, Inc.** (10118)

★2467★
Calhoun County Historical Museum - Library (Hist)
U.S. Hwy. 20 Phone: (712)297-8139
Rockwell City, IA 50579 Judy Webb, Cur.
Subjects: Local history, genealogy. **Special Collections:** Rare book collection. **Holdings:** 3000 books; 400 genealogical records; 5000 county obituary notices; 80 scrapbooks; clippings; county and school records; telephone books; cemetery records. **Services:** Library open to public under supervision.

★2468★
Calhoun County Museum - Archives and Library (Hist)
303 Butler St. Phone: (803)874-3964
St. Matthews, SC 29135 Debbie Roland, Dir.
Founded: 1952. **Staff:** Prof 1. **Subjects:** Genealogy, local history, archeology, geology. **Special Collections:** Lawrence Keitt papers; Geiger Collection; Olin M. Dantzler papers (microfilm); Rev. Paul Turquand sermons (microfilm); 1850 Census of Orangeburgh District; cemetery, Bible, and will records. **Holdings:** 430 books; 320 bound periodical volumes; 200 plats and grants; 100 private papers; 50 oral histories, 1952-1975. **Subscriptions:** 12 journals and other serials. **Services:** Interlibrary loan; copying; library open to the public.

★2469★
(Cali) Biblioteca Centro Colombo-Americano - USIS Collection (Educ)
Calle 13N, No. 8-45
Cali, Colombia
Remarks: Maintained or supported by the U.S. Information Agency. Focus is on materials that will assist peoples outside the United States to learn about the United States, its people, history, culture, political processes, and social milieux.

★2470★
California Academy of Sciences - Library (Env-Cons, Biol Sci)
Golden Gate Park Phone: (415)750-7102
San Francisco, CA 94118-9961 Tom Moritz, Academy Libn.
Founded: 1853. **Staff:** Prof 5.2; Other 3.8. **Subjects:** Anthropology, aquatic sciences and aquariology, astronomy, biodiversity, biogeography, botany, conservation/ecology, entomology, evolutionary biology, geology, herpetology, ichthyology, invertebrate zoology, mammalogy, marine biology, natural history, ornithology, paleontology, systematics. **Special Collections:** Academy archives; manuscript collection; media; fine arts; Biodiversity Resource Center. **Holdings:** 180,000 volumes; 75,000 maps; 145,000 slides; 1 million pictures; 100 video recordings. **Subscriptions:** 2400 journals and other serials. **Services:** Interlibrary loan; copying; library open to the public. **Automated Operations:** MELVYL. **Computerized Information Services:** OCLC, DIALOG Information Services, ENVIRONET, RLIN; CD-ROMs; ECONET, OnTyme Electronic Message Network Service, SCIENCEnet, InterNet, BITNET (electronic mail services). Performs searches on fee basis. **Networks/Consortia:** Member of CLASS, Bay Area Library and Information Network. **Publications:** Accessions List, irregular. **Remarks:** FAX: (415)750-7106. Electronic mail address(es): CASLIB@CMSA.BERKELEY.EDU (InterNet); CLASS.CALSCI (OnTyme Electronic Message Network Service); CAS.LIBRARY (SCIENCEnet); CASLIB@UCBCMSA (BITNET); CAOS (ECONET). Alternate telephone number(s): (415)750-7122 (Special Collections); (415)750-7361 (Biodiversity Resource Center). **Staff:** Richard Pallowick, Asst.Libn., Tech.Serv.; Adam Schiff, Assoc.Libn., User Serv.; Pennington Ahlstrand, Asst.Libn., Spec.Coll.; Barbara Butler, Coord.Biodiversity Rsrc.Ctr.

★2471★
California Air Resources Board - Library (Env-Cons)
Box 2815 Phone: (916)323-8377
Sacramento, CA 95812 Mark T. Edwards, Libn.
Founded: 1972. **Staff:** Prof 2. **Subjects:** Air pollution, air quality, environment. **Special Collections:** Air Pollution Technical Information Center reports (120,000 titles on microfiche); NTIS reports (air pollution; 20,000 on microfiche). **Holdings:** 6000 books. **Subscriptions:** 310 journals and other serials; 13 newspapers. **Services:** Interlibrary loan; copying; library open to the public. **Computerized Information Services:** DIALOG Information Services. **Remarks:** Located at 1800 15th St., Sacramento, CA 95814. **Remarks:** FAX: (916)322-4357.

California Archeological Inventory
See: **Sonoma State University - Northwest Information Center** (15373)

★2472★
California Baptist College - Annie Gabriel Library (Rel-Phil)
8432 Magnolia Ave. Phone: (714)689-5771
Riverside, CA 92504 Stephen Gateley, Dir.
Founded: 1951. **Staff:** Prof 3; Other 3. **Subjects:** Religion education, Southern Baptist Polity and history, theology. **Special Collections:** Hymnal Collection (1500 volumes). **Holdings:** 70,000 books; 11,000 bound periodical volumes; 6900 microfiche; 5100 reels of microfilm. **Services:** Interlibrary loan; copying; library open to the public. **Computerized Information Services:** OCLC EPIC. Contact Person: June Reeder, Ref.Libn. **Remarks:** FAX: (714)351-1808.

California Career Information System
See: **Eureka, The California Career Information System** (5477)

★2473★
California College of Arts and Crafts - Meyer Library (Art)
5212 Broadway Phone: (510)653-8118
Oakland, CA 94618 Vanroy R. Burdick, Dir. of Libs.
Founded: 1907. **Staff:** Prof 3; Other 2. **Subjects:** Fine arts, graphic design, architecture, crafts. **Special Collections:** Jo Sinel Collection (industrial design). **Holdings:** 35,000 volumes; 570 theses. **Subscriptions:** 240 journals and other serials. **Services:** Interlibrary loan; copying. **Computerized Information Services:** OCLC. **Remarks:** FAX: (510)655-3541. **Staff:** Suzanne Degler, Assoc.Libn.; Michael Lordi, Arch. & Design Libn.

★2474★
California College of Podiatric Medicine - Schmidt Medical Library (Med)
Rincon Annex, Box 7855 Phone: (415)292-0409
San Francisco, CA 94120 Ronald E. Schultz, Lib.Dir.
Founded: 1914. **Staff:** Prof 1; Other 2. **Subjects:** Clinical medicine, basic science. **Special Collections:** Podiatry and lower extremity materials collection (500 items); orthopedics collection (1500 volumes); sports medicine collection (250 volumes). **Holdings:** 5000 books; 20,000 bound periodical volumes; 200 AV programs; 5 VF drawers of reprints; 6 VF drawers of city state file. **Subscriptions:** 195 journals and other serials. **Services:** Interlibrary loan; copying; library open to the public with restrictions. **Automated Operations:** Integrated library system. **Computerized Information Services:** MEDLINE, DIALOG Information Services, CD Plus. Performs searches on fee basis. **Networks/Consortia:** Member of National Network of Libraries of Medicine - Pacific Southwest Region, San Francisco Biomedical Library Network. **Publications:** Newsletter; acquisitions list, quarterly; serial holdings list, annual; handbook, biennial; AV holdings list, annual. **Remarks:** Located at 1835 Ellis, San Francisco, CA 94115. **Remarks:** FAX: (415)292-0439.

★2475★
California Family Study Center - Library (Soc Sci)
5433 Laurel Canyon Blvd. Phone: (818)509-5959
North Hollywood, CA 91607-2114 Mark Stover, Dir.
Founded: 1980. **Staff:** Prof 1; Other 4. **Subjects:** Marriage and family counseling, psychotherapy, psychology, research methods. **Holdings:** 5000 books; 1000 professional papers; 110 journals; 40 journal titles on microfiche; 500 audio cassettes; 175 video cassettes; 21 films; 6 VF drawers. **Subscriptions:** 150 journals and other serials. **Services:** Library open to the public on fee basis. **Automated Operations:** Computerized public access catalog, cataloging, circulation, and acquisitions. **Computerized Information Services:** DIALOG Information Services; CD-ROMs; internal database; InterNet (electronic mail service). **Networks/Consortia:** Member of OCLC Pacific Network. **Remarks:** FAX: (818)762-6547. Electronic mail address(es): enq4mes@mvs.oac.ucla.edu (InterNet).

★2476★
California Federal Savings and Loan Association - Management Library
5700 Wilshire Blvd.
Los Angeles, CA 90036
Defunct.

★2477★
California Historical Society - History Center (Hist)
1120 Old Mill Rd. Phone: (213)449-5450
San Marino, CA 91108 Roy McJunkin, Photo.Cur.
Founded: 1978. **Staff:** Prof 3. **Subjects:** Local and state history. **Special Collections:** Title Insurance and Trust Collection (TICOR); Los Angeles Area Chamber of Commerce Collection (75,000 photographs). **Holdings:** Figures not available. **Services:** Photographs available on order; center open to the public. **Publications:** California History, quarterly; Courier (newsletter). **Special Indexes:** Index to California History. **Remarks:** Collection currently housed at University of Southern California, Department of Special Collections, University Library, Los Angeles, CA 90089-0182.

★2478★
California Historical Society - The North Baker Library in Schubert Hall
2099 Pacific Ave. Phone: (415)567-1848
San Francisco, CA 94109-2235 Michael W. Harvey, Lib./Archv.Dir.
Founded: 1922. **Staff:** 3. **Subjects:** California history, business history, theater, women in California, printing and publishing on the Pacific Coast. **Special Collections:** Edward C. Kemble Collections on Western Printing and Publishing (3500 volumes); Historic American Building Survey; Archive of Northern California American Civil Liberties Union (40 linear feet); Archives of People's Temple (Jonestown, 70 linear feet). **Holdings:** 50,000 volumes; 3000 bound periodical volumes; 4000 manuscript collections; 500,000 photographs; 39,000 photographic negatives; 3500 maps; 312 boxes and 17 VF drawers of ephemera (including 800 posters, 300 broadsides, and 200 architectural drawings). **Services:** Library open to the public by appointment via written request. **Automated Operations:** MELVYL. **Computerized Information Services:** RLIN; internal databases. **Networks/Consortia:** Member of Bay Area Library and Information Network. **Remarks:** FAX: (415)567-2394. **Staff:** Robert MacKimmie, Cur.Dir., Photo.; Jeffrey A. Barr, Libn., Tech./Photo.Serv.

★2479★
California Institute of the Arts - Library (Art, Mus, Theater)
24700 McBean Pkwy. Phone: (805)253-7885
Valencia, CA 91355 Frederick B. Gardner, Dean
Founded: 1969. **Staff:** Prof 5; Other 8. **Subjects:** Art, design, music, theater, dance, film/video. **Special Collections:** Artists' Books Collection; rare book collection on the development of motion pictures (750 books); LAICA Artists Registry Archive. **Holdings:** 73,242 books; 7502 bound periodical volumes; 2811 films and videos; 96,920 slides; 7528 reels of microfilm; 10,634 exhibition catalogs; 13,112 sound recordings; 12,610 scores. **Subscriptions:** 565 journals and other serials; 22 newspapers. **Services:** Interlibrary loan; copying; library open to the public for reference use only. **Automated Operations:** Computerized cataloging. **Computerized Information Services:** DIALOG Information Services, OCLC EPIC; Plays in Collections, Exhibition Catalogs, Music Scores in Collections (internal databases). Performs searches on fee basis. Contact Person: Margie Hanft, Ref. & Film Libn. **Networks/Consortia:** Member of Total Interlibrary Exchange (TIE), Performing Arts Libraries Network of Greater Los Angeles (PALNET), Santa Clarita InterLibrary Network (SCILNET). **Remarks:** FAX: (805)254-4561. **Staff:** Joan Anderson, Cat./Music Libn.; Evy Horigan, Art/Slide Libn.; Lucy Harrison, Theatre/Dance Libn.

★2480★
California Institute of Integral Studies - Library (Rel-Phil, Area-Ethnic)
765 Ashbury Phone: (415)753-6100
San Francisco, CA 94117 Bruce Flath, Lib.Dir.
Founded: 1968. **Staff:** Prof 1; Other 4. **Subjects:** Comparative philosophy and religion, especially Hinduism, Yoga, Buddhism, Zen, theosophy and parapsychology; psychology and counseling; drama therapy; organizational development; anthropology. **Special Collections:** Works of Sri Aurobindo, Gandhi, Haridas Chandhuri, Alan Watts, and Scott Rogo. **Holdings:** 30,000 books; 200 masters' theses and doctoral dissertations. **Subscriptions:** 130 journals and other serials. **Services:** Interlibrary loan; borrowing privileges for public on fee basis. **Computerized Information Services:** BRS Information Technologies, DIALOG Information Services; internal database. **Networks/Consortia:** Member of Northern California Consortium of Psychology Libraries (NCCPL). **Publications:** List of books in Alan Watts Collection. **Staff:** Fariba Bogzaran, Acq.Coord.; Monika Landenhamer, Cat.Coord.; Thomas Browne, Circ.Coord.; Mary Spoerer, Lib.Asst.

★2481★
California Institute of Public Affairs - Library (Soc Sci)
517 19th St.
P.O. Box 189040 Phone: (916)442-2472
Sacramento, CA 95818 T.C. Trzyna, Pres./Dir.
Founded: 1969. **Staff:** Prof 1; Other 1. **Subjects:** California - current affairs, description, environmental issues; environmental, energy, natural resource policy; California and worldwide law and organizations; global problems. **Holdings:** 1200 volumes; 125 file boxes of reports and clippings. **Subscriptions:** 200 journals and other serials. **Services:** Library not open to the public. **Computerized Information Services:** EcoNet (electronic mail service). **Publications:** California Information Guides Series; bibliographies; directories. **Remarks:** FAX: (916)442-2478. Electronic mail address(es): CIPA (EcoNet). The institute is an affiliate of The Claremont Graduate School.

★2482★
California Institute of Technology - Aeronautics Library (Sci-Engr)
1201 E. California Blvd. Phone: (818)356-4521
Pasadena, CA 91125 Virginia N. Anderson, Libn.
Founded: 1940. **Staff:** Prof 1; Other 1. **Subjects:** Aeronautics, fluid and solid mechanics, acoustics, jet propulsion, hydrodynamics. **Special Collections:** National Advisory Committee for Aeronautics (NACA) and NASA reports; Advisory Group for Aerospace Research and Development (AGARD) reports; Aeronautical Research Council reports. **Holdings:** 8742 books; 7256 bound periodical volumes; 355,018 microfiche; 260,150 reports. **Subscriptions:** 164 journals and other serials. **Services:** Interlibrary loan; copying; library open to the public for reference use only. **Computerized Information Services:** DIALOG Information Services, NASA/RECON. Performs searches on fee basis. **Publications:** Additions to the Library, monthly. **Remarks:** FAX: (818)449-2677.

★2483★
California Institute of Technology - Applied Physics/Electrical Engineering Library (Sci-Engr)
116-81 Steele Laboratories, Rm. 114 Phone: (818)356-4851
Pasadena, CA 91125 Paula C. Samazan, Prin.Lib.Asst.
Founded: 1958. **Staff:** 1. **Subjects:** Applied physics, solid state physics, electricity and magnetism, semiconductors, quantum electronics, electronics. **Holdings:** 1572 books; 1729 bound periodical volumes; 300 doctoral dissertations. **Subscriptions:** 61 journals and other serials. **Services:** Interlibrary loan; copying; library open to the public for reference use only. **Computerized Information Services:** Internal database. **Remarks:** FAX: (818)792-7540.

★2484★
California Institute of Technology - Astrophysics Library (Sci-Engr)
1201 E. California Blvd., Mail Code 105-24 Phone: (818)356-4008
Pasadena, CA 91125 Helen Z. Knudsen, Libn.
Founded: 1947. **Staff:** Prof 1; Other 1. **Subjects:** Astronomy, astrophysics. **Special Collections:** Palomar Sky Survey prints (1870 prints; 800 overlays). **Holdings:** 10,103 books; 8862 bound periodical volumes; 290 theses and dissertations; 850 unbound reports; 50 microforms; 2300 observatory publications and pamphlets; 2866 slides; 37 films; 994 microfiche; 43 sets of infrared prints. **Subscriptions:** 104 journals and other serials. **Services:** Library not open to the public; mail and telephone reference available. **Automated Operations:** Computerized public access catalog. **Computerized Information Services:** SIMBAD; ASTRODATA, NED (internal databases). **Remarks:** FAX: (818)568-1517. Telex: 188192 Caltech PSD; 675425 Caltech PSD. Figures given include holdings for branch libraries at Palomar Mountain Observatory, Owens Valley Radio Observatory, and Big Bear Solar Observatory.

★ 2485 ★
California Institute of Technology - Chemical Engineering Library (Sci-Engr)
202 Spalding Laboratory Phone: (818)356-6423
Pasadena, CA 91125 Dana Roth, Libn.
Staff: 1. **Subjects:** Chemical engineering, process control, surface science, biotechnology, polymer science, air pollution. **Holdings:** 24 books; 3455 bound periodical volumes. **Subscriptions:** 88 journals and other serials. **Services:** Interlibrary loan; library open to the public by appointment. **Computerized Information Services:** DIALOG Information Services, STN International; CLAS, TOC/DOC (internal databases). **Remarks:** FAX: (818)792-7540.

★ 2486 ★
California Institute of Technology - Computer Science Library (Comp Sci)
1201 E. California Blvd.
Mail Code 256-80 Phone: (818)356-6704
Pasadena, CA 91125 Nancy Zachariasen, Libn.
Founded: 1977. **Staff:** Prof 1; Other 1. **Subjects:** Computer science and engineering, digital electronics. **Special Collections:** Computer Science Technical Report Collection (210 reports). **Holdings:** 3154 books; 1159 bound periodical volumes; 3098 technical reports; 90 manuals. **Subscriptions:** 121 journals and other serials. **Services:** Interlibrary loan; copying; SDI; library open to the public for reference use only. **Computerized Information Services:** DIALOG Information Services; internal database; electronic mail service. **Special Catalogs:** Computer Science Technical Report List. **Remarks:** FAX: (818)792-7540.

★ 2487 ★
California Institute of Technology - Earthquake Engineering Research Library (Sci-Engr)
201 Thomas Laboratory Phone: (818)356-4227
Pasadena, CA 91125 Donna Covarrubias, Asst.Libn.
Founded: 1968. **Staff:** 2. **Subjects:** Earthquake engineering, vibration theory, structural mechanics, finite element analysis, seismology, disaster mitigation. **Holdings:** 17,000 books; 1100 bound periodical volumes; 7000 technical reports; 24,000 photographs, slides, maps; 550 seismographic records. **Subscriptions:** 147 journals and other serials. **Services:** Interlibrary loan; copying; library open to the public for reference use only. **Computerized Information Services:** Internal database. **Publications:** Publications list, monthly; serials list; reports list.

★ 2488 ★
California Institute of Technology - Environmental Engineering Library (Env-Cons)
136 W.M. Keck Laboratory (138-78) Phone: (818)356-4381
Pasadena, CA 91125 Rayma Harrison, Libn.
Founded: 1968. **Staff:** Prof 1; Other 1. **Subjects:** Aerosol physics, air quality management and modeling, aquatic and atmospheric chemistry, coastal engineering, hydraulic engineering, wastewater treatment and disposal. **Holdings:** 4645 books; 1911 bound periodical volumes; 23,218 technical and government reports; 157 volumes of dissertations. **Subscriptions:** 96 journals and other serials. **Services:** Library open to the public with restrictions on lending.

★ 2489 ★
California Institute of Technology - Geology and Planetary Sciences Library (Sci-Engr)
201 North Mudd Bldg. Phone: (818)356-6699
Pasadena, CA 91125 Jim O'Donnell, Geol./Planetary Sci.Libn.
Staff: Prof 1; Other 1. **Subjects:** Earth sciences, geology, mineralogy, geophysics, geochemistry, planetary science, seismology. **Holdings:** 15,560 books; 21,738 bound periodical volumes; maps. **Subscriptions:** 401 journals and other serials. **Services:** Interlibrary loan; copying; library open to the public. **Computerized Information Services:** DIALOG Information Services, STN International; internal database; InterNet, BITNET (electronic mail services). **Remarks:** FAX: (818)568-0935. Electronic mail address(es): JIMODO@CALTECH.EDU (InterNet).

★ 2490 ★
California Institute of Technology - Industrial Relations Center - Management Library (Bus-Fin)
383 S. Hill (3-90) Phone: (818)356-4048
Pasadena, CA 91125 Barbara Huff-Duff, Mgt.Libn.
Founded: 1939. **Staff:** Prof 1; Other 1. **Subjects:** Productivity/quality management; management of technology and innovation; new product development; new technological business ventures; implementation of advanced manufacturing systems; technical professionals - managerial and leadership skills development. **Holdings:** 2026 books; 1466 bound periodical volumes; 5 VF drawers of management-related materials; selected corporate annual reports; Conference Board reports and series. **Subscriptions:** 60 journals. **Services:** Interlibrary loan (through Millikan Library); library not open to the general public. **Automated Operations:** Computerized public access catalog, cataloging, and acquisitions. **Computerized Information Services:** DIALOG Information Services, OCLC, RLIN, ORION, MELVYL; internal databases; BITNET (electronic mail service). Performs searches on fee basis. **Publications:** Recent Acquisitions, bimonthly; bibliography series. **Remarks:** FAX: (818)795-7174. Electronic mail address(es): HUFFDUFF@ROMEO.CALTECH.EDU (BITNET).

★ 2491 ★
California Institute of Technology - Jet Propulsion Laboratory - Library (Sci-Engr)
111-113
4800 Oak Grove Dr. Phone: (818)354-4200
Pasadena, CA 91109 D. Adel Wilder, Mgr., Lib.
Founded: 1948. **Staff:** Prof 18; Other 19. **Subjects:** Astronautics, space sciences, astronomy, engineering, communications. **Special Collections:** Oceanic remote sensing collection. **Holdings:** 101,210 books; 39,085 bound periodical volumes; 45,220 technical reports; 1.2 million microforms. **Subscriptions:** 2700 journals and other serials. **Services:** Interlibrary loan. **Automated Operations:** Computerized cataloging and serials. **Computerized Information Services:** DIALOG Information Services, NASA/RECON. **Networks/Consortia:** Member of NASA Aerospace Research Information Network (ARIN). **Publications:** Library Additions, biweekly - for internal distribution only. **Remarks:** (818)393-6752. **Staff:** Judith M. Castagno, Supv., Info.Serv.; Edward S. Jollie, Jr., Supv., Tech.Serv.; Justine Weiher, Serv., Doc. Review.

★ 2492 ★
California Institute of Technology - Millikan Library (Sci-Engr, Biol Sci, Soc Sci)
1201 E. California Blvd. Phone: (818)356-6405
Pasadena, CA 91125 Glenn L. Brudvig, Dir. of Libs.
Staff: Prof 17; Other 44. **Subjects:** Biology, chemistry, engineering, mathematics, physics, humanities, social sciences. **Special Collections:** History of science. **Holdings:** 228,078 books; 137,543 bound periodical volumes; 115,283 microforms; 2022 linear feet of documents; 577,031 institute archival materials. **Subscriptions:** 4450 journals and other serials. **Services:** Interlibrary loan; copying; document delivery; library open to the public for reference use only. **Automated Operations:** Computerized cataloging, acquisitions, serials, circulation, and ILL. **Computerized Information Services:** DIALOG Information Services, OCLC, PFDS Online, RLIN, BRS Information Technologies, DTIC, MEDLINE, ORION, MELVYL; BITNET (electronic mail service). **Networks/Consortia:** Member of CLASS. **Publications:** Serials and Journals in the CIT Libraries, annual - for sale. **Remarks:** FAX: (818)795-1547. Electronic mail address(es): BRUDUIG@IAGO.CALTECH.EDU (BITNET). **Staff:** Kimberly Douglas, Hd., Rd.Svcs.; Dana L. Roth, Hd., Sci. & Engr.Lib.; Teresita Legaspi, Hd., ILL Dept.; Janet J. Jenks, Hd., Hum. & Soc.Sci.Lib.; Dr. Judith Goodstein, Inst.Archv.; Vivian Hay, Hd., Tech.Serv.

California Legion of Honor Library
See: **Fine Arts Museums of San Francisco - Library** (5703)

★ 2493 ★
California Lutheran University - Pearson Library - Special Collections (Rel-Phil, Soc Sci)
60 W. Olsen Rd. Phone: (805)493-3250
Thousand Oaks, CA 91360-2787 Kenneth E. Pflueger
Founded: 1961. **Staff:** 12. **Special Collections:** Scandinavian Lutheranism and history (400 items). **Holdings:** 110,000 U.S. federal government documents. **Services:** Interlibrary loan; copying; library open to the public with restrictions. **Automated Operations:** Computerized public access catalog. **Computerized Information Services:** DIALOG Information Services, OCLC; internal databases. **Remarks:** FAX: (805)493-3842.

★2494★
California Maritime Academy Library (Sci-Engr, Trans)
Box 1392 Phone: (707)648-4265
Vallejo, CA 94590-0644 Paul W. O'Bannon, Sr.Libn.
Founded: 1959. **Staff:** Prof 2; Other 2. **Subjects:** Marine engineering and technology, navigation, ship operations, marine transportation, cargo handling. **Holdings:** 25,000 books; 20,000 technical reports on microfiche; 3000 bound periodical volumes; 1800 microforms of periodicals. **Subscriptions:** 385 journals and other serials; 10 newspapers. **Services:** Interlibrary loan; copying; library open to the public. **Automated Operations:** Computerized cataloging. **Computerized Information Services:** OCLC, DIALOG Information Services. **Networks/Consortia:** Member of CLASS. **Remarks:** FAX: (707)648-4240. **Staff:** Darcus Thomas, Libn.

★2495★
California Medical Association - Socioeconomic Library (Bus-Fin)
Box 7690 Phone: (415)882-5133
San Francisco, CA 94120-7690 Susan Salisbury, Adm., Info.Serv.
Founded: 1959. **Staff:** Prof 1; Other 1. **Subjects:** Medical socioeconomics, health insurance, public assistance. **Holdings:** 3600 books and pamphlets. **Subscriptions:** 195 journals and other serials. **Services:** Interlibrary loan; copying; library open to members only. **Computerized Information Services:** DIALOG Information Services, MEDLARS. **Networks/Consortia:** Member of San Francisco Biomedical Library Network, Northern California and Nevada Medical Library Group (NCNMLG). **Publications:** Selected List of Acquisitions, quarterly. **Special Indexes:** Index to CMA Policy (book). **Remarks:** FAX: (415)882-5116. Alternate telephone number(s): 541-0900.

★2496★
California Missionary Baptist Institute & Seminary - Library (Rel-Phil)
9246 Rosser St.
Box 848 Phone: (213)925-4082
Bellflower, CA 90706 Kathy Wood
Founded: 1957. **Subjects:** Theology, history. **Special Collections:** Church history. **Holdings:** 7500 books; periodicals on microfilm; association minutes; 35 other cataloged items.

California Museum of Photography
See: **University of California, Riverside** (18404)

★2497★
California Pacific Medical Center - California Campus - Emge Medical Library (Med)
PO Box 7999 Phone: (415)750-6072
San Francisco, CA 94120 Peggy Tahir, Lib.Mgr.
Founded: 1959. **Staff:** Prof 1.5; Other 1. **Subjects:** Medicine, allied health sciences. **Holdings:** 4000 books; 7500 bound periodical volumes; 600 audiotapes. **Subscriptions:** 400 journals and other serials. **Services:** Interlibrary loan; library not open to the public. **Computerized Information Services:** MEDLINE, DIALOG Information Services, BRS Information Technologies; OnTyme Electronic Message Network Service (electronic mail service). **Networks/Consortia:** Member of San Francisco Biomedical Library Network, Northern California and Nevada Medical Library Group (NCNMLG). **Remarks:** FAX: (415)750-5026. Electronic mail address(es): CHS/EMGE (OnTyme Electronic Message Network Service). Library located at 3700 California St., San Francisco, CA 94118. **Formed by the merger of:** Northern California Health Center and Pacific Presbyterian Medical Center/University of the Pacific.

★2498★
California Pacific Medical Center/University of the Pacific School of Dentistry - Pacific Campus - Health Sciences Library (Med)
PO Box 7999 Phone: (415)923-3240
San Francisco, CA 94120 Peggy Tahir, Lib.Mgr.
Staff: Prof 2; Other 2. **Subjects:** Medicine, dentistry, ophthalmology. **Holdings:** 11,193 books; 63,290 bound periodical volumes; 1024 audiocassettes; 328 videotapes. **Subscriptions:** 824 journals and other serials. **Services:** Interlibrary loan; library not open to the public. **Computerized Information Services:** MEDLARS, DIALOG Information Services. Performs searches on fee basis. **Remarks:** FAX: (415)923-6597. Library located at 2395 Sacramento St., San Francisco, CA. **Formed by the merger of:** Pacific Presbyterian Medical Center/University of the Pacific and Northern California Health Center. **Staff:** Douglas Varner, Libn., Pacific Campus.

California Petroleum Industry Collection
See: **Long Beach Public Library** (9279)

★2499★
California Polytechnic State University - Environmental Design Resource Library (Plan, Art)
3801 W. Temple Ave., Bldg. 7 Phone: (714)869-2665
Pomona, CA 91768 Kathy Morgan, Slide Cur.
Staff: Prof 2; Other 2. **Subjects:** Architecture, landscape architecture, urban and regional planning. **Special Collections:** Craig Ellwood Collection (800 drawings and professional papers); Raymond Gaio Collection (marketing of professional design services; 1300 items); Construction Documents and Materials of Construction Collection (500 construction drawings, product literature, specifications, samples); school archives (300 examples of student work, including models); Neutra Travel Sketches (105 pastel travel sketches by Richard Neutra); Ralph Walker Collection (privately published poems and writings of Ralph Walker); Raphel Soriano Collection (AIA papers and drawings); Jean Rienecke papers. **Holdings:** 7521 books; 60,000 slides. **Subscriptions:** 125 journals and other serials. **Services:** Collection open to the public for reference use only. **Staff:** Pat Lin, Archv.; Art Hacker, Dir.

★2500★
California Polytechnic State University - Robert E. Kennedy Library (Sci-Engr)
San Luis Obispo, CA 93407 Phone: (805)756-2344
Dr. David B. Walch, Dean
Founded: 1903. **Staff:** Prof 21; Other 38. **Subjects:** Engineering and technology, agriculture, architecture, home economics, business, science, social sciences, humanities. **Special Collections:** Barton Collection of Landscape Architecture (55,000 items); Julia Morgan papers (10,250 items); Hearst Castle Collection (8500 items); Diablo Canyon Nuclear Plant Depository (11,442 items); California promotional and travel literature (3000 items); Western Fairs Collection (100,000 items). **Holdings:** 612,000 books; 100,000 bound periodical volumes; 139,000 other cataloged items; 450,000 government documents; 2.8 million microforms; 1500 linear feet of university archival materials. **Subscriptions:** 6247 journals and other serials; 107 newspapers. **Services:** Interlibrary loan; copying; library open to the public for reference use only on fee basis. **Automated Operations:** Computerized cataloging, circulation, and serials. **Computerized Information Services:** OCLC, DIALOG Information Services, MEDLINE, BRS Information Technologies, RLIN, WILSONLINE, CLSI, Inc; InterNet, BITNET (electronic mail services). **Networks/Consortia:** Member of Total Interlibrary Exchange (TIE), CLASS. **Publications:** Annual Report; Information Guides; Library Update; bibliography series. **Special Catalogs:** Periodical and Serials Holdings. **Remarks:** FAX: (805)756-1415. Electronic mail address(es): DU525@CALPOLY (BITNET); library@calpoly.edu (InterNet).

★2501★
California Province of the Society of Jesus - Jesuit Center Library (Rel-Phil)
300 College Ave.
Box 128 Phone: (408)354-9240
Los Gatos, CA 95031 Rev. Edward T. Burke, S.J., Libn.
Founded: 1887. **Staff:** Prof 1; Other 1. **Subjects:** Catholic theology, ecclesiastical history, Jesuitica. **Special Collections:** Jesuitica. **Holdings:** 40,000 books. **Subscriptions:** 42 journals and other serials. **Services:** Interlibrary loan (limited); library open to the public by appointment. **Remarks:** Jointly maintained with Sacred Heart Jesuit Center.

California Public Employee Relations Library
See: **University of California, Berkeley - California Public Employee Relations Library** (18308)

★2502★
California Research Corporation - Library (Bus-Fin)
2719 Wilshire Blvd., Suite 200 Phone: (310)829-9865
Santa Monica, CA 90403 Cyndi Chrysler, Libn.
Subjects: Banks, savings and loan institutions, thrift and loan institutions. **Holdings:** 275 books; 4000 reports. **Subscriptions:** 35 journals and other serials. **Services:** Library not open to the public. **Publications:** The CRC Report. **Remarks:** FAX: (213)829-7375.

★2503★
California Research & Technology, Inc. - Library (Sci-Engr)
20943 Devonshire St. Phone: (818)709-3705
Chatsworth, CA 91311 Pam Doll, Libn.
Subjects: Structural engineering, physical sciences. **Holdings:** 3500 books; 3000 reports. **Subscriptions:** 10 journals and other serials. **Services:** Library not open to the public.

★2504★
California School for the Blind - Library Media Center (Aud-Vis)
500 Walnut Ave. Phone: (510)794-3854
Fremont, CA 94536 Alice M. Bartholomew, Libn.
Founded: 1860. **Staff:** 2. **Subjects:** Educational and recreational books and media for pre-kindergarten and high school level blind and multi-handicapped children. **Holdings:** 4700 braille and print books; 200 professional books; 2200 records and tapes; 200 models, realia, maps, charts, kits; 51 boxes of pamphlets; specialized equipment for the handicapped. **Subscriptions:** 20 journals and other serials. **Services:** Center not open to the public. **Remarks:** FAX: (510)794-3813.

★2505★
California School of Professional Psychology - Berkeley/Alameda Campus - Rudolph Harwich Library (Soc Sci, Med)
1005 Atlantic Ave. Phone: (510)523-2300
Alameda, CA 94501 Harry Hosel, Dir. of Lib.Serv.
Founded: 1969. **Staff:** Prof 1; Other 5. **Subjects:** Clinical psychology, organizational psychology. **Special Collections:** Psychological assessment. **Holdings:** 14,500 books; 6000 bound periodical volumes; 350 tapes; 1000 dissertations. **Subscriptions:** 375 journals and other serials. **Services:** Interlibrary loan; library not open to the public. **Computerized Information Services:** BRS Information Technologies, DIALOG Information Services, RLIN; CD-ROM (PsycLIT, MEDLINE, Excerpta Medica CD: Psychiatry); OnTyme Electronic Message Network Service, DOCLINE (electronic mail services). Performs searches on fee basis. **Networks/Consortia:** Member of National Network of Libraries of Medicine - Pacific Southwest Region, CLASS, Northern California Consortium of Psychology Libraries (NCCPL). **Remarks:** FAX: (510)523-5943. Electronic mail address(es): CSPB (OnTyme Electronic Message Network Service).

★2506★
California School of Professional Psychology - Ingeborg S. Kauffman Library (Soc Sci, Med)
1350 M St. Phone: (209)486-8424
Fresno, CA 93721 Dorothy A. Spencer, Ph.D., Dir.
Founded: 1973. **Staff:** Prof 2; Other 3. **Subjects:** Psychology, organizational behavior. **Special Collections:** Test collection (110 printed documents; 630 microfiche). **Holdings:** 10,000 books; 4000 bound periodical volumes; 1334 microforms; 315 audio cassettes. **Subscriptions:** 250 journals and other serials. **Services:** Interlibrary loan; copying; library open to the public for reference use only; open to mental health professionals without restrictions. **Automated Operations:** Computerized public access catalog, cataloging, acquisitions, serials, and circulation. **Computerized Information Services:** BRS Information Technologies, DIALOG Information Services, MEDLARS, DOCLINE; OnTyme Electronic Message Network Service (electronic mail service). **Networks/Consortia:** Member of Area Wide Library Network (AWLNET), 49-99 Cooperative Library System. **Remarks:** FAX: (209)237-7529. Electronic mail address(es): CSPSY (OnTyme Electronic Message Network Service). **Staff:** Louise A. Colbert, Ref.Libn.

★2507★
California School of Professional Psychology - Los Angeles Campus Library (Med, Soc Sci)
1000 S. Fremont Ave. Phone: (818)284-2777
Alhambra, CA 91803-1360 Tobeylynn Birch, Dir. of Lib.
Founded: 1970. **Staff:** Prof 2; Other 2. **Subjects:** Psychology - clinical, industrial/organizational, health, community; public policy; women's issues; homosexuality and lesbianism; minority mental health. **Holdings:** 20,000 books; 2000 bound periodical volumes; 4000 microfiche; 1800 dissertations; 80 reels of microfilm; 450 audiotapes; 125 videocassettes; 7 films. **Subscriptions:** 330 journals and other serials. **Services:** Interlibrary loan; copying; library open to the public for reference use only. **Automated Operations:** Computerized Interlibrary loan (DOCLINE). **Computerized Information Services:** BRS Information Technologies, DIALOG Information Services. Performs searches on fee basis. **Networks/Consortia:** Member of CLASS. **Remarks:** FAX: (818)284-1682.

★2508★
California School of Professional Psychology - San Diego Library (Med, Soc Sci)
6212 Ferris Sq. Phone: (619)452-1664
San Diego, CA 92121-3205 Ada Burns, Lib.Dir.
Founded: 1972. **Staff:** 1. **Subjects:** Psychology. **Holdings:** 19,500 books; 1800 bound periodical volumes; 1200 cassette tapes. **Subscriptions:** 256 journals and other serials. **Services:** Interlibrary loan; library open to local professionals and students for reference use only. **Computerized Information Services:** BRS Information Technologies, RLIN, DOCLINE, California Union List of Periodicals (CULP); CD-ROMs (PsycLIT, Dissertation Abstracts Online). Performs searches on fee basis for campus community only. **Networks/Consortia:** Member of OCLC Pacific Network. **Remarks:** FAX: (619)452-0331.

California Social Welfare History Archives
See: **University of Southern California - Social Work Library** (19347)

★2509★
California State Archives (Hist)
Archives Bldg., Rm. 130
1020 O St. Phone: (916)653-0066
Sacramento, CA 95814 John F. Burns, Chf. of Archv.
Founded: 1850. **Staff:** Prof 10; Other 11. **Subjects:** California government and politics. **Special Collections:** Spanish land grants (19 volumes); Earl Warren papers (550 cubic feet); Robert F. Kennedy Assassination Investigation papers (60 cubic feet); State government Oral History Program transcripts (60 volumes). **Holdings:** 60,000 cubic feet of documents, photographs, microforms, maps, audiotapes, films, videotapes, computer materials, and artifacts. **Subscriptions:** 20 journals and other serials. **Services:** Copying; archives open to the public. **Automated Operations:** Computerized cataloging. **Computerized Information Services:** RLIN. **Publications:** California Originals (newsletter), quarterly - available upon request. **Remarks:** Maintained by California State Secretary of State. **Remarks:** FAX: (916)653-0084. **Staff:** Joseph Samora, Archv. II; Genevieve Troka, Archv. II; Laren Metzer, Archv. II; David Snyder, Archv. II; May Lee Tom, Archv. I; Nancy Zimmelman, Archv. I; Teena Stern, Archv. II.

★2510★
California State Automobile Association - Library (Trans)
P.O. Box 1860 Phone: (415)565-2300
San Francisco, CA 94101-1860 Pauline Jones Tighe, Libn.
Staff: Prof 1; Other 2. **Subjects:** Automobiles, traffic safety, driver education, automobile safety, traffic engineering, pedestrians, bicycles, motor vehicle accident statistics, highways, freeways, insurance. **Holdings:** Books; unbound reports; newspaper clippings; government documents. **Subscriptions:** 275 journals and other serials. **Services:** Library open to the public by request. **Computerized Information Services:** DIALOG Information Services.

★2511★
California State Banking Department - Library
111 Pine St., Suite 1100
San Francisco, CA 94111
Subjects: Banking, law, statistics. **Special Collections:** California Superintendent of Banks Annual Reports, 1880 to present. **Holdings:** 3000 books; 100 annual reports of state-chartered banks. **Remarks:** Currently inactive.

★2512★
California State Board of Equalization - Law Library (Law)
1020 N St., Rm. 265
Box 942879 Phone: (916)445-7356
Sacramento, CA 94279-0001 Robert Owens, Sr.Libn.
Staff: Prof 1. **Subjects:** Tax law - federal, state, local. **Holdings:** 10,000 volumes. **Services:** Library not open to the public. **Computerized Information Services:** LEXIS, NEXIS.

★2513★
California State Census Data Center - Library (Soc Sci)
915 L St., 8th Fl. Phone: (916)323-2201
Sacramento, CA 95814 Richard Lovelady, Mgr.
Founded: 1979. **Staff:** Prof 5. **Subjects:** Census, demography, housing, population. **Holdings:** 700 machine-readable files. **Services:** Copying; library open to the public. **Computerized Information Services:** Internal database. **Publications:** Data Source Handbook, (Dec.1989). **Remarks:** Data center is a cooperative effort between the U.S. Bureau of the Census and the California State Department of Finance - Population Research Unit. **Staff:** Nancy Austin, Res.Anl.

★2514★
(California State) Colorado River Board of California - Library (Env-Cons)
770 Fairmont Ave., Suite 100 Phone: (818)543-4676
Glendale, CA 91203-1035 J.C. Jay Chen, Sr. Hydraulic Engr.
Founded: 1937. **Staff:** 1. **Subjects:** Colorado River, California water rights, hydrology, water resources, conservation, engineering, agriculture, salinity. **Holdings:** 12,500 books; 300 pamphlets; 500 documents and reports; 60 VF drawers of maps and drafts. **Subscriptions:** 40 journals and other serials. **Services:** Interlibrary loan; library open to the public. **Publications:** Annual Report to California State Library. **Remarks:** FAX: (818)543-4685. **Formerly:** Located in Los Angeles, CA.

★2515★
California State Court of Appeal, 1st Appellate District - Law Library (Law)
303 2nd St., Suite 600 S. Phone: (415)396-9758
San Francisco, CA 94107 Jane W. Evans, Law Libn.
Staff: Prof 1; Other 1. **Subjects:** Law. **Holdings:** 50,000 books. **Subscriptions:** 175 journals and other serials. **Services:** Interlibrary loan; library not open to the public. **Computerized Information Services:** LEXIS, WESTLAW, DIALOG Information Services, RLIN. **Remarks:** FAX: (415)396-9668.

★2516★
California State Court of Appeal, 2nd Appellate District - Law Library (Law)
300 S. Spring St., Rm. 3547 Phone: (213)897-5113
Los Angeles, CA 90013 C. David Carlburg, Law Libn.
Founded: 1967. **Staff:** Prof 2; Other 1. **Subjects:** Law. **Holdings:** 90,000 books. **Subscriptions:** 100 journals and other serials. **Services:** Library not open to the public. **Computerized Information Services:** WESTLAW, LEXIS, NEXIS, DIALOG Information Services. **Staff:** Mary J. Forrest, Asst.Libn.

★2517★
California State Court of Appeal, 3rd Appellate District - Law Library (Law)
Library & Courts Bldg., Rm. 119
914 Capitol Mall Phone: (916)323-0850
Sacramento, CA 95814 Linda Wallihan, Law Libn.
Staff: Prof 1; Other 1. **Subjects:** California law. **Holdings:** 40,000 books; 500 microfiche. **Services:** Library not open to the public. **Computerized Information Services:** LEXIS, WESTLAW, DIALOG Information Services.

★2518★
California State Court of Appeal, 4th Appellate District, Division One - Law Library (Law)
750 B St., Suite 500 Phone: (619)237-6023
San Diego, CA 92101 Nanna Kathleen Frye, Law Libn.
Staff: Prof 1; Other 1. **Subjects:** Law. **Special Collections:** California law. **Holdings:** 24,000 volumes; 1 VF drawer of pamphlets; 2500 microfiche. **Subscriptions:** 42 journals and other serials. **Services:** Library not open to the public. **Computerized Information Services:** LEXIS, WESTLAW, DIALOG Information Services, VU/TEXT Information Services. **Remarks:** FAX: (619)237-7098.

★2519★
California State Court of Appeal, 4th Appellate District, Division Two - Law Library (Law)
303 W. 5th St. Phone: (714)383-4088
San Bernardino, CA 92401 Terry Lynch, Libn.
Founded: 1966. **Staff:** 2. **Subjects:** Law. **Holdings:** 30,000 books; 720 bound periodical volumes. **Services:** Library not open to the public. **Computerized Information Services:** DIALOG Information Services, WESTLAW, LEXIS. **Remarks:** FAX: (714)383-4660.

★2520★
California State Court of Appeal, 5th Appellate District - Law Library (Law)
2525 Capitol Phone: (209)445-5491
Fresno, CA 93721 Kathleen Pearce, Law Libn.
Staff: 1. **Subjects:** Law. **Holdings:** Figures not available. **Services:** Library open to court staff only.

★2521★
California (State) Department of Alcohol and Drug Programs - Prevention Resource Center (Med)
1700 K St., Rm. 102 Phone: (800)879-2772
Sacramento, CA 95814 Ira Bray, Libn.
Staff: Prof 1; Other 3. **Subjects:** Alcohol and drug abuse, prevention. **Holdings:** 500 books; 1000 bound periodical volumes; 3500 reprints, clippings, reports; 200 films; 90 titles on microfilm. **Subscriptions:** 25 journals and other serials. **Services:** Interlibrary loan; copying; library open to the public. **Automated Operations:** Computerized public access catalog and cataloging. **Computerized Information Services:** DIALOG Information Services, BRS Information Technologies. **Networks/Consortia:** Member of Regional Alcohol and Drug Abuse Resource Network (RADAR). **Special Catalogs:** Film Catalog; clearinghouse catalog. **Formerly:** Located in Oakland, CA.

★2522★
California (State) Department of Commerce - Library (Bus-Fin)
801 K St., Suite 1600 Phone: (916)324-5853
Sacramento, CA 95814 Ms. Yumi L. Nagao, Sr.Libn.
Founded: 1977. **Subjects:** Economic and tourism statistics for California. **Holdings:** 2500 volumes. **Subscriptions:** 140 journals and other serials; 11 newspapers. **Services:** Library not open to the public. **Automated Operations:** Computerized cataloging. **Computerized Information Services:** DIALOG Information Services. **Publications:** California Economic Information Sources; California Business Directories.

★2523★
California (State) Department of Conservation - Division of Mines and Geology - Library (Sci-Engr)
660 Bercut Dr. Phone: (916)327-1850
Sacramento, CA 95814-0131 Sylvia L. Bender-Lamb, Sr.Libn.
Founded: 1880. **Staff:** Prof 2. **Subjects:** Geology, mineralogy, mining engineering, petroleum. **Special Collections:** Gold rush and early California mining. **Holdings:** 18,000 books; 7000 bound periodical volumes; 100,000 other cataloged items; 16,000 maps. **Subscriptions:** 200 journals and other serials. **Services:** Interlibrary loan; copying; library open to the public for reference use only. **Automated Operations:** Computerized cataloging, acquisitions, serials, and circulation. **Computerized Information Services:** CD-ROMs (Earth Science Library, Publications of the U.S. Geological Survey, Geological Reference File); internal database. **Remarks:** FAX: (916)327-1853. A branch library is maintained at 1145 Market St., 3rd Fl., San Francisco, CA 94103. Contact Person: Keith Blean, Libn. Telephone: (415)557-1828.

★2524★
California (State) Department of Conservation - Division of Mines and Geology - Library (Sci-Engr)
1145 Market St., 3rd Fl. Phone: (415)557-1828
San Francisco, CA 94103-1513 Keith C. Blean, Libn.
Founded: 1880. **Staff:** Prof 1. **Subjects:** Geology, mines and mining, geologic hazards. **Special Collections:** Alquist-Priolo Act special study zone maps. **Holdings:** 20,000 books; 10,000 reports; 20,000 maps. **Services:** Interlibrary loan; copying; library open to the public. **Automated Operations:** Computerized cataloging. **Computerized Information Services:** GeoRef, USGS. **Remarks:** Library serves as a United States Geological Survey depository. FAX: (415)557-1435.
Formerly: Located in Pleasant Hill, CA.

★2525★
California (State) Department of Corporations - Law Library (Law)
3700 Wilshire Blvd., 5th Fl. Phone: (213)736-3632
Los Angeles, CA 90010 Sheri V. Silverton, Sr.Libn.
Staff: Prof 1; Other 1. **Subjects:** Law. **Special Collections:** Securities. **Holdings:** 9000 books; 250 periodicals; 200 AV programs. **Subscriptions:** 25 journals and other serials. **Services:** Library open to personnel of other state agencies. **Computerized Information Services:** LEXIS, NEXIS. **Remarks:** Maintains branch libraries in Sacramento, San Francisco, and San Diego.

California (State) Department of Developmental Services - Camarillo State Hospital
See: **Camarillo State Hospital & Developmental Center** (2593)

★2526★
California (State) Department of Developmental Services - Staff Library (Med)
Agnews Developmental Center
3500 Zanker Rd.
San Jose, CA 95134 Phone: (408)432-8500
Founded: 1948. **Subjects:** Mental retardation, developmental disabilities, neurology, psychology, psychiatric nursing, rehabilitation therapies. **Holdings:** 4000 books; 1020 bound periodical volumes; 125 videotapes. **Subscriptions:** 40 journals and other serials. **Services:** Interlibrary loan; copying; library open to state employees, students, parents, community. **Networks/Consortia:** Member of Medical Library Consortium of Santa Clara Valley, South Bay Cooperative Library System (SBCLS). **Publications:** Acquisitions bibliography update; orientation booklet, annual.

California (State) Department of Developmental Services - Stockton Developmental Center
See: **Stockton Developmental Center** (15803)

California (State) Department of Education - Office of Child Development - Resource and Referral Service
See: **Mexican-American Opportunity Foundation - Resource and Referral Service** (10238)

★2527★
California (State) Department of Education - School for the Deaf Library (Educ)
39350 Gallaudet Dr. Phone: (510)794-3666
Fremont, CA 94538 Joyanne K. Burdett, Libn.
Founded: 1860. **Staff:** Prof 1. **Subjects:** High interest, low vocabulary books suitable for K-12 deaf students. **Special Collections:** Education of the deaf (500 books). **Holdings:** 12,000 books. **Subscriptions:** 12 journals and other serials; 3 newspapers. **Services:** Library open to the public for reference use only; collection circulates to in-house staff only. **Remarks:** Alternate telephone number(s): 794-3725.

California (State) Department of Finance - California State Census Data Center
See: **California State Census Data Center - Library** (2513)

California (State) Department of Food & Agriculture - Pest Management Division Library
See: **California (State) Department of Pesticide Regulation - Library** (2535)

★2528★
California (State) Department of Health Services - Vector Surveillance and Control - Environmental Management Branch - Library (Biol Sci)
2151 Berkeley Way, Rm. 619 Phone: (510)540-2356
Berkeley, CA 94704 Franklin Ennik
Founded: 1947. **Subjects:** Zoonoses, medical entomology, vertebrate ecology, waste management, biostatistics, health education. **Holdings:** 2500 volumes; 65,000 reports and reprints. **Services:** Library open to the public with restrictions. **Remarks:** (510)540-3666. Small technical libraries are located in field offices in Los Angeles, Sacramento, San Bernardino, Santa Rosa, San Diego, and Redding, California.

★2529★
California (State) Department of Housing and Community Development - Library (Plan)
IMS D-29, Rm. 430
P.O. Box 952055 Phone: (916)322-7995
Sacramento, CA 94252-2055 Barbara A. Martinez, Sr.Libn.
Founded: 1987. **Staff:** 1. **Subjects:** Housing, planning, community development. **Special Collections:** Department publications archive. **Holdings:** 4000 books. **Subscriptions:** 275 journals. **Services:** Library open to the public with restrictions. **Computerized Information Services:** BRS Information Technologies; internal databases. **Remarks:** Library located at 1800 3rd St., Rm. 430, Sacramento, CA.

★2530★
California (State) Department of Industrial Relations - Division of Labor Statistics & Research - Research Library
P.O. Box 420603
San Francisco, CA 94142
Founded: 1945. **Subjects:** Wage settlements, work stoppages, work injuries and illnesses, and occupational diseases in California; work injuries in selected industries. **Holdings:** Figures not available. **Special Indexes:** California Consumer Price Index. **Remarks:** Currently inactive.

★2531★
California (State) Department of Justice - Attorney General's Office - Law Library (Law)
300 S. Spring St., 7th Fl. N. Phone: (213)897-2342
Los Angeles, CA 90013 Janet T. Raffalow, Supv.Libn.
Staff: Prof 2; Other 3. **Subjects:** Law. **Holdings:** 39,000 volumes. **Subscriptions:** 4 newspapers. **Services:** Library not open to the public. **Automated Operations:** MELVYL. **Computerized Information Services:** LEXIS. **Remarks:** FAX: (213)897-2805.

★2532★
California (State) Department of Justice - Attorney General's Office - Law Library (Law)
110 West A St., Suite 600 Phone: (619)237-7642
San Diego, CA 92101 Fay Henexson, Sr.Libn.
Founded: 1972. **Staff:** Prof 1; Other 1. **Subjects:** California and United States law. **Special Collections:** Opinions of the California Attorneys General, 1919 to present. **Holdings:** 25,000 books; 900 bound periodical volumes; 100 linear feet of California government documents; 60 linear feet of microfiche. **Subscriptions:** 56 journals and other serials. **Services:** Interlibrary loan; library not open to the public. **Computerized Information Services:** LEXIS. **Special Indexes:** Index to opinions of the California Attorney General.

★2533★
California (State) Department of Justice - Attorney General's Office - Law Library (Law)
455 Golden Gate Ave., Rm. 6248 Phone: (415)703-1847
San Francisco, CA 94102 Michael D. Jones, Sr.Libn.
Staff: Prof 1; Other 3. **Subjects:** Law, government. **Special Collections:** California Attorney General's opinions and letters of advice. **Holdings:** 25,000 books; 2100 bound periodical volumes; 1000 documents. **Subscriptions:** 258 journals and other serials; 7 newspapers. **Services:** Interlibrary loan; library not open to the public. **Computerized Information Services:** LEXIS. **Special Indexes:** Index of Attorney General's opinions, letters of advice, and office memoranda. **Remarks:** FAX: (415)703-1853.

California (State) Department of Mental Health - Metropolitan State Hospital
See: **Metropolitan State Hospital** (10221)

California (State) Department of Mental Health - Patton State Hospital
See: **Patton State Hospital** (12795)

California (State) Department of Parks and Recreation - California State Railroad Museum
See: **California State Railroad Museum** (2553)

★2534★
California (State) Department of Parks and Recreation - Hearst San Simeon State Historical Monument - Hearst Castle Staff Library (Hist)
750 Hearst Castle Rd. Phone: (805)927-2076
San Simeon, CA 93452 Judy Anderson, Lib.Coord.
Founded: 1969. **Staff:** 4. **Subjects:** William Randolph Hearst; Hearst Castle; art history and criticism; architectural history; museum studies; Hollywood; journalism and publishing; nature studies; historic preservation; Hearst family; California history; turn-of-the-century politics. **Special Collections:** Hearst Castle Oral History Project (250 audio tapes; interview transcriptions); Hollywood features and documentaries (50 videotapes); Hearst art collection records. **Holdings:** 2000 books; VF drawers; reports and studies; operating records. **Subscriptions:** 30 journals and other serials. **Services:** Library open to the public for telephone reference questions only. **Automated Operations:** Computerized cataloging, acquisitions, and circulation.

★2535★
California (State) Department of Pesticide Regulation - Library (Agri)
1220 N St.
Box 942871 Phone: (916)654-1202
Sacramento, CA 94271-0001 Chizuko Kawamoto, Supv.Libn.
Founded: 1981. **Staff:** Prof 5; Other 8. **Subjects:** Pesticides. **Special Collections:** Pesticide registration - support data. **Holdings:** 29,500 volumes. **Subscriptions:** 204 journals and other serials. **Services:** Library not open to the public. **Automated Operations:** Computerized cataloging, acquisitions, serials, circulation, and indexing. **Computerized Information Services:** DIALOG Information Services, RLIN; Pesticide Data Index Database (internal database). **Remarks:** FAX: (916)654-1416. Pesticide registration/support data is available to the public on a fee basis under FIFRA and California Public Records Act guidelines; contact library for further information. **Formerly:** California (State) Department of Food & Agriculture - Pest Management Division Library.

★2536★
California (State) Department of Transportation - CalTrans District 4 Library (Trans)
150 Oak St., Rm. 56
Box 7310 Phone: (415)557-0567
San Francisco, CA 94120 Alice Y. Whitten, Lib.Tech.Asst.
Founded: 1972. **Staff:** Prof 1. **Subjects:** Transportation planning, highway engineering, environmental planning, hydraulics, regional government, land use. **Special Collections:** California Highway and Public Works Publications, 1924-1966; California Highway Statutes, 1929 to present; budget reports, 1925 to present; specifications, 1925 to present; all Transportation Research Board (TRB) publications; California Standard plans, 1966 to present; California State Department of Transportation departmental manuals; environmental impact statements from the nine Bay Area counties. **Holdings:** 9880 books; 2000 bound periodical volumes; 2 shelves of clippings; 2 VF drawers. **Subscriptions:** 161 journals and other serials. **Services:** Interlibrary loan; copying; library open to the public by appointment. **Publications:** News from the Library and List of Publications Received, bimonthly. **Remarks:** FAX: (415)557-1759. **Staff:** Alice Y. Whitten.

★2537★
California (State) Department of Transportation - District 11 Library (Trans)
San Juan St.
P.O. Box 85406 Phone: (619)688-6644
San Diego, CA 92186-5406 Mary Cogswell, Libn.
Staff: 1. **Subjects:** Multimodal transportation, planning, engineering. **Special Collections:** Highway/Transportation Research Board of National Academy of Science material; California Highways, 1925-1967. **Holdings:** 3000 volumes. **Services:** Interlibrary loan; library open to the public for reference use only. **Publications:** Bibliography of publications received, monthly. **Remarks:** FAX: (619)688-3204.

★2538★
California (State) Department of Transportation - Legal Division Library (Law)
1120 N St., Rm. 1315
Box 1438 Phone: (916)654-2630
Sacramento, CA 95807 Lorna J. Flesher, Supv.Libn.
Staff: Prof 1; Other 1. **Subjects:** Torts, contracts, environmental law, multimodal transportation, real property. **Holdings:** Figures not available. **Services:** Library not open to the public. **Automated Operations:** Computerized cataloging and serials. **Computerized Information Services:** WESTLAW. **Remarks:** Maintains branch libraries in San Francisco, Los Angeles, and San Diego. **Remarks:** FAX: (916)654-6128.

★2539★
California (State) Department of Transportation - Materials & Research Library (Sci-Engr, Trans)
5900 Folsom Blvd.
Sacramento, CA 95819 Phone: (916)739-2452
Founded: 1965. **Staff:** Prof 1; Other 1. **Subjects:** Materials specifications, highway equipment testing, pollution measurement, soil mechanics, highway safety structures, geotechnical engineering. **Special Collections:** Road specifications of all U.S. states; complete American Society for Testing and Materials standards; F.H. Hveem papers. **Holdings:** 19,000 books, reports, bound periodical volumes; 4 VF drawers of pamphlets; 200 microfiche; 2000 other cataloged items. **Subscriptions:** 200 journals and other serials. **Services:** Interlibrary loan; copying; SDI; library open to the public for reference use only. **Automated Operations:** Computerized cataloging and serials. **Computerized Information Services:** DIALOG Information Services. **Publications:** List of publications - available upon request. **Remarks:** FAX: (916)739-2822.

★2540★
California (State) Department of Transportation - Transportation Library (Trans)
1120 N St. Phone: (916)654-4601
Sacramento, CA 95807 Edith Darknell, Supv.Libn.
Staff: Prof 4; Other 2. **Subjects:** Transportation planning, highway operations, highway and bridge design, public transportation. **Special Collections:** Departmental archives. **Holdings:** 50,000 volumes. **Subscriptions:** 300 journals and other serials. **Services:** Interlibrary loan; copying; library open to the public with restrictions. **Automated Operations:** Computerized public access catalog (SYDNEY). **Computerized Information Services:** DIALOG Information Services, OCLC. **Publications:** Library News and List of Publications Received, quarterly - for internal distribution only. **Remarks:** FAX: (916)654-6011. **Staff:** Laurel Clark, Libn.; Diane Johnson, Libn.; Carol Gilbert, Libn.

★2541★
California (State) Department of Water Resources - Law Library (Law)
1416 9th St., Rm. 1118-13 Phone: (916)653-8001
Sacramento, CA 95814 Mary Ann Parker, Sr.Libn.
Founded: 1966. **Staff:** Prof 1; Other 1. **Subjects:** Federal and state water law, water resources development. **Holdings:** 16,750 volumes; 550 government documents. **Subscriptions:** 38 journals and other serials. **Services:** Interlibrary loan; copying; library open to the public for reference use only. **Computerized Information Services:** WESTLAW. **Remarks:** FAX: (916)653-0952.

★2542★
California (State) Employment Development Department - Labor Market Information Division - Library (Bus-Fin)
7000 Franklin Blvd., No. 1100 Phone: (916)427-4693
Sacramento, CA 95823 Mary F. Hicks, Libn.
Staff: 1. **Subjects:** Labor market, unemployment insurance. **Holdings:** 5774 volumes. **Subscriptions:** 17 journals and other serials. **Services:** Library open to the public by appointment. **Automated Operations:** Computerized cataloging, serials, and circulation. **Computerized Information Services:** DIALOG Information Services. **Publications:** Employment Development Department Labor Market Information Publications Directory. **Remarks:** FAX: (916)323-6674.

★2543★
California (State) Energy Commission - Library (Sci-Engr)
1516 9th St. Phone: (916)324-3006
Sacramento, CA 95814 Diana Fay Watkins, Sr.Libn.
Founded: 1975. **Staff:** Prof 1; Other 1. **Subjects:** General energy, electric utilities, natural gas, petroleum, nuclear and solar power, alternative sources of energy. **Special Collections:** Collection of works produced or contracted by the commission; transcripts of commission hearings. **Holdings:** 20,000 books. **Subscriptions:** 350 journals and other serials. **Services:** Interlibrary loan; copying; library open to the public. **Automated Operations:** Integrated library system (SYDNEY). **Computerized Information Services:** DIALOG Information Services, OCLC. **Publications:** Monthly acquisitions list; semiannual serials list.

California State Environmental Protection Agency -California State Water Resources Control Board
See: **California State Water Resources Control Board** (2578)

★2544★
California (State) Governor's Office - Office of Planning & Research - Information Center (Plan)
1400 10th St., Ste. 15
Sacramento, CA 95814 Phone: (916)322-6312
Founded: 1973. **Staff:** 1. **Subjects:** Land use, zoning, planning, state government. **Holdings:** 2000 books; 500 reports. **Subscriptions:** 40 journals and other serials; 20 newspapers. **Services:** Interlibrary loan; copying; center open to the public. **Automated Operations:** Computerized public access catalog and indexing. **Publications:** Sources: An Annotated Bibliography for California Planners. **Remarks:** FAX: (916)322-3785.

★2545★
California State Lands Commission - Boundary Investigation Map Library (Geog-Map)
1807 13th St. Phone: (916)455-5086
Sacramento, CA 95814 Roy Minnick, Supv.
Founded: 1937. **Staff:** Prof 2; Other 2. **Subjects:** Property boundaries, public lands, hydrography, topography, record maps. **Special Collections:** Historical United States Geological Survey quads, pre-1930 (California); negatives of hydrographic and topographic sheets of California coast, 1850-1934. **Holdings:** 3000 books. **Subscriptions:** 6 journals and other serials. **Services:** Library open to the public by appointment. **Publications:** Rancho Land Grants in California; Bibliography of Hydrographic and Topographic Charts in California; Basic Geodesy; Land Title Law in California; Laws for the California Surveyor; Public Land Survey - History, Methods, Retracements.

★2546★
California State Library (Info Sci)
Library & Courts Bldg.
914 Capitol Mall
Box 942837 Phone: (916)654-0183
Sacramento, CA 94237-0001 Gary E. Strong, State Libn.
Founded: 1850. **Staff:** Prof 77; Other 109. **Subjects:** General research collection in support of state government, Californiana, law, genealogy, business, education, applied science and technology, population, public administration, statistics, water resources. **Special Collections:** Regional library of books for the blind and physically handicapped; talking book phonograph records and cassettes; braille books. **Holdings:** 695,845 volumes; 733,476 documents; 2.4 million microforms; 74,700 maps and charts; 11 16mm films; 160 video recordings; 262,048 audio recordings; federal and state government document depository. **Subscriptions:** 9668 journals, serials, and newspapers. **Services:** Interlibrary loan; copying; consultant service for public libraries; library open to the public. **Automated Operations:** Computerized public access catalog, cataloging, acquisitions, serials, and circulation. **Computerized Information Services:** DIALOG Information Services, BRS Information Technologies, NewsNet, Inc., Legi-Tech, ORBIT Search Service, Mead Data Central, NLM, VU/TEXT Information Services, DataTimes; OnTyme Electronic Message Network Service (electronic mail service). **Publications:** List of publications - available on request. **Special Indexes:** California State Publications, monthly (hardcopy; cumulations on COM). **Remarks:** FAX: (916)654-0064. Electronic mail address(es): CSLILL (OnTyme Electronic Message Network Service). Includes the holdings of the State Law Library. **Staff:** David Price, Asst. State Libn.; Yolanda J. Cuesta, Chf. of Lib.Dev.; Barbara Will, Fed.Prog.Coord.; Sheila F. Thornton, Chf., State Lib.Serv.; Gary Kurutz, Supv., Spec.Coll.; Jay Cunningham, Supv., Tech.Serv.; Kathy Hudson, Info.Tech.Coord.

★2547★
California State Library - Sutro Library (Hist)
480 Winston Dr. Phone: (415)557-0421
San Francisco, CA 94132 Clyde Janes, Supv.Libn.
Founded: 1917. **Staff:** Prof 2; Other 9. **Subjects:** American genealogy and local history, English history, history of science and technology, Americana, bibliography, voyages and travels, Mexican history, Hebraica, natural history. **Special Collections:** Papers of Sir Joseph Banks, 1760-1820. **Holdings:** 150,000 volumes; 20,000 manuscripts. **Subscriptions:** 87 journals and other serials. **Services:** Interlibrary loan; copying; library open to the public. **Automated Operations:** Computerized cataloging. **Publications:** Anatomy of a Library (brochure on the collection); New Arrivals in American Local History and Genealogy, quarterly - free upon request. **Remarks:** Library specializes in works published prior to 1900. FAX: (415)557-9325. **Staff:** Frank J. Glover, Ref.Libn.

★2548★
California State Medical Facility - Medical Staff Library (Med)
1600 California Dr. Phone: (707)448-6841
Vacaville, CA 95696 Victoria Bayubay, Libn.
Founded: 1950. **Staff:** 1. **Subjects:** Psychiatry, medicine, surgery, penology, criminology, psychology, social work, nursing, hospital administration. **Holdings:** 6000 books; 130 bound periodical volumes; research materials relating to criminology and case work; reports from other state and national agencies; releases from federal, state, local agencies interested in inmate care and welfare and community adjustment. **Subscriptions:** 149 journals and other serials. **Services:** Interlibrary loan; research; library open to the public for reference use only with consent of the superintendent. **Publications:** Bibliographies.

★2549★
California State Office of Legislative Counsel - Library (Law)
3021 State Capitol Phone: (916)445-2609
Sacramento, CA 95814 Marguerite Beveridge, Libn.
Founded: 1949. **Staff:** Prof 1; Other 10. **Subjects:** Law. **Special Collections:** Publications of the Legislature of California. **Holdings:** 26,500 books; 400 bound periodical volumes; 7000 other cataloged items; 6 boxes of ultrafiche of the National Reporter System, 1st series; California bills, 1850 to present, in microform. **Subscriptions:** 182 journals and other serials. **Services:** Library not open to the public. **Computerized Information Services:** LEXIS; internal database.

★2550★
California State Office of the State Architect - Architecture/Engineering Library (Plan)
400 P St., 5th Fl. Phone: (916)445-8661
Sacramento, CA 95814 Rose A. Granados, Tech.Libn.
Founded: 1958. **Staff:** Prof 1. **Subjects:** Construction industry standards, architecture, electrical and mechanical engineering, building products, interior design. **Special Collections:** Architectural samples (6000). **Holdings:** 400 books; 30 bound periodical volumes; 5470 catalogs; titles 1-26 of the California Code of Regulations; IHS microfilm service. **Subscriptions:** 40 journals and other serials. **Services:** Interlibrary loan; copying; library open to other state agencies. **Computerized Information Services:** Internal databases. **Remarks:** FAX: (916)327-3369; (916)445-3521.

California State Parks System - La Purisima Mission
See: **La Purisima Mission** (8853)

★2551★
California State Polytechnic University - Library - W.K. Kellogg Arabian Horse Library (Rec)
3801 W. Temple Ave. Phone: (714)869-3081
Pomona, CA 91768-4080 Mellissa J. Paul, Cur.
Founded: 1975. **Staff:** Prof 1. **Subjects:** Arabian horses - history, breeding, use, pedigrees, literature. **Special Collections:** W.K. Kellogg Ranch papers; Library of Gladys Brown Edwards. **Holdings:** 6000 books; 350 bound periodical volumes; 4 VF drawers of club newsletters; 2 VF drawers of farm brochures; 30 videotapes; photographs; show programs; auction catalogs. **Subscriptions:** 48 journals and other serials. **Services:** Copying; library open to the public for reference use only. **Automated Operations:** Computerized public access catalog, acquisitions and serials. **Computerized Information Services:** Internal database; InterNet (electronic mail service). **Publications:** The Arabian Horse Bibliography; library brochure. **Remarks:** FAX: (714)869-6922. Electronic mail address(es): MJPAUL@CSUPomona.EDU (InterNet).

★2552★
California State Postsecondary Education Commission - Library
1020 12th St., 3rd Fl.
Sacramento, CA 95814
Defunct.

★2553★
California State Railroad Museum - Library (Hist, Trans)
111 I St. Phone: (916)323-8073
Sacramento, CA 95814 Stephen E. Drew, Cur.
Founded: 1981. **Staff:** Prof 3. **Subjects:** History of railroads in California, Nevada, and the West. **Special Collections:** Corporate records of Central

Pacific, Southern Pacific, and Western Pacific railroads and their subsidiary companies; Atchison, Topeka & Santa Fe Railway collection (rolling stock drawings, 1884-1940; maps, 1880-1983; surveyors' and engineers' notebooks, 1884-1920); Railway & Locomotive Historical Society archival and photograph collection; Baldwin Locomotive Works engine specification books, 1869-1938 (microfilm); Lima Locomotive Works construction drawings; Gerald M. Best papers and photograph collection; Pullman Company negatives; C.P. Huntington papers (microfilm); papers and collections of the Pacific Coast Chapter of the Railway & Locomotive Historical Society; California State Railroad Museum documents (Museum's development and restoration of the locomotives and rolling stock on exhibit; total of 6000 cubic feet). **Holdings:** 10,000 books; 500 periodical titles; 1 million photographs, timetables, maps, drawings, and railroad ephemera. **Subscriptions:** 90 journals and other serials. **Services:** Copying; library open to the public for reference use only. **Computerized Information Services:** Internal databases. **Remarks:** FAX: (916)327-5655. Operated by California State Department of Parks and Recreation. **Staff:** Blaine Lamb, Archv.; Ellen Halteman, Libn.

★2554★
California (State) Regional Water Quality Control Board - San Francisco Bay Region - Library (Env-Cons)
2101 Webster St., 5th Fl. Phone: (510)464-1255
Oakland, CA 94612 Steven R. Ritchie, Hd. of Reg.
Subjects: Water quality studies of surface and ground waters in San Francisco Bay Area. **Holdings:** 3600 studies and reports. **Services:** Copying; library open to the public for reference use only.

★2555★
California State Resources Agency - Library (Biol Sci, Rec)
1416 9th St., Rm. 117 Phone: (916)653-2225
Sacramento, CA 95814 Madeleine A. Darcy, Sr.Libn.
Founded: 1927. **Staff:** Prof 1; Other 2. **Subjects:** Freshwater fisheries, game and game birds, forestry, park management, soil conservation, boats and boating, recreation, water pollution, engineering. **Holdings:** 50,000 volumes; 10 VF drawers of reports. **Subscriptions:** 650 journals and other serials. **Services:** Interlibrary loan; copying; library open to the public for reference use only. **Networks/Consortia:** Member of Forest Service Information Network. **Publications:** List of accessions, quarterly - for internal distribution and requesting libraries. **Remarks:** Library serves Departments of Fish and Game, Forestry, Parks & Recreation, Conservation, Water Resources, and Water Resources Control Board.

★2556★
California State Supreme Court Library (Law)
303 2nd St.
South Tower, Rm. 8047 Phone: (415)396-9439
San Francisco, CA 94107 Karen Toran, Law Libn.
Founded: 1868. **Staff:** Prof 2; Other 2. **Subjects:** Law. **Holdings:** 150,000 volumes. **Services:** Library not open to the public. **Computerized Information Services:** WESTLAW, LEXIS, DIALOG Information Services, RLIN, VU/TEXT Information Services. **Networks/Consortia:** Member of Bay Area Library and Information Network. **Remarks:** FAX: (415)904-9465. **Staff:** Janet Bogenschultz, Asst.Libn.

★2557★
California State University - Desert Studies Center - Library (Biol Sci, Hist)
P.O. Box 490 Phone: (619)733-4266
Baker, CA 92309 Robert Fulton, D.S.C. Mgr.
Founded: 1976. **Staff:** 1. **Subjects:** Natural sciences, Mojave Desert, desert literature, local history, local archeology, reference material, local research. **Holdings:** 450 books; 100 reports; 50 scientific reprints; 50 maps. **Subscriptions:** 4 journals and other serials. **Services:** Library open to the public upon registration with Desert Studies Center manager. **Remarks:** The Center is a university field station in the Mojave Desert.

★2558★
California State University, Bakersfield - California Well Sample Repository (Energy)
9001 Stockdale Hwy. Phone: (805)664-2324
Bakersfield, CA 93311-1099 Russ H. Robinson, Cur.
Founded: 1975. **Staff:** Prof 1. **Subjects:** California oil, gas, geothermal cores, mining, engineering. **Special Collections:** Well samples (10,000); California well records (microfiche, microfilm, and print). **Holdings:** 300 books; 100 bound periodical volumes; California oil field summaries; papers; bulletins. **Services:** Repository open to the public. **Special Catalogs:** California Well Sample Repository Catalog of Well Samples, 5th edition.

★2559★
California State University, Chico - Meriam Library - Special Collections (Hist)
First & Hazel Sts. Phone: (916)898-6342
Chico, CA 95929 William A. Jones, Spec.Coll.Libn.
Founded: 1976. **Staff:** Prof 1.5. **Special Collections:** Northeastern California Collection; regional information and records. **Holdings:** Books; periodicals; manuscripts; photographs; local government records. **Subscriptions:** 50 journals and other serials; 35 newspapers. **Services:** Library open to the public. **Computerized Information Services:** Internal database. **Publications:** Finding aids to photographs and manuscript collections. **Remarks:** FAX: (916)898-4443. **Staff:** Mary Ellen Bailey.

★2560★
California State University, Fresno - Armenian Studies Program - Sarkis & Meline Kalfayan Center for Armenian Studies - Sahatdjian Library (Area-Ethnic)
Fresno, CA 93740 Phone: (209)278-2669
Dr. Dickran Kouymjian, Dir., Ctr. for Armenian Stud.
Founded: 1988. **Subjects:** Armenia - history, literature, language, general; Armenians in the United States. **Special Collections:** Martin Collection (materials on Near East relief). **Holdings:** 2000 books; 10 bound periodical volumes; film and record archival items. **Subscriptions:** 4 journals and other serials; 14 newspapers. **Services:** Library open to the public for reference use only. **Publications:** Hye Sharzhoom (newspaper). **Special Indexes:** Index of Armenian Art, Vol. I and II. **Remarks:** FAX: (209)278-6758.

★2561★
California State University, Fresno - Henry Madden Library - Department of Special Collections (Hum)
Fresno, CA 93740 Phone: (209)278-2595
Ronald J. Mahoney, Hd.
Founded: 1951. **Staff:** Prof 1; Other 1. **Subjects:** Fairs, history, viticulture, William Saroyan, lumbering, olives, federal irrigation water limitation, Utopia in Mexico, local history, architecture, genealogy, Sierra National Forest. **Special Collections:** Donald G. Larson Collection of International Exhibitions and Fairs (7500 items); Harry Pidgeon Collection (645 negatives and prints); Viticulture and Enology Collection (7540 items); William Saroyan Collection (725 items); Roy J. Woodward Memorial Library of Californiana (15,000 items); Credit Foncier of Sinaloa Company Collection (587 photographs; 14,000 other items); Joseph A. Lowande Collection of Worldwide Rationing (9 books; 2 linear feet); Mineral King Collection (2 VF drawers); Alexander Pronin Collection of Russian Postcards, 1890-1920 (1500); Harold G. Schutt Collection on Lumbering in Tulare County (300 photographs; 6 VF drawers); Brock-Harris-McLane Families Collection (5 linear feet, 200 photographs); Lawrence K. Cone (Condrajian) Architecture Collection (185 drawings and blueprints, 50 renderings, 52 volumes of diaries); June English Local History and Genealogy Collection (60 books, 500 photographs, 12 linear feet); June English/Sierra National Forest (California) Collection (14 linear feet); National Land for People Collections (24 VF drawers). **Holdings:** 22,000 books; 560 bound periodical volumes; 2500 negatives. **Services:** Copying; department open to the public for reference use only. **Automated Operations:** Computerized cataloging. **Computerized Information Services:** OCLC. **Networks/Consortia:** Member of Area Wide Library Network (AWLNET), CLASS, Research Libraries Information Network (RLIN). **Special Indexes:** San Joaquin Valley Index; Photographs of Panama-Pacific International Exposition Index; Enology Collection Index; Larson Exhibition Collection Index (all on cards); San Joaquin Valley Photograph Index; biographical index of Fresno and Madera Counties (California; both books); June English/Sierra National Forest (California) Index (cards). **Remarks:** FAX: (209)278-2099.

★2562★
California State University, Fullerton - Library - Freedom Center (Soc Sci)
Box 4150 Phone: (714)773-3445
Fullerton, CA 92634 Sharon K. Perry, Univ.Archv. & Spec.Coll.Libn.
Founded: 1965. **Staff:** Prof 1; Other 1. **Subjects:** 20th century - politics, sociology, religion, contemporary culture, alternative life styles, counter cultures. **Special Collections:** Holocaust; Spanish Civil War; disarmament; anti-Vietnam War movement; civil rights; civil liberties; right wing extremism. **Holdings:** 8000 pamphlets; 4079 unbound periodical titles; 2000 folders of ephemera. **Subscriptions:** 300 periodicals. **Services:** Interlibrary loan (limited); copying; center open to the public with restrictions. **Remarks:** FAX: (714)773-2439.

★ 2563 ★

California State University, Fullerton - Museum of Anthropology - Library (Soc Sci)
Fullerton, CA 92634 Phone: (714)773-3977
Constance Cameron, Cur.
Founded: 1973. **Staff:** 1. **Subjects:** Southern California - ethnology, archeology; archeological analysis; California archeology; Southwest; cultural anthropology. **Special Collections:** The Masterkey (1927 to present; complete set); Pacific Coastal Archaeological Society Quarterly (1965 to present; complete set); Journal of California & Great Basin Anthropology (1974 to present; complete set). **Holdings:** 1000 books; 2000 manuscripts. **Subscriptions:** 5 journals and other serials. **Services:** Library open to the public for reference use only. **Publications:** Archeological Research Facility papers, irregular. **Special Catalogs:** Museum catalogs.

★ 2564 ★

California State University, Fullerton - Oral History Program (Hist)
The Library
800 N. State College Blvd. Phone: (714)773-3580
Fullerton, CA 92634 Gail Gutierrez, Archv.
Founded: 1968. **Staff:** Prof 2. **Subjects:** Local, community, and family history; ethnic groups: Japanese Americans, Chinese Americans, African Americans, Native Americans, Mexican Americans, Swedish Americans; biography; political and university history; Philippine studies; Southeast Utah uranium; Mormon colony. **Holdings:** 825 volumes; 4000 interviews (audio); 15 masters' thesis. **Subscriptions:** 4 journals and other serials. **Services:** Program open to the public by appointment. **Special Catalogs:** Catalog of Oral History Collection, 1985 (addition, 1991).

★ 2565 ★

California State University, Fullerton - University Archives and Special Collections (Hist, Hum)
Box 4150 Phone: (714)773-3444
Fullerton, CA 92634 Sharon K. Perry, Univ.Archv. & Spec.Coll.Libn.
Founded: 1967. **Staff:** Prof 2; Other 2. **Subjects:** University archives, local and regional history, science fiction, press and fine printing, angling. **Special Collections:** Kerridge Angling Collection; Fairfax Proudfit Walkup Theater Collection; press collection; Science Fiction Writers of America depository; archives of popular culture; James Boyer May/Jan Amsberry Poetry Collection. **Holdings:** 4896 linear feet of archival materials; 140,896 other cataloged items. **Subscriptions:** 627 journals and other serials; 10 newspapers. **Services:** Interlibrary loan (limited); copying; collections open to the public. **Automated Operations:** Computerized cataloging. **Remarks:** FAX: (714)773-2439. **Staff:** Issa Fasheh, Assoc.Libn.

★ 2566 ★

California State University, Fullerton - University Archives and Special Collections - Roy V. Boswell Collection for the History of Cartography (Geog-Map)
Library
800 N. State College Blvd.
Box 4150 Phone: (714)773-3444
Fullerton, CA 92634 Sharon K. Perry, Univ.Archv. & Spec.Coll.Libn.
Founded: 1971. **Staff:** Prof 1; Other 2. **Subjects:** Maps; history of cartography; voyaging and exploration prior to 1900. **Holdings:** 3089 books; 722 pamphlets and periodicals; 1525 pre-1901 maps. **Subscriptions:** 35 journals and other serials. **Services:** Interlibrary loan (limited); copying; library open to the public. **Special Catalogs:** Catalogs of map exhibits. **Remarks:** FAX: (714)773-2439.

★ 2567 ★

California State University, Hayward - Music Library (Mus)
Hayward, CA 94542 Phone: (510)881-3778
Ray Reeder, Mus.Libn.
Founded: 1959. **Staff:** Prof 1; Other 3. **Subjects:** Western concert music, folk music, ethnomusicology, music education, jazz. **Holdings:** 12,136 books; 1410 bound periodical volumes; 22,513 scores; 514 microforms; 18,344 phonograph records; 306 tapes. **Subscriptions:** 141 journals and other serials. **Services:** Interlibrary loan; copying; library open to the public for reference use only. **Automated Operations:** Computerized cataloging, acquisitions, and circulation. **Computerized Information Services:** BRS Information Technologies, DIALOG Information Services. **Networks/Consortia:** Member of CLASS, Bay Area Library and Information Network. **Publications:** Quodlibet, 3/year - for internal distribution only. **Special Indexes:** Index to recorded songs and arias (card).

★ 2568 ★

California State University, Long Beach - Special Collections Library (Mus, Hist)
1250 Bellflower Blvd. Phone: (213)985-4087
Long Beach, CA 90840 Irene Still Meyer, Supv., Spec.Coll., Archv.
Subjects: Political history, California literature, local history, music and the arts. **Special Collections:** Wesley Kuhnle materials and records (research in early keyboard music, performance, tuning); oral history tapes concerning cultural development in southern California, 1930-1950 (total of 30 linear feet); Dorothy Healey Collection of radical politics in Southern California, 1940-1970; Pasadena Playhouse Collection of Los Angeles playbills, scrapbooks, playscripts; Long Beach History Collection (including Joan Hotchkis Collection of Bixby Family papers); university archives; author collections: S.T. Coleridge, Robinson Jeffers, Mary Austin, Upton Sinclair, Charles Bukowski; Los Angeles area poetry; Gerald Locklin poetry; small press collection. **Services:** Copying; library open to the public. **Remarks:** FAX: (213)985-1703. **Staff:** Larry Davis, Archv.; Kristie French, Archv.

★ 2569 ★

California State University, Northridge - Geography Map Library (Geog-Map)
18111 Nordhoff St. Phone: (818)885-3465
Northridge, CA 91330 Michael Swift, Map Cur.
Founded: 1961. **Staff:** Prof 2. **Subjects:** Topographic and thematic maps. **Special Collections:** Sanborn Fire Insurance Maps of California and western United States (145,000 sheets). **Holdings:** 325,000 map sheets. **Subscriptions:** 10 journals and other serials. **Services:** Library open to the public. **Special Catalogs:** Catalog of Sanborn Atlases at California State University, Northridge. **Staff:** Kris Tacsik, Asst.Cur.

★ 2570 ★

California State University, Northridge - Instructional Materials Laboratory - Library (Educ)
18111 Nordhoff St.
PO Box 1289 Phone: (818)885-2501
Northridge, CA 91328-1289 Karin Duran, Ph.D., Dir.
Founded: 1965. **Staff:** Prof 1; Other 1. **Subjects:** Curriculum materials for all subjects, K-12. **Special Collections:** Bilingual-bicultural curriculum materials (850 items). **Holdings:** 15,000 books; 3000 filmstrips and sound filmstrips; 2000 phonograph records and cassettes; 2000 transparencies, slides, kits, games; 150 microcomputer software programs; 100 videocassettes. **Services:** Copying; curriculum previewing; laboratory open to the public with fee for borrowing. **Special Catalogs:** Song file catalog (card).

★ 2571 ★

California State University, Northridge - Library - Health Science Collection
18111 Nordhoff St.
Northridge, CA 91330
Founded: 1965. **Subjects:** Health education, nutrition, occupational health, sanitation, child and maternity care, medical statistics, preventive medicine, public health administration, physiology, communicative disorders. **Holdings:** 45,000 books; 13,000 bound periodical volumes. **Remarks:** Currently inactive.

★ 2572 ★

California State University, Northridge - Oviatt Library - Special Collections Department (Hum)
18111 Nordhoff St. Phone: (818)885-2832
Northridge, CA 91330 Tony Gardner, Spec.Coll.Libn.
Founded: 1958. **Staff:** Prof 1; Other 1. **Subjects:** Local history, theater programs, contemporary fiction and poetry, radio and film scripts, gender studies, printing and publishing, Japanese American internment, music, 19th century Europe, slavery. **Special Collections:** California Tourism and Promotional Literature Collection (1860-1939); Los Angeles court transcripts (1885-1904); early 19th century American and English theatre programs; NBC radio plays (1935-1943); Milton Geiger radio and film scripts; Thomas and Barbara McDermott Collection of 20th Century American and English Literature; Gwen Briston papers; Bullough Collection on Human Sexuality; Guernsey Collection on British History (1815-1915); Patrick Collection of 19th and Early 20th Century Russian Pamphlets; Edwin Booth Collection; World War II Japanese-American relocation camp newsletters; migratory farm labor camp papers (1930s); George Cruikshank Collection; Emanuel Haldeman-Julius Little and Big

Blue Books (2200 titles); Thomas B. Mosher books; Aaron Cohen Collection on Women Music Composers; Ray Martin music scores (manuscripts); Francis Gilbert Webb correspondence (1889-1934). **Holdings:** 14,000 books; 100 bound periodical volumes; 2500 manuscripts. **Services:** Department open to the public. **Automated Operations:** Computerized cataloging, circulation, and serials. **Computerized Information Services:** OCLC, DIALOG Information Services, MEDLINE; OnTyme Electronic Message Network Service, SprintMail, Dialnet (electronic mail services). **Remarks:** FAX: (818)885-2676.

★2573★
California State University, Northridge - Urban Archives Center (Hist, Soc Sci)
Oviatt Library, Rm. 4
Northridge, CA 91330 Phone: (818)885-2487
Founded: 1978. **Staff:** Prof 2; Other 4. **Subjects:** Los Angeles County and San Fernando Valley history, Chambers of Commerce, education, labor and guild history, political history, minority and ethnic groups, women's studies, social service organizations, environment, journalism. **Special Collections:** California Association for the Education of Young Children (10 linear feet); California Federation of Teachers, AFT, AFL-CIO (60 linear feet); Senator Thomas C. Carrell Collection (12 linear feet); Congressman James C. Corman papers (300 linear feet); The Greater Los Angeles Visitors and Convention Bureau (57 linear feet); International Longshoremen's and Warehousemen's Union, Local 13 (40 linear feet); League of Women Voters, Los Angeles Chapter (30 linear feet); Lesser-Silberberg Collection of the Jewish Federation Council of Los Angeles, Community Relations Committee (200 linear feet); Los Angeles County Federation of Labor, AFL-CIO (40 linear feet); Max Mont Collection (Jewish Labor Committee; 12 linear feet); Dr. Julian Nava Collection (40 linear feet); The Los Angeles Newspaper Guild (25 linear feet); The United Way of Los Angeles (50 linear feet); The YWCA of Los Angeles Collection (22 linear feet); Bustop Campaign Collection (86 linear feet); Paul M. Goldner (UAW) Collection (14 linear feet); The Jewish Family Service Collection (13.5 linear feet); Agness M. Underwood Collection (12 linear feet); Valley Industry and Commerce Association (8.5 linear feet); Victor Van Bourg Papers (1.2 linear feet); American Aeronaut, 1941-1977 (IAM); Labor News (Long Beach Labor Council), 1926-1941; Dorothy Boberg Collection (15 linear feet); Rockwell International Corp., Rocketdyne Division, Santa Susana Field Laboratories Activity Reports (1985 to present; 15 linear feet); John and LaRee Caughey's ACLU Papers on School Integration (1 linear foot); James A. Stanley Papers on Transportation in Los Angeles (12 linear feet). **Holdings:** 2100 linear feet of documents, minutes, labor newspapers; photographs; oral histories. **Services:** Copying; microfilming; center open to the public with restrictions on some collections. **Computerized Information Services:** OCLC; GEAC (internal database). **Publications:** The UAC Newsletter, 3/year; finding guides to collections. **Staff:** Robert G. Marshall, Archv.

★2574★
California State University, Sacramento - Library - Science & Technology Reference Department (Sci-Engr, Biol Sci)
2000 Jed Smith Dr. Phone: (916)278-4636
Sacramento, CA 95819-2695 Joseph Kramer, Hd.
Founded: 1953. **Staff:** Prof 4. **Subjects:** Biology and environment, engineering, geology, chemistry, physics, mathematics, computer science, nursing, speech pathology, home economics. **Special Collections:** Powder Diffraction File (X-ray); Sadtler Standard Spectra (8 series). **Holdings:** 171,938 books; 63,528 bound periodical volumes; 23,000 microforms and AV programs; 11,100 geologic maps of California and neighboring states; 5800 pamphlets; 8800 clippings. **Subscriptions:** 3114 journals. **Services:** Interlibrary loan; copying; department open to the public. **Automated Operations:** Computerized cataloging, acquisitions, serials, and circulation. **Computerized Information Services:** BRS Information Technologies, DIALOG Information Services, STN International. **Networks/Consortia:** Member of Mountain Valley Library System. **Publications:** Subject bibliographies. **Remarks:** FAX: (916)278-6798. **Staff:** Deborah Metzger, Ref.Libn.; Eileen Heaser, Ref.Libn.

★2575★
California State University, Sacramento - Library Media Center (Aud-Vis)
2000 Jed Smith Dr. Phone: (916)278-7302
Sacramento, CA 95819 Judy Jones, Act.Lib.Hd.
Founded: 1974. **Staff:** 2. **Special Collections:** Harry Sweet Collection (16mm film of TV news, channel 13, Stockton; 1967-1981). **Holdings:** 2300 videocassettes; 200 filmstrips; 250 slide/tape sets; 2300 audio cassettes; 1632 language audio cassettes; 2300 16mm films. **Services:** AV programs available for reference use only. **Publications:** Subject media bibliographies.

★2576★
California State University, Stanislaus - Library - Special Collections (Hist)
Turlock, CA 95380 Phone: (209)667-3232
John K. Amrhein, Dean, Lib.Serv.
Founded: 1960. **Staff:** 25. **Special Collections:** Assyriana - Sayad Collection (150 volumes in Assyrian language); North San Joaquin Valley local history. **Holdings:** 277,000 books; 10,000 bound periodical volumes; 770,000 microfiche; 30,000 reels of microfilm. **Subscriptions:** 3900 journals and other serials; 12 newspapers. **Services:** Interlibrary loan; copying; collections open to the public. **Automated Operations:** Computerized public access catalog, serials, circulation, and management data. **Computerized Information Services:** DIALOG Information Services, OCLC, RLIN. Performs searches free of charge for faculty and students. Contact Person: Paula Crawford, Ref.Libn., 667-3233. **Networks/Consortia:** Member of 49-99 Cooperative Library System. **Remarks:** FAX: (209)667-3164. **Staff:** Laura M. Boyer, Ref.Libn.; Patrick Hall, Ref.Libn.; Peter C. Mollema, Jr., Coll.Dev.Libn.; J. Carlyle Parker, Univ.Archv.; Priscilla S. Peters, Ser./Sys.Libn.; Bob Santos, Ref.Libn.

★2577★
California State University and Colleges - Moss Landing Marine Laboratories - Library (Biol Sci)
Box 450 Phone: (408)755-8654
Moss Landing, CA 95039 Sheila Baldridge, Libn.
Founded: 1966. **Staff:** Prof 1; Other 1. **Subjects:** Oceanography, marine mammals and birds, marine biology and geology, trace metals research, marine chemistry. **Special Collections:** Central California Collection (online). **Holdings:** 7580 books; 2450 bound periodical volumes; 200 nautical charts; 469 topographical maps; 1200 technical reports; 250 theses. **Subscriptions:** 92 journals and other serials. **Services:** Interlibrary loan (fee); copying; library open to the public with restrictions. **Automated Operations:** Computerized cataloging. **Computerized Information Services:** DIALOG Information Services. **Remarks:** FAX: (408)753-2826.

★2578★
California State Water Resources Control Board - Library (Law)
Box 100 Phone: (916)657-2412
Sacramento, CA 95812 Terrance Heiser, Leg.Asst.
Founded: 1967. **Staff:** 1. **Subjects:** Law - water, environmental. **Special Collections:** History of Water Resources Control Board; Regulatory History of California Water Supply and Use; California Water Quality Orders; California Water Rights Decisions and Orders; legal opinions and memoranda. **Holdings:** 7500 volumes; 500 bound periodical volumes; 6500 reports; 10,000 archival items; 500 microfiche; 120 videotapes. **Subscriptions:** 300 journals and other serials; 3 newspapers. **Services:** Interlibrary loan; copying; library open to the public by appointment only. **Automated Operations:** Computerized cataloging and acquisitions. **Computerized Information Services:** LEXIS, WESTLAW, DIALOG Information Services; internal database. Performs searches free of charge. **Special Indexes:** Index of State Water Resources Control Board Water Quality Orders (card and online). **Remarks:** Division of the California State Environmental Protection Agency. Library located at 901 P St., Sacramento, CA 95814. FAX: (916)657-0932.

★2579★
California Thoroughbred Breeders Association - Carleton F. Burke Memorial Library (Rec, Biol Sci)
201 Colorado Place
P.O. Box 750 Phone: (818)445-7800
Arcadia, CA 91007-2604 Marla A. Conway, Libn.
Founded: 1937. **Staff:** Prof 1. **Subjects:** Horses - racing, breeding, veterinary, training, handicapping, fiction. **Special Collections:** Edward E. Lasker Collection of Foreign Racing Records (2000 volumes); C.C. Mosely Collection on American Breeding; Kent Cochran Collection. **Holdings:** 10,000 books; 1500 bound periodical volumes; 600 microfiche; 30 videotapes. **Subscriptions:** 67 journals and other serials. **Services:** Copying; library open to the public for reference use only. **Computerized Information Services:** Bloodstock Research Information Services, Inc., Equine Line. **Special Indexes:** Index by dams to sales catalogs (card). **Remarks:** FAX: (818)574-0852. Toll-free telephone number(s): (800)225-2822.

★ 2580 ★
California Western School of Law - Library (Law)
350 Cedar St. Phone: (619)239-0391
San Diego, CA 92101 Chin Kim, Lib.Dir.
Founded: 1924. **Staff:** Prof 7; Other 18. **Subjects:** Law - international and comparative. **Holdings:** 116,285 books; 78,128 books in microform. **Subscriptions:** 2955 journals and other serials; 10 newspapers. **Services:** Interlibrary loan (fee); copying. **Automated Operations:** Computerized cataloging. **Computerized Information Services:** WESTLAW, LEXIS, NEXIS, OCLC, EPIC. **Publications:** Monthly Acquisitions List. **Remarks:** FAX: (619)696-9999. **Staff:** James Dopp, Dir., Tech.Serv.; Louis W. Bookheim, Dir., Pub.Serv.; Mary E. Garcia, Assoc.Dir.; Linda Weathers, Comp.Serv./Ref.Libn.; George Wilk, Asst.Ref.Libn.; Jane Petitmermet, Acq.Libn.

★ 2581 ★
Callaway Educational Association - Coleman Library (Educ)
701 Lincoln St. Phone: (404)882-0946
LaGrange, GA 30240 M. Christopher Boner, Dir.
Founded: 1955. **Staff:** Prof 1; Other 10. **Subjects:** Children's literature, literacy research, home and family. **Special Collections:** Georgia Collection (325 monographs); rare book collection (175 monographs). **Holdings:** 96,900 volumes; 110 bound periodical volumes; 4625 reels of microfilm of newspapers and periodicals; 1500 microfiche; 5960 phonograph records; 3614 filmstrips; 15 VF drawers; 10 films; 1272 cassettes; 1086 videocassettes. **Subscriptions:** 274 journals and other serials; 8 newspapers. **Services:** Library open to members of the Callaway Educational Association. **Special Indexes:** Literacy Reference File (card); Index to Georgia Magazines (card); LaGrange Daily News Index.

Callery Chemical Company
See: **Mine Safety Appliances Company - MSA Research Corporation** (10436)

Gertrude Callihan Memorial Library
See: **First United Methodist Church** (5810)

Calliopean Society Library
See: **Bridgeport Public Library - Historical Collections** (2116)

CALRECO, Inc.
See: **WESTRECO, Inc.** (20347)

★ 2582 ★
Calspan Corporation - Technical Information Center (Sci-Engr)
Box 400
4455 Genesee St. Phone: (716)632-7500
Buffalo, NY 14225 Susan Doughtie, Mgr.
Founded: 1946. **Staff:** Prof 1; Other 3. **Subjects:** Aerodynamics, aeronautics, electronics, transportation, computer sciences, meteorology, aerospace sciences, applied sciences, applied physics. **Special Collections:** Complete output in microfiche of American Institute of Aeronautics and Astronautics reports; National Advisory Committee for Aeronautics (NACA) Collection, 1915-1958; Society of Automotive Engineers (complete papers); NTIS microfiche (600,000); IEEE Conference Proceedings (30 years); military standards and specifications (complete set; microfilm). **Holdings:** 22,000 books; 564 reels of microfilm and 14,000 microfiche backfiles of periodicals; 234,000 hardcopy reports; 617,000 reports on microfiche. **Subscriptions:** 372 journals and other serials. **Services:** Interlibrary loan; center not open to the public. **Computerized Information Services:** DIALOG Information Services, PFDS Online, DTIC, NASA/RECON, MEDLINE. **Networks/Consortia:** Member of Western New York Library Resources Council (WNYLRC).

Calumet Regional Archives
See: **Indiana University--Northwest** (7808)

Calumet Room
See: **Hammond Historical Society** (6873)

★ 2583 ★
Calvary Baptist Church - Library (Rel-Phil)
3921 Baltimore Phone: (816)531-1208
Kansas City, MO 64111 Carroll O'Neal, Libn.
Staff: Prof 2; Other 2. **Subjects:** Religion, history of the Southern Baptist church, children's religious literature, Bible, missions in foreign countries. **Holdings:** 2000 books. **Subscriptions:** 15 journals and other serials. **Services:** Interlibrary loan; library open to the public for reference use only.

★ 2584 ★
Calvary Baptist Church - Media Library (Rel-Phil)
1009 W. Alameda
Box 127 Phone: (505)622-2553
Roswell, NM 88201 Betty Kennedy, Dir., Lib.Serv.
Founded: 1962. **Staff:** 4. **Subjects:** Religion, social sciences, biography, arts, philosophy, history. **Special Collections:** Complete history of Calvary Baptist Church, 1938 to present. **Holdings:** 2879 books; 21 bound periodical volumes; 22 AV programs; 9 VF drawers. **Subscriptions:** 10 journals and other serials. **Services:** Library open to the public with restrictions. **Automated Operations:** Computerized cataloging and circulation. **Publications:** Bookworm News From Your Media Library, annual - for internal distribution only. **Staff:** Alpha Stewart, Asst.Dir.

★ 2585 ★
Calvary Baptist Theological Seminary - Library (Rel-Phil)
1380 Valley Forge Rd. Phone: (215)368-7538
Lansdale, PA 19446 Clint J. Banz, Libn.
Founded: 1975. **Staff:** Prof 1; Other 4. **Subjects:** Theology, Biblical studies. **Holdings:** 55,000 books; 13,000 bound periodical volumes; 40,000 microforms; 1200 tapes. **Subscriptions:** 525 journals and other serials. **Services:** Copying; library open to the public with restrictions. **Automated Operations:** Computerized cataloging, acquisitions, and serials.

★ 2586 ★
Calvary Bible College - Hilda Kroeker Library (Rel-Phil)
15800 Calvary Rd. Phone: (816)322-0110
Kansas City, MO 64147 Marilynn Zeller, Hd.Libn.
Founded: 1932. **Staff:** Prof 1; Other 5. **Subjects:** Bible, practical theology. **Holdings:** 57,800 books; 2262 bound periodical volumes; 2665 microfilm and microfiche of book and periodical titles; 146 bound graduate theses; 54 VF drawers. **Subscriptions:** 307 journals and other serials. **Services:** Interlibrary loan; copying; library open to the public for reference use only. **Publications:** Calvary Communique (newsletter), semiannual.

★ 2587 ★
Calvary Episcopal Church - Library (Rel-Phil)
123 S. 9th St. Phone: (314)449-3194
Columbia, MO 65201 Charles Brown, Parish Libn.
Founded: 1975. **Staff:** Prof 3; Other 2. **Subjects:** Bible interpretation, church history, Anglicanism, social ethics, Christian belief and practice, 20th century theology. **Holdings:** 1450 books; 75 cassettes. **Subscriptions:** 6 journals and other serials. **Services:** Library open to local visitors. **Publications:** The Salter (newsletter), monthly - for internal distribution only.

★ 2588 ★
Calvary Hospital - Medical Library (Med)
1740 Eastchester Rd. Phone: (212)518-2229
Bronx, NY 10461-9955 Dorothy M. Maucione, Med.Libn.
Founded: 1963. **Staff:** Prof 1; Other 1. **Subjects:** Medicine, cancer, nutrition, ethics, nursing. **Holdings:** 2079 books; medical journal articles; 100 microfiche, slides, audio- and videotapes. **Subscriptions:** 265 journals and other serials. **Services:** Interlibrary loan; library not open to the public. **Automated Operations:** Computerized cataloging, acquisitions, and circulation. **Computerized Information Services:** Internal databases. **Networks/Consortia:** Member of National Network of Libraries of Medicine - Middle Atlantic Region, Manhattan-Bronx Health Sciences Library Consortia, New York Metropolitan Reference and Research Library Agency. **Remarks:** FAX: (212)518-2676.

Calvert County Genealogical Society
See: **Calvert County Historical Society - Library** (2589)

★2589★
Calvert County Historical Society - Library (Hist)
Prince Fredrick Library Bldg.
30 Duke St. Phone: (301)535-2452
Prince Frederick, MD 20678 Gloria V. Gatewood, Cur.
Founded: 1977. **Staff:** 1. **Subjects:** Genealogy, history, Maryland, Maryland counties. **Special Collections:** Calvert Journal and Calvert Gazette, 1876-1931 (microfilm). **Holdings:** 450 books; documents; photographs. **Services:** Copying; library open to the public. **Publications:** Stein's History of Calvert County; Arthur Storer: Forgotten Man of Science. **Remarks:** The Calvert County Historical Society operates in conjunction with the Calvert County Genealogical Society.

Eleanor Calvert Memorial Library
See: **Kitchener-Waterloo Art Gallery** (8747)

★2590★
Calvert Environmental, Inc./APT - Library (Sci-Engr)
5985 Santa Fe Phone: (619)272-0050
San Diego, CA 92109 Shui-Chow Yung, Res.Dir.
Subjects: Aerosol science, fluids, chemistry. **Holdings:** 700 books; 300 bound periodical volumes; 3000 reports. **Services:** Library not open to the public. **Formerly:** Calvert, Inc./APT.

★2591★
Calvert Marine Museum - Library (Sci-Engr, Hist)
Box 97 Phone: (410)326-2042
Solomons, MD 20688 Paul L. Berry, Libn.
Founded: 1975. **Staff:** Prof 1. **Subjects:** Maritime history, Miocene and vertebrate paleontology, geology, marine biology, local history. **Special Collections:** Buddenhagen Collection (comprehensive Atlantic Coastal Plain geology and paleontology); M.M. Davis Collection (shipbuilding); J.C. Lore and Sons Oyster Packing Company Collection (business records); Watermen of Patuxent River Region Collection (oral history tapes; photographs; slides); Warren Denton Company Collection (business records); Marion V. Brewington research files on Chesapeake Bay maritime history (cards). **Holdings:** 3500 books; 200 bound periodical volumes; 1100 unbound periodicals; 150 maps and charts; 1000 local newspaper clippings; 9200 slides; 11,000 photographs; 15 linear feet of business archives. **Subscriptions:** 35 journals and other serials. **Services:** Copying; library open to the public for reference use only. **Computerized Information Services:** Internal databases.

★2592★
Calvin College - Seminary - Library (Rel-Phil)
3207 Burton St., S.E. Phone: (616)957-7197
Grand Rapids, MI 49546 Marvin E. Monsma, Dir.
Founded: 1856. **Staff:** Prof 8.5; Other 26. **Subjects:** Religion, philosophy, English literature, French literature and language, Dutch language and literature, history. **Special Collections:** Calvin and Calvinism; Archives of the Christian Reformed Church. **Holdings:** 360,000 books; 95,000 bound periodical volumes; 100,000 government documents; 450,000 microforms. **Subscriptions:** 2830 journals and other serials; 20 newspapers. **Services:** Interlibrary loan; copying; library open to the public. **Automated Operations:** Computerized public access catalog, cataloging, circulation, serials and acquisitions (DYNIX). **Computerized Information Services:** DIALOG Information Services, OCLC; CD-ROMs (WILSONDISC, ERIC, PsycLIT). **Networks/Consortia:** Member of Michigan Library Consortium (MLC). **Publications:** Origins, irregular - by subscription. **Special Indexes:** Card index to major publications (serials) of the Christian Reformed Church.**Remarks:** FAX: (616)957-6470. **Staff:** Conrad J. Bult, Asst.Dir., Ref.; Harry Boonstra, Asst.Dir., Theological Libn.; Paul Fields, Theological Libn.; Glenn Remelts, Sys.Libn.; Stephen Lambers, Govt.Doc./Info.Serv.; Francene Lewis, Hd., Cat.; Herbert Brinks, Cur., Heritage Hall; Connie Van Sledright, Hd., Circ.; Jo Duyst, Acq.; Richard Gamble, Dir., Meeter Ctr. for Calvin Stud.

Camara Brasileira do Livro
See: **Brazilian Chamber of Publishing** (2099)

Camara de Comercio Espanola
See: **Spanish Chamber of Commerce** (15569)

Camara de Comercio Espanola en los Estados Unidos
See: **Spain-United States Chamber of Commerce - Library** (15568)

Camara Nacional de Agricultura y Agroindustria
See: **Costa Rica - National Chamber of Agriculture** (4349)

★2593★
Camarillo State Hospital & Developmental Center - Professional Library (Med)
1878 S. Lewis Rd.
Box 6022 Phone: (805)484-3661
Camarillo, CA 93011-6022 Mrs. Nagiko Sato Kiser, Sr.Libn.
Founded: 1936. **Staff:** Prof 1; Other 1. **Subjects:** Psychiatric and psychological treatment, neurology, internal medicine, nursing services, public health, behavioral science. **Holdings:** 6980 books; 910 bound periodical volumes; 7090 unbound volumes of periodicals; 21 linear feet of journals; 2 VF drawers. **Subscriptions:** 141 journals and other serials. **Services:** Interlibrary loan; copying; library open to the public. **Computerized Information Services:** DOCLINE (electronic mail service). **Networks/Consortia:** Member of National Network of Libraries of Medicine - Pacific Southwest Region, CLASS. **Publications:** Monthly and annual reports - restricted circulation; acquisition lists; journal holdings list, annual. **Remarks:** FAX: (805)389-2700. Maintained by California State Department of Developmental Services.

★2594★
Cambria County Free Law Library (Law)
Courthouse Phone: (814)472-5440
Ebensburg, PA 15931 Jeanne M. Wolf, Law Libn.
Founded: 1906. **Staff:** Prof 1. **Subjects:** Law. **Holdings:** 35,000 volumes. **Services:** Library open to the public.

★2595★
Cambria County Historical Society - Museum & Library (Hist)
615 N. Center St. Phone: (814)472-6674
Ebensburg, PA 15931 Sara Leishman, Cur.
Founded: 1925. **Staff:** 1. **Subjects:** Genealogy, history of Cambria County, general history. **Holdings:** 2000 volumes. **Services:** Copying; library open to the public for reference use only. **Publications:** Heritage (newsletter), quarterly - to members.

★2596★
Cambria County Library - Preschool Adventure Library (Educ)
248 Main St. Phone: (814)536-5131
Johnstown, PA 15901 Sue Hensel, Children's Libn.
Staff: Prof 1; Other 1. **Holdings:** Toys; games; puzzles; cassettes; record players; videotapes. **Remarks:** FAX: (814)536-6905.

★2597★
Cambrian College - Learning Resources Centre (Educ)
1400 Barrydowne Rd., Station A Phone: (705)566-8101
Sudbury, ON, Canada P3A 3V8 Mr. Chris Bartlett, Dir., LRC
Founded: 1967. **Staff:** Prof 2; Other 15. **Subjects:** Science, technology, business, health sciences, applied arts, industrial training, support programs. **Special Collections:** Art (169 items); Cambriana Archives (9 VF drawers). **Holdings:** 40,725 books; 5292 bound periodical volumes; 44 VF drawers of pamphlets and clippings; 293 microfiche; 1821 recordings; 157 film loops; 357 films; 295 filmstrips; 155 kits; 207 reels of microfilm; 937 scores; 133 slide sets; 1945 videotapes; 4653 uncataloged government publications, including 1312 Statistics Canada publications. **Subscriptions:** 664 journals and other serials; 17 newspapers. **Services:** Interlibrary loan; copying; center open to the public with restrictions. **Automated Operations:** Computerized acquisitions. **Computerized Information Services:** Envoy 100 (electronic mail services). **Networks/Consortia:** Member of The Bibliocentre. **Publications:** New Acquisitions List, monthly; Learning Resource Centre Brochure. **Special Catalogs:** Film, Video & Software Catalog. **Special Indexes:** Periodicals List; Vertical File List; Company Annual Reports Listing (sheets). **Remarks:** FAX: (705)671-7329. **Staff:** Diane Henry, Hd.Libn.

★ 2598 ★
Cambridge Acoustical Associates, Inc. - Library (Sci-Engr)
80 Sherman St. Phone: (617)491-1421
Cambridge, MA 02140 Bonnie Whitney, Libn./Adm.
Staff: Prof 1. **Subjects:** Acoustics, vibration, physics, computers, engineering. **Holdings:** 1000 books; 150 bound periodical volumes; 2000 other cataloged items. **Subscriptions:** 10 journals and other serials. **Services:** Library not open to the public. **Remarks:** FAX: (617)491-1424.

★ 2599 ★
Cambridge Energy Research Associates - Library (Energy)
20 University Rd.
Charles Sq. Phone: (617)497-6446
Cambridge, MA 02138 Barbara Blodgett, Libn.
Staff: Prof 1. **Subjects:** Energy - oil, gas, coal, nuclear; utilities; economics; politics. **Holdings:** 600 books; 200 other cataloged items. **Subscriptions:** 95 journals and other serials; 5 newspapers. **Services:** Library open to employees and clients.

★ 2600 ★
Cambridge Historical Commission - Library (Hist)
City Hall Annex
57 Inman St. Phone: (617)349-4683
Cambridge, MA 02139 Charles M. Sullivan, Exec.Dir.
Founded: 1964. **Staff:** Prof 4; Other 1. **Subjects:** Architectural history and development of Cambridge. **Holdings:** 300 books; 13,000 building inventory records, 1963-1977; maps of Cambridge, 1633-1930; 19,000 35mm negatives; 3500 negatives from city records, 1919-1958; 3500 early views of Cambridge. **Services:** Copying; library open to the public. **Publications:** Survey of Architectural History in Cambridge, 1965-1977 (5 volumes); Maintaining Your Old House in Cambridge, 1987; Photographic History of Cambridge, 1984; East Cambridge, 1988. **Special Indexes:** Holdings organized by geographic location; card index of all Cambridge architects and builders. **Remarks:** FAX: (617)349-4669. **Staff:** Sarah J. Zimmerman, Arch.Hist.; Susan E. Maycock, Survey Dir.; Nancy L. Doonan, Asst.Dir.

★ 2601 ★
Cambridge Historical Society - Library (Hist)
159 Brattle St. Phone: (617)547-4252
Cambridge, MA 02138 Warren M. Little, Exec.Dir.
Founded: 1969. **Staff:** Prof 2. **Subjects:** Local history. **Special Collections:** Letters of Ole Bull; New England Brick Company Archives. **Holdings:** 500 books; 250 other cataloged items. **Services:** Copying; library open to the public. **Publications:** Cambridge Historical Society Proceedings - individual copies or by subscription. **Staff:** Marjorie Gutheim, Libn.

★ 2602 ★
Cambridge Hospital - Medical Library (Med)
1493 Cambridge St. Phone: (617)498-1439
Cambridge, MA 02139 Gina Chen, Med.Libn.
Staff: Prof 1. **Subjects:** Medicine, surgery, health sciences. **Holdings:** 550 books; 2000 bound periodical volumes. **Subscriptions:** 70 journals and other serials. **Services:** Interlibrary loan; library not open to the public. **Computerized Information Services:** MEDLARS, PaperChase.

★ 2603 ★
Cambridge Mental Health Center - Resource Center (Med)
County Rd. 35 Phone: (614)439-1371
Cambridge, OH 43725 Noreen M. Kenney, Dir., Lib.Serv.
Staff: Prof 1. **Subjects:** Mental health, psychology, psychiatry, mental retardation, programming. **Holdings:** 701 books; AV programs. **Subscriptions:** 70 journals and other serials. **Services:** Interlibrary loan; copying; center open to the public with restrictions. **Publications:** Acquisitions list, quarterly. **Formerly:** Cambridge Mental Health & Developmental Center - Resource Center.

Cambridge Military Library
See: **Canada - National Defence** (2777)

★ 2604 ★
Cambridge School Department - Teachers' Resource Center (Educ)
459 Broadway Phone: (617)349-6400
Cambridge, MA 02138 Sheila Morshead, Libn./Media Spec.
Founded: 1969. **Staff:** Prof 1; Other 2. **Subjects:** Education. **Holdings:** 3500 books; 20,000 AV programs; 500 pamphlets; 500 microcomputer programs. **Subscriptions:** 110 journals and other serials. **Services:** Media production; video editing; center open to the public for reference use only. **Computerized Information Services:** DIALOG Information Services, HOLLIS; PeaceNet (electronic mail service). **Remarks:** FAX: (617)349-6897.

★ 2605 ★
Cambridge Systematics, Inc. - Library (Trans)
222 3rd St. Phone: (617)354-0167
Cambridge, MA 02142 Roanne Neuwirth, Libn.
Subjects: Transportation planning, economic development. **Holdings:** 150 books; 2000 reports. **Subscriptions:** 20 journals and other serials. **Services:** Library not open to the public. **Computerized Information Services:** Dow Jones News/Retrieval, CompuServe Information Service; MCI Mail (electronic mail service).

★ 2606 ★
Camden Archives and Museum (Hist)
1314 Broad St. Phone: (803)425-6050
Camden, SC 29020 Agnes B. Corbett, Dir.
Founded: 1973. **Staff:** Prof 3. **Subjects:** History - local, state, national, military; genealogy. **Holdings:** 4000 books; 75 bound periodical volumes; 120 reels of microfilm; manuscripts; newspapers; maps; city records; photographic collections; records of community institutions; local artifacts. **Subscriptions:** 7 journals and other serials. **Services:** Copying; archives open to the public for reference use only. **Staff:** Joseph Matheson, Asst.Dir.

Camden-Carroll Library
See: **Morehead State University - Camden-Carroll Library** (10725)

★ 2607 ★
Camden County Bar Association - Law Library (Law)
Hall of Justice
101 S. Fifth St.
Camden, NJ 08103 Phone: (609)757-5032
Subjects: Law. **Holdings:** 20,000 books; 100 bound periodical volumes; U.S. and state statutes. **Services:** Library open to the public for reference use only. **Remarks:** Alternate telephone number(s): (609)964-3420.

★ 2608 ★
Camden County Historical Society - Library (Hist)
Park Blvd. & Euclid Ave. Phone: (609)964-3333
Camden, NJ 08103 Toni Gutwein, Libn.
Founded: 1899. **Staff:** Prof 1. **Subjects:** History - Camden, Camden County, New Jersey, Pennsylvania, U.S.; decorative arts; Walt Whitman; genealogy; biography. **Holdings:** 20,000 books; 20 VF drawers; 587 reels of microfilm of newspapers; manuscripts; building contracts; maps; photographs; deeds. **Subscriptions:** 15 journals and other serials. **Services:** Copying; library open to the public on a fee basis. **Publications:** Bulletin, annual; newsletter, quarterly. **Staff:** Carole A. Wood, Dir.

★ 2609 ★
Camden County Library - Regional Film and Video Service - Library (Aud-Vis)
Echelon Urban Center
203 Laurel Rd. Phone: (609)772-1642
Voorhees, NJ 08043 Patricia Hodson, AV Libn.
Founded: 1970. **Staff:** Prof 1; Other 4. **Subjects:** Films - entertainment, social documentaries, film art, health and safety, classic features, cartoons. **Special Collections:** State Department films; National Gallery of Art. **Holdings:** 1900 16mm films; 1600 videotapes. **Services:** Interlibrary loan; library open to members of the South Jersey Regional Film Library Co-operative. **Automated Operations:** Computerized cataloging. **Networks/Consortia:** Member of New Jersey State Library Regional Film Centers, South Jersey Regional Library Cooperative. **Special Catalogs:** Catalogs, annual. **Formerly:** South Jersey Regional Film Library.

★2610★
Camden Historical Commission - Historic Camden Revolutionary War Park (Hist)
S. Broad St., Box 710 Phone: (803)432-9841
Camden, SC 29020 Joanna B. Craig, Dir.
Founded: 1970. **Staff:** Prof 2; Other 1. **Subjects:** American Revolutionary War, local history, Indians. **Holdings:** 200 volumes; 20 archeological reports; manuscript material pertaining to Camden from settlement in 1733 to present. **Subscriptions:** 10 journals and other serials. **Services:** Open to the public for reference use only.

★2611★
Camden-Rockport Historical Society - Archives (Hist)
Old Conway House and Cramer Museum
Box 747 Phone: (207)236-2257
Rockport, ME 04856 Marlene Hall, Dir.
Founded: 1969. **Staff:** 2. **Subjects:** History - Camden, Rockport. **Special Collections:** Costumes; area memorabilia. **Holdings:** 1000 archival materials including ships' logs and records, photographs, other historical materials. **Services:** Archives open to the public during the summer months. **Formerly:** Located in Camden, ME.

★2612★
Camelot Therapeutic Horsemanship - Camelot Library (Rec)
523 W. 2nd. St. Phone: (602)289-4106
Winslow, AZ 86047 Karen Berggren, Libn.
Founded: 1985. **Staff:** Prof 1. **Subjects:** Equines, therapeutic horsemanship, domestic animals, therapeutic use of animals, nature, chivalry, King Arthur. **Special Collections:** The Flinn Foundation Collection. **Holdings:** 300 books. **Services:** Interlibrary loan; copying; library open to the public by appointment. **Publications:** The Camelot Chronicles, biennial.

Angus L. Cameron Medical Library
See: **Trinity Medical Center - Angus L. Cameron Medical Library** (16515)

★2613★
Cameron County Historical Society - Little Museum (Hist)
102 W. 4th St. Phone: (814)486-2162
Emporium, PA 15834 Sandra R. Hornung, Pres.
Staff: 2. **Subjects:** History of Cameron County, logging, early industry; genealogy. **Special Collections:** Gen. Joseph T. McNarney, USAF (books; pictures; papers); Tom Mix, silent film star (artifacts; papers; photographs); Sylvania Electric Corp.; Panama Canal; early dynamite industry. **Holdings:** Cameron County documents; maps; 3 VF drawers of newspaper clippings and documents; all tombstone inscriptions in 38 cemeteries and some church records on microfilm; early Cameron County newspapers on microfilm. **Services:** Museum open to the public on a limited schedule.

★2614★
Cameron Forge Company - Library (Sci-Engr)
PO Box 1212 Phone: (713)856-3332
Houston, TX 77251-1212 Norma A. Willoughby, Libn.
Founded: 1977. **Staff:** Prof 1. **Subjects:** Alloys, engineering, metallurgy, forging processes. **Special Collections:** Metals Abstracts (1932 to present). **Holdings:** 3000 books; 1000 bound periodical volumes. **Subscriptions:** 100 journals and other serials. **Services:** Library open to librarians only. **Computerized Information Services:** DIALOG Information Services. **Remarks:** FAX: (713)856-3315.

★2615★
Cameroon - Ministry of Higher Education, Computer Services and Scientific Research - Institut de Recherches Medicales et d'Etudes des Plantes Medicinales (IMPM) - Service de la Bibliotheque de la Documentation et des Publications (Med)
Yaounde, Cameroon Phone: 302865
Francois Bene Mbama, Chf. of Serv.
Founded: 1979. **Staff:** Prof 3; Other 7. **Subjects:** Medicine, nutrition, medicinal plants. **Holdings:** 400 books; 40 bound periodical volumes; 300 reports; 50 microfiche; 350 photos and diapositives; 4000 monographs; 70 archival items; 700 theses. **Subscriptions:** 42 journals and other serials. **Services:** Interlibrary loan; copying; SDI; library open to the public for reference use only. **Computerized Information Services:** BABICAM (internal database). **Publications:** Science and Technology Review/Health Science Series; Cahiers de l'IMPM; National Medical Bibliography of Cameroon. **Remarks:** Telex: 8418 KN.

★2616★
Cameroon Institute of International Relations - Library (Soc Sci)
B.P. 1637 Phone: 310305
Yaounde, Cameroon Samuel Foncham, Libn.
Staff: 8. **Subjects:** International relations; political science; international law; diplomacy; economic, financial and technical problems affecting present and future relations of African states as well as other countries. **Holdings:** 15,000 volumes; 6357 documents on international organizations. **Subscriptions:** 542 journals and other serials. **Services:** Interlibrary loan; library open to the public upon authorization of the director of studies and with library card. **Remarks:** Telex: 8384 KN. Maintained by University of Yaounde. **Also Known As:** Institut des Relations Internationales du Cameroun. **Staff:** Louis-Marie Ngoumou, Doc.

★2617★
Camp Dresser & McKee, Inc. - Herman G. Dresser Library (Env-Cons)
10 Cambridge Ctr. Phone: (617)252-8145
Boston, MA 02142 Virginia L. Carroll, Libn.
Founded: 1963. **Staff:** Prof 1; Other 1. **Subjects:** Environmental engineering, waste disposal, wastewater and solid waste management, water supply, water resources, hazardous wastes. **Special Collections:** Water and sanitation for health in developing countries (microfiche). **Holdings:** 12,000 books; 900 bound periodical volumes; 4000 reports; 4500 report data/computations; 2000 pamphlets; 600 reprints of articles written by employees; 3500 microfiche. **Subscriptions:** 201 journals and other serials. **Services:** Interlibrary loan; copying; library open to the public by appointment only. **Automated Operations:** Computerized circulation. **Computerized Information Services:** DIALOG Information Services, ORBIT Search Service, Chemical Information Systems, Inc. (CIS), Technical Database Services (TDS), Ground Water On-Line, BT North America, ASCE (American Society of Civil Engineers); internal database. Performs searches on fee basis. **Networks/Consortia:** Member of NELINET, Inc. **Publications:** Acquisitions list, monthly - for internal distribution only. **Special Indexes:** Report Index; computation index (both on rolodex). **Remarks:** FAX: (617)621-2565. **Staff:** Katie Smith, Asst.Libn.

★2618★
Camp Hill Hospital - Health Sciences Library (Med)
1763 Robie St. Phone: (902)420-2287
Halifax, NS, Canada B3H 3G2 Verona Leslie, Lib.Asst.
Staff: 1. **Subjects:** Medicine, surgery, psychiatry, nursing, gerontology, psychology, pharmacology. **Holdings:** 2000 books; 100 bound periodical volumes; tapes. **Subscriptions:** 200 journals and other serials. **Services:** Interlibrary loan; copying; library open to the public for reference use only. **Computerized Information Services:** MEDLARS, CAN/OLE; Envoy 100 (electronic mail service). **Remarks:** FAX: (902)420-2168. Electronic mail address(es): CHH.LIB (Envoy 100).

★2619★
Camp Hill Medical Centre - Regional Drug Information Service (Med)
1763 Robie St. Phone: (902)420-2211
Halifax, NS, Canada B3H 3G2 C. Brian Tuttle, Dir.
Founded: 1975. **Staff:** Prof 3; Other 1. **Subjects:** Therapeutics, pharmacology, toxicology, institutional and professional pharmacy practice. **Holdings:** 2000 files. **Subscriptions:** 18 journals and other serials. **Services:** Service open to health care professionals in Nova Scotia and pharmacists in New Brunswick and Prince Edward Island. **Computerized Information Services:** MEDLARS, Micromedex, Inc., Iowa Drug Information Service Database (IDIS); internal database. **Publications:** The Distillate, quarterly; Drug Formulary Decisions, quarterly; Network, quarterly. **Remarks:** FAX: (902)420-2612. **Formerly:** Camp Hill Hospital. **Formerly:** Its Provincial Drug Information Service. **Staff:** Donna H. Wheeler-Usher, Drug Info.Pharm.; Margaret A. Willan, Drug Info.Pharm.

Charles MacFie Campbell Memorial Library
See: **Massachusetts Mental Health Center** (9823)

John Bulow Campbell Library
See: **Columbia Theological Seminary** (3998)

Campbell Library
See: **St. Joseph's University - Academy of Food Marketing** (14421)

★2620★
Campbell-Mithun-Esty - Library & Information Services (Bus-Fin)
222 S. 9th St. Phone: (612)347-1509
Minneapolis, MN 55402 Virginia Ferestad, V.P., Dir.
Founded: 1953. **Staff:** Prof 3; Other 6. **Subjects:** Advertising, marketing. **Holdings:** 1000 books; 2000 volumes of client records; 500 files of pamphlets and clippings; 500 competitive advertising files; 1200 picture files. **Subscriptions:** 1500 journals and other serials. **Services:** Interlibrary loan; copying; permission to use library may be requested. **Computerized Information Services:** DIALOG Information Services, Mead Data Central, DataTimes, Dow Jones News/Retrieval, VU/TEXT Information Services, M.A.I.D. **Publications:** Bulletin, bimonthly - for internal distribution only. **Remarks:** FAX: (612)347-1515. **Staff:** Peggy Sjolander, Ref.Libn.; Phyllis Lindberg, Libn.

★2621★
Campbell-Mithun-Esty - Research Information Center (Bus-Fin)
737 N. Michigan Ave. Phone: (312)266-5445
Chicago, IL 60611 Rebecca Shavit, Info.Spec.
Founded: 1962. **Staff:** Prof 1. **Subjects:** Advertising, marketing, business, food industry. **Holdings:** 1500 books; 500 government documents; 174 VF drawers of clippings, pamphlets, pictures, and annual reports. **Subscriptions:** 250 journals and other serials; 5 newspapers. **Services:** Interlibrary loan; copying; center open to the public by request. **Computerized Information Services:** DIALOG Information Services, DataTimes. **Networks/Consortia:** Member of Chicago Library System. **Special Indexes:** Information File Index (card); Corporation File Index (card).

Paul A. Campbell International Library of Man and Space
See: **Trinity University - Elizabeth Coates Maddux Library - Special Collections** (16521)

★2622★
Campbell River Museum & Archives - Reference Library (Hist)
1235 Island Hwy.
Campbell River, BC, Canada V9W 2C7 Phone: (604)287-3103
Founded: 1958. **Subjects:** History - Northern Vancouver Island, Northwest Coast native Indian culture and history. **Special Collections:** Native culture; local diaries and memorabilia. **Holdings:** 1300 books; 200 oral history tapes; archival documents; videotapes. **Subscriptions:** 27 journals and other serials. **Services:** Copying; library open to the public with restrictions. **Remarks:** FAX: (604)286-6490.

★2623★
Campbell Soup Company - Research Information Center (Biol Sci, Food-Bev)
Campbell Place, Box 57U Phone: (609)342-4926
Camden, NJ 09103-1799 CarolAnn Vincent, Res.Libn.
Founded: 1941. **Staff:** Prof 1; Other 2. **Subjects:** Food technology, biochemistry, microbiology, nutrition, home economics. **Holdings:** 5000 books; 2200 bound periodical volumes; 1500 pamphlets; 2500 patents. **Subscriptions:** 200 journals and other serials. **Services:** Interlibrary loan; library not open to the public. **Automated Operations:** Computerized acquisitions and serials. **Computerized Information Services:** DIALOG Information Services, NEXIS, Leatherhead Food Research Association. **Networks/Consortia:** Member of New Jersey Library Network. **Publications:** Library Bulletin, monthly. **Remarks:** FAX: (609)342-6324.

★2624★
Campbell Taggart, Inc. - Technical Center - Library (Food-Bev)
3401 Haggar Way
Dallas, TX 75235 Phone: (214)358-9211
Subjects: Food plant sanitation, chemistry, microbiology, nutrition, food technology and processing, cereal chemistry, machinery, marketing. **Special Collections:** U.S. Government data and regulations. **Holdings:** Figures not available. **Subscriptions:** 92 journals and other serials. **Services:** Interlibrary loan; library not open to the public. **Remarks:** FAX: (214)358-1499. **Formerly:** Its Research Division - Library.

★2625★
Campbell University - School of Law - Law Library (Law)
Box 458 Phone: (919)893-4111
Buies Creek, NC 27506 Karen C. Sorvari, Law Libn.
Founded: 1976. **Staff:** Prof 3; Other 5. **Subjects:** Law. **Holdings:** 83,400 books and bound periodical volumes; 3000 other cataloged items; 57,000 volumes in microform, including state and federal Supreme Court records and briefs, U.N. treaties, English ruling cases, English reports, U.S. agency reports; AV programs. **Subscriptions:** 500 journals and other serials; 6 newspapers. **Services:** Copying; library open to the public. **Computerized Information Services:** DIALOG Information Services, WESTLAW, LEXIS. Performs searches on fee basis for North Carolina attorneys. **Remarks:** FAX: (919)893-4850. **Staff:** Olivia Weeks, Ref.Libn.; John Allison, Tech.Serv.Libn.

★2626★
(Campinas) Centro Cultural Brasil-Estados Unidos - USIS Collection (Educ)
Ave. Julio de Mesquita, 606
Caixa Postal 408 Phone: 192 526888
13100 Campinas, SP, Brazil Teresa R.P. Camargo, Chf.Libn.
Founded: 1963. **Staff:** 2. **Holdings:** 7476 books. **Subscriptions:** 30 journals and other serials; 2 newspapers. **Services:** Library open to the public. **Remarks:** FAX: 192 513664. Maintained or supported by the U.S. Information Agency. Focus is on materials that will assist peoples outside the United States to learn about the United States, its people, history, culture, political processes, and social milieux. **Staff:** Marina Trevisan.

★2627★
Campion College - Library (Rel-Phil)
University of Regina Phone: (306)586-4242
Regina, SK, Canada S4S 0A2 Myfanwy Truscott, Libn.
Founded: 1917. **Staff:** Prof 1; Other 2. **Subjects:** Religious studies, theology, philosophy, English literature, Canadian and medieval history, psychology. **Special Collections:** Jesuitica (1000 volumes); women and religion. **Holdings:** 50,000 books; 4900 bound periodical volumes; 194 phonograph records; 10,000 microfiche; 148 maps. **Subscriptions:** 200 journals and other serials; 5 newspapers. **Services:** Interlibrary loan (through University of Regina); copying; library open to the public. **Automated Operations:** NOTIS. **Remarks:** FAX: (306)359-1251.

★2628★
Campney & Murphy - Library (Law)
595 Burrard St., 16th Fl.
P.O. Box 49190 Phone: (604)688-8022
Vancouver, BC, Canada V7X 1K9 Pam Clancy, Libn.
Founded: 1932. **Staff:** Prof 1. **Subjects:** Canadian law. **Holdings:** 1600 books. **Subscriptions:** 367 journals and other serials. **Services:** Interlibrary loan; library not open to the public. **Computerized Information Services:** QL Systems, CAN/LAW, WESTLAW, LEXIS, NEXIS, Info Globe, Infomart Online, DIALOG Information Services; QUICKMAIL, Envoy 100 (electronic mail services). **Publications:** Newsletter, irregular - for internal distribution only. **Remarks:** FAX: (604)688-0829. Telex: 04-53320. Electronic mail address(es): Admin/CAMPNEY.MURPHY (Envoy 100).

Campus Martius Museum
See: **Ohio Historical Society** (12271)

Camrose Lutheran University
See: **Augustana University College** (1299)

★2629★
Charles Camsell General Hospital - Peter Wilcock Library (Med)
12804 114th Ave. Phone: (403)453-5581
Edmonton, AB, Canada T5M 3A4 Gail Moores
Staff: Prof 1; Other 2. **Subjects:** Medicine, nursing, paramedical sciences, hospital administration. **Holdings:** 1500 books; 2300 bound periodical volumes; 1000 cassettes; 2 VF drawers of pamphlets and reports. **Subscriptions:** 250 journals and other serials. **Services:** Interlibrary loan; copying; library open to the public for reference use only on request. **Automated Operations:** Computerized cataloging. **Computerized Information Services:** MEDLARS, DIALOG Information Services; Envoy 100 (electronic mail service). **Remarks:** FAX: (403)453-6565. Electronic mail address(es): CAMSELL.LIB (Envoy 100).

★ 2630 ★
Camunian Center for Prehistoric and Ethnologic Studies - Library (Soc Sci, Hist)
25044 Capo di Ponte Phone: 364 42091
Valcomonica, (BS), Italy Ariela Fradkin Anati, Libn.
Founded: 1964. **Staff:** 2. **Subjects:** Archeology, prehistoric art, ethnology, history of religions. **Special Collections:** Archives (documentation for studies in prehistoric art). **Holdings:** 35,000 volumes; 100,000 slides; site descriptions and research reports. **Subscriptions:** 650 journals and other serials. **Services:** Copying; library open to members and research students. **Computerized Information Services:** UNESCO's ISIS (internal database). **Remarks:** FAX: 364 42572. Telex: 301504. **Also Known As:** Centro Camuno di Studi Preistorici e Etnologici.

Albert Camus Archives
See: **University of Wisconsin--Milwaukee - Golda Meir Library** (19631)

★ 2631 ★
Canada - Agriculture Canada - Animal & Plant Health Directorate - Library (Med)
3851 Chemin Fallowfield Rd.
P.O. Box 11300, Sta. H Phone: (613)998-9320
Nepean, ON, Canada K2H 8P9 P. Atherton, Libn.
Founded: 1902. **Staff:** Prof 1; Other 1. **Subjects:** Veterinary medicine, virology, immunology, bacteriology. **Holdings:** 18,500 volumes. **Subscriptions:** 183 journals and other serials. **Services:** Interlibrary loan; copying; SDI; library open to the public for reference use only. **Automated Operations:** Computerized cataloging, acquisitions, circulation, and ILL. **Computerized Information Services:** Agrinet (electronic mail service). **Remarks:** FAX: (613)952-2285. **Formerly:** Animal Diseases Research Institute - Library. **Staff:** G. Eldridge.

★ 2632 ★
Canada - Agriculture Canada - Animal Research Centre Library (Biol Sci)
Genetics Bldg.
Ottawa, ON, Canada K1A 0C6 Phone: (613)993-6002
Staff: 2. **Subjects:** Animal science and nutrition, genetics, physiology, biochemistry. **Holdings:** 3000 books; 4200 bound periodical volumes. **Subscriptions:** 200 journals and other serials. **Services:** Interlibrary loan; SDI; library open to the public for reference use only. **Automated Operations:** Computerized cataloging. **Computerized Information Services:** Agrinet (electronic mail service).

★ 2633 ★
Canada - Agriculture Canada - Canadian Agriculture Library (Agri)
Sir John Carling Bldg., Rm. 245 Phone: (613)995-7829
Ottawa, ON, Canada K1A 0C5 V.G. Desroche, Dir., CAL
Founded: 1910. **Staff:** Prof 41; Other 43. **Subjects:** Agriculture and allied sciences, economics, veterinary medicine, chemistry, biochemistry, nutrition, management science. **Special Collections:** Chapais Collection (personal library of first Minister of Agriculture, Hon. Jean-Charles Chapais, and his son, Jean-Charles); Food and Agriculture Organization publications. **Holdings:** 1 million volumes; 20,000 microforms; 7700 translations. **Subscriptions:** 22,400 journals and other serials. **Services:** Interlibrary loan; copying; central library open to the public for reference use only. **Automated Operations:** Computerized public access catalog, cataloging, acquisitions, serials, and circulation. **Computerized Information Services:** CAN/SDI, CAN/OLE, DIALOG Information Services, QL Systems, MEDLINE, Info Globe, Prima Telematic Inc., DOBIS. **Publications:** Publications of the Canada Department of Agriculture, 1867-1974; Agricultural Periodicals Published in Canada, 1836-1960; Chapais Collection. **Special Catalogs:** Union List of Serials in Canada Department of Agriculture Libraries; Catalogue of the Buller Memorial Library (located in Research Station, Winnipeg library); Union Catalog of Library Holdings. **Remarks:** Maintains 28 branch libraries. FAX: (613)952-3813. **Also Known As:** Canada - Ministere de l'Agriculture - Bibliotheque Canadienne de l'Agriculture. **Staff:** J. Wu, Asst.Dir., Cent.Lib.Serv.; M. Cutler, Asst.Dir., Reg.Serv.; J. Stitt, Chf., Acq.Serv.; J. Gazeley, Chf., Tech.Serv.; E. Daniel, Chf., Pub.Serv.; D. Rabow, Chf., SDI Serv.; D. Kichuk, Reg.Coord., West.

★ 2634 ★
Canada - Agriculture Canada - Canadian Grain Commission - Library (Agri)
303 Main St., Rm. 300 Phone: (204)983-0878
Winnipeg, MB, Canada R3C 3G8 E. Simundsson, Libn.
Founded: 1913. **Staff:** Prof 1; Other 1.5. **Subjects:** Cereal chemistry, cereals, oilseeds, grain industry and trade, baking, brewing, milling. **Holdings:** 3000 books; 8000 bound periodical volumes; 1000 pamphlets. **Subscriptions:** 300 journals and other serials; 15 newspapers. **Services:** Interlibrary loan; copying; SDI; library open to the public for reference use only. **Automated Operations:** Computerized cataloging. **Computerized Information Services:** DIALOG Information Services, CAN/OLE, AGRICAT, QL Systems; Envoy 100, Agrinet (electronic mail services). **Remarks:** FAX: (204)983-2751. Electronic mail address(es): CGC.LIBRARY (Envoy 100). **Also Known As:** Commission Canadienne des Grains. **Staff:** Cheryl MacDonald-Deda, Lib.Techn.

★ 2635 ★
Canada - Agriculture Canada - Delhi Research Station - Library (Agri)
P.O. Box 186 Phone: (519)582-1950
Delhi, ON, Canada N4B 2W9 Robert Duff, Libn.
Founded: 1933. **Staff:** Prof 1. **Subjects:** Tobacco, peanuts, plant science, soil science, crop protection, genetics, chemistry, biochemistry, physiology. **Special Collections:** Tobacco Research Collection (4 VF drawers). **Holdings:** 1500 books; 3000 bound periodical volumes. **Subscriptions:** 71 journals and other serials; 6 newspapers. **Services:** Interlibrary loan; copying; SDI; library open to the public for reference use only. **Automated Operations:** Computerized cataloging and acquisitions. **Computerized Information Services:** AGRICAT. **Remarks:** FAX: (519)582-4223.

★ 2636 ★
Canada - Agriculture Canada - Entomology Research Library (Biol Sci, Sci-Engr)
K.W. Neatby Bldg., Rm. 4061
Central Experimental Farm Phone: (613)996-1665
Ottawa, ON, Canada K1A 0C6 S. Sherman, Libn.
Founded: 1919. **Staff:** Prof 1; Other 1. **Subjects:** Entomology, natural history, biology, evolution, paleontology. **Holdings:** 10,000 books; 13,000 bound periodical volumes; 10,000 reprints; 5000 government documents. **Subscriptions:** 250 journals and other serials. **Services:** Interlibrary loan; copying; SDI; library open to the public for reference use only. **Automated Operations:** Computerized cataloging. **Computerized Information Services:** Agrinet (electronic mail service). **Remarks:** FAX: (613)995-1823.

★ 2637 ★
Canada - Agriculture Canada - Experimental Farm Library (Agri)
P.O. Box 3398
801, Rte. 344 Phone: (514)589-2171
L'Assomption, PQ, Canada J0K 1G0 Pierre DiCampo
Subjects: Horticulture. **Holdings:** 2500 books; 400 bound periodical volumes; 500 reports. **Subscriptions:** 80 journals and other serials. **Services:** Interlibrary loan; SDI; library open to the public for reference use only. **Computerized Information Services:** CAN/OLE, CABCD; internal database. **Remarks:** FAX: (514)589-4027.

★ 2638 ★
Canada - Agriculture Canada - Experimental Farm Library (Biol Sci)
1642 Rang 2, W. Phone: (418)856-3141
La Pocatiere, PQ, Canada G0R 1Z0 J. Deschenes
Staff: 1. **Subjects:** Plant pathology, mycology, biochemistry, plant physiology, general agriculture, plant breeding, botany, entomology, bacteriology. **Holdings:** 950 books; 1215 bound periodical volumes; 250 maps; 1200 aerial photographs; 150 boxes of reports; 425 boxes of reprints and bulletins. **Subscriptions:** 52 journals and other serials. **Services:** Interlibrary loan; library open to agronomists and research workers. **Remarks:** FAX: (418)856-5374.

★ 2639 ★
Canada - Agriculture Canada - Experimental Farm Library (Agri)
Box 760 Phone: (306)695-2274
Indian Head, SK, Canada S0G 2K0 David Gehl, Off. in Charge
Founded: 1889. **Subjects:** Agronomy, cereal production, soils, general crop production, herbicides, weeds. **Special Collections:** History of Station - experimental records. **Holdings:** Figures not available. **Subscriptions:** 8 journals and other serials. **Services:** Interlibrary loan; library open to the public for reference use only. **Remarks:** Operates as part of the Research Station, Regina - Library. **Remarks:** FAX: (306)695-3445.

★ 2640 ★
Canada - Agriculture Canada - Food Research and Development Centre - Library (Sci-Engr)
3600 Casavant Blvd., W. Phone: (514)773-1105
St. Hyacinthe, PQ, Canada J2S 8E3 Francine Bernard, Libn.
Founded: 1985. **Staff:** Prof 1; Other 1. **Subjects:** Food science, biotechnology, packaging, meat science. **Holdings:** 1000 books; 200 bound periodical volumes. **Subscriptions:** 250 journals and other serials; 5 newspapers. **Services:** Interlibrary loan; copying; SDI; library open to the public for reference use only. **Computerized Information Services:** DIALOG Information Services, CAN/OLE; CD-ROMs (FSTA, AGRICOLA). **Publications:** Agricat. **Remarks:** FAX: (514)773-8461.

★ 2641 ★
Canada - Agriculture Canada - Health of Animals Laboratory - Library (Med)
4 College St. Phone: (506)536-0135
Sackville, NB, Canada E0A 3C0 Dr. R.A. Heckert, Lib.Hd.
Founded: 1954. **Subjects:** Veterinary medicine. **Holdings:** 500 volumes. **Subscriptions:** 61 journals and other serials. **Services:** Library not open to the public. **Computerized Information Services:** Current Contents Search. **Remarks:** FAX: (506)536-1801. Electronic mail address(es): EM 609 SACK.

★ 2642 ★
Canada - Agriculture Canada - Library, Shared Services (Agri)
1955 Brood St.
Box 8035 Phone: (306)780-7075
Regina, SK, Canada S4P 4C7 Susan Yanosik, Info.Spec.
Subjects: Agricultural marketing and economics. **Holdings:** 500 books; 200 bound periodical volumes; 3000 bulletins and reports. **Subscriptions:** 50 journals and other serials; 6 newspapers. **Services:** Interlibrary loan; library open to the public by permission.

★ 2643 ★
Canada - Agriculture Canada - London Research Centre Library (Sci-Engr, Biol Sci)
1400 Western Rd. Phone: (519)645-4452
London, ON, Canada N6G 2V4 Dorothy Drew, Libn.
Founded: 1951. **Staff:** Prof 1. **Subjects:** Chemistry, entomology, plant pathology, fumigation, plant physiology, microbiology. **Holdings:** 4000 books; 7000 bound periodical volumes. **Subscriptions:** 150 journals and other serials. **Services:** Interlibrary loan; copying; SDI; library open to qualified persons. **Computerized Information Services:** CAN/OLE, DIALOG Information Services; CD-ROMs (CCINFO, AGRICOLA, CAB Abstracts). **Networks/Consortia:** Member of Canadian Agriculture Library System.

★ 2644 ★
Canada - Agriculture Canada - Neatby Library (Sci-Engr, Biol Sci)
K.W. Neatby Bldg., Rm. 3032
Central Experimental Farm Phone: (613)995-5011
Ottawa, ON, Canada K1A 0C6 Marcel Charette
Founded: 1960. **Staff:** 2. **Subjects:** Agrometeorology, bacteriology, nitrogen fixation, environmental sciences, soil, soil sciences. **Holdings:** 6000 books; 7000 bound periodical volumes; 1000 microcards of Beilstein's Handbuch der Organischen Chemie; soil surveys of the United States and Canada. **Subscriptions:** 260 journals and other serials. **Services:** Interlibrary loan; copying; SDI; library open to the public for reference use only. **Automated Operations:** Computerized cataloging. **Publications:** List of Acquisitions, monthly. **Staff:** M. Graham, ILL; Gail Waters.

★ 2645 ★
Canada - Agriculture Canada - Plant Research Library (Biol Sci)
C.E.F. Bldg. 49 Phone: (613)996-1665
Ottawa, ON, Canada K1A 0C6 Eva Gavora, Libn.
Founded: 1887. **Staff:** Prof 1; Other 1. **Subjects:** Botany, taxonomy, mycology. **Special Collections:** Linnaean Collection, including early botany publications by Carl Linnaeus and revised editions by other botanists, mainly 1748-1825. **Holdings:** 11,000 books; 15,000 bound periodical volumes; 14,000 microfiche of early taxonomic works and eleven European herbaria. **Subscriptions:** 210 journals and other serials. **Services:** Interlibrary loan; copying; SDI; library open to the public. **Remarks:** FAX: (613)952-3813.

★ 2646 ★
Canada - Agriculture Canada - Research Station, Agassiz - Library (Agri)
P.O. Box 1000
Agassiz, BC, Canada V0M 1A0 Phone: (604)796-2221
Staff: Prof 1. **Subjects:** Agriculture, weeds, plants, soils, poultry, dairy cattle, nutrition. **Holdings:** 2500 books; 600 bound periodical volumes; 6000 unbound serials; 1000 Microfiche. **Subscriptions:** 270 journals and other serials. **Services:** Interlibrary loan; copying; library open to the public for reference use only. **Automated Operations:** Computerized public access catalog, cataloging, acquisitions, and serials. **Computerized Information Services:** Agrinet (electronic mail service). **Remarks:** FAX: (604)796-2221.

★ 2647 ★
Canada - Agriculture Canada - Research Station, Beaverlodge - Library (Agri)
Box 29 Phone: (403)354-2212
Beaverlodge, AB, Canada T0H 0C0 Linda Christiansen, Libn.
Staff: Prof 1. **Subjects:** Cereal and oilseed breeding, plant management, forage crops, pasture management, soil fertility, soil management, agrometeorology, apiculture. **Holdings:** 5000 volumes. **Subscriptions:** 120 journals and other serials. **Services:** Interlibrary loan; library open to the public. **Computerized Information Services:** AGRICAT; Agrinet (electronic mail service). **Remarks:** FAX: (403)354-8171. Electronic mail address(es): LBABEAG (Agrinet).

★ 2648 ★
Canada - Agriculture Canada - Research Station, Brandon - Library (Agri)
RR 3, Box 1000A Phone: (204)726-7650
Brandon, MB, Canada R7A 5Y3 Carol Enns
Founded: 1984. **Staff:** Prof 1. **Subjects:** Barley breeding and genetics; swine genetics, breeding, nutrition; plant pesticides; meat science; forage agronomy; beef genetics and breeding; corn and sorghum breeding; plant growth regulators; agronomy. **Holdings:** 1500 books; 2200 bound periodical volumes; newsletters; reports; station's scientific publications. **Subscriptions:** 150 journals and other serials; 10 newspapers. **Services:** Interlibrary loan; copying; library open to the public. **Computerized Information Services:** DIALOG Information Services, CAN/OLE; internal database; CD-ROM; Datapac, AGRINET (electronic mail services). **Publications:** Review of Results, annual; Newsnotes, monthly. **Remarks:** FAX: (204)728-3858. Electronic mail address(es): OTTA::LBMBAG (AGRINET).

★ 2649 ★
Canada - Agriculture Canada - Research Station, Charlottetown - Library (Biol Sci)
P.O. Box 1210 Phone: (902)566-6861
Charlottetown, PE, Canada C1A 7M8 Barrie Stanfield, Libn.
Founded: 1961. **Staff:** Prof 1. **Subjects:** Plant physiology and pathology, entomology, pest control, weed control, forage and cereal crops, cattle, soil science, potatoes. **Holdings:** 2500 books; 2000 bound periodical volumes; 200 boxes of government publications; 7 VF drawers of clippings and pamphlets. **Subscriptions:** 250 journals and other serials. **Services:** Interlibrary loan; copying; library open to the public for reference use only. **Automated Operations:** Computerized public access catalog and cataloging. **Computerized Information Services:** CAN/OLE, DIALOG Information Services; AGRINET, Envoy 100 (electronic mail services). **Remarks:** FAX: (902)566-6821. Electronic mail address(es): OTTA::LBPCAG (AGRINET); ILL.PCAG (Envoy 100).

★ 2650 ★
Canada - Agriculture Canada - Research Station, Fredericton - Library (Agri, Biol Sci)
Box 20280 Phone: (506)452-3260
Fredericton, NB, Canada E3B 4Z7 Richard Anderson, Libn.
Founded: 1952. **Staff:** Prof 1.5. **Subjects:** Agriculture, botany, zoology, soil science. **Holdings:** 5000 books; 4500 bound periodical volumes; 18,000 pamphlets and reprints. **Subscriptions:** 300 journals and other serials. **Services:** Interlibrary loan; copying; library open to the public by permission. **Computerized Information Services:** DIALOG Information Services, CAN/OLE; VUCAT (internal database). **Networks/Consortia:** Member of Canadian Agriculture Library System. **Remarks:** FAX: (506)452-3316.

★2651★
Canada - Agriculture Canada - Research Station, Harrow - Library (Agri)
Harrow, ON, Canada N0R 1G0 Phone: (519)738-2251
Eric A. Champagne, Libn.
Staff: Prof 1. **Subjects:** Agriculture and allied topics. **Holdings:** 2000 books; 1800 bound periodical volumes; 300 government publications; 4 VF drawers. **Subscriptions:** 200 journals and other serials. **Services:** Interlibrary loan; SDI; library open to the public for reference use only. **Computerized Information Services:** DIALOG Information Services, CAN/OLE; Agrinet (electronic mail service).

★2652★
Canada - Agriculture Canada - Research Station, Kamloops - Library (Agri)
3015 Ord Rd. Phone: (604)376-5565
Kamloops, BC, Canada V2B 8A9 Dr. K. Broersma, Dir.
Founded: 1962. **Staff:** 1. **Subjects:** Forage crops, range management, soils and fertilizers, cattle nutrition. **Holdings:** 1800 books; 2000 bound periodical volumes; research papers; reports; reprints; manuscripts; dissertations. **Subscriptions:** 186 journals and other serials. **Services:** Library open to the public with restrictions. **Remarks:** FAX: (604)376-7334. All inquiries concerning this collection should be addressed to the Main Library in Ottawa.

★2653★
Canada - Agriculture Canada - Research Station, Kentville - Library (Biol Sci)
Kentville, NS, Canada B4N 1J5 Phone: (902)678-2171
Jerry Miner, Libn.
Founded: 1953. **Staff:** Prof 1; Other 1. **Subjects:** Entomology, plant pathology, chemistry, fruit processing, field crops, small fruits, poultry, statistics, physiology of plant life. **Holdings:** 2500 books; 10,000 bound periodical volumes; 4000 reports. **Subscriptions:** 350 journals and other serials. **Services:** Interlibrary loan; SDI; library open to the public for reference use only. **Computerized Information Services:** DIALOG Information Services, CAN/OLE; Envoy 100 (electronic mail service). **Remarks:** FAX: (902)679-2311. Electronic mail address(es): ILL.NSKR (Envoy 100).

★2654★
Canada - Agriculture Canada - Research Station, Lacombe - Library (Agri)
Bag Service 5000 Phone: (403)782-3316
Lacombe, AB, Canada T0C 1S0 Dixie Anderson, Libn.
Founded: 1907. **Staff:** 1. **Subjects:** Agriculture, cereal pathology, soil science, meat science, swine nutrition and breeding. **Holdings:** 1000 books; 1500 bound periodical volumes. **Subscriptions:** 80 journals and other serials; 10 newspapers. **Services:** Interlibrary loan; copying; SDI; library open to the public with restrictions. **Automated Operations:** Computerized public access catalog and cataloging. **Computerized Information Services:** DIALOG Information Services, CAN/OLE. **Remarks:** FAX: (403)782-6120.

★2655★
Canada - Agriculture Canada - Research Station, Lethbridge - Library (Agri, Biol Sci)
P.O. Box 3000, Main Phone: (403)327-4561
Lethbridge, AB, Canada T1J 4B1 Cheryl M. Ronning Mains, Libn.
Founded: 1950. **Staff:** Prof 1; Other 1.5. **Subjects:** Agriculture, biology, entomology, biochemistry, animal science, plant science, soil science, irrigation. **Holdings:** 14,000 books; 8000 bound periodical volumes; 18,000 unbound periodicals; 170,000 unbound reports and bulletins; 2000 reprints; 100 reels of microfilm, 2000 slides. **Subscriptions:** 600 journals and other serials; 3 newspapers. **Services:** Interlibrary loan; SDI; library open to the public with restrictions. **Automated Operations:** Computerized public access catalog and cataloging. **Computerized Information Services:** CAN/SDI, DIALOG Information Services, CAN/OLE; internal database; Agrinet (electronic mail service). **Publications:** Periodicals currently recieved at the Library, Lethbridge Research Station, irregular - available on request.

★2656★
Canada - Agriculture Canada - Research Station, Morden - Library (Biol Sci)
P.O. Box 3001 Phone: (204)822-4471
Morden, MB, Canada R0G 1J0 Cheryl Scharf, Sec.
Subjects: Biology, genetics, agronomy, plant pathology and physiology, horticulture. **Holdings:** 400 books; 500 bound periodical volumes; 50 shelf feet of annual reports and bulletins of agriculture research institutions. **Subscriptions:** 50 journals and other serials. **Services:** Library open to the public by appointment. **Computerized Information Services:** AGRINET ((electronic mail service)). **Remarks:** FAX: (204)822-6841. Electronic mail address(es): MORDRA::AG362MAIL (AGRINET). All inquiries concerning this collection should be addressed to the main library in Ottawa.

★2657★
Canada - Agriculture Canada - Research Station, Regina - Library (Agri)
5000 Wascana Pkwy.
Box 440 Phone: (306)780-7431
Regina, SK, Canada S4P 3A2 Susan Yanosik, Lib.Techn.
Staff: 1. **Subjects:** Weed control and ecology, herbicides, biological control of weeds. **Special Collections:** Reports on weed control in Western Canada, 1928 to present. **Holdings:** 800 books; 2100 bound periodical volumes; government publications. **Subscriptions:** 60 journals and other serials. **Services:** Interlibrary loan; copying; SDI; library open to the public for reference use only. **Computerized Information Services:** DIALOG Information Services, CAN/OLE. **Remarks:** FAX: (306)780-7453.

★2658★
Canada - Agriculture Canada - Research Station, St. Jean - Library (Agri, Biol Sci)
430, blvd. Gouin
P.O. Box 457 Phone: (514)346-4494
St. Jean-Sur-Richelieu, PQ, Canada J3B 3E6 Ian Wallace, Libn.
Founded: 1952. **Staff:** Prof 1; Other 1.5. **Subjects:** Entomology, botany, agriculture, soil science, horticulture. **Holdings:** 10,000 books; 3000 bound periodical volumes; 300 bound abstract volumes. **Subscriptions:** 1200 journals and other serials. **Services:** Interlibrary loan; SDI; translation. **Automated Operations:** Computerized cataloging, serials, and circulation. **Computerized Information Services:** DIALOG Information Services, CAN/OLE; Envoy 100 (electronic mail service). **Remarks:** FAX: (514)346-7740. Electronic mail address(es): RES335 (Envoy 100).

★2659★
Canada - Agriculture Canada - Research Station, St. John's West - Library (Biol Sci)
Brookfield Rd.
P.O. Box 7098 Phone: (709)772-4619
St. John's, NF, Canada A1E 3Y3 Heather Myers, Libn.
Staff: Prof 1. **Subjects:** Horticulture, plant breeding and pathology, entomology, agronomy. **Holdings:** 700 books; 400 bound periodical volumes; 325 Agriculture Canada publications; 75 boxes of pamphlets and Agriculture Canada reports. **Subscriptions:** 130 journals and other serials. **Services:** Interlibrary loan; copying; library open to the public for reference use only. **Automated Operations:** Computerized public access catalog, cataloging, and departmental ILL. **Computerized Information Services:** Agrinet (electronic mail service).

★2660★
Canada - Agriculture Canada - Research Station, Ste. Foy - Library (Agri)
2560 Hochelaga Blvd. Phone: (418)657-7980
Ste. Foy, PQ, Canada G1V 2J3 Suzanne Cote
Founded: 1970. **Staff:** 1. **Subjects:** Plant physiology and pathology, cereal and forage breeding, soil conservation, cold resistance, molecular biology. **Holdings:** 6000 books; 5000 bound periodical volumes; 20,000 unbound periodicals; 4000 microfiche; 250 maps. **Subscriptions:** 120 journals and other serials. **Services:** Interlibrary loan; copying; library open to the public for reference use only. **Automated Operations:** Computerized public access catalog and cataloging. **Computerized Information Services:** DIALOG Information Services, CAN/OLE; AGRICAT (internal database). **Networks/Consortia:** Member of Canadian Agriculture Library System. **Publications:** Accession List, irregular - for internal distribution only; list of French language agricultural journals published in Quebec, irregular - for internal distribution and to agricultural community leaders. **Special Catalogs:** Union catalog of research officers' textbooks. **Remarks:** FAX: (418)648-2402.

★ 2661 ★
Canada - Agriculture Canada - Research Station, Saskatoon - Library (Agri)
107 Science Pl. Phone: (306)975-7014
Saskatoon, SK, Canada S7N 0X2 Van Keane, Libn.
Founded: 1957. **Staff:** Prof 1; Other 1. **Subjects:** Agriculture, entomology, crop science, plant breeding, plant pathology, oil seeds, pedology, biotechnology. **Special Collections:** Safety information. **Holdings:** 9000 books; serials in microform. **Subscriptions:** 350 journals and other serials. **Services:** Interlibrary loan; SDI; library open to the public with restrictions. **Automated Operations:** Computerized public access catalog. **Computerized Information Services:** CAN/OLE, DIALOG Information Services; CD-ROMs; Agrinet (electronic mail service). **Publications:** Bibliographies (online), irregular; acquisitions list, quarterly; newsletter, bimonthly. **Remarks:** FAX: (306)242-1839.

★ 2662 ★
Canada - Agriculture Canada - Research Station, Summerland - Library (Agri)
Summerland, BC, Canada V0H 1Z0 Phone: (604)494-7711
M.A. Watson, Libn.
Founded: 1951. **Staff:** Prof 1. **Subjects:** Horticulture, entomology, plant pathology, food processing, pomology, irrigation, plant nutrition, viticulture, oenology. **Holdings:** 2000 books; 8100 bound periodical volumes; 5200 unbound periodicals; 20,500 pamphlets. **Subscriptions:** 103 journals and other serials. **Services:** Interlibrary loan; copying; SDI; library open to the public for reference use only. **Automated Operations:** Computerized public access catalog and cataloging. **Special Indexes:** Quick Reference Index (online). **Remarks:** FAX: (604)494-0755.

★ 2663 ★
Canada - Agriculture Canada - Research Station, Swift Current - Library (Agri)
Box 1030 Phone: (306)773-4621
Swift Current, SK, Canada S9H 3X2 Karen E. Wilton, Libn.
Founded: 1921. **Staff:** Prof 1. **Subjects:** Cereal breeding, soil science, forage and range management, animal nutrition, irrigation, agrometeorology, agricultural engineering. **Holdings:** 1500 books; 2800 bound periodical volumes; 200 annual reports; 380 pamphlet boxes; 9000 microfiche. **Subscriptions:** 270 journals and other serials; 5 newspapers. **Services:** Interlibrary loan; copying; SDI; library open to the public with restrictions. **Automated Operations:** Computerized cataloging. **Publications:** Article Alert, weekly; Publication Alert, irregular; Journals Currently Received, annual - all for internal distribution only. **Special Indexes:** Swift Current Research Station Scientific Publications Index (computer printout). **Remarks:** FAX: (306)773-9123.

★ 2664 ★
Canada - Agriculture Canada - Research Station, Vancouver - Library (Agri)
6660 N.W. Marine Dr. Phone: (604)224-4355
Vancouver, BC, Canada V6T 1X2 Tony Matsumoto, Libn.
Founded: 1960. **Staff:** Prof 1; Other 1. **Subjects:** Plant pathology, virus chemistry and physiology, entomology, pedology and soil survey. **Special Collections:** Entomological Society of British Columbia Collection (130 books). **Holdings:** 1000 books. **Subscriptions:** 65 journals and other serials. **Services:** Interlibrary loan; copying; SDI; library open to the public with restrictions. **Automated Operations:** Computerized public access catalog, cataloging, and serials. **Computerized Information Services:** DIALOG Information Services, CAN/OLE. **Networks/Consortia:** Member of Canadian Agriculture Library System. **Remarks:** FAX: (604)666-4994.

★ 2665 ★
Canada - Agriculture Canada - Research Station, Vineland Station - Library (Agri)
PO Box 6000 Phone: (416)562-4113
Vineland Station, ON, Canada L0R 2E0 Ms. Sheridan Alder, Libn.
Staff: Prof 1. **Subjects:** Crop protection, primarily horticultural crops; entomology; plant pathology; nematology. **Holdings:** 1250 books; 1800 bound periodical volumes; 345 unbound abstracts; 650 Agriculture Canada and Ontario Ministry of Agriculture & Food publications; 161 unbound annual reports. **Subscriptions:** 60 journals and other serials. **Services:** Interlibrary loan; copying; SDI; library open to the public by appointment. **Automated Operations:** Computerized cataloging and documents. **Computerized Information Services:** CAN/OLE, DIALOG Information Services, Pesticide Research Information System (PRIS), Canadian Centre for Occupational Health & Safety; Agrinet (electronic mail service). **Networks/Consortia:** Member of Canadian Agriculture Library System. **Remarks:** FAX: (416)562-4335.

★ 2666 ★
Canada - Agriculture Canada - Research Station, Winnipeg - Library (Agri, Biol Sci)
195 Dafoe Rd. Phone: (204)983-5533
Winnipeg, MB, Canada R3T 2M9 Mike Malyk, Libn.
Founded: 1957. **Staff:** Prof 2; Other 1. **Subjects:** Cereal breeding and pathology, stored products entomology and mycology, cereal chemistry, integrated pest control, molecular biology. **Special Collections:** Buller Memorial Library; botany and entomology reprint collections. **Holdings:** 7500 books; 6000 bound periodical volumes; 12,000 government reports; 30,000 reprints; 250 boxes of government bulletins; 1000 pamphlet boxes of unbound journals. **Subscriptions:** 300 journals and other serials; 5 newspapers. **Services:** Interlibrary loan; copying; SDI; library open to the public. **Automated Operations:** Computerized cataloging. **Computerized Information Services:** CAN/OLE, DIALOG Information Services; AGRICAT (internal database); Agrinet (electronic mail service). **Networks/Consortia:** Member of Canadian Agriculture Library System. **Special Catalogs:** Buller Memorial Library Catalog (book); Botany and Entomology Reprints (card); Staff Publications (online). **Remarks:** FAX: (204)983-4604.

Canada - Atmospheric Environment Service
See: **Canada - Environment Canada** (2703)

Canada - Bibliotheque Nationale du Canada
See: **Canada - National Library of Canada** (2803)

Canada - Bibliotheque du Parlement
See: **Canada - Library of Parliament** (2764)

Canada - Bureau du Surintendent des Institutions Financieres
See: **Canada - Office of the Superintendent of Financial Institutions** (2833)

★ 2667 ★
Canada - Canada Centre for Remote Sensing - Technical Information Service (Sci-Engr)
1547 Merivale Rd., 4th Fl. Phone: (613)952-0500
Ottawa, ON, Canada K1A 0Y7 Brian McGurrin, Hd.
Founded: 1972. **Staff:** 6; Other 6. **Subjects:** Remote sensing, scanning and imaging systems, pattern recognition, atmospheric optics, earth sciences, global change, geographic information systems. **Holdings:** 3000 books; 80,000 documents. **Subscriptions:** 110 journals and newsletters. **Services:** Interlibrary loan; copying; SDI; service open to the public. **Automated Operations:** Computerized cataloging and acquisitions. **Computerized Information Services:** PFDS Online, CAN/OLE, UTLAS, RESORS (Remote Sensing On-Line Retrieval System). Performs searches on fee basis. Contact Person: Louis Marcotte, RESORS Mgr., 952-2706. **Publications:** RESORS Keyword Dictionaries, irregular - to online users; Remote Sensing in Canada (newsletter), quarterly. **Remarks:** FAX: (613)952-7353. Telex: 053 3777. **Staff:** Lidia Taylor, Libn.

★ 2668 ★
Canada - Canadian Advisory Council on the Status of Women - Library (Soc Sci)
110 O'Connor St.
Box 1541, Sta. B Phone: (613)995-8285
Ottawa, ON, Canada K1P 5R5 Sharon Pipon, Libn.
Founded: 1974. **Staff:** Prof 1; Other 2. **Subjects:** Economic, political, legal, constitutional, and social status of women in Canada; women's health, education, and employment. **Special Collections:** Newsletters of Canadian women's groups; briefs and reports on status of women's issues (8000); council publications and background papers (350 titles). **Holdings:** 12,000 books; 42 VF drawers of clippings, manuscripts, dissertations. **Subscriptions:** 450 journals and other serials. **Services:** Interlibrary loan; copying; library open to the public. **Computerized Information Services:** Internal database. **Publications:** Selective list of acquisitions, monthly; selected tables of contents of feminist research journals and other serials - both for internal distribution only. **Remarks:** FAX: (613)992-1715. **Also Known As:** Conseil Consultatif Canadien sur la Situation de la Femme.

★2669★
Canada - Canadian Embassy - Library (Area-Ethnic)
501 Pennsylvania Ave., N.W. Phone: (202)682-1740
Washington, DC 20001 Mrs. Angela Kilkenny, Chf.Libn.
Founded: 1947. **Staff:** Prof 2; Other 2. **Subjects:** Canadiana, economics, biography, government, international affairs, Canadian-U.S. relations. **Special Collections:** Newspaper clippings and press releases (700 topics); Canadian Government document depository (6000 documents). **Holdings:** 8000 books; 80 VF drawers of material on Canadian subjects; 385 reels of microfilm; 2300 microfiche. **Subscriptions:** 400 journals and other serials; 25 newspapers. **Services:** Interlibrary loan; copying (limited); library open to the public by appointment. **Computerized Information Services:** NEXIS, Info Globe, Infomart Online, QL Systems. **Remarks:** Telex: 89664. **Staff:** Barbara Chinn Donohue, Ref.Libn.

★2670★
Canada - Canadian International Development Agency - Development Information Centre (Soc Sci)
Place du Centre
200 Promenade du Portage Phone: (819)994-5006
Hull, PQ, Canada K1A 0G4 Nicole Sansfacon, Chf.
Founded: 1965. **Staff:** Prof 2; Other 8. **Subjects:** International development, project management. **Holdings:** 5000 books. **Subscriptions:** 1200 journals and other serials. **Services:** Interlibrary loan; copying; center open to the public with restrictions. **Computerized Information Services:** DIALOG Information Services, CAN/OLE, QL Systems, Info Globe, IST-Informatheque Inc. **Publications:** Focus (accession list of monographs), monthly; Documents (list of confidential material), monthly - to agency officers only. **Also Known As:** Agence Canadienne de Developpement International.

Canada - Canadian Parks Service - Point Pelee National Park
See: **Point Pelee National Park** (13158)

★2671★
Canada - Canadian Radio-Television and Telecommunications Commission - Library (Info Sci)
Ottawa, ON, Canada K1A 0N2 Phone: (819)997-4484
Emmett B. Will, Libn.
Founded: 1968. **Staff:** Prof 1; Other 2. **Subjects:** Broadcasting, mass media, telecommunications, communications. **Special Collections:** CRTC decisions, public notices, and orders. **Holdings:** 8000 books; pamphlets. **Subscriptions:** 300 journals and other serials. **Services:** Interlibrary loan; copying; library open to the public. **Computerized Information Services:** DIALOG Information Services, PFDS Online, CAN/OLE, DOBIS Canadian Online Library System, QL Systems, CAN/LAW, Infomart Online, Info Globe, WILSONLINE, Questel; Envoy 100 (electronic mail service). **Publications:** Accessions List, monthly. **Remarks:** Library located at 1 Promenade du Portage, 2nd F., Hull, PQ. FAX: (819)994-0218. Electronic mail address(es): ILL.OORT (Envoy 100). **Also Known As:** Conseil de la Radiodiffusion et des Telecommunications Canadiennes.

Canada - Canadian Wildlife Service
See: **Canada - Environment Canada, Conservation & Protection - Canadian Wildlife Service** (2715)

Canada - Commission de la Fonction Publique
See: **Canada - Public Service Commission** (2836)

Canada - Commission de Reforme du Droit
See: **Canada - Law Reform Commission of Canada** (2763)

★2672★
Canada - Communications Canada - Canadian Conservation Institute - Library (Art)
Ottawa, ON, Canada K1A 0C8 Phone: (613)998-3721
Alicia Prata, Chief Libn.
Founded: 1973. **Staff:** Prof 4; Other 3. **Subjects:** Conservation and preservation of historic and art objects. **Special Collections:** Museology. **Holdings:** 9000 books; 10,000 volumes of journals; 10,000 pamphlets and reprints. **Subscriptions:** 300 journals. **Services:** Interlibrary loan; library open to serious scholars for reference use only. **Automated Operations:** Computerized cataloging. **Computerized Information Services:** Conservation Information Network. **Publications:** Acquisitions list. **Special Indexes:** Museology Index. **Remarks:** FAX: (613)998-4721. **Also Known As:** Institut Canadien de Conservation. **Staff:** Vicki L. Davis, Ref.; Elizabeth Kirby, Ref.; Tabassum Grover, Cat.; Maureen Clark, ILL; Gile Hetu, ILL.

★2673★
Canada - Communications Canada - Canadian Heritage Information Network - Resource Center (Info Sci)
Journal Tower South, 20th Fl.
365 Laurier Ave., W.
Ottawa, ON, Canada K1A OC8 Phone: (613)992-3333
Founded: 1972. **Subjects:** Canadian museum collections, computerization, collections management, reference database management. **Holdings:** 1000 bound volumes; 175 audio tapes; 25 videotapes; 280 vertical files **Subscriptions:** 120 journals and other serials. **Services:** Interlibrary loan; copying; SDI; center open to researchers, museology students, and museum professionals only. **Computerized Information Services:** Canadian Heritage Information Network (CHIN), Conservation Information Network (CIN); 5 CD-ROMs. Performs searches on fee basis. **Remarks:** FAX: (613)952-2318. **Staff:** Deborah F. Jewett, Doc.Res.

★2674★
Canada - Communications Canada - Communications Research Centre Library (Sci-Engr, Info Sci)
Box 11490, Sta. H Phone: (613)998-2202
Ottawa, ON, Canada K2H 8S2 C. LaPlante, Hd., CRC Lib.
Founded: 1950. **Staff:** Prof 1; Other 3. **Subjects:** Telecommunications; engineering - aerospace, electrical, electronic; computer science; physics; astronomy. **Holdings:** 10,000 books; 1106 bound periodical volumes; 231 technical reports. **Subscriptions:** 450 journals and other serials. **Services:** Interlibrary loan; library not open to the public. **Automated Operations:** Computerized public access catalog and cataloging. **Computerized Information Services:** CAN/OLE, DIALOG Information Services, DOBIS, Questel; Envoy 100 (electronic mail service). **Remarks:** FAX: (613)998-2433. Electronic mail address(es): ILL.CRC (Envoy 100).

★2675★
Canada - Communications Canada - Library and Information Retrieval Services (Info Sci)
300 Slater St., Rm. 1420 Phone: (613)990-4937
Ottawa, ON, Canada K1A 0C8 Claire Renaud-Frigon, Hd.
Founded: 1969. **Staff:** Prof 3; Other 7. **Subjects:** Telecommunications, computer and satellite communications, cable television, videotex, office of the future, arts and culture, broadcasting. **Special Collections:** International Telecommunications Union (ITU) publications; Comite Consultatif International Telegraphique et Telephonique (CCITT) publications. **Holdings:** 15,000 books; 2200 technical reports; 5500 microfiche; 300 reels of microfilm. **Subscriptions:** 900 journals and other serials; 10 newspapers. **Services:** Interlibrary loan; copying; library open to the public for reference use only. **Automated Operations:** Computerized public access catalog, cataloging, serials, and routing. **Computerized Information Services:** CAN/SDI, CAN/OLE, DIALOG Information Services, Info Globe, DOBIS Canadian Online Library System; Envoy 100 (electronic mail service). **Publications:** Acquisitions and conferences lists. **Special Catalogs:** Union catalogue (COM); union list of periodicals. **Remarks:** FAX: (613)990-7016. Telex: 053-3342. Electronic mail address(es): OOCO.LIB (Envoy 100). **Staff:** Mrs. Z. Vandoros, Hd., Tech.Serv.; Monique Perrier, Hd., HQ Lib.

Canada - Conseil National de Recherches
See: **Canada - National Research Council - Canada Institute for Scientific and Technical Information (CISTI)** (2814)

★2676★
Canada - Consumer and Corporate Affairs Canada - Departmental Library (Bus-Fin, Law)
Ottawa, ON, Canada K1A 0C9 Phone: (819)997-1632
Edith Core, Chf.Libn.
Founded: 1968. **Staff:** Prof 5; Other 7. **Subjects:** Consumer protection, restrictive trade practices, corporate and commercial law, intellectual property, management. **Holdings:** 30,000 books; 12,000 bound periodical volumes; 30,000 government documents; 6000 corporate annual reports. **Subscriptions:** 1500 journals and other serials; 50 newspapers. **Services:** Interlibrary loan; copying; library open to the public. **Automated Operations:** Computerized cataloging, serials, and indexing. **Computerized Information Services:** DIALOG Information Services, QL Systems, Info Globe, WESTLAW, LEXIS, NEXIS, The Financial Post DataGroup, Infomart Online, UTLAS, CAN/OLE, STM Systems Corporation; Envoy 100 (electronic mail service). **Publications:** Bulletin, monthly. **Remarks:** FAX: (819)997-2378. Electronic mail address(es): ILL.OOCI (Envoy 100). **Also Known As:** Consommation et Corporations Canada. **Staff:** J. Marosi, Hd., Ref./Rd.Serv.; G. Lepkey, Hd., Tech.Serv.; P. Audet, Cat.; R. Honey, Rd.Serv.Techn.; M. St.-Jean, Rd.Serv.Techn.

★2677★
Canada - Consumer and Corporate Affairs Canada - Patent and Copyright Office Search Room (Law)
50 Victoria St. Phone: (819)997-2968
Hull, PQ, Canada K1A 0C9 Richard LeBel, Hd.
Holdings: Patents; microfiche; microfilm. **Services:** Interlibrary loan; copying; room open to the public. **Remarks:** FAX: (819)997-2721.

★2678★
Canada - Consumer and Corporate Affairs Canada - Patent Library (Law)
Place du Portage I, 11th Fl. Phone: (613)997-2964
Ottawa, ON, Canada K1A 0C9 Pat Smith, Hd.
Founded: 1973. **Staff:** 1. **Subjects:** Patents of the world, patent acts and rules, copyrights, trademarks. **Holdings:** 1000 books. **Subscriptions:** 150 journals and other serials. **Services:** Interlibrary loan; copying; library open to the public. **Computerized Information Services:** DIALOG Information Services, QL Systems, WESTLAW, LEXIS, NEXIS, Info Globe, Infomart Online, CAN/OLE. **Publications:** Canadian Patent Office Record. **Remarks:** FAX: (819)997-2378.

★2679★
Canada - Defence and Civil Institute of Environmental Medicine - Scientific Information Centre (Med, Sci-Engr)
1133 Sheppard Ave., W.
P.O. Box 2000 Phone: (416)635-2070
Downsview, ON, Canada M3M 3B9 Stewart Harrison, Act.Hd.
Founded: 1952. **Staff:** Prof 1; Other 2. **Subjects:** Aviation medicine, environmental physiology, biochemistry, biophysics, biostatistics, human engineering, electronics, aircraft accident investigation, computer systems. **Special Collections:** Canadian Aviation Medicine (16,000 reports). **Holdings:** 8000 books; 8000 bound periodical volumes; 20,000 reports; 2000 microforms. **Subscriptions:** 150 journals and other serials. **Services:** Interlibrary loan; copying; center open to the public with restrictions. **Automated Operations:** Computerized public access catalog. **Computerized Information Services:** CAN/OLE, MEDLINE, DIALOG Information Services. **Publications:** Bibliography of all reports published by Defence Research Establishment Toronto and Defence Research Medical Laboratories, 1951-1971; Recent Acquisitions, irregular - for internal distribution only. **Remarks:** Maintained by Canada - National Defence.

★2680★
Canada - Defence Research Establishment Atlantic - Library (Sci-Engr, Mil)
P.O. Box 1012 Phone: (902)426-3100
Dartmouth, NS, Canada B2Y 3Z7 Donna I. Richardson, Hd., Info.Serv.
Founded: 1946. **Staff:** Prof 1; Other 3. **Subjects:** Underwater acoustics, electrical and mechanical engineering, computer science, materials science, naval architecture. **Holdings:** 5000 books; 2800 bound periodical volumes; 24,000 research reports. **Subscriptions:** 257 journals and other serials; 5 newspapers. **Services:** Interlibrary loan; library open to the public with restrictions. **Automated Operations:** Computerized public access catalog, cataloging, circulation, and subject indexing (TECHLIBplus). **Computerized Information Services:** CAN/OLE, DIALOG Information Services, UTLAS; Envoy 100, DRENET (electronic mail service). **Remarks:** FAX: (902)426-9654. Electronic mail address(es): DREA.INFO.SVCS (Envoy 100); Richardson@ASP.DREA.DND.CA (DRENET). The Defence Research Establishments are administered by the Research and Development Branch of Canada - National Defence.

★2681★
Canada - Defence Research Establishment Ottawa - Library (Sci-Engr)
Ottawa, ON, Canada K1A 0Z4 Phone: (613)998-2657
S.G. McIntyre, Head, Info.Svcs.
Founded: 1950. **Staff:** Prof 1; Other 2. **Subjects:** Chemistry, physics, engineering, electronics, computer sciences. **Holdings:** 7000 books; 340 periodical titles; 25,000 other cataloged items. **Subscriptions:** 275 journals and other serials. **Services:** Interlibrary loan; library not open to the public. **Automated Operations:** Computerized public access catalog, cataloging, and circulation. **Computerized Information Services:** DIALOG Information Services, CAN/OLE, STN International; internal database; Envoy 100 (electronic mail service). **Publications:** Accession lists. **Remarks:** FAX: (613)998-2675.

★2682★
Canada - Defence Research Establishment Pacific - Library (Sci-Engr)
Forces Mail Office Phone: (604)363-2921
Victoria, BC, Canada V0S 1B0 Barbara J. Witt, Libn.
Founded: 1948. **Staff:** Prof 1; Other 1. **Subjects:** Physics, mathematics, computer programming, oceanography, metallurgy, chemical analysis, corrosion prevention, electrical engineering. **Holdings:** 6500 books; 1420 bound periodical volumes; 17,225 manuscript reports, pamphlets, reprints. **Subscriptions:** 220 journals and other serials. **Services:** Interlibrary loan; library not open to the public. **Computerized Information Services:** CAN/OLE, DIALOG Information Services.

★2683★
Canada - Defence Research Establishment Suffield - Information Services (Sci-Engr, Mil)
Box 4000 Phone: (403)544-4000
Medicine Hat, AB, Canada T1A 8K6 Anne M. Dickason, Hd., Info.Serv.
Founded: 1941. **Staff:** Prof 2; Other 1. **Subjects:** Chemistry, biology, electronics, military science, medicine. **Holdings:** 25,000 volumes; 50,000 technical and defence documents; 1200 Suffield publications; archives. **Subscriptions:** 325 journals and other serials. **Services:** Interlibrary loan; copying; SDI; library open to the public with restrictions. **Automated Operations:** Computerized serials. **Computerized Information Services:** CAN/OLE, Chemical Abstracts Service (CAS), DOBIS Canadian Online System, DIALOG Information Services; Envoy 100 (electronic mail service). **Publications:** Serials list, annual; research papers, irregular. **Remarks:** FAX: (403)544-3388. Electronic mail address(es): DRES.LIBRARY (Envoy 100). **Formerly:** Located in Ralston, AB, Canada.

★2684★
Canada - Defence Research Establishment Valcartier - Library (Sci-Engr, Mil)
P.O. Box 8800 Phone: (418)844-4262
Courcelette, PQ, Canada G0A 1R0 Lise Chaillez, Libn.
Founded: 1945. **Staff:** Prof 1; Other 6. **Subjects:** Electro-optics, physics, chemistry, general sciences, mechanical engineering, military science. **Holdings:** 20,000 books; 3000 bound periodical volumes; 30,000 reports, patents, documents; 50,000 microforms. **Subscriptions:** 500 journals and other serials. **Services:** Interlibrary loan; library not open to the public. **Computerized Information Services:** Envoy 100 (electronic mail service). **Publications:** Users Manual - for internal distribution only. **Special Catalogs:** Documents catalog (online). **Remarks:** FAX: (418)844-4624. **Also Known As:** DREV.

Canada - Defense Nationale
See: **Canada - National Defence** (2782)

★2685★
Canada - Department of Finance - Treasury Board Library (Bus-Fin)
L'Esplanade Laurier, East Tower, 11th Fl.
140 O'Connor St. Phone: (613)996-5491
Ottawa, ON, Canada K1A 0G5 J.E.T. Reid, Chf.Libn.
Founded: 1947. **Staff:** Prof 7; Other 10. **Subjects:** Finance, economics, management, personnel management, public accounts, public administration. **Holdings:** 30,000 volumes. **Subscriptions:** 800 journals and other serials; 18 newspapers. **Services:** Interlibrary loan; copying; SDI; library open to the public with restrictions; priority given to departmental clients. **Automated Operations:** Computerized public access catalog, cataloging, acquisitions, serials, circulation, and ILL. **Computerized Information Services:** DIALOG Information Services, Info Globe, QL Systems, DOBIS Canadian Online Library System, REUTERS, Infomart Online, The Financial Post DataGroup; Envoy 100 (electronic mail service). **Publications:** What's New, biweekly. **Remarks:** FAX: (613)992-6411. Telex: 053-3336 FIN/TB OTT. Electronic mail address(es): ILL.OOF (Envoy 100). **Also Known As:** Canada - Ministere des Finances - Conseil du Tresor du Canada. **Staff:** Diane Lalonde-Roy, ILL; Bonnie Fraser, Act.Dp.Chf., Client Serv.; Eileen Bays-Coutts, Dp.Chf., Tech.Serv.

Canada - Department of Forestry
See: **Canada - Forestry Canada** (2738)

Canada - Department of Indian & Northern Development
See: **Canada - Indian & Northern Affairs Canada** (2757)

Canada - Department of Industry, Science & Technology - Canadian Industrial Innovation Centre/Waterloo
See: **Canadian Industrial Innovation Centre/Waterloo** (2939)

★2686★
Canada - Department of Industry, Science & Technology - Government Documentation Centre (Bus-Fin)
800 Square Victoria, Suite 3800
C.P. 247 Phone: (514)283-7274
Montreal, PQ, Canada H4Z 1E8 Nicole Beaudry, Chf.
Founded: 1975. **Staff:** 2. **Subjects:** Statistics, economics, regional development, science and technology, finances, marketing. **Special Collections:** Collection of Statistics Canada and industrial studies. **Holdings:** 10,000 volumes; government and annual reports. **Subscriptions:** 275 journals and other serials. **Services:** Interlibrary loan; center open to the public on a limited schedule. **Automated Operations:** Computerized public access catalog, cataloging, acquisitions, serials, circulation, and other functions. **Computerized Information Services:** DIALOG Information Services, Questel, CAN/OLE, DOBIS Canadian Online Library System, Data-Star. **Publications:** Acquisitions Bulletin, monthly. **Remarks:** FAX: (514)283-3302. Telex: 055-60768. **Staff:** Claire Lavoie, ILL.

★2687★
Canada - Department of Industry, Science & Technology - Library (Bus-Fin)
235 Queen St. Phone: (613)954-2728
Ottawa, ON, Canada K1A 0H5 Rise Segall, Mgr., Lib.Serv.
Staff: 11. **Subjects:** Business, industry, industrial policy and development, science and technology policy, trade, economic policy. **Holdings:** Figures not available. **Services:** Interlibrary loan; copying; library open to the public. **Automated Operations:** Computerized cataloging, acquisitions, and serials. **Computerized Information Services:** DIALOG Information Services, Info Globe, Infomart Online, Reuters, PROFILE Information; Envoy 100 (electronic mail service). **Publications:** Recent Additions; bulletin. **Remarks:** FAX: (613)954-1894. Electronic mail address(es): ISIC.LIBRARY (Envoy 100).

★2688★
Canada - Department of Industry, Science & Technology - Tourism Reference and Documentation Centre (Bus-Fin)
235 Queen St., Rm. 400D Phone: (613)954-3943
Ottawa, ON, Canada K1A 0H6 Margery Denofreo, Coord.
Founded: 1938. **Staff:** Prof 1; Other 2. **Subjects:** Tourism. **Special Collections:** Canadian tourism research and statistics; international tourism statistics. **Holdings:** 8000 research and statistical reports; 12 VF drawers of archives; 6 VF drawers of reports. **Subscriptions:** 240 journals and other serials; 5 newspapers. **Services:** Interlibrary loan; copying; center open to the public with restrictions. **Automated Operations:** Computerized cataloging and circulation. **Computerized Information Services:** DOBIS Canadian Online Library System; internal database. Performs searches free of charge. Contact Person: Rheal Viau, Data Anl. **Publications:** New Acquisitions, quarterly - distributed internally and to mailing list. **Special Indexes:** Index to substantive, non-ephemeral publications (online). **Remarks:** FAX: (613)952-7906. Telex: 053-4123.

★2689★
Canada - Department of Justice - Library (Law)
928 Royal Trust Tower Phone: (403)495-2973
Edmonton, AB, Canada T5J 2Z2 Suzan A. Hebditch, Law Libn.
Staff: 2. **Subjects:** Law - Canadian, English. **Holdings:** 1500 books; 8500 bound periodical volumes; manuscripts; statutes and gazettes of Canada, Alberta, Saskatchewan, and the Northwest Territories. **Subscriptions:** 127 journals and other serials. **Services:** Interlibrary loan (limited); library not open to the public. **Automated Operations:** INMAGIC. **Computerized Information Services:** QL Systems, CAN/LAW, WESTLAW; internal databases; BITNET (electronic mail service). **Publications:** News From the Law Library, newsletter - for internal distribution only. **Remarks:** FAX: (403)495-2964; (403)495-4915. Electronic mail address(es): USERDOJE@UALTAMTS (BITNET).

★2690★
Canada - Department of Justice - Library (Law)
1055 W. Georgia St., Rm. 2800
P.O. Box 11118, Royal Ctr. Phone: (604)666-0549
Vancouver, BC, Canada V6E 3P9 Judy Deavy, Law Libn.
Founded: 1968. **Staff:** Prof 1; Other 1. **Subjects:** Law. **Holdings:** 1000 books; 9000 bound periodical volumes. **Subscriptions:** 150 journals and other serials. **Services:** Interlibrary loan; library not open to the public. **Computerized Information Services:** QL Systems, CAN/LAW, WESTLAW; QUICKMAIL (electronic mail service). **Remarks:** FAX: (604)666-2760; (604)775-5942.

★2691★
Canada - Department of Justice - Library (Law)
Justice Bldg.
Kent & Wellington Sts. Phone: (613)957-4611
Ottawa, ON, Canada K1A 0H8 Mireille McCullough, Dir., Lib.Serv.
Staff: Prof 6; Other 12. **Subjects:** Law. **Holdings:** 90,000 volumes. **Subscriptions:** 1100 journals and other serials; 4 newspapers. **Services:** Interlibrary loan; library not open to the public. **Automated Operations:** Computerized cataloging, acquisitions, and serials. **Computerized Information Services:** QL Systems, WESTLAW, SOQUIJ, DOBIS Canadian Online Library System, DIALOG Information Services, LEXIS, UTLAS, CAN/LAW; Legal Research Service (internal database). **Publications:** Library bulletin, monthly. **Remarks:** FAX: (613)952-5792. Telex: 053-3603. **Also Known As:** Canada - Ministere de la Justice. **Staff:** Alison Whiddon, Hd., Ref. & Rd.Serv.; Edite Abols, Hd., Cat. Unit.

★2692★
Canada - Department of Justice - Library (Law)
Complexe Guy Favreau
200 Dorchester Blvd., W. Phone: (514)283-6674
Montreal, PQ, Canada H2Z 1X4 Andre Archambault, Libn.
Founded: 1982. **Staff:** Prof 1; Other 1. **Subjects:** Law, law enforcement. **Holdings:** 10,500 books; 16,000 bound periodical volumes; 60 loose-leaf binders; microfiche. **Subscriptions:** 210 journals and other serials. **Services:** Library not open to the public. **Automated Operations:** Computerized cataloging and acquisitions. **Computerized Information Services:** QL Systems, WESTLAW, SOQUIJ, LEXIS; QUICKMAIL (electronic mail service). **Remarks:** FAX: (514)283-3856.

★2693★
Canada - Economic Council of Canada - Library (Bus-Fin)
PO Box 527 Phone: (613)952-1833
Ottawa, ON, Canada K1P 5V6 Leonard Bonavero, Libn.
Founded: 1964. **Staff:** Prof 1; Other 3. **Subjects:** Economics, finance, statistics, social sciences. **Holdings:** 25,000 items; microforms; selective depository for Statistics Canada publications. **Subscriptions:** 1000 journals and other serials; 18 newspapers. **Services:** Interlibrary loan; copying; SDI; library open to the public. **Automated Operations:** Computerized cataloging, serials, acquisitions, circulation, and ILL. **Computerized Information Services:** DIALOG Information Services, Info Globe, CAN/OLE, The Financial Post DataGroup, Infomart Online, DOBIS Canadian Online Library System, OECD (Organisation for Economic Co-Operation and Development). **Publications:** Accession list, monthly. **Remarks:** Library located at 320 Queen St., Place de Ville, Tower A, 16th Fl., Ottawa, ON. FAX: (613)952-2171. **Also Known As:** Conseil Economique du Canada.

★2694★
Canada - Employment & Immigration Canada - Library (Soc Sci)
Place du Portage, Phase IV Phone: (819)994-2603
Ottawa, ON, Canada K1A 0J9 P.E. Sunder-Raj, Dir., Lib.Serv.
Founded: 1966. **Staff:** Prof 7; Other 9. **Subjects:** Adult education, immigration, labor economics, management, income maintenance, social sciences. **Holdings:** 85,000 books and bound periodical volumes; 250 reels of microfilm; microforms. **Subscriptions:** 2000 journals and other serials. **Services:** Interlibrary loan; copying; library open to the public for reference use only. **Automated Operations:** Computerized public access catalog, cataloging, acquisitions, serials, and circulation. **Computerized Information Services:** QL Systems, DIALOG Information Services, UTLAS, DOBIS Canadian Online Library System, Infomart Online, Info Globe; Envoy 100 (electronic mail service). **Publications:** Accession List, monthly. **Remarks:** Library located at Place du Portage, Phase IV, 150 Promenade du Portage, Hull, PQ. FAX: (819)953-5482. Electronic mail address(es): ILL.OOMI (Envoy 100). **Also Known As:** Emploi et Immigration Canada. **Staff:** Mrs. M. Nowosielski, Hd., Tech.Serv.; Mrs. D. Monroe, Hd., Info. & Serv.

★2695★
Canada - Employment & Immigration Canada - Ontario Regional Library (Soc Sci)
4900 Yonge St., Suite 700 Phone: (416)224-4858
North York, ON, Canada M2N 6A8 Flaka R. Hersom, Libn.
Subjects: Immigration, employment. **Special Collections:** Immigration statistics, departmental publications. **Holdings:** 6000 books; clippings file. **Subscriptions:** 201 journals and other serials. **Services:** Library open to the public by appointment. **Publications:** Acquisitions list, irregular. **Remarks:** FAX: (416)224-4860.

★2696★
Canada - Employment & Immigration Canada - Quebec Regional Library (Soc Sci, Bus-Fin)
1441, rue St-Urbain, Ground Fl. Phone: (514)283-1386
Montreal, PQ, Canada H2X 2M6 Jacinthe Castonguay, Reg.Chf., Lib.Serv.
Founded: 1967. **Staff:** Prof 1; Other 2. **Subjects:** Manpower, immigration, unemployment insurance, counseling, employment, economics. **Holdings:** 10,000 books and government documents; 60 bound periodical volumes. **Subscriptions:** 150 journals and other serials; 6 newspapers. **Services:** Interlibrary loan; copying; SDI; library open to the public on a limited schedule. **Computerized Information Services:** DIALOG Information Services, DOBIS Canadian Online Library System. **Publications:** Liste des Nouvelles Acquisitions, 4/year - free upon request. **Remarks:** FAX: (514)283-1386.

★2697★
Canada - Employment & Immigration Canada - Vancouver Regional Office - Economic Services - Library
P.O. Box 11145, Royal Centre Phone: (604)666-6328
Vancouver, BC, Canada V6E 2P8 Vera Jones, Libn.
Remarks: No further information was supplied by respondent.

★2698★
Canada - Energy, Mines & Resources Canada - Canada Centre for Mapping - Geographical Services Division - Map Resource Centre (Geog-Map)
615 Booth St. Phone: (613)995-2124
Ottawa, ON, Canada K1A 0E9 Diane Lacasse, Geog./Map Libn.
Founded: 1947. **Staff:** Prof 1. **Subjects:** Canadian atlases, thematic cartography, topography of Canada, geography, history. **Holdings:** 30,000 maps; 500 atlases; gazetteers; bibliographies of cartography, hydrographic charts, aeronautical charts, small-scale thematic mapping. **Services:** Interlibrary loan. **Remarks:** A listing of Canadian digital cartographic databases is planned. FAX: (613)943-8282.

★2699★
Canada - Energy, Mines & Resources Canada - CANMET - Library and Documentation Services Division (Sci-Engr, Energy)
555 Booth St. Phone: (613)995-4132
Ottawa, ON, Canada K1A 0G1 James E. Kanasy, Dir.
Founded: 1913. **Staff:** Prof 6; Other 13. **Subjects:** Mining and mining technology, mineralogy, mineral processing, metals and materials technology, energy technology. **Holdings:** 250,000 volumes of serials, books, reports, and translations; 14,000 items on microform. **Subscriptions:** 3900 journals and other serials. **Services:** Interlibrary loan; copying; translation; library open to the public with restrictions. **Automated Operations:** Computerized public access catalog, cataloging, acquisitions, serials, circulation and ILL. **Computerized Information Services:** DIALOG Information Services, ORBIT Search Service, CAN/OLE, QL Systems, CAN/SDI; internal databases; Envoy 100 (electronic mail service). **Publications:** Accession List, monthly - for sale; Current Awareness Bulletin in Mining and Mineral Processing, semimonthly - available by subscription. **Special Indexes:** Index to CANMET Publications, annual. **Remarks:** CANMET is an acronym for Canada Centre for Mineral and Energy Technology. FAX: (613)995-8730; (613)952-2587. Telex: 053-3395. Electronic mail address(es): CANMET.LIBRARY (Envoy 100). **Staff:** Mrs. K. Nagy, Hd., Rd.Serv.; Mr. J. Ho, Hd., Tech.Serv.; Mr. C.M. Mason, Hd., Doc.Serv.

Canada - Energy, Mines & Resources Canada - Geological Survey of Canada
See: **Canada - Geological Survey of Canada** (2747)

★2700★
Canada - Energy, Mines & Resources Canada - Headquarters Library (Energy)
580 Booth St. Phone: (613)996-8282
Ottawa, ON, Canada K1A 0E4 F.B. Scollie, Chf.Libn.
Founded: 1958. **Staff:** Prof 4; Other 5. **Subjects:** Mineral and energy economics, policy, taxation, legislation and statistics, energy conservation. **Special Collections:** Energyfiche, 1973-1983; Statistics Canada microfiche collection, 1867-1983; Mineral Resources Branch and Mineral Policy Sector publications; provincial geological reports; Energy Sector publications. **Holdings:** 85,000 books and bound periodical volumes; 5000 reports; 156 shelf feet of microforms. **Subscriptions:** 1000 journals and other serials. **Services:** Interlibrary loan; copying; library open to the public at librarian's discretion. **Automated Operations:** Computerized cataloging and acquisitions. **Computerized Information Services:** DIALOG Information Services, CAN/OLE, QL Systems, Info Globe, The Financial Post Information Service, UTLAS; internal databases; Envoy 100 (electronic mail service). **Publications:** Accession list, monthly - limited distribution. **Remarks:** FAX: (613)996-1024. **Also Known As:** Canada - Ministere de l'Energie, des Mines et des Ressources - Bibliotheque Centrale. **Staff:** P. Gibson, Asst.Hd., Pub.Serv.; M. Doyon, Asst.Hd., Tech.Serv.

Canada - Energy, Mines & Resources Canada - Institute of Ocean Sciences
See: **Institute of Ocean Sciences - Library** (7960)

★2701★
Canada - Energy, Mines & Resources Canada - Surveys & Mapping Library (Geog-Map)
615 Booth St. Phone: (613)995-4071
Ottawa, ON, Canada K1A 0E9 Rosemary Swan, Hd.Libn.
Founded: 1962. **Staff:** Prof 1; Other 2. **Subjects:** Geodesy, photogrammetry, cartography, toponymy, Canadian geography and history. **Holdings:** 35,000 books; 12,000 bound periodical volumes. **Subscriptions:** 400 journals and other serials. **Services:** Interlibrary loan; copying; library open to the public with permission of librarian. **Computerized Information Services:** UTLAS, DIALOG Information Services, CAN/OLE, DOBIS Canadian Online Library System. Performs searches. **Publications:** Acquisitions list. **Remarks:** FAX: (613)943-1549. Telex: 053-3117.

★2702★
Canada - Energy, Mines & Resources Canada - Surveys, Mapping & Remote Sensing Sector - National Air Photo Library (Sci-Engr)
615 Booth St., No. 180 Phone: (613)995-4560
Ottawa, ON, Canada K1A 0E9 W. Voller, Chf.
Special Collections: Photography for Canada, 1925 to present. **Holdings:** 4.5 million photographs; 15,000 index maps. **Services:** Reproduction of aerial photographs; library open to the public. **Special Catalogs:** Air photography index maps, catalogs, and brochures. **Remarks:** FAX: (613)995-4568. Telex: 053-4328. **Formerly:** Its Surveys & Mapping Branch.

★2703★
Canada - Environment Canada - Atmospheric Environment Service - Atlantic Regional Library (Sci-Engr)
5th Fl., 1496 Bedford Hwy. Phone: (902)426-9278
Bedford, NS, Canada B4A 1E5 Joan Backer, Libn.
Founded: 1974. **Staff:** 1. **Subjects:** Meteorology, climatology. **Holdings:** 450 books; 1000 bound periodical volumes; 1000 microfiche of climatological data; 200 shelf feet of unbound reports, periodicals, and summaries. **Subscriptions:** 30 journals and other serials. **Services:** Copying; library open to the public by appointment. **Remarks:** FAX: (902)426-9158.

★2704★
Canada - Environment Canada - Atmospheric Environment Service - Central Region Library (Sci-Engr)
266 Graham Ave., Suite 1000
Winnipeg, MB, Canada R3C 3V4 Phone: (204)983-2024
Subjects: Meteorology, climatology. **Holdings:** 250 books; 500 bound periodical volumes; 2000 scientific papers; 100 bound volumes of Canadian weather data; 1000 technical circulars. **Subscriptions:** 20 journals and other serials. **Services:** Library open to the public for reference use only. **Automated Operations:** INMAGIC. **Remarks:** FAX: (204)983-4884.

★2705★
Canada - Environment Canada - Atmospheric Environment Service - Library (Sci-Engr)
4905 Dufferin St. Phone: (416)739-5702
Downsview, ON, Canada M3H 5T4 Maria Latyszewskyj, Libn.
Founded: 1871. **Staff:** Prof 2; Other 5. **Subjects:** Meteorology, climatology, atmospheric sciences. **Special Collections:** Meteorological records for Canadian stations, 1873 to present; meteorological records for Toronto, 1839 to present; depository collection of World Meteorological Organization published documents. **Holdings:** 20,000 books; 10,000 bound periodical volumes; 65,000 world climatic data documents; 1800 bound Canadian weather records; 9200 research and technical reports; 16 VF drawers of pamphlets; 14 VF drawers; 23 drawers of National Technical Information Service microfiche. **Subscriptions:** 654 journals and other serials. **Services:** Interlibrary loan; copying; library open for reference with limited borrowing. **Automated Operations:** Computerized cataloging, acquisitions, serials, and circulation. **Computerized Information Services:** DIALOG Information Services, Info Globe, DOBIS Canadian Online Library System, CAN/OLE, ELIAS (Environmental Libraries Automated System) Data Base; Envoy 100 (electronic mail service). **Publications:** Selected List of Accessions, bimonthly; serials list - both to all members of AES and others on request. **Remarks:** FAX: (416)739-4212. Electronic mail address(es): ILL.OTM (Envoy 100). The Atmospheric Environment Service is part of Environment Canada. **Also Known As:** Canada - Service de l'Environnement Atmospherique. **Staff:** D. Sanderson, Cat.Libn.

★2706★
Canada - Environment Canada - Atmospheric Environment Service - Quebec Region - Bibliotheque Regionale (Sci-Engr)
100 Blvd. Alexis-Nihon, 3rd Fl.
St. Laurent, PQ, Canada H4M 2N8 Phone: (514)873-2111
Founded: 1950. **Subjects:** Meteorology, weather forecasting, climatology. **Holdings:** 200 books; 50 bound periodical volumes; 1 drawer of microfiche. **Services:** On-site consultations. **Remarks:** Library is accessible on a restricted basis. Toll-free telephone number(s): (800)463-4311.

★2707★
Canada - Environment Canada - Atmospheric Environment Service - Western Region Library (Sci-Engr)
Twin Atria, Rm. 240
4999 98th Ave. Phone: (403)495-3143
Edmonton, AB, Canada T6B 2X3 Miriam Samji, Sec.
Founded: 1960. **Subjects:** Atmospheric sciences, physics, climatology. **Holdings:** 810 books; 521 bound periodical volumes; 1500 unbound reports; 370 unbound periodicals; 2500 pamphlets. **Subscriptions:** 39 journals and other serials. **Services:** Library not open to the public. **Remarks:** FAX: (403)468-7950.

★2708★
Canada - Environment Canada - Canadian Meteorological Centre/ Numerical Prediction Research - Library (Env-Cons)
2121 N. Service Rd., Rm. 508 Phone: (514)421-4750
Dorval, PQ, Canada H9P 1J3 Marie Serlemd, Libn.
Remarks: No further information was supplied by respondent.

★2709★
Canada - Environment Canada - Canadian Parks Service - Ontario Regional Library (Hist)
111 Water St., E. Phone: (613)938-5787
Cornwall, ON, Canada K6H 6S3 Joan M. Lipscombe, Libn.
Staff: Prof 1; Other 1. **Subjects:** Natural history, Canadian history, industrial arts, archeology. **Special Collections:** National historic sites reports and manuscripts. **Holdings:** 16,000 books; 150 bound periodical volumes. **Subscriptions:** 350 journals and other serials. **Services:** Interlibrary loan; copying; library open to the public with restrictions. **Computerized Information Services:** DOBIS Canadian Online Library System, DIALOG Information Services, CAN/OLE, ELIAS; Envoy 100 (electronic mail service). **Remarks:** FAX: (613)938-5785. Electronic mail address(es): PARKS.ILL.OCN (Envoy 100).

★2710★
Canada - Environment Canada - Canadian Parks Service - Prarie & Northern Regional Library (Env-Cons)
457 Main St. Phone: (204)983-5941
Winnipeg, MB, Canada R3B 3E8 Maxine McMillan, Lib.Spec.
Founded: 1973. **Staff:** Prof 1; Other 1. **Subjects:** National parks and historic sites, Canadian prairie, wildlife and historic conservation, ecology. **Holdings:** 12,000 books; 10,000 periodical volumes; 6 drawers of microforms. **Subscriptions:** 250 journals and other serials. **Services:** Interlibrary loan; copying (limited); library open to the public for reference use only. **Automated Operations:** Computerized cataloging. **Computerized Information Services:** CAN/OLE, DIALOG Information Services, ELIAS (Environmental Libraries Automated System) Data Base; Envoy 100 (electronic mail service). **Publications:** Acquisitions, quarterly; Current Contents, weekly - both for internal distribution only. **Remarks:** FAX: (204)983-2014. Electronic mail address(es): PARKS.ILLMWIAP (Envoy 100).

★2711★
Canada - Environment Canada - Canadian Parks Service - Western Regional Library (Env-Cons)
220 4th Ave., S.E., Rm. 551 Phone: (403)292-4455
Calgary, AB, Canada T2P 3H8 David Palmer, Libn.
Founded: 1973. **Staff:** Prof 2. **Subjects:** Park planning, interpretation, and conservation; Western Canadian history; natural history; historical and archaeological research. **Holdings:** 6000 books; 8000 internal reports; 400 microfiche; 10 reels of microfilm; 120 films. **Subscriptions:** 200 journals and other serials. **Services:** Interlibrary loan; library open to the public for reference use only. **Computerized Information Services:** DOBIS Canadian Online Library System, DIALOG Information Services, CAN/OLE. **Publications:** Monthly acquisitions list. **Remarks:** FAX: (403)292-4746. **Staff:** Maggie Hawes, Lib.Techn.

★2712★
Canada - Environment Canada - Departmental Library (Env-Cons)
351 St. Joseph Blvd., 2nd Fl.
Hull Quebec Phone: (819)997-1767
Ottawa, ON, Canada K1A 0H3 Mrs. M. Czanyo, Dept.Libn.
Founded: 1973. **Staff:** Prof 8; Other 13. **Subjects:** Land use planning, national parks and historic sites, pollution prevention and control, water resources, environmental planning and management, wildlife. **Holdings:** 88,500 books; 47,000 bound periodical volumes; 690 reels of microfilm; 10,000 reports on microfiche from U.S. Environmental Protection Agency; Environment Canada publications depository. **Subscriptions:** 3900 journals and other serials; 25 newspapers. **Services:** Interlibrary loan; copying; SDI; translation of scientific and technical material; library open to the public for reference use only. **Automated Operations:** Computerized public access catalog, cataloging, acquisitions, serials, and circulation. **Computerized Information Services:** DIALOG Information Services, MEDLINE, Prima Telematic Inc., Info Globe, DOBIS Canadian Online Library System, CAN/OLE, QL Systems, PFDS Online, RESORS (Remote Sensing On-Line Retrieval System), ELIAS (Environmental Libraries Automated System) Data Base, RLIN; Termium (internal database). **Publications:** Acquisitions List, bimonthly; Library Services (brochure); BIBLIO (Environment Canada Library Translation Series). **Remarks:** FAX: (819)997-1929. **Also Known As:** Canada - Ministere de l'Environnement.

★2713★
Canada - Environment Canada - Departmental Library, Chaudiere Branch (Rec, Env-Cons)
Ottawa, ON, Canada K1A 0H3 Phone: (819)997-6679
Peter Le Roy, Br.Libn.
Founded: 1980. **Staff:** Prof 1; Other 2. **Subjects:** Archeology, Canadian history, conservation and restoration, outdoor recreation, tourism, parks and reserves, architecture. **Special Collections:** Canadiana; collection of early architectural books (microfilm). **Holdings:** 36,594 books; Canadian Parks Service publications depository; trade catalogs on microfiche; American architectural books on microfilm; Historic American Buildings Survey on microfiche. **Subscriptions:** 304 journals and other serials. **Services:** Interlibrary loan; copying; SDI; library open to the public. **Automated Operations:** Computerized cataloging, acquisitions, serials, and circulation. **Computerized Information Services:** DIALOG Information Services, RLIN, DOBIS Canadian Online Library System, UTLAS, RESORS (Remote Sensing On-Line Retrieval System), CAN/OLE, QL Systems, Questel, Info Globe, Infomart Online, MEDLARS, Prima Telematic Inc., ELIAS (Environmental Libraries Automated System) Data Base; Conservation Information Network, Envoy 100 (electronic mail services). **Publications:** Acquisitions List, bimonthly - available on request. **Remarks:** FAX: (819)997-2206. Electronic mail address(es): ILL.OOPAC (Envoy 100).

★2714★
Canada - Environment Canada, Conservation & Protection - Atlantic Region Library (Env-Cons)
45 Alderney Dr., Queen Square, 15th Fl. Phone: (902)426-7219
Dartmouth, NS, Canada B2Y 2N6 Dawn Taylor-Prime, Reg.Libn.
Founded: 1981. **Staff:** Prof 1; Other 1. **Subjects:** Environmental sciences, water pollution, air pollution, water quality, land, environmental engineering. **Special Collections:** Flood Damage Reduction Program; Ocean Dumping collection; LRTAP Collection; EPA publications on microfiche; hazardous waste collection; State of the Environment Collection; marine environmental quality studies; Environment/Economy collection. **Holdings:** 28,000 books; 400,000 reports on microfiche; 2 drawers of journals on microfilm; 1 drawer of journals on microfiche. **Subscriptions:** 250 journals; 40 newspapers; other series titles. **Services:** Interlibrary loan; copying; SDI; library open to the public for reference use only. **Automated Operations:** Computerized cataloging. **Computerized Information Services:** DIALOG Information Services, CAN/OLE, DOBIS Canadian Online Library System, iNET 2000, ELIAS (Environment Libraries Automated System); Envoy 100, iNET 2000 (electronic mail services). **Publications:** Acquisitions list, bimonthly; annotated bibliographies, irregular; newsletter, irregular - for internal distribution only. **Special Indexes:** Indexes to special collections (print, card, and fiche). **Remarks:** Alternate telephone number(s): (902)426-7232. FAX: (902)426-7219.

★2715★
Canada - Environment Canada, Conservation & Protection - Canadian Wildlife Service - Atlantic Region Library (Env-Cons)
Box 1590 Phone: (506)536-3025
Sackville, NB, Canada E0A 3C0 Jean Sealy, Libn.
Founded: 1970. **Staff:** 1. **Subjects:** Birds, mammals, conservation, habitat protection and management, pollution, national parks. **Holdings:** 1000 books; 40 bound periodical volumes; 60 boxes of manuscript reports; 70 boxes of reprints and reports; 300 national parks publications; 2800 microforms. **Subscriptions:** 60 journals and other serials. **Services:** Interlibrary loan; copying; library open to the public with restrictions. **Remarks:** FAX: (506)536-3528 **Also Known As:** Canada - Service Canadien de la Faune.

★2716★
Canada - Environment Canada, Conservation & Protection - Canadian Wildlife Service - Ontario Region Library (Env-Cons)
49 Camelot Dr. Phone: (613)952-2406
Nepean, ON, Canada K1A 0H3 Danuta Derdak, Act.Libn.
Staff: Prof 1. **Subjects:** Ornithology, mammalogy, wildlife management, environmental impact (wildlife). **Holdings:** 2000 books; 140 bound periodical volumes; 500 reports. **Subscriptions:** 74 journals and other serials. **Services:** Interlibrary loan; copying; library open to qualified users for reference use only. **Computerized Information Services:** DOBIS. **Remarks:** FAX: (613)952-9027.

★2717★
Canada - Environment Canada, Conservation & Protection - Canadian Wildlife Service - Prairie Migratory Bird Research Centre - Library (Env-Cons)
115 Perimeter Rd. Phone: (306)975-4096
Saskatoon, SK, Canada S7N 0X4 Pat Yeudall, Libn.
Founded: 1966. **Staff:** 1. **Subjects:** Birds, conservation, natural resources. **Holdings:** Manuscripts; satellite photographs; maps; microfilm. **Subscriptions:** 96 journals and other serials. **Services:** Interlibrary loan; copying; library open to the public with restrictions. **Automated Operations:** Computerized cataloging. **Remarks:** Library is part of the Western and Northern Region of the Canadian Wildlife Service, with headquarters in Edmonton, AB. **Remarks:** FAX: (306)975-4089.

★2718★
Canada - Environment Canada, Conservation & Protection - Library (Env-Cons)
100 Hamilton Blvd.
Box 6010 Phone: (403)667-3407
Whitehorse, YT, Canada Y1A 5L7 Wendy Chambers, Libn.
Founded: 1978. **Staff:** Prof 1. **Subjects:** Water and air pollution, hydrocarbon development, environmental impact of pipelines, Beaufort Sea, residential wood smoke, hazardous substances. **Holdings:** 2000 books; 100 microfiche; 50 video cassettes; 2500 slides. **Subscriptions:** 31 journals and other serials. **Services:** Interlibrary loan; copying; library open to the public with restrictions. **Remarks:** FAX: (403)667-7962.

★2719★
Canada - Environment Canada, Conservation & Protection - Ontario Region Library (Env-Cons)
25 St. Clair Ave., E., 7th Fl. Phone: (416)973-0893
Toronto, ON, Canada M4T 1M2 Susan Griffin, Libn.
Founded: 1975. **Staff:** Prof 1. **Subjects:** Air and water pollution control and prevention, waste management, toxic chemicals, hazardous materials, environmental policy and law. **Special Collections:** Environmental Protection Service reports; consultants reports for Ontario region. **Holdings:** 7600 books; 1000 microfiche. **Subscriptions:** 90 journals and other serials. **Services:** Interlibrary loan; copying; SDI; library open to the public. **Automated Operations:** Computerized cataloging. **Computerized Information Services:** DIALOG Information Services, QL Systems, CAN/OLE, DOBIS. **Remarks:** FAX: (416)973-8342.

★2720★
Canada - Environment Canada, Conservation & Protection - Pacific Region Library (Env-Cons)
224 W. Esplanade Phone: (604)666-5914
North Vancouver, BC, Canada V7M 3H7 Andrew Fabro, Libn.
Founded: 1972. **Staff:** Prof 1. **Subjects:** Pollution - air, water, land. **Holdings:** 6750 monographs; 2000 microforms; Canadian and U.S. government environmental reports. **Subscriptions:** 125 journals and other serials. **Services:** Interlibrary loan; copying; library open to the public for reference use; loans to government employees. **Computerized Information Services:** PFDS Online, DIALOG Information Services, CAN/OLE, DOBIS Canadian Online Library System; Envoy 100 (electronic mail service). **Publications:** EPS Reports, irregular. **Remarks:** FAX: (604)666-9107. Electronic mail address(es): EPSPACIFIC (Envoy 100).

★2721★
Canada - Environment Canada, Conservation & Protection - Quebec Region Library (Env-Cons)
1141, route de l'Eglise, 7th Fl.
P.O. Box 10100 Phone: (418)649-6546
Ste. Foy, PQ, Canada G1V 4H5 Cecile Morin, Libn.
Founded: 1976. **Staff:** 4. **Subjects:** Migratory birds and their habitats, waterfowl management, acid rain, environmental policy and planning, environmental impact assessment, aquatic toxicology, water and air pollution. **Holdings:** 9000 monographs. **Subscriptions:** 200 journals and other serials. **Services:** Interlibrary loan; copying; library open to the public. **Automated Operations:** Computerized cataloging and acquisitions. **Computerized Information Services:** Internal database; Envoy 100 (electronic mail service). **Remarks:** Maintains branch libraries in Quebec City and Montreal. FAX: (418)648-4613. Electronic mail address(es): QQE.PEB (Envoy 100, Quebec City); QMEE.PEB (Envoy 100, Montreal). **Staff:** Dominique Trudeau, Montreal Br.Techn.; Carmen Joseph, Quebec City Br.Techn.

★2722★
Canada - Environment Canada, Conservation & Protection - Western and Northern Region Library (Env-Cons, Biol Sci)
4999 98th Ave., Rm. 210 Phone: (403)468-8951
Edmonton, AB, Canada T6B 2X3 Teresa Fraser, Lib.Techn.
Staff: Prof 1. **Subjects:** Ornithology, botany, mammalogy, wildlife conservation, ecology, natural resources, land use, endangered species, environmental pollution, monitoring and control, toxic waste management. **Holdings:** 23,000 books; 1600 bound periodical volumes; 4500 manuscripts; 1500 government documents. **Subscriptions:** 450 journals and other serials. **Services:** Interlibrary loan; library open to the public with restrictions. **Automated Operations:** Computerized cataloging. **Computerized Information Services:** ELIAS. **Publications:** Accessions list, monthly. **Remarks:** FAX: (403)495-2615.

Canada - Environment Canada, Parks - Fortress of Louisbourg National Historic Park
See: **Fortress of Louisbourg National Historic Park** (6027)

Canada - Environment Canada, Parks Service - Fort Malden National Historic Park
See: **Fort Malden National Historic Park** (6008)

★2723★
Canada - External Affairs Canada - Legal Library (Law)
125 Sussex Dr. Phone: (613)996-9134
Ottawa, ON, Canada K1A 0G2 Ruth M. Thompson, Dir.
Subjects: Law. **Remarks:** No further information was supplied by respondent.

★2724★
Canada - External Affairs and International Trade Canada - Library (Soc Sci, Bus-Fin)
Lester B. Pearson Bldg.
Sussex Dr. Phone: (613)996-8691
Ottawa, ON, Canada K1A 0G2 Ruth Margaret Thompson, Dir.
Founded: 1931. **Staff:** Prof 11; Other 19. **Subjects:** International relations, international law, international economics, trade, international organizations. **Special Collections:** International documents; international law. **Holdings:** 50,000 books; 30,000 bound periodical volumes; 800,000 documents; 400,000 microforms; 800 maps; 600 reference dossiers. **Subscriptions:** 3000 journals and other serials; 86 newspapers. **Services:** Interlibrary loan; copying; library open to the public with restrictions. **Automated Operations:** Computerized cataloging, acquisitions, and serials. **Computerized Information Services:** UTLAS; Envoy 100 (electronic mail service). **Publications:** Acquisitions List, semimonthly. **Remarks:** FAX: (613)952-1013. Alternate telephone number(s): 992-6150, (reference). Electronic mail address(es): ILL.OOE (Envoy 100). **Also Known As:** Affaires Exterieures et Commerce International Canada.

★2725★
Canada - Federal Court of Canada - Library (Law)
Supreme Court Bldg. Phone: (613)995-1382
Ottawa, ON, Canada K1A 0H9 Rosalie Fox, Hd.Libn.
Founded: 1971. **Staff:** 7. **Subjects:** Law. **Holdings:** Figures not available. **Services:** Library open to the public by appointment. **Computerized Information Services:** QL Systems, LEXIS, WESTLAW, DIALOG Information Services, Societe Quebecoise d'Information Juridique (SOQUIJ), CAN/LAW, Info Globe, Infomart Online; electronic mail service. **Remarks:** FAX: (613)954-7714. **Staff:** Louise Houston, Cat./Sys.Libn.

★2726★
Canada - Fisheries & Oceans - Arctic Biological Station Library
555 St. Pierre Blvd.
Ste. Anne de Bellevue, PQ, Canada H9X 3R4
Defunct. Absorbed by Canada - Fisheries & Oceans - Institut Maurice-LaMontagne - Library.

★2727★
Canada - Fisheries & Oceans - Biological Station Library (Biol Sci)
St. Andrews, NB, Canada E0G 2X0 Phone: (506)529-8854
Marilynn Rudi, Libn.
Founded: 1908. **Staff:** 2. **Subjects:** Fisheries, aquatic biology, chemistry, aquaculture. **Holdings:** 6000 books; 8500 bound periodical volumes; 420 boxes of pamphlets. **Subscriptions:** 715 journals and other serials. **Services:** Interlibrary loan; copying; library open to qualified researchers. **Computerized Information Services:** DIALOG Information Services, CAN/OLE, DOBIS Canadian Online Library System; Envoy 100 (electronic mail service). **Publications:** Circulars and technical reports, irregular. **Remarks:** FAX: (506)529-4274. Electronic mail address(es): ILL.NBAB (Envoy 100).

★2728★
Canada - Fisheries & Oceans - Central & Arctic Region - Sea Lamprey Control Centre - Library (Biol Sci)
Canal Dr., Ship Canal P.O. Phone: (705)949-1102
Sault Ste. Marie, ON, Canada P6A 1P0 Anna Little, Off.Serv.Supv.
Founded: 1965. **Subjects:** Lamprey biology, fish and fishing, vertebrate zoology, general biology, fisheries management and research. **Holdings:** 300 books; 300 unbound periodicals; 1500 separates; 250 Fisheries Research Board manuscript reports; 650 Sea Lamprey Control Centre annual reports; 400 unbound reports. **Subscriptions:** 30 journals and other serials. **Services:** Library open to the public by appointment only for reference use. **Computerized Information Services:** CompuServe Information Service (electronic mail service). **Remarks:** FAX: (705)949-2739.

★2729★
Canada - Fisheries & Oceans - Fisheries Management Regional Library (Biol Sci)
555 W. Hastings St. Phone: (604)666-3851
Vancouver, BC, Canada V6B 5G3 Paulette Westlake, Hd., Rec. & Lib.Serv.
Founded: 1962. **Staff:** 2. **Subjects:** Fisheries management, habitat management, resource enhancement, biology, economics, aquaculture. **Holdings:** 2000 books; 250 bound periodical volumes; 100 shelves of reports and government documents; 450 translations; 1000 microfiche. **Subscriptions:** 30 journals. **Services:** Interlibrary loan; library not open to the public. **Computerized Information Services:** DIALOG Information Services, CAN/OLE; Envoy 100 (electronic mail service). **Remarks:** FAX: (604)666-3450. Electronic mail address(es): ILL.BUAFI (Envoy 100). **Staff:** Marcia H. Van Wely.

★2730★
Canada - Fisheries & Oceans - Fisheries Research Branch, Gulf Region - Gulf Fisheries Center - Library (Biol Sci)
P.O. Box 5030 Phone: (506)851-6264
Moncton, NB, Canada E1C 9B6 Paulette Levesque, Libn.
Founded: 1981. **Staff:** Prof 1. **Subjects:** Marine statistics and population dynamics. **Special Collections:** Fisheries. **Holdings:** 6000 volumes. **Subscriptions:** 260 journals and other serials. **Services:** Library not open to the public. **Computerized Information Services:** DIALOG Information Services, CAN/OLE; CD-ROM; WAVES (internal database); Envoy 100 (electronic mail service). **Publications:** List of publications - available on request. **Remarks:** FAX: (506)851-7732. Electronic mail address(es): DFO.LIB.MONCTON (Envoy 100). Telex: 014-2607. **Staff:** Gisele Richard, Asst.Libn.

★2731★
Canada - Fisheries & Oceans - Freshwater Institute Library (Biol Sci)
501 University Crescent Phone: (204)983-5170
Winnipeg, MB, Canada R3T 2N6 K. Eric Marshall, Hd., Lib.Serv.
Founded: 1966. **Staff:** Prof 1; Other 2. **Subjects:** Fisheries, limnology. **Special Collections:** Fritsch Collection of illustrations of freshwater algae (microfiche); Arctic Petroleum Operators Association reports (microfiche). **Holdings:** 22,000 books; 60,000 bound periodical volumes; 12,000 pamphlets; 200 pamphlet boxes of reports; 20,000 microfiche; 300 reels of microfilm; 15,000 cards of abstracts and indexes. **Subscriptions:** 500 journals and other serials. **Services:** Interlibrary loan; copying; SDI; library open to the public. **Automated Operations:** Computerized cataloging. **Computerized Information Services:** DIALOG Information Services, CAN/OLE, STN International; WAVES (internal database); Envoy 100, SCIENCEnet (electronic mail services). Performs searches on fee basis. **Publications:** New Publications in the Library, monthly - for internal distribution only. **Remarks:** FAX: (204)983-6285. Electronic mail address(es): DFO.LIB.WINNIPEG (administration, Envoy 100); ILL.MWFW (ILL, Envoy 100); E.MARSHALL (SCIENCEnet).

★2732★
Canada - Fisheries & Oceans - Headquarters Library (Biol Sci)
200 Kent St., 10th Fl. W. Phone: (613)993-2926
Ottawa, ON, Canada K1A 0E6 H.A. Cameron, Mgr.
Staff: Prof 3; Other 3. **Subjects:** Fisheries, marine sciences. **Holdings:** 20,000 books; 1000 bound periodical volumes. **Subscriptions:** 1400 journals and other serials; 10 newspapers. **Services:** Interlibrary loan; copying; SDI; library open to the public with restrictions on borrowing. **Computerized Information Services:** DIALOG Information Services, CAN/OLE, Info Globe, Infomart Online, QL Systems; Envoy 100 (electronic mail service). **Publications:** Acquisitions, bimonthly. **Remarks:** FAX: (613)996-9055. Electronic mail address(es): DFO.LIB.OTTAWA; ILL.DFO (both Envoy 100). **Also Known As:** Canada - Peches et Oceans. **Staff:** J. Weerasinghe, Ref.; S.A. Farooqui, Cat.; D. Lasalle, ILL.

★2733★
Canada - Fisheries & Oceans - Institut Maurice-LaMontagne - Library (Biol Sci)
850, route de la Mer
P.O. Box 1000 Phone: (418)775-6552
Quebec, PQ, Canada G5H 3Z4 Guy Michaud, Libn.
Staff: Prof 1; Other 2. **Subjects:** Fisheries; aquaculture; oceanography - chemical, physical, biological; biology - marine life, parasitology; cartography; hydrography. **Holdings:** 20,000 books; 8000 microfiche; 35

films. **Subscriptions:** 250 journals and other serials; 20 newspapers. **Services:** Interlibrary loan; copying; library open to the public. **Automated Operations:** Computerized cataloging. **Computerized Information Services:** DIALOG Information Services, CAN/OLE, DOBIS Canadian Online Library System, UTLAS; WAVES, VAGUES internal databases; Envoy 100 (electronic mail service). **Publications:** List of Acquisitions, bimonthly. **Remarks:** FAX: (418)775-0542. Electronic mail address(es): DFO.LIB.QUEBEC (Envoy 100).

Canada - Fisheries & Oceans - Institute of Ocean Sciences
See: **Institute of Ocean Sciences - Library** (7960)

★2734★
Canada - Fisheries & Oceans - Newfoundland Regional Library (Biol Sci)
P.O. Box 5667 Phone: (709)772-2022
St. John's, NF, Canada A1C 5X1 Audrey Conroy, Reg.Libn.
Founded: 1940. **Staff:** 4. **Subjects:** Marine biology, freshwater resource development, fisheries, pollution. **Holdings:** 9200 books; 1500 linear feet of serials. **Subscriptions:** 775 journals and other serials. **Services:** Interlibrary loan; copying; SDI; library open to the public. **Computerized Information Services:** DIALOG Information Services, CAN/OLE; WAVES, ASFA (internal databases); Envoy 100 (electronic mail service). **Remarks:** FAX: (709)772-2156. Telex: 0164 698.

★2735★
Canada - Fisheries & Oceans - Pacific Biological Station - Library (Biol Sci)
Nanaimo, BC, Canada V9R 5K6 Phone: (604)756-7071
G. Miller, Hd., Lib.Serv.
Founded: 1913. **Staff:** Prof 2; Other 1. **Subjects:** Fish biology, fish culture, marine ecology, biological oceanography. **Holdings:** 3600 books; 35,000 bound periodical volumes; 80,000 reports. **Subscriptions:** 2400 journals and other serials. **Services:** Interlibrary loan; copying; SDI; library open to the public with restrictions. **Automated Operations:** Computerized cataloging. **Computerized Information Services:** DIALOG Information Services, CAN/OLE; Envoy 100 (electronic mail service). **Remarks:** Alternate telephone number(s): 756-7070. FAX: (604)756-7053. Telex: 04-46128. Electronic mail address(es): DFO.LIB.NANAIMO (Envoy 100). **Staff:** P.L. Olson, Tech.Serv.Libn.

★2736★
Canada - Fisheries & Oceans - Scotia-Fundy Regional Library - Halifax Fisheries Library (Biol Sci, Env-Cons)
P.O. Box 550 Phone: (902)426-7160
Halifax, NS, Canada B3J 2S7 Lori Collins
Founded: 1968. **Staff:** Prof 1; Other 1. **Subjects:** Fisheries, environmental control, food technology. **Special Collections:** Atlantic Salmon. **Holdings:** 13,000 books; 2800 bound periodical volumes; 40,000 technical reports; 20,000 microfiche; 500 reels of microfilm. **Subscriptions:** 1000 journals and other serials; 20 newspapers. **Services:** Interlibrary loan; copying; SDI; library open to the public with restrictions. **Computerized Information Services:** CAN/OLE, DIALOG Information Services, QL Systems, WILSONLINE; WAVES (internal database); Envoy 100, SCIENCEnet (electronic mail services). **Remarks:** FAX: (902)426-2698. Telex: 019-21891. Electronic mail address(es): ILL.NSHF (Envoy 100 - interlibrary loans); DFO.LIB.HALIFAX (Envoy 100 - all other messages); BEDFORD.INST (Attn. Halifax Library; SCIENCEnet).

★2737★
Canada - Fisheries & Oceans - West Vancouver Laboratory - Library (Biol Sci)
4160 Marine Dr. Phone: (604)666-4813
West Vancouver, BC, Canada V7V 1N6 MeiShuen Fok, Libn.
Founded: 1970. **Staff:** 1. **Subjects:** Fisheries research, aquatic environment and habitat. **Holdings:** 2000 volumes. **Subscriptions:** 250 journals and other serials. **Services:** Interlibrary loan; copying; SDI; library open to the public with restrictions. **Automated Operations:** Computerized cataloging. **Computerized Information Services:** DIALOG Information Services, CAN/OLE; WAVES (internal database); Envoy 100 (electronic mail service). **Remarks:** FAX: (604)666-3497. Electronic mail address(es): DFO.LIB.WESTVAN (Envoy 100).

★2738★
Canada - Forestry Canada - Great Lakes Forestry Centre - Library (Biol Sci)
P.O. Box 490 Phone: (705)949-9461
Sault Ste. Marie, ON, Canada P6A 5M7 Sandra Burt, Libn.
Staff: Prof 1; Other 2. **Subjects:** Forestry, entomology, biochemistry, physiology, bioclimatology. **Holdings:** 8000 volumes. **Subscriptions:** 450 journals and other serials. **Services:** Interlibrary loan; copying; SDI; translation; library open to the public with restrictions. **Automated Operations:** Computerized cataloging, acquisitions, and circulation. **Computerized Information Services:** DIALOG Information Services, CAN/OLE; Envoy 100 (electronic mail service). **Publications:** Accessions list, monthly - available upon request; Serials Holdings List. **Remarks:** FAX: (705)759-5700.

★2739★
Canada - Forestry Canada - Laurentian Forestry Centre - Library (Biol Sci)
1055, rue du Peps
C.P. 3800 Phone: (418)648-4850
Ste. Foy, PQ, Canada G1V 4C7 Gilles Bizier, Libn.
Founded: 1952. **Staff:** Prof 1; Other 1. **Subjects:** Forestry, entomology, plant pathology, silviculture, pedology, ecology. **Holdings:** 7000 books; 3000 bound periodical volumes; 12,000 serials; 9 VF drawers of researchers' scientific works. **Subscriptions:** 200 journals and other serials. **Services:** Interlibrary loan; copying; library open to the public for reference use only. **Automated Operations:** Computerized cataloging, acquisitions, and circulation. **Computerized Information Services:** Online systems; Envoy 100 (electronic mail service). **Publications:** List of scientific publications, irregular. **Remarks:** FAX: (418)648-5849. Electronic mail address(es): QQMF.BIB (Envoy 100). **Also Known As:** Centre de Foresterie des Laurentides.

★2740★
Canada - Forestry Canada - Maritimes Forestry Centre - Library (Biol Sci)
Regent St.
P.O. Box 4000 Phone: (506)452-3541
Fredericton, NB, Canada E3B 5P7 Barry Barner, Libn.
Founded: 1911. **Staff:** Prof 1; Other 2. **Subjects:** Forestry, forest ecology, forest genetics, silviculture, forest pathology, forest entomology, forest economics. **Special Collections:** Forestry Canada documents. **Holdings:** 8000 books; 8000 periodical volumes; 60,000 documents; 5000 microforms, manuscripts. **Subscriptions:** 300 journals. **Services:** Interlibrary loan (fee); library open to the public. **Automated Operations:** Computerized cataloging, acquisitions, and circulation (SYDNEY). **Computerized Information Services:** DIALOG Information Services, CAN/OLE, DOBIS Canadian Online Library System; Envoy 100 (electronic mail service). **Remarks:** FAX: (506)452-3525. Electronic mail address(es): ILL.NBFE (Envoy 100). Library located at the H.J. Flemming Forestry Complex, Regent St. S., Fredericton, NB.

★2741★
Canada - Forestry Canada - Newfoundland and Labrador Region - Library (Biol Sci)
P.O. Box 6028 Phone: (709)772-4672
St. John's, NF, Canada A1C 5X8 Catherine E. Philpott, Libn.
Founded: 1950. **Staff:** 1. **Subjects:** Forestry, entomology, environmental research. **Holdings:** 3500 books; 1270 bound periodical volumes. **Subscriptions:** 143 journals and other serials. **Services:** Interlibrary loan; copying; SDI; library open to the public. **Remarks:** FAX: (709)772-2576.

★2742★
Canada - Forestry Canada - Northwest Region - Northern Forestry Centre - Library (Biol Sci)
5320 122nd St. Phone: (403)435-7324
Edmonton, AB, Canada T6H 3S5 David J.S. Robinson, Libn.
Founded: 1952. **Staff:** Prof 1; Other 1. **Subjects:** Forestry, entomology, mycology, soil science, hydrology, environmental pollution. **Holdings:** 5000 books; 5000 bound periodical volumes; 35,000 reports and government publications; 3000 reprints and pamphlets; 248 microforms. **Subscriptions:** 165 journals and other serials. **Services:** Interlibrary loan; copying, library open to the public for reference; loans made to qualified researchers. **Computerized Information Services:** Envoy 100 (electronic mail service). **Publications:** Accessions lists, irregular - to mailing list. **Remarks:** Alternate telephone number(s): (403)435-7323. Telex: 037-2117. FAX: (403)435-7359. Electronic mail address(es): NOFC.ILL (Envoy 100).

★2743★
Canada - Forestry Canada - Pacific and Yukon Region - Pacific Forestry Centre - Library (Biol Sci)
506 W. Burnside Rd. Phone: (604)363-0600
Victoria, BC, Canada V8Z 1M5 Alice Solyma, Hd., Lib.Serv.
Founded: 1940. **Staff:** Prof 1; Other 2. **Subjects:** Forest science, land and environmental research, economics, entomology, fire research, hydrology, mensuration, meteorology, mycology, plant pathology. **Holdings:** 20,000 books and bound periodical volumes; 55,000 reports and government documents. **Subscriptions:** 325 journals and other serials. **Services:** Interlibrary loan; copying; SDI; library open to the public. **Automated Operations:** Computerized public access catalog, cataloging, acquisitions, and circulation. **Computerized Information Services:** DIALOG Information Services, Info Globe, Infomart Online, CAN/OLE, BRS Information Technologies; internal database; DIALMAIL, Envoy 100 (electronic mail services). **Remarks:** Alternate telephone number(s): 363-0637; 363-0680. FAX: (604)363-0775. Electronic mail address(es): ILL.BVIF (Envoy 100). **Formerly:** Its Pacific and Yukon Forestry Centre - Library.

★2744★
Canada - Forestry Canada - Petawawa National Forestry Institute - Library (Biol Sci)
Chalk River, ON, Canada K0J 1J0 Phone: (613)589-2880
Mary Mitchell, Libn.
Founded: 1920. **Staff:** Prof 1; Other 1. **Subjects:** Forestry. **Holdings:** 6000 volumes; 24,000 bound periodical volumes; 15,000 nonbook items; 1500 other cataloged items. **Subscriptions:** 243 journals and other serials. **Services:** Interlibrary loan; copying; SDI; library open to the public with restrictions. **Automated Operations:** Computerized public access catalog, cataloging, circulation, and acquisitions. **Computerized Information Services:** DOBIS Canadian Online Library System, CAN/OLE, DIALOG Information Services, RESORS (Remote Sensing On-Line Retrieval System); Envoy 100 (electronic mail service). **Publications:** Accessions List, monthly. **Remarks:** FAX: (613)589-2275. Electronic mail address(es): OCKE (Envoy 100).

Canada - Gendarmerie Royale du Canada
See: **Royal Canadian Mounted Police - Canadian Police College - Law Enforcement Reference Centre** (14108)

★2745★
Canada - Geological Survey of Canada - Cordilleran Geoscience Library (Sci-Engr)
100 W. Pender St., 5th Fl. Phone: (604)666-3812
Vancouver, BC, Canada V6B 1R8 Mary Akehurst, Chf.Libn.
Founded: 1973. **Staff:** Prof 1; Other 1. **Subjects:** Earth sciences with emphasis on the Western Cordillera and marine work on the Pacific Coast. **Special Collections:** Reports and maps of the Geological Survey of Canada, Department of Energy, Mines & Resources, Environment Canada, Indian & Northern Affairs, and Fisheries and Oceans; publications from U.S. Geological Survey, U.S. Bureau of Mines, U.S. State Geological Surveys, B.C. Ministry of Energy, Mines & Petroleum Resources, and B.C. Ministry of Environment. **Holdings:** 104,000 volumes; 12,000 maps; 25 VF drawers of unbound reports; 1200 theses; microforms. **Subscriptions:** 1000 journals and other serials; 900 government serials. **Services:** Copying (limited); library open to the public with restrictions. **Computerized Information Services:** Geoscan; internal databases. **Remarks:** FAX: (604)666-1124.

★2746★
Canada - Geological Survey of Canada - Institute of Sedimentary & Petroleum Geology - Library (Sci-Engr)
3303 33rd St., N.W. Phone: (403)292-7165
Calgary, AB, Canada T2L 2A7 John McIsaac, Hd.Libn.
Founded: 1966. **Staff:** Prof 2; Other 2. **Subjects:** Geology - general, sedimentary, petroleum; paleontology; micropaleontology. **Holdings:** 100,000 books; 2000 translations; 12 cabinets of maps. **Subscriptions:** 654 journals and other serials. **Services:** Library open to the public for reference use only. **Automated Operations:** Computerized public access catalog, cataloging, and acquisitions. **Computerized Information Services:** CAN/OLE, DIALOG Information Services, PFDS Online; Envoy 100 (electronic mail service). **Publications:** Monthly Accessions List. **Remarks:** FAX: (403)292-5377. **Staff:** Edward Hau, Asst.Libn.

★2747★
Canada - Geological Survey of Canada - Library (Sci-Engr)
601 Booth St., Rm. 350 Phone: (613)996-3919
Ottawa, ON, Canada K1A 0E8 Koushal Sehdeav, Chf., Lib. & Bibliog.Serv.
Founded: 1844. **Staff:** Prof 10; Other 10. **Subjects:** Geology, paleontology, geochemistry, geophysics, physical geography, sedimentology. **Holdings:** 400,000 volumes; 254,000 maps; 2300 open files of unpublished GSC documents announced to users; 52,400 microforms; 750,000 photographs; 3000 translations. **Subscriptions:** 4000 journals and other serials. **Services:** Interlibrary loan; copying; SDI (for Canadian users); library open to the public with restrictions. **Automated Operations:** Computerized cataloging and acquisitions. **Computerized Information Services:** DIALOG Information Services, , Questel, ORBIT Search Service, CAN/OLE, UTLAS, QL Systems; GEOSCAN (internal database); Envoy 100 (electronic mail service). Performs searches on fee basis. Contact Person: Judith Wilks. **Publications:** Accession List, bimonthly; List of Translations, irregular. **Remarks:** FAX: (613)996-9990. Telex: 053-3117. Electronic mail address(es): GSC.LIB (Envoy 100). The Geological Survey of Canada is part of Energy, Mines & Resources Canada. **Staff:** Mrs. L.A. Frieday, Hd., Automated Oper.; Mrs. E. Frebold, Hd., Info.Serv.; Mrs. M. Slachta, Hd., Ref. & Circ. ; Ms. E. Smith, Acq.; Mr. D.E. Tedford, ILL; Mrs. B. Chen, Map Lib.

★2748★
Canada - Geological Survey of Canada - Library - Geophysics Collection (Sci-Engr)
1 Observatory Crescent
Ottawa, ON, Canada K1A 0Y3 Phone: (613)995-5558
Founded: 1905. **Staff:** 2. **Subjects:** Geophysics, seismology, gravity, rock physics, geomagnetism, geodynamics, paleomagnetism, permafrost, earth tides, meteorite craters, planetology. **Holdings:** 6000 books; 35,000 bound periodical volumes; 15,000 pamphlets, reports, reprints. **Subscriptions:** 1100 journals and other serials. **Services:** Interlibrary loan; library open to the public with restrictions. **Automated Operations:** Computerized cataloging and acquisitions. **Computerized Information Services:** DIALOG Information Services, CAN/OLE, Pergamon, Inc. UTLAS; Envoy 100 (electronic mail service). **Publications:** Serials list, irregular. **Remarks:** FAX: (613)952-9088. Electronic mail address(es): GEOPHYS.LIB (Envoy 100).

★2749★
Canada - Health and Welfare Canada - Departmental Library (Med, Soc Sci)
Jeanne Mance Bldg., 5th Fl.
Tunney's Pasture Phone: (613)954-8591
Ottawa, ON, Canada K1A 0K9 Ms. Marty H. Lovelock, Dept.Libn.
Founded: 1991. **Staff:** Prof 4; Other 10. **Subjects:** Health administration; education and policy; healthcare - children, women, handicapped, natives, elderly; social welfare; gerontology; demography; income support and social security; family violence; child care; substance abuse. **Holdings:** 70,000 report and monograph titles. **Subscriptions:** 1200 journals and other serials. **Services:** Interlibrary loan; copying; library open to the public by appointment. **Automated Operations:** Computerized public access catalog, cataloging, acquisitions, serials, and circulation. **Computerized Information Services:** BRS Information Technologies, DIALOG Information Services, CAN/OLE, QL Systems, Info Globe, Infomart Online, MEDLARS, DOBIS Canadian Online Library System; CD-ROMs; Envoy 100 (electronic mail service). **Publications:** Acquisitions list, bimonthly; periodicals list, annual; Family Violence Update, irregular; Library Remote Access and Search Guide - available upon request. **Remarks:** FAX: (613)957-3379. Electronic mail address(es): OONHHS (Envoy 100). Contains holdings of the former Canada - Health and Welfare Canada - Policy, Planning & Information Branch and Health Services and Promotion Information Network. **Staff:** Abha Goomar, ILL; Robin Nagy, Ref.; Jean King, Acq.; Paule DeGrace, Coll.Dev.; Shawn Aitken, Online Spec.

★2750★
Canada - Health and Welfare Canada - Health Protection Branch - Library Services (Biol Sci, Med)
Sir F.G. Banting Research Centre, 3rd Fl., W.
Ross Ave., Tunney's Pasture Phone: (613)957-1026
Ottawa, ON, Canada K1A 0L2 Susan Higgins, Chf., Lib.Serv.
Founded: 1969. **Staff:** Prof 11; Other 13. **Subjects:** Pharmacology, pharmaceutical chemistry, food science, nutrition research, microbiology, toxicology, medical sciences, public health, epidemiology, environmental health, radiation protection, drug abuse. **Holdings:** 15,000 books; 500

microforms. **Subscriptions:** 1500 journals. **Services:** Interlibrary loan; copying; SDI; library open to the public for reference use only. **Automated Operations:** Computerized public access catalog, cataloging, and ILL. **Computerized Information Services:** DOBIS Canadian Online Library System, DIALOG Information Services, BRS Information Technologies, STN International, PFDS Online, UTLAS, MEDLARS, Info Globe, Infomart Online, QL Systems; Envoy 100 (electronic mail service). **Publications:** Annual report; newsletter. **Special Indexes:** HPB Publications Index. **Remarks:** FAX: (613)957-1907. Electronic mail address(es): OONHBR (Envoy 100). The Health Protection Branch Libraries are organized as a library network, with separate locations in the Laboratory Centre for Disease Control (LCDC) Building (957-1362), the Environmental Health Directorate Building (957-1725), the Sir Frederick G. Banting Research Centre (957-1022), the Federal Centre for AIDS (954-3256) all on Tunney's Pasture, and the Drug Library at Place Vanier (954-8669). **Also Known As:** Sante et Bien-Etre Social Canada. **Staff:** Terry Chernis, Mgr., Banting Lib.; Carol-Anne O'Brien, Env. Health; Elizabeth Aitken, LCDC.

★2751★
Canada - Health and Welfare Canada - Health Protection Branch - Regional Library (Food-Bev)
3155 Willingdon Green Phone: (604)666-3147
Burnaby, BC, Canada V5G 4P2 Elizabeth Hardacre, Libn.
Founded: 1964. **Staff:** 1. **Subjects:** Food inspection and analysis, microbiology, pesticides, pharmaceuticals, illicit drug analysis. **Holdings:** 2500 books; 1000 bound periodical volumes. **Subscriptions:** 100 journals and other serials. **Services:** Interlibrary loan; copying; library open to the public by permission only. **Computerized Information Services:** DIALOG Information Services. **Remarks:** FAX: (604)666-3149.

★2752★
Canada - Health and Welfare Canada - Health Protection Branch - Regional Library (Food-Bev, Sci-Engr)
2301 Midland Ave. Phone: (604)666-3350
Scarborough, ON, Canada M1P 4R7 S. Brockhurst, Lib.Techn.
Staff: 1. **Subjects:** Food analysis, food and drug legislation, microbiology, chemistry, pharmacology, toxicology, cosmetics, pesticides, narcotics. **Holdings:** 2500 books; 212 bound periodical volumes. **Subscriptions:** 97 journals and other serials. **Services:** Library open to the public for reference use only. **Formerly:** Located in Scarborough, ON.

★2753★
Canada - Health and Welfare Canada - Health Protection Branch - Regional Library (Food-Bev, Sci-Engr)
1001, Blvd. St. Laurent, W., Ch. 345 Phone: (514)646-1353
Longueuil, PQ, Canada J4K 1C7 France Lachapelle, Libn.
Founded: 1971. **Staff:** 1. **Subjects:** Food and drugs, organic chemistry, forensic chemistry, nutrition, medical devices, pesticides, pharmacology, cosmetics, microbiology. **Holdings:** 2100 books; 600 bound periodical volumes; 3500 pamphlets and other cataloged items. **Subscriptions:** 150 journals and other serials. **Services:** Interlibrary loan; copying; library open to the public by appointment. **Automated Operations:** Computerized cataloging and serials. **Remarks:** FAX: (514)928-4102.

★2754★
Canada - Health and Welfare Canada - Policy, Planning & Information Branch - Library
Brooke Claxton Bldg., 2nd Fl. N
Tunney's Pasture
Ottawa, ON, Canada K1A 0K9
Defunct. Merged with Health Services and Promotion Information Network to form Canada - Health and Welfare Canada - Departmental Library.

★2755★
Canada - Immigration Refugee Board - Documentation Center (Law)
240 Bank St. Phone: (613)996-0741
Ottawa, ON, Canada K1A 0K1 Barbara Camfield, Rsrc.Ctr.Coord.
Founded: 1988. **Staff:** 4. **Subjects:** Human rights, immigration, refugees. **Holdings:** 2200 books. **Subscriptions:** 200 journals and other serials; 26 newspapers. **Services:** Center open to the public for reference use only. **Computerized Information Services:** DOBIS Canadian Online Library System, DIALOG Information Services, NEXIS, LEXIS, Questel; internal databases. **Remarks:** FAX: (613)954-1228.

★2756★
Canada - Indian & Northern Affairs Canada - Departmental Library (Area-Ethnic, Hist)
Ottawa, ON, Canada K1A 0H4 Phone: (819)997-0811
Sue Hanley, Dept.Libn.
Founded: 1966. **Staff:** Prof 8; Other 5. **Subjects:** Native lands, revenues, trusts, economic development, and self-government; Canadian North; Canadian history and exploration; Indian and Inuit culture, education, and housing. **Special Collections:** Arctic and rare book collection. **Holdings:** 51,000 titles in 200,000 volumes; 20,000 bound periodical volumes; 3500 special government documents; 3000 reels of microfilm; 15 drawers of microfiche; Canadian native and northern newspapers. **Subscriptions:** 1200 journals and other serials; 20 newspapers. **Services:** Interlibrary loan; copying; SDI; library open to the public for reference use only. **Automated Operations:** VTLS. **Computerized Information Services:** DIALOG Information Services, QL Systems, Info Globe, Infomart Online, UTLAS, CAN/OLE, DOBIS Canadian Online Library System, SDM, Inc., CAN/LAW; Envoy 100 (electronic mail service). **Publications:** Accessions List, monthly; brochure; Native and Northern Periodical List; bibliographies. **Remarks:** Library located at Terrasses de la Chaudiere, Hull, PQ. FAX: (819)953-5491; (819)997-0514; (819)997-1587. Telex: 053-3711. Electronic mail address(es): INA.ILL (Envoy 100). **Staff:** Dan Denault, Mgr., Tech.Serv.; Julia Finn, Mgr., Client Serv.

★2757★
Canada - Indian & Northern Affairs Canada - Regional Library (Area-Ethnic)
1100-275 Portage Ave., 8th Fl. Phone: (204)983-4928
Winnipeg, MB, Canada R3B 3A3 Sandi Krynski, Libn.
Founded: 1980. **Staff:** 1. **Subjects:** Indian history and issues. **Special Collections:** Newspaper clipping files by subject, issues and band names. **Holdings:** 2000 books; government documents. **Subscriptions:** 10 newspapers. **Services:** Interlibrary loan; copying; library open to the public; inquiries accepted in writing. **Special Catalogs:** Audio-visual catalog. **Remarks:** FAX: (204)983-7820. **Also Known As:** Department of Indian & Northern Development.

★2758★
Canada - Indian & Northern Affairs Canada - Technical Library (Sci-Engr, Env-Cons)
P.O. Box 1500 Phone: (403)920-8144
Yellowknife, NT, Canada X1A 2R3 Donald Albright, Reg.Libn.
Founded: 1973. **Staff:** Prof 1; Other 1. **Subjects:** Earth and environmental sciences. **Special Collections:** Geology theses of the Northwest Territories (200); Cold Regions Research & Engineering Laboratory (CRREL) Publications (400). **Holdings:** 15,000 books; 700 bound periodical volumes; 2000 government documents; 90 reels of microfilm; 75 microfiche sets; 50 sheet maps; 730 boxes of unbound periodicals. **Subscriptions:** 300 journals and other serials; 15 newspapers. **Services:** Interlibrary loan; copying; library open to the public. **Computerized Information Services:** CAN/OLE; CD-ROMs (Microlog: Canadian Research Index, CD-ROM BiblioDisc, WLN LaserCat, PolarPac). **Publications:** Recent Acquisitions, irregular; I.N.A.C. Technical Library is People and Service and You (pamphlet). **Remarks:** Library is located at 4914 50th St., Bellanca Bldg., Yellowknife, NT. Alternate telephone number(s): 920-8252. FAX: (403)873-5763.

★2759★
Canada - Labour Canada - Central Region Resource Centre (Bus-Fin)
MacDonald Bldg., Rm. 400
344 Edmonton St. Phone: (204)983-7229
Winnipeg, MB, Canada R3B 2Y1 Janice Forzley, Tech.Svcs.Asst.
Founded: 1980. **Staff:** 1. **Subjects:** Occupational safety, labor legislation, equal pay. **Holdings:** 2005 volumes; 50 pamphlets; 32 video cassettes; 39 slide sets; 10 transparencies; 29 file boxes of adjudication decisions; 69 legal opinion binders. **Subscriptions:** 20 journals and other serials. **Services:** Copying; center open to the public with restrictions. **Publications:** Library Bulletin, weekly - for internal distribution only. **Remarks:** FAX: (204)983-2117.

★2760★
Canada - Labour Canada - Library Services (Bus-Fin)
Ottawa, ON, Canada K1A 0J2 Phone: (819)997-3540
Leslie Hamel, Chf.Libn.
Founded: 1900. **Staff:** Prof 9; Other 6. **Subjects:** Industrial relations, unions, working women, occupational safety and health, fair employment practices,

employment relationships. **Special Collections:** Canadian labor history; labor union newspapers and proceedings; international labor publications. **Holdings:** 200,000 books; 10,000 bound periodical volumes; 1600 reels of microfilm of American and Canadian labor union newspapers. **Subscriptions:** 1200 journals and other serials; 100 newspapers. **Services:** Interlibrary loan; copying; SDI; library open to the public for reference use only. **Automated Operations:** Computerized cataloging and acquisitions. **Computerized Information Services:** PFDS Online, DIALOG Information Services, BRS Information Technologies, CAN/OLE, Informart, Info Globe, QL Systems; LABORLINE (internal database); Envoy 100 (electronic mail service). Performs searches free of charge for internal database. **Publications:** Library Bulletin; Laborline Thesaurus, irregular. **Special Indexes:** Periodicals index, 1970-1981. **Remarks:** Alternate telephone number(s): 997-3541. FAX: (819)997-1664. Telex: 819 997 3453. Electronic mail address(es): OOL.ILL (Envoy 100). **Also Known As:** Travail Canada. **Staff:** H. Apouchtine, Hd. Client Serv.; J. Cameron, Hd.Tech.Serv.

★2761★
Canada - Labour Canada - Library Services - Occupational Safety and Health Reference Centre (Med, Sci-Engr)
Ottawa, ON, Canada K1A 0J2 Phone: (819)997-8458
Helen Apouchtine, Hd. of Client Serv.
Founded: 1967. **Staff:** Prof 1; Other 1. **Subjects:** Occupational safety and health, industrial hygiene, safety engineering, ergonomics, fire prevention and protection. **Special Collections:** Standards; occupational safety and health legislations. **Holdings:** 10,000 books; standards; VF; material safety data sheets. **Subscriptions:** 250 journals and other serials. **Services:** Interlibrary loan; copying; SDI; center open to the public. **Automated Operations:** Computerized cataloging. **Computerized Information Services:** DIALOG Information Services, BRS Information Technologies, MEDLARS, Infomart Online, QL Systems, Questel, CAN/OLE, Canadian Centre for Occupational Health & Safety; LABORLINE (internal database). Performs searches free of charge on LABORLINE. **Networks/Consortia:** Member of PB Quill, FEDLINK. **Publications:** Occupational Safety and Health - A Bibliography (updated periodically); Library Bulletin. **Special Indexes:** Index of Canadian periodicals in OSH field. **Remarks:** Centre located at 165 Hotel de Ville, Hull, PQ. FAX: (819)997-1664. Telex: 0533664. **Staff:** Nicole Boodreault, Cat.Techn.

★2762★
Canada - Labour Relations Board - Research and Reference Centre (Law, Bus-Fin)
C.D. Howe Bldg., 4th Fl. West
240 Sparks St. Phone: (613)996-9466
Ottawa, ON, Canada K1A 0X8 Gloria R. Anderson, Dir.
Founded: 1973. **Staff:** Prof 2; Other 2. **Subjects:** Labor law, collective bargaining, labor relations. **Holdings:** 4000 monographs. **Subscriptions:** 550 journals and other serials; 10 newspapers. **Services:** Interlibrary loan; copying; SDI; library open to the public for reference use only. **Computerized Information Services:** DIALOG Information Services, Info Globe, Infomart Online, DOBIS Canadian Online Library System, The Financial Post DataGroup, WILSONLINE, CAN/LAW, CAN/OLE, INFODEX, STM Systems Corporation, QL Systems; internal database; Envoy 100 (electronic mail service). **Publications:** Library bulletin, quarterly; Recent Acquisitions, monthly. **Remarks:** FAX: (613)995-9493. Electronic mail address(es): ILL.OOLRB (Envoy 100). **Also Known As:** Conseil Canadien des Relations du Travail. **Staff:** Joy Patel, Dp.Dir.

★2763★
Canada - Law Reform Commission of Canada - Library (Law)
130 Albert St., Rm. 809 Phone: (613)995-8648
Ottawa, ON, Canada K1A 0L6 Judith Rubin, Libn.
Founded: 1972. **Staff:** Prof 1; Other 2. **Subjects:** Law - criminal, administrative, health. **Special Collections:** Reports, study papers, and research papers from other Law Reform Commissions. **Holdings:** 3650 books; 5532 bound periodical volumes; 560 other cataloged items. **Subscriptions:** 306 journals and other serials; 5 newspapers. **Services:** Interlibrary loan. **Computerized Information Services:** DIALOG Information Services, QL Systems, WESTLAW, LEXIS, DOBIS Canadian Online Library System, CAN/LAW; Envoy 100 (electronic mail service). **Remarks:** FAX: (613)996-8599. Electronic mail address(es): CBANET (Envoy 100). **Also Known As:** Canada - Commission de Reforme du Droit.

★2764★
Canada - Library of Parliament (Hist, Law)
Parliament Bldgs. Phone: (613)992-3122
Ottawa, ON, Canada K1A 0A9 Erik J. Spicer, Parliamentary Libn.
Founded: 1867. **Staff:** Prof 122; Other 127. **Subjects:** Parliamentary history and procedure, government and politics, foreign affairs, economics and finance, law, history, social welfare, Canadiana. **Special Collections:** United Kingdom parliamentary papers (3322 linear feet); U.S. Congressional publications (2781 linear feet); U.N. depository items (French and English; 2844 linear feet); Australia and New Zealand federal parliamentary publications (382 linear feet); Canadian political pamphlets. **Holdings:** 641,000 books and bound periodical volumes; 539,194 microforms; 8609 files of clippings; 10,348 unpublished research reports; 4650 video and audio cassettes; Library of Parliament/National Archives of Canada oral history interview project. **Subscriptions:** 2640 periodicals; 603 newspapers. **Services:** Interlibrary loan; copying; library open to the public for reference use only. **Automated Operations:** Computerized cataloging, acquisitions, and indexing. **Computerized Information Services:** CAN/SDI, WILSONLINE, iNET 2000, CAN/LAW, Dun & Bradstreet Business Credit Services, CANSIM, Infomart Online, CAN/OLE, DIALOG Information Services, QL Systems, Info Globe, DOBIS Canadian Online Library System, REUTERS, VU/TEXT Information Services, FT PROFILE, UTLAS, OCLC, WESTLAW, BRS Information Technologies, Dow Jones News/Retrieval, Questel, STM Systems Corporation, LEXIS, NEXIS; MINISIS, NIL (internal databases). **Publications:** Articles, weekly; Library of Parliament Guide to Services (revised as required); Periodicals and Newspapers in the Collections of the Library of Parliament; Annual Report of the Parliamentary Librarian; Current Issue Reviews, updated monthly; background papers; legislative summaries; Quorum, daily during session; bibliographies and selected compilations - all distributed to Senators, Members of Parliament, and interested libraries. **Special Indexes:** Indexes to Proceedings of Senate Committees, sessional (published by Supply and Services); index to boards, commissions, task forces, and councils; clipping file subject headings; index to ministers' speeches. **Remarks:** Alternate telephone number(s): 995-1166. FAX: (613)992-1269. Maintains 3 branch libraries and 2 reading rooms in the parliamentary precinct; participates in joint conservation projects with Canadian Conservation Institute and National Library of Canada. **Staff:** Richard Pare, Assoc. Parliamentary Libn.; M. Montgomery, Dir., Info. & Tech.Serv.Br.; Hugh Finsten, Dir., Res.Br.; J.J. Cardinal, Dir., Adm. & Personnel Br.

Canada - Ministere de l'Agriculture
See: **Canada - Agriculture Canada** (2631)

Canada - Ministere de l'Energie, des Mines et des Ressources
See: **Canada - Energy, Mines & Resources Canada** (2700)

Canada - Ministere de l'Environnement
See: **Canada - Environment Canada** (2703)

Canada - Ministere des Finances
See: **Canada - Department of Finance** (2685)

Canada - Ministere de la Justice
See: **Canada - Department of Justice** (2691)

Canada - Ministere du Revenu National
See: **Canada - Revenue Canada** (2841)

Canada - Ministere du Solliciteur General
See: **Canada - Solicitor General Canada** (2849)

★2765★
Canada - Mortgage and Housing Corporation - Canadian Housing Information Centre (Soc Sci, Plan)
700 Montreal Rd. Phone: (613)748-2362
Ottawa, ON, Canada K1A 0P7 Leslie Jones, Mgr.
Founded: 1946. **Staff:** Prof 5; Other 8. **Subjects:** Housing, urban planning, community development, energy conservation, mortgages, residential

rehabilitation. **Special Collections:** Municipal information and maps (6000 items); collection of slides and photographs of housing (100,000). **Holdings:** 70,000 books; 10,000 bound periodical volumes; 1000 vertical files; 6000 microfiche; 2000 maps; 2000 external research reports. **Subscriptions:** 1500 journals and other serials; 7 newspapers. **Services:** Interlibrary loan; copying; center open to the public for reference use only. **Automated Operations:** Computerized cataloging. **Computerized Information Services:** DIALOG Information Services, PFDS Online, BRS Information Technologies, Info Globe, CAN/OLE, QL Systems, Prima Telematic Inc., DOBIS Canadian Online Library System, Questel, ESA/IRS, Infomart Online; Airbase (internal database); GEMDES (electronic mail service). **Publications:** Acquisitions list, monthly; Recent Research Funded by CMHC, quarterly; Serials List, annual; Compendium of Research, annual; bibliographies on housing topics (150 titles). **Special Indexes:** Canadian housing index (book). **Remarks:** FAX: (613)748-4069. **Also Known As:** Societe Canadienne d'Hypotheques et de Logement. **Staff:** Deanna MacDonald, Chf., Ref.Serv.

★2766★
Canada - National Archives of Canada - Archival Community Program Division - Canadian Postal Archives Library (Rec, Hist)
365 Laurier Ave., W. Phone: (613)992-9350
Ottawa, ON, Canada K1A 0N3 Balvinder Kahlon, Lib. & Ref.Cons.
Founded: 1977. **Staff:** Prof 1; Other 1. **Subjects:** Philately, postal history. **Special Collections:** Canadian photographic postal history; Universal Postal Union Book Collection. **Holdings:** 9000 volumes; 2400 bound periodical volumes; archival materials; microfilm. **Subscriptions:** 250 journals and other serials. **Services:** Interlibrary loan; copying; library open to the public. **Automated Operations:** Computerized cataloging. **Computerized Information Services:** UTLAS. **Remarks:** FAX: (613)992-3744.

★2767★
Canada - National Archives of Canada - Cartographic & Architectural Archives Division
395 Wellington St.
Ottawa, ON, Canada K1A 0N3
Defunct. Merged with National Archives of Canada - Moving Image & Sound Archives to form National Archives of Canada - Cartographic & Audio-Visual Archives Division.

★2768★
Canada - National Archives of Canada - Cartographic & Audio-Visual Archives Division (Aud-Vis, Plan, Geog-Map)
395 Wellington St. Phone: (613)995-1311
Ottawa, ON, Canada K1A 0N3 Betty Kidd, Dir.
Staff: Prof 22; Other 20. **Subjects:** History cartography of Canada; current mapping Canada; foreign current mapping; architecture; engineering; film; television; recorded sound. **Special Collections:** National Architectural Archives; Atlantic Neptune; rare atlases; private cartographic collections; government cartographic, architectural, and engineering records; holdings of the National Film Board and Canadian Broadcasting Corporation; Crawley Collection. **Holdings:** 2 million maps, plans, charts, atlases, globes; 53,000 hours of film; 106,000 hours of television programs; and other sound recordings; still photographs; architectural drawings; engineering plans; records; files. **Subscriptions:** 343 journals and other serials. **Services:** Interlibrary loan; copying; collections open for research. **Computerized Information Services:** UTLAS; internal databases; Envoy 100 (electronic mail service). **Publications:** Departmental annual report; Film/Video Canadiana; Carto-Canadiana; Beyond the Printed Word; Documents that Move and Speak; various publications - list available on request. **Remarks:** FAX: (613)995-4451 (Cartographic sector); (613)995-6575 (AV sector). Telex: 953 3367. Alternate telephone number(s): (613)995-6575 (AV sector). Electronic mail address(es): NAPPB (Envoy 100). TAV sector located at 344 Wellington St. Contains holdings of the former Canada - National Archives of Canada - Moving Image & Sound Archives and Canada - National Archives of Canada - Cartographic & Architectural Archives Division. **Staff:** Louis Cardinal, Chf., Coll.Sect.; Velma Parker, Asst.Chf., Pub.Serv.Description Sect.; Tom Nagy, Asst.Chf., Coll.Mgmt.Sect.; David Brown, Mgr., Geomatics Prog.; Ed Dahl, Early Cart.Spec.; Jana Vosikovska, Asst.Chf., Coll.Sect.; Andris Kesteris, Asst.Chf., Pub.Serv. Description Sect.

★2769★
Canada - National Archives of Canada - Documentary Art and Photography Division (Aud-Vis)
395 Wellington St. Phone: (613)992-3884
Ottawa, ON, Canada K1A 0N3 Lilly Koltun, Dir.
Founded: 1986. **Staff:** Prof 28; Other 16. **Subjects:** Canadian history, history of photography, documentary art, philately, caricature. **Holdings:** 15 million photographs; 250,000 works of art; 800,000 philatelic items. **Services:** Copying; collection open to the public. **Automated Operations:** Computerized cataloging. **Computerized Information Services:** Internal database. **Publications:** Guide to Canadian Photographic Archives (book). **Special Catalogs:** Visual catalog (card); ArchiVISTA optical catalog of cartoons (images and descriptions). **Remarks:** FAX: (613)995-6226. Division includes the Canadian Postal Archives as well as the Canadian Museum of Caricature.

★2770★
Canada - National Archives of Canada - Government Archives Division (Hist)
395 Wellington St. Phone: (613)996-8507
Ottawa, ON, Canada K1A 0N3 Eldon Frost, Dir.
Founded: 1986. **Staff:** Prof 40; Other 46. **Subjects:** Activities of the Government of Canada, 1750-1991. **Holdings:** 57 kilometers of records; 20,000 reels of microfilm; 4000 machine-readable data files. **Services:** Interlibrary loan (microfilm only); copying; archives open to the public with restrictions on some material. **Publications:** Inventories (updated as required). **Remarks:** FAX: (613)995-6217. **Staff:** J.W. O'Brien, Chf., State & Mil.Rec.; T. Cook, Chf., Soc. & Nat.Res.Rec.; W. McMahon, Chf., Access Sect.

★2771★
Canada - National Archives of Canada - Manuscript Division (Hist)
395 Wellington St. Phone: (613)996-8498
Ottawa, ON, Canada K1A 0N3 Harold Naugler, Dir.
Founded: 1872. **Staff:** Prof 41; Other 17. **Subjects:** Canadian and allied North American and European history. **Holdings:** 66 million documents; 25,000 reels of microfilm. **Services:** Interinstitutional loan (microfilm only); copying; research rooms open to the public with restrictions on certain material. **Publications:** General Inventory Series (microfiche); Finding Aids (microfiche and print); Literary Archives Guide (1988); Archival Sources for the Study of Finnish Canadians (1989); Archival Sources for the Study of German Language Groups in Canada (1989); Archival Sources for the Study of Canadian Jewry (1987); A Guide to Sources for the Study of Ukrainian Candians (1984); Archival Sources for the Study of Polish Canadians (1987); Women's Archives Guide (1991); Labour History Guide; Guide to Documentation in Great Britain and Eire Relating to Canada. **Special Catalogs:** Main Entry Catalogue (microfiche). **Remarks:** FAX: (613)943-8112. **Staff:** Peter DeLottinville, Political Archv.Serv.; Judi Cumming, Pub.Archv.Serv.; Charles MacKinnon, Canadian Soc.Archv.Serv.; Paul Fortier, Cons. & Sys.Mgt.Serv.

★2772★
Canada - National Archives of Canada - Moving Image & Sound Archives
395 Wellington St.
Ottawa, ON, Canada K1A 0N3
Defunct. Merged with National Archives of Canada - Cartographic & Architectural Archives Division to form National Archives of Canada - Cartographic & Audio-Visual Archives Division.

★2773★
Canada - National Aviation Museum - Library (Sci-Engr)
PO Box 9724
Ottawa Terminal Phone: (613)993-2303
Ottawa, ON, Canada K1G 5A3 John Barton, Libn.
Founded: 1987. **Staff:** 2. **Subjects:** Aviation. **Holdings:** 4000 books; 4000 bound periodical volumes; 4500 aeronautical technical manuals. **Subscriptions:** 150 journals and other serials; 2 newspapers. **Services:** Interlibrary loan; copying; library open to the public by appointment. **Automated Operations:** Computerized public access catalog. **Remarks:** FAX: (613)990-3655.

★2774★
Canada - National Capital Commission - Library (Plan)
161 Laurier Ave., W., 6th Fl. Phone: (613)239-5123
Ottawa, ON, Canada K1P 6J6 Gwyneth Hughes, Libn.
Staff: 2. **Subjects:** Urban planning. **Holdings:** Figures not available. **Subscriptions:** 200 journals and other serials; 5 newspapers. **Services:** Interlibrary loan; library open to the public. **Computerized Information Services:** DOBIS Canadian Online Library System. **Remarks:** FAX: (613)239-5274.

★2775★
Canada - National Defence - Air Technical Library (Mil, Sci-Engr)
Bldg. 155W, CFB Ottawa (N) Phone: (613)993-2105
Ottawa, ON, Canada K1A 0K2 L. McKim, Hd., NDLRS
Founded: 1952. **Staff:** 3. **Subjects:** Engineering - aircraft, electrical; aircraft structural engineering; computers - languages, programming; logistics. **Special Collections:** Canadian Forces Technical Orders; federal supply catalogs; Canadian Forces publications; Canadian Forces Catalog of Materiel; U.S. Air Force Technical Orders (140,000 items total). **Holdings:** 7500 books. **Subscriptions:** 100 journals and other serials. **Services:** Interlibrary loan; copying; library open to those who establish a need-to-know, with restrictions on classified material. **Computerized Information Services:** DOBIS Canadian Online Library System; Envoy 100 (electronic mail service).

★2776★
Canada - National Defence - Athabasca Library (Educ)
Box 1430 Phone: (403)594-8990
Medley, AB, Canada T0A 2M0 Kevan Rhead, Hd.Libn.
Founded: 1970. **Staff:** Prof 2; Other 1. **Subjects:** Curriculum for K-9 English and French. **Holdings:** 30,000 books; 100 bound periodical volumes; pamphlets and nonprint materials. **Subscriptions:** 114 journals and other serials.

★2777★
Canada - National Defence - Cambridge Military Library (Mil)
Royal Artillery Park
1565 Queen St. Phone: (902)427-7193
Halifax, NS, Canada B3J 2H9 MCpl D.L. Egan, Libn./Cust.
Staff: Prof 1. **Subjects:** Military history, biography, art, and science; strategy; 19th century travel; naval history. **Special Collections:** Corfu Collection. **Holdings:** 15,000 books; 500 bound periodical volumes. **Subscriptions:** 20 journals and other serials. **Services:** Interlibrary loan; library open to the public for reference use only. **Remarks:** Library evolved from an officers' reading room established in 1817.

★2778★
Canada - National Defence - Canadian Forces Base Halifax - Maritime Command Reference Library (Mil)
Halifax, NS, Canada B3K 2X0 Phone: (902)427-8398
S. Barron, Base Libn.
Remarks: No further information was supplied by respondent.

★2779★
Canada - National Defence - Canadian Forces College - Keith Hodson Memorial Library (Mil, Soc Sci)
215 Yonge Blvd. Phone: (416)482-6846
Toronto, ON, Canada M5M 3H9 Cathy Murphy, Chf.Libn.
Staff: Prof 4; Other 3. **Subjects:** Military and naval arts and sciences, international relations, social sciences. **Holdings:** 35,000 books; 2000 bound periodical volumes; 2500 government documents; 2500 reels of microfilm. **Subscriptions:** 250 journals and other serials. **Services:** Library not open to the public. **Computerized Information Services:** QL Systems, Info Globe, DIALOG Information Services, CAN/OLE, UTLAS. **Remarks:** Includes the holdings of the Canadian Forces College - Staff School Library.

★2780★
Canada - National Defence - Chief Construction and Properties Library
101 Colonel By Drive
8th North Tower
Ottawa, ON, Canada K1A 0K2
Defunct.

Canada - National Defence - College Militaire Royal de St-Jean
See: **College Militaire Royal de St-Jean** (3898)

★2781★
Canada - National Defence - Communications and Electronics Engineering Library (Comp Sci)
Canadian Bldg., 14th Fl.
219 Laurier Ave., W. Phone: (613)996-6296
Ottawa, ON, Canada K1A 0K2 M. Levesque, Hd.
Staff: 3. **Subjects:** Computers, computer programming, electronics, data processing. **Holdings:** 5500 books; 1000 technical reports. **Subscriptions:** 135 journals and other serials. **Services:** Interlibrary loan; library not open to the public. **Computerized Information Services:** DOBIS Canadian Online Library System; Envoy 100 (electronic mail service).

Canada - National Defence - Defence and Civil Institute of Environmental Medicine
See: **Canada - Defence and Civil Institute of Environmental Medicine** (2679)

Canada - National Defence - Defence Research Establishment
See: **Canada - Defence Research Establishment** (2680)

★2782★
Canada - National Defence - Directorate of History - Library (Mil, Hist)
2429 Holly Ln. Phone: (613)998-7062
Ottawa, ON, Canada K1A 0K2 R. Laurin, Hd.
Founded: 1919. **Staff:** 1. **Subjects:** History of Canadian Armed Forces, military history of Canada, military science, naval history, aircraft technology. **Special Collections:** Document collection; pamphlet collection; biographical files; map collection. **Holdings:** 10,000 books; 2800 bound periodical volumes. **Subscriptions:** 108 journals and other serials. **Services:** Interlibrary loan; copying; library not open to the public. **Computerized Information Services:** DOBIS Canadian Online Library System; internal database; Envoy 100 (electronic mail service). **Also Known As:** Canada - Defense Nationale - Service Historique.

★2783★
Canada - National Defence - Fort Frontenac Library (Mil)
Fort Frontenac Phone: (613)541-5829
Kingston, ON, Canada K7K 5L0 Serge Campion, Chf.Libn.
Founded: 1947. **Staff:** Prof 3; Other 5. **Subjects:** Military art and science, international relations, political and economic sciences, sociology. **Special Collections:** Military Strategy and World Politics. **Holdings:** 95,000 books; 2994 bound periodical volumes; 24 VF drawers. **Subscriptions:** 400 journals and other serials; 25 newspapers. **Services:** Interlibrary loan; copying; SDI; library open to the public by written request. **Automated Operations:** Computerized public access catalog, cataloging, serials, and circulation. **Computerized Information Services:** DIALOG Information Services, iNET 2000; iNET 2000 (electronic mail service). Performs searches free of charge. **Publications:** New acquisitions. **Remarks:** Alternate telephone number(s): 541-5815. FAX: (613)546-0589. Electronic mail address(es): CAMPION.SERGE.G (iNET 2000). Fort Frontenac Library serves the National Defence College of Canada and Canadian Land Forces Command and Staff College. **Staff:** David Willis, Hd., Tech.Serv.; Glenyss Turner, Hd., Rd.Adv.Serv.

★2784★
Canada - National Defence - Judge Advocate General Library (Law)
Constitution Bldg., 11th Fl.
305 Rideau St. Phone: (613)992-2613
Ottawa, ON, Canada K1A 0K2 William Nesbitt, Chf., JAG Lib.
Founded: 1950. **Staff:** 2. **Subjects:** Law - general, military, international. **Special Collections:** Regulations and Orders - Canadian Army, Air Force, and Navy and Canadian Forces since integration. **Holdings:** 7000 volumes; House of Commons Debates, 1939 to present; Statutes of Canada since confederation, 1867 to present; Federal Statutory Orders and Regulations, 1955 to present. **Subscriptions:** 40 journals and other serials. **Services:** Library open to the public for reference use only. **Computerized Information Services:** CAN/LAW, WESTLAW, QL Systems, DOBIS Canadian Online Library System; Envoy 100 (electronic mail service). **Publications:** Canada Court Martial Appeal Reports, Volumes I, II, III and Part I of Volume IV with current service updates.

★2785★
Canada - National Defence - Land Technical Library (Mil)
Louis St. Laurent Bldg., 3rd Fl.
555, blvd. de la Carriere Phone: (613)997-9573
Hull, PQ, Canada K1A 0K2 H. Blouin, Hd.
Staff: 2. **Subjects:** Military vehicles, clothing, equipment, general stores; artillery and weapons; communications and electronics. **Holdings:** 2200 books; 15,000 technical reports. **Subscriptions:** 90 journals and other serials. **Services:** Interlibrary loan; library not open to the public. **Computerized Information Services:** DOBIS Canadian Online Library System; Envoy 100 (electronic mail service).

★2786★
Canada - National Defence - Maritime Technical Library/NDR LS 3-5 (Mil, Sci-Engr)
Louis St. Laurent Bldg., 3rd Fl.
555, blvd. de la Carriere Phone: (613)994-9200
Hull, PQ, Canada K1A 0K2 D. Shaver, Hd.
Staff: 2. **Subjects:** Naval architecture, ship maintenance, undersea engineering and detection. **Holdings:** 1900 books; 7000 technical reports. **Subscriptions:** 62 journals and other serials. **Services:** Interlibrary loan; library not open to the public. **Computerized Information Services:** DOBIS Canadian Online Library System; Envoy 100 (electronic mail service).

★2787★
Canada - National Defence - Mobile Command HQ Library (Mil)
St. Hubert, PQ, Canada J3Y 5T5 Phone: (514)462-7242
Mary Finlay, Chf.Libn.
Staff: Prof 1; Other 1. **Subjects:** Military science. **Holdings:** 10,000 volumes. **Subscriptions:** 100 journals and other serials. **Services:** Interlibrary loan; library not open to the public. **Computerized Information Services:** Envoy 100 (electronic mail service). **Publications:** Accession list, irregular. **Remarks:** Electronic mail address(es): PEB.QSTHUM (Envoy 100).

★2788★
Canada - National Defence - National Defence Medical Centre - Medical Library (Med)
Alta Vista Dr. Phone: (613)738-5211
Ottawa, ON, Canada K1A 0K6 Philip B. Allan, Chf.Med.Libn.
Founded: 1961. **Staff:** Prof 1; Other 1. **Subjects:** Medicine, nursing. **Special Collections:** Military medical history (500 volumes). **Holdings:** 4200 books; 9800 bound periodical volumes; 1250 video and audio cassettes. **Subscriptions:** 295 journals and other serials. **Services:** Interlibrary loan; copying; library open to the public with restrictions. **Computerized Information Services:** MEDLARS. **Remarks:** FAX: (613)993-7719.

★2789★
Canada - National Defence - Northern Region Headquarters Library (Mil, Area-Ethnic)
Evans Block
P.O. Box 6666 Phone: (403)873-4011
Yellowknife, NT, Canada X1A 2R3 Tony Sunderland, Lib.Ck.
Founded: 1970. **Staff:** 1. **Subjects:** Exploration, expeditions, Northern travel, native peoples, sociology, Northern reference, military history, geography. **Holdings:** 1000 volumes; 350 magazines; 800 reports. **Subscriptions:** 40 journals and other serials; 27 newspapers. **Services:** Interlibrary loan; copying; library open to the public with restrictions. **Remarks:** Library is a backup for Northern Region Operation Information Service.

★2790★
Canada - National Defence - Perkes Library (Mil)
101 Colonel By Drive, 2 North Tower Phone: (613)996-0831
Ottawa, ON, Canada K1A 0K2 Martine Patriarcky, Dept.Libn.
Founded: 1903. **Staff:** Prof 8; Other 27. **Subjects:** Military art and science, disarmament and peacekeeping, naval science, aeronautics, political science, management, computer science. **Special Collections:** Charles H. Stewart Collection of Military Canadiana. **Holdings:** 105,000 books; 8000 bound periodical volumes; 1500 linear feet of government documents. **Subscriptions:** 2018 journals and other serials. **Services:** Interlibrary loan; copying; library open to members of other federal government libraries. **Automated Operations:** Computerized cataloging. **Computerized Information Services:** UTLAS; Envoy 100 (electronic mail service). **Remarks:** FAX: (613)995-8176. **Also Known As:** Canada - Defense Nationale. **Staff:** M. Meechan, Hd., Rd.Serv.Sect.; J. Cameron, Hd., Branch Libs.; A. Civan, Hd., Cat.; B. Grier, Hd., Acq.; P. Greig, Hd., Coll.Dev.

Canada - National Defence - Royal Canadian Ordnance Corps Museum
See: **(Royal Canadian) Ordnance Corps Museum** (14110)

Canada - National Defence - Royal Military College of Canada
See: **Royal Military College of Canada** (14123)

Canada - National Defence - Royal Roads Military College
See: **Royal Roads Military College** (14132)

★2791★
Canada - National Energy Board - Library (Energy)
311 6th Ave., S.W. Phone: (403)299-3561
Calgary, AB, Canada T2P 3H2 Helen T. Booth, Chf.
Founded: 1959. **Staff:** Prof 2; Other 4. **Subjects:** Energy - technology, economics, policy, regulation; petroleum and natural gas pipeline technology; electric utilities. **Special Collections:** NEB Hearing Documents (10,000). **Holdings:** 7000 books. **Subscriptions:** 400 journals and other serials; 8 newspapers. **Services:** Interlibrary loan; copying; library open to the public. **Automated Operations:** Computerized public access catalog, cataloging, acquisitions, serials, and circulation. **Computerized Information Services:** CAN/OLE, Infomart Online, Info Globe, DIALOG Information Services, QL Systems, PFDS Online, CAN/SDI; CAN/OLE (electronic mail service). **Publications:** Library Accession List, monthly; Current Periodicals List, irregular. **Remarks:** FAX: (403)292-5503. **Formerly:** Located in Ottawa, ON. **Also Known As:** Canada - Office National de l'Energie.

★2792★
Canada - National Farm Products Marketing Council - Library (Agri)
270 Albert St., 13th Fl.
PO Box 3430, Sta. D Phone: (613)995-6752
Ottawa, ON, Canada K1P 6L4 Crystal Babey, Libn.
Subjects: Agriculture. **Special Collections:** Supply managed commodities. **Holdings:** 200 books; 200 reports. **Remarks:** FAX: (613)995-2097. Telex: 760-1353.

★2793★
Canada - National Film Board of Canada - Archives (Theater)
P.O. Box 6100, Sta. A Phone: (514)283-9080
Montreal, PQ, Canada H3C 3H5 Bernard Lutz, Archv.
Staff: 2. **Subjects:** National Film Board films and filmmakers. **Holdings:** 1200 cubic feet of documents. **Services:** Copying; archives open to the public by appointment for reference use only.

★2794★
Canada - National Film Board of Canada - Edmonton District Office - Film & Video Library
9700 Jasper Ave., Rm. 120
Edmonton, AB, Canada T5J 4C3
Founded: 1940. **Subjects:** Canada - the land, history, industry, native people; creative arts; literature; health and medicine; science; social science; sports and recreation. **Special Collections:** Films and videos in French and English. **Holdings:** 6200 16mm films. **Remarks:** Currently inactive.

★2795★
Canada - National Film Board of Canada - Film Library (Aud-Vis)
1251 Avenue of the Americas, 16th Fl. Phone: (212)586-5131
New York, NY 10020 Jane Gutteridge, U.S. Sales Mgr.
Staff: 4. **Subjects:** Film, video. **Holdings:** 4300 16mm films; 4300 video cassettes. **Services:** Audiovisual distributor; maintains collection of films and videotapes available for preview, rental, and sale in the United States. **Special Catalogs:** Catalog of current titles. **Remarks:** FAX: (212)575-2382. See additional listings for National Film Board of Canada under Canada - National Film Board of Canada.

★2796★
Canada - National Film Board of Canada - Film Library (Theater)
424 21st St., E. Phone: (306)975-4245
Saskatoon, SK, Canada S7K 0C2 Lucie Joyal, AV Supv.
Staff: Prof 2; Other 2. **Subjects:** Canadian studies, creative arts, social science, health and medicine, recreation. **Holdings:** 3500 films; 900 video cassettes; 20 VF drawers of information sheets. **Services:** Interlibrary loan; video rental; library open to the public. **Computerized Information Services:** FORMAT. Performs searches on fee basis.

★2797★
Canada - National Film Board of Canada - Film Preview Library (Theater)
3155 Cote de Liesse Rd. Phone: (514)283-9437
P.O. Box 6100, Sta. A Marielle D. Cartier, Libn./Hd., AV
Montreal, PQ, Canada H3C 3H5 Coll.
Founded: 1939. **Staff:** Prof 3; Other 2. **Subjects:** History, industry, health and medicine, social sciences, sports and recreation, social geography, animation. **Special Collections:** Archival films (9200); festival films (815 35mm films; 1758 16mm films); Canadian Broadcasting Corporation (CBC) films (300); Radio-Canada films (300); sponsored films (1000); films by Independent Canadian Filmmakers (150). **Holdings:** 14,217 16mm films; 5252 35mm films; 5550 3/4 and 1/2 inch videotapes. **Services:** Library not open to the public. **Computerized Information Services:** Internal database. **Remarks:** FAX: (514)283-5729. Telex: 063666. to 20: GOC 148.

★2798★
Canada - National Film Board of Canada - Film and Video Library (Theater)
245 Main St. Phone: (204)983-4131
Winnipeg, MB, Canada R3C 1A7 Roberta Boily, Sr.Libn.
Staff: Prof 1; Other 4. **Subjects:** Social issues, women's issues, health, nature and ecology, Native issues, history. **Holdings:** 3000 films; 1000 video cassettes. **Services:** Interlibrary loan; SDI; library open to the public. **Automated Operations:** Computerized cataloging, acquisitions, and circulation. **Computerized Information Services:** FORMAT. Performs searches free of charge. **Special Catalogs:** National Film Board of Canada Film and Video Catalogue (English & French; hardcopy and online). **Special Indexes:** Index of Canadian productions. **Remarks:** Alternate telephone number(s): 983-4696. FAX: (204)983-0742.

★2799★
Canada - National Film Board of Canada - Library (Aud-Vis)
100-1045 Howe St. Phone: (604)666-0716
Vancouver, BC, Canada V6Z 2B1 James Roberts, AV Lib.Supv.
Founded: 1939. **Staff:** 5. **Holdings:** 10,000 films and videotapes. **Subscriptions:** 3 journals and other serials. **Services:** Library open to the public. **Computerized Information Services:** Produces Film-Video Canadiana; Envoy 100 (electronic mail service). **Remarks:** FAX: (604)666-1569. Toll-free telephone number(s): (800)661-9867. Electronic mail address(es): Roberts.J (Envoy 100).

★2800★
Canada - National Film Board of Canada - Reference Library
5475 Spring Garden Rd.
Halifax, NS, Canada B3J 1G2
Subjects: Film, video, maritime culture, Canadian literature, photography. **Special Collections:** Notes on documentary; film studies; women in film. **Holdings:** 356 volumes; 50 internal reports and catalogs; 20 government reports. **Remarks:** FAX: (902)426-8901. Currently inactive due to fire damage.

★2801★
Canada - National Film Board of Canada - Reference Library (Theater)
P.O. Box 6100, Sta. A Phone: (514)283-9045
Montreal, PQ, Canada H3C 3H5 Rose-Aimee Todd, Hd.
Founded: 1940. **Staff:** Prof 2; Other 3. **Subjects:** Film and filmmaking, television, Canadian history, communication. **Holdings:** 15,000 books; 5000 periodicals; 36 VF drawers; 10 drawers of maps; 500 reels of microfilm; 4000 microfiche. **Subscriptions:** 900 journals and other serials. **Services:** Interlibrary loan; copying; library open to the public by appointment. **Automated Operations:** Computerized cataloging. **Computerized Information Services:** DIALOG Information Services, UTLAS, DOBIS Canadian Online Library System, Infomart Online, Info Globe; RAPIDOC (internal database); Envoy 100 (electronic mail service). **Publications:** What's New, bimonthly - for internal distribution only. **Remarks:** Library located at 3155 Cote de Liesse Rd., Montreal, PQ H4N 2N4. FAX: (514)283-5729. **Also Known As:** Canada - Office National du Film. **Staff:** Patricia Butler, Assoc.Libn.

★2802★
Canada - National Gallery of Canada - Library (Art)
380 Sussex Dr.
P.O. Box 427, Sta. A Phone: (613)990-0586
Ottawa, ON, Canada K1N 9N4 Murray Waddington, Chf.Libn.
Founded: 1918. **Staff:** 13. **Subjects:** Post-medieval Western art, Canadian art, photography. **Special Collections:** Canadiana Collection (Canadian art; 25,000 titles); Canadian art documentation (60,000 files); restoration and conservation (1000 titles); prints and drawings (8000 titles); archives (1100 linear feet). **Holdings:** 100,000 books and bound periodical volumes; 225,000 photographs and slides. **Subscriptions:** 1000 journals and other serials. **Services:** Interlibrary loan; library open to the public by appointment. **Automated Operations:** Computerized cataloging. **Computerized Information Services:** DIALOG Information Services, RLIN, UTLAS. **Special Indexes:** Artists in Canada: A Union List of Artist's Files. **Remarks:** Alternate telephone number(s): (613)990-0589 (ILL); (613)990-0587 (ILL). FAX: (613)990-9818. **Also Known As:** Musee des Beaux-arts du Canada. **Staff:** Roy Engfield, Dp.Libn.

★2803★
Canada - National Library of Canada (Info Sci)
395 Wellington St. Phone: (613)995-9481
Ottawa, ON, Canada K1A 0N4 Marianne Scott, Natl.Libn.
Founded: 1953. **Staff:** 498. **Subjects:** Canadiana, humanities, social sciences. **Special Collections:** Canadian materials (including government publications, manuscripts, newspapers, periodicals, monographs, sound recordings, educational kits); children's literature; library and information sciences; music; rare books; rare Hebraica and Judaica Collections. **Holdings:** 1.3 million volumes; 123,000 sound recordings; 4.8 million microforms; 2.8 million government documents. **Subscriptions:** 27,451 titles; 1315 newspapers (including microforms received on legal deposit). **Services:** Interlibrary loan; copying; library open to the public for reference use only. **Automated Operations:** Computerized cataloging, ILL, indexing, acquisitions, serials, and circulation. **Computerized Information Services:** BADADUQ, BRS Information Technologies, CAN/LAW, CAN/OLE, Conservation Information Network, Data-Star, DIALOG Information Services, OCLC EPIC, Dunserve II, Info Globe, Infomart Online, OCLC, FT PROFILE, QL Systems , RLIN, Questel, SDM (Services Documentaires Multimedia, Inc.), UTLAS, VU/TEXT Information Services, WILSONLINE; produces Canadian Conspectus Online, DOBIS Canadian Online Library System, MRDS (MARC Records Distribution Service), CANREG (Canadian Register of Research and Researchers in the Social Sciences); NLCATBN (Canadiana-National Library Catalogue); Envoy 100, ALANET (electronic mail services). **Publications:** Canadiana (national bibliography; print, microfiche, online); Canadian Directories, 1790-1987: Bibliography and Place-Name Index; Canadian ISBN Publisher's Directory; Canadian Subject Headings; Canadian Theses; Canadian Translations 1988; National Library News, 10/year. **Special Catalogs:** Catalogue of Publications, annual; Union List of Serials in the Social Sciences and the Humanities held by Canadian Libraries (CANUCS); Union List of Canadian Newspapers; CANUC-H (Canadian Union Catalogue of Library Materials for the Print-Disabled). **Remarks:** FAX: (613)996-7941. Telex: 053 4311. Electronic mail address(es): OONL.ILL, OONL.REF (Envoy 100); CANADA.LDC, CANADA.ORDER, CANADA.NLSCOTT (ALANET). **Also Known As:** Bibliotheque Nationale du Canada. **Staff:** Ingrid Parent, Act.Dir., Acq. & Bibliog.Serv.; Gwynneth Evans, Dir., Ext.Rel.; Louis Forget, Dir.Info.Tech.Serv.; Marc Gagnon, Dir., Adm.Serv.; Tom Delsey, Dir., Policy and Plan.; R. Blair, Act.Dir., Pub.Serv.Br.

★2804★
Canada - National Library of Canada - Canadian Book Exchange Centre (CBEC) (Hum, Sci-Engr)
85 Bentley Ave. Phone: (613)952-8902
Ottawa, ON, Canada K1A 0N4 Pierre Gamache, Act.Chf.
Founded: 1973. **Staff:** Prof 1; Other 9. **Subjects:** Social sciences, humanities, science, technology, medicine, Canadian history and literature. **Holdings:** 150,000 books; 2.2 million periodical volumes; 820,000 official publications. **Services:** Center open to member institutions. **Publications:** Canadian Book Exchange Centre (booklet) - by request. **Special Catalogs:** Monographs exchange lists; periodicals exchange lists; Canadian official publications exchange list; foreign and international official publications exchange list. **Remarks:** Alternate telephone number(s): 952-8902. FAX: (613)954-9891. **Staff:** Rick Blouin, Hd., Per. & Off.Pubns.

★2805★
Canada - National Library of Canada - Children's Literature Service (Hum)
395 Wellington St. Phone: (613)996-2300
Ottawa, ON, Canada K1A 0N4 Irene E. Aubrey, Chf.
Founded: 1975. **Staff:** Prof 2; Other 1. **Subjects:** Children's and young adults' literature, developing and improving library services for patrons under the age of 16 years. **Special Collections:** Canadian children's and young adults' literature in English, French, and other languages (30,100 volumes); professional children's and young adults' literature (3756 volumes in English, French, and other languages); non-Canadian major award-winning children's and young adults' books, classics, and folklore (2010 volumes). **Holdings:** 35,866 books. **Subscriptions:** 10 journals and other serials. **Services:** Interlibrary loan; copying; service open to the public. **Computerized Information Services:** DOBIS Canadian Online Library System; Envoy 100 (electronic mail service). **Publications:** Supplement to Notable Canadian Children's Books, annual; subject bibliographies, irregular. **Remarks:** FAX: (613)996-4424. Telex: 053 4311. Electronic mail address(es): OONL.CLS (Envoy 100). **Staff:** Mary Collis, Ch.Lit.Libn.

★2806★
Canada - National Library of Canada - Library Development Centre (Info Sci)
395 Wellington St. Phone: (613)995-8717
Ottawa, ON, Canada K1A 0N4 Michael Williamson
Founded: 1970. **Staff:** Prof 7; Other 7. **Subjects:** Library and information science - Canada, automation, new technologies, administration and management, planning, library services for the disabled, resource sharing, standards, statistics; Canadian repository for IPLA publications; secretariat for Council of Federal Libraries. **Holdings:** 1500 monographs; 400 periodical titles; 1430 reports; 692 standards; 90 films and videos; 1000 sound cassettes; 3600 microforms; 4000 IFLA papers; 9000 files containing pamphlets, clippings, unpublished speeches and papers. **Subscriptions:** 467 journals and other serials. **Services:** Interlibrary loan; copying; center open to the public. **Computerized Information Services:** DIALOG Information Services, CAN/OLE, Info Globe, EPIC, WILSONLINE, Conservation Information Network; DOBIS Canadian Online Library System; internal databases; CD-ROMs (LISA, ERIC, Library Literature, TERMDOK, BiblioDisc); ALANET (electronic mail service). **Publications:** Canadian Library/Information Science Research Projects, annual; LDC Bibliographies, irregular; Recent Acquisitions in the Field of Library and Information Science, bimonthly - restricted distribution; Liaison (Council of Federal Libraries newsletter), quarterly; Handbook of Library Services for Disabled Canadians; Libraries for All; Accessible Canadian Library. **Special Indexes:** Research file (library research in Canada); DIREFS file (Canadian library and information science index); CANUC-H (Canadian Union Catalogue of Library Materials for the Print Disabled); CANWIP (Registry of Canadian Works in Progress). **Remarks:** FAX: (613)943-2946. **Staff:** Doug Hodges, Mgr., Liaison Serv.; Susan Haigh, Act.Hd., Pub.Serv.; Wendy Scott, Hd., Coll.; Jean-Marie Briere, Liaison Off.; Diane Bays, Liaison Off.; Carolynn Robertson, Sys.

★2807★
Canada - National Library of Canada - Literary Manuscripts Collection (Hum)
395 Wellington St. Phone: (613)995-3364
Ottawa, ON, Canada K1A 0N4 Claude LeMoine, Cur.
Staff: Prof 3. **Subjects:** Manuscripts and papers of Canadian authors and organizations including small literary presses, private presses, and the book arts. **Holdings:** 155 collections of manuscripts, including the papers of Bernard Amtmann (antiquarian bookseller), Clare Bice (author, illustrator), Blackfish Press, Marie-Claire Blais (novelist), Arthur Stanley Bourinot (poet, literary historian), George Bowering (poet, editor), Elizabeth Cleaver (illustrator), Gary Geddes (poet, editor), Rejean Ducharme (novelist), Andre Giroux (novelist, writer for television), Robert Harlow (novelist), Jack Hodgins (novelist), W.P. Kinsella (novelist, story writer), Marie LeFranc (writer), Roger Lemelin (novelist, writer for television), Daphne Marlatt (poet), Claire Martin (author, translator), Michael Ondaatje (poet, novelist), Oolichan Books, Guy Robert (writer, publisher), Gabrielle Roy (novelist), Laura Salverson (writer), Chris Scott (novelist), Elizabeth Smart (poet, story writer), Elizabeth Spencer (novelist, story writer), Guy Sylvestre (critic, literary historian), Robert Sward (poet publisher), Phyllis Webb (poet), J.M. Yates (poet, editor); Michel Tremblay; Susanna Moodie; Coach House Press; House of Anansi; James Houston (writer and illustrator). **Services:** Copying; collection open to the public. **Computerized Information Services:** DOBIS Canadian Online Library System; Envoy 100 (electronic mail service). **Publications:** Literary Manuscripts at the National Library of Canada, 2nd ed. **Remarks:** Alternate telephone number(s): 996-1318. FAX: (613)996-4424. Telex: 053 4311. Electronic mail address(es): LEMOINE.CJ (Envoy 100). **Staff:** Linda Hoad, Mss.Libn.; Lorna Knight, Mss.Libn.

★2808★
Canada - National Library of Canada - Multilingual Biblioservice (Hum)
Ottawa, ON, Canada K1A 0N4 Phone: (819)997-9930
Marie F. Zielinska, Chf.
Founded: 1973. **Staff:** Prof 3; Other 7. **Subjects:** Fiction, biographies, children's literature, folklore. **Holdings:** 400,000 volumes. **Subscriptions:** 130 journals and other serials. **Services:** Interlibrary loan; long-term loans to Canadian public libraries through designated deposit centers (32 languages available); library not open to the public. **Computerized Information Services:** MINISIS (internal database); Envoy 100 (electronic mail service). **Publications:** Guide to suppliers of commercially available books-on-cassette in languages other than English or French. **Special Catalogs:** Author, title, shelflist catalog in each non-Roman-script language (card); catalog of large-print books; catalog of books-on-cassette. **Remarks:** The Multilingual Biblioservice also contracts with 19 part-time language specialists. It is located at 25 Eddy St., 2nd Fl., Hull, PQ. FAX: (819)953-6984. Telex: 0534311. Electronic mail address(es): OONL.MBS (Envoy 100). **Staff:** Irena L. Bell, Asst.Chf.; Virginia Ballance, Hd., Cat. and Automation.

★2809★
Canada - National Library of Canada - Music Division (Mus)
395 Wellington St. Phone: (613)996-3377
Ottawa, ON, Canada K1A 0N4 Dr. S. Timothy Maloney, Chf.
Founded: 1970. **Staff:** 8. **Subjects:** Music in Canada, Canadian musical heritage. **Special Collections:** Percy Scholes Collection (200 linear feet of clippings, pamphlets, pictures); Percival Price Campanology Collection (200 linear feet); papers of Canadian composer Healey Willan (1880-1968), educator Claude Champagne (1891-1965), conductor Sir Ernest MacMillan (1893-1973), pianist Glenn Gould (1932-1982), other Canadian musicians and musical organizations. **Holdings:** 50,000 books and scores; 1560 periodical titles; 120,000 Canadian sound recordings; 48 VF drawers of files on Canadian music and musicians; 3500 linear feet of manuscript and archival collections; 77,000 pieces of sheet music. **Subscriptions:** 410 journals and other serials. **Services:** Interlibrary loan; copying; dubbing of sound recordings; division open to the public. **Computerized Information Services:** OCLC EPIC, UTLAS, DOBIS Canadian Online Library System; CD-ROMs; internal databases; Envoy 100 (electronic mail service). **Special Catalogs:** Union catalog of Canadian music, pre-1950 (data sheets); microfiche catalog of 45rpm and 78rpm recordings with Canadian content held by the National Library Music Division; finding aids for archival papers. **Special Indexes:** Index to articles about Canadian musical subjects in Canadian music periodicals (card). **Remarks:** FAX: (613)996-4424. Telex: 053 4311. Electronic mail address(es): OONL.MUS (Envoy 100). **Staff:** Maria Calderisi Bryce, Hd., Printed Coll.; Dr. Stephen Willis, Hd., Mss.Coll.

★2810★
Canada - National Library of Canada - Reference and Information Services Division (Info Sci)
395 Wellington St. Phone: (613)995-9481
Ottawa, ON, Canada K1A 0N4 Barbara Camfield, Div.Chf.
Founded: 1972. **Staff:** Prof 22; Other 14. **Subjects:** National reference, information, and referral service in the social sciences and humanities, with an emphasis on Canadian studies. **Special Collections:** Canadian city directories (10,000 volumes); national bibliographies. **Holdings:** 50,000 volumes; 300 reels of microfilm; 157,000 microfiche for approximately 100 titles. **Subscriptions:** 3850 journals and other serials. **Services:** Reference, information, and referral services to libraries and individual researchers on site, by mail (conventional and electronic), telephone, telex, or FAX; advisory service on bibliographic compilation; division open to the public after contacting local libraries. **Computerized Information Services:** BADADUQ, BRS Information Technologies, CAN/LAW, CAN/OLE, DataTimes, DIALOG Information Services, DOBIS Canadian Online Library System, Data-Star, Dow Jones News/Retrieval, OCLC EPIC, Info Globe, Infomart Online, OCLC, QL Systems, RLIN, SDM (Services Documentaires Multimedia, Inc.), Questel, UTLAS, VU/TEXT Information Services, WILSONLINE; CD-ROMs (BiblioDisc, Bibliographie Nationale Francaise Depuis 1975, Books in Print Plus, DAVID, CHOIX, Dialog OnDisc, Canadian Business & Current Affairs, GPO Monthly Catalog, Ulrich's Plus, British Library General Catalogue of Printed Books to 1975, CD:Education, DISCLOSURE, PAIS, Social Science Citation Index, StatCan: Reference Disc, TERMDOK, UN Publications, Waves); Envoy 100 (electronic mail service). Performs searches on fee basis. **Publications:** Bibliographic Style Manual; Canadian City Directories, 1790-1987: A Bibliography and Place-Name Index; Canadian Directories: A Guide to Interlibrary Loan and Reproduction Policies; Canadian Translations; Directory of Special Collections of

Research Value in Canadian Libraries, 1992; Guide de Redaction bibliographique; Provincial Royal Commissions and Commissions of Inquiry, 1867-1982; Theses in Canada: A Bibliographic Guide. **Remarks:** FAX: (613)943-1112. Telex: 053 4311. Electronic mail address(es): OONL.REF (Envoy 100). **Staff:** Cecilia Muir, Hd., Pub.Serv.Sect.; Alice McClymont, Hd., Coll.Mgt.Sect.; F. Gaudet, Act.Hd., Sys. & Res.Sup.Sect.

★2811★
Canada - National Library of Canada - Reference and Information Services Division - Newspaper Service (Info Sci)
395 Wellington St. Phone: (613)996-1338
Ottawa, ON, Canada K1A 0N4 Sandra Burrows, Newspaper Ref.Spec.
Founded: 1967. **Staff:** 1. **Subjects:** Canadian and foreign newspapers, Canadian ethnic newspapers and serials. **Holdings:** 200,000 reels of microfilm of newspapers; 13,000 microprint cards; 18,000 bound volumes of early newspapers. **Subscriptions:** 632 newspapers. **Services:** Interlibrary loan; copying; library open to the public after consulting local libraries. **Computerized Information Services:** DOBIS Canadian Online Library System, UTLAS, OCLC EPIC, Infomart Online, Info Globe; Envoy 100 (electronic mail service). **Special Catalogs:** Union list of Canadian newspapers, 1991; Checklist of Canadian ethnic serials, 1981; Checklist of indexes to Canadian newspapers, 1987. **Remarks:** FAX: (613)943-1112. Telex: 053 4311. Electronic mail address(es): OONL.REF (Envoy 100).

★2812★
Canada - National Library of Canada - Reference and Information Services Division - Official Publications (Info Sci)
395 Wellington St. Phone: (613)996-7452
Ottawa, ON, Canada K1A 0N4 Betty Deavy, Govt. & Law Spec.
Founded: 1967. **Staff:** 1. **Special Collections:** Depository for Canadian Federal and Provincial publications; sales publications of Great Britain, India, France, U.S. Congressional and statistical microform sets, UNESCO, European Communities, OECD, League of Nations, U.N., OAS, Pan American Institute of Geography and History, WIPO; Canadian Indian Rights Collection (historical, parliamentary, legal, socioeconomic documentation on native claims from Canada, United States, Australia, New Zealand); Parliament of Canada Unpublished Sessional Papers, 1916 to present; Parliament of Canada Committee Reports, 1935 to present; Federal Royal Commission Reports, 1867 to present; documents from Federal Provincial Conferences of First Ministers, 1887-1976; Canadian Pre-Confederation Statutes, including British Columbia (1859-1871), New Brunswick (1786-1870), Newfoundland (1833-1867), Nova Scotia (1758-1867), Prince Edward Island (1744-1868); Canadian Parliamentary Proceedings and Sessional Papers, 1841 to present; Documents de la Session du Quebec, 1869 to present; Census of Canada, 1851 to present. **Holdings:** 2 million government documents in hardcopy and 2 million in microform from Canada, foreign countries, international governmental organizations. **Services:** Interlibrary loan; copying; division open to the public with restrictions. **Computerized Information Services:** Envoy 100 (electronic mail service). **Remarks:** FAX: (613)943-1112. Telex: 053 4311. Electronic mail address(es): OONL.REF (Envoy 100). **Staff:** Norma Gauld.

★2813★
Canada - National Library of Canada - Special Collections (Rare Book)
395 Wellington St. Phone: (613)996-1318
Ottawa, ON, Canada K1A 0N4 Claude LeMoire, Hd.Cur.
Staff: Prof 6; Other 1. **Special Collections:** Rare Canadiana including native-language materials and Canadian limited editions and livres d'artistes; Jacob M. Lowy Collection (rare Hebraica and Judaica); Saul Hayes Collection of Hebraic Manuscripts and Microforms; Literary Manuscript Collection (manuscripts and papers of Canadian authors and organizations including small literary presses, private presses, the book arts, and illustrations of Canadian children's literature). **Holdings:** 25,000 items. **Services:** Copying (limited); division open to the public. **Computerized Information Services:** DOBIS Canadian Online Library System; Envoy 100 (electronic mail service). **Special Catalogs:** Published catalog of the collection of native North American language books; Literary Manuscripts at the National Library of Canada/Les Manuscrits Litteraires a la Bibliotheque Nationale du Canada (1990). **Remarks:** FAX: (613)996-4424. Telex: 053 4311. Electronic mail address(es): LeMoine.C (Envoy 100). **Formerly:** Its Rare Book Division. **Staff:** Cheryl N. Jaffee, Cur., Lowy Coll.; Dr. Joyce Banks, Rare Bks./Coll.; Lorna Knight, Cur., Lit.Mss.Coll.

Canada - National Museums of Canada - Canadian Museum of Civilization
See: **Canadian Museum of Civilization - Library** (2962)

Canada - National Museums of Canada - Canadian War Museum
See: **Canadian War Museum - Library** (3000)

★2814★
Canada - National Research Council - Canada Institute for Scientific and Technical Information (CISTI) (Sci-Engr)
Montreal Rd. Phone: (613)993-1600
Ottawa, ON, Canada K1A 0S2 Margot Montgomery, Dir.Gen.
Staff: Prof 68; Other 141. **Subjects:** Science and technology, medicine. **Holdings:** 475,000 books; 2 million microfiche. **Subscriptions:** 55,000 journals and other serials. **Services:** Interlibrary loan; copying; SDI; library open to the public. **Automated Operations:** Computerized cataloging. **Computerized Information Services:** CAN/SDI, CAN/OLE, CAN/SND, DOBIS Canadian Online Library System, DIALOG Information Services, PFDS Online, BRS Information Technologies, MEDLARS, Institute for Scientific Information, Info Globe, Questel, ESA/IRS, LEXIS, NEXIS, WILSONLINE, INSIGHT; Envoy 100 (electronic mail service). Performs searches on fee basis. Contact Person: K. Wallace, 993-2013. **Publications:** List of publications - available on request. **Special Catalogs:** Union List of Scientific Serials in Canadian Libraries. **Remarks:** FAX: (613)952-9112. CISTI operates 14 branch libraries within the National Research Council. **Also Known As:** Institut Canadien de l'Information Scientifique et Technique.

Canada - National Research Council - CISTI - Aeronautical & Mechanical Engineering Branch - Library
See: **Canada - National Research Council - CISTI - J.H. Parkin Branch - Library** (2822)

★2815★
Canada - National Research Council - CISTI - Biotechnology Branch (Biol Sci)
6100 Royalmount Ave. Phone: (514)496-6117
Montreal, PQ, Canada H4P 2R2 Sylvie Belzile, Hd.
Founded: 1985. **Staff:** 2. **Subjects:** Biotechnology; engineering - genetic, protein, biochemical; fermentation; molecular immunology. **Holdings:** 3200 volumes. **Subscriptions:** 450 journals and other serials. **Services:** Branch open to researchers with permission. **Computerized Information Services:** CAN/OLE, DIALOG Information Services, STN International, MEDLARS; Envoy 100 (electronic mail service). **Remarks:** FAX: (514)496-6232. Electronic mail address(es): CISTI.IRBM (Envoy 100). CISTI is the acronym for the Canada Institute for Scientific and Technical Information.

Canada - National Research Council - CISTI - Chemistry Branch
See: **Canada - National Research Council - CISTI - Environmental Chemistry Branch** (2818)

★2816★
Canada - National Research Council - CISTI - Dominion Astrophysical Observatory (Sci-Engr)
5071 W. Saanich Rd. Phone: (604)363-0020
Victoria, BC, Canada V8X 4M6 Eric S. LeBlanc, Lib.Hd.
Founded: 1929. **Staff:** Prof 1. **Subjects:** Astronomy, astrophysics, optical design. **Holdings:** 3200 theses; 700 conference papers; 9500 monographs; 700 observatory research reports. **Subscriptions:** 70 journals and other serials. **Services:** Library open to the public. **Computerized Information Services:** CAN/OLE, DOBIS Canadian Online Library System, DIALOG Information Services; Envoy 100, InterNet (electronic mail services). **Remarks:** FAX: (604)363-0045. Telex: 0497295. Electronic mail address(es): CISTI.DAOV (Envoy 100); NRCDAO.NRC.CA. (InterNet). CISTI is the acronym for the Canada Institute for Scientific and Technical Information.

★2817★
Canada - National Research Council - CISTI - Dominion Radio Astrophysical Observatory (Sci-Engr)
P.O. Box 248 Phone: (604)493-2277
Penticton, BC, Canada V2A 6K3 Elizabeth Jones, Adm.Off.
Founded: 1960. **Subjects:** Astronomy, radio astronomy, astrophysics, physics, engineering, computer science, electronics, standards. **Holdings:** 3000 books; 80 bound periodical volumes. **Subscriptions:** 104 journals and other serials. **Services:** Interlibrary loan; branch not open to the public. **Computerized Information Services:** CAN/OLE, DOBIS Canadian Online Library System; Envoy 100, InterNet (electronic mail services). **Remarks:** FAX: (604)493-7767. Electronic mail address(es): CISTI.DRAO (Envoy 100); SEC@DRAO.NRC.CA (InterNet). CISTI is the acronym for the Canada Institute for Scientific and Technical Information. **Staff:** Erika Rohner, Adm.Off.

Canada - National Research Council - CISTI - Electrical Engineering Branch
See: **Canada - National Research Council - CISTI - McNaughton Branch** (2824)

★2818★
Canada - National Research Council - CISTI - Environmental Chemistry Branch (Sci-Engr)
Bldg. M-12
Montreal Rd. Phone: (613)993-2266
Ottawa, ON, Canada K1A 0R6 Lee-Yong Tan, Hd.
Staff: Prof 1; Other 1. **Subjects:** Environmental protection - toxics in batteries, solid wastes, functional polymers; process technology - membrane separation, combustion emissions, sludges, toxic destruction; environmental measurement - analytical methods, modeling, atmospheric contaminants and sensors; chemical characterization; cluster and supramolecular projects. **Special Collections:** Complete Chemical Abstracts, 1907 to present. **Holdings:** 7800 books, conference proceedings, and reports; 850 serials. **Subscriptions:** 170 journals and other serials. **Services:** Interlibrary loan; branch open to the public with restrictions. **Automated Operations:** Computerized public access catalog. **Computerized Information Services:** CAN/OLE, UTLAS; Envoy 100 (electronic mail service). **Remarks:** FAX: (613)952-7275. Electronic mail address(es): CISTI.EC (Envoy 100). CISTI is the acronym for the Canada Institute for Scientific and Technical Information. **Formerly:** Its Chemistry Branch.

★2819★
Canada - National Research Council - CISTI - Industrial Materials Branch (Sci-Engr)
75, blvd. de Mortagne Phone: (514)641-2280
Boucherville, PQ, Canada J4B 6Y4 Louise Venne, Hd.
Founded: 1979. **Staff:** Prof 1; Other 1. **Subjects:** Plastics, polymeric and metallic composites, metals and ceramics, instrumentation and sensors, computer integrated materials processing. **Holdings:** 24,000 volumes. **Subscriptions:** 350 journals and other serials. **Services:** Interlibrary loan; branch open to the public with restrictions. **Computerized Information Services:** CAN/OLE, DOBIS Canadian Online Library System, DIALOG Information Services; internal database; Envoy 100 (electronic mail service). **Remarks:** FAX: (514)641-4627 (c/o Library). Electronic mail address(es): CISTI.IGMM (Envoy 100). CISTI is the acronym for Canada Institute for Scientific and Technical Information. **Also Known As:** Institut des Materiaux Industriels (IMI).

★2820★
Canada - National Research Council - CISTI - Institute for Marine Biosciences Branch (Sci-Engr, Biol Sci)
1411 Oxford St. Phone: (902)426-8250
Halifax, NS, Canada B3H 3Z1 Annabelle Taylor, Hd.
Founded: 1951. **Staff:** Prof 1; Other 1. **Subjects:** Marine bioscience, biological chemistry, analytical chemistry. **Holdings:** 6300 books; 15,000 bound periodical volumes. **Subscriptions:** 250 journals and other serials. **Services:** Interlibrary loan; copying; branch open to the public with permission. **Computerized Information Services:** CAN/OLE, DIALOG Information Services; Envoy 100 (electronic mail service). **Remarks:** FAX: (902)426-9413. Electronic mail address(es): CISTI.MBH (Envoy 100). CISTI is the acronym for the Canadian Institute for Scientific and Technical Information. **Formerly:** Its Institute for Marine Biosciences Branch.

★2821★
Canada - National Research Council - CISTI - Institute for Research in Construction Branch (Sci-Engr, Plan)
Montreal Rd. Phone: (613)993-2466
Ottawa, ON, Canada K1A 0R6 Scott Mellon, Act.Hd.
Founded: 1948. **Staff:** Prof 3; Other 2. **Subjects:** Construction, soil mechanics, acoustics, building services, fire research, building codes, building structures, materials, snow and ice research. **Holdings:** 100,000 books; 200,000 reports. **Subscriptions:** 800 journals and other serials. **Services:** Interlibrary loan; copying; branch open to the public. **Automated Operations:** Computerized public access catalog and cataloging. **Computerized Information Services:** CAN/OLE, PFDS Online, DIALOG Information Services; Envoy 100 (electronic mail service). **Publications:** Recent acquisitions, monthly - available on request. **Remarks:** FAX: (613)954-5984. Electronic mail address(es): CISTI.IRC (Envoy 100). CISTI is the acronym for the Canada Institute for Scientific and Technical Information. **Staff:** Vicki Ganguli, Ref. & Cat.Libn.; Joan Collins, Ref.Libn.

★2822★
Canada - National Research Council - CISTI - J.H. Parkin Branch - Library (Sci-Engr)
Montreal Rd., Bldg M-2 Phone: (613)993-2431
Ottawa, ON, Canada K1A 0R6 Morna Tuttle, Hd.
Founded: 1941. **Staff:** Prof 2; Other 6. **Subjects:** Aeronautics, mechanical and structural engineering, railway and marine transportation, tribology, fuels and lubricants, hydraulics. **Special Collections:** Unclassified NASA publications (depository). **Holdings:** 61,000 books; 10,000 bound periodical volumes; 750,000 technical reports; NASA microfiche, 1962 to present; Advisory Group for Aerospace Research and Development, American Society of Mechanical Engineers (ASME), Society of Manufacturing Engineers (SME), Supersonic Aircraft Engine, and American Institute of Aeronautics and Astronautics reprints, 1963 to present. **Subscriptions:** 1500 journals and other serials. **Services:** Interlibrary loan; copying; branch open to the public. **Computerized Information Services:** DIALOG Information Services, CAN/OLE, CAN/SDI; Envoy 100 (electronic mail service). **Remarks:** FAX: (613)952-7158. Electronic mail address(es): CISTI.PRKN (Envoy 100). CISTI is the acronym for the Canada Institute for Scientific and Technical Information. **Formerly:** Its Aeronautical & Mechanical Engineering Branch - Library. **Staff:** John Leonardo, Ref.

★2823★
Canada - National Research Council - CISTI - Marine Dynamics Branch (Sci-Engr)
P.O. Box 12093, Sta. A Phone: (709)772-2468
St. John's, NF, Canada A1B 3T5 David Clark, Libn.
Staff: Prof 1. **Subjects:** Naval architecture, ice properties, offshore structures, hydrodynamics. **Holdings:** 8000 books. **Subscriptions:** 200 journals and other serials. **Services:** Interlibrary loan; branch open to the public with permission. **Automated Operations:** Computerized public access catalog and acquisitions. **Computerized Information Services:** CAN/OLE, DIALOG Information Services, BOATS (BMT Abstracts Online), MARNA, SHIPDES; CD-ROM (Arctic & Antarctic Regions); Envoy 100, InterNet, BITNET (electronic mail services). **Remarks:** Alternate telephone number(s): (709)772-4116. FAX: (709)772-2462. Electronic mail address(es): CISTI.IMDS (Envoy 100); DCLARK@MINNIE.IMD.NRC.CA (InterNet); DCLARK@INDIGO.NRC.CA (BITNET). CISTI is the acronym for the Canada Institute for Scientific and Technical Information.

★2824★
Canada - National Research Council - CISTI - McNaughton Branch (Sci-Engr)
Montreal Rd., Bldg. M-50 Phone: (613)993-2006
Ottawa, ON, Canada K1A 0R6 Jennifer Campbell, Hd.
Founded: 1954. **Staff:** Prof 1; Other 1. **Subjects:** Applied physics, power engineering, robotics, artifical intelligence, information technology, electronics. **Holdings:** 5000 books; 6000 bound periodical volumes. **Subscriptions:** 300 journals and other serials. **Services:** Interlibrary loan; copying; SDI; branch open to the public with restrictions. **Automated Operations:** Computerized public access catalog and serials (INNOPAC). **Computerized Information Services:** CAN/OLE; Envoy 100, InterNet (electronic mail services). **Remarks:** Electronic mail address(es): CISTI.MCN (Envoy 100); LIBRARY@IIT.NRC.CA (InterNet). CISTI is the acronym for the Canada Institute for Scientific and Technical Information. **Formerly:** Its Electrical Engineering Branch.

★2825★
Canada - National Research Council - CISTI - National Measurement Standards Branch (Sci-Engr)
Montreal Rd., Bldg. M-36 Phone: (613)993-2483
Ottawa, ON, Canada K1A 0R6 Raymond Jacyna, Hd.
Founded: 1962. **Staff:** Prof 1; Other 1. **Subjects:** Measurement standards; heat and thermometry; optics; photometrics and radiometry; time and frequency; acoustics; semiconductor physics; solid state science; metrology; ionizing radiation; electrical standards. **Special Collections:** BIPM (Bureau International des Poids et Mesures) publications. **Holdings:** 17,500 books. **Subscriptions:** 450 journals and other serials. **Services:** Interlibrary loan; copying; SDI; branch open to the public upon referral by Main Library. **Automated Operations:** Computerized public access catalog, acquisitions, and ordering. **Computerized Information Services:** CAN/OLE, DIALOG Information Services, CAN/SDI; Envoy 100 (electronic mail service). **Remarks:** Alternate telephone number(s): 993-6400. FAX: (613)952-1394. Electronic mail address(es): CISTI.NMS (Envoy 100). CISTI is the acronym for the Canada Institute for Scientific and Technical Information. **Formerly:** Its Physics Branch.

Canada - National Research Council - CISTI - Physics Branch
See: **Canada - National Research Council - CISTI - National Measurement Standards Branch** (2825)

★2826★
Canada - National Research Council - CISTI - Plant Biotechnology Branch (Biol Sci)
110 Gymnasium Rd. Phone: (306)975-5256
Saskatoon, SK, Canada S7N 0W9 Flora Chen, Hd.
Founded: 1948. **Staff:** Prof 1; Other 1. **Subjects:** Crop biotechnology, conifer biotechnology, stress tolerance genes, regulation of gene expression in plants, legume biotechnology, bio-organic chemistry, seed oil modification, plant cell metabolism, transgenic plants. **Holdings:** 9420 books; 5079 pamphlets, patents, documents; 90 translations; 25 drawers of microcards; 152 reels of microfilm; 45 titles on microfiche; 2827 indexed reprints. **Subscriptions:** 267 journals. **Services:** Branch open to institute staff and faculty and students of University of Saskatchewan. **Computerized Information Services:** DOBIS Canadian Online Library System, CAN/OLE, DIALOG Information Services, STN International. **Publications:** Library newsletter, irregular. **Remarks:** CISTI is the acronym for the Canada Institute for Scientific and Technical Information.

★2827★
Canada - National Research Council - CISTI - Sussex Branch (Sci-Engr)
100 Sussex Dr. Phone: (613)990-6027
Ottawa, ON, Canada K1A 0R6 Dianne Kharouba, Hd.
Staff: Prof 1; Other 2. **Subjects:** Biology, chemistry, physics, astrophysics. **Special Collections:** Astronomy collection (12,000 books and serials). **Holdings:** 75,000 volumes. **Subscriptions:** 1300 journals and other serials. **Services:** Interlibrary loan; SDI; branch open to the public with restrictions. **Automated Operations:** Computerized cataloging. **Computerized Information Services:** CAN/OLE, UTLAS, DOBIS Canadian Online Library System, MEDLARS, DIALOG Information Services, CCINFOline; Envoy 100, InterNet (electronic mail services). **Remarks:** FAX: (613)952-0974. Electronic mail address(es): CISTI.SUSS (Envoy 100); LIBRARY@BIOLOGYSX.LAN.NRC.CA (InterNet). CISTI is the acronym for the Canada Institute for Scientific and Technical Information.

★2828★
Canada - National Research Council - CISTI - Uplands Branch (Sci-Engr)
Bldg. U61, Uplands Campus Phone: (613)998-3327
Ottawa, ON, Canada K1A 0R6 Debbie Braun, Hd.
Founded: 1953. **Staff:** Prof 1; Other 1. **Subjects:** Aeronautics, mechanical engineering, electronics, mathematics, computer science. **Special Collections:** Collection of documents from the National Advisory Committee for Aeronautics/NASA, the Advisory Group for Aerospace Research & Development (AGARD), and the American Institute of Aeronautics and Astronautics reprints (1970 to present). **Holdings:** 8400 books; 3400 bound periodical volumes; 140,000 other cataloged items. **Subscriptions:** 230 journals. **Services:** Interlibrary loan; branch open to the public. **Automated Operations:** Computerized public access catalog. **Computerized Information Services:** CAN/OLE, UTLAS; Envoy 100 (electronic mail service). **Remarks:** FAX: (613)952-1704. Electronic mail address(es): CISTI.UPLDS (Envoy 100). CISTI is the acronym for the Canada Institute for Scientific and Technical Information.

★2829★
Canada - National Transportation Agency of Canada - Library (Trans)
Ottawa, ON, Canada K1A 0N9 Phone: (819)997-7160
Roseanne Pareanen, Libn.
Staff: Prof 2; Other 1. **Subjects:** Transport policy, transportation economics, administrative law. **Holdings:** 25,000 books and bound periodical volumes. **Subscriptions:** 250 journals and other serials. **Services:** Interlibrary loan; copying; library open to the public with restrictions. **Computerized Information Services:** CAN/OLE, CAN/LAW, QL Systems, DIALOG Information Services; Envoy 100 (electronic mail service). Performs searches on fee basis. **Publications:** Accession List, bimonthly. **Remarks:** Alternate telephone number(s): (819)997-7642. FAX: (819)953-9815. Electronic mail address(es): NTA.LIBRARY (Envoy 100). **Also Known As:** Office National des Transports du Canada. **Staff:** A. Rochefort.

★2830★
Canada - Newfoundland Offshore Petroleum Board - Library (Energy)
TD Place, 5th Fl.
140 Water St. Phone: (709)778-1400
St. John's, NF, Canada A1C 6H6 Eileen Blanchard, Libn.
Founded: 1986. **Staff:** 1.5. **Subjects:** Offshore petroleum industry and allied subjects. **Holdings:** 3000 books; 1000 reports. **Subscriptions:** 50 journals and other serials; 15 newspapers. **Services:** Interlibrary loan; copying; library open to the public on request. **Automated Operations:** Computerized public access catalog. **Computerized Information Services:** Envoy 100 (electronic mail service). **Remarks:** FAX: (709)778-1473. Telex: 016 4031. Electronic mail address(es): ICE.MAN (Envoy 100).

★2831★
Canada - Office of the Auditor General - Information and Library Services (Bus-Fin)
240 Sparks St., 11th Fl., W. Phone: (613)995-3766
Ottawa, ON, Canada K1A 0G6 Shayla Mindell, Mgr.
Founded: 1977. **Staff:** Prof 4; Other 4. **Subjects:** Accounting, auditing, public administration, finance, management. **Special Collections:** U.S. General Accounting Office publications; annual reports of the Office of the Auditor General. **Holdings:** 9000 books; 213 meters of uncatalogued material; 153 meters of microfiche. **Subscriptions:** 384 journals and other serials; 12 newspapers. **Services:** Interlibrary loan; copying; SDI; library open to the public by appointment. **Automated Operations:** Computerized public access catalog, cataloging, and serials. **Computerized Information Services:** DIALOG Information Services, PFDS Online, CAN/OLE, Info Globe, Infomart Online, QL Systems; Envoy 100 (electronic mail service). **Special Catalogs:** Recent Acquisitions, monthly - available on request. **Remarks:** FAX: (613)952-5131. Electronic mail address(es): LIBRARY.AGO (Envoy 100). **Staff:** Gail Rawlings, Hd., Tech.Serv. & Sys.; Judy Chamberland, Hd., Client Serv.; Cathy Ray, Cat.Libn.

★2832★
Canada - Office of the Commissioner of Official Languages - Library (Hum)
110 O'Connor St., 13th Fl. Phone: (613)995-0403
Ottawa, ON, Canada K1A 0T8 Rosemarie Benoit, Libn.
Staff: Prof 1; Other 2. **Subjects:** Bilingualism in Canada and other countries, languages, languages in education, official languages, demolinguistics, sociolinguistics. **Holdings:** 11,000 books. **Subscriptions:** 120 journals and other serials; 23 newspapers. **Services:** Interlibrary loan; copying; library open to the public. **Computerized Information Services:** DOBIS Canadian Online Library System, DIALOG Information Services, CAN/OLE, TERMDOK TERMIUM; Envoy 100 (electronic mail service). **Remarks:** FAX: (613)993-5082. Electronic mail address(es): ILL.OOCOL (Envoy 100). **Staff:** Sylvie Parent, Lib.Techn.

Canada - Office National de l'Energie
See: **Canada - National Energy Board** (2791)

Canada - Office National du Film
See: **Canada - National Film Board of Canada** (2793)

★2833★
Canada - Office of the Superintendent of Financial Institutions - Library (Bus-Fin)
255 Albert St., 14th Fl. Phone: (613)990-7729
Ottawa, ON, Canada K1A 0H2 Luanne Larose, Lib.Techn.
Staff: Prof 1. **Subjects:** Insurance, finance, banks and banking. **Holdings:** 6400 books. **Subscriptions:** 250 journals and other serials; 10 newspapers. **Services:** Interlibrary loan; copying; library open to the public with restrictions. **Remarks:** FAX: (613)952-8219. **Also Known As:** Canada - Bureau du Surintendent des Institutions Financieres.

Canada - Peches et Oceans
See: **Canada - Fisheries & Oceans** (2732)

★2834★
Canada - Prairie Farm Rehabilitation Administration - Library (Env-Cons, Sci-Engr)
Motherwell Bldg.
1901 Victoria Ave. Phone: (306)780-5100
Regina, SK, Canada S4P 0R5 Charlene Dusyk, Hd.
Founded: 1966. **Staff:** Prof 1; Other 2. **Subjects:** Water engineering, resource management and conservation, soil science, hydrology, drought. **Holdings:** 20,000 books; 1400 bound periodical volumes; 1000 pamphlets. **Subscriptions:** 500 journals and other serials; **Services:** Interlibrary loan; copying; library open to the public. **Automated Operations:** Computerized cataloging and serials. **Computerized Information Services:** CAN/OLE, DIALOG Information Services; Envoy 100 (electronic mail service). **Publications:** Library Newsletter, bimonthly. **Remarks:** FAX: (306)780-5018. Electronic mail address(es): PFRA.LIB (Envoy 100).

★2835★
Canada - Privy Council Office - Library (Soc Sci)
85 Sparks St., Suite 1000
Ottawa, ON, Canada K1A 0A3 Phone: (613)957-5125
Staff: Prof 1; Other 3. **Subjects:** Political science, history, government. **Holdings:** 10,000 volumes. **Subscriptions:** 350 journals and other serials; 30 newspapers. **Services:** Interlibrary loan; copying; open to the public with security clearance. **Computerized Information Services:** DIALOG Information Services, Infomart Online, Reuters, DOBIS Canadian Online Library System, QL Systems, Info Globe, NEXIS, CAN/LAW. Performs searches on fee basis. **Remarks:** FAX: (613)957-5043.

★2836★
Canada - Public Service Commission - Library Services Division (Bus-Fin)
B1123, West Tower
300 Laurier Ave., W. Phone: (613)992-4068
Ottawa, ON, Canada K1A 0M7 Ron Pelton
Founded: 1977. **Staff:** Prof 5; Other 12. **Subjects:** Public administration, training, personnel management, linguistics. **Special Collections:** History of the Public Service. **Holdings:** 21,345 books; 300 videocassettes; 1308 films. **Subscriptions:** 700 journals and other serials. **Services:** Interlibrary loan; library open to the public for reference use only. **Automated Operations:** Computerized cataloging and circulation. **Computerized Information Services:** DIALOG Information Services, DOBIS, Termium, Info Globe, Questel, SDM, Banque de Terminologie du Quebec. **Publications:** New items, irregular - for internal distribution only. **Special Catalogs:** Film and video catalog; Self-Learning Catalogue; Service/Empowerment Catalogue. **Remarks:** FAX: (613)992-4329. **Also Known As:** Canada - Commission de la Fonction publique. **Staff:** J. Patterson, Hd.Proc. & Sys.; G. Renaud, Hd., Client Serv.

★2837★
Canada - Public Service Staff Relations Board - Library (Bus-Fin)
Sta. B, P.O. Box 1525 Phone: (613)990-1814
Ottawa, ON, Canada K1P 5V2 Richard Harkin, Chf., Lib.Serv.
Founded: 1967. **Staff:** Prof 2; Other 3. **Subjects:** Industrial and labor relations in the public sector, arbitration, collective bargaining, public administration, wages and working conditions. **Holdings:** 3800 books. **Subscriptions:** 920 journals and other serials; 8 newspapers. **Services:** Interlibrary loan; copying; library open to the public. **Automated Operations:** Computerized cataloging. **Computerized Information Services:** PSSRB Decisions (internal database). **Publications:** Acquisitions List, bimonthly. **Special Indexes:** Index to PSSRB Decisions. **Remarks:** FAX: (613)990-1849.

★2838★
Canada - Public Works Canada - Library Services (Sci-Engr, Plan)
Sir Charles Tupper Bldg.
Riverside Dr. Phone: (613)736-2400
Ottawa, ON, Canada K1A 0M2 P.A. Madaire, Hd., Lib.Serv.
Founded: 1955. **Staff:** Prof 2; Other 2. **Subjects:** Engineering - civil, mechanical, electrical; architecture and design; realty and property management; urban planning and design; energy conservation. **Special Collections:** Publications produced by or for the Department of Public Works (1000 titles). **Holdings:** 15,000 books; 2000 bound periodical volumes; 4000 federal government documents; 100 linear feet of statistics; 100 linear feet of standards; 4000 microfiche. **Subscriptions:** 600 journals and other serials; 5 newspapers. **Services:** Interlibrary loan; copying; SDI; library open to the public with restrictions on some material. **Computerized Information Services:** PFDS Online, DIALOG Information Services, QL Systems, CAN/OLE, Info Globe, DOBIS Canadian Online Library System, Infomart Online; Envoy 100 (electronic mail service). **Publications:** Bibliographies. **Remarks:** FAX: (613)736-2401. **Also Known As:** Travaux Publics Canada. **Staff:** Marilyn Dyck, Ref.Libn.; Barbara Cope, ILL.

★2839★
Canada - Revenue Canada - Customs & Excise - College Library (Bus-Fin)
Rigaud, PQ, Canada J0P 1P0 Phone: (514)451-6711
Lucie Lamarche, Lib.Ck.
Staff: Prof 1; Other 1. **Subjects:** Customs and excise, training and development, education. **Holdings:** 1500 volumes. **Subscriptions:** 100 journals and other serials; 8 newspapers. **Services:** Interlibrary loan; library not open to the public. **Remarks:** FAX: (514)451-0144.

★2840★
Canada - Revenue Canada - Customs & Excise - Legal Services Library (Law)
3rd Fl., Connaught Bldg.
MacKenzie Ave. Phone: (613)954-6290
Ottawa, ON, Canada K1A 0L5 Fiona A. McPherson
Staff: 1. **Subjects:** Law - administrative, customs, excise; Canadian Goods and Services Tax. **Holdings:** 1000 volumes; government documents. **Services:** Library not open to the public.

★2841★
Canada - Revenue Canada - Customs & Excise - Library (Bus-Fin)
Connaught Bldg., 2nd Fl. Phone: (613)957-9195
Ottawa, ON, Canada K1A 0L5 Dianne L. Parsonage, Dept.Libn.
Founded: 1952. **Staff:** Prof 3; Other 5. **Subjects:** Public finance, public administration, commerce and trade, sales tax, goods and services tax. **Special Collections:** Customs and excise administration. **Holdings:** 20,000 books; 3000 other cataloged items. **Subscriptions:** 600 journals and other serials; 22 newspapers. **Services:** Interlibrary loan; copying; library open to the public with prior permission. **Automated Operations:** Computerized acquisitions, cataloging, and ILL. **Computerized Information Services:** DIALOG Information Services, Infomart Online, QL Systems; internal database. **Publications:** Library Accessions List, monthly; Periodical List, annual - for internal distribution only. **Remarks:** FAX: (613)954-1765. Telex: 053 3330. **Also Known As:** Canada - Ministere du Revenu National - Douanes et Accise. **Staff:** Suneeta Chander, Hd., Cat.Sect.; Margaret McClintock, Client Serv.

★2842★
Canada - Revenue Canada - Customs & Excise - Scientific and Technical Information Centre (Sci-Engr)
79 Bentley Ave. Phone: (613)998-8510
Ottawa, ON, Canada K1A 0L5 Ted Racine, Hd., STI Ctr.
Founded: 1974. **Staff:** Prof 1; Other 1. **Subjects:** Analytical and applied chemistry, chemical technology. **Special Collections:** Chemical Manufacturers Literature Files (950 folders); International and National Trade Classifications, Tariffs, Customs Co-operation Council Committees Notes (200 volumes). **Holdings:** 2775 books; 3000 bound periodical volumes; 250 internal technical and research reports. **Subscriptions:** 120 journals and other serials. **Services:** Interlibrary loan; copying; SDI; center open to the public with prior approval. **Computerized Information Services:** DIALOG Information Services, QL Systems, CAN/OLE, STN International, DOBIS Canadian Online Library System; LASS (internal database). **Remarks:** FAX: (613)952-7825. Part of Laboratory & Scientific Services Directorate of Revenue Canada.

★2843★
Canada - Revenue Canada - Montreal District Office - Taxation Library (Bus-Fin)
305 Rene Levesque, W. Phone: (514)283-7725
Montreal, PQ, Canada H2Z 1A6 Adriana Carabin, Libn.
Founded: 1982. **Staff:** Prof 2. **Subjects:** Finance, taxation, business. **Holdings:** 3000 books. **Subscriptions:** 200 journals and other serials; 15 newspapers. **Services:** Interlibrary loan; copying; library open to the public. **Automated Operations:** Computerized cataloging and acquisitions. **Computerized Information Services:** QL Systems, DIALOG Information Services, SOQUIJ (Societe Quebecoise d'Information Juridique), Infomart Online. **Staff:** Maureen Subranni, Lib.Techn.

★2844★
Canada - Revenue Canada - Taxation Library (Bus-Fin)
Ottawa, ON, Canada K1A 0L8 Phone: (613)957-2290
Lorraine Wilkinson, Chf.Libn.
Founded: 1953. **Staff:** Prof 7; Other 10. **Subjects:** Taxation, law, accounting, electronic data processing, management, personnel management. **Holdings:** 50,000 books and microfiche; 13,400 titles including non-catalogued departmental materials. **Subscriptions:** 1600 journals and other serials. **Services:** Interlibrary loan; copying; SDI; library open to the public by appointment. **Automated Operations:** Computerized cataloging, acquisitions, and serials. **Computerized Information Services:** BRS Information Technologies, CAN/LAW, Infomart Online, DIALOG Information Services, Info Globe, QL Systems, WESTLAW, Canadian Tax Online, LEXIS, NEXIS, Reuter Pricelink. **Publications:** List of new acquisitions, monthly; list of serials currently received, annual; library guide - all available on request. **Remarks:** FAX: (613)957-7476. Library maintains branches in Montreal, Quebec, Calgary, and Vancouver. **Staff:** Mary Butterill, Hd., Tech.Serv.; Sandra Mayers, Hd., Client Serv.

Canada - Royal Canadian Mounted Police
See: **Royal Canadian Mounted Police** (14109)

★2845★
Canada - Science Council of Canada - Library
100 Metcalfe St.
Ottawa, ON, Canada K1P 5M1
Defunct.

★2846★
Canada - Science Institute of the Northwest Territories - Inuvik Research Centre - Library (Sci-Engr)
P.O. Box 1430 Phone: (403)979-3838
Inuvik, NT, Canada X0E 0T0 Gary White, Mgr.
Founded: 1963. **Staff:** Prof 1; Other 2. **Subjects:** General scientific subjects, Western Arctic region, Northern region. **Holdings:** 2000 books; 58 films; microfilm; maps. **Subscriptions:** 70 journals and other serials; 12 newspapers. **Services:** Interlibrary loan; copying; library open to the public. **Remarks:** FAX: (403)979-3570.

★2847★
Canada - Secretary of State - Departmental Library (Soc Sci, Area-Ethnic)
15 Eddy St., 2nd Fl. Phone: (819)997-3981
Hull, PQ, Canada K1A 0M5 Rejean Heroux, Chf.Libn.
Founded: 1966. **Staff:** Prof 8; Other 25. **Subjects:** Social sciences, higher education, Canadian identity, bilingualism, ethnic groups, human rights. **Holdings:** 78,500 books; 4000 departmental documents; 90 AV items; 19,000 microfiche; 1000 linear feet of documents. **Subscriptions:** 780 journals and other serials. **Services:** Interlibrary loan; SDI; library open to the public with restrictions on circulation. **Automated Operations:** Computerized cataloging and acquisitions. **Computerized Information Services:** DIALOG Information Services, Info Globe, QL Systems, DOBIS Canadian Online Library System, WESTLAW, SDM, CAN/OLE, Infomart Online, Questel, UTLAS, WILSONLINE; CRDI/MINISIS (internal database). **Publications:** Accessions List, bimonthly; Periodical List, annual. **Remarks:** FAX: (819)997-7836. Telex: 053-3384. **Also Known As:** Canada - Secretariat d'Etat. **Staff:** Ruth MacEachern, Tech.Serv.; Louis Belanger, Info./Ref.; Lise Sabourin, Lib. Network.

★2848★
Canada - Secretary of State - Translation Bureau - Library (Info Sci)
200 W. Rene-Levesque Blvd., Rm. 307 Phone: (514)283-7519
Montreal, PQ, Canada H2Z 1X4 Lucie Rebelo, Libn.
Founded: 1978. **Staff:** Prof 1; Other 3. **Subjects:** Translation, computer science, economics, management, technology, agriculture, medicine, government. **Special Collections:** Dictionaries, lexicons, vocabularies. **Holdings:** 14,000 books; 500 standards; 400 annual reports; 1500 documents and pamphlets. **Subscriptions:** 50 journals and other serials. **Services:** Interlibrary loan; copying; library open to the public with prior telephone contact. **Automated Operations:** Computerized cataloging. **Computerized Information Services:** UTLAS, DOBIS Canadian Online Library System. **Remarks:** FAX: (514)283-3877. **Staff:** Marie Lacoste, Lib.Techn.

Canada - Service Canadien de la Faune
See: **Canada - Environment Canada, Conservation & Protection - Canadian Wildlife Service** (2715)

Canada - Service de l'Environnement Atmospherique
See: **Canada - Environment Canada** (2703)

★2849★
Canada - Solicitor General Canada - Ministry Library & Reference Centre (Law)
340 Laurier Ave., W., 11th Fl. Phone: (613)991-2787
Ottawa, ON, Canada K1A 0P8 Heather Moore, Chf.Libn.
Founded: 1969. **Staff:** Prof 3; Other 3. **Subjects:** Criminology, corrections, parole, police/law enforcement, terrorism, crime victims, crime prevention. **Special Collections:** National Criminal Justice Reference Service (NCJRS) Microfiche Program (14,000 microfiche); NCCD Abstracts and Full-Text Documents (microfiche); Council of State publications (microfiche); Law Reform Commission of Canada documents (microfiche); Australian Law Reform Commission (microfiche); Canadian Press Newsfile (microfiche); MICROLOG Collection (Canadian federal and provincial government documents on microfiche). **Holdings:** 34,000 books; 5000 bound periodical volumes; 500 videocassettes. **Subscriptions:** 690 journals and other serials. **Services:** Interlibrary loan; copying; library open to the public upon referral. **Automated Operations:** Computerized cataloging and acquisitions. **Computerized Information Services:** DIALOG Information Services, UTLAS, QL Systems, Infomart Online, CAN/OLE; Envoy 100 (electronic mail service). **Publications:** Guide to Library Services; Select bibliographies/ reading lists - for internal distribution only; Acquisitions List, monthly - to mailing list; AV Catalogue, annual - on request and to mailing list; Investigations and Enquiries into the Federal Penal System, 1841-1988, irregular - on request. **Remarks:** FAX: (613)993-7062. Electronic mail address(es): MSG.LIB.ILL (Envoy 100). **Also Known As:** Canada - Ministere du Solliciteur General. **Staff:** France Grenier, Ref.Serv.; Padma Krishnamurti, Tech.Serv.

★2850★
Canada - Statistics Canada - Advisory Services - Alberta and Northwest Territories (Soc Sci)
Park Sq., 8th Fl. Phone: (403)495-3027
10001 Bellamy Hill Bruce Meyers, Ass't Dir. Advisory
Edmonton, AB, Canada T5J 3B6 Services
Founded: 1967. **Staff:** 4. **Subjects:** Canadian economic and social activity statistics. **Holdings:** Statistics Canada publications (about 1200 titles published annually); selected other federal and provincial government publications; census microforms and maps. **Services:** Copying; center open to the public for reference use only and to purchase publications. **Computerized Information Services:** CANSIM. Performs searches on fee basis. **Remarks:** Toll-free telephone number(s): for Alberta residents is (800)282-3907. Residents of Northwest Territories may call (403)495-3028 collect. FAX: (403)495-3026.

★2851★
Canada - Statistics Canada - Advisory Services - British Columbia and the Yukon (Soc Sci)
Sinclair Centre
3rd Fl., Federal Bldg., Suite 440F
757 W. Hastings St. Phone: (604)666-3691
Vancouver, BC, Canada V6C 3C9 Rita Green, Asst.Dir.Adv.Serv.
Founded: 1970. **Staff:** 8. **Subjects:** Canadian economic and social activity statistics. **Holdings:** Statistics Canada publications (about 1200 titles

published annually); selected other federal and provincial government publications; census microforms and maps. **Services:** Copying; center open to the public for reference use only. **Computerized Information Services:** CANSIM. Performs searches on fee basis. **Remarks:** Toll-free telephone number(s): (800)663-1551 (in southern and central British Columbia); for northern British Columbia and Yukon Territory residents, the number is Zenith 08913. FAX: (604)666-6680.

★2852★
Canada - Statistics Canada - Advisory Services - Manitoba (Soc Sci)
MacDonald Bldg.
344 Edmonton St., Suite 300 Phone: (204)983-4020
Winnipeg, MB, Canada R3B 3L9 Bernie Gloyn, Asst.Dir. Advisory Serv.
Founded: 1970. **Staff:** 3. **Subjects:** Canadian economic and social activity statistics. **Holdings:** Statistics Canada publications (about 1200 titles published annually); selected other federal and provincial government publications; census microforms and maps. **Services:** Copying; center open to the public for reference use only and to purchase publications. **Computerized Information Services:** CANSIM. Performs searches on fee basis. **Remarks:** Toll-free telephone number(s): (800)542-3404 (in Manitoba). FAX: (204)983-7543.

★2853★
Canada - Statistics Canada - Advisory Services - Maritime Provinces (Soc Sci)
North American Life Centre Phone: (902)426-5331
1770 Market St. Andrew Maw, Asst. Dir. Advisory Services
Halifax, NS, Canada B3J 3M3
Founded: 1972. **Staff:** 5. **Subjects:** Canadian economic and social activity statistics. **Holdings:** Statistics Canada publications (about 1200 titles published annually); selected other federal and provincial government publications; census microforms and maps. **Services:** Copying; center open to the public for reference use only and to purchase publications. **Computerized Information Services:** CANSIM. Performs searches on fee basis. **Remarks:** Toll-free telephone number(s): (800)565-7192 (for Maritimes residents). FAX: (902)426-9538.

★2854★
Canada - Statistics Canada - Advisory Services - National Capital Region (Soc Sci)
R.H. Coats Bldg. Lobby
Tunney's Pasture Phone: (613)951-8116
Ottawa, ON, Canada K1A 0T6 Helene Lavoie, Mgr.
Founded: 1965. **Staff:** 10. **Subjects:** Canadian economic and social activity statistics. **Holdings:** Statistics Canada publications; selected federal and provincial government publications; census microforms and maps. **Services:** Copying; center open to the public for reference use only and to purchase publications. **Computerized Information Services:** CANSIM. Performs searches on fee basis. **Remarks:** FAX: (613)951-0581.

★2855★
Canada - Statistics Canada - Advisory Services - Newfoundland and Labrador (Soc Sci)
Viking Bldg., 3rd Fl., Crosbie Rd.
Box 8556
St. John's, NF, Canada A1B 3P2 Phone: (709)772-4073
Founded: 1975. **Staff:** 2. **Subjects:** Canadian economic and social activity statistics. **Holdings:** Statistics Canada publications (about 1200 titles published annually); selected other federal and provincial government publications; census microforms and maps. **Services:** Copying; center open to the public for reference use only and to purchase publications. **Computerized Information Services:** CANSIM. Performs searches on fee basis. **Remarks:** Toll-free telephone number(s): (800)563-4255. FAX: (709)772-6433.

★2856★
Canada - Statistics Canada - Advisory Services - Ontario (Soc Sci)
25 St. Clair Ave., E., 10th Fl. Phone: (416)973-6586
Toronto, ON, Canada M4T 1M4 Gregg Connolly, Dir. of Advisory Services
Founded: 1968. **Staff:** 17. **Subjects:** Canadian economic and social activity statistics. **Holdings:** Statistics Canada publications (about 1200 titles published annually); selected other federal and provincial government publications; census microforms and maps. **Services:** Copying; center open to the public for reference use only and to purchase publications. **Computerized Information Services:** CANSIM. Performs searches on fee basis. **Remarks:** Toll-free telephone number(s): (800)263-1136 (in Ontario). FAX: (416)973-7475.

★2857★
Canada - Statistics Canada - Advisory Services - Quebec (Soc Sci)
Complexe Guy Favreau
200 Rene Levesque Blvd., W. Phone: (514)283-5725
Montreal, PQ, Canada H2Z 1X4 Y. Deslauriers, Asst.Dir.Adv.Serv.
Founded: 1968. **Staff:** 15. **Subjects:** Canadian economic and social activity statistics. **Holdings:** Statistics Canada publications (about 1200 titles published annually); selected other federal and provincial government publications; census microforms and maps. **Services:** Copying; center open to the public for reference use only and to purchase publications. **Computerized Information Services:** CANSIM. Performs searches on fee basis. **Remarks:** Toll-free telephone number(s): (800)361-2831. FAX: (514)283-9350.

★2858★
Canada - Statistics Canada - Advisory Services - Saskatchewan (Soc Sci)
Avord Tower, 9th Fl.
2002 Victoria Ave.
Regina, SK, Canada S4P 0R7 Phone: (306)780-5405
Founded: 1975. **Staff:** 3. **Subjects:** Canadian economic and social activity statistics. **Holdings:** Statistics Canada publications (about 1200 titles published annually); selected other federal and provincial government publications; census microforms and maps. **Services:** Copying; center open to the public for reference use only and to purchase publications. **Computerized Information Services:** CANSIM. Performs searches on fee basis. **Remarks:** Toll-free telephone number(s): (800)667-7164 (in Saskatchewan). FAX: (306)780-5403.

★2859★
Canada - Statistics Canada - Advisory Services - Southern Alberta (Soc Sci)
First Street Plaza, Suite 401
138 4th Ave. S.E.
Calgary, AB, Canada T2G 4Z6 Phone: (403)292-6717
Founded: 1987. **Staff:** 3. **Subjects:** Canadian economic and social activity statistics. **Holdings:** Statistics Canada publications; selected federal and provincial government publications; census microforms and maps. **Services:** Copying; center open to the public for reference use only and to purchase publications. **Computerized Information Services:** CANSIM. Performs searches on fee basis. **Remarks:** Toll-free telephone number(s): (800)472-9708. FAX: (403)292-4958.

★2860★
Canada - Statistics Canada - Library (Soc Sci)
R.H. Coats Bldg., 2nd Fl.
Tunney's Pasture Phone: (613)951-8219
Ottawa, ON, Canada K1A 0T6 M.J. Maffini, Dir., Lib.Serv.
Founded: 1918. **Staff:** Prof 9; Other 15. **Subjects:** Economics, demography, mathematics, statistics, statistical methodology, social sciences. **Special Collections:** Official foreign statistics; historical collection of Statistics Canada publications. **Holdings:** 250,000 volumes. **Subscriptions:** 3400 journals and other serials. **Services:** Interlibrary loan; copying; library open to the public. **Automated Operations:** Computerized public access catalog, cataloging, circulation, serials, and acquisitions. **Computerized Information Services:** DIALOG Information Services, BRS Information Technologies, CAN/OLE, Infomart Online, QL Systems, DOBIS Canadian Online Library System, Info Globe, MEDLARS; Envoy 100 (electronic mail service). **Publications:** Accessions List, monthly; Current Contents of Periodicals, monthly; List of Supplementary Documents; Guide to managing Statistics Canada publications in libraries. **Special Catalogs:** Master title file for all publications issued by Statistics Canada since its inception in 1918; card file of research papers; Statistics Canada Catalogue, annual; Statistics Canada Catalogue. **Remarks:** FAX: (613)951-0939. Electronic mail address(es): ILL.OOS (Envoy 100). **Staff:** Tara Naraynsingh, Hd., Sys. and Res.Sup.; Fay Hjartarson, Hd., Bibliog.Prod.; Tony Moren, Hd., Tech.Serv.

★2861★
Canada - Supply and Services Canada - Consulting and Audit Canada - Information Resource Centre (Bus-Fin)
112 Kent St., 10th Fl. Phone: (613)996-3348
Ottawa, ON, Canada K1A 0S5 Marie-Claire Girouard, Lib.Techn.
Staff: 1. **Subjects:** Business, finance, public administration, management consulting. **Holdings:** 5000 books. **Subscriptions:** 151 journals and other serials. **Services:** Interlibrary loan; copying; library open to the public. **Computerized Information Services:** DOBIS Canadian Online Library System. **Remarks:** FAX: (613)952-8295. **Formerly:** Its Bureau of Management Consulting.

★2862★
Canada - Supply and Services Canada - Library (Bus-Fin)
Place du Portage 3, (1-E)
11 Laurier St.
Hull, PQ, Canada K1A 0S5 Phone: (819)956-3460
Founded: 1962. **Staff:** Prof 2; Other 6. **Subjects:** Management, accounting and finance, data processing, purchasing, public administration. **Special Collections:** Statistics Canada publications (complete set); Canadian Government standards. **Holdings:** 40,000 books. **Subscriptions:** 385 journals and other serials; 25 newspapers. **Services:** Interlibrary loan; library open to the public for reference use only. **Automated Operations:** Computerized cataloging. **Computerized Information Services:** DOBIS Canadian Online System. **Publications:** Library accessions list, irregular; The Reporter (newsletter), monthly; Information Bulletin, irregular; R & D Bulletin, monthly; Government Business Opportunities, weekly - all for internal distribution only. **Remarks:** FAX: (819)997-9776; (819)997-0080. Telex: 053 3703. **Staff:** P. Kalloo, Ref.Libn.; S. Seguin-Forget, Chf. Purchasing Off.

★2863★
Canada - Supreme Court of Canada - Library (Law)
Supreme Court Bldg.
Kent & Wellington Sts. Phone: (613)996-8120
Ottawa, ON, Canada K1A 0J1 F. Diane Teeple, Dir., Lib. & Res.Serv.
Founded: 1875. **Staff:** Prof 12; Other 17. **Subjects:** Civil and common law. **Holdings:** 353,200 volumes; 123,759 microfiche; 5875 reels of microfilm; 268 audio cassettes; 25 videotapes. **Subscriptions:** 4000 journals and other serials. **Services:** Interlibrary loan; copying; SDI; library open to qualified researchers. **Automated Operations:** Computerized public access catalog and cataloging. **Computerized Information Services:** QL Systems, WESTLAW, LEXIS, DOBIS Canadian Online Library System, UTLAS, Societe Quebecoise d'Information Juridque (SOQUIJ), CAN/LAW, DIALOG Information Services, Info Globe, Infomart Online, Questel, SDM, REUTERS, CBANET; QUICKMAIL (electronic mail service). **Publications:** Books Received, monthly; Law Journal Contents, weekly - for internal distribution only; Library Guide, annual; Law Reports Contents, weekly - for internal distribution only; Library Guide for Law Clerks, annual. **Special Indexes:** Index of unreported Supreme Court judgments by style of cause (card). **Remarks:** FAX: (613)996-3063. **Also Known As:** Cour Supreme du Canada. **Staff:** Odele Berthiaume, Chf., Res.Serv.; Rosemary Murray-Lachapelle, Chf., Tech.Serv. & Sys.; Patricia Spry, Chf., Info. & Rd.Serv.

★2864★
Canada - Tax Court of Canada - Tax Library (Law)
Centennial Towers
200 Kent St. Phone: (613)992-1704
Ottawa, ON, Canada K1A 0M1 Denis Roussel, Lib.Techn.
Founded: 1962. **Staff:** Prof 2; Other 1. **Subjects:** Income tax law, tax regulation, accounting. **Holdings:** 1450 books; 7000 bound periodical volumes. **Subscriptions:** 65 journals and other serials. **Services:** Interlibrary loan; library open to the public with restrictions. **Automated Operations:** Computerized cataloging and acquisitions. **Computerized Information Services:** QL Systems, LEXIS, DOBIS Canadian Online Library System. **Remarks:** FAX: (613)957-9034. The Tax Court of Canada is a Court of Record and its library is maintained to assist judges in determining the merits of cases. **Also Known As:** Cour Canadienne de l'Impot. **Staff:** Chantal Beauregard, Sr.Lib.Ck.

★2865★
Canada - Telesat Canada - Information Resource Centre (Info Sci)
1601 Telesat Ct. Phone: (613)748-0123
Gloucester, ON, Canada K1B 5P4 Marian Eagen, Rsrc.Ctr.Mgr.
Founded: 1970. **Staff:** Prof 2; Other 4. **Subjects:** Satellite communications, business and management. **Holdings:** 5000 books; 8000 documents; Telesat papers; annual reports. **Subscriptions:** 800 journals and other serials. **Services:** Interlibrary loan; library not open to the public. **Automated Operations:** Computerized cataloging, acquisitions, serials, and circulation. **Computerized Information Services:** DIALOG Information Services, Info Globe, DOBIS Canadian Online Library System, CAN/OLE, The Financial Post DataGroup, Infomart Online, NewsNet, Inc., Dun & Bradstreet Business Credit Services; internal database; Envoy 100 (electronic mail service). **Publications:** Accession list, bimonthly; Telesat papers, semiannual. **Remarks:** FAX: (613)748-8712. Telex: 053-4184. Electronic mail address(es): ANIK (Envoy 100). **Formerly:** Its Corporate Library. **Staff:** Steve Roby, Info.Serv.Coord.

★2866★
Canada - Transport Canada - Air Navigation Library (Trans)
Canada Place, 12th Fl.
1100-9700 Jasper Ave.
Edmonton, AB, Canada T5J 4E6 Phone: (403)495-3990
Founded: 1970. **Staff:** 1. **Subjects:** Aviation electronics and telecommunications, data communications, radar, navigational aids. **Special Collections:** Standards and procedures governing Air Navigation personnel; headquarter and regional reports on navigational aids and airport equipment. **Holdings:** 200 books; 4100 government documents; 10,000 microfiche; equipment manuals. **Subscriptions:** 30 journals and other serials. **Services:** Interlibrary loan; SDI; library open to the public for reference use only. **Automated Operations:** Computerized cataloging. **Computerized Information Services:** DIALOG Information Services, CAN/OLE, DOBIS Canadian Online Library System; TCN (internal database); Envoy 100 (electronic mail service). **Publications:** Accession list. **Remarks:** FAX: (403)495-3880.

★2867★
Canada - Transport Canada - Airworthiness Technical Reference Centre (Trans)
200 Kent St., Rm. 640
Centennial Towers Phone: (613)952-4401
Ottawa, ON, Canada K1A 0N8 Susan Lamanna, Libn.
Founded: 1977. **Staff:** Prof 1; Other 3. **Subjects:** Aircraft, air regulations, aircraft maintenance and service. **Holdings:** 50 books; 20 bound periodical volumes; 4500 other cataloged items; 200 reels of microfilm; 58 drawers of microfiche. **Subscriptions:** 34 journals and other serials. **Services:** Center open to the public for reference use only. **Automated Operations:** Computerized cataloging and acquisitions. **Computerized Information Services:** DIALOG Information Services, CAN/OLE. **Remarks:** FAX: (613)996-9178. Telex: 053 3130.

★2868★
Canada - Transport Canada - Atlantic Region Library (Trans)
95 Foundry St. Phone: (506)851-7360
P.O. Box 42 Christine Midwinter,
Moncton, NB, Canada E1C 8K6 Act.Reg.Lib.Coord.
Founded: 1984. **Staff:** Prof 1. **Subjects:** Transportation. **Holdings:** 598 books; 1 box of government documents on microfiche. **Subscriptions:** 23 journals and other serials. **Services:** Interlibrary loan; copying; library open to the public for reference use only. **Automated Operations:** Computerized cataloging. **Computerized Information Services:** CAN/OLE, DOBIS Canadian Online Library System. **Publications:** CONTACT (newsletter). **Remarks:** FAX: (506)851-3018.

★2869★
Canada - Transport Canada - Aviation Regulation Library (Trans)
1100, 9700 Jasper Ave.
Edmonton, AB, Canada T5J 4E6 Phone: (403)495-5223
Staff: Prof 1; **Subjects:** Aeronautics. **Special Collections:** Agency archives (aircraft manuals; 11 drawers of microfiche). **Holdings:** 4700 books; 24 drawers of microfiche. **Subscriptions:** 69 journals and other serials. **Services:** Interlibrary loan (limited); copying; library open to the public with restrictions. **Computerized Information Services:** DIALOG Information Services, CAN/OLE; Envoy 100 (electronic mail service). Performs searches on fee basis.

★2870★
Canada - Transport Canada - Canadian Coast Guard - Centre Regional de Documentation (Trans)
104 Dalhousie, Rm. 110 Phone: (418)648-5250
Quebec, PQ, Canada G1K 4B8 Jean Tremblay, Libn.
Founded: 1983. **Staff:** Prof 1. **Subjects:** Maritime transportation, dredging, shipping, seamanship, inland water transport, navigation. **Special Collections:** Transport Canada publications. **Holdings:** 6000 books. **Subscriptions:** 175 journals and other serials. **Services:** Center open to the public. **Automated Operations:** Computerized cataloging, acquisitions, serials, and circulation. **Remarks:** FAX: (418)648-4236.

★2871★
Canada - Transport Canada - Canadian Coast Guard - Eastern Region Library
Harvey Rd.
Box 1300
St. John's, NF, Canada A1C 6H8
Remarks: Currently inactive.

★2872★
Canada - Transport Canada - Canadian Coast Guard College - Library (Trans)
P.O. Box 4500 Phone: (902)564-3660
Sydney, NS, Canada B1P 6L1 David N. MacSween, Libn.
Founded: 1965. **Staff:** Prof 2; Other 2. **Subjects:** Marine and mechanical engineering, navigation, technology. **Special Collections:** Magnetic compass; magnetism of ships (30 books). **Holdings:** 29,000 books; 2000 bound periodical volumes; 300 films; 300 videotapes. **Subscriptions:** 300 journals and other serials. **Services:** Interlibrary loan; copying; library open to the public at librarian's discretion. **Automated Operations:** Computerized cataloging and acquisitions. **Computerized Information Services:** CAN/OLE, iNET 2000, DOBIS Canadian Online Library System; DIALOG Information Services. **Publications:** New Acquisitions, irregular; Serials, annual; AV List, annual. **Remarks:** FAX: (902)564-3672. **Also Known As:** College de la Garde Cotiere Canadienne. **Staff:** Louise McKenna, Asst.Libn.

★2873★
Canada - Transport Canada - Central Region Library and Information Centre (Trans)
333 Main St., 16th Fl.
P.O. Box 8550 Phone: (204)983-6853
Winnipeg, MB, Canada R3C 0P6 Terry Jorba, Reg.Libn.
Founded: 1985. **Staff:** Prof 1. **Subjects:** Air transportation, transportation policy. **Special Collections:** Central Region publications. **Holdings:** 950 books; 80 shelves of government reports and publications. **Subscriptions:** 187 journals and other serials; 5 newspapers. **Services:** Interlibrary loan; reading room for the public. **Automated Operations:** Computerized public access catalog, cataloging, and ILL. **Computerized Information Services:** CAN/OLE, CCINFOdisc, DIALOG Information Services. **Publications:** Recent Acquisitions, irregular - for internal distribution only. **Remarks:** FAX: (204)984-2255.

★2874★
Canada - Transport Canada - Library & Information Services (Trans)
Place de Ville, Tower C Phone: (613)998-5127
Ottawa, ON, Canada K1A 0N5 Jacques Cadieux, Chf.
Founded: 1935. **Staff:** Prof 3; Other 10. **Subjects:** Transportation - air, marine, surface; civil and electrical engineering. **Special Collections:** List of Lights and Fog Signals (Canada), 1902 to present; List of Shipping (Canada), 1901 to present; Notices to Mariners (Canada), 1902 to present; Lloyd's Register, 1905 to present. **Holdings:** 11,000 books and bound periodical volumes; 95,000 government documents and technical reports; 4000 reels of microfilm; 330,000 microfiche. **Subscriptions:** 1200 journals and other serials. **Services:** Interlibrary loan; copying; SDI; library open to the public for reference use only. **Automated Operations:** Computerized cataloging. **Computerized Information Services:** DIALOG Information Services, PFDS Online, CAN/OLE, QL Systems, Infomart Online, Info Globe, DOBIS Canadian Online Library System; Transport Canada Library Information System (TCLIS; internal database); Envoy 100 (electronic mail service). Performs searches on fee basis. **Remarks:** FAX: (613)954-4731. Telex: 053-3130 DOT OTT. Electronic mail address(es): A.HUOT (Envoy 100). **Formerly:** Its Library & Information Centre. **Also Known As:** Transport Canada - Centre de Documentation. **Staff:** Walter Tsang, Hd., Pub.Serv. & Commun.

★2875★
Canada - Transport Canada - Maritimes Region Library (Sci-Engr)
44 Portland St., Suite 202
P.O. Box 1013 Phone: (902)426-5182
Dartmouth, NS, Canada B2Y 4K2 Gary Keirstead, Libn.Techn.
Founded: 1973. **Staff:** Prof 1; Other 1. **Subjects:** Marine safety and engineering, maritime law, oil pollution and its prevention, naval architecture, oceanography, seamanship and navigation, management. **Holdings:** 5000 books; 2000 microfiche; VF drawers of reports, clippings, marine equipment brochures, catalogs. **Subscriptions:** 100 serials. **Services:** Interlibrary loan; copying; library open to the public with restrictions. **Computerized Information Services:** CAN/OLE, QL Systems, DIALOG Information Services, DOBIS Canadian Online Library System; ENVOY 100 (electronic mail service). Performs searches on fee basis. **Remarks:** FAX: (902)426-8337. Electronic mail address(es): ILL.NSHMT (Envoy 100).

★2876★
Canada - Transport Canada - Ontario Region Library (Trans)
4900 Yonge St., Suite 300 Phone: (416)224-3619
North York, ON, Canada M2N 6A5 Eng K. Ching, Reg.Libn.
Founded: 1977. **Staff:** Prof 1. **Subjects:** Air transportation, navigation, and regulation; airport planning. **Special Collections:** Toronto area airports team documents. **Holdings:** 800 books; 7000 reports; 700 microfiche reports. **Subscriptions:** 70 journals and other serials. **Services:** Interlibrary loan; copying; SDI; library open to the public for reference use only. **Automated Operations:** Computerized cataloging. **Computerized Information Services:** DIALOG Information Services, CAN/OLE, DOBIS Canadian Online Library System, Canadian Transportation Documentation System. **Networks/Consortia:** Member of Council of Federal Libraries (CFL). **Publications:** Acquisitions, irregular - for internal distribution only. **Remarks:** FAX: (416)224-3767.

★2877★
Canada - Transport Canada - Regional Library (Trans)
800 Burrard St., Suite 620 Phone: (604)666-5868
Vancouver, BC, Canada V6Z 2J8 J. Jill Rowland, Reg.Libn.
Founded: 1982. **Staff:** Prof 2. **Subjects:** Aviation and marine transportation. **Special Collections:** AK documents (400); International Civil Aviation Organization (ICAO) documents. **Holdings:** 3000 monographs and government documents. **Subscriptions:** 225 journals and other serials; 5 newspapers. **Services:** Interlibrary loan; copying; SDI; library open to the public. **Automated Operations:** Computerized cataloging and serials. **Computerized Information Services:** DIALOG Information Services, CAN/OLE, Infomart Online, DOBIS/LIBIS; Envoy 100 (electronic mail service). **Remarks:** Alternate telephone number(s): 666-5869. FAX: (604)666-6476. Telex: 04-54320. Electronic mail address(es): J.ROWLAND (Envoy 100). **Staff:** Jean Lederer, Libn.

★2878★
Canada - Transport Canada - Training Institute - Technical Information Centre - Library (Sci-Engr)
1950 Montreal Rd.
Bag Service 5400
Cornwall, ON, Canada K6H 6L2 Phone: (613)936-5018
Staff: Prof 3; Other 2. **Subjects:** Transportation, electronics, management, electronic data processing, aeronautics, naval arts and sciences, educational technology. **Holdings:** 4500 volumes; 3500 transportation document titles. **Subscriptions:** 200 journals and other serials; 20 newspapers. **Services:** Interlibrary loan. **Computerized Information Services:** CAN/OLE, DOBIS Canadian Online Library System, DIALOG Information Services.

★2879★
Canada - Transport Canada - Transportation Development Centre - Judith Nogrady Library (Trans)
Guy Favreau Complex
Suite 601, West Tower
200 Rene Levesque Blvd., W. Phone: (514)283-0007
Montreal, PQ, Canada H2Z 1X4 Georgia Ludgate, Hd.Libn.
Founded: 1971. **Staff:** Prof 4; Other 1. **Subjects:** Transportation. **Holdings:** 14,000 books; 3000 periodical volumes; 2500 technical reports; 15,000 slides; 250 videotapes; 4000 photographs. **Subscriptions:** 400 journals and other serials; 5 newspapers. **Services:** Interlibrary loan; library open to the public for reference use only. **Automated Operations:** Computerized cataloging, acquisitions, and serials. **Computerized Information Services:** DIALOG Information Services, CAN/OLE. **Publications:** Recent Acquisitions, quarterly; Serials Currently Received, biennial. **Remarks:** FAX: (514)283-7158. **Also Known As:** Centre de developpement des transports - Bibliotheque Judith Nogrady. **Staff:** Hung Nguyen, Cat.; Meredith Giffin, Acq.; Elaine Joffre, AV.

★2880★
Canada - Transport Canada - Western Regional Library (Trans)
11th Fl., Zone 4
9700 Jasper Ave. Phone: (403)495-3801
Edmonton, AB, Canada T5J 4E6 P.J. Nelson, Regional Libn.
Founded: 1974. **Staff:** Prof 1; Other 3. **Subjects:** Air transportation; airports and construction; telecommunications; engineering; civil aeronautics; social and economic conditions of Alberta, Northwest Territories, and Yukon; management; personnel. **Holdings:** 30,000 monographs and government documents; 8 VF drawers of clippings and pamphlets. **Subscriptions:** 300 journals and other serials; 30 newspapers. **Services:** Interlibrary loan; library

open to the public for reference use only. **Automated Operations:** Computerized cataloging. **Computerized Information Services:** DIALOG Information Services, CAN/OLE, DOBIS Canadian Online Library System; Transport Canada Document System (internal database); Envoy 100 (electronic mail service). **Special Catalogs:** Union catalog of TC library holdings. **Remarks:** FAX: (403)495-4035.

★ 2881 ★
Canada - Transportation Safety Board of Canada - Library (Trans)
PO Box 9120
Alta Vista Terminal Phone: (819)994-8020
Ottawa, ON, Canada K1G 3T8 Lorna Adcock, Lib.Techn.
Founded: 1978. **Staff:** Prof 1. **Subjects:** Transportation - aviation, marine, rail, pipeline. **Special Collections:** Flight Safety Foundation publications; International Civil Aviation Organization (ICAO) publications; Aircraft Technical Publishers Microfiche Library; AGARD reports; international accident reports. **Holdings:** 3500 books. **Subscriptions:** 115 journals and other serials. **Services:** Interlibrary loan; copying; library not open to the public. **Computerized Information Services:** CAN/OLE, DIALOG Information Services, DOBIS Canadian Online Library System. **Remarks:** FAX: (819)997-2239. Telex: 053-4487.

★ 2882 ★
Canada - Veterans Affairs Canada - Library (Mil, Soc Sci)
P.O. Box 7700 Phone: (902)566-8988
Charlottetown, PE, Canada C1A 8M9 M.J. Gaudet, Libn.
Founded: 1944. **Staff:** 2. **Subjects:** Canadian military history, management and personnel, social welfare, psychology. **Holdings:** 6500 books; 17,000 other print items. **Subscriptions:** 254 journals and other serials. **Services:** Interlibrary loan; copying; library open to the public for reference use only. **Computerized Information Services:** DOBIS Canadian Online Library System; Envoy 100 (electronic mail service). **Publications:** Accession list, quarterly. **Remarks:** FAX: (902)566-8525. Electronic mail address(es): ILL.PCV (Envoy 100). **Also Known As:** Affaires des Anciens Combattants Canada.

★ 2883 ★
Canada Centre for Inland Waters - Library (Sci-Engr, Biol Sci)
867 Lakeshore Rd.
Box 5050 Phone: (416)336-4982
Burlington, ON, Canada L7R 4A6 Eve Dowie, Hd., Lib.Serv.
Founded: 1968. **Staff:** Prof 2; Other 3. **Subjects:** Limnology, water research, water pollution, hydraulics, sanitary engineering. **Holdings:** 28,000 books; 120,000 unbound periodicals; 250 dissertations; 18 drawers of microforms. **Subscriptions:** 300 journals and other serials. **Services:** Interlibrary loan; copying; library open by appointment to persons engaged in water research. **Computerized Information Services:** CAN/OLE, DIALOG Information Services. **Remarks:** FAX: (416)336-4989. Electronic mail address(es): OBUC.

Canada Centre for Mapping
See: **Canada - Energy, Mines & Resources Canada - Canada Centre for Mapping** (2698)

Canada Centre for Mineral and Energy Technology
See: **Canada - Energy, Mines & Resources Canada - CANMET** (2699)

Canada Centre for Remote Sensing
See: **Canada - Canada Centre for Remote Sensing** (2667)

★ 2884 ★
Canada College - Russell L. Stimson Ophthalmic Reference Library (Med)
4200 Farm Hill Blvd. Phone: (415)306-3293
Redwood City, CA 94061 Anne L. Nicholls, Coord.
Staff: 1. **Subjects:** Ophthalmology, ophthalmic dispensing and optics, geometrical optics, eye examination, refraction. **Holdings:** 800 books; 30 bound periodical volumes. **Services:** Copying; library open to the public by appointment for reference use.

★ 2885 ★
Canada Council - Arts Research Library (Art)
99 Metcalfe
P.O. Box 1047 Phone: (613)598-4341
Ottawa, ON, Canada K1P 5V8 Gisele Ouellette-Gigault, Adm.Off.
Founded: 1978. **Subjects:** Arts. **Special Collections:** Environment; copyright and artistic sectors (4000 titles). **Holdings:** Books; bound periodical volumes; reports; manuscripts. **Subscriptions:** 37 journals and other serials. **Services:** Library open to the public by appointment. **Publications:** Arts Research Bibliography. **Remarks:** FAX: (613)598-4390. **Formerly:** Its Research and Evaluation Section - Library.

Canada Institute for Scientific and Technical Information (CISTI)
See: **Canada - National Research Council - Canada Institute for Scientific and Technical Information (CISTI)** (2814)

★ 2886 ★
Canada Latin American Resource Centre (Area-Ethnic, Soc Sci)
382 Harbord St. Phone: (416)533-9940
Toronto, ON, Canada M6G 1H9 Aida Morris, Libn.
Founded: 1966. **Staff:** Prof 1. **Subjects:** Latin America, Central America, human rights, Canada's international policy, trade unions, development. **Holdings:** 5000 books. **Subscriptions:** 400 journals and other serials. **Services:** Copying; center open to the public. **Computerized Information Services:** Internal database. **Remarks:** FAX: (416)533-4579.

★ 2887 ★
Canada Life Assurance Company - Corporate Library (Bus-Fin)
330 University Ave. Phone: (416)597-1456
Toronto, ON, Canada M5G 1R8 Nathalie Richard, Libn.
Founded: 1931. **Staff:** 5. **Subjects:** Insurance, allied fields. **Holdings:** 10,500 volumes; 32 VF drawers. **Subscriptions:** 145 journals and other serials. **Services:** Library open to representatives of other insurance companies and members of Special Libraries Association. **Formed by the merger of:** Its Library and Investment Library.

★ 2888 ★
Canada Post Corporation - Corporate Library (Bus-Fin)
Bldg. A, Sta. 124 Phone: (613)734-7928
Ottawa, ON, Canada K1A 0B1 Bruce Moreland, Off., Lib.Serv.
Founded: 1948. **Staff:** Prof 2; Other 3. **Subjects:** Management, labor relations, public administration, postal operations, postal history, engineering, computer science, law, marketing. **Special Collections:** Union Postale Universelle and foreign postal administration publications. **Holdings:** 17,000 monographs; 100 audiocassettes; 500 videocassettes: **Subscriptions:** 1000 periodicals; 12 newspapers. **Services:** Interlibrary loan; copying; library open to the public by appointment. **Automated Operations:** Computerized cataloging (DOBIS). **Computerized Information Services:** DIALOG Information Services, QL Systems, Info Globe, Infomart Online, UTLAS; Envoy 100 (electronic mail service). **Publications:** Accessions report, monthly. **Remarks:** FAX: (613)734-7186.

★ 2889 ★
Canada Safety Council (CSC) - Library
2750 Stevenage Dr., Unit 6
Ottawa, ON, Canada K1G 3N2
Founded: 1968. **Subjects:** Safety - public, occupational, traffic, motorcycle. **Special Collections:** Occupational Safety Data Sheets - Technical Information. **Holdings:** 5000 books; 1500 safety pamphlets; 2500 safety posters. **Remarks:** Currently inactive.

Canada Wire and Cable, Ltd.
See: **Alcatel Canada Wire Inc.** (325)

★ 2890 ★
Canada's Sports Hall of Fame - John W. Davies Library (Rec)
Exhibition Pl. Phone: (416)595-1046
Toronto, ON, Canada M6K 3C3 Cheryl Rielly, Cur.
Founded: 1978. **Staff:** 1. **Subjects:** Canadian sports. **Special Collections:** Canada at the Olympics, 1932-1988; Canadian participation in the Commonwealth Games, Pan American Games, Amateur Athletic Union of Canada; scrapbooks of Barbara Ann Scott and "Torchy" Peden; track and field meet results, 1945-1976. **Holdings:** 200 books. **Services:** Copying; library open to the public by appointment. **Remarks:** FAX: (416)595-1228.

Mariam Coffin Canaday Library
See: **Bryn Mawr College** (2304)

Ward M. Canaday Center
See: **University of Toledo** (19425)

Ward M. Canaday Library
See: **The Good Hope School** (6546)

Canadian Advisory Council on the Status of Women
See: **Canada - Canadian Advisory Council on the Status of Women** (2668)

★2891★
Canadian Airlines - Engineering Library (Sci-Engr)
One Grant McConachie Way
Vancouver International Airport Phone: (604)270-5211
Vancouver, BC, Canada V7B 1V1 Terry Jones, Mgr.
Founded: 1942. **Staff:** 1. **Subjects:** Aviation, engineering, government regulations. **Holdings:** 7000 books; 300 unbound periodicals; 40,000 engineering drawings; 2300 microfiche of maintenance manuals, overhaul manuals, service bulletins, and stock catalogs; business and government documents. **Subscriptions:** 15 journals and other serials. **Services:** Interlibrary loan; copying; library open to the public with prior approval.

★2892★
Canadian Amateur Musicians-Musiciens Amateurs du Canada - Music Library (Mus)
4450 Sherbrooke St., W. Phone: (514)932-8755
Montreal, PQ, Canada H3Z 1E6 Claire Mallin, Adm.
Subjects: Sacred and secular vocal music, orchestral music and concertos, chamber music, recorder music, instrumental music. **Holdings:** 6000 titles. **Services:** Mail order service available in the United States and Canada; library open to the public on a limited schedule. **Special Catalogs:** Catalogs - free to members. **Remarks:** Library is a collection of performance music for amateurs and professionals, individuals and groups.

Canadian Architectural Archives
See: **University of Calgary - Mackimmie Library - Humanities/Arts/ Social Sciences Area** (18292)

★2893★
Canadian Arctic Resources Committee - Douglas Pimlot Memorial Library (Plan)
1 Nicholas St., Suite 412 Phone: (613)236-7379
Ottawa, ON, Canada K1P 7B7 Ann Ray, Ed.
Founded: 1979. **Staff:** 1. **Subjects:** Resource development, northern sovereignty, land claims, hydro development, women's issues, wildlife, land-use planning. **Holdings:** 500 books. **Subscriptions:** 20 journals and other serials; 5 newspapers. **Services:** Interlibrary loan; copying; library open to the public for reference use only. **Remarks:** FAX: (613)232-4665.

Canadian Association for Community Living - G. Allan Roeher Institute
See: **G. Allan Roeher Institute** (14029)

★2894★
Canadian Automobile Association - Library (Trans)
1775 Courtwood Crescent Phone: (613)226-7631
Ottawa, ON, Canada K2C 3J2 L. Chevrier, Libn.
Subjects: Automobile transportation; travel and tourism; traffic - engineering, accidents, and safety; automobile societies; emergency road service. **Special Collections:** Transportation research record series. **Holdings:** 5000 books; 3000 slides; 60 film/video materials; tourbooks. **Subscriptions:** 503 journals and other serials. **Services:** Library not open to the public. **Remarks:** FAX: (613)225-7383.

★2895★
Canadian Bankers Association - Library (Bus-Fin)
2 First Canadian Place, Suite 600
Box 348 Phone: (416)362-6092
Toronto, ON, Canada M5X 1E1 Brian Davidson, Libn.
Staff: Prof 3; Other 1. **Subjects:** Financial institutions. **Special Collections:** Bank annual reports and ratings; CBA publications; banking history. **Holdings:** 10,000 books and documents; 12 VF drawers of subject files. **Subscriptions:** 475 journals and newsletters. **Services:** Interlibrary loan. **Computerized Information Services:** DIALOG Information Services, The Financial Post Information Service, Info Globe, Infomart Online, Mead Data Central, WILSONLINE, QL Systems, Ltd., Reuters TEXTLINE; internal database. **Publications:** What's New (acquisitions list) - for internal distribution only. **Remarks:** FAX: (416)362-7705.

Canadian Baptist Archives
See: **Baptist Convention of Ontario and Quebec - Canadian Baptist Archives** (1498)

★2896★
Canadian Bible College/Canadian Theological Seminary - Archibald Foundation Library (Rel-Phil)
4400 Fourth Ave. Phone: (306)545-1515
Regina, SK, Canada S4T 0H8 H.D. (Sandy) Ayer, Dir., Lib.Serv.
Founded: 1941. **Staff:** Prof 2; Other 6. **Subjects:** Bible, missiology, theology, church growth and history, pastoral theology, Christian education. **Special Collections:** History and thought of the Christian and missionary alliance. **Holdings:** 55,000 books; 3017 bound periodical volumes; 2800 AV programs; 3000 microfiche; 12 drawers of pamphlets. **Subscriptions:** 618 journals and other serials. **Services:** Interlibrary loan; copying; library open to the public with restrictions. **Automated Operations:** Computerized public access catalog, cataloging and acquisitions. **Remarks:** FAX: (306)545-0210. **Staff:** Anne McGillivray, Asst.Libn.

Canadian Book Exchange Centre (CBEC)
See: **Canada - National Library of Canada** (2804)

★2897★
Canadian Book Information Centre
1622 W. 7th Ave.
Vancouver, BC, Canada V6J 1S5
Defunct.

★2898★
Canadian Book Information Centre - Atlantic Region
1741 Barrington St., 4th Fl.
Halifax, NS, Canada B3J 2A4
Defunct.

★2899★
Canadian Book Information Centre - National Office (Publ)
260 King St., E. Phone: (416)362-6555
Toronto, ON, Canada M5A 1K3 Mary Newitt, Natl.Dir.
Founded: 1975. **Staff:** 4. **Subjects:** Marketing and promotion of Canadian books. **Holdings:** 4000 books. **Subscriptions:** 61 journals and other serials. **Services:** Center open to the public. **Computerized Information Services:** Canadian Media List, Telebook, Bookings (internal databases). Performs searches on fee basis. Contact Person: Mark Daniels. **Publications:** For Immediate Release (newsletter), bimonthly - available by subscription; CBIC Media List 1991-92 - for sale. **Special Catalogs:** Canadian Books for Children & Young Adults; Environmental Books; Women's Studies Catalogue; Books About First Nations and Aboriginal Peoples; Literature Catalogue - all available upon request. **Remarks:** The Canadian Book Information Centre is a trade association that develops promotional and marketing programs for Canadian-owned book publishers. Maintained by the Association of Canadian Publishers. FAX: (416)361-0643. **Also Known As:** CBIC. **Staff:** Patti McCabe, Prog.Coord.; Genny Urquhart, Prog.Coord.

★2900★
Canadian Book Publishers' Council - Library (Publ)
215 Merton St., Suite 203
Toronto, ON, Canada M4S 1B1 Phone: (416)322-7011
Subjects: Canadian publishing, education statistics, publishing trade. **Holdings:** 1000 books and bound periodical volumes.

★2901★
Canadian Broadcasting Corporation - Engineering Library (Info Sci)
7925 Cote St. Luc Rd. Phone: (514)485-5546
Montreal, PQ, Canada H4W 1R5 Lysanne St-Laurent, Lib.Techn.
Founded: 1954. **Staff:** Prof 1. **Subjects:** Radio and television, engineering, communications, photography, management. **Holdings:** 2000 volumes. **Subscriptions:** 170 journals and other serials. **Services:** Interlibrary loan; copying; library open to the public by request. **Automated Operations:** Computerized cataloging, acquisitions, and serials. **Computerized Information Services:** DIALOG Information Services, CAN/OLE. **Remarks:** FAX: (514)485-5885.

★2902★
Canadian Broadcasting Corporation - Library (Info Sci)
C.P. 6000 Phone: (514)597-6265
Montreal, PQ, Canada H3C 3A8 Angele Pintal, Hd.Libn.
Founded: 1944. **Staff:** Prof 3; Other 7. **Subjects:** Broadcasting, Canadiana, communication, performing arts, fine arts, current events. **Holdings:** 38,000 books; 24 VF drawers of clippings, pamphlets; 40 VF drawers of pictures; 2222 reels of microfilm of journals and newspapers. **Subscriptions:** 678 journals and other serials; 16 newspapers. **Services:** Interlibrary loan; library not open to the public. **Automated Operations:** Computerized serials. **Computerized Information Services:** Info Globe, DIALOG Information Services, Canada Systems Group (CSG), Canadian Financial Database, The Financial Post Information Service, Infomart Online, Questel, TEXTLINE, WILSONLINE. **Publications:** New acquisitions list - for internal distribution only. **Remarks:** FAX: (514)597-5551. **Also Known As:** Societe Radio-Canada; CBC. **Staff:** Yvon C. Paquin; Michelle Tymocko; Elisabeth Theotikos.

★2903★
Canadian Broadcasting Corporation - Music Library (Mus)
P.O. Box 500, Sta. A. Phone: (416)975-5901
Toronto, ON, Canada M5W 1E6 Rosemary Downing, Supv., Music Lib.
Founded: 1936. **Staff:** Prof 2; Other 9. **Subjects:** Sheet music; music literature and history. **Special Collections:** CBC commissioned works (620 works); scores/parts for TV/radio background music; Canadiana; popular sheet music, 1900-1955 (30,000 titles). **Holdings:** 1500 books; 600 bound periodical volumes; 10 VF drawers of clippings under 4000 music headings; 8 VF drawers of publishers' catalogs; 115 VF drawers of CBC archival arrangements; 250,000 phonograph records; compact discs. **Subscriptions:** 58 journals and other serials. **Services:** Interlibrary loan; library open to music professionals. **Automated Operations:** Computerized cataloging, acquisitions, serials, and circulation. **Special Catalogs:** Catalog of CBC commissions. **Remarks:** Sheet music located at 90 Sumach Street, Toronto, ON. Phonograph records and compact discs housed at 100 Carlton St., Toronto, ON. Library contains the holdings of the former Canadian Broadcasting Corporation - Record Library. **Staff:** Gordon Richardson, Sr.Mus.Libn./Cat.; Jan Cornish, Mus.Libn./Ref.; Rose Fujita, Mus.Libn./Circ.; Dean Ackison, Mus.Libn./Acq.

★2904★
Canadian Broadcasting Corporation - Music & Record Library (Mus)
5600 Sackville St.
Box 3000 Phone: (902)420-4405
Halifax, NS, Canada B3J 3E9 Caroline Grant, Sr.Rec.Libn.
Founded: 1936. **Staff:** 2. **Subjects:** Music. **Holdings:** 200 books; 40,000 phonograph records; 7000 pieces of sheet music and scores. **Subscriptions:** 12 journals and other serials. **Services:** Library open to the public by appointment for serious reference use only. **Automated Operations:** Computerized cataloging, acquisitions, and circulation. **Special Catalogs:** Catalogs of sound recordings - classical music, popular music, irregular - for internal distribution only. **Remarks:** FAX: (902)420-4414.

★2905★
Canadian Broadcasting Corporation - Music Services Library (Mus)
1400 Blvd. Rene Levesque E. Phone: (514)597-6400
Montreal, PQ, Canada H2L 2M2 Louise Champeau, Hd., Music Serv.
Founded: 1936. **Subjects:** Music, music rights. **Special Collections:** 78rpm phonograph records (60,000). **Holdings:** 380,000 phonograph records; 190,000 sheet music titles; 60,000 compact discs. **Subscriptions:** 35 journals and other serials. **Services:** Library not open to the public. **Automated Operations:** Computerized circulation. **Computerized Information Services:** Internal database. **Remarks:** FAX: (514)597-5551. **Staff:** Charlotte Ferland, Supv., Mus. Copyrights; Guy Peloquin, Supv., Mus./Rec.Lib.

★2906★
Canadian Broadcasting Corporation - Radio Archives (Info Sci)
Box 500, Sta. A Phone: (416)975-5880
Toronto, ON, Canada M5W 1E6 Wayne Willoughby, Hd., Radio Archv.
Founded: 1960. **Staff:** Prof 4; Other 7. **Subjects:** News reference topics - national and international politics, events, personalities, and current trends; pop culture; serious music and drama. **Special Collections:** TV and radio news logs (427 microfiche); CBC Times (471 microfiche); CBC program schedules (849 microfiche); radio program logs (361 microfiche). **Holdings:** 1544 books; 100 bound periodical volumes; 199,992 magnetic tapes. **Subscriptions:** 6 journals and other serials. **Services:** Archives open to performers, contracted institutions, graduate students, and serious scholars when material is not available elsewhere. **Automated Operations:** Computerized cataloging. **Computerized Information Services:** Internal databases; CBC E-MAIL (electronic mail service). **Remarks:** FAX: (416)975-7081. Telex: 06-21776 CBC COM TOR. **Staff:** Mary Sharp, Hd.Libn.; Gail Donald, Hd.Res.

★2907★
Canadian Broadcasting Corporation - Record Library (Mus)
541 Portage Ave. Phone: (204)788-3600
Winnipeg, MB, Canada R3C 2H1 Mary A. Worobec, Sr.Libn.
Founded: 1948. **Staff:** Prof 1. **Subjects:** Music, music industry. **Holdings:** 35,000 recordings. **Services:** Library not open to the public. **Remarks:** FAX: (204)788-3685.

★2908★
Canadian Broadcasting Corporation - Reference Library (Info Sci)
365 Church St.
Box 500, Sta. A Phone: (416)975-3244
Toronto, ON, Canada M5W 1E6 Leone Earls, Supv.
Staff: Prof 5; Other 5. **Subjects:** Radio and television broadcasting, Canadiana, current affairs, drama. **Holdings:** 12,000 books; 8000 files of newspaper clippings. **Subscriptions:** 200 journals and other serials; 10 newspapers. **Services:** Interlibrary loan; copying; library open to the public for research on CBC or broadcasting in Canada. **Automated Operations:** Computerized serials. **Computerized Information Services:** Dow Jones News/Retrieval, VU/TEXT Information Services, QL Systems, DIALOG Information Services, Info Globe, LEXIS, NEXIS, STM Systems Corporation, The Financial Post DataGroup, PROFILE Information, Infomart Online. **Publications:** Bibliotalk, irregular - for internal distribution only. **Remarks:** FAX: (416)975-3555. **Staff:** Louise Goldberg, Libn.; Lynda Barnett, Libn.; Anne Mercer, Libn.

★2909★
Canadian Broadcasting Corporation - TV Current Affairs Library (Info Sci)
Box 500, Sta. A. Phone: (416)975-6727
Toronto, ON, Canada M5W 1E6 Diana Redegeld, Supv.
Founded: 1975. **Staff:** Prof 1. **Subjects:** Canada - politics, current affairs, history. **Holdings:** 500 books; 3200 videocassettes. **Subscriptions:** 85 journals and other serials; 30 newspapers. **Services:** Library not open to the public. **Computerized Information Services:** DIALOG Information Services, Info Globe, NEXIS, LEXIS, VU/TEXT Information Services, The Financial Post DataGroup, Infomart Online, QL Systems, PROFILE Information; WIRES (internal database). **Remarks:** FAX: (416)975-6640.

★2910★
Canadian Broadcasting Corporation - TV News Library (Info Sci)
700 Hamilton St. Phone: (604)662-6855
Vancouver, BC, Canada V6B 2R5 Colin Preston, News Libn.
Founded: 1953. **Staff:** 2. **Subjects:** British Columbia news, current affairs, drama and variety television programs and inserts. **Holdings:** 35,000 reels of film; 10,000 videotapes. **Services:** Library open to the public by appointment. **Computerized Information Services:** Internal database. **Remarks:** FAX: (604)662-6878.

★ 2911 ★
Canadian Cancer Society - Library (Med)
193 Sherbrook St.
Winnipeg, MB, Canada R3C 2B7 Phone: (204)774-7483
Remarks: FAX: (204)786-6286. No further information was supplied by respondent.

★ 2912 ★
Canadian Centre for Ecumenism - Library (Rel-Phil)
2065 Sherbrooke St., W. Phone: (514)937-9176
Montreal, PQ, Canada H3H 1G6 Bernice Baranowski, Lib.Coord. & Res.
Founded: 1963. **Staff:** Prof 4; Other 9. **Subjects:** Ecumenism, ecumenical movement, interfaith dialogue, interdenominational dialogue, Christian churches, world religions. **Special Collections:** World Council of Churches collection (books and periodicals); research dossier collection (particular church/religion approaches to authority, ethics, the role of women, social justice, human rights; 300). **Holdings:** 6000 volumes. **Subscriptions:** 200 journals and other serials; 20 newspapers. **Services:** Copying; library open to the public with restrictions. **Publications:** Ecumenism/Oecumenisme, 4/year - by subscription. **Remarks:** FAX: (514)935-5497. **Also Known As:** Centre Canadien d'Oecumenisme. **Staff:** Lucile Laroche, C.N.D., Doc.; Marguerite M. D'Avignon, Lib.Techn.

★ 2913 ★
Canadian Centre for Occupational Health and Safety (Med)
250 Main St., E. Phone: (416)572-4400
Hamilton, ON, Canada L8N 1H6 Peter Lukas, Hd.Libn.
Founded: 1978. **Subjects:** Occupational health and safety. **Special Collections:** Centre international d'informations de securite et d'hygiene du travail, International Labour Office (CIS/ILO) microfiche, 1969 to present. **Holdings:** 24,000 volumes; 222,000 microfiche. **Subscriptions:** 863 journals and other serials. **Services:** Center responds to inquiries; provides both publications service and computerized information service, workshops, and customized membership services. **Computerized Information Services:** Canadian Centre for Occupational Health & Safety, CCINFOdisc, CCINFOline. **Publications:** Annual report; At the Centre, 3/year; Liaison, bimonthly; safety infograms; ergonomic infograms; medical infograms; proceedings of workshops; summary documents on occupational health and safety; list of additional summary publications - available on request. **Remarks:** FAX: (416)572-4500. **Staff:** P.K. Abeytunga, Proj.Dev./Coord.; Kash Manchuk, Comptroller; Anne Graveraux, Dir.,Inquiries Serv.; Eleanor Irwin, Dir.,Oper.Sup.

★ 2914 ★
Canadian Centre for Philanthropy - Library (Bus-Fin)
1329 Bay St., Suite 200 Phone: (416)515-0764
Toronto, ON, Canada M5R 2C4 Rose Van Rotterdam, Dir. for Ntl.Rsrc.Ctr.
Subjects: Philanthropy, fundraising, marketing, voluntarism, management, computers, government legislation. **Holdings:** 1500 volumes. **Subscriptions:** 20 journals and other serials. **Services:** Library open to the public on a limited schedule. **Automated Operations:** Computerized cataloging. **Computerized Information Services:** Philioscan - Canadian foundations (internal database). Performs searches on fee basis. **Publications:** Bibliographies (online); Canadian Directory to Foundations. **Remarks:** FAX: (416)368-0328.

★ 2915 ★
The Canadian Children's Book Centre - Children's Literature Special Collection (Hum)
35 Spadina Rd. Phone: (416)975-0010
Toronto, ON, Canada M5R 2S9 Carol McDougall, Libn.
Founded: 1976. **Staff:** Prof 1. **Special Collections:** Canadian children's literature. **Holdings:** 2000 books; archival items. **Subscriptions:** 50 journals and other serials. **Services:** Center open to the public for reference use only. **Publications:** The Children's Book News (newsletter), quarterly - available on request; Canadian Classics; Awards List. **Special Catalogs:** Our Choice Catalogue. **Remarks:** FAX: (416)975-1839.

★ 2916 ★
Canadian Circumpolar Library (Geog-Map)
Rm. B-03 Cameron
University of Alberta Phone: (403)492-4409
Edmonton, AB, Canada T6G 2J8 Ms. Robin Minion, Hd.Libn.
Founded: 1960. **Staff:** Prof 2; Other 4. **Subjects:** All subjects (including fiction) as they relate to the arctic and cold regions of the world, with particular emphasis on the west Canadian arctic and Alaska. **Special Collections:** Native and northern newspapers; consultant reports on pipelines, MacKenzie Highway, and community development in Northwest Territories; Louis Romanet papers on Hudson Bay Factor; documents used in the compilation of the Peace Athabasca Delta Project; Northern Masters and PhD theses. **Holdings:** 120,000 volumes, including pamphlets; 40 films and videotapes; 47 filmstrips; 190 sound recordings; 1100 reels of microfilm; 20,000 microfiche. **Subscriptions:** 808 journals and other serials. **Services:** Interlibrary loan; copying; library open to the public. **Automated Operations:** Computerized cataloging. **Computerized Information Services:** CAN/OLE, QL Systems; produces Boreal Library Catalog; BITNET, Envoy 100 (electronic mail services). **Publications:** Library Bulletin, monthly - by subscription or on exchange; Northern Titles KWIC Index, monthly - on exchange or by subscription (available online through QL Systems); Circumpolar Research Series of monographs - (available on exchange or purchase); occasional publications; annual report. **Special Indexes:** KWIC Index to newspaper clippings; Northern Titles KWIC index. **Remarks:** FAX: (403)492-4327. Telex: 492-4327. Electronic mail address(es): BINS@UALTAMTS (BITNET); ILL.AEU (Envoy 100).

★ 2917 ★
Canadian Co-operative Association - Library (Bus-Fin)
400-275 Bank St. Phone: (613)238-6711
Ottawa, ON, Canada K2P 2L6 Carol Hunter, Libn.
Founded: 1966. **Staff:** 1. **Subjects:** Cooperatives, credit unions, employee ownership, international development. **Special Collections:** Cooperative pioneers audiotape library (oral histories). **Holdings:** 4000 books; 25 films; 110 videotapes; 154 audiotapes; 12 kits; 37 VF drawers. **Subscriptions:** 82 journals and other serials; 60 newsletters. **Services:** Interlibrary loan; copying; library open to the public with restrictions. **Automated Operations:** Computerized public access catalog and cataloging. **Computerized Information Services:** DIALOG Information Services, Infomart Online, DOBIS Canadian Online Library System, IDRC; Envoy 100 (electronic mail service). **Publications:** Library Services Bulletin, quarterly - to interested researchers, volunteers, employees of cooperatives. **Special Catalogs:** Audiovisual Catalogue - available upon request. **Remarks:** FAX: (613)567-0658. Telex: 053 4406. Electronic mail address(es): CCA.OTT (Envoy 100).

Canadian Coast Guard College
See: **Canada - Transport Canada - Canadian Coast Guard College** (2872)

Canadian Conservation Institute
See: **Canada - Communications Canada - Canadian Conservation Institute** (2672)

★ 2918 ★
Canadian Consulate General - Information Centre (Area-Ethnic)
1251 Avenue of the Americas Phone: (212)768-2400
New York, NY 10020 Curtis L. Field, Lib.Dir.
Founded: 1945. **Staff:** Prof 2; Other 2. **Subjects:** Canadian government and politics, business, industry, trade, history, geography, literature, art, education, law, Canada-U.S. relations. **Special Collections:** Parliamentary Papers, 1867 to present; Canadian Government Publications (selective depository); Statistics Canada (full depository); Annual reports of Canadian companies; Financial Post Corporation Service; federal and provincial statutes. **Holdings:** 7500 books; 10,000 government documents; 44,324 microfiche; 2745 reels of microfilm; 30 drawers of news clippings and pamphlet files; 2 drawers of biography files; 13 drawers of corporation annual reports. **Subscriptions:** 233 journals and other serials; 21 newspapers. **Services:** Interlibrary loan; copying; library open to the public on limited schedule. **Computerized Information Services:** DIALOG Information Services, NEXIS, Info Globe, Dow Jones News/Retrieval, The Financial Post DataGroup, Infomart Online. **Publications:** Library News, bimonthly - for internal distribution only. **Remarks:** FAX:(212)768-2440. Telex: 62014481-DOMCAN NYK. Maintained by Canada - External Affairs Canada. **Staff:** Lorna Cheriton, Asst.Libn.

Canadian Council on Children and Youth
See: **Children Enfants Jeunesse Youth** (3561)

★2919★
Canadian Council on Social Development - Resource Centre (Soc Sci)
55 Parkdale Ave.
Box 3505, Sta. C Phone: (613)728-1865
Ottawa, ON, Canada K1Y 4G1 Odette Barrington, Rsrc.Ctr.Off.
Founded: 1921. **Staff:** Prof 1. **Subjects:** Social welfare, social policy, housing, justice, employment. **Special Collections:** Historical Canada Social Welfare Collection. **Holdings:** 20,000 books; 7 drawers of subject files. **Subscriptions:** 50 journals and other serials. **Services:** Interlibrary loan; copying; center open to the public by appointment for reference use only and on a limited schedule. **Automated Operations:** Computerized cataloging, and serials. **Computerized Information Services:** DOBIS Canadian Online Library System, CAN/OLE, iNET 2000, BRS Information Technologies, Infomart Online; Envoy 100 (electronic mail service). **Publications:** Perception, 4/year; Vis-a-vis, 4/year; Overview, quarterly; Initiative, 4/year. **Remarks:** FAX: (613)728-9387. Electronic mail address(es): C.C.S.D. (Envoy 100). **Also Known As:** Conseil Canadien de Developpement Social.

★2920★
Canadian County Historical Museum - Library (Trans)
300 S. Grand
El Reno, OK 73036 Phone: (405)262-5121
Founded: 1970. **Staff:** 4. **Subjects:** History of Canadian County; Chicago, Rock Island & Pacific Railway; American railroads; medicine; school textbooks. **Holdings:** 500 books; 300 other cataloged items; 4 VF drawers of clippings; 3 VF drawers of documents; 30 cassette Tapes; 4 VF drawers of old photographs. **Services:** Library open to the public for reference use only. **Publications:** Bulletin, irregular.

★2921★
Canadian Deaf & Hard of Hearing Forum - Resource Library (Med)
2435 Holly Ln., Suite 205 Phone: (613)526-4867
Ottawa, ON, Canada K1V 7P2 Yvette Kereluk, Hd.
Subjects: Hearing impairement - legal rights, education, technical aids. **Holdings:** Figures not available. **Remarks:** FAX: (613)526-4718.

★2922★
Canadian Dental Association - Sydney Wood Bradley Memorial Library (Med)
1815 Alta Vista Dr. Phone: (613)523-1770
Ottawa, ON, Canada K1N 6E7 Martha Vaughan, Libn.
Founded: 1950. **Staff:** Prof 2; Other 2. **Subjects:** Dentistry, dental health, dental hygiene, dental research, business, medicine. **Holdings:** 5100 books; 1320 bound periodical volumes; internal documents; governmnet reports. **Subscriptions:** 207 journals and other serials. **Services:** Interlibrary loan; copying; SDI; library open to the public with restrictions. **Computerized Information Services:** MEDLINE; Envoy 100 (electronic mail service). Performs searches on fee basis. **Publications:** Bibliographies. **Remarks:** FAX: (613)523-7736. **Staff:** Marsha Maslove, Lib.Techn.

Canadian Dermatological Association Archives
See: **McGill University - Osler Library** (9908)

★2923★
Canadian Diabetes Association - National Office Archives (Med)
78 Bond St. Phone: (416)362-4440
Toronto, ON, Canada M5B 2J8 Marian Cooke, Libn.-Archv.
Founded: 1981. **Subjects:** Diabetes. **Holdings:** 50 books; association minutes and annual reports; pamphlets; films; cassettes; scrapbooks. **Services:** Archives open to the public with permission.

★2924★
Canadian Education Association - Library (Educ)
252 Bloor St., W., Suite 8-200 Phone: (416)924-7721
Toronto, ON, Canada M5S 1V5 Diane Sibbett, Libn.
Founded: 1957. **Staff:** Prof 2. **Subjects:** Elementary and secondary education in Canada. **Holdings:** 4000 books; 36 VF drawers of clippings and pamphlets. **Subscriptions:** 300 journals and other serials. **Services:** Interlibrary loan; library open to the public. **Remarks:** FAX: (416)924-3188. **Also Known As:** Association Canadienne d'Education.

Canadian Energy Research Institute - I.N. McKinnon Memorial Library
See: **I.N. McKinnon Memorial Library** (9933)

★2925★
Canadian Environmental Law Association - Library (Law, Env-Cons)
517 College St., Suite 401 Phone: (416)960-2284
Toronto, ON, Canada M6G 4A2 Mary Vise, Libn.
Founded: 1975. **Staff:** 1. **Subjects:** Canadian environmental law, Great Lakes - pollution (including legal aspects), pesticides, forestry; environmental aspects of free trade. **Holdings:** 1200 books; 6500 reports. **Subscriptions:** 160 journals and other serials. **Services:** Interlibrary loan; copying (limited); library open to the public. **Automated Operations:** Computerized public access catalog. **Remarks:** FAX: (416)960-9392. **Staff:** Christine Beckermann, Asst.Libn.

★2926★
Canadian Ethnic Studies Association - Research Unit for Canadian Ethnic Studies (Area-Ethnic)
University of Calgary
2500 University Dr., N.W. Phone: (403)220-7257
Calgary, AB, Canada T2N 1N4 Dr. Howard Palmer, Dir.
Staff: Prof 10. **Subjects:** Ethnicity in academia, history, sociology, anthropology, political science, and education. **Special Collections:** Ethnic newspapers and publications. **Holdings:** Figures not available. **Subscriptions:** 12 journals and other serials; 35 newspapers. **Services:** Research unit open to researchers. **Automated Operations:** Computerized acquisitions. **Publications:** Canadian Ethnic Studies Journal; bibliography, annual. **Special Indexes:** Index of articles received; index of book reviews for publication. **Remarks:** FAX: (403)282-8606. Telex: 03 821545.

★2927★
Canadian Exporters' Association - Library (Bus-Fin)
99 Bank St., Suite 250 Phone: (613)238-8888
Ottawa, ON, Canada K1P 6B9 J. D. Moore
Founded: 1943. **Staff:** 2. **Subjects:** Trade statistics, regional geographic and economic groups, international organizations, international transport, export and international business, foreign investment. **Holdings:** 5000 books. **Services:** Interlibrary loan; copying; library open to members and open to the public at librarian's discretion. **Remarks:** FAX: (613)563-9218.

★2928★
Canadian Federation of Independent Business (CFIB) - Research Library (Bus-Fin)
4141 Yonge St. Phone: (416)222-8022
Toronto, ON, Canada M2P 2A6 Katalin Coorsh, Mgr., Lib.Serv.
Staff: Prof 1.5; Other 2. **Subjects:** Small business, entreprenuership, economic policy, politics and government. **Special Collections:** International Small Business Conference proceedings. **Holdings:** 4000 volumes; 20 VF drawers of subject files; annual reports. **Subscriptions:** 300 journals and other serials; 6 newspapers. **Services:** Interlibrary loan; copying; library open to the public by appointment only. **Computerized Information Services:** DIALOG Information Services, Info Globe, Infomart Online. **Publications:** Library newsletter - for internal distribution only; research materials and publications on small business in Canada, irregular - for internal distribution only. **Remarks:** FAX: (416)222-4337. **Staff:** Ryla Snider Lightman, Lib.Cons.

★2929★
Canadian Film Institute - National Science Film Library
115 Torbay Rd., Unit 9
Markham, ON, Canada L3R 2M9
Founded: 1961. **Subjects:** Health and medicine, earth sciences, physical and engineering sciences, behavioral and biological sciences, geography and history, arts, performing arts and film. **Holdings:** 6000 16mm film and videotape titles. **Remarks:** Maintained by L.M. Media Marketing Services Ltd. Currently inactive. **Also Known As:** Institut Canadien du Film.

Canadian Forces College
See: **Canada - National Defence - Canadian Forces College** (2779)

★ 2930 ★
Canadian Foundation for Children, Youth and the Law - Justice for Children and Youth Resource Centre (Law)
720 Spadina Ave., Suite 405 Phone: (416)920-1633
Toronto, ON, Canada M5S 2T9 Doreen Way, Exec.Asst.
Founded: 1978. **Staff:** 1. **Subjects:** Children's rights and legal representation, education, child welfare and abuse, medical and foster care, family law. **Holdings:** 2000 books; 355 bound periodical volumes; clipping files; subject files; government reports; organization information files; government documents. **Subscriptions:** 230 journals and other serials. **Services:** Interlibrary loan; copying; center open to the public. **Publications:** Newsletter, 2/year. **Remarks:** FAX: (416)920-5855.

★ 2931 ★
Canadian Foundation for Economic Education - Resource Centre (Bus-Fin)
2 St. Clair W., No. 501 Phone: (416)968-2236
Toronto, ON, Canada M4V 1L5 Judith Jackson, Rsrc.Ctr.Dir.
Founded: 1977. **Staff:** Prof 1. **Subjects:** Economics, economic education. **Holdings:** 2000 books; 5 VF drawers of clippings. **Subscriptions:** 165 journals and other serials. **Services:** Interlibrary loan; copying; center open to the public by appointment. **Special Indexes:** Index of journal articles received in resource centre (card). **Remarks:** FAX: (416)968-0488.

★ 2932 ★
Canadian Gas Association - Library and Information Centre (Energy)
55 Scarsdale Rd. Phone: (416)447-6465
Don Mills, ON, Canada M3B 2R3 B. Cayley
Founded: 1984. **Staff:** Prof 1. **Subjects:** Gas industry policy, energy statistics, gas appliance and equipment standards, indoor air quality, natural gas vehicles. **Special Collections:** Canadian gas utility advertisements. **Holdings:** 1080 books. **Subscriptions:** 115 journals and other serials. **Services:** Interlibrary loan; copying; library open to the public by appointment. **Automated Operations:** Computerized cataloging. **Computerized Information Services:** CAN/OLE, DIALOG Information Services, Info Globe, Infomart Online, QL Systems; Envoy 100 (electronic mail service). Performs searches on fee basis. **Publications:** Bibliography of gas-related literature, irregular - distributed to Canadian Gas Association member libraries. **Remarks:** FAX: (416)447-7067.

★ 2933 ★
Canadian Gay Archives - James Fraser Library (Soc Sci)
Sta. A, Box 639 Phone: (416)921-6310
Toronto, ON, Canada M5W 1G2 Harold Averill, Pres.
Founded: 1973. **Staff:** Prof 9. **Subjects:** Homosexuality, lesbianism, gay liberation movement, censorship. **Special Collections:** Records of lesbian and gay organizations and individuals (260 linear meters); 2000 sound recordings; 1600 posters; 1000 artifacts (includes baseball uniforms, T-shirts, banners, pins, and matchbook covers). **Holdings:** 5000 books; 8 linear meters of clippings; 375 hours of audiotapes; 80 hours of videotapes; 3000 lesbian and gay periodical titles; 1900 other periodical titles; 5000 photographs; 12,500 vertical files. **Subscriptions:** 350 journals and other serials. **Services:** Copying; library open to the public. **Publications:** Gay Archivist (newsletter), irregular; publications series (12 titles - bibliographies, manuals, historical sketches); brochures. **Special Indexes:** Index to published material (card); partial index to Body Politic; partial index to clippings; finding aids, inventories to somearchives and poster collection.

★ 2934 ★
Canadian General Electric Company, Ltd. - Engineering Library (Sci-Engr)
107 Park St., N. Phone: (705)748-7745
Peterborough, ON, Canada K9J 7B5 Donald Friar
Staff: Prof 1. **Subjects:** Science and technology, engineering. **Holdings:** American Institute of Electrical Engineers (AIEE) and Institute of Electrical and Electronics Engineers (IEEE) transactions; Conference Internationale des Grands Reseaux Electriques/International Conference on Large High Tension Electric Systems (CIGRE) reports. **Subscriptions:** 203 journals and other serials. **Services:** Library not open to the public. **Publications:** Library newsletter. **Remarks:** Alternate telephone number(s): (705)748-7861. FAX: (705)748-7859.

Canadian Health Libraries Association Archives
See: **McGill University - Osler Library** (9908)

★ 2935 ★
Canadian Hearing Society - Library (Med)
271 Spadina Rd. Phone: (416)964-9595
Toronto, ON, Canada M5R 2V3 Marion Baker, Libn.
Subjects: Hearing impairment, education of the deaf, social work and rehabilitation in the field of hearing loss. **Holdings:** 600 books; 3 VF drawers of reports and reprints. **Subscriptions:** 22 journals and other serials. **Services:** Copying; library open to the public with restrictions. **Computerized Information Services:** Envoy 100 (electronic mail service). **Remarks:** FAX: (146)964-2066. TDD: 964-0023.

Canadian Housing Information Centre
See: **Canada - Mortgage and Housing Corporation** (2765)

★ 2936 ★
Canadian Human Rights Commission - Main Library (Soc Sci, Law)
1300-320 Queen St.
Ottawa, ON, Canada K1A 1E1 Phone: (613)995-9481
Founded: 1978. **Staff:** Prof 1; Other 1. **Subjects:** Human and civil rights, pay equity, employment discrimination. **Special Collections:** CHRC tribunal transcripts. **Holdings:** 5000 books. **Subscriptions:** 150 journals and other serials. **Services:** Interlibrary loan; library open to the public for reference use only. **Automated Operations:** Computerized public access catalog. **Computerized Information Services:** DIALOG Information Services, Infomart Online, Info Globe, DOBIS Canadian Online Library System; Envoy 100 (electronic mail service). **Remarks:** FAX: (613)996-9661. Electronic mail address(es): LIBRARY.CHRC (Envoy 100).

★ 2937 ★
Canadian Hunter Exploration, Ltd. - Library (Sci-Engr)
435 4th Ave., S.W. Phone: (403)260-1716
Calgary, AB, Canada T2P 3A8 Maureen Miller, Lib.Coord.
Subjects: Earth sciences, petroleum engineering. **Holdings:** 5000 books. **Subscriptions:** 250 journals and other serials. **Services:** Interlibrary loan; library not open to the public. **Computerized Information Services:** DIALOG Information Services, ORBIT Search Service, Info Globe, Infomart Online, DOBIS Canadian Online Library System. **Remarks:** FAX: (403)260-1899.

★ 2938 ★
Canadian Imperial Bank of Commerce - Business Information (Bus-Fin)
Head Office - Commerce Court Phone: (416)980-3053
Toronto, ON, Canada M5L 1A2 Cynthea Penman, Mgr.
Founded: 1971. **Staff:** Prof 7; Other 6. **Subjects:** Banks and banking, finance, industry, business, economics. **Special Collections:** Annual reports of Canadian chartered banks, 1867 to present. **Holdings:** 22,000 titles; 1500 files of clippings and pamphlets; 30 newspapers titles on microform; Statistics Canada publications; Canadian corporate reports on microfiche. **Subscriptions:** 3000 serials including annuals. **Services:** Center open to officers of the corporation and corporate members (fee). **Automated Operations:** Computerized cataloging, circulation, acquisitions, and serials. **Computerized Information Services:** DIALOG Information Services, Info Globe, Infomart Online, Dow Jones News/Retrieval, VU/TEXT Information Services, InvesText, Mead Data Central, REUTERS; CD-ROMs (DISCLOSURE, Lotus One Source, Moody's International, Statistics Canada Catalogue Online). **Publications:** BIRM Bulletin; Monthly News and Acquisitions List - for internal distribution only. **Remarks:** FAX: (416)861-3666. Library located at 25 King St. W., Commerce Court N., 7th Fl., Toronto, ON. **Staff:** Philomena Pun, Asst.Mgr.

★ 2939 ★
Canadian Industrial Innovation Centre/Waterloo - Resource Centre (Sci-Engr)
156 Columbia St., W. Phone: (519)885-5870
Waterloo, ON, Canada N2L 3L3 Carol Stewart, Libn.
Founded: 1981. **Staff:** 1. **Subjects:** Technological innovation, invention, entrepreneurship, beginning businesses, patents, licensing. **Holdings:** 600 books and bound periodical volumes. **Subscriptions:** 20 journals and other serials; 5 newspapers. **Services:** Copying; center open to the public for reference use only. **Automated Operations:** Computerized cataloging. **Computerized Information Services:** DIALOG Information Services, Info Globe, iNET 2000; Spires (University of Waterloo internal database); COSY (electronic mail service). Performs searches on fee basis. Contact Person: Gary Svoboda, Mktg.Mgr. **Remarks:** FAX: (519)885-5729. Toll-free telephone number(s): (800)265-4559. Center operated with support from the University of Waterloo and Canada - Department of Industry, Science & Technology.

★2940★
Canadian Institute of Chartered Accountants - Studies & Standards Department Library (Bus-Fin)
150 Bloor St., W. Phone: (416)927-2375
Toronto, ON, Canada M5S 2Y2 Gerald B. Gerard, Libn.
Founded: 1980. **Staff:** 1. **Subjects:** Accounting, auditing. **Holdings:** 5000 volumes. **Subscriptions:** 85 journals and other serials; 5 newspapers. **Services:** Library not open to the public. **Remarks:** FAX: (416)962-3375.

★2941★
Canadian Institute of Credit and Financial Management - Research and Lending Library (Bus-Fin)
5090 Explorer Dr., Suite 501 Phone: (416)629-9805
Mississauga, ON, Canada L4W 3T9 D. Nichols, Exec.Dir.
Founded: 1968. **Staff:** 1. **Subjects:** Credit and financial management, commercial law, accounting, economics, financial statement analysis, business administration, marketing. **Holdings:** 3500 volumes. **Subscriptions:** 44 journals and other serials. **Services:** Library open to members only. **Remarks:** FAX: (416)629-9809.

★2942★
Canadian Institute of Guided Ground Transport - Information Centre (Trans)
Queen's University Phone: (613)545-2810
Kingston, ON, Canada K7L 3N6 Alice Pignal, Info.Off.
Founded: 1972. **Staff:** Prof 1. **Subjects:** Railroads - hazardous materials transport by rail, track/train dynamics, railway costs, energy. **Special Collections:** C.I.G.G.T. Railway Library Series. **Holdings:** 15,000 volumes of technical report literature; microfiche. **Subscriptions:** 100 journals and other serials. **Services:** Interlibrary loan; copying; center open to the public. **Automated Operations:** Computerized cataloging. **Computerized Information Services:** Online systems. **Publications:** C.I.G.G.T. Newsletter; abstract list; publication list. **Special Indexes:** Pre-catalog Information List, weekly - for internal distribution only; C.I.G.G.T. Reports, irregular - for sale. **Remarks:** FAX: (613)545-3856.

★2943★
Canadian Institute of Hypnotism - Library (Med)
110 Greystone Phone: (514)426-1010
Pointe Claire, PQ, Canada H9R 5T6 Maxine Kershaw, Coord.
Founded: 1954. **Staff:** 1. **Subjects:** Hypnosis - medical, dental, historical. **Holdings:** 1100 books; 45 bound periodical volumes. **Subscriptions:** 5 journals and other serials. **Services:** Interlibrary loan; library open to the public with restrictions. **Remarks:** FAX: (514)426-4680.

★2944★
Canadian Institute of International Affairs - Library (Soc Sci)
15 King's College Circle Phone: (416)979-1851
Toronto, ON, Canada M5S 2V9 Jane R. Barrett, Libn.
Founded: 1945. **Staff:** Prof 1; Other 2. **Subjects:** International relations, politics, Canadian foreign relations. **Holdings:** 20,000 books; 3000 bound periodical volumes; 9000 pamphlets; 120 drawers of clippings. **Subscriptions:** 75 journals and other serials; 10 newspapers. **Services:** Interlibrary loan; copying; library open to the public. **Automated Operations:** Computerized cataloging. **Computerized Information Services:** Canadian foreign relations internal database (available online via DIALOG Information Services.); Envoy 100 (electronic mail service). Performs searches on fee basis. **Publications:** Bibliography of works on Canadian foreign relations, 1976-1980, Supplement, 1981-1985. **Remarks:** FAX: (416)979-8575. Electronic mail address(es): CIIA.LIB (Envoy 100).

Canadian Institute of Resources Law
See: **University of Calgary** (18286)

★2945★
Canadian Institute of Steel Construction - Head Office Library (Plan)
201 Consumers Rd., Suite 300
Willowdale, ON, Canada M2J 4G8 Phone: (416)491-4552
Founded: 1942. **Holdings:** 5000 books; technical reports. **Services:** Library open to the public. **Remarks:** FAX: (416)491-6461.

Canadian International College - David Thompson Library
See: **David Thompson Library** (16317)

Canadian International Development Agency
See: **Canada - Canadian International Development Agency** (2670)

★2946★
Canadian Jewellers Institute - Gerstein/Tiffany Library (Sci-Engr)
20 Eglinton Ave., W., Suite 1203
P.O. Box 2021 Phone: (416)480-1424
Toronto, ON, Canada M4R 1K8 Susan Tunney, Inst.Coord.
Staff: Prof 2. **Subjects:** Precious metals, gemstones, watches, management, salesmanship. **Holdings:** 400 books; 385 bound periodical volumes; 30 16mm films; 45 videotapes; trade publications; government reports. **Subscriptions:** 16 journals and other serials. **Services:** Interlibrary loan (limited); library open to members. **Remarks:** FAX: (416)480-2342.

★2947★
Canadian Jewish Congress - Jewish Federation of Greater Toronto - Ontario Region Archives (Area-Ethnic)
4600 Bathurst St. Phone: (416)635-2883
Willowdale, ON, Canada M2R 3V2 Dr. Stephen A. Speisman, Dir.
Founded: 1973. **Staff:** Prof 2; Other 20. **Subjects:** Jews in Ontario. **Holdings:** 6000 photographs; minutes and correspondence; microfilm; oral history tapes; memorabilia. **Services:** Interlibrary loan (limited); copying; archives open to the public. **Automated Operations:** Computerized cataloging (INMAGIC). **Computerized Information Services:** Internal database. **Remarks:** FAX: (416)635-1408. **Formerly:** Canadian Jewish Congress - Toronto Jewish Congress. **Staff:** Mrs. Brooky Robins, Asst. to Dir.

★2948★
Canadian Jewish Congress - Jewish Historical Society of Western Canada - Archives (Area-Ethnic)
404-365 Hargrave St. Phone: (204)942-4822
Winnipeg, MB, Canada R3B 2K3 Bonnie Tregobov, Archv.
Founded: 1968. **Staff:** 2. **Subjects:** History of the Jewish people of Western Canada. **Holdings:** 150 linear feet of documents; 4550 photographs and negatives; 450 oral history tapes and transcripts. **Subscriptions:** 6 journals and other serials. **Services:** Archives open to the public on request. **Special Indexes:** Newspaper index of local Yiddish and Anglo-Jewish press (online).

★2949★
Canadian Jewish Congress - National Archives (Area-Ethnic)
1590 Ave. Docteur Penfield Phone: (514)931-7531
Montreal, PQ, Canada H3G 1C5 Janice Rosen, Dir./Archv.
Founded: 1919. **Staff:** Prof 2; Other 2. **Subjects:** Jewish Canadiana. **Holdings:** Records of the Canadian Jewish Congress; large collection of personal and institutional archives relating to Canadian Jewish community. **Services:** Copying; archives open to the public by appointment. **Computerized Information Services:** Internal database. **Publications:** Canadian Jewish Archives, irregular; National Archives Newsletter. **Remarks:** FAX: (514)931-0548. **Staff:** David Rome, Hist.

Canadian Jewish Congress - Toronto Jewish Congress
See: **Canadian Jewish Congress - Jewish Federation of Greater Toronto** (2947)

Canadian Land Forces Command and Staff College
See: **Canada - National Defence - Fort Frontenac Library** (2783)

★2950★
Canadian Legal Information Centre - Resource Centre
161 Laurier Ave., W., 5th Fl.
Ottawa, ON, Canada K1P 1P3
Defunct.

★2951★
Canadian Legal Information Centre - Resource Centre (Law)
600 Eglinton Ave., E., Suite 205 Phone: (416)483-3802
Toronto, ON, Canada M4P 1P3 Anna Visy, Libn.
Founded: 1984. **Staff:** 2. **Subjects:** Access to justice; public legal education; plain language; law-related education. **Holdings:** 8000 monographs. **Subscriptions:** 200 journals and other serials; 2 newspapers. **Services:** Interlibrary loan; copying; SDI; library open to the public. **Computerized Information Services:** DIALOG Information Services, Infomart Online; internal databases. **Publications:** List of publications - available on request. **Remarks:** FAX: (416)483-4436. **Staff:** Tammy Ferrell, Lib.Techn.

Canadian Library of Family Medicine
See: **College of Family Physicians of Canada** (3891)

★2952★
Canadian Lutheran Bible Institute - Library (Rel-Phil)
4837 52A St. Phone: (403)672-4454
Camrose, AB, Canada T4V 1W5 Joyce Rasmussen, Libn.
Staff: Prof 1. **Subjects:** Biblical studies, biblical theology, biblical archaeology, mission studies, practical theology, church history. **Holdings:** 10,000 books; 43 bound periodical volumes; 576 audio cassettes. **Subscriptions:** 68 journals and other serials. **Services:** Library open to the public.

★2953★
Canadian Marconi Company - Kanata - Library (Sci-Engr)
415 Legget Dr.
Box 249 Phone: (613)592-6500
Kanata, ON, Canada K2K 2B2 Lois Brimacombe, Hd.Libn.
Founded: 1985. **Staff:** Prof 1. **Subjects:** Engineering, aeronautics, telecommunications, microwave engineering. **Holdings:** 1150 volumes. **Subscriptions:** 120 journals and other serials. **Services:** Interlibrary loan; library not open to the public. **Computerized Information Services:** CAN/OLE, iNET 2000, DIALOG Information Services. **Remarks:** FAX: (613)592-7427. Telex: 053-4805 (ARCON OTT).

★2954★
Canadian Marconi Company - Montreal - Library (Sci-Engr)
2442 Trenton Ave.
Box 35 Phone: (514)341-7630
Montreal, PQ, Canada H3P 1Y9 Mary Thomson-Oliver, Libn.
Staff: Prof 1. **Subjects:** Engineering, aeronautics, telecommunications, microwave engineering. **Holdings:** 4500 books; 1500 bound periodical volumes. **Subscriptions:** 100 journals and other serials. **Services:** Interlibrary loan; library not open to the public. **Automated Operations:** Computerized public access catalog and cataloging. **Computerized Information Services:** DIALOG Information Services, CAN/OLE. **Remarks:** FAX: (514)340-3100. Telex: 05 827822.

Canadian Marketing Associates
See: **Tandem International Inc.** (16004)

★2955★
Canadian Meat Council - Technical Library (Food-Bev)
5233 Dundas St., W., Suite 304 Phone: (416)239-8411
Islington, ON, Canada M9B 1A6 Veena Shankar, Libn.
Founded: 1975. **Staff:** 1. **Subjects:** Microbiology, nutrition, meat science, additives, meat research, sanitation. **Holdings:** 900 books; CMC annual reports. **Subscriptions:** 50 journals and other serials. **Services:** Library open to CMC members only. **Remarks:** FAX: (416)239-2416.

★2956★
Canadian Medical Association - Library (Med)
1867 Alta Vista Dr.
P.O. Box 8650 Phone: (613)731-9331
Ottawa, ON, Canada K1G 0G8 Kathleen Beaudoin, Libn.
Founded: 1955. **Staff:** Prof 2. **Subjects:** Medicine. **Holdings:** 900 books; 1250 bound periodical volumes; 900 other cataloged items. **Subscriptions:** 400 journals and other serials. **Services:** Interlibrary loan; copying; library open to physicians and other libraries. **Computerized Information Services:** MEDLARS, BRS Information Technologies, DOBIS Canadian Online Library System, iNET 2000, CAN/OLE, Infomart Online, CAN/LAW, QUIC/LAW. **Special Indexes:** Index to Canadian Medical Association Journal, semiannual; index to Canadian Journal of Surgery, annual. **Remarks:** FAX: (613)731-9013.

★2957★
Canadian Memorial Chiropractic College - C.C. Clemmer Health Sciences Library (Med)
1900 Bayview Ave. Phone: (416)482-2340
Toronto, ON, Canada M4G 3E6 Marilyn E. Schafer, Dir., Lib.Serv.
Founded: 1945. **Staff:** Prof 4; Other 5. **Subjects:** Chiropractic, orthopedics, sports medicine, nutrition, radiology, neurology. **Special Collections:** History of chiropractic collection (1000 books). **Holdings:** 13,300 books; 5600 bound periodical volumes; 6000 reprints; 25,667 slides; 401 slide-tape presentations; 540 x-ray transparencies; 2004 audiocassettes; 374 videocassettes; 81 videotapes; 69 films; 36 phonograph records; 25 charts; 27 anatomical models; 20 computer assisted instructions (CAI). **Subscriptions:** 419 journals and other serials. **Services:** Interlibrary loan; copying; library open to the public for reference use only. **Computerized Information Services:** MEDLARS, DIALOG Information Services, CAN/OLE, Data-Star; OnTyme Electronic Message Network Service, Envoy 100 (electronic mail services). Performs searches on fee basis. **Networks/Consortia:** Member of Chiropractic Library Consortium (CLIBCON). **Publications:** Chiropractic Research Abstracts Collection (CRAC), annual. **Remarks:** FAX: (416)482-9745. Electronic mail address(es): CMCC (Envoy 100). **Staff:** Margaret Butkovic, AV Libn.; Subash Gandhi, Tech.Serv.Libn.; Mary Boite, Ref.Libn.; Valda Srede, Ref.Libn.

★2958★
Canadian Mennonite Bible College - Library (Rel-Phil)
600 Shaftesbury Blvd. Phone: (204)888-6781
Winnipeg, MB, Canada R3P 0M4 Paul Friesen, Libn.
Founded: 1947. **Staff:** 2. **Holdings:** 41,000 books. **Subscriptions:** 210 journals and other serials; 10 newspapers. **Services:** Interlibrary loan; library open to the public. **Computerized Information Services:** BIB-BASE (internal database).

★2959★
Canadian Mental Health Association - Windsor-Essex County Branch Library (Med)
880 Ouellette Ave., Suite 901 Phone: (519)255-7440
Windsor, ON, Canada N9A 1C7 Patricia Hayward, Mgr., Educ. & Prevention
Founded: 1980. **Subjects:** Bereavement, mental health, stress. **Holdings:** 500 books; 40 AV programs. **Subscriptions:** 5 journals and other serials. **Services:** Copying; library open to the public with restrictions. **Publications:** Nexus (newsletter). **Remarks:** FAX: (519)255-7817.

★2960★
Canadian Mental Health Association, Alberta Division - Suicide Information and Education Centre (Soc Sci)
No. 201 1615 10th Ave., S.W. Phone: (403)245-3900
Calgary, AB, Canada T3C 0J7 G.G. Harrington, Dir.
Founded: 1982. **Staff:** Prof 2; Other 1. **Subjects:** Suicidal behaviors, suicide prevention, bereavement. **Holdings:** 17,000 articles, manuscripts, documents, films, tapes, theses, cassettes; information kits. **Subscriptions:** 14 journals and other serials. **Services:** Interlibrary loan; document delivery; center open to the public. **Computerized Information Services:** iNET 2000, Suicide Information and Education Centre (SIEC). Performs searches on fee basis. **Publications:** SIEC Monthly Clipping Service; SIEC Current Awareness Bulletin, quarterly - both by subscription; bibliographies (online); selected reading lists; print information kits - for sale; Suicide in Older Adults: Selected Readings; Youth Suicide Awareness: Presenter's Handbook; SIEC User's Manual (includes SIEC Theasurus of Subject Terms & Guide to Searching). **Special Catalogs:** Youth Suicide Audiovisual Catalog - for sale. Film and video list. **Staff:** Karen Kiddey, Lib.Coord.

Canadian Meteorological Centre/Numerical Prediction Research
See: **Canada - Environment Canada** (2708)

★2961★
Canadian Military Engineers Museum - Research Library
M.P.O. 612
Canadian Forces Base
Chilliwack, BC, Canada V0X 2E0
Founded: 1956. **Subjects:** Military engineering, military history, Corps of Engineers history. **Holdings:** 2000 books; 1000 bound periodical volumes; 1000 pamphlets; 10 boxes of documents; 150 maps; 12 drawers of photographs. **Remarks:** Currently inactive.

Canadian Museum of Caricature
See: **Canada - National Archives of Canada - Documentary Art and Photography Division** (2769)

★**2962**★
Canadian Museum of Civilization - Library (Soc Sci, Area-Ethnic)
100 Laurier St.
P.O. Box 3100, Station B Phone: (819)776-7173
Hull, PQ, Canada J8X 4H2 Manon Guilbert, Act.Chf.Libn.
Founded: 1842. **Staff:** Prof 4; Other 9. **Subjects:** Anthropology, archeology, folk culture, material history, Canadian history, ethnology. **Holdings:** 5900 linear feet of books and periodicals; 400,000 photographs and slides; pamphlets; microforms; films; videotapes. **Subscriptions:** 950 journals and other serials. **Services:** Interlibrary loan; copying; SDI; library open to the public for reference use only. **Automated Operations:** Computerized cataloging, acquisitions, and serials. **Computerized Information Services:** DIALOG Information Services, CAN/OLE, DOBIS Canadian Online Library System, UTLAS. Performs searches on fee basis. **Remarks:** FAX: (819)776-8300. Alternate telephone number(s): (819)776-7174. **Formerly:** Canada - National Museums of Canada - Canadian Museum of Civilization. **Also Known As:** Musee Canadien des Civilisations. **Staff:** Margaret Orr, Hd., Tech.Serv.; Chris Kirby, Hd., Photo.; Brigette LaFonde, Ref.Libn.

★**2963**★
Canadian Museum of Nature - Library & Archives (Sci-Engr, Hist)
P.O. Box 3443, Sta. D Phone: (613)998-3923
Ottawa, ON, Canada K1P 6P4 Arch W.L. Stewart, Hd.Libn.
Founded: 1842. **Staff:** Prof 3; Other 7. **Subjects:** Natural sciences - botany, zoology, paleontology, mineral sciences, zooarchaeology. **Special Collections:** C.S. Sternberg Collection (vertebrate paleontology; 6000 reprints); J.F. Grayson Collection (5000 reprints, books, periodicals, catalogs, transparencies); R.M. Anderson Collection (mammalogy and ornithology; 2000 items); Canadian Arctic Expedition, 1913-1918; photographs (73,700); Nature Art (1100). **Holdings:** 70,000 books; 36,000 bound periodical volumes; 12 drawers of newspaper clippings; pamphlets; microforms. **Subscriptions:** 1700 journals and other serials. **Services:** Interlibrary loan; copying; SDI; library open to the public for reference use only. **Automated Operations:** Computerized cataloging and serials. **Computerized Information Services:** DIALOG Information Services, CAN/OLE, UTLAS, DOBIS Canadian Online Library System, STM Systems Corporation, Banque de Terminologie du Quebec (BTQ); Envoy 100 (electronic mail service). Performs searches. **Publications:** Acquisitions list, monthly. **Remarks:** FAX: (613)998-1065. Electronic mail address(es): ILL.OONMNS (Envoy 100). **Also Known As:** Musee Canadien de la Nature. **Staff:** Patrice Stevenson, Hd., Tech.Serv.; Mireille Boudreau, Photo./Ref. Libn.

★**2964**★
Canadian Museums Association - Documentation Centre (Hum)
280 Metcalfe St., Suite 400
Ottawa, ON, Canada K2P 1R7 Phone: (613)233-5653
Founded: 1974. **Staff:** Prof 1. **Subjects:** Museology. **Holdings:** 1500 volumes. **Services:** Copying; center open to the public. **Computerized Information Services:** Directory of Canadian Museums (internal database); Envoy 100 (electronic mail service). **Publications:** CMA Bibliography, biennial; Museum Studies Programmes in Canada, Official Directory of Canadian Museums. **Remarks:** FAX: (613)233-5438.

★**2965**★
Canadian Music Centre - British Columbia Regional Office (Mus)
2021 W. 4th Ave., No. 200 Phone: (604)734-4622
Vancouver, BC, Canada V6J 1N3 Colin Miles, Reg.Dir.
Founded: 1977. **Staff:** Prof 1; Other 1. **Subjects:** Music by Canadian composers. **Holdings:** 12,000 published and unpublished scores; 200 files on Canadian composers; 1700 recordings and cassettes; 250 information files on Canadian music. **Subscriptions:** 20 journals and other serials. **Services:** Interlibrary loan; copying; library open to the public. **Automated Operations:** Computerized cataloging. **Computerized Information Services:** Envoy 100 (electronic mail service). **Remarks:** Electronic mail address(es): CMC.VAN (Envoy 100). **Also Known As:** Centre de Musique Canadienne. **Staff:** Judith Pierce, Adm.Asst.

★**2966**★
Canadian Music Centre - Ettore Mazzoleni Library (Mus)
20 St. Joseph St. Phone: (416)961-6601
Toronto, ON, Canada M4Y 1J9 Mark Hand, Natl.Libn.
Founded: 1959. **Staff:** Prof 2; Other 3.5. **Subjects:** Music by Canadian composers. **Holdings:** 11,000 published and unpublished scores; 500 discs and 2000 tapes of Canadian music; 334 files of Canadian composers' biographies, program notes, publicity. **Subscriptions:** 10 journals and other serials. **Services:** Interlibrary loan; copying (of unpublished works with copyright holder's permission only); direct loans of scores to musicians and others throughout the world; library open to the public. **Automated Operations:** Computerized public access catalog and cataloging. **Computerized Information Services:** Envoy 100 (electronic mail service). **Publications:** Acquisitions, annual - free upon request; information lists; Canadian Orchestral, Chamber, and Keyboard Music. **Remarks:** FAX: (416)961-7198. Electronic mail address(es): CMC.NAT (Envoy 100). "The Canadian Music Centre exists to promote, disseminate and make readily available the music of Canadian composers, both in Canada and abroad." **Also Known As:** Centre de Musique Canadienne. **Staff:** Simone Auger, Exec.Dir.

★**2967**★
Canadian Music Centre - Library (Mus)
430, rue St-Pierre, Suite 300 Phone: (514)849-9175
Montreal, PQ, Canada H2Y 2M5 Mireille Gagne, Reg.Dir.
Founded: 1973. **Staff:** Prof 4; Other 1. **Subjects:** Music, Canadian composers, musical societies. **Special Collections:** Music scores by Quebec and Canadian composers. **Holdings:** 10,000 scores; 3000 audiocassettes and tapes; 1000 discs. **Services:** Interlibrary loan; copying; library open to the public. **Computerized Information Services:** Four Dimensions (internal database); Envoy 100 (electronic mail service). **Special Catalogs:** Acquisitions catalogs. **Also Known As:** Centre de Musique Canadienne. **Staff:** Robert Gravel, Libn.

★**2968**★
Canadian Music Centre - Prairie Region Library (Mus)
911 Library Tower
2500 University Dr., N.W. Phone: (403)220-7403
Calgary, AB, Canada T2N 1N4 John Reid, Reg.Dir.
Founded: 1980. **Staff:** 2. **Subjects:** Canadian music. **Holdings:** 11,000 published and unpublished scores; 3000 discs and tapes of Canadian music; biographies and program notes on Canadian composers. **Subscriptions:** 20 journals and other serials. **Services:** Interlibrary loan; copying; library open to the public. **Computerized Information Services:** Fourth Dimension (internal database); Envoy 100 (electronic mail service). **Publications:** Prairie Sounds (magazine), 4/year; list of other publications - available on request. **Remarks:** FAX: (403)282-6837. Electronic mail address(es): CMC.CAL (Envoy 100).

★**2969**★
Canadian National Institute for the Blind - Library for the Blind (Aud-Vis)
1929 Bayview Ave. Phone: (416)480-7520
Toronto, ON, Canada M4G 3E8 Rosemary Kavanagh, Exec.Dir.
Founded: 1906. **Staff:** Prof 9; Other 80. **Subjects:** General and scholarly topics. **Special Collections:** Sherman Swift Reference Library (print collection on blindness; 2000 books); braille collection of music scores (18,000). **Holdings:** 10,000 titles in braille; 14,000 titles on audiotape. **Subscriptions:** 62 journals and other serials in braille and on tape. **Services:** Interlibrary loan; talking books available for sale to public libraries; special format materials available to handicapped persons only. **Automated Operations:** Computerized cataloging and circulation. **Computerized Information Services:** Envoy 100 (electronic mail service). **Publications:** CNIB Library Newsletter; acquisitions list. **Special Catalogs:** Catalogs of the braille and talking books collections (print, audio, braille, computer disc formats); braille music collection. **Remarks:** FAX: (416)480-7700. **Formerly:** Its National Library Services. **Also Known As:** CNIB; Institut Canadien pour les Aveugles (INCA). **Staff:** Lynn Leith, Mgr., Recording Studio; Jay Campbell, Mgr., Braille; Barbara Freeze, Dir., Prod./Proc.; Janice Hayes, Dir., Client Serv.; John Beard, Dir., Sys./Oper.

★2970★
Canadian National Institute for the Blind - Quebec Division Library (Aud-Vis)
1010 St. Catherine E., Suite P-100 Phone: (514)284-2040
Montreal, PQ, Canada H2L 2G3 France Lemay, Proj.Libn.
Founded: 1965. **Staff:** 3. **Subjects:** General collection in French. **Holdings:** Sound reading material. **Services:** Textbooks read on tape; cassette reproducing; library open to registered blind persons only. **Computerized Information Services:** Envoy 100 (electronic mail service). **Remarks:** Library exchanges French sound reading material with others in Canada and the U.S. FAX: (514)284-2512. Electronic mail address(es): INCA.BIBLIO (Envoy 100). **Also Known As:** Institut National Canadien pour les Aveugles.

★2971★
Canadian National Railways - Dechief Research Library (Trans, Bus-Fin)
1060 University
B.P. 8100 Phone: (514)399-8025
Montreal, PQ, Canada H3C 3N4 Gilda Martinello, Sys.Libn.
Founded: 1923. **Staff:** Prof 4; Other 1. **Subjects:** Railroad engineering, operation, economics; management; industrial relations. **Holdings:** 37,000 books; 8600 bound periodical volumes; 1700 technical reports; 6500 microforms. **Subscriptions:** 900 journals and other serials. **Services:** Interlibrary loan; library not open to the public. **Automated Operations:** Computerized acquisitions, cataloging, circulation, and serials. **Computerized Information Services:** DIALOG Information Services, Infomart Online, CAN/OLE, Info Globe, Dow Jones News/Retrieval; internal databases. **Publications:** Current Awareness Bulletin, monthly. **Remarks:** FAX: (514)399-8258. **Also Known As:** Chemins de Fer Nationaux du Canada. **Staff:** Fiona Murray, Info.Serv.Libn.

★2972★
Canadian National Railways - Photographic Library (Aud-Vis, Trans)
P.O. Box 8100 Phone: (514)399-5465
Montreal, PQ, Canada H3C 3N4 Connie Romani, Photo Libn.
Founded: 1930. **Staff:** Prof 1. **Subjects:** Railway transportation. **Special Collections:** Historical Railways (includes pictures dating back to the late 1800s). **Holdings:** 1000 photograph albums of pictures; 300,000 black/white negatives; 35,000 color negatives; 50,000 color transparencies. **Services:** Photographic reproduction; library open to the public by appointment only. **Computerized Information Services:** Internal databases. **Remarks:** FAX: (514)399-5344. **Also Known As:** Chemins de Fer Nationaux du Canada.

★2973★
Canadian National Railways - Public Affairs Department Library
935 Lagauchetiere St., W.
Sta. A, P.O. Box 8100
Montreal, PQ, Canada H3C 3N4
Defunct.

Canadian Newspapers Ltd. - Victoria Times-Colonist
See: **Victoria Times-Colonist** (19829)

★2974★
Canadian Numismatic Association - Library (Rec)
118 Cameron St. Phone: (705)737-0845
Moncton, NB, Canada E1C 5Y6 Geoffrey G. Bell, Libn.
Founded: 1950. **Staff:** Prof 1. **Subjects:** Numismatics. **Special Collections:** Canadian Antiquarian and Numismatic Journal, 1872-1933. **Holdings:** 3500 books. **Subscriptions:** 58 journals and other serials. **Services:** Library open to the public with restrictions. **Special Catalogs:** Catalog of audio visual holdings - for sale. **Formerly:** Located in Cookstown, ON.

★2975★
Canadian Nurses Association - Helen K. Mussallem Library (Med)
50 The Driveway Phone: (613)237-2133
Ottawa, ON, Canada K2P 1E2 Elizabeth Hawkins Brady, Lib.Mgr.
Founded: 1964. **Staff:** Prof 2; Other 4. **Subjects:** Nursing, history of nursing. **Special Collections:** Repository Collection of Canadian Nursing Studies; provincial nursing legislation; Archives of Canadian Nursing; Canadian nursing education program information. **Holdings:** 16,000 books and documents; photographs. **Subscriptions:** 500 journals and other serials. **Services:** Interlibrary loan; copying; SDI; library open to the public. **Computerized Information Services:** MEDLARS, DOBIS Canadian Online Library System, CAN/OLE; electronic mail service. Contact Person: Martha Ippersiel, Ref.Libn. **Publications:** List of publications - available on request. **Special Indexes:** Index of Canadian Nursing Research (book); Guide to the Historical Collections of the Canadian Nurses Association (book). **Remarks:** FAX: (613)237-3520.

★2976★
Canadian Occidental Petroleum, Ltd. - Library (Energy)
635 8th Ave., S.W., Suite 1500 Phone: (403)234-6437
Calgary, AB, Canada T2P 3Z1 Marlene Robertson, Libn.
Founded: 1979. **Staff:** 1. **Subjects:** Oil, gas. **Holdings:** 2500 books. **Subscriptions:** 250 journals and other serials. **Services:** Interlibrary loan; library not open to the public. **Computerized Information Services:** DIALOG Information Services, ORBIT Search Service, Info Globe, Dow Jones News/Retrieval, QL Systems, CAN/OLE, Infomart Online. **Remarks:** FAX: (403)263-8673. Telex: 03821516.

★2977★
Canadian Olympic Association - Library/Information Services (Rec)
Olympic House, Cite du Havre Phone: (514)861-3371
Montreal, PQ, Canada H3C 3R4 Sylvia Doucette, Info.Ctr.Coord.
Founded: 1970. **Staff:** Prof 1. **Subjects:** Olympics, amateur sports, Pan American Games. **Holdings:** 1000 books; 100 boxes of reports, clippings, reprints; films; still photographs. **Subscriptions:** 225 journals and other serials. **Services:** Interlibrary loan; copying; library open to the public with restrictions. **Remarks:** FAX: (514)861-2896. Telex: (021)0524858 CANOLYCOM MTL.

★2978★
Canadian Opera Company - Opera Resource Centre (Mus)
227 Front St., E. Phone: (416)363-6671
Toronto, ON, Canada M5A 1E8 Christopher Morris, Archv.
Founded: 1974. **Staff:** Prof 1; Other 1. **Subjects:** History of the Canadian Opera Company, 1950 to present; history of opera in Toronto. **Special Collections:** Records of Herman Geiger-Torel (72 linear feet of document cases; 1 display case); records of Vida Hampton Peene (12 document cases); Karl Emil Pincott Phonograph Collection (1300 operatic recordings). **Holdings:** 400 volumes; 19 bound volumes of minutes; 12 bound volumes of programs; 94 libretti; 10 file drawers, 85 document cases, 81 feet, and 10 cartons of: correspondence, contracts, agreements, financial materials, brochures, posters, flyers, artwork releases, reviews, biographies, fund-raising materials, cast lists, schedules, set models, set and costume designs, stage plans and house, souvenir and tour programs; 44 scrapbooks of media items; 12,000 photographs and slides; 24 feet of audio- and videotapes; 4 films; posters, 1959 to present. **Subscriptions:** 20 journals and other serials. **Services:** Copying; center open to the public by appointment. **Special Indexes:** Indexes to corporate, administrative, and artistic records, 1950 to present; Canadian Opera Company's seasons, repertoire, tours, and artists; boards of directors, officers, committees, 1950 to present; AV programs and photographs (all on cards).

★2979★
Canadian Pacific Forest Products Research Ltd. - Library
179 Main St., W.
Hawkesbury, ON, Canada K6A 2H4
Defunct.

★2980★
Canadian Paraplegic Association - Information Center (Med)
1500 Don Mills Rd.
Don Mills, ON, Canada M3B 3K4 Phone: (416)391-0203
Founded: 1977. **Staff:** Prof 1. **Subjects:** Spinal cord injury and rehabilitation; social, political, technical concerns of the handicapped. **Holdings:** 1200 volumes; 1200 reprints. **Subscriptions:** 60 journals and newsletters. **Services:** Interlibrary loan; copying; SDI; library open to the public by referral. **Publications:** Up-date, irregular; New Materials.

★2981★
Canadian Paraplegic Association, Manitoba Inc. - Library (Med)
825 Sherbrook St. Phone: (204)786-4753
Winnipeg, MB, Canada R3A 1M5 Lucy DeLuca, Libn.
Subjects: Spinal cord injury. **Holdings:** 500 books; reports; archives. **Subscriptions:** 52 journals and other serials. **Services:** Interlibrary loan; copying; library open to the public. **Remarks:** FAX: (204)786-1140.

Canadian Parks Service
See: **Canada - Environment Canada - Canadian Parks Service** (2709)

★2982★
Canadian Petroleum Association - Library (Energy)
150 6th Ave., S.W., Suite 3800 Phone: (403)269-6721
Calgary, AB, Canada T2P 2Y7 Diana Parnell, Libn.
Services: Library open to the public with permission. **Remarks:** FAX: (403)261-4622.

Canadian Postal Archives
See: **Canada - National Archives of Canada - Documentary Art and Photography Division** (2769)

★2983★
Canadian Press - Library (Publ)
36 King St., E. Phone: (416)364-0321
Toronto, ON, Canada M5C 2L9 Asma Khan, Libn.
Founded: 1932. **Staff:** 1. **Subjects:** Canadian news events and biography, World War II, newspaper reference topics. **Holdings:** 250 books; 48 VF drawers. **Subscriptions:** 9 journals and other serials. **Services:** Library not open to the public. **Computerized Information Services:** Canadian Press Newstex (CPN), QL Systems. Performs searches on fee basis. **Remarks:** FAX: (416)364-0207. Toll-free telephone number(s): (800)387-0899 (online searches).

★2984★
Canadian Psychoanalytic Society - Library (Med)
7000 Cote des Neiges Rd. Phone: (514)738-6105
Montreal, PQ, Canada H3S 2C1 Nadia Gargour, Adm.Dir.
Founded: 1967. **Staff:** 2. **Subjects:** Psychoanalysis. **Holdings:** 5357 books. **Subscriptions:** 50 journals and other serials. **Services:** Library not open to the public. **Also Known As:** Societe Canadienne de Psychanalyse.

★2985★
Canadian Pulp and Paper Association - Library (Sci-Engr)
Sun Life Bldg., 19th Fl.
1155 Metcalfe St. Phone: (514)866-6621
Montreal, PQ, Canada H3B 4T6 Karen Fountain, Libn.
Staff: Prof 1; Other 1. **Subjects:** Pulp and paper in Canada and U.S., Canadian government statistics, environmental issues, printing industry, forestry. **Special Collections:** Early Canadian pulp and paper material. **Holdings:** 1500 books. **Subscriptions:** 250 journals and other serials; 10 newspapers. **Services:** Interlibrary loan; copying; library open to the public. **Remarks:** FAX: (514)866-3035.

Canadian Radio-Television and Telecommunications Commission
See: **Canada - Canadian Radio-Television and Telecommunications Commission** (2671)

★2986★
Canadian Railroad Historical Association - Library (Trans)
120 St. Pierre Phone: (514)638-1522
St. Constant, PQ, Canada J5A 2G2 Dr. R.V.V. Nicholls, Archv./Libn.
Founded: 1932. **Staff:** Prof 1; Other 1. **Subjects:** Canadian railway and tramway history, technology, and operation. **Special Collections:** Sir William Van Horne Collection. **Holdings:** 2500 books; 200 bound periodical volumes; 150 feet of archival material; 40,000 mechanical drawings. **Subscriptions:** 30 journals and other serials. **Services:** Library open to the public by appointment.

★2987★
Canadian Red Cross Society - National Office - Library (Soc Sci)
1800 Alta Vista Dr. Phone: (613)739-2573
Ottawa, ON, Canada K1G 4J5 Ann M. Butryn, Mgr., Off.Serv./Libn.
Founded: 1961. **Staff:** 2. **Subjects:** Canadian Red Cross Society, International Committee of the Red Cross, International Federation of Red Cross and Red Crescent Societies, transfusion medicine. **Special Collections:** International humanitarian law (60 volumes). **Holdings:** 1500 books; 600 bound periodical volumes; 100 boxes of archival material; 50 boxes of pamphlets, clippings, press releases. **Subscriptions:** 200 journals and other serials. **Services:** Interlibrary loan; library open to the public by appointment. **Remarks:** Alternate telephone number(s): 739-2372. FAX: (613)731-2574. Telex: 05-33784 CANCROSSOTT.

★2988★
Canadian Red Cross Society, Manitoba Division - Library (Soc Sci)
200-360 Broadway Phone: (204)982-7300
Winnipeg, MB, Canada R3C 0T6 C. King, Commnr.
Subjects: Red Cross. **Holdings:** 2000 books. **Subscriptions:** 12 journals and other serials. **Services:** Copying; library open to the public for reference use only. **Remarks:** FAX: (204)942-8367.

★2989★
Canadian Rehabilitation Council for the Disabled - CRCD Resource Centre
45 Sheppard Ave., E., Suite 801
Toronto, ON, Canada M2N 5W9
Founded: 1962. **Subjects:** Physical disabilities, rehabilitation. **Holdings:** 4000 books. **Remarks:** Currently inactive.

★2990★
Canadian Restaurant & Foodservices Association - Resource Centre (Food-Bev)
80 Bloor St., W., Suite 1201 Phone: (416)923-8416
Toronto, ON, Canada M5S 2V1 Kevin P. Tuttle, Info. & Res.Asst.
Founded: 1972. **Staff:** Prof 1. **Subjects:** Food service, quantity cooking, legislation, administration, management, statistics, training, customer attitude surveys. **Holdings:** 1000 books; 15 VF drawers. **Subscriptions:** 100 journals and other serials. **Services:** Copying; center open to the public on fee basis. **Computerized Information Services:** Compusearch Market and Social Research Ltd. Data Base, Marketing Information Data Systems, Inc. (MIDS). Performs searches on fee basis. **Publications:** Info Stats, monthly - to members. **Special Indexes:** Index of feature articles appearing in two major Canadian trade journals (book). **Remarks:** Toll-free telephone number(s): (800)387-5649. FAX: (416)923-1450.

Canadian Society of Mayflower Descendants - Library
See: **North York Public Library - Canadiana Department** (11961)

★2991★
Canadian Standards Association - Information Centre (Sci-Engr)
178 Rexdale Blvd. Phone: (416)747-4058
Rexdale, ON, Canada M9W 1R3 Michael Lewis, Mgr.
Founded: 1970. **Staff:** Prof 4. **Subjects:** Engineering, product safety, quality control, certification of products, electrical engineering, consumerism. **Special Collections:** Engineering standards (600,000). **Holdings:** 2000 books; 1800 technical information files. **Subscriptions:** 200 journals and other serials. **Services:** Interlibrary loan; center open to the public. **Automated Operations:** Computerized cataloging. **Computerized Information Services:** DIALOG Information Services, BRS Information Technologies, CAN/OLE, QL Systems, Infomart Online, Info Globe, LEXIS, NEXIS, Canadian Systems Group (CSG); Envoy 100 (electronic mail service). **Special Indexes:** Archival CSA standards index. **Remarks:** FAX: (416)747-2475. Electronic mail address(es): ILL.CSA (Envoy 100). Telex: 06-989344. **Also Known As:** Association Canadienne de Normalisation (ACNOR).

★2992★
Canadian Tax Foundation - Library (Bus-Fin)
1 Queen St. E., No. 1800 Phone: (416)863-9784
Toronto, ON, Canada M5C 2Y2 Ron MacLeod, Libn.
Founded: 1946. **Staff:** Prof 1; Other 1. **Subjects:** Canadian and international taxation, public finance, government expenditures in Canada (including provincial), local government. **Special Collections:** Taxation services (looseleaf); federal and provincial budgets and public accounts. **Holdings:** 22,000 books; 2900 bound periodical volumes; 5000 pamphlets; 12 drawers of Royal Commission briefs; 16 drawers of Statistics Canada material. **Subscriptions:** 250 journals and other serials. **Services:** Copying; library open to the public for reference use only. **Remarks:** FAX: (416)863-9585. **Also Known As:** Association Canadienne d'Etudes Fiscales.

★2993★
Canadian Teachers' Federation - George G. Croskery Memorial Library (Educ)
110 Argyle Ave. Phone: (613)232-1505
Ottawa, ON, Canada K2P 1B4 Geraldine Gilliss, Dir., Res. & Info.Serv.
Founded: 1953. **Staff:** Prof 2; Other 2. **Subjects:** Education, research, economics and finance, teachers, teacher welfare, curriculum, labor relations, sociology, psychology, educational law and litigation. **Special Collections:** Collective agreements; educational legislation; policy handbooks. **Holdings:** 15,000 books; 24 VF drawers; 220 reels of microfilm of back periodicals. **Subscriptions:** 250 journals and other serials; 10 newspapers. **Services:** Interlibrary loan; library not open to the public. **Automated Operations:** Computerized acquisitions. **Computerized Information Services:** DIALOG Information Services, QL Systems, Info Globe, Infomart Online, The Financial Post DataGroup. **Remarks:** FAX: (613)232-1886. Telex: 0636700906. **Also Known As:** Federation Canadienne des Enseignants. **Staff:** Marita Moll, Libn.

★2994★
Canadian Telephone Employees' Association - Library (Bus-Fin)
360 Place du Canada Phone: (514)861-9963
Montreal, PQ, Canada H3B 2N2 Miss E.A. Fenton, Gen.Sec.
Founded: 1945. **Staff:** Prof 1. **Subjects:** Labor relations, trade unions. **Holdings:** 200 books; CTEA publications. **Subscriptions:** 25 journals and other serials.

Canadian Theological Seminary
See: **Canadian Bible College/Canadian Theological Seminary** (2896)

★2995★
Canadian Thoroughbred Horse Society - Library (Rec)
Box 172 Phone: (416)675-3602
Rexdale, ON, Canada M9W 5L1 Nigel P.H. Wallace, Gen.Mgr.
Staff: Prof 1. **Subjects:** Thoroughbred horses. **Holdings:** Broodmare record books; daily racing form chart books; name charts on microfiche; pedigrees. **Subscriptions:** 12 journals and other serials. **Services:** Library open to the public. **Remarks:** FAX: (416)675-9405.

★2996★
Canadian Tobacco Manufacturers Council - Information Center (Med)
1808 Sherbrooke St., W., 2nd Fl.
Montreal, PQ, Canada H3H 1E5 Selma D. Trevick, Coord., Lib.Serv.
Founded: 1971. **Staff:** Prof 2. **Subjects:** Smoking and health, tobacco, environment, pollution, biology, agriculture. **Holdings:** 545 books; 46 bound periodical volumes; 180 binders of clippings; 8 VF drawers of motion pictures and tapes; 80 boxes of reports; 20 boxes of pamphlets. **Subscriptions:** 284 journals and other serials; 20 newspapers. **Services:** Interlibrary loan; copying; center open to the public by appointment only. **Automated Operations:** Computerized cataloging. **Computerized Information Services:** DIALOG Information Services, CAN/OLE, Info Globe, QL Systems, Infomart Online, iNET 2000, The Financial Post Information Service, Publinet Data Base; Envoy 100 (electronic mail service). **Remarks:** FAX: (514)937-6380. Telex: 05-268827 CANTOBMAN.

★2997★
Canadian Trotting Association - Library (Rec)
2150 Meadowvale Blvd. Phone: (416)858-3060
Mississauga, ON, Canada L5N 6R6 Elynne Lewis, Libn.
Staff: Prof 1. **Subjects:** Harness racing, standardbred breeding. **Special Collections:** Worldwide stud books; photographs; current and historical turf journals; historical race programs; horse, driver, and trainer statistics. **Holdings:** Books; microfiche; audio and video cassetter. **Services:** Library open to the public. **Computerized Information Services:** Internal database. Performs searches on fee basis. **Publications:** Trot Magazine, monthly - for sale (free to members). **Remarks:** FAX: (416)858-3111.

★2998★
Canadian Union College - Library (Rel-Phil)
Box 430 Phone: (403)782-3381
College Heights, AB, Canada T0C 0Z0 Keith H. Clouten, Lib.Serv.Dir.
Staff: Prof 2; Other 3. **Subjects:** Religion, social sciences, science. **Special Collections:** Seventh-Day Adventist history and publications. **Holdings:** 55,000 books; 5000 bound periodical volumes; films; tapes; records; curriculum materials; 300 maps. **Subscriptions:** 500 journals and other serials; 9 newspapers. **Services:** Interlibrary loan; library open to the public. **Automated Operations:** Computerized public access catalog, cataloging, acquisitions, and serials. **Computerized Information Services:** DIALOG Information Services; Envoy 100 (electronic mail service). Performs searches on fee basis. Contact Person: Joyce Van Scheik, Pub.Serv.Libn. **Remarks:** FAX: (403)782-3977. Electronic mail address(es): ILL.ACHCU(Envoy 100).

★2999★
Canadian Utilities Limited - Library Services (Energy)
10035 105th St. Phone: (403)420-7039
Edmonton, AB, Canada T5J 2V6 Renee Hartel, Libn.
Founded: 1972. **Staff:** Prof 3. **Subjects:** Public utilities, gas and electricity, engineering, management. **Holdings:** 10,000 books; 500 annual reports; 200 standards. **Subscriptions:** 500 journals and other serials. **Services:** Interlibrary loan; copying; library open to the public with restrictions. **Automated Operations:** Computerized cataloging and serials. **Computerized Information Services:** DIALOG Information Services, Info Globe, CAN/OLE, The Financial Post DataGroup, Infomart Online; Envoy 100 (electronic mail service). **Publications:** New Arrivals, bimonthly. **Remarks:** FAX: (403)420-7400. Electronic mail address(es): CUL/D.FROH (Envoy 100). **Staff:** Suzanne Weir, Asst.Libn.; Carolyn Evans, Lib.Techn.

★3000★
Canadian War Museum - Library (Mil)
330 Sussex Dr. Phone: (613)996-4708
Ottawa, ON, Canada K1A 0M8 Jean Langdon-Ford, Libn.
Founded: 1969. **Staff:** 2. **Subjects:** Canadian military history, weapons, insignia, uniforms, military decorations. **Special Collections:** World War II newspaper clippings (80 VF drawers); Canadian Militia and Canadian Army Orders, 1899-1910 and 1914 to present; War Office list in changes of war materiel, 1883-1965 (incomplete). **Holdings:** 15,000 volumes, including bound periodical volumes and Canadian armed forces manuals. **Subscriptions:** 70 journals and other serials. **Services:** Interlibrary loan; library open to the public for reference use only. **Automated Operations:** Computerized cataloging and acquisitions. **Computerized Information Services:** DOBIS, UTLAS. **Publications:** Accessions list, 4/year. **Remarks:** FAX: (613)954-1016. **Formerly:** Canada - National Museums of Canada - Canadian War Museum. **Also Known As:** Musee Canadien de la Guerre. **Staff:** Carol Ann Kennedy.

★3001★
Canadian Western Natural Gas Company Limited - Library (Energy)
909 11th Ave., S.W. Phone: (403)245-7403
Calgary, AB, Canada T2R 1L8 Shelley J. Rosser, Libn.
Founded: 1977. **Staff:** Prof 1. **Subjects:** Public utilities, gas. **Holdings:** 3200 books; 9 VF drawers of annual reports. **Subscriptions:** 150 journals and other serials. **Services:** Interlibrary loan; library open to the public with restrictions. **Computerized Information Services:** DIALOG Information Services. **Remarks:** This library is a branch of the Canadian Utilities Limited main library in Edmonton. **Remarks:** FAX: (403)245-7400.

★3002★
Canadian Wheat Board - Library (Agri)
423 Main St.
Box 816 Phone: (204)983-3437
Winnipeg, MB, Canada R3C 2P5 M. Ruth Reedman, Libn.
Founded: 1981. **Staff:** Prof 1; Other 3. **Subjects:** Grain trade, agricultural economics. **Holdings:** 4500 books. **Subscriptions:** 1000 journals and other serials. **Services:** Interlibrary loan; library open to the public. **Automated Operations:** Computerized cataloging and serials. **Computerized Information Services:** DIALOG Information Services, CAN/OLE, UTLAS, AES Canada, AgriData Network, Infomart Online, Info Globe; Envoy 100, (electronic mail services). **Publications:** Selected list of recent acquisitions, monthly - distributed internally and to selected libraries and individuals. **Special Indexes:** Index to Grain Matters (online). **Remarks:** FAX: (204)983-4031. Telex: 07-57801. Electronic mail address(es): CWB.LIB (Envoy 100).

★3003★
Canadian Wildlife Federation - Resource Centre (Env-Cons)
2740 Queensview Dr. Phone: (613)721-2286
Ottawa, ON, Canada K2B 1A2 Mrs. Luba Mycio-Mommers, Pub.Aff.
Founded: 1961. **Staff:** 2. **Subjects:** Wildlife education, outdoor recreation, conservation, environment, natural history, energy. **Special Collections:** Canadian Wildlife Federation Archives. **Holdings:** Figures not available. **Subscriptions:** 50 journals and other serials. **Services:** Library open to the public for reference use only. **Publications:** List of publications - available on request. **Remarks:** FAX: (613)721-2902.

Canadian Wildlife Service
See: **Canada - Environment Canada, Conservation & Protection - Canadian Wildlife Service** (2715)

★3004★
Canadian Women's Movement Archives (Soc Sci)
PO Box 128, Sta. P
Toronto, ON, Canada M5S 2S7 Phone: (416)597-8865
Founded: 1977. **Staff:** 2. **Subjects:** Women's groups; lesbian groups; women's conferences, festivals, demonstrations, issues. **Holdings:** 350 books; 750 periodicals and newsletters; 2500 group files; individual files; ephemera; buttons; T-shirts; photographs; slides; tapes. **Subscriptions:** 150 journals and other serials; 20 newspapers. **Services:** Copying; archives open to the public. **Publications:** Lesbian and Gay Holdings at the CWMA, 1987; A Descriptive Inventory of the Sound Recordings at the C.W.M.A., 1988. **Also Known As:** Archives Canadiennes du Mouvement des Femmes. **Staff:** Margaret Fulford, Proj.Archv.

★3005★
Canadian Wood Council - Library (Sci-Engr)
55 Metcalfe St., Suite 1550 Phone: (613)235-7221
Ottawa, ON, Canada K1P 6L5 A. Mattila, Libn.
Staff: Prof 10; Other 4. **Subjects:** Wood design, products, building codes, product standards. **Holdings:** 5000 technical publications; 6 slide-cassette programs. **Services:** Library open to the public with prior permission. **Automated Operations:** INMAGIC. **Publications:** List of publications - available on request. **Remarks:** FAX: (613)235-9911.

Canadiana Collection of Children's Books
See: **Toronto Public Library** (16414)

Canadore College - Library
See: **North Bay College Education Centre - Library** (11873)

Canal Park Marine Museum
See: **U.S. Army - Corps of Engineers - Detroit District** (16937)

★3006★
Canal Society of New Jersey - Museum - Library (Hist)
P.O. Box 737 Phone: (908)722-9556
Morristown, NJ 07963-0737 Myra Snook
Subjects: New Jersey canals, 1824-1930. **Holdings:** Legislative documents; photographs; glass slides; engineering drawings; boat passage records; manuscripts. **Services:** Library open to the public by appointment. **Remarks:** Museum located in the Waterloo Village Restoration, Stanhope, New Jersey.

★3007★
(Canberra) American Center - USIS Library (Educ)
Natl. Press Club Bldg., Suite 1
16 Natl. Circuit
Barton, ACT 2600, Australia Rosemary Dickson, Lib.Dir.
Founded: 1976. **Staff:** 3. **Subjects:** United States - government, politics, defense, trade, economics, foreign affairs. **Special Collections:** U.S. federal legislation. **Holdings:** 2000 books. **Subscriptions:** 100 journals and other serials; 5 newspapers. **Services:** Copying, library open to the public. **Computerized Information Services:** DIALOG Information Services, LEGI-SLATE, PDQ. **Remarks:** Maintained or supported by the U.S. Information Agency. Focus is on materials that will assist peoples outside the United States to learn about the United States, its people, history, culture, political processes, and social milieux. **Staff:** Roslyn Orr, Ref.Libn.

★3008★
Canby Community Health Services - Medical Library (Med)
112 St. Olaf Ave., S.
Canby, MN 56220 Phone: (507)223-7277
Subjects: Medicine, health, hospitals. **Holdings:** 1100 books. **Subscriptions:** 10 journals and other serials; 4 newspapers. **Services:** Library open to the public by special permission. **Remarks:** FAX: (507)223-7465.

The Cancer Information Service
See: **Sylvester Comprehensive Cancer Center** (15948)

★3009★
Candler General Hospital - Medical Library (Med)
5353 Reynolds St. Phone: (912)356-6011
Savannah, GA 31412 Mary V. Fielder, Mgr., Lib.Serv.
Founded: 1972. **Staff:** Prof 1. **Subjects:** Medicine, nursing, hospital administration, rehabilitation. **Holdings:** 1425 books; 1900 bound periodical volumes; 2 VF drawers of subject files. **Subscriptions:** 185 journals and other serials. **Services:** Interlibrary loan; library not open to the public. **Computerized Information Services:** BRS Information Technologies. Performs searches on fee basis for non-staff members. **Networks/Consortia:** Member of Southeast Georgia Health Sciences Library Consortium (SEGHSLC), Georgia Interactive Network for Medical Information (GaIN). **Remarks:** FAX: (912)356-6567.

★3010★
Canfield Memorial Library - Russell Vermontiana Collection (Hist)
Arlington, VT 05250 Phone: (802)375-6307
Mary Lou Thomas, Dir.
Founded: 1956. **Staff:** 4. **Subjects:** History of Vermont, including counties adjoining Vermont in New York, Massachusetts, and New Hampshire. **Special Collections:** Dorothy Canfield Fisher papers. **Holdings:** 8000 books; maps; 4500 pamphlets; 400 manuscript account books, journals, diaries; 5500 manuscript letters, deeds, court records; 2000 photographs. **Services:** Collection open to the public on Tuesdays and by appointment.

CANMET
See: **Canada - Energy, Mines & Resources Canada - CANMET** (2699)

★3011★
CanOcean Engineering Ltd. - Engineering Library (Sci-Engr)
One Grosvnor Sq.
New Westminster, BC, Canada V3M 5S1 Phone: (604)524-4451
Staff: Prof 1. **Subjects:** Engineering - petroleum, marine, arctic; diving technology. **Special Collections:** Canadian Arctic environmental conditions; marine engineering in ice conditions. **Holdings:** 1418 volumes; 300 conference proceedings; 150 internal reports; 350 industrial standards; 600 vendor catalogs. **Subscriptions:** 59 journals and other serials. **Services:** Interlibrary loan; copying; library open to the public with restrictions. **Computerized Information Services:** Online systems. **Publications:** Bibliographies.

★3012★
Canspec Group Inc. - Branch Office Library (Sci-Engr)
3650 21st St., N.E., No. 4 Phone: (403)291-3126
Calgary, AB, Canada T2E 6V6 Jennie Davison, Lib.Techn.
Founded: 1980. **Staff:** Prof 1. **Subjects:** Metallurgy, nondestructive testing, welding, quality assurance, chemical analysis, heat treating, metallography. **Special Collections:** Metallurgical, nondestructive testing, and product specifications (900). **Holdings:** 550 books; 500 reports; 600 technical reports; 10 reels of microfilm and 1000 microfiche of engineering and technical reports. **Subscriptions:** 51 journals and other serials. **Services:** Interlibrary loan; library not open to the public. **Publications:** HME Library Bulletin, monthly. **Remarks:** FAX: (403)250-1015. **Formerly:** Hanson Materials Engineering.

★3013★
Canspec Group Inc. - Library (Sci-Engr)
7450 18th St. Phone: (403)440-2131
Edmonton, AB, Canada T6P 1N8 Connie Vogler, Lib.Techn.
Founded: 1966. **Staff:** Prof 1. **Subjects:** Metallurgy, metallography, welding technology, materials engineering, chemical analysis, nondestructive testing, heat treating. **Special Collections:** Metallurgical and nondestructive testing specifications (900). **Holdings:** 1000 books; 300 handbooks; 1600 technical files; 9000 consulting engineering reports. **Subscriptions:** 100 journals and other serials; 15 newspapers. **Services:** Interlibrary loan; library not open to the public. **Publications:** Library Information Bulletin, monthly - to staff. **Remarks:** FAX: (403)440-1167. **Formerly:** Hanson Materials Engineering - Main Office Library.

Cantacuzino Institute
See: **Romania - Ministry of Health - Cantacuzino Institute** (14048)

★3014★
Canterbury Cathedral Library-Printed Books (Rel-Phil, Hist)
11 The Precincts Phone: 227 458950
Canterbury, Kent CT1 2EH, England Sheila Hingley, Cathedral Libn.
Staff: 4. **Subjects:** Slavery, church history, theology, paleography, early printing and science. **Special Collections:** Mendham Collection (15th-19th century anti-Papist materials; 6000 titles); Elham and Preston Parish Libraries. **Holdings:** 40,000 books; 1000 bound periodical volumes; 19th century pamphlets. **Subscriptions:** 10 journals and other serials. **Services:** Library open to the public by appointment with letter of introduction and identification. **Automated Operations:** Computerized catalog. **Computerized Information Services:** Online systems. **Publications:** Information leaflets. **Remarks:** FAX: 227 762897. Canterbury Cathedral - Archives is maintained separately and is located at 11 The Precincts, Canterbury, Kent CT1 2EG; Mrs. C Hodgson is the archivist.

★3015★
Canterra Engineering, Ltd. - Library (Sci-Engr)
6700 9 St., N.E.
Calgary, AB, Canada T2E 8K6 Phone: (403)295-7676
Subjects: Mechanical design - drills, off-road vehicles, construction equipment. **Holdings:** 100 volumes; 1200 papers. **Computerized Information Services:** Internal database (commercial catalogs of 2000 companies). **Remarks:** Telex: 03821214.

Cantigny First Division Foundation
See: **First Division Museum & Library** (5775)

★3016★
Canton Art Institute - Purdy Memorial Library (Art)
1001 Market Ave., N. Phone: (216)453-7666
Canton, OH 44702 M.J. Albacete, Exec.Dir.
Staff: 1. **Subjects:** Art. **Holdings:** 2000 books. **Subscriptions:** 25 journals and other serials. **Services:** Library open to the public for reference use only.

★3017★
Canton Historical Society - Library (Hist)
11 Front St. Phone: (203)693-2793
Collinsville, CT 06022 Jane L. Goedecke, Libn.
Founded: 1976. **Staff:** Prof 1; Other 1. **Subjects:** Local and state history, Victoriana, Collins Manufacturing Company. **Special Collections:** Collins Company (manufacturers of edge tools) of Collinsville, Connecticut, 1826-1966 (books; manuscripts; brochures; ledgers; patterns). **Holdings:** 250 books; 73 years of annual reports; 30 deeds; 10 scrapbooks; 150 manuscripts; 50 unbound magazines of historical interest; 1000 photographs; census for Canton, CT, 1790-1910, on microfilm. **Services:** Library open to the public for reference use only. **Publications:** Newsletter - to members.

★3018★
Canton Historical Society - Library
1400 Washington St.
Canton, MA 02021 Phone: (617)821-5027
Subjects: Indian relics, household implements, farm implements, military material, woolen textiles. **Special Collections:** Official town records, 1636 to present; records and maps of towns of Stoughton and Sharon. **Holdings:** 558 books; 11 patents; 600 clippings; 380 pamphlets and documents; 300 programs and manuscripts; 5000 artifacts and photographs. **Services:** Library not open to the public.

★3019★
Canton-Potsdam Hospital - Medical Library (Med)
50 Leroy St. Phone: (315)265-3300
Potsdam, NY 13676 Mark Uebler, Libn.
Subjects: Medicine. **Holdings:** 243 books. **Subscriptions:** 27 journals and other serials. **Services:** Interlibrary loan; library not open to the public. **Computerized Information Services:** BRS Information Technologies. **Networks/Consortia:** Member of North Country Reference and Research Resources Council (NCRRRC).

★3020★
Canton Repository Library (Law)
500 Market St., S. Phone: (216)454-5611
Canton, OH 44702 Annie Jones, Libn.
Subjects: Ohio revised code. **Holdings:** Microfilm, newspaper articles, clippings. **Services:** Library not open to the public. **Remarks:** FAX: (216)454-5610.

★3021★
Cape Ann Historical Association - Library (Hist)
27 Pleasant St. Phone: (508)283-0455
Gloucester, MA 01930 Judith McCulloch, Adm.
Subjects: Cape Ann - fishing industry, history, art history, genealogy. **Special Collections:** Gordon Thomas Collection (photographs of fishing schooners and the Gloucester waterfront, 1870-1930; 4000). **Holdings:** 2000 books; 75 volumes of manuscripts and day books; 3 drawers of clippings; 4 drawers of Cape Ann Artists Archive. **Services:** Library open to the public for reference use only. **Publications:** Listing of Cape Ann artists. **Special Indexes:** Indexes to photographic and manuscript holdings (card). **Staff:** Britt Crews; Marion Harding.

★3022★
Cape Breton Miners' Museum - Library (Hist)
Quarry Point Phone: (902)849-4522
Glace Bay, NS, Canada B1A 5T8 Thomas Miller, Cat.
Founded: 1967. **Staff:** 1. **Subjects:** Mining, geology, history, engineering, transportation. **Special Collections:** Institute of Mining Engineers, 1889-1938 (94 volumes); Mines of Nova Scotia reports, 1880 to present; Geological Survey of Canada, 1876-1903 (24 volumes). **Holdings:** 834 books; 187 newspapers; 150 magnetic tapes; 55 documents. **Services:** Interlibrary loan; library open to the public with restrictions.

★3023★
Cape Breton Regional Hospital - School of Nursing Library (Med)
409 King's Rd. Phone: (902)562-2322
Sydney, NS, Canada B1S 1B4 Patricia Keough, Libn.
Founded: 1963. **Staff:** Prof 1. **Subjects:** Health sciences, medicine, nursing, obstetrics, gynecology, pediatrics, anatomy, physiology, nutrition, psychiatry. **Holdings:** 2466 books; 5 bound periodical volumes. **Subscriptions:** 84 journals and other serials. **Services:** Interlibrary loan; copying; library open to the public at librarian's discretion. **Remarks:** FAX: (902)562-8593. **Formerly:** Sydney Community Health Centre - Health Sciences Library.

★3024★
Cape Cod Museum of Natural History - Clarence L. Hay Library (Biol Sci)
Rte. 6-A
Drawer R
Brewster, MA 02631 Phone: (508)896-3867
Founded: 1975. **Staff:** Prof 1; Other 15. **Subjects:** Natural history, zoology, botany, geology, ornithology, nature crafts. **Special Collections:** Archeology collection (300 volumes); Cape Cod Collection (100 volumes); teachers' collection (200 volumes). **Holdings:** 5000 books; 4 VF drawers; 2 drawers of picture files; 75 audiotapes; 10 videotapes. **Subscriptions:** 54 journals and other serials; 6 newspapers. **Services:** Interlibrary loan; copying; SDI; library open to the public with restrictions on borrowing. **Automated Operations:** Computerized cataloging. **Computerized Information Services:** Internal databases. **Publications:** Cape Naturalist, annual; newsletter, 6/year - both to members.

Cape Cod National Seashore
See: **U.S. Natl. Park Service** (17679)

★3025★
Cape Fear Valley Medical Center - Library Services (Med)
Box 2000 Phone: (919)323-6601
Fayetteville, NC 28302 Pat Hammond, Lib.Dir.
Founded: 1975. **Staff:** Prof 1; Other 1. **Subjects:** Medicine, surgery, nursing, rehabilitation, allied health sciences, consumer health. **Special Collections:** Consumer Health Library (CHL). **Holdings:** 1500 books. **Subscriptions:** 200 journals and other serials. **Services:** Interlibrary loan; copying; SDI; library open to the public for reference use only. **Computerized Information Services:** BRS Information Technologies, NLM. Performs searches on fee basis. **Networks/Consortia:** Member of Cape Fear Health Sciences Information Consortium (CFHSIC), National Network of Libraries of Medicine - Southeastern/Atlantic Region, South Central Health Information Network of North Carolina (SCHIN of NC). **Remarks:** FAX: (919)433-7710.

Cape Hateras National Seashore Library
See: **North Carolina (State) Department of Cultural Resources - Division of Archives and History** (11884)

Cape Hatteras National Seashore
See: **U.S. Natl. Park Service** (17680)

Cape Lookout National Seashore
See: **U.S. Natl. Park Service** (17681)

★3026★
Cape May County Historical & Genealogical Society - Library (Hist)
DN 707
Rte. 9 Phone: (609)465-3535
Cape May Court House, NJ 08210 Ione Williams, Libn.
Founded: 1927. **Staff:** Prof 3; Other 2. **Subjects:** Local history and genealogy. **Special Collections:** H. Clifford Campion, Jr. Memorial Collection; Edward M. Post and Lewis T. Stevens Memorial Collection; Edmunds Collection. **Holdings:** 500 books; 20 bound periodical volumes; manuscripts; clippings; 31 volumes of New Jersey archives; Star and Wave newspapers, 1866-1971, on microfilm. **Services:** Copying; library open to nonmembers on fee basis. **Special Indexes:** Newspaper indexes. **Staff:** Somers Corson, Act.Cur.

★3027★
Cape Natural History Club - Library (Biol Sci)
P.O. Box 16 Phone: 21 246967
Rondebosch 7700, Republic of South Africa G. Peel
Founded: 1922. **Staff:** 1. **Subjects:** South African natural history. **Holdings:** 1000 volumes. **Services:** Library open to members only.

★3028★
(Cape Town) American Cultural Center - USIS Library (Educ)
Scott's Bldg., 2nd Fl.
10 Plein St.
Cape Town 8001, Republic of South Africa
Remarks: Maintained or supported by the U.S. Information Agency. Focus is on materials that will assist peoples outside the United States to learn about the United States, its people, history, culture, political processes, and social milieux.

Capen Memorial Library
See: **Second Presbyterian Church** (15008)

★3029★
The Capital - Library (Publ)
2000 Capital Dr. Phone: (301)268-5000
Annapolis, MD 21401 Janice C. Wolod
Staff: Prof 1. **Subjects:** Newspaper reference topics. **Holdings:** Bound volumes of newspaper (1940 to present); microfilm of newspaper (1976 to present). **Services:** Library open to the public with restrictions. **Computerized Information Services:** VU/TEXT Information Services.

Capital Bible Seminary
See: **Washington Bible College/Capital Bible Seminary** (19991)

Capital Cities/ABC, Inc. - ABC Publishing - Chilton Company
See: **Chilton Company** (3601)

Capital Cities/ABC, Inc. - Kansas City Star Newspapers
See: **Kansas City Star Newspaper** (8551)

Capital Construction Commission of China - Construction and Building Library
See: **China Building Technology Development Center** (3603)

★3030★
Capital District Library Council for Reference and Research - Bibliographic Center (Info Sci)
2255 Story Ave. Phone: (518)382-2001
Schenectady, NY 12309-5315 Charles D. Custer, Exec.Dir.
Founded: 1968. **Staff:** Prof 6; Other 6. **Subjects:** Library networks and consortia, interlibrary cooperation, cooperative acquisitions, data files, library automation and administration. **Special Collections:** CDLC Union Catalog (1 million titles) and the data cards and holdings of the CDLC Union List of Serials (29,000 titles). **Holdings:** 1500 volumes; 10 VF drawers of reports, directories, subject-related materials. **Subscriptions:** 80 journals and other serials. **Services:** Interlibrary loan; copying; center open by appointment to area and referred researchers. **Automated Operations:** Computerized cataloging and ILL. **Computerized Information Services:** OCLC, BiblioFile, RLIN; produces CaDiLaC (Capital District Library Access Catalog; CD-ROM); ALANET (electronic mail service). **Networks/Consortia:** Member of SUNY/OCLC Library Network, New York State Interlibrary Loan Network (NYSILL). **Publications:** ReCap (newsletter); reports and directories - to institutional and personal members, limited distribution to similar groups. **Special Catalogs:** Union List of Serials and Supplements; Directory of Collection Strengths; Union List of Newspapers; Computer Data Base Directory. **Remarks:** FAX: (518)382-3826. This is the bibliographic center for 16 academic libraries, 3 public library systems (66 public libraries), 4 school library systems, and 29 special libraries which are members of the council. **Staff:** Marie E. Noonan, ILL Libn.; J. James Mancuso, Prog.Serv.Libn.; Carol D. Wait, Ser.Libn.; Suzanne Rahn, Cat.Libn.; Madeline Fiedler, SAVE Liaison; Jenny Wang, HLSP Cons.

★3031★
Capital District Psychiatric Center - Library (Med)
75 New Scotland Ave. Phone: (518)447-9611
Albany, NY 12208 Gail Botta, Libn.
Founded: 1978. **Staff:** Prof 1; Other 5. **Subjects:** Psychiatry, psychology. **Holdings:** 6193 books; 6190 bound periodical volumes. **Subscriptions:** 175 journals and other serials. **Services:** Interlibrary loan; copying; SDI; library open to the public for reference use only. **Automated Operations:** Computerized public access catalog and cataloging. **Computerized Information Services:** BRS Information Technologies, NLM, OCLC; CD-ROM (Silver Platter). Performs searches on fee basis. **Networks/Consortia:** Member of National Network of Libraries of Medicine - Middle Atlantic Region, Capital District Library Council for Reference & Research Resources (CDLC). **Remarks:** A branch library of Schaffer Library Health Sciences, Albany Medical College. Operated by Albany Medical College under contract with the Capital District Psychiatric Center. **Staff:** Virginia Jaffin, Supv.

★3032★
Capital Group Inc. - Research Library (Bus-Fin)
333 S. Hope St., 52nd Fl. Phone: (213)486-9261
Los Angeles, CA 90071 Vickie Halverson Taylor, V.P.
Staff: Prof 1; Other 5. **Subjects:** Investment management, corporation records, business and economic conditions, finance. **Holdings:** 1500 books; 500 bound periodical volumes; 6000 company files; 50 industry files. **Subscriptions:** 450 journals and other serials; 25 newspapers. **Services:** Interlibrary loan; copying; library open to SLA members and other librarians. **Computerized Information Services:** DIALOG Information Services, Spectrum Ownership Profiles Online, LEXIS, NEXIS, Dow Jones News/Retrieval, VU/TEXT Information Services, Datatimes, Reuter TEXTLINE, Citicorp Database Services, Global Report; internal database. **Publications:** Monthly acquisitions list - for internal distribution only. **Special Indexes:** Index of internal reports. **Remarks:** FAX: (213)486-9217. **Formerly:** Capital Group Research Inc.

★3033★
Capital University - Chemistry Library (Sci-Engr)
2199 E. Main St. Phone: (614)236-6614
Columbus, OH 43209 Albert F. Maag, Univ.Libn.
Founded: 1959. **Staff:** Prof 1; Other 1. **Subjects:** Chemistry. **Holdings:** 2300 books; 2800 bound periodical volumes. **Subscriptions:** 21 journals and other serials. **Services:** Copying; library open to the public for reference use only. **Computerized Information Services:** DIALOG Information Services, Chemical Abstracts Service (CAS). Performs searches on fee basis. **Networks/Consortia:** Member of OHIONET. **Remarks:** FAX: (614)236-6490.

★3034★
Capital University - Law School Library (Law)
665 S. High St. Phone: (614)445-8836
Columbus, OH 43215 Donald A. Hughes, Jr., J.D., Dir.
Staff: Prof 10; Other 6. **Subjects:** Law - American, Canadian, British; jurisprudence; legal philosophy. **Holdings:** 215,000 volumes. **Subscriptions:** 2000 journals and other serials; 6 newspapers. **Services:** Interlibrary loan; copying; library open to the public for reference use only. **Automated Operations:** Computerized cataloging. **Computerized Information Services:** WESTLAW, LEXIS. **Networks/Consortia:** Member of OHIONET. **Remarks:** FAX: (614)445-7125. **Staff:** Jacqueline Orlando, J.D., Hd., Pub.Serv.; Phyllis Post, Hd., Tech.Serv.

★3035★
Capitol College - John G. Puente Library (Sci-Engr, Comp Sci)
11301 Springfield Rd. Phone: (301)953-0060
Laurel, MD 20708 Susan Boerner, Libn.
Founded: 1932. **Staff:** Prof 1; Other 7. **Subjects:** Electronics, computer science, telecommunications, optoelectronics. **Special Collections:** Electronic Product Manufacturer Data Books (500). **Holdings:** 9000 books; 200 bound periodical volumes; 10 VF drawers; 122 filmstrips; 133 audio cassettes; 6000 microfiche; 100 reels of microfilm; 94 phonograph records. **Subscriptions:** 90 journals and other serials. **Services:** Interlibrary loan; copying; SDI; library open to the public with restrictions. **Computerized Information Services:** DIALOG Information Services. **Networks/Consortia:** Member of Interlibrary Users Association (IUA), Maryland Interlibrary Organization (MILO). **Remarks:** FAX: (301)953-3876. **Staff:** Tae-Hwa Kim, Lib.Mgr.

★3036★
Caplin & Drysdale - Library (Law)
1 Thomas Circle Phone: (202)862-5073
Washington, DC 20005 Karen M. Stephenson, Law Libn.
Founded: 1964. **Staff:** Prof 2. **Subjects:** Law. **Holdings:** 12,000 books; 3000 bound periodical volumes. **Services:** Interlibrary loan; library not open to the public. **Staff:** Ann Cromwell, Leg.Libn.

Capulin Volcano National Monument
See: **U.S. Natl. Park Service** (17682)

★3037★
(Caracas) Centro Venezolano-Americano - USIS Collection (Educ)
Calle Cerro Quintero
Las Mercedes
Caracas, Venezuela
Remarks: Maintained or supported by the U.S. Information Agency. Focus is on materials that will assist peoples outside the United States to learn about the United States, its people, history, culture, political processes, and social milieux.

Caravan for Commuters, Inc.
See: **Massachusetts State Transportation Library** (9834)

★3038★
Carbon County Law Library (Law)
Carbon County Courthouse
P.O. Box 207 Phone: (717)325-3111
Jim Thorpe, PA 18229-0207 Mary Alice Herman, Libn.
Staff: 1. **Subjects:** Law. **Holdings:** 14,143 volumes. **Subscriptions:** 33 journals and other serials. **Services:** Library open to the public. **Computerized Information Services:** WESTLAW.

★3039★
Carbon/Graphite Group, Inc. - Technical Library (Sci-Engr)
4861 Packard Rd. Phone: (716)286-0321
Niagara Falls, NY 14304 Joanne Gothard, Info.Spec.
Founded: 1960. **Staff:** 1. **Subjects:** Carbon, graphite, electrodes. **Holdings:** 5000 books; 1550 bound periodical volumes; 2185 technical reports; 4400 reprints; 8000 U.S. patents; 600 foreign patents; microfilm; microcards. **Subscriptions:** 25 journals and other serials. **Services:** Interlibrary loan; copying; library open to the public for reference use only on request. **Computerized Information Services:** ORBIT Search Service; internal database. **Remarks:** FAX: (716)286-0322.

★3040★
Carder Gray DDB Needham - Information Centre
77 Bloor St., W.
Toronto, ON, Canada M5S 1M2
Defunct.

Cardeza Foundation
See: **Thomas Jefferson University - Cardeza Foundation** (8359)

★3041★
Cardion Electronics, Inc. - Library (Bus-Fin, Comp Sci)
Long Island Expressway Phone: (516)921-7300
Woodbury, NY 11797 Antoinette Cignarella, Mktg.Info.Spec.
Founded: 1960. **Staff:** Prof 1. **Subjects:** General business, radar, fiber optics, microwave theory, computers. **Holdings:** 2000 books; 150 bound periodical volumes. **Subscriptions:** 153 journals and other serials. **Services:** Library not open to the public. **Automated Operations:** Computerized circulation and serials. **Computerized Information Services:** DIALOG Information Services; QA-Tech Manuals (internal database). **Networks/Consortia:** Member of Long Island Library Resources Council. **Publications:** Newsletter - for internal distribution only. **Special Catalogs:** Computer software; technical reports (both printouts). **Remarks:** FAX: (516)921-7330. Telex: 221683 CARD.

★3042★
Career Development Services - Career Resource Library (Educ)
14 Franklin St., Suite 1200 Phone: (716)325-2274
Rochester, NY 14604 Karen S. Kral, Mgr., Info. & Rsrcs.
Staff: Prof 1. **Subjects:** Vocational guidance, career change, career management and development, outplacement and spouse relocation. **Holdings:** 900 books; 7000 articles in vertical files; Employer Information File on 800 local companies and organizations. **Subscriptions:** 35 journals and other serials. **Services:** Interlibrary loan; copying; consulting; library open to the public. **Computerized Information Services:** DIALOG Information Services, Dow Jones News/Retrieval. **Publications:** Annotated subject bibliographies. **Special Indexes:** Index to local Employer Information File (online). **Remarks:** FAX: (716)325-2133.

Career and Employment Information Center
See: **Detroit Public Library - Philosophy, Religion and Education Department** (4827)

Hugh L. Carey Collection
See: **St. John's University** (14355)

★3043★
William Carey International University - Kenneth Scott Latourette Library (Rel-Phil, Soc Sci)
1539 E. Howard St. Phone: (818)797-1200
Pasadena, CA 91104 Leroy Judd, Lib.Coord.
Founded: 1979. **Staff:** Prof 1; Other 2. **Subjects:** Christian (Protestant) missions, anthropology, area studies, applied linguistics, English as a second language, community development. **Holdings:** 45,000 books; 20 drawers of microfiche; 18 drawers of microfilm; Human Relations Area Files (HRAF) on microfiche. **Subscriptions:** 350 journals and other serials. **Services:** Interlibrary loan; copying; library open to the public for reference use only. **Computerized Information Services:** DIALOG Information Services, ORION, MELVYL. Performs searches on fee basis. **Remarks:** Alternate telephone number(s): (818)398-2155. FAX: (818)398-2260.

William Carey Library
See: **New Orleans Baptist Theological Seminary - John T. Christian Library** (11538)

★3044★
Cargill, Inc. - Information Center (Agri, Bus-Fin)
Box 5670 Phone: (612)475-6498
Minneapolis, MN 55440 Julia Peterson, Mgr.
Founded: 1956. **Staff:** Prof 7; Other 3. **Subjects:** Grain storage and handling; commodity trading; agribusiness; finance; marketing; biochemistry; hybrid

corn breeding and genetics; animal feeding and nutrition; vegetable oil processing and chemistry; agricultural and food products; market research. **Holdings:** 30,000 books; 500 bound periodical volumes; 250 other cataloged items; 9000 internal research reports; 2000 general information files; 16,000 documents; 6 drawers of microforms. **Subscriptions:** 900 journals and other serials; 20 newspapers. **Services:** Interlibrary loan; center not open to the public. **Automated Operations:** Computerized cataloging and serials. **Computerized Information Services:** DIALOG Information Services, PFDS Online, Dow Jones News/Retrieval, NLM, OCLC, Mead Data Central, BRS Information Technologies, DataTimes, DunsPrint, NewsNet, Inc., Teltech Inc., STN International, Market Analysis and Information Database (MAID), University Microfilms International (UMI), Dun & Bradstreet Business Credit Services, Dun's Conquest, Global Scan, Leatherhead Food Research Associates; internal database. **Networks/ Consortia:** Member of MINITEX Library Information Network. **Publications:** Monthly summary reports on research work - to management; special bibliographies - to company personnel; Cargill Information Center News, quarterly. **Remarks:** FAX: (612)475-5228. **Staff:** Kathi Kohli, Sr.Res.Libn.; Sidnie Ross, Res.Libn.; Mary Louise Lose, Res.Libn.; Margaret Drews, Res.Libn.; Peter Sidney, Res.Libn.; Cindy Acton, Asst.Ref.Libn

★3045★
Caribbean Center for Advanced Studies - Library (Soc Sci)
Box 3711, Old San Juan Sta. Phone: (809)725-6500
San Juan, PR 00904-3711 Sra. Nilsa Vargas, Lib.Dir.
Founded: 1961. **Staff:** Prof 3; Other 6. **Subjects:** Psychology, social studies, Caribbean studies. **Holdings:** 10,286 books; 842 bound periodical volumes. **Subscriptions:** 131 journals and other serials; 5 newspapers. **Services:** Interlibrary loan; copying; library open to the public. **Computerized Information Services:** DIALOG Information Services. **Remarks:** FAX: (809)721-7187. Located at Calle Tanca, Esq. Luna, San Juan, PR. **Staff:** Iraida Matos, Libn.; Aurelio Huertas, Libn.

★3046★
Caribbean Community Secretariat - Documentation Centre (Soc Sci)
Bank of Guyana Building
PO Box 10827 Phone: 2 692819
Georgetown, Guyana Maureen Newton, Sr. Doc./Off.-in-Charge
Founded: 1970. **Staff:** 8. **Subjects:** Regional integration, trade, agriculture, energy sources, fuels, environment, industry, food, nutrition, women's affairs, public health, sanitation. **Special Collections:** Official documents of the Caribbean Community, United Nations, and its specialized agencies (UNCTAD, ECLAC, GATT, UNIDO, and UNESCO). **Holdings:** 34,683 books, pamphlets, and documents. **Subscriptions:** 850 journals and other serials; 19 newspapers. **Services:** Interlibrary loan; copying (limited); library open to bona fide researchers. **Computerized Information Services:** Internal databases. **Publications:** C.C.S. Current Awareness Service: New Additions and Articles. **Special Indexes:** Caribbean Common Market Council: index to documents. **Remarks:** FAX: 2 67816; 2 66091; 2 64493. Telex: 2263 CARISEC GY. **Also Known As:** CARICOM. **Staff:** Indrowty Dianand; Joy Duncan.

★3047★
Caribbean Culture Center - Library (Area-Ethnic)
408 W. 58th St. Phone: (212)307-7420
New York, NY 10019 C. Daniel Dawson, Dir., Spec.Proj.
Founded: 1976. **Staff:** 1. **Subjects:** Influence of African traditions in the cultures of the Americas. **Holdings:** Photographs; videotapes. **Services:** Copying; library open to the public by appointment. **Publications:** Caribe Magazine; occasional publications. **Remarks:** FAX: (212)315-1086.

★3048★
Caribbean Family Planning Affiliation - Library (Soc Sci)
Airport and Factory Rd.
P.O. Box 419 Phone: (809)462-4171
St. Johns, Antigua-Barbuda Daisy A. Lake, Doc.Off.
Founded: 1980. **Staff:** Prof 1; Other 1. **Subjects:** Family planning, teenage pregnancy, AIDS, birth control, adolescents, population, demography. **Special Collections:** Adolescent pregnancy and contraceptive surveys in the Caribbean; Dr. Tirbani P. Jagdes Collection (24 books). **Holdings:** 700 books; 30 reports. **Subscriptions:** 8 journals and other serials. **Services:** SDI; library open to the public for reference use only. **Computerized Information Services:** Internal database. **Publications:** Bibliography on Men and Family Planning; Current Awareness Bulletin. **Remarks:** FAX: (809)462-1187.

Caribbean Food and Nutrition Institute
See: **Pan American Health Organization** (12716)

★3049★
Caribbean Industrial Research Institute - Technical Information and Systems (Sci-Engr)
Tunapuna Post Office Phone: (809)663-4171
Trinidad, Trinidad and Tobago Barbara Gumbs, Hd., TI & S
Founded: 1970. **Subjects:** Analytical and industrial chemistry; food technology; microbiology; biochemistry; materials technology; engineering - chemical, electronic, mechanical, industrial, civil; information science; patents and copyright. **Holdings:** 27,000 volumes. **Subscriptions:** 100 journals and other serials. **Services:** Technology searches. **Computerized Information Services:** Internal database. Performs searches free of charge. **Publications:** Technochat (newsletter); fact sheets. **Remarks:** FAX: (809)663 4180. Telex: 24438 CARIRI WG. **Formed by the merger of:** Its Technical Information Service and Data Processing Centre.

Caribbean Regional Library
See: **University of Puerto Rico - Library System - Caribbean and Latin American Studies Collection** (19239)

★3050★
Carle Foundation Hospital - Library (Med)
611 W. Park St. Phone: (217)383-3011
Urbana, IL 61801 Anita D. Johnson, Lib.Mgr.
Founded: 1931. **Staff:** Prof 1; Other 3. **Subjects:** Medicine, medical specialties, nursing, allied health, health care administration. **Holdings:** 2500 books; 9000 bound periodical volumes. **Subscriptions:** 245 journals and other serials. **Services:** Interlibrary loan; document delivery; library open to the public with restrictions. **Computerized Information Services:** MEDLINE, BRS Information Technologies. **Networks/Consortia:** Member of East Central Illinois Consortium, National Network of Libraries of Medicine - Greater Midwest Region, ILLINET. **Remarks:** FAX: (217)383-3452.

★3051★
Carleton Board of Education - Library/Resource Centre (Educ)
133 Greenbank Rd. Phone: (613)721-1820
Nepean, ON, Canada K2H 6L3 Guylaine Bourdon, Lib.Supv.
Staff: Prof 2; Other 1. **Subjects:** General and special education, French immersion. **Holdings:** 25,000 books; curriculum documents. **Subscriptions:** 203 journals and other serials. **Services:** Interlibrary loan. **Computerized Information Services:** BRS Information Technologies, WILSONLINE, Info Globe, Infomart Online, DOBIS Canadian Online Library System. **Remarks:** FAX: (613)820-6968.

★3052★
Carleton College - Science Library (Sci-Engr)
Northfield, MN 55057 Phone: (507)663-4415
Charles F. Priore, Jr., Sci.Libn.
Founded: 1978. **Staff:** Prof 1; Other 1. **Subjects:** Geology, physics, biology, chemistry. **Holdings:** 8000 books; 11,000 bound periodical volumes; microforms. **Subscriptions:** 237 journals and other serials. **Services:** Interlibrary loan; copying; SDI; library open to the public with restrictions. **Automated Operations:** Computerized cataloging. **Computerized Information Services:** DIALOG Information Services, STN International. Performs searches free of charge. **Networks/Consortia:** Member of MINITEX Library Information Network. **Publications:** Acquisitions Bulletin, monthly.

★3053★
Carleton Memorial Hospital - Library (Med)
Box 400 Phone: (506)328-3341
Woodstock, NB, Canada E0J 2B0 Joanne E. Rosevear, Adm.
Founded: 1977. **Staff:** Prof 1; Other 1. **Subjects:** Medicine, management, computers. **Special Collections:** Archives. **Holdings:** 3500 books; 90 cassettes. **Subscriptions:** 146 journals and other serials; 5 newspapers. **Services:** Interlibrary loan; copying; library open to the public.

★3054★
Carleton University - Institute of Soviet and East European Studies - East-West Project - Documentation Centre (Soc Sci)
Social Sciences Research Bldg., Rm. 109 Phone: (613)788-6600
Ottawa, ON, Canada K1S 5B6 Prof. C.H. McMillan
Founded: 1973. **Subjects:** East-West trade and investment, East European regional integration, East-South economic relations. **Holdings:** Periodicals; occasional papers; unpublished monographs; reports from research institutes and international organizations. **Services:** Center open to the public by appointment. **Publications:** The East-West Business Directory. **Remarks:** FAX: (613) 788-3506.

★3055★
Carleton University - Macodrum Library - Map Library (Geog-Map)
D299 Loeb Bldg.
Colonel By Drive Phone: (613)788-2600
Ottawa, ON, Canada K1S 5B6 Barbara E. Farrell, Map Libn.
Founded: 1966. **Staff:** Prof 1; Other 5. **Subjects:** Maps, atlases, cartography. **Special Collections:** Zaborski Collection of Maps of USSR and Eastern Europe (8000). **Holdings:** 1656 books; 140,000 sheet maps; 2050 atlases; 11,000 aerial photographs; 400 wall maps; 25 reels of microfilm of atlases and maps; 7000 maps and gazetteers on microfiche; 3055 slides; 2000 cartographic reference works. **Subscriptions:** 33 journals and other serials. **Services:** Interlibrary loan; copying; library open to the public. **Computerized Information Services:** CUBE (internal database); BITNET, Envoy 100 (electronic mail services). **Publications:** Acquisition lists; search aids, both irregular - both for internal distribution only. **Remarks:** FAX: (613)788-3909. Electronic mail address(es): BARBARA–FARRELL@CARLETON.CA (BITNET); CARLETON.U.LIB (Envoy 100).

★3056★
Carleton University - Norman Paterson School of International Affairs - Resource Centre (Soc Sci)
Colonel By Drive Phone: (613)788-2600
Ottawa, ON, Canada K1S 5B6 Vivian Cummins, Coord.
Staff: Prof 1; Other 3. **Subjects:** International affairs, conflict analysis, international development, global and regional political economy, foreign policy, strategy and security. **Special Collections:** Unpublished papers from conferences and research organizations (1500 papers). **Holdings:** 1000 books; 700 theses; 3500 pamphlets. **Subscriptions:** 400 journals and other serials; 10 newspapers. **Services:** SDI; center open to the public for reference use only. **Computerized Information Services:** DIALOG Information Services, MINISIS, CAN/OLE; internal database. **Publications:** Carleton International Proceedings, annual - on request; Canada Among Nations, annual - for sale; Bibliography series, irregular - on request; bibliography on international trade policy - for internal distribution only.

★3057★
Carlisle Hospital - Medical Library (Med)
246 Parker St.
P.O. Box 310 Phone: (717)245-5184
Carlisle, PA 17013-0310 Judith Welch, Staff Libn.
Subjects: Medicine, nursing. **Holdings:** 700 books. **Subscriptions:** 120 journals and other serials; 2 newspapers. **Services:** Interlibrary loan; copying; SDI; library open to the public on a limited schedule for reference use only. **Computerized Information Services:** MEDLARS, BRS Information Technologies, BRS/COLLEAGUE. Performs searches on fee basis. **Networks/Consortia:** Member of Central Pennsylvania Health Sciences Library Association (CPHSLA). **Remarks:** FAX: (717)249-1562.

Carlsbad Caverns National Park
See: **U.S. Natl. Park Service** (17684)

★3058★
Carlsbad City Library - Genealogy and Local History Division (Hist)
1250 Carlsbad Village Dr. Phone: (619)434-2931
Carlsbad, CA 92008 Ray F. Brookhart, Div.Hd.
Founded: 1977. **Staff:** 2. **Special Collections:** Genealogy (30,000 volumes); local history (2500 photographs). **Services:** Interlibrary loan; copying; department open to the public. **Automated Operations:** Computerized public access catalog, cataloging, and circulation. **Networks/Consortia:** Member of Serra Cooperative Network. **Remarks:** FAX: (619)729-2050.

Carlsen Memorial Library
See: **St. Olaf Lutheran Church** (14553)

★3059★
Carlsmith Ball Wichman Murray Case Mukai & Ichiki - Library (Law)
2200 Pacific Tower
Bishop Square
1001 Bishop St. Phone: (808)523-2500
Honolulu, HI 96813 Swee Lian Berkey, Libn.
Staff: Prof 1; Other 1. **Subjects:** Law. **Holdings:** 11,300 books; 100 bound periodical volumes; 10 VF drawers of legislative material; 1 VF drawer of pamphlets; 3 shelves of pamphlets. **Subscriptions:** 225 journals and other serials. **Services:** Library not open to the public. **Computerized Information Services:** WESTLAW, LEXIS, NEXIS, DIALOG Information Services. **Remarks:** FAX: (808)523-0842. Telex: CWCMI HR. **Formed by the merger of:** Carlsmith, Wichman, Case, Mukai & Ichiki and Ball, Hunt, Hart, Brown & Baerwitz.

★3060★
Carlson Companies - Resource Center (Bus-Fin)
P.O. Box 59159 Phone: (612)449-2543
Minneapolis, MN 55459-8201 Julie Setnosky, Mgr.
Founded: 1989. **Staff:** Prof 2; Other 1. **Subjects:** Business and finance, advertising, marketing, premium promotions, incentives, travel agencies, hotels and restaurants. **Holdings:** Figures not available. **Subscriptions:** 215 journals and other serials; 6 newspapers. **Services:** Library not open to the public. **Computerized Information Services:** DIALOG Information Services, LEXIS, NEXIS, DataTimes, VU/TEXT Information Services, InvesText, Dow Jones News/Retrieval, Reuter TEXTLINE, WILSONLINE. **Remarks:** FAX: (612)449-2546. **Staff:** Janet Lee.

Carlson Foundation Memorial Library
See: **Park City Hospital** (12742)

Carlson Library
See: **University of Rochester** (19275)

Loren D. Carlson Health Sciences Library
See: **University of California, Davis** (18353)

★3061★
Carlson Marketing Group/E.F. MacDonald Motivation - Market Research Information Center
111 N. Main St.
Dayton, OH 45401
Defunct.

Rena M. Carlson Library
See: **Clarion University of Pennsylvania** (3759)

★3062★
Carlton County Historical Society - Library (Hist)
406 Cloquet Ave. Phone: (218)879-1938
Cloquet, MN 55720 Ellen Quinn, Dir.
Founded: 1948. **Staff:** 4. **Subjects:** Carlton County, logging and lumbering, Ojibwa Indians, settlements, railroads. **Holdings:** 200 books and pamphlets; 65 boxes of archival materials and maps; 8 AV programs; 11 VF drawers; newspapers (microfilm); census records (microfilm). **Subscriptions:** 3 journals and other serials; 3 newspapers. **Services:** Copying; library open to the public.

★3063★
Carlton, Fields, Ward, Emmanuel, Smith & Cutler, P.A. - Library (Law)
One Harbour Place
Box 3239 Phone: (813)223-7000
Tampa, FL 33601 Anne V. Ellis, Ch.Libn.
Staff: Prof 2; Other 3. **Subjects:** Law. **Holdings:** 30,000 volumes; memoranda; briefs. **Subscriptions:** 120 journals and other serials; 10 newspapers. **Services:** Interlibrary loan; library not open to the public. **Computerized Information Services:** WESTLAW, LEXIS, DIALOG Information Services, VU/TEXT Information Services, DataTimes, CompuServe Information Service, Information America, Prentice Hall Online. **Remarks:** Maintains branch libraries in Orlando, Pensacola, Tallahassee, and West Palm Beach, FL. **Staff:** Shirley V. Lentz, Assoc.Libn.

★3064★
Carmelite Collection (Rel-Phil)
1600 Webster St., N.E. Phone: (202)526-1221
Washington, DC 20017 Rev. D. George Kennedy, O.Carm.- Libn.
Founded: 1948. **Staff:** Prof 1. **Subjects:** Carmelite order - history, Teresa of Avila, biography. **Special Collections:** Baptist of Mantua. **Holdings:** 7700 books; 995 bound periodical volumes; 100 reels of microfilm of medieval texts. **Subscriptions:** 33 journals and other serials. **Services:** Interlibrary loan; copying; collection open to researchers from universities. **Special Catalogs:** Printed Catalog (1958); Printed Catalog II: Teresa of Avila (1982). **Remarks:** Maintained by the Carmelite Order of the Roman Catholic Church.

★3065★
Carmelite Monastery - Library and Archives (Rel-Phil)
1318 Dulaney Valley Rd. Phone: (301)823-7415
Baltimore, MD 21204 Sr. Constance Fitz Gerald, O.C.D., Archv.
Founded: 1790. **Staff:** 2. **Subjects:** Discalced Carmelite history and spirituality, Scripture, Catholic spirituality and theology, Roman Catholic missals and breviaries, biographies of the saints, Maryland history. **Special Collections:** Works of St. Teresa of Avila and St. John of the Cross in various languages; archives of the first community of Roman Catholic nuns in the Thirteen original states (founded in 1790) and other material relating to the history of the Catholic Church in the United States; Durham collection (extensive papers related to Southern Maryland lawsuit); Restorers of Southern Maryland. **Holdings:** 45,000 volumes. **Subscriptions:** 55 journals and other serials. **Services:** Library generally not open to the public; archives open to the public by appointment. **Computerized Information Services:** Online systems. **Staff:** Sr. Nancy Miller, Libn.

★3066★
Carmelite Monastery - Library of the Immaculate Heart of Mary (Rel-Phil)
Beckley Hill Phone: (802)476-8362
Barre, VT 05641 Sr. Jeanne M. Gonyon, Libn.
Founded: 1950. **Staff:** Prof 1. **Subjects:** Scripture, modern theology, philosophy, psychology, Carmelite spirituality, ecclesiology, social sciences, literature, biography of saints. **Special Collections:** Works of St. John of the Cross and St. Teresa of Jesus. **Holdings:** 8000 books; 400 bound periodical volumes; 6 VF drawers of reports of General Chapters, special meetings, unpublished material related to post-Vatican II renewal. **Subscriptions:** 40 journals and other serials; 10 newspapers. **Services:** Interlibrary loan; library open to the public with restrictions.

★3067★
Carmichael-Lynch Advertising - Information Center (Bus-Fin)
800 Hennepin Ave. Phone: (612)334-6000
Minneapolis, MN 55403 Michele Cherif, Mgr.
Founded: 1990. **Staff:** Prof 1. **Subjects:** Advertising. **Holdings:** Figures not available. **Subscriptions:** 1400 journals and other serials; 7 newspapers. **Services:** Copying; center open to the public with restrictions. **Computerized Information Services:** DIALOG Information Services, Data-Star. **Remarks:** FAX: (612)334-6216.

Marcel Carne Film Archive
See: **French Library in Boston, Inc.** (6149)

★3068★
Carnegie Endowment for International Peace - Library (Soc Sci)
2400 N St., N.W. Phone: (202)862-7970
Washington, DC 20037 Jennifer L. Little, Libn.
Staff: Prof 1; Other 2. **Subjects:** International affairs, foreign relations. **Holdings:** 8000 books; 90 bound periodical volumes; 10 lateral file drawers of uncataloged pamphlets; New York Times, 1981-1991, on microfiche. **Subscriptions:** 200 journals and other serials; 10 newspapers. **Services:** Interlibrary loan; library not open to the public. **Computerized Information Services:** DIALOG Information Services, NEXIS, OCLC, EPIC, DataTimes, INFO-SOUTH Latin American Information System. **Networks/Consortia:** Member of Consortium of Foundation Libraries (CFL), CAPCON Library Network. **Remarks:** FAX: (202)862-2610.

★3069★
Carnegie Foundation for the Advancement of Teaching - Information Center (Educ)
5 Ivy Ln. Phone: (609)452-1780
Princeton, NJ 08540 Hinda Feige Greenberg, Dir.
Founded: 1967. **Staff:** Prof 1. **Subjects:** All levels of education; public policy. **Holdings:** 5000 books; 1500 pamphlets and booklets; 80 volumes of foundation's annual reports; 300 volumes of foundation publications. **Subscriptions:** 100 journals and other serials. **Services:** Copying; center open to the public by appointment for reference use. **Automated Operations:** Computerized cataloging, acquisitions, and circulation. **Computerized Information Services:** DIALOG Information Services, WILSONLINE, NEXIS. **Remarks:** FAX: (609)520-1712.

★3070★
Carnegie Institution of Washington - Department of Embryology - Library (Biol Sci)
115 W. University Pkwy. Phone: (301)467-1414
Baltimore, MD 21210 John Watt, Libn.
Staff: Prof 1. **Subjects:** Embryology, biochemistry. **Holdings:** 300 books; 1800 bound periodical volumes; 775 periodicals. **Subscriptions:** 55 journals and other serials. **Services:** Copying (limited); library open to the public. **Remarks:** FAX: (301)243-6311.

★3071★
Carnegie Institution of Washington - Department of Plant Biology - Library (Biol Sci)
290 Panama St. Phone: (415)325-1521
Stanford, CA 94305 Dr. Winslow R. Briggs, Dir.
Founded: 1930. **Staff:** 20. **Subjects:** Botany, plant physiology, biophysics, plant ecology, photosynthesis. **Special Collections:** Institute publications (200); reprint collections for photosynthesis and plant taxonomy. **Holdings:** 2000 books; 1130 bound periodical volumes; 64 volumes in Jens Clausen Memorial Library; 73 bound yearbooks. **Services:** Library not open to the public. **Remarks:** FAX: (415)325-6857.

★3072★
Carnegie Institution of Washington - Department of Terrestrial Magnetism and Geophysical Laboratory Library (Sci-Engr)
5241 Broad Branch Rd., N.W. Phone: (202)686-4370
Washington, DC 20015-1395 Shaun J. Hardy, Libn.
Founded: 1904. **Staff:** 2.5. **Subjects:** Geophysics, geochemistry, seismology, petrology, mineralogy, crystallography, astrophysics, planetary physics, terrestrial magnetism. **Special Collections:** History of electricity and magnetism; history of volcanology; petrology; physical chemistry. **Holdings:** 40,000 books, bound periodical volumes, reports, maps; 110 VF drawers of pamphlets, offprints, clippings, dissertations. **Subscriptions:** 300 journals and other serials. **Services:** Interlibrary loan; library open to the public with restrictions. **Computerized Information Services:** OCLC, DIALOG Information Services. Performs searches. **Networks/Consortia:** Member of CAPCON Library Network. **Publications:** Carnegie Institution of Washington Year Book; Annual Report of the Director, Geophysical Laboratory; scientific staff reports. **Remarks:** FAX: (202)364-8726, (202)686-2419. Alternate telephone number(s): (202)686-2410. **Formed by the merger of:** Carnegie Institution of Washington - Geophysical Laboratory Library and Terrestrial Magnetism Department Library. **Staff:** Lavonne Lela, Asst.Libn.

Carnegie Institution of Washington - Geophysical Laboratory Library
See: **Carnegie Institution of Washington** (3072)

★3073★
Carnegie Institution of Washington - Library (Sci-Engr)
1530 P St., N.W. Phone: (202)387-6411
Washington, DC 20005 Ray Bowers, Ed./Pub.Off.
Founded: 1903. **Staff:** Prof 2. **Subjects:** Astronomy, geophysics, botany, embryology, genetics, archeology. **Holdings:** 1000 books; 195 bound periodical volumes of SCIENCE and NATURE. **Services:** Interlibrary loan; library open to the public with restrictions. **Remarks:** Library serves almost exclusively as depository for Carnegie Institution of Washington publications.

★3074★
Carnegie Institution of Washington - Observatories - Library (Sci-Engr)
813 Santa Barbara St. Phone: (818)304-0234
Pasadena, CA 91101 Joan Gantz, Libn.
Founded: 1905. **Staff:** Prof 1. **Subjects:** Astronomy, astrophysics, physics, mathematics. **Holdings:** 26,000 volumes; 100 bound periodical volumes; observatory publications. **Subscriptions:** 100 journals and other serials. **Services:** Copying; library open to the public for reference use only by appointment. **Remarks:** FAX: (818)795-8136. Telex: 1561318. An alternate telephone number is 577-1122. Electronic mail address(es): 6036::JOAN (Space Physics Analysis Network (SPAN)); JOAN@OCIW.@HAMLET.CALTECH.EDU (BITNET). **Also Known As:** The Observatories of the Carnegie Institution of Washington.

Carnegie Institution of Washington - Terrestrial Magnetism Department Library
See: **Carnegie Institution of Washington** (3072)

★3075★
Carnegie Library of Pittsburgh - Business Department (Bus-Fin)
One Mellon Bank Center
East Plaza, Level B
500 Grant St. Phone: (412)281-5945
Pittsburgh, PA 15219 Pam Craychee, Dept.Hd.
Founded: 1924. **Staff:** Prof 7; Other 3. **Subjects:** Investments, small business, management, marketing, insurance, advertising, accounting, real estate. **Special Collections:** Financial directories of public corporations (includes historical Moody's manuals); trade and state industrial directories; indexes and files on Pittsburgh companies. **Holdings:** 11,479 volumes; VF materials; microfilm; looseleaf services. **Subscriptions:** 200 journals, serials, and newspapers. **Services:** Interlibrary loan; department open to the public. **Automated Operations:** Computerized cataloging. **Computerized Information Services:** DIALOG Information Services, Dow Jones News/Retrieval, WESTLAW, VU/TEXT Information Services, InfoTrac; CD-ROM. Performs searches on fee basis. Contact Person: Dorothy Kabakeris, Sr. Staff Libn. **Networks/Consortia:** Member of Pittsburgh Regional Library Center (PRLC), Oakland Library Consortium. **Publications:** Annotated new titles list, monthly; small business bibliographies, annual. **Special Indexes:** Pittsburgh Company Index. **Remarks:** FAX: (412)471-1724. **Staff:** Blanche Abel, Sr. Staff Libn.; Natalie Lustig, Staff Libn.; Susan Carpenter, Staff Libn.

★3076★
Carnegie Library of Pittsburgh - Children's Department (Hum)
4400 Forbes Ave. Phone: (412)622-3122
Pittsburgh, PA 15213 Dallas Clautice, Dept.Hd.
Founded: 1898. **Staff:** Prof 5; Other 4. **Subjects:** Literature for children through age 12. **Special Collections:** Literature Portraying Disabilities Collection; Alice Wirth Wirsing Collection; historical collection; Child Sexual Abuse Resources Collection. **Holdings:** 55,000 books; 100 bound periodical volumes. **Subscriptions:** 25 journals and other serials. **Services:** Department open to the public, with some restrictions on the historical collection. **Computerized Information Services:** OCLC. **Networks/Consortia:** Member of Pittsburgh Regional Library Center (PRLC). **Remarks:** FAX: (412)621-1267. **Staff:** Helene Tremaine, Sr. Staff Libn.; Andrea Jones, Libn.; Jane McCullough, Libn.

★3077★
Carnegie Library of Pittsburgh - Humanities Department (Hum)
4400 Forbes Ave. Phone: (412)622-3119
Pittsburgh, PA 15213 Denise S. Sticha, Dept.Hd.
Founded: 1989. **Staff:** Prof 10; Other 6. **Subjects:** Literature, language, philosophy, religion, sports and recreation, psychology, folklore and custom, cooking. **Special Collections:** Gypsy Collection; Workplace Center (collection of employment retraining and vocational guidance); Gillespie Collection (endow collection selected to resemble a well-maintained home library); Andrew W. Mellon International Collection of contemporary poetry. **Holdings:** Books; 20 VF drawers of clippings and pamphlets; 1100 videocassettes; 3500 audiocassettes; 3000 spoken word recordings. **Subscriptions:** 120 journals and other serials. **Services:** Interlibrary loan; copying; department open to the public. **Automated Operations:** Computerized public access catalog, cataloging, acquisitions, and circulation. **Computerized Information Services:** OCLC; InfoTrac; Ulisys (internal database). Performs searches on fee basis. **Networks/Consortia:** Member of Pittsburgh Regional Library Center (PRLC), Oakland Library Consortium. **Remarks:** FAX: (412)621-1267. **Staff:** Amanda Albright, Asst.Hd.; Vera Green, Sr. Staff Libn.; David Uptegraff, Sr. Staff Libn.; Elizabeth Bergmann, Libn.; Marjorie Franklin, Libn.; Laurie Anderson, Libn.; Deborah Matthews, Libn.; Marian Streiff, Libn.

★3078★
Carnegie Library of Pittsburgh - Music and Art Department (Mus, Art)
4400 Forbes Ave. Phone: (412)622-3105
Pittsburgh, PA 15213 Kathryn Logan, Dept.Hd.
Founded: 1938. **Staff:** Prof 7; Other 19. **Subjects:** Music, art, architecture, interior design, collectibles, dance. **Special Collections:** Pittsburghiana (music and art); Bernd Architectural Collection; Fashion Group Costume Collection; Boyd Memorial Collection (music and musicology); Merz Music Library (19th century American and German music journals); Pittsburgh Jazz and Popular Music Resource Collection; Wichmann Organ Music Collection. **Holdings:** 110,000 music books and scores; 63,000 art books; 1750 dance books; 39,000 sound recordings; 280,000 mounted pictures; 78,000 slides; 69 VF drawers. **Subscriptions:** 320 journals and other serials. **Services:** Interlibrary loan; copying; department open to the public. **Automated Operations:** Computerized cataloging and circulation. **Computerized Information Services:** OCLC, DIALOG Information Services. **Networks/Consortia:** Member of Pittsburgh Regional Library Center (PRLC), Oakland Library Consortium. **Remarks:** FAX: (412)621-1267. **Staff:** Kirby Dilworth, Asst.Dept.Hd.; Katherine Kepes Snovak, Libn.; A. Catherine Tack, Libn.; Cheryl O'Neill, Libn.; John Forbis, Libn.

★3079★
Carnegie Library of Pittsburgh - Pennsylvania Department (Hist)
4400 Forbes Ave. Phone: (412)622-3154
Pittsburgh, PA 15213 Maria Zini, Hd.
Founded: 1928. **Staff:** Prof 4; Other 5. **Subjects:** Pennsylvania history, biography, economics, and sociology, with emphasis on Pittsburgh and western Pennsylvania; genealogy; heraldry. **Special Collections:** Carnegie Collection (books and pamphlets written by and about Andrew Carnegie); Isaac Craig manuscripts; Pittsburgh Photographic Library. **Holdings:** 30,000 volumes; 100 VF drawers of clippings and pamphlets; 57,000 photographs; 11,000 reels of microfilm. **Subscriptions:** 46 journals and other serials. **Services:** Copying. **Automated Operations:** Computerized public access catalog, and cataloging. **Computerized Information Services:** OCLC, VU/TEXT Information Services. **Networks/Consortia:** Member of Pittsburgh Regional Library Center (PRLC), Oakland Library Consortium. **Remarks:** FAX: (412)621-1267. **Staff:** Marilyn Holt, Asst.Hd.; Ann M. Loyd, Libn.; Adrianne McConville, Libn.

★3080★
Carnegie Library of Pittsburgh - Science and Technology Department (Sci-Engr, Biol Sci)
4400 Forbes Ave. Phone: (412)622-3138
Pittsburgh, PA 15213 James E. Bobick, Hd.
Founded: 1895. **Staff:** Prof 12; Other 22. **Subjects:** Chemistry, physics, astronomy, computer science, engineering, technology, geology, health, medicine, metallurgy, botany, biology, zoology. **Special Collections:** Complete sets of U.S. and British patent specifications and drawings; plant patents; topographical maps (complete set); selected geologic maps, folios of the geologic atlas of the U.S.; soil surveys and maps; American National Standards (ANSI); British Standards (BSI); German Standards (DIN; in English translation); Department of Defense Adopted Industry Standards; U.S. military and federal specifications; Brutcher translations; ISI translations; AEC translations; AEC reports; NASA reports; ERDA reports. **Holdings:** 385,000 books; 425,000 bound periodical volumes; 875,000 reels of microfilm and microfiche; 150,000 technical reports; 100,000 government documents; 22,000 historical trade catalogs. **Subscriptions:** 2000 journals and other serials. **Services:** Interlibrary loan; copying; department open to the public. **Automated Operations:** Computerized cataloging and circulation. **Computerized Information Services:** DIALOG Information Services, OCLC, PFDS Online, Classification and Search Support Information System (CASSIS), STN International; InfoTrac. Performs searches on fee basis. Contact Person: David Murdock, Sr.Libn. **Networks/Consortia:** Member of Pittsburgh Regional Library Center (PRLC), Oakland Library Consortium. **Publications:** Science and Technology, a Purchase Guide for Public Libraries, annual. **Special Indexes:** Index to Handicraft Books, 1974-1984 (book). **Remarks:** FAX: (412)621-1267. **Staff:** Joan Anderson, Sr.Libn.; Naomi Balaban, Libn.; Jan Comfort, Libn.; Susan Horvath, Libn.; Diane Eldridge, Libn.; Dorothy Melamed, Libn.; Kristine Mielcarek, Libn.; Margery Peffer, Libn.; Donna Strawbridge, Libn.; Gregory Pomrenke, Libn.

★3081★
Carnegie Library of Pittsburgh - Social Sciences Department (Soc Sci)
4400 Forbes Ave. Phone: (412)622-3175
Pittsburgh, PA 15213 Sheila T. Jackson, Dept.Hd.
Founded: 1989. **Staff:** Prof 7; Other 8. **Subjects:** History and geography, political science, economics and business, sociology, education, law. **Special**

Collections: Worthington Welsh Collection of Wales and Americana; selective U.S. Government depository library. **Holdings:** 285,000 books. **Subscriptions:** 490 journals and other serials; 30 newspapers. **Services:** Interlibrary loan; copying; department open to the public. **Automated Operations:** Computerized cataloging, acquisitions, and circulation. **Computerized Information Services:** DIALOG Information Services, VU/TEXT Information Services, OCLC; CAROLINE (internal database). Performs searches on fee basis. **Networks/Consortia:** Member of Pittsburgh Regional Library Center (PRLC), Oakland Library Consortium. **Remarks:** FAX: (412)621-1267. **Staff:** Barbara Rosenfield, Asst.Hd.; Mary E. Gildroy, Libn.; Michael Marino, Sr.Libn.; Pat Geary, Sr.Libn.; D. Nora Barreca, Libn.

★3082★
Carnegie-Mellon University - Center for Excellence in Optical Data Processing - Library (Comp Sci)
Dept. of Electrical and Computer Engineering — Phone: (412)268-2464
Pittsburgh, PA 15213 — Marlene Layton, Libn.
Founded: 1984. **Subjects:** Optical data processing, optical pattern recognition, optical signal processing, and optical computing. **Holdings:** 400 research publications. **Remarks:** FAX: (412)268-6345.

★3083★
Carnegie Mellon University - Hunt Institute for Botanical Documentation - Library (Biol Sci)
Pittsburgh, PA 15213 — Phone: (412)268-2434
Robert W. Kiger, Dir.
Founded: 1960. **Staff:** Prof 7; Other 8. **Subjects:** Botanical history; plant taxonomy, including 15th-17th century herbals; extensive collection of 18th and 19th century colorplate works, floras, monographic works, and other works on natural history, plant exploration and introduction. **Special Collections:** Botanical art and illustration (30,000 paintings, drawings, prints); botanical portraiture (25,000); botanical biographies (20,000); bibliography of botanical biographies (200,000 citations); Strandell Collection of Linnaeana (3500 titles; 3600 clippings); library of Michel Adanson (127 books; 260 holographic letters). **Holdings:** 23,000 books. **Subscriptions:** 270 journals and other serials; 2 newspapers. **Services:** Interlibrary loan; copying; institute open to the public for reference use only. **Computerized Information Services:** OCLC. **Networks/Consortia:** Member of Pittsburgh Regional Library Center (PRLC). **Publications:** International Register of Specialists and Current Research in Plant Systematics; Plant Taxonomic Database Standar ds (numbered series); Bulletin of the Hunt Institute for Botanical Documentation; Guide to Archives; Huntia; Bibliographia Periodicum Huntianum. **Special Catalogs:** Exhibition catalogs; Catalog of Botanical Books in the Collection of Rachel McMasters Miller Hunt, 1477-1800; Catalog of Portrait Collection; Catalog of Art Collection. **Remarks:** FAX: (412)268-5677. **Staff:** T.D. Jacobsen, Asst.Dir.; Charlotte A. Tancin, Libn.; Sarah Yoder Leroy, Asst.Libn. James J. White, Cur. of Art; Gavin D.R. Bridson, Bibliog.; Anita L. Karg, Archv.

★3084★
Carnegie-Mellon University - University Libraries - Special Collections (Hum)
Hunt Library — Phone: (412)268-6622
Pittsburgh, PA 15213 — M.C. Johnsen, Spec.Coll.Libn.
Founded: 1960. **Staff:** Prof 1; Other 1. **Subjects:** History of printing, 19th century English literature, landmark books of science. **Special Collections:** Anne Lyon Haight Collection of C.C. Moore's "Twas the Night Before Christmas" (400 editions); Frances Hooper Kate Greenaway Collection. **Holdings:** 12,000 books. **Services:** Library open to the public. **Special Catalogs:** Exhibit catalogs. **Remarks:** FAX: (412)268-6944.

★3085★
Carnegie Museum of Natural History - Library (Sci-Engr, Biol Sci)
4400 Forbes Ave. — Phone: (412)622-3264
Pittsburgh, PA 15213 — Elizabeth Kwater, Libn.
Founded: 1898. **Staff:** Prof 3. **Subjects:** Anthropology, archeology, entomology, ornithology, geology, mammalogy, botany, herpetology, paleontology, malacology, mineralogy. **Special Collections:** Otto E. Jennings Library (botany); Western Pennsylvania Botanical Society Library; Hugh Kahl Library (entomology); George A. Ehrman Library (entomology); B. Preston Clark Library (entomology); John Hamilton Library (entomology); E.R. Eller Library (geology and paleontology); John E. Guilday Library and Reprint Collection (geology and paleontology); O.A. Peterson Reprint Collection (geology and paleontology); J.B. Hatcher Reprint Collection (geology and paleontology); Albert C.L.G. Gunther Reprint Collection (herpetology); Arnold E. Ortmann Library (invertebrates); George E. Clapp Conchology Library; Victor Sterki Library (invertebrates); Boone and Crockett Club Library (mammalogy); J. Kenneth Doutt Memorial Library (mammalogy); W.E. Clyde Todd Ornithological Reprint Collection; John P. Robin Library (ornithology); G. Bernard Van Cleve Library (ornithology); W.J. Holland Library (natural history); Andrey Avinoff Library (natural history); J.J. Stevenson Library (natural history). **Holdings:** 128,000 volumes; 3000 serial titles; reprint collection; archival materials; manuscripts. **Subscriptions:** 1000 journals and other serials. **Services:** Interlibrary loan; copying; library open to the public by appointment. **Automated Operations:** Computerized cataloging. **Computerized Information Services:** OCLC. **Networks/Consortia:** Member of Pittsburgh Regional Library Center (PRLC). **Remarks:** FAX: (412)622-8837. **Staff:** Marianne Kasica, Cat.Libn.; Susan Rettger, Gifts & Exch.Libn.

★3086★
Carnegie Public Library of Clarksdale and Coahoma County - Delta Blues Museum Collection (Hist, Mus)
114 Delta Ave.
Box 280 — Phone: (601)624-4461
Clarksdale, MS 38614 — Sid F. Graves, Jr., Dir.
Founded: 1914. **Staff:** Prof 6; Other 5. **Subjects:** Blues music; history - local, state, regional, black. **Holdings:** 15,000 books, periodicals, phonograph records, photographs, videotapes. **Services:** Interlibrary loan; copying; collection open to the public with restrictions. **Publications:** Clarksdale & Coahoma County: A History, 1982. **Remarks:** FAX: (601)627-7263.

★3087★
Carney Hospital - Colpoys Library (Med)
2100 Dorchester Ave. — Phone: (617)296-4000
Boston, MA 02124-5666 — Catherine I. Moore, Med.Libn.
Staff: Prof 1. **Subjects:** Medicine. **Holdings:** 1200 books; 6000 bound periodical volumes; tapes. **Subscriptions:** 230 journals and other serials; 10 newspapers. **Services:** Interlibrary loan; library not open to the public. **Computerized Information Services:** BRS Information Technologies, LEXIS, DIALOG Information Services, NLM; CD-ROM (MEDLINE). Performs searches free of charge. **Networks/Consortia:** Member of Boston Biomedical Library Consortium, Massachusetts Health Sciences Libraries Network (MaHSLiN). **Remarks:** FAX: (617)296-9513.

★3088★
Carolina Art Association - Gibbes Museum of Art - Library (Art)
135 Meeting St. — Phone: (803)722-2706
Charleston, SC 29401 — Angela Mack, Cur., Coll.
Staff: 1. **Subjects:** Art, architecture. **Special Collections:** Files on South Carolina artists; photographic collections showing development of Charleston. **Holdings:** 5000 books. **Subscriptions:** 12 journals and other serials. **Services:** Copying; library open to the public by appointment. **Remarks:** FAX: (803)723-1721.

★3089★
Carolina Library Services, Inc. (Info Sci)
209 N. Columbia St. — Phone: (919)929-4870
Chapel Hill, NC 27514 — Kate Millard, Dir.
Founded: 1977. **Staff:** Prof 4; Other 7. **Subjects:** Biotechnology, medicine, information science. **Holdings:** 1000 books; 500 government reports; 50 dissertations on microfilm. **Subscriptions:** 20 journals and other serials. **Services:** Copying; SDI; document delivery; information services (fee); services open to the public. **Computerized Information Services:** DIALOG Information Services, OCLC; DIALORDER (electronic mail service). Performs searches on fee basis. **Special Catalogs:** Catalog of world wide sources of all types of publications (card). **Remarks:** FAX: (919)933-1253. **Staff:** Rick Oxendine, Doc. Delivery

★3090★
Carolina Population Center - Library (Soc Sci)
University of North Carolina at Chapel Hill
CB No. 8120 — Phone: (919)962-3081
Chapel Hill, NC 27516-3997 — Patricia E. Shipman, Hd.Libn.
Founded: 1967. **Staff:** Prof 3; Other 4. **Subjects:** Population dynamics, policy, education; abortion; family planning; fertility. **Special Collections:** Collected papers of the Population Associations of America, 1968 to present;

Bibliography File (350). **Holdings:** 9000 books; 1500 bound periodical volumes; 40,000 analytics; 15,000 documents, technical reports, manuscripts; 90 documents on microfiche. **Subscriptions:** 375 journals and other serials. **Services:** Interlibrary loan; copying; library open to the public. **Automated Operations:** Computerized public access catalog. **Computerized Information Services:** DIALOG Information Services, MEDLINE, POPLINE; BITNET (electronic mail service). **Remarks:** FAX: (919)966-6638. Electronic mail address(es): CLWARD@UNCVM1 (BITNET). **Staff:** Cheryl Ward, Asst.Hd.Libn.; Laurie Leadbetter, Ref.Libn.

★3091★
Carolina Power & Light Company - Library (Energy)
411 Fayetteville St.
Box 1551 Phone: (919)546-6790
Raleigh, NC 27602 A.P. Carmichael, Corp.Libn.
Founded: 1970. **Staff:** Prof 2; Other 2. **Subjects:** Engineering - electrical, mechanical, nuclear, civil, environmental; codes and standards; energy economics. **Special Collections:** Electric Power Research Institute (EPRI) reports; nuclear facility PSARs and FSARs; NRC regulatory documents. **Holdings:** 8800 books; 65,000 other cataloged items. **Subscriptions:** 225 journals and other serials. **Services:** Interlibrary loan; copying; SDI; library open to the public by prior arrangement. **Computerized Information Services:** DIALOG Information Services, Knight-Ridder Unicom, Edison Electric Institute (EEI), Electric Power Research Institute (EPRI). **Publications:** Energy News Review, weekly; BiblioBulletin (acquisitions list), monthly - both for internal distribution only. **Remarks:** FAX: (919)546-7678. Telex: 910 380 3760 CPL RALNC.

Carondelet Health Services, Inc. - St. Mary's Hospital & Health Center
See: **St. Mary's Hospital & Health Center** (14528)

Carpenter Center for the Visual Arts
See: **Harvard University** (6951)

Coy C. Carpenter Library
See: **Wake Forest University - Bowman Gray School of Medicine** (19940)

★3092★
Guy Carpenter & Company, Inc. - Library and Information Services (Bus-Fin)
2 World Trade Center, 54th Fl. Phone: (212)323-1800
New York, NY 10048 Sheila L. Sterling, Asst. V.P.
Founded: 1980. **Staff:** Prof 2; Other 1. **Subjects:** Property and casualty insurance, business. **Special Collections:** Reinsurance collection. **Holdings:** 3000 books; 20 drawers of microfilm. **Subscriptions:** 125 journals and other serials; 10 newspapers. **Services:** Interlibrary loan; copying; library open to SLA members by appointment. **Computerized Information Services:** DIALOG Information Services, Dow Jones News/Retrieval, Dun & Bradstreet Business Credit Services, Mead Data Central, REUTERS, WILSONLINE, VU/TEXT Information Services, DataTimes. **Staff:** Valerie Logan, Assoc.Libn.

★3093★
Carpenter Technology Corporation - Research and Development Center Library (Sci-Engr)
Box 14662 Phone: (215)371-2583
Reading, PA 19612-4662 Wendy M. Schmehl, Libn.
Founded: 1950. **Staff:** Prof 1. **Subjects:** Ferrous metallurgy, metal working, chemistry. **Holdings:** 4800 books; 10,000 bound periodical volumes; 8500 hardcopy reports and pamphlets; 10,000 microfiche of reports and pamphlets. **Subscriptions:** 170 journals and other serials. **Services:** Interlibrary loan. **Automated Operations:** Computerized serials. **Computerized Information Services:** DIALOG Information Services, ORBIT Search Service. **Networks/Consortia:** Member of Berks County Library Association (BCLA). **Publications:** Patent Abstract Bulletin, weekly. **Remarks:** FAX: (215)371-3256.

★3094★
Emily Carr College of Art and Design - Library (Art, Aud-Vis)
1399 Johnston St.
Granville Island Phone: (604)844-3840
Vancouver, BC, Canada V6H 3R9 Ken Chamberlain, Hd.Libn.
Founded: 1926. **Staff:** Prof 2; Other 4.5. **Subjects:** 20th century visual arts. **Holdings:** 11,500 books; 100,100 slides; 221 slide sets; 2000 exhibition catalogs; 505 videotapes; 415 sound recordings; 47 films. **Subscriptions:** 125 journals and other serials. **Services:** Library not open to the public. **Computerized Information Services:** Envoy 100 (electronic mail service). **Publications:** Guide to the AV Library, annual - available upon request; Videotape Catalog, annual - available to instructors upon request. **Special Indexes:** Indexes to audio, video, slide set, and exhibition catalog holdings. **Remarks:** FAX: (604)844-3801. Alternate telephone number(s): (604)844-2804 (AV). Electronic mail address(es): ECCA (Envoy 100).

Carr Health Sciences Library
See: **Somerville Hospital** (15365)

Peter Carras Library
See: **Christian Health Care Center** (3633)

Gertrude S. Carraway Library
See: **North Carolina (State) Department of Cultural Resources** (11887)

★3095★
Carraway Methodist Medical Center - Medical Library (Med)
1600 N. 26th St. Phone: (205)226-6265
Birmingham, AL 35234 Mrs. Bobby H. Powell, Med.Libn.
Founded: 1942. **Staff:** Prof 1. **Subjects:** Medicine, surgery, nursing, allied health sciences. **Special Collections:** Pastoral care collection (421 volumes). **Holdings:** 1293 books; 7805 bound periodical volumes. **Subscriptions:** 214 journals and other serials. **Services:** Interlibrary loan (limited); library not open to the public. **Automated Operations:** Computerized ILL (DOCLINE). **Computerized Information Services:** MEDLINE. **Networks/Consortia:** Member of Jefferson County Hospital Librarians' Association, Alabama Health Libraries Association (ALHELA). **Remarks:** FAX: (205)226-5357.

Brandon Carrell, M.D., Medical Library
See: **Texas Scottish Rite Hospital for Children** (16229)

★3096★
Carrier Corporation - Logan Lewis Library (Sci-Engr)
Bldg. TR-4
Box 4808 Phone: (315)432-6306
Syracuse, NY 13221-4808 Flora P. Rockburn, Libn.
Founded: 1942. **Staff:** Prof 1. **Subjects:** Air conditioning, heating, refrigeration, ventilation, acoustics, electrical engineering, mechanical engineering, chemistry and chemical engineering, air and water pollution. **Special Collections:** Archives of Willis Carrier; Carrier Corporation history; history of air conditioning. **Holdings:** 6000 books; 2900 bound periodical volumes. **Subscriptions:** 350 journals and other serials. **Services:** Interlibrary loan; copying; SDI. **Computerized Information Services:** DIALOG Information Services, PFDS Online, NEXIS; internal database. **Networks/Consortia:** Member of Central New York Library Resources Council (CENTRO). **Publications:** Bi-monthly Bulletin; Periodicals Received, annual - both to area libraries upon request. **Remarks:** A subsidiary of United Technologies Corporation. Library located on Carrier Parkway, Syracuse, NY 13221-0000. **Remarks:** FAX: (315)432-6741.

★3097★
Carrier Foundation - Nolan D.C. Lewis Library (Med)
Box 147 Phone: (908)281-1412
Belle Mead, NJ 08502 Lynne Cohn, Dir.
Staff: Prof 2; Other 1. **Subjects:** Psychiatry, psychotherapy, psychiatric nursing, family therapy, psychology, adjunctive therapies. **Special Collections:** Nolan Lewis Collection. **Holdings:** 3000 books; 600 audio and video cassettes. **Subscriptions:** 150 journals and other serials. **Services:** Interlibrary loan; copying; SDI; library open to the public by appointment for reference use. **Automated Operations:** Computerized cataloging and circulation. **Computerized Information Services:** BRS Information Technologies; DOCLINE, MESSAGES (electronic mail services). Performs searches on fee basis. **Networks/Consortia:** Member of Central Jersey Health Science Libraries Association (CJHSLA), Health Sciences Library Association of New Jersey (HSLANJ), MEDCORE, BHSL. **Remarks:** FAX: (908)874-3386.

★3098★
Carrington, Coleman, Sloman & Blumenthal - Library (Law)
200 Crescent Ct., Suite 1500 Phone: (214)855-3530
Dallas, TX 75201 Sue H. Johnson, Libn.
Staff: 1. **Subjects:** Law. **Holdings:** 15,500 volumes. **Subscriptions:** 50 journals and other serials. **Services:** Library not open to the public. **Computerized Information Services:** LEXIS, WESTLAW, Information America, DataTimes. **Remarks:** FAX: (214)855-1333.

★3099★
Carroll College - Jack and Sallie Corette Library (Rel-Phil, Hum)
Helena, MT 59625-0099 Phone: (406)442-1295
Lois A. Fitzpatrick, Dir.
Founded: 1928. **Staff:** Prof 3; Other 2. **Subjects:** Drama, literary criticism, social work, philosophy, theology, biomedicine. **Holdings:** 101,000 books; 16 VF drawers of archival material relating to the Catholic Church in Montana; 675 microfiche on slavery in America; 800 magnetic tapes; 10,000 microforms; 3000 phonograph records; 100 videotapes. **Subscriptions:** 420 journals and other serials; 16 newspapers. **Services:** Interlibrary loan; copying; library open to the public for reference use only. **Automated Operations:** Computerized cataloging, serials, circulation, and ILL. **Computerized Information Services:** OCLC, DIALOG Information Services, BRS Information Technologies, MEDLINE, OCLC EPIC, EasyNet. **Networks/Consortia:** Member of Helena Area Health Sciences Library Consortium (HAHSLC), Bibliographical Center for Research, Rocky Mountain Region, Inc. (BCR), Northwest Association of Private Colleges & Universities (NAPCU). **Remarks:** FAX: (406)443-3964. **Staff:** John Thomas, Ref.Libn.; Robert Tiessen, Per./Govt.Docs.Libn.; Peggy Kude, Circ.Mgr.; Cathi Burgoyne, Tech.Serv.Supv.

★3100★
Carroll County Bar Association - Library (Law)
Court House Phone: (301)857-2672
Westminster, MD 21157 Terry L. Hinkel, Libn.
Staff: 1. **Subjects:** Law. **Holdings:** 10,000 volumes. **Services:** Library not open to the public.

★3101★
Carroll County Farm Museum - Landon Burns Memorial Library (Agri)
500 S. Center St. Phone: (301)848-7775
Westminster, MD 21157 Lyndi McNulty, Cur.
Founded: 1965. **Staff:** 2. **Subjects:** Agriculture, farm machinery, Victorian life. **Holdings:** 500 books. **Services:** Library open to the public with restrictions.

★3102★
John Carroll University - Seismological Library (Sci-Engr)
Cleveland, OH 44118 Phone: (216)397-4657
Val Finan, Libn.
Founded: 1905. **Staff:** Prof 2. **Subjects:** Seismological data, geophysics. **Special Collections:** Seismological bulletins from approximately 300 observatories throughout the world (10,000). **Holdings:** 200 books; 1000 bound periodical volumes. **Services:** Interlibrary loan; library not open to the public.

★3103★
Carson County Square House Museum - Information Center (Hist)
Box 276 Phone: (806)537-3524
Panhandle, TX 79068 Dr. Paul Catz, Dir.
Founded: 1967. **Staff:** 1. **Subjects:** Carson County and Texas Panhandle history, pioneer health and medicine, museology, Texana, American Indians, art. **Special Collections:** Artist morgue of Ben Carlton Mead (illustrator; 12 linear feet); pioneer school textbooks (70); music, 1910-1940; rare books on Texana. **Holdings:** 875 books; 36 bound periodical volumes; 7809 documents; 10,655 artifacts, including 5 photographs, maps, business and personal communications, postcards, legal and offical correspondence. **Subscriptions:** 26 journals and other serials; 6 newspapers. **Services:** Copying; center open to the public for reference use only. **Automated Operations:** Computerized cataloging and acquisitions. **Staff:** David Hoover, Reg.

Kit Carson Foundation
See: **Kit Carson Historic Museums - Library** (3104)

★3104★
Kit Carson Historic Museums - Library (Hist)
P.O. Drawer CCC Phone: (505)758-5440
Taos, NM 87571 Neil Poese, Dir.
Founded: 1952. **Staff:** 1. **Subjects:** Early fur trade, Western Americana, Spanish-Colonial history, archeology, allied subjects. **Special Collections:** Collection of literature on Kit Carson (250 items). **Holdings:** 3880 books; 5591 bound periodical volumes; 701 pamphlets; 2 VF drawers of uncataloged pamphlets; 8541 photographs and negatives; 919 maps; deeds; documents; letters; papers; manuscripts. **Subscriptions:** 23 journals and other serials. **Services:** Copying; photograph duplication; library open to the public for reference use only. **Formerly:** Kit Carson Foundation. **Staff:** Char Graebner, Archv.

★3105★
Carson-Newman College - Stephens-Burnett Memorial Library - Special Collections (Rel-Phil, Area-Ethnic)
Russell Ave. Phone: (615)475-9061
Jefferson City, TN 37760 Dr. Stanley H. Benson, Dir.
Founded: 1851. **Staff:** 20. **Subjects:** Baptist history and heritage, local history, Appalachian life and culture. **Special Collections:** East Tennessee Baptist Historical Collection. **Holdings:** 185,000 volumes; U.S. government documents; AV materials. **Subscriptions:** 1000 journals and other serials; 24 newspapers. **Services:** Interlibrary loan; copying; collections open to the public for reference use only. **Automated Operations:** Computerized public access catalog and cataloging. **Computerized Information Services:** BRS Information Technologies, OCLC, STN International; CD-ROMs. **Networks/Consortia:** Member of SOLINET, Knoxville Area Health Sciences Library Consortium (KAHSLC). **Remarks:** FAX: (615)471-3502. **Staff:** Imogene Brewer, Cat.Libn.; Barbara Hartman, Ref.Libn.; Mary Evelyn Lynn, Per.Libn.; George Anah Self, Info.Serv.Libn.; Bruce Whitney, Media Serv.

★3106★
Rachel Carson Council, Inc. - Library (Biol Sci)
8940 Jones Mill Rd. Phone: (301)652-1877
Chevy Chase, MD 20815 Shirley A. Briggs, Exec.Dir.
Founded: 1965. **Staff:** 1. **Subjects:** Pesticides, toxic substances, government regulation, pest management programs. **Special Collections:** Government regulatory documents; Rachel Carson's personal library; pesticide toxicology collection. **Holdings:** 2000 books; 1500 documents and unbound reports; 50 drawers of specialized files; Environmental Protection Agency Pesticide Product Information and Registry of Toxic Effects of Chemical Substances materials on microfiche. **Subscriptions:** 85 journals and other serials. **Services:** Copying (limited); library open to the public by appointment. **Computerized Information Services:** Internal database. **Publications:** Publications on pesticides, toxic substances, and alternatives to use of pesticides, irregular - by subscription and for sale. **Special Indexes:** Index to pesticides by common name, chemical name, trade names, and CAS number (card).

★3107★
Carson-Tahoe Hospital - Lahontan Basin Medical Library (Med)
775 Fleischmann Way
Box 2168 Phone: (702)882-1361
Carson City, NV 89702-2168 Elaine L. Laessle, Libn.
Founded: 1973. **Staff:** Prof 1. **Subjects:** Clinical medicine, health care. **Holdings:** 1000 books; unbound periodicals; 202 folders of medical files. **Subscriptions:** 190 journals and other serials. **Services:** Interlibrary loan; copying; SDI; library open to the public for reference use only. **Computerized Information Services:** MEDLINE, DOCLINE, DIALOG Information Services; OnTyme Electronic Message Network Service (electronic mail service). Performs searches. **Networks/Consortia:** Member of Northern California and Nevada Medical Library Group (NCNMLG).

Cartagena Agreement Board
See: **Andean Group - Cartagena Agreement Board - Documentation Center** (837)

★3108★
(Cartagena) Biblioteca Centro Colombo-Americano - USIS Collection (Educ)
Calle de la Factoria, No. 36-27
Cartagena, Colombia Phone: 953 641714
Founded: 1961. **Staff:** 1. **Subjects:** English language, economics, narcotics, United States arts, literature. **Holdings:** 3000 books; vertical file drawers. **Subscriptions:** 15 journals and other serials. **Services:** Library open to the public. **Computerized Information Services:** Internal database. **Remarks:** FAX: 953 651887. Maintained or supported by the U.S. Information Agency. Focus is on materials that will assist peoples outside the United States to learn about the United States, its people, history, culture, political processes, and social milieux.

★3109★
Amon Carter Museum - Library (Art)
3501 Camp Bowie Blvd.
Box 2365 Phone: (817)738-1933
Fort Worth, TX 76113-2365 Milan R. Hughston, Libn.
Founded: 1961. **Staff:** Prof 2; Other 1. **Subjects:** Western Americana, American art, history of photography. **Special Collections:** American newspapers before 1900 (6000 reels of microfilm); M. Knoedler & Company, Inc. Library (26,000 volumes of exhibition and art auction catalogs on microfiche). **Holdings:** 30,000 books; 4800 bound periodical volumes. **Subscriptions:** 125 journals and other serials. **Services:** Interlibrary loan (microforms only); copying (limited); library open to the public by appointment. **Computerized Information Services:** DIALOG Information Services, ArtQuest, RLIN, Conservation Information Network; RLG (electronic mail service). **Remarks:** FAX: (817)377-8523. Electronic mail address(es): BM.ACC (RLG). **Staff:** Sherman Clarke, Asst.Libn.

★3110★
Carter & Burgess, Inc. Engineers & Planners - Library (Sci-Engr)
1100 Macon Phone: (817)335-2611
Fort Worth, TX 76102 Marian White, Libn.
Staff: Prof 1; Other 5. **Subjects:** Engineering - hydraulic, environmental, airport, highway, planning. **Special Collections:** FAA engineering specifications (150); Fort Worth engineering specifications; federal specifications and guidelines. **Holdings:** 2000 books; 1800 manufacturers' specifications; American Society for Testing and Materials set. **Subscriptions:** 180 journals and other serials; 10 newspapers. **Services:** Copying; library not open to the public. **Special Catalogs:** Catalog for technical reference material (card); CSI Manufacturer's Products Specifiers Catalogs.

Dr. Linden J. Carter Library
See: **Berkshire Christian College** (1747)

Gray Carter Library
See: **Greenwich Hospital Association** (6748)

Jimmy Carter Library
See: **U.S. Presidential Libraries** (17926)

★3111★
Larue D. Carter Memorial Hospital - Medical Library (Med)
1315 W. 10th St. Phone: (317)634-8401
Indianapolis, IN 46202 Philip I. Enz, Adm.Libn.
Founded: 1953. **Staff:** Prof 2. **Subjects:** Psychiatry, psychology, social work, psychiatric nursing, rehabilitation therapies, mental health. **Special Collections:** History of Mental Health. **Holdings:** 18,000 volumes; 200 audiotapes; 4 drawers of staff publications. **Subscriptions:** 236 journals and other serials. **Services:** Interlibrary loan; copying; library open to the public for reference use only. **Networks/Consortia:** Member of National Network of Libraries of Medicine - Greater Midwest Region. **Staff:** Judith K. Smith, Libn.

★3112★
Carter, Ledyard and Milburn - Library (Law)
2 Wall St. Phone: (212)732-3200
New York, NY 10005 Julius M. Pomerantz, Libn.
Staff: Prof 1; Other 2. **Subjects:** Law, philosophy of law. **Holdings:** 15,500 volumes. **Subscriptions:** 25 journals and other serials.

★3113★
Carter-Wallace, Inc. - Library (Med)
Half-Acre Rd. Phone: (609)655-6000
Cranbury, NJ 08512-0000 Arthur Hilscher, Dir.
Founded: 1948. **Staff:** Prof 3; Other 9. **Subjects:** Pharmacology, experimental medicine, organic chemistry, medicine, toiletries, diagnostics. **Special Collections:** Substituted Alkanediols (26,000 documents). **Holdings:** 3500 books; 1800 bound periodical volumes; 47,000 reports, pamphlets, documents. **Subscriptions:** 350 journals and other serials. **Services:** Interlibrary loan; copying; library open to special librarians. **Computerized Information Services:** DIALOG Information Services. **Networks/Consortia:** Member of MEDCORE. **Publications:** Current Product Abstracts, monthly. **Staff:** Rose Bonini, Doc.Mgr.; Dolores Ureneck, Lib.Mgr.

★3114★
William Carter College & Evangelical Theological Seminary - Wagner-Kevetter Library
2306 E. Ash St.
Goldsboro, NC 27534
Founded: 1952. **Staff:** Prof 4; Other 4. **Subjects:** Religion, liberal arts, philosophy, psychology, political science, sociology. **Holdings:** 20,000 books. **Remarks:** Currently inactive.

Carter's Ink Company - Technical Library
See: **Avery Dennison Company** (1375)

★3115★
G. Thomas Cartier and Associates - Library
311 Middle Rd.
Falmouth, ME 04105
Defunct.

Cartoon, Graphic, and Photographic Arts Research Library
See: **Ohio State University - Cartoon, Graphic, and Photographic Arts Research Library** (12299)

★3116★
Cartwright, Slobodin - Law Library (Law)
101 California St., 26th Fl. Phone: (415)433-0440
San Francisco, CA 94111 Cynthia S. McClellan, Law Libn.
Founded: 1984. **Staff:** Prof 1. **Subjects:** Law, product safety, medicine. **Holdings:** 7000 books and nonbook items. **Subscriptions:** 30 journals and other serials; 5 newspapers. **Services:** Interlibrary loan; library not open to the public. **Computerized Information Services:** DIALOG Information Services, MEDLINE, RLIN, WESTLAW; internal databases. **Remarks:** FAX: (415)391-5845.

★3117★
Carver Bible College - Library (Rel-Phil)
437 Nelson St., S.W. Phone: (404)527-4529
Atlanta, GA 30313 Helen Crecraft, Act.Libn.
Founded: 1943. **Staff:** Prof 2; Other 3. **Subjects:** Biblical expositions, doctrine, theology, evangelism, languages, social science, psychology, missions, counseling, church history, Christian education, world religions, prophecy and eschatology. **Holdings:** 16,783 books. **Subscriptions:** 39 journals and other serials. **Services:** Library not open to the public. **Staff:** Ruth Scheltema.

★3118★
Carver County Historical Society, Inc. - Library (Hist)
119 S. Cherry St.
Waconia, MN 55387 Phone: (612)442-4234
Founded: 1940. **Staff:** Prof 1. **Subjects:** Carver County history. **Special Collections:** Early lending libraries of Swedes and Germans in the locality. **Holdings:** 500 books; 10,000 photographs; 400 reels of microfilm of newspapers; censuses. **Subscriptions:** 2 journals and other serials. **Services:** Interlibrary loan (limited); copying; library open to the public. **Special Indexes:** Index of Carver Co. Newspapers, 1862 to present (in progress).

George Washington Carver Correspondence Collection
See: **Alabama State University - University Library & Learning Resources - Archives & Special Collections** (192)

George Washington Carver National Monument
See: **U.S. Natl. Park Service** (17719)

★3119★
Cary Medical Center - Health Science Library (Med)
Van Buren Rd.
MRA Box 37 Phone: (207)498-3111
Caribou, ME 04736 Donna E. Cote-Thibodeau, Libn.
SStaff: 1. **Subjects:** Medicine. **Holdings:** 700 volumes. **Subscriptions:** 90 journals and other serials. **Services:** Interlibrary loan; copying; library open to the public for reference use only.

Melbert B. Cary, Jr. Graphic Arts Collection
See: **Rochester Institute of Technology** (13981)

★3120★
Casa Grande Valley Historical Society - Museum Library (Hist)
110 W. Florence Blvd. Phone: (602)836-2223
Casa Grande, AZ 85222 Kay Benedict, Dir.
Founded: 1964. **Staff:** 4. **Subjects:** Local history. **Holdings:** 500 volumes; manuscripts; artifacts. **Services:** Library open to the public for reference use only. **Publications:** Monographs on local history. **Special Indexes:** Index to local newspaper.

Casa de Velazquez
See: **France - Ministere de l'Education - Velazquez House** (6066)

Lourdes Casal Library
See: **Center for Cuban Studies, Inc.** (3229)

Pablo Casals International Cello Library
See: **Arizona State University - Music Library** (1017)

★3121★
Cascade County Historical Society - Archives and Information Center (Hist)
1400 1st Ave., N. Phone: (406)452-3462
Great Falls, MT 59401 Cindy Kittredge, Dir.
Founded: 1976. **Staff:** Prof 4. **Subjects:** State and local history. **Special Collections:** Great Falls Building Survey; MacDonald Collection (350 pages of transcribed letters, 1903-1907); Robert Vaughn Collection (35 items); Cascade County maps (25); county immigration and naturalization records (80 volumes). **Holdings:** 2000 books; 700 bound newspapers; 12,000 photographs; 4 VF drawers of pamphlets; 4 VF drawers of clippings; 40 oral history tapes. **Subscriptions:** 2 journals and other serials. **Services:** Copying; center open to the public with restrictions. **Special Indexes:** Index to Great Falls Tribune, 1891-1916 and 1917-1954.

CASE
See: **Council for Advancement and Support of Education** (4356)

Everett Needham Case Library
See: **Colgate University** (3880)

★3122★
J.I. Case Company - Library (Sci-Engr)
7S 600 County Line Rd. Phone: (708)887-3974
Burr Ridge, IL 60521 Alice E. Packard, Libn.
Founded: 1985. **Staff:** Prof 1. **Subjects:** Engineering - agricultural, automotive. **Holdings:** 1500 books; 250 bound periodical volumes. **Services:** Interlibrary loan; library not open to the public. **Computerized Information Services:** DIALOG Information Services, ORBIT Search Service. **Networks/Consortia:** Member of Suburban Library System (SLS). **Remarks:** FAX: (708)789-7187.

Leland D. Case Library for Western Historical Studies
See: **Black Hills State University - E.Y. Berry Library-Learning Center - Special Collections** (1876)

Case Western Reserve University - Cleveland Health Sciences Library
See: **Cleveland Health Sciences Library** (3804)

★3123★
Case Western Reserve University - Elderly Care Research Center - Library (Soc Sci)
Mather Memorial, Rm. 226 Phone: (216)368-2700
Cleveland, OH 44106 Eva Kahana, Ph.D., Dir., Res. Center
Founded: 1968. **Staff:** Prof 1. **Subjects:** Sociology of aging, gerontology, medical sociology, environmental psychology/sociology. **Special Collections:** Reprints of papers presented at Gerontological Society of America meetings for past ten years. **Holdings:** 500 books; 300 bound periodical volumes; 200 other cataloged items. **Services:** Center open to students of Case Western Reserve University. **Remarks:** FAX: (216)368-2676.

Case Western Reserve University - FES Information Center
See: **FES Information Center - Library** (5675)

★3124★
Case Western Reserve University - Kulas Music Library (Mus)
Haydn Hall
11118 Bellflower Rd. Phone: (216)368-2403
Cleveland, OH 44106 Stephen Toombs, Music Libn.
Staff: Prof 1. **Subjects:** Early music performance practice, historical musicology. **Special Collections:** Radio Canada International recordings depository (750 titles). **Holdings:** 11,000 books; 4000 bound periodical volumes; 12,500 scores; 10,500 sound recordings; 600 microforms. **Subscriptions:** 80 journals and other serials. **Services:** Interlibrary loan; copying; library open to the public for reference use only. **Automated Operations:** Computerized public access catalog, cataloging, acquisitions, serials, circulation, and ILL. **Computerized Information Services:** DIALOG Information Services. Performs searches on fee basis. Contact Reference Department. **Networks/Consortia:** Member of NEOMARL, Cleveland Area Metropolitan Library System (CAMLS). **Remarks:** FAX: (216)368-4272.

★3125★
Case Western Reserve University - Law School Library (Law)
11075 East Blvd. Phone: (216)368-2792
Cleveland, OH 44106 Kathleen M. Carrick, Dir.
Founded: 1892. **Staff:** Prof 9; Other 15. **Subjects:** Law, international law, medical jurisprudence. **Special Collections:** American statute collection; foreign and international law. **Holdings:** 241,607 books; 47,482 microcards; 2012 reels of microfilm; 240,796 microfiche; 501 VF materials; 1700 unbound reports, pamphlets, documents. **Subscriptions:** 3660 journals and other serials; 12 newspapers. **Services:** Interlibrary loan; copying; library open to the public. **Automated Operations:** Computerized cataloging and circulation. **Computerized Information Services:** LEXIS, OCLC, WESTLAW, DIALOG Information Services, BRS Information Technologies, NEXIS; InterNet, BITNET (electronic mail services). **Networks/Consortia:** Member of Ohio Regional Consortium of Law Libraries (ORCLL). **Publications:** Acquisitions list, monthly; Just In Case; bibliographies. **Remarks:** FAX: (216)368-6144. Electronic mail address(es): CWRUID@PO.CWRU.EDU (InterNet); CWRUID@PO.CWRU.EDU.@CUNYVM (BITNET). **Staff:** Christine Corcos, Hd.Pub.Serv./Coll.Dev.Off.; Randall Wilcox, Rd.Serv.Libn.; Sonia Solomonoff, Cat.; Judith Kaul, Comp./Ref.; Joe Hinger, Ser.Libn.; Mary Hudson, Hd., Tech.Serv.; Cheryl Cheatham, Media/Ref.Libn.

★3126★
Case Western Reserve University - Lillian and Milford Harris Library (Soc Sci)
Mandel School of Applied Social Sciences
11235 Bellflower Rd. Phone: (216)368-2302
Cleveland, OH 44106-7164 Arthur S. Biagianti, Dir./Libn.
Founded: 1927. **Staff:** Prof 1; Other 2. **Subjects:** Social work, social welfare, poverty, alcoholism, corrections, aging, child welfare, minority group relations, community organization, psychiatry and mental health. **Holdings:** 22,000 books; 1500 bound periodical volumes; 7000 pamphlets and monographs; 533 microforms; 274 AV programs. **Subscriptions:** 309 journals and other serials. **Services:** Interlibrary loan; copying; library open to the public for reference use only. **Automated Operations:** Computerized public access catalog, cataloging, and circulation. **Computerized Information Services:** DIALOG Information Services, OCLC. **Networks/ Consortia:** Member of Cleveland Area Metropolitan Library System (CAMLS). **Publications:** Acquisitions list. **Special Catalogs:** Catalogs of pamphlet material and minority collection (cards). **Remarks:** FAX: (216)368-2106. Electronic mail address(es): asb2@po.cwru.edu (InterNet); asb2%po.cwru.edu@cunyvm (BITNET).

★3127★
Case Western Reserve University - University Archives (Hist)
Quail Bldg., Rm. 317 Phone: (216)368-3320
Cleveland, OH 44106-7229 Dennis Harrison, Univ.Archv.
Staff: Prof 4; Other 1. **Subjects:** University history, education, faculty papers. **Holdings:** 8500 linear feet of records, photographs, nontextual records. **Services:** Copying; archives open to the public. **Computerized Information Services:** Internal databases. Performs searches free of charge. **Remarks:** FAX: (216)368-3364. **Staff:** Jill Tatem, Asst.Univ.Archv.; Eleanor O'Sullivan, Archv.; Helen Yackshaw, Archv.

★3128★
Case Western Reserve University - Warner and Swasey Observatory - Library (Sci-Engr)
Cleveland, OH 44106 Phone: (216)368-6701
William Claspy, Asst.
Founded: 1921. **Subjects:** Astronomy, astrophysics, physics. **Special Collections:** Astrographic catalogs; Palomar Sky Survey Atlas; European Southern Observatory/Science Research Council Atlas of the Southern Sky; U.S. and foreign observatory publications. **Holdings:** 1500 books; 4000 bound periodical volumes; 480 linear feet of observatory publications. **Subscriptions:** 210 journals and other serials. **Services:** Interlibrary loan; library open to the public. **Computerized Information Services:** CD-ROMs (Guide Star Catalog, Einstein Observatory Database of HRI X-ray Images, Einstein Observatory Catalog of IPC X-ray Sources, Einstein Observatory Slew Survey); InterNet (electronic mail service). **Remarks:** FAX: (216)368-3565. Electronic mail address(es): WPC@PO.CWRU.EDU (InterNet).

★3129★
Casemate Museum - Library (Hist)
Box 341 Phone: (804)727-3935
Fort Monroe, VA 23651 Dennis P. Mroczkowski, Dir.
Founded: 1951. **Staff:** Prof 5. **Subjects:** Civil War, military history, peninsula Virginia, Jefferson Davis, Fort Monroe and U.S. Army Coast Artillery. **Holdings:** 1300 volumes; 509 reels of microfilm; 36 boxes of manuscripts. **Subscriptions:** 14 journals and other serials. **Services:** Copying; library open to the public for reference use only by appointment. **Publications:** Tales of Old Fort Monroe; Casemate Papers; Museum Guidebook. **Staff:** David J. Johnson, Archv.; Kathy A. Rothrock, Spec.; Carol J. Hanson, Musm. Aide; William C. Matthews, Exhibit Spec.

★3130★
Casey County Public Library - Genealogy Collection (Hist)
Rt. 1, Box A Phone: (606)787-9381
Liberty, KY 42539 Jan J. Ranks, Dist.Libn.
Subjects: Genealogy. **Holdings:** 830 books; 50 AV programs; 100 nonbook items; 150 reels of microfilm; 22 videocassettes; 302 VF; 86 audiotapes. **Services:** Copying; collection open to the public. **Publications:** Kentucky Kinfolks; Casey County Public Library Genealogical Holdings. **Staff:** Patty Black, Geneal.Res.

Casey Memorial Library
See: **U.S. Army Post - Fort Hood - Community Recreation Division** (17065)

★3131★
Casper College - Library - Special Collections (Hist)
125 College Dr. Phone: (307)268-2269
Casper, WY 82601 Lynnette Anderson, Dir.
Founded: 1945. **Staff:** Prof 4; Other 9. **Subjects:** History - Wyoming, Natrona county, Casper city. **Special Collections:** Monographs and historical maps collection; Frances Seeley Webb Photo Collection; Robert David Historical Collection; Chuck Morrison Photo Collection. **Holdings:** 3867 books; 107 bound periodical volumes; 28 archival items; 10 videotapes; 17 tapes; 2 sound recordings; 33 reels of microfilm. **Services:** Interlibrary loan; library open to the public. **Automated Operations:** Computerized cataloging, acquisitions, circulation, and indexing. **Computerized Information Services:** WESTLAW. **Networks/Consortia:** Member of Colorado Alliance of Research Libraries (CARL). **Remarks:** FAX: (307)268-2682. **Staff:** Jeannette Murrell, Pub.Serv.; Donna Kolarich, Tech.Serv.; Sunny Munns, Ref.

★3132★
Cass County Historical Society and Museum - Library (Hist)
1004 E. Market St. Phone: (219)753-3866
Logansport, IN 46947 Bruce Stuart, Cur.
Subjects: History - Cass County, general; genealogy. **Special Collections:** Civil War records; Wabash-Erie Canal Collection. **Holdings:** 7500 books; 25 bound periodical volumes; 10 AV programs; 75 manuscripts. **Subscriptions:** 2 journals and other serials. **Services:** Copying; library open to the public with restrictions.

★3133★
Cassels Blaikie and Company, Ltd. - Library
33 Yonge St., Suite 200 Phone: (416)941-7500
Toronto, ON, Canada M5E 1S8 Louanne Cumberbatch, Libn.
Remarks: No further information was supplied by respondent.

★3134★
Cassels, Brock, and Blackwell - Library (Law)
40 King St., W., Suite 2100 Phone: (416)869-5436
Toronto, ON, Canada M5H 1B5 Clare Lyons, Libn.
Staff: 4. **Subjects:** Law. **Holdings:** Figures not available. **Services:** Interlibrary loan; library not open to the public. **Computerized Information Services:** QL Systems, Info Globe, DIALOG Information Services, STM Systems Corporation, CAN/LAW, CBANET, WESTLAW, LEXIS, NEXIS. **Remarks:** FAX: (416)360-8877. Telex: 06-23415.

★3135★
Cassia County Historical Society - Reference Room (Hist)
P.O. Box 331 Phone: (208)678-7172
Burley, ID 83318 Rachel Martindale, Cur.
Subjects: Local history. **Holdings:** Books; journals. **Services:** Room open to the public for reference use only on a limited schedule.

Castillo de San Marcos National Monument
See: **U.S. Natl. Park Service - Castillo de San Marcos Natl. Monument & Fort Matanzas Natl. Monument** (17685)

★3136★
Castleton State College - Calvin Coolidge Library - Learning Resources Center - Special Collections (Hist, Info Sci)
Castleton, VT 05735 Phone: (802)468-5611
Patrick Max, Lib.Dir.
Staff: 9. **Special Collections:** Vermontiana (4000 items). **Holdings:** 24,000 U.S. Government documents (depository). **Subscriptions:** 867 journals and other serials; 11 newspapers. **Services:** Interlibrary loan; copying; collections open to the public. **Computerized Information Services:** DIALOG Information Services, BRS Information Technologies. **Networks/Consortia:** Member of NELINET, Inc. **Remarks:** FAX: (802)468-2421.

M.C. & Mattie Caston Law Library
See: **Baylor University** (1607)

Catalina Marine Science Center
See: **University of Southern California - Catalina Marine Science Center** (19323)

Catalog World: America's Mail Order Theater
See: **Harris Catalog Library - Catalog World: America's Mail Order Theater** (6914)

★3137★
Catalyst - Information Center (Soc Sci)
250 Park Ave., S., 5th Fl. Phone: (212)777-8900
New York, NY 10003-1459 Mary C. Mattis, V.Pres. Res.
Founded: 1975. **Staff:** 3. **Subjects:** Corporate women. **Special Collections:** Work and family (two career families); leadership development and management. **Holdings:** 500 books; 800 vertical files of periodical articles, government documents, studies. **Subscriptions:** 200 journals and other serials. **Services:** Interlibrary loan; copying; center open to corporations, contributors, and members by appointment only. **Computerized Information Services:** DIALOG Information Services. **Remarks:** FAX: (212)477-4252. **Staff:** Wendy Hirschberg, Dir.; Anne Tierney, Info.Spec.; Sandra McNeill, Info.Ctr.Coord.; Cybele Merrick, Info.Spec.

★3138★
Catalytica, Inc. - Information Center (Sci-Engr)
430 Ferguson Dr. Phone: (415)960-3000
Mountain View, CA 94043-5272 Cliff Mills, Info.Ctr.Mgr.
Founded: 1976. **Staff:** Prof 2; Other 3. **Subjects:** Catalysis, chemical engineering, biotechnology, catalysts. **Special Collections:** U.S. and foreign patents (catalysis and chemical engineering; 7000). **Holdings:** 3000 books; 100 bound periodical volumes. **Subscriptions:** 161 journals and other serials. **Services:** Interlibrary loan; center not open to the public. **Computerized Information Services:** DIALOG Information Services, STN International, Syracuse Research Corporation, ORBIT Search Service, VU/TEXT Information Services, DataTimes, LEXIS, NEXIS, MEDLARS; ALANET (electronic mail service). **Networks/Consortia:** Member of SOUTHNET, CLASS. **Remarks:** FAX: (415)960-0127. Telex: 176775. Electronic mail address(es): ALA1827 (ALANET).

★3139★
Catawba County Historical Association - Library (Hist)
Box 73 Phone: (704)465-0383
Newton, NC 28658 Sidney Halma, Dir.
Founded: 1949. **Staff:** Prof 3; Other 2. **Subjects:** Local history, genealogy. **Special Collections:** Mrs. D.M. Eaton Collection of correspondence and decorative arts reference books; Clapp Family Civil War Correspondence, 1857-1912; Cilley Correspondence. **Holdings:** 1600 volumes; 860 bound periodical volumes; 2100 other cataloged items. **Subscriptions:** 18 journals and other serials. **Services:** Copying; library open to the public for reference use only. **Publications:** Past Times, bimonthly.

★3140★
Catawba-Wateree AHEC - Library (Med)
1020 W. Meeting
Box 1045 Phone: (803)286-4121
Lancaster, SC 29720 Audrey Powers, Med.Libn.
Founded: 1978. **Staff:** Prof 1. **Subjects:** Medicine. **Holdings:** 300 books; 150 periodical volumes; 150 AV programs. **Subscriptions:** 125 journals and other serials. **Services:** Interlibrary loan; copying; library open to the public by appointment. **Automated Operations:** Computerized cataloging and circulation. **Computerized Information Services:** MEDLARS, DIALOG Information Services. Performs searches on fee basis. **Networks/Consortia:** Member of South Carolina Health Information Network (SCHIN). **Remarks:** FAX: (803)286-4165.

★3141★
Caterpillar Inc. - Business Resource Center (Bus-Fin)
100 N.E. Adams St. Phone: (309)675-4622
Peoria, IL 61629-7110 Amy Wolf, Bus.Info.Supv.
Founded: 1949. **Staff:** Prof 2; Other 2. **Subjects:** Business, management, statistics, marketing, corporations, trade. **Holdings:** 5000 books; 40 VF drawers of pamphlets; annual reports. **Subscriptions:** 500 journals and other serials; 7 newspapers. **Services:** Interlibrary loan; copying; center open to the public by prior arrangement. **Automated Operations:** Computerized cataloging, circulation, and ILL. **Computerized Information Services:** DIALOG Information Services, NEXIS, Human Resource Information Network (HRIN), Data-Star, DataTimes. **Networks/Consortia:** Member of Illinois Valley Library System, ILLINET. **Publications:** Business Update, quarterly; Serials Holding List, annual - both for internal distribution only. **Remarks:** FAX: (309)675-5948. **Staff:** Lea McCall, Bus.Info.Anl.

Caterpillar Inc. - Solar Turbines Incorporated
See: **Solar Turbines Incorporated** (15353)

★3142★
Caterpillar Inc. - Technical Information Center (Sci-Engr)
100 N.E. Adams St. Phone: (309)578-6118
Peoria, IL 61629 Kay Cloyes, Tech.Libn.
Founded: 1940. **Staff:** Prof 3; Other 3. **Subjects:** Mechanical engineering, metallurgy, enginology, soil mechanics. **Holdings:** 15,000 volumes; 127 VF drawers of technical society papers and government reports; 8 VF drawers of bibliographies; 10 VF drawers of translations; 29 VF drawers of university publications; 297 VF drawers of internal reports. **Subscriptions:** 600 journals and other serials. **Services:** Interlibrary loan; center open to the public on request. **Automated Operations:** Computerized cataloging and serials. **Computerized Information Services:** DIALOG Information Services, BRS Information Technologies, OCLC; internal databases. **Networks/Consortia:** Member of Illinois Valley Library System. **Publications:** TIC Update, monthly - for internal distribution only. **Remarks:** FAX: (309)578-6733.

Blanche Cathcart Memorial Library
See: **Hope Reformed Church** (7383)

★3143★
Cathedral Church of St. John the Divine - Cathedral Library (Rel-Phil)
1047 Amsterdam Ave. Phone: (212)316-7495
New York, NY 10025 Madeleine L'Engle Franklin, Writer in Residence
Staff: Prof 1. **Subjects:** Religion, philosophy, theology, psychology, mythology and theological fantasy, church history, biography, ecclesiastical architecture. **Special Collections:** Bibles (200 volumes). **Holdings:** 15,000 books; 3000 unbound periodicals. **Subscriptions:** 15 journals and other serials. **Services:** Interlibrary loan; copying; library open to the public.

Willa Cather Historical Center
See: **Nebraska State Historical Society** (11381)

Martin P. Catherwood Library
See: **Cornell University - New York State School of Industrial and Labor Relations** (4326)

Catholic Archives of Texas
See: **Texas Catholic Conference** (16206)

Catholic Association for International Peace Archives
See: **Marquette University - Department of Special Collections and University Archives - Manuscript Collections Memorial Library** (9709)

★3144★
Catholic Center at New York University - Catholic Center Library (Rel-Phil)
58 Washington Square, S. Phone: (212)674-7236
New York, NY 10012-1094 Fr. Raymond Daley
Founded: 1952. **Subjects:** Religion, theology, ethics, scripture, philosophy, Apologetics, spirituality. **Special Collections:** John Henry Cardinal Newman (130 books). **Holdings:** 4000 books.

★3145★
Catholic Central Union of America - Central Bureau Library (Soc Sci, Rel-Phil)
3835 Westminster Pl. Phone: (314)371-1653
St. Louis, MO 63108 Rev. John H. Miller, C.S.C., Dir.
Founded: 1908. **Staff:** 1. **Subjects:** Cooperatives, social action, biography, theology, philosophy, church history. **Special Collections:** German-Americana. **Holdings:** 42,200 books; 5000 bound periodical volumes; 2000 pamphlets; 1200 reels of microfilm. **Subscriptions:** 41 journals and other serials. **Services:** Copying; library open to the public by appointment. **Publications:** Social Justice Review, bimonthly.

★3146★
Catholic Diocese of Covington - Archives (Rel-Phil)
The Catholic Center
947 Donaldson Rd.
Box 18548 Phone: (606)283-6307
Erlanger, KY 41018-0548 Sr. Mary Philip Trauth, S.N.D., Ph.D., Archv.
Staff: 1. **Subjects:** History of the Catholic Church in eastern Kentucky, 1853-1988; in northeastern Kentucky, 1853 to present. **Holdings:** 1221 linear feet and 310 volumes of correspondence, personnel records, parish reports, financial ledgers, blueprints and architectural drawings. **Services:** Archives open on a limited schedule.

★3147★
Catholic Diocese of Spokane (Rel-Phil)
Box 1453 Phone: (509)456-7100
Spokane, WA 99201 Rev. Edward J. Kowrach, Archv.
Staff: Prof 2. **Subjects:** History, religion. **Special Collections:** Eastern Washington Catholic Church records. **Holdings:** 15,000 volumes; 1000 bound periodical volumes; 5000 reels of microfilm of records of Eastern Washington; 5000 nonbook items. **Subscriptions:** 13 journals and other serials. **Services:** Copying; archives open to the public. **Computerized Information Services:** Internal database. Performs searches free of charge. Contact Person: Fr. Ted Bradley, Archv., 659-0437.

Catholic Education Centre Library
See: **Metropolitan (Toronto) Separate School Board** (10232)

Catholic Foreign Mission Society of America
See: **Maryknoll School of Theology - Library** (9745)

★3148★
Catholic Health Association of the United States - Information Resource Center (Med)
4455 Woodson Rd. Phone: (314)427-2500
St. Louis, MO 63134 Mark Unger, Dir.
Staff: Prof 1. **Subjects:** Administrative aspects of health care facilities, advocacy, statistics, surveys, Catholic religion, business. **Holdings:** Figures not available. **Subscriptions:** 195 journals and other serials; 20 newspapers. **Services:** Center open to members only.

★3149★
Catholic Medical Center - Health Science Library (Med)
100 McGregor St. Phone: (603)668-3545
Manchester, NH 03102 Marcia K. Allen, Dir., Lib.Serv.
Founded: 1979. **Staff:** Prof 1; Other 2. **Subjects:** Medicine, nursing, allied health sciences, health care management, medical ethics. **Special Collections:** Psychology; psychiatry; geriatrics. **Holdings:** 3160 books; 480 bound periodical volumes. **Subscriptions:** 240 journals and other serials. **Services:** Video and slide production; closed-circuit TV educational programs; library open to students, affiliated agencies, medical staff, and hospital personnel. **Computerized Information Services:** MEDLINE, BRS Information Technologies, Union Catalog of Medical Periodicals (UCMP); CD-ROM; DOCLINE (electronic mail service). **Networks/Consortia:** Member of National Network of Libraries of Medicine - New England Region, Merrimack Valley/Lakes Region Health Science Librarians, BHSL. **Remarks:** FAX: (603)668-5348.

★3150★
Catholic Medical Center of Brooklyn & Queens, Inc. - Central Medical Library (Med)
88-25 153rd St. Phone: (718)657-6800
Jamaica, NY 11432 Joan A. Napolitano, Dir.
Founded: 1969. **Staff:** Prof 2; Other 3. **Subjects:** Medicine, surgery, orthopedics, ophthalmology, family practice, dentistry. **Holdings:** 4000 books; 5400 bound periodical volumes; 4 VF drawers; 1100 Audio-Digest tapes; 100 MEDCOM slides; microforms; 200 videocassettes. **Subscriptions:** 250 journals and other serials. **Services:** Interlibrary loan; copying; library open to the public with identification. **Computerized Information Services:** MEDLINE, BRS Information Technologies. **Networks/Consortia:** Member of Brooklyn-Queens-Staten Island Health Sciences Librarians (BQSI), Medical Library Center of New York (MLCNY), Medical & Scientific Libraries of Long Island (MEDLI). **Special Catalogs:** CMC Periodical Union List. **Remarks:** CMC includes Mary Immaculate, Jamaica; St. John's, Queens; St. Joseph's, Queens; St. Mary's, Brooklyn. Library is affiliated with Cornell University Medical College Library. FAX: (718)657-5422. **Staff:** Ann Pierce, Libn.; Brigitte Delinnis, ILL; Sara Freeman, AV.

Catholic School Commission of Montreal
See: **Commission des Ecoles Catholiques de Montreal - Bibliotheque Centrale** (4055)

★3151★
Catholic Seminary Foundation of Indianapolis - Library (Rel-Phil)
4615 N. Michigan Rd. Phone: (317)925-9095
Indianapolis, IN 46208-2399 Rev. Charles Henry, O.S.B.
Founded: 1968. **Staff:** Prof 3. **Subjects:** Religion and theology, sociology, history, literature, biography. **Holdings:** 45,000 books; 657 bound periodical volumes; 800 phonograph records; 215 tapes. **Subscriptions:** 136 journals and other serials. **Services:** Interlibrary loan; copying; library open to the public with restrictions. **Networks/Consortia:** Member of Central Indiana Area Library Services Authority (CIALSA). **Also Known As:** St. Maur Hospitality. **Staff:** Tamara L. Dryer, Asst.Dir.; Donna Bush, Libn.

Catholic Telecommunication Network of America (CTNA) Library
See: **Diocese of St. Cloud - Catholic Education Ministries - Media Center** (4884)

★3152★
Catholic Theological Union at Chicago - Library (Rel-Phil)
5401 S. Cornell Ave. Phone: (312)324-8000
Chicago, IL 60615 Rev. Kenneth O'Malley, C.P., Lib.Dir.
Founded: 1968. **Staff:** Prof 3; Other 3. **Subjects:** Catholic theology, scripture, canon law, missiology, patristics, homiletics. **Special Collections:** Franciscan Order (history, documents, spirituality). **Holdings:** 76,314 books; 20,000 bound periodical volumes; 560 AV programs. **Subscriptions:** 540 journals and other serials; 16 newspapers. **Services:** Interlibrary loan; copying; library open to the public with restrictions. **Automated Operations:** Computerized cataloging and circulation. **Computerized Information Services:** OCLC. **Networks/Consortia:** Member of Association of Chicago Theological Schools Library Council, Chicago Library System, ILLINET. **Staff:** Jan Boyle, Hd., Tech.Serv.; Deborah Cocanig, Cat.; Gerrie Boberg, ILL.

★3153★
Catholic Universe Bulletin - Library (Publ)
1027 Superior Ave.
Cleveland, OH 44114-2556 Phone: (216)696-6525
Subjects: Religious and lay leaders, welfare and educational institutions, churches, schools. **Holdings:** 98 bound periodical volumes; 60,500 photographs; 350,000 clippings. **Subscriptions:** 40 newspapers. **Services:** Copying; library open to the public by appointment. **Remarks:** FAX: (216)696-6519.

★3154★
Catholic University of America - Chemistry Library (Sci-Engr)
301 Maloney Bldg. Phone: (202)319-5389
Washington, DC 20064 Patricia Ortega, Hd.
Staff: 1. **Subjects:** Chemistry, allied sciences. **Holdings:** 6715 books; 16,843 bound periodical volumes. **Subscriptions:** 111 journals and other serials. **Services:** Interlibrary loan; copying; library open to the public with restrictions. **Networks/Consortia:** Member of CAPCON Library Network, Consortium of Universities of the Washington Metropolitan Area. **Remarks:** FAX: (202)319-4735.

★3155★
Catholic University of America - Clementine Library (Rel-Phil)
Mullen Library, Rm. 104 Phone: (202)319-5091
Washington, DC 20064 Carolyn T. Lee, Cur.
Staff: Prof 1. **Subjects:** Pre-1800 theology; Jansenism; law; classical, European, Eastern languages and literature; Rome and the states of the church; missions; hagiography. **Special Collections:** Clementine Foster Stearns Collection on the Knights of Malta (400 titles); catechisms (1300 volumes); Catholic pamphlets (20 VF drawers); American Catholic local history (2000 books and pamphlets). **Holdings:** 30,000 books. **Services:** Copying (limited); library open to the public with restrictions. **Networks/Consortia:** Member of CAPCON Library Network, Consortium of Universities of the Washington Metropolitan Area, Washington Theological Consortium. **Remarks:** FAX: (202)319-4735.

★3156★
Catholic University of America - Department of Archives and Manuscripts (Hist, Rel-Phil)
Mullen Library, Rm. 4 Phone: (202)319-5065
Washington, DC 20064 Dr. Anthony Zito, Univ.Archv.
Founded: 1948. **Staff:** Prof 3; Other 2. **Subjects:** 19th and 20th century American labor history; American Catholic Church history. **Special Collections:** Terence V. Powderly Papers; John Mitchell Papers; Lawrence F. Flick Papers; John Brophy Papers; John W. Hayes Papers; "Mother" Mary Harris Jones Papers; Philip Murray Papers; Aloysius Cardinal Muench Papers; Peter Guilday Papers; John A. Ryan Papers; National Catholic Welfare Conference Papers. **Holdings:** 9041 cubic feet of manuscripts. **Services:** Microfilming; copying; department open to scholars. **Computerized Information Services:** MEDLARS, BRS Information Technologies, PFDS Online, DIALOG Information Services, WILSONLINE, Questel, OCLC. **Networks/Consortia:** Member of CAPCON Library Network, Consortium of Universities of the Washington Metropolitan Area, Washington Theological Consortium. **Publications:** Finding aids for some papers. **Special Indexes:** Index to photographs of Archbishop Martin J. Connors papers. **Remarks:** FAX: (202)319-4735.

★3157★
Catholic University of America - Engineering/Architecture/Mathematics Library (Sci-Engr)
200 Pangborn Bldg. Phone: (202)319-5167
Washington, DC 20064 William Guy
Staff: Prof 1; Other 2. **Subjects:** Engineering - aerospace, atmospheric, civil, mechanical, nuclear science, electrical; architecture and planning; mathematics. **Holdings:** 22,819 books; 11,798 bound periodical volumes. **Subscriptions:** 445 journals and other serials. **Services:** Interlibrary loan; copying; library open to the public. **Networks/Consortia:** Member of CAPCON Library Network, Consortium of Universities of the Washington Metropolitan Area. **Remarks:** FAX: (202)319-4735.

★3158★
Catholic University of America - Library and Information Science Library (Info Sci)
132 Marist Bldg.
620 Michigan Ave., N.E. Phone: (202)319-5092
Washington, DC 20064 Patsy Haley Stann, Hd.
Staff: Prof 1; Other 2. **Subjects:** Library science, information science, history of books, information retrieval, automation, book selection, cataloging. **Holdings:** 11,399 books; 3338 bound periodical volumes; 931 reels of microfilm; 200 VF materials; 2000 theses and research papers; annual reports; library school catalogs; handbooks. **Subscriptions:** 302 journals and other serials. **Services:** Interlibrary loan; copying; library open to the public with restrictions. **Networks/Consortia:** Member of CAPCON Library Network, Consortium of Universities of the Washington Metropolitan Area, Washington Theological Consortium. **Remarks:** FAX: (202)319-6101.

★3159★
Catholic University of America - Music Library (Mus)
101 Ward Music Bldg. Phone: (202)319-5424
Washington, DC 20064 Barbara D. Henry, Hd.
Founded: 1952. **Staff:** Prof 1; Other 2. **Subjects:** Musicology, music education, performance. **Special Collections:** Grentzer Spivacke Music Collection (Music Education); Latin American music collection. **Holdings:** 19,248 books; 3785 bound periodical volumes; 10,127 pieces of music; 13,894 sound recordings; 1453 tapes; 811 compact discs. **Subscriptions:** 130 journals. **Services:** Interlibrary loan; copying; library open to the public with restrictions. **Networks/Consortia:** Member of CAPCON Library Network, Consortium of Universities of the Washington Metropolitan Area. **Publications:** Major Holdings, every 5 years; periodical titles list, annual. **Remarks:** FAX: (202)319-4735.

★3160★
Catholic University of America - Nursing/Biology Library (Med, Biol Sci)
Washington, DC 20064 Phone: (202)319-5411
N.L. Powell, Libn.
Staff: Prof 1; Other 2. **Subjects:** Nursing, medicine, social and physical sciences, biological and botanical sciences. **Holdings:** 37,826 books; 14,943 bound periodical volumes; 3142 reels of microfilm; 2727 theses. **Subscriptions:** 351 journals and other serials. **Services:** Interlibrary loan; copying; library open to the public with restrictions. **Networks/Consortia:** Member of CAPCON Library Network, Consortium of Universities of the Washington Metropolitan Area, Washington Theological Consortium. **Remarks:** FAX: (202)319-4735.

★3161★
Catholic University of America - Oliveira Lima Library (Area-Ethnic, Hist)
Washington, DC 20064 Phone: (202)319-5059
Jacqueline Varjao-Atkinson, Libn.
Founded: 1916. **Staff:** Prof 1. **Subjects:** Brazil and Portugal - history, literature, church history, economic history, medical history; Portugal's colonial expansion and diplomatic history; Brazilian travel; European biography; Brazilian and African ethnography; native languages of Brazil, Africa, Argentina, Chile, Paraguay, Spain; Portuguese Africa; substantial materials on Spain, Spanish America, Great Britain, France, Germany, Italy, Japan, China. **Special Collections:** Lima Family papers; Tracts on the Portuguese Inquisition; collection of pamphlets on 19th century Portuguese liberalism; Dutch pamphlets on 17th century Brazil; Portuguese Restoration, 1640-1668; Society of Jesus; 19th century Brazilian newspapers; Portuguese newspapers of early liberal period. **Holdings:** 55,606 books; 1600 bound periodical volumes; 121,529 pages of manuscripts. **Subscriptions:** 10 journals and other serials. **Services:** Copying (limited); library open to the public by appointment for reference use only. **Computerized Information Services:** OCLC. **Networks/Consortia:** Member of CAPCON Library Network, Consortium of Universities of the Washington Metropolitan Area. **Publications:** A Conspectus of the Oliveira Lima Library and its holdings (printed in both English and Portuguese); The Friends of the Oliveira Lima Library Newsletter; The Oliveira Lima Library (pamphlet) - for internal distribution only; Oliveira Lima and the Catholic University of America; Bibliographical and Historical Description of the Rarest Books in the Oliveira Lima Collection at the Catholic University of America (1 volume; 1927); A Guide to the Manuscripts in the Lima Library, The Catholic University of America, Washington, DC (34 pages; 1971). **Remarks:** FAX: (202)319-4735. **Staff:** Thomas Cohen, Cur.

★3162★
Catholic University of America - Physics Library (Sci-Engr)
208 Keane Bldg. Phone: (202)319-5320
Washington, DC 20064 Patricia Ortega
Staff: 1. **Subjects:** Physics. **Holdings:** 6251 books; 11,761 bound periodical volumes. **Subscriptions:** 83 journals and other serials. **Services:** Interlibrary loan; copying; library open to the public with restrictions. **Networks/Consortia:** Member of CAPCON Library Network, Consortium of Universities of the Washington Metropolitan Area, Washington Theological Consortium. **Remarks:** FAX: (202)319-4735.

★3163★
Catholic University of America - Religious Studies/Philosophy/Humanities Division Library (Rel-Phil, Hum)
Mullen Library, Rm. 300 Phone: (202)319-5088
Washington, DC 20064 Bruce Miller, Coord.
Staff: Prof 3; Other 1.5. **Subjects:** Theology, philosophy, canon law, religion, biblical studies, Christian literature, church history, art, ancient and medieval history, Greek and Latin, English, comparative literature, modern languages, speech and drama. **Special Collections:** Catholic Americana (10,000 volumes). **Holdings:** 296,151 books; 50,000 bound periodical volumes. **Subscriptions:** 778 journals and other serials. **Services:** Interlibrary loan; copying; library open to the public with restrictions. **Computerized Information Services:** MEDLARS, BRS Information Technologies, PFDS Online, DIALOG Information Services, WILSONLINE, Questel, OCLC. **Networks/Consortia:** Member of CAPCON Library Network, Consortium of Universities of the Washington Metropolitan Area, Washington Theological Consortium. **Remarks:** FAX: (202)319-4735.

★3164★
Catholic University of America - School of Law - Robert J. White Law Library (Law)
620 Michigan Ave. Phone: (202)319-5155
Washington, DC 20064 Prof. Stephen G. Margeton, Dir.
Founded: 1965. **Staff:** Prof 8; Other 8. **Subjects:** Law. **Special Collections:** Religion and the law (500 volumes). **Holdings:** 156,000 volumes. **Subscriptions:** 2250 journals and other serials. **Services:** Interlibrary loan; copying; library open to the public with restrictions. **Networks/Consortia:** Member of Consortium of Universities of the Washington Metropolitan Area, CAPCON Library Network. **Remarks:** FAX: (202)319-4447. **Staff:** Patrick Petit, Assoc. Law Libn./Hd., Pub.Serv.; Jean Berard, Asst.Libn./Hd., Tech.Serv.; James Josey, Ref.Libn.; Diana Botluk, Ref.Libn.; Mark Hammond, Ref.Libn.; Brian Baker, Circ.Libn.; Rhea Wilson, Cat.

★3165★
Catholic University of America - Semitics - Institute of Christian Oriental Research (ICOR) Library (Hum, Rel-Phil)
Mullen Library, Rm. 18 Phone: (202)319-5084
Washington, DC 20064 Monica Blanchard, Hd.
Founded: 1895. **Staff:** Prof 1. **Subjects:** Coptic, Syriac, Arabic, Biblical Hebrew, Cuneiform languages; languages and literature of the Bible in the ancient and Near East; languages and literatures of the Christian Near East; Christian Orient; theology. **Special Collections:** Collection of the Institute of Christian Oriental Research, begun from the personal library of the founder, Monsignor H. Hyvernat (circa 25,000 items). **Holdings:** 35,000 volumes; 145 volumes of photographs of Coptic manuscripts in Paris and Naples; 112 volumes of photographs of Coptic manuscripts in Pierpont Morgan Library; 52 VF drawers of offprints and department members' papers; 89 volumes of bound miscellanea (Christian Orient studies); 150 manuscripts (including Arabic, Persian, Turkish, Syriac). **Subscriptions:** 169 journals and other serials. **Services:** Interlibrary loan; copying; library open to the public with restrictions. **Networks/Consortia:** Member of CAPCON Library Network, Consortium of Universities of the Washington Metropolitan Area, Washington Theological Consortium. **Remarks:** FAX: (202)319-4735.

★3166★
Catholic University of Leuven - Faculty Library of Letters and Philosophy (Hum)
Blijde-Inkomststraat 21 Phone: 16 284900
B-3000 Leuven, Belgium Dr. M. De Smedt
Founded: 1974. **Staff:** 12. **Subjects:** Languages, literature, classical studies, history, art history, oriental studies. **Holdings:** 250,000 books; 50,000 bound periodical volumes. **Subscriptions:** 1500 journals and other serials; 15 newspapers. **Services:** Copying; library open to the public. **Remarks:** FAX: 16 285025. **Also Known As:** Katholieke Universiteit Leuven - Faculteitsbibliotheek Letteren en Wijsbegeerte.

★3167★
Catholic University of North - Library and Documentation Unit (Sci-Engr)
Avenida Angamos, 0610
C.P. 1280 Phone: 55241148
Antofagasta, Chile Drahomira Srytrova Tomasova
Founded: 1858. **Staff:** 37. **Subjects:** Exact sciences, engineering, architecture, economy, humanities. **Special Collections:** Chilean history (1300 items); thesis collection (2600); historical archives (10 items). **Holdings:** 75,000 books; 52,000 bound periodical volumes; 7900 documents; 17,450 AV programs. **Subscriptions:** 277 journals and other serials; 7 newspapers. **Services:** Interlibrary loan; copying; SDI; unit open to the public with restrictions. **Computerized Information Services:** RENIB (internal database). **Special Catalogs:** Repertorios: Serie I, Repertorio Bibliografico; Repertorios: Serie II, Repertorio Documental (bibliographic catalogs of information about the reality of northern Chile). **Remarks:** FAX: 55 241724. Telex: 225097 UNORTE CL. **Formerly:** University of North. **Also Known As:** Universidad Catolica del Norte - Unidad de Biblioteca y Documentacion. **Staff:** Isabel Bahamondes; Patricia Briones; Liliana Cordero; Alejandro Chau; Martha Guerrero; Hada Ildefonso; Maria Mardones; Claudio Mena; Angela Peragallo; Robert Sepulveda.

★3168★
Catholic University of Puerto Rico - Monsignor Fremiot Torres Oliver Law Library (Law)
Las Americas Ave. Phone: (809)841-2000
Ponce, PR 00732 Noelia Padua-Flores, Dir.
Founded: 1961. **Staff:** Prof 6; Other 8. **Subjects:** Law - civil, criminal, constitutional; torts. **Special Collections:** U.S. Government Publications and United Nations documents; Puerto Rico Collection. **Holdings:** 113,436 books; 215 reels of microfilm; 87 cassettes; 38,548 volume-equivalents of microfiche. **Subscriptions:** 2220 journals and other serials; 19 newspapers. **Services:** Interlibrary loan; library open to the public for reference use only. **Automated Operations:** Computerized cataloging, acquisitions, and serials (NOTIS). **Computerized Information Services:** WESTLAW, LEXIS, OCLC, MICROJURIS; CD-ROM (Compuley); internal databases. **Networks/Consortia:** Member of SOLINET. **Publications:** Sumario de Revistas, irregular; Boletin Informativo (list of new acquisitions), quarterly - both free upon request. **Remarks:** FAX: (809)841-4620. **Staff:** Gregorio Mejill, Cat.Libn.; Teresita Guillermard, Ref. & Circ.Dept.Dir.; Julia Velez, Acq.Dept.Dir.; Milton Delgado, Cat.Dept.Dir.; Alvaro Santiago, Per./Docs.Dir.

★3169★
Catholics United for Life (Soc Sci, Rel-Phil)
c/o Dennis Musk
3050 Gap Knob Rd.
New Hope, KY 40052 Phone: (502)325-3061
Subjects: Catholic moral and social teachings - family life, marriage, the value of human life, natural family planning; alternatives to abortion; theology; papal teachings; hagiology; and related subjects. **Holdings:** 10,000 volumes. **Services:** Library open to the public at librarian's discretion. **Remarks:** FAX: (502)325-3091.

George B. Catlin Memorial Library
See: **Detroit News** (4812)

Catlin House Library and Archives
See: **Lackawanna Historical Society** (8869)

★3170★
Cattaraugus County Memorial and Historical Museum - Library (Hist)
Court St. Phone: (716)938-9111
Little Valley, NY 14755 Lorna J. Spencer, Cur.
Founded: 1914. **Staff:** 2. **Subjects:** Local history. **Holdings:** 300 books; 60 bound periodical volumes; 10 maps; 110 reels of microfilm; cemetery lists. **Subscriptions:** 5 journals and other serials. **Services:** Copying; library open to the public. **Special Indexes:** Index to Cattaraugus County census, 1810-1905 (book).

Richard B. Cattell Memorial Library
See: **Lahey Clinic Medical Center** (8879)

★3171★
CAUSA Institute - Library
401 5th Ave.
New York, NY 10016
Founded: 1980. **Staff:** 1. **Subjects:** Religion, politics, economics, history. **Holdings:** 17,000 volumes. **Services:** Library not open to the public. **Remarks:** Currently inactive.

★3172★
CAUSE - Library (Educ)
4840 Pearl E. Circle, Suite 302E Phone: (303)449-4430
Boulder, CO 80301-2454 Jane N. Ryland, Pres.
Staff: Prof 6; Other 6. **Subjects:** Planning, evaluation, and management of computing and information technology in higher education. **Holdings:** Figures not available. **Services:** Copying; library open to members only. **Computerized Information Services:** Online systems; BITNET (electronic mail service). **Publications:** List of publications - available upon request. **Special Indexes:** Exchange Library Index (a subject listing of articles and documents available to members through the library). **Remarks:** FAX: (303)440-0461.

Cavagna Library
See: **University of Illinois - Map and Geography Library** (18683)

Caven Library
See: **University of Toronto - Knox College** (19454)

Mary Cavitt Memorial Library
See: **U.S. English - Mary Cavitt Memorial Library** (17455)

Edgar Cayce Foundation
See: **Association for Research and Enlightenment - Edgar Cayce Foundation - Library** (1168)

★3173★
Caylor-Nickel Medical Center - Library (Med)
1 Caylor-Nickel Square Phone: (219)824-3500
Bluffton, IN 46714 Patricia Niblick, Med.Libn.
Founded: 1915. **Staff:** Prof 1. **Subjects:** Surgery, internal medicine, pathology, radiology, pediatrics, obstetrics, gynecology, urology, nursing, pharmacology, endocrinology. **Special Collections:** Complete set of the Collected Papers in Medicine and Surgery from the Mayo Clinic and the Mayo Foundation. **Holdings:** 9782 books; 5126 bound periodical volumes; 1 VF drawer of staff reprints; 902 tapes; 10 films. **Subscriptions:** 417 journals and other serials. **Services:** Interlibrary loan; copying; library open to the public with restrictions. **Automated Operations:** Computerized cataloging and serials. **Networks/Consortia:** Member of National Network of Libraries of Medicine - Greater Midwest Region, Northeastern Indiana Health Science Library Consortium, Tri-ALSA. **Publications:** New Acquisitions list.

★3174★
Cayuga County Historian - Library (Hist)
Historic Old Post Office Bldg.
157 Genesee St. Phone: (315)253-1300
Auburn, NY 13021 Thomas G. Eldred, County Hist.
Founded: 1969. **Staff:** 3. **Subjects:** Local history, genealogy. **Holdings:** 300 books; 500 bound periodical volumes; 50 boxes and 27 VF drawers of reports, manuscripts, letters, broadsides, clippings; 700 reels of microfilm of newspapers; 1500 reels of microfilm of records; photographs. **Subscriptions:** 16 journals and other serials. **Services:** Copying; library open to the public for reference use only. **Publications:** Cayuga Gazette. **Remarks:** Alternate telephone number(s): 253-1190. **Staff:** Malcolm O. Goodelle, Archv.

★3175★
The Cayuga Museum - Library (Hist)
203 Genesee St. Phone: (315)253-8051
Auburn, NY 13021 Peter L. Gabak, Dir.
Founded: 1936. **Staff:** Prof 2. **Subjects:** Central New York Indian and Cayuga County history, early sound motion pictures. **Special Collections:** General John S. Clark Collection of Indian history; Auburn Theological Seminary; Civil War; Case Film Research Laboratory materials; Cayuga County Historical Society collections and archives (1876-1973). **Holdings:** 3000 books; bound periodical volumes. **Services:** Copying; library open to the public during museum hours.

CBC
See: **Canadian Broadcasting Corporation** (2901)

CBIC
See: **Canadian Book Information Centre** (2899)

★3176★
CBS Inc. - CBS News Audio Archives (Info Sci)
524 W. 57th St. Phone: (212)975-6489
New York, NY 10019 Steven McCane
Staff: Prof 2. **Subjects:** Presidential addresses, CBS News special reports, NASA space missions, public figures interviews, political conventions, daily news broadcasts, network programs. **Holdings:** 200,000 audiotapes. **Services:** Copying; library open to the public with restrictions. **Staff:** Pamela Blittersdorf, Audiotape Libn.; Gerald Mazza, Audiotape Libn.

★3177★
CBS Inc. - CBS News Reference Library (Info Sci)
524 W. 57th St. Phone: (212)975-2917
New York, NY 10019 Laura B. Kapnick, Dir.
Founded: 1940. **Staff:** Prof 5; Other 4. **Subjects:** Radio, television, biography, current events, government, politics. **Special Collections:** CBS News program transcripts. **Holdings:** 28,000 books; 1000 bound periodical volumes; 15,000 clippings files; 5000 reels of microfilm; 30,000 microfiche. **Subscriptions:** 270 journals and other serials; 10 newspapers. **Services:** Interlibrary loan; copying; library open to serious researchers by appointment. **Computerized Information Services:** DIALOG Information Services, VU/TEXT Information Services, NEXIS. **Staff:** Carole D. Parnes, Mgr., Indus.Info.; Cryder H. Bankes, III, Mgr., Lib.Serv.; Sara Wolozin, Mgr., Newspaper Serv.

★3178★
CBS Inc. - Law Library (Law)
51 W. 52nd St., 36th Fl. Phone: (212)975-4260
New York, NY 10019 Marilee N. Martel, Mgr., Info.Serv.
Staff: Prof 1. **Subjects:** Communications, copyright, cable television, entertainment law, broadcasting. **Holdings:** 4800 books; 9 bound periodical volumes. **Subscriptions:** 30 journals and other serials; 5 newspapers. **Services:** Copying; library open to the public by appointment - LLAGNY and SLA members only. **Automated Operations:** Computerized cataloging, serials, and circulation. **Computerized Information Services:** LEXIS, NEXIS, DIALOG Information Services. **Remarks:** FAX: (212)975-7292; (212)975-2185.

CBS Records Inc. - Archives
See: **Sony Music Archives** (15378)

★3179★
CCH Computax, Inc. - Technical Library (Bus-Fin)
Worldway Postal Center
Box 92938 Phone: (213)543-3445
Los Angeles, CA 90009 Angela Li, Lib.Mgr.
Founded: 1980. **Staff:** Prof 1. **Subjects:** Taxation. **Holdings:** 3000 books; 165 VF drawers of documents. **Subscriptions:** 30 journals and other serials. **Services:** Interlibrary loan; copying; document distribution; library not open to the public. **Automated Operations:** Computerized cataloging and serials. **Computerized Information Services:** CCH Computax (internal database). Performs searches. **Publications:** Computalk, quarterly - for internal distribution only. **Remarks:** FAX: (213)543-6430.

★3180★
CD Research, Ltd. - Library Services (Info Sci)
8 Dexter Saunders Rd. Phone: (401)273-4070
North Scituate, RI 02857 Derryl R. Johnson, Info. Broker
Subjects: Library and information services, patents. **Special Collections:** Image File (400,000 pictures and clippings); Chronology File; Quotation File. **Holdings:** 3000 volumes. **Services:** SDI; library not open to the public. **Automated Operations:** Computerized indexing to files. **Remarks:** CD Research, Ltd. provides library organization services, computerized and traditional information retrieval, article abstracting, and monitoring of professional literature in all subject areas especially legal. **Formerly:** Located in Providence, RI.

★3181★
(Cebu City) USIS Library (Educ)
Osmena Blvd.
Cebu City 6401, Philippines
Remarks: Maintained or supported by the U.S. Information Agency. Focus is on materials that will assist peoples outside the United States to learn about the United States, its people, history, culture, political processes, and social milieux.

★3182★
Cedar Crest College - Women's Center - Library (Soc Sci)
100 College Dr. Phone: (215)437-4471
Allentown, PA 18104 Patricia Sacks, Dir.
Staff: Prof 1; Other 3. **Subjects:** Psychology and sociology of women, job opportunities, education, the women's movement, elderly women. **Holdings:** 300 books; college guides; occupational reference materials. **Services:** Library open to the public.

★3183★
Cedar Crest and Muhlenberg College Libraries (Soc Sci, Hum)
Allentown, PA 18104 Phone: (215)437-4471
Patricia Ann Sacks, Dir. of Libs.
Founded: 1867. **Staff:** Prof 9; Other 14. **Subjects:** Sciences, social and behavioral sciences, humanities, American poetry, social services, arts, religious studies, British and American history, Russia, women's studies, German language and literature. **Special Collections:** Muhlenberg Papers; Pennsylvania Germans (2000 items); American Women Poets Collection; 19th century African Exploration and Travel (300 titles); American Indians; music; fencing (200 titles); Herstory: Women's History collection; Cornell University collection of Women's Rights Pamphlets; Marjorie Wright Miller Poetry Collection; Psychical Research (700 titles); Abram Samuels U.S. Sheet Music Collection (23,033). **Holdings:** 306,487 volumes; 175,906 U.S. Government documents (depository); 47,800 microforms. **Subscriptions:** 1307 periodicals. **Services:** Interlibrary loan; copying; libraries open to the public with restrictions on borrowing. **Automated Operations:** Computerized public access catalog (LS/2000), cataloging, and circulation. **Computerized Information Services:** OCLC, BRS Information Technologies, DIALOG Information Services, WILSONLINE, MEDLARS/Bioethics. **Networks/Consortia:** Member of Lehigh Valley Association of Independent Colleges, Inc. (LVAIC), PALINET. **Publications:** Acquisitions List, monthly; bibliography series, occasional; Serials Holdings List. **Special Catalogs:** Pennsylvania German collection (card). **Remarks:** Holdings represent Muhlenberg College - Harry C. Trexler Library (telephone: (215)821-3500) and Cedar Crest College - Cressman Library (telephone: (215)437-4471). FAX: (215)821-3511. **Staff:** Diane Melnychuk, Hd., Acq.Serv.; Heidy Wieder, Local Sys.Tech.Asst.; Barbara Howard, AV Serv.; Marianne Bundra, Lending Serv.; Mary Beth Freeh, Ref./Instr.Serv.

★3184★
Cedar Falls Historical Society - Rownd Historical Library (Hist)
Cedar Falls Victorian House Museum
303 Franklin St. Phone: (319)266-5149
Cedar Falls, IA 50613 Rosemary Beach, Exec.Dir.
Founded: 1968. **Staff:** Prof 4. **Subjects:** Local, state, U.S. history; natural ice industry; 19th century agriculture. **Special Collections:** Books by Cedar Falls authors (100 volumes); Cedar Falls Record, 1897-1950 (165 volumes); Diamonds Bulletin, 1932-1953 (25 volumes); probate records of Black Hawk County, 1853-1930. **Holdings:** 400 books; 250 bound periodical volumes; 75 Roger Leavitt notebooks; 200 oral history tapes; 65 scrapbooks; 324 issues of The Palimpsest magazine, 1950 to present; 3 file cabinets of information files; 1 file cabinet of photographs. **Services:** Library open to the public for reference use only. **Publications:** List of publications - available on request.

★3185★
Cedar Rapids Gazette - Library (Publ)
500 3rd Ave., S.E. Phone: (319)398-8328
Cedar Rapids, IA 52406 Bridget Janus
Staff: 2. **Subjects:** Newspaper reference topics. **Holdings:** News clippings; photographs. **Services:** Library not open to the public. **Automated Operations:** Stauffer's News Library System. **Remarks:** FAX: (319)398-5846.

★3186★
Cedar Rapids Museum of Art - Herbert S. Stamats Art Library (Art)
410 3rd Ave., S.E.
Cedar Rapids, IA 52401 Phone: (319)366-7503
Founded: 1967. **Staff:** 1. **Subjects:** Art history, architecture, archeology, studio art, crafts, gardening. **Special Collections:** Grant Wood Archives; Marvin Cone Archives; James Swann Archives; Malvina Hoffman Archives; Bertha Jaques Archives; Mauricio Lasansky Archives. **Holdings:** 1000 books; 50 bound periodical volumes; museum catalogs; 2 VF drawers of clippings. **Subscriptions:** 60 journals and other serials. **Services:** Interlibrary loan (limited); library open to the public for reference use only. **Remarks:** FAX: (319)366-4111.

★3187★
Cedar Springs Foundation - Library (Hum)
43378 Cedar Springs Rd. Phone: (209)855-2438
Auberry, CA 93602 William H. Young, Libn.
Founded: 1974. **Staff:** Prof 1. **Subjects:** Education, psychology, humanities, religion, philosophy. **Special Collections:** Agnosticism; free thought; humanism; peace; thanatology. **Holdings:** 5000 books; 50 cassette tapes; 30 boxes of reprints; 150 VF folders of clippings. **Subscriptions:** 120 journals and other serials. **Services:** Interlibrary loan; copying; library open to the public by appointment. **Automated Operations:** Computerized public access catalog. **Publications:** Newsletter, quarterly; occasional papers and bibliographies.

★3188★
Cedarcrest Regional Hospital - Medical Library
525 Russell Rd.
Newington, CT 06111
Defunct.

★3189★
Cedars-Sinai Medical Center - Health Sciences Information Center (Med)
8700 Beverly Blvd.
Box 48956 Phone: (213)855-3751
Los Angeles, CA 90048 Ellen Wilson Green, Dir. of Libs.
Founded: 1953. **Staff:** Prof 4; Other 5. **Subjects:** Clinical medicine. **Holdings:** 10,000 books; microfilm. **Subscriptions:** 561 journals and other serials. **Services:** Interlibrary loan; copying; center open to the public for reference use only. **Computerized Information Services:** MEDLINE, DIALOG Information Services, BRS Information Technologies. **Remarks:** FAX: (213)967-0138. **Staff:** Phyllis Soben, Med.Libn.; William Jacobs, Med.Libn.; Susan A. Kaisaki, Med.Libn.

★3190★
CEGA Services, Inc. - Information Services Department (Educ)
Box 81826 Phone: (402)464-0602
Lincoln, NE 68501-1826 Su Perk Davis, Dir., Info.Serv.
Founded: 1978. **Staff:** Prof 3; Other 2. **Subjects:** Literacy, corrections and criminal justice, illiteracy. **Holdings:** 12,000 literacy programs; 40,000 human services programs. **Services:** Clearinghouse open to subscribers. **Publications:** The Written Word (newsletter), monthly; Corrections Compendium; Corrections International; Survival Sourcebook; lists of correctional facilities, jails, departments of corrections, and parole/probation officers. **Remarks:** Serves as a Coalition for Literacy Information Center and a Project Literacy U.S. clearinghouse. FAX: (402)464-5931. **Formerly:** Contact Center - Clearinghouse/Information. **Staff:** Emily Herrick, Literacy; Mary Marlette, Ed.

★3191★
CEGEP de l'Abitibi-Temiscamingue - Bibliotheque (Hist, Area-Ethnic)
425 College Blvd.
Box 8000 Phone: (819)762-0931
Rouyn-Noranda, PQ, Canada J9X 5M5 Serge Allard, Dir.
Founded: 1953. **Subjects:** Northwest Quebec (Abitibi-Temiscamingue). **Holdings:** 64,091 books. **Subscriptions:** 247 journals and other serials. **Services:** Interlibrary loan; copying; library open to the public with restrictions. **Automated Operations:** Computerized cataloging, acquisitions, serials, and circulation. **Computerized Information Services:** DIALOG Information Services, BADADUQ; Envoy 100 (electronic mail service). **Remarks:** CEGEP is an acronym for College d'Enseignement General et Professionel. FAX: (819)762-3815. Electronic mail address(es): PEB.QRUQR (Envoy 100).

★3192★
CEGEP St-Jean-sur-Richelieu - Bibliotheque (Hist, Hum)
30, blvd. du Seminaire
C.P. 1018 Phone: (514)347-5301
St. Jean-sur-Richelieu, PQ, Canada J3B 7B1 Michel Robert, Chf.Libn.
Founded: 1968. **Staff:** Prof 2; Other 5. **Subjects:** History of Quebec, Quebec literature. **Holdings:** 75,042 books; 9427 bound periodical volumes; 22,156 slides; 2489 cassettes, tapes, phonograph records; 1057 films; 202 reels of microfilm. **Subscriptions:** 247 journals and other serials; 5 newspapers. **Services:** Interlibrary loan; copying; library open to the public. **Automated Operations:** Computerized cataloging. **Networks/Consortia:** Member of Reseau Normalise et Automatise des Ressources Documentaires (RENARD). **Publications:** Listes des nouveautes, monthly. **Remarks:** CEGEP is an acronym for College d'Enseignement General et Professionnel. FAX: (514)347-3329. **Staff:** Robert Dufort, Ref.Libn.

CEGEP de St-Laurent - College de Musique Sainte-Croix
See: **College de Musique Sainte-Croix** (3899)

★3193★
CEGEP de Ste-Foy - Centre d'Enseignement et de Recherche en Foresterie de Ste-Foy Inc. (Agri)
2410, chemin Ste-Foy Phone: (418)659-4225
Ste. Foy, PQ, Canada G1V 1T3 Demis Dubreuil, Info.Dir.
Founded: 1985. **Staff:** Prof 6; Other 6. **Subjects:** Forest management, harvesting, construction; wood product transformation; urban forestry. **Holdings:** 506 volumes; 10 unbound reports; 10 reels of microfilm; 10 magnetic tapes. **Subscriptions:** 15 journals and other serials. **Services:** Center open to the public with restrictions. **Computerized Information Services:** FORINVENT (Forestry Inventory System; internal database). Contact Person: David Pruneau, Comp.Techn. **Publications:** Catalogue des interventious sylvicoles; Notions d'entomology foresriere. **Remarks:** CEGEP is an acronym for College d'Enseignement General et Professionel. FAX: (418)657-3529.

★3194★
CEGEP de Trois-Rivieres - Bibliotheque (Hum)
3500 de Courval
C.P. 97 Phone: (819)376-1721
Trois-Rivieres, PQ, Canada G9A 5E6 Denis Simard, Dir.
Founded: 1968. **Staff:** Prof 3; Other 16. **Subjects:** Literature, humanities, philosophy, pure and applied sciences, history, geography, linguistics. **Special Collections:** Materiautheque (architecture, applied arts, electrotechnique); Pates et Papiers. **Holdings:** 105,000 books; 20,000 bound periodical volumes; 90,614 documents; AV programs. **Subscriptions:** 415 journals and other serials; 3 newspapers. **Services:** Interlibrary loan; copying; SDI; library open to the public. **Automated Operations:** Computerized public access catalog, cataloging, acquisitions, serials, and circulation. **Computerized Information Services:** Questel, DIALOG Information Services; CADOT (Catalogue Automatise des Documents a Trois Rivieres; internal database). Performs searches free of charge. **Networks/Consortia:** Member of ADATE, Reseau Normalise et Automatise des Ressources Documentaires (RENARD). **Publications:** Liste des periodiques actifs et non actifs (1800 titles). **Special Catalogs:** Cataloque de la cinematheque. **Remarks:** CEGEP is an acronym for College d'Enseignement General et Professionnel. FAX: (819)376-4420; 376-2595. **Staff:** Le Duy Quy, Tech.Serv.; Odile Gendron; Daniele Baillargeon, Ref.; Pierre Germain, Loan.

★3195★
CEGEP du Vieux-Montreal - Centre de Ressources Didactiques (Art)
255 Ontario St., E.
Station N, P.O. Box 1444 Phone: (514)982-3437
Montreal, PQ, Canada H2X 3M8 Suzane Giroux, Dir.
Staff: Prof 3; Other 10. **Subjects:** History of arts, applied arts, applied science and technology, applied human science, humanities, literature. **Special Collections:** Audiovisual collection. **Holdings:** 91,000 books. **Subscriptions:** 400 journals and other serials. **Services:** Interlibrary loan; copying; center open to the public for reference use only. **Publications:** Documents recus au service des acquisitions, 10/year; Bonjour (newsletter) - both for internal distribution only. **Remarks:** CEGEP is an acronym for College d'Enseignement General et Professionnel. **Also Known As:** College du Vieux-Montreal. **Staff:** Gerard Dubord, Ref.; Michel Hache, Ref.; Serge Poulin, Ref.

Celanese Corporation - Celanese Specialties Operations
See: **Hoechst Celanese Corporation - Engineering Plastics Division** (7308)

★3196★
Celebrity Access - Film/TV Information Center (Theater)
20 Sunnyside Ave., Suite A, No. 241 Phone: (415)389-8133
Mill Valley, CA 94941 Thomas Burford, Pub.
Founded: 1980. **Staff:** 2. **Subjects:** Celebrities, filmography, actor/actress biography. **Special Collections:** Autographs of the rich and famous (photographs, cards, books, magazines, posters, album pages); collectibles price guides; movie and TV reference books. **Holdings:** 300 books. **Services:** Center not open to the public; performs searches by mail on fee basis. **Publications:** Celebrity Access - The Directory - for sale. **Formerly:** Thomas Burford Ltd.

★3197★
Celebrity Service International, Inc. - Library (Theater)
1780 Broadway, Suite 300 Phone: (212)245-1460
New York, NY 10019 Frances Van
Founded: 1939. **Staff:** 16. **Subjects:** Public figures - theatrical and musical entertainers, newsmakers and corporate personalities, internationally recognized social, fashion, and cultural leaders. **Holdings:** 750 books; 210,000 documents. **Subscriptions:** 40 journals and other serials. **Services:** Library not open to the public. **Remarks:** FAX: (212)397-4626. Maintains branch offices in Los Angeles, London, Paris, and Rome. **Staff:** Nancy Preiser; Eve Rapess; Carol Schiff.

★3198★
(Celinograd) Selskochozjajstvennyj Institut - Biblioteka (Agri, Soc Sci, Biol Sci, Sci-Engr)
ul. Mira 73 Phone: 24990
Celinograd, Russia Elisaveta Eshimovna Romanenko
Founded: 1958. **Staff:** Prof 31; Other 10. **Subjects:** Agriculture, economics, electrification, mechanization, biotechnology, architecture. **Holdings:** 562,000 books; 58,050 bound periodical volumes; 1270 reports; 45 reels of microfilm; 19,600 other cataloged items. **Subscriptions:** 360 journals and other serials; 65 newspapers. **Services:** Interlibrary loan; library open to the public with restrictions. **Special Indexes:** Index of articles (card).

★3199★
The Celtic Evangelical Church - Community of St. Columba - Library (Rel-Phil)
Box 90880
Honolulu, HI 96835-0880 Rt.Rev. Wayne W. Gau, Abbot
Staff: 1. **Subjects:** Early Celtic Christian Church - history, liturgy, theology, modern revivals; liturgy of the Gallican-type and Anglican rites. **Holdings:** 400 books; 50 unpublished papers. **Services:** Interlibrary loan; copying; library open to the public with restrictions. **Publications:** The Celtic Evangelist, 2/year. **Staff:** James H. Donalson, Canon Liturgist.

★3200★
Celtrix Laboratories, Inc. - Library (Biol Sci)
2500 Faber Pl. Phone: (415)813-4090
Palo Alto, CA 94303 Maria Hylkema, Tech.Info.Spec.
Founded: 1982. **Staff:** Prof 1; Other 2. **Subjects:** Biochemistry, chemical engineering, dermatology, plastic surgery, immunology, dentistry, orthopedics. **Holdings:** 2500 books; 750 other cataloged items. **Subscriptions:** 160 journals and other serials. **Services:** Interlibrary loan. **Computerized Information Services:** DIALOG Information Services; internal database. **Networks/Consortia:** Member of Northern California and Nevada Medical Library Group (NCNMLG). **Publications:** Infomatrix (current awareness digest), weekly. **Remarks:** Library serves both Collagen Corporation and Celtrix Laboratories, Inc. (former subsidiary of Collagen Corp). **Remarks:** FAX: (415)856-0533.

★3201★
Centenary Hospital - C.D. Farquharson Health Sciences Library (Med)
2867 Ellesmere Rd. Phone: (416)284-8131
Scarborough, ON, Canada M1E 4B9 Vadla Poplak, Hd.Libn.
Founded: 1970. **Staff:** Prof 1; Other 3. **Subjects:** Medicine, pediatrics, surgery, obstetrics, gynecology, anesthesia, psychiatry. **Holdings:** 1500 books. **Subscriptions:** 100 journals and other serials. **Services:** Interlibrary loan; library not open to the public. **Computerized Information Services:** CD-ROM (MEDLINE, CINAHL). **Remarks:** FAX: (416)281-7323.

★3202★
Centennial College of Applied Arts & Technology - Ashtonbee Campus Resource Centre (Educ)
Sta. A, P.O. Box 631 Phone: (416)752-4444
Scarborough, ON, Canada M1K 5E9 Ron Wood, Dir.
Founded: 1969. **Staff:** Prof 2; Other 4. **Subjects:** Automotive technology, aircraft/avionics. **Holdings:** 16,616 volumes. **Subscriptions:** 142 periodicals. **Services:** Interlibrary loan; center open to the public. **Automated Operations:** Computerized circulation. **Computerized Information Services:** DOBIS Canadian Online Library System, DIALOG Information Services. Performs searches on fee basis. Contact Person: Mary Lou Lamont, Libn., ext. 4607. **Publications:** Guide to the Resource Centre. **Special Catalogs:** Videotape catalog; film catalog. **Remarks:** Centre located at 75 Ashtonbee Rd., Scarborough, ON. FAX: (416)759-4075 (Attn: Resource Centre).

★3203★
Centennial College of Applied Arts & Technology - Progress Campus Resource Centre (Educ)
Sta. A, P.O. Box 631 Phone: (416)439-7180
Scarborough, ON, Canada M1K 5E9 Mary-Lu Brennan, Dir.
Founded: 1977. **Staff:** Prof 3; Other 10. **Subjects:** Business, engineering, law, robotics, fluid power. **Holdings:** 26,012 volumes. **Subscriptions:** 248 periodicals. **Services:** Interlibrary loan; center open to the public. **Automated Operations:** Computerized circulation. **Computerized Information Services:** DOBIS Canadian Online Library System, DIALOG Information Services. Performs searches on fee basis. Contact Person: Linda Choptiany, Libn., ext. 2604. **Publications:** Guide to the Resource Centre. **Special Catalogs:** Videotape catalog. **Remarks:** Centre located at 41 Progress Court, Scarborough, ON M1L 3Z6. **Remarks:** FAX: (416)431-2597 (Attn: Resource Centre). Centre located at 41 Progress Court, Scarborough, ON. **Staff:** Annetta Protain, Exec.Dir., Rsrc.Ctr.; Linda Choptiany, Pub.Serv.Libn.

★3204★
Centennial College of Applied Arts & Technology - Warden Woods Campus Resource Centre (Educ)
Sta. A, P.O. Box 631 Phone: (416)694-3241
Scarborough, ON, Canada M1K 5E9 Ron Wood, Dir.
Founded: 1966. **Staff:** Prof 2; Other 7. **Subjects:** Nursing, social sciences and humanities, travel, fashion, early childhood education, social services. **Holdings:** 32,411 volumes. **Subscriptions:** 230 periodicals. **Services:** Interlibrary loan; center open to the public. **Automated Operations:** Computerized circulation. **Computerized Information Services:** DOBIS Canadian Online Library System, Info Globe. Performs searches on fee basis. Contact Person: Holly Prue, Libn., 694-3241, ext. 3604. **Publications:** Guide to the Resource Centre. **Special Catalogs:** Videotape, nursing, and film catalogs. **Remarks:** Centre located at 651 Warden Ave., Scarborough, ON. 3Z6. FAX: (416)694-2664 (Attn: Resource Centre). **Staff:** Holly Prue, Pub.Serv.Libn.

Centennial Museum Research Room
See: **Royal Canadian Mounted Police** (14109)

★3205★
Center for Advanced Studies on Modern Africa and Asia - Library (Area-Ethnic)
13, rue du Four Phone: 1 43 26 96 90
F-75006 Paris, France Anne Malecot, Libn.
Founded: 1936. **Staff:** 3. **Subjects:** Africa, Asia, the Pacific Basin, the Caribbean - social, political, administrative, and economic problems; sociopolitical and anthropological traditions. **Special Collections:** Charles-Andre Julien Fund - Memoires du CHEAM (written by former trainees of the Center). **Holdings:** 15,000 volumes. **Subscriptions:** 220 journals and other serials. **Services:** Interlibrary loan; copying; library open to professors, researchers, and doctorate students. **Remarks:** FAX: 1 40510358. Maintained by National Foundation of Political Sciences/Fondation Nationale des Sciences Politiques. **Also Known As:** Centre de Hautes Etudes sur l'Afrique et l'Asie Modernes. **Staff:** Veronique Bodin; Frederique Parpaillon.

★3206★
Center for Advanced Study in the Behavioral Sciences - Library (Soc Sci)
202 Junipero Serra Blvd. Phone: (415)321-2052
Stanford, CA 94305 Margaret Amara, Libn.
Founded: 1954. **Staff:** Prof 2. **Subjects:** Anthropology, history, philosophy, political science, psychology, sociology. **Special Collections:** Ralph W. Tyler Collection (1000 publications representing works conceived, initiated, or completed by Fellows during their stay at the center). **Holdings:** 6000 books. **Subscriptions:** 290 journals and other serials; 18 newspapers. **Services:** Library not open to the public. **Computerized Information Services:** DIALOG Information Services, RLIN. **Special Catalogs:** Catalog of the Ralph W. Tyler Collection. **Remarks:** FAX: (415)321-1192.

Center for Advanced Study in Health Care Fiscal Management Organization and Control
See: **University of Wisconsin--Madison** (19620)

★3207★
Center for the Advancement of Human Co-operation - Library
Box 15778
Gainesville, FL 32604 Phone: (904)378-4067
Founded: 1984. **Staff:** 2. **Subjects:** Russian and Soviet history, politics, economics, science, philosophy, theology, art. **Holdings:** 3000 volumes. **Subscriptions:** 16 journals and other serials; 3 newspapers. **Services:** Library open to the public by appointment. **Staff:** Renee-Marie Croose Parry, Coord.; Kenneth Croose Parry.

Centre Africain de Formation et de Recherche Administratives pour le Developpement
See: **African Training and Research Centre in Administration for Development - Division of Documentation and Information** (129)

Center for African Oral Data
See: **Indiana University - Archives of Traditional Music** (7776)

★3208★
Center for American Archeology - Research Library (Soc Sci)
P.O. Box 366 Phone: (618)653-4316
Kampsville, IL 62053 Kenneth B. Farnsworth, Dir., Contract Archeo.Prog.
Founded: 1958. **Subjects:** Archeology; excavation, analysis, preservation of archeological sites. **Holdings:** 15,000 volumes. **Subscriptions:** 100 journals and other serials. **Services:** Library open to the public for reference use only; check-out privileges to students and staff.

★3209★
Center for the American Woman & Politics - Library (Soc Sci)
Eagleton Institute, Rutgers University
Wood Lawn, Neilson Campus Phone: (908)932-9384
New Brunswick, NJ 08901 Kathy Kleeman, Sr.Prog.Assoc.
Founded: 1971. **Staff:** 5. **Subjects:** Women and American politics and government. **Holdings:** 700 books; 2000 papers, pamphlets, clippings. **Subscriptions:** 75 journals and other serials. **Services:** Copying; library open to the public on request. **Publications:** List of publications - available on request. **Remarks:** CAWP is a research and education center committed to increasing knowledge about American women's participation in government and politics. FAX: (908)932-6778. **Staff:** Ruth B. Mandel, Dir.

Centre d'Animation de Developpement et de Recherche en Education - Bibliotheque
See: **Centre de Documentation de l'Enseignement Prive - Bibliotheque** (3234)

★3210★
Center for Anthropological Studies - Library (Hist)
Box 14576 Phone: (505)296-4836
Albuquerque, NM 87191-0576 Albert E. Ward, Dir.
Founded: 1976. **Staff:** 2. **Subjects:** Southwestern archeology, ethnology, and history; Spanish colonial history. **Special Collections:** Richard and Marietta Wetherill Collection; Southwestern environmental impact statements and studies. **Holdings:** 2000 books; 1000 bound periodical volumes; 250 other cataloged items. **Subscriptions:** 12 journals and other serials. **Services:** Copying; library open to the public by appointment. **Publications:** List of publications - available on request. **Remarks:** FAX: (505)255-6467.

★3211★
Center for Applications of Psychological Type, Inc. - Isabel Briggs Myers Memorial Library (Soc Sci)
2720 6th St., N.W., Suite A Phone: (904)375-0160
Gainesville, FL 32609 Gerald P. Macdaid, Dir. of Res.
Founded: 1981. **Subjects:** Myers-Briggs Type Indicator, Jungian psychology, typology, general psychology. **Holdings:** 159 books; 350 bound periodical volumes; 1200 research reports; 450 dissertations. **Subscriptions:** 36 journals and other serials. **Services:** Copying; library open to the public for reference use only. **Publications:** Myers-Briggs Type Indicator Bibliography, semiannual - for sale. **Remarks:** FAX: (904)378-0503.

★3212★
Center for Applied Prevention Research - Library (Med)
4760 Walnut St., Suite 106 Phone: (303)443-5696
Boulder, CO 80301 Tessa Davis
Founded: 1987. **Staff:** Prof 1. **Subjects:** Substance abuse prevention. **Special Collections:** Student Assistance Program Resources; Youth Leadership Program Resources; evaluation instrument file. **Holdings:** 2500 books; 500 reports. **Subscriptions:** 100 journals and other serials. **Services:** Copying; library open to the public. **Networks/Consortia:** Member of Regional Alcohol and Drug Abuse Resource Network (RADAR). **Publications:** What's New in Resources, quarterly - for distribution in Colorado only. **Remarks:** FAX: (303)443-4373. Toll-free telephone number(s): (800)972-4636.

★3213★
Center for Applied Research in the Apostolate - Archives and Research Library (Rel-Phil)
Georgetown University
P.O. Box 1601 Phone: (202)687-8080
Washington, DC 20057 Rev. Msgr. Edward C. Foster, Exec.Dir.
Founded: 1965. **Staff:** 6. **Subjects:** Church personnel projections and management studies, religious life, parish development, pastoral research and planning, overseas ministry, health ministry. **Special Collections:** Seminary Directories, 1965 to present; diocesan surveys; Religious Life; 1982 values data (printout). **Holdings:** 2000 monographs; 200 titles of CARA publications, 1965 to present. **Subscriptions:** 600 journals and other serials. **Services:** Library open to the public with restrictions. **Publications:** Religious formation directory; seminary directory; seminary forum. **Remarks:** FAX: (202)687-8083. **Staff:** Sr. Eleace King, IHM, D.Ed.; C. Joseph O'Hara, Ph.D.

★3214★
Center for Auto Safety - Safety Research Service (SRS) - Library (Trans)
2001 S St., N.W., Suite 410 Phone: (202)328-7700
Washington, DC 20009 Christine Lauer, Res.
Founded: 1973. **Subjects:** Automotive and highway safety, product liability. **Holdings:** 4000 volumes; reports. **Services:** Library not open to the public. **Remarks:** Library has access to a database of 100,000 consumer complaints. **Formerly:** Its Product Liability Research Service (PLRS). **Staff:** Russell Shew, Res.

★3215★
The Center for Bead Research - Library (Art)
4 Essex St. Phone: (518)523-1794
Lake Placid, NY 12946 Peter Francis, Jr., Dir.
Founded: 1984. **Staff:** Prof 1; Other 1. **Subjects:** Beads, traditional ornamentation, materials science, jewelry, glass. **Special Collections:** Francis Bead Research Notes (22 volumes); archives (3700 photographs); bead-making tools; study collection of beads. **Holdings:** 425 books; 50 bound periodical volumes; 4000 reprints, articles, documents. **Subscriptions:** 18 journals and other serials. **Services:** Copying; library open to the public by appointment. **Computerized Information Services:** India Bead Data Bank (internal database). Performs searches on fee basis. **Publications:** Papers of The Center for Bead Research, irregular - for sale; Contributions of the Center for Bead Research, irregular - for sale; The Bead Bibliography (online); Margaretologist (newsletter), biennial - to members and patrons. **Special Indexes:** Purchase His Pilgrimes Index; Bead Index to the National Geographic (both printouts).

Center for Byzantine & Modern Greek Studies
See: **Queens College of City University of New York** (13639)

Centre for Canadian Historical Horticulture Studies
See: **Royal Botanical Gardens - Library** (14105)

★3216★
Centre Canadien d'Etudes et de Cooperation Internationale - Bibliotheque Specialisee (Soc Sci)
180, rue Ste-Catherine, E. Phone: (514)875-9911
Montreal, PQ, Canada H2X 1K9 Robert Hazel
Founded: 1958. **Staff:** Prof 2. **Subjects:** Developing nations in Africa, Latin America, and Asia. **Holdings:** 20,000 books. **Subscriptions:** 300 journals and other serials. **Services:** Interlibrary loan; copying; library open to the public. **Publications:** List of new books, quarterly. **Staff:** Carmen Houle, Lib.Techn.; Laurent Cauchon, Lib.Techn.

Centre Canadien d'Oecumenisme
See: **Canadian Centre for Ecumenism** (2912)

★3217★
Center for Chinese Research Materials - Information Center (Area-Ethnic)
Box 3090 Phone: (703)281-7731
Oakton, VA 22124 Pingfeng Chi, Dir.
Founded: 1968. **Staff:** Prof 2; Other 1. **Subjects:** 20th century China. **Holdings:** 3000 rare book and periodical titles in xerographic and offset form; 6000 reels of microfilm. **Services:** Copying; center open to the public for reference use only. **Publications:** Newsletter, irregular - available on request.

★3218★
Centre for Christian Studies - Library (Rel-Phil)
77 Charles St., W. Phone: (416)923-1168
Toronto, ON, Canada M5S 1K5 Shelagh S. Telford, Libn.
Founded: 1954. **Staff:** Prof 1. **Subjects:** Religious education, pastoral care, youth ministry, feminist theology, social ministry. **Holdings:** 5000 volumes; 15 VF drawers of pamphlets, articles, and pictures. **Subscriptions:** 40 journals and other serials. **Services:** Library open to the public for reference use only (borrowing privileges restricted to students, staff, and graduates).

★3219★
Centre College - Grace Doherty Library - Special Collections (Rare Book, Hist)
600 W. Walnut St. Phone: (606)236-5211
Danville, KY 40422-1394 Stanley Campbell, Dir.
Special Collections: Rare Book Collection (3600 volumes); Centre College Archives. **Holdings:** 64,000 volumes of government documents. **Subscriptions:** 750 journals and other serials; 40 newspapers. **Services:** Interlibrary loan; copying; collections open to the public. **Automated Operations:** Computerized cataloging. **Computerized Information Services:** OCLC, DIALOG Information Services, WILSONLINE, BRS Information Technologies, VU/TEXT Information Services. Performs searches on fee basis. Contact Person: Mary Beth Garriott, 236-5211. **Networks/Consortia:** Member of SOLINET, Council of Independent Kentucky Colleges & Universities. **Special Catalogs:** Catalogs of Rare Book Collection and College Archives (card). **Remarks:** FAX: (606)236-7925. **Staff:** Robert Glass, Asst.Dir./Hd., Spec.Coll.

★3220★
Centre Community Hospital - Esker W. Cullen Health Sciences Library (Med)
1800 E. Park Ave. Phone: (814)234-6191
State College, PA 16803-6797 Gloria Durbin Venett, Libn.
Founded: 1981. **Staff:** Prof 1; Other 1. **Subjects:** Medicine, nursing, management, health administration. **Holdings:** 1414 books; 90 bound periodical volumes; 430 audiocassettes; 19 films; 127 multimedia kits; 15 slides; 111 videotapes. **Subscriptions:** 111 journals and other serials. **Services:** Interlibrary loan; copying; SDI; library open to the public for reference use only. **Automated Operations:** Computerized cataloging and ILL. **Computerized Information Services:** MEDLARS, DIALOG Information Services; internal database; DOCLINE (electronic mail service). Performs searches on fee basis. **Networks/Consortia:** Member of Central Pennsylvania Health Sciences Library Association (CPHSLA), BHSL. **Remarks:** FAX: (814)231-7031. Alternate telephone number(s): 234-6725; 234-6191.

★3221★
Center for Computer/Law - Library (Law)
Box 3549 Phone: (310)544-7372
Manhattan Beach, CA 90266 Michael D. Scott, Exec.Dir.
Founded: 1977. **Staff:** Prof 1; Other 1. **Subjects:** Law - computer, communication, information; automation. **Holdings:** 2000 books; 150 bound periodical volumes; 2000 pamphlets and reprints; 500 microfiche. **Subscriptions:** 50 journals and other serials; 8 newspapers. **Services:** Library open to the public by appointment. **Automated Operations:** Computerized cataloging and serials. **Remarks:** FAX: (310)544-4965.

★3222★
Center of Concern - Resource Center (Soc Sci)
3700 13th St., N.E. Phone: (202)635-2757
Washington, DC 20017 Jim Hug, S.J., Exec.Dir.
Subjects: International social justice issues, international development, international debt, welfare state, Catholic health care, women, labor, social theology. **Holdings:** Figures not available. **Services:** Library not open to the public. **Publications:** CENTER FOCUS (Newsletter), bimonthly. **Remarks:** The Center of Concern is an independent, interdisciplinary team engaged in social analysis, theological reflection, policy advocacy, and public education on issues of peace and justice. The Center also holds nongovernmental consultative status with the United Nations.

Center for Connecticut Studies
See: **Eastern Connecticut State University** (5144)

★3223★
Center for Continuing Study of California Economy - Library (Bus-Fin)
610 University Ave. Phone: (415)321-8551
Palo Alto, CA 94301-2019 Nancy Levy
Founded: 1969. **Subjects:** California - economic statistics, demographics, and issues. **Holdings:** 10,000 volumes. **Subscriptions:** 25 journals and other serials; 5 newspapers. **Services:** Library not open to the public. **Computerized Information Services:** California Counties & Cities (internal database). **Publications:** CCSCE Projection Series: California Economic Growth, California Population Characteristics, California County Projections.

★3224★
Centre de Cooperation Internationale en Recherche Agronomique pour le Developpement - Centre d'Information et de Documentation en Agronomie des Regions Chaudes - Bibliotheque et Documentation Centrales (Agri)
Avenue du Val de Montferrand
BP 5035 Phone: 1 67615800
F-34032 Montpellier, France Jean-Francois Giovannetti, Dir.
Founded: 1962. **Subjects:** Tropical agriculture, agronomical research, rural development, agrarian systems, rural economics and sociology, tropical vegetable and animal production, forests, aid for developing countries. **Holdings:** 10,000 volumes; 2735 periodical collections; 5000 microfiche. **Subscriptions:** 1400 journals and other serials. **Services:** Copying; SDI; library open to the public. **Computerized Information Services:** AGRIS, IAALD, IBISCUS, CCN, ADBS, ARIOD; CD-ROM (SESAME). **Publications:** AGRITROP. **Special Catalogs:** Catalogue des acquisitions de la bibliotheque; catalogue des periodiques recus au CIDRAC. **Remarks:** FAX: 1 67615820. Telex: 480 762 F. **Also Known As:** International Cooperation Center of Agricultural Research for Development; CIRAD - CIDARC.

Centre de Cooperation Internationale en Recherche Agronomique pour le Developpement - Institut de Recherches sur les Fruits et Agrumes
See: **International Cooperation Center of Agricultural Research for Development - Institute of Research on Fruits and Citrus Fruits** (8087)

★3225★
Centre County Law Library (Law)
Centre County Courthouse, Rm. 305 Phone: (814)355-6727
Bellefonte, PA 16823 Maxine Ishler, Court Adm.
Subjects: Law. **Holdings:** 500 books; 20,000 bound periodical volumes. **Subscriptions:** 150 journals and other serials. **Services:** Interlibrary loan; copying; library open to the public.

★3226★
Centre de Creation Industrielle - Service Documentation (Art, Plan)
Centre Georges Pompidou
F-75191 Paris Cedex 4, France Phone: 4 2771233
Founded: 1973. **Subjects:** Design - industrial, graphic, urban; architecture. **Holdings:** 14,500 volumes; photographs. **Subscriptions:** 250 journals and other serials. **Services:** Service open to architects, urban designers, students, government agencies, and users of the Pompidou Centre. **Computerized Information Services:** Produces CCiDOC Data Base. **Remarks:** FAX: 4 2772949. Telex: 212 726 CNAC GP.

★3227★
Center for Creative Leadership - Library (Soc Sci)
5000 Laurinda Dr.
P.O. Box 26300 Phone: (919)288-7210
Greensboro, NC 27438-6300 Frank H. Freeman, Lib.Dir.
Founded: 1969. **Staff:** Prof 2; Other 2. **Subjects:** Leadership, management, organizational behavior, innovation, social psychology, industrial psychology. **Special Collections:** Psychological assessment (500 documents); performance appraisal (250 documents). **Holdings:** 5000 books; 400 bound periodical volumes; 600 dissertations and reports; 500 technical reports; 5000 reprints and unpublished papers. **Subscriptions:** 170 journals and other serials; 5 newspapers. **Services:** Interlibrary loan; copying; SDI; library open to center participants or visiting scholars. **Automated Operations:** Computerized acquisitions, cataloging, serials, and circulation. **Computerized Information Services:** DIALOG Information Services, Dow Jones News/Retrieval, WILSONLINE, BRS Information Technologies, OCLC; FROLIC (internal database); CompuServe Information Service (electronic mail service). **Networks/Consortia:** Member of North Carolina Information Network (NCIN). **Publications:** Acquisitions list, monthly - for internal distribution only; topical bibliographies, irregular - by request; Leadership Education Sourcebook, semiannual. **Special Catalogs:** Leadership/Management (card). **Remarks:** FAX: (919)288-3999. Telex: 3772224. Electronic mail address(es): 76067,2475 (CompuServe Information Service). **Staff:** Peggy Cartner; Carol Keck.

Center of the Creative and Performing Arts - Archives
See: **State University of New York at Buffalo - Music Library** (15740)

★3228★
Center for Creative Studies - Library (Art)
201 E. Kirby Phone: (313)872-3118
Detroit, MI 48202 Jean Peyrat, Libn.
Founded: 1966. **Staff:** Prof 2. **Subjects:** Art. **Special Collections:** Art History (51,000 slides). **Holdings:** 20,000 books; 319 bound periodical volumes; 80,000 flat pictures. **Subscriptions:** 75 journals and other serials. **Services:** Library open to the public for reference use only. **Formerly:** Center for Creative Studies/College of Art & Design - Library.

★3229★
Center for Cuban Studies, Inc. - Lourdes Casal Library (Area-Ethnic)
124 W. 23rd St. Phone: (212)242-0559
New York, NY 10011 Jerome Nickel, Libn.
Subjects: Cuba - culture, society, economy, history with emphasis on period 1959 to present; Jose Marti. **Special Collections:** Graphics and photographic archives; Cuban feature and documentary films. **Holdings:** 4000 books. **Subscriptions:** 23 journals and other serials. **Services:** Copying; library open to members, students, and scholars. **Publications:** Cuba Update, quarterly; CCS Newsletter, occasional. **Remarks:** FAX: (212)242-1937.

★3230★
Center for Cultural Survival - Library (Soc Sci)
11 Divinity Ave. Phone: (617)496-8786
Cambridge, MA 02138 Mary Herbert, Asst.Dir.
Staff: 3. **Subjects:** Indigenous populations, ethnic minorities, human rights, development, social impact, culture change. **Holdings:** 10,000 clippings; 500 unpublished social impact assessments; 1000 reports and documents. **Subscriptions:** 150 journals and other serials; 20 newspapers. **Services:** Library open to the public. **Publications:** Quarterly magazine; occasional reports. **Remarks:** FAX: (617)496-8787. Center is the research division of Cultural Survival, Inc.

★3231★
Center for Defense Information - Library (Mil)
1500 Massachusetts Ave., N.W. Phone: (202)862-0700
Washington, DC 20005 Kathryn Schultz, Res.Libn.
Founded: 1972. **Staff:** 2. **Subjects:** Defense information, Defense Department budgets, foreign affairs, military posture, nuclear weapons, arms control. **Special Collections:** Stockholm International Peace Research Institute (SIPRI) yearbooks (6 linear feet); Arms Control and Disarmament Agency's Documents on Disarmament (27 volumes); The Military Balance (27 volumes) and Strategic Survey (both from the International Institute for Strategic Studies); defense-related Congressional Budget studies (3 linear feet); defense-related General Accounting Office reports (12 linear feet);

Center for Defense Information's Defense Monitor (138 issues); America's Defense Monitor video cassettes (195 episodes); Jane's Yearbooks (8 linear feet); DOD Budget Documents, 1927 to present (10 linear feet). **Holdings:** 4500 books; 4500 congressional hearing reports; Central Intelligence Agency reference materials (10 linear feet); Defense Department posture statements and reports to Congress (6 linear feet); 40 VF drawers of defense information; 700 audio and video cassettes; 300 pamphlets, reports, and manuscripts. **Subscriptions:** 130 journals and other serials; 5 newspapers. **Services:** Interlibrary loan; copying; library open to the public. **Remarks:** The "Defense Monitor" and "America's Defense Monitor" are available for a fee. FAX: (202)862-0708. Telex: 904059 WSH(CDI). **Staff:** Goldia Shaw, Lib.Asst.

★3232★
Centre de Documentation Benjamin Franklin - (Paris) USIS Library (Educ)
2, rue St. Florentin
F-75001 Paris, France
Remarks: Maintained or supported by the U.S. Information Agency. Focus is on materials that will assist peoples outside the United States to learn about the United States, its people, history, culture, political processes, and social milieux.

★3233★
Centre de Documentation sur l'Education des Adultes et Condition Feminine (CDEACF) (Educ)
1265 Berri, No. 340 Phone: (514)844-3674
Montreal, PQ, Canada H2L 4X4 Rosalie Ndejuru, Coord., Chf.Libn.
Founded: 1966. **Staff:** Prof 2; Other 10. **Subjects:** Adult education, womens issues, literacy, professional training, popular education, communication. **Special Collections:** Current issues records (1250 files); organizations working in adult education and women's issues throughout the world (560 files); literacy education collection. **Holdings:** 17,000 books; 1000 bound periodical titles; 2000 manuscripts and reports; 1 box microfiche; 1 box videotapes. **Subscriptions:** 450 journals and other serials. **Services:** Interlibrary loan; copying; SDI; center open to the public. **Automated Operations:** Computerized cataloging, acquisitions, serials, and circulation. **Computerized Information Services:** CDEACF, ALFA, CPDM (internal databases). **Publications:** Documentation Plus: documents recents 1990; guide d'utilisation. **Special Catalogs:** 560 Organismes oeuvrant dans les champs de l'education des adultes et la condition feminine. **Remarks:** FAX: (514)844-1598. **Formerly:** Institut Canadien d'Education des Adultes, Relais-Femmes et RGPAQ. **Staff:** Therese LeBlanc, Ref.Libn.

Centre de Documentation pour l'Education en Europe
See: **Documentation Centre for Education in Europe** (4938)

★3234★
Centre de Documentation de l'Enseignement Prive - Bibliotheque (Educ)
1940, blvd. Henri-Bourassa, Est Phone: (514)381-8891
Montreal, PQ, Canada H2B 1S2 Guy Dion, Dir.Gen.
Founded: 1968. **Staff:** 2. **Subjects:** Private education. **Holdings:** 3000 documents; bound periodical volumes. **Subscriptions:** 105 journals and other serials. **Services:** Library open to teachers and researchers. **Remarks:** FAX: (514)381-4086. **Staff:** Roland Desrosiers; Monique Pillon.

Centre de Documentation Internationale des Industries Utilisatrices de Produits Agricoles
See: **International Documentation Center for Industries Using Agricultural Products** (8100)

Center for Documentation on Refugees - Library
See: **United Nations High Commissioner for Refugees** (16773)

Centre de Documentation pour le Sport
See: **Sport Information Resource Centre** (15593)

Center for Dredging Studies
See: **Texas A&M University** (16192)

★3235★
Center for Early Education/College for Developmental Studies - Laura M. Ellis Memorial Library (Educ)
563 N. Alfred St. Phone: (213)651-0707
West Hollywood, CA 90048 Lucy E. Greene, Libn.
Founded: 1968. **Staff:** Prof 1; Other 1. **Subjects:** Psychology; education - elementary, preschool, teacher, special; psychoanalysis; sociology; human development; parenting. **Holdings:** 8600 books. **Subscriptions:** 100 journals and other serials. **Services:** Interlibrary loan; copying; library open to the public on request. **Remarks:** FAX: (213)651-0860.

Center for Eastern Christian Studies
See: **University of Scranton - Center For Eastern Christian Studies** (19300)

★3236★
Center on Education and Training for Employment - Research Library (Educ)
Ohio State University
1900 Kenny Rd. Phone: (614)292-4353
Columbus, OH 43210 Steve Chambers, Libn.
Founded: 1966. **Staff:** Prof 1; Other 1. **Subjects:** Education - vocational, adult, career; educational evaluation; youth unemployment; special populations. **Holdings:** 60,000 books; 4500 bound periodical volumes; 330,000 microforms; 12,000 dissertations; 1500 instruments. **Subscriptions:** 200 journals and other serials; 5 newspapers. **Services:** Library not open to the public. **Automated Operations:** Computerized cataloging and acquisitions. **Computerized Information Services:** DIALOG Information Services, BRS Information Technologies; Resources in Vocational Education (RIVE), Library Control System (LCS; internal databases). **Publications:** SDI, monthly; Periodical List, annual; Guide to the Instrument File; newsletter - for internal distribution only. **Special Catalogs:** Data collection instrument file (card).

★3237★
Center for Emergency Medicine of Western Pennsylvania - Library (Med)
230 McKee Pl., Suite 500 Phone: (412)578-3200
Pittsburgh, PA 15213 P.M. Paris, MD, Chf.Med.Off.
Staff: Prof 2; Other 5. **Subjects:** Emergency medicine, pre-hospital care, critical care medicine. **Holdings:** 300 books; 500 bound periodical volumes. **Subscriptions:** 50 journals and other serials. **Services:** Library open to the public with restrictions. **Remarks:** FAX: (412)578-3241. **Staff:** E.I. Weinberg, Chf.Exc.Off.

Center for Energy and Environment Research
See: **University of Puerto Rico - Mayaguez Campus Library - Research and Development Center of the Caribbean** (19254)

Centre d'Enseignement et de Recherche en Foresterie de Ste-Foy Inc.
See: **CEGEP de Ste-Foy** (3193)

★3238★
Center for Environmental Information, Inc. - Air Resources Information Clearinghouse (ARIC) (Env-Cons)
46 Prince St.
Rochester, NY 14607-1016 Phone: (716)271-3550
Founded: 1982. **Staff:** 3. **Subjects:** Acid deposition and its ecological, socioeconomic, and political impact; atmospheric sciences; control technologies; global climate change (greenhouse effect, ozone depletion, and related phenomenon) - scientific, technical and policy information; indoor air pollution; air toxic emissions. **Holdings:** 2000 books and technical reports; 6 VF drawers of newspaper clippings, articles, brochures. **Subscriptions:** 50 journals and other serials. **Services:** Telephone/mail reference and referral; clearinghouse open to the public for reference use only. **Computerized Information Services:** DIALOG Information Services, MEDLARS. Performs searches on fee basis. **Networks/Consortia:** Member of Rochester Regional Library Council (RRLC). **Publications:** Acid Precipitation Digest; Global Climate Change Digest (both current awareness bulletins); ARIC Bibliographic Series (specialized bibliographies on related issues); list of additional publications - available upon request. **Remarks:** FAX: (716)271-0606. **Staff:** Carol Beal, Dir., Info.Spec.; Chris Fredette, Info.Spec.; Susan Doron, Mgr. of Info.Serv.

★3239★
Center for Environmental Information, Inc. - CEI Library (Env-Cons)
46 Prince St.
Rochester, NY 14607-1016 Phone: (716)271-3550
Founded: 1974. **Staff:** 18. **Subjects:** Natural resources, conservation, acid rain, greenhouse effect, environment, energy, environmental education. **Special Collections:** Acid Rain Reference Collection (1000 shelved items; 5 VF drawers). **Holdings:** 6500 books and technical reports; 30 VF drawers of newspaper clippings, journal reprints, pamphlets, brochures, flyers. **Subscriptions:** 180 journals and other serials. **Services:** Telephone/mail reference and referral; library open to the public for reference use only. **Computerized Information Services:** DIALOG Information Services, NLM. Performs searches on fee basis. **Networks/Consortia:** Member of Rochester Regional Library Council (RRLC). **Publications:** Directory of Environmental Agencies & Organizations; CEI Sphere - to members; Acid Precipitation Digest; Global Climate Change Digest; bibliographies - catalog available upon request. **Remarks:** FAX: (716)271-0606. **Staff:** Chris Fredette, Info.Spec.; Carole Beal, Dir./Info.Spec.

Centre d'Etudes Acadiennes
See: **Universite de Moncton** (18072)

Centre d'Etudes Franco-Terreneuviennes
See: **Memorial University of Newfoundland** (10049)

Centre d'Etudes et Recherches de Charbonnages de France
See: **National Insitute of Industrial Environment and Hazards** (11203)

★3240★
Centre d'Etudes Verniennes - Mediatheque (Hist)
15, rue de l'Heronniere Phone: 40 41 95 95
F-44041 Nantes Cedex, France Ms. Bertrand, Dir.
Founded: 1969. **Staff:** 1. **Subjects:** Jules Verne - life and works. **Holdings:** 2500 books; 120 bound periodical volumes; 3200 documents; 22 reels of microfilm of manuscripts, letters, and books; 116 manuscripts. **Services:** Interlibrary loan; copying; library open to the public by appointment. **Publications:** Cahiers de Centre d'Etudes Verniennes. **Special Catalogs:** Catalogue des Manuscrits. **Staff:** Mme. Sainlot, Co-Cons.; Colette Gallois, Libn.

Center for Excellence in Optical Data Processing
See: **Carnegie-Mellon University** (3082)

Center for Family Studies
See: **The Family Institute - Crowley Library** (5589)

★3241★
Center for Forensic Economic Studies - Information Center (Bus-Fin)
1608 Walnut St., Suite 1200 Phone: (215)546-5600
Philadelphia, PA 19103 Kathleen M. Dewane, Info.Serv.Mgr.
Founded: 1987. **Staff:** Prof 1; Other 1. **Subjects:** Economics, demography, business, finance. **Holdings:** 400 books; 5000 reports. **Subscriptions:** 75 journals and other serials; 3 newspapers. **Services:** Interlibrary loan; copying; SDI; center open to the public by appointment. **Computerized Information Services:** DIALOG Information Services. **Remarks:** FAX: (215)732-8158.

Center for Forensic Psychiatry
See: **Michigan (State) Department of Mental Health** (10300)

Centre de Foresterie des Laurentides
See: **Canada - Forestry Canada - Laurentian Forestry Centre** (2739)

★3242★
Center for Governmental Research, Inc. - Library (Soc Sci, Plan)
37 S. Washington St. Phone: (716)325-6360
Rochester, NY 14608-9990 Peter Young, Libn.
Founded: 1915. **Staff:** Prof 1. **Subjects:** Government finance, local government, criminal justice, human services, community services, urban studies, economics, education, environment, planning, administration, health, housing, transportation, infrastructure, research, methodology, theory, taxation, public finance. **Special Collections:** New York State Statistics. **Holdings:** 1060 internal reports, 1915 to present; local budgets; ACIR publications. **Subscriptions:** 100 journals and other serials. **Services:** Interlibrary loan; copying; library open to the public with restrictions. **Computerized Information Services:** DIALOG Information Services, OCLC. Performs searches on fee basis. **Networks/Consortia:** Member of Rochester Regional Library Council (RRLC). **Remarks:** FAX: (716)325-2612. Affiliated with New York State Data Center.

★3243★
Center for the Great Lakes - Great Lakes Information Service (Sci-Engr)
35 E. Wacker, Suite 1870 Phone: (312)263-0785
Chicago, IL 60601 Paul Botts, Info.Serv.Dir.
Founded: 1983. **Staff:** 3. **Subjects:** Great Lakes - water quality, water diversion, water use, management, natural resources, economy. **Holdings:** 200 books; 600 reports; subject files; fact sheets. **Subscriptions:** 50 journals and other serials. **Services:** Copying; library open to the public by appointment. **Publications:** The Great Lakes Reporter (newsletter), bimonthly. **Formerly:** Its Library.

Center for Great Plains Studies
See: **University of Nebraska, Lincoln** (18995)

Center for Gulf Studies
See: **Bienville Historical Society** (1835)

Centre de Hautes Etudes sur l'Afrique et l'Asie Modernes
See: **Center for Advanced Studies on Modern Africa and Asia** (3205)

★3244★
Center for Health Affairs - Greater Cleveland Hospital Association Library (Med)
Playhouse Square
1226 Huron Rd. Phone: (216)696-6900
Cleveland, OH 44115 Dorothy R. Leicht, Asst.Libn.
Staff: 1. **Subjects:** Administration of health care facilities; hospital administration; health services - planning, education, statistics, demographics; association management. **Special Collections:** Metropolitan Health Planning Corporation Archives; Greater Cleveland Hospital Association Archives. **Holdings:** 5000 books; 70 bound periodical volumes; 50 shelves of other cataloged items; 10 VF drawers of reports and newsletters; annual reports. **Subscriptions:** 261 journals and other serials. **Services:** Interlibrary loan; copying; library open to the public by appointment. **Remarks:** FAX: (216)696-1837.

Center for Health Management Studies
See: **Rush University** (14149)

★3245★
Center for the History of American Needlework - Library (Rec)
Box 359 Phone: (412)586-5325
Valencia, PA 16059 Mary Ann Geiger, Ed.
Founded: 1975. **Staff:** Prof 1. **Subjects:** Needlework, embroidery, lacemaking, textile fabrics, weaving, spinning, costume. **Holdings:** 3500 volumes; 3500 slides; textile collection. **Services:** Library open to the public for reference use only. **Publications:** Bibliographies and reference books on textile subjects; Victorian patterns on knit & crochet.

Center for the History of Foot Care and Footwear
See: **Pennsylvania College of Podiatric Medicine** (12839)

Center for History of Physics
See: **American Institute of Physics - Center for History of Physics** (641)

Center for Holocaust Studies
See: **A Living Memorial to the Holocaust - Museum of Jewish Heritage - Documentation & Research Library** (9231)

Centre Hospitalier Christ-Roi - Bibliotheque Medicale
See: **Christ-Roi Hospital - Library** (3628)

★3246★
Centre Hospitalier Cooke - Bibliotheque Medicale et Administrative (Med)
3450, rue Ste-Marguerite Phone: (819)375-7713
Trois-Rivieres, PQ, Canada G8Z 1X3 Claudette Groleau, Biblio.
Staff: Prof 1. **Subjects:** Medicine, allied health sciences, administration. **Holdings:** 5000 volumes. **Subscriptions:** 145 journals and other serials. **Services:** Interlibrary loan; library not open to the public. **Special Catalogs:** Catalogue Collectif des Periodiques des Bibliotheques de Sante et des Services Sociaux de la Region 04.

★3247★
Centre Hospitalier Cote-des-Neiges - Bibliotheque (Med)
4565, chemin de la Reine-Marie Phone: (514)340-1424
Montreal, PQ, Canada H3W 1W5 Louise Bourbonnais, Chf.Libn.
Founded: 1947. **Staff:** Prof 1; Other 1. **Subjects:** Geriatrics, chronic care and allied specialties, neurolinguistics, brain disorders. **Holdings:** 4000 books. **Subscriptions:** 185 journals and other serials; 14 newspapers. **Services:** Interlibrary loan; copying; center open to the public for reference use only. **Computerized Information Services:** MEDLARS; Ad Hoc Biblio (internal database). **Networks/Consortia:** Member of Association des Bibliotheques de la Sante Affiliees a l'Universite de Montreal (ABSAUM). **Remarks:** FAX: (514)340-3500. **Staff:** Josee Legault, Techn.

★3248★
Centre Hospitalier Hotel-Dieu de Gaspe - Centre de Documentation (Med)
C.P. 120 Phone: (418)368-3301
Havre de Gaspe, PQ, Canada G0C 1R0 Mathilda Adams, Resp.
Founded: 1962. **Staff:** 1. **Subjects:** Medicine, surgery, pharmacy, radiology, cardiology, nursing, obstetrics. **Holdings:** 1000 books. **Subscriptions:** 85 journals and other serials. **Services:** Interlibrary loan; copying; center open to local health institution only. **Computerized Information Services:** BRS/COLLEAGUE. **Publications:** Radar, 3/year - for internal distribution only. **Remarks:** FAX: (418)368-6850.

★3249★
Centre Hospitalier Hotel-Dieu de Sherbrooke - Bibliotheque (Med)
580 S. Bowen St. Phone: (819)569-2551
Sherbrooke, PQ, Canada J1G 2E8 Nicole Fontaine, Doc.Techn.
Founded: 1954. **Staff:** 1. **Subjects:** Medicine, medical specialties, hospital administration, nursing. **Holdings:** 2700 books; 3800 unbound and bound periodical volumes; 980 cassettes; 30 videotapes. **Subscriptions:** 161 journals and other serials. **Services:** Interlibrary loan; copying; library open to medical personnel and students. **Remarks:** FAX: (819)822-6764.

★3250★
Centre Hospitalier Jacques-Viger - Centre de Documentation (Med)
1051 St. Hubert St.
Montreal, PQ, Canada H2L 3Y5 Phone: (514)842-7181
Founded: 1960. **Staff:** 1. **Subjects:** Geriatrics, gerontology, medicine, long term care, nursing. **Holdings:** 300 books; 600 bound periodical volumes; 200 brochures. **Subscriptions:** 50 journals and other serials. **Services:** Interlibrary loan; center not open to the public.

★3251★
Centre Hospitalier de la Region de l'Amiante - Bibliotheque Medicale (Med)
1717 rue Notre-Dame N. Phone: (418)338-7777
Thetford Mines, PQ, Canada G6G 2V4 Jacinthe Ouellet, Biblio.
Founded: 1971. **Staff:** Prof 1. **Subjects:** Medicine, nursing, administration. **Holdings:** 2000 books; AV programs. **Subscriptions:** 252 journals and other serials. **Services:** Library open to the public with restrictions. **Special Indexes:** Index of French periodicals (card). **Remarks:** FAX: (418)335-7673.

★3252★
Centre Hospitalier Regional de Lanaudiere - Bibliotheque Medicale (Med)
1000 Ste-Anne Blvd. Phone: (514)759-8222
Joliette, PQ, Canada J6E 6J2 Francine Garneau, Biblio.
Staff: Prof 1; Other 1. **Subjects:** Medicine, psychiatry, addictions, psychology, social work, nursing, hospital administration. **Holdings:** 15,000 volumes; 393 other cataloged items; 400 cassettes. **Subscriptions:** 250 journals and other serials. **Services:** Interlibrary loan; copying; library open to the public for reference use only. **Remarks:** FAX: (514)759-7969.

★3253★
Centre Hospitalier Robert-Giffard - Bibliotheque Professionnelle (Med)
2601, de la Canardiere Phone: (418)663-5300
Beauport, PQ, Canada G1J 2G3 Yolande Plamondon, Techn.
Founded: 1927. **Staff:** Prof 1; Other 2. **Subjects:** Psychiatry, neurology, general medicine, psychology, social sciences, nursing. **Holdings:** 9750 books; 5000 bound periodical volumes; 35 magnetic tapes; 150 videocassettes. **Subscriptions:** 110 journals and other serials. **Services:** Interlibrary loan; copying; library open to the public for reference use only. **Computerized Information Services:** MEDLINE.

★3254★
Centre Hospitalier St-Joseph - Bibliotheque Medicale et Administrative (Med)
731, rue Ste-Julie Phone: (819)379-8112
Trois-Rivieres, PQ, Canada G9A 1Y1 Solange De Rouyn, Chf.
Founded: 1961. **Staff:** Prof 1. **Subjects:** Medicine, administration. **Holdings:** 4773 books; 1277 bound periodical volumes. **Subscriptions:** 231 journals and other serials. **Services:** Interlibrary loan (fee); copying; library open to the public for reference use only. **Remarks:** FAX: (819)372-3581.

Centre Hospitalier Thoracique de Montreal
See: **Montreal Chest Hospital Centre** (10695)

★3255★
Centre Hospitalier de l'Universite Laval - Bibliotheque des Sciences de la Sante (Med)
2705, blvd. Sir Wilfred Laurier Phone: (418)656-8188
Ste. Foy, PQ, Canada G1V 4G2 Beatrice Dionne, Chf.
Staff: 2. **Subjects:** Medicine, allied health sciences. **Holdings:** 5000 books; 1300 bound periodical volumes. **Subscriptions:** 400 journals and other serials. **Services:** Interlibrary loan; copying; library open to the public on fee basis. **Special Catalogs:** Catalog of health sciences periodicals of the Quebec region.

★3256★
Centre Hospitalier de Verdun - Bibliotheque Medicale (Med)
4000 Blvd. LaSalle Phone: (514)765-8121
Verdun, PQ, Canada H4G 2A3 Mrs. Andree N. Mandeville, Libn.
Staff: Prof 1; Other 2. **Subjects:** Medicine. **Holdings:** 2000 books; 8200 bound periodical volumes. **Subscriptions:** 150 journals and other serials. **Services:** Library open to the public with restrictions.

Centre for Human Settlements
See: **United Nations - Centre for Human Settlements (Habitat)** (16750)

★3257★
Center for Humane Options in Childbirth Experiences (CHOICE) - Library (Med)
5426 Madison St.
Hilliard, OH 43026 Abby Kinne, Founder
Founded: 1977. **Staff:** Prof 4; Other 8. **Subjects:** Home birth, Lamaze method, natural childbirth, breast feeding, birth alternatives, nutrition, midwifery, Monitrice program for hospital coaches. **Holdings:** 400 books; films; pamphlets; statistical reports. **Services:** Library open to the public.

★3258★
Center for Immigration Policy and Refugee Assistance - Library (Soc Sci)
Georgetown University
Hoya Sta., Box 2298 Phone: (202)298-0213
Washington, DC 20057 Mary Ann Larkin
Founded: 1981. **Staff:** 2. **Subjects:** U.S. immigration, international migration. **Holdings:** 2000 volumes. **Services:** Library open to the public. **Computerized Information Services:** Internal database. **Publications:** HMP Newsletter, irregular - free upon request; papers on international migration, irregular. **Remarks:** FAX: (202)338-0572.

Centre d'Information et de Documentation en Agronomie des Regions Chaudes
See: **Centre de Cooperation Internationale en Recherche Agronomique pour le Developpement - Centre d'Information et de Documentation en Agronomie des Regions Chaudes** (3224)

Center for Information and Numerical Data Analysis and Synthesis
See: **Purdue University - CINDAS** (13536)

★3259★
Centre International des Civilisations Bantu - Library (Area-Ethnic)
B.P. 700 Phone: 723314
Libreville, Gabon Pierre Dandjinov, Hd., Info & Doc.
Founded: 1985. **Staff:** 8. **Subjects:** Bantu culture and origins. **Holdings:** 7000 volumes. **Subscriptions:** 70 journals and other serials; 10 newspapers. **Services:** Copying; SDI; library open to the public with restrictions on borrowing. **Computerized Information Services:** DOCUM, ANNU (internal databases). **Publications:** Acquisition lists; Ethnic Lexicon. **Special Catalogs:** Thematic catalogs. **Staff:** Raphael Essaba; Jean Baptist Adjogobo; Jeannette Divagou.

Centre International de Documentation Parlementaire (CIDP)
See: **International Centre for Parliamentary Documentation** (8073)

Centre International de l'Enfance
See: **International Children's Centre - Documentation Department** (8080)

★3260★
Center for International Financial Analysis and Research, Inc. (CIFAR) (Bus-Fin)
211 College Rd., E. Phone: (609)520-9333
Princeton, NJ 08540 Dr. Vinod B. Bavishi, Exec.Dir.
Founded: 1984. **Staff:** Prof 2; Other 5. **Subjects:** International finance and accounting. **Holdings:** Books; annual and quarterly reports from 10,000 leading companies worldwide; global company financial directories; foreign stock exchange publications; worldwide stock prices; periodicals; dictionaries; dissertations; other cataloged items; worldwide business newspapers. **Services:** Copying; center open to the public. **Automated Operations:** Computerized public access catalog and cataloging. **Computerized Information Services:** International Companies Financial Database. **Remarks:** FAX: (609)520-0905. Telex: 6716479. **Staff:** Arlene W. Goldhammer, Mgr., Ref.Serv.

★3261★
Centre International de Hautes Etudes Agronomiques Mediterraneennes - Institut Agronomique Mediterraneen - Centre de Documentation Mediterraneen (Agri)
3191 Route de Mende
B.P. 5056
F-34033 Montpellier Cedex 1, Phone: 67 632880
France Mrs. M.L. Leclerc, Hd. of Doc.Ctr.
Founded: 1963. **Staff:** Prof 3; Other 2. **Subjects:** Mediterranean countries, international economics, agricultural policy, rural development, agro-industry, statistics. **Holdings:** 43,000 books; 1640 microfiche; 1175 AV items. **Subscriptions:** 310 journals and other serials; 3 newspapers. **Services:** Interlibrary loan; copying; library open to the public with accession card. **Computerized Information Services:** DIALOG Information Services, Europeenne de Donnees, SUNIST; MEDIT, EDUCAGRI, CIHEAM (internal databases). **Publications:** Docmed (bibliography of Mediterranean documents), annual; Liste Bimestrielle des Acquisitions; bibliographies (agricultural policy, food industry, range management). **Remarks:** FAX: 67542527. Telex: 480 783 F.

★3262★
Center for International Policy (Soc Sci)
1755 Massachusetts Ave., N.W., Suite 324 Phone: (202)232-3317
Washington, DC 20036 William Goodfellow, Dir.
Founded: 1975. **Staff:** Prof 4; Other 2. **Subjects:** United States human rights policy and economic and military aid, Central American Peace Process. **Special Collections:** Collection of documents pertaining to peace negotiations in Central America, especially Contadora and Arias plans; human rights portfolio explaining laws affecting foreign aid. **Holdings:** Figures not available. **Subscriptions:** 20 journals and other serials. **Services:** Center open to the public with permission. **Remarks:** FAX: (202)232-3440. **Staff:** Jim Morrell, Res.Dir.; Robert White, Pres.

Centre International de Recherche en Amenagement Linguistique
See: **Universite Laval** (18067)

★3263★
Centre Introducing Literature and Samples of New Foreign Products - Technical Library (Bus-Fin)
1 Fu Xing Men Wai St.
P.O. Box 1420
Beijing 100027, People's Republic of China Phone: 1 481704
Subjects: Foreign trade in China. **Holdings:** 10,000 volumes. **Remarks:** Telex: 210214 CEXHN CN.

★3264★
Center for Investigative Reporting - Library (Info Sci)
530 Howard St., 2nd Fl. Phone: (415)543-1200
San Francisco, CA 94105 Dan Noyes, Mng.Ed.
Founded: 1977. **Staff:** 12. **Subjects:** Regulatory agencies, agriculture, environment, military issues, health and safety, freedom of information, Asian crime. **Special Collections:** Investigative methodology collection. **Holdings:** 1000 books and methodology files; 200 videotapes. **Subscriptions:** 50 journals and other serials; 6 newspapers. **Services:** Copying (limited); library open to the public at librarian's discretion. **Publications:** Bibliography, annual - free upon request; Investigative Reports, annual - for sale. **Remarks:** FAX: (415)543-8311. **Staff:** Barbara Newcombe, Libn.

Center for Korean Studies
See: **University of Hawaii - Center for Korean Studies** (18618)

★3265★
Centre for Latin American Monetary Studies - Library (Bus-Fin)
Durango 54
Delegacion Cuauhtemoc
06700 Mexico City DF, Mexico Phone: 5 5330300
Subjects: Latin American economics - monetary and financial policies and procedures. **Holdings:** 125,900 reviews, magazines, and other items. **Services:** Interlibrary loan; library open to the public. **Remarks:** FAX: 5 5146554. Cable: CEMLA. Telex: 1771229 CEMLME. **Staff:** Claudio M. Antonovich; Genoveva de Maria y Campos; Alejandra Galicia Becerril.

Center for Latin American and Tropical Art
See: **University of Florida** (18562)

Center for Legislative Archives (NNL)
See: **National Archives & Records Administration** (11025)

★3266★
Center for Libertarian Studies (Soc Sci)
Box 4091 Phone: (415)692-8456
Burlingame, CA 94011-4091 Burton Blumert, Pres.
Subjects: Libertarianism. **Holdings:** 2000 books; 300 unbound periodicals. **Subscriptions:** 12 journals and other serials. **Services:** Center open to the public. **Remarks:** FAX: (415)342-9164.

Center for Magnetic Recording Research
See: **University of California, San Diego** (18415)

Center for Manufacturing Productivity and Technology Transfer
See: **Rensselaer Polytechnic Institute** (13819)

★3267★
Center for Mathematics and Computer Science - Library (Sci-Engr, Comp Sci)
Kruislaan 413 Phone: 20 5929333
NL-1098 SJ Amsterdam, Netherlands Frank A. Roos, Libn.
Founded: 1946. **Staff:** 8.5. **Subjects:** Pure and numerical mathematics, applied statistics, mathematical statistics, operations research, systems analysis, computer science. **Holdings:** 150,000 volumes. **Subscriptions:** 1400 journals. **Services:** Interlibrary loan; copying; SDI; library open to the public. **Computerized Information Services:** DIALOG Information Services, ESA/IRS, STN International; USENET (electronic mail service). **Remarks:** FAX: 20 5924199. Telex: 12571 MACTR NL. Electronic mail address(es): karin@avi.nl; ay@cwi.nl; faroos@cwi.nl (USENET). Library is the central library on mathematics and computer science in the Netherlands. Center is maintained by Netherlands Organization for Scientific Research - Stichting Mathematisch Centrum. **Also Known As:** Centrum voor Wiskunde en Informatica (CIS); Shichting Mathematisch Centrum.

★3268★
Center for Medical Consumers and Health Information - Consumer's Medical Library (Med)
237 Thompson St. Phone: (212)674-7105
New York, NY 10012 Arthur Levin, Dir.
Founded: 1977. **Staff:** 3. **Subjects:** Medicine, health, nutrition. **Holdings:** 1500 books; subject files. **Subscriptions:** 58 journals and other serials. **Services:** Library open to the public. **Publications:** HEALTHFACTS, monthly - by subscription.

Center for Medieval and Early Renaissance Studies
See: **State University of New York at Binghamton** (15729)

Center for Mennonite Brethren Studies
See: **Fresno Pacific College & Mennonite Brethren Biblical Seminary - Hiebert Library** (6162)

★3269★
Center for Mental Health - Library (Med)
2020 Brown St.
Box 1258 Phone: (317)649-8161
Anderson, IN 46015 Rebecca Wallace, Libn.
Staff: 1. **Subjects:** Family therapy, violence, stress management, psychiatry, psychology, social work. **Holdings:** 600 books. **Subscriptions:** 15 journals and other serials; 7 newspapers. **Services:** Interlibrary loan; library. **Remarks:** FAX: (317)641-8238.

Center for Meteorite Studies
See: **Arizona State University** (1010)

★3270★
Center for Migration Studies - CMS Library (Soc Sci, Area-Ethnic)
209 Flagg Place Phone: (718)351-8800
Staten Island, NY 10304-1199 Diana J. Zimmerman, Hd., CMS Lib.
Founded: 1964. **Staff:** Prof 1; Other 3. **Subjects:** International migration, refugees, ethnicity, ethnic groups in the U.S. **Special Collections:** CMS refugee holdings (2500 entries); 86 archival collections pertaining primarily to the Italian-American experience including L'Archivio del Commissariato Generale dell'Emigrazione (84 reels of microfilm); L'Archivio del Prelato per l'Emigrazione Italiana (28 reels of microfilm); ethnic press (microfilm). **Holdings:** 22,500 volumes; 3600 reports; 285 reels of microfilm of archival material; 500 dissertations on microfilm; manuscripts. **Subscriptions:** 250 journals and other serials; 40 newspapers; 180 newsletters. **Services:** Copying; center open to the public. **Publications:** Directory of International Study Centers, Research Programs and Library Resources, 1987; Refugees: Holdings of the Center for Migration Studies Library/Archives, 1987; Guides to CMS Archives, 1974-1988. **Remarks:** FAX: (718)667-4598.

★3271★
Center for Modern Psychoanalytic Studies - Library (Med)
16 W. 10th St. Phone: (212)260-7050
New York, NY 10011 Cyril Z. Meadow, Dir.
Founded: 1971. **Staff:** Prof 2; Other 2. **Subjects:** Psychoanalysis, psychology, psychiatry, sociology, anthropology. **Special Collections:** Bound psychoanalytic research projects of center's graduates and other institute graduates' research. **Holdings:** 5000 books; 300 lecture tapes. **Subscriptions:** 16 journals and other serials. **Services:** Library open for research by appointment.

★3272★
Center for Molecular Nutrition and Sensory Disorders - Library (Sci-Engr)
Taste and Smell Clinic
5125 MacArthur Blvd., N.W. Phone: (202)364-4180
Washington, DC 20016 Robert I. Henkin
Founded: 1970. **Staff:** Prof 1; Other 1. **Subjects:** Taste and smell physiology and pathology. **Holdings:** 150 books; 300 bound periodical volumes; 400 reports; 3000 xerox copies of books and periodicals related to issues of taste and olfaction. **Subscriptions:** 3 journals and other serials. **Services:** Library open to the public with restrictions. **Remarks:** Library is said to be one of the largest collection of information related to taste and smell in the United States.

Centre for Monarchical Studies
See: **Monarchist League of Canada - Centre for Monarchical Studies - King George III Memorial Library** (10601)

Centre de Musique Canadienne
See: **Canadian Music Centre** (2965)

Centre National d'Etudes des Telecommunications - Service de Documentation Interministerielle
See: **France - National Telecommunications Research Center - Interministerial Documentation Service** (6071)

★3273★
Centre National de la Recherche Scientifique - Bibliotheque de Sociologie du CNRS (Soc Sci)
59, 61 rue Pouchet Phone: 1 40 25 11 80
F-75849 Paris Cedex 17, France Blandine Veith, Libn.
Staff: Prof 11. **Subjects:** Sociology. **Holdings:** 40,000 books. **Subscriptions:** 620 journals and other serials. **Services:** Interlibrary loan; copying; library open to social science researchers and students. **Special Catalogs:** Catalogue Collectif des Ouvrages Etrangers; Catalogue Collectif National (periodiques). **Remarks:** FAX: 1 42 28 95 44. **Staff:** Francoise Picard, Libn.; Marie Noelle Postic, Libn.; Jean Claude Darbois, Libn.; Beatrice De Peyret, Libn.

Center for National Security Studies
See: **American Civil Liberties Union - ACLU/CNSS Library** (525)

★3274★
Center for Naval Analyses - Library (Mil, Sci-Engr)
4401 Ford Ave.
Alexandria, VA 22302-0268 Phone: (703)824-2096
Staff: Prof 3; Other 2. **Subjects:** Naval science, systems analysis, statistics, mathematics, military science, operations research, economics. **Holdings:** 18,000 books; 1000 bound periodical volumes; 2000 Congressional documents. **Subscriptions:** 400 journals and other serials; 8 newspapers. **Services:** Interlibrary loan; library not open to the public. **Automated Operations:** Computerized cataloging and serials. **Computerized Information Services:** DIALOG Information Services, NEXIS, OCLC, Faxon. **Networks/Consortia:** Member of CAPCON Library Network, Interlibrary Users Association (IUA). **Publications:** New Books, monthly; List of Journal Holdings, quarterly. **Remarks:** Center is a federally funded research and development center. FAX: (703)824-2949. **Staff:** James T. Higgins, Ref.Libn.; Alyson Danowski, ILL.

★3275★
Center for Neurodevelopmental Studies, Inc. - Library (Med)
8434 N. 39th Ave.
Phoenix, AZ 85051-4778 Phone: (602)433-1400
Founded: 1978. **Subjects:** Autism, sensory systems, neurodevelopment, special education. **Holdings:** 350 volumes.

Centre for Newfoundland Studies
See: **Memorial University of Newfoundland - Queen Elizabeth II Library** (10055)

★3276★
Center for Northern Studies (CNS) - Library (Sci-Engr)
Town Hill Rd. Phone: (802)888-4331
Wolcott, VT 05680 Lisa Delepine, Libn.
Founded: 1971. **Staff:** Prof 3. **Subjects:** Arctic and subarctic cultures, quaternary paleoecology, social systems of Arctic and subarctic, archeology of indigenous peoples of the Arctic and subarctic, resource law and policy, physical systems of northern regions. **Special Collections:** History of Arctic exploration. **Holdings:** 13,000 books; 60 newsletter files; 60 reels of microfilm; 1000 reprints of scientific papers; 5000 specimen herbarium; 650 maps. **Subscriptions:** 130 journals and other serials; 5 newspapers. **Services:** Interlibrary loan; copying; library open to the public with restrictions. **Staff:** Dr. Steven B. Young, Dir.

★3277★
Centre for Pacific Development and Training - Learning Resources Centre (Soc Sci)
Middle Head Rd. Phone: 2 9609563
Mosman, NSW 2091, Australia Craig Boaden, Mgr., Rsrcs.Dev. Unit
Founded: 1946. **Staff:** 3. **Subjects:** Developing countries, economic development, education, management, rural development, public administration. **Special Collections:** Rare book collection (500); Hallstrom Pacific Library. **Holdings:** 25,000 books; 10,000 bound periodical volumes; 1000 AV programs and microforms. **Subscriptions:** 250 journals and other serials; 10 newspapers. **Services:** Interlibrary loan; copying; SDI; library open to the public. **Computerized Information Services:** ABN (Australian Bibliographic Network), OZLINE: Australian Information Network; internal database. **Remarks:** FAX: 2 9602942. Telex: AA27293. A part of the Australian International Development Assistance Bureau (AIDAB). **Staff:** Janis Papanicolaou.

Center for Pacific Northwest Studies
See: **Western Washington University** (20305)

★3278★
Centre Populaire de Documentation (Soc Sci)
1265, Berri, Bureau 840 Phone: (514)845-3490
Montreal, PQ, Canada H2L 4X4 Carl Gauthier, Coord./Libn.
Founded: 1977. **Staff:** Prof 1; Other 3. **Subjects:** Working and social conditions. **Special Collections:** Unions and Popular Groups, 1970 to present (2000 posters); popular groups archives. **Holdings:** 10,000 books; 610 bound periodical volumes; 400 thematic files; 20 reels of microfilm. **Subscriptions:** 80 journals and other serials; 10 newspapers. **Services:** Copying; center open to the public. **Automated Operations:** Computerized cataloging. **Computerized Information Services:** Internal databases. **Publications:** Revue de Presse du CPD, monthly; bibliographies. **Remarks:** FAX: (514)844-1598.

★3279★
Center for Population Options - Resource Center (Soc Sci)
1025 Vermont Ave., N.W., Suite 210 Phone: (202)347-5700
Washington, DC 20005 Janet Riessman, Pub.Educ.Coord.
Founded: 1982. **Staff:** 1. **Subjects:** Adolescent fertility issues - sexuality education, birth control, teenage pregnancy and child bearing, teenage pregnancy prevention, health, sexually transmitted diseases and human immunodeficiency virus (HIV) among adolescents, condom availability; school-based clinics; adolescent reproductive health. **Holdings:** 2500 volumes. **Subscriptions:** 150 journals and other serials; 2 newspapers. **Services:** Library open to the public by appointment. **Publications:** List of publications - available on request. **Remarks:** FAX: (202)347-2263.

★3280★
Center to Prevent Handgun Violence - Library (Soc Sci, Law)
1225 Eye St., N.W., Suite 1100 Phone: (202)289-7319
Washington, DC 20005 Vanessa Scherzer, Asst.Dir. of Pub.Educ.
Founded: 1983. **Staff:** Prof 1. **Subjects:** Handgun violence, teenage suicide, firearms litigation, crime, accidental shootings, Second Amendment, gun control, foreign gun control laws, children and guns. **Holdings:** 1000 articles; 8 VF; videotapes. **Subscriptions:** 6 journals and other serials. **Services:** Copying; SDI; library open to the public by appointment. **Computerized Information Services:** Internal database. **Remarks:** FAX: (202)408-1851.

★3281★
Center for Process Studies - Library (Rel-Phil)
1325 N. College Ave.
Claremont, CA 91711 Phone: (714)626-3521
Founded: 1973. **Staff:** Prof 2. **Subjects:** Holistic worldview, organicism, systematic philosophy, philosophical metaphysics, panentheism, neo-classical theism, constructive postmodern theology and world order. **Special Collections:** Alfred North Whitehead Collection (primary materials); Charles Hartshorne Collection; Daniel Day Williams Collection. **Holdings:** 1430 books; 5800 articles; 335 dissertations. **Subscriptions:** 18 journals and other serials. **Services:** Copying; library open to the public. **Publications:** Alfred North Whitehead: A Primary-Secondary Bibliography, 1977. **Remarks:** Affiliated with the School of Theology at Claremont and The Claremont Graduate School. **Staff:** John Quiring, Libn.

Center for Public Affairs Research - Library
See: **University of Nebraska, Omaha - Center for Public Affairs Research - Library** (19006)

★3282★
Centre de Readaptation Constance-Lethbridge - Medical Library (Med)
7005, blvd. de Maisonneuve, W. Phone: (514)487-1770
Montreal, PQ, Canada H4B 1T3 Jane Petrov, Libn.
Staff: Prof 1. **Subjects:** Rehabilitation medicine, physical and occupational therapy, vocational rehabilitation, psychology, speech. **Holdings:** 2500 books; 1000 bound periodical volumes. **Subscriptions:** 80 journals and other serials. **Services:** Interlibrary loan; copying; library open to the public. **Networks/Consortia:** Member of McGill Medical and Health Libraries Association (MMHLA). **Also Known As:** Constance-Lethbridge Rehabilitation Centre.

Centre de Recherche et d'Etudes sur les Societes Mediterraneennes
See: **Institut de Recherches et d'Etudes sur le Monde Arabe et Musulman** (7885)

★3283★
Centre de Recherche Industrielle du Quebec - Industrie Information (Sci-Engr)
8475, rue Christophe Colomb
P.O. Box 2000
Montreal, PQ, Canada H2P 2X1 Phone: (514)383-3250
Founded: 1985. **Subjects:** Electronics, robotics, industrial research, automation. **Special Collections:** Canadian patents. **Holdings:** 4000 books. **Subscriptions:** 250 journals and other serials; 5 newspapers. **Services:** Interlibrary loan; copying; SDI; open to the public on contract basis. **Automated Operations:** Computerized cataloging and circulation. **Computerized Information Services:** DIALOG Information Services, PFDS Online, BRS Information Technologies, Questel, CAN/OLE, STN International, Food RA Online Scientific and Technical Information (FROSTI), European KOMPASS Online (EKOL), Data-Star, SDM Inc.; Banque d'Information Industrielle (internal database); Envoy 100 (electronic mail service). Performs searches on fee basis. Contact Person: Carola Lamouraux, Libn. **Publications:** Acquisitions list. **Remarks:** FAX: (514)383-3238. Telex: 05-827887. Electronic mail address(es): QMCRI.PEB (Envoy 100).

★3284★
Centre de Recherche Industrielle du Quebec - Ste-Foy Branch - Industrie Information (Sci-Engr)
333, rue Franquet Phone: (418)659-1550
Ste. Foy, PQ, Canada G1V 4C7 Madeleine Savard, Chef de Groupe
Founded: 1970. **Staff:** Prof 6; Other 1. **Subjects:** Industrial research - materials, mechanics, biotechnology, energy; chemistry; wood technology; metallurgy. **Special Collections:** Industrial standards. **Holdings:** 16,000 books; standards. **Subscriptions:** 600 journals and other serials; 10 newspapers. **Services:** Interlibrary loan; copying; SDI; open to the public on a contractual basis. **Automated Operations:** Computerized public access catalog, cataloging, serials, and circulation. **Computerized Information Services:** DIALOG Information Services, PFDS Online, STN International, Infomart Online, BRS Information Technologies, CAN/OLE, QL Systems, Questel, Information Retrieval Service (IRS), European KOMPASS Online (EKOL), Food RA Online Scientific and Technical Information (FROSTI), Data-Star, SDM Inc.; Banque d'Information Industrielle, SOURCES (internal databases); Envoy 100 (electronic mail service). Performs searches on fee basis. **Publications:** Liste des nouvelles acquisitions. **Remarks:** FAX: (418)652-2225. Telex: 051-31569. Electronic mail address(es): QSFCR.PEB (Envoy 100). **Also Known As:** Industrial Research Center of Quebec.

★3285★
Centre de Recherche Lionel-Groulx (Hist)
261, Bloomfield Phone: (514)271-4759
Outremont, PQ, Canada H2V 3R6 Jean-Pierre Chalifoux
Founded: 1976. **Staff:** 6. **Subjects:** History, Canadian history, French literature, methodology, pedagogy, sociology, philosophy. **Special Collections:** Revue d'histoire de l'Amerique francaise. **Holdings:** 10,000 books; 200 unbound periodicals; 5000 small volumes of writings, classified and in envelopes. **Subscriptions:** 152 journals and other serials. **Services:** Copying; center open to the public with restrictions. **Computerized Information Services:** CDS-ISIS (internal database). **Remarks:** FAX: (514)271-6369.

Centre de Recherche Oceanographiques de Dakar-Thiaroye
See: **Dakar-Thiaroye Center for Oceanographic Research** (4526)

★3286★
Centre de Recherches en Relations Humaines - Bibliotheque (Soc Sci)
2715 Cote St. Catherine Rd. Phone: (514)738-8076
Montreal, PQ, Canada H3T 1B6 Noel Mailloux, Dir./Prof. Emeritus
Founded: 1950. **Staff:** 1. **Subjects:** Psychology, social sciences, criminology. **Holdings:** 35,000 books; 12,000 bound periodical volumes. **Subscriptions:** 250 journals and other serials. **Services:** Library open to the public with restrictions.

★3287★
Center for Reformation Research - Library (Hist)
6477 San Bonita Ave. Phone: (314)727-6655
St. Louis, MO 63105 Dr. William Maltby, Exec.Dir.
Founded: 1957. **Staff:** Prof 1; Other 3. **Subjects:** History - Reformation, Renaissance, early modern, late medieval. **Special Collections:** Manuscripts on microfilm; political archives of Philip of Hesse; Simmler Collection (Zurich Reformation); Baum Collection (Strassburg Reformation). **Holdings:** 2500 books; 1650 reels of microfilm; 1500 microcards. **Subscriptions:** 10 journals and other serials. **Services:** Interlibrary loan; copying; library open to the public. **Publications:** Sixteenth Century Bibliography.

★3288★
Center for Religion, Ethics & Social Policy - Anne Carry Durland Memorial Alternatives Library (Soc Sci)
127 Anabel Taylor Hall
Cornell University Phone: (607)255-6486
Ithaca, NY 14853 Lynn Andersen, Libn.
Founded: 1974. **Staff:** Prof 2; Other 2. **Subjects:** Afro-America, alternative education, farming & organic gardening, gay & lesbian issues, holistic health, international issues, Native America, disarmament, empowerment, environmental issues, human rights, new age movement, psychology, sexuality, gender, spiritualtiy, women's studies. **Special Collections:** Eco-justice, environment, peace movement, Native Americans, counter-culture; South African investment (2200 periodicals, newsletters, and ephemera). **Holdings:** 6700 books; 550 audio and AV tapes. **Subscriptions:** 260 journals and other serials. **Services:** Interlibrary loan; copying; library open to the public; reserve services for groups committed to contemporary issues; special lending to incarcerated individuals. **Computerized Information Services:** Q&A (internal database).

Center for Renaissance Studies
See: **Concentus Musicus - Center for Renaissance Studies** (4109)

Center for Research and Documentation of East European Jewry
See: **Hebrew University of Jerusalem - Society for Research on Jewish Communities** (7104)

★3289★
Center for Research Libraries (Info Sci)
6050 S. Kenwood Ave. Phone: (312)955-4545
Chicago, IL 60637 Donald B. Simpson, Pres.
Founded: 1949. **Staff:** Prof 16; Other 45. **Subjects:** Foreign doctoral dissertations; U.S. and foreign newspapers; foreign scientific and technical journals; archival materials on microfilm; state documents; infrequently used research materials. **Special Collections:** Russian Academy of Science publications, 1958 to present. **Holdings:** 3 million volumes; 58,000 children's books; backfiles of 241,000 college catalogs for 2000 schools; 85,000 primary and secondary textbooks; 600,000 foreign doctoral dissertations. **Subscriptions:** 13,400 journals and other serials; 300 newspapers. **Services:** Interlibrary loan; copying; center open to personnel of member institutions. **Computerized Information Services:** OCLC, RLIN; ALANET (electronic mail service). **Publications:** Focus newsletter; Handbook. **Remarks:** FAX: (312)955-4339. Electronic mail address(es): ALA1553 (ALANET). Functions as a resource center for member libraries of Center for Research Libraries (CRL). **Staff:** Emma Davis, Dir., Access Serv.; Marjorie Bloss, Dir., Tech.Serv.; Ray Boylan, Dir., Coll.Resrcs.; Marlys Rudeen, Hd., Acq.Dept.; Patricia Finney, Hd., Stack Mgt.; Esther Smith, Coll.Dev.Libn.; Linda Naru, Plan./Dev.Off.; Andrew Bullen, Hd., Circ.Dept.

★3290★
Center for the Rights of the Terminally Ill - Resource Library (Soc Sci)
3308 Glade Creek Dr. Phone: (817)656-5143
Hurst, TX 76054 Julie A. Grimstad, Exec.Dir.
Founded: 1985. **Staff:** 1. **Subjects:** Euthanasia and infanticide, "Right to Die" court cases, patients' rights, suicide, death and dying, death education, care of the elderly. **Special Collections:** Dr. Joseph R. Stanton Collection (speeches, articles, and letters; 1970-1991); overviews of all "Right to Die" court cases since 1975; analysis and information on 43 living will-related laws. **Holdings:** 50 books; 17 bound periodical volumes; 15,000 newspaper and magazine articles; 20 AV programs. **Subscriptions:** 5 journals and other serials; 4 newspapers. **Services:** Copying; library open to the public by appointment. **Publications:** CRTI REPORT (newsletter); Can Cancer Pain Be Relieved (booklet); Suffering: A Key to the Meaning of Life (booklet); Living Will (brochure). **Remarks:** The Center was founded in 1985 to oppose euthanasia and assisted suicide, and to protect vulnerable patients.

★3291★
Center for Russian & East European Jewry - Students Struggle for Soviet Jewry - Archives (Area-Ethnic)
210 W. 91st St. Phone: (212)799-8900
New York, NY 10024 Glenn Richter, Natl.Coord.
Founded: 1964. **Staff:** Prof 2; Other 2. **Subjects:** Conditions and emigration of Soviet Jews. **Special Collections:** Biographical data on Soviet Jewish refuseniks and prisoners of conscience (organized by city). **Holdings:** 50 books; files; clippings. **Subscriptions:** 15 newspapers. **Services:** Copying; archives open to the public by appointment. **Publications:** Newsletter, 3/year - to the public; list of other publications - available upon request. **Staff:** Henry Gerber, Asst.Natl.Coord.

★3292★
Center for Safety in the Arts - Library (Sci-Engr)
5 Beekman St., Ste. 1030 Phone: (212)227-6220
New York, NY 10038 Dr. Michael McCann, Ph.D.
Founded: 1977. **Subjects:** Hazards in the visual arts, performing arts, educational facilities, and museums. **Holdings:** Figures not available. **Services:** Library open to the public.

★3293★
Center for Science and Environment - Library (Sci-Engr, Env-Cons)
807 Vishal Bhavan
95 Nehru Place
New Delhi 110 019, Delhi, India Phone: 11 6433394
Subjects: Science and technology in environment and development. **Holdings:** 30,000 volumes. **Also Known As:** Vigyan and Paryavaran Kendra.

Center for Science and International Affairs
See: **Harvard University - John F. Kennedy School of Government - Library** (6977)

★3294★
Center for Scientific Anomalies Research - CSAR Library (Sci-Engr)
5010 Willis Rd. Phone: (517)522-3551
Grass Lake, MI 49240 Marcello Truzzi, Dir.
Founded: 1983. **Staff:** Prof 1. **Subjects:** Scientific anomalies, psychical research, cryptozoology, UFO's, occultism, philosophy of science. **Holdings:** 8000 books; 1000 unbound periodicals; 200 audiotapes; 50 videotapes. **Subscriptions:** 20 journals and other serials. **Services:** Library open to serious researchers with permission of Director. **Publications:** Zetetic Scholar, irregular. **Remarks:** FAX: (517)522-3555.

Center for Seafarers' Rights
See: **Seamen's Church Institute of New York** (14983)

★3295★
Center for Senility Studies - Library (Med)
161 N. Dithridge St.
Pittsburgh, PA 15213 Phone: (412)683-7111
Subjects: Alzheimer's Disease, dementias, schizophrenia, brain circulation. **Holdings:** Clippings; books; research correspondence. **Services:** Library open to the public by appointment.

★3296★
Centre de Services Sociaux du Montreal Metropolitan - Centre de Documentation (Soc Sci)
1001, blvd. de Maisonneuve, E. Phone: (514)527-7261
Montreal, PQ, Canada H2L 4R5 Helene Neilson
Founded: 1955. **Staff:** Prof 1; Other 1. **Subjects:** Social service, child welfare, juvenile delinquency, child abuse, aged, psychotherapy. **Holdings:** 13,500 books; 300 periodical titles; 12 VF drawers of subject files. **Subscriptions:** 75 journals and other serials. **Services:** Interlibrary loan; copying; library open to the public at librarian's discretion. **Automated Operations:** Computerized circulation and acquisitions. **Remarks:** FAX: (514)527-4925.

★3297★
Centre de Services Sociaux de Quebec - Centre de Documentation (Soc Sci)
540 Charest Blvd., E. Phone: (418)529-7351
Quebec, PQ, Canada G1K 8L6 Lydia Chencinska, Responsable
Founded: 1975. **Staff:** Prof 2; Other 1. **Subjects:** Social service, psychology, sociology. **Special Collections:** Local history. **Holdings:** 7000 books; 150 documentary records; 70 video cassettes. **Subscriptions:** 124 journals and other serials. **Services:** Interlibrary loan; copying; SDI; center open to the public with restrictions. **Automated Operations:** Computerized cataloging, acquisitions, and circulation. **Staff:** Noelline Labrie, Doc.

Centre de Services Sociaux de Ville Marie
See: **Ville Marie Social Service Centre** (19848)

★3298★
Center on Social Welfare Policy and Law - Library (Law)
275 7th Ave., 6th Fl. Phone: (212)633-6967
New York, NY 10001 Ramon C. Curva, Dir.
Founded: 1967. **Staff:** 1. **Subjects:** Law, public assistance programs, poverty, legal services. **Holdings:** 3000 books; federal public assistance materials; 105 VF drawers of pamphlets, law reports, statutes, unpublished litigation papers. **Subscriptions:** 80 journals and other serials. **Services:** Copying; library open to the public by appointment only. **Computerized Information Services:** WESTLAW. **Publications:** Library Bulletin. **Remarks:** Primarily for the use of its staff attorneys, library is a grantee of Legal Services Corporation. FAX: (212)633-6371.

★3299★
Center for Socialist History - Library (Soc Sci, Bus-Fin)
2633 Etna St. Phone: (510)843-4658
Berkeley, CA 94704 Ernest Haberkern
Founded: 1981. **Subjects:** Socialist and labor history. **Holdings:** 20,000 books. **Services:** Library open to the public at librarian's discretion. **Publications:** Interbulletin.

★3300★
Center for Southern Folklore - Archives (Area-Ethnic, Hist)
152 Beale St. Phone: (901)525-3655
Memphis, TN 38103 Richard Raichelson, Folklorist
Founded: 1972. **Staff:** Prof 8. **Subjects:** Folklife and ethnic cultures of the Mid-South, folk music and religion, folktales, crafts, folk art and architecture, occupational lore, blues music, ethnic culture, Memphis and Mississippi River history. **Special Collections:** The Reverend L.O. Taylor Collection (documentation of Memphis black community from the late 1920s to 1977); oral histories of Beale Street entertainers and businessmen, and of the Memphis Jewish community. **Holdings:** 1000 books; 3500 unbound periodical volumes; 2000 newsletters; 1200 phonograph records; 40,000 slides; 200,000 feet of film; 40,000 photographs; 5000 hours of audiotapes. **Services:** Copying; archives open to the public by appointment. **Publications:** Images of the South: Visits with Eudora Welty and Walker Evans (first in the series); Center for Southern Folklore Update, quarterly - to members and media. **Special Catalogs:** American Folklore Films and Videotapes: A Catalog, volume 2. **Special Indexes:** American Folklore Films and Videotapes: An Index, volume 1. **Remarks:** This is "a nonprofit multimedia folklife center documenting the people and traditions of the South and producing films, records, illustrated books, slide and tape programs, concert series, conferences, and folklife festivals which present these people and traditions to large general audiences, educators, and public media." **Staff:** Judy Peiser, Exec.Dir.; Bob Pest, Mktg.Dir.; Robert Jones, Photo.

Center for Southwest Research
See: **University of New Mexico - Special Collections Department** (19047)

★3301★
Center for Strategy Research, Inc. - Library (Bus-Fin)
101 Arch St. Phone: (617)345-9500
Boston, MA 02110 Lester Wilson, Off.Mgr.
Subjects: Industrial research. **Holdings:** 200 books; 800 reports. **Subscriptions:** 10 journals and other serials. **Services:** Library not open to the public.

Center for Studies on Non-European Countries
See: **Poland - Polish Academy of Sciences** (13167)

★3302★
Center for the Study of Aging, Inc. - Library (Soc Sci)
706 Madison Ave. Phone: (518)465-6927
Albany, NY 12208 Sara Harris, Exec.Dir.
Founded: 1957. **Staff:** 3. **Subjects:** Gerontology and geriatrics, physical activity and aging, mental health and illness, environment, housing, medicine, social sciences, caregiving. **Holdings:** 4500 volumes. **Subscriptions:** 10 journals and other serials. **Services:** Library open to the public by appointment. **Special Catalogs:** Catalog I - Health, Fitness, Wellness, Recreation, Activities, Rehabilitation; Catalog II - Selected books on aging for professional and lay persons; Catalog III - Books on mental health and mental illness (including Alzheimer's), psychiatry, alcoholism, developmental disability, social work counseling, death and dying; lists of books dealing with caregiving assessment, AIDS, women, geriatric medicine, nursing, and allied health fields. **Remarks:** FAX: (518)462-1339. **Staff:** Dorothea Mantis, Mgr.

Center for the Study of Comparative Folklore and Mythology - Wayland D. Hand Library of Folklore and Mythology
See: **University of California, Los Angeles - Wayland D. Hand Library of Folklore and Mythology** (18401)

Center for the Study of the Consumer Movement
See: **Consumers Union of United States, Inc. - Library** (4248)

★3303★
Centre for the Study of Cooperatives - Co-operative Resource Centre (Bus-Fin)
Diefenbaker Centre
University of Saskatchewan Phone: (306)966-6195
Saskatoon, SK, Canada S7N 0W0 June M. Bold
Founded: 1984. **Staff:** 2. **Subjects:** Cooperatives, economics, social sciences. **Holdings:** 3000 books. **Subscriptions:** 54 journals and other serials. **Services:** Interlibrary loan; copying; center open to the public. **Automated Operations:** Computerized public access catalog and cataloging. **Computerized Information Services:** Internal database. **Remarks:** FAX: (306)966-8517. **Staff:** Leslie Polsom.

Center for the Study of Data Processing
See: **Washington University - School of Technology and Information Management - STIM/CSDP Library** (20072)

★3304★
Center for the Study of Ethics in the Professions - Library (Soc Sci)
IIT Center
Illinois Institute of Technology
3300 S. Federal St. Phone: (312)567-3017
Chicago, IL 60616 Dr. Sohair Wastawy ElBaz, Libn./Info.Res.
Founded: 1976. **Staff:** 4. **Subjects:** Professional ethics, codes, education, self-regulation, and autonomy; social responsibility, history, and sociology of professions; individual responsibility in organizations; public regulation and policy. **Special Collections:** Codes of ethics collection (800 items); referral bank of more than 400 programs and organizations (both national and international) concerned with professional ethics and allied issues. **Holdings:** 1800 books; 26 videotapes; 350 conference papers, court decisions, journal reprints, bibliographies. **Subscriptions:** 46 journals; 91 newsletters. **Services:** Copying; library open to the public. **Computerized Information Services:** DIALOG Information Services; internal databases; InterNet (electronic mail service). **Publications:** Occasional papers series, irregular; Perspectives on the Professions (newsletter), semiannual - both free upon request. **Special Catalogs:** Compilation of Statements Relating to Standards of Professional Responsibility and Freedom (b booklet); referral bank (booklet). **Remarks:** FAX: (312)567-3493. Alternate telephone number(s): 567-6913. Electronic mail address(es): CSEPELBAZ@KARL.IIT.EDU (InterNet).

Center for the Study of Federalism
See: **Temple University** (16128)

★3305★
Center for the Study of the History of Nursing (Hist)
University of Pennsylvania
307 Nursing Education Bldg. Phone: (215)898-4502
Philadelphia, PA 19104-6096 David M. Weinberg, Cur.
Founded: 1985. **Staff:** 3. **Subjects:** History of nursing, with emphasis on the Mid-Atlantic region. **Special Collections:** Manuscript collections (470 linear feet of materials including records of hospitals, schools of nursing, nursing alumni associations, voluntary non-profit associations, professional associations, and military associations); personal papers of individual practitioners, collectors, and researchers; Philadelphia General Hospital, Mercy-Douglass Hospital, and Visiting Nurse Society of Philadelphia photographic images (3000); textbooks, manuals, and histories (1000 volumes). **Holdings:** Organizational records, personal papers, printed materials, photographic images, oral histories, artifacts, magnetic media. **Services:** Center open to the public. **Computerized Information Services:** RLIN; BITNET (electronic mail service). Performs searches. **Publications:** The Chronicle (newsletter). **Remarks:** FAX: (215)898-6320. Electronic mail address(es): BM.PSA@RLG (BITNET). Depository for primary source materials pertinent to the development of nursing and health care in the Mid-Atlantic region and as a national center for visiting nurse association materials. Center is located at the University of Pennsylvania School of Nursing. It is, at the same time, a self-supporting entity overseen by its own governing board.

★3306★
Center for the Study of Human Rights - Library (Soc Sci)
1108 International Affairs Bldg.
Columbia University
New York, NY 10027 Phone: (212)854-2479
Founded: 1978. **Staff:** 3. **Subjects:** Human rights, interdisciplinary research and teaching. **Holdings:** 600 books; 50 periodicals; 1000 articles, reports, papers; 6 VF drawers; 200 course curricula. **Subscriptions:** 20 journals and other serials. **Services:** Library open to the public for reference use only. **Publications:** Human Rights Bibliography. **Remarks:** FAX: (212)749-0397. Telex: 220094.

★3307★
Center for the Study of Market Alternatives - Library (Bus-Fin)
2285 University Dr. Phone: (208)368-7811
Boise, ID 83706 D. Allen Dalton, Dir.
Founded: 1976. **Staff:** 1. **Subjects:** Free enterprise, economics, political science, freedom philosophy. **Holdings:** 1216 volumes; 61 videotapes; 500 audiotapes. **Subscriptions:** 15 journals and other serials. **Services:** Library open to the public.

★3308★
Center for the Study of the Presidency - Library (Soc Sci)
208 E. 75th St. Phone: (212)249-1200
New York, NY 10021 Maria Rossi, Libn.
Founded: 1965. **Staff:** Prof 2; Other 2. **Subjects:** American Presidency, U.S. Congress. **Holdings:** 3000 books; 1000 bound periodical volumes; 200 reels of microfilm. **Subscriptions:** 15 journals and other serials. **Services:** Copying; library open to the public. **Computerized Information Services:** Internal database. **Remarks:** FAX: (212)628-9503. **Staff:** Judith Hurd, Asst.Libn.

Center for the Study of Rural Librarianship
See: **Clarion University of Pennsylvania - College of Library Science** (3758)

Center for the Study of Science in Society
See: **Virginia Polytechnic Institute and State University** (19871)

Centre Suisse Recherche, de'Analyse et de Synthese d'Information
See: **CENTREDOC** (3316)

★3309★
Center for Sustainable Agriculture - Library (Agri)
2318 Bree Ln. Phone: (916)756-7177
Davis, CA 95616 Karen Van Epen, Res.
Founded: 1979. **Subjects:** Agriculture, land, forestry, water, natural resources. **Holdings:** 6000 volumes. **Services:** Library not open to the public. **Remarks:** FAX: (916)756-7188. Affiliated with Farallones Institute.

Center for the Teaching of Michigan History
See: **Historical Society of Michigan** (7273)

★3310★
Center for Thanatology Research - Library (Soc Sci)
391 Atlantic Ave. Phone: (718)858-3026
Brooklyn, NY 11217 Roberta Halporn, Dir.
Founded: 1982. **Staff:** Prof 1. **Subjects:** Aging, dying, death, bereavement, gravestone studies. **Holdings:** 1000 books; 40 bound periodical volumes; videotapes; audiocassettes; photographs; rubbings. **Subscriptions:** 6 journals and other serials. **Services:** Copying; library open to the public by appointment. **Automated Operations:** Computerized cataloging. **Publications:** Subject bibliographies, 20/year - available upon request.

Center for Translation Studies - Translation Library
See: **University of Texas at Dallas** (19409)

Centre on Transnational Corporations
See: **United Nations** (16751)

Center for Ulcer Research and Education
See: **CURE Foundation** (4485)

★3311★
Center for U.S.-Mexican Studies - Research Library (Area-Ethnic, Soc Sci)
University of California, San Diego
10111 N. Torrey Pines Rd., (0510) Phone: (619)534-4309
La Jolla, CA 92093-0510 Tamara Riquelme, Res.Libn.
Founded: 1979. **Staff:** 2. **Subjects:** Mexico, U.S.-Mexican relations, immigration, border studies, Mexican economy, trade and finance. **Special Collections:** Tape recordings of over 150 interdisciplinary seminars on Mexico and U.S.-Mexican Relations; Free Trade Agreement; ephemeral materials file (project proposals and descriptions; papers written by visiting research fellows, academic staff members, and faculty research associates; 100); Mexican government documents; Mexican newspapers and journals. **Holdings:** 1200 books; Mexico-related clippings from U.S. and Mexican newspapers, 1979 to present. **Subscriptions:** 46 journals; 24 newsletters; 12 newspapers. **Services:** Copying; library open to the public for reference use only. **Remarks:** FAX: (619)534-6447.

★3312★
Center for Urban Horticulture - Elisabeth C. Miller Horticulture Library (Biol Sci)
University of Washington
GF-15 Phone: (206)543-8616
Seattle, WA 98195 Laura Lipton, Hd.Libn.
Founded: 1984. **Staff:** Prof 1; Other 1. **Subjects:** Horticulture, arboreta and botanical gardens, urban forestry, gardening. **Holdings:** 5000 books; 1000 bound periodical volumes. **Subscriptions:** 300 journals and other serials. **Services:** Copying; library open to the public for reference use only. **Computerized Information Services:** DIALOG Information Services, OCLC. **Networks/Consortia:** Member of Council on Botanical Horticultural Libraries. **Staff:** Valerie Easton, Libn.; Martha Ferguson, Tech.

★3313★
Center on War & the Child (Soc Sci)
35 Benton St.
Box 487 Phone: (501)253-8900
Eureka Springs, AR 72632 Richard J. Parker, Exec.Dir.
Founded: 1983. **Subjects:** Children as soldiers, military training, war toys, children as victims in civil and international conflict, socialization of children to violence. **Holdings:** 1200 volumes; topical files of unbound, unpublished items; news clippings; photographs and slides. **Services:** Copying; library open to the public. **Publications:** WarChild Monitor International (newsletter), quarterly; Center Updates; Action Alerts - all to members.

★3314★
Center for War, Peace, and the News Media - Archive of News Media Coverage (Info Sci)
New York University
10 Washington Pl., 4th Fl. Phone: (212)998-7960
New York, NY 10003 Dee Ella Spears, Res.Anl.
Founded: 1985. **Staff:** Prof 4; Other 2. **Subjects:** Media coverage of U.S.-Soviet relations, U.S. defense policy issues, nuclear issues, the Soviet Union and U.S. foreign policy; media criticism. **Special Collections:** Newspaper and newsmagazine collection, 1985 to present; videotape collection of network evening news, November 1987 to present; library of specialized publications on defense and Soviet issues. **Holdings:** 200,000 clippings; 800 videotapes. **Subscriptions:** 24 journals and other serials; 8 newspapers. **Services:** SDI; archives open to the public by appointment. **Computerized Information Services:** Internal database. **Publications:** Deadline, bimonthly - available through membership, free to working journalists; Occasional paper series, 3/year; conference proceedings, irregular. **Remarks:** FAX: (212)995-4040. Telex: 235128 NYU UR. **Staff:** Michael Schiffer, Anl.; Robert Karl Manoff, Dir.; Judy Weddle, Dir. of Spec.Proj.

★3315★
Center for Wetland Resources - Information Services and Archives
CWR Bldg., Rm. 103
Louisiana State University
Baton Rouge, LA 70803
Founded: 1982. **Subjects:** Marine and wetland sciences, coastal ecology, fisheries, wetland soil chemistry, nearshore oceanography and climatology. **Special Collections:** Richard J. Russell Collection (geomorphology, earth sciences); Marine Education Microfilm Series (MEMS). **Holdings:** 500 books; 10,000 technical reports and reprints; 300 data tapes; 500 aerial photographs of Louisiana; 3500 maps; 15,000 microfiche; archives. **Remarks:** Currently inactive.

★3316★
CENTREDOC - Library (Sci-Engr)
Rue Breguet 2 Phone: 38 254181
CH-20007 Neuchatel, Switzerland Bernard Chapuis, Dir.
Subjects: Science, technology, economics, patents. **Holdings:** 6000 bound volumes; 95,000 patent documents. **Subscriptions:** 200 journals and other serials. **Services:** Current awareness; document delivery. **Computerized Information Services:** DIALOG Information Services, ESA/IRS, Hungarian Economic Information Service (ECHO), Infotrade, International Patent Documentation Center (INPADOC), INKADAT (Informationssystem Karlsruhe), Data-Star, ORBIT Search Service, STN International, Questel. Performs searches on fee basis. **Remarks:** FAX: 38 254873. Telex: 952 655 CSEM. **Also Known As:** Centre Suisse Recherche, de'Analyse et de Synthese d'Information.

★3317★
Centerior Energy Corporation - Law Library (Law)
55 Public Square
Box 5000 Phone: (216)479-4607
Cleveland, OH 44113 David W. Whitehead, Gen.Couns.
Staff: Prof 1. **Subjects:** General law. **Holdings:** 4100 books. **Services:** Library not open to the public. **Automated Operations:** Computerized indexing. **Computerized Information Services:** LEXIS, NEXIS. **Remarks:** FAX: (216)687-6540. **Formerly:** Cleveland Electric Illuminating Company.

★3318★
Centerior Energy Corporation - Library (Energy)
205 St. Clair Ave., N.W., Rm. 479
P.O. Box 6776 Phone: (216)479-4764
Cleveland, OH 44101 Jean G. Ocampo, Libn.
Founded: 1947. **Staff:** 4. **Subjects:** Electric power engineering, energy, public utilities, management. **Special Collections:** Electric Power Research Institute Reports. **Holdings:** 3250 books; 625 bound periodical volumes; 500 items in pamphlet file; 5000 items in business services files; 2000 microfiche. **Subscriptions:** 250 journals and other serials. **Services:** Interlibrary loan; copying; library open to the public by appointment. **Automated Operations:** Computerized public access catalog, acquisitions, and circulation. **Computerized Information Services:** DIALOG Information Services, Edison Electric Institute (EEI). **Networks/Consortia:** Member of Cleveland Area Metropolitan Library System (CAMLS). **Publications:** Library Bulletin, bimonthly; Acquisition List, monthly. **Special Indexes:** Electric Power Research Institute (EPRI) Reports index (card). **Remarks:** FAX: (216)479-1665.

★3319★
Centerior Energy Corporation - Perry Nuclear Power Plant - PNPP Information & Resource Center (Energy)
10 Center Rd., TEC-219 Phone: (216)259-3737
Perry, OH 44081 Sharon Yaworski, Hd.
Founded: 1984. **Staff:** Prof 2. **Subjects:** Nuclear energy, electric utilities. **Holdings:** 9605 books; industry standards of 19 associations on microfilm; Electric Power Research Institute (EPRI) research reports; regulations; 568 training videotapes; slides; photographs. **Subscriptions:** 87 journals and other serials. **Services:** Center open to the public with restrictions. **Automated Operations:** Computerized cataloging and circulation. **Publications:** Perry Perspective (newsletter) - to the public. **Remarks:** FAX: (216)259-3452.

Centers for Disease Control
See: **U.S. Centers for Disease Control** (17125)

★3320★
Centinela Hospital Medical Center - Edwin W. Dean Memorial Library (Med)
555 E. Hardy St.
Box 720 Phone: (213)673-4660
Inglewood, CA 90307 Marilyn K. Slater, Ph.D., Hea.Sci.Libn.
Founded: 1972. **Staff:** Prof 1; Other 1. **Subjects:** Sports medicine, orthopedics, clinical medicine, nursing. **Holdings:** 6000 books; 8200 bound periodical volumes. **Subscriptions:** 250 journals and other serials. **Services:** Interlibrary loan; library not open to the public. **Automated Operations:** Computerized cataloging, acquisitions, serials, and circulation. **Computerized Information Services:** MEDLINE, DIALOG Information Services, BRS Information Technologies, LEXIS, NEXIS; OnTyme Electronic Message Network Service (electronic mail service). **Remarks:** FAX: (213)672-7167.

Centra Health, Inc. - Lynchburg General Marshall Lodge Hospital
See: **Lynchburg General Marshall Lodge Hospital** (9474)

Centra Health, Inc. - Virginia Baptist Hospital
See: **Virginia Baptist Hospital** (19858)

★3321★
Central Agency for Jewish Education - Adler-Shinensky Library (Area-Ethnic)
4200 Biscayne Blvd. Phone: (305)576-4030
Miami, FL 33137 Shirley Wolfe, Dir.
Founded: 1948. **Staff:** Prof 2; Other 2. **Subjects:** Israel, education, Hebrew language, Holocaust, Yiddish language, Judaica, Jewish ethnics, Bible. **Special Collections:** Biblical personalities. **Holdings:** 30,000 volumes; 50 file boxes of pamphlets; 1500 filmstrips; 200 tapes; 200 videotapes. **Subscriptions:** 70 journals and other serials; 8 newspapers. **Services:** Interlibrary loan; copying; library open to the public. **Automated Operations:** Computerized cataloging, acquisitions, serials, and circulation (ALEPH). **Special Catalogs:** Audiovisual Catalog, annual - to schools. **Remarks:** FAX: (305)576-0307. **Staff:** Lillian Ross, Community Serv.Dir.

★3322★
Central Agency for Jewish Education of Greater Philadelphia - Jacob and Frances Seidman Educational Resource Center (Area-Ethnic)
7500 A West Ave. Phone: (215)635-8940
Melrose Park, PA 19126 Nancy M. Messinger, Dir.
Founded: 1979. **Staff:** Prof 4. **Subjects:** Jewish history, holidays, customs; Hebrew language and literature; Bible; ethics; prayer. **Special Collections:** Israel Resources (2 VF drawers; 400 documents); Jewish instructional games (100 teacher-made and commercial games); Principal's resources; Holocaust materials; music resources collection (records and cassette tapes). **Holdings:** 1900 books; 5500 documents; 15 VF drawers of instructional materials; 400 videotapes. **Subscriptions:** 30 journals and other serials. **Services:** Copying and laminating; center open to the public. **Computerized Information Services:** Internal database. **Publications:** HIGHLIGHTS, 3/year - to all Jewish religious school teachers in the Philadelphia area; bibliographies. **Special Indexes:** Subject, age, and method cross-index. **Remarks:** FAX: (215)635-8946. **Formerly:** Its Elsie and William Chomsky Educational Resource Center (CERC). **Staff:** Marcia Goldberg, Cat.Libn.; Sallie Olson, Prog.Coord.; Helen Pearlman, Cons./Cat./Indexer; Ephie Seitz, Res.Asst.

★3323★
Central America Resource Center (Area-Ethnic)
Box 2327 Phone: (512)476-9841
Austin, TX 78768 Charlotte McCann, Libn.
Founded: 1983. **Staff:** Prof 2. **Subjects:** Central America, United States policy, human rights, refugees, United States immigration law. **Holdings:** 1000 books; 290 bound periodical volumes; 3 VF drawers of unpublished manuscripts; 7 VF drawers of newspaper clippings and pamphlets. **Subscriptions:** 65 journals and other serials. **Services:** Copying; SDI; open to the public for reference use only. **Computerized Information Services:** Internal database; PeaceNet (electronic mail service). Performs searches on fee basis. **Publications:** Directory of Central America Organizations; Central America NewsPak (compilation of news on Central America), biweekly. **Remarks:** FAX: (512)476-0130. Electronic mail address(es): CARC (PeaceNet). **Formerly:** Its Information Bank. **Staff:** Jill Gronquist, Dir.

★3324★
Central America Resource Center - Penny Lernoux Memorial Library on Latin America (Area-Ethnic)
317 17th Ave., S.E. Phone: (612)627-9445
Minneapolis, MN 55414 Pam Keesey, Libn.
Founded: 1983. **Subjects:** Central America - society, history, literature, politics, human rights, U.S. foreign policy; Latin America; liberation theology; women. **Holdings:** 2600 books; 45 AV programs; government documents; human rights reports; personal testimonies; VF material. **Subscriptions:** 70 journals and other serials. **Services:** Copying; center open to the public. **Publications:** Centroamerica: the Month in Review (news journal), monthly; Directory of Central America Classroom Resources K-12; Annotated Bibliograpy of Library Resources on Central America. **Remarks:** Is said to serve as a clearinghouse for information not readily available in the mainstream media; offers titles in Spanish and English. Center is said to be the largest publicly accessible collection of Central America materials in the upper Midwest. FAX: (612)627-9450. **Formerly:** Located in St. Paul, MN.

★3325★
Central American Research Institute for Industry - Documentation and Information Division - Manuel Noriega Morales Library (Sci-Engr)
Avenida La Reforma, 4-47, Zona 10 Phone: 2 310631
01010 Guatemala City, Guatemala Rocio M. Marban, Hd., Doc. & Info.Div.
Founded: 1956. **Staff:** Prof 4; Other 4. **Subjects:** Technology, food industry, biotechnology, pulp and paper, industrial counseling. **Special Collections:** Central American standards (1140). **Holdings:** 40,000 books; 900 bound periodical volumes; reports; documents; reprints; microfiche; catalogs; directories; AV programs; diskettes. **Subscriptions:** 200 journals and other serials. **Services:** Interlibrary loan; copying; division open to the public for reference use only. **Automated Operations:** Computerized cataloging. **Computerized Information Services:** DIALOG Information Services, PFDS Online, Questel, STN International; internal database; DIALMAIL, BITNET, ECONET (electronic mail services). Performs searches on fee basis. **Publications:** List of publications - available on request. **Remarks:** Institute was established by the governments of Costa Rica, El Salvador, Guatemala, Honduras, and Nicaragua, and maintains an office in each country. FAX: 2 317470. Telex: 5312 ICAITI GU. **Also Known As:** Instituto Centroamericano de Investigacion y Tecnologia Industrial (ICAITI). **Staff:** Rosa Regina de De La Vega, Libn.

Central Archives for Empirical Social Research
See: **University of Cologne - Central Archives for Empirical Social Research** (18487)

★3326★
Central Arkansas Library System - Reference Services Department - Library (Hum)
700 Louisiana Phone: (501)370-5952
Little Rock, AR 72201 Phillip L. Jones, Ref.Serv.
Staff: Prof 4; Other 5. **Special Collections:** Arkansas history and literature (3400 items); genealogy collection (3300 items); Foundation Center Regional collection; sheet music, 1900-1945. **Holdings:** 130,000 federal documents; 25,000 state and local documents; 1600 maps. **Subscriptions:** 800 journals and other serials; 50 newspapers. **Services:** Interlibrary loan; copying; department open to the public with restrictions. **Automated Operations:** Computerized cataloging. **Computerized Information Services:** OCLC. **Networks/Consortia:** Member of AMIGOS Bibliographic Council, Inc. **Special Indexes:** State and local documents; genealogy collection (both on cards). **Remarks:** FAX: (501)375-7451. **Staff:** Sarah Ziegenbein, Assoc.Ref.Libn.; Jennifer Chilcoat, Assoc.Ref.Libn.; Raleigh Petersen, Ref.Libn.

★3327★
Central Baptist Church - Media Center (Rel-Phil)
420 N. Roy Phone: (612)646-2751
St. Paul, MN 55104 Cleo Kasten, Libn.
Founded: 1947. **Staff:** 6. **Subjects:** Bible, Christian life and education, devotions, missions, biography. **Holdings:** 4500 books; slides; filmstrips; phonograph records; maps; pamphlets; audio- and videotapes; denominational papers. **Subscriptions:** 10 journals and other serials. **Services:** Center open to the public with restrictions.

★3328★
Central Baptist Seminary - Dr. W. Gordon Brown Memorial Library (Rel-Phil)
6 Gormley Industrial Ave.
Box 28 Phone: (416)888-9600
Gormley, ON, Canada L0H 1G0 Tom Huehn, Libn.
Founded: 1949. **Staff:** Prof 1. **Subjects:** Theology, Christian education, church history, Canadian Baptists. **Holdings:** 22,500 volumes; 1400 microfiche; slides; cassettes. **Subscriptions:** 85 journals and other serials. **Services:** Library open to the public on a fee basis. **Computerized Information Services:** iNet 2000, Envoy 100 (electronic mail services). **Remarks:** FAX: (416)888-9603. **Formerly:** Located in Toronto, ON.

★3329★
Central Baptist Theological Seminary - Library (Rel-Phil)
741 N. 31st St. Phone: (913)371-8110
Kansas City, KS 66102-3964 Larry Blazer, Libn. & Assoc.Prof.
Founded: 1901. **Staff:** Prof 3; Other 5. **Subjects:** Theology, particularly Protestant; Baptist doctrine and history. **Special Collections:** Fred E. Young Qumran Collection; Anabaptist Foundation Collection. **Holdings:** 70,081 books; 9793 bound periodical volumes; 6 VF drawers of pamphlets; 10,082 microforms; 7059 AV materials. **Subscriptions:** 347 journals and other serials. **Services:** Interlibrary loan; copying; library open to the public with restrictions on borrowing. **Remarks:** FAX: (913)371-8110. **Staff:** Miss Arel T. Lewis, Asst.Libn.; Kathy Darcy, Tech.Serv.Libn.

★3330★
Central Bible College - Pearlman Memorial Library (Rel-Phil)
3000 N. Grant Phone: (417)833-2551
Springfield, MO 65803 Lynn Robert Anderson, Lib.Dir.
Founded: 1922. **Staff:** Prof 2; Other 22. **Subjects:** Bible and theology, missions, church history, religious education, American history, religious music, psychology. **Special Collections:** Assemblies of God Collection. **Holdings:** 93,811 books; 4161 bound periodical volumes; 77 VF drawers of clippings and pamphlets; 123 periodical titles on microfiche; 285 linear feet of archival materials; 4206 AV programs. **Subscriptions:** 418 journals and other serials. **Services:** Interlibrary loan; copying; library open to the public for reference use only. **Automated Operations:** Computerized cataloging and acquisitions. **Computerized Information Services:** OCLC. **Networks/Consortia:** Member of Assemblies of God Library Consortium, Missouri Library Network Corp. (MLNC). **Remarks:** FAX: (417)833-5141. **Staff:** Alice Murphy, Tech.Serv.Libn.; Debra Brown, Acq.Libn.; Tim Johnson, AV.

★3331★
Central Carolina Community College - Learning Resource Center (Educ)
1105 Kelly Dr. Phone: (919)775-5401
Sanford, NC 27330 Frances Andrews, Assoc. Dean Lrng.Rsrcs.
Founded: 1965. **Staff:** Prof 3; Other 4. **Subjects:** Electronics, auto and motorcycle mechanics, tool and die making, veterinary medicine, nursing, law enforcement, business administration, radio-television broadcasting, secretarial science, paralegal technology, laser-electro optics, cosmetology, instrumentation. **Special Collections:** Veterinary medical technology (1265 books; 16 periodicals); law library collection (1650 volumes); nursing and medical library (915 volumes; 16 periodicals). **Holdings:** 24,382 books; 9 VF drawers of pamphlets and clippings; 3568 records, tapes, films, slides; 2599 microforms. **Subscriptions:** 306 journals and other serials; 16 newspapers. **Services:** Interlibrary loan; copying; center open to the public. **Automated Operations:** Computerized public access catalog, cataloging, acquisitions, and serials. **Computerized Information Services:** DIALOG Information Services. Performs searches on fee basis. **Networks/Consortia:** Member of North Carolina Area Health Education Centers Program Library and Information Services Network, North Carolina Information Network (NCIN). **Remarks:** FAX: (919)775-1221. **Staff:** Gwen L. Glover, Libn.; Linda Halstead, Libn.; Marian Bridges, ILL Libn.; Ethel Badgett, Acq.; Martha Luck, Film Libn.

★3332★
Central Chamber of Commerce of Finland - Library (Bus-Fin)
Postilokero 1000
SF-00101 Helsinki, Finland Phone: 0 650133
Subjects: Finland - business and foreign trade. **Holdings:** 7000 volumes; 400 periodicals; archives. **Computerized Information Services:** Internal database. **Remarks:** FAX: 0 650303. Telex: 123814 chamb SF. **Also Known As:** Chambre de Commerce Centrale de Finlande.

★3333★
Central Christian Church - Library (Rel-Phil)
205 E. Short St.
Box 1459 Phone: (606)233-1551
Lexington, KY 40591 Walter A. Hehl, Hd.
Founded: 1951. **Staff:** Prof 1. **Subjects:** Religion, philosophy, biography. **Holdings:** 6100 books. **Services:** Library open to the public. **Staff:** Ann McConnell, Libn.

★3334★
Central Christian College of the Bible - Library (Rel-Phil)
911 Urbandale Dr., E. Phone: (816)263-3900
Moberly, MO 65270 Gareth L. Reese, Libn.
Founded: 1957. **Staff:** Prof 1; Other 3. **Subjects:** Theology. **Special Collections:** Walter S. Coble mission files. **Holdings:** 26,039 books; 2637 bound periodical volumes; 1421 unbound periodicals; 78 book titles on microfiche; 4 periodical titles in microform; 4824 microfiche; 119 linear feet of clippings, pamphlets, archival documents; 24 VF drawers; 3098 audio- and videotapes and phonograph records. **Subscriptions:** 194 journals and other serials. **Services:** Interlibrary loan; copying; library open to the public. **Computerized Information Services:** BiblioFile (internal database). **Networks/Consortia:** Member of Missouri Library Network Corp. (MLNC).

★3335★
Central City Business Institute - Victoria Nelli Memorial Library (Bus-Fin)
953 James St. Phone: (315)472-6233
Syracuse, NY 13203 Mary Lee Shanahan
Subjects: Business. **Holdings:** 2500 books; 9 AV programs. **Subscriptions:** 93 journals and other serials; 7 newspapers. **Services:** Interlibrary loan; library not open to the public. **Networks/Consortia:** Member of Central New York Library Resources Council (CENTRO). **Remarks:** FAX: (315)472-6201.

★3336★
Central Connecticut State University - Department of Geography - Map Depository (Geog-Map)
1615 Stanley St. Phone: (203)827-7218
New Britain, CT 06050 Dr. James N. Snaden, Dir.
Founded: 1968. **Staff:** Prof 2; Other 1. **Subjects:** Topography. **Special Collections:** Defense Mapping Agency and U.S. Geological Survey Depository. **Holdings:** 50 books; 25,000 flat maps; topographic maps; aeronautical and nautical charts; gazetteers. **Services:** Copying; depository open to the public for reference use only. **Computerized Information Services:** BITNET (electronic mail service). **Special Indexes:** Index to maps. **Remarks:** FAX: (203)827-7200. Electronic mail address(es): SNADEN@CTSTATEU (BITNET). **Staff:** Lisa Graves, Libn.

★3337★
Central Connecticut State University - Elihu Burritt Library - Special Collections (Hum)
Wells St. Phone: (203)827-7524
New Britain, CT 06050 Frank Gagliardi, Assoc.Dir.
Founded: 1849. **Staff:** Prof 1; Other 2. **Special Collections:** Connecticut Polish American Archive and Manuscript Collection (475 linear feet of documents); Herbert D. Welte papers (40 linear feet); papers of Middletown & Berlin Turnpike Co. (2 linear feet); records of the First Church of Christ, New Britain, 1758-1900 (2 linear feet); World's Fair Collection (120 items); Bookseller's Catalog Collection (10,000); Elihu Burritt Collection (400 items); Mark Twain Collection (500 items); Thomas Hardy Collection (600 items); Bruce Rogers Collection (285 items); Polish Heritage Collection (8300 items); Dutch language children's books (275 items); Frederic W. Goudy Collection (200 items); Walter Hart Blumenthal Collection (700 items); University Archives (6000 archival materials); children's historical collection (1900 items); Private Press Collection (600 items). **Holdings:** 19,000 books; 1000 bound periodical volumes. **Services:** Interlibrary loan; copying; collections open to the public. **Automated Operations:** Computerized cataloging and circulation. **Computerized Information Services:** BRS Information Technologies, DIALOG Information Services, OCLC. Performs searches on fee basis. Contact Person: Emily Chasse, 827-7649. **Networks/Consortia:** Member of NELINET, Inc., Capital Region Library Council (CRLC). **Remarks:** FAX: (203)827-7961. **Staff:** Ewa Wolynska.

★3338★
The Central Conservatory of China - Bibliotheca (Mus)
43 Baojia Jie Phone: 1 665336
Beijing, People's Republic of China Song Kai, Dp.Libn.
Founded: 1950. **Staff:** 26. **Subjects:** Music, music theory, composition, conducting, national music and instruments, piano, orchestra and vocal music, opera in Chinese, Russian, Japanese, English, and other foreign languages. **Holdings:** 250,000 volumes; 275 periodicals; 150,000 AV programs and microforms; scores. **Services:** Copying. **Publications:** Selected Works on Chinese and Foreign Musicians; Selected Works on the Performing Art of Vocal Music.

★3339★
Central DuPage Hospital - Medical Library (Med)
25 N. Winfield Rd. Phone: (708)682-1600
Winfield, IL 60190 Dorothy B. Rowe, Libn.
Founded: 1974. **Staff:** Prof 2. **Subjects:** Medicine, nursing, allied health sciences. **Holdings:** 4000 books; unbound periodicals; 8 VF drawers. **Subscriptions:** 400 journals and other serials. **Services:** Interlibrary loan; copying; library open to the public for reference use only. **Computerized Information Services:** MEDLINE, MEDLARS, DIALOG Information Services. Performs searches on fee basis. **Networks/Consortia:** Member of DuPage Library System, Fox Valley Health Science Library Consortium (FVHSL), National Network of Libraries of Medicine - Greater Midwest Region. **Remarks:** FAX: (708)682-0028. **Staff:** Gloria Sullivan, Asst.Libn.

★3340★
Central General Hospital - Medical Library (Med)
888 Old Country Rd. Phone: (516)681-8900
Plainview, NY 11803 Paula Goldfader, Libn.
Remarks: No further information was supplied by respondent.

★3341★
Central Illinois Landmarks Foundation - Architectural Archives (Art, Plan)
Peoria Public Library
107 N.E. Monroe St. Phone: (309)672-8858
Peoria, IL 61602 Joyce M. Johnson, Cons./Presrv.
Subjects: Peoria area architecture. **Special Collections:** Architectural blueprints, drawings, and other material exceeding 20,000 sheets for more than 800 buildings by 200 different firms. **Holdings:** Figures not available. **Services:** Copying; open to the public by appointment.

★3342★
Central Institute for the Deaf - Professional Library (Med)
818 S. Euclid Phone: (314)652-3200
St. Louis, MO 63110 Mary M. Sicking, Libn.
Founded: 1929. **Staff:** Prof 1. **Subjects:** Audiology, early childhood education, behavioral sciences, speech pathology, physiology, otolaryngology, education of the deaf, noise control, electroacoustics, digital instrumentation, aural rehabilitation, neurophysiology. **Special Collections:** The CID/Max A. Goldstein Collection (evolution of nonelectric hearing aids and early editions of books dealing with speech and hearing); Research Department Publications (978). **Holdings:** 9058 books; 1035 bound periodical volumes; 137 dissertations; 109 drawers of clippings; 12 reels of microfilm; 20 videotapes. **Subscriptions:** 76 journals. **Services:** Interlibrary loan; copying; library open to the public for reference use only. **Remarks:** Library located in the Hearing Clinics & Research Bldg., 909 S. Taylor, St. Louis, MO 63110. The CID/Max A. Goldstein Collection is housed at Washington University - School of Medicine Library.

★3343★
Central Islip Psychiatric Center - Health Science Library (Med)
Carlton Ave., Med. Surg. Bldg. Phone: (516)234-6262
Central Islip, NY 11722 Libn.
Founded: 1973. **Staff:** Prof 1; Other 1. **Subjects:** Psychiatry, nursing, psychology, rehabilitation, retardation, developmental disabilities, geriatrics. **Special Collections:** John G. Walker Psychology Collection (180 items); old medicine and surgery textbooks (70). **Holdings:** 9011 books; 1257 bound periodical volumes; 20 VF drawers; 28 AV programs. **Subscriptions:** 188 journals and other serials. **Services:** Interlibrary loan; copying; library open to the public for reference use only but LILRC patrons have borrowing privileges. **Computerized Information Services:** Internal database. **Networks/Consortia:** Member of Long Island Library Resources Council, Suffolk Cooperative Library System. **Publications:** Accessions, monthly - for internal distribution only; Annual Report and Monthly Report (statistics).

Central Library of St. Lucia
See: **St. Lucia - Central Library of St. Lucia** (14469)

★3344★
Central Louisiana State Hospital - Medical and Professional Library (Med)
Box 5031 Phone: (318)484-6363
Pineville, LA 71361-5031 Benton Carol McGee, Med.Libn.
Founded: 1958. **Staff:** Prof 1; Other 2. **Subjects:** Psychiatry, psychology, social work, occupational therapy, psychiatric nursing, psychiatric hospital administration. **Holdings:** 4000 books; 3500 bound periodical volumes; 12 VF drawers of pamphlets and reports. **Subscriptions:** 182 journals and other serials. **Services:** Interlibrary loan; copying; library open to the public. **Computerized Information Services:** DIALOG Information Services. Performs searches on fee basis. **Publications:** Current Contents of Journals Received, weekly; Bibliographies - to hospital staff.

★3345★
Central Maine Medical Center - Health Science Library (Med)
300 Main St.
Box 4500 Phone: (207)795-2560
Lewiston, ME 04240-0309 Maryanne Greven, Lib.Dir.
Founded: 1977. **Staff:** Prof 3; Other 2. **Subjects:** Biomedicine, health care administration. **Special Collections:** Consumer Health Information collection. **Holdings:** 1500 books; 3300 bound periodical volumes. **Subscriptions:** 425 journals and other serials; 8 newspapers. **Services:** Interlibrary loan; copying; SDI; library open to the public. **Computerized Information Services:** NLM, DIALOG Information Services, BRS Information Technologies, Institute for Scientific Information (ISI), WILSONLINE; CD-ROMs (MEDLINE, CINAHL). Performs searches on fee basis. **Networks/Consortia:** Member of Medical Library Center of New York (MLCNY), Health Science Library and Information Cooperative of Maine (HSLIC). **Publications:** Info-To-Go (newsletter and acquisition list), quarterly. **Remarks:** FAX: (207)795-2569 **Staff:** Barbara Harness, Staff Libn.; Maureen Fournier, Staff Libn.

★3346★
Central Maine Power Company - Library Services (Energy)
Edison Dr. Phone: (207)623-3521
Augusta, ME 04336 Alan S. King, Corp.Libn.
Founded: 1978. **Staff:** Prof 2; Other 5. **Subjects:** Public utilities, energy, engineering, Canadian studies, regulation, rate design. **Special Collections:** Engineering drawings and photographs (50,000); Utility Annual Reports (5000); Energy Management Consumer Collection (1500 items). **Holdings:** 10,000 books; 15,000 reels of microfilm; 400,000 microfiche; 5000 other cataloged items. **Subscriptions:** 527 journals and other serials; 23 newspapers. **Services:** Interlibrary loan; copying; SDI; library open to the public. **Automated Operations:** Computerized public access catalog, cataloging, acquisitions, serials, and circulation. **Computerized Information Services:** DIALOG Information Services, WILSONLINE, Utility Data Institute, Reuters Information Services (Canada) Limited, LEXIS, Dow Jones News/Retrieval, NEXIS, WESTLAW, OCLC, Reuter TEXTLINE, QL Systems; Sources in Energy Management Planning (SEMP) (internal database); Knight-Ridder Unicom News, DIALMAIL (electronic mail services). Performs searches free of charge. **Networks/Consortia:** Member of NELINET, Inc. **Publications:** Contents, monthly; NOTABENE, quarterly; EMF Keeptrack, daily newsclips - all for internal distribution only. **Remarks:** FAX: (207)623-9384. **Staff:** Fred McKinley, Ser.Libn.; Elizabeth Brooks, Spec.Serv.Libn.; Alison Plummer, Acq.; Fran Hargreaves, Shared Serv.

★3347★
Central Michigan University - Brooks Astronomical Observatory - Library (Sci-Engr)
Physics Dept. Phone: (517)774-3320
Mt. Pleasant, MI 48859 Wayne Osborn, Observatory Dir.
Founded: 1970. **Subjects:** Astronomy. **Holdings:** 100 books; 600 bound periodical volumes; 20 reports. **Subscriptions:** 5 journals and other serials. **Services:** Library open to the public by appointment.

★3348★
Central Michigan University - Clarke Historical Library (Hist)
Mt. Pleasant, MI 48859 Phone: (517)774-3352
Frank Boles, Dir.
Founded: 1955. **Staff:** Prof 3; Other 4. **Subjects:** Michigan, Old Northwest Territory, early travel in the Midwest, Afro-Americana, history of slavery, Native Americans, children's literature, angling. **Special Collections:** Lucile Clarke Memorial Children's Library (6768 volumes); Wilbert Wright Collection Afro-Americana (5000 volumes); Reed T. Draper Angling Collection (1261 volumes); Presidential Campaign Biography Collection (778 volumes); university archives. **Holdings:** 60,000 books; 1440 maps; 3274 manuscripts; 1100 broadsides; 26,400 photographs; 8072 microforms; 3564 pieces of sheet music; 900 newspapers; 12,000 pieces of ephemera; 50 tape recordings; 100 phonograph records. **Subscriptions:** 103 journals and other serials. **Services:** Library open to the public. **Automated Operations:** Computerized public access catalog and cataloging. **Networks/Consortia:** Member of Michigan Library Consortium (MLC). **Publications:** Annual report - to mailing list; Resource Guides; occasional books and bibliographies; Michigan Historical Review, semiannual - by subscription. **Special Indexes:** Indexes to: newspapers on microfilm; Mt. Pleasant death records; manuscripts on microfilm; women's history; Twain Collection. **Remarks:** FAX: (517)774-4499. **Staff:** Krista E. Clumpner, Tech.Serv.; Evelyn Leasher, Pub.Serv.; Mary L. Huggard, Microforms.

★3349★
Central Minnesota Historical Center - Library (Hist)
St. Cloud State University Phone: (612)255-3254
St. Cloud, MN 56301 David H. Overy, Dir.
Founded: 1967. **Staff:** 2. **Subjects:** Church history, business, Minnesota politics and government, oral history, railroad and labor history, World War II military history. **Special Collections:** Rural Church Oral History Project; World War II Veterans Oral History Project. **Holdings:** 230 linear feet of local history materials. **Services:** Copying; library open to the public. **Remarks:** Maintained by St. Cloud State University.

★3350★
Central Missouri State University - Ward Edwards Library - Special Collections (Hist)
Warrensburg, MO 64093 Phone: (816)543-4151
Dorie Brookshier, Spec.Coll.Libn.
Founded: 1937. **Staff:** Prof 2; Other 1. **Special Collections:** Missouri - history, geology, literature, geneology, authors; Izaak Walton's Compleat Angler; Missouri Speleology Society Speleology Collection; Virginia Scott Miner Collection of Contemporary Poetry; Children/Young Adult Collection; Research Collection in Literature for Children and Young Adults; W. Espy History of the Death Penalty for Missouri and Kansas. **Services:** Copying; collections open to the public for reference use only. **Automated Operations:** Computerized public access catalog (NOTIS, LUIS). **Computerized Information Services:** OCLC. **Networks/Consortia:** Member of Kansas City Metropolitan Library Network (KCMLN), Missouri Library Network Corp. (MLNC). **Remarks:** FAX: (816)543-8001. **Staff:** Ophelia Gilbert, Cur., Hist.Ch.Lit.Co ll.

★3351★
Central Nevada Historical Society - Museum Library (Hist)
P.O. Box 326
Logan Field Rd. Phone: (702)482-9676
Tonopah, NV 89049 William J. Metscher, Dir.
Founded: 1980. **Staff:** 1. **Subjects:** Central Nevada history - Nye and Esmeralda Counties. **Holdings:** 600 books; 30 AV programs; 10 microform and nonbook items; 15 manuscripts; 20,000 photographs; 500 maps. **Services:** Copying; library open to the public for reference use only. **Publications:** Central Nevada's Glorious Past. **Staff:** Nancy Marshall, Asst.Cur.

★3352★
Central New Jersey Home News - Library (Publ)
123 How Ln.
P.O. Box 551 Phone: (908)246-5529
New Brunswick, NJ 08903 Betty Selingo, Libn.
Founded: 1950. **Staff:** 2. **Subjects:** Newspaper reference topics, state and local news. **Holdings:** 700 books; 1 million clippings; photographs. **Subscriptions:** 15 journals and other serials; 18 newspapers. **Services:** Library not open to the public. **Computerized Information Services:** Internal database. **Remarks:** FAX: (908)937-6046. Alternate telephone number(s): (908)246-5625. **Formerly:** Home News Publishing Company. **Staff:** Patricia Mangione.

★3353★
Central New York Regional Planning Board - Library & Information Center (Env-Cons)
90 Presidential Plaza, Suite 122 Phone: (315)422-8276
Syracuse, NY 13202 Thomas Wight, Plan./Res.Assoc.
Founded: 1966. **Staff:** 1. **Subjects:** Water quality, land use planning, environmental and hazardous waste management, transportation, human resources, public utilities, grants assistance. **Special Collections:** U.S. Bureau of Census Products (500 items on U.S. census material); U.S. Census maps (150). **Holdings:** 3000 books; 900 bound periodical volumes; 200 maps; 800 pamphlets; 1000 natural resources maps; 500 transportation maps; 150 local, state, federal regulations; 6 selected planning-regional council newsletters. **Subscriptions:** 7 journals and other serials; 4 newspapers. **Services:** Copying; library open to the public by appointment. **Remarks:** FAX: (315)422-9051.

★3354★
Central Newfoundland Regional Health Center - Hospital Library (Med)
Union St. Phone: (709)292-2228
Grand Falls, NF, Canada A2A 2E1 Ellen Lewis, Libn.
Subjects: Medicine. **Holdings:** Figures not available. **Services:** Library open to post-secondary-level students. **Remarks:** No further information was supplied by respondent.

★3355★
Central Ohio Transit Authority - COTA Library
1600 McKinley Ave.
Columbus, OH 43222
Defunct.

Central Opera Service
See: **OPERA America Information Service** (12502)

★3356★
Central Power and Light Company - CPL Library (Energy)
P.O. Box 2121 Phone: (512)881-5503
Corpus Christi, TX 78403 Bettye J. Lucas, Info.Res.Spec.
Founded: 1980. **Staff:** Prof 1; Other 1. **Subjects:** Electric utilities, business and economics, communications and public relations. **Special Collections:** Historical photograph collection, 1916 to present (10,000 black/white photographs); company history. **Holdings:** 600 books; 7500 Electric Power Research Institute (EPRI) reports on microfiche; 12 drawers of subject files; 100 technical reports. **Subscriptions:** 85 journals and other serials; 10 newspapers. **Services:** Interlibrary loan; copying; library open to the public at librarian's discretion. **Computerized Information Services:** DIALOG Information Services, Knight-Ridder Unicom News, Dow Jones News/ Retrieval, URAP, NEXIS. **Remarks:** FAX: (512)880-6006. Library located at 539 N. Carancahua St., Rm. 10307, Corpus Christi, TX 78401.

★3357★
Central Presbyterian Church - Library (Rel-Phil)
12455 S.W. 104 St. Phone: (305)598-1239
Miami, FL 33816 Ms. Mickey Osburn
Founded: 1986. **Subjects:** Religion, education, social sciences. **Holdings:** 880 books; 111 videotapes. **Subscriptions:** 14 journals and other serials. **Services:** Library open to the Presbyterian community.

★3358★
Central Presbyterian Church - Library (Rel-Phil)
1100 W. Capitol
Jackson, MS 39203 Phone: (601)353-2757
Staff: Prof 1; Other 5. **Subjects:** Religion, Presbyterian Church. **Holdings:** 4000 books. **Services:** Library not open to the public.

★3359★
Central Presbyterian Church - Library (Rel-Phil)
3501 Campbell Phone: (816)931-2515
Kansas City, MO 64109 Mary E. Arney, Libn.
Staff: 1. **Subjects:** Religion, children's literature, peacemaking. **Special Collections:** Presbyterian Church history and curriculum; religion; peacemaking; children's literature; autographed book collection. **Holdings:** 6326 volumes; 9 shelves of posters and large pictures; 9 VF drawers of religious materials; 4 boxes of sewing patterns; large print materials. **Subscriptions:** 15 journals and other serials. **Services:** Copying; library open to the public. **Computerized Information Services:** Internal database. **Publications:** Bibliographies and reviews, weekly.

★3360★
Central Presbyterian Church - Library (Rel-Phil)
46 Park St. Phone: (201)744-5340
Montclair, NJ 07042 Mrs. C. Molinaro, Lib.Comm.
Founded: 1977. **Staff:** 2. **Subjects:** Theology, family relations, children's literature. **Holdings:** 2500 books. **Services:** Library not open to the public.

★3361★
Central Presbyterian Church - Library (Rel-Phil)
3788 Richmond Ave. Phone: (713)621-2424
Houston, TX 77027 J.J. Britton, Libn.
Staff: 1. **Subjects:** Religion, education. **Holdings:** 4000 books. **Subscriptions:** 12 journals and other serials. **Services:** Interlibrary loan; library open to the public on request.

★3362★
Central & South West Services - Corporate Library (Energy)
1616 Woodall Rodgers Phone: (214)754-1150
Dallas, TX 75202 Loyse Whisman, Supv., Lib.Serv.
Founded: 1980. **Staff:** Prof 2; Other 1. **Subjects:** Electric power and utility business, environment. **Special Collections:** Electric Power Research Institute (EPRI) technical reports (16 drawers of microfiche; 250 videotapes; 2500 papers). **Holdings:** 4000 books; 30 bound periodical volumes; 100 computer software packages. **Subscriptions:** 300 journals and other serials. **Services:** Interlibrary loan; copying; library open to other libraries. **Automated Operations:** Computerized cataloging, acquisitions, and serials. **Computerized Information Services:** DIALOG Information Services, DataTimes, NewsNet, Inc., WESTLAW, WILSONLINE, OCLC EPIC; Knight-Ridder Unicom (electronic mail service). **Remarks:** FAX: (214)754-1033. **Staff:** Misty Gay, Text Sys.Libn.

★3363★
Central Soya Company, Inc. - Feed Research Library (Agri)
1200 N. 2nd St. Phone: (219)724-1304
Decatur, IN 46733 Dr. R.L. Schoelkopf
Founded: 1980. **Staff:** Prof 1. **Subjects:** Animal nutrition and health. **Holdings:** 800 books; 21 journals and other serials; 40 titles of conference proceedings; 9 drawers of agribusiness documents; 2 cabinets of university/ Agriculture Extension Service files; 18 reels of microfilm of Central Soya Feed Research reports. **Subscriptions:** 123 journals and other serials. **Services:** Interlibrary loan; library open to the public with corporate approval. **Computerized Information Services:** BRS Information Technologies. **Networks/Consortia:** Member of Tri-ALSA, INCOLSA. **Remarks:** FAX: (219)724-1247. **Staff:** Tara K. Cook.

★3364★
Central Soya Company, Inc. - Food Research Library (Food-Bev)
Fort Wayne National Bank Bldg.
P.O. Box 1400 Phone: (219)425-5906
Fort Wayne, IN 46801-1400 Valesca Wilson, Res.Libn.
Founded: 1940. **Staff:** Prof 1. **Subjects:** Soybeans, nutrition, proteins, chemistry, food science. **Holdings:** 6500 books; 5067 bound periodical volumes; 3 VF drawers of pamphlets; 119 reels of microfilm. **Subscriptions:** 100 journals and other serials. **Services:** Interlibrary loan. **Computerized Information Services:** DIALOG Information Services. **Remarks:** FAX: (219)425-5838.

★3365★
Central State Hospital - Libraries (Med)
Milledgeville, GA 31062-9989 Phone: (912)453-6889
Susan Lemme, Dir. of Libs.
Founded: 1961. **Staff:** Prof 2. **Subjects:** Psychiatry, neurology, medicine, nursing, psychology, social work, allied health sciences, religion. **Holdings:** 8100 volumes. **Subscriptions:** 90 journals and other serials. **Services:** Interlibrary loan; library open to the public with restrictions. **Computerized Information Services:** BRS Information Technologies. **Networks/ Consortia:** Member of Health Science Libraries Consortium of Central Georgia (HSLCG), Georgia Interactive Network for Medical Information (GaIN), Georgia Health Sciences Library Association (GHSLA), Georgia Online Database (GOLD), Central Georgia Associated Libraries (CGAL). **Remarks:** Alternate telephone number(s): (912)453-4153; 453-4371. **Staff:** Kathy Warner.

★3366★
Central State Hospital - Medical Library (Med)
3000 W. Washington St. Phone: (317)639-3927
Indianapolis, IN 46222 Bette A. Kinsley, Libn.
Founded: 1954. **Staff:** Prof 1; Other 1. **Subjects:** Psychiatry, psychology, nursing, business and management, geriatrics, mental retardation, social work. **Holdings:** 7500 books; 3000 bound periodical volumes; 300 archival materials; 116 video cassettes; 450 audio cassettes; 22 VF drawers. **Subscriptions:** 152 journals and other serials. **Services:** Interlibrary loan; copying; SDI; library open to the public for reference use only. **Networks/ Consortia:** Member of Central Indiana Area Library Services Authority (CIALSA), Central Indiana Health Science Library Consortium. **Publications:** Tables of Contents; acquisitions lists - for internal distribution only.

★3367★
Central State Hospital - Medical Library (Med)
Box 4030 Phone: (804)524-7517
Petersburg, VA 23803 Jennifer Amador, Lib.Dir.
Staff: Prof 1; Other 6. **Subjects:** Psychiatry, psychiatric nursing, social work, clinical psychology, mental retardation. **Holdings:** 98,000 books; 2000 bound periodical volumes. **Subscriptions:** 150 journals and other serials. **Services:** Interlibrary loan; copying; library open to the public. **Automated Operations:** Computerized ILL (DOCLINE). **Computerized Information Services:** DIALOG Information Services; CD-ROMs (PsycLIT, MEDLINE). Performs searches on fee basis. **Publications:** New Acquisitions List, monthly - free. **Remarks:** FAX: (804)524-7308.

Central State Hospital - Professional Library
See: **Griffin Memorial Hospital** (6758)

Central State University
See: **University of Central Oklahoma** (18446)

★3368★
Central State University - Library - Map Collection (Geog-Map)
100 N. University Phone: (405)341-2980
Edmond, OK 73060-0192 Fritz A. Buckallew, Map Libn.
Founded: 1972. **Staff:** Prof 1; Other 3. **Subjects:** Maps. **Special Collections:** Axis Powers Topographic Mapping (4000). **Holdings:** 53,095 maps. **Services:** Interlibrary loan; copying; SDI; collection open to the public. **Automated Operations:** Computerized cataloging, acquisitions, and serials. **Computerized Information Services:** BRS Information Technologies, DIALOG Information Services, OCLC, DataTimes, Northwestern Online Total Integrated Systems (NOTIS). **Networks/Consortia:** Member of AMIGOS Bibliographic Council, Inc. **Special Catalogs:** Central State University Map Collection: A Subject Analysis (book).

★3369★
Central States Institute of Addictions - Addiction Material Center - Library (Med)
721 N. LaSalle St. Phone: (312)266-1056
Chicago, IL 60610 Dr. Dan Hendershott, Libn.
Founded: 1963. **Staff:** 3. **Subjects:** Alcohol and alcoholism, alcohol safety education, addictions, drug abuse education, drugs and driving. **Holdings:** 3500 books; 500 government publications; 600 pamphlets; 200 films on alcohol and drug abuse; abstract files. **Subscriptions:** 76 journals and other serials. **Services:** Interlibrary loan; center open to the public for reference use only.

Central Statistical Office of Finland
See: **Finland - Central Statistical Office of Finland** (5705)

★3370★
Central Suffolk Hospital - Medical Library (Med)
1300 Roanoke Ave. Phone: (516)548-6445
Riverhead, NY 11901 Anne Kirsch, Med.Libn.
Founded: 1973. **Staff:** Prof 1. **Subjects:** Medicine, nursing, surgery, allied health and hospital fields. **Holdings:** 800 books; 275 bound periodical volumes; 200 cassettes; 4 VF drawers of pamphlets. **Subscriptions:** 125 journals and other serials. **Services:** Interlibrary loan; copying; library for research use by referral. **Networks/Consortia:** Member of Medical & Scientific Libraries of Long Island (MEDLI), Long Island Library Resources Council, BHSL. **Remarks:** FAX: (516)727-8890.

★3371★
Central Synagogue of Nassau County - Helen Blau Memorial Library (Rel-Phil)
430 DeMott Ave. Phone: (516)766-4300
Rockville Centre, NY 11570 Miriam Schonwald, Libn.
Founded: 1959. **Staff:** Prof 2. **Subjects:** Religion, comparative religion, sociology, history, biography. **Special Collections:** Holocaust related literature. **Holdings:** 4200 books; 200 bound periodical volumes; 200 filmstrips; maps; phonograph records; cassettes; slides. **Subscriptions:** 3 journals and other serials. **Services:** Interlibrary loan; copying; library open to the public.

★3372★
The Central Union of Agricultural Cooperatives - Library (Agri)
1-8-3, Otemachi
Chiyoda-ku Nokyo Bldg. Phone: 3 32457578
Tokyo 100, Japan Mrs. Atsuko Hareyama
Founded: 1965. **Staff:** Prof 2. **Subjects:** Agricultural cooperatives, agriculture, agricultural economics. **Holdings:** 40,000 books; 600 bound periodical volumes. **Services:** Library not open to the public. **Publications:** Information of new registrations, monthly. **Remarks:** FAX: 3 52557356.

★3373★
Central Union of Agricultural Producers - Library (Agri)
Simonkatu 6
Postilokero 510
SF-00101 Helsinki, Finland Phone: 0 131151
Staff: 1.5. **Subjects:** Farming. **Holdings:** 10,000 volumes. **Subscriptions:** 200 journals and other serials; 20 newspapers. **Services:** Interlibrary loan; copying; library open to the public by appointment. **Computerized Information Services:** DIALOG Information Services, ESA/IRS, Data-Star, FT PROFILE. **Remarks:** FAX: 0 13115425. Telex: 122474 MTK SF. **Also Known As:** Maataloustuottajain Keskusliitto. **Staff:** Virve Myllymaki; Eeva Laurila, Libn.

★3374★
Central United Methodist Church - Library (Rel-Phil)
616 Jackson St., S.E. Phone: (205)353-6664
Decatur, AL 35601 Clydia D. DeFreese
Founded: 1959. **Subjects:** Bible, Methodist Church history, Bible history, devotional literature. **Holdings:** Books; 50 archival items; United Methodist Church reading list. **Subscriptions:** 11 journals and other serials. **Services:** Library open to the public. **Staff:** Margaret Cuthreu; Nina Gamble.

★3375★
Central United Methodist Church - Library (Rel-Phil)
1615 Copper, N.E. Phone: (505)243-7834
Albuquerque, NM 87106 Jean Dulaff, Libn.
Founded: 1961. **Subjects:** Church work, Bible, doctrinal theology, personal religion, Methodism, social issues. **Holdings:** 2374 books; 2 VF drawers; filmstrips. **Subscriptions:** 15 journals and other serials. **Services:** Library open to the public with restrictions. **Publications:** Acquisitions list, quarterly; bibliographies.

★3376★
Central United Methodist Church - Library (Rel-Phil)
925 N. 18th St. Phone: (817)752-7653
Waco, TX 76707 Mrs. R.L. Roberts, Jr., Libn.
Staff: Prof 1. **Subjects:** Religion, Bible, Christian doctrine, Jesus, devotional literature, religious art, worship, missions, religious education and leadership, career opportunities, evangelism, Methodism, social sciences, applied science, literature, history, travel, geography, biography. **Holdings:** 2500 books; hymnals; sheet music; conference and district reports; filmstrips; pamphlets; slides; AV maps. **Services:** Interlibrary loan; library not open to the public. **Formerly:** Trinity United Methodist Church. **Formed by the merger of:** Brookview United Methodist Church, St. John's United Methodist Church, and Trinity United Methodist Church.

★3377★
Central Vermont Hospital - Medical Library (Med)
Box 547 Phone: (802)229-9121
Barre, VT 05641 Betty-Jean Eastman, Med.Libn.
Staff: 1. **Subjects:** Medicine, surgery, nursing, allied health sciences. **Holdings:** 500 books. **Subscriptions:** 60 journals and other serials. **Services:** Interlibrary loan; library open to persons in health science fields.

★3378★
Central Vermont Public Service Corporation - Library Services (Energy)
77 Grove St. Phone: (802)773-2711
Rutland, VT 05701 Linda G. Cameron, Mgr., Lib.Serv. & Rec.
Founded: 1952. **Staff:** Prof 1; Other 1. **Subjects:** Energy, business, management, electrical engineering, utility law and regulation. **Holdings:** 2400 books; 50 bound periodical volumes; 40 VF drawers of pamphlets. **Subscriptions:** 150 journals and other serials. **Services:** Interlibrary loan; service open to the public by appointment. **Automated Operations:** Computerized serials, circulation, and routing. **Computerized Information Services:** DIALOG Information Services, NEXIS, LEXIS, Dow Jones News/Retrieval, NewsNet, Inc. **Publications:** Library Services Update, bimonthly - for internal distribution only.

★3379★
Central Virginia Training Center - Professional Library (Med)
Box 1098
Lynchburg, VA 24505 Phone: (804)947-6171
Founded: 1941. **Staff:** Prof 1. **Subjects:** Mental retardation, epilepsy, psychology, medicine, social work, special education. **Holdings:** 5000 books; 2200 bound periodical volumes; 85 audiotapes; 225 slides; reports; articles; clippings. **Subscriptions:** 130 journals and other serials. **Services:** Interlibrary loan; copying; library open to the public for reference use only. **Computerized Information Services:** Access to online systems. **Networks/Consortia:** Member of Lynchburg Area Library Cooperative. **Publications:** List of journal holdings, annual - for internal distribution only. **Staff:** Frances G. Imure.

★3380★
Central Washington Hospital - Heminger Health Sciences Library (Med)
1300 Fuller St.
P.O. Box 1887 Phone: (509)662-1511
Wenatchee, WA 98807-1887 Jane Belt, Med.Libn.
Founded: 1972. **Staff:** Prof 1. **Subjects:** Nursing, medicine, paramedical sciences, hospital administration and management. **Holdings:** 2000 books; 30 bound periodical volumes; 25 tapes. **Subscriptions:** 75 journals and other serials. **Services:** Interlibrary loan; copying; library open to the public. **Computerized Information Services:** MEDLARS, NLM. Performs searches on fee basis. **Networks/Consortia:** Member of Heminger (Ross A.) Health Sciences Library Consortium, National Network of Libraries of Medicine (NN/LM). **Publications:** Resources Newsletter, bimonthly.

★3381★
Central Washington University - Library - Special Collections
Ellensburg, WA 98926-9989 Phone: (509)963-1777
Special Collections: Curriculum collection (80 early 20th century textbooks, 1797 picture books, 9964 children's books, 7860 curriculum guides, 10,610 textbooks); map collection (85,187); media archives (1066 16mm films); music collection (5850 books, 920 bound periodical volumes, 12,792 phonograph records, 5735 magnetic tapes, 56 sets of collected works, 4500 scores, 20 volumes of microfilm, 215 cassettes, 113 compact discs); documents collection (529,370 U.S., state, foreign, United Nations, and international documents). **Services:** Interlibrary loan; library open to the public.

★3382★
Central Wisconsin Center for Developmentally Disabled - Library Information Center (Med)
317 Knutson Dr. Phone: (608)249-2151
Madison, WI 53704 Geraldine Matthews, Libn.
Subjects: Developmental disabilities. **Holdings:** 12,000 books; 4000 bound periodical volumes; reports; manuscripts; archives; microfiche; microfilm. **Subscriptions:** 50 journals and other serials. **Services:** Interlibrary loan; copying; library open to the public. **Remarks:** FAX: (608)249-0878.

★3383★
Centrale de l'Enseignement du Quebec - Centre de Documentation (Educ)
1170 boul. Lebourgneuf
Bureau 300 Phone: (418)627-8888
Quebec, PQ, Canada G2K 2G1 Guy Duchesne
Staff: Prof 1; Other 6. **Subjects:** Education, social sciences. **Holdings:** 13,000 books, unbound reports, documents, papers; 250 reels of microfilm; 15,000 current CEQ documents. **Subscriptions:** 350 journals and other serials. **Services:** Interlibrary loan; copying; library open to the public with restrictions. **Automated Operations:** Computerized cataloging and circulation. **Computerized Information Services:** DIALOG Information Services, Questel; DOCEQ (internal database). **Remarks:** FAX: (418)627-9999.

Centralforbundet for Alkohol- och Narkotikaupplysning
See: **Swedish Council for Information on Alcohol and Other Drugs** (15919)

★3384★
(Centralia) Chronicle - Library (Publ)
321 N. Pearl St. Phone: (206)736-3311
Centralia, WA 98531 Linda Stewart
Subjects: Newspaper reference topics. **Holdings:** Copies of newspaper. **Services:** Library open to the public for reference use only. **Remarks:** FAX: (206)736-1568.

★3385★
Centralnyj Naucno-Issledovatelskij Eksperimentalnyj i Proektnyj Institut po Selskomu Stroitelstvu (CNIEPselstroj) - Naucno-Techniceskaja Biblioteka (Plan)
ul. Aprelevskaja 65 Phone: 4365153
SU-143360 Aprelevka 2, Russia Lidia Wasilevna Lihachova
Founded: 1962. **Staff:** Prof 2; Other 2. **Subjects:** Agricultural engineering; building - general, agricultural, materials, economics, management; architecture; interior design. **Holdings:** 35,000 books; 2000 bound periodical volumes. **Subscriptions:** 100 journals and other serials; 15 newspapers. **Services:** Interlibrary loan; copying.

★3386★
Centro Andino de Accion Popular - Library (Agri)
D. Martin de Utreras 733 y Selve Alegre
Aptdo. 17-15-00173-B Phone: 2 522763
Quito, Ecuador Francisco Rhon Davila, Exec.Dir.
Founded: 1978. **Staff:** 3. **Subjects:** Socioeconomic and agricultural technology; alternative methods of development; development in Native Andean communities; health; economy; history; national statistics. **Holdings:** 15,000 volumes. **Subscriptions:** 10 journals and other serials. **Services:** Copying; library open to the public with restrictions. **Computerized Information Services:** MICRO ISIS (internal database). **Remarks:** FAX: 2 568452. Telex: 21190 ECLOF-ED.

Centro de Biblioteca e Informacion Cientifica Enrique Mejia Ruiz
See: **Universidad de Caldas** (17983)

Centro Camuno di Studi Preistorici e Etnologici
See: **Camunian Center for Prehistoric and Ethnologic Studies** (2630)

Centro de Documentacao de Hansenologia e Dermatologia Sanitaria Luiza Keffer
See: **Brasil - Secretaria de Estado da Saude - Coordenacao dos Institutos de Pesquisa** (2084)

★3387★
Centro de Estudios Avanzados de Puerto Rico y El Caribe - Biblioteca (Area-Ethnic)
Calle Cristo No. 52
Apartado S-4467 Phone: (809)723-4481
San Juan, PR 00904 Carmen Sylvia Arroyo, Hd.Libn.
Founded: 1976. **Staff:** Prof 1; Other 3. **Subjects:** Puerto Rico and the Caribbean - archeology, literature, history, folklore. **Special Collections:** Oral history tape collection (local history); Cerro Maravilla trial tape collection; Puerto Rican artists brochures and programs; Spanish discovery of the West Indies (books and maps). **Holdings:** 12,500 books; 1500 audiotapes. **Subscriptions:** 92 journals and other serials. **Services:** Interlibrary loan; copying; library open to the public for reference use only.

Centro de Estudios de Historia y Organizacion de la Ciencia "Carlos J. Finlay"
See: **Cuban Academy of Sciences - Center for the Study of the History and Organization of Science** (4465)

★3388★
Centro de Estudios Interplanetarios - Library (Sci-Engr)
Balmes 86
Entlo. 2A
E-08006 Barcelona, Spain Phone: 3 2158621
Subjects: UFO sightings - Spain, Portugal. **Holdings:** 520 volumes. **Computerized Information Services:** Internal database.

Centro de Estudios Puertorriquenos
See: **Hunter College of City University of New York - Centro de Estudios Puertorriquenos** (7561)

Centro de Informacion Tecnologica Industrial
See: **Laboratorios Nacionales de Fomento Industrial** (8861)

Centro Interamericano para el Desarrollo Regional
See: **Inter-American Center for Regional Development** (8023)

Centro Interamericano de Investigacion y Documentacion sobre Formacion Profesional
See: **Inter-American Center for Research and Documentation on Vocational Training** (8024)

Centro Internacional de Agricultura Tropical
See: **International Center for Tropical Agriculture** (8078)

Centro Internacional de la Infancia
See: **International Children's Centre - Documentation Department** (8080)

Centro Internacional de la Papa
See: **International Potato Center - Information Unit** (8175)

Centro de Investigacion y Desarrollo "Ing. Juan C. Van Wyk"
See: **Ing. Juan C. Van Wyck Center for Research and Development** (19751)

★3389★
Centro de Investigacion y de Promocion Amazonica - Library (Soc Sci)
Ricardo Palma 666 D Phone: 14 464823
Lima 18, Peru Rosa Panizo Uriarte, Libn.
Subjects: Amazonian rights, rural development. **Holdings:** 3290 books, periodicals, and articles. **Subscriptions:** 5 journals and other serials. **Services:** Interlibrary loan; SDI; library open to the public. **Remarks:** Alternate telephone number(s): 14 458661.

Centro de Investigaciones Historicas (CIH)
See: **University of Puerto Rico - Library System - Historical Research Center** (19241)

★3390★
Centro de la Mujer Peruana Flora Tristan - Library (Soc Sci)
Biblioteca Flora Tristan
Parque Hernan Velarde 42
Lima 1, Peru Phone: 14 248008
Subjects: Women's rights in Peru; women - legislation, health, sexuality; women's roles in history. **Holdings:** 4000 volumes.

Centro de Mujeres de Nigeria
See: **Women's Centre of Nigeria** (20557)

Centro Nacional de Documentacion Cientifica y Tecnologica
See: **Bolivia - National Scientific and Technological Documentation Center** (1949)

Centro Nacional de Informacao Documental Agricola
See: **Brazil - Ministry of Agriculture - National Center for Agricultural Documentary Information - Library** (2093)

Centro Nacional de Referencia del Uruguay
See: **Uruguay - Biblioteca Nacional - Centro Nacional de Documentacion Cientifica, Tecnica y Economica** (19696)

Centro Panamericano de Ingeniera Sanitaria y Ciencias del Ambiente
See: **Pan American Health Organization - Pan American Center for Sanitary Engineering & Environmental Sciences - REPIDISCA Network** (12719)

Centro de Pesquisas e Desenvolvimento Leopoldo A. Miguez de Mello
See: **Leopoldo A. Miguez de Mello Research and Development Center** (10384)

Centrum voor Wiskunde en Informatica
See: **Center for Mathematics and Computer Science** (3267)

★3391★
Centurion Hospital of Carrollwood - Medical Library (Med)
7171 N. Dale Mabry Hwy. Phone: (813)932-2222
Tampa, FL 33614 Linda Cox, Med.Educ.Coord., Hd.Libn.
Founded: 1982. **Staff:** Prof 2. **Subjects:** Medicine, nursing, and allied health sciences. **Holdings:** 350 books. **Subscriptions:** 70 journals and other serials. **Services:** Copying; library not open to the public. **Staff:** Claire Kennally, Reg.Libn.Cons.; Dorothy Kodish, Libn.

★3392★
Century Association - Library (Art)
7 W. 43rd St. Phone: (212)944-0090
New York, NY 10036 W. Gregory Gallagher, Libn.
Founded: 1847. **Staff:** Prof 1. **Subjects:** History, art, architecture, literature. **Special Collections:** Platt Architectural Library; Centuriana. **Holdings:** 25,000 volumes. **Subscriptions:** 100 journals and other serials; 9 newspapers. **Services:** Library not open to the public.

★3393★
Century Companies of America - Corporate Library (Bus-Fin, Law)
2000 Heritage Way Phone: (319)352-1000
Waverly, IA 50677 Marietta K. Sargeant, Libn.
Staff: Prof 1. **Subjects:** Law, business, insurance. **Holdings:** 9000 books. **Subscriptions:** 700 journals and other serials. **Services:** Library not open to the public. **Computerized Information Services:** DIALOG Information Services, LEXIS, NEXIS, BRS Information Technologies. **Remarks:** FAX: (319)352-5843.

★3394★
CER Corporation - Library (Energy)
950 Grier Dr. Phone: (702)361-2700
Las Vegas, NV 89119 Ella J. Jackson, Libn.
Founded: 1980. **Staff:** Prof 1. **Subjects:** Natural gas and unconventional gas recovery, petroleum engineering and geology, geothermal energy, peaceful use of nuclear energy, hazardous waste management. **Special Collections:** Tight gas sands (1500 reports and reprints). **Holdings:** 1500 books; 2000 technical reports; 150 project notebooks; 2500 well logs; 21,000 microfiche. **Subscriptions:** 150 journals and other serials. **Services:** Interlibrary loan; copying (limited); library open to the public with restrictions. **Automated Operations:** Computerized cataloging. **Computerized Information Services:** DIALOG Information Services, Integrated Technical Information System (ITIS), PFDS Online, DataTimes; Easylink (electronic mail service). **Remarks:** FAX: (702)361-7766.

★3395★
CERN - European Organization for Nuclear Research - Scientific Information Service (CERN AS-SI) (Sci-Engr)
CH-1211 Geneva 23, Switzerland Phone: 22 7672454
Dr. Stephan Schwarz, Ph.D.
Founded: 1954. **Staff:** Prof 11; Other 12. **Subjects:** Particle physics (high energy physics) and and allied subjects in science and technology. **Special Collections:** Pauli Collection (correspondence, manuscripts, private library); CERN Historical Archive. **Holdings:** 50,000 volumes; 200,000 preprints and reports. **Subscriptions:** 700 titles. **Services:** Interlibrary loan; SDI; service open to scientists and engineers working in areas related to particle physics. **Automated Operations:** ALEPH. **Computerized Information Services:** STN International, ESA/IRS, Data-Star, DIALOG Information Services, Questel; International preprints database (updated daily); PARTICLE PROPERTIES REACTION DATA (internal database); BITNET (electronic mail service). Performs searches free of charge. Contact Person: Eliane Chaney, telephone: 22 7674483. **Publications:** Various library accessions lists; manuals for databases; Directory of High Energy Physics Institutes. **Remarks:** Organization is a center for basic research (not concerned with the development of nuclear power or weapons.) FAX: 22 7828611.

★3396★
Cerro Tololo Inter-American Observatory - Library (Sci-Engr)
Casilla 603 Phone: 213352
La Serena, Chile Eugenia Barraza, Libn.
Subjects: Astronomy. **Holdings:** 12,300 volumes. **Services:** Library not open to the public. **Computerized Information Services:** Electronic mail service. **Remarks:** FAX: 51 213352, ext. 342. Telex: 602301 AURA CT. Operated by Association of Universities for Research in Astronomy, Inc. (AURA). **Also Known As:** Observatorio Interamericano de Cerro Tololo.

★3397★
Certainteed Corporation - Corporate Library/Information Center (Sci-Engr)
1400 Union Meeting Rd.
Blue Bell, PA 19422 Phone: (215)341-6283
Founded: 1978. **Staff:** Prof 2; Other 1. **Subjects:** Insulation, roofing concepts, pipes, business and management, science and technology, glass manufacture. **Holdings:** 2000 books; 1000 bound periodical volumes; 50 standards and specifications. **Subscriptions:** 375 journals and other serials; 6 newspapers. **Services:** Interlibrary loan; library not open to the public. **Computerized Information Services:** DIALOG Information Services, PFDS Online, Info Globe, NewsNet, Inc., Chemical Abstracts Service (CAS), Occupational Health Services, Inc. (OHS). **Networks/Consortia:** Member of PALINET, Philadelphia Area Reference Librarians Information Exchange (PARLIE). **Remarks:** FAX: (215)341-6429. **Staff:** Trudy Eaton, Asst.Libn.

★3398★
Ceskoslovenska Akademie Ved (CSAV) - Ustav Geotechniky (Sci-Engr)
Puskinovo 9 Phone: 422-3121749
CS-160 00 Prague, Czechoslovakia Dr. Jan Kozak, CSC, Archv.Hd.
Founded: 1986. **Staff:** Prof 1. **Subjects:** Earthquakes. **Special Collections:** Pre-photographical depictions of the consequences of 83 earthquakes, 1348-1908 (403 engravings, drawings, paintings). **Holdings:** 50 books; 50 reports; 490 archival items. **Remarks:** FAX: 422-842134.

★3399★
Cessna Aircraft Company - Aircraft Division - Engineering Library (Sci-Engr)
P.O. Box 7704
Wichita, KS 67277 Phone: (316)946-6575
Subjects: Aerodynamics. **Holdings:** 3500 volumes. **Services:** Library not open to the public.

Cetus Corporation
See: **Cessna Aircraft Company - Aircraft Division - Engineering Library** (3399)

Cetus Corporation
See: **Chiron Corporation - Information Services Center** (3618)

★3400★
Ceylon Chamber of Commerce - Library (Bus-Fin)
50 Nawam Mawatha
P.O. Box 274
Colombo 2, Sri Lanka Phone: 1 421745
Subjects: Sri Lanka - manufacturing, importing, exporting. **Holdings:** 15,000 volumes. **Computerized Information Services:** Internal databases. **Remarks:** FAX: 1 449352. Telex: 21492 GLOBAL CE.

★3401★
CH2M Hill, Inc. - Corvallis Regional Office Library (Env-Cons)
2300 N.W. Walnut Blvd. Phone: (503)752-4271
Corvallis, OR 97330-3596 Tony Salmon, Libn.
Staff: Prof 1; Other 2. **Subjects:** Engineering, environmental science, wastewater technology, geology. **Holdings:** 5000 books; 550 bound periodical volumes; 4000 manufacturers' catalogs; 20 boxes of archival material; 20,000 internal reports. **Subscriptions:** 200 journals and other serials; 15 newspapers. **Services:** Interlibrary loan; copying; library open to the public with restrictions. **Computerized Information Services:** DIALOG Information Services, CIS. **Special Catalogs:** Catalog to manufacturers' catalogs (card, book); catalog to internally generated materials (card). **Staff:** James F. Counihan, Lib.Supv.

★3402★
CH2M Hill, Inc. - Information Center (Sci-Engr)
2525 Air Park
P.O. Box 49-2478 Phone: (916)243-5831
Redding, CA 96049 Virginia Merryman, Libn.
Founded: 1968. **Staff:** Prof 1. **Subjects:** Engineering - sanitary, structural, agricultural; California weather; water resources. **Special Collections:** North American Weather Charts, 1942 to present; California rainfall records, 1956 to present. **Holdings:** 5000 books; 3000 U.S. Geological Survey topographical maps; 300 geological reports and maps; 100 California Department of Water Resources bulletins; 2000 project reports. **Subscriptions:** 45 journals and other serials. **Services:** Interlibrary loan; copying; center open to the public by appointment. **Computerized Information Services:** DIALOG Information Services. **Remarks:** FAX: (916)243-1654.

★3403★
CH2M Hill, Inc. - Information Resource Center (Env-Cons)
1216 Arch St. Phone: (215)563-4220
Philadelphia, PA 19107 Eileen C. Mathias
Founded: 1974. **Staff:** Prof 1. **Subjects:** Environmental planning, solid waste, engineering, hazardous waste mitigation. **Holdings:** 4000 books. **Subscriptions:** 120 journals and other serials; 2 newspapers. **Services:** Center not open to the public. **Computerized Information Services:** DIALOG Information Services, TOXNET, MAX Online Demographic Data Management and Reporting System, STN International. **Remarks:** FAX: (215)563-3828. **Formerly:** Rogers, Golden and Halpern, Inc.

★3404★
CH2M Hill, Inc. - Library (Sci-Engr)
6425 Christie Ave., Suite 500 Phone: (510)652-2426
Emeryville, CA 94608-1006 Mary Byrne, Libn.
Staff: Prof 1. **Subjects:** Engineering - water, wastewater, hazardous waste. **Holdings:** 2000 books; company reports and contract documents; National Technical Information Service (NTIS) reports. **Subscriptions:** 100 journals and other serials; 10 newspapers. **Services:** Library open to the public by permission. **Computerized Information Services:** DIALOG Information Services, OCLC. **Remarks:** FAX: (510)652-0482.

★3405★
CH2M Hill, Inc. - Library (Sci-Engr)
3840 Rosin Ct., Rm. 110 Phone: (916)920-0300
Sacramento, CA 95834-1633 Joy Hills, Libn.
Founded: 1973. **Staff:** Prof 1. **Subjects:** Water resources, energy, sanitation engineering, environmental planning, civil engineering, structural engineering, hazardous waste. **Holdings:** 1500 books; 50 unbound periodicals; 1500 technical reports, proposals, contract documents, vendor catalogs. **Subscriptions:** 50 journals and other serials; 15 newspapers. **Services:** Interlibrary loan; library not open to the public. **Remarks:** FAX: (916)920-8463.

★3406★
CH2M Hill, Inc. - Library (Sci-Engr)
825 N.E. Multnomah, Suite 1300 Phone: (503)235-5000
Portland, OR 97232 Barbara L. Stollberg, Libn.
Founded: 1970. **Staff:** Prof 1; Other 1. **Subjects:** Engineering - water, wastewater, environmental, hazardous waste, industrial processes, geotechnical; planning, economics. **Holdings:** 10,000 books; 7000 internal reports. **Subscriptions:** 70 journals and other serials; 25 newspapers. **Services:** Interlibrary loan; copying; library open to the public with restrictions. **Computerized Information Services:** DIALOG Information Services; internal database. **Remarks:** FAX: (503)295-4446.

★3407★
CH2M Hill, Inc. - Library (Env-Cons)
Box 4400 Phone: (703)471-6405
Reston, VA 22090 Suzanne L. Montgomery, Lib.Mgr.
Founded: 1971. **Staff:** Prof 1; Other 2. **Subjects:** Hazardous wastes, water and wastewater treatment, civil engineering. **Holdings:** 5500 books; manufacturers' catalogs. **Subscriptions:** 94 journals and other serials. **Services:** Interlibrary loan; library not open to the public. **Automated Operations:** Computerized acquisitions and serials. **Computerized Information Services:** DIALOG Information Services, OCLC EPIC. **Networks/Consortia:** Member of OCLC Pacific Network. **Publications:** Reston Review (newsletter), weekly. **Remarks:** FAX: (703)481-0980.

★3408★
CH2M Hill, Inc. - Rocky Mountain Regional Office - Library (Sci-Engr)
Box 22508 Phone: (303)771-0900
Denver, CO 80222 Audrey Mars, Libn.
Staff: Prof 1; Other 1. **Subjects:** Water and wastewater, civil and mechanical engineering, climatology, mining. **Holdings:** 5500 volumes; 2000 technical reports; 1100 trade catalogs; 300 Environmental Protection Agency documents; 300 U.S. Geological Survey topographical maps; 1000 archival materials. **Subscriptions:** 150 journals and other serials; 10 newspapers. **Services:** Interlibrary loan; copying; library open to other CH2M Hill libraries. **Automated Operations:** Computerized acquisitions, serials, and circulation. **Remarks:** FAX: (303)741-4053.

★3409★
CH2M Hill, Inc. - Southeast Regional Office - Technical Library (Env-Cons)
7201 N.W. 11th Place
P.O. Box 147009 Phone: (904)331-2442
Gainesville, FL 32614-7009 Hang T. SooHoo, Sr.Rec.Mgt.Spec.
Founded: 1968. **Staff:** Prof 1; Other 2. **Subjects:** Water supply, wastewater treatment and disposal, domestic and industrial waste treatment, solid and hazardous wastes disposal, environmental sciences, construction management. **Holdings:** 6200 books; 243 bound periodical volumes; 2600 engineering reports; 2500 specifications; 500 reels of microfilm; 5200 microfiche; AV equipment; maps. **Subscriptions:** 200 journals and other serials. **Services:** Interlibrary loan; center not open to the public. **Automated Operations:** Computerized cataloging. **Computerized Information Services:** DIALOG Information Services, BRS Information Technologies, OCLC. Performs searches on fee basis. **Publications:** Acquisition list, annual; newsletter, periodically. **Special Catalogs:** Catalog of bound company reports (card); catalog of bound specifications (card); catalog of original project drawings (card); catalog of manufacturers' catalogs (online). **Remarks:** FAX: (904)331-5320. Telex: 756070.

★3410★
CH2M Hill, Inc. - Technical Information Center (Sci-Engr)
777 108th Ave., N.E. Phone: (206)453-5000
Bellevue, WA 98004-6922 Kay M. Boyett, Lib.Sys.Coord.
Founded: 1973. **Staff:** Prof 1; Other 1. **Subjects:** Engineering. **Holdings:** 15,000 books. **Subscriptions:** 575 journals and other serials; 35 newspapers. **Services:** Interlibrary loan; center not open to the public. **Automated Operations:** Computerized serials. **Computerized Information Services:** DIALOG Information Services, Chemical Information Systems, Inc. (CIS), OCLC. **Networks/Consortia:** Member of Western Library Network (WLN). **Remarks:** FAX: (206)462-5957. Telex: 185234 ch2m mut.

Chaco Culture National Historical Park
See: **U.S. Natl. Park Service** (17686)

★3411★
Chadbourne & Parke - Library (Law)
30 Rockefeller Plaza, 24th Fl. Phone: (212)408-5286
New York, NY 10112 Catherine A. Pennington, Dir.
Founded: 1892. **Staff:** Prof 6; Other 5. **Subjects:** Law. **Holdings:** 50,000 books; 750 bound periodical volumes; 100 VF drawers. **Subscriptions:** 400 journals and other serials; 20 newspapers. **Services:** Interlibrary loan; copying; library open to members of American Association of Law Libraries and Special Libraries Association. **Computerized Information Services:** WESTLAW, DIALOG Information Services, LEXIS, Dow Jones News/Retrieval, Dun & Bradstreet Business Credit Services, RLIN. **Networks/Consortia:** Member of Research Libraries Information Network (RLIN). **Publications:** Library Newsletter, monthly; Tax Cat, annual. **Remarks:** FAX: (212)541-5369. **Staff:** Fran Fredrick, Ref.Libn.; Phyllis Poda, Tax Libn.; Lillian Arcuri, Assoc.Libn. for Pub.Serv.; Anna Smallen, Assoc.Libn. for Tech.Serv.; Alexandra Radushkevich, Foreign & Intl.Libn.

Chain Store Age
See: **Lebhar-Friedman, Inc.** (9038)

★3412★
Chait Salomon - Bibliotheque/Library (Law)
1 Place Ville Marie, Suite 1900-1 Phone: (514)879-1353
Montreal, PQ, Canada H3B 2C3 Pauline Housden, Libn.
Founded: 1928. **Staff:** Prof 1. **Subjects:** Law, corporate law, real estate law, litigation. **Holdings:** 1300 books; 5250 bound periodical volumes. **Subscriptions:** 166 journals and other serials. **Services:** Interlibrary loan; copying; SDI; library open to the public with restrictions. **Computerized Information Services:** SOQUIJ (Societe Quebecoise d'Information Juridique), CAN/LAW, The Financial Post DataGroup, STM Systems Corporation; Manac Systems (internal database). **Remarks:** FAX: (514)879-1460.

Challis Resource Centre
See: **Confederation College of Applied Arts & Technology** (4137)

★3413★
Dr. Everett Chalmers Hospital - Dr. Garfield Moffatt Health Sciences Library (Med)
P.O. Box 9000 Phone: (506)452-5432
Fredericton, NB, Canada E3B 5N5 Paul Clark, Libn.
Founded: 1977. **Staff:** Prof 1. **Subjects:** Medicine, nursing, allied health sciences. **Holdings:** 1500 books; 700 bound periodical volumes. **Subscriptions:** 200 journals and other serials. **Services:** Interlibrary loan; copying; SDI; library open to the public by appointment. **Computerized Information Services:** MEDLINE, CAN/OLE; Envoy 100 (electronic mail service). Performs searches on fee basis. **Remarks:** FAX: (506)452-5947. Electronic mail address(es): ILL.NBFDEC (Envoy 100).

★3414★
Chamber of Commerce of Hawaii - Information Office (Bus-Fin)
735 Bishop St., Suite 220 Phone: (808)522-8800
Honolulu, HI 96813 Mikel Humerickhouse, Supv.
Founded: 1948. **Staff:** 1. **Subjects:** Statistics; commercial, trade, business information. **Special Collections:** Lists of Chamber of Commerce members providing special services. **Holdings:** 6000 pamphlets and reports; 8 VF drawers of newspaper clippings; directories; buyers' guides. **Subscriptions:** 10 journals and other serials. **Services:** Interlibrary loan; copying; office open to the public. **Publications:** Trade Tips, biweekly; Hawaii Facts and Figures, annual; Living and Working in Hawaii, irregular; Directory of Manufacturers, State of Hawaii, biennial; Directory of Shopping Centers, irregular. **Remarks:** FAX: (808)522-8836.

★3415★
Chamber of Commerce and Industry (Bolivia) - Library (Bus-Fin)
Suarez de Figueroa 127, No. 3 y 4
Casilla 180
Santa Cruz, Bolivia Phone: 3 334555
Founded: 1980. **Staff:** 1. **Subjects:** Bolivian economic development. **Holdings:** 1500 volumes. **Subscriptions:** 50 journals and other serials; 5 newspapers. **Services:** Library open to the public for reference use only. **Publications:** Guia de Industria, Comercio y Servicios; Santa Cruz en Cifras; Manual de Normas Bolivianas para Comercio Exterior. **Remarks:** FAX: 3 342353. Telex: 4298 CAINCO BV. **Also Known As:** Camara de Industria y Comercio. **Staff:** Victor Ojeda Chilo.

★3416★
Chamber of Commerce, Industry and Trades of Burkina - Library (Bus-Fin)
B.P. 502
Ouagadougou 01, Burkina Faso Phone: 306114
Subjects: Burkina Faso commerce. **Holdings:** 2500 volumes. **Subscriptions:** 45 journals and other serials; 10 newspapers. **Services:** Interlibrary loan; copying; library open to the public. **Remarks:** FAX: 306116. Alternate telephone number(s): 301266. Telex: 5268BF. **Also Known As:** Chambre de Commerce, d'Industrie et d'Artisanat du Burkina. **Staff:** Jean Baptist Kinane, Chef de Serv.; Boubacar Duedradoo, Doc.; Joriane Kyeleine, Doc.

★3417★
Chamber of Commerce of the United States of America - National Chamber Foundation Library (Bus-Fin)
1615 H St., N.W. Phone: (202)463-5448
Washington, DC 20062 Jacqueline Tyson, Libn.
Founded: 1917. **Staff:** Prof 1. **Subjects:** Economics, business. **Special Collections:** Nation's Business Magazine, 1912 to present (microfilm). **Holdings:** 5000 books; 30 VF drawers. **Subscriptions:** 100 journals and other serials; 5 newspapers. **Services:** Interlibrary loan; library open to the public by appointment. **Remarks:** FAX: (202)463-3114.

★3418★
Chamber of Mines of Eastern British Columbia - Bureau of Information (Sci-Engr)
215 Hall St. Phone: (604)352-5242
Nelson, BC, Canada V1L 5X4 L. Addie, Mgr.
Founded: 1920. **Staff:** 1. **Subjects:** British Columbian and Canadian mining - statistics, history, safety, regulations; geology; prospecting. **Special Collections:** British Columbia Ministry of Energy, Mines & Petroleum Resources reports, 1896 to present; Geological Survey of Canada material, 1876-1972 (650 items). **Holdings:** 2000 books; 1500 bound periodical volumes; 600 other cataloged items; 12 volumes of press reports and archives; 200 pamphlets; 1200 maps. **Subscriptions:** 30 journals and other serials; 5 newspapers. **Services:** Copying; bureau open to the public. **Remarks:** FAX: (604)352-3013.

★3419★
Chamber of Mines of South Africa - Head Office - Library (Sci-Engr)
P.O. Box 61809 Phone: 11 8388211
Marshalltown 2107, Republic of South Africa Jeannette Hofsajer, Libn.
Founded: 1886. **Staff:** Prof 2; Other 3. **Subjects:** Mining, geology, labor. **Special Collections:** Comro Research Reports (3000); South African Institute of Mining and Metallurgy publications (2000). **Holdings:** 15,000 books; 25,000 bound periodical volumes; 10,000 reports; archival items; microfilm. **Subscriptions:** 400 journals and other serials; 20 newspapers. **Services:** Interlibrary loan; copying; SDI; library open to the public. **Computerized Information Services:** DIALOG Information Services; SABINET (internal database). **Remarks:** FAX: 11 8341884.

Chamberlain GARD
See: **Electrocom GARD** (5289)

Chambre de Comerce et d'Industrie de l'Ile Maurice
See: **Mauritius Chamber of Commerce and Industry** (9851)

Chambre de Commerce Central de Finlande
See: **Central Chamber of Commerce of Finland** (3332)

★3420★
Chambre des Notaires du Quebec - Centre de Documentation (Law)
630 Rene-Levesque Blvd. W., Suite 1700 Phone: (514)879-1793
Montreal, PQ, Canada H3B 1T6 Celine Amnotte, Libn.
Founded: 1975. **Staff:** Prof 2; Other 7. **Subjects:** Law, civil and commercial law, fiscal policy. **Holdings:** 3500 books; 1000 bound periodical volumes; 1000 other cataloged items. **Subscriptions:** 300 journals and other serials; 15 newspapers. **Services:** Center not open to the public. **Automated Operations:** Computerized cataloging, acquisitions, and serials. **Computerized Information Services:** SOQUIJ (Societe Quebecoise d'Information Juridique). Performs searches on fee basis. **Remarks:** FAX: (514)879-1923.

Chamizal National Memorial
See: **U.S. Natl. Park Service** (17687)

★3421★
Champaign County Historical Archives (Hist)
The Urbana Free Library
201 S. Race St. Phone: (217)367-4025
Urbana, IL 61801-3283 Jean Koch, Dir.
Founded: 1956. **Staff:** Prof 2; Other 4. **Subjects:** Champaign County history, genealogy of Illinois and the eastern United States. **Holdings:** 7242 books; 2115 bound periodical volumes; 3919 reels of microfilm; 9706 microfiche; 190 VF drawers of photographs, family information, clippings, manuscripts, documents, marriage records, chancery court records, probate records; guardianship records and abstracts; 300 oral history tapes. **Subscriptions:** 275 journals and other serials. **Services:** Copying; archives open to the public for reference use only; private researchers available. **Automated Operations:** Computerized cataloging. **Networks/Consortia:** Member of Lincoln Trail Libraries System (LTLS). **Publications:** Champaign County Historical Archives Historical Publications Series: 1858 Alexander Bowman Map of Urbana and West Urbana; Combined 1893, 1913 and 1929 Atlases of Champaign County; Early History and Pioneers of Champaign County, 1891; 1863 Alexander Bowman Map of Champaign County; Ivesdale: A Photographic Essay; Upon A Quiet Landscape: The Photographs of Frank Sadorus; The History of Champaign County, 1905; From Salt Fork to Chickamauga. **Special Indexes:** Name indexes to Champaign County birth records, marriage license applications, cemetery inscriptions, funeral home records, monument company records, obituaries, probates, chancery court records; name and subject indexes for reprints in Historical Publications Series. **Remarks:** FAX: (217)367-4061. **Staff:** Howard Grueneberg, Cat.Libn.; Jean Gordon, Archv.Asst.; Michele McNabb, Archv.Asst.

★3422★
Champaign County Historical Museum - Library (Hist)
709 W. University Ave. Phone: (217)356-1010
Champaign, IL 61820 Linda Lauchner, Cur.
Founded: 1974. **Staff:** 5. **Subjects:** Local history. **Holdings:** 800 books; Museum publications; Champaign-Urbana city directories, 1899-1960; University of Illinois yearbooks; AV programs; resource materials on renovation of old homes; 125 audiotapes; 3500 slides; oral histories. **Services:** Library open to the public by appointment on a limited schedule. **Publications:** Historic Sites in Champaign County; Historic Sites in Champaign-Urbana; Grass Roots Preservation.

★3423★
Champaign County Law Library (Law)
County Court House Phone: (513)652-2222
Urbana, OH 43078 Judy K. Burnett, Libn.
Staff: 1. **Subjects:** Law. **Holdings:** 10,500 volumes. **Services:** Library open to the public with restrictions.

★3424★
Champaign-Urbana News-Gazette - Library (Publ)
P.O. Box 677 Phone: (217)351-5228
Champaign, IL 61824-0677 Carolyn J. Vance, Chf.Libn.
Founded: 1946. **Staff:** Prof 1; Other 1. **Subjects:** Local news; Illinois State Government news; Newspaper clipping file of Champaign, Urbana, Danville, Champaign county, and Vermilion county, Illinois State government. **Holdings:** 400 books; 1.21 million newspaper clippings, 1946 to present; 44,000 photographs; 95 maps; 12 VF drawers of pamphlets and brochures; News-Gazette, 1953 to present, on microfilm. **Subscriptions:** 20 journals and other serials; 8 newspapers. **Services:** Interlibrary loan; copying (limited); library open to the public by telephone only. **Special Indexes:** Local Editorial Index, 1979-1987. **Remarks:** FAX: (217)351-5295 (Attn.: Library).

★3425★
Champion International - Business Information (Bus-Fin)
One Champion Plaza Phone: (203)358-7692
Stamford, CT 06921 Charles Shih, Mgr.
Staff: Prof 2; Other 1. **Subjects:** Business, paper, forestry. **Holdings:** 1800 books; 150 bound periodical volumes; 100 research reports; 850 annual reports; microfiche. **Subscriptions:** 150 journals and other serials; 6 newspapers. **Services:** Interlibrary loan; not open to the public. **Computerized Information Services:** DIALOG Information Services, NEXIS, Dow Jones News/Retrieval, Info Globe. **Networks/Consortia:** Member of Southwestern Connecticut Library Council (SWLC). **Publications:** Quarterly newsletter - for internal distribution only; holdings booklet, annual. **Remarks:** FAX: (203)358-6444. **Staff:** Carolyn Hart, Bus.Info.Anl.

★3426★
Champion International - Technical Information Center (Sci-Engr)
W. Nyack Rd. Phone: (914)578-7102
West Nyack, NY 10994 Shirley A. Rigney, Tech.Info.Supv.
Staff: Prof 2; Other 1. **Subjects:** Pulp and paper, wood and wood chemistry. **Holdings:** 2000 volumes; 75 VF drawers. **Subscriptions:** 227 journals and other serials. **Services:** Interlibrary loan; center open to the public by appointment. **Computerized Information Services:** DIALOG Information Services, PFDS Online, NLM, Chemical Abstracts Service (CAS). **Staff:** Ronnie Cohen, Libn.

Stephen Chan Library of Fine Arts
See: **New York University - Institute of Fine Arts** (11725)

★3427★
A Chance to Grow - Kretsch Brain Injury Resource Library (Med)
3700 Bryant Ave., N. Phone: (612)521-2266
Minneapolis, MN 55412 Emmett Davis, Lib.Dir.
Founded: 1982. **Staff:** Prof 4. **Subjects:** Brain injury, cerebral palsy, autism, learning disabilities, Down syndrome/genetics, brain allergy. **Special Collections:** Mailable kits of traveling mini-libraries about brain injury and related issues. **Holdings:** 2000 volumes. **Services:** Interlibrary loan; library open to the public. **Computerized Information Services:** Internal database. **Publications:** Library newsletter, quarterly; Bibliography. **Staff:** K. DeBoer, Dir. ACTG.

Chancellor Walworth Library of the Court of Chancery
See: **New York State Supreme Court - Appellate Division, 4th Judicial Department - Law Library** (11713)

Chandler Memorial Library and Ethnic Center
See: **Nashua Public Library** (10998)

★3428★
Chandler, Wood, Harrington & Maffly - Library (Law)
111 Sutter St., 19th Fl. Phone: (415)421-5484
San Francisco, CA 94104 Sumy Anhorn, Libn.
Subjects: Law. **Holdings:** Figures not available. **Services:** Library not open to the public. **Remarks:** FAX: (415)986-4874.

Channel Islands Archive
See: **Santa Barbara Museum of Natural History - Library** (14802)

Chanute Technical Training Center
See: **U.S. Air Force Hospital** (16898)

★3429★
Chaparral Genealogical Society - Library (Hist)
310 N. Live Oak
P.O. Box 606 Phone: (713)255-9081
Tomball, TX 77375 Ella Louise Hill, Libn.
Founded: 1973. **Staff:** 18. **Subjects:** Genealogy, local history. **Holdings:** 2000 books; 675 bound periodical volumes; 275 reels of microfilm of census and county records; 2 VF drawers. **Subscriptions:** 80 journals and other serials. **Services:** Interlibrary loan; copying; library open to the public. **Publications:** Roadrunner, quarterly. **Special Indexes:** Indexes to early county censuses; Index to Waller County, Texas Cemeteries; index to marriage records from the following sixteen Texas counties: Austin, Brazos, Burleson, Fayette, Ft. Bend, Galveston, Grimes, Harris, Jefferson, Lee, Madison, Milam, Trinity, Washington, Waller, Montgomery.

★3430★
Chapel of the Cross (Episcopal) - Library (Rel-Phil)
304 E. Franklin St.
Chapel Hill, NC 27514 Phone: (919)929-2193
Subjects: Religion. **Holdings:** 1200 books. **Subscriptions:** 4 journals and other serials. **Services:** Library not open to the public.

Howard I. Chapelle Memorial Library
See: **Chesapeake Bay Maritime Museum** (3483)

★3431★
Chapelwood United Methodist Church - Pathfinders Memorial Resource Library (Rel-Phil)
11140 Greenbay Phone: (713)465-3467
Houston, TX 77024 Ann Mobley, Dir.
Staff: Prof 2; Other 4. **Subjects:** Bible, children, Christian life and education, juvenile fiction, devotions. **Holdings:** 8400 books; 193 filmstrips; 227 cassettes; 50 video cassettes; 111 phonograph records; 116 AV programs. **Subscriptions:** 16 journals and other serials. **Services:** Library open to the public with restrictions. **Staff:** Dona Badgett, Libn.; Marguerite Brice, Asst.Libn.

F. Stuart Chapin, Jr. Planning Library
See: **University of North Carolina at Chapel Hill** (19059)

Chapin Library
See: **Williams College** (20446)

Chaplin Memorial Library
See: **Norwich University** (12122)

★3432★
Chapman and Cutler - Law Library (Law)
111 W. Monroe St., 16th Fl. Phone: (312)845-3749
Chicago, IL 60603-4080 Denis S. Kowalewski, Libn.
Staff: Prof 5; Other 6. **Subjects:** Law. **Holdings:** 30,000 volumes; loose-leaf services. **Subscriptions:** 70 journals and other serials; 15 newspapers. **Services:** Interlibrary loan; library not open to the public. **Computerized Information Services:** Dun & Bradstreet Business Credit Services, LEXIS, WESTLAW, DIALOG Information Services, Legislative Information System (LIS), VU/TEXT Information Services, DataTimes, OCLC, LEGI-SLATE. **Special Indexes:** Index to internal research on legal topics; index to client letters on banking topics (both online). **Remarks:** FAX: (312)701-6620. **Staff:** David Fanta, Asst.Libn.; Jamie Stewart, Asst.Libn.; Robert Luberda, Asst.Libn.

★3433★
Chapman Historical Museum - Library (Hist)
348 Glen St. Phone: (518)793-2826
Glens Falls, NY 12801 John L. Polnak, Dir.
Founded: 1967. **Staff:** 4. **Subjects:** Local and social history, Adirondacks. **Special Collections:** Broad Street School Collection, 1937-1974 (3 cubic feet); Charles E. Bullard papers, 1855-1947 (3.5 cubic feet); genealogy collection, 1760 to present (4 cubic feet); Glens Falls Police Department records, 1905-1928; Glens Falls Public School Collection, 1881-1962 (21 cubic feet); Orcutt family correspondence, 1861-1886; Hopkins-Sheldon family papers, 1845-1900; George Sands papers, 1840-1870 (3 cubic feet); business records collection, 1800-1940 (18 volumes); Seneca Ray Stoddard Collection (25 cubic feet of photographs); Glens Falls Insurance Company business records, 1849-1968 (55 cubic feet); YMCA business records, 1887-1969 (30 VF drawers). **Holdings:** 700 books; 20,000 photographs; archives. **Services:** Copying; library open to researchers by appointment. **Formerly:** Glens Falls Queensbury Historical Association, Inc. **Staff:** Flora Ingalls, Libn.

Chapman Library - Philbrook Museum of Art
See: **Philbrook Museum of Art** (12997)

★3434★
Chapman Research Group, Inc. - Library (Sci-Engr)
5601 S. Broadway, Suite 306 Phone: (303)730-2226
Littleton, CO 80121 Marilyn Chapman, Pres.
Founded: 1969. **Subjects:** Technology transfer, economics, management, new venture development. **Holdings:** 2000 volumes. **Subscriptions:** 12 journals and other serials; 3 newspapers. **Services:** Library open by specific arrangement only. **Remarks:** FAX: (303)730-2372.

★3435★
Charfoos & Christensen, P.C. - Library (Law)
4000 Penobscot Bldg. Phone: (313)963-8080
Detroit, MI 48226 Nora L.M. Shumake, Dir. of Libs.
Founded: 1972. **Staff:** Prof 1; Other 2. **Subjects:** Law, medicine. **Holdings:** 560 books; 51 bound periodical volumes; 65 other cataloged items. **Subscriptions:** 44 journals and other serials. **Services:** Interlibrary loan; library not open to the public. **Automated Operations:** Computerized cataloging. **Computerized Information Services:** BRS Information Technologies, DIALOG Information Services, Dow Jones News/Retrieval, NLM, LEXIS, NEXIS, WESTLAW; internal database. **Networks/Consortia:** Member of Detroit Associated Libraries, National Network of Libraries of Medicine - Greater Midwest Region. **Remarks:** FAX: (313)963-0243.

★3436★
Charity-Delgado School of Nursing - Library (Med)
450 S. Claiborne Ave. Phone: (504)568-6430
New Orleans, LA 70112 Anne B. Howard, Lib.Coord.
Staff: Prof 2; Other 2. **Subjects:** Nursing. **Holdings:** 7500 books; 2000 bound periodical volumes. **Subscriptions:** 110 journals and other serials. **Services:** Interlibrary loan; copying; library open to the public. **Staff:** Phyllis Ward, Libn.

★3437★
Charles County Circuit Court - Law Library (Law)
Charles County Courthouse
P.O. Box 3060
Washington & Charles Sts. Phone: (301)932-3322
La Plata, MD 20646 Kathy Mazzola, Libn.
Staff: Prof 1. **Subjects:** Maryland and federal law. **Special Collections:** Laws of Maryland, 1822 to present. **Holdings:** 10,000 volumes; 10 microfiche; other cataloged items. **Subscriptions:** 13 journals and other serials. **Services:** Copying; library open to the public for reference use only. **Computerized Information Services:** WESTLAW.

Charles County Community College - Southern Maryland Studies Center
See: **Southern Maryland Studies Center** (15498)

Prince Charles Education Resource Centre - Library Media Services
See: **Winnipeg School Division No. 1** (20491)

★3438★
Charles River Associates, Inc. - Library (Energy, Trans)
Box 708 Phone: (617)266-0500
Boston, MA 02117 Christian F. Stueart, Lib.Mgr.
Staff: Prof 2. **Subjects:** Economics, transportation, energy, metallurgy, environment, industrial organization. **Holdings:** 20,000 volumes. **Subscriptions:** 300 journals and other serials; 5 newspapers. **Services:** Interlibrary loan; library not open to the public. **Automated Operations:** Computerized cataloging. **Computerized Information Services:** DIALOG Information Services, NEXIS, OCLC. **Networks/Consortia:** Member of NELINET, Inc. **Remarks:** FAX: (617)266-0698. Telex: 706922.

★3439★
Charles River Broadcasting Company - WCRB Library (Mus)
750 South St.
Box 9173 Phone: (617)893-7080
Waltham, MA 02254-9173 George C. Brown, Mus.Dir.
Founded: 1948. **Staff:** Prof 1. **Subjects:** Classical music recordings; live performance tapes of Boston Symphony Orchestra, Boston Pops, New York Philharmonic; music from Marlboro, Koussevitzky series. **Holdings:** 50,000 phonograph records; 7000 compact discs. **Subscriptions:** 5 journals and other serials. **Services:** Library not open to the public. **Networks/Consortia:** Member of Boston Area Music Libraries (BAML).

★3440★
Charles River Museum of Industry - Library (Sci-Engr)
154 Moody St. Phone: (617)893-5410
Waltham, MA 02154 Karen M. LeBlanc, Dir.
Subjects: Horology, machine tools, automotive history, local history. **Special Collections:** Waltham Watch Company; W.H. Nichols Company; Waltham Screw Company; Atwood Collection; Raytheon Collection; William Davis Collection. **Holdings:** 2500 books; 20 bound periodical volumes; 500 machine drawings and patents; 20 AV programs; 7 manuscript collections. **Services:** Copying; library open to the public for reference use only.

Charleston Evening Post/News and Courier
See: **Charleston Post and Courier** (3444)

★3441★
Charleston Gazette-Sunday Gazette Mail - Library (Publ)
1001 Virginia St., E. Phone: (304)348-5140
Charleston, WV 25301 Ron Miller, Hd.Libn.
Founded: 1960. **Staff:** Prof 4. **Subjects:** Newspaper reference topics, West Virginia. **Holdings:** 36 bound periodical volumes; 1416 reels of microfilm and 40,000 microjackets of Charleston Gazette, 1888 to present, and Charleston Daily Mail, 1914 to present. **Services:** Library not open to the public. **Staff:** Linda Colvin, Asst.; Alison Stanley, Asst.; Christine Kelly, Asst.

★3442★
Charleston Library Society (Hist)
164 King St. Phone: (803)723-9912
Charleston, SC 29401 Catherine E. Sadler, Libn.
Founded: 1748. **Staff:** Prof 5; Other 3. **Subjects:** Genealogy, history, literature. **Special Collections:** South Caroliniana; Charleston newspapers, 1732 to present; 18th century books and periodicals; architecture and furniture; Jewish history; botany; South Carolina history. **Holdings:** 95,000 volumes; 1600 reels of microfilm. **Subscriptions:** 120 journals and other serials; 10 newspapers. **Services:** Interlibrary loan; copying; library open to the public. **Staff:** Dedree Syracuse, Asst.Libn.; Patricia G. Bennett, Asst.Libn.; Janice L. Grimes, Sec./Asst.; LeeAnn Floss, Asst.Libn.

★3443★
Charleston Museum - Library (Hist, Biol Sci)
360 Meeting St. Phone: (803)722-2996
Charleston, SC 29403 K. Sharon Bennett, Archv./Libn.
Founded: 1773. **Staff:** Prof 1; Other 2. **Subjects:** Natural history of South Carolina, history of South Carolina, decorative arts, historic archeology. **Special Collections:** Print collection of South Carolina artists (200); Gov. William Aiken House Collection (5000 volumes); Manigault House Collection (300 volumes); Heyward-Washington House Collection (400 volumes). **Holdings:** 10,000 books; 10,000 bound periodical volumes; 400 early maps of South Carolina area; 300 documents; 200 pamphlets; 10 boxes of manuscripts. **Subscriptions:** 50 journals and other serials. **Services:** Interlibrary loan; copying; library open to nonmembers on fee basis.

★3444★
Charleston Post and Courier - Library (Publ)
134 Columbus St. Phone: (803)577-7111
Charleston, SC 29403 Mary S. Crockett, Chf.Libn.
Founded: 1946. **Staff:** Prof 3; Other 1. **Subjects:** Newspaper reference topics. **Special Collections:** News and Courier, 1803-1991 (on microfilm); Evening Post, 1894-1991; Post and Courier, 1991 to present; Charleston City Year Books, 1880 to present. **Holdings:** 1500 books; 350 bound periodical volumes; 205 VF drawers of newspaper clippings and microclips; 8 shelves of pamphlets; 23 drawers of photograph files. **Subscriptions:** 60 newspapers. **Special Indexes:** Index to historic houses. **Remarks:** FAX: (803)723-4893. Published by Evening Post Publishing Company. **Formerly:** Charleston Evening Post/News and Courier - Post/Courier Library. **Staff:** Pamela Smith, Libn.; Lathorina Perry, Photo Libn.

Charleston Sunday Gazette Mail
See: **Charleston Gazette-Sunday Gazette Mail** (3441)

Jean Charlot Collection
See: **University of Hawaii - Special Collections** (18627)

★3445★
Charlotte Law Library Associates - Charlotte Law Library
730 E. Trade St., Suite 600
Charlotte, NC 28202-3076
Defunct. Holdings absorbed by Mecklenburg County Law & Government Library.

★3446★
Charlotte and Mecklenburg County Public Library - Robinson-Spangler Carolina Room (Hist)
310 N. Tryon St. Phone: (704)336-2980
Charlotte, NC 28202-2176 Patricia Ryckman, Mgr.
Founded: 1956. **Staff:** Prof 5; Other 3. **Subjects:** Local and regional history, genealogy. **Special Collections:** Harry Golden Collection (129 boxes of local author's manuscripts, working papers, tapes); Charlotte Music Archives; local newspaper, 1956-1985 (7 million negatives). **Holdings:** 18,000 books; 364 bound periodical volumes; 120 VF drawers of clippings and genealogical materials; 4800 reels of microfilm of Federal Population Schedules; 2125 reels of microfilm of local newspapers; 360 reels of microfilm of county records; local and state documents. **Subscriptions:** 226 journals and other serials. **Services:** Interlibrary loan; copying; room open to the public. **Computerized Information Services:** OCLC, VU/TEXT Information Services. Performs searches free of charge. **Networks/Consortia:** Member of SOLINET, Metrolina Library Association. **Remarks:** FAX: (704)336-2677. **Staff:** Lew Herman, Libn.; Valerie Burnie, Libn.; Sheila Bumgarner, Libn.; Rosemary Lands, Libn.

★3447★
Charlotte-Mecklenburg Schools - Curriculum Research Center (Educ)
428 W. Boulevard
Charlotte, NC 28203 Phone: (704)376-0122
Founded: 1957. **Staff:** Prof 1; Other 2. **Subjects:** Education. **Special Collections:** Curriculum Development Library (on microfiche). **Holdings:** 14,964 books; unbound journals; 8 drawers of current publishers catalogs; backfiles of 185 journals on microfilm; 4 VF drawers of pamphlets; curriculum guides; ERIC Documents (complete set); 275 video cassettes; 261 16mm films. **Subscriptions:** 287 journals and other serials. **Services:** Copying; center open to the public for reference use only. **Automated Operations:** Computerized public access catalog (DYNIX). **Computerized Information Services:** BRS Information Technologies; CD-ROMs (ERIC, Books in Print Plus, Book Review Digest, Education Index). **Publications:** Bibliographies. **Staff:** Barbara M. Waymer, Inservice Coord./Media; Barbara Epps, Media Techn.; Cathi Cooper, Media Techn.

Charlotte Museum of History - Hezekiah Alexander Homesite
See: **Hezekiah Alexander Foundation** (340)

★3448★
Charlotte Observer - Library (Publ)
600 S. Tryon St.
Box 32188 Phone: (704)358-5217
Charlotte, NC 28232 Sara Gesler Klemmer, Hd.Libn.
Founded: 1956. **Staff:** Prof 1; Other 6. **Subjects:** Newspaper reference topics. **Holdings:** 1000 VF drawers of clippings; 375 VF drawers of pictures; 30 drawers of microfilm. **Subscriptions:** 10 journals and other serials. **Services:** Library not open to the public; research services available on a fee basis. **Computerized Information Services:** VU/TEXT Information Services, DIALOG Information Services. **Remarks:** FAX: (704)358-5036. Published by Knight Publishing Company, Inc.

★3449★
Charlton County Historical Society - Library (Hist)
P.O. Box 575 Phone: (912)496-7401
Folkston, GA 31537 Lois B. Mays, Pres.
Founded: 1975. **Subjects:** Local history, genealogy. **Special Collections:** Okefenokee Collection (history of Okefenokee Swamp, and area animals, birds, fish, and plants; books, leaflets, essays, pictures). **Holdings:** 100 books. **Services:** Copying; library open to the public by appointment. **Publications:** Printed Census of Charlton County: 1860 and 1910; abstracts of 1908, 1910, 1912 Charlton County Herald, weekly newspaper.

★3450★
Charlton Park Historic Village & Museum - Library (Hist)
2545 S. Charlton Park Rd. Phone: (616)945-3775
Hastings, MI 49058 Sara Feldbauer, Cur. of Coll.
Founded: 1936. **Staff:** 1. **Subjects:** Local history, crafts, agriculture. **Special Collections:** 1900 census data; late 19th centure newspapers; late 19th to mid-20th century regional photographs; advertising art; postcards; family papers; museum journals. **Holdings:** 300 bound periodical volumes. **Services:** Copying; library open to the public by appointment.

Chartered Institute of Marketing
See: **Infomark** (7841)

★3451★
Chartered Institute of Transport - Library (Trans)
80 Portland Pl. Phone: 71 6369952
London W1N 4DP, England Sue Woolley
Subjects: Transportation, physical distribution. **Holdings:** 53,000 volumes. **Subscriptions:** 303 journals and other serials. **Services:** Library open to the public for reference use only. **Remarks:** FAX: 71 6370511.

Chase Collection
See: **Bradley University - Virginius H. Chase Special Collections Center - Chase Collection** (2060)

Emory A. Chase Memorial Library
See: **New York State Supreme Court - 3rd Judicial District** (11688)

★3452★
Chase Manhattan Bank, N.A. - Library (Bus-Fin)
33 Maiden Ln., 27th Fl. Phone: (212)968-3415
New York, NY 10081 Jean Hrichus, Mgr.
Founded: 1955. **Staff:** Prof 4; Other 5. **Subjects:** Banking, finance, industry, domestic and foreign corporations, economics, data processing. **Holdings:** 14,000 books; 250 bound periodical volumes; 110 VF drawers; 60 periodical titles on microfilm; Wall Street Journal, 1969 to present, on microfiche; New York Times, 1922 to present, on microfilm. **Subscriptions:** 500 journals and other serials. **Services:** Interlibrary loan; center not open to the public. **Automated Operations:** Computerized cataloging and serials. **Computerized Information Services:** NEXIS, OCLC, DIALOG Information Services, VU/TEXT Information Services, BRS Information Technologies, TEXTLINE, Dow Jones News/Retrieval, InvesText, Spectrum Ownership Profiles Online. **Remarks:** FAX: (212)968-3437.

Salmon P. Chase College of Law
See: **Northern Kentucky University** (12006)

Virginius H. Chase Special Collections Center
See: **Bradley University** (2058)

William Merritt Chase Archives
See: **Parrish Art Museum - Library** (12764)

★3453★
Chatfield Brass Band Inc. - Music Lending Library (Mus)
81 Library Ln.
P.O. Box 578 Phone: (507)867-3275
Chatfield, MN 55923 Meindert Zylstra, Mgr.
Founded: 1971. **Staff:** 6. **Subjects:** Music - band, dance band and orchestra, popular, piano, instrumental, vocal. **Special Collections:** Jan Bily Collection (small orchestra music); composer histories; old and out of print band music. **Holdings:** 101 books; 50,000 pieces of indexed music; 1800 boxes of unindexed music; 200 other cataloged items. **Subscriptions:** 3 journals and other serials. **Services:** Interlibrary loan; copying; library open to the public, with service charges applied to borrowing - fee schedules available on request. **Publications:** Newsletter, irregular; library history, free upon request. **Staff:** Barbara Pettey, Hd. Lending Libn.

★3454★
Chatsworth Historical Society - Frank H. Schepler, Jr. Memorial Library
10385 Shadow Oak Dr.
Chatsworth, CA 91313
Subjects: History of Chatsworth, the San Fernando Valley, and California, 1885 to present. **Holdings:** 260 manuscripts, slides, photographs, oral history tapes, documents. **Remarks:** Currently inactive.

★3455★
Chattanooga-Hamilton County Bicentennial Library - Local History and Genealogical Collections (Hist)
1001 Broad St. Phone: (615)757-5317
Chattanooga, TN 37402 Clara W. Swann, Dept.Hd.
Founded: 1888. **Staff:** Prof 1; Other 4. **Subjects:** Southeast U.S. genealogy; local and state history. **Holdings:** 24,645 books; 311 manuscript collections; 160 VF drawers of clippings and photographs; 8180 reels of microfilm of county records and local newspapers; 8192 microfiche. **Subscriptions:** 128 journals and other serials. **Services:** Copying; collections open to the public for reference use only. **Automated Operations:** Computerized cataloging. **Computerized Information Services:** OCLC. **Networks/Consortia:** Member of SOLINET. **Publications:** Collections brochure, irregular; Guide to Manuscript Collections, irregular. **Special Indexes:** Family surname index for materials in the department (card); local newspaper obituary indexes, 1897 to present. **Staff:** Ned Irwin.

★3456★
Chattanooga-Hamilton County Regional Planning Commission - Library (Plan)
City Hall Annex, Rm. 200
100 E. 11th St. Phone: (615)757-5216
Chattanooga, TN 37402 Deborah Maddox, Libn.
Subjects: Conditions, growth, and change in urban and regional areas. **Holdings:** 1150 books; 8 VF drawers of clippings; 480 loose-leaf notebooks; 46 drawers of maps; 1980 U.S. Census for Tennessee. **Subscriptions:** 20 journals and other serials. **Services:** Library open to the public for reference use only.

★3457★
Chattanooga Times - Library (Publ)
117 E. 10th St.
Box 951 Phone: (615)756-1234
Chattanooga, TN 37402 Mr. Chris Hardesty, Libn.
Founded: 1963. **Staff:** Prof 2. **Subjects:** Newspaper reference topics. **Holdings:** 500 books; 51,000 subject and biographical clipping files; 80 VF drawers of pictures; newspaper, 1879 to present, on microfilm; 300 pamphlets. **Subscriptions:** 15 newspapers. **Services:** Copying; library open to other libraries and to journalists for reference use only and by appointment with management approval. **Remarks:** FAX: (615)267-4036. **Staff:** David Hamilton, Asst.Libn.

★3458★
Chattem Inc. - Chemicals - Research Library (Sci-Engr)
1715 W. 38th St. Phone: (615)821-4571
Chattanooga, TN 37409-1248 Tilda Wall, Libn.
Founded: 1915. **Staff:** 2. **Subjects:** Chemistry, engineering, medicine, pharmaceuticals. **Special Collections:** Antique herbals and antique almanacs. **Holdings:** 2100 books; 2200 bound periodical volumes; 200 pamphlets; 670 patents. **Subscriptions:** 92 journals and other serials; 34 newspapers. **Services:** Copying; library open to the public for reference use only on request. **Remarks:** FAX: (615)821-6132. Telex: 558-463.

Milton J. Chatton Medical Library
See: **Santa Clara Valley Medical Center - Milton J. Chatton Medical Library** (14811)

★3459★
Chautauqua County Historical Society - Library (Hist)
Village Park
Box 7 Phone: (716)326-2977
Westfield, NY 14787 Michelle Henry, Dir.
Founded: 1883. **Staff:** 1. **Subjects:** History of Chautauqua County. **Special Collections:** Tourgee papers; Civil War Muster Rolls of Chautauqua County; Foote Papers; Cushing Papers; Genealogy of Chautauqua County. **Holdings:** 2000 books. **Services:** Library open to the public with restrictions. **Publications:** History of Chautauqua County, 1938-1978; Patriot Soldiers of 1775-1783 (volumes I & II); Veterans of the War for American Independence of Chautauqua County - all for sale. **Special Catalogs:** Local history collection (card); Foote papers (card). **Special Indexes:** Tourgee papers (book).

★3460★
Chautauqua County Law Library (Law)
Gerace Office Bldg.
Attn: Law Library
Mayville, NY 14757 Phone: (716)753-4129
Staff: 1. **Subjects:** Law, local legislation. **Special Collections:** Local history collection. **Holdings:** 12,314 volumes. **Services:** Interlibrary loan; library open to the public for reference use only. **Networks/Consortia:** Member of Chautauqua-Cattaraugus Library System.

Chautauqua Institution - Smith Memorial Library
See: **Smith Memorial Library** (15250)

★3461★
Chaves County District Court - Library (Law)
Box 1776 Phone: (505)622-2565
Roswell, NM 88201 Jean Willis, Ct.Adm.
Staff: Prof 1. **Subjects:** Law. **Holdings:** 10,000 volumes. **Services:** Library open to the public for reference use only. **Computerized Information Services:** WESTLAW. **Remarks:** FAX: (505)624-9506. Information concerning the library may be obtained by contacting the District Court office.

★3462★
Chedoke-McMaster Hospitals - Chedoke Hospital Library (Med)
Box 2000, Sta. A Phone: (416)521-2100
Hamilton, ON, Canada L8N 3Z5 Lois M. Wyndham, Chf.Libn.
Staff: Prof 1; Other 1. **Subjects:** Rehabilitation medicine, geriatrics, child psychology and psychiatry, alcohol and drug abuse. **Holdings:** 2500 books. **Subscriptions:** 251 journals and other serials. **Services:** Interlibrary loan; library open to the public by appointment. **Computerized Information Services:** DIALOG Information Services, MEDLINE, CAN/OLE. **Networks/Consortia:** Member of Hamilton/Wentworth District Health Library Network. **Remarks:** FAX: (416)521-7938.

★3463★
Cheekwood Botanical Gardens - Library (Biol Sci)
Cheekwood-Forrest Park Dr. Phone: (615)353-2148
Nashville, TN 37205 Muriel H. Connell, Libn.
Founded: 1971. **Staff:** Prof 1; Other 2. **Subjects:** Horticulture, landscape architecture, plant science, ecology, wildflowers, garden design, botanical art, orchids, herbs, natural history. **Holdings:** 4300 books; 260 bound periodical volumes; 62 slide programs; videocassettes; flower and seed catalogs. **Subscriptions:** 108 journals and other serials. **Services:** Interlibrary loan; copying; library open to the public with restrictions. **Also Known As:** Tennessee Botanical Gardens & Fine Arts Center - Botanical Gardens Library.

Cheekwood Museum
See: **Tennessee Botanical Gardens & Fine Arts Center** (16154)

★3464★
Chelmsford Historical Society - Barrett-Byam Homestead Library (Hist)
40 Byam Rd. Phone: (508)256-2311
Chelmsford, MA 01824 Rebecca Warren, Cur.
Founded: 1930. **Subjects:** Chelmsford and Massachusetts history, Civil War and Revolution, early agriculture. **Special Collections:** Historical music and school books. **Holdings:** Reports; pamphlets; deeds. **Subscriptions:** 10 journals and other serials. **Services:** Library open to the public on limited schedule, mid-April to mid-December.

★3465★
Chelsea School of Art - Library (Art)
Manresa Rd. Phone: 71 3513844
London SW3 6LS, England Dr. Stephen Bury
Founded: 1963. **Staff:** Prof 3; Other 3. **Subjects:** Modern art history, contemporary art. **Special Collections:** Exhibition catalogues (40,000); artists' books (800); art periodicals (1000); art cuttings and ephemera (30,000 items); British Black Art Archive. **Holdings:** 75,000 books; 10,000 bound periodical volumes; 60,000 archival items; 2000 microfiche; 500 reels of microfilm; 170,000 slides. **Subscriptions:** 300 journals and other serials; 2 newspapers. **Services:** Interlibrary loan; copying; SDI; library open to the public. **Automated Operations:** Computerized public access catalog, cataloging, serials, acquisitions, and circulation (BLCMP). **Publications:** Women's Art and Artists; Afro-Caribbean and Asian Art in Britain; Postmodernism; Public Art. **Remarks:** FAX: 71 3528721.

★3466★
Chem-Nuclear Systems, Inc. - Information Center (Env-Cons)
140 Stoneridge Dr. Phone: (803)256-0450
Columbia, SC 29210 Amy C. Gossett, Libn.
Founded: 1981. **Staff:** Prof 1. **Subjects:** Radioactive waste management, nuclear engineering, government regulations, radiation protection. **Special Collections:** Nuclear Regulatory Commission materials. **Holdings:** 250 books; 2000 technical reports; 300 reports on microfiche; 10 VF drawers of subject files. **Subscriptions:** 200 journals and other serials. **Services:** Interlibrary loan; center not open to the public. **Computerized Information Services:** DIALOG Information Services. **Remarks:** FAX: (803)799-4470.

★3467★
Chem Systems Inc. - Information Center (Sci-Engr)
303 S. Broadway Phone: (914)631-2828
Tarrytown, NY 10591 Maryann M. Grandy, Dir., Info. & Comm.
Founded: 1964. **Staff:** Prof 5; Other 3. **Subjects:** Petrochemicals, chemical engineering, energy, specialty chemicals. **Holdings:** 1100 books; 3000 technical reports and conference proceedings; 175 VF drawers of technical data; pamphlets; U.S. and foreign patents. **Subscriptions:** 200 journals and other serials. **Services:** Interlibrary loan; center not open to the public. **Computerized Information Services:** DIALOG Information Services, PFDS Online, BRS Information Technologies, Dow Jones News/Retrieval, Data-Star, NEXIS, STN International. **Remarks:** FAX: (914)631-8851. Telex: 221844. **Staff:** Kristene Sullivan, Search Coord.; Denise Komonchak, Tech.Serv.; Esther Cheng, Databases; Jocelyn Rosen, Indexing; Ella Barsky, Res./Anl.

★3468★
Chem Systems Ltd. - Library (Sci-Engr)
28 St. James's Sq. Phone: 71 839 4652
London SW1Y 4JH, England Elizabeth Coles, Mgr., Info.Serv.
Founded: 1964. **Staff:** Prof 3. **Subjects:** Chemistry, energy, chemical engineering, plastics, resins, rubber, textiles, refining, petrochemicals, fertilizers. **Holdings:** 1000 bound volumes; internal reports. **Subscriptions:** 200 journals and other serials. **Services:** Library not open to the public. **Computerized Information Services:** DIALOG Information Services, ESA/IRS, Mead Data Central, ORBIT Search Service, STN International, Data-Star, FT PROFILE, Dun & Bradstreet Business Credit Services, Kompass, BRS Information Technologies, TRADSTAT, GBI, PFDS Online; internal database. **Remarks:** FAX: 71 930 1504. Telex: 916636. **Formerly:** Chem Systems International Ltd. **Staff:** Paul Duncan; Dawn Wright.

★3469★
Chemical Abstracts Service - Library Services Department (Info Sci, Sci-Engr)
Box 3012 Phone: (614)447-3600
Columbus, OH 43210 Robert S. Tannehill, Jr., Mgr., Lib.Serv.
Founded: 1954. **Staff:** Prof 15; Other 32. **Subjects:** Library and information science, chemistry, chemical engineering, chemical information sciences. **Special Collections:** Collection of primary chemical sciences literature (serials, proceedings of meetings, patents, technical reports, edited collections). **Holdings:** 20,000 books; 30,000 serial titles. **Subscriptions:** 9000 journals and other serials. **Services:** Interlibrary loan; copying; SDI; library open to the public with restrictions. **Automated Operations:** Computerized cataloging. **Computerized Information Services:** DIALOG Information Services, PFDS Online, LEXIS, WESTLAW, BRS Information Technologies, STN International; InterNet (electronic mail service). **Networks/Consortia:** Member of OHIONET, Columbus Area Libraries Information Council of Ohio (CALICO). **Publications:** Meeting Alert, bimonthly - both for internal distribution only. **Special Catalogs:** DDS Directory of Publications - available upon request. **Special Indexes:** International CODEN Directory (microfiche); CAS Source Index (print; computer-readable); CASSI KWOC Title Index (microfiche). **Remarks:** This collection of primary chemical sciences literature is said to be the most comprehensive in the world. Chemical Abstracts Service is a division of the American Chemical Society, Inc. FAX: (614)447-3647. Electronic mail address(es): rst65@cas.bitnet@cunyvm.cuny.edu (InterNet). Telex: MCI 684 2086. **Staff:** Michael Cirivello, Acq.Prod.Mgr.; Leon Blauvelt, Bibliog.Info.Mgr.; Marian Nichol, Doc.Serv.Mgr.

★3470★
Chemical Bank - Business Information Center (Bus-Fin)
277 Park Ave., 5th Fl. Phone: (212)310-7806
New York, NY 10172 Melinda Scott, V.P. & Mgr.
Founded: 1966. **Staff:** Prof 9; Other 6. **Subjects:** Banking, finance, economics, management. **Holdings:** 2000 books; 150 bound periodical

volumes; 800 periodical titles; 650,000 microforms; 174 VF drawers. **Subscriptions:** 1600 journals and other serials; 10 newspapers. **Services:** Interlibrary loan; library not open to the public. **Automated Operations:** Computerized cataloging, serials, and circulation. **Computerized Information Services:** DIALOG Information Services, Dow Jones News/ Retrieval, Data Resources (DRI), Investment Dealers Digest, TEXTLINE, NEXIS, VU/TEXT Information Services; internal database. **Remarks:** FAX: (212)755-8737. **Staff:** Helen Traina, Asst. V.P. & Mgr.; Nora Lidell, Info.Spec.; Maureen O'Donnell, Info.Spec.; Howard Jaeger, Info.Spec.

★3471★
Chemical Industry Institute of Toxicology - CIIT Information Services (Sci-Engr, Biol Sci)
P.O. Box 12137 Phone: (919)541-2070
Research Triangle Park, NC 27709 Willanna A. Griffin, Libn.
Founded: 1979. **Staff:** Prof 1; Other 1. **Subjects:** Toxicology, industrial chemicals, biochemistry, epidemiology, cell biology, analytical chemistry. **Holdings:** 8000 books; CIIT reports. **Subscriptions:** 307 journals and other serials. **Services:** Interlibrary loan; services open to the public. **Automated Operations:** Computerized cataloging, acquisitions, and serials. **Computerized Information Services:** DIALOG Information Services, MEDLARS, STN International. **Special Indexes:** Subject index to CIIT staff publications, monthly. **Remarks:** FAX: (919)541-9015.

Chemical International Information Center
See: **Chemists' Club Library** (3473)

★3472★
Chemical Manufacturers Association - Library (Sci-Engr)
2501 M St., N.W. Phone: (202)887-1100
Washington, DC 20037-1303 Rose Clark, Libn.
Subjects: Chemical industry. **Holdings:** 1000 books; 60 VF drawers.

Chemical Thermodynamics Data Center
See: **U.S. Natl. Institute of Standards and Technology** (17614)

Chemical Warfare/Chemical and Biological Defense Information Analysis Center
See: **Battelle Memorial Institute** (1565)

Chemins de Fer Nationaux du Canada
See: **Canadian National Railways** (2971)

Chemir Laboratories
See: **Spectra Search** (15578)

The Chemists' Club - National Foundation for History of Chemistry
See: **University of Pennsylvania - National Foundation for History of Chemistry - Library** (19190)

★3473★
Chemists' Club Library - Chemical International Information Center (Sci-Engr)
295 Madison Ave., 27th Fl. Phone: (212)679-6383
New York, NY 10017 Elsie Lim, Libn.
Founded: 1898. **Staff:** Prof 2; Other 3. **Subjects:** Pure and applied chemistry, chemical engineering, pharmacology, toxicology. **Special Collections:** Biographies and portraits of chemists; chemical companies (vertical files). **Holdings:** 65,000 volumes; microfilm. **Subscriptions:** 150 journals and other serials. **Services:** Copying; translation; center open to the public. **Automated Operations:** Computerized accounting. **Computerized Information Services:** MEDLARS, DIALOG Information Services, PFDS Online, Chemical Abstracts Service (CAS). Performs searches on fee basis. **Publications:** Chemical Monographs Review; Library News. **Special Catalogs:** Serial Holding List of Chemists' Club Library. **Remarks:** FAX: (212)779-0349. **Staff:** Mildred Hunt, Ref.Libn.

★3474★
Chemlab Service of Amarillo - Library
6420 River Rd.
Amarillo, TX 79108
Founded: 1960. **Subjects:** Water, wastewater control and treatment, hazardous wastes. **Holdings:** 350 books; 200 reports. **Remarks:** Currently inactive.

★3475★
Chemung County Historical Society, Inc. - Mrs. Arthur W. Booth Library (Hist)
415 E. Water St. Phone: (607)734-4167
Elmira, NY 14901 Constance Barone, Dir.
Founded: 1923. **Staff:** 1. **Subjects:** New York State and local history, local authors, genealogies. **Special Collections:** Chemung County historical journals, 1955 to present; Chemung County historical records, maps, atlases; county historical records; Elmira city directories, 1857 to present; all minutes of Elmira City Council and County Board of Supervisors. **Holdings:** 1800 volumes; letters; 20,000 manuscripts; 10,000 photographs; historical pamphlets; 300 scrapbooks. **Services:** Copying; library open to the public (fee charged); open to groups and students for research by appointment on fee basis. **Computerized Information Services:** OCLC; Timeless Collections (internal database). **Publications:** Chemung Historical Journal.

★3476★
Chen-Northern, Inc. - Library (Sci-Engr)
370 Benjamin Lane
P.O. Box 7777 Phone: (208)377-2100
Boise, ID 83707 Joan Peterson, Info.Spec.
Subjects: Chemistry, geotechnical and material engineering, nondestructive testing, construction and materials quality control, laboratories. **Holdings:** 40,000 volumes. **Remarks:** FAX: (208)376-5349. **Formerly:** Northern Engineering & Testing, Inc.

★3477★
Chenango Memorial Hospital - Medical Library (Med)
179 N. Broad St. Phone: (607)335-4159
Norwich, NY 13815-1097 Ann L. Slocum, Lib.Serv.Mgr.
Founded: 1953. **Staff:** Prof 1. **Subjects:** Medicine, nursing, and allied health sciences. **Holdings:** 800 books; 570 bound periodical volumes. **Subscriptions:** 203 journals and other serials. **Services:** Interlibrary loan; copying; library open to the public by appointment. **Automated Operations:** Computerized ILL. **Computerized Information Services:** MEDLINE, OCLC; DOCLINE (electronic mail service). **Networks/Consortia:** Member of South Central Research Library Council (SCRLC). **Remarks:** Alternate telephone number(s): 335-4111. FAX: (607)334-2024.

Anne Bunce Cheney Library
See: **University of Hartford - William H. Mortensen Library** (18615)

Karl Cherkasky Social Medicine Library
See: **Montefiore Medical Center** (10663)

★3478★
Cherokee County Historical Society - Research Center (Hist)
Box 247 Phone: (712)436-2624
Cleghorn, IA 51014 Anne Wilberding, Pres.
Subjects: Local history, genealogy. **Special Collections:** Original pioneer materials and World War II data for Cherokee County; Collection of genealogical research data. **Holdings:** Figures not available. **Services:** Copying; center open to the public by appointment. **Publications:** Newsletter, quarterly.

Cherokee Garden Club Library
See: **Atlanta Historical Society - Archives/Library** (1246)

★3479★
Cherokee National Historical Society, Inc. - Cherokee National Archives (Hist)
Box 515
TSA-LA-GI Phone: (918)456-6007
Tahlequah, OK 74465 Tom Mooney, Archv.
Founded: 1963. **Staff:** 1. **Subjects:** Cherokee history. **Special Collections:** W.W. Keeler (Principal Chief of Cherokees) papers; Cherokee National Executive Committee minutes, 1948 (origin) to 1970 (disbandment); Cherokee Nation papers, 1969-1975; Earl Boyd Pierce (Counsel General of the Cherokee Nation) papers, 1928-1983; manuscript collections. **Holdings:** 3000 books; 500 bound periodical volumes; 147 reels of microfilm; 5 VF drawers of pamphlets; 7 VF drawers of papers and committee minutes. **Subscriptions:** 20 journals and other serials. **Services:** Copying; archives open to the public on request.

★3480★
Cherokee Regional Library - Georgia History & Genealogical Room (Hist, Area-Ethnic)
305 S. Duke St.
Box 707 Phone: (404)638-2992
LaFayette, GA 30728 Brian Stoutenburg, Dir.
Staff: Prof 3. **Subjects:** Local history, genealogy, Cherokee Indians. **Holdings:** 990 books; 80 bound periodical volumes; 15 maps; 380 reels of microfilm (including county census data); 4 VF drawers of family histories; 3 VF drawer of local history materials. **Subscriptions:** 12 journals and other serials. **Services:** Copying; library open to the public. **Publications:** Bibliographies of county histories. **Special Catalogs:** Early Walker County History. **Special Indexes:** Deed Index I of Walker County; Index to Walker County History; Query Index (card); index to South Walker County cemeteries; partial index to Walker County Messenger (local newspaper). **Remarks:** FAX: (404)638-4028. **Staff:** Russell D. Murphy, Tech.Serv.; Robert Manning, HQ Libn.

★3481★
Cherokee Strip Land Rush Museum - Docking Research Center Archives Library (Hist)
S. Summit Street Rd.
P.O. Box 1002 Phone: (316)442-6750
Arkansas City, KS 67005 Liz Oakes, Exec.Dir.
Founded: 1966. **Staff:** Prof 1; Other 1. **Subjects:** Local history, genealogy. **Special Collections:** Speeches and pictures of Governor Robert Docking. **Holdings:** Books; bound periodical volumes; pamphlets on historical events; unbound reports; newspapers; patents; maps; pictures; letters; manuscripts; clippings; dissertations; 6 reels of microfilm; 10 tapes. **Services:** Copying; research upon request; library open to the public for reference use only. **Remarks:** Library contains the holdings of the Cowley County Genealogical Society.

★3482★
Cherry Hospital - Learning Resource Center (Med)
Box 8000 Phone: (919)731-3447
Goldsboro, NC 27530 Maxim Tabory, Libn.
Staff: Prof 1; Other 1. **Subjects:** Psychiatry, medicine, nursing, psychology, social work, allied health sciences. **Holdings:** 2000 books; 800 bound periodical volumes; 986 AV programs. **Subscriptions:** 95 journals and other serials. **Services:** Interlibrary loan; center open to state employees and health care workers. **Publications:** List of new acquisitions, quarterly - for internal distribution only. **Special Catalogs:** AV catalog (book).

★3483★
Chesapeake Bay Maritime Museum - Howard I. Chapelle Memorial Library (Hist)
Box 636 Phone: (301)745-2916
St. Michaels, MD 21663 Joan Chlan, Libn.
Founded: 1968. **Staff:** 2. **Subjects:** Chesapeake Bay history and marine life; boat construction, maintenance, handling; waterfowl; voyages and travel; naval and sailing craft history; ship models; steamboat history. **Holdings:** 3400 volumes. **Subscriptions:** 12 journals and other serials. **Services:** Library open to the public with restrictions. **Remarks:** FAX: (301)745-6088.

Chesapeake Biological Laboratory
See: **University of Maryland - Center for Environmental & Estuarine Studies** (18798)

Chesapeake & Ohio Canal National Historical Park
See: **U.S. Natl. Park Service - Chesapeake & Ohio Canal National Historical Park** (17688)

★3484★
Chesapeake & Ohio Historical Society, Inc. - C&O Archival Collection (Hist, Trans)
P.O. Box 79 Phone: (703)862-2210
Clifton Forge, VA 24422 Thomas W. Dixon, Jr., Pres., C&O Hist.Soc.,Inc.
Founded: 1969. **Staff:** 2. **Subjects:** C&O Railway history - steam/diesel locomotives, passenger and freight cars, operations, buildings, structures, right-of-way. **Special Collections:** C&O Railway operations in the Steam Age and early Diesel era (50,000 negatives); C&O Railway and Hocking Valley Railway engineering and mechanical drawings collections (100,000 items). **Holdings:** 200 books; 150 bound periodical volumes; 5000 pamphlets, manuscripts, research notes. **Services:** Collection open to the public on a limited schedule. **Publications:** C&O Freight Cars, 1937; C&O Diesel Review; Pere Marquette Motive Power; C&O Alleghany Subdivision; Yearly C&O Historical Calendar; Chessie's Road; Riding that New River Train; C&O Huntington Division; Pere Marquette in 1945; miscellaneous publications. **Special Indexes:** Index to photographs and drawings by subject and location (online). **Staff:** Margaret M. Berry, Bus.Mgr.

★3485★
Chesebrough-Pond's, USA - Research Library (Sci-Engr)
40 Merritt Blvd. Phone: (203)381-4312
Trumbull, CT 06611 Mary Suprynowicz, Res.Libn.
Founded: 1959. **Staff:** Prof 2. **Subjects:** Chemistry, cosmetic science, pharmacology, dentistry. **Holdings:** 5000 books; 2000 bound periodical volumes; 20 lateral file drawers of patents, reprints, pamphlets; 40 cartridges of microfilm; 20 boxes of microfiche. **Subscriptions:** 250 journals and other serials. **Services:** Interlibrary loan; copying. **Automated Operations:** Computerized cataloging, acquisitions, serials, and circulation. **Computerized Information Services:** DIALOG Information Services, TOXLINE, MEDLINE, NEXIS, Data-Star. **Remarks:** FAX: (203)381-4212. **Formerly:** Chesebrough-Pond's, Inc. **Staff:** Kathleen McGrath, Asst.Libn.

★3486★
Cheshire Hospital - MacGrath Family Medical Library (Med)
580 Court St. Phone: (603)352-4111
Keene, NH 03431 Jean Slepian, Libn.
Founded: 1963. **Staff:** Prof 1; Other 1. **Subjects:** Medicine, nursing, and allied health sciences. **Holdings:** 1000 books; 1600 bound periodical volumes; 165 indices; 8 VF drawers of pamphlets. **Subscriptions:** 160 journals and other serials; 5 newspapers. **Services:** Interlibrary loan; copying; library open to the public. **Computerized Information Services:** MEDLINE, BRS Information Technologies. Performs searches on fee basis. **Networks/Consortia:** Member of National Network of Libraries of Medicine - New England Region.

★3487★
Chester County Archives and Records Services (Hist)
117 W. Gay St. Phone: (215)344-6760
West Chester, PA 19380 Jeffrey Rollison, Dir.
Founded: 1982. **Staff:** Prof 4. **Subjects:** Local history, county government and politics, genealogy. **Holdings:** 2000 cubic feet of historic county government records. **Services:** Copying; archives open to the public. **Special Catalogs:** Guide to Records of the Court of Common Pleas Chester County, Pennsylvania, 1681-1900 (book); Guide to the Records of the Court of Quarter Sessions, Chester County, 1681-1969. **Special Indexes:** Indexes to selected record series. **Remarks:** FAX: (215)692-4357. Jointly maintained by Chester County Historical Society and Chester County. **Staff:** Laurie A. Rofini, Archv.; Barbara L. Weir, Asst.Archv.

Chester County Cabinet Library
See: **West Chester University - Francis Harvey Green Library** (20186)

★3488★
Chester County Historical Society - Library (Hist)
225 N. High St. Phone: (215)692-4800
West Chester, PA 19380 Rosemary B. Philips, Libn.
Founded: 1893. **Staff:** Prof 4. **Subjects:** Local history and politics, genealogy, decorative arts, church history. **Special Collections:** Albert Cook Myers' William Penn historical collection (196 volumes and several boxes of Myers' personal papers); Robert F. Brinton postal history collection (1000 items); almanacs (500 items); large collection of Chester County newspapers (1809 to present); historical photographs; Christian Brinton art history collection. **Holdings:** Books; periodicals; 140 VF drawers of newspaper clippings; 250 reels of microfilm; 70,000 photographs. **Subscriptions:** 159 journals and other serials; 11 newspapers. **Services:** Copying; library open to nonmembers on fee basis. **Computerized Information Services:** OCLC. **Special Indexes:** Name index to Chester County tax lists, 1699-1758, 1775-1783 (card); list of Chester County men on Revolutionary War rolls (card); Indexes to photo collection (ondisc). **Remarks:** FAX: (215)692-4357. **Staff:** Marion P. Strode, Asst.Libn.; Wesley Sollenberger, Asst.Libn. ; Pamela Powell, Photo Archv.

★3489★
Chester County Hospital - Medical Staff Library (Med)
701 E. Marshall St. Phone: (215)431-5204
West Chester, PA 19380 Anne W. Harrington, Med. Staff Libn.
Staff: Prof 1. **Subjects:** Medicine, surgery. **Holdings:** 250 books; 730 bound periodical volumes and other cataloged items. **Subscriptions:** 112 journals and other serials. **Services:** Interlibrary loan; copying; SDI; library open to the public by appointment and with permission of administrator or librarian. **Computerized Information Services:** MEDLINE; internal database. **Networks/Consortia:** Member of BHSL, Consortium for Health Information & Library Services (CHI). **Remarks:** FAX: (215)696-8411.

★3490★
Chester County Hospital - School of Nursing Library (Med)
701 E. Marshall St.
West Chester, PA 19380 Phone: (215)431-5222
Founded: 1897. **Staff:** Prof 2. **Subjects:** Nursing, medicine, natural science, education, nutrition, psychology, social science. **Special Collections:** History of nursing. **Holdings:** 1800 books; 150 bound periodical volumes; pamphlets; filmstrips; phonograph records; audio and video cassettes; CAI programs. **Subscriptions:** 50 journals and other serials. **Services:** Interlibrary loan; copying; library open to the public for reference use only. **Computerized Information Services:** CD-ROM (Nursing & Allied Health (CINAHL)-CD). **Networks/Consortia:** Member of National Network of Libraries of Medicine - Middle Atlantic Region, Consortium for Health Information & Library Services (CHI), BHSL. **Remarks:** FAX: (215)696-8620. **Staff:** Virginia Moll, Libn.; Inger Wallin, Libn.

★3491★
Chester County Law Library (Law)
15 W. Gay St. Phone: (215)344-6166
West Chester, PA 19380 Jeannie Naftzger, Law Libn.
Founded: 1862. **Staff:** Prof 1; Other 1. **Subjects:** Law. **Holdings:** 24,000 books; 150 bound periodical volumes; 1 VF drawer of pamphlets; 3 VF drawers of Chester County Township and Borough Ordinances. **Subscriptions:** 30 journals and other serials. **Services:** Interlibrary loan; copying; library open to the public for reference use only. **Computerized Information Services:** WESTLAW. **Special Indexes:** Index to Chester County Township and Borough Ordinances.

J & W Chester Subscription Library
See: **University of Sussex - University Library** (19360)

Lord Chesterfield Collection
See: **San Diego State University** (14718)

★3492★
Chesterwood - Museum Library (Art)
Box 827 Phone: (413)298-3579
Stockbridge, MA 01262-0827 Wanda Magdeleine Styka, Archv.
Founded: 1969. **Staff:** Prof 4. **Subjects:** Sculpture, art, architecture, history of art, landscape architecture, decorative arts, historic preservation, conservation, history, museum administration, American diplomacy. **Special Collections:** Daniel Chester French collection of photographs, correspondence, papers, blueprints, drawings, books, and memorabilia (10,000 items); correspondence of Henry Flagg French (father of Daniel Chester French; 1 volume); papers of Margaret French Cresson and William Penn Cresson; literary manuscripts of Mary Adams French. **Holdings:** 6000 volumes; 7000 slides; 30 videotapes; 19 oral history tapes of friends and relatives of Daniel Chester French; photographs; 44 reels of microfilm of Daniel Chester French Family Papers in Library of Congress; 100,000 archival items. **Subscriptions:** 3 journals and other serials. **Services:** Copying; library open to scholars by appointment. **Publications:** The Chesterwood Pedestal (newsletter) - to Friends of Chesterwood; Chesterwood: A Guidebook for Students (pamphlet); Chesterwood: A Guidebook for Teachers (pamphlet). **Special Catalogs:** Annual exhibit catalogs. **Remarks:** Maintained by the National Trust for Historic Preservation. **Staff:** Paul W. Ivory, Dir. of Chesterwood; Susan Frisch Lehrer, Asst.Dir.; Linda Wesselman Jackson, Cur.

★3493★
Chestnut Hill College - Logue Library - Special Collections (Area-Ethnic, Educ)
Germantown & Northwestern Aves. Phone: (215)248-7055
Philadelphia, PA 19118-2695 Helen M. Hayes, Lib.Dir.
Founded: 1924. **Staff:** 6. **Holdings:** Irish Collection (Irish literature and history; 4820 volumes); Educational Materials Collection (textbooks and children's literature; 4628 volumes). **Subscriptions:** 40 journals and other serials. **Services:** Interlibrary loan; copying; collections open to the public with borrowing only through interlibrary loan. **Automated Operations:** Computerized cataloging and ILL. **Computerized Information Services:** OCLC, DIALOG Information Services, ERIC; CD-ROM (PsycLIT) . **Networks/Consortia:** Member of PALINET, Tri-State College Library Cooperative (TCLC). **Remarks:** FAX: (215)248-7056. **Staff:** Sr. Maria Regina, Educ.Mtls.Libn.

★3494★
Chestnut Hill Hospital - Medical Library (Med)
8835 Germantown Ave. Phone: (215)248-8206
Philadelphia, PA 19118-2767 Susan G. Mowery, Med.Libn.
Staff: Prof 1. **Subjects:** Medicine, nursing, consumer health. **Special Collections:** Archives. **Holdings:** 3000 books; 500 bound periodical volumes; 153 filmstrips. **Subscriptions:** 152 journals and other serials. **Services:** Interlibrary loan; copying; SDI; library open to the public by physician's referral only. **Computerized Information Services:** BRS Information Technologies. **Networks/Consortia:** Member of Delaware Valley Information Consortium (DEVIC). **Publications:** Informed, quarterly - for internal distribution only. **Special Catalogs:** Union List of Serials, annual - to members only.

★3495★
Chevron Canada Resources - Library (Energy, Sci-Engr)
500 5th Ave., S.W. Phone: (403)234-5577
Calgary, AB, Canada T2P 0L7 Zahina Iqbal, Libn.
Founded: 1954. **Staff:** Prof 1; Other 2. **Subjects:** Geology, environmental studies, geophysics, petroleum engineering, business. **Special Collections:** Law Library; Tax collection; Geological Survey of Canada papers, late 1800s to present (bulletins; papers; maps; memoirs). **Holdings:** 15,000 books and items in series; 600 videotapes. **Subscriptions:** 875 journals and other serials. **Services:** Interlibrary loan; current awareness; library not open to the public. **Automated Operations:** Computerized cataloging, acquisitions, serials, and circulation. **Computerized Information Services:** DIALOG Information Services, PFDS Online, CAN/OLE, Info Globe, CA Online, Dun & Bradstreet Business Credit Services, CBANET, Infomart Online. **Networks/Consortia:** Member of Chevron Libraries Network. **Publications:** Library News, quarterly - for internal distribution only. **Remarks:** FAX: (403)234-5947. Telex: 03821 645.

★3496★
Chevron Chemical Company - Library and Information Center (Energy, Bus-Fin)
Box 2100 Phone: (713)754-2276
Houston, TX 77252 Stanley E. Brewer, Chf.Libn.
Founded: 1974. **Staff:** Prof 4; Other 2. **Subjects:** Petroleum industry, petrochemical business, marketing, exploration and production, geology. **Special Collections:** Annual Reports (300 companies in petroleum and allied industries). **Holdings:** 35,000 books; 750 bound periodical volumes; 42,000 unbound periodical volumes; N.Y. Times, 1969 to present, on microfiche; NTIS microfiche in energy-related areas; 11,500 U.S. government documents; 15,000 U.S. Geological Survey and state geological survey maps. **Subscriptions:** 400 journals and other serials; 10 newspapers. **Services:** Interlibrary loan; library open to the public by appointment. **Automated Operations:** Computerized cataloging. **Computerized Information Services:** DIALOG Information Services, PFDS Online, STN International, Mead Data Central, VU/TEXT Information Services. **Publications:** Acquisitions List, bimonthly - for internal distribution only. **Remarks:** Alternate telephone number(s): 754-2271; 754-2272; 754-2274. FAX: (713)754-2288. **Staff:** Judith M. Van Horn, Res.Libn.; Susan C. Stewart, Libn.; Linda R. McClain, Libn.

★3497★
Chevron Chemical Company - Ortho Research & Development - Library (Agri)
15049 San Pablo Ave.
Box 4010 Phone: (510)231-6372
Richmond, CA 94804 John R. O'Neill, Lib.Spec.
Founded: 1984. **Staff:** Prof 1. **Subjects:** Pesticide science, agricultural chemicals, organic chemistry, plant sciences, toxicology, agriculture. **Special Collections:** Ortho Archives. **Holdings:** 4000 books; 4000 bound periodical volumes; 4000 material safety data sheets; 2300 reels of microfilm of patents; 4000 reels of microfilm of journals; 10,000 microfiche; laboratory notebooks; Environmental Protection Agency pesticide label files; patents; product labels; marketing studies. **Subscriptions:** 50 journals and other serials; 2 newspapers. **Services:** Library not open to the public. **Automated Operations:** Computerized cataloging, serials, and routing. **Computerized Information Services:** DIALOG Information Services, Maxwell Online, Inc., STN International, National Pesticide Information Retrieval System, Questel; internal databases. **Networks/Consortia:** Member of Chevron Libraries Network. **Special Catalogs:** Journal holdings list; laboratory notebooks; material safety data sheets. **Remarks:** FAX: (510)231-6425.

★3498★
Chevron Corporation - Corporate Law Department - Library (Law)
555 Market St., Rm. 4055 Phone: (415)894-1714
San Francisco, CA 94105 Jill E. Shankman, Law Libn.
Staff: Prof 1. **Subjects:** Patents, trademarks, law, licensing. **Holdings:** 4000 books; 500 bound periodical volumes; microfilm. **Subscriptions:** 76 journals and other serials. **Services:** Interlibrary loan; copying; library open to the public at librarian's discretion. **Automated Operations:** Computerized serials. **Computerized Information Services:** LEXIS, DIALOG Information Services, RLIN, DataTimes, VU/TEXT Information Services. **Remarks:** FAX: (415)894-2144.

★3499★
Chevron Corporation - Corporate Library (Bus-Fin, Energy)
225 Bush St., Rm. 1410 Phone: (415)894-2946
San Francisco, CA 94104 Margaret J. Linden, Mgr.
Founded: 1917. **Staff:** Prof 8; Other 13. **Subjects:** Petroleum and natural gas economics and technology, energy policy, other energy resources. **Special Collections:** Corporate archives. **Holdings:** Figures not available. **Subscriptions:** 2000 journals and other serials. **Services:** Library open to the public for reference use only by special request. **Automated Operations:** Computerized public access catalog, cataloging, acquisitions, and routing. **Computerized Information Services:** RLIN, NEXIS, LEXIS, ORBIT Search Service, BRS Information Technologies, Info Globe, VU/TEXT Information Services, WILSONLINE, DIALOG Information Services, Dow Jones News/Retrieval, NewsNet, Inc., DataTimes; internal database; OnTyme Electronic Message Network Service (electronic mail service). **Networks/Consortia:** Member of CLASS. **Remarks:** FAX: (415)894-6805. Electronic mail address(es): CCL (OnTyme Electronic Message Network Service). **Staff:** Elena Herdman, Supv., Tech.Serv.; Marie Tilson, Sr.Ref.Libn.

Chevron Environmental Health Center, Inc. - Information Services
See: **Chevron Research and Technology Company** (3503)

★3500★
Chevron Exploration & Production Services Company - Library (Sci-Engr)
2811 Hayes Rd.
Box 42832 Phone: (713)596-2026
Houston, TX 77242-2832 Betty J. Parton, Libn.
Founded: 1966. **Staff:** Prof 1; Other 3. **Subjects:** Geophysics, geology, mathematics. **Holdings:** 1500 volumes. **Subscriptions:** 43 journals and other serials. **Services:** Interlibrary loan; library not open to the public.

★3501★
Chevron Oil Field Research Company - Technical Information Services (Energy, Sci-Engr)
P.O. Box 446 Phone: (310)694-7500
La Habra, CA 90631 Ann S. Coppin, Supv.
Founded: 1947. **Staff:** Prof 3; Other 6. **Subjects:** Geology, geochemistry, geophysics, petroleum engineering, oceanography, paleontology, physics, chemistry, mathematics. **Holdings:** 29,000 books; 18,500 bound periodical volumes; 6000 geologic maps; 2000 reels of microfilm; 36,000 microfiche; 400 patents. **Subscriptions:** 1050 journals and other serials. **Services:** Interlibrary loan; copying; SDI; translations; collection open to the public by appointment or referral. **Automated Operations:** Computerized cataloging, acquisitions, serials, and circulation. **Computerized Information Services:** DIALOG Information Services, ORBIT Search Service, STN International, RLIN, OCLC EPIC, ORION. **Publications:** Current Awareness Bulletin, semimonthly - for internal distribution only. **Remarks:** FAX: (310)694-7433. **Staff:** E. Susan Palmer, Tech.Info.Spec.; Patricia E. Lutkin, Assoc.Res.Libn.

★3502★
Chevron Overseas Petroleum Inc. - Chevron Park Technical Library (Energy)
6001 Bollinger Canyon Rd., Rm. E1300
P.O. Box 5040 Phone: (510)842-4426
San Ramon, CA 94583-0940 Mary Ann Whitney, Chf.Libn.
Staff: Prof 5; Other 9. **Subjects:** Petroleum geology, international business, computers and information technology, petroleum engineering, mineral resources. **Special Collections:** Maps and charts (10,000). **Holdings:** 65,000 books. **Subscriptions:** 545 journals and other serials. **Services:** Interlibrary loan; copying; SDI; library open to the public with restrictions. **Automated Operations:** Computerized public access catalog, acquisitions, routing, and cataloging. **Computerized Information Services:** DIALOG Information Services, ORBIT Search Service, BRS Information Technologies, WILSONLINE, Reuters, LEXIS, NEXIS, MELVYL; internal database; OnTyme Electronic Message Network Service, DIALMAIL (electronic mail services). **Publications:** Library Update, monthly. **Remarks:** FAX: (510)842-5261.

★3503★
Chevron Research and Technology Company - Environmental Health Information Center (Env-Cons)
1003 W. Cutting Blvd., Suite 120 Phone: (510)242-7053
P.O. Box 4054 Connie L. Riley, Team Ldr.,
Richmond, CA 94804-0054 Info.Rsrcs. Team
Staff: Prof 1; Other 5. **Subjects:** Toxicology, environmental health, chemical regulation, risk assessment. **Holdings:** 3500 books. **Subscriptions:** 100 journals and other serials. **Services:** Interlibrary loan; copying; SDI. **Computerized Information Services:** DIALOG Information Services, NLM, PFDS Online, BRS Information Technologies, Chemical Information Systems, Inc. (CIS), Integrated Risk Information System (IRIS), Environmental Fate Data Bases, QSAR, STN International, Technical Database Services (TDS). **Networks/Consortia:** Member of Bay Area Library and Information System (BALIS). **Remarks:** FAX: (510)242-7022. **Formerly:** Chevron Environmental Health Center, Inc. - Information Services.

★3504★
Chevron Research and Technology Company - Technical Information Center (Energy, Sci-Engr)
100 Chevron Way
Box 1627
Richmond, CA 94802-0627 Phone: (510)242-4755
Founded: 1920. **Staff:** Prof 9; Other 17. **Subjects:** Chemistry, petroleum refining, petrochemicals, engineering, fuels, lubricants. **Holdings:** 18,000 books; 9000 bound periodical volumes; preprints of meeting papers of the Society of Automotive Engineers and American Society of Chemical Engineers; 3 million U.S. and foreign patents; 60,000 pamphlets; 20 file drawers of trade literature; 525,000 documents of company reports and correspondence; 4.28 million pages of documents on microfilm. **Subscriptions:** 1300 journals and other serials. **Services:** Interlibrary loan; copying; translations; SDI profiles; center open to the public by special request. **Automated Operations:** Computerized cataloging, acquisitions, serials, and circulation. **Computerized Information Services:** DIALOG Information Services, PFDS Online, RLIN, Chemical Abstracts Service (CAS), STN International; OnTyme Electronic Message Network Service, DIALMAIL (electronic mail services). **Networks/Consortia:** Member of Research Libraries Information Network (RLIN), CLASS. **Publications:** Library Alert, monthly; Publications - Chevron Research Company, annual. **Remarks:** FAX: (510)242-5621. Telex: 176967 (W.U.). Electronic mail address(es): CRC (OnTyme Electronic Message Network Service). **Staff:** F.D. Lopez, Team Ldr., Tech.Serv.; S.L. Modrick, Team Ldr., Ref.; L.R. White, Team Ldr., Rec.; J.W. Armstrong, Res.Transl.; R.K. Dikeman, Info.Anl.; N.E. Lambert, Info.Anl.; E.F. Edelstein, Info.Anl.; A. Rosanoff, Info.Anl.; M.J. Paolini, Info.Anl.

Chevron "Standard Hour" Collection
See: **San Francisco Performing Arts Library and Museum - Library** (14737)

★3505★
Chevron USA Inc. - Eastern Exploration Business Unit - Learning Resource Center (Sci-Engr)
935 Gravier St. Phone: (504)592-6292
New Orleans, LA 70112 B.G. (Bob) Hatten, Libn.
Staff: Prof 1; Other 5. **Subjects:** Geology, engineering, business. **Holdings:** 10,000 books; 104 bound periodical volumes; 3000 other cataloged items. **Subscriptions:** 1077 journals and other serials; 90 newspapers. **Services:** Interlibrary loan; center not open to the public. **Automated Operations:** Computerized cataloging and serials. **Computerized Information Services:** PFDS Online, DIALOG Information Services; Libinfo (internal database); EBSCONET (electronic mail service).

★3506★
Chevron USA Inc. - Law Library (Law)
P.O. Box 4553 Phone: (713)754-3330
Houston, TX 77210 Frederick A. Riemann, Chf. Law Libn.
Founded: 1933. **Staff:** Prof 2. **Subjects:** Law. **Holdings:** 50,000 books; 1000 bound periodical volumes; 200 cassette tapes. **Subscriptions:** 500 journals and other serials; 10 newspapers. **Services:** Interlibrary loan; library open to the public by appointment. **Automated Operations:** Computerized cataloging. **Computerized Information Services:** LEXIS, WESTLAW. **Publications:** Acquisitions List, monthly - for internal distribution only. **Remarks:** FAX: (713)754-3326. **Staff:** Nan M. Dubbelde, Asst.Libn.

★3507★
Chevy Chase Baptist Church - Sebring Memorial Library (Rel-Phil)
5671 Western Ave., N.W. Phone: (202)966-8662
Washington, DC 20015 Margaret Spurling, Libn.
Staff: Prof 1. **Subjects:** Religion, biography, missions, children's literature. **Holdings:** 2800 books; 2 VF drawers of pictures; 1 VF drawer of archival materials; AV programs. **Subscriptions:** 10 journals and other serials. **Services:** Interlibrary loan (limited); library open to the public for reference use only.

★3508★
Cheyenne Mountain Zoological Park - Library (Biol Sci)
4250 Cheyenne Mt. Zoo Rd. Phone: (719)633-9927
Colorado Springs, CO 80906-5728 Kevin P. Tanski, Educ.Cur.
Staff: Prof 2. **Subjects:** Zoology, biology, veterinary medicine, botany. **Holdings:** 550 books; zoo publications. **Subscriptions:** 16 journals and other serials. **Services:** Library not open to the public. **Remarks:** FAX: (719)633-2254.

★3509★
Cheyney University of Pennsylvania - Leslie Pinckney Hill Library - Special Collections (Area-Ethnic)
Cheyney, PA 19319 Phone: (215)399-2203
Founded: 1837. **Staff:** 11. **Subjects:** Education, economics, business, English and American literature, humanities, industrial management and technology, social and behavioral scienes, textiles. **Special Collections:** Afro-American Collection (3534 volumes); Cheyney Archives and the William Dorsey Collection of Notebooks and Books on Afro-American History (2500 items). **Holdings:** 231,865 volumes; 311,479 ERIC documents; 435,905 microform units; 60,898 documents. **Subscriptions:** 1016 journals and other serials; 31 newspapers. **Services:** Interlibrary loan; copying; collections open to the public with restrictions. **Automated Operations:** Computerized cataloging. **Computerized Information Services:** CD-ROMs. **Networks/Consortia:** Member of Tri-State College Library Cooperative (TCLC), PALINET, State System of Higher Education Libraries Council (SSHELCO). **Remarks:** FAX: (215)399-2491. **Staff:** Helen Boyd, Hd., Cat.Dept.; William Dorf, Hd., Acq.Dept.; Karen Humbert, Hd., Circ.Dept.; Alla Reddy, Hd., Ref.Dept.; Charlotte Taylor, Hd., Ser.Dept.

John W. Chi Memorial Medical Library
See: **Ingham Medical Center Corporation** (7853)

Chi Lambda Cult/Occult Research Center
See: **Lincoln Christian College & Seminary - Jessie C. Eury Library** (9173)

★3510★
CHI Research, Inc. - Library (Info Sci)
10 White Horse Pike
Haddon Heights, NJ 08035 Phone: (609)546-0600
Staff: Prof 3; Other 1. **Subjects:** Bibliometrics, science and technology indicators, science, social sciences. **Special Collections:** Bibliometrics collection (75 books; approximately 750 papers); U.S. patents and patent citations, 1971 to present (600,000). **Holdings:** 1000 books; 3000 papers in subject areas; 250 reels of magnetic computer tapes. **Subscriptions:** 20 journals and other serials. **Services:** Library open to the public by appointment. **Computerized Information Services:** Internal database. **Special Indexes:** Extensive scientific publication and citation data. **Remarks:** FAX: (609)546-9633.

★3511★
(Chiang Mai) USIS Library (Educ)
24 Rajdamnoen Rd. Phone: 53 214120
Chiang Mai 50000, Thailand Elizabeth McKay, Dir.
Founded: 1968. **Staff:** 1. **Holdings:** 2629 books; 43 bound periodical volumes. **Subscriptions:** 3 newspapers. **Services:** SDI; library open to the public. **Publications:** New book and VCR list. **Remarks:** FAX: 53 211377. Maintained or supported by the U.S. Information Agency. Focus is on materials that will assist peoples outside the United States to learn about the United States, its people, history, culture, political processes, and social milieux. **Staff:** Sanguan Chantalay.

★3512★
Chicago Academy of Sciences - Matthew Laughlin Memorial Library (Sci-Engr, Biol Sci)
2001 N. Clark St. Phone: (312)549-0606
Chicago, IL 60614 Louise T. Lunak, Libn.
Founded: 1857. **Staff:** Prof 1; Other 2. **Subjects:** Ornithology, geology, biological science, physical sciences. **Holdings:** 30,000 volumes. **Subscriptions:** 150 journals and other serials. **Services:** Interlibrary loan; library open to the public with director's permission.

Chicago Aerial Industries
See: **CAI** (2443)

★3513★
Chicago Bar Association - Library
321 S. Plymouth Court
Chicago, IL 60604
Defunct.

Chicago Bible Society
See: **American Bible Society - Library** (502)

★3514★
Chicago Board of Education - Chicago Public Schools Professional Library
1819 W. Pershing Rd., 4C N
Chicago, IL 60601
Founded: 1935. **Subjects:** Elementary and secondary education. **Special Collections:** Proceedings and Annual Reports of the Chicago Board of Education; Curriculum Department Archives. **Holdings:** 27,500 books; 29,000 microforms; 53 videocassettes; 244 tapes; 48 VF drawers. **Remarks:** Currently inactive.

★3515★
Chicago Board of Trade - Education Department - Library (Bus-Fin)
141 W. Jackson Blvd. Phone: (312)435-3552
Chicago, IL 60604 Rita J. Macellaio, Hd.Libn.
Founded: 1969. **Staff:** Prof 2. **Subjects:** Commodity exchanges, futures trading, financial instruments, agricultural economics, options, business and finance. **Special Collections:** Statistical Annuals of the Board of Trade, 1858 to present; prices of commodities, 1858 to present; collection of Futures and Treasury Bills prices, 1956 to present. **Holdings:** 3900 books; 700 bound periodical volumes; 20 videotapes; 100 other cataloged items; 13 VF drawers of government reports, newsletters, exchange statistics; unbound reports. **Subscriptions:** 550 journals and other serials; 22 newspapers. **Services:** Interlibrary loan; library open to the public on a limited schedule. **Automated Operations:** Computerized cataloging, acquisitions, and serials. **Computerized Information Services:** OCLC, DIALOG Information Services. **Networks/Consortia:** Member of ILLINET. **Publications:** The Chicago Board of Trade Commodity Bibliography; bibliographies, annual. **Staff:** Deborah Lynch, Asst.Libn.

★3516★
Chicago Botanic Garden - Library (Biol Sci)
Box 400 Phone: (708)835-8200
Glencoe, IL 60022 Virginia A. Henrichs, Libn.
Staff: Prof 2. **Subjects:** Horticulture, botany, agriculture, nature studies. **Holdings:** 12,000 books; 17 VF drawers. **Subscriptions:** 200 journals and other serials. **Services:** Interlibrary loan; copying; library open to the public for reference use only. **Automated Operations:** Computerized cataloging. **Computerized Information Services:** OCLC, DIALOG Information Services. **Remarks:** FAX: (708)835-4484. **Staff:** Sally Lohr, Asst.Libn.

★3517★
Chicago City-Wide College - Dawson Technical Institute Library (Educ)
3901 S. State St. Phone: (312)451-2087
Chicago, IL 60609 Robert Palagi, LRC Mgr.
Founded: 1972. **Staff:** Prof 2; Other 1. **Subjects:** Nursing, industrial arts, business. **Special Collections:** Adult education (1000 volumes). **Holdings:** 11,000 books. **Subscriptions:** 110 journals and other serials; 5 newspapers. **Services:** Library open to the public for reference use only. **Remarks:** FAX: (312)451-2160. **Staff:** Effie B. Tyler, Educ.Mtls.Coord.

★3518★
Chicago College of Osteopathic Medicine - Alumni Memorial Library (Med)
555 31st St. Phone: (708)515-6200
Downers Grove, IL 60515 Sandra A. Worley, Dir. of Lib.Serv.
Founded: 1913. **Staff:** Prof 5; Other 13. **Subjects:** Medicine, allied health sciences, osteopathy. **Special Collections:** Osteopathy; History of Medicine. **Holdings:** 20,207 books; 31,260 bound periodical volumes; 9176 audiotapes; 1014 videotapes; 40,410 slides; 15 videodiscs. **Subscriptions:** 850 journals and other serials; 5 newspapers. **Services:** Interlibrary loan; copying; SDI; library open to the public for reference use. **Automated Operations:** Computerized cataloging and acquisitions. **Computerized Information Services:** OCLC, MEDLINE, PFDS Online, BRS Information Technologies, DIALOG Information Services. Performs searches on fee basis. **Networks/Consortia:** Member of ILLINET, National Network of Libraries of Medicine - Greater Midwest Region. **Publications:** Library newsletter, quarterly - for internal distribution and to mailing list. **Formerly:** Located in Chicago, IL. **Staff:** Mary Ann Huslig, Asst.Dir.; Pui Chan, Assoc.Cat.

★3519★
Chicago College of Osteopathic Medicine - Olympia Fields Osteopathic Medical Center Library (Med)
20201 S. Crawford Phone: (708)747-4000
Olympia Fields, IL 60461 Sandra A. Worley, Dir.
Founded: 1978. **Staff:** 1.5. **Subjects:** Medicine, nursing. **Holdings:** 2500 books; 4800 bound periodical volumes; 225 videotapes. **Subscriptions:** 200 journals and other serials. **Services:** Interlibrary loan; copying; SDI; current awareness; PC workstations; library open to the public for reference use only. **Computerized Information Services:** MEDLARS, BRS Information Technologies. **Networks/Consortia:** Member of Chicago and South Consortium. **Publications:** Newsletter. **Remarks:** FAX: (708)515-6195. Library is a branch library of the Chicago College of Osteopathic Medicine - Alumni Memorial Library. **Staff:** Paul Blobaum, Libn.

★3520★
Chicago County Historical Society - Library (Hist)
Taylors Falls Public Library
Taylors Falls, MN 55084 Marilyn Rimestad, Libn.
Founded: 1871. **Subjects:** St. Croix Valley and Taylors Falls history. **Holdings:** 10,859 books. **Subscriptions:** 23 journals and other serials. **Services:** Library open to the public on a limited schedule.

★3521★
Chicago Department of Human Services - Library (Soc Sci)
500 Peshtigo Court, N. Phone: (312)744-3988
Chicago, IL 60611 Janice Bradshaw, Supv.
Staff: Prof 1; Other 3. **Subjects:** Human services. **Holdings:** 1300 volumes; technical manuals. **Subscriptions:** 200 journals and other serials. **Services:** Interlibrary loan; copying; library open to the public for reference use only.

★3522★
Chicago Historical Society - Research Collections (Hist)
Clark St. at North Ave. Phone: (312)642-4600
Chicago, IL 60614 Janice McNeill, Libn.
Founded: 1856. **Staff:** 16. **Subjects:** History - Chicago, Illinois, Civil War, Lincoln. **Special Collections:** Chicago directories; trade catalogs; advertising cards (4000); theater programs (12,550); sheet music (5500); personal papers and records of Chicago individuals and organizations from the city's early days to the present (15,800 linear feet); negatives and prints from Chicago newspaper morgues, 1900-1965 (250,000); historic American city prints; J. Norman Jensen Collection of Lake and River Disasters, 1679-1947 (8500 cards). **Holdings:** 112,700 books and pamphlets; 10,000 bound periodical volumes; 3500 volumes of newspapers; 16,000 broadsides and posters; 9860 maps; 725 atlases; 37 VF drawers of clippings; 40,000 pieces of miscellanea; 11,000 reels of microfilm; 300,000 architectural drawings; 53,000 prints; 1 million photographs; 12,000 reels of newsfilm. **Computerized Information Services:** OCLC. **Staff:** Archie Motley, Cur., Archv. & Mss.; Larry Viskochil, Cur., Prints & Photos.; Wim de Wit, Cur., Arch.Coll.

★3523★
Chicago Institute for Psychoanalysis - McLean Library (Med)
180 N. Michigan Ave. Phone: (312)726-6300
Chicago, IL 60601 Heidi Rosenberg, Libn.
Founded: 1932. **Staff:** Prof 1; Other 3. **Subjects:** Psychoanalysis, psychosomatic medicine, psychiatry, allied social and behavioral sciences. **Special Collections:** Maxwell Gitelson Film Library (200 titles); Franz Alexander Archives of Psychoanalytic History. **Holdings:** 13,000 books; 2000 bound periodical volumes; 6 VF drawers of psychoanalytic society meeting archives; 8 VF drawers of staff writing archives; 30 VF drawers of reprints and pamphlets; 2000 reels of microfilm. **Subscriptions:** 200 journals and other serials. **Services:** Interlibrary loan; copying; library open to the public for annual fee. **Computerized Information Services:** Online systems. Performs searches on fee basis. **Special Catalogs:** Gitelson Film Library Catalog. **Special Indexes:** Chicago Psychoanalytic Literature Index, 1920-1970 (3 volumes; 1971); quarterly subject index, 1971 to 1988. **Also Known As:** Institute for Psychoanalysis.

Chicago Jazz Archive
See: **University of Chicago - Music Collection** (18455)

Chicago Jewish Archives
See: **Spertus College of Judaica - Norman and Helen Asher Library** (15584)

Chicago Kent Law School
See: **Illinois Institute of Technology** (7674)

Chicago Medical School
See: **University of Health Sciences-Chicago Medical School** (18633)

★3524★
Chicago Mercantile Exchange - Library/Resource Center (Bus-Fin)
30 S. Wacker Dr. Phone: (312)930-8239
Chicago, IL 60606 Bruce Q. Frost, Mgr.
Founded: 1977. **Staff:** Prof 2; Other 3. **Subjects:** Futures, options on futures. **Holdings:** 3500 books; 250 bound periodical volumes; 15 VF drawers. **Subscriptions:** 400 journals and other serials; 25 newspapers. **Services:** Interlibrary loan; library open to the public. **Automated Operations:** Computerized cataloging, acquisitions, serials, and circulation. **Computerized Information Services:** DIALOG Information Services, NEXIS, LEXIS, OCLC, InvesText, VU/TEXT Information Services, Reuters, DataTimes. **Networks/Consortia:** Member of Chicago Library System. **Publications:** Bibliography. **Special Indexes:** Index to Daily Clips (online). **Remarks:** FAX: (312)466-7436. **Staff:** Joan Daley, Archv./Res.Spec.; Kathryn Samuels, Circ./ILL; Elizabeth Lekan, Prod.Ed.

Chicago Metropolitan Sanitary District
See: **Metropolitan Water Reclamation District of Greater Chicago** (10235)

★3525★
Chicago Municipal Reference Library (Soc Sci)
City Hall, Rm. 1004 Phone: (312)744-4992
Chicago, IL 60602 Joyce Malden, Libn.
Staff: Prof 11; Other 11. **Subjects:** Municipal affairs - city planning, criminology, public finance, housing, public administration, public personnel. **Special Collections:** City of Chicago documents. **Holdings:** 45,000 titles; 84 VF drawers of newspaper clippings; 48 VF drawers of pamphlets; maps; microfilm. **Subscriptions:** 1300 journals and other serials; 40 newspapers. **Services:** Interlibrary loan; copying; library open to the public for reference use only. **Automated Operations:** Computerized cataloging. **Computerized Information Services:** OCLC, DIALOG Information Services, DataTimes, LEGI-SLATE, VU/TEXT Information Services, WILSONLINE, LOGIN. **Networks/Consortia:** Member of ILLINET. **Publications:** Recent Additions, Municipal Reference Library, monthly; Checklist of Publications of the City of Chicago, quarterly; Facts about Chicago, annual - all free upon request.

Chicago Musical College Archives
See: **Roosevelt University - Music Library** (14058)

★3526★
Chicago Park District - Garfield Park Conservatory (Agri)
300 N. Central Park Blvd. Phone: (312)533-1281
Chicago, IL 60624 Jagdish P. Nautiyal, Horticulturist
Subjects: Horticulture. **Special Collections:** Horticultural reference books. **Holdings:** 350 books; slides. **Services:** Library not open to the public.

★3527★
Chicago Public Library - Carter G. Woodson Regional Library - Vivian G. Harsh Research Collection of Afro-American History & Literature (Area-Ethnic)
9525 S. Halsted St. Phone: (312)747-6910
Chicago, IL 60628 Robert Miller, Cur.
Founded: 1932. **Staff:** Prof 4; Other 1. **Subjects:** Afro-Americans - history, religion, sociology, art, literature, music. **Special Collections:** Illinois Writers Project; Heritage Press Archives; Carl Sang Collection of Afro-American History, 1684 to present; Charlemae Hill Rollins Collection of Children's Literature; Era Bell Thompson Collection; Ben Burns Collection; David P. Ross Collection of Reprints in Afro-Americana and Africana; Horace Revels Cayton Collection. **Holdings:** 70,000 books; 565 bound periodical volumes; 5000 linear feet of other cataloged items; 10,180 pamphlets; 1146 phonograph records; 1500 cassette tapes; 10,170 reels of microfilm. **Subscriptions:** 70 journals and other serials; 30 newspapers. **Services:** Interlibrary loan; copying; library open to the public. **Automated Operations:** Computerized cataloging. **Computerized Information Services:** OCLC. **Networks/Consortia:** Member of ILLINET. **Publications:** Serials Holding List, biennial; Malcolm X, a Selected Bibliography, biennial; Richard Wright, a Selected Bibliography; Harold Washington, a Selected Bibliography; Microfilm Holdings, annual; Dr. Martin Luther King, Jr., a Selected Bibliography, biennial; Jazz at Harsh, biennial; Mary Mcleod Bethune Bio-Bibliography; Carter Godwin Woodson Bio-Bibliography; Gwendolyn Brooks: A Selected Bibliography; Serials Holdings List; Chicago and the African American: A Selected Bibliography. **Special Catalogs:** The Dictionary Catalog of the Vivian G. Harsh Collection; Afro-American History & Literature (book); The Chicago Afro-American Union Analytic Catalog (book); Union Catalog of Black Music Holdings in Selected Chicago Libraries (online). **Remarks:** FAX: (312)747-3396. **Staff:** Edward Manney, Libn. III; Beverly Cook, Libn. II; Dorothy Lyles, Libn. I; Michael Flug, Archv.

★3528★
Chicago Public Library Central Library - Arts and Letters Division - Literature and Language Department (Hum)
Harold Washington Library Center
400 S. State St. Phone: (312)747-4700
Chicago, IL 60605 Rosemary Dawood, Hd., Lit. & Lang.
Staff: Prof 23; Other 19. **Subjects:** Literature - American, English, foreign; language study; linguistics; foreign languages. **Special Collections:** Wright's American Fiction (novels; on microfilm); Library of English Literature (microfilm); La Fin de Siecle literary magazine (microfilm); Spanish drama of the Golden Age (3500 plays on microfilm). **Holdings:** 556,880 books; 2775 bound periodical volumes; 42,183 books in microform; 27,696 periodical volumes in microform; 802 foreign telephone directories; 7560 language learning audiocassettes; 375 language learning videocassettes; 12 audiocassettes magazine titles; 150 audiocassettes; 510 videocassettes (foreign). **Subscriptions:** 1342 journals and other serials; 186 foreign language newspapers. **Services:** Interlibrary loan; copying; language laboratory; department open to the public. **Automated Operations:** Computerized cataloging, acquisitions, serials, and circulation. **Computerized Information Services:** OCLC. **Networks/Consortia:** Member of ILLINET. **Special Catalogs:** Foreign language card catalog; Spanish Information Center (community and general information data files); annotated catalog of 825 foreign language periodicals and newspapers. **Remarks:** FAX: (312)747-4745. **Staff:** M. Patricia Young, Hd., Lit. & Lang.Info.Ctr.; William McElwain, Hd., Foreign Lang.Info.Ctr.; Nancy E. Harvey, Hd., Lit.Sect.; Beverly Goerke, Hd., Fiction/Browsing Sect.; Elizabeth Alaras, Asst.Hd., Foreign Lang.Info.Ctr.; Lia Londono, Hd., Spanish Info.Serv.; Marian Pagan, Hd., Lang.Lab.; Leonard Sopka, Ser.Libn.; Wayne Schaefer, Dept.Comp.Coord.; Joyce Meggett, Fiction Rsrc.Coll./Last Copy Fiction.

★3529★
Chicago Public Library Central Library - Business/Science/Technology Division (Bus-Fin, Sci-Engr)
Harold Washington Library Center
400 S. State St.
Chicago, IL 60605 David R. Rouse, BST Div.Chf.
Founded: 1977. **Staff:** Prof 27; Other 11. **Subjects:** Small business, marketing, technology, corporate reports, investments, management, personnel, patents, physical and biological sciences, medicine, health, computer science, careers, environmental information, gardening, cookbooks. **Special Collections:** U.S. and British Patents complete (38,265 volumes and 5581 reels of U.S. patents); gazettes complete; domestic and foreign automobile manuals; radio, TV, electrical, schematics; industrial, corporate, product directories; career information; science fair projects; standards and specifications, including International Organization for Standardization (ISO; on microfilm). **Holdings:** 290,000 books; 45,000 bound periodical volumes; Securities and Exchange Commission (SEC) reports; 8 VF drawers of federal specifications and standards; 20 VF drawers of American an National Standards Institute standards; 50 VF drawers of pamphlets and corporate annual reports. **Subscriptions:** 2400 journals and other serials; 8 newspapers. **Services:** Interlibrary loan; copying; division open to the public. **Automated Operations:** Computerized cataloging. **Computerized Information Services:** DIALOG Information Services, ORBIT Search Service, BRS Information Technologies, Dow Jones News/

Retrieval, Mead Data Central, OCLC, VU/TEXT Information Services, LEGI-SLATE, DataTimes, WILSONLINE, NewsNet, Inc., Burrelle's. **Networks/Consortia:** Member of ILLINET. **Publications:** Bibliographies on special subjects; brochures. **Remarks:** The Business Information Center's telephone number is (312)747-4400, the Science and Technology Information Center's telephone number is 747-4450, and the Computer-Assisted Reference Center's telephone number is 747-4470. **Staff:** Diane Richmond, Sci./Tech.Info.Hd.; Robert Bibbee, Bus.Info.Hd.; Marcia Dellenbach, Comp.Ref.Ctr.Hd.; Lauro Zupko, Per.Hd.

★3530★
Chicago Public Library Central Library - General Information Services Division - Bibliographic & ILL Center (Info Sci)
Harold Washington Library Center
400 S. State St. Phone: (312)747-4351
Chicago, IL 60605 Valerie Samuelson, Hd.
Founded: 1977. **Staff:** Prof 14; Other 12. **Subjects:** Bibliographies - national, trade, selective. **Holdings:** 12,912 books. **Subscriptions:** 15 journals and other serials. **Services:** Interlibrary loan; center not open to the public. **Automated Operations:** Computerized cataloging. **Computerized Information Services:** OCLC. **Networks/Consortia:** Member of ILLINET, Chicago Library System. **Remarks:** FAX: (312)747-4918. **Staff:** Kristin Lipkowski, First Asst.; John Mead; Joseph Rice; Laurel Sher.

★3531★
Chicago Public Library Central Library - General Information Services Division - Information Center (Info Sci)
Harold Washington Library Center
400 S. State St. Phone: (312)747-4300
Chicago, IL 60605 Paula W. Saitis, Info.Ctr.Hd.
Founded: 1971. **Staff:** Prof 13; Other 3. **Subjects:** Ready reference material in all subjects. **Holdings:** 1690 titles; 92 card catalog drawers of biographical/obituary information; 50 card catalog drawers of Chicago curio information; 60 card catalog drawers of general information; 3000 domestic telephone directories; 225 foreign telephone directories. **Subscriptions:** 17 journals and other serials; 3 newspapers. **Services:** Telephone reference; DIAL-LAW (747-4304), a collection of tape-recorded messages giving general information about Illinois law and the legal system; DIAL-PET (747-4336), giving general information about pet health and care; Address Service (747-4330), address information from out-of-town directories. **Computerized Information Services:** DIALOG Information Services, NEXIS, VU/TEXT Information Services, DataTimes. **Publications:** Chicagoland Clubs Directory. **Staff:** Carolyn Mulac, First Asst.; Susan Bantz-Gustafson, Coll.Dev.; Kevin Davey, Files Hd.; Patricia Gaines, Database Proj.Coord.

★3532★
Chicago Public Library Central Library - General Information Services Division - Newspapers & General Periodicals Center (Publ)
Harold Washington Library Center
400 S. State St. Phone: (312)747-4300
Chicago, IL 60605 Margaret Clark, Hd.
Staff: Prof 4; Other 7. **Subjects:** Newspapers, periodicals, reference tools. **Special Collections:** Chicago newspapers, 1833 to present; New York Times (indexed); London Times (indexed); Microphoto "Early American Newspapers"; Microphoto Underground Newspaper Collection; Foreign Language Press Survey. **Holdings:** 3350 books; 33,223 bound periodical volumes; 37,237 microforms, newspaper indexes, almanacs. **Subscriptions:** 96 journals and other serials; 290 newspapers. **Services:** Interlibrary loan; center open to the public. **Automated Operations:** Computerized cataloging and circulation. **Computerized Information Services:** NEXIS, DIALOG Information Services, VU/TEXT Information Services, WILSONLINE, DataTimes. **Networks/Consortia:** Member of ILLINET. **Special Catalogs:** Chicago Public Library Serials Holdings List. **Staff:** Maggie Harrington, First Asst.

★3533★
Chicago Public Library Central Library - Government Publications Department (Info Sci)
Harold Washington Library Center
400 S. State St. Phone: (312)747-4500
Chicago, IL 60605 Roberta Palen, Hd.Libn.
Founded: 1979. **Staff:** Prof 7; Other 7.5. **Subjects:** United States, Illinois, and Chicago documents. **Special Collections:** Congressional Information Service's CIS microfiche library; American Statistics Index microfiche library; Index to International Statistics microfiche library; CIS/Greenwood Press hearings, 1869 (microfiche); CIS/Greenwood Press committee prints (microfiche); U.S. depository library, 1876 to present. **Holdings:** 783,000 documents; 1.3 million microforms; 82,000 maps. **Services:** Interlibrary loan; copying; department open to the public. **Computerized Information Services:** DIALOG Information Services, Legislative Information System (LIS), OCLC, LEGI-SLATE. **Networks/Consortia:** Member of ILLINET. **Publications:** Department brochure; pathfinders, irregular. **Remarks:** FAX: (312)747-4516. **Staff:** Lynne Kiviluoma, Asst.Hd.; Jan Brooks, Libn.; Patrick Corriere, Libn.; Colleen Vander Hye, Libn.; William Gordon, Libn.; Jane Baker, Libn.

★3534★
Chicago Public Library Central Library - Professional Library (Info Sci)
Harold Washington Library Center
400 S. State St. Phone: (312)747-4760
Chicago, IL 60605 Teresa Nunchuck, Hd.
Founded: 1976. **Staff:** 1.5. **Subjects:** Library science, Chicago Public Library, Chicago Library System. **Special Collections:** History of Chicago Public Library; Harold Washington Library Center Design/Building. **Holdings:** 11,400 books; 2000 bound periodical volumes; 270 audio cassettes; 300 microforms; 54 current library school catalogs; ARL Systems & Procedures Exchange Center Kits; 42 VF drawers of unbound reports, clippings, pamphlets, brochures. **Subscriptions:** 210 journals and other serials. **Services:** Interlibrary loan; research; library open to the public. **Automated Operations:** Computerized cataloging and acquisitions. **Computerized Information Services:** OCLC, DIALOG Information Services, WILSONLINE, BRS Information Technologies, VU/TEXT Information Services, DataTimes. **Networks/Consortia:** Member of ILLINET. **Publications:** Serials listing; department brochure. **Remarks:** FAX: (312)747-4762. **Staff:** Anita Owens, Libn. I.

★3535★
Chicago Public Library Central Library - Social Sciences Division (Soc Sci)
Harold Washington Library Center
400 S. State St. Phone: (312)747-4600
Chicago, IL 60605 Diane Purtill, Div.Chf.
Founded: 1975. **Staff:** Prof 14; Other 6. **Subjects:** Sociology, history, education, religion, psychology, philosophy, political science, sports, anthropology, law, genealogy, travel. **Special Collections:** Newsbank-Urban Affairs Library; Library of American Civilization (12,500 microfiche); Migne's Patrologia Cursus Completus (221 volumes on microfiche). **Holdings:** 368,760 books; 41,441 bound periodical volumes; 541,109 microforms; 4901 pamphlets; 4600 college catalogs on microfiche; 2645 maps; ERIC microfiche; 230 microcomputer disks. **Subscriptions:** 1921 journals and other serials. **Services:** Interlibrary loan; copying; division open to the public. **Automated Operations:** Computerized cataloging, acquisitions, serials, and circulation. **Computerized Information Services:** OCLC. **Networks/Consortia:** Member of ILLINET. **Special Indexes:** Chicago History Index (card). **Remarks:** The Social Sciences and History Information Center's telephone number is (312)747-4600; the Education and Philosophy Information Center's telephone number is 747-4690. FAX: (312)747-4646. **Staff:** Walter Grantham, Asst.Div.Chf. & Hd., Soc.Sci.Info.Ctr.; Joseph Grod, Hd., Soc.Sci.Sect.; Virginia Meeker, Hd., Educ.Sect.; Jennifer Shapp, Hd., Educ./Philosophy Sect.; Sharman Meehan, Hd., Philosophy & Rel.; James Stewart, Hd., Hist.Sect.

★3536★
Chicago Public Library Central Library - Special Collections Department (Rare Book, Hist, Hum)
Harold Washington Library Center
400 S. State St.
Chicago, IL 60605 Phone: (312)747-4960
Founded: 1975. **Staff:** Prof 7; Other 1. **Subjects:** Civil War; Chicago history; Chicago theater; Chicago authors, book arts. **Special Collections:** Grand Army of the Republic Collection (1500 items); World's Columbian Exposition (470 items; 1200 manuscripts); Chicago Theater Archives (600 linear feet); Chicago Public Library Archives (1000 linear feet); Lebold Miniature Book Collection (170 volumes); Neighborhood History Collection (600 linear feet). **Holdings:** 29,965 books; 973 bound periodical volumes; 2000 linear feet of archival materials; 9000 photographs; 1100 historical artifacts; miscellaneous manuscript collections. **Subscriptions:** 48 journals and other serials. **Services:** Copying; division open to the public with identification. **Automated Operations:** Computerized cataloging. **Computerized Information Services:** OCLC. **Networks/Consortia:** Member of ILLINET. **Publications:** Treasures of the Chicago Public Library - for sale. **Remarks:** FAX: (312)747-4960. **Staff:** Constance J. Gordon, Cat.; Glenn Humphreys, Cat.; Kathy Hussey-Arntson, Musm.Spec.; Lauren Bufferd, Theatre Archv.; Andrea Mark, Archv.; Galen R. Wilson, Asst.Cur.

★3537★
Chicago Public Library Cultural Center - Film/Video Center (Aud-Vis)
Harold Washington Library Center
400 S. State St. Phone: (312)747-4100
Chicago, IL 60605 Barbara L. Flynn, Hd.
Founded: 1951. **Staff:** Prof 4; Other 9. **Subjects:** Motion picture distribution, television, cable and home video. **Holdings:** 422 books; 357 pamphlets; 5068 16mm sound films; 1419 8mm silent films; 31,340 slides; motion picture reviews from local newspapers, 1964 to present; 8508 audiocassettes; 6153 VHS videocassettes; 1500 Beta videocassettes; 7042 spoken word recordings; 140 multimedia sets; 26 posters. **Subscriptions:** 15 journals and other serials. **Services:** Interlibrary loan; copying. **Automated Operations:** Computerized cataloging. **Computerized Information Services:** OCLC. **Networks/Consortia:** Member of ILLINET. **Publications:** List of new 16mm films, bimonthly; annotated filmographies. **Special Catalogs:** 16mm film catalog in book form, 1981, updated with bimonthly list; 8mm film list; slide list; videocassettes; Books on Tape annotated catalog. **Remarks:** FAX: (312)747-4126; (312)704-1972.

★3538★
Chicago Public Library Cultural Center - Thomas Hughes Children's Library (Hum)
Harold Washington Library Center
400 S. State St. Phone: (312)747-4200
Chicago, IL 60605 Laura B. Culberg, Hd.
Founded: 1910. **Staff:** Prof 8; Other 6. **Subjects:** Children's books, preschool through 8th grade; books about children's books for adults; children's books in foreign languages. **Special Collections:** Retrospective collection of early children's books; out of print materials and illustrated classics, folk and fairy tales; Chicago and Illinois Authors and Illustrators (6000 volumes); St. Nicholas magazine, 1873-1931. **Holdings:** 73,135 books; 543 bound periodical volumes; 1882 sound recordings for children; 4996 paperbacks; 698 pamphlets; 1140 audio/bookkits, videotapes, software, filmstrips, other nonbook materials; 45 volumes of dissertations. **Subscriptions:** 98 journals and other serials. **Services:** Interlibrary loan; copying; regularly scheduled children's programs; class visits to the public library; librarians' visits to elementary schools; library open to the public. **Automated Operations:** Computerized cataloging, acquisitions, and serials. **Computerized Information Services:** OCLC. **Networks/Consortia:** Member of ILLINET. **Publications:** Calendar of Ev ents; Summer Fun Programs; Brochure of Department; Monthly Program Flyer - all free upon request; subject and graded reading lists. **Remarks:** FAX: (312)747-4223. **Staff:** Oleh SaJewych, Libn.; Marsha Huddleston, Libn.; Jane Sorenson, Libn.; Irma Jean Patterson, Lib.Assoc.; Shannon Arends, Libn.; Mary Fran Bajt, Libn.; Malore Brown, Libn.

★3539★
Chicago Public Library Cultural Center - Visual & Performing Arts - Art Information Center (Art, Theater)
Harold Washington Library Center
400 S. State St. Phone: (312)747-4800
Chicago, IL 60605 Rosalinda Hack, Hd., Vis. & Perf. Arts
Founded: 1897. **Staff:** Prof 8; Other 10. **Subjects:** Fine and applied art, architecture, decorative arts, crafts, dance, motion pictures, radio, television, theater arts, photography, costume. **Special Collections:** Picture Collection, mounted and unmounted (secondary sources; over 1 million); Folk Dance collection (50 loose-leaf volumes); Chicago Stagebills, 1937 to present. **Holdings:** 97,551 books; 9278 bound periodical volumes; 6 VF drawers of Chicago Artists file; 99 reels of microfilm of Sears Roebuck catalogs; 277 dance videotapes; 6 VF drawers of pamphlets; 661 volumes on microfilm; 7186 periodical volumes on microfilm; 6192 monographs on microfiche. **Subscriptions:** 714 journals and other serials. **Services:** Interlibrary loan; copying; viewing room; slide maker available for public use; center open to the public. **Automated Operations:** Computerized cataloging. **Computerized Information Services:** OCLC. **Networks/Consortia:** Member of ILLINET. **Publications:** Occasional annotated reading lists and/or bibliographies. **Special Indexes:** Indexes to paintings, Chicago architecture. **Remarks:** FAX: (312)747-4832. **Staff:** Yvonne Brown, Hd., Art Info.Ctr.; Karen Kuntz, First Asst.; Margarete K. Gross, Pict.Libn.; Laura Morgan, Ser.Libn.

★3540★
Chicago Public Library Cultural Center - Visual & Performing Arts - Music Information Center (Mus)
Harold Washington Library Center
400 S. State St. Phone: (312)747-4850
Chicago, IL 60605 Rosalinda Hack, Hd., Vis. & Perf. Arts
Founded: 1915. **Staff:** Prof 8; Other 10. **Subjects:** History and theory of music, biographies of musicians and composers, music education, opera, musical comedy, sacred music, popular music, discography, music business, musical instruments, vocal and instrumental pedagogy, music therapy, folk music, composition and orchestration, arranging. **Special Collections:** Chicago music programs, 1873 to present; "Old Pops" collection of U.S. popular songs in original sheet music covers, 1830-1980s (10,702); Silberstein chamber music collection (2700 items); Balaban & Katz Theatre Orchestra Collection (10,860 dance band scores; 6057 classical scores; 5525 pieces of sheet music; 312 production scores); Chicago Blues Archives (recordings, photographs, videotapes, monographs). **Holdings:** 27,936 books; 5941 bound periodical volumes; 32,879 bound volumes of music; 15,837 pieces of music; 15 VF drawers of pamphlets and clippings; 6102 microfiche of music; 1986 reels of microfilm of periodicals; 93,701 phonograph records, compact discs, audiocassettes; 1183 music videos; 13,543 uncataloged recordings; 47,943 uncataloged scores. **Subscriptions:** 642 journals and other serials. **Services:** Interlibrary loan; copying; listening center; practice rooms (3); viewing room; center open to the public. **Automated Operations:** Computerized cataloging. **Computerized Information Services:** OCLC; CONTACT (Illinois Music Database; internal database); Dialcom, Inc. (electronic mail service). **Networks/Consortia:** Member of ILLINET. **Publications:** Occasional annotated reading lists and/or bibliographies. **Special Indexes:** Indexes to songs, record titles, and piano, violin, and organ pieces in collections (card). **Remarks:** FAX: (312)747-4832. Electronic mail address(es): MUSIC-INFO-US (Dialcom, Inc.). **Staff:** Richard Schwegel, Hd., Music Info.Ctr.; Alain Wolfe, Score Libn.; Jeannette Casey, Recorded Sound Libn.; Gerald Zimmerman, Spec.Proj.; Elaine Halama, Bks./Ser.Libn.

Chicago Public Schools Professional Library
See: **Chicago Board of Education** (3514)

★3541★
Chicago-Read Mental Health Center - Professional Library (Med)
4200 N. Oak Park Ave. Phone: (312)794-3746
Chicago, IL 60634 Ruth Greenberg, Libn.
Staff: Prof 1; Other 1. **Subjects:** Psychiatry, psychology, medicine, mental retardation, mental health, crisis intervention. **Holdings:** 6000 books; 6000 bound periodical volumes; 2000 unbound materials; 150 bibliographies. **Subscriptions:** 134 journals and other serials. **Services:** Interlibrary loan; copying (limited); library open to staff members only. **Networks/Consortia:** Member of National Network of Libraries of Medicine - Greater Midwest Region, Illinois Department of Mental Health and Developmental Disabilities Library Services Network (LISN), Chicago Library System. **Remarks:** Alternate telephone number(s): 794-4000.

★3542★
Chicago School of Professional Psychology - Library (Med)
806 S. Plymouth Ct., 2nd Fl. Phone: (312)786-9444
Chicago, IL 60605 Phyllis Schub, Libn.
Founded: 1979. **Staff:** Prof 1; Other 3. **Subjects:** Psychology - clinical, theoretical; psychotherapy; psychoanalysis; sociology. **Holdings:** 8200 books; 150 bound periodical volumes; 5300 cards of microfiche. **Subscriptions:** 200 journals and other serials. **Services:** Interlibrary loan; copying; library open to the public by appointment. **Computerized Information Services:** BRS/After Dark, SilverPlatter Information, Inc. **Remarks:** FAX: (312)786-9611.

★3543★
Chicago Sinai Congregation - Emil G. Hirsch Library (Rel-Phil)
5350 S. Shore Dr. Phone: (312)288-1600
Chicago, IL 60615 Bella Sandler, Libn.
Founded: 1950. **Staff:** Prof 1. **Subjects:** Judaica, Reform Judaism. **Special Collections:** Archives of Chicago Sinai Congregation, 1861 to present. **Holdings:** 4800 books; 50 bound periodical volumes; 50 other cataloged items. **Subscriptions:** 29 journals and other serials. **Services:** Library open to the public.

★3544★
Chicago State University - The Paul and Emily Douglas Library - Materials Center (Educ)
E. 95th St. & King Dr. Phone: (312)995-2276
Chicago, IL 60628 Carol L. Bentley, Hd. of Ctr.
Founded: 1867. **Staff:** Prof 2; Other 2. **Subjects:** Children's literature. **Holdings:** 50,542 books; curriculum guides; textbooks; kits; standardized tests; pictures and study prints; units and lesson plans. **Subscriptions:** 24 journals and other serials. **Services:** Interlibrary loan; center open to the public for reference use only. **Automated Operations:** Computerized cataloging and circulation. **Computerized Information Services:** DIALOG Information Services, BRS Information Technologies, OCLC. **Networks/Consortia:** Member of ILLINET, National Network of Libraries of Medicine - Greater Midwest Region, Center for Research Libraries (CRL). **Staff:** Beverly Meyer.

★3545★
Chicago Sun-Times - Editorial Library (Publ)
401 N. Wabash Ave. Phone: (312)321-2593
Chicago, IL 60611 Terri M. Golembiewski, Lib.Dir.
Founded: 1876. **Staff:** Prof 5; Other 5. **Subjects:** Newspaper reference topics, current events, local government, political science, photography, graphic arts. **Special Collections:** Newspaper clippings and microfilm, 1876 to present. **Holdings:** 3300 books; online newspaper full text file, 1985 to present; 600,000 files of clippings; 350,000 files of photographs; 260,000 negatives; 20 VF drawers of pamphlets. **Subscriptions:** 41 journals and other serials; 11 newspapers. **Services:** Library not open to the public. **Computerized Information Services:** DIALOG Information Services, DataTimes, VU/TEXT Information Services, Information America, NEXIS. **Networks/Consortia:** Member of Chicago Library System. **Special Indexes:** Newspaper index, 1976-1985 (online). **Staff:** Diana Boriss, Ref.Libn.; Judith Halper, Ref.Libn.; Virginia Davis, Ref.Libn.; Paulette Cage, Ref.Libn.

★3546★
Chicago Testing Laboratory, Inc. - Library (Sci-Engr)
3360 Commercial Ave. Phone: (708)498-6400
Northbrook, IL 60062 Richard Root, Pres.
Subjects: Bituminous materials, paper, plastics. **Holdings:** 200 books; 500 reports. **Subscriptions:** 15 journals and other serials. **Services:** Library not open to the public.

★3547★
Chicago Theological Seminary - Hammond Library (Rel-Phil)
5757 S. University Ave. Phone: (312)752-5757
Chicago, IL 60637 Rev. Neil W. Gerdes, Libn.
Founded: 1855. **Staff:** Prof 3; Other 6. **Subjects:** Theology, Bible, social ethics, personality and religion, Congregational Church history, sociology and religion. **Special Collections:** Lowenbach Collection of Congregational and Puritan history (8000 volumes); Anton Boisen Collection (papers and books on psychiatry, psychology, religion; 8000 volumes). **Holdings:** 107,259 volumes; 12,000 volumes of church records from Midwest Congregational churches and societies; 785 microforms; 705 AV programs. **Subscriptions:** 225 journals and other serials. **Services:** Interlibrary loan; copying; library open to the public with approval of librarian. **Automated Operations:** Computerized cataloging. **Computerized Information Services:** Online systems. **Networks/Consortia:** Member of ILLINET. **Special Catalogs:** Chicago Union Card Catalog of Chicago Cluster Schools, the University of Chicago divinity collection and Newberry Library (microfiche). **Remarks:** FAX: (312)752-5925. **Staff:** Joan Blocher, Asst.Libn.; Roberta Schaafsma, Tech.Asst.

★3548★
Chicago Title Insurance Company - Law Library (Law)
2 N. LaSalle St., 8th Fl. Phone: (312)630-2458
Chicago, IL 60602-3768 John A. Kareken
Staff: Prof 2. **Subjects:** Property. **Remarks:** FAX: (312)630-2960.

★3549★
Chicago Transit Authority - Harold S. Anthon Memorial Library (Trans)
Merchandise Mart Plaza
Box 3555 Phone: (312)664-7200
Chicago, IL 60654 Lillian D. Culbertson, Supv., Lib.Serv.
Founded: 1967. **Staff:** Prof 2; Other 2. **Subjects:** Urban transportation, transportation planning and engineering, business administration. **Holdings:** 20,000 books. **Subscriptions:** 550 journals and other serials. **Services:** Interlibrary loan; copying; Current Awareness Service; library open to the public for reference use only by appointment. **Automated Operations:** Computerized cataloging and ILL. **Computerized Information Services:** OCLC. **Networks/Consortia:** Member of ILLINET, Chicago Library System. **Publications:** Acquisitions list. **Staff:** Violette Y. Brooks, Ref.Libn.

★3550★
Chicago Tribune - Editorial Information Center (Publ)
435 N. Michigan Ave. Phone: (312)222-3871
Chicago, IL 60611 John F. Jansson, Ed., Info.Sys.
Founded: 1910. **Staff:** Prof 21; Other 1. **Subjects:** Newspaper reference topics, Chicago, Illinois, Midwest. **Holdings:** 8000 books; 16 million newspaper clippings; 9 million photographs; 3 million envelopes of negatives; Chicago Tribune, 1847 to present (including Paris edition, on microfilm); Chicago American & Today, 1950-1974, on microfilm. **Subscriptions:** 150 journals and other serials; 8 newspapers. **Services:** Center not open to the public. **Computerized Information Services:** DIALOG Information Services, Dow Jones News/Retrieval, NEXIS, LEXIS, VU/TEXT Information Services, AgriData Network, DataTimes, Info Globe, NewsNet, Inc.; produces the Chicago Tribune on CD-ROM. **Remarks:** Published by the Chicago Tribune Company. **Staff:** Karen Blair, Mgr., Res.; Richard Rott, Mgr., Online Sys.; Mary Wilson, Mgr., Photo. & Graphics.

★3551★
Chicago Tribune - Marketing Information Center (Bus-Fin)
435 N. Michigan, 2nd Fl. Phone: (312)222-3188
Chicago, IL 60611 Lynne Kerger, Mgr.
Founded: 1964. **Staff:** Prof 2. **Subjects:** Advertising, retailing, Chicago market, marketing research, newspapers and competing media. **Holdings:** 500 books; syndicated media data. **Subscriptions:** 90 journals and other serials. **Services:** Library open to the public by appointment. **Computerized Information Services:** VU/TEXT Information Services, DIALOG Information Services, DataTimes, NEXIS. **Networks/Consortia:** Member of Chicago Library System. **Publications:** New Store Openings, quarterly - by subscription. **Remarks:** FAX: (312)222-3935. **Staff:** Mari Colello.

★3552★
Chicago Tribune Press Service - Washington Bureau - Library (Publ)
1615 L St., N.W., Suite 300 Phone: (202)785-9430
Washington, DC 20036 Linda Harrington, Res.
Staff: Prof 1; Other 1. **Subjects:** Politics, foreign affairs, economics, defense, history. **Holdings:** 2000 books; 1000 government documents; presidential documents. **Subscriptions:** 50 journals and other serials; 10 newspapers. **Services:** Library not open to the public. **Computerized Information Services:** VU/TEXT Information Services, DIALOG Information Services, FEC.

★3553★
Chicago Zoological Society - Library (Biol Sci)
8400 W. 31st St. Phone: (708)485-0263
Brookfield, IL 60513 Mary S. Rabb, Libn.
Founded: 1964. **Staff:** Prof 2. **Subjects:** Natural history, animal behavior, zoology. **Holdings:** 9000 books; 3000 bound periodical volumes; slides; photographs. **Subscriptions:** 310 journals and other serials. **Services:** Interlibrary loan; copying; library open to the public with restrictions. **Publications:** Zoo Guide; Brookfield Bison; Brookfield Bandarlog.

★3554★
Chicana Research & Learning Center, Inc. - Library (Area-Ethnic)
1502 Norris Dr. Phone: (512)444-7595
Austin, TX 78704 Martha P. Cotera, Dir.
Founded: 1974. **Staff:** 1. **Subjects:** Hispanic women. **Holdings:** 400 books; 500 reports. **Services:** Copying; library open to the public. **Computerized Information Services:** Biographic database on Hispanic women worldwide (internal database). **Special Catalogs:** Catalog of publications. **Remarks:** FAX: (512)477-1767.

Chicano Library Resource Center
See: **San Jose State University - Wahlquist Library** (14761)

Chickamauga-Chattanooga National Military Park
See: **U.S. Natl. Park Service** (17689)

Chickasaw Council House Library
See: **Oklahoma Historical Society** (12349)

Chickasaw National Recreation Area
See: **U.S. Natl. Park Service - Chickasaw Natl. Recreation Area** (17690)

★3555★
CHIER Information Center (Med)
320 W. 15th St. Phone: (213)742-5872
Los Angeles, CA 90015 Cynthia Perkins, Dir., Lib. & Info.Serv.
Founded: 1977. **Staff:** Prof 1; Other 1. **Subjects:** Clinical medicine, oncology, hospital management, nursing. **Holdings:** 3180 books; 3500 bound periodical volumes; 500 audio cassettes. **Subscriptions:** 282 journals and other serials. **Services:** Interlibrary loan; library not open to the public. **Computerized Information Services:** MEDLARS, BRS Information Technologies. Performs searches on fee basis. Telephone 742-5872. **Remarks:** FAX: (213)742-5875.

★3556★
(Chihuahua) Instituto Mexicano-Norteamericano de Relaciones Culturales - USIS Collection (Educ)
V. Guerrero, No. 616
31000 Chihuahua, Chih., Mexico
Remarks: Maintained or supported by the U.S. Information Agency. Focus is on materials that will assist peoples outside the United States to learn about the United States, its people, history, culture, political processes, and social milieux.

★3557★
Child Custody Services of Philadelphia, Inc. - Resource Center (Soc Sci)
P.O. Box 202 Phone: (215)576-0177
Glenside, PA 19038-0202 Dr. Ken Lewis, Dir.
Founded: 1978. **Staff:** Prof 2; Other 1. **Subjects:** Child custody, single-parent families, divorce, child-snatching, mental health and law. **Special Collections:** Father's rights movement; women's liberation. **Holdings:** 828 books; 50 bound periodical volumes; 16 dissertation abstracts; 25 special reports; 12 grant narratives; 28 television and radio news documentaries; 50 monographs. **Subscriptions:** 75 journals and other serials; 58 newspapers. **Services:** Copying; center open to the public by appointment. **Computerized Information Services:** MCI Mail (electronic mail service). **Publications:** CCES Workshop Series; CCES Monograph Series. **Remarks:** Electronic mail address(es): CUSTODY 354-0356 (MCI Mail).

★3558★
Child & Family Services - Library (Soc Sci)
1680 Albany Ave. Phone: (203)297-0558
Hartford, CT 06105 Hong-Chan Li
Staff: Prof 1. **Subjects:** Child welfare, family services, psychology, child psychiatry, social work, child development. **Holdings:** 4000 books; 1200 pamphlets; 120 microfiche; 12 videocassettes; 300 audiocassettes. **Subscriptions:** 60 journals and other serials. **Services:** Interlibrary loan; library open to the public by appointment.

★3559★
Child Trends, Inc. - Library (Soc Sci)
2100 M St., N.W., Rm. 610 Phone: (202)223-6288
Washington, DC 20037-1207 Dr. Nicholas Zill, Exec.Dir.
Founded: 1979. **Staff:** 13. **Subjects:** Physical, social, emotional, and psychological development of children; influence of family, school, peers, neighborhood, religion, media on children; teen pregnancy; family strengths; statistics. **Holdings:** Statistics and reports from U.S. Bureau of the Census, National Center for Health Statistics, National Center for Education Statistics. **Services:** Library not open to the public. **Remarks:** FAX: (202)728-4142.

★3560★
Child Welfare League of America - Information Service - Dorothy L. Bernhard Library (Soc Sci)
440 First St., N.W., Suite 310 Phone: (202)638-2952
Washington, DC 20001-2085 Lisa A. Merkel, Libn.
Founded: 1920. **Staff:** Prof 1. **Subjects:** Child welfare, social work, social welfare, child development, health care, youth issues. **Special Collections:** Archives of the Child Welfare League of America. **Holdings:** 5000 books; 30 VF drawers of USHHS publications on child welfare; 600 research reports; 70 VF drawers. **Subscriptions:** 90 journals and other serials. **Services:** Library open to member agencies and organizations. **Computerized Information Services:** Internal database. **Publications:** Subject bibliographies. **Special Catalogs:** AV catalog. **Remarks:** FAX: (202)638-4004.

★3561★
Children Enfants Jeunesse Youth - Resource Centre (Soc Sci)
55 Parkdale Ave., 3rd Fl. Phone: (613)722-0133
Ottawa, ON, Canada K1Y 1E5 Elizabeth Bourque, Hd.
Founded: 1992. **Staff:** 1. **Subjects:** Children and youth - health, law, education, culture, recreation, agencies, native, environment, child welfare. **Holdings:** 15,000 books and bound periodical volumes; reports; briefs; essays; directories; statistics; inventory of programs. **Subscriptions:** 235 journals and other serials; 10 newspapers; list of subscriptions and topics available for a fee. **Services:** Center open to the public. **Computerized Information Services:** Internal database. Performs searches on fee basis. **Remarks:** FAX: (613)722-4829. CETY maintains a database of voluntary sector organizations involved with the Young Offenders Act. **Formerly:** Canadian Council on Children and Youth.

★3562★
Children of the Green Earth - Green Earth Collection (Env-Cons)
P.O. Box 31087
Seattle, WA 98103-1087 Michael Soule, Dir.
Subjects: Tree folklore and mythology, youth tree planting, children's tree books, tree care and planting. **Holdings:** 100 books; 6 AV programs. **Services:** Interlibrary loan; copying; collection open to the public.

★3563★
Children's Aid Society of Ottawa - Library (Soc Sci)
1370 Bank St. Phone: (613)733-0670
Ottawa, ON, Canada K1H 7Y3 Janice Horton, Staff Training/Dev.
Subjects: Child welfare, child protection, foster and residential care. **Holdings:** 1200 books; reports; archives. **Subscriptions:** 45 journals and other serials. **Services:** Library not open to the public. **Remarks:** FAX: (613)737-1874.

★3564★
Children's Book Council - Library (Hum)
568 Broadway Phone: (212)966-1990
New York, NY 10012 Paula Quint, Exec.V.P.
Founded: 1945. **Staff:** 1. **Subjects:** Children's books, books about children's books. **Special Collections:** Selected prizewinning children's books. **Holdings:** 7000 books. **Subscriptions:** 30 journals and other serials. **Services:** Library open to the public for reference use only.

★3565★
Children's Book Council of Iran - Library (Hum)
Enghelab, Sevazar No. 69 Phone: 21 6408074
Tehran, Iran Mrs. Nasrin-Dokht Em Khorasani, Libn.
Subjects: Children's and young adult literature. **Special Collections:** Clippings 1970-1991. **Holdings:** 12,930 books and reference works; 32 periodical titles; 690 documents; 36 thesis titles; 500 posters; 12 disks; 132 tapes. **Subscriptions:** 20 journals and other serials. **Services:** SDI; library open to the public by membership or recommendation.

★3566★
Children's Hospital - Forbes Medical Library (Med)
1056 E. 19th Ave. Phone: (303)861-6400
Denver, CO 80218 Anne S. Klenk, Med.Libn.
Staff: Prof 1; Other 2. **Subjects:** Pediatrics, nursing with emphasis on pediatrics, nonprofessional information on child care and common

childhood diseases. **Special Collections:** Archives of pediatrics in Rocky Mountain area. **Holdings:** 3500 books; 5000 bound periodical volumes. **Subscriptions:** 320 journals and other serials. **Services:** Interlibrary loan; library open to the public by appointment. **Computerized Information Services:** BRS Information Technologies, MEDLARS, DIALOG Information Services; TenTime (electronic mail service). Performs searches for hospital staff only. **Networks/Consortia:** Member of National Network of Libraries of Medicine - Midcontinental Region, Colorado Council of Medical Librarians. **Remarks:** FAX: (303)861-6786.

★3567★
Children's Hospital - Library (Med)
700 Children's Drive Phone: (614)461-2713
Columbus, OH 43205 Linda De Muro, Libn.
Founded: 1953. **Staff:** Prof 1; Other 2. **Subjects:** Pediatrics, allied health sciences. **Holdings:** 4200 books; 8500 bound periodical volumes. **Subscriptions:** 300 journals and other serials. **Services:** Interlibrary loan; copying; library open to the public for reference use only. **Automated Operations:** Computerized cataloging, serials, and circulation. **Computerized Information Services:** BRS Information Technologies, MEDLINE, DIALOG Information Services. **Networks/Consortia:** Member of Central Ohio Hospital Library Consortium. **Remarks:** FAX: (614)460-8140.

★3568★
Children's Hospital of Buffalo - Medical Library (Med)
219 Bryant St. Phone: (716)878-7304
Buffalo, NY 14222 Lucy Wargo, Lib.Dir.
Founded: 1940. **Staff:** Prof 1; Other 1. **Subjects:** Pediatrics, general medicine. **Holdings:** 1856 books; 10,393 bound periodical volumes. **Subscriptions:** 343 journals and other serials. **Services:** Interlibrary loan; copying; library open to the public. **Computerized Information Services:** Online systems. **Networks/Consortia:** Member of Library Consortium of Health Institutions in Buffalo (LCHIB), Western New York Library Resources Council (WNYLRC).

Children's Hospital of the East Bay
See: **Children's Hospital Medical Center of Northern California** (3577)

★3569★
Children's Hospital of Eastern Ontario - Dominick J. Conway Library (Med)
401 Smyth Rd. Phone: (613)737-2206
Ottawa, ON, Canada K1H 8L1 Patricia Johnston, Dir., Lib.Serv.
Founded: 1974. **Staff:** Prof 1; Other 2. **Subjects:** Pediatrics, nursing, allied health sciences, general medicine, hospital management. **Holdings:** 8500 books; 3500 bound periodical volumes; 6 VF drawers of pamphlets and reprints; 850 AV programs. **Subscriptions:** 400 journals and other serials. **Services:** Interlibrary loan; copying; SDI; library open to the public. **Computerized Information Services:** MEDLARS, DIALOG Information Services, iNET 2000; Envoy 100 (electronic mail service). Performs searches on fee basis. **Networks/Consortia:** Member of O.H.A. Region 9 Hospital Libraries. **Publications:** CHEO Hospital Acquisitions List, quarterly. **Remarks:** FAX: (613)738-3216. Electronic mail address(es): CHEO.LIB (Envoy 100). **Formerly:** Its Medical Library.

★3570★
Children's Hospital & Health Center - Health Sciences Library (Med)
8001 Frost St. Phone: (619)576-1700
San Diego, CA 92123 Anna Habetler, Mgr.
Founded: 1955. **Staff:** Prof 2; Other 1. **Subjects:** Pediatrics. **Special Collections:** Family Library (patient education materials for parents and children). **Holdings:** 2500 books; 3000 bound periodical volumes; 700 audiotapes. **Subscriptions:** 285 journals and other serials. **Services:** Interlibrary loan; SDI; library open to the public for reference use only. **Automated Operations:** Computerized acquisitions, cataloging, and ILL (DOCLINE). **Computerized Information Services:** NLM, BRS Information Technologies, DIALOG Information Services, OCLC, OCLC EPIC. Contact Person: Charlotte McClamma, Med.Libn., 576-1700, ext. 5690. **Publications:** Periodicals Holdings List; Acquisitions List, both irregular. **Remarks:** FAX: (619)495-4934.

★3571★
Children's Hospital, Inc. - Medical Library (Med)
3825 Greenspring Ave. Phone: (301)462-6800
Baltimore, MD 21211 Rita Billstone, Volunteer Libn.
Staff: 1. **Subjects:** Orthopedics, plastic surgery, pediatrics, medicine. **Holdings:** 745 books; 260 bound periodical volumes. **Subscriptions:** 7 journals and other serials. **Services:** Interlibrary loan; copying; library open to staff and allied health professionals. **Remarks:** FAX: (301)669-7910.

★3572★
Children's Hospital, Inc. - Medical-Nursing Library (Med)
345 N. Smith Ave. Phone: (612)220-6145
St. Paul, MN 55102 Nancy W. Battaglia, Dir.
Founded: 1960. **Staff:** Prof 1. **Subjects:** Pediatrics, pediatric endocrinology, pediatric nursing, growth and development. **Holdings:** 1000 books; 600 bound periodical volumes; 2 VF drawers of reprints and photoduplicated articles; 100 Audio-Digest tapes on pediatrics. **Subscriptions:** 100 journals and other serials. **Services:** Interlibrary loan; library open to qualified students and researchers for reference. **Computerized Information Services:** DIALOG Information Services, MEDLINE. Performs searches on fee basis. **Networks/Consortia:** Member of National Network of Libraries of Medicine - Greater Midwest Region, Twin Cities Biomedical Consortium (TCBC).

★3573★
Children's Hospital of the King's Daughters - Medical Library (Med)
800 W. Olney Rd. Phone: (804)628-7232
Norfolk, VA 23507 C.W. Gowen, Jr., M.D.
Founded: 1979. **Staff:** Prof 1; Other 1. **Subjects:** Pediatrics. **Special Collections:** Maria Alexander Memorial Collection (endocrinology and metabolism; 23 books). **Holdings:** 432 books; 263 bound periodical volumes; 300 audio cassettes; 18 video cassettes; 5 slide collections on pediatric specialties. **Subscriptions:** 31 journals and other serials. **Services:** Interlibrary loan; library not open to the public. **Remarks:** FAX: (804)627-6541.

★3574★
Children's Hospital of Los Angeles - Medical Library (Med)
4650 Sunset Blvd. Phone: (213)669-2254
Los Angeles, CA 90027 Doreen B. Keough, Med.Libn.
Staff: Prof 1; Other 2. **Subjects:** Pediatrics. **Holdings:** 5000 books; 4000 bound periodical volumes; 1250 reels of microfilm. **Subscriptions:** 350 journals and other serials. **Services:** Interlibrary loan; SDI; library open to health professionals. **Automated Operations:** Computerized cataloging, serials, and circulation. **Computerized Information Services:** MEDLINE, DIALOG Information Services. **Remarks:** FAX: (213)662-7019.

★3575★
Children's Hospital & Medical Center - Hospital Library (Med)
4800 Sand Point Way N.E.
P.O. Box 5371 Phone: (206)526-2118
Seattle, WA 98105 Tamara A. Turner, Dir.
Founded: 1946. **Staff:** Prof 3. **Subjects:** Pediatrics. **Special Collections:** Resident's teaching files. **Holdings:** 3500 books; 4500 bound periodical volumes. **Subscriptions:** 800 journals and other serials. **Services:** Interlibrary loan; copying; SDI; library open to the public for reference use only. **Computerized Information Services:** MEDLINE, DIALOG Information Services, BRS Information Technologies; CD-ROM (LASERCAT); OnTyme Electronic Message Network Service (electronic mail service). Performs searches on fee basis. **Networks/Consortia:** Member of Seattle Area Hospital Library Consortium (SAHLC). **Remarks:** Alternate telephone number(s): (206)526-2098. FAX: (206)527-3838. Electronic mail address(es): COHMC (OnTyme Electronic Message Network Service). **Staff:** Kathleen McCrory, Libn.I; Susan Klawansky, Libn. I.

★3576★
Children's Hospital Medical Center - Mary A. Hower Medical Library (Med)
281 Locust St. Phone: (216)379-8250
Akron, OH 44308 Julie Thom, Dir.
Staff: Prof 1; Other 3. **Subjects:** Medicine, pediatrics. **Special Collections:** Classics in Medicine Series. **Holdings:** 2833 books; 5000 bound periodical volumes. **Subscriptions:** 306 journals and other serials. **Services:** Interlibrary loan; library not open to the public. **Automated Operations:** Computerized cataloging. **Computerized Information Services:** BRS Information Technologies, NLM, DIALOG Information Services. **Networks/Consortia:** Member of NEOUCOM Council Associated Hospital Librarians. **Remarks:** FAX: (216)258-3158. **Staff:** Laura Marcinkosky, Med.Lib.Asst.

★3577★
Children's Hospital Medical Center of Northern California - Health Sciences Library (Med)
747 52nd St. Phone: (510)428-3448
Oakland, CA 94609 Leonard P. Shapiro, Med.Libn.
Founded: 1938. **Staff:** 4. **Subjects:** Pediatrics, neonatology, adolescent medicine, pediatric nursing, child development, child psychology. **Holdings:** 2800 books; 7200 bound periodical volumes; 250 Audio-Digest tapes; 400 videotapes. **Subscriptions:** 400 journals and other serials. **Services:** Interlibrary loan; SDI; library open to the public by appointment. **Automated Operations:** Computerized public access catalog, acquisitions, serials, and circulation. **Computerized Information Services:** MEDLINE, BRS Information Technologies; OnTyme Electronic Message Network Service (electronic mail service). Performs searches free of charge. **Publications:** Children's Hospital Library Newsletter & Acquisitions List, 3/Year; Children's Hospital Serials Holdings List, annual - both available on request. **Remarks:** FAX: (510)601-3963. Electronic mail address(es): CLASS.CHILD.HOSP (OnTyme Electronic Message Network Service). **Also Known As:** Children's Hospital of the East Bay. **Staff:** Ronald P. Anderson, Media Spec.

★3578★
Children's Hospital of Michigan - Medical Library (Med)
3901 Beaubien Phone: (313)745-5322
Detroit, MI 48201 Michele S. Klein, Dir., Lib.Serv.
Staff: Prof 1.5; Other 2.5. **Subjects:** Pediatrics, growth and development, genetics, pediatric clinical research. **Holdings:** 3000 books; 8000 bound periodical volumes; 40 audiotapes. **Subscriptions:** 305 journals and other serials. **Services:** Interlibrary loan; LATCH (Literature Attached To Charts); SDI; library not open to the public. **Automated Operations:** Computerized public access catalog, cataloging, and circulation. **Computerized Information Services:** OCLC, DIALOG Information Services, MEDLINE, BRS Information Technologies, VU/TEXT Information Services, WILSONLINE; CD-ROM (MEDLINE). **Remarks:** FAX: (313)993-0148. **Staff:** Cathy H. Eames.

★3579★
Children's Hospital/National Medical Center - Hospital Library (Med)
111 Michigan Ave., N.W. Phone: (202)745-3195
Washington, DC 20010 Deborah D. Gilbert, Dir.
Staff: Prof 3; Other 2. **Subjects:** Pediatrics, child development, nursing, dentistry, psychiatry, ophthalmology. **Holdings:** 2953 books; 8254 bound periodical volumes; 300 AV programs. **Subscriptions:** 550 journals and other serials. **Services:** Interlibrary loan; copying; LATCH (Literature Attached To Charts); library open to the public by appointment. **Automated Operations:** Computerized cataloging. **Computerized Information Services:** NLM, BRS Information Technologies, DIALOG Information Services. **Remarks:** FAX: (202)939-4492. **Staff:** Shirley Knobloch, Asst.Libn.; Lyn Ingersoll, Family Libn.

★3580★
Children's Hospital of Oklahoma - CHO Medical Library (Med)
Box 26307 Phone: (405)271-5699
Oklahoma City, OK 73126 Jean Cavett, Dir.
Founded: 1973. **Staff:** Prof 1; Other 1. **Subjects:** Pediatrics. **Holdings:** 900 books; 1900 bound periodical volumes. **Subscriptions:** 120 journals and other serials. **Services:** Interlibrary loan; SDI. **Computerized Information Services:** MEDLINE; DOCLINE (electronic mail service). **Networks/Consortia:** Member of Greater Oklahoma City Area Health Sciences Library Consortium (GOAL), Oklahoma Health Sciences Library Association (OHSLA), BHSL, ALLCeD.

★3581★
Children's Hospital of Oklahoma - Family Resource Center (Med)
940 N.E. 13th St., Rm. 3N 109
Box 26307 Phone: (405)271-5525
Oklahoma City, OK 73126 Madalyn McCollom, Dir.
Founded: 1985. **Staff:** Prof 2. **Subjects:** Lay medical information, parenting/child care, community resource files, general health care, caring for the chronically ill, preparation/hospitalization. **Special Collections:** Community resources for handicapped children and children with special health needs. **Holdings:** 900 titles; 1 vertical file; 90 videotapes; 30 audio cassettes. **Subscriptions:** 16 journals and other serials; 8 newsletters. **Services:** Copying; center open to the public. **Automated Operations:** Computerized cataloging. **Networks/Consortia:** Member of Metropolitan Libraries Network of Central Oklahoma Inc. (MetroNet). **Publications:** Newsletter, quarterly - for internal distribution only; Bibliography - free to Oklahoma residents. **Remarks:** FAX: (405)271-3017. Maintained by Oklahoma Medical Center.

★3582★
Children's Hospital of Philadelphia - Medical Library (Med)
34th & Civic Center Blvd. Phone: (215)590-2317
Philadelphia, PA 19104-4399 Mrs. Swaran Lata Chopra, Adm.Supv./Dir.
Founded: 1956. **Staff:** Prof 1; Other 1. **Subjects:** Pediatrics, medicine, nursing. **Holdings:** 4400 books; 7200 bound periodical volumes; 6 VF drawers of clippings and pamphlets; audio cassettes; video cassettes. **Subscriptions:** 200 journals and other serials. **Services:** Interlibrary loan; copying; library open to the public. **Remarks:** FAX: (215)662-9517.

★3583★
Children's Hospital of Pittsburgh - Blaxter Memorial Library (Med)
3705 5th Ave. at De Soto Phone: (412)692-5288
Pittsburgh, PA 15213-2583 Nancy Dunn, Libn.
Staff: Prof 2; Other 1. **Subjects:** Pediatric medicine. **Holdings:** 1000 books; 2600 bound periodical volumes. **Subscriptions:** 200 journals and other serials. **Services:** Interlibrary loan; copying; library open to the public with restrictions. **Computerized Information Services:** NLM, DIALOG Information Services, BRS Information Technologies.

★3584★
Children's Hospital Research Foundation - Edward L. Pratt Library (Med)
Elland & Bethesda Avenues Phone: (513)559-4300
Cincinnati, OH 45229 Barbarie F. Hill, Lib.Dir.
Founded: 1931. **Staff:** Prof 2; Other 1.5. **Subjects:** Pediatrics, genetics, medicine. **Holdings:** 4500 books; 12,000 bound periodical volumes; 250 videotapes. **Subscriptions:** 280 journals and other serials. **Services:** Interlibrary loan; copying; SDI; library open to physicians and other local research personnel for reference use only. **Computerized Information Services:** MEDLINE, DIALOG Information Services, OCLC, BRS Information Technologies, NLM; internal database. **Networks/Consortia:** Member of National Network of Libraries of Medicine - Greater Midwest Region. **Publications:** Studies of the Children's Hospital Research Foundation. **Remarks:** FAX: (513)559-9669. **Staff:** Valerie Purvis.

★3585★
Children's Hospital of Wisconsin - Health Sciences Library (Med)
9000 W. Wisconsin Phone: (414)266-2000
Milwaukee, WI 53201 Molly Youngkin, Br.Libn.
Staff: Prof 1. **Subjects:** Pediatrics, nursing, medicine. **Holdings:** 1300 books; 2300 bound periodical volumes. **Subscriptions:** 190 journals and other serials. **Services:** Interlibrary loan; copying; library open to the public with permission. **Computerized Information Services:** BRS Information Technologies, NLM. Performs searches on fee basis. **Networks/Consortia:** Member of Southeastern Wisconsin Health Science Library Consortium (SWHSL).

★3586★
Children's Medical Center - Library (Med)
One Children's Plaza Phone: (513)226-8307
Dayton, OH 45404 Jane R. Bottoms, Libn.
Founded: 1967. **Staff:** Prof 1; Other 1. **Subjects:** Pediatrics, allied health sciences. **Holdings:** 2000 books; 5000 bound periodical volumes. **Subscriptions:** 240 journals and other serials. **Services:** Interlibrary loan; library not open to the public.

★3587★
Children's Medical Center of Dallas - Lauren Taylor Reardon Family Library (Med)
1935 Amelia St. Phone: (214)920-2280
Dallas, TX 75235 Sally Francis, Dir., Ch. Life Dept.
Founded: 1983. **Staff:** Prof 1. **Subjects:** Health, cancer, child development, children's literature, medicine, death and bereavement. **Special Collections:** Children's books on health-related topics (120). **Holdings:** 1000 books; pamphlets; brochures. **Services:** Library not open to the public. **Publications:** Information brochure. **Remarks:** Library collection provides "adults and children with information about chronic diseases and coping with illness."

★3588★
Children's Memorial Hospital - Joseph Brennemann Library (Med)
2300 Children's Plaza Phone: (312)880-4505
Chicago, IL 60614 Meg Ward, Dir.
Founded: 1935. **Staff:** Prof 3; Other 3. **Subjects:** Pediatrics, surgery, genetics, child psychiatry. **Holdings:** 5400 books; 28,000 bound periodical volumes. **Subscriptions:** 500 journals and other serials. **Services:** Interlibrary loan; library not open to the public. **Automated Operations:** Computerized cataloging and serials. **Computerized Information Services:** NLM, OCLC, BRS Information Technologies, DIALOG Information Services. **Networks/Consortia:** Member of National Network of Libraries of Medicine - Greater Midwest Region. **Publications:** Acquisitions/Newsletter, bimonthly - to hospital departments, employees, and outside libraries on request.

★3589★
Children's Mercy Hospital - Medical Library (Med)
2401 Gillham Rd. Phone: (816)234-3800
Kansas City, MO 64108 Anne R. Palmer, Mgr., Lib.Serv.
Founded: 1913. **Staff:** Prof 1; Other 2. **Subjects:** Pediatrics. **Special Collections:** William L. Bradford, M.D., Library of the History of Pediatrics (300 volumes). **Holdings:** 1300 books; 8100 bound periodical volumes. **Subscriptions:** 225 journals and other serials. **Services:** Interlibrary loan; copying; SDI. **Automated Operations:** Computerized public access catalog. **Computerized Information Services:** MEDLARS, BRS Information Technologies; CD-ROM (MEDLINE, CINAHL Health Planning and Administrative Data Base). **Networks/Consortia:** Member of Kansas City Library Network, Inc. (KCLN). **Special Catalogs:** Children's Mercy Hospital Serial Holdings. **Remarks:** FAX: (816)234-3125.

★3590★
Children's Museum, Boston - Resource Center (Area-Ethnic, Hist)
Museum Wharf
300 Congress St.
Boston, MA 02210 Phone: (617)426-6500
Founded: 1913. **Staff:** Prof 1; Other 2. **Subjects:** Multicultural education, Native Americans, East Asia, natural and physical sciences, special needs. **Special Collections:** Curriculum and display kits developed by museum staff. **Holdings:** 10,000 books. **Subscriptions:** 60 journals and other serials. **Services:** Interlibrary loan; center open to the public for reference use only. **Computerized Information Services:** BRS Information Technologies, OCLC. **Remarks:** FAX: (617)426-1944.

★3591★
Children's Museum of Indianapolis - Rauh Memorial Library (Hist)
3000 N. Meridian St.
Box 3000 Phone: (317)924-5431
Indianapolis, IN 46206 Gregg Jackson, Libn./Archv.
Founded: 1975. **Staff:** Prof 1. **Subjects:** American history, American Indians, antiques, folk art, Indiana history, dolls, toys, museum studies, science, world cultures, education theory. **Special Collections:** Children's books (300). **Holdings:** 6000 books; 200 bound periodical volumes; 500 vertical file materials. **Subscriptions:** 65 journals and other serials. **Services:** Interlibrary loan; copying; library open to the public with restrictions. **Automated Operations:** Computerized cataloging and circulation. **Computerized Information Services:** OCLC. **Networks/Consortia:** Member of Central Indiana Area Library Services Authority (CIALSA), INCOLSA. **Remarks:** FAX: (317)921-4019.

★3592★
Children's Museum of Oak Ridge - Regional Appalachian Center - Media Center/Library (Hist)
461 W. Outer Dr. Phone: (615)482-1074
Oak Ridge, TN 37830 Jane Barnes Alderfer, Archv./Libn.
Founded: 1979. **Staff:** Prof 1. **Subjects:** Appalachia, local history. **Special Collections:** Cole Family Collection (aviation, armed services, world flight, social history, family; 2.5 linear feet of photographs); William G. Pollard Collection (religion, physics, nuclear history; 1.3 linear feet of books, chronology, papers, and journal articles). **Holdings:** 2200 books; 500 audiocassettes; 75 videotapes; 80 maps; 7 linear feet of slides; 6.5 linear feet of local history photographs and manuscripts; 8 linear feet of VF material. **Subscriptions:** 29 journals and other serials. **Services:** Copying; library open to the public by appointment. **Automated Operations:** Computerized cataloging. **Publications:** An Encyclopedia of East Tennessee; Ridges & Valleys; An Appalachian Studies Teacher's Manual; These are Our Voices: The Story of Oak Ridge, 1942-1970; Anderson County, Tennessee: A Pictorial History; Oak Ridge and Me.

Children's Psychiatric Research Institute
See: **Dr. Joseph Pozsonyi Memorial Library** (13285)

★3593★
Children's Rehabilitation Centre - Medical Library (Med)
Box 1403 Phone: (709)754-1970
St. John's, NF, Canada A1C 5N5 Kathleen Legge, Libn.
Holdings: 200 books. **Subscriptions:** 75 journals and other serials. **Services:** Library not open to the public.

★3594★
Children's Specialized Hospital - Medical Library (Med)
150 New Providence Rd. Phone: (908)233-3720
Mountainside, NJ 07091 Anne Glasser, Med.Libn.
Staff: Prof 1. **Subjects:** Pediatrics, rehabilitation, nursing. **Holdings:** 3000 books; 14 VF drawers; 320 audio cassettes; 105 filmstrip kits; 450 slides. **Subscriptions:** 150 journals and other serials. **Services:** Interlibrary loan; copying; library open to the public on limited schedule. **Computerized Information Services:** NLM; DOCLINE (electronic mail service). **Networks/Consortia:** Member of Cosmopolitan Biomedical Library Consortium (CBLC), BHSL, Health Sciences Library Association of New Jersey (HSLANJ). **Remarks:** FAX: (908)233-4176.

Chile - Biblioteca Nacional de Chile
See: **Chile - National Library of Chile** (3598)

★3595★
Chile - Congreso Nacional - Biblioteca Central (Soc Sci)
Compania 1147, Clasificador 1199 Phone: 2 6715331
Santiago, Chile Ximena Feliu, Dir.
Founded: 1883. **Staff:** Prof 90; Other 40. **Subjects:** Social sciences, politics, legislative process, law, economics. **Special Collections:** Rare and valuable books collection; map collection; music collection. **Holdings:** 200,000 books; 300,000 bound periodical volumes; newspaper clippings (1950 to present); 30 titles of microfiche. **Subscriptions:** 650 journals and other serials; 50 newspapers. **Services:** Interlibrary loan; copying; library open to the public. **Computerized Information Services:** Internal database. **Publications:** Studies and Research Series; New Arrivals; Selective Periodicals Abstracts. **Remarks:** Alternate telephone number(s): 2 6968062. FAX: 2 6726575.

★3596★
Chile - Ministry of Public Health - Public Health Institute of Chile - Library (Med)
Casilla 48
Avenida Marathon 1000 Phone: 2 490021
Santiago, Chile Maria Teresa Orostica, Libn.
Subjects: Clinical microbiology and immunology, medical bacteriology, virology, bromatology, bacteriology of tuberculosis, serology of syphilis. **Holdings:** 10,000 volumes. **Also Known As:** Instituto de Salud Publica de Chile.

★3597★
Chile - National Commission for Scientific and Technological Research - Directorate for Information - Technical Library (Sci-Engr)
C.P. 297-V
Canada 308 Phone: 2 2744537
Santiago, Chile Ana Maria Prat, Dir. of Info.
Subjects: Science, technical information and documentation. **Holdings:** 5000 volumes. **Subscriptions:** 150 journals and other serials. **Services:** Copying; microfilming; translation. **Computerized Information Services:** Database of documents produced through research projects financed by parent organization, other internal databases. **Publications:** Serie Informacion y Documentacion, irregular; Serie Directorios; Serie Bibliografica. **Remarks:** FAX: 2 496729. Telex: 340191 CNCT CK.

★3598★
Chile - National Library of Chile (Hist, Hum)
Avda B. O'Higgins 651
Clasificador 1400 Phone: 2 338957
Santiago, Chile Ursula Schadlich Sch., Lib.Coord.
Founded: 1813. **Staff:** Prof 50; Other 100. **Subjects:** Human sciences, Latin American history, Chilean history, education, social sciences, literature,

Chilean authors. **Special Collections:** Chilean Periodica Collection; travelers' diaries; collections on Medina, Barros Arana, Feliu (60,000 titles). **Holdings:** 3.5 million books; 1600 microfiche; 10,000 reels of microfilm. **Services:** Copying; library open to the public. **Computerized Information Services:** Internal database. **Publications:** Bibliografia Chilena; Referencias Criticas, Sobre Autores Chilenos; Chile y su Cultura; Revista Mapocho; Monografias. **Remarks:** FAX: 2 381975. **Also Known As:** Chile - Biblioteca Nacional de Chile. **Staff:** Francisco Benimeli; Marjorie Pena; Maria A. Palma; Bety Zernott; Liliana Montesinos; Maria Tomicic; Paulina Sanhueza; Fernando Castro; Manuel Cornejo.

★3599★
Chilkat Valley Historical Society - Sheldon Museum & Cultural Center (Hist)
Box 269 Phone: (907)766-2366
Haines, AK 99827 Rebecca Nelson, Asst.Cur.
Founded: 1925. **Staff:** 4. **Subjects:** Tlingit art and culture; Alaskan history. **Special Collections:** Porcupine Mining Company account books, 1897-1916; logbooks from two harbor boats, 1910-1930. **Holdings:** 1150 books; 5600 feet of home movies; Haines and Skagway newspapers on microfilm; AV programs on historical and resource subjects; photographs, 1897 to present; autographed correspondence; journals, manuscripts, deeds from circa 1900; maps; charts; 27 linear feet of blueprints. **Subscriptions:** 12 journals and other serials. **Services:** Center open to the public for reference use only.

★3600★
Chilliwack Archives (Hist)
9291 Corbould St. Phone: (604)795-9255
Chilliwack, BC, Canada V2P 4A6 Ron Denman, Dir.
Founded: 1958. **Staff:** Prof 3. **Subjects:** Local history and genealogy. **Special Collections:** Chilliwack Progress newspaper (88 reels of microfilm; 5000 original copies). **Holdings:** 1500 books; 200 sound recordings; 350 maps; 25,000 pictorial images; 50 paintings, drawings, and prints; 39 meters of government records; 65 meters of manuscript collections. **Subscriptions:** 16 journals and other serials. **Services:** Copying; library open to the public with restrictions. **Publications:** Chilliwack Museum & Historical Society Newsletter, quarterly. **Special Catalogs:** Internal catalogs of books, manuscripts, collections, and maps. **Special Indexes:** Indexes of manuscript collections and pictures. **Staff:** Jim Bowman, Archv.; Louise Shaw, Cur.

★3601★
Chilton Company - Marketing & Advertising Information Center (Bus-Fin, Publ)
One Chilton Way Phone: (215)964-4497
Radnor, PA 19089 Christine Sweely, Mgr.
Founded: 1957. **Staff:** Prof 2; Other 1. **Subjects:** Advertising, marketing, publishing. **Holdings:** 1000 books; 40 VF drawers of pamphlets, articles, government statistical reports (filed by subject); 240 reels of microfilm of Chilton publications. **Subscriptions:** 110 journals and other serials. **Services:** Interlibrary loan; copying; center open to the public with restrictions. **Computerized Information Services:** DIALOG Information Services, PFDS Online, Dow Jones News/Retrieval, NEXIS, VU/TEXT Information Services. **Remarks:** FAX: (215)964-4100. Subsidiary of ABC Publishing, a division of Capital Cities/ABC, Inc. **Staff:** Alison Gleichman, Ref.Libn.

★3602★
Chilton Memorial Hospital - Medical Library (Med)
97 West Parkway Phone: (201)831-5058
Pompton Plains, NJ 07444 Janice Sweeton, Mgr.
Founded: 1970. **Staff:** Prof 1. **Subjects:** Medicine, allied health sciences. **Holdings:** 2500 books; 3000 bound periodical volumes; 165 video cassettes. **Subscriptions:** 120 journals and other serials. **Services:** Interlibrary loan; library not open to the public. **Computerized Information Services:** MEDLINE. **Networks/Consortia:** Member of Bergen Passaic Regional Library Cooperative. **Publications:** Bibliographies. **Remarks:** FAX: (201)831-5041.

China - National Geological Library
See: **People's Republic of China - National Geological Library** (12928)

China - The National Library of China
See: **People's Republic of China - The National Library of China** (12929)

★3603★
China Building Technology Development Center - China Library of Building Arts and Science (Plan)
19 Chegongzhuang St.
Western Suburb Phone: 1 8992679
Beijing 100044, People's Republic of China Liu Yu-an, Libn.
Founded: 1956. **Staff:** 17. **Subjects:** Building construction and engineering, architecture, allied sciences and technologies. **Holdings:** 220,000 volumes; 1230 periodicals; 1500 technical materials. **Services:** Interlibrary loan; copying; library open to engineers, architects, researchers, and workers in construction, production, education, information, and administration. **Computerized Information Services:** Internal database. **Remarks:** Telex: 22087 CBTDC CN. **Formerly:** Capital Construction Commission of China - Construction and Building Library.

★3604★
China Encyclopaedia Publishing House - Library (Info Sci, Publ)
A1 East Waiguan Jie
Andingmenwai
Beijing, People's Republic of China Phone: 1 464389
Founded: 1979. **Staff:** 15. **Subjects:** Encyclopedias, reference books, yearbooks, directories, guides, chronological tables, and dictionaries published around the world. **Holdings:** 40,000 volumes; 600 periodicals. **Services:** Interlibrary loan; copying. **Publications:** Encyclopaedic Knowledge; Encyclopaedic Reference Materials; Encyclopaedic Yearbook.

China Library of Building Arts and Science
See: **China Building Technology Development Center** (3603)

★3605★
China Medical University - Library (Med)
No 3, Sec 5 Nanjing Jie
Shenyang 110001, Liaoning, Phone: 24 376229
People's Republic of China Mr. Dizhi Xiong, Dir.
Founded: 1914. **Staff:** Prof 20; Other 28. **Subjects:** Medicine and allied sciences. **Holdings:** 330,000 books; 115,000 bound periodical volumes; 2048 volumes of microfiche. **Subscriptions:** 1927 journals and other serials; 33 newspapers. **Services:** Interlibrary loan; copying; SDI; library open to the public upon special contract. **Computerized Information Services:** CD-ROM (MEDLINE). Contact Person: Miss Chang Wen-yu. **Staff:** Mr. Qimen Dien, Dp.Dir.; Ms. Li Ma, Dp.Dir.

★3606★
China Nationality Library (Area-Ethnic)
49 Fuxingmen Nei St. Phone: 653231-510
Beijing 100031, People's Republic of China Li Jiuqi, Chf.Libn.
Founded: 1959. **Staff:** 50. **Subjects:** Chinese publications. **Special Collections:** 24 Chinese minority languages, with emphasis on Tibetan language (160,416 volumes); manuscripts in gold and silver; sutras written on palm leaves; rubbings from stone and bronze tablets; district histories. **Holdings:** 531,214 volumes. **Subscriptions:** 2400 journals and other serials; 130 newspapers. **Services:** Copying. **Special Catalogs:** Catalog of Publications Held by the Library; Chronicle of National Affairs; Collections in Ancient Tibetan. **Formerly:** Nationalities Culture Palace - Library. **Staff:** Zhang Xiufeng, Dep.Libn.

★3607★
China Textile University - Library (Sci-Engr)
1882 West Yan'an Lu Phone: 2599800
Shanghai, People's Republic of China Tang Bao-Ning, Libn.
Founded: 1951. **Staff:** 46. **Subjects:** Cotton and wool textile engineering, mechanical engineering, knitting, textiles, textile industry management, textile machinery, automation, instrumentation, synthetic fibers, dyeing and finishing, environmental control, chemical engineering. **Holdings:** 384,317 volumes; 2965 periodicals; 1047 technical reports; 360 AV programs and microforms. **Services:** Copying. **Formerly:** East China Institute of Textile Science and Technology.

★3608★
Chinatown Building and Education Foundation - Chinese Cultural and Community Center (Area-Ethnic)
125 N. Tenth St.
Philadelphia, PA 19107 Phone: (215)923-6767
Subjects: Chinese language publications. **Holdings:** Figures not available. **Services:** Library not open to the public.

★3609★
Chinese Academy of Medical Sciences and Peking Union Medical College - Library (Med)
9 Dongdan Santiao Phone: 5128183
Beijing 100730, People's Republic of China Lu Rushan, Dir.
Founded: 1921. **Staff:** 70. **Subjects:** Biology, basic and clinical medicine, environmental hygiene, nutrition, drugs. **Special Collections:** Thread-bound books on traditional Chinese medicine. **Holdings:** 180,881 books; 315,143 bound periodical volumes; 820 theses; 1240 technical reports; 455 cassettes; microforms; videotapes. **Subscriptions:** 2120 periodicals. **Services:** Interlibrary loan; copying; library open to the public. **Computerized Information Services:** MEDLARS; CD-ROM (MEDLINE). **Special Catalogs:** Union catalog of periodicals in foreign languages subscribed to by medical and medicinal colleges in all of China, annual. **Remarks:** FAX: 5128176. Telex: 222689 CAMS CN.

Chinese Academy of Sciences - Documentation and Information Center
See: **Academia Sinica - Library** (30)

Chinese Academy of Sciences - Guangzhou Institute of Energy Conversion
See: **Guangzhou Institute of Energy Conversion** (6790)

★3610★
Chinese Academy of Sciences - Institute of Oceanology - Library (Sci-Engr, Biol Sci)
7 Nanhai Rd. Phone: 532 279062204
Qingdao, People's Republic of China Peng Haiqing, Hd. of Lib.
Staff: Prof 12. **Subjects:** Physical oceanography; marine - geology, geophysics, biology, environment, chemistry; instrumentation. **Holdings:** 87,617 books; 47,980 bound periodical volumes; 31,149 unbound reports. **Subscriptions:** 950 journals and other serials; 20 newspapers. **Services:** Interlibrary loan; copying; library open to the public. **Publications:** Bulletin of New Books. **Special Catalogs:** Catalog of periodical holdings; catalog of conference proceedings holdings. **Special Indexes:** Special technical reports index (card); conference proceedings index (card). **Remarks:** FAX: 532 270882. Telex: 32222 ISS CN. **Staff:** Min-hu Xu, Sr.Libn.; Guiying Shi, Sr.Libn.; Bizeng Wang, Sr.Libn.; Keli Yang; Xiubin Wang; Huiyuan Ma; Guizhi Huang.

★3611★
Chinese Academy of Social Sciences - Institute of Nationality Studies - Library (Area-Ethnic)
27 Bai Shi Qiao Rd. Phone: 1 8328877
Beijing 100081, People's Republic of China Huang Guozheng, Assoc.Res. Fellow
Founded: 1958. **Staff:** 17. **Subjects:** Ethnology; nationality histories, languages, cultures, economies, laws, education, writings, literatures, customs; world nationalities; anthropology; race relations; religions; national policies; ethnic liberation movements; sociology. **Special Collections:** Sketches of Main-tsze (16 volumes). **Holdings:** 400,000 volumes. **Subscriptions:** 600 journals and other serials; 100 newspapers. **Services:** Interlibrary loan; copying; SDI; library open to the public at librarian's discretion. **Staff:** Jia-zi Jin; Hong-mei Lu; Tas Hong; Li-sheng Niu; Zhong Wei; Min Zhang; Yan-feng Wang; Naijun Shi; Ying Dong; Xiu-ying Zhao; Li Zhang; Xue-yan Cao; Lo Zha; Ming Cheng.

Chinese Cultural and Community Center
See: **Chinatown Building and Education Foundation** (3608)

★3612★
Chinese Historical Society of America - Archives (Area-Ethnic)
650 Commercial St.
San Francisco, CA 94111 Phone: (415)391-1188
Subjects: Chinese in America, late 19th century to present. **Special Collections:** Records of the Chinatown Factfinding Committee; archives of the Chinese Constitutionalist Party. **Holdings:** Newspaper clippings; photographs; manuscripts. **Publications:** Monthly newsletter, 10/year; Chinese America: History and Perspectives, annual. **Remarks:** Archives are located in the Asian American Studies Library, 101 Wheeler Hall, University of California, Berkeley.

★3613★
Chinese Information and Culture Center - Library (Area-Ethnic)
1230 Avenue of the Americas Phone: (212)373-1834
New York, NY 10020-1579 James Chang, Dir.
Founded: 1991. **Subjects:** Political, economic, cultural, social development and contemporary foreign relations of the Republic of China; China - history, language, literature, art, philosophy, religion; foreign relations. **Special Collections:** Republic of China Government Document collection. **Holdings:** 30,000 items including reference, folio, juvenile and microfilm collections. **Subscriptions:** 300 journals and other serials; 45 newspapers (published in Republic of China and the United States). **Services:** Library open to the public. **Computerized Information Services:** RLIN, DataTimes, Central News Agency. **Remarks:** FAX: (212)373-1866. Alternate telephone number(s): (212)373-1841. **Formerly:** Chinese Cultural Center - Information & Communication Division - Library. **Staff:** Vicky Tseng, Coord.; Shi-Ru Lin, Libn.; Verna Tang, Libn; Anna Liou, Libn.; Lan-May Chen, Lib.Asst.; Alice Liao, Lib.Asst.; Wan-Pi Yang, Lib.Asst.

Chinese Language and Research Center
See: **National University of Singapore** (11319)

★3614★
Chinese Nationalist League of Canada - Library (Area-Ethnic)
529 Gore Ave. Phone: (604)681-6022
Vancouver, BC, Canada V6A 2Z6 James K. Cheng, Chf.Libn.
Founded: 1961. **Staff:** Prof 4; Other 6. **Subjects:** China - history, politics, society; China Town and Canadian-Chinese history. **Special Collections:** History of the Chinese Nationalist League of Canada. **Holdings:** 31,000 books; 1000 bound periodical volumes. **Subscriptions:** 145 journals and other serials; 12 newspapers. **Services:** Interlibrary loan; copying; library open to the public. **Staff:** Y.L. Wong, Supv., Pub.Serv.; Charlie Chan, Supv., Tech.Serv.

★3615★
Chinese University of Hong Kong - University Library System (Hum)
N.T. Phone: 0 6097301
Shatin, Hong Kong Frederick Chang, Act.Univ.Libn.
Founded: 1963. **Staff:** 165. **Subjects:** General collection. **Special Collections:** Fine arts and archeology (6000 book and periodical titles); pre-1949 Chinese periodicals; 19th century blockprints and Chinese writings (2000 volumes and reprints); masters theses and Ph.D. dissertations. **Holdings:** 861,000 books; 139,000 bound periodical volumes; 114,700 microforms. **Subscriptions:** 7244 journals and other serials; 69 newspapers. **Services:** Interlibrary loan; copying; library open to the public with restrictions. **Computerized Information Services:** DIALOG Information Services, FT PROFILE. **Publications:** An Annotated Guide to Serial Publications of the Hong Kong Government; Serials of Hong Kong: 1845-1979; Newspapers of Hong Kong: 1841-1979; History of Medicine: An Annotated Bibliography of Titles at the Chinese University. **Special Catalogs:** Union Catalogue of Serials; Union Catalogue of Audio Visual Materials; Asian Fine Arts Collection: Union Catalogue: The Chinese University of Hong Kong; Catalogue of the Chinese Rare Books in the Libraries of the Chinese University of Hong Kong. **Remarks:** FAX: 0 6036952. Telex: 50301 CUHK HX. **Staff:** Nancy Chan, Sub-Libn.; Meliza Ng, Sub-Libn.; Rita Wong, Sub-Libn.; Pamela Lee, Sub-Libn.; Mr. C. Liu, Sub-Libn.; Mr. T.H. Chow, Asst.Libn.; Mr. C.L. Lee, Asst.Libn.; Mr. C.C. Wong, Asst.Libn.; Mr. K.C. Yue, Asst.Libn.; May Chau, Asst.Libn.; Vincent Cheung, Asst.Libn.; Maggie Choi, Asst.Libn.; Mrs. W.K. Lam, Asst.Libn.; Mr. K.K. Lew, Asst.Libn.; Rita Lo, Asst.Libn.; Edith Wu, Asst.Libn.; John Wu, Asst.Libn.; Miss S.H. Yu, Asst.Libn.; Lucia Ho, Asst.Libn.; Mr. C.W. Lam, Asst.Libn.; Fanny Chan, Asst.Libn.; Shirley Leung, Asst.Libn.; Ann Chiu.

★3616★
Chippewa Valley Museum, Inc. - Library (Hist)
9 Carson Park Dr.
Box 1204 Phone: (715)834-7871
Eau Claire, WI 54702 Eldbjorg Tobin
Founded: 1964. **Staff:** 2. **Subjects:** History - local, area, state. **Special Collections:** Oral history tapes (125). **Holdings:** 1500 books; 10 VF drawers of clippings; 20,000 photographs of early scenes and citizens; manuscripts; obituary file of 2500 names; biographical file of 500 names; 700 documents; 200 maps. **Subscriptions:** 15 journals and other serials. **Services:** Copying; library open to the public for reference use only. **Automated Operations:** Computerized indexing. **Publications:** Guide to Archives and Manuscripts in Chippewa Valley Museum (cooperative project with Eau Claire Public Library and University of Wisconsin, Eau Claire).

★3617★
Chippewa Valley Technical College - Technology Resource Center-Library (Educ)
620 W. Clairemont Ave. Phone: (715)833-6285
Eau Claire, WI 54701 Eileen Emberson, Lib.Serv.Mgr.
Founded: 1966. **Staff:** Prof 1; Other 6.75. **Subjects:** Electronics, fluid power, health occupations, quantity foods, data processing, police science, accounting, business education, law, automotive technology. **Special Collections:** Repository for the National Clearinghouse on Aging's Service Center for Aging Information (SCAN). **Holdings:** 33,199 books; 10,050 other cataloged items; 4000 microfiche on aging. **Subscriptions:** 675 journals and other serials; 42 newspapers. **Services:** Interlibrary loan; copying; center open to the public. **Computerized Information Services:** DIALOG Information Services, OCLC; CD-ROMs. **Publications:** Brochures; bibliographies - both available on request. **Special Catalogs:** AV listing; computer software listing. **Remarks:** FAX: (715)833-6470.

★3618★
Chiron Corporation - Information Services Center (Biol Sci)
1400 53rd St. Phone: (510)420-3279
Emeryville, CA 94608 George F. McGregor, Dir., Info.Serv.
Founded: 1978. **Staff:** Prof 2; Other 3. **Subjects:** Biotechnology. **Holdings:** 9600 volumes. **Subscriptions:** 550 journals and other serials. **Services:** Interlibrary loan; copying (articles); PC center for employee use; journal routing; document delivery. **Automated Operations:** Computerized public access catalog, cataloging, acquisitions, serials, and circulation. **Computerized Information Services:** DIALOG Information Services, PFDS Online, NLM, RLIN, LEXIS, NEXIS, Data-Star, STN International; internal databases. **Remarks:** FAX: (510)420-4134. Telex: 4992659. **Formerly:** Cetus Corpration Information Services Center. **Staff:** Gretchen Peterson, Info.Spec.

★3619★
Chisholm Trail Museum - Archives and Library (Hist)
502 N. Washington Ave. Phone: (316)326-3820
Wellington, KS 67152 Anita Busch, Libn.
Staff: Prof 1. **Subjects:** Pioneer history - Kansas, Wellington, Sumner county. **Special Collections:** Kansas Collection (100 volumes); antique and rare books; sheet music (100 pieces). **Holdings:** 500 books; 200 other cataloged items; 700 archival materials. **Services:** Copying; library open to the public for reference use only.

Chittenden Pianoforte Library
See: **Vassar College - George Sherman Dickinson Music Library** (19788)

★3620★
Choate, Hall and Stewart - Law Library (Law)
Exchange Place
53 State St. Phone: (617)227-5020
Boston, MA 02109 Eva Murphy, Hd.Libn.
Staff: Prof 2; Other 2. **Subjects:** Law. **Holdings:** 15,000 volumes; 550 microfiche. **Subscriptions:** 275 journals and other serials. **Services:** Interlibrary loan; library not open to the public. **Computerized Information Services:** LEXIS, WESTLAW, DIALOG Information Services, Dow Jones News/Retrieval, VU/TEXT Information Services, Information America, LEGI-SLATE, Maxwell Macmillan Taxes Online; Current USC. **Remarks:** FAX: (617)227-7566. Telex: 289374. **Staff:** Mary Rogalski, Asst.Libn.

Elsie and William Chomsky Educational Resource Center
See: **Central Agency for Jewish Education of Greater Philadelphia** (3322)

★3621★
Chongqing Design Institute - The Information Material Group (Plan, Sci-Engr)
26 Gongren Jie
Daxigou, Central District
Chongqing, Sichuan Province, Phone: 51942
People's Republic of China Wei Qide, Libn.
Founded: 1951. **Staff:** 6. **Subjects:** Building design and structure, heating, ventilation, water supply and drainage, electricity, municipal administration. **Special Collections:** Ancient and modern architecture; photography; fine arts; building structure data. **Holdings:** 15,611 volumes; 60,551 technical reports; microforms; AV programs. **Subscriptions:** 186 journals and other serials. **Services:** Copying.

★3622★
Christ Church - Library (Rel-Phil)
25 Broadway Phone: (716)454-3878
Rochester, NY 14607 Robert W. Barnes, Libn.
Founded: 1983. **Staff:** 4. **Subjects:** Religion, ethics, biography. **Holdings:** 300 books; unbound periodicals. **Subscriptions:** 5 journals and other serials. **Services:** Library open to the public.

★3623★
Christ Church American Center - USIS Library (Educ)
Sun Alliance Bldg., 4th Fl.
106 Gloucester St.
P.O. Box 4221
Christ Church, New Zealand
Remarks: Maintained or supported by the U.S. Information Agency. Focus is on materials that will assist peoples outside the United States to learn about the United States, its people, history, culture, political processes, and social milieux.

Christ Church Cathedral - Diocese of Fredericton Archives
See: **Diocese of Fredericton - Synod Archives** (4877)

★3624★
Christ Episcopal Church - Library (Rel-Phil)
P.O. Box 1374
Dover, DE 19903 Phone: (302)734-5731
Founded: 1930. **Subjects:** Theology, Bible, history. **Holdings:** 700 books; 65 reports. **Services:** Library not open to the public.

★3625★
Christ Episcopal Church - Richard W. Dunne Library (Rel-Phil)
35 Harris Rd. Phone: (203)673-9630
Avon, CT 06001 Sally C. Levin, Libn.
Founded: 1980. **Subjects:** Religion, spirituality, children's literature, psychology, religious adult literature, family, child development, grief, healing. **Special Collections:** Church needlework collection. **Holdings:** 911 books; videocassettes; audiocassettes. **Subscriptions:** 2 journals and other serials. **Services:** Library open to the public. **Automated Operations:** Computerized cataloging (under development).

Christ Hospital
See: **Evangelical Health Systems** (5494)

★3626★
Christ Hospital - School of Nursing Library (Med)
176 Palisade Ave. Phone: (201)795-8200
Jersey City, NJ 07306 Katherine Vargo, Libn.
Founded: 1890. **Staff:** Prof 1. **Subjects:** Nursing. **Holdings:** 2356 volumes. **Subscriptions:** 55 journals and other serials. **Services:** Interlibrary loan; copying; library open to the public by appointment for reference use. **Networks/Consortia:** Member of Health Sciences Library Association of New Jersey (HSLANJ), BHSL, New Jersey Library Network.

★3627★
Christ the King Seminary - Library (Rel-Phil)
711 Knox Rd. Phone: (716)652-8959
East Aurora, NY 14052 Rev. Bonaventure F. Hayes, O.F.M., Lib.Dir.
Founded: 1951. **Staff:** Prof 3; Other 1. **Subjects:** Religion, theology. **Special Collections:** Msgr. James Bray Collection (750 volumes); early French Canadian and Niagara Frontier history. **Holdings:** 103,205 books; 18,537 bound periodical volumes; 133 nonbook items; 346 reels of taped lectures; 148 reels of microfilm; 659 cassette tapes; 3259 microfiche. **Subscriptions:** 440 journals and other serials. **Services:** Interlibrary loan; copying; library open to the public. **Automated Operations:** Computerized cataloging. **Computerized Information Services:** OCLC. **Networks/Consortia:** Member of Western New York Library Resources Council (WNYLRC). **Remarks:** FAX: (716)652-8903. **Staff:** Sr. Tiburtia Gorecki, FSSJ, Per.Libn./ILL; Teresa Lubienecki, Cat.Libn.

★3628★
Christ-Roi Hospital - Library (Med)
300 blvd. W-Hamel Phone: (418)682-1711
Vanier, PQ, Canada G1M 2R9 Gratien Gelinas, Biblio.
Founded: 1965. **Staff:** Prof 1. **Subjects:** Medicine, nursing, pharmacy, allied health sciences. **Holdings:** 1000 books. **Subscriptions:** 80 journals and other serials. **Services:** Interlibrary loan; copying; library open to the public by appointment and for reference use only.

★3629★
Christ Seminary - Seminex Library (Rel-Phil)
c/o Episcopal Theological Seminary of the Southwest
Box 2247 Phone: (512)472-4134
Austin, TX 78768 Lucille Hager, Dir.
Founded: 1974. **Staff:** Prof 1. **Subjects:** Biblical studies, Lutheran theology, church history, Judaica. **Holdings:** 37,000 books. **Subscriptions:** 169 journals and other serials. **Services:** Interlibrary loan; copying; library open to the public. **Automated Operations:** Computerized cataloging. **Computerized Information Services:** Online systems. **Networks/Consortia:** Member of AMIGOS Bibliographic Council, Inc.

★3630★
Christ United Methodist Church - Helen Stahler Library (Rel-Phil)
380 Mineola Ave. Phone: (216)836-5563
Akron, OH 44320 Helen H. Stahler, Libn.
Founded: 1959. **Staff:** Prof 1; Other 5. **Subjects:** Religion, Methodism, biography, children's literature. **Holdings:** 2100 books; 4 VF drawers of pamphlets; 2 VF drawers of filmstrips; AV programs. **Subscriptions:** 11 journals and other serials. **Services:** Library open to the public with restrictions.

★3631★
Christ United Methodist Church - Library (Rel-Phil)
44 Highland Rd.
Bethel Park, PA 15102 Phone: (412)835-6621
Staff: Prof 1. **Subjects:** Religion. **Holdings:** 3600 books; 300 filmstrips; 40 phonograph records; 50 audiotapes; 80 slides. **Services:** Library not open to the public.

★3632★
Christian Family Renewal - Library (Rel-Phil)
P.O. Box 73
Clovis, CA 93613 Phone: (209)297-7818
Subjects: Applied Christianity - business, politics, educational counseling. **Holdings:** 6000 volumes. **Remarks:** Toll-free telephone number(s): (800)345-7646.

★3633★
Christian Health Care Center - Peter Carras Library (Med)
301 Sicomac Ave.
Wyckoff, NJ 07481 Phone: (201)848-5200
Subjects: Medicine, nursing, psychiatry. **Holdings:** Figures not available. **Services:** Copying; library open to the public. **Remarks:** FAX: (201)848-9758.

John T. Christian Library
See: **New Orleans Baptist Theological Seminary - John T. Christian Library** (11538)

★3634★
Christian Medical Foundation International - Library (Med)
7522 N. Hines Ave. Phone: (813)932-3688
Tampa, FL 33614 Lyn Thornton, Asst.Dir.
Subjects: Christian medical and ethical principles, spiritual care of the ill. **Holdings:** 2500 volumes; biographical archives.

★3635★
Christian and Missionary Alliance - Albert B. Simpson Historical Library & Archives (Rel-Phil)
P.O. Box 35000 Phone: (719)599-5999
Colorado Springs, CO 80935 J.C. Wenninger, Dir., Educ.
Subjects: Christian and Missionary Alliance history, 1800s to present; missions; hymnody; biography; foreign language Bibles. **Special Collections:** Writings of A.B. Simpson (C&MA founder). **Holdings:** 3517 books; A.B. Simpson's magazines, 1800 to present, on microfiche. **Subscriptions:** 45 journals and other serials. **Services:** Copying; library open to the public for reference use only. **Remarks:** Library located at 8595 Explorer Dr., Colorado Springs, CO 80920.

★3636★
Christian Overcomers - Lending Library (Rel-Phil)
246 3rd Ave. Phone: (201)358-0055
Westwood, NJ 07675 Michael Shultz, Dir.
Subjects: Disabled adults, Christianity. **Holdings:** 857 books. **Services:** Interlibrary loan; library open to the handicapped. **Staff:** Janet Thomson, Libn.

★3637★
Christian Record Services, Inc. - Lending Library (Aud-Vis)
P.O. Box 6097
4444 S. 52nd St. Phone: (402)488-0981
Lincoln, NE 68506 Kathy Fogg, Supv., Mktg./Lib.Serv.
Founded: 1899. **Staff:** Prof 1; Other 8. **Subjects:** The Bible, Christianity, religion, history, music, nature. **Holdings:** 1054 English cassette titles; 247 English braille titles; large print booklets; 40 music cassette titles; 39 Spanish cassette titles; 10 full-vision book titles; 11 Bible courses. **Subscriptions:** 8 journals and other serials. **Services:** Library open to legally blind and visually handicapped or those with physical handicaps which prevent them from following normal reading practices; materials sent free on 30-day loan basis with renewal privileges. **Publications:** List of publications - available on request. **Remarks:** Said to be one of the world's largest printers of inspirational braille. **Also Known As:** CRS, International.

★3638★
Christian Science Monitor - Research Library (Publ)
1 Norway St. Phone: (617)450-2680
Boston, MA 02115 Mary McGee, Libn.
Founded: 1908. **Staff:** Prof 3; Other 2. **Subjects:** Newspaper reference topics, history, literature. **Holdings:** 10,000 books; 100 editorial research reports; 3 million clippings. **Subscriptions:** 50 journals and other serials. **Services:** Interlibrary loan (local only); library not open to the public. **Computerized Information Services:** NEXIS, VU/TEXT Information Services, Dow Jones News/Retrieval, Info Globe, Washington Alert Services, Dialcom Inc., DIALOG Information Services. **Remarks:** Published by Christian Science Publishing Society.

★3639★
Christian Theological Seminary - Library (Rel-Phil)
1000 W. 42nd St.
Box 88267 Phone: (317)924-1331
Indianapolis, IN 46208-0267 David Bundy
Founded: 1941. **Staff:** Prof 3; Other 5. **Subjects:** Religion, theology. **Special Collections:** Disciples of Christ historical materials. **Holdings:** 120,000 books; 8100 bound periodical volumes; 40 VF drawers of pamphlets. **Subscriptions:** 938 journals and other serials; 10 newspapers. **Services:** Interlibrary loan; copying; library open to the public for reference use only. **Automated Operations:** Computerized cataloging. **Networks/Consortia:** Member of Central Indiana Area Library Services Authority (CIALSA), INCOLSA. **Publications:** Encounter, quarterly - by subscription. **Remarks:** FAX: (317)923-1961. **Staff:** Jeff Hoffman, Assoc.Libn., Tech.Serv.; Richard Doolen, Assoc.Libn., Rd.Serv.

★3640★
Christian Union Bible College - Library (Rel-Phil)
1110 N. Washington St.
Box 27 Phone: (513)981-2897
Greenfield, OH 45123 Norma Kellough, Sec.
Founded: 1979. **Staff:** 1. **Subjects:** Bible, pastoral ministries, Christian education, theology, languages, missions. **Special Collections:** Christian Union historical materials; general and state council minutes. **Holdings:** 5900 books; 30 magnetic tapes; Christian Union Witness magazines, photographs, books. **Subscriptions:** 10 journals and other serials; 3 newspapers. **Services:** Copying; library open to local ministers and religious workers. **Automated Operations:** Computerized cataloging and acquisitions. **Computerized Information Services:** Internal database. **Special Indexes:** Index to Christian Union Witness (printout). **Formerly:** Christian Union School of the Bible - Library.

Christian Women's Exchange - Hermann-Grima House
See: **Hermann-Grima House** (7160)

Christiana Hospital Library
See: **Medical Center of Delaware** (9990)

Christie Education Library
See: **Brandon University** (2077)

★3641★
Christmas Seal and Charity Stamp Society - Library (Rec)
P.O. Box 35696-0696 Phone: (312)493-4208
Edina, MN 55439 Richard Roberts, Hist./Libn.
Founded: 1931. **Subjects:** Christmas seals of the world, especially the United States; charity seals of the world. **Special Collections:** Complete file of Seal News (and predecessor titles) representing official publications of the society from 1931 to present (1 VF drawer). **Holdings:** 3 VF drawers of pamphlets, clippings, hobby newsletters describing seals and issuing societies; new issues of many nations and funds, errors, rarities, values, collections, exhibits of such. **Services:** Interlibrary loan; copying; questions answered by mail. **Publications:** Newsletter - to members and subscribers or by exchange.

★3642★
Chromalloy American Corporation - Turbine Support Division Library
30 Dart Rd.
Attn: Tech Data
Shenondoah, GA 30265 Phone: (404)254-6200
Remarks: No further information was supplied by respondent.

★3643★
Chronicle of Higher Education - Library (Educ, Publ)
1255 23rd St., N.W., Suite 700 Phone: (202)466-1036
Washington, DC 20037 Edith Uunila Taylor, Sr.Ed.
Founded: 1966. **Staff:** 3. **Subjects:** Higher education. **Holdings:** 2500 books; 1500 booklets; newspaper and magazine clippings. **Subscriptions:** 250 journals and other serials; 50 newspapers. **Services:** Interlibrary loan; copying; library open to the public by appointment. **Remarks:** FAX: (202)296-2691. Telex: 892505.

★3644★
Chrysler Motors - Chrysler Information Resources Center (Sci-Engr)
418-05-36
12000 Chrysler Dr. Phone: (313)956-4881
Highland Park, MI 48288 Barbara M. Fronczak, Dir.
Founded: 1933. **Staff:** Prof 3; Other 2. **Subjects:** Automotive engineering. **Holdings:** 5000 books; 15,000 bound periodical volumes; 57,000 reports and preprints; service manuals in various formats, including CD-ROM. **Subscriptions:** 450 journals and other serials. **Services:** Interlibrary loan; copying; SDI; center open to the public by appointment. **Automated Operations:** Computerized cataloging and acquisitions. **Computerized Information Services:** DIALOG Information Services, ORBIT Search Service, NEXIS, LEXIS. **Networks/Consortia:** Member of Michigan Library Consortium (MLC). **Remarks:** FAX: (313)252-7858. **Staff:** Dorothy Tekelly, Asst.; Carol Mullin, Asst.; Joan Zoppi, Asst.

★3645★
Chrysler Museum - Jean Outland Chrysler Library (Art)
Olney Rd. & Mowbray Arch Phone: (804)622-1211
Norfolk, VA 23510 Rena Hudgins, Hd.Libn.
Founded: 1933. **Staff:** Prof 3; Other 4. **Subjects:** Art history, glass, decorative arts. **Holdings:** 40,000 books; 1000 bound periodical volumes; 25,000 auction and exhibition catalogs; 80 VF drawers; 20,000 auction catalogs and 6000 exhibition catalogs on microfiche. **Subscriptions:** 300 journals and other serials. **Services:** Interlibrary loan; copying; library open to the public. **Automated Operations:** Computerized cataloging. **Computerized Information Services:** OCLC. **Networks/Consortia:** Member of SOLINET. **Remarks:** FAX: (804)623-5282. **Staff:** Rosemary Dumais, Tech.Serv.Libn.; Lynda Wright, Ref.Libn.

Chudozestvennyj Institut Litovskoj SSR - Biblioteka
See: **Vilnius Art Academy - Library** (19849)

★3646★
Chugoku National Agricultural Experiment Station - Library (Agri)
6-12-1
Nishifukazu-cho Phone: 849 234100
Fukuyama 721, Hiroshima, Japan Mr. Isamer Matayama
Founded: 1968. **Staff:** Prof 1; Other 2. **Subjects:** Mechanization, crops, livestock, post-harvest technology, biotechnology, soil conservation. **Holdings:** 25,000 books; 2500 bound periodical volumes. **Subscriptions:** 2000 journals and other serials; 4 newspapers. **Services:** Interlibrary loan; library not open to the public. **Computerized Information Services:** DIALOG Information Services. Contact Person: Miss Yuriko Unome. **Publications:** Chugoku National Agricultural Experiment Station Bulletin. **Remarks:** 849 247893. **Also Known As:** Chugoku Nogyo Shikenjo - Shiryoka.

Chugoku Nogyo Shikenjo - Shiryoka
See: **Chugoku National Agricultural Experiment Station** (3646)

★3647★
CHUM/City - City Pulse News Library (Info Sci)
299 Queen St., W. Phone: (416)591-5757
Toronto, ON, Canada M5V 2Z5 Denise Korol, Hd.Libn.
Founded: 1978. **Staff:** Prof 1; Other 3. **Subjects:** News - local, international, series. **Holdings:** 150 books; 15,000 video cassettes; 500 phonograph records; 40 VF drawers. **Subscriptions:** 20 journals and other serials; 4 newspapers. **Services:** Library open to the public with permission of news director. **Computerized Information Services:** Internal databases. **Special Catalogs:** News footage catalog. **Remarks:** FAX: (416)593-6397.

★3648★
Church Bible Studies - Library (Rel-Phil)
191 Mayhew Way
Walnut Creek, CA 94596 Phone: (510)937-7286
Founded: 1971. **Subjects:** Theology, education. **Holdings:** 200 books. **Services:** Library not open to the public.

★3649★
Church of the Brethren General Board - Brethren Historical Library and Archives (Rel-Phil)
1451 Dundee Ave. Phone: (708)742-5100
Elgin, IL 60120 Kenneth M. Shaffer, Jr., Dir.
Founded: 1936. **Staff:** Prof 1; Other 1. **Subjects:** Church of the Brethren history, German Baptist Brethren history. **Holdings:** 5556 volumes; 1726 serial volumes; 2000 cubic feet of archival materials and manuscript collections; 20,000 photographs; 2200 audiotapes; 530 reels of microfilm; 190 microfiche; 76 films; 30 videotapes; 100 phonograph records. **Services:** Interlibrary loan; copying; library open to the public by appointment. **Automated Operations:** Computerized public access catalog and cataloging. **Computerized Information Services:** MCI Mail (electronic mail service). **Networks/Consortia:** Member of ILLINET, North Suburban Library System (NSLS). **Publications:** Guide to the Brethren in Europe; Guide to Research in Brethren History; Guide for Local Church Historians; Guide to Research in Brethren Family History (all are pamphlets) - all free upon request. **Remarks:** FAX: (708)742-6103. **Staff:** Rosalita J. Leonard, Lib.Techn.

Church of Christ Disciples Archives
See: **University of Toronto - Victoria University - Library** (19463)

Church Divinity School of the Pacific
See: **Graduate Theological Union** (6613)

Church of England - General Synod - Council for the Care of Churches
See: **Council for the Care of Churches** (4360)

★3650★
Church of the Incarnation - Marmion Library (Rel-Phil)
3966 McKinney Ave. Phone: (214)521-5101
Dallas, TX 75204-2099 Rebekah Mathis, Act.Libn.
Founded: 1955. **Staff:** 2. **Subjects:** Religion, history, biography, fiction, children's literature. **Holdings:** 11,000 books; 400 cassette tapes; videotapes. **Subscriptions:** 4 journals and other serials. **Services:** Library open to the public for reference use only. **Staff:** Willa Johnson.

★3651★
Church of Jesus Christ of Latter-Day Saints - Albuquerque South Stake Family History Center (Hist)
6100 Katson, N.E. Phone: (505)266-4867
Albuquerque, NM 87109 Maurice L. Philpott, Lib.Dir.
Staff: 5. **Subjects:** Genealogy, social history, heraldry, geography. **Special Collections:** Catholic church, cemetery, mortuary, probate, marriage records of New Mexico. **Holdings:** 950 books; 700 reels of microfilm of U.S. Census Records; 155 reels of microfilm of Boyd's Marriage Index; 600 reels of microfilm of U.S. records; microfilm of many New Mexico church records. **Services:** Copying; access to the microfilm collection of the main center in Salt Lake City; center open to the public. **Special Indexes:** International Genealogical Index (microfiche); family registry. **Remarks:** Center located at 5709 Haines, N.E., Albuquerque, NM, 87110.

★3652★
Church of Jesus Christ of Latter-Day Saints - Boston Family History Center (Hist)
P.O. Box 138 Phone: (617)235-2164
Weston, MA 02193 Elizabeth Bentall, Dir.
Founded: 1971. **Staff:** Prof 1. **Subjects:** Genealogy, family histories. **Holdings:** 500 books; 50 bound periodical volumes; 10 manuscripts; 81 million names on microfiche; microfilm. **Services:** Copying; access to the microfilm collection of the main center in Salt Lake City; center open to the public. **Computerized Information Services:** CD-ROM.

★3653★
Church of Jesus Christ of Latter Day Saints - Boulder City Family History Center (Hist)
528 Hopi Pl. Phone: (702)293-3304
Boulder City, NV 89005 Margo Snowden, Libn.
Founded: 1984. **Staff:** 12. **Subjects:** Genealogy. **Holdings:** Books; microfilm; microfiche of holdings of Salt Lake City Genealogical Library. **Services:** Access to microfilm and microfiche collections of the main center in Salt Lake City; center open to the public.

★3654★
Church of Jesus Christ of Latter-Day Saints - Calgary Institute of Religion - Library (Rel-Phil)
3120 32nd Ave., N.W. Phone: (403)282-5516
Calgary, AB, Canada T2N 1N7 H. Bruce Roghaar, Dir.
Founded: 1968. **Staff:** 4. **Subjects:** Religion. **Holdings:** 700 volumes. **Subscriptions:** 3 journals and other serials. **Services:** Copying; center open to the public.

★3655★
Church of Jesus Christ of Latter-Day Saints - Cleveland, Ohio Stake Family History Center (Hist)
24931 Westwood Rd.
c/o Ira Myers Phone: (216)777-1518
Westlake, OH 44145 Ira T. Myers, Hd.Libn.
Founded: 1966. **Staff:** Prof 1; Other 20. **Subjects:** Genealogy. **Special Collections:** Collection of names from all over the world, primarily 1600-1969 (80 million names; on microfiche); family registry index and collection. **Holdings:** 88 reels of microfilm of U.S., British, Canadian collections; 112 reels of microfilm of non-English speaking countries (continental European, Afro-Asian, Latin American, Iberian Peninsula, Scandinavian Collections); 52 reels of microfilm of family names. **Services:** Access to the microfilm collection of the main center in Salt Lake City; center open to the public. **Special Indexes:** Accelerated index system to names on census and mortality records from 1600s to 1900.

★3656★
Church of Jesus Christ of Latter-Day Saints - Detroit Family History Center (Hist)
425 N. Woodward Phone: (313)647-5671
Bloomfield Hills, MI 48103 Jeffrey Kulesus, Dir.
Founded: 1970. **Subjects:** Genealogy. **Holdings:** 165 books; 148 bound periodical volumes; International Genealogical Index (88 million names). **Services:** Interlibrary loan; copying; access to the microfilm collection of the main center in Salt Lake City; center open to the public. **Special Indexes:** Index to Wayne County, MI, Probate Records; index to indefinite loan film collection. **Staff:** Ruth Urie, Films & Acq.

★3657★
Church of Jesus Christ of Latter-Day Saints - El Paso Family History Center (Hist)
3651 Douglas Ave. Phone: (915)565-9711
El Paso, TX 79903 H. Leroy Taylor, Libn.
Founded: 1966. **Staff:** Prof 5. **Subjects:** Genealogy. **Holdings:** 352 books; 56 bound periodical volumes. **Services:** Copying; access to the microfilm collection of the main center in Salt Lake City; center open to the public. **Staff:** Lovell K. Lovett, Asst.Libn.; Grace Wade, Asst.Libn.; Patricia Fish, Asst.Libn.; John McHann, Asst.Libn.; Elaine McHann, Asst.Libn.

★3658★
Church of Jesus Christ of Latter-Day Saints - Eugene, Oregon Family History Center (Hist)
3550 W. 18th Ave. Phone: (503)343-3741
Eugene, OR 97402 Leon R. Barnwell, Libn.
Founded: 1968. **Staff:** Prof 1; Other 45. **Subjects:** Genealogy. **Special Collections:** County censuses for the state of Oregon; 1850 census for all states (microfilm); index to 1850 census for all states; 1860 and 1870 census indexes and film for most states. **Holdings:** 2800 books; 400 bound periodical volumes; 5 VF drawers; 3 VF drawers of family histories; 3000 reels of microfilm; 200 maps. **Subscriptions:** 10 journals and other serials. **Services:** Copying; access to the microfilm collection of the main center in Salt Lake City; center open to the public. **Automated Operations:** Computerized personal ancestral file. **Computerized Information Services:** Internal database; CD-ROM (FamilySearch). **Special Indexes:** Surname Index.

★3659★
Church of Jesus Christ of Latter-Day Saints - Eureka Stake Family History Center (Hist)
P.O. Box 6399 Phone: (707)443-7411
Eureka, CA 95502 Alan S. Cookson, Dir.
Founded: 1974. **Staff:** 10. **Subjects:** Genealogy. **Special Collections:** California cemetery records (microfilm); Trinity, Shasta, Tehema, and Madoc Counties' vital records; Humboldt county census records. **Holdings:** Books; bound periodical volumes; local obituaries; directories; microfiche. **Subscriptions:** 3 journals and other serials. **Services:** Access to the microfilm collection of the main center in Salt Lake City; center open to the public. **Computerized Information Services:** Ancestral Search (internal database). **Remarks:** Center located at 2806 Dolbeer St., Eureka, CA.

★3660★
Church of Jesus Christ of Latter-Day Saints - Family History Library (Hist)
35 N.W. Temple Phone: (801)240-2331
Salt Lake City, UT 84150 David M. Mayfield, Dir.
Founded: 1894. **Staff:** Prof 120; Other 98. **Subjects:** Genealogy, family history, church and civil records, local history. **Special Collections:** Family Group Records Collection (8 million family reconstitution forms from the U.S. and foreign countries); oral genealogy tapes; international collection of manuscripts identifying individuals in historic populations (microfilm); International Genealogical Index (150 million names; microfiche). **Holdings:** 240,000 volumes; 3000 bound periodical volumes; 1.7 million reels of microfilm; 350,000 microfiche. **Subscriptions:** 135 journals and other serials. **Services:** Copying; orientation film; research classes; center open to the public. **Automated Operations:** Computerized cataloging, acquisitions, and circulation to 1600 branch family history centers. **Computerized Information Services:** Produces Family Search CD-ROM. **Publications:** Genealogical Research Papers, irregular; News of the Family History Library - to genealogical societies. **Special Catalogs:** Family History Library Catalog (COM & CD-ROM). **Special Indexes:** International Genealogical Index (150 million names; COM). **Remarks:** Branch family history centers having access to most films are added to the system on a continuing basis. **Staff:** Stephen Kendall, Mgr., Lib.Serv; Glade Nelson, Mgr., Family Hist.Ctr.Sup.; Janet Dipastena, Mgr., Lib.Sys.; Thomas E. Daniels, Mgr., P.R.

★3661★
Church of Jesus Christ of Latter-Day Saints - Helena Family History Center (Hist)
Forest Park Estates
Clancy, MT 59634 Phone: (406)443-0716
Founded: 1962. **Staff:** 28. **Subjects:** Genealogy. **Special Collections:** 1880, 1900, 1910 Montana census. **Holdings:** 119 books; 540 reels of microfilm; accelerated indexing systems on microfiche; 2 drawers of microfiche. **Services:** Interlibrary loan; copying; access to the microfilm collection of the main center in Salt Lake City; center open to the public. **Computerized Information Services:** CD-ROMs (International Genealogical Index, The Ancestral File, Social Security Index, Military Index of those killed or missing in action in the Korean and Vietnam Wars, 1950-1975). **Staff:** Gary Luther, Co-Dir.; Marcia Luther, Co-Dir.

★3662★
Church of Jesus Christ of Latter-Day Saints - Historical Department - Church Library-Archives (Rel-Phil)
50 E. North Temple St.
Salt Lake City, UT 84150 Phone: (801)240-2745
Staff: Prof 37; Other 15. **Subjects:** Mormonism. **Special Collections:** Publications, manuscripts, records of and pertaining to the Mormon Church. **Holdings:** 170,000 books, pamphlets, bound periodical volumes; 290,000 minute books and other handwritten volumes; 150,000 reels of microfilm; 70,000 microfiche; 12,000 transcriptions and tapes; 500 videotapes; 8000 manuscript histories; 1 million manuscripts. **Subscriptions:** 180 journals and other serials; 12 newspapers. **Services:** Copying; library open to approved researchers. **Special Catalogs:** Manuscript Catalog, Registers, Inventories and indexes of holdings of Library-Archives. **Staff:** Grant Anderson, Lib.Dir.; Steven Sorensen, Archv.Dir.

★3663★
Church of Jesus Christ of Latter-Day Saints - Jacksonville, Florida Family History Center (Hist)
4087 Hendricks Ave. Phone: (904)743-0527
Jacksonville, FL 32207 Vela M. Milton, Dir.
Staff: Prof 1. **Subjects:** Genealogy, local history. **Special Collections:** Early Jacksonville newspaper clippings; local pedigree file. **Holdings:** 671 volumes; 1203 reels of microfilm; 25 drawers of newspaper vital statistics. **Services:** Copying; center open to the public with restrictions.

★3664★
Church of Jesus Christ of Latter-Day Saints - Laie Family History Center (Hist)
55-600 Naniloa Loop Phone: (808)293-2133
Laie, HI 96762 David H. Miles, Libn.
Founded: 1965. **Subjects:** Genealogy. **Special Collections:** Hawaiian and Polynesian genealogies; International Genealogical Index (100 million names; microfiche). **Holdings:** 200 books; 1900 and 1910 Hawaii Census; 1300 reels of microfilm; church records. **Subscriptions:** 2 journals and other serials. **Services:** Copying; access to the microfilm collection of the main center in Salt Lake City; center open to the public. **Computerized Information Services:** CD-ROM (FamilySearch); access to complete catalog of Salt Lake Library (9 million names on CD-ROM).

★3665★
Church of Jesus Christ of Latter-Day Saints - Lansing Family History Center (Hist)
431 E. Saginaw
Box 801 Phone: (517)332-2932
East Lansing, MI 48823 Azalia Benjamin, Br.Libn.
Founded: 1970. **Subjects:** Genealogy. **Holdings:** 76 reels of microfilm of gazetteers; 1048 reels of microfilm of family group sheets; index file to the computer holdings of the Genealogical Department of the Salt Lake City Family History Center; Family Registry; 141 reels of microfilm of Loiselle's Marriage Index of Quebec; 116 reels of microfilm of vital and probate records of Ingham County, Michigan; 11 reels of microfilm of vital records of Clinton County, Michigan; 350 reels of microfilm of vital records of other counties in Michigan. **Services:** Copying; access to microfilm collection of the main center in Salt Lake City; center open to the public.

★3666★
Church of Jesus Christ of Latter-Day Saints - Las Vegas Family History Center (Hist)
509 S. 9th St. Phone: (702)382-9695
Las Vegas, NV 89101-7010 Earl C. Brunner, Jr., Dir.
Founded: 1966. **Subjects:** Genealogy, county history. **Special Collections:** All western states' U.S. censuses; complete U.S. census, 1910. **Holdings:** 6000 books; 1200 bound periodical volumes; 7000 reels of microfilm; 20,000 microfiche. **Subscriptions:** 20 journals and other serials. **Services:** Copying; center open to the public. **Computerized Information Services:** CD-ROMs. **Special Indexes:** Index to 1870 U.S. Census of Nevada; Nevada Obituary Index from 1900 (incomplete). **Remarks:** FAX: (702)382-1597. **Staff:** Kenneth W. Bell, Assoc.Dir.; Ronald J. Langford, Assoc.Dir.

★3667★
Church of Jesus Christ of Latter-Day Saints - Los Angeles Family History Center (Hist)
10741 Santa Monica Blvd. Phone: (213)474-9990
Los Angeles, CA 90025 Bert Scoll, Pres./Libn.
Founded: 1964. **Staff:** Prof 14. **Subjects:** Genealogy, local and county history. **Special Collections:** U.S. Census, 1790-1910; Index to St. Catherine's House vital records, 1837-1903; Soundex 1880, 1900, 1910 census; Hamburg Passenger List; Index to Pension Records, National Archives; Index to Passenger Lists, National Archives; Civil Registration Indexes to Births, Marriages and Deaths for Ireland, 1864-1958; Civil Registration Indexes to Births, Marriages and Deaths for Scotland, 1855-1920s; Surname Indexes to Land Records of Ireland, 1708-1904 (complete); Land Records of Ireland, 1708-1832 (complete); Genealogical Manuscripts Collection of Ireland. **Holdings:** 11,500 books; 1800 bound periodical volumes; 60,000 reels of microfilm; 62 VF drawers of U.S. gazetteer files; 22 index sets. **Subscriptions:** 60 journals and other serials. **Services:** Copying; microfilm copying; member of the borrowing program of the Genealogical Society, Salt Lake City, UT; genealogical consultant services; center open to the public. **Special Indexes:** Gazetteer card file of small or nonexistent towns; subject and locality index of periodicals. **Remarks:** Alternate telephone number(s): 474-2202. FAX: (213)474-2262.

★3668★
Church of Jesus Christ of Latter-Day Saints - Lovell, Wyoming Family History Center (Hist)
Box 7 Phone: (307)548-2963
Byron, WY 82412 Christy E. Petrich, Libn.
Founded: 1965. **Staff:** 15. **Subjects:** Genealogy, history, biography. **Holdings:** 325 books; 200 bound periodical volumes; 20 unbound cemetery records; 1 set of unbound mortuary records; 10 folders of unbound obituary clippings; genealogy microforms. **Services:** Copying; center open to the public.

★3669★
Church of Jesus Christ of Latter-Day Saints - Mesa Family History Center (Hist)
464 E. 1st Ave. Phone: (602)964-1200
Mesa, AZ 85204 Ronald L. Livingston, Dir.
Founded: 1930. **Staff:** Prof 1. **Subjects:** Genealogy. **Holdings:** 18,000 books; 40,000 reels of microfilm; 90,000 microfiche; family histories; 10,000 indexed pedigree charts. **Subscriptions:** 78 journals and other serials. **Services:** Copying; center open to the public. **Computerized Information Services:** CD-ROM (FamilySearch). **Remarks:** FAX: (602)964-7137.

★3670★
Church of Jesus Christ of Latter-Day Saints - Philadelphia Pennsylvania Stake - Family History Center (Hist)
721 Paxon Hollow Rd. Phone: (215)356-8507
Broomall, PA 19008 George W. Schock, Dir.
Founded: 1973. **Staff:** 1. **Subjects:** Genealogy. **Holdings:** 200 books; 42,000 microfiche; 200 reels of microfilm. **Services:** Access to microfilm and microfiche records of the main Library in Salt Lake City; center open to the public. **Computerized Information Services:** Internal databases.

★3671★
Church of Jesus Christ of Latter-Day Saints - Richland Regional Family History Center (Hist)
400 Catskill Phone: (509)946-6637
Richland, WA 99352 Richard P. Allen, Dir.
Founded: 1967. **Staff:** 40. **Subjects:** Genealogy. **Holdings:** 1200 books; 500 bound periodical volumes; 4000 reels of microfilm; 13,000 microfiche. **Services:** Interlibrary loan; copying; access to the microfilm collection of the main library in Salt Lake City; center open to the public. **Automated Operations:** Computerized cataloging, acquisitions, and circulation. **Computerized Information Services:** Internal databases.

★3672★
Church of Jesus Christ of Latter-Day Saints - Roswell Family History Center (Hist)
39 Lost Trail Rd. Phone: (505)623-3363
Roswell, NM 88201 Murray H. Sharp, Dir.
Founded: 1975. **Staff:** 6. **Subjects:** Genealogy, Roswell history. **Holdings:** 150 books. **Services:** Interlibrary loan; center open to the public. **Publications:** Newsletter - for internal distribution only. **Staff:** Teddy Lindsey, Libn.; James Applegate, Libn.; Hazel Waggoner, Libn.

★3673★
Church of Jesus Christ of Latter-Day Saints - Safford-Thatcher Stakes - Family History Center (Hist)
1803 S. 8th Ave. Phone: (602)428-3194
Safford, AZ 85546 Lorin W. Moffett, Dir.
Founded: 1939. **Staff:** 50. **Subjects:** Genealogy. **Special Collections:** Indian Tribes (pamphlets); World Conference, 1969 (18 volumes); World Conference, 1981 (13 volumes); Genealogical Society Series (12 volumes). **Holdings:** 5000 books; 1087 bound periodical volumes; 3000 films; microfiche for genealogical research. **Subscriptions:** 21 journals and other serials. **Services:** Interlibrary loan; copying; center open to the public. **Computerized Information Services:** Ancestral Search, Computers, Personal Ancestral File (internal databases).

★3674★
Church of Jesus Christ of Latter-Day Saints - St. George Family History Center (Hist)
410 South 200 East Phone: (801)673-4591
St. George, UT 84770 Calvin Gardner, Dir.
Staff: Prof 2. **Subjects:** Genealogy and history. **Special Collections:** Church records for Southern Utah, Northern Nevada, and Northern Arizona (microfilm). **Holdings:** 5000 volumes; 2000 reels of microfilm; 4000 microfiche. **Services:** Copying; center open to the public. **Special Indexes:** Obituary Index for Mountain West.

★3675★
Church of Jesus Christ of Latter-Day Saints - San Diego Multi-Regional Family History Center (Hist)
3705 10th Ave. Phone: (619)295-9808
San Diego, CA 92103 Violet Hartman, Chf.Libn.
Founded: 1965. **Staff:** 50. **Subjects:** Genealogy, local history. **Holdings:** 12,000 volumes; 21,000 reels of microfilm; 25,000 microfiche. **Subscriptions:** 95 journals and other serials. **Services:** Copying; access to the microfilm collection of the main center in Salt Lake City; center open to the public. **Computerized Information Services:** FamilySearch. **Remarks:** Alternate telephone number(s): 295-0882.

★3676★
Church of Jesus Christ of Latter-Day Saints - Tacoma Branch Family History Center (Hist)
1102 S. Pearl
Tacoma, WA 98465 Phone: (206)564-1103
Founded: 1976. **Staff:** 55. **Subjects:** Genealogy and local history. **Special Collections:** Family pedigree charts (800); family genealogies (180). **Holdings:** 600 volumes; 7400 reels of microfilm; 25 VF drawers of western Washington obituaries; 3 VF drawers of genealogical materials; hanging file of surnames; census records; films. **Services:** Interlibrary loan (fee); copying; access to the microfilm collection of the main center in Salt Lake City; center open to the public. **Staff:** Ken Lukens, Libn.; Marty Lukens, Libn.

★3677★
Church of Jesus Christ of Latter-Day Saints - Tampa Stake Family History Center (Hist)
1313 Divot Ln. Phone: (813)971-2869
Tampa, FL 33612 James B. Williams, Libn.
Founded: 1968. **Staff:** 30. **Subjects:** Local history, genealogy. **Special Collections:** Mortuary and cemetery records of Hillsborough County, FL. **Holdings:** 2200 books; 9000 reels of microfilm; 1000 unbound periodicals; 2500 clippings, maps, manuscripts; 12 drawers of microfiche of the International Family History Index; U.S. census, 1790-1850, Heads of Household Index. **Subscriptions:** 2 journals and other serials. **Services:** Copying; access to the microfilm collection of the main center in Salt Lake City; center open to the public. **Computerized Information Services:** FamilySearch.

★3678★
Church of Jesus Christ of Latter-Day Saints - Toronto Family History Library (Hist)
95 Melbert Rd.
Box 247 Phone: (416)621-4607
Etobicoke, ON, Canada M9C 4V3 E.G. Lansitie, Libn.
Founded: 1970. **Staff:** 15. **Subjects:** Genealogy. **Holdings:** Figures not available. **Services:** Library open to the public.

★3679★
Church of Jesus Christ of Latter-Day Saints - Ventura Family History Center (Hist)
3051 Loma Vista Rd. Phone: (805)643-5607
Ventura, CA 93003 David B. Combe, Dir.
Subjects: Genealogy. **Holdings:** 600 books; 500 reels of microfilm; 20,000 microfiche. **Subscriptions:** 10 journals and other serials. **Services:** Copying; microfiche/microfilm copying; access to microfilm collection of the main center in Salt Lake City; center open to the public. **Remarks:** A branch library is maintained at 411 San Antonio St., Ojai, CA 93023; telephone: (805)646-6307.

★3680★
Church of Jesus Christ of Latter-Day Saints - Visalia, California Stake Family History Center (Hist)
3835 Judy Ln. Phone: (209)732-3712
Visalia, CA 93277 Jessie M. Jones, Dir.
Founded: 1984. **Subjects:** Genealogy. **Special Collections:** Torrey Collection. **Holdings:** Card Catalog of the Salt Lake Index (MCC) on microfilm; Genealogical Library Catalog (GLC) on microfiche; International Genealogical Index (IGI); Accelerated Index System to U.S. Census (AIS); Family Register; Sutro File. **Services:** Interlibrary loan; copying; library open to the public. **Publications:** The Pedigree Chart (newsletter), bimonthly - to church members and to others upon request.

★3681★
Church of Jesus Christ of Latter-Day Saints - West Palm Beach, Florida Stake Family History Center (Hist)
1099 S.W. 9th Ave. Phone: (407)395-6644
Boca Raton, FL 33486 Donald W. Jennings, Jr., Dir.
Founded: 1965. **Staff:** Prof 2. **Subjects:** Genealogical research. **Holdings:** 500 books; 3000 reels of microfilm; International Genealogical Index (IGI); catalog of Salt Lake Family History Library on microfiche; family registery. **Subscriptions:** 6 journals and other serials. **Services:** Copying; access to microfilm collection of the main center in Salt Lake City; center open to the public on a limited schedule. **Computerized Information Services:** FamilySearch. **Publications:** Listing of films. **Remarks:** Library located at 1530 W. Camino Real, Boca Raton, FL 33486. **Staff:** Phyllis Heiss; Mary Bordeman.

★3682★
Church of Jesus Christ of Latter-Day Saints - Worcester Family History Center (Hist)
67 Chester St. Phone: (508)852-7000
Worcester, MA 01606 Delene Holbrook, Dir.
Subjects: Genealogy. **Remarks:** No further information was supplied by respondent.

★3683★
Church of the Lighted Window - Library (Rel-Phil)
1200 Foothill Blvd. Phone: (818)790-1185
La Canada, CA 91011 Roberta M. Parsons
Founded: 1965. **Subjects:** Christian living, Bible, devotions, family, biography, poetry, literature. **Holdings:** 1000 books. **Services:** Library open to the public on a limited schedule.

★3684★
Church Media Center (Rel-Phil)
63 Green St. Phone: (603)224-7020
Concord, NH 03301 Doris M. Dunbar, Dir.
Founded: 1976. **Staff:** Prof 1. **Subjects:** Religious education, theology, peace and justice, spirituality, church history, stewardship, religious drama, marriage and family, church seasons. **Holdings:** 2500 books; 16 bound periodical volumes; 800 reports; 250 videotapes; 800 filmstrips; 900 audiocassettes; games; charts. **Subscriptions:** 25 journals and other serials; 3 newspapers. **Services:** Library open to the public on fee basis. **Special Catalogs:** Catalog; video catalog - both with monthly updates. **Remarks:** Center is maintained by the New Hampshire branches of the Episcopal Church and United Church of Christ.

★3685★
Church of the Nazarene - International Headquarters - Resource Center/ SSM Library (Rel-Phil)
6401 The Paseo Phone: (816)333-7000
Kansas City, MO 64131 Karen Champion, Libn.
Staff: Prof 1. **Subjects:** Bible, religious education, missions. **Holdings:** 8000 books; 20 VF drawers of pamphlets; 1 VF drawer of scores; 100 cassette tapes. **Subscriptions:** 100 journals and other serials. **Services:** Center not open to the public.

★3686★
Churchill County Museum Association - Churchill County Museum & Archives - Archives (Hist)
1050 S. Maine St. Phone: (702)423-3677
Fallon, NV 89406 Myrl Nygren, Act.Dir.
Founded: 1968. **Staff:** 4.5. **Subjects:** Nevada history, museum administration, local history. **Special Collections:** Willie Capucci Collection (Nevada; 20 linear feet of documents, letters, postcards, legal papers, and other items); Churchill County government records, 1860 to present; City of Fallon records, 1907 to present. **Holdings:** 1000 books. **Services:** Copying; archives open to the public for reference use only.

Winston Churchill Memorial and Library
See: **Westminster College** (20328)

★3687★
CIBA Corning Diagnostics Corporation - Gilford Technical Library (Sci-Engr)
132 Artino St. Phone: (216)775-9343
Oberlin, OH 44074 Marjorie Mulder, Libn.
Founded: 1971. **Staff:** Prof 1. **Subjects:** Biochemistry, electronics engineering, optics. **Special Collections:** Gilford Archives. **Holdings:** 3000 books; 100 bound periodical volumes; 28 VF drawers of archival material. **Subscriptions:** 150 journals and other serials. **Services:** Interlibrary loan; copying; library open to the public by appointment. **Computerized Information Services:** DIALOG Information Services, Dow Jones News/ Retrieval. Performs searches on fee basis. **Networks/Consortia:** Member of Cleveland Area Metropolitan Library System (CAMLS). **Remarks:** FAX: (216)774-3939 (Attn.: Library). Telex: 433 2091.

★3688★
CIBA Corning Diagnostics Corporation - Steinberg Information Center (Med, Bus-Fin)
63 North St. Phone: (508)359-3538
Medfield, MA 02052 Kathleen E. McCabe, Supv.Info.Ctr.
Founded: 1978. **Staff:** Prof 3. **Subjects:** Clinical medicine, market research, engineering, biotechnology, business. **Special Collections:** Market research collection (medical instruments and diagnostics markets; 3500 items); competitor files. **Holdings:** 3000 books; 2200 bound periodical volumes; 24,000 patents; 850 internal research reports. **Subscriptions:** 205 journals and other serials. **Services:** Interlibrary loan; center not open to the public. **Automated Operations:** Computerized cataloging, serials, and circulation. **Computerized Information Services:** DIALOG Information Services, PFDS Online. **Networks/Consortia:** Member of NELINET, Inc. **Publications:** Acquisitions list, monthly; market reports, quarterly; Competition Digest, biweekly; Current Contents, weekly; Competitor Profiles, quarterly; newsletter - for internal distribution only. **Special Catalogs:** Patent Catalog; Research Reports Catalog; Competitor Files Catalog (all online). **Remarks:** FAX: (508)359-3442.

★3689★
CIBA-GEIGY (Canada) Ltd. - Pharmaceutical Library (Med)
6860 Century Ave. Phone: (416)821-4420
Mississauga, ON, Canada L5N 2W5 Heather Dansereau, Med.Libn.
Staff: Prof 1; Other 1. **Subjects:** Medicine, pharmacy, pharmacology, business. **Special Collections:** CIBA-GEIGY products; CIBA and GEIGY publications. **Holdings:** 3000 volumes; 70,000 microfiche. **Subscriptions:** 260 journals and other serials. **Services:** Interlibrary loan; copying. **Remarks:** FAX: (416)821-0755.

★3690★
CIBA-GEIGY Corporation - Biotechnology Library (Sci-Engr, Agri)
3054 Cornwallis Dr. Phone: (919)541-8500
Research Triangle Park, NC 27709 Katharine S. Thomas, Info.Sci.
Founded: 1985. **Staff:** Prof 1; Other 1. **Subjects:** Agriculture, biotechnology. **Holdings:** 2800 books; 175 manuscripts; 3000 patents; 1300 archival items; 166 reels of microfilm. **Subscriptions:** 153 journals and other serials. **Services:** Library not open to the public. **Automated Operations:** Computerized public access catalog, cataloging, acquisitions, serials, and circulation. **Computerized Information Services:** DIALOG Information Services, STN International, ORBIT Search Service, TOXNET; BIBLIOTECH (internal database). **Networks/Consortia:** Member of SOLINET. **Remarks:** FAX: (919)541-8585.

★3691★
CIBA-GEIGY Corporation - Corporate Library (Sci-Engr)
Saw Mill River Rd. Phone: (914)479-2397
Ardsley, NY 10502 Paul M. McIlvaine, Supv.Lib.Serv.
Founded: 1956. **Staff:** Prof 2; Other 2. **Subjects:** Organic chemistry, plastics and polymers, business administration and management. **Holdings:** 7000 books; 10,000 bound periodical volumes; 1500 reports; 4000 reels of microfilm; 1100 microfiche. **Subscriptions:** 825 journals and other serials. **Services:** Interlibrary loan; library not open to the public. **Automated Operations:** Computerized serials. **Computerized Information Services:** DIALOG Information Services, PFDS Online, NLM, Dow Jones News/ Retrieval. **Publications:** Infoscope, bimonthly - for internal distribution only. **Remarks:** FAX: (914)479-4788.

★3692★
CIBA-GEIGY Corporation - Pharmaceuticals Division - Scientific Information Center (Med)
566 Morris Ave. Phone: (908)277-4826
Summit, NJ 07901 Lynette C. Schneider, Dir.
Founded: 1937. **Staff:** Prof 13; Other 10. **Subjects:** Medicine, chemistry, pharmacology, pharmacy, business. **Holdings:** 5000 books; 24,000 bound periodical volumes; 2260 reels of microfilm of journal holdings; 500,000 unpublished proprietary documents. **Subscriptions:** 900 journals and other serials. **Services:** Interlibrary loan; library not open to the public. **Automated Operations:** Computerized public access catalog, cataloging, serials, and circulation. **Computerized Information Services:** BRS Information Technologies, DIALOG Information Services, PFDS Online, MEDLINE, Questel, STN International, IMSBASE, Data-Star, VU/TEXT Information Services; internal database. **Networks/Consortia:** Member of Medical Library Center of New York (MLCNY), PALINET. **Publications:** News and New Book List; Project Team Updates, weekly; Current Bulletins, monthly; Literature Updates, weekly; Competitor Profiles, monthly. **Remarks:** FAX: (908)277-7999. **Staff:** Anne E. Garty, Asst.Dir.; Anthony Fedell, Mgr., Pharm.Rec.Ctr.

★3693★
CIBA-GEIGY Corporation - Research & Development Information Services (Sci-Engr, Agri)
410 Swing Rd.
Box 18300 Phone: (919)632-2815
Greensboro, NC 27419 Leslie Levine, Mgr.
Founded: 1974. **Staff:** Prof 2. **Subjects:** Agricultural chemicals, dyestuffs, paper chemistry, organic chemistry, biochemistry, agriculture, veterinary science. **Holdings:** 15,000 books; 13,000 bound periodical volumes; 3500 reels of microfilm. **Subscriptions:** 800 journals and other serials. **Services:** Interlibrary loan; service not open to the public. **Automated Operations:** Computerized public access catalog, cataloging, acquisitions, serials, and circulation. **Computerized Information Services:** LEXIS, MEDLINE, BRS Information Technologies, Chemical Abstracts Service (CAS), DIALOG Information Services, ORBIT Search Service, Dow Jones News/Retrieval; Bibliotech (internal database). **Networks/Consortia:** Member of SOLINET. **Publications:** What's New, monthly - to other Ciba-Geigy libraries. **Remarks:** FAX: (919)299-8318. **Staff:** Eunice Lynne Jacques, Lib.Serv.; Paul F. Lee, Libn., ILL.

★3694★
CIBA-GEIGY Corporation - Technical Information Center (Biol Sci, Med)
400 Farmington Ave. Phone: (203)674-6312
Farmington, CT 06032 Joanna W. Eickenhorst, Supv., Info.Serv.
Founded: 1979. **Staff:** Prof 3. **Subjects:** Toxicology, environmental health, mutagenicity, metabolism, pharmacokinetics. **Holdings:** 4000 books. **Subscriptions:** 140 journals and other serials. **Services:** Interlibrary loan; SDI. **Computerized Information Services:** NLM, PFDS Online, DIALOG Information Services, OCLC. **Networks/Consortia:** Member of Capital Region Library Council (CRLC). **Publications:** Acquisitions list, monthly; Journal Holdings List; Style Manual. **Special Indexes:** Technical Reports Index; Reprints Collection Index. **Remarks:** FAX: (203)676-9443.

★3695★
CIGNA Corporation - Investment Library (Bus-Fin)
900 Cottage Grove Rd., SM18 Phone: (203)726-3257
Bloomfield, CT 06002 Patricia Slevinsky, Dir., Bus.Rsrc.Ctr.
Founded: 1919. **Staff:** Prof 8; Other 8. **Subjects:** Life and health insurance, pensions, law, business management, economics, investments. **Holdings:** 20,000 volumes; 2000 annual reports. **Subscriptions:** 150 journals and other serials; 10 newspapers. **Services:** Interlibrary loan; copying; library open to the public by appointment. **Computerized Information Services:** DIALOG Information Services, PFDS Online, LEXIS, NEXIS, WESTLAW, OCLC, BRS Information Technologies, Dow Jones News/Retrieval, WILSONLINE. **Networks/Consortia:** Member of Capital Region Library Council (CRLC). **Formerly:** Its Hartford Business Library. **Staff:** Jessie Snyder, Info.Spec.; Barbara Wilkie, Info.Spec.

★3696★
CIGNA Corporation - Law Library (W-26L) (Law)
Hartford, CT 06152 Phone: (203)726-6024
Suzanne Broque, Law Libn.
Staff: Prof 1; Other 1. **Subjects:** Law - investment, life and health insurance. **Holdings:** 30,000 volumes. **Subscriptions:** 3 newspapers. **Services:** Interlibrary loan; copying; SDI. **Computerized Information Services:** LEXIS, NEXIS, WESTLAW, VU/TEXT Information Services, WILSONLINE, Dow Jones News/Retrieval, DIALOG Information Services. **Publications:** CIGNA Hartford Law Library News, irregular - for internal distribution only. **Remarks:** Library located at 900 Cottage Grove Rd., Bloomfield, CT 06002. FAX: (203)726-6770.

★3697★
CIGNA Corporation - Philadelphia Research Library (Bus-Fin)
2 Liberty Pl.
1601 Chestnut Pl. Phone: (215)761-4146
Philadelphia, PA 19192 Christine Flynn, Mgr.
Founded: 1947. **Staff:** Prof 2; Other 2. **Subjects:** Insurance, management, occupational and environmental safety and health. **Holdings:** 15,000 books; 2100 bound periodical volumes. **Subscriptions:** 400 journals and other serials. **Services:** Interlibrary loan; library not open to the public. **Automated Operations:** Computerized acquisitions and serials. **Computerized Information Services:** DIALOG Information Services, Dow Jones News/Retrieval, Mead Data Central, VU/TEXT Information Services. **Remarks:** FAX:(215)761-5588. **Staff:** Elizabeth Sellner, Info.Spec.

★3698★
Cincinnati Art Museum - Mary R. Schiff Library (Art)
Eden Park Phone: (513)721-5204
Cincinnati, OH 45202 Mona L. Chapin, Hd.Libn.
Founded: 1881. **Staff:** Prof 3; Other 2. **Subjects:** Art. **Special Collections:** Museum Archives; Cincinnati art; artists from Cincinnati and surrounding area. **Holdings:** 54,000 volumes; 1320 feet of U.S. and foreign museum, gallery, exhibition catalogs; 250,000 pamphlets and clippings; 16,500 mounted pictures. **Subscriptions:** 350 journals and other serials. **Services:** Interlibrary loan; copying; library open to the public. **Networks/Consortia:** Member of Greater Cincinnati Library Consortium (GCLC). **Special Catalogs:** File of exhibitions and artists shown at the museum since 1886 (card). **Special Indexes:** Art index from 19th century Cincinnati newspapers. **Remarks:** FAX: (513)721-0129. **Staff:** Cathy Shaffer, Asst.Libn./Ref.; Peggy Runge, Asst.Libn./Cat.

Cincinnati Children's Hospital - University Affiliated Cincinnati Center for Developmental Disorders
See: **University Affiliated Cincinnati Center for Developmental Disorders** (18147)

★3699★
Cincinnati City Planning Department - Office of Planning and Management Support - Library (Plan)
City Hall, Rm. 141
801 Plum St. Phone: (513)352-3441
Cincinnati, OH 45202 Felix Bere, Info.Spec./City Plan.
Subjects: Cincinnati urban affairs and statistics. **Special Collections:** Cincinnati development projects and support programs (2000 vertical files). **Holdings:** 2255 local government documents; 12,000 slides; 800 data files. **Services:** Copying; library open to the public for reference use only. **Automated Operations:** Computerized management reports. **Computerized Information Services:** Internal database. **Formerly:** Cincinnati City Planning Commission.

★3700★
Cincinnati College of Mortuary Science - Library (Sci-Engr)
Cohen Center
3860 Pacific Ave. Phone: (513)745-3631
Cincinnati, OH 45207-1033 Dan L. Flory, Pres.
Founded: 1882. **Staff:** 1. **Subjects:** Mortuary science, funeral service, thanatology, death and dying, embalming, public health. **Special Collections:** Materials on support groups for grieving persons (Sudden Infant Death Syndrome groups, Widow-to-Widow, Hospice Care, Compassionate Friends). **Holdings:** 5000 books; 1000 bound periodical volumes; filmstrips; cassettes. **Subscriptions:** 30 journals and other serials. **Services:** Library open to the public for reference use only. **Automated Operations:** Computerized cataloging.

★3701★
Cincinnati Electronics Corporation - Technical Library
2630 Glendale-Milford Rd.
Cincinnati, OH 45241
Defunct.

★3702★
Cincinnati Enquirer Newspaper - Library
617 Vine St. Phone: (513)721-2700
Cincinnati, OH 45202 Ray Zwick, Libn.
Subjects: Newspaper reference topics. **Remarks:** No further information was supplied by respondent.

★3703★
Cincinnati Historical Society - Library (Hist)
The Museum Center
Cincinnati Union Terminal
1301 Western Ave. Phone: (513)287-7030
Cincinnati, OH 45203-1129 Laura L. Chace, Libn.
Founded: 1831. **Staff:** Prof 9. Other 10. **Subjects:** Northwest Territory, Miami Purchase, Hamilton County and Cincinnati metropolitan area, genealogy. **Special Collections:** James Albert Green Collection of William

Henry Harrison; Peter G. Thomson Collection of Ohioana; Cornelius J. Hauck Collections (arboreta, rare books). **Holdings:** 90,000 volumes; 7500 linear feet of manuscripts; 500,000 photographs; 14,000 slides; 2500 maps; 5000 reels of microfilm; 1300 broadsides; 350 linear feet of clippings. **Subscriptions:** 300 journals and other serials. **Services:** Copying; library open to the public for reference use only. **Automated Operations:** Computerized cataloging. **Computerized Information Services:** OCLC. **Networks/Consortia:** Member of Greater Cincinnati Library Consortium (GCLC). **Publications:** Bulletin, quarterly. **Special Indexes:** Metropolitan Cincinnati vital statistics (card); local history index for Metropolitan Cincinnati (card). **Remarks:** FAX: (513)287-7095. **Staff:** Gale E. Peterson, Dir.; Barbara J. Dawson, Ref.Libn.; Jonathan Dembo, Mss.Supv.; Scott L. Gampfer, Cons.Spec. ; Linda J. Bailey, Asst.Libn., Photo.; Roger Beasley, Cat.

Cincinnati Institute of Fine Arts - Taft Museum Library
See: **Taft Museum - Library** (15984)

★3704★
Cincinnati Law Library Association (Law)
601 Courthouse — Phone: (513)632-8445
Cincinnati, OH 45202 — Carol E. Meyer, Law Libn.
Founded: 1834. **Staff:** Prof 2; Other 8. **Subjects:** Law. **Special Collections:** Ohio and U.S. Supreme Court Briefs and Records; Ohio Law History; State Session Laws. **Holdings:** 218,000 books; 27,000 bound periodical volumes; 15,000 reels of microfilm; 800 drawers of microfiche; 100 cassettes; SEC No-Action Letters; Federal Register, 1971 to present; IRS Private Letter Rulings; Code of Federal Regulations, 1936 to present. **Subscriptions:** 948 journals and other serials; 14 newspapers. **Services:** Interlibrary loan; library open to the public for reference use only. **Automated Operations:** Computerized cataloging and serials. **Computerized Information Services:** WESTLAW, Rotunda Information Systems; InfoTrac. **Networks/Consortia:** Member of Greater Cincinnati Library Consortium (GCLC), Ohio Regional Consortium of Law Libraries (ORCLL). **Publications:** Ohio Legal Resource Bibliography. **Remarks:** Alternate telephone number(s): 632-8371.

★3705★
Cincinnati Milacron Inc. - Information Resource Center (Sci-Engr)
4701 Marburg Ave. — Phone: (513)841-8589
Cincinnati, OH 45209-1025 — Alice Patience, Info.Mgr.
Founded: 1968. **Staff:** Prof 1; Other 2. **Subjects:** Machine tools, metalworking, electronic controls, materials science, robotics, plastics processing machinery, automated manufacturing, systems integration. **Holdings:** 8000 books; 17,000 other cataloged items; 300 cubic feet of company archives; 1450 reels of microfilm. **Subscriptions:** 500 journals and other serials; 25 newspapers. **Automated Operations:** Computerized public access catalog, cataloging, acquisitions, serials, circulation, and routing. **Computerized Information Services:** DIALOG Information Services, Dow Jones News/Retrieval; CD-ROMs (Standard & Poor's COMPUSTAT Services, Inc., Computer Library, Microsoft Bookshelf, Thomas Register). Performs searches on fee basis. **Publications:** Checklist, biweekly. **Remarks:** FAX: (513)841-8059.

★3706★
Cincinnati Museum of Natural History - Library (Biol Sci)
1720 Gilbert Ave. — Phone: (513)621-3890
Cincinnati, OH 45202 — Sandra V. Pesce, Libn.
Staff: 1. **Subjects:** Natural history. **Holdings:** 7500 books; 2500 periodical volumes. **Subscriptions:** 80 journals and other serials. **Services:** Interlibrary loan; copying; library open to museum members and specialists by appointment only. **Computerized Information Services:** OCLC. **Networks/Consortia:** Member of OHIONET.

★3707★
Cincinnati Post - Library (Publ)
125 E. Court St. — Phone: (513)352-2000
Cincinnati, OH 45202 — Rob Hahn, Libn.
Founded: 1930. **Staff:** Prof 2. **Subjects:** Newspaper reference topics. **Holdings:** 750 books; 280 VF drawers of pictures; 56 VF drawers of clippings; microfilm, 1882 to present. **Services:** Library not open to the public. **Remarks:** Published by E.W. Scripps Co.

★3708★
Cincinnati Psychoanalytic Institute - Frederic T. Kapp Memorial Library (Med)
3001 Highland Ave. — Phone: (513)961-8886
Cincinnati, OH 45219 — Alice Hurlebaus, Libn.
Founded: 1981. **Subjects:** Psychoanalysis, psychiatry, mental health. **Holdings:** 3000 volumes; 300 reprints; 40 audiocassettes. **Subscriptions:** 45 journals and other serials. **Services:** Interlibrary loan; copying; library open to the public with restrictions. **Computerized Information Services:** BRS Information Technologies, MEDLINE; Jourlit (internal database). Performs searches on fee basis.

★3709★
Cincinnati Public Schools - Professional Library (Educ)
1908 Seymour Ave. — Phone: (513)531-5589
Cincinnati, OH 45237 — Beth Millbourn, Libn.
Staff: Prof 1; Other 1. **Subjects:** Education. **Special Collections:** Review collection of supplementary books approved by teacher committees for use in classrooms in support of curriculum. **Holdings:** 8261 books; 618 reels of microfilm; 24,493 microfiche. **Subscriptions:** 182 journals and other serials. **Services:** Interlibrary loan; library open to the public by special permission. **Special Catalogs:** Supplementary Books Bulletin (titles approved for school purchase), annual.

★3710★
Cincinnati Zoo and Botanical Garden - Library (Biol Sci)
3400 Vine St. — Phone: (513)559-7737
Cincinnati, OH 45220 — Bea Orendorff, Lib.Coord.
Founded: 1977. **Subjects:** Zoology, biology, natural history, environmental science, animal husbandry, botany. **Special Collections:** Zoological Realia; animal inventory; animal picture file; animal information; wildlife rescue program. **Holdings:** 3100 books; 100 bound periodical volumes; 10,000 slides; 30 educational kits; bibliographies. **Subscriptions:** 35 journals and other serials. **Services:** Copying; library open to the public by appointment. **Special Indexes:** Index to slide collection.

CINDAS
See: **Purdue University - CINDAS** (13536)

CINDAS - Ceramics Information Analysis Center
See: **Purdue University** (13534)

CINDAS - High Temperature Materials - Mechanical, Electronic and Thermophysical Properties Information Analysis Center
See: **Purdue University** (13535)

CINDAS - Metals Information Analysis Center
See: **Purdue University** (13537)

★3711★
Cinema Arts, Inc. - Motion Picture Archives (Aud-Vis, Art)
Box 70 — Phone: (717)676-4145
South Sterling, PA 18460 — Beverly Allen, Archv.
Subjects: Kinograms (1915-1931); telenews (1947-1953); industry (1910-1950s); transportation (1900-1950s); WW I & II newsreels and miscellaneous; feature pictures (1905-1965). **Holdings:** 30.1 million feet of motion picture film; 1 million still photographs and lobby cards pertaining to the motion picture industry (1900-1970). **Services:** Copying; archives open to the public on fee basis. **Remarks:** Films are cataloged by subject, such as agriculture, bathing beauties, circus, crime, dance, expeditions, fires, gags, immigrants, military, motion picture production, personalities, prohibition, sports, stunts, telephone, and zoos. FAX: (717)676-9194.

★3712★
Cinematheque Ontario - Film Reference Library (Theater)
70 Carlton St. — Phone: (416)967-1517
Toronto, ON, Canada M5B 1L7 — Susan M. Murray, Dir. of Doc.
Founded: 1990. **Staff:** Prof 4. **Subjects:** All aspects of the cinema. **Special Collections:** Silent Film Music Selections for Piano (100). **Holdings:** 20,000 books; 900 bound periodical volumes; 100 unpublished screenplays; 5000 soundtracks of motion pictures; 200 BBC recordings on motion pictures; extensive files by subject, film title, and biography for all aspects of filmmaking and the industry; 5000 posters; 600 video cassettes; 25,000 photographic stills; 2000 slides; 12 laser discs. **Subscriptions:** 125 journals and other serials. **Services:** Copying; clipping service; library open to the public for reference use only. **Remarks:** FAX: (416)967-0628. Telex: 06 219724, Attn: Library. **Formed by the merger of:** Ontario Film Institute and Festival of Festivals. **Staff:** Rosemary Ullyot, Lib.Techn.; Michael W. Anderson, Lib.Techn.

★3713★
Cinematheque Quebecoise - Archives & Film Museum (Theater)
335 Blvd. de Maisonneuve, E.
Montreal, PQ, Canada H2X 1K1 Phone: (514)842-9763
Founded: 1963. **Staff:** 25. **Subjects:** Canadian cinema, animation, film history. **Special Collections:** Documents and equipment illustrating the history of cinema, 1870 to present (500 apparatus). **Holdings:** 25,000 films; 300,000 photographs; 13,000 posters; animation documents. **Subscriptions:** 450 journals and other serials. **Services:** Archives open to the public with restrictions. **Computerized Information Services:** FORMAT; STAR (internal database). **Publications:** Revue de la Cinematheque, bimonthly - by subscription; brochures on Canadian and foreign cinema and filmmakers - for sale. **Remarks:** FAX: (514)842-1816. **Staff:** Robert Daudelin, Dir. of Cons.; Stephane Leclerc, Dir. of Adm.; Gisele Cote, Acq.; Louise Beaudet, Hd. of Animation; Rene Beauclair, Libn.

★3714★
Cinematheque Quebecoise - Centre de Documentation Cinematographique (Theater)
335 Blvd. de Maisonneuve, E. Phone: (514)842-9763
Montreal, PQ, Canada H2X 1K1 Rene Beauclair, Hd.Libn.
Founded: 1963. **Staff:** Prof 1; Other 7. **Subjects:** Canadian and international cinema, television, video. **Holdings:** 40,000 books; 125,000 bound periodical volumes; 300,000 clippings and pamphlets on actors, directors, films; 600 reels of microfilm; 100,000 vertical files on films, film personalities, festivals, and associations; 300 videocassettes of film classics. **Subscriptions:** 450 journals and other serials; 20 newspapers. **Services:** Copying; center open to the public. **Computerized Information Services:** Online systems. Performs searches free of charge. Contact Person: Julie Dubuc, Ref. **Publications:** Dossiers thematiques from press clippings; Annual Bibliography of Quebec Cinema; subject bibliographies related to the public screenings at the Cinematheque. **Special Indexes:** Indexes of films, personalities, subjects (card). **Remarks:** FAX: (514)842-1816. **Staff:** Jean-Yves Croteau, Ref.; Julienne Bourdreau, Ref.

CIRAD - CIDARC
See: **Centre de Cooperation Internationale en Recherche Agronomique pour le Developpement - Centre d'Information et de Documentation en Agronomie des Regions Chaudes** (3224)

★3715★
Circus Historical Society - Library (Hist)
2515 Dorset Rd. Phone: (614)294-5361
Columbus, OH 43221 Fred D. Pfening, Jr.
Founded: 1954. **Subjects:** Circusiana. **Holdings:** Figures not available. **Services:** Library not open to the public.

★3716★
Circus World Museum - Robert L. Parkinson Library & Research Center (Hist)
426 Water St. Phone: (608)356-8341
Baraboo, WI 53913 Fred Dahlinger, Jr., Archv./Hist.
Founded: 1970. **Staff:** Prof 2. **Subjects:** Circus, Wild West. **Holdings:** 1200 books; 300 bound periodical volumes; 60,000 photographic prints; 30,000 negatives; 5000 pieces of circus band music; 7000 lithographs; 300 pieces of original circus lithograph art; 1900 circus programs; 400 route books; business records; statistical and biographical files. **Services:** Interlibrary loan; copying (both limited); center open to the public. **Networks/Consortia:** Member of Multitype Advisory Library Committee (MALC). **Publications:** Circuses Currently in Operation; List of Loanable Circus Books; Circus Movies for Loan by Mail. **Special Indexes:** Index to 400,000 names of people in the circus field. **Remarks:** Owned by State Historical Society of Wisconsin. Library located at 415 Lynn St., Baraboo, WI 53913. FAX: (608)356-1800. **Staff:** William McCarthy, Res.Hist.

CISTI
See: **Canada - National Research Council - Canada Institute for Scientific and Technical Information (CISTI)** (2814)

★3717★
CIT Group, Inc. - Law Library (Law)
650 CIT Dr. Phone: (201)740-5412
Livingston, NJ 07039 Dawn Zeffiro, Leg.Lib.
Subjects: Law, banks and banking, equipment leasing. **Holdings:** 4000 books. **Subscriptions:** 50 journals and other serials; 3 newspapers. **Services:** Library not open to the public. **Computerized Information Services:** DIALOG Information Services. **Remarks:** FAX: (201)740-5087.

★3718★
Citadel Assurance - Library (Bus-Fin)
1075 Bay St. Phone: (416)928-8539
Toronto, ON, Canada M5S 2W5 Janet Steryannis
Founded: 1972. **Staff:** 1. **Subjects:** Insurance, insurance law, business, management, finance. **Special Collections:** Finance. **Holdings:** 500 books; 200 unbound periodical volumes; 13 VF drawers of reprints, annual reports, clippings. **Subscriptions:** 40 journals and other serials. **Services:** Interlibrary loan; copying. **Computerized Information Services:** DIALOG Information Services, Info Globe, The Financial Post Information Service, Infomart Online. **Networks/Consortia:** Member of Network of Insurance Libraries in Toronto. **Publications:** Social Security Benefits in Canada, annual - for internal distribution only. **Remarks:** FAX: (416)928-1553. Citadel Assurance is a subsidiary of Winterthur Swiss Insurance Co.

★3719★
Citadel Military College of South Carolina - Archives/Museum (Hist, Mil)
The Citadel Phone: (803)792-6846
Charleston, SC 29409 Jane Yates, Dir./Archv.-Musm.
Staff: Prof 2. **Subjects:** The Citadel; military history. **Special Collections:** General Mark W. Clark Collection; VADM Friedrich Ruge; Bruce Catton; General Ellison Capers; The Citadel. **Holdings:** 1000 linear feet of material. **Services:** Copying; archives open to the public by appointment. **Staff:** Mary Jo Dellucci, Musm.Cur.

★3720★
Citadel Military College of South Carolina - Daniel Library (Mil)
The Citadel Phone: (803)792-5116
Charleston, SC 29409 Zelma G. Palestrant, Dir.
Founded: 1842. **Staff:** Prof 7; Other 11. **Subjects:** General academic subjects with special emphasis on the military sciences and South Carolina. **Holdings:** 167,731 books; 9402 bound periodical volumes; 86,741 government documents; 983,538 microforms; 628 AV items. **Subscriptions:** 1377 journals and other serials; 17 newspapers. **Services:** Interlibrary loan; copying; library open to the public for reference use only. **Automated Operations:** Computerized public access catalog, cataloging, acquisitions, circulation, and ILL. **Computerized Information Services:** OCLC, DIALOG Information Services, BRS Information Technologies, OCLC EPIC; CD-ROMs; BITNET, InterNet (electronic mail services). **Publications:** Bibliographies. **Remarks:** FAX: (803)792-5190. Electronic mail address(es): LIBRARY@CITADEL (BITNET); LIBRARY@VAX.CITADEL.EDU (InterNet). **Staff:** J. Edward Maynard, Circ.; Sherman E. Pyatt, Docs.; Herbert Nath, Ref.; Alan Johns, Cat.; Elizabeth W. Carter, Info.Serv.; Olga Paradis, Acq.

★3721★
Cite de la Sante de Laval - Centre de Documentation (Med)
1755, blvd. Rene Laennec Phone: (514)975-5493
Laval, PQ, Canada H7M 3L9 France Pontbriand, Libn.
Founded: 1978. **Staff:** Prof 1. **Subjects:** Medicine, nursing, community health. **Holdings:** 5000 books; 4000 bound periodical volumes. **Subscriptions:** 275 journals and other serials. **Services:** Interlibrary loan; copying; center open to the public for reference use only. **Computerized Information Services:** DIALOG Information Services, MEDLINE; Envoy 100, QLACS (electronic mail services). **Networks/Consortia:** Member of Association des Bibliotheques de la Sante Affiliees a l'Universite de Montreal (ABSAUM). **Publications:** Biblionouvelles, monthly. **Remarks:** Alternate telephone number(s): 668-1010. **Staff:** Lise Labelle, Techn.

★3722★
Citibank, N.A. - Citicorp Law Library (Law)
425 Park Ave., 2nd Fl. Phone: (212)559-2503
New York, NY 10043 Amparo Reyes, Law Libn.
Staff: Prof 1; Other 1. **Subjects:** Law, securities, banking, international banking. **Holdings:** 5500 books; 45 bound periodical volumes; legal memoranda; microfilm. **Subscriptions:** 35 journals and other serials. **Services:** Interlibrary loan; library not open to the public. **Computerized Information Services:** LEXIS, NEXIS. **Publications:** Library Bulletins: Law Periodicals, Continuing Education. **Remarks:** Alternate telephone number(s): 559-8990. FAX: (212)793-4402.

★3723★
Citicorp/Citibank - Citiinformation (Bus-Fin)
399 Park Ave., 4th Fl.
Zone 6 Phone: (212)559-1000
New York, NY 10043 Josephine Arencibia, Sr.Ref.Libn.
Founded: 1906. **Staff:** Prof 5; Other 11. **Subjects:** Banking, investment, finance, management, business, economics. **Special Collections:** Reports on obsolete companies; Securities and Exchange Commission (SEC) filing companies; international annual reports. **Holdings:** 20,000 books; 45,000 bound periodical volumes; 950 VF drawers of corporate materials; 10K reports on New York Stock Exchange and American Stock Exchange, 1969 to present. **Subscriptions:** 500 journals and other serials. **Services:** Interlibrary loan; library open to clients. **Computerized Information Services:** DIALOG Information Services, Dow Jones News/Retrieval, NEXIS, Data Resources (DRI), Dun & Bradstreet Business Credit Services, ADP Network Services, Reuters Performs searches on fee basis. **Publications:** Recent Additions List, bimonthly - for internal distribution only. **Remarks:** Toll-free telephone number(s): (800)248-4637. **Staff:** Adrian Overholser, Mgr.; Ann Carolan, Info.Spec.; James Fichter, Info.Spec.

★3724★
Citicorp/TTI - Technical Library (Comp Sci)
3100 Ocean Park Blvd. Phone: (213)450-9111
Santa Monica, CA 90405 Bonnie Ruehs-Lutz, Info.Mgr.
Staff: Prof 1. **Subjects:** Computer science, mathematics, banking. **Special Collections:** Electronic Funds Transfer (EFT). **Holdings:** 1000 books; 100 bound periodical volumes; internal documents. **Subscriptions:** 93 journals and other serials. **Services:** Interlibrary loan; center not open to the public.

CITIS Ltd.
See: **Construction Industry Translation and Information Services, Ltd.** (4234)

★3725★
Citizens Against Tobacco Smoke - Library
Box 36236
Cincinnati, OH 45236 Ahron Leichtman, Pres.
Founded: 1985. **Subjects:** Smoking, health, nonsmokers' rights. **Holdings:** 300 volumes. **Remarks:** Currently inactive.

★3726★
Citizens Association for Sound Energy (CASE) - Library (Energy)
1426 S. Polk St. Phone: (214)946-9446
Dallas, TX 75224 Juanita Ellis, Pres.
Subjects: Energy, nuclear energy and waste. **Special Collections:** U.S. Nuclear Regulatory Commission information. **Holdings:** Figures not available. **Services:** Copying (limited); library open to the public with restrictions. **Publications:** Newsletter, irregular.

Citizen's Clearinghouse for Hazardous Wastes
See: **Tufts University - Nils Yngve Wessell Library** (16552)

★3727★
Citizens Clearinghouse for Hazardous Wastes - Library (Env-Cons)
P.O. Box 6806
Falls Church, VA 22040 Phone: (703)237-2249
Subjects: Waste management technology, physical effects of contact with toxic chemicals and hazardous wastes, environmental concerns. **Holdings:** 2500 volumes. **Subscriptions:** 600 journals and other serials. **Services:** Library open to the public by appointment.

★3728★
Citizens Housing and Planning Council of New York - Library (Plan)
218 W. 40th St., 12th Fl. Phone: (212)391-9030
New York, NY 10018-1509 Ruth Dickler, Libn.
Founded: 1937. **Staff:** 1. **Subjects:** Housing, planning. **Holdings:** 6000 books; 26 VF drawers. **Subscriptions:** 13 journals and other serials. **Services:** Copying; library open to the public for reference use only. **Remarks:** FAX: (212)391-9033.

Citizens to Preserve Jubilee College - Library
See: **Bradley University - Virginius H. Chase Special Collections Center - Chase Collection** (2060)

★3729★
Citizens' Research Foundation - Library (Soc Sci)
University of Southern California Research Annex
3716 S. Hope St. Phone: (213)743-5211
Los Angeles, CA 90007 Herbert E. Alexander, Dir.
Subjects: Political finance, fund-raising methods, campaign expenditures, group and individual financial participation in the electoral process. **Holdings:** 2000 volumes; files of research data. **Services:** Copying (limited); library open to the public for reference use only. **Remarks:** FAX: (213)743-3130.

★3730★
Citizens Union Foundation of the City of New York - Library (Soc Sci)
198 Broadway Phone: (212)227-0342
New York, NY 10038 Jeannette Kahlenberg, Exec.Dir.
Founded: 1897. **Subjects:** New York City politics and government since the turn of the century; elections, 1910 to present; candidate information. **Holdings:** Books; documents. **Services:** Library open to the public by appointment. **Remarks:** FAX: (212)227-0345.

Citrus Research & Development Technical Library
See: **Coca-Cola Company - Coca-Cola Foods** (3854)

City College / CUNY
See: **City College of City University of New York** (3731)

★3731★
City College of City University of New York - Architecture Library (Plan)
408 Shepard Hall
Convent Ave. at 140th St. Phone: (212)650-8767
New York, NY 10031 Judy Connorton, Chf.
Founded: 1967. **Staff:** Prof 1; Other 8. **Subjects:** Architecture, urban planning, landscape architecture, structural technology. **Holdings:** 20,000 books; 5500 bound periodical volumes; pictures, newspaper and periodical clippings. **Subscriptions:** 60 journals and other serials. **Services:** Interlibrary loan; copying; library open to the public for reference use only. **Automated Operations:** Computerized public access catalog, circulation, and acquisitions (NOTIS). **Special Catalogs:** Union List of New York City Locations for Periodicals in the Avery Index (30 page pamphlet).

★3732★
City College of City University of New York - College Archives (Educ)
Cohen Library
North Academic Center
Convent Ave. & W. 138th St. Phone: (212)650-5367
New York, NY 10031 Barbara Jane Dunlap, Chf., Archv. & Spec.Coll.
Founded: 1960. **Staff:** Prof 1; Other 1. **Subjects:** Publications of and about City College, including official records and papers; selected publications of alumni and faculty; biographical material on alumni; private papers and other memorabilia of alumni and faculty; student life - clubs, publications, activities. **Special Collections:** Papers of Cleveland Abbe, Charles Baskerville, R.R. Bowker, Alfred G. Compton, Abraham Goldforb, Townsend Harris, Ira Marion, Lewis F. Mott, Henry Neumann, Edward M. Shepard, and Everett Wheeler; official publications of the City University and Board of Higher Education. **Holdings:** 2000 linear feet of official and alumni records, bound, boxed, oversize, and in vertical files; 140 reels of microfilm; 110 phonograph records; 13,000 photographs; 400 blueprints. **Services:** Copying (limited); archives open to the public. **Computerized Information Services:** BITNET (electronic mail service). **Publications:** Guides to some portions of the collection. **Special Indexes:** Indexes to select college publications; register of Townsend Harris Papers - free upon request. **Remarks:** Electronic mail address(es): LIBBD@CCNY (BITNET).

★3733★
City College of City University of New York - Music Library (Mus)
Cohen Library
North Academic Center
Convent Ave. & W. 138th St. Phone: (212)650-7174
New York, NY 10031 Melva Peterson, Chf.
Founded: 1948. **Staff:** Prof 2; Other 1. **Subjects:** Music. **Holdings:** 9750 volumes; 15,680 scores; 12,890 phonograph records and compact discs; 550 titles in microform. **Subscriptions:** 165 journals and other serials. **Services:** Interlibrary loan; copying; library open to the public for reference use only. **Automated Operations:** Computerized public access catalog, cataloging, and acquisitions (NOTIS). **Staff:** Ruth Henderson, Libn.

★3734★
City College of City University of New York - Science/Engineering Division (Sci-Engr, Biol Sci)
Science Bldg., Rm. J-29 Phone: (212)650-8246
New York, NY 10031 Anabel C. Meister, Chf.
Founded: 1936. **Staff:** Prof 3; Other 2. **Subjects:** Biology; chemistry; earth sciences; mathematics; oceanography; physics; nursing; medicine; computer sciences; technology; engineering - chemical, civil, electrical, mechanical. **Holdings:** 124,900 books; 91,675 bound periodical volumes; 1150 pamphlets and catalogs; 3855 reels of microfilm of journals. **Subscriptions:** 1194 journals and other serials. **Services:** Interlibrary loan; copying; library open to the public with proper ID. **Automated Operations:** Computerized public access catalog, acquisitions, and circulation (NOTIS). **Computerized Information Services:** BRS Information Technologies, DIALOG Information Services, STN International. **Networks/Consortia:** Member of Medical Library Center of New York (MLCNY). **Staff:** Estelle Davis, Ref.Libn.; Philip Barnett, Ref.Libn.

★3735★
City College of City University of New York - Special Collections (Rare Book, Hum)
Cohen Library
North Academic Center
Convent Ave. & W. 138th St. Phone: (212)650-5367
New York, NY 10031 Barbara Jane Dunlap, Chf., Archv. & Spec.Coll.
Founded: 1960. **Staff:** Prof 1; Other 1. **Subjects:** English literature, drama, social welfare. **Special Collections:** City College Phonographic Library of Contemporary Poets (books and recordings of poets active 1932-1942); English Civil War pamphlets; W.B. Yeats; library of Morris Raphael Cohen; Russell Sage Collection (labor and social welfare prior to 1965; 100,000 pamphlets, annual reports, conference proceedings, serials); Restoration and Eighteenth Century Drama. **Holdings:** 7000 books. **Services:** Copying (limited); collections open to the public. **Computerized Information Services:** BITNET (electronic mail service). **Remarks:** Electronic mail address(es): LIBBD@CCNY (BITNET).

City College Phonographic Library of Contemporary Poetry
See: **City College of City University of New York - Special Collections** (3735)

★3736★
City College of San Francisco - Hotel and Restaurant Department - Alice Statler Library (Bus-Fin, Food-Bev)
50 Phelan Ave. Phone: (415)239-3460
San Francisco, CA 94112 Rose Towns, Slater Libn.
Founded: 1964. **Staff:** Prof 1. **Subjects:** Public hospitality industries - hotels, motels, restaurants, catering services, cafeterias, school lunches; cookery and nutrition; tourism; wines and other beverages. **Special Collections:** American Hotel & Motel Association materials (nearly complete set of texts, student manuals, instructors guides); menu collection from all over the world (2000); leading magazines in the field, 1897 to present (bound volumes and microfilm). **Holdings:** 7000 books; 900 bound periodical volumes; 7000 pamphlets; 16mm training films; videotapes. **Subscriptions:** 100 journals and other serials. **Services:** Copying; library open to the public for reference use only. **Automated Operations:** Computerized cataloging. **Publications:** Yearly acquisition lists; special subject lists - available on request. **Special Indexes:** Subject index to selected periodicals (online). **Remarks:** Alternate telephone number(s): 239-3000.

★3737★
City of Commerce Public Library (Bus-Fin, Sci-Engr)
5655 Jillson St. Phone: (213)722-6660
Commerce, CA 90040-1485 Robert W. Conover, Dir.
Founded: 1961. **Staff:** Prof 11; Other 34. **Subjects:** Business management, industrial standards and specifications, coatings technology, investment, law, paint industry. **Holdings:** 103,000 books; industrial directories. **Subscriptions:** 350 journals and other serials. **Services:** Interlibrary loan; copying; library open to the public. **Automated Operations:** Computerized cataloging. **Computerized Information Services:** OCLC, InfoTrac, DIALOG Information Services, OCLC EPIC. **Networks/Consortia:** Member of Metropolitan Cooperative Library System (MCLS). **Publications:** Paint Bibliography. **Remarks:** FAX: (213)724-1978. **Staff:** Carrie W. Pachon, Asst.Dir.; Corinne Bradbury, Tech.Serv.; Armida Oliva, Ch.Serv.; Yolanda Cardenas-Parra, Circ.; Marie A. Kaneko, Ref.

★3738★
City of Detroit - Law Department - Library (Law)
1010 City-County Bldg. 2
Woodward Ave. Phone: (313)224-4550
Detroit, MI 48226 Thomas R. Killian
Staff: Prof 1. **Subjects:** Municipal law. **Holdings:** 20,000 books; 500 microfiche. **Subscriptions:** 20 journals and other serials. **Services:** Library not open to the public. **Computerized Information Services:** LEXIS.

★3739★
City of Hope National Medical Center - Graff Medical and Scientific Library (Med)
1500 E. Duarte Rd. Phone: (818)301-8497
Duarte, CA 91010 Anne Dillibe, Dir., Lib.Serv.
Founded: 1954. **Staff:** Prof 2; Other 3. **Subjects:** Neuroscience, immunology, biomedicine, medical genetics, biochemistry, biology, pediatrics, cancer pathology. **Holdings:** 5000 books; 45,000 bound periodical volumes. **Subscriptions:** 1000 journals and other serials. **Services:** Interlibrary loan; copying; SDI; library open to the public. **Computerized Information Services:** DIALOG Information Services, BRS Information Technologies, NLM, ORBIT Search Service, Mead Data Central, OCLC, Chemical Information Systems, Inc. (CIS), STN International, WILSONLINE, Life Science Network, SPIN; InterNet (electronic mail service). **Remarks:** FAX: (818)357-1929. Telex: 910-585-1832. Electronic mail address(es): LIBRARY%COH@USC.EDU (InterNet). **Staff:** John L. Carrigan, Info.Spec.

★3740★
City of Industry - Ralph W. Miller Golf Library/Museum - Library (Rec)
One Industry Hills Pkwy.
P.O. Box 3287
City of Industry, CA 91744 Phone: (818)854-2354
Founded: 1977. **Staff:** Prof 2; Other 1. **Subjects:** Golf - history, instruction; Scottish history; turf maintenance; golf course achitecture. **Special Collections:** Golf memorabilia and other museum materials (1100). **Holdings:** 5200 books; 530 bound periodical volumes; 5300 photographs; 4300 VF articles; 2500 bound articles on golf, 1890 to present; 1 VF drawer of archival materials; 400 videotapes; 220 framed artworks; newspaper clippings, 1900 to present (hardcopy and microfiche). **Subscriptions:** 20 journals and other serials. **Services:** Copying; library open to the public for reference use only. **Special Indexes:** Subject index for newspaper clippings; subject and author index for magazine articles (both bound). **Remarks:** FAX: (818)854-2305. **Staff:** Marge Dewey, Lib.Mgr.; Saundra Sheffer, Libn.

★3741★
City of London Business Library (Bus-Fin)
Brewers' Hall Garden Phone: 71 6388215
London EC2V 5BX, England Garry Humphreys
Staff: Prof 8; Other 7. **Subjects:** Current financial data, finance, business, companies, market research. **Holdings:** 900 books; 1500 reports; 3000 directories. **Subscriptions:** 900 journals and other serials; 100 newspapers. **Services:** Interlibrary loan; copying; SDI; library open to the public; groups of students must telephone in advance. **Special Indexes:** List of periodicals (online).

★3742★
City of Midland - Grace A. Dow Memorial Library - Special Collections (Art, Hist)
1710 W. St. Andrews Dr. Phone: (517)835-7151
Midland, MI 48640-2698 Rosemarie Byers, Lib.Dir.
Founded: 1955. **Staff:** 35.5. **Special Collections:** Fine Arts collection (10,300 volumes); local and state history (1300 volumes); genealogy (850 volumes); art reproductions (250). **Holdings:** 235,100 books; 150 bound periodical volumes; 1000 reports; 59,700 microfiche; 1800 reels of microfilm. **Subscriptions:** 500 journals and other serials; 30 newspapers. **Services:** Interlibrary loan; copying; collections open to the public. **Automated Operations:** Computerized acquisitions and circulation. **Computerized Information Services:** DIALOG Information Services; CD-ROMs (Magazine Index, Newspaper Index); internal database; OnTyme Electronic Message Network Service (electronic mail service). Performs searches on fee basis. Contact Person: Eileen Finzel, Ref.Libn. **Networks/Consortia:** Member of White Pine Library Cooperative, Michigan Library Consortium (MLC). **Publications:** Newsletter, monthly. **Special Indexes:** Cemetery index prepared by the Midland Genealogical Society; local obituary index (online); local newspaper index. **Remarks:** FAX: (517)835-9791.

★3743★
(City of) Overland Park - Planning Commission - Research Department Library (Plan)
8500 Santa Fe Dr.
Overland Park, KS 66212 John Rod, Lib.Hd.
Subjects: City planning; land use and development. **Holdings:** 950 books.

City Pulse News Library
See: **CHUM/City - City Pulse News Library** (3647)

★3744★
(City of) Sacramento History & Science Division - Sacramento Archives & Museum Collection Center (Hist)
551 Sequoia Pacific Blvd. Phone: (916)264-7072
Sacramento, CA 95814-0229 James E. Henley, Mgr.
Founded: 1953. **Staff:** Prof 5; Other 2. **Subjects:** Regional history, printing, theater, ethnic history, photography. **Special Collections:** McClatchy Collection (Gold Rush, printing, California theater; 500 linear feet); Natomas Collection (water, gold mining; 150 linear feet); California Almond Growers Association Collection (business records). **Holdings:** 5000 books; 1.5 million photographs; 5200 linear feet of government records; 150 VF drawers of regional maps; lithographs; 9 million feet of local NBC-TV affiliate news film, 1955-1973; 1600 linear feet of personal and business records; 19th century newspapers. **Subscriptions:** 15 journals and other serials. **Services:** Copying; archives open to the public by appointment. **Computerized Information Services:** Internal database. **Special Indexes:** Finding aids to the collection. **Staff:** Sherry A. Hatch, Registrar; Charlene Gilbert, Archv.; Patty Gregory, Cur. of Hist

★3745★
City of Toronto Archives (Hist)
City Hall Phone: (416)392-7483
100 Queen St., W. Robert Halifax, Dir. of Rec./City
Toronto, ON, Canada M5H 2N2 Archv.
Founded: 1960. **Staff:** Prof 10; Other 2. **Subjects:** Corporation of the City of Toronto. **Holdings:** 7000 cubic feet of government records, papers of elected officials, maps, photographs, papers of individuals and organizations related to the City of Toronto. **Services:** Copying; archives open to the public with restrictions. **Computerized Information Services:** Access to online systems. **Publications:** Guide to fine art collection; guide to record group collections. **Special Catalogs:** Market Gallery exhibition catalogs. **Staff:** Victor L. Russell, Archv.Mgr.

City University of New York - Baruch College
See: **Bernard Baruch College of City University of New York** (1548)

City University of New York - Brooklyn College
See: **Brooklyn College of City University of New York** (2230)

City University of New York - City College
See: **City College of City University of New York** (3731)

City University of New York - Graduate School and University Center
See: **Graduate School and University Center of the City University of New York** (6612)

City University of New York - Hunter College
See: **Hunter College of City University of New York** (7562)

City University of New York - John Jay College of Criminal Justice
See: **John Jay College of Criminal Justice of CUNY** (8345)

City University of New York - Mt. Sinai School of Medicine
See: **Mount Sinai School of Medicine of City University of New York** (10819)

City University of New York - New York City Technical College
See: **New York City Technical College of City University of New York** (11567)

City University of New York - Queens College
See: **Queens College of City University of New York** (13637)

Cityline Information Service
See: **Oakland Public Library** (12205)

★3746★
Civic Garden Centre - Library (Biol Sci)
777 Lawrence Ave., E. Phone: (416)445-1552
North York, ON, Canada M3C 1P2 Pamela MacKenzie, Libn.
Founded: 1964. **Staff:** Prof 1; Other 2. **Subjects:** Horticulture, flower arranging, garden design, herbs, botany, natural history, Canadiana, orchids. **Special Collections:** Historical Canadian books on horticulture. **Holdings:** 6500 books; 9 VF drawers. **Subscriptions:** 55 journals and other serials. **Services:** Interlibrary loan; copying; library open to the public for reference use only. **Publications:** Trellis, 10/year - to members.

Civil Division WRAT Research Room
See: **Arizona (State) Attorney General - Water Rights Adjudication Team (WRAT) Research Room** (993)

★3747★
The Civil War Library & Museum (Hist)
1805 Pine St. Phone: (215)735-8196
Philadelphia, PA 19103 Russ A. Pritchard, Dir.
Founded: 1888. **Staff:** 2. **Subjects:** Civil War, slavery, politics, Reconstruction. **Special Collections:** Abraham Lincoln Collection (750 books and pamphlets). **Holdings:** 14,000 books; 100 bound periodical volumes; pamphlets; manuscripts; photographs; archives; portraits. **Services:** Copying; library open to the public. **Publications:** Newsletter, quarterly. **Formerly:** Military Order of the Loyal Legion of the United States - The Civil War Library & Museum. **Staff:** Constance E. Williams, Libn.

Civil War and Upstate New York History Library
See: **Madison County Historical Society** (9518)

★3748★
Clackamas County, Oregon - Alden E. Miller Law Library (Law)
Clackamas County Courthouse, Rm. 101 Phone: (503)655-8248
Oregon City, OR 97045 Ailsa Mackenzie Werner, Law Libn.
Staff: Prof 1. **Subjects:** Law. **Holdings:** 1000 books; 16,000 bound periodical volumes. **Subscriptions:** 100 journals and other serials. **Services:** Interlibrary loan; copying; library open to the public for reference use only. **Special Indexes:** Cumulative Index to Oregon Law Review, annual. **Remarks:** FAX: (503)655-8229.

★3749★
Clairol, Inc. - Research Library (Sci-Engr)
2 Blachley Rd. Phone: (203)357-5001
Stamford, CT 06922 Linda Massoni, Libn.
Staff: Prof 1. **Subjects:** Chemistry and technology of cosmetics, hair dyes and dyeing, personal care, appliances. **Holdings:** 10,000 books; 6000 bound periodical volumes; 30 titles on microfilm. **Subscriptions:** 350 journals and other serials. **Services:** Library open to the public with restrictions. **Computerized Information Services:** DIALOG Information Services, NLM, Chemical Information Systems, Inc. (CIS), Chemical Abstracts Service (CAS), STN International. **Staff:** Ginger Hevey, Info.Coord.

★3750★
Clapp & Eisenberg - Law Library (Law)
1 Newark Ctr. Phone: (201)642-3900
Newark, NJ 07102 Karen P. Schuh, Libn.
Staff: Prof 1; Other 1. **Subjects:** Law, litigation. **Holdings:** Figures not available. **Services:** Interlibrary loan; copying; SDI; library open to library professionals. **Computerized Information Services:** DIALOG Information Services, LEXIS, Dun & Bradstreet Business Credit Services, WESTLAW. **Remarks:** FAX: (201)642-7413.

George E. Clapp Conchology Library
See: **Carnegie Museum of Natural History - Library** (3085)

Margaret Clapp Library
See: **Wellesley College** (20153)

Mary Norton Clapp Library
See: **Occidental College** (12232)

★3751★
Clapp and Mayne, Inc. - Library (Bus-Fin)
1606 Ponce de Leon Ave.
San Juan, PR 00909 Phone: (809)721-3800
Subjects: Marketing research, economics. **Holdings:** 4000 books; 1000 reports. **Subscriptions:** 10 journals and other serials. **Services:** Library open to University of Puerto Rico students. **Remarks:** FAX: (809)721-3812.

★3752★
The Claremont Colleges - Ella Strong Denison Library (Hum)
Scripps College
1030 Columbia. Ave. Phone: (714)621-8000
Claremont, CA 91711 Judy Harvey Sahak, Libn.
Founded: 1931. **Staff:** Prof 2; Other 2. **Subjects:** Humanities and fine arts. **Special Collections:** Perkins and Kirby Collection (history of the book and book arts); Macpherson Collection (women); Metcalf Collection (Gertrude Stein); Pacific Coast Browning Foundation (Browning); Hanna Collection (Southwest); Miller-Howard Collection (Latin America); Ament Collection (Melville); Louise Seymour Jones Collection (4600 bookplates); original and revised versions of Richard W. Armour (62 titles, including 44 manuscripts); Scripps College Archives (including Alexander and Hartley Burr, Scripps, Ellen Browning). **Holdings:** 100,129 books. **Subscriptions:** 106 journals and other serials. **Services:** Interlibrary loan; copying; library open to the public with restrictions. **Automated Operations:** Computerized cataloging, acquisitions, serials, and circulation. **Computerized Information Services:** OCLC. **Remarks:** FAX: (714)621-4733. One of the participating libraries of The Claremont Colleges - Libraries.

The Claremont Colleges - Francis Bacon Foundation, Inc.
See: **Francis Bacon Foundation, Inc. - Francis Bacon Library** (1401)

★3753★
The Claremont Colleges - Honnold/Mudd Library - Special Collections (Hum, Soc Sci)
800 N. Dartmouth St. Phone: (714)621-8150
Claremont, CA 91711 Bonnie J. Clemens, Dir.
Founded: 1952. **Staff:** Prof 16; Other 45. **Special Collections:** California and Western Americana (7169 volumes); Water Resources Development of Southern California (2641 volumes); Philbrick Library of Dramatic Literature and Theater History (10,000 items); Oxford and its Colleges (4881 volumes); Mrs. Humphry Ward (1800 items); Florentine Renaissance (3795 volumes); Hymnology (4005 volumes); Northern Europe and Scandinavia (4053 volumes); Oriental languages and literature (74,417 volumes). **Services:** Copying; libraries open to the public with restrictions. **Automated Operations:** Computerized cataloging, acquisitions, serials, and circulation. **Computerized Information Services:** OCLC; CD-ROMs. **Remarks:** FAX: (714)621-4733. The Claremont Colleges are composed of Pomona College, Claremont Graduate School, Scripps College, Claremont McKenna College, Harvey Mudd College, Pitzer College. **Staff:** Alberta Walker, Assoc.Dir. of Libs.; Judy Harvey Sahak, Asst.Dir.; Bartley Harloe, Asst.Dir.; Wanda Knight, Sys.Mgr.

★3754★
The Claremont Colleges - Norman F. Sprague Memorial Library (Sci-Engr)
Harvey Mudd College Phone: (714)621-8000
Claremont, CA 91711 Kim Moffhart, Libn.
Founded: 1972. **Staff:** Prof 1; Other 2. **Subjects:** Science, history of science, engineering. **Special Collections:** The "De Re Metallica" Library of President and Mrs. Herbert Hoover (1010 volumes; 21 manuscripts; 441 letters); Carruthers' History of Aviation Collection (4000 volumes). **Holdings:** 76,227 volumes; 110 reels of microfilm; 27,000 technical reports; 15,000 microfiche; 35 film loops; 1050 pamphlets. **Subscriptions:** 663 journals and other serials. **Services:** Interlibrary loan; copying; library open to the public with restrictions. **Automated Operations:** Computerized cataloging, acquisitions, serials, and circulation. **Computerized Information Services:** OCLC. **Special Catalogs:** Bibliotheca De Re Metallica, 1980. **Remarks:** FAX: (714)621-4733. One of the participating libraries of the The Claremont Colleges - Libraries.

The Claremont Graduate School - California Institute of Public Affairs
See: **California Institute of Public Affairs** (2481)

The Claremont Graduate School - Center for Process Studies
See: **Center for Process Studies** (3281)

★3755★
The Claremont Graduate School - George G. Stone Center for Children's Books (Hum)
131 E. 10th St. Phone: (714)621-8000
Claremont, CA 91711-6188 Doty Hale, Dir.
Founded: 1965. **Staff:** Prof 2; Other 1. **Subjects:** Children's literature; materials about children's literature; old children's books. **Holdings:** 20,000 books. **Subscriptions:** 26 journals and other serials. **Services:** Interlibrary loan; center open to the public with annual fee for borrowing privileges. **Publications:** Unicorn Booklist, annual; Gifts to Open Again and Again, annual - to members, classes, and the public. **Remarks:** FAX: (714)621-8390.

★3756★
Claremont McKenna College - Seeley G. Mudd Science Library (Sci-Engr, Biol Sci)
Pomona College
Pomona Science Library
640 W. College Ave. Phone: (714)621-8000
Claremont, CA 91711 Brian Ebersole, Libn.
Founded: 1983. **Staff:** Prof 1; Other 2. **Subjects:** Botany, chemistry, geology, mathematics, physics-astronomy, zoology. **Holdings:** 91,907 volumes; 500 reels of microfilm; 3000 microfiche. **Subscriptions:** 686 journals and other serials. **Services:** Interlibrary loan; copying; library open to the public with restrictions. **Automated Operations:** Computerized cataloging, acquisitions, serials, and circulation. **Computerized Information Services:** OCLC. **Remarks:** FAX: (714)621-4733.

★3757★
Clarion County Historical Society - Library/Museum (Hist)
18 Grant St. Phone: (814)226-4450
Clarion, PA 16214 Michael A. Bertheaud, Dir./Cur.
Founded: 1955. **Staff:** 1. **Subjects:** Genealogy, Pennsylvania history. **Holdings:** 1500 books; bound newspapers, 1894-1929; pictures; pamphlets; documents; correspondence; church and cemetery records; 300 family trees; census indexes; archival material. **Subscriptions:** 24 journals and other serials. **Services:** Copying; genealogical research; library open to the public with restrictions.

★3758★
Clarion University of Pennsylvania - College of Library Science - Center for the Study of Rural Librarianship - Library (Info Sci)
Clarion, PA 16214 Phone: (814)226-2383
Dr. Bernard Vavrek, Coord.
Founded: 1978. **Staff:** Prof 3; Other 5. **Subjects:** Rural and small libraries and librarianship, bookmobile activities, adult literacy, reference services. **Holdings:** Library statistics, annual reports, newsletters from various state library agencies and systems. **Services:** Interlibrary loan; copying; SDI; library open to the public. **Computerized Information Services:** OCLC. **Networks/Consortia:** Member of Pittsburgh Regional Library Center (PRLC). **Publications:** Developing a Marketing Program for Libraries (book); Reference Service in Rural Public Libraries (book); Rural Libraries (journal), semiannual; list of bibliographies - available on request; Rural and Small Library Services Newsletter, bimonthly; Budgeting Manual for Small Libraries; Jobline, for rural and small library positions, monthly; Conference proceedings - The Rural Bookmobile, 1985 and 1986. **Remarks:** FAX: (814)226-2150.

★3759★
Clarion University of Pennsylvania - Rena M. Carlson Library (Educ)
Clarion, PA 16214-1232 Phone: (814)226-2343
Gerard B. McCabe, Dir. of Libs.
Founded: 1867. **Staff:** Prof 14; Other 16. **Subjects:** Business administration, education, teacher education, library science, special education. **Special Collections:** British Commonwealth History Collection. **Holdings:** 308,969 books; 42,740 bound periodical volumes; 1.1 million microforms; 4348 audio recordings; 2776 maps and charts. **Subscriptions:** 1684 journals and newspapers. **Services:** Interlibrary loan; copying; library open to the public. **Automated Operations:** Computerized public access catalog. **Computerized Information Services:** OCLC, DIALOG Information Services. Contact Person: Deon Knickerbocker, Ref.Libn., 226-2303. **Networks/Consortia:** Member of Pittsburgh Regional Library Center (PRLC), Northwest Interlibrary Cooperative of Pennsylvania (NICOP). **Remarks:** Figures include holdings of library at Venango Campus, Oil City, PA. FAX: (814)226-1862. **Staff:** Debra Decker, Ser.Libn.; C. Richard Snow, Venango Campus Hd.Libn.; J. Kenneth Wyse, Cat.; Janice Horn, Hd., Tech.Serv.; Connie Gamaluddin, Hd.Ref.Libn.; Nancy Palma, Venago Campus Libn.; Shirley Johnson, Cat.Libn.; Bruce Webb, Lrng.Rsrcs.; Roger Horn, Coll.Libn.; Elaine Moore, Lrng.Rsrcs.; James McDaniel, Ref.Libn.

★3760★
Claritas Corporation - Library (Bus-Fin)
201 N. Union St. Phone: (703)683-8300
Alexandria, VA 22314 Patrick Jones, Libn.
Subjects: Geo-demographics and small-area demography. **Holdings:** 5000 books; 1000 microfiche. **Subscriptions:** 40 journals and other serials. **Computerized Information Services:** Produces PRIZM and P$YCLE. Performs searches on fee basis. **Remarks:** FAX: (703)683-8309. Claritas is a subsidiary of Verenigde Nederlandse Uitgeversbedrijven.

★3761★
Clark Atlanta University - School of Library & Information Studies - Library (Info Sci)
223 James P. Brawley Dr., S.W. Phone: (404)880-8691
Atlanta, GA 30314 Almeta Gould Woodson, Libn.
Founded: 1941. **Staff:** Prof 1; Other 8. **Subjects:** Library and information sciences. **Special Collections:** Children's books; Afro-American studies; ethnic studies. **Holdings:** 22,384 books; 3442 bound periodical volumes; 12 VF drawers; microfilm; microcards; filmstrips; motion pictures; tapes; phonograph records. **Subscriptions:** 143 journals and other serials. **Services:** Interlibrary loan; library open to the public with restrictions. **Computerized Information Services:** Electronic mail. **Remarks:** FAX: (404)880-8222.

★3762★
Clark Atlanta University - Southern Center for Studies in Public Policy - Research Library (Soc Sci)
JP Brawley Dr.
Fairstreet S.W. Phone: (404)880-8000
Atlanta, GA 30314 Rebecca Ivey, Res.Libn.
Founded: 1968. **Staff:** Prof 2; Other 2. **Subjects:** Economic development, public policy, transportation, employment and labor, blacks and civil rights, poverty. **Special Collections:** Robert Brown Collection; Andrew Brimmer Papers (15). **Holdings:** 5000 books; 325 bound periodical volumes; 6 VF drawers of clippings; 10 tapes each of the National Longitudinal Survey, the Panel Study of Income Dynamics, 1980 Census Report. **Subscriptions:** 185 journals and other serials; 6 newspapers. **Services:** Interlibrary loan; copying; library open to the public for reference use only. **Automated Operations:** Computerized cataloging. **Computerized Information Services:** DIALOG Information Services. **Networks/Consortia:** Member of Georgia Online Database (GOLD). **Publications:** So You Are Doing Research, biennial; Working Papers Series - for sale. **Special Indexes:** Index of journal articles dealing with public policy issues. **Remarks:** FAX: (404)880-8222.

★3763★
Clark Atlanta University Center - Robert W. Woodruff Library - Division of Archives and Special Collections (Area-Ethnic, Hist)
111 James P. Brawley Dr., S.W. Phone: (404)522-8980
Atlanta, GA 30314 Wilson Flemister, Dir.
Founded: 1982. **Staff:** Prof 5; Other 3. **Subjects:** The Afro-American Experience; Afro-Americana in the southeastern United States; materials by and about peoples of African descent. **Special Collections:** Thayer-Lincoln Collection (125 manuscripts, pictures, and artifacts recording the career of Abraham Lincoln); manuscript collections representing outstanding persons in Afro-American history including Arthur Ashe, Clarence A. Bacote, John Brown, Thomas Clarkson, Paul Laurence Dunbar, Grace Towns Hamilton, C. Eric Lincoln, Rose McLendon, Paul and Eslanda Goode Robeson, Henry O. Tanner, George A. Towns, Andrew Young; Countee Cullen-Harold Jackman Collection (black artists and writers); Maud Cuney Hare Music and Musicians Manuscript Collection; Henry P. Slaughter Collection (pre-mid-20th century Afro-American history); archival holdings for academic institutions in the Atlanta University Center consortium (Atlanta University, Clark College, The Interdenominational Theological Center and component seminaries: Gammon Theological Seminary (Methodist), Morehouse School of Religion (Baptist), Charles H. Mason Theological Seminary (Church of God in Christ), Phillips School of Theology (Christian Methodist Episcopal), Johnson C. Smith Seminary, Inc. (Presbyterian), Turner Theological Seminary (African Methodist Episcopal), Morehouse College, Morris Brown College, and Spelman College); archival holdings from race relations and socioeconomic organizations in the South: the Neighborhood Union in Atlanta, Commission on Interracial Cooperation, Association of Southern Women for the Prevention of Lynching, Southern Regional Council, Southern Conference for Human Welfare (manuscripts and archives total approximately 5000 cubic feet); American Missionary Association papers; George Washington Carver papers, 1864-1943; Freedman's Bureau correspondence; Hoyt Fuller Collection on the Afro-American Experience; John and Lugenia Burns Hope Papers, 1888-1947; Martin Luther King, Jr. Memorabilia Collection, 1954 to present; Carl Van Vechten Photograph Collection of internationally known persons of African descent; Black Abolitionists papers, 1830-1865 (microfilm); slavery and antislavery pamphlets from the libraries of Salmon P. Chase and John P. Hale, 1840s and 1850s (microfilm); papers of the Congress of Racial Equality (CORE), records of the Fair Employment Practice Committee, 1941-1946 (microfilm); Johnstown Archeological Collection, 1912-1982 (microfilm); Pennsylvania Abolition Society papers, 1775-1975 (microfilm); Gerrit Smith papers, 1775-1924 (microfilm); Peter Smith papers, 1763-1850 (microfilm); papers of the Student Nonviolent Coordinating Committee (SNCC), 1959-1972 (microfilm); Tuskegee Institute News Clipping File, 1899-1966 (microfilm). **Holdings:** 22,000 books; 1000 bound periodical volumes; 313 college and university catalogs; 94 VF drawers of subject files; 59 audiotapes; 76 microfiche; dissertations on Negros, 1931-1966 on microfilm; Atlanta University and The Interdenominational Theological Center graduate theses and dissertations; pamphlets. **Services:** Interlibrary loan; copying (limited); library open to the public for reference use only for a fee. **Computerized Information Services:** DIALOG Information Services, BRS Information Technologies. **Networks/Consortia:** Member of CCLC, University Center in Georgia, Inc., Georgia Online Database (GOLD). **Publications:** Graduate Theses of Atlanta University; Guide to Manuscripts and Archives in the Negro Collection of Trevor Arnett Library. **Staff:** Jessie B. Ebanks, Libn.-Archv.; Gloria J. Mims, Libn., Spec.Pubns. & VF; Jayasri Misra, Libn.-Archv.; Dovie T. Patrick, Libn.-Archv.

B. Preston Clark Library
See: **Carnegie Museum of Natural History - Library** (3085)

★3764★
Clark County District Health Department - Health Education Resource Center (Med)
625 Shadow Ln.
Box 4426
Las Vegas, NV 89127 Phone: (702)383-1218
Founded: 1962. **Staff:** Prof 2. **Subjects:** Health promotion. **Holdings:** 3 VF drawers of health reprints; health pamphlets; news clippings; filmstrips;

videotapes; 16mm films. **Subscriptions:** 2 newspapers. **Services:** Interlibrary loan; copying (limited); film loans; center open to the public for reference use only. **Remarks:** FAX: (702)384-5342. **Staff:** Cheri Foster, Hea.Educ.; J. Palmer, Hea.Educ.; Michael Bernstein, Hea.Educ.; Mary Smith, Film Lib.; Marlene Johnson, Pamphlets.

★3765★
Clark County Historical Society - Library (Hist)
Box 2157 Phone: (513)324-0657
Springfield, OH 45501-2157 Floyd A. Barmann, Dir.
Founded: 1897. **Staff:** 1. **Subjects:** Clark County and Ohio history. **Special Collections:** Springfield city directories, 1852 to present; newspapers, 1829 to present. **Holdings:** 1000 books; 7500 archival materials. **Subscriptions:** 10 journals and other serials. **Services:** Copying; library open to the public. **Publications:** Newsletter, bimonthly. **Special Catalogs:** Books, cemetery inscriptions, archival material, early businesses (card).

★3766★
Clark County Historical Society - Pioneer Museum - Library (Hist)
430 W. 4th
P.O. Box 862 Phone: (316)635-2227
Ashland, KS 67831 Floretta Carter, Cur.
Founded: 1968. **Staff:** 1. **Subjects:** County and state history. **Special Collections:** Early cattle era pictorial records; Kansas State Historical Society volumes, 1891 to present (214). **Holdings:** 10 VF drawers of manuscripts; Clark County newspapers, 1884 to present. **Subscriptions:** 4 journals and other serials. **Services:** Library not open to the public. **Publications:** Early Clark County, Kansas (6 volumes); Kings and Queens of the Range.

★3767★
Clark County Law Library (Law)
304 E. Carson Phone: (702)455-4696
Las Vegas, NV 89101 Frank Alan Herch, J.D., Dir.
Founded: 1923. **Staff:** Prof 1; Other 4. **Subjects:** Law, legislative history. **Holdings:** 50,000 volumes, including all available Nevada case, statutory, and legislative material, U.S. Supreme Court and federal cases, federal codes, cases and statutes, legal encyclopedias, periodicals, texts and treatises, loose-leaf services, form books, city and county codes; U.S. Tax Court Reporter Decisions and regional reporters on microfiche. **Subscriptions:** 218 journals and other serials; 5 newspapers. **Services:** Interlibrary loan; copying; library open to the public with restrictions. **Automated Operations:** Computerized public access catalog. **Computerized Information Services:** WESTLAW; CD-ROM (LaserGuide). **Publications:** Clark County Law Library News & Notes, monthly; Selected Recent Acquisitions, quarterly. **Special Indexes:** Legal Digests and Citators; Index to Legal Periodicals; Nevada Digest; Nevada Advance Opinions. **Remarks:** FAX: (702)455-5120. **Staff:** Ann Jarrell.

★3768★
Clark County Law Library (Law)
Court House
Box 5000 Phone: (206)699-2268
Vancouver, WA 98668 Rosemary Lewin
Staff: Prof 1. **Subjects:** Law. **Holdings:** 16,000 volumes. **Services:** Library open to the public on a limited schedule. **Special Indexes:** Washington AGO index.

★3769★
Clark County Parks and Recreation Department - Clark County Museum (Hist)
1830 S. Boulder Hwy. Phone: (702)455-7955
Henderson, NV 89015 Mark Ryzdynski, Musm.Cur.
Founded: 1979. **Staff:** Prof 4; Other 8. **Subjects:** History - southern Nevada, Clark County, Henderson, Las Vegas, Boulder City. **Special Collections:** Photograph collection. **Holdings:** 200 books; 100 bound periodical volumes; southern Nevada newspapers. **Subscriptions:** 3 journals and other serials, 3 newspapers. **Services:** Copying; museum open to the public. **Computerized Information Services:** Internal database. Performs searches on fee basis. **Remarks:** FAX: (702)455-7948. **Staff:** Dawna Jolliff, Cur. of Exhibits; Jan Ventre, Musm.Off.Mgr.; Christie Leavitt, Cur. of Educ.

Dr. Leslie J. Clark Memorial Library
See: **Hemet Valley Hospital District** (7127)

Dr. Thomas Clark Health Services Library
See: **Good Samaritan Hospital** (6548)

Edith M. Clark History Room
See: **Rowan Public Library** (14089)

Clark Field Archive
See: **Maxwell Museum Association - Maxwell Museum of Anthropology** (9853)

Harold Terry Clark Library
See: **Cleveland Museum of Natural History** (3814)

J. Reuben Clark Law School Library
See: **Brigham Young University** (20804)

★3770★
Clark, Klein and Beaumont - Law Library (Law)
1600 First Federal Bldg.
1001 Woodward Ave. Phone: (313)965-8300
Detroit, MI 48226 Kathleen A. Gamache, Libn.
Staff: Prof 2. **Subjects:** Law - tax, antitrust and securities, corporate, real estate, labor, trial, interstate commerce, wills and trusts, environment. **Holdings:** 20,000 books; 137 newsletter titles. **Subscriptions:** 154 journals and other serials. **Services:** Interlibrary loan; library not open to the public. **Computerized Information Services:** DIALOG Information Services, BRS Information Technologies, LEXIS, WESTLAW, VU/TEXT Information Services, Dow Jones News/Retrieval. **Networks/Consortia:** Member of Detroit Associated Libraries Region of Cooperation (DALROC). **Remarks:** Alternate telephone number(s): 965-8277. FAX: (313)962-4348; (313)962-0136. **Staff:** Carola Fisher, Asst.Libn.

★3771★
Clark, Ladner, Fortenbaugh & Young - Library (Law)
One Commerce Square
2005 Market St. Phone: (215)241-1883
Philadelphia, PA 19103 Heide-Marie Bliss, Lib.Dir.
Staff: 2. **Subjects:** Law, products liability, bankruptcy, trademarks, tax, admiralty. **Holdings:** Figures not available. **Services:** Interlibrary loan; library not open to the public. **Automated Operations:** Computerized cataloging. **Computerized Information Services:** WESTLAW, LEXIS, NEXIS, Dow Jones News/Retrieval, DIALOG Information Services, VU/TEXT Information Services, Compu-Mark U.S. On-Line, Information America, Dun & Bradstreet Business Credit Services; Memo, Expert (internal databases). **Networks/Consortia:** Member of PALINET. **Remarks:** FAX: (215)241-1857.

★3772★
Clark Memorial Hospital - Medical Library (Med)
1220 Missouri Ave. Phone: (812)283-2358
Jeffersonville, IN 47131-0069 Kathleen Lynn, Libn.
Founded: 1971. **Staff:** Prof 1. **Subjects:** Medicine, nursing. **Holdings:** 300 books; 100 bound periodical volumes; 2 VF drawers of pamphlet material; 200 video cassettes; 1 video cassette series; 2 audio cassette series. **Subscriptions:** 57 journals and other serials. **Services:** Interlibrary loan; library not open to the public. **Networks/Consortia:** Member of Kentucky Health Sciences Library Consortium, Southeastern Indiana Area Library Services Authority (SIALSA). **Remarks:** FAX: (812)283-2688.

Clark Science Library
See: **Smith College** (15232)

★3773★
Sterling and Francine Clark Art Institute - Library (Art)
225 South St.
Box 8 Phone: (413)458-9545
Williamstown, MA 01267 Sarah S. Gibson, Libn.
Founded: 1962. **Staff:** Prof 6; Other 6. **Subjects:** European and American art. **Special Collections:** Juynboll collection (850,000 reproductions of works of art); Mary Ann Beinecke decorative art collection; Duveen Library and Archive. **Holdings:** 100,000 volumes; 28,000 auction sales catalogs; 110,000 slides. **Subscriptions:** 615 journals and other serials. **Services:** Interlibrary loan; copying; library open to the public. **Automated Operations:** Computerized acquisitions and cataloging. **Computerized Information Services:** DIALOG Information Services; BITNET (electronic mail service). **Networks/Consortia:** Member of Research Libraries Information Network (RLIN). **Special Indexes:** Index of auction sales catalogs (card). **Remarks:** FAX: (413)458-8503. Electronic mail address(es): BM.CAL@RLG (BITNET). **Staff:** Susan Roeper, Assoc.Libn.; Peter Erickson, Cat. & Ser.Libn.; Paige Carter, Cat.Libn.; J. Dustin Wees, Photo & Slide Libn.; Elizabeth Kieffer, Slide Cat.

★3774★
Theda Clark Regional Medical Center - Health Sciences Library (Med)
130 2nd St. Phone: (414)729-2190
Neenah, WI 54956 Mary Horan, Libn.
Staff: Prof 1. **Subjects:** Medicine. **Holdings:** 1200 books; 1500 bound periodical volumes. **Subscriptions:** 350 journals and other serials. **Services:** Interlibrary loan; copying; library open to the public with restrictions. **Automated Operations:** Computerized cataloging, acquisitions, and serials. **Computerized Information Services:** DIALOG Information Services, MEDLARS. **Networks/Consortia:** Member of Fox River Valley Area Library Consortium (FRVALC), Fox Valley Library Council. **Remarks:** FAX: (414)729-2131.

★3775★
Clark, Thomas, Winters, & Newton - Library (Law)
1200 Texas Commerce Bank Bldg.
700 Lavaca Phone: (512)472-8800
Austin, TX 78701 Deborah K. Meleski, Law Libn.
Staff: Prof 1; Other 1. **Subjects:** Law, banking law, medicine. **Holdings:** 13,000 books; 500 bound periodical volumes. **Subscriptions:** 200 journals and other serials; 8 newspapers. **Services:** Interlibrary loan; copying; library open to the public for reference use only. **Automated Operations:** Computerized cataloging, acquisitions, and journal routing. **Computerized Information Services:** DIALOG Information Services, LEXIS, NEXIS; Library Catalog, Routing List, Expert Witnesses Deposition Database (internal databases). Performs searches on fee basis. **Publications:** Newsletter - for internal distribution only. **Special Indexes:** Indexes of internal work product. **Remarks:** FAX: (512)474-1129.

Tom Clark Archives
See: **University of Southern California - Library - Department of Special Collections - American Literature Collection** (19338)

★3776★
Clark University - Guy H. Burnham Map and Aerial Photograph Library (Geog-Map)
950 Main St. Phone: (508)793-7322
Worcester, MA 01610-1477 Beverly Presley, Map/Geog.Libn.
Founded: 1920. **Staff:** Prof 1; Other 1.9. **Subjects:** Maps, atlases, gazetteers, cartography, remote sensing. **Special Collections:** Maps of Africa; maps and aerial photos of Massachusetts; William Libbey Lantern slide collection; J.K. Wright Reading Room (departmental library of geographic materials). **Holdings:** 2600 volumes; 184,000 maps; 7500 aerial photographs and other remote sensing images; 195 wall maps. **Subscriptions:** 89 journals and other serials. **Services:** Interlibrary loan; copying; library open to the public. **Automated Operations:** Computerized public access catalog and cataloging. **Computerized Information Services:** EPIC; BITNET, InterNet (electronic mail services). **Networks/Consortia:** Member of Worcester Area Cooperating Libraries (WACL), NELINET, Inc., Colorado Alliance of Research Libraries (CARL). **Publications:** Map Library Guide; subject bibliographies. **Remarks:** FAX: (508)793-8881. Electronic mail address(es): bpresley@clarku (BITNET); bpresley@clarku.edu (InterNet).

William Andrews Clark Memorial Library
See: **University of California, Los Angeles - William Andrews Clark Memorial Library** (18402)

William J. Clark Library
See: **Virginia Union University** (19899)

Wilson W. Clark Memorial Library
See: **University of Portland** (19230)

Bruce C. Clarke Community Library
See: **U.S. Army Post - Training Center Engineer & Fort Leonard Wood** (17075)

Bruce C. Clarke Engineering School - Library
See: **U.S. Army** (16925)

Clarke Historical Library, Central Michigan University
See: **Central Michigan University - Clarke Historical Library** (3348)

★3777★
Clarke Institute of Psychiatry - Farrar Library (Med)
250 College St. Phone: (416)979-6820
Toronto, ON, Canada M5T 1R8 Diane Thomas, Hd., Lib.Serv.
Staff: 3. **Subjects:** Psychiatry, psychology, psychiatric nursing, neuroendocrinology, neurochemistry, occupational therapy, social work. **Holdings:** 6500 books; 12,000 bound periodical volumes; 10 VF drawers of reprints; 12 VF drawers of staff publications; 2 VF drawers of government documents. **Subscriptions:** 333 journals and other serials. **Services:** Interlibrary loan; library not open to the public. **Computerized Information Services:** CD-ROMs (MEDLINE, PsycLIT, CINAHL, Social Work Abstracts); diskettes (Current Contents: Life Sciences, Current Contents: Social & Behavioral Sciences). **Publications:** Clarke in Press; Mirrors of the Mind. **Remarks:** FAX: (416)979-2243. **Staff:** Joan Barnes; Siobahn McCready.

John Henrik Clarke Africana Library
See: **Cornell University - John Henrik Clarke Africana Library** (4314)

Lucile Clarke Memorial Children's Library
See: **Central Michigan University - Clarke Historical Library** (3348)

★3778★
Bishop Clarkson Memorial Hospital - Pathology/Medical Staff Library
Dewey & 44th
Omaha, NE 68105
Subjects: Medicine, pathology, laboratory diagnosis. **Holdings:** 450 books; 1200 bound periodical volumes. **Remarks:** Currently inactive.

★3779★
Clarkson University - Andrew S. Schuler Educational Resources Center (Sci-Engr)
Potsdam, NY 13699 Phone: (315)268-2292
J. Natalia Stahl, Assoc.Dir. ERC
Founded: 1980. **Staff:** Prof 5; Other 8. **Subjects:** Engineering - chemical, civil, environmental, mechanical, aeronautical, industrial, electrical, computer; chemistry; physics; biology; mathematics; management; humanities; social sciences. **Special Collections:** NASA Publication Program; corporate reports. **Holdings:** 94,667 books; 64,440 bound periodical volumes; 38,109 technical reports; 829 dissertations; 2692 masters' theses; 279 maps; 1058 phonograph records; 10,860 reels of microfilm; 232,742 microfiche. **Subscriptions:** 2670 journals and other serials. **Services:** Interlibrary loan; copying; SDI; center open to the public with identification. **Automated Operations:** Computerized public access catalog, cataloging, acquisitions, serials, and circulation. **Computerized Information Services:** OCLC, DIALOG Information Services, BRS Information Technologies, Chemical Abstracts Service (CAS), WILSONLINE, Knowledge Index, VU/TEXT Information Services, STN International, OCLC EPIC, News$ource, ORBIT Search Service, BRS/After Dark, Infomart Online; BITNET, New York State Education and Research Network (NYSERNet), InterNet (electronic mail services). Performs searches on fee basis. Contact Person: Gayle C. Berry, Hd.,Ref., 268-2297. **Networks/Consortia:** Member of North Country Reference and Research Resources Council (NCRRRC), Associated Colleges of the St. Lawrence Valley, Inc. (ACSLV), SUNY/OCLC Library Network. **Publications:** ERC News. **Remarks:** FAX: (315)268-6570. Electronic mail address(es): ADMINLNS@CLVM.CLARKSON.EDU (InterNet). **Staff:** James S. Nolte, ILL Libn.; Jean L. Scappator, Cat.Libn.; Byron V. Whitney, Hd., Bibliog. Control.

★3780★
Clarksville Leaf-Chronicle Company - Library (Publ)
Box 829 Phone: (615)552-1808
Clarksville, TN 37041-0829 Loni L. Ward, Libn.
Founded: 1968. **Staff:** Prof 1. **Subjects:** Newspaper reference topics. **Holdings:** 700 books; 1 drawer of maps; newspaper clippings; microfilm. **Subscriptions:** 15 newspapers. **Services:** Library not open to the public. **Special Catalogs:** Catalog to newspaper clippings on file and on microfilm (card).

Class of 1904 Science Library
See: **Oberlin College** (12217)

★3781★
Classic AMX Club, International - AMX Library (Rec)
7963 Depew St. Phone: (303)428-8760
Arvada, CO 80003 Larry G. Mitchell, Cur.
Founded: 1974. **Staff:** 1. **Subjects:** Sales and promotional material relating to American Motors' AMX automobile. **Holdings:** Sales and promotional books, folders, flyers; 4 VF drawers; 200 loose-leaf binders; 273 collectors items. **Services:** Copying; SDI; library open to the public with restrictions.

Classified Abstract Archive of the Alcohol Literature
See: **Rutgers University - Rutgers Center of Alcohol Studies** (14172)

Jens Clausen Memorial Library
See: **Carnegie Institution of Washington - Department of Plant Biology - Library** (3071)

★3782★
Clausen, Miller, Gorman, Caffrey & Witous - Library (Law)
10 S. LaSalle St. Phone: (312)606-7534
Chicago, IL 60603-1098 Nancy L. Tuohy, Lib.Dir.
Staff: Prof 3; Other 5. **Subjects:** Law - insurance, environmental, medical. **Holdings:** 20,000 books; 2000 bound periodical volumes; 500 reports; 2500 microfiche. **Subscriptions:** 500 journals and other serials; 9 newspapers. **Services:** Interlibrary loan; library not open to the public. **Computerized Information Services:** DIALOG Information Services, Dow Jones News/ Retrieval, Dun & Bradstreet Business Credit Services, LEXIS, WESTLAW, DataTimes, Information America. **Remarks:** FAX: (312)606-7777. **Staff:** Kelly M. Moore, Ref.Libn.; Janice A. Collins, Cat.

★3783★
Clay County Archives & Historical Library (Hist)
210 E. Franklin
Box 99
Liberty, MO 64068 Phone: (816)781-3611
Founded: 1979. **Staff:** 7. **Subjects:** Genealogy, local history, Civil War. **Special Collections:** Clay County probate records, 1821-1983; marriage index; Alexander Doniphan Chapter, Daughters of the American Revolution Collection; Nadine Hodges books on Missouri heritage; cemetery listings, 1830-1870 (federal census); family histories (40). **Services:** Copying; archives open to the public on fee basis. **Remarks:** The Clay County Archives & Historical Library houses the library of the Genealogical Society of Liberty.

★3784★
Clay County Historical Society - Archives (Hist)
202 1st Ave., N.
P.O. Box 501
Moorhead, MN 56560 Phone: (218)233-4604
Founded: 1932. **Staff:** Prof 1. **Subjects:** Minnesota; Clay County and its cities and villages. **Special Collections:** Town, church, county histories (5 file drawers); autobiographical and biographical records of early Clay County pioneers (5 file drawers); glass negatives taken by pioneer photographers O.E. Flaten and S.P. Wange (12,000). **Holdings:** 1000 volumes; 5 VF drawers of documents, pamphlets, clippings. **Subscriptions:** 15 journals and other serials. **Services:** Copying; archives open to the public for reference use only. **Publications:** Newsletter, bimonthly. **Staff:** Mark Peihl, Archv.

★3785★
Clayton Environmental Consultants, Inc. - Library and Information Center (Env-Cons, Med)
22345 Roethel Dr. Phone: (313)344-1770
Novi, MI 48050 Marjorie Corey, Libn.
Staff: Prof 1; Other 2. **Subjects:** Industrial hygiene, toxicology, analytical chemistry, environmental pollution, waste management, environmental engineering. **Special Collections:** Environmental Protection Agency (EPA), Occupational Safety and Health Administration (OSHA), National Institute for Occupational Safety and Health (NIOSH) government documents collection. **Holdings:** 5000 books; 200 bound periodical volumes; 3000 other cataloged items. **Subscriptions:** 101 journals and other serials. **Services:** Library not open to the public. **Automated Operations:** Computerized cataloging. **Computerized Information Services:** DIALOG Information Services, Questel, MEDLARS. Performs searches on fee basis. **Networks/ Consortia:** Member of Oakland Wayne Interlibrary Network (OWIN). **Remarks:** FAX: (313)344-2654.

Clayton Library
See: **Houston Public Library** (7459)

★3786★
Clearbrook Center - Lekotek (Educ)
3705 Pheasant Dr. Phone: (708)392-2812
Rolling Meadows, IL 60008 Sheila Lullo, Dir.
Founded: 1983. **Staff:** Prof 3; Other 1. **Subjects:** Toys which encourage interactice play, infant stimulation, development of fine and gross motor skills, and speech development and which may be adapted for developmentally delayed children. **Holdings:** Figures not available. **Services:** Lekotek open to special needs population. **Remarks:** Lekotek, a library of toys and adaptive equipment, emphasizes the development of parent-child relationships using toys as an instrument. **Staff:** Kelly Berliner, Lekotek Ldr.; Sue Water, Lekotek Ldr.

★3787★
Clearfield Law Library (Law)
Court House Phone: (814)765-2641
Clearfield, PA 16830 Jacki Kendrick, Law Libn.
Subjects: Law. **Holdings:** 8000 volumes. **Services:** Library open to the public.

★3788★
Clearinghouse on Child Abuse and Neglect Information (Soc Sci)
P.O. Box 1182 Phone: (703)385-7565
Washington, DC 20013 Caroline Hughes, Proj.Mgr.
Founded: 1975. **Staff:** Prof 4; Other 2. **Subjects:** Child abuse and neglect, child protective services. **Special Collections:** State statutes; directory of program directories. **Holdings:** 12,000 books, articles, and reports. **Subscriptions:** 30 journals and other serials. **Services:** Copying; clearinghouse open to the public by appointment. **Computerized Information Services:** DIALOG Information Services. Performs searches on fee basis. **Publications:** Listing of the National Center on Child Abuse and Neglect publications - available upon request. **Special Catalogs:** Child Abuse and Neglect and Family Violence Audiovisual Catalog. **Remarks:** FAX: (703)506-0384. Maintained by the U.S. Department of Health & Human Services - National Center on Child Abuse and Neglect (NCCAN) and the Office of Policy, Planning and Legislation (OPPL).

★3789★
Clearinghouse on Development Communication - Library (Info Sci)
c/o Institute for International Research
1815 N. Ft. Myer Dr., Suite 600 Phone: (703)527-5546
Arlington, VA 22209 Earl McLetchie, Libn.
Founded: 1972. **Staff:** Prof 4. **Subjects:** Development communication, communication strategies, Third World education, developing countries, communication technology, health, population, agriculture, environment. **Holdings:** 3000 books; 12,000 reports; videotapes. **Subscriptions:** 200 journals and other serials. **Services:** Copying; library open to the public. **Computerized Information Services:** IDRC; internal databases; MCI Mail (electronic mail service). Performs searches. **Publications:** Development Communication Report (newsletter), quarterly. **Special Catalogs:** Catalog of Publications and Audio Visuals. **Remarks:** FAX: (703)527-4661. Electronic mail address(es): IIRVA (MCI Mail).

Clearinghouse on Family Resource and Support Programs
See: **Family Resource Coalition** (5591)

★3790★
Clearinghouse on Family Violence Information (Soc Sci)
P.O. Box 1182
Washington, DC 20013 Phone: (703)385-7565
Founded: 1987. **Staff:** Prof 4; Other 2. **Subjects:** Spouse abuse, elder abuse, sibling abuse, parent abuse. **Holdings:** 700 books, articles, and reports. **Subscriptions:** 10 journals and other serials. **Services:** Copying; clearinghouse open to the public by appointment. **Computerized Information Services:** DIALOG Information Services; Database of National Organizations Concerned with Family Violence (internal database). Performs searches on fee basis. **Publications:** List of publications - available upon request. **Special Catalogs:** Child Abuse and Neglect and Family Violence Audiovisual Catalog. **Remarks:** FAX: (703)385-3206. Maintained by the U.S. Department of Health & Human Services - National Center on Child Abuse and Neglect (NCCAN) and the Office of Policy, Planning and Legislation (OPPL). **Staff:** Caroline Hughes, Proj.Mgr.

Clearinghouse on Health Indexes
See: **National Center for Health Statistics** (11103)

★3791★
Clearinghouse for Sociological Literature (Soc Sci)
Dept. of Sociology
Northern Illinois Univ. Phone: (815)753-6433
DeKalb, IL 60115-2891 Hugo O. Engelmann, Ed.
Founded: 1965. **Staff:** 1. **Subjects:** Sociology, social psychology, allied social sciences. **Holdings:** 100 articles and books on microfilm. **Services:** Copying; clearinghouse open to public. **Remarks:** Appropriate manuscripts will be accepted from anyone. Manuscripts on deposit are available on request in full sized printout upon payment of a user's fee.

★3792★
Cleary, Gottlieb, Steen & Hamilton - Library (Law)
1 Liberty Plaza Phone: (212)225-3444
New York, NY 10006 Karol M. Sokol, Dir. of Lib.Serv.
Founded: 1946. **Staff:** Prof 4; Other 8. **Subjects:** Law. **Holdings:** 25,000 volumes. **Services:** Library not open to the public. **Computerized Information Services:** DIALOG Information Services, LEXIS, WESTLAW, Dow Jones News/Retrieval, IDD Information Services (IDDIS), VU/TEXT Information Services, Reuters. **Remarks:** FAX: (212)225-3449. **Staff:** Ellen Ingerson; Patricia Pardo; Lydia Celis.

Nathan and Henry B. Cleaves Law Library
See: **Cumberland Bar Association** (4472)

Clementine Library
See: **Catholic University of America** (3155)

William L. Clements Library
See: **University of Michigan** (18888)

C.C. Clemmer Health Sciences Library
See: **Canadian Memorial Chiropractic College** (2957)

★3793★
Clemson University - Emery A. Gunnin Architectural Library (Art, Plan)
College of Architecture
Lee Hall Phone: (803)656-3933
Clemson, SC 29634-0501 Deborah S. Johnson
Staff: 6. **Subjects:** Art, architecture, building science, city and regional planning. **Special Collections:** Slide collection (80,000). **Holdings:** 28,900 books; 5600 bound periodical volumes; 2000 city and regional planning documents. **Subscriptions:** 250 journals and other serials. **Services:** Interlibrary loan; copying; library open to the public. **Automated Operations:** Computerized cataloging and circulation. **Computerized Information Services:** DIALOG Information Services, RLIN. **Networks/Consortia:** Member of SOLINET. **Publications:** Monthly acquisitions list; selected bibliography of art and architecture reference materials. **Special Catalogs:** Catalog of slide collection.

★3794★
Clemson University - Robert Muldrow Cooper Library (Sci-Engr, Agri)
Clemson, SC 29634-3001 Phone: (803)656-3026
Joseph F. Boykin, Jr., Dir.
Founded: 1893. **Staff:** Prof 30; Other 70. **Subjects:** Agriculture, engineering, chemistry, physics, mathematics, textiles, architecture. **Special Collections:** J. Strom Thurmond Papers; John C. Calhoun Papers; James F. Byrnes Papers; Edgar A. Brown Papers; Benjamin R. Tillman Papers. **Holdings:** 736,249 volumes; 24,217 reels of microfilm; 1.7 million microfiche; 31,449 microcards; 18,439 maps. **Subscriptions:** 7214 journals and other serials. **Services:** Interlibrary loan; copying; library open to the public. **Automated Operations:** Computerized cataloging, acquisitions, serials, and circulation (NOTIS). **Computerized Information Services:** DIALOG Information Services, OCLC, BRS Information Technologies, RLIN; internal database; BITNET, InterNet (electronic mail services). Performs searches on fee basis. Contact Person: Martha Lyle. **Networks/Consortia:** Member of SOLINET. **Publications:** Annual list of current periodicals and continuations received (alphabetical and classified); indexes, abstract journals, and selected statistical sources found in the library. **Special Indexes:** Magazine index; newspaper index; trade & industry index; computer index; management contents. **Remarks:** FAX: (803)656-3025. Electronic mail address(es): JBOYKIN@CLUST1.A1.CLEMSON.EDU (BITNET). **Staff:** Deborah Babel Adm.Serv.Libn.; Peggy Cover, Ref.Serv.; Michael Kohl, Spec.Coll.Libn.; Maureen Harris, Pub.Docs.; Marsha McCurley, Cat.; JoAnne Deeken, Acq.; Deana Astle, Tech.Serv.; Deborah Johnson, Arch.

Clendening History of Medicine Library
See: **University of Kansas** (18732)

★3795★
Clermont County Law Library Association (Law)
Courthouse
Main St. Phone: (513)732-7109
Batavia, OH 45103 Carol A. Suhre, Law Libn.
Founded: 1933. **Staff:** Prof 1; Other 2. **Subjects:** Ohio law, taxation, bankruptcy, medicine. **Holdings:** 18,000 books; 10,000 ultrafiche. **Subscriptions:** 29 journals and other serials; 6 newspapers. **Services:** Interlibrary loan; copying; faxing; library open to the public for reference use only. **Automated Operations:** Computerized cataloging. **Computerized Information Services:** DIALOG Information Services, WESTLAW, OCLC, Hannah Information Systems. **Networks/Consortia:** Member of OHIONET. **Remarks:** FAX: (513)732-0974.

Cleveland Board of Education - Max S. Hayes Vocational School
See: **Max S. Hayes Vocational School** (7059)

★3796★
Cleveland Center for Economic Education - Library (Bus-Fin)
John Carroll University Phone: (216)397-4384
Cleveland, OH 44118 Mary Krohmer, Dev.Dir.
Founded: 1973. **Staff:** 4. **Subjects:** Economics, economic education. **Holdings:** 3000 volumes. **Services:** Library open to the public with restrictions. **Remarks:** FAX: (216)397-4256.

★3797★
Cleveland Chiropractic College - Learning Resource Centers (Med)
590 N. Vermont Phone: (213)660-6166
Los Angeles, CA 90004 Marian Hicks, Dir. of Lrng.Rsrc.Ctr.
Founded: 1908. **Staff:** Prof 2; Other 4. **Subjects:** Chiropractic and manipulative medicine, basic human life sciences, diagnosis, physical therapy, orthopedics. **Special Collections:** History of chiropractic. **Holdings:** 14,000 books; 3895 bound periodical volumes; 16 periodicals on microfiche; 3332 x-rays; 1114 slide sets; 580 videocassettes; 3731 audiocassettes; 16 16mm films. **Subscriptions:** 314 journals and other serials. **Services:** Interlibrary loan; copying; centers open to the public for reference use only. **Computerized Information Services:** DIALOG Information Services, OCLC, BookQuest, SerialsQuest; DOCLINE (electronic mail service). Performs searches on fee basis. **Networks/Consortia:** Member of Chiropractic Library Consortium (CLIBCON). **Remarks:** Alternate telephone number(s): (213)660-9450. FAX: (213)665-1931. Electronic mail address(es): 90004B (DOCLINE).

★3798★
Cleveland Chiropractic College - Ruth R. Cleveland Memorial Library (Med)
6401 Rockhill Rd. Phone: (816)333-8230
Kansas City, MO 64131 Marcia M. Thomas, Lib.Dir.
Founded: 1976. **Staff:** Prof 1; Other 2. **Subjects:** Health sciences, roentgenology, chiropractic, orthopedics, diagnosis, acupuncture. **Special Collections:** Chiropractic practice, history, philosophy (400 volumes). **Holdings:** 8600 books; 350 bound periodical volumes; 4100 radiographic films; 5000 radiographic slides; 8000 slides and tapes; 14 drawers of journals on microfiche. **Subscriptions:** 210 journals and other serials. **Services:** Interlibrary loan; copying; library open to the public for reference use only. **Computerized Information Services:** DIALOG Information Services; OCLC; DOCLINE, OnTyme Electronic Message Network Service (electronic mail services). Performs searches on fee basis. **Networks/Consortia:** Member of Kansas City Library Network, Inc. (KCLN), Chiropractic Library Consortium (CLIBCON). **Publications:** New Books, 3/year - for internal distribution only; Library News, monthly.

★3799★
Cleveland Clinic Foundation - Library Services Department (Med)
9500 Euclid Ave. Phone: (216)444-5697
Cleveland, OH 44195-5243 Gretchen Hallerberg, Mgr., Lib.Serv.Dept.
Founded: 1921. **Staff:** Prof 4.5; Other 4.5. **Subjects:** Medical sciences, nursing. **Holdings:** 8500 books; 28,000 bound periodical volumes. **Subscriptions:** 800 journals and other serials. **Services:** Interlibrary loan; library not open to the public. **Automated Operations:** Computerized serials and circulation. **Computerized Information Services:** MEDLINE, BRS Information Technologies, DIALOG Information Services, MEDLARS, CD Plus. **Networks/Consortia:** Member of National Network of Libraries of Medicine - Greater Midwest Region, Cleveland Area Metropolitan Library System (CAMLS). **Remarks:** FAX: (216)444-0271. **Staff:** Marian Dorner, Med.Libn.; Jodith Janes, Med.Libn.; Devera Kastner, Med.Libn.; Brenda Benik, Med.Libn.

★3800★
Cleveland College of Art & Design - Library (Art)
Green Lane
Linthorpe, Middlesbrough TS5 7RJ, England Phone: 642 821441
Adrian D. Bull, Tutor-Libn.
Founded: 1966. **Staff:** Prof 1; Other 3.5. **Subjects:** Art, design, history of art and design. **Special Collections:** Iconography of the railway collection (200 illustrations, 1000 slides). **Holdings:** 24,000 books; 200 bound periodical volumes; 300 microfiche; 250,000 slides. **Subscriptions:** 120 journals and other serials; 3 newspapers. **Services:** Interlibrary loan; copying; library open to the public for reference use only. **Publications:** Library Handbook, annual; Periodicals Holding List, semiannual; acquisitions list, biennial. **Remarks:** FAX: 642 823467.

★3801★
Cleveland College of Jewish Studies - Aaron Garber Library (Area-Ethnic)
26500 Shaker Blvd. Phone: (216)464-5581
Beachwood, OH 44122-7197 Jean Loeb Lettofsky, Dir., Lib.Serv.
Staff: Prof 1; Other 1. **Subjects:** Judaica. **Special Collections:** Holocaust materials; Hebrew literature. **Holdings:** 20,000 volumes. **Subscriptions:** 100 journals and other serials. **Services:** Interlibrary loan; copying; library open to residents of Metropolitan Cleveland.

★3802★
Cleveland Council on World Affairs - Library (Soc Sci)
539 Hanna Bldg.
1422 Euclid Ave. Phone: (216)781-3730
Cleveland, OH 44115 Christine Lucas, Prog.Off.
Founded: 1924. **Staff:** 5. **Subjects:** Foreign affairs. **Special Collections:** U.S. Department of State's policy statements and background notes on individual countries. **Holdings:** 360 bound periodical volumes; 100 reports. **Subscriptions:** 4 journals and other serials; 3 newspapers. **Services:** Library open to the public. **Remarks:** FAX: (216)781-2729.

★3803★
Cleveland Department of Law Library (Law)
100 City Hall
601 Lakeside Ave. Phone: (216)664-2656
Cleveland, OH 44114 Karen E. Martines, Libn.
Founded: 1942. **Staff:** Prof 2; Other 2. **Subjects:** Federal, Ohio and City of Cleveland law; municipal corporation law; municipal codes and ordinances. **Holdings:** 20,000 volumes. **Subscriptions:** 25 journals and other serials. **Services:** Copying; library open to the public with restrictions. **Remarks:** FAX: (216)623-6948. Maintained by Cleveland Public Library - Public Administration Library. **Staff:** Diane Mathews.

Cleveland Electric Illuminating Company
See: **Centerior Energy Corporation** (3317)

Grover Cleveland Library
See: **Princeton University - Rare Books and Special Collections** (13386)

★3804★
Cleveland Health Sciences Library (Med)
2119 Abington Rd. Phone: (216)368-3427
Cleveland, OH 44106 Robert G. Cheshier, Dir.
Founded: 1965. **Staff:** Prof 15; Other 21. **Subjects:** Medicine, dentistry, nursing, biology, nutrition. **Holdings:** 135,607 books; 219,396 bound periodical volumes; 2051 AV programs; 100 microforms. **Subscriptions:** 2841 journals and other serials. **Services:** Interlibrary loan; copying; SDI; library open to the public for reference use only. **Automated Operations:** Computerized public access catalog, cataloging, acquisitions, serials, and circulation. **Computerized Information Services:** MEDLINE, OCLC, BRS Information Technologies, DIALOG Information Services, PFDS Online Performs searches on fee basis. **Networks/Consortia:** Member of National Network of Libraries of Medicine - Greater Midwest Region, Cleveland Area Metropolitan Library System (CAMLS), NEOMARL. **Remarks:** FAX: (216)368-3008. Library holdings are divided among the Allen Memorial Library, Health Center Library, Dittrick Museum of Historical Medicine. Maintained by Case Western Reserve University and Cleveland Medical Library Association.

★3805★
Cleveland Health Sciences Library - Allen Memorial Library (Med)
11000 Euclid Ave. Phone: (216)368-3640
Cleveland, OH 44106 Lillian S. Levine, Asst.Dir.
Staff: Prof 7. **Subjects:** Medicine. **Special Collections:** History of Medicine; Darwin; Freud. **Holdings:** 76,356 books; 107,793 bound periodical volumes. **Subscriptions:** 1332 journals and other serials. **Services:** Interlibrary loan; copying; SDI; library open to the public for reference use only. **Computerized Information Services:** OCLC, MEDLINE, DIALOG Information Services, BRS Information Technologies. **Networks/Consortia:** Member of National Network of Libraries of Medicine - Greater Midwest Region, Cleveland Area Metropolitan Library System (CAMLS), NEOMARL. **Remarks:** Alternate telephone number(s): 368-3745. FAX: (216)368-6421. **Staff:** Carole Hughes, Ref.Libn.; Susan Hill; Dzwinka Komarjanski, Hd., Ref.; Joseph Hagloch, Circuit Libn.; Glen Jenkins, Archv. & Rare Bks.Libn.

★3806★
Cleveland Health Sciences Library - Health Center Library (Med)
2119 Abington Rd. Phone: (216)368-4540
Cleveland, OH 44106 Robert G. Cheshier, Dir.
Staff: Prof 6. **Subjects:** Medicine, nursing, dentistry, nutrition, biology. **Holdings:** 108,096 serials; 56,711 monographs; 2048 AV programs. **Subscriptions:** 1509 journals and other serials. **Services:** Interlibrary loan; copying; SDI; library open to the public for reference use only. **Computerized Information Services:** OCLC, MEDLINE, MEDLARS, BRS Information Technologies, DIALOG Information Services, PFDS Online. **Networks/Consortia:** Member of National Network of Libraries of Medicine - Greater Midwest Region, Cleveland Area Metropolitan Library System (CAMLS), NEOMARL. **Remarks:** FAX: (216)368-3008. **Staff:** Karen Burt, Hd.Cat.Libn.; Kathy Meneely, Coll.Dev.-Ser.; Virginia Saha, Asst.Dir., Coll.Dev.; Kathleen Blazar, Hd.Ref.Libn./AV; June Hund, Ref.Libn.

★3807★
Cleveland Health Sciences Library - Medical History Division (Med)
11000 Euclid Ave. Phone: (216)368-3648
Cleveland, OH 44106 Dr. Patsy A. Gerstner, Chf.Cur.
Staff: Prof 5. **Subjects:** History of medicine. **Special Collections:** Dittrick Museum of Medical History; Nicolaus Pol Collection of Incunabula (40); Sigmund Freud Collection (500); Harold N. Cole Collection of Venereals (200); Charles Darwin Collection of Books and Manuscripts (400 titles; 136 manuscripts); Marshall Collection of Herbals (400); historical biology (2000); Archives of Northern Ohio Medical History; Classics in Medicine. **Holdings:** 35,000 books; 75,000 artifacts. **Services:** Copying; library open to the public. **Automated Operations:** Computerized cataloging and serials. **Computerized Information Services:** OCLC. **Remarks:** Alternate telephone number(s): 368-6390. FAX: (216)368-6421 **Staff:** James Edmonson, Cur.; Glen Jenkins, Rare Bk.Libn./Archv.; Jennifer Simmons, Coll.Mgr.

★3808★
Cleveland Hearing and Speech Center - Lucile Dauby Gries Memorial Library
11206 Euclid Ave.
Cleveland, OH 44106
Subjects: Audiology, speech, language, deafness, rehabilitation, psychology. **Special Collections:** Technical journals, 1889 to present; AV file. **Holdings:** 1200 books; 490 bound periodical volumes; 90 dissertations; 4 VF drawers of reprints, abstracts, former comprehensive examinations. **Remarks:** Currently inactive.

★3809★
Cleveland Institute of Art - Jessica R. Gund Memorial Library (Art)
11141 East Blvd. Phone: (216)421-7440
Cleveland, OH 44106 Cristine C. Rom, Lib.Dir.
Founded: 1882. **Staff:** Prof 3; Other 3.5. **Subjects:** Fine arts, crafts, industrial design, general design, history of architecture, graphic arts, art history, textiles, metals. **Special Collections:** Artists' books (700). **Holdings:** 45,000 books; 10,000 bound periodical volumes; 80,000 slides; 4000 pictures; 37 volumes and boxes of archival materials; 4000 reels of microfilm; 15,000 microfiche. **Subscriptions:** 320 journals and other serials; 2 newspapers. **Services:** Interlibrary loan; copying; library open to the public. **Automated Operations:** Computerized cataloging. **Computerized Information Services:** OCLC. **Networks/Consortia:** Member of Cleveland Area Metropolitan Library System (CAMLS). **Remarks:** FAX: (216)421-7439. **Staff:** Hyosoo Lee, Tech.Serv.Libn.; M. Michelle Rossman, Slide Libn.

★3810★
Cleveland Institute of Music - Library (Mus)
11021 East Blvd. Phone: (216)795-3114
Cleveland, OH 44106 Jean S. Toombs, Dir.
Founded: 1922. **Staff:** Prof 3; Other 1. **Subjects:** Music - performance materials, scores, analytical works, bibliographies, biographies. **Holdings:** 44,954 books and scores; 15,105 sound recordings. **Subscriptions:** 105 journals and other serials; 2 newspapers. **Services:** Interlibrary loan; library open to the public for reference use only. **Automated Operations:** Computerized public access catalog, cataloging, and circulation. **Computerized Information Services:** OCLC. **Networks/Consortia:** Member of Cleveland Area Metropolitan Library System (CAMLS), OHIONET. **Remarks:** FAX: (216)791-3063. **Staff:** Janet Winzenburger, Acq.; Paul Schlenk, Ref.

★3811★
Cleveland Law Library Association (Law)
404 Cuyahoga County Court House Phone: (216)861-5070
Cleveland, OH 44113 Jan Ryan Novak, Dir.
Founded: 1869. **Staff:** Prof 4; Other 9. **Subjects:** Law - state, federal, British, Canadian. **Special Collections:** State session laws; Ohio State Supreme Court records and briefs, 1910 to present. **Holdings:** 140,000 volumes; 30,000 bound periodical volumes; 150,000 microfiche. **Subscriptions:** 6000 journals and other serials; 5 newspapers. **Services:** Interlibrary loan (to member libraries); library not open to the public. **Automated Operations:** Computerized public access catalog, cataloging, circulation, acquisitions, serials, and accounting. **Computerized Information Services:** LEXIS, WESTLAW, VU/TEXT Information Services, DataTimes, Hannah Information Systems, DIALOG Information Services, OCLC; internal databases. **Publications:** Newsletter, quarterly - to members; Research Guide Series. **Remarks:** FAX: (216)861-1606. **Staff:** Eric Hess, Tech.Serv.Libn.; Rand J. Diamond, Pub.Serv.Libn.; Juliane A. Novak, Circ.Serv.Libn.

Cleveland Medical Library Association - Cleveland Health Sciences Library
See: **Cleveland Health Sciences Library** (3804)

★3812★
Cleveland Metroparks Zoo - Library (Sci-Engr)
3900 Brookside Park Dr. Phone: (216)661-6500
Cleveland, OH 44109 Charles R. Voracek, Sr.Educ.Spec.
Founded: 1882. **Staff:** Prof 1. **Subjects:** Mammalogy, ornithology, herpetology, zoo management, zoology, aquarium science, invertebrates. **Holdings:** 2500 books. **Subscriptions:** 32 journals and other serials. **Services:** Library open to the public by appointment for reference use. **Remarks:** FAX: (216)661-3312.

★3813★
Cleveland Museum of Art - Ingalls Library (Art)
11150 East Blvd. Phone: (216)421-7340
Cleveland, OH 44106 Ann B. Abid, Hd.Libn.
Founded: 1916. **Staff:** Prof 9; Other 13. **Subjects:** Art, architecture, decorative arts, oriental art. **Special Collections:** Sothebys, Christies, and Parke-Bernet sales catalogs; Gernsheim photographs; Berenson Archive; D.I.A.L; Conway Library; Witt Library. **Holdings:** 167,000 volumes; 380,000 slides; 350,000 photograph reference collection; 100 VF of artist clippings; 45,520 microfiche; 656 reels of microfilm. **Subscriptions:** 2000 journals and other serials. **Services:** Copying; library open to the public on a limited schedule. **Automated Operations:** Computerized public access catalog, cataloging, acquisitions, serials, and circulation. **Computerized Information Services:** RLIN, DIALOG Information Services; RLG, BITNET (electronic mail service). **Special Catalogs:** ARLO Union list of serials and periodicals, 1974. **Remarks:** FAX: (216)421-0411. Electronic mail address(es): BM.CMA (RLG); BM.CMA@RLG (BITNET). **Staff:** Georgina Toth, Ref.Libn.; Louis Adrean, Asst.Libn. for Pub.Serv.; Sara Jane Pearman, Slide Libn.; Eleanor Scheifele, Photo.Libn.; Elizabeth Lantz, Asst.Libn. for Tech.Serv.; Richard Kromstedt, Ser.Libn.

★3814★
Cleveland Museum of Natural History - Harold Terry Clark Library (Sci-Engr, Biol Sci)
1 Wade Oval Dr., University Circle Phone: (216)231-4600
Cleveland, OH 44106-1767 Wendy Wasman, Libn.
Founded: 1921. **Staff:** Prof 1; Other 1. **Subjects:** Natural history, ornithology, geology, astronomy, anthropology, zoology, entomology, botany, ichthyology, archeology. **Special Collections:** Rare books (over 500). **Holdings:** 8000 books; 35,000 bound and unbound periodical volumes; 18 VF drawers of pamphlets; slide collections; periodical recordings for the blind and visually impaired. **Subscriptions:** 300 journals and other serials. **Services:** Interlibrary loan; copying; library open to the public for reference use only. **Remarks:** FAX: (216)231-5919.

★3815★
Cleveland Psychiatric Institute - Karnosh Medical Library (Med)
1708 Aiken Ave. Phone: (216)661-6200
Cleveland, OH 44109 Michael Petit, Libn.
Staff: Prof 1. **Subjects:** Psychology, psychiatry, psychoanalysis, medicine, sociology, clinical neurology, psychological nursing, social work. **Holdings:** 5740 books; 1819 bound periodical volumes; 5 VF drawers of pamphlets; 301 cassette tapes; 16 reels of tape; 64 slides. **Subscriptions:** 60 journals and other serials. **Services:** Interlibrary loan; copying; library open to the public for reference use only on request. **Computerized Information Services:** NLM. **Remarks:** FAX: (216)398-4884 (Attn: Library).

★3816★
Cleveland Psychoanalytic Institute - Library (Med)
11328 Euclid Ave., No. 205 Phone: (216)229-2111
Cleveland, OH 44106 Jane Zimring, Libn.
Founded: 1962. **Staff:** Prof 1. **Subjects:** Psychoanalysis, child therapy. **Special Collections:** Concordance to the Psychological Works of Sigmund Freud; Complete Psychological Works of Sigmund Freud (Standard Edition); Chicago Psychoanalytic Literature Index. **Holdings:** 1700 books; 440 bound periodical volumes; 170 tape recordings of scientific psychoanalytic meetings; 8 shelves of unbound periodicals; 10 boxes of reprints; 25 boxes of unpublished papers. **Subscriptions:** 15 journals and other serials. **Services:** Copying; library open to persons interested in psychoanalysis. **Computerized Information Services:** Internal database.

★3817★
Cleveland Public Library - Audio-Video Department (Aud-Vis)
325 Superior Ave. Phone: (216)623-2942
Cleveland, OH 44114-1271 Arnold McClain, Dept.Hd.
Founded: 1869. **Staff:** Prof 2; Other 5. **Holdings:** 4850 16mm films; 6548 sound recordings; 3730 videocassettes; 3564 software programs; 814 slides. **Services:** Library open to the public. **Automated Operations:** Computerized public access catalog, cataloging, acquisitions, and circulation. **Computerized Information Services:** OCLC, DIALOG Information Services, BRS Information Technologies, OhioPI, (Ohio Public Information Utility), Hannah Information Systems, U.S. Patent Classification System, PFDS Online, WILSONLINE; CD-ROMs (CIRR on Disc, ABI/INFORM Ondisc). **Networks/Consortia:** Member of OHIONET, Cleveland Area Metropolitan Library System (CAMLS), NEOMARL, North Central Library Cooperative (NCLC). **Staff:** Kathy L. Broz.

★3818★
Cleveland Public Library - Business, Economics & Labor Department (Bus-Fin)
325 Superior Ave. Phone: (216)623-7008
Cleveland, OH 44114-1271 Julius Bremer, Dept.Hd.
Founded: 1869. **Staff:** Prof 6; Other 7. **Subjects:** Investments and finance, marketing and advertising, insurance, accounting, real estate, communications, labor, taxation, salesmanship, banking, transportation. **Special Collections:** Trade directories (1095). **Holdings:** 128,822 volumes; 18,693 bound periodical volumes; 470,573 microfiche; 672 reels of microfilm; 336 VF drawers of economic and business subject files, corporation files, company annual reports; annual reports for companies on the New York, over-the-counter, and American Stock Exchanges on microfiche; 100 loose-leaf services on investments, taxation, labor, employment. **Subscriptions:** 2328 journals and other serials; 9 newspapers. **Services:** Interlibrary loan; copying; department open to the public. **Automated Operations:** Computerized public access catalog, cataloging, acquisitions, and circulation. **Computerized Information Services:** OCLC, DIALOG Information Services, BRS Information Technologies, OhioPI (Ohio Public Information Utility), Hannah Information Systems, U.S. Patent Classification System, PFDS Online, WILSONLINE; CD-ROMs (CIRR, ABI/INFORM, Laser Disclosure). **Networks/Consortia:** Member of OHIONET, Cleveland Area Metropolitan Library System (CAMLS), NEOMARL, North Central Library Cooperative (NCLC). **Special Indexes:** Corporation File Index (card). **Remarks:** FAX: (216)623-7008. Staff: Mary Ellen Kollar; Johnny L. Parsons; Natalie S. Sidel; Teresa A. Smith; Geraldine B. Tiedman.

★3819★
Cleveland Public Library - Children's Literature Department (Hum)
325 Superior Ave. Phone: (216)623-2834
Cleveland, OH 44114-1271 Ruth M. Hadlow, Dept.Hd.
Founded: 1869. **Staff:** Prof 1; Other 2. **Subjects:** Children's materials. **Special Collections:** Collection of Early Children's Books (1453 volumes); Lewis Carroll Collection (books by and about the author; 150 volumes); Rosenbach Collection of Early American Children's Books (microfiche). **Holdings:** 40,044 volumes; 674 bound periodical volumes; 1056 microfiche; 45rpm records; phonograph records; book/record and book/cassette combinations; comics. **Subscriptions:** 60 journals and other serials. **Services:** Interlibrary loan; copying; department open to the public. **Automated Operations:** Computerized public access catalog, cataloging, acquisitions, and circulation. **Computerized Information Services:** OCLC, DIALOG Information Services, BRS Information Technologies, Hannah Legislative Service, PFDS Online, U.S. Patent Classification System, OhioPI (Ohio Public Information Utility), WILSONLINE. **Networks/Consortia:** Member of OHIONET, NEOMARL, Cleveland Area Metropolitan Library System (CAMLS), North Central Library Cooperative (NCLC). **Special Indexes:** Author and illustrator index; subject index: preschool through grade two.

★3820★
Cleveland Public Library - Cleveland Research Center (Bus-Fin)
325 Superior Ave., 4th Fl. Phone: (216)623-2999
Cleveland, OH 44114-1271 Angela B. Bowie, Agency Hd.
Founded: 1987. **Staff:** 3. **Subjects:** Marketing, business and industry, competitive intelligence, management. **Holdings:** 1500 databases; government and industry contacts. **Services:** Research; document delivery; third-party inquiries; center open to the public. **Automated Operations:** Computerized public access catalog. **Computerized Information Services:** LEXIS, Federal Assistance Programs Retrieval System (FAPRS), Economic Bulletin Board (EBB), DIALOG Information Services, BRS Information Technologies, Hannah Information Systems, NEXIS, PFDS Online, Dow Jones News/Retrieval, TRADSTAT, WILSONLINE, VU/TEXT Information Services, Dun & Bradstreet Business Credit Services, DataTimes, Data-Star, OhioPI; DIALMAIL (electronic mail service). Performs searches on fee basis. **Networks/Consortia:** Member of Cleveland Area Metropolitan Library System (CAMLS), OHIONET, NEOMARL, North Central Library Cooperative (NCLC). **Remarks:** FAX: (216)623-6987.

★3821★
Cleveland Public Library - Documents Collection (Info Sci)
325 Superior Ave. Phone: (216)623-2870
Cleveland, OH 44114-1271 Siegfried Weinhold, Dept.Hd.
Founded: 1869. **Staff:** Prof 2; Other 2. **Subjects:** United States Government publications. **Holdings:** Government Printing Office (GPO) depository, 1886 to present; patent depository, 1790 to present (microfilm); U.S. Serial Set, 1789-1969 (microfiche); Major Studies & Issue Briefs of the Congressional Research Service, 1916 to present (microfilm); Presidential Executive Orders and Proclamations, 1789-1983 (microfiche); U.S. Census, decennial and nondecennial, 1790 to present (microform); U.S. NASA depository, 1968 to present (microfiche); U.S. Bureau of Mines publications, 1910 to present (microfiche); National Technical Information Service (NTIS) subscription to Selected Research in Microfiche (SRIM), science and technology, 1975 to present (microfiche); Atomic Energy Commission (AEC) and U.S. Department of Energy (DOE) Depository, 1940s to present (microform and hardcopy); U.S. Congressional Committee Hearings, 23rd Congress, 1833 to present (microfiche); American Statistics Index/Abstracts, 1974 to present (microfiche); 10,171 bound periodical volumes; 59,800 microcards; 2.01 million microfiche; 12,051 reels of microfilm. **Services:** Interlibrary loan (limited); copying; collection open to the public. **Automated Operations:** Computerized public access catalog, cataloging, acquisitions, and circulation. **Computerized Information Services:** OCLC, DIALOG Information Services, BRS Information Technologies, OhioPI (Ohio Public Information Utility), U.S. Patent Classification System, CASSIS, Hannah Information Systems, PFDS Online, WILSONLINE; CD-ROMs (CIRR, ADI/INFORM, Congressional Information Service Masterfile, MARCIVE). **Networks/Consortia:** Member of OHIONET, Cleveland Area Metropolitan Library System (CAMLS), NEOMARL, North Central Library Cooperative (NCLC). **Remarks:** FAX: (216)623-7030. **Staff:** Robin Gray.

★3822★
Cleveland Public Library - Fine Arts and Special Collections Department - Fine Arts Section (Art, Mus)
325 Superior Ave. Phone: (216)623-2848
Cleveland, OH 44114-1271 Alice N. Loranth, Dept.Hd.
Founded: 1869. **Staff:** Prof 4; Other 3. **Subjects:** Art, architecture, sculpture, painting, music. **Special Collections:** Cleveland Architectural plans (1432 items); Cleveland Graphics collection (1043 items); Johann H. Beck, Charles V. Rychlick, Frederick K. Grossman, Cleveland City Club Anvil-Revues Music Archives (112 linear feet); art and music files (137 2 VF drawers); dance band orchestrations (3072). **Holdings:** 174,687 volumes; 10,959 bound periodical volumes; 20,500 pieces of sheet music; 28,886 sound recordings. **Subscriptions:** 523 journals and other serials. **Services:** Interlibrary loan; copying; section open to the public. **Automated Operations:** Computerized public access catalog, cataloging, acquisitions, and circulation. **Computerized Information Services:** OCLC, DIALOG Information Services, BRS Information Technologies, OhioPI (Ohio Public Information Utility), Hannah Legislative Service, U.S. Patent and Classification System, PFDS Online, WILSONLINE; CD-ROMs (CIRR, ABI/INFORM). **Networks/Consortia:** Member of OHIONET, NEOMARL, Cleveland Area Metropolitan Library System (CAMLS), North Central Library Cooperative (NCLC). **Publications:** Descriptive pamphlets of holdings. **Special Indexes:** Indexes to songs, hymns, sheet music; indexes to art and artists, music subjects, and musicians represented in vertical files. **Remarks:** FAX: (216)623-7050. **Staff:** Ellen Olson; Kathleen Shamp; Joan Maurushat.

★3823★
Cleveland Public Library - Fine Arts and Special Collections Department - Special Collections Section - John G. White Collection and Rare Books (Rare Book, Hum)
325 Superior Ave. Phone: (216)623-2818
Cleveland, OH 44114-1271 Alice N. Loranth, Dept.Hd.
Founded: 1869. **Staff:** Prof 2; Other 2. **Special Collections:** Orientalia (58,780 volumes); folklore (45,010 volumes); chess and checkers and

auxiliary subjects (30,317 volumes); rare books (15,561 volumes); East India Company manuscript collection of official documents and correspondence, 1741-1859 (over 30,000 pages and 200 titles); languages and linguistics (15,360 volumes); India and Southeast Asia (4000 volumes); Near Eastern archeology (7665 volumes); early travel and voyages to the Orient and Africa (7678 volumes); Egyptology (5580 volumes); Chinese, Japanese, and Tibetan religion and philosophy (5440 volumes); Arabic and Persian literature (5695 volumes); Omar Khayyam (1055 editions in 48 languages); Arabian Nights (760 volumes in 57 languages); Sanskrit literature (3311 volumes); Judaica (1730 volumes); manuscript catalogs (720 volumes); Madagascar (510 volumes); proverbs (2870 volumes); gypsies (741 volumes); chapbooks (1730 volumes); Robert Hays Gries Tobacco Collection (1376 volumes); Occult sciences (2625 volumes); witchcraft (1700 volumes); Medieval romance literature (3170 volumes); Celtic and Icelandic language and saga literature (1120 volumes); Tegner (225 19th century editions); Rabelais (245 16th-18th century editions); Castiglione (102 volumes); Vida (106 volumes); Derrydale Press (182 volumes); Cleveland Author Collection (2026 volumes); Cleveland Imprint Collection (458 volumes); 18th-19th century prostitution collection (299 volumes); early children's books (1485 volumes); political pamphlets, 1611 to 20th century (1851); Margaret Klipple Memorial Archives of African Folktales; Newbell Niles Puckett Memorial Archives of Ohio Superstitions and Popular Beliefs, Black Names in America, Religious Beliefs of the Southern Negro, and Canadian Lumberjack Songs. **Holdings:** 165,991 volumes; 1500 bound manuscripts; 342 boxes and 59 VF drawers of clippings and pictorial material on chess; 147 tapes; 2587 reels of microfilm. **Subscriptions:** 799 journals and other serials. **Services:** Interlibrary loan; copying; exhibits; lectures; collection open to the public with valid identification. **Automated Operations:** Computerized public access catalog, cataloging, acquisitions, and circulation. **Computerized Information Services:** OCLC, DIALOG Information Services, BRS Information Technologies, OhioPI (Ohio Public Information Utility), Hannah Information Systems, U.S. Patent Classification System, PFDS Online, WILSONLINE; CD-ROMs (CIRR, ABI/INFORM). **Networks/Consortia:** Member of OHIONET, NEOMARL, Cleveland Area Metropolitan Library System (CAMLS), North Central Library Cooperative (NCLC). **Publications:** Descriptive pamphlets of holdings, irregular; John G. White Department of Folklore, Orientalia and Chess (2nd ed., 1978). **Special Catalogs:** Black Names in America: Origin and Usage (1975); A Catalog of Folklore, Folklife and Folk Songs (1978); Catalog of the Chess Collection (including checkers), 1964; Popular Beliefs and Superstitions Compendium of American Folklore: From the Ohio Collection of Newbell Niles Puckett (1981). **Special Indexes:** Index to chess biography, tournaments, and historic chess columns; French, Spanish, and Italian folksong and ballad index. **Staff:** Motoko Reece.

★3824★
Cleveland Public Library - Foreign Literature Department (Hum)
325 Superior Ave. Phone: (216)623-2895
Cleveland, OH 44114-1271 Natalia B. Bezugloff, Dept.Hd.
Founded: 1869. **Staff:** Prof 4; Other 2. **Subjects:** Collections in 39 modern languages which include classics and standard works with emphasis on belles-lettres, literary history, biography; books on learning languages; encyclopedias; dictionaries. **Holdings:** 211,908 volumes; 5518 bound periodical volumes; 5502 sound recordings. **Subscriptions:** 147 journals and other serials. **Services:** Interlibrary loan; copying; file of teachers and translators of foreign languages; department open to the public. **Automated Operations:** Computerized public access catalog, cataloging, acquisitions, and circulation. **Computerized Information Services:** OCLC, DIALOG Information Services, BRS Information Technologies, OhioPI (Ohio Public Information Utility), Hannah Information Systems, U.S. Patent Classification System, PFDS Online, WILSONLINE; CD-ROMs (CIRR, ABI/INFORM). **Networks/Consortia:** Member of OHIONET, NEOMARL, Cleveland Area Metropolitan Library System (CAMLS), North Central Library Cooperative (NCLC). **Publications:** Booklists; descriptive brochures, all irregular. **Special Catalogs:** Catalogs by languages. **Special Indexes:** Old indexes to poetry, short stories, literary criticism. **Staff:** Bente C. Bob; Areta H. Nadozirny; Mark M. Stanczak.

★3825★
Cleveland Public Library - General Reference Department (Info Sci)
325 Superior Ave. Phone: (216)623-2856
Cleveland, OH 44114-1271 Donald Tipka, Dept.Hd.
Founded: 1869. **Staff:** Prof 5; Other 17. **Subjects:** Bibliography, cartography and maps, encyclopedias, newspapers, general reference. **Special Collections:** Obituary file of newspaper death notices. **Holdings:** 49,408 volumes; 29,719 bound periodical volumes; 27 VF drawers; 131,627 sheet maps; 86,223 microfiche of periodicals; 66,145 reels of microfilm of periodicals and newspapers; 74,012 micro-opaque cards. **Subscriptions:** 500 journals and other serials; 160 newspapers. **Services:** Interlibrary loan; department open to the public. **Automated Operations:** Computerized public access catalog, cataloging, acquisitions, and circulation. **Computerized Information Services:** OCLC, DIALOG Information Services, BRS Information Technologies, OhioPI (Ohio Public Information Utility), Hannah Information Systems, U.S. Patent Classification System, PFDS Online, WILSONLINE; CD-ROMs (CIRR, ABI/INFORM). **Networks/Consortia:** Member of OHIONET, NEOMARL, Cleveland Area Metropolitan Library System (CAMLS), North Central Library Cooperative (NCLC). **Publications:** Cleveland News Index, monthly. **Remarks:** FAX: (216)623-7043. **Staff:** Renee DeCourville; Margaret A. Dennis; Maureen C. Farrell; Linda Wyler.

★3826★
Cleveland Public Library - History and Geography Department (Hist, Geog-Map)
325 Superior Ave. Phone: (216)623-2864
Cleveland, OH 44114-1271 JoAnn Petrello, Dept.Hd.
Founded: 1869. **Staff:** Prof 4; Other 6. **Subjects:** History - ancient, medieval, modern; archaeology; local history; genealogy; heraldry; geography; black history; exploration and travel; numismatics. **Special Collections:** Photograph Collection (900,337); British learned society serials; 19th century travel narratives; English parish register collection. **Holdings:** 215,317 volumes; 12,232 bound periodical volumes; 18,800 Cleveland pictures on microfiche; 6000 maps and brochures with current travel data; local history clipping file; Coat-of-Arms file; 1092 World Wars I and II posters. **Subscriptions:** 935 journals and other serials. **Services:** Interlibrary loan; copying; department open to the public. **Automated Operations:** Computerized public access catalog, cataloging, acquisitions, and circulation. **Computerized Information Services:** OCLC, DIALOG Information Services, BRS Information Technologies, OhioPI (Ohio Public Information Utility), Hannah Information Systems, U.S. Patent Classification System, PFDS Online, WILSONLINE; CD-ROMs (CIRR, ABI/INFORM). **Networks/Consortia:** Member of OHIONET, NEOMARL, Cleveland Area Metropolitan Library System (CAMLS), North Central Library Cooperative (NCLC). **Special Indexes:** Photograph Collection index (movie stills and posters captured on an optical disk). **Staff:** Ronald B. Spagnoli; Christopher Wood; Maureen T. Mullin.

★3827★
Cleveland Public Library - Literature Department (Hum, Theater)
325 Superior Ave. Phone: (216)623-2881
Cleveland, OH 44114-1271 Evelyn M. Ward, Dept.Hd.
Founded: 1869. **Staff:** Prof 4; Other 2. **Subjects:** Fiction, drama and theater, film, radio, television, poetry, essays, humor and satire, oratory and public speaking, craft of writing, literary criticism and biography, classical Greek and Latin, linguistics, journalism, book trade, printing, publishing, library and information science. **Special Collections:** Shakespeare and early English play collection; American drama, including Barrett W. Clark Collection of old paperbacks; William F. McDermott Memorial Theatre Collection; Weidenthal Collection of theatrical memorabilia; Wertheimer theatre programs; W. Ward Marsh cinema archives. **Holdings:** 330,811 volumes; 10,547 bound periodical volumes; 22,000 theater programs and playbills; 76,000 photographs; 16,000 titles of microprint editions of plays and miscellanea. **Subscriptions:** 615 journals and other serials. **Services:** Interlibrary loan; copying; department open to the public. **Automated Operations:** Computerized public access catalog, cataloging, acquisitions, and circulation. **Computerized Information Services:** OCLC, DIALOG Information Services, BRS Information Technologies, OhioPI (Ohio Public Information Utility), Hannah Information Systems, U.S. Patent Classification System, PFDS Online, WILSONLINE; CD-ROMs (CIRR, ABI/INFORM). **Networks/Consortia:** Member of OHIONET, NEOMARL, Cleveland Area Metropolitan Library System (CAMLS), North Central Library Cooperative (NCLC). **Publications:** Book lists and descriptive brochures, irregular. **Special Indexes:** Card indexes to clippings, theater programs, and pictures. **Staff:** Evelyn K. Prince; Deborah W. Charvat; Mark L. Moore.

★3828★
Cleveland Public Library - Popular Library Department (Rec)
325 Superior Ave. Phone: (216)623-2842
Cleveland, OH 44114-1271 John Philip Ferguson, Dept.Hd.
Founded: 1869. **Staff:** Prof 2; Other 2. **Subjects:** Popular fiction and nonfiction, popular magazines. **Holdings:** 14,533 volumes. **Services:** Books-by-Mail; department open to the public. **Automated Operations:** Computerized public access catalog, cataloging, acquisitions, and

circulation. **Computerized Information Services:** OCLC, DIALOG Information Services, BRS Information Technologies, OhioPI (Ohio Public Information Utility), Hannah Information Systems, U.S. Patent Classification System, PFDS Online, WILSONLINE; CD-ROMs (CIRR, ABI/INFORM). **Networks/Consortia:** Member of OHIONET, NEOMARL, Cleveland Area Metropolitan Library System (CAMLS), North Central Library Cooperative (NCLC). **Staff:** Richard T. Fox.

★3829★
Cleveland Public Library - Public Administration Library (Soc Sci)
601 Lakeside Ave., Rm. 100 Phone: (216)623-2919
Cleveland, OH 44114-1271 Karen E. Martines, Dept.Hd.
Founded: 1869. **Staff:** Prof 2; Other 2. **Subjects:** Law - federal, Ohio; municipal corporate law; municipal codes and ordinances. **Special Collections:** City of Cleveland Collection (6000 volumes); Urban Documents (microfiche). **Holdings:** 17,738 volumes; 901 bound periodical volumes; 2457 bound serial volumes; 32 VF drawers of Cleveland subject file; 38,376 documents; 49,175 microfiche; 1502 reels of microfilm. **Subscriptions:** 660 journals and other serials; 8 newspapers. **Services:** Interlibrary loan; copying; library open to the public. **Automated Operations:** Computerized public access catalog, cataloging, acquisitions, and circulation. **Computerized Information Services:** OCLC, DIALOG Information Services, BRS Information Technologies, OhioPI (Ohio Public Information Utility), Hannah Information Systems, U.S. Patent Classification System, PFDS Online, WILSONLINE; CD-ROMs (CIRR, ABI/INFORM). **Networks/Consortia:** Member of OHIONET, North Central Library Cooperative (NCLC), Cleveland Area Metropolitan Library System (CAMLS), NEOMARL. **Publications:** Recent Acquisitions, quarterly - available upon request. **Remarks:** FAX: (216)623-6948. Maintains Cleveland Department of Law Library. **Staff:** Diane J. Mathews.

Cleveland Public Library - Public Administration Library - Cleveland Department of Law Library
See: **Cleveland Department of Law Library** (3803)

★3830★
Cleveland Public Library - Science and Technology Department (Sci-Engr)
325 Superior Ave. Phone: (216)623-2932
Cleveland, OH 44114-1271 Jean Z. Piety, Hd.
Founded: 1869. **Staff:** Prof 5; Other 9. **Subjects:** Engineering, science, metallurgy, aeronautics, mechanics, geology, environment, agriculture, history of science and technology, natural history, handicrafts, photography. **Special Collections:** Standards and specifications; dog stud books; Great Lakes Basin; cookbooks. **Holdings:** 308,593 volumes; 98,323 bound periodical volumes; 29,606 microfiche; 891 reels of microfilm. **Subscriptions:** 1965 journals and other serials. **Services:** Interlibrary loan; copying; department open to the public. **Automated Operations:** Computerized public access catalog, cataloging, acquisitions, and circulation. **Computerized Information Services:** OCLC, DIALOG Information Services, BRS Information Technologies, U.S. Patent Classification System, PFDS Online, WILSONLINE; CD-ROMs (Health Reference Center, General Science Index, Applied Science & Technology Index, MEDLINE, NTIS Bibliographic Data Base, Geological Reference File, Mitchell On-Demand). **Networks/Consortia:** Member of OHIONET, NEOMARL, Cleveland Area Metropolitan Library System (CAMLS), North Central Library Cooperative (NCLC). **Special Indexes:** Card indexes to automobiles, Great Lakes, history, standards, and specifications. **Remarks:** FAX: (216)623-7029. **Staff:** Penelope J. O'Connor; Kathryn E. Cseplo; Karen D. Long; Barbara J. Rasgaitis.

★3831★
Cleveland Public Library - Social Sciences Department (Soc Sci)
325 Superior Ave. Phone: (216)623-2860
Cleveland, OH 44114-1271 Thelma J. Morris, Dept.Hd.
Founded: 1869. **Staff:** Prof 5; Other 6. **Subjects:** Government, education, general and child psychology, League of Nations, United Nations, Great Britain Parliamentary Papers, Ohio documents, political and social sciences, religion, philosophy, law, logic, ethics, social welfare, crime, juvenile delinquency, costumes, sports, dance, public administration. **Special Collections:** Cleveland School Desegregation (public records and documents); Charles W. Mears collection of baseball scrapbooks records, yearbooks, and historical association documents. **Holdings:** 308,725 volumes; 46,053 bound periodical volumes; 85,853 microfiche; 48,850 microcards. **Subscriptions:** 1749 journals and other serials. **Services:** Interlibrary loan; copying; department open to the public. **Automated Operations:** Computerized public access catalog, cataloging, acquisitions, and circulation. **Computerized Information Services:** OCLC, DIALOG Information Services, BRS Information Technologies, OhioPI (Ohio Public Information Utility), Hannah Information Systems, PFDS Online, WILSONLINE; CD-ROMs (CIRR, ABI/INFORM). **Networks/Consortia:** Member of OHIONET, NEOMARL, Cleveland Area Metropolitan Library System (CAMLS), North Central Library Cooperative (NCLC). **Remarks:** FAX: (216)623-7064. **Staff:** Pamela L. Boesiger; Barbara A. Morton; Dorothy M. Skladanowski; Gail L. Morse.

Cleveland Research Center
See: **Cleveland Public Library** (3820)

Ruth R. Cleveland Memorial Library
See: **Cleveland Chiropractic College** (3798)

★3832★
Cleveland State University - Joseph W. Bartunek III Law Library (Law)
1801 Euclid Ave. Phone: (216)687-2250
Cleveland, OH 44115 Scott Finet, Dir.
Founded: 1897. **Staff:** Prof 7; Other 12. **Subjects:** Law. **Special Collections:** U.S. Government documents selective depository; Ohio and U.S. Supreme Court Records and Briefs (on microfilm). **Holdings:** 340,000 volumes. **Subscriptions:** 2946 journals and other serials. **Services:** Interlibrary loan; copying; library open to the public. **Computerized Information Services:** LEXIS, NEXIS, WESTLAW, DIALOG Information Services, OCLC, Hannah Information Systems, RLIN, Northwestern Online Total Integrated Systems (NOTIS), VU/TEXT Information Services, DataTimes, BRS Information Technologies, CompuServe Information Service, MEDIS,. **Publications:** User Guide; Monthly Acquisitions List; Contents of Current Periodicals. **Remarks:** FAX: (216)687-6881. **Staff:** Joseph S. Rosenfeld, Automation Libn.; Marie Rehmar, Ref.Serv.Libn.; Bae Smith, Acq./Ser.Libn.; Laura Ray, Media/Ref. Libn.; Ellen Quinn, Info.Serv.Libn.; Katherine Malmquist, Assoc.Dir.; Nancy Hanacek, Cat.Mgr.

Ernest G. Cleverdon Library
See: **First Alabama Bank of Mobile** (5725)

★3833★
Climax Metals - Library (Bus-Fin, Sci-Engr)
101 Merritt 7 Corporate Park Phone: (203)845-3090
Norwalk, CT 06854-5113 Mary A. McPherson, Libn.
Founded: 1951. **Staff:** Prof 1. **Subjects:** Metallurgy, mining, geology, business and finance, law, economic statistics, management. **Holdings:** 2000 books; 40 drawers of microforms; company reports; 200 annual reports; 10 VF drawers. **Subscriptions:** 350 journals and other serials; 10 newspapers. **Services:** Interlibrary loan; copying; library open to SLA members by appointment. **Computerized Information Services:** WILSONLINE, DIALOG Information Services, Dow Jones News/Retrieval, EPIC, InvesText, DataTimes, Global Scan. **Publications:** Recent Acquisitions, monthly. **Remarks:** FAX: (203)845-2994. **Formerly:** Located in Greenwich, CT.

Cline-Keller Library
See: **Bartholomew County Historical Society** (1543)

Cline Library
See: **Northern Arizona University** (11991)

Cline-Tunnell Library
See: **Western Conservative Baptist Seminary** (20241)

★3834★
Clinical Research Associates - Library (Med, Sci-Engr)
50 Madison Ave. Phone: (212)685-8788
New York, NY 10010 Carol Dorsey, Libn.
Subjects: Chemistry, pharmacology. **Holdings:** 15,000 books. **Subscriptions:** 25 journals and other serials. **Services:** Library not open to the public.

★3835★
Clinical Research Foundation - Library (Med)
11250 Corporate Ave. Phone: (913)752-8600
Leneza, KS 66219-1392 Dr. John Plachetka, CEO
Founded: 1984. **Staff:** 1. **Subjects:** Pharmaceutical research, pharmacology, medicine. **Holdings:** 600 books; 100 bound periodical volumes. **Subscriptions:** 80 journals and other serials. **Services:** Services not open to the public. **Remarks:** FAX: (816)231-0233. **Formerly:** Quincy Research Center - Information Services located in Kansas City, KS.

★3836★
Clinical Research Institute of Montreal/ - Medical Library (Med)
110 Pine Ave., W. Phone: (514)987-5599
Montreal, PQ, Canada H2W 1R7 Lorraine Bielmann, Doc.
Founded: 1967. **Staff:** Prof 2; Other 4. **Subjects:** Medicine, allied health sciences. **Holdings:** 2600 books; 1100 bound periodical volumes; 222,421 reprints. **Subscriptions:** 123 journals and other serials. **Services:** Library not open to the public. **Computerized Information Services:** MEDLINE; Envoy 100 (electronic mail service). **Remarks:** FAX: (514)987-5675. Electronic mail address(es): QMIRC (Envoy 100). Affiliated with the Universite de Montreal. **Also Known As:** Institut de de Recherches Cliniques de Montreal - Centre de Documentation. **Staff:** John Smyth, Asst.Libn.

★3837★
Clinton County Historical Society - Archives (Hist)
4700 Brook Rd.
Lansing, MI 48906
Subjects: Clinton County - genealogy, history, architecture; Central Michigan history. **Special Collections:** Clinton County newspapers (10,000); county tax records, 1881-1940; vintage scrapbooks (80); photograph collection; local histories (50); family histories (200); newspapers, censuses, county records (100 rolls). **Services:** Copying; archives open to the public on a limited schedule. **Formerly:** Located in DeWitt, MI. **Staff:** Myrna VanEpps, Archv.

★3838★
Clinton County Historical Society - Genealogy Library (Hist)
149 E. Locust St., Box 529
Wilmington, OH 45177 Phone: (513)382-4684
Founded: 1948. **Subjects:** Clinton County history and family genealogy, local Quaker history, local author's works. **Special Collections:** Manuscripts and documents by Quaker sculptor Eli Harvey; photographic archives. **Holdings:** Figures not available. **Subscriptions:** 6 journals and other serials; 12 newspapers. **Services:** Copying; library open to the public. **Publications:** Rombach Place Recorder (newsletter), monthly - for internal distribution only. **Staff:** Virginia Smith, Chm.

★3839★
Clinton County Law Library (Law)
Court House Phone: (717)893-4013
Lock Haven, PA 17745 Carol Kwiatek, Lib.Dir.
Subjects: Law. **Remarks:** No further information was supplied by respondent.

★3840★
Clinton River Watershed Council - Library (Sci-Engr)
8215 Hall Rd. Phone: (313)739-1122
Utica, MI 48087 Peggy B. Johnson, Exec.Sec.
Founded: 1973. **Staff:** 2. **Subjects:** Water - quality, management, recreation, associated land uses. **Special Collections:** Reports on the Clinton River. **Holdings:** 500 books; special reports; engineering reports; dissertations; data collections. **Subscriptions:** 25 journals and other serials. **Services:** Copying; library open to the public. **Publications:** Newsletter, quarterly; annual report - to mailing list; reports on special topics.

★3841★
Cliveden - Library (Law)
6401 Germantown Ave. Phone: (215)848-1777
Philadelphia, PA 19144 Jennifer Esler, Dir.
Staff: 6. **Special Collections:** 18th and 19th century law library of Benjamin Chew. **Holdings:** 1000 books; 200 bound periodical volumes; 3000 manuscripts. **Services:** Copying; library open to the public with prior written permission. **Remarks:** Maintained by National Trust for Historic Preservation. Portions of Chew Family Library on loan from the Library Company of Philadelphia.

Cloisters Library
See: **Metropolitan Museum of Art - Cloisters Library** (10209)

★3842★
Clorox Company - Technical Center Library (Sci-Engr)
7200 Johnson Dr.
Pleasanton, CA 94566 Phone: (510)847-6343
Staff: Prof 2; Other 2. **Subjects:** Chemistry, chemical specialties, food, microbiology, toxicology. **Holdings:** 3500 books; 1800 bound periodical volumes; 1800 reports. **Subscriptions:** 402 journals and other serials. **Services:** Interlibrary loan; library not open to the public. **Automated Operations:** Computerized cataloging and serials. **Computerized Information Services:** DIALOG Information Services, BRS Information Technologies, Chemical Abstracts Service (CAS), Questel, Chemical Information Systems, Inc. (CIS), Dow Jones News/Retrieval, NLM, Mead Data Central; internal database. **Networks/Consortia:** Member of CLASS. **Publications:** What's New In House, quarterly - research and corporate distribution. **Staff:** Isom Harrison; Sumedha Shende.

Clothier Nursing Library
See: **Bryn Mawr Hospital** (2305)

★3843★
Cloud County Historical Society - Library (Hist)
Cloud County Historical Museum
635 Broadway Phone: (913)243-2866
Concordia, KS 66901 Brad J. Chapin, Cur.
Founded: 1959. **Staff:** Prof 2; Other 1. **Subjects:** Local history. **Special Collections:** Concordia Blade Empire, 1870-1980 (on microfilm); Royal Family books and scrapbooks (113 volumes); collection of old medical books. **Holdings:** 900 books; 50 bound periodical volumes; 10 cubic feet of historical files; atlases; newspapers, 1884-1950; 9 drawers of birth, death, and marriage records; 3 drawers of unbound manuscripts. **Subscriptions:** 13 journals and other serials. **Services:** Library open to the public for reference use only. **Publications:** Cloud Comments, irregular.

O.J. Cloughly Alumni Library
See: **St. Louis College of Pharmacy** (14436)

★3844★
Clover Park Technical College - F.V. Miner Resource Center (Educ)
4500 Steilacoom Blvd., S.W. Phone: (206)589-5571
Tacoma, WA 98499-4098 Kathy Blair, Libn.
Holdings: 85,000 books. **Subscriptions:** 600 journals and other serials; 10 newspapers. **Services:** Interlibrary loan; copying; faxing; center open to the public. **Computerized Information Services:** DIALOG Information Services. **Remarks:** FAX: (206)589-5726. **Formerly:** Clover Park Vocational Technical Institute - Resource Center.

Clover Park Vocational Technical Institue
See: **Clover Park Technical College** (3844)

★3845★
Club Alpino Italiano - Biblioteca Nazionale (Sci-Engr)
Via Barbaroux 1
I-10122 Turin, Italy Phone: 11 533031
Founded: 1863. **Staff:** Prof 1; Other 1. **Subjects:** Alpinism, geology, glaciology, etnography, geography, speleology, botany. **Special Collections:** Alpine Journal - Les Alpes collection; American Alpine Journal collection. **Holdings:** 12,500 books; 10,000 bound periodical volumes. **Subscriptions:** 16 journals and other serials. **Services:** Library not open to the public. **Special Catalogs:** Catalogo a Stampa per Autori - Argomenti - Zone Geografich.

★3846★
Club Managers Association of America - Research and Publications Department (Bus-Fin)
1733 King St. Phone: (703)739-9500
Alexandria, VA 22314 Karen L. Miller, Mgr., Res. & Pubns.
Founded: 1927. **Staff:** 22. **Subjects:** Club management operations, private club administration, employment in club industry. **Holdings:** 250 books; 50 bound periodical volumes. **Subscriptions:** 25 journals. **Services:** Department not open to the public. **Special Catalogs:** Professional Development Catalog of programs, services, and publications - for sale.

★3847★
CNA Insurance Companies - Library (Bus-Fin)
CNA Plaza - 3 S.
Van Buren and Wabash Phone: (312)822-7630
Chicago, IL 60685 Sandra Masson, Libn.
Founded: 1958. **Staff:** Prof 3; Other 3. **Subjects:** Insurance, business. **Holdings:** 16,000 books. **Subscriptions:** 400 journals and other serials; 7 newspapers. **Services:** Interlibrary loan; library open to the public by appointment. **Automated Operations:** Computerized cataloging, acquisitions, serials, and circulation. **Computerized Information Services:** DIALOG Information Services, LEXIS, NEXIS, VU/TEXT Information Services, DataTimes, MEDLARS, BestLink Insurance News, ACCI/HIAA, Insurance Information Institute (III). **Networks/Consortia:** Member of Chicago Library System. **Remarks:** Alternate telephone number(s): 822-7631. FAX: (312)822-6419. **Staff:** Arlene Krizanic, Asst.Libn.

CNIB
See: **Canadian National Institute for the Blind - Library for the Blind** (2969)

★3848★
CNR, Inc. - Library (Info Sci)
220-3 Reservoir St. Phone: (617)449-4902
Needham, MA 02194 Andrea Kroll, Adm.Mgr.
Subjects: Communications technology, information science. **Holdings:** 350 books; 4000 reports; microfiche. **Subscriptions:** 300 journals and other serials. **Services:** Library not open to the public. **Remarks:** FAX: (617)449-5046.

★3849★
CNR Ministries - Library
Box 18
Edgemont, PA 19028
Subjects: Bible. **Holdings:** Figures not available. **Remarks:** Currently inactive.

Coady International Institute
See: **St. Francis Xavier University - Coady International Institute** (14317)

★3850★
Coal Association of Canada - Information Services (Energy)
205 9th Ave., S.E., Suite 502 Phone: (403)262-1544
Calgary, AB, Canada T2G 0R3 Becci Brown
Subjects: Coal. **Holdings:** Figures not available. **Services:** Interlibrary loan; library not open to the public. **Remarks:** FAX: (403)265-7604.

Coal Mining Research and Development Center of France - Library
See: **National Insitute of Industrial Environment and Hazards** (11203)

Coalbed Methane Information Center
See: **University of Alabama - Natural Gas Supply Information Center** (18165)

S. Carroll Coale Library
See: **Bethesda United Methodist Church** (1793)

★3851★
Coalition on Resource Recovery and the Environment - Library (Env-Cons)
U.S. Conference of Mayors
1620 I St., N.W., 4th Fl., Suite 600 Phone: (202)293-7330
Washington, DC 20006 David Gatton, Tech.Dir.
Subjects: Resource recovery, waste management, and related environmental issues. **Holdings:** 1000 technical reports. **Remarks:** Coalition believes that successful waste management is an "integrated utilization of many technologies which, taken as a whole, are best selected by an informed public and informed public officials." FAX: (202)293-2352.

★3852★
Coastal Ecosystems Management - Library (Env-Cons)
120 N. Rupert St. Phone: (817)870-1199
Fort Worth, TX 76107 Elizabeth L. Parker, Libn.
Subjects: Geoscience, environmental science, wildlife management, mineral resources exploration and management, plant and animal systematics and ecology. **Holdings:** 10,000 books, reprints, and journals; 1000 charts. **Computerized Information Services:** Internal database (2.5 million variate values Gulf Coast habitats). **Also Known As:** ECOsystems Management.

Coastal Engineering Information Analysis Center
See: **U.S. Army - Engineer Waterways Experiment Station** (16966)

Coastal Plain Experiment Station Library
See: **University of Georgia** (18593)

★3853★
J.F. Coates, Inc. - Library (Bus-Fin)
3738 Kanawha St., N.W.
Washington, DC 20015 Phone: (202)966-9307
Founded: 1979. **Subjects:** Forecasting; strategic and short- and long-range planning; technology and public policy; the future. **Holdings:** 5000 books; 500 reports. **Subscriptions:** 150 journals and other serials; 5 newspapers. **Services:** Interlibrary loan; library not open to the public. **Remarks:** FAX: (202)966-8349.

★3854★
Coca-Cola Company - Coca-Cola Foods - Citrus Research & Development Technical Library (Food-Bev)
261 Orange Ave.
Box 1268 Phone: (407)886-1568
Plymouth, FL 32768 Joyce N. Dykes, Libn.
Staff: 1. **Subjects:** Chemistry, food technology. **Holdings:** 900 books; 2 VF drawers of patents. **Subscriptions:** 50 journals and other serials. **Services:** Library not open to the public. **Remarks:** FAX: (407)886-6030.

★3855★
Coca-Cola Company - Coca-Cola USA - Marketing Information Center (Food-Bev)
Drawer 1734 Phone: (404)676-3314
Atlanta, GA 30301 Judy A. Cassell, Libn.
Founded: 1968. **Staff:** Prof 1. **Subjects:** Soft drinks and beverages, marketing, advertising. **Holdings:** 1000 books; 5650 documents and reports; 8 drawers of microfilm and microfiche. **Subscriptions:** 200 journals and other serials. **Services:** Interlibrary loan. **Automated Operations:** Computerized serials. **Computerized Information Services:** DIALOG Information Services, NEXIS, DataTimes, VU/TEXT Information Services; MIC document file (internal database). **Networks/Consortia:** Member of Georgia Online Database (GOLD), SOLINET. **Special Indexes:** Document file subject index. **Remarks:** FAX: (404)676-4190. Center located at 310 North Ave., Atlanta, GA 30313.

★3856★
Coca-Cola Company - Global Intelligence Resources (Food-Bev)
NAT 15
P.O. Drawer 1734 Phone: (404)676-4856
Atlanta, GA 30301 Marcia B. Abrams, Mgr.
Founded: 1967. **Staff:** Prof 1; Other 1. **Subjects:** Soft drinks and beverages, international marketing indicators, population and demographics data, packaging and advertising. **Special Collections:** Proprietary company reports (6000). **Holdings:** 250 books. **Subscriptions:** 42 journals and other serials. **Services:** Interlibrary loan; copying; SDI; library open to the public by appointment. **Computerized Information Services:** DIALOG Information Services, InvesText; FINDER (internal database). **Publications:** New in the Library, monthly; International Market Research Digest, quarterly - both for internal distribution only. **Special Indexes:** Standardized Index System (SIS) Thesaurus to FINDER. **Remarks:** FAX: (404)515-1024. **Formerly:** Its Marketing Information Resources International.

★3857★
Coca-Cola Company - Law Library (Law)
P.O. Drawer 1734 Phone: (404)676-2096
Atlanta, GA 30301 Barbara A. Beach, Mgr., Law Lib.
Founded: 1976. **Staff:** Prof 3. **Subjects:** Antitrust and trade regulations; food and drug laws; corporation law; Securities and Exchange Commission; labor and employee benefits; patents, trademarks, and copyright; international law. **Special Collections:** Roy D. Stubbs Collection (40 volumes). **Holdings:** 15,000 books; 800 bound periodical volumes; Federal Register, 1970 to present, on microfiche; Code of Federal Regulations, 1977 to present, on microfiche; FTC Decisions on microfiche. **Subscriptions:** 200 journals and other serials; 10 newspapers. **Services:** Interlibrary loan; copying; SDI; library open to the public with restrictions. **Automated Operations:** Computerized cataloging and serials. **Computerized Information Services:** LEXIS, NEXIS, DIALOG Information Services, Dow Jones News/Retrieval, EUROBASES. **Networks/Consortia:** Member of SOLINET. **Remarks:** FAX: (404)676-7636. **Staff:** Susan H. Suggs, Ref.Libn.; Sara B. Allen, Cat.Ref.

Coca-Cola Company - Marketing Information Resources International
See: **Coca-Cola Company - Global Intelligence Resources** (3856)

★3858★
Coca-Cola Company - Technical Information Services (Food-Bev)
P.O. Drawer 1734 Phone: (404)676-2008
Atlanta, GA 30301 Margareta Martin, Mgr.
Founded: 1967. **Staff:** Prof 3; Other 2. **Subjects:** Beverages, soft drinks, fruit juices, food technology, nutrition, chemistry, engineering. **Holdings:** 9500 books; 3800 bound periodical volumes; 16,000 reprints, patents, and MSDS's; 2300 internal reports. **Subscriptions:** 350 journals and other serials. **Services:** Interlibrary loan; copying; Information Services open to the public for reference use by request only. **Automated Operations:** Computerized public access catalog. **Computerized Information Services:** DIALOG Information Services, ORBIT Search Service, Data-Star, STN International, NLM, NERAC, WILSONLINE, OCLC; internal databases. **Networks/Consortia:** Member of SOLINET. **Publications:** Information Bulletin, monthly - for internal distribution only. **Special Indexes:** Online index of internal reports and literature searches. **Remarks:** FAX: (404)515-2572. Library located at 1 Coca-Cola Plaza, N.W., Atlanta, GA 30313. **Staff:** Kenneth Koubek, Info.Serv.Spec.; Brigitte Ridling, Info.Sci.

Coca-Cola USA
See: **Coca-Cola Company - Coca-Cola USA** (3855)

★3859★
Cochise County Superior Court - Law Library (Law)
Courthouse
P.O. Drawer P Phone: (602)432-9339
Bisbee, AZ 85603-0050 Lucia J. Ventura, Libn.
Founded: 1932. **Staff:** 1. **Subjects:** Law. **Holdings:** 20,000 volumes. **Subscriptions:** 29 journals and other serials. **Services:** Interlibrary loan; copying; library open to the public for reference use only.

John Cochran Division Library
See: **U.S. Dept. of Veterans Affairs (MO-St. Louis) - Library Service (142D) - John Cochran Division Library** (17362)

Mary Helen Cochran Library
See: **Sweet Briar College** (15932)

Cockerell Collection
See: **Dalhousie University** (4538)

★3860★
Cocoa Research Institute of Ghana - Library (Food-Bev, Agri)
P.O. Box 8 Phone: Tafo 51
Tafo-Akim, Ghana Mr. E.K. Tetteh, Chf.Lib.Off.
Founded: 1938. **Staff:** 4. **Subjects:** Cocoa, coffee, cola, sheanut, and tallow - breeding, agronomy, soil nutrition, plant pathology, entomology, physiology, biochemistry. **Holdings:** 14,317 volumes. **Subscriptions:** 459 journals and other serials. **Services:** Interlibrary loan; copying; SDI; library open to researchers and students. **Computerized Information Services:** Cocoa (internal database). **Publications:** Bibliographies.

★3861★
Coconino County Law Library (Law)
100 E. Birch
County Court House Phone: (602)779-6656
Flagstaff, AZ 86001 Jule Grippin, Sr., Law Libn.
Staff: 1. **Subjects:** Law. **Holdings:** 15,000 volumes. **Services:** Copying; library open to the public.

★3862★
Code, Hunter - Barristers and Solicitors - Law Library (Law)
736 6th Ave., S.W., Suite 2200 Phone: (403)298-1044
Calgary, AB, Canada T2P 3W1 Jennifer Martison, Libn.
Staff: 3. **Subjects:** Law. **Holdings:** 10,000 volumes. **Subscriptions:** 3 newspapers. **Services:** Interlibrary loan; library not open to the public. **Computerized Information Services:** QL Systems, CAN/LAW, Info Globe, LEXIS, WESTLAW, Infomart Online, Canadian Tax Online. **Remarks:** FAX: (403)263-9193.

Codex Corporation
See: **Motorola Codex** (10783)

★3863★
CODUS Ltd. - Library (Sci-Engr)
196-198 West St.
Sheffield S1 4ET, England Phone: 742 761252
Subjects: Quality control and standards for electronic components. **Holdings:** 2000 books; publications of component approval organizations. **Computerized Information Services:** Produces CODUS data base. **Remarks:** FAX: 742 750318. Telex: 547216 UGSHEF G.

Cody Memorial Library
See: **University of Toronto - Wycliffe College - Leonard Library** (19464)

★3864★
Coen Company, Inc. - Technical Library (Sci-Engr)
1510 Rollins Rd. Phone: (415)697-0440
Burlingame, CA 94010-2306 Sherman Eaton, Chm. of Bd.
Staff: Prof 1. **Subjects:** Engineering, combustion, energy. **Holdings:** 400 books; 500 bound periodical volumes; 100 codes and standards. **Subscriptions:** 12 journals and other serials. **Services:** Library not open to the public.

Loring Coes, Jr. Library
See: **Norton Company - Northborough Research Center** (12097)

★3865★
Coffield Ungaretti & Harris - Library (Law)
3500 Three First National Plaza Phone: (312)977-4499
Chicago, IL 60602 John M. Klasey
Founded: 1980. **Staff:** Prof 1; Other 3. **Subjects:** Law - securities, taxation, real estate, corporations, bankruptcy, environmental, health care, labor, litigation, public finance, estate planning. **Holdings:** 14,000 books; 30 bound periodical volumes; 700 reports on microfiche; U.S. Internal Revenue Service Private Letter Rulings, 1978-1980, on microfiche; U.S. Securities and Exchange Commission No-Action Letters, 1982, on microfiche; 500 legislative history documents; 1000 work-product documents. **Subscriptions:** 193 journals and other serials; 9 newspapers. **Services:** Interlibrary loan; copying; SDI; legal research. **Computerized Information Services:** LEXIS, DIALOG Information Services, WESTLAW, Information America, DataTimes; internal database. Performs searches on fee basis. **Networks/Consortia:** Member of Chicago Library System. **Special Catalogs:** Precedent file (online, printout). **Remarks:** FAX: (312)977-4405. **Formerly:** Coffield Ungaretti Harris & Slavin.

★3866★
COGEMA Canada Ltee. - Library (Sci-Engr)
P.O. Box 9204
817-825 45th St., W. Phone: (306)244-2554
Saskatoon, SK, Canada S7K 3X5 Lois Harte, Libn.
Staff: Prof 1. **Subjects:** Geology, uranium deposits, earth sciences. **Holdings:** 2700 books; 115 periodicals; 8000 maps; 1900 reports; 800 microfiche. **Subscriptions:** 103 journals and other serials. **Services:** Interlibrary loan (limited); library not open to the public. **Remarks:** FAX: (306)653-3883.

★3867★
Cogins, Inc. - Technical Information Services (Biol Sci, Sci-Engr)
2330 Circadian Way Phone: (707)576-6221
Santa Rosa, CA 95407 Dr. W.J. Mayer, Dir., Info.Serv.
Founded: 1937. **Staff:** Prof 4. **Subjects:** Bioremediation, environmental technology, protein, genetic engineering. **Holdings:** 5500 books; 10,000 bound periodical volumes; 218 reels of microfilm of laboratory notebooks; 8000 microfiche of company reports; 2000 reels of microfilm of periodicals and documents; 1125 reels of microfilm of patents. **Subscriptions:** 100 journals and other serials. **Services:** Interlibrary loan; SDI; library open to the public with advance request and approval by management. **Automated Operations:** Computerized cataloging and serials. **Computerized Information Services:** DIALOG Information Services, PFDS Online, STN International, OCLC. **Publications:** Bioremediation Report (newsletter). **Special Indexes:** Folro (index for HRC reports). **Remarks:** FAX: (707)575-7833. **Formerly:** Henkel Research Corporation - Library. **Staff:** Phil Mattison, Patent Liaison; Hunter McCleary, Info.Spec.; Sam Hom, Info.Spec.

★3868★
Cogswell College - Library & Learning Services (Sci-Engr)
10420 Bubb Rd. Phone: (408)252-5550
Cupertino, CA 95014 Lorna Corbetta-Noyes, Libn.
Founded: 1971. **Staff:** Prof 1; Other 1. **Subjects:** Electronics, computer technology, mechanical engineering technology, industrial and fire safety, electrical engineering, quality assurance, music technology, software engineering, computer and video imaging. **Holdings:** 13,000 books. **Subscriptions:** 90 journals and other serials; 5 newspapers. **Services:** Interlibrary loan; copying; library open to the public for reference use only. **Computerized Information Services:** DIALOG Information Services. **Networks/Consortia:** Member of San Francisco Consortium, CLASS. **Publications:** Cogswell Contact, bimonthly - to alumni, staff, and faculty. **Special Catalogs:** Audio-Visual Catalog. **Remarks:** FAX: (408)253-2413. **Also Known As:** Cogswell Polytechnical College.

Cogswell Music Library
See: **Indiana University of Pennsylvania** (7810)

George M. Cohan Collection
See: **Museum of the City of New York - Theatre Collection** (10892)

★3869★
Cohasset Historical Society - Library (Hist)
14 Summer St. Phone: (617)383-6930
Cohasset, MA 02025 David H. Wadsworth, Sr.Cur.
Founded: 1928. **Staff:** 1. **Subjects:** Cohasset area history; local and area maritime history; genealogy. **Special Collections:** Arthur Mahoney Collection; Henry F. Howe Collection (history - local, area, theater). **Holdings:** 650 books. **Services:** Library open to the public for reference use only. **Computerized Information Services:** Internal database. **Remarks:** Operates in conjunction with Historical Society Archives of Local and Area History. Affiliated with Cohasset Historic Trust.

Albert D. Cohen Management Library
See: **University of Manitoba** (18784)

L. Lewis Cohen Memorial Medical Library
See: **Louis A. Weiss Memorial Hospital** (20143)

Morris Raphael Cohen Library
See: **City College of City University of New York - Special Collections** (3735)

Ralph Cohen Memorial Library
See: **Isaac M. Wise Temple** (20536)

★3870★
Cohen, Shapiro, Polisher, Shiekman and Cohen - Library (Law)
Princeton Pike Corporate Ctr.
1009 Lenox Dr., Bldg. 4 Phone: (609)895-6268
Lawrenceville, NJ 08648 Lorri L. Miksa, Libn.
Staff: Prof 2; Other 1. **Subjects:** Law. **Holdings:** 5000 volumes. **Subscriptions:** 50 journals and other serials; 4 newspapers. **Services:** Library not open to the public. **Computerized Information Services:** WESTLAW, LEXIS; internal databases. **Remarks:** FAX: (609)895-1329. **Staff:** Jeanne Tomar, Doc.Env.Libn.; Ann McCarron, Libn.Asst.

★3871★
Cohen, Shapiro, Polisher, Shiekman and Cohen - Library (Law)
12 S. 12th St.
Philadelphia, PA 19107 Phone: (215)351-2005
Staff: Prof 2; Other 2. **Subjects:** Law. **Holdings:** 11,000 books; 235 bound periodical volumes. **Subscriptions:** 100 journals and other serials; 16 newspapers. **Services:** Interlibrary loan; library not open to the public. **Computerized Information Services:** LEXIS, WESTLAW, VU/TEXT Information Services, DIALOG Information Services, DataTimes, CompuServe Information Service, Information America. **Remarks:** FAX: (215)592-4329. **Staff:** Dorisn Ireton, Libn.

Charles Cohn Memorial Library
See: **North Shore Synagogue** (11949)

★3872★
Colby College - Miller Library - Special Collections (Hum, Hist)
Waterville, ME 04901 Phone: (207)872-3284
Patience-Anne W. Lenk, Interim Act.Cur.
Founded: 1938. **Staff:** 1. **Special Collections:** American regional literature collection (includes works of Sarah Orne Jewett, Laura Richards, Kenneth Roberts, Ben Ames Williams, Booth Tarkington; complete set of Mosher Press publications); Colby College Archives; Edwin Arlington Robinson Collection (1500 printed and manuscript items); James Augustine Healy Collection of Irish Literature (6000 volumes); Thomas Hardy Collection (300 printed and manuscript items); Thomas Mann Collection (200 printed items); Bern Porter Collection of Contemporary Letters (2000 printed volumes; 7000 letters and manuscripts); British section (all titles published by Kelmscott Press; 300 different editions of the Rubaiyat; Violet Paget/Vernon Lee assemblage; John Masefield Collection); 19th century juvenile literature collection (1000 Jacob Abbott items; bound set of Tiptop Weekly; works of Kate Douglas Wiggin; antique textbooks); Harold Trowbridge Pulsifer Library (late 19th and early 20th century poetry); Thomas Sargent Perry's private library; Irish literary renaissance and contemporary Irish literature. **Holdings:** 37,250 books; 100 bound periodical volumes; 288,000 letters and manuscripts; 728 reels of microfilm. **Subscriptions:** 10 journals and other serials. **Services:** Copying; collections open to the public. **Computerized Information Services:** OCLC; internal database; InterNet (electronic mail service). **Publications:** Guide to James Augustine Healy Collection. **Remarks:** FAX: (207)872-3555. Electronic mail address(es): PALENK@COLBY.EDU. (InterNet).

William E. Colby Memorial Library
See: **Sierra Club** (15159)

★3873★
Cold Spring Harbor Laboratory - Main Library (Biol Sci, Med)
Box 100 Phone: (516)367-8352
Cold Spring Harbor, NY 11724 Susan Cooper, Dir., Libs./Dir, Pub.Aff.
Founded: 1906. **Staff:** Prof 1.5; Other 4.5. **Subjects:** Biological sciences, genetics, cancer research, cell science, neurobiology, virology. **Special Collections:** Carnegie Collection (genetics, eugenics, biochemistry historical collection; 3628 volumes). **Holdings:** 8600 books; 23,000 bound periodical volumes; 24 VF drawers of archives, letters, clippings; 4 boxes of pamphlets. **Subscriptions:** 621 journals and other serials. **Services:** Interlibrary loan; copying; library open to the public by appointment with librarian only. **Computerized Information Services:** DIALOG Information Services, MEDLARS. **Networks/Consortia:** Member of Long Island Library Resources Council, National Network of Libraries of Medicine - Middle Atlantic Region. **Remarks:** Original eugenics work of historical interest and much of the definitive work in genetics was done at this site. FAX: (516)367-8532. **Staff:** Genemary Falvey, Hd., Lib.Serv.; Laura Hyman, Adm.Mgr.; Wanda Stolen, ILL.

Bruce M. Cole Memorial Library
See: **St. Joseph's Hospital & Health Center** (14410)

Clinton L. Cole Marine Library
See: **University of Maine - Raymond H. Fogler Library - Special Collections Department** (18779)

★3874★
Cole County Historical Society - Museum and Library (Hist)
109 Madison St.
Jefferson City, MO 65101 Phone: (314)635-1850
Founded: 1941. **Subjects:** History - Cole County, Jefferson City; genealogy. **Holdings:** 600 books; 50 bound periodical volumes; 25 scrapbooks; 100 documents and manuscripts; 2000 pictures; 15 inaugural ball gowns of former governors' wives. **Services:** Library not open to the public.

Matt Cole Memorial Library
See: **Williams College - Center for Environmental Studies** (20445)

Cole Memorial Library of the Physics and Astronomy Departments
See: **Ohio State University** (12303)

★3875★
Colebrook Historical Society, Inc. - Library and Archives (Hist)
Box 85 Phone: (203)379-3509
Colebrook, CT 06021 Elizabeth McNeill, Cur.
Founded: 1953. **Staff:** 1. **Subjects:** Local history, local authors, genealogy, early settlers and industries. **Special Collections:** Colebrook River history; Colebrook district schools history. **Holdings:** 600 books; 70 linear feet of town and church records, account books, early maps, cemetery headstone information, photographs, pictures. **Services:** Collections open to the public for reference use only on a limited schedule, Memorial Day through Columbus Day; otherwise by appointment. **Special Indexes:** Index to scrapbooks (card); index to 19th century Colebrook residents; Index to Irving Manchester: The Colebrook History (1935); - for sale; index to millsites.

Coleccion Tloque Nahuaque
See: **University of California, Santa Barbara - Library - Chicano Studies Collection** (18431)

★3876★
Colegio de Abogados de Barcelona - Biblioteca (Law)
Mallorca 283 Phone: 3 4872814
E-08037 Barcelona, Spain Jose Mendez Perez
Founded: 1833. **Staff:** Prof 5; Other 4. **Subjects:** Law. **Special Collections:** Incunabula, manuscripts, and first editions by Catalan lawyers (13); Boletin Oficial del Estado, 1720 to present; Diario Oficial de las Cortes Generales (Spanish Congress Official Journal), 1808 to present. **Holdings:** 250,000 books; 843 bound periodical volumes; microfiche; microfilm. **Subscriptions:** 376 journals and other serials; 2 newspapers. **Services:** Library not open to the public. **Automated Operations:** Computerized cataloging. **Computerized Information Services:** CELEX, BOE. Contact Person: Patricia Sanpera, Libn./Doc. **Remarks:** FAX: 93 4871128.

Coleman Library
See: **Callaway Educational Association** (2581)

Coleman Library
See: **Florida A&M University - School of Business & Industry** (5862)

★3877★
W.B. Coleman Company - Library (Sci-Engr)
1 Pavilion Ave.
Riverside, NJ 08075 Phone: (609)461-2800
Founded: 1922. **Staff:** 1. **Subjects:** Metallurgy, materials analysis. **Holdings:** 500 books; 18,000 reports. **Subscriptions:** 30 journals and other serials; 3 newspapers. **Services:** Library not open to the public. **Remarks:** FAX: (609)764-8206.

Coler Memorial Hospital
See: **New York City Health and Hospitals Corporation** (11560)

★3878★
Coles, Gilbert Associates - Library
2800-400 3rd Ave., S.W. Phone: (403)266-9500
Calgary, AB, Canada T2P 4H2 Eileen Millard, Libn.
Remarks: No further information was supplied by respondent.

★3879★
Colgate Palmolive Company - Technical Information Center (Sci-Engr)
909 River Rd. Phone: (908)878-7573
Piscataway, NJ 08854 Monica Grover, Sect.Hd.
Founded: 1936. **Staff:** Prof 1; Other 2. **Subjects:** Soaps and detergents, fats and oils, dentifrices, cosmetics, perfumes and essential oils, environmental pollution, foods, chemistry. **Holdings:** 20,000 books; 10,000 bound periodical volumes; 16,000 periodical volumes on 4000 reels of microfilm; 250 VF drawers of internal reports; 10 VF drawers of archival materials. **Subscriptions:** 500 journals and other serials. **Services:** Interlibrary loan; copying; SDI; center open to the public with restrictions. **Computerized Information Services:** DIALOG Information Services, Maxwell Online, Inc., BRS Information Technologies, LEXIS, NEXIS, NLM, Dow Jones News/Retrieval, MIS; CD-ROMs (MEDLINE, TOXLINE, MicroPatent). **Publications:** Notes & Abstracts Bulletin, monthly; Search Alerts. **Special Indexes:** Indexes to internal documents and compounds (online). **Remarks:** FAX: (908)878-7128.

Colgate Rochester Divinity School/Bexley Hall/Crozer Theological Seminary - Ambrose Swasey Library
See: **Ambrose Swasey Library** (15904)

Samuel Colgate Historical Library
See: **American Baptist Historical Society - American Baptist-Samuel Colgate Historical Library** (498)

★3880★
Colgate University - Everett Needham Case Library - Special Collections Department (Hist, Hum, Rare Book)
13 Oak Dr. Phone: (315)824-7305
Hamilton, NY 13346-1398 Melissa McAfee, Spec.Coll.Libn.
Founded: 1947. **Staff:** Prof 1; Other 2. **Subjects:** Literature - American and British literature, New York state history, history of printing. **Special Collections:** University archives; Henry A. Colgate Collection of Joseph Conrad; Earl Daniels Collection of T.S. Eliot; Thomas Iiams Collection on Books about Books; Elmer Sheets Collection of fine bindings; the Norman H. Strouse Collection of fine printing; the Richard S. Weiner Collection of George Bernard Shaw; Powys Family Collection; History of Radio and Television collection; History of the State of New York collection. **Holdings:** 12,000 books; 6000 linear feet of archival materials. **Subscriptions:** 7 journals and other serials. **Services:** Copying (limited); archives open to the public. **Automated Operations:** Computerized public access catalog and cataloging. **Computerized Information Services:** Internal database. **Remarks:** FAX: (315)824-1704.

★3881★
Collard and Company - Library (Info Sci)
48 Hastings Rd. Phone: (908)464-6000
Berkeley Heights, NJ 07922 R. Collard, Pres.
Subjects: Information systems. **Holdings:** 5000 books; 5000 reports. **Subscriptions:** 130 journals and other serials. **Services:** Library not open to the public.

Collectif d'Echanges pour la Technologie Appropriee
See: **Exchange Group for Appropriate Technology** (5517)

★3882★
Collector Car Appraisers Association - Library (Rec)
24 Myrtle Ave. Phone: (716)855-1931
Buffalo, NY 14204 Jim Sandoro
Founded: 1980. **Subjects:** Car appraisal and restoration. **Holdings:** 3740 volumes; factory manuals; sales literature; photographs. **Remarks:** FAX: (716)856-7135.

★3883★
Collectors Club - Library (Rec)
22 E. 35th St. Phone: (212)683-0559
New York, NY 10016 Bruce Rutherford, Libn.
Founded: 1896. **Subjects:** Philately, postal history. **Holdings:** 100,000 items. **Subscriptions:** 150 journals and other serials. **Services:** Interlibrary loan (fee); copying; library open to the public for reference use only by appointment; members may borrow books.

★3884★
Collectors Club of Chicago - Library (Rec)
1029 N. Dearborn St. Phone: (312)642-7981
Chicago, IL 60610 Lester E. Winick, Lib.Comm.
Founded: 1945. **Staff:** 1. **Subjects:** Philately. **Holdings:** 4000 books; 2000 bound periodical volumes. **Subscriptions:** 100 journals and other serials. **Services:** Interlibrary loan; library open to the public. **Publications:** Books on postal history.

★3885★
College of Aeronautics - George A. Vaughn, Jr. Memorial Library (Sci-Engr)
LaGuardia Airport Sta. Phone: (718)429-6600
Flushing, NY 11371 JoAnn Jayne, Dir.
Founded: 1955. **Staff:** Prof 3; Other 2. **Subjects:** Aeronautics, engineering, physical science, mathematics, computers. **Special Collections:** NASA Reports, SAE Reports, Aircraft Maintenance Manuals (28,332). **Holdings:** 35,714 books; 1787 bound periodical volumes; 131,846 microforms; 954 AV programs. **Subscriptions:** 381 journals and other serials; 12 newspapers. **Services:** Interlibrary loan; copying; library open to the public by appointment. **Computerized Information Services:** DIALOG Information Services, WILSONLINE, AVCOM. **Networks/Consortia:** Member of New York Metropolitan Reference and Research Library Agency. **Remarks:** FAX: (718)429-0256. **Staff:** Barbara Feldman, Asst.Libn.; William Assad, Evening Libn.

College of the Americas - Museum of the Americas
See: **Museum of the Americas** (10887)

College of Art & Design
See: **Center for Creative Studies** (3228)

College Band Directors National Association Archives
See: **University of Maryland, College Park Libraries - Music Library** (18821)

College Canadien de Police - Centre du Documentation Policiere
See: **Royal Canadian Mounted Police - Canadian Police College - Law Enforcement Reference Centre** (14108)

★3886★
College Center of the Finger Lakes - Library
22 W. 3rd St.
Box 180
Corning, NY 14830
Founded: 1965. **Subjects:** Business, education, engineering. **Holdings:** 10,000 books. **Remarks:** Currently inactive.

★3887★
College of Charleston - Robert Scott Small Library - Special Collections (Hist)
66 George St. Phone: (803)792-5530
Charleston, SC 29424 Gail Garfinkle, Coord. of Spec.Coll.
Staff: Prof 2. **Subjects:** Charleston, South Carolina Lowcountry. **Special Collections:** Wendell Mitchell Levi Library & Archives (pigeon fancier); Scientific Apparatus of the College of Charleston, 1800-1940. **Holdings:** 25,000 books; 1000 bound periodical volumes; 600 linear feet of other cataloged items. **Services:** Copying; collections open to the public with restrictions. **Automated Operations:** Computerized cataloging. **Computerized Information Services:** DIALOG Information Services. Performs searches on fee basis. Contact Person: Phillip Powell. **Networks/Consortia:** Member of Charleston Academic Libraries Consortium. **Remarks:** FAX: (803)792-8019. **Staff:** Oliver Smalls, Archv.

★3888★
College of the Desert - Library (Soc Sci)
43-500 Monterey Ave.
Palm Desert, CA 92260 Phone: (619)773-2563
Founded: 1962. **Special Collections:** Desert Collection (400 volumes). **Services:** Interlibrary loan; copying; library open to the public. **Computerized Information Services:** ERIC; internal databases. **Remarks:** FAX: (619)568-5955.

College for Developmental Studies
See: **Center for Early Education/College for Developmental Studies** (3235)

★3889★
College Dominicain de Philosophie et de Theologie - Bibliotheque (Rel-Phil)
96 Empress Ave. Phone: (613)233-5696
Ottawa, ON, Canada K1R 7G3 Denis Regimbald, Chf.Libn./Info.Dir.
Staff: Prof 3. **Subjects:** Theology, Near Eastern studies, Biblical studies, philosophy, medieval studies. **Holdings:** 85,000 books; 14,675 bound periodical volumes. **Subscriptions:** 10 journals and other serials; 500 newspapers. **Services:** Interlibrary loan; copying; library open to the public. **Remarks:** FAX: (613)233-6064. **Also Known As:** Dominican College of Philosophy and Theology. **Staff:** Angelo Ouellet, Asst.Libn.; Annette Smart, Asst.Libn.

★3890★
College Edouard Montpetit - Ecole Nationale d'Aerotechnique - Bibliotheque (Sci-Engr, Comp Sci)
5555, place de la Savane Phone: (514)678-3560
St. Hubert, PQ, Canada J3Y 5K2 Marielle Raymond, Chf.Libn.
Founded: 1964. **Staff:** Prof 1; Other 2. **Subjects:** Aeronautics, computer assisted design and manufacturing. **Special Collections:** Aeronautics (10,000). **Holdings:** 17,300 books; 2205 bound periodical volumes; 4000 microfiche. **Subscriptions:** 200 journals and other serials. **Services:** Interlibrary loan; copying; library open to the public. **Automated Operations:** Computerized cataloging and acquisitions. **Computerized Information Services:** MULTILIS (internal database). **Remarks:** FAX: (514)678-3240.

College d'Enseignement General et Professionnel
See: **CEGEP de Trois-Rivieres** (3194)

★3891★
College of Family Physicians of Canada - Canadian Library of Family Medicine (Med)
Natural Sciences Centre, Rm. 170 C
University of Western Ontario Phone: (519)661-3170
London, ON, Canada N6A 5B7 Lynn Dunikowski, Libn.
Founded: 1972. **Staff:** Prof 1; Other 3. **Subjects:** Family medicine, general practice. **Services:** Copying; library consultation; services available to CFPC members and health agencies and personnel interested in family medicine. **Computerized Information Services:** MEDLARS, BRS Information Technologies, DIALOG Information Services, CAN/OLE; Envoy 100, NETNORTH (electronic mail services). **Publications:** A Library for Family Physicians: Recommended List of Books and Journals. **Special Indexes:** Family Medicine Literature Index (FAMLI), annual. **Remarks:** The Canadian Library of Family Medicine bases its services at the Sciences Library of the University of Western Ontario and uses the library's facilities and collection. FAX: (519)661-3292. Electronic mail address(es): L.DUNIKOWSKI (Envoy 100).

College Football Hall of Fame
See: **National Football Foundation** (11169)

College de la Garde Cotiere Canadienne
See: **Canada - Transport Canada - Canadian Coast Guard College** (2872)

★3892★
College of Great Falls - Library (Rel-Phil)
1301 20th St., S. Phone: (406)761-8210
Great Falls, MT 59404 Una M. Koontz, Lib.Dir.
Founded: 1932. **Staff:** Prof 2; Other 4. **Subjects:** Religion, education. **Special Collections:** Microbook Library of American Civilization (12,474 microfiche); Bertsche Collection (Montana and local history). **Holdings:** 74,071 books; 13,234 bound periodical volumes; 31,922 microforms; 512 AV programs; 2241 phonograph records; 1552 scores; 1155 cassettes. **Subscriptions:** 434 journals and other serials; 10 newspapers. **Services:** Interlibrary loan; copying; library open to the public with restrictions. **Computerized Information Services:** DIALOG Information Services, WLN; CD-ROMs (Academic Index, LaserCAT, HealthPLAN-CD). Performs searches on fee basis. **Remarks:** FAX: (406)454-0113. **Staff:** Susan Lee, Rd.Serv.Libn.

★3893★
College of Health Sciences - Learning Resources Center (Med)
920 S. Jefferson St., Rm. 611 Phone: (703)985-8270
Roanoke, VA 24016 Nan Seamans, Dir.
Staff: 3. **Subjects:** Nursing, allied health. **Holdings:** 5000 books; 600 bound periodical volumes. **Subscriptions:** 175 journals and other serials. **Services:** Interlibrary loan; copying; SDI; center open to the public for reference use only. **Computerized Information Services:** DIALOG Information Services, MEDLARS. Performs searches on fee basis. **Networks/Consortia:** Member of Southwestern Virginia Health Information Librarians (SWVAHILI). **Remarks:** Affiliated with Community Hospital of Roanoke Valley.

★3894★
College of the Holy Cross - Fenwick Music Library (Mus)
Worcester, MA 01610 Phone: (508)793-2295
Lisa M. Redpath, Mus.Libn.
Founded: 1978. **Staff:** Prof 1; Other 1. **Subjects:** Classical music, jazz, ethnomusicology. **Special Collections:** Farmerie Collection (jazz recordings); Hennessy Collection (opera recordings). **Holdings:** 3900 books; 320 bound periodical volumes; 4100 scores; 14,000 phonograph records; 330 videotapes. **Subscriptions:** 40 journals and other serials. **Services:** Interlibrary loan; library open to the public with librarian's permission. **Automated Operations:** Computerized cataloging. **Computerized Information Services:** OCLC, DIALOG Information Services; BITNET (electronic mail service). **Networks/Consortia:** Member of NELINET, Inc., Worcester Area Cooperating Libraries (WACL). **Remarks:** Electronic mail address(es): redpath@hlycross (BITNET).

★3895★
College of the Holy Cross - O'Callahan Science Library (Sci-Engr)
Worcester, MA 01610 Phone: (508)793-2643
Tony Stankus, Sci.Libn.
Founded: 1958. **Staff:** Prof 1; Other 2. **Subjects:** Mathematics, biology, chemistry, physics, history of science, biographies of scientists, astronomy, earth science, neuroscience, ethical and social implications of science and medicine, computer science. **Holdings:** 31,029 books; 38,000 bound periodical volumes. **Subscriptions:** 604 journals and other serials. **Services:** Interlibrary loan; copying; SDI; library open to the public with restrictions. **Computerized Information Services:** DIALOG Information Services, OCLC; CD-ROM (Compact Cambridge Life Sciences Collection); BITNET, InterNet (electronic mail services). **Networks/Consortia:** Member of NELINET, Inc., Worcester Area Cooperating Libraries (WACL). **Remarks:** FAX: (508)793-2372. Electronic mail address(es): LIB-STANKUS@HLYCROSS (BITNET). **Staff:** Carolyn Mills, Asst.Sci.Libn.

★3896★
College for Human Services - Library (Soc Sci)
345 Hudson St., 14th Fl. Phone: (212)989-2002
New York, NY 10014 Hibbert W. Moss, Hd.Libn.
Staff: Prof 2; Other 4. **Subjects:** Human services, social sciences, business, management. **Holdings:** 16,000 books; 3000 reels of microfilm. **Subscriptions:** 232 journals and other serials; 6 newspapers. **Services:** Interlibrary loan; copying; library open to the public for reference use only. **Automated Operations:** Computerized cataloging and acquisitions. **Computerized Information Services:** DIALOG Information Services, University Microfilms International (UMI) Newspaper Abstracts; CD-ROMs (ERIC, Sociofile, BIP). Performs searches on fee basis. Contact Person: Robert McCullum, Asst., Ref.Serv. 989-2002, ext. 213. **Networks/Consortia:** Member of New York Metropolitan Reference and Research Library Agency. **Remarks:** FAX: (212)627-5104. **Staff:** Michael Hillman.

★3897★
College of Insurance - Insurance Society of New York - Kathryn and Shelby Cullom Davis Library (Bus-Fin)
101 Murray St. Phone: (212)962-4111
New York, NY 10007 Don Spicehandler, Chf.Libn.
Founded: 1901. **Staff:** Prof 8. **Subjects:** Insurance - casualty, fire, health, inland marine, life, marine, suretyship, unemployment, workmen's compensation, allied fields; fire and accident prevention; earthquakes; actuarial science. **Special Collections:** William Winter Marine Library (marine insurance); Heber B. Churchill earthquake collection. **Holdings:** 84,423 books; 16,453 bound periodical volumes; 64,732 pamphlets, clippings, speeches. **Subscriptions:** 464 journals and other serials; 10 newspapers. **Services:** Interlibrary loan; copying; library open to the public for reference and research. **Computerized Information Services:** RLIN, LEXIS, NEXIS. **Networks/Consortia:** Member of New York Metropolitan Reference and Research Library Agency. **Publications:** Insurance Society of New York Recent Additions; Books Added to the Ecker Library; Trivial Pursuit: Insurance. **Remarks:** FAX: (212)964-3381. **Staff:** Mark Jablin, Assoc.Libn.; Donna Vetere, Liberal Arts Libn.; Arati Bhattacharji, Ser.Cat; Glady Hodapp, Chf.Ser.Libn.; Charlotte Karcher, Evening Libn.; Renee Sanders, Chf.Cat.; Galina Sassian, Monographic Cat.

College of Law at San Fernando Valley
See: **University of La Verne** (18763)

★3898★
College Militaire Royal de St-Jean - Library (Mil, Area-Ethnic)
Richelain, PQ, Canada J0J 1R0 Phone: (514)358-6602
Gretchen Cheung, Chf.Libn.
Founded: 1952. **Staff:** Prof 4; Other 5. **Subjects:** French Canadian literature, military science, Canadiana, Canadian history, sciences. **Holdings:** 113,245 books; 26,544 bound periodical volumes; 5041 government publications; French Canadian newspapers on microfilm; 5200 reels of microfilm; 5700 microfiche. **Subscriptions:** 899 journals and other serials. **Services:** Interlibrary loan; copying; library open to professors, staff and families, and officer cadets. **Computerized Information Services:** DIALOG Information Services, DOBIS Canadian Online Library System, UTLAS; CUBE (Carleton Library System; internal database); Envoy 100 (electronic mail service). **Publications:** Accession Lists, monthly. **Remarks:** FAX: (514)358-6799. Electronic mail address(es): PEB.QSTJ (Envoy 100). Maintained by Canada - National Defence. **Staff:** L. Racicot, Tech.Serv.Libn.; Lise Lafleche, Acq.Libn.; Paul Tremblay, Ref.Libn.

★3899★
College de Musique Sainte-Croix - Bibliotheque (Mus)
637 Sainte-Croix Blvd. Phone: (514)747-6521
St. Laurent, PQ, Canada H4L 3X7 Isabelle Paquette, Dir.
Founded: 1968. **Staff:** Prof 2. **Subjects:** Music. **Special Collections:** Gregorian Chant number 800 with paleographic signs (Solesmes). **Holdings:** 4840 books; 1050 bound periodical volumes; 6500 scores; Gregorian Chant on microfilm; theses; documents on Canadian composers; tapes. **Subscriptions:** 42 journals and other serials. **Services:** Copying; library open to the public with restrictions. **Remarks:** College de Musique Sainte-Croix is part of the CEGEP de Saint-Laurent. **Staff:** Catherine Jolicoeur, Asst.Libn.

★3900★
College of Notre Dame - Notre Dame Library (Hum)
1500 Ralston Ave. Phone: (415)593-1601
Belmont, CA 94002 Linda A. Driver, Lib.Dir.
Founded: 1868. **Staff:** Prof 3.5; Other 1.5. **Subjects:** English and American literature, religion, art, history, French and Spanish literature, music. **Special Collections:** Archives of modern Christian art (19,000 slides); Californiana (1270 volumes). **Holdings:** 84,390 books; 13,500 bound periodical volumes; 16,487 microforms; 128 AV programs; 8000 sound recordings; 6800 scores. **Subscriptions:** 550 journals and other serials. **Services:** Interlibrary loan; copying; library open to the public for reference use only. **Computerized Information Services:** DIALOG Information Services, RLIN. **Staff:** Mary Guedon, Ref.; Judy Castillo, Acq., Ser., & ILL.

★3901★
College of the Ozarks - Ralph Foster Museum - Lois Brownell Research Library (Hist)
Point Lookout, MO 65726 Phone: (417)334-6411
Robert S. Esworthy, Dir.
Founded: 1971. **Subjects:** Firearms, archeology, Ozarks regional history, antiques, fine art, natural history. **Holdings:** 1500 books; 300 bound periodical volumes; 5 VF drawers of archives. **Subscriptions:** 25 journals and other serials; 7 newspapers. **Services:** Library open to the public with permission of director. **Remarks:** FAX: (417)335-2618.

★3902★
College of Physicians of Philadelphia - Library (Med)
19 S. 22nd St.
Philadelphia, PA 19103 Phone: (215)561-6050
Founded: 1787. **Staff:** Prof 7; Other 14. **Subjects:** Medicine, medical specialties, consumer health, history of medicine. **Special Collections:** Incunabula (427); 16th-19th century works (65,000). **Holdings:** 145,000 monographs; 190,000 bound periodical volumes; theses; dissertations; 1500 manuscript record groups; 10,000 portraits, engravings, pictures; 10,000 autographs. **Subscriptions:** 700 journals and other serials. **Services:** Interlibrary loan; copying; library consultation; library open to the public for reading and copying; other privileges restricted to Fellows of the College. **Computerized Information Services:** OCLC, MEDLINE, DIALOG Information Services, BRS Information Technologies, WILSONLINE, MDX Health Digest; CD-ROM (MEDLINE). Performs searches on fee basis. **Networks/Consortia:** Member of PALINET, National Network of Libraries of Medicine - Middle Atlantic Region, Health Sciences Libraries Consortium (HSLC), Philadelphia Area Consortium of Special Collections Libraries (PACSCL). **Publications:** Currently Received Serials. **Special Indexes:** Card file of portraits. **Remarks:** FAX: (215)561-6477. **Staff:** Andrea Kenyon, Dir. of Lib. for Pub.Serv.; Thomas Horrocks, Dir. of Lib. for Hist.Serv.; Patricia H. Wilson, Coord. for Ref.Serv.; Marjorie Smink, Assoc.Libn. for Coll.Mgt.; Kate Anthony, Doc. Delivery Coord.; Jack Eckert, Cur. of Archv. & Mss.

★3903★
College of Physicians and Surgeons of British Columbia - Medical Library Service (Med)
1383 W. 8th Ave. Phone: (604)733-6671
Vancouver, BC, Canada V6H 4C4 Jim Henderson, Dir.
Founded: 1960. **Staff:** Prof 4; Other 7. **Subjects:** Medicine, medical history, medical biography. **Special Collections:** Vancouver Medical Association Historical Collection; British Columbia Archives of Medicine. **Holdings:** 10,000 books; 70,000 bound periodical volumes; 1500 pamphlets; 8 VF drawers of archival materials; 3 shelves of reports; 1800 audiotapes; 100 video cassettes; 30 interactive computer discs. **Subscriptions:** 650 journals and other serials. **Services:** Interlibrary loan; copying; SDI; library open to the public for reference use only. **Automated Operations:** Computerized acquisitions, cataloging, serials, and statistics. **Computerized Information Services:** MEDLINE, BRS Information Technologies, CAN/OLE; Envoy 100, InterNet (electronic mail services). **Publications:** Books for Hospital Libraries, annual - to British Columbia hospitals. **Remarks:** FAX: (604)737-8582. Electronic mail address(es): BCMLS (Envoy 100); jim@cbdn.ca (InterNet). **Also Known As:** British Columbia Medical Library Service. **Staff:** Adrienne Clark, Asst.Libn.; Linda Einblau, Ref.Libn.; Judy Neill, Cat.; Diane Walley, ILL.

★3904★
College Placement Council, Inc. - Information Center (Educ)
62 Highland Ave. Phone: (215)868-1421
Bethlehem, PA 18017 Rhea A. Nagle, Coord.
Staff: Prof 1. **Subjects:** Career planning and development, recruiting and placement, education statistics. **Holdings:** 3000 volumes; 15 shelves of files. **Subscriptions:** 49 journals and other serials. **Services:** Center open to the public.

★3905★
College of Preachers - Library (Rel-Phil)
3510 Woodley Rd., N.W. Phone: (202)537-6387
Washington, DC 20016 Rev. Dr. Erica B. Wood, Int.Pres. & Dir. of Studies
Founded: 1929. **Subjects:** Religion. **Holdings:** 10,000 volumes. **Subscriptions:** 70 journals and other serials. **Services:** Library open to the public by appointment. **Special Indexes:** Index to Fellows of the College of Preachers' Theses. **Remarks:** Alternate telephone number(s): 537-6380. FAX: (202)364-6600. **Staff:** Lenore Bellinger, Libn.

★3906★
College Retirement Equities Fund - CREF Research Library (Bus-Fin)
730 3rd Ave. Phone: (212)916-4007
New York, NY 10017 Linda Krauss Bashover, Libn.
Founded: 1973. **Staff:** Prof 1; Other 4. **Subjects:** Investments, finance. **Holdings:** 1086 books; 33 drawers of microfiche; 270 VF drawers of corporation records; 8 drawers of microfilm. **Subscriptions:** 450 journals and other serials; 30 newspapers. **Services:** Interlibrary loan; library open to SLA members. **Computerized Information Services:** DIALOG Information Services, NEXIS.

College du Sacre-Coeur Archives
See: **University of Sudbury - Jesuit Archives** (19358)

★3907★
College of St. Catherine - Library - Ade Bethune Collection (Art)
2004 Randolph Ave. Phone: (612)690-6650
St. Paul, MN 55105 Janet Kinney, Lib.Dir.
Founded: 1905. **Staff:** Prof 1; Other 1. **Subjects:** Ade Bethune, sacred art, liturgy and art, women artists, liturgical movement, Catholic church history, Catholic radicalism, Catholic Worker Movement. **Special Collections:** Ade Bethune Collection. **Holdings:** 23 VF drawers; 10 map drawers. **Services:** Copying; library open to the public and researchers with permission of director. **Remarks:** FAX: (612)690-6024.

★3908★
College of St. Catherine - Library - Ruth Sawyer Collection (Hum, Rare Book)
Saint Catherine Library, Rare Book Rm.
2004 Randolph Ave. Phone: (612)690-6553
St. Paul, MN 55105 Sr. Mary William Brady, CSJ, Archv./Cur.
Staff: Prof 2. **Subjects:** Ruth Sawyer, children's literature, history and art of storytelling, folklore. **Special Collections:** Original manuscripts and drawings from several of Ruth Sawyer's books (2399 books, 265 letters); honorary medals - Newbery, Wilder, Regina; artifacts of storybook characters; Charlotte Hill Slade Collection (fine binding and printing; Orientalia, first and limited editions; 2337 books); the Sister Antonia McHugh Collection (autographed works of literary merit, local authors and authors associated with the college; 779 books; 3027 letters); Florence and Alfred Muellerleile Collection (books made by Alfred Muellerleile, master printer: printing; rare and precious medieval manuscript leaves, bibles, and incunabula; 902 books). **Holdings:** 6417 books; 3232 letters. **Services:** Copying; collection open to the public with restrictions. **Automated Operations:** Computerized cataloging. **Computerized Information Services:** DIALOG Information Services, OCLC. **Networks/Consortia:** Member of MINITEX Library Information Network, Cooperating Libraries in Consortium (CLIC). **Publications:** The Ruth Sawyer Bibliography - for internal distribution only. **Remarks:** This is a complete collection of Ruth Sawyer's writings, copies of works translated into foreign languages, correspondence, and other personal memorabilia. FAX: (612)690-6024.

★3909★
College of St. Catherine - Library - Women's Collection (Soc Sci)
Saint Catherine Library
2004 Randolph Ave. Phone: (612)690-6648
St. Paul, MN 55105 Janet Kinney, Lib.Dir.
Founded: 1964. **Staff:** Prof 1. **Subjects:** Sociological and economic studies on women published in the early 20th century; psychological liberation of women; history, education, status of women in all phases of public and private life. **Special Collections:** Herstory (collection of 300 women's journals, newspapers, newsletters, 1956-1971; 23 reels of microfilm); U.S. Dept. of Labor, Women's Bureau Bulletin, 1918-1954 (microfiche). **Holdings:** 5400 books; 20 bound periodical volumes; 8 VF drawers of pamphlets and clippings. **Subscriptions:** 40 journals and other serials. **Services:** Interlibrary loan; copying; collection open to the public for reference use only. **Automated Operations:** Computerized cataloging. **Computerized Information Services:** DIALOG Information Services, OCLC. **Networks/Consortia:** Member of MINITEX Library Information Network, Cooperating Libraries in Consortium (CLIC). **Remarks:** FAX: (612)690-6024.

★3910★
College of St. Catherine - Performing Arts Library (Mus, Theater)
2004 Randolph Ave. Phone: (612)690-6696
St. Paul, MN 55105 Donald Bemis Jones, Libn.
Founded: 1970. **Staff:** Prof 1; Other 1. **Subjects:** Music, theater and drama, speech communication. **Holdings:** 10,000 books and scores; 6500 phonograph records. **Subscriptions:** 30 journals and other serials. **Services:** Interlibrary loan; listening facilities for Compact Discs, audiocassettes, and phonograph records; library open to the public with restrictions. **Automated Operations:** Computerized cataloging. **Computerized Information Services:** OCLC. **Networks/Consortia:** Member of Cooperating Libraries in Consortium (CLIC). **Remarks:** FAX: (612)690-6024.

★3911★
College of Saint Mary - Library - Special Collections (Hum)
1901 S. 72nd St. Phone: (402)399-2471
Omaha, NE 68124 Sr. Susan Severin, Dir.
Founded: 1923. **Staff:** Prof 3; Other 2. **Subjects:** Spirituality, literature, education. **Special Collections:** Women's Studies (5000 volumes). **Holdings:** Figures not available. **Services:** Interlibrary loan; copying; collections open to the public with restrictions. **Computerized Information Services:** CINAHL Information Systems. **Networks/Consortia:** Member of NEBASE. **Remarks:** FAX: (402)399-2686. **Staff:** Linda Schritter, Ref.Libn.; Robert Hromek, AV Coord.

★3912★
College of St. Thomas - O'Shaughnessy Library - Special Collections (Area-Ethnic)
2115 Summit Ave. Phone: (612)647-5726
St. Paul, MN 55105 John B. Davenport, Spec.Coll.Coord.
Founded: 1983. **Staff:** Prof 2. **Subjects:** Ireland, Scotland, and Wales - language, history, literature, folklore, religion. **Special Collections:** Celtic Collection (8000 volumes); French court historical memoirs, diaries, letters; Hilaire Belloc; Anglicanism. **Holdings:** 2000 cataloged volumes. **Subscriptions:** 7 journals and other serials. **Services:** Copying; collection open to the public 20 hours a week and upon written request. **Computerized Information Services:** OCLC. **Networks/Consortia:** Member of Cooperating Libraries in Consortium (CLIC), MINITEX Library Information Network. **Staff:** John B. Davenport; James D. Kellen.

★3913★
College of St. Thomas - School of Divinity - Archbishop Ireland Memorial Library (Rel-Phil)
2260 Summit Ave. Phone: (612)647-5501
St. Paul, MN 55105 Mary Martin, Theol.Libn./Dir.
Founded: 1894. **Staff:** Prof 3; Other 3. **Subjects:** Biblical studies, Catholic theology, patrology, scholastic philosophy, U.S. Catholic Church history, canon law. **Special Collections:** Archbishop Ireland papers (microfilm); Patrologia Graeca; Patrologia Latina; Sources Chretiennes. **Holdings:** 66,900 books; 13,750 bound periodical volumes. **Subscriptions:** 415 journals and other serials; 30 newspapers. **Services:** Interlibrary loan; copying; library open to the public. **Computerized Information Services:** CD-ROM (WILSONDISC - Religion Index One); InterNet (electronic mail service). **Networks/Consortia:** Member of Minnesota Theological Libraries Association (MTLA). **Special Catalogs:** Catalog of consortium serials collection (printed); Union Catalog of Consortium Monographic Collection (CD-ROM). **Remarks:** Electronic mail address(es): IN%memartin@stthomas.edu (InterNet). **Staff:** Margaret Mary Bannigan, Coord. of Serv.; Betty Bigelbach,Ref.Libn.

College of the San Francisco Art Institute
See: **San Francisco Art Institute** (14726)

★3914★
College of the Southwest - Scarborough Memorial Library - Special Collections (Educ)
6610 Lovington Hwy. Phone: (505)392-6561
Hobbs, NM 88240 John McCance, Lib.Dir.
Founded: 1962. **Staff:** Prof 1; Other 2. **Subjects:** Education, southwestern United States, U.S. Civil War. **Holdings:** Southwest Heritage Collection (4500 volumes); New Mexico State Textbook Evaluation Center Collection (23,000 volumes). **Subscriptions:** 248 journals and other serials; 15 newspapers. **Services:** Interlibrary loan; copying; collections open to the public. **Remarks:** FAX: (505)392-6006.

★3915★
College de Ste-Anne-de-la-Pocatiere - Bibliotheque (Hist, Hum)
100, ave. Painchaud Phone: (418)856-3012
La Pocatiere, PQ, Canada G0R 1Z0 Marcel Mignault, Hd.
Founded: 1829. **Staff:** Prof 1; Other 1. **Subjects:** History of Canada, French-Canadian and French literature, regional history. **Holdings:** 80,000 books; 25,000 bound periodical volumes; 2000 pamphlets. **Subscriptions:** 150 journals and other serials. **Services:** Interlibrary loan; library open to the public for reference use only.

★3916★
College de Ste-Anne-de-la-Pocatiere - Societe Historique-de-la-Cote-du-Sud - Bibliotheque (Hist)
C.P. 937 Phone: (418)856-2104
La Pocatiere, PQ, Canada G0R 1Z0 Guy Theberge, Pres.
Founded: 1948. **Staff:** Prof 2. **Subjects:** History - regional, church, Canada, Quebec; genealogy. **Holdings:** 1200 books; 500 bound periodical volumes; 120 archival boxes; 400 pamphlets. **Services:** Library open to the public. **Automated Operations:** Computerized publications list. **Publications:** Cahiers d'Histoire (1-21st ed.), 3/year; Le Javelier (historical magazine). **Special Indexes:** Index de la Gazette des Campagnes (1st ed., 1861-1895; 2nd ed., 1940-1956).

★3917★
College Universitaire de St. Boniface - Bibliotheque Alfred-Monnin (Hum)
200, Av de la Cathedrale Phone: (204)233-0210
Saint-Boniface, MB, Canada R2H 0H7 Marcel Boulet, Hd.Libn.
Founded: 1818. **Staff:** Prof 3; Other 6. **Subjects:** French and French-Canadian literature, education, social sciences, history, religion, philosophy. **Holdings:** 97,000 books; 12,800 bound periodical volumes; 1200 reels of microfilm; 11,000 microfiche; 4253 AV programs. **Subscriptions:** 625 journals and other serials; 9 newspapers. **Services:** Interlibrary loan; copying; library open to the public with restrictions. **Automated Operations:** Computerized public access catalog, cataloging, and circulation. **Computerized Information Services:** DIALOG Information Services, IST-Informatheque Inc.; Envoy 100 (electronic mail service). **Remarks:** The majority of holdings are in French. FAX: (204)237-3240. Electronic mail address(es): PEB.MSC (Envoy 100). **Staff:** Marcel Lemieux, Tech.Serv.; Madeleine Samuda, Ref.

College du Vieux-Montreal
See: **CEGEP du Vieux-Montreal** (3195)

★3918★
College of William and Mary - Earl Gregg Swem Library - Special Collections (Hist)
Williamsburg, VA 23185 Phone: (804)221-3090
Nancy H. Marshall, Univ.Libn.
Founded: 1693. **Staff:** 6. **Subjects:** Virginia history, U.S. history to 1830, dogs and hunting, history of American printing. **Holdings:** University Archives Collection (3000 linear feet); Virginia Historical Manuscripts, 17th-20th centuries (1,000,000); Tucker-Coleman Collection, 1675-1956 (1500 volumes; 30,000 manuscripts); Peter Chapin Collection on dogs (3100 items). **Services:** Copying; collections open to the public. **Automated Operations:** Computerized cataloging. **Computerized Information Services:** OCLC; BITNET InterNet (electronic mail services). **Networks/Consortia:** Member of SOLINET. **Publications:** Library Contributions (numbered series), irregular. **Remarks:** FAX: (804)221-3088. Electronic mail address(es): WMVMI (BITNET); WMUMI.CC.NUM.EDU (InterNet). **Staff:** Kay J. Domine, Univ.Archv./Asst.Libn., Spec.Coll.; Margaret C. Cook, Cur., Mss./Rare Bks.

College of William and Mary - Institute of Early American History and Culture
See: **Institute of Early American History and Culture** (7930)

★3919★
College of William and Mary - Marshall-Wythe Law Library (Law)
Williamsburg, VA 23187 Phone: (804)221-3255
James S. Heller, Law Libn.
Staff: Prof 5; Other 8. **Subjects:** Law. **Special Collections:** Environmental law; taxation; Roman law; Thomas Jefferson Law Library. **Holdings:** 159,364 volumes; 108,497 volumes in microform; 421 AV programs. **Subscriptions:** 4316 journals and other serials; 10 newspapers. **Services:** Interlibrary loan; copying; library open to the public. **Automated Operations:** Computerized public access catalog, cataloging, and circulation. **Computerized Information Services:** LEXIS, NEXIS, DIALOG Information Services, OCLC, WESTLAW. **Networks/Consortia:** Member of SOLINET, COSELL. **Remarks:** FAX: (804)221-3261. **Staff:** Martha Rush, Assoc. Law Libn.; Sue Welch, Hd., Tech.Serv.; Susan Trask, Ref.Libn.; Mary Grace Hune, Ref.Libn.

★3920★
Collegiate Reformed Dutch Church - Library (Hist)
45 John St. Phone: (212)233-1960
New York, NY 10038 Maria Hollenga, Libn.
Founded: 1633. **Staff:** 2. **Subjects:** Genealogical data, 1633 to present. **Special Collections:** Minutes of board meetings, 1633 to present. **Holdings:** 45 books; archival materials; documents. **Subscriptions:** 20 journals and other serials. **Services:** Interlibrary loan; copying; library open to the public. **Publications:** Year Book. **Remarks:** FAX: (212)406-1856.

★3921★
Collier State Park Logging Museum - Library (Hist)
PO Box 5156 Phone: (503)884-5766
Klamath Falls, OR 97601 Lowell Jones, Cur.
Founded: 1946. **Staff:** Prof 1. **Subjects:** Logging, forestry, fisheries, Klamath Indians. **Special Collections:** Life of Jim McCrank, 96-year old lumberjack; Life of Jack Kimball Cruiser; logging equipment (650 pieces); Indian stone artifacts. **Holdings:** 50 books; logging magazines and newspapers; 3000 logging photographs; equipment catalogs; 20 tapes of autobiographies of loggers; Klamath Indian-English Dictionary dated 1870. **Services:** Library not open to the public. **Automated Operations:** Computerized cataloging. **Special Indexes:** Geological study of Collier State Park; Indexes of 600 exhibits. **Remarks:** Maintained by Oregon State Department of Transportation - State Parks and Recreation Division.

Collins Archive of Catalan Art and Architecture
See: **Art Institute of Chicago - Ryerson and Burnham Libraries** (1082)

Collins Collection of the Dance
See: **Birmingham Public and Jefferson County Free Library** (1854)

Donald Collins Memorial Library
See: **American Society of Abdominal Surgeons** (741)

V.C.C. Collum Carnac and Mother-Goddess Research Archive
See: **University of San Francisco - Special Collections Department/ Donohue Rare Book Room** (19290)

Howard Colman Library
See: **Rockford College** (14003)

★3922★
Cologne Library on German-Jewish History
Josef Haubrich Hof 1 Phone: 221 232349
W-5000 Cologne 1, Germany Dr. Monika Richarz, Ph.D.
Founded: 1959. **Staff:** Prof 2; Other 2. **Subjects:** German-Jewish history, Zionism, Palestine, Israel. **Special Collections:** German-Jewish Community Histories collection (1500 vols.); The Image of Jews in German Literature collection (1200 vols.); German-Jewish periodicals (420 titles). **Holdings:** 40,000 books; 6000 bound periodical volumes. **Subscriptions:** 98 journals and other serials; 10 newspapers. **Services:** Interlibrary loan; copying; library open to the public. **Publications:** Survey of Current Research on German-Jewish History, triennial. **Special Catalogs:** Catalog of Community Histories, 1988. **Also Known As:** Germania Judaica - Kolner Bibliothek zur Geschichte des Deutschen Judentums e.V.

★3923★
Colombia - Instituto Colombiano Agropecuario - Biblioteca Agropecuaria de Colombia (Agri)
Apdo Aereo 151123 Eldorado
Bogota, Colombia Phone: 1 2673008
Founded: 1968. **Staff:** Prof 6; Other 14. **Subjects:** Agriculture, veterinary medicine, rural development, technology transfer, agricultural biotechnology, multiple crops. **Special Collections:** Hemeroteca; Coleccion Colombiana Agropecuaria; Coleccion de Audiotutoriales. **Holdings:** 40,000 books; 1700 bound periodical volumes; 10,580 reports; 5900 microfiche; 140 audiotutoriales. **Subscriptions:** 254 journals and other serials. **Services:** Interlibrary loan; copying; SDI; library open to the public. **Computerized Information Services:** AGRIS, AGRICOLA; Base de datos del Ica (internal database). **Publications:** Bibliografias Especializadas. **Remarks:** FAX: 1 2673008.

★3924★
Colombia - Ministry of Mines & Petroleum - Institute for Nuclear Affairs - Library (Energy)
Avenida Eldorado, cra. 50
Apdo. Aereo 8595 Phone: 12220600
Bogota, Colombia Cecilia Briceno de Monroy, Hd.Libn.
Founded: 1958. **Staff:** 5. **Subjects:** Peaceful uses of nuclear energy in health physics and nuclear medicine, industry, biochemistry, hydrology and sedimentology, geology, nuclear safety, metallurgy, reactors, chemistry, physics, electronics, uranium exploration, agriculture, solar energy. **Special Collections:** IAEA Publications. **Holdings:** 135,000 volumes. **Subscriptions:** 50 journals and other serials; 5 newspapers. **Services:** Interlibrary loan; copying; SDI; library open to the public. **Computerized Information Services:** INIS (CD-ROM). **Remarks:** FAX: 12220173. Telex: 42416 IAN BG CO. **Also Known As:** Instituto de Asuntos Nucleares - Centro de Documentacion e Informacion Nuclear.

Colombia - National Ministry of Education - Colombian Fund for Scientific Research and Special Projects of Francisco Jose de Caldas
See: **Colombian Fund for Scientific Research and Special Projects of Francisco Jose de Caldas** (3927)

★3925★
Colombian Academy of Exact, Physical and Natural Sciences - Luis Lopez de Mesa Library (Sci-Engr)
Carrera 3 A No. 17-34, Piso 3
Apdo. Aereo 44.763 Phone: 13414805
Bogota, Colombia Prof. Carlos-Eduardo Calderon-Gomez, Lib.Dir.
Founded: 1958. **Subjects:** Natural sciences, mathematics, physics, geology, astronomy, history of sciences in Colombia. **Holdings:** 24,500 volumes. **Subscriptions:** 300 journals and other serials. **Services:** Library open to serious researchers only. **Computerized Information Services:** ACOCI (internal database). **Publications:** Revista de la Academia Colombiana de Ciencias Exactas, Fisicas y Naturales. **Remarks:** FAX: 2838552. Maintained by Colombia - Ministry of Education. **Also Known As:** Academia Colombiana de Ciencias Exactas, Fisicas y Naturales/Biblioteca Luis Lopez de Mesa. **Staff:** Dr. Luis-Eduardo Mora-Osejo, Pres. of the Academy; Dr. Jose A. Lozano, Exec.Sec.; Bertha Mesa-Montealegre, Libn.

★3926★
Colombian Association for Human Rights - Library (Soc Sci)
Apdo. Aereo 16985 Phone: 1 2585796
Bogota, Colombia Luis E. Agudelo Ramirez, Gen.Dir.
Founded: 1980. **Staff:** 2. **Subjects:** Human rights. **Special Collections:** Human Rights International Law. **Holdings:** 950 volumes. **Services:** Library open to students. **Also Known As:** Asociacion Colombiano Pro Derechos Humanos (ACDHUM).

★3927★
Colombian Fund for Scientific Research and Special Projects of Francisco Jose de Caldas - National Information System (Sci-Engr)
Apdo. Aereo 051580
Bogota, Colombia Phone: 2169800
Subjects: Scientific and technological policy. **Holdings:** 1500 books; 10 bound periodical volumes; 2000 reports. **Services:** Interlibrary loan; copying; open to the public. **Computerized Information Services:** DIALOG Information Services; internal databases. **Publications:** Colombia: Ciencia y Tecnologia, 3/year; Ciencia, Tecnologia y Desarrollo, irregular. **Remarks:** Maintained by Colombia - National Ministry of Education. **Remarks:** FAX: 2744460. Telex: 44305 FOCOL CO. **Also Known As:** Fondo Colombiano de Investigaciones Cientificas y Proyectos Especiales "Francisco Jose de Caldas."

★3928★
Colombiere Center - Library (Rel-Phil)
P.O. Box 139 Phone: (313)625-5611
Clarkston, MI 48347 Rev. Stephen A. Meder, S.J., Libn.
Founded: 1959. **Staff:** 1. **Subjects:** Bible study, spiritual and ascetical works, spiritual exercises, Society of Jesus history and documents, theology, Greek and Latin classics. **Holdings:** 28,000 books; 4000 bound periodical volumes; 1 file drawer of spiritual exercises; 1 file drawer of U.S. Catholic Conference publications. **Subscriptions:** 70 journals and other serials. **Remarks:** Information refers to combined collections of the Dinan and Tertians Libraries.

★3929★
(Colombo) American Center - USIS Library (Educ)
39 Sir Ernest de Silva Mawatha
Post Box 1245
Colombo 7, Sri Lanka
Remarks: Maintained or supported by the U.S. Information Agency. Focus is on materials that will assist peoples outside the United States to learn about the United States, its people, history, culture, political processes, and social milieux.

★3930★
Colonial Penn Group, Inc. - Market Research Department Library (Bus-Fin)
Colonial Penn Plaza
19th & Market Streets Phone: (215)988-3796
Philadelphia, PA 19181 Amy Stone, Libn.
Founded: 1975. **Staff:** Prof 1. **Subjects:** Insurance, senior citizen market, marketing, direct mail advertising, statistics. **Holdings:** 1500 books; 10 VF drawers of government document files; 80 VF drawers of general, company, project files. **Subscriptions:** 300 journals and other serials; 8 newspapers. **Services:** Interlibrary loan; library not open to the public. **Automated Operations:** Computerized cataloging and serials. **Computerized Information Services:** DIALOG Information Services, VU/TEXT Information Services, Dow Jones News/Retrieval, INVESTEXT, BestLink Insurance News, NEXIS. **Special Indexes:** Index to research reports. **Remarks:** FAX: (215)988-8163.

Colonial Williamsburg Foundation - Institute of Early American History and Culture
See: **Institute of Early American History and Culture** (7930)

★3931★
Colonial Williamsburg Foundation Library - Abby Aldrich Rockefeller Folk Art Center - Library (Art)
307 S. England St.
Williamsburg, VA 23187 Phone: (804)220-7671
Founded: 1957. **Staff:** 1. **Subjects:** American folk art. **Special Collections:** 19th century childrens books. **Holdings:** 4500 books; 120 linear feet of bound periodicals (20 titles). **Services:** Library open to the public by appointment. **Special Catalogs:** Exhibition and collection catalogs.

★3932★
Colonial Williamsburg Foundation Library - Archaeology Library (Hist, Soc Sci)
303 Botetourt St. Phone: (804)220-7336
Williamsburg, VA 23187 Patricia Samford
Subjects: Archeology - Colonial and Early American periods; Williamsburg, Virginia. **Holdings:** 1600 books; 50 linear feet of bound periodicals (15 titles); 60 linear feet of uncataloged reports. **Services:** Library open to the public by appointment.

★3933★
Colonial Williamsburg Foundation Library - Audiovisual Library (Aud-Vis)
415 N. Boundary St. Phone: (804)220-7418
Williamsburg, VA 23187 Mary Keeling, AV Serv.Libn.
Special Collections: Colonial life and material culture; museum programs; architectural photographs of Virginia/Chesapeake region buildings; English and American decorative arts; 19th century folk art; Colonial Williamsburg Foundation restoration and programs; lecture series videotapes. **Holdings:** 150,000 black and white photographs; 120,000 slides; 600 videotapes; 50 phonograph recordings; 80 reel-to-reel films; 50 filmstrips. **Services:** Photoreproduction; library open to the public by appointment. **Staff:** Suzanne Brown, AV Cat.Libn.; Cathy Grosfils, AV Ed.Libn.

★3934★
Colonial Williamsburg Foundation Library - Central Library (Hist)
415 N. Boundary St.
P.O. Box 1776 Phone: (804)220-7423
Williamsburg, VA 23187-1776 Susan Berg, Dir.
Founded: 1933. **Staff:** Prof 14; Other 9. **Subjects:** History of the Williamsburg/ Virginia/ Chesapeake Region in the Colonial and Early American periods - African Americans, architecture, economics, government, material culture, music, social life and customs; historic preservation and museum studies. **Special Collections:** Research query files, 1927 to present; house histories and research reports for Colonial Williamsburg. **Holdings:** 26,000 books; 600 linear feet of bound periodicals (450 titles); 950 research reports; 200 linear feet of reference file materials. **Services:** Interlibrary loan; library open to the public. **Automated Operations:** Computerized public access catalog, cataloging, acquisitions, and circulation. **Computerized Information Services:** DIALOG Information Services, EPIC, RLIN, CIN, OCLC. **Networks/Consortia:** Member of SOLINET. **Publications:** A Guide to Colonial Williamsburg Foundation Libraries, (out of print); Colonial Williamsburg: the Journal of the Colonial Williamsburg Foundation, quarterly. **Remarks:** FAX: **Remarks:** FAX: (804)221-8902. **Staff:** Liz Ackert, Cir./Ref.Libn.; Lois Danuser, Circ.Lib.Asst.; Mary Haskell, Automation and Tech.Serv.Libn.; Julie Conlee, Cat.Libn./Automation; Serena Paisley, Cat.Libn./Authority Cont.; Annette Parham, Acq.Libn.

★3935★
Colonial Williamsburg Foundation Library - Decorative Arts Library (Art)
Lafayette & Botetourt St. Phone: (804)220-7523
Williamsburg, VA 23187 Susan Shames, Decorative Arts Libn.
Subjects: American and English decorative arts of the Colonial and Early American periods. **Special Collections:** 18th and 19th century decorative arts books. **Holdings:** 14,000 books; 480 linear feet of bound periodicals (310 titles); 12,000 auction sales catalogs; 500 reports. **Services:** Library open to the public by appointment.

★3936★
Colonial Williamsburg Foundation Library - Historic Trades Library (Hist)
Margaret Hunter Workshop
Duke of Gloucester St.
Williamsburg, VA 23187 Phone: (804)220-7106
Subjects: Colonial and Early American historic trades. **Special Collections:** Wolcott Collection. **Holdings:** 2500 books. **Services:** Library open to the public by appointment. **Staff:** Linda Wenger; Diane Hudgins.

★3937★
Colonial Williamsburg Foundation Library - Information Systems Library (Comp Sci)
427 Franklin St. Phone: (804)220-7304
Williamsburg, VA 23178 Joan McIntosh
Subjects: Computer hardware and software. **Holdings:** 100 books; 30 videotapes; 40 software packages. **Services:** Library open to the public by appointment.

★3938★
Colonial Williamsburg Foundation Library - Special Collections (Art, Hum, Rare Book)
415 N. Boundary St. Phone: (804)220-7420
Williamsburg, VA 23187-1776 John Ingram, Cur. of Spec.Coll.
Special Collections: 18th century Williamsburg imprints; 18th century music; A. Lawrence Kocher Collection of Architecture Books; Alden Hopkins Collection of Landscape Architecture Books; Webb-Prentis Collection of books owned in 18th century Williamsburg; Robert Anderson Papers; William Blathwayt Papers; Francis Nicholson Papers; John Norton & Sons Papers; Shirley Plantation Research Collection. **Holdings:** 8000 books; 1100 dissertations; 950 reports; 4600 microforms; 2500 maps; 41,000 manuscripts; 5000 photographs; 60,000 architectural, landscape and archeological drawings. **Services:** Copying. **Automated Operations:** Computerized public access catalog, cataloging, acquisitions, and circulation. **Publications:** The William Blathwayt Papers at Colonial Williamsburg, 1631-1722; The Colonial Williamsburg Research Collections in Microform. **Staff:** Greg Williams, Assoc.Cur. of Spec.Coll.; George Yetter, Assoc.Cur. of Arch. Drawings.

Colorado Career Information System
See: **The Education Diffusion Group** (5252)

★3939★
Colorado Chautauqua Association - Archives and History Room (Area-Ethnic, Hist)
Chautauqua Park Phone: (303)442-3282
Boulder, CO 80302 Elaine Scanlon, Exec.Dir.
Founded: 1991. **Subjects:** Chautauquas. **Special Collections:** Archives of the Colorado Chautauqua Association; printed materials and photographs pertaining to other Chautauquas. **Holdings:** 32 linear feet of printed materials; 800 photographic images; blueprints; maps; ephemera. **Services:** Archives and History Room open to the public by appointment on a limited schedule.

★3940★
Colorado College - Charles Leaming Tutt Library - Special Collections (Hist)
1021 N. Cascade Phone: (719)389-6668
Colorado Springs, CO 80903 John Sheridan, Spec.Coll.Libn./College Archv.
Founded: 1876. **Staff:** Prof 3; Other 1. **Subjects:** History - Colorado, Colorado College, 19th and 20th century American West, printing; Abraham Lincoln. **Special Collections:** Colorado College Collection (1200 volumes; 1350 linear feet of archival material); Colorado (10,000 volumes); rare books (1700 volumes); special editions (3000 volumes); Justice Chess Collection (300 volumes); Alice Bemis Taylor Collection of historical manuscripts (300 items); Archer Butler Hulbert papers (13 feet); Charles C. Mierow papers (12 feet); Helen Hunt Jackson papers (7 feet); Donald Jackson Collection of Fine Printing (60 items); William S. Jackson papers (37 feet); Spencer Penrose papers (53 feet); Thomas Nelson Haskell papers (8 feet); Theodore Roosevelt letters (57 items); Edward Royal Warren papers (12 feet); Philip Washburn papers (6 feet); Charles Collins Collection of historical manuscripts (57 items); oral history interviews (109 items); Robert W. & Elinor L. Hendee Abraham Lincoln Collection (2500 volumes; 75 feet of Lincolniana). **Holdings:** 30,000 books; 350 bound periodical volumes; 640 linear feet of manuscripts; 518 oral history tapes; 53,000 photographs; 70 feet of ephemera; 81 historical tapes. **Subscriptions:** 1400 journals and other serials; 45 newspapers. **Services:** Copying; collections open to the public with restrictions. **Automated Operations:** Computerized cataloging, acquisitions, and circulation. **Computerized Information Services:** DIALOG Information Services, OCLC; internal database. **Networks/Consortia:** Member of Bibliographical Center for Research, Rocky Mountain Region, Inc. (BCR). **Publications:** Guides to manuscript collections. **Special Indexes:** Index to tape collection; index to photograph collection. **Remarks:** FAX: (719)389-6859. **Staff:** Judith R. Finley, Dir., Oral Hist.Proj./Photo.Cur.; Virginia R. Kiefer, Spec.Coll.Asst.

Colorado Geological Survey Library
See: **Colorado (State) Department of Natural Resources** (3957)

★3941★
Colorado Historical Society - Stephen H. Hart Library (Hist)
Colorado State History Museum
1300 Broadway Phone: (303)866-2305
Denver, CO 80203 Katherine Kane, Dir., Coll.Serv.
Founded: 1879. **Staff:** Prof 6; Other 5. **Subjects:** Colorado and business history, railroads, mining, cattle industry, social and cultural movements. **Special Collections:** William Henry Jackson Collection of photographs west of the Mississippi River (10,000); Colorado Midland and Denver Rio Grande Railroad Collections; mining records; H.A.W. Tabor papers; Dawson scrapbooks. **Holdings:** 47,000 volumes; 1500 manuscript collections; 29,334 reels of microfilm; 1000 serial titles; 14,500 reels of television newsfilm; 1000 newspapers titles; 2500 maps and atlases; 350,000 photographs and negatives. **Subscriptions:** 140 journals and other serials; 164 newspapers. **Services:** Copying; mail and phone reference service; library open to the public. **Publications:** Guide to Manuscript Collections; Calendars, occasional. **Special Catalogs:** Jackson Photograph Collection Catalogs; Oral Histories Catalog; Mining Inventory; manuscripts collection catalog. **Special Indexes:** Western Cattle Range Industry Study Index ; WPA Index; Dawson Index (all on card). **Remarks:** FAX: (303)866-5739. **Staff:** Patrick Fraker, Ref.Libn.; Stan Oliner, Cur., Bks. & Mss.; Eric Paddock, Cur., Photo.; Rebecca Lintz, Chf.Libn.

Colorado Library Association Archives
See: **University of Colorado--Boulder - Western Historical Collections/University Archives** (18508)

★3942★
Colorado Mental Health Center at Fort Logan - Medical Library (Med)
3520 W. Oxford Ave. Phone: (303)762-4388
Denver, CO 80236 Kathleen Elder, Dir., Lib.Serv.
Founded: 1963. **Staff:** Prof 1. **Subjects:** Psychiatry, psychology, behavioral sciences. **Holdings:** 5000 books; 3213 bound periodical volumes. **Subscriptions:** 96 journals and other serials. **Services:** Interlibrary loan; copying; library open to the public for reference use only. **Networks/Consortia:** Member of Colorado Council of Medical Librarians, Central Colorado Library System (CCLS). **Remarks:** FAX: (303)762-4332. **Formerly:** Fort Logan Mental Health Center.

★3943★
Colorado Mental Health Institute at Pueblo - Professional Library (Med)
1600 W. 24th St.
Pueblo, CO 81003 Phone: (719)546-4677
Founded: 1925. **Staff:** Prof 2; Other 1. **Subjects:** Psychiatry, mental health, psychology, surgery, internal medicine, social work. **Holdings:** 6000 books. **Subscriptions:** 150 journals and other serials. **Services:** Interlibrary loan; copying; library open to the public with restrictions. **Computerized Information Services:** MEDLARS, BRS Information Technologies, Human Resource Information Network (HRIN). **Networks/Consortia:** Member of Arkansas Valley Regional Library Service System, National Network of Libraries of Medicine - Midcontinental Region. **Formerly:** Colorado State Hospital - Professional Library. **Staff:** Carol Ann Smith, Libn.

★3944★
Colorado Mining Association - Library (Sci-Engr)
1340 Colorado State Bank Bldg.
1600 Broadway Phone: (303)894-0536
Denver, CO 80202 S.A. Hunter
Staff: 3. **Subjects:** Mining operations and management, metals, government. **Special Collections:** Mining Year Books, 1969-1984; mining magazines; Colorado Miner magazine. **Holdings:** Figures not available. **Subscriptions:** 18 journals and other serials. **Services:** Copying; library open to the public for reference use only. **Remarks:** FAX: (303)894-8416.

★3945★
Colorado Railroad Historical Foundation/Colorado Railroad Museum - Library (Trans)
17155 W. 44th Ave.
Box 10 Phone: (303)279-4591
Golden, CO 80402-0010 Charles Albi, Exec.Dir.
Founded: 1958. **Staff:** 5. **Subjects:** Railroad history of the United States and Canada with emphasis on Colorado and the Rocky Mountain West. **Special Collections:** Files, office and operating records of Rio Grande Southern Railroad; Denver & Rio Grande Western, Colorado, and Southern Gilpin Railroads; Denver Tramway. **Holdings:** 3000 books; 650 bound periodical volumes; documents. **Subscriptions:** 36 journals and other serials. **Services:** Library open to the public by appointment. **Publications:** Iron Horse News, 6/year; Colo Rail Annual.

Colorado River Board of California
See: **(California State) Colorado River Board of California** (2514)

★3946★
Colorado School for the Deaf and the Blind - Media Center (Educ, Aud-Vis)
33 N. Institute St. Phone: (719)578-2206
Colorado Springs, CO 80903 Janet L. Fleharty, Media Spec.
Founded: 1874. **Staff:** Prof 2; Other 1. **Subjects:** Books of interest to deaf and blind children; professional books on deafness and blindness for staff and parents. **Holdings:** 10,000 books; 200 periodical volumes. **Subscriptions:** 51 journals and other serials. **Services:** Center open to the public. **Special Indexes:** Colorado Index, quarterly - to the public. **Remarks:** FAX: (719)578-2239. **Staff:** Marianne Arnold, Libn.; Beth Davidson, Educ.Tech.

★3947★
Colorado School of Mines - Arthur Lakes Library (Sci-Engr, Energy)
Golden, CO 80401 Phone: (303)273-3690
Joanne V. Lerud, Dir.
Founded: 1874. **Staff:** Prof 10; Other 11. **Subjects:** Geology, mining, geophysics, petroleum, metallurgy, chemistry, mathematics, physics, mineral economics, chemical and petroleum refining. **Special Collections:** U.S. Government Selective Depository; Original Mine Reports (2000); Colorado Mining History (1500 items); Boettcher Collection on Energy, Environment, Public Policy (10,072 items); Natural Gas Supply Information Center. **Holdings:** 136,260 books; 52,000 bound periodical volumes; 165,332 geologic, mineral, topographic, Government Printing Office (GPO), Defense Mapping Agency, U.S. Geological Survey, National Ocean Survey maps; house organs; trade publications; 6570 theses; 860 reels of microfilm; 66,433 microfiche. **Subscriptions:** 2940 journals and other serials; 21 newspapers. **Services:** Interlibrary loan; copying; library open to the public. **Automated Operations:** Computerized cataloging, acquisitions, and circulation. **Computerized Information Services:** DIALOG Information Services, PFDS Online; internal database; OnTyme Electronic Message Network Service (electronic mail service). Performs searches on fee basis. Contact Person: Ann Lerew, Asst.Dir., Info.Serv., 273-3687. **Networks/Consortia:** Member of Bibliographical Center for Research, Rocky Mountain Region, Inc. (BCR), Colorado Alliance of Research Libraries (CARL), Central Colorado Library System (CCLS). **Remarks:** FAX: (303)273-3199. Telex: 910-934-0190. **Staff:** Robert Sorgenfrei, Acq./Coll.Dev.; Lisa Dunn, Ref.Libn.; Rosalia Rooney, U.S. Govt.Docs. & Maps; Gail Fernald, Ref.Libn.; Gay Ellen Roesch, Cat.Hd.; Christine Ericson, Cat.Libn.; Judy Larson, Circ.Hd.; Deborah Grealy, Natural Gas Supply Info.Ctr.; Mary F. Safford, U.S. Govt.Pubns.Libn.

★3948★
Colorado Ski Museum - Ski Hall of Fame - Historical Library (Rec)
P.O. Box 1976 Phone: (303)476-1876
Vail, CO 81658 Christine Steeg Scrip, Exec.Dir.
Staff: 2. **Subjects:** Colorado and national ski history. **Special Collections:** 10th Mountain Division artifacts. **Holdings:** 150 books; 200 bound periodical volumes; 30 AV programs. **Services:** Copying; library open to museum members. **Remarks:** FAX: (303)476-1879. Library located in the Colorado Ski Heritage Center, 241 S. Frontage Rd., Vail Village Transportation Center, Vail, CO.

★3949★
Colorado Springs Fine Arts Center - Reference Library and Taylor Museum Library (Art)
30 W. Dale St. Phone: (719)634-5581
Colorado Springs, CO 80903 Roderick Dew, Libn.
Founded: 1936. **Staff:** Prof 1; Other 1. **Subjects:** Art history, drawing, painting, sculpture, crafts, architecture, photography, graphic arts and printing, anthropology of the Southwest, museums and private collections. **Special Collections:** Santos; Indians of the Southwest; Latin American folk and Colonial art. **Holdings:** 27,000 books; 950 bound periodical volumes; 12 shelves of biographical files; 20 shelves of museum publications. **Subscriptions:** 50 journals and other serials. **Services:** Art reference service; library open to the public with restrictions on circulation.

★3950★
Colorado Springs Gazette Telegraph - Library (Publ)
30 S. Prospect
Box 1779 Phone: (719)636-0182
Colorado Springs, CO 80901 Phil Witherow, Res.Dir.
Staff: Prof 3; Other 1. **Subjects:** Newspaper reference topics. **Holdings:** 200 books and bound periodical volumes; 30 file drawers of photographs; newspaper clippings (microfiche). **Services:** Library open to the public with restrictions. **Computerized Information Services:** DIALOG Information Services, NEXIS, DataTimes, VU/TEXT Information Services; internal database. **Remarks:** FAX: (719)636-0202. The Telegraph is published by Freedom Newspapers. **Staff:** Paula Davis; Victor Greto.

★3951★
Colorado Springs Pioneers Museum - Starsmore Center For Local History (Hist)
215 S. Tejon St. Phone: (719)578-6650
Colorado Springs, CO 80903 Sharron G. Uhler, Archv.
Founded: 1938. **Staff:** Prof 1; Other 1. **Subjects:** Colorado history, local genealogy. **Special Collections:** Francis W. Cragin Far West Notebooks; Colorado historical manuscripts; William J. Palmer letters and diaries; historical photographs of the Pike's Peak region (25,000). **Holdings:** 2500 books; 300 bound periodical volumes. **Subscriptions:** 10 journals and other serials; 5 newspapers. **Services:** Copying; center open to the public. **Computerized Information Services:** Internal database. Performs searches free of charge. **Networks/Consortia:** Member of Plains and Peaks Regional Library Service System.

★3952★
Colorado Springs Public Schools - District No. 11 - Professional Resource Center (Educ)
1115 N. El Paso St. Phone: (719)520-2190
Colorado Springs, CO 80903 Sheryl O'Bryan, Techn.
Founded: 1959. **Staff:** Prof 2; Other 1. **Subjects:** Education. **Holdings:** 7490 books; 6073 nonprint materials. **Subscriptions:** 67 journals and other serials. **Services:** Center open to the public with restrictions.

★3953★
Colorado State Bank - Law Library (Law)
1600 Broadway, Rm. 1015 Phone: (303)837-0287
Denver, CO 80202 Lenore Allen, Libn.
Subjects: Law - Colorado, labor, tax, oil and gas. **Holdings:** 14,500 books; 100 bound periodical volumes. **Services:** Library not open to the public. **Automated Operations:** Computerized cataloging.

★3954★
Colorado (State) Department of Education - Instructional Materials Center for the Visually Handicapped (Aud-Vis, Educ)
1015 High St. Phone: (719)578-2196
Colorado Springs, CO 80903 Lucia A. Hasty, Cons.
Founded: 1971. **Staff:** Prof 1; Other 2. **Special Collections:** Large print and braille textbooks used by visually handicapped students in Colorado schools, K-12. **Holdings:** 5000 books; braille and large print books. **Subscriptions:** 10 journals and other serials. **Services:** Resources and materials service for the visually handicapped; center not open to the public. **Computerized Information Services:** SpecialNet (electronic mail service). **Publications:** Handbook of Resources and Materials for the Visually Handicapped in Colorado. **Remarks:** FAX: (719)578-2239. Electronic mail address(es): CO.SE (SpecialNet). **Formerly:** Located in Denver, CO.

★3955★
Colorado (State) Department of Education - Resource Center (Educ)
201 E. Colfax Ave., Rm. 106 Phone: (303)866-6618
Denver, CO 80203 Christine Hamilton-Pennell, Libn.
Founded: 1985. **Staff:** Prof 1.5; Other 2. **Subjects:** Education, library science, adult education, management. **Special Collections:** Early Childhood; AIDS Education; Race and Sex Equity. **Holdings:** 6500 volumes. **Subscriptions:** 500 journals and other serials. **Services:** Interlibrary loan; copying; center open to the public for browsing only. **Automated Operations:** Computerized cataloging, acquisitions, and serials. **Computerized Information Services:** DIALOG Information Services, WILSONLINE; Performs searches. **Networks/Consortia:** Member of Bibliographical Center for Research, Rocky Mountain Region, Inc. (BCR), Colorado Alliance of Research Libraries (CARL). **Publications:** Directory of Environmental Education Resources (DEER); School Model Programs - both available online through CARL. **Remarks:** FAX: (303)830-0793. **Staff:** Debra Grieb, Libn.

★3956★
Colorado (State) Department of Labor & Employment - Labor Market Information Library (Bus-Fin)
251 E. 12th Ave. Phone: (303)937-4935
Denver, CO 80203 Kenneth A. Anderson, Economist
Staff: Prof 1; Other 1. **Subjects:** Labor market information. **Special Collections:** Colorado Labor Force Review Series, 1964 to present. **Holdings:** 200 books; 2000 unbound reports; 1000 unbound periodicals; all official Colorado labor force estimates. **Subscriptions:** 20 journals and other serials. **Services:** Library open to the public for reference use only.

★3957★
Colorado (State) Department of Natural Resources - Colorado Geological Survey Library (Sci-Engr)
1313 Sherman, Rm. 715 Phone: (303)866-2611
Denver, CO 80203 Suzanne Tourtelot, Staff Asst.
Founded: 1969. **Staff:** 1. **Subjects:** Geology, geophysics. **Special Collections:** Colorado geology (500 volumes). **Holdings:** 2500 books; 500 bound periodical volumes; 1000 government documents; 1000 technical reports; 1000 maps; depository for U.S. Geological Survey and U.S. Department of Energy. **Subscriptions:** 15 journals and other serials. **Services:** Copying; library open to the public with restrictions. **Publications:** List of publications - available upon request. **Remarks:** FAX: (303)866-2115.

Colorado (State) Department of Regulatory Agencies Office of Energy Conservation
See: **Colorado (State) Office of Energy Conservation** (3966)

★3958★
Colorado (State) Department of Social Service - Library (Soc Sci)
1575 Sherman St. Phone: (303)866-4086
Denver, CO 80203-1714 Dorothy B. Shaughnessy, Libn.
Founded: 1945. **Staff:** Prof 1. **Subjects:** Social work, public and social welfare, psychology, sociology, child welfare, adoption, foster care, aged, child development, handicapped, crime and juvenile delinquency, group work and community organizations. **Holdings:** 9418 volumes; 3 VF drawers of pamphlets; 275 AV software programs. **Subscriptions:** 79 journals and other serials. **Services:** Interlibrary loan; copying; library open to the public. **Networks/Consortia:** Member of Central Colorado Library System (CCLS). **Publications:** Library Outlook, quarterly - for internal distribution only.

★3959★
Colorado State District Court, 2nd Judicial District - Law Library (Law)
1437 Bannock St., Rm. 389 Phone: (303)640-2233
Denver, CO 80202 Jo Ann Viola Salazar, Law Libn.
Founded: 1926. **Staff:** Prof 1. **Subjects:** Law. **Holdings:** 18,000 books; 1650 volumes on ultrafiche. **Subscriptions:** 11 journals and other serials. **Services:** Copying; library open to the public.

★3960★
Colorado State District Court, 6th Judicial District - Law Library (Law)
Box 3340 Phone: (303)259-0258
Durango, CO 81301 Al H. Haas, Chf. Judge
Staff: Prof 2. **Subjects:** Law. **Holdings:** 210,000 volumes. **Services:** Copying; library open to the public by special arrangement. **Staff:** Carolyn A. Wilber, Res.Atty.

★3961★
Colorado (State) Division of Highways - Tech Transfer (Trans)
4340 E. Louisiana Ave., Rm. L203 Phone: (303)757-9220
Denver, CO 80222 Beth Moore, Adm.Off.
Founded: 1949. **Staff:** Prof 1; Other 1. **Subjects:** Highway engineering, road planning and design, road and street research, road construction and maintenance, soils and materials, traffic safety and engineering, highway law, bridges and tunneling. **Holdings:** 100 books; 80 bound periodical volumes; 12,000 paperbound reports; 20 unbound periodicals. **Services:** Copying; open to the public. **Automated Operations:** Computerized cataloging. **Computerized Information Services:** DIALOG Information Services; electronic mail service. **Publications:** CDOH Research Newsletter, quarterly; Tech Transfer Topics.

★3962★
Colorado (State) Division of State Archives and Public Records (Hist)
Dept. of Administration
1313 Sherman St., Rm. 1B20 Phone: (303)866-2055
Denver, CO 80203 Terry Ketelsen, State Archv.
Founded: 1943. **Staff:** 12. **Subjects:** Noncurrent official public records and printed publications of the Territory and State of Colorado. **Holdings:** 78,000 cubic feet of public records. **Services:** Copying; certification; open to all who wish to consult records for legitimate purposes. **Publications:** Guide to the Resources of the Colorado State Archives (loose-leaf), updated periodically; brochures. **Remarks:** FAX: (303)620-4949. **Staff:** Greg Adame; James Chipman; Erin Christiensen; Jim Parker; Linda Watson; Vera Welham; Karen Zoltenko.

★3963★
Colorado (State) Division of Wildlife - Library (Env-Cons)
6060 Broadway Phone: (303)291-7319
Denver, CO 80216 Rita C. Green, Libn.
Staff: 1. **Subjects:** Wildlife, conservation, ecology, mammals and birds. **Holdings:** 1000 books; 500 bound periodical volumes; 540 films. **Subscriptions:** 15 journals and other serials. **Services:** Copying; library open to students or personnel in field.

★3964★
Colorado (State) Division of Wildlife - Research Center Library (Biol Sci)
317 W. Prospect Phone: (303)484-2836
Fort Collins, CO 80526 Jacqueline Boss, Libn.
Founded: 1967. **Staff:** Prof 1. **Subjects:** Wildlife, biology and management, fish biology, fishery management. **Special Collections:** Federal Aid in Fish and Wildlife Restoration, Colorado. **Holdings:** 4976 books; 600 bound periodical volumes; 3000 pamphlets and federal aid reports; 161 16mm films; 94 videocassettes; 44 slide kits. **Subscriptions:** 73 journals and other serials. **Services:** Interlibrary loan; library open to the public with restrictions. **Computerized Information Services:** DIALOG Information Services, Fish and Wildlife Reference Service Database. **Networks/Consortia:** Member of High Plains Regional Library Service System, Colorado Alliance of Research Libraries (CARL). **Publications:** Colorado Division of Wildlife Special Report; Technical Publication; Division Report Series, all irregular - all to libraries and other state and federal agencies. **Remarks:** FAX: (303)490-2621. **Staff:** Mary Colleen Hanna, Cat.

Colorado State Hospital - Professional Library
See: **Colorado Mental Health Institute at Pueblo** (3943)

Colorado State Judicial Department - El Paso County Law Library
See: **El Paso County Law Library** (5280)

★3965★
Colorado State Library - Colorado State Publications Library (Info Sci)
State Office Bldg., Rm. 314
201 E. Colfax Ave. Phone: (303)866-6728
Denver, CO 80203 Maureen Crocker, Libn.Prog.Mgr.
Founded: 1980. **Staff:** Prof 1; Other 2. **Subjects:** State publications. **Holdings:** 11,000 volumes. **Services:** Interlibrary loan; copying; library open to the public. **Automated Operations:** Computerized public access catalog and cataloging. **Computerized Information Services:** OCLC. **Networks/Consortia:** Member of Bibliographical Center for Research, Rocky Mountain Region, Inc. (BCR), Colorado Alliance of Research Libraries (CARL). **Publications:** Accesions checklist; microfiche checklist; Selective Bibliography Series; Colorado State Publications Classification Schedule. **Remarks:** FAX: (303)830-0793. **Staff:** Margie Wait, Cat.

★3966★
Colorado (State) Office of Energy Conservation - Library (Energy)
1675 Broadway, Suite 1300 Phone: (303)620-4292
Denver, CO 80202-4613 Martha J. Blackwell, Database Spec.
Founded: 1977. **Staff:** Prof 1; Other 1. **Subjects:** Energy consumption and conservation, recycling. **Holdings:** 1000 volumes. **Subscriptions:** 303 journals and other serials; 3 newspapers. **Services:** Copying; library open to the public. **Computerized Information Services:** Internal databases. **Publications:** Energy Talk; Senior Powerline; Weather Data; RecyleNet; Developments. **Remarks:** FAX: (303)620-4288. **Formerly:** Colorado (State) Department of Regulatory Agencies Office of Energy Conservation.

★3967★
Colorado State Supreme Court Law Library (Law)
State Judicial Bldg.
2 E. 14th Ave. Phone: (303)837-3720
Denver, CO 80203 Frances D. Campbell, Dir.
Staff: Prof 3; Other 2. **Subjects:** Law. **Holdings:** 74,000 books; 5000 bound periodical volumes; 750 reels of microfilm; 9500 volumes on microfiche. **Subscriptions:** 2250 journals and other serials. **Services:** Copying; library open to the public. **Automated Operations:** Computerized cataloging. **Computerized Information Services:** WESTLAW. Performs searches on fee basis. Contact Person: Martha Campbell, Libn. **Networks/Consortia:** Member of Bibliographical Center for Research, Rocky Mountain Region, Inc. (BCR). **Staff:** Linda Gruenthal, Libn.

★3968★
Colorado State University - Atmospheric Science Branch Library (Sci-Engr)
Foothills Campus
Fort Collins, CO 80523
Phone: (303)491-8532
Elizabeth A. Fuseler-McDowell, Hd., Sci./Tech.Dept.
Founded: 1985. **Staff:** 1. **Subjects:** Meteorology, climatology, air pollution, oceanography, geophysics, satellites and remote sensing in meteorology, radar. **Holdings:** 3000 books; 1500 bound periodical volumes; 2500 documents and technical reports; 250 reels of microfilm; 10 VF drawers of reprints; 300 volumes on microfiche. **Subscriptions:** 62 journals and other serials. **Services:** Interlibrary loan; copying; library open to the public. **Automated Operations:** Computerized cataloging. **Computerized Information Services:** DIALOG Information Services, BRS Information Technologies. Performs searches on fee basis. Contact Person: Michael Culbertson, Sci. & Tech.Libn., 491-1874; 491-1887. **Networks/Consortia:** Member of Research Libraries Information Network (RLIN), Colorado Alliance of Research Libraries (CARL). **Remarks:** FAX: (303)491-8449. **Staff:** Michael Culbertson, Engr.Libn.

★3969★
Colorado State University - Engineering Sciences Branch Library (Sci-Engr)
Fort Collins, CO 80523
Phone: (303)491-8694
Elizabeth A. Fuseler, Hd., Sci./Tech.Dept.
Founded: 1961. **Staff:** Prof 1; Other 1. **Subjects:** Water resources, hydraulics, hydrology, fluid mechanics, lasers and quantum electronics, energy. **Special Collections:** Delft Hydraulics Laboratory Documentation Data; Asian Institute of Technology theses; E.W. Lane special collection on hydrology. **Holdings:** 4650 books; 3550 bound periodical volumes; 7600 documents; 5 VF drawers of reprints. **Subscriptions:** 95 journals and other serials. **Services:** Interlibrary loan; copying; library open to the public. **Computerized Information Services:** DIALOG Information Services, STN International, BRS Information Technologies, Integrated Technical Information System (ITIS); InterNet (electronic mail service). Performs searches on fee basis. **Networks/Consortia:** Member of Research Libraries Information Network (RLIN). **Publications:** Energy from the Wind (annotated bibliography). **Special Indexes:** WASAR (Water and Soil in Arid Regions), An Index to Selected Materials in Colorado State University Libraries. **Remarks:** FAX: (303)491-1195. Electronic mail address(es): LWESS@VINES.COLOSTATE.EDU (InterNet). **Staff:** Michael Culbertson.

★3970★
Colorado State University - Germans from Russia Project Library (Area-Ethnic)
University Libraries
Fort Collins, CO 80523
Phone: (303)491-1844
John Newman, Proj.Archv.
Staff: 1. **Subjects:** Germans from Russia. **Holdings:** 880 books; 45 bound periodical volumes; 100 manuscripts. **Services:** Interlibrary loan; copying; library open to public by prior arrangement. **Special Catalogs:** Germans from Russia in Colorado (1978).

★3971★
Colorado State University - Natural Resource Ecology Laboratory - Library (Env-Cons)
Fort Collins, CO 80523
Phone: (303)491-1991
Founded: 1967. **Subjects:** Grassland ecology, soils, systems analysis. **Holdings:** 1000 volumes. **Services:** Library not open to the public. **Computerized Information Services:** InterNet (electronic mail service). **Remarks:** FAX: (303)491-1965. Electronic mail address(es): DAVE@POA.NREL.COLO.STATE.EDU (InterNet).

★3972★
Colorado State University - Veterinary Teaching Hospital - Branch Library (Med)
300 W. Drake Rd.
Fort Collins, CO 80523
Phone: (303)491-1213
Elizabeth A. Fuseler, Hd., Sci./Tech.Dept.
Founded: 1979. **Staff:** Prof 1; Other 2. **Subjects:** Veterinary medicine. **Special Collections:** Poisonous plants (200 pieces). **Holdings:** 1950 books; 3100 bound periodical volumes. **Subscriptions:** 183 journals and other serials. **Services:** Interlibrary loan; library open to the public with restrictions. **Computerized Information Services:** DIALOG Information Services, BRS Information Technologies, OCLC, NLM, STN International; InterNet (electronic mail service). Performs searches on fee basis. **Networks/Consortia:** Member of Research Libraries Information Network (RLIN). **Remarks:** FAX: (303)491-1195. Electronic mail address(es): BFUSELER@VINES.COLOSTATE.EDU (InterNet).

★3973★
Colorado State University - Vietnam War Literature Collection (Hist)
University Libraries
Fort Collins, CO 80523
Phone: (303)491-1844
John Newman, Spec.Coll.Libn.
Founded: 1975. **Staff:** Prof 1; Other 1. **Subjects:** Vietnam War - fiction, poetry, plays. **Holdings:** 2000 books; 100 bound periodical volumes; 500 other cataloged items. **Services:** Interlibrary loan; copying; collection open to the public by appointment. **Computerized Information Services:** Internal database. **Publications:** Vietnam War Literature (1988).

★3974★
Colorado State University - William E. Morgan Library (Sci-Engr, Biol Sci)
Fort Collins, CO 80523
Phone: (303)491-1838
Joan L. Chambers, Dir. of Lib.
Founded: 1870. **Staff:** Prof 43; Other 98. **Subjects:** Hydraulic engineering, irrigation, water resources, soil mechanics, radiology and radiation biology, agronomy, horticulture, microbiology, mycology, parasitology, veterinary medicine, genetics, forestry. **Special Collections:** University Libraries; Colorado Agricultural Archives; Imaginary Wars; Vietnam War fiction collection. **Holdings:** 1.6 million volumes; 1.4 million microforms; 32,000 maps; 7500 audio reproductions. **Subscriptions:** 20,000 journals and other serials; 170 newspapers. **Services:** Interlibrary loan; copying; SDI; library open to the public. **Automated Operations:** Computerized public access catalog and circulation. **Computerized Information Services:** DIALOG Information Services, OCLC, BRS Information Technologies, NLM, STN International, WILSONLINE; CD-ROMs. Contact Person: Michael Culbertson, Sci./Tech., 491-1874, or Jennifer Monath, Soc.Sci./Hum., 491-1860. **Networks/Consortia:** Member of Bibliographical Center for Research, Rocky Mountain Region, Inc. (BCR), Research Libraries Information Network (RLIN), Center for Research Libraries (CRL). **Publications:** Library Series, irregular. **Special Catalogs:** Serials Book Catalog.

Colpoys Library
See: **Carney Hospital** (3087)

★3975★
Colquitt Regional Medical Center - Health Sciences Library (Med)
P.O. Box 40
Moultrie, GA 31776
Phone: (912)890-3460
Susan Statom, Med.Libn.
Founded: 1979. **Staff:** Prof 1. **Subjects:** Medicine, nursing, and allied health sciences. **Holdings:** 200 books; 350 bound periodical volumes. **Subscriptions:** 57 journals and other serials. **Services:** Interlibrary loan; copying; SDI; library open to the public at librarian's discretion. **Computerized Information Services:** NLM, BRS/COLLEAGUE. **Networks/Consortia:** Member of Georgia Interactive Network for Medical Information (GaIN). **Remarks:** FAX: (912)890-2173.

Colt Industries
See: **Coltec Industries - FM Engine Division Library** (3976)

Colt Industries - Crucible Research Center
See: **Crucible Materials Corporation** (4452)

Coltec Industries - Delavan Inc
See: **Delavan Inc.** (4712)

★3976★
Coltec Industries - FM Engine Division Library (Sci-Engr)
701 Lawton Ave.
Beloit, WI 53511
Phone: (608)364-4411
Sue Garry, Libn.
Founded: 1960. **Subjects:** Metallurgy, diesel engines. **Holdings:** 1200 books; 200 bound periodical volumes; 1500 unbound professional reports and papers. **Subscriptions:** 30 journals and other serials. **Services:** Library not open to the public. **Formerly:** Colt Industries.

★3977★
Colton Hall Museum - Library (Hist)
Civic Center Phone: (408)375-9944
Monterey, CA 93940 Susan Klusmire, Cur.
Staff: Prof 2. **Subjects:** California and local history. **Holdings:** 1500 books; 3000 documents; clipping files; early textbooks. **Subscriptions:** 11 journals and other serials. **Services:** Copying; library open to the public with restrictions on some materials. **Remarks:** Maintained by the city of Monterey. Bilingual materials are available pertaining to the 1849 California Constitutional Convention. **Remarks:** FAX: (408)646-3702.

Harold S. Colton Memorial Library
See: **Museum of Northern Arizona** (10916)

★3978★
Columbia Bible College - G. Allen Fleece Library (Rel-Phil)
7435 Monticello Rd.
Box 3122 Phone: (803)754-4100
Columbia, SC 29230 David Mash, Dir.
Founded: 1923. **Staff:** Prof 1; Other 9. **Subjects:** Bible, theology, missions, sanctification, education, music. **Special Collections:** Visual aids for religious education and Christian service; missionary curios; sanctification. **Holdings:** 96,078 volumes; 13,478 AV programs; 3048 cassette tapes; 1010 phonograph records; 40 VF drawers of pamphlets; 6 VF drawers of pictures. **Subscriptions:** 627 journals and other serials. **Services:** Interlibrary loan; copying; center open to the public. **Automated Operations:** Computerized cataloging, acquisitions, serials, and ILL. **Computerized Information Services:** OCLC, BRS Information Technologies; CD-ROM (ERIC). Performs searches on fee basis. **Networks/Consortia:** Member of SOLINET, South Carolina Library Network. **Staff:** Marilyn Morrison; JoAnn Rhodes.

★3979★
Columbia Christian College - Library - Special Collections (Rel-Phil)
9101 E. Burnside St. Phone: (503)255-7060
Portland, OR 97216 Mary B. Gunselman, Act.Hd.Libn.
Founded: 1956. **Staff:** Prof 2; Other 1. **Special Collections:** First Century Christianity to the Restoration movement (2000). **Holdings:** 31,000 books; 26,000 microfiche. **Subscriptions:** 245 journals and other serials; 2 newspapers. **Services:** Interlibrary loan; copying; collections open to the public.

★3980★
Columbia College-Hollywood - Joseph E. Bluth Memorial Library (Theater)
925 N. LaBrea Ave. Phone: (213)851-0550
Hollywood, CA 90038 Kurt G. Wolfe, Libn.
Founded: 1978. **Staff:** Prof 1; Other 1. **Subjects:** Television, motion pictures, theater, broadcast journalism, art history, electronics, computers. **Special Collections:** Screenplays and television plays (1250); television production, writing, history; motion picture production, writing, history, biography. **Holdings:** 4400 books; 160 video cassettes; technical journals. **Subscriptions:** 26 newspapers and magazines. **Services:** Library not open to the public. **Remarks:** FAX: (213)851-6401.

Columbia College Library
See: **Columbia University - Columbia College Library** (4010)

★3981★
Columbia County Historical Society - Columbia County Museum (Hist)
5 Albany Ave.
P.O. Box 311 Phone: (518)758-9265
Kinderhook, NY 12106 Sharon S. Palmer, Exec.Dir.
Founded: 1926. **Staff:** Prof 2; Other 1. **Subjects:** Regional, county, American history; genealogy; art history; architecture; decorative arts. **Holdings:** 3000 books; antiques. **Services:** Copying; museum open to the public.

★3982★
Columbia County Historical Society - Edwin M. Barton Library (Hist)
P.O. Box 197
Orangeville, PA 17859 Phone: (717)683-6011
Founded: 1914. **Staff:** 10. **Subjects:** Columbia County history, local history and genealogy. **Special Collections:** Late 19th century personal and small business accounts and correspondence of the county. **Holdings:** 1000 books; 50 bound periodical volumes; 200 bound manuscripts and 20 linear feet of unbound manuscripts; 50 scrapbooks; 12 linear feet of pamphlet files cataloged by subject and area; 3 linear feet of Works Progress Administration (WPA) files of mid-1930s historical and genealogical compilations; 1200 photographs and maps. **Services:** Copying; library open to the public. **Publications:** The Columbian; historical leaflets. **Special Indexes:** List of area newspapers (booklet).

★3983★
Columbia County Historical Society - Museum (Hist)
Old County Courthouse Phone: (503)397-2368
St. Helens, OR 97051 Billie S. Ivey, Cur.
Founded: 1969. **Staff:** Prof 2. **Subjects:** History of Columbia County, genealogy. **Holdings:** 450 books; 150 bound periodical volumes; deeds and contracts; maps; local pictures; magazines; newspapers; scrapbooks. **Services:** Copying; museum open to the public for reference use only. **Publications:** Columbia County History, annual.

★3984★
Columbia Daily Tribune - Library (Publ)
101 N. 4th St.
P.O. Box 798 Phone: (314)874-6483
Columbia, MO 66205 Jan Summers, News Libn.
Founded: 1975. **Staff:** Prof 1. **Holdings:** News clipping file; news photo file; reference collection. **Services:** Copying; library open to the public. **Remarks:** FAX: (314)874-6413.

★3985★
Columbia Falls Aluminum Company - Library (Sci-Engr)
2000 Aluminum Dr.
Box 10 Phone: (406)892-3261
Columbia Falls, MT 59912 Karen Green, Chem.Techn.
Founded: 1955. **Staff:** Prof 2. **Subjects:** Chemistry - inorganic, metals and metallurgy, environmental control, raw materials data; technical analytical data; management; technical writing. **Special Collections:** Aluminum and aluminum casting and principles; environmental control. **Holdings:** 1000 books; 50 bound periodical volumes; 5 drawers of prints and negatives; 1700 pamphlets and patents; 200 trade catalogs. **Subscriptions:** 30 journals and other serials. **Services:** Interlibrary loan; copying; library open to the public by request. **Special Catalogs:** Patent and document catalog. **Staff:** Donald F. Ryan, Tech.Supt.

★3986★
Columbia Gas System Service Corporation - Law Library (Law)
20 Montchanin Rd. Phone: (302)429-5320
Wilmington, DE 19807 Kathryn C. Bossler, Law Libn.
Staff: Prof 1. **Subjects:** Law - utility, corporate, general. **Holdings:** 5328 books; 52 periodical titles; 5 VF drawers. **Services:** Library not open to the public. **Computerized Information Services:** LEXIS, WESTLAW. **Remarks:** FAX: (302)429-5461.

★3987★
Columbia Gas System Service Corporation - Research Library
1600 Dublin Rd.
Columbus, OH 43215
Defunct.

★3988★
Columbia Gas Transmission Corporation - Law Library (Law)
Box 1273 Phone: (304)357-2554
Charleston, WV 25325 Sandra K. Neylon, Law Lib.Adm.
Staff: Prof 2. **Subjects:** Law - general, oil, gas, property, contracts, statutes. **Holdings:** 11,000 volumes; 346 VF drawers of law files. **Subscriptions:** 150 journals and other serials; 12 newspapers. **Services:** Library not open to the public.

★3989★
Columbia Gulf Transmission Company - Engineering Library (Sci-Engr)
Box 683 Phone: (713)267-4100
Houston, TX 77001 Vance Benoit, Engr.Libn.
Founded: 1959. **Staff:** Prof 1. **Subjects:** Engineering - natural gas, petroleum, general; business and management; information sciences. **Holdings:** 3700 books; 300 bound periodical volumes; 500 manufacturers' catalogs; 4 VF drawers of maps; 4 VF drawers of clippings; 4 VF drawers of pictures; 15,052 microforms; 400 Columbia Gas and Columbia Gulf publications; government documents; standards. **Subscriptions:** 201 journals and other serials. **Services:** Interlibrary loan; copying; library open to the public. **Automated Operations:** Computerized cataloging and acquisitions. **Computerized Information Services:** PFDS Online; internal database. **Publications:** Library Bulletin, bimonthly - for internal distribution only. **Remarks:** Library located at 3805 W. Alabama, Houston, TX 77027-5290.

★3990★
Columbia Hospital - College of Nursing - Library (Med)
2121 E. Newport Ave. Phone: (414)961-3533
Milwaukee, WI 53211 Shirley S. Chan, Libn.
Staff: Prof 1; Other 2. **Subjects:** Nurses and nursing, nursing education, pharmacology, community health, psychology, sociology, nutrition. **Special Collections:** Historical Collection; National League for Nursing (NLN) Collection (294 publications); American Nurses Association (ANA) Collection. **Holdings:** 4500 books; 511 bound periodical volumes; pamphlets on 129 subjects; 65 slide/tape sets; 65 filmstrip/record sets; 90 filmstrip/cassette sets; 60 audio cassettes; 388 slides; 15 faculty theses; 4 VF drawers of pamphlets; 3 VF drawers of book/AV catalogs; 139 transparencies; 11 videotapes; 19 anatomical models; 2 charts; 1 skeleton. **Subscriptions:** 100 journals and other serials. **Services:** Interlibrary loan; copying; SDI; library open to the public for reference use only. **Networks/Consortia:** Member of Southeastern Wisconsin Health Science Library Consortium (SWHSL), Library Council of Metropolitan Milwaukee, Inc. (LCOMM), National Network of Libraries of Medicine - Greater Midwest Region. **Publications:** AV Software List, annual; Current Awareness on nursing journals - both for internal distribution only; Journal Holding List, annual; Accessions List; Booklists, monthly; Annual Report.

★3991★
Columbia Hospital - Medical Library (Med)
2025 E. Newport Ave. Phone: (414)961-3858
Milwaukee, WI 53211 Ruth Holst, Dir., Lib.Serv.
Founded: 1942. **Staff:** Prof 2; Other 3. **Subjects:** Medicine, nursing, hospital administration, consumer health. **Special Collections:** Clinical medicine and nursing (150,000 reprints). **Holdings:** 2000 books; 8000 bound periodical volumes; 450 audio cassettes. **Subscriptions:** 300 journals and other serials. **Services:** Interlibrary loan; copying; SDI; library open to the public by request. **Computerized Information Services:** BRS Information Technologies, NLM, DIALOG Information Services, WILSONLINE. **Networks/Consortia:** Member of Southeastern Wisconsin Health Science Library Consortium (SWHSL), Library Council of Metropolitan Milwaukee, Inc. (LCOMM), National Network of Libraries of Medicine - Greater Midwest Region. **Remarks:** FAX: (414)961-8712. **Staff:** Jane Koenig, Libn.

★3992★
Columbia Hospital for Women Medical Center - Medical Library (Med)
2425 L St., N.W. Phone: (202)293-6560
Washington, DC 20037 Elizabeth M. Haggart, Libn.
Founded: 1981. **Staff:** Prof 1. **Subjects:** Obstetrics and gynecology. **Holdings:** 1800 books. **Subscriptions:** 280 journals and other serials. **Services:** Interlibrary loan; library not open to the public. **Computerized Information Services:** MEDLINE.

Columbia Missourian
See: **University of Missouri--Columbia** (18961)

★3993★
Columbia Museum of Art - Library (Art)
1112 Bull St. Phone: (803)343-2155
Columbia, SC 29201 Elizabeth B. Rich, Hd.
Founded: 1950. **Staff:** Prof 1; Other 4. **Subjects:** American art; European art, Renaissance through 20th century; biography of artists. **Holdings:** 12,000 volumes; 6 VF drawers of pamphlets. **Subscriptions:** 49 journals and other serials. **Services:** Interlibrary loan; copying; library open to the public for reference use only. **Remarks:** FAX: (803)343-2150.

★3994★
Columbia Organic Chemical Co., Inc. - Library
Box 1045
Camden, SC 29020
Defunct.

Columbia-Presbyterian Medical Center of New York - Edward S. Harkness Eye Institute
See: **Edward S. Harkness Eye Institute** (6905)

★3995★
Columbia Research Corporation - Repository (Mil)
2531 Jefferson Davis Hwy., Suite 100 Phone: (703)841-1445
Arlington, VA 22202 Dawn R. Sanborn, Libn.
Staff: Prof 1. **Subjects:** Naval weapons and technology. **Special Collections:** Military specifications, standards and handbooks; NASA Aeronautical Engineering Continuing Bibliography with Indexes; International Aerospace Abstracts Indexes; Jane's Fighting Ships; Scientific & Technical Aerospace Reports Indexes; Government-Industry Data Exchange Program Reports. **Holdings:** 70 volumes; 5000 documents; 2000 classified government documents; 5000 unclassified government documents; 30 documents on microfiche. **Services:** Repository not open to the public. **Automated Operations:** Computerized cataloging. **Computerized Information Services:** Internal database.

★3996★
Columbia River Fisheries Private Collection (Biol Sci)
P.O. Box 83 Phone: (206)795-3920
Skamokawa, WA 98647 Irene Martin, Libn./Owner
Staff: Prof 1. **Subjects:** Columbia River and Alaska salmon fisheries, Columbia river history. **Holdings:** 530 books; 10 VF drawers of manuscripts, photographs, pamphlets, cannery labels, scrapbooks, clippings, engravings; salmon fishery artifacts; video- and audiotapes. **Subscriptions:** 10 journals and other serials. **Services:** Copying; collection open to the public by appointment only; reference and research done on request.

★3997★
Columbia River Maritime Museum, Inc. - Library (Hist)
1792 Marine Dr. Phone: (503)325-2323
Astoria, OR 97103 Anne Witty, Cur.
Founded: 1982. **Staff:** Prof 1. **Subjects:** Maritime and Pacific Northwest history. **Special Collections:** Astoria Marine Construction Company plan and photograph files; Haskins Collection of fur trade journals and papers; Columbia River Packers Association/Bumble Bee Seafoods corporate archives. **Holdings:** 5610 books; 155 bound periodical volumes; 10,500 marine photographs; 15 file cabinets. **Subscriptions:** 194 journals and other serials. **Services:** Copying; library open to the public by appointment for reference use only. **Publications:** The Quarterdeck (newsletter), quarterly - to museum members.

★3998★
Columbia Theological Seminary - John Bulow Campbell Library (Rel-Phil)
701 Columbia Dr. Phone: (404)378-8821
Decatur, GA 30031-0520 Dr. James A. Overbeck, Lib.Dir.
Founded: 1828. **Staff:** Prof 4; Other 1. **Subjects:** Biblical studies, church history, systematic theology, practical church work. **Special Collections:** Thomas M. Smyth rare book collection (includes newspapers of the Civil War period). **Holdings:** 115,000 books; 15,000 bound periodical volumes. **Subscriptions:** 540 journals and other serials. **Services:** Interlibrary loan; copying; library open to the public on limited schedule. **Automated Operations:** Computerized cataloging and acquisitions. **Computerized Information Services:** BRS Information Technologies, DIALOG Information Services. Performs searches on fee basis. Contact Person: Dr. Christine Wenderoth. **Networks/Consortia:** Member of University Center in Georgia, Inc., Atlanta Theological Library Association. **Publications:** Library Newsletter - for internal distribution only. **Remarks:** FAX: (404)377-9696. **Staff:** Ruthanne Huff, Tech.Serv.; Colleen Higgs, Circ.

★3999★
Columbia Union College - Theofield G. Weis Library (Rel-Phil)
7600 Flower Ave. Phone: (301)891-4217
Takoma Park, MD 20912-7796 Margaret J. von Hake, Libn.
Founded: 1904. **Staff:** Prof 3; Other 3. **Subjects:** Religion, education, health sciences, history, natural sciences, psychology. **Special Collections:** Heritage Room (Seventh-Day Adventist manuscripts; book rarities; mementos; theses and dissertations); Curriculum Library Collection (children's books; textbooks; curriculum guides; resource units). **Holdings:** 123,000 volumes; 34 VF drawers of reports, manuscripts, clippings. **Subscriptions:** 412 journals and other serials. **Services:** Interlibrary loan; copying; library open to the public with references. **Automated Operations:** Computerized cataloging. **Computerized Information Services:** OCLC. **Networks/Consortia:** Member of CAPCON Library Network. **Publications:** Booklist, quarterly - to faculty, students, selected libraries; Newsletter, irregular - to faculty and students. **Special Indexes:** Author, title, subject index to selected Seventh-Day Adventist serial publications (271,000 cards). **Remarks:** FAX: (301)270-1618. **Staff:** Stanley Cottrell, Cat.; Kathy Hecht, Circ./ILL; Debby Szasz, Curric.Lib./Acq.; Corliss Vander Mei, Ref. Libn. ; Joan Vander Mei, Ser.; Lee Marie Wisel, Cat.Libn.

★4000★
Columbia University - Ambrose Monell Engineering Library (Sci-Engr)
422 Mudd Phone: (212)854-3206
New York, NY 10027 Ujwal Ranadive, Ref./Coll.Dev.Libn.
Founded: 1883. **Staff:** Prof 1; Other 6. **Subjects:** Engineering - chemical, civil, electrical, industrial, mechanical, nuclear; mining; metallurgy; applied mathematics; computer science; operations research. **Special Collections:** Archival material of New York Tunnel Authority; Regional Technical Report Center; DOE, NASA, and NTIS technical reports (over 1 million on microfiche). **Holdings:** 206,000 volumes; 7700 reels of microfilm. **Subscriptions:** 1375 journals and other serials. **Services:** Library open to Columbia University affiliates. **Automated Operations:** Computerized public access catalog, serials, and circulation. **Computerized Information Services:** DIALOG Information Services, STN International, OCLC, RLIN, Ei Page One; CD-ROMs; InterNet, BITNET (electronic mail services). **Networks/Consortia:** Member of Research Libraries Information Network (RLIN), Center for Research Libraries (CRL). **Remarks:** Alternate telephone number(s): 854-2976. Electronic mail address(es): UR2@CUNIXF.CC.COLUMBIA.EDU (InterNet); UR2@CUNIXF (BITNET).

★4001★
Columbia University - Augustus C. Long Health Sciences Library (Med)
701 W. 168th St. Phone: (212)305-3692
New York, NY 10032 Susan Jacobson, Act.Dir.
Founded: 1928. **Staff:** Prof 20; Other 36. **Subjects:** Anatomy; biochemistry; clinical medicine; dentistry; medical history and practice; microbiology; neurology; nursing; oncology; pathology; pharmacology; physiology; public health; surgery - general, orthopedic, plastic; thanatology. **Special Collections:** Jerome P. Webster Library of Plastic Surgery; George Sumner Huntington Collection (anatomy); John Green Curtis Collection (physiology); Sigmund Freud Library; Florence Nightingale Collection; Orton Collection (learning disorders); Hyman Collection in the History of Anesthesia. **Holdings:** 445,000 volumes; 2562 AV programs. **Subscriptions:** 4414 journals and other serials. **Services:** Interlibrary loan; library not open to the public. **Automated Operations:** Computerized public access catalog, cataloging, acquisitions, serials, and ILL (DOCLINE). **Computerized Information Services:** DIALOG Information Services, NLM, BRS Information Technologies, RLIN, CLIO (Columbia Libraries Information Online); internal database. **Networks/Consortia:** Member of Research Libraries Information Network (RLIN), New York Metropolitan Reference and Research Library Agency, Medical Library Center of New York (MLCNY). **Publications:** Information News, quarterly. **Remarks:** FAX: (212)234-0595.

★4002★
Columbia University - Avery Architectural and Fine Arts Library (Art, Plan)
New York, NY 10027 Phone: (212)854-3501
Angela Giral, Libn.
Founded: 1890. **Staff:** Prof 10; Other 11. **Subjects:** Architecture, painting, sculpture, decorative arts, urban planning, archeology, real estate development. **Special Collections:** Collection of original architectural drawings - Upjohn, A.J. Davis, Renwick, F.L. Wright, Lienau, Sullivan, Greene and Greene. **Holdings:** 250,000 volumes; 400,000 manuscripts, letters, clippings, drawings. **Subscriptions:** 1200 journals and other serials. **Services:** Copying; library open to the public with restrictions. **Automated Operations:** Computerized cataloging and acquisitions. **Computerized Information Services:** DIALOG Information Services, CIN; CD-ROM (Art Index); produces Avery Index to Architectural Periodicals. **Networks/Consortia:** Member of Research Libraries Information Network (RLIN), New York Metropolitan Reference and Research Library Agency. **Special Catalogs:** Avery Catalog. **Special Indexes:** Avery Index to Architectural Periodicals; AVIADOR CAvery Videodisc Index of Architectural Drawings on RLIN; Avery Index (online, hardcopy), with supplements. **Staff:** William O'Malley, Arch.; Janet Parks, Drawings Cur.; Paula Gabbard, Fine Arts; Katharine Chibnik, Access & Sup.Serv.; Kathe Chipman, Indexer/Ref.Libn.; Ted Goodman, Index Ed.; Barbara Sykes-Austin, Urban Plan. & Indexer/Ref.Libn.; Deborah Kempe, Indexer/Ref.Libn.; Katharine Keller, Indexer/Ref.Libn.

★4003★
Columbia University - Biological Sciences Library (Biol Sci)
601 Fairchild Bldg. Phone: (212)854-4715
New York, NY 10027 Kathleen Kehoe, Ref./Coll.Dev.Libn.
Founded: 1912. **Staff:** Prof 1; Other 1. **Subjects:** Experimental zoology, neurosciences, genetics, molecular biology, cytology, histology, animal and plant physiology, biochemistry, cell biology. **Holdings:** 46,000 volumes. **Subscriptions:** 330 journals and other serials. **Services:** Library not open to the public. **Automated Operations:** Computerized cataloging and acquisitions. **Computerized Information Services:** DIALOG Information Services, RLIN, BRS Information Technologies, NLM; InterNet, BITNET (electronic mail services). Performs searches on fee basis. **Networks/Consortia:** Member of Research Libraries Information Network (RLIN), Center for Research Libraries (CRL), New York Metropolitan Reference and Research Library Agency. **Remarks:** Electronic mail address(es): Kehoe@cunixf (BITNET).

★4004★
Columbia University - Burgess-Carpenter Library (Hum, Soc Sci)
406 Butler Library Phone: (212)854-4710
New York, NY 10027 Victor Fernandez, Supv.
Staff: Prof 1; Other 10. **Subjects:** Social sciences, history, language and literature, classics in Greek and Latin. **Holdings:** 135,000 volumes; 25,000 Columbia masters' essays; 3500 dissertations. **Services:** Interlibrary loan; copying; library open to the public. **Automated Operations:** Computerized public access catalog and circulation. **Networks/Consortia:** Member of Research Libraries Information Network (RLIN), Center for Research Libraries (CRL), New York Metropolitan Reference and Research Library Agency. **Special Indexes:** Card indexes to Columbia masters' essays.

★4005★
Columbia University - Butler Library (Hist, Hum, Area-Ethnic)
225A Butler Library Phone: (212)854-7602
New York, NY 10027 Daphne G. Estwick, Hd., Access & Circ.
Staff: 59. **Subjects:** Literature, humanities, history. **Holdings:** 1.6 million volumes. **Subscriptions:** 4000 journals and other serials. **Services:** Interlibrary loan; copying; library open with limited access. **Automated Operations:** Computerized public access catalog, cataloging, acquisitions, and circulation. **Computerized Information Services:** Online systems; InterNet, BITNET (electronic mail services). **Networks/Consortia:** Member of Research Libraries Information Network (RLIN), Center for Research Libraries (CRL), New York Metropolitan Reference and Research Library Agency. **Remarks:** Electronic mail address(es): estwick@cunixf (BITNET); estwick@cunixf.cc.columbia.edu (InterNet).

★4006★
Columbia University - C.V. Starr East Asian Library (Area-Ethnic)
300 Kent Hall
116th St. & Amsterdam Ave. Phone: (212)854-4318
New York, NY 10027 Dr. Amy Vladeck Heinrich, Act. East Asian Libn.
Founded: 1902. **Staff:** Prof 9; Other 11. **Subjects:** China, Japan, Korea - humanities, history, social sciences, art history. **Special Collections:** Chinese local histories and genealogies; Japanese woodblock - printed books; Korean collection of Yi Song-ui. **Holdings:** Chinese - 214,370 books and 54,344 bound periodical volumes; Japanese - 166,233 books and 41,968 bound periodical volumes; Korean - 28,970 books and 7309 bound periodical volumes; Western languages - 41,293 books and 10,483 bound periodical volumes; 10,594 reels of microfilm; 10,905 microfiche. **Subscriptions:** 3517 journals and other serials; 52 newspapers. **Services:** Interlibrary loan; copying; library open to the public for reference use only. **Automated Operations:** Computerized public access catalog (CLIO) and cataloging. **Networks/Consortia:** Member of Center for Research Libraries (CRL), New York Metropolitan Reference and Research Library Agency, Research Libraries Information Network (RLIN). **Remarks:** FAX: (212)662-6286. **Staff:** Charles Wu, Hd., Tech.Serv.; Kenji Niki, Bibliog./Ref.Libn., Japanese; Fran LaFleur, Bibliog./Ref.Libn., Chinese; Amy Lee, Bibliog./Ref.Libn, Korean; Eddie Wang, Chinese Cat.; Yasuko Makino, Japanese Cat.

★4007★
Columbia University - Center for Ethnomusicology (Mus)
417 Dodge Hall Phone: (212)854-1247
New York, NY 10027 Prof. Dieter Christensen, Dir.
Founded: 1964. **Staff:** Prof 1; Other 2. **Subjects:** Ethnomusicology. **Special Collections:** Laura Boulton Collection of Liturgical and Traditional Music; Collection of contemporary and traditional Turkish music; Flamenco Collection (videotapes); Omah Collection. **Holdings:** 130 books; 70 bound periodical volumes; 50,000 tape recordings, 300 video recordings. **Subscriptions:** 2 journals and other serials. **Services:** Center open to the public with restrictions. **Automated Operations:** Computerized cataloging. **Special Indexes:** Card index and documentation.

★4008★
Columbia University - Center for Population & Family Health - Library/Information Program (Soc Sci)
60 Haven Ave., B-3 Phone: (212)305-6960
New York, NY 10032 Susan K. Pasquariella, Ph.D, Hd.Libn.
Founded: 1968. **Staff:** Prof 2; Other 3. **Subjects:** Family planning, evaluative methodology, operations research, demography. **Special Collections:** Developing countries family planning program evaluations. **Holdings:** 7000 books; 30,000 published and unpublished reports, manuscripts, reprints, documents. **Subscriptions:** 200 journals and other serials. **Services:** Interlibrary loan; copying; SDI; library open to the public with restrictions. **Computerized Information Services:** Contributes to POPLINE database. **Networks/Consortia:** Member of APLIC International Census Network. **Publications:** POPLINE Thesaurus; CPFH Working Papers. **Remarks:** Center for Population & Family Health is a part of International Institute for the Study of Human Reproduction, Columbia University. FAX: (212)305-7024. Telex: 971913 POPFAMHLTH. **Staff:** Carole Oshinsky, Ref.Libn.

★4009★
Columbia University - Chemistry Library (Sci-Engr)
454 Chandler Hall Phone: (212)854-4709
New York, NY 10027 Elida B. Stein, Ref./Coll.Dev.Libn.
Founded: 1900. **Staff:** Prof 1; Other 1. **Subjects:** Chemistry - organic, physical, theoretical, inorganic; biochemistry. **Holdings:** 42,000 volumes. **Subscriptions:** 325 journals and other serials. **Services:** Library not open to the public. **Automated Operations:** Computerized cataloging and acquisitions. **Computerized Information Services:** Chemical Abstracts Service (CAS), DIALOG Information Services, BRS Information Technologies, RLIN; InterNet (electronic mail service). **Networks/Consortia:** Member of New York Metropolitan Reference and Research Library Agency, Research Libraries Information Network (RLIN). **Remarks:** Electronic mail address(es): STEIN@CUNIXF.CC.COLUMBIA.EDU (InterNet).

★4010★
Columbia University - Columbia College Library (Soc Sci, Hum)
225 Butler Library Phone: (212)854-3534
New York, NY 10027 Evelyn Ghoram, Supv.
Founded: 1907. **Staff:** Prof 1; Other 13. **Subjects:** Humanities, social sciences, American history and literature, economics, English literature, philosophy. **Holdings:** 44,000 volumes. **Services:** Interlibrary loan; copying. **Automated Operations:** Computerized public access catalog. **Networks/Consortia:** Member of Center for Research Libraries (CRL), New York Metropolitan Reference and Research Library Agency, Research Libraries Information Network (RLIN).

★4011★
Columbia University - Columbiana (Hist)
210 Low Memorial Library Phone: (212)854-3786
New York, NY 10027 Hollee Haswell, Cur.
Founded: 1883. **Staff:** Prof 1; Other 2. **Subjects:** Columbia University history and biography. **Special Collections:** Columbia University archives; King's College Room (contains original library of King's College from Colonial America; portraits; furniture, decorative arts, and other memorabilia). **Holdings:** 28,000 books; 369,000 paper ephemera; 3000 photographs. **Services:** Copying. **Networks/Consortia:** Member of Center for Research Libraries (CRL), New York Metropolitan Reference and Research Library Agency, Research Libraries Information Network (RLIN).

★4012★
Columbia University - Comprehensive Cancer Center - Library (Med)
701 W. 168th St. Phone: (212)305-6948
New York, NY 10032 Betty Rose Moore, Lib.Serv.Coord.
Founded: 1952. **Staff:** Prof 1. **Subjects:** Cancer. **Services:** Interlibrary loan. **Remarks:** Holdings are housed in and services are provided by the Augustus C. Long Health Sciences Library.

★4013★
Columbia University - Department of Art History & Archaeology - Visual Resources Collection - Photograph Library (Art, Aud-Vis)
820-825 Schermerhorn Hall Phone: (212)854-3044
New York, NY 10027 Linda Strauss, Cur., Vis.Rsrcs.Coll.
Founded: 1952. **Staff:** Prof 1; Other 8. **Subjects:** Art - Primitive and Pre-Columbian, Near Eastern, Far Eastern, Greek, Roman, early Christian, Medieval, Renaissance, Baroque, 19th and 20th century. **Special Collections:** Berenson I-Tatti Archive (50,000 photographs); Dial Iconographic Index (12,580); Haseloff Archive (20,000); Bartsch Collection (10,640); Gaignieres Collection (3420); Arthur Kingsley Porter Collection (4000); Ware Collection; Courtauld Collection; Marburger Index on microfiche; Windsor Castle drawings; Chatsworth Collection; all James Austin offerings; special Alinari offerings; Bibles Moralisees in Vienna and Toledo; Arndt Einzelaufnamen (5100 photographs); Rudolph Wittkower Collection (5 VF drawers); Millard Meiss Collection (15 VF drawers). **Holdings:** 155,000 photographs; 15,000 gallery announcements. **Services:** Collection open to scholars with proper identification only for reference use.

★4014★
Columbia University - Geology Library (Sci-Engr)
601 Schermerhorn Hall Phone: (212)854-4713
New York, NY 10027 Susan Klimley, Libn.
Founded: 1912. **Staff:** Prof 1; Other 1. **Subjects:** Geology, mineralogy, stratigraphy, geophysics, geochemistry, remote sensing, petrology, sedimentology, economic geology. **Special Collections:** State and foreign geological survey collection. **Holdings:** 86,000 volumes. **Subscriptions:** 1400 journals and other serials. **Services:** Library open to the public open to the public with restrictions. **Automated Operations:** Computerized cataloging and acquisitions. **Networks/Consortia:** Member of Research Libraries Information Network (RLIN). **Publications:** Acquisitions list.

★4015★
Columbia University - Herbert H. Lehman Library (Soc Sci, Geog-Map)
International Affairs Bldg.
420 W. 118th St. Phone: (212)854-4170
New York, NY 10027 Jane Winland
Founded: 1965. **Staff:** Prof 4; Other 13. **Subjects:** Political science, international affairs, sociology, anthropology, geography. **Special Collections:** Documents Service Center (90,000 standard printed materials; 640,000 microforms); PL 480 materials (50,000 volumes); Soviet Nationalities Collection (13,446 volumes); foreign newspapers (110). **Holdings:** 290,000 volumes; 83,000 maps; 165,000 microforms; 15 sections of Rand Corporation Reports; 6 microfiche drawers of Human Relations Area Files (HRAF) microfiles; 102 VF drawers of Bureau of Applied Social Research Archives. **Subscriptions:** 1600 journals and other serials; 110 newspapers. **Services:** Interlibrary loan; copying; SDI; library open to the public with restrictions. **Automated Operations:** Computerized public access catalog, circulation, cataloging, and acquisitions. **Computerized Information Services:** DIALOG Information Services, BRS Information Technologies, RLIN. **Networks/Consortia:** Member of Research Libraries Information Network (RLIN), New York Metropolitan Reference and Research Library Agency, New York State Interlibrary Loan Network (NYSILL). **Remarks:** Library has Reading Center for the Visually Disabled. Equipment includes 520 Visualtek Voyager enlarging machines, IBM PCs with adaptive software, an IBM large print typewriter, and a "talking" calculator. **Staff:** William Middleton, Hd., Doc.Serv.Ctr.; Diane Goon, Ref.Libn.; Jerry Breeze, Ref.Libn.; William Young, Soc.Sci.Bibl.

★4016★
Columbia University - Lamont-Doherty Geological Observatory - Geoscience Library (Sci-Engr)
Palisades, NY 10964 Phone: (914)359-2900
Susan Klimley, Libn.
Founded: 1960. **Staff:** Prof 1; Other 2. **Subjects:** Geophysics, geochemistry, oceanography, marine biology, seismology, meteorology. **Holdings:** 20,000 volumes. **Subscriptions:** 525 journals and other serials. **Services:** Copying; library open to the public with restrictions. **Computerized Information Services:** DIALOG Information Services. **Networks/Consortia:** Member of New York Metropolitan Reference and Research Library Agency, Research Libraries Information Network (RLIN).

★4017★
Columbia University - Law Library (Law)
Law School
435 W. 116th St. Phone: (212)854-3737
New York, NY 10027-7297 James L. Hoover, Law Libn.
Founded: 1910. **Staff:** Prof 16; Other 25. **Subjects:** Law - Anglo-American, foreign, international, Roman, medieval; criminology; trials; legal biography. **Special Collections:** League of Nations and United Nations documents; John Jay and James Kent collections on U.S. and English legal history. **Holdings:** 723,000 volumes; 500 linear feet of manuscripts and archival materials; 16,600 reels of microfilm; 429,500 microfiche; 10 magnetic tapes; 25 videotapes. **Subscriptions:** 6100 journals and other serials. **Services:** Interlibrary loan; copying; SDI; document delivery; library open to the public with advance permission from librarian. **Automated Operations:** Computerized public access catalog, cataloging, acquisitions, serials, and circulation. **Computerized Information Services:** LEXIS, WESTLAW, DIALOG Information Services, NEXIS, OCLC; RLIN, InterNet (electronic mail services). Performs searches on fee basis. Contact Person: Debra Wilson, 854-7851. **Networks/Consortia:** Member of Research Libraries Information Network (RLIN). **Remarks:** FAX: (212)854-3295. Electronic mail address(es): LAWREF@LAWMAIL.LAW.COLUMBIA.EDU (InterNet). **Staff:** Joanne Armstrong, Hd., Pub.Serv.; Kent McKeever, Assoc. Law Libn.; Bess Michaels, Hd., Access Serv.; Whitney Bagnall, Spec.Coll.

★4018★
Columbia University - Mathematics/Science Library (Sci-Engr)
303 Mathematics Phone: (212)854-4712
New York, NY 10027 Mei-Ling Lo, Math./Sci.Libn.
Staff: Prof 1; Other 1. **Subjects:** Pure mathematics, algebra, number theory, geometry, topology, probability, history of science, mathematical statistics, general science. **Holdings:** 105,000 volumes; academy publications. **Subscriptions:** 550 journals and other serials. **Services:** Library not open to the public. **Automated Operations:** Computerized cataloging and acquisitions. **Computerized Information Services:** DIALOG Information Services, BRS Information Technologies, RLIN; InterNet (electronic mail service). Performs searches on fee basis. **Networks/Consortia:** Member of Research Libraries Information Network (RLIN). **Publications:** Acquisitions list. **Remarks:** ml52@cunixf.cc.columbia.edu (InterNet).

★4019★
Columbia University - Music Library (Mus)
701 Dodge Phone: (212)854-4711
New York, NY 10027 Elizabeth Davis, Libn.
Founded: 1931. **Staff:** Prof 1; Other 4. **Subjects:** Music - analysis, interpretation, appreciation, bibliography, history, criticism, theory; musical instruments; musical notation; musicians; church music; ethnomusicology; composition. **Holdings:** 65,000 scores and literature; 20,000 phonograph records and tapes; 1000 compact discs; 2000 reels of microfilm; 3957 microcards. **Subscriptions:** 300 journals and other serials. **Services:** Interlibrary loan. **Automated Operations:** Computerized public access catalog(CLIO). **Computerized Information Services:** DIALOG Information Services. **Networks/Consortia:** Member of Center for Research Libraries (CRL), New York Metropolitan Reference and Research Library Agency, Research Libraries Information Network (RLIN).

★4020★
Columbia University - Oral History Research Office (Hist)
Butler Library
Box 20 Phone: (212)854-2273
New York, NY 10027 Ronald J. Grele, Dir.
Founded: 1948. **Staff:** Prof 3; Other 30. **Subjects:** National affairs, New York history, international relations, culture and the arts, social welfare, business and labor, philanthropy, Afro-American community, law, medicine, education, journalism, religion. **Special Collections:** The New Deal (50,000 pp.); Eisenhower Administration (36,000 pp.); Social Security, origins through Medicare (10,650 pp.); popular arts (7800 pp.); history of Carnegie Corporation (9928 pp.); aviation history (5400 pp.); radio pioneers (4765 pp.); Vietnam Veterans (3720 pp.); Columbia Crisis of 1968 (2450 pp.); psychoanalytic movement (2000 pp.); Nobel Laureates (1500 pp.); Women's History and Population Issues (2500 pp.); Occupation of Japan (1500 pp.); Bennington College Summer School of the Dance (5600 pp.); Adlai E. Stevenson (5600 pp.); Southern Intellectual Leaders (1500 pp.); World Bank (1400 pp.); Robert A. Taft (1600 pp.); United Negro College Fund (2500 pp.); United States-Iranian Relations (1455 pp.); Allard K. Lowenstein Project (2500 pp.); American Craftspeople (5000 pp.).; The Sixties (7500 pp.). **Holdings:** 6000 volumes of edited transcript; 3400 reels and cassettes of tapes, 1963 to present; microforms of one third of the collection; supporting papers accompany some memoirs; data on other oral history holdings and centers worldwide. **Services:** Research service available; copying (limited); collection open to the public with restrictions. The office provides books on oral history - for sale. **Automated Operations:** Computerized cataloging. **Computerized Information Services:** RLIN. **Networks/Consortia:** Member of Research Libraries Information Network (RLIN). **Publications:** Oral History, annual report, 1949-1977; The Oral History Collection of Columbia University, 4th edition, 1979 (out of print). **Staff:** Mary Marshall Clark, Act.Asst.Dir.; Alice Rwabazaire, Adm.Asst.

★4021★
Columbia University - Physics Library (Sci-Engr)
810 Pupin Laboratories Phone: (212)854-3943
New York, NY 10027 Kathleen Kehoe, Ref./Coll.Dev.Libn.
Founded: 1898. **Staff:** Prof 1; Other 1. **Subjects:** Physics - theoretical, high energy, particle, mathematical; astrophysics; x-ray astronomy; theoretical astronomy. **Holdings:** 28,000 volumes. **Subscriptions:** 400 journals and other serials. **Services:** Library not open to the public. **Automated Operations:** Computerized cataloging and acquisitions. **Computerized Information Services:** DIALOG Information Services, BRS Information Technologies, RLIN. Performs searches on fee basis. **Networks/Consortia:** Member of Research Libraries Information Network (RLIN). **Publications:** Acquisitions list.

★4022★
Columbia University - Psychology Library (Soc Sci)
409 Schermerhorn Hall Phone: (212)854-5658
New York, NY 10027 Leigh Hallingby, Ref./Coll.Dev.Libn.
Founded: 1912. **Staff:** Prof 1; Other 1. **Subjects:** Research and experimental psychology - animal physiology, cognition, learning, memory, perception, personality, psycholinguistics, sensory-motor research, vision. **Holdings:** 31,000 volumes; 3000 microforms. **Subscriptions:** 325 journals and other serials. **Services:** Library not open to the public. **Automated Operations:** Computerized public access catalog, cataloging, and acquisitions. **Computerized Information Services:** DIALOG Information Services, BRS Information Technologies, RLIN, OCLC; CD-ROM (PsycLIT); InterNet (electronic mail service). Performs searches on fee basis. **Networks/Consortia:** Member of Research Libraries Information Network (RLIN), New York Metropolitan Reference and Research Library Agency. **Remarks:** Electronic mail address(es): lh7@cunixf.cc.columbia.edu (InterNet).

★4023★
Columbia University - Rare Book and Manuscript Library (Rare Book)
Butler Library, 6th Fl. Phone: (212)854-2231
New York, NY 10027 Kenneth A. Lohf, Libn.
Founded: 1930. **Staff:** Prof 8; Other 7. **Subjects:** General rare book collections selected from the University Libraries. **Special Collections:** Manuscript Collection (American and English literature, American publishing, international affairs, oral history, economic and banking history: 26 million manuscripts and papers); Plimpton Library (history of textbooks from the manuscript period, calligraphy, mathematics, English and Latin grammars); David Eugene Smith Mathematical Library; Dale Library of Weights and Measures; Spinoza Collection; Seligman Library (history of economics); Epstean Collection (photography); Kilroe Collection (Tammaniana); Joan of Arc; Mary, Queen of Scots; Bakhmeteff Archive of Russian and East European History and Culture (Russian history, literature, social life of the 19th and 20th centuries; development of the Soviet Union and its relation to the U.S.: 1.2 million archival materials); Columbiana; Gonzalez Lodge Collection; Book Arts Collection; Herbert H. Lehman Papers; Park Benjamin Collection; Random House Papers and Library; Brander Matthews Dramatic Library. **Holdings:** 500,000 books; 2200 collections of correpondence and papers. **Services:** Library open to qualified researchers. **Automated Operations:** Computerized cataloging. **Computerized Information Services:** RLIN; BITNET (electronic mail service). **Networks/Consortia:** Member of Center for Research Libraries (CRL), New York Metropolitan Reference and Research Library Agency, Research Libraries Information Network (RLIN). **Publications:** Columbia Library Columns, 3/year - by subscription. **Remarks:** FAX: (212)222-0331. Electronic mail address(es): LOHF@CUNIXF.CC.COLUMBIA.EDU (BITNET). **Staff:** Bernard R. Crystal, Asst.Libn. for Mss.; Rudolph Ellenbogen, Asst.Libn. for Rare Bks.

★4024★
Columbia University - School of the Arts - Research Center for Arts and Culture - Archives (Art)
615 Dodge Hall Phone: (212)854-5869
New York, NY 10027 J. Jeffri, Dir.
Founded: 1985. **Staff:** Prof 1.5; Other 5. **Subjects:** Artists - economic condition, human and social service needs information, demographics, education; discrete studies; arts institutions. **Holdings:** Reports; oral histories. **Services:** Library open to the public with restrictions. **Computerized Information Services:** Internal databases. **Publications:** TEXTS (for commercial publication). **Remarks:** FAX: (212)854-1309.

★4025★
Columbia University - School of Library Service Library (Info Sci)
606 Butler Library Phone: (212)854-3543
New York, NY 10027 Olha della Cava, Libn.
Founded: 1926. **Staff:** Prof 1; Other 6. **Subjects:** All aspects of librarianship and information science, library history, administration, bibliography, documentation, library schools and training, publishing, history of books and printing. **Special Collections:** Graphic Arts Collection (14,000 volumes). **Holdings:** 102,000 volumes. **Subscriptions:** 3200 journals and other serials. **Services:** Interlibrary loan; copying. **Computerized Information Services:** CD-ROM. **Networks/Consortia:** Member of New York Metropolitan Reference and Research Library Agency, Research Libraries Information Network (RLIN). **Publications:** Selected Acquisitions List - limited circulation.

★4026★
Columbia University - Sulzberger Journalism Library (Info Sci)
304 Journalism Bldg.
Broadway & 116th St. Phone: (212)854-3860
New York, NY 10027 Sheila Carney, Libn.
Founded: 1913. **Staff:** Prof 1; Other 2. **Subjects:** Journalism, current events. **Special Collections:** Pulitzer Prizes in Journalism (on microfilm). **Holdings:** 15,000 volumes; 731 VF drawers of clippings. **Subscriptions:** 61 journals and other serials; 44 newspapers. **Services:** Interlibrary loan; copying; library open to faculty and students. **Automated Operations:** Computerized public access catalog. **Computerized Information Services:** DataTimes, NEXIS, VU/TEXT Information Services; InterNet (electronic mail service). **Networks/Consortia:** Member of Research Libraries Information Network (RLIN), New York Metropolitan Reference and Research Library Agency. **Remarks:** Electronic mail address(es): CARNEY@CUNIXF.CC.COLUMBIA.EDU (InterNet).

★4027★
Columbia University - Thomas J. Watson Library of Business and Economics (Bus-Fin)
130 Uris Hall Phone: (212)854-4000
New York, NY 10027 Jill Parchuck, Bus.Libn.
Founded: 1920. **Staff:** Prof 3; Other 20. **Subjects:** Financial management, money and capital markets, marketing, international business, business and economic history, operations research, management science, economics, banking, labor and industrial relations, advertising, agriculture, transportation. **Special Collections:** Marvyn Scudder Financial Collection. **Holdings:** 374,363 volumes; 691,417 microforms; working papers of U.S. business schools. **Subscriptions:** 3141 journals and other serials. **Services:** Interlibrary loan; copying; library open to the public with restrictions. **Automated Operations:** Computerized public access catalog, acquisitions, and circulation. **Computerized Information Services:** DIALOG Information Services, BRS Information Technologies, Dow Jones News/ Retrieval, Nikkei Telecom, ABI/INFORM, NEXIS, Disclosure Incorporated. **Networks/Consortia:** Member of Research Libraries Information Network (RLIN), New York State Interlibrary Loan Network (NYSILL), New York Metropolitan Reference and Research Library Agency. **Special Catalogs:** Annual reports in microform (card); bound annual reports (book). **Special Indexes:** Index to New York Stock Exchange listing applications, 1959 to present (card). **Staff:** James Coen, Coll.Dev./ Ref.Libn.; Lilita Gusts, Ref.Libn.; Larry Meyers, Access Supv.

★4028★
Columbia University - Whitney M. Young, Jr. Memorial Library of Social Work (Soc Sci, Med)
309 International Affairs Bldg.
420 W. 118th St. Phone: (212)854-5159
New York, NY 10027 Laura Delaney Brody, Soc. Work Libn.
Founded: 1898. **Staff:** Prof 1. **Subjects:** Social work; community organization; social policy development and administration; health, mental health, mental retardation; social services - family and children, day care, legal; aging; corrections and court services - probation, parole, diversionary treatment; alcoholism and drug addiction; industrial social welfare and manpower programs; urban education; intergroup relations; social and physical rehabilitation. **Special Collections:** The Mary Richmond Archives; The Homer Folks Archives; The Whitney M. Young, Jr. Papers; The Dorothy Hutchinson Collection on the Child; The Brookdale Collection on Gerontology. **Holdings:** 136,000 volumes; masters' theses; dissertations; agency reports. **Subscriptions:** 646 journals and other serials. **Services:** Interlibrary loan; copying. **Automated Operations:** Computerized public access catalog. **Computerized Information Services:** DIALOG Information Services, BRS Information Technologies; InterNet, BITNET (electronic mail services). Performs searches on fee basis. **Networks/Consortia:** Member of New York Metropolitan Reference and Research Library Agency, Research Libraries Information Network (RLIN). **Remarks:** Electronic mail address(es): ld16@CUNIXF.CC.COLUMBIA.EDU (InterNet); ld16@CUNIXF (BITNET).

★4029★
Columbian Newspaper Library (Publ)
701 W. 8th St.
Box 180 Phone: (206)694-3391
Vancouver, WA 98666 Norma Harris, Libn.
Subjects: Newspaper reference topics. **Remarks:** No further information was supplied by respondent.

★4030★
Columbiana County Law Library (Law)
Court House Phone: (216)424-9511
Lisbon, OH 44432 Barbara Thoman, Libn.
Staff: 1. **Subjects:** Law. **Holdings:** 15,000 volumes. **Services:** Library not open to the public.

★4031★
Columbus-Cabrini Medical Center - Columbus Hospital Medical Library (Med)
2520 N. Lakeview Ave. Phone: (312)883-7341
Chicago, IL 60614 James L. Finnerty, Ph.D., Dir., Lib.
Founded: 1975. **Staff:** Prof 1. **Subjects:** Clinical medicine, medical research, basic sciences in medicine; health care administration. **Holdings:** 3600 books; 2200 bound periodical volumes; 250 videotapes. **Subscriptions:** 200 journals and other serials; 5 newspapers. **Services:** Interlibrary loan; library not open to the public (call for information). **Computerized Information Services:** BRS Information Technologies, MEDLINE, CD-Plus; DOCLINE (electronic mail service). **Networks/Consortia:** Member of Metropolitan Consortium of Chicago, Chicago Library System, ILLINET, National Network of Libraries of Medicine (NN/LM). **Publications:** Serial Holdings List; Subject Guide to Serials; Subject Guide to Videotapes, all annual. **Remarks:** FAX: (312)296-1809.

Christopher Columbus Library
See: **International Columbian Quincentenary Alliance, Ltd.** (8085)

★4032★
Columbus College of Art and Design - Packard Library (Art)
107 N. Ninth St. Phone: (614)224-9101
Columbus, OH 43215 Chilin Yu, Hd.Libn.
Founded: 1879. **Staff:** Prof 3; Other 3. **Subjects:** Fine arts, architecture, literature, design, photography. **Holdings:** 32,000 books; 3100 bound periodical volumes; 50,400 slides; 35,500 pictures and prints. **Subscriptions:** 236 journals and other serials; 7 newspapers. **Services:** Interlibrary loan; copying; library open to the public for reference use only. **Automated Operations:** Computerized circulation. **Staff:** Gail Storer, Libn. II; Elizabeth Strautz, Libn. I.

★4033★
Columbus Dispatch - Editorial Library (Publ)
34 S. Third St. Phone: (614)461-5039
Columbus, OH 43216 James Hunter, Libn.
Founded: 1960. **Staff:** Prof 1; Other 5. **Subjects:** Newspaper reference topics. **Holdings:** 1000 books; 30 bound periodical volumes; 2000 reels of microfilm; newspaper clippings; 500,000 photographs. **Subscriptions:** 20 journals and other serials; 15 newspapers. **Services:** Library not open to the public. **Computerized Information Services:** DIALOG Information Services, NEXIS, Dow Jones News/Retrieval, VU/TEXT Information Services, MEDLINE, DataTimes; internal database. **Networks/Consortia:** Member of Columbus Area Libraries Information Council of Ohio (CALICO).

★4034★
Columbus Hospital - Health Sciences Library (Med)
Box 5013 Phone: (406)771-5631
Great Falls, MT 59403 Katherine V. Chew, Dir.
Founded: 1963. **Staff:** Prof 1; Other 2. **Subjects:** Medicine, nursing, science, oncology, orthopedics. **Holdings:** 8580 books; 10,000 bound periodical volumes; 6 VF drawers of pamphlets; 6 catalog drawers of drug description slips. **Subscriptions:** 550 journals and other serials. **Services:** Interlibrary loan; copying; library open to the public. **Computerized Information Services:** MEDLINE, DIALOG Information Services; CD-ROM (LaserCat); OnTyme Electronic Message Network Service (electronic mail service). **Networks/Consortia:** Member of Western Library Network (WLN). **Remarks:** FAX: (406)771-5550. Electronic mail address(es): CLMBS (OnTyme Electronic Message Network Service).

★4035★
Columbus Hospital - Medical Library (Med)
495 N. 13th St. Phone: (201)268-4862
Newark, NJ 07107-1397 Paula Fuselli
Staff: 1. **Subjects:** Medicine, nursing. **Holdings:** 745 books; 1186 bound periodical volumes; NCME video tapes; tapes; microfiche. **Subscriptions:** 75 journals and other serials. **Services:** Interlibrary loan; library not open to the public. **Computerized Information Services:** NLM. **Networks/Consortia:** Member of Cosmopolitan Biomedical Library Consortium (CBLC). **Remarks:** FAX: (201)268-4865.

Columbus Hospital Medical Library
See: **Columbus-Cabrini Medical Center** (4031)

★4036★
Columbus Law Library Association (Law)
369 S. High St., 10th Fl. Phone: (614)221-4181
Columbus, OH 43215 Keith Blough, Lib.Dir.
Founded: 1887. **Staff:** Prof 2; Other 5. **Subjects:** Ohio and U.S. law. **Holdings:** 60,000 volumes; 5500 volumes on microfiche; 269 audiotape titles; 20 videocassettes titles. **Subscriptions:** 1600 journals and other serials; 6 newspapers. **Services:** Copying; library open to the public for reference use only. **Automated Operations:** Computerized cataloging, serials, acquisitions, and circulation. **Computerized Information Services:** WESTLAW. Performs searches on fee basis for local residents. **Networks/Consortia:** Member of OHIONET. **Publications:** Columbus Law Library Quarterly; acquisitions list, quarterly - local distribution. **Remarks:** FAX: (614)221-2115. **Staff:** Andrew Brann, Assoc. Law Libn.

★4037★
Columbus Ledger-Enquirer - Library (Publ)
17 W. 12th St. Phone: (404)324-5526
Columbus, GA 31902 Patricia F. Thrower, Libn.
Founded: 1948. **Staff:** Prof 1; Other 1. **Subjects:** Newspaper reference topics. **Holdings:** Clippings; pamphlets; newspapers, 1832 to present, on microfilm; microcards of old clippings. **Subscriptions:** 18 journals and other serials; 22 newspapers. **Services:** Library not open to the public. **Remarks:** FAX: (404)576-6236.

Columbus Memorial Library
See: **Organization of American States** (12558)

★4038★
Columbus Museum of Art - Resource Center (Art)
480 E. Broad St. Phone: (614)221-6801
Columbus, OH 43215 Annette J. Oren, Libn.
Staff: Prof 2; Other 6. **Subjects:** Art, art history. **Special Collections:** Seymour Luckoff Memorial Collection (books on artists in the Sirak Collection). **Holdings:** 4500 books; 10 VF drawers; 10 drawers of exhibition catalogs; 15,000 slides. **Subscriptions:** 30 journals and other serials. **Services:** Copying; slides; educational slide packets; library open to museum members and local teachers and college students by appointment for reference use only. **Remarks:** FAX: (614)221-0226.

★4039★
Columbus Public Schools - Professional Library (Educ)
889 E. 17th Ave. Phone: (614)225-2815
Columbus, OH 43211 Michael A. Burke, Dir.
Staff: 1. **Subjects:** Education. **Holdings:** 5000 volumes. **Subscriptions:** 57 journals and other serials. **Services:** Library not open to the public; media reference. **Automated Operations:** Computerized cataloging. **Computerized Information Services:** OCLC. **Networks/Consortia:** Member of OHIONET. **Remarks:** FAX: (614)365-5817. **Staff:** Noralee Smith.

★4040★
Columbus State Community College - Educational Resources Center (Educ)
550 E. Spring St.
Box 1609 Phone: (614)227-2463
Columbus, OH 43215 Linda Landis, Dean of Educ.Rsrcs.
Founded: 1968. **Staff:** Prof 6; Other 9. **Subjects:** Health, engineering, arts and sciences, business, public service technologies. **Holdings:** 20,950 books; 38,367 AV programs; 215 pamphlets; 2888 reels of microfilm. **Subscriptions:** 444 journals and other serials; 12 newspapers. **Services:** Copying; center open to the public with courtesy card. **Automated Operations:** Computerized cataloging and circulation. **Computerized Information Services:** DIALOG Information Services, PFDS Online, BRS Information Technologies, OCLC, VU/TEXT Information Services, WILSONLINE, LS/2000. **Networks/Consortia:** Member of OHIONET, Columbus Area Libraries Information Council of Ohio (CALICO). **Publications:** Handbook. **Special Catalogs:** Film Catalog, irregular. **Remarks:** FAX: (614)227-2457. **Formerly:** Columbus Technical Institute - Educational Resources Center. **Staff:** JoAnn Luzader, Supv., Lib.Serv.; Claire Fohl, Tech.Serv.Coord.; Jane Goostree, Ref.Libn.; Laurinda Dukat, Cat.Libn.

Columbus Technical Institute - Educational Resources Center
See: **Columbus State Community College** (4040)

★4041★
COM/Energy Services Co. - Library (Energy)
1 Main St.
Box 9150 Phone: (617)225-4381
Cambridge, MA 02142 Esther A. Reppucci, Supv., Lib./Rec.Ctr.
Founded: 1958. **Staff:** Prof 1; Other 8. **Subjects:** Energy, finance, management, rates, regulations. **Holdings:** 1000 books. **Subscriptions:** 125 journals and other serials. **Services:** Interlibrary loan; copying; library open to the public by appointment. **Also Known As:** Commonwealth Energy System.

★4042★
Comanche Crossing Museum - Library (Hist)
Box 647 Phone: (303)622-4690
Strasburg, CO 80136 Sandy Miller, Cur.
Subjects: Local history, transcontinental railroad history. **Special Collections:** Old school records. **Holdings:** Books; government documents. **Services:** Library open to the public for reference use only.

Combustion Engineering, Inc. - Power Systems Group - Public and Technical Information Center
See: **ABB Combustion Engineering, Inc.** (5)

Betty Comden - Adolph Green Collection
See: **Museum of the City of New York - Theatre Collection** (10892)

Comegys Library
See: **Smithsonian Institution Libraries - Special Collections Department** (15285)

★4043★
Comerica Incorporated - Research Library (Bus-Fin)
Detroit, MI 48275-1134 Phone: (313)222-9377
Beth Stanton, Mgr., Res.Lib.
Founded: 1974. **Staff:** Prof 3; Other 2. **Subjects:** Banking, economics, business, industry, accounting. **Holdings:** 20,000 books; 900 unbound

periodical titles; 200 VF drawers of corporate and bank annual reports; 80 VF drawers of pamphlets and clippings; 15 VF drawers of industry investment reports. **Subscriptions:** 900 journals and other serials; 35 newspapers. **Services:** Interlibrary loan; library open to the public by request. **Automated Operations:** Computerized public access catalog, acquisitions, serials, and circulation. **Computerized Information Services:** Dow Jones News/Retrieval, DIALOG Information Services, VU/TEXT Information Services, Lotus One Source; CD-ROM (Dun's Million Dollar Disc). **Publications:** Library Notes: Recent Additions to the Comerica Incorporated Research Library, monthly. **Staff:** Stephanie Eagles, Libn.; Linda Swift, Libn.

★4044★
Comics Magazine Association of America - Library (Art)
355 Lexington Ave.
New York, NY 10017 Phone: (212)661-4261
Subjects: Comics magazines. **Holdings:** 100 books; 2000 periodicals; 2 VF drawers. **Services:** Library not open to the public. **Remarks:** FAX: (212)370-9047.

★4045★
Cominco Ltd. - Central Technical Library (Sci-Engr)
Technical Research Centre
P.O. Box 2000 Phone: (604)364-4408
Trail, BC, Canada V1R 4S4 S.R. (Stan) Greenwood, Info.Spec.
Founded: 1925. **Staff:** Prof 1; Other 1. **Subjects:** Chemistry, extractive metallurgy, mining and milling, engineering. **Holdings:** 6000 books; 12,000 bound periodical volumes; 2000 pamphlets; 15,000 technical patents; 2000 U.S. Bureau of Mines reports and circulars; Chemical Abstracts, 1906 to present; U.S. Patent Office Gazette, 1897 to present; Canadian Patent Office Record, 1907 to present. **Subscriptions:** 250 journals and other serials; 8 newspapers. **Services:** Interlibrary loan; copying; library open to the public by personal arrangement with library supervisor. **Automated Operations:** Computerized circulation. **Computerized Information Services:** Online systems, DIALOG Information Services, QL Systems. Performs searches on fee basis. **Remarks:** FAX: (604)364-4400.

★4046★
Cominco Ltd. - Corporate/Legal Library (Bus-Fin)
200 Burrard St. Phone: (604)685-3055
Vancouver, BC, Canada V6C 3L7 Frieda M. Schilling, Libn.
Staff: Prof 1; Other 1. **Subjects:** Business, finance, statistics, law. **Holdings:** 7000 books; 2500 reports and other cataloged items. **Subscriptions:** 75 journals and other serials; 10 newspapers. **Services:** Interlibrary loan; copying; services open to the public by arrangement with librarian. **Automated Operations:** Computerized public access catalog and cataloging. **Computerized Information Services:** Info Globe, NewsNet, Inc., Dow Jones News/Retrieval, QL Systems, DIALOG Information Services, CAN/OLE, Infomart Online, CAN/LAW, STM Systems Corporation, VU/TEXT Information Services. **Remarks:** FAX: (604)884-2509. **Formerly:** Its Information Services.

★4047★
Cominco Ltd. - Product Technology Centre Library (Sci-Engr)
Sheridan Park Phone: (416)822-2022
Mississauga, ON, Canada L5K 1B4 Pat Doyle, Info.Spec.
Founded: 1964. **Staff:** Prof 1. **Subjects:** Lead, zinc, corrosion, metallurgy, electrochemistry. **Holdings:** 2500 volumes; 10,000 pamphlets. **Subscriptions:** 150 journals and other serials. **Services:** Interlibrary loan; library not open to the public. **Computerized Information Services:** Chemical Abstracts Service (CAS), DIALOG Information Services, PFDS Online, CAN/OLE; IBM-PC (internal database). **Networks/Consortia:** Member of Sheridan Park Association. **Remarks:** FAX: (416)822-2882.

Comision Nacional de Seguridad Nuclear y Salvaguardias
See: **Mexico - National Commission on Nuclear Safety and Safeguards** (10241)

Comite Central des Armateurs de France
See: **French National Shipowners Association** (6150)

Comite Intergouvernemental de Recherches Urbaines et Regionales - Service de Documentation
See: **Intergovernmental Committee on Urban and Regional Research (ICURR) - Information Exchange Service** (8042)

★4048★
Commander U.S. Army - Dugway Proving Ground - Technical Library (Mil, Sci-Engr)
ATTN: STEDP-SD-TA-F JOD-I
Dugway, UT 84022-5000 Phone: (801)831-3565
Founded: 1950. **Staff:** Other 3. **Subjects:** Chemistry, biology, chemical/biological warfare. **Special Collections:** Classified and unclassified documents related to chemical/biological testing (access limited to U.S. Government agencies and their contractors). **Holdings:** 6000 books; 250 bound periodical volumes; 30,000 bound technical reports; 15,000 microforms. **Subscriptions:** 65 journals and other serials. **Services:** Interlibrary loan; library not open to the public. **Automated Operations:** Computerized public access catalog, cataloging, serials, and circulation. **Computerized Information Services:** DIALOG Information Services, DTIC, OCLC. **Remarks:** FAX: (801)831-2397.

★4049★
The Commercial Appeal - News Library (Publ)
495 Union Ave. Phone: (901)529-2781
Memphis, TN 38103 Virginia Everett, Lib.Dir.
Founded: 1986. **Staff:** Prof 4; Other 2. **Subjects:** Newspaper reference topics. **Holdings:** News clippings; photographs; reference books; The Commercial Appeal, 1945 to present; Memphis Press-Scimitar on microfilm. **Subscriptions:** 125 journals and other serials; 40 newspapers. **Services:** Library not open to the public. **Computerized Information Services:** NEXIS, LEXIS, DIALOG Information Services, DataTimes, VU/TEXT Information Services; internal database. Performs searches on fee basis. **Special Indexes:** Index to The Commerical Appeal (online). **Remarks:** Published by Scripps Howard Publishing Company. **Staff:** Rosemary Nelms, Ref.Libn.; Greg Paraham, Ref.Libn.; Janet Smith, Ref.Libn.

★4050★
Commercial Testing and Engineering Company - Library (Sci-Engr)
1919 S. Highland Ave., Suite 210 B Phone: (708)953-9300
Lombard, IL 60148 George Engelke, Mgr.
Subjects: Raw materials testing techniques and specifications. **Holdings:** 1000 books; 1000 reports. **Services:** Library not open to the public. **Remarks:** FAX: (312)953-9306.

★4051★
Commercial Testing Laboratories - Library
22 Lipan St.
Denver, CO 80223
Subjects: Construction material specifications, geotechnical science. **Holdings:** 500 books; 500 reports. **Remarks:** Currently inactive.

★4052★
Commercial Union Insurance Companies - Risk Control Technical Resource Center (Bus-Fin)
1 Beacon St.
Boston, MA 02108 Phone: (617)725-6062
Founded: 1979. **Subjects:** Insurance, safety, risk control. **Holdings:** 2000 books; 250 AV programs; 5 VF drawers. **Subscriptions:** 20 journals and other serials. **Services:** Center not open to the public. **Automated Operations:** Computerized cataloging. **Computerized Information Services:** DIALOG Information Services, Dow Jones News/Retrieval.

Commissariat a l'Energie Atomique - Centre d'Etudes de Saclay - Mission Information Scientific et Technique (MIST)
See: **France - Atomic Energy Commission - Saclay Research Center - MIST** (6060)

Commission Canadienne des Grains
See: **Canada - Agriculture Canada - Canadian Grain Commission - Library** (2634)

★4053★
Commission on Chicago Landmarks - Library (Plan)
320 N. Clark St., Rm. 516 Phone: (312)744-3200
Chicago, IL 60610 William McLanahan, Dir.
Founded: 1968. **Staff:** 12. **Subjects:** Chicago history and architecture. **Special Collections:** Chicago Historic Resources Survey maps and data forms (City of Chicago building-by-building survey); old building permit records. **Holdings:** 300 books; 120 reports. **Subscriptions:** 10 journals and other serials. **Services:** Library open to the public.

★4054★
Commission on Civil Rights - National Clearinghouse Library (Soc Sci)
1121 Vermont Ave., N.W. Phone: (202)376-8110
Washington, DC 20425 Barbara J. Fontana, Libn.
Founded: 1957. **Staff:** Prof 1; Other 1. **Subjects:** Civil rights, economics, education, sex discrimination, sociology, law. **Special Collections:** The aged and the handicapped; commission publications. **Holdings:** 65,000 books; 1100 bound periodical volumes; 1200 state and federal codes and statutes; 110 legal periodical titles; 500 reels of microfilm of minority periodicals; 300 journals on microfiche. **Subscriptions:** 300 journals and newspapers. **Services:** Interlibrary loan; copying; library open to the public for reference use only. **Automated Operations:** Computerized cataloging. **Computerized Information Services:** DIALOG Information Services, OCLC, LEXIS, NEXIS. **Publications:** Monthly acquisitions list; bibliographies. **Remarks:** FAX: (202)376-8315.

Commission de la Construction du Quebec
See: **(Quebec Province) Commission de la Construction du Quebec** (13582)

★4055★
Commission des Ecoles Catholiques de Montreal - Bibliotheque Centrale (Educ)
3737 Sherbrooke E.
Montreal, PQ, Canada H1X 3B3 Phone: (514)596-6586
Founded: 1931. **Staff:** 2. **Subjects:** Education, psychology, philosophy. **Special Collections:** Textbooks used in the schools of Montreal (1500). **Holdings:** 40,000 volumes. **Services:** Copying; library open to the public with restrictions. **Also Known As:** Catholic School Commission of Montreal.

Commission d'Energie Electrique du Nouveau Brunswick
See: **New Brunswick Electric Power Commission** (11448)

★4056★
Commission of the European Communities - Library (Bus-Fin)
200, rue de la Loi Phone: 2 235111
B-1049 Brussels, Belgium Eric Gaskell
Founded: 1959. **Subjects:** Economics, law, government, Europe, science and technology. **Holdings:** 210,000 books; 100,000 bound periodical volumes; 10,000 reports; 165,000 microfiche; 2500 theses. **Subscriptions:** 8000 journals and other serials. **Services:** Interlibrary loan; copying; library open to postgraduate students and anyone, who for professional reasons, needs access to EC documentation. **Computerized Information Services:** Produces European Community Library Automated System (ECLAS). Contact Person: Margaret Braune, Database Adm. **Publications:** Bulletin, monthly; series of Biblio dossiers; Thesaurus; Dictionary of EC Acronyms. **Staff:** Marvja Gutiennez, Hd., Rd.Serv.

★4057★
Commission of the European Communities - Library (Bus-Fin)
39 Molesworth St. Phone: 1 712244
Dublin 2, Ireland Tim Kelly, Hd. of Info.Serv.
Founded: 1974. **Staff:** Prof 1; Other 2. **Subjects:** European community - agriculture, energy, education, development, law. **Special Collections:** European community publications. **Holdings:** 20,000 books; 5000 reports; microfiche. **Subscriptions:** 10 journals and other serials. **Services:** Interlibrary loan; copying; library open to the public. **Computerized Information Services:** SCAD, CELEX, RAPID. **Remarks:** FAX: 1 712657. Telex: EUCO E1 93827.

★4058★
Commission of the European Communities - Specialized Department for Terminology and Computer Applications - Library (Sci-Engr)
Batiment Jean Monnet A2/101 Phone: 43012389
L-2920 Luxembourg, Luxembourg Mr. P. Hoffman, Hd.
Subjects: Terminology - agriculture, coal and steel technology, medicine, occupational health, nuclear science, transport, industry, official nomenclatures, economics, community regulations, data processing, civil engineering, information and documentation sciences. **Holdings:** 7500 bound periodical volumes. **Subscriptions:** 200 journals and other serials. **Services:** Library open to terminologists and translators. **Computerized Information Services:** Produces Eurodicautom. Performs searches on fee basis. **Remarks:** Provides scientific and technical terms, definitions, contextual phrases, and abbreviations in the official languages of the European Communities.

★4059★
Commission for the Preservation of Natural and Historical Monuments and Relics - Documentation Centre (Plan)
P.O. Box 124 Phone: 320481
Livingstone, Zambia Benson Njobvu
Founded: 1987. **Staff:** 1. **Subjects:** Historic preservation. **Holdings:** 1300 volumes. **Subscriptions:** 10 journals and other serials; 2 newspapers. **Services:** Interlibrary loan; copying; library open to the public by appointment.

Commission Sericicole Internationale
See: **International Sericultural Commission** (8186)

Committee of Small Press Editors and Publishers Archive
See: **Temple University - Central Library System - Contemporary Culture Collection** (16133)

★4060★
Commodity Futures Trading Commission - Library (Bus-Fin, Law)
2033 K St., N.W., Rm. 540 Phone: (202)254-5901
Washington, DC 20581 John Fragale, Adm.Libn.
Staff: Prof 1; Other 3. **Subjects:** Law, futures and options trading, economics, business, regulation. **Special Collections:** Legislative Histories: Commodity Exchange Act, 1936; Futures Trading Act, 1978; Commodity Futures Trading Commission Act, 1974; Futures Trading Act, 1982 and 1986. **Holdings:** 11,000 books; 1000 bound periodical volumes; microforms. **Subscriptions:** 550 journals and other serials; 12 newspapers. **Services:** Interlibrary loan; library not open to the public. **Automated Operations:** Computerized cataloging, serials, circulation, and acquisitions. **Computerized Information Services:** OCLC, WESTLAW, LEXIS, LEGI-SLATE. **Networks/Consortia:** Member of FEDLINK. **Remarks:** FAX: (202)254-6265.

★4061★
Commodity Research Bureau - Library (Bus-Fin)
75 Wall St., 23rd Fl. Phone: (212)504-7754
New York, NY 10005 Jim Nevler, Contact
Subjects: Commodity futures. **Holdings:** 400 books; 400 reports. **Subscriptions:** 27 journals and other serials. **Services:** Library not open to the public.

Commonwealth Court of Pennsylvania
See: **(Pennsylvania State) Commonwealth Court of Pennsylvania** (12856)

★4062★
Commonwealth Edison Company - Library (Energy)
P.O. Box 767-35 FNE. Phone: (312)294-3066
Chicago, IL 60690 Barbara R. Kelly, Supv., Lib.Serv.
Founded: 1902. **Staff:** Prof 2; Other 3. **Subjects:** Public utilities, nuclear and electrical engineering, management. **Holdings:** 22 VF drawers of public utility reports; 59 VF drawers of pamphlets; 50 maps; microfiche. **Subscriptions:** 365 journals and other serials. **Services:** Interlibrary loan; library open to the public for reference use only. **Computerized Information Services:** DIALOG Information Services. Performs searches on fee basis. **Networks/Consortia:** Member of Chicago Library System, ILLINET. **Publications:** Library Bulletin, bimonthly. **Staff:** Grace M. Pertell, Libn.

★4063★
Commonwealth Edison Company - Production Training Center - Learning Resource Center (Energy)
36400 S. Essex Rd.
Wilmington, IL 60481 Phone: (815)458-3411
Founded: 1982. **Staff:** Prof 1; Other 1. **Subjects:** Nuclear and fossil energy plant training. **Holdings:** 100 books; 60 video cassettes. **Subscriptions:** 22 journals and other serials. **Services:** Interlibrary loan; copying; center open to the public for reference use only by appointment. **Computerized Information Services:** DIALOG Information Services, EdVENT. Performs searches on fee basis. **Networks/Consortia:** Member of Bur Oak Library System. **Remarks:** FAX: (815)458-3411.

Commonwealth Energy System
See: **COM/Energy Services Co.** (4041)

★4064★
The Commonwealth Institute - Commonwealth Resource Centre (Area-Ethnic)
Kensington High St.
London W8 6NQ, England Phone: 71 603 4535
Staff: Prof 3. **Subjects:** The Commonwealth - arts and literature, trade and development, education, community relations, commodities, languages, agriculture, sociology. **Holdings:** 60,000 AV programs. **Subscriptions:** 600 journals and other serials. **Services:** Interlibrary loan; copying; center open to the public. **Publications:** Commonwealth Bibliographies; reading lists; lists of materials; information leaflets. **Special Catalogs:** Exhibition catalogs. **Remarks:** FAX: 71 6027374. **Staff:** Karen Peters, Libn.; Marie Bastiampillai, Asst.Libn.

★4065★
Commonwealth Laboratory, Inc. - Library (Sci-Engr)
Chemists Bldg.
2209 E. Broad St. Phone: (804)648-8358
Richmond, VA 23223 Edwin Cox, III, Hd.
Subjects: Chemical engineering and analysis. **Holdings:** 1000 books; 2000 reports. **Subscriptions:** 35 journals and other serials. **Services:** Library open to the public with restrictions. **Remarks:** FAX: (804)644-5820. Maintained by Edwin Cox Associates.

Commonwealth of Massachusetts
See: **Massachusetts State**

★4066★
Commonwealth Microfilm Products - Library Service (Publ)
3395 American Dr., Unit 11 Phone: (416)671-4173
Mississauga, ON, Canada L4V 1T5 A. Gordon Holmes, Mgr.Lib.Serv.
Founded: 1952. **Staff:** Prof 4; Other 9. **Subjects:** Newspapers, periodicals. **Special Collections:** Canadian Military Gazette; Glenbow Collection; Gospel Herald. **Holdings:** Newspapers and periodicals on microfilm. **Subscriptions:** 87 newspapers. **Services:** Library not open to the public. **Remarks:** FAX: (416)671-8361. **Staff:** Douglas Johnston, Gen.Mgr.

Commonwealth of Pennsylvania
See: **Pennsylvania State**

★4067★
Commonwealth Research Group, Inc. - Library
230 Beacon St.
Boston, MA 02116
Subjects: Energy supply and demand; transportation economics. **Holdings:** 400 books; 300 reports. **Remarks:** FAX: Currently inactive.

Commonwealth Scientific and Industrial Research Organization
See: **Australia - Commonwealth Scientific and Industrial Research Organization (CSIRO)** (1323)

★4068★
Commonwealth Secretariat - Library (Soc Sci)
Marlborough House
Pall Mall Phone: 71 8393411
London SW1Y 5HX, England Eileen Murtagh
Founded: 1965. **Staff:** 5. **Subjects:** The Commonwealth - development issues, economics, industry, agriculture, education, law, science, youth, health, women and development. **Holdings:** 12,000 volumes. **Subscriptions:** 5000 journals and other serials; newspapers. **Services:** Interlibrary loan; copying; library open to scholars working in the development field with permission from the librarian. **Computerized Information Services:** Internal databases. **Remarks:** FAX: 71 9300827. Telex: 27678. Cable: COMSECGEN LONDON SW1.

★4069★
Commonwealth Technology, Inc. - Library
5380-B Eisenhower Ave.
Alexandria, VA 22304
Defunct.

Communications Canada
See: **Canada - Communications Canada** (2674)

★4070★
Communications Institute - Communications Library (Info Sci)
Lockbox 472139, Marina Sta. Phone: (415)626-5050
San Francisco, CA 94147-2139 Theodore S. Connelly, Dir.
Founded: 1965. **Staff:** Prof 3; Other 1. **Subjects:** Communications - education, cable television, history, languages, media; children's art. **Special Collections:** Abraham Collection (corporate America in 1976); Pfleuger Collection (history of communications in U.S.); Communications in the Nazi World; Communications in the World of a Subculture. **Holdings:** 20,000 books; 300 bound periodical volumes; 100 reports; 500 archival items. **Subscriptions:** 121 journals and other serials; 10 newspapers. **Services:** Library open to the public by appointment to professionals and students. **Computerized Information Services:** CATV (internal database). Contact Person: Philippe Greenleaf. **Publications:** BCTV: Bibliography on Cable Television, (non-cumulative) annual; CINCOM: Courses in Communications, annual - both available on a fee basis.

★4071★
Communications Satellite Corporation - COMSAT North Library (Sci-Engr)
22300 Comsat Dr. Phone: (301)428-4512
Clarksburg, MD 20871 Merilee Worsey, Libn., Info.Ctr.
Founded: 1967. **Staff:** Prof 1; Other 1. **Subjects:** Satellite communication, electronics engineering, computer science. **Special Collections:** Microfilm collection of military specifications. **Holdings:** 14,000 books; 40,000 technical reports. **Subscriptions:** 380 journals and other serials. **Services:** Interlibrary loan; library open to the public by appointment. **Automated Operations:** Computerized cataloging, acquisitions, serials, and circulation. **Computerized Information Services:** DIALOG Information Services, NASA/RECON, NEXIS, NewsNet, Inc.; internal database. **Networks/Consortia:** Member of Interlibrary Users Association (IUA). **Publications:** Information News, monthly; New Book List; journal holdings list. **Remarks:** FAX: (301)428-7747.

★4072★
Communications Workers of America - CWA Research Library (Bus-Fin)
501 3rd St., N.W. Phone: (202)434-1199
Washington, DC 20001 Nancy Dysart
Founded: 1975. **Staff:** Prof 1. **Subjects:** Telecommunications, economics, labor relations. **Holdings:** 2000 books; 10 VF drawers. **Subscriptions:** 150 journals and other serials. **Services:** Interlibrary loan; library open to the public on request. **Computerized Information Services:** DIALOG Information Services, NewsNet, Inc., Dow Jones News/Retrieval, LEXIS, NEXIS. **Remarks:** FAX: (202)434-1201. **Formerly:** Its CWA Information Library.

★4073★
Community Associates of Connecticut, Inc. - Professional Resource Center (Med)
25 Hillside Ave. Phone: (203)274-9241
Oakville, CT 06779-1735 Keith F. Helmer, Pres./C.E.O.
Subjects: Physically and severely handicapped, communication training, special education, parent training, therapeutic training. **Special Collections:** Severely physically handicapped. **Holdings:** 150 books; 100 other cataloged items. **Services:** Center open to the public with restrictions. **Remarks:** FAX: (203)274-2388.

Community College of Baltimore
See: **New Community College of Baltimore - Libraries/Media Services** (11461)

★4074★
Community College of Philadelphia - Educational Resources Center (Educ)
1700 Spring Garden St. Phone: (215)751-8383
Philadelphia, PA 19130 Dr. Addie J. Butler, Dean
Founded: 1965. **Staff:** Prof 6; Other 30. **Subjects:** Education in community colleges. **Holdings:** 87,533 books; 7210 microforms. **Subscriptions:** 430 journals and other serials; 7 newspapers. **Services:** Interlibrary loan; copying; center open to TCLC members. **Automated Operations:** Computerized cataloging, acquisitions, and circulation. **Computerized Information Services:** BRS Information Technologies, OCLC, VU/TEXT Information Services, ERIC. **Networks/Consortia:** Member of PALINET, Tri-State College Library Cooperative (TCLC). **Remarks:** FAX: (215)751-8762. **Staff:** Donald Jones, Dept.Hd.; Aimee Weis, ILL; Joan Johnson, Acq.; C. Shu-erh Fu, Cat.

★4075★
Community Environmental Council - Gildea Resource Center
930 Miramonte Dr.
Santa Barbara, CA 93109
Defunct.

★4076★
Community-General Hospital of Greater Syracuse - Medical Library (Med)
Broad Rd. Phone: (315)492-5500
Syracuse, NY 13215 Diana Wendell, MLS, AHIP Lib.Dir.
Founded: 1966. **Staff:** Prof 1; Other 1. **Subjects:** General surgery and medicine, nursing. **Holdings:** 4000 books; 3000 bound periodical volumes; 2 drawers of microfiche; 5 VF drawers of pamphlets and clippings; video cassettes. **Subscriptions:** 305 journals and other serials. **Services:** Interlibrary loan; copying; SDI; library open to the public at librarian's discretion. **Automated Operations:** Computerized cataloging and ILL. **Computerized Information Services:** MEDLARS, BRS Information Technologies. Performs searches on fee basis for outside individuals. **Networks/Consortia:** Member of National Network of Libraries of Medicine - Middle Atlantic Region, Central New York Library Resources Council (CENTRO). **Publications:** Community-General Hospital Staff Library Bulletin, quarterly. **Special Catalogs:** Union list of serials, annual. **Remarks:** FAX: (315)492-5329.

★4077★
Community General Hospital of Sullivan County - Health Sciences Library (Med)
Bushville Rd.
Box 800 Phone: (914)794-3300
Harris, NY 12742-0800 Mary Allison Farley, Libn.
Founded: 1978. **Staff:** Prof 1. **Subjects:** Medicine, nursing, pharmacology, medical specialties, allied health sciences. **Holdings:** 550 books; 450 bound periodical volumes. **Subscriptions:** 75 journals and other serials. **Services:** Interlibrary loan; copying; library open to the public with restrictions. **Computerized Information Services:** NLM. Performs searches on fee basis. **Networks/Consortia:** Member of Health Information Libraries of Westchester (HILOW), Southeastern New York Library Resources Council (SENYLRC). **Remarks:** FAX: (914)794-6596.

★4078★
Community Hospital - Medical Library (Med)
3325 Chanate Rd. Phone: (707)576-4675
Santa Rosa, CA 95404 Joan Chilton, Med.Libn.
Founded: 1962. **Staff:** Prof 1. **Subjects:** Medicine. **Holdings:** 3000 books; 6500 bound periodical volumes; Audio-Digest tapes; video cassettes. **Subscriptions:** 182 journals and other serials. **Services:** Interlibrary loan; library open to the public. **Computerized Information Services:** MEDLARS.

★4079★
Community Hospital at Glen Cove - Medical Library (Med)
St. Andrews Ln. Phone: (516)676-5000
Glen Cove, NY 11542 Kathryn M. Gegan, Libn.
Staff: Prof 1. **Subjects:** Medicine. **Holdings:** Figures not available. **Subscriptions:** 89 journals and other serials. **Services:** Interlibrary loan; copying; library open to the public at librarian's discretion. **Networks/Consortia:** Member of Medical & Scientific Libraries of Long Island (MEDLI), Long Island Library Resources Council.

★4080★
Community Hospital Indianapolis - Library (Med)
1500 N. Ritter Ave. Phone: (317)353-5591
Indianapolis, IN 46219 Sheila Hofstetter, Mgr.
Staff: Prof 2; Other 1. **Subjects:** Medicine, nursing, allied health sciences. **Holdings:** 2000 books; 3000 bound periodical volumes. **Subscriptions:** 360 journals and other serials. **Services:** Interlibrary loan; copying; SDI; library open to the public. **Computerized Information Services:** BRS Information Technologies, DIALOG Information Services, NLM. **Networks/Consortia:** Member of Central Indiana Area Library Services Authority (CIALSA), Central Indiana Health Science Library Consortium, National Network of Libraries of Medicine - Greater Midwest Region, INCOLSA. **Staff:** Sr. Marianne Mader, Staff Libn.

★4081★
Community Hospital of the Monterey Peninsula - Medical Library (Med)
Box HH Phone: (408)625-4550
Monterey, CA 93942 Julia Richardson
Staff: Prof 1. **Subjects:** Medicine, allied health sciences. **Holdings:** 1030 books; 1700 bound periodical volumes; 650 audiotapes. **Subscriptions:** 130 journals and other serials. **Services:** Interlibrary loan; library not open to the public. **Computerized Information Services:** MEDLINE. **Networks/Consortia:** Member of National Network of Libraries of Medicine - Pacific Southwest Region. **Publications:** Monthly newsletter.

★4082★
Community Hospital of Springfield & Clark County - Health Sciences Library (Med)
2615 E. High St. Phone: (513)325-0531
Springfield, OH 45501 Joyce Davis, Libn.
Staff: Prof 1. **Subjects:** Medicine, nursing. **Holdings:** 3900 books; 2100 bound periodical volumes. **Subscriptions:** 120 journals and other serials. **Services:** Interlibrary loan; library not open to the public. **Computerized Information Services:** MEDLARS; DOCLINE (electronic mail service).

★4083★
Community Hospitals of Central California, Inc. - Medical Library (Med)
Box 1232 Phone: (209)442-3968
Fresno, CA 93715 Roberto Urzua, Mgr., Lib.Serv.
Staff: Prof 1; Other 1. **Subjects:** Medicine, nursing, and allied health sciences. **Holdings:** 7000 books; 12 VF drawers of pamphlets and clippings; microfilm backfiles. **Subscriptions:** 656 journals and other serials. **Services:** Interlibrary loan; library open to the public by referral only. **Computerized Information Services:** BRS Information Technologies, MEDLINE, DIALOG Information Services; OnTyme Electronic Message Network Service (electronic mail service). Performs searches on fee basis. **Networks/Consortia:** Member of Area Wide Library Network (AWLNET), Northern California and Nevada Medical Library Group (NCNMLG). **Remarks:** FAX: (209)442-6451. Electronic mail address(es): FCHMC (OnTyme Electronic Message Network Service).

★4084★
Community Information Centre of Metropolitan Toronto (Soc Sci)
590 Jarvis St., 5th Fl. Phone: (416)392-0505
Toronto, ON, Canada M4Y 2J4 Joan Christensen, Exec.Dir.
Staff: Prof 20; Other 3. **Subjects:** Community information, health, welfare, employment, government services, senior services. **Holdings:** 4000 documents. **Services:** Center open to the public. **Computerized Information Services:** Community Information Database (internal database). **Publications:** Directory of Community Services in Metropolitan Toronto, annual; Directory of Child Care Services in Metropolitan Toronto, annual - both available by mail; list of additional publications - available upon request. **Remarks:** FAX: (416)392-4404. **Staff:** Beth White, Coord.Res. & Pubns.

★4085★
Community Legal Services, Inc. - Law Library (Law)
1324 Locust St. Phone: (215)893-5368
Philadelphia, PA 19107 Darlene Moore, Libn.
Staff: Prof 1; Other 1. **Subjects:** Civil and poverty law. **Holdings:** 15,000 books; 300 bound periodical volumes; 8 VF drawers. **Subscriptions:** 60 journals and other serials. **Services:** Interlibrary loan; library open to the public by appointment. **Computerized Information Services:** LEXIS, NEXIS, DIALOG Information Services, VU/TEXT Information Services, WESTLAW. **Remarks:** Alternate telephone number(s): 893-5371. FAX: (215)893-5350.

★4086★
Community Medical Center - Hospital Library (Med)
1800 Mulberry St. Phone: (717)969-8197
Scranton, PA 18510 Ann Duesing, Hd.Libn.
Founded: 1972. **Staff:** Prof 1.5; Other 1.5. **Subjects:** Internal medicine, neonatology, oncology, pulmonary medicine, perinatology, cardiology. **Holdings:** 1500 books; 3000 reels of microfilm. **Subscriptions:** 200 journals and other serials; 3 newspapers. **Services:** Interlibrary loan; copying; library open to the public at librarian's discretion for reference use only. **Automated Operations:** Computerized serials. **Computerized Information Services:** DIALOG Information Services, MEDLINE. **Networks/Consortia:** Member of BHSL, Health Information Library Network of Northeastern Pennsylvania (HILNNEP). **Remarks:** FAX: (717)969-8902. **Staff:** Corrine McNabb, Libn.

★4087★
Community Medical Center - School of Nursing Library (Med)
315 Colfax Ave. Phone: (717)969-8973
Scranton, PA 18510 Ann Duesing, Hd.Libn.
Staff: Prof 1; Other 1. **Subjects:** Nursing, medicine, health administration. **Holdings:** 2500 books; 50 bound periodical volumes; 30 periodical titles on microfilm. **Subscriptions:** 125 journals and other serials. **Services:** Interlibrary loan; copying; library open to the public for reference use only. **Automated Operations:** Computerized serials and circulation. **Computerized Information Services:** MEDLINE, DIALOG Information Services. Performs searches on fee basis. **Networks/Consortia:** Member of Health Information Library Network of Northeastern Pennsylvania (HILNNEP), BHSL. **Remarks:** FAX: (717)969-8902.

★4088★
Community Memorial Hospital - McKay Memorial Library (Med)
W180 N8085 Town Hall Rd.
Box 408 Phone: (414)251-1000
Menomonee Falls, WI 53051-0408 B.J. Keppel, Med.Libn.
Founded: 1977. **Subjects:** Medicine, nursing, health care. **Holdings:** 375 books; 50 bound periodical volumes; 1859 slides; 156 microfiche; 217 videocassettes; 10 audiocassettes. **Subscriptions:** 225 journals and other serials. **Services:** Interlibrary loan; copying; SDI; library open to the public for reference use only. **Computerized Information Services:** DIALOG Information Services, BRS Information Technologies, MEDLARS. Performs searches on fee basis. **Networks/Consortia:** Member of Southeastern Wisconsin Health Science Library Consortium (SWHSL), Waukesha County Federated Library System, Library Council of Metropolitan Milwaukee, Inc. (LCOMM), National Network of Libraries of Medicine - Greater Midwest Region. **Publications:** Acquisitions List, quarterly; Serial Holdings List, annual; Videocassette List, semiannual. **Remarks:** FAX: (414)251-0789.

★4089★
Community Mutual Insurance Company-Blue Cross/Blue Shield - Communications Resource Center (Bus-Fin)
1351 William Howard Taft Rd., CK1-231 Phone: (513)872-8460
Cincinnati, OH 45206 Maureen McKee, Rsrc.Ctr.Coord.
Founded: 1970. **Staff:** Prof 1; Other 1. **Subjects:** Insurance, health care costs, health maintenance organizations, health education, management. **Special Collections:** Annual reports from other Blue Cross plans; health insurance statistics, 1950 to present; enrollment and utilization reports from other Blue Cross plans, 1950 to present. **Holdings:** 900 books; 150 reports; 50 VF drawers of newspaper and magazine articles. **Subscriptions:** 120 journals and other serials; 8 newspapers. **Services:** Interlibrary loan; copying; library open to the public with restrictions. **Automated Operations:** Computerized acquisitions and circulation. **Computerized Information Services:** NEXIS, LEXIS. **Remarks:** FAX: (513)872-3060.

★4090★
Community Relations-Social Development Commission - Research Library (Soc Sci)
231 W. Wisconsin Ave. Phone: (414)272-5600
Milwaukee, WI 53203 Signe Waller, Res.Spec.
Founded: 1964. **Staff:** Prof 1; Other 1. **Subjects:** Poverty/social welfare, aging, employment and training, health, criminal justice, education. **Holdings:** 1000 books; 50 bound periodical volumes; 20 VF drawers; census and statistics collection; agency archives. **Subscriptions:** 40 journals and other serials; 6 newspapers. **Services:** Interlibrary loan; library open to the public by appointment. **Networks/Consortia:** Member of Library Council of Metropolitan Milwaukee, Inc. (LCOMM). **Publications:** Memorandum of new library materials, irregular - for internal distribution only. **Remarks:** FAX: (414)272-7982.

★4091★
Community Resources For Children - Resource & Toy Library (Educ)
1754 Second, Suite A Phone: (707)253-0376
Napa, CA 94559 Michelle Kunkel, Rsrc.Libn.
Founded: 1979. **Staff:** Prof 1; Other 2. **Subjects:** Toys - infant, toddler, puzzles, large and small motor skill development, puppets, dramatic play, educational. **Holdings:** 515 books; 900 toys; puzzles; puppets; cassettes; phonograph records; musical instruments. **Subscriptions:** 13 journals and other serials. **Services:** Copying; library open to the public. **Publications:** Rainbow Newsletter, monthly - to members and available by request. **Special Indexes:** Toy inventory; picture index. **Remarks:** FAX: (707)253-2735.

★4092★
Community Service, Inc. - Library (Soc Sci)
114 E. Whiteman St. Phone: (513)767-2161
Yellow Springs, OH 45387 Jane Morgan, Exec.Dir.
Founded: 1940. **Staff:** 2. **Subjects:** Communities - small , utopian, intentional; rural sociology; folk societies; communes; economics; education, land trusts. **Special Collections:** Twentieth century intentional communities. **Holdings:** 1000 volumes; 24 VF drawers of community development material, including commune newsletters from the 1950s and miscellaneous literature from communes and intentional communities. **Subscriptions:** 25 journals and other serials. **Services:** Library open to the public for reference use only. **Remarks:** Alternate telephone number(s): (513)767-1461.

★4093★
Community United Methodist Church - Library (Rel-Phil)
20 N. Center St. Phone: (708)355-1483
Naperville, IL 60540 Forrest Rice, Ch., Lib.Comm.
Founded: 1950. **Subjects:** Christianity, Evangelical United Brethren Church, Naperville (IL) area, United Methodist Church, Northern Illinois area Evangelical United Brethren churches. **Special Collections:** Peace with Justice Collection (100 volumes). **Holdings:** 4000 books; 50 archival boxes; 25 videotapes. **Subscriptions:** 9 journals and other serials. **Services:** Library open to the public; some materials for reference use only.

★4094★
Como Zoo - Library (Biol Sci)
Midway Pkwy. & Kaufman Dr. Phone: (612)488-4041
St. Paul, MN 55103 Kristi Wells, Dir.
Founded: 1955. **Staff:** Prof 1. **Subjects:** Animal studies, zoo-related studies. **Holdings:** 500 books. **Services:** Library open to staff, docents, and board members only. **Special Indexes:** Animal inventory.

★4095★
Compagnie de Jesus - Bibliotheque de Theologie (Rel-Phil)
5605 Decelles Ave. Phone: (514)737-1465
Montreal, PQ, Canada H3T 1W4 Claude-Roger Nadeau, S.J., Dir.
Founded: 1882. **Staff:** Prof 1; Other 5. **Subjects:** Theology, scripture, patristics, church history, canon law, history of religions, philosophy. **Special Collections:** Canadiana; 16th-18th century theological books; rare books from the "Ancien College des Jesuites de Quebec," established in 1635. **Holdings:** 195,000 volumes; 475 bound periodical volumes. **Subscriptions:** 400 journals and other serials. **Services:** Interlibrary loan; copying; library open to the public with restrictions.

★4096★
Compagnie de Jesus - Jesuits Library and Archives (Rel-Phil)
175, blvd. des Hauteurs
C.P. 130 Phone: (514)438-3593
St. Jerome, PQ, Canada J7Z 5T8 Joseph Cossette, S.J., Lib.Dir.
Founded: 1852. **Staff:** Prof 2; Other 1. **Subjects:** Religious sciences, church history, theology, literature, spirituality, Scripture. **Special Collections:** Archives of the Society of Jesus, French Canada (976 linear feet, including 122 reels of microfilm); history of Canada. **Holdings:** 79,683 volumes; 125 reels of microfilm; microcards; 150 other cataloged items. **Subscriptions:** 125 journals and other serials. **Services:** Copying; library open to the public for reference use only. **Publications:** Cahiers d'histoire des Jesuites, 6/year; Monumenta Historica Societatis, 5th. Jesu; Monumenta Novae Franciae. **Staff:** I. Contant, Asst.Libn.

★4097★
Compass, Inc. - Library (Comp Sci)
550 Edgewater Dr. Phone: (617)245-9540
Wakefield, MA 01880-1253 Arlene M. McGrane, Libn.
Founded: 1961. **Staff:** Prof 1; Other 2. **Subjects:** Computers, mathematics of computation. **Holdings:** 2190 books; 150 volumes and 20 VF drawers of documents; 349 microfiche; 210 volumes of conferences, proceedings, tutorials; 26 VF drawers of technical reports. **Subscriptions:** 140 journals and other serials. **Services:** Interlibrary loan; library not open to the public. **Computerized Information Services:** DIALOG Information Services. **Publications:** Bibliography of Selected Publications.

★4098★
Complexe Scientifique du Quebec - Service de Documentation et de Bibliotheque (Sci-Engr, Agri)
2700 Einstein C-1-100 Phone: (418)643-9730
Ste. Foy, PQ, Canada G1P 3W8 M. Levesque, Hd.Libn.
Founded: 1971. **Staff:** Prof 1; Other 4. **Subjects:** Forestry, agriculture, minerals. **Holdings:** 10,000 books; 900 bound periodical volumes. **Subscriptions:** 250 journals and other serials; 5 newspapers. **Services:** Interlibrary loan; copying; SDI; library open to the public. **Automated Operations:** Computerized cataloging. **Computerized Information Services:** DIALOG Information Services, CAN/OLE. **Publications:** Acquisitions Recentes; INFO-CRM; Sommaire des Periodiques (MAPAQ). **Remarks:** FAX: (418)643-3361. Telex: 051-31589 SBCS QBC.

★4099★
Compliance Systems Publications, Inc. - Library (Plan)
3071 Peachtree Rd., N.E.
Atlanta, GA 30305 Phone: (404)231-1003
Subjects: Manufactured housing, mobile homes, building codes and standards, energy costs. **Holdings:** 3000 items. **Remarks:** Alternate telephone number(s): (404)233-4125.

Compliance Theory Data Base and Library
See: **Pennsylvania (State) Department of Public Welfare - Office of Children, Youth & Families - Research Center** (12864)

★4100★
Compton Community College - Library - Black History Collection (Area-Ethnic)
1111 E. Artesia Blvd. Phone: (213)637-2660
Compton, CA 90221 Saul J. Panski, Hd.Libn.
Founded: 1927. **Staff:** Prof 2.5; Other 1. **Subjects:** Black history. **Holdings:** 40,074 books; 6668 microforms. **Subscriptions:** 193 journals and other serials; 3 newspapers. **Services:** Interlibrary loan; collection open to the public for reference use only. **Networks/Consortia:** Member of Metronet. **Remarks:** FAX: (213)638-2401. **Staff:** Estina Pratt, Asst.Libn.

★4101★
Compu-Mark U.S. - Library (Bus-Fin)
7201 Wisconsin Ave.
Bethesda, MD 20814 Phone: (617)479-1600
Staff: Prof 7. **Subjects:** Trademarks - U.S., state, international. **Holdings:** Business and trade directories; books; microfiche. **Services:** Library not open to the public. **Computerized Information Services:** Produces trademark databases. Performs searches on fee basis. **Remarks:** FAX: (617)786-8273. Toll-free telephone number(s): (800)421-7800. Telex: 440 388 COMUS.

★4102★
Computer Aided Manufacturing-International, Inc. (CAM-I) - Library (Comp Sci)
1250 E. Copeland Rd., Suite 500 Phone: (817)860-1654
Arlington, TX 76011 Nancy Thomas, Lib.Coord.
Staff: 1. **Subjects:** Computer-aided manufacturing and design - numerical control, automatically programmed tools (APT), process planning, geometric modeling, quality assurance and standards, sculptured surfaces; factory management; cost management systems; computer integrated enterprise; product optimization. **Special Collections:** APT documentation and prototype software; CAM-I's Automated Process Planning (CAPP) system and other process planning materials; CIM Architecture Documentation and Cost Management System videos "The Productivity Paradox" (1988) and cost management conceptual design; DMIS "Dimensional Measuring Interface Specifications" Standard. **Holdings:** 2000 books; 55 original magnetic tapes. **Services:** Copying; library open to the public with restrictions. **Special Catalogs:** Catalog of Publications and Prototype Software (microfiche, magnetic tapes, videotapes and discs). **Remarks:** CAM-I is a nonprofit industrial research and development organization, engaged in the research and development of CIM technology. CAM-I's member organizations, located throughout North America, Europe, Japan, and Australia, provide funds and manpower to support such research and receive the benefits of new developments immediately upon completion. After evaluation, the prototype developments (reports and software) are released to the public and may then be obtained from CAM-I's library. Proceedings of international conferences and seminars are also available. FAX: (817)275-6450.

Computer Modelling Group - I.N. McKinnon Memorial Library
See: **I.N. McKinnon Memorial Library** (9933)

★4103★
Computer Sciences Corporation - Systems Sciences Division - Technical Information Center (Comp Sci)
4600 Powder Mill Rd. Phone: (301)937-0760
Beltsville, MD 20705 Tenna Morse, Mgr.
Staff: Prof 3. **Subjects:** Computer science, aerospace, management, mathematics. **Holdings:** 2500 books; reports on microfiche; programming manuals. **Subscriptions:** 150 journals. **Services:** Interlibrary loan; center not open to the public. **Computerized Information Services:** OCLC. **Networks/Consortia:** Member of Interlibrary Users Association (IUA). **Special Catalogs:** Catalog of corporation reports.

★4104★
Computer Sciences Corporation - Technical Library (Comp Sci)
2100 Grand Ave. Phone: (213)615-1709
El Segundo, CA 90245 Michael L. Shapiro, Res.Asst.
Founded: 1962. **Staff:** Prof 1; Other 1. **Subjects:** Data processing, communications, information retrieval, programming, systems analysis, business, management, operations research, systems integration. **Holdings:** 2200 books; 1150 bound periodical volumes; 7000 unbound reports; 16,200 microfiche. **Subscriptions:** 232 journals and other serials. **Services:** Interlibrary loan; copying; library not open to the public. **Automated Operations:** Computerized, cataloging, serials, and circulation. **Computerized Information Services:** DIALOG Information Services, BRS Information Technologies. **Special Catalogs:** Book catalog to CSC technical reports and program documentation. **Special Indexes:** KWIC index to books, all serials and document holdings. **Remarks:** FAX: (213)322-6109.

★4105★
Computer Sciences Corporation - Virginia Technology Center Library (Comp Sci, Info Sci)
3170 Fairview Park Dr., m/c 222 Phone: (703)641-2009
Falls Church, VA 22042 Dorothy Barrett, Mgr., Info.Rsrcs.
Founded: 1963. **Staff:** Prof 3; Other 3. **Subjects:** Computers, communications, electronic engineering, operations research, management science. **Holdings:** 12,000 books; 200 bound periodical volumes; 50,000 documents and reports; 10,000 microfiche; 300 reels of microfilm. **Subscriptions:** 350 journals and other serials; 12 newspapers. **Services:** Interlibrary loan; library not open to the public. **Computerized Information Services:** DIALOG Information Services, DTIC, OCLC, LEXIS, NEXIS; CD-ROMs. **Networks/Consortia:** Member of Interlibrary Users Association (IUA), CAPCON Library Network CAPCON. **Special Indexes:** COMDEX (Computerized Documents Index) index to company reports. **Remarks:** FAX: (703)849-1001. **Formerly:** Its M/C 222 Library Services.

★4106★
Computing Devices Co. - Technical Library (Sci-Engr)
Box 8508 Phone: (613)596-7273
Ottawa, ON, Canada K1G 3M9 Elaine M. Tigges, Libn.
Staff: Prof 1; Other 1. **Subjects:** Defense electronics. **Holdings:** 8000 books; 66 VF drawers of documents; reports; government and industry standards. **Subscriptions:** 240 journals and other serials. **Services:** Library not open to the public. **Automated Operations:** Computerized cataloging. **Computerized Information Services:** DIALOG Information Services, CAN/OLE.

★4107★
Comunidad Budista Soto Zen - Biblioteca (Rel-Phil)
Moro Zeit 11-6 A
E-46001 Valencia, Spain Phone: 6 3913868
Subjects: Zen Buddhism, religion. **Holdings:** 500 volumes.

★4108★
CONAC - Library
Binational Center for Education
2717 Ontario Rd., N.W., Suite 200
Washington, DC 20009
Founded: 1972. **Subjects:** Higher education, Chicano literature, curriculum development, functional literacy, teacher and parent training. **Special Collections:** Fomento Literario - Chicano Literature (324 items). **Holdings:** 12,000 volumes; 60 reports. **Remarks:** Currently inactive. **Also Known As:** El Congreso Nacional de Asuntos Colegiales.

Conagra, Inc.
See: **Armour Swift-Eckrich** (1055)

Conant Library
See: **Nichols College** (11801)

★4109★
Concentus Musicus - Center for Renaissance Studies - Library (Mus)
1219 University Ave., S.E. Phone: (612)379-4463
Minneapolis, MN 55414 Marcia Dunsmore, Adm.Dir.
Founded: 1966. **Subjects:** Renaissance music, dance, and instruments. **Holdings:** 2000 volumes; replicas of medieval and Renaissance instruments; period costumes. **Services:** Library open to the public by special arrangement.

★4110★
Conception Abbey and Seminary - Library (Rel-Phil)
Conception, MO 64433-0501 Phone: (816)944-2803
Founded: 1873. **Staff:** Prof 3; Other 3. **Subjects:** Roman Catholic Church, philosophy, patrology, monasticism. **Special Collections:** 16th-19th century theological books (2600 volumes). **Holdings:** 99,797 books; 19,833 bound periodical volumes; 12 VF drawers of pamphlets; 13,333 art and travel slides; 3353 music recordings; 3500 rare books and incunabula; 1223 tape recordings; 200 filmstrips; 401 reels of microfilm. **Subscriptions:** 342 journals and other serials. **Services:** Interlibrary loan; copying; library open to the public with librarian's approval. **Computerized Information Services:** OCLC. **Staff:** Sr. Agnes Irene Huser, CSJ, Asst.Libn.; Jack Nevelle, Asst.Libn.

★4111★
Concord Environmental Corporation - Library (Env-Cons)
2 Tippett Rd. Phone: (416)630-6331
Downsview, ON, Canada M3H 2V2 Cathy Lindsey-King, Libn. & Info.Off.
Founded: 1979. **Staff:** Prof 1. **Subjects:** Air pollution, hazardous substances, atmospheric and environmental science, meteorology, occupational hygiene and health, risk assessment. **Holdings:** 100 books; 150 bound periodical volumes; 2000 reports; 650 microfiche. **Subscriptions:** 150 journals and other serials. **Services:** Interlibrary loan; copying; library open to the public by appointment. **Computerized Information Services:** DIALOG Information Services, MEDLARS, Chemical Information Systems, Inc. (CIS), Integrated Risk Information System (IRIS), International Register of Potentially Toxic Chemicals (IRPTC), CAN/OLE, Syracuse Research Environmental Fate Data Bases; PC MACNET (electronic mail service). **Remarks:** FAX: (416)630-0506. Electronic mail address(es): CONCORDTOR (PC MACNET).

★4112★
Concord Museum - Library (Hist)
200 Lexington Rd.
P.O. Box 146 Phone: (508)369-9609
Concord, MA 01742 Charmian Clark, Libn.
Founded: 1939. **Staff:** 3. **Subjects:** Local history, decorative arts, early American furnishings. **Holdings:** 1000 books. **Subscriptions:** 10 journals and other serials. **Services:** Library open to staff, museum members, and scholars by prior arrangement.

★4113★
Concordia College - Buenger Memorial Library (Rel-Phil)
275 N. Syndicate Phone: (612)641-8240
St. Paul, MN 55104 Glenn W. Offermann, Hd.Libn.
Founded: 1893. **Staff:** Prof 4; Other 3. **Subjects:** Elementary education, religious education, church music, business. **Holdings:** 100,000 books; 12,000 periodical volumes, mostly in microform; 5000 nonbook materials; 500 motion pictures and videotapes; 3000 audio recordings; 1700 filmstrips; 3500 slides. **Subscriptions:** 450 journals and other serials; 6 newspapers. **Services:** Interlibrary loan; copying; library open to the public with restrictions. **Computerized Information Services:** DIALOG Information Services; internal database. **Networks/Consortia:** Member of Cooperating Libraries in Consortium (CLIC), MINITEX Library Information Network, Metronet. **Remarks:** FAX: (612)659-0207. **Staff:** Charlotte Knoche, Cat./Ref.Libn.; Martha Burkart, Curric.Coord.; Jeff Burkart, AV Dir.

★4114★
Concordia College - Link Library (Educ)
800 N. Columbia Ave. Phone: (402)643-7258
Seward, NE 68434 Myron Boettcher, Dir.
Founded: 1912. **Staff:** Prof 4; Other 7. **Subjects:** Education and religion. **Special Collections:** Koschmann Memorial Collection of Children's Literature. **Holdings:** 182,000 volumes; 12,000 microforms; 15,000 nonprint materials. **Subscriptions:** 800 journals and other serials. **Services:** Interlibrary loan; copying; library open to the public. **Automated Operations:** Computerized cataloging. **Computerized Information Services:** OCLC. **Networks/Consortia:** Member of NEBASE. **Remarks:** FAX: (402)643-4218. **Staff:** Marjorie Meier, Pub.Serv.Libn.; Ray Huebschman, Coord., AV; Glenn Ohlmann, Tech.Serv.Libn.

Concordia College - Lutheran Church - Missouri Synod - Michigan District Archives
See: **Lutheran Church - Missouri Synod - Michigan District Archives** (9450)

★4115★
Concordia Historical Institute - Department of Archives and History (Rel-Phil)
801 DeMun Ave. Phone: (314)721-5934
St. Louis, MO 63105 August R. Suelflow, Dir.
Founded: 1927. **Staff:** Prof 3; Other 13. **Subjects:** Lutheranism in America. **Special Collections:** Archives of The Lutheran Church - Missouri Synod; Archives of the National Evangelical Lutheran Church; Archives of the Synod of Evangelical Lutheran Churches; Lutheran congregational histories; Evangelical Lutheran Synodical Conference Archives; Lutheran

Foreign Mission resources; Lutheran Hour Broadcast discs; files and manuscripts of Lutheran leaders; Lutheran theological literature. **Holdings:** 58,000 books; 7800 bound periodical volumes; 2.5 million archival, document, manuscript materials; 178,000 feet of microfilm; 4700 phonograph records, discs, tapes; 340 sets of slides and filmstrips; 5000 photographs, pictures, museum materials. **Subscriptions:** 130 journals and other serials; 35 newspapers. **Services:** Interlibrary loan (fee); copying; assistance in reference, research, bibliography, book identification, translation; department open to the public. **Networks/Consortia:** Member of St. Louis Regional Library Network. **Publications:** Concordia Historical Institute Quarterly; Historical Footnotes; Regional Archivist. **Special Indexes:** Index to Microfilm Holdings, 2 volumes. **Staff:** Marvin A. Huggins, Asst.Dir., Archv. and Lib.; Roy A. Ledbetter, Ref. and Res.Asst.

★4116★
Concordia Hospital - Library (Med)
1095 Concordia Ave. Phone: (204)661-7163
Winnipeg, MB, Canada R2K 3S8 Edith Konoplenko, Lib.Techn.
Founded: 1979. **Staff:** Prof 1. **Subjects:** Medicine, nursing. **Holdings:** 3000 books. **Subscriptions:** 63 journals and other serials. **Services:** Interlibrary loan; library open to the public for reference use only. **Remarks:** FAX: (204)663-7301.

★4117★
Concordia Seminary - Library (Rel-Phil)
801 DeMun Ave. Phone: (314)721-5934
St. Louis, MO 63105 David O. Berger, Dir., Lib.Serv.
Founded: 1839. **Staff:** Prof 2; Other 6. **Subjects:** Biblical studies, theology, patristics, Reformation and church history, hymnology and liturgics, sacred music. **Special Collections:** Lutherana (16th and 17th century Lutheran reformers and dogmaticians). **Holdings:** 167,955 books; 32,150 bound periodical volumes; 3450 reels of microfilm; 1615 phonodiscs; 861 filmstrips; 41,509 microfiche; 5015 cassettes; 706 microcards; 7174 slides. **Subscriptions:** 911 journals and other serials. **Services:** Interlibrary loan; copying; library open to the public for reference use only. **Automated Operations:** Computerized public access catalog (CD-ROM); circulation, and acquisitions. **Computerized Information Services:** BRS Information Technologies. Performs searches on fee basis. Contact Person: Robert Roethemeyer, Coord., Pub.Serv. **Networks/Consortia:** Member of St. Louis Regional Library Network, Missouri Library Network Corp. (MLNC). **Remarks:** FAX: (314)721-5903. **Staff:** Joann Mirly, Asst.Dir.; Mark Bliese, Coord., Tech.Serv.

★4118★
Concordia Theological Seminary - Archives (Rel-Phil)
6600 N. Clinton Phone: (219)481-2100
Fort Wayne, IN 46825 Otto Krupski, Archv.
Founded: 1846. **Subjects:** Concordia Theological Seminary, 1846 to present; history of the Lutheran Church, Missouri Synod. **Holdings:** 110 linear feet; 15 VF drawers; 100 business and academic records, publications, faculty writings, student records, photographs, architectural plans for campus buildings, slides, and motion pictures. **Services:** Copying; archives open to the public. **Remarks:** FAX: (219)481-2126.

★4119★
Concordia Theological Seminary - Library (Rel-Phil)
6600 N. Clinton Phone: (219)481-2100
Fort Wayne, IN 46825 Rev. Paul Jackson, Hd.Libn.
Founded: 1846. **Staff:** Prof 3; Other 6. **Subjects:** Lutheran theology, church history, Lutherana, missions. **Special Collections:** 16th-17th century Lutheran Orthodoxy; Hermann Sasse Collection. **Holdings:** 133,706 books; 7192 microforms; 6515 AV programs; 4549 other cataloged items. **Subscriptions:** 757 journals and other serials; 10 newspapers. **Services:** Interlibrary loan; copying; library open to the public. **Automated Operations:** Computerized cataloging, acquisitions, and serials. **Computerized Information Services:** OCLC, DIALOG Information Services. **Networks/Consortia:** Member of INCOLSA, Tri-ALSA. **Remarks:** FAX: (219)481-2126. **Staff:** Lois Guebart, Tech.Serv.Libn.; James Lanning, Cat.

★4120★
Concordia University - Klinck Memorial Library (Rel-Phil)
7400 Augusta St. Phone: (708)209-3050
River Forest, IL 60305-1499 Henry R. Latzke, Dir., Lib.Serv./Media Serv.
Founded: 1864. **Staff:** Prof 5; Other 4. **Subjects:** Education, religion, psychology, church music. **Special Collections:** Hymnal collection. **Holdings:** 133,761 books; 16,648 bound periodical volumes; 12,698 curriculum laboratory materials; 2039 reels of microfilm; 446,818 microfiche; ERIC documents on microfiche (complete); 1980 U.S. Census computer tapes. **Subscriptions:** 595 journals; 5 newspapers. **Services:** Interlibrary loan; copying; library open to the public. **Automated Operations:** Computerized cataloging. **Computerized Information Services:** OCLC, DIALOG Information Services; CD-ROMs (ERIC, BIP Plus, Academic Abstracts). Performs searches on fee basis. **Networks/Consortia:** Member of ILLINET, Suburban Library System (SLS), LIBRAS Inc. **Remarks:** FAX: (708)209-3175. **Staff:** Audrey Roberts, Per.Libn.; Elizabeth Vihnanek, Curric. & Ref.Libn.; Richard Richter, Dir., Television; Marilyn Wenzel, Tech.Serv./Pub.Serv.

★4121★
Concordia University - Loyola Campus - Georges P. Vanier Library (Soc Sci, Hum)
7141 Sherbrooke St., W. Phone: (514)848-7769
Montreal, PQ, Canada H4B 1R6 Judy Appleby, Hd., Vanier.Lib.
Staff: Prof 6; Other 27. **Subjects:** Science - general, social, exercise; humanities; communication arts; commerce; library studies; theatre; dance; music. **Special Collections:** Africa Collection; D'Arcy McGee Collection of Irish Material; Masonic Collection (400 items); Rudnyc'ki Archives; Hilaire Belloc Collection. **Holdings:** 475,000 volumes; 103,000 microfiche and microfilm. **Subscriptions:** 1906 journals and other serials. **Services:** Interlibrary loan; copying; library open to the public with restrictions on borrowing. **Automated Operations:** Computerized cataloging, circulation, and serials. **Computerized Information Services:** BRS Information Technologies, PFDS Online, DIALOG Information Services, QL Systems, UTLAS, International Development Research Centre (IDRC), Info Globe, Infomart Online, WILSONLINE; CD-ROMs (PsycLIT, ABI/INFORM, Canadian Business and Current Affairs (CBCA), Social Sciences Index, Humanities Index, SPORT Discus); Envoy 100 (electronic mail service). Performs searches on fee basis. **Remarks:** FAX: (514)848-2804. Electronic mail address(es): ILL.QML (Envoy 100). **Staff:** Sonia Poulin, Ref.Libn.; Howard Perron, Ref.Libn.; Marvin Orbach, Ref.Libn.; Helena Gamiero, Ref.Libn.; Luigina Vileno, Ref.Libn.; Christopher Bober, Ref.Libn.

★4122★
Concordia University - Sir George Williams Campus - Conservatory of Cinematographic Art - Library (Theater)
1455 de Maisonneuve Blvd., W., Suite 109 Phone: (514)848-2424
Montreal, PQ, Canada H3G 1M8 Serge Losique, Dir.
Subjects: History of the cinema. **Holdings:** 1000 volumes; film collection. **Remarks:** Alternate telephone number(s): (514)848-3878 FAX: (514)848-3886.

★4123★
Concordia University - Sir George Williams Campus - Guidance Information Centre (Educ)
1455 de Maisonneuve Blvd., W. Phone: (514)848-3556
Montreal, PQ, Canada H3G 1M8 Marlis Hubbard, Libn.
Founded: 1966. **Staff:** Prof 2; Other 4. **Subjects:** Educational planning, careers and career planning, financial aid, student life, study skills, personal development, job-hunting skills. **Special Collections:** Women and Careers (200 books); Disabled. **Holdings:** 5000 books; 200 pamphlet boxes on careers; 3 VF drawers and 37 pamphlet boxes on financial aid; employer file of recruiting literature from 500 companies. **Subscriptions:** 57 journals and other serials. **Services:** Copying; center open to the public. **Automated Operations:** INMAGIC. **Computerized Information Services:** Internal database. **Publications:** Acquisitions List; Blueprint for a Guidance Information Centre; bibliographies (online). **Special Indexes:** Indexes to occupational and vocational collections. **Remarks:** FAX: (514)848-3494. Maintained by Concordia Guidance Services. **Staff:** Susan Hawke, Libn.

★4124★
Concordia University - Sir George Williams Campus - Science & Engineering Library (Sci-Engr)
1455 de Maisonneuve Blvd., W. Phone: (514)848-7721
Montreal, PQ, Canada H3G 1M8 Zuzana Jirkovsky, Hd.
Founded: 1966. **Staff:** Prof 5; Other 17. **Subjects:** Science, engineering, computer science. **Holdings:** Figures not available. **Services:** Interlibrary loan; copying; SDI; library open to the public with restrictions on borrowing. **Automated Operations:** Computerized cataloging, serials, and circulation. **Computerized Information Services:** BRS Information Technologies, ORBIT Search Service, QL Systems, IST-Informatheque Inc., Chemical Abstracts Service (CAS), UTLAS, CAN/OLE, Data-Star, DIALOG Information Services, DOBIS Canadian Online Library System, The Financial Post DataGroup, Info Globe, Infomart Online, STN International, WILSONLINE; Refcatts (internal database). Performs searches on fee basis. **Publications:** Serials Holdings List. **Staff:** Lee Harris, Ref.Libn.; Dubravka Kapa, Ref.Libn.; Mary Tansey, Ref.Supv.; Gheri Celin, Circ.Supv.; Ruth Noble, Ref.Libn.; Carol Coughlin, Ref.Libn.

Concrete Technology Information Analysis Center
See: **U.S. Army - Engineer Waterways Experiment Station** (16967)

★4125★
Concurrent Computer Corporation - Library (Comp Sci)
1 Technology Way Phone: (508)392-2990
Westford, MA 01886 Dave Davis, Libn.
Founded: 1988. **Staff:** 1. **Subjects:** Computer science, engineering, computer industry. **Holdings:** 400 books; 100 videotapes; 25 MRDF. **Subscriptions:** 200 journals and other serials; 30 newspapers. **Services:** Interlibrary loan; copying; SDI; library not open to the public. **Automated Operations:** Computerized cataloging. **Computerized Information Services:** DIALOG Information Services, OCLC; InterNet (electronic mail service). **Remarks:** FAX: (508)392-2494. Electronic mail address(es): DAVED@WESTFORD.CCUR.COM (InterNet).

★4126★
Concurrent Computer Corporation - Library (Comp Sci)
106 Apple St. Phone: (201)870-4500
Tinton Falls, NJ 07724 Dave Davis, Libn.
Founded: 1977. **Subjects:** Computer science, electrical engineering, math, management. **Holdings:** 2000 books. **Subscriptions:** 150 journals and other serials. **Services:** Copying; SDI; library open to the public by appointment. **Computerized Information Services:** DIALOG Information Services. **Remarks:** FAX: (201)870-5889.

★4127★
Conde Nast Publications, Inc. - Library (Publ, Art)
350 Madison Ave., 11th Fl. Phone: (212)880-8343
New York, NY 10017 Cynthia Cathcart, Sr.Libn.
Founded: 1935. **Staff:** Prof 3. **Subjects:** Fashion, houses, gardens, home furnishings, interior design, health, personalities. **Special Collections:** Bound volumes of House & Garden, Vogue, Vanity Fair, Glamour, Mademoiselle, Brides, Self, Gentlemen's Quarterly (complete sets). **Holdings:** 5100 volumes. **Subscriptions:** 100 journals and other serials; 5 newspapers. **Services:** Copying; library open to the public by appointment. **Special Indexes:** Index to Vogue, 1892 to present; index to Vanity Fair, 1913-1936. **Staff:** Annette Ohnikian.

★4128★
Condell Memorial Hospital - Fohrman Library (Med)
900 S. Garfield Ave.
Libertyville, IL 60048 Phone: (708)362-2900
Founded: 1963. **Staff:** 1. **Subjects:** Medicine, surgery. **Holdings:** 1000 volumes. **Subscriptions:** 100 journals and other serials. **Services:** Interlibrary loan. **Networks/Consortia:** Member of Northeastern Illinois Library Consortium, National Network of Libraries of Medicine - Greater Midwest Region, North Suburban Library System (NSLS).

★4129★
Condon & Forsyth - Library (Law)
1251 Avenue of the Americas Phone: (212)757-6870
New York, NY 10020 Antoinette Tatta, Libn.
Founded: 1922. **Staff:** Prof 1. **Subjects:** Law. **Special Collections:** Aviation law (350 cataloged items). **Holdings:** 13,000 books; 250 bound periodical volumes. **Subscriptions:** 76 journals; 144 serials; 6 newspapers. **Services:** Interlibrary loan; library not open to the public. **Computerized Information Services:** DIALOG Information Services, WESTLAW.

Cone Library
See: **Teikyo Marycrest University** (16056)

Marvin Cone Archives
See: **Cedar Rapids Museum of Art - Herbert S. Stamats Art Library** (3186)

★4130★
Cone Mills Corporation - Library (Bus-Fin)
1106 Maple St. Phone: (919)379-6215
Greensboro, NC 27405 Ellen Bailey, Libn.
Founded: 1944. **Staff:** Prof 1. **Subjects:** Textile technology, marketing, industrial relations, management, chemistry. **Holdings:** 3965 books; 5910 patents. **Subscriptions:** 100 journals and other serials; 6 newspapers. **Services:** Interlibrary loan; copying; library open to the public with company approval. **Computerized Information Services:** DIALOG Information Services; CD-ROMs. **Remarks:** FAX: (919)379-6423.

★4131★
Moses H. Cone Memorial Hospital - Medical Library (Med)
1200 N. Elm St. Phone: (919)379-4484
Greensboro, NC 27420 Leslie G. Mackler, Dir., Med.Lib.
Founded: 1953. **Staff:** 4. **Subjects:** Medicine, medical specialities. **Holdings:** 3800 books; 8000 bound periodical volumes; 1400 AV programs. **Subscriptions:** 200 journals and other serials. **Services:** Interlibrary loan; copying; SDI; library open to the public for reference use only. **Computerized Information Services:** MEDLARS, BRS Information Technologies. Performs searches on fee basis.

★4132★
Conemaugh Valley Memorial Hospital - Health Sciences Library (Med)
1086 Franklin St. Phone: (814)533-9111
Johnstown, PA 15905-4398 Fred L. Wilson, Jr., Dir., Hea.Sci.Lib.
Staff: Prof 2. **Subjects:** Medicine, nursing, allied health sciences. **Special Collections:** Hospital archives. **Holdings:** 5506 books; 7345 bound periodical volumes; 450 Audio-Digest tapes; 136 videotapes. **Subscriptions:** 340 journals and other serials. **Services:** Interlibrary loan; library not open to the public. **Automated Operations:** Computerized cataloging, serials, and circulation. **Computerized Information Services:** NLM, DIALOG Information Services; DOCLINE (electronic mail service). **Networks/Consortia:** Member of Central Pennsylvania Health Sciences Library Association (CPHSLA). **Publications:** Monthly holdings update. **Remarks:** FAX: (814)533-3244. **Staff:** Catherine Geiser, Lib.Techn.; Mark Kush, AV Techn.

★4133★
Coney Island Hospital - Harold Fink Memorial Library (Med)
2601 Ocean Pkwy. Phone: (718)615-4299
Brooklyn, NY 11235 Munir U. Din, Dir.
Founded: 1951. **Staff:** Prof 1; Other 1.5. **Subjects:** Medicine, nursing, pharmacy, psychiatry, podiatry, hospital administration. **Holdings:** 5700 books; 17,000 bound periodical volumes; 350 video cassettes; 200 slide/tape sets; 150 slide sets with pamphlets. **Subscriptions:** 325 journals and other serials. **Services:** Interlibrary loan; library not open to the public. **Automated Operations:** Computerized serials and circulation. **Computerized Information Services:** NLM; CD-ROM. **Networks/Consortia:** Member of Brooklyn-Queens-Staten Island Health Sciences Librarians (BQSI), BHSL, New York Metropolitan Reference and Research Library Agency. **Remarks:** FAX: (718)615-5385.

Confederacion Nacional de Trabajadores Dominicanos
See: **National Confederation of Dominican Workers** (11128)

★4134★
Confederate Memorial Literary Society - Museum of the Confederacy - Eleanor S. Brockenbrough Library (Hist)
1201 S. Clay St. Phone: (804) 644-7150
Richmond, VA 23219 Guy Swanson, Dir. of Lib. and Res.
Founded: 1890. **Staff:** Prof 1. **Subjects:** Confederate military history, Confederate civil history, history of the South. **Special Collections:** Confederate manuscripts, imprints, numismatics; Jefferson Davis letters; maps; photographs; ephemera. **Holdings:** Figures not available. **Services:** Copying; library open to the public by appointment. **Publications:** Journal, biennial. **Special Catalogs:** Catalog, biennial. **Remarks:** FAX: (804)644-7150.

Confederate Memorial Museum
See: **United Daughters of the Confederacy - Shropshire Upton Chapter** (16705)

★4135★
Confederation des Caisses Populaires et d'Economie Desjardins du Quebec - Service de Documentation de Reference (Bus-Fin)
100, ave. des Commandeurs Phone: (418)835-4441
Levis, PQ, Canada G6V 7N5 Ginette Bruneau, Chf.
Founded: 1971. **Staff:** Prof 3; Other 4. **Subjects:** Cooperation, finance, economy, education. **Holdings:** 37,000 books. **Subscriptions:** 500 journals and other serials. **Services:** Interlibrary loan; copying; center open to the public. **Remarks:** FAX: (418)833-5873.

★4136★
Confederation Centre Art Gallery and Museum - Art Resource Centre (Art)
P.O. Box 848 Phone: (902)628-6111
Charlottetown, PE, Canada C1A 7L9 Ted Fraser, Gallery Dir.
Founded: 1964. **Subjects:** Art, architecture, sculpture. **Holdings:** 4000 books; unbound periodicals; 4000 color slides; slide/tape sets on historical and modern art; filmstrips on Canadian art. **Subscriptions:** 10 journals and other serials. **Services:** Library open to the public by appointment. **Remarks:** FAX: (902)566-4648. **Formerly:** Its Art Reference Library.

★4137★
Confederation College of Applied Arts & Technology - Challis Resource Centre (Educ)
Box 398, Sta. F Phone: (807)475-6204
Thunder Bay, ON, Canada P7C 4W1 Laraine Tapak, Dir.
Founded: 1967. **Staff:** Prof 1; Other 14. **Subjects:** Applied arts, business, technology, health sciences, distance education. **Holdings:** 34,000 books; 10,000 AV programs. **Subscriptions:** 600 journals and other serials; 50 newspapers. **Services:** Interlibrary loan; copying; center open to the public with restrictions. **Automated Operations:** Computerized public access catalog, acquisitions, and circulation. **Computerized Information Services:** DIALOG Information Services, Info Globe, WILSONLINE, DOBIS Canadian Online Library System; CD-ROMs (ERIC, Canadian Business and Current Affairs). **Remarks:** FAX: (807)622-3258.

★4138★
Confederation Life Insurance Company - Information Resources (Bus-Fin)
260 Interstate North Pkwy.
Box 105103 Phone: (404)859-3057
Atlanta, GA 30348 Michael Aiken, Asst.Mgr., Info.Rsrcs.
Founded: 1982. **Staff:** Prof 1. **Subjects:** Life insurance, actuarial science, business management, insurance law. **Special Collections:** Insurance law (500 volumes). **Holdings:** 1500 books; 100 bound periodical volumes; Life Office Management Association (LOMA) texts. **Subscriptions:** 55 journals and other serials; 5 newspapers. **Services:** Interlibrary loan; copying; open to the public with permission. **Computerized Information Services:** LEXIS, NEXIS, WILSONLINE, Dow Jones News/Retrieval, DIALOG Information Services.

★4139★
Confederation Life Insurance Company - Library (Bus-Fin)
321 Bloor St., E. Phone: (416)323-8326
Toronto, ON, Canada M4W 1H1 Lynne M. Sugden, Libn.
Founded: 1871. **Staff:** Prof 1; Other 2. **Subjects:** Actuarial science, group insurance, investments, law, management, marketing, personnel administration. **Holdings:** 10,000 books; 130 bound periodical volumes; 10 VF drawers of Life Insurance Marketing and Research Association (LIMRA) and Life Office Management Association (LOMA) reports; 17 VF drawers of U.S. and Canadian legislation; 5 VF drawers of association material; 1 VF drawer of maps; 2000 pamphlets. **Subscriptions:** 300 journals and other serials. **Services:** Interlibrary loan; copying; library open to librarians in insurance field. **Automated Operations:** Computerized cataloging, acquisitions, serials, and circulation. **Computerized Information Services:** Internal databases. **Publications:** Acquisitions to the Business Library, bimonthly; Synopsis of Periodicals, annual - both for internal distribution only. **Remarks:** FAX: (416)323-4191.

★4140★
Conference Board of Canada - Information Services & Resource Centre (Bus-Fin)
255 Smyth Rd. Phone: (613)526-3280
Ottawa, ON, Canada K1H 8M7 Zoe Baxter Buchanan, Mgr., Info.Serv.
Founded: 1916. **Staff:** Prof 2; Other 2. **Subjects:** Management practice, statistics, economics, financial services, international business, tourism, compensation, business and the environment, education. **Special Collections:** Complete holdings of the Conference Board (Canadian, American, European). **Holdings:** 10,000 books; Canadian and U.S. Government publications; newsletters. **Subscriptions:** 320 journals and other serials; 25 newspapers. **Services:** Interlibrary loan; center not open to the public. **Automated Operations:** Computerized cataloging, acquisitions, serials, and circulation (INMAGIC). **Computerized Information Services:** DIALOG Information Services, Info Globe, Infomart Online. Performs searches on fee basis. **Special Indexes:** Cumulative index, annual (book). **Remarks:** FAX: (613)526-4857.

★4141★
Conference Board, Inc. - Information Service (Bus-Fin)
845 3rd Ave. Phone: (212)759-0900
New York, NY 10022 Ellen Ackerman, Dir.
Founded: 1916. **Staff:** Prof 8; Other 5. **Subjects:** Economics; business management. **Holdings:** 15,000 books and pamphlets; 25 periodical titles in microform. **Subscriptions:** 1200 journals and other serials. **Services:** Interlibrary loan (to members); copying; open only to Conference Board members and faculty. **Computerized Information Services:** DIALOG Information Services, Dow Jones News/Retrieval, NEXIS. **Special Indexes:** Cumulative Index to Conference Board Publications. **Remarks:** FAX: (212)980-7014. Telex: 237282 and 234465. **Staff:** Carol Estoppey, Asst.Dir.; Rita Korn, Info.Spec.; Rita Kay Meyer, Info.Spec.; Deborah Hendel, Info.Spec.; Kathleen Gaskin, Info.Spec.; Diane Shimek, Sr.Info.Spec.; Hilma Ebanks, Sr.Info.Spec.

Conference of Manitoba and Northwestern Ontario Archives
See: **University of Winnipeg - Library - Special Collections** (19568)

★4142★
Conference des Recteurs et des Principaux des Universites du Quebec - Centre de Documentation (Educ)
300, rue Leo Pariseau, Suite 1200
Succursale Place du Parc, C.P. 952 Phone: (514)288-8524
Montreal, PQ, Canada H2W 2N1 Roger Charland, Libn.
Founded: 1967. **Staff:** Prof 1. **Subjects:** Education, communication, industrial relations, library science, economics. **Holdings:** 6500 books; 300 bound periodical volumes. **Subscriptions:** 300 journals and other serials; 20 newspapers. **Services:** Interlibrary loan; center open to the public. **Computerized Information Services:** Internal databases. **Remarks:** FAX: (514)288-0554. Telex: 055-60944. **Also Known As:** Conference of Rectors and Principals of Quebec Universities.

★4143★
Conflict Resolution Center International - Library (Soc Sci)
7101 Hamilton Ave. Phone: (412)371-9884
Pittsburgh, PA 15208-1828 Paul Wahrhaftig, Pres.
Founded: 1973. **Staff:** 1. **Subjects:** Conflict resolution, arbitration, mediation. **Holdings:** 100 books; 1500 reports. **Services:** Copying; library open to the public. **Automated Operations:** Computerized annotated index. **Computerized Information Services:** ConflictNet (electronic mail service). **Remarks:** FAX: (412)371-9885.

★4144★
Congoleum Corporation - Technical Research Library (Sci-Engr)
Box 3127 Phone: (609)584-3329
Trenton, NJ 08619 Daniel W. Schutter, Lab.Mgr.
Founded: 1920. **Subjects:** Plastics, chemistry, paper, floor coverings, coatings. **Holdings:** 1500 books; official patent gazettes (current year). **Subscriptions:** 35 journals and other serials. **Services:** Library not open to the public. **Remarks:** FAX: (609)584-3305.

★4145★
Congregation Adath Jeshurun - Gottlieb Memorial Library (Rel-Phil)
York & Ashbourne Rds.
Elkins Park, PA 19117 Phone: (215)635-1337
Staff: Prof 1; Other 2. **Subjects:** Judaica, religion, Bible. **Holdings:** 4000 books; 6 VF drawers of clippings; 50 phonograph records. **Services:** Interlibrary loan; copying; library open to the public with restrictions.

★4146★
Congregation Agudas Achim - Bernard Rubinstein Library (Rel-Phil)
1201 Donaldson Ave. Phone: (512)736-4216
San Antonio, TX 78228 Marie Bartman, Libn.
Staff: 1. **Subjects:** Judaica. **Holdings:** 4000 volumes; magazines of Jewish content; 20 phonograph records. **Services:** Copying; library open to the public for reference use only.

★4147★
Congregation of the Alexian Brothers - Provincial Archives (Rel-Phil)
600 Alexian Way Phone: (708)981-3608
Elk Grove Village, IL 60007 Bro. Roy Godwin, C.F.A., Prov.Archv.
Founded: 1971. **Staff:** Prof 1; Other 1. **Subjects:** History of the Alexian Brothers, Roman Catholic Church history. **Special Collections:** Hospitals, nursing homes, church history from areas served by the Alexians (1027 linear feet). **Holdings:** Figures not available. **Subscriptions:** 11 journals and other serials. **Services:** Archives open to the public with restrictions. **Remarks:** FAX: (708)981-5561. Alternate telephone number(s): 640-7550.

★4148★
Congregation Beth Achim - Joseph Katkowsky Library (Rel-Phil)
21100 12 Mile Rd., W. Phone: (313)352-8670
Southfield, MI 48076 Dr. Israel Wiener, Chf.Libn.
Founded: 1960. **Staff:** Prof 2. **Subjects:** Judaica, Jewish theology and liturgy, Bible/Old Testament, cantorial liturgy, Jewish history. **Special Collections:** Classic Jewish Theology; Classic Cantorial Liturgy; B. Isaac Collection (children's books); Gerdin Yiddish Collection. **Holdings:** 13,500 books; 80 records of liturgical music in Hebrew and Yiddish; 75 pamphlets. **Subscriptions:** 25 journals and other serials; 6 newspapers. **Services:** Interlibrary loan; copying; library open to the public. **Automated Operations:** Computerized public access catalog. **Staff:** Judith Lawson, Asst.Libn.

★4149★
Congregation Beth Am - Dorothy G. Feldman Library (Rel-Phil)
3557 Washington Blvd. Phone: (216)321-1000
Cleveland Heights, OH 44118 Mrs. Louis L. Powers, Libn.
Founded: 1935. **Staff:** Prof 1. **Subjects:** Judaica. **Special Collections:** Children's literature. **Holdings:** 7000 volumes; records. **Subscriptions:** 22 journals and other serials. **Services:** Interlibrary loan; library open to the public.

★4150★
Congregation Beth Am - Library (Rel-Phil)
26790 Arastradero Rd. Phone: (415)493-4661
Los Altos Hills, CA 94022 Diane Rauchwerger, Libn.
Founded: 1961. **Staff:** 2. **Subjects:** Judaica. **Holdings:** 2500 books. **Subscriptions:** 20 journals and other serials. **Services:** Library open to the public subject to approval. **Staff:** Christine Liddicoat, Asst.Libn.

★4151★
Congregation Beth-El Zedeck - Library (Rel-Phil)
600 W. 70th St. Phone: (317)253-3441
Indianapolis, IN 46260 Constance L. Yaffe, Libn.
Founded: 1958. **Staff:** Prof 1. **Subjects:** Judaism, Jewish literature. **Holdings:** 3000 books. **Subscriptions:** 12 journals and other serials. **Services:** Library open to the public. **Remarks:** FAX: (317)259-6849.

★4152★
Congregation Beth Emeth - Judaica Library (Rel-Phil)
100 Academy Rd. Phone: (518)436-9761
Albany, NY 12208 Sylvia Braun, Libn.
Founded: 1975. **Subjects:** Judaica. **Holdings:** 2000 Books; archival items. **Subscriptions:** 6 journals and other serials; 2 newspapers. **Services:** Library open to the public.

★4153★
Congregation Beth Jacob-Beth Israel - Segal-Dion Family Library (Rel-Phil)
850 Evesham Rd. Phone: (609)751-1191
Cherry Hill, NJ 08003 Lester Hering, Rabbi
Founded: 1956. **Staff:** 1. **Subjects:** Judaica. **Holdings:** 5500 books. **Subscriptions:** 15 journals and other serials. **Services:** Library open to the public. **Formerly:** Congregation Beth Jacob - Goodwin Family Library, located in Merchantville, NJ.

★4154★
Congregation Beth Shalom - Rabbi Mordecai S. Halpern Memorial Library (Rel-Phil)
14601 W. Lincoln Rd. Phone: (313)547-7970
Oak Park, MI 48237 Eleanor Smith, Libn.
Founded: 1966. **Staff:** Prof 1. **Subjects:** Judaica. **Holdings:** 8000 books; 200 phonograph records; 200 Hebrew language story books. **Subscriptions:** 13 journals and other serials. **Services:** Library open to the public.

★4155★
Congregation B'nai Israel - Isidore Bloch Memorial Library (Rel-Phil)
4401 Indian School Rd., N.E. Phone: (505)266-0155
Albuquerque, NM 87110 Irving H. Held, Libn.
Staff: 2. **Subjects:** Judaica. **Special Collections:** Yiddish and Hebrew rare books. **Holdings:** 3600 books. **Services:** Copying; library open to the public with restrictions.

★4156★
Congregation Brith Shalom - Jewish Center - Morris P. Radov Library (Rel-Phil)
3207 State St.
Erie, PA 16508 Phone: (814)454-2431
Founded: 1950. **Staff:** Prof 5. **Subjects:** Talmud, Bible, Judaica, Midrash, rabbinics, mysticism, Kabbalah, Chasidism. **Holdings:** 2500 books. **Services:** Interlibrary loan; copying; library not open to the public. **Computerized Information Services:** Online system.

★4157★
Congregation Emanu-El - Ivan M. Stettenheim Library (Rel-Phil)
1 E. 65th St. Phone: (212)744-1400
New York, NY 10021-6596 Salome Cory
Founded: 1906. **Subjects:** Judaica. **Holdings:** 20,000 books. **Subscriptions:** 55 periodicals and newsletters.

★4158★
Congregation Emanu-El B'ne Jeshurun - Rabbi Dudley Weinberg Library (Rel-Phil)
2419 E. Kenwood Blvd. Phone: (414)964-4100
Milwaukee, WI 53211 Paula H. Fine, Libn.
Founded: 1930. **Staff:** Prof 1; Other 2. **Subjects:** Judaica, Talmud, general reference. **Special Collections:** Jewish children's books (1500). **Holdings:** 9000 books and other cataloged items. **Subscriptions:** 30 journals and other serials. **Services:** Interlibrary loan; copying; library open to the public by recommendation with identification.

Congregation of the Holy Name
See: **Dominican Sisters of San Rafael** (4949)

★4159★
Congregation Keneseth Israel - Library (Rel-Phil)
2227 Chew St. Phone: (215)435-9074
Allentown, PA 18104 Anne Stakelon, Libn.
Staff: Prof 1. **Subjects:** Judaica, religion, Biblical history, literature. **Special Collections:** Judaica (adult and juvenile). **Holdings:** 4700 books; recordings. **Subscriptions:** 15 journals and other serials. **Services:** Library open to the public.

★4160★
Congregation Kins of West Rogers Park - Jordan E. Feuer Library (Rel-Phil)
2800 W. North Shore Phone: (312)761-4000
Chicago, IL 60645 Bee Greenstein, Libn.
Founded: 1961. **Staff:** Prof 1; Other 5. **Subjects:** Religion and Hebraica. **Special Collections:** Judaica (180 phonograph records). **Holdings:** 4500 books; 60 filmstrips. **Subscriptions:** 13 journals and other serials. **Services:** Library open to the public. **Staff:** Ellen Friedman, Libn.

★4161★
Congregation Mikveh Israel - Archives (Hist)
Independence Mall East Phone: (215)922-5446
Philadelphia, PA 19106 Florence S. Finkel, Pres., K.K.M.I. Archv. Trust
Subjects: Origins and development of the Philadelphia Jewish community. **Holdings:** 40,000 minute books, inter- and intra-community correspondence, statistics on birth, marriage, and death, accounts, demographic information, genealogical source data, and other cataloged items. **Services:** Archives open to the public by appointment.

★4162★
Congregation Mishkan Israel - Library (Rel-Phil)
785 Ridge Rd. Phone: (203)288-3877
Hamden, CT 06517 Linda K. Cohen
Staff: 1. **Subjects:** Judaica. **Special Collections:** Congregation archives. **Holdings:** 5000 books. **Subscriptions:** 10 journals and other serials; 3 newspapers. **Services:** Interlibrary loan; library open to the public by arrangement.

★4163★
Congregation Mishkan Tefila - Harry and Anna Feinberg Library (Rel-Phil)
300 Hammond Pond Pkwy. Phone: (617)332-7770
Chestnut Hill, MA 02167 Louise Lieberman, Libn.
Founded: 1920. **Staff:** Prof 1; Other 2. **Subjects:** Judaica. **Holdings:** 4000 books. **Services:** Library open to the public by permission.

★4164★
Congregation Rodeph Shalom - Library (Rel-Phil)
1338 Mount Vernon St.
Philadelphia, PA 19123 Phone: (215)627-6747
Founded: 1802. **Staff:** Prof 1; Other 1. **Subjects:** Judaica; Jewish history and religion, especially American. **Special Collections:** Roberta Lee Magaziner Music Memorial (Jewish music: 340 books and pieces of sheet music). **Holdings:** 8720 books; 8 VF drawers of clippings and pamphlets. **Subscriptions:** 24 journals and other serials. **Services:** Interlibrary loan; library open to the public by appointment. **Remarks:** Branch library located at 8201 High School Rd., Elkins Park, PA. **Staff:** Yelena Elkind.

★4165★
Congregation Rodfei Zedek - J.S. Hoffman Memorial Library (Rel-Phil)
5200 Hyde Park Blvd. Phone: (312)752-2770
Chicago, IL 60615 Henrietta Schultz, Libn.
Founded: 1950. **Staff:** Prof 1; Other 1. **Subjects:** Judaica, Americana, Lincolniana. **Holdings:** 8000 books; phonograph records. **Subscriptions:** 30 journals and other serials. **Services:** Library open to the public.

★4166★
Congregation Shaarey Zedek - Library and Media Center (Rel-Phil)
27375 Bell Rd. Phone: (313)357-5544
Southfield, MI 48034 Joan Braun, Dir.
Staff: Prof 4. **Subjects:** Hebraica and Judaica, children's literature. **Special Collections:** Cantor Sonenklar Music Collection (75 items); Irwin T. Holtzman Israeli Literature (50 items). **Holdings:** 27,500 volumes; 20 VF drawers of pamphlets, clippings, pictures; 6 drawers of audio cassettes; 200 phonograph records; educational and archival materials. **Subscriptions:** 30 journals and other serials. **Services:** Copying; library open to the public with restrictions. **Automated Operations:** Computerized cataloging. **Staff:** Evelyn Schreier, Libn.; Sharon Cohen, Libn.

★4167★
Congregation Shalom - Sherman Pastor Memorial Library (Rel-Phil)
7630 N. Santa Monica Blvd. Phone: (414)352-9288
Milwaukee, WI 53217 Sally G. Weber, Libn.
Founded: 1970. **Staff:** Prof 1; Other 1. **Subjects:** Bible, Jewish history, Israel, Jewish biography and holidays. **Holdings:** 5000 books. **Subscriptions:** 6 journals and other serials; 3 newspapers. **Services:** Interlibrary loan; copying; library open to the public with restrictions.

★4168★
Congregation Shearith Israel - Sophie and Ivan Salomon Library Collection (Rel-Phil)
8 W. 70th St. Phone: (212)873-0300
New York, NY 10023 Dr. Janice Ovadiah, Exec.Dir.
Founded: 1956. **Staff:** Prof 1. **Subjects:** Judaica, Hebraica. **Special Collections:** American Jewish Archive. **Holdings:** 5500 books. **Subscriptions:** 15 journals and other serials. **Services:** Library open to the public by appointment.

★4169★
Congregation Solel - Library (Rel-Phil)
1301 Clavey Rd.
Highland Park, IL 60035 Phone: (708)433-3555
Founded: 1960. **Staff:** Prof 10. **Subjects:** Jewish history and philosophy, Bible, Talmud, Midrash, prophets, Israel. **Special Collections:** Art books; Hagaddot; Holocaust photographs and maps of towns destroyed. **Holdings:** 8000 books. **Subscriptions:** 28 journals and other serials. **Services:** Library open to the public. **Staff:** M.W. Hanig, Lib. Co-Chm.; N. Belrose, Lib. Co-Chm.

Congreso de los Diputados
See: **Spain - Congress of Deputies** (15559)

El Congreso Nacional de Asuntos Colegiales
See: **CONAC** (4108)

Congress Watch Library
See: **Public Citizen** (13472)

★4170★
Congressional Budget Office - Library (Bus-Fin)
House Office Bldg., Annex 2
2nd & D Sts., S.W. Phone: (202)226-2635
Washington, DC 20515 Jane T. Sessa, Libn.
Staff: Prof 2; Other 1. **Subjects:** Economics, federal budget, congressional budget process, economic policy. **Holdings:** 10,000 books; 800 bound periodical volumes; 1000 economics working papers; Serial Set, 86th Congress to present, on microfiche. **Subscriptions:** 354 journals and other serials. **Services:** Interlibrary loan; copying; library open to the public. **Automated Operations:** Computerized circulation. **Computerized Information Services:** DIALOG Information Services, NEXIS; CD-ROM. **Publications:** Serials received by the Congressional Budget Office Library, irregular. **Remarks:** FAX: (202)225-1484.

★4171★
Congressional Clearinghouse on the Future (Sci-Engr)
H2-555 House Annex 2 Phone: (202)226-3434
Washington, DC 20515 Elaine Wicker, Ed.
Subjects: Demographic, technological, and economic trends. **Holdings:** Figures not available. **Services:** Clearinghouse services available to members of Congress and congressional staff. **Publications:** What's Next (newsletter), quarterly; Emerging Issues - to members of Congress. **Remarks:** FAX: (202)225-0972. Publications are reprinted and available to the public for a fee through the Congressional Institute for the Future, 412 First St., Washington D.C. 20003. Telephone: (202)863-1700.

★4172★
Congressional Information Service, Inc. (Publ)
4520 East-West Hwy., Suite 800 Phone: (301)654-1550
Bethesda, MD 20814 Paul P. Massa, Pres.
Founded: 1970. **Subjects:** U.S. congressional, judiciary, and executive branches of government; federal regulations; statistics; library history; diplomatic history; history of science. **Holdings:** Congressional publications, 1789 to present; U.S. government statistical publications; selected statistical publications from U.S. sources other than the federal government; Supreme Court publications; U.S. administrative publications; statistical publications from major international intergovernmental organizations. **Services:** Service not open to the public. **Computerized Information Services:** DIALOG Information Services. **Special Indexes:** CIS/Index, monthly with quarterly and annual cumulation; American Statistics Index, annual with monthly and quarterly supplements; Statistical Reference Index, monthly with quarterly and annual cumulation; Index to International Statistics, monthly with quarterly and annual cumulation; CIS Federal Register Index, weekly with monthly and semiannual cumulations; ASI Microfiche Library; CIS Microfiche Library; SRI Microfiche Library; U.S. Supreme Court Records & Briefs on Microfiche; IIS Microfiche Library; retrospective CIS indexes with companion microfiche collections - U.S. Congressional Committee Prints, U.S. Serial Set, U.S. Congressional Committee Hearings, Unpublished U.S. Senate Committee Hearings; Index to the Code of Federal Regulations, annual; Index to Presidential Executive Orders & Proclamations (microfiche). **Remarks:** CIS created the first standard indexes to congressional publications and to U.S. Government statistics. It collects, analyzes, abstracts, and microfilms the publications indexed.

Congressional Information Service, Inc. - University Publications of America
See: **University Publications of America - Library** (19233)

★4173★
Congressional Quarterly, Inc. - Editorial Research Reports Library (Publ)
1414 22nd St., N.W. Phone: (202)887-8569
Washington, DC 20037 Kathleen E. Walton, Hd.Libn.
Staff: Prof 3; Other 3. **Subjects:** U.S. Congress, legislation, politics, economics, foreign relations, history. **Special Collections:** Archival collection of all Congressional Quarterly, Inc. and Congressional Quarterly Press publications; political clipping file (65 newspapers clipped). **Holdings:** 8000 books; 100 bound periodical volumes; Congressional Information Service (CIS), 1973 to present, on microfiche; New York Times, 1960 to present, on microfilm. **Subscriptions:** 210 journals and other serials; 65 newspapers. **Services:** Interlibrary loan; copying; SDI; library open to CQ subscribers by appointment. **Automated Operations:** Computerized cataloging. **Computerized Information Services:** DIALOG Information Services, NEXIS, Washington Alert Service, DataTimes, Federal Election Commission Direct Access Program, VU/TEXT Information Services, NewsNet, Inc., Dow Jones News/Retrieval; Dialnet (electronic mail service). **Publications:** Library News, monthly - for internal distribution only. **Special Indexes:** CQ Index. **Remarks:** FAX: (202)223-0843. **Staff:** Michael Williams, Libn.

Congressional Research Service
See: **Library of Congress** (9111)

U.S. Conn Library
See: **Wayne State College** (20116)

★4174★
Connaught Laboratories, Ltd. - Balmer Neilly Library (Med, Biol Sci)
1755 Steeles Ave., W. Phone: (416)667-2662
Willowdale, ON, Canada M2R 3T4 Hugh McNaught, Libn.
Founded: 1921. **Staff:** Prof 1; Other 2. **Subjects:** Immunology, virology, bacteriology. **Special Collections:** Archives. **Holdings:** 23,000 volumes. **Subscriptions:** 250 journals and other serials. **Services:** Interlibrary loan; copying; library open to the public by appointment. **Computerized Information Services:** DIALOG Information Services, CAN/OLE, The Financial Post DataGroup, Info Globe, Infomart Online. **Publications:** Acquisitions List, quarterly - for internal distribution only. **Remarks:** FAX: (416)667-2850.

★4175★
Connecticut Aeronautical Historical Association - New England Air Museum Reference Library (Hist)
Bradley International Airport Phone: (203)623-3305
Windsor Locks, CT 06096 John W. Ramsay, Dir., Hist. & Info.
Founded: 1965. **Staff:** Prof 2. **Subjects:** Aeronautical history. **Special Collections:** Sikorsky Collection; Burnelli Collection; early New England aviation history. **Holdings:** 3500 books; 45,000 bound and unbound periodicals; 2500 technical manuals; 20,000 photographs and slides; art work; microforms. **Subscriptions:** 1 journals and other serials; 1 newspapers. **Services:** Copying (limited); library open to the public by appointment. **Computerized Information Services:** Internal database. **Publications:** New England Air Museum Newsletter, quarterly. **Staff:** Harvey Lippencott, Archv.

★4176★
Connecticut Agricultural Experiment Station - Osborne Library (Agri, Biol Sci)
123 Huntington St.
Box 1106 Phone: (203)789-7265
New Haven, CT 06504 Paul Gough, Libn.
Founded: 1875. **Staff:** 1. **Subjects:** Botany, chemistry, entomology, soils. **Special Collections:** U.S. Department of Agriculture documents and publications depository. **Holdings:** 23,050 volumes. **Subscriptions:** 401 journals and other serials. **Services:** Interlibrary loan; copying; library open to qualified researchers. **Computerized Information Services:** DIALOG Information Services. **Remarks:** FAX: (203)789-7232.

★4177★
Connecticut Audubon Society - Fairfield Nature Center - Library (Biol Sci)
2325 Burr St. Phone: (203)259-6305
Fairfield, CT 06430 Sherman Kent, Exec.Dir.
Founded: 1898. **Subjects:** Ornithology, botany, herpetology, mammalogy, natural history. **Holdings:** 5000 books; 2500 ornithology journals. **Services:** Library open to members and volunteers for reference use only. **Remarks:** FAX: (203)254-7673.

★4178★
Connecticut College - Charles E. Shain Library - Special Collections (Hum)
Mohegan Ave. Phone: (203)439-2650
New London, CT 06320 Mary Kent, Spec.Coll.Libn.
Staff: 1. **Subjects:** Literature, history, art history, history of books and printing, children's literature, philosophy. **Special Collections:** Coudert Collection of Oriental Art (500 volumes); Downs Collection of fish and angling (1400 volumes); Helen O. Gildersleeve Collection of 19th and 20th century children's literature (2500 volumes); Simmons Collection of John Masefield; Palmer Collection of Americana, history, and theater (1750 volumes); Wyman Ballad Collection (350 volumes); first editions of Faulkner, Frost, O'Neill, Stein, Yeats; manuscripts and papers of Prudence Crandall, Alice Hamilton, Richard Mansfield, Belle Moskowitz, Eugene O'Neill, Frances Perkins, Lydia Sigourney; New London County History (200 volumes); Susanne K. Langer Collection (500 volumes); William Meredith Collection (100 volumes); Carl and Alma Wies Collection of the Book Arts (400 volumes); Connecticut College Archives. **Holdings:** 12,500 books; 770 bound periodical volumes; 830 little magazines. **Services:** Collections open to the public on limited schedule during academic year, otherwise by appointment. **Automated Operations:** Computerized cataloging and acquisitions. **Computerized Information Services:** OCLC, DIALOG Information Services, BRS Information Technologies. **Networks/Consortia:** Member of NELINET, Inc., CTW Consortium. **Special Catalogs:** Palmer Collection Catalog (card). CTW (Connecticut College, Trinity College (Hartford), Weslegan University). **Remarks:** FAX: (203)442-0761.

★4179★
Connecticut College - Greer Music Library (Mus)
New London, CT 06320-4196 Phone: (203)439-2711
Carolyn Johnson, Mus.Libn.
Founded: 1969. **Staff:** Prof 1; Other 1. **Subjects:** Music. **Special Collections:** American tunebooks of the 19th century (100); Richard C. Shelley Jazz and Blues Recordings Collection (2770 phonograph records); John H. Hilliar Collection of Opera Recordings (1500 phonograph records). **Holdings:** 6000 books; 900 bound periodical volumes; 14,000 sound recordings; 10,000 scores; 250 magnetic tapes. **Subscriptions:** 96 journals and other serials. **Services:** Interlibrary loan; copying; library open to the public for reference use. **Automated Operations:** Computerized cataloging, circulation, and acquisitions (NOTIS). **Computerized Information Services:** OCLC. **Networks/Consortia:** Member of NELINET, Inc., CTW Consortium. **Remarks:** Alternate telephone number(s): (203)439-2651.

★4180★
Connecticut Electric Railway Association, Inc. - Library Department (Trans)
Box 360
East Windsor, CT 06088 Phone: (203)627-6540
Founded: 1940. **Staff:** 1. **Subjects:** Transportation, electric railways, trolley data. **Holdings:** 2005 books; 370 bound periodical volumes; Interstate Commerce Commission reports; pictures; magazines; maps; time-tables; builders' plans. **Services:** Collection open to the public by special request. **Remarks:** FAX: (203)627-6510.

Connecticut Historical Commission - Prudence Crandall Museum
See: **Prudence Crandall Museum** (4409)

★4181★
Connecticut Historical Society - Library (Hist)
1 Elizabeth St. Phone: (203)236-5621
Hartford, CT 06105 Everett C. Wilkie, Jr., Hd., Libn.
Founded: 1825. **Staff:** Prof 7; Other 5. **Subjects:** New England and Connecticut history and genealogy, colonial sources. **Special Collections:** Connecticut imprints, city directories, maps and atlases, photographs and prints, almanacs, children's books, sermons, broadsides, trade catalogs, historical and genealogical manuscripts, account books, and diaries. **Holdings:** 100,000 books; 400 bound periodical volumes; 2 million manuscripts; 1500 volumes of 18th and early 19th century newspapers. **Subscriptions:** 62 journals and other serials. **Services:** Copying; library open to the public. **Automated Operations:** Computerized cataloging. **Computerized Information Services:** OCLC. Performs searches on fee basis. Contact Person: Everett C. Wilkie, Jr., Rare Bks. & Mss.Cur., 236-0861. **Networks/Consortia:** Member of NELINET, Inc. **Publications:** Bulletin, quarterly; annual reports; monographs and occasional publications. **Special Indexes:** Connecticut imprints by date and place of publication; chronological index of manuscripts; index to Connecticut Courant, 1764-1820. **Remarks:** FAX: (203)236-2664. **Staff:** Ruth Blair, Mss.Cat.; Gary Wait, Bk.Cat.; Judith Johnson, Ref.Libn.; Alesandra Schmidt, Ref.Libn.

The Connecticut Horticultural Society Library
See: **Wethersfield Historical Society - Old Academy Museum Library** (20354)

★4182★
Connecticut Missionary Society - Connecticut Conference Archives (Rel-Phil)
125 Sherman St. Phone: (203)233-5564
Hartford, CT 06105 Allen F. Tinkham, Archv.
Staff: Prof 1. **Subjects:** United Church of Christ churches in Connecticut. **Special Collections:** Historical records on its Connecticut churches; letters and journals of Missionaries of Connecticut Missionary Society, 1800 to present; file on Connecticut Congregational clergy. **Holdings:** 1500 books; 40 bound periodical volumes; uncataloged books and tracts. **Services:** Archives open to the public with restrictions.

★4183★
Connecticut Mutual Life Insurance Company - Corporate Library (Bus-Fin)
140 Garden St. Phone: (203)987-2473
Hartford, CT 06154 Andrea Garbus, Libn.
Founded: 1957. **Staff:** Prof 1; Other 2. **Subjects:** Life insurance, business, law. **Special Collections:** Company archives; company publications. **Holdings:** 6000 volumes; 24 VF drawers of archival material. **Subscriptions:** 111 journals; 180 serials. **Services:** Interlibrary loan; copying; SDI; services open to the public at librarian's discretion. **Computerized Information Services:** DIALOG Information Services, BRS Information Technologies, VU/TEXT Information Services, Dow Jones News/Retrieval. **Publications:** Periodical Review, weekly; Key Issues Report, weekly - all for internal distribution only. **Remarks:** FAX: (203)987-6800. **Staff:** Winifred Bell, Consultant; Jeanne Ford, Asst.Libn.

★4184★
Connecticut Region Education Council - Metro Media Library (Educ)
1 Barnard La. Phone: (203)242-8883
Bloomfield, CT 06002 Rebecca Haller
Staff: 1. **Subjects:** Public school curriculum. **Holdings:** Films; videos. **Services:** Copying; library open to the public for rentals.

★4185★
Connecticut River Watershed Council - Library (Env-Cons)
125 Combs Rd.
Easthampton, MA 01027 Phone: (413)584-0057
Staff: Prof 3; Other 2. **Subjects:** Water resources, water law, Connecticut River studies. **Holdings:** 1000 books. **Services:** Copying; library open to the public for reference use only.

★4186★
Connecticut Society of Genealogy - Library (Hist)
P.O. Box 435 Phone: (203)569-0002
Glastonbury, CT 06033 Jacquelyn L. Ricker, Exec.Sec.
Founded: 1968. **Staff:** 2. **Subjects:** Genealogy. **Holdings:** Books; manuscripts; microfiche; microfilm. **Services:** Copying; library open to the public. **Remarks:** Library located at 175 Maple St., East Hartford, CT 06118.

★4187★
Connecticut State Board of Education - J.M. Wright Technical School - Library (Educ)
Box 1416
Scalzi Park Phone: (203)324-7363
Stamford, CT 06904 Mrs. Omaa Chukwurah
Founded: 1919. **Staff:** 1. **Subjects:** Automobile repair, auto body repair, plumbing, carpentry, hairdressing, cosmetology, drafting, electricity, electronics, fashion technology, computer technology, machine tool and die, licensed practical nursing, certified nursing aide, graphics, culinary arts. **Special Collections:** Professional books relative to teaching, especially vocational subjects. **Holdings:** 5356 books; 269 pamphlets; 400 pamphlets; 252 files of magazines; 8 VF drawers of monographs, excerpts, catalogs. **Subscriptions:** 82 journals and other serials. **Services:** Interlibrary loan; library not open to the public. **Computerized Information Services:** Internal databases. **Remarks:** FAX: (203)324-1196.

★4188★
Connecticut State Department on Aging - Library (Soc Sci)
175 Main St.
Hartford, CT 06106 Phone: (203)566-7728
Staff: Prof 1; Other 1. **Subjects:** Long term care, housing, demographics. **Holdings:** 1600 books; 10 drawers of National Clearinghouse on Aging reports on microfiche. **Subscriptions:** 30 journals and other serials. **Services:** Copying; library open to the public by appointment for reference use.

★4189★
Connecticut (State) Department of Health Services - Stanley H. Osborn Medical Library
150 Washington St.
Hartford, CT 06106
Founded: 1923. **Subjects:** Public health, medicine. **Special Collections:** Connecticut statutes and legislation. **Holdings:** 50 books; 200 Public Health Service publications. **Remarks:** Currently inactive.

★4190★
Connecticut State Department of Higher Education - Research and Information Services Division - Library (Educ)
61 Woodland St.
Hartford, CT 06105 Phone: (203)566-4645
Founded: 1982. **Subjects:** Higher education - enrollment, degree production, employment, policy development, budgeting. **Holdings:** 2000 volumes. **Automated Operations:** Computerized cataloging, acquisitions, serials, and circulation. **Computerized Information Services:** VAX-VMS (internal database); electronic mail service. **Remarks:** FAX: (203)566-7865.

★4191★
Connecticut State Department of Mental Retardation, Region 2 - Probus Club Resource Center (Med)
270 Farmington Ave., Suite 260 Phone: (203)679-8406
Farmington, CT 06032-1909 Greg Damato, Dir.Trng. & Staff Dev.
Founded: 1974. **Subjects:** Mental retardation, developmental disabilities, behavior modification, team functioning, emotional disturbance, physical handicaps. **Special Collections:** Gross motor and fine motor skills. **Holdings:** 1000 books; 200 bound periodical volumes; 300 other cataloged items; 40 AV programs. **Subscriptions:** 3 journals and other serials. **Services:** Center open to the public. **Remarks:** FAX: (203)674-9808.

★4192★
Connecticut (State) Judicial Department - Law Library at Bridgeport (Law)
Court House
1061 Main St., 7th Fl. Phone: (203)579-6237
Bridgeport, CT 06604 Willie E. Jackson, Supv. Law Libn.
Founded: 1877. **Staff:** Prof 2; Other 1. **Subjects:** Law - admiralty, bailments, debtor-creditor, evidence, pleadings, negligence, zoning, wills and estates; Connecticut legislation, 1980 to present. **Special Collections:** Connecticut Collection, colonial days to the present. **Holdings:** 40,000 books. **Subscriptions:** 92 law journals. **Services:** Interlibrary loan; library open to the public for reference use only. **Computerized Information Services:** WESTLAW; CD-ROM. **Remarks:** Branches of the State Law Library System are located in Stamford, Danbury, Hartford, New Haven, Waterbury, Middletown, Rockville, Litchfield, Putnam, Willimantic, Norwich, and New London. **Remarks:** FAX: (203)579-6512. **Staff:** Louise Baldyga, Libn.II.

★4193★
Connecticut (State) Judicial Department - Law Library at Hartford (Law)
95 Washington St. Phone: (203)566-3900
Hartford, CT 06106 Lawrence G. Cheeseman, Supv. Law Libn.
Founded: 1854. **Staff:** Prof 1. **Subjects:** Law. **Holdings:** 35,000 volumes. **Subscriptions:** 55 journals and other serials. **Services:** Interlibrary loan; copying; library open to the public. **Computerized Information Services:** Internal database. **Remarks:** FAX: (203)566-7825.

★4194★
Connecticut (State) Judicial Department - Law Library at Litchfield (Law)
Court House, West St.
P.O. Box 428 Phone: (203)567-0598
Litchfield, CT 06759 Peter M. Jenkins, Libn.
Founded: 1976. **Staff:** 1. **Subjects:** Law. **Holdings:** 10,000 volumes. **Subscriptions:** 130 journals and other serials. **Services:** Copying; library open to the public.

★4195★
Connecticut (State) Judicial Department - Law Library at New Haven (Law)
County Courthouse
235 Church St. Phone: (203)789-7889
New Haven, CT 06510 Martha J. Sullivan, Supv. Law Libn.
Founded: 1848. **Staff:** Prof 2; Other 1. **Subjects:** Law. **Holdings:** 50,000 volumes. **Subscriptions:** 320 journals and other serials. **Services:** Copying; library open to the public. **Remarks:** FAX: (203)789-7889. **Staff:** Ann Christmann.

★4196★
Connecticut (State) Judicial Department - Law Library at Putnam (Law)
Court House
155 Church St. Phone: (203)928-3716
Putnam, CT 06260 Donna R. Izbicki, Libn.
Staff: Prof 1. **Subjects:** Law. **Holdings:** 13,000 books. **Subscriptions:** 150 journals and other serials. **Services:** Copying; library open to the public.

★4197★
Connecticut (State) Judicial Department - Law Library at Rockville (Law)
Court House
Brooklyn St. Phone: (203)872-3824
Rockville, CT 06066 Roseann Canny, Libn.
Staff: 1. **Subjects:** Law. **Holdings:** 15,000 books. **Services:** Interlibrary loan; copying; library open to the public.

★4198★
Connecticut (State) Judicial Department - Law Library at Stamford (Law)
Court House
123 Hoyt St. Phone: (203)359-1114
Stamford, CT 06905 Jonathan C. Stock, Supv. Law Libn.
Staff: Prof 2; Other 1. **Subjects:** Law. **Holdings:** 24,914 books. **Services:** Interlibrary loan; copying; library open to the public. **Publications:** Connecticut State Library-Law Library/Stamford (newsletter), quarterly - to attorneys and corporations. **Special Catalogs:** Subject Catalog (card, book). **Remarks:** FAX: (203)359-1114. **Staff:** Caroline Faas, Law Libn. II.

★4199★
Connecticut (State) Judicial Department - Law Library at Waterbury (Law)
Court House
300 Grand St. Phone: (203)754-2644
Waterbury, CT 06702 Mary B. Fuller, Libn.
Staff: 1. **Subjects:** Law. **Holdings:** 38,000 volumes. **Subscriptions:** 34 journals and other serials. **Services:** Library open to the public. **Remarks:** FAX: (203)754-2644. Contains the holdings of the Waterbury Bar Library.

★4200★
Connecticut State Library (Info Sci)
231 Capitol Ave. Phone: (203)566-4777
Hartford, CT 06106 Richard G. Akeroyd, Jr., State Libn.
Founded: 1854. **Staff:** Prof 43; Other 94. **Subjects:** Connecticut, local history and genealogy, state and federal law, politics and government, legislative reference. **Special Collections:** Barbour Index of Connecticut Vital Records to 1850; indexes to original sources of genealogical data; Connecticut newspapers, town documents; State Archives (includes records of Judicial Dept., Governor's Office, General Assembly, and several executive branch agencies); local government records; non-government records from individuals, families, businesses, and organizations; Connecticut legislative proceedings and hearings; early automobile catalogs; early Connecticut manufacturers' catalogs; almanacs. **Holdings:** 700,000 books; 30,000 bound periodical volumes; 28,000 cubic feet of archival records; newspaper clipping files, 1927 to present; 6000 reels of microfilm; 6000 maps; regional federal documents depository of 1.5 million documents; state documents depository of 50,000 state documents. **Subscriptions:** 1100 journals and other serials; 100 newspapers. **Services:** Interlibrary loan; copying; library open to the public. **Automated Operations:** Computerized public access catalog, acquisitions, cataloging, and ILL. **Computerized Information Services:** OCLC, DIALOG Information Services, BRS Information Technologies, RLIN, WILSONLINE, LEXIS, WESTLAW; internal database. **Networks/Consortia:** Member of NELINET, Inc. **Publications:** Checklist of Publications of Connecticut State Agencies; Agency Newsletter, bimonthly. **Special Indexes:** Index to Connecticut Legislative Journals, 1911 to present. **Remarks:** FAX: (203)566-8940. **Staff:** Zena Kovack, Assoc. State Libn. for Progs.; Patricia L. Owens, Hd., Lib.Serv.Div.; Mark Jones, State Archv.; Ken Rieke, Hd., Rec.Ctr.; Eunice DiBella, Pub.Rec.Adm.; Theodore O. Wohlsen, Hd., Hist. & Geneal.; Jane Ouderkirk, Hd., Pat.Serv.Div.; Leon Shatkin, Hd., ILL; Lynne Newell, Hd., Pres.Off.; Mary Merrill, Dir., Middletown Lib.Serv.Ctr.; Sharon Brettschneider, Dir., Willimantic Lib.Serv.Ctr.

★4201★
Connecticut State Library (Aud-Vis)
Middletown Library Service Center
786 S. Main St. Phone: (203)344-2645
Middletown, CT 06457 Mary Engels, Supv.
Staff: 3. **Special Collections:** Travel and recreation, children's films. **Holdings:** 2200 16mm film titles; children's, nonfiction, professional librarianship videos (800 titles). **Services:** Service available to public libraries, state institutions, state agencies, organizations, clubs. **Automated Operations:** Computerized circulation. **Remarks:** Alternate telephone number(s): 344-2002. FAX: (203)344-2537.

★4202★
Connecticut State Library - Law Library at Danbury (Law)
Superior Courthouse
146 White St. Phone: (203)797-2731
Danbury, CT 06810 Cheryl S. Bennin
Founded: 1919. **Staff:** Prof 1. **Subjects:** Law. **Special Collections:** Government legislative histories collection; Connecticut reference materials collection. **Holdings:** 19,400 books; 50 bound periodical volumes; 17,790 microfiche. **Subscriptions:** 20 journals and other serials; 2 newspapers. **Services:** Library open to the public. **Computerized Information Services:** CD-ROM (Connecticut Casebase). **Remarks:** FAX: (203)797-2731.

★4203★
Connecticut State Library - Library for the Blind and Physically Handicapped (Aud-Vis)
198 West St. Phone: (203)566-2151
Rocky Hill, CT 06067 Carol A. Taylor, Dir.
Founded: 1968. **Staff:** Prof 2; Other 16. **Holdings:** 175,000 braille and talking books. **Services:** Interlibrary loan; library open to visually impaired or physically handicapped residents of Connecticut. **Automated Operations:** Computerized serials and circulation. **Special Catalogs:** CTC Connecticut Cassettes: A catalog of locally produced cassette books available from the Connecticut State Library for the Blind and Physically Handicapped. **Remarks:** Service may be conducted by mail or telephone. Books and playback equipment are sent postage free. Toll-free telephone number(s): (800)842-4516. **Remarks:** FAX: (203)566-6669.

★4204★
Connecticut State Museum of Natural History - Library (Biol Sci)
University of Connecticut
U-23 Phone: (203)486-4460
Storrs, CT 06269-3023 Carl W. Rettenmeyer, Musm.Dir.
Founded: 1983. **Subjects:** Birds, vertebrates, natural history. **Holdings:** 3000 books; field guides. **Services:** Interlibrary loan; copying; library open to the public by appointment. **Remarks:** FAX: (203)486-6364.

★4205★
Connecticut State Office of Policy and Management - Library (Plan)
80 Washington St. Phone: (203)566-2800
Hartford, CT 06106 Ronald G. Fontaine, Libn.
Founded: 1978. **Staff:** Prof 1. **Subjects:** Energy, state budgets, planning. **Holdings:** Figures not available. **Services:** Interlibrary loan; library open to the public. **Automated Operations:** Computerized public access catalog. **Remarks:** FAX: (203)566-6295.

★4206★
Connecticut Valley Historical Museum - Library and Archives (Hist)
194 State St. Phone: (413)732-3080
Springfield, MA 01103 Guy A. McLain, Hd., Lib. & Archv.Coll.
Founded: 1988. **Staff:** Prof 4; Other 2. **Subjects:** Connecticut Valley history, Springfield history 1636 to present, New England genealogy, Springfield business history. **Special Collections:** Roger Putnam papers (1920-1972; 96 linear feet); 17th-20th century Springfield and Connecticut Valley manuscripts; Ames Sword Co. Collection (1829-1885; 8 linear feet); Massachusetts Mutual Life Insurance Company Collection (1851 to present; 100 linear feet); Monarch Insurance Co. Collection (1900 to present; 85 linear feet); Springfield Fire and Marine Insurance Co. Collection (1870-1960; 80 linear feet); John Pynchon account books (1651-1713). **Holdings:** 23,000 books; 2000 bound periodical volumes; 25,000 photographs; 1600 linear feet of archival records; 300 feet of vertical files, atlases, and maps; 5000 microform records. **Subscriptions:** 40 journals and other serials; 15 newspapers. **Services:** Copying; department open to the public. **Automated Operations:** Computerized cataloging. **Publications:** Pathfinders for Italian, Jewish, Irish, Polish, and Afro-Afro American genealogy; archives guides for all archives collections. **Special Indexes:** Springfield History Index (card). **Formed by the merger of:** Springfield City Library - Genealogy and Local History Department and Connecticut Valley Historical Museum. **Staff:** Margaret Humberston, Libn.; Valerie McQuillan, Libn.; Renay Jihad, Libn.; Cindy Murphy, Libn.

★4207★
Connecticut Valley Hospital - Hallock Medical Library (Med)
Box 351 Phone: (203)344-2304
Middletown, CT 06457 Pauline Kruk, Med.Libn.
Founded: 1946. **Staff:** Prof 1. **Subjects:** Psychiatry, neurology, medicine. **Holdings:** 4500 books; 2500 bound periodical volumes. **Subscriptions:** 77 journals and other serials. **Services:** Interlibrary loan; library open to medical and psychology students and physicians.

★4208★
Connecticut Valley Hospital - Willis Royle Library (Med)
Merrit Hall
Tynan Dr. Phone: (203)344-2449
Middletown, CT 06457 Storm Somers
Founded: 1980. **Staff:** Prof 1. **Subjects:** Self-improvement, recreation, life skills. **Special Collections:** Audio collection (110 recordings); living and coping skills resource collection (180 audio visual items, booklets, curriculum guides, and games). **Holdings:** 3000 books. **Subscriptions:** 25 journals and other serials; 3 newspapers. **Services:** Interlibrary loan; library not open to the public.

★4209★
John T. Conner Center for U.S./U.S.S.R. Reconciliation - Library (Rel-Phil)
122 North St. Phone: (317)743-7483
West Lafayette, IN 47906 Donald L. Nead, Adm.
Founded: 1983. **Staff:** 1. **Subjects:** Religious life in the U.S.S.R. **Holdings:** 175 volumes. **Services:** Library open to the public by appointment.

★4210★
Conner Prairie - Research Department Library (Hist)
13400 Allisonville Rd.
Noblesville, IN 46060 Phone: (317)776-6000
Founded: 1964. **Staff:** Prof 2. **Subjects:** History of the old Northwest, Jacksonian America, central Indiana to 1850 - culture, architecture, ideas, institutions. **Special Collections:** William Conner papers (6 linear feet). **Holdings:** 4500 books; maps; newspapers; journals; account books; local government documents, hardcopy and microfilm. **Subscriptions:** 25 journals and other serials; 30 newspapers. **Services:** Library open to the public on approval. **Staff:** Timothy R. Crumrin, Hist./Archv.

Connexxus Womens Center
See: **June Mazer Lesbian Library** (9862)

Charles J. Connick Stained Glass Archives
See: **Boston Public Library - Fine Arts Department** (1992)

Cyril Connolly Library
See: **University of Tulsa - McFarlin Library** (19466)

★4211★
Conoco, Inc. - Law Library (Law)
600 N. Dairy Ashford St. Phone: (713)293-3056
Houston, TX 77079-1175 Pamela R. Jenkins, Lib.Asst.
Staff: 1. **Subjects:** U.S. law - cases and statutes, oil and gas law, international law. **Special Collections:** Backfile of Federal Register and Code of Federal Regulations (complete set on microfiche). **Holdings:** 30,000 books; 500 bound periodical volumes; legal department memos and briefs. **Subscriptions:** 125 journals and other serials; 12 newspapers. **Services:** Interlibrary loan; copying; SDI; center open with librarian's permission. **Automated Operations:** Computerized cataloging. **Computerized Information Services:** LEXIS, NEXIS, WESTLAW, DIALOG Information Services, Dow Jones News/Retrieval, OCLC. **Networks/Consortia:** Member of AMIGOS Bibliographic Council, Inc. **Publications:** Acquisitions list/newsletter - for internal distribution only. **Remarks:** FAX: (713)293-1054.

★4212★
Conoco, Inc. - Research and Engineering - Technical Information Services (Energy)
1000 S. Pine
PO Box 1267 Phone: (405)767-2334
Ponca City, OK 74603 Patsy S. Hoskins, Supv.
Founded: 1952. **Staff:** Prof 1; Other 3. **Subjects:** Petroleum, chemicals. **Holdings:** 11,000 books; 20,000 bound periodical volumes; 3000 pamphlets; 100,000 patents; 3000 reports in VF; API Abstracts, Petroleum Abstracts (University of Tulsa), Chemical Abstracts, U.S. Patents, 1952 to present, and U.S. Patent Gazette on microfilm; 30,500 Proprietary Research Reports (online). **Subscriptions:** 360 journals and other serials. **Services:** Interlibrary loan; copying; contracted SDI; contracted translations; services open to the public on request. **Computerized Information Services:** PFDS Online, DIALOG Information Services, NLM, STN International; internal database. **Publications:** Library Bulletin, semimonthly. **Remarks:** FAX: (405)767-2182. **Staff:** John F. Foell, Sr.Info.Spec.

Frances R. Conole Archive of Sound Recordings
See: **State University of New York at Binghamton - Special Collections** (15731)

Joseph Conrad Society
See: **The Polish Library** (13182)

Conrad Technical Library
See: **U.S. Army - TRADOC - Signal Center & Fort Gordon** (17023)

★4213★
Consad Research Corporation - Library (Soc Sci, Plan)
121 N. Highland Ave. Phone: (412)363-5500
Pittsburgh, PA 15206 Sheila Steger, Libn.
Founded: 1963. **Staff:** 1. **Subjects:** Social science methodology, statistics, urban planning, drug abuse, occupational safety and health. **Holdings:** 10,000 books; 10,000 reports. **Subscriptions:** 54 journals and other serials. **Services:** Library open to the public with restrictions. **Computerized Information Services:** DIALOG Information Services. **Remarks:** FAX: (412)363-5509.

Consciousness Village - Inspiration University
See: **Inspiration University** (7861)

Conseil Canadien de Developpement Social
See: **Canadian Council on Social Development** (2919)

Conseil Canadien des Normes
See: **Standards Council of Canada** (15641)

Conseil Canadien des Relations du Travail
See: **Canada - Labour Relations Board** (2762)

Conseil Consultatif Canadien sur la Situation de la Femme
See: **Canada - Canadian Advisory Council on the Status of Women** (2668)

Conseil Economique du Canada
See: **Canada - Economic Council of Canada** (2693)

Conseil Oecumenique des Eglises
See: **World Council of Churches** (20613)

Conseil Oleicole International
See: **International Olive Oil Council** (8164)

Conseil de la Radiodiffusion et des Telecommunications Canadiennes
See: **Canada - Canadian Radio-Television and Telecommunications Commission** (2671)

★4214★
Conseil des Universites du Quebec - Centre de Documentation (Educ)
2700 Laurier Blvd.
Tour Frontenac, 8th Fl. Phone: (418)646-5821
Ste. Foy, PQ, Canada G1V 2L8 Michele Lavoie, Doc.
Founded: 1970. **Staff:** Prof 1. **Subjects:** Higher education, science, technology. **Special Collections:** Canadian university statistics (Statistics Canada); Quebec university statistics; Quebec and Ontario university catalogs. **Holdings:** 7000 books; 120 bound periodical volumes. **Services:** Interlibrary loan; copying; center open to the public. **Automated Operations:** Computerized cataloging. **Computerized Information Services:** UTLAS. **Publications:** Acquisitions list, monthly - limited distribution. **Remarks:** FAX: (418)643-0932.

Consejo Oleicola Internacional
See: **International Olive Oil Council** (8164)

Conselho Nacional de Desenvolvimento Cientifico e Tecnologico - Instituto Brasileiro de Informacao em Ciencia e Tecnologia
See: **Brazil - National Council of Scientific and Technological Development - Brazilian Institute for Information in Science and Technology** (2095)

★4215★
The Conservancy, Inc. - Conservancy Nature Center Library (Biol Sci)
1450 Merrihue Dr. Phone: (813)262-0304
Naples, FL 33942 William G. Harding, Dir. of Ed.
Founded: 1982. **Staff:** 2. **Subjects:** Natural history of Florida, marine science, Florida and tropical botany, ornithology, ecology, conservation, paleontology. **Holdings:** 3000 books; 4 VF drawers; 11 cases; 500 other cataloged items. **Subscriptions:** 7 journals and other serials. **Services:** Library open to the public for reference use only.

★4216★
Conservation Council of Ontario - Library (Env-Cons)
489 College St., Suite 506
Toronto, ON, Canada M6G 1A5 Phone: (416)969-9637
Founded: 1952. **Subjects:** Conservation, water quality, parks, land use planning, energy, agriculture, forestry, air quality, community action, economics, sustainable development, environmental law, mining, natural heritage, northern development, population, transportation, waste management, wildlife. **Holdings:** 1000 books. **Subscriptions:** 30 journals and other serials. **Services:** Copying; library open to the public by appointment. **Computerized Information Services:** Internal datases. **Publications:** List of publications - available on request. **Remarks:** FAX: (416)960-8053.

★4217★
Conservation Districts Foundation - Davis Conservation Library (Env-Cons)
408 E. Main St.
Box 776 Phone: (713)332-3402
League City, TX 77574-0776 Ruth Chenhall, Educ.-Info.Spec.
Founded: 1962. **Staff:** Prof 1. **Subjects:** Conservation, natural resources, soil, water, agriculture, forests, city and town planning, conservation of wild life, water resources development, ecology. **Special Collections:** History of soil and water conservation districts movement in America. **Holdings:** 1500 books; 55 bound periodical volumes; 300 pamphlets; 50 VF drawers of history of the National Association of Conservation Districts and conservation. **Subscriptions:** 16 journals and other serials. **Services:** Interlibrary loan; copying; library open to the public by appointment. **Remarks:** FAX: (713)332-5259.

Conservation Foundation
See: **World Wildlife Fund-U.S.** (20636)

★4218★
Conservation and Renewable Energy Inquiry and Referral Service - Library (Energy)
Advanced Sciences, Inc.
2000 N. 15th St., Suite 407 Phone: (703)243-4900
Arlington, VA 22201 Jon Findley, Proj.Mgr.
Founded: 1976. **Staff:** Prof 9; Other 3. **Subjects:** Energy conservation, renewable energy, solar heating and cooling, solar water heating. **Holdings:** 1200 books and pamphlets; 2000 reports; 5700 articles; 2000 clippings. **Subscriptions:** 70 journals and other serials. **Services:** Library not open to the public. **Automated Operations:** Computerized cataloging. **Computerized Information Services:** DIALOG Information Services, Integrated Technical Information System (ITIS). **Publications:** Pamphlets; fact sheets; bibliographies - all available on request. **Remarks:** Toll-free telephone number(s): (800)523-2929. The Conservation and Renewable Energy Inquiry and Referral Service operates under contract to the U.S. Department of Energy.

★4219★
Conservatoire d'Art Dramatique de Quebec - Bibliotheque (Theater)
31, Mont-Carmel Phone: (418)643-9351
Quebec, PQ, Canada G1R 4A6 Georgette Laki, Bibliothecaire
Staff: Prof 1; Other 2. **Subjects:** All aspects of the theater, dramatic criticism. **Holdings:** 12,000 books; 320 bound periodical volumes; 4000 slides in 80 series; 4000 unbound periodicals. **Subscriptions:** 20 journals and other serials. **Services:** Interlibrary loan; library open to the public for consultation with limited borrowing. **Special Indexes:** Index to number of characters in each play (card). **Remarks:** All holdings are in French.

★4220★
Conservatoire de Musique de Montreal - Centre de Documentation (Mus)
100, rue Notre-Dame est Phone: (514)873-7481
Montreal, PQ, Canada H2Y 1C1 Nicole Boisclair, Directrice
Founded: 1942. **Staff:** Prof 1; Other 4. **Subjects:** Music. **Special Collections:** Emil Cooper; Jean Deslauriers; Arthur Garami; Wilfrid Pelletier. **Holdings:** 57,120 books and scores; 9570 sound recordings; 297 magnetic tapes; 250 compact discs; 361 cassettes; 52 videocassettes; 100 slides; 23 microfilms. **Subscriptions:** 111 periodicals. **Services:** Interlibrary loan; center open to the public with restrictions. **Automated Operations:** Computerized cataloging. **Computerized Information Services:** UTLAS. **Publications:** Brochures on services and research strategy; lists of new acquisitions. **Remarks:** FAX: (514)873-7943. **Also Known As:** Montreal Conservatory of Music - Documentation Centre.

★4221★
Conservatoire de Musique du Quebec - Bibliotheque (Mus)
587 Radisson St.
C.P. 1146 Phone: (819)371-6748
Trois-Rivieres, PQ, Canada G9A 5K8 Guy Lefebvre, Biblio.
Subjects: Music. **Holdings:** Music ephemera, books, dictionaries. **Remarks:** FAX: (819)371-6955.

Conservatoire National des Arts et Metiers - Institut National des Techniques de la Documentation
See: **National Conservatory of Arts and Crafts - National Institute for Information Science** (11133)

Conservatoire de Paris Archives
See: **Boston University - Music Library** (2015)

★4222★
Conservatorio de Musica de Puerto Rico - Biblioteca (Mus)
P.O. Box 41227, Minillas Sta. Phone: (809)751-0160
Santurce, PR 00940-1227 Elsa Mariani, Hd.Libn.
Founded: 1962. **Staff:** Prof 2; Other 2. **Subjects:** Music. **Special Collections:** Complete works of Brahms, Bach, Romero, and Ramos; Puerto Rican Collection. **Holdings:** 5689 books; 19,191 scores and parts; 960 orchestral music scores and parts; 430 pieces of choral music; 11 binders of microfiche; 70 albums of clippings; 500 librettos, college and publishers' catalogs; 5372 phonograph records; band music. **Subscriptions:** 82 journals and other serials. **Services:** Interlibrary loan; copying; library open to the public for reference use only. **Remarks:** FAX: (809)758-8268. **Staff:** Damaris Cordero Rios, Libn.

Conservatory of Cinematographic Art
See: **Concordia University - Sir George Williams Campus** (4122)

Consiglio Oleicolo Internazionale
See: **International Olive Oil Council** (8164)

★4223★
Consoer Townsend & Associates - Library and Information Center (Sci-Engr, Plan)
3 Illinois Center
303 E. Wacker Dr., Suite 600 Phone: (312)938-0300
Chicago, IL 60601 Carol DeBiak, Libn./Mgr.
Founded: 1930. **Staff:** Prof 1. **Subjects:** Engineering - structural, civil; transportation; water; wastewater; solid wastes. **Holdings:** 10,000 books; 150 bound periodical volumes; 1800 manufacturing catalogs; 2650 company owned project reports; 28 VF drawers of pamphlets; 8000 microfiche. **Subscriptions:** 40 journals and other serials. **Services:** Interlibrary loan; library not open to the public. **Computerized Information Services:** DIALOG Information Services. **Networks/Consortia:** Member of ILLINET. **Special Catalogs:** Company reports, Contract Specifications, Design Calculations. **Remarks:** Member of AECOM Technology Corporation. FAX: (312)938-1109.

★4224★
Consolidated Biotechnology, Inc. - Library (Biol Sci)
1413 W. Indiana Ave. Phone: (219)295-6767
Elkhart, IN 46515 Dr. John Marshall
Subjects: Biochemistry, biotechnology. **Holdings:** 800 books; 1500 reports. **Subscriptions:** 30 journals and other serials. **Services:** Library open to the public.

★4225★
Consolidated Edison Company of New York, Inc. - Library (Energy)
4 Irving Pl., Rm. 1650-S Phone: (212)460-4228
New York, NY 10003 Steven Jaffe, Libn.
Founded: 1906. **Staff:** Prof 2; Other 1. **Subjects:** Electricity, gas, public utility economics, atomic power. **Holdings:** 10,000 books; 10,000 bound periodical volumes; 40 cabinets of pamphlets on labor and political science; microforms. **Subscriptions:** 310 journals and other serials. **Services:** Interlibrary loan; copying; library open to the public by appointment. **Computerized Information Services:** DIALOG Information Services, PFDS Online, NEXIS, Control Data Corporation (CDC), Electric Power Database (EPD/RDIS), BRS Information Technologies. **Publications:** Con Edison Library Bulletin, monthly. **Staff:** Peter James Dietrich, Assoc.Libn.

★4226★
Consolidated Natural Gas Service Co., Inc. - Research Department Library (Energy)
4141 Rockside Rd., Suite 230 Phone: (216)736-6077
Cleveland, OH 44131-2537 Carol A. Brown, Mgr., Lib.Serv.
Staff: Prof 1; Other 2.5. **Subjects:** Natural gas, liquefied natural gas, public utilities, management. **Holdings:** 4000 books; 1500 periodical volumes on microfilm; 3500 other cataloged items; 45 vertical files; 80,000 government documents on microfiche. **Subscriptions:** 200 journals and other serials. **Services:** Interlibrary loan; copying; SDI; library open to the public by appointment. **Automated Operations:** Computerized acquisitions, cataloging, serials, and circulation. **Computerized Information Services:** DIALOG Information Services, ORBIT Search Service, A.G.A. GasNet, Gasline, OCLC, Dun & Bradstreet Business Credit Services, VU/TEXT Information Services, DataTimes, Dow Jones News/Retrieval. Performs searches on fee basis. **Networks/Consortia:** Member of Cleveland Area Metropolitan Library System (CAMLS), American Gas Association - Library Services (AGA-LSC). **Publications:** Library Acquisition List, bimonthly; subject bibliographies. **Remarks:** FAX: (216)447-6076.

★4227★
Consolidated Papers, Inc. - Research and Development Library (Sci-Engr)
Box 8050 Phone: (715)422-2543
Wisconsin Rapids, WI 54495-8050 Delia C. Aschenbrenner, Lib.Supv.
Founded: 1959. **Staff:** Prof 2; Other 1. **Subjects:** Pulp paper technology, graphic arts, management, engineering, environment. **Holdings:** 9000 books; 900 bound periodical volumes; 3000 reprints; 12 drawers of patents. **Subscriptions:** 700 journals and other serials; 12 newspapers. **Services:** Library open to the public with restrictions. **Automated Operations:** Computerized cataloging, serials, and circulation. **Computerized Information Services:** DIALOG Information Services, PFDS Online, WILSONLINE. **Publications:** From the Stacks (newsletter), quarterly - for internal distribution only. **Staff:** Cynthia VanErt, Asst.Libn.Supv.

★4228★
Consolidated Rail Corporation - Law Library (Law)
1138 Six Penn Center Plaza Phone: (215)977-5044
Philadelphia, PA 19103 Sandra I. Compo, Law Libn.
Staff: Prof 1. **Subjects:** Law, railroads, interstate commerce. **Special Collections:** Railroad materials. **Holdings:** 20,000 books. **Services:** Interlibrary loan; library not open to the public. **Computerized Information Services:** WESTLAW, DIALOG Information Services. **Remarks:** FAX: (215)977-4817.

★4229★
Consolidation Coal Company - R & D Division - Technical Resource Center (Energy)
4000 Brownsville Rd. Phone: (412)854-6688
Library, PA 15129 Jacqueline E. Hedderman, Info.Spec.
Founded: 1947. **Staff:** Prof 1. **Subjects:** Coal and fuel chemistry and technology. **Special Collections:** Bureau of Mines' IC's and RI's. **Holdings:** 10,000 books; 2500 bound periodical volumes; selected government microfiche and reports. **Subscriptions:** 150 journals and other serials. **Services:** Library not open to the public. **Computerized Information Services:** DIALOG Information Services, OCLC. **Remarks:** FAX: (412)854-6613.

★4230★
Consolidation Coal Company - Technical Library (Sci-Engr, Energy)
Consol Plaza
1800 Washington Rd. Phone: (412)831-4513
Pittsburgh, PA 15241 Elinor Rodgers, Libn.
Founded: 1973. **Staff:** 1. **Subjects:** Coal mining and processing, geology, engineering, environmental concerns. **Holdings:** 5600 books; 2000 volumes of exploration reports; 420 engineering reports; coal company files of 214 U.S. companies; 515 state maps. **Subscriptions:** 15 journals and other serials. **Services:** Interlibrary loan; library open to the public by appointment. **Publications:** Explore-Information (newsletter), monthly. **Special Indexes:** Computer index for exploration project reports.

Consommation et Corporations Canada
See: **Canada - Consumer and Corporate Affairs Canada** (2676)

Constance-Lethbridge Rehabilitation Centre
See: **Centre de Readaptation Constance-Lethbridge** (3282)

★4231★
The Constant Society - Library (Comp Sci)
4244 University Way, N.E.
Box 45513 Phone: (206)633-5186
Seattle, WA 98145 Ted S. Davis
Founded: 1975. **Subjects:** Computer science, mathematics, physics. **Holdings:** 102 volumes; 9000-entry bibliography. **Subscriptions:** 20 journals and other serials. **Services:** Library not open to the public. **Computerized Information Services:** Internal database.

Mother M. Constantine Memorial Library
See: **Mount Carmel Health** (10799)

★4232★
Constitution Island Association, Inc. - Warner House Library (Hist)
Box 41 Phone: (914)446-8676
West Point, NY 10996 Nancy Morris, Exec.Dir.
Founded: 1916. **Staff:** 1. **Subjects:** Warner family library, including books written by Susan and Anna Warner. **Holdings:** 2000 books; 300 periodicals; 8 VF drawers of Warner correspondence, family records, manuscripts, drawings, photographs. **Services:** Library open to the public by appointment. **Publications:** Annual report; bibliography of Warner books, 1976; biography of Susan and Anna Warner, 1978.

★4233★
Construction Consultants, Inc. - Library (Sci-Engr)
900 Pallister Phone: (313)874-2770
Detroit, MI 48202 Joan M. Boram, Libn.
Founded: 1974. **Staff:** Prof 1; Other 1. **Subjects:** Construction, waterproofing, roofing, concrete. **Special Collections:** Legal documents related to roofing failures. **Holdings:** 500 books. **Subscriptions:** 24 journals and other serials. **Services:** Interlibrary loan; copying; library open to the public with restrictions. **Remarks:** FAX: (313)874-1693.

★4234★
Construction Industry Translation and Information Services, Ltd. - Research Institute/Information Center (Sci-Engr)
2 Rosemount Terrace
Blackrock Phone: 1 2886227
Dublin, Ireland D.P. Murphy, Hd., Info.Ctr.
Founded: 1972. **Staff:** 8 Prof. **Subjects:** Engineering - civil, structural, hydraulic; hydrology; foundations; soil mechanics; highways; tunnels; dams. **Holdings:** 1000 books. **Subscriptions:** 500 journals and other serials. **Services:** Center not open to the public. **Computerized Information Services:** Produces CITIS CD-ROM. **Publications:** International Civil Engineering Abstracts; Software Abstracts for Engineers. **Remarks:** FAX: 1 2885971. **Also Known As:** CITIS Ltd.

★4235★
Construction Safety Association of Ontario - Information Resource Group (Plan)
74 Victoria St., 10th Fl. Phone: (416)366-1501
Toronto, ON, Canada M5C 2A5 Cyrele Shoub, Libn.
Founded: 1980. **Staff:** 2. **Subjects:** Occupational health and safety; construction safety. **Holdings:** 2500 books. **Subscriptions:** 251 journals and other serials. **Services:** Copying; library open to the public by appointment. **Computerized Information Services:** DIALOG Information Services, MEDLARS, ORBIT Search Service, Canadian Centre for Occupational Health and Safety (CCOHS); internal database. **Remarks:** FAX: (416)366-2302. **Staff:** Patricia Dean.

★4236★
Consulate-General of the Federal Republic of Germany - Library (Soc Sci)
PO Box 363 Phone: (403)422-6175
Edmonton, AB, Canada T5J 2J6 Josef Friess, Libn.
Remarks: No further information was supplied by respondent.

★4237★
Consulate General of India - Information Service of India Library (Area-Ethnic)
3 E. 64th St. Phone: (212)879-7800
New York, NY 10021 Mrs. Pushpa Gupta, Libn.
Founded: 1958. **Staff:** Prof 1; Other 1. **Subjects:** India - all fields of information. **Special Collections:** Collected works of Mahatma Gandhi (55 volumes). **Holdings:** 6636 books; ministry's annual report; clippings from Indian newspapers. **Subscriptions:** 40 journals and other serials; 15 newspapers. **Services:** Library open to the public.

★4238★
Consulate General of Ireland - Library (Area-Ethnic)
515 Madison Ave.
New York, NY 10022 Phone: (212)319-2555
Subjects: Historical, political, cultural, social, and general information on Ireland. **Holdings:** Figures not available. **Services:** Library open to the public with restrictions.

★4239★
Consulate General of Israel - Lt. David Tamir Library and Reading Room (Area-Ethnic)
800 2nd Ave. Phone: (212)351-5200
New York, NY 10017 Evelyn Musher, Dir., Community Rel.
Founded: 1948. **Staff:** 1. **Subjects:** Israel, Middle East. **Holdings:** Figures not available. **Services:** Library not open to the public. **Special Catalogs:** Israel Speakers Bureau Catalog; Films of Israel Catalog. **Remarks:** Alternate telephone number(s): (212)351-5333 (recorded information and news about Israel).

★4240★
Consulate-General of Japan - Japanese Consulate Library (Area-Ethnic)
2480 ManuLife Place
10180 101st St. Phone: (403)422-3752
Edmonton, AB, Canada T5J 3S4 Tomiko Ohuchi, Ck.
Staff: 1. **Subjects:** Japanese history, culture, economics. **Holdings:** 1000 books; 500 bound periodical volumes; 500 government reports; 128 films; 1000 slides; 300 maps, annual reports, pamphlets. **Subscriptions:** 120 journals and other serials; 7 newspapers. **Services:** Library open to the public. **Remarks:** Alternate telephone number(s): 423-4750.

★4241★
Consultants in Engineering Acoustics - Library
25 Drumm St., No. 202
San Francisco, CA 94111
Subjects: Acoustical engineering, noise control and applications. **Holdings:** 400 volumes. **Remarks:** Currently inactive.

★4242★
Consultative Association of Guyanese Industry - Library (Bus-Fin)
78 Church St.
P.O. Box 10730
Georgetown, Guyana Phone: 2 57170
Staff: 2. **Subjects:** Guyanese industry. **Holdings:** 3000 volumes. **Services:** Library open to members only. **Remarks:** FAX: 2 64603. Telex: CAGI.

Consultative Group on International Agricultural Research - International Institute of Tropical Agriculture
See: **International Institute of Tropical Agriculture** (8135)

Consultative Group on International Agricultural Research - International Laboratory for Research on Animal Diseases
See: **International Laboratory for Research on Animal Diseases** (8141)

Consultative Group on International Agricultural Research - International Rice Research Institute
See: **International Rice Research Institute** (8182)

Consumer and Corporate Affairs Canada
See: **Canada - Consumer and Corporate Affairs Canada** (2676)

Consumer Health Information Library
See: **Bronson Methodist Hospital - Health Sciences Library** (2209)

Consumer Health Library
See: **Cape Fear Valley Medical Center - Library Services** (3025)

Consumer Movement Archives
See: **Kansas State University - University Archives** (8573)

★4243★
Consumer Product Safety Commission - Library (Sci-Engr, Bus-Fin)
5401 Westbard Ave., 4th Fl. Phone: (301)492-6544
Washington, DC 20207 Hoor Siddiqui, Libn.
Founded: 1973. **Staff:** Prof 1; Other 1. **Subjects:** Consumer product safety and standards, administrative law, product testing, business and economics, science and technology. **Special Collections:** Standards Collection; Indexed Document Collection; CPSC Records and Archives (11 cubic feet). **Holdings:** 12,000 books; 15,000 indexed documents and news clippings on product safety; 300 journals, 1970-1979, on microfilm. **Subscriptions:** 300 journals and other serials; 5 newspapers. **Services:** Interlibrary loan; copying; library open to the public. **Automated Operations:** Computerized cataloging and ILL. **Computerized Information Services:** OCLC, DIALOG Information Services, MEDLINE, NEXIS, LEXIS, WESTLAW, DunsPrint; internal database. **Networks/Consortia:** Member of FEDLINK. **Publications:** User's Guide to Library and Information Resources; Information Update (newsletter/new accessions list), monthly. **Special Indexes:** KWIC Index to the Indexed Document Collection. **Remarks:** FAX: (301)492-6924.

★4244★
Consumer Product Safety Commission - National Injury Information Clearinghouse (Soc Sci)
Westwood Towers Bldg., Rm. 625
5401 Westbard Ave. Phone: (301)504-0424
Washington, DC 20207 Joel I. Friedman, Dir.
Founded: 1973. **Staff:** Prof 6; Other 3. **Subjects:** Injury data from accidents associated with consumer products; epidemiology of accidents. **Special Collections:** Injury data from more than four million consumer product-associated accidents reported through the National Electronic Injury Surveillance System (NEISS); reports on in-depth investigations of accidents associated with consumer products; reports of incidents associated with consumer products such as consumer complaints, newspaper clippings, medical examiner and coroner alert programs; reports on death certificates. **Holdings:** 100 staff studies and special reports on consumer product-associated injuries. **Services:** Answers inquiries for information. **Computerized Information Services:** Online systems. **Publications:** NEISS Data Highlights, annual - currently free upon request. **Staff:** Joyce Coonley, Tech.Info.Spec.; Hope L. Barrett, Tech.Info.Spec.; Pat Duvall, Tech.Info.Spec.; Idelle Smith, Tech.Info.Spec.; Vicky Leonard, Tech.Info.Spec.

★4245★
Consumers Association of Canada, Manitoba Division - Library (Bus-Fin)
222 Osborne St., S., Rm. 21 Phone: (204)452-2572
Winnipeg, MB, Canada R3L 1Z3 Gloria Desorcy, Exec.Asst.
Founded: 1967. **Staff:** 1. **Subjects:** Product information, consumer education, consumer issues. **Holdings:** 70 books; reports; manuscripts; archives; government publications and reports. **Subscriptions:** 9 journals and other serials. **Services:** Copying; library open to the public. **Special Indexes:** Hassle Helpers, index of agencies to contact about consumer problems.

Consumer's Medical Library
See: **Center for Medical Consumers and Health Information - Consumer's Medical Library** (3268)

★4246★
Consumers Power Company - Law Library (Law)
212 W. Michigan Ave. Phone: (517)788-1088
Jackson, MI 49201-2280 Helen K. Sova, Libn.
Staff: Prof 1. **Subjects:** Federal and Michigan Statutes and administrative law materials, energy, environment, labor, public utilities. **Special Collections:** Company history. **Holdings:** 20,000 books; 250 reports, newsletters, pamphlets. **Subscriptions:** 60 journals and other serials. **Services:** Library open to the public with restrictions. **Computerized Information Services:** LEXIS. **Publications:** Letter regarding new material, irregular. **Remarks:** FAX: (517)788-0045.

★4247★
Consumers Power Company - Library Services (Energy)
1945 Parnall Rd. Phone: (517)788-0541
Jackson, MI 49201 Catherine A. Smith, Libn.
Founded: 1977. **Staff:** Prof 1. **Subjects:** Energy - electric, gas, nuclear; environment; management. **Special Collections:** Electric Power Research Institute (EPRI) reports; Nuclear Regulatory Commission reports (NUREG). **Holdings:** 4500 books and bound periodical volumes; 20,000 reports, pamphlets, and standards. **Subscriptions:** 225 journals and other serials. **Services:** Interlibrary loan; library open to the public with restrictions. **Computerized Information Services:** DIALOG Information Services, NEXIS, WILSONLINE, VU/TEXT Information Services, ORBIT Search Service; A.G.A. GasNet, EEI Knight-Ridder Unicom (electronic mail services). **Networks/Consortia:** Member of Capital Area Library Network (Calnet), Michigan Library Consortium (MLC). **Publications:** Library Lines, quarterly - internal distribution and to librarians on request. **Remarks:** FAX: (517)788-0728. Electronic mail address(es): EEI075 (Knight-Ridder Unicom).

★4248★
Consumers Union of United States, Inc. - Library (Bus-Fin)
101 Truman Ave. Phone: (914)378-2260
Yonkers, NY 10703-1057 Sara Ingram, Hd., Lib.Div.
Founded: 1936. **Staff:** Prof 6; Other 4. **Subjects:** Consumer goods, standards and specifications, consumer economics, history of the consumer movement,

health and medicine. **Holdings:** 5000 books; 1500 volumes of periodicals on microfilm; 20,000 unbound journals; 15,000 pamphlets; 215 VF drawers of laboratory test project data, company documents, correspondence; archives. **Subscriptions:** 800 journals and other serials. **Services:** Interlibrary loan. **Automated Operations:** Computerized serials and acquisitions. **Computerized Information Services:** DIALOG Information Services, NLM, NEXIS, NewsNet, Inc. **Publications:** Consumer Reports News Digest, semimonthly - by subscription. **Special Indexes:** Consumer Reports indexes; indexes to CR Travel Letter, CR On Health, Zillions. **Remarks:** Contains the holdings of the Center for the Study of the Consumer Movement. FAX: (914)378-2900. **Formerly:** Located in Mount Vernon, NY. **Staff:** Elizabeth Hamilton, Sr.Res.Libn.; Mary Ann Larkin, Sr.Res.Libn.; Ellen Carney, Res.Libn.; Evelyn J. Riedel, Sr.Res.Libn.; Joan Jackson, Res.Libn.

Contact Center - Clearinghouse/Information
See: **CEGA Services, Inc. - Information Services Department** (3190)

★4249★
Contel Federal Systems Inc. - Information Management Systems Division - Technical Library (Info Sci)
31717 La Tienda Dr.
Mail Code 202
Westlake Village, CA 91359 Phone: (818)706-4000
Founded: 1958. **Staff:** Prof 1. **Subjects:** Communications, computer technology, electronics, engineering, management, microwaves, artificial intelligence. **Holdings:** 1000 books; 1500 bound periodical volumes; 8 drawers of microfiche. **Subscriptions:** 202 journals and other serials; 11 newspapers. **Services:** Interlibrary loan; copying; library open to the public by appointment. **Automated Operations:** Computerized cataloging, acquisitions, serials, and circulation. **Computerized Information Services:** DTIC, U.S. National Technical Information Service (NTIS), DIALOG Information Services; EasyLink (electronic mail service). **Special Indexes:** Eaton Corporation patents. **Remarks:** FAX: (818)706-5050. **Formerly:** Eaton Corporation - Information Management Systems Division.

Contel Technology Center
See: **GTE Government Systems - Technical Library** (6776)

★4250★
Contemporary Crafts Association - Library (Art)
3934 S.W. Corbett Ave. Phone: (503)223-2654
Portland, OR 97201 Beulah Parisi, Act.Libn.
Founded: 1971. **Staff:** Prof 1; Other 2. **Subjects:** Ceramics and pottery, weaving and textiles, Pacific Northwest craftsmen, contemporary designers, metalwork and jewelry, contemporary glass, sculpture, woodworking, architecture. **Holdings:** 420 books; 74 bound and 125 unbound periodical volumes; 235 exhibition catalogs.

Contemporary Music Project (CMP) Lending Service
See: **University of Maryland, College Park Libraries - Music Library** (18821)

★4251★
Continental Bank - Research and Information Services Division (Bus-Fin)
231 S. LaSalle St. Phone: (312)923-6927
Chicago, IL 60697 Janet S. Reed, Mgr., V.P.
Founded: 1925. **Staff:** Prof 7; Other 7. **Subjects:** Banking, industry, finance, management. **Holdings:** 8000 books. **Subscriptions:** 1200 journals and other serials. **Services:** Interlibrary loan; division open to bank personnel. **Automated Operations:** Computerized cataloging and acquisitions. **Computerized Information Services:** DIALOG Information Services, Dow Jones News/Retrieval, VU/TEXT Information Services, LEXIS, NEXIS, Data Resources (DRI), Info Globe, DataTimes, FactSet Data Systems, Inc., REUTERS. **Networks/Consortia:** Member of Chicago Library System. **Staff:** Susan J. Glodkowski, Res.Mgr.; Peggy L. Popa, Info.Spec.; Alicia R. Forton, Sr.Info.Anl.; Eileen Pyne, Sr.Info.Anl.; Andrea Hall, Sr.Info.Anl.; Robert Hopkins, Sr.Info.Anl.

Continuous Electron Beam Accelerator Facility Library
See: **Southeastern Universities Research Association** (15452)

★4252★
(Contonou) Centre Culturel Americain - USIS Library (Educ)
Blvd. de France Pres du Conseil de L'Entente
B.P. 2014
Contonou, Benin
Remarks: Maintained or supported by the U.S. Information Agency. Focus is on materials that will assist peoples outside the United States to learn about the United States, its people, history, culture, political processes, and social milieux.

★4253★
Contra Costa Child Care Council - Toy and Resource Library (Educ)
300 E. Leland Rd., Suite 106 Phone: (510)427-5437
Pittsburg, CA 94565 Mickey Williams, Area Mgr.
Staff: Prof 3. **Subjects:** Toys, games, parenting, child care and development, children's activities and literature. **Holdings:** Books; toys; parenting magizines; children's and parenting videotapes. **Services:** Copying; library open to the public. **Automated Operations:** Computerized cataloging and circulation. **Staff:** Dora Thomas, Rsrc./Ref.Coord.; Bea Espinoza, Rsrc./Ref.Coord.

★4254★
Contra Costa County Law Library (Law)
1020 Ward St., 1st Fl. Phone: (510)646-2783
Martinez, CA 94553-1276 Jean Steffensen, Law Libn.
Founded: 1854. **Staff:** 6. **Subjects:** Law. **Holdings:** 50,000 volumes. **Subscriptions:** 400 journals and other serials; 10 newspapers. **Services:** Copying; faxing; library open to the public. **Computerized Information Services:** WESTLAW. **Remarks:** FAX: (510)646-2438. A branch law library, containing 17,000 volumes, is located at 100 37th St., Richmond, CA 94805.

★4255★
Contra Costa County Office of Education - Information Center & Professional Library (Educ)
77 Santa Barbara Rd. Phone: (510)942-3397
Pleasant Hill, CA 94523-4215 Kleanthy Gonos, Mgr., Educ.Info.
Staff: Prof 1; Other 2. **Subjects:** Teaching methodology, administration, educational research, special education. **Special Collections:** Collection of research documents. **Holdings:** 4000 books; 350,000 ERIC microfiche; 3000 textbooks in sample textbook collection; 750 documents; 1750 juvenile review books. **Subscriptions:** 250 journals and other serials. **Services:** Copying; center is open to outside users in area only. **Computerized Information Services:** ERIC. **Remarks:** FAX: (510)942-3480.

★4256★
Contra Costa Times - Library (Publ)
2640 Shadelands Dr.
Box 5088 Phone: (510)935-2525
Walnut Creek, CA 94596 Elyse A. Eisner, Libn.
Founded: 1978. **Staff:** Prof 2; Other 1. **Subjects:** Newspaper reference topics. **Holdings:** 500 books; 120 VF drawers of clippings; 54 VF drawers of photographs; 12 drawers of microfilm of Contra Costa Times, 1913 to present; 3 drawers of microfilm of Concord Transcript, 1905-1982. **Subscriptions:** 20 journals and other serials; 15 newspapers. **Services:** Copying; SDI; library open to the public by appointment. **Computerized Information Services:** DIALOG Information Services, DataTimes. **Remarks:** FAX: (510)943-8362. Library is maintained by Lesher Communications. **Staff:** Kathy Drewke, Photo Libn.

★4257★
Control Data Corporation - Santa Clara Operations Library (Comp Sci)
5101 Patrick Henry Dr. Phone: (408)496-4100
Santa Clara, CA 95054 Richard J. Clifton, Dir.
Founded: 1967. **Staff:** Prof 1. **Subjects:** Computer science and programming, communications, business. **Holdings:** 1517 books; 170 bound periodical volumes; 301 government reports on computers; 357 microfiche of government reports. **Subscriptions:** 101 journals and other serials. **Services:** Interlibrary loan; library not open to the public. **Automated Operations:** Computerized cataloging. **Remarks:** FAX: (408)496-4106. **Formerly:** Located in Sunnyvale, CA.

Controlled Fusion Atomic Data Center
See: **Oak Ridge National Laboratory** (12186)

★4258★
Controls for Environmental Pollution, Inc. - Library (Sci-Engr)
P.O. Box 5351
Santa Fe, NM 87502 Phone: (505)982-9841
Subjects: Materials analysis, organic and inorganic chemistry, bioassay, hazardous waste, mixed waste analysis. **Holdings:** 1000 books; 3000 reports. **Subscriptions:** 25 journals and other serials. **Services:** Library not open to the public. **Remarks:** Toll-free telephone number(s): (800)545-2189 (outside of New Mexico). FAX: (505)982-9289. Library located at 1925 Rosina St., Santa Fe, NM, 87501.

Convalescent Hospital for Children
See: **Crestwood Children's Hospital** (4431)

★4259★
Converse College - Music Library (Mus)
580 E. Main St. Phone: (803)596-9074
Spartanburg, SC 29302-0006 Darlene E. Fawver, Mus.Libn.
Founded: 1905. **Staff:** Prof 1; Other 2. **Subjects:** Music. **Special Collections:** Lily Strickland Collection (manuscripts; printed music; poetry; sketches; memorabilia); Radiana Pazmor Collection (personal correspondence including letters from Aaron Copland, Charles Ives, Darius Milhaud, Maurice Ravel, and Virgil Thomson); rare books and manuscripts (collection of autographed books, scores, and manuscripts including those of former deans of the School of Music). **Holdings:** 10,000 books; 16,000 scores; 20,000 sound recordings. **Subscriptions:** 140 journals and other serials. **Services:** Interlibrary loan; copying; library open to the public. **Automated Operations:** Computerized cataloging and ILL. **Computerized Information Services:** OCLC, DIALOG Information Services; CD-ROMs (ERIC, Periodical Abstracts). **Networks/Consortia:** Member of SOLINET. **Publications:** New Music Library Acquisitions, monthly - for internal distribution only.

★4260★
Converse Consultants - Library (Sci-Engr)
3 Century Dr.
Parsippany, NJ 07054 Phone: (201)605-5200
Staff: 1. **Subjects:** Geology, soil mechanics, allied sciences. **Holdings:** 3000 volumes. **Subscriptions:** 25 journals and other serials. **Services:** Library open to the public by appointment.

★4261★
Converse Consultants Inc. - Corporate Library (Sci-Engr)
3393 E. Foothill Blvd. Phone: (818)796-8200
Pasadena, CA 91107 Jan McMahon, Corp.Libn.
Founded: 1980. **Staff:** Prof 1. **Subjects:** Engineering - geotechnical, earthquake, mathematics; soils; foundations; groundwater hydrology. **Holdings:** 1000 books; 200 government reports in microform; 100 company reports; 1 file drawer of clippings. **Subscriptions:** 52 journals and other serials. **Services:** Interlibrary loan (limited); library not open to the public. **Computerized Information Services:** PFDS Online. **Remarks:** Alternate telephone number(s): (818)440-0800. FAX: (818)795-3394.

★4262★
Converse County Memorial Hospital - William A. Hinrichs Medical Library (Med)
111 S. 5th St. Phone: (307)358-2122
Douglas, WY 82633 Barbara Pickinpaugh, Med.Lib.Mgr.
Founded: 1979. **Staff:** 1. **Subjects:** Medicine, surgery. **Holdings:** 220 books; 6 bound periodical volumes. **Subscriptions:** 22 journals and other serials. **Services:** Interlibrary loan; copying; library open to health care personnel. **Automated Operations:** Computerized cataloging and serials. **Networks/Consortia:** Member of Health Sciences Information Network (HSIN). **Remarks:** FAX: (307)358-9216.

J.G. Converse Memorial Medical Library
See: **Winter Haven Hospital** (20499)

Dominick J. Conway Library
See: **Children's Hospital of Eastern Ontario** (3569)

★4263★
E.A. Conway Memorial Hospital - Medical Library (Med)
Box 1881 Phone: (318)388-7644
Monroe, LA 71201 Pamela D. Ashley, Med.Libn.
Founded: 1941. **Staff:** Prof 1. **Subjects:** Medicine and allied health sciences. **Holdings:** 650 volumes; 120 AV items. **Subscriptions:** 69 journals and other serials. **Services:** Interlibrary loan; copying; library open to outside users with physician's order. **Automated Operations:** NOTIS. **Computerized Information Services:** MEDLINE. **Networks/Consortia:** Member of National Network of Libraries of Medicine - South Central Region. **Remarks:** FAX: (318)388-7649.

Conway Library
See: **Cleveland Museum of Art - Ingalls Library** (3813)

Conwellana-Templana Collection
See: **Temple University - Central Library System** (16134)

★4264★
Charles Cook Theological School - Mary Mildred McCarthy Library (Rel-Phil)
708 S. Lindon Ln. Phone: (602)968-9354
Tempe, AZ 85281 Mark Thomas, Libn.
Staff: Prof 1; Other 1. **Subjects:** Religion, Native Americans. **Special Collections:** Fey Collection (100 books); Indian Collection (1500 books); archives. **Holdings:** 11,000 books; 8 VF drawers. **Subscriptions:** 56 journals and other serials. **Services:** Copying; library open to the public. **Computerized Information Services:** Ecunet (electronic mail service).

★4265★
Cook County Historical Society - Grand Marais Library
Grand Marais, MN 55604
Subjects: Pioneer life stories; community histories; history of organizations, schools, churches, industries. **Special Collections:** Thomsonites (400 items mounted in special show cases). **Holdings:** Files of information on lumbering, fishing, organizations, school, churches, pioneers, industries; 40 transcriptions; newspapers and census on microfilm. **Remarks:** Currently inactive.

★4266★
Cook County Hospital - Health Science Library (Med)
1900 W. Polk St. Phone: (312)633-7787
Chicago, IL 60612 Grace Auer, Coord., Libs.
Staff: Prof 1; Other 2. **Subjects:** Nursing, allied health sciences, management. **Holdings:** 3582 books. **Subscriptions:** 74 journals and other serials. **Services:** Interlibrary loan. **Computerized Information Services:** MEDLARS (through Tice Memorial Library). **Staff:** Estela Escudero, Libn.

★4267★
Cook County Hospital - Tice Memorial Library (Med)
720 S. Wolcott St. Phone: (312)633-6724
Chicago, IL 60612 Estela B. Escudero, Lib.Coord.
Founded: 1953. **Staff:** Prof 2; Other 4. **Subjects:** Medicine, surgery. **Special Collections:** Frederick Tice Collection of rare books in medicine. **Holdings:** 3500 books; 6500 bound periodical volumes; AV programs. **Subscriptions:** 365 journals and other serials. **Services:** Interlibrary loan; library not open to the public. **Computerized Information Services:** MEDLARS. Performs searches free of charge. **Networks/Consortia:** Member of Metropolitan Consortium of Chicago, National Network of Libraries of Medicine - Greater Midwest Region. **Remarks:** Maintained by the Cook County Board. **Staff:** Carmen L. Salvador, Cat.Libn.

★4268★
Cook County Law Library (Law)
2900 Richard J. Daley Center Phone: (312)443-5423
Chicago, IL 60602 Bennie E. Martin, Exec. Law Libn.
Founded: 1966. **Staff:** Prof 20. **Subjects:** Law - Anglo-American, foreign, international. **Holdings:** 228,302 books; 15,000 bound periodical volumes. **Subscriptions:** 1000 journals and other serials; 20 newspapers; CIS Legislative History Service in microform. **Services:** Interlibrary loan; SDI; library open to the public with restrictions. **Automated Operations:** NOTIS. **Computerized Information Services:** RLIN, LEXIS, WESTLAW, Illinois Legislative Information System, CQ Washington Alert. **Publications:** Acquisitions List, bimonthly; Newsletter, 6/year. **Special Catalogs:** Union Card Catalog. **Remarks:** Maintains seven branch libraries. **Staff:** Montell Davenport, Ref.Libn.; Frederic C. Pearson, Circ.Libn.; Alfred Kulys, Cat.Libn.; Antonio Naranjo, Foreign Law Libn.; Linda Zaba, Chf.Acq.Libn.

★4269★
Cook County State's Attorney's Office Library (Law)
500 Richard J. Daley Center Phone: (312)443-3048
Chicago, IL 60602 Darlene M. Davies, Hd.Libn.
Staff: Prof 1; Other 6. **Subjects:** Law. **Holdings:** 30,000 books; 6000 bound periodical volumes. **Subscriptions:** 110 journals and other serials. **Services:** Library not open to the public. **Computerized Information Services:** LEXIS. **Remarks:** FAX: (312)443-3000. **Staff:** Antigony Lambros, Libn.; Marilyn Shannon, Libn.; Georgia Trotter, Libn.

★4270★
James Cook University of North Queensland - Library (Area-Ethnic, Biol Sci, Sci-Engr)
Townsville, QLD 4811, Australia Phone: 77 814472
John McKinlay, Univ.Libn.
Staff: Prof 15; Other 50. **Subjects:** General collection. **Special Collections:** North Queensland history and literature; marine science; tropics; science and technology. **Holdings:** 350,000 books; 170,000 bound periodical volumes; 65,000 AV programs; 30,000 microforms. **Subscriptions:** 6200 journals and other serials. **Services:** Interlibrary loan; copying; library open to the public. **Automated Operations:** Dynix. **Computerized Information Services:** DIALOG Information Services, MEDLINE, AUSTRALIS, STN International, Australian Bibliographic Network (ABN), INFOLINE, ESA/IRS, Ozline; electronic mail service. Performs searches on fee basis. **Publications:** Library Guide; Library Catalogue; Annual Report. **Special Indexes:** Serials List. **Remarks:** FAX: 77 756691.

Oscar G. Cook Memorial Library
See: **Oxford United Methodist Church** (12644)

★4271★
Cook, Snowdon - Library (Law)
340 12th Ave., S.W., Suite 900 Phone: (403)261-0990
Calgary, AB, Canada T2P 2M7 Ann Wright, Libn.
Subjects: Law. **Holdings:** Figures not available. **Services:** Library not open to the public. **Remarks:** FAX: (403)263-8782.

J.C. Cooke Library
See: **Northwest Bible College - J.C. Cooke Library** (12042)

Cooke Media Group Incorporated - Los Angeles Daily News
See: **Los Angeles Daily News** (9339)

Phyllis Cooksey Resource Center
See: **Planned Parenthood of Minnesota** (13126)

Frank B. Cookson Music Library
See: **University of Connecticut** (18516)

Arthur Braddan Coole Library on Oriental Numismatics
See: **American Numismatic Association - Library** (699)

★4272★
Cooley, Godward, Castro, Huddleson & Tatum - Library (Law)
1 Maritime Plaza, 20th Fl. Phone: (415)981-5252
San Francisco, CA 94111-3580 Yvonne Boyer, Libn.
Staff: Prof 2; Other 1. **Subjects:** Law. **Holdings:** 18,000 books. **Services:** Interlibrary loan; library open to attorneys and clients only. **Computerized Information Services:** LEXIS, DIALOG Information Services, WESTLAW, Information America, Dun & Bradstreet Business Credit Services, DataTimes, Dow Jones News/Retrieval. **Remarks:** FAX: (415)951-3698. A branch library is maintained at 5 Palo Alto Square, 4th Fl., 3000 El Camino Real, Palo Alto, CA 94306. **Staff:** Margaret Baer, Asst.Libn.

★4273★
Thomas M. Cooley Law School - Library (Law)
217 S. Capitol Ave.
Box 13038 Phone: (517)371-5140
Lansing, MI 48901 Judith Anspach, Dir. of Lib.Serv.
Founded: 1973. **Staff:** Prof 8; Other 9. **Subjects:** Law. **Special Collections:** Federal Document Depository Collection. **Holdings:** 120,757 books; 126,340 volumes on microfiche; 758,038 microfiche; 3158 reels of microfilm. **Subscriptions:** 3614 journals and other serials; 18 newspapers. **Services:** Interlibrary loan; copying; library open to the public. **Automated Operations:** Computerized public access catalog (INNOVACQ) and cataloging. **Computerized Information Services:** DIALOG Information Services, WESTLAW, Auto-Cite, LEXIS, WILSONLINE. Contact Person: Aletha Honsowitz, Lawyer, Libn., 371-5140, ext. 611. **Networks/Consortia:** Member of Capital Area Library Network (Calnet), Michigan Library Consortium (MLC). **Publications:** Library User's Guide. **Remarks:** FAX: (517)334-5714. **Staff:** Sheryl Summers, Dp.Dir., Lib.Serv.; Pamela Craig, Lawyer, Libn.; Alettra Hansowitz, Lawyer, Libn.; Ann Lucas, Ser.Libn.; Rita Marsala, Info.Serv.Libn.; John Michaud, Info.Serv.Libn.; William Olsen, Cat.Libn.

Calvin Coolidge Library
See: **Castleton State College** (3136)

★4274★
Coolidge Center for Environmental Leadership - Library (Env-Cons)
1675 Massachusetts Ave. Phone: (617)864-5085
Cambridge, MA 02138 Catherine Crumbley, Prog.Coord.
Founded: 1983. **Subjects:** Environmental issues of developing countries, international development. **Holdings:** 3000 books; 1000 documents. **Subscriptions:** 100 journals and other serials. **Services:** Library open to the public with restrictions. **Automated Operations:** Computerized public access catalog and cataloging (INMAGIC). **Remarks:** FAX: (617)864-6503.

Cooper-Hewitt Collection
See: **Cooper Union - Library** (4277)

Cooper-Hewitt Museum of Design
See: **Smithsonian Institution Libraries - Cooper-Hewitt Museum of Design - Doris & Henry Dreyfuss Memorial Study Center** (15274)

★4275★
Cooper Hospital/University Medical Center - Reuben L. Sharp Health Science Library (Med)
1 Cooper Plaza Phone: (609)342-2525
Camden, NJ 08103 Joan Fierberg, Dir.
Founded: 1971. **Staff:** Prof 4; Other 6. **Subjects:** Medicine, nursing, allied health sciences, patient education. **Special Collections:** History of medicine in Camden County; Cooper Hospital history of medicine (250 volumes). **Holdings:** 15,095 textbooks, bound journals, AV materials, computer software. **Subscriptions:** 475 journals and other serials. **Services:** Interlibrary loan; copying; LATCH; Computer workstations; library open to the public for reference use only. **Automated Operations:** Computerized cataloging, serials, and circulation. **Computerized Information Services:** MEDLARS, BRS Information Technologies, DIALOG Information Services. Performs searches on fee basis; miniMedline searching offered free of charge. **Networks/Consortia:** Member of Southwest New Jersey Consortium for Health Information Services. **Special Catalogs:** Union List of Hospital Audiovisual Programs. **Remarks:** A consumer Health Education Center, located with in the library, provides free pamphlets on varied topics in English and Spanish. FAX: (609)342-9588. **Staff:** Barbara Miller, Ref.Libn.; Randy Brenner, Ref.Libn.

★4276★
Cooper Laboratories, Inc. - Information Center
Box 7264
Mountain View, CA 94039
Founded: 1987. **Subjects:** Immunology, biotechnology, pulmonary medicine, chemistry. **Holdings:** 300 books. **Remarks:** Currently inactive.

Robert Muldrow Cooper Library
See: **Clemson University** (3794)

Thomas Cooper Library
See: **University of South Carolina** (19312)

★4277★
Cooper Union - Library (Art, Sci-Engr)
41 Cooper Sq. Phone: (212)353-4186
New York, NY 10003 Elizabeth A. Vajda, Hd.Libn.
Founded: 1859. **Staff:** Prof 4; Other 4. **Subjects:** Architecture, art, engineering. **Special Collections:** Cooper-Hewitt Collection (papers of Peter Cooper and Abram S. Hewitt and partial school archives; 150,000 pieces; 600 linear feet). **Holdings:** 87,500 books; 15,500 bound periodical volumes; 50,000 slides. **Subscriptions:** 375 journals and other serials. **Services:** Interlibrary loan; library not open to the public. **Automated Operations:** Computerized public access catalog, cataloging, acquisitions, and circulation. **Computerized Information Services:** DIALOG Information Services, WILSONLINE, RLIN, Avery Index to Architectural Periodicals. **Networks/Consortia:** Member of Research Library Association of South Manhattan. **Publications:** Acquisitions List, quarterly. **Remarks:** FAX: (212)353-4345. **Staff:** Herbert Bott, Asst. to the Hd.Libn; Ulla Volk, Libn., Art & Arch.; Carol Salomon, Asst.Libn., Engr./Sci.; Tom Micchelli, Asst.Libn., Slides

Cooperative Children's Book Center (CCBC)
See: **University of Wisconsin--Madison - Cooperative Children's Book Center (CCBC)** (19590)

★4278★
Cooperative Educational Service Agency (CESA) No. 10 - Instructional Media Center (Aud-Vis)
725 W. Park Ave. Phone: (715)723-0341
Chippewa Falls, WI 54729 Susan Frederick, Lib. Media Spec.
Staff: Prof 1; Other 2. **Subjects:** Special education, education, home economics, nutrition, human growth and development, computer education, science, math, technology. **Holdings:** 18,500 AV programs and books. **Subscriptions:** 50 journals and other serials. **Services:** Interlibrary loan; copying; center open to CESA 10 schools. **Automated Operations:** Computerized cataloging and circulation. **Computerized Information Services:** DIALOG Information Services; CD-ROM (ERIC); internal database; electronic mail service. **Publications:** The Quest Quarterly - to members. **Remarks:** FAX: (715)723-0341. Center serves the 30 CESA No. 10 school districts.

★4279★
Cooperative Housing Foundation - Library (Plan)
P.O. Box 91280
Washington, DC 20090 Phone: (301)587-4700
Subjects: Cooperative and selfhelp housing for low- and moderate-income groups. **Holdings:** 5000 volumes. **Remarks:** FAX: (301)587-2626. Telex: 440271 CHFUI.

★4280★
Cooperative League of the Republic of China - Library (Bus-Fin)
11-2 Fuchow St. Phone: 2 3219343
Taipei, Taiwan Wen-pinn Tsai, Libn.
Staff: 9. **Subjects:** Cooperatives, economics. **Holdings:** 10,000 volumes. **Services:** Interlibrary loan; copying; library open to the public. **Remarks:** FAX: 2 3517918.

★4281★
Coopers Creek Chemical Corporation - Library (Sci-Engr)
River Rd. Phone: (215)828-0375
West Conshohocken, PA 19428 Glen Kornfeind
Subjects: Bitumines. **Holdings:** 75 books; 200 reports. **Subscriptions:** 10 journals and other serials. **Services:** Library not open to the public.

★4282★
Coopers & Lybrand - Central Library (Bus-Fin)
203 N. LaSalle St. Phone: (312)701-5684
Chicago, IL 60601 Mallory Otten, Supv.
Founded: 1977. **Staff:** Prof 2. **Subjects:** Accounting, auditing, business. **Special Collections:** Complete American Institute of Certified Public Accountants (AICPA) Audit Guide Series (32) and Statements on Auditing Standards Series (63); complete Financial Accounting Standards Board (FASB) Statements of Financial Accounting Standards Series (105) and FASB Interpretations Series (38); Wall Street Journal, 1979 to present, on microfilm; Fortune and Forbes 500 annual reports file. **Holdings:** 4500 books; 45 audio- and videotapes; 40,000 periodicals on microfiche. **Subscriptions:** 200 journals and other serials; 10 newsletters. **Services:** Interlibrary loan; copying; library open to the public by appointment. **Computerized Information Services:** DIALOG Information Services, Dun & Bradstreet Business Credit Services, NEXIS, LEXIS. **Publications:** New Acquisitions List, monthly. **Remarks:** FAX: (312)701-6533; (312)701-6534. **Staff:** Paula Villanueva.

★4283★
Coopers & Lybrand - Corporate Library (Bus-Fin)
2400 Eleven Penn Center Phone: (215)963-8200
Philadelphia, PA 19103 Maxine S. Boodis, Lib.Mgr.
Founded: 1961. **Staff:** Prof 1; Other 3. **Subjects:** Accounting, auditing, taxation, real estate. **Holdings:** 600 books; Moody's manuals; management letters; annual reports; business directories; maps; vertical file. **Subscriptions:** 350 journals and other serials; 15 newspapers; 58 newsletters. **Services:** Interlibrary loan; library open to the public with restrictions. **Computerized Information Services:** DIALOG Information Services, LEXIS, NEXIS, Dun & Bradstreet Business Credit Services, MAX Online Demographic Data Management and Reporting System, Dow Jones News/Retrieval; CD-ROMs (Disclosure Incorporated, ABI/INFORM, Moody's, Newspaper Abstracts, Philadelphia Inquirer); internal database. **Publications:** News from the Library, 3/year - for internal distribution only. **Remarks:** FAX: (215)963-8821.

Coopers & Lybrand - Healthcare Library
See: **Herman Smith Associates/Coopers & Lybrand - Healthcare Library** (15244)

★4284★
Coopers & Lybrand - Information Centre (Bus-Fin)
145 King St., W., 24th Fl. Phone: (416)869-1130
Toronto, ON, Canada M5H 1V8 Mary Hum, Mgr.
Founded: 1966. **Staff:** Prof 3; Other 1. **Subjects:** Accounting, business, auditing, management consulting. **Holdings:** 6000 books; 3000 confidential client reports; 1000 annual reports; Consumer and Corporate Affairs filings; Statistics Canada microfiche. **Subscriptions:** 300 journals and other serials; 7 newspapers. **Services:** Interlibrary loan; copying; SDI. **Computerized Information Services:** DIALOG Information Services, Info Globe, Dow Jones News/Retrieval, Dun & Bradstreet Business Credit Services, FT PROFILE, InvesText, NEXIS, LEXIS, The Financial Post DataGroup, Infomart Online, STM Systems Corporation, REUTERS, QUIC/LAW. **Remarks:** FAX: (416)863-0926. Telex 06-23590. **Staff:** Brian Goldthorp; Barbara Edwards; Angela Carito.

★4285★
Coopers & Lybrand - Information Centre (Bus-Fin)
1170 Peel St. Phone: (514)876-1500
Montreal, PQ, Canada H3B 4T2 Danielle Martin, Hd.Libn.
Staff: 3. **Subjects:** Accounting, auditing, taxation, management. **Holdings:** 2000 books. **Subscriptions:** 225 journals and other serials. **Services:** Interlibrary loan; center not open to the public. **Computerized Information Services:** DIALOG Information Services. **Remarks:** FAX: (514)876-1502.

★4286★
Coopers & Lybrand - Library (Bus-Fin)
1000 W. 6th St. Phone: (213)481-1000
Los Angeles, CA 90017 Mabel Cross, Libn.
Staff: Prof 2. **Subjects:** Accounting, auditing, taxation, finance, management. **Special Collections:** Annual reports of 2000 companies. **Holdings:** 2000 books. **Subscriptions:** 250 journals and other serials. **Services:** Interlibrary loan; copying; library open to clients and librarians by appointment. **Computerized Information Services:** DIALOG Information Services, LEXIS, NEXIS. **Publications:** Acquisitions List, monthly.

★4287★
Coopers & Lybrand - Library (Bus-Fin)
333 Market St. Phone: (415)957-3172
San Francisco, CA 94105 Wayne Gribling, Libn./Rec.Supv.
Founded: 1974. **Staff:** Prof 1; Other 1. **Subjects:** Accounting, auditing, taxation, management consulting. **Holdings:** 2400 books; 1200 annual reports. **Subscriptions:** 200 journals and other serials. **Services:** Interlibrary loan; library open by appointment to researchers in the field. **Computerized Information Services:** DIALOG Information Services, Dow Jones News/Retrieval, DataTimes, LEXIS, NEXIS, InvesText, NewsNet, Inc., DunsPrint, PFDS Online, VU/TEXT Information Services, CCH (Commerce Clearing House, Inc.), Merger and Corporate Transactions Database; RBase Budget File (internal database). **Networks/Consortia:** Member of Bay Area Library and Information System (BALIS). **Remarks:** FAX: (415)957-3394.

★4288★
Coopers & Lybrand - Library (Bus-Fin)
1 Post Office Sq. Phone: (617)574-5491
Boston, MA 02109 Amy Pietrowski, Hd.Libn.
Founded: 1945. **Staff:** Prof 3; Other 3. **Subjects:** Taxation, accounting. **Holdings:** 4500 books; 600 bound periodical volumes; 200 services. **Subscriptions:** 300 journals and other serials; 15 newspapers. **Services:** Interlibrary loan; library not open to the public. **Computerized Information Services:** DIALOG Information Services, LEXIS, NEXIS, National Automated Accounting Research System (NAARS), Dun & Bradstreet Business Credit Services, Dow Jones News/Retrieval, VU/TEXT Information Services, CompuServe Information Service **Publications:** Notes from the Library, monthly - quarterly. **Remarks:** FAX: (617)542-1297. **Staff:** Gregor Smart, Asst.Libn.; Joyce Sulkey, Asst.Libn.

★4289★
Coopers & Lybrand - Library 5 North (Bus-Fin, Law)
1800 M St., N.W. Phone: (202)822-4368
Washington, DC 20036 Valerie Solomon, Hd.Libn.
Staff: Prof 1; Other 1. **Subjects:** Tax law, accounting, auditing, economics. **Special Collections:** Legislative histories of revenue/tax acts, 1918 to present. **Holdings:** 4000 books; 400 bound periodical volumes; 500 other cataloged items. **Subscriptions:** 254 journals and other serials. **Services:** Interlibrary loan; copying; library open to the public by appointment. **Computerized Information Services:** LEXIS, NEXIS, DIALOG Information Services, DataTimes, Dun & Bradstreet Business Credit Services, Dow Jones News/Retrieval, CCH ACCESS. **Publications:** Coopers & Lybrand publications and brochures compendium. **Remarks:** FAX: (202)296-8933.

★4290★
Coopers & Lybrand - National Library (Bus-Fin)
1251 Avenue of the Americas Phone: (212)536-2858
New York, NY 10020 James D. Walz, Mgr.
Founded: 1959. **Staff:** Prof 4; Other 5. **Subjects:** Accounting. **Holdings:** 13,000 volumes. **Subscriptions:** 600 journals and other serials. **Services:** Interlibrary loan; library not open to the public. **Automated Operations:** Computerized public access catalog, cataloging, and serials. **Computerized Information Services:** Mead Data Central, DIALOG Information Services, Dow Jones News/Retrieval, ADP Network Services, Inc., CompuServe Information Service, REUTERS, NewsNet, Inc., Info Globe, WILSONLINE, VU/TEXT Information Services, InvesText, Interactive Data Services, Inc., ORBIT Search Service; CD-ROMs (Laser D/SEC, Business Periodicals Ondisc, Disclosure/Worldscope, Moody's Company Data, Standard & Poor's Corporations, Newspaper Abstracts, Business Dateline, Computer Select). **Remarks:** FAX: (212)536-3567. **Staff:** Jacqueline Kilberg, Ref.Libn.; Judith Kincannon, Asst.Ref.Libn.; Christine Bruzzese, Asst.Libn./Cat.

Coordenacao dos Institutos de Pesquisa
See: **Brasil - Secretaria de Estado da Saude - Coordenacao dos Institutos de Pesquisa** (2084)

★4291★
Adolph Coors Company - Technical Library (Food-Bev)
Mail BC520 Phone: (303)277-3506
Golden, CO 80401 Stephen Boss, Libn.
Staff: Prof 1. **Subjects:** Brewing, microbiology, chemistry, law, engineering. **Special Collections:** Coors History Collection. **Holdings:** 5000 books; 40,000 internal reports; patents; clippings; pamphlets. **Subscriptions:** 400 journals and other serials; 15 newspapers. **Services:** Copying; library open to the public with restrictions. **Publications:** Library Bulletin, monthly. **Remarks:** FAX: (303)277-6064.

Copeland Memorial Library
See: **Florida Baptist Schools, Inc.** (5869)

★4292★
(Copenhagen) American Library - USIS LIbrary (Educ)
Dag Hammerskjolds Alle 24
DK-2100 Copenhagen, Denmark
Remarks: Maintained or supported by the U.S. Information Agency. Focus is on materials that will assist peoples outside the United States to learn about the United States, its people, history, culture, political processes, and social milieux.

★4293★
Copley Newspapers, Inc. - The James S. Copley Library (Hist)
Box 1530 Phone: (619)454-0411
La Jolla, CA 92038 Carol Beales, Mgr.
Founded: 1966. **Staff:** Prof 6; Other 1. **Subjects:** American Revolution, American Southwest, Mark Twain, Benito Juarez, John Charles Fremont, U.S. presidents, English and American authors' correspondence (late 19th and early 20th century). **Special Collections:** Autographs of the signers of the Declaration of Independence; American Revolutionary War documents and letters. **Holdings:** 15,000 books; 5500 letters, documents, manuscripts. **Subscriptions:** 3 newspapers. **Services:** Copying; library open to the public on a limited schedule. **Computerized Information Services:** OCLC. **Publications:** A Promise Kept/The Story of the James S. Copley Library, 1984. **Remarks:** Library located at 1134 Kline St., La Jolla, CA 92037. FAX: (619)454-5014. **Staff:** Marian Holleman, Libn.; Harold Kopelke, Cons.; Lauralee Bennett, Cons.; Ron Vanderhye, OCLC Cat.

★4294★
Copper Development Association Inc. - Copper Data Center (Sci-Engr)
Greenwich Office Park 2 Phone: (203)625-8210
Box 1840 William T. Black, Mgr., Tech. &
Greenwich, CT 06836-1840 Market Data
Founded: 1965. **Staff:** Prof 3. **Subjects:** Copper technology from refining of metal through end-use performance of copper and copper alloys; competitive materials. **Holdings:** 50,000 documents. **Computerized Information Services:** Internal database. **Publications:** Extracts of Copper Technology, Thesaurus of Terms on Copper Technology - to members; Patent Brief; Accessions List. **Remarks:** FAX: (203)625-0174. Toll-free telephone number(s): (800)CDA-DATA.

Copyright Public Information Office
See: **Library of Congress** (9112)

Ted Corbitt Archives
See: **New York Road Runners Club - Albert H. Gordon Library** (11639)

★4295★
Corcoran Gallery of Art - Corcoran Archives (Art)
17th St. & New York Ave., N.W.
Washington, DC 20006 Phone: (202)638-3211
Subjects: American art. **Special Collections:** Records of the Corcoran Gallery of Art. **Holdings:** 800 linear feet of cataloged items. **Services:** Copying; archives open to the public by appointment. **Remarks:** FAX: (202)737-5414.

★4296★
Corcoran Gallery and School of Art - Library (Art)
17th St. & New York Ave., N.W. Phone: (202)628-9484
Washington, DC 20006 Ann Maginnis, Libn.
Founded: 1982. **Staff:** Prof 1; Other 1. **Subjects:** Contemporary art, art techniques, photography. **Holdings:** 14,000 books; 850 bound periodical volumes; exhibition catalogs. **Subscriptions:** 140 journals and other serials. **Services:** Interlibrary loan; copying; library open to the public by appointment. **Automated Operations:** Computerized cataloging. **Remarks:** FAX: (202)737-2664.

★4297★
Cordova Historical Society, Inc. - Archives (Hist)
Cordova Museum
Box 391 Phone: (907)424-6665
Cordova, AK 99574 Lavon Branshaw, Musm. Attendant
Founded: 1966. **Staff:** 1. **Subjects:** Cordova history, early 1900s to present; the railroad era, fishing. **Special Collections:** Cordova Times newspapers, 1906 to present (microfilm). **Holdings:** Manuscript maps and photographs of the Copper River, the Northwest Railway, Cordova; charts; technical drawings; aerial photographs; correspondence of state and local officials. **Services:** Archives open to the public when attendant is present.

★4298★
Core Laboratories, Inc. - Library (Sci-Engr)
Box 1407
Houston, TX 77251-1407 Phone: (713)972-6635
Staff: Prof 1. **Subjects:** Petroleum engineering, geology, chemistry, mathematics. **Holdings:** 1800 books; 1000 bound periodical volumes; 500 technical reports and papers. **Subscriptions:** 50 journals and other serials. **Services:** Interlibrary loan; library not open to the public. **Computerized Information Services:** DIALOG Information Services, PFDS Online. **Publications:** Library Log, quarterly - for internal distribution only. **Remarks:** Library located at 10201 Westheimer, Bldg. 1A, Rm. 100, Houston, TX 77042. FAX: (713)972-6660.

★4299★
CoreSTATES Bank, N.A. - Marketing Information Center (Bus-Fin)
510 Walnut St., 7th Fl. 1-9-7-51 Phone: (215)786-8579
Philadelphia, PA 19106 Ginny Bevilacqua, Mktg.Off.
Founded: 1973. **Staff:** 1. **Subjects:** Marketing, banking. **Holdings:** 500 books. **Subscriptions:** 100 journals and other serials. **Services:** Interlibrary loan; center not open to the public. **Computerized Information Services:** NEXIS, LEXIS. **Remarks:** FAX: (215)973-7753. **Formed by the merger of:** First Pennsylvania Bank, N.A. - Marketing Information Center and CoreSTATES to form CoreSTATES Bank, N.A.

Jack and Sallie Corette Library
See: **Carroll College - Jack and Sallie Corette Library** (3099)

D. Leonard Corgan Library
See: **King's College - D. Leonard Corgan Library** (8721)

★4300★
Cornell College - Chemistry Library (Sci-Engr)
West Science Center Phone: (319)895-4000
Mount Vernon, IA 52314 Dr. Addison Ault, Dir., Lib.Serv.
Staff: 2. **Subjects:** Chemistry. **Holdings:** 4503 volumes. **Services:** Interlibrary loan; copying; library open to the public. **Computerized Information Services:** DIALOG Information Services, PFDS Online, BRS Information Technologies, OCLC. Performs searches on fee basis. Contact Person: Sue Lifson, Ref. & Circ.Libn. **Networks/Consortia:** Member of Iowa Computer Assisted Network (ICAN). **Staff:** Carol Brokel, Asst.Dir.

★4301★
Cornell Institute for Social and Economic Research (CISER) - CISER Data Archive (Soc Sci, Info Sci)
Cornell University
260 Caldwell Hall Phone: (607)255-1359
Ithaca, NY 14853 Ann S. Gray, Data Archv.
Founded: 1982. **Staff:** Prof 1; Other 2. **Subjects:** Social sciences, census, economics, labor statistics, New York state, social surveys and indicators. **Holdings:** 1600 magnetic computer tapes and data documentation. **Services:** Contract programming; data extraction; archive open to the public with restrictions. **Computerized Information Services:** CD-ROMs; internal database; BITNET, InterNet (electronic mail services). Contact Person: Yoko Akiba, Archv.Supv.Spec. **Publications:** CISER Data Archive Holdings, 3/year - to Cornell community. **Special Catalogs:** Data Archive Holdings (online). **Remarks:** FAX: (607)255-9353. Electronic mail address(es): AG5@CORNELLA (BITNET); AG5@CORNELLA.CIT.CORNELL.EDU (InterNet). The archive serves as a centralized information center and clearinghouse for the acquisition, storage, access, and dissemination of primarily social and economic data in machine-readable format.

Julian and Virginia Cornell Library
See: **Vermont Law School - Julian and Virginia Cornell Library** (19805)

Cornell Library of Science and Engineering
See: **Swarthmore College** (15900)

Cornell Medical Center
See: **New York Hospital-Cornell Medical Center - Medical Archives** (11579)

Cornell Mill Museum
See: **Missisquoi Historical Society** (10509)

Cornell Modern Indonesia Project
See: **Cornell University - Southeast Asia Program** (4332)

★4302★
Cornell University - Albert R. Mann Library (Agri, Biol Sci, Food-Bev)
Ithaca, NY 14853-4301 Phone: (607)255-2285
Jan Olsen, Libn.
Founded: 1952. **Staff:** Prof 24; Other 40. **Subjects:** Agriculture, biological sciences, human ecology, nutrition. **Special Collections:** Everett Franklin Phillips Beekeeping Collection (5200 volumes); James E. Rice Poultry Library (5700 volumes); Language of Flowers (185 volumes); Lace and Lacemaking (267 volumes). **Holdings:** 626,200 volumes; 3100 maps; 512,000 microforms. **Subscriptions:** 9900 journals and other serials. **Services:** Interlibrary loan; copying; SDI; library open to the public. **Automated Operations:** Computerized public access catalog, cataloging, acquisitions, and circulation. **Computerized Information Services:** BRS Information Technologies, DIALOG Information Services; BITNET (electronic mail service). **Networks/Consortia:** Member of Research Libraries Information Network (RLIN). **Remarks:** FAX: (607)255-0850. Library serves the New York State College of Agriculture & Life Sciences, the New York State College of Human Ecology, the Division of Biological Sciences, and the Division of Nutritional Sciences. **Remarks:** Electronic mail address(es): MANX@CORNELLC (BITNET). **Staff:** Samuel Demas, Hd., Coll.Dev.; Janet McCue, Hd., Tech.Serv.; Susan Barnes, Hd., Pub.Serv.; Howard Curtis, Hd., Info.Tech.

★4303★
Cornell University - Arecibo Observatory - Library (Sci-Engr)
Box 995 Phone: (809)878-2612
Arecibo, PR 00613 Carmen G. Segarra, Libn.
Founded: 1963. **Staff:** Prof 2. **Subjects:** Astronomy, radio and radar astronomy, upper atmosphere, physics, computer science, engineering. **Special Collections:** Center for Radiophysics and Space Research reports (880); Arecibo Observatory reports (29); National Astronomy and Ionosphere Center reports (250); Palomar Observatory Sky Survey. **Holdings:** 2500 books; 3000 bound periodical volumes; 130 theses; reprints; maps; charts; slides. **Subscriptions:** 100 journals and other serials. **Services:** Interlibrary loan; copying; computing; library open to the public with permission. **Automated Operations:** Computerized cataloging. **Remarks:** FAX: (809)878-1861. **Formerly:** Its National Astronomy & Ionosphere Center Library.

★4304★
Cornell University - Bailey Hortorium Library (Biol Sci)
Albert R. Mann Library, Rm. 462 Phone: (607)255-2131
Ithaca, NY 14853-4301 J.I. Davis, Libn.
Staff: 1. **Subjects:** Taxonomic botany and horticulture. **Special Collections:** Worldwide collection of seed and plant lists and catalogs from botanical gardens and commercial sources; card file of sources for plant materials. **Holdings:** 12,000 volumes; 20,000 reprints on taxonomic botany and allied subjects; 8000 photographs of type specimens and other important specimens in European herbaria. **Subscriptions:** 214 journals and other serials. **Services:** Interlibrary loan; library open to the public. **Remarks:** Library serves the New York State College of Agriculture & Life Sciences at Cornell University.

★4305★
Cornell University - Cornell Laboratory for Environmental Applications of Remote Sensing (CLEARS) - Remote Sensing and Map Library (Geog-Map)
464 Hollister Hall Phone: (607)255-0800
Ithaca, NY 14853 Eugenia M. Barnaba, Tech.Mgr.
Founded: 1984. **Staff:** Prof 4. **Subjects:** Remote sensing, aerial photographs, satellite imagery, topographic maps. **Special Collections:** 1968 Land Use Inventory of New York State (aerial photographs; maps; data books); U.S. Department of Interior National Wetlands Maps for New York State. **Holdings:** 3000 volumes; 200,000 aircraft and spacecraft images; 8000 maps; 2000 volumes of statistical data on land use. **Services:** Copying; library open to the public by appointmment for reference use only. **Remarks:** FAX: (607)255-0238.

★4306★
Cornell University - Department of Manuscripts and University Archives (Hist, Plan)
101 John M. Olin Library Phone: (607)255-3530
Ithaca, NY 14853-5301 H. Thomas Hickerson, Chm.
Founded: 1942. **Staff:** Prof 5; Other 10. **Subjects:** Cornell University history, city and regional planning, 19th and 20th century politics, social and civil service reform, land policy, agriculture, railroads, forest products, diplomatic history, medicine, human sexuality, ornithology, manufacturing, New York state history. **Holdings:** 28,217 cubic feet of archives, manuscripts, ephemera; 4079 reels of microfilm; 6650 tape recordings; 80,000 photographs and films. **Subscriptions:** 90 journals and other serials. **Services:** Interlibrary loan; copying; department open to the public. **Automated Operations:** Computerized public access catalog, cataloging, and circulation. **Computerized Information Services:** BITNET (electronic mail service). **Networks/Consortia:** Member of Research Libraries Information Network (RLIN). **Publications:** Documentation Newsletter, biennial - by subscription. **Remarks:** FAX: (607)255-9346. Electronic mail address(es): BM.CCA@RLG (BITNET). **Staff:** Gould Colman, Univ.Archv.; Herbert Finch, Archv.; Elaine Engst, Assoc.Archv.; Brenda Marston, Sr.Asst.Archv.

★4307★
Cornell University - Engineering Library (Sci-Engr)
Carpenter Hall Phone: (607)255-4318
Ithaca, NY 14853-2201 John Saylor, Libn.
Founded: 1937. **Staff:** Prof 3; Other 6. **Subjects:** Engineering - aerospace, chemical, civil, electrical, industrial, mechanical, nuclear; theoretical and applied mechanics; space science and technology; water resources development; computer science; operations research; energy; materials science; earth science. **Special Collections:** NTIS Reports; American Society of Mechanical Engineers Technical Papers; Society of Automotive Engineers Papers. **Holdings:** 294,000 volumes; 1.45 million microforms. **Subscriptions:** 4600 journals and other serials. **Services:** Interlibrary loan; copying; library open to the public with restrictions. **Automated Operations:** Computerized public access catalog, cataloging, acquisitions, and circulation. **Computerized Information Services:** DIALOG Information Services, BRS Information Technologies, STN International, PFDS Online. **Networks/Consortia:** Member of Research Libraries Information Network (RLIN). **Remarks:** Electronic mail address(es): EGR@CORNELL (BITNET). **Staff:** Jill Powell, Ref.Libn.; Mary Patterson, Ref.Libn.; Joanne Leary, Circ. Reserve Supv.

★4308★
Cornell University - Entomology Library (Biol Sci)
Comstock Hall Phone: (607)255-3265
Ithaca, NY 14853-2601 Edwin Spragg, Entomology Libn.
Founded: 1914. **Staff:** Prof 1; Other 3. **Subjects:** General and applied entomology, medical entomology, parasitology. **Special Collections:** Collected reprints of important entomological writers; collected reprints for each order of insects. **Holdings:** 35,000 volumes. **Subscriptions:** 600 journals and other serials. **Services:** Interlibrary loan; copying; library open to the public. **Automated Operations:** Computerized public access catalog, cataloging, acquisitions, and circulation. **Computerized Information Services:** BRS Information Technologies, DIALOG Information Services; BITNET (electronic mail service). Performs searches on fee basis. **Networks/Consortia:** Member of Research Libraries Information Network (RLIN). **Special Indexes:** Author index to reprint collections (card). **Remarks:** Electronic mail address(es): MANX@CORNELLC (BITNET).

★4309★
Cornell University - Fine Arts Library (Art, Plan)
Sibley Dome Phone: (607)255-3710
Ithaca, NY 14853-6701 Judith E. Holliday, Libn.
Founded: 1871. **Staff:** Prof 2; Other 4. **Subjects:** Art, architecture, city planning, landscape architecture. **Holdings:** 143,000 volumes; 6400 microforms. **Subscriptions:** 1900 journals and other serials. **Services:** Interlibrary loan; copying. **Automated Operations:** Computerized public access catalog, cataloging, acquisitions, and circulation. **Networks/Consortia:** Member of Research Libraries Information Network (RLIN). **Special Indexes:** Avery Index to Architectural Periodicals. **Staff:** Pat Sullivan, Assoc.Libn.

★4310★
Cornell University - Fiske Icelandic Collection (Area-Ethnic)
217 John M. Olin Library Phone: (607)255-6462
Ithaca, NY 14853-5301 P.M. Mitchell, Cur.
Founded: 1905. **Staff:** Prof 2. **Subjects:** Iceland - flora and fauna, geography, geology, history, literature and language, natural resources, statistics; early Scandinavian history; Old Norse literature, language, mythology. **Special Collections:** Fiskeana, runology. **Holdings:** 36,000 volumes; 530 reels of microfilm; 25,000 letters; 600 maps. **Subscriptions:** 80 journals and other serials. **Services:** Interlibrary loan (limited); copying; collection open to the public with restrictions on circulation. **Automated Operations:** Computerized public access catalog, cataloging, acquisitions, and circulation. **Networks/Consortia:** Member of Research Libraries Information Network (RLIN). **Publications:** Islandica, irregular - by subscription, on exchange, or for sale from Cornell University Press. **Special Catalogs:** Catalogue of the Icelandic Collection Bequeathed by Willard Fiske, 1914 and its Supplements, 1927 and 1943; Catalogue of Runic Literature, 1918. **Remarks:** FAX: (607)255-9346.

★4311★
Cornell University - Flower Veterinary Library (Med)
Schurman Hall Phone: (607)253-3510
Ithaca, NY 14853-6401 Susanne K. Whitaker, Vet.Med.Libn.
Founded: 1897. **Staff:** Prof 2; Other 8. **Subjects:** Veterinary medicine and supporting biomedical subjects. **Holdings:** 80,500 volumes; 30,000 AV items. **Subscriptions:** 1300 journals and other serials. **Services:** Interlibrary loan; copying; SDI; library open to the public for reference use only. **Automated Operations:** Computerized public access catalog, cataloging, acquisitions, and circulation. **Computerized Information Services:** NLM, DIALOG Information Services, BRS Information Technologies. Performs searches on fee basis. **Networks/Consortia:** Member of Research Libraries Information Network (RLIN). **Publications:** Newsletter, quarterly - internal and limited outside distribution. **Remarks:** FAX: (607)253-3708. Library serves the New York State College of Veterinary Medicine at Cornell University. **Staff:** Nancy Cummings, Ref.Libn.

★4312★
Cornell University - Herbert F. Johnson Museum of Art - Reference Library (Art)
Ithaca, NY 14853-4001 Phone: (607)255-6464
Nancy Allyn Jarzombek, Assoc.Cur.
Founded: 1973. **Staff:** Prof 1. **Subjects:** Art, artists. **Holdings:** 1000 books; 23 VF drawers of artists' files; auction and exhibition catalogs; catalogs of museum's collections and exhibitions. **Subscriptions:** 15 journals and other serials. **Services:** Library open to the public with restrictions. **Remarks:** FAX: (607)255-9940.

★4313★
Cornell University - History of Science Collections (Sci-Engr, Hist)
215 John M. Olin Library Phone: (607)255-4033
Ithaca, NY 14853-5301 David W. Corson, Hist. of Sci.Libn.
Founded: 1961. **Staff:** Prof 2; Other 2. **Subjects:** History of the biological and physical sciences, medicine, and technology, 16th-19th centuries. **Special Collections:** Adelmann Collection (history of embryology and anatomy; 5400 volumes); Boyle Collection (writings of Robert Boyle; 175 volumes); Baldassare Boncompagni Archives (history of mathematics and physical sciences; 3400 items); Benoist LaForte Archives (late 18th century chemistry; 3000 manuscript items); Cooper Collection (19th century American civil engineering; 350 items); Hill Collection (18th-19th century North American ornithology; 380 volumes); Hollister Collection (history of civil engineering; 300 volumes); Lavoisier Collection (18th and early 19th century chemistry; 2000 volumes, 525 manuscript items); medical dissertations (16th-19th centuries, mainly German; 6500 items); rare books. **Holdings:** 35,000 books. **Subscriptions:** 9 journals and other serials. **Services:** Copying (limited); collections open to the public with restrictions on circulation. **Automated Operations:** Computerized public access catalog, cataloging, acquisitions, and circulation. **Networks/Consortia:** Member of Research Libraries Information Network (RLIN). **Special Catalogs:** Catalog of manuscripts; catalogs by provenance, publisher, printer, and imprint date (all card). **Remarks:** FAX: (607)255-9346. **Staff:** Margaret Rogers, Adm.Supv.; Laura Linke, Sr.Spec.Coll.Asst.

★4314★
Cornell University - John Henrik Clarke Africana Library (Area-Ethnic)
310 Triphammer Rd. Phone: (607)255-5229
Ithaca, NY 14850-2599 Thomas Weissinger, Libn.
Founded: 1972. **Staff:** Prof 1; Other 3. **Subjects:** African, Afro-American, Caribbean peoples - history, culture, lifestyles, and economic, social, and political development. **Special Collections:** Civil Rights Microfilm Collection (940 microforms). **Holdings:** 13,800 books; 12 file drawers of clippings; 250 videocassettes. **Subscriptions:** 104 journals and other serials; 15 newspapers. **Services:** Interlibrary loan; library open to the public. **Automated Operations:** Computerized public access catalog, cataloging, acquisitions, and circulation. **Computerized Information Services:** DIALOG Information Services, RLIN. **Networks/Consortia:** Member of Research Libraries Information Network (RLIN). **Remarks:** Alternate telephone number(s): 255-3822. FAX: (607)255-0784.

★4315★
Cornell University - John M. Echols Collection on Southeast Asia (Area-Ethnic)
107-E John M. Olin Library Phone: (607)255-4189
Ithaca, NY 14853-5301 John H. Badgley, Cur.
Staff: Prof 3; Other 7. **Subjects:** Southeast Asia. **Holdings:** 210,000 monographs; 20,000 serials; 850 backfile newspapers; 142,000 microforms; 1600 maps. **Subscriptions:** 4000 journals and other serials; 91 newspapers. **Services:** Interlibrary loan; copying; collection open to the public for reference use only. **Automated Operations:** public access catalog, cataloging, acquisitions, and circulation. **Computerized Information Services:** BITNET (electronic mail service). **Networks/Consortia:** Member of Research Libraries Information Network (RLIN). **Publications:** Accessions list, monthly - by subscription. **Special Catalogs:** Southeast Asia Catalog (10 volume book catalog), published 1976-1983. **Remarks:** FAX: (607)255-9346. Telex: WUI6713054 Cornell ITCA (specify Echols, Olin Library). Electronic mail address(es): AJR@CORNELLC (BITNET). **Staff:** Allen Riedy, S.E. Asia Libn.; Mary Crawford, Adm.Supv.

★4316★
Cornell University - Johnson Graduate School of Management - Library (Bus-Fin)
Malott Hall Phone: (607)255-3389
Ithaca, NY 14853-4201 Donald Schnedeker, Dir.
Founded: 1949. **Staff:** Prof 3; Other 5. **Subjects:** Business administration and management science, finance, investment, accounting, marketing, managerial economics, operations management and information systems, behavioral science, personnel, quantitative analysis. **Special Collections:** Corporation reports (600,000 microtext editions). **Holdings:** 161,000 volumes; 9000 pamphlets; 664,000 microforms. **Subscriptions:** 2300 journals and other serials. **Services:** Interlibrary loan. **Automated Operations:** Computerized public access catalog, cataloging, acquisitions, and circulation. **Computerized Information Services:** DIALOG Information Services, BRS Information Technologies, Dow Jones News/Retrieval, U.S. Department of Commerce, First Call; CD-ROMs (Lotus CD/Corporate, COMPUSTAT PC Plus, ABI/INFORM, BPI); BITNET (electronic mail service). Performs searches on fee basis. **Networks/Consortia:** Member of Research Libraries Information Network (RLIN). **Publications:** College and University Business Library Statistics, 1988-1989; Occasional bibliographies - to other schools of management. **Remarks:** FAX: (607)255-8633. Electronic mail address(es): DONS@CRNLGSM (BITNET). **Staff:** Lynn Brown, Ref.Libn.; Meryl White, Ref.Libn.

★4317★
Cornell University - Laboratory of Ornithology - Library (Biol Sci)
159 Sapsucker Woods Rd. Phone: (607)254-2403
Ithaca, NY 14850-1999 Todd A. Culver, Educ.Spec.
Staff: 2. **Subjects:** Ornithology. **Special Collections:** Books illustrated by Louis A. Fuertes (100). **Holdings:** 3500 books; 430 periodical titles. **Subscriptions:** 200 journals and other serials. **Services:** Copying; library open to the public on a fee basis. **Remarks:** FAX: (607)254-2415. **Staff:** Tim Dillon.

★4318★
Cornell University - Laboratory of Ornithology - Library of Natural Sounds (Biol Sci, Aud-Vis)
159 Sapsucker Woods Rd. Phone: (607)254-2404
Ithaca, NY 14850-1999 Greg Budney, Cur.
Founded: 1948. **Staff:** Prof 2; Other 7. **Subjects:** Vocalizations - bird, amphibian, mammal; environmental sounds. **Holdings:** 70,000 sound recordings. **Subscriptions:** 3 journals and other serials. **Services:** Copying; library open to the public by appointment. **Remarks:** FAX: (607)254-2415.

★4319★
Cornell University - Law Library (Law)
Myron Taylor Hall Phone: (607)255-7236
Ithaca, NY 14853-4901 Jane L. Hammond, Law Libn.
Founded: 1887. **Staff:** Prof 7; Other 16. **Subjects:** Law. **Holdings:** 399,163 volumes; 4961 reels of microfilm; 333,087 microfiche. **Subscriptions:** 5176 journals and other serials; 7 newspapers. **Services:** Interlibrary loan; copying; library open to the public with restrictions. **Automated Operations:** Computerized public access catalog, cataloging, acquisitions, and serials. **Computerized Information Services:** LEXIS, NEXIS, WESTLAW. **Networks/Consortia:** Member of New York State Interlibrary Loan Network (NYSILL), South Central Research Library Council (SCRLC), Research Libraries Information Network (RLIN). **Remarks:** FAX: (607)255-7193.

★4320★
Cornell University - Maps, Microtexts, Newspapers Department (Geog-Map)
015 John M. Olin Library Phone: (607)255-5258
Ithaca, NY 14853-5301 Caroline Spicer, Libn.
Founded: 1961. **Staff:** Prof 3; Other 2. **Holdings:** 190,000 sheet maps; 10,000 volumes; 2.1 million microforms. **Subscriptions:** 443 newspapers. **Services:** Copying; department open to the public. **Automated Operations:** Computerized public access catalog, cataloging, circulation and acquisitions. **Computerized Information Services:** CD-ROMs (NewsBank Electronic Index, Newspaper Abstracts Ondisc). **Networks/Consortia:** Member of Research Libraries Information Network (RLIN). **Special Catalogs:** Microtexts in Cornell University Libraries (book). **Remarks:** FAX: (607)255-9346. **Staff:** Carmen Blankinship, Sr.Asst.Libn.

★4321★
Cornell University - Mathematics Library (Sci-Engr)
White Hall Phone: (607)255-5076
Ithaca, NY 14853-7901 Steven W. Rockey, Libn.
Founded: 1870. **Staff:** 3. **Subjects:** Pure mathematics, applied mathematics, mathematical statistics, mathematical logic, history of mathematics. **Holdings:** 40,000 volumes. **Subscriptions:** 570 journals and other serials. **Services:** Interlibrary loan; copying; library open to the public for reference use only. **Automated Operations:** Computerized public access catalog, cataloging, circulation, and acquisitions. **Computerized Information Services:** DIALOG Information Services, STN International; BITNET (electronic mail service). **Networks/Consortia:** Member of Research Libraries Information Network (RLIN). **Remarks:** Electronic mail address(es): LIBRARY@MSSUN%MSI.CORNELL.EDU (BITNET).

★4322★
Cornell University - Media Services Distribution Center (Sci-Engr, Aud-Vis)
7 Business and Technology Park Phone: (607)255-7660
Ithaca, NY 14850 Carol Doolittle, Mgr.
Founded: 1948. **Staff:** Prof 3; Other 7. **Subjects:** Agriculture safety, human ecology, natural resources, youth development, food and nutrition, animal science, sociology, science, family studies. **Holdings:** 2000 publications; 200 16mm films; 180 35mm slide sets; 300 videotapes; 30 audiotapes. **Services:** Interlibrary loan (fee); center open to the public. **Networks/Consortia:** Member of Consortium of College and University Media Centers (CCUMC), American Film & Video Association. **Publications:** AV, computer software and publications catalogs - available upon request. **Remarks:** FAX: (607)255-9946.

Cornell University - Medical College - New York Hospital-Cornell Medical Center - Medical Archives
See: **New York Hospital-Cornell Medical Center - Medical Archives** (11579)

★4323★
Cornell University - Medical College - Samuel J. Wood Library - C.V. Starr Biomedical Information Center (Med)
1300 York Ave. Phone: (212)746-6050
New York, NY 10021 Robert M. Braude, Ph.D., Dir.
Founded: 1899. **Staff:** Prof 9; Other 26. **Subjects:** Medicine, nursing. **Special Collections:** New York Hospital Archives; Cornell Medical Center Archives. **Holdings:** 52,000 books; 93,186 bound periodical volumes; 5119 microfiche; 470 audio recordings; 394 videocassettes; 37 reels of microfilm; 26,500 iconographic images, photographs, and prints. **Subscriptions:** 1616 journals and other serials. **Services:** Interlibrary loan; SDI (limited); center open to health professionals on a fee basis. **Automated Operations:** Computerized public access catalog, cataloging, acquisitions, serials, and circulation. **Computerized Information Services:** OCLC, RLIN, BRS Information Technologies, DIALOG Information Services, NLM, miniMEDLINE; CD-ROM (MedFive); internal database. **Networks/Consortia:** Member of Medical Library Center of New York (MLCNY), New York Metropolitan Reference and Research Library Agency, National Network of Libraries of Medicine - Middle Atlantic Region. **Publications:** Vital Signs: Hx & Px (newsletter, online). **Remarks:** FAX: (212)746-6494. Alternate telephone number(s): 746-6055 (reference services). Affiliated with New York Hospital. **Staff:** Carolyn Anne Reid, Assoc.Dir.; Mira Myhre, Hd., Cat.; Mark E. Funk, Hd., Coll.Dev.; Octavio Morales, Hd., Comp.Serv. Jacqueline Picciano, Hd., Access Serv.; Adele A. Lerner, Archv.; Diane G. Thomson, Hd., Educ. & Info.Serv.; Jeanne Strausman; Catherine Warren; Helen-Ann Brown, Hd.,Lib.Rel.

★4324★
Cornell University - Music Library (Mus)
225 Lincoln Hall Phone: (607)255-4011
Ithaca, NY 14853-4101 Lenore Coral, Mus.Libn.
Founded: 1958. **Staff:** Prof 2; Other 5. **Subjects:** Musicology, music, opera, chamber music, contemporary music and dance. **Special Collections:** Vocal music published in U.S., 18th-20th century (12,150 items); early 16th century music (microfilm); 18th century chamber music; Archive of Field Recordings (251). **Holdings:** 100,000 books, scores, bound periodical volumes; 38,000 phonograph records. **Subscriptions:** 720 journals and other serials. **Services:** Interlibrary loan; library open to the public. **Automated Operations:** Computerized public access catalog, cataloging, acquisitions, and circulation. **Networks/Consortia:** Member of Research Libraries Information Network (RLIN). **Special Catalogs:** Materials relating to Alessandro Scarlatti's operas (book catalog); Archive of Field Recordings (book catalog). **Special Indexes:** Index to sheet music. **Staff:** James Cassaro, Assoc.Mus.Libn.

★4325★
Cornell University - New York State Agricultural Experiment Station - Library (Agri, Food-Bev)
Geneva, NY 14456 Phone: (315)787-2214
Mary Van Buren, Libn.
Founded: 1882. **Staff:** Prof 1; Other 1. **Subjects:** Agriculture, fruit and vegetable breeding, food science, wines, seed investigation, entomology, plant pathology. **Special Collections:** Large collection of books and journals on grapes and wine. **Holdings:** 49,000 volumes. **Subscriptions:** 1000 journals and other serials. **Services:** Interlibrary loan; copying; library open to the public. **Computerized Information Services:** DIALOG Information Services, BRS Information Technologies, RLIN. **Networks/Consortia:** Member of Research Libraries Information Network (RLIN). **Publications:** New in the Library - for internal distribution only. **Remarks:** FAX: (315)787-2397. **Staff:** Ardeen L. White, Asst.Libn.

★4326★
Cornell University - New York State School of Industrial and Labor Relations - Martin P. Catherwood Library (Bus-Fin)
Ives Hall Phone: (607)255-2184
Ithaca, NY 14851-0952 Shirley F. Harper, Libn.
Founded: 1945. **Staff:** Prof 12; Other 16. **Subjects:** Labor-management relations, labor law and legislation, labor organization, industrial and labor conditions, labor economics, human resources, social security, personnel administration, supervision, industrial psychology, industrial safety, international labor conditions and problems, organization behavior. **Special Collections:** Labor union journals, proceedings, and constitutions; Labor Management Documentation Center (manuscripts and current documents). **Holdings:** 175,000 volumes; 250,000 pamphlets and documents; 34,000 microforms; 12,500 linear feet of manuscripts. **Subscriptions:** 1000 journals; 2500 serials. **Services:** Copying; document delivery; library open to the public with restrictions. **Automated Operations:** Computerized public access catalog, cataloging, acquisitions, and circulation. **Computerized Information Services:** DIALOG Information Services, BRS Information Technologies, Dow Jones News/Retrieval, The Source Information Network, LEXIS, Questel, Human Resource Information Network (HRIN), CompuServe Information Service, VU/TEXT Information Services, NewsNet, Inc., Labor Relations Press (LRP); DIALMAIL (electronic mail service); Performs searches on fee basis. Contact Person: Constance Finlay, Ref.Libn., 255-2184. **Networks/Consortia:** Member of Research Libraries Information Network (RLIN). **Publications:** Acquisitions List, monthly; finding guides for some manuscript collections. **Remarks:** FAX: (607)255-9641. Electronic mail address(es): 11595 (DIALMAIL). **Staff:** Richard Strassberg, Assoc.Libn./Dir.LMDC Ctr.; Carolyn Zimmerman, Hd.Circ. & Reserve; Linda Lowry, Ref.Libn.; Martha Hodges, Ref.Archv.; M. Constance Buckley, Doc.Ctr.; Phillip Dankert, Coll.Dev.; Chung N. Kim, Cat.Libn.; John Goddard, Cat.; Gail Neely, Cat.; Stephen Helmer, Res. Aide.

★4327★
Cornell University - New York State School of Industrial and Labor Relations - Sanford V. Lenz Library (Bus-Fin)
15 E. 26th St. Phone: (212)340-2845
New York, NY 10010-1565 Donna L. Schulman, Dir.
Founded: 1979. **Staff:** Prof 1; Other 3. **Subjects:** Industrial relations, labor relations, collective bargaining, arbitration, women and work. **Special Collections:** Trade Union Women (1000 books; 200 subject files). **Holdings:** 6000 books. **Subscriptions:** 125 journals and other serials; 65 newspapers. **Services:** Interlibrary loan; copying; SDI; library open to the public for reference use only. **Computerized Information Services:** DIALOG Information Services, BRS Information Technologies, Dow Jones News/Retrieval, RLIN. Performs searches on fee basis. **Networks/Consortia:** Member of New York Metropolitan Reference and Research Library Agency. **Publications:** Acquisitions list, irregular. **Remarks:** FAX: (212)340-2822.

★4328★
Cornell University - Physical Sciences Library (Sci-Engr)
Clark Hall Phone: (607)255-4016
Ithaca, NY 14853-2501 Patricia O'Neill, Libn.
Founded: 1965. **Staff:** Prof 3; Other 7. **Subjects:** Astronomy; chemistry - analytical, inorganic, organic; physics - applied, experimental, theoretical; biochemistry; biophysics; crystallography; electron microscopy; optics; quantum theory. **Special Collections:** X-ray powder diffraction cards of American Society for Testing and Materials; spectral indexes of Sadtler Research and Texas A&M University Thermodynamics Research Center. **Holdings:** 90,000 volumes; 21,000 microforms. **Subscriptions:** 850 journals and other serials. **Services:** Interlibrary loan; copying. **Automated Operations:** Computerized public access catalog, cataloging, circulation and acquisitions. **Computerized Information Services:** DIALOG Information Services, STN International, Chemical Abstracts Service (CAS). Performs searches on fee basis. **Networks/Consortia:** Member of Research Libraries Information Network (RLIN). **Staff:** Mary E. Thomas, Assoc.Libn.; Susan E. Markowitz, Assoc.Libn.

★4329★
Cornell University - Program on Participation and Labor-Managed Systems - Documentation Center (Bus-Fin)
490 Uris Hall
Ithaca, NY 14853-4867 Phone: (607)255-4867
Founded: 1978. **Staff:** Prof 1. **Subjects:** Workers' self-management, participation, control; production cooperatives; self-help. **Holdings:** 250 books; 900 manuscripts; 50 dissertations; 3700 bibliographic citations with abstracts. **Services:** Copying; reference search services (fee); center open to the public with restrictions. **Publications:** PPLMS Annual Report. **Remarks:** FAX: (607)255-2818.

★4330★
Cornell University - Rare Books Department (Rare Book)
106 John M. Olin Library Phone: (607)255-4211
Ithaca, NY 14853-5301 Mark Dimunation, Libn.
Founded: 1865. **Staff:** Prof 2; Other 4. **Subjects:** Antislavery, Daniel and Philip Berrigan, Charles X of France, Dante, Robert Dodsley, Ford Madox Ford, Franco-Americana, French Revolution, Samuel Johnson, James Joyce, Marquis de Lafayette, Wyndham Lewis, A.J. Liebling, Comte de Maurepas, George Jean Nathan, Petrarch, Alexander Pope, George Bernard Shaw, Jonathan Swift, E.B. White, Witchcraft, William Wordsworth, William Stringfellow, Laura (Riding) Jackson, Paul Goodman, Rudyard Kipling, Valerius Maximus, Theodore Drieser, Lydia Maria Child, John Steinbeck, Abraham Lincoln, Baron Charles Louis de Montesquieu, selected 20th century authors, selected Luther and Protestant Reformation material. **Holdings:** 131,000 books; 1.6 million manuscripts. **Subscriptions:** 4 journals and other serials. **Services:** Copying; department open to the public. **Networks/Consortia:** Member of Research Libraries Information Network (RLIN). **Remarks:** FAX: (607)255-9346. **Staff:** James Tyler, Asst. Rare Bks.Libn.

Cornell University - School of Hotel Administration Library
See: **Cornell University - Stouffer Hotels Library** (4333)

★4331★
Cornell University - Shoals Marine Laboratory - Library (Biol Sci)
G14 Stimson Hall Phone: (607)255-3717
Ithaca, NY 14853-7101 John B. Heiser, Dir., Lab.
Staff: 1. **Subjects:** Marine biology and geology, oceanography, meteorology, physical science. **Holdings:** 1000 books; pamphlets; articles; theses. **Services:** Library open to the public with restrictions on circulation. **Remarks:** Library located on Appledore Island, Isles of Shoals, ME. **Remarks:** FAX: (607)255-0742.

★4332★
Cornell University - Southeast Asia Program - Cornell Modern Indonesia Project (Area-Ethnic)
102 West Ave. Phone: (607)255-4359
Ithaca, NY 14850-3982 Audrey Kahin, Ed.
Staff: 3. **Subjects:** Indonesia, Southeast Asia. **Special Collections:** Publications of Cornell Modern Indonesia Project (69 volumes); publications of Southeast Asia Program (138 volumes); Indonesia Press Survey, 1955-1963 (5 volumes); Indonesia Current Affairs (6 volumes); Report on Indonesia (5 volumes); Far Eastern Economic Review, 1968 to present; New York Times newspaper clippings of Southeast Asia and Korea, 1975 to present; Foreign Broadcast Information Service: Daily Report on Asia and Pacific, 1981 to present. **Holdings:** 300 books; 200 bound periodical volumes. **Subscriptions:** 16 journals and other serials. **Services:** Library open to the public with permission. **Publications:** Indonesia, semiannual - by subscription; irregular publications. **Remarks:** FAX: (607)254-5000.

★4333★
Cornell University - Stouffer Hotels Library (Bus-Fin, Food-Bev)
Statler Hall Phone: (607)255-3673
Ithaca, NY 14853-6901 Katherine Laurence, Libn.
Founded: 1950. **Staff:** Prof 2.5; Other 4.75. **Subjects:** Hotel, motel, and restaurant administration; personnel administration; accounting; food and food chemistry; food facilities engineering; sanitation; advertising; sales promotion; public relations; marketing; environmental law; real estate; tourist industry; resort development. **Special Collections:** Menu Collection; rare cookbooks. **Holdings:** 25,000 volumes; 7000 microforms. **Subscriptions:** 497 journals and other serials. **Services:** Interlibrary loan; copying; library open to the public with restrictions. **Automated Operations:** Computerized public access catalog, cataloging, circulation, and acquisitions. **Computerized Information Services:** DIALOG Information Services, BRS Information Technologies; Consortium of Hospitality Research Information Services (internal database). Performs searches on fee basis. **Networks/Consortia:** Member of Research Libraries Information Network (RLIN). **Publications:** The Hospitality Index: The Index of the Lodging and Restaurant Industry, quarterly. **Remarks:** FAX: (607)255-4179. **Formerly:** Its School of Hotel Administration Library. **Staff:** Nancy Young, Ref.Libn.; Bill Coons, Ref.Libn.

★4334★
Cornell University - Wason Collection on East Asia (Area-Ethnic)
107 John M. Olin Library
Ithaca, NY 14853-5301 Phone: (607)255-4357
Founded: 1918. **Staff:** Prof 2; Other 4. **Subjects:** China, Japan, Korea, Tibet, Central Asia. **Special Collections:** Collection of Tun-huang manuscripts of Pelliot, Stein, and Peking collections (microfilm). **Holdings:** 421,000 volumes and microforms. **Subscriptions:** 2843 journals and other serials; 30 newspapers. **Services:** Interlibrary loan; copying; collection open to the public with restrictions. **Automated Operations:** Computerized public access catalog, cataloging, acquisitions, and circulation (Western Languages). **Computerized Information Services:** RLIN; OCLC CJK350. **Networks/Consortia:** Member of Research Libraries Information Network (RLIN). **Publications:** Griffis Collection of Japanese Books: An Annotated Bibliography, 1982. **Special Catalogs:** Catalog of the Wason Collection on China and the Chinese, 9 volumes, 1980 and 1985. **Remarks:** FAX: (607)255-9346. **Staff:** Satoshi Akiba, Asst.Cur.

Corning Glass Works - Hazleton Wisconsin
See: **Hazleton Wisconsin** (7071)

★4335★
Corning Incorporated - Technical Information Center (Sci-Engr)
Sullivan Park Phone: (607)974-3359
Corning, NY 14831 Richard A. Dreifuss, Lib.Supv.
Founded: 1936. **Staff:** Prof 2; Other 3. **Subjects:** Glass technology, ceramics, physics, chemistry, electronics. **Holdings:** 20,000 books; 24,000 bound periodical volumes; 18,000 internal company technical reports; 2500 translations. **Subscriptions:** 400 journals and other serials. **Services:** Center not open to the public. **Computerized Information Services:** DIALOG Information Services, STN International, PFDS Online, Dow Jones News/Retrieval; internal database. **Publications:** TICNOTES (newsletter) - for internal distribution only. **Remarks:** FAX: (607)962-6067. **Formerly:** Corning Glass Works. **Staff:** Marianna Stewart.

★4336★
Corning Museum of Glass - The Leonard S. and Juliette K. Rakow Library (Art, Sci-Engr)
1 Museum Way Phone: (607)927-5371
Corning, NY 14830-2253 Norma P.H. Jenkins, Hd.Libn.
Founded: 1951. **Staff:** Prof 4; Other 3. **Subjects:** Art, history, archeology of glass; glass manufacture and technology prior to 1900; glass painting and staining; history of science and technology; decorative arts; conservation. **Special Collections:** Rare books, incunabula, early manuscripts dealing with art and history of glass; glass manufacturers' trade catalogs on microfiche (4000). **Holdings:** 51,000 books; 12,000 bound periodical volumes; 800 documents; 155,000 2x2 colored transparent slides; 33 VF drawers of ephemera; 700 fine art prints and photographs; 93 boxes of company records of defunct glass firms; 1 drawer of patents; 600 reels of microfilm; 425 films (converted to videotapes). **Subscriptions:** 740 journals and other serials. **Services:** Interlibrary loan; copying; library open to the public for reference use only. **Automated Operations:** Computerized cataloging. **Computerized Information Services:** OCLC; OBCAT (internal database). **Networks/Consortia:** Member of South Central Research Library Council (SCRLC). **Publications:** Journal of Glass Studies, annual; New Glass Review, annual - both available by subscription; Acquisitions List, monthly - for internal distribution only. **Special Catalogs:** Exhibition catalogs, irregular - for sale. **Remarks:** FAX: (607)937-3352. **Staff:** Virginia Wright, Assoc.Libn.; Gail Bardhan, AV Libn.; Elizabeth Hylen, Acq.Libn.

Warren H. Corning Library
See: **Holden Arboretum** (7323)

★4337★
Cornish College - Library (Art)
710 E. Roy St. Phone: (206)323-1400
Seattle, WA 98102 Ronald G. McComb, Lib.Dir.
Founded: 1974. **Staff:** Prof 1; Other 2. **Subjects:** Fine arts, design, music, dance, theater, liberal arts. **Holdings:** 12,000 books; 25,000 slides; 1900 scores; **Subscriptions:** 100 journals and other serials. **Services:** Viewing/listening facility; library open to the public with restrictions. **Staff:** Sean Kennedy.

Coronado National Memorial
See: **U.S. Natl. Park Service** (17692)

Coronel Memorial Library
See: **Royal Roads Military College** (14132)

★4338★
Corporation Professionnelle des Medecins du Quebec - Informatheque (Med)
1440, rue Sainte-Catherine, W., Rm. 914 Phone: (514)878-4441
Montreal, PQ, Canada H3G 1S5 Helene Landry, Lib.Techn.
Staff: Prof 2. **Subjects:** Social medicine, legal medicine, health insurance, medical education, medical ethics, hospital administration, state medicine. **Special Collections:** Medical laws. **Holdings:** Books; periodicals; federal, provincial, U.S. Government publications. **Subscriptions:** 136 journals and other serials; 19 newspapers. **Services:** Interlibrary loan; library not open to the public. **Remarks:** FAX: (514)878-4379. **Also Known As:** Professional Corporation of Physicians of Quebec. **Staff:** Guylaine Lavigne, Lib.Techn.

★4339★
Corporation du Seminaire St-Joseph de Trois-Rivieres - Archives du Seminaire de Trois-Rivieres (Hist)
858, rue Laviolette Phone: (819)376-4459
Trois-Rivieres, PQ, Canada G9A 5S3 Suzanne Girard, Resp.
Founded: 1918. ST Prof 1. **Subjects:** Local history and genealogy, Canadiana. **Special Collections:** Hart Family papers (100,000 documents); Collection Montarville Boucher de la Bruere (10,000 documents); Monsignor Albert Tessier papers (10,000 documents); Fonds d'archives prives (570 items). **Holdings:** 12,000 books; 2000 bound periodical volumes; 28 filing cabinets; 1 filing cabinet of microfiche; 49 reels of microfilm; 20 films; 230 audiotapes. **Subscriptions:** 15 journals and other serials. **Services:** Copying; archives open to the public. **Special Catalogs:** Etat General des Fonds et Collections Conserves aux Archives du Seminaire de Trois Rivieres, 1991 (book and microfiche). **Remarks:** FAX: (819)378-0607. **Staff:** Christian Lalancette, Doc.Techn.

Corpus Christi Art Foundation - Art Museum of South Texas
See: **Art Museum of South Texas** (1086)

★4340★
Corpus Christi Caller-Times - Library (Publ)
Box 9136 Phone: (512)884-2011
Corpus Christi, TX 78469-9136 Margaret J. Neu, Hd.Libn.
Founded: 1954. **Staff:** Prof 1; Other 2. **Subjects:** Newspaper reference topics. **Holdings:** Books; microfilm; clippings; photographs; maps. **Services:** Library open with limited public access. **Computerized Information Services:** DataTimes, DIALOG Information Services. **Remarks:** FAX: (512)886-3732. Library located at 820 Lower N. Broadway, Corpus Christi, TX 78401.

★4341★
Corpus Christi Museum - Staff Library (Biol Sci, Hist)
1900 N. Chaparral Phone: (512)883-2862
Corpus Christi, TX 78401 Patricia Murphy, Libn.
Founded: 1967. **Staff:** Prof 1. **Subjects:** Archeology, natural history, museology, malacology, anthropology, ornithology, botany. **Special Collections:** Juveniles Series Collection; Netting Periodicals Collection; Museological Collection; Law Collection (19th century). **Holdings:** 10,000 volumes; 48 VF drawers; 20 map case drawers; 180 sound recordings; microfilm; microfiche. **Subscriptions:** 93 journals and other serials. **Services:** Interlibrary loan; library open to the public with restrictions.

Archbishop Corrigan Memorial Library
See: **St. Joseph's Seminary** (14419)

★4342★
Corry Area Historical Society - Tiffany Archives (Hist)
Box 107 Phone: (814)664-4749
Corry, PA 16407 Vera Tiffany, Libn.
Subjects: Climax locomotives, local history, Corry authors. **Special Collections:** Collection of objects manufactured in Corry, 1860 to present. **Holdings:** 100 volumes; 200 old newspapers; city directories. **Services:** Copying; library open to the public for reference use only. **Remarks:** Alternate telephone number(s): 664-4530.

★4343★
Cortana Corporation - Library (Sci-Engr)
520 N. Washington St., Suite 200 Phone: (703)534-8000
Falls Church, VA 22046 Signe E. Zimmerman, Libn.
Subjects: Foreign technology, marine engineering, hydrodynamics, composite materials, drag reduction. **Special Collections:** Marine bionics. **Holdings:** 700 books; 1110 patents and documents; 1180 excerpts, abstracts, and translated foreign-language material; unbound periodicals. **Subscriptions:** 60 journals and other serials; 4 newspapers. **Services:** Interlibrary loan; library open to the public by appointment at president's discretion. **Computerized Information Services:** DIALOG Information Services, CompuServe Information Service. **Remarks:** FAX: (703)534-8005.

★4344★
Corte dei Conti - Biblioteca (Law)
Viale Mazzini 105 Phone: 6 38762272
I-00165 Rome, Italy Maria Grazia Terminiello, Dir.
Founded: 1862. **Staff:** 30. **Subjects:** Public law, public accountancy, social sciences, administrative law. **Special Collections:** Ancient codes collection. **Holdings:** 150,000 books. **Subscriptions:** 1100 journals and other serials. **Services:** Copying; library open to civil servants, academicians and researchers only. **Computerized Information Services:** BASIS (internal database); CD-ROM. **Publications:** Bollettino della Documentazione di Fonte Amministrativa; Bollettino delle Accessioni; Bollettino di Informazione Sulla Stampa Periodica.

★4345★
Cortez Public Library - Southwest Collection (Hist)
802 E. Montezuma Phone: (303)565-8117
Cortez, CO 81321 Maryellen Brubaker, Lib.Dir.
Subjects: Local history. **Holdings:** Figures not available. **Services:** Interlibrary loan; copying; collection open to the public. **Remarks:** FAX: (303)565-8122.

★4346★
Cortland County Historical Society - Library (Hist)
25 Homer Ave. Phone: (607)756-6071
Cortland, NY 13045 Shirley G. Heppell, Libn.
Founded: 1925. **Staff:** Prof 1; Other 2. **Subjects:** Cortland County history and genealogy. **Holdings:** 2118 books; 91 bound periodical volumes; 310 reels of microfilm; 620 cubic feet of manuscripts; 55 linear feet of cemetery records and vital records; 225 journal and serial titles; 148 maps; 3000 photographs; 24 oral history tapes. **Services:** Copying; library open to the public. **Special Indexes:** 1810 population finding list; 1820-1910 federal census of Cortland County; 1855, 1865, 1875 New York census of Cortland County; 1900 federal census index of Cortland County.

Paul V. Corusy Memorial Library
See: **International Association of Assessing Officers - Research and Technical Services Department** (8053)

★4347★
Corvallis Clinic - Medical Library (Med)
3680 N.W. Samaritan Dr. Phone: (503)754-1150
Corvallis, OR 97330 Gail Drlica, Med.Libn.
Founded: 1949. **Staff:** Prof 1. **Subjects:** Clinical medicine. **Holdings:** 6000 books; 7000 bound periodical volumes; 2500 tapes; 4000 slides. **Subscriptions:** 200 journals and other serials. **Services:** Interlibrary loan; copying; library open to local medical, paramedical, and college personnel. **Networks/Consortia:** Member of Marine-Valley Health Information Network (MarVHIN), Oregon Health Sciences Libraries Association (OHSLA).

★4348★
Corvus Systems, Inc. - Technical Library
8150 Leesburg Pike
Vienna, VA 22180
Defunct.

★4349★
Costa Rica - National Chamber of Agriculture - Library (Agri)
P.O. Box 1671-1000
San Jose, Costa Rica Phone: 216864
Subjects: Costa Rican agriculture, foreign commerce. **Holdings:** 1500 volumes. **Services:** Interlibrary loan; copying; SDI; library open to the public. **Remarks:** FAX: 338658. Telex: 3489 CAGRI CR. **Also Known As:** Camara Nacional de Agricultura y Agroindustria.

★4350★
Cote d'Ivoire - Bibliotheque Nationale (Hum)
B.P. V 180 Phone: 21 38 72
Abidjan, Cote d'Ivoire Odette Gnahore, Dir.
Founded: 1971. **Staff:** Prof 25; Other 33. **Subjects:** Social sciences, applied sciences, literature, fine arts. **Holdings:** 31,471 books; 1637 bound periodical volumes; 695 reports. **Subscriptions:** 120 journals and other serials; 56 newspapers. **Services:** Library open to the public. **Publications:** Bibliographie de la Cote d'Ivoire Guide du Lecteur.

★4351★
Cottage Hospital - David L. Reeves Medical Library (Med)
Box 689 Phone: (805)569-7240
Santa Barbara, CA 93102 Lucy Thomas, Lib.Dir.
Founded: 1942. **Staff:** Prof 4. **Subjects:** Medicine, surgery. **Holdings:** 3500 books; 7500 bound periodical volumes; 200 other cataloged items. **Subscriptions:** 250 journals and other serials. **Services:** Interlibrary loan; copying; library open to the public for reference use only. **Computerized Information Services:** BRS Information Technologies, MEDLARS, National Library of Medicine. Performs searches on fee basis. **Networks/Consortia:** Member of National Network of Libraries of Medicine - Pacific Southwest Region, Total Interlibrary Exchange (TIE). **Remarks:** FAX: (805)569-7588. **Staff:** Patricia Feldman, Libn.; M. Lou Smitheram, Libn.; Mary R. Turtle, Libn.

★4352★
Cottage Hospital of Grosse Pointe - Medical Library (Med)
159 Kercheval Ave. Phone: (313)884-8600
Grosse Pointe Farms, MI 48236 Carol Attar, Lib.Dir.
Staff: Prof 1; Other 1. **Subjects:** Medicine, nursing, and allied health sciences. **Holdings:** 1272 books; 4 VF drawers of clippings and pamphlets; video cassettes; audio cassettes. **Subscriptions:** 145 journals and other serials. **Services:** Interlibrary loan; copying. **Computerized Information Services:** MEDLINE, BRS Information Technologies, DIALOG Information Services.

★4353★
Cottonlandia Educational and Recreational Foundation, Inc. - Rowell A. Billups Memorial Library (Soc Sci)
Highway 82, W. Phone: (601)453-0925
Greenwood, MS 38930 Peggy H. McCormick, Exec.Dir.
Founded: 1988. **Staff:** 1. **Subjects:** Archeology, regional history, regional authors. **Special Collections:** Delta Writers Library; Mississippi authors. **Holdings:** 500 books; 3 manuscripts. **Subscriptions:** 12 journals and other serials. **Services:** Copying; library open to the public for reference use only. **Automated Operations:** Computerized cataloging and acquisitions. **Publications:** Humber-McWilliams Site; Early Sixteenth Century Glass Beads in the Spanish Colonial Trade; The Southeastern Ceremonial Complex: Artifacts and Analysis (exhibition catalog). **Remarks:** FAX: (601)453-6680. **Staff:** Irene Billups.

★4354★
Cottonwood County Historical Society - Library (Hist)
812 4th Ave. Phone: (507)831-1134
Windom, MN 56101 Garnet E. Booze, Adm.
Founded: 1901. **Staff:** Prof 1; Other 2. **Subjects:** County history. **Holdings:** Clippings and pamphlets; 2 filing cases of obituaries and history; local newspapers on microfilm. **Services:** Copying; library open to the public. **Publications:** History of Cottonwood County, 1870-1970 - for sale.

John N. Couch Biology Library
See: **University of North Carolina at Chapel Hill** (19067)

Couchman Memorial Library
See: **University of Dubuque Theological Seminary - Library** (18555)

★4355★
Coudert Brothers - Library (Law)
200 Park Ave. Phone: (212)880-4796
New York, NY 10166 Jane C. Rubens, Att. in Charge
Staff: Prof 6; Other 5. **Subjects:** Law. **Holdings:** 32,000 books; 900 bound periodical volumes. **Subscriptions:** 125 journals and other serials; 26 newspapers. **Services:** Interlibrary loan (local); library open to clients and members of Special Libraries Association. **Computerized Information Services:** DIALOG Information Services, LEXIS, WESTLAW. **Remarks:** FAX: (212)557-8137. **Staff:** Nora Gardner, Asst.Libn.; Vija Doks, Hd., Ref.; Rebecca Wright, Ref.Libn.; Arati Bhattacharji, Cat.Libn.; Gregory Deloatch, ILL Libn.; Paulette Schneider, Automation Libn.

Coulee Dam National Recreation Area
See: **U.S. Natl. Park Service - Coulee Dam Natl. Recreation Area** (17693)

★4356★
Council for Advancement and Support of Education - Reference Center (Educ)
Eleven Dupont Circle, N.W., Suite 400 Phone: (202)328-5900
Washington, DC 20036 Susan VanGilder, Ref.Ctr.Mgr.
Founded: 1974. **Staff:** Prof 1; Other 1. **Subjects:** Alumni administration, educational fund raising, government relations, institutional relations, executive management, student recruitment. **Holdings:** Books; periodicals; reports; studies; speeches; surveys; college, university, and independent school publications and literature. **Subscriptions:** 52 journals and other serials. **Services:** Center open to the public for reference use only by appointment. **Computerized Information Services:** DIALOG Information Services; internal database.

★4357★
Council for Alternatives to Stereotyping in Entertainment - Library (Soc Sci)
139 Corson Ave.
Staten Island, NY 10301 Phone: (718)720-5378
Subjects: Entertainment - stereotyping, self-image, reality perception, receptivity to accurate performance feedback. **Holdings:** 1000 volumes.

★4358★
Council of American Embroiderers - CAE Library (Art)
Carnegie Office Park
600 Bell Ave. Phone: (412)279-0299
Carnegie, PA 15106 Lynne Wohleber, Libn.
Founded: 1969. **Staff:** Prof 2. **Subjects:** Embroidery, art, color, crafts, design, quilting, lace, needle arts and allied areas. **Special Collections:** American Fabrics Magazine, volumes 5-77, 1948-1967; index for volumes 1-68, 1946-1965. **Holdings:** 2000 books; study samplers; VF drawers. **Subscriptions:** 7 journals and other serials. **Services:** Copying; library open to members of organization, serious researchers, and correspondence students. **Automated Operations:** Computerized cataloging. **Publications:** Booklist by author - for sale to authorized users. **Formerly:** National Standards Council of American Embroiderers - NSCAE Library. **Staff:** Marinda Stretavsky, Asst.Libn.

★4359★
Council Bluffs Daily Nonpareil - Library (Info Sci)
117 Pearl St.
Council Bluffs, IA 51503 Phone: (712)328-1811
Subjects: Newspaper history. **Holdings:** Figures not available. **Remarks:** FAX: (712)328-1597.

★4360★
Council for the Care of Churches - Library (Rel-Phil, Art)
83 London Wall Phone: 071 638-0971
London EC2M 5NA, England Janet Seeley, Libn.
Staff: Prof 1. **Subjects:** Ecclesiastical art and architecture, Anglican churches and cathedrals in England, conservation. **Special Collections:** National Survey of English Churches (guidebooks; photographs). **Holdings:** 12,000 books; 30 microforms; 20,000 files; 135,000 photographs; 11,000 slides. **Subscriptions:** 120 journals and other serials. **Services:** Interlibrary loan; copying; library open to the public by appointment. **Special Catalogs:** Slide library catalog. **Remarks:** FAX: (071)638-0184. Maintained by the General Synod of the Church of England.

★4361★
Council of Consulting Organizations, Inc. - Library
521 5th Ave.
New York, NY 10175
Defunct.

★4362★
Council for Court Excellence - Library (Law)
1025 Vermont Ave., N.W., Suite 510
Washington, DC 20005 Phone: (202)783-7736
Founded: 1982. **Staff:** 3. **Subjects:** Local and federal courts - administration of justice, communication between citizens and courts. **Special Collections:** Court management studies in Nation's Capital Jury Reform, civil delay, child abuse. **Holdings:** 4000 volumes. **Subscriptions:** 5 journals and other serials; 4 newspapers. **Services:** Library open to the public at librarian's discretion.

★4363★
Council on the Environment of New York City - Library (Plan)
51 Chambers St., Rm. 228 Phone: (212)566-0990
New York, NY 10007 Sophie Dolgin, Libn.
Founded: 1975. **Staff:** 1. **Subjects:** Horticulture, landscaping, urban technology, environmental education, architecture, playgrounds, recreation. **Holdings:** 1050 books; 3 VF drawers clippings; 2 boxes of card files; garden and tool catalogs. **Subscriptions:** 8 journals and other serials. **Services:** Interlibrary loan; copying; library open to the public for reference use only.

Council of Europe - Documentation Centre for Education in Europe
See: **Documentation Centre for Education in Europe** (4938)

★4364★
Council of Europe - Documentation Section (Soc Sci)
B.P. 431 R6 Phone: 88 412025
F-67006 Strasbourg Cedex, France David Clow
Founded: 1949. **Staff:** 15. **Subjects:** Unity in Europe - governmental cooperation; parliamentary democracy, human rights, media, international law, local government, environment, migration, social affairs, public health, international organizations, culture, education. **Holdings:** 150,000 volumes. **Subscriptions:** 800 journals and other serials; 80 newspapers. **Services:** Interlibrary loan; copying; library open to the public with restrictions. **Automated Operations:** Computerized public access catalog. **Computerized Information Services:** BLAISE, CATEL, CELEX, ECHO, ESA/IRS, EUROBASES, EPOQUE, Europenne des Donnes, POLIS, RAPID, FT PROFILE, SCAD. **Publications:** Bibliographic Bulletins; acquisitions list; East-West bulletin. **Remarks:** FAX: 88 412780. Telex: STRASBOURG 870943. **Staff:** Tim Lisney; Joelle Bouteiller.

★4365★
Council on Foreign Relations - Library (Soc Sci)
58 E. 68th St. Phone: (212)734-0400
New York, NY 10021 Virginia Etheridge, Dir., Lib.Serv.
Founded: 1930. **Staff:** Prof 4; Other 3. **Subjects:** International relations, international organizations, economics, political science. **Special Collections:** Documentation on the United Nations and the various European Communities. **Holdings:** 40,000 volumes; 105,000 United Nations and specialized agency documents; 340 VF drawers of clipping files. **Subscriptions:** 360 journals and other serials; 16 newspapers. **Services:** Interlibrary loan; copying; library open to the public if approved by the librarian. **Automated Operations:** Computerized public access catalog (MILCS). **Computerized Information Services:** NEXIS, DIALOG Information Services, Dow Jones News/Retrieval, OCLC, LEXIS, WILSONLINE, CIDS. **Networks/Consortia:** Member of New York Metropolitan Reference and Research Library Agency, Consortium of Foundation Libraries (CFL). **Remarks:** FAX: (212)861-1789. **Staff:** Janis Kreslins, Asst.Dir., Lib.Serv.; Barbara Miller, Doc. & Archv.; Marcia Sprules, Ref./Comp.Sys.Libn.

★4366★
Council of Governments of the Central Naugatuck Valley - Library (Plan)
20 E. Main St. Phone: (203)757-0535
Waterbury, CT 06702 Peter Dorpalen, Exec.Dir.
Founded: 1960. **Staff:** 5. **Subjects:** Planning, land use planning, demography, housing, transportation, recycling, solar energy. **Special Collections:** U.S. Census of Population and Housing, 1950-1990. **Holdings:** 3500 books, bound periodical volumes, reports; 1 box of microfiche. **Subscriptions:** 25 journals and other serials. **Services:** Copying; library open to the public by appointment. **Computerized Information Services:** CD-ROM (1990 U.S. Census). **Publications:** List of publications - available on request. **Remarks:** FAX: (203)756-7688.

★4367★
Council of Jewish Federations - Library (Soc Sci)
730 Broadway Phone: (212)475-5000
New York, NY 10003 Martin Kraar, Exec.V.P.
Staff: 1. **Subjects:** Jewish social welfare, community organization. **Holdings:** 300 books; 237 VF drawers of pamphlets, reports, speeches, studies, local agency material, correspondence, minutes. **Subscriptions:** 135 journals and other serials; 55 newspapers. **Services:** Interlibrary loan; library not open to the public. **Publications:** Major Council Publications, A Selected Bibliography, biennial.

★4368★
Council of the Maritime Premiers - Atlantic Coastal Resource Information Centre - Library (Biol Sci)
16 Station St.
Box 310
Amherst, NS, Canada B4H 3Z5 Phone: (902)667-7231
Founded: 1982. **Staff:** Prof 1. **Subjects:** Atlantic region - aquaculture, coastal zone management, engineering, fisheries, estuaries, marine sciences, oceanography, remote sensing, recreation, erosion, power development, offshore oil, gas and mineral development and exploration, laws and regulations, environmental protection. **Special Collections:** Topographic, hydrographic, and resource oriented map collections of the Atlantic region. **Holdings:** 1200 books; unbound periodicals; government documents; VF drawers; maps; research reports. **Subscriptions:** 29 journals and other serials. **Services:** Interlibrary loan; copying; user orientation; center open to the public with restrictions. **Computerized Information Services:** CAN/OLE, Remote Sensing On-line Retrieval System (RESORS), WATDOC. Performs searches on fee basis. **Publications:** Bibliographies; library manual; fact sheets; periodicals list; information circulars. **Special Indexes:** Indexes of special subject collections. **Remarks:** FAX: (902)667-6008.

★4369★
Council of Maritime Premiers - Land Registration and Information Service - Surveys & Mapping Division - LRIS Map Library (Geog-Map)
120 Water St. Phone: (902)436-2107
Summerside, PE, Canada C1N 1A9 Louise Goodwin, Client Serv.Techn.
Founded: 1973. **Staff:** 1. **Subjects:** Maritime coverage of base maps, NTS maps, coordinate monument information. **Holdings:** 800 microfiche. **Services:** Interlibrary loan; copying; coordinate transformations and computations; library not open to the public. **Automated Operations:** Computerized cataloging and circulation. **Computerized Information Services:** CompuServe Information Service; MicroVAX, CARIS (internal databases). Performs searches on fee basis. **Special Indexes:** Index to Urban and Resource Mapping. **Remarks:** FAX: (902)436-1519.

★4370★
Council on National Literatures - Information Center (Hum)
Box 81 Phone: (718)767-8380
Whitestone, NY 11357 Anne Paolucci, Pres./Exec.Dir.
Founded: 1974. **Staff:** 2. **Subjects:** Integration of Western and non-Western literatures; overviews of national literatures. **Special Collections:** Special commemorative volumes. **Holdings:** 5000 volumes. **Subscriptions:** 1000 journals and other serials. **Services:** Center not open to the public. **Publications:** Review of National Literatures, annual; CNL/World Report, annual; CNL/Review of Books, 6/year; list of publications - available upon request. **Staff:** Dr. R.C. Clark, Bk. Review Ed.; Dr. H. Paolucci, Coord.;. Dolores Frank, Mgr.

Council of Planning Librarians
See: **Merriam Center Library** (10161)

Council for Scientific and Industrial Research (of South Africa)
See: **South Africa - Council for Scientific and Industrial Research** (15382)

★4371★
Council of State Governments - States Information Center (Soc Sci)
Iron Works Pike
Box 11910 Phone: (606)252-2291
Lexington, KY 40578-1910 Ed Garner, Mgr., States Info.Ctr.
Staff: Prof 3. **Subjects:** State government organization and administration, legislative processes and procedures, intergovernmental relations. **Holdings:** 20,000 documents; checklists of state libraries from 50 states; state bluebooks and budgets. **Subscriptions:** 206 journals and other serials; 8 newspapers. **Services:** Interlibrary loan. **Automated Operations:** Computerized cataloging and circulation. **Computerized Information Services:** Integrated State Information System (ISIS) (internal database). **Publications:** State Government Research Checklist, bimonthly. **Remarks:** FAX: (606)231-1858. **Staff:** Mary Bone, Libn.; Lise Smith-Peters, Info.Spec.

★4372★
Count Dracula Fan Club - Research Library (Rec)
Penthouse N.
29 Washington Square, W. Phone: (212)982-6754
New York, NY 10011 Dr. Jeanne Youngson, Pres.
Founded: 1970. **Staff:** 4. **Subjects:** Vampirism, lycanthropy, horror. **Special Collections:** Frankenstein, Stoker, The Shadow, and other adventure/mystery series. **Holdings:** 25,000 volumes. **Services:** Library not open to the public. **Remarks:** Library is used by The Vampire Research Referral Center, Vampire Research Foundation, Vampire Information Bureau and the special vampire research division of the CDFC.

★4373★
Country Doctor Museum - Library (Med)
Vance St.
Box 34
Bailey, NC 27807 Phone: (919)235-4165
Staff: 1. **Subjects:** Medicine, pharmacy. **Holdings:** 800 volumes. **Services:** Library open to the public by appointment.

★4374★
Country Music Foundation - Library and Media Center (Mus)
4 Music Square E. Phone: (615)256-1639
Nashville, TN 37203 Charlie Seemann, Dp.Dir.
Staff: Prof 8. **Subjects:** Country and popular music, music publishing and recording, recorded sound technology, music copyright. **Special Collections:** Acuff Collection (films, books, photographs, clippings, tapes, manuscripts documenting the career of Roy Acuff); National Academy of Recording Arts & Sciences (700 records, tapes, printed material related to NARAS-Award nominees). **Holdings:** 7500 books; 1500 bound periodical volumes; 150,000 recorded discs; 5000 audio- and videotapes; 1000 16mm films; 4000 pieces of sheet music; 1200 vertical file folders; 35,000 photographs. **Subscriptions:** 400 journals and other serials; 10 newspapers. **Services:** Copying; library open to the public by appointment. **Computerized Information Services:** DIALOG Information Services, VU/TEXT Information Services. **Remarks:** FAX: (615)255-2245. **Staff:** Linda Gross, Hd., Tech.Serv.; Ronnie Pugh, Ref.Libn.; Bob Pinson, Principal Res.; Patti Hughes, Lib.Sec.; Alan Stoker, Audio/Video Engr.; Becky Bell, Sr.Tech.Serv.Libn.; John Rumble, Hist.

★4375★
Country Music Showcase International, Inc. - Library (Mus)
P.O. Box 368 Phone: (515)989-3748
Carlisle, IA 50047 Harold L. Luick, Pres.
Founded: 1984. **Staff:** Prof 2. **Subjects:** Iowa recording artists and songwriters; historic recording artists; music industry - seminars, recording process, consulting, management, career development, songwriting; music and entertainment law. **Special Collections:** Country music record collection, 1949-1987 (8000 items); Hank Williams Original Albums Collection; Kajac Record Corporation Collection, 1960-1978 (450 45rpm phonograph records and 527 record albums). **Holdings:** 460 books; videotapes. **Subscriptions:** 23 journals and other serials; 10 newspapers. **Services:** Library open to the public by appointment. **Publications:** Country Music Showcase International Entertainment News, 4/year - free upon request. **Remarks:** Alternate telephone number(s): 989-3676. **Staff:** Barbara Lancaster, V.P.

★4376★
Countryside Home - Staff Library (Med)
1425 Wisconsin Dr. Phone: (414)674-3170
Jefferson, WI 53549 Catherine M. Rueth, Sec./Libn.
Founded: 1971. **Staff:** 1. **Subjects:** Medicine, nursing, and allied health sciences. **Holdings:** 1011 books. **Subscriptions:** 28 journals and other serials. **Services:** Interlibrary loan; library not open to the public. **Remarks:** FAX: (414)674-6075.

Francis A. Countway Library
See: **Harvard University - Schools of Medicine, Dental Medicine & Public Health - Boston Medical Library** (6996)

★4377★
County of Carleton Law Association - Law Library (Law)
Court House
161 Elgin St., Rm. 2004 Phone: (613)233-7386
Ottawa, ON, Canada K2P 2K1 Karen MacLaurin, Libn. & Asst.Treas.
Founded: 1888. **Staff:** Prof 2; Other 2. **Subjects:** Law - general, case. **Holdings:** 15,000 books; 115 periodical titles; 140 Canadian law report series titles; 25 British law report series titles, provincial report series; topical report series. **Subscriptions:** 200 serials. **Services:** Library not open to the public. **Automated Operations:** Computerized cataloging, acquisitions, and serials. **Computerized Information Services:** QL Systems, CAN/LAW, Infomart Online. **Remarks:** FAX: (613)238-3788. **Staff:** Verna Preston, Ref.Libn.

★4378★
County of Los Angeles Public Library - American Indian Resource Center (Area-Ethnic)
Huntington Park Library
6518 Miles Ave. Phone: (213)583-1461
Huntington Park, CA 90255 Tom Lippert, Libn.
Founded: 1979. **Staff:** Prof 1; Other 2. **Subjects:** Indians of North America, including Southwest, Plains, Woodlands, and California Indians - history, tribal cultural histories, fine arts, religion, literature, laws and treaties. **Special Collections:** Federal Census Records (1880-1940); Current Events Files (652 subject headings; 12 VF drawers); Information and Referral File. **Holdings:** 9000 books; 35 16mm films; 65 titles in microform; 68 videocassettes; 400 audiocassettes; 300 federal and state documents. **Subscriptions:** 70 periodical titles. **Services:** Interlibrary loan; copying; center open to the public. **Computerized Information Services:** DIALOG Information Services. **Remarks:** FAX: (213)587-2061.

★4379★
County of Los Angeles Public Library - Asian Pacific Resource Center (Area-Ethnic)
Montebello Library
1550 W. Beverly Blvd. Phone: (213)722-2650
Montebello, CA 90640 Corrina Chuang, Libn.
Founded: 1979. **Staff:** Prof 1; Other 2. **Subjects:** Asian Pacific Americans, Asian languages, Eastern Asian and Pacific countries. **Special Collections:** Assembly Centers and Relocation Centers publications (Japanese Americans in World War II; microfilm); U.S. Armed Forces in Vietnam, 1954-1975 (21 reels of microfilm). **Holdings:** 13,397 books; 74 periodical titles; 943 AV program titles; 5 VF drawers. **Subscriptions:** 74 journals and other serials; 15 newspapers. **Services:** Interlibrary loan; copying; center open to the public. **Publications:** Subject bibliographies (40). **Remarks:** FAX: (213)722-3018.

★4380★
County of Los Angeles Public Library - Black Resource Center (Area-Ethnic, Hist)
A.C. Bilbrew Library
150 E. El Segundo Blvd. Phone: (213)538-3350
Los Angeles, CA 90061 Louise Parsons, Commun.Lib.Mgr.
Founded: 1974. **Staff:** Prof 1; Other 2. **Subjects:** History and culture of African-Americans, black music and musical artists. **Special Collections:** Pictures/posters of famous black Americans (260). **Holdings:** 8500 books; 65 bound periodical volumes; 3500 clippings; 2576 reels of microfilm; 1182 microfiche; 360 videocassettes; 378 audiocassettes; 405 phonograph records. **Subscriptions:** 120 journals and other serials; 20 newspapers. **Services:** Interlibrary loan; copying; center open to the public for reference use only. **Automated Operations:** Computerized public access catalog. **Remarks:** FAX: (213)327-0824. **Also Known As:** A.C. Bilbrew Library.

★4381★
County of Los Angeles Public Library - Californiana Collection (Hist)
Rosemead Public Library
8800 Valley Blvd. Phone: (818)573-5220
Rosemead, CA 91770 Sally Colby, Libn.
Staff: Prof 1. **Subjects:** California history. **Special Collections:** Masters' theses on California subjects (500); California Census, 1850-1880, 1900, 1910 (microfilm); Soundex, 1880, 1900, 1910. **Holdings:** 12,000 books; Los Angeles Star, 1851-1879, on microfilm; Alta California, 1849-1891, on microfilm. **Subscriptions:** 30 journals and other serials. **Services:** Interlibrary loan; copying; collection open to the public. **Remarks:** FAX: (818)280-8523.

★4382★
County of Los Angeles Public Library - Chicano Resource Center (Area-Ethnic, Hist)
East Los Angeles Library
4801 E. 3rd St.
Los Angeles, CA 90022 Phone: (213)263-5087
Founded: 1976. **Staff:** Prof 1; Other 2. **Subjects:** Chicano studies; history and culture of Mexican Americans in the United States - politics, folklore, customs, education, art, language, health; history of Mexico. **Holdings:** 7000 books; 3 cabinet of microfilm; 180 videocassettes; 140 16mm films; 2 cabinets of pamphlets; 20 slide sets; 100 phonograph records; 150 sets of prints; 43 filmstrips; 125 audiocassettes. **Subscriptions:** 55 journals and other serials. **Services:** Interlibrary loan; center open to the public. **Computerized Information Services:** Internal databases. **Publications:** Bibliographies on Chicano and Mexican culture and history. **Special Indexes:** Periodical index (cards). **Remarks:** FAX: (213)264-5465.

★4383★
County of Los Angeles Public Library - Community Access Library Line (CALL) (Soc Sci)
2150 W. 120th St.
Hawthorne, CA 90250 Phone: (213)725-0764
Founded: 1979. **Staff:** Prof 7; Other 2. **Subjects:** Community agencies and literacy centers. **Holdings:** 2000 books; 20 VF drawers. **Subscriptions:** 65 journals and other serials; 16 newspapers. **Services:** Multilingual telephone information and referral for Southern California; Southern California Literacy Hotline; library open to the public for telephone service only. **Computerized Information Services:** DIALOG Information Services, VU/TEXT Information Services, OCLC; Star System (internal database). **Remarks:** Toll-free telephone number(s): (800)372-6641 (Southern California only). FAX: (213)722-3018. **Formerly:** Located in Montebello, CA. **Staff:** David Wysocki, CALL Libn.; Robert Timmerman, CALL Libn.; Joseph McCarthy, CALL Libn.; Lydia Lee, CALL Libn.; Melody Holzman, CALL Libn.; Joan Mead, CALL Libn.

★4384★
County of Los Angeles Public Library - Consumer Health Information Program & Services (CHIPS) (Med)
Carson Public Library
151 E. Carson St. Phone: (213)830-0909
Carson, CA 90745 Ellen Mulkern, CHIPS Libn.
Founded: 1977. **Staff:** Prof 1; Other 2. **Subjects:** Health, medicine. **Holdings:** 6500 books; 350 video cassettes; 150 films; 24 VF drawers of pamphlets. **Subscriptions:** 35 journals and other serials. **Services:** Interlibrary loan; copying; services open to the public. **Automated Operations:** Computerized cataloging and acquisitions. **Computerized Information Services:** OnTyme Electronic Message Network Service, EMS (Electronic Mail System; electronic mail services). **Publications:** Health bibliographies, irregular. **Remarks:** FAX: (213)830-6181. CHIPS operates Tel-med Health and Legal Line, telephone (213)549-9000.

★4385★
County of York Law Association - Court House Library (Law)
361 University Ave. Phone: (416)327-5700
Toronto, ON, Canada M5G 1T3 Anne C. Matthewman, Libn./Adm.
Founded: 1885. **Staff:** Prof 3; Other 3. **Subjects:** Law. **Holdings:** 25,000 volumes. **Services:** Library not open to the public. **Computerized Information Services:** QL Systems, CAN/LAW, WESTLAW, LEXIS, NEXIS. **Remarks:** FAX: (416)947-9148. **Staff:** Martha Leger; Sharon Day-Feldman.

Cour Canadienne de l'Impot
See: **Canada - Tax Court of Canada** (2864)

Cour Supreme du Canada
See: **Canada - Supreme Court of Canada** (2863)

★4386★
The Courier - Library (Publ)
Box 609 Phone: (419)422-5151
Findlay, OH 45839-0609 Alicia Waldman, Libn.
Founded: 1886. **Staff:** 1. **Subjects:** Newspaper reference topics. **Holdings:** The Courier, 1846 to present, on microfilm. **Services:** Library not open to the public. Material available at Findlay/Hancock County Public Library. **Special Indexes:** Daily listing of news stories (card).

★4387★
Courier-Journal - Library (Publ)
525 W. Broadway Phone: (502)582-4184
Louisville, KY 40202 Doris J. Batliner, Chf.Libn.
Founded: 1920. **Staff:** Prof 3; Other 11. **Subjects:** Newspaper reference topics, coal, pollution, horseracing, mining. **Special Collections:** Newspaper clippings (5 million); photograph collection (350,000); Courier-Journal, November 1868 to present (microfilm); Louisville Times, May 1884 to February 14, 1987 (microfilm). **Holdings:** 4700 books; 15,000 pamphlets; 350,000 clippings on microfilm. **Subscriptions:** 50 journals and other serials; 15 newspapers. **Services:** Interlibrary loan; library open to the public on fee basis. **Computerized Information Services:** DIALOG Information Services, DataTimes; Info-KY News Retrieval System (internal database). Performs searches on fee basis from material published before March, 1988 only. Contact Person: Sharon Bidwell, Ref.Libn., 582-4184. **Networks/Consortia:** Member of Kentucky Library Network, Inc. (KLN). **Publications:** Acquisitions Bulletin. **Remarks:** FAX: (502)582-4075. **Staff:** Leonard Tharp, Libn., Info-KY/Sys./BASIS Sys.; Pat Chapman, Asst.Ref.Libn.; Patty Smith, Asst.Sys.Libn.

Courville-Abbott Memorial Library
See: **White Memorial Medical Center - Courville-Abbott Memorial Library** (20383)

H.T. Coutts Library
See: **University of Alberta** (18194)

★4388★
Couvent des Dominicains - Bibliotheque de l'Ecole Biblique et Archeologique Francaise de Jerusalem (Rel-Phil)
6 Nablus Rd.
P.O. Box 19053 Phone: 2 28 24 99
91190 Jerusalem, Israel Marcel Sigrist, Ph.D.
Subjects: Bible, archeology and epigraphy of the ancient Near East. **Holdings:** 80,000 books; 300 bound periodical volumes. **Services:** Copying; library open to the public with restrictions. **Publications:** Revue biblique; Etudes Bibliques; Cahiers de la Revue biblique. **Remarks:** FAX: 2 28 25 67.

★4389★
Covenant Medical Center - Champaign Campus Library
407 S. Fourth St.
Box 4003
Champaign, IL 61820
Defunct. Holdingds absorbed by Covenant Medical Center - Library in Urbana, IL.

★4390★
Covenant Medical Center - Library (Med)
1400 W. Park St. Phone: (217)337-2283
Urbana, IL 61801 Nancy Bishop, Mgr.
Staff: Prof 1. **Subjects:** Clinical medicine, nursing, allied health sciences. **Holdings:** 1000 books; 500 bound periodical volumes; 10 boxes of archival materials. **Subscriptions:** 175 journals and other serials. **Services:** Interlibrary loan; copying; SDI; library open to the public for reference use only. **Automated Operations:** Computerized cataloging. **Computerized Information Services:** MEDLARS, DIALOG Information Services; CLSI (internal database). **Networks/Consortia:** Member of ILLINET, National Network of Libraries of Medicine - Greater Midwest Region, East Central Illinois Consortium.

★4391★
Covenant Theological Seminary - J. Oliver Buswell, Jr. Library (Rel-Phil)
12330 Conway Rd., Creve Coeur Phone: (314)434-4044
St. Louis, MO 63141 James C. Pakala
Founded: 1955. **Staff:** 5. **Subjects:** Bible, theology, church history, practical theology. **Special Collections:** Blackburn Library; Presbyteriana; English Puritans. **Holdings:** 56,678 books; 3866 bound periodical volumes; 3759 microforms; 847 cassettes; 4 VF drawers of pamphlets; theses; recordings. **Subscriptions:** 352 journals and other serials. **Services:** Interlibrary loan; copying; library open to qualified persons on request. **Automated Operations:** Computerized cataloging. **Computerized Information Services:** DIALOG Information Services. Performs searches on fee basis. **Networks/Consortia:** Member of St. Louis Regional Library Network. **Remarks:** FAX: (314)434-4819.

★4392★
Covington and Burling - Library (Law)
1201 Pennsylvania Ave., N.W. Phone: (202)662-6184
Washington, DC 20004 Roberta I. Shaffer, Lib.Dir.
Staff: Prof 8; Other 14. **Subjects:** Law - taxation, antitrust, labor, administrative, corporation, aviation. **Special Collections:** Legislative histories of selected federal laws. **Holdings:** 68,000 books; 2000 bound periodical volumes; 40 VF drawers. **Subscriptions:** 400 journals and other serials. **Services:** Interlibrary loan; copying; library not open to the public. **Automated Operations:** Computerized cataloging. **Computerized Information Services:** DIALOG Information Services, LEXIS, WESTLAW, Dow Jones News/Retrieval, OCLC. **Networks/Consortia:** Member of CAPCON Library Network. **Remarks:** FAX: (202)662-6291. **Staff:** Ms. M. Dzurinko, Bibliog.Serv.; Ms. C. White, Asst.Libn., Spec.Coll.; Ms. J. Yablon, Res.Serv.; Ms. Y. Brown, Ref.Libn.; Ms. M. King, ILL; Ms. B. Smith, Accounts & Acq.

★4393★
Covington Virginian - Library (Publ)
343 Monroe Ave. Phone: (703)962-2121
Covington, VA 24426 Horton P. Beirne, Ed.
Founded: 1920. **Subjects:** Newspaper reference topics. **Special Collections:** Covington Virginian, 1920-1988; Covington Virginian, 1958 to present (microfilm); Virginian Review, 1989 to present. **Remarks:** FAX: (703)962-5072.

Cowan Memorial Library
See: **Anglican Church Army in Canada** (866)

★4394★
Cowboy Artists of America Museum - Library (Art)
Box 1716 Phone: (512)896-2553
Kerrville, TX 78029 Mary Meyers
Founded: 1983. **Staff:** Prof 1. **Subjects:** Art of the American West - contemporary and historical; Cowboy Artists of America; North American Indians; frontier and pioneer life; cattle and sheep ranching; fur trade. **Special Collections:** Books, catalogs, pamphlets, photographs and other cataloged works by and about the Cowboy Artists of America. **Holdings:** 2000 books; 2000 unbound periodicals; 150 unbound museum catalogs. **Services:** Copying; telephone and mail research; library open to the public by appointment (museum entrance fee required). **Special Indexes:** Listing of periodical, newspaper, and museum coverage of CAA members (printout). **Remarks:** Library located at 1550 Bandera Hwy., Kerrville, TX 78028.

★4395★
Coweta County Genealogical Society - Library (Hist)
P.O. Box 1014 Phone: (404)251-2877
Newnan, GA 30264 Norma Gunby, Pres.
Founded: 1981. **Staff:** Prof 7; Other 9. **Subjects:** Genealogy, state and local history. **Special Collections:** Local histories; census. **Holdings:** Books; magazines; microfilm; family charts and sheets; newspapers and other genealogical material. **Services:** Copying; library open to the public. **Staff:** Jonesy Mulalley, Hd.Libn.

Cowles Foundation for Research in Economics
See: **Yale University** (20707)

Cowles Library
See: **Drake University** (4997)

Cowles Publishing Company - Spokesman-Review and Spokane Chronicle
See: **(Spokane) Spokesman-Review and Spokane Chronicle** (15592)

Cowley County Genealogical Society
See: **Cherokee Strip Land Rush Museum - Docking Research Center Archives Library** (3481)

★4396★
Cox, Castle & Nicholson - Library (Law, Bus-Fin)
2049 Century Park, E., No. 2800 Phone: (310)277-4222
Los Angeles, CA 90067 Janet Kasabian, Law Libn.
Founded: 1968. **Staff:** 1. **Subjects:** Law, real estate. **Holdings:** 17,000 books; 1000 bound periodical volumes. **Subscriptions:** 240 journals and other serials; 10 newspapers. **Services:** Interlibrary loan; library not open to the public. **Automated Operations:** Computerized circulation. **Computerized Information Services:** NEXIS, DIALOG Information Services, DataTimes, Dow Jones News/Retrieval, WESTLAW. Performs searches on fee basis. **Remarks:** FAX: (310)277-7889.

Edwin Cox Associates - Commonwealth Laboratory, Inc.
See: **Commonwealth Laboratory, Inc.** (4065)

Cox Library
See: **Black Hills State University - E.Y. Berry Library-Learning Center - Special Collections** (1876)

★4397★
Cox Medical Centers - Libraries (Med)
1423 N. Jefferson Ave. Phone: (417)836-3460
Springfield, MO 65802 Wilma Bunch, Supv., Lib.Serv.
Founded: 1907. **Staff:** Prof 2; Other 3.5. **Subjects:** Medicine, nursing, allied health. **Special Collections:** History of medicine collection; history of nursing collection. **Holdings:** 2757 titles; 3684 volumes. **Subscriptions:** 220 journals and other serials. **Services:** Interlibrary loan; copying; medical book ordering service; library open to the public by appointment. **Automated Operations:** DTI Data Trek. **Computerized Information Services:** DIALOG Information Services, BRS Information Technologies, MEDLARS, Mead Data Central MICROMEDEX. **Networks/Consortia:** Member of National Network of Libraries of Medicine - Midcontinental Region. **Publications:** InforMed: Newsletter of Information in Medicine. **Remarks:** FAX: (417)836-8937; (417)885-6199. The Cox Medical Centers' Libraries are the North Library which is located at 1423 N. Jefferson Ave., Springfield, MO, 65802 and the David Miller Memorial Library which is located at 3801 S. National Ave., Springfield, MO 65807. Contains the holdings of the former Burge School of Nursing Library. **Staff:** Karen A. Davis, Libn., North Lib.; Mitzi Murphy, Libn., David Miller Memorial Lib.

★4398★
Cozen & O'Connor - Library (Bus-Fin)
1900 Market St. Phone: (215)665-2136
Philadelphia, PA 19103 Evelyn Nanes, Lib.Dir.
Staff: 3. **Subjects:** Insurance, engineering, fire, taxation, corporate law. **Holdings:** 13,000 books. **Subscriptions:** 20 journals and other serials; 5 newspapers. **Services:** Interlibrary loan; copying; library not open to the public. **Computerized Information Services:** DIALOG Information Services, WESTLAW, LEXIS, VU/TEXT Information Services; Expert Witness (internal database). **Remarks:** FAX: (215)665-2013.

★4399★
CP Rail - Corporate Library/Information Centre (Trans, Bus-Fin)
P.O. Box 6042, Sta. A Phone: (514)395-6617
Montreal, PQ, Canada H3C 3E4 Carol Lacourte, Corp.Libn.
Founded: 1972. **Staff:** Prof 3; Other 6. **Subjects:** Transportation, business. **Holdings:** 13,000 books; 2000 annual report titles; 450 Statistics Canada titles. **Subscriptions:** 750 journals and other serials. **Services:** Interlibrary loan; copying; library open to the public by appointment only. **Automated Operations:** Computerized public access catalog, cataloging, acquisitions, and serials. **Computerized Information Services:** DIALOG Information Services, Info Globe, CAN/OLE, Infomart Online, Dow Jones News/Retrieval, QL Systems; Envoy 100 (electronic mail service). **Publications:** Recent Additions, monthly. **Remarks:** FAX: (514)395-7959. **Staff:** V. Leblanc, Res.Libn.; H. Berardinucci, Supv., Cat. & Acq.

★4400★
CPC International - Best Foods Research Center - Information Center (Food-Bev)
1120 Commerce Ave.
Box 1534 Phone: (908)688-9000
Union, NJ 07083 Anne Troop, Mgr., Info.Serv.
Founded: 1970. **Staff:** Prof 5; Other 1. **Subjects:** Nutrition, food technology, cookery, food microbiology, food analysis. **Holdings:** 6000 books; company reports and patents on microfiche. **Subscriptions:** 300 journals and other serials. **Services:** Interlibrary loan. **Automated Operations:** Computerized cataloging and acquisitions. **Computerized Information Services:** DIALOG Information Services, MEDLINE, STN International; internal databases. **Publications:** Monthly list of acquisitions; annual periodicals holdings list. **Remarks:** FAX: (908)851-4660. **Staff:** Diane Malakoff, Info.Spec.; Jeanne Brown, Info.Spec.; Elizabeth Turick, Info.Spec.; Roseanne Rossi, Info.Spec.; Lisa Schwartz, Tech.

★4401★
CPC International - Moffett Technical Library (Food-Bev)
6500 S. Archer Rd.
Box 345 Phone: (708)563-6849
Argo, IL 60501 Joy-Louise Caruso, Mgr., Info.Serv.
Founded: 1939. **Staff:** Prof 2; Other 1. **Subjects:** Chemistry, chemical engineering, food chemistry, general business topics. **Special Collections:** Carbohydrate chemistry (125 volumes and 5 periodicals). **Holdings:** 3200 books; 3500 bound periodical volumes; 75 VF drawers of pamphlets; 35 VF drawers of patents; 800 microfilm cassettes of periodicals; 300 VF drawers of internal reports; 100 VF drawers of internal correspondence; 10 VF drawers of archives. **Subscriptions:** 191 journals and other serials. **Services:** Library not open to the public. **Automated Operations:** Computerized cataloging, acquisitions, serials, and circulation. **Computerized Information Services:** DIALOG Information Services, STN International; CAIRS (internal database). **Networks/Consortia:** Member of Suburban Library System (SLS).

John Grant Crabbe Library
See: **Eastern Kentucky University** (5146)

★4402★
Craft and Folk Art Museum - Research Library (Art)
6067 Wilshire Blvd. Phone: (213)934-7239
Los Angeles, CA 90036 Joan M. Benedetti, Musm.Libn.
Founded: 1975. **Staff:** Prof 1; Other 2. **Subjects:** Folk art, contemporary crafts, design, masks. **Special Collections:** Slide Registry of Contemporary Craftspeople; L.A. Community Research Project (slides, audiotapes, reports on 28 ethnic folk artists in Los Angeles); contemporary craft artists' biographical materials (8 VF drawers); museum archives. **Holdings:** 6000 books; 35,000 slides; 1 VF drawer of clippings; brochures and ephemera; 8 lateral file drawers of archival materials; 5 VF drawers of archival materials; information and referral files. **Subscriptions:** 130 journals and other serials. **Services:** Library and slide registry open to the public by appointment for reference use only. **Computerized Information Services:** Internal database (exhibition information). **Remarks:** Alternate telephone number(s): 937-5544. FAX: (213)937-5576.

Crafts-Farrow State Hospital
See: **South Carolina (State) Department of Mental Health** (15404)

★4403★
Crafts Guild of Manitoba - Library (Art)
183 Kennedy St. Phone: (204)943-6281
Winnipeg, MB, Canada R3C 1S6 Moira Wilson, Chm.
Founded: 1928. **Staff:** 4. **Subjects:** Crafts - weaving, pottery, embroidery, knitting, crochet, quilting. **Holdings:** 1600 volumes; 700 slides. **Subscriptions:** 10 journals and other serials. **Services:** Library not open to the public.

★4404★
Craftsmen Corporation - Library (Sci-Engr)
725 Rte. 347
Smithtown, NY 11787 Phone: (516)360-7870
Subjects: Engineering. **Holdings:** 500 books; 4000 reports. **Subscriptions:** 20 journals and other serials. **Services:** Library not open to the public. **Remarks:** FAX: (516)360-0417.

Cragmont Medical Library
See: **Madison State Hospital** (9528)

Craig Memorial Library
See: **Miami Valley Hospital** (10272)

Vera Craig Pictorial Archive of American Interiors
See: **U.S. Natl. Park Service - Harpers Ferry Center Library** (17729)

Donald W. Craik Engineering Library
See: **University of Manitoba** (18787)

★4405★
Crain Communications, Inc. - Information Center (Publ, Bus-Fin)
740 N. Rush St. Phone: (312)649-5328
Chicago, IL 60611-2590 Mark Mandle
Founded: 1930. **Staff:** Prof 2; Other 4. **Subjects:** Advertising, marketing. **Holdings:** 1900 books; 260 bound periodical volumes; clipping file. **Subscriptions:** 150 journals and other serials. **Services:** Library not open to the public. **Computerized Information Services:** DIALOG Information Services, NEXIS, VU/TEXT Information Services, DataTimes. **Special Indexes:** Index to Crain's Chicago Business and other periodicals (card and microfiche). **Remarks:** Second office located at 220 E. 42nd St., New York, NY 10017. Telephone: (212)210-0184.

★4406★
H.E. Cramer Company, Inc. - Library (Sci-Engr)
136 W. Burton Ave.
Salt Lake City, UT 84115-2611 Phone: (801)486-0121
Subjects: Atmospheric physics, meteorology, mathematics, statistics, computer science. **Holdings:** 500 books; 1100 reports. **Subscriptions:** 10 journals and other serials. **Services:** Library not open to the public.

★4407★
Cranbrook Academy of Art - Library (Art)
500 Lone Pine Rd.
Box 801 Phone: (313)645-3355
Bloomfield Hills, MI 48303-0801 Judy Dyki, Lib.Dir.
Founded: 1932. **Staff:** Prof 3; Other 6. **Subjects:** History of art, photography, painting, ceramics, architecture, fiber/textiles, sculpture, metalsmithing, printmaking, design. **Special Collections:** Cranbrook Press publications; Fine Binding Collection; exhibit catalog collection; lectures by visiting artists (500 cassette tapes). **Holdings:** 25,000 books; 18 VF drawers of clippings on artists and art; 5 VF drawers of clippings on CAA alumni and staff; 14 VF drawers of exhibit catalogs on artists; 32,500 slides. **Subscriptions:** 150 journals and other serials; 8 newspapers. **Services:** Interlibrary loan; copying; library open to the public for reference use only. **Computerized Information Services:** DIALOG Information Services, WILSONLINE, OCLC. **Networks/Consortia:** Member of Michigan Library Consortium (MLC). **Remarks:** FAX: (313)646-0046. **Staff:** Diane Gunn, Slide Cur.; Maris Cannon, Tech.Serv.

★4408★
Cranbrook Institute of Science - Library (Sci-Engr)
500 Lone Pine Rd.
P.O Box 801 Phone: (313)645-3255
Bloomfield Hills, MI 48303-0801 Gretchen Young-Weiner, Libn.
Founded: 1935. **Staff:** Prof 1. **Subjects:** Anthropology, ethnology, natural sciences, physics, astronomy. **Holdings:** 17,500 books; 25 VF drawers of pamphlets; 2000 maps; phonograph records. **Subscriptions:** 210 journals and other serials. **Services:** Interlibrary loan; copying; library open to the public. **Publications:** Annual Report - free to libraries on request; Newsletter, 6/year - free to members and libraries or by exchange; bulletins, irregular. **Remarks:** FAX: (313)642-0803.

Ella Johnson Crandall Memorial Library
See: **Union College** (16649)

★4409★
Prudence Crandall Museum - Library (Hist)
Box 47 Phone: (203)546-9916
Canterbury, CT 06331 Kazimiera Kozlowski, Musm.Cur.
Staff: Prof 1. **Subjects:** Black history, life of Prudence Crandall, state and local history, women's history. **Holdings:** 1000 books. **Services:** Library open to the public by appointment for reference use only. **Remarks:** Maintained by Connecticut Historical Commission.

Charles Crane Memorial Library
See: **University of British Columbia** (18257)

★4410★
Crane Company - Hydro-Aire Division - Technical Library (Sci-Engr)
P.O. Box 7722 Phone: (818)842-6121
Burbank, CA 91510 Joanne Mandeville, Libn.
Founded: 1955. **Staff:** 1. **Subjects:** Aeronautics, engineering. **Special Collections:** Federal Aviation Administration reports; American Society for Testing and Materials; Air Force reports; NASA documents; American Society for Nondestructive Testing. **Holdings:** 1000 volumes; 1000 cataloged reports; 45 VF drawers of government specifications and handbooks; 86 VF drawers of miscellaneous reports and documents; 35 VF drawers of customer documents. **Services:** Interlibrary loan; library not open to the public. **Remarks:** Library located at 3000 Winona Ave., Burbank, CA 91504.

★4411★
Crane Defense Systems - Library (Sci-Engr)
Rte. 20, Box 1126 Phone: (409)539-4545
Conroe, TX 77301 Cecile Covington, Libn.
Staff: Prof 1. **Subjects:** Basic and applied technologies. **Holdings:** 2200 books; 4500 reports, patents, documents. **Subscriptions:** 153 journals and other serials. **Remarks:** FAX: (409)539-4532.

★4412★
J. W. Crane Memorial Library (Med)
2109 Portage Ave. Phone: (204)831-2152
Winnipeg, MB, Canada R3J 0L3 Judy Inglis, Dir.
Staff: Prof 1; Other 2. **Subjects:** Geriatrics, long-term care. **Holdings:** 6000 books. **Subscriptions:** 185 journals and other serials. **Services:** Interlibrary loan; copying; SDI; library open for student practicums. **Computerized Information Services:** BRS Information Technologies; AGECAN (internal database); CD-ROMs (MEDLINE, CINAHL, HealthPlan). Performs searches. **Publications:** Agelit (bibliography), monthly; Special Bibliography Series, monthly. **Remarks:** FAX: (204)888-5574.

Crane Music Library
See: **State University College at Potsdam** (15713)

★4413★
Cranford Historical Society - Museum Library (Hist)
124 N. Union Ave. Phone: (908)276-0082
Cranford, NJ 07016 Patricia Pavlak, Cur.
Founded: 1927. **Staff:** Prof 1. **Subjects:** Local history, Indian artifacts, paintings. **Special Collections:** Harrison Huster Indian Collection; Victorian Parlor; early agricultural and household implements; Canton export china. **Holdings:** Books; pictures; clippings; articles; maps; oral history tapes; scrapbooks. **Subscriptions:** 6 journals and other serials. **Services:** Library open to the public for reference use only. **Publications:** 300 Years at Crane's Ford.

★4414★
Cranford United Methodist Church - Library (Rel-Phil)
201 E. Lincoln Ave. Phone: (201)276-0936
Cranford, NJ 07016 Laura Engel, Libn.
Founded: 1960. **Staff:** Prof 1; Other 1. **Subjects:** Religion, history, philosophy, psychology, children's books. **Holdings:** 3600 books; 300 unbound reports and pamphlets; picture file. **Subscriptions:** 4 journals and other serials. **Services:** Library not open to the public.

Sir Thomas Crapper Memorial Archives
See: **International Brotherhood of Old Bastards, Inc.** (8066)

Crater Lake National Park
See: **U.S. Natl. Park Service** (17694)

Craters of the Moon National Monument
See: **U.S. Natl. Park Service** (17695)

★4415★
Cravath, Swaine, & Moore - Law Library (Law)
Worldwide Plaza
825 Eighth Ave. Phone: (212)474-3500
New York, NY 10019 Arlene Eis, Dir., Lib.Serv.
Founded: 1819. **Staff:** Prof 9; Other 16. **Subjects:** Law. **Special Collections:** Corporate precedent files (100 VF drawers); tender offer library (60 VF drawers); government documents (100 VF drawers). **Holdings:** 50,000 books; 600 VF drawers. **Subscriptions:** 4000 journals and other serials; 15 newspapers. **Services:** Interlibrary loan; library not open to the public. **Automated Operations:** Computerized public access catalog, serials, circulation, routing, and ILL. **Computerized Information Services:** DIALOG Information Services, Dun & Bradstreet Business Credit Services, WESTLAW, LEGI-SLATE, LEXIS, IDD Information Services, Inc. (IDDIS), DataTimes, Reuter TEXTLINE, Dow Jones News/Retrieval, RLIN, OCLC, VU/TEXT Information Services, NewsNet, Inc., Quotron Systems, Inc. **Special Indexes:** Proxy, Tender Offer, and Prospectus Index. **Remarks:** FAX: (212)474-3556. **Staff:** Elsbeth Moller, Asst.Dir., Lib.Serv.; Katherine Kenworthy, Hd., Tech.Serv.

Craven-Pamlico-Carteret Regional Library - Bogue Banks Library
See: **Bogue Banks Library** (1943)

Craver and Craver, Inc. - Spectra Search
See: **Spectra Search** (15578)

C.C. Crawford Memorial Library
See: **Dallas Christian College** (4544)

★4416★
Crawford County Law Library (Law)
Court House, Rm. 212
903 Diamond Park
Meadville, PA 16335 Phone: (814)336-1151
Staff: 1. **Subjects:** Law. **Holdings:** 16,375 books; 145 bound periodical volumes; 2000 volumes on ultrafiche. **Services:** Library open to the public for reference use only.

★4417★
F. Marion Crawford Memorial Society - Bibliotheca Crawfordiana (Hum)
Saracinesca House
3610 Meadowbrook Ave. Phone: (615)292-9695
Nashville, TN 37205 John C. Moran, Dir.
Founded: 1975. **Staff:** Prof 1. **Subjects:** Fantastic literature, modern Romanticism (post-1850). **Special Collections:** Francis Marion Crawford, 1854-1909 (425 items); Francis Marion Crawford letters (printed, on disk). **Holdings:** 1150 books; 430 letters, photocopied or on microfilm; 5 original letters; 3 theses; 100 pieces of miscellanea. **Subscriptions:** 12 journals and other serials. **Services:** Copying; library open to the public by appointment. **Publications:** The Worthies Library (series of books); The Romantist (journal).

★4418★
Fred Roberts Crawford Witness to the Holocaust Project - Library (Hist)
Emory University Phone: (404)329-6428
Atlanta, GA 30322 Terry Anderson, Libn.
Founded: 1978. **Staff:** Prof 1. **Subjects:** The Holocaust. **Holdings:** 200 books; 142 audiotapes; 13 videotapes; 113 transcripts; 405 photographs; 100 slides; 73 speeches, articles, pamphlets. **Services:** Library open to the public.

Woodruff L. Crawford Branch Library of the Health Sciences
See: **University of Illinois at Chicago - College of Medicine at Rockford** (18696)

★4419★
Crazy Horse Memorial - Library (Area-Ethnic)
University of North America
Avenue of the Chiefs Phone: (605)673-4681
Crazy Horse, SD 57730-9998 Jessie Y. Sundstrom, Libn.
Founded: 1947. **Staff:** Prof 1. **Subjects:** American Indians, art. **Holdings:** 14,000 books. **Services:** Library not open to the public.

★4420★
Creare, Inc. - Library (Sci-Engr)
P.O. Box 71 Phone: (603)643-3800
Hanover, NH 03755 Dorothy A. Gannon, Lib.Mgr.
Founded: 1961. **Staff:** Prof 1; Other 3. **Subjects:** Fluid mechanics and machinery, heat transfer, multiphase flow, gas turbines, computers, cryogenics, computational fluid dynamics. **Holdings:** 2700 books; 33,000 other cataloged items; 500 patents; 1600 company reports and proposals. **Subscriptions:** 200 journals and other serials. **Services:** Library open to the public with restrictions. **Automated Operations:** Computerized cataloging, acquisitions, serials, and circulation. **Computerized Information Services:** DIALOG Information Services, OCLC EPIC. **Publications:** Acquisitions list, monthly - for internal distribution only. **Remarks:** FAX: (603)643-4657.

★4421★
Creation-Science Research Center - Information Center (Rel-Phil)
Box 23195
San Diego, CA 92123 Phone: (619)569-8673
Founded: 1971. **Staff:** Prof 3; Other 2. **Subjects:** Creation-science and history. **Holdings:** 1800 books; clippings. **Services:** Center not open to the public.

★4422★
Creative Education Foundation - Library (Educ)
1050 Union Rd.
Buffalo, NY 14224 Phone: (716)675-3181
Founded: 1954. **Staff:** 6. **Subjects:** Creative behavior, decision-making, problem solving. **Holdings:** 2500 volumes; 1500 reels of microfilm; doctoral theses. **Services:** Library not open to the public. **Remarks:** FAX: (716)675-3209.

Creative Studies Library
See: **State University College at Buffalo** (15704)

★4423★
Credit Union National Association - Information Resource Center (Bus-Fin)
5710 W. Mineral Point Rd.
Box 431 Phone: (608)231-4170
Madison, WI 53701 Anne Reynolds, Mgr.
Founded: 1958. **Staff:** Prof 2; Other 1. **Subjects:** Credit unions, economics, business, finance. **Special Collections:** Edward A. Filene papers; Roy F. Bergengren papers; history of the credit union movement. **Holdings:** 2000 books; 6000 historical items; 4000 credit union documents; 10,000 historical documents; minutes of Credit Union National Association, World Council of Credit Unions, CUNA Supply Corporation and annual reports of state, provincial, national credit union leagues on microfilm, 1000 photographs. **Subscriptions:** 400 journals and newsletters. **Services:** Interlibrary loan; copying; SDI; center open to the public by appointment. **Automated Operations:** Computerized cataloging and serials. **Computerized Information Services:** DIALOG Information Services, NEXIS, Dow Jones News/Retrieval, NewsNet, Inc., Dun & Bradstreet Business Credit Services. **Networks/Consortia:** Member of South Central Library System. **Special Catalogs:** Cross-indexed catalog of historical credit union documents. **Remarks:** FAX: (608)231-1869. **Staff:** Gabriel Kirkpatrick, Archv.

★4424★
Creedmoor Psychiatric Center - Health Sciences Library (Med)
80-45 Winchester Blvd. Phone: (718)464-7500
Queens Village, NY 11427 Pushpa Bhati, Sr.Libn.
Staff: Prof 1; Other 1. **Subjects:** Psychiatry, psychology, medicine, sociology, hospital administration. **Holdings:** 14,550 books; 2210 bound periodical volumes; 2409 other cataloged items; 3298 pamphlets. **Subscriptions:** 175 journals and other serials. **Services:** Interlibrary loan; library open to the public by appointment. **Computerized Information Services:** Online systems. **Networks/Consortia:** Member of Brooklyn-Queens-Staten Island Health Sciences Librarians (BQSI), National Network of Libraries of Medicine - Middle Atlantic Region, Medical & Scientific Libraries of Long Island (MEDLI), New York Metropolitan Reference and Research Library Agency. **Special Indexes:** List of new acquisitions by subject (pamphlet); list of current subscription journals. **Remarks:** Maintained by the New York State Office of Mental Health.

★4425★
Creek Indian Memorial Association - Creek Council House Museum - Library (Hist)
Town Square
106 W. 6th St. Phone: (918)756-2324
Okmulgee, OK 74447 Tommy A. Steinsick, Dir.
Founded: 1930. **Staff:** Prof 1. **Subjects:** Oklahoma history, Creek Indian history and culture. **Holdings:** 200 books; 60 bound periodical volumes; 2 VF drawers of clippings and biography notes; 150 documents and records of the Creek Nation. **Services:** Library open to the public with permission of director.

★4426★
Creighton University - Health Sciences Library (Med)
California at 24th St.
Omaha, NE 68178 Phone: (402)280-5108
Founded: 1910. **Staff:** Prof 6; Other 18. **Subjects:** Medicine, pharmacy, dentistry, nursing, and allied health sciences. **Special Collections:** Von Schulte Rare Book Collection; Levine Collection (history of scurvy); National Football League (NFL) Charities Research Collection of Autism. **Holdings:** 31,830 books; 58,623 bound periodical volumes; 4338 AV programs; 63,179 microforms. **Subscriptions:** 1443 journals and other serials; 6 newspapers. **Services:** Interlibrary loan; copying; SDI; library open to the public. **Automated Operations:** Computerized public access catalog, cataloging, circulation, and serials. **Computerized Information Services:** MEDLINE, BRS Information Technologies, OCLC; CD-ROM. Performs searches on fee basis. Contact Person: Richard Jizba, Ref.Libn. **Networks/Consortia:** Member of NEBASE, National Network of Libraries of Medicine - Midcontinental Region. **Publications:** New Accessions List, monthly - to faculty. **Remarks:** FAX: (402)280-5134. **Staff:** Geraldine Dell, Circ.Libn.; Nannette Bedrosky, Tech.Serv.Libn.; Jane Stehlik Romack, AV Libn.

★4427★
Creighton University - Reinert/Alumni Memorial Library (Rel-Phil)
2500 California St. Phone: (402)280-2705
Omaha, NE 68178 Ray B. Means, Lib.Dir.
Founded: 1878. **Staff:** Prof 9; Other 11. **Subjects:** Religion, philosophy. **Special Collections:** Japanese history and culture. **Holdings:** 330,000 books; 44,000 bound periodical volumes; 39,000 books on microfiche; 73,500 U.S. government documents; 647,000 microfiche; 1800 cassettes; 6900 reels of film. **Subscriptions:** 1585 journals and other serials; 35 newspapers. **Services:** Interlibrary loan; copying; library open to the public. **Automated Operations:** Computerized public access catalog, cataloging, and serials. **Computerized Information Services:** DIALOG Information Services, OCLC. **Networks/Consortia:** Member of NEBASE. **Remarks:** FAX: (402)280-2435. **Staff:** LaVina Swanek, Hd., Ser.; Mary Nash, Hd., Ref.; Gerry Chase, Hd., Circ.; Lauralee Grabe, Hd., Tech.Serv.

John Crerar Library
See: **University of Chicago - John Crerar Library** (18452)

Cresap - Library
See: **Towers Perrin Co.** (16438)

★4428★
Crescent Avenue Presbyterian Church - Library (Rel-Phil)
716 Watchung Ave.
Plainfield, NJ 07060
Subjects: Religion, American history. **Holdings:** 3000 books. **Remarks:** Currently inactive.

★4429★
Cresset Chemical Company - Library (Sci-Engr)
P.O. Box 367 Phone: (419)669-2041
Weston, OH 43569 Sally Newman, Adm.Asst.
Founded: 1989. **Subjects:** Concrete. **Holdings:** 200 books; 300 reports. **Subscriptions:** 30 journals and other serials. **Services:** Library not open to the public. **Remarks:** FAX: (419)669-2200.

Cressman Library
See: **Cedar Crest and Muhlenberg College Libraries** (3183)

★4430★
Crestar Bank - Information Center (Bus-Fin)
Box 26665 Phone: (804)782-7452
Richmond, VA 23261 Sue N. Miller, Mgr., Info.Serv.
Founded: 1970. **Staff:** Prof 3. **Subjects:** Banking, finance, economics, statistics, accounting, management, economic statistics of Southeastern U.S., international banking and economic data. **Holdings:** 10,000 books; 50 VF drawers of annual reports of banks and bank holding companies; 10 drawers of international economic and financial data; 20 drawers of banking-related subjects. **Subscriptions:** 600 journals and other serials; 10 newspapers. **Services:** Interlibrary loan; copying; center open to students and customers by appointment. **Automated Operations:** Computerized cataloging and serials. **Computerized Information Services:** DIALOG Information Services, Dow Jones News/Retrieval, TEXTLINE, NEXIS, VU/TEXT. **Publications:** Books 'n Things (informational sheet), monthly - to banks and holding company management personnel. **Remarks:** FAX: (804)782-5262. **Staff:** Tina Schmitt, Tech.Serv.Spec.; Ann Mountcastle, Info.Ctr.Asst.

★4431★
Crestwood Children's Hospital - Arthur M. Lowenthal Library (Med)
2075 Scottsville Rd. Phone: (716)436-4442
Rochester, NY 14623 Marilyn Kalmbacher, Libn.
Founded: 1967. **Staff:** Prof 1. **Subjects:** Child psychiatry, clinical psychology, community and child mental health, psychiatric social work. **Holdings:** 2050 books; 500 bound periodical volumes. **Subscriptions:** 70 journals and other serials. **Services:** Interlibrary loan; copying; library open to the public. **Networks/Consortia:** Member of Rochester Regional Library Council (RRLC). **Remarks:** FAX: (716)436-0169. **Formerly:** Convalescent Hospital for Children.

★4432★
Crime & Justice Foundation - Mascarello Library of Criminal Justice (Law)
95 Berkeley St., 2nd Fl. Phone: (617)426-9800
Boston, MA 02116 Cynthia Brophy, Proj.Dir.
Founded: 1977. **Subjects:** Criminal justice, correction, probation, parole, courts, police. **Special Collections:** Early Prison Societies in Boston, 1820s to present; annotated laws of Massachusetts. **Holdings:** 2500 volumes; 9 films. **Subscriptions:** 22 journals and other serials. **Services:** Library open to the public for reference use only. **Publications:** Comparative Analysis of Adult Correctional Standards; Comparative Analysis of Standards for Juvenile Probation and After Care Services; Comparative Analysis of Standards for Administration of Correctional Agencies; Legal Review of Correctional Standards (1986); Evaluation of the Hampden County Day Reporting Center (1988); Court Mediation Program of the Crime & Justice Foundation (1989); Shifting the Debate on Crime: A Study of Public Opinion & New Approaches to Fighting Crime (1991); The Crisis in Corrections & Sentencing in Massachusetts (1991); Managing the Develo pment of Community Corrections (1990).

★4433★
The Criswell College - Wallace Library (Rel-Phil)
4010 Gaston Ave. Phone: (214)742-3111
Dallas, TX 75246 Dawn Pilcher, Libn.
Founded: 1979. **Staff:** Prof 1; Other 15. **Subjects:** Theology, Baptists, Anabaptists, Bible commentaries, church history, history, literature. **Special Collections:** Baptist history; Dr. W.A. Criswell manuscripts; Dr. George W. Truett memorabilia; archaeological collection; First Baptist Church, Dallas, Texas scrapbooks. **Holdings:** 67,012 books; 10,000 bound periodical volumes; 2000 cassette tapes; 4300 microforms. **Subscriptions:** 600 journals and other serials. **Services:** Interlibrary loan; copying; library open to the public with restrictions. **Automated Operations:** Computerized cataloging and ILL. **Computerized Information Services:** OCLC.

Critical Mass Energy Project
See: **Public Citizen** (13473)

★4434★
Critikon, Inc. - R & D Information Services Library (Med, Sci-Engr)
4110 George Rd. Phone: (813)887-2000
Tampa, FL 33634-7498 Jeffrey A. Baker, Supv., Info.Serv.
Founded: 1981. **Staff:** Prof 1; Other 1. **Subjects:** Biomedical engineering, medicine, electronics, chemistry, biochemistry. **Holdings:** 2600 books. **Subscriptions:** 100 journals and other serials. **Services:** Interlibrary loan; library open to health care professionals. **Automated Operations:** Computerized cataloging. **Computerized Information Services:** DIALOG Information Services, ORBIT Search Service, BRS Information Technologies, NLM, NEXIS. **Remarks:** FAX: (813)887-2554. Critikon, Inc. is a division of Johnson and Johnson.

★4435★
Croatian Serbian Slovene Genealogical Society - Library (Area-Ethnic)
2527 San Carlos Ave. Phone: (415)592-1190
San Carlos, CA 94070 Adam S. Eterovich, Dir.
Staff: 4. **Subjects:** Genealogy, heraldry, census, U.S. history prior to 1900. **Special Collections:** 120,000 index cards on individuals in the U.S. prior to 1910. **Holdings:** 2000 books; 20 bound periodical volumes; 20 drawers of index cards; 30 manuscripts. **Subscriptions:** 10 journals and other serials; 5 newspapers. **Services:** Library open to the public by appointment. **Publications:** Bulletins; monographs.

Betty Crocker Food & Publications Information Center
See: **General Mills, Inc.** (6327)

Crocker Business and Accounting Libraries
See: **University of Southern California** (19324)

Crocker House Museum
See: **Macomb County Historical Society - Crocker House Museum** (9506)

Sabin and Lena Crocker Library
See: **Macomb County Historical Society - Crocker House Museum** (9506)

★4436★
Crompton & Knowles Corporation - Dyes and Chemicals Division - Gibraltar Research Library (Sci-Engr)
Box 341 Phone: (215)582-8765
Reading, PA 19603 Florence Sheehan, Info.Chem.
Staff: Prof 1. **Subjects:** Dyes, organic chemistry, textiles. **Holdings:** 1350 books; 1300 bound periodical volumes; 19 VF drawers of patents; 4 VF drawers of trade literature. **Subscriptions:** 28 journals and other serials. **Services:** Interlibrary loan; copying (both limited); library open to the public by appointment. **Computerized Information Services:** DIALOG Information Services, PFDS Online, Chemical Information Systems, Inc. (CIS). **Networks/Consortia:** Member of Berks County Library Association (BCLA). **Special Catalogs:** Dye patents (card); dye structures (card). **Remarks:** FAX: (215)582-6665.

Betty Cronk Memorial Library
See: **Rochester Business Institute** (13976)

Crop Science Society of America - American Society of Agronomy
See: **American Society of Agronomy** (742)

★4437★
Crosby County Pioneer Memorial - CCPM Historical Collection/ Museum Library (Hist)
101 Main St.
Box 386 Phone: (806)675-2331
Crosbyton, TX 79322 Verna Anne Wheeler, Exec.Dir.
Founded: 1958. **Staff:** Prof 1. **Subjects:** West Texas history. **Holdings:** 3171 volumes; 5 vertical files; The Crosbyton Review, 1909 to present, on microfilm. **Subscriptions:** 17 journals and other serials. **Services:** Copying; library open to the public for reference use only. **Publications:** Newsletter, quarterly. **Special Indexes:** Index to the Crosbyton Review; index to photography collection; index to oral histories.

★4438★
Crosby, Heafey, Roach & May - Law Library (Law)
1999 Harrison St. Phone: (510)763-2000
Oakland, CA 94612 Nora L. Skrukrud, Libn.
Founded: 1969. **Staff:** Prof 3; Other 4. **Subjects:** Civil litigation, taxation, labor law, medical jurisprudence, environmental law, intellectual property, products liability. **Holdings:** 20,000 books; 150 bound periodical volumes. **Subscriptions:** 400 journals and other serials; 13 newspapers. **Services:** Interlibrary loan; library not open to the public. **Automated Operations:** Computerized public access catalog, cataloging, acquisitions, and serials. **Computerized Information Services:** DIALOG Information Services, LEXIS, WESTLAW, DataTimes, DataQuick, Information America, Maxwell Macmillan Taxes Online, VU/TEXT Information Services, REUTERS. **Remarks:** FAX: (510)273-8898.

Crosby Library
See: **Gonzaga University** (6544)

George C. Croskery Memorial Library
See: **Canadian Teachers' Federation** (2993)

★4439★
Cross Cancer Institute - Library (Med)
11560 University Ave. Phone: (403)492-8593
Edmonton, AB, Canada T6G 1Z2 Juliana Zia, Libn.
Founded: 1968. **Staff:** Prof 1. **Subjects:** Neoplastic diseases, cancer research. **Holdings:** 4000 books; 860 bound periodical volumes; 2 drawers of pamphlets; government documents. **Subscriptions:** 160 journals and other serials. **Services:** Interlibrary loan; copying; library open to medical and health care personnel only. **Computerized Information Services:** MEDLINE, DIALOG Information Services. **Remarks:** FAX: (403)492-0884.

Charle Cross Goodrich Information Center
See: **B.F. Goodrich Company - Research and Development Center** (6567)

★4440★
Crosswicks Public Library - Local History Collection (Hist)
Box 147 Phone: (609)298-6271
Crosswicks, NJ 08515 Alice Bumbera, Libn.
Staff: Prof 1; Other 1. **Subjects:** Local history and genealogy. **Holdings:** 10,000 books. **Services:** Interlibrary loan; collection open to the public with restrictions.

★4441★
Crouch Enterprises, Inc. - Consumer Housing Library (Plan)
11166 Main St. Phone: (703)768-4741
Fairfax, VA 22030 Tracy Hill, Oper.Mgr.
Founded: 1985. **Staff:** 9. **Subjects:** New and resale housing, real estate procedures and services, schools and daycare, new construction projects. **Holdings:** Planning and zoning maps; county master plans; real estate manuals. **Services:** Copying; library open to the public. **Computerized Information Services:** Online systems. **Publications:** Directory of Homes & Services. **Remarks:** A branch library is maintained at 12501 Property Dr., Silver Spring, MD 20904.

Crouch Music Library
See: **Baylor University** (1604)

★4442★
Crouse-Irving Memorial Hospital - Library (Med)
736 Irving Ave. Phone: (315)470-7380
Syracuse, NY 13210 Wendy Skinner, Dir., Lib.Serv.
Founded: 1913. **Staff:** Prof 5; Other 15. **Subjects:** Nursing, medicine. **Holdings:** 3000 books; 1500 bound periodical volumes; 1500 AV programs. **Subscriptions:** 235 journals and other serials. **Services:** Interlibrary loan; copying; library open to the public for reference use only. **Automated Operations:** Computerized cataloging and ILL. **Computerized Information Services:** MEDLARS, DIALOG Information Services, OCLC. **Networks/ Consortia:** Member of Central New York Library Resources Council (CENTRO). **Remarks:** An alternate phone number is 470-7861. FAX: (315)470-7443. **Staff:** Karen Fenner, Libn.; Kristine Hogan, Libn.; Virginia Watson, Libn.; Diane Hawkins, Libn.

★4443★
Crow Wing County Historical Society - Library (Hist)
320 Laurel St.
Box 722 Phone: (218)829-3268
Brainerd, MN 56401 Pamela A. Brunfelt, Exec.Dir.
Staff: Prof 1. **Subjects:** Local history. **Special Collections:** Works Progress Administration (WPA) biographies of local residents; Joe Marchel Resort Photograph Collection. **Holdings:** Maps; diaries; historical scrapbooks and photograph albums; oral history collection; county newspapers; Brainerd city directories, 1901-1974. **Subscriptions:** 10 journals and other serials; 3 newspapers. **Services:** Copying; library open to the public with restrictions. **Computerized Information Services:** Internal database. **Networks/ Consortia:** Member of Northern Lights Library Network (NLLN). **Special Indexes:** Index to WPA Biographies; index to archives/photographs (card).

Orville W. Crowder Memorial Library
See: **World Nature Association** (20627)

Crowell Learning Resource Center
See: **Moody Bible Institute** (10706)

★4444★
Crowell & Moring - Library (Law)
1001 Pennsylvania Ave., N.W. Phone: (202)624-2828
Washington, DC 20004-2505 Ellen M. Callinan, Mgr., Res.Serv.
Founded: 1979. **Staff:** Prof 5; Other 6. **Subjects:** Law - corporate, environmental, energy; government contracts; transportation; taxation. **Special Collections:** Legislative histories (200 titles). **Holdings:** 35,000 books; 1600 bound periodical volumes; 6000 microfiche; 100 video cassettes; 1000 volumes of Congressional hearings and reports. **Subscriptions:** 150 journals and other serials; 8 newspapers. **Services:** Interlibrary loan; SDI; library open by appointment only. **Computerized Information Services:** LEXIS, NEXIS, Dow Jones News/Retrieval, DataTimes, WESTLAW, DIALOG Information Services, WILSONLINE, LEGI-SLATE. **Publications:** C&M Hillights. **Special Indexes:** Legal Memoranda File (card). **Staff:** Lisa Hensley, Comp.Serv.; Bich-Ha Nguyen, Tech.Serv.; Margo Chisholm, Ref.Serv.; Mary Shackelton, Leg.Serv.

Crowley Library
See: **The Family Institute - Crowley Library** (5589)

★4445★
Crowley Ridge Regional Library - Local History Collection (Hist)
315 W. Oak Phone: (501)935-5133
Jonesboro, AR 72401 Rusty Dancer, Ref.Libn.
Subjects: Arkansas history, 1790 to present; genealogy of northeastern Arkansas, southeastern Missouri, western Tennessee. **Holdings:** 500 linear feet of area and family histories, census records, cemetery records, genealogical research materials. **Services:** Copying; collection open to the public. **Remarks:** FAX: (501)935-7987.

★4446★
Crown College - Peter Watne Memorial Library (Rel-Phil)
6425 County Rd. 30 Phone: (612)446-4240
St. Bonifacius, MN 55375-9001 Roger A. van Oosten, Dir., Lib.Serv.
Founded: 1916. **Staff:** Prof 1; Other 6. **Subjects:** Bible and theology, history, teacher education, Christian education, missions. **Special Collections:** Howard O. Jones Evangelism Collection (200 volumes); college archives (500 volumes, 8 VF drawers); teacher education children's library (9600 volumes). **Holdings:** 85,000 books; 6000 bound periodical volumes; 2000 volumes unbound periodicals; 70,000 microprint volumes; 30 VF drawers of pamphlets and documents; 4000 AV items; 63 periodical titles on microfiche. **Subscriptions:** 345 journals and other serials; 5 newspapers. **Services:** Interlibrary loan; copying; library open to the public with restrictions. **Automated Operations:** Computerized cataloging. **Computerized Information Services:** OCLC. **Networks/Consortia:** Member of MINITEX Library Information Network. **Remarks:** FAX: (612)446-4149. **Formerly:** St. Paul Bible College.

Crown Gardens and Archives
See: **Whitfield-Murray Historical Society** (20387)

★4447★
Crown Life Insurance Company - Corporate Information Centre (Bus-Fin)
120 Bloor St., E. Phone: (416)928-4650
Toronto, ON, Canada M4W 1B8 Susan Cameron, Corp.Libn.
Founded: 1900. **Staff:** Prof 1. **Subjects:** Life and health insurance, management, financial services, computers. **Special Collections:** Canadian Life and Health Insurance Association and Life Insurance Marketing and Research Association publications; Annual Reports of Superintendent of Insurance of Canada; annual reports of life insurance companies. **Holdings:** 4000 books; 1 file drawer of microfiche. **Subscriptions:** 150 journals and other serials; 6 newspapers. **Services:** Interlibrary loan; copying; center open to the public by appointment. **Automated Operations:** Computerized cataloging, serials, and journal routing. **Computerized Information Services:** DIALOG Information Services, Info Globe, BRS Information Technologies, LEXIS, NEXIS, Infomart Online. **Publications:** Update, quarterly - to company employees and selected libraries in Toronto. **Remarks:** FAX: (416)928-5817.

★4448★
Crown Life Insurance Company - Law Library (Law)
120 Bloor St., E. Phone: (416)928-4563
Toronto, ON, Canada M4W 1B8 Mari White, Law Libn.
Founded: 1973. **Staff:** 2. **Subjects:** Law - life insurance, labor, corporation, securities, taxation. **Holdings:** 5000 volumes. **Subscriptions:** 400 loose-leaf services. **Services:** Interlibrary loan (limited); library not open to the public. **Automated Operations:** Computerized cataloging, acquisitions, serials, and circulation. **Computerized Information Services:** QL Systems, LEXIS, WESTLAW, CAN/LAW, NEXIS; internal databases; QUICKMAIL (electronic mail service). **Publications:** Acquisition list, monthly. **Special Indexes:** Index to American Council of Life Insurance (ACLI) General/Legislative/Special Bulletins; Index to Canadian Life & Health Insurance Association Circulars. **Remarks:** FAX: (416)928-2414. **Staff:** Marie Hindley, Lib.Techn.

Crown Zellerbach Corporation
See: **James River Corporation** (8323)

★4449★
Crownsville Hospital Center - Staff Library (Med)
Crownsville, MD 21032 Phone: (301)987-6200
Susan S. Merrill, Libn.
Founded: 1954. **Staff:** Prof 1; Other 1. **Subjects:** Psychiatry, psychology, behavior therapy, family therapy, nursing, social services. **Holdings:** 1200 books; 15 file boxes; 250 VF items; 40 audiotapes; unbound periodicals. **Subscriptions:** 20 journals and other serials. **Services:** Interlibrary loan (limited); copying; SDI; library open to the public for reference use only. **Computerized Information Services:** Access to MEDLARS, DIALOG Information Services. **Networks/Consortia:** Member of Maryland Association of Health Science Librarians (MAHSL). **Special Catalogs:** MAHSL Catalog (Union List of Biomedical Serials).

★4450★
Crozer Chester Medical Center - Medical Library (Med)
1 Medical Center Blvd. Phone: (215)447-2600
Upland, PA 19013 Judith E. Ziegler, Lib.Dir.
Founded: 1966. **Staff:** Prof 1; Other 2. **Subjects:** Medicine, nursing, allied health sciences. **Special Collections:** Burns and trauma collections. **Holdings:** 3000 books; 8500 bound periodical volumes. **Subscriptions:** 450 journals and other serials. **Services:** Interlibrary loan; copying; SDI; library open to the public for reference use only. **Computerized Information Services:** BRS Information Technologies, DIALOG Information Services, NLM, MEDLARS; CD-ROM; DOCLINE (electronic mail service). Performs searches on fee basis. **Networks/Consortia:** Member of Consortium for Health Information & Library Services (CHI), National Network of Libraries of Medicine - Middle Atlantic Region, BHSL. **Publications:** CCMC Journal List; newsletter, quarterly; acquisitions list. **Remarks:** FAX: (215)447-6162. **Formerly:** Located in Chester, PA.

★4451★
CRSS, Inc. - Pena Library (Plan)
1177 W. Loop S.
Box 22427 Phone: (713)552-2271
Houston, TX 77027 Nancy Acker Fleshman, Res.Libn.
Founded: 1968. **Staff:** Prof 1; Other 1. **Subjects:** Architecture, engineering, environment, planning, landscape architecture, interior and graphic design, management. **Holdings:** 2500 books; 500 bound periodical volumes; 335 CRS reports; 30 VF drawers research files. **Subscriptions:** 65 journals and other serials. **Services:** Interlibrary loan; copying; SDI; library open to the public by appointment. **Computerized Information Services:** PFDS Online, LEXIS, NEXIS, DIALOG Information Services, VU/TEXT Information Services, DataTimes; DIALMAIL (electronic mail service). **Remarks:** FAX: (713)552-2054.

★4452★
Crucible Materials Corporation - Crucible Research Center - Library (Sci-Engr)
P.O. Box 88 Phone: (412)923-2955
Pittsburgh, PA 15230 Patricia J. Aducci, Tech.Libn. & Info.Spec.
Subjects: Tool steels; super alloys; permanent magnets; titanium and titanium alloys; particle metallurgy; powder-metal and alloys; product and process research, development and engineering. **Holdings:** 3500 books; 2500 periodical volumes; internal technical reports; 30 VF cabinets of technical documents; government reports; patents; mineral statistics; American Iron and Steel Institute (AISI) literature; company archives; internal reports on microfiche. **Subscriptions:** 120 journals and other serials. **Services:** Interlibrary loan; library not open to the public. **Computerized Information Services:** DIALOG Information Services, PFDS Online, BRS Information Technologies, WILSONLINE. Performs searches on fee basis. **Remarks:** FAX: (412)788-4665. **Formerly:** Colt Industries - Crucible Research Center.

★4453★
Crum and Forster Commercial Insurance - Business Information Center (Bus-Fin)
211 Mt. Airy Rd. Phone: (908)953-3326
Basking Ridge, NJ 07920 Toby E. Hecht, Supv.
Founded: 1971. **Staff:** Prof 1. **Subjects:** Property and casualty insurance, personnel, investment, management, training, data processing. **Special Collections:** Company historical materials (10 cartons). **Holdings:** 5000 books; 8 VF drawers of clippings. **Subscriptions:** 400 journals and other serials; 6 newspapers. **Services:** Interlibrary loan; copying; SDI. **Automated Operations:** Computerized cataloging, acquisitions, serials, and circulation. **Computerized Information Services:** DIALOG Information Services,

NEXIS, LEXIS, WESTLAW, Dow Jones News/Retrieval, VU/TEXT Information Services; DIALMAIL (electronic mail service). Performs searches on fee basis. **Networks/Consortia:** Member of Northwest Regional Library Cooperative. **Publications:** Information Exchange, quarterly; AV directory, irregular - both for internal distribution only. **Remarks:** FAX: (908)953-9121.

Frederick W. Crumb Memorial Library
See: **State University College at Potsdam** (15714)

★4454★
Crummy, Del Deo, Dolan, Griffinger & Vecchione - Library (Law)
1 Riverfront Plaza Phone: (201)596-4500
Newark, NJ 07102-5311 Sylvia Reuben
Staff: Prof 3; Other 5. **Subjects:** Law, trial advocacy, insolvency, corporate law, taxation. **Holdings:** 40,000 books. **Subscriptions:** 60 journals and other serials; 8 newspapers. **Services:** Interlibrary loan; library not open to the public. **Automated Operations:** Computerized public access catalog. **Computerized Information Services:** WESTLAW, LEXIS, DIALOG Information Services. **Remarks:** FAX: (201)596-0545.

Crundale Rectorial Library
See: **University of London - Wye College - Library** (18766)

Crusade of Mercy
See: **United Way/Crusade of Mercy** (17968)

★4455★
Crystal Systems, Inc. - Library (Sci-Engr)
27 Congress St. Phone: (508)745-0088
Salem, MA 01970 Peggy Mullane, Asst. to Pres.
Founded: 1971. **Staff:** 25. **Subjects:** Crystals. **Holdings:** 300 books; 500 reports. **Subscriptions:** 50 journals and other serials. **Services:** Library not open to the public. **Remarks:** FAX: (508)744-5059. Telex TWX 710 347 1523.

★4456★
CSA Fraternal Life - Czechoslovak Heritage Museum, Library and Archives (Area-Ethnic)
2701 S. Harlem Ave.
Box 249 Phone: (708)795-5800
Berwyn, IL 60402-0249 Lillian K. Chorvat, Libn./Musm.Cur.
Founded: 1974. **Staff:** Prof 1; Other 1. **Subjects:** Czechoslovakian classics; world classic literature in Czech; history - Czech, Moravian, Slovak; contributions of Czech Americans. **Special Collections:** Archives of the Czechoslovak Society of America (CSA); fraternal publications; Czechoslovak artifacts (authentic folk costumes and instruments of Czechoslovakia); original minutes of the society, 1854 to present (15,000 volumes); sheet music of Bohemia, Moravia, Slovakia; pictures of American Sokol (physical culture organization) in Chicago, 1893 to present; history of Czech, Moravian, and Slovak immigration, 1643 to present; trade unions established by Czechs in Chicago, 1886 to present. **Holdings:** 50,000 books; 50,000 bound periodical volumes; 25 unbound reports; 1500 archival volumes; 65 oral histories; 2 reels of 35mm film. **Subscriptions:** 15 journals and other serials; 5 newspapers. **Services:** Interlibrary loan; copying; library open to the public with supervision of museum personnel. **Automated Operations:** Computerized public access catalog and cataloging. **Publications:** Journal, monthly. **Remarks:** Toll-free telephone number(s): (800)543-3272. FAX: (708)795-0217. **Staff:** Lillian K. Chowat.

CSIRO
See: **Australia - Commonwealth Scientific and Industrial Research Organization (CSIRO)** (1323)

★4457★
CSX Transportation, Inc. - Law Library (Law)
500 Water St., J 150 Phone: (904)359-1237
Jacksonville, FL 32202 Brenda Rowe, Off.Mgr.
Subjects: Law. **Holdings:** 10,000 volumes. **Services:** Library not open to the public.

★4458★
CTB Macmillan/McGraw-Hill Test Publishing Company - Library/ Reference Resource Center (Educ, Publ)
2500 Garden Rd. Phone: (408)649-7920
Monterey, CA 93940 Chase Weaver, Libn./Archv.
Founded: 1965. **Staff:** 2. **Subjects:** Education, educational psychology, statistics, psychology, electronic learning, economics, mathematics. **Special Collections:** Test archives. **Holdings:** 6500 books; 100 bound periodical volumes; 800 research reports. **Subscriptions:** 95 journals and other serials; 6 newspapers. **Services:** Interlibrary loan; copying; library open to graduate students with restrictions on some materials. **Automated Operations:** Computerized acquisitions, cataloging, circulation, and serials (Columbia). **Remarks:** FAX: (408)649-7825.

★4459★
CTL Engineering, Inc. - Library (Sci-Engr)
2860 Fisher Rd. Phone: (614)276-8123
Columbus, OH 43204 Dr. Osama Abdulshafi
Founded: 1927. **Subjects:** Civil engineering. **Holdings:** 5000 books; 3000 reports. **Subscriptions:** 10 journals and other serials. **Services:** Library not open to the public. **Remarks:** FAX: (614)276-6377.

CTTC Hospital - Medical Library
See: **U.S. Air Force Hospital** (16898)

Cuba - Archivo Nacional
See: **Cuban Academy of Sciences** (4466)

★4460★
Cuba - Ministerio de la Agricultura - Centro de Informacion y Documentacion Agropecuario (Agri)
Calle 11, no.1057 E/ 12 y 14, Vedado
Plaza de la Rev. Phone: 30 1672
Havana 4149, Cuba Gloria Ponjuan Dante
Subjects: Farming. **Holdings:** 13,962 books; 5344 bound periodical volumes; 13 patents; 710 documents; 273 scientific research reports; 150 theses; 5710 translations; 1000 articles; 184 other cataloged items. **Services:** Interlibrary loan; copying; SDI; translating. **Remarks:** Alternate telephone numbers are 3-9116, 3-3256, 3-5619, and 306743. Telex: 0511007.

★4461★
Cuba - Ministerio de la Agricultura - Instituto de Investigaciones Tabacaleras - Biblioteca Central (Agri, Sci-Engr)
Carretera Tumbadero KM 8 1/2 Phone: 3055
San Antonio de los Banos, Cuba Maria del Carmen Gutierrez, Lic.
Subjects: Tobacco research. **Holdings:** Figures not available. **Services:** Translating. **Remarks:** Alternate telephone number(s): 2778. **Formerly:** Its Centro Experimental de Tabaco.

★4462★
Cuba - Ministerio de la Agricultura - Instituto de Suelos de Cuba - Biblioteca (Agri)
Antigua Carretera de Vento KM 8 1/2
Capdevilla, Boyeros Phone: 44 4680
Havana 8022, Cuba Nirva D. Fonseca Sanchez, Tec.
Subjects: Soil research. **Holdings:** 3395 books; 6517 periodicals; 85 theses; 200 reference books. **Services:** Interlibrary loan; SDI; translations; biblioteca open to the public on a limited schedule. **Remarks:** Alternate telephone number(s): 44 3038; 44 3039; 44 4680.

★4463★
Cuba - Ministerio del Azucar - Instituto Cubano de Investigaciones Azucareras - Departamento de Informacion Cientifica-Tecnica (Agri)
ICINAZ
P.O. Box 10154
Quivican Phone: 057 55445
Havana, Cuba Lucia Cruz, Lib.Hd.
Founded: 1973. **Staff:** 7. **Subjects:** Sugar. **Holdings:** 2397 books; 225 bound periodical volumes; 140 scientific research reports; 29 theses; 469 translations; 2935 documents; 281 other cataloged items. **Subscriptions:** 119 journals and other serials. **Services:** Interlibrary loan; SDI; translating; literature surveying. **Computerized Information Services:** Internal database. **Remarks:** Alternate telephone number(s): 057 222610. Telex: 51-1446 DNMCC-CU. **Staff:** Rosa M. Perez, Russian Transl.; Hector Pesquero, English Transl.; Jose A. Tabares, Info.; Rodolfo Milas, Info.

★4464★
Cuba - Ministerio de Cultura - Biblioteca Nacional Jose Marti (Info Sci)
Avenida de Independencia
Plaza de la Revolucion Phone: 79-6091-98
Havana, Cuba Dra. Marta Terry Gonzalez, Hd.
Subjects: General collection. **Special Collections:** 16th-19th century rare documents, books, periodicals, incunabula. **Holdings:** 2.22 million volumes; 19,335 scores; 10,400 posters; 12,500 maps; 22,967 slides; 9757 phonograph records; 73,028 photographs; 48,954 manuscripts. **Subscriptions:** 1500 journals and other serials; 800 newspapers. **Services:** Interlibrary loan; copying; SDI; library open to the public. **Computerized Information Services:** BOLCULT (internal database). **Publications:** Revista de la Biblioteca Nacional Jose Marti; Bibliografia Cubana; bibliographic bulletins in the fields of fine arts, music, theater, dance, literature, and general cultural problems; Bibliotecas. **Special Indexes:** Indice General de Publicaciones Periodicas Cubanas; Indice Acumulativo de la Bibliografia Cubana. **Remarks:** Telex: 51 1963.

Cuba - National Archives
See: **Cuban Academy of Sciences** (4466)

Cuba Company Archives
See: **University of Maryland, College Park Libraries - McKeldin Library - Historical Manuscripts and Archives Department** (18818)

★4465★
Cuban Academy of Sciences - Center for the Study of the History and Organization of Science - C.J. Finlay Library (Sci-Engr)
460 entre Amargura y Teniente Rey
Apartado 70 Phone: 60 2084
Havana, Cuba Lidia C. Patallo Bernardez, Libn.
Staff: Prof 6; Other 4. **Subjects:** Science of science; science policy; history, organization, and economy of science. **Special Collections:** History of science (6000 volumes); Cuba (6000 volumes); old and rare books (2500 volumes). **Holdings:** 100,812 books and pamphlets; 60,162 serials. **Services:** Interlibrary loan; SDI; library open to the public. **Publications:** Conferencias y estudios de Historia y Organizacion de la Ciencia. **Also Known As:** Academia de Ciencias de Cuba - Centro de Estudios de Historia y Organizacion de la Ciencia "Carlos J. Finlay."

★4466★
Cuban Academy of Sciences - National Archives (Area-Ethnic)
Compostela no. 906 esq. a San Isisdro Phone: 31-2414
Havana, Cuba Berarda C. Salabarria Abraham, Dir.
Holdings: 2972 books; 300 bound periodical volumes. **Services:** Copying. **Remarks:** Alternate telephone number(s): 31-1361. **Also Known As:** Academia de Ciencias de Cuba - Archivo Nacional.

★4467★
Cuban American National Foundation - Library (Area-Ethnic)
1000 Thomas Jefferson St., Suite 505 Phone: (202)265-2822
Washington, DC 20007 Tom Cox, Rec.Dir.
Staff: 6. **Subjects:** Cuban politics, economics, and culture, Latin America. **Holdings:** 500 volumes. **Services:** Copying; library open to the public by appointment. **Remarks:** FAX: (202)338-0308.

Cubberley Education Library
See: **Stanford University** (15646)

★4468★
Cubic Defense Systems, Inc. - Technical Library (Sci-Engr)
P.O. Box 85587 Phone: (619)277-6780
San Diego, CA 92186 Kathleen M. Cook, Mgr., Tech.Lib.
Founded: 1968. **Staff:** Prof 1. **Subjects:** Electronics, aeronautics, management, mathematics, physics, communications, radar, computer science. **Holdings:** 5000 books; 1500 bound periodical volumes; 26,000 reports on microfiche; 5800 hardcopy reports; 1000 maps. **Subscriptions:** 280 journals and other serials. **Services:** Interlibrary loan; copying; SDI; library open to the public by appointment. **Automated Operations:** Computerized cataloging, acquisitions, serials, and circulation. **Computerized Information Services:** DIALOG Information Services, BRS Information Technologies, RLIN, DTIC, ORBIT Search Service, NASA/RECON. **Networks/Consortia:** Member of CLASS. **Publications:** Acquisitions List, monthly. **Remarks:** FAX: (619)277-1878.

Frank L. Cubley Library
See: **Paul Smith's College of Arts and Sciences** (12797)

E.M. Cudahy Memorial Library
See: **Loyola University of Chicago** (9420)

★4469★
CUH2A, Inc. - Library (Plan)
600 Alexander Rd. Phone: (609)452-1212
Princeton, NJ 08453-5240 Susan Moss, Mgr., Info.Rsrcs.
Founded: 1981. **Staff:** Prof 1. **Subjects:** Architecture, engineering, graphic arts, interior design. **Holdings:** 2000 books; 1300 archival boxes; 500 cartridges of microfilm. **Subscriptions:** 124 journals and other serials; 2 newspapers. **Services:** Interlibrary loan; copying; SDI; library open to the public for reference use only. **Automated Operations:** Computerized cataloging. **Remarks:** FAX: (609)452-1943.

William S. Culbertson Library
See: **National Presbyterian Church** (11252)

Culham Laboratory
See: **Great Britain - Atomic Energy Authority - AEA Technology - Culham/Harwell Library** (6663)

★4470★
Culinary Institute of America - Katharine Angell Library (Food-Bev)
651 S. Albany Post Rd. Phone: (914)452-9600
Hyde Park, NY 12538-1499 Eileen de Vries, Libn.
Founded: 1972. **Staff:** Prof 2; Other 2. **Subjects:** Cookery, food service, restaurant management. **Special Collections:** Louis P. DeGouy notebooks (261). **Holdings:** 40,000 volumes; 3400 menus; 6000 pamphlets. **Subscriptions:** 140 journals and other serials. **Services:** Interlibrary loan; copying; library open to the public by appointment. **Networks/Consortia:** Member of Southeastern New York Library Resources Council (SENYLRC). **Staff:** Gertrude D. Trani, Asst.Libn.

Esker W. Cullen Health Sciences Library
See: **Centre Community Hospital** (3220)

Cullen Eye Institute Library
See: **Baylor College of Medicine - Department of Ophthalmology** (1600)

Howard S. Cullman Library
See: **Tobacco Merchants Association of the U.S.** (16380)

Cultural Survival, Inc.
See: **Center for Cultural Survival** (3230)

★4471★
Culver Pictures, Inc. - Library (Aud-Vis)
150 W. 22nd St., No. 300 Phone: (212)645-1672
New York, NY 10011-2421 Harriet Lois Culver, Pres.
Founded: 1926. **Staff:** Prof 6. **Special Collections:** Chansonetta Emmons; Seidman Americana Collection; Mishkin Opera Collection. **Holdings:** 5000 books; 1000 bound periodical volumes; over 9 million photographs, prints, and engravings. **Services:** Library not open to the public. **Remarks:** Illustrated materials are available to publishers and advertisers for reproduction on a fee basis. FAX: (212)627-9112. **Staff:** Douglas A. Peckham, Mng.Dir.; Peter Tomlinson; Allen Reuben; Timothy Feleppa.

★4472★
Cumberland Bar Association - Nathan and Henry B. Cleaves Law Library (Law)
County Court House
142 Federal St. Phone: (207)773-9712
Portland, ME 04101 Nancy Rabasca, Libn.
Founded: 1811. **Staff:** Prof 1; Other 1. **Subjects:** Law. **Special Collections:** Briefs and records of the Supreme Judicial Court of Maine. **Holdings:** 31,154 volumes. **Subscriptions:** 126 journals and other serials. **Services:** Interlibrary loan; copying; library open to the public.

★4473★
Cumberland County Department of Planning and Development - Library (Plan)
c/o Cumberland County Library
800 E. Commerce St. Phone: (609)453-2175
Bridgeton, NJ 08302 Nancy Forrester, Libn.
Founded: 1965. **Staff:** 1. **Subjects:** Planning theory and history, land and land utilization, statistics, traffic and transportation, utilities and housing, agriculture and agricultural retention, parks and recreation, government finance and administration, community facilities, history and preservation. **Holdings:** 300 volumes; 150 pamphlets; 20 file boxes of newsletters and reports; 200 maps. **Subscriptions:** 10 journals and other serials. **Services:** Interlibrary loan; copying; library open to the public. **Publications:** Annual reports; newsletters, irregular - to all county officials. **Remarks:** FAX: (609)541-0967. Library is an affiliate of New Jersey State Data Center.

★4474★
Cumberland County Historical Society - Pirate House Library (Hist)
Box 16 Phone: (609)455-8580
Greenwich, NJ 08323 Carl L. West, Hd.Libn.
Founded: 1908. **Subjects:** History and genealogy of New Jersey and Cumberland County. **Special Collections:** Photographs of Cumberland County (1000); deeds, 1674-1850 (500); survey maps (800); Washington Whig Newspapers (bound, 1815-1837); Bridgeton Chronicle (bound, 1853-1858, 1863-1865, 1880-1883); New Jersey Patriot (bound, 1869-1891); U.S. Census of Cape May and Cumberland County, 1830-1880 (microfilm); Cumberland County Directories, 1869-1925. **Holdings:** 1500 books; 4 VF drawers of family genealogical data; 5 VF drawers of historical data; 2 VF drawers of maps and charts; 1 map case; deeds; family sheets; ledgers; Bible records; sheriff books. **Services:** Copying; library open to the public on a limited schedule. **Special Indexes:** Index of South Jersey families (card); index to deeds and maps (cards). **Staff:** Carl L. West, Libn.

★4475★
Cumberland County Historical Society & Hamilton Library (Hist)
21 N. Pitt St.
Box 626 Phone: (717)249-7610
Carlisle, PA 17013 Janet M. Hocker, Libn.
Founded: 1874. **Staff:** 7. **Subjects:** Cumberland County history, Pennsylvania history. **Special Collections:** Local newspapers, 1785 to present (microfilm; microfiche; bound volumes); Carlisle Indian Industrial School memorabilia, 1879-1918; papers of Robert Whitehill, Judge James Hamilton, George Stevenson, Samuel Postlethwaite; business records of Cumberland County firms; A.A. Photograph Collection; genealogy files (3000). **Holdings:** 7000 books; 700 linear feet of Cumberland County documents including tax lists, 1750-1906; 200 linear feet of manuscripts; 40 VF drawers; 270 maps; 900 reels of microfilm; 125 microcards; 12,000 photographs. **Subscriptions:** 10 journals and other serials. **Services:** Copying; library open to the public.

★4476★
Cumberland County Law Library (Law)
County Court House
W. Broad & Fayette Sts. Phone: (609)451-8000
Bridgeton, NJ 08302 Lynn Merle
Founded: 1909. **Staff:** Prof 1. **Subjects:** Law. **Holdings:** 10,000 books; 1000 bound periodical volumes; 200 other cataloged items. **Services:** Library open to the public. **Remarks:** FAX: (609)455-9490.

★4477★
Cumberland County Law Library (Law)
Court House
S. Hanover St. Phone: (717)240-6208
Carlisle, PA 17013 Ronna Boyles, Libn.
Staff: 1. **Subjects:** Law. **Holdings:** 18,018 volumes. **Services:** Library open to the public with restrictions.

★4478★
Cumberland County Public Library - North Carolina Foreign Language Center (Hum)
300 Maiden Lane
Fayetteville, NC 28301 Phone: (919)483-5022
Founded: 1976. **Staff:** Prof 2; Other 3. **Subjects:** European and Asian languages; English as a second language. **Holdings:** 39,061 books; 1151 phonograph records; 1465 audiocassettes and filmstrips; 637 videocassettes. **Subscriptions:** 60 journals and other serials. **Services:** Interlibrary loan; center open to the public. **Automated Operations:** Computerized cataloging and circulation. **Computerized Information Services:** Internal database. **Networks/Consortia:** Member of SOLINET **Publications:** Newsletter, quarterly - free upon request. **Remarks:** FAX: (919)483-8644. **Staff:** Francis Newton, Jr.

Cumberland Gap National Historical Park
See: **U.S. Natl. Park Service** (17696)

Cumberland School of Law
See: **Samford University - Cumberland School of Law** (14661)

★4479★
Cumberland Science Museum - Dyer Memorial Library (Biol Sci)
800 Ridley Blvd. Phone: (615)862-5160
Nashville, TN 37203 Jean Simpson, Dir., Adm.
Founded: 1945. **Subjects:** Natural history. **Holdings:** 3500 books. **Subscriptions:** 40 journals and other serials.

Thayer Cumings Library and Archives
See: **Strawbery Banke Museum** (15827)

★4480★
Cummer Gallery of Art - Library (Art)
829 Riverside Ave. Phone: (904)356-6857
Jacksonville, FL 32204 Lenore Byrd, Chm., Lib.Comm.
Founded: 1961. **Subjects:** American Impressionism, Western and Eastern visual arts. **Special Collections:** European porcelains, especially Meissen (600 volumes of rare sales catalogs, clippings, photographs). **Holdings:** 3200 books; 1200 bound periodical volumes; 10,000 art slides. **Subscriptions:** 14 journals and other serials. **Services:** Copying; library open to the public with restrictions.

Dorothy Cummings Memorial Library
See: **American Indian Bible College** (625)

Nathan Cummings Center
See: **Memorial Sloan-Kettering Cancer Center - Medical Library - Nathan Cummings Center** (10048)

★4481★
Cummington Historical Commission - Kingman Tavern Historical Museum - Lyman Library (Hist)
Main St. Phone: (413)634-5335
Cummington, MA 01026 Merrie Bergmann, Ch.
Founded: 1968. **Subjects:** Genealogy, local history. **Special Collections:** Hattie Hamlen glass negatives and prints (250 photos of Cummington, 1900). **Holdings:** 300 books; diaries; ledgers. **Services:** Copying; library open to the public on a limited schedule.

★4482★
Cummins Engine Co., Inc. - Libraries (Sci-Engr)
M/C 50120, Box 3005 Phone: (812)377-7201
Columbus, IN 47201 W.E. Poor, Lib.Serv.Mgr.
Staff: Prof 1; Other 2. **Subjects:** Diesel engineering. **Holdings:** 8000 books; 1000 bound periodical volumes; 20,000 research reports; 25,000 society technical papers; 3000 patents; 1000 reels of microfilm. **Subscriptions:** 400 journals and other serials; 6 newspapers. **Services:** Interlibrary loan; library open to the public by appointment. **Automated Operations:** Computerized acquisitions, serials, and circulation. **Computerized Information Services:** DIALOG Information Services, NEXIS, Dow Jones News/Retrieval, Dun & Bradstreet Business Credit Services. **Remarks:** FAX: (812)377-7032.

J.W. Cummins Memorial Library
See: **Farmland Industries, Inc.** (5602)

★4483★
CUNA Mutual Insurance Group - Library & Research Center (Bus-Fin)
Box 33430 Phone: (313)357-8100
Detroit, MI 48232-5430 Dianne Zyskowski, Supv.
Founded: 1978. **Staff:** 1. **Subjects:** Insurance, credit unions, banking. **Holdings:** 7000 books; 5000 legal volumes. **Subscriptions:** 350 journals and other serials; 5 newspapers. **Services:** Interlibrary loan; library not open to the public. **Computerized Information Services:** DIALOG Information Services. **Networks/Consortia:** Member of Oakland Wayne Interlibrary Network (OWIN).

CUNY - Baruch College
See: **Bernard Baruch College of City University of New York** (1548)

CUNY - Baruch College - National Center for the Study of Collective Bargaining in Higher Education and the Professions
See: **National Center for the Study of Collective Bargaining in Higher Education and the Professions** (11109)

CUNY - Brooklyn College
See: **Brooklyn College of City University of New York** (2230)

CUNY - Brooklyn College of City University of New York
See: **Brooklyn College of City University of New York** (2230)

CUNY - City College Library
See: **City College of City University of New York** (3731)

CUNY - Graduate School and University Center
See: **Graduate School and University Center of the City University of New York** (6612)

CUNY - Hunter College
See: **Hunter College of City University of New York** (7562)

CUNY - John Jay College of Criminal Justice
See: **John Jay College of Criminal Justice of CUNY** (8345)

CUNY - Mt. Sinai School of Medicine
See: **Mount Sinai School of Medicine of City University of New York** (10819)

CUNY - Queens College
See: **Queens College of City University of New York** (13637)

★4484★
Curative Rehabilitation Center - Learning Resource Center (Med)
1000 N. 92nd St. Phone: (414)259-1414
Wauwatosa, WI 53226 Terry Bochte, Libn.
Founded: 1976. **Staff:** Prof 1. **Subjects:** Physical medicine and rehabilitation, psychology, pediatrics, brain injury rehabilitation, orthopedics. **Special Collections:** Videotapes on aspects of physical therapy and neurodevelopmental treatment (50). **Holdings:** 1200 books; 800 bound periodical volumes. **Subscriptions:** 80 journals and other serials. **Services:** Interlibrary loan; copying; center open to the public by appointment. **Automated Operations:** Computerized ILL (DOCLINE). **Computerized Information Services:** BRS Information Technologies. **Networks/Consortia:** Member of Southeastern Wisconsin Health Science Library Consortium (SWHSL), Library Council of Metropolitan Milwaukee, Inc. (LCOMM).

★4485★
CURE Foundation - Library (Med)
P.O. Box 84513 Phone: (213)825-5091
Los Angeles, CA 90073 David Rimer, Dir.
Subjects: Gastrointestinal diseases, peptic ulcers. **Holdings:** Books; 500 bound periodical volumes; 1000 original manuscripts and research reports. **Services:** Copying; library open to the public only with special permission. **Remarks:** Provides support to the Center for Ulcer Research and Education.

★4486★
(Curitiba) Centro Cultural Brasil-Estados Unidos - USIS Colletion (Educ)
Rua Amintas de Barros, 99
Ed. Itatiaia
Caixa Postal 3328
80000 Curitiba, Paraiba, Brazil
Remarks: Maintained or supported by the U.S. Information Agency. Focus is on materials that will assist peoples outside the United States to learn about the United States, its people, history, culture, political processes, and social milieux.

★4487★
Curly-Coated Retriever Club of America - Archives (Rec)
2628 Huckleberry Butte Phone: (208)476-7031
Orofino, ID 83544 Marillyn Caldwell, Archv.
Founded: 1979. **Staff:** 1. **Subjects:** Curly-Coated Retrievers - breeding, care, exhibiting, history. **Holdings:** Bibliographical information; pedigree and picture files; medical information; club proceedings; awards records. **Services:** Copying; library open to the public by appointment.

★4488★
Curry College - Louis R. Levin Memorial Library - Special Collections (Educ)
1071 Blue Hill Ave. Phone: (617)333-0500
Milton, MA 02186 Catharine King, Dir.
Subjects: Communication, learning disabilities. **Holdings:** 38,943 U.S. Government documents. **Subscriptions:** 560 journals and other serials. **Services:** Interlibrary loan; copying; library open to the public. **Automated Operations:** Computerized cataloging. **Computerized Information Services:** OCLC, BRS Information Technologies, WILSONLINE. **Networks/Consortia:** Member of NELINET, Inc. **Publications:** Bibliographic Instruction, Orientation - for internal distribution only. **Staff:** Gail Shank, Hd., Rd.Serv. & Govt.Doc.; Elaine Bevniev, Hd., Tech.Serv.

John Curtin School of Medical Research
See: **Australian National University - University Library** (1344)

★4489★
Charles S. Curtis Memorial Hospital - Medical Library (Med)
St. Anthony, NF, Canada A0K 4S0 Phone: (709)454-3333
Joan Hillier, Libn.
Staff: 1. **Subjects:** Medicine. **Holdings:** 200 books. **Subscriptions:** 70 journals and other serials. **Services:** Library not open to the public. **Remarks:** FAX: (709)454-2052.

★4490★
Helene Curtis Industries, Inc. - Corporate Library (Sci-Engr)
401 W. North Ave. Phone: (312)292-2285
Chicago, IL 60639 Laura Claggett, Mgr.
Founded: 1957. **Staff:** Prof 2; Other 2. **Subjects:** Cosmetics, chemistry, textiles, dermatology, toxicology, marketing, management, computers. **Special Collections:** Company archives; U.S. and foreign patents. **Holdings:** 4000 books; 20 reels of microfilm; 2 microfiche; annual and 10K reports; 3600 patents; 3 VF drawers of pamphlets. **Subscriptions:** 450 journals and other serials; 6 newspapers. **Services:** Interlibrary loan; SDI; library not open to the public. **Automated Operations:** Computerized cataloging, acquisitions, serials, and ILL. **Computerized Information Services:** DIALOG Information Services, The Source Information Network, PFDS Online, STN International, NLM, BRS Information Technologies, WILSONLINE, LEXIS, NEXIS, VU/TEXT Information Services, DataTimes; internal database. **Networks/Consortia:** Member of ILLINET. **Publications:** Newsletter, bimonthly - for internal distribution only. **Remarks:** FAX: (312)292-2295. **Staff:** Loretta Rudaitis, Info.Spec.

★4491★
Curtis Institute of Music - Library (Mus)
Knapp Hall
1720 Locust St. Phone: (215)893-5265
Philadelphia, PA 19103 Elizabeth Walker, Libn.
Founded: 1925. **Staff:** Prof 3; Other 4. **Subjects:** Music - orchestral, chamber, solo instrumental, vocal. **Special Collections:** Charles H. Jarvis Memorial Collection (19th century piano, solo, and chamber music; 1700 items); Leopold Stokowski Collection of Orchestral Music (1500 items). **Holdings:** 10,000 books; 65,000 scores; 7000 phonograph records; 3500 tapes; 800 compact discs. **Subscriptions:** 50 journals and other serials. **Services:** Interlibrary loan; library open to the public by appointment only. **Computerized Information Services:** OCLC. **Networks/Consortia:** Member of PALINET **Remarks:** FAX: (215)893-0194. **Staff:** Dr. Kenton T. Meyer, Asst.Libn.; Peter L. Eisenberg, Cat.Libn.

★4492★
Curtis, Mallet-Prevost, Colt and Mosle - Library (Law)
101 Park Ave. Phone: (212)696-6138
New York, NY 10178 Janet P. Tidwell, Libn.
Founded: 1897. **Staff:** Prof 2; Other 4. **Subjects:** Anglo-American law. **Special Collections:** Legislation of Central and Latin America. **Holdings:** 30,000 books; 2000 bound periodical volumes; 20 VF drawers of pamphlet material; 800 reels of microfilm; microfiche. **Subscriptions:** 500 journals and other serials; 10 newspapers. **Services:** Interlibrary loan; library open to members of Special Libraries Association and Law Library Association of Greater New York. **Automated Operations:** Computerized circulation. **Computerized Information Services:** LEXIS, DIALOG Information Services, WESTLAW, Dow Jones News/Retrieval. **Special Indexes:** Index to Laws of Latin American Countries (book). **Staff:** Gary Jaskula, Assoc.Libn.

Mary Beth Curtis Health Science Library
See: **Elmbrook Memorial Hospital** (5307)

★4493★
Glenn H. Curtiss Museum of Local History - Minor Swarthout Memorial Library (Hist)
41 Lake St.
Box 326 Phone: (607)569-2160
Hammondsport, NY 14840 Lindsley A. Dunn, Sr.Cur.
Founded: 1975. **Staff:** 1. **Subjects:** Aeronautics, local history. **Holdings:** 2000 books; 6000 periodicals; 600 early Curtiss aviation photographs. **Subscriptions:** 15 journals and other serials. **Services:** Copying; library open to the public by appointment.

★4494★
Cardinal Cushing General Hospital - Staff Library (Med)
235 N. Pearl St. Phone: (617)588-4000
Brockton, MA 02401 Nancy Sezak, Med.Libn.
Staff: 1. **Subjects:** Medicine. **Holdings:** 864 books; 1060 bound periodical volumes; 434 unbound journals; 2 drawers of pamphlets and reprints. **Subscriptions:** 108 journals and other serials. **Services:** Interlibrary loan; copying (limited); library open to the public with permission. **Computerized Information Services:** NLM, BRS Information Technologies. Performs searches on fee basis. **Networks/Consortia:** Member of Southeastern Massachusetts Consortium of Health Science Libraries (SEMCO), Massachusetts Health Sciences Libraries Network (MaHSLiN), North Atlantic Health Science Libraries (NAHSL).

Harvey Cushing/John Hay Whitney Medical Library
See: **Yale University** (20715)

★4495★
Cushing Hospital - Staff Library
Dudley Rd.
Box 9008
Framingham, MA 01701-9008
Founded: 1959. **Subjects:** Geriatrics, aging, psychology, medicine. **Holdings:** 2500 books; 1000 bound periodical volumes. **Remarks:** Currently inactive.

★4496★
Charlotte Cushman Club - Theatre Research Library (Theater)
239 S. Camac St. Phone: (215)735-4676
Philadelphia, PA 19107 Jean Rapp, Lib.Chm.
Founded: 1907. **Staff:** Prof 1. **Subjects:** History of the stage and city theaters. **Holdings:** 3000 books; 25 bound volumes of Theatre Arts; 112 scrapbooks; 2000 clippings and letters; 5000 programs; 100 pieces of theatrical memorabilia; plays; theatrical biographies; programs and playbills; pictures and picture books on stage and cinema. **Services:** Library open to the public for reference use only.

Cushwa-Leighton Library
See: **St. Mary's College** (14509)

Custer Battlefield National Monument
See: **U.S. Natl. Park Service** (17697)

★4497★
Custer County Historical Society - Library (Hist)
225 S. 10th Ave. Phone: (308)872-2203
Broken Bow, NE 68822 Mary Landkamer, Res.
Founded: 1960. **Staff:** Prof 3; Other 3. **Subjects:** History - state, local; genealogy. **Special Collections:** Census of the 81 cemeteries in Custer County, Nebraska. **Holdings:** 200 books; 110 volumes of bound newspapers; 700 photographs; 50 maps; 221 reels of microfilm; 24 VF drawers of obituaries and biographical materials. **Subscriptions:** 2 journals and other serials. **Services:** Copying; library open to the public. **Publications:** Custer County Times Newsletter, 2/year - to members. **Special Indexes:** Index to Butcher Photograph Collection, city and county histories, obituaries, and cemeteries, 1874 to present. **Staff:** Grace Varney, Dir.; Phillip Gardner.

★4498★
Custer County Law Library (Law)
Courthouse Phone: (308)872-6481
Broken Bow, NE 68822 William Steffens, Pres., Custer County Bar Assn.
Subjects: Law. **Holdings:** Figures not available. **Services:** Library open to judges and lawyers of Custer County.

General George Armstrong Custer Collection
See: **Monroe County Library System** (10623)

Cutler Army Community Hospital
See: **U.S. Army Hospitals** (17037)

Cutter Library and Information Services
See: **Miles, Inc.** (10388)

★4499★
Cuyahoga County Planning Commission - Library (Plan)
323 Lakeside Ave. W., Suite 400 Phone: (216)443-3700
Cleveland, OH 44113 Terri Garsteck, Libn.
Founded: 1947. **Staff:** Prof 30. **Subjects:** Regional and urban planning, population, transportation, housing, employment, economic and community development. **Holdings:** 1000 books; 50 bound periodical volumes; VF drawers of documents and pamphlets; 3 cases of archives; 550 CPC reports. **Subscriptions:** 25 journals and other serials; 5 newspapers. **Services:** Interlibrary loan; copying; library open to the public for reference use only. **Publications:** Community and regional reports; County Data Newsletter. **Remarks:** FAX: (216)443-3737.

★4500★
Cuyahoga County Public Library - Fairview Park Regional Branch - Special Collections (Hist)
4449 W. 213th St. Phone: (216)581-5833
Fairview Park, OH 44126 John Lonsak, Regional Mgr.
ST 9. **Special Collections:** Genealogy/local history (642 linear feet; 210 periodical titles; microforms). **Services:** Interlibrary loan; copying; collections open to the public. **Computerized Information Services:** DIALOG Information Services, WILSONLINE, WESTLAW, OCLC. Performs searches on fee basis (limited free searching). **Networks/ Consortia:** Member of Cleveland Area Metropolitan Library System (CAMLS) **Special Catalogs:** Genealogy/Local History Source File (card); Cuyahoga County Ancestor File (card). **Special Indexes:** 1880 and 1900 Cleveland Street/Ward Index (card); Index to Fairview Herald, 1947-1958 (card). **Remarks:** FAX: (216)333-0697. **Staff:** John S. Bellamy, III, Hist.Spec.; Barbara Musselman, Local Hist./Geneal.Spec.; Gary Claxton, Adult.Serv.Mgr.

★4501★
CVD, Inc. - Library (Sci-Engr)
185 New Boston St. Phone: (617)933-9243
Woburn, MA 01801 Jit Joela, Res.Sci.
Subjects: Infrared optics. **Holdings:** 750 books; 2000 reports. **Subscriptions:** 18 journals and other serials. **Services:** Library not open to the public.

★4502★
CVI, Inc. - Library (Sci-Engr)
4200 Lyman Ct. Phone: (614)876-7381
Hilliard, OH 43026-1293 Steve L. Hensley, Mgr., V.I.P. & Cat. Items
Subjects: Cryogenic and vacuum technology. **Holdings:** 1200 books; 1000 reports. **Subscriptions:** 25 journals and other serials. **Services:** Library not open to the public. **Remarks:** FAX: (614)876-5648. Telex: 245 383.

★4503★
CVPH Medical Center - Medical Library (Med)
100 Beekman St. Phone: (518)562-7325
Plattsburgh, NY 12901 Christina Ransom, Med.Libn.
Founded: 1972. **Staff:** Prof 1; Other 1. **Subjects:** Medicine, nursing, health care. **Holdings:** 550 books. **Subscriptions:** 149 journals and other serials. **Services:** Interlibrary loan; copying; SDI; library open to the public by appointment. **Automated Operations:** Computerized serials. **Computerized Information Services:** BRS Information Technologies, NLM; HOBO (electronic mail service). **Networks/Consortia:** Member of North Country Reference and Research Resources Council (NCRRRC), Health Science Libraries of New Hampshire & Vermont (HSL-NH/VT). **Publications:** Newsletter, quarterly. **Remarks:** FAX: (518)562-7129.

★4504★
Cylburn Arboretum Association - Library (Biol Sci)
4915 Greenspring Ave. Phone: (301)396-0180
Baltimore, MD 21209 Adelaide C. Rackemann, Libn.
Staff: Prof 2. **Subjects:** Horticulture, gardening, wild flowers, trees, shrubs. **Special Collections:** Rock gardening. **Holdings:** 1600 books; 2 VF drawers of clippings and pamphlets; seed catalogs. **Services:** Library open to the public on a limited schedule.

★4505★
Cyprus - Ministry of Finance - Department of Statistics and Research - Library (Soc Sci, Bus-Fin)
13 Byron Ave. Phone: 2 303286
Nicosia 162, Cyprus Chr. Demosthenous, Sr. Clerical Off.
Founded: 1960. **Subjects:** Demography, agriculture, trade, industry, economics, statistics. **Special Collections:** Publications of United Nations, International Labour Office, Economic Commission for Europe; statistics of selected countries worldwide. **Holdings:** 11,500 books; statistical yearbooks. **Subscriptions:** 3 journals and other serials; 5 newspapers. **Services:** Interlibrary loan; copying; library open to the public with restrictions. **Remarks:** FAX: 2 366080. Telex: 3399 MINFIN CY.

★4506★
Cyprus Minerals Company - Library/Information Center (Law, Bus-Fin, Sci-Engr)
9100 E. Mineral Circle Phone: (303)643-5365
Englewood, CO 80112 Marriott W. Smart, Dir.
Founded: 1979. **Staff:** Prof 4; Other 2. **Subjects:** Law, business, geology, mining, engineering. **Holdings:** 60,000 books; 160 bound periodical volumes; 7 VF drawers of company information. **Subscriptions:** 1000 journals and other serials; 20 newspapers. **Services:** Interlibrary loan; SDI; library open to the public by appointment. **Automated Operations:** Computerized cataloging. **Computerized Information Services:** DIALOG Information Services, Dow Jones News/Retrieval, WILSONLINE, WESTLAW, InvesText, DataTimes, Reuter Country Reports; DENCAT (internal database). **Remarks:** FAX: (303)643-5298. **Staff:** Trudy Gayner, Asst.Libn./Tech.Serv.; Katherine Faris, Info.Spec.; Fran Schrag, Asst.Libn./Ser. & ILL.

★4507★
Cytogen Corp. - R & D Library (Med)
201 College Rd., E., CN-5309 Phone: (609)987-8237
Princeton, NJ 08540-5309 Bonnie Myers
Founded: 1981. **Staff:** Prof 1. **Subjects:** Cancer research, biotechnology. **Holdings:** 650 books. **Subscriptions:** 205 journals and other serials. **Services:** Interlibrary loan; library not open to the public. **Computerized Information Services:** DIALOG Information Services, STN International; internal databases. **Remarks:** FAX: (609)452-7211.

Czechoslovak Heritage Museum, Library and Archives
See: **CSA Fraternal Life** (4456)

★4508★
Czechoslovakia - Academy of Applied Arts - Library (Art)
nam Krasnoarmejcu 80 Phone: 2 21395121
CS-116 93 Prague, Czechoslovakia Eva Vrtiskova, Ph.D.
Founded: 1885. **Staff:** Prof 2. **Subjects:** Arts. **Holdings:** 56,490 books; 65 bound periodical volumes. **Subscriptions:** 66 journals and other serials; 7 newspapers. **Services:** Interlibrary loan; copying; SDI; library open to the public. **Remarks:** FAX: 2 2326884. **Also Known As:** Vysoka Skola Umeleckoprumyslova - Knihovna.

★4509★
Czechoslovakia - Aeronautical Research and Test Institute - Library (Trans)
Beranovych 130 Phone: 2 6847580
CS-199 05 Prague 9, Czechoslovakia Ing. Ladislav Vymetal
Founded: 1922. **Subjects:** Aviation, airplane design, materials testing, composites. **Special Collections:** Aircraft directories, periodicals, and standards collection. **Holdings:** 21,587 books; 42,444 reports; 559 microfiche. **Subscriptions:** 343 journals and other serials; 2 newspapers. **Services:** Interlibrary loan; copying; SDI; library open to the public. **Computerized Information Services:** Internal database. **Publications:** Accession books; Institute reports. **Remarks:** FAX: 2 6835905. Telex: 12 18 93. **Also Known As:** Vyzkumny a Zkusebni Letecky Ustav.

★4510★
Czechoslovakia - Geological Office - Czechoslovakian Geological Survey Library of Prague (Sci-Engr)
Malostranske nam. 19 Phone: 2 533641
CS-118 21 Prague 1, Czechoslovakia Jaroslav Novotny, Ph.D., Libn.
Founded: 1919. **Subjects:** Prof 6; Other 1. **Subjects:** Geology, hydrogeology, geochemical prospecting, mineralogy, petrology, paleontology, chemical analysis. **Holdings:** 35,000 books; 13,650 monographs; 78,894 journals; 38,797 reprints; 3827 microfiche; maps; reports; microfilm; microcards; 1353 other cataloged items. **Subscriptions:** 1100 journals and other serials. **Services:** Copying; library open to the public. **Computerized Information Services:** PASCAL-GEODE. **Publications:** News; Mineralogicko geologicka bilbiografie CSSR za rok 1989. **Remarks:** FAX: 2 533564. Telex: 122540.

★4511★
Czechoslovakia - Institute of Scientific and Technical Information for Agriculture - Central Agricultural and Forestry Library (Agri)
Slezska 7 Phone: 2 257541
CS-120 56 Prague 2, Czechoslovakia Dr. Ivo Hoch, Ph.D.
Founded: 1926. **Staff:** Prof 44. **Subjects:** Plant production, plant protection, agricultural economics, animal production, veterinary medicine, mechanization of agriculture, forestry, protection of the environment. **Special Collections:** Agricultural Council for the Kingdom of Bohemia; Patriotic Economic Society in Bohemia. **Holdings:** 750,000 books; 62,000 bound periodical volumes; 33,000 reports; 11,000 dissertations; 13,000 firm publications. **Subscriptions:** 1350 journals and other serials. **Services:** Interlibrary loan; copying; library open to the public. **Computerized Information Services:** DIALOG Information Services, Data-Star, FIZ-INKA; AGROINDEX (internal database). Performs searches. Contact Persons: Engr. Szekelyova; Engr. Slezakova. **Publications:** Selection of new accessions of foreign agricultural literature in UZLK-UVTIZ collection; agricultural literature, list of journals subscribed to by the UZLK; bulletin of Czechoslovak FAO Committee; review of retrievals and subject bibliographies; AGROINFORM. **Remarks:** FAX: 257090. Telex: UVTIZ-c 121295.

★4512★
Czechoslovakia - Knihovna Narodniho Muzea - Library (Hist, Hum)
Vaclavske nam. 68 Phone: 2 269451
CS-115 79 Prague 1, Czechoslovakia Dr. Helga Turkova, Dir. of Lib.
Founded: 1818. **Staff:** Prof 40. **Subjects:** History, librarianship, literature, museology, philology, natural science. **Special Collections:** Castle Libraries Collection (1.6 million books). **Holdings:** 1.5 million books; 180,000 bound periodical volumes. **Subscriptions:** 500 journals and other serials. **Services:** Interlibrary loan; copying; SDI; library open to the public for reference use only. **Publications:** Catalog of the Exhibition on Knihovna Narodniho Muzea - Library in the Museum of the Book located in the Zdar nad Sazavou; Historia litterarum and Library History, quarterly. **Remarks:** FAX: 2 2369489. **Staff:** Mgr. Alena Skwarlova, Cat.Serv.; Dr. Pavel Brodsky, Dept. of Mss.; Jana Jaksova, Dept. of Old Prints; Dr. Eva Stejskalova, Dept. of Per.; Dr. Jitka Simakova; Dr. Petr Masek, Castle Libs.; Dr. Eva Rysava, Dept. of Bk. Culture; Dr. Jarmila Kucerova, Acq. & Exch.Sect.

★4513★
Czechoslovakia - Ministry of the Environment - Water Research Institute - Information Center (Biol Sci, Sci-Engr)
Podbabska 30 Phone: 2 31167419
CS-160 62 Prague 6, Czechoslovakia Ms. N. Wannerova, MSc.
Founded: 1920. **Staff:** Prof 9. **Subjects:** Hydraulics, hydrology, sanitary engineering, waste treatment, chemistry, physics, water supply, water pollution control, dam design. **Holdings:** 62,000 books; 465,000 bound periodical volumes. **Subscriptions:** 45 journals and other serials; 3 newspapers. **Services:** Interlibrary loan; copying; center open to the public. **Computerized Information Services:** VODA/WATER (journal articles, conference reports; internal database). **Publications:** Prace a studie, annual; Vyzkum pro praxi, annual; VTEI, irregular. **Special Catalogs:** Hydrologicka bibliografie za rok, annual (book). **Remarks:** FAX: 2 3114805. Telex: 122517. **Formerly:** Czechoslovakia - Ministry of Forestry and Water. **Also Known As:** Vyzkumny Ustav Vodohospodarsky - Informacni Stredisko. **Staff:** Ms. M. Jelenova, Doc.; Ms. J. Kalouskova, Libn.; Ms. L. Tachova, Libn.; Ms. M. Kuckova, Libn.; Ms. H. Moravcova, Ed.

Czechoslovakia - Ministry of Forestry and Water Management
See: **Czechoslovakia - Ministry of the Environment - Water Research Institute** (4513)

★4514★
Czechoslovakia - National Gallery of Prague - Library (Art)
Hradcanske nam. 15 Phone: 2 3524413
CS-119 04 Prague 1, Czechoslovakia Tomas Pergler, Magister
Staff: 5. **Subjects:** Visual arts - history, theory; art. **Special Collections:** Old Prints. **Holdings:** 65,000 books; 760 bound periodical volumes. **Subscriptions:** 2 newspapers. **Services:** Interlibrary loan; copying; library open to foreign scholars and students specializing in visual arts. **Publications:** Lists of acquisitions - annual as a book, monthly as a catalog. **Also Known As:** Knihovna Narodni Galerie u Praze. **Staff:** Milan Lyoka, Ph.D.

★4515★
Czechoslovakia - National Library of Medicine (Med)
Sokolska 31 Phone: 2 99956
CS-121 32 Prague 2, Czechoslovakia Otakar Pinkas
Founded: 1949. **Staff:** 102. **Subjects:** Biomedicine, public health, health-related legislation. **Holdings:** 230,000 volumes; microfiche. **Subscriptions:** 1560 journals and other serials. **Services:** Interlibrary loan; copying; SDI; library open to the public. **Computerized Information Services:** Excerpta Medica, Czechoslovak Medical Literature Data Base. Performs searches free of charge. **Publications:** Bibliographies and abstracts of domestic and foreign literature; Bibliographia Medica Cechoslovaca, monthly. **Remarks:** Telex: 121 293. **Formerly:** Institute for Medical Information - State Medical Library. **Also Known As:** Narodni Lekarska Knihovna.

★4516★
Czechoslovakia - Regional Museum - Library
Zamecke nam 14 Phone: 41728876
CS-415 00 Teplice, Czechoslovakia Dusan Spicka, Dir. of the Musm.
Founded: 1897. **Staff:** 2. **Subjects:** Natural history, archeology, history, art. **Special Collections:** Literature of Northwest Bohemia. **Holdings:** 60,000 books; 500 bound periodical volumes; 10 manuscripts. **Subscriptions:** 110 journals and other serials; 40 newspapers. **Services:** Interlibrary loan; library open to the public. **Publications:** News and studies; monograph studies; Archeological Research in Northwest Bohemia. **Also Known As:** Czechoslovakia - Regionalni Muzeum.

D

★4517★
D & S Petroleum Consulting Group Ltd. - Library (Energy)
125 9th Ave., S.E., Suite 500 Phone: (403)268-6503
Calgary, AB, Canada T2G 0P6 Ann Bryden, Libn.
Staff: Prof 1. **Subjects:** Petroleum consulting. **Subscriptions:** 28 journals and other serials. **Services:** Library not open to the public. **Remarks:** FAX: (403)269-7265. Telex: 03-824649. No further information was supplied by respondent.

★4518★
D & Z, Inc. - Library (Sci-Engr)
1818 Market St., 21st Fl. Phone: (215)299-8222
Philadelphia, PA 19103 Ms. Sandy Davis, Libn.
Founded: 1945. **Staff:** Prof 1. **Subjects:** Engineering - mechanical, chemical, electrical, instrumentation. **Holdings:** 2200 books; 22 VF drawers of specifications, technical reports; manufacturers' catalogs; standards; building codes. **Subscriptions:** 100 journals and other serials. **Services:** Library open to the public by appointment. **Computerized Information Services:** DIALOG Information Services. **Networks/Consortia:** Member of Industrial Libraries Network. **Remarks:** FAX: (215)299-2236.

★4519★
(Dacca) American Cultural Center - USIS Library (Educ)
House No. 8, Rd. No. 9
Dhanmondi R.A.
Dacca, Bangladesh
Remarks: Maintained or supported by the U.S. Information Agency. Focus is on materials that will assist peoples outside the United States to learn about the United States, its people, history, culture, political processes, and social milieux.

★4520★
Dacotah Prairie Museum - Archives (Hist)
21 S. Main St.
Box 395 Phone: (605)622-7117
Aberdeen, SD 57402-0395 Merry Coleman, Dir.
Founded: 1969. **Staff:** 5.5. **Subjects:** History of Brown County and the northeastern region of South Dakota, 1797 to present. **Holdings:** Ledgers; photographs; school records; oral histories; records of organizations and businesses; letters and manuscripts of missionaries in the area, 1860-1880. **Services:** Copying; archives open to the public by appointment. **Computerized Information Services:** Internal databases.

★4521★
Dade County Law Library System (Law)
2101 County Courthouse
73 W. Flagler St. Phone: (305)375-5422
Miami, FL 33130 Wilbur McDuff, Lib.Dir.
Founded: 1937. **Staff:** Prof 7; Other 8. **Subjects:** Law. **Special Collections:** All Florida territorial and state statutes and session laws, 1800 to present; instructional law audiocassettes; English and Canadian statutes and case reports. **Holdings:** 121,000 volumes; microforms. **Subscriptions:** 650 journals and other serials. **Services:** Copying; library open to the public at librarian's discretion. **Computerized Information Services:** WESTLAW, DIALOG Information Services, BRS Information Technologies, Veralex 2. Performs searches on fee basis. **Remarks:** Maintains 4 branch libraries. System maintained by 11th Judicial Circuit Court. Library located at 321 County Courthouse, 73 W. Flagler St. **Staff:** Robert B. Wallace, Law Libn.; Barbara Hunt, Asst.Lib.Adm.; Lauretta Buck, Hd., Tech.Serv.

★4522★
Dade County Law Library System - Auxiliary Branch (Law)
420 Lincoln Rd., Suite 245 Phone: (305)538-0314
Miami Beach, FL 33139 Johanna Porpiglia, Br.Libn.
Staff: Prof 1. **Subjects:** Law. **Holdings:** 19,500 books. **Services:** Copying; library open to the public with restrictions. **Computerized Information Services:** WESTLAW.

Elizabeth Dafoe Library
See: **University of Manitoba** (18789)

Dr. Joseph D'Agrosa Medical Library
See: **Brookhaven Memorial Hospital Medical Center** (2217)

Dahlgren Memorial Library
See: **Georgetown University - Medical Center** (6378)

Adelle Dailey Music Library
See: **University of Kentucky** (18742)

Daily News of Los Angeles
See: **Los Angeles Daily News** (9339)

★4523★
Dain Bosworth, Inc. - Research Library (Bus-Fin)
100 Dain Tower Phone: (612)371-2774
Minneapolis, MN 55402 Diane Wiederhoeft, Res.Libn.
Founded: 1970. **Staff:** Prof 1; Other 1. **Subjects:** Publicly owned companies, business. **Holdings:** 6000 files on public companies; 3000 current annual reports. **Subscriptions:** 40 journals and other serials; 6 newspapers. **Services:** Library not open to the public. **Computerized Information Services:** DataTimes.

Jonas Dainauskas History Library
See: **Lithuanian Research and Studies Center, Inc. - Libraries** (9211)

Carl Dair Archive
See: **Massey College - Robertson Davies Library** (9839)

★4524★
Dairyland Power Cooperative - Library (Sci-Engr)
3200 East Ave. S. Phone: (608)788-4000
La Crosse, WI 54601 Shirley Matthes, Rec.Mgr.
Staff: Prof 1; Other 1. **Subjects:** Rural electrification, energy industry, engineering, public utilities, business. **Holdings:** 1200 volumes. **Subscriptions:** 380 journals and other serials. **Services:** Library not open to the public except by special request. **Automated Operations:** Computerized cataloging.

Daishowa Chemicals Inc.
See: **Lignotech (U.S.) Inc.** (9161)

★4525★
(Dakar) Centre Culturel Americain - USIS Library (Educ)
Immeuble BIAO
2, Place de l'Independance
Post Box 49
Dakar, Senegal
Remarks: Maintained or supported by the U.S. Information Agency. Focus is on materials that will assist peoples outside the United States to learn about the United States, its people, history, culture, political processes, and social milieux.

★4526★
Dakar-Thiaroye Center for Oceanographic Research - Library (Biol Sci)
Route de Rufisque, Km. 10
B.P. 2241 Phone: 340536
Dakar, Senegal Florent Diouf, Documentaliste
Staff: 1. **Subjects:** Marine stocks, ecosystems, environment, marine economics, oceanography. **Holdings:** 24,800 volumes. **Subscriptions:** 62 journals and other serials. **Services:** Interlibrary loan; copying; SDI; library open with the permission of the director. **Computerized Information Services:** ASFA-HORIZON, RESADOC (internal databases); BITNET (electronic mail service). **Remarks:** FAX: 324307. Alternate telephone number(s): 340534. Telex: 5468 ORSTONSG. Electronic mail address(es): fdiouf@crodt.orstom.fr (BITNET). Maintained by Agricultural Research Institute of Senegal. **Also Known As:** Centre de Recherche Oceanographiques de Dakar-Thiaroye.

★4527★
Dakota County Historical Society - Research Center (Hist)
130 3rd Ave., N. Phone: (612)451-6260
South St. Paul, MN 55075 Irelise Brasch, Dir.
Founded: 1939. **Staff:** 3. **Subjects:** State, county, and local history. **Holdings:** 500 volumes; county newspapers and census on microfilm; photographs; maps. **Subscriptions:** 4 journals and other serials; 8 newspapers. **Services:** Copying; center open to the public for reference use only.

★4528★
Dakota Hospital - Library (Med)
1720 S. University Dr.
Box 6014 Phone: (701)280-4187
Fargo, ND 58108-6014 Ardis Haaland, Med.Libn.
Founded: 1979. **Staff:** Prof 1. **Subjects:** Internal medicine, obstetrics and gynecology, physical medicine and rehabilitation, nursing, surgery, pediatrics. **Holdings:** 2000 books; 3500 bound periodical volumes; 600 AV program titles. **Subscriptions:** 285 journals and other serials. **Services:** Interlibrary loan; copying; library open to students from affiliated institutions. **Computerized Information Services:** BRS Information Technologies, MEDLINE; EasyLink, DOCLINE (electronic mail services). Performs searches on fee basis. **Networks/Consortia:** Member of Valley Medical Network (VMN). **Remarks:** FAX: (701)280-4674. Electronic mail address(es): 62013716 (EasyLink); 58103A (DOCLINE).

★4529★
Dakota State University - Karl E. Mundt Library (Educ)
Madison, SD 57042-1799 Phone: (605)256-5203
Ethelle S. Bean, Dir., Asst.Prof.
Founded: 1881. **Staff:** Prof 3; Other 2. **Subjects:** Education, computers, South Dakota. **Special Collections:** Karl E. Mundt Archives (2500 linear feet). **Holdings:** 77,500 books; 15,450 bound periodical volumes; 200 reels of microfilm of Indian Affairs in Dakota, 1850-1890; complete kinescopes of the Army-McCarthy Hearings; CD-ROM. **Subscriptions:** 600 journals and other serials; 16 newspapers. **Services:** Interlibrary loan; copying; library open to the public. **Automated Operations:** Computerized public access catalog, cataloging, serials, and circulation. **Computerized Information Services:** OCLC, ERIC, DIALOG Information Services; CD-ROM (Computer Library); InfoTrac; internal database; BITNET EasyLink (electronic mail services). Performs searches on fee basis. Contact Person: Mark Eriksen, Pub.Serv.Libn./Asst.Prof., 256-5319. **Networks/Consortia:** Member of MINITEX Library Information Network. **Publications:** Inside the Library, irregular - for internal distribution only. **Remarks:** FAX: (605)256-5208. Electronic mail address(es): ETHELLE@SDNET (BITNET). **Staff:** Rise Smith, Tech.Serv.Libn./Assoc.Prof.; Bonnie Olson, Archv.

Edgar Dale Educational Media & Instructional Materials Laboratory
See: **Ohio State University** (12305)

Dale Library of Weights and Measures
See: **Columbia University - Rare Book and Manuscript Library** (4023)

★4530★
Dalhousie University - Australian Literature Collection (Hum)
Halifax, NS, Canada B3H 4H8 Phone: (902)494-3615
Dr. William Birdsall, Univ.Libn.
Subjects: Australian literature - poetry, prose, and small literary magazines. **Special Collections:** Items published prior to 1960; items from the collections of George Mackaness and Kenneth Slessor; inscribed limited editions; fine bindings. **Holdings:** 4500 titles in 4800 volumes; 25 nonbook items. **Services:** Interlibrary loan (limited); copying; collection open to the public. **Staff:** Karen Smith, Hd., Spec.Serv.

★4531★
Dalhousie University - Canadian Literature Collection (Hum)
Halifax, NS, Canada B3H 4H8 Phone: (902)494-3615
Karen Smith, Hd., Spec.Coll.
Staff: Prof 1; Other 2. **Subjects:** Canadian literature, Nova Scotiana. **Special Collections:** Canadian Little Presses (10,000 volumes); Canadian Almanacs (600 volumes); Sir T.C. Haliburton Collection (150 volumes). **Subscriptions:** 44 journals and other serials; 2 newspapers. **Services:** Collection open to the public for reference use only. **Computerized Information Services:** Envoy 100 (electronic mail service). **Remarks:** FAX: (902)494-2319. Electronic mail address(es): ADM.KILLAM (Envoy 100).

★4532★
Dalhousie University - Maritime School of Social Work - Library (Soc Sci)
6420 Coburg Rd. Phone: (902)494-6433
Halifax, NS, Canada B3H 3J5 Linda MacLeod, Libn.
Founded: 1941. **Staff:** 1. **Subjects:** Social work, social welfare, sociology, psychology, counseling, community development. **Holdings:** 21,900 books and bound periodical volumes; 12 VF drawers. **Subscriptions:** 65 journals and other serials. **Services:** Interlibrary loan; copying; library open to the public. **Automated Operations:** Computerized cataloging and serials. **Remarks:** FAX: (902)494-6709.

★4533★
Dalhousie University - Oceans Institute of Canada - Library (Trans)
1236 Henry St., 5th Fl.
Halifax, NS, Canada B3H 3J5 Phone: (902)494-3879
Founded: 1978. **Subjects:** Transportation and transportation industry; ports, harbors, and waterways; shipping industry; cargo systems; marine natural resources; oil, gas, and liquefied natural gas exploration and development; marine and maritime laws and policy; marine environmental quality; resource development and management. **Holdings:** 2462 books; 90 bound periodical volumes. **Subscriptions:** 40 journals and other serials. **Services:** Copying; library open to the public by appointment. **Remarks:** FAX: (902)494-1334. Telex: UKB 7491.

★4534★
Dalhousie University - School for Resource and Environmental Studies - Library (Env-Cons)
1312 Robie St. Phone: (902)494-1359
Halifax, NS, Canada B3H 3E2 Mrs. J.G. Reade, Libn.
Founded: 1978. **Staff:** Prof 1; Other 1. **Subjects:** Environmental conservation, management, impact assessment; energy and the environment; fisheries; marine resource policy. **Holdings:** 5000 books; 15,000 unbound items. **Subscriptions:** 6 journals and other serials. **Services:** Copying; library open to the public for reference use only. **Automated Operations:** Computerized cataloging. **Computerized Information Services:** Envoy 100 (electronic mail service). **Remarks:** FAX: (902)494-3728. Electronic mail address(es): SRES (Envoy 100).

★4535★
Dalhousie University - School for Resource and Environmental Studies - Southeast Asian Environmental Collection (Env-Cons)
1312 Robie St. Phone: (902)494-1217
Halifax, NS, Canada B3H 2E2 Barbara Patton, Intl.Proj.Info.Off.
Founded: 1979. **Staff:** 3. **Subjects:** Environment - Indonesia, Southeast Asia, Philippines. **Holdings:** 10,000 books and documents; 25 AV programs. **Subscriptions:** 60 journals; 140 newsletters. **Services:** Interlibrary loan; copying; SDI; collection open to the public. **Automated Operations:** Computerized public access catalog, acquisitions, and cataloging. **Computerized Information Services:** KWOC Index; Envoy 100 (electronic mail service). Performs searches free of charge. Contact Person: Carol David. **Publications:** EMDI Environmental Reports; Ecology of Indonesia series. **Remarks:** Alternate telephone number(s): (902)494-6738. FAX: (902)494-3728. Telex: 019-21863. Electronic mail address(es): SRES (Envoy 100). **Staff:** Nick Gao.

★4536★
Dalhousie University - Science Services (Sci-Engr, Biol Sci)
Halifax, NS, Canada B3H 4H8 Phone: (902)494-2384
Sylvia J. Fullerton, Asst.Univ.Libn., Sci.Serv.
Staff: Prof 5; Other 3. **Subjects:** Biology, chemistry, psychology, physics, computer science, geology, oceanography, atmospheric sciences. **Special Collections:** Map collection (63,350 maps; 11,500 aerial photographs). **Holdings:** 69,875 books; 75,400 bound periodical volumes; 35,500 documents. **Subscriptions:** 2400 journals and other serials. **Services:** Interlibrary loan; SDI; library open to the public. **Automated Operations:** Computerized public access catalog, cataloging, acquisitions and circulation. **Computerized Information Services:** CAN/OLE, DIALOG Information Services; CD-ROM; Envoy 100, BITNET (electronic mail services). Performs searches on fee basis. Contact Person: Patricia Lutley, Coord., Pub.Serv. **Remarks:** FAX: (902)494-2319. Telex: 01921863. Electronic mail address(es): ILL.MACDONALD (Envoy 100); SFULL@ADM.DAL.CA (BITNET). **Staff:** Frederick Kennedy, Libn.; Sharon Longard, Libn.; Rosemary Mackenzie, Libn.

★4537★
Dalhousie University - Sir James Dunn Law Library (Law)
Weldon Law Bldg. Phone: (902)494-2124
Halifax, NS, Canada B3H 4H9 Christian L. Wiktor, Law Libn.
Founded: 1883. **Staff:** Prof 5; Other 12. **Subjects:** Law - Canadian, English, Commonwealth, American. **Special Collections:** Maritime law; international law. **Holdings:** 150,000 volumes. **Subscriptions:** 3350 journals and other serials. **Services:** Interlibrary loan; copying; library open to the public with restrictions. **Publications:** Marine Affairs Bibliography. **Remarks:** FAX: (902)494-6669. Alternate telephone number(s): 494-2125; 494-2640. **Staff:** Linda S. Aiken, Acq.Libn.; Jane M. MacDonald, Ref.Libn.; Jill Mahony-Plummer, Pub.Serv.Libn.; Joan Simpson, Cat.

★4538★
Dalhousie University - Special Collections (Publ, Rare Book, Hum)
University Library Phone: (902)494-3615
Halifax, NS, Canada B3H 4H8 Karen Smith, Hd., Spec.Coll.
Founded: 1936. **Staff:** Prof 1; Other 1. **Special Collections:** The Cockerell Collection - representative bindings of the 15th to 18th centuries assembled by Douglas Cockerell, the famous English bookbinder (104 volumes); Oscar Wilde Collection (305 volumes); Rare Book Collection (10,000 volumes). **Services:** Collection open to the public for reference use only. **Computerized Information Services:** Envoy 100 (electronic mail service). **Remarks:** FAX: (902)494-2319. Electronic mail address(es): ADM.KILLAM (Envoy 100).

★4539★
Dalhousie University - Special Collections - Bacon Collection (Hum)
University Library Phone: (902)494-3615
Halifax, NS, Canada B3H 4H8 Karen Smith, Hd., Spec.Coll.
Founded: 1972. **Staff:** Prof 1; Other 2. **Subjects:** Pre-1750 monographs by and about Sir Francis Bacon. **Holdings:** 300 volumes; 180 17th century imprints. **Services:** Collection open to the public for reference use only. **Computerized Information Services:** Envoy 100 (electronic mail service). **Special Catalogs:** A Short Title Catalogue of the Dalhousie Bacon Collection, 1978. **Remarks:** FAX: (902)494-2319. Electronic mail address(es): ADM.KILLAM (Envoy 100).

★4540★
Dalhousie University - Special Collections - Kipling Collection (Hum)
University Library Phone: (902)494-3615
Halifax, NS, Canada B3H 4H8 Karen Smith, Hd., Spec.Coll.
Founded: 1954. **Staff:** Prof 1; Other 2. **Subjects:** Kiplingiana. **Holdings:** 2000 books; 400 bound periodical volumes; 1000 other cataloged items; 653 unbound periodicals; 37 literary manuscripts; 64 musical selections; 226 photostats and clippings; 850 letters; 100 illustrations; 2400 newspaper items. **Services:** Collection open to the public for reference use only. **Computerized Information Services:** Envoy 100 (electronic mail service). **Publications:** Rudyard Kipling: A Bibliographic Catalogue, 1959. **Remarks:** FAX: (902)494-2319. Electronic mail address(es): ADM.KILLAM (Envoy 100).

★4541★
Dalhousie University - W.K. Kellogg Health Sciences Library (Med)
Sir Charles Tupper Medical Bldg. Phone: (902)494-2458
Halifax, NS, Canada B3H 4H7 J. Elizabeth Sutherland, Hea.Sci.Libn.
Founded: 1889. **Staff:** Prof 6; Other 23. **Subjects:** Medicine, dentistry, nursing, pharmacy, physiotherapy, health services administration, physical education, human communication disorders, occupational therapy. **Holdings:** 153,900 volumes; 2500 audiotapes, videotapes, slide-tape programs. **Subscriptions:** 2487 journals and other serials. **Services:** Interlibrary loan; copying; Regional Loan and Information Service; library open to the public. **Automated Operations:** Computerized cataloging, serials, acquisitions, and circulation. **Computerized Information Services:** MEDLINE, CAN/OLE, CAN/SDI, DIALOG Information Services; CD-ROM (MEDLINE, CINAHL, International Pharmaceutical Abstracts, SPORT Discus, IDIS Drug File); Envoy 100, InterNet, NetNorth (electronic mail services). **Remarks:** FAX: (902)494-3750. Electronic mail address(es): ADM.KELLOGG (Envoy 100); JESUTHER@AC.DAL.CA (InterNet). **Staff:** Bill Owen, Hd., Pub.Serv.; Judith Coughlan-Lambly, Hd., Tech.Serv.; Patrick Ellis, Hd., Lending Serv.; Hughena MacMillan, Hd., ILL.

★4542★
Dalian Institute of Technology - Library (Sci-Engr)
40 Luanjincun
Dalian, Liaoning Province, People's Republic of China Phone: 42102
Wu Ruifeng, Lib.Hd.
Founded: 1949. **Staff:** 102. **Subjects:** Applied mathematics; physics; engineering mechanics; machine building technology and machine appliance; machinery design and manufacturing; crane conveyor and construction; machinery; metallic materials; internal combustion engines; turbine engines; applied thermal engineering; radio technique; automatic control; industrial and electrical automation; computer software; computer applications; engineering - foundry, ship and ocean, hydraulic, coastal, offshore, structural, transportation, chemical, environmental; architecture; ideological and political education; engineering of urbanization; foreign languages; process control and automation; applied chemistry; corrosion and protection; chemical equipment machinery; inorganic chemical technology; petrochemical technology; fine chemicals technology; polymer materials; coal processing technology; systems engineering; industrial business management; library and information science. **Holdings:** 1.48 million volumes; 6927 periodicals; 960 AV programs; microforms. **Subscriptions:** 5025 journals and other serials; 287 newspapers. **Services:** Interlibrary loan; copying. **Publications:** Book and Information Work; Library and Readers; New Books; Scientific and Technical Reference Material; Translations of Scientific and Technical Literatures. **Special Catalogs:** Catalog of Chinese and Foreign Scientific and Technical Periodicals Held by the Library; Catalog of New Acquisitions of Scientific and Technical Publications.

★4543★
Dallas Area Rapid Transit - DART Resource Center (Trans)
601 Pacific Ave. Phone: (214)658-6411
Dallas, TX 75202 Patricia Lee, Tech.Rec.Spec.
Founded: 1986. **Staff:** Prof 1. **Subjects:** Mass transit, management, engineering, architecture, planning. **Holdings:** 1500 books; 300 reports and studies; 20 sets of standards and specifications on microfiche. **Subscriptions:** 65 journals and other serials; 2 newspapers. **Services:** Interlibrary loan; library open to the public by appointment. **Automated Operations:** Computerized acquisitions, cataloging, serials, and circulation. **Computerized Information Services:** DIALOG Information Services, Startext; internal databases. **Publications:** Transfer (newsletter), monthly - to the public; Connections (newsletter), monthly - for internal distribution only. **Remarks:** FAX: (214)658-6234.

★4544★
Dallas Christian College - C.C. Crawford Memorial Library (Rel-Phil)
2700 Christian Pkwy. Phone: (214)241-3371
Dallas, TX 75234 John M. Wade, Libn.
Founded: 1950. **Staff:** Prof 1; Other 1. **Subjects:** Theology. **Special Collections:** Restoration Library (history of Churches of Christ). **Holdings:** 23,253 books; 1636 audio cassette tapes. **Subscriptions:** 132 journals and other serials. **Services:** Interlibrary loan; copying; library open to the public with specific needs. **Automated Operations:** Computerized cataloging. **Computerized Information Services:** OCLC. **Networks/Consortia:** Member of AMIGOS Bibliographic Council, Inc. **Remarks:** FAX: (214)241-8021.

★4545★
Dallas Civic Garden Center - Horticulture Library (Agri)
Fair Park
3601 Martin Luther King Blvd.
P.O. Box 152537 Phone: (214)428-7476
Dallas, TX 75315 M. Cheever, Dir. of Horticulture
Founded: 1941. **Subjects:** Gardening, botany, floriculture, greenhouse management, flower arranging, pest control. **Holdings:** Figures not available. **Services:** Library not open to the public; accessible on a restricted basis only.

★4546★
Dallas County Circuit Court - Library (Law)
Dallas County Courthouse
Box 1158 Phone: (205)874-2526
Selma, AL 36701 Catherine C. Gilmer, Libn.
Subjects: Law. **Special Collections:** Rare law books. **Holdings:** 9945 books. **Services:** Interlibrary loan; copying; library open to the public for reference use only.

★4547★
Dallas County Community College District - Bill J. Priest Institute for Economic Development - Learning Resource Center (Educ)
1402 Corinth Phone: (214)565-5779
Dallas, TX 75215 Cynthia A. Teter, LRC Dir.
Founded: 1973. **Staff:** Prof 2. **Subjects:** Reference; occupational technical disciplines. **Special Collections:** Government contracting and small business development. **Holdings:** 1545 books; 101 machine-readable data files; 128 films; 17 audiotapes; 179 bound periodical volumes. **Subscriptions:** 34 journals and other serials. **Services:** Center not open to the public. **Automated Operations:** NOTIS. **Remarks:** FAX: (214)565-5857. **Formerly:** Its DCCCD Jobs Training Center.

★4548★
Dallas County Heritage Society - Library (Hist)
1717 Gano St.
Dallas, TX 75215 Phone: (214)421-5141
Subjects: Texas history, Dallas history, decorative arts, architecture. **Special Collections:** Dallas postcards (2000). **Holdings:** 2000 books; 10 bound periodical volumes; 1000 archival items; 100 reels of microfilm; 700 photographs; manuscripts. **Subscriptions:** 10 journals and other serials. **Services:** Copying; library open to the public by appointment.

★4549★
Dallas County Historical Society - Historical and Genealogical Library (Hist)
Rte. 2, Box 126 Phone: (417)345-7297
Buffalo, MO 65622 Leni Howe, Corresponding Sec.
Subjects: Family and county history. **Holdings:** 200 books; 20 documents; 10 manuscripts. **Services:** Library open to the public by appointment.

★4550★
Dallas County Law Library (Law)
Government Ctr., 2nd Fl.
600 Commerce St. Phone: (214)653-7481
Dallas, TX 75202-4606 Traphene Hickman, Dir.
Founded: 1933. **Staff:** Prof 5; Other 10. **Subjects:** Law, Texas State government. **Special Collections:** State Bar of Texas and Dallas Bar Association continuing legal education materials (print and audio-video); professional responsibility and ethics collection. **Holdings:** 91,359 volumes; 3500 bound periodical volumes; 98,172 microfiche; 1341 film rolls; 4017 audio cassettes; 136 videocassettes; 350 pamphlet boxes of Texas legislative bills, 1983-1990; pre-NRS state reports on microfilm; Federal Register, Code of Federal Regulations, Texas Register, Texas Attorney General opinions, U.S. Supreme Court records and briefs, and Texas State Supreme Court briefs on microfiche. **Subscriptions:** 1536 journals and other serials. **Services:** Interlibrary loan; copying; library open to the public for reference use only. **Automated Operations:** Computerized cataloging and ILL. **Computerized Information Services:** WESTLAW, DataTimes, VU/TEXT Information Services, Dow Jones News/Retrieval, OCLC, LEGI-SLATE. Performs searches on fee basis. Contact Person: Marcia Stoklosa, Cat. & ILL, 653-6013. **Networks/Consortia:** Member of AMIGOS Bibliographic Council, Inc. **Publications:** Dallas County Law Library Monthly Aquisitions list - free upon request. **Remarks:** FAX: (214)653-6103. Maintains branch libraries in Dallas, Garland, Grand Prairie, and Richardson, TX. The Criminal Law Library is located at 133 N. Industrial Blvd., 1st Fl., Dallas, TX, 75207-4313; tel 653-4313. The Belo Branch is located at 2101 Ross Ave., Dallas, TX 75201; tel 754-4730. **Staff:** Marcia Stoklosa, Tech.Serv.; Mary Rankin, Assoc.Dir.&Acq.; June Clee, Br.Mgr., Main Lib.; Rodney Johnson, Ser., Main Lib.; Marcia Baker, Br.Mgr., Criminal Law Lib.; Sharon Williams, Br.Mgr., Belo Br.

★4551★
Dallas County Law Library - Richardson Branch (Law)
Richardson Public Library
900 Civic Center Dr. Phone: (214)238-4000
Richardson, TX 75080 Julianne Lovelace, Lib.Dir.
Founded: 1980. **Staff:** 4. **Subjects:** Texas law, U.S. law. **Holdings:** 4500 books; 24 trays of microfiche. **Subscriptions:** 5 journals and other serials. **Services:** Copying; library open to the public. **Computerized Information Services:** DIALOG Information Services. **Staff:** Steven M. Benson, Libn.

★4552★
Dallas-Fort Worth Medical Center - Library (Med)
2709 Hospital Blvd. Phone: (214)641-5000
Grand Prairie, TX 75051 Kathy Broyles, Libn.
Founded: 1964. **Staff:** Prof 1. **Subjects:** Medicine. **Holdings:** 250 books; 236 bound periodical volumes; 264 audiotapes; 46 videotapes. **Subscriptions:** 43 journals and other serials. **Services:** Library open to the public for reference use only. **Computerized Information Services:** MiniMEDLINE. **Remarks:** FAX: (214)641-8035.

★4553★
Dallas Historical Society - G.B. Dealey Library and Research Center (Hist)
Hall of State, Fair Park
Box 150038 Phone: (214)421-4500
Dallas, TX 75315 Michael V. Hazel, Dir. of Res.
Founded: 1922. **Staff:** Prof 3. **Subjects:** Dallas, Texas, Southwestern, and U.S. history. **Special Collections:** Sarah Horton Cockrell, Charles E. Arnold, and Johnson Photograph Collections; Henry Stark Photograph Collection (Views in Texas, 1895; 255 photographs); Caruth Collection (4 linear feet); Reverchon Collection (1 linear foot); Howard Library Collection; papers of Hatton W. Sumners, G.B. Dealey, Elmer Scott, William H. Gaston, R.L. Thornton, Thomas B. Love, and Joseph W. Bailey. **Holdings:** 14,000 books; 10,000 bound periodical volumes; 2 million archival materials. **Services:** Copying; center open to the public. **Publications:** When Dallas Became a City: Letters of John Milton McCoy, 1870-1881; Guide to Fair Park; All Together! World War I Posters of the Allied Nations; Dallas Rediscovered; Legacies (journal), semiannual. **Remarks:** FAX: (214)421-7500.

★4554★
Dallas Morning News - Reference Department (Publ)
Communications Ctr.
Box 655237 Phone: (214)977-8302
Dallas, TX 75265 Judy Sall, Ref.Ed.
Founded: 1917. **Staff:** Prof 5; Other 10. **Subjects:** Newspaper reference topics. **Special Collections:** Texana and local Dallas history (600 books). **Holdings:** 5000 books; 150,000 pictures; 9 million clippings. **Subscriptions:** 115 newspapers and periodicals. **Services:** Department open to other libraries on a limited basis. **Computerized Information Services:** DIALOG Information Services, VU/TEXT Information Services, NEXIS, DataTimes, Dow Jones News/Retrieval; internal database. **Remarks:** FAX: (214)977-8319. **Staff:** Jerome Sims, Photo Libn.; T. Alan Doss, Night Libn.; Judy Metcalf, Electronic Media Ed.

★4555★
Dallas Museum of Art - Library (Art)
1717 N. Harwood
Dallas, TX 75201 Phone: (214)922-1276
Founded: 1936. **Staff:** Prof 2. **Subjects:** Art history, painting, sculpture, drawing, prints, decorative arts, pre-Columbian and African art. **Holdings:** 25,000 books; 1000 bound periodical volumes; 60 VF drawers of artist files; art museum annual reports; auction catalogs, 1950 to present. **Subscriptions:** 106 journals and other serials. **Services:** Copying; library open to the public for reference use only. **Computerized Information Services:** OCLC. **Networks/Consortia:** Member of AMIGOS Bibliographic Council, Inc. **Remarks:** FAX: (214)954-0174. Telex: 734 025 DMA UR.

★4556★
Dallas Museum of Natural History - Mudge Rare Book Library (Biol Sci)
P.O. Box 150433 Phone: (214)670-8476
Dallas, TX 75315 Jim Peterson
Staff: .5. **Subjects:** Ornithology; travel. **Special Collections:** 19th Century illustrated elephant folios. **Holdings:** 4000 books; 1000 bound periodical volumes. **Subscriptions:** 6 journals and other serials. **Services:** Library open to the public by appointment. **Remarks:** FAX: (214)428-4356.

Dallas/Norman Library
See: **Summer Institute of Linguistics** (15859)

★4557★
(Dallas) Office of the City Secretary - Dallas Municipal Archives and Records Center (Hist)
City Hall
1500 Marilla Phone: (214)670-3741
Dallas, TX 75201 Robert Sloan, City Sec.
Subjects: History of the city of Dallas, 1871 to present. **Holdings:** 3000 cubic feet of government records of the Dallas City Council and city departments, City Council, board and commission minute books, ordinances, resolutions, land instruments, zoning maps and files, special committee reports, tax rolls and plats, annual reports and budgets, building card appraisals, city charters and codes, bond registers, audit reports, and tape recordings of City Council meetings. **Services:** Copying; archives open to the public during business hours (appointment preferred).

Dallas Park and Recreation Department - Division of Cultural Affairs - The Science Place
See: **The Science Place** (14941)

★4558★
Dallas Power and Light Company - Research Library
1506 Commerce St., Rm. 7E
Dallas, TX 75201
Defunct.

★4559★
Dallas Public Library - J. Erik Jonsson Central Library - Business and Technology Division (Bus-Fin, Sci-Engr)
1515 Young St. Phone: (214)670-1608
Dallas, TX 75201 Sarabeth Allen, Div.Mgr.
Founded: 1955. **Staff:** Prof 12; Other 9. **Subjects:** Business, economics, management, energy, hospitality, technology, health sciences, engineering, construction, domestic sciences, transportation, data processing. **Special Collections:** Business History Collection; automobile shop manuals; corporate reports; business and industrial trade directories; standards and specifications. **Holdings:** 143,000 books; 36,000 bound periodical volumes; 13,000 microcards; 700,000 microfiche; 20,000 reels of microfilm; 18 VF drawers of clippings and pamphlets; 2000 audio cassettes; 255 videocassettes. **Subscriptions:** 2000 journals and other serials; 20 newspapers. **Services:** Interlibrary loan; copying; telephone reference; division open to the public. **Automated Operations:** Computerized cataloging. **Computerized Information Services:** DIALOG Information Services, Dow Jones News/Retrieval, DataTimes, BRS Information Technologies; CD-ROMs (InfoTrac, Health Reference Center, Disclosure Incorporated). Performs searches on fee basis. Contact Person: Carla La Croix, Asst. to Div.Mgr. **Special Catalogs:** Book catalog of library's Business History Collection. **Remarks:** Alternate telephone number(s): 670-1400. **Staff:** Lloyd Loving, Libn.; Marian Waite, Asst. to Div.Mgr.; Loring Sumner, Libn.; Tim Sibley, Libn.; Loretta Klassen, Libn.

★4560★
Dallas Public Library - J. Erik Jonsson Central Library - Children's Center (Hum)
1515 Young St. Phone: (214)670-1400
Dallas, TX 75201 Kathy Toon, Div.Mgr.
Founded: 1987. **Staff:** Prof 4; Other 7. **Subjects:** Children's literature. **Special Collections:** Texana; historical collection of children's books; alphabet books; fairy tales and legends; Mother Goose. **Holdings:** 93,000 books; 1023 bound periodical volumes. **Subscriptions:** 89 journals and other serials. **Services:** Interlibrary loan; copying; center open to the public. **Automated Operations:** Computerized public access catalog, cataloging, and circulation. **Networks/Consortia:** Member of Northeast Texas Library System (NETLS). **Remarks:** FAX: (214)670-7839. **Staff:** Phyllis Ray, Asst.Mgr.

★4561★
Dallas Public Library - J. Erik Jonsson Central Library - Fine Arts Division (Art, Mus, Theater)
1515 Young St. Phone: (214)670-1643
Dallas, TX 75201 Roger Carroll, Div.Mgr.
Founded: 1955. **Staff:** Prof 7; Other 10. **Subjects:** Theater, music, painting, fashion, sculpture, architecture, prints and printmaking, dance, photography, crafts, video, sports. **Special Collections:** Margo Jones Theatre Collection (75 cubic feet); W.E. Hill Theatre; John Rosenfield Collection; Dallas Theater Center Collection; Marion Flagg Papers (music educator); Lawrence Kelly Collection of Opera Renderings; Dallas Little Theatre; Interstate Theatre Collection (300 cubic feet); Juana De Laban Dance Collection; Player Theatre Archives and Video; Margaret Rutherford Film Collection; Margaret Mitchell Collection (archives related to Gone with the Wind); Texas Federation of Music Clubs Music Manuscript Archive. **Holdings:** 136,109 books; 7731 pieces of sheet music; 45,000 recordings; 389 cassette tapes; 429 videocassettes; 15,182 music scores; 510,222 vertical and picture file items in theater, art, and music. **Subscriptions:** 2940 journals and other serials. **Services:** Interlibrary loan; copying; library open to the public with restrictions. **Automated Operations:** Computerized cataloging and circulation. **Computerized Information Services:** DIALOG Information Services, DataTimes, WILSONLINE; InfoTrac. **Remarks:** Alternate telephone number(s): 670-1400. FAX: (214)670-7839. **Staff:** Robert Eason, Theater Libn.; Donna Mendro, Recordings Libn.; John Elfers, Mus.Libn.; Sharon Herfurth, Asst.Mgr.; John McAnally, Sports Libn.; Valerie Pinkney, Art Libn.

★4562★
Dallas Public Library - J. Erik Jonsson Central Library - Fine Books Division (Publ)
1515 Young St. Phone: (214)670-1444
Dallas, TX 75201 Marvin H. Stone, Mgr.
Founded: 1956. **Staff:** Prof 1. **Subjects:** History of printing and the book. **Holdings:** 2650 books. **Subscriptions:** 14 journals and other serials. **Services:** Division open to the public by appointment.

★4563★
Dallas Public Library - J. Erik Jonsson Central Library - Genealogy Collection (Hist)
1515 Young St. Phone: (214)670-1433
Dallas, TX 75201 Lloyd DeWitt Bockstruck, Supv.
Staff: Prof 1; Other 7. **Subjects:** Genealogy, heraldry, onomatology, local history. **Holdings:** 59,533 books; 26,530 reels of microfilm; 1237 microcards; 46,372 microfiche. **Subscriptions:** 700 journals and other serials. **Services:** Copying; collection open to the public.

★4564★
Dallas Public Library - J. Erik Jonsson Central Library - General Reference Division (Info Sci)
1515 Young St. Phone: (214)670-1700
Dallas, TX 75201 La Verne Brown, Mgr.
Founded: 1901. **Staff:** Prof 5; Other 17. **Holdings:** 1900 volumes; 35,600 microfiche. **Subscriptions:** 150 journals and other serials. **Services:** Department open to the public. **Automated Operations:** Computerized cataloging and serials. **Computerized Information Services:** OCLC, Dow Jones News/Retrieval; internal database. **Networks/Consortia:** Member of AMIGOS Bibliographic Council, Inc., Project TexNet Interlibrary Loan Network (TexNet), Northeast Texas Library System (NETLS). **Special Indexes:** Central Research Library Periodicals List. **Remarks:** FAX: (214)670-7839. **Staff:** Gary Jennings; Ben Rodriguez; Carol Armstrong; Sara Harvey.

★4565★
Dallas Public Library - J. Erik Jonsson Central Library - Government Information Center - Government Publications Collections (Info Sci)
1515 Young St. Phone: (214)670-1468
Dallas, TX 75201 Marie R. Hartman, Mgr.
Founded: 1978. **Staff:** Prof 5; Other 6. **Subjects:** Official publications - United States, Texas, international, United Nations and affiliates; maps; atlases. **Special Collections:** U.S. Patents depository, 1790 to present; U.S. Geological Survey depository; Texas documents depository, NASA depository. **Holdings:** 10,000 books; 6000 bound periodical volumes; 750,000 U.S. Government publications; 10,000 Texas state publications; 10,000 international government documents; 3000 reels of microfilm; 25,000 maps; 150,000 microfiche; geological publications from most of the 50 states. **Subscriptions:** 400 journals and other serials. **Services:** Interlibrary loan (limited); copying; division open to the public. **Automated Operations:** Computerized cataloging and circulation. **Computerized Information Services:** DIALOG Information Services, U.S. Patent Classification System, BRS Information Technologies, PFDS Online. Performs searches on fee basis. Contact Person: Johanna Johnson, Asst.Mgr./Patent Libn. **Networks/Consortia:** Member of AMIGOS Bibliographic Council, Inc., Northeast Texas Library System (NETLS). **Remarks:** (214)670-7839. **Staff:** Carol Stanglin, Atlases/Intl.Docs.Libn.; Kathy Coppage, Texas Docs./Maps Libn.; Charlotte Bagh, U.S. Docs.Libn.; Darlene Brimmage, Maps

★4566★
Dallas Public Library - J. Erik Jonsson Central Library - Government Information Center - Urban Information Collections (Plan)
1515 Young St. Phone: (214)670-1487
Dallas, TX 75201 Marie R. Hartman, Mgr.
Founded: 1982. **Staff:** Prof 1; Other 3. **Subjects:** City service management and administration, public administration, grants, urban planning, transportation, citizen participation and awareness. **Special Collections:** Foundation Center Collection; City of Dallas documents. **Holdings:** 20,000 books; 1500 bound periodical volumes; 72,000 microfiche; 13 videocassettes. **Subscriptions:** 250 journals and other serials. **Services:** Interlibrary loan; copying; center open to the public. **Computerized Information Services:** DIALOG Information Services, LOGIN. Performs searches on fee basis. **Publications:** Directory of Dallas County Foundations; Urban Information Review. **Special Catalogs:** APL/CAT (A Public Library Community Access Tool; online database of 4000 local community organizations). **Remarks:** FAX: (214)670-7839. **Staff:** Calvin Wallace, APL/Cat.Libn.; Edward Walton, Grants Libn.; Cynthia Mayo, Mun.Ref.

★4567★
Dallas Public Library - J. Erik Jonsson Central Library - History and Social Sciences Division (Hist, Soc Sci)
1515 Young St. Phone: (214)670-1424
Dallas, TX 75201 Heather Williams, Mgr.
Founded: 1973. **Staff:** Prof 6; Other 7. **Subjects:** History and travel, law, political science, education, psychology, sociology, social welfare, biography, military and naval sciences, public administration. **Special Collections:** College catalogs (6400, on microfiche). **Holdings:** 141,362 books; 28,300 bound periodical volumes; 382,684 microfiche; 10,100 reels of microfilm; 52 VF drawers of travel material and pamphlets. **Subscriptions:** 745 journals and other serials. **Services:** Interlibrary loan; copying; division open to the public. **Computerized Information Services:** DIALOG Information Services, BRS Information Technologies. Performs searches on fee basis. Contact Person: David Bader, Libn. or Carolyn Starks, Libn. **Remarks:** Includes the holdings of the U.S. Office of Education - Region VI - Educational Resources Information Center. **Staff:** Nellie Kendall, Libn.; Michael K. Smith, Libn.; Paul K. Oswalt, Asst.Mgr.

★4568★
Dallas Public Library - J. Erik Jonsson Central Library - Humanities Division (Hum)
1515 Young St. Phone: (214)670-1668
Dallas, TX 75201 Frances Bell, Div.Mgr.
Founded: 1901. **Staff:** Prof 8; Other 7. **Subjects:** Literary criticism, bibliography, language, fiction, drama, journalism, poetry, library science, essays, philosophy, religion. **Holdings:** 211,000 books; 13,600 bound periodical volumes. **Subscriptions:** 570 journals and other serials. **Services:** Interlibrary loan; copying. **Special Indexes:** Play index which provides author-title analytics for anthologies not included in standard indexes (card). **Staff:** Ronald Boyd, Asst.Mgr.; Pat Ferguson, Libn.; Stephen Housewright, Libn.; Jesse Jensen, Libn.; Murel McGrath, Libn.; Yolanda Davis-Yancy, Prof.Asst.; Michael Hicks, Prof.Asst.

★4569★
Dallas Public Library - J. Erik Jonsson Central Library - Texas/Dallas History and Archives Division (Hist)
1515 Young St. Phone: (214)670-1435
Dallas, TX 75201 Marvin H. Stone, Mgr.
Founded: 1979. **Staff:** Prof 4; Other 4. **Subjects:** Dallas and Texas history and area studies. **Special Collections:** Historic photographs by Denny, Johnny, and Durwood Hayes, John Mazziotta, George McAfee, Frank Rogers, Squire Haskins, and Dallas city photographers. 2540 archival collections, including: Mayor Wes Wise City Council Files (12 cubic feet); Neiman-Marcus (325 cubic feet); Dallas County Records (450 cubic feet); Sanger-Harris Collection (76 cubic feet); Childrens Medical Center (15 cubic feet); Juanita Craft Collection (60 cubic feet); Texas Pacific Land Trust (261 volumes; 18 cubic feet); Bruce Alger Congressional papers (60 cubic feet); Zonta Club of Dallas (20 cubic feet); Clint Peoples Collection (U.S. Marshal; 30 cubic feet); Mary Bywaters Dance Collection (100 cubic feet); Anita Martinez Collection (30 cubi c feet). **Holdings:** 36,000 volumes; 27 cabinets of newspapers clippings; 13,000 microforms; 325 oral history interviews; 400 cubic feet of local history archives; 400,000 historic photgraphs, 5000 Maps. **Subscriptions:** 255 journals and other serials; 30 newspapers. **Services:** Copying; photograph copying; division open to the public. **Automated Operations:** Computerized cataloging. **Computerized Information Services:** DataTimes. **Networks/Consortia:** Member of AMIGOS Bibliographic Council, Inc., Northeast Texas Library System (NETLS). **Staff:** Joan Dobson, Asst.Mgr. & Local Hist.Spec.; Michael D. Smith, Map Libn.; Sharon Van Dorn, Per.Libn.; Jimm Foster, Photog.Archv.; Carol Roark, Archv.

★4570★
Dallas Theological Seminary - Turpin Library (Rel-Phil)
3909 Swiss Ave. Phone: (214)841-3758
Dallas, TX 75204 Robert D. Ibach, Dir.
Founded: 1924. **Staff:** Prof 6.5; Other 13.5. **Subjects:** Theology, Bible, Biblical languages, Christian literature, church history, world missions, Christian education, practical theology, devotional literature. **Holdings:** 142,000 volumes; 4500 tapes and cassettes; 38,388 microforms. **Subscriptions:** 1094 journals and other serials. **Services:** Interlibrary loan; copying; library open to the public with annual fee required for checking out books. **Automated Operations:** Computerized public access catalog. **Computerized Information Services:** DIALOG Information Services, BRS Information Technologies, OCLC. **Networks/Consortia:** Member of AMIGOS Bibliographic Council, Inc. **Remarks:** FAX: (214)841-3642. **Staff:** Marvin Hunn, Asst.Dir.; John M. Beverage, Pub.Serv.Libn.; Steven Perry, Tech.Serv.Libn.; Philip Johnson, Coll.Dev.Libn.

★4571★
Dallas Times-Herald - Library (Publ)
1101 Pacific St.
Box 655445 Phone: (214)720-6240
Dallas, TX 75265 Eve McCullar, Libn.
Founded: 1973. **Staff:** Prof 5. **Subjects:** Newspaper reference topics. **Holdings:** 900 books; newspaper, 1886 to present, on microfilm. **Subscriptions:** 10 journals and other serials; 5 newspapers. **Services:** Library not open to the public. **Computerized Information Services:** NEXIS, VU/TEXT Information Services, DataTimes, Business Dateline. **Remarks:** FAX: (214)720-6841.

★4572★
Leo A. Daly Company - Alfred A. Yee Division - Library (Sci-Engr)
Honfed Tower, Suite 1000
1357 Kapiolani Blvd. Phone: (808)521-8889
Honolulu, HI 96814 Marian Galola, Libn.
Founded: 1960. **Staff:** Prof 1. **Subjects:** Structural engineering, precast and prestressed concrete, architecture, planning, interior design. **Holdings:** 2500 books; 33 bound periodical volumes; 46 VF drawers of clippings, archives, photographs, manufacturers' literature; slides; maps. **Subscriptions:** 75 journals and other serials; 6 newspapers. **Services:** Library not open to the public; reference services for librarians and qualified researchers. **Computerized Information Services:** DIALOG Information Services. **Special Indexes:** Index of product information (online). **Remarks:** FAX: (808)521-3757.

★4573★
(Damascus) American Cultural Center - USIS Library (Educ)
87 Ata Ayoubi St.
Malki
Post Box 29
Damascus, Syrian Arab Republic
Remarks: Maintained or supported by the U.S. Information Agency. Focus is on materials that will assist peoples outside the United States to learn about the United States, its people, history, culture, political processes, and social milieux.

★4574★
Dames & Moore - Library (Sci-Engr)
911 Wilshire Blvd., Suite 700 Phone: (213)683-0471
Los Angeles, CA 90017 Ann W. Shea, Libn.
Founded: 1966. **Staff:** Prof 1. **Subjects:** Soil mechanics and foundation engineering, oceanography, geology. **Holdings:** 7000 books; 500 pamphlets; 34 VF drawers of pamphlets (uncataloged); 10,000 maps. **Subscriptions:** 200 journals and other serials. **Services:** Interlibrary loan; library not open to the public. **Computerized Information Services:** DIALOG Information Services, PFDS Online, Occupational Health Services, Inc. (OHS). **Networks/Consortia:** Member of CLASS. **Remarks:** FAX: (213)628-0015.

★4575★
Dames & Moore - Library (Sci-Engr)
6 Peidmont Center, Suite 500
3525 Peidmont Rd. Phone: (404)262-2915
Atlanta, GA 30305 Margaret Phelps, Adm.Sec.
Founded: 1974. **Subjects:** Civil engineering, nuclear power plants, meteorology, geology, water resources, biology, environment, pollution. **Holdings:** 3500 books; 150 environmental reports; 4 VF drawers of technical material; 1500 maps. **Subscriptions:** 53 journals and other serials. **Services:** Interlibrary loan; library not open to the public. **Computerized Information Services:** DIALOG Information Services, Georgia Online Database (GOLD). **Remarks:** FAX: (404)233-2271.

★4576★
Dames & Moore - Library (Sci-Engr)
7101 Wisconsin Ave., Suite 700 Phone: (301)652-2215
Bethesda, MD 20814 Anne Darlington, Libn.
Founded: 1975. **Staff:** Prof 1. **Subjects:** Geology, civil engineering, environmental science, toxicology. **Special Collections:** Maps. **Holdings:** 3500 books; 2500 geological survey bulletins and reports. **Subscriptions:** 175 journals and other serials. **Services:** Library not open to the public. **Computerized Information Services:** DIALOG Information Services, TOXNET, Chemical Information Systems, Inc. (CIS), Ground Water On-Line.

★4577★
Dames & Moore - Library (Sci-Engr)
500 Market Place Tower
2025 1st Ave. Phone: (206)728-0744
Seattle, WA 98121 George Draffan, Libn.
Founded: 1968. **Staff:** Prof 1. **Subjects:** Geology, hydrology, fisheries biology, geotechnical engineering, environmental legislation. **Holdings:** 3000 books; 1000 technical reports; maps. **Subscriptions:** 135 journals and other serials. **Services:** Interlibrary loan; library not open to the public. **Automated Operations:** Computerized cataloging. **Computerized Information Services:** DIALOG Information Services, OCLC. **Remarks:** FAX: (206)448-7994.

★4578★
Dames & Moore - Library Services (Sci-Engr)
221 Main St., Suite 600 Phone: (415)896-5858
San Francisco, CA 94105-1917 Julie Italiano, Info.Spec./Libn.
Staff: Prof 1. **Subjects:** Hazardous wastes, geology, civil engineering, economics, earthquakes, earthquake engineering, soils. **Special Collections:** Soil surveys (California); Alquist-Priolo maps (central California); hazardous waste documents and reports (500). **Holdings:** 1000 books; 1200 reports. **Subscriptions:** 40 journals and other serials. **Services:** Interlibrary loan; copying. **Computerized Information Services:** DIALOG Information Services; VAX (internal database). Performs searches on fee basis for Dames & Moore personnel. **Remarks:** FAX: (415)882-9261.

D'Amour Library
See: **Western New England College** (20280)

★4579★
Dan River, Inc. - Research Library (Sci-Engr)
P.O. Box 261
Danville, VA 24541 Phone: (804)799-7103
Subjects: Textiles, organic chemistry. **Holdings:** 1000 books; 300 bound periodical volumes. **Subscriptions:** 50 journals and other serials. **Services:** Library open to the public by appointment.

Dana Biomedical Library
See: **Dartmouth College** (4608)

Charles A. Dana Law Library
See: **Stetson University - College of Law** (15783)

Charles A. Dana Medical Library
See: **University of Vermont - Charles A. Dana Medical Library** (19479)

★4580★
Dana College - C.A. Dana-Life Library (Area-Ethnic, Hum)
College Dr. Phone: (402)426-7301
Blair, NE 68008 Ruth J. Rasmussen, Lib.Dir.
Founded: 1884. **Staff:** Prof 2; Other 3. **Subjects:** Danish literature and language; history; humanities. **Special Collections:** Lauritz Melchior Memorial (records; scores; tapes; scrapbooks; artifacts; paintings). **Holdings:** 148,000 books; microfilm; phonograph records. **Subscriptions:** 534 journals and other serials; 12 newspapers. **Services:** Interlibrary loan; library open to the public. **Automated Operations:** Computerized cataloging. **Computerized Information Services:** OCLC, NeLCMS (Nebraska Libraries Communication System), DIALOG Information Services. **Remarks:** Library is said to have one of the best collections of Danish literature in translation and in the original language in the U.S. FAX: (402)426-7332. **Staff:** Sharon Jensen, Asst.Dir.

★4581★
Dana-Farber Cancer Institute - Professional Staff Library (Med)
44 Binney St. Phone: (617)732-3508
Boston, MA 02115 Christine W. Fleuriel, Libn.
Founded: 1980. **Staff:** Prof 1; Other 1. **Subjects:** Cancer research. **Holdings:** 1400 books; 1500 bound periodical volumes. **Subscriptions:** 110 journals and other serials. **Services:** Interlibrary loan; SDI; library not open to the public. **Computerized Information Services:** NLM, DIALOG Information Services. **Publications:** Centerline (newsletter) - available on request. **Remarks:** FAX: (617)735-8989.

John Cotton Dana Library
See: **Woodstock Historical Society, Inc.** (20580)

Naylor Dana Institute for Disease Prevention
See: **American Health Foundation** (604)

★4582★
Danbury Hospital - Health Sciences Library (Med)
24 Hospital Ave. Phone: (203)797-7279
Danbury, CT 06810 Michael J. Schott, Dir.
Staff: Prof 1; Other 4. **Subjects:** Medicine, nursing, hospitals, allied health sciences. **Holdings:** 3720 books; 5060 bound periodical volumes; 781 AV programs; 2 VF drawers of reports; 40 cases of pamphlets; 12 VF drawers of clippings. **Subscriptions:** 432 journals and other serials. **Services:** Interlibrary loan; copying; SDI; library open to the public for reference use only. **Automated Operations:** Computerized ILL. **Computerized Information Services:** MEDLINE, BRS Information Technologies. Performs searches on fee basis. **Networks/Consortia:** Member of Northwestern Connecticut Health Science Library Consortium (NW-CT-HSL), Connecticut Association of Health Science Libraries (CAHSL). **Publications:** Library Line, monthly.

★4583★
Danbury Scott-Fanton Museum and Historical Society - Library (Hist)
43 Main St. Phone: (203)743-5200
Danbury, CT 06810 Lucye Boland, Dir.
Staff: Prof 1. **Subjects:** Town and state history, genealogy, hat industry and other local industries. **Holdings:** 800 books; 50 bound periodical volumes; manuscripts; diaries; deeds; maps; negatives and prints of local scenes, 1875 to present. **Services:** Copying; library open to the public with restrictions.

★4584★
Dance Films Association, Inc. (Aud-Vis, Theater)
1133 Broadway, Rm. 507 Phone: (212)727-0764
New York, NY 10010 Susan Braun, Exec.Dir.
Founded: 1956. **Subjects:** Dance on film and videotape. **Holdings:** Films on dance. **Services:** Film and videotape projection; film rental library for members - public may purchase most of the films in the library; annual competitive dance film and videotape festival in New York City. **Publications:** News Bulletin, bimonthly - to members. **Special Catalogs:** Dance Film and Video Guide, 1991.

★4585★
Dance Notation Bureau - Library and Archive (Theater)
31-33 W. 21st St., 3rd Fl. Phone: (212)807-7899
New York, NY 10010 Lisa Machlin, Libn.
Founded: 1940. **Staff:** Prof 1. **Subjects:** Dance notation - Labanotation, Benesh Movement, Eshkol-Wachman Movement; Kinetography-Laban; notation theory and reconstruction. **Special Collections:** DNB Archive (332 scores). **Holdings:** 600 books; 3000 scores; 300 videotapes; 400 audiotapes; 50 films; 200 photographs; 1000 other cataloged items. **Services:** Interlibrary loan (limited); copying; library open to the public by appointment. **Special Catalogs:** Notated Theatrical Dances Catalog, irregular - free upon request.

★4586★
Dane County Law Library (Law)
315 City-County Bldg.
210 Martin Luther King Jr. Blvd. Phone: (608)266-6316
Madison, WI 53709 Ann Waidelich, Libn.
Founded: 1957. **Staff:** Prof 1; Other 1. **Subjects:** Law. **Special Collections:** Madison and Dane County government documents. **Holdings:** 8000 volumes. **Subscriptions:** 4 journals and other serials. **Services:** Interlibrary loan; copying; SDI; library open to the public for reference use only. **Computerized Information Services:** LEXIS, NEXIS. **Networks/Consortia:** Member of South Central Library System. **Remarks:** FAX: (608)266-6305.

★4587★
Dane County Regional Planning Commission - Library (Plan)
City-County Bldg., Rm. 523
Madison, WI 53709 Phone: (608)266-4137
Founded: 1964. **Subjects:** Transportation, land use and development, census and population, water resources. **Holdings:** 3900 government reports; 3000 maps. **Subscriptions:** 14 journals and other serials; 110 newsletters. **Services:** Interlibrary loan; library open to the public.

★4588★
Danforth Museum of Art - Marks Fine Arts Library (Art)
123 Union Ave.
Framingham, MA 01701 Phone: (508)620-0050
Founded: 1976. **Subjects:** Art, artists, art history, decorative arts. **Holdings:** 4000 books. **Services:** Copying; fills research requests; library open to the public for reference use only.

D'Angelo Law Library
See: **University of Chicago - D'Angelo Law Library** (18447)

Allen Mercer Daniel Law Library
See: **Howard University** (7471)

Daniel Library
See: **Citadel Military College of South Carolina** (3720)

Lois H. Daniel Memorial Library
See: **Tennessee State University - Lois H. Daniel Memorial Library** (16172)

★4589★
Daniel, Mann, Johnson and Mendenhall - Library (Plan)
3250 Wilshire Blvd. Phone: (213)381-3663
Los Angeles, CA 90010 Mickey Conrad, Mgr., Info.Serv.
Staff: Prof 2. **Subjects:** Area statistics and information; transportation; architecture; planning; recreation; environment; water resources; engineering - civil, structural, mechanical. **Holdings:** 7500 books; 800 maps; 19,000 35mm slides; Transportation Research Board reports. **Subscriptions:** 250 journals and other serials. **Services:** Interlibrary loan; copying; library open to the public for reference use only by appointment. **Publications:** What's New in the DMJM Library. **Remarks:** FAX: (213)383-3656.

★4590★
Danish Association for International Cooperation - Library (Soc Sci)
Landgreven 7 Phone: 33 326244
DK-1301 Copenhagen K, Denmark Helle Leth-Moller, Chf.Libn.
Founded: 1968. **Staff:** 6. **Subjects:** Development - economic, political, social; Third World development. **Holdings:** 32,000 volumes and magazines. **Subscriptions:** 400 journals and other serials. **Services:** Interlibrary loan; copying; SDI; library open to the public. **Computerized Information Services:** Internal databases. **Publications:** MS Biblioteksnyt (Library News); U-Vejviser (Third World Directory). **Remarks:** FAX: 33 156243. Telex: 15928 MS DK. **Also Known As:** Mellemfolkeligt Samvirke. **Staff:** Hanne Tingleff; Vagn Plenge; Thomas Kamp.

Danish Baptist General Conference of America - Archives
See: **American Baptist Historical Society - American Baptist-Samuel Colgate Historical Library** (498)

Danish Federation of Trade Unions
See: **The Labour Movement** (8862)

Danish Fisheries Technology Institute - Documentation Department
See: **Danish Institute for Fisheries Technology and Aquaculture** (4592)

★4591★
Danish Information Office (Area-Ethnic)
Royal Danish Embassy
3200 Whitehaven St., N.W. Phone: (202)234-4300
Washington, DC 20008-3683 Bent Skou, Min./Couns., Hd., Info.
Founded: 1945. **Subjects:** Denmark, Danish society. **Holdings:** Factsheets. **Services:** Office not open to the public, but will respond to telephone and written inquiries. **Remarks:** Alternate telephone number(s): 797-5300. FAX: (202)328-1470.

★4592★
Danish Institute for Fisheries Technology and Aquaculture - Library (Biol Sci)
North Sea Centre
P.O. Box 93 Phone: 9 8944300
DK-9850 Hirtshals, Denmark Thorkild Pedersen, Libn.
Staff: 1. **Subjects:** Fishery topics - fishery biology, fishing gear, fishing methods, economic and marketing analyses, marine biology, aquaculture. **Holdings:** 4000 books. **Subscriptions:** 264 journals and other serials. **Computerized Information Services:** Online systems; produces FISHLINE. Performs searches on fee basis. **Remarks:** FAX: 9 8942226. Telex: 67 757 FTI DK. **Formerly:** Danish Fisheries Technology Institute - Documentation Department.

The Danish Veterinary and Agricultural Library
See: **The Royal Veterinary and Agricultural University** (14139)

Danmarks Biblioteksskoles Bibliotek
See: **Royal School of Librarianship** (14133)

Danmarks Geologiske Undersogelse
See: **Geological Survey of Denmark** (6365)

Danmarks Paedagogiske Bibliotek - Danmarks Laererhosjskole
See: **Denmark - National Library of Education - The Royal Danish School of Educational Studies** (4766)

Danmarks Tekniske Bibliotek
See: **Denmark - National Technological Library of Denmark** (4767)

★4593★
Danny Foundation - Library (Med)
3160F Danville Blvd.
P.O. Box 680 Phone: (415)833-2669
Alamo, CA 94507 Jack Walsh
Founded: 1987. **Subjects:** Crib safety, juvenile products. **Holdings:** 170 bound periodical volumes. **Subscriptions:** 7 journals and other serials; 2 newspapers. **Services:** Library open to the public.

★4594★
Danville Public Library (Hist)
511 Patton St. Phone: (804)799-5195
Danville, VA 24541 Denise Johnson
Founded: 1928. **Staff:** Prof 5; Other 12. **Subjects:** Local genealogy, local history. **Holdings:** 115,105 books; 49,394 microform. **Subscriptions:** 165 journals and other serials; 18 newspapers. **Services:** Interlibrary loan; copying; open to the public with restrictions. **Remarks:** FAX: (804)799-5221.

★4595★
Danville Public Library - Archives (Hist)
307 N. Vermilion St. Phone: (217)446-7420
Danville, IL 61832 Roberta D. Allen, Dir.Ref./Dir.Archv.
Founded: 1883. **Staff:** 1. **Subjects:** East Central Illinois and West Central Indiana genealogy; Vermilion County history. **Holdings:** 3000 books; 100 bound periodical volumes; 1610 unbound periodical volumes; 811 reels of microfilm; 1095 nonbook items. **Subscriptions:** 12 journals and other serials. **Services:** Interlibrary loan; copying; archives open to the public for reference use only. **Networks/Consortia:** Member of ILLINET, Lincoln Trail Libraries System (LTLS). **Remarks:** FAX: (217)446-0865. Alternate telephone number(s): (217)446-9725.

Danzvardis Consular Archive
See: **Lithuanian Research and Studies Center, Inc. - Lithuanian World Archives, Inc.** (9212)

★4596★
DAP Inc. - Technical Library (Sci-Engr)
Box 277 Phone: (513)667-4461
Dayton, OH 45401-0277 Frances S. Repperger, Tech.Info.Coord.
Founded: 1981. **Staff:** 1. **Subjects:** Adhesives, sealants, coatings, wood preservatives, building construction, chemistry, microbiology. **Special Collections:** Test methods; raw materials; industry and government specifications. **Holdings:** 5000 books; reports; patents; specifications; archives; microfiche. **Subscriptions:** 100 journals and other serials. **Services:** Interlibrary loan; library not open to the public. **Computerized Information Services:** DIALOG Information Services, ORBIT Search Service, STN International, Dow Jones News/Retrieval, NLM, OCLC EPIC, NPIRS (National Pesticide Information Retrieval System). **Remarks:** FAX: (513)254-1672.

★4597★
Dar America Casablanca - USIS Library (Educ)
10, Place Bel Air Phone: 2221460
Casablanca, Morocco Mina Jaouad, Chf.Libn.
Founded: 1982. **Staff:** 2. **Holdings:** Books; bound periodical volumes; videotapes. **Subscriptions:** 36 journals and other serials. **Services:** Interlibrary loan; library open to the public. **Remarks:** FAX: 204127. **Remarks:** Maintained or supported by the U.S. Information Agency. Focus is on materials that will assist peoples outside the United States to learn about the United States, its people, history, culture, political processes, and social milieux.

★4598★
Dar America Marrakech - USIS Library (Educ)
Avenue Chouhada
L'Hivernage
Marrakech, Morocco
Remarks: Maintained or supported by the U.S. Information Agency. Focus is on materials that will assist peoples outside the United States to learn about the United States, its people, history, culture, political processes, and social milieux.

★4599★
Dar America Rabat - USIS Library (Educ)
35 Avenue Al Fahs
Rabat-Souissi
Rabat, Morocco
Remarks: Maintained or supported by the U.S. Information Agency. Focus is on materials that will assist peoples outside the United States to learn about the United States, its people, history, culture, political processes, and social milieux.

★4600★
(Dar es Salaam) American Center - USIS Library (Educ)
Samora Ave.
P.O. Box 9170
Dar es Salaam, United Republic of Tanzania
Remarks: Maintained or supported by the U.S. Information Agency. Focus is on materials that will assist peoples outside the United States to learn about the United States, its people, history, culture, political processes, and social milieux.

★4601★
William O. Darby Ranger Memorial Foundation, Inc. - Library (Hist)
Box 1625 Phone: (501)782-3388
Fort Smith, AK 72902 Emory S. Dockery, Jr., Exec.Dir.
Founded: 1977. **Staff:** 1. **Subjects:** William O. Darby, Rangers. **Special Collections:** Personal items of General Darby and his parents. **Holdings:** 1500 items. **Services:** Copying; library open to the public. **Remarks:** Library located at 311 General Darby St. FAX: (501)783-7590.

★4602★
D'Arcy Masius Benton & Bowles - Information Center (Bus-Fin)
1725 N. Woodward Ave.
P.O. Box 811 Phone: (313)258-8533
Bloomfield Hills, MI 48303 Rita Rochlen, Dir.
Founded: 1952. **Staff:** Prof 3; Other 4. **Subjects:** Marketing, advertising. **Holdings:** 8000 books; 200,000 pictures. **Subscriptions:** 500 journals and other serials; 8 newspapers. **Services:** Copying (limited). **Automated Operations:** Computerized circulation. **Computerized Information Services:** DIALOG Information Services, Mead Data Central. **Publications:** What's New - for internal distribution only. **Formerly:** Its Library Information Services. **Staff:** Harriet Siden, Libn.; Suzanne Lichtman, Libn.

★4603★
D'Arcy Masius Benton & Bowles - Information Center (Bus-Fin)
1 Memorial Dr. Phone: (314)622-9425
St. Louis, MO 63102 Jean Kammer, Libn.
Staff: Prof 2; Other 2. **Subjects:** Advertising. **Holdings:** 750 volumes; 375 VF drawers of pamphlets and clippings. **Subscriptions:** 750 journals and other serials. **Remarks:** FAX: (314)342-3584.

Colgate Darden Graduate School of Business Administration
See: **University of Virginia** (19501)

★4604★
E.C. Dargan Research Library (Rel-Phil)
127 Ninth Ave., N. Phone: (615)251-2133
Nashville, TN 37234 Howard Gallimore, Mgr.
Founded: 1933. **Staff:** Prof 4; Other 5. **Subjects:** Baptist church, religious education, religion, theology. **Holdings:** 37,580 books; 1100 feet of archival material. **Subscriptions:** 594 journals and other serials; 9 newspapers. **Services:** Interlibrary loan; copying; library open to the public for reference use only. **Computerized Information Services:** Datadex (internal database). **Networks/Consortia:** Member of SOLINET. **Publications:** Selected Guide to Archival and Manuscript Collections in the Dargan-Carver Library, 1984. **Remarks:** Maintained by Southern Baptist Convention - Sunday School Board. FAX: (615)251-3866. **Staff:** Elaine Bryant, Cat./Acq.Libn.; Janice Lampley, Spec.Proj.Libn.; Ray Minardi, Archv./Res.Libn.; Kevin Jarrell, AV Spec.

★4605★
Darien Historical Society - Library (Hist)
45 Old Kings Hwy., N.
Darien, CT 06829 Phone: (203)655-9233
Staff: 1. **Subjects:** Local history. **Special Collections:** Darien archival collection (account books; diaries; photographs). **Holdings:** 1200 books; 20 linear feet, 60 boxes, and 2 file cases of other cataloged items. **Services:** Copying; library open to the public.

★4606★
Dark Shadows Fan Club - Library (Rec)
P.O. Box 69A04
West Hollywood, CA 90069 Phone: (213)650-5112
Subjects: Dark Shadows television series. **Holdings:** 1000 volumes; photographs.

Ira C. Darling Center Library
See: **University of Maine** (18777)

Louise Darling Biomedical Library
See: **University of California, Los Angeles - Louise Darling Biomedical Library** (18390)

Roger Darling Memorial Library
See: **Ashland Theological Seminary** (1113)

Samuel Taylor Darling Memorial Library
See: **Gorgas Army Community Hospital** (6579)

★4607★
Darlington County Historical Commission - Darlington County Archives (Hist)
104 Hewitt St. Phone: (803)398-4710
Darlington, SC 29532 Horace Fraser Rudisill, Hist.
Staff: 2. **Subjects:** Local history and genealogy. **Holdings:** Books; documents; pamphlets; journals; early county court records. **Services:** Copying; library open to the public. **Special Indexes:** Index to church and land record groups (card and notebook).

Darlington Memorial Library
See: **University of Pittsburgh** (19209)

William Darlington Library
See: **West Chester University - Francis Harvey Green Library** (20186)

Darnall Army Hospital
See: **U.S. Army Hospitals** (17039)

William L. Darnall Library
See: **U.S. Navy - National Naval Medical Command - Naval Dental School - National Naval Dental Clinic** (17806)

★4608★
Dartmouth College - Dana Biomedical Library (Med)
Dartmouth-Hitchcock Medical Ctr. Phone: (603)650-7658
Hanover, NH 03756 Daniel T. Richards, Libn.
Founded: 1797. **Staff:** Prof 9; Other 10. **Subjects:** Medicine, life sciences, nursing, agriculture. **Special Collections:** Conner Collection of Rare Medical Classics; Raymond Pearl Longevity Collection; Henry A. Schroeder papers (11,281 items); Henry Kumm Index on Poliomyelitis and Tropical Medicine; Dartmouth Medical School Eye Institute Reprint File. **Holdings:** 195,220 volumes; Dartmouth Medical School faculty reprints; 6601 AV programs; microforms; subject pamphlets; dissertations. **Subscriptions:** 3036 journals and other serials. **Services:** Interlibrary loan; copying; SDI; library open to the public. **Automated Operations:** Computerized cataloging, acquisitions, and serials. **Computerized Information Services:** OCLC, MEDLINE, DIALOG Information Services, BRS Information Technologies, RLIN. Performs searches on fee basis. **Networks/Consortia:** Member of National Network of Libraries of Medicine (NN/LM), NELINET, Inc., Research Libraries Information Network (RLIN). **Publications:** Dana Nurse Interface; Dana Interface, monthly - free upon request. **Special Catalogs:** AV catalog (online). **Remarks:** FAX: (603)650-8683. **Staff:** Thomas Mead; Frederick Pond; Constance Rinaldo; Sheila Gorman; Cynthia Taylor; Margaret Mout seous; Marjorie Westerfield.

★4609★
Dartmouth College - Feldberg Library (Bus-Fin, Sci-Engr, Biol Sci)
Hanover, NH 03755 Phone: (603)646-2191
James R. Fries, Libn.
Founded: 1972. **Staff:** Prof 4; Other 5. **Subjects:** Business administration and management; engineering - biomedical, electrical, mechanical; environmental/natural resource systems analysis and policy design; cold regions science and engineering; computer applications and information systems. **Special Collections:** Thayer Collection (books in mathematics, civil engineering, and military engineering donated by General Thayer; 1565 volumes). **Holdings:** 101,328 volumes; 7626 reels of microfilm; 779,416 microfiche. **Subscriptions:** 2803 journals and other serials. **Services:** Interlibrary loan; copying; library open to the public. **Automated Operations:** Computerized cataloging, acquisitions, and serials. **Computerized Information Services:** DIALOG Information Services, PFDS Online, BRS Information Technologies, Integrated Technical Information System (ITIS), OCLC, NEXIS, Dow Jones News/Retrieval. **Remarks:** FAX: (603)646-2384. **Staff:** Jonathan Brown; Karen Sluzenski; Bette Snyder.

★4610★
Dartmouth College - Kresge Physical Sciences Library (Sci-Engr)
Hanover, NH 03755 Phone: (603)646-3563
Susan C. George, Libn.
Founded: 1974. **Staff:** Prof 3; Other 3. **Subjects:** Chemistry, earth sciences, physics, astronomy, climatology. **Holdings:** 99,466 volumes. **Subscriptions:** 1633 journals and other serials. **Services:** Interlibrary loan (fee); copying; library open to the public. **Automated Operations:** Computerized cataloging, acquisitions, and serials. **Computerized Information Services:** OCLC, DIALOG Information Services, BRS Information Technologies, Questel, DARC Pluridata System (DPDS). **Networks/Consortia:** Member of NELINET, Inc., Research Libraries Information Network (RLIN). **Remarks:** FAX: (603)646-3681. **Staff:** Barbara DeFelice.

★4611★
Dartmouth College - Map Section (Geog-Map, Sci-Engr)
Baker Library Phone: (603)646-2579
Hanover, NH 03755 John F. Berthelsen, Spec.Subj.Asst.
Founded: 1946. **Staff:** 1. **Subjects:** Topography, geology, oceanography, local history, historical cartography, New England. **Special Collections:** New Hampshire; polar regions; Soviet Russia. **Holdings:** 159,732 maps; 3200 reference books and atlases; 28 globes; 560 relief models; 285 aerial photographs; 300 rolled wall maps; pre-1900 maps and atlases; nautical charts. **Subscriptions:** 15 journals and other serials. **Services:** Interlibrary loan; copying; section open to the public. **Automated Operations:** Computerized cataloging, acquisitions, and serials. **Computerized Information Services:** DIALOG Information Services, BRS Information Technologies, OCLC. **Networks/Consortia:** Member of NELINET, Inc., Research Libraries Information Network (RLIN). **Publications:** A Guide to the Map Room; List of Known Maps of New Hampshire to 1800. **Remarks:** FAX: (603)646-2167. Library serves as a Map Depository for the Defense Mapping Agency, the U.S. Geological Survey, the Canadian Department of Energy, Mines and Resources, and U.S. Government publications.

★4612★
Dartmouth College - Oriental Collection (Area-Ethnic)
Baker Library
Hanover, NH 03755 Phone: (603)646-3605
Staff: 1. **Subjects:** East Asia - history, literature, philosophy, religion, language, bibliography (in Chinese and Japanese). **Special Collections:** Complete set of Ku Chin T'u Shu Chi Cheng of the Ching dynasty (2000 volumes in 200 Orient wrapped cases). **Holdings:** 60,000 volumes. **Subscriptions:** 63 journals and other serials. **Services:** Interlibrary loan; copying; SDI; collection open to the public with restrictions. **Automated Operations:** Computerized cataloging and serials. **Computerized Information Services:** RLIN; BITNET (electronic mail service). **Networks/Consortia:** Member of Research Libraries Information Network (RLIN), NELINET, Inc. **Remarks:** FAX: (603)646-2167.

★4613★
Dartmouth College - Paddock Music Library (Mus)
Hanover, NH 03755 Phone: (603)646-3234
Patricia B. Fisken, Libn.
Founded: 1975. **Staff:** Prof 1; Other 2. **Subjects:** Music. **Holdings:** 47,559 books and scores; 15,448 phonograph records. **Subscriptions:** 264 journals and other serials. **Services:** Interlibrary loan; copying; library open to the public for reference use only. **Automated Operations:** Computerized cataloging, acquisitions, and serials. **Computerized Information Services:** DIALOG Information Services, BRS Information Technologies, OCLC. **Networks/Consortia:** Member of NELINET, Inc., Research Libraries Information Network (RLIN). **Remarks:** FAX: (603)646-1219.

★4614★
Dartmouth College - Sanborn House English Library (Hum)
Hanover, NH 03755 Phone: (603)646-2312
Founded: 1929. **Staff:** 1. **Subjects:** English and American literature. **Special Collections:** Shakespeare collection; spoken word phonograph record collection; works by English-American poets published since 1912 (1500 volumes). **Holdings:** 6986 books; 433 sound recordings. **Subscriptions:** 42 journals and other serials. **Services:** Library open to the public. **Automated Operations:** Computerized cataloging, acquisitions, and serials. **Computerized Information Services:** DIALOG Information Services, BRS Information Technologies, OCLC. **Networks/Consortia:** Member of NELINET, Inc., Research Libraries Information Network (RLIN). **Staff:** Gloria Densmore, Br.Lib.Adm.Asst.

★4615★
Dartmouth College - Sherman Art Library (Art)
Carpenter Hall Phone: (603)646-2305
Hanover, NH 03755 Barbara Reed, Libn.
Staff: Prof 1; Other 3. **Subjects:** Art, architecture, photography. **Holdings:** 77,826 volumes. **Subscriptions:** 512 journals and other serials. **Services:** Interlibrary loan; library open to the public with restrictions. **Automated Operations:** Computerized cataloging, acquisitions, and serials. **Computerized Information Services:** DIALOG Information Services, BRS Information Technologies, OCLC. **Networks/Consortia:** Member of NELINET, Inc., Research Libraries Information Network (RLIN). **Remarks:** FAX: (603)646-1218.

★4616★
Dartmouth College - Special Collections (Hum, Hist, Publ)
Dartmouth College Library Phone: (603)646-2037
Hanover, NH 03755 Philip N. Cronenwett, Spec.Coll.Libn.
Staff: Prof 3; Other 7. **Subjects:** American calligraphy; bookplates; broadsides; Dartmouth Archives and local history; Abenaki Indians; Don Quixote; American, English, French, and German plays; George Ticknor; Great Awakening; Hanover genealogy; movie scripts; New England illustrated books, 1769-1869; New England railroads; New Hampshire history and imprints; Polar regions and explorers; private presses; sheet music; Spanish civilization and plays; theater (primarily American); White Mountains. **Holdings:** Vilhjalmur Stefansson correspondence and papers; principal collection of works by and about authors and statesmen - Sherman Adams, Josiah Bartlett, Robert P. Bass, Rupert Brooke, Robert Burns, Witter Bynner, Erskine Caldwell, Salmon P. Chase, Rufus Choate, Winston Churchill (American novelist), Grenville Clark, Joseph Conrad, Stephen Crane, Silas Dinsmore, Richard Eberhart, Corey Ford, Robert Frost, John Galsworthy, Robert Bontine Cunninghame Graham, Ramon Guthrie, John P. Hale, James G. Huneker, Aldous Huxley, J.J. Lankes, T.E. Lawrence, E.V. Lucas, Benton, Percy, Steele MacKaye, David McClure, Herman Melville, H.L. Mencken, Henry Miller, Eugene O'Neill, Kenneth Roberts, Count Rumford, Rudolph Ruzicka, Augustus Saint Gaudens, William Shakespeare, Wallace Stevens, Genevieve Taggard, Isaiah Thomas, Charles W. Tobey, Daniel Webster, Eleazar Wheelock, Weeks family of Lancaster, NH, Nathaniel Whitaker, Ben Ames Williams, Levi Woodbury, Charles A. Young. **Services:** Copying; collections open to the public. **Automated Operations:** Computerized cataloging, acquisitions, and serials. **Computerized Information Services:** OCLC. **Networks/Consortia:** Member of NELINET, Inc., Research Libraries Information Network (RLIN). **Publications:** Resource guides; microform publications. **Remarks:** FAX: (603)646-3702. **Staff:** Kenneth C. Cramer, Coll.Archv.; Stanley W. Brown, Cur. of Rare Bks.

★4617★
Dartnell Corporation - Publishing-Research Library (Publ)
4660 N. Ravenswood Ave. Phone: (312)561-4000
Chicago, IL 60640 Juanita Roberts, Libn.
Founded: 1963. **Staff:** Prof 1. **Subjects:** Publishing, salesmanship, sales management, customer service, direct mail, human resources. **Holdings:** 2700 volumes. **Subscriptions:** 475 journals and other serials; 11 newspapers. **Services:** Interlibrary loan; copying; library open to the public on request.

Darwin Library
See: **University of Cambridge - Library** (18441)

★4618★
Darwinian Institute of Botany - Library (Biol Sci)
Labarden 200
Casilla Correo 22 Phone: 1 7474748
1642 San Isidro, Argentina Elena Silnicky De Vizer, Libn.
Founded: 1912. **Staff:** Prof 3. **Subjects:** Argentine flora, systematic botany, phytogeography, plant anatomy and cytogenetics, palynology. **Holdings:** 50,000 volumes. **Subscriptions:** 655 journals and other serials. **Services:** Interlibrary loan; copying; library open to students, scientists, and professionals. **Computerized Information Services:** InterNet (electronic mail service). **Remarks:** Alternate telephone number(s): 1 7434800. FAX: 1 7474748. Electronic mail address(es): POSTMASTER@IBODA.EDU.AR (InterNet). Affiliated with the National Academy of Sciences of Buenos Aires and the National Council of Scientific and Technical Research. **Also Known As:** Instituto de Botanica "Darwinion." **Staff:** Nelly E. Werner de Zanlongo.

Data Center on Atomic Transition Probabilities
See: **U.S. Natl. Institute of Standards and Technology** (17615)

★4619★
Data General Corporation - Corporate Library (Sci-Engr, Comp Sci)
4400 Computer Dr., M.S. C-236 Phone: (508)870-5825
Westborough, MA 01580 Cheryl Cove, Sr.Res.Libn.
Founded: 1977. **Staff:** Prof 1. **Subjects:** Computer science, engineering, mathematics, business. **Holdings:** 2500 books. **Subscriptions:** 250 journals and other serials; 10 newspapers. **Services:** Interlibrary loan; library not open to the public. **Computerized Information Services:** OCLC, DIALOG, Mead Data Central; CD-ROM (Lotus One Source, INSPEC Ondisc, Faulkner Technical Reports Infodisk, Computer Library). **Networks/Consortia:** Member of NELINET, Inc. **Publications:** Newsletter.

★4620★
Data Memory Systems, Inc. - Historical Evaluation & Research (HERO) Library (Mil)
10366-B Democracy Ln. Phone: (703)591-3674
Fairfax, VA 22030 Brian R. Bader, Libn.
Founded: 1962. **Staff:** Prof 5. **Subjects:** Military history, Middle East wars. **Special Collections:** Weiner Collection (military law). **Holdings:** 1900 books. **Subscriptions:** 10 journals and other serials. **Services:** Interlibrary loan; library not open to the public. **Remarks:** FAX: (703)591-6109.

★4621★
Data Systems Analysts Inc. - Technical Library (Comp Sci)
4300 Haddonfield Rd. Phone: (609)665-6088
Pennsauken, NJ 08109 Elizabeth Colabrese, Libn.
Staff: Prof 1. **Subjects:** Data processing, data communications, computer programming, computer networks, telecommunications. **Holdings:** 3500 books; 1000 bound periodical volumes; 35 VF drawers of computer manuals; 80 VF drawers of reports. **Subscriptions:** 90 journals and other serials. **Services:** Interlibrary loan; library not open to the public. **Computerized Information Services:** DIALOG Information Services. **Remarks:** FAX: (609)665-6672.

★4622★
DataCenter (Bus-Fin)
464 19th St. Phone: (510)835-4692
Oakland, CA 94612 Ruth Sill, Act.Libn.
Founded: 1977. **Staff:** Prof 6; Other 6. **Subjects:** Corporations, labor, national and international economies, industry, military, Latin America, human rights. **Holdings:** 3500 books; 140 VF drawers of files on 15,000 corporations; 260 VF drawers of public interest and public policy issues files; 145,000 articles on Latin America. **Subscriptions:** 350 journals and other serials; 40 newspapers. **Services:** Copying; center open to the public on fee basis. **Automated Operations:** Computerized public access catalog (MELVYL). **Computerized Information Services:** DIALOG Information Services, DataTimes, NEXIS, TOXNET, PeaceNet; Data Center File Indexes (internal database). Performs searches on fee basis. Contact Person: Andy Kivel, Search Serv. **Publications:** ISLA (Information Services Latin America), monthly; Corporate Responsibility Monitor, bimonthly - all by subscription; press profiles and updates; corporate profiles. **Special Catalogs:** Periodical catalog. **Special Indexes:** Files indexes. **Remarks:** FAX: (510)835-3017. **Staff:** Nancy Gruber; Zoia Horn; Leon Sompolinsky; Andy Kivell.

★4623★
DataChase Inc. - Library (Bus-Fin)
500 Market St.
Portsmouth, NH 03801 Phone: (800)852-0258
Subjects: Business information - areas, companies, industries, markets, products, emerging technologies. **Holdings:** 2000 books; data base documentation. **Subscriptions:** 20 journals and other serials. **Computerized Information Services:** Online systems; internal database; MCI Mail (electronic mail service). Performs searches on fee basis. **Remarks:** FAX: (312)943-8707. Toll-free telephone number(s): (800)852-0258. Telex: WUI 6501721928 MCI. Electronic mail address(es): DATACHASE (MCI Mail).

DATANET
See: **Minnesota State Department of Administration - DATANET** (10476)

★4624★
Dataque International - Technical Information Center (Sci-Engr, Food-Bev)
P.O. Box 11177
Chicago, IL 60611-0177 Andrew Bickers, V.P.
Staff: Prof 3; Other 2. **Subjects:** Chemistry, food technology, engineering, trend analysis, toxicology, business. **Holdings:** Business periodicals; online files; clippings files. **Services:** Interlibrary loan; copying; SDI. **Computerized Information Services:** DIALOG Information Services, PFDS Online, NLM; DATAQUE (internal database). Performs searches on fee basis. Contact Person: Dan Drazen, Tech.Serv.Mgr. **Publications:** Echofacts (trend analysis newsletter) - to clients. **Special Indexes:** Index of food technology patents (online); indexes of issues management topics and current searches. **Remarks:** FAX: (312)944-6708. **Staff:** Rosalie Alicea, Doc.Anl.; Ramesh Dadlani, Doc.Anl.

★4625★
Dataquest - Information Resource Center (Comp Sci)
1290 Ridder Park Dr. Phone: (408)437-8600
San Jose, CA 95131 Susan M. Waldstein, Corp.Libn.
Founded: 1986. **Staff:** 4. **Subjects:** Computers, peripherals, telecommunications, semiconductors. **Special Collections:** High tech company financial reports. **Holdings:** 700 reports. **Subscriptions:** 500 journals and other serials. **Services:** Library not open to the public. **Computerized Information Services:** DIALOG Information Services, NEXIS, LEXIS, Dow Jones News/Retrieval, NewsNet, Inc., Data-Star, Questel; CompuServe Information Service, DIALMAIL (electronic mail services). **Remarks:** A Dun & Bradstreet Company. FAX: (408)437-0292. Telex: 171973. **Remarks:** FAX: (408)437-0292. **Formerly:** Its Library. **Staff:** Ann Anderson; Patty Grimm.

★4626★
Datasonics, Inc. - Library (Sci-Engr)
1400 Rte. 28A
P.O. Box 8 Phone: (508)563-9311
Cataumet, MA 02534 Margo Newcomb, Sales Coord.
Subjects: Acoustics, sediment dynamics, environmental remote sensing, acoustic fish stock assessment. **Holdings:** 200 books; 300 reports. **Subscriptions:** 20 journals and other serials. **Services:** Library not open to the public.

★4627★
Datatape Incorporated - Library (Sci-Engr)
360 Sierra Madre Villa
P.O. Bin 7014 Phone: (818)796-9381
Pasadena, CA 91109-2934 Sharon Bullers, Mgr., Lib.Serv.
Founded: 1953. **Staff:** 1. **Subjects:** Chemistry, physics, electronics, photography, business, instrumentation, recording methods, mathematics. **Holdings:** 8000 books; 100 bound periodical volumes; 8000 technical reports. **Subscriptions:** 102 journals and other serials. **Services:** Interlibrary loan; copying; library open to the public for limited use on request. **Remarks:** Datatape Incorporated is a subsidiary of Eastman Kodak Company.

Daughters of the American Revolution
See: **National Society, Daughters of the American Revolution** (11289)

★4628★
Daughters of the Republic of Texas - Library (Hist)
Box 1401 Phone: (512)225-1071
San Antonio, TX 78295-1401 Ann Fears Crawford, Ph.D., Dir.
Founded: 1945. **Staff:** Prof 4; Other 3. **Subjects:** History - Texas Republic, Alamo, San Antonio, Texas. **Special Collections:** William E. Howard Collection; Theodore Gentilz Collection; John W. Smith Collection; Bustillo Collection; Cassiano-Perez Collection; Spanish Kings and Viceroys; John James Collection; Grandjean Photograph Collection. **Holdings:** 17,500 books; 2500 manuscripts and archival materials; 250 feet of clippings; 50 reels of microfilm; 30,000 photographs; 1000 maps. **Subscriptions:** 65 journals and other serials. **Services:** Copying; library open to the public for research only. **Networks/Consortia:** Member of Council of Research & Academic Libraries (CORAL). **Publications:** Library brochure. **Remarks:** Alternate telephone number(s): 225-8155. **Staff:** Martha Utterback, Asst.Dir.; Jeannette Phinney, Libn.

★4629★
Daughters of Union Veterans of the Civil War - National Headquarters Library & Museum (Hist)
503 S. Walnut St. Phone: (217)544-0616
Springfield, IL 62704 Vivian Gertz, Natl.Treas.
Staff: Prof 1. **Subjects:** Civil War. **Holdings:** Paintings; glass windows; Civil War guns. **Services:** Library open to the public on limited schedule and by appointment.

★4630★
Dauphin County Historical Society - Archives/Library/Museum (Hist)
219 S. Front St. Phone: (717)233-3462
Harrisburg, PA 17104 Warren W. Wirebach, Libn.
Founded: 1869. **Staff:** 1. **Subjects:** Local history and genealogy, Civil War. **Special Collections:** Simon Cameron papers (2 drawers of microfilm); Bucher papers; Rev. John Elder papers; Joseph Wallace papers; Kelker Collection; DeWitt papers; Charles C. Rawn papers; Zuckerman Photograph Collection; McFarland photographs. **Holdings:** 500 books; 150 bound periodical volumes; 500 manuscripts; 500 patents. **Services:** Library open to the public. **Staff:** Christopher Fritsch, Archv.

★4631★
Dauphin County Law Library (Law)
Dauphin County Court House
Front & Market Sts. Phone: (717)255-2797
Harrisburg, PA 17101 Tracey E. Gill, Libn.
Founded: 1865. **Staff:** 2. **Subjects:** Law. **Holdings:** 34,000 volumes. **Subscriptions:** 7 newspapers. **Services:** Copying; library open to the public for reference use only.

★4632★
(Davao City) USIS Library (Educ)
Davao City Chamber of Commerce Bldg.
J.P. Laurel Ave. Phone: 82 63533
Davao City 8000, Philippines Frank Whitaker
Founded: 1949. **Staff:** 2. **Subjects:** Americana. **Special Collections:** Study in the U.S. **Holdings:** 5000 books; 3000 microfiche; 461 video recordings; 2500 pamphlets; 400 school catalogs. **Subscriptions:** 62 journals and other serials; 5 newspapers. **Services:** Copying; SDI; library open to the public with restrictions. **Remarks:** FAX: 82 62858. Maintained or supported by the U.S. Information Agency. Focus is on materials that will assist peoples outside the United States to learn about the United States, its people, history, culture, political processes, and social milieux. **Staff:** Robert E. Asense, Libn.

Chalmer Davee Library
See: **University of Wisconsin--River Falls** (19647)

★4633★
Davenport College - Kalamazoo Branch - Thomas F. Reed Memorial Library (Bus-Fin)
4123 W. Main St. Phone: (616)382-2835
Kalamazoo, MI 49007 Judith J. Bosshart, Dir.
Founded: 1981. **Staff:** Prof 2; Other 4. **Subjects:** Business, data processing, administrative services, travel, tourism, accounting, humanities. **Holdings:** 7000 books; 17,500 microfiche; 475 videotapes. **Subscriptions:** 325 journals and other serials; 8 newspapers. **Services:** Interlibrary loan; copying; library open to the public for reference use only. **Automated Operations:** Computerized cataloging and circulation. **Computerized Information Services:** LEXIS, NEXIS. **Networks/Consortia:** Member of Southwest Michigan Library Network (SMLN), Michigan Library Consortium (MLC). **Special Catalogs:** Audio-visual catalog. **Remarks:** FAX: (616)382-3541. **Formerly:** Davenport College of Business. **Staff:** Yun-Huei Huang; Joseph Salamun.

★4634★
Davenport Medical Center - Medical Staff Library (Med)
1111 W. Kimberly Rd. Phone: (319)383-0243
Davenport, IA 52806 Julia Hopewell
Staff: Prof 1. **Subjects:** Medicine, nursing, hospital administration. **Holdings:** 350 books; 250 bound periodical volumes; 200 AV titles. **Subscriptions:** 53 journals and other serials. **Services:** Interlibrary loan; copying; SDI; library open to the public by appointment. **Computerized Information Services:** NLM. Performs searches on fee basis. **Networks/Consortia:** Member of Quad City Area Biomedical Consortium, National Network of Libraries of Medicine - Greater Midwest Region. **Remarks:** FAX: (319)383-0243.

★4635★
Davenport Museum of Art - Research Library (Art)
1737 W. 12th St. Phone: (319)326-7804
Davenport, IA 52804 Sheryl Haut, Libn.
Founded: 1925. **Staff:** Prof 1. **Subjects:** Art history, American art. **Holdings:** 5000 books; 5000 pamphlets. **Subscriptions:** 20 journals and other serials. **Services:** Copying; library open to the public. **Automated Operations:** Computerized cataloging. **Remarks:** FAX: (319)326-7736.

★4636★
David Library of the American Revolution (Hist)
River Rd., Rte. 32
Box 748 Phone: (215)493-6776
Washington Crossing, PA 18977 David J. Fowler, Res.Dir./Acq.Libn.
Founded: 1959. **Staff:** Prof 3; Other 2. **Subjects:** American History, 1750-1800. **Special Collections:** Sol Feinstone Collection of the American Revolution (original letters and manuscripts). **Holdings:** 3500 books; 10,000 reels of microfilm. **Subscriptions:** 25 journals and other serials. **Services:** Copying; library open to the public. **Special Catalogs:** Abstracts of New Jersey Manuscripts in Sol Feinstone Collection (book); Guide to the Sol Feinstone Manuscript Collection; guide to microform holdings - free upon request. **Special Indexes:** Index to microfilm edition of Sol Feinstone Collection (book).

★4637★
Charles Davidoff Association - Library (Sci-Engr)
5 Secatoag Ave. Phone: (516)883-3700
Port Washington, NY 11050 Charles Davidoff
Subjects: Electroplating, chemistry, metallurgy, waste disposal. **Holdings:** 200 books; 500 reports. **Subscriptions:** 15 journals and other serials. **Services:** Library not open to the public.

John W. Davies Library
See: **Canada's Sports Hall of Fame** (2890)

★4638★
Davies Medical Center - O.W. Jones Medical Library (Med)
Castro & Duboce St. Phone: (415)565-6352
San Francisco, CA 94114 Anne Shew, Med.Libn.
Staff: Prof 1. **Subjects:** Biomedical sciences. **Holdings:** 1200 books; 4600 bound periodical volumes; 208 audio cassettes; 135 videotapes. **Subscriptions:** 152 journals and other serials. **Services:** Interlibrary loan; library not open to the public. **Automated Operations:** Computerized cataloging, serials, and circulation. **Computerized Information Services:** MEDLARS, DIALOG Information Services, PFDS Online; DOCLINE (electronic mail service). **Networks/Consortia:** Member of National Network of Libraries of Medicine - Pacific Southwest Region, San Francisco Biomedical Library Network. **Publications:** Acquisitions list, irregular; serials holdings - available on request; bibliographies - available on request. **Remarks:** Alternate telephone number(s): (415)565-6779.

Robertson Davies Library
See: **Massey College - Robertson Davies Library** (9839)

★4639★
Davies, Ward & Beck - Library (Law)
One First Canadian Place, 43rd Fl.
P.O. Box 63 Phone: (416)863-0900
Toronto, ON, Canada M5X 1B1 Marla Sterritt, Libn.
Staff: 4. **Subjects:** Law. **Holdings:** Figures not available. **Services:** Interlibrary loan; library not open to the public. **Computerized Information Services:** Internal database. **Remarks:** FAX: (416)863-0871. **Staff:** Jane Freeman.

Davis Centre Library
See: **University of Waterloo** (19544)

★4640★
Chester Davis Memorial Library (Rec)
5121 Park Blvd. Phone: (609)522-2569
Wildwood, NJ 08260-0121 Glenn W. Dye
Founded: 1950. **Staff:** 1. **Subjects:** Precancelled stamps of the United States, Canada, Great Britain, and Europe; birds and wild flowers of the United States; color photographs of wild flowers in the Bert Hoover Arboretum and others. **Holdings:** 5000 books; 2000 bound periodical volumes; 500 3x5 color prints; 5000 negatives; 100 black/white negatives of early New Jersey post offices. **Subscriptions:** 20 journals and other serials; 5 newspapers. **Services:** Copying; library open to the public by appointment. **Computerized Information Services:** Access to online systems. **Publications:** List of publications - available on request. **Remarks:** Maintained by National Association of Precancel Collectors, Inc.

★4641★
Davis Community (Presbyterian) Church - Resource Center Library (Rel-Phil)
412 C St. Phone: (916)753-2894
Davis, CA 95616 Mary Lou Willett, Libn.
Founded: 1962. **Subjects:** Religion. **Holdings:** 3000 books. **Subscriptions:** 20 journals and other serials. **Services:** Library open to the public with restrictions.

★4642★
Davis & Company - Law Library (Law)
2800 Park Place
666 Burrard St. Phone: (604)687-9444
Vancouver, BC, Canada V6C 2Z7 Joan Mulholland, Libn.
Founded: 1892. **Staff:** Prof 1; Other 2. **Subjects:** Law. **Holdings:** 15,000 books; 350 bound periodical volumes. **Subscriptions:** 400 journals and other serials. **Services:** Library not open to the public. **Automated Operations:** Integrated library system. **Computerized Information Services:** QL Systems, Info Globe, Infomart Online, The Financial Post DataGroup, CAN/LAW, LEXIS, WESTLAW, DIALOG Information Services, INSIGHT; QUICKMAIL (electronic mail service). **Remarks:** FAX: (604)687-1612. Telex: 04-508528.

Davis Conservation Library
See: **Conservation Districts Foundation** (4217)

★4643★
Davis Consultants - Library (Sci-Engr)
Voelbel Rd. Phone: (609)448-0161
Highstown, NJ 08520 Martha Davis, Dir.
Subjects: Engineering, printing science, paper technology, history. **Special Collections:** Technical Association of the Pulp and Paper Industry and American Society of Mechanical Engineers journals (30 years); Science Operations Support Equipment journals (40 years). **Subscriptions:** 40 journals and other serials. **Services:** Library not open to the public.

Emert L. Davis Memorial Library
See: **U.S. Army - TRADOC - Patton Museum of Cavalry & Armor** (17020)

★4644★
Davis Friends Meeting - Library (Rel-Phil)
345 L. St.
Davis, CA 95616 Noel Peattie
Founded: 1973. **Staff:** Prof 1. **Subjects:** Quaker studies, peace, social concerns. **Holdings:** 1000 books; 30 bound periodical volumes; audiocassettes; videotapes; globes. **Subscriptions:** 40 journals and other serials. **Services:** Library open to the public after meeting for worship.

★4645★
Davis, Graham & Stubbs - Law Library (Law)
370 17th St. Phone: (303)892-9400
Denver, CO 80202 Ann Evans, Mgr., Lib. & Info.Res.
Staff: Prof 4; Other 2. **Subjects:** Law. **Holdings:** 30,000 volumes. **Subscriptions:** 353 journals and other serials; 13 newspapers. **Services:** Interlibrary loan; library not open to the public. **Automated Operations:** Computerized cataloging. **Computerized Information Services:** LEXIS, NEXIS, DIALOG Information Services; produces LEGISTATE (Legislative Monitoring Service for Colorado). **Remarks:** FAX: (303)893-1379. **Staff:** Camille M. Davis, Info.Rsrcs.Anl.; Mary Farner, Res.Libn.; John Price, Ref.Libn.

Harwell Goodwin Davis Library
See: **Samford University - Harwell Goodwin Davis Library** (14663)

★4646★
J.M. Davis Gun Museum - Research Library (Hist)
333 N. Lynn Riggs Blvd.
Box 966 Phone: (918)341-5707
Claremore, OK 74017 Lee T. Good, Chf.Adm.Off.
Founded: 1969. **Subjects:** Firearms, edged weapons, American Indian artifacts, steins, musical instruments. **Holdings:** 1110 books; 30 bound periodical volumes; old gun catalogs; World War I posters; pins, buttons, and badges. **Subscriptions:** 15 journals and other serials. **Services:** Library open to the public for reference use only.

Kathryn and Shelby Cullom Davis Library
See: **College of Insurance - Insurance Society of New York - Kathryn and Shelby Cullom Davis Library** (3897)

Lady Davis Institute for Medical Research
See: **Sir Mortimer B. Davis Jewish General Hospital** (4650)

Davis Library
See: **Mote Marine Laboratory** (10771)

Davis Library
See: **Temple Emanu-El** (16099)

Davis Memorial Library
See: **Methodist College** (10179)

Michael M. Davis Reading Room
See: **Association of University Programs in Health Administration - Resource Center for Health Services Administration Education** (1172)

Paul Price Davis History Room
See: **Yadkin County Public Library** (20690)

★4647★
Davis Polk & Wardwell - Law Library (Law)
1300 Eye St., N.W. Phone: (202)962-7400
Washington, DC 20005 Kathleen S. Martin, Libn.
Founded: 1981. **Staff:** 3. **Subjects:** Law - general, banking, corporate, tax. **Special Collections:** Legislative histories for banking and taxation. **Holdings:** 12,000 books; 200 periodicals; 150 videotapes; microfiche. **Subscriptions:** 125 journals and other serials; 8 newspapers. **Services:** Interlibrary loan; SDI; library open to the public by appointment. **Automated Operations:** Computerized cataloging. **Computerized Information Services:** LEXIS, NEXIS, WESTLAW, DIALOG Information Services, BRS Information Technologies, Dow Jones News/Retrieval, PHINet FedTax Database, LEGI-SLATE, OCLC, PFDS Online, Reuters, InfoText; Docufind (internal database). **Publications:** Library Bulletin - for internal distribution only. **Special Indexes:** GAO Reports Index. **Remarks:** FAX: (202)962-7111. **Staff:** Stephen Mellin, Asst.Libn.; Kathleen McNahon, Tech.Serv.

★4648★
Davis Polk & Wardwell - Library (Law)
1 Chase Manhattan Plaza Phone: (212)530-4267
New York, NY 10005 Daniel Hanson, Chf.Libn.
Founded: 1881. **Staff:** Prof 8; Other 14. **Subjects:** Law - tax, antitrust, international, corporate. **Special Collections:** Opinions & Memoranda of Law; United States Supreme Court Briefs. **Holdings:** 70,000 volumes. **Subscriptions:** 900 journals and other serials; 25 newspapers. **Services:** Interlibrary loan; library not open to the public. **Automated Operations:** Computerized public access catalog, and cataloging. **Computerized Information Services:** Spectrum Ownership Profiles Online, NewsNet, Inc., CompuServe Information Service Information Network, LEGI-SLATE, WILSONLINE, ADP Network Services, Inc., LRS, Securities Data Company, Inc., OCLC, DIALOG Information Services, PFDS Online, LEXIS, WESTLAW, Dow Jones News/Retrieval. **Publications:** DPW Library Bulletin. **Special Catalogs:** Memoranda of law. **Remarks:** FAX: (212)530-4800; (212)530-4039. **Staff:** Karen Gillis, Online Serv.Libn.; Bonnie Schwartz, Corp.Libn.; Benjamin Toby, Ref.Libn.; Catherine Fitzgerald, Tech.Serv.Libn.

★4649★
Sir Mortimer B. Davis Jewish General Hospital - Institute of Community & Family Psychiatry - Library (Med)
4333 Cote St. Catherine Rd. Phone: (514)340-8210
Montreal, PQ, Canada H3T 1E4 Ruth Stilman, Libn.
Founded: 1969. **Staff:** Prof 1; Other 1. **Subjects:** Psychiatry, psychotherapy, family therapy, community mental health, psychopharmacology. **Holdings:** 5500 books; 1700 bound periodical volumes; 300 VF materials; 580 audiotapes. **Subscriptions:** 83 journals and other serials. **Services:** Interlibrary loan; copying; library open to the public for consultation. **Automated Operations:** Computerized acquisitions. **Computerized Information Services:** BRS Information Technologies, MEDLINE; Envoy 100 (electronic mail service). **Networks/Consortia:** Member of McGill Medical and Health Libraries Association (MMHLA), Montreal Health Libraries Association (MHLA). **Remarks:** FAX: (514)340-7507. Electronic mail address(es): ILL.QMJGI (Envoy 100).

★4650★
Sir Mortimer B. Davis Jewish General Hospital - Lady Davis Institute for Medical Research - Research Library (Med)
3755 Cote St. Catherine Rd. Phone: (514)340-8222
Montreal, PQ, Canada H3T 1E2 Arlene Greenberg, Chf.Med.Libn.
Founded: 1969. **Subjects:** Biochemistry, molecular biology, cancer research, cell genetics, medical research, diabetes. **Holdings:** Books housed at hospital's main library. **Subscriptions:** 70 journals and other serials. **Services:** Interlibrary loan; copying; library open to the public for consultation only. **Computerized Information Services:** BRS Information Technologies, CAN/OLE, NLM, MEDLARS; Envoy 100 (electronic mail service). **Networks/Consortia:** Member of McGill Medical and Health Libraries Association (MMHLA), Montreal Health Libraries Association (MHLA), Canadian Health Libraries Association. **Remarks:** Library staff and services are coordinated through the Sir Mortimer B. Davis Jewish General Hospital - Medical Library. FAX: (514)340-7552. Electronic mail address(es): ILL.QMJGL (Envoy 100).

★4651★
Sir Mortimer B. Davis Jewish General Hospital - Medical Library (Med)
3755 Cote St. Catherine Rd. Phone: (514)340-8222
Montreal, PQ, Canada H3T 1E2 Arlene Greenberg, Chf.Med.Libn.
Founded: 1950. **Staff:** Prof 1; Other 3. **Subjects:** Medicine, nursing, allied health sciences, administration. **Holdings:** 30,000 books and bound periodical volumes. **Subscriptions:** 650 journals and other serials. **Services:** Interlibrary loan; copying; library open to the public for reference use only. **Computerized Information Services:** BRS Information Technologies, NLM, MEDLARS, CAN/OLE; Envoy 100 (electronic mail service). **Networks/Consortia:** Member of McGill Medical and Health Libraries Association (MMHLA), Montreal Health Libraries Association (MHLA), Canadian Health Libraries Association. **Publications:** Library Newsletter, biannual; recent acquisitions list, bimonthly, - both for internal distribution and upon request. **Remarks:** FAX: (514)340-7552. Electronic mail address(es): ILL.QMJG (Envoy 100). **Staff:** Paula Calestagne; Liz Breier; Francoise Soubeyrand; Chris Stevenson.

Stanley K. Davis Library
See: **Albany General Hospital** (225)

William T. Davis Education Center
See: **Staten Island Institute of Arts and Sciences** (15762)

★4652★
Dawes Arboretum - Library (Agri, Biol Sci)
7770 Jacksontown Rd., S.E. Phone: (614)323-2355
Newark, OH 43055 Alan D. Cook, Dir., Extended Serv.
Founded: 1929. **Staff:** 2. **Subjects:** Horticulture, botany, ecology, nature, forestry. **Holdings:** 5000 books. **Subscriptions:** 28 journals and other serials. **Services:** Copying; library open to members for reference use only.

Charles Gates Dawes Home
See: **Evanston Historical Society** (5506)

★4653★
Dawgwood Research Library (Hum)
601 Ymbacion St. Phone: (512)526-4406
Refugio, TX 78377 Kathleen Huson Maxwell, Cur.
Founded: 1938. **Staff:** Prof 1; Other 1. **Subjects:** Texana, history, philosophy, genealogy, historical correspondence and maps. **Special Collections:** Greek philosophy collection (emphasis on Pythagoras); Napoleon collection; Texas map collection; newspaper collections; classical music collection. **Holdings:** 25,000 books, bound historical periodicals, magazines, bound and unbound manuscripts, documents; 42 book cases; 5 filing cabinets; map vault. **Services:** Library open to the public by appointment. **Also Known As:** Hobart Huson's Dawgwood Research Library.

Dana Dawson Library
See: **St. Paul School of Theology** (14569)

J.M. Dawson Church-State Research Center
See: **Baylor University** (1606)

Dawson Technical Institute Library
See: **Chicago City-Wide College** (3517)

Timothy C. Day Technical Library
See: **University of Cincinnati - OMI College of Applied Science** (18480)

★4654★
Dayton Art Institute - Library (Art)
Forest & Riverview Aves.
Box 941 Phone: (513)223-5277
Dayton, OH 45401 Jane A. Dunwoodie, Hd.Libn.
Staff: Prof 2; Other 1. **Subjects:** Art and architecture. **Special Collections:** Lott Memorial Architectural Library. **Holdings:** 26,362 volumes; 24,023 slides; 335 VF drawers of museum and auction catalogs and bulletins; 820 microfiche. **Subscriptions:** 111 journals and other serials. **Services:** Interlibrary loan (copies only); copying; library open to the public for reference use only. **Networks/Consortia:** Member of Southwestern Ohio Council for Higher Education (SOCHE). **Special Catalogs:** Ohio-Kentucky Cooperative Libraries Union List of Serials. **Remarks:** FAX: (513)223-3140. **Staff:** Alice Saidel, Ref.Libn.

★4655★
Dayton Hudson Corporation - Research/Information Center (Bus-Fin)
777 Nicollet Mall Phone: (612)370-6769
Minneapolis, MN 55402 Marcy Carrel
Staff: 1.5. **Subjects:** Retailing, business. **Special Collections:** Competitor Files (more than 200 companies); retail slide library; corporte archives. **Holdings:** 500 books; business and retail directories. **Subscriptions:** 200 journals, newspapers, and other serials. **Services:** Interlibrary loan; current awareness tracking. **Automated Operations:** Computerized cataloging and serials. **Computerized Information Services:** DIALOG Information Services, Dow Jones News/Retrieval, VU/TEXT Information Services, DataTimes, InvesText; CD-ROMs (CD/Corporate, Business Dateline). **Publications:** Trend Bulletin, monthly; Strategic Developments, weekly. **Remarks:** FAX: (612)370-5513.

★4656★
Dayton Mental Health Center - Staff Library (Med)
2611 Wayne Ave. Phone: (513)258-0440
Dayton, OH 45420 Leonard Skonecki, Libn.
Founded: 1950. **Staff:** Prof 1. **Subjects:** Psychiatry, psychology, medicine, social work. **Holdings:** 660 books. **Subscriptions:** 17 journals and other serials. **Services:** Interlibrary loan; library not open to the public.

★4657★
Dayton and Montgomery County Public Library - Adult Services Department (Rec)
215 E. Third St. Phone: (513)227-9500
Dayton, OH 45402-2103 Glenna Reynolds, Dept.Hd.
Founded: 1847. **Staff:** Prof 17; Other 9. **Subjects:** General collection. **Special Collections:** Dayton and Montgomery County history, genealogy; Women's Suffrage Collection; Shaker Collection; Dayton and Montgomery County photographs (2000 items); large print (4200 items); foreign languages (French, German, Italian, Spanish, Vietnamese, Slavic; 4000 items); sheet music (12 VF drawers); adult literacy and English as a second language (1200 titles). **Holdings:** 500,000 books. **Services:** Interlibrary loan; copying; department open to the public. **Automated Operations:** Computerized cataloging and circulation. **Computerized Information Services:** OCLC, DIALOG Information Services. **Networks/Consortia:** Member of OHIONET. **Publications:** BITS (Business Industry Technology Service), 10/year; Dayton/Miami Valley Clearinghouse, annual. **Special Indexes:** Local organizations; Montgomery County genealogy index; sheet music index. **Remarks:** TTY: (513)224-9433.

★4658★
Dayton and Montgomery County Public Library - Audio-Visual Division (Aud-Vis)
215 E. Third St. Phone: (513)227-9500
Dayton, OH 45402-2103 Theodore J. Nunn, Div.Hd.
Founded: 1973. **Staff:** Prof 1; Other 9. **Holdings:** 3000 16mm films; 800 filmstrips; 7000 slides; 6000 phonograph records; 18,000 audio cassettes; 8700 video cassettes; 8500 compact discs. **Services:** Center open to the public. **Special Catalogs:** 16mm Film Catalog; Books-on-Audio-Cassette.

★4659★
Dayton and Montgomery County Public Library - Magazine Room (Bus-Fin)
215 E. Third St. Phone: (513)227-9500
Dayton, OH 45402-2103 Kevin Smith, Div.Hd.
Founded: 1987. **Staff:** Prof 4; Other 6. **Subjects:** Business and industry, general collection. **Special Collections:** 19th-century local newspapers; local newspaper clippings, 1940-1985. **Holdings:** Bound periodicals; microfilm. **Subscriptions:** 1200 journals and other serials. **Services:** Copying, library open to the public. **Automated Operations:** Computerized cataloging and circulation. **Computerized Information Services:** DIALOG Information Services, WILSONLINE. **Networks/Consortia:** Member of OHIONET. **Special Indexes:** Local Newspaper Index, 1985 to present (online). **Remarks:** FAX: (513)227-9548; (513)227-9549.

★4660★
Dayton Newspapers Inc. - Reference Library (Publ)
37 S. Ludlow St. Phone: (513)225-2201
Dayton, OH 45402 Michael Passo, Lib.Dir.
Founded: 1979. **Staff:** Prof 1; Other 5. **Subjects:** Newspaper reference topics. **Special Collections:** Dayton Journal Herald/Dayton Daily News, 1837 to present (microfilm). **Holdings:** 3500 books; 3500 pamphlets; newspaper clippings; microfiche; pictures; photographs. **Subscriptions:** 25 journals and other serials. **Services:** Copying; library open to the public by appointment. **Computerized Information Services:** NEXIS, VU/TEXT Information Services; internal database. **Remarks:** FAX: (513)225-2989.

★4661★
Dayton Progress Corporation - Library (Sci-Engr)
500 Progress Rd.
Dayton, OH 45449-2351 Phone: (513)859-5111
Subjects: Die technology. **Holdings:** 50 books; 2000 reports. **Subscriptions:** 10 journals and other serials. **Services:** Library not open to the public. **Remarks:** FAX: (513)859-5353.

★4662★
Daytons Bluff Area Early Childhood & Family Education Program - Toy & Book Library
262 Bates Ave.
St. Paul, MN 55106
Defunct.

Dazian Library of Theatrical Design
See: **Museum of the City of New York - Theatre Collection** (10892)

★4663★
DDB Needham/West - Information Center (Bus-Fin)
5900 Wilshire Blvd. Phone: (213)937-5100
Los Angeles, CA 90036 Lois S. Steinmann, Mgr., Info.Serv.
Founded: 1980. **Staff:** Prof 1. **Subjects:** Advertising, marketing, business. **Holdings:** 500 books; 200 market reports; 1 VF drawer of pamphlets; 14 VF drawers of subject clipping files. **Subscriptions:** 82 journals and other serials. **Services:** Copying (limited); telephone reference for other librarians; library open to clients only. **Computerized Information Services:** DIALOG Information Services, Mead Data Central, DataTimes. **Remarks:** FAX: (213)936-4038.

★4664★
DDB Needham Worldwide, Inc. - Information Center (Bus-Fin)
303 E. Wacker Dr. Phone: (312)861-0200
Chicago, IL 60601 Grace A. Villamora, V.P. & Dir. of Info.Ctr.
Founded: 1948. **Staff:** Prof 3; Other 5. **Subjects:** Advertising, marketing research. **Special Collections:** New product files; vintage catalogs; lifestyle reports; songbooks. **Holdings:** 5000 books; 200 VF drawers of pictures and print advertisements; 25 VF drawers of subject clippings; 35 VF drawers of corporation files and annual reports; 100 pamphlet boxes of consumer analysis material. **Subscriptions:** 300 journals and other serials; 6 newspapers. **Services:** Interlibrary loan; SDI; center not open to the public except for prearranged student group tours. **Automated Operations:** Computerized cataloging, acquisitions, and serials. **Computerized Information Services:** DIALOG Information Services, MAID Systems Ltd., Dow Jones News/Retrieval, NEXIS, VU/TEXT Information Services, OCLC, PRODUCTSCAN, DataTimes; Computerized Research Library (internal database). Performs searches on fee basis. **Networks/Consortia:** Member of Chicago Library System, ILLINET. **Publications:** Bookends, monthly; Reference Shelf, monthly; CRL Index, every six months. **Remarks:** FAX: (312)819-1868. **Staff:** Sandra Garber, Sr.Info.Spec.; Nikki Chura, Sr.Info.Spec.

★4665★
DDB Needham Worldwide, Inc. - Information Center (Bus-Fin)
437 Madison Ave. Phone: (212)415-2546
New York, NY 10022 Alice Bromley, V.P./Dir., Info.Ctr.
Founded: 1962. **Staff:** Prof 4; Other 3. **Subjects:** Advertising, marketing, finance. **Holdings:** 9000 books; 100 bound periodical volumes; 50 VF drawers of pictures; 150 VF drawers of subject files; 500 reels of microfilm. **Subscriptions:** 304 journals and other serials. **Services:** Interlibrary loan; center not open to the public. **Computerized Information Services:** DIALOG Information Services, NEXIS, Dow Jones News/Retrieval, TEXTLINE, InvesText, DataTimes, MAID.

Frank V. De Bellis Collection
See: **San Francisco State University** (14742)

Cantor Gerald De Bruin Music, Tapes and Record Library
See: **Temple Beth El of Greater Buffalo - Library** (16088)

Francisco Jose de Caldas Colombian Fund for Scientific Research and Special Projects
See: **Colombian Fund for Scientific Research and Special Projects of Francisco Jose de Caldas** (3927)

★4666★
De Forest Research, Inc. - Library (Theater)
1645 N. Vine St., Suite 701 Phone: (213)469-2271
Hollywood, CA 90028 Kellam De Forest, Pres.
Staff: Prof 3; Other 10. **Subjects:** Research material for motion pictures and television. **Holdings:** 32,000 books; 2000 bound periodical volumes; 4000 files of photographs and clippings; 8000 motion picture and television scripts. **Subscriptions:** 19 journals and other serials. **Services:** Library open to the public on fee basis. **Remarks:** FAX: (213)856-0375. This is a private research organization which provides legal and authenticating information for the movie and television industry.

De Golyer Library
See: **Southern Methodist University - De Golyer Library** (15499)

★4667★
Paul De Haen International, Inc. - Drug Information Systems and Services
2750 S. Shoshone St.
Englewood, CO 80110
Defunct.

De Havilland Aircraft Company of Canada - Engineering Library
See: **Boeing of Canada Ltd. - De Havilland Division** (1937)

De Kalb County Board of Education - Fernbank Science Center
See: **Fernbank Science Center** (5669)

★4668★
De Kalb Medical Center - Health Sciences Library (Med)
2701 N. Decatur Rd. Phone: (404)501-5638
Decatur, GA 30033 Marilyn Barry, Dir.
Founded: 1974. **Staff:** Prof 1; Other 1. **Subjects:** Clinical medicine, nursing, allied health. **Holdings:** 1000 books; 6000 periodical volumes. **Subscriptions:** 240 journals. **Services:** Interlibrary loan; library not open to the public. **Computerized Information Services:** MEDLARS, BRS Information Technologies; CD-ROMs (MEDLINE, CINAHL); Georgia Online Database (GOLD); DOCLINE, MICROMEDEX (electronic mail services). **Networks/Consortia:** Member of Atlanta Health Science Libraries Consortium (AHSLC). **Remarks:** FAX: (404)501-5093.

★4669★
De Kalb Plant Genetics - Research Library (Agri)
3100 Sycamore Rd. Phone: (815)758-3461
DeKalb, IL 60115 Dr. Charles F. Krull, V.P.
Founded: 1965. **Staff:** 1. **Subjects:** Agriculture. **Holdings:** Figures not available. **Services:** Library not open to the public. **Remarks:** A division of De Kalb Genetics Corp.

Clarence De La Chapelle Medical Library
See: **Bellevue Hospital** (1696)

Simon Lucuix Rio De La Plata Library
See: **University of Texas at Austin - Benson Latin American Collection** (19380)

De La Salle Institute of Moraga - Library for Lasallian Studies
See: **St. Mary's College of California - Library - Special Collections** (14511)

Loyd De Lap Law Library
See: **Klamath County Library** (8755)

★4670★
De Paul Health Center - Medical Library (Med)
12303 DePaul Dr. Phone: (314)344-6397
Bridgeton, MO 63044 Joan A. Laneman, Lib.Dir.
Staff: Prof 3. **Subjects:** Medicine, nursing, psychiatry, management, staff and patient education. **Holdings:** 9500 books; 4000 bound periodical volumes; 300 other cataloged items; videotapes. **Subscriptions:** 262 journals and other serials. **Services:** Interlibrary loan; copying; library open to medical and nursing students. **Computerized Information Services:** MEDLARS, NLM. Performs searches on fee basis. **Networks/Consortia:** Member of National Network of Libraries of Medicine (NN/LM), Saint Louis Medical Librarians Consortia. **Staff:** Sr. Teresa Marie Henry, D.C., Lib.Asst.; Norma S. Gross, Bibliotherapist.

De Paul Library
See: **Saint Mary College - De Paul Library - Special Collections Center** (14500)

★4671★
De Paul Medical Center - Boone Memorial Library (Med)
150 Kingsley Ln. Phone: (804)889-5270
Norfolk, VA 23505 Jeanne L. Morris, Med.Libn.
Founded: 1944. **Staff:** Prof 1. **Subjects:** Medicine. **Holdings:** 1809 books; 2948 bound periodical volumes; 595 Audio-Digest tapes. **Subscriptions:** 136 journals and other serials. **Services:** Interlibrary loan. **Remarks:** FAX: (804)889-5881.

★4672★
De Paul Medical Center - School of Nursing Library (Med)
150 Kingsley Ln. Phone: (804)889-5386
Norfolk, VA 23505 Elinor B. Arsic, Libn.
Staff: Prof 1. **Subjects:** Medicine and religion. **Special Collections:** Historical nursing books. **Holdings:** 4317 books; 540 bound periodical volumes; 3724 AV programs; 9 VF drawers of clippings and pamphlets. **Subscriptions:** 80 journals and other serials. **Services:** Interlibrary loan; library open to hospital personnel with restrictions. **Publications:** New books and audiovisuals list, bimonthly - to faculty and students; Audiovisual Resource Guide (book).

★4673★
De Paul University - Lincoln Park Campus Library - Special Collections Department (Hum)
2323 N. Seminary Phone: (312)362-8088
Chicago, IL 60614 Kathryn DeGraff, Spec.Coll.Libn.
Founded: 1975. **Staff:** Prof 1; Other 1. **Subjects:** French Revolution, humanities. **Special Collections:** Napoleon Collection (4000 volumes); rare books (2000 volumes); Dickens Collection (590 volumes); sports (900 volumes); book arts (170 volumes); Horace Collection (212 volumes). **Holdings:** 7872 books; 598 bound periodical volumes; 70 manuscripts. **Services:** Copying; department open to the public. **Automated Operations:** Computerized cataloging, serials, and circulation. **Computerized Information Services:** BRS Information Technologies, OCLC. **Networks/Consortia:** Member of ILLINET. **Special Catalogs:** Napoleon Library Catalog (1941); revised addenda (1978). **Remarks:** FAX: (312)362-6187.

Edmond de Rothschild Library
See: **Park Avenue Synagogue** (12741)

De Sales Hall School of Theology - Library
See: **Oblates Theology Library** (12229)

De Sandvigske Samlinger - Biblioteket
See: **Sandvig Collections - Library** (14786)

De Soto National Memorial
See: **U.S. Natl. Park Service** (17698)

Juan De Valdes Library
See: **Evangelical Seminary of Puerto Rico** (5505)

★4674★
De Vry Institute of Technology - Learning Resource Center (Sci-Engr)
3300 N. Campbell Ave. Phone: (312)929-8500
Chicago, IL 60618 Julie A. Engel, Dir.
Staff: Prof 1; Other 8. **Subjects:** Business, electronics, computer science. **Special Collections:** Sams Photofact Service, 1946 to present; data books and specifications manuals. **Holdings:** 9116 volumes. **Subscriptions:** 214 journals and other serials. **Services:** Interlibrary loan; copying; center open to the public for reference use only. **Computerized Information Services:** DIALOG Information Services. **Networks/Consortia:** Member of Chicago Library System, ILLINET. **Remarks:** FAX: (312)348-1780.

★4675★
De Vry Institute of Technology - Learning Resource Center (Sci-Engr)
11224 Holmes Rd. Phone: (816)941-0430
Kansas City, MO 64131 Connie Jean Migliazzo, Dir.
Staff: Prof 1; Other 3. **Subjects:** Engineering, computer information systems, business, education, telecommunications. **Special Collections:** Data books. **Holdings:** 8437 books; 157 AV programs; 20 maps; 33,933 microfiche. **Subscriptions:** 134 journals and other serials. **Services:** Copying; center open to the public for reference use only. **Computerized Information Services:** DIALOG Information Services. **Special Catalogs:** Catalog of Data Books.

★4676★
De Vry Institute of Technology - Learning Resource Center (Sci-Engr)
1350 Alum Creek Dr. Phone: (614)253-7291
Columbus, OH 43209 Christine S. Roeder, Dir.
Founded: 1970. **Staff:** Prof 1; Other 1. **Subjects:** Electronics technology, computer science, business operations. **Special Collections:** Sam's Photofacts. **Holdings:** 13,000 books. **Subscriptions:** 190 journals and other serials. **Services:** Copying; library open to the public for reference use only. **Automated Operations:** Computerized cataloging. **Computerized Information Services:** DIALOG Information Services.

★4677★
De Vry Institute of Technology - Learning Resource Center (Sci-Engr)
4250 N. Beltline Rd. Phone: (214)258-6767
Irving, TX 75038-4299 Carolyn Cochran, Dir., LRC
Founded: 1969. **Staff:** Prof 1; Other 3. **Subjects:** Electronics, computer science, business information. **Holdings:** 7000 books; 8173 microfiche; 24 film loops; 15 videotapes; computer software; Case-Oriented Studies Information Retrieval System (COSIRS) materials. **Subscriptions:** 200 journals and other serials. **Services:** Copying; information services for handicapped; center open to the public for reference use only. **Computerized Information Services:** DIALOG Information Services. **Remarks:** FAX: (214)659-1748.

M.H. De Young Memorial Museum Library
See: **Fine Arts Museums of San Francisco - Library** (5703)

★4678★
Deacon Barclays de Zoete Wedd - Library
304 Bay St. Phone: (416)350-3200
Toronto, ON, Canada M5H 2P2 Lillian Haibeck, Libn.
Founded: 1987. **Staff:** 1. **Holdings: Holdings:** 4000 reports. **Subscriptions:** 50 journals and other serials; 10 newspapers. **Services:** Library not open to the public. **Remarks:** FAX: (416)865-9513. **Formerly:** Deacon, Morgan, McEwen, Inc.

★4679★
Deaconess Community Lutheran Church of America - Lutheran Deaconess Community Library (Rel-Phil)
801 Merion Square Rd. Phone: (215)642-8838
Gladwyne, PA 19035 Sr. Catharine Stirewalt, Libn.
Founded: 1946. **Subjects:** Religion, theology, Christian education, church history, Bible, psychology, education, social work, women's work in the church. **Special Collections:** Historical and archival collection of Deaconess Community, LCA (26 VF drawers; 95 documentary storage boxes; 2 memorabilia cabinets; 150 volumes). **Holdings:** 9000 volumes; 30 pamphlet cases of audiovisual and curriculum material for Christian education; 6 VF drawers of miscellanea. **Subscriptions:** 38 journals and other serials. **Services:** Library not open to the public.

★4680★
Deaconess Hospital - Drusch Professional Library (Med)
6150 Oakland Ave. Phone: (314)768-3137
St. Louis, MO 63139 Carol Iglauer, Chf.Libn.
Founded: 1943. **Staff:** Prof 1; Other 3. **Subjects:** Nursing, medicine. **Holdings:** 2812 books; 2824 bound periodical volumes; 188 videotapes; 416 audio cassettes; 66 instructional computer diskettes; 252 filmstrips; 2123 slides; 806 microfiche. **Subscriptions:** 202 journals and other serials. **Services:** Interlibrary loan; SDI; library open to health sciences professionals and students. **Automated Operations:** Computerized cataloging and ILL. **Computerized Information Services:** BRS Information Technologies, DIALOG Information Services, NLM. **Networks/Consortia:** Member of St. Louis Regional Library Network, National Network of Libraries of Medicine - Midcontinental Region. **Publications:** Acquisitions List, quarterly.

★4681★
Deaconess Hospital - Health Science Library (Med)
600 Mary St. Phone: (812)426-3385
Evansville, IN 47747 Jean Weir, Med.Libn.
Founded: 1969. **Staff:** Prof 1; Other 1. **Subjects:** Nursing education, clinical medicine, allied health sciences. **Holdings:** 11,000 books; 2000 AV programs. **Subscriptions:** 300 journals and other serials; 5 newspapers. **Services:** Interlibrary loan; copying; current awareness; library open to health personnel with permission. **Computerized Information Services:** NLM. **Networks/Consortia:** Member of Evansville Area Libraries Consortium.

G.B. Dealey Library and Research Center
See: **Dallas Historical Society** (4553)

Edwin W. Dean Memorial Library
See: **Centinela Hospital Medical Center** (3320)

Mallette Dean Archive
See: **University of San Francisco - Special Collections Department/ Donohue Rare Book Room** (19290)

Dean Memorial Library
See: **American Museum of Natural History - Department of Ichthyology** (686)

★4682★
Dean Witter Reynolds, Inc. - Library (Bus-Fin)
2 World Trade Center Phone: (212)392-2745
New York, NY 10048 Barbara C. White, Chf.Libn.
Founded: 1988. **Staff:** Prof 4; Other 10. **Subjects:** Finance, investments, corporation records, economic conditions. **Holdings:** 5000 books. **Subscriptions:** 600 journals and other serials. **Services:** Interlibrary loan; copying; library not open to the public. **Automated Operations:** Computerized serials. **Computerized Information Services:** Dow Jones News/Retrieval, DIALOG Information Services, PFDS Online, NEXIS, Info Globe, TEXTLINE, Vickers Stock Research Corporation, INVESTEXT, Dun & Bradstreet Business Credit Services, NewsNet, Inc., Spectrum Ownership Profiles Online, VU/TEXT Information Services, DataTimes; internal databases. **Special Indexes:** Index to DWR Research Reports (online). **Remarks:** FAX: (212)392-4524. **Staff:** Merill Losick, Assoc.Libn.; Andrea Goodman, Ref.Libn.; Denise Ueason, Ref.Libn.

John B. Deans Memorial Library
See: **Union County Historical Society** (16651)

★4683★
Dearborn & Ewing - Law Library (Law)
1 Sovran Pl., Suite 1200 Phone: (615)259-3560
Nashville, TN 37239-1200 Sharon L. Hom, Libn.
Founded: 1972. **Staff:** Prof 1. **Subjects:** Law. **Holdings:** 7100 books; 155 bound periodical volumes. **Subscriptions:** 65 journals and other serials. **Services:** Library not open to the public. **Computerized Information Services:** LEXIS; Research Bank (internal database). **Publications:** Library Inventory List. **Remarks:** FAX: (615)259-0157; 259-0177.

Frederick M. Dearborn Medical Library
See: **Metropolitan Hospital Center** (10204)

Dearborn Historical Commission
See: **Dearborn Historical Museum - Historical Records & Archives** (4684)

★4684★
Dearborn Historical Museum - Historical Records & Archives (Hist)
915 S. Brady St. Phone: (313)565-3000
Dearborn, MI 48124 Helen K. Mamalakis, Archv.Spec.
Founded: 1950. **Staff:** Prof 2; Other 2. **Subjects:** Dearborn history. **Special Collections:** Orville L. Hubbard Collection; local celebrities collections; mayoral files; local events files. **Holdings:** 2600 books; 382 bound periodical volumes; 15 VF drawers and 16 storage cabinets of manuscripts; 50 VF drawers of clippings, pamphlets, photographs, maps; 15 storage cabinets of diaries, documents, archival materials; 424 reels of microfilm of local newspapers and records; 16,000 feet of tape of oral histories; several collections of local celebrities. **Subscriptions:** 35 journals and other serials. **Services:** Copying; library open to the public for reference use only. **Publications:** Museum Quarterly; Annual Report; Dearborn Historian. **Special Catalogs:** Manuscript, history, newspaper, and photo catalogs (card). **Remarks:** Maintained by the Dearborn Historical Commission. **Staff:** Donald V. Baut, Cur. of Res.

Death Valley National Monument
See: **U.S. Natl. Park Service** (17699)

Hiram E. Deats Memorial Library
See: **Hunterdon County Historical Society** (7565)

★4685★
Debevoise & Plimpton - Law Library (Law)
875 3rd Ave. Phone: (212)909-6275
New York, NY 10022 Denis R. O'Connor, Mgr.Lib.Serv.
Staff: Prof 8; Other 8. **Subjects:** Law. **Holdings:** 70,000 books; 300 bound periodical volumes; 3000 pamphlets. **Subscriptions:** 50 journals and other serials; 25 newspapers. **Services:** Interlibrary loan; library open to clients; SLA members and others may visit by appointment. **Automated Operations:** Computerized cataloging, acquisitions, serials, circulation, and budgeting. **Computerized Information Services:** DIALOG Information Services, Dow Jones News/Retrieval, Spectrum Ownership Profiles Online, WESTLAW, LEXIS, Maxwell Macmillan Taxes Online, DataTimes, VU/TEXT Information Services, Information America, Disclosure Incorporated, EPIC, Comtex. **Remarks:** FAX: (212)909-6836. Telex: 148377. **Staff:** Druet Cameron, Assoc.Libn.; Helen Lawless, Coord., Ref.Serv.; Scott Wilson, Tax Libn.; Maura Forman, Corp.Libn.; Chris Lauzau, Gen.Ref.;

★4686★
Deborah Heart and Lung Center - Medical Library (Med)
200 Trenton Rd. Phone: (609)893-6611
Browns Mills, NJ 08015 Carol A. Harris, Med.Libn.
Founded: 1971. **Staff:** Prof 2. **Subjects:** Cardiology, respiratory diseases, cardiothoracic surgery, medicine, pathology, nursing. **Holdings:** 3500 books; 2000 bound periodical volumes; AV programs. **Subscriptions:** 175 journals and other serials. **Services:** Interlibrary loan; library not open to the public. **Computerized Information Services:** MEDLARS; MED/MAIL (electronic mail service). **Networks/Consortia:** Member of National Network of Libraries of Medicine - Middle Atlantic Region, Society for Cooperative Healthcare and Related Education (SCHARE).

★4687★
Debreceni Orvostudomanyi Egyetem - KENEZY Konyvtar (Med)
Nagyerdei Krt 98 Phone: 52 13847
H-4012 Debrecen, Hungary Marta Viragos
Founded: 1947. **Staff:** Prof 11; Other 13. **Subjects:** Medicine, and allied subjects. **Holdings:** 83,471 books; 67,073 bound periodical volumes. **Subscriptions:** 900 journals and other serials. **Services:** Interlibrary loan; copying; SDI; library open to professionals only. **Computerized Information Services:** DIALOG Information Services, Data-Star, MEDLINE, Current Contents Search, Pro-Cite; floppy disc (Micro-ISIS). Contact Person: Katalin Soos; Katalin Somogyi. **Publications:** List of book acquisitions; bibliography of publications at the university. **Remarks:** FAX: 52 13847. **Also Known As:** Debrecen University of Medicine.

Eugene V. Debs Collection
See: **Indiana State University - Department of Rare Books and Special Collections** (7772)

★4688★
Decatur Department of Community Development - Planning Library (Plan)
One Civic Center Plaza
Decatur, IL 62523
Phone: (217)424-2778
George Weaver, Plan.Dir.
Subjects: Land use planning, transportation, housing, economics, urban redevelopment, demographics, community facilities studies, natural resources and environment. **Holdings:** 75 books; 1500 other cataloged items; 25 pieces of census material; 100 Illinois Geological Survey reports; 10 dissertations; 100 unbound periodicals. **Subscriptions:** 14 journals and other serials. **Services:** Library open to qualified researchers.

★4689★
Decatur Genealogical Society - Library (Hist)
356 N. Main St.
Box 1548
Decatur, IL 62525-1548
Phone: (217)429-0135
Founded: 1965. **Staff:** 12. **Subjects:** Genealogy. **Special Collections:** Stephen Decatur Chapter D.A.R. Library (600 books). **Holdings:** 45,000 books; 15,000 bound periodical volumes; 2000 microfiche; census on microfilm; birth, marriage, court, and death and cemetery records; family histories. **Subscriptions:** 160 journals and other serials. **Services:** Copying; library open to the public on fee basis. **Publications:** Central Illinois Quarterly.

★4690★
Decatur Herald and Review - Library (Publ)
601 E. William St.
Box 311
Decatur, IL 62525
Phone: (217)429-5151
Bob Fallstrom, Lib.Supv.
Founded: 1890. **Staff:** 7. **Subjects:** Newspaper reference topics, local history. **Holdings:** 1500 books; 929,600 clippings; 90,000 photographs and maps; Decatur newspapers, 1873 to present, on microfilm. **Subscriptions:** 50 newspapers. **Services:** Interlibrary loan; copying; library may be consulted for information unavailable elsewhere; research (fee). **Special Indexes:** Obituary index (card). **Remarks:** FAX: (217)421-6913.

★4691★
Decatur Memorial Hospital - Health Science Library (Med)
2300 N. Edward St.
Decatur, IL 62526
Phone: (217)877-8121
Karen J. Stoner, Libn.
Staff: Prof 1; Other 1. **Subjects:** Nursing, general medicine. **Holdings:** 2500 books; 2800 bound periodical volumes; AV programs. **Subscriptions:** 140 journals and other serials. **Services:** Interlibrary loan; copying; library open to the public for reference use only. **Computerized Information Services:** DIALOG Information Services, MEDLARS, PDQ; CD-ROMs. **Networks/Consortia:** Member of National Network of Libraries of Medicine - Greater Midwest Region, ILLINET, Rolling Prairie Library System (RPLS), Capital Area Consortium (CAC). **Remarks:** FAX: (217)877-6217.

Stephen Decatur Collection
See: **Millikin University** (10405)

★4692★
DECHEMA - I & D Information Systems and Data Banks Department - Library (Sci-Engr)
Theodor-Heuss-Allee 25
W-6000 Frankfurt am Main 97, Germany
Phone: 69 7564244
Dr. Reiner Eckermann, Dept.Hd.
Staff: Prof 2. **Subjects:** Chemical engineering and biotechnology - equipment manufacturing, plant design and construction, materials and corrosion, computer-aided design, mathematical models and methods, laboratory techniques, analytical chemistry, safety, dangerous materials, pollution control, energy and raw materials supply and conservation, chemical reaction engineering, unit operations, processes and products, biotechnology, genetic engineering. **Holdings:** 21,000 volumes. **Subscriptions:** 400 journals and other serials. **Services:** SDI; inquiry service; department open to the public. **Automated Operations:** Computerized cataloging. **Computerized Information Services:** STN International, INKADAT, Data-Star; department produces DECHEMA Chemical Engineering and Biotechnology Abstracts Data Bank (DECHEMA), DECHEMA Biotechnology Equipment Suppliers Databank (BIOQUIP), European Coal Data Bank (COALDATA), DECHEMA Equipment Suppliers Data Base (DEQUIP), DECHEMA Research Institutions Databank (DERES), DECHEMA Environmental Technology Equipment Databank (DETEQ), DECHEMA Thermophysical Property Data Bank (DETHERM), Chemical Safety Databank (CHEMSAFE), DECHEMA Corrosion Data Base (DECOR). Performs searches on fee basis. Contact Person: Dr. David Ilten, 7564-248. **Publications:** DECHEMA Chemistry Data Series; DECHEMA Corrosion Handbook; DECHEMA Monograph Series; publications in all areas of chemical engineering and biotechnology. **Special Catalogs:** Publications catalog. **Remarks:** DECHEMA is an acronym for Deutsche Gesellschaft fur Chemisches Apparatewesen, Chemische Technik und Biotechnologie e.V. The library is part of the I & D Department, which produces the above databases. FAX: 69 7564 201. Telex: 412 490 DCHA D. **Staff:** Dagmar Lower, Supv.

★4693★
Dechert, Price and Rhoads - Library (Law)
4000 Bell Atlantic Tower
1717 Arch St.
Philadelphia, PA 19103-2793
Phone: (215)994-2453
Susan G. Alford, Libn.
Staff: Prof 3; Other 3. **Subjects:** Law. **Holdings:** 25,000 books; 1300 bound periodical volumes; 13 VF drawers of annual reports and proxy statements. **Subscriptions:** 200 journals and other serials. **Services:** Interlibrary loan; library not open to the public. **Computerized Information Services:** LEXIS, WESTLAW, DIALOG Information Services, VU/TEXT Information Services, Dow Jones News/Retrieval. **Remarks:** FAX: (215)994-2222. **Staff:** Elizabeth A. McNerlin, Asst.Libn.; Suzanne Campbell, Sys.Libn.

Dechief Research Library
See: **Canadian National Railways** (2971)

★4694★
Decision Information Services, Ltd. - Library (Info Sci)
2130 Hanover St.
Palo Alto, CA 94306
Phone: (415)856-3666
Ulla Mick, Pres.
Staff: 1. **Subjects:** Management of information work; information needs and behaviors; information technology; microcomputers; participatory planning; policy studies. **Holdings:** 500 books; 5000 papers and reports. **Subscriptions:** 200 journals and other serials. **Computerized Information Services:** Internal databases.

Decker Library
See: **Maryland Institute, College of Art** (9751)

★4695★
Dedham Historical Society - Library (Hist)
612 High St.
PO Box 215
Dedham, MA 02026
Phone: (617)326-1385
Robert B. Hanson, Exec.Dir.
Founded: 1859. **Staff:** 4. **Subjects:** Dedham and Eastern Massachusetts history, New England genealogy. **Special Collections:** Fisher Ames Papers, 1758-1808 (400); Nathaniel Ames Diary (1758-1822) and Almanacs (1726-1774); Horace Mann lecture notes, 1796-1859; regional collections of surveyor's plans, 1740-1900; IGI Massachusetts VR microfilm collection. **Holdings:** 8000 volumes; account books; documents; manuscripts; newspapers; local histories; genealogical information. **Subscriptions:** 10 journals and other serials. **Services:** Copying; library open to the public.

Jean Crew Deeks Memorial Library
See: **Scarborough City Health Department - Health Resource Centre** (14894)

Deep Canyon Desert Research Center
See: **University of California, Riverside** (18405)

★4696★
Deer Isle-Stonington Historical Society - Library (Trans, Hist)
Deer Isle, ME 04627
Phone: (207)348-2886
Genice Welcome, Exec.Sec.
Founded: 1959. **Staff:** 13. **Subjects:** Marine vessels, steamboats and yachts, early children's books and school books. **Special Collections:** Area customhouse books (30); Richardson Collection of steamboat photographs; Dr. Noyes Collection of "Genealogical History of Families of Deer Isle, Maine" (43 volumes; 70 volumes of miscellanea). **Holdings:** 200 books; early scrapbooks; file of clippings on local subjects; diaries; photographs. **Services:** Library open to the public from June through September. **Publications:** Newsletter, annual.

★4697★
Deere & Company - Law Library (Law)
John Deere Rd.
Moline, IL 61265 Phone: (309)752-4287
Subjects: Law. **Holdings:** 5700 volumes. **Services:** Library not open to the public. **Computerized Information Services:** WESTLAW. Performs searches on fee basis.

★4698★
Deere & Company - Library (Agri, Sci-Engr)
John Deere Rd. Phone: (309)765-4733
Moline, IL 61265 Betty S. Hagberg, Mgr., Lib.Serv.
Founded: 1958. **Staff:** Prof 3; Other 7. **Subjects:** Agriculture, engineering, business, economics, management, materials science. **Special Collections:** Deere & Company history. **Holdings:** 25,000 books; 500 bound periodical volumes; federal documents; 18 drawers of microfiche; 1000 reels of microfilm. **Subscriptions:** 2500 journals and other serials; 14 newspapers. **Services:** Interlibrary loan; copying; library open to the public by appointment for reference use. **Automated Operations:** Computerized cataloging, acquisitions, serials, and circulation. **Computerized Information Services:** PFDS Online, OCLC, MEDLARS, DIALOG Information Services, NEXIS, Info Globe, Dow Jones News/Retrieval, Reuter TEXTLINE, Dun's Direct Access, OCLC EPIC, CompuServe Information Service. **Networks/Consortia:** Member of ILLINET. **Publications:** Staying Ahead: Reading for Self-Development, irregular. **Special Indexes:** Online index to archival holdings. **Remarks:** FAX: (309)765-4088. **Staff:** Les Stegh, Archv.; Diana Polk, Sr.Ref.Libn.

★4699★
Deere & Company - Technical Center Library (Sci-Engr)
3300 River Dr. Phone: (309)765-3883
Moline, IL 61265 Mrs. Doni Kernan, Libn.
Subjects: Engineering, materials science, metallurgy, chemistry. **Holdings:** 5000 books; 200 bound periodical volumes; 1520 hardcopy technical reports; 1790 reports on microfiche; 230 videotapes. **Subscriptions:** 175 journals and other serials. **Services:** Interlibrary loan. **Automated Operations:** Computerized circulation. **Computerized Information Services:** TELTECH. **Remarks:** Alternate telephone number(s): 765-3710.

★4700★
John Deere Tractor Works - Library (Sci-Engr)
Product Engineering Ctr.
6725 Cedar Hts. Dr. Phone: (319)292-8000
Cedar Falls, IA 50613 Dianna M. Goodrich, Libn.
Staff: Prof 2. **Subjects:** Applied mechanics, internal combustion engines, fuels and lubricants, materials. **Holdings:** 3000 volumes; technical reports and manuals; patents. **Subscriptions:** 200 journals and other serials. **Services:** Interlibrary loan; copying; library open to the public with restrictions. **Computerized Information Services:** DIALOG Information Services, OCLC.

Defence Research Establishment
See: **Canada - Defence Research Establishment** (2680)

Defence Research Establishment Valcartier
See: **Canada - Defence Research Establishment Valcartier** (2684)

★4701★
Defence Science and Technology Organisation - Materials Research Laboratories - Library (Mil, Sci-Engr)
P.O. Box 50 Phone: 3 319 4499
Ascot Vale, VIC 3032, Australia Malcolm McPherson, Sr.Libn.
Subjects: Materials - metallic, polymer, ceramic, composite; protection of personnel and equipment; explosives, armor, and ammunition; ship structures and engineering; underwater systems. **Holdings:** 50,000 volumes; 100,000 reports. **Subscriptions:** 500 journals and other serials. **Services:** Interlibrary loan; library not open to the public. **Computerized Information Services:** DIALOG Information Services, STN International, ORBIT Search Service, AUSINET, Australian Defence Libraries Database (DISNET); internal databases (defense reports); ILANET (electronic mail service). **Remarks:** FAX: 3 318 4536. Telex: AA35230. Electronic mail address(es): V MRL (ILANET).

★4702★
Defense for Children International -- United States of America - Library (Soc Sci)
210 Forsyth St.
New York, NY 10002 Phone: (212)353-0951
Subjects: Child maltreatment and abuse, children's rights legislation, children and war, refugees, juvenile justice. **Holdings:** 1000 volumes; statistical materials.

Defense Construction Supply Center
See: **U.S. Defense Logistics Agency** (17167)

Defense General Supply Center
See: **U.S. Defense Logistics Agency** (17169)

Defense Industrial Plant Equipment Center
See: **U.S. Dept. of Defense** (17223)

Defense Industrial Supply Center
See: **U.S. Defense Logistics Agency** (17170)

Defense Logistics Services Center
See: **U.S. Defense Logistics Agency** (17171)

Defense Personnel Support Center
See: **U.S. Defense Logistics Agency** (17172)

Defense Pest Management Information Analysis Center
See: **U.S. Dept. of Defense - Armed Forces Pest Management Board** (17222)

★4703★
Defense Research Institute, Inc. - Brief Bank (Law)
750 N. Lake Shore Dr., Suite 500 Phone: (312)944-0575
Chicago, IL 60611 Pamela Kaplan, Asst.Res.Dir.
Founded: 1961. **Staff:** Prof 12; Other 12. **Subjects:** Briefs filed in appellate cases, civil litigation. **Special Collections:** Tort Liability Research Library; insurance law. **Holdings:** 2000 briefs (case files). **Subscriptions:** 50 journals and other serials. **Services:** DRI Research Services for members; not open to the public. **Automated Operations:** Computerized cataloging. **Computerized Information Services:** Internal database. Performs searches on fee basis to members only. **Publications:** Annual Brief Bank Indexes, semiannual supplements. **Special Indexes:** Brief Bank Indexes listed by legal subject. **Remarks:** FAX: (312)944-2003.

★4704★
Defense Systems, Inc. - Library (Info Sci)
1521 West Branch Phone: (703)883-2630
McLean, VA 22102 Deborah Carter
Staff: Prof 1. **Subjects:** Communication and computer systems, international politics and defense, military arts and sciences. **Special Collections:** Terrorism; human factors in computer systems. **Holdings:** 175 books; 700 unbound materials. **Subscriptions:** 21 journals and other serials. **Services:** Interlibrary loan; copying; library open to the public by appointment for reference use only. **Computerized Information Services:** DIALOG Information Services, NEXIS. **Remarks:** FAX: (703)883-0672.

★4705★
Defense Systems Management College - Library (Mil)
Bldg. 226 Phone: (703)664-2900
Fort Belvoir, VA 22060-5426 Helen H. Haltzel, Dir.
Founded: 1971. **Staff:** 7. **Subjects:** Weapon systems acquisition management, program management, total quality management. **Holdings:** 13,000 books; 10,000 reports. **Subscriptions:** 300 journals and other serials; 20 newspapers. **Services:** Interlibrary loan. **Automated Operations:** Computerized public access catalog, cataloging, and circulation. **Computerized Information Services:** DIALOG Information Services, LEGI-SLATE, DTIC. **Networks/Consortia:** Member of FEDLINK. **Remarks:** FAX: (703)780-1785. A branch of the U.S. Department of Defense. **Staff:** Maryellen Tipper, Ref. & Rd.Serv.; Gloria Holland, Tech.Serv.

★4706★
H.J. Degenkolb Associates, Engineers - Library (Sci-Engr)
350 Sansome St., Suite 900 Phone: (415)392-6952
San Francisco, CA 94104 Wess-John Murdough, Libn.
Founded: 1979. **Staff:** 1.**Subjects:** Earthquake engineering, structural engineering, geology, seismology, special construction, building laws and standards. **Holdings:** 3500 books; 150 bound periodical volumes; 5000 unbound technical reports; 3500 reports on microfiche; 500 maps; 30 boxes of clippings; 4 VF drawers; 6 VF drawers of manufacturers' catalogs; 250 bound manufacturers' catalogs; 5000 slides. **Subscriptions:** 160 journals and other serials. **Services:** Interlibrary loan; copying; library open to the public by appointment for reference use. **Automated Operations:** Computerized cataloging. **Computerized Information Services:** DIALOG Information Services. **Networks/Consortia:** Member of CLASS. **Remarks:** FAX: (415)981-3157.

George A. Degenshein, M.D. Memorial Library
See: **Maimonides Medical Center** (9547)

★4707★
Degolyer and MacNaughton - Library (Energy)
One Energy Square, Suite 400
4925 Greenville Ave. Phone: (214)368-6391
Dallas, TX 75206 Eleanor Maclay, Libn.
Founded: 1939. **Staff:** Prof 1. **Subjects:** Petroleum and natural gas, economics, geology, engineering. **Holdings:** 18,000 books; 3900 bound periodical volumes; 21,500 pamphlets; 4500 geologic maps; 90 pamphlet boxes of preprints. **Subscriptions:** 100 journals and other serials. **Services:** Interlibrary loan; copying; library open to the public by appointment. **Remarks:** FAX: (214)369-4061. Telex: 73 0485.

Leo Dehon Library
See: **Sacred Heart School of Theology** (14207)

★4708★
Del Mar College - Music Library
Music Dept.
Baldwin Blvd.
Corpus Christi, TX 78404
Defunct. Holdings absorbed by Del Mar College - William F. White, Jr. Library.

★4709★
Del Norte Baptist Church - Library (Rel-Phil)
5800 Montgomery Blvd., N.E. Phone: (505)881-9711
Albuquerque, NM 87109 Dorothy Conner, Res.Asst.
Subjects: Religion, history. **Holdings:** Figures not available. **Services:** Library open to the public with the permission of the church office.

★4710★
Del Norte County Historical Society - Library (Hist)
577 H St. Phone: (707)464-3922
Crescent City, CA 95531 Anne C. Steven, Libn.
Founded: 1967. **Subjects:** History of Del Norte County and California, local Indians, logging, lighthouses, fishing. **Holdings:** 1056 books; 2000 personal papers, diaries, other materials; historic photographs; Yurok and Tolowa Indian artifacts; newspapers. **Subscriptions:** 345 journals and other serials. **Services:** Copying; SDI; library open to the public for reference use only.

★4711★
Del Norte County Law Library (Law)
Courthouse
450 H St. Phone: (707)464-7217
Crescent City, CA 95531 Margot E. McGuire, Law Libn.
Subjects: Law. **Holdings:** 6653 volumes. **Services:** Library open to the public for reference use only.

Josefina del Toro Fulladosa Collection
See: **University of Puerto Rico - Library System - Josefina de Toro Fulladosa Collection** (19242)

Thomas E. Delahanty Law Library
See: **Maine (State) Administrative Office of the Courts - Thomas E. Delahanty Law Library** (9556)

★4712★
Delavan Inc. - Engineering Library (Sci-Engr)
P.O. Box 65100 Phone: (515)274-1561
West Des Moines, IA 50265-0100 Gwen Hartman, Libn.
Founded: 1955. **Staff:** 1. **Subjects:** Liquid atomization, spray nozzles, fuel injectors, fuel combustion, fluid flow and hydraulics, pumps, engineering design, properties of materials. **Holdings:** 1000 books; 500 bound periodical volumes; 12,000 papers and articles; manufacturers' catalogs; 1800 patents related to company products; 1000 technical reports (for company use); microfilm; microfiche; motion pictures. **Subscriptions:** 100 journals and other serials. **Services:** Library principally for organization use. **Publications:** Library bulletin - for internal distribution only. **Special Catalogs:** Index card files based on author, title, and key words. **Remarks:** FAX: (515)271-7205. A division of Coltec Industries.

★4713★
Delaware Academy of Medicine, Inc. - Lewis B. Flinn Library (Med)
1925 Lovering Ave. Phone: (302)656-6398
Wilmington, DE 19806 Gail P. Gill, Libn., Dir.
Founded: 1930. **Staff:** Prof 3; Other 2. **Subjects:** Medicine. **Special Collections:** 50 state medical journals (15-year holding). **Holdings:** 4000 books; 9800 bound periodical volumes. **Subscriptions:** 245 journals and other serials. **Services:** Interlibrary loan; copying; library open to the public for reference use only. **Automated Operations:** Computerized cataloging. **Computerized Information Services:** MEDLARS, DIALOG Information Services, OCLC; DOCLINE, LOANSOME DOC (electronic mail services). Performs searches on fee basis. **Networks/Consortia:** Member of Wilmington Area Biomedical Library Consortium (WABLC), Delaware Library Consortium (DLC), Libraries in the New Castle County System (LINCS), Health Sciences Libraries Consortium (HSLC), National Network of Libraries of Medicine (NN/LM). **Remarks:** Alternate telephone number(s): (302)656-1629. FAX: (302)656-0470.

★4714★
Delaware Agricultural Museum - Library (Agri)
866 N. DuPont Hwy. Phone: (302)734-1618
Dover, DE 19901 Hope Z. Schladen, Dir.
Founded: 1974. **Staff:** 2. **Subjects:** History of agriculture in Delaware, history of agriculture. **Special Collections:** Original ledgers and diaries of early Delaware farmers and merchants; early maps of the Delmarva areas; 19th century farm and home periodicals; USDA yearbooks (nearly complete set); early cookbooks; interviews with elder Delaware farmers and homemakers (audiotapes); Delaware Department of Transporation archeological surveys; extension service program collection; Voices of American Homemakers collection. **Holdings:** 1600 volumes. **Subscriptions:** 12 journals and other serials. **Services:** Copying; library open to the public. **Staff:** Mary Harnish-Kopco, Cur.

★4715★
Delaware Art Museum - Helen Farr Sloan Library (Art)
2301 Kentmere Pkwy. Phone: (302)571-9590
Wilmington, DE 19806 Iris Snyder, Hd.Libn.
Founded: 1912. **Staff:** Prof 1; Other 3. **Subjects:** American art history, history of illustration, pre-Raphaelites. **Special Collections:** Bancroft Pre-Raphaelite Library (1000 volumes); Howard Pyle Library (1000 volumes); N.C. Wyeth Collection (150 volumes); John Sloan Memorial Library (2500 volumes); John Sloan, Everett Shinn, Jerome Myers, Frank Schoonover collections. **Holdings:** 35,000 books; 360 bound periodical volumes; 60 shelves of unbound periodicals; 800 reels of microfilm of illustrated periodicals, 1890-1940; 52 VF drawers of pamphlets and clippings; 20 shelves of auction catalogs. **Subscriptions:** 50 journals and other serials. **Services:** Interlibrary loan; copying; library open to the public with advance approval required for use of special collections. **Computerized Information Services:** RLIN. **Remarks:** FAX: (302)571-0220.

★4716★
Delaware County Daily Times - Library (Publ)
500 Mildred Ave. Phone: (215)622-8821
Primos, PA 19018 Peggy Chance
Founded: 1952. **Staff:** Prof 1; Other 1. **Subjects:** Newspaper reference topics. **Holdings:** Delaware County Daily Times, 1876 to present; photographs. **Services:** Copying; library open to the public.

★4717★
Delaware County Historical Society - Library (Hist)
85 N. Malin Rd. Phone: (215)359-1148
Broomall, PA 19008 Christine Templin, Adm.
Founded: 1895. **Staff:** 3. **Subjects:** Delaware County history and genealogy. **Special Collections:** 1790-1910 Census of Delaware County, indexed 1790-1870; Baker Collection of local historic data (105 notebooks); atlas books of early land holdings; Pennsylvania and New Jersey archives; Chester Times, 1876-1970; out-of-print newspapers, 1840-1935. **Holdings:** 5000 books; 140 bound periodical volumes; 4500 files of clippings and pictures. **Services:** Copying; library open to the public. **Formerly:** John G. Pew Memorial Library located in Chester, PA.

★4718★
Delaware County Law Library (Law)
91 Court House
N. Sandusky St. Phone: (614)368-1775
Delaware, OH 43015 Maryanne W. Stewart, Libn.
Founded: 1900. **Staff:** 1. **Subjects:** Law. **Holdings:** 18,000 volumes. **Subscriptions:** 6 newspapers. **Services:** Library open to the public with librarian present. **Computerized Information Services:** WESTLAW.

★4719★
Delaware County Law Library (Law)
Courthouse Phone: (215)891-4462
Media, PA 19063 Charlotte H. Hewlings, Libn.
Founded: 1902. **Staff:** 1. **Subjects:** Law. **Holdings:** 30,000 volumes. **Subscriptions:** 56 journals and other serials. **Services:** Copying; library open to the public.

★4720★
Delaware County Planning Department - Planning Information Services (Plan)
Toal Bldg.
Second & Orange Sts. Phone: (215)891-5205
Media, PA 19063 Jill Hammond, Libn.
Founded: 1968. **Staff:** Prof 3. **Subjects:** Land use, population and demography, mapping of area, zoning and planning, economic statistics, environmental resources, data about minor civil division, housing. **Holdings:** 1500 books; 100 bound periodical volumes; 5000 binders of report material from government sources; 150 microfiche; 8 VF drawers. **Subscriptions:** 70 journals and other serials. **Services:** Interlibrary loan; copying; SDI; library open to the public. **Publications:** Acquisition lists, bimonthly - to area libraries. **Staff:** Jill Ann Kelly, Plan.Info.Spec.

Delaware Indian Resource Center
See: **Westchester County Department of Parks, Recreation and Conservation** (20228)

★4721★
Delaware Museum of Natural History - Library (Biol Sci)
4840 Kennett Pike, Rte. 52
Box 3937 Phone: (302)658-9111
Wilmington, DE 19807 Gene K. Hess, Coll.Mgr.
Staff: 1. **Subjects:** Malacology (mollusks), ornithology, mammalogy, natural history. **Special Collections:** Books by and about Linnaeus (600 books; 200 reprints). **Holdings:** 5000 books; 1000 bound periodical volumes; 10,000 unbound reprints on mollusks; 4000 unbound reprints on birds. **Subscriptions:** 100 journals and other serials. **Services:** Copying; library open to the public by prior arrangement. **Publications:** Indo-Pacific Mollusca, irregular; Nemouria, irregular; Living Volutes (1970); Philippine Birds (1971); South Pacific Birds (1976); Exotic Conchology (1976); Woodpeckers of the World (1982). **Special Indexes:** Index Nudibranchia (1971).

★4722★
Delaware River Basin Commission - Technical Library (Env-Cons)
25 State Police Dr.
Box 7360 Phone: (609)883-9500
Trenton, NJ 08628 Betty A. Lin, Libn.
Founded: 1962. **Staff:** Prof 1. **Subjects:** Delaware River, water resources, water pollution, aquatic biology, geology, hydrology. **Holdings:** 1500 books; 10,000 technical reports; 1 map case; 500 slides. **Subscriptions:** 65 journals and other serials. **Services:** Interlibrary loan; copying; library open to the public by appointment. **Computerized Information Services:** DIALOG Information Services. **Remarks:** FAX: (609)883-9522.

Delaware State Archives
See: **Delaware (State) Division of Historical & Cultural Affairs** (4730)

Delaware (State) Bureau of Museums and Historic Sites - E.R. Johnson Memorial Collection
See: **Delaware State Museums - Johnson Victrola Museum** (4736)

★4723★
Delaware State College - William C. Jason Library - Learning Center (Hist)
1200 N. Du Pont Hwy Phone: (302)739-5111
Dover, DE 19901 Gertrude Winston Jackson
Staff: Prof 25; Other 1. **Subjects:** Business, nursing, education, science, Delaware history, historical research. **Special Collections:** Historical Resource Collection; Delaware Collection. **Holdings:** Figures not available. **Subscriptions:** 1111 journals and other serials; 28 newspapers. **Services:** Interlibrary loan; library open to the public. **Computerized Information Services:** DIALOG Information Services; CD-ROMs (ABI/INFORM, Applied Science & Technology Index, Biography Index, Books in Print Plus, Business Periodicals Index, CIRR, CINAHL, ERIC, Education Index, GPO on SilverPlatter, General Science Index, Grolier Electronic Encyclopedia, Humanities Index, International Encyclopedia of Education, Le Pac, MLA International Bibliography, McGraw-Hill Dictionary of Scientific & Technical Terms, MEDLINE, NewsBank Electronic Index, Pravda, PsycLit, Science Helper K-8, Social Science Index, Sociofile, World Atlas); InfoTrac. Contact Person: Mrs. Rosamond Panda. **Remarks:** Alternate telephone number(s): (302)739-5112. FAX: (302)739-3533.

★4724★
Delaware (State) Department of Health & Social Services - Division of Public Health - Library
P.O. Box 637
Dover, DE 19903
Defunct.

★4725★
Delaware (State) Department of Public Instruction - Library Information Center (Educ)
Townsend Bldg.
Box 1402 Phone: (302)739-4692
Dover, DE 19903 Thomas F. Brennan, Dir.
Founded: 1970. **Staff:** Prof 1; Other 1. **Subjects:** Educational administration and supervision; school finance; school plant planning; school law. **Special Collections:** Laws of Delaware; Delaware Code Annotated; Delaware history of education; ERIC microfiche (complete set). **Holdings:** 5000 books; 140 periodicals; minutes of the State Board of Education; department reports; information files. **Subscriptions:** 200 journals and other serials; 15 newspapers. **Services:** Interlibrary loan; copying; library open to the public. **Computerized Information Services:** DIALOG Information Services. **Networks/Consortia:** Member of Kent Library Network (KLN). **Publications:** Compilation of School Laws of Delaware, updated periodically - to school personnel. **Remarks:** FAX: (302)736-9092.

★4726★
Delaware (State) Department of Public Instruction - State Film Library (Aud-Vis)
Edgehill Shopping Ctr.
43 S. DuPont Hwy. Phone: (302)739-4685
Dover, DE 19903 Doris Vrhovac, Lib.Spec.
Staff: 2. **Holdings:** Films; videos. **Services:** Library open to schools, institutes of higher education, and those with educational need. **Remarks:** FAX: (302)739-3092. **Staff:** Doris M. Vrhovac, Libn.

★4727★
Delaware (State) Department of Transportation - Library (Trans)
Administrative Bldg.
Rte. 113, Box 778 Phone: (302)739-4157
Dover, DE 19903 Juliana Cheng, Libn.
Staff: 1. **Subjects:** Traffic studies, highway design, mass transportation. **Special Collections:** Transportation Research Board Reports. **Holdings:** 300 books; 8000 reports. **Services:** Interlibrary loan; library open to the public with restrictions. **Networks/Consortia:** Member of Kent Library Network (KLN).

★4728★
Delaware (State) Development Office - Delaware Tourisim Office (Rec)
99 Kings Hwy.
P.O. Box 1401 Phone: (302)739-4271
Dover, DE 19903 John J. Casey, Jr., Dir.
Staff: Prof 3; Other 4. **Subjects:** State of Delaware - travel information, tourism, promotional and statistical material. **Holdings:** Books; maps; brochures. **Services:** Office open to the public. **Remarks:** Toll-free telephone number(s): (800)282-8667 (in Delaware); (800)441-8846 (outside Delaware). FAX: (302)739-5749. **Staff:** Catherine Wheeler, Dir., Tourism Off.

★4729★
Delaware (State) Development Office - Technical Library
99 Kings Hwy.
Box 1401
Dover, DE 19901
Founded: 1981. **Subjects:** Business development, planning, land use, statistics, economics. **Holdings:** 480 volumes; studies; pamphlets. **Remarks:** Houses the State Data Center. Currently inactive.

★4730★
Delaware (State) Division of Historical & Cultural Affairs - Delaware State Archives (Hist)
Hall of Records Phone: (302)739-5318
Dover, DE 19901 Howard P. Lowell, Act. State Archv./Rec.Adm.
Founded: 1905. **Staff:** Prof 5; Other 7. **Subjects:** Delaware history and government, county and city records. **Special Collections:** Tatnall Tombstone Collection (2 volumes); Turner Genealogical Collection (21 cubic feet); transcribed church records (35 volumes). **Holdings:** 3000 books; 5000 maps and architectural drawings; 19,000 cubic feet of state and local records; 75,000 photographs and slides; 75,000 reels of microfilm. **Services:** Copying; archives open to the public. **Networks/Consortia:** Member of Kent Library Network (KLN). **Publications:** Delaware Documentation (annual checklist of state publications) - national distribution. **Remarks:** FAX: (302)739-6710. **Staff:** Joanne A. Mattern, Dp. State Archv.; Randy Goss, Coord., Accessioning and Proc.; Bruce Haase, Archv.

★4731★
Delaware (State) Division of Libraries - State Library (Info Sci)
43 S. DuPont Hwy. Phone: (302)739-4748
Dover, DE 19903 Tom W. Sloan, Dir. & State Libn.
Founded: 1901. **Staff:** Prof 7; Other 12. **Subjects:** Reference, library science, biography, social sciences, local history. **Special Collections:** Delaware state documents. **Holdings:** 40,598 books; 60 periodical titles on microfilm; 5400 reels of microfilm; 10,000 talking books and cassettes. **Subscriptions:** 10 newspapers. **Services:** Interlibrary loan; library services to the blind and physically handicapped; library open to the public. **Automated Operations:** LBPH-READS. **Computerized Information Services:** OCLC, LEXIS, NEXIS; CD-ROMs. **Networks/Consortia:** Member of PALINET. **Publications:** Annual Reports of Delaware Public Libraries, LSCA Annual Program, and Long Range Library Development Plan. **Remarks:** FAX: (302)739-6787. **Staff:** Jane Gafvert, Adm.Libn.; Anne Norman, Adm.Libn.; Jane Tupin, Sr.Libn.

★4732★
Delaware State General Assembly - Legislative Library (Law)
Box 1401 Phone: (302)739-5808
Dover, DE 19901 Ruth Ann Melson, Libn.
Founded: 1967. **Staff:** Prof 1. **Subjects:** Delaware law and legislation. **Holdings:** 7000 books; 10,000 legal materials, statutes, legislative reports. **Subscriptions:** 20 journals and other serials; 8 newspapers. **Services:** Interlibrary loan; copying; library open to the public during the months July-December. **Computerized Information Services:** Bill search (internal database). Performs searches free of charge. **Publications:** Laws of Delaware, biennial; Legislative Digest, annual; leadership brochure, biennial. **Special Indexes:** Index to code changes, daily while assembly is in session. **Remarks:** FAX: (302)739-3895.

★4733★
Delaware State Geological Survey - Library (Sci-Engr)
University of Delaware Phone: (302)451-2833
Newark, DE 19716 Robert R. Jordan, State Geologist
Subjects: Geology, mineral and water resources, seismology, well sampling, cartography. **Special Collections:** Core and sample library (25,000 items); repository for geophysical logs and seismic sections. **Holdings:** Figures not available. **Services:** Library open to the public by appointment for reference use. **Remarks:** FAX: (302)292-3579. **Staff:** Thomas E. Pickett, Assoc.Dir.

★4734★
Delaware State Hospital - Medical Library (Med)
1902 N. Dupont Hwy. Phone: (302)421-6368
New Castle, DE 19720 James M. McCloskey, Sr.Libn.
Staff: Prof 1. **Subjects:** Psychiatry, psychology, medicine, social work, nursing, pastoral care. **Special Collections:** Delaware State Hospital Archives. **Holdings:** 4000 books; 1240 bound periodical volumes. **Subscriptions:** 125 journals and other serials. **Services:** Interlibrary loan; library open to the public for reference use only. **Computerized Information Services:** BRS Information Technologies, MEDLINE. **Networks/Consortia:** Member of Wilmington Area Biomedical Library Consortium (WABLC), National Network of Libraries of Medicine - Middle Atlantic Region, Libraries in the New Castle County System (LINCS). **Publications:** Library Current. **Remarks:** FAX: (302)421-6503.

★4735★
Delaware State Law Library in Kent County (Law)
Kent County Courthouse
Dover, DE 19901 Phone: (302)739-5467
Staff: Prof 1; Other 1. **Subjects:** Law. **Holdings:** 39,000 volumes. **Subscriptions:** 35 journals and other serials.

★4736★
Delaware State Museums - Johnson Victrola Museum (Aud-Vis)
102 S. State St.
PO Box 1401 Phone: (302)739-3262
Dover, DE 19903 Ann Baker Horsey, Cur. of Coll.
Founded: 1967. **Staff:** 1. **Subjects:** Sound recording industry, Victor Talking Machine Company. **Special Collections:** Victor phonographs, records, catalogs; papers of E.R. Johnson. **Holdings:** Books; reference materials. **Services:** Library open to the public for reference use only. **Computerized Information Services:** Internal database. **Publications:** Enrico Caruso: A Discography. **Remarks:** Collection located at the Delaware State Museum, 316 S. Governors Ave. Alternate telephone number(s): 739-5316. FAX: (302)739-6712. **Formerly:** Delaware (State) Bureau of Museums and Historic Sites - E.R. Johnson Memorial Collection.

★4737★
Delaware Valley College of Science and Agriculture - Joseph Krauskopf Memorial Library (Agri)
Doylestown, PA 18901 Phone: (215)345-1500
Constance R. Shook, Dir., Lib.Serv.
Founded: 1924. **Staff:** Prof 4; Other 7. **Subjects:** Agribusiness, agronomy, animal science, computer information systems management, dairy science, English literature, equine science, food industry, horticulture, ornamental horticulture, poultry husbandry, biology, chemistry, business administration. **Special Collections:** Memorial Collection of Judaica. **Holdings:** 58,000 volumes; 11,000 bound periodical volumes; U.S. Department of Agriculture and State Agricultural Experiment Station bulletins (subject indexed); 2000 reels of microfilm; 41,100 microfiche. **Subscriptions:** 690 journals. **Services:** Interlibrary loan; copying; library open to the public for reference use only. **Automated Operations:** Computerized cataloging and acquisitions. **Computerized Information Services:** OCLC, BRS Information Technologies. **Networks/Consortia:** Member of Council on Botanical Horticultural Libraries, Tri-State College Library Cooperative (TCLC). **Remarks:** FAX: (215)345-1711. **Staff:** Karen Byrne, Cat./Ref.Libn.; June Bitzer, Acq./Ref.Libn.; Janet Klaessig, Per./Ref.Libn.

★4738★
Delaware Valley Hospital - Library (Med)
1 Titus Place Phone: (607)865-4101
Walton, NY 13856 Marian Platt, Libn.
Staff: Prof 1; Other 1. **Subjects:** Medicine, allied health sciences. **Holdings:** 257 volumes. **Subscriptions:** 40 journals and other serials. **Services:** Interlibrary loan; library not open to the public. **Computerized Information Services:** OCLC, MARC. **Networks/Consortia:** Member of South Central Research Library Council (SCRLC).

★4739★
Delaware Valley Medical Center - John A. Whyte Medical Library (Med)
200 Oxford Valley Rd. Phone: (215)949-5160
Langhorne, PA 19047 Ann B. Lalaiotes, Lib.Dir.
Staff: Prof 1. **Subjects:** Medicine. **Holdings:** 810 books; 115 bound periodical volumes; 550 cassettes and videotapes. **Subscriptions:** 115 journals and other serials. **Services:** Interlibrary loan; library not open to the public. **Computerized Information Services:** NLM; DOCLINE (electronic mail service). **Networks/Consortia:** Member of National Network of Libraries of Medicine - Middle Atlantic Region, Delaware Valley Information Consortium (DEVIC). **Remarks:** FAX: (215)945-8314.

★4740★
Delcan Corporation - Library (Sci-Engr)
133 Wynford Dr. Phone: (416)441-4111
North York, ON, Canada M3C 1K1 Kelly Mazzuca, Lib.Tech.
Founded: 1982. **Staff:** Prof 1; Other 1.5. **Subjects:** Engineering, architecture, planning, contract administration, transportation, systems. **Special Collections:** Delcan reports and proposals (2500). **Holdings:** 3000 books; 1600 reports; 1000 proposals. **Subscriptions:** 145 journals and other serials. **Services:** Interlibrary loan; library not open to the public. **Automated Operations:** Computerized cataloging, serials, and circulation (INMAGIC). **Computerized Information Services:** DIALOG Information Services, QL Systems, CAN/OLE; internal database. **Special Catalogs:** Delcan reports and proposals. **Remarks:** FAX: (416)441-4131.

Delco Chassis Market Research Department
See: **General Motors Corporation - Delco Chassis Market Research Department** (6335)

★4741★
Delco Electronics - Delco Systems Operations - Technical Library (Sci-Engr)
E 104
6767 Hollister Ave. Phone: (805)961-7080
Goleta, CA 93117-3018 Kenneth C. Crombie, Tech.Libn.
Founded: 1960. **Staff:** Prof 1. **Subjects:** Physics, astronautics, aeronautics, mathematics, electronics, electrical engineering. **Holdings:** 3100 books; 8900 bound periodical volumes. **Subscriptions:** 200 journals and other serials; 10 newspapers. **Services:** Interlibrary loan; library not open to the public. **Computerized Information Services:** DIALOG Information Services. **Remarks:** FAX: (805)961-7383. Delco Electronics is a subsidiary of G.M. Hughes Electronics.

★4742★
Delco Electronics Corporation - Information Resource Center (Sci-Engr)
1 Corporate Center Phone: (317)451-0385
Kokomo, IN 46902-9002 Gloria Kohler, Adm.
Founded: 1961. **Staff:** Prof 2. **Subjects:** Electronics, semiconductors, acoustics, mechanics, physics, metallurgy, chemistry, mathematics, communications, research management. **Holdings:** 3500 books; 550 bound periodical volumes; 6000 technical reports. **Subscriptions:** 300 journals and other serials. **Services:** Interlibrary loan; library not open to the public but use for reference may be requested. **Automated Operations:** Computerized public access catalog, cataloging, acquisitions, serials, and circulation. **Computerized Information Services:** DIALOG Information Services, OCLC. **Networks/Consortia:** Member of INCOLSA. **Remarks:** FAX: (317)451-0542. **Staff:** Dorothy Hubbard, Coord.; Shirley Pickering, Coord.

★4743★
Delegation for Friendship Among Women - Library (Soc Sci)
2219 Caroline Ln. Phone: (612)455-5620
South St. Paul, MN 55075 Mary Pomeroy, Delegation Sec.
Founded: 1970. **Staff:** 1. **Subjects:** Activities of women in the Third World. **Special Collections:** Womens' organizations in third world or developing countries. **Holdings:** 1000 books; 30 other cataloged items. **Subscriptions:** 20 journals and other serials; 6 newspapers. **Services:** Library open to the public by appointment.

★4744★
Delex Systems, Inc. - Information Center (Mil)
1953 Gallows Rd., Suite 700 Phone: (703)734-8300
Vienna, VA 22182-3991 Victoria Harriston, Info.Ctr.Mgr.
Founded: 1978. **Staff:** Prof 1; Other 1. **Subjects:** Naval warfare, computer science. **Holdings:** 1500 books; 8500 reports; 200 maps; 5000 microfiche. **Subscriptions:** 120 journals and other serials. **Services:** Interlibrary loan; library not open to the public. **Computerized Information Services:** DIALOG Information Services, DTIC (DROLS), LEXIS, NEXIS; internal databases; CD-ROM (DODISS Plus). **Publications:** Current Periodicals Holdings. **Remarks:** FAX: (703)734-9303.

Delhom-Gambrell Reference Library
See: **Mint Museum - Library** (10498)

★4745★
Dellcrest Children's Centre - Library (Soc Sci)
1645 Sheppard Ave., W. Phone: (416)633-0515
Downsview, ON, Canada M3M 2X4 Lois Elliott, Libn.
Founded: 1978. **Staff:** Prof 1. **Subjects:** Child psychotherapy, welfare, and development; parenting and family therapy. **Holdings:** 1124 volumes; 41 cassettes; 36 VF drawers of pamphlets. **Subscriptions:** 30 journals and other serials. **Services:** Library open to the public with restrictions.

Deloitte Haskins & Sells Tax Research Room
See: **University of Minnesota - Business Reference Service** (18897)

★4746★
Deloitte & Touche - Business Information Centre (Bus-Fin)
BCE Place
181 Bay St., Suite 1400 Phone: (416)601-6150
Toronto, ON, Canada M5J 2T3 Lilian Gilmour, Libn.
Staff: 6. **Subjects:** Accounting, auditing, business. **Special Collections:** Annual reports. **Holdings:** 7000 books. **Subscriptions:** 300 journals and other serials; 7 newspapers. **Services:** Interlibrary loan; library not open to the public. **Automated Operations:** Computerized cataloging and serials. **Computerized Information Services:** Info Globe, DIALOG Information Services, Infomart Online, Mead Data Central, Reuters, ADP Brokerage Information Services Group, The Conference Board, Inc., WESTLAW, InvesText, INSIGHT. **Remarks:** FAX: (416)601-6151. **Staff:** Juanita Richardson; Anne Lessard; Kerry Buller.

★4747★
Deloitte & Touche - Information Center (Bus-Fin)
1633 Broadway Phone: (212)492-2410
New York, NY 10019 Trudy Katz, Asst.Libn.
Staff: Prof 2; Other 3. **Subjects:** Accounting, business, management. **Holdings:** 5000 books. **Subscriptions:** 300 journals and other serials; 10 newspapers. **Services:** Interlibrary loan; center open to SLA members. **Automated Operations:** Computerized cataloging, acquisitions, and serials. **Computerized Information Services:** DIALOG Information Services, NEXIS, Dow Jones News/Retrieval, Reuter TEXTLINE, System Development Corporation (SDC), National Planning Data Corporation (NPDC). **Remarks:** FAX: (212)489-6944. **Staff:** Sally Hand, Ref.Libn.

★4748★
Deloitte & Touche - Library (Bus-Fin)
1000 Wilshire Blvd., 12th Fl. Phone: (213)688-5359
Los Angeles, CA 90017-2471 Kathleen Tice, Hd. Libn.
Staff: Prof 2; Other 1. **Subjects:** Auditing, taxation, management services, actuarial science, employee benefits, valuation. **Holdings:** Figures not available. **Services:** Library not open to the public. **Automated Operations:** Computerized circulation. **Computerized Information Services:** LEXIS, DIALOG Information Services, DataTimes, InvesText. **Publications:** Newsletters; booklets. **Remarks:** FAX: (213)688-0100. **Staff:** Anita Szafran, Ref.Libn.

★4749★
Deloitte & Touche - Library (Bus-Fin)
1001 Pennsylvania Ave., N.W., Suite 350 Phone: (202)879-5304
Washington, DC 20004-2505 Judith A. Parvez, Libn.
Founded: 1977. **Staff:** Prof 1. **Subjects:** Accounting, auditing, banking, data processing, management, taxation. **Holdings:** 500 books. **Subscriptions:** 104 journals and other serials. **Services:** Interlibrary loan; library open to the public by special arrangement. **Computerized Information Services:** DIALOG Information Services, LEXIS, NEXIS, DataTimes. **Remarks:** FAX: (202)879-5309.

★4750★
Deloitte & Touche - Library (Bus-Fin)
4300 Norwest Ctr.
90 S. 7th St. Phone: (612)344-0226
Minneapolis, MN 55402 Richard G. Reynen, Libn.
Founded: 1976. **Staff:** Prof 1; Other 2. **Subjects:** Accounting, auditing, taxation. **Holdings:** 3000 books; 45 bound periodical volumes. **Subscriptions:** 300 journals and other serials; 5 newspapers. **Services:** Interlibrary loan; copying; library open to the public with restrictions. **Computerized Information Services:** DIALOG Information Services, Dow Jones News/Retrieval, LEXIS, NEXIS, DataTimes; DIALMAIL (electronic mail service). **Remarks:** FAX: (612)339-6202; (612)375-5418.

★4751★
Deloitte & Touche - Library (Bus-Fin)
333 Clay, Suite 2300
Houston, TX 77002 Phone: (713)756-2416
Staff: Prof 1; Other 1. **Subjects:** Taxation, accounting, auditing, management consulting. **Special Collections:** All State Tax Reporters. **Holdings:** 9000 books; 75 bound periodical volumes; 3 VF drawers of annual reports. **Subscriptions:** 150 journals and other serials; 15 newspapers. **Services:** Interlibrary loan; copying. **Computerized Information Services:** LEXIS, DIALOG Information Services. **Remarks:** FAX: (713)756-2001.

★4752★
Deloitte & Touche - Library (Bus-Fin)
Scotia Centre, Suite 2400
700 2nd St., S.W. Phone: (403)267-1783
Calgary, AB, Canada T2P 0S7 Heather Gellner, Lib.Tech.
Staff: Prof 1. **Subjects:** Accounting, auditing, taxation. **Holdings:** 2400 books. **Subscriptions:** 140 journals and other serials; 4 newspapers. **Services:** Interlibrary loan; copying; SDI. **Automated Operations:** Computerized cataloging and serials. **Computerized Information Services:** Info Globe, DIALOG Information Services, Infomart Online, QL Systems, WILSONLINE, CAN/OLE, Canadian Tax Online; internal database; Envoy 100 (electronic mail service). **Remarks:** FAX: (403)264-2871. Maintains branch library at 1167 Kensington Crescent, N.W., Calgary, AB T2N 1X7.

★4753★
Deloitte & Touche - Library and Information Center (Bus-Fin)
50 Fremont St. Phone: (415)393-9735
San Francisco, CA 94105 Mary Torres, Lib.Mgr.
Founded: 1975. **Staff:** Prof 3. **Subjects:** Accounting, taxation, auditing, real estate, computers. **Holdings:** 3000 books. **Subscriptions:** 200 journals and newspapers. **Services:** Interlibrary loan; library not open to the public. **Computerized Information Services:** DIALOG Information Services, Dow Jones News/Retrieval, VU/TEXT Information Services, DataTimes, LEXIS, Dun & Bradstreet Business Credit Services. **Remarks:** FAX: (415)393-4304. **Staff:** David O'Connor; Marianna Keanne.

★4754★
Deloitte & Touche - Library and Information Center (Bus-Fin)
1055 Dunsmuir Phone: (604)669-4466
Vancouver, BC, Canada C7X 1P4 C. Iona Douglas, Libn.
Staff: Prof 1. **Subjects:** Accounting, auditing, taxation, industry. **Holdings:** 2000 books; annual reports; stock, exchange rate, and dividend records. **Subscriptions:** 65 journals and other serials; 6 newspapers. **Services:** Interlibrary loan; library open to the public with restrictions. **Computerized Information Services:** DIALOG Information Services, Infomart Online, QL Systems, Info Globe. **Remarks:** FAX: (604)685-0395.

★4755★
Deloitte & Touche - National Information Center (Bus-Fin)
1 World Trade Center Phone: (212)669-5000
New York, NY 10048 Rhea Tabakin, Mgr.
Staff: Prof 5; Other 5. **Subjects:** Accounting, business. **Holdings:** 5000 volumes. **Subscriptions:** 400 journals and other serials; 7 newspapers. **Services:** Interlibrary loan; copying; library open to SLA members. **Automated Operations:** Computerized cataloging and routing. **Computerized Information Services:** DIALOG Information Services, PFDS Online, Mead Data Central, ADP Network Services, Inc., Dow Jones News/Retrieval, InvesText, Spectrum Ownership Profiles Online; CD-ROMs. Performs searches on fee basis. **Publications:** Subject bibliographies - for internal distribution only. **Remarks:** FAX: (212)669-5160. **Formed by the merger of:** Deloitte Haskins & Sells and Touche Ross and Company.

★4756★
Deloitte & Touche - Research Center (Bus-Fin)
180 N. Stetson Phone: (312)946-3616
Chicago, IL 60601 Therese Cotillas, Mgr.
Staff: Prof 2; Other 3. **Subjects:** Accounting, auditing, taxation, business and finance, management, electronic data processing/information technology. **Holdings:** 2500 books; 1000 corporate annual reports. **Subscriptions:** 250 journals and other serials; 15 newspapers. **Services:** Interlibrary loan; copying; library open to the public by appointment. **Automated Operations:** Computerized acquisitions and serials. **Computerized Information Services:** DIALOG Information Services, Dow Jones News/Retrieval, LEXIS, NEXIS, National Automated Accounting Research System (NAARS), DataTimes, VU/TEXT Information Services, Reuters, ADP Network Services, Inc., SDC (System Development Corporation), MAID (Market Analysis and Information Database). **Publications:** Library acquisitions list, bimonthly - for internal distribution only; Library Services Brochure - available on request. **Remarks:** FAX: (312)946-2600. **Staff:** Barbara Dolmon.

★4757★
Deloitte & Touche - Tax Resource Centre (Bus-Fin)
BCE Place
181 Bay St., Suite 1400 Phone: (416)601-6150
Toronto, ON, Canada M5J 2V1 Mina Woodruff, Mgr.
Staff: 3. **Subjects:** Income taxation - personal, corporate; international taxation; sales and commodity tax. **Holdings:** 7000 books; 18 bound periodical volumes; 400 reports. **Subscriptions:** 384 journals and other serials. **Services:** Interlibrary loan; library not open to the public. **Automated Operations:** Computerized cataloging. **Computerized Information Services:** CAN/LAW, Infomart Online, Info Globe, QL Systems, WESTLAW, LEXIS, NEXIS, Canadian Tax Online, STM Systems Corporation, Business Opportunities Sourcing System (BOSS), The Financial Post DataGroup. **Remarks:** FAX: (416)601-6151. **Staff:** Elizabeth Dingman, Info.Spec.; Michele Dietrich, Lib.Techn.

Delta Blues Museum Collection
See: **Carnegie Public Library of Clarksdale and Coahoma County** (3086)

Delta Omicron Music Composers Library
See: **Public Library of Cincinnati and Hamilton County - Art and Music Department** (13477)

★4758★
Delta Projects Inc. - Library
Box 5244, Sta. A Phone: (403)258-6527
Calgary, AB, Canada T2H 2N7 Carol A. Seebruch, Info.Rsrcs.Coord.
Founded: 1977. **Subjects:** Engineering, technology, business, management. **Holdings:** Reports; patents; books; journals; standards; government documents. **Services:** Library not open to the public. **Computerized Information Services:** DIALOG Information Services, CAN/OLE. **Remarks:** FAX: (403)255-1421. Telex: 038-22509.

Delta Regional Primate Research Center
See: **Tulane University** (16566)

★4759★
Delta Waterfowl and Wetlands Research Station - David Winton Bell Memorial Library (Biol Sci)
R.R. 1
Portage La Prairie, MB, Canada R1N 3A1 Phone: (204)239-1900
Founded: 1951. **Staff:** 1. **Subjects:** Ornithology, wetland biology, ecology, animal behavior, natural history, botany. **Holdings:** 4500 books; 3500 bound periodical volumes; 250 upublished theses; 500 government reports; 12,000 offprints. **Subscriptions:** 95 journals and other serials. **Services:** Interlibrary loan; copying; library open to the public with restrictions. **Remarks:** FAX: (204)239-5950.

Delta Writers Library
See: **Cottonlandia Educational and Recreational Foundation, Inc. - Rowell A. Billups Memorial Library** (4353)

★4760★
Deltiologists of America - Library (Rec)
Box 8 Phone: (215)485-8572
Norwood, PA 19074 James L. Lowe, Dir.
Founded: 1960. **Staff:** 1. **Subjects:** Deltiology (publishing and collecting of picture postcards), 1870 to present. **Special Collections:** Picture postcard publications. **Holdings:** 250 books; 400 bound periodical volumes; 3000 clippings in 5 file drawers; 600,000 picture postcards in 300 file drawers. **Subscriptions:** 20 journals and other serials. **Services:** Interlibrary loan; library not open to the public. **Publications:** Postcard Classics, bimonthly - limited circulation; Bibliography of Postcard Literature; Standard Postcard Catalog; Lincoln Postcard Catalog; Pictures in the Post; Picture Postcards of the Golden Age; Detroit Publishing Company Collector's Guide.

★4761★
Demeure Historique - Library (Hist)
57, quai de la Tournelle Phone: 1 43290286
F-75005 Paris, France Marquis De Breteuil, Exec.Off.
Founded: 1924. **Subjects:** French historic landmarks. **Holdings:** 500 volumes.

Cecil B. DeMille Collection
See: **Academy of Motion Picture Arts and Sciences - Margaret Herrick Library** (35)

★4762★
Democratic National Committee - Research Library (Soc Sci)
430 S. Capitol St., S.E. Phone: (202)863-8000
Washington, DC 20003 Mark Steitz, Dir., Res.
Staff: Prof 6. **Subjects:** Party and national politics. **Special Collections:** Democratic National Convention proceedings, 1856 to present; Democratic Party publications, 1856 to present; Democratic National Committee working files, 1950 to present. **Holdings:** 500 books. **Subscriptions:** 34 journals and other serials. **Services:** Library not open to the public. **Remarks:** FAX: (202)863-8028.

Carol Dempster Collection
See: **Museum of Modern Art - Film Stills Archive** (10908)

Denali National Park and Preserve
See: **U.S. Natl. Park Service** (17700)

★4763★
Dene-Nation - Library
Northway Bldg.
Box 2338
Yellowknife, NT, Canada X1A 2P7 Phone: (403)873-4081
Remarks: Alternate telephone number(s): 873-4082. No further information was supplied by respondent.

Ella Strong Denison Library
See: **The Claremont Colleges - Ella Strong Denison Library** (3752)

Denison Memorial Library
See: **University of Colorado Health Sciences Center** (18511)

★4764★
Denison Mines Ltd. - Library
650 W. Georgia St.
Box 11575
Vancouver, BC, Canada V6B 4N7
Defunct.

★4765★
Denison Mines Ltd. - Library
Royal Bank Plaza
South Tower, Suite 3400
P.O. Box 40
Toronto, ON, Canada M5J 2K2
Defunct.

Denmark - Geological Survey of Denmark
See: **Geological Survey of Denmark** (6365)

Denmark - Ministry of Environment - Geological Survey of Denmark
See: **Geological Survey of Denmark** (6365)

★4766★
Denmark - National Library of Education - The Royal Danish School of Educational Studies (Educ)
Emdrupvej 101 Phone: 3 9696633
DK-2400 Copenhagen NV, Denmark Mette Stockmarr, Chf.Libn.
Founded: 1887. **Staff:** Prof 58; Other 5. **Subjects:** Theory of education, national and international systems of education, educational psychology, developmental psychology. **Special Collections:** Danish and foreign literature for children and young people collection (60,000 volumes of fiction; 6000 volumes of non-fiction; 60 periodicals). **Holdings:** 904,590 books; 457,017 microfiche; 232 reels of microfilm. **Subscriptions:** 5457 journals and other serials; 25 newspapers. **Services:** Interlibrary loan; copying; library open to the public. **Publications:** PEPSY. **Remarks:** FAX: 3 9660082. **Also Known As:** Danmarks Paedagogiske Bibliotek - Danmarks Laererhosjskole. **Staff:** Birgitte Rischel, Libn.

★4767★
Denmark - National Technological Library of Denmark (Sci-Engr)
Anker Engelunds Vej 1 Phone: 42883088
DK-2800 Lyngby, Denmark Inger Hoy Nielsen, Libn.
Founded: 1942. **Staff:** 82. **Subjects:** Science, technology. **Holdings:** 700,000 books, conference proceedings, dissertations, and research reports. **Subscriptions:** 4000 journals and other serials. **Services:** Interlibrary loan; library open to the public. **Automated Operations:** Computerized cataloging and serials. **Computerized Information Services:** Produces Automated Library Information System (ALIS). **Special Catalogs:** Subject catalog containing all monographs and dissertations in participating technological libraries; serials holdings list. **Remarks:** FAX: 42883040. Telex: 37148 DTBC DK. **Also Known As:** Danmarks Tekniske Bibliotek - DTB.

★4768★
Denmark - Royal Danish Air Force - Library (Mil, Trans)
Jonstrupvej 286 Phone: 45 42978003
DK-3500 Jonstrup, Denmark Ingemann Rasmussen, LTC
Founded: 1951. **Staff:** Prof 1; Other 4. **Subjects:** Aviation history, civil and military aircraft, air defense. **Special Collections:** All the World Aircraft magazine, 1909 to present; Flight International Magazine, 1918 to present. **Holdings:** 24,000 books. **Subscriptions:** 173 journals and other serials. **Services:** Interlibrary loan; library open to the public. **Computerized Information Services:** ALBA, ALIS, AUBOLINE, BASIS, COSMOS, DANDOU; TINLIB (internal database). **Publications:** TILGANG. **Remarks:** FAX: 45 42875109.

★4769★
Denmark - Royal Danish Navy - Library (Mil)
Overgaden oven Vandet 62b Phone: 3 1547382
DK-1415 Copenhagen K, Denmark A. Holm, Commander
Founded: 1765. **Staff:** Prof 1; Other 3. **Subjects:** Naval history. **Special Collections:** Greenland and Artic affairs collection; Sea-voyages and expeditions collection. **Holdings:** 32,000 books. **Subscriptions:** 50 journals and other serials. **Services:** Interlibrary loan; copying; library open to the public. **Automated Operations:** TINLib.

★4770★
Denmark - Royal Library (Hum, Art, Publ)
P.O. Box 2149 Phone: 3 3930111
DK-1016 Copenhagen K, Denmark
Erland Kolding Nielsen, Dir.Gen.
Founded: 1653. **Staff:** Prof 141.5; Other 161.5. **Subjects:** Theology, humanities, social sciences. **Special Collections:** Department of Judaica and Hebraica (85,000 books and serial publications; 488 current serials; 500 manuscripts); Manuscript Department (56,1890 Danish and Western manuscripts; 5000 microforms; 1977 AV items); Drama Collection (13,500 manuscripts; 13,300 books); Music Department (239,395 print items; 10,185 manuscripts; 711 microforms; 143 AV items); Orchestra Collection (7000 print items; 9500 manuscripts); Map Collection (251,000 maps; 7000 atlases; 27 globes); Print and Photograph Collection (1 million portraits; 1.3 million topographical sheets including 800,000 postcards; 530,000 historical pictures and albums; 3.5 million aerial photographs; 1 million items in Muller's Pinakotek, Silhouette Collections, Newspaper Archives, Ex-libris); Oriental Department (4400 manuscripts; 52,300 books; 385 current serials); Office of International Publications (50,000 books; 160,000 documents; 100,000 microforms; 1100 current serials). **Holdings:** 3.4 million books, serials and serial publications (including 4500 incunabula and 40,000 bound periodical volumes); 168,000 microforms; 7000 AV items; 4000 linear meters of pamphlets. **Subscriptions:** 11,000 foreign journals and other serials. **Services:** Interlibrary loan; copying; library open to the public. **Computerized Information Services:** BLAISE, BRS Information Technologies, DAFA Data AB, Deutsches Bibliotheksinstitut (DBI), DIALOG Information Services, DIMDI, ECHO, ESA/IRS, HELECON Online Service, ORBIT Search Service, Questel, WILSONLINE and 22 other databases. Performs searches. Contact Person: Virginia Laursen, Libn. **Publications:** Publications on the Royal Library today and in the future; The Royal Library's history; bibliographies; catalogs. **Remarks:** FAX: 3 3932218. Telex: 15009. **Also Known As:** Kongelige Bibliotek. **Staff:** Birgitte Huidt, Sectional Libn.

★4771★
Denmark - Royal Military - Library (Mil)
Kastellet 42 Phone: 3 3112233
DK-2100 Copenhagen O, Denmark Carl Ibh, LTC
Founded: 1785. **Staff:** Prof 16. **Subjects:** Defense policy; army - history, equipment, research, technology, leadership. **Holdings:** 180,000 books; 320 bound periodical volumes; 765 microfiche. **Services:** Interlibrary loan; library open to the public. **Publications:** News from Royal Military Library (in Danish). **Remarks:** FAX: 3 3911482.

Denmark - Royal Museum of Fine Arts
See: **Royal Museum of Fine Arts (of Denmark) - Department of Paintings - Library** (14124)

Denmark - Royal School of Librarianship
See: **Royal School of Librarianship** (14133)

Denmark - The Royal Veterinary and Agricultural University
See: **The Royal Veterinary and Agricultural University** (14139)

Dennison Manufacturing Company
See: **Avery Dennison Company** (1375)

★4772★
Denny's - Documentation Library (Comp Sci)
203 E. Main St.
Spartanburg, SC 29319 Phone: (803)597-8000
Founded: 1972. **Staff:** Prof 2. **Subjects:** Computers. **Holdings:** 500 books. **Services:** Library not open to the public. **Automated Operations:** Computerized cataloging. **Remarks:** Library located at 3345 Michelson Dr., Suite 200, Irvine CA 92715. **Formerly:** Located in La Mirada, CA.

★4773★
Denton Record-Chronicle - Library (Publ)
PO Box 369 Phone: (817)387-3811
Denton, TX 76202 Julia Lehman
Staff: Prof 1. **Subjects:** Newspaper reference topics. **Holdings:** Microfilm (1908 to present). **Services:** Copying; library open to the public. **Remarks:** FAX: (214)434-1414; (214)434-2400.

★4774★
Denver Art Museum - Frederic H. Douglas Library of Anthropology and Art (Art, Area-Ethnic)
100 W. 14th Ave. Pkwy. Phone: (303)640-1613
Denver, CO 80204 Margaret Goodrich, Libn.
Founded: 1929. **Staff:** 1.5. **Subjects:** American Indians, African and Oceanic art, anthropology, primitive art. **Special Collections:** American Indians. **Holdings:** 6000 volumes; 144 linear feet of clippings; 840 linear feet of journals, serials, and monographs; U.S. government documents from the 19th and early 20th centuries. **Services:** Copying; library open to the public. **Automated Operations:** Computerized cataloging. **Computerized Information Services:** OCLC. **Networks/Consortia:** Member of Central Colorado Library System (CCLS), Bibliographical Center for Research, Rocky Mountain Region, Inc. (BCR). **Remarks:** FAX: (303)640-5513.

★4775★
Denver Botanic Gardens - Helen Fowler Library (Biol Sci)
909 York St. Phone: (303)370-8014
Denver, CO 80206 Solange G. Gignac, Libn.
Founded: 1948. **Staff:** Prof 2. **Subjects:** Horticulture, botany. **Special Collections:** Watercolors of Colorado and wild flowers; Waring Collection (rare horticulture and botany books). **Holdings:** 19,915 books; 400 bound periodical volumes; 8000 pamphlets; 300 brochures describing botanic gardens; 675 slides; 150 index seminum lists. **Subscriptions:** 431 journals and other serials. **Services:** Interlibrary loan; copying; library open to the public but only members may borrow. **Computerized Information Services:** OCLC. **Networks/Consortia:** Member of Central Colorado Library System (CCLS). **Publications:** Library Lines, bimonthly; accessions list, monthly. **Special Indexes:** Index to Green Thumb, quarterly. **Remarks:** FAX: (303)331-4013. **Staff:** Ellen Mackey, Asst.Libn.

★4776★
Denver Conservative Baptist Seminary - Carey S. Thomas Library (Rel-Phil)
University Park Sta., Box 10000 Phone: (303)761-2482
Denver, CO 80210 Sarah Miller, Libn.
Founded: 1950. **Staff:** Prof 3; Other 7. **Subjects:** Bible, theology, missions, church history, Christian education, homiletics, philosophy, pastoral theology. **Holdings:** 120,000 volumes; filmstrips; microfilm; slides; cassette and reel tapes; pamphlets. **Subscriptions:** 525 journals and other serials. **Services:** Interlibrary loan; copying; library open to the public on fee basis. **Automated Operations:** Computerized cataloging. **Computerized Information Services:** OCLC, BRS Information Technologies. Performs searches on fee basis. Contact Person: Robin Ottoson, Ref./Cat. **Networks/Consortia:** Member of Bibliographical Center for Research, Rocky Mountain Region, Inc. (BCR). **Remarks:** FAX: (303)761-8060. Alternate telephone number(s): (303)781-8691 (evenings and Saturdays). **Staff:** Jeannette France, Asst.Libn.

★4777★
Denver General Hospital - Medical Library (Med)
777 Bannock St. Phone: (303)893-7421
Denver, CO 80204-4507 Rebecca Berg, Dir., Med.Lib.
Founded: 1939. **Staff:** Prof 1; Other 1. **Subjects:** Clinical medicine, nursing, surgery. **Holdings:** 1200 books; 10,500 bound periodical volumes. **Subscriptions:** 195 journals. **Services:** Interlibrary loan; copying; library open to the public with restrictions. **Automated Operations:** ILL. **Computerized Information Services:** MEDLARS; DOCLINE (electronic mail service). **Networks/Consortia:** Member of Colorado Council of Medical Librarians, National Network of Libraries of Medicine - Midcontinental Region. **Staff:** Sharry Stewart DiQuinzio.

★4778★
Denver Medical Library (Med)
1719 E. 19th Ave. Phone: (303)839-6670
Denver, CO 80218 Mary De Mund, Lib.Dir.
SFounded: 1871. **Staff:** Prof 3; Other 2. **Subjects:** Medicine, dentistry, history of medicine, nursing, socioeconomics, health administration. **Special Collections:** Hubert Work Collection (neuropsychiatry; 4200 volumes). **Holdings:** 7272 books; 27,200 bound periodical volumes. **Subscriptions:** 400 journals and other serials. **Services:** Interlibrary loan; copying; library open to the public with permission from society member. **Automated Operations:** Computerized public access catalog, acquisitions, serials, and circulation. **Computerized Information Services:** NLM, DIALOG Information Services, BRS Information Technologies; CD-ROM (MEDLINE). Performs online searches. **Remarks:** Contains the holdings of the former Presbyterian Denver Hospital - Bradford Memorial Library. FAX: (303)863-8112. **Staff:** Pat Byler, Pub.Serv.Libn.; Dorothy Struble, Tech.Serv.Libn.

★4779★
Denver Museum of Natural History - Library (Biol Sci, Soc Sci)
City Park Phone: (303)370-6361
Denver, CO 80205 Kristine Haglund, Hd., Lib./Archv.
Founded: 1900. **Staff:** 3. **Subjects:** Anthropology, archeology, geology, paleontology, ornithology, astronomy. **Holdings:** 24,000 volumes; 750 cubic feet of archives and manuscripts; 100,000 photographs. **Subscriptions:** 90 journals and other serials. **Services:** Interlibrary loan; copying; library open to the public with restrictions. **Automated Operations:** Computerized public access catalog and cataloging. **Computerized Information Services:** OCLC, OCLC EPIC, DIALOG Information Services. **Networks/Consortia:** Member of Central Colorado Library System (CCLS). **Remarks:** FAX: (303)331-6492. **Staff:** Liz Clancy, Photo Archv.; Katherine B. Gully, Libn.

★4780★
Denver Post - Newsroom Library (Publ)
1560 Broadway Phone: (303)820-1443
Denver, CO 80202 Victoria L. Makings, Libn.
Staff: Prof 2; Other 5. **Subjects:** Newspaper reference topics. **Holdings:** 200 volumes. **Services:** Library not open to the public. **Computerized Information Services:** DataTimes. **Special Indexes:** Index of Denver Post articles, 1901-1981 (2 million cards).

★4781★
Denver Public Library - Business, Science & Government Publications Department (Bus-Fin, Sci-Engr)
1357 Broadway Phone: (303)640-8847
Denver, CO 80203 Michael Espinosa, Dept.Mgr.
Founded: 1889. **Staff:** Prof 12; Other 9. **Subjects:** Business, technology, pure science. **Special Collections:** Automobile repair manuals; U.S. Patents depository (Official Gazettes; all patents, 1789 to present). **Holdings:** 270,000 volumes; regional depository for U.S. Government documents; telephone books; specialized business directories; Standards and Specifications Collection. **Subscriptions:** 919 journals and other serials; 9 newspapers. **Services:** Interlibrary loan; copying; department open to the public. **Automated Operations:** Computerized cataloging, acquisitions, serials, and circulation. **Computerized Information Services:** DIALOG Information Services, ORBIT Search Service U.S. Patent Classification System. Performs searches on fee basis. **Networks/Consortia:** Member of Colorado Alliance of Research Libraries (CARL). **Remarks:** FAX: (303)640-8817. **Staff:** Elena Wenzel, Coll.Spec.

★4782★
Denver Public Library - Folk Music Collection, Friends of Music (Mus)
1357 Broadway Phone: (303)640-8830
Denver, CO 80203 James X. Kroll, Dept.Mgr.
Subjects: Folk music with emphasis on ballads and Anglo-American tradition; ethnomusicology; contemporary folk music. **Holdings:** 2900 books and song collections; 47 bound periodical volumes. **Subscriptions:** 15 journals and other serials. **Services:** Interlibrary loan (limited); copying; collection open to the public for reference use only. **Remarks:** FAX: (303)640-8814. Collection is part of the Humanities Department.

★4783★
Denver Public Library - Genealogy Department (Hist)
1357 Broadway Phone: (303)640-8870
Denver, CO 80203 James Jeffrey, Coll.Spec.
Founded: 1910. **Staff:** Prof 8. **Subjects:** County, state, town histories; census schedules, 1790-1910; genealogy; military rosters; heraldry. **Special Collections:** Denver obituaries, 1939 to present (21 reels of microfilm; 15 volumes; 15 file drawers; 34 microfiche); genealogical manuscripts and clippings (13 VF drawers); genealogical charts (2 map cases); Drapar Manusript Collection (134 reels of microfilm); Corbin Collection (New England; 60 reels of microfilm); Barbour Collection (Connecticut; 98 reels of microfilm); Archives of the Catholic Archdiocese of Santa Fe, 1678-1976 (90 reels of microfilm); Spanish Archives of New Mexico, 1621-1821 (22 reels of microfilm); Mexican Archives of New Mexico, 1821-1846 (42 reels of microfilm); Territorial Archives of New Mexico, 1846-1914 (189 reels of microfilm). **Holdings:** 40,000 books; 3250 bound periodical volumes; 5200 reels of microfilm of census schedules and other material; 30,000 microcards and microfiche; vital records; census indexes; 7 VF drawers of Denver Tramway personnel records; 150 audiocassettes; Foundation Center Collection (Foundation Center publications; U.S. tax form 990 for Colorado foundations). **Subscriptions:** 250 journals and other serials. **Services:** Interlibrary loan; copying; genealogical research. **Networks/Consortia:** Member of Colorado Alliance of Research Libraries (CARL). **Special Catalogs:** FHLC Family History Library Catalog. **Special Indexes:** Index to obituaries published in 2 major Denver newspapers (1939-present); index to anniversary announcements published in 2 major Denver newspapers; family name file; coat of arms file; IGI (International Genealogical Index) (all on microfiche). **Remarks:** FAX: (303)640-8818.

★4784★
Denver Public Library - Special Collections Room (Hist, Hum)
1357 Broadway Phone: (303)640-8880
Denver, CO 80203-2165 Eleanor M. Gehres, Mgr.
Holdings: Archery Collection (230 books; 34 bound periodical volumes); Eugene Field Collection (400 books; 950 manuscripts); Ross-Barrett Historical Aeronautics Collection (12,100 books; 900 bound periodical volumes; 5 VF drawers of pamphlets; 600 pictures; 12 linear feet of manuscripts; 48 films); 105 World War I and II posters (105); Collection of Fine Printing (1700 books); Rippey-Rivers Collection of Hooper & Co. (carriages and coach-built automobiles; 300 photographs and other items); George Elbert Burr (450 etchings and watercolors; 3 linear feet of manuscripts and notebooks); Howard Zahniser Memorial Wilderness Collection (250 books); Wright and Mcgill Fishing Collection (300 books). **Subscriptions:** 25 journals and other serials. **Services:** Interlibrary loan; copying (both limited); room open to the public with restrictions. **Computerized Information Services:** DIALOG Information Services, OCLC. **Networks/Consortia:** Member of Colorado Alliance of Research Libraries (CARL). **Remarks:** FAX: (303)640-8887. Maintained by Denver Public Library - Western History Department. **Staff:** Kay Wisnia.

★4785★
Denver Public Library - Western History Department (Hist)
1357 Broadway Phone: (303)640-8880
Denver, CO 80203-2165 Eleanor M. Gehres, Mgr.
Founded: 1935. **Staff:** Prof 8; Other 6. **Subjects:** History of U.S. west of Mississippi River with special emphasis on Rocky Mountain region. **Special Collections:** Western states mining collection; Spanish land grants; western railroads; Nate Salsbury-Buffalo Bill Collection; Western newspapers on microfilm; Frontier Theater Collection; Western Art Collection. **Holdings:** 85,000 books and pamphlets; 400,000 prints and photographs; 182 VF drawers of clippings; 5000 maps; 13,000 reels of microfilm; 1800 manuscript collections. **Subscriptions:** 300 journals and other serials. **Services:** Interlibrary loan (limited); copying; department open to the public. **Computerized Information Services:** DIALOG Information Services, OCLC. **Networks/Consortia:** Member of Colorado Alliance of Research Libraries (CARL). **Publications:** Occasional books and catalogs; Oral History Workshop Guide; Nothing Is Long Ago: A Documentary History of Colorado 1776/1976. **Special Catalogs:** Colorado Photographers, 1858-1940; David Barry pictures published catalog; Otto Perry Railroad published catalog (volumes 1 and 2). **Special Indexes:** General Western Index (6 million entries). **Remarks:** FAX: (303)640-8887. **Staff:** Agostino D. Mastrogiuseppe; Lisa Backman; Lynn Taylor; Nancy Chase; Kay Wisnia; Barbara Walton; Philip J. Panum.

★4786★
Denver Public School District 1 - Professional Library (Educ)
3800 York St., Bldg.1, Unit B Phone: (303)837-1000
Denver, CO 80205 Phyllis Dodd, Supv.
Founded: 1923. **Staff:** Prof 2; Other 6. **Subjects:** Educational materials for teachers, pupils, curriculum. **Special Collections:** Multi-ethnic print and nonprint media; instruction in the use of the library/IMC (nonprint); materials to be used with gifted, talented, creative students. **Holdings:** 77,000 books; 403 bound periodical volumes; microforms; 7000 nonprint materials. **Subscriptions:** 152 journals and other serials. **Services:** Interlibrary loan; copying; software evaluation center; library open to the public with restrictions. **Remarks:** FAX: (303)293-9816.

★4787★
Denver Zoological Garden - Library (Biol Sci)
2900 E. 23rd Ave. Phone: (303)331-4114
Denver, CO 80205 John Wortman, Gen.Cur.
Founded: 1970. **Subjects:** Animal husbandry, endangered species, natural history, veterinary medicine, business. **Holdings:** 1500 books; 150 bound periodical volumes; 2000 annual reports, guidebooks from other zoos, other cataloged items. **Subscriptions:** 150 journals and other serials. **Services:** Library open to the public for reference use only. **Remarks:** FAX: (303)331-4125.

Department of National Archives (of Sri Lanka)
See: **Sri Lanka - Department of National Archives** (15625)

Department of Veterans Affairs
See: **U.S. Dept. of Veterans Affairs** (17283)

★4788★
DePaul University - Law Library (Law)
25 E. Jackson Blvd. Phone: (312)362-8121
Chicago, IL 60604 Judith A. Gaskell, Dir.
Founded: 1915. **Staff:** Prof 9; Other 10. **Subjects:** Anglo-American law. **Special Collections:** Tax law; health law; human rights law; Municipal Codes for Chicago area and Illinois municipalities with populations over 40,000. **Holdings:** 156,021 volumes; 119,040 volumes in microform. **Subscriptions:** 4880 journals and other serials. **Services:** Interlibrary loan; library open to the public. **Automated Operations:** Computerized public access catalog, cataloging, acquisitions, serials, and circulation. **Computerized Information Services:** WESTLAW, LEXIS, DIALOG Information Services; BITNET (electronic mail service). **Networks/ Consortia:** Member of ILLINET. **Remarks:** FAX: (312)362-6908. Electronic mail address(es): LAWJAG@DEPAUL (BITNET). **Staff:** Mary Lu Linnane, Hd., Tech.Serv.; Milta Hall, Hd., Pub.Serv.; Raminta Sinkus, Hd., Cat.Serv.; Walter Baumann, Cat./Gov.Doc.Libn.; James Goodridge, Sr.Ref.Libn.; Firouzeh Logan, Circ.Mgr.; Lenore Boehm, Acq.Mgr.

★4789★
DePauw University - Archives of DePauw University and Indiana United Methodism and Special Collections of DePauw University (Rel-Phil, Hist)
Roy O. West Library Phone: (317)658-4406
Greencastle, IN 46135 Wesley W. Wilson, Archv.
Founded: 1951. **Staff:** Prof 1; Other 4. **Subjects:** DePauw University history, United Methodist Church of Indiana. **Special Collections:** Histories of Indiana United Methodist Churches and early Methodist Church records of Indiana; history of the United Methodist Church and its antecedents; DePauw University records from founding in 1837 to present; Governor James Whitcomb Book Collection; Records of Society of Professional Journalists; Greencastle city records; Putnam County records. **Holdings:** 8000 books; 350 bound periodical volumes; 250 volumes of Methodist Conference minutes; 1800 church histories of Indiana Methodism; 2000 cubic feet of manuscripts of the history of the university and the church; 1400 tape recordings; 650 reels of microfilm; 600,000 photographs. **Subscriptions:** 3 journals and other serials. **Services:** Interlibrary loan (microfilm only); copying; genealogical research service on a fee basis; archives open to the public. **Computerized Information Services:** OCLC; BITNET (electronic mail service). **Publications:** Annual Report; Newsletter, annual - both to donors, alumni, United Methodist Churches in Indiana, Methodist archives, libraries in Indiana. **Remarks:** Electronic mail address(es): WWWILSON@DEPAUW

Depot Park Museum
See: **Sonoma Valley Historical Society** (15374)

Helen L. DeRoy Medical Library
See: **Providence Hospital** (13446)

★4790★
Des Moines Art Center - Library (Art)
4700 Grand Ave. Phone: (515)277-4405
Des Moines, IA 50312-2099 Margaret Buckley, Libn.
Founded: 1948. **Staff:** Prof 1. **Subjects:** Painting, graphics, sculpture, architecture, art history, textiles, drawing, ceramics, photography. **Holdings:** 11,200 books; 505 bound periodical volumes; 24 VF drawers of publications on individual artists; 24 VF drawers of museum catalogs, art collection catalogs, allied materials. **Subscriptions:** 21 journals and other serials. **Services:** Library open to the public by appointment for reference use only.

★4791★
Des Moines Botanical Center - Berkowitz Library (Biol Sci)
909 E. River Dr. Phone: (515)283-4148
Des Moines, IA 50316 Matt Rosen, Dir.
Subjects: Gardening, horticulture. **Special Collections:** Des Moines Garden Club Collection (old English gardening books). **Holdings:** 1000 books; 10 AV programs. **Services:** Library not open to the public.

★4792★
Des Moines Register - Library (Publ)
715 Locust St. Phone: (515)284-8442
Des Moines, IA 50304 Phyllis Wolfe
Founded: 1924. **Staff:** Prof 1; Other 6. **Subjects:** Newspaper reference topics. **Holdings:** 500 books; clippings; photographs. **Services:** Library open to the public; research work done on fee basis only. **Computerized Information Services:** DataTimes; TRI-ME (index only, internal database).

★4793★
Des Plaines Historical Society - John Byrne Memorial Library (Hist)
789 Pearson St. Phone: (708)391-5399
Des Plaines, IL 60016 Joy A. Matthiessen, Musm.Dir.
Founded: 1967. **Staff:** 6. **Subjects:** Local history. **Special Collections:** Dr. C.A. Earle Collection (24 boxes). **Holdings:** 550 books; 7 VF drawers of clippings; 4 boxes of documents; 4000 photographs; 15 boxes of documents; microfilm; magnetic tapes; maps; Des Plaines and Maine Township archival materials; Maine Township census, 1840-1880, 1900, 1910. **Services:** Copying; library open to the public by appointment on weekdays only.

Deschatelets Library
See: **Oblate Fathers - Bibliotheque Deschatelets** (12227)

★4794★
Descript - Library (Sci-Engr)
LR Ranch
7328 O'Rourke Ln. Phone: (915)821-9398
El Paso, TX 79934 Scott Pearson
Staff: 1. **Subjects:** Physics, mathematics, control theory, weapons technology, economics. **Holdings:** 3000 books; 2000 reports. **Subscriptions:** 40 journals and other serials. **Services:** Library not open to the public. **Staff:** Terri Eveland, Libn.; Puring Quiambao, Libn.

★4795★
Deseret News Publishing Co. - Deseret News Library (Publ)
30 East 100 S.
Box 1257 Phone: (801)237-2155
Salt Lake City, UT 84110 Colleen Randall, Hd.Libn.
Founded: 1957. **Staff:** 4. **Subjects:** Newspaper reference topics. **Holdings:** Newspaper clippings; pictures; negatives; reference books; microfilm. **Services:** Library not open to the public. **Computerized Information Services:** VU/TEXT Information Services; Atex (internal database). **Remarks:** FAX: (801)237-2121. **Staff:** Jean Watkins, Asst.Libn.; Emmie Rutledge, Comp.Asst.; Linda Handy, Rsrcs.

★4796★
Desert Botanical Garden - Richter Library (Biol Sci)
Papago Park
1201 N. Galvin Pkwy. Phone: (602)941-1225
Phoenix, AZ 85008 Jane B. Cole, Libn.
Founded: 1937. **Staff:** Prof 1. **Subjects:** Cacti and other succulents, desert trees and shrubs, arid land plants, native plant conservation, desert ecology, desert restoration. **Special Collections:** M.C. Richter Collection; botanical print collection (600). **Holdings:** 10,000 volumes; 270 bound periodical volumes; 3000 unbound periodicals; 6000 35mm slides; 650 VF materials. **Subscriptions:** 61 journals. **Services:** Interlibrary loan; copying; library open to the public for reference use only on weekdays. **Computerized Information Services:** Arizona State University Catalog. **Networks/Consortia:** Member of Council on Botanical Horticultural Libraries, Colorado Alliance of Research Libraries (CARL). **Publications:** Sonoran Quarterly; Agave, irregular. **Special Indexes:** Plant Records and Library Index (online). **Remarks:** FAX: (602)949-1220.

Desert Research Institute
See: **University of Nevada--Reno** (19013)

★4797★
Design Associates - Library (Sci-Engr)
134 Chesterfield Rd. Phone: (804)380-0760
Hampton, VA 23661 James Morgan
Subjects: Cryogenics engineering, cryogenic wind tunnels, nuclear reactor plants, wastewater treatment, marine products. **Holdings:** 2500 technical catalogs.

★4798★
Desjardins Ducharme - Law Library (Law)
600 W. de la Gauchetiere, Suite 2400 Phone: (514)878-9411
Montreal, PQ, Canada H3B 4L8 Jacques Cartier, Law Libn.
Staff: Prof 1; Other 2. **Subjects:** Law - corporate, tax, bankruptcy, labor, insurance; general liability. **Special Collections:** Canadian Jurisprudence (2000 volumes). **Holdings:** 7000 books; 1000 bound periodical volumes; 25,000 reports on microfiche. **Subscriptions:** 100 journals and other serials; 5 newspapers. **Services:** Library not open to the public. **Remarks:** FAX: (514)878-9092. Telex: 05-25202.

Donald Deskey Archive
See: **Smithsonian Institution Libraries - Cooper-Hewitt Museum of Design - Doris & Henry Dreyfuss Memorial Study Center** (15274)

J.N. Desmarais Library
See: **Laurentian University - J.N. Desmarais Library - Special Collections, Rare Books, and Archives** (8978)

★4799★
Alice Curtis Desmond & Hamilton Fish - Library (Biol Sci, Env-Cons)
Rte. 9D & 403
Box 265 Phone: (914)424-3020
Garrison, NY 10524 Geraldine S. Baldwin, Libn.
Founded: 1980. **Staff:** 3. **Subjects:** Hudson River. **Special Collections:** Hamilton Fish Collection; History of Hudson River (800 volumes). **Holdings:** 15,000 books. **Subscriptions:** 100 journals and other serials. **Services:** Interlibrary loan; copying; library open to the public. **Computerized Information Services:** DIALOG Information Services; Hudson River Reference Collection (internal database). **Staff:** Karen E. Sager, Ch.Libn.

Det Danske Baptistsamfund
See: **Baptist Union of Denmark** (1518)

★4800★
Det Kongelige Danske Kunstakademi - Kunstakademiets Bibliotek (Art)
Kongens Nytorv 1 Phone: 33 128659
DK-1050 Copenhagen K, Denmark Hakon Lund, Chf.Libn.
Founded: 1754. **Staff:** Prof 8; Other 9. **Subjects:** Art, architecture, photography. **Holdings:** 127,644 volumes; 126,098 architectural drawings; 157,313 slides; 355,143 photographs; 13,352 nonbook items. **Subscriptions:** 461 journals and other serials. **Services:** Interlibrary loan; copying; library open to the public. **Computerized Information Services:** UNI-C; Rex (internal database). **Publications:** Bibliografi over danskve Kunst; Skrifter udgivet Kunstakademiets Bibliotek (series). **Remarks:** FAX: 33 140662. **Staff:** Emma Salling, Res.Libn.

★4801★
Detrex Corp. - Library (Sci-Engr)
4000 Town Center, Suite 1100 Phone: (313)358-5800
Southfield, MI 48075-1506 Sharon Bakaian, Libn.
Subjects: Chemistry and chemical engineering. **Holdings:** 2800 volumes. **Services:** Library not open to the public. **Remarks:** FAX: (313)358-5803.

Louis M. Detro Memorial Library
See: **Great Lakes Bible College** (6694)

★4802★
Detroit Baptist Theological Seminary - Library (Rel-Phil, Hum)
4801 Allen Rd. Phone: (313)381-0111
Allen Park, MI 48101 Margaretta L. Grosjean
Founded: 1976. **Staff:** Prof 1; Other 1. **Subjects:** Biblical studies, Hebrew and Greek language, church history, theology, homiletics. **Holdings:** 20,000 books; 1180 bound periodical volumes. **Subscriptions:** 143 journals and other serials. **Services:** Interlibrary loan; library open to the public with restrictions.

★4803★
Detroit Bar Association Foundation - Library (Law)
2380 Penobscot Bldg. Phone: (313)961-3507
Detroit, MI 48226 Jeffrey C. Brennan, Asst.Exec.Dir.
Founded: 1853. **Staff:** Prof 3; Other 3. **Subjects:** Law. **Special Collections:** Michigan law and treatises. **Holdings:** 68,000 books; 10,000 bound periodical volumes; 40,000 other cataloged items. **Subscriptions:** 93 journals and other serials; 5 newspapers. **Services:** Copying. **Computerized Information Services:** WESTLAW. **Networks/Consortia:** Member of Michigan Library Consortium (MLC). **Publications:** Practitioners Handbook; jury verdicts; results; 36th District Court Practice and Procedure Handbook. **Remarks:** FAX: (313)965-0842. **Staff:** James Singer, Tech.Serv.Libn.; Heather Farnan, Libn.

Detroit (City of) Law Department - Library
See: **City of Detroit - Law Department - Library** (3738)

★4804★
Detroit College of Law - Library (Law)
130 E. Elizabeth St. Phone: (313)226-0157
Detroit, MI 48201 Mario A. Ceresa, Hd.Libn.
Founded: 1891. **Staff:** Prof 5; Other 4. **Subjects:** Law. **Holdings:** 85,626 volumes; 103,037 volumes in microform. **Subscriptions:** 2615 journals and other serials. **Services:** Interlibrary loan; copying; library open to the public with restrictions. **Computerized Information Services:** LEXIS, WESTLAW, OCLC, NEXIS. **Publications:** Acquisitions list, bimonthly. **Remarks:** FAX: (313)965-5097. **Staff:** Hildur Hanna, Assoc.Libn.,Circ.; Amy Eaton, Ser. & Budget Libn.; Lorraine K. Lorne, Assoc.Libn., Tech.Serv.; Gretchen Van Dam, Asst.Libn.

★4805★
Detroit Edison Company - Fermi 2 Power Plant - NOC Information Center (Energy)
116 EF2 NOC
6400 N. Dixie Hwy. Phone: (313)586-4073
Newport, MI 48166 Jennifer West, Libn.
Founded: 1981. **Staff:** Prof 1. **Subjects:** Nuclear power, electric utilities. **Holdings:** 800 books; 160 bound periodical volumes; 5000 reports; 45 drawers of documents; 56 drawers of microfilm; 50 drawers of microfiche. **Subscriptions:** 30 journals and other serials. **Services:** Interlibrary loan; center not open to the public. **Automated Operations:** Computerized cataloging. **Computerized Information Services:** DIALOG Information Services, OCLC; internal database. **Networks/Consortia:** Member of Michigan Library Consortium (MLC).

★4806★
Detroit Edison Company - Reference Services (Energy)
2000 2nd Ave. Phone: (313)237-9216
Detroit, MI 48226 Marilyn J. Baird, Supv.
Founded: 1915. **Staff:** Prof 2; Other 3. **Subjects:** Public utilities, electrical and mechanical engineering, business management. **Holdings:** 5000 books;

videotapes; industry standards on microfiche; audiotapes. **Subscriptions:** 500 journals and other serials. **Services:** Interlibrary loan; copying; SDI; services open to the public by appointment. **Automated Operations:** Computerized cataloging, acquisitions, circulation, and ILL. **Computerized Information Services:** OCLC, Human Resource Information Network (HRIN), DataTimes, DIALOG Information Services, NEXIS, VU/TEXT Information Services, Dun & Bradstreet Business Credit Services; DIALMAIL (electronic mail service). **Networks/Consortia:** Member of Michigan Library Consortium (MLC). **Publications:** FYI newsletter, monthly. **Remarks:** FAX: (313)237-8011. **Staff:** Alice A. Pepper, Res.Anl.

★4807★
Detroit Free Press - Library (Publ)
321 W. Lafayette Phone: (313)222-6840
Detroit, MI 48226 Bernadine Aubert, Chief Libn.
Founded: 1925. **Staff:** Prof 7; Other 4. **Subjects:** Newspaper reference topics. **Holdings:** 4000 books; clippings, 1971-1981, on microfilm; Free Press, 1925 to present, on microfilm; 1 million photographs. **Subscriptions:** 50 journals and other serials; 15 newspapers. **Services:** Library not open to the public. **Computerized Information Services:** DataTimes, VU/TEXT Information Services, NEXIS, DIALOG Information Services; CD-ROM (Free Press full text online retrieval; internal database). **Remarks:** FAX: (313)222-8778. **Staff:** Doris Weinberger-Blechman, Libn.; Ann Mieczkowski, Asst.Chf.Libn.; Chris Kucharski, Libn.; Patrice Williams, Libn.; Apollinaris Mwila, Libn.; Christine Schmuckal, Libn.; Sean Varner, Libn.

★4808★
Detroit Garden Center - Library (Biol Sci)
Moross House, 2nd Fl.
1460 E. Jefferson Ave. Phone: (313)259-6363
Detroit, MI 48207 Margaret Grazier, Libn.
Founded: 1932. **Staff:** Prof 1. **Subjects:** Horticulture, and floral culture. **Holdings:** 5000 books. **Subscriptions:** 10 journals and other serials. **Services:** Library open to the public for research. **Publications:** Detroit Garden Center Bulletin. **Remarks:** Moross House, the oldest known brick residence in Detroit, has been restored under the auspices of the Detroit Historical Commission and is the headquarters of the Detroit Garden Center.

★4809★
Detroit Institute of Arts - Research Library (Art)
5200 Woodward Ave. Phone: (313)833-7926
Detroit, MI 48202 Constance Wall, Libn.
Founded: 1905. **Staff:** Prof 2; Other 3. **Subjects:** Painting, sculpture, furniture, decorative arts, history of art, architecture. **Special Collections:** Paul McPharlin Collection of puppetry and theater material; Grace Whitney Hoff Collection of fine bindings; Albert Kahn Architecture Library. **Holdings:** 65,000 books; 6500 bound periodical volumes; 1500 bulletins; 40,000 2x2 slides; 27,000 3x4 slides; 166,000 pamphlets and museum and sale catalogs; 83,000 photographs. **Subscriptions:** 263 journals and other serials. **Services:** Interlibrary loan; copying; library open to the public. **Automated Operations:** Computerized cataloging. **Networks/Consortia:** Member of Michigan Library Consortium (MLC). **Special Indexes:** D.I.A. Bulletin Index; American and Foreign Art Institution File; microfilm clipping file. **Staff:** Lynne Garza, Asst.Libn.

★4810★
Detroit Macomb Hospital Corporation - Detroit Riverview Hospital - Hospital Library (Med)
7733 E. Jefferson Phone: (313)499-4123
Detroit, MI 48214 Donna Marshall, Corp.Dir. of Libs.
Staff: Prof 2; Other 1. **Subjects:** Medicine. **Holdings:** 2600 books; 2000 bound periodical volumes. **Subscriptions:** 290 journals and other serials. **Services:** Interlibrary loan; copying; SDI; List of publications - available on request open to the public by appointment. **Computerized Information Services:** NLM, BRS Information Technologies, DIALOG Information Services, WILSONLINE. **Publications:** Libraryline, bimonthly. **Staff:** Meg Carpenter, Libn.

★4811★
Detroit Macomb Hospital Corporation - Macomb Hospital Center Library (Med)
11800 12 Mile Rd. Phone: (313)573-5117
Warren, MI 48093 Donna Marshall, Corp.Dir. of Libs.
Founded: 1974. **Staff:** Prof 2; Other 1. **Subjects:** Medicine, surgery, obstetrics and gynecology, oral surgery, respiratory medicine. **Holdings:** 2600 books; 2000 bound periodical volumes; 5 VF drawers. **Subscriptions:** 290 journals and other serials. **Services:** Interlibrary loan; library open to the public. **Automated Operations:** Computerized cataloging. **Computerized Information Services:** NLM, BRS Information Technologies, DIALOG Information Services, OCLC, WILSONLINE. **Remarks:** FAX: (313)573-5803. **Staff:** Margaret Carpenter, Asst.Libn.

★4812★
Detroit News - George B. Catlin Memorial Library (Publ)
615 Lafayette W.
Detroit, MI 48226 Phone: (313)222-2110
Founded: 1917. **Staff:** Prof 3; Other 6. **Subjects:** Newspaper reference topics. **Holdings:** 20,000 books; 3 million clippings; 1 million photographs; 5000 pamphlets; microfilm. **Subscriptions:** 50 journals and other serials; 6 newspapers. **Services:** Interlibrary loan; library not open to the public. **Computerized Information Services:** NEXIS, VU/TEXT Information Services, DataTimes. **Staff:** Patricia K. Zacharias Hd., Ed.Lib. & Ref.Depts.; Vivian M. Baulch, Lib.Adm.

★4813★
Detroit Osteopathic Hospital - Library (Med)
12523 3rd Ave. Phone: (313)252-4830
Highland Park, MI 48203 Gayle A. Williams, Dir.
Founded: 1944. **Staff:** Prof 2; Other 1. **Subjects:** Internal medicine, orthopedics, surgery, nephrology, cardiology, oncology. **Special Collections:** Osteopathic literature. **Holdings:** 1700 books; 4200 bound periodical volumes; 400 audio cassettes. **Subscriptions:** 188 journals and other serials. **Services:** Interlibrary loan; library not open to the public. **Automated Operations:** Computerized circulation. **Computerized Information Services:** BRS Information Technologies, OCLC, MEDLARS, DIALOG Information Services, WILSONLINE, American Osteopathic Network (AONET), INTERACT. **Networks/Consortia:** Member of National Network of Libraries of Medicine - Greater Midwest Region, Michigan Library Consortium (MLC), Michigan Health Sciences Libraries Association (MHSLA). **Staff:** Christopher J. Hunt, Libn.

★4814★
Detroit Psychiatric Institute - Library (Med)
1151 Taylor Phone: (313)874-7551
Detroit, MI 48202 Rita H. Bigman, Libn.
Staff: Prof 1; Other 1. **Subjects:** Psychiatry, psychoanalysis, social work, psychology, psychiatric nursing, general medicine. **Holdings:** 3300 books; 350 bound periodical volumes; 14 VF drawers of psychoanalysis and psychiatry articles. **Subscriptions:** 89 journals and other serials. **Services:** Interlibrary loan; library not open to the public. **Automated Operations:** Computerized cataloging, acquisitions, serials, and circulation. **Computerized Information Services:** BRS Information Technologies, NLM, DIALOG Information Services. **Networks/Consortia:** Member of Michigan Library Consortium (MLC).

★4815★
Detroit Public Library - Art and Literature Department (Art)
5201 Woodward Ave. Phone: (313)833-1470
Detroit, MI 48202-4093 Shirley Solvick, Chf.
Founded: 1989. **Staff:** Prof 6; Other 2. **Subjects:** Art, architecture, handicrafts, design, drawing, cartooning, pottery and porcelain, prints, photography, literary history and criticism, drama, poetry, essays and belles lettres, public speaking, language and linguistics, folklore. **Special Collections:** Picture file (600,000 separate pictures covering all subjects); reference collection of foreign language dictionaries; children's literature reference and research collection. **Holdings:** 230,000 books; 22,000 bound periodical volumes; 750 color prints; 60 VF drawers of clippings and pamphlets. **Subscriptions:** 700 journals and other serials. **Services:** Interlibrary loan; copying; department open to the public. **Automated Operations:** Computerized cataloging. **Computerized Information Services:** DIALOG Information Services, VU/TEXT Information Services. Performs searches on fee basis. Contact Person: Jean Comport, First Asst. **Networks/Consortia:** Member of Detroit Associated Libraries Region of Cooperation (DALROC). **Special Indexes:** Play index; index of poetry by subject and individual poems; index to biography and criticism of artists, architects, dramatists, poets, novelists, and other writers; citations on specific buildings, especially those in the Detroit area (all card); picture heading list. **Remarks:** FAX: (313)833-1474.

★4816★
Detroit Public Library - Burton Historical Collection (Hist)
5201 Woodward Ave. Phone: (313)833-1480
Detroit, MI 48202 Noel S. VanGorden, Chf.
Founded: 1914. **Staff:** Prof 8; Other 2. **Subjects:** History - Detroit, Michigan, Old Northwest, local, Great Lakes; genealogy. **Special Collections:** Edgar DeWitt Jones - Lincoln Collection; Ernie Harwell Sports Collection (19,500 guides, periodicals, record books, yearbooks, rule books). **Holdings:** 260,000 volumes; 12,000 pamphlets; 4800 bound volumes of newspapers; 5060 feet of manuscripts and personal papers; 10,500 feet of archival materials; 20,000 reels of microfilm; 10,000 microfiche; 1100 microcards; 50,000 pictures; 4000 maps; 5000 glass negatives; 6800 scrapbooks; 1000 color transparencies; 1000 lantern slides; 4050 maps; 325 broadsides. **Subscriptions:** 500 journals and other serials. **Services:** Copying (limited); collection open to the public. **Publications:** Guide to the Manuscripts in the Burton Historical Collection, Detroit Public Library; Genealogical Guide to the Burton Historical Collection. **Special Indexes:** Manuscripts reported in National Union List of Manuscripts. **Staff:** John Gibson, Mss.Spec.; Benedict Markowski, Fld.Archv.; Deborah Evans, Fld.Archv.

★4817★
Detroit Public Library - Business and Finance Department (Bus-Fin)
5201 Woodward Ave. Phone: (313)833-1420
Detroit, MI 48202 Marva Greenwood-Smail, Chf.
Founded: 1924. **Staff:** Prof 6; Other 2. **Subjects:** Corporations, accounting, insurance, banking, advertising, real estate, business administration, investments, securities quotations, marketing. **Special Collections:** Corporation annual reports (hardcopy and microfiche); trade directories. **Holdings:** 57,000 books; 9000 bound periodical volumes; 35 VF drawers; U.S. and foreign telephone directories. **Subscriptions:** 650 journals and other serials; 15 newspapers. **Services:** Interlibrary loan; copying; department open to the public. **Computerized Information Services:** DIALOG Information Services, Dow Jones News/Retrieval, VU/TEXT Information Services. **Remarks:** FAX: (313)833-1425.

★4818★
Detroit Public Library - Film Department (Aud-Vis)
5201 Woodward Ave. Phone: (313)833-1495
Detroit, MI 48202 Grace Larson, Chf.
Founded: 1947. **Staff:** Prof 3; Other 3. **Subjects:** Film - educational, children's, feature, foreign, black studies. **Holdings:** 13,000 videocassettes. **Subscriptions:** 5 journals and other serials. **Services:** Library open to the public. **Automated Operations:** Computerized circulation. **Computerized Information Services:** VIDSTAR (internal database). **Publications:** Annotated Lists on Parenting and Substance Abuse. **Special Catalogs:** Video Catalog.

★4819★
Detroit Public Library - Foreign Language Collection (Hum)
Downtown Library
121 Gratiot Phone: (313)224-0580
Detroit, MI 48226 Wlodek Zaryczny, Foreign Lang.Spec.
Founded: 1866. **Staff:** Prof 2. **Subjects:** Works in 52 foreign languages on all subjects. **Holdings:** 75,000 books. **Subscriptions:** 100 journals and other serials; 50 newspapers. **Services:** Interlibrary loan; copying; deposit collections available to Michigan public libraries upon request. **Computerized Information Services:** VU/TEXT Information Services, DIALOG Information Services. **Publications:** Periodic lists of new books in specific languages - internal distribution and to others upon request. **Remarks:** FAX: (313)961-0918. **Staff:** Parvin Bolourchi.

★4820★
Detroit Public Library - General Information Department (Info Sci)
5201 Woodward Ave. Phone: (313)833-1400
Detroit, MI 48202 Terry Gahman, Chf.
Founded: 1948. **Staff:** Prof 12; Other 3. **Subjects:** Bibliography, library science, sports, home economics, gardening. **Special Collections:** Early American newspapers (320 reels of microfilm); American Periodical Series I-III (2800 reels of microfilm). **Holdings:** 123,000 books; 31,500 bound periodical volumes; 14,400 reels of microfilm; 17 vertical file cabinets of pamphlets and clippings. **Subscriptions:** 704 journals and other serials. **Services:** Interlibrary loan; copying; TIP Services (information and referral); department open to the public. **Computerized Information Services:** DIALOG Information Services, VU/TEXT Information Services, Academic Abstracts; InfoTrac; internal database. Performs searches on fee basis. **Remarks:** FAX: (313)833-1404.

★4821★
Detroit Public Library - General Information Department - TIP Service (Info Sci)
5201 Woodward Ave. Phone: (313)833-4000
Detroit, MI 48202 Terry Gahman, Chf.
Founded: 1972. **Subjects:** Community information and referral in the areas of drug abuse, senior citizen housing, legal aid, health care, counseling, recreational activities, emergency food and shelter, other community topics. **Holdings:** Information on 2000 agencies; directories; pamphlets. **Services:** Service open to the public. **Computerized Information Services:** TIP referral file (internal database). **Publications:** List of publications - available on request. **Remarks:** TDD: (313)833-1403.

★4822★
Detroit Public Library - History and Travel Department (Hist, Geog-Map)
5201 Woodward Ave. Phone: (313)833-1445
Detroit, MI 48202 James Tong, Chf.
Founded: 1949. **Staff:** Prof 5; Other 2. **Subjects:** Political and social history, archeology, Indians, geography, travel, biography. **Special Collections:** Map Collection (250,000 sheet maps; 4000 atlases). **Holdings:** 214,000 volumes; 92 VF drawers of travel pamphlets; 10 VF drawers of map publishers catalogs; 44 VF drawers; 8 Biography clippings. **Subscriptions:** 362 journals and other serials. **Services:** Interlibrary loan; copying. **Automated Operations:** Computerized cataloging (maps). **Computerized Information Services:** DIALOG Information Services, VU/TEXT Information Services. Performs searches on fee basis. **Special Catalogs:** Map card catalog (area and subject arrangement). **Staff:** Michael Knes, Map Spec.

★4823★
Detroit Public Library - Labor Collection (Bus-Fin)
5201 Woodward Ave. Phone: (313)833-1440
Detroit, MI 48202 Paula Kaczmarek, Chf.
Subjects: History of U.S. and foreign labor movement and individual unions; U.S. and foreign labor laws and legislation; collective bargaining and arbitration; labor relations; statistics on wages, hours of labor. **Special Collections:** Labor union contracts and agreements; labor union constitutions; labor union convention proceedings. **Holdings:** 20,500 books; 1600 bound periodical volumes; 8000 cataloged pamphlets; 16 VF drawers of uncataloged pamphlets and clippings; 1020 reels of microfilm, 2700 microfiche; **Subscriptions:** 100 journals and other serials; 130 newspapers. **Services:** Interlibrary loan; copying; collection open to the public. **Computerized Information Services:** DIALOG Information Services, LOGIN, VU/TEXT Information Services, Hannah Information Systems. **Remarks:** Collection housed in Sociology and Economics Department.

★4824★
Detroit Public Library - Municipal Reference Library (Soc Sci)
City County Bldg., Rm. 1004
2 Woodward Ave. Phone: (313)224-3885
Detroit, MI 48226 Richard Maciejewski, Chf.
Founded: 1945. **Staff:** Prof 2; Other 2. **Subjects:** Public administration, municipal government, transportation, city planning, public health, urban sociology, police, fire, housing, human resources. **Special Collections:** City of Detroit and Wayne County documents, latest 25 years; municipal documents exchange with 19 similar libraries in the country; grantsmanship center including information on government and foundation funding sources and proposal writing; newspaper clippings on Detroit and Wayne County subjects, 1965 to present. **Holdings:** 35,000 volumes; 92 legal drawers of pamphlets; 175,000 clippings. **Subscriptions:** 300 journals and other serials. **Services:** Interlibrary loan; copying (both limited); library open to the public for reference use only. **Computerized Information Services:** DIALOG Information Services, LOGIN, VU/TEXT Information Services, Hannah Information Systems. Performs searches on fee basis. **Publications:** MRL Bulletin, bimonthly - to city and county employees and interested government agencies. **Remarks:** FAX: (313)964-6958.

★4825★
Detroit Public Library - Music and Performing Arts Department (Mus, Theater)
5201 Woodward Ave. Phone: (313)833-1460
Detroit, MI 48202 Agatha Pfeiffer Kalkanis, Chf.
Founded: 1921. **Staff:** Prof 5; Other 2. **Subjects:** Music, theater, moving pictures, radio and television, broadcasting, dance, bullfighting, circus, rodeo. **Special Collections:** E. Azalia Hackley Collection (blacks in the

performing arts); Michigan Collection (music by Michigan composers or with Michigan associations). **Holdings:** 40,000 books; 7917 bound periodical volumes; 56,000 scores; 30,000 recordings; 20,000 popular sheet music titles; 150 VF drawers; 6 VF drawers of photographs; 2000 cassettes; 1033 reels of microfilm. **Subscriptions:** 344 journals and other serials. **Services:** Interlibrary loan; copying; department open to the public. **Computerized Information Services:** DIALOG Information Services, VU/TEXT Information Services.

★4826★
Detroit Public Library - National Automotive History Collection (Trans)
5201 Woodward Ave. Phone: (313)833-1456
Detroit, MI 48202 Ronald Grantz, Cur.
Founded: 1953. **Staff:** Prof 1.5. Other 1. **Subjects:** Automobiles - history, technology, finance, law, biographies, advertising; men and companies associated with auto industry; carriage making and design; trucks; buses; motorcycles; bicycles. **Special Collections:** Papers of pioneer automakers; records of corporations; races; accessory companies; legal cases. **Holdings:** 26,000 books; 8710 bound periodical volumes; 183,000 photographs; 117,000 advertising catalogs for vehicles and accessories; 89,000 advertisements, pamphlets, clippings, sheet music, blueprints, phonograph records, race programs, miscellanea. **Subscriptions:** 182 journals and other serials. **Services:** Photographic service; copying; collection open to the public with staff supervision. **Computerized Information Services:** DIALOG Information Services, VU/TEXT Information Services. **Publications:** Wheels; Journal of the National Automotive History Collection. **Special Catalogs:** Subject guide to the holdings of the Automotive History Collection of the Detroit Public Library. History Collection. **Remarks:** FAX: (313)833-1429. **Staff:** Mark Patrick, Asst.Libn.

★4827★
Detroit Public Library - Philosophy, Religion and Education Department (Rel-Phil)
5201 Woodward Ave. Phone: (313)833-1430
Detroit, MI 48202 Geraldine Frenette, Chf.
Founded: 1950. **Staff:** Prof 6; Other 2. **Subjects:** Philosophy, psychology, psychiatry, religion, education, career guidance. **Special Collections:** Career and Employment Information Center. **Holdings:** 108,000 books; 9400 bound periodical volumes; 3200 government documents and reports; 260 boxes of occupations pamphlets; 426 boxes of school catalogs; 80 VF drawers of clippings and pamphlets. **Subscriptions:** 260 journals and other serials; 6 newspapers. **Services:** Interlibrary loan; copying; department open to the public. **Computerized Information Services:** DIALOG Information Services, VU/TEXT Information Services. **Networks/Consortia:** Member of Michigan Occupational Information Center. **Special Indexes:** Index to occupations collection (card); index to vertical file (card).

★4828★
Detroit Public Library - Rare Book Room (Rare Book)
5201 Woodward Ave. Phone: (313)833-1476
Detroit, MI 48202 Janet B. Whitson, Chf.
Founded: 1948. **Staff:** Prof 1; Other 1. **Subjects:** Rare books in all subject areas; autographs; the book arts, including binding and design; book collecting, selling, and values; calligraphy; conservation and preservation; cookery; first editions; illuminated manuscripts; presses and printers; printing and typography. **Special Collections:** Americana; early atlases; early printed books; fine bindings; historic children's literature; Samuel L. Clemens; cookbooks; Kate Greenaway; Aldous Huxley; incunabula; D.H. Lawrence; T.E. Lawrence; medieval manuscripts; modern press books; Evaline Ness; Eugene O'Neill; Laura Ingalls Wilder. **Holdings:** 27,700 books; 1400 bound periodical volumes; 1750 autographs; 19,000 book dealer catalogs; 1100 pamphlets; 9000 bookplates; 260 literary manuscripts and letters. **Subscriptions:** 78 journals and other serials. **Services:** Interlibrary loan; copying; room open to the public.

★4829★
Detroit Public Library - Sociology and Economics Department (Soc Sci, Bus-Fin)
5201 Woodward Ave. Phone: (313)833-1440
Detroit, MI 48202 Paula Kaczmarek, Chf.
Founded: 1945. **Staff:** Prof 8; Other 3. **Subjects:** Sociology, social work, economics, labor, political science, international relations, public administration, law, public health, city planning. **Holdings:** 233,000 books; 15,000 bound periodical volumes; 900 bound newspapers; 95,000 paper items; 10,800 reels of microfilm; 171 VF drawers of pamphlets, clippings, and releases; 400,000 microfiche. **Subscriptions:** 750 journals and other serials; 60 newspapers. **Services:** Interlibrary loan; copying. **Computerized Information Services:** VU/TEXT Information Services, DIALOG Information Services, LOGIN, Hannah Information Systems. **Remarks:** Houses the Labor Collection and regional U.S. Documents Depository.

★4830★
Detroit Public Library - Technology and Science Department (Sci-Engr)
5201 Woodward Ave. Phone: (313)833-1450
Detroit, MI 48202 Barbara Klont, Chf.
Founded: 1917. **Staff:** Prof 7; Other 3. **Subjects:** Metals and metal technology; engineering - automotive, mechanical, civil, electronic, nuclear; biological sciences; space sciences; computer science. **Holdings:** 296,140 books; 102,656 bound periodical volumes; U.S. patent collection; 396,353 government reports; 46 VF drawers of pamphlets and trade catalogs; 349,982 microcards and microfiche. **Subscriptions:** 1640 journals and other serials. **Services:** Interlibrary loan; copying; NTIS documents ordering; department open to the public. **Computerized Information Services:** U.S. Patent Office Classification System, DIALOG Information Services, VU/TEXT Information Services. **Staff:** Carol Wischmeyer, Subject Spec.; Lilian Stefano, Act. Patent Depository Lib.Rep.

★4831★
Detroit Public Schools - Professional Library (Educ)
5057 Woodward Ave., Rm. 869
Detroit, MI 48202 Phone: (313)494-1626
Founded: 1966. **Staff:** 1. **Subjects:** Education. **Holdings:** 5000 volumes; 1000 pamphlets. **Subscriptions:** 100 journals and other serials. **Services:** Copying; library open to the public for reference use only.

★4832★
Detroit Receiving Hospital & University Health Center - Library (Med)
4201 St. Antoine Phone: (313)745-4475
Detroit, MI 48201 Cherrie M. Mudloff, Libn.
Staff: Prof 1; Other 1. **Subjects:** Medicine. **Holdings:** 3000 books. **Subscriptions:** 286 journals and other serials. **Services:** Interlibrary loan; copying; library open to hospital personnel and Metropolitan Detroit Medical Library Group members. **Computerized Information Services:** NLM, WILSONLINE, DIALOG Information Services, BRS Information Technologies, OCLC. **Networks/Consortia:** Member of National Network of Libraries of Medicine - Greater Midwest Region, Detroit Associated Libraries Region of Cooperation (DALROC). **Remarks:** FAX: (313)993-0497.

Detroit Riverview Hospital
See: **Detroit Macomb Hospital Corporation** (4810)

★4833★
Detroit Symphony Orchestra - Library (Mus)
Orchestra Hall
3711 Woodward Ave. Phone: (313)833-0627
Detroit, MI 48201 Elkhonon Yoffe, Libn.
Founded: 1919. **Staff:** Prof 2. **Subjects:** Orchestral scores and parts. **Special Collections:** Original prints and manuscripts. **Holdings:** Figures not available. **Services:** Library not open to the public. **Remarks:** FAX: (313)833-3046. **Staff:** Charles Weaver, Asst.Libn.

★4834★
Detroit University Club - Library (Hist)
1411 E. Jefferson Phone: (313)567-9280
Detroit, MI 48207 Dorothy Turri, Mgr.
Subjects: Detroit and Michigan history and fiction. **Holdings:** 5000 books. **Subscriptions:** 47 journals and other serials. **Services:** Library open to members only.

Andre Deutsch Archive
See: **University of Tulsa - McFarlin Library** (19466)

★4835★
Deutsch, Kerrigan and Stiles - Law Library (Law)
755 Magazine St. Phone: (504)581-5141
New Orleans, LA 70130 Pat Sarsfield, Libn.
Staff: Prof 1. **Subjects:** Law - federal, state, admiralty, labor, tax, aviation; insurance; contracts. **Special Collections:** Collection of Great Britain legal materials (1382 volumes). **Holdings:** 30,000 volumes. **Subscriptions:** 59 journals and other serials; 6 newspapers. **Services:** Library not open to the public. **Computerized Information Services:** LEXIS, NEXIS. **Remarks:** FAX: (504)566-1201. Telex: 584358. **Staff:** Gwen P. Stricklin

Deutsche Bibliothek
See: **Germany - Deutsche Bibliothek** (6440)

★4836★
Deutsche Forschungsanstalt fur Luft- und Raumfahrt e.V. - Abt. Bibliothekswesen (Sci-Engr)
Bunsenstrasse 10 Phone: 551 7092150
W-3400 Goettingen, Germany Mr. H. Futterer
Founded: 1978. **Staff:** Prof 2; Other 18. **Subjects:** Aerospace. **Holdings:** 110,000 books; 40,000 bound periodical volumes; 180,000 reports. **Subscriptions:** 1600 journals and other serials; 20 newspapers. **Services:** Library open to the public for reference use only. **Computerized Information Services:** STN International, ESA/IRS. Contact Person: Mr. G. Freyschmidt, telephone: 2203 6013293. **Remarks:** FAX: 551 7092169.

Deutsche Gesellschaft fur Chemisches Apparatewesen, Chemische Technik und Biotechnologie e.V.
See: **DECHEMA** (4692)

Deutsche Stiftung fur Internationale Entwicklung
See: **German Foundation for International Development** (6426)

Deutsches Archaeologisches Institut
See: **German Archaeological Institute** (6419)

Deutsches Elektronen-Synchrotron
See: **German Electron-Synchrotron - DESY Scientific Documentation and Information Service** (6425)

Deutsches Hydrographisches Institut
See: **Bundesamt fur Seeschiffahrt und Hydrographie** (2360)

Deutsches Institut fur Internationale Padagogische Forschung
See: **German Institute for International Educational Research** (6429)

Deutsches Kunststoff-Institut - Dienstleistungen Information und Dokumentation
See: **German Plastics Institute - Information and Documentation Services** (6432)

★4837★
Deutschheim State Historic Site - Library (Area-Ethnic)
109 W. 2nd Phone: (314)486-2200
Hermann, MO 65041 Erin McCawley Renn, Ph.D., Hist. Site Adm.
Founded: 1979. **Staff:** 3. **Subjects:** 19th century Germans and 19th century Missouri Germans - art, architecture, daily life. **Special Collections:** 19th century German rare books collection; art collection (modern German books). **Holdings:** 600 books; periodicals; newspapers; day books; letters; photographs. **Subscriptions:** 10 journals and other serials. **Services:** Library open to qualified researchers. **Special Catalogs:** Catalog of holdings. **Remarks:** Operated by the Missouri (State) Department of Natural Resources - Division of Parks, Recreation & Historic Preservation.

★4838★
Deutschlandfunk - Dokumentation und Archive (Info Sci)
Raderberggurtel 40 Phone: 221 3452578
W-5000 Cologne 51, Germany Dr. Dieter Siebenkas
Founded: 1962. **Subjects:** Radio. **Holdings:** 60,000 books; 10,000 microfiche; 1000 reels of microfilm. **Services:** Library open to the public. **Computerized Information Services:** IBAS (internal database). **Publications:** Verzeichnis der Neuerwerbungen. **Remarks:** FAX: 221 3452823.

★4839★
Developing Countries Farm Radio Network - Library (Soc Sci)
40 Dundas St. W.
Box 12, Suite 227B Phone: (416)593-3751
Toronto, ON, Canada M5G 2C2 Joan Beckley, Libn.
Founded: 1980. **Subjects:** Developing world, agriculture, health, appropriate technology. **Holdings:** 800 books. **Subscriptions:** 300 journals and other serials. **Services:** Library open to the public by appointment. **Automated Operations:** INMAGIC. **Remarks:** Library serves primarily as a resource used in preparing information packages produced by Developing Countries Farm Radio Network (DCFRN). FAX: (416)593-3752. **Staff:** Joan Clayton.

★4840★
Development and Technical Assistance Center - Library (Bus-Fin)
70 Audubon St. Phone: (203)772-1345
New Haven, CT 06510 Laura Margolin, Pubns.Mgr.
Founded: 1982. **Staff:** Prof 2; Other 2. **Subjects:** Corporate and foundation philanthropy, nonprofit management. **Holdings:** 100 books. **Subscriptions:** 12 journals and other serials. **Services:** Copying; library open to the public by appointment. **Computerized Information Services:** Internal database. **Publications:** Connecticut Foundation Directory; Corporate Philanthropy in New England; Grant Announcement Service; Corporate Philanthropy in Connecticut; Corporate Philanthropy in Rhode Island; Budgeting Guide for Nonprofit Administrators and Volunteers; Proposal Writer's Guide. **Remarks:** Toll-free telephone number(s): (800)788-5598.

Developmental Center for Handicapped Persons
See: **Utah State University** (19715)

Devereaux Library
See: **South Dakota School of Mines and Technology** (15417)

★4841★
Devereux Foundation - Professional Library (Soc Sci)
19 S. Waterloo Rd.
Box 400 Phone: (215)296-6901
Devon, PA 19333 Joyce Matheson, Libn.
Founded: 1957. **Staff:** Prof 1; Other 1. **Subjects:** Clinical psychology, special education, psychiatry, child care, vocational rehabilitation, psychoanalysis. **Special Collections:** Clinical training audiotape library (100). **Holdings:** 3500 books; 150 bound periodical volumes; 6 multimedia training programs. **Subscriptions:** 145 journals and other serials. **Services:** Interlibrary loan; copying; library open to professionals. **Automated Operations:** Computerized cataloging. **Computerized Information Services:** DIALOG Information Services, OCLC; DOCLINE (electronic mail service). Performs searches on fee basis. **Networks/Consortia:** Member of PALINET, Delaware Valley Information Consortium (DEVIC), National Network of Libraries of Medicine - Middle Atlantic Region. **Remarks:** FAX: (215)296-6909. **Staff:** Mary Caparro, ILL.

George F. DeVine Music Library
See: **University of Tennessee at Knoxville** (19368)

Devonian Library
See: **Western Canadian Universities - Marine Biological Society** (20236)

★4842★
Devres, Inc. - Library (Soc Sci)
7201 Wisconsin Ave., Suite 500
Bethesda, MD 20814 Phone: (301)951-5546
Founded: 1978. **Subjects:** International development and developing nations - agriculture, rural development, small enterprise, nutrition, natural resources and energy, education, management information systems, institutional development. **Holdings:** 700 volumes. **Services:** Library not open to the public. **Remarks:** Telex: 440184 (DEVR UI). FAX: (301)652-5934.

★4843★
Dewey Ballantine - Library (Law)
1301 Avenue of the Americas Phone: (212)259-6000
New York, NY 10019 Gitelle Seer, Dir., Lib.Serv.
Staff: Prof 5; Other 14. **Subjects:** Law - antitrust, securities, taxation, real property, trusts and estates, corporate, bankruptcy, intellectual property. **Holdings:** 50,000 volumes. **Services:** Interlibrary loan; library open to members of SLA by appointment. **Automated Operations:** Computerized cataloging. **Computerized Information Services:** LEXIS, NEXIS, WESTLAW, DIALOG Information Services, PFDS Online, Dow Jones News/Retrieval, Reuters, VU/TEXT Information Services, DataTimes, Info Globe, LEGI-SLATE. **Publications:** Library Information Bulletin, monthly - available to reciprocating libraries. **Remarks:** FAX: (212)259-6679. Telex: 12-6825. **Formerly:** Dewey, Ballantine, Bushby, Palmer & Wood. **Staff:** Ellen Kaufman, Assoc.Dir.; Shirley E. Diamond, Corp.Libn.; Dawn Dublin, Tech.Serv.Libn.; Anne Cummings, Ref.Libn.

Governor Thomas E. Dewey Graduate Library for Public Affairs and Policy
See: **State University of New York at Albany - Governor Thomas E. Dewey Graduate Library for Public Affairs and Policy** (15727)

Dewey Library
See: **Massachusetts Institute of Technology** (9801)

★4844★
Dewitt Historical Society of Tompkins County - Archive/Library/Museum (Hist)
116 N. Cayuga St. Phone: (607)273-8284
Ithaca, NY 14850 Margaret C. Hobbie, Dir.
Founded: 1935. **Staff:** Prof 4; Other 4. **Subjects:** Local history, genealogy. **Special Collections:** Ithaca Imprints (500 volumes); Verne Morton Photographs, 1896-1945. **Holdings:** 2360 books; 347 bound periodical volumes; 900 linear feet of archival materials and manuscripts; 1500 maps; 100,000 photographs; 10,000 glass plate negatives; 300 scrapbooks (indexed); genealogy letter files; microfilm. **Services:** Copying; library open to the public. **Publications:** Newsletter, quarterly - to members. **Staff:** Susan Robey, Archv.

★4845★
Dexter Corporation - Dexter Nonwovens Division - Technical Information Center (Sci-Engr)
Two Elm St. Phone: (203)623-9801
Windsor Locks, CT 06096 Fred N. Masters, Jr., Mgr.
Founded: 1965. **Staff:** Prof 1; Other 1. **Subjects:** Papermaking, synthetic fiber papers, nonwoven fabrics papers. **Holdings:** Figures not available. **Services:** Library open to the public by appointment. **Remarks:** FAX: (203)623-5339.

★4846★
Dezign House - Library (Art)
Box 284 Phone: (216)294-2778
Jefferson, OH 44047 Ramon Jan Elias, Dir.
Founded: 1962. **Subjects:** Art history, design, theater, mechanical music, family history. **Special Collections:** Hawkesworth family papers; special travel section (Russia, China, Czechoslovakia, Portugal, France, England, Spain, Denmark, West Germany, Austria; photographs and pamphlets, books, and maps). **Holdings:** 12,000 books. **Services:** Library not open to the public.

★4847★
DHS/CMHS - Health Sciences Library (Med)
Administration Bldg., Rm. 100
St. Elizabeths Campus
2700 Martin Luther King, Jr. Ave., S.E.
Washington, DC 20032 Phone: (202)373-7175
Staff: Prof 2; Other 2. **Subjects:** Psychiatry, occupational therapy, general medicine, Protestant and Catholic chaplaincy, neurology, dance therapy, dentistry, therapeutic recreation, clinical psychology, social work, speech pathology and audiology, psychiatric nursing, psychoanalysis, psychodrama. **Special Collections:** William Alanson White Library. **Holdings:** 20,000 books; 18,000 bound periodical volumes. **Subscriptions:** 300 journals and other serials. **Services:** Interlibrary loan; copying; library open to the public for reference use only with librarian's permission. **Automated Operations:** Computerized cataloging. **Computerized Information Services:** PsycINFO, MEDLINE. **Networks/Consortia:** Member of District of Columbia Health Sciences Information Network (DOCHSIN). **Publications:** Library News, bimonthly - for internal distribution only. **Staff:** Velora A. Jernigan, ILL.

★4848★
Dial Corporation - Dial Technical Administrative Center (Food-Bev)
15101 N. Scottsdale Rd. Phone: (602)998-6120
Scottsdale, AZ 85260-2101 Linda Monroe, Sr.Info.Spec./Libn.
Founded: 1976. **Staff:** 1. **Subjects:** Food sciences; microbiology; nutrition; shelf stable foods; packaging; chemistry; soaps; detergents; cosmetics; products for personal care, household, and laundry. **Holdings:** 9400 books; 8200 bound periodical volumes; 7000 pamphlets. **Subscriptions:** 250 journals and other serials. **Services:** Interlibrary loan; copying; center open to the public by appointment. **Automated Operations:** Computerized cataloging. **Computerized Information Services:** DIALOG Information Services, PFDS Online, BRS Information Technologies, OCLC, Chemical Information Systems, Inc. (CIS), MEDLINE, Dow Jones News/Retrieval, NLM, Chemical Abstracts Service (CAS). **Networks/Consortia:** Member of AMIGOS Bibliographic Council, Inc. **Publications:** Accession Bulletin, bimonthly; list of serials and journals. **Remarks:** FAX: (602)998-6227.

★4849★
Dial Corporation - Law Department Library (Law)
Dial Tower, No. 2212
1850 N. Central Ave. Phone: (602)207-5746
Phoenix, AZ 85077 Margaret E. Hoffman, Adm.
Subjects: Law. **Holdings:** 3000 volumes. **Services:** Library not open to the public. **Remarks:** FAX: (602)207-5480. **Formerly:** Greyhound Corporation.

★4850★
DIALOG Information Services, Inc. (Comp Sci)
3460 Hillview Ave. Phone: (415)858-3785
Palo Alto, CA 94304 Patrick J. Tierney, Pres.
Subjects: Chemistry, science and technology, engineering, social sciences and humanities, business, economics, medicine, popular magazine literature, research in progress, law. **Holdings:** 250 million computer accessible citations and abstracts on subject fields listed above. **Services:** Computer-based online retrieval and SDI support services; training seminar in online searching of DIALOG databases, DIALORDER. **Computerized Information Services:** DIALOGLINK; DIALOG OnDisc; DIALMAIL (electronic mail service). **Publications:** Chronolog, monthly - to users of service; Searching DIALOG: The Complete Guide; user's manual; DIALOG Databases documentation chapters. **Remarks:** Toll-free telephone number(s): (800)3-DIALOG (334-2564). FAX: (415)858-7069. Telex: 334499 DIALOG 8 PLA. Branch offices are maintained in Boston, Los Angeles, New York City, Washington, DC, Philadelphia, Chicago, Houston; international representatives are located in London, Tokyo, Toronto, Seoul, Sydney, Mexico City, Buenos Aires, Sao Paulo, Copenhagen, Cairo, Helsinki, Oxford, Paris, Hong Kong, Tel-Aviv, Oslo, Riyadh, Barcelona, Solna (Sweden), Neuchatel (Switzerland), Santiago (Chile), Bielefed (Germany), Bangalore (India). **Staff:** Richard Ream, V.P., Mktg. & Customer Serv.; Robert Donati, Dir., Domestic Fld.Oper.; Libby Trudell, Dir., Marketing; Georg Romero, Mgr., Customer Serv.

Harry Diamond Laboratories
See: **U.S. Army - Laboratory Command** (16982)

Diana Press Archive
See: **June Mazer Lesbian Library** (9862)

★4851★
A.B. Dick Company - Library
5700 W. Touhy Ave.
Chicago, IL 60648
Founded: 1945. **Subjects:** Chemistry, business, electronics, graphic arts. **Holdings:** 3300 books; 2300 bound periodical volumes; 30 VF drawers of patents; 16 VF drawers of pamphlets and clippings. **Remarks:** Currently inactive.

O.D. Dickerson Memorial Library
See: **American Institute for Chartered Property Casualty Underwriters - Insurance Institute of America - Library** (634)

Donald R. Dickey Library of Vertebrate Zoology
See: **University of California, Los Angeles - Louise Darling Biomedical Library** (18390)

James Dickey Collection
See: **University of West Florida** (19550)

John W. Dickhaut Library
See: **Methodist Theological School in Ohio** (10190)

★4852★
Dickinson College - Library - Special Collections (Hist)
College Library Phone: (717)245-1399
Carlisle, PA 17013 George Hing, Archv./Cur.
Founded: 1784. **Staff:** 2. **Subjects:** College archives; historical and literary manuscripts; rare books. **Special Collections:** Papers of Founders, James Buchanan, Roger Brooke Taney, Joseph Priestley, Carl Sandburg, John Drinkwater, Moncure Conway, Robert Bridges (American editor); Books from the Library of Isaac Norris, 1671-1735; John F. Kennedy Collection (6600 items). **Holdings:** 20,000 volumes; 1000 feet of manuscripts and archival materials. **Subscriptions:** 6 journals and other serials. **Services:** Copying; collections open to the public. **Computerized Information Services:** OCLC; BITNET (electronic mail service). **Publications:** Guide to the Archives and Manuscripts Collection of Dickinson College (1972); John and Mary's Journal. **Remarks:** FAX: (717)243-6573. Electronic mail address(es): HING@DICKINSN (BITNET). **Staff:** Marie Booth Ferre, Asst.Cur.

George Sherman Dickinson Music Library
See: **Vassar College - George Sherman Dickinson Music Library** (19788)

★4853★
Dickinson Press - Library (Publ)
127 1st St., W. Phone: (701)225-8111
Dickinson, ND 58601 Linda Sailer
Subjects: Newspaper reference topics. **Holdings:** Dickinson Press (complete file; 1883 to present). **Remarks:** FAX: (701)225-4205.

★4854★
Dickinson School of Law - Sheely-Lee Law Library (Law)
150 S. College St. Phone: (717)243-4611
Carlisle, PA 17013 James R. Fox, Law Libn. & Prof.
Founded: 1834. **Staff:** Prof 7; Other 8. **Subjects:** Law. **Special Collections:** Intellectual property law; Jewish, Israeli, Italian law; law and medicine. **Holdings:** 270,000 volumes; 20 VF drawers of records and briefs of the U.S. Supreme Court in microform; 365 shelves of records and briefs of Pennsylvania Supreme, Superior, Commonwealth Courts. **Subscriptions:** 1238 journals and other serials; 10 newspapers. **Services:** Interlibrary loan; copying; library open to the public for reference use only. **Automated Operations:** Computerized cataloging. **Computerized Information Services:** LEXIS, WESTLAW, OCLC. **Networks/Consortia:** Member of PALINET, Mid-Atlantic Law Library Cooperative (MALLCO). **Publications:** Selected acquisitions, irregular. **Remarks:** FAX: (717)243-4443. **Staff:** Cecily Giardina, Govt.Doc.Libn.; Mark Podvia, ILL; Debra Jones, Cat.; Judy Swarthout, Reader Serv.; Gail Partin, Ref.Libn.; Margot West, Archv.

★4855★
Dickinson State University - Stoxen Library (Educ)
Dickinson, ND 58601 Phone: (701)227-2135
Bernnett Reinke, Lib.Dir.
Founded: 1918. **Staff:** Prof 4. **Subjects:** Education. **Special Collections:** Theodore Roosevelt Collection (200 volumes). **Holdings:** 75,000 volumes. **Subscriptions:** 600 journals and other serials; 16 newspapers. **Services:** Interlibrary loan; copying; library open to the public. **Automated Operations:** Computerized public access catalog, cataloging, and ILL. **Computerized Information Services:** DIALOG Information Services, OCLC; EasyLink (electronic mail service). Performs searches on fee basis. Contact Person: Lillian Sorenson, ILL & Cat. or Eileen Kopron, Circ. **Networks/Consortia:** Member of MINITEX Library Information Network, North Dakota Network for Knowledge, ODIN (Online Dakota Information Network). **Remarks:** FAX: (701)227-2006. **Staff:** James Martz, Acq.Libn.; Lillian Sormson, ILL & Tech.Spec.; Eileen Kopren, Circ. & Ref.

★4856★
Dickinson, Wright, Moon, Van Dusen & Freeman - Information Center (Law)
800 First National Bldg. Phone: (313)223-3500
Detroit, MI 48226 Mark A. Heinrich, Hd.Libn.
Founded: 1878. **Staff:** Prof 3; Other 3. **Subjects:** Law - general civil practice, corporation, taxation, banking, estate planning, product liability, labor, international trade. **Holdings:** 20,000 volumes. **Subscriptions:** 500 journals and other serials. **Services:** Interlibrary loan; center not open to the public. **Automated Operations:** Computerized cataloging. **Computerized Information Services:** LEXIS, WESTLAW, VU/TEXT Information Services, DIALOG Information Services, Dow Jones News/Retrieval, Questor; internal database. **Networks/Consortia:** Member of Detroit Associated Libraries Region of Cooperation (DALROC), Michigan Library Consortium (MLC). **Remarks:** Branch libraries located at 525 N. Woodward Ave., Box 509, Bloomfield Hills, MI 48013; 121 E. Allegan St., Lansing, MI 48933; 1901 L St., N.W., Suite 801, Washington, DC 20036; 300 Ottawa Ave., N.W., Suite 650, Grand Rapids, MI 49503; 30 N. LaSalle, Suite 2000, Chicago, IL 60602. FAX: (313)223-3598. **Staff:** Carol M. Darga, Tech.Serv.Libn.; Mary Barrett, Br.Libn.

★4857★
Dickson Mounds Museum - Library (Hist)
R.R. 1, Box 185 Phone: (309)547-3721
Lewiston, IL 61542 Dr. Judith Franke, Musm.Dir.
Founded: 1927. ST 1. **Subjects:** Archeology - Illinois, general; anthropology; prehistoric Indians; Indian arts; Illinois state history; local history; natural history; museum studies. **Special Collections:** Rare books (archeology, medicine, history). **Holdings:** 1200 books; 220 bound periodical volumes; 5 AV programs. **Subscriptions:** 38 journals and other serials; 2 newspapers. **Services:** Library open to the public for reference use only. **Remarks:** FAX: (309)343-0150. Is a branch of the Illinois State Museum. **Staff:** Duane Esarey, Coll.Mgr.; Jeanette Vaultonburg, Act.Libn.; Andrea Keller, Cons.

★4858★
DiCyan Library (Med)
1486 E. 33rd St.
Brooklyn, NY 11234 Phone: (718)252-8844
Subjects: Pharmacology, psychopharmacology, neuropharmacology, psychiatry, therapeutics, biochemistry, drugs. **Holdings:** 3000 volumes. **Services:** Library not open to the public.

★4859★
Diebold Group, Inc. - Information Services Library (Comp Sci)
2 Depot Plaza, Suite 203 Phone: (914)242-0580
Bedford Hills, NY 10507 Jean McAcy
Founded: 1954. **Staff:** Prof 1; Other 1. **Subjects:** Management, data processing, computer and management information systems, communications, business, automation, telecommunications. **Holdings:** 3500 books; 3000 annual reports and pamphlets; 500 computer manufacturers' catalogs; 1500 clipping files. **Subscriptions:** 102 journals and other serials. **Services:** Interlibrary loan; library not open to the public. **Computerized Information Services:** DIALOG Information Services. **Formerly:** Located in New York, NY.

Oskar Diethelm Historical Library
See: **New York Hospital-Cornell Medical Center** (11580)

★4860★
Dietrich Collection (Area-Ethnic, Hum)
West Farms Rd.
RR1, Box 335 Phone: (603)632-7156
Enfield, NH 03748 Dr. R. Krystyna Dietrich, Dir.
Founded: 1962. **Staff:** Prof 1. **Subjects:** Alexander Orlowski, Polish art, American literature in Poland, Daniel Chodowiecki, Polish reference materials. **Special Collections:** Paintings, drawings, graphics of Alexander Orlowski, 1777-1832; etchings of Daniel Chodowiecki, 1726-1801; etchings of Jean Pierre Norblin de la Gourdaine, 1745-1830; Polish translations of American literature. **Holdings:** 10,000 volumes; 2000 works of art; 5000 uncataloged items. **Services:** Reference; copying; collection open to the public by appointment. **Publications:** Alexander Orlowski in America: a bibliography; U.S. Literature in Poland, 1790-1960 (typed bibliography, 1600 pages). **Special Catalogs:** Works by and about Alexander Orlowski outside of Poland and Russia, in the Dietrich Collection, and elsewhere in America (1700 cards); works by and about Daniel Chodowiecki in the collection (1900 cards). **Remarks:** This is said to be the largest American collection of works by and about Orlowski, as well as the only collection of American literature in Polish in the U.S.

Howard Dietz Collection
See: **Museum of the City of New York - Theatre Collection** (10892)

Diffusion in Metals Data Center
See: **U.S. Natl. Institute of Standards and Technology - Metallurgy Division** (17620)

★4861★
Dighton Historical Society - Museum Library (Hist)
1217 Williams St.
Dighton, MA 02715 Elaine Varley, Cur.
Founded: 1968. **Subjects:** Local history - Bristol County, Dighton, Somerset, and Rehoboth, Massachusetts; genealogy. **Holdings:** Books; documents; scrapbooks; clipping files. **Services:** Library open to the public by appointment for reference use only. **Remarks:** The curator may be reached at (508)669-5514.

★4862★
Digital Automation Associates, Inc. - Library (Comp Sci)
310 W. Gypsy Lane Rd. Phone: (419)352-7526
Bowling Green, OH 43402 Teresa Berg, Contact
Subjects: Electronics, communications, data acquisition and control systems, robotics, electronic/fiber optics. **Holdings:** 2000 volumes.

★4863★
Digital Equipment Corporation - Andover Library
165 Dascomb Rd. Phone: (508)493-5111
Andover, MA 01810 Richard Maxfield, Info.Sys.Anl.
Defunt.

★4864★
Digital Equipment Corporation - Corporate Market Research Center (Comp Sci)
2 Results Way Phone: (508)467-5943
Marlboro, MA 01752 Barbara Klein, Mgr.
Founded: 1983. **Staff:** Prof 14; Other 2. **Subjects:** Computer industry. **Holdings:** 1000 market research reports; planning services. **Subscriptions:** 150 journals and other serials. **Services:** Interlibrary loan (DEC only); center not open to the public. **Automated Operations:** Computerized public access catalog, cataloging, serials, and circulation. **Computerized Information Services:** DIALOG Information Services, Dun & Bradstreet Business Credit Services, Dow Jones News/Retrieval, Computer Intelligence Corporation (CIC), Reuter TEXTLINE, InvesText, NEXIS. **Networks/Consortia:** Member of Digital Library Network, NELINET, Inc. **Publications:** MRC Memo, bimonthly - for internal distribution only. **Remarks:** FAX: (508)467-3069. **Staff:** Rene Davis, Info.Cons.; Carol Hill, Info.Cons.; Chris Di Pietro, Res.Serv.Supv.; Cassie Marrone, Comm.Prog.; Patti Arsenault, Trng. Prog.; Priscilla Littlefield, Info.Cons.; Joyce Gevirtzman, Info.Cons.; Sonia Miletti, Info.Cons.; Judi Tebo, Info.Cons.; Sue Ann McLean, Cat.; Jackie Finn, Oper.Supv.

★4865★
Digital Equipment Corporation - Maynard Area Information Services (Comp Sci)
146 Main St., MLO 4-3/A20 Phone: (617)493-6231
Maynard, MA 01754-2571 Janice Eifrig, Mgr.
Founded: 1974. **Staff:** Prof 10; Other 6. **Subjects:** Computer science, electronics, electrical engineering, management, business. **Holdings:** 14,000 books; 1000 bound periodical volumes; 1200 AV programs; 2000 volumes of company literature; 2000 volumes of technical reports. **Subscriptions:** 800 journals and other serials; 20 newspapers. **Services:** Interlibrary loan; services not open to the public. **Automated Operations:** Computerized cataloging, acquisitions, serials, and circulation. **Computerized Information Services:** OCLC, DIALOG Information Services, BRS Information Technologies, NEXIS, Dow Jones News/Retrieval, DunsPrint; internal database. **Networks/Consortia:** Member of NELINET, Inc., Digital Library Network. **Publications:** Library newsletter, monthly; periodicals list, annual; abstracts newsletter, bimonthly. **Staff:** Carol Henley, Sys.Coord.; Marguerite Vierkant, Doc. Delivery Task Ldr.; Liz Slade, Cat. Task Ldr.; Beth Owen, Res.Asst. Task Ldr.; Lynn Sellar, Acq. Task Ldr.

★4866★
Digital Equipment Corporation - Merrimack Library Services (Comp Sci)
MK01-1/K11
Digital Dr. Phone: (603)884-5482
Merrimack, NH 03054-0430 Nancy J. Sullivan, Lib.Mgr.
Staff: 6. **Subjects:** Computer science, engineering, marketing. **Holdings:** 3000 books; 1000 other cataloged items. **Subscriptions:** 200 journals and other serials; 10 newspapers. **Services:** library not open to the public. **Automated Operations:** Computerized cataloging, acquisitions, and circulation. **Computerized Information Services:** DIALOG Information Services. **Staff:** B. Johnson, Circ.Libn.; H. Ferrigno, Cat. & Ref.Libn.; B. Vorbeau, Ser.Libn.; C. Roberts, Circ. & Ref.Libn.; R. Tullis, Acq. & Tech.Serv.Libn.

★4867★
Digital Equipment Corporation - Networks and Communications Library (Comp Sci)
550 King St., LKG1-2/J10 Phone: (508)486-7067
Littleton, MA 01460 Janet Hebert, Info.Serv.Mgr.
Founded: 1978. **Staff:** Prof 4; Other 2. **Subjects:** Networks, communications. **Holdings:** 3000 books; 2000 other cataloged items; technical reports; pamphlets; AV programs. **Subscriptions:** 200 journals and other serials; 15 newspapers. **Services:** Interlibrary loan; library not open to the public. **Automated Operations:** Computerized cataloging and circulation. **Computerized Information Services:** DIALOG Information Services, InvesText, Dow Jones News/Retrieval, NEXIS. **Networks/Consortia:** Member of NELINET, Inc. **Staff:** Martha Sullivan, Circ.; Sharon Allman, Acq.; Ann Kallock, Market Info.Spec.; Ellen Gilliam, Tech.Info.Spec.; Kathy Fagelman, Cat.

★4868★
Digital Equipment Corporation - Shrewsbury Library (Sci-Engr)
333 South St., SHR1-3/G18
Shrewsbury, MA 01545-4112 Phone: (508)841-3400
Founded: 1983. **Staff:** Prof 2. **Subjects:** Engineering, management, manufacturing, quality. **Holdings:** 8500 books; technical reports; standards; patents. **Subscriptions:** 270 journals and other serials. **Services:** Interlibrary loan; library not open to the public. **Automated Operations:** Computerized cataloging, circulation, and ILL. **Computerized Information Services:** DIALOG Information Services, OCLC; internal database. **Networks/Consortia:** Member of Digital Library Network, NELINET, Inc. **Remarks:** FAX: (508)841-3738. **Staff:** Carole Piggford, Tech.Libn.; Peter Andrews, Tech.Libn.

★4869★
Digital Equipment Corporation - Spit Brook Library (Comp Sci)
110 Spit Brook Rd. Phone: (603)881-1058
Nashua, NH 03062 Catherine Sloan, Sr.Tech.Libn.
Founded: 1980. **Staff:** Prof 2; Other 1. **Subjects:** Software engineering, programming languages, technical documentation. **Holdings:** 1200 books; 1000 manuals; 500 reports; 250 AV programs; 3 VF drawers. **Subscriptions:** 200 journals and other serials; 20 newspapers. **Services:** Interlibrary loan; library not open to the public. **Automated Operations:** Computerized cataloging and circulation. **Computerized Information Services:** DIALOG Information Services; DIALMAIL, Ethernet (electronic mail services). Performs searches on fee basis. **Networks/Consortia:** Member of NELINET, Inc., Digital Library Network. **Staff:** Derek Kozikowski, Sys.Libn.

★4870★
M.M. Dillon, Ltd. - Library (Sci-Engr)
100 Sheppard Ave., E.
Box 1850, Station A Phone: (416)229-4646
Willowdale, ON, Canada M2N 6N5 Mary J. Gibson, Libn.
Staff: 1. **Subjects:** Engineering, environmental and planning. **Holdings:** Books; reports; microfiche; microfilm. **Subscriptions:** 100 journals and other serials. **Services:** Interlibrary loan; copying; library not open to the public. **Remarks:** FAX: (416)229-4292.

★4871★
Dillon, Read & Company, Inc. - Library (Bus-Fin)
535 Madison Ave. Phone: (212)906-7000
New York, NY 10022-4212 Nancy J. Bowles, Lib.Dir.
Founded: 1966. **Staff:** Prof 6; Other 11. **Subjects:** Corporate and municipal finance; securities regulations. **Holdings:** 3000 books; 500 shelves of corporate and municipal reports; 84 shelves of subject files. **Subscriptions:** 900 journals and other serials. **Services:** Interlibrary loan (New York City only); copying; library open to librarians on special request only. **Computerized Information Services:** DIALOG Information Services, NEXIS, LEXIS, TEXTLINE, Spectrum Ownership Profiles Online, Dow Jones News/Retrieval, Securities Database, Data Resources (DRI). **Remarks:** FAX: (212)758-9377. **Staff:** Rita Schaffer, Assoc.Libn., Res.

★4872★
Dilworth, Paxson, Kalish & Kauffman - Library (Law)
2600 The Fidelity Bldg. Phone: (215)875-7112
Philadelphia, PA 19109 Patricia A. Wyatt, Lib.Dir.
Staff: 4. **Subjects:** Law. **Holdings:** 20,000 books; 30 bound periodical volumes. **Subscriptions:** 40 journals and other serials; 15 newspapers. **Services:** Library not open to the public. **Computerized Information Services:** DIALOG Information Services, LEXIS, NEXIS, WESTLAW, Information America, Dow Jones News/Retrieval, Dun & Bradstreet Business Credit Services, LEGI-SLATE, Information America, DataTimes, VU/TEXT Information Services. **Remarks:** FAX: (215)875-8540; (215)875-7234. Telex: 831-320.

Georgi Dimitrov Higher Institute of Physical Culture
See: **Bulgaria - National Sports Academy** (2350)

Dinan & Tertians Libraries
See: **Colombiere Center - Library** (3928)

Dinosaur National Monument
See: **U.S. Natl. Park Service** (17701)

★4873★
Dinosaur State Park - Library (Biol Sci)
West St. Phone: (203)529-8423
Rocky Hill, CT 06067 Brenda Sauer, Sr.Ck.
Subjects: Paleontology, geology, natural history, museums. **Holdings:** 1000 books; 40 AV programs. **Subscriptions:** 12 journals and other serials. **Services:** Library not open to the public. **Automated Operations:** Librarian's Helper.

★4874★
Dinsmore & Shohl - Library (Law)
255 E. 5th St. Phone: (513)977-8338
Cincinnati, OH 45202-3172 Anne K. Abate, Libn.
Staff: Prof 1; Other 2. **Subjects:** Law. **Holdings:** 22,000 volumes. **Services:** Interlibrary loan; library not open to the public. **Computerized Information Services:** LEXIS, WESTLAW, DIALOG Information Services, DataTimes, Compu-Mark, TriState Online; InterNet (electronic mail service). **Remarks:** FAX: (513)977-8141. Electronic mail address(es): usr3919@tso.uc.edu (InterNet).

★4875★
Diocese of Allentown - Pro-Life Library (Soc Sci)
1135 Stefko Blvd. Phone: (215)691-0380
Bethlehem, PA 18017 Suzanne Mello
Staff: Prof 1; Other 1. **Subjects:** Bioethics, abortion, sexuality, death and dying. **Special Collections:** United States Catholic Conference Documentary Service; Origins Documentary Service. **Holdings:** 700 volumes; 600 audiotapes; 40 videotapes; 100 pamphlets and booklets; 50 government statistics and reports; newspaper clippings. **Subscriptions:** 11 journals and other serials. **Services:** Interlibrary loan; copying; library open to the public. **Publications:** Pamphlets and tracts, irregular; curriculum publications.

★4876★
Diocese of Amarillo - Diocesan Archives (Rel-Phil)
1800 N. Spring St.
Box 5644 Phone: (806)383-2243
Amarillo, TX 79117-5644 Sr. Christine Jensen, Archv.
Subjects: History of the Roman Catholic church in western Texas, 1876 to present. **Holdings:** Archival materials: account books; letters; parish histories; parish records of baptisms, marriages, deaths; manuscripts. **Services:** Copying; archives open to serious students of church history.

Diocese of Calgary
See: **Anglican Church of Canada** (868)

★4877★
Diocese of Fredericton - Synod Archives (Rel-Phil, Hist)
c/o Provincial Archives of New Brunswick
P.O. Box 6000 Phone: (506)453-2122
Fredericton, NB, Canada E3B 5H1 Harvey Malmberg, Diocesan Archv.
Founded: 1892. **Staff:** 1. **Subjects:** New Brunswick parochial history, 16th and 17th century theology, Church of England history, 17th century church architecture, church music. **Special Collections:** Bishop John Medley Collection; New Brunswick parish records (90 parishes). **Holdings:** 4000 books. **Services:** Archives open to the public; Medley Library open to the public by appointment open to the public **Remarks:** Alternate telephone number(s): 450-8500. The archives are housed at the Provincial Archives of New Brunswick in Fredericton, N.B. Medley Library is housed at Christ Church Cathedral Hall located at 168 Church St., Fredericton, N.B.

★4878★
Diocese of La Crosse - Archives (Rel-Phil)
P.O. Box 4004 Phone: (608)788-7700
La Crosse, WI 54602-4004 Rev. Michael J. Gorman, Chancellor/Archv.
Staff: 2. **Subjects:** History of the Catholic Church in the Diocese of La Crosse, 1868 to present. **Holdings:** 45 linear feet of ecclesiastical records, documents, letters. **Services:** Archives not open to the public. **Remarks:** FAX: (608)788-8413.

★4879★
Diocese of Lafayette, Louisiana - Archives (Rel-Phil)
Box 3387 Phone: (318)261-5639
Lafayette, LA 70502 Regina Arnaud, M.L.S., Archv.
Founded: 1918. **Staff:** Prof 1; Other 2. **Subjects:** Diocese parishes and Southwest Louisiana religious history. **Special Collections:** Bishop Maurice Schexnayder papers, 1895-1981 (50 linear feet). **Holdings:** 500 books; 2000 linear feet of archival materials; 200 reels of microfilm of sacramental records, 1756-1978. **Subscriptions:** 15 journals and other serials. **Services:** Interlibrary loan; copying; archives open to the public with restrictions. **Special Indexes:** Correspondence of the Most Rev. Jules Jeanmard, 1st Bishop of Lafayette, 1918-1956; correspondence of the Most Rev. Bishop Gerard Frey, 3rd Bishop of Lafayette, 1973-1989; holdings file index (all online).

Diocese of Montreal
See: **Anglican Church of Canada - Diocese of Montreal - Archives** (869)

Diocese of New Westminster
See: **Anglican Church of Canada - Ecclesiastical Province of British Columbia & Diocese of New Westminster** (870)

★4880★
Diocese of Ogdensburg - Archives (Rel-Phil)
622 Washington St.
P.O. Box 369 Phone: (315)393-2920
Ogdensburg, NY 13669 Rev. Lawrence E. Cotter, Archv.
Founded: 1872. **Staff:** Prof 1; Other 1. **Subjects:** Church history. **Special Collections:** Journal of Father Picquet, founder of Fort LaPresentation (later Ogdensburg). **Holdings:** Books; correspondence; ecclesiastical records of the diocese. **Services:** Copying; archives open to the public with restrictions.

★4881★
Diocese of Phoenix - Kino Institute Library
1224 E. Northern Phone: (602)997-7397
Phoenix, AZ 85020 Sr. Bibiane Roy, Libn.
Founded: 1972. **Staff:** 1. **Holdings:** 10,000 books; 2000 audio tapes. **Subscriptions:** 150 journals and other serials; 6 newspapers. **Services:** Copying; library open to the public.

★4882★
Diocese of Pittsburgh - Learning Media Center (Rel-Phil)
111 Boulevard of the Allies Phone: (412)456-3121
Pittsburgh, PA 15222 Carole M. Obrokta, Dir.
Founded: 1968. **Staff:** Prof 1; Other 2. **Subjects:** Religious education, theology, educational methods. **Holdings:** 5000 books; 1500 cassette tapes; 600 videotapes; 500 16mm films; 3500 filmstrips. **Subscriptions:** 80 journals and other serials. **Services:** Center open to the public with restrictions. **Publications:** Media Messages of C.C.D.

★4883★
Diocese of Rochester - Catholic Family Center - Department of Justice & Peace - Library
50 Chestnut St.
Rochester, NY 14604
Defunct.

★4884★
Diocese of St. Cloud - Catholic Education Ministries - Media Center (Rel-Phil)
305 7th Ave., N.
St. Cloud, MN 56301 Phone: (612)252-1021
Founded: 1953. **Staff:** Prof 2; Other 2. **Subjects:** Religion, Bible, family issues, personal growth, social concerns, global awareness, Christian living. **Special Collections:** Catholic Telecommunication Network of America (CTNA) Library (1300 videotapes); MECC computer software programs, K-12 (all subject areas; restricted for use by diocesan schools). **Holdings:** 5000 books; 200 films; 1200 sound filmstrips; 200 phonograph records; 500 cassette tapes; 1500 video cassettes. **Subscriptions:** 5 journals and other serials. **Services:** Interlibrary loan; center open to the public with restrictions. **Computerized Information Services:** Internal database. Performs searches on fee basis. **Special Catalogs:** Media Catalog, every 4 years with annual supplement - available upon request. **Special Indexes:** CTNA listings. **Remarks:** FAX: (612)251-0259. **Formerly:** Its Bureau of Education - Media Center. **Staff:** Pamela Walz, Media Coord.; Timothy Welch, Media Cons.

★4885★
Diocese of Savannah - Chancery Archives & Diocesan Archives (Rel-Phil)
Catholic Pastoral Center
601 E. Liberty St.
Savannah, GA 31401-5196 Phone: (912)238-2320
Founded: 1973. **Staff:** 1. **Subjects:** Diocese of Savannah, 1796 to present. **Special Collections:** Diocesan archives (journals; personal and official letters; scrapbooks; typescripts; papers related to the growth of the Catholic Church during the Spanish and French colonization of Georgia; stories of the experiences of early missionaries with the Indian tribes of Georgia; 200 linear feet). **Holdings:** 80 books; 104 reels of microfilm. **Subscriptions:** 4 journals and other serials. **Services:** Copying; center open to the public by appointment with archivist's approval. **Computerized Information Services:** Genealogical Research (internal database). **Remarks:** FAX: (912)238-2335.

★4886★
Diocese of Tucson - Regina Cleri Resource Library
8800 E. 22nd St.
Tucson, AZ 85710
Subjects: Theology, sacred scripture, spirituality, family life, church history and renewal. **Special Collections:** Spanish language materials (700 books; 20 AV programs). **Holdings:** 15,000 books; 200 filmstrips; 25 films. **Remarks:** Currently inactive.

★4887★
Diocese of Wilmington - Office of Total Education - Resource Center
1626 N. Union St. Phone: (302)573-3136
Wilmington, DE 19806 Scott Stone, Resource Coord.
Staff: Prof 1; Other 1. **Subjects:** Catholic theology, religious education, liturgical formation. **Special Collections:** AV programs on the sacraments, the life of Jesus, the Bible, liturgical celebrations (220 16mm films; 900 audio cassettes; 5000 slides; 900 video cassettes; 3000 filmstrips; 200 phonograph records). **Holdings:** 9000 books; 110 bound periodical volumes. **Subscriptions:** 42 journals and other serials. **Services:** Interlibrary loan; copying; center open to the public. **Networks/Consortia:** Member of Libraries in the New Castle County System (LINCS). **Publications:** Catalog update, semiannual - by subscription; newsletter, bimonthly - to members. **Special Catalogs:** AV Catalog (book). **Staff:** M.J. Quinlan, Asst.Coord.

★4888★
Diosygori Gepgyar - Muszaki Konyvtar (Sci-Engr)
Pf 503 Phone: 46 59211
H-3544 Miskolc, Hungary Sinkovics Belane
Founded: 1947. **Staff:** Prof 4. **Subjects:** Machine industry, metalworking, wire-drawing, pumps, computers, cable machines. **Special Collections:** Prospectuses on light punch cards (6000); patent specifications by numbers of patents and UDS (8000); translations (12,700). **Holdings:** 49,000 books; 2680 bound periodical volumes; 1380 microfiche; 1220 research reports. **Subscriptions:** 155 journals and other serials; 8 newspapers. **Services:** Interlibrary loan; library not open to the public. **Remarks:** FAX: 46 51652. Telex: 06-2334; 06-2241.

★4889★
Diozesanarchiv Wien (Rel-Phil)
Wollzeile 2 Phone: 222 51552239
A-1010 Vienna, Austria Dr. Annemarie Fenzel, Dir.
Founded: 1936. **Staff:** Prof 2. **Subjects:** Roman Catholic church, Archdiocese of Vienna. **Special Collections:** Prayer books (3000); indexes of the dioceses in the Austro-Hungarian monarchy from 1860-1940. **Holdings:** 15,000 books; 35,000 bound periodical volumes; 400 reels of microfilm. **Subscriptions:** 400 journals and other serials; 30 newspapers. **Services:** Interlibrary loan; copying; archives open to the public. **Computerized Information Services:** Internal database. **Publications:** Beitrage zur Wiener Diozesangeschichte, 3/year.

Paul Dirac Science Library
See: **Florida State University - Paul Dirac Science Library** (5917)

★4890★
Direct Marketing Association, Inc. - Information Central (Bus-Fin)
11 W. 42nd St. Phone: (212)768-7277
New York, NY 10036-8096 Ann Zeller, V.P., Info. & Spec.Proj.
Founded: 1946. **Staff:** Prof 7; Other 2. **Subjects:** Direct response advertising and marketing, including media applications (direct mail, catalog, telemarketing, print, television), markets (business-to-business, consumer, financial services, circulation, fund raising), and management basics. **Holdings:** 500 volumes; 2500 bound portfolios of direct marketing campaigns; 1500 microfiched records; 1200-topic resource collection, including articles, speeches, seminar notes, research reports; cassettes; slides. **Subscriptions:** 110 journals and other serials. **Services:** Center open to non-members on fee basis. **Computerized Information Services:** DIALOG Information Services, NEXIS; Direct Link (internal database). Performs searches on fee basis. **Publications:** Service Directories; Statistical Fact Book; Start-Up Resource Guides. **Remarks:** FAX: (212)398-6725. **Staff:** Nilda Castillo, Mgr., Info.Ctrl.Adm.; Lynne Wellenbusher, Mgr., Info.Ctrl.Rsrcs.; Anthony Giacchetto, Info.Spec.; Christine Heaphy, Asst.Mgr., Direct Link Database Serv.; Allison Cosmedy, Asst.Mgr., Pubns.Dev. & Prod.; Rhonda Gadson, Recs.Adm.

Direction des Archives du Senegal
See: **Senegal - Direction des Archives du Senegal** (15036)

★4891★
Everett McKinley Dirksen Congressional Leadership Research Center (Hist)
301 S. 4th St., Suite A Phone: (309)347-7113
Pekin, IL 61554-4219 John J. Kornacki, Ph.D, Exec.Dir.
Founded: 1963. **Staff:** Prof 3. **Subjects:** U.S. Congressional leadership, Everett McKinley Dirksen, U.S. Congress, Harold Himmel Velde. **Special Collections:** Dirksen Papers, circa 1933-1969 (1800 linear feet); Velde Papers, circa 1949-1956 (16 linear feet). **Holdings:** 2000 linear feet of archival materials; 1500 pieces of memorabilia; 8000 photographs. **Subscriptions:** 7000 journals and other serials. **Services:** Exhibit hall open to the public; archives open to researchers by appointment. **Publications:** The Dirksen Center Congress (information about Center programs and the U.S. Congress and its leadership), quarterly - free upon request; annual report; Network (newsletter for teachers), semiannual. **Remarks:** FAX: (309)347-7113. **Staff:** Linda M. Sams, Adm.Asst./Ed.; Stan Mendenhall, Educ.Assoc. 0 0

★4892★
Disada Productions Ltd. - Walt Disney Memorial Library (Theater)
5788 Notre Dame de Grace Ave. Phone: (514)489-0527
Montreal, PQ, Canada H4A 1M4 Peter Adamakos, Pres.
Founded: 1967. **Staff:** 1. **Subjects:** Motion pictures, animation. **Holdings:** 600 books; 4000 bound periodical volumes; 2000 other cataloged items; 800 films and tapes; 5000 pieces of original artwork; 2000 posters, photographs, pressbooks; 400 special film materials. **Subscriptions:** 18 journals and other serials. **Services:** Copying; screening facilities; library open to the public by appointment.

Disaster Research Center
See: **University of Delaware** (18541)

★4893★
Disciples of Christ Historical Society - Library (Hist, Rel-Phil)
1101 19th Ave., S. Phone: (615)327-1444
Nashville, TN 37212 David I. McWhirter, Dir.
Founded: 1941. **Staff:** Prof 2. **Subjects:** Christian Church, Disciples of Christ, Churches of Christ. **Holdings:** 30,000 volumes; 150 record groups of archival materials; 800 collections of personal papers; manuscripts; microfilm; phonograph records. **Subscriptions:** 270 journals and other serials. **Services:** Interlibrary loan; copying; library open to members. **Automated Operations:** Computerized cataloging. **Networks/Consortia:** Member of SOLINET. **Publications:** Discipliana, quarterly - to members; Preliminary Guide to Black Materials in the Disciples of Christ Historical Society (book); list of additional publications - available upon request. **Special Indexes:** Index to the Christian Record; Index to World Call. **Staff:** May F. Reed, Lib.Asst.

★4894★
Walt Disney Attractions - Information Services Technical Resource Center (Comp Sci)
PO Box 10,000 Phone: (407)828-4254
Lake Buena Vista, FL 32830-1000 Carol C. Hotz, Adm.
Founded: 1986. **Staff:** Prof 1; Other 1. **Subjects:** Computer science, human resources, general business. **Special Collections:** Computer Science collection (7000 items). **Holdings:** 500 books; 2000 reports; 100 microfiche; 3000 computer documents; 200 AV items. **Subscriptions:** 400 journals and other serials; 2 newspapers. **Services:** Center not open to the public. **Automated Operations:** Data Trek, Inc. **Computerized Information Services:** DIALOG Information Services, NEXIS, Gartner Online, Dow Jones News/Retrieval; CD-ROM (Computer Library). **Special Indexes:** Documentation Index; Journal Index. **Remarks:** Alternate telephone number(s): (407)828-4255. **Staff:** Karen Knipling, Info.Spec.Assoc.

★4895★
The Walt Disney Company - Archives (Hist)
500 S. Buena Vista St. Phone: (818)560-5424
Burbank, CA 91521 David R. Smith, Archv.
Founded: 1970. **Staff:** Prof 2; Other 4. **Subjects:** Walt Disney, Disneyland, Walt Disney World. **Holdings:** 5000 square feet of archival material, correspondence, publications, music, photographs, character merchandise, film, production files, original artwork. **Services:** Copying (limited); archives open to the public by appointment. **Staff:** Robert Tieman, Asst.Archv.

★4896★
Walt Disney Imagineering - Information Research Center (Art)
1401 Flower St. Phone: (818)544-7263
Glendale, CA 91201 Joen B. Kommer, Mgr., Info.Res.Ctr.
Founded: 1963. **Staff:** Prof 7; Other 6. **Subjects:** Architecture, art, business, design, history, travel, costume. **Holdings:** 50,000 books; clippings file. **Subscriptions:** 500 journals and other serials. **Services:** Library not open to the public. **Computerized Information Services:** NEXIS, DIALOG Information Services, Dow Jones News/Retrieval, BASELINE, VU/TEXT Information Services, DataTimes. **Special Indexes:** Picture Index (card). **Remarks:** FAX: (818)544-7845. **Staff:** Aileen Kutaka-Barkley, Info.Spec.; Saundra Murray, Info.Spec.; Susan Gibberman, Res./Cat.; Ann Shaller, Cat./Abstractor; Susan Hendrickson, Info.Spec.

Walt Disney Memorial Library
See: **Disada Productions Ltd.** (4892)

★4897★
Distilled Spirits Council of the U.S., Inc. - Library (Food-Bev)
1250 Eye St., N.W., 8th Fl. Phone: (202)628-3544
Washington, DC 20005 Matthew J. Vellucci, Lib.Dir.
Founded: 1973. **Staff:** Prof 1; Other 1. **Subjects:** Distilled spirits industry, prohibition, temperance movement, alcoholism, liquor laws, alcohol and health/safety issues, moderate drinking, drinking customs. **Special Collections:** Market studies. **Holdings:** 3000 volumes; 72 VF drawers of information on subjects and organizations. **Subscriptions:** 225 journals and other serials. **Services:** Interlibrary loan; copying; library open to researchers with prior approval. **Publications:** Library Distillates, irregular - for internal distribution only. **Remarks:** FAX: (202)682-8888.

★4898★
District of Columbia Corporation Counsel Law Library (Law)
District Bldg., Rm. 302
14th St. & Pennsylvania Ave., N.W. Phone: (202)727-6274
Washington, DC 20004 Deborah M. Cannon, Law Libn.
Founded: 1932. **Staff:** Prof 1; Other 1. **Subjects:** Law. **Holdings:** 30,000 volumes. **Services:** Interlibrary loan; library not open to the public. **Automated Operations:** Computerized acquisitions and serials. **Computerized Information Services:** WESTLAW.

★4899★
District of Columbia Court of Appeals - Library (Law)
500 Indiana Ave., N.W., 6th Fl. Phone: (202)879-2767
Washington, DC 20001 Harriet E. Rotter, Libn.
Founded: 1976. **Staff:** Prof 1. **Subjects:** Appellate practice. **Holdings:** 20,000 books; 875 bound periodical volumes. **Subscriptions:** 64 journals and other serials. **Services:** Interlibrary loan; library not open to the public. **Computerized Information Services:** WESTLAW, LEXIS, NEXIS.

★4900★
District of Columbia Department of Housing and Community Development - Library (Plan)
51 N St., N.E., Rm. 346 Phone: (202)535-1769
Washington, DC 20002 Anne L. Meglis, Libn.
Founded: 1966. **Staff:** Prof 1. **Subjects:** Urban renewal, housing, city planning, community development, historic preservation, urban affairs. **Special Collections:** Archives (1000 items on the District of Columbia Redevelopment Land Agency and Department of Housing); photograph collection of before-and-after photographs of urban renewal project areas, 1950 to present (6 VF drawers). **Holdings:** 3000 books; newspaper clippings on all urban renewal project areas, 1954-1981 (partially indexed). **Subscriptions:** 100 journals and other serials. **Services:** Interlibrary loan; copying; library open to the public with restrictions.

★4901★
District of Columbia General Hospital - Medical Library (Med)
19th St. & Massachusetts Ave., S.E. Phone: (202)675-5348
Washington, DC 20003 Lavonda K. Broadnax, Chf.Libn.
Staff: Prof 2; Other 2. **Subjects:** Medicine, nursing, allied health sciences. **Holdings:** 11,000 books; 12,000 bound periodical volumes. **Subscriptions:** 599 journals and other serials. **Services:** Interlibrary loan; library not open to the public. **Automated Operations:** Computerized serials. **Computerized Information Services:** MEDLINE, DIALOG Information Services. **Networks/Consortia:** Member of District of Columbia Health Sciences Information Network (DOCHSIN). **Publications:** Acquisitions list, quarterly. **Special Catalogs:** Alphabetical and subject lists of journal holdings. **Remarks:** FAX: (202)675-7819.

★4902★
District of Columbia Public Library - Art Division (Art)
Martin Luther King Memorial Library
901 G St., N.W. Phone: (202)727-1291
Washington, DC 20001 Bonnie C. Kryszak, Chf.
Founded: 1927. **Staff:** Prof 3. **Subjects:** Art history, painting, architecture, interior design, drawing, sculpture, artists, city planning, landscape architecture, arts and crafts, aesthetics, graphic arts, photography, stamps, coins, paper money. **Special Collections:** Material on 845 artists in the District of Columbia Metropolitan area; Local Art Techniques and Crafts File. **Holdings:** 33,500 books; 800 bound periodical volumes; 81,519 mounted pictures; 124 VF drawers of pamphlets, clippings, exhibition catalogs; circulating picture collection. **Subscriptions:** 96 journals and other serials. **Services:** Interlibrary loan. **Automated Operations:** Computerized public access catalog and circulation. **Computerized Information Services:** DIALOG Information Services, DataTimes. **Remarks:** FAX: (202)727-1129. **Staff:** Virginia Wertz, Libn. II; Sarah E. McBryde, Libn. II.

★4903★
District of Columbia Public Library - Audiovisual Division (Aud-Vis)
Martin Luther King Memorial Library
901 G St., N.W. Phone: (202)727-1265
Washington, DC 20001 Eric White, Chf. AV Libn.
Founded: 1957. **Staff:** Prof 3; Other 3. **Holdings:** 134 books; 3096 reels of film; 805 phonorecords; 1247 books on tape; 193 audio cassettes; 5812 video cassettes. **Subscriptions:** 16 journals and other serials. **Services:** Division open to the public. **Publications:** Regular film programs. **Special Catalogs:** Film Catalog; Video Catalog. **Staff:** Turner Freeman, Libn. I; Bruce Snyder, Libn. II.

★4904★
District of Columbia Public Library - Biography Division (Hist)
Martin Luther King Memorial Library
901 G St., N.W. Phone: (202)727-2079
Washington, DC 20001 Bonnie Jo Dopp, Chf.
Founded: 1950. **Staff:** Prof 3. **Subjects:** Biography, heraldry, genealogy. **Holdings:** 36,065 books; 90 VF drawers of pamphlets and clippings. **Subscriptions:** 10 journals and other serials. **Services:** Interlibrary loan. **Publications:** List of Black Americans. **Staff:** Marian Holt, Libn. II; Judith Zvonkin, Libn. II.

★4905★
District of Columbia Public Library - Black Studies Division (Area-Ethnic)
Martin Luther King Memorial Library
901 G St., N.W. Phone: (202)727-1211
Washington, DC 20001 Alice B. Robinson, Chf.
Founded: 1971. **Staff:** Prof 3. **Subjects:** Slavery in the U.S. and Caribbean, biography, business, social conditions, literature, history, science, technology, civil rights. **Special Collections:** Beatrice Murphy Foundation (1860 books); Juvenile Reference Collection (715 books). **Holdings:** 20,655 books; 24 bound periodical volumes; 350 reels of microfilm; 30 VF drawers. **Subscriptions:** 112 journals and other serials; 58 newspapers. **Services:** Copying; division open to the public for reference use only. **Publications:** Booklists on special subject, irregular - free. **Special Indexes:** Index of Black literary magazines (card). **Remarks:** FAX: (202)727-1129. **Staff:** Charles Hicks, Libn. II; Joe Lewis, Libn. II.

★4906★
District of Columbia Public Library - Business, Economics and Vocations Division (Bus-Fin)
Martin Luther King Memorial Library
901 G St., N.W. Phone: (202)727-1171
Washington, DC 20001 Mr. Mirza N. Baig, Chf.
Founded: 1907. **Staff:** Prof 3. **Subjects:** Statistics, economics, vocations, investment, real estate, import, export, accounting, taxation, business report writing, organizational behavior, commerce, management, marketing, labor, transportation. **Special Collections:** U.S. Census, 1790 to present; company annual reports; Small Business Center (SBC); Mini Employment Information Center (MEIC). **Holdings:** 43,271 books; 1150 bound periodical volumes; 450 business directories; 6000 pamphlets; 400 telephone directories; 5148 reels of microfilm; 88 microcards; 7628 microfiche. **Subscriptions:** 425 journals and other serials; 35 newspapers and financial services. **Services:** Interlibrary loan; copying; division open to the public. **Computerized Information Services:** DIALOG Information Services, Economic Bulletin Board, DataTimes, InfoTrac. **Special Indexes:** Title index to American Management Association and Conference Board publications (card). **Staff:** Jane Cates, Libn. II; Patricia Wood, Libn. II

★4907★
District of Columbia Public Library - Children's Division (Hum)
Martin Luther King Memorial Library
901 G St., N.W. Phone: (202)727-1248
Washington, DC 20001 Rose Timmons, Chf.
Founded: 1896. **Staff:** Prof 4. **Subjects:** Children's literature. **Special Collections:** Illustrators Collection, 19th century to present (11,500 volumes); historical children's books and periodicals (1500 books; 558 bound periodical volumes); source collection for children's literature (200 volumes). **Holdings:** 62,700 books; 603 bound periodical volumes; 937 phonograph records; 323 filmstrips. **Subscriptions:** 46 journals and other serials. **Services:** Division open to the public. **Publications:** Graded and subject reading lists, irregular - free. **Staff:** Beulah Holbert, Libn. II; Maria Harris, Libn. II; Rebecca Fritz, Libn. II.

★4908★
District of Columbia Public Library - History, Travel and Geography Division (Hist, Geog-Map)
Martin Luther King Memorial Library
901 G St., N.W. Phone: (202)727-1161
Washington, DC 20001 Eleanor A. Bartlett, Chf.
Founded: 1949. **Staff:** Prof 3. **Subjects:** History, geography, travel. **Holdings:** 57,109 books; 44 VF drawers of pamphlets and clippings; 2995 reels of microfilm; 737 microcards; 3004 microfiche. **Subscriptions:** 103 journals and other serials. **Services:** Interlibrary loan. **Staff:** Nineta Rozen, Libn. II; Ethel L. Sumpter, Libn. II.

★4909★
District of Columbia Public Library - Language, Literature and Foreign Language Division (Hum)
Martin Luther King Memorial Library
901 G St., N.W.
Washington, DC 20001 Phone: (202)727-1281
Founded: 1949. **Staff:** Prof 3. **Subjects:** Poetry, drama, general and literary essays, literary history and criticism, philology, journalism, library science, foreign languages, language instruction. **Holdings:** 59,292 books; 78 bound periodical volumes; 900 pamphlets; 1131 microforms. **Subscriptions:** 132 journals and other serials. **Services:** Library open to the public. **Automated Operations:** Integrated library system (CLSI). **Computerized Information Services:** DIALOG Information Services, LC Direct, OCLC EPIC; InfoTrac. **Networks/Consortia:** Member of FEDLINK. **Staff:** Barbara Gloriod, Libn. II; Alexander Geyger, Libn. II.

★4910★
District of Columbia Public Library - Library for the Blind and Physically Handicapped (Aud-Vis)
Martin Luther King Memorial Library
901 G St., N.W. Phone: (202)727-2142
Washington, DC 20001 Grace Lyons, Chf.
Founded: 1973. **Staff:** Prof 3; Other 8. **Subjects:** Popular and general material in special formats; information on legislation and services for the disabled; volunteer production of graduate and post-secondary school and work-related materials in recorded formats; reference material on aging and the handicapped. **Holdings:** 4200 books; 2700 phonograph records; 179,000 recorded books; 11,890 large-print books; 4500 books in braille. **Subscriptions:** 109 journals and other serials (55 print and braille, 54 recorded). **Services:** Interlibrary loan; certification required with talking book materials; production of taped materials for disabled; Senior Bookmobile Service to elderly; institutions and homebound service; Washington Lifelong Learning Center. **Computerized Information Services:** NLS/NET, READS/NLS (internal databases). **Publications:** Newsletter, quarterly - large-print distributed to blind and disabled readers and local and national organizations serving the disabled. **Remarks:** FAX: (202)727-1129. **Staff:** Edith Lewis, Libn.; Betty J. George, Libn., Sr. Mobile Serv.

★4911★
District of Columbia Public Library - Music and Recreation Division (Mus, Rec)
Martin Luther King Memorial Library
901 G St., N.W. Phone: (202)727-1285
Washington, DC 20001 Victor P. Dyni, Chf.
Founded: 1934. **Staff:** Prof 4. **Subjects:** Music, recreation. **Special Collections:** Hans Kindler Collection of orchestral scores and parts. **Holdings:** 17,500 books; 1000 bound periodical volumes; 22,835 sound recordings; 4916 pieces of sheet music; 29,485 scores; 750 orchestral sets; 147 reels of microfilm. **Subscriptions:** 104 journals and other serials. **Special Indexes:** Song index. **Staff:** Julia Marshall, Libn. II; Cathy Dixon, Libn. II.

★4912★
District of Columbia Public Library - Philosophy, Psychology and Religion Division (Rel-Phil, Soc Sci)
Martin Luther King Memorial Library
901 G St., N.W. Phone: (202)727-1251
Washington, DC 20001 Vicky Thompkins, Asst.Libn.
Founded: 1956. **Staff:** Prof 3. **Subjects:** Religion, psychology, philosophy. **Holdings:** 44,860 books; 350 bound periodical volumes; 60 reports; 60 clippings; 8 VF drawers of pamphlets; 1180 reels of microfilm. **Subscriptions:** 75 journals and other serials. **Services:** Interlibrary loan. **Automated Operations:** Integrated library system (CLSI). **Special Indexes:** Indexes to sermons, periodicals, mythology, psychologists, and philosophers. **Staff:** Eleanor Dore, Asst.Chf.; Warren Glick, Libn. II.

★4913★
District of Columbia Public Library - Sociology, Government and Education Division (Soc Sci)
Martin Luther King Memorial Library
901 G St., N.W. Phone: (202)727-1261
Washington, DC 20001 Paul T. Mills, Chf.
Founded: 1927. **Staff:** Prof 3. **Subjects:** Social sciences, sociology, education, customs, folklore, military science, government, political science, costume. **Special Collections:** Adult Basic Education (6321 volumes). **Holdings:** 78,829 books; 1227 bound periodical volumes; 100 VF drawers of pamphlets; 2722 reels of microfilm; 12,084 microfiche. **Subscriptions:** 172 journals and other serials. **Services:** Interlibrary loan. **Computerized Information Services:** Internal database. **Publications:** How to Prepare for the High School Equivalency Exam - free to patrons; DC Adult Literacy programs. **Staff:** Laura Keen, Libn. II; Thomas Woody, Libn. II.

★4914★
District of Columbia Public Library - Technology and Science Division (Sci-Engr)
Martin Luther King Memorial Library
901 G St., N.W. Phone: (202)727-1175
Washington, DC 20001 Lessie O. Mtewa, Asst.Libn.
Founded: 1907. **Staff:** Prof 4. **Subjects:** Mathematics, computer science, biology, domestic arts, earth science, chemistry, physics, engineering, agriculture, gardening, medicine, psychiatry, astronomy, consumer information, health, veterinary science. **Holdings:** 81,200 books; 2500 bound periodical volumes; 5300 microforms; 65 VF drawers. **Subscriptions:** 300 journals and other serials. **Services:** Interlibrary loan; copying; library open to the public. **Computerized Information Services:** DIALOG Information Services, DataTimes, InfoTrac; Health Reference (internal database). **Staff:** Diane Henry, Asst.Chf.; Jeffrey King, Libn. II; Barbara Roberts, Libn. II.

★4915★
District of Columbia Public Library - Telephone Reference Division (Hum)
Martin Luther King Memorial Library
901 G St., N.W. Phone: (202)727-1126
Washington, DC 20001 Bill Stephenson, Chf.
Founded: 1973. **Staff:** Prof 3. **Special Collections:** World Almanacs (1868 to present). **Holdings:** 1356 books; 25 VF drawers; bound periodical volumes. **Subscriptions:** 7 journals and other serials; 3 newspapers. **Remarks:** FAX: (202)727-1129. **Staff:** Dorothy Gray, Libn. II; Janette Graham, Libn. II.

★4916★
District of Columbia Public Library - Washingtoniana Division (Hist)
Martin Luther King Memorial Library
901 G St., N.W. Phone: (202)727-1213
Washington, DC 20001 Roxanna Deane, Chf.
Founded: 1907. **Staff:** Prof 6; Other 3. **Subjects:** District of Columbia - history, current affairs, government, biography, organizations. **Special Collections:** History of Washington, DC from its founding to the present; Washington Star Library (13 million clippings; 1 million photographs). **Holdings:** 16,183 books; 676 bound periodical volumes; 1 million newspaper clippings and pamphlets; 6039 reels of microfilm; 20,000 mounted pictures; 2000 maps; 218 oral history tapes. **Subscriptions:** 55 journals and other serials. **Services:** Copying; division open to the public. **Computerized Information Services:** DIALOG Information Services, DataTimes; Collections DC (internal database). **Publications:** Annual Checklist of D.C. Government Publications. **Staff:** Mary Ternes, Asst.Chf.; Karen Blackman-Mills, Libn. II; Matthew Gilmore, Libn. II; Leroy Graham, Archv.; Rhoda Adkins, Tech.; Doris Young, Tech.; Lavette Coney, Presrv.Techn.

★4917★
District of Columbia Public Library - Young Adult Services Division (Hum)
Martin Luther King Memorial Library
901 G St., N.W. Phone: (202)727-5535
Washington, DC 20001 Michael T. Wallace, Chf.
Founded: 1982. **Staff:** Prof 2; Other 1. **Subjects:** Young adult fiction. **Special Collections:** Popular albums, filmstrips,and videocassetes. **Holdings:** 12,500 books; 370 phonorecords; 220 filmstrips; 31 videocassetes. **Subscriptions:** 25 journals and other serials. **Computerized Information Services:** Grolier's Electronic Encyclopedia, Compton's MultiMedia Encyclopedia. **Publications:** Booklists of fiction and other subjects, irregular - free. **Special Catalogs:** YASD Book Catalog of Paperback Titles. **Staff:** Felecia Jackson, Libn. II; Alma Murphy, Gen.Adv.

★4918★
District of Columbia Public Schools - Division of Professional Development and Training - Research Information Center
Goding Elementary School, Rm. 405
10th & F Sts., N.E.
Washington, DC 20002
Defunct.

★4919★
District of Columbia School of Law - Library (Law)
719 13th St., N.W. Phone: (202)727-5358
Washington, DC 20005 Glen-Peter Ahlers, Sr., Libn.
Founded: 1988. **Staff:** Prof 6. **Subjects:** Law. **Holdings:** 108,000 volumes. **Subscriptions:** 430 journals and other serials; 18 newspapers. **Services:** Interlibrary loan; copying; library open to the public. **Automated Operations:** Computerized cataloging. **Computerized Information Services:** WESTLAW, LEXIS, NEXIS, DIALOG Information Services. **Networks/Consortia:** Member of CAPCON Library Network. **Publications:** Acquisitions, library guide. **Remarks:** FAX: (202)727-2381. **Staff:** Eduardo Caparas; Mildred Bailey; Michael Petit.

★4920★
District of Columbia Superior Court - Library (Law)
500 Indiana Ave., N.W. Phone: (202)879-1435
Washington, DC 20001 Letty Limbach, Libn.
Staff: Prof 1; Other 2. **Subjects:** Criminal law, District of Columbia law, family law. **Special Collections:** Civil and criminal jury instructions for most of the states; court annual reports; biographical file of Superior Court judges. **Holdings:** 20,000 books; 450 bound periodical volumes; 25 VF drawers. **Subscriptions:** 53 journals and other serials. **Services:** Interlibrary loan; library open to the public by appointment. **Computerized Information Services:** WESTLAW, LEXIS; internal database.

District One Technical Institute - Library - Educational Resource Center
See: **Chippewa Valley Technical College - Technology Resource Center-Library** (3617)

★4921★
Dittberner Associates, Inc. - Library (Comp Sci)
4903 Auburn Ave. Phone: (301)652-8350
Bethesda, MD 20814 Ingrid C.D. Mayr, Libn.
Founded: 1965. **Staff:** Prof 1. **Subjects:** Computers, telephone switching equipment, national and international business statistics. **Holdings:** 700 books; 13 VF drawers of industry files; 60 VF drawers of telecommunication market and technology information. **Subscriptions:** 85 journals and other serials. **Services:** Library not open to the public. **Remarks:** Library is used primarily in conjunction with consulting services performed by the corporation. FAX: (301)657-8084.

Howard Dittrick Museum of Historical Medicine
See: **Cleveland Health Sciences Library - Medical History Division** (3807)

★4922★
Diversified Research Laboratories, Ltd. - Information Resource Centre (Food-Bev)
1047 Yonge St. Phone: (416)922-5100
Toronto, ON, Canada M4W 2L2 Lusi Wong, Info.Mgr.
Founded: 1976. **Staff:** 3. **Subjects:** Food science and technology. **Holdings:** 5000 volumes. **Subscriptions:** 250 journals and other serials. **Services:** Interlibrary loan; copying; SDI; center open to the public by appointment only. **Automated Operations:** Computerized cataloging, acquisitions, serials, and circulation. **Computerized Information Services:** DIALOG Information Services, NEXIS, CAN/OLE. Performs searches on fee basis. **Networks/Consortia:** Member of Sheridan Park Association. **Publications:** Frontiers (newsletter), bimonthly - to clients. **Remarks:** FAX: (416)922-4318. **Also Known As:** Weston Research Centre.

★4923★
Divine Providence Hospital - Medical Library (Med)
1100 Grampian Blvd. Phone: (717)326-8153
Williamsport, PA 17701 Bobbi Masten, Dir., Med.Rec.
Founded: 1951. **Subjects:** Medicine. **Holdings:** 781 books; 1200 bound periodical volumes. **Subscriptions:** 40 journals and other serials. **Services:** Interlibrary loan.

★4924★
Divine Word Seminary of St. Augustine - Library (Rel-Phil, Area-Ethnic)
199 Seminary Dr.
Bay St. Louis, MS 39520 Phone: (601)467-6414
Founded: 1923. **Subjects:** Afro-American history and literature, ethnology, theology, social sciences, pure and applied sciences, literature, geography, history. **Holdings:** 8000 volumes; 500 bound periodical volumes. **Services:** Library open to the public for research purposes only. **Remarks:** Includes the holdings of St. Augustine Retreat Center - Library, telephone: 467-9837.

★4925★
Dorothea Dix Hospital - Walter A. Sikes Learning Resource Center (Med)
820 S. Boylan Ave.
Box 7597 Phone: (919)733-5111
Raleigh, NC 27611 Spanola M. Eubanks, Dir., Lib.Serv.
Founded: 1957. **Staff:** Prof 2. **Subjects:** Psychiatry, psychiatric nursing, social service, psychology, neurology. **Holdings:** 10,000 books; 4500 bound periodical volumes; 350 reels of microfilm; 950 cassette tapes. **Subscriptions:** 125 journals and other serials. **Services:** Interlibrary loan; copying; library open to the public for reference use only. **Computerized Information Services:** DIALOG Information Services; CD-ROM (MEDLINE).**Networks/Consortia:** Member of Resources for Health Information (REHI). **Special Catalogs:** AV holdings catalog. **Remarks:** FAX: (919)733-9781. Maintains Learning Lab equipped with AV equipment and materials. **Formerly:** Its P.T. Fuller Staff Library. **Staff:** Ella Williams, Media Spec.

Dorothea Dix Library and Museum
See: **Harrisburg State Hospital - Library Services** (6925)

★4926★
Dix Hills Jewish Center - Library
Vanderbilt Pkwy. at Deforest Rd. Phone: (516)499-6645
Dix Hills, NY 11746 Nancy Savas, Libn.
Remarks: No further information was supplied by respondent.

★4927★
Dixo Engineering - Library (Sci-Engr)
158 Central Ave.
Box 7038 Phone: (201)845-6000
Rochelle Park, NJ 07662 Jerome B. Schapiro, Pres.
Founded: 1926. **Subjects:** Drycleaning - procedures, consumer standards policy, applications. **Holdings:** Test data; national and international standardization information on consumer affairs, detergents, textiles, care labeling. **Services:** Library not open to the public. **Remarks:** FAX: (201)845-6004.

★4928★
Dixon Gallery and Gardens - Library (Art)
4339 Park Ave. Phone: (901)761-5250
Memphis, TN 38117 Sheila K. Tabakoff, Cur. of Coll.
Founded: 1976. **Staff:** 1. **Subjects:** Impressionist art, horticulture, porcelain, art history. **Special Collections:** Stout Collection of porcelain books (300). **Holdings:** 3500 volumes. **Subscriptions:** 15 journals and other serials. **Services:** Copying; library open to the public by appointment. **Remarks:** FAX: (901)682-0943. **Staff:** Sue Turpin, Libn.

Dixson Library
See: **State Library of New South Wales - Special Collections** (15688)

★4929★
DNAX Research Institute of Molecular and Cellular Biology - Library (Biol Sci)
901 California Ave. Phone: (415)496-1285
Palo Alto, CA 94304-1104 Nancy S. Fadis, Lib.Mgr.
Founded: 1981. **Staff:** Prof 2; Other 1. **Subjects:** Immunology, molecular biology, genetic engineering, patents, parasitology, virology. **Holdings:** 800 books. **Subscriptions:** 168 journals and other serials. **Services:** Library not open to the public. **Automated Operations:** Computerized cataloging, acquisitions, and serials. **Computerized Information Services:** DIALOG Information Services, Research Alert; CD-ROMs (MEDLINE, Current Contents). DIALMAIL (electronic mail service). **Remarks:** FAX: (415)496-1200. Telex: 469133. Electronic mail address(es): DNAX (DIALMAIL). **Staff:** Roberta E. Ling, Assoc.Libn.

★4930★
Doall Company - Library
245 N. Laurel Ave.
Des Plaines, IL 60016
Subjects: Machine tool operation, cutting tools, gauging equipment, metallurgy, metrology. **Holdings:** Books; films; photographs; data and other nonprint material. **Remarks:** Currently inactive.

★4931★
Doane Information Services - Information Center (Agri)
11701 Borman Dr., Suite 100 Phone: (314)569-2700
St. Louis, MO 63146 Toni Anderson, Libn.
Founded: 1947. **Staff:** 1. **Subjects:** Agriculture, economics, business management, law. **Holdings:** 2000 books; 1000 bound periodical volumes; 10,000 college, state, U.S.D.A. publications; 30 VF drawers of subject files; 8 VF drawers of state agricultural statistics; government documents; agricultural college publications. **Subscriptions:** 700 journals and other serials. **Services:** Center open to the public by appointment. **Automated Operations:** Computerized cataloging. **Remarks:** Doane Information Services is a division of Doane Agricultural Services.

Ray Doblitz Memorial Library
See: **Ohev Shalom Synagogue** (12261)

★4932★
Dobra Iron and Steel Research Institute - Library (Sci-Engr)
CS-739 51 Dobra, Czechoslovakia Phone: 658 23421
Boris Skandera, Hd.
Founded: 1963. **Staff:** Prof 24. **Subjects:** Metallurgy, steel production, extraction and treatment of metals, powder metallurgy, nonferrous metals, automation in the field of metallurgy, economics. **Holdings:** 900,000 volumes; 400,000 special materials. **Subscriptions:** 11,500 journals and other serials. **Services:** Interlibrary loan; copying; SDI; library open to the public. **Computerized Information Services:** DIALOG Information Services, PFDS Online, Data-Star, STN International; METAL (200,000 entries; internal database). Performs searches on fee basis. **Publications:** Hutnicke aktuality, 12/year - international exchange. **Remarks:** FAX: 658 23016; 658 23046. Telex: 52691. **Also Known As:** Vyzkumny Ustav Hutnictvi Zeleza, Dobra.

Milton B. Dobrin Library
See: **University of Houston - Allied Geophysical Laboratories** (18639)

Docking Research Center Archives Library
See: **Cherokee Strip Land Rush Museum - Docking Research Center Archives Library** (3481)

Doctors Hospital - Eckman Medical Library
See: **Beth Israel Hospital North** (1770)

★4933★
Doctors Hospital - Health Sciences Library (Med)
340 College St., 6th Fl. Phone: (416)963-5464
Toronto, ON, Canada M5T 3A9 Sharon Virtue, Mgr./Libn.
Staff: Prof 1. **Subjects:** Clinical medicine, nursing, hospital administration. **Holdings:** 1500 books; 500 cassettes. **Subscriptions:** 250 journals and other serials; 2 newspapers. **Services:** Interlibrary loan. **Computerized Information Services:** MEDLARS, DIALOG Information Services, DOBIS Canadian Online Library System; Envoy 100 (electronic mail service). **Publications:** Acquisitions list, quarterly - for internal distribution only. **Remarks:** Electronic mail address(es): ILL.OTDHS (Envoy 100).

★4934★
Doctors' Hospital - Medical Library (Med)
5000 University Dr. Phone: (305)669-2334
Coral Gables, FL 33146 Sandra E. Poston, Lib.Dir.
Founded: 1954. **Staff:** Prof 1. **Subjects:** Medicine, surgery, neurology and neurosurgery, ophthalmology. **Holdings:** 1156 books; 852 bound periodical volumes; video and audio cassettes. **Subscriptions:** 79 journals and other serials. **Services:** Interlibrary loan; library not open to the public. **Networks/Consortia:** Member of Miami Health Sciences Library Consortium (MHSLC). **Remarks:** FAX: (305)669-2286.

★4935★
Doctors Hospital - W.S. Konold Memorial Library (Med)
1087 Dennison Ave., LIBID 43201B
Columbus, OH 43201 Phone: (614)297-4113
Founded: 1973. **Staff:** Prof 1; Other 1. **Subjects:** Osteopathy, medicine, nursing. **Holdings:** 3000 books; 10,000 bound periodical volumes; 300 slide sets; 500 videotapes; 900 audiotapes. **Subscriptions:** 225 journals and other serials. **Services:** Interlibrary loan; copying; SDI; library open to the public for reference use only. **Computerized Information Services:** MEDLINE; DOCLINE (electronic mail service). **Networks/Consortia:** Member of National Network of Libraries of Medicine - Greater Midwest Region, Central Ohio Hospital Library Consortium. **Publications:** Journal of the Columbus Clinical Groups, quarterly - to staff and medical students. **Remarks:** FAX: (614)294-5322.

★4936★
Doctors Hospital Inc. of Stark County - Medical Library (Med)
400 Austin Ave., N.W. Phone: (216)837-7371
Massillon, OH 44646 Valerie Haren, Chf.Med.Libn.
Staff: Prof 1; Other 1. **Subjects:** Medicine, osteopathy. **Holdings:** 1500 books; 2900 bound periodical volumes. **Subscriptions:** 150 journals and other serials. **Services:** Interlibrary loan; library accepts requests from other libraries. **Automated Operations:** Computerized ILL. **Computerized Information Services:** BRS Information Technologies; DOCLINE (electronic mail service). **Remarks:** FAX: (216)837-7379.

★4937★
Doctors' Medical Center - Professional Library (Med)
1441 Florida Ave.
Box 4138 Phone: (209)576-3782
Modesto, CA 95352 Margaret F. Luebke, Med.Libn.
Founded: 1966. **Staff:** Prof 1; Other 1. **Subjects:** Medicine, nursing. **Holdings:** 600 books; 400 bound periodical volumes. **Subscriptions:** 160 journals and other serials. **Services:** Interlibrary loan; copying; SDI; library not open to the public. **Computerized Information Services:** MEDLINE, BRS Information Technologies. **Networks/Consortia:** Member of 49-99 Cooperative Library System. **Remarks:** FAX: (209)576-3781.

★4938★
Documentation Centre for Education in Europe (Educ)
Council of Europe
B.P. 431 R6 Phone: 88 412593
F-67006 Strasbourg Cedex, France Wilson Barrett
Founded: 1964. **Staff:** 2.5. **Subjects:** Education. **Special Collections:** Council of Europe publications (in the field of education). **Holdings:** 23,000 volumes. **Subscriptions:** 350 journals and other serials. **Services:** Interlibrary loan; copying; SDI; center open to the public. **Computerized Information Services:** Internal database. **Publications:** Newsletter/Faits nouveaux. **Remarks:** FAX: 88 412780. Telex: 870943. The Centre is financed by the Council of Europe. **Also Known As:** Centre de Documentation pour l'Education en Europe.

Austin A. Dodge Pharmacy Library
See: **University of Mississippi - John Davis Williams Library** (18951)

★4939★
Dodge County Historical Society - Library (Hist)
P.O. Box 433 Phone: (507)635-5508
Mantorville, MN 55955 Margot L. Ballard, Musm.Dir.
Subjects: Minnesota and early American history, the military. **Special Collections:** School text books; religious texts and hymnals. **Holdings:** 2000 books; 200 manuscripts; documents; newspapers. **Subscriptions:** 5 newspapers. **Services:** Copying; library open to the public for reference use only.

★4940★
Dodge County Historical Society - May Museum - Library (Hist)
P.O. Box 766 Phone: (402)721-4515
Fremont, NE 68025 Loell R. Jorgensen, Musm.Dir.
Founded: 1970. **Staff:** 1. **Subjects:** Dodge County history, historic preservation, 19th century decorative arts. **Special Collections:** Historical photographs (1000). **Holdings:** 1220 volumes; 1 VF drawer of maps; 12 file boxes of documents; 2 manuscripts. **Subscriptions:** 14 journals and other serials. **Services:** Copying; library open to the public.

★4941★
Ronald T. Dodge Company - Library (Sci-Engr)
55 Westpark Rd. Phone: (513)439-4497
Dayton, OH 45459 Kathleen M. Willis, Off.Mgr.
Founded: 1979. **Staff:** Prof 1. **Subjects:** Microencapsulation, controlled release, chemistry, materials engineering, product development. **Special Collections:** Electroluminescent lighting and displays (800 patents; 50 early technical papers). **Holdings:** 500 books; 300 reports; 1000 patents. **Subscriptions:** 100 journals and other serials; 10 newspapers. **Services:** Copying; library open to the public by appointment at librarian's discretion. **Computerized Information Services:** ORBIT Search Service. **Special Catalogs:** Electroluminescent lighting. **Remarks:** FAX: (513)439-1704.

★4942★
Dofasco Inc. - Information Services (Sci-Engr)
1330 Burlington St., E.
P.O. Box 2460 Phone: (416)544-3761
Hamilton, ON, Canada L8N 3J5 Linda Pauloski, Libn.
Founded: 1961. **Staff:** Prof 1; Other 1. **Subjects:** Business, steel industry. **Special Collections:** British Iron and Steel Industry and Brutcher metallurgical translations; metallurgical patents (4 VF drawers). **Holdings:** 2000 books; 31 bound periodical volumes; annual reports. **Subscriptions:** 200 journals and other serials; 7 newspapers. **Services:** Interlibrary loan; copying (both limited); open to the public on application to librarian. **Computerized Information Services:** Info Globe, Infomart Online, The Financial Post DataGroup, Data-Star, DIALOG Information Services. **Special Catalogs:** Dofasco Held Periodical Listing. **Remarks:** FAX: (416)548-4630.

★4943★
Dofasco Inc. - Technical Information Centre (Sci-Engr)
1390 Burlington St., E.
Box 2460 Phone: (416)548-4726
Hamilton, ON, Canada L8N 3J5 Ann M. Duff, Res.Libn.
Founded: 1976. **Staff:** Prof 1; Other 1. **Subjects:** Iron and steel production, finishing processes, corrosion, coal, coke. **Holdings:** Books; bound periodical volumes; microfilm; patents; reports. **Services:** Interlibrary loan; SDI; center open to the public by appointment. **Automated Operations:** Computerized cataloging, acquisitions, serials, and circulation. **Computerized Information Services:** DIALOG Information Services, CAN/OLE, STN International, PFDS Online, Data-Star; internal databases; DIALMAIL, Envoy 100 (electronic mail services). **Networks/Consortia:** Member of Sheridan Park Association. **Remarks:** FAX: (416)548-4653. Telex: 061-8682.

Edward Laurence Doheny Memorial Library
See: **St. John's Seminary** (14349)

★4944★
Estelle Doheny Eye Institute - Kenneth T. Norris, Jr. Visual Science Library (Med)
1355 San Pablo St. Phone: (213)342-6644
Los Angeles, CA 90033 Ann Dawson, Act.Libn.
Staff: Prof 1; Other 1. **Subjects:** Ophthalmology. **Holdings:** 1500 books; 1000 bound periodical volumes. **Subscriptions:** 95 journals and other serials. **Services:** Interlibrary loan; library not open to the public. **Computerized Information Services:** BRS Information Technologies, PFDS Online, DIALOG Information Services, NLM.

Grace Doherty Library
See: **Centre College** (3219)

James Alan Doherty Municipal Reference Library
See: **Los Angeles Public Library** (9349)

Dokumentation Kraftfahrwesen
See: **Motor Vehicle Documentation** (10777)

★4945★
Dolby Laboratories, Inc. - Technical Library (Sci-Engr)
100 Potrero Ave. Phone: (415)558-0359
San Francisco, CA 94103 Rita Evans, Info.Spec.
Founded: 1967. **Staff:** Prof 1; Other 1. **Subjects:** Noise reduction, signal processing, electronics. **Special Collections:** Archives (history of Dolby Laboratories, Ray Dolby, noise reduction; 1600 clippings; 50 patents; 300 photographs; 1200 slides; 36 volumes of company publications). **Holdings:** 900 books; 125 bound periodical volumes; 1800 preprints. **Subscriptions:** 150 journals and other serials. **Services:** Interlibrary loan; copying; SDI; library open to the public by appointment. **Computerized Information Services:** DIALOG Information Services, DataTimes, NewsNet, Inc.; internal databases; DIALMAIL (electronic mail service). **Publications:** Bibliography on noise reduction, Dolby Laboratories, Ray Dolby (online); current awareness bulletin, monthly; Acquisitions, bimonthly - both for internal distribution only. **Special Indexes:** Index to clippings on Dolby Laboratories and Ray Dolby (online). **Remarks:** FAX: (415)863-1373.

Dolmen Press Archives
See: **Wake Forest University - Z. Smith Reynolds Library** (19942)

★4946★
Dolphin Marine Research Library (Biol Sci)
308 Washington St.
Box 310 Phone: (509)996-2286
Winthrop, WA 98862-0310 Frances F. Brewster, Libn.
Holdings: 6200 books; reports; manuscripts. **Services:** Copying; library open to the public by appointment.

★4947★
Dominican College Library (Rel-Phil)
487 Michigan Ave., N.E. Phone: (202)529-5300
Washington, DC 20017-1584 Rev. J. Raymond Vandegrift, O.P., Libn.
Founded: 1905. **Staff:** Prof 2; Other 2. **Subjects:** Scholastic and modern theology, Thomistic and modern philosophy, scripture, patristics. **Special Collections:** Dominicana (Dominican Order history and authors); Thomas Aquinas; Dominican Dissertations; rare books. **Holdings:** 53,049 books; 12,007 bound periodical volumes; 29 reels of microfilm; 220 microfiche; 192 audio cassettes. **Subscriptions:** 317 journals and other serials. **Services:** Interlibrary loan; copying; library open to the public. **Automated Operations:** Computerized cataloging and ILL. **Networks/Consortia:** Member of Washington Theological Consortium, CAPCON Library Network. **Special Catalogs:** Analytical Catalog of Dominican Authors. **Remarks:** Maintained by the Dominican House of Studies.

Dominican College of Philosophy and Theology
See: **College Dominicain de Philosophie et de Theologie** (3889)

Dominican House of Studies - Dominican College Library
See: **Dominican College Library** (4947)

Dominican Republic - National Confederation of Dominican Workers
See: **National Confederation of Dominican Workers** (11128)

★4948★
Dominican Santa Cruz Hospital - Medical Library (Med)
1555 Soquel Dr. Phone: (408)462-7738
Santa Cruz, CA 95065 Candace Walker, Med.Libn.
Founded: 1975. **Staff:** Prof 1; Other 3. **Subjects:** Medicine, nursing, health. **Holdings:** 1000 books; 2500 bound periodical volumes; 500 videotapes. **Subscriptions:** 75 journals and other serials. **Services:** Interlibrary loan; copying; library open to the public for reference use only. **Computerized Information Services:** MEDLINE. Performs searches on fee basis.

Dominican School of Philosophy and Theology
See: **Graduate Theological Union** (6613)

★4949★
Dominican Sisters of San Rafael - Congregation of the Holy Name - Archives (Rel-Phil)
Dominican Convent of San Rafael
1520 Grand Ave. Phone: (415)454-9221
San Rafael, CA 94901-2236 Sr. M. Martin Barry, O.P., Archv.
Founded: 1930. **Staff:** 2. **Subjects:** History of the congregation. **Holdings:** 175 linear feet of archival materials, including letters, ledgers, publications, photographs, clippings. **Subscriptions:** 3 journals and other serials. **Services:** Copying; archives open to the public by appointment.

★4950★
Domino Sugar Corporation - Research and Development Library (Food-Bev)
266 Kent Ave. Phone: (718)387-6800
Brooklyn, NY 11211 Gerald J. Patout, Jr., Corp.Libn.
Founded: 1948. **Staff:** Prof 2. **Subjects:** Sugar technology, analytical chemistry, food technology, chemical engineering. **Special Collections:** Historical sugar monographs and serial titles. **Holdings:** 3000 books; 100 bound periodical volumes; 20 VF drawers of pamphlets; 100 reels of microfilm; 40 VF drawers of internal reports; 35mm slides. **Subscriptions:** 100 journals and other serials. **Services:** Interlibrary loan; library not open to the public. **Automated Operations:** INMAGIC. **Computerized Information Services:** Proprietary Amstar Research (internal database). **Publications:** Bibliographies - for internal distribution only. **Remarks:** FAX: (718)599-0354. **Formerly:** Amstar Corporation. **Staff:** Paulette Meltzer, Assoc.Libn.

★4951★
Domtar, Inc. - Information Services (Sci-Engr)
C.P. 300 Phone: (514)457-8260
Senneville, PQ, Canada H9X 3L7 Barbara G. Bolton, Libn.
Founded: 1963. **Staff:** Prof 1. **Subjects:** Pulp and paper, chemical engineering, environment. **Holdings:** 1600 books; 3200 bound periodical volumes; 500 pamphlets. **Subscriptions:** 200 journals and other serials. **Services:** Interlibrary loan; copying; library open to the public for reference use only by request. **Computerized Information Services:** DIALOG Information Services, PFDS Online, CAN/OLE, STN International. **Publications:** Periodicals list - available on request. **Special Indexes:** Index to internal reports. **Remarks:** FAX: (514)457-4527. **Formerly:** Its Research Centre Library.

★4952★
Donaldson Company, Inc. - Information Center (Sci-Engr)
P.O. Box 1299 Phone: (612)887-3019
Minneapolis, MN 55440 Barbara A. Standing, Info.Rsrcs.Adm.
Founded: 1969. **Staff:** Prof 1. **Subjects:** Filtration, pollution engineering, particle technology, control systems, acoustics, hydraulics and pneumatics, aerodynamics and fluid mechanics, business. **Holdings:** 7000 books; 20,000 internal reports; 3000 external reports. **Subscriptions:** 300 journals and other serials. **Services:** Interlibrary loan; center not open to the public. **Automated Operations:** Computerized journal routing. **Computerized Information Services:** DIALOG Information Services; internal database. **Remarks:** FAX: (612)887-3155.

★4953★
Donaldson, Lufkin & Jenrette, Inc. - Corporate Information Center (Bus-Fin)
140 Broadway Phone: (212)504-3704
New York, NY 10005 Susan W. Littin, V.P.
Founded: 1962. **Staff:** Prof 5; Other 10. **Subjects:** Business, finance, investments. **Special Collections:** Financial history of the American Revolution. **Holdings:** 2000 books; 400 bound periodical volumes; 60,000 microfiche. **Subscriptions:** 400 journals and other serials; 19 newspapers. **Services:** Interlibrary loan; center not open to the public. **Automated Operations:** Computerized cataloging, acquisitions, serials, circulation, and corporate document check-in. **Computerized Information Services:** Dun & Bradstreet Business Credit Services, IDD Information Services, Inc., Securities Data Company, Inc., IBES (Institutional Brokers Estimate System), DIALOG Information Services, Dow Jones News/Retrieval, Info Globe, Spectrum Ownership Profiles Online, ADP Network Services, Inc., NEXIS, InvesText, NewsNet, Inc., Disclosure Incorporated, Securities Data Company, Inc, Reuters, DRI/McGraw-Hill. Performs searches on fee basis. **Remarks:** FAX: (212)504-3816. **Staff:** Joel Neuberg, Sr.Info.Spec.; Richard Redmond, Info.Spec.; Louise Sandford, Info.Spec.; Paul Smaldone, Info.Spec.

Donaldson, Lufkin & Jenrette, Inc. - Pershing & Company Inc.
See: **Pershing & Company Inc.** (12952)

★4954★
W.B. Doner and Company Advertising - Research Library (Bus-Fin)
25900 Northwestern Hwy. Phone: (313)827-8269
Southfield, MI 48075 Joan Leb, Res.Libn.
Founded: 1970. **Staff:** Prof 1; Other 2. **Subjects:** Business, advertising. **Holdings:** 220 books; research reports. **Subscriptions:** 178 journals and other serials; 6 newspapers. **Services:** Library not open to the public. **Computerized Information Services:** DIALOG Information Services, NEXIS, Info Globe, DataTimes. **Networks/Consortia:** Member of Council on Resource Development (CORD). **Remarks:** FAX: (313)827-8399.

Donnell Library Center
See: **New York Public Library - Donnell Library Center** (11602)

★4955★
R.R. Donnelley & Sons, Co. - Corporate Library (Bus-Fin)
2223 S. King Dr. Phone: (312)326-7149
Chicago, IL 60616 Mike Poznanovich, Info.Spec.
Founded: 1985. **Staff:** Prof 1; Other 1. **Subjects:** Business, commercial printing, publishing, direct marketing. **Holdings:** 400 books; market studies and reports; corporate and subject files. **Subscriptions:** 142 journals and other serials. **Services:** Library not open to the public. **Computerized Information Services:** NewsNet, Inc., DIALOG Information Services. **Remarks:** FAX: (312)326-8543. **Formerly:** Its Marketing Library.

★4956★
R.R. Donnelley & Sons, Co. - Technical Library (Sci-Engr)
750 Warrenville Rd. Phone: (708)810-5242
Lisle, IL 60532 Carol Brade, Tech.Libn.
Founded: 1989. **Subjects:** Printing, graphic arts, electronic engineering, computer engineering, manufacturing technology. **Holdings:** 1880 volumes; 180 unbound magazine titles. **Subscriptions:** 181 journals and other serials. **Services:** Interlibrary loan; library not open to the public. **Computerized Information Services:** DIALOG Information Services, PFDS Online; ALANET (electronic mail service). **Publications:** CAB (Current Awareness Bulletin). **Remarks:** Electronic mail address(es): ALA1884 (ALANET).

★4957★
Donnelly Corporation - Library (Bus-Fin)
414 E. 40th St. Phone: (616)786-5095
Holland, MI 49423 Nancy Yetman, Tech.Libn.
Founded: 1972. **Staff:** Prof 1. **Subjects:** Business, management, glass, plastics, physics, vacuum technology, chemistry, transportation. **Holdings:** 5000 books; 2000 unbound periodicals; 10 drawers of patents for automobile rearview mirrors; 8 drawers of reports. **Subscriptions:** 225 journals and other serials. **Services:** Interlibrary loan; copying; library open to the public with permission. **Automated Operations:** Computerized cataloging and serials. **Computerized Information Services:** DIALOG Information Services. **Networks/Consortia:** Member of Lakeland Area Library Network (LAKENET). **Special Catalogs:** Periodical holdings. **Remarks:** "Donnelly Corporation is one of the foremost U.S. authorities in automotive rear vision." FAX: (616)786-5185.

★4958★
Donohue & Associates, Inc. - Library (Sci-Engr)
P.O. Box 1067 Phone: (414)458-8711
Sheboygan, WI 53082-1067 John J. Condon, Lib.Dir.
Staff: Prof 1; Other 3. **Subjects:** Water resources, environmental engineering, transportation, architecture. **Holdings:** 21,000 books. **Subscriptions:** 450 journals and other serials; 30 newspapers. **Services:** Interlibrary loan; library not open to the public. **Automated Operations:** Computerized cataloging. **Computerized Information Services:** DIALOG Information Services, NewsNet, Inc., BRS Information Technologies, Dow Jones News/Retrieval, Groundwater Information Center Database, STN International, Chemical Information Systems, Inc. (CIS). Performs searches on fee basis. Contact Person: John Condon. **Networks/Consortia:** Member of Northeast Wisconsin Intertype Libraries (NEWIL), Library Council of Metropolitan Milwaukee, Inc. (LCOMM). **Publications:** Catalog Drawer, monthly - for internal distribution only. **Remarks:** FAX: (414)458-0537.

Countess Bernardine Murphy Donohue Rare Book Room
See: **University of San Francisco - Special Collections Department/ Donohue Rare Book Room** (19290)

★4959★
Donors Forum of Chicago - Library (Bus-Fin)
53 W. Jackson, Suite 430 Phone: (312)431-0265
Chicago, IL 60604 Gayle S. Barr, Dir., Lib.Serv.
Founded: 1972. **Staff:** Prof 1; Other 2. **Subjects:** Philanthropy, grants and funding, foundations and corporate giving, nonprofit organizations. **Special Collections:** Federal tax returns (form 990PF) for private foundations in seven midwest states and major national foundations elsewhere (100,000 microfiche); information on nonprofit organizations in the Chicago area; consultants' file; nonprofit newsletters; files on private foundations and corporate giving including annual reports. **Holdings:** 2000 books; 32 VF drawers. **Subscriptions:** 82 journals and other serials. **Services:** Copying; library open to the public. **Computerized Information Services:** Members Grant Database, Illinois Foundations Database (internal databases). **Publications:** Directory of Illinois Foundations, biennial; Directory of Members & Library Partners. **Special Catalogs:** Donors Forum Members Grants List. **Remarks:** FAX: (312)431-1113.

Donors Forum of Forsyth County
See: **Winston-Salem Foundation** (20494)

★4960★
Donovan, Leisure, Newton & Irvine - Library (Law)
30 Rockefeller Plaza, 39th Fl. Phone: (212)632-3022
New York, NY 10112 Albert P. Borner, Libn.
Staff: Prof 1; Other 3. **Subjects:** Law. **Special Collections:** Antitrust briefs and pleadings. **Holdings:** 21,000 volumes; 10 VF drawers of pamphlets. **Services:** Interlibrary loan; library open to clients and SLA members.

Donovan Technical Library
See: **U.S. Army - TRADOC - Infantry School** (17012)

Donovick Library
See: **American Type Culture Collection** (780)

Dooley Library
See: **Joslin Diabetes Center, Inc.** (8484)

★4961★
Dorchester County Public Library - Dorchester County Historical Society Collection (Hist)
303 Gay St. Phone: (301)228-7331
Cambridge, MD 21613 Jean Del Sordo, Dir.
Founded: 1922. **Staff:** 13.5. **Subjects:** Genealogy, local history, Maryland history. **Special Collections:** Maryland Historical Magazine; abstracts from the Land Records of Dorchester County, Maryland; Archives of Maryland; Dorchester County Genealogical Magazine. **Holdings:** 500 books; 90 microforms; Bibles; scrapbooks; ephemera; census records; local newspapers; fire insurance maps; family histories; other items. **Subscriptions:** 118 journals and other serials. **Services:** Copying; collection open to the public. **Remarks:** FAX: (301)228-6313. **Staff:** Susan Steele, Asst.Dir.; Cheryl Michael, Hd., Adult Serv.; Nancy Nagler, Libn.

★4962★
Dorchester Historical Society - Robinson-Lehane Library (Hist)
195 Boston St. Phone: (617)265-7802
Dorchester, MA 02125 Richard McKinnon, Cur.
Staff: Prof 1; Other 5. **Subjects:** Local history, genealogy, architecture. **Special Collections:** Huebener Brick Collection; Badlam Collection of Revolutionary War papers; Baker Chocolate Company collection (2 Hollinger boxes); Fowle Collection of the Civil War; Dorchester Athenaeum Collection; Huebener Photograph Collection; Luther Briggs architectural drawing collection; books and manuscripts of Capen Whitney, Lewis, Taylor Adams, Follen Adams; Lucy Stone Collection; Dorchester Womans Club Collection; Athena Club Collection; Putnam Nail Company; collection of photographs of Dorchester, MA , 1850 to present. **Holdings:** 1500 books; 5000 manuscripts; 100 newspapers and clippings. **Services:** Interlibrary loan; copying; library open to the public by appointment. **Computerized Information Services:** Performs searches on fee basis. **Publications:** Newsletter, bimonthly - to members. **Special Catalogs:** Catalogs to manuscript and photograph col lections.

★4963★
Dordt College - Archives and Dutch Memorial Collection (Area-Ethnic)
498 4th Ave., N.E. Phone: (712)722-3771
Sioux Center, IA 51250 Louise M. Hulst, Archv.
Founded: 1972. **Staff:** 1.5. **Subjects:** Life, culture, institutions of Dutch settlers in Iowa, Wisconsin, Minnesota, North and South Dakota, parts of Canada; college history; Christian Reformed Church. **Special Collections:** Dordt College archives; Abraham Kuyper Collection; rare books collection. **Holdings:** 2500 books; 5500 church and Christian school records, letters, diaries, genealogies, oral history tapes. **Services:** Collection not open to the public. **Automated Operations:** Computerized public access catalog. **Computerized Information Services:** DIALOG Information Services, EPIC.

★4964★
Dormant Brain Research and Development Laboratory - Library (Med)
Laughing Coyote Mountain
Box 10
Black Hawk, CO 80422 Mr. T.D. Lingo, Dir.
Founded: 1957. **Staff:** 2. **Subjects:** Neural cybernetics. **Holdings:** 5000 volumes. **Services:** Library not open to the public. **Remarks:** Laboratory researches "techniques for individuals to utilize more of the brain, 90% of which is dormant, to increase intelligence, creativity, health, and longevity. Also seeks to assist parents in teaching children to use 100% of the brain."

★4965★
Dorr-Oliver Incorported - Technical Library (Sci-Engr)
612 Wheeler's Farm Rd.
P.O. Box 3819 Phone: (203)876-5537
Milford, CT 06460-8719 William D. Kallaway, Libn.
Founded: 1937. **Staff:** Prof 1. **Subjects:** Solid/liquid separation, pulp, paper, minerals, food, pharmaceuticals, chemical processing. **Special Collections:** American Society for Testing and Materials standards. **Holdings:** 9000 books; internal reports; manuals. **Subscriptions:** 250 journals and other serials. **Services:** Library open to SLA members and by appointment. **Computerized Information Services:** DIALOG Information Services. **Networks/Consortia:** Member of Southwestern Connecticut Library Council (SWLC). **Publications:** New Book List, irregular. **Remarks:** FAX: (203)876-5432.

★4966★
Dorset Natural History & Archaeological Society - Library (Hist)
Dorset County Museum
West St.
Dorchester DT1 1XA, England Phone: 305262735
Founded: 1845. **Staff:** 6. **Subjects:** Dorset County, local history, geology, archeology, natural history, literature, arts. **Special Collections:** Thomas Hardy Collection; William Barnes Collection; Sylvia Townsend Warner Collection. **Holdings:** 30,000 books; 10,000 bound periodical volumes; 1000 reports; 20,000 archives. **Subscriptions:** 120 journals and other serials; 3 newspapers. **Services:** Copying; library open to the public by appointment. **Publications:** Annual proceedings; regular monographs; Sunday books, leaflets, booklets.

★4967★
Dorsey & Whitney - Law Library (Law)
2200 First Bank Pl. E. Phone: (612)340-2613
Minneapolis, MN 55402 Ann M. Carter, Dir., Lib. & Info.Rsrcs.
Founded: 1912. **Staff:** Prof 8; Other 6. **Subjects:** Law. **Holdings:** 45,000 volumes; 100 cassette tapes; 5725 volumes on microfilm. **Subscriptions:** 650 journals and other serials; 20 newspapers. **Services:** Library not open to the public. **Automated Operations:** Computerized cataloging, acquisitions, and serials. **Computerized Information Services:** Dun & Bradstreet Business Credit Services, LEXIS, WESTLAW, DIALOG Information Services, NEXIS, Dow Jones News/Retrieval, RLIN, VU/TEXT Information Services, NewsNet, Inc., DataTimes. **Networks/Consortia:** Member of CLASS. **Publications:** Library newsletter - for internal distribution only. **Remarks:** FAX: (612)340-2868; 340-2768. **Staff:** Nina Platt, Lib.Supv.; Gretchen Walker, Ref.Libn.; Naomi Reed, Ref.Libn.; Barbara Haeny, Ref.Libn.; Heather Newman, Info.Spec.; Michelle Johns, Cat.; Juliann Olhrich, D.C. Office Ref.Libn.

Dossin Great Lakes Museum Information Center
See: **Great Lakes Maritime Institute** (6698)

James Dotta Anthropology Library
See: **Redding Museum & Art Center - Research Library** (13763)

The Robert D. Doty Health Sciences Library
See: **Holston Valley Hospital and Medical Center - The Robert D. Doty Health Sciences Library** (7341)

★4968★
(Douala) Centre Culturel Americain - USIS Library (Educ)
Ave. du Pres. Ahmadou Ahidjo
Post Box 4045
Douala-Akwa, Cameroon
Remarks: Maintained or supported by the U.S. Information Agency. Focus is on materials that will assist peoples outside the United States to learn about the United States, its people, history, culture, political processes, and social milieux.

Douglas Aircraft Company
See: **McDonnell Douglas Corporation** (9883)

★4969★
Douglas County Historical Society - Archives (Hist)
906 E. Harbor View Pkwy. Phone: (715)394-5712
Superior, WI 54880 Rachel E. Martin, Exec.Dir.
Founded: 1902. **Staff:** Prof 2. **Subjects:** History of Superior, Douglas County, Lake Superior; political, economic, industrial, social, cultural aspects of the area. **Holdings:** 823 books; 16,500 photographs; 2500 maps of the area. **Services:** Copying (limited); copying of photographs; library open to the public for reference use only. **Formerly:** Its Fairlawn Museum Library. **Staff:** Teddy Meronek, Chm., Archv.Comm.

Douglas County Historical Society - Library/Archives Center
See: **Historical Society of Douglas County** (7267)

★4970★
Douglas County Hospital - Health Sciences Library (Med)
111 17th Ave., E. Phone: (612)762-6090
Alexandria, MN 56308 Mary Johnson, Lib.Mgr.
Staff: 1. **Subjects:** Medicine, nursing. **Holdings:** 300 books. **Subscriptions:** 90 journals and other serials. **Services:** Interlibrary loan; copying; faxing; library open to students for reference use only. **Networks/Consortia:** Member of Northern Lights Library Network (NLLN), Valley Medical Network (VMN), Michigan Health Sciences Libraries Association (MHSLA).

★4971★
Douglas County Law Library (Law)
Hall of Justice
17th & Farnam Phone: (402)444-7174
Omaha, NE 68183 Carol Gendler, Dir.
Founded: 1905. **Staff:** Prof 1. **Subjects:** Law. **Holdings:** 25,000 volumes. **Services:** Copying; library open to the public with restrictions. **Computerized Information Services:** WESTLAW, DIALOG Information Services, LEXIS, PHINet FedTax Database, Nebraska Legislature Shared Information Systems; internal database; DOCLINE (electronic mail service). Performs searches on fee basis. **Publications:** Nebraska Bankruptcy Service, monthly - by subscription. **Special Indexes:** Index to eighth circuit slip opinions; Nebraska advance sheet; Nebraska Bankruptcy Service; Nebraska Workmen's Compensation Rehearing Decisions. **Remarks:** FAX: (402)341-0213. **Staff:** Sandy Lundholm.

★4972★
Douglas County Law Library (Law)
1313 Belknap St.
Court House Phone: (715)394-0207
Superior, WI 54880 Jan Haack, Libn.
Staff: 1. **Subjects:** Law. **Holdings:** 10,500 volumes. **Services:** Library open to the public. **Remarks:** FAX: (715)394-3858.

★4973★
Douglas County Museum - Lavola Bakken Memorial Library (Hist)
Box 1550 Phone: (503)440-4507
Roseburg, OR 97470 Frederick R. Reenstjerna, Res.Libn.
Founded: 1969. **Staff:** Prof 1. **Subjects:** Douglas County history, Umpqua Indians, logging, sawmills and grist mills, marine history, mining, development of area towns, railroads, agriculture. **Special Collections:** Herbarium collection of Douglas County. **Holdings:** 2000 books; 200 vertical files of letters, diaries, manuscripts, census, cemetery records; 400 oral histories; 175 genealogies. **Subscriptions:** 30 journals and other serials. **Services:** Copying; library open to the public for reference use only. **Computerized Information Services:** Argus (internal database).

Frederic H. Douglas Library of Anthropology and Art
See: **Denver Art Museum** (4774)

★4974★
Douglas Hospital Centre - Staff Library (Med)
6875 LaSalle Blvd. Phone: (514)762-3029
Montreal, PQ, Canada H4H 1R3 Elaine Mancina, Chf.Libn.
Staff: 2. **Subjects:** Psychiatry, psychopharmacology, psychology, child psychiatry, psychiatric nursing, rehabilitation. **Holdings:** 4000 books; 4400 bound periodical volumes; bibliographies. **Subscriptions:** 210 journals and other serials. **Services:** Interlibrary loan; copying; library open to the public by appointment for consultation only.

Jane H. Douglas Memorial Library
See: **Amateur Astronomers Association - Jane H. Douglas Memorial Library** (444)

Paul and Emily Douglas Library
See: **Chicago State University** (3544)

★4975★
Douglass Boulevard Christian Church - Library (Rel-Phil)
2005 Douglass Blvd. Phone: (502)452-2629
Louisville, KY 40205 Clara C. Cruikshank, Libn.
Founded: 1940. **Staff:** Prof 1. **Subjects:** Religion, Bible study, family and community, fiction. **Holdings:** 2500 volumes; family life and community action pamphlets. **Services:** Library not open to the public.

Frederick Douglass National Historic Site
See: **U.S. Natl. Park Service - Frederick Douglass National Historic Site - Library** (17716)

Douglass-Truth Branch Library
See: **Seattle Public Library** (14998)

J. Kenneth Dout Memorial Library
See: **Carnegie Museum of Natural History - Library** (3085)

★4976★
Dover Publications, Inc. - Pictorial Archives Library (Art)
31 E. 2nd St. Phone: (516)294-7000
Mineola, NY 11501 John W. Grafton, Asst. to Pres.
Staff: Prof 1. **Subjects:** Pre-1900 portraits, natural history, photographs, 19th century trades and manufacturers. **Special Collections:** American portraits (20,000 portraits of Americans in all walks of life who lived prior to 1900); European portraits (30,000 portraits of Europeans in all walks of life who lived prior to 1900). **Holdings:** 400 books; 200 bound periodical volumes. **Services:** Library not open to the public. **Remarks:** Toll-free telephone number(s): (800)642-6226 (New York residents); (800)223-3130 (non-residents).

★4977★
Dow Chemical Canada Inc. - Modeland Centre Library (Sci-Engr)
P.O. Box 1012 Phone: (519)339-3143
Sarnia, ON, Canada N7T 7K7 Julie N. Welsh, Mgr.
Founded: 1956. **Staff:** Prof 2; Other 4. **Subjects:** Chemistry, engineering, business. **Holdings:** 5000 books; 500 bound periodical titles; microfiche report collection; technical reports. **Subscriptions:** 489 journals and other serials. **Services:** Interlibrary loan; copying; SDI. **Computerized Information Services:** DIALOG Information Services, PFDS Online, Info Globe, Infomart Online, STN International, OCLC EPIC, PLASPEC. **Networks/Consortia:** Member of Michigan Library Consortium (MLC). **Remarks:** FAX: (519)339-3868.

★4978★
Dow Chemical Canada Inc. - Sarnia Division Library (Sci-Engr)
P.O. Box 3030 Phone: (519)339-5179
Sarnia, ON, Canada N7T 7M1 Jane Hames, Info.Spec.
Staff: Prof 1. **Subjects:** Chemistry, engineering. **Computerized Information Services:** DIALOG Information Services, STN International, ORBIT Search Service. **Remarks:** FAX: (519)339-4392.

★4979★
Dow Chemical Canada Inc. - Western Canada Division - Library (Sci-Engr)
Bag Service 16, Hwy. 15 Phone: (403)998-5628
Fort Saskatchewan, AB, Canada T8L 2P4 Marg M. Critchley, Lib.Coord.
Founded: 1979. **Staff:** 2. **Subjects:** Chemistry, engineering. **Special Collections:** Chemical Abstracts, 1920-1966. **Holdings:** 2000 books. **Subscriptions:** 133 journals and other serials. **Services:** Interlibrary loan; library not open to the public. **Automated Operations:** Computerized circulation. **Computerized Information Services:** DIALOG Information Services, Chemical Abstracts Service (CAS), STN International, ORBIT Search Service CAN/OLE; Envoy 100 (electronic mail service). **Remarks:** FAX: (403)998-6709. Electronic mail address(es): DOW.FORT.SASK (Envoy 100).

★4980★
Dow Chemical Company - Legal Library (Law)
2030 Willard H. Dow Ctr. Phone: (517)636-6648
Midland, MI 48674 Doris L. Steiner, Supv.
Staff: Prof 1; Other 2. **Subjects:** Law. **Holdings:** 11,000 books. **Subscriptions:** 58 journals and other serials. **Services:** Library open to the public by permission. **Automated Operations:** Computerized serials. **Computerized Information Services:** LEXIS, NEXIS, WESTLAW. **Remarks:** FAX: (517)636-3771.

★4981★
Dow Chemical Company - Technical Information Services - Central Report Index (Sci-Engr)
566 Bldg. Phone: (517)636-9342
Midland, MI 48667 Suzanne V. McKinley, Mgr.
Founded: 1945. **Staff:** Prof 4; Other 6. **Subjects:** Chemistry, engineering, agriculture, polymers, market research. **Special Collections:** Proprietary technology reports. **Holdings:** 250,000 proprietary technical research and development reports; 310,000 chemical registry items. **Services:** Department not open to public. **Automated Operations:** Computerized processing of all materials for storage and retrieval. **Computerized Information Services:** Online systems. **Special Indexes:** Indexes, guides, and bulletins to the proprietary collection (hardcopy, microform). **Staff:** M.L. Dilling; A.L. Clemons; W.W. Meyer; C.J. Del Valle, Supv.Oper.

★4982★
Dow Chemical Company - Technical Information Services - Chemical Library (Sci-Engr)
566 Bldg.
Box 1704 Phone: (517)636-1098
Midland, MI 48641-1704 Suzanne V. McKinley, Mgr.
Founded: 1920. **Staff:** Prof 10; Other 6. **Subjects:** Chemistry, plastics, agriculture, process engineering, chemical engineering, metallurgy, physics, biology, business. **Holdings:** 25,000 books; 1800 journal titles; 45,000 cartridges of microfilm of 250 journal titles. **Subscriptions:** 700 journals and other serials. **Services:** Interlibrary loan; copying; translation; library open to the public by appointment. **Automated Operations:** Computerized cataloging, serials, and circulation. **Computerized Information Services:** Online systems. Performs searches on fee basis. **Special Catalogs:** Union List of Serials for Dow Division Libraries' Holdings. **Remarks:** FAX: (517)636-2524. **Staff:** A.G. Buske; J.A. Bays; F.K. Voci; A.E. Rogers, Supv.Oper.; I.L. Knox, Search Team Ldr.; J.L. Curnutt; S.R. Smith; A.C. Gregg; J.H. Connor; R.H. Pederson.

★4983★
Dow Chemical U.S.A. - Applied Information Sciences (Sci-Engr)
B-1210 Bldg. Phone: (409)238-3512
Freeport, TX 77541-3259 Andrea H. Hazlitt, Mgr.
Founded: 1944. **Staff:** Prof 5; Other 5. **Subjects:** Chemistry, physical sciences, chemical engineering. **Holdings:** 12,000 books; 20,000 bound periodical volumes; 1000 pamphlets; 120,000 company reports. **Subscriptions:** 425 journals and other serials. **Services:** Interlibrary loan; copying; library open to the public by appointment. **Automated Operations:** Computerized cataloging, serials, and holdings list. **Computerized Information Services:** OCLC, DIALOG Information Services, PFDS Online, NLM, STN International; internal databases. **Networks/Consortia:** Member of AMIGOS Bibliographic Council, Inc. **Remarks:** FAX: (409)238-0915; 238-0336. **Staff:** G.M. McNamee, Res.Ldr.; C.F. Wolfe, Proj.Ldr.; T.F. Bailey, Res.Ldr.; N.E. Boaz, Libn.

★4984★
Dow Chemical U.S.A. - Business Information Center (Bus-Fin)
2020 Willard H. Dow Ctr. Phone: (517)636-3779
Midland, MI 48674 Phae H. Dorman, Mgr.
Founded: 1968. **Staff:** Prof 2; Other 2. **Subjects:** Business, economics, chemical business intelligence, plastics business intelligence, marketing research, international investment, management, finance. **Special Collections:** Chemical economics and marketing; Executive Speech File. **Holdings:** 6000 books; annual reports; 60 journals on microfilm. **Subscriptions:** 300 journals and other serials; 10 newspapers. **Services:** Interlibrary loan; center open to the public with restrictions. **Computerized Information Services:** DIALOG Information Services, Dow Jones News/Retrieval, NEXIS, BRS Information Technologies, VU/TEXT Information Services. **Networks/Consortia:** Member of Michigan Library Consortium (MLC). **Publications:** New Items Bulletin, monthly. **Remarks:** FAX: (517)636-8135.

★4985★
Dow Chemical U.S.A. - Engineering/Technical Information Resources Group - Library (Sci-Engr)
Information Ctr. Bin 2B1
400 W. Sam Houston Pkwy., S.
Box 1299 Phone: (713)978-2694
Houston, TX 77042-1299 Ray Bartells, Supv.
Founded: 1963. **Staff:** Prof 3. **Subjects:** Engineering - mechanical, process, electrical, civil, chemical, environmental; geology. **Special Collections:** Historical mechanical and civil engineering; geology library; vendor data library; Dow design archives; Dow standards international collection; law library. **Holdings:** 15,000 books; 1500 bound periodical volumes; TIS files; 200 unbound reports; 500,000 reels of microfilm; engineering design datafile. **Subscriptions:** 302 journals and other serials. **Services:** Interlibrary loan; copying; SDI (both limited); library open to the public. **Automated Operations:** Computerized public access catalog, cataloging, acquisitions, serials, and circulation. **Computerized Information Services:** TIS Information System (internal database). **Publications:** Information Services: UPDATE, monthly; Technical Information: UPDATE, as needed - both for internal distribution only. **Special Catalogs:** ISIS: Information Services Information Services. **Special Indexes:** Indexes to vendors, design data, subscriptions (hardcopy, machine readable). **Staff:** L. Mueller.

★4986★
Dow Chemical U.S.A. - Louisiana Division - Library (Sci-Engr)
Box 400 Phone: (504)389-1627
Plaquemine, LA 70764-0400 Linda N. Bourgoyne, Supv.
Staff: 3. **Subjects:** Chemistry, physical sciences, plastics, chemical engineering, process chemistry. **Holdings:** 5500 books; 2900 bound periodical volumes; chemical abstracts; U.S. chemical patents; official gazette. **Subscriptions:** 138 journals and other serials. **Services:** Library not open to the public. **Automated Operations:** Computerized acquisitions, serials, and circulation. **Computerized Information Services:** DIALOG Information Services, PFDS Online; internal databases. **Remarks:** FAX: (504)389-1666.

★4987★
Dow Chemical U.S.A. - Western Research and Development Library (Sci-Engr)
2800 Mitchell Dr. Phone: (510)944-2064
Walnut Creek, CA 94598 Mary Lao, Libn./Proj.Ldr.
Staff: Prof 1; Other 3. **Subjects:** Chemistry, engineering, agricultural sciences. **Holdings:** 20,000 volumes; reports; patents; documents; industrial literature. **Subscriptions:** 425 journals and other serials. **Services:** Library not open to the public. **Remarks:** (510)944-2155. A branch library is maintained at Box 1398, Pittsburg, CA 94565.

★4988★
Dow Corning Corporation - Business Intelligence Center (Bus-Fin)
Box 0994 CO-2302
Midland, MI 48686-0994 Phone: (517)496-5733
Founded: 1965. **Staff:** Prof 1; Other 1. **Subjects:** Business, marketing, management. **Holdings:** 300 books; 1000 reports; 100 pamphlets; 100 maps. **Subscriptions:** 78 journals and other serials. **Services:** Interlibrary loan; SDI; center open to the public by appointment for reference use only. **Automated Operations:** Computerized cataloging and circulation. **Computerized Information Services:** DIALOG Information Services, Dow Jones News/Retrieval; internal database. **Networks/Consortia:** Member of Michigan Library Consortium (MLC). **Publications:** New Titles.

★4989★
Dow Corning Corporation - Technical Information Services - Information and Training Center (Sci-Engr)
Midland, MI 48686-0994 Phone: (517)496-4958
Lori T. Karnath, Libn.
Founded: 1948. **Staff:** Prof 1; Other 2. **Subjects:** Chemistry, organosilicon chemistry, polymer chemistry. **Holdings:** 2500 books; 2100 bound periodical volumes; 320 dissertations; 1500 cartridges of microfilm of periodicals; 150 hardcopy and 1500 microfiche government contract reports. **Subscriptions:** 150 journals and other serials. **Services:** Interlibrary loan; copying; library open to researchers by special arrangement. **Automated Operations:** Computerized cataloging, circulation, and ILL. **Computerized Information Services:** DIALOG Information Services, PFDS Online, NLM; TIS Information Systems (internal database). **Networks/Consortia:** Member of Michigan Library Consortium (MLC), White Pine Library Cooperative. **Publications:** Bi-Weekly Library Bulletin; List of Contract Reports - for internal distribution only. **Remarks:** FAX: (517)496-5121. **Staff:** Carla S. Clark, ILL.Serv.

Grace A. Dow Memorial Library
See: **City of Midland - Grace A. Dow Memorial Library** (3742)

★4990★
Dow Jones & Co. - Library (Bus-Fin)
200 Liberty St. Phone: (212)416-2676
New York, NY 10281 Lottie Lindberg, Hd.Libn.
Staff: Prof 2; Other 7. **Subjects:** Business, finance, investment. **Special Collections:** Clipping file of Wall Street Journal, 1968-1987. **Holdings:** Figures not available. **Services:** Interlibrary loan; library not open to the public. **Automated Operations:** Computerized cataloging and circulation. **Computerized Information Services:** Dow Jones News/Retrieval. **Special Indexes:** The Wall Street Journal Index, monthly with annual cumulations; Barron's Index, annual. **Staff:** Elizabeth Yeh, Asst.Libn.

★4991★
Dow, Lohnes & Albertson - Law Library (Law)
1255 23rd St., N.W., Suite 275 Phone: (202)857-2650
Washington, DC 20037 Ellen H. Mulquin, Dir., Info.Serv.
Staff: Prof 4; Other 1. **Subjects:** Corporate and tax law, employee benefits, litigation, international trade. **Holdings:** 15,000 volumes. **Subscriptions:** 29 journals and other serials. **Services:** Interlibrary loan; library open to the public with prior permission. **Computerized Information Services:** LEXIS, WESTLAW. **Remarks:** FAX: (202)857-2900. **Staff:** Elinor Russell, Lib.Supv.; Michael McWhite, Info.Spec.; Patricia Callahan, Info.Spec.; Helen Tulloch, Info.Spec.

Fr. William Dowell Parish Library
See: **St. Jude Catholic Church - Fr. William Dowell Parish Library** (14423)

William A. Downes Archives
See: **Mystic River Historical Society - William A. Downes Archives** (10947)

★4992★
Downey Avenue Christian Church - Christian Education Committee - Library for Adults & Youth (Rel-Phil)
111 S. Downey Ave. Phone: (317)359-5304
Indianapolis, IN 46219 Frances M. West, Libn.
Subjects: Religion, geography, missions, church and society, biography, fiction. **Holdings:** 900 books. **Services:** Library open to the public with restrictions.

★4993★
Downey Historical Society - Downey History Center (Hist)
12540 Rives Ave.
Box 554 Phone: (213)862-2777
Downey, CA 90241 Barbara Callarman, Dir.
Founded: 1967. **Staff:** 4. **Subjects:** Local history, Governor John G. Downey, genealogy. **Special Collections:** Genealogical Records for Los Nietos Valley pioneers; insurance registers; school account books. **Holdings:** 750 books; records of Downey Cemetery with tombstone inscriptions; 8 VF drawers of records, clippings, photographs; 1850-1910 census on microfilm; Sanborn maps of Downey, 1887-1907, on microfilm; original Sanborn maps of Downey, 1925-1932; original records of Los Angeles County District Attorney's Registers of Arrest, 1883-1919; original records of Los Nietos & Downey Townships court dockets, 1871-1952. **Subscriptions:** 10 journals and other serials. **Services:** Copying; center open to the public. **Publications:** A Brief History of John G. Downey; Newsletter, monthly.

★4994★
Downtown Research and Development Center - Library (Plan)
215 Park Ave. S., Suite 1301
New York, NY 10003-1603 Phone: (212)228-0246
Founded: 1954. **Subjects:** City planning, urban renewal, parking, traffic, mass transportation, marketing, urban design, land use and values, regional planning, zoning, subdivisions, urban economics, landscape architecture, electric vehicles, and related urban issues. **Special Collections:** Central business districts (in- and out-of-print books and slides). **Holdings:** 3500 books, journals, reports, maps, charts, slides, and photographs. **Subscriptions:** 2 newspapers. **Services:** Library not open to the public.

Drache Law Library
See: **University of Winnipeg - Library - Special Collections** (19568)

★4995★
Drackett Company - Information Resource Center (Sci-Engr)
5020 Spring Grove Ave. Phone: (513)632-1449
Cincinnati, OH 45232 Cindy Meisner, Info.Rsrc.Mgr.
Founded: 1925. **Staff:** Prof 1; Other 2. **Subjects:** Science and technology, business and finance. **Holdings:** 3000 books; 8800 patents; 100 technical reports; 310 cartridges of microfilm. **Subscriptions:** 110 journals and other serials; 6 newspapers. **Services:** Interlibrary loan; copying. **Computerized Information Services:** DIALOG Information Services, PFDS Online. **Remarks:** FAX: (513)632-1276. A division of Bristol-Myers Squibb.

★4996★
Dracula Unlimited - Bram Stoker Memorial Association - Library (Hum)
Penthouse N.
29 Washington Square, W. Phone: (212)982-6754
New York, NY 10011 Dr. Jeanne Youngson, Founder
Founded: 1985. **Staff:** 2. **Subjects:** Bram Stoker. **Special Collections:** Bram Stoker first editions; worldwide editions of Dracula. **Holdings:** 425 books; 12 documents; photographs of Bram Stoker, his relatives, and places associated with Stoker; memorabilia. **Services:** Library open to members of the Bram Stoker Memorial Association only; also used for research referrals.

J.F. Drake Memorial Learning Resources Center
See: **Alabama A & M University - J.F. Drake Memorial Learning Resources Center** (180)

Drake Memorial Library
See: **State University College at Brockport** (15702)

★4997★
Drake University - Cowles Library - Special Collections (Hist)
28th St. & University Ave. Phone: (515)271-2989
Des Moines, IA 50311 J. Elias Jones, Bibliog./Archv.
Founded: 1968. **Staff:** 1.5. **Subjects:** State, local, university history; Iowa authors. **Special Collections:** Disciples of Christ Historical Collection (200 titles); Philip Duffield Stong papers (1200 pieces of correspondence); Gardner (Mike) Cowles Jr. papers; literary manuscripts and other papers of Susan Glaspell, MacKinlay Kantor, Thomas Duncan; university archives. **Holdings:** 55 VF drawers; 1525 other cataloged items. **Services:** Interlibrary loan; copying; collections open to the public for reference use only. **Remarks:** FAX: (515)271-3933. **Staff:** Mark Stumme; Inga Hoifedlt.

★4998★
Drake University - Law Library (Law)
Carnegie Hall
27th & Carpenter Phone: (515)271-2141
Des Moines, IA 50311 John D. Edwards, Dir.
Founded: 1875. **Staff:** Prof 4; Other 6. **Subjects:** Law. **Special Collections:** Foreign law, including English law; agricultural law; Constitutional law. **Holdings:** 150,000 books; 19,789 bound periodical volumes; 4633 government documents; 375 audio recordings; 24 video recordings; 410 titles in microform. **Subscriptions:** 3030 journals and other serials; 8 newspapers. **Services:** Interlibrary loan; copying; library open to the public with permission. **Automated Operations:** Computerized cataloging (DRA). **Computerized Information Services:** LEXIS, OCLC, WESTLAW. **Networks/Consortia:** Member of Bibliographical Center for Research, Rocky Mountain Region, Inc. (BCR), Mid-America Law School Library Consortium. **Publications:** Current Acquisitions List, monthly; newsletter. **Special Catalogs:** Periodicals holdings list. **Remarks:** FAX: (515)271-2530. **Staff:** Kaye Stoppel, Assoc.Libn.; Lisa Hermann, Pub.Serv.Libn.; Julie Thomas, Tech.Serv.Libn.

Drake Well Museum
See: **Pennsylvania (State) Historical & Museum Commission** (12876)

★4999★
Charles Stark Draper Laboratory, Inc. - Technical Information Center (Sci-Engr, Comp Sci)
555 Technology Sq., Mail Sta. 74 Phone: (617)258-3555
Cambridge, MA 02139 M. Hope Coffman, Dir.
Founded: 1972. **Staff:** Prof 6; Other 5. **Subjects:** Flight control, inertial guidance, aerospace technology, computer science. **Special Collections:** Technical Report Literature Collection in Aerospace Technology. **Holdings:** 5000 books; 64,000 technical reports; 17,200 archival materials; 900 theses. **Subscriptions:** 200 journals and other serials. **Services:** Interlibrary loan; center not open to the public. **Automated Operations:** Computerized cataloging and acquisitions. **Computerized Information Services:** DIALOG Information Services, DTIC, NASA/RECON, NEXIS, OCLC, COMPENDEX PLUS, Computer Select, Ei Page One; CD-ROMs; internal database. **Networks/Consortia:** Member of NELINET, Inc. **Publications:** TIC Bulletin, monthly - for internal distribution only. **Remarks:** FAX: (617)258-2826. **Staff:** Laurie Rotman, Acq.Libn.; Evelyn Burger, Ref.Libn.; Gary D. Ambush, Chf.Doc. Control; Peg Spinner, Cat.

Draper Fund
See: **Population Crisis Committee/Draper Fund** (13220)

Draper Hall Library
See: **Metropolitan Hospital Center** (10203)

Herman G. Dresser Library
See: **Camp Dresser & McKee, Inc.** (2617)

★5000★
Dresser Industries, Inc. - Dresser Pump Division - Information Center (Sci-Engr)
401 Worthington Ave. Phone: (201)484-1234
Harrison, NJ 07029 Tracy Mason, Libn.
Staff: Prof 1. **Subjects:** Turbomachinery, fluid engineering, pumps and compressors, flow measurement, lubrication. **Special Collections:** Von Karman Institute of Fluid Dynamics Lecture Series; British Hydromechanics Research Association research reports, 1947 to present (500 reports on microfiche). **Holdings:** 2300 books; 10 VF drawers; 100 Electric Power Research Institute (EPRI) reports; 20 journals on microfiche. **Subscriptions:** 70 journals and other serials. **Services:** Center not open to the public. **Automated Operations:** Computerized cataloging, acquisitions, and document indexing. **Computerized Information Services:** DIALOG Information Services, PFDS Online, Data-Star, INFO-LINE; DTI/Data Trek (internal database). **Publications:** Technical News Bulletin, quarterly - for internal distribution only. **Remarks:** FAX: (201)485-8724.

DREV
See: **Canada - Defence Research Establishment Valcartier** (2684)

★5001★
Drew County Historical Society - Museum and Archives (Hist)
404 S. Main St. Phone: (501)367-7446
Monticello, AR 71655 Ruby Jeter, Archv.
Staff: Prof 3. **Subjects:** History - Monticello, Drew County, Southeast Arkansas, Arkansas. **Holdings:** 250 books; 60 bound periodical volumes; 248 cassette tapes; 16 VF drawers of clippings, pamphlets, letters; 35 reels of microfilm; 25 maps; family histories; original Goodspeeds; textile collection; quilts and looms; early printing press; Indian artifacts. **Services:** Copying; archives open to the public for reference use only. **Staff:** Mrs. Melba Dunn.

★5002★
Drew University - Library (Rel-Phil, Hum)
Madison, NJ 07940 Phone: (201)408-3588
Dr. Caroline M. Coughlin, Dir.
Founded: 1867. **Staff:** Prof 14; Other 26. **Subjects:** Theology, religion, history, Methodistica, English and American literature, patristics, liberal arts, Biblical archeology, art, United Nations, European Common Market. **Special Collections:** U.S. Depository Collection (162,000 documents); Tyerman Collection of Methodist Pamphlets; Tipple and Maser Collections of Wesleyana; Methodist Manuscript Collection; David Creamer Hymnology Collection; Walter Koehler Collection in Reformation History. **Holdings:** 391,554 books; 63,000 bound periodical volumes; 218,161 microforms; 2000 phonograph records; 500 videotapes; 125 VF drawers of manuscripts; 48,720 pamphlets. **Subscriptions:** 1870 journals and other serials; 30 newspapers. **Services:** Interlibrary loan; copying; library open to the public for reference use only; annual fee for borrowers. **Automated Operations:** Computerized cataloging, acquisitions, and ILL. **Computerized Information Services:** DIALOG Information Services, OCLC. **Special Catalogs:** Methodist Union Catalog published since 1975 (book). **Remarks:** Alternate telephone number(s): 408-3471. **Staff:** Jean Schoenthaler, Asst.Dir./Hd., Tech.Serv.; Kenneth E. Rowe, Methodist Libn.; Pam Snelson, Hd., Access Serv.

★5003★
Drexel University - Center for Insulation Technology - Library (Sci-Engr)
32nd and Chestnut Sts. Phone: (215)895-1833
Philadelphia, PA 19104 Dr. Harold Lorsch, Dir.
Subjects: Insulation. **Holdings:** Figures not available.

★5004★
Drexel University - Science and Technology Library
32nd & Chestnut Sts.
Philadelphia, PA 19104
Defunct. Holdings absorbed by Drexel University - W.W. Hagerty Library.

★5005★
Drexel University - W.W. Hagerty Library - Special Collections (Hist)
32nd & Chestnut Sts. Phone: (215)895-2755
Philadelphia, PA 19104 Ann Preston, Spec.Coll.Libn.
Founded: 1891. Special Collection: Drexeliana (material concerning the university, the Drexel family, faculty and student publications). **Holdings:** 910 linear feet of archival materials. **Services:** Interlibrary loan; copying; collections open to the public for reference use only. **Automated Operations:** Computerized cataloging and ILL. **Computerized Information Services:** DIALOG Information Services, PFDS Online, BRS Information Technologies, Dow Jones News/Retrieval, OCLC, VU/TEXT Information Services, Data-Star, Maxwell Macmillan Taxes Online; CD-ROMs (Applied Science & Technology Index, MEDLINE, Business Periodicals Index, ABI/INFORM, GPO, PsycLIT, Disclosure Incorporated, Business Dateline); electronic mail service. **Networks/Consortia:** Member of PALINET. **Remarks:** FAX: (215)895-1601. **Staff:** Anita Samuel, Govt.Docs.Libn.; Joy Collins, Hd.

★5006★
Dreyfus Corporation - Library and Information Services (Bus-Fin)
200 Park Ave. Phone: (212)922-6087
New York, NY 10166 Cytheria Theodos, Dir., Lib. & Info.Serv.
Founded: 1962. **Staff:** Prof 4; Other 9. **Subjects:** Mutual funds, corporations, business, finance. **Holdings:** 1500 books; 57,000 microfiche; 4000 files of corporation records; 100 drawers of subject files. **Subscriptions:** 400 journals and other serials; 20 newspapers. **Services:** Interlibrary loan; library not open to the public. **Automated Operations:** Computerized cataloging, acquisitions, and serials. **Computerized Information Services:** DIALOG Information Services, Dow Jones News/Retrieval, ORBIT Search Service, NEXIS, LEXIS, VU/TEXT Information Services, DataTimes, NewsNet, Inc. **Remarks:** Alternate telephone number(s): (212)922-6082. FAX: (212)922-6092. **Staff:** Cathy Sciascia, Supv., Ref.Serv.; Deirche Marrs, Info.Spec.; Judith Pinsker, Info.Spec.; Bonnie Rose, Supv., Tech.Serv.

Doris & Henry Dreyfuss Memorial Study Center
See: **Smithsonian Institution Libraries - Cooper-Hewitt Museum of Design - Doris & Henry Dreyfuss Memorial Study Center** (15274)

Felix J. Dreyous Library
See: **New Orleans Museum of Art** (11539)

★5007★
DRI/McGraw-Hill, Inc. - Library (Bus-Fin)
29 Hartwell Ave. Phone: (617)860-6968
Lexington, MA 02173 Jack Howard, Libn.
Staff: 1. **Subjects:** Economics. **Holdings:** 100 books; 500 reports. **Subscriptions:** 50 journals and other serials. **Services:** Library not open to the public. **Remarks:** FAX: (617)860-6332.

★5008★
Drinker, Biddle & Reath - Law Library (Law)
1100 Philadelphia Natl. Bank Bldg.
Broad & Chestnut Sts. Phone: (215)988-2951
Philadelphia, PA 19107 Nancy H. Nance, Libn.
Staff: Prof 1; Other 4. **Subjects:** Law. **Holdings:** 18,000 volumes. **Subscriptions:** 12 newspapers. **Services:** Interlibrary loan; copying; library open to the public for reference use only on request. **Automated Operations:** Computerized circulation, check-in, and accounts. **Computerized Information Services:** LEXIS, DIALOG Information Services, WILSONLINE, VU/TEXT Information Services, Dow Jones News/Retrieval, Dun & Bradstreet Business Credit Services, Reuters, CompuServe Information Service, WESTLAW. **Networks/Consortia:** Member of PALINET. **Remarks:** FAX: (215)988-2757.

Dr. Philip Drinker Library
See: **Harvard University - School of Public Health - Kresge Center Library** (6995)

Drinker Library of Choral Music
See: **Free Library of Philadelphia - Music Department - Drinker Library of Choral Music** (6120)

Robert Dunning Dripps Library of Anesthesia
See: **Hospital of the University of Pennsylvania** (7424)

★5009★
Driscoll Foundation Children's Hospital - Medical Library (Med)
3533 Alameda
Box 6530 Phone: (512)854-5341
Corpus Christi, TX 78411 Becky Melton, Med.Libn.
Staff: 1. **Subjects:** General pediatrics, neonatology, pediatric surgery and cardiology. **Holdings:** 330 books; 4000 bound periodical volumes. **Subscriptions:** 80 journals and other serials. **Services:** Library open to professionals. **Networks/Consortia:** Member of Coastal Bend Health Sciences Library Consortium (CBHSLC).

Dritte Welt Haus
See: **Third World House** (16308)

Drugs and Crime Data Center and Clearinghouse
See: **U.S. Dept. of Justice - Bureau of Justice Statistics** (17251)

★5010★
Drummond Island Historical Society - Drummond Island Historical Museum - Library
Drummond Island, MI 49726
Founded: 1963. **Subjects:** Drummond Island history, family history. **Special Collections:** Family albums and portraits. **Holdings:** Books; township records; birth and death certificates; scrapbooks; memorabilia. **Remarks:** Currently inactive.

John Drummond Archives
See: **Frank Lloyd Wright Home and Studio Foundation - Research Center** (20641)

Drusch Professional Library
See: **Deaconess Hospital** (4680)

Dryden Business Library
See: **Prudential Insurance Company of America** (13460)

Dryden Flight Research Facility
See: **NASA - Ames Research Center** (10979)

★5011★
DSIR Lincoln Library (Biol Sci)
Ellesmere Junction Rd.
Private Bag Phone: 3 3252511
Lincoln, New Zealand R.E. McNaughton
Founded: 1960. **Staff:** Prof 2; Other 1. **Subjects:** Botany; agriculture; plant breeding; plant genetics; grain - processing, milling, baking; entomology. **Holdings:** 14,000 books; 3500 periodical titles. **Subscriptions:** 589 journals and other serials. **Services:** Interlibrary loan; copying; library open to the public for reference use only. **Computerized Information Services:** DIALOG Information Services, KIWINET; internal databases. Contact Person: M.R. Bowen, Dp.Libn. **Remarks:** FAX: 3 3252074.

★5012★
Du Page County Law Library (Law)
Jucicial Center
505 N. County Farm Rd. Phone: (708)682-7337
Wheaton, IL 60187 Charlean Eggert, Hd. Law Libn.
Staff: Prof 1; Other 3. **Subjects:** Law, Illinois law, federal law. **Special Collections:** Illinois Revised Statutes, 1816 to present. **Holdings:** 24,000 volumes; Illinois Institute for Continuing Legal Education publications. **Subscriptions:** 32 journals and other serials; 15 newspapers. **Services:** Copying; library open to the public for reference use only.

★5013★
Du Page Library System - System Center (Info Sci)
127 S. 1st St.
Box 268 Phone: (708)232-8457
Geneva, IL 60134 Pamela Feather, Exec.Dir.
Founded: 1966. **Staff:** Prof 1; Other 25. **Subjects:** Library science, plays. **Holdings:** 28,493 books; 883 pieces of framed art; 2200 pieces of sheet music; 2737 children's materials. **Subscriptions:** 410 journals and other serials. **Services:** Interlibrary loan; copying; delivery; center open to the public. **Automated Operations:** Computerized cataloging and circulation. **Computerized Information Services:** DIALOG Information Services; internal database. Performs searches on fee basis. Contact Person: Carol Morrison, Info. Network Cons. **Networks/Consortia:** Member of ILLINET. **Publications:** Dlessence, monthly - to library staffs and public library trustees; Miscellany, biweekly - to library staffs. **Remarks:** DuPage Library System is a cooperative organization of 123 academic, public, school, and special libraries. FAX: (708)232-0699. **Staff:** Frances Lovelace, Youth & Spec.Serv.Cons.; Marilyn Shulski, Bus.Mgr.; Diann Haggerty, Comp.Supv.

★5014★
Alfred I. Du Pont Institute - Medical Library (Med)
Box 269 Phone: (302)651-5821
Wilmington, DE 19899 Carl Nolting, Med.Libn.
Founded: 1940. **Staff:** Prof 1. **Subjects:** Orthopedics, pediatrics, biochemistry, genetics. **Holdings:** 5000 books; 16,000 bound periodical volumes. **Subscriptions:** 300 journals and other serials. **Services:** Interlibrary loan; library open to the public for reference use only. **Computerized Information Services:** MEDLARS, BRS Information Technologies. Performs searches on fee basis. **Networks/Consortia:** Member of Wilmington Area Biomedical Library Consortium (WABLC), Libraries in the New Castle County System (LINCS), National Network of Libraries of Medicine - Middle Atlantic Region, Delaware Library Consortium (DLC).

Du Pont-Ball Library
See: **Stetson University - Du Pont-Ball Library** (15784)

★5015★
Du Pont Canada, Inc. - Central Library (Bus-Fin)
Streetsville Postal Sta., Box 2300 Phone: (416)821-5782
Mississauga, ON, Canada L5M 2J4 Joan Leedale, Libn.
Founded: 1954. **Staff:** 2. **Subjects:** Business, management, marketing, economics, statistics, chemicals and chemical industry, textile fibers industry, plastics industry, government. **Holdings:** 10,000 books; 28 VF drawers of annual reports; 32 VF drawers of Statistics Canada reports. **Subscriptions:** 251 journals and other serials; 8 newspapers. **Services:** Library not open to the public. **Automated Operations:** Computerized cataloging and serials. **Computerized Information Services:** Info Globe, QL Systems, PFDS Online, DIALOG Information Services, Infomart Online, The Financial Post DataGroup. **Remarks:** FAX: (416)821-5110.

★5016★
Du Pont Canada, Inc. - Information Center (Sci-Engr)
P.O. Box 611 Phone: (613)348-4338
Maitland, ON, Canada K0E 1P0 Sue Shipman, Libn.
Founded: 1953. **Staff:** 1. **Subjects:** Chemical engineering, chemical plant operation, organic chemistry, management, occupational health, synthetic fiber manufacture, environment, computers. **Holdings:** 2300 books; 1450 bound periodical volumes; 6929 reports, patents, other cataloged items. **Subscriptions:** 153 journals and other serials. **Services:** Interlibrary loan; copying; SDI; library open to the public with clearance from management. **Automated Operations:** Computerized serials. **Computerized Information Services:** DIALOG Information Services, CAN/OLE, BRS Information Technologies, PFDS Online. **Publications:** New Books and Reports, quarterly; Procedures Manual, irregular - limited distribution. **Remarks:** FAX: (613)348-4200.

★5017★
Du Pont Canada, Inc. - Legal & Patent Library (Law)
Streetsville Postal Sta., Box 2200
Mississauga, ON, Canada L5M 2H3 Phone: (416)821-5782
Founded: 1954. **Staff:** Prof 1. **Subjects:** Intellectual property, corporate law, environmental law. **Holdings:** 3000 books. **Subscriptions:** 100 journals and other serials. **Services:** Interlibrary loan; library not open to the public. **Computerized Information Services:** DIALOG Information Services, ORBIT Search Service, QL Systems, STM Systems Corporation. **Remarks:** FAX: (416)821-5110. **Formerly:** Its Patents Library.

★5018★
Du Pont Canada, Inc. - Research Centre Library (Sci-Engr)
P.O. Box 5000 Phone: (613)548-5254
Kingston, ON, Canada K7L 5A5 S. Toronyi, Res.Sci.-Info.Off.
Founded: 1954. **Staff:** Prof 1; Other 1. **Subjects:** Chemistry, chemical engineering, mathematics, electronics, physics, computers, plastics, management, economics, textile fibers, occupational health and safety. **Holdings:** 8000 books; 4500 bound periodical volumes; 25 VF drawers of unbound materials; 145 VF drawers of internal reports. **Subscriptions:** 250 journals and other serials. **Services:** Interlibrary loan; library not open to the public. **Computerized Information Services:** DIALOG Information Services, STN International.

★5019★
E.I. Du Pont de Nemours & Company, Inc. - Benger Laboratory - Library (Sci-Engr)
400 Du Pont Blvd. Phone: (703)949-2000
Waynesboro, VA 22980 Becky Moomau, Libn.
Founded: 1947. **Staff:** 1. **Subjects:** Polymer chemistry, fiber technology. **Holdings:** 5000 books; 3500 bound periodical volumes; 1700 pamphlets. **Subscriptions:** 100 journals and other serials. **Services:** Interlibrary loan; copying; library open to the public by appointment.

★5020★
E.I. Du Pont de Nemours & Company, Inc. - Dacron Research Laboratory (Sci-Engr)
Box 800
Kinston, NC 28501 Phone: (919)522-6111
Founded: 1954. **Staff:** 1. **Subjects:** Textile fibers, polymers and polymerization, organic chemistry, textile industry, fabrics. **Holdings:** 6600 books; 1750 bound periodical volumes. **Subscriptions:** 150 journals and other serials; 5 newspapers. **Services:** Laboratory not open to the public. **Automated Operations:** Computerized cataloging. **Computerized Information Services:** DIALOG Information Services, Chemical Abstracts Service (CAS).

★5021★
E.I. Du Pont de Nemours & Company, Inc. - Du Pont Chemicals Library (Sci-Engr)
Sabine River Works
Box 1089 Phone: (409)886-6418
Orange, TX 77630 Patsy Holland, Tech.Libn.
Staff: Prof 1. **Subjects:** Chemistry, chemical engineering. **Holdings:** 5000 books; 1000 bound periodical volumes. **Subscriptions:** 150 journals and other serials. **Services:** Library open to the public by appointment. **Automated Operations:** Computerized circulation. **Computerized Information Services:** DIALOG Information Services, PFDS Online, STN International. **Remarks:** FAX: (409)886-6264.

★5022★
E.I. Du Pont de Nemours & Company, Inc. - Haskell Laboratory for Toxicology & Industrial Medicine - Library (Med)
Elkton Rd.
Box 50 Phone: (302)366-5225
Newark, DE 19714 Nancy S. Selzer, Site Libn.
Founded: 1935. **Staff:** Prof 1; Other 2. **Subjects:** Industrial medicine and toxicology. **Holdings:** 5500 books; 15,500 bound periodical volumes. **Subscriptions:** 265 journals and other serials. **Services:** Interlibrary loan; copying; library open to qualified persons. **Automated Operations:** Computerized cataloging. **Computerized Information Services:** DIALOG Information Services, PFDS Online, BRS Information Technologies, MEDLARS. **Networks/Consortia:** Member of National Network of Libraries of Medicine - Middle Atlantic Region, Wilmington Area Biomedical Library Consortium (WABLC), Delaware Library Consortium (DLC), PALINET. **Remarks:** FAX: (302)366-5732.

★5023★
E.I. Du Pont de Nemours & Company, Inc. - Imaging Systems Department - Information Center (Sci-Engr)
Chief Quake Rd. Phone: (908)257-4600
Parlin, NJ 08859-0000 Peggy J. Joplin, Supv.
Founded: 1940. **Staff:** Prof 1; Other 2. **Subjects:** Photography, graphic arts, chemistry, physics, polymers, plastics. **Holdings:** 2500 books; 5500 bound periodical volumes; 120 trade catalogs and directories; 70 VF drawers of company reports; 55 VF drawers of pamphlets, translations, photocopies; 10 VF drawers of trade literature; 154 reels of microfilm; 3500 microcards. **Subscriptions:** 175 journals and other serials. **Services:** Interlibrary loan; center not open to the public. **Computerized Information Services:** DIALOG Information Services, STN International, PFDS Online. **Publications:** Additions to the Library, monthly - for internal distribution only.

★5024★
E.I. Du Pont de Nemours & Company, Inc. - Legal Department Library (Law)
Montchanin Bldg., MG-3 Phone: (302)774-3307
Wilmington, DE 19898 M. Jane DiCecco, Law Libn.
Founded: 1935. **Staff:** Prof 1; Other 1. **Subjects:** Law. **Holdings:** 18,000 books; 800 bound periodical volumes; 100 pamphlets; 61 reels of microfilm; 26 video cassettes. **Subscriptions:** 208 journals and other serials. **Services:** Library open to the public with permission. **Automated Operations:** Computerized cataloging. **Computerized Information Services:** LEXIS, NEXIS, DIALOG Information Services, WESTLAW. **Networks/Consortia:** Member of Delaware Library Consortium (DLC).

★5025★
E.I. Du Pont de Nemours & Company, Inc. - Marshall Laboratory Library (Sci-Engr)
3500 Grays Ferry Ave.
Box 3886 Phone: (215)339-6314
Philadelphia, PA 19146 Virginia L. Maier, Libn.
Founded: 1951. **Staff:** Prof 1; Other 2. **Subjects:** Polymer chemistry, organic coatings, organic chemistry, chemical engineering. **Holdings:** 4000 books; 1000 bound periodical volumes; 2000 departmental technical reports (1000 on microfilm). **Subscriptions:** 240 journals and other serials. **Services:** Interlibrary loan; library not open to the public. **Computerized Information Services:** DIALOG Information Services. **Publications:** Library Bulletin, bimonthly - for internal distribution only.

★5026★
E.I. Du Pont de Nemours & Company, Inc. - NEN Products - Library (Sci-Engr, Med)
549 Albany St. Phone: (617)350-9699
Boston, MA 02118 John Hawkins, Supv., Lib.Serv.
Founded: 1964. **Staff:** Prof 2; Other 3. **Subjects:** Chemistry, nuclear medicine, pharmacology. **Holdings:** 15,000 books; 20,000 bound periodical volumes; 3000 reports. **Subscriptions:** 310 journals and other serials. **Services:** Interlibrary loan; copying; library open to the public by appointment. **Automated Operations:** Computerized public access catalog, cataloging, acquisitions, serials, and circulation. **Computerized Information Services:** DIALOG Information Services, PFDS Online, BRS Information Technologies, Data-Star, BIOSIS Connection, STN International. **Remarks:** Alternate telephone number(s): (508)671-8972. FAX: (617)350-9658. **Staff:** Margaret Hanson, ILL Libn.

★5027★
E.I. Du Pont de Nemours & Company, Inc. - Stine Laboratory Library (Med)
Elkton Rd.
Box 30 Phone: (302)366-5353
Newark, DE 19714 Nancy S. Selzer, Site Libn.
Founded: 1947. **Staff:** Prof 1; Other 2. **Subjects:** Pharmacology, drug metabolism, biochemistry, agriculture, biology. **Holdings:** 1000 books; 2000 bound periodical volumes. **Subscriptions:** 265 journals and other serials. **Services:** Interlibrary loan; copying; SDI; library open to the public with restrictions. **Automated Operations:** Computerized cataloging. **Computerized Information Services:** DIALOG Information Services. **Networks/Consortia:** Member of Wilmington Area Biomedical Library Consortium (WABLC), Libraries in the New Castle County System (LINCS). **Remarks:** FAX: (302)366-5739.

★5028★
E.I. Du Pont de Nemours & Company, Inc. - Technical Library Network (Sci-Engr, Bus-Fin)
P.O. Box 80014 Phone: (302)992-2666
Wilmington, DE 19880-0014 Lois H. Bronstein, Supv., TLN
Founded: 1919. **Staff:** Prof 35; Other 68. **Subjects:** Agricultural chemicals, business and economics, chemistry, biomedicine, electronics, engineering, fibers, films, imaging, industrial relations, management, marketing, pigments, plastics, polymers. **Special Collections:** Corporate annual reports; safety standards and specifications. **Holdings:** 97,000 books; 35,000 bound periodical volumes; journals in microform; 235 shelves of pamphlets. **Subscriptions:** 4181 journals and other serials. **Services:** Interlibrary loan; library not open to the public. **Computerized Information Services:** DIALOG Information Services, ORBIT Search Service, NEXIS, OCLC, Chemical Abstracts Service (CAS), Dow Jones News/Retrieval, MEDLINE, Occupational Health Services, Inc. (OHS), BRS Information Technologies. **Networks/Consortia:** Member of PALINET, Wilmington Area Biomedical Library Consortium (WABLC). **Remarks:** FAX: (302)992-6758. Technical Library network includes the following branch libraries: Business Information Center, (302)774-9738; Glasgow Research Laboratory Library, (302)451-3537; Jackson Laboratory Library, (609)540-4232; Louviers Library (302)366-4242; Pioneering Lab Information Center, (302)695-3451; Polymer Information Center, (302)695-4223; Fibers & Composites Development Centers Library (302)999-4168; Lavoisier Library, (302)695-3391. **Staff:** Emmett D. Calhoun, Supv., Bus.Info.Ctr.; Carolyn K. Markwood, Supv., Jackson Lab.; Evelyn L. Brownlee, Supv., Lavoisier Lib.; Nurdan Atalay-Heckrotte, Supv., PRL Info.Ctr.; Louise G. Glogoff, Supv., Polymer Info.Ctr.; Dushanka G. Keane, Supv., F & CDC Lib.; Joan D. Hogan, Supv., Glasgow Res.Lab.Lib.; Ellyn C. Moore, Supv., Acq.; Linda M. Brannan, Supv., Louviers Lib.; Eleanor C. Turner, Supv., ILL; Catherine E. Brown, Supv.Cat.

★5029★
E.I. Du Pont de Nemours & Company, Inc. - Victoria Plant Library (Sci-Engr)
Old Bloomington Rd. Phone: (512)572-1111
Victoria, TX 77901 Debbie A. Ganem, Libn.
Founded: 1950. **Staff:** 1. **Subjects:** Chemistry, mathematics, engineering, management. **Holdings:** 3250 volumes; 75 volumes of engineering standards and codes; 800 reels of microfilm. **Subscriptions:** 150 journals and other serials. **Services:** Library not open to the public.

★5030★
E.I. Du Pont de Nemours & Company, Inc. - Washington Laboratory Library
Box 1217
Parkersburg, WV 26102 Phone: (304)863-4528
Remarks: FAX: (304)863-2681. No further information was supplied by respondent.

Jessie Ball Du Pont Memorial Library
See: **Stratford Hall Plantation** (15821)

★5031★
Du Pont Merck Pharmaceutical Co. - Information Services (Med)
Information Center, Rm. 2202 Phone: (302)892-7413
Wilmington, DE 19880-0027 Terri Licari, Mgr., Info.Serv.Ctr.
Founded: 1978. **Staff:** Prof 13; Other 23. **Subjects:** Pharmacology, biomedicine, chemistry, computer science, information science, business, patents. **Special Collections:** Annual Reports of Pharmaceutical Companies; Physician's Desk Reference (1950 to present). **Holdings:** 10,000 books; 2500 bound periodical volumes. **Subscriptions:** 500 journals and other serials. **Services:** Interlibrary loan; center not open to the public. **Automated Operations:** Computerized cataloging, serials, document delivery, current awareness, and ILL (DOCLINE). **Computerized Information Services:** Questel, NewsNet, Inc., STN International, OCLC EPIC, TOXNET, First Call, Reuters, DIALOG Information Services, BRS Information Technologies, NLM, NEXIS, Data-Star; AMANDA, DRAKE (internal databases); All-in-One (electronic mail service). **Networks/Consortia:** Member of Wilmington Area Biomedical Library Consortium (WABLC). **Publications:** Pharmaceutical product notes; competitive surveillance bulletins. **Remarks:** FAX: (302)892-1686. Maintains five information centers and one corporate archibal facility located at four sites in Delaware, Pennsylvania, and Massachusetts. **Staff:** June Fifty, Sr.Info.Anl.; Karen Stesis, Sr.Inf.Anl.; Patti Johns, Sr.Info.Anl.; Marie Gould, Info.Coord.; Gennie Diamond, Info.Coord.; Beverly Copeland, Info.Asst.; Monica Weiss, Info.Anl.; Sharon Johnston, Info.Coord.; Mary Talmadge, Sr.Info.Anl.; Suzanne Sykes, Info.Anl.; Regina Lawler, Info.Coord.; Linda Grim, Info.Coord.; Pauline Leeds, Supv. Billerica Site; Peter Mattei, Info.Sci.; Wendy Bruhn, Info.Coord.; Betsy Dandrow, Info.Coord.; Paulette Carter-Scott, Info.Asst.; Tina Maloney, Info.Coord.

★5032★
Duane, Morris & Heckscher - Law Library (Law)
1 Liberty Pl. Phone: (215)979-1720
Philadelphia, PA 19103-7396 JoEllen Berger, Libn.
Founded: 1904. **Staff:** Prof 2; Other 3. **Subjects:** Law. **Holdings:** 19,000 books; 4000 bound periodical volumes; 15 VF drawers of maps, reports, pamphlets. **Subscriptions:** 220 journals and other serials; 6 newspapers. **Services:** Interlibrary loan; copying; SDI; library open to the public with restrictions. **Computerized Information Services:** DIALOG Information Services, VU/TEXT Information Services, WESTLAW, LEXIS, NEXIS, EPIC, OCLC. **Networks/Consortia:** Member of PALINET. **Remarks:** FAX: (215)979-1020. **Staff:** David W. Falk, Asst.Libn.

Lawrence Duba Research Library
See: **Behringer-Crawford Museum** (1652)

A. Stephen Dubois Library
See: **Gowanda Psychiatric Center** (6587)

Marvin Duchow Music Library
See: **McGill University** (9907)

★5033★
Ducks Unlimited Canada - Library (Env-Cons)
1190 Waverley St. Phone: (204)477-1760
Winnipeg, MB, Canada R3T 2E2 Margaret Haworth-Brockman, Biol.
Founded: 1938. **Staff:** Prof 1. **Subjects:** Wetland management, waterfowl biology, conservation, wildlife habitat development, remote sensing, wetland ecology. **Special Collections:** Complete collection of "The Auk"; Proceedings of North American Wildlife Conference; Journal of Wildlife Management; "Wetlands" (journal of wetland scientists); The Wildlife Society Bulletin; Wildfowl. **Holdings:** 1000 books; 125 bound periodical volumes; 1000 Canadian and American government reports and manuscripts. **Subscriptions:** 8 journals and other serials; 15 newspapers. **Services:** Interlibrary loan; copying; library open to the public by appointment. **Computerized Information Services:** Performs searches free of charge. **Remarks:** FAX: (204)452-7560.

★5034★
Dudley Observatory - Library (Sci-Engr)
69 Union Ave. Phone: (518)382-7583
Schenectady, NY 12308 Rita A. Spenser, Act.Libn.
Founded: 1852. **Subjects:** Astronomy, astrophysics, space science, physics, mathematics. **Special Collections:** Rare books in astronomy (250). **Holdings:** 5500 books; 10,000 bound periodical volumes; 8500 unbound serials; 6000 pamphlets, reports, specifications, and standards; 13 VF drawers of star atlases; 2 VF drawers of astronomical pictures. **Subscriptions:** 250 journals and other serials. **Services:** Interlibrary loan; copying; library open to the public. **Networks/Consortia:** Member of Capital District Library Council for Reference & Research Resources (CDLC).

★5035★
Duff and Phelps, Inc. - Research Library (Bus-Fin)
55 E. Monroe St., Suite 3600 Phone: (312)263-2610
Chicago, IL 60603 Janice F. Chindlund, Asst. V.P.
Founded: 1932. **Staff:** Prof 2; Other 4. **Subjects:** Financial analysis, public utilities, industry analysis, economics. **Holdings:** 700 books; U.S. Securities and Exchange Commission (SEC) microfiche; annual reports for 5000 companies. **Subscriptions:** 1200 journals and other serials. **Services:** Interlibrary loan; library not open to the public. **Automated Operations:** Computerized serials. **Computerized Information Services:** Online systems. **Remarks:** FAX: (312)263-4529. **Staff:** John W. Marcus. .

★5036★
Duke Power Company - David Nabow Library (Sci-Engr, Bus-Fin)
526 S. Church St., Rm. ECO6H Phone: (704)373-4095
Charlotte, NC 28201-1006 Audrey W. Caldwell, Supv.
Founded: 1967. **Staff:** Prof 2; Other 5. **Subjects:** Engineering - civil, electrical, mechanical, nuclear; environment; social sciences - economics, management, finance, industry; science - information systems management. **Special Collections:** Nuclear Regulatory Commission reports and standards; Electric Power Research Institute reports; American National Standards Institute, National Electrical Manufacturers Association, and Institute of Electrical and Electronics Engineers standards (20,000 microfiche; 7500 documents on microfiche). **Holdings:** 58,000 books; 90 bound periodical volumes; 20,000 standards; 12 drawers of periodicals on microfiche. **Subscriptions:** 502 journals and other serials. **Services:** Interlibrary loan; SDI; library open to the public. **Automated Operations:** Computerized cataloging, serials, standards, and circulation. **Computerized Information Services:** DIALOG Information Services, VU/TEXT Information Services, EPRINET; Edison Electric Institute (EEI) (electronic mail service). **Publications:** Acquisitions List, monthly; Safety Analysis Reports, quarterly; Periodicals List, quarterly. **Remarks:** FAX: (704)373-7826. **Staff:** Frank Dagenhart; Linda Skinner; Rita Miller; Pamela Palmer; Joye Christenbury; Mark Alexander.

★5037★
Duke Power Company - Information Systems Library (Comp Sci)
401 S. College St. Phone: (704)382-0107
Charlotte, NC 28202 Linda W. Skinner, Libn.
Founded: 1984. **Staff:** Prof 1. **Subjects:** Computer technology. **Holdings:** 500 books. **Subscriptions:** 75 journals and other serials; 10 newspapers. **Services:** Interlibrary loan; copying; library open to the public with restrictions. **Automated Operations:** Computerized public access catalog and circulation. **Computerized Information Services:** DIALOG Information Services, EEI (Edison Electric Institute). **Publications:** I/S Library Bulletin, irregular - for internal distribution only. **Remarks:** FAX: (704)382-0790.

★5038★
Duke Power Company - Legal Department - Law Library (Law)
422 S. Church St. Phone: (704)382-8138
Charlotte, NC 28242-0001 Cynthia C. Smith, Libn.
Founded: 1950. **Staff:** Prof 1. **Subjects:** Law - public utilities, regulatory, environmental, labor. **Special Collections:** Federal Register, Code of Federal Regulations; Southeastern Reporter; Federal Reporter, Federal Supplement; General Statutes of North Carolina; Code of Laws of South Carolina; Federal Energy Regulatory Commission (FERC) Opinions, Orders, and Decisions; North Carolina Administrative Code. **Holdings:** 4000 books. **Subscriptions:** 54 journals and other serials. **Services:** Interlibrary loan; copying; library open to the public with restrictions. **Computerized Information Services:** LEXIS, NEXIS; internal database. **Publications:** New Acquisitions, irregular - for internal distribution only. **Remarks:** FAX: (704)382-8137.

★5039★
Duke University - A.S. Vesic Engineering Library (Sci-Engr)
Durham, NC 27706 Phone: (919)660-5368
Eric J. Smith, Engr.Libn.
Founded: 1923. **Staff:** Prof 1; Other 3. **Subjects:** Engineering - mechanical, electrical, biochemical, civil, environmental, biomedical; materials science; computer science. **Holdings:** 96,540 volumes; 28,500 NASA Research Reports. **Subscriptions:** 1450 journals and other serials. **Services:** Interlibrary loan; copying; library open to the public with restrictions. **Automated Operations:** Computerized cataloging, acquisitions, and serials. **Computerized Information Services:** DIALOG Information Services, BRS Information Technologies, OCLC. **Networks/Consortia:** Member of SOLINET.

★5040★
Duke University - Biology-Forestry Library (Biol Sci)
Durham, NC 27706 Phone: (919)684-2381
David M. Talbert
Founded: 1938. **Staff:** Prof 1; Other 2. **Subjects:** Botany, zoology, forestry, environmental studies, soils, meteorology. **Holdings:** 169,000 volumes. **Subscriptions:** 1800 journals and other serials. **Services:** Interlibrary loan; copying; library open to the public. **Automated Operations:** Computerized cataloging, acquisitions, and serials (through central library). **Computerized Information Services:** DIALOG Information Services, STN International, MEDLARS; CD-ROMs (AGRICOLA, Biological Abstracts, Enviro/Energyline Abstracts Plus, CRIS); BITNET (electronic mail service). Performs searches on fee basis. **Remarks:** Electronic mail address(es): BIOFOR@DUKEMVS (BITNET).

★5041★
Duke University - Center for Demographic Studies - Reference Library (Soc Sci)
2117 Campus Dr. Phone: (919)684-6126
Durham, NC 27706 Sue P. Hicks, Libn.
Founded: 1964. **Staff:** Prof 6. **Subjects:** Demography; human ecology; census, vital statistics, other data sources; methods of research and analysis; population dynamics; urban and regional studies; economics of population size and distribution; migration studies; gerontology. **Special Collections:** Joseph J. Spengler Collection (population and allied topics; several thousand books, periodicals, serials, reprints, clippings from the library of Professor Emeritus Spengler); Mortality Migration Reprint (reference files, 500 entries each); National Center for Health Statistics Mortality Data; 1960, 1970, and 1980 Public Use Samples; reprint files on aging, migration, human ecology. **Holdings:** 5000 books; 300 bound periodical volumes; 2000 census volumes; 30 dissertations; 125 maps; 350 microfiche; documents; program documentation. **Subscriptions:** 50 journals and other serials. **Services:** Library open to outside users actively engaged in demographic research. **Publications:** Reprint series - available on request; bibliography on aging and population modeling (online). **Special Catalogs:** ABC's - Annotated Bibliographic Compiling System. **Remarks:** FAX: (919)684-3861. **Staff:** George C. Myers, Dir. of Ctr.; Kenneth G. Manton, Asst.Dir.

★5042★
Duke University - Chemistry Library (Sci-Engr)
Durham, NC 27706 Phone: (919)660-1578
Kitty Porter, Libn.
Founded: 1927. **Staff:** Prof 1. **Subjects:** Chemistry, allied sciences. **Special Collections:** Sadtler Standard Spectra collections (UV, IR-Grating, NMR, C-13, Raman); API and TRC Catalogs of Standard Spectra. **Holdings:** 47,043 volumes. **Subscriptions:** 600 journals and other serials. **Services:** SDI; document delivery; library open to the public. **Computerized Information Services:** DIALOG Information Services, BRS Information Technologies, STN International, OCLC; BITNET (electronic mail service). Performs searches on fee basis. **Networks/Consortia:** Member of SOLINET. **Publications:** Recent Acquisitions List, monthly. **Remarks:** FAX: (919)681-8666. Electronic mail address(es): DKPCHEM@DUKEMVS (BITNET).

★5043★
Duke University - Divinity School Library (Rel-Phil)
Durham, NC 27706 Phone: (919)684-8111
Roger Lloyd, Libn.
Founded: 1927. **Staff:** Prof 2; Other 3. **Subjects:** Religion, the Wesleys and Methodism, American Christianity, Quakerism, Roman Catholicism, Judaism, Hinduism, Buddhism, Islam, religious art and architecture, history of the transmission of Biblical text, archeology of the Near East, medieval mysticism. **Holdings:** 276,982 volumes. **Subscriptions:** 625 journals and other serials. **Services:** Interlibrary loan; copying; library open to the public. **Automated Operations:** Computerized cataloging, acquisitions, and serials (through central library). **Staff:** Harriet V. Leonard, Ref.Libn.

★5044★
Duke University - Marine Laboratory - A.S. Pearse Memorial Library (Biol Sci)
Piver's Island Phone: (919)728-2111
Beaufort, NC 28516 Dr. Joseph Ramus, Lib.Rep.
Founded: 1954. **Staff:** Prof 1. **Subjects:** Marine biology, oceanography, geology, biochemistry. **Holdings:** 17,000 volumes. **Subscriptions:** 135 journals and other serials. **Services:** Interlibrary loan; copying; library open to the public for reference use only. **Automated Operations:** Computerized cataloging, acquisitions, serials, and circulation. **Computerized Information Services:** OCLC. **Publications:** Serial Publications (1991) - available upon request. **Remarks:** FAX: (919)728-2514. **Staff:** Susan Kenney, Lib.Assoc.

★5045★
Duke University - Math-Physics Library (Sci-Engr)
233 Physics Bldg. Phone: (919)684-8118
Durham, NC 27706 Mary Ann W. Southern, Libn.
Founded: 1939. **Staff:** Prof 1; Other 2. **Subjects:** Mathematics, physics, statistics, astronomy, astrophysics. **Special Collections:** University of Ulm Microwave Catalog. **Holdings:** 91,952 volumes. **Subscriptions:** 595 journals. **Services:** Interlibrary loan; copying; library open to the public. **Automated Operations:** Computerized public access catalog, cataloging, acquisitions, and periodical check-in (INNOVACQ). **Computerized Information Services:** DIALOG Information Services, OCLC, BRS Information Technologies; BITNET, InterNet (electronic mail services). Performs searches on fee basis for users affiliated with Duke. **Networks/Consortia:** Member of SOLINET, Triangle Research Libraries Network (TRLN). **Remarks:** Electronic mail address(es): DUKPAM@DUKEMVS (BITNET); mplib@phy.duke.edu (InterNet).

★5046★
Duke University - Medical Center Library (Med)
Durham, NC 27710 Phone: (919)684-2092
Susan J. Feinglos, Act.Dir.
Founded: 1930. **Staff:** Prof 13; Other 24. **Subjects:** Medicine, allied health sciences. **Special Collections:** Josiah C. Trent Collection (history of medicine). **Holdings:** 254,000 volumes. **Subscriptions:** 4837 journals and other serials. **Services:** Interlibrary loan; copying; document delivery; SDI; library open to the public with librarian's permission. **Automated Operations:** Computerized cataloging, acquisitions, and serials. **Computerized Information Services:** BRS Information Technologies, DIALOG Information Services, NLM, OCLC, CD-Plus; BITNET (electronic mail service). Performs searches on fee basis. Self-service CD-ROM searching available free of charge. **Networks/Consortia:** Member of SOLINET, Triangle Research Libraries Network (TRLN). **Special Catalogs:** North Carolina Union List of Biomedical Serials (NORCUL). **Remarks:** FAX: (919)684-5906. Electronic mail address(es): WIETH001@DUKEMC (BITNET).

★5047★
Duke University - Music Library (Mus)
College Sta., Box 6695 Phone: (919)684-6449
Durham, NC 27708 John E. Druesedow, Dir.
Founded: 1974. **Staff:** Prof 2; Other 2. **Subjects:** Music. **Special Collections:** Alexander Weinmann Collection (18th and 19th century musical imprints, with emphasis on Strauss); Robert Ward Archives; Riethus Collection (Central and Eastern Europe history and biography). **Holdings:** 80,000 books, scores, periodicals; 9400 microforms; 16,000 sound and video recordings; music literature. **Subscriptions:** 400 journals and other serials. **Services:** Interlibrary loan; library open to the public for reference use only. **Automated Operations:** Computerized public access catalog. **Computerized Information Services:** DIALOG Information Services; CD-ROM; BITNET, InterNet (electronic mail services). **Special Indexes:** Card index to manuscript inventories and descriptions. **Remarks:** FAX: (919)681-8678. Electronic mail address(es): JED@ECSVAX; JED@UNCECS.EDU (InterNet);JED@ECSVAX (BITNET). **Staff:** Timothy J. Cherubini, Asst.Dir.

★5048★
Duke University - School of Law Library (Law)
Durham, NC 27706 Phone: (919)684-2847
Richard Danner, Dir.
Staff: Prof 9; Other 13. **Subjects:** Law. **Holdings:** 414,401 volumes. **Subscriptions:** 6258 journals and other serials. **Services:** Interlibrary loan; copying; library open to the public for reference use only. **Automated Operations:** Computerized public access catalog, cataloging, circulation, acquisitions, and ILL. **Computerized Information Services:** LEXIS, NEXIS, WESTLAW, RLIN, OCLC, DIALOG Information Services, Dow Jones News/Retrieval. **Networks/Consortia:** Member of SOLINET, Triangle Research Libraries Network (TRLN). **Publications:** D.U.L.L. News, monthly. **Remarks:** FAX: (919)684-8770. **Staff:** Claire Germain, Assoc.Dir.; Hope Breeze, Hd., Tech.Serv.; Janeen Denson, Circ.Libn.; Doris Hinson, Cat.; Janet Sinder, Ref.Libn.; Gretchen Wolf, Acq.Libn.; Meg Collins, Ref.Libn.; Ken Hirsh, Ref.Libn.

★5049★
Duke University - Special Collections Department (Hum)
344 Perkins Library Phone: (919)684-3372
Durham, NC 27706 Robert L. Byrd, Dir., Spec.Coll.
Staff: Prof 17; Other 8. **Subjects:** Southern history and literature; U.S. history; history of advertising; history of economic theory; British history and literature, women's studies; English and American literature; Utopian literature; Wesleyana and Methodistica; German Baroque literature; parapsychology; juvenile literature; Nazi and Fascist propaganda and literature; American popular sheet music. **Special Collections:** J. Walter Thompson Company Archives (2 million items); Socialist Party of America records (250,000 items); Labor Archives (CIO Operation Dixie records); George Washington Flowers Collection of Southern Americana; William B. Hamilton Collection of British Manuscripts; Confederate Imprint Collection; Walt Whitman Collection; Frank Baker Collection of Wesleyana and British Methodistica; Harold Jantz Collections of German Baroque and German-American Literature; Glen Negley Collection of Utopian Literature; Alexander Weinmann Collection of Viennese Music; Abram and Frances Pascher Kanof Collection of Jewish Art, Archaeology, and Symbolism; Kenneth Willis Clark Collection of Greek Manuscripts; Duke Papyri Collection. **Holdings:** 137,000 books; 11,000 maps, broadsides, and pieces of sheet music; 9.5 million manuscripts. **Services:** Copying. **Publications:** Guide to the Cataloged Collections in the Manuscript Department of the William R. Perkins Library (1980; 1005 pages). **Special Catalogs:** Autograph, subject, geographic, and picture files (card) for manuscript collections. **Special Indexes:** Indexes to broadsides, juvenile literature, trade catalogs, World War II publications, provenance and ownership, signed bookbindings, publishers, printers, (card; online) **Remarks:** FAX: (919)684-2855. **Staff:** Steven L. Hensen, Asst.Dir.; Linda McCurdy, Hd., Pub.Serv.; M. Susan Taraba, Hd., Rare Mtls.Cat.; Sharon E. Knapp, Hd., Ms.Proc. & Cat.; Virginia Daley, Women's Studies Archv.; Ellen G. Gartrell, Advertising Hist.Spec.; J. Samuel Hammond, Rare Bk.Libn.

★5050★
Duke University - University Archives (Hist)
341 Perkins Phone: (919)684-5637
Durham, NC 27706 William E. King, Univ.Archv.
Founded: 1972. **Staff:** Prof 2. **Subjects:** University history and records; 19th century Methodism. **Special Collections:** Triangle Universities Computation Center; William McDougall papers (psychology); Fritz London papers (physics); Calvin Bryce Hoover papers (economics); Alice Mary Baldwin papers (women's education). **Holdings:** 3000 books; 475 bound periodical volumes; 13,000 dissertations; 7000 linear feet of records, manuscripts, and photographs. **Subscriptions:** 28 journals and other serials. **Services:** Copying; archives open to the public. **Computerized Information Services:** Internal databases. **Staff:** Thomas F. Harkins, Assoc.Univ.Archv.

★5051★
Dukes County Historical Society - Library (Hist)
Cooke & School Sts.
Box 827 Phone: (508)627-4441
Edgartown, MA 02539 Ann C. Allen, Libn.
Founded: 1922. **Staff:** 4. **Subjects:** History of Martha's Vineyard, genealogy, whaling history, shipping, maritime history, history of Island Indians, literature by Island authors. **Special Collections:** Whaling and other logbooks; account books. **Holdings:** 3000 volumes; 225 boxes of archival material; customs office account books; records; deeds; correspondence; photographs; oral histories; videotapes. **Subscriptions:** 39 journals and other serials. **Services:** Copying; library open to the public. **Publications:** Dukes County Intelligencer, quarterly. **Staff:** Marian R. Halperin, Dir.

★5052★
Dukes Law Library (Law)
P.O. Box 1267
Edgartown, MA 02539 Phone: (508)627-3751
Subjects: Law. **Holdings:** Figures not available. **Services:** Library open to the public for reference use only. **Remarks:** Part of the Massachusetts State Trial Court;. Marnie Warner, Law Library Coordinator.

Dulany Library
See: **William Woods College** (20577)

★5053★
Dull Knife Memorial College - Dr. John Woodenlegs Memorial Library (Area-Ethnic)
Box 98 Phone: (406)477-8293
Lame Deer, MT 59043-0098 Joni A. Williams, Lib.Dir.
Founded: 1979. **Staff:** Prof 1; Other 2. **Subjects:** Cheyenne history, sociology, psychology, human services. **Special Collections:** Cheyenne Collection (65 oral histories). **Holdings:** 10,000 books. **Subscriptions:** 120 journals and other serials; 7 newspapers. **Services:** Interlibrary loan; copying; library open to the public with restrictions. **Automated Operations:** Computerized cataloging.

★5054★
Duluth News-Tribune - Library (Publ)
Box 169000 Phone: (218)723-5309
Duluth, MN 55816-9000 June Rudd, Libn.
Founded: 1960. **Staff:** Prof 1. **Subjects:** Newspaper reference topics. **Holdings:** 300 books; 1 million newspaper clippings; 1150 reels of microfilm; 100,000 photographs. **Services:** Library not open to the public. **Remarks:** Library located at 424 W. 1st St., Duluth, MN 55802.

Dumbarton Oaks Research Library and Collection
See: **Harvard University - Dumbarton Oaks Research Library and Collection** (6963)

★5055★
Gabriel Dumont Institute of Native Studies and Applied Research - Library (Area-Ethnic)
121 Broadway Ave. Phone: (306)522-5691
Regina, SK, Canada S4N 0Z6 John Murray, Coord.
Founded: 1980. **Staff:** Prof 3; Other 2. **Subjects:** Metis and aboriginal studies and education, Metis. **Special Collections:** Aboriginal History Archives. **Holdings:** 30,000 books. **Subscriptions:** 200 journals and other serials. **Services:** Interlibrary loan; copying; library open to the public. **Automated Operations:** Integrated library system (NOTIS). **Computerized Information Services:** GDI Database (internal database). **Remarks:** FAX: (306)565-0809. Branch libraries are maintained in the following cities throughout Saskatchewan: Prince Albert, Saskatoon, Regina, Ile a la Crosse. **Staff:** Bette Desjarlais, Prince Albert Libn.; Marilyn Belhunser, Regina Libn.; Pat Kelly, Proc.Tech. Regina.

John J. Dumphy Memorial Library
See: **St. Vincent Hospital** (14610)

Dun & Bradstreet Corporation - Dataquest
See: **Dataquest** (4625)

Isadora Duncan Collection
See: **San Francisco Performing Arts Library and Museum - Library** (14737)

Dunham Hall Library
See: **Windham Textile and History Museum** (20476)

★5056★
Dunham Tavern Museum - Library (Rec)
6709 Euclid Ave. Phone: (216)431-1060
Cleveland, OH 44103 Elizabeth Martel, Libn.
Staff: 1. **Subjects:** Antique collecting; history of Cleveland and Ohio. **Special Collections:** Antiques Magazine, 1922 to present. **Holdings:** 1000 books. **Services:** Library open to members only. **Remarks:** Maintained by Society of Collectors, Inc.

★5057★
Dunhill - Business Research Library (Bus-Fin)
1100 Park Central Blvd., S. Phone: (305)974-7800
Pompano Beach, FL 33064 Ruth Balaban, Libn.
Staff: Prof 2. **Subjects:** Manufacturing, wholesalers, retailers, religious market, clubs and organizations, finance, associations and members, service organizations. **Holdings:** Trade directories. **Services:** Library not open to the public. **Remarks:** A subsidiary of Dunhill International List Company, Inc. FAX: (305)974-0443.

Elaine G. Dunitz Hospice Library
See: **Reading Hospital & Medical Center - Medical Library** (13746)

★5058★
Dunlap and Associates Inc. - Library (Soc Sci)
17 Washington St. Phone: (203)866-8464
Norwalk, CT 06854 Frances Maloon, Dir.
Founded: 1948. **Staff:** Prof 1. **Subjects:** Psychology, human factors, statistics, military science, drug abuse, accidents, alcohol-related accidents. **Holdings:** 2500 books; 100 bound periodical volumes; 80 VF drawers of reports, government documents, pamphlets. **Subscriptions:** 50 journals and other serials; 5 newspapers. **Services:** Interlibrary loan; copying; library open to the public by appointment. **Remarks:** FAX: (203)866-0799.

★5059★
Dunn-Behre Dolbear, Inc. - Library (Sci-Engr)
275 Madison Ave.
New York, NY 10016 Phone: (212)684-4150
Subjects: Mineral economics, mining engineering, mine development. **Holdings:** 300 books; 1000 reports. **Subscriptions:** 15 journals and other serials. **Services:** Library not open to the public. **Remarks:** FAX: (212)684-4438.

★5060★
Dunn Geoscience Corporation - Information Resources (Sci-Engr)
12 Metro Park Rd. Phone: (518)458-1313
Albany, NY 12205 Laurie Sutherland-Nehring, Sr.Info.Rsrcs.Spec.
Founded: 1960. **Staff:** Prof 1; Other 1. **Subjects:** Geology, toxicology, hydrology, hazardous materials, environmental law. **Special Collections:** New York State geology; soil surveys; map collection; ground water surveys. **Holdings:** 1000 books; 4000 other cataloged items; internal reports. **Subscriptions:** 130 journals and other serials. **Services:** SDI; center open to the public with permission of director. **Automated Operations:** Computerized public access catalog. **Computerized Information Services:** DIALOG Information Services, BRS Information Technologies, Chemical Abstracts Service (CAS), Ground Water On-Line, NLM, TOXNET; MESSAGES, DIALMAIL (electronic mail services). Performs searches on fee basis. **Networks/Consortia:** Member of Capital District Library Council for Reference & Research Resources (CDLC). **Remarks:** FAX: (518)458-2472.

Sir James Dunn Law Library
See: **Dalhousie University - Sir James Dunn Law Library** (4537)

Richard W. Dunne Library
See: **Christ Episcopal Church - Richard W. Dunne Library** (3625)

Guy B. Dunning Library
See: **Nebraska Christian College - Library - Special Collections** (11371)

Duns Scotus Library
See: **Lourdes College - Duns Scotus Library** (9402)

★5061★
Duns Scotus Library
20000 W. 9 Mile Rd.
Southfield, MI 48075
Defunct.

★5062★
Dunwoody Institute - John A. Butler Learning Center (Educ)
818 Wayzata Blvd. Phone: (612)374-5800
Minneapolis, MN 55403 Kristina Oberstar, Lib.Adm.
Founded: 1914. **Staff:** Prof 1; Other 2. **Subjects:** Printing, mechanical and architectural drafting, electronics, refrigeration, baking, electrical and mechanical engineering, welding, auto mechanics. **Holdings:** 12,000 books. **Subscriptions:** 60 journals and other serials. **Services:** Center not open to the public. **Formerly:** Dunwoody Industrial Institute. **Staff:** Lori Caouette.

★5063★
Duplin County Historical Society - Leora H. McEachern Library of Local History (Hist)
P.O. Box 130 Phone: (919)289-2654
Rose Hill, NC 28458 William Dallas Herruig
Founded: 1932. **Staff:** 1. **Subjects:** Genealogy, local history. **Holdings:** Books; reports; archival materials; microfiche; microfilm; family correspondence files. **Services:** Copying; library open to the public on a limited schedule. **Computerized Information Services:** Internal database. **Publications:** Footnotes (magazine), quarterly.

Dupuis Hall Library
See: **Queen's University at Kingston** (13648)

★5064★
Duquesne University - Law Library (Law)
900 Locust St. Phone: (412)434-5017
Pittsburgh, PA 15282 Frank Yining Liu, Dir./Prof. of Law
Founded: 1911. **Staff:** Prof 5. **Subjects:** Law. **Holdings:** 139,931 volumes; 34,039 volumes in microform. **Subscriptions:** 1858 journals and other serials. **Services:** Interlibrary loan. **Computerized Information Services:** LEXIS, NEXIS, WESTLAW, OCLC. **Networks/Consortia:** Member of Mid-Atlantic Law Library Cooperative (MALLCO). **Publications:** Acquisitions List, monthly; Duquesne University Law Library Information Guide, annual - both for internal distribution only; Duquesne University Law Library Notes. **Remarks:** FAX: (412)434-6294. **Staff:** Agnes F. Robinson, Asst. Law Libn.; Doris M.E. Corsello, Cat.; Rao Dittakavi, Ref.Libn.; Mark Falk, AV Comp.Serv.Libn.

★5065★
Duquesne University - Tamburitzans Cultural Center (Area-Ethnic)
1801 Boulevard of the Allies Phone: (412)434-5185
Pittsburgh, PA 15219 Ronald F. Rendulic, Asst.Mng.Dir.
Founded: 1954. **Staff:** Prof 1. **Subjects:** Eastern Europe - folk culture, folk music, folk dance, costume, musical instruments, history. **Special Collections:** James Clarke Collection (history and culture of Russia and Bulgaria; 10,000 books, journals, papers); E. Eddy Nadel Collection (books; recordings; costumes); LaMeri Costume Collection (700 pieces). **Holdings:** 25,000 books; 11,000 phonograph records; 1000 audiotapes; 400 films; 4500 slides. **Subscriptions:** 56 journals and other serials; 21 newspapers. **Services:** Center open to the public for reference use only.

★5066★
Duracell WTC - Technical Information Center (Sci-Engr)
37 A St. Phone: (617)449-7600
Needham Heights, MA 02194-2806 E. Hera-Jones, Mgr., Tech.Info.Serv.
Founded: 1969. **Staff:** Prof 2; Other 1. **Subjects:** Electrochemistry, physical chemistry, metallurgy, materials science, environmental science, computer science. **Holdings:** 4500 books; 2140 bound periodical volumes; 4000 reprints and pamphlets; 16 VF drawers of battery patents; 3000 government contract reports; 4 VF drawers of literature searches; 2000 microforms. **Subscriptions:** 197 journals and other serials. **Services:** Center open to the public for reference use only by request. **Computerized Information Services:** Mead Data Central, PFDS Online, DIALOG Information Services, Occupational Health Services, Inc. (OHS); internal database. **Publications:** TIC Bulletin, monthly - for internal distribution only. **Remarks:** FAX: (617)449-4825. **Staff:** Rita Lai-yee Lo; Carol Mock.

★5067★
Durant Family Registry - Library (Rec)
2700 Timber Ln. Phone: (414)499-8797
Green Bay, WI 54313-5899 Jeff Gillis, Pres.
Founded: 1976. **Staff:** 1. **Subjects:** Automobiles - Durant, DeVaux, Star, Flint, Rugby, Canadian Frontenac. **Special Collections:** Sales literature, owners manuals, factory photographs, allied information for cars produced by W.C. Durant, 1921-1932. **Holdings:** Figures not available. **Services:** Copying; library open to the public. **Publications:** Durant's Standard, quarterly.

★5068★
(Durban) American Cultural Center - USIS Library (Educ)
2902 Durban Bay House
333 Smith St.
Durban 4001, Republic of South Africa
Remarks: Maintained or supported by the U.S. Information Agency. Focus is on materials that will assist peoples outside the United States to learn about the United States, its people, history, culture, political processes, and social milieux.

★5069★
Durham College of Applied Arts and Technology - Main Library & Simcoe Resource Centre (Educ)
Simcoe St., N.
Box 385 Phone: (416)576-0210
Oshawa, ON, Canada L1H 7L7 Susan Barclay-Pereira, Dir., Lrng.Rsrcs.
Founded: 1967. **Staff:** Prof 2; Other 10. **Subjects:** Technology, business, applied arts, health sciences. **Holdings:** 40,000 books; 1800 bound periodical volumes; 1300 federal and provincial government documents; 5300 slides; 2000 pamphlets; 620 filmstrips; 339 records; 1580 tapes and videocassettes. **Subscriptions:** 400 journals and other serials; 8 newspapers. **Services:** Interlibrary loan; copying; center open to local and regional library system users. **Automated Operations:** Computerized public access catalog, cataloging, acquisitions, and circulation. **Computerized Information Services:** Internal database (Mandarin); CD-ROMs (EBSCO, Grolier Encyclopedia, Canadian Business and Current Affairs, Magazine Article Summaries). **Special Catalogs:** Annotated Video Catalog. **Remarks:** FAX: (416)436-9774. **Staff:** Carol Mittlestead, Ref.Serv.

★5070★
Durham County Hospital Corporation - Watts School of Nursing - Library (Med)
3643 N. Roxboro Rd. Phone: (919)470-7346
Durham, NC 27704 Priscilla W. Hoover, Libn.
Founded: 1895. **Staff:** Prof 1; Other 1. **Subjects:** Nursing and nursing education, pediatrics, obstetrics and gynecology, sociology and psychology. **Holdings:** 5333 books; 249 bound periodical volumes; 4 VF drawers; 20 boxes of pamphlets. **Subscriptions:** 59 journals and other serials. **Services:** Interlibrary loan; copying; library open to hospital personnel and nursing students only.

★5071★
Durham Herald-Sun Newspaper - Library (Publ)
2828 Pickett Rd. Phone: (919)419-6520
Durham, NC 27705 Ruth J. Monnig, Lib.Dir.
Founded: 1976. **Staff:** Prof 1; Other 8. **Subjects:** Newspaper reference topics. **Special Collections:** Durham Herald-Sun Newspaper Microfilm Collection, 1890 to present. **Holdings:** 5500 books; 2 million clippings; 500,000 photographs; 120 VF drawers; Duke University Index to Herald-Sun newspapers, 1930-1981; 14,500 microfiche. **Subscriptions:** 70 journals and other serials; 35 newspapers. **Services:** Library not open to the public. **Computerized Information Services:** NEXIS, VU/TEXT Information Services; IND-EX (index to local news, 1981 to present; internal database). **Remarks:** FAX: (919)419-6873.

★5072★
Durkee-French Foods, Inc. - Technical Library (Food-Bev)
1655 Valley Rd.
P.O. Box 942 Phone: (201)633-3662
Wayne, NJ 07474-0942 Joy Johnsen, Libn./Info.Spec.
Staff: Prof 1. **Subjects:** Food technology, chemistry, microbiology, packaging. **Holdings:** 500 books; 480 bound periodical volumes; 5 VF drawers of reprints. **Subscriptions:** 60 journals and other serials. **Services:** Interlibrary loan. **Computerized Information Services:** DIALOG Information Services. **Networks/Consortia:** Member of Bergen Passaic Regional Library Cooperative. **Publications:** Library newsletter, monthly - for internal distribution only. **Remarks:** FAX: (201)633-2960.

Anne Carry Durland Memorial Alternatives Library
See: **Center for Religion, Ethics & Social Policy** (3288)

★5073★
DuSable Museum of African American History - Library (Area-Ethnic)
740 E. 56th Place Phone: (312)947-0600
Chicago, IL 60637 Dr. Gwen Robinson, Dir.
Founded: 1961. **Staff:** Prof 2; Other 3. **Subjects:** Black history, sociology, politics, religion, fiction, biography; Africana. **Holdings:** 3000 volumes; 500 other cataloged items; 100 oral history tapes; 50 manuscripts; 85 VF drawers of clippings. **Services:** Library not open to the public. **Publications:** Calendar, annual. **Staff:** Eugene Feldman, Dir. of Res. & Pubn.; Maurice S. Marks, Dp.Dir.; Ramon B. Price, Cur.

★5074★
Duta Wacana Christian University - Faculty of Theology - Library (Rel-Phil)
Jl. Dr. Wahidin 17 Phone: 274 3606
Yogyakarta 55222, Indonesia Mr. Karmito, M.Th.
Founded: 1962. **Staff:** Prof 3; Other 5. **Subjects:** Christianity, Eastern philosophy, sociology, religions, Islam, modern philosophy, Indonesia. **Special Collections:** New Religious Movements in Primal Societies collection (1800 microfiche); Javanese mysticism and philosophy collection (450 volumes). **Holdings:** 24,000 books; 3000 bound periodical volumes; 160 reports; 2800 microfiche; theses; dissertations. **Subscriptions:** 172 journals and other serials; 6 newspapers. **Services:** Interlibrary loan; copying; library open to members only. **Publications:** Guide for Using the Library. **Special Indexes:** Author-Title Index to Selected Articles of the Daily Kompas & Suara Pembaruan. **Remarks:** FAX: 274 3235. Telex: 25486 UKDW IA.

★5075★
Dutchess County Department of Planning - Information Center (Plan)
27 High St. Phone: (914)485-9681
Poughkeepsie, NY 12601 Carolyn T. Purcell, P.R. Spec.
Founded: 1980. **Staff:** Prof 1. **Subjects:** Land use, transportation, environmental and urban planning, parks and recreation, housing and energy, refuse disposal, natural resources, zoning, water. **Special Collections:** Complete 1980 census for Dutchess County; 1990 census for Dutchess, Ulster, and Sullivan counties; American Society of Planning Officials Reports; Urban Land Institute reports. **Holdings:** 5000 books; 30 county and municipal master plans; New York State statistical yearbooks; 10,000 slides; 1200 pamphlets and unpublished reports; selected 1970 U.S., state, and county census data. **Subscriptions:** 15 journals and other serials. **Services:** Copying; center open to the public for reference use only. **Computerized Information Services:** Info New York (internal database). **Publications:** County data book; land use and housing reports. **Remarks:** FAX: (914)485-9686.

★5076★
Dutchess County Genealogical Society - Library (Hist)
LDS Church
Spackenkill Rd. Phone: (914)454-1614
Poughkeepsie, NY 12603 Linda Koehler, Libn.
Founded: 1975. **Subjects:** Genealogy, history, heraldry. **Holdings:** 269 books; 232 pamphlets; 3 reels of microfilm of 1790 census; 71 reels of microfilm of 1810 census; Dutchess county census of 1800 and 1830-1910 (ten year intervals) on microfilm. **Subscriptions:** 21 journals and other serials. **Services:** Library open to the public. **Publications:** The Dutchess, quarterly.

Addison M. Duval Library
See: **Georgia (State) Department of Human Resources - Georgia Mental Health Institute** (6399)

★5077★
Duval County Law Library (Law)
102 Court House Phone: (904)630-2560
Jacksonville, FL 32202 Jack T. Sheng, Law Libn.
Founded: 1939. **Staff:** Prof 1; Other 3. **Subjects:** Law - Florida, U.S.; state statutes. **Special Collections:** Old English law. **Holdings:** 45,000 books; 6100 bound periodical volumes; 1200 other cataloged items; 20 maps; 125 tapes. **Subscriptions:** 164 journals and other serials; 6 newspapers. **Services:** Copying; library open to county residents.

Duveen Library and Archive
See: **Sterling and Francine Clark Art Institute - Library** (3773)

F.W. and Bessie Dye Memorial Library
See: **Texas Woman's University** (16281)

Dyer Institute of Interdisciplinary Studies
See: **U.S. Army - Military History Institute** (16995)

Dyer Memorial Library
See: **Cumberland Science Museum** (4479)

Dyer Observatory
See: **Vanderbilt University - Jean and Alexander Heard Library** (19771)

★5078★
Dyke College - Library Resource Center - Spencerian Archives (Hist)
112 Prospect Ave., SE Phone: (216)696-9000
Cleveland, OH 44115 Dr. Donna Trivison, Dir.
Staff: Prof 2; Other 2. **Subjects:** History of Dyke College and its founders, 1848 to present; business education. **Special Collections:** College archives; letters of Platt Rogers Spencer and his descendants; Spencerian script specimens; photograph collection; original drawings by Penman; neo-Sumerian artifact collection. **Holdings:** 35 cubic feet of archival material; memorabilia. **Services:** Collection open to the public for reference use only on a limited basis and by prior arrangement. **Networks/Consortia:** Member of Cleveland Area Metropolitan Library System (CAMLS). **Remarks:** FAX: (216)696-6430. **Staff:** Milan Milkovic, Asst.Dir., Tech.Serv.

★5079★
Dykema, Gossett - Law Library (Law)
400 Renaissance Ctr., 35th Fl. Phone: (313)568-6716
Detroit, MI 48243 Sylvia Snay, Hd.Libn.
Staff: Prof 4; Other 5. **Subjects:** Law - tax, estate, corporate, securities, labor/employment, environmental, intellectual property; litigation. **Special Collections:** Tax legislative materials. **Holdings:** 50,000 books; 2000 bound periodical volumes; AV programs; 100 audiotapes; 100 videotapes. **Subscriptions:** 500 journals and other serials; 30 newspapers. **Services:** Interlibrary loan; library open to the public at librarian's discretion. **Computerized Information Services:** LEXIS, WESTLAW, DIALOG Information Services, Dow Jones News/Retrieval, VU/TEXT Information Services, Hannah Legislative Service. **Remarks:** FAX: (313)568-6594. **Staff:** Donna Loyd, Acq.Libn.; Karen Mullin, Cat.

Archie R. Dykes Library of the Health Sciences
See: **University of Kansas** (18733)

★5080★
Dylon Industries, Inc. - Library (Sci-Engr)
7700 Clinton Rd.
Cleveland, OH 44144 Phone: (216)651-1300
Founded: 1967. **Subjects:** Lubricants, release agents, cements, graphites, forging lubricants, die casting release agents. **Holdings:** 3000 volumes. **Subscriptions:** 52 journals and other serials. **Services:** Library not open to the public. **Computerized Information Services:** DIALOG Information Services. **Remarks:** FAX: (216)651-1777.

★5081★
Dynamics Research Corporation - Library (Sci-Engr)
60 Frontage Rd. Phone: (508)475-9090
Andover, MA 01810 Sheila Elfman, Libn.
Founded: 1962. **Staff:** Prof 1; Other 1. **Subjects:** Inertial navigation systems, computer programming, guidance and control, human factors. **Holdings:** 5000 books; 8000 documents, pamphlets, periodicals. **Subscriptions:** 100 journals and other serials. **Services:** Interlibrary loan; library not open to the public. **Computerized Information Services:** DIALOG Information Services, OCLC. NERAC. **Networks/Consortia:** Member of NELINET, Inc. **Remarks:** FAX: (508)470-0201.

★5082★
Dynamics Technology - Library (Sci-Engr)
21311 Hawthorne Blvd., Suite 300 Phone: (213)543-5433
Torrance, CA 90503 Seruia Thompson, Libn.
Subjects: Fluid mechanics, physical oceanography, fiber optic sensors, instrumentation simulation, electromagnetics, geophysics, remote sensing, vehicle aerodynamics, hydrodynamics. **Holdings:** 1500 books; 3000 reports. **Subscriptions:** 50 journals and other serials. **Services:** Library not open to the public. **Remarks:** FAX: (213)543-2117.

★5083★
Dynetics, Inc. - Library (Sci-Engr)
PO Drawer B Phone: (205)922-9230
Huntsville, AL 35814-5050 Pedro Prezberry, Res. Data Anl.
Founded: 1974. **Subjects:** Radar, optics, antenna, technology. **Holdings:** 2500 books; 200 bound periodical volumes; 10 reports; 50 microfiche; 50 reels of microfilm. **Remarks:** FAX: (205)922-9260. Library located at 1000 Explorer Blvd., Huntsville, AL.

E

★5084★
E-Systems, Inc. - Division Library (CBN 38) (Sci-Engr)
Box 6056 Phone: (903)457-4320
Greenville, TX 75403-6056 Joleta Moore, Supv.
Founded: 1960. **Staff:** Prof 1; Other 2. **Subjects:** Electronics, mathematics, physics, research and development, airborne equipment. **Holdings:** 5000 books; 1525 periodical volumes; 50,000 military specifications and standards; 2000 Armed Services Technical Information Agency (ASTIA) documents; 2500 technical manuals; 24,000 reports. **Subscriptions:** 300 journals and other serials. **Services:** Interlibrary loan; library not open to the public. **Automated Operations:** Computerized public access catalog, cataloging, and circulation. **Computerized Information Services:** DIALOG Information Services, DTIC. **Remarks:** FAX: (903)457-4413.

★5085★
E-Systems, Inc. - ECI Division - Technical Information Center (Sci-Engr)
1501 72nd St., N.
Box 12248 Phone: (813)381-2000
St. Petersburg, FL 33733-2248 Susan Weiss, Sr.Tech.Libn.
Founded: 1958. **Staff:** 2. **Subjects:** Electronics, communications, electrical engineering, management, computer science. **Holdings:** 6000 books; 1000 bound periodical volumes; 12,000 documents. **Subscriptions:** 250 journals and other serials. **Services:** Interlibrary loan; center not open to the public. **Automated Operations:** Computerized cataloging and circulation. **Computerized Information Services:** DIALOG Information Services, DTIC, Aerospace Online. **Remarks:** FAX: (813)381-2000, ext. 4801.

★5086★
E-Systems, Inc. - Garland Division - Library Information Services (Sci-Engr)
Box 660023 Phone: (214)272-0515
Dallas, TX 75266-0023 Deborah O'Dell, Sr.Tech.Libn.
Founded: 1952. **Staff:** 2. **Subjects:** Electronics, communications, automation, engineering systems, data processing, display systems, optics. **Holdings:** 10,000 books; 725 bound periodical volumes; 10,000 technical reports; 500 microfiche. **Subscriptions:** 300 journals and other serials. **Services:** Interlibrary loan; library not open to the public. **Automated Operations:** Computerized cataloging, serials, and circulation. **Computerized Information Services:** DIALOG Information Services, DTIC.

★5087★
E-Systems, Inc. - Melpar Division - Technical Library (Sci-Engr)
7700 Arlington Blvd. Phone: (703)560-5000
Falls Church, VA 22046 John Suggs, Div.Libn.
Staff: Prof 2. **Subjects:** Electronic engineering, communications. **Holdings:** 300 books; vendor catalogs; military standards and specifications. **Subscriptions:** 150 journals and other serials. **Services:** Interlibrary loan; copying; SDI. **Computerized Information Services:** DIALOG Information Services, DTIC. **Networks/Consortia:** Member of Interlibrary Users Association (IUA). **Remarks:** FAX: (703)280-4627. Telex: 89-9494.

★5088★
EA Engineering, Science, and Technology, Inc. - Library (Env-Cons, Biol Sci)
15 Loveton Circle Phone: (301)771-4950
Sparks, MD 21152 Kathleen E. Cohen, Mgr., Lib.Serv.
Founded: 1973. **Staff:** 1. **Subjects:** Environmental science, health sciences, biology. **Holdings:** 15,000 books; 50 bound periodical volumes; 25,000 other cataloged items. **Subscriptions:** 65 journals and other serials; 5 newspapers. **Services:** Interlibrary loan; copying; library open to the public with approval of librarian. **Computerized Information Services:** DIALOG Information Services, NLM.

★5089★
EAA - Aviation Foundation - Library (Sci-Engr)
EAA Aviation Center
P.O. Box 3065 Phone: (414)426-4848
Oshkosh, WI 54903-3065 Dennis H. Parks, Lib./Archv.Dir.
Founded: 1972. **Staff:** 2. **Subjects:** Aeronautical history, aircraft design, amateur construction, sport aviation. **Special Collections:** Aircraft plans (600 sets); scale aircraft drawings (10,000); aeronautical ephemera. **Holdings:** 7000 books; 3000 bound periodical volumes; technical reports; technical manuals; photographs; historic aviation videotapes. **Subscriptions:** 150 journals and other serials. **Services:** Copying; library open to the public. **Automated Operations:** Computerized cataloging and journal indexing. **Computerized Information Services:** DIALOG Information Services. **Special Catalogs:** Radtke photo archives (online and book). **Special Indexes:** Index to published scale aircraft drawings; index to aircraft articles published in Sport Aviation, 1953-1989 (both online and book). **Remarks:** FAX: (414)426-4828.

Eachdraidh Archives
See: **University College of Cape Breton - Beaton Institute** (18484)

Eagle Publishing Company - Berkshire Eagle
See: **Berkshire Eagle** (1748)

Eagle Ridge Hospital Library - Royal Columbian Hospital
See: **Royal Columbian Hospital** (14116)

★5090★
Eagle-Tribune - Library (Publ)
Box 100 Phone: (508)685-1000
Lawrence, MA 01842 Linda Iannalfo, Lib.Dir.
Staff: Prof 1. **Subjects:** Newspaper reference topics. **Holdings:** 200 books; newspaper on microfilm; 65,000 clipping files. **Services:** Copying; library open to public with permission of librarian; requests in writing are accepted. **Remarks:** Library located at 100 Turnpike St., Lawrence, MA 01845.

★5091★
Eagleville Hospital - Henry S. Louchheim Library (Med)
100 Eagleville Rd. Phone: (215)539-6000
Eagleville, PA 19408 Kathryn Dobbs, Mgr. of Lib.Serv.
Founded: 1971. **Staff:** Prof 1; Other 1. **Subjects:** Alcoholism, drug addiction, psychology, psychiatry, sociology, social work. **Special Collections:** History and philosophy of community living; black history; women; staff publications. **Holdings:** 6000 books; 10 drawers of archival materials and reprints; 750 audiocassettes; 90 videotapes. **Subscriptions:** 116 journals and other serials. **Services:** Interlibrary loan; copying; library open to the public for reference use only with approval of librarian. **Computerized Information Services:** BRS Information Technologies. **Networks/Consortia:** Member of Consortium for Health Information & Library Services (CHI), Delaware Valley Information Consortium (DEVIC). **Publications:** Bibliographies. **Special Indexes:** Indexes to directories, reprints, and staff publications. **Remarks:** FAX: (215)539-5123.

★5092★
EAI Corporation - Library (Mil)
1308 Continental Dr., Suite J Phone: (301)676-1449
Abingdon, MD 21009 Eric I. Salehi, V.P.
Founded: 1980. **Staff:** Prof 1; Other 3. **Subjects:** Chemical biological warfare, chemical agent demilitarization and environmental monitoring, mathematical modeling, emergency management, security systems. **Holdings:** 200 books; 800 technical reports; selected government documents. **Subscriptions:** 10 journals and other serials. **Services:** Library not open to the public. **Computerized Information Services:** DTIC, DIALOG Information Services, CBIAC. **Remarks:** FAX: (301)671-7241.

Amelia Earhart Library
See: **Atchison County Historical Society - Amelia Earhart Library** (1224)

★ 5093 ★
Amelia Earhart Society - Library (Hist)
P.O. Box 182 Phone: (510)947-2865
Bethayers, PA 19006 Barbara Wiley, Res.Coord.
Staff: 5. **Subjects:** Amelia Earhart, Fred Noonan, World War II, pre-World War II military intelligence, aviation. **Holdings:** 121 volumes; 56 documents; 17 microform and nonbook items; 2 manuscripts. **Services:** Interlibrary loan; copying; SDI; library open to the public.

★ 5094 ★
Earlham College - Ernest A. Wildman Science Library (Sci-Engr, Biol Sci)
Box 72 Phone: (317)983-1245
Richmond, IN 47374 Sara Penhale, Sci.Libn.
Founded: 1970. **Staff:** Prof 1; Other 4. **Subjects:** Biology, chemistry, geology, mathematics, physics. **Holdings:** 25,000 books; 13,000 bound periodical volumes; 29,000 microforms; 22,000 government documents; 14,000 maps. **Subscriptions:** 337 journals and other serials. **Services:** Interlibrary loan; copying; library open to the public. **Automated Operations:** Computerized public access catalog and cataloging. **Computerized Information Services:** DIALOG Information Services, STN International; CD-ROM (Silver Patter, WILSONDISC); BITNET (electronic mail service). **Remarks:** Electronic mail address(es): sarap@earlham (BITNET).

★ 5095 ★
Earlham College - Joseph Moore Museum - Hadley Library (Biol Sci)
Box E-68 Phone: (317)983-1303
Richmond, IN 47374 John B. Iverson, Musm.Dir.
Subjects: Ornithology, mammals. **Holdings:** 1000 books; 200 bound periodical volumes. **Services:** Library open to the public with restrictions.

★ 5096 ★
Earlham College - Quaker Collection (Rel-Phil)
Lilly Library Phone: (317)983-1511
Richmond, IN 47374 Thomas Hamm, Archv.
Founded: 1909. **Staff:** Prof 1; Other 1. **Subjects:** Society of Friends (Quakers); Earlham College. **Special Collections:** Indian Affairs; collections of Chas. F. Coffin, Allen Jay, Barnabas C. Hobbs, Thomas E. Jones, David M. Edwards, William C. Dennis, Landrum Bolling, Josiah Parker, Elbert Russell, Marcus Mote, Clifford Crump, Esther Griffin White, Harlow Lindley; Earlham College Historical Collection; Willard Heiss; Homer L. Morris; Eli & Mahalah Jay; Joseph Moore; Indiana Yearly Meeting of Friends. **Holdings:** 12,000 books; 550 bound periodical volumes; 5000 pamphlets, manuscripts, photographs; 60 volumes of printed and bound theses; 250 audiocassettes; 1200 volumes of Quaker genealogy. **Subscriptions:** 70 journals and other serials. **Services:** Interlibrary loan (limited); copying; collection open to the public. **Automated Operations:** Computerized cataloging. **Networks/Consortia:** Member of INCOLSA. **Special Catalogs:** Catalog of archival materials (card). **Remarks:** FAX: (317)983-1304.

★ 5097 ★
Early American Industries Association - Library (Hist)
c/o Eugene Fox
275 Kent Place Blvd. Phone: (908)277-6922
Summit, NJ 07901 Terry A. McNealy, Libn.
Staff: 1. **Subjects:** Early American tools and technology. **Special Collections:** Ephemera Collection; collection on early tools. **Holdings:** 1750 books; 750 catalogs and broadsides; 25 videotapes. **Services:** Copying; library open to the public; members and friends of the association have borrowing privileges. **Remarks:** Library located at Bucks County Historical Society, Pine St., Doylestown, PA 18901.

★ 5098 ★
Early Childhood Family Education - Resource Center (Educ)
Lewiston Elementary School Phone: (507)523-2194
Lewiston, MN 55952 Retha Finger, Parent Fac.
Staff: Prof 2; Other 1. **Subjects:** Parenting, child development, children's literature and activities. **Special Collections:** Toys, records, and puzzles (500). **Holdings:** 580 books. **Services:** Center open to people in the school district. **Remarks:** Part of collection is located in the Altura Elementary School, Altura, MN 55910.

★ 5099 ★
Early Childhood Family Education - Toy Lending Library (Educ)
110 S. Greeley, No. 103 Phone: (612)430-3760
Stillwater, MN 55082-5699 Mary C. Harcey, Coord.
Staff: Prof 1; Other 1. **Subjects:** Infant, preschool, and elementary educational toys and games; children and parenting. **Holdings:** Books; 200 toys. **Services:** Library open to the public. **Special Catalogs:** Toy and book catalog. **Remarks:** Maintained by Stillwater District 834.

★ 5100 ★
Early Sites Research Society - Library (Soc Sci)
Long Hill Phone: (508)948-2410
Rowley, MA 01969 James Whittall, Archeo.Dir.
Founded: 1973. **Subjects:** Archeology, stone work. **Holdings:** 1000 volumes of written materials and AV programs. **Services:** Library not open to the public.

★ 5101 ★
Wyatt Earp Birthplace and Museum - Library (Hist)
1020 E. Detroit Ave. Phone: (309)734-6419
Monmouth, IL 61462 Melba Matson, Cur.
Founded: 1986. **Staff:** 1. **Subjects:** Wyatt Earp. **Holdings:** 28 books; 150 documents; 21 AV programs; 10 manuscripts. **Subscriptions:** 5 journals and other serials. **Services:** Library open to the public on a limited schedule. **Publications:** Wyatt Earp, Native Son.

★ 5102 ★
Earth Ecology Foundation - Library (Env-Cons)
612 N. 2nd St. Phone: (209)442-3034
Fresno, CA 93702 Erik Wunstell, Dir.
Founded: 1980. **Subjects:** Nature, ecology, science, technology, geography. **Special Collections:** Panama Pacific World's Fair and Exposition (construction plans, photos, books, and news clippings; 1915); Fresno State College and University (building plans, construction photos, yearbooks, and letters; 1915-1970); Underground Gardens (designs and history; 1917-1945); American Magazine Covers Collection (1780-1980); National Geographic (magazines, maps, and books; 1945-1990); Science Year Annuals (1965-1990); The Geometric Progression of Space and Time (original scientific paper; 1979); The Unified Field Pattern of Earth's Solar Orbit (original scientific paper; 1990); Earth Ecology Foundation Papers and Letters (1971-1990). **Holdings:** 5000 volumes. **Services:** Library open to the public by appointment.

★ 5103 ★
Earth Island Institute - Library (Env-Cons)
300 Broadway, Suite 28 Phone: (415)788-3666
San Francisco, CA 94133 Petra Loesch
Founded: 1985. **Subjects:** Environment. **Holdings:** 2000 volumes. **Services:** Library open to the public by appointment. **Remarks:** FAX: (415)788-7324.

Earth Resources Observation Systems Data Center
See: **U.S. Geological Survey** (17529)

★ 5104 ★
Earth Spirit Community - Library (Rel-Phil)
Box 365 Phone: (617)395-1023
Medford, MA 02155 Andras Corban Arthen, Dir.
Founded: 1983. **Subjects:** Nature spirituality, alternative lifestyles and communities, natural healing. **Holdings:** 5000 volumes.

★ 5105 ★
Earth Technology Corp. - Library/Information Center
100 W. Broadway, Suite 5000
Long Beach, CA 90802
Defunct.

★5106★
Earthmind - Library (Energy)
Box 743
Mariposa, CA 95338
Founded: 1972. **Staff:** Prof 2. **Subjects:** Alternative energy sources - wind, water, electric power; electric vehicles. **Holdings:** 1000 books. **Subscriptions:** 20 journals and other serials. **Services:** Library open to the public by appointment. **Publications:** Wind & Windspinners; The Homebuilt Wind-Generated Electricity Handbook; Electric Vehicles. **Staff:** Julia May, Pres.; Michael Hacklman, Pres.

★5107★
Earthwatch - Library (Soc Sci)
680 Mt. Auburn St.
Box 403 Phone: (617)926-8200
Watertown, MA 02172 Brian Rosborough, Pres.
Founded: 1971. **Staff:** Prof 45; Other 10. **Subjects:** Archeology, animal behavior, art history, ecology, ornithology, marine science, anthropology. **Special Collections:** Expedition archives. **Holdings:** Figures not available. **Subscriptions:** 100 journals and other serials. **Services:** Library not open to the public. **Computerized Information Services:** DIALOG Information Services. **Staff:** Tina Hass, Libn.

★5108★
Earthworm, Inc. - Recycling Information Center (Env-Cons)
35 Medford St. Phone: (617)628-1844
Somerville, MA 02143 Jeffrey Coyne, Pres.
Founded: 1970. **Staff:** 4. **Subjects:** Recycling, resource recovery, solid waste management, environmental quality, pollution, environmental education, hazardous waste. **Holdings:** 100 volumes; recycling trade journals, newsletters, publications, and manuals; publications from Environmental Protection Agency and environmental and commercial organizations; Earthworm News. **Subscriptions:** 8 journals and other serials. **Services:** Slide shows; center open to the public by appointment. **Publications:** Earthworm Recycling Guide, for sale - to mailing list. **Formerly:** Located in Boston, MA.

East Asian Business and Development Research Archive
See: **University of California, Davis - Institute of Governmental Affairs - Library** (18352)

★5109★
East Bay Genealogical Society - Library (Hist)
405 14th St., Terrace Level Phone: (510)451-9599
Oakland, CA 94612 Lois J. Kline, Libn.
Founded: 1982. **Staff:** Prof 1. **Subjects:** Genealogy. **Special Collections:** East Bay Area Genealogical Societies Newsletters. **Holdings:** 100 books; surname file. **Subscriptions:** 12 newsletters. **Services:** Library open to the public for reference use only. **Publications:** Live Oak (newsletter), monthly - to members.

★5110★
East Brunswick Public Library - Holocaust Studies Collection (Hist)
2 Jean Walling Civic Center Phone: (908)390-6767
East Brunswick, NJ 08816 Sharon Karmazin, Dir.
Subjects: The Holocaust. **Holdings:** 300 monograph titles; 5 videocassettes. **Services:** Interlibrary loan; copying; collection open to the public for reference use only. **Automated Operations:** Computerized acquisitions and circulation. **Special Catalogs:** Catalog of Holocaust Studies Collection (annotated book catalog). **Remarks:** FAX: (201)390-6796. **Staff:** Kathryn O'Rourke, Hd., Adult Serv.; Susan Kheel, Hd., Ref.

★5111★
East Brunswick Public Library - Mystery Classics Collection (Hum)
2 Jean Walling Civic Center Phone: (201)390-6767
East Brunswick, NJ 08816 Sharon Karmazin, Dir.
Subjects: Classic mysteries. **Holdings:** 200 monograph titles. **Services:** Interlibrary loan; copying; collection open to the public for reference use only. **Automated Operations:** Computerized acquisitions and circulation. **Special Catalogs:** Catalog of the Mystery Classics Collection. **Remarks:** FAX: (201)390-6796. **Staff:** Kathryn O'Rourke, Hd., Adult Serv.; Susan Kheel, Hd., Ref.

★5112★
East Carolina University - Health Sciences Library (Med)
Greenville, NC 27854-4354 Phone: (919)551-2212
JoAnn Bell, Ph.D., Dir.
Founded: 1969. **Staff:** Prof 14; Other 24. **Subjects:** Medicine, allied health sciences, social welfare. **Holdings:** 61,659 books; 62,587 bound periodical volumes; 16,682 reels of microfilm; 3795 nonprint materials. **Subscriptions:** 1990 journals and other serials. **Services:** Interlibrary loan; copying; library open to the public. **Automated Operations:** Computerized cataloging and circulation. **Computerized Information Services:** DIALOG Information Services, BRS Information Technologies, NLM, OCLC; OCLC LINK, BITNET (electronic mail services). Performs searches on fee basis. **Networks/Consortia:** Member of SOLINET. **Publications:** New Book & AV Titles, monthly; Library Handbook; Information On-Call, bimonthly. **Special Catalogs:** Nonprint Media Catalog. **Remarks:** Alternate telephone number(s): 551-2222. FAX: (919)551-2224. Electronic mail address(es): HSLBELL@ECSVAX (BITNET).

★5113★
East Carolina University - Joyner Library - Map Collection (Geog-Map)
BO6A Joynck Bldg. Phone: (919)757-6533
Greenville, NC 27858-4353 Ralph L. Scott, Hd., Docs.
Founded: 1963. **Staff:** Prof 3; Other 2. **Subjects:** Maps - topographical (USGS), geologic; charts - nautical, hydrographic, aeronautical. **Special Collections:** Depository for maps from the U.S. Department of Defense Mapping Agency, U.S. Geological Survey, National Ocean Service, Government Printing Office. **Holdings:** 78,000 maps. **Services:** Library open to the public. **Computerized Information Services:** CD-ROM (Marcive: Government Documents); internal database; BITNET (electronic mail service). **Remarks:** FAX: (919)757-6618. Electronic mail address(es): LBSCOTT@ECUVM1 (BITNET); SCOTT@ECSVAX (BITNET). **Staff:** June Parker; Michael Cotter; Katrina Blount.

★5114★
East Carolina University - Joyner Library - Special Collections Department (Hist)
Greenville, NC 27858 Phone: (919)757-6671
Donald R. Lennon, Coord. of Spec.Coll.
Founded: 1966. **Staff:** Prof 4; Other 4. **Subjects:** History - North Carolina, military, missionary, tobacco, East Carolina University, international communism. **Holdings:** 2.25 million manuscripts and archival materials; 19,000 volumes; 250 oral history tapes and transcripts; 100 reels of microfilm; 8500 microfiche. **Subscriptions:** 100 journals and other serials; 60 newspapers. **Services:** Copying; department open to the public. **Publications:** East Carolina Manuscript Collection Bulletins, 1967-1987; Guide to Military History Resources in the East Carolina Manuscript Collection; Guide to Women's History Resources in the East Carolina Manuscript Collection; Guide to Asian Resources in the East Carolina Manuscript Collection. **Special Catalogs:** Registers of Narrative Descriptions. **Remarks:** FAX: (919)757-6618. **Formerly:** Its Archives & Manuscripts Department. **Staff:** Mary Boccaccio, Cur.; Maurice York, N.C. Libn.

★5115★
East Carolina University - Music Library (Mus)
A.J. Fletcher Music Center Phone: (919)757-6250
Greenville, NC 27858 Roberta Chodacki, Asst.Prof./Act.Hd.
Staff: Prof 2; Other 5. **Subjects:** Music. **Holdings:** 27,590 books, scores and bound periodical volumes; 3000 recital and concert tapes; 11,200 sound recordings; 1135 reels of microfilm; 1725 microforms. **Subscriptions:** 292 journals and other serials. **Services:** Interlibrary loan; copying; SDI; library open to the public. **Automated Operations:** Computerized public access catalog, cataloging, and circulation. **Computerized Information Services:** DIALOG Information Services, BRS Information Technologies; internal database; BITNET, EasyLink (electronic mail services). Performs searches on fee basis. **Networks/Consortia:** Member of SOLINET. **Publications:** Full Score (newsletter), bimonthly - local distribution. **Special Indexes:** Song index; BAND-AID (band music discography); index to children's songs (all online). **Remarks:** FAX: (919)757-6618.

★5116★
East Central Legal Services - Library (Law)
1010 W. 8th St., No. 2
Anderson, IN 46016 Phone: (317)644-2816
Founded: 1977. **Staff:** 8. **Subjects:** Law - federal, Indiana, family, administrative, poverty, consumer. **Holdings:** 1516 books; 24 bound periodical volumes. **Services:** Library open to attorneys.

East China Institute of Textile Science and Technology
See: **China Textile University** (3607)

★5117★
East County Jewish Community Center - Samuel & Rebecca Astor Judaica Library (Area-Ethnic)
4079 54th St. Phone: (619)583-3300
San Diego, CA 92105 Mollie S. Harris, Hd.Libn.
Founded: 1960. **Staff:** Prof 1; Other 1. **Subjects:** Judaica. **Special Collections:** Holocaust Collection; special Israel and research sections. **Holdings:** 10,000 volumes, including books in Yiddish, Hebrew, German, and Spanish; Russian books and pamphlets; 24 audio- and videotapes. **Subscriptions:** 32 journals and other serials. **Services:** Interlibrary loan; copying; library open to the public. **Publications:** Annual report; book lists; bibliographies; pamphlets - all free upon request to libraries. **Formerly:** Jewish Community Center.

★5118★
East Dallas Christian Church - Haggard Memorial Library (Rel-Phil)
Box 710329 Phone: (214)824-8185
Dallas, TX 75371-0329 Mrs. Alfred C. Grosse, Lib.Chm.
Founded: 1950. **Staff:** Prof 1; Other 6. **Subjects:** Religion, missions, education, recreation, literature, art, Americana, psychology, science. **Special Collections:** The Christian Church (Disciples of Christ) history, theology, and work in the world. **Holdings:** 15,500 books; 300 filmstrips with scripts and/or records; 5 cassette tapes. **Services:** Library open to community residents for planned activities. **Remarks:** Located at 629 N. Peak St., Dallas, TX 75246.

★5119★
East European Institute, Munich - Library (Hist, Area-Ethnic)
Scheinerstrasse 11 Phone: 89 98 38 21
W-8000 Munich 80, Germany Dr. Otto Boess, Chf.Libn.
Founded: 1952. **Subjects:** History and economy of Russia, Soviet Union, and Poland. **Holdings:** 145,000 volumes. **Subscriptions:** 688 journals and other serials; 38 newspapers. **Services:** Interlibrary loan; copying; library open to the public. **Remarks:** Affiliated with the Foundation for Research on Eastern Europe and the Bavarian State Ministry for Science. **Also Known As:** Osteuropa-Institut Munchen.

★5120★
East Hampton Library - Long Island Collection (Hist)
159 Main St. Phone: (516)324-0222
East Hampton, NY 11937 Dorothy T. King, Libn.
Founded: 1930. **Staff:** Prof 1. **Subjects:** Long Island history, biography, genealogy; Long Island imprints; books by Long Island authors. **Special Collections:** Thomas Moran Biographical Art Collection; memorabilia and other material related to T. Moran (1837-1926), his wife, brothers, son; Herbert F. Seversmith Collection, 1904-1967 (Long Island genealogy; 395 items); Jeannette Edwards Rattray Collection (shipwrecks of Long Island; East Hampton Genealogy). **Holdings:** 3500 books; 300 bound periodical volumes; 90 VF drawers of reports, manuscripts, clippings, pamphlets, documents, maps; 102 reels of microfilm of Long Island newspapers, Whaling Log Books, Suffolk County Federal Census, 1820-1880, 1900. **Subscriptions:** 11 journals and other serials. **Services:** Copying; collection open to the public. **Special Catalogs:** Catalog to Long Island Collection; Thomas Moran Biographical Collection; Herbert F. Seversmith Collection (all on cards and microfilm); East Hampton Star Index (book).

★5121★
East Liberty Presbyterian Church - Library (Rel-Phil)
116 S. Highland Mall Phone: (412)441-3800
Pittsburgh, PA 15206 Sheryn Peters, Libn.
Staff: Prof 1. **Subjects:** Religion and theology. **Holdings:** 1375 volumes. **Subscriptions:** 10 journals and other serials. **Services:** Library open to the public with restrictions.

★5122★
East Market St. Christian Church - Library (Rel-Phil)
864 E. Market St. Phone: (216)923-2326
Akron, OH 44305 Cleo Houchin
Founded: 1988. **Staff:** Prof 1. **Subjects:** Religion, literature, applied science, fine arts, history, philosophy. **Holdings:** 700 books.

★5123★
East Orange General Hospital - Medical Library (Med)
300 Central Ave. Phone: (201)266-8520
East Orange, NJ 07018-2819 Cindy Santamaria, Mgr. of Lib.Serv.
Founded: 1974. **Staff:** Prof 2. **Subjects:** Medicine, mental health, allied health sciences. **Holdings:** 1200 books. **Subscriptions:** 85 journals and other serials. **Services:** Interlibrary loan; copying; SDI; current awareness; LATCH; library open to the public for reference service on request. **Automated Operations:** Computerized ILL (DOCLINE). **Computerized Information Services:** BRS Information Technologies, MEDLARS. **Networks/Consortia:** Member of Cosmopolitan Biomedical Library Consortium (CBLC), Health Sciences Library Association of New Jersey (HSLANJ), BHSL. **Remarks:** FAX: (201)266-8469. **Staff:** Avis Towns, Libn.Asst.

Sarita Kennedy East Law Library
See: **St. Mary's University** (14541)

★5124★
East Stroudsburg University - Kemp Library (Educ)
East Stroudsburg, PA 18301-2999 Phone: (717)424-3465
George V. Summers, Dir. of Lib.
Staff: Prof 12. **Subjects:** Health and physical education, education, history, political science, sociology, biology. **Holdings:** 312,770 books; 57,356 bound periodical volumes; 66,996 government documents; 10,501 microcards; 293,297 microprints; 733,133 microfiche; 34,393 reels of microfilm; ERIC microfiche; early American imprints and early English books in microform. **Subscriptions:** 2200 journals and other serials; 26 newspapers. **Services:** Interlibrary loan; copying; library open to the public for reference use only. **Automated Operations:** Computerized cataloging and circulation (PALS). **Computerized Information Services:** OCLC. **Networks/Consortia:** Member of PALINET, Interlibrary Delivery Service of Pennsylvania (IDS). **Remarks:** FAX: (717)424-3151. **Staff:** Patricia J. Jersey, Ref./ILL Libn.; Leslie Berger, Ref./ILL Libn.; A. Angelini, Hd.Cat.; Paul Graham, Asst.Cat.; Judith M. Feller, Doc.Libn.; John B. Lalley, Hd., Acq.; M. Paul Beaty, Per.Libn.; A. Susan Bromer, Curric.Mtls.Libn.; M. Kay LaVelle, Ref.Libn.; Yun Xia, Sys.Libn.

★5125★
East Tennessee Baptist Hospital - Health Sciences Library (Med)
Box 1788 Phone: (615)632-5618
Knoxville, TN 37901 Mary C. Congleton, Libn.
Founded: 1949. **Staff:** 2.**Subjects:** Nursing, allied health sciences, cardiology, gerontology, oncology. **Holdings:** 2684 books. **Subscriptions:** 189 journals and other serials. **Services:** Interlibrary loan; library open to area professionals only. **Automated Operations:** Computerized cataloging. **Computerized Information Services:** BRS Information Technologies, DIALOG Information Services, OCLC, MEDLINE; DOCLINE (electronic mail service). **Networks/Consortia:** Member of Knoxville Area Health Sciences Library Consortium (KAHSLC), Tennessee Health Science Library Association (THeSLA). **Publications:** Acquisitions list, monthly - to hospital departments, physicians, and area schools. **Special Catalogs:** AV catalog. **Special Indexes:** AV index. **Staff:** Marilyn Harrell, Asst.Libn.

★5126★
East Tennessee Discovery Center - Library (Sci-Engr)
P.O. Box 6204 Phone: (615)637-1121
Knoxville, TN 37914-0204 Mike Arms, Dir.
Founded: 1976. **Staff:** Prof 6; Other 6. **Subjects:** Science, nature, history and culture, technology, arts and crafts. **Special Collections:** Old tools (200); dolls (300); costumes (25); fossils (300); rocks and minerals (5000); Indian artifacts (100); man-made artifacts (20,000); shells (5000); stuffed animals (300); charts (300). **Holdings:** 1200 books; 200 manuscripts; 15,000 slides; 300 pamphlets; 2500 postcards; 10 VF drawers; 32 videotapes; 10 compact discs; 1 laser disc. **Subscriptions:** 30 journals and other serials. **Services:** Library open to the public for reference use only.

★5127★
East Tennessee State University - Archives of Appalachia (Hist)
Sherrod Library Phone: (615)929-4338
Johnson City, TN 37614 Norma Myers, Asst.Dir., Archv. & Spec.Coll.
Staff: Prof 3; Other 2. **Subjects:** Appalachia - history, economic development, material culture, folklore; Tennessee history and educational

institutions. **Special Collections:** Congress for Appalachian Development Collection; Burton-Manning Folklore Collection; Broadside Television, Inc., Collection; Clinchfield Railroad Collection; Magnet Mills Collection; Washington County, Tennessee County Court records; Appalachian Photographic Archives; East Tennessee State University papers; East Tennessee Light and Power Company records (102 linear feet); Appalachian Preaching Mission records (3 linear feet; 377 audiotapes); Elizabethton Star negatives (30,000); Kenneth Murray photographs. **Holdings:** 2800 books; 94 linear feet of vertical files; 3000 linear feet of archival materials and manuscripts; 3200 audiotapes; 1400 videotapes; 315 linear feet of photographs. **Services:** Copying; archives open to the public. **Automated Operations:** Computerized cataloging and subject indexing. **Computerized Information Services:** Archival Computerized Subject Access System (internal database). **Publications:** Archives of Appalachia Newsletter, 3/year - by free subscription; A Guide to Audio and Video Recordings Available from the Archives of Appalachia (volume III, special supplement) - free upon request. **Remarks:** Contains the holdings of the former Coal Employment Project (CEP) - Archives. **Staff:** Dr. Marie Tedesco, Pub.Serv.Archv.; Scott Schwartz, Tech.Serv.Arch.

East Tennessee State University - James H. Quillen College of Medicine - Holston Valley Hospital and Medical Center
See: **Holston Valley Hospital and Medical Center - The Robert D. Doty Health Sciences Library** (7341)

★5128★
East Tennessee State University - Medical Library (Med)
James H. Quillen College of Medicine
Box 70, 693 Phone: (615)929-6252
Johnson City, TN 37614-0693 Janet S. Fisher, Asst. Dean
Founded: 1975. **Staff:** Prof 5; Other 14. **Subjects:** Medicine. **Special Collections:** Hardy Long Collection (history of medicine). **Holdings:** 38,121 books; 35,100 bound periodical volumes; 6885 AV programs; government documents; microforms; vertical files. **Subscriptions:** 816 journals and other serials. **Services:** Interlibrary loan; copying; SDI; library open to the public with restrictions. **Automated Operations:** Computerized cataloging and serials. **Computerized Information Services:** BRS Information Technologies, DIALOG Information Services, NLM, Faxon, OCLC; CD-ROM (MEDLINE); OnTyme Electronic Message Network Service (electronic mail service). **Networks/Consortia:** Member of Tri-Cities Area Health Sciences Libraries Consortium. **Publications:** Actus Medicus, bimonthly; Library Guide, annual - to mailing list. **Remarks:** FAX: (615)461-7025. Electronic mail address(es): ETSU (OnTyme Electronic Message Network Service). **Staff:** Martha Whaley, Hist. of Med.Libn.; Betsy Williams, Asst.Libn.; Patsy Stranberg, Hd., ILL/Circ.; Martha Earl, Ref. Libn.; Kelly Hensley, Media/Microcumpter Serv.Libn.

★5129★
East Texas Baptist University - Mamye Jarrett Learning Center (Educ, Hist)
1209 N. Grove Phone: (903)935-7963
Marshall, TX 75670 Rose Mary Magrill, Dir.
Founded: 1917. **Staff:** Prof 5; Other 1. **Subjects:** Teacher education, Texana. **Special Collections:** Lentz Collection of manuscripts on Harrison County (125); Millard Cope Collection of Texana. **Holdings:** 106,551 books; 15,439 bound periodical volumes, 426 reels of microfilm; 70 microcards; 2138 microfiche. **Subscriptions:** 572 journals and other serials; 9 newspapers. **Services:** Interlibrary loan; copying; center open to graduates, area teachers, ministers, and East Texas history researchers. **Computerized Information Services:** DIALOG Information Services. Performs searches on fee basis. Contact Person: Narine Brooks, Ref.Libn. **Networks/Consortia:** Member of AMIGOS Bibliographic Council, Inc. **Remarks:** FAX: (903)935-3447. **Staff:** Gene Futrell, Curric.Libn.; Dorothy Meadows, Circ.Libn.; Carolyn Peterson, Cat.

★5130★
East Texas Legal Services - Library (Law)
414 E. Pillar Phone: (409)560-1455
Nacogdoches, TX 75961 Lana Caswell Garcia, Law Libn.
Founded: 1979. **Staff:** Prof 1; Other 7. **Subjects:** Law, poverty law. **Holdings:** 25,000 books; 33 bound periodical volumes; 3 VF drawers of poverty files; 232 briefs; 1 filing drawer of forms; 30 tapes. **Subscriptions:** 100 journals and other serials; 25 newspapers. **Services:** Library open to area bar associations and their representatives. **Computerized Information Services:** WESTLAW. **Publications:** ETLS Library Newsletter, monthly - to professional staff of program. **Remarks:** Alternate telephone number(s): (903)893-4401. Branch libraries are located in Beaumont, Huntsville, Longview, Paris, Texarkana, and Tyler.

★5131★
East Texas State University - James Gilliam Gee Library (Educ)
East Texas Sta. Phone: (903)886-5717
Commerce, TX 75429-2951 Mary E. Cook, Dir. of Lib.Serv.
Founded: 1889. **Staff:** Prof 14; Other 23. **Subjects:** Teacher education, liberal arts and sciences, Texas history, business. **Special Collections:** Historical textbooks; early imprints; Texana, especially Texas county histories; collection of pamphlets on printing by Douglas McMurtrie. **Holdings:** 521,618 books; 142,611 bound periodical volumes; 360,687 U.S. Government documents; 109,589 books in microform; 300,302 ERIC microfiche; 19,054 VF materials. **Subscriptions:** 2111 journals and other serials; 41 newspapers. **Services:** Interlibrary loan; copying; library open to the public. **Automated Operations:** Computerized cataloging, acquisitions, and circulation. **Computerized Information Services:** DIALOG Information Services, DataTimes, WILSONLINE, BRS Information Technologies, OCLC; CD-ROM (ERIC, PsycLIT); Info Track. Performs searches on fee basis. Contact Person: Diane Downing, Hd., Ref.Dept., 886-5719. **Networks/Consortia:** Member of AMIGOS Bibliographic Council, Inc., Association for Higher Education of North Texas (AHE). **Publications:** Ex Libris, monthly - select mailing list. **Special Catalogs:** Shelf list (magnetic tape, printout) - available on request. **Remarks:** FAX: (903)886-5723. **Staff:** Donald R. Kerr, Assoc.Dir.; Scott Downing, ILL Libn.

★5132★
East Texas State University - Oral History Program (Hist)
James Gilliam Gee Library
East Texas Sta. Phone: (903)886-5737
Commerce, TX 75429-2953 Dr. James Conrad, Coord. of Oral Hist.
Founded: 1968. **Staff:** Prof 1; Other 1. **Subjects:** History of East Texas - railroad, cotton, blacks, medicine; Texas social work; institutional history. **Special Collections:** Senator A.M. Aikin, Jr. project; Fletcher Warren project; Southwest Dairy project; Dallas Mayors project; Cooper Lake Project; Caddo Lake project. **Holdings:** 301 volumes; 890 cassette tapes of interviews. **Subscriptions:** 3 journals and other serials. **Services:** Copying; program open to the public with restrictions. **Automated Operations:** Computerized cataloging. **Special Catalogs:** Oral history catalog. **Remarks:** FAX: (903)886-5039.

★5133★
East-West Center - Institute of Culture and Communication - CCPC - Resource Materials Collection (Soc Sci)
John A. Burns Hall, Rm. 4063 Phone: (808)944-7345
Honolulu, HI 96848 Sumiye Konoshima, Res.Info.Spec.
Staff: Prof 3; Other 3. **Subjects:** Sociocultural and economic effects of communication and information technologies; development of mass media and its role in international relations; communication and socioeconomic development; cultural change; social relations in multicultural context; cross-cultural contact and interpersonal relations; international relations and economics; development of Asian and Pacific countries. **Holdings:** 16,000 books; 12,000 documents, reports, reprints, conference papers, project descriptions; 1500 AV programs; country/agency files; vertical files. **Subscriptions:** 580 journals and other serials and newsletters; 7 newspapers. **Services:** Interlibrary loan; copying; SDI; collection open to the public with restrictions. **Computerized Information Services:** DIALOG Information Services; internal database. **Publications:** Bibliographies. **Remarks:** CCPC is the abbreviation for the Communication Institute, Culture Learning Institute , Pacific Islands Development Program, and Center-Wide Programs. FAX: (808)944-7670. **Staff:** Polly Chan, Jr. RMC Spec.; Victoria Rumenapp, Jr. RMC Spec.

★5134★
East-West Center - Resource Materials Collection (Soc Sci)
JAB 2005
East-West Rd. Phone: (808)944-7451
Honolulu, HI 96848 Phyllis Tabusa, Res.Info.Spec.
Founded: 1969. **Staff:** Prof 3; Other 2. **Subjects:** Demography and population studies; environmental policy; mineral and energy resources; economic development policy; geographic focus on Asia and the Pacific. **Special Collections:** Census and government publications of Asian and Pacific countries. **Holdings:** 24,000 books; 14,000 reprints/papers; 180 reels of microfilm; 6 tapes; maps. **Subscriptions:** 500 journals and other serials; 10 newspapers. **Services:** Interlibrary loan; copying; current awareness; collection open to the public. **Automated Operations:** Computerized public access catalog, cataloging, and circulation. **Computerized Information Services:** DIALOG Information Services, OCLC; BITNET (electronic mail

service). **Publications:** Accession List, 5-6/year. **Special Catalogs:** Online catalog. **Remarks:** FAX: (808)944-7490. Telex: 230 989171. Electronic mail address(es): TABUSAP@EWC (BITNET). **Formerly:** Its EAPI PI RSI Research Materials Collection. **Staff:** Jerilyn Sumida, Jr. RMC Spec.; Terese Leber, Jr. RMC Spec.

★5135★
East-West Gateway Coordinating Council - Reference Area (Plan)
911 Washington Ave. Phone: (314)421-4220
St. Louis, MO 63101 Katherine Mack, Info.Serv.Coord.
Founded: 1966. **Staff:** Prof 1. **Subjects:** Transportation, regional comprehensive planning, environmental planning, solid waste, regional census data, housing. **Holdings:** 5000 books; 8 VF drawers of pamphlets; regional maps. **Subscriptions:** 200 journals and other serials. **Services:** Interlibrary loan; copying; library open to the public by appointment. **Special Indexes:** Index of agency-produced publications. **Remarks:** FAX: (314)231-6120.

★5136★
East York Board of Education - Professional Library (Educ)
840 Coxwell Ave. Phone: (416)396-2000
Toronto, ON, Canada M4C 2V3 Martha Pluscauskas, Coord.
Founded: 1973. **Staff:** Prof 1. **Subjects:** Education. **Holdings:** 8000 books. **Subscriptions:** 252 journals and other serials. **Services:** Interlibrary loan; copying; library open to employees of the Board of Education, residents of East York, and student teachers.

★5137★
Eastchester Historical Society - Angelo H. Bianchi Library (Hist)
Box 37 Phone: (914)793-1900
Eastchester, NY 10709 Madeline D. Schaeffer, Libn.
Staff: Prof 1. **Subjects:** Juvenile literature, 1795-1905; local and general history. **Special Collections:** Juvenile textbooks, 1790-1900; transcribed records of the town of Eastchester, 1664-1870 (10 volumes); records of St. Paul's National Shrine of the Bill of Rights, Eastchester (3 volumes). **Holdings:** 8000 books; manuscripts; diaries; maps. **Subscriptions:** 25 journals and other serials. **Services:** Copying; library open to the public with restrictions.

★5138★
EASTCONN - Resource Library (Educ)
376 Hartford Tpke. Phone: (203)455-0707
North Windham, CT 06256 Linda Welchman, Dir.
Staff: Prof 1; Other 1. **Subjects:** Elementary and secondary education. **Special Collections:** Nonprint curriculum support materials; curriculum development and teacher support materials. **Holdings:** 500 videotapes; 1000 software programs; 50 print and nonprint materials on nutrition. **Services:** Library not open to the public. **Publications:** EASTCONN Newsletter, quarterly - to member schools and other interested persons. **Special Catalogs:** Software and videotape catalogs. **Remarks:** Library offers a delivery system to member schools. **Remarks:** FAX: (203)455-0691.

★5139★
Easter Seal Ability Council - Library (Med)
11010-101 St., No. 216 Phone: (403)429-0137
Edmonton, AB, Canada T5H 4B8 Gwen Sanderson, Lib.Techn.
Founded: 1986. **Staff:** 1. **Subjects:** Barrier-free design, disabilities, aids and devices for the disabled, attitudes and awareness. **Holdings:** 800 books. **Subscriptions:** 20 journals and other serials. **Services:** Interlibrary loan; copying; library open to the public. **Automated Operations:** Columbia Automated Library System. **Remarks:** FAX: (403)426-3352.

★5140★
Easter Seal Rehabilitation Center of Southwestern Connecticut - Francis M. Harrison Memorial Library (Med)
26 Palmer's Hill Rd. Phone: (203)325-1544
Stamford, CT 06902 Deborah Menchek, V.P.
Founded: 1961. **Staff:** 1. **Subjects:** Rehabilitation. **Holdings:** 500 books; 240 bound periodical volumes; 6 VF drawers of pamphlets and brochures; 3 shelves of reports and catalogs. **Subscriptions:** 18 journals and other serials. **Services:** Interlibrary loan; library open to the public for reference and research by appointment.

★5141★
The Easter Seal Society - Resource Centre (Med)
200-250 Ferrand Dr., Suite 200 Phone: (416)421-8377
Don Mills, ON, Canada M3C 3P2 Georgina Westdyk, Volunteer Serv.Coord.
Founded: 1983. **Staff:** Prof 1; Other 1. **Subjects:** Physical disabilities; housing, transportation, education, and special services for the disabled. **Holdings:** 1000 books; 30 other cataloged items. **Subscriptions:** 41 journals and other serials. **Services:** Copying; center open to the public for reference use only. **Publications:** List of publications - available on request. **Remarks:** FAX: (416)696-1035.

★5142★
Eastern Baptist Theological Seminary - Library (Rel-Phil)
6 Lancaster Ave. Phone: (215)645-9318
Wynnewood, PA 19096 Dr. William J. Hand, Act.Dir.
Founded: 1925. **Staff:** Prof 2; Other 2. **Subjects:** Theology and allied subjects. **Special Collections:** Russell H. MacBride Collection of Philosophy, Religion and Classical Literature (3750 volumes); J. Pius Barbor Collection in Black Church Studies (1157 volumes); Hispanic Studies Collection (2361 volumes). **Holdings:** 111,247 books; 11,385 bound periodical volumes. **Subscriptions:** 399 journals and other serials. **Services:** Interlibrary loan; copying; library open to graduate students and ministers. **Automated Operations:** Computerized cataloging and acquisitions. **Computerized Information Services:** OCLC. **Networks/Consortia:** Member of PALINET, Southeastern Pennsylvania Theological Library Association (SEPTLA). **Remarks:** FAX: (215)649-3834. **Formerly:** Located in Philadelphia, PA. **Staff:** Rev. R. David Koch, Assoc.Libn./Tech.Serv.

★5143★
Eastern Christian College - Library (Rel-Phil)
2410 Creswell Rd.
Box 629 Phone: (301)879-9300
Bel Air, MD 21014 Vera J. Benson, Lib.Supv.
Staff: 3. **Subjects:** Religion. **Holdings:** 15,111 books; 75 bound periodical volumes; 8 drawers of Christian Church/Churches of Christ agency materials. **Subscriptions:** 177 journals and other serials. **Services:** Interlibrary loan; library open to the public.

★5144★
Eastern Connecticut State University - Center for Connecticut Studies (Hist)
J. Eugene Smith Library Phone: (203)456-5443
Willimantic, CT 06226 B. Tucker, Dir.
Founded: 1970. **Staff:** Prof 1; Other 1. **Subjects:** Connecticut - education, politics, religion, economic development, town history, folklore. **Special Collections:** Depository Windham Town Records and Archives, 1700-1980; New London Day, 1881-1920; Hartford Courant, 1837-1923, 1933-1946; Missionary Society of Connecticut Papers, 1759-1948. **Holdings:** 2618 books; 62 bound periodical volumes; 300 folders; 339 volumes of town annual reports; 96 folders of Connecticut dissertations and theses. **Subscriptions:** 40 journals and other serials. **Services:** Interlibrary loan; copying; center open to the public. **Publications:** Connecticut History.

★5145★
Eastern Idaho Regional Medical Center - Health Sciences Library (Med)
Box 2077 Phone: (208)529-6077
Idaho Falls, ID 83403-2077 Coleen C. Winward, Med.Libn.
Founded: 1971. **Staff:** Prof 1. **Subjects:** Clinical medicine, nursing, hospital administration. **Special Collections:** Historical medicine and nursing. **Holdings:** 500 books; 100 videotapes. **Subscriptions:** 200 journals and other serials; 5 newspapers. **Services:** Interlibrary loan; copying; library open to the public with restrictions (fee may be required). **Computerized Information Services:** MEDLARS; DOCLINE, OnTyme Electronic Message Network Service (electronic mail services). Performs limited searches on a fee basis. **Networks/Consortia:** Member of Southeast Idaho Health Information Consortium, National Network of Libraries of Medicine - Pacific Northwest Region, Idaho Health Information Association. **Publications:** CITATION, 2/year. **Remarks:** FAX: (208)529-7099. Electronic mail address(es): EIRMC (DOCLINE); CLASS.EIRMC (OnTyme Electronic Message Network Service).

Eastern Illinois University - Horizons
See: **Horizons (The Illinois Career Information System)** (7410)

Eastern Instructional Support Center
See: **Pennsylvania Resources and Information Center for Special Education** (12853)

★5146★
Eastern Kentucky University - John Grant Crabbe Library - Government Documents (Info Sci)
Richmond, KY 40475 Phone: (606)622-1791
Sharon Marsh, Libn.
Founded: 1967. **Staff:** 7. **Subjects:** Federal, state, and international government publications. **Special Collections:** Transportation Research Board (2000 titles); Gulfcoast Research Laboratory, Mississippi (500 titles). **Holdings:** 169,567 books; 15,750 bound periodical volumes; 919,195 nonbook items. **Subscriptions:** 1000 journals and other serials. **Services:** Interlibrary loan; copying; SDI; open to the public. **Computerized Information Services:** ERIC; BITNET (electronic mail service). Performs searches on fee basis. **Publications:** Subject bibliographies. **Remarks:** Provides subject analyses of selected periodical journal articles. FAX: (606)622-1174. Electronic mail address(es): libmarsh@eku (BITNET). **Staff:** Vickey Baggott.

★5147★
Eastern Kentucky University - John Grant Crabbe Library - John Wilson Townsend Room (Hist)
Richmond, KY 40475 Phone: (606)622-1792
Jerry Parrish Dimitrov, Libn.
Founded: 1930. **Staff:** Prof 1; Other 1. **Subjects:** Kentucky and Kentuckians, genealogy. **Special Collections:** Kentucky collection of autographed first editions by Kentuckians or about Kentucky. **Holdings:** 20,969 books; 409 bound periodical volumes; 120 linear feet of manuscripts; 16 VF drawers of clippings; 314 reels of microfilm; 2767 sheets of microprint; 7859 microfiche. **Subscriptions:** 16 journals and other serials. **Computerized Information Services:** Richmond Cemetery records (internal database). **Special Indexes:** Indexes and finding guides to manuscript collections. **Remarks:** FAX: (606)622-1174.

★5148★
Eastern Kentucky University - John Grant Crabbe Library - Learning Resources Center (Educ)
Richmond, KY 40475 Phone: (606)622-1794
Marilee Gabbard, Libn.
Subjects: Learning and teaching materials for kindergarten through 12th grade. **Special Collections:** Curriculum guides (3179); textbooks (6177); professional books (8242). **Holdings:** 28,558 books; 50,539 AV items. **Services:** Copying; center open to the public with restrictions. **Publications:** Subject bibliographies; new book lists. **Remarks:** FAX: (606)622-1415. **Staff:** Joyce Creek.

★5149★
Eastern Kentucky University - Law Enforcement Library (Law)
Stratton Bldg. Phone: (606)622-1798
Richmond, KY 40475 Verna Casey, Libn.
Founded: 1975. **Staff:** Prof 1; Other 1. **Subjects:** Law enforcement, fire science, security, loss prevention, traffic safety, criminal law, correctional services, police administration, criminal justice. **Holdings:** 21,457 volumes; 218 theses; 14,372 microfiche; 170 reels of microfilm; 190 videotapes. **Subscriptions:** 155 journals and other serials. **Services:** Interlibrary loan; copying; library open to the public with restrictions. **Automated Operations:** Computerized cataloging. **Computerized Information Services:** OCLC; WESTLAW. **Networks/Consortia:** Member of SOLINET, Kentucky Library Network, Inc. (KLN). **Remarks:** FAX: (606)622-1174.

★5150★
Eastern Kentucky University - Music Library (Mus)
Foster Music Bldg. Phone: (606)622-1795
Richmond, KY 40475 Elizabeth K. Baker, Libn.
Founded: 1969. **Staff:** Prof 1; Other 2. **Subjects:** Music, music history, music theory, music therapy, drama. **Holdings:** 20,962 books; 754 bound periodical volumes; 8151 recordings; 867 tapes; 112 videocassettes; 1414 reels of microfilm; 3014 microfiche; 400 compact discs. **Subscriptions:** 163 journals and other serials. **Services:** Interlibrary loan. **Computerized Information Services:** OCLC. **Networks/Consortia:** Member of SOLINET, Kentucky Library Network, Inc. (KLN). **Remarks:** FAX: (606)622-1174.

★5151★
Eastern Kentucky University - University Archives (Hist)
Cammack Bldg., Rm. 26 Phone: (606)622-2820
Richmond, KY 40475 Charles C. Hay, III, Dir.
Founded: 1976. **Staff:** Prof 1; Other 1. **Subjects:** History - university, local, leisure and athletics in Kentucky; environmental and conservation movements in Kentucky. **Special Collections:** Governor Keen Johnson papers (30 cubic feet); Rodes Shackelford papers (10 cubic feet); Lilly Family papers (15 cubic feet); Hanger Family papers (5 cubic feet); William L. Wallace papers (15 cubic feet); Kentucky High School Athletic Association papers and films (80 cubic feet); Central University of Kentucky records (6 cubic feet); Association for Intercollegiate Athletics for Women (AIAW), Southern Region II Collection (13 cubic feet); Kentucky Parks & Recreation Society records (6 cubic feet); Kentucky Industrial Education Association records (9 cubic feet); Sierra Club records (1 cubic foot); Richmond Chamber of Commerce (8 cubic feet); Pre-1920 Richmond and Madison County newspaper collection (20 cubic feet); OVC athletic records (15 cubic feet); Fort Boonesborough State Park Association records (3 cubic feet); League of Women Voters of Richmond (5.5 cubic feet); American Correctional Association prison photograph collection (2 cubic feet); Kentucky State Poetry Society records (4 cubic feet); Crooke Family Papers (earliest land surveys of Madison County; 3 cubic feet); Robert F. Collins papers (12 cubic feet); EKU institutional records (1000 cubic feet); personal papers of EKU faculty and alumni (50 cubic feet); Oral History Project Tapes: Kentucky Power Structure (500 tapes); Kentucky Coal Camps (170 tapes); Congressman Carl Perkins Project (70 tapes); Kentucky Prison System (65 tapes); Depression Era (200 tapes); Kentucky River (125 tapes); Governor Bert Combs Project (75 tapes). **Holdings:** 900 cubic feet of archival materials; 2350 cassettes and tapes; 50 films and videotapes. **Services:** Copying; AV production facilities; archives open to the public with restrictions on the use of some collections. **Publications:** Informational literature; finding guides - both to state agencies and appropriate organizations. **Special Indexes:** Index to the collections; index to EKU Board of Regents minutes; index to Faculty Senate minutes; index to the Eastern Progress (student newspaper). **Remarks:** FAX: (606)622-1020.

★5152★
Eastern Maine Medical Center - Parrot Health Sciences Library (Med)
489 State St. Phone: (207)945-8228
Bangor, ME 04401 Suellen Jagels, Lib.Dir.
Staff: Prof 4; Other 4. **Subjects:** Medicine, surgery, obstetrics, gynecology, pediatrics, orthopedics, neurology. **Special Collections:** Nursing Education Collection; Alcohol Abuse Collection. **Holdings:** 7500 book titles; 11,065 bound periodical volumes; 8 VF drawers of archival material. **Subscriptions:** 500 journals and other serials. **Services:** Interlibrary loan; copying; library open to the public with fee for services. **Automated Operations:** Computerized ILL (DOCLINE). **Computerized Information Services:** MEDLARS, BRS Information Technologies, DIALOG Information Services; DIALMAIL (electronic mail service). Performs searches on fee basis. **Networks/Consortia:** Member of Health Science Library and Information Cooperative of Maine (HSLIC), BHSL. **Remarks:** FAX: (207)945-8233 - for emergency only. **Staff:** Wendy Troiano, Asst.Libn.; Coleen Coble, Asst.Libn.; Beverly Hayes, Asst.Libn.

★5153★
Eastern Maine Vocational Technical Institute - Library (Educ)
354 Hogan Rd. Phone: (207)941-4600
Bangor, ME 04401 Karen Reilly, Libn.
Staff: Prof 1; Other 1. **Subjects:** Building construction, electrical power, machine tool technology, automotive technology, business management, medical laboratory technology, electronics, foods, medical radiography, nursing, welding, refrigeration and air conditioning, developmental studies, continuing education. **Special Collections:** American Welding Society depository (128 volumes). **Holdings:** 9500 books; 105 bound periodical volumes. **Subscriptions:** 175 journals and other serials; 10 newspapers. **Services:** Interlibrary loan; copying; SDI; library open to the public. **Computerized Information Services:** CD-ROM (MaineCat). **Networks/Consortia:** Member of Health Science Library and Information Cooperative of Maine (HSLIC). **Remarks:** FAX: (207)941-4608.

★5154★
Eastern Mennonite College and Seminary - Menno Simons Historical Library and Archives (Hist, Rel-Phil)
Harrisonburg, VA 22801-2462 Phone: (703)432-4178
Lois B. Bowman, Assoc.Dir.
Founded: 1943. **Staff:** Prof 1; Other 1. **Subjects:** Anabaptist and Mennonite history, German culture in Eastern United States, history of the Shenandoah

Valley, genealogy. **Holdings:** 19,607 volumes; 272 reels of microfilm; 216 microfiche; 780 reels of magnetic tape; 811 linear feet of manuscript and archival material; 63 VF drawers and 45 linear feet of general files. **Subscriptions:** 390 journals and other serials; 22 newspapers. **Services:** Interlibrary loan; copying (both limited); library open to the public for reference use only. **Automated Operations:** Computerized cataloging. **Networks/Consortia:** Member of SOLINET. **Publications:** Historical Library Bulletin, irregular. **Remarks:** FAX: (703)432-4444. **Staff:** Harold E. Huber, Asst.

★5155★
Eastern Michigan University - Archives/Special Collections (Hist)
University Library Phone: (313)487-3423
Ypsilanti, MI 48197 Carolyn Kirkendall, Archv.Libn.
Staff: Prof 1; Other 1. **Subjects:** History of Eastern Michigan University. **Holdings:** 3952 linear feet and 190 VF drawers of university publications, photographs, correspondence, papers, ephemera; 175 linear feet record albums. **Subscriptions:** 8 journals and other serials; 2 newspapers. **Services:** Archives open to the public on a limited schedule. **Networks/Consortia:** Member of Michigan Library Consortium (MLC). **Remarks:** FAX: (313)487-8861.

★5156★
Eastern Michigan University - Government Documents Collection - University Library (Info Sci)
Ypsilanti, MI 48197 Phone: (313)487-2280
Clare Beck, Govt.Doc.Libn.
Founded: 1966. **Staff:** Prof 1; Other 1. **Subjects:** U.S. Government and population, economics, education, health, social conditions. **Holdings:** 188,000 U.S. Government publications (selective depository). **Services:** Interlibrary loan; copying; collection open to the public. **Computerized Information Services:** InterNet (electronic mail service). **Remarks:** FAX: (313)487-8861. Electronic mail address(es): LIB–BECK@EMUNIX.EMICH.EDU (InterNet).

★5157★
Eastern Michigan University - Instructional Materials Center (Educ)
University Library Phone: (313)487-0490
Ypsilanti, MI 48197 Carolyn Kirkendall, Libn.
Staff: Prof 1; Other 1. **Subjects:** Kindergarten-secondary school instructional materials for examination and use by students in education. **Holdings:** 50,000 pamphlets, posters, media kits, games, pictures, curriculum guides, textbooks. **Services:** Center open to the public for reference use only. **Networks/Consortia:** Member of Michigan Library Consortium (MLC). **Remarks:** FAX: (313)487-8861.

★5158★
Eastern Michigan University - LOEX National Library Instruction Clearinghouse (Info Sci)
Library, Rm. 217 D Phone: (313)487-0168
Ypsilanti, MI 48197 Linda Shirato, Dir.
Founded: 1972. **Staff:** Prof 1; Other 1. **Subjects:** Library instruction. **Special Collections:** NOTIS user instruction materials **Holdings:** 37,000 sample instruction materials; videotapes; CAI software. **Services:** Interlibrary loan (to members); copying; clearinghouse open to the public by appointment. **Computerized Information Services:** National Bibliographic Instruction Database; Speakers Database (internal databases). **Publications:** LOEX News (newsletter), quarterly - by subscription. **Remarks:** FAX: (313)487-8861.

★5159★
Eastern Michigan University - Map Library (Geog-Map)
University Library Phone: (313)487-3191
Ypsilanti, MI 48197 Joanne Hansen, Sci. & Tech.Libn.
Staff: Prof 1; Other 1. **Special Collections:** Michigan wetlands; Defense Mapping Agency (D.M.A.) depository; U.S. Geological Survey; Great Lakes charts. **Holdings:** 46,000 maps; atlases; 18,000 tourist and road maps; gazetteers. **Services:** Copying; library open to the public. **Networks/Consortia:** Member of Michigan Library Consortium (MLC). **Special Indexes:** Subject Index to Geographic Notes. **Remarks:** FAX: (313)487-8861.

★5160★
Eastern Montana College - Library - Special Collections (Hist)
1500 N. 30th St. Phone: (406)657-2262
Billings, MT 59101-0298 Jane Howell, Dir., Lib.Serv.
Special Collections: Custer Collection (formerly held at Custer Battlefield National Monument; 100 volumes; 71 boxes); Dora C. White Memorial Collection (local correspondence and works, Billings and Yellowstone County; 3100 volumes; 700 pictures and photographs); federal and Montana documents (154,365). **Services:** Interlibrary loan; copying; collections open to the public. **Automated Operations:** Computerized cataloging, acquisitions, and serials. **Computerized Information Services:** BRS Information Technologies. **Networks/Consortia:** Member of Western Library Network (WLN).

★5161★
Eastern Nebraska Genealogical Society - Library (Hist)
Box 541 Phone: (402)721-9553
Fremont, NE 68025-0541 Claire Mares, Ed.
Founded: 1971. **Subjects:** Local history, genealogy. **Special Collections:** Czech newspaper abstracts and translations, 1911-1918; Ship Passenger List to Baltimore, 1874; Colfax County Marriages, 1869-1879; Omaha Mortuary Death List, 1891-1893. **Holdings:** 500 books; genealogies and pedigree sheets. **Subscriptions:** 100 journals and other serials. **Services:** Library open to the public by appointment. **Publications:** List of publications and indexes available upon request.

★5162★
Eastern New Mexico University - Film Library (Aud-Vis)
Portales, NM 88130 Phone: (505)562-2602
Wanda Graham, Dir.
Staff: Prof 2; Other 10. **Subjects:** General collection. **Holdings:** 4000 16mm films; 1000 video cassettes. **Services:** Library open to the public. **Special Catalogs:** Catalog of films and video cassettes.

★5163★
Eastern New Mexico University - Golden Library - Special Collections (Hum, Hist)
Portales, NM 88130 Phone: (505)562-2636
C. Edwin Dowlin, Lib.Dir.
Founded: 1968. **Staff:** Prof 2; Other 9. **Subjects:** Science fiction; Roosevelt County, New Mexico; southwest history; historical services. **Special Collections:** Jack Williamson Science Fiction Library (10,989 volumes; 447 science fiction oral history tapes; 152 cubic feet of archival materials; 727 periodical titles); Southwest and Local History Library, includes Roosevelt County, New Mexico history (556 cubic feet of papers; 719 oral histories; 5818 photographs); University Archives (950 cubic feet); Senator Harold Runnels papers (256 cubic feet); Lyric Theatre and Dance Collection (281 books; 87 bound periodical volumes; 56 phonograph records; 54 boxes of listed items). **Subscriptions:** 7 journals and other serials. **Services:** Interlibrary loan; copying; collections open to the public with restrictions. **Networks/Consortia:** Member of AMIGOS Bibliographic Council, Inc. **Publications:** Registers of the uncataloged papers. **Remarks:** FAX: (505)562-2647. **Staff:** Mary J. Walker, Hist.Serv.Libn.

★5164★
Eastern Oregon Psychiatric Center - Medical Library (Med)
2600 Westgate Phone: (503)276-0810
Pendleton, OR 97801 Cathy Britain, Libn.
Founded: 1919. **Staff:** Prof 1. **Subjects:** Mental health, allied health sciences. **Holdings:** 1700 volumes. **Subscriptions:** 10 journals and other serials. **Services:** Interlibrary loan; library open to the public with restrictions. **Remarks:** FAX: (503)276-1147.

Eastern Pennsylvania Psychiatric Institute
See: **Medical College of Pennsylvania** (9998)

★5165★
Eastern Shore Hospital Center - Professional Library (Med)
Box 800 Phone: (301)228-0800
Cambridge, MD 21613 Estella C. Clendaniel, Supv., Lib. & Files
Founded: 1953. **Staff:** 1. **Subjects:** Psychiatry, medicine, nursing. **Holdings:** 2669 books; 361 bound periodical volumes; 4 VF drawers of pamphlets. **Subscriptions:** 39 journals and other serials. **Services:** Interlibrary loan; copying; library open to the public with restrictions. **Computerized Information Services:** MEDLARS. **Networks/Consortia:** Member of Maryland Association of Health Science Librarians (MAHSL). **Remarks:** Maintained by Maryland State Department of Health & Mental Hygiene.

★5166★
Eastern State Hospital - Library Services - Staff Library (Med)
4601 Ironbound Rd.
P.O. Box 8791 Phone: (804)253-5457
Williamsburg, VA 23187-3701 R. Blanton McLean, Lib.Dir.
Founded: 1841. **Staff:** Prof 1; Other 1. **Subjects:** Psychiatry, psychology, medicine, nursing. **Special Collections:** Galt Papers, 19th century (1850 items). **Holdings:** 2000 books; 825 bound periodical volumes; 1310 AV programs. **Subscriptions:** 114 journals. **Services:** Interlibrary loan; copying; library open to the public for reference use only. **Automated Operations:** Computerized ILL (DOCLINE). **Computerized Information Services:** DIALOG Information Services, OCLC; CD-ROM (MEDLINE). **Special Catalogs:** AV holdings catalog. **Remarks:** FAX: (804)253-7078.

★5167★
Eastern State Hospital - Resource Library (Med)
627 W. 4th St. Phone: (606)355-1431
Lexington, KY 40508-9990 Sonja Zaumeyer, Dir. of Staff Dev.
Staff: Prof 1. **Subjects:** Psychiatry, psychology, mental illness, nurnsing. **Holdings:** 1050 volumes. **Subscriptions:** 20 journals and other serials. **Services:** Interlibrary loan; library not open to the public.

Eastern State Hospital Library
See: **Washington State Library** (20036)

★5168★
Eastern State School and Hospital - Staff Library (Med)
3740 Old Lincoln Hwy. Phone: (215)953-6122
Trevose, PA 19053-4992 Gretchen E. Clark, Libn.
Founded: 1963. **Staff:** Prof 1; Other 1. **Subjects:** Child psychiatry, nursing, psychology, social services, special education. **Holdings:** 3344 volumes; 59 dissertations; 292 pamphlets. **Subscriptions:** 69 journals and other serials. **Services:** Interlibrary loan; copying; library open to the public for reference use only. **Remarks:** FAX: (215)953-6144.

★5169★
Eastern Technical Associates - Library (Env-Cons)
Box 58495 Phone: (919)834-2970
Raleigh, NC 27658 Glenna Clark
Subjects: Air emissions, opacity measurement of stationary sources. **Holdings:** 900 reports and government publications.

★5170★
Eastern Virginia Medical School - Moorman Memorial Library (Med)
700 W. Olney Rd.
Box 1980 Phone: (804)446-5845
Norfolk, VA 23501 Anne O. Cramer, Dir./Asst. Dean
Founded: 1972. **Staff:** Prof 7; Other 13.75. **Subjects:** Medicine, allied health sciences, behavioral sciences. **Holdings:** 18,787 books; 42,010 bound periodical volumes; 3557 microforms; 1909 media titles; 7331 unbound periodical volumes. **Subscriptions:** 1156 journals and other serials. **Services:** Interlibrary loan; copying; SDI; library open to the public. **Automated Operations:** Computerized public access catalog, cataloging, acquisitions, serials, and circulation. **Computerized Information Services:** BRS Information Technologies, MEDLARS, miniMEDLINE, WILSONLINE, DIALOG Information Services; CD-ROM (MEDLINE); BITNET, DOCLINE, MAILMAN (electronic mail services). Performs searches on fee basis. **Networks/Consortia:** Member of SOLINET, National Network of Libraries of Medicine - Southeastern/Atlantic Region, Virginia Tidewater Consortium for Higher Education. **Publications:** Inform (newsletter), quarterly. **Remarks:** Alternate telephone number(s): 446-5848 (ILL), 446-5840 (ADM.). Electronic mail address(es): 23501A (DOCLINE); HARRIS@EVMSVMS (BITNET). **Staff:** Richard J. Harris, Sys.Coord.; Kerrie S. Shaw, Pub.Serv.Coord.; Ethel Pollock, Lrng.Rsrcs.Coord.; Renee Mansheim, Tech.Serv.Coord.; JoLinda Shaw, Ref.Libn.; Margaret Demchuk, Ref.Libn.

★5171★
Eastern Washington State Historical Society - Research Library and Special Collections (Hist)
Cheney Cowles Museum
W. 2316 1st Ave. Phone: (509)456-3931
Spokane, WA 99204 Glenn Mason, Dir.
Founded: 1916. **Staff:** Prof 2. **Subjects:** History of Eastern Washington, Spokane, the Inland Empire; Inland Empire mining; Eastern Washington social, agricultural, women's history; Spokane business history; Native American plateau cultures. **Special Collections:** Spokane Flour Mill, 1892-1947 (88 linear feet); Expo '74 (280 linear feet); Spokane Chamber of Commerce, 1898-1975 (62 linear feet); Inland Empire mining history manuscripts, 1880-1980 (200 linear feet); photographs, 1878 to present (150,000); Cutter Architectural Collection (300 sets of plans, 1888-1923); Libby Photo Collection (60,000 images of Spokane, 1900-1960); 450 manuscript collections relating to eastern Washington and northern Idaho. **Holdings:** 7000 books; 100,000 historical photographs; 140 bound periodical volumes; 2100 linear feet of manuscripts; 45 VF drawers of newspaper clippings; 750 oral history tapes; 35 videotapes; 3 music tapes; 9 reels of microfilm; 12 drawers of maps. **Subscriptions:** 18 journals and other serials. **Services:** Copying (limited); library open to the public by appointment. **Publications:** Libby's Spokane: A visual retrospect (1980); A Guide to the Cutter Collection (architecture); Frank Palmer Scenic Photographs (1987); A Night of Terror, Devastation, and Awful Woe: The Spokane Fire of 1889 (1989). **Special Catalogs:** Catalogue of Manuscript Collections (1987). **Special Indexes:** Pacific Northwesterner Index, 1957-1966 (volumes 1-20).

★5172★
Eastern Washington University - Geography Department - Map Library (Geog-Map)
Cheney, WA 99004 Phone: (509)359-2477
David S. Anderson, Cart.
Founded: 1910. **Staff:** 1. **Subjects:** Maps - U.S., world, regional. **Holdings:** 100,000 maps. **Services:** Library open to the public.

★5173★
Eastern Washington University - Instructional Media Center
Cheney, WA 99004
Defunct.

★5174★
Eastern Washington University - Library - Archives and Special Collections (Hist, Art)
MS 84 Phone: (509)359-2475
Cheney, WA 99004 V. Louise Saylor, Dean of Libs.
Founded: 1915. **Staff:** Prof 2; Other 2. **Subjects:** Pacific Northwest history, science fiction, county and municipal records, religious architecture. **Special Collections:** C.S. Kingston Pacific Northwest Collection (23,700 volumes); A.T. Perry Science Fiction Collection (3100 volumes); Ye Galleon Press Collection (18 linear feet); Harold C. Whitehouse Collection of Ecclesiastical Architecture (27 linear feet); Herman J. Deutsch Pacific Northwest Pamphlet and Clipping Collection (140 cubic feet); University Archives (1600 cubic feet). **Holdings:** 26,800 books; 1300 bound periodical volumes. **Subscriptions:** 100 journals and other serials; 30 newspapers. **Services:** Interlibrary loan; copying; collections open to the public. **Computerized Information Services:** DIALOG Information Services, OCLC, WILSONLINE, MEDLINE; CD-ROM (ERIC, PsychLIT, USDOCS, ABI-Inform, PAIS, EPIC). Performs searches on fee basis. Contact Person: Lee Alkire, 359-2263. **Special Indexes:** Spokesman Review Newspaper Index (1988 to present). **Remarks:** FAX: (509)359-6456. **Staff:** Jay Weston Rea, Univ.Archv.; Chas. V. Mutschler, Asst.Archv.

★5175★
Eastern Washington University - Music Library (Mus)
Music Bldg., Mail Stop 100 Phone: (509)359-2501
Cheney, WA 99004 Karen Schatz, Libn.
Founded: 1950. **Staff:** Prof 1; Other 4. **Subjects:** Music. **Holdings:** 8500 phonograph records; 9000 scores; 242 boxes of music on microfilm; 200 compact discs. **Services:** Interlibrary loan; library open to the public.

Eastern Washington University - Spokane Medical Library
See: **Spokane Medical Library** (15591)

Eastman Arbitration Library
See: **American Arbitration Association** (474)

Eastman Chemical Company
See: **Eastman Kodak Company - Eastman Chemical Company** (5180)

★5176★
Eastman Dental Center - Basil G. Bibby Library (Med)
625 Elmwood Ave. Phone: (716)275-5010
Rochester, NY 14620 June Glaser, Libn.
Staff: Prof 1; Other 1. **Subjects:** Dentistry. **Holdings:** 3150 books; 5600 bound periodical volumes. **Subscriptions:** 150 journals and other serials. **Services:** Interlibrary loan; SDI; library open to health professionals by appointment. **Computerized Information Services:** MEDLARS; CD-ROM. **Networks/Consortia:** Member of Rochester Regional Library Council (RRLC). **Publications:** EDC Library Gazette, quarterly. **Remarks:** FAX: (716)244-8705.

George Eastman House
See: **International Museum of Photography at George Eastman House** (8158)

★5177★
Eastman Kodak Company - Building 69 Library (Sci-Engr)
B69, Fl. 1, Kodak Phone: (716)722-2356
Rochester, NY 14650-1917 Ray Curtin, Libn.
Founded: 1948. **Staff:** Prof 1; Other 1. **Subjects:** Electronic imagery; human factors; photography; engineering - chemical, electrical, mechanical. **Holdings:** 3500 books. **Subscriptions:** 347 journals and other serials. **Services:** Interlibrary loan; copying; SDI; library open to the public by appointment. **Automated Operations:** Computerized public access catalog, serials, and circulation. **Computerized Information Services:** DIALOG Information Services, NEXIS, PFDS Online, ORBIT Search Service; KDOC (internal database). **Networks/Consortia:** Member of Rochester Regional Library Council (RRLC). **Remarks:** FAX: (716)477-8161. Contains the holdings of the former Eastman Kodak Company - InfoSource Engineering.

★5178★
Eastman Kodak Company - Business Information Center (Bus-Fin)
343 State St. Phone: (716)724-3041
Rochester, NY 14650 M. Lois Gauch, Dir.
Founded: 1919. **Staff:** Prof 1; Other 3. **Subjects:** General business, photography. **Special Collections:** Company archives. **Holdings:** 7000 books. **Subscriptions:** 300 journals and other serials; 6 newspapers. **Services:** Interlibrary loan; center not open to the public. **Automated Operations:** Computerized cataloging and journal circulation. **Computerized Information Services:** Online systems. **Networks/Consortia:** Member of Rochester Regional Library Council (RRLC). **Publications:** What's New List, monthly - for internal distribution only. **Remarks:** FAX: (716)724-0663.

★5179★
Eastman Kodak Company - Colorado Division - Engineering and Information Services Library (Sci-Engr)
Weld County Rd. 66 Phone: (303)686-4383
Windsor, CO 80551 George Reed, Supv.
Founded: 1970. **Staff:** 1. **Subjects:** Engineering, construction. **Holdings:** 750 books. **Subscriptions:** 40 journals and other serials. **Services:** Library not open to the public.

Eastman Kodak Company - Datatape Incorporated
See: **Datatape Incorporated** (4627)

★5180★
Eastman Kodak Company - Eastman Chemical Company - Technical Information Center (Sci-Engr)
P.O. Box 1972
Bldg. 150B Phone: (615)229-2530
Kingsport, TN 37662-5150 Gerald S. Cassell, Mgr.
Staff: Prof 9; Other 22. **Services:** Library open to the public with permission. **Automated Operations:** Computerized cataloging, acquisitions, circulation (Faxon) and JLL. **Computerized Information Services:** OCLC; access to 500 online databases from 20 vendors. **Remarks:** The Technical Information Center is the overall entity which supervises, and is comprised of, the individual libraries listed below. Alternate telephone number(s): 229-6110. FAX: (615)229-4558. Telex: 671 5569. **Staff:** Michael W. Ubaldini, Asst.Mgr.

★5181★
Eastman Kodak Company - Eastman Chemical Company - Technical Information Center - Business Library (Bus-Fin)
P.O. Box 431
Bldg. 280 Phone: (615)229-6117
Kingsport, TN 37662-5280 M. Gail Preslar, Libn.
Founded: 1947. **Staff:** 2. **Subjects:** Business management, industrial relations, marketing, economics. **Holdings:** 2500 books; telephone directories on microfiche; state industrial directories; company annual reports. **Subscriptions:** 300 journals and other serials. **Services:** Interlibrary loan; SDI; library open to the public with prior approval. **Automated Operations:** Computerized cataloging, acquisitions, circulation, and ILL. **Computerized Information Services:** OCLC, access to 20 database vendors. **Remarks:** Alternate telephone number(s): 229-2071. FAX: (615)229-2145. Telex: 671 5569.

★5182★
Eastman Kodak Company - Eastman Chemical Company - Technical Information Center - Engineering Library (Sci-Engr)
P.O. Box 511
Bldg. 54D Phone: (615)229-2237
Kingsport, TN 37662-5054 Jean D. Coffman, Libn.
Founded: 1961. **Staff:** 2. **Subjects:** All engineering disciplines with emphasis on chemical engineering. **Holdings:** 3000 books; 100,000 vendor catalogs on microfilm; industry standards. **Subscriptions:** 200 journals and other serials. **Services:** Interlibrary loan; SDI; library open to the public with prior approval. **Automated Operations:** Computerized cataloging, acquisitions, serials, circulation, and ILL. **Computerized Information Services:** OCLC, access to 20 database vendors. **Remarks:** Alternate telephone number(s): 229-2972. FAX: (615)229-6099.

★5183★
Eastman Kodak Company - Eastman Chemical Company - Technical Information Center - Medical Library (Sci-Engr)
Bldg. 215, Box 1975 Phone: (615)229-6097
Kingsport, TN 37662-5215 Lillian L. Lewis, Libn.
Founded: 1959. **Subjects:** Industrial medicine, industrial hygiene, employee assistance programs. **Special Collections:** Index Medicus. **Holdings:** 2000 books. **Subscriptions:** 90 journals and other serials. **Services:** Interlibrary loan; SDI; library open to the public with prior approval. **Automated Operations:** Computerized cataloging, acquisitions, serials, circulation, and ILL. **Computerized Information Services:** OCLC and access to 20 database vendors. **Remarks:** Alternate telephone number(s): 229-6109. FAX: (615)229-4558. Telex: 671 5569.

★5184★
Eastman Kodak Company - Eastman Chemical Company - Technical Information Center - Product Safety Library (Sci-Engr)
P.O. Box 511
Bldg. 54D Phone: (615)229-6109
Kingsport, TN 37662-5054 Lillian L. Lewis, Libn.
Founded: 1984. **Subjects:** Product safety, product toxicology, environmental control. **Holdings:** 900 books; Federal Register on microfilm. **Subscriptions:** 40 journals and other serials. **Services:** Interlibrary loan; SDI; library open to the public with prior approval. **Automated Operations:** Computerized cataloging, acquisitions, serials, circulation, and ILL. **Computerized Information Services:** OCLC, access to 20 database vendors. **Remarks:** Alternate telephone number(s): (615)229-3648. FAX: (615)229-4558. Telex: 671 5569.

★5185★
Eastman Kodak Company - Eastman Chemical Company - Technical Information Center - Research Library (Sci-Engr)
P.O. Box 1972
Bldg. 150B Phone: (615)229-6111
Kingsport, TN 37662-5150 Mary F. Fanslow, Libn.
Founded: 1944. **Staff:** 4. **Subjects:** Organic chemistry; polymer science; pharmaceutical chemistry; agricultural chemistry; fiber, textile, and plastics technology. **Holdings:** 15,500 books; 3 million U.S. and foreign patents; 85,000 vendor catalogs on microfilm; Beilstein; Chemical Abstracts; government reports. **Subscriptions:** 1050 journals and other serials. **Services:** Interlibrary loan; copying; center open to the public for reference use with approval. **Automated Operations:** Computerized cataloging, acquisitions, serials, circulation, and ILL. **Computerized Information Services:** OCLC, access to 20 database vendors. **Remarks:** FAX: (615)229-4558. Telex: 671 5569.

★5186★
Eastman Kodak Company - Eastman Chemical Company - Texas Eastman Division - Research & Development Library (Sci-Engr)
Box 7444 Phone: (903)237-6117
Longview, TX 75607 Donna Kesterson, Libn.
Founded: 1952. **Staff:** Prof 1. **Subjects:** Chemistry, chemical engineering, business. **Holdings:** 15,000 books; U.S. chemical patents, August 1966 to present, on microfilm. **Subscriptions:** 200 journals and other serials. **Services:** Interlibrary loan; library open to the public with restrictions. **Formerly:** Eastman Kodak Company - Texas Eastman Company.

★5187★
Eastman Kodak Company - InfoSource - Corporate Health, Safety, and Environment Library (Med)
Kodak Park, Bldg. 320 Phone: (716)588-3619
Rochester, NY 14652-3615 Richard Bartl, Libn., InfoSource CHSE Lib.
Founded: 1952. **Staff:** 1. **Subjects:** Toxicology, occupational medicine, environmental sciences, biosciences, ergonomics. **Holdings:** 5000 books and government publications; 5000 bound periodical volumes. **Subscriptions:** 300 journals and other serials. **Automated Operations:** Computerized cataloging. **Networks/Consortia:** Member of Rochester Regional Library Council (RRLC). **Remarks:** FAX: (716)588-9705. **Staff:** Mary Hedges.

★5188★
Eastman Kodak Company - InfoSource KAD - Library 35213 (Rel-Phil)
Rochester, NY 14653 Phone: (716)726-3418
Ray Curtin, Site Mgr.
Founded: 1944. **Staff:** Prof 2; Other 1. **Subjects:** Engineering, electronics, materials, mathematics, metallurgy, applied optics, plastics, aerospace. **Special Collections:** Institute of Electrical and Electronic Engineers (IEEE) publications. **Holdings:** 17,000 books. **Subscriptions:** 600 journals and other serials. **Services:** Interlibrary loan; library not open to the public. **Automated Operations:** Computerized cataloging, acquisitions, serials, and circulation. **Computerized Information Services:** DIALOG Information Services, OCLC, ORBIT Search Service. **Networks/Consortia:** Member of Rochester Regional Library Council (RRLC). **Remarks:** FAX: (716)726-7307. **Staff:** Kathryn A Starr.

★5189★
Eastman Kodak Company - InfoSource Kodak Park Library (Sci-Engr, Comp Sci)
Kodak Park, Bldg. 56, 4th Fl.
Mail Code: 23302 Phone: (716)477-5943
Rochester, NY 14652 Janet R. Prentice, Site Mgr.
Staff: Prof 1; Other 2. **Subjects:** Computer science, statistics, industrial engineering, behavioral science, management, consulting. **Holdings:** 5000 books. **Subscriptions:** 300 journals and other serials; 5 newspapers. **Services:** Interlibrary loan; library not open to the public. **Automated Operations:** Computerized cataloging, acquisitions, serials, and circulation. **Computerized Information Services:** DIALOG Information Services, BRS Information Technologies, NEXIS, Dow Jones News/Retrieval, Dun & Bradstreet Business Credit Services, OCLC. **Networks/Consortia:** Member of Rochester Regional Library Council (RRLC), Monroe County Library System (MCLS).

Eastman Kodak Company - L & F Products
See: **L & F Products** (8843)

★5190★
Eastman Kodak Company - Research Library (Sci-Engr, Art)
02224 2-83-RL Phone: (716)722-2723
Rochester, NY 14650 Richard Bartl, Lib.Mgr.
Founded: 1912. **Staff:** Prof 3; Other 5. **Subjects:** Photography, chemistry, physics, electronics, biotechnology. **Special Collections:** Old photographic books and journals. **Holdings:** 30,000 books; 10,000 bound periodical volumes; 12,000 volumes on microfilm; 11,000 translations. **Subscriptions:** 1300 journals and other serials. **Services:** Interlibrary loan; copying; library open to the public by appointment. **Automated Operations:** Computerized cataloging, acquisitions, serials, and ILL. **Computerized Information Services:** DIALOG Information Services, OCLC, PFDS Online, BRS Information Technologies, NEXIS, Chemical Abstracts Service (CAS); internal database. **Networks/Consortia:** Member of Rochester Regional Library Council (RRLC). **Remarks:** FAX: (716)477-1909. **Staff:** Jeffrey Yu, Ref.Libn.

Eastman Kodak Company - Sterling Drug, Inc.
See: **Sterling Drug, Inc.** (15778)

Eastman Memorial Foundation - Lauren Rogers Museum of Art
See: **Lauren Rogers Museum of Art** (14032)

Eastman School of Music
See: **University of Rochester - Eastman School of Music** (19279)

★5191★
Eastminster Presbyterian Church - Library (Rel-Phil)
106 N. Riverside Dr. Phone: (407)723-8371
Indialantic, FL 32903 Gratia Richman, Libn.
Staff: 4. **Subjects:** Religion. **Holdings:** 2750 volumes. **Services:** Library open to the public.

★5192★
Eastmoreland General Hospital - Health Sciences Library (Med)
2900 S.E. Steele St. Phone: (503)234-0411
Portland, OR 97202 Dolores Judkins, Libn.
Subjects: Osteopathic medicine, medicine, nursing. **Holdings:** 489 books; 510 cassette tapes; 17 slide/tape kits. **Subscriptions:** 50 journals and other serials. **Services:** Interlibrary loan; copying; SDI; library open to the public with librarian's permission. **Computerized Information Services:** MEDLINE, NLM; OnTyme Electronic Message Network Service (electronic mail service). **Networks/Consortia:** Member of Oregon Health Information Online (ORHION), Portland Area Health Sciences Librarians.

★5193★
Easton Hospital - Medical Library (Med)
250 S. 21st St. Phone: (215)250-4130
Easton, PA 18042 Kristine Keifer, Libn.
Staff: Prof 1; Other 1. **Subjects:** Internal medicine, surgery, obstetrics, pediatrics, geriatrics, physical therapy. **Holdings:** 1000 books; 5500 bound periodical volumes. **Subscriptions:** 230 journals and other serials. **Services:** Interlibrary loan; copying; library open to the public. **Computerized Information Services:** MEDLINE, BRS Information Technologies; Knowledge Finder (internal database). **Networks/Consortia:** Member of BHSL, Cooperating Hospital Libraries of the Lehigh Valley Area. **Remarks:** FAX: (215)250-4905.

★5194★
Eaton Corporation - Corporate Research & Development Library (Sci-Engr)
Box 766 Phone: (313)354-6979
Southfield, MI 48037 Cheryl E. Pfeifer, Res.Libn.
Founded: 1963. **Staff:** Prof 1.5; Other 1. **Subjects:** Automotive and mechanical engineering, metallurgy. **Holdings:** 4200 books; 1700 bound periodical volumes; 75 VF drawers of internal reports, federal government reports, clippings, and translations. **Subscriptions:** 320 journals and other serials. **Services:** Interlibrary loan (limited); copying; SDI; library open by referral. **Computerized Information Services:** DIALOG Information Services, OCLC, PFDS Online, WILSONLINE, BRS Information Technologies, RLIN, PRS Corporate Information Services; internal database. **Networks/Consortia:** Member of Michigan Library Consortium (MLC). **Publications:** 30 Minutes a Day (listing of acquisitions), monthly - for internal distribution only; INFO-ALERT, corporate news bulletin, weekly - to management. **Remarks:** Library located at 26201 Northwestern Hwy., Southfield, MI 48076. FAX: (313)354-2739. **Staff:** Freda Bowling, Libn.

Eaton Corporation - Information Management Systems Division
See: **Contel Federal Systems Inc.** (4249)

★5195★
Eaton Corporation - Milwaukee Technical Library (Sci-Engr)
4201 N. 27th St. Phone: (414)449-6886
Milwaukee, WI 53216 Cynthia Berndt, Res.Libn.
Founded: 1960. **Staff:** Prof 1; Other 1. **Subjects:** Control systems; engineering- electrical, electronic, mechanical; management. **Holdings:** 3500 books. **Subscriptions:** 300 serials. **Services:** Interlibrary loan; SDI; library open to the public with restrictions. **Automated Operations:** Computerized public access catalog and cataloging. **Computerized Information Services:** DIALOG Information Services. **Networks/Consortia:** Member of Library Council of Metropolitan Milwaukee, Inc. (LCOMM). **Publications:** Eaton Enquirer, monthly. **Special Catalogs:** IHS. **Remarks:** FAX: (414)449-6221.

★5196★
Ebara Seisakujo - Shiryoshitsu (Sci-Engr)
11-1 Haneda
Asahicho, Ota-ku Phone: 3 37436278
Tokyo 144, Japan Mr. Nobuhiro Harasawa
Founded: 1964. **Staff:** Prof 2; Other 1. **Subjects:** Hydraulic engineering. **Holdings:** 25,000 books. **Subscriptions:** 500 journals and other serials; 15 newspapers. **Services:** Library not open to the public. **Computerized Information Services:** DIALOG Information Services. Contact Person: Mr. Akira Kurosu, Asst.Mgr. **Remarks:** FAX: 3 37453356. Telex: EBARATYO J22988.

★5197★
Ebasco Services, Inc. - Corporate Library (Sci-Engr)
2 World Trade Center, 92nd Fl. Phone: (212)839-2021
New York, NY 10048 Gloria Aks, Supv., Libs.
Staff: Prof 3; Other 5. **Subjects:** Engineering, construction, energy, environment, hazardous waste management, business. **Holdings:** 12,500 volumes; industry standards and vendor catalogs on microfilm. **Subscriptions:** 400 journals and other serials. **Services:** Interlibrary loan; library open to SLA members only. **Automated Operations:** Computerized cataloging, circulation, and serials. **Computerized Information Services:** DIALOG Information Services, VU/TEXT Information Services, NewsNet, Inc., Dun & Bradstreet Business Credit Services, NEXIS, Integrated Technical Information System (ITIS); internal database; CD-ROMs (DIALOG OnDisc, COMPENDEX PLUS, NTIS OnDisc, Selected Water Resources Abstracts). Performs searches on fee basis. **Publications:** Newsletter/Acquisitions List - for internal distribution only. **Special Catalogs:** Periodicals catalog. **Remarks:** FAX: (212)839-3551. **Staff:** Amy Van Brunt, Ref.; Noreen Coleman, Ref.

★5198★
Friedrich Ebert Foundation - Library (Bus-Fin, Hist)
Godesberger Allee 149 Phone: 228 8830
W-5300 Bonn 2, Germany Horst Ziska, Chf.Libn.
Founded: 1969. **Staff:** Prof 34. **Subjects:** German and international labor history, social history, political party and trade union publications. **Holdings:** 300,000 books; 70,000 bound periodical volumes. **Subscriptions:** 3000 journals and other serials; 250 newspapers. **Services:** Interlibrary loan; copying; library open to the public. **Publications:** Bibliographie zur Geschichte der deutschen Arbeiterbewegung, annual. **Remarks:** FAX: 228 883530. **Formerly:** Research Institute of the Friedrich Ebert Foundation - Library of Social Democracy. **Also Known As:** Bibliothek der Friedrich-Ebert-Stiftung.

★5199★
Friedrich Ebert Stiftung - Karl Marx Haus Studienzentrum - Bibliothek und Dokumentation (Soc Sci)
Johannisstr 28 Phone: 651 43011
W-5500 Treves, Germany K.L. Konig
Founded: 1968. **Subjects:** Writings and works of Marx and Engels; history - socialism, Marxism, communism, revolutionary socialist working men's movement; social and economic history of the 19th century. **Special Collections:** Adams Collection. **Holdings:** 50,000 books; 170 bound periodical volumes; archives; microfiche; microfilm. **Subscriptions:** 100 journals and other serials. **Services:** Interlibrary loan; copying; library open to the public.

Hope Fox Eccles Clinical Library
See: **University of Utah - Spencer S. Eccles Health Sciences Library** (19477)

Spencer S. Eccles Health Sciences Library
See: **University of Utah - Spencer S. Eccles Health Sciences Library** (19477)

Ecclesiastical Province of British Columbia & Diocese of New Westminster
See: **Anglican Church of Canada - Ecclesiastical Province of British Columbia & Diocese of New Westminster** (870)

Elchanan Echikson Memorial Library
See: **Temple Sharey Tefilo-Israel** (16123)

John M. Echols Collection on Southeast Asia
See: **Cornell University - John M. Echols Collection on Southeast Asia** (4315)

★5200★
Eckenfelder Inc. - Library (Sci-Engr)
227 French Landing Dr. Phone: (615)255-2288
Nashville, TN 37228 Ted M. Bugg, Libn.
Staff: 1. **Subjects:** Waste water treatment, solid and hazardous waste management, hydrogeology, risk assessment. **Holdings:** 1600 books and government documents; 1000 in-house technical reports. **Subscriptions:** 30 journals and other serials. **Services:** Interlibrary loan; library not open to the public. **Computerized Information Services:** DIALOG Information Services, IRIS, QSAR, TOXNET, STORET. **Remarks:** FAX: (615)256-8332.

★5201★
Eckert, Seamans, Cherin & Mellott - Library (Law)
600 Grant St., 42nd Fl. Phone: (412)566-5922
Pittsburgh, PA 15219 Martha MacKelvey, Lib.Dir.
Staff: 3. **Subjects:** Law. **Holdings:** 20,000 books. **Services:** Library not open to the public. **Automated Operations:** INMAGIC. **Computerized Information Services:** DIALOG Information Services, Information America, LEXIS, WESTLAW; internal database. **Staff:** Joanne Mast.

Eckfeldt Memorial Medical Library
See: **Monadnock Community Hospital** (10599)

Eckman Medical Library
See: **Beth Israel Hospital North** (1770)

★5202★
Eco-Inventors & Eco-Entrepeneurs Chapter - Renewable Energy Information Center (Energy)
3201 Corte Malpaso
Unit 304 Phone: (805)484-9786
Camarillo, CA 93012 Alan A. Tratner, Dir.
Founded: 1978. **Staff:** Prof 3. **Subjects:** Renewable energy and geothermal energy research and development. **Special Collections:** Renewable Energy News Digest (complete set); Geothermal World Directory, 1972-1986. **Holdings:** 500 volumes; Geothermal Energy Monthly Journal, 1973-1986, on microfiche; maps; slides. **Subscriptions:** 10 journals and other serials. **Services:** Copying; accepts mail requests for information. **Computerized Information Services:** Internal database. **Special Indexes:** Geothermal Energy, cumulative index; Geothermal World Directory index.

★5203★
Ecolab, Inc. - Corporate Information Center (Sci-Engr)
840 Sibley Memorial Hwy. Phone: (612)451-5651
St. Paul, MN 55118 Dona M. Sontag Bradt, Mgr.
Founded: 1947. **Staff:** Prof 2; Other 2. **Subjects:** Surfactant and organic chemistry, cleaning technologies, dairy and food technology, environmental affairs. **Holdings:** 10,000 books; 900 bound periodical volumes; 10,000 reports, patents, standards; vendor catalogs on microfilm. **Subscriptions:** 628 journals and other serials. **Services:** Interlibrary loan; copying; SDI; center open to professionals in allied fields. **Automated Operations:** Computerized cataloging, serials, and circulation. **Computerized Information Services:** DIALOG Information Services, PFDS Online, STN International. **Remarks:** FAX: (612)451-2574. **Staff:** Nancy A. Fenton, Assoc.Libn.; Ann W. Specktor, Asst.Libn.

★5204★
Ecole Francaise d'Athenes - Bibliotheque (Hist)
Odos Didotou 6 Phone: 1 3612518
GR-106 80 Athens, Greece Marie Dominique Nenna
Founded: 1846. **Staff:** Prof 8. **Subjects:** Greek and Roman archeology, ancient history, philology. **Holdings:** 80,000 books; 500 reels of microfilm. **Subscriptions:** 540 journals and other serials. **Services:** Copying; library open to the public. **Computerized Information Services:** BiblioFile, ISIS; CCO-CNRS (internal database). **Remarks:** FAX: 1 3632101.

★5205★
Ecole des Hautes Etudes Commerciales de Montreal - Bibliotheque Patrick Allen (Bus-Fin)
5255 Decelles Ave. Phone: (514)340-6220
Montreal, PQ, Canada H3T 1V6 Maurice Lemelin, Dir.
Founded: 1910. **Staff:** Prof 10; Other 32. **Subjects:** Human management, finance, marketing, advertising, production management, accounting, auditing, business economics, quantitative methods, operation research, human organization, industrial relations. **Holdings:** 180,000 books; 115,000 bound periodical volumes; 3000 reels of microfilm. **Subscriptions:** 7222 journals and other serials. **Services:** Interlibrary loan; copying; library open to the public with restrictions on borrowing. **Automated Operations:** Computerized cataloging and circulation. **Computerized Information Services:** DIALOG Information Services, PFDS Online; internal database. **Publications:** New Acquisitions, monthly. **Special Catalogs:** Catalog of periodicals (online). **Remarks:** Affiliated with Universite de Montreal. FAX: (514)340-5639. **Staff:** Louise Goulet, Chf., Cat.; Gerald Boudreau, Asst.Dir./Chf., Ref.Dept.; Francine Celleir, Chf., Acq.Dept.

Ecole Nationale d'Aerotechnique
See: **College Edouard Montpetit - Ecole Nationale d'Aerotechnique** (3890)

★5206★
Ecole Nationale de Genie Rural, des Eaux et des Forets (ENGREF) - Centre de Documentation (Agri, Env-Cons)
19 av du Maine
F-75732 Paris Cedex 15, France Phone: 1 4549880
Founded: 1972. **Subjects:** Environment, economics, agriculture, hydrology. **Holdings:** 30,000 books; 50 bound periodical volumes; 2000 archival materials; 9000 microfiche. **Subscriptions:** 200 journals and other serials; 10 newspapers. **Services:** Interlibrary loan; library open to the public. **Computerized Information Services:** ESA/IRS. **Publications:** Bulletin bibliographique (biannually). **Remarks:** FAX: 1 45498827. Telex: 1 45498888.

★5207★
Ecole Nationale Superieure Agronomique de Rennes (ENSAR) - Bibliotheque Centrale (Agri)
65 rue de Saint Brieuc Phone: 99 287571
F-35042 Rennes Cedex, France Marie-Jeanne Rougelot, Bibliothecaire
Founded: 1830. **Staff:** Prof 2. **Subjects:** Agronomy, environment. **Special Collections:** Old books on agronomy and sciences. **Holdings:** 30,000 books. **Subscriptions:** 400 journals and other serials. **Automated Operations:** Computerized cataloging. **Remarks:** FAX: 99287510.

Ecole Polytechnique Federale de Lausanne
See: **Swiss Federal Institute of Technology, Lausanne** (15937)

★5208★
Ecole Polytechnique Federale de Lausanne - Departement de Mathematiques - Bibliotheque (Sci-Engr)
MA Ecublens Phone: 21 6932534
CH-1015 Lausanne, Switzerland Mrs. M. Gervaix
Founded: 1970. **Staff:** 1.5. **Subjects:** Mathematics. **Holdings:** 21,500 books; 8000 bound periodical volumes. **Subscriptions:** 308 journals and other serials. **Services:** Library open to the public. **Remarks:** FAX: 21 6934303.

★5209★
Ecole Polytechnique de Montreal - Bibliotheque (Sci-Engr)
C.P. 6079, Succursale A Phone: (514)340-4847
Montreal, PQ, Canada H3C 3A7 Olivier Paradis, Dir.
Founded: 1873. **Staff:** Prof 11; Other 30. **Subjects:** Engineering. **Special Collections:** Technical standards, industrial catalogs. **Holdings:** 168,000 books; 120,000 bound periodical volumes; 16,200 maps. **Subscriptions:** 2776 journals and other serials. **Services:** Interlibrary loan; copying; SDI; library open to the public with restrictions. **Automated Operations:** Computerized public access catalog, cataloging, acquisitions, serials, and circulation. **Computerized Information Services:** STN International, WILSONLINE, CAN/OLE, ORBIT Search Service, DIALOG Information Services, Questel, MINISIS; Envoy 100, BITNET (electronic mail services). Performs searches on fee basis. Contact Person: Marie-Helene Dupuis, Fee-Based Serv., 340-4213. **Publications:** Infotech, irregular; list of acquisitions, monthly. **Remarks:** FAX: (514)340-4026. Electronic mail address(es): QMEP.B.DIR (Envoy 100); i000@POLYTEC1 (BITNET). Affiliated with Universite de Montreal. **Staff:** Claire Pelletier, Tech.Serv.; Louise Thibaudeau, Doc. Access Serv.; Minh-Thu Nguyen, Automated Serv.; Nicole Lemyre, Info. Access Serv.

★5210★
Ecological Institute, Civil Association - Library (Biol Sci)
Km. 2.5 Carretera Antigua a Coatepec
Apartado Postal No. 63 Phone: 281 72974
91000 Xalapa, Veracruz, Mexico Felisa Herrador, Hd.
Founded: 1976. **Staff:** Prof 3; Other 1. **Subjects:** Ecology, botany, biology, zoology, silviculture. **Holdings:** 17,000 books; 1500 technical reports; 500 maps; 12,026 microfiche; 33 records. **Subscriptions:** 150 journals and other serials. **Services:** Copying; library open to local researchers and universities; open to others upon application. **Automated Operations:** Computerized cataloging. **Publications:** Nuevas Adquisiciones, semiannual. **Also Known As:** Instituto de Ecologia, A.C. - Bilioteca. **Staff:** Patricia Ortiz; Delfino Hernandez, Pub.Serv.; Isabel Lasserre, Tech.Libn.

★5211★
Ecology Action Centre - Resource Centre (Env-Cons)
3115 Veith St., 3rd Fl.
Halifax, NS, Canada B3K 3G9 Phone: (902)454-7828
Founded: 1971. **Subjects:** Resource industries, pollution, energy, biospheric changes, institutional responses to environmental issues, human habitat and society. **Holdings:** 6000 items. **Subscriptions:** 58 newsletters and other serials. **Services:** Copying; center open to the public for reference use only. **Automated Operations:** Computerized cataloging. **Computerized Information Services:** Omnis (internal database). **Remarks:** FAX: (902)454-4766.

★5212★
Ecology Center - Library (Env-Cons)
2530 San Pablo Ave. Phone: (510)548-2221
Berkeley, CA 94702 Dave Kershner, Info.Coord.
Founded: 1969. **Staff:** 1. **Subjects:** Solid waste, energy, San Francisco Bay area environment, air pollution, water resources, land use planning, environmental education. **Special Collections:** Solid Waste Management. **Holdings:** 2000 volumes; 20 vertical files. **Subscriptions:** 50 journals and other serials. **Services:** Copying; library open to the public for reference use only; borrowing privileges for members. **Computerized Information Services:** EcoNet (electronic mail service). **Publications:** Ecology Center Terrain, monthly - to members and by subscription. **Special Indexes:** Indexes of books and periodicals.

★5213★
Ecology & Environment, Inc. - Library (Env-Cons)
368 Pleasantview Dr. Phone: (716)684-8060
Lancaster, NY 14086 Theresa L. Wolfe, Info.Spec.
Staff: 1. **Subjects:** Environment, hazardous wastes. **Holdings:** 5500 books. **Subscriptions:** 250 journals and other serials. **Services:** Interlibrary loan; library not open to the public. **Networks/Consortia:** Member of Western New York Library Resources Council (WNYLRC). **Remarks:** FAX: (716)684-0844.

★5214★
Economic Associates, Inc. - Library
2025 Pennsylvania Ave., N.W.
Washington, DC 20006
Defunct.

Economic Comission for Latin America and the Caribbean
See: **United Nations Economic Commission for Latin America and the Caribbean** (16759)

Economic Council of Canada
See: **Canada - Economic Council of Canada** (2693)

★5215★
Economic Development Council of Northeastern Pennsylvania - James Pettinger Memorial Library (Bus-Fin)
1151 Oak St. Phone: (717)655-5581
Pittston, PA 18640-3795 Lynne Breza, Res.Libn.
Founded: 1965. **Staff:** 25. **Subjects:** Economic analysis, economic development planning. **Holdings:** 3000 volumes. **Subscriptions:** 22 newspapers. **Services:** Copying; library open to the public. **Computerized Information Services:** DIALOG Information Services; internal databases; DEVIN (electronic bulletin board). **Publications:** State of the Region, annual; statistical reports on Northeastern Pennsylvania. **Remarks:** FAX: (717)654-5137. Affiliated with Foundation Center and the Pennsylvania Energy Office.

Economic and Social Commission for Asia and the Pacific
See: **United Nations Economic and Social Commission for Asia and the Pacific** (16761)

Economic and Social Commission for Western Asia
See: **United Nations Economic and Social Commission for Western Asia** (16762)

★5216★
Economics Research Associates - Library (Bus-Fin)
10990 Wilshire Blvd., No. 1600 Phone: (310)477-9585
Los Angeles, CA 90024 Julie A. Robinson, Libn.
Founded: 1968. **Staff:** Prof 1. **Subjects:** Real estate development, land use, housing, recreation, tourism, urban affairs. **Holdings:** 600 volumes; 1500 government publications; 10,000 internal reports; 75 VF drawers of geographic data; 25 VF drawers of newspaper clippings and brochures. **Subscriptions:** 504 journals and other serials. **Services:** Interlibrary loan (limited). **Computerized Information Services:** Internal database. **Remarks:** FAX: (310)478-1950.

★5217★
Economics and Technology, Inc. - Library (Info Sci)
1 Washington Mall Phone: (617)227-0900
Boston, MA 02108 Michele A. Dignum
Founded: 1972. **Staff:** Prof 2; Other 1. **Subjects:** Telecommunication tariffs. **Special Collections:** History of telecommuniction carrier tariffs at federal and state level. **Holdings:** 200 reels of microfilm; tariffs of 150 jurisdictions. **Services:** Library open to the public by appointment only. **Remarks:** FAX: (617)227-5535.

★5218★
Ecosystems International, Inc. - Library (Sci-Engr)
Box 225 Phone: (301)621-7430
Gambrills, MD 21054 Sadie Castruccio, Oper.Mgr.
Founded: 1972. **Staff:** 1. **Subjects:** Electronics, computer systems design, physics, economics, mathematics, engineering, the environment. **Holdings:** 20,000 volumes. **Subscriptions:** 9 journals and other serials. **Services:** Library open to the public at librarian's discretion. **Computerized Information Services:** DIALOG Information Services, NASA/RECON. **Remarks:** FAX: (301)923-0457. Telex: 9103802778.

ECOsystems Management
See: **Coastal Ecosystems Management** (3852)

★5219★
ECRI - Library (Med)
5200 Butler Pike Phone: (215)825-6000
Plymouth Meeting, PA 19462 Lillian A. Linton, Libn.
Founded: 1969. **Staff:** Prof 2; Other 3. **Subjects:** Medical devices, biomedical engineering, hospital safety. **Special Collections:** Health Devices Evaluation Services (medical and medical device manufacturing literature). **Holdings:** 2200 books; 470 VF drawers of technical reports and evaluation data. **Subscriptions:** 800 journals and other serials. **Services:** Interlibrary loan; library not open to the public. **Automated Operations:** Computerized cataloging and circulation. **Computerized Information Services:** DIALOG Information Services, NLM, BRS Information Technologies; Health Devices Thesaurus (internal database). **Networks/Consortia:** Member of National Network of Libraries of Medicine - Middle Atlantic Region, Delaware Valley Information Consortium (DEVIC). **Publications:** Health Devices; Health Devices Alerts; Health Devices Sourcebook, annual - for sale; Health Care Standards, annual. **Remarks:** FAX: (215)834-7366. **Also Known As:** Emergency Care Research Institute. **Staff:** Justine Adams, Cat.Libn.

★5220★
ECS Power Systems, Inc. - Library (Sci-Engr)
150 Isabella St., Suite 201 Phone: (613)236-3920
Ottawa, ON, Canada K1S 5A3 Lena Sverdlova, Info.Spec.
Founded: 1985. **Staff:** Prof 1. **Subjects:** Physical sciences, nuclear reactor and energy plant design, naval architecture, marine engineering, maintenance engineering. **Holdings:** 500 books. **Subscriptions:** 150 journals and other serials. **Services:** Interlibrary loan; copying; library open to the public by special permission. **Computerized Information Services:** CAN/OLE, DOBIS Canadian Online Library System. **Remarks:** FAX: (613)236-5614. Telex: 053 4499.

★5221★
Ector County Library - Southwest History/Genealogy Department (Hist)
321 W. 5th St. Phone: (915)332-0634
Odessa, TX 79761 Barbara Horton, Lib.Dir.
Founded: 1938. **Staff:** 3. **Subjects:** Southwest history (Oklahoma, New Mexico, Arizona, Texas); United States and world genealogy; Texas city and county histories; Texas biographies. **Holdings:** 10,500 books; 1500 bound periodical volumes; 4400 reels of microfilm; 9000 microfiche; 10,500 Texas state documents. **Subscriptions:** 150 journals and other serials. **Services:** Copying; department open to the public. **Automated Operations:** Computerized cataloging and serials. **Staff:** Betty Theda, S.W. Hist./Geneal.Dept.Hd.

★5222★
Ecuadorian Institute of Natural Sciences - Library (Biol Sci, Env-Cons)
Casilla 408, Center Phone: 2 215497
Quito, Ecuador Dr. Grace Acosta, Libn.
Founded: 1940. **Staff:** 3. **Subjects:** Natural resources, phytogeography, soil conservation, forestry, natural sciences, biology, ecology, conservation. **Holdings:** 46,000 volumes. **Subscriptions:** 102 journals and other serials; 10 newspapers. **Services:** Interlibrary loan; library open to scientific researchers and university students. **Remarks:** Affiliated with Ecuador - Ministry of Public Education and Culture and the Ministry of Agriculture. **Also Known As:** Instituto Ecuatoriano de Ciencias Naturales. **Staff:** Wilson Acosta; Bolivar Sylva.

★5223★
Ecumenical Library (Rel-Phil)
475 Riverside Dr., Rm. 900 Phone: (212)870-3804
New York, NY 10115 Betty Ljungberg, Libn.
Founded: 1978. **Staff:** Prof 1. **Subjects:** Missions, theology, social issues, ecumenical relations. **Special Collections:** H. Paul Douglass Collection of Religious Research Reports (2000); Denominational Yearbooks (1000). **Holdings:** 14,000 books; 50 file drawers of pamphlets and clippings. **Subscriptions:** 100 journals and other serials. **Services:** Interlibrary loan; copying; library open to the public by appointment. **Remarks:** Created in 1978 by the merger of the Research Library of the National Council of Churches with the United Mission Library of the United Methodist and United Presbyterian Churches. Library is administered by an ecumenical committee composed of representatives of organizations in the Interchurch Center.

Ecumenical Music & Liturgy Resource Library
See: **Liturgy Library** (9228)

★5224★
Ecumenical Theological Center - Reference Library (Rel-Phil)
8425 W. McNichols Phone: (313)342-4600
Detroit, MI 48221 Dr. Robert Werenski, Libn.
Subjects: Theology, personal and spiritual growth, organizational development. **Holdings:** 5000 books. **Services:** Library not open to the public.

★5225★
ED TEL - Resource Centre
10044 108th St., 2nd Fl.
P.O. Box 20500 Phone: (403)441-2485
Edmonton, AB, Canada T5J 2R4 Kathy Fitzpatrick, Libn.
Holdings: 3800 books; archival materials. **Subscriptions:** 250 journals and other serials; 4 newspapers. **Services:** Interlibrary loan; copying; library not open to the public. **Remarks:** FAX: (403)423-0921.

★5226★
E.B. Eddy Forest Products, Ltd. - Library (Sci-Engr)
P.O. Box 600 Phone: (613)782-2645
Hull, PQ, Canada J8X 3Y7 G. Regimbald, Libn.
Founded: 1946. **Staff:** 1. **Subjects:** Pulp and paper manufacture, physics, chemistry. **Holdings:** 500 volumes. **Subscriptions:** 100 journals and other serials. **Services:** Library not open to the public. **Remarks:** FAX: (613)782-2515.

Eddy Genealogical and Historical Collection
See: **Hoyt Public Library** (7485)

Eden Archives
See: **Evangelical and Reformed Historical Society** (5502)

★5227★
Eden Hospital Medical Center - Medical & Dental Staff Library (Med)
19933 Lake Chabot Rd.
Castro Valley, CA 94546
Subjects: Medicine. **Holdings:** Figures not available. **Remarks:** Currently inactive.

★5228★
Eden Theological Seminary - Luhr Library (Rel-Phil)
475 E. Lockwood Ave. Phone: (314)961-3627
St. Louis, MO 63119 Karen M. Luebbert, Dir.
Founded: 1850. **Staff:** Prof 7.5; Other 10.5. **Subjects:** Religion, philosophy, theology. **Special Collections:** Reformed Church history and catechisms. **Holdings:** 73,857 books; 9199 bound periodical volumes. **Subscriptions:** 263 journals; 6 newspapers. **Services:** Interlibrary loan; copying; library open to the public. **Automated Operations:** Computerized cataloging. **Computerized Information Services:** BRS Information Technologies, DIALOG Information Services, OCLC. **Networks/Consortia:** Member of Missouri Library Network Corp. (MLNC), St. Louis Regional Library Network. **Remarks:** FAX: (314)968-7113. **Staff:** Ellen Eliceiri, Ref.Libn.; Barbara Hause, Circ.Supv.; Suzanne Walls, AV; Maya Grach, Acq.Libn.; Susan Wautzok, Cat.Libn.

★5229★
(Eden) Town Historian's Office - Library (Hist)
2795 E. Church St.
Eden, NY 14057 Norma Hardy Webb, Town Hist.
Staff: 1. **Subjects:** Local history and genealogy. **Holdings:** 300 books; 30 scrapbooks; 8 boxes of deeds, tax records, road warrants, tavern licenses, school district records; 10 photograph albums; 11 drawers of local history and genealogy files; 110 reels of microfilm. **Subscriptions:** 15 journals and other serials. **Services:** Copying; library open to the public by appointment. **Special Indexes:** Indexes to town records, church records, scrapbooks, daybooks, histories of town, 1847-1851 vital records, original deeds, cemetery inscriptions, death notices, gazetteers (all on cards).

Edgell Communications, Inc.
See: **Advanstar Communications, Inc.** (93)

★5230★
Edgewater Baptist Church - Library (Rel-Phil)
5501 Chicago Ave.
Minneapolis, MN 55417 Phone: (612)827-3803
Subjects: Religion. **Holdings:** 800 books; tapes; records; flannelgraphs. **Services:** Library open to the public for reference use only. **Staff:** Bruce Colebank; Karna Haugen.

★5231★
Edgewater Medical Center - Medical Library (Med)
5700 N. Ashland Ave. Phone: (312)878-6000
Chicago, IL 60660 Lucy Carrera, Med.Libn.
Staff: Prof 1. **Subjects:** Internal medicine, cardiology, surgery, orthopedics, obstetrics, oncology. **Holdings:** 1000 books; 4500 bound periodical volumes; 200 Audio-Digest tapes. **Subscriptions:** 130 journals and other serials. **Services:** Interlibrary loan; copying; library open to the public with restrictions. **Computerized Information Services:** BRS Information Technologies; DOCLINE (electronic mail service). Performs searches on fee basis. **Networks/Consortia:** Member of Metropolitan Consortium of Chicago, National Network of Libraries of Medicine - Greater Midwest Region, ILLINET, Chicago Library System. **Publications:** Periodicals Holding List, annual; Directory of Metropolitan Consortium of Chicago - to members. **Remarks:** Alternate telephone number(s): (312)989-8600. FAX: (312)878-8894. **Formerly:** Edgewater Hospital - Medical Library.

★5232★
Edinboro University of Pennsylvania - Baron-Forness Library (Hum, Hist)
Edinboro, PA 16444 Phone: (814)732-2780
Barbara Grippe, Act.Dir.
Founded: 1867. **Staff:** Prof 16; Other 12. **Subjects:** Art, history, literature. **Special Collections:** Southeast Asia; Erie Indians. **Holdings:** 323,619 books; 82,889 bound periodical volumes; 21,511 federal, state, U.N. documents; 1.2 million microforms. **Subscriptions:** 6292 journals and other serials; 14 newspapers. **Services:** Interlibrary loan; copying; SDI; library open to the public with restrictions. **Automated Operations:** Computerized public access catalog, serials, and circulation. **Computerized Information Services:** DIALOG Information Services, OCLC. **Networks/Consortia:** Member of Pittsburgh Regional Library Center (PRLC), Northwest Interlibrary Cooperative of Pennsylvania (NICOP), State System of Higher Education Libraries Council (SSHELCO). **Remarks:** FAX: (814)732-2883. **Staff:** Susan Hennip, ILL.

★5233★
Edinburgh College of Art - Library (Art)
Lauriston Pl Phone: 31 2299311255
Edinburgh EH3 9DF, Scotland Glenn Craig, Chf.Libn.
Founded: 1907. **Staff:** Prof 4; Other 9. **Subjects:** Fine art, design and crafts, architecture, planning and housing. **Special Collections:** Architectural reference collection. **Holdings:** 87,000 books; 21,000 bound periodical volumes; 1000 microfiche; 520 reels of microfilm; 138,000 slides. **Subscriptions:** 381 journals and other serials. **Services:** Interlibrary loan; copying; library open to the public for reference use only. **Automated Operations:** Computerized public access catalog. **Computerized Information Services:** DIALOG Information Services; SALBIN (internal database); JANET (electronic mail service). Contact Person: Wilson Smith. **Publications:** New Accessions. **Remarks:** FAX: 31 2290089.

★5234★
Edinburgh School of Agriculture - Library (Agri)
Kings Bldgs.
W. Mains Rd. Phone: 31 6671041
Edinburgh EH9 3JG, Scotland Ruth M. Johnson, Libn.
Subjects: Agriculture and horticulture - land use, rural development, socioeconomics, education, computers, agricultural policy, and allied subjects. **Holdings:** 12,000 books; 20,000 pamphlets. **Subscriptions:** 430 journals and other serials. **Services:** SDI; library open to the public. **Computerized Information Services:** Produces Agdex database. **Remarks:** FAX: 31 6672601. Telex: 727617. **Staff:** Marilyn Mullay, Asst.Libn.

★5235★
Edison Electric Institute - Library (Energy)
701 Pennsylvania Ave., N.W. Phone: (202)508-5623
Washington, DC 20004-2696 Ethel Tiberg, Mgr., Lib.Serv.
Founded: 1917. **Staff:** Prof 3; Other 3. **Subjects:** Electric utilities, energy, environment. **Holdings:** 16,243 volumes; 512 bound periodical volumes; 143 VF drawers; government documents; technical reports. **Subscriptions:** 664 journals and other serials. **Services:** Interlibrary loan; library open to the public by appointment. **Automated Operations:** Computerized cataloging and routing. **Computerized Information Services:** ORBIT Search Service, DIALOG Information Services, BRS Information Technologies, VU/TEXT Information Services, OCLC, WILSONLINE, EEI UNICOM. **Publications:** Library bibliographies. **Remarks:** FAX: (202)508-5794. **Staff:** Susan Farkas, Gen.Ref.Libn.; Jackie Johnson, Leg.Ref.Libn.

Edison Institute Archives
See: **Henry Ford Museum and Greenfield Village** (5964)

Edison National Historic Site
See: **U.S. Natl. Park Service** (17702)

★5236★
Thomas Edison Winter Home - Library (Hist)
2350 MacGregor Blvd. Phone: (813)334-7419
Fort Myers, FL 33901 Gary E. Thomas, Asst.Mgr.
Founded: 1948. **Staff:** 1. **Subjects:** Thomas A. Edison, history of the phonograph. **Special Collections:** Edison biographies; Henry Ford history. **Holdings:** 250 pieces of correspondence, journals, logbooks, manuscripts, experiment logbooks, interoffice correspondence, business records, photographs, technical drawings, original phonograph recordings. **Services:** Library not open to the public. **Remarks:** FAX: (813)332-6684. **Staff:** Mary C. Fitzpatrick, Asst.Mgr.

★5237★
Editor & Publisher, Co. - Editorial/Information/Service (Publ)
11 W. 19th St. Phone: (212)675-4380
New York, NY 10011-4234 Shqipe Malushi, Ed./Info./Spec.
Founded: 1901. **Staff:** Prof 2. **Subjects:** Journalism, newspapers. **Holdings:** 500 books; bound volumes of Editor & Publisher, 1901 to present; 200 reels of microfilm. **Subscriptions:** 10 journals and other serials; 10 newspapers. **Services:** Copying; library open to the public by appointment. **Automated Operations:** Computerized CG. **Special Indexes:** Periodical index (card). **Remarks:** FAX: (212)929-1259. **Formerly:** Its Library.

★5238★
Edmonton Art Gallery - Reference Library (Art)
2 Sir Winston Churchill Square
Edmonton, AB, Canada T5J 2C1 Phone: (403)422-6223
Founded: 1924. **Subjects:** Contemporary art and artists (including Canadian), art history, art education. **Special Collections:** Old exhibition catalogs, 1900-1950 (20). **Holdings:** 13,000 volumes; 40,000 slides; 120 videotapes; 34 drawers of clippings of artist biographical information; 400 microfiche. **Subscriptions:** 26 periodicals; 75 newsletters and bulletins. **Services:** Interlibrary loan; library not open to the public. **Computerized Information Services:** Canadian Heritage Information Network (CHIN). **Remarks:** FAX: (403)426-3105.

★5239★
Edmonton Autism Society - Information Centre (Med)
7515A Mount Lawn Rd. Phone: (403)479-0088
Edmonton, AB, Canada T5B 4J1 Joyce Barber, Pres.
Subjects: Autism, behavior management. **Holdings:** 200 items (books, audiocassettes, video recordings, pamphlets). **Subscriptions:** 18 journals and other serials. **Services:** Library open to the public with restrictions. **Publications:** UPDATE (newsletter), quarterly.

★5240★
Edmonton Catholic Schools - Professional Library (Educ)
9807 106th St. Phone: (403)441-6123
Edmonton, AB, Canada T5K 1C2 C. Hornby, Res.Libn.
Staff: 2. **Subjects:** Education, Catholicism. **Holdings:** 5000 books. **Subscriptions:** 200 journals and other serials. **Services:** Library not open to the public.

★5241★
Edmonton City Archives (Hist)
10105 112th Ave. Phone: (403)428-4761
Edmonton, AB, Canada T5G 0H1 Helen LaRose, Supv., Archv.
Founded: 1973. **Staff:** 5. **Subjects:** Alberta and Edmonton history. **Holdings:** 5000 books; 2500 City of Edmonton reports; 300 maps; 25,000 photographs; city records; manuscripts; plans. **Subscriptions:** 11 journals and other serials. **Services:** Copying; archives open to the public for reference use only.

★5242★
Edmonton (City) Planning & Development Department - Library (Plan)
The Boardwalk
10310 102nd Ave., N.W., 2nd Fl. Phone: (403)428-2665
Edmonton, AB, Canada T5J 2X6 Katherina Hui, Lib.Techn.
Founded: 1965. **Staff:** Prof 1. **Subjects:** Planning, urban design, land use, housing and population, economics, public administration and finance, personnel. **Special Collections:** Slide collection (2060). **Holdings:** 5000 books and reports; aerial photographs of Edmonton. **Subscriptions:** 129 journals and other serials. **Services:** Interlibrary loan; copying; library open to the public for reference use only. **Publications:** News from the Planning Library (newsletter/acquisitions list), monthly - to mailing list. **Special Indexes:** MOLLI index to document collection. **Remarks:** FAX: (403)428-4665.

★5243★
Edmonton City Transportation - Transit Research Centre (Sci-Engr)
Mitchell Division
11904 154th St. Phone: (403)428-2988
Edmonton, AB, Canada T5V 1J2 Irene Caine, Res.Off.
Founded: 1983. **Staff:** Prof 1; Other 1. **Subjects:** Transportation; light rail transit; planning and development; transit planning studies and systems; safety and training centers; bus operations; environment; geotechnology. **Special Collections:** Transportation research and services reports (1000). **Holdings:** 2000 books. **Subscriptions:** 100 journals and other serials; 10 newspapers. **Services:** Interlibrary loan; library not open to the public. **Automated Operations:** Computerized cataloging, serials, and circulation. **Computerized Information Services:** DIALOG Information Services, PFDS Online, CAN/OLE, MEDLARS. **Publications:** Library Bulletin, bimonthly - for internal distribution only. **Remarks:** FAX: (403)428-4752.

★5244★
Edmonton Community and Family Services Department - Staff Library (Soc Sci)
Centennial Library, 5th Fl.
7 Sir Winston Churchill Square Phone: (403)496-5835
Edmonton, AB, Canada T5J 2V4 Noreen Wilson, Libn.
Staff: Prof 1. **Subjects:** Social services, welfare services, social and urban planning, community organization, poverty, preventive social service. **Holdings:** 5000 books; 230 reports. **Subscriptions:** 120 journals and other serials; 20 newspapers. **Services:** Library open to the public for consultation only. **Automated Operations:** Computerized cataloging. **Automated Operations:** Computerized public access catalog, cataloging, and acquisitions. **Remarks:** FAX: (403)428-4556.

★5245★
Edmonton Journal - Library (Publ)
P.O. Box 2421 Phone: (403)429-5263
Edmonton, AB, Canada T5J 2S6 Patricia Garneau, Hd.Libn.
Founded: 1903. **Staff:** 10. **Subjects:** Newspaper reference topics, current events. **Holdings:** 500 volumes; clippings; photographs; newspaper, 1903 to present, on microfilm. **Services:** Library not open to the public. **Computerized Information Services:** Infomart Online; INFO-KY (internal database). **Special Indexes:** Index of newspaper clippings. **Remarks:** FAX: (403)429-5500. The Journal is published by Southam Publishing Co.

★5246★
Edmonton Police - Library (Law)
9620 103A Ave., 4th Fl. Phone: (403)421-3459
Edmonton, AB, Canada T5H 0H7 Janice Broverman, Libn.
Founded: 1979. **Staff:** 1. **Subjects:** Police science. **Holdings:** 6000 books. **Subscriptions:** 150 journals and other serials; 4 newspapers. **Services:** Interlibrary loan; library not open to the public. **Computerized Information Services:** DIALOG Information Services. **Remarks:** FAX: (403)425-9963.

★5247★
Edmonton Power - Library (Energy)
Capitol Square, 11th Fl.
10065 Jasper Ave. Phone: (403)448-3373
Edmonton, AB, Canada T5J 3B1 Georgina DeMeyer, Libn.
Founded: 1972. **Staff:** 2. **Subjects:** Electrical and electronics engineering, power transmission and distribution, energy resources and conservation. **Holdings:** 3500 books; 450 bound periodical volumes; 2200 reports and documents; 800 manufacturers' catalogs; 3000 standards; 3 VF drawers of technical papers. **Subscriptions:** 300 journals and other serials. **Services:** Interlibrary loan; copying; library open to the public by appointment. **Computerized Information Services:** DIALOG Information Services, CAN/OLE. **Special Indexes:** Manufacturers' catalogs indexed by subject and manufacturer. **Remarks:** FAX: (403)448-3059.

★5248★
Edmonton Public Schools - Professional Library (Educ)
One Kingsway Phone: (403)429-8323
Edmonton, AB, Canada T5H 4G9 Marilyn Elliott, Libn.
Founded: 1961. **Staff:** Prof 1; Other 2. **Subjects:** Education. **Special Collections:** Award winning children's literature; local curriculum guides. **Holdings:** 8800 books; 260 dissertations; 13 drawers of pamphlets and unbound reports; microfiche; 250 cassette tapes; videotapes. **Subscriptions:** 433 journals and other serials. **Services:** Interlibrary loan; library open to the public with restrictions. **Computerized Information Services:** ERIC; CD-ROMs (ERIC on Silverplatter, Books in Print With Book Reviews Plus, Ulrich's Plus, Comptons Multimedia Encyclopedia, Information Finder, Microsoft Bookshelf, Grolier Electronic Encyclopedia). **Remarks:** FAX: (403)429-8318.

★5249★
Edmonton Sun - Newspaper Library (Publ)
4990 92nd Ave., No. 250 Phone: (403)468-0261
Edmonton, AB, Canada T6B 3A1 John M. Sinclair, Chf.Libn.
Founded: 1978. **Staff:** Prof 1; Other 6. **Subjects:** Newspaper reference topics, current affairs. **Special Collections:** Local hard news; Commonwealth Games, 1978; Wayne Gretzky, Edmonton Oilers, and Edmonton Eskimos clippings and photographs. **Holdings:** 800 books; 2 million clippings; 20,000 microfiche; 200,000 photographs; all editions of Edmonton Sun on microfilm. **Services:** Copying; library open to the public through telephone access only. **Computerized Information Services:** Infomart Online. **Publications:** Edmonton Sun on microfilm, monthly. **Remarks:** FAX: (403)468-0139. Alternate telephone number(s): (403)468-0147. **Staff:** Bruce Grant, Asst.Chf.Libn.

★5250★
Jennie Edmundson Memorial Hospital - School of Nursing - Library (Med)
933 E. Pierce St. Phone: (712)328-6130
Council Bluffs, IA 51501 Christine Kirby, Libn.
Founded: 1959. **Staff:** Prof 1; Other 1. **Subjects:** Nursing, medicine, paramedical sciences. **Holdings:** 8499 books; 2710 bound periodical volumes; 19 VF drawers of pamphlets and clippings; government documents; AV and computer-aided instruction programs. **Subscriptions:** 250 journals and other serials; 5 newspapers. **Services:** Interlibrary loan; copying; library open to the public for reference use only. **Computerized Information Services:** MEDLINE, BRS Information Technologies. Performs searches on fee basis. **Networks/Consortia:** Member of National Network of Libraries of Medicine - Greater Midwest Region, ICON. **Publications:** Student Handbook/Orientation Manual; Annual Report; Library Corner - Dimensions. **Special Catalogs:** AV catalog; serials catalog. **Remarks:** An alternate telephone number is 328-6203. FAX: (712)328-6283; 328-6002.

★5251★
EDO Corporation - Barnes Engineering Division - Library (Sci-Engr)
88 Long Hill Cross Rd.
Box 867 Phone: (203)926-1777
Shelton, CT 06484 Belle B. Shipe, Libn.
Founded: 1962. **Staff:** 1. **Subjects:** Electro-optics, engineering. **Holdings:** 500 books. **Subscriptions:** 15 journals and other serials. **Services:** Interlibrary loan; library not open to the public. **Computerized Information Services:** DIALOG Information Services. **Remarks:** FAX: (203)926-1030. Telex: 6819115.

★5252★
The Education Diffusion Group - Colorado Career Information System (Educ)
3800 York St.
Unit B Phone: (303)764-3936
Denver, CO 80205 Charles Beck, Jr., Dir.
Staff: 3. **Subjects:** Colorado occupations, employers, training programs, schools; national schools; wage and employment outlook; financial aid; job search skills; apprenticeships. **Computerized Information Services:** Internal database. **Remarks:** This is a computerized career information system which is updated annually and available by subscription. Delivery options include mainframe tapes, IBM hard disk, and floppy disks with printed volumes of information. **Remarks:** FAX: (303)764-3935.

★5253★
Educational Broadcasting Corporation - Thirteen/WNET Reference Services (Info Sci)
356 W. 58th St.
New York, NY 10019 Phone: (212)560-3063
Founded: 1972. **Staff:** Prof 3. **Subjects:** Current events. **Special Collections:** Thirteen program guides, 1963 to present. **Holdings:** 2200 books; 900 bound periodical volumes; 216 VF drawers of news clippings; 2225 reels of microfilm of newspapers. **Subscriptions:** 200 journals and other serials; 6 newspapers. **Services:** Interlibrary loan; copying; library open to the public by appointment on fee basis. **Computerized Information Services:** DIALOG Information Services, NEXIS, VU/TEXT Information Services, WILSONLINE, DataTimes. **Remarks:** FAX: (212)582-3297. **Staff:** Jane Bealer, Assoc.Mgr., Corp.Res.; Harriett Obus, Ref. & Prog.Res.; Margery Frohlinger, Assoc.Mgr.Corp.Res.

★5254★
Educational Center for Life (Soc Sci)
Professional Bldg., Suite 19
909 Woodward Ave. Phone: (313)338-1910
Pontiac, MI 48341-2977 Phyllis Sullivan, R.N., B.S.N., Dir.
Founded: 1974. **Staff:** 2. **Subjects:** Abortion, infanticide, euthanasia, chastity, medical ethics, alternatives to abortion. **Holdings:** 220 books; 12 bound periodical volumes; 9 VF drawers; films; videotapes; audiotapes. **Subscriptions:** 20 journals and other serials. **Services:** Center open to the public. **Automated Operations:** Computerized public access catalog. **Publications:** Pregnancy Services of Southeastern Michigan Directory; Teen Alert Card; coloring books. **Special Catalogs:** Pro-Life Resource Catalog.

★5255★
Educational Communications - Environmental Library (Env-Cons)
P.O. Box 35559 Phone: (310)559-9160
Los Angeles, CA 90035 Nancy Pearlman, Exec.Prod.
Founded: 1972. **Staff:** Prof 2. **Subjects:** Environment, ecological education, media production, pollution, land use, resource management, wildlife preservation, population, urban affairs, planning, energy sources, waste, open space, historic preservation, toxic substances, ocean and coastal

protection, desert and forest management. **Special Collections:** ECONEWS (television series; 225 videocassettes); Environmental Directions (radio series; 750 audiocassettes); Environmental Viewpoints radio series (50 audio-cassettes). **Holdings:** 400 books; 7000 unbound magazines; 200 booklets and pamphlets; 7000 informational sheets and newsletters; VF drawers; simulation games, posters, other cataloged items. **Subscriptions:** 125 magazines and newsletters. **Services:** Reference materials open to the public on request. **Computerized Information Services:** Directory of Environmental Organizations (5000 names and addresses; internal database) - for sale. **Publications:** The Compendium-Guide to the World's Environmental Crisis (newsletter), bimonthly; 1992 Directory of Environmental Organizations, 16th edition (comprehensive list of international, national, state, county, and city groups). **Remarks:** Holdings are decentralized; materials are available from committee coordinators and at selected libraries, galleries, and educational centers in Southland or by mail order.

★5256★
Educational Concerns for Hunger Organization - Library (Agri)
17430 Durrance Rd. Phone: (813)543-3246
North Fort Myers, FL 33917 Dr. Martin L. Price
Founded: 1979. **Staff:** Prof 4; Other 6. **Subjects:** Tropical agriculture, agronomy, agroforestry, horticulture, appropriate technology, rural development. **Holdings:** 1200 books; microfiche; microfilm; videotapes. **Subscriptions:** 20 journals and other serials. **Services:** Library open primarily to studying missionaries and students. **Publications:** ECHO development notes; ECHO news; annotated listing of seeds.

★5257★
Educational Fund to End Handgun Violence - Firearms Litigation Clearinghouse (Law)
Box 72
110 Maryland Ave., N.E.
Washington, DC 20002 Phone: (202)743-2340
Founded: 1977. **Subjects:** Handguns, firearms liability. **Holdings:** 2000 bound periodical volumes; 300 documents; 1000 pages of brochures and descriptions; 10,000 pages of depositions, pleadings, and correspondence. **Services:** Clearinghouse open to members only. **Remarks:** FAX: (202)544-7213.

Educational Institute of Scotland Library
See: **Scotland - National Library of Scotland** (14953)

★5258★
Educational Leadership Institute - Library (Educ)
2205 N. Summit Phone: (414)289-0706
Milwaukee, WI 53202 Dr. Jeremy Jon Lietz, Dir.
Founded: 1980. **Subjects:** General and special education administration, school law, demography, staff development, curriculum. **Holdings:** 695 books; 237 reports and manuscripts. **Services:** Copying.

★5259★
Educational Management Corporation - Art Institute of Philadelphia - Library (Art)
1622 Chestnut St. Phone: (215)567-7080
Philadelphia, PA 19103 Paul V. Patanella, Libn.
Staff: 3. **Subjects:** Commercial art - photography, interior design, visual communication, fashion merchandising; music and video business. **Holdings:** 3500 books. **Subscriptions:** 90 journals and other serials. **Services:** Library not open to the public; circulation services provided for students and faculty.

Educational Policies Clearinghouse
See: **National School Boards Association** (11280)

★5260★
Educational Records Bureau - Library (Educ)
140 W. 65th St. Phone: (212)873-9108
New York, NY 10023 Dr. David Hall, III, Pres.
Founded: 1970. **Subjects:** Educational testing. **Holdings:** 500 books; 500 research reports; 1 million test scores. **Services:** Library open to qualified persons with permission only. **Remarks:** FAX: (617)237-4869.

★5261★
Educational Research Service - Library (Educ)
2000 Clarendon Blvd. Phone: (703)243-2100
Arlington, VA 22201 Josephine Franklin, Coord., Info.Serv.
Founded: 1973. **Staff:** Prof 10; Other 1. **Subjects:** Educational administration, policy, practices; school management. **Holdings:** 15,000 books, reports, booklets, documents; 248 file drawers of journal articles, clippings, newsletters. **Subscriptions:** 140 journals and other serials. **Services:** Copying; library open to the public with restrictions. **Computerized Information Services:** Online systems. **Publications:** ERS Bulletin, monthly (September-June) - by subscription; ERS Information Aids; ERS Reports; ERS Research Briefs; ERS Monographs; ERS Concerns in Education; ERS School Research Forum; ERS Spectrum - all for sale. **Staff:** Mary Edith Norman, Asst. Coord., Info.Serv.

Educational Resources Information Center
See: **ERIC Clearinghouse on Adult, Career, and Vocational Education** (5395)

★5262★
Educational Testing Service - Carl Campbell Brigham Library and Test Collection (Educ)
Rosedale Rd. Phone: (609)734-5737
Princeton, NJ 08541 Marilyn Halpern, Mgr. of Libs.
Staff: Prof 4; Other 5. **Subjects:** Psychology; education; psychometrics; measurement instruments; tests - educational, achievement and personality, interest and aptitude, sensory-motor, and vocational. **Holdings:** 12,200 books; 10,000 bound periodical volumes; 6000 technical reports; 17,300 tests; test manuals; 200 annotated test bibliographies; 800 tests on microfiche. **Subscriptions:** 300 journals and other serials; 9 newspapers. **Services:** Interlibrary loan; library open to the public for reference use only with restrictions on use of test collection. **Automated Operations:** Computerized public access catalog and cataloging. **Computerized Information Services:** DIALOG Information Services, BRS Information Technologies; produces ETS Test Collection. **Networks/Consortia:** Member of CLASS. **Publications:** Pamphlets on library and literature search services; News on Tests, quarterly - by subscription; Tests in Microfiche, annual; annotated bibliographies of tests by type or subject. **Special Catalogs:** Periodical holdings. **Remarks:** FAX: (609)734-5410. **Staff:** Bonnie Eskra, Info.Spec.; Alicia Magee, Info.Spec.; Karen McQuillen, Info.Spec.

★5263★
Edward-Dean Museum - Art Reference Library (Art)
9401 Oak Glen Rd. Phone: (714)845-2626
Cherry Valley, CA 92223 Jan Holmlund, Dir.
Founded: 1964. **Staff:** Prof 1; Other 1. **Subjects:** Furniture, decorative arts, sculpture, architecture, costume design, history. **Holdings:** 1200 books. **Services:** Library open to the public by special permission. **Remarks:** Maintained by Riverside County Museum Department.

★5264★
Edward Hospital - Medical Library (Med)
801 S. Washington St. Phone: (708)527-3937
Naperville, IL 60566 Janette Trofimuk, Dir.
Founded: 1955. **Staff:** Prof 1. **Subjects:** Medicine, allied health, nursing. **Holdings:** 2000 books. **Subscriptions:** 200 journals and other serials. **Services:** Interlibrary loan; library open to the public. **Automated Operations:** Computerized cataloging. **Computerized Information Services:** BRS Information Technologies, DIALOG Information Services, MEDLARS, CD PLUS. **Networks/Consortia:** Member of Fox Valley Health Science Library Consortium (FVHSL). **Remarks:** FAX: (708)355-9703.

★5265★
Edwards County Historical Society - Library (Hist)
212 W. Main St.
P.O. Box 205 Phone: (618)445-2631
Albion, IL 62806 Terry L. Harper, Pres.
Founded: 1949. **Subjects:** Genealogy, history. **Holdings:** 693 books; 37 nonbook items. **Subscriptions:** 3 newspapers. **Services:** Copying; library open to the public.

★5266★
Jacob Edwards Library - Special Collections (Hist)
236 Main St. Phone: (508)764-5426
Southbridge, MA 01550 Harry R. Williams, Dir.
Founded: 1914. **Staff:** Prof 2; Other 6. **Special Collections:** Dirlam Collection on whaling and the Arctic; local history. **Holdings:** 67,500 books; 295 bound periodical volumes. **Subscriptions:** 191 journals and other serials; 17 newspapers. **Services:** Interlibrary loan; copying; collections open to the public. **Automated Operations:** Computerized cataloging and circulation. **Networks/Consortia:** Member of C/W MARS, Inc. **Remarks:** FAX: (508)764-8391. **Staff:** Evelyn Petrelli, Asst.Libn.; Mary White, Children's Libn.

Jonathan Edwards Library
See: **Princeton University - Rare Books and Special Collections** (13386)

Library of Gladys Brown Edwards
See: **California State Polytechnic University - Library** (2551)

Ward Edwards Library
See: **Central Missouri State University** (3350)

Myron Eells Library of Northwest History
See: **Whitman College** (20389)

EEOC
See: **U.S. Equal Employment Opportunity Commission** (17483)

Effigy Mounds National Monument
See: **U.S. Natl. Park Service** (17703)

Joseph F. Egan Memorial Supreme Court Law Library
See: **New York State Supreme Court - 4th Judicial District** (11693)

★5267★
EG&G/EM - Technical Information Center (Sci-Engr)
P.O. Box 1912 M/S C1-16 Phone: (702)295-0547
North Las Vegas, NV 89025 Jeffrey A. Gordon, Tech.Info.Adm.
Founded: 1955. **Staff:** Prof 1; Other 1. **Subjects:** Electronic engineering, physics, nuclear engineering, photography/imaging, management, environmental studies, computer imaging. **Holdings:** 10,000 books; 1500 bound periodical volumes. **Subscriptions:** 64 journals and other serials. **Services:** Interlibrary loan; copying; center open for limited research only by corporation personnel. **Automated Operations:** Computerized cataloging, acquisitions, serials, and circulation. **Computerized Information Services:** DIALOG Information Services, LEXIS, NEXIS, Integrated Technical Information System (ITIS), OCLC. **Formerly:** Its Research Reference Center.

★5268★
EG&G Idaho, Inc. - Idaho National Engineering Laboratory - INEL Technical Library (Sci-Engr, Energy)
Box 1625, MS 2300 Phone: (208)526-1185
Idaho Falls, ID 83415-2300 Brent N. Jacobsen, Lib.Mgr.
Founded: 1952. **Staff:** Prof 10; Other 11. **Subjects:** Nuclear energy and technology, metallurgy and material science, chemistry and chemical engineering, physics, reactor engineering and safety, fluid mechanics and heat transfer, engineering, mathematics, computer science, biotechnology, radioactive waste management, earth and environmental sciences, electronics and instrumentation, health physics and nuclear biology, occupational safety and health, business and management, nuclear physics, optics and lasers. **Special Collections:** U.S. Atomic Energy Commission (AEC), U.S. Energy Research and Development Administration (ERDA), U.S. Department of Energy (DOE) Reports (900,000, hardcopy and microfiche); power reactor docket information (150,000 items on microfiche). **Holdings:** 46,000 books; 2100 periodical titles. **Subscriptions:** 1100 journals and other serials. **Services:** Interlibrary loan; copying; library open to the public with restrictions. **Automated Operations:** Computerized cataloging, acquisitions, serials, and circulation. **Computerized Information Services:** DIALOG Information Services, Integrated Technical Information System (ITIS), BRS Information Technologies, LEXIS, NEXIS, EPIC OCLC, LEXPAT, NASA/RECON, STN International, Chemical Abstracts Service (CAS), United States Department of Energy (USDOE), U.S. Department of Defense; OnTyme Electronic Message Network Service (electronic mail service). **Networks/Consortia:** Member of National Network of Libraries of Medicine - Pacific Northwest Region. **Publications:** INEL Technical Library Update, monthly - local distribution. **Special Catalogs:** Technical Library Journal Holdings; The INEL Technical Library (brochure). **Remarks:** FAX: (208)526-0211. Electronic mail address(es): INELEGGID.CLASS (OnTyme Electronic Message Network Service). EG&G Idaho, Inc. operates under contract to the U.S. Department of Energy. **Staff:** Heather M. Redding, Ref.; David P. Klepich, Ref.; Lila Pelot, ILL; Marie Suhre, Acq./Law Libn.; Gene Giesbrecht, Ref./Chem. & Physics; Jackie Loop, Ref.; Sandy Biermann, Ref./Acq.; Nancy Ottewitte, Cat.; Ray Born, Prog.

★5269★
EG&G, Inc. - Corporate Headquarters - Business & Financial Reference Library (Bus-Fin)
45 William St. Phone: (617)237-5100
Wellesley, MA 02181-4054 Raymond J. Champoux
Founded: 1970. **Staff:** Prof 1; Other 1. **Subjects:** Business reference. **Holdings:** 50 books; 50 bound periodical volumes; 500 credit reports. **Subscriptions:** 95 journals and other serials; 5 newspapers. **Services:** Library open to the public by specific request. **Computerized Information Services:** Dun & Bradstreet Business Credit Services; internal databases. **Remarks:** FAX: (617)431-4115. Electronic mail address(es): 321-6798 (MCI Mail).

★5270★
EG&G, Inc. - Washington Analytical Services Center - Library & Market Research Center (Sci-Engr)
1396 Piccard Dr. Phone: (301)840-3243
Rockville, MD 20850 Maria Shih, Mgr.
Staff: Prof 2; Other 1. **Subjects:** Electrical engineering, acoustics, physics, mathematics, oceanography, environmental sciences. **Holdings:** 3000 books; 175 bound periodical volumes; 11,000 military specifications and standards; 1300 technical reports; 980 visual search microfilm files. **Subscriptions:** 85 journals and other serials; 20 newspapers. **Services:** Interlibrary loan; center not open to the public. **Automated Operations:** Computerized cataloging. **Computerized Information Services:** DIALOG Information Services; internal databases. **Publications:** Engineering Information Bulletin, quarterly - for internal distribution only. **Remarks:** FAX: (301)258-9522.

★5271★
EG&G Mound Applied Technologies - Mound Library (Sci-Engr)
Box 3000 Phone: (513)865-4152
Miamisburg, OH 45343-3000 Susan J. Moore, Supv., Lib.
Staff: Prof 2; Other 2. **Subjects:** Chemistry, physics, engineering, nuclear energy, mathematics. **Special Collections:** Nuclear energy documents issued by U.S. Department of Energy, 1964 to present (550,000 titles on microfiche). **Holdings:** 22,160 books; 10,600 bound periodical volumes; 500,000 government reports on microfiche; 3000 laboratory originated reports; 2000 volumes of technical journals on microfilm. **Subscriptions:** 600 journals and other serials. **Services:** Interlibrary loan; center not open to the public. **Computerized Information Services:** DIALOG Information Services, Integrated Technical Information System (ITIS), DTIC, NASA/RECON, STN International. **Remarks:** FAX: (513)865-4817. **Staff:** Beverly Peters, ILL

George William Eggers Archive
See: **State University College at Buffalo - Burchfield Art Center - Research Library** (15703)

★5272★
Egyptian Red Crescent Society - Library (Med)
29 El Galaa St.
Cairo, Egypt Phone: 2 750558
Subjects: Health, welfare, disaster relief. **Holdings:** 1000 volumes; biographical archives. **Remarks:** Telex: 93249.

Ehinger Library
See: **West Chester University - Francis Harvey Green Library** (20186)

Edward Ehrenkrantz/Elchanan Echikson Memorial Library
See: **Temple Sharey Tefilo-Israel** (16123)

Frederick L. Ehrman Medical Library
See: **New York University - Medical Center** (11727)

George A. Ehrman Library
See: **Carnegie Museum of Natural History - Library** (3085)

Eidgenoessisches Institut fuer Reaktorforschung
See: **Paul Scherrer Institute** (14907)

Eidgenoessisches Institut fuer Schnee- und Lawinenforschung
See: **Switzerland - Federal Research Institute for Forest, Snow and Landscape - Federal Institute for Snow and Avalanche Research** (15940)

Eidgenossische Technische Hochschule
See: **Swiss Federal Institute of Technology, Zurich** (15938)

1839 Courthouse Museum
See: **Berrien County Historical Association** (1758)

★5273★
EIMCO Process Equipment Company - Technical Library
669 W. 2nd St.
Salt Lake City, UT 84101-1604
Founded: 1976. **Subjects:** Water treatment, waste management, solid/liquid separation technology. **Special Collections:** Manufacturers' catalogs. **Holdings:** 1550 books; 500 bound periodical volumes; 500 documents; 40 VF drawers of technical files. **Remarks:** Currently inactive.

Albert Einstein College of Medicine
See: **Yeshiva University - Albert Einstein College of Medicine** (20751)

Albert Einstein Medical Center - Mt. Sinai-Daroff Division
See: **Mt. Sinai Hospital** (10814)

★5274★
Albert Einstein Medical Center - Northern Division - Luria Medical Library (Med)
York & Tabor Roads — Phone: (215)456-6345
Philadelphia, PA 19141 — Marion H. Silverman, Dir.
Founded: 1951. **Staff:** Prof 2; Other 3. **Subjects:** Medicine. **Holdings:** 2000 books; 16,000 bound periodical volumes. **Subscriptions:** 300 journals and other serials. **Services:** Interlibrary loan; copying; library open to the public for reference use only with identification. **Computerized Information Services:** MEDLARS, BRS Information Technologies, DIALOG Information Services. **Networks/Consortia:** Member of National Network of Libraries of Medicine - Middle Atlantic Region, Delaware Valley Information Consortium (DEVIC), BHSL. **Remarks:** FAX: (215)456-8267. Alternate telephone number(s): 456-6346. **Staff:** Florence Rosenthal, Coord. Media Ctr.

Einstein Institute of Mathematics and Computer Science - Library
See: **Hebrew University of Jerusalem** (7100)

★5275★
EIP Associates - Library (Env-Cons)
601 Montgomery St., Suite 500 — Phone: (415)362-1500
San Francisco, CA 94111 — Cathleen G. Brown, Libn.
Founded: 1972. **Staff:** Prof 1. **Subjects:** Environment, natural resources, pollution, hydrology, geology, community planning. **Special Collections:** San Francisco environmental reports. **Holdings:** 6000 reports and other cataloged items. **Subscriptions:** 72 journals and other serials. **Services:** Interlibrary loan; library not open to the public. **Remarks:** FAX: (415)362-1954.

Eisenberg Medical Staff Library
See: **Sinai Hospital of Baltimore, Inc.** (15185)

D.D. Eisenhower Army Medical Center
See: **U.S. Army Hospitals** (17038)

Dwight D. Eisenhower Library
See: **U.S. Presidential Libraries** (17921)

★5276★
Mamie Doud Eisenhower Birthplace Foundation, Inc. - Museum & Library (Hist)
709 Carroll St.
P.O. Box 55 — Phone: (515)432-1896
Boone, IA 50036 — Larry Adams, Cur.
Founded: 1977. **Staff:** Prof 1. **Subjects:** Eisenhower (Mamie Doud and Dwight D.), Doud, and Carlson family history; political history of the Eisenhower era; military history of World War II; Eisenhower College. **Holdings:** 1000 books; 3000 unbound letters, manuscripts, clippings, photographs, slides, sound recordings, philatelic and numismatic items, periodicals, newspapers, campaign and inaugural materials, records pertaining to the restoration of the birthplace. **Subscriptions:** 10 journals and other serials. **Services:** Copying; library open to the public on a limited schedule and with restrictions on certain items. **Special Indexes:** Manuscript Index. **Remarks:** Alternate telephone number(s): 432-1931.

★5277★
Eisenhower Medical Center - Del E. Webb Memorial Medical Information Center (Med)
39000 Bob Hope Dr. — Phone: (619)773-1400
Rancho Mirage, CA 92270 — Barbara E. Potts, MLS
Founded: 1973. **Staff:** Prof 1; Other 1. **Subjects:** Medicine, health sciences. **Special Collections:** History of medicine. **Holdings:** 6500 books; 4000 bound periodical volumes; 250 AV program titles. **Subscriptions:** 300 journals and other serials. **Services:** Interlibrary loan; center not open to the public. **Computerized Information Services:** MEDLINE, DIALOG Information Services. **Networks/Consortia:** Member of Inland Empire Medical Library Cooperative (IEMLC).

Milton S. Eisenhower Library
See: **Johns Hopkins University - Milton S. Eisenhower Library** (8420)

★5278★
El Dorado County Law Library (Law)
550 Main St., Suite A — Phone: (916)621-6423
Placerville, CA 95667 — Marcus N. Prenk, Law Lib.Adm.
Staff: Prof 1. **Subjects:** California and federal law. **Holdings:** 10,300 volumes; 220 other cataloged items. **Services:** Copying; library open to the public. **Computerized Information Services:** LEXIS.

★5279★
El Monte Historical Society Museum - Library (Hist)
3150 Tyler Ave. — Phone: (818)444-3813
El Monte, CA 91731 — Lillian Freer Potter, Libn.
Founded: 1958. **Staff:** Prof 4. **Subjects:** History - local, state, regional, national. **Holdings:** 3000 books; 500 bound periodical volumes; 2000 uncataloged items; manuscripts; photographs; films ; diaries. **Services:** Copying; library open to the public with restrictions. **Publications:** The Landmark, quarterly. **Staff:** Tary Ballard, Comp./Res.; Marie Schaefer, Cur.; Fred Love, Building Engr./Res.

★5280★
El Paso County Law Library (Law)
104 Judicial Bldg.
20 E. Vermijo Phone: (719)630-2880
Colorado Springs, CO 80903 Molly Walker, Law Libn.
Founded: 1973. **Staff:** Prof 1. **Subjects:** Law - corporate, state, tax, inheritance, labor, pension plan. **Holdings:** 20,000 volumes. **Subscriptions:** 40 journals and other serials. **Services:** Interlibrary loan; copying; library open to the public for reference use only. **Computerized Information Services:** WESTLAW, VU/TEXT Information Services, DIALOG Information Services, OCLC. Performs searches on fee basis. **Remarks:** Jointly maintained by Colorado State Judicial Department and El Paso County Bar Association. **Remarks:** FAX: (719)630-3389.

★5281★
El Paso County Law Library (Law)
500 E. San Antonio St. Phone: (915)546-2245
El Paso, TX 79901 Lynn E. Sanchez, Libn.
Founded: 1950. **Staff:** Prof 2; Other 1. **Subjects:** Law. **Holdings:** 24,422 volumes. **Subscriptions:** 49 journals and other serials. **Services:** Interlibrary loan; copying; library open to the public for reference use only. **Staff:** Gigi L. Goode, Asst.Libn.

El Paso Herald-Post
See: **El Paso Times, Inc.** (5287)

★5282★
El Paso Museum of Art - Library (Art)
1211 Montana Ave.
El Paso, TX 79902-5588 Phone: (915)541-4040
Subjects: Art, art history, history, anthropology. **Holdings:** 3000 books. **Subscriptions:** 10 journals and other serials. **Services:** Library open to the public for reference use only.

★5283★
El Paso Natural Gas Company - Engineering & Technical Information Center (Energy)
Box 1492 Phone: (915)541-3085
El Paso, TX 79978 Anne S. Wise, Coord.
Founded: 1974. **Staff:** 1. **Subjects:** Natural gas transmission, gas industry and technology, alternate fuels, business and economics. **Holdings:** 2000 books. **Subscriptions:** 100 journals and other serials. **Services:** Interlibrary loan; copying; SDI; center open to the public by appointment. **Computerized Information Services:** DIALOG Information Services, PFDS Online; A.G.A. GasNet (electronic mail service). **Publications:** Bulletin; serials list, biennial. **Remarks:** Alternate telephone number(s): 541-3067. FAX: (915)541-3155.

★5284★
El Paso Public Library - Genealogy Section (Hist)
501 N. Oregon St. Phone: (915)543-5475
El Paso, TX 79901 Ramiro S. Salazar, Dir. of Libs.
Staff: Prof 1; Other 2. **Subjects:** Genealogy. **Special Collections:** Daughters of the American Revolution Lineage Books; official records of the Union and Confederate Armies. **Holdings:** 4500 books; 825 bound periodical volumes; 5 VF drawers; 391 reels of microfilm. **Subscriptions:** 59 journals and other serials. **Services:** Interlibrary loan; copying; section open to the public. **Automated Operations:** Computerized cataloging. **Computerized Information Services:** OCLC. **Networks/Consortia:** Member of AMIGOS Bibliographic Council, Inc. **Remarks:** FAX: (915)543-5410. **Staff:** Ann Marshall May, Docs./Geneal.Libn.

★5285★
El Paso Public Library - Southwest Collection (Hist)
501 N. Oregon St. Phone: (915)543-5440
El Paso, TX 79901 Wayne Daniel, Southwest Libn.
Founded: 1906. **Staff:** Prof 1; Other 2. **Subjects:** El Paso, Texas; New Mexico; Arizona; Mexican Revolution. **Special Collections:** Aultman Collection (6000 negatives and prints); Trost Architectural Collection (150 sets of plans; 600 photographs); Rusk-Edwards papers. **Holdings:** 25,000 books; 3000 bound periodical volumes; 20,000 photographs, negatives, prints; 400 architectural plans; 300 linear feet of archival materials and manuscripts; 80 VF drawers. **Subscriptions:** 95 journals and other serials. **Services:** Interlibrary loan; copying; collection open to the public. **Special Indexes:** Index to El Paso newspapers, 1881 to present. **Remarks:** FAX: (915)543-5410.

★5286★
El Paso Times - Library (Publ)
401 Mills Ave. Phone: (915)546-6179
El Paso, TX 79901 Judy Soles
Founded: 1940. **Staff:** Prof 1. **Subjects:** Newspaper reference topics. **Holdings:** Newspaper clippings. **Services:** Library not open to the public. **Remarks:** FAX: (915)546-6415.

★5287★
El Paso Times, Inc. - Library (Publ)
Box 20 Phone: (915)546-6263
El Paso, TX 79999 Judy Soles, Chf.Libn.
Staff: Prof 1; Other 1. **Subjects:** Newspaper reference topics. **Holdings:** 200 books; vertical files on 1500 subjects; 1200 rolls of newspaper. **Special Indexes:** Index to Herald-Post, January 1985 to December 1986 (card), January 1987 to present; 1989 monthly and cumulative index, through December 1991 (online). **Formerly:** El Paso Herald-Post.

Frederick Elbel Library
See: **Northern Indiana Historical Society** (12004)

Elbin Library
See: **West Liberty State College** (20195)

Elconin Center Library
See: **West Coast University** (20189)

★5288★
Electric Power Research Institute - Technical Library (Energy)
3412 Hillview Ave. Phone: (415)855-2354
Palo Alto, CA 94304 Stephen B. Parker, Libn.
Founded: 1974. **Staff:** Prof 2; Other 3. **Subjects:** Energy, engineering, environmental studies, nuclear power, electric power generation and transmission. **Special Collections:** EPRI reports and videos; foreign report collection. **Holdings:** 10,000 books; 10,000 microfiche; U.S. utility annual reports. **Subscriptions:** 750 journals and other serials; 7 newspapers. **Services:** Interlibrary loan; copying; SDI; library open to sponsored users only. **Automated Operations:** Computerized cataloging, acquisitions, serials, circulation, and routing. **Computerized Information Services:** DIALOG Information Services, RLIN; internal databases; OnTyme Electronic Message Network Service (electronic mail service). **Networks/Consortia:** Member of CLASS. **Publications:** Library Currents, 6/year - for internal distribution only. **Remarks:** FAX: (415)855-1080. Electronic mail address(es): EPRI (OnTyme Electronic Message Network Service II).

Electrochemical Society - National Foundation for History of Chemistry
See: **University of Pennsylvania - National Foundation for History of Chemistry - Library** (19190)

★5289★
Electrocom GARD - Library (Sci-Engr)
7449 N. Natchez Ave. Phone: (708)647-9000
Niles, IL 60648 Ida Carter, Tech.Libn.
Founded: 1965. **Staff:** Prof 1. **Subjects:** Engineering, energy applications, manufacturing technology, materials engineering, mechanics research, instrumentation and controls, nondestructive testing. **Holdings:** 4800 volumes; 12 drawers of military and federal standards and specifications; 700 technical reports. **Subscriptions:** 175 journals and other serials. **Services:** Interlibrary loan; library open to the public with prior approval. **Computerized Information Services:** DIALOG Information Services, DTIC. **Networks/Consortia:** Member of North Suburban Library System (NSLS), ILLINET. **Publications:** New Arrivals, monthly - for internal distribution only. **Remarks:** FAX: (708)647-8678. **Formerly:** Chamberlain GARD Division - Library.

Electromagnetic Compatibility Analysis Center
See: **IIT Research Institute - Electromagnetic Compatibility Analysis Center** (7660)

Electromagnetic Systems Laboratories
See: **ESL/Subsidiary of TRW, Inc.** (5439)

★5290★
Electronic Industries Association - Marketing Services Research Center (Sci-Engr)
2001 Pennsylvania Ave., N.W. Phone: (202)457-8739
Washington, DC 20006-1813 Michelle C. Bing, Mgr.
Founded: 1984. **Staff:** Prof 1; Other 1. **Subjects:** Electronics industry, consumer electronics industry. **Holdings:** 2000 books and reports; 350 subject files. **Subscriptions:** 150 journals and other serials; 2 newspapers. **Services:** Research available on a fee basis to non-members. **Computerized Information Services:** DIALOG Information Services, NewsNet, Inc., NEXIS, DataTimes. **Publications:** Research Center UPDATE (overview of news and research in the electronics industry), monthly - available by subscription. **Remarks:** FAX: (202)457-8745.

★5291★
Electronics Museum - De Forest Memorial Archive
Foothill College
El Monte Rd. at I-280
Los Altos Hills, CA 94022
Defunct.

★5292★
Electronics and Space Corporation - Technical Library (Sci-Engr)
8100 W. Florissant Ave. Phone: (314)553-3334
St. Louis, MO 63136 Chris Cooksey, Libn.
Staff: Prof 1; Other 1. **Subjects:** Engineering, physics, mathematics, computers, data processing, systems management. **Special Collections:** Military specifications and standards. **Holdings:** Figures not available.

★5293★
Electronics and Telecommunications Research Institute - ETRI Technical Information Center (Sci-Engr, Info Sci)
P.O. Box 8
Daedog Danji Phone: 861-4455
Daejeon 305-606, Republic of Korea Min-Ho Key, Dir., Tech.Info.Ctr.
Staff: 51. **Subjects:** Information technology, telecommunications, computer science, automation, elctronics, semiconductors. **Holdings:** 65,000 volumes. **Subscriptions:** 700. **Services:** Interlibrary loan; copying; center open to the public. **Computerized Information Services:** DIALOG Information Services, BRS Information Technologies; KIETLINE, ETLARS (internal databases). **Remarks:** FAX: 042-861-1033. Telex: K45532. Maintained by Korea - Ministry of Science and Technology.

★5294★
The Electrosynthesis Company, Inc. - Library (Sci-Engr)
P.O. Box 430 Phone: (716)684-0513
East Amherst, NY 14051 H.R. Weinberg
Founded: 1977. **Subjects:** Electrochemistry, electrosynthesis, batteries, fuel cells, corrosion, pollution control. **Holdings:** 2500 volumes. **Subscriptions:** 26 journals and other serials. **Services:** Interlibrary loan; library open to clients only. **Computerized Information Services:** Internal database. **Remarks:** FAX: (716)684-0511.

★5295★
Elf Aquitaine, Inc. - Library (Sci-Engr)
280 Park Ave., 36th Fl.
New York, NY 10017 Phone: (212)922-3000
Subjects: Mining engineering, natural resources, chemistry, metallurgy, chemical engineering. **Holdings:** 2000 books; bound U.S. patents; legal files. **Subscriptions:** 53 journals and other serials. **Services:** Interlibrary loan; copying; library open to the public. **Formerly:** Located in Stamford, CT.

★5296★
ELF ATOCHEM North America Inc. - Library (Sci-Engr)
900 First Ave. Phone: (215)337-6548
King of Prussia, PA 19406 Louis P. Torre
Founded: 1944. **Staff:** Prof 6; Other 3. **Subjects:** Chemistry. **Holdings:** 10,000 books; 20,000 bound periodical volumes. **Subscriptions:** 400 journals and other serials. **Services:** Library not open to the public. **Remarks:** FAX: (215)337-6784. **Formerly:** ATOCHEM North America Inc. **Staff:** Susan Hunsicker; Leah Yocum; Kathryn M. Donovan; Barbara Cavallo; John Hack.

★5297★
Elf Exploration, Inc. - Library (Energy)
1000 Louisiana, Suite 3800
First Interstate Bank Plaza Phone: (713)739-2021
Houston, TX 77002 Alan D. Powell, Supv., Doc.
Founded: 1978. **Staff:** Prof 2. **Subjects:** Petroleum - exploration, production, industry and trade; geology; computer science. **Holdings:** 5000 books; 100 bound periodical volumes; 2000 maps and satellite photographs; 100 reports. **Subscriptions:** 160 journals and other serials; 5 newspapers. **Services:** Interlibrary loan; copying; SDI; library open to the public by appointment. **Automated Operations:** Computerized cataloging and circulation. **Computerized Information Services:** DIALOG Information Services, PFDS Online, NEXIS, Dow Jones News/Retrieval, Dwight's Energydata, Inc., Petroleum Information Corporation (PI), DataTimes, VU/TEXT Information Services; internal database; Missive, DIALMAIL (electronic mail services). **Publications:** Daily News Summary - for internal distribution only; new acquisitions, monthly. **Remarks:** Alternate telephone number(s): 739-2018. FAX: (713)650-3621. Telex: 790 587 PETRAKI HOU. Electronic mail address(es): ELF AQUITAINE PETROLEUM (DIALMAIL). **Formerly:** Elf Aquitaine Petroleum. **Staff:** Elizabeth A. Evans, Sr.Libn.

Elftman Memorial Library
See: **Salvation Army School for Officers Training** (14657)

★5298★
Elgin Mental Health Center - Library (Med)
750 S. State St. Phone: (708)742-1040
Elgin, IL 60123 Jennifer Ford, Lib.Dir.
Founded: 1872. **Staff:** Prof 1; Other 3. **Subjects:** Psychology, psychiatry, medicine, social work, nursing. **Holdings:** 15,000 books; 900 bound periodical volumes; 500 audiocassettes; 25 VF drawers; 4 VF drawers of bibliographies. **Subscriptions:** 140 journals and other serials; 12 newspapers. **Services:** Interlibrary loan; copying; SDI; library open to the public with restrictions on borrowing. **Automated Operations:** Computerized serials. **Networks/Consortia:** Member of National Network of Libraries of Medicine - Greater Midwest Region, Fox Valley Health Science Library Consortium (FVHSL), Illinois Department of Mental Health and Developmental Disabilities Library Services Network (LISN). **Publications:** Serials Holdings List, annual. **Remarks:** FAX: (708)742-1063. Maintained by Illinois State Department of Mental Health and Developmental Disabilities. **Formerly:** Its Anton Boisen Professional Library.

John Eliot Library
See: **United Church of Christ First Congregational Church of Woodstock - John Eliot Library** (16699)

Eliot Elisofon Archives
See: **Smithsonian Institution - National Museum of African Art** (15264)

★5299★
Elizabeth General Medical Center - Charles H. Schlichter, M.D. Health Science Library (Med)
925 E. Jersey St. Phone: (908)558-8092
Elizabeth, NJ 07201 Catherine M. Boss, Dir.
Staff: Prof 2. **Subjects:** Nursing, medicine. **Holdings:** 4332 books; 3023 microfilm and bound periodical volumes. **Subscriptions:** 230 journals and other serials. **Services:** Interlibrary loan; copying; library open to the public with restrictions. **Computerized Information Services:** MEDLARS, BRS Information Technologies; MESSAGES (electronic mail service). Performs searches on fee basis. **Networks/Consortia:** Member of Cosmopolitan Biomedical Library Consortium (CBLC), BHSL, Health Sciences Library Association of New Jersey (HSLANJ). **Special Catalogs:** Catalog of audiovisuals (card, book). **Remarks:** FAX: (908)820-8974. **Staff:** Donald Miller, Asst.Dir.

Elizabethan Club Collection
See: **Yale University** (20711)

★5300★
Elizabethtown College - The High Library - Archives (Hist)
Elizabethtown, PA 17022-2298 Phone: (717)367-1151
Dr. Nelson P. Bard, Jr., Dir.
Founded: 1899. **Staff:** 12.5. **Special Collections:** Archives of Elizabethtown College; Brethren Heritage Room (materials relating to the Church of the Brethren). **Holdings:** 129,530 books; 20,000 bound periodical volumes; 388 manuscripts; 62,951 microfiche; 7458 reels of microfilm; 29,352 media items. **Subscriptions:** 1100 journals and other serials; 11 newspapers. **Services:** Interlibrary loan; copying; archives open to the public for reference use only. **Automated Operations:** Computerized , public access catalog, cataloging and ILL. **Computerized Information Services:** OCLC, DIALOG Information Services, Academic Index; CD-ROM (Intelligent Catalog). **Networks/Consortia:** Member of PALINET, Associated College Libraries of Central Pennsylvania (ACLCP). **Remarks:** FAX: (717)367-7567. **Formerly:** Zug Memorial Library. **Staff:** Peter J. DePuydt; Hedwig T. Durnbaugh; E. Margaret Gabel; Naomi L. Hershey; Sylvia Tiffany Morra.

★5301★
Elk County Law Library (Law)
Court House Phone: (814)776-1161
Ridgway, PA 15853 Martha Keller Masson, Lib.Dir.
Subjects: Law. **Remarks:** No further information was supplied by respondent.

★5302★
Elko Medical Clinic - Library
762 14th St.
Elko, NV 89801
Defunct.

Elks Library
See: **Barlow Respiratory Hospital** (1531)

E. R. Eller Library
See: **Carnegie Museum of Natural History - Library** (3085)

Duke Ellington Collection
See: **Smithsonian Institution - National Museum of American History - Archives Center** (15269)

★5303★
Elliot Hospital - Medical Library (Med)
955 Auburn St. Phone: (603)669-5300
Manchester, NH 03103 Judy Reingold, Dir.
Founded: 1976. **Staff:** Prof 1; Other 1. **Subjects:** Medicine, nursing, health administration. **Holdings:** 1500 books; 5000 bound periodical volumes; 1000 microfiche. **Subscriptions:** 300 journals and other serials. **Services:** Interlibrary loan; library not open to the public. **Computerized Information Services:** MEDLARS, BRS/COLLEAGUE, WILSONLINE. **Remarks:** FAX: (603)627-0561.

★5304★
Elliott Company - Library (Sci-Engr)
N. Fourth St. Phone: (412)527-8054
Jeannette, PA 15644 Joan Costers, Sec.
Staff: Prof 1. **Subjects:** Turbines, compressors. **Holdings:** 2300 books; 4200 pamphlets; 900 company technical reports and memoranda; 300 microfiche. **Subscriptions:** 50 journals and other serials. **Services:** Interlibrary loan; library not open to the public.

★5305★
Ellis County Historical Society - Archives (Hist)
100 W. 7th St. Phone: (913)628-2624
Hays, KS 67601 Janet Johannes, Archv.
Founded: 1971. **Staff:** Prof 1. **Subjects:** Local history, Volga-German migration. **Special Collections:** Records of the Munjor Town and Grazing Company (.5 linear feet); miscellaneous papers of former U.S. Congresswoman Kathryn O'Loughlin McCarthy (.5 linear feet); Volga-German Centennial photograph collection (2000); Guercio Studio photography collection (25,000 negatives and prints). **Holdings:** 64,000 documents and photographs. **Services:** Copying; archives open to the public with restrictions. **Publications:** Homesteader, quarterly - to members. **Staff:** Jo Riedel, Musm.Dir.

Dean B. Ellis Library
See: **Arkansas State University** (1033)

★5306★
Ellis Hospital - MacMillan Library (Med)
1101 Nott St. Phone: (518)382-4381
Schenectady, NY 12308 Christopher Stater, Dir.
Founded: 1930. **Staff:** Prof 1; Other 2. **Subjects:** Medicine, nursing, hospital administration, allied health. **Special Collections:** Hospital Satellite Network (video collection; 1600 items). **Holdings:** 2000 books; 5000 bound periodical volumes. **Subscriptions:** 180 journals and other serials. **Services:** Interlibrary loan; library not open to the public. **Computerized Information Services:** MEDLARS, BRS Information Technologies. **Networks/Consortia:** Member of Capital District Library Council for Reference & Research Resources (CDLC). **Remarks:** FAX: (518)382-4029.

Ellis Island Library
See: **U.S. Natl. Park Service - Statue of Liberty-Ellis Island Library** (17782)

Laura M. Ellis Memorial Library
See: **Center for Early Education/College for Developmental Studies** (3235)

Richard Ellis Library and Archive
See: **Temple University - Central Library System - Rare Book & Manuscript Collection** (16137)

George Elliston Poetry Collection
See: **University of Cincinnati** (18471)

Ellwanger & Barry Horticultural Library
See: **University of Rochester - Department of Rare Books and Special Collections** (19278)

ELM Trust
See: **American Watchmakers Institute** (785)

★5307★
Elmbrook Memorial Hospital - Mary Beth Curtis Health Science Library (Med)
19333 W. North Ave. Phone: (414)785-2091
Brookfield, WI 53045 Mary Rheineck, Med.Libn.
Staff: Prof 1. **Subjects:** Medicine, nursing, hospital administration. **Holdings:** 1600 books; 35 boxes of pamphlets; 4 VF drawers; 200 reels of microfilm of periodicals. **Subscriptions:** 130 journals and other serials. **Services:** Interlibrary loan; copying; library open to the public for reference use only. **Computerized Information Services:** BRS Information Technologies, MEDLARS; DOCLINE (electronic mail service). **Networks/Consortia:** Member of Southeastern Wisconsin Health Science Library Consortium (SWHSL). **Remarks:** FAX: (414)785-9162.

★5308★
Elmhurst Historical Museum - Library (Hist)
120 E. Park Ave. Phone: (708)833-1457
Elmhurst, IL 60126 Brian F. Bergheger, Dir.
Staff: 3. **Subjects:** History of Elmhurst and DuPage County, genealogy, museology. **Holdings:** 350 books; 142 reels of microfilm of local newspapers and state and federal censuses of DuPage County; 1400 slides; 100 oral history tapes and cassettes; 300 linear feet of archival materials, manuscripts, maps, photographs. **Subscriptions:** 15 journals and other serials. **Services:** Copying; library open to the public for reference use only. **Special Catalogs:** Guide to Research Collections of Elmhurst Historical Museum (loose-leaf); manuscript and iconographic catalog (card).

Elmhurst Hospital Center
See: **Mount Sinai Services** (10820)

★5309★
Elmhurst Memorial Hospital - Marquardt Memorial Library (Med)
200 Berteau Ave. Phone: (708)833-1400
Elmhurst, IL 60126 Pauline Ng, Dir.
Staff: Prof 1; Other 14. **Subjects:** Medicine, allied health sciences. **Holdings:** 2480 books; 2689 audiotapes; 769 videotapes; 800 files of pamphlets. **Subscriptions:** 250 journals and other serials. **Services:** Interlibrary loan; library not open to the public. **Automated Operations:** Computerized cataloging. **Computerized Information Services:** MEDLARS, DIALOG Information Services, BRS Information Technologies. **Networks/Consortia:** Member of National Network of Libraries of Medicine - Greater Midwest Region, Suburban Library System (SLS), Illinois Health Libraries Consortium, Fox Valley Health Science Library Consortium (FVHSL). **Publications:** New Acquisitions, monthly - for internal distribution only. **Remarks:** FAX: (312)833-9312.

★5310★
Elmira Psychiatric Center - Professional Library (Med)
Caller 1527 Phone: (607)737-4769
Elmira, NY 14902 Consuelo R. Madumba, Act.Dir., Educ. & Trng.
Founded: 1973. **Staff:** 1. **Subjects:** Psychiatry, psychology, sociology. **Holdings:** 2416 books; 798 AV programs. **Subscriptions:** 58 journals and other serials. **Services:** Interlibrary loan; copying; library open to the public. **Special Catalogs:** Catalog of AV holdings.

★5311★
Elmira Star Gazette - Library (Publ)
201 Baldwin St.
Box 285 Phone: (607)734-5151
Elmira, NY 14902-9976 Peggy Ridosh, Libn.
Staff: 1. **Subjects:** Newspaper reference topics. **Special Collections:** Newspaper, 1835 to present, on microfilm. **Holdings:** 50 books; 9 VF drawers of photographs; 130 VF drawers of clippings. **Services:** Library open to the public with restrictions. **Remarks:** FAX: (607)733-4408.

★5312★
Elrick and Lavidge, Inc. - Library (Bus-Fin)
3 Westbrook Corporate Center, Suite 600 Phone: (708)449-5300
Westchester, IL 60154 Mrs. Pat Taylor, Libn.
Founded: 1965. **Staff:** 1. **Subjects:** Market research, marketing, consumer behavior, business and management, industry, statistics. **Special Collections:** Primary research reports (6000); industrial market research reference books. **Holdings:** 300 books; 7 VF drawers of pamphlets; 2 drawers of maps; 100 directories; 283 telephone directories; census publications. **Subscriptions:** 50 journals and other serials. **Services:** Interlibrary loan; library not open to the public. **Computerized Information Services:** DIALOG Information Services. **Special Catalogs:** Catalog to primary research reports (card); catalog to reference supplements. **Remarks:** A subsidiary of Equifax, Inc. FAX: (312)726-7511.

★5313★
ELTECH Systems Corporation - Library (Sci-Engr)
625 East St. Phone: (216)357-4000
Fairport Harbor, OH 44077 Sheryl Kinley-Alligood, Info.Serv.Spec.
Subjects: Electrochemical technology - membrane cells, aluminum/air power sources, battery systems, electrodes, air cathodes, electrochemical catalysts, ceramics, asbestos replacement materials, ferrites, electrode coatings. **Holdings:** 15,000 volumes. **Remarks:** FAX: (216)357-4077. Subsidiaries are Electrode Corporation (Chardon, OH) and Elgard Corporation (Chardon, OH).

★5314★
Elvis, This One's For You Fan Club - Library (Mus)
1905 Paramount Ave. Phone: (512)462-9093
Austin, TX 78704 Casey Korenek, Pres.
Founded: 1986. **Staff:** Prof 1. **Subjects:** Elvis Presley. **Holdings:** 150 books; 200 bound periodical volumes. **Subscriptions:** 25 newsletters. **Services:** Interlibrary loan; library open to the public with restrictions. **Automated Operations:** Computerized cataloging. **Publications:** Newsletter - for internal distribution only.

★5315★
Walter Elwood Museum - Library (Biol Sci)
300 Guy Park Ave. Phone: (518)843-5151
Amsterdam, NY 12010 Mary Margaret Gage, Dir.
Founded: 1940. **Staff:** Prof 1; Other 1. **Subjects:** Wildlife, religion, history, government. **Holdings:** 1500 books. **Services:** Library open to the public for reference use only. **Remarks:** Maintained by Mohawk Valley Heritage Association, Inc.

★5316★
Elwyn Institutes - Elwyn Staff Library (Med)
111 Elwyn Rd. Phone: (215)891-2084
Elwyn, PA 19063 Joyce Lentz, Libn.
Founded: 1968. **Staff:** Prof 1. **Subjects:** Mental retardation, special education, vocational rehabilitation, psychology, medicine. **Holdings:** 2500 volumes; 8 VF drawers of reprints, reports, bibliographies, and brochures. **Subscriptions:** 50 journals and other serials. **Services:** Interlibrary loan; copying; library open to the public for reference use only. **Networks/Consortia:** Member of Consortium for Health Information & Library Services (CHI). **Publications:** Acquisitions, 3/year - to staff members. **Remarks:** FAX: (215)891-2088.

Elyria Chronicle-Telegram
See: **Lorain County Printing & Publishing Company** (9304)

★5317★
Elyria Memorial Hospital - Library (Med)
630 E. River St. Phone: (216)323-3221
Elyria, OH 44035 Linda Masek, Hd.Libn.
Founded: 1975. **Staff:** Prof 1; Other 3. **Subjects:** Orthopedics, nursing, pediatrics. **Holdings:** 3783 books; 3102 bound periodical volumes; 20 VF drawers of pamphlets, reports, clippings, bibliographies, AV programs. **Subscriptions:** 260 journals and other serials. **Services:** Interlibrary loan; library not open to the public. **Computerized Information Services:** MEDLINE. **Networks/Consortia:** Member of National Network of Libraries of Medicine - Greater Midwest Region.

★5318★
Elysium Archives (Soc Sci)
5436 Fernwood Ave. Phone: (213)455-1000
Los Angeles, CA 90027 Ralph Gerowitz, Res.Libn.
Founded: 1969. **Staff:** Prof 2. **Subjects:** Nudism, naturism, human potential. **Special Collections:** Lange Collection; Price Collection. **Holdings:** 5000 books; 2000 bound periodical volumes; AV programs; videotapes; motion pictures. **Subscriptions:** 20 journals and other serials; 6 newspapers. **Services:** Archives open to the public by appointment on fee basis. **Publications:** Journal of the Senses. **Remarks:** FAX: (213)455-2007.

★5319★
Emanuel Congregation - Joseph Taussig Memorial Library (Rel-Phil)
5959 N. Sheridan Rd. Phone: (312)561-5173
Chicago, IL 60660 Rose S. Levenson
Founded: 1930. **Staff:** Prof 1. **Subjects:** Judaica, Judaism, children's Jewish literature, theology. **Special Collections:** Israel collection (200 books); outreach collection (100 books explaining Judaism). **Holdings:** 2000 books; 50 reports. **Subscriptions:** 20 journals and other serials; 3 newspapers. **Services:** Library open to the public at librarian's discretion.

★5320★
Emanuel Hospital & Health Center - Library Services (Med)
2801 N. Gantenbein Ave. Phone: (503)280-3558
Portland, OR 97227 Ford Schmidt, Dir.
Staff: Prof 1; Other 2. **Subjects:** Medicine, nursing, allied health sciences. **Special Collections:** Burn care; surgery; trauma care. **Holdings:** 2000 books. **Subscriptions:** 250 journals and other serials. **Services:** Interlibrary loan; SDI; library open to the public for reference use only. **Computerized Information Services:** MEDLARS, BRS Information Technologies; DOCLINE, OnTyme Electronic Message Network Service (electronic mail services). **Networks/Consortia:** Member of Oregon Health Information Online (ORHION). **Remarks:** Includes the holdings of the School of Nursing Library. FAX: (503)280-3757.

★5321★
Emanuel Medical Center - Medical Library (Med)
825 Delbon Ave.
Box 2120 Phone: (209)667-4200
Turlock, CA 95381-2120 Donna Cardoza, Lib.Ck.
Staff: 1. **Subjects:** Medicine, allied health sciences. **Holdings:** 836 books; 210 bound periodical volumes. **Subscriptions:** 115 journals and other serials. **Services:** Interlibrary loan; copying; library open for professional use. **Networks/Consortia:** Member of National Network of Libraries of Medicine - Pacific Southwest Region, 49-99 Cooperative Library System, FEDLINK, North San Joaquin Health Sciences Library Consortium.

★5322★
Embassy of France - Press and Information Service - Documentation Center (Area-Ethnic)
4101 Reservoir Rd. N.W.
Washington, DC 20007-2182 Phone: (202)944-6060
Staff: Prof 7. **Subjects:** France - general, domestic politics, foreign policy, economics, social policy, press. **Special Collections:** Le Monde collection; major French publications; Journal Officiel; French Resistance collection; French Colonial Empire collection; French reference guides; French political journals. **Holdings:** Figures not available. **Services:** Copying; center open to the public by appointment. **Computerized Information Services:** Produces News From France (available online through NewsNet, Inc.). **Publications:** News From France; Facts on France; France Magazine. **Remarks:** FAX: (202)944-6072.

★5323★
Embassy of India - Library of the Information Service of India (Area-Ethnic)
2107 Massachusetts Ave., N.W. Phone: (202)939-7000
Washington, DC 20008 Lata Deshdande, Libn.
Staff: Prof 3. **Subjects:** India - philosophy, religion, history, geography, literature, food and agriculture, economics, political science. **Special Collections:** Rabindranath Tagore collection; Mahatma Gandhi collection; Sri Aurobindo collection. **Holdings:** 11,200 volumes. **Subscriptions:** 110 journals and other serials; 40 newspapers. **Services:** Interlibrary loan; library open to the public.

★5324★
Embassy of New Zealand - Library (Area-Ethnic)
37 Observatory Circle, N.W. Phone: (202)328-4800
Washington, DC 20008 Mei Taare, Pub.Aff.Off.
Founded: 1953. **Staff:** Prof 3. **Subjects:** New Zealand - history, literature, geography, foreign policy, Polynesian peoples. **Special Collections:** Maori people; South Pacific Islands. **Holdings:** 2100 volumes. **Services:** Interlibrary loan; library open to the public. **Publications:** New Zealand Update, monthly.

★5325★
Embassy of Sweden - Library-Information Center (Area-Ethnic)
Watergate 600, Suite 1200
600 New Hampshire Ave., N.W. Phone: (202)944-5600
Washington, DC 20037 Larilyn Andre, Libn.
Staff: 1. **Subjects:** Sweden - social policy, ethnology, government, history, education, literature. **Holdings:** 4000 books and bound periodical volumes; yearly publications by the Swedish government including the Yearbook of Nordic Statistics. **Services:** Library not open to the public. **Remarks:** FAX: (202)625-6046. Telex: RCA 248347 SUSK UR.

★5326★
Embroiderers' Guild of America - Library (Rec)
335 W. Broadway, Suite 100 Phone: (502)589-6956
Louisville, KY 40202 Marijean Booske, Libn.
Staff: 2. **Subjects:** Embroidery. **Subjects:** Needle arts and design. **Holdings:** 4000 books; videotapes; pamphlet file. **Services:** Library open to the public; borrowing privileges reserved for members only. **Publications:** Needle Arts, quarterly.

★5327★
Embry Riddle Aeronautical University - Jack R. Hunt Memorial Library (Sci-Engr)
Daytona Beach, FL 32114 Phone: (904)226-6595
Richard E. Waddell, Lib.Dir.
Founded: 1965. **Staff:** Prof 11; Other 9. **Subjects:** Aviation, management, aeronautical engineering. **Special Collections:** Aviation history (10,000 volumes). **Holdings:** 44,300 books; 5700 bound periodical volumes; 21,000 documents; 115,000 reports on microfiche; 2750 AV programs; 1530 journal titles; 5000 reels of microfilm. **Subscriptions:** 961 journals and other serials. **Services:** Interlibrary loan; copying; library open to the public. **Automated Operations:** Computerized public access catalog, cataloging, acquisitions, and circulation. **Computerized Information Services:** DIALOG Information Services. **Networks/Consortia:** Member of SOLINET, Florida Library Network (FLN), Central Florida Library Consortium (CFLC). **Special Catalogs:** Periodicals Holdings List; Media Catalog. **Remarks:** FAX: (904)226-6368. **Staff:** Kathleen Citro, Ref.Serv.; Thomas Tipsword, Sys./Tech.Serv.; Jacqueline Henning, Media/Circ.

Emergency Care Research Institute
See: **ECRI** (5219)

★5328★
Emerson College - Library (Info Sci)
150 Beacon St. Phone: (617)578-8670
Boston, MA 02116 Mickey Moskowitz, Dir.
Founded: 1892. **Staff:** Prof 8; Other 12. **Subjects:** Speech communication, mass communications, speech pathology, theater arts. **Holdings:** 146,000 books; 4309 bound periodical volumes; 1011 phonotapes; 4167 phonograph records; 14,198 microforms; 978 videotapes; 101 filmstrips; 5480 slides; 157 films; 7 models. **Subscriptions:** 1100 journals and other serials. **Services:** Interlibrary loan; library open to the public with college identification card or letter of introduction from other library. **Automated Operations:** Computerized public access catalog, cataloging, circulation, acquisitions, and ILL. **Computerized Information Services:** DIALOG Information Services, OCLC; BITNET (electronic mail service). **Networks/Consortia:** Member of NELINET, Inc., Fenway Library Consortium (FLC). **Remarks:** FAX: (617)578-8509. Electronic mail address(es): MMOSKOWITZ@EMERSON (BITNET). **Staff:** Elizabeth Bezera, Assoc.Dir., Pub.Serv.; Joanne Schmidt, Asst.Dir., Bibliog.Serv.; David Murphy, Hd. of Media; Robert Fleming, Archv.; Ross Schennum, Circ.Mgr.

Ruth Emerson Library
See: **American Institute of Baking** (630)

Emge Medical Library
See: **California Pacific Medical Center - California Campus** (2497)

★5329★
Emmaus Bible College - Library (Rel-Phil)
2570 Asbury Rd. Phone: (312)383-7000
Dubuque, IA 52001-3044 John Rush, Libn.
Founded: 1941. **Staff:** Prof 1. **Subjects:** Biblical studies. **Special Collections:** Plymouth Brethren Writings (books; pamphlets; periodicals). **Holdings:** 43,000 books and AV programs; 6000 bound periodical volumes. **Subscriptions:** 250 journals and other serials. **Services:** Interlibrary loan; copying; library open to the public with restrictions.

★5330★
Emory and Henry College - Appalachian Oral History Collection (Hist)
Emory, VA 24327-0947 Phone: (703)944-4121
Thelma J. Hutchins, Dir.
Staff: 1. **Subjects:** Southwest Virginia, East Tennessee, social and economic history, agricultural and mining history, personal memoirs. **Holdings:** 1400 hours of tapes; 680 transcripts. **Services:** Copying; collection open to the public for reference use only. **Computerized Information Services:** DIALOG Information Services, OCLC. **Networks/Consortia:** Member of SOLINET. **Remarks:** FAX: (703)944-4592.

Emory University - Crawford Long Hospital
See: **Crawford Long Hospital of Emory University** (9284)

★5331★
Emory University - Documents Center (Info Sci)
Woodruff Library Phone: (404)727-6880
Atlanta, GA 30322 Elizabeth A. McBride, Hd., Doc.Ctr.
Founded: 1956. **Staff:** Prof 1; Other 4. **Subjects:** Publications of the U.S. Government (1789 to present), the U.N., and the League of Nations; Organization of American States official records; selected publications of foreign governments. **Holdings:** 14,500 linear feet of books and bound periodical volumes; 1000 linear feet of microforms; 532,000 microfiche; 8 VF drawers. 1210 journals and other serials. **Services:** Interlibrary loan; copying; U.S. collection open to the public. **Computerized Information Services:** OCLC, DIALOG Information Services, PFDS Online; CD-ROMs. Performs searches on fee basis. **Networks/Consortia:** Member of Georgia Online Database (GOLD), Research Libraries Information Network (RLIN), SOLINET. **Publications:** List of publications - available upon request.

Emory University - Georgia Humanites Council - Georgia Humanities Resource Center
See: **Georgia Humanities Council** (6386)

★5332★
Emory University - James Samuel Guy Library (Sci-Engr)
Atkins Hall
1515 Pierce Dr. Phone: (404)727-6618
Atlanta, GA 30322 Donna Hudson, Hd., Chemistry Lib.
Founded: 1951. **Staff:** Prof 1; Other 2. **Subjects:** Chemistry - organic, physical, analytical, inorganic. **Holdings:** 12,500 books; 12,000 bound periodical volumes; 9000 microforms. **Subscriptions:** 205 journals and other serials. **Services:** Interlibrary loan; library open to the public. **Computerized Information Services:** DIALOG Information Services, OCLC, STN International. **Networks/Consortia:** Member of Georgia Online Database (GOLD), Research Libraries Information Network (RLIN), University Center in Georgia, Inc. **Remarks:** FAX: (404)727-0054.

★5333★
Emory University - Museum of Art and Archaeology - Library (Hist)
Michael C. Carlos Hall Phone: (404)727-6123
Atlanta, GA 30322 Elizabeth Hornor, Coord., Educ.Prog.
Subjects: Egypt, Greece and Rome, ancient America, Mesopotamia, archaeology. **Holdings:** 300 books; 100 documents. **Services:** Library not open to the public. **Remarks:** Alternate telephone number(s): (404)727-4282. FAX: (404)727-4292.

★5334★
Emory University - Pitts Theology Library (Rel-Phil)
Theology Bldg. Phone: (404)727-4166
Atlanta, GA 30322 Channing R. Jeschke, Libn.
Founded: 1914. **Staff:** Prof 7; Other 11. **Subjects:** Theology. **Special Collections:** Wesleyana Collection (2700 volumes); hymnology (8800 volumes); theology (58,876 volumes); Cardinal Henry Edward Manning Library (4300 books; 1500 manuscripts); Richard C. Kessler Reformation Collection (1300 print and manuscript items). **Holdings:** 439,035 volumes; 6700 United Methodist Conference Reports; 4116 reels of microfilm; 79,713 microfiche. **Subscriptions:** 1706 journals and other serials. **Services:** Interlibrary loan; copying; library open to the public. **Automated Operations:** Computerized public access catalog, cataloging, and acquisitions. **Computerized Information Services:** OCLC, RLIN. **Staff:** David Chen, Asst.Libn., Tech.Serv.; Cynthia G. Runyon, Asst.Libn., Pub.Serv.; Achilla I. Erdican, Cat.Libn.; Fred A. Grater, Cat.Libn.; Jackie W. Ammerman, Cur., Archv. & Mss.; Matt Patrick Graham, Ref.Libn.

★5335★
Emory University - School of Law Library (Law)
Gambrell Hall Phone: (404)727-6824
Atlanta, GA 30322 Robin K. Mills, Law Libn.
Founded: 1916. **Staff:** Prof 8; Other 13. **Subjects:** Law. **Holdings:** 262,905 volumes. **Subscriptions:** 5392 journals and other serials. **Services:** Interlibrary loan; copying; library open to members of Bench and Bar. **Automated Operations:** Computerized public access catalog, cataloging, and acquisitions. **Computerized Information Services:** DIALOG Information Services, OCLC, LEXIS, NEXIS, WESTLAW, Legal Trac. **Networks/Consortia:** Member of SOLINET. **Remarks:** FAX: (404)727-6820. **Staff:** Deborah Mann Keene, Assoc.Dir.; Cindy Wang, Acq.; Joice Elam, Ser.; Jane Tuttle, Ref.; Pamela Deemer, Cat.Libn.; Frank Heintz, Pub.Serv.; Jaime Henriquez, Comp.Serv.

★5336★
Emory University - School of Medicine - Health Sciences Center Library (Med)
Atlanta, GA 30322 Phone: (404)727-5820
Carol A. Burns, Dir.
Founded: 1923. **Staff:** Prof 13. **Subjects:** Medicine, dentistry, nursing, public health. **Holdings:** 66,506 books; 113,804 bound periodical volumes; 4143 AV programs. **Subscriptions:** 3095 journals and other serials. **Services:** Interlibrary loan; copying; library open to health professionals in the metropolitan area. **Automated Operations:** Computerized public access catalog, cataloging, circulation, and acquisitions. **Computerized Information Services:** BRS Information Technologies, MEDLINE, DIALOG Information Services; DOCLINE, BITNET (electronic mail services). Performs searches on fee basis. Contact Person: Beth Siegel, Ref.Libn. **Networks/Consortia:** Member of University Center in Georgia, Inc., Atlanta Health Science Libraries Consortium (AHSLC), Consortium of Southern Biomedical Libraries (CONBLS). **Publications:** Book Ends. **Remarks:** FAX: (404)727-5827. Electronic mail address(es): LIBCB@EMUVM1 (BITNET). **Staff:** E. Louise Warren, Coll.Mgt.; Sandra Franklin, Assoc.Dir.; Elaine Keefer, Ref.Libn.; Linda Garr Markwell, Grady Br.Libn.; Joan E. Spring, Cat.; J. Steven Foote, Ser.Cat.; Kathryn J. Torrente, Hd., Ref.Dept.; Michael Greer, ILL Supv.; Bonita Bryan, Circ.Supv.; Barbara Ruelle, Acq.Libn.; Carolyn Brown, Ref.Libn.

★5337★
Emory University - Science Library (Sci-Engr)
Woodruff Library Phone: (404)727-6885
Atlanta, GA 30322 Elaine Wagner, Science Ref.Libn.
Founded: 1955. **Staff:** Prof 3; Other 4. **Subjects:** Biology, psychology, physics, geology, mathematics, computer science, sociology of medicine. **Holdings:** 61,000 books. **Subscriptions:** 2000 journals and other serials. **Services:** Interlibrary loan; library not open to the public. **Automated Operations:** Computerized cataloging and circulation. **Computerized Information Services:** DIALOG Information Services, BRS Information Technologies, DOBIS Canadian Online Library System, STN International, RLIN, OCLC. **Networks/Consortia:** Member of Georgia Online Database (GOLD), Research Libraries Information Network (RLIN), University Center in Georgia, Inc., Center for Research Libraries (CRL). **Publications:** Selected References in Psychology (1988); Guide to Library Resources and Services in the Biological Sciences (1984); Guide to Energy Information (1981); Library Resources for Authors of Scientific Papers (1981); Library Resources for the Study of Communicative Disorders (1982); Guide to Resources in Geology (1985); Selected References in Computer Sciences (1988); Selected References in Mathematics (1988); Selected References in Ecology (1990).

★5338★
Emory University - Special Collections Department (Hist, Rel-Phil)
Woodruff Library Phone: (404)727-6887
Atlanta, GA 30322 Linda M. Matthews, Hd., Spec.Coll.
Founded: 1926. **Staff:** Prof 4; Other 6. **Subjects:** Methodism, Confederate history, Southern history, Southern journalists, Southern literature, Southern women, British and Irish literature, American and Asian Communism, Emory archives. **Special Collections:** Joel Chandler Harris Collection; Julian LaRose Harris papers; Ralph McGill papers; William Butler Yeats; Lady Gregory and Sir William Gregory; Derek Mahon; Seamus Heaney; Ted Hughes; Theodore Draper; Philip Jaffe; Richard H. Rich; William B. Hartsfield; Robert W. Woodruff; Floyd C. Watkins Literary Manuscripts Collection, including letters and manuscripts of Robert Penn Warren, Madison Jones, Carson McCullers, and Raymond Andrews; Victorian literature; Yellowbacks; French Revolution pamphlets; Confederate imprints; Belgian Collection. **Holdings:** 30,000 books; 300 bound periodical volumes; 800 maps; 7500 linear feet of manuscripts; 7000 volumes of Emory University dissertations and theses; 325 reels of microfilm. **Services:** Interlibrary loan (microfilm only); copying; department open to qualified researchers. **Automated Operations:** Computerized public access catalog and cataloging. **Computerized Information Services:** RLIN, OCLC; BITNET (electronic mail service). **Networks/Consortia:** Member of SOLINET, Research Libraries Information Network (RLIN). **Publications:** Manuscript Sources for Civil War History: A Descriptive List of Holdings in the Special Collections Department (1990); Manuscript Sources for Methodist History: A Descriptive List of Holdings in the Special Collections Department (1990); Manuscript Sources for Women's History: A Descriptive List of Holdings in the Special Collections Department (revised 1987); A Guide to Manuscript Sources in the Special Collections Department for Atlanta (1978); Lucy M. Stanton, Artist (1975); Guide to the Charles Holmes Herty Papers (1981); John Hill Hewitt, Sources and Bibliography (1981); A Guide to Manuscript Sources for China, Japan and

Korea (1983). **Remarks:** FAX: (404)727-0053. Electronic mail address(es): LIBBDB@EMUVM1 (BITNET). **Staff:** Virginia J.H. Cain, Proc.Archv.; Beverly D. Bishop, Ref.Archv.; Linda H. Visk, Cat.

★5339★
Emory University - Yerkes Regional Primate Center - Library (Biol Sci)
Atlanta, GA 30322 Phone: (404)727-7764
Nellie Johns, Libn.
Founded: 1945. **Staff:** Prof 1. **Subjects:** Primatology. **Special Collections:** Rare books on primates; collected reprints on primates (3000). **Holdings:** 3000 books; 2000 bound periodical volumes; 1500 bound faculty publications, 1925 to present. **Subscriptions:** 60 journals and other serials. **Services:** Interlibrary loan; library not open to the public. **Computerized Information Services:** DIALOG Information Services, VU/TEXT Information Services, OCLC, DOBIS Canadian Online Library System, RLIN. **Networks/Consortia:** Member of Atlanta Health Science Libraries Consortium (AHSLC), Georgia Online Database (GOLD). **Publications:** Yerkes bibliography, 1925 to present. **Remarks:** FAX: (404)727-7845.

★5340★
Empire Blue Cross Blue Shield - Archives & Corporate Library (Bus-Fin)
3 Park Ave., Mezzanine Phone: (212)251-2385
New York, NY 10016 Daphne Chang, Corp.Libn.
Founded: 1983. **Staff:** Prof 2; Other 3. **Subjects:** Health insurance, medical economics, health industry. **Special Collections:** C. Rufus Rorem Collection; J. Douglas Colman Collection; Louis Pink papers; Dr. Frederick Elliott papers. **Holdings:** 5000 books; 15 bound periodical volumes; 2282 reels of microfilm; corporate archives. **Subscriptions:** 300 journals and other serials; 15 newspapers. **Services:** Interlibrary loan; copying; SDI; archives open to the public with special permission. **Automated Operations:** Computerized cataloging. **Computerized Information Services:** NEXIS, DIALOG Information Services, Dow Jones News/Retrieval, WILSONLINE. **Networks/Consortia:** Member of New York Metropolitan Reference and Research Library Agency, SUNY/OCLC Library Network. **Publications:** Newsclips, daily; Custom Contents, weekly; Journal List; New Book List, monthly. **Remarks:** Alternate telephone number(s): (212)251-2386; (212)251-2384; (212)251-2239, archives only. FAX: (212)481-7230. **Staff:** Albert Marotta, Asst.Libn.; Margaret Willis, ILL/Law Libn.; Beverly Dishon, Archv.

★5341★
Empire Health Services - Health Information Center (Med)
P.O. Box 248 Phone: (509)458-7398
Spokane, WA 99210-0248 Robin Braun, Libn.
Staff: 3. **Subjects:** Cardiology, internal medicine, obstetrics, pediatrics. **Special Collections:** SIDS collection; grief. **Holdings:** Figures not available. **Services:** Interlibrary loan; SDI. **Computerized Information Services:** DIALOG Information Services, MEDLINE; OnTyme Electronic Message Network Service (electronic mail service). Performs searches on fee basis. **Remarks:** FAX: (509)458-7790; (509)838-7977. Electronic mail address(es): DEACONESSMC (OnTyme Electronic Message Network Service). **Staff:** Arleen Libertini.

Emploi et Immigration Canada
See: **Canada - Employment & Immigration Canada** (2694)

★5342★
Employee Benefit Research Institute - Library (Bus-Fin)
2121 K St., N.W., Suite 600 Phone: (202)775-6349
Washington, DC 20037-1896 Jeanette B. Hull, Hd.Libn.
Founded: 1978. **Staff:** Prof 2. **Subjects:** Pension plans, health care benefits, employee benefits, retirement income. **Holdings:** 3700 books and reports; 2500 government documents; 3000 microfiche. **Subscriptions:** 220 journals and other serials; 5 newspapers. **Services:** Interlibrary loan; library open to member firms. **Automated Operations:** Computerized cataloging. **Computerized Information Services:** DIALOG Information Services, Human Resource Information Network (HRIN). **Remarks:** FAX: (202)775-6312. **Staff:** Gail G. Rust, Asst.Libn.

★5343★
Employers Casualty Company - Engineering Department - Technical Resource Center (Sci-Engr)
Box 2759
Dallas, TX 75221 Phone: (214)760-6315
Founded: 1975. **Staff:** Prof 1; Other 1. **Subjects:** Safety engineering, industrial hygiene, traffic safety. **Holdings:** 400 books; 2400 technical reports and pamphlets; 200 AV materials. **Subscriptions:** 35 journals and other serials. **Services:** Interlibrary loan; copying; center open to the public by appointment. **Automated Operations:** Computerized cataloging. **Computerized Information Services:** DIALOG Information Services; internal databases. **Special Indexes:** Information Center Index. **Formerly:** Employers Insurance of Texas.

Employer's Insurance of Texas
See: **Employers Casualty Company - Engineering Department - Technical Resource Center** (5343)

★5344★
Employers Reinsurance Corporation - June Austin Parrish Memorial Library (Bus-Fin)
5200 Metcalf
Box 2991 Phone: (913)676-5681
Overland Park, KS 66201 Marilyn Downs, Libn.
Founded: 1940. **Staff:** Prof 1; Other 1. **Subjects:** Reinsurance, insurance, law. **Special Collections:** Collection of clippings on domestic and international reinsurance. **Holdings:** 10,000 books; 100 bound periodical volumes; 80 VF drawers of pamphlets, bulletins, and proceedings from insurance associations, bureaus, and organizations. **Subscriptions:** 104 journals and other serials. **Services:** Interlibrary loan; copying; library open to the public with restrictions. **Computerized Information Services:** WESTLAW. **Remarks:** FAX: (913)676-5221.

Employment & Immigration Canada
See: **Canada - Employment & Immigration Canada** (2694)

★5345★
Emporia State University - Butcher Toy Lending Library (Educ)
1200 Commercial Phone: (316)343-5360
Emporia, KS 66801 Jeanne Frederickson, Media Spec.
Staff: Prof 1; Other 6. **Subjects:** Early childhood education and skills development. **Holdings:** 30 books; construction blocks; games; puzzles. **Services:** Library open to licensed day care centers, campus laboratory school, and the campus community.

★5346★
Emporia State University - William Allen White Library - Special Collections (Hum)
1200 Commercial Phone: (316)343-5037
Emporia, KS 66801 Dr. Henry R. Stewart, Univ.Libn.
Founded: 1952. **Staff:** Prof 1; Other 1.5. **Special Collections:** William Allen White Collection (48.6 linear feet of manuscripts; 283 photographic prints; 242 volumes; 10.5 linear feet of correspondence; 15 linear feet of newspapers and periodical articles and clippings; 450 pieces of memorabilia); Mary White Collection (186 items); Normaliana Collection (1419 volumes; 36,727 other unaccessioned materials; 35 reels of microfilm; archival items); May Massee Collection (1400 volumes; 5000 works of art; 18 linear feet of other materials); Lois Lenski Collection (299 items); Children's Literature Collection (32,255 books; 361 bound periodical volumes); Rare Book Collection (1396 books; 248 bound periodical volumes); Dunning Antique Collection; W.A. White Children's Book Award Collection (778 volumes; 90 archival items; 9 reels of microfilm) and Archives (93 linear feet); Elizabeth Yates Collection (205 items); Ruth Garver Gagliardo Collection (1822 volumes; 4.5 linear feet of other materials); Historical Children's Literature Collection (521 books; 159 bound periodical volumes); 3096 ESU theses and research papers. **Subscriptions:** 12 journals and other serials. **Services:** Interlibrary loan; copying (both limited); SDI; collections open to the public but do not circulate with the exception of Children's Literature and the collection of theses and research papers. **Automated Operations:** Computerized public access catalog, cataloging, and circulation. **Computerized Information Services:** DIALOG Information Services, OCLC. Performs searches on fee basis. **Networks/Consortia:** Member of Bibliographical Center for Research, Rocky Mountain Region, Inc. (BCR). **Publications:** A Bibliography of Willam Allen White (1969; 2 volumes); The May Massee Collection: Creative Publishing for Children, 1923-1963, A Checklist (1979); The William Allen White Children's Book Award, Books on the Master Lists, 1952-1953 through 1987-1988 (1987) - all for sale. **Special Catalogs:** May Massee Collection (card); Normaliana (card); Ruth Garver Gagliardo (card); collection of theses and research papers (card). **Remarks:** FAX: (316)343-5997. **Staff:** Mary E. Bogan, Spec.Coll.Libn.

Empresa Brasileira de Pesquisa Agropecuaria - Centro Nacional de Pesquisa de Tecnologia Agroindustrial de Alimentos
See: **Brazilian Agricultural Research Corporation - National Center for Agricultural and Agro-Industrial Food Technology** (2097)

Empresa Brasileira de Pesquisa Agropecuaria - Centro de Pesquisa Agropecuaria Tropico Umido
See: **Brazilian Agricultural Research Corporation - Agricultural Research Center for the Humid Tropics** (2096)

★5347★
Encore Computer Corp. - Information Resource Center (Comp Sci)
6901 W. Sunrise Blvd., MS 408 Phone: (305)797-5933
Fort Lauderdale, FL 33313 L. Susan Hayes, Mgr., Corp.Libn.
Founded: 1977. **Staff:** Prof 1; Other 1. **Subjects:** Computers, electrical engineering, marketing. **Holdings:** 3500 volumes; 2500 microforms. **Subscriptions:** 150 journals and other serials. **Services:** Interlibrary loan; copying; SDI; center open to the public by appointment. **Automated Operations:** Computerized cataloging, acquisitions, serials, and circulation (Data Trek). **Computerized Information Services:** DIALOG Information Services, REMO; internal database; InterNet (electronic mail service). **Remarks:** FAX: (305)797-5940. Electronic mail address(es): shayes@encore.com (InterNet).

★5348★
Encyclopaedia Britannica, Inc. - Editorial Library (Publ)
310 S. Michigan Ave. Phone: (312)347-7402
Chicago, IL 60604 Terry Miller, Hd.Libn.
Founded: 1933. **Staff:** Prof 3; Other 2. **Subjects:** Reference, foreign statistics. **Holdings:** 42,000 volumes; 5000 unbound geographical and statistical publications; 2500 reels of microfilm. **Subscriptions:** 2500 journals and other serials; 8 newspapers. **Services:** Interlibrary loan; copying; library open to the public by appointment. **Computerized Information Services:** DIALOG Information Services, NEXIS, OCLC. **Remarks:** FAX: (312)347-7914. **Staff:** Shantha Uddin, Assoc.Libn.; Robert Lewis, Asst.Libn.; David Foster, Cur., Geog.

★5349★
ENDA America Latina - Library (Plan)
Naciones Unidas
Apdo. Aereo 091369
Bogota, Colombia Phone: 1 288-2876
Subjects: Third World - urban development, technology, public sanitation. **Holdings:** 5000 volumes; documents.

★5350★
Energy Conservation Coalition - Information Center (Energy)
1525 New Hampshire Ave., N.W. Phone: (301)891-1100
Washington, DC 20036 Nancy Hirsh, Dir.
Founded: 1981. **Subjects:** Energy and energy conservation, federal legislation. **Holdings:** 500 books, publications, reports, periodicals. **Services:** Center not open to the public. **Remarks:** FAX: (301)891-2218.

Energy Conversion Systems
See: **ECS Power Systems, Inc. - Library** (5220)

★5351★
Energy & Environmental Management, Inc. (E2M) - Library (Env-Cons)
Box 71 Phone: (412)733-0022
Murrysville, PA 15668 Larry L. Simmons, Pres.
Founded: 1981. **Subjects:** Environmental compliance in the electric utility, metals production, mining, chemical, petroleum, sanitation, and manufacturing industries. **Holdings:** 1000 books. **Computerized Information Services:** Internal databases.

Energy, Mines & Resources Canada
See: **Canada - Energy, Mines & Resources Canada** (2700)

William P. Engel Library
See: **Temple Emanu-El** (16103)

★5352★
Engelhard Corporation - Technical Information Center (Sci-Engr)
25 Middlesex/Essex Tpke. Phone: (908)205-5271
Iselin, NJ 08830-0770 Roger L. Meyer, Mgr., Tech.Info.Serv.
Staff: Prof 3; Other 3. **Subjects:** Pigments; additives; kaolin; clays; catalysts; specialty chemicals; fabrication of noble metals - platinum, gold, silver. **Holdings:** 25,000 books; 5000 bound periodical volumes; 1000 other cataloged items; 20,000 special reports; 50,000 foreign patents; complete U.S. patents, 1974 to present. **Subscriptions:** 450 journals and other serials. **Services:** Interlibrary loan; copying; center open to the public with prior approval. **Computerized Information Services:** Online systems. **Publications:** Review of Current Technical Literature and Patent Bulletin, monthly. **Remarks:** FAX: (908)205-5300. **Formerly:** Located in Edison, NJ. **Staff:** Maurica Fedors, Sr.Tech.Info.Spec.; Maryann Sobin, Libn.

★5353★
Engineering Societies Library (Sci-Engr)
United Engineering Center
345 E. 47th St. Phone: (212)705-7611
New York, NY 10017 Davida Scharf, Dir.
Founded: 1913. **Staff:** Prof 9; Other 23. **Subjects:** Engineering - chemical, civil, electrical, mechanical, mining; history of engineering; fuels; metallurgy. **Special Collections:** Current and superceded standards; conference proceedings; history of technology collection. **Holdings:** 300,000 books; 10,000 maps. **Subscriptions:** 5500 journals and other serials. **Services:** Document delivery; research service; library open to the public. **Computerized Information Services:** DIALOG Information Services, OCLC, STN International, BRS Information Technologies, ORBIT Search Service; DIALMAIL, CompuServe Information Service, MCI Mail (electronic mail services). Performs searches. **Networks/Consortia:** Member of New York State Interlibrary Loan Network (NYSILL), New York Metropolitan Reference and Research Library Agency. **Publications:** Engineering Publications Advisor, monthly. **Remarks:** FAX: (212)753-9568; (212)486-1086. **Staff:** Roscoe Thompson, Assoc.Dir.; Richard Steele, Assoc.Dir.; Carmina McGovern, Mgr.

★5354★
Engineers' Club of Dayton - Library (Sci-Engr)
110 E. Monument Ave. Phone: (513)228-2148
Dayton, OH 45402 Susan Marks, Asst.Mgr.
Founded: 1918. **Staff:** 1. **Subjects:** Engineering - electrical, civil, mechanical; mathematics; aviation and space technology; chemistry; physics. **Holdings:** 3500 books; 1950 bound periodical volumes; 150 pamphlets; 300 pamphlets (uncataloged); 460 reels of microfilm. **Subscriptions:** 10 journals and other serials. **Services:** Interlibrary loan; copying; library open to the public with restrictions. **Networks/Consortia:** Member of Southwestern Ohio Council for Higher Education (SOCHE). **Remarks:** FAX: (513)228-4794.

★5355★
Engineers International, Inc. - Library
98 E. Naperville Rd., Suite 101
Westmont, IL 60559-1595
Defunct.

England - National Meteorological Library
See: **Great Britain - National Meteorological Library & Archive** (6687)

England - Royal College of Nursing
See: **Royal College of Nursing** (14111)

England - Royal College of Physicians of London
See: **Royal College of Physicians of London** (14113)

England - Royal College of Surgeons of England
See: **Royal College of Surgeons of England** (14114)

England - Royal College of Veterinary Surgeons
See: **Royal College of Veterinary Surgeons** (14115)

England - Royal Greenwich Observatory
See: **Royal Greenwich Observatory - Library** (14119)

England - Royal Institute of International Affairs
See: **Royal Institute of International Affairs** (14122)

England - Royal Society of Medicine
See: **Royal Society of Medicine** (14136)

Joseph W. England Library
See: **Philadelphia College of Pharmacy and Science** (12980)

★5356★
Englewood Hospital - Medical Library and Regional Consumer Health Information Center (Med)
350 Engle St. Phone: (201)894-3070
Englewood, NJ 07631 Katherine L. Lindner, Dir.
Staff: Prof 2; Other 2. **Subjects:** Medicine, nursing, and allied health sciences. **Special Collections:** Internal medicine and surgery AV programs; Consumer Health Collection. **Holdings:** 3000 books; 10,000 bound periodical volumes. **Subscriptions:** 400 journals and other serials. **Services:** Interlibrary loan; copying; library open to the public by appointment. **Computerized Information Services:** MEDLINE. **Networks/Consortia:** Member of Bergen Passaic Regional Library Cooperative. **Special Catalogs:** Catalog of audiovisual materials; listing of health education resources for patients and community members. **Remarks:** FAX: (201)894-9049. Consumer health information center for Bergen and Passaic Counties, NJ. **Formerly:** Its Learning Center Library. **Staff:** Mr. Jan Hudgens, Cat.

★5357★
Englewood Hospital - School of Nursing Library (Med)
350 Engle St. Phone: (201)894-3145
Englewood, NJ 07631 Lia Sabbagh, Libn.
Founded: 1896. **Staff:** Prof 1. **Subjects:** Nursing, history of nursing. **Special Collections:** Archives on the history of nursing (rare books). **Holdings:** 6000 books; 328 bound periodical volumes; 325 cassette and filmstrip titles; 50 film titles; 20 slides and cassettes; 60 other cataloged items. **Subscriptions:** 70 journals and other serials. **Services:** Interlibrary loan; copying; SDI; library open to the public. **Networks/Consortia:** Member of Health Sciences Library Association of New Jersey (HSLANJ), BHSL. **Remarks:** FAX: (201)894-9049.

★5358★
English Folk Dance and Song Society - Vaughan Williams Memorial Library (Mus)
Cecil Sharp House
2 Regent's Pk. Rd. Phone: 71 485 2206
London NW1 7AY, England Malcolm Taylor, Libn.
Subjects: Traditional music, song, dance, and customs; storytelling; social history; folk revivals. **Special Collections:** 20th century collections of traditional music, including Percy Grainger, Cecil Sharp, Ralph Vaughan Williams, James Carpenter, Mike Yates, and British Broadcasting Corporation (BBC; manuscripts; field recordings). **Holdings:** 15,000 books; 100 bound periodical volumes; 175 microforms; 25 manuscripts. **Services:** Interlibrary loan (limited); copying; library open to the public on fee basis. **Publications:** A List of Books for the Study of Folk Song; A List of Books for the Study of English Folk Dancing; Folk Music Collected in the British Isles: Some Manuscript and Recorded Collections Accessible to the Public; additional publications available - all for sale. **Special Catalogs:** Catalogs of: photographs, periodicals, leaflets, Cecil Sharp's informants, films, videos; Sound Library catalog. **Special Indexes:** Indexes to: song titles, dance titles, tune titles, folk plays.

★5359★
English, McCaughan and O'Bryan - Law Library (Law)
Box 14098 Phone: (305)462-3300
Fort Lauderdale, FL 33302 Angela R. Stramiello, Libn.
Staff: Prof 1. **Subjects:** Law. **Holdings:** 5000 volumes. **Services:** Library not open to the public. **Computerized Information Services:** Compuserve, Inc., WESTLAW, DIALOG Information Services, VU/TEXT Information Services, LEXIS. **Remarks:** FAX: (305)763-2439.

English as a Second Language Learning Resources Centre
See: **Alberta Advanced Education - Alberta Vocational College - ESL Learning Resources Centre** (231)

★5360★
English-Speaking Union of the U.S.A. - Ruth M. Shellens Memorial Library (Area-Ethnic)
16 E. 69th St. Phone: (212)879-6800
New York, NY 10021 Linda Cramer, Dir.
Founded: 1942. **Staff:** Prof 1. **Subjects:** Great Britain. **Special Collections:** Winifred Nerney Collection (biographies and autobiographies of English authors writing from 1900 to 1964). **Holdings:** 7500 books. **Subscriptions:** 18 journals and other serials. **Services:** Library open to the public for research and study. **Remarks:** FAX: (212)772-2886.

★5361★
English-Speaking Union of the U.S.A. - Washington D.C. Branch Library (Area-Ethnic)
2131 S St., N.W. Phone: (202)234-4602
Washington, DC 20008 Arthur P. Bean, Libn.
Staff: 1. **Subjects:** English and Commonwealth history and social studies, travel, biography, fiction. **Holdings:** 1100 volumes. **Services:** Library open to the public for reference use on request.

★5362★
Enron Corporation - Law Library (Law)
1400 Smith Phone: (713)853-5322
Houston, TX 77002-7369 Majorie Wright, Supv., Corp. & Law Depts.
Subjects: Law. **Holdings:** 5000 volumes. **Services:** Library not open to the public. **Remarks:** FAX: (713)853-5426.

★5363★
Ensanian Physicochemical Institute - Information Center for Gravitation Chemistry (Sci-Engr)
Box 98 Phone: (814)225-3296
Eldred, PA 16731 Elizabeth A. Ensanian, Chf.Libn.
Founded: 1968. **Staff:** Prof 3. **Subjects:** Gravitation, nonlinear thermodynamics, exobiology, cosmology, unifield fields, chemistry, relativistic physics, biology, engineering. **Special Collections:** Reports of zero gravity drop tower experiments. **Holdings:** 1300 books; 2000 bound periodical volumes; 850 reports; 400 reprints on gravity phenomena; 350 microfiche. **Subscriptions:** 43 journals and other serials; 5 newspapers. **Services:** Will answer brief inquiries and make referrals; center open to the public with restrictions. **Publications:** Literature Survey, quarterly - for internal distribution only; Annual Review of Gravitational Chemistry - for internal distribution only; Journal of the Ensanian Physicochemical Institute (book). **Staff:** Armand O. Ensanian, Ref.Libn.; Bernard Caplan, Res.Spec.; Tamara Ensanian, Res.Spec.

★5364★
ENSCO, Inc. - Technical Library (Trans)
5400 Port Royal Rd. Phone: (703)321-9000
Springfield, VA 22151 Irene Minich, Mgr./Libn.
Staff: Prof 1. **Subjects:** Railroad and highway safety technology, signal processing, computer technology, seismic detection. **Special Collections:** Railroad technology (1200 volumes). **Holdings:** 4000 volumes. **Subscriptions:** 150 journals and other serials. **Services:** Interlibrary loan; library not open to the public. **Computerized Information Services:** DTIC, DIALOG Information Services. **Remarks:** FAX: (703)321-4529.

★5365★
ENSR Consulting & Engineering - Environmental Contracting Center Library (Env-Cons)
Box 2105 Phone: (303)493-8878
Fort Collins, CO 80522 Beth Mullan, Libn.
Founded: 1972. **Staff:** 1. **Subjects:** Ecology, pollution, environmental science, energy, impact assessment, mining reclamation. **Special Collections:** Oil shale; hazardous waste characterization and clean-up; environmental impact statements; federal and state regulations and guidelines for the Rocky Mountain region; oil spills. **Holdings:** 3500 books; 200 bound technical reports; 700 technical reports; 500 maps; reprints. **Subscriptions:** 200 journals and other serials; 10 newspapers. **Services:** Interlibrary loan; copying; SDI; library open to the public for reference use only. **Computerized Information Services:** Online systems. **Special Indexes:** Reprint literature for benthos, fishes, ornithology, mammology, water quality, hydrology, air quality, vegetation. **Remarks:** Library located at 1716 Heath Pkwy., Fort Collins, CO 80524.

★5366★
ENSR Consulting & Engineering - Information Center (Env-Cons)
35 Nagog Park Phone: (508)635-9500
Acton, MA 01720 Deanna C. Robinson, Mgr.
Founded: 1972. **Staff:** Prof 2. **Subjects:** Hazardous waste, environmental engineering, air and water pollution, air toxics, risk assessment, chemistry, meteorology. **Holdings:** 5000 books; 15,000 scientific and technical reports; microfiche collection. **Subscriptions:** 250 journals and other serials. **Services:** Interlibrary loan; copying; SDI. **Automated Operations:** Computerized cataloging and circulation. **Computerized Information Services:** DIALOG Information Services, DunsPrint, STN International, OCLC, MEDLARS. **Publications:** Accessions list - for internal distribution only. **Remarks:** A division of American NUKEM. FAX: (508)635-9180. **Staff:** Joyce Overoye, Asst.Libn.

★5367★
ENSR Consulting & Engineering - Library (Env-Cons)
1220 Avenida Acaso Phone: (805)388-3775
Camarillo, CA 93012-8727 N/A
Founded: 1977. **Staff:** 1. **Subjects:** Air pollution, environmental chemistry, environmental impact, hazardous waste. **Holdings:** 200 books; 1200 technical reports, state documents, and environmental impact statements; 1350 company reports; 550 Environmental Protection Agency reports; 1200 microfiche; 320 U.S. Geological Survey maps. **Subscriptions:** 60 journals and other serials. **Services:** Interlibrary loan; library not open to the public. **Computerized Information Services:** DIALOG Information Services, OCLC. **Publications:** Library newsletter, monthly - for internal distribution only. **Remarks:** FAX: (805)388-3577.

★5368★
ENSR Health Sciences - Library/Information Center (Med)
1320 Harbor Bay Pkwy., Suite 100 Phone: (510)865-1888
Alameda, CA 94501 Glenn London, Mgr., Info.Serv.
Subjects: Occupational medicine, industrial hygiene, epidemiology, environment, risk assessment, consulting, engineering, environmental health. **Holdings:** 1500 books; 1000 reports. **Subscriptions:** 100 journals and other serials. **Services:** Library not open to the public. **Computerized Information Services:** MEDLARS, DIALOG Information Services, BRS Information Technologies, STN International, DataTimes, LEXIS, NewsNet, Inc. **Remarks:** FAX: (510)748-6799. **Staff:** Tanya K. Stout, Info.Spec.

★5369★
Ente Nazionale Italiano di Unificazione - Library (Sci-Engr)
Piazza Armando Diaz 2
I-20123 Milan, (MI), Italy Phone: 2 72001141
Subjects: Industrial standards. **Holdings:** 3000 volumes. **Computerized Information Services:** Internal database. **Remarks:** Serves as the official Italian agency for standards. Telex: 312481 UNI I.

★5370★
Enterprise Cape Breton Corporation - Library
Box 1750 Phone: (902)564-3616
Sydney, NS, Canada B1P 6T7 Edmund MacEachern, Central Rec.Off.
Staff: 1. **Services:** library not open to the public. **Remarks:** FAX: (902)564-3825.

★5371★
Enterprise Newfoundland and Labrador - Business Resource Centre (Bus-Fin)
Viking Bldg.
136 Crosbie Rd. Phone: (709)729-7150
St. John's, NF, Canada A1B 3K3 Ruth Parsons, Dir., Lib.Serv.
Founded: 1973. **Staff:** 5.5. **Subjects:** Marketing, small business, economic and rural development. **Holdings:** 800 books; 20 VF drawers of subject files; Standard Industrial Classification (SIC) directories. **Subscriptions:** 300 journals and other serials. **Services:** Interlibrary loan; copying; SDI; center open to the public. **Computerized Information Services:** CAN/OLE, DIALOG Information Services, BRS Information Technologies, The Financial Post DataGroup, Info Globe; CD-ROMs; Envoy 100 (electronic mail service). **Remarks:** FAX: (709)729-7183. **Formerly:** Newfoundland and Labrador Development Corporation Ltd.

★5372★
Entomological Society of America - Archives (Biol Sci)
9301 Annapolis Rd. Phone: (301)731-4535
Lanham, MD 20706-3115 W. Darryl Hansen, Exec.Dir.
Founded: 1974. **Staff:** Prof 1. **Subjects:** Entomology - medical, economic, environmental, systematic. **Special Collections:** History of the Entomological Society of America and its members, 1954 to present. **Holdings:** 90 linear feet of historical records, records of meetings, minutes, correspondence; research materials. **Services:** Interlibrary loan; copying; archives open to members. **Computerized Information Services:** Internal database. **Remarks:** FAX: (301)731-4538.

★5373★
Envirologic Data - Corporate Library
295 Forest Ave.
Portland, ME 04101
Defunct.

★5374★
Environic Foundation International, Inc. - Library and Files (Plan, Env-Cons)
916 St. Vincent St. Phone: (219)233-3357
South Bend, IN 46617-1443 Patrick Horsbrugh, Chm.
Founded: 1970. **Staff:** 4. **Subjects:** Urban planning, geotecture (subterranean accommodation), thalatecture (construction in the shallows), hypostecture (high structures), limnotecture (design of lakes), nesotecture (design of islands), synecotecture (structures that accommodate vegetation in association with human requirements), synecopolis (design of cities using synecological principles), poietic encyclement (remaking all that is made - the ultimate technological achievement), person/plant proxemics (the values of close interrelationships between vegetation and human well-being). **Special Collections:** John Bunge Papers; Thames Barrage Project, 1927-1957; High Paddington (London) Papers, 1950-1954; New Barbican (London) Papers, 1954-1955. **Holdings:** 6000 books. **Subscriptions:** 64 journals and other serials. **Services:** Library open to the public for reference use only on request. **Remarks:** FAX: (219)233-3357.

Environment Agency (of Japan) - National Institute for Environmental Studies
See: **Japan - Environment Agency - National Institute for Environmental Studies - Environmental Information Center** (8329)

Environment Canada
See: **Canada - Environment Canada** (2703)

★5375★
Environmental Action Coalition - Library/Resource Center (Env-Cons)
625 Broadway, 2nd Fl. Phone: (212)677-1601
New York, NY 10012 Jennie Tichenor, Libn.
Founded: 1970. **Staff:** Prof 4; Other 3. **Subjects:** Energy, water pollution, solid waste, ecology, environmental education, consumer information. **Holdings:** 3000 books; reports; VF drawers. **Subscriptions:** 13 journals and other serials. **Services:** Library open to the public with borrowing privileges reserved for members. **Publications:** ECO News; ECO-facts; Cycle; Waste Paper (periodicals); It's Your Environment (book); Plant a Tree for Arbor Day; City Trees, Country Trees; Woods and Water; Don't Waste Waste (curricula); Plastics: America's Packaging Dilemma.

★5376★
Environmental Coalition on Nuclear Power - Library (Energy)
433 Orlando Ave.
State College, PA 16803 Phone: (814)237-3900
Founded: 1968. **Subjects:** Nuclear power; radioactive waste; radiation and health; energy alternatives to nuclear power - educational, legal, and political aspects; energy policy. **Special Collections:** Leo Goodman Memorial Collection - Nuclear Energy. **Holdings:** 2000 documents. **Services:** Library open to the public by appointment.

★5377★
Environmental Educational Center - Library (Biol Sci)
190 Lord Stirling Rd. Phone: (201)766-2489
Basking Ridge, NJ 07920 Margaret Ryan
Founded: 1976. **Staff:** Prof 1. **Subjects:** Wildlife, nature, ecology, outdoor activities. **Special Collections:** Mushroom collection (100 books of Mycological Society); children's literature collection (200 books). **Holdings:** 1000 books; 100 videotapes. **Subscriptions:** 65 journals and other serials. **Services:** Library open to the public for reference use only. **Remarks:** FAX: (201)766-ANTS.

★5378★
Environmental Law Institute - Library (Law, Env-Cons)
1616 P St., N.W., Suite 200 Phone: (202)939-3814
Washington, DC 20036 Lynda L. Larsen, Chf.Libn.
Founded: 1970. **Staff:** Prof 1; Other 1. **Subjects:** Environmental law, toxic substances, natural resources, wetlands, air and water pollution. **Holdings:** 15,000 books. **Subscriptions:** 400 journals and other serials. **Services:** Interlibrary loan; library open to the public by appointment. **Computerized Information Services:** DIALOG Information Services, LEXIS, NEXIS, WESTLAW. **Special Indexes:** Subject index to environmental law articles in selected law journals (card). **Remarks:** FAX: (202)328-5002.

Environmental Law Institute - National Wetlands Technical Council
See: **National Wetlands Technical Council** (11323)

★5379★
Environmental Library of Sarasota County (Env-Cons)
7112 Curtiss Ave. Phone: (813)924-9677
Sarasota, FL 34231 Linda R. Idelberger, Libn.
Founded: 1986. **Staff:** Prof 1. **Subjects:** Environmental science, water resources, ecology, solid and hazardous waste, conservation, recycling, natural history. **Holdings:** 2600 books; 250 bound periodical volumes; 1500 microfiche; 5000 government documents; 2500 topographic and coastal maps. **Subscriptions:** 100 journals and other serials. **Services:** Interlibrary loan; copying; library open to the public. **Computerized Information Services:** DIALOG Information Services, OCLC. **Networks/Consortia:** Member of Florida Library Network (FLN), Tampa Bay Library Consortium, Inc. (TBLC), SOLINET. **Remarks:** Environmental Library of Sarasota County is a member of the Sarasota County Public Library System. FAX: (813)923-4011.

Environmental Protection Agency
See: **U.S. Environmental Protection Agency** (17456)

★5380★
Environmental Research Associates, Inc. - Library (Env-Cons)
P.O. Box 219 Phone: (215)449-7400
Villanova, PA 19085 Dr. M.H. Levin, Libn.
Subjects: Environmental engineering and planning, health and safety, water resource management. **Holdings:** 1000 volumes.

★5381★
Environmental Research Institute of Michigan - ERIM Information Resource Center (Sci-Engr)
Box 134001 Phone: (313)994-1200
Ann Arbor, MI 48113 Corliss H. Allender, Mgr.
Founded: 1977. **Staff:** Prof 2; Other 3. **Subjects:** Remote sensing, infrared and electro-optical technology, allied sciences. **Holdings:** 12,000 books; 1500 bound periodical volumes; 3000 maps; LANDSAT, radar, aerial photographs. **Subscriptions:** 350 journals and other serials. **Services:** Interlibrary loan; center not open to the public. **Automated Operations:** Computerized cataloging, acquisitions, and serials. **Computerized Information Services:** DIALOG Information Services, DTIC. **Networks/Consortia:** Member of Michigan Library Consortium (MLC). **Publications:** ERIM Bibliography, irregular - available on request; Information Center Acquisitions, monthly - for internal distribution only. **Remarks:** FAX: (313)662-0893. **Staff:** Nina M. Harris, Info.Spec.

★5382★
Environmental Research Institute of Michigan - Infrared Information Analysis Center (IRIA) (Sci-Engr)
Box 134001 Phone: (313)994-1200
Ann Arbor, MI 48113-4001 Dr. Joseph Accetta, Dir.
Founded: 1956. **Staff:** Prof 5; Other 4. **Subjects:** Infrared and electro-optical technology and associated topics. **Holdings:** 400 books; 50,000 technical reports. **Services:** Center open to visitors with security clearance. **Computerized Information Services:** DIALOG Information Services, DTIC. **Publications:** Proceedings of IRIS; annotated bibliographies; state-of-the-art reports; The Infrared Handbook. **Special Indexes:** Bibliographies for subscribers (printout). **Remarks:** FAX: (313)994-5550. Center is a U.S. Department of Defense information analysis center, providing bibliographic and other information services to authorized requesters. **Staff:** Tony LaRocca Mgr.

★5383★
Environmental Science & Engineering, Inc. - Library (Env-Cons)
S. Overlook Phone: (203)929-6764
Amherst, NH 03031 Kathy Andrews, Libn.
Founded: 1987. **Staff:** 2. **Subjects:** Environmental risk management and compliance audits, hazardous waste management and minimization, air and water pollution control, underground storage tank management, environmental assessments for real estate transfers. **Holdings:** 4000 volumes. **Subscriptions:** 45 journals and other serials. **Services:** Library not open to the public. **Computerized Information Services:** Internal database. **Publications:** Acquisition list. **Remarks:** FAX: (203)926-0108.

★5384★
Environmental Science Services - Library (Env-Cons)
532 Atwells Ave.
Providence, RI 02909 Phone: (401)421-0398
Subjects: Environmental science; chemical, biological, physical effects of various activities on the atmosphere, soils, and water resources. **Holdings:** 10,000 volumes. **Remarks:** FAX: (401)421-0396. Parent organization is Thibault & Associates, Inc.

EPA
See: **U.S. Environmental Protection Agency** (17456)

Ephrata Cloister
See: **Pennsylvania (State) Historical & Museum Commission** (12877)

Epilepsy Foundation of America - National Epilepsy Library
See: **National Epilepsy Library** (11161)

Episcopal Church - Episcopal Diocese of New Hampshire - Church Media Center
See: **Church Media Center** (3684)

★5385★
Episcopal Church Executive Council - Henry Knox Sherrill Resource Center (Rel-Phil)
Episcopal Church Ctr.
815 2nd Ave. Phone: (212)867-8400
New York, NY 10017 Avis E. Harvey, Rsrcs./Info.Off.
Staff: 1. **Subjects:** Episcopal church. **Holdings:** Figures not available. **Services:** Center open to the public for reference use only.

★5386★
Episcopal Church of the Holy Faith - Parish Library (Rel-Phil)
311 E. Palace Ave. Phone: (505)982-4447
Santa Fe, NM 87501 Rev. Philip Wainwright, Lib.Hd.
Founded: 1949. **Staff:** 8. **Subjects:** Comparative religion, arts and symbolism, Bible, altar, festivals, drama, music, theology, church history. **Special Collections:** History of Anglicanism in the Southwest. **Holdings:** 5000 books; unbound magazines. **Subscriptions:** 10 journals and other serials. **Services:** Interlibrary loan; copying; library open to the public with circulation by mail. **Publications:** Lent and Advent Book Lists, annual; Newsletter, quarterly.

Episcopal Church in the U.S.A.
See: **Protestant Episcopal Church** (13434)

Episcopal Diocese of . . .
See: **Protestant Episcopal Church**

Episcopal Divinity School - Library
See: **Weston School of Theology - Library** (20343)

★5387★
Episcopal Health Services, Inc. - St. John's Episcopal Hospital - Smithtown Medical Library (Med)
Rte. 25A Phone: (516)862-3186
Smithtown, NY 11785 Laura Righter, Adm.
Founded: 1966. **Staff:** 1. **Subjects:** Medicine, health care administration. **Holdings:** 400 books. **Subscriptions:** 100 journals and other serials. **Services:** Interlibrary loan; library not open to the public. **Networks/Consortia:** Member of Long Island Library Resources Council. **Remarks:** FAX: (516)862-3179. **Staff:** Carol Carini.

★5388★
Episcopal Health Services of Long Island - St. John's Episcopal Hospital (South Shore Division) - Medical Library (Med)
327 Beach 19th St. Phone: (718)868-7699
Far Rockaway, NY 11691 Kalpana Desai, Chf.Med.Libn.
Founded: 1974. **Staff:** Prof 1; Other 1. **Subjects:** Medicine, pediatrics, surgery, obstetrics/gynecology, psychiatry, nursing. **Holdings:** 800 books; 2000 bound periodical volumes; audio cassettes. **Subscriptions:** 124 journals and other serials. **Services:** Interlibrary loan; copying; library open to students. **Computerized Information Services:** MEDLARS; CD-ROM (MEDLINE); DOCLINE (electronic mail service). **Networks/Consortia:** Member of Brooklyn-Queens-Staten Island Health Sciences Librarians (BQSI), Medical & Scientific Libraries of Long Island (MEDLI), BHSL. **Remarks:** FAX: (718)327-8948. Alternate telephone number(s): (718)868-7698.

★5389★
Episcopal Hospital - Medical Library (Med)
Front St. & Lehigh Ave. Phone: (215)427-7487
Philadelphia, PA 19125 Nina P. Long, Dir., Lib.Serv.
Founded: 1970. **Staff:** Prof 2; Other 1. **Subjects:** Medicine, nursing, cardiology. **Special Collections:** Hospital archive records dating from 1851. **Holdings:** 3054 books; 4112 bound periodical volumes; AV programs, software programs. **Subscriptions:** 210 journals and other serials. **Services:** Interlibrary loan; copying; library open to the public for reference use only. **Computerized Information Services:** MEDLARS. Performs searches on fee basis. **Networks/Consortia:** Member of Delaware Valley Information Consortium (DEVIC), BHSL, National Network of Libraries of Medicine - Middle Atlantic Region. **Remarks:** FAX: (215)427-7490.

★5390★
Episcopal Theological Seminary of the Southwest - Library (Rel-Phil)
Box 2247 Phone: (512)472-4134
Austin, TX 78768 Harold H. Booher, Libn.
Founded: 1953. **Staff:** Prof 2; Other 2. **Subjects:** Theology, English Church history, biblical criticism, church history (other than English), church and culture, pastoral care, ethics, philosophy, politics, sociology. **Special Collections:** Black Collection of fine editions of nineteenth century English and American literature; Winterbotham Collection (history, geography, language, literature, art, culture of Spanish America). **Holdings:** 86,133 books; 5639 bound periodical volumes. **Subscriptions:** 319 journals and other serials. **Services:** Interlibrary loan; copying; library open to the public. **Automated Operations:** Computerized cataloging and ILL. **Computerized Information Services:** OCLC. **Networks/Consortia:** Member of AMIGOS Bibliographic Council, Inc. **Staff:** Robert E. Cogswell, Cat.; Patricia M. Booher, Circ.Libn.

★5391★
Epitestudomanyi Intezet - Szakkonyvtar (Plan)
David Ferenc 6
PF 71 Phone: 1 852544
H-1518 Budapest, Hungary Ilona Pasztor
Founded: 1949. **Staff:** Prof 1. **Subjects:** Architecture; engineering - civil, structural, sanitary, electrical; construction; building repair. **Holdings:** 49,000 books; 4000 bound periodical volumes; 4550 reports. **Subscriptions:** 79 journals and other serials; 6 newspapers. **Services:** Interlibrary loan; copying; library open to the public (except research reports). **Remarks:** FAX: 1 1663766. Telex: 22-4285 eti h.

Epitesugyi es Varosfejlesteztesi Miniszterium - Epitesugyi Tajekoztatasi Kozpont
See: **Hungary - Ministry for Transport, Communication and Construction** (7554)

★5392★
Epoch Research Corporation - Library (Info Sci)
2-7-12-106 Nakano
Nakano-ku
Tokyo 164, Japan Phone: 33 3821384
Subjects: Office automation, new technology, information industry, library automation. **Holdings:** 1000 books. **Subscriptions:** 20 journals and other serials. **Services:** Document delivery. **Computerized Information Services:** DIALOG Information Services, BRS Information Technologies, Nikkei Economic Electronic Databank Service - Information Retrieval (NEEDS-IR), JICST On-line Information Service; HINET. Performs searches on fee basis. **Remarks:** FAX: 33 3838411.

Eppley Institute for Research in Cancer & Allied Diseases - Library
See: **University of Nebraska at Omaha - Medical Center - McGoogan Library of Medicine** (19010)

Max Epstein Archive
See: **University of Chicago - Department of Art** (18450)

★5393★
Epworth Fellowship Church, Inc. - Library (Rel-Phil)
RD 1, P.O. Box 65 1/2 Phone: (302)875-4488
Laurel, DE 19956 Pam James
Founded: 1979. **Staff:** Prof 15; Other 5. **Subjects:** Religion. **Holdings:** 4000 books. **Subscriptions:** 6 journals and other serials. **Services:** Library open to the public with restrictions.

Equal Employment Opportunity Commission
See: **U.S. Equal Employment Opportunity Commission** (17483)

★5394★
Equifax, Inc. - Corporate Information Resources H-36 (Bus-Fin)
Box 4081 Phone: (404)885-8320
Atlanta, GA 30302 Michael McDavid, Mgr.
Founded: 1910. **Staff:** Prof 2; Other 2. **Subjects:** Management, marketing, economics, insurance, general business, employee development. **Special Collections:** American Management Association and Conference Board studies and reports (19 VF drawers); company archives. **Holdings:** 2000 books; telephone directories. **Subscriptions:** 350 journals and other serials; 10 newspapers. **Services:** Interlibrary loan; copying; SDI; resources open to the public by appointment. **Computerized Information Services:** DIALOG Information Services, Dow Jones News/Retrieval, NewsNet, Inc., PFDS Online, VU/TEXT Information Services, DataTimes, NEXIS, LEXIS. **Networks/Consortia:** Member of Georgia Online Database (GOLD), SOLINET. **Remarks:** FAX: (404)885-8369. **Staff:** Terry Gordon.

Equifax, Inc. - Elrick and Lavidge, Inc.
See: **Elrick and Lavidge, Inc.** (5312)

Equine Research Library
See: **Kentucky Horse Park** (8661)

Erdelyi Vilagszovetseg
See: **Transylvanian World Federation** (16464)

Ergonomics Information Analysis Centre
See: **University of Birmingham - School of Manufacturing and Mechanical Engineering - Ergonomics Information Analysis Centre - Library** (18249)

★5395★
ERIC Clearinghouse on Adult, Career, and Vocational Education - Center on Education and Training for Employment (Educ)
Ohio State University
1900 Kenny Rd. Phone: (614)292-4353
Columbus, OH 43210-1090 Susan Imel, Dir.
Founded: 1966. **Staff:** Prof 6; Other 3. **Subjects:** Education - adult, career, vocational. **Holdings:** 60,000 books; 300,000 ERIC microfiche. **Subscriptions:** 100 journals and other serials. **Services:** Library open to the public at librarian's discretion. **Computerized Information Services:** DIALOG Information Services, BRS Information Technologies; Dialcom, Inc. (electronic mail service). **Publications:** List of publications - available on request. **Remarks:** ERIC is an acronym for Educational Resources Information Center. Toll-free telephone number(s): (800)848-4815. FAX: (614)292-1260. Electronic mail address(es): 44: AVO0003 (Dialcom, Inc.). **Formerly:** Its National Center for Research in Vocational Education.

★5396★
ERIC Clearinghouse on Counseling and Personnel Services - Learning Resources Center (Educ)
School of Education Bldg., Rm. 2108
University of Michigan Phone: (313)764-9492
Ann Arbor, MI 48109-1259 Garry R. Walz, Dir.
Founded: 1966. **Staff:** Prof 9. **Subjects:** Guidance, counseling, student and educational psychology, helping services. **Holdings:** 500 books; 310,000 microfiche. **Subscriptions:** 70 journals and other serials. **Services:** Center open to the public. **Computerized Information Services:** BRS Information Technologies, DIALOG Information Services; CD-ROM (DIALOG OnDisc); MultiLink (electronic mail service). Performs searches on fee basis. Contact Person: Barbara Hogan Karvonen, User Serv.Spec. **Publications:** Monographs; special papers; digests; information briefs; annotated minibibliographies; newsletters. **Remarks:** FAX: (313)747-2425. **Also Known As:** ERIC/CAPS.

★5397★
ERIC Clearinghouse on Educational Management (Educ)
College of Education
University of Oregon
1787 Agate St. Phone: (503)346-5043
Eugene, OR 97403 Dr. Philip K. Piele, Prof./Dir.
Founded: 1966. **Staff:** Prof 9; Other 6. **Subjects:** Education - management, facilities, planning, evaluation; schools - administration, organization, finance, building design and construction. **Holdings:** 600 books; 315,000 ERIC documents on microfiche; 22,000 ERIC documents on educational management on microfiche. **Subscriptions:** 35 journals and other serials. **Services:** Clearinghouse open to the public with restrictions. **Computerized Information Services:** DIALOG Information Services. **Publications:** Bibliographies; reviews; monographs; books; newsletter, quarterly. **Remarks:** FAX: (503)346-5890. **Staff:** Stuart C. Smith, Asst.Dir./Ed.

★5398★
ERIC Clearinghouse on Elementary and Early Childhood Education (Educ)
University of Illinois
805 W. Pennsylvania Ave. Phone: (217)333-1386
Urbana, IL 61801 Lilian G. Katz, Ph.D., Dir.
Founded: 1967. **Staff:** Prof 6; Other 2. **Subjects:** Early childhood education, elementary education, day care, parent education, infants, child development and education through early adolescence. **Holdings:** ERIC microfiche collection; VF drawers; small resource library of early childhood materials. **Subscriptions:** 150 journals and other serials. **Services:** Information and reference service; clearinghouse open to the public for reference use only. **Automated Operations:** Computerized document processing. **Computerized Information Services:** ERIC, DIALOG Information Services, BRS Information Technologies, PLATO; CD-ROM; BITNET (electronic mail service). **Networks/Consortia:** Member of Lincoln Trail Libraries System (LTLS). **Publications:** ERIC/EECE Newsletter; resource lists and digests - free upon request; list of additional publications - for sale, available upon request. **Remarks:** FAX: (217)333-3767. Electronic mail address(es): ericeece@ux1 (BITNET). **Staff:** Dianne Rothenberg, Assoc.Dir.; Norma K. Howard, User.Serv.

★5399★
ERIC Clearinghouse on Handicapped & Gifted Children - CEC Information Services (Educ)
Council for Exceptional Children
1920 Association Dr. Phone: (703)620-3660
Reston, VA 22091 Frederick Weintraub, Dir.
Founded: 1966. **Staff:** Prof 10; Other 2. **Subjects:** Exceptional child education, handicapped, gifted, special education. **Holdings:** 48,000 bound documents and microfiche; ERIC microfiche collection; private collection on microfiche; ECER collection. **Subscriptions:** 250 journals and other serials. **Services:** Copying; services open to the public for reference use only. **Computerized Information Services:** DIALOG Information Services, BRS Information Technologies; SpecialNet (electronic mail service). Performs searches on fee basis. **Remarks:** FAX: (703)264-9494. **Staff:** Kathleen McLane, Assoc.Dir.; Jean Boston, Assoc.Dir.

★5400★
ERIC Clearinghouse on Higher Education (Educ)
George Washington University
School of Education & Human Development
One Dupont Circle, Suite 630 Phone: (202)296-2597
Washington, DC 20036 Dr. Jonathan D. Fife, Dir.
Founded: 1968. **Staff:** Prof 5. **Subjects:** Higher education. **Holdings:** 14,000 cataloged items, primarily reports; ERIC microfiche collection. **Subscriptions:** 47 journals and other serials. **Services:** Copying; clearinghouse open to the public. **Computerized Information Services:** DIALOG Information Services. **Publications:** ASHE - ERIC Higher Education Report Series, 8/year; Administrator's Update, 3/year. **Remarks:** FAX: (202)296-8379. **Staff:** Judi Conrad, Assoc.Dir.

★5401★
ERIC Clearinghouse on Information Resources (Info Sci)
030 Huntington Hall
Syracuse University Phone: (315)443-3640
Syracuse, NY 13244-2340 Dr. Michael Eisenberg, Dir.
Founded: 1974. **Staff:** Prof 4; Other 3. **Subjects:** Library and information science - management, and use of libraries and information centers, technology and automation, information policy, information literacy, information storage and retrieval, censorship, networking; educational technology - design and development, computer assisted instruction, media, distance education, simulation and gaming. **Holdings:** 3600 books; 350,000 ERIC documents on microfiche. **Subscriptions:** 84 journals. **Services:** Copying; clearinghouse open to the public. **Computerized Information Services:** DIALOG Information Services; MICROsearch (internal database); BITNET, MultiLink Inc. (electronic mail services). Performs searches on fee basis. **Publications:** ERIC/IR Update (newsletter), semiannual - free upon request; trends and issues analyses, synthesis papers, and user services products in scope area. **Remarks:** One of 16 clearinghouses in the Educational Resources Information Center system. FAX: (315)443-5732. Electronic mail address(es): ERIC@SUVM (BITNET). **Staff:** Donald P. Ely, Assoc.Dir.; Barbara Minor, Pubn.Coord; Jane Klausmeier Janis, Oper.Coord.; Nancy R. Preston, User Serv.Coord.

★5402★
ERIC Clearinghouse for Junior Colleges (Educ)
8118 Math Sciences Bldg.
University of California, Los Angeles Phone: (213)825-3931
Los Angeles, CA 90024 Arthur M. Cohen, Dir.
Founded: 1966. **Staff:** Prof 4; Other 4. **Subjects:** Research on planning and operation of community, junior, and two-year colleges - administration, students, staff, instruction, curriculum. **Holdings:** 10,000 research reports. **Subscriptions:** 11 journals and other serials. **Services:** SDI; clearinghouse open to the public for reference use only. **Computerized Information**

Services: DIALOG Information Services, BRS Information Technologies; CD-ROMs (Silver Platter, Dialog ondisc). **Publications:** New Directions for Community Colleges, quarterly - by subscription; ERIC Digests - available on request; newsletter - available on request; occasional monographs. **Special Indexes:** Index of the Junior Colleges' holdings (card). **Remarks:** FAX: (213)206-8095. **Staff:** Anita Colby, Assoc.Dir.; Diane Hirshberg, User Serv.Spec.

★5403★
ERIC Clearinghouse on Languages and Linguistics (Hum, Educ)
Center for Applied Linguistics
1118 22nd St., N.W. Phone: (202)429-9551
Washington, DC 20037 Charles Stansfield, Dir.
Founded: 1966. **Staff:** Prof 6; Other 1. **Subjects:** Foreign languages, theoretical and applied linguistics, second language instruction, first and second language acquisition, bilingualism, bilingual education, English as a second/foreign language. **Holdings:** 310,000 ERIC microfiche; 65 state foreign language and English as a second language newsletters. **Subscriptions:** 50 journals and other serials. **Services:** Copying; clearinghouse open to the public. **Computerized Information Services:** DIALOG Information Services; BITNET (electronic mail service). Performs searches on fee basis. Contact Person: Craig Packard, User Serv.Coord. **Publications:** Language in Education: Theory and Practice Series; ERIC/CLL News Bulletin. **Remarks:** FAX: (202)659-5641. Telex: 892773 CENTAPLING. Electronic mail address(es): CAL@GUVAX (BITNET). **Staff:** Jeanne L. Rennie, Assoc.Dir.

★5404★
ERIC Clearinghouse on Reading and Communication Skills (Educ)
Smith Research Ctr.
Indiana University
2805 E. 10th St. Phone: (812)855-5847
Bloomington, IN 47408 Dr. Carl Smith, Dir.
Founded: 1966. **Staff:** Prof 14; Other 7. **Subjects:** Reading, English and language arts, journalism education, speech and mass communication, theater and drama. **Holdings:** 500 books; 300,000 documents on microfiche. **Subscriptions:** 75 journals and other serials. **Services:** Library open to the public by appointment. **Computerized Information Services:** CD-ROM (ERIC); BITNET (electronic mail service). Performs searches on fee basis. Contact Person: Gail Londergan, Asst.Dir. **Publications:** Digests, 10-12/year; monographs; bibliographies; brochures. **Special Indexes:** Resources in Education; Current Index to Journals in Education. **Remarks:** FAX: (812)855-7901. Electronic mail address(es): ERICRCS (BITNET). **Staff:** Ellie Macfarlane, Assoc.Dir.; Nola Aiex, Asst.Dir., Processing; Warren Lewis, Asst.Dir., Pubns.

★5405★
ERIC Clearinghouse on Rural Education and Small Schools (Educ)
1031 Quarrier St.
Box 1348
Charleston, WV 25325 Phone: (800)624-9120
Founded: 1966. **Staff:** 7. **Subjects:** Education - rural, small schools, Mexican American, American Indian, Alaska Native, migrant, outdoor. **Holdings:** 300,000 documents on ERIC microfiche. **Subscriptions:** 32 journals and other serials. **Services:** Clearinghouse open to the public for reference use only. **Computerized Information Services:** DIALOG Information Services, BRS Information Technologies; CD-ROM (ERIC); internal database; GTE (electronic mail service). Performs searches free of charge (ERIC files only). **Publications:** Newsletter, 3/year; Information Analysis Products. **Remarks:** Toll-free telephone number(s): (800)624-9120; (800)344-6646 (in West Virginia). FAX: (304)347-0487. Electronic mail address(es): CRESS.ERIC (GTE). **Also Known As:** CRESS. **Staff:** Craig B. Howley, Co-Dir.; C. Todd Strohmenger, Co-Dir.; Gary Huang, Asst.Dir.; Phyllis Stowers, Coord., Acq.; Pam Coe, Indian Ed.Spec.; Berma Lanham, Coord. User Serv.; Pat Cahape, Pubns.Coord.

★5406★
ERIC Clearinghouse for Science, Mathematics and Environmental Education (Educ, Sci-Engr)
Ohio State University
1200 Chambers Rd. Phone: (614)292-6717
Columbus, OH 43212 Dr. David L. Haury, Dir.
Founded: 1966. **Staff:** Prof 7. **Subjects:** Curriculum, teacher education, instruction, learning, research reporting and methodology in the areas of science, mathematics, and environmental education. **Holdings:** 100,000 documents. **Subscriptions:** 100 journals and other serials. **Services:** Copying; SDI; abstracting and indexing; consulting; clearinghouse open to the public. **Computerized Information Services:** ERIC; CD-ROM (DIALOG OnDisc). Performs searches on fee basis. **Publications:** Newsletter, bibliographies, digests, research reviews, directories, instructional activities manuals (15-20/year). **Remarks:** FAX: (614)292-0263. **Staff:** Dawn D. Puglisi, Asst.Dir.; Gail L. Messineo, Database Coord.; Linda A. Milbourne, Off.Mgr.

★5407★
ERIC Clearinghouse for Social Studies/Social Science Education (Educ)
Social Studies Development Center
Indiana University
2805 E. 10th St. Phone: (812)855-3838
Bloomington, IN 47405 John J. Patrick, Dir.
Founded: 1970. **Staff:** Prof 3; Other 10. **Subjects:** Social studies and social science education - content, teaching strategies, research, programs, teachers, education as a social science, social studies and the community, anthropology, archeology, economics, geography, sociology, history, social psychology, psychology, philosophy, political science. **Holdings:** 5000 books, resources, games, simulations, filmstrips, and curriculum guides. **Subscriptions:** 82 journals and other serials. **Services:** Clearinghouse not open to the public. **Computerized Information Services:** ERIC; BITNET (electronic mail service). Performs searches on fee basis. **Publications:** Keeping Up, annual - free on request. **Remarks:** FAX: (812)855-7901. Electronic mail address(es): RISINGER@IUBACS (BITNET). **Staff:** Jane Henson; C. Fredrick Risinger; Vickie Schlene.

★5408★
ERIC Clearinghouse on Teacher Education (Educ)
American Assn. of Colleges for Teacher Education
One Dupont Circle, Suite 610 Phone: (202)293-2450
Washington, DC 20036 Dorothy K. Stewart, Info.Spec.
Staff: Prof 6; Other 2. **Subjects:** Teacher education; health, physical, recreation, and dance education. **Holdings:** 200,000 microfiche; ERIC indexes and abstracts. **Subscriptions:** 27 journals and other serials. **Services:** Copying; clearinghouse open to the public. **Computerized Information Services:** DIALOG Information Services; CD-ROMs (DIALOG OnDisc, OCLC, SilverPlatter). **Remarks:** FAX: (202)457-8095.

★5409★
ERIC Clearinghouse on Tests, Measurement and Evaluation (Educ)
American Institutes for Research
3333 K St., N.W., Suite 200 Phone: (202)342-5060
Washington, DC 20007 Dr. Lawrence M. Rudner, Dir.
Founded: 1966. **Staff:** Prof 2; Other 3. **Subjects:** Tests, measurement, and evaluation; research methodology; human growth and development; learning theory. **Special Collections:** ERIC/TME reports, highlights, annotated bibliographies, digests, and updates; complete collection of Resources in Education (RIE) and Current Index to Journals in Education (CIJE). **Holdings:** 267,000 ERIC documents on microfiche. **Services:** Abstracting; workshops; indexing; clearinghouse open to the public. **Computerized Information Services:** DIALOG Information Services, BRS Information Technologies. Performs searches on fee basis. Contact Person: Lynn Davey, User Serv.Coord. **Publications:** Current publications list - free upon request. **Remarks:** FAX: (202)342-5033. **Staff:** Deborah Jean Vitale, Adm. & Doc.Coord.

★5410★
ERIC Clearinghouse on Urban Education (Educ)
Institute for Urban and Minority Education
Teachers College, Columbia University
Box 40 Phone: (212)678-3433
New York, NY 10027 Dr. Erwin Flaxman, Dir.
Founded: 1965. **Staff:** Prof 8; Other 4. **Subjects:** Education of urban and minority children and youths; psychology; sociology. **Holdings:** 1000 books; 15,500 reports, manuscripts, and other documentation; 205,000 titles in ERIC microfiche collection. **Subscriptions:** 60 journals and other serials. **Services:** Reference services by mail in the form of prepared bibliographies and other ERIC/CUE publications; clearinghouse open to the public by appointment. **Computerized Information Services:** DIALOG Information Services, PFDS Online, BRS Information Technologies, CD-ROM (SilverPlatter). Performs searches on fee basis. Contact Person: Dr. Michael Webb, Assoc.Dir. **Publications:** Trends and Issues Series - for sale; Urban Diversity Series, irregular - for sale; ERIC/CUE Digests, irregular - single copies free upon request with a self-addressed stamped envelope. **Remarks:** FAX: (212)678-4048. **Also Known As:** ERIC/CUE. **Staff:** Wendy Schwartz, Mng.Ed. & Acq.Coord.; Karen Wallace, Info.Spec.; Dr. Carol Ascher, Writer; Patti White, Info.Spec.; Luvon Roberson, Outreach Coord.; Peter Cuasay, Res.Asst./Asst. to the Dir.

★5411★
ERIC Processing and Reference Facility (Educ)
1301 Piccard Dr., Suite 300 Phone: (301)258-5500
Rockville, MD 20850-4305 Ted Brandhorst, Dir.
Founded: 1966. **Staff:** Prof 11; Other 7. **Subjects:** Education, lexicography, document and information processing, abstracting, indexing, reference. **Special Collections:** Complete collection of ERIC Clearinghouse products; complete ERIC microfiche collection. **Holdings:** 500 volumes. **Subscriptions:** 25 journals and other serials. **Services:** Information processing services; facility open to the public with restrictions. **Computerized Information Services:** ERIC database in machine-readable form available. **Publications:** Resources in Education, monthly abstract journal; updates to the ERIC Processing Manual, Directory of ERIC System Components, the ERIC System Documentation; Bibliography of ERIC Clearinghouse Publications. **Special Indexes:** ERIC Thesaurus; Source Directory; Contract/Grant Number Index; Report Number Index; Clearinghouse Number/ED Number Cross Reference Listing; Title Index - all for sale. **Remarks:** FAX: (301)948-3695. This is a centralized editing and information processing facility maintaining the ERIC database and serving all components of the ERIC network. It is operated for the U.S. Department of Education by ARC Professional Services Group - Information Systems Division.

Erich-Schneider-Bibliothek
See: **Germany - National Library of Economics in Germany** (6451)

Erickson Education Foundation - J2CP Information Services
See: **J2CP Information Services** (8299)

★5412★
Milton Erickson Foundation, Inc. - Archives (Med)
3606 N. 24th St.
Phoenix, AZ 85016 Phone: (602)956-6196
Staff: Prof 1. **Subjects:** Hypnotherapy, pain control. **Special Collections:** Dr. Erickson's therapeutic methods. **Holdings:** 100 books; 160 videotapes; 702 audiotapes; memorabilia. **Services:** Archives limited to health professionals by appointment only.

★5413★
Erico Products, Inc. - Information Resources Center (Sci-Engr)
34600 Solon Rd. Phone: (216)248-0100
Solon, OH 44139 Maria M. Ackley, Dir.
Staff: 1. **Subjects:** Engineering, science and technology, materials, metals, research and development, sales, marketing, personnel. **Holdings:** 6000 books; 2000 patents; 500 manuscripts; standards; specifications. **Subscriptions:** 100 journals and other serials; 5 newspapers. **Services:** ILL; copying; center open to the public open to the public with restrictions. **Computerized Information Services:** DIALOG Information Services, ORBIT Search Service, STN International.

★5414★
Erie Business Center South - Library (Bus-Fin)
700 Moravia St. Phone: (412)658-9066
New Castle, PA 16101 Irene G. Marburger, Dir.
Subjects: Business administration - accounting, sales, advertising, marketing, travel and tourism; secretarial science - executive, legal, medical, travel/tourism; management information systems; computers. **Holdings:** 1100 books. **Subscriptions:** 10 journals and other serials. **Services:** Library not open to the public. **Formerly:** New Castle Business School. **Staff:** Barbara T. Klenotic.

★5415★
Erie Canal Museum - Resource Center (Hist)
318 Erie Blvd., E. Phone: (315)471-0593
Syracuse, NY 13202 Donald Wilson, Curator
Founded: 1962. **Staff:** Prof 4. **Subjects:** Erie Canal and New York State Canal System, 1817 to present; U.S. and foreign canals - history, economics, engineering, construction, operations; Syracuse local history. **Special Collections:** W.H. Campbell Collection (750 sketches with text of historic subjects in Central New York); Rossman Panama Canal Collection; St. Lawrence Seaway Collection (construction of the seaway, 1942-1958). **Holdings:** 1200 volumes; 15,000 photographs; 2000 film negatives; 200 linear feet of manuscript material; 2500 maps and plans; 800 prints; 1600 government documents; slides. **Subscriptions:** 58 journals and other serials. **Services:** Copying; center open to the public by appointment only.

★5416★
Erie County Historical Society - Library & Archives (Hist)
417 State St. Phone: (814)454-1813
Erie, PA 16501 Annita A. Andrick, Libn./Archv.
Founded: 1903. **Staff:** Prof 2; Other 2. **Subjects:** History - Erie County, western Pennsylvania, Lake Erie region; genealogy; historic preservation. **Special Collections:** Battles Family Papers; Gideon Ball Collection; Battles Bank Collection; Mary Benedict Collection; Harry Burleigh Collection; C. Paxton Cody Collection; Judah Colt Collection; Rudolph Conrader Collection; Erie Academy Papers; Erie Imprint Collection; Erie Oil Company Collection; Erie Philharmonic Papers; Erie Street Railway Papers; Oliver Hazard Perry Ferguson Collection; GAR Post 67 Papers; Adam Grimler Collection; Hammermill Paper Co. Inc. Collection; Irving Literary Institute Collection; Josiah Kellogg Collection; Koehler Brewery/Erie Brewing Company, Inc. Papers; Maurice Kolpien Collection; Litton Shipyard Papers; David B. McCreary Papers; Nagle Steam Engine & Boiler Works Collection; 145th Regiment Papers; Pennsylvania Population Company Papers; Oren Reed Family Papers; William L. Scott Collection; Norman T . Sobel Collection; Tavern Licenses. **Holdings:** 3350 volumes; 105 bound periodical volumes; 650 maps and measured drawings; 297 reels of microfilm; 56 linear feet of newspapers clippings, typescripts, and reports; 228 linear feet of manuscripts; 15,500 photographs, slides, and postcards; 11,557 glass plate negatives; 145 linear feet of other archival materials. **Subscriptions:** 47 journals and other serials. **Services:** Copying; library open to the public. **Networks/Consortia:** Member of Northwest Interlibrary Cooperative of Pennsylvania (NICOP), Pittsburgh Regional Library Center (PRLC). **Publications:** Journal of Erie Studies, semiannual - to members and by exchange. **Special Catalogs:** Dictionary catalog.

★5417★
Erie County Law Library (Law)
Court House
140 W. 6th St. Phone: (814)451-6319
Erie, PA 16501 Max C. Peaster, Libn.
Staff: Prof 1. **Subjects:** Law. **Holdings:** 21,155 volumes; 7800 microforms. **Subscriptions:** 66 journals and other serials. **Services:** Interlibrary loan; copying; library open to the public for reference use only. **Computerized Information Services:** WESTLAW. **Networks/Consortia:** Member of Northwest Interlibrary Cooperative of Pennsylvania (NICOP). **Remarks:** FAX: (814)451-6320.

★5418★
Erie County Law Library Association - Library (Law)
Court House, 1st Fl.
323 Columbus Ave. Phone: (419)626-4823
Sandusky, OH 44870 Carolyn W. Delli Bovi, MLS, JD
Founded: 1890. **Staff:** 1. **Subjects:** Law. **Holdings:** 15,000 volumes. **Services:** Interlibrary loan; library open to the public by appointment. **Remarks:** FAX: (419)626-4826.

★5419★
Erie County Medical Center - Medical Library (Med)
462 Grider St. Phone: (716)898-3939
Buffalo, NY 14215 Edward J. Leisner, Sr.Med.Libn.
Founded: 1921. **Staff:** Prof 2; Other 2. **Subjects:** Medicine, orthopedics, cardiology, neurology, surgery, nursing. **Holdings:** 2300 books; 16,000 bound periodical volumes; 1150 AV programs; 4 VF drawers of reprints and pamphlets. **Subscriptions:** 382 journals and other serials. **Services:** Interlibrary loan; copying; library open to the public for reference use only. **Computerized Information Services:** BRS Information Technologies, OCLC. **Networks/Consortia:** Member of National Network of Libraries of Medicine - Middle Atlantic Region, Western New York Library Resources Council (WNYLRC), Library Consortium of Health Institutions in Buffalo (LCHIB). **Special Catalogs:** Learning Resources Center Media Catalog, annual. **Staff:** Susan Craft, Med.Libn.

Erik H. Erikson Library
See: **San Francisco Psychoanalytic Institute** (14739)

★5420★
Erikson Institute - Library (Soc Sci)
25 W. Chicago Ave. Phone: (312)280-7302
Chicago, IL 60610 Maija B. May, Libn.
Founded: 1966. **Staff:** Prof 1. **Subjects:** Child development, psychology, sociology, anthropology. **Holdings:** 2500 books; 3 VF drawers of pamphlets; films; filmstrips; tapes. **Subscriptions:** 13 journals and other serials. **Services:** Interlibrary loan; copying; library open to the public for reference use only.

Erlander Home Museum
See: **Swedish Historical Society of Rockford** (15922)

★5421★
Erlanger Medical Center - Medical Library (Med)
975 E. 3rd St. Phone: (615)778-7246
Chattanooga, TN 37403 Belva Jennings, Lib.Mgr.
Founded: 1940. **Staff:** Prof 1; Other 4. **Subjects:** Surgery, obstetrics and gynecology, pediatrics, ophthalmology, internal medicine, plastic surgery, oncology, nursing. **Special Collections:** William Moore Bogart Memorial Collection (historic, southern, and general medicine; 500 items); History of Medicine Collection. **Holdings:** 6608 books; 25,500 bound periodical volumes; 4 VF drawers of archival materials; 4 VF drawers of pamphlets; 1345 cassette tapes. **Subscriptions:** 562 journals and other serials. **Services:** Interlibrary loan; copying; library open to the public for reference use only. **Automated Operations:** Computerized cataloging and acquisitions. **Computerized Information Services:** MEDLARS; DOCLINE (electronic mail service). Performs searches on fee basis. **Networks/Consortia:** Member of Tennessee Health Science Library Association (THeSLA), Health Education Library Program (HELP), SOLINET. **Publications:** Bibliographies; accessions lists; new books lists, monthly. **Special Indexes:** Index of bibliographies (card). **Remarks:** FAX: (615)778-7247. **Staff:** Ruth Kee, Asst.Libn.; Myra Beaty, Asst.Libn.; Rose Mary Bearden, Asst.Libn.; Claudia Love, Sec.III.

Ernst & Whinney Tax Library
See: **Brigham Young University - Glenn and Olive Nielson Library** (20802)

★5422★
Ernst & Young - Information Center (Bus-Fin)
200 Clarendon St. Phone: (617)859-6307
Boston, MA 02116 Ann M. Kenny, Libn.
Staff: Prof 1; Other 2. **Subjects:** Taxation, accounting, general business. **Special Collections:** Board of Tax Appeals. **Holdings:** 2000 books. **Subscriptions:** 185 journals and other serials; 6 newspapers. **Services:** Center not open to the public. **Computerized Information Services:** DIALOG Information Services, Mead Data Central, Dun & Bradstreet Business Credit Services, Dow Jones News/Retrieval, InvesText, SDI Mergers and Corporate Transactions. Performs searches on fee basis. **Publications:** Information Center Update, quarterly. **Remarks:** FAX: (617)266-5843. Telex: 921849 ERNST BSM.

★5423★
Ernst & Young - Information Center (Bus-Fin)
787 7th Ave. Phone: (212)773-5961
New York, NY 10019 Janet How Accardo, Mgr., Lib.Serv.
Founded: 1965. **Staff:** Prof 6; Other 2. **Subjects:** Accounting, business, taxation. **Holdings:** 10,000 volumes. **Subscriptions:** 500 journals and other serials. **Services:** Interlibrary loan; center not open to the public. **Automated Operations:** Computerized cataloging. **Computerized Information Services:** DIALOG Information Services, Mead Data Central, Interactive Data Services, Inc., Global Report, Dow Jones News/Retrieval, CompuServe Information Service, Financial Times Business Reports. **Networks/Consortia:** Member of SUNY/OCLC Library Network. **Publications:** Update. **Remarks:** FAX: (212)489-1745. Telex: 147214 ERNST NYK. **Staff:** Miriam Redrick; Mitchell Feir; Sylvia Sanderlin.

★5424★
Ernst & Young - International Tax Library (Bus-Fin)
787 7th Ave., 22nd Fl. Phone: (212)773-6469
New York, NY 10019 Bernice Selden, Intl. Tax Libn.
Founded: 1980. **Staff:** 1. **Subjects:** International taxation. **Holdings:** 2000 volumes. **Subscriptions:** 160 journals and other serials. **Services:** ILL; copying; library not open to the public. **Automated Operations:** Computerized public access catalog. **Computerized Information Services:** LEXIS, NEXIS. **Remarks:** FAX: (212)773-5584. **Staff:** Helen Walsh, Asst.

★5425★
Ernst & Young - Library (Bus-Fin)
515 S. Flower St., No. 2000 Phone: (213)977-4216
Los Angeles, CA 90071 Jeffrey M. Lambert, Hd.Libn.
Staff: Prof 2; Other 1. **Subjects:** Accounting, business, electronic data processing, health care, tax, executive compensation, financial services, marketing. **Holdings:** 3500 books. **Subscriptions:** 310 journals and other serials; 15 newspapers. **Services:** Interlibrary loan; library not open to the public. **Automated Operations:** Computerized cataloging. **Computerized Information Services:** DIALOG Information Services, Mead Data Central, DataTimes, Dun & Bradstreet Business Credit Services. **Networks/Consortia:** Member of Metronet. **Remarks:** FAX: (213)680-9430. **Staff:** Anita Sfarian, Tax Libn.

★5426★
Ernst & Young - Library (Bus-Fin)
330 N. Wabash
One IBM Plaza Phone: (312)368-1800
Chicago, IL 60611 Jack Holcomb, Libn.
Staff: 2. **Subjects:** Accounting, taxation. **Holdings:** Figures not available. **Services:** Interlibrary loan; library not open to the public.

★5427★
Ernst & Young - Library (Bus-Fin)
1 Detroit Center
500 Woodward Ave., No. 1700 Phone: (313)596-7100
Detroit, MI 48226 Jan Farrace, Hd.Libn.
Staff: Prof 1; Other 1. **Subjects:** Accounting, taxation, auditing, health care, consulting information, general business. **Holdings:** Figures not available. **Subscriptions:** 300 journals and other serials. **Services:** Interlibrary loan; library not open to the public. **Automated Operations:** Computerized cataloging, acquisitions, serials, and circulation. **Computerized Information Services:** LEXIS, NEXIS.

★5428★
Ernst & Young - Library (Bus-Fin)
277 Park Ave. Phone: (212)773-1975
New York, NY 10172 Janet How Accardo
Founded: 1953. **Staff:** Prof 3.5; Other 4. **Subjects:** Accounting and auditing, management consulting, taxation. **Holdings:** 5500 books. **Subscriptions:** 500 journals and other serials. **Services:** Interlibrary loan; copying; library open to clients and SLA members. **Automated Operations:** Computerized cataloging and serials. **Computerized Information Services:** NEXIS, PFDS Online, Dow Jones News/Retrieval, DIALOG Information Services, CompuServe Information Service, Dun & Bradstreet Business Credit Services. **Publications:** Acquisitions List, quarterly - to staff and other accounting firms. **Remarks:** FAX: (212)773-3441. **Staff:** Mitchell Feir, Asst.Libn.; Ellen Loughlin, Asst.Libn.; Marge Lynn, Cat.

★5429★
Ernst & Young - Library (Bus-Fin)
2121 San Jacinto St., Suite 400 Phone: (214)969-8411
Dallas, TX 75201 Tommy M. Yardley, Libn.
Staff: Prof 1; Other 2. **Subjects:** Accounting, tax accounting, auditing. **Special Collections:** Annual reports; tax subject file. **Holdings:** 6900 books; 1000 bound periodical volumes. **Subscriptions:** 400 journals and other serials; 6 newspapers. **Services:** Interlibrary loan; copying; library open to the public with librarian's approval. **Automated Operations:** Computerized acquisitions and serials. **Computerized Information Services:** DIALOG Information Services, LEXIS, WESTLAW, Dow Jones News/Retrieval, Maxwell Macmillan Taxes Online, DataTimes, National Planning Data Corporation (NPDC), CCH Access; internal database. **Publications:** INFO-LINK - for internal distribution only. **Remarks:** FAX: (214)969-8530.

★5430★
Ernst & Young - Library (Bus-Fin)
111 E. Kilbourn Ave., Suite 900 Phone: (414)274-8778
Milwaukee, WI 53202 Neil Hootkin, Libn.
Staff: 1. **Subjects:** Taxation, tax law, accounting, auditing. **Holdings:** 1200 books. **Subscriptions:** 35 journals and other serials. **Services:** Interlibrary loan; copying; SDI; library open to the public with administrative approval. **Computerized Information Services:** LEXIS. Performs searches on fee basis for clients only. **Remarks:** FAX: (414)273-1645; (414)273-4648.

★5431★
Ernst & Young - Library (Bus-Fin)
707 7th Ave., S.W., 13th Fl. Phone: (403)290-4183
Calgary, AB, Canada T2P 3H6 Joan Faulk, Mgr., Lib.Serv.
Founded: 1980. **Staff:** Prof 1; Other 1. **Subjects:** Business, finance, accounting, auditing, taxation, human resource management. **Holdings:** 2100 books; 175 clippings files; 600 annual reports of 390 companies; 150 prospectuses. **Subscriptions:** 120 journals and other serials; 5 newspapers. **Services:** Interlibrary loan; copying (limited); SDI; library open to other libraries. **Automated Operations:** Computerized cataloging, acquisitions, and serials. **Computerized Information Services:** DIALOG Information Services, QL Systems, Info Globe, Infomart Online, CT Online Systems, INSIGHT Monthly Economic Report. **Publications:** Key Economic Indicators; Information Bulletin quarterly - both for internal distribution only. **Special Indexes:** Annual report index (online). **Remarks:** FAX: (403)290-4265.

★5432★
Ernst & Young - Library (Bus-Fin)
1 Place Ville Marie, Suite 2400 Phone: (514)875-6060
Montreal, PQ, Canada H3B 3M9 Margaret Cameron, Libn.
Founded: 1971. **Staff:** 1. **Subjects:** Accounting, tax, management consulting. **Holdings:** 3000 books; 600 annual reports. **Subscriptions:** 120 journals and other serials; 10 newspapers. **Services:** Interlibrary loan; library not open to the public. **Remarks:** FAX: (514)871-8713.

★5433★
Ernst & Young - National Library (Bus-Fin)
Royal Trust Tower
Box 251, Toronto Dominion Centre Phone: (416)864-1234
Toronto, ON, Canada M5K 1J7 Anita A. Currie, Mgr., Lib.Serv.
Founded: 1961. **Staff:** Prof 2; Other 4. **Subjects:** Accounting, management consulting, economics, marketing. **Special Collections:** Financial reports of Canadian companies (1800); complete Statistics Canada collection. **Holdings:** 10,000 volumes. **Subscriptions:** 450 journals and other serials. **Services:** Interlibrary loan; library not open to the public. **Computerized Information Services:** DIALOG Information Services, PFDS Online, Info Globe, DunsPrint, Dow Jones News/Retrieval, Canada Systems Group (CSG), Infomart Online, LEXIS, NEXIS, WILSONLINE, Marketscan, Reuters Information Services (Canada). **Publications:** Library Bulletin, quarterly; periodicals list. **Remarks:** FAX: (416)864-1174. **Staff:** Wendy Brennan, Ref.Libn.

★5434★
Ernst & Young - National Office Library (Bus-Fin)
2000 National City Center Phone: (216)861-5000
Cleveland, OH 44114 Naomi Clifford, Natl.Off.Libn.
Founded: 1960. **Staff:** Prof 3; Other 1. **Subjects:** Accounting, auditing, management. **Special Collections:** American Institute of Certified Public Accountants and Financial Accounting Standards Board publications. **Holdings:** 6000 volumes; 20 VF drawers; 6000 annual reports. **Subscriptions:** 400 journals and other serials; 15 newspapers. **Services:** Interlibrary loan; copying; library open to the public by appointment. **Automated Operations:** Computerized cataloging and ILL. **Computerized Information Services:** DIALOG Information Services, Dow Jones News/ Retrieval, VU/TEXT Information Services, LEXIS, NEXIS; internal database. **Networks/Consortia:** Member of OHIONET. **Remarks:** FAX: (216)861-8315. **Staff:** Kathy Fabianich, Asst.Libn.; Danean Putman, Asst.Libn.

EROS Data Center
See: **U.S. Geological Survey** (17529)

★5435★
Erstes Oesterreichisches Motorrad - und Technik Museum - Sammlung Ehn - Bibliothek (Trans)
Museumgasse 6 Phone: 02984 2151
A-3730 Eggenburg, Austria Friedrich Ehn, Dir.
Founded: 1980. **Staff:** 3. **Subjects:** Motorcycles, traffic. **Special Collections:** Austrian Motor collection. **Holdings:** 300 books; 50 bound periodical volumes; 500 documents; 20 manuscripts; photographs. **Services:** Library not open to the public. **Publications:** Die Motorroller und Mopeds der Wiener Firm Lohner.

★5436★
Escambia County Health Department - Library (Med)
Box 12604 Phone: (904)435-6550
Pensacola, FL 32574-2604 Linda Mills, Hea.Educ.Supv.
Subjects: Health, public health. **Holdings:** Vertical files. **Services:** Library open to the public. **Remarks:** Library located at 2251 N. Palafox St., Pensacola, FL 32501.

★5437★
Escondido Historical Society - Museum Library (Hist)
P.O. Box 263 Phone: (619)743-8207
Escondido, CA 92025 Janean Young, Chm., Lib.
Founded: 1976. **Staff:** 2. **Subjects:** Local and California history, restoration and historical preservation. **Special Collections:** Historical/cultural survey (7 volumes); Harold Bell Wright Collection; San Pasqual Battle. **Holdings:** 980 books; 24 bound periodical volumes; 3 AV programs; 1 roll of maps; 75 oral history tapes; city directories, 1886 to present; 160 local high school annuals; 20 local history scrapbooks; newspaper clipping file; pamphlets; photographs; ephemera. **Subscriptions:** 12 journals and other serials. **Services:** Copying; library open to the public for reference use only. **Staff:** Chris O'Connor, Reg.

★5438★
Esherick Homsey Dodge and Davis - Library (Plan)
2789 25th St. Phone: (415)285-9193
San Francisco, CA 94110 Susan M. Koskinen, Libn.
Founded: 1946. **Staff:** Prof 1; Other 2. **Subjects:** Architecture, planning. **Holdings:** 2600 books; 50,000 slides and photographs; 2200 product literature catalogs; 16 VF drawers of product literature; blueprints; archives. **Subscriptions:** 140 journals and other serials. **Services:** Library not open to the public. **Computerized Information Services:** DIALOG Information Services; 4th Dimension (internal database).

ESL Learning Resources Centre
See: **Alberta Advanced Education - Alberta Vocational College - ESL Learning Resources Centre** (231)

★5439★
ESL/Subsidiary of TRW, Inc. - Research Library (Sci-Engr)
495 Java Dr.
Box 3510 Phone: (408)738-2888
Sunnyvale, CA 94088-3510 Verna Van Velzer, Chf.Libn.
Founded: 1966. **Staff:** Prof 1; Other 1. **Subjects:** Electronics, communications, computer science, physics, mathematics, military science. **Holdings:** 20,000 volumes. **Subscriptions:** 275 journals and other serials. **Services:** Interlibrary loan; library not open to the public. **Automated Operations:** Computerized acquisitions, serials, circulation, and financial records. **Computerized Information Services:** DIALOG Information Services, DTIC; OnTyme Electronic Message Network Service (electronic mail service). **Networks/Consortia:** Member of CLASS. **Remarks:** FAX: (408)743-6304. **Also Known As:** Electromagnetic Systems Laboratories. **Staff:** Carol Reichner, Info.Spec.

★5440★
Esoteric Philosophy Center, Inc. - Library
10085 Westpark, Suite B
Houston, TX 77042
Founded: 1970. **Subjects:** Metaphysics, occult doctrine, sound, color, vibration, astrology, numerology, tarot, palmistry, yoga. **Holdings:** 2460 books. **Remarks:** Currently inactive.

★5441★
Esperantic Studies Foundation - Library (Hum)
3900 Northampton St., N.W. Phone: (202)362-3963
Washington, DC 20015 E. James Lieberman, Dir.
Founded: 1968. **Staff:** 1. **Subjects:** Esperanto, international communication. **Holdings:** 500 books; 30 file boxes of unbound U.S., European, and Asian journals in Esperanto. **Subscriptions:** 5 journals and other serials. **Services:** Library open to the public by appointment. **Publications:** Esperanto and International Language Problems: A Research Bibliography (4th edition; 1977); newsletter; Esperantic Studies, 2/year. **Remarks:** FAX: (202)363-6899.

★5442★
Esperanto Cultural Centre - Library (Hum)
Postiers 27, Case Postale 779 Phone: 39 267407
CH-2301 La Chaux-De-Fonds, Switzerland Mario Lepine, Adm.
Founded: 1968. **Subjects:** Esperanto. **Holdings:** 10,000 volumes. **Also Known As:** Kultura Centro Esperantista.

★5443★
Esperanto League for North America - Esperanto Information Service (Hum)
Box 1129 Phone: (510)653-0998
El Cerrito, CA 94530 Mike Donohoo, Dir.
Staff: Prof 2. **Subjects:** Book service listing over 1000 titles in Esperanto for sale in many subjects including language, history, interlinguistics, prose, drama, poetry, biography, politics, philosophy, science, geography, travel, music. **Special Catalogs:** Book catalog published by Esperanto Book Service with occasional appendices. **Also Known As:** ELNA.

★5444★
Espey Manufacturing & Electronics Corporation - Component Specifications Library (Sci-Engr)
Ballston and Congress Aves.
Box 422 Phone: (518)584-4100
Saratoga Springs, NY 12866 Bernard J. Smith, Libn.
Subjects: Electronics, engineering, finishing materials. **Holdings:** 5000 volumes; government and military specifications. **Services:** Interlibrary loan; copying; library open to the public with restrictions. **Automated Operations:** Computerized cataloging. **Remarks:** FAX: (518)584-4330.

★5445★
Essex County Historical Society - Brewster Library (Hist)
Court St.
Elizabethtown, NY 12932 Phone: (518)873-6466
Founded: 1956. **Subjects:** Adirondack history, folklore, literature; Indians of North America; Northern New York guidebooks; Essex County, New York. **Holdings:** 3038 books; 91 bound periodical volumes; 5000 pamphlets; 24 VF drawers of ephemera; 350 manuscripts; 32 reels of microfilm; 78 newspaper titles; 350 maps; 162 microforms and AV programs; 34 drawers of cemetery records. **Services:** Copying (limited); library open to the public by appointment. **Special Indexes:** Index to cemetery records; index to place names; index to newspaper articles; North Country index.

★5446★
Essex County Hospital Center - Hamilton Memorial Library (Med)
Box 500 Phone: (201)228-8002
Cedar Grove, NJ 07009 Elizabeth B. Guarducci, Med.Libn.
Founded: 1958. **Staff:** 3. **Subjects:** Psychiatry, psychology, mental health, psychotherapy, medicine, social work. **Holdings:** 2500 books. **Subscriptions:** 100 journals and other serials; 7 newspapers. **Services:** Interlibrary loan; copying; library open to the public with restrictions. **Networks/Consortia:** Member of Cosmopolitan Biomedical Library Consortium (CBLC). **Publications:** Acquisitions list, quarterly.

★5447★
Essex County Law Library (Law)
512 County Courts Bldg.
50 W. Market St. Phone: (201)621-4871
Newark, NJ 07102 Debra Womack, Libn.
Founded: 1896. **Staff:** 2. **Subjects:** Law. **Holdings:** 20,000 volumes. **Services:** Library open to county judges and attorneys.

★5448★
Essex Institute - James Duncan Phillips Library (Hist)
132 Essex St. Phone: (508)744-3390
Salem, MA 01970 William T. La Moy, Dir. of Lib.
Founded: 1821. **Staff:** Prof 3; Other 2. **Subjects:** Essex County history, New England maritime history and culture, early American history, genealogy. **Special Collections:** Almanacs; juvenile literature; trade catalogs; western books on imperial China; American fine and decorative arts; Hawthorne; Whittier. **Holdings:** 400,000 books; bound periodical volumes; early American broadsides; directories; newspapers (complete for Salem); manuscript business records and personal papers of merchants and families; logbooks; journals; diaries; manuscripts of American literary figures; maps; photographs. **Subscriptions:** 60 journals and other serials. **Services:** Copying; photographic orders; library open to the public on fee basis. **Publications:** Essex Institute Historical Collections, quarterly - by subscription. **Remarks:** FAX: (508)744-0036. **Staff:** Jane Ward, Cur. of Mss.; Mary Fabiszewski, Cat.; Nancy Heywood, Photo.Coll.

★5449★
Essex Law Association - Library (Law)
County Court House
245 Windsor Ave. Phone: (519)252-8418
Windsor, ON, Canada N9A 1J2 Douglas A. Hewitt, Libn.
Staff: 2. **Subjects:** Law. **Holdings:** 12,000 volumes. **Services:** Copying; library open to university law students for reference use only. **Computerized Information Services:** Online systems. **Remarks:** FAX: (519)252-9686.

★5450★
Essex Law Library (Law)
Superior Court House
34 Federal St. Phone: (508)741-0674
Salem, MA 01970 Richard E. Adamo, Law Libn.
Staff: Prof 1; Other 1. **Subjects:** Massachusetts and New England law, federal cases and statutes. **Special Collections:** Maritime law and law of the seas cases. **Holdings:** 34,000 books; 10,000 bound periodical volumes; law archives; Massachusetts statutes. **Services:** Interlibrary loan; copying; library open to the public. **Automated Operations:** Computerized acquisitions. **Remarks:** Part of the Massachusetts State Trial Court; Marnie Warner, Law Library Coordinator.

★5451★
Essex Shipbuilding Museum - Archives (Hist)
P.O. Box 277 Phone: (508)768-7541
Essex, MA 01929 Jim Witham, Cur.
Founded: 1976. **Staff:** 2. **Subjects:** Shipbuilding in Essex, genealogy, early American industries, maritime history and economics. **Special Collections:** Choate Family papers; Burnham Family papers; Essex shipyards, vessels, and fittings collection (correspondence, bills, photographs, and plans). **Holdings:** 260 books; 2000 photographs; 3 videotapes; 300 slides; 5000 other nonbook items. **Subscriptions:** 12 journals and other serials. **Services:** Copying; library open to the public. **Computerized Information Services:** Internal database. Performs searches on fee basis. Contact Person: Diana H. Stockton, Adm. **Special Catalogs:** A Catalog of the Vessels, Boats and Other Craft Built in the Town of Essex, 1870-1980 - for sale. **Remarks:** "Dedicated to the shipbuiders of Essex, MA, the museum maintains a collection of tools, documents and other materials preserving the history of local shipbuilding from 1668 to present day."

★5452★
Esso Chemical, Alberta Limited - Information Centre (Sci-Engr)
Agricultural Chemicals Complex
P.O. Box 28000 Phone: (403)998-5856
Edmonton, AB, Canada T5J 4R4 Patricia Jigolyk, Lib.Techn.
Founded: 1980. **Staff:** 1. **Subjects:** Chemistry, engineering, agronomy. **Holdings:** 3000 books; reports, codes and standards. **Subscriptions:** 98 journals and other serials. **Services:** Interlibrary loan; SDI; library not open to the public. **Computerized Information Services:** Online systems. **Remarks:** FAX: (403)998-6237. Library located at Redwater, AB.

★5453★
Esso Chemical Canada - Library
P.O. Box 2406 Phone: (403)420-8703
Edmonton, AB, Canada T5J 3R8 Patricia Jigolyk, Libn.
Remarks: Library located at Esso Tower, 14th Fl., 10060 Jasper Ave., Edmonton, AB, Canada, T5J 3R8. No further information was supplied by respondent.

★5454★
Esso Chemical Canada - Library (Sci-Engr)
4711 Yonge St. Phone: (416)733-5413
Toronto, ON, Canada M5W 1K3 Beth Boudreau, Libn.
Founded: 1965. **Staff:** Prof 1. **Subjects:** Petrochemical industry. **Special Collections:** SRI Chemical Economics Handbook; world petrochemicals. **Holdings:** 3200 books. **Subscriptions:** 95 journals and other serials. **Services:** Interlibrary loan; copying; SDI; library open to the public by appointment. **Automated Operations:** Computerized cataloging and serials (INMAGIC). **Computerized Information Services:** DIALOG Information Services, Info Globe, CAN/OLE; TELEMAIL, Envoy 100 (electronic mail services). **Publications:** Update, quarterly. **Remarks:** FAX: (416)733-5339. Electronic mail address(es): BA.BOUDREAU (TELEMAIL; Envoy 100).

★5455★
Esso Petroleum Canada - Information Centre (Energy)
90 Wynford Dr., Rm. 4106 Phone: (416)441-7858
North York, ON, Canada M3C 1K5 Les Czarnota, Info.Spec.
Founded: 1982. **Staff:** Prof 1; Other 1. **Subjects:** Petroleum - technology, engineering; petrochemical technology; chemical engineering. **Special Collections:** Standards of the American Petroleum Institute (API), American Society for Testing and Materials (ASTM), and Canadian Standards Association (CSA). **Holdings:** 1500 books. **Subscriptions:** 100 journals and other serials. **Services:** Interlibrary loan; center not open to the public. **Automated Operations:** Computerized cataloging and serials. **Computerized Information Services:** DIALOG Information Services. **Remarks:** Alternate telephone number(s): (416)441-7735. FAX: (416)441-7700.

★5456★
Esso Petroleum Canada - Research Technical Information Centre (Energy)
Box 3022 Phone: (519)339-2470
Sarnia, ON, Canada N7T 7M1 S.L. O'Brien, Info.Spec.
Staff: Prof 1; Other 3. **Subjects:** Chemistry, petroleum, petrochemicals, polymers, chemical engineering, energy. **Holdings:** 12,000 books; 10,000 bound periodical volumes; 40,000 company research reports; U.S. chemical patents; chemical abstracts, 1907 to present; American Petroleum Institute literature and patents, 1964 to present. **Subscriptions:** 300 journals and other serials. **Services:** Interlibrary loan; SDI; center open to students. **Automated Operations:** Computerized cataloging, acquisitions, serials, and circulation. **Computerized Information Services:** DIALOG Information Services, PFDS Online, CAN/OLE, Canadian Centre for Occupational Health & Safety, STN International; internal database; Envoy 100 (electronic mail service). **Publications:** Newsletter, monthly; Acquisition List - for internal distribution only. **Remarks:** FAX: (519)339-4436. Electronic mail address(es): NM.BOURQUE (Envoy 100).

★5457★
Esso Resources Canada Limited - Law Library (Law)
237 4th Ave., S.W., 35th Fl.
Calgary, AB, Canada T2P 0H6 Phone: (403)237-2890
Staff: 1. **Subjects:** Law. **Holdings:** 1114 books; 173 bound periodical volumes; 462 reports. **Subscriptions:** 173 journals and other serials; 3 newspapers. **Services:** Interlibrary loan; copying; library not open to the public. **Computerized Information Services:** QL Systems, CAN/LAW; internal database. **Remarks:** Alternate telephone number(s): 237-3737. FAX: (403)237-2786.

★5458★
Esso Resources Canada Limited - Library Information Centre (Energy)
237 4th Ave., S.W.
Calgary, AB, Canada T2P 0H6 Phone: (403)237-4520
Founded: 1957. **Staff:** Prof 5; Other 6. **Subjects:** Petroleum exploration, production, and research; business; minerals. **Special Collections:** Engineering standards; Northern Environmental Information. **Holdings:** 20,000 books; 6000 bound periodical volumes; 9000 external reports; 20,000 internal reports. **Subscriptions:** 500 journals and other serials. **Services:** Interlibrary loan. **Automated Operations:** Computerized public access catalog, cataloging, acquisitions, serials, and circulation. **Computerized Information Services:** DIALOG Information Services, PFDS Online, Data-Star, CANSIM, CAN/OLE, Info Globe, SPIRES, QL Systems; TIGER (internal database); Envoy 100 (electronic mail service). **Publications:** Current Awareness, biweekly. **Special Indexes:** Internal computer-produced indexes. **Remarks:** Alternate telephone number(s): 237-3737. A subsidiary of Imperial Oil, Ltd. **Staff:** Dan Pauli, Online Spec.; Teresa Zwierzchowski, Ref.Libn.

★5459★
Esso Resources Canada Limited - Research Library (Sci-Engr)
3535 Research Rd., N.W. Phone: (403)284-7417
Calgary, AB, Canada T2L 2K8 Abe S. Cohen, Libn.
Founded: 1956. **Staff:** Prof 1. **Subjects:** Chemistry, chemical engineering, physics, petroleum engineering, ice engineering, oceanography. **Holdings:** 9000 books; 6000 company reports; 1000 patents. **Subscriptions:** 200 journals and other serials. **Services:** Interlibrary loan; SDI; library open to the public with restrictions. **Automated Operations:** Computerized cataloging, acquisitions, and circulation. **Computerized Information Services:** CAN/OLE, DIALOG Information Services, ORBIT Search Service, STN International, QL Systems, Info Globe, Infomart Online; BITNET, Envoy 100 (electronic mail services). **Remarks:** FAX: (403)284-7589. Electronic mail address(es): ILL. ESSO.RESEARCH (Envoy 100); ascohen@eren; (BITNET).

Estacion Experimental Agro-Industrial Obispo Colombres
See: **Obispo Colombres Agro-Industrial Experiment Station** (12226)

★5460★
Estacion Experimental Agro Industrial Obispo Colombres - Biblioteca Alfredo Guzman (Agri)
Casilla de Correo No. 9 Phone: 81 266561
4101 Las Talitas, Tucuman, Argentina Eduardo Rothe
Staff: Prof 1; Other 3. **Subjects:** Sugar cane, sugar and derivatives, citrus industry, horticulture, animal production. **Holdings:** 5712 books; 14,895 bound periodical volumes. **Subscriptions:** 55 journals and other serials. **Services:** Interlibrary loan; copying; library open to the public for reference use only. **Publications:** Bibliography (1909-1979); Bibliography (1980-1990, under development).

★5461★
Esterline Angus Instrument Corporation - Company Library (Sci-Engr)
1201 Main St. Phone: (317)244-7611
Indianapolis, IN 46224-6533 Kelli R. Norris, Libn.
Founded: 1964. **Staff:** 1. **Subjects:** Electrical and mechanical instruments. **Holdings:** 757 books. **Subscriptions:** 20 journals and other serials. **Services:** Interlibrary loan; library open to the public by appointment only. **Remarks:** FAX: (317)247-4749. An Esterline Company.

Margaret Estes Library
See: **LeTourneau University - Margaret Estes Library** (9072)

W.L. Estes, Jr. Memorial Library
See: **St. Luke's Hospital of Bethlehem, Pennsylvania** (14483)

ESTIS/INFORM
See: **University of Minnesota - ESTIS/INFORM** (18909)

★5462★
Estonian Agricultural University - Library (Agri)
ul. Rija 12 Phone: 5472
Tartu, Estonia Tina Tohure
Founded: 1952. **Staff:** Prof 10; Other 18. **Subjects:** Agriculture, cattle-breeding, veterinary science, mechanization. **Holdings:** 480,469 books; 2362 bound periodical volumes; 5143 reports; 2011 archival items; 1200 reels of microfilm. **Subscriptions:** 363 journals and other serials; 48 newspapers. **Services:** Interlibrary loan; library open to the public. **Also Known As:** Estonskaja Selskochnozjajstvennaja, Akademija - Biblioteka.

★5463★
Estonian Music Center, U.S.A. - Musical Library (Area-Ethnic)
68-50 Juno St. Phone: (718)261-9618
Forest Hills, NY 11375 Juta Kurman, Pres.
Founded: 1956. **Staff:** 2. **Subjects:** Estonian and international music. **Special Collections:** Ethnic Estonian collection. **Holdings:** Sheet music; albums; biographies; photographs; cassette tapes; binders. **Subscriptions:** 2 journals and other serials. **Services:** Center open to the public by appointment. **Publications:** Biographies of composers and interpreters (Estonian and English). **Staff:** Jaan Kurman.

Estonskaja Selskochozjajstvennaja Akademija Biblioteka
See: **Estonian Agricultural University** (5462)

★5464★
Estorff Reference Library (Area-Ethnic)
Peter Muller St.
Private Bag 13349 Phone: 61 293203
Windhoek 9000, Namibia Mr. J. Loubser
Staff: Prof 2; Other 5. **Special Collections:** Namibiana Collection; Africana Collection; United Nations Collection. **Holdings:** 42,000 books; 54 microfiche; 24 microfilm titles; 114 maps. **Subscriptions:** 114 journals and other serials. **Services:** Interlibrary loan; library not open to the public. **Computerized Information Services:** SABINET; NAMLIT (internal database). Contact Person: Mrs. M. Boer. **Remarks:** FAX: 61 229808.

★5465★
Estudio Teologico Agustiniano - Padres Agustinos - Biblioteca (Rel-Phil)
Paseo de Filipinos 7
E-47007 Valladolid, Spain Phone: 306800
Founded: 1810. **Staff:** Prof 2; Other 2. **Subjects:** Theology, church history, philosophy. **Special Collections:** Philippines books (10,000); Augustinian books (3000). **Holdings:** 140,000 books; 20,000 bound periodical volumes. **Subscriptions:** 500 journals and other serials. **Services:** Copying; library open to the public. **Publications:** Updated checklist of Filipiniana at Valladolid. **Remarks:** FAX: 397896. **Also Known As:** Augustinian Philippines Library.

★5466★
Esztergomi Foszekesegyhazi Konyvtar
Pazmany u.2. Phone: 527
H-2500 Esztergom, Hungary Dr. Matyas Erdos, Dir.
Staff: 2. **Subjects:** Religion. **Special Collections:** Batthiany; Mayer; Fugger. **Holdings:** 250,000 volumes; 1000 bound periodical volumes. **Subscriptions:** 16 journals and other serials. **Services:** Interlibrary loan; copying; library open to the public with restrictions.

★5467★
Ethicon, Inc. - Scientific Information Services (Sci-Engr)
P.O. Box 151 Phone: (201)218-3272
Somerville, NJ 08876-0151 Dr. Charles G. Fritz, Dir.
Founded: 1956. **Staff:** Prof 3; Other 3. **Subjects:** Biological and physical sciences, sterilization, polymer chemistry, surgery, controlled drug delivery, pharmaceutical science. **Holdings:** 9000 books; 25,000 bound periodical volumes; 12 VF drawers of U.S. and foreign patents. **Subscriptions:** 400 journals and other serials. **Services:** Interlibrary loan. **Automated Operations:** Computerized acquisitions and circulation. **Computerized Information Services:** NLM, U.S. Patents Files, STN International, DIALOG Information Services, Dow Jones News/Retrieval, BRS Information Technologies; internal databases. **Networks/Consortia:** Member of MEDCORE. **Publications:** Current Literature, weekly; Scientific Information Reports, monthly - both for internal distribution only. **Remarks:** FAX: (201)218-3558. **Staff:** Norma K. Stavetski, Sect.Mgr., Res.Lib.; Susan Kantor, Assoc.Libn.

★5468★
Ethics and Public Policy Center - Library (Rel-Phil)
1015 15th St., N.W., Suite 900 Phone: (202)682-1200
Washington, DC 20005 Bettie P. Gray
Founded: 1976. **Staff:** Prof 5; Other 7. **Subjects:** Current events, Catholic studies, education studies, Protestant studies, legal studies, foreign affairs. **Holdings:** 200 books; 57 bound periodical volumes; 23 reports. **Subscriptions:** 57 journals and other serials; 4 newspapers. **Services:** Library not open to the public. **Publications:** Newsletters. **Remarks:** FAX: (202)408-0632.

Ethiopia - Ministry of Culture - The National Library and Archives of Ethiopia
See: **Ethiopia - The National Library and Archives of Ethiopia** (5469)

★5469★
Ethiopia - The National Library and Archives of Ethiopia (Area-Ethnic, Info Sci)
P.O. Box 717 Phone: 44 22 41
Addis Ababa, Ethiopia Almaz Mengistu, Asst.Libn.
Subjects: Ethiopiana, education, science and technology. **Special Collections:** Ethiopian manuscripts (1650); rare books; Ethiopiana (clippings; cuttings; bound newspapers). **Holdings:** 60,000 books; 10,000 bound periodical volumes; 40,000 patents and documents; 200 microforms; UN publications. **Services:** Interlibrary loan; copying; library open to the public. **Publications:** Ethiopian Publications, semiannual. **Special Indexes:** Index of Periodicals, semiannual. **Remarks:** Maintained by Ethiopia - Ministry of Culture. **Staff:** Arefaine Belay, Dept.Hd.

★5470★
Ethnic American Council - Library (Soc Sci)
820 Lathrop Phone: (708)366-1000
River Forest, IL 60305 Michael Burny
Founded: 1984. **Staff:** 1. **Subjects:** American ethnic groups, politics and government, liberty, communism, free market economics, entrepreneurship. **Special Collections:** Austrian economics collection. **Holdings:** 500 books; 25 reports. **Subscriptions:** 15 journals and other serials; 5 newspapers. **Services:** Library open to the public by appointment; must apply in writing.

Ethnomusicology Archive
See: **University of California, Los Angeles - Ethnomusicology Archive** (18383)

★5471★
Ethyl Corporation - Information and Library Services (Sci-Engr)
Box 14799 Phone: (504)768-5779
Baton Rouge, LA 70898-4799 Ferol A. Foos, Libn.
Founded: 1940. **Staff:** Prof 4; Other 3. **Subjects:** Chemistry, chemical engineering, business. **Holdings:** 20,000 books; 8000 bound periodical volumes. **Subscriptions:** 1200 journals and other serials. **Services:** Interlibrary loan (limited). **Automated Operations:** Computerized cataloging, acquisitions, serials, and circulation. **Computerized Information Services:** DIALOG Information Services, DataTimes, VU/TEXT Information Services, STN International, Dow Jones News/Retrieval, PIERS (Port Import/Export Reporting Service), Data-Star, National Pesticide Information Retrieval System (NPIRS). **Remarks:** FAX: (504)768-5990. Telex: 784583. **Staff:** Louise O. Pearce, Tech.Serv.; Sandra B. Williford, Bus.Ref.; Carolyn M. Beaver, Tech.Ref.

★5472★
Etobicoke Board of Education - Resource Library (Educ)
1 Civic Centre Court Phone: (416)394-7309
Etobicoke, ON, Canada M9C 2B3 Alice Churchman, Coord.
Founded: 1969. **Staff:** Prof 2.5; Other 3.5. **Subjects:** Education, psychology, social sciences, curriculum subjects. **Holdings:** 30,000 books; 13 VF drawers of clippings. **Subscriptions:** 452 journals and other serials. **Services:** Copying; library open to the public. **Computerized Information Services:** DIALOG Information Services, PFDS Online, BRS Information Technologies, Infomart Online, Info Globe. **Remarks:** FAX: (416)394-7397. **Staff:** Barbara Green, Prog.Adv.; Andre Vietinghoff, Libn.

★5473★
Etobicoke General Hospital - Medical Library (Med)
101 Humber College Blvd. Phone: (416)744-3334
Rexdale, ON, Canada M9V 1R8 Joyce Gitt, Lib.Techn.
Founded: 1973. **Staff:** Prof 1. **Subjects:** Medicine, allied health sciences. **Holdings:** 3700 books; 178 bound periodical volumes. **Subscriptions:** 75 journals and other serials. **Services:** Interlibrary loan; library open to affiliated students.

★5474★
Etobicoke Planning Department - Library (Plan)
Etobicoke City Hall
3rd Fl., N Block
399 The West Mall Phone: (416)394-8242
Etobicoke, ON, Canada M9C 2Y2 Roseann Senatore, Lib.Techn.
Founded: 1976. **Staff:** 1. **Subjects:** Urban planning, environment, land use. **Holdings:** 1500 books; related bylaws; related statutes; regional official plans. **Subscriptions:** 80 journals and other serials. **Services:** Library open to the public with restrictions. **Automated Operations:** Computerized cataloging.

★5475★
Etruscan Foundation - Library (Area-Ethnic)
161 Country Club Dr. Phone: (313)886-6654
Grosse Pointe Farms, MI 48236 Count Ferdinand Cinelli, Pres.
Founded: 1958. **Staff:** 1. **Subjects:** Classical archeology, history of Etruscan civilization. **Holdings:** 800 volumes. **Subscriptions:** 201 journals and other serials. **Services:** Interlibrary loan; library open to students and scholars. **Publications:** Newsletter, annual; Etruscan (scholarly publication).

★5476★
ETS, Inc. - Library (Env-Cons)
1401 Municipal Rd.
Roanoke, VA 24012-1309 Phone: (703)265-0004
Subjects: Air pollution and energy - systems design, particulate and gaseous emissions control, pollutant monitoring, control equipment cost. **Holdings:** 20,000 documents. **Computerized Information Services:** Internal database (coal-fired boilers and incinerators). **Remarks:** FAX: (703)774-8883. Parent organization is ETS International.

★5477★
Eureka, The California Career Information System (Educ)
P.O. Box 647 Phone: (510)235-3883
Richmond, CA 94808-0647 M. Sumyyah Bilal, Exec.Dir.
Founded: 1976. **Staff:** Prof 8; Other 4. **Subjects:** Career exploration, occupational and school information, job search and financial aid, programs of study and training, skills assessment. **Holdings:** Figures not available. **Services:** Copying; system provides mail-order printouts. **Computerized Information Services:** Career Information System (CIS; internal database). Performs searches on fee basis. Contact Person: Lisa Mapp. **Publications:** EUREKA; Job Search Guide; OWN - Working for Yourself in California; Micro-skills; Skills; Career Finder - all annual; Financial Aid Guide, semimonthly.

★5478★
Euroconsult - Bibliotheek (Agri)
Beaulieustraat 22
Postbus 41 Phone: 85 577512
NL-6800 AK Arnhem, Netherlands Mrs. Moniek van de Ven
Founded: 1977. **Staff:** Prof 1. **Subjects:** Agriculture, rural development, water mangement, anthropology, institutional development, natural resources and the environment. **Special Collections:** Topographical map collection (1000). **Holdings:** 10,000 books; 10,000 reports. **Subscriptions:** 125 journals and other serials; 2 newspapers. **Services:** Library not open to the public. **Remarks:** FAX: 85 577577. Telex: 45097 euro nl.

★5479★
European Academy of Facial Surgery - Library (Med)
97 Harley St. Phone: 71 935 3171
London W1N IDF, England P. Adlington
Founded: 1977. **Subjects:** Facial plastic surgery. **Holdings:** Videotapes.

★5480★
European Baptist Federation - International Baptist Theological Seminary - Library (Rel-Phil)
Gheistrasse 31 Phone: 1 7240010
CH-8803 Ruschlikon, Switzerland Marie H. Walker, MLS
Staff: 2.5. **Subjects:** Theology, missions, understanding between Baptists and other Christians. **Special Collections:** Anabaptists of the Reformation. **Holdings:** 52,000 volumes. **Subscriptions:** 358 journals and other serials. **Remarks:** FAX: 1 7243148.

★5481★
European Center for Applied Economic Research - Library (Bus-Fin)
Steinengraben 42 Phone: 61 22 32 00
CH-4012 Basel, Switzerland Mr. Bodenstedt, Libn.
Subjects: Applied economics, innovation and new technology, market research, marketing, management consulting, economic analysis and policy consulting, regional policy and local authorities, technical infrastructure, energy, water, transportation, health policy. **Holdings:** 50,000 volumes. **Remarks:** FAX: 61 22 40 69. Telex: 963 323 PROG.

★5482★
European Center for Study and Information - Library (Hum)
Twaalfmaandenstraat 1, 1e verdiep Phone: 3 2312266
B-2000 Antwerp, Belgium R. Verschooten, Dir.
Founded: 1963. **Subjects:** European issues, economics, federation, defense policies, social problems, European culture. **Holdings:** 50,000 volumes. **Subscriptions:** 50 journals and other serials. **Services:** Library open on a limited schedule. **Formerly:** European Center for Research and Information Exchange - Library. **Also Known As:** Europees Studie & Informatie Centrumnew (ESIC).

★5483★
European Communities Court of Justice - Library (Law)
P.O. Box 1406 Phone: 43031
L-2925 Luxembourg, Luxembourg Dr. Christian Kohler
Founded: 1953. **Staff:** Prof 7; Other 13. **Subjects:** Law - community, international, national, comparative; theory of law. **Holdings:** 100,000 volumes; 30 microfiche. **Subscriptions:** 550 journals and other serials. **Services:** Library open to the public at librarian's discretion. **Publications:** Bibliographie Courante; Legal Bibliography of European Integration. **Remarks:** FAX: 43032424. Telex 2771 CJINFO LU.

★5484★
European Community Information Service - Library (Soc Sci)
2100 M St., N.W., Suite 707 Phone: (202)862-9500
Washington, DC 20037 Barbara Sloan, Hd., Pub. Inquiries
Founded: 1963. **Staff:** Prof 3; Other 2. **Subjects:** International relations and economics, trade affairs, European affairs, political science, international monetary affairs. **Special Collections:** Information on and official documents of the European Economic Community, the European Coal and Steel Community, and the European Atomic Energy Community. **Holdings:** 40,000 books; 2700 pamphlets; VF materials on over 1300 subjects. **Services:** Interlibrary loan (limited); copying; library open to the public by appointment. **Publications:** Europe Magazine, bimonthly. **Remarks:** FAX: (202)429-1766.

★5485★
European FORUM on Development Service - Library (Soc Sci)
Thomas-Mann-Strasse 52 Phone: 228 654160
W-5300 Bonn 1, Germany Bernard Gilson, Exec.Sec.
Founded: 1964. **Staff:** 2. **Subjects:** Cooperation between national volunteer organizations in developing countries. **Holdings:** 1000 volumes. **Remarks:** FAX: 228 650414. **Formerly:** Regional Conference on International Voluntary Service.

★5486★
European Free Trade Association - Library (Bus-Fin)
9-11, rue de Varembe
CH-1211 Geneva 20, Switzerland Phone: 22 7349000
Subjects: Trade in Western Europe (Austria, Finland, Iceland, Norway, and Switzerland); economics; statistics. **Holdings:** 14,000 volumes. **Remarks:** FAX: 22 7339291. Telex: 22 660 EFTA CH. Telegram: EFTASEC.

★5487★
European Human Rights - Library (Soc Sci)
Marknadsvagen 289
S-183 34 Taby, Sweden Phone: 8 7681398
Subjects: Freedom of speech, human rights, violations of human rights in Europe, social sciences, religion. **Holdings:** 30,000 volumes; slides; videotapes; audiotapes.

★5488★
European Institute of Environmental Cybernetics - Library (Sci-Engr, Biol Sci)
GR-162 32 Athens, Greece Phone: 1 363 5951
B.D. Georgeascu, Dir., Libn.
Founded: 1970. **Subjects:** Automation, biosciences, biotechnology, energy, information science, environmental and health control, management, nuclear studies, pollution control, space sciences. **Holdings:** 90,000 volumes. **Subscriptions:** 3000 journals and other serials. **Services:** Interlibrary loan; library not open to the public.

European Organization for Nuclear Research
See: **CERN - European Organization for Nuclear Research - Scientific Information Service (CERN AS-SI)** (3395)

★5489★
European Parliament - Library (Soc Sci, Bus-Fin, Law)
European Centre Phone: 4300
Kirchberg, Luxembourg Mario Tonelotto
Staff: Prof 13; Other 28. **Subjects:** Political science, European community, European law, European Parliament. **Holdings:** 130,000 books. **Subscriptions:** 1600 journals and other serials; 35 newspapers. **Services:** Interlibrary loan; copying; library open to the public at librarian's discretion. **Automated Operations:** Computerized cataloging (PEGASE). **Computerized Information Services:** BELINDIS, BLAISE, BPA, CED, Datacentralen, DPA, ECHO, Data-Star, Profile, Telesystemes S.A., GCAM, GENIOS, JURIDIAL, EPOQUE (European Parliament Official Documents). **Remarks:** FAX: 437260.

★5490★
European Regional Clearinghouse for Community Work - Library (Soc Sci)
179, rue du Debarcadere Phone: 71 366273
B-6001 Marcinelle, Belgium Mrs. Bertiaux
Founded: 1976. **Subjects:** Social work, gerontology, community development. **Holdings:** 1500 volumes. **Services:** Library open to the public. **Computerized Information Services:** Internal database. **Remarks:** FAX: 71 47 11 04.

★5491★
European Space Agency - Europpean Space Research and Technology Center - Library and Information Services (Sci-Engr)
P.O. Box 299 Phone: 1719 83015
2200AG Noordwijk, Netherlands Dr. D.I. Raitt
Founded: 1962. **Staff:** 4. **Subjects:** Astronomy, astrophysics, plasma physics, advanced space technology, telecommunications, life sciences, material sciences, launcher technology, remote sensing, computers, electronics, space vehicles, physics, engineering. **Holdings:** 25,000 volumes; 1 million microfiche; 20,000 reports and standards. **Subscriptions:** 850 journals and other serials. **Services:** Interlibrary loan; library not open to the public. **Computerized Information Services:** DIALOG Information Services, ESA/IRS, ECHO, Questel, STN International, Data-Star, NewsNet, Inc.; ALANET, DIALMAIL, DataMail, BITNET, CompuServe Information Service (electronic mail services). **Remarks:** FAX: 1719 85429. Telex: 39098 ESTC NL. Electronic mail address(es): LIBRARY@ESTEC (BITNET). The European Space Agency comprises four principal components: 1. ESA Headquarters, located in Paris, France; 2. European Space Research and Technology Center (ESTEC), located in Noordwijk, The Netherlands; 3. European Space Operations Center (ESOC), located in Darmstadt, Germany; and 4. European Space Research Institute (ESRIN), located in Rome, Italy. **Also Known As:** ESTEC. **Staff:** Miss L. Valentin.

European Space Research and Technology Center
See: **European Space Agency** (5491)

Europees Studie & Informatie Centrumnew (ESIC)
See: **European Center for Study and Information** (5482)

Jessie C. Eury Library
See: **Lincoln Christian College & Seminary - Jessie C. Eury Library** (9173)

William L. Eury Appalachian Collection
See: **Appalachian State University** (916)

★5492★
Evaluation Associates, Inc. - Library (Sci-Engr)
GSB Bldg.
1 Belmont Ave. Phone: (215)667-3761
Bala Cynwyd, PA 19004 Gui Saatdjien, Dir., Info.Serv.
Subjects: Electronics engineering, circuit breakers, product development. **Holdings:** 5000 volumes. **Remarks:** FAX: (215)667-4704.

★5493★
Evangelical Covenant Church of America - Covenant Library and Historical Library (Rel-Phil)
5125 N. Spaulding Ave. Phone: (312)478-2696
Chicago, IL 60625-4987 Timothy J. Johnson, Archv.
Founded: 1935. **Staff:** Prof 1; Other 2. **Subjects:** Historical denominational records of the Covenant and allied denominations; historical records of local Covenant Churches. **Special Collections:** Local church records; pictures of church pioneers; newspapers and church records (microfilm); denominational and regional conference headquarters correspondence and records (900 document boxes). **Holdings:** 4500 books; 600 bound periodical volumes; 325 pamphlets; 1661 document boxes of clippings, diaries, correspondence, music, and departmental publications; 750 reels of microfilm; 10,000 photographs. **Subscriptions:** 12 journals and other serials. **Services:** Copying; microfilm printing; library open to the public by appointment. **Computerized Information Services:** Photograph Inventory database; Covenant Chronology database (internal databases).**Publications:** Covenant Heritage Society Newsletter, quarterly - for internal distribution only. **Special Indexes:** Index to people in photographs; union list of periodicals (both printed and online); author/subject in dex to Covenant Quarterly (online); author index to Aurora.

Evangelical Friends Church, Eastern Region - Society of Friends - Ohio Yearly Meeting
See: **Society of Friends - Ohio Yearly Meeting** (15324)

★5494★
Evangelical Health Systems - Christ Hospital - Health Sciences Library (Med)
4440 W. 95th St. Phone: (708)346-5127
Oak Lawn, IL 60453 Janice E. Kelly, Chf.Libn.
Founded: 1978. **Staff:** Prof 2; Other 3. **Subjects:** Medicine. **Holdings:** 7200 books; 5500 bound periodical volumes; 150 video cassettes; 475 audio cassettes. **Subscriptions:** 320 journals and other serials. **Services:** Interlibrary loan; SDI; library open to the public for reference use only by special permission. **Automated Operations:** Computerized cataloging, serials, acquisitions, and circulation. **Computerized Information Services:** NLM, BRS Information Technologies. Performs searches on fee basis. **Networks/Consortia:** Member of Chicago and South Consortium, Suburban Library System (SLS). **Remarks:** FAX: (708)346-5127; 346-5145. **Staff:** Mary Hanlon, Libn.

★5495★
Evangelical Lutheran Church in America - ELCA Archives (Rel-Phil)
8765 W. Higgins Rd. Phone: (312)380-2818
Chicago, IL 60631 Elisabeth Wittman, Dir. for Archv.
Founded: 1987. **Staff:** Prof 3.5; Other 2. **Subjects:** Lutheran Church, theology, immigration history, family history and biography, world missions, Lutheran cooperation. **Special Collections:** Official records of the Evangelical Lutheran Church in America, its immediate predecessors, the American Lutheran Church (ALC), the Association of Evangelical Lutheran Churches (AELC) and its Synods, and the Lutheran Church in America; Archives of Cooperative Lutheranism, including records of the Lutheran Council in the U.S.A., its predecessor, the National Lutheran Council; LCUSA Oral History Collection; records of 34 related inter-Lutheran agencies and organizations; Christ Seminary-Seminex and Evangelical Lutherans in Mission; personal papers of over 150 Lutheran church leaders. **Holdings:** 7500 linear feet of books; bound and unbound periodicals; records and manuscripts; microfilm; microfiche; photographs; audio and video recordings. **Subscriptions:** 100 journals and other serials. **Services:** Copying; archives open to the public. **Computerized Information Services:** OCLC. **Networks/Consortia:** Member of ILLINET. **Publications:** Preserving Yesterday for Tomorrow: A Guide to the LCA Archives (1977); Guides to the Oral History Collections, LCUSA (1984, 1987); Introductory Guide to Lutheran Archives, LCUSA (1981). **Special Indexes:** Index to 4000 congregations. **Remarks:** FAX: (312)380-1465. Alternate telephone number(s): 380-2819. **Staff:** Thomas C. Rick, Asst.Archv.; Maureen O'Brien Will, Archv. Media Spec.; Steven E. Bean, Archv.Spec.

★5496★
Evangelical Lutheran Church in America - ELCA Region III Archives (Rel-Phil)
2481 Como Ave. Phone: (612)641-3205
St. Paul, MN 55108 Paul Daniels, Archv.
Founded: 1988. **Staff:** Prof 2. **Subjects:** Lutheran Church, theology, immigration history, family history and biography, world missions. **Special Collections:** Official records of the Evangelical Lutheran Church in America and its nine Region III Synods (1988 to present); records of the predecessors of the ELCA: the Free Lutheran Church (1893-1963), the American Lutheran Church (ALC), the Association of Evangelical Lutheran Churches (AELC, 1917-60), and their predecessors (1840 to present); Immigrant American Lutheranism (emphasis on Scandinavian and German, 1840 to present); Global Mission Collection (China, Japan, Taiwan, Madagascar, South Africa, India, Iraq); Home Missions Collection; personal papers of Lutheran church leaders. **Holdings:** 3000 linear feet of archival materials; oral history tapes and transcripts. **Services:** Copying; archives open to persons with legitimate research requests. **Remarks:** Alternate telephone number(s): (612)641-3238. Archives located at Luther Northwestern Seminary - Library.

★5497★
Evangelical Lutheran Church in America - Florida Synod - Audio-Visual Library (Aud-Vis, Rel-Phil)
3838 W. Cypress St. Phone: (813)876-7660
Tampa, FL 33607 Joan M. Mathre, Libn.
Staff: 1. **Subjects:** Christian education, stewardship, missions. **Holdings:** 25 books; 50 films; 20 filmstrips; 50 cassettes; 20 phonograph records; 200 videotapes. **Services:** Library open to the public with restrictions. **Remarks:** FAX: (813)870-0826.

★5498★
Evangelical Lutheran Church in America - Library-Resource Center (Rel-Phil)
8765 W. Higgins Rd.
Chicago, IL 60631 Phone: (312)380-2811
Founded: 1988. **Staff:** Prof 1. **Subjects:** Theology, Lutheran Church, ecumenism, American and world Lutheranism. **Holdings:** 5000 books; 100 videotapes. **Subscriptions:** 150 journals and other serials; 10 newspapers. **Services:** Interlibrary loan; copying; library open to the public for reference use only. **Automated Operations:** Computerized cataloging. **Computerized Information Services:** BRS Information Technologies; CD-ROMs; TCN (electronic mail service). **Networks/Consortia:** Member of ILLINET. **Remarks:** FAX: (312)380-1465. **Staff:** Claire H. Buettner, Rec.Mgt.

★5499★
Evangelical Lutheran Church in America - Metropolitan New York Synod - Archives (Rel-Phil)
Wagner College
631 Howard Ave.
Staten Island, NY 10301
Subjects: Lutheran Church in New Netherland, New York, New Jersey, and New England, 1649-1960; Lutheran Church in New York City area, 1960 to present. **Holdings:** 400 linear feet of biographical and historical materials; synod minutes; manuscript research studies; synod correspondence; diaries of church leaders. **Services:** Copying; archives open to serious researchers by appointment only.

★5500★
Evangelical Lutheran Church in America - North Carolina Synod - Archives (Rel-Phil)
1988 Lutheran Synod Dr. Phone: (704)633-4861
Salisbury, NC 28144 George L. Rhyne, Archv.
Founded: 1803. **Staff:** 1. **Subjects:** Lutheran Church. **Special Collections:** Congregational records, 1774 to present; Papers of Pastors Collection; synod proceedings for the North Carolina and Tennessee Synods, 1803 to present. **Holdings:** 650 volumes; 300 linear feet of archival materials; 9 VF drawers of historical files; 260 reels of microfilm. **Services:** Copying (limited); archives open to the public.

★5501★
Evangelical Lutheran Church in America - Publishing House - Library (Rel-Phil, Publ)
426 S. 5th St.
Minneapolis, MN 55440 Phone: (612)330-3343
Staff: 1. **Subjects:** Theology and religion. **Special Collections:** Books published by Augsburg Fortress Publishers and its predecessors. **Holdings:** 3000 books; 50 bound periodical volumes. **Subscriptions:** 288 journals and other serials. **Services:** Library not open to the public.

Evangelical Lutheran Synodical Conference Archives
See: **Concordia Historical Institute - Department of Archives and History** (4115)

★5502★
Evangelical and Reformed Historical Society - Eden Archives (Hist, Rel-Phil)
475 E. Lockwood Ave. Phone: (314)961-3627
Webster Groves, MO 63119-3192 Prof. Lowell H. Zuck, Dir.
Founded: 1925. **Staff:** Prof 2; Other 1. **Subjects:** Evangelical Synod of North America, Evangelical & Reformed Church, United Church of Christ in relationship to German Protestant churches and missions in the U.S. and elsewhere, especially midwestern U.S. **Special Collections:** Records of Evangelical Synod of North America churches. **Holdings:** 4400 volumes; 200 VF drawers of reports, manuscripts, archival materials; 35 volumes of photoduplicated German-American immigration-mission documents; 125 reels of microfilm of church records. **Services:** Interlibrary loan; copying; archives open to the public with restrictions on limited schedule; genealogical service on fee basis. **Publications:** Newsletter, biennial (in cooperation with Evangelical & Reformed Historical Society, Lancaster Theological Seminary, Lancaster, PA, 17603 and Historical Council, United Church of Christ, 700 Prospect Ave., Cleveland, OH 44115). **Staff:** Mrs. Ahme Quist, Archv.

★5503★
Evangelical and Reformed Historical Society - Lancaster Central Archives and Library (Rel-Phil)
Lancaster Theological Seminary
555 W. James St. Phone: (717)393-0654
Lancaster, PA 17603 Kay K. Schellhase, Archv.
Founded: 1863. **Staff:** Prof 1; Other 2. **Subjects:** Reformed Church in the United States; Evangelical and Reformed Church; United Church of Christ; Mercersburg theology. **Special Collections:** Reformed Church in the United States (transcribed church records of the 18th century, especially in southeastern Pennsylvania). **Holdings:** 6200 books; 840 bound periodical volumes; 211 manuscript boxes and 120 VF drawers of reports, manuscripts, and archival materials; 337 reels of microfilm of church records; 450 AV programs; 12,500 ministerial files; 3800 church and institutional files. **Services:** Copying; library open to the public. **Remarks:** Includes the archives of the United Church of Christ.

★5504★
Evangelical School of Theology - Rostad Library (Rel-Phil)
121 S. College St. Phone: (717)866-5775
Myerstown, PA 17067 Terry M. Heisey, Libn.
Staff: Prof 1; Other 1. **Subjects:** Theology, Biblical studies, church history, pastoral psychology, Christian education. **Special Collections:** Publications relating to the Evangelical Congregational Church and the United Evangelical Church. **Holdings:** 48,000 books; 8000 bound periodical volumes. **Subscriptions:** 300 journals and other serials. **Services:** Interlibrary loan; copying; library open to the public. **Computerized Information Services:** DIALOG Information Services. Performs searches on fee basis. **Networks/Consortia:** Member of Southeastern Pennsylvania Theological Library Association (SEPTLA).

★5505★
Evangelical Seminary of Puerto Rico - Juan de Valdes Library (Rel-Phil)
Ave. Ponce de Leon 776 Phone: (809)758-4141
Hato Rey, PR 00918 Jeanene M. Coleson, Dir.
Founded: 1958. **Staff:** Prof 2; Other 1. **Subjects:** Theology, religious education, Bible, study of history of religions. **Special Collections:** Works of Spanish reformers of the 16th century; Protestantism in Puerto Rico. **Holdings:** 48,000 books; 2287 bound periodical volumes; 590 microforms; 64 boxes of historical documents. **Subscriptions:** 327 journals and other serials; 8 newspapers. **Services:** Interlibrary loan; copying; library open to the public for reference use only. **Special Indexes:** Index to Puerto Rico Evangelico, 1912-1973 (online). **Remarks:** FAX: (809)751-0847. **Also Known As:** Seminario Evangelico de Puerto Rico. **Staff:** Gloria M. Mercado; Maricarmen Laureano.

Evans Army Community Hospital
See: **U.S. Army Hospitals - Evans Army Community Hospital** (17040)

Evans Library
See: **Florida Institute of Technology - Evans Library** (5876)

Lulu Evanson Resource Library
See: **North Dakota Farmers Union** (11919)

★5506★
Evanston Historical Society - Charles Gates Dawes Home - Research Room and Library (Hist)
225 Greenwood St. Phone: (708)475-3410
Evanston, IL 60201 Richard P. Hartung, Exec.Dir.
Founded: 1898. **Staff:** 1. **Subjects:** History of Evanston and Illinois. **Special Collections:** Biographical materials on Charles G. Dawes, 1865-1951. **Holdings:** 2500 books; 250 bound periodical volumes; 11,000 photographs; 2500 slides; clippings; local government documents and reports; Evanston newspapers, 1872 to present. **Subscriptions:** 10 journals and other serials. **Services:** Copying; library open to the public. **Staff:** Mark Burnette, Ref.Archv.

★5507★
Evanston Hospital - J.L. and Helen Kellogg Cancer Care Center - Library (Med)
2650 Ridge Ave. Phone: (708)570-2108
Evanston, IL 60201 K. Bauman, Med.Sec.
Founded: 1974. **Subjects:** Oncology. **Holdings:** 750 volumes. **Services:** Library not open to the public. **Remarks:** FAX: (708)570-2918.

★5508★
Evanston Hospital - Webster Library (Med)
2650 Ridge Ave. Phone: (708)570-2665
Evanston, IL 60201 Dalia S. Kleinmuntz, Dir.
Founded: 1912. **Staff:** Prof 2.5; Other 2. **Subjects:** Medicine, nursing, allied health sciences. **Holdings:** 5000 books; 14,000 bound periodical volumes. **Subscriptions:** 400 journals and other serials. **Services:** Interlibrary loan; copying; SDI; library open to selected public by appointment. **Computerized Information Services:** DIALOG Information Services, BRS Information Technologies, MEDLINE; CD-ROMs (CINHAL). **Networks/Consortia:** Member of North Suburban Library System (NSLS), Metropolitan Consortium of Chicago, National Network of Libraries of Medicine (NN/LM). **Publications:** Newsletter, quarterly. **Remarks:** FAX: (708)570-2926. **Staff:** Linda Feinberg, Libn.; Eva Eisenstein, Libn.; Susan Swanson, Coord.

★5509★
Evansville Museum of Arts and Science - Library (Art)
411 S.E. Riverside Dr. Phone: (812)425-2406
Evansville, IN 47713 Mary McNamee Schnepper, Cur. of Coll.
Founded: 1927. **Staff:** 3. **Subjects:** Art, history, anthropology, science, technology, natural history, architecture, antiques. **Special Collections:** Henry B. Walker, Jr. Memorial Art Library; Evansville and Vanderburgh County, Indiana history archives (19 VF drawers); art archives (13 VF drawers of catalogs, show notices, biographical manuscripts). **Holdings:** 3500 books; 2000 unbound periodicals; letters; documents; maps. **Subscriptions:** 30 journals and other serials. **Services:** Copying; library open to the public for reference use only. **Remarks:** FAX: (812)421-7507.

★5510★
Evansville Psychiatric Children's Center - Staff Library (Med)
3330 E. Morgan Ave. Phone: (812)477-6436
Evansville, IN 47715 Michele Haynes, Med.Rec.Adm./Libn.
Founded: 1966. **Staff:** 1. **Subjects:** Psychotherapy, child development, recreation therapy, psychopathology, education, nursing. **Special Collections:** Children's psychiatric diseases (400 volumes). **Holdings:** Figures not available. **Subscriptions:** 4 journals and other serials. **Services:** Interlibrary loan; copying; library open to professionals and students in allied fields. **Networks/Consortia:** Member of Evansville Area Libraries Consortium. **Remarks:** FAX: (812)474-4248.

★5511★
Evening Observer - Library (Publ)
8-10 E. 2nd St. Phone: (716)366-3000
Dunkirk, NY 14048-0391 Louise Ratkoski, Libn.
Founded: 1882. **Staff:** 1. **Subjects:** Newspaper reference topics, Dunkirk and area events. **Holdings:** Newspapers, 1882 to present, on microfilm. **Services:** Library open to the public by permission. **Remarks:** FAX: (716)366-3005.

Evening Post Publishing Company - Charleston Evening Post/News and Courier
See: **Charleston Post and Courier** (3444)

★5512★
Eveready Battery Company, Inc. - Technical Information Center (Sci-Engr)
25225 Detroit Rd. Phone: (216)835-7641
Westlake, OH 44145 Claire Marie Langkau, Mgr., Tech.Info.
Founded: 1956. **Staff:** Prof 4; Other 4. **Subjects:** Batteries, electrochemistry. **Holdings:** 10,000 books; 10,000 documents; 30,000 patents. **Subscriptions:** 350 journals and other serials. **Services:** Center not open to the public. **Computerized Information Services:** DIALOG Information Services, PFDS Online, Dow Jones News/Retrieval, STN International; internal databases. **Publications:** Review of Literature, weekly - for internal distribution only. **Remarks:** FAX: (216)835-7772. **Staff:** Michael F. Allan, Staff Info.Spec.; Elaine M. Balfe, Info.Spec.; Michelle A. Drabik, Info.Chem.

★5513★
Everett Public Library - Northwest History Collection (Hist)
2702 Hoyt Phone: (206)259-8762
Everett, WA 98201-3556 Mark Nesse, Dir.
Founded: 1977. **Staff:** 2. **Subjects:** History of Everett and Snohomish County, late 1800s to present. **Special Collections:** Edwin Parker's research notes for Timber, a historical novel of the Pacific Northwest; Sumner Iron Works account books and business records and photographs; Everett Pulp and Paper Company business records, photographs, movies; Darius Kinsey monographs and photographs of logging in the 19th and 20th centuries; Oscar Carlson exhibit files and trial depositions for the Everett Massacre, 1916; John Juleen Studio photographs (1920-1940); photographs of the Everett area, 1891-1940 (10,000 items); oral history interviews with local old-timers. **Holdings:** 12,000 original photographic prints, negatives, and reels of early movie footage. **Services:** Interlibrary loan; copying; collection open to the public by appointment. **Automated Operations:** Computerized cataloging and circulation. **Remarks:** FAX: (206)258-6831. **Staff:** David Dilgard, Lib.Spec.; Margaret Riddle, Lib.Spec.

Everglades National Park
See: **U.S. Natl. Park Service** (17704)

Everson Museum of Art - Library - Syracuse China Center for the Study of American Ceramics - Archives of American Ceramics
See: **Everson Museum of Art** (5514)

★5514★
Everson Museum of Art - Richard V. Smith Art Reference Library (Art)
401 Harrison St. Phone: (315)474-6064
Syracuse, NY 13202 April Oswald, Libn./Archv.
Founded: 1968. **Staff:** Prof 1. **Subjects:** Contemporary and traditional American painting and sculpture, world ceramics, Asian and African art, film, photography, video, sculpture, architecture, museum education. **Holdings:** 10,000 books and exhibition and museum catalogs; 6000 slides. **Subscriptions:** 40 journals and other serials. **Services:** Interlibrary loan; library open to members for reference use only. **Computerized Information Services:** American Ceramics (internal database). **Remarks:** FAX: (315)474-6943. **Formerly:** Everson Museum of Art Library - Syracuse China Center for the Study of American Ceramics - Archive of American Ceramics.

★5515★
Dianne Evert Photography, Inc. - Slide Library (Aud-Vis)
5509 Park Ave., S. Phone: (612)868-0585
Minneapolis, MN 55417 Dianne Evert, Pres.
Founded: 1978. **Staff:** Prof 1. **Subjects:** General with emphasis on Minnesota scenes and activities, amateur sports. **Holdings:** 5000 slides. **Services:** Copying; library open to the public.

★5516★
Everywoman Opportunity Center, Inc. - Library (Educ)
237 Main St., Suite 330 Phone: (716)847-1120
Buffalo, NY 14203 Karen Williams, Human Serv. Aide
Subjects: Career and vocational guidance. **Holdings:** 350 volumes. **Services:** Library not open to the public. **Publications:** Newsletter, 3-4/year.

Ewing Memorial Library
See: **First Presbyterian Church** (5786)

★5517★
Exchange Group for Appropriate Technology - Library (Sci-Engr)
18, rue de la Sablonniere
B-1000 Brussels, Belgium Phone: 2 2181896
Founded: 1980. **Staff:** 8. **Subjects:** Technical items and their adaptation to social, cultural, and economic environment of Third World countries; development issues; drug/development issues; renewable energy; evaluation methodology. **Holdings:** 5000 volumes. **Services:** Copying; library open to the public. **Computerized Information Services:** Internal databases. **Remarks:** FAX: 2 2231495. **Also Known As:** Collectif d'Echanges pour la Technologie Appropriee. **Staff:** F. Douxchamps, Gen.Sec.; J. Lederman, Libn.

Executive Office of the President
See: **U.S. Executive Office of the President** (17484)

★5518★
Executive Yuan - Council of Agriculture - Agricultural Science Information Center (Agri)
3F, 14 Wen-Chou St. Phone: 2 3626222
Taipei 10616, Taiwan Wan-Jiun Wu, Dir.
Staff: 30. **Subjects:** Agriculture, forestry, fisheries, animal husbandry, food science. **Holdings:** 6499 books; 1260 bound periodical volumes. **Subscriptions:** 460 journals and other serials; 10 newspapers. **Services:** Copying; SDI; center open to the public. **Computerized Information Services:** Agricultural Science & Technology Information Management System (ASTIMS), DIALOG Information Services, BRS Information Technologies, PFDS Online, DIMDI, STN International, ESA/IRS. Performs searches on fee basis. Contact Person: Evelyn Tan, Libn. **Publications:** ASIC Universal Information Service System; List of Agricultural Journals/Periodicals; Bibliography of Agricultural Literature. **Remarks:** FAX: 2 3632459. **Also Known As:** ASIC.

Frederick Exley Archive
See: **University of Rochester - Department of Rare Books and Special Collections** (19278)

Exodus Trust Archives of Erotology
See: **Institute for Advanced Study of Human Sexuality - Exodus Trust Archives of Erotology - Research Library** (7896)

★5519★
Experience, Inc. - Information Center (Agri)
1200 2nd Ave., S., Suite 400 Phone: (612)338-7844
Minneapolis, MN 55403 Judith K. Blumenfeld, Info.Mgr.
Founded: 1981. **Staff:** Prof 1. **Subjects:** Agriculture, agribusiness, rural development, food processing. **Special Collections:** USDA and state agricultural documents. **Holdings:** 200 books; 1500 internal project reports; county files on agriculture and economics worldwide. **Subscriptions:** 104 journals and other serials. **Services:** Interlibrary loan; copying; center open to the public with permission of information manager. **Computerized Information Services:** DIALOG Information Services; internal database. Performs searches on fee basis. **Special Indexes:** Internal reports index. **Remarks:** FAX: (612)338-8005. Telex: 467326 EXPERIENCE CI.

★5520★
Experiment in International Living - School for International Training - Donald B. Watt Library (Soc Sci)
Kipling Rd. Phone: (802)257-7751
Brattleboro, VT 05301 Shirley Capron, Pub.Serv.Libn.
Founded: 1968. **Staff:** Prof 2; Other 1. **Subjects:** Social sciences, education, languages and linguistics, area studies, educational research, psychology, French, Spanish. **Special Collections:** Linguistics. **Holdings:** 30,000 books; 1000 microfiche on language, teaching, linguistics, education; 4 VF drawers; masters' theses and essays; pamphlets; reports; case studies; files on international organizations in the social science field. **Subscriptions:** 300 journals and other serials; 18 newspapers. **Services:** Interlibrary loan; copying; library open to the public for reference use only. **Staff:** Michael Green, Tech.Serv.Libn.

★5521★
Explorers Club - James B. Ford Library (Geog-Map, Hist)
46 E. 70th St. Phone: (212)628-8383
New York, NY 10021 Janet E. Baldwin, Cur. of. Coll.
Founded: 1904. **Staff:** Prof 1. **Subjects:** Geography, natural history, ethnology, the Arctic. **Special Collections:** Admiral Robert E. Peary Collection; 18th century travel. **Holdings:** 20,000 books; 1000 bound periodical volumes. **Subscriptions:** 100 journals and other serials. **Services:** Library open to researchers by appointment. **Remarks:** FAX: (212)288-4449.

★5522★
Export Development Corporation - Library (Bus-Fin)
151 O'Connor St. Phone: (613)598-2701
Ottawa, ON, Canada K1A 1K3 Ann James, Libn.
Founded: 1973. **Staff:** Prof 1; Other 2. **Subjects:** Economics, international banking and finance, commerce. **Special Collections:** Annual reports of official export credit agencies (100 volumes). **Holdings:** 3000 volumes; 6000 annual reports. **Subscriptions:** 500 journals and other serials; 21 newspapers. **Services:** Interlibrary loan; copying; SDI; library open to the public by appointment. **Automated Operations:** Computerized serials. **Computerized Information Services:** DIALOG Information Services, Info Globe, DOBIS Canadian Online Library System, Reuter TEXTLINE, Infomart Online. **Publications:** Acquisitions list; list of periodicals received - both for internal distribution only. **Remarks:** FAX: (613)237-2690.

★5523★
Export-Import Bank of the United States - Library (Bus-Fin)
811 Vermont Ave., N.W. Phone: (202)566-8320
Washington, DC 20571 Pat Martinez, Libn.
Founded: 1946. **Staff:** Prof 1; Other 1. **Subjects:** Banking, economics, finance, commerce, trade statistics, exports. **Special Collections:** Economist Intelligence Unit (EIU) collection of quarterly economic reviews. **Holdings:** 2000 books; 1000 other cataloged items; 20 VF drawers of congressional materials; 5 VF drawers of clippings; 2 VF drawers of press releases. **Subscriptions:** 750 journals and other serials; 20 newspapers. **Services:** Interlibrary loan; SDI; library open to the public for reference use only with permission. **Automated Operations:** Computerized cataloging and serials. **Computerized Information Services:** DIALOG Information Services, OCLC. **Networks/Consortia:** Member of FEDLINK. **Publications:** Bibliographies on financial statements or other subjects of interest; Acquisitions List, monthly - for internal distribution only. **Remarks:** FAX: (202)566-7524. **Staff:** Denice M. Peoples, Lib.Techn.

★5524★
Express-News Corporation - Library (Publ)
Box 2171 Phone: (512)225-7411
San Antonio, TX 78297-2171 Judy Zipp, Hd.Libn.
Founded: 1865. **Staff:** Prof 4. **Subjects:** Newspaper reference topics. **Holdings:** Pictures and graphics; San Antonio Express, 1865-1991, and San Antonio News, 1918-1984, on microfilm; newspaper clippings, 1954-1991. **Subscriptions:** 20 newspapers. **Services:** Copying; library open to the public by appointment with a fee. **Staff:** Wanda Lackey; Rachel Gutierrez; Rosalinda Valdez.

External Affairs and International Trade Canada
See: **Canada - External Affairs and International Trade Canada** (2724)

★5525★
Extreme North Agricultural Research Institute - Biblioteka (Agri)
Komsomolskaya St. 1 Phone: 40148
SU-663302 Norilsk, Russia Olga Gregorievna Krylova
Founded: 1937. **Staff:** Prof 2; Other 1. **Subjects:** Reindeer husbandry, game animal biology, veterinary medicine, northern plant growing, plant and animal protection. **Special Collections:** Northern Agriculture of the 20th Century; Geographic Travels and Studies of the 19th-20th Centuries. **Holdings:** 50,000 books; 20,000 bound periodical volumes; 1000 reports. **Subscriptions:** 120 journals and other serials; 20 newspapers. **Services:** Interlibrary loan; library open to the public. **Publications:** Reindeer Husbandry. **Special Indexes:** Index of the Institute Research Workers.

★5526★
Extrusion Engineers - Library (Sci-Engr)
858 Princeton Ct. Phone: (908)369-7260
Neshanic Station, NJ 08853-9686 Dr. David W. Riley, Pres.
Founded: 1980. **Subjects:** Friction and viscosity over wide range of temperatures, velocities, pressures, shear rates. **Holdings:** 400 books. **Subscriptions:** 6 journals and other serials. **Services:** Copying; library open to the public by appointment. **Remarks:** FAX: (908)369-7260.

★5527★
Exxon Biomedical Sciences, Inc. - Library (Med)
Mettlers Rd.
CN 2350 Phone: (201)873-6091
East Millstone, NJ 08875-2350 Janice R. Seager, Libn.
Founded: 1952. **Staff:** Prof 7; Other 6. **Subjects:** Toxicology, industrial hygiene, epidemiology, occupational medicine. **Holdings:** 5000 books; 8000 bound periodical volumes; 6000 government reports; clippings; pamphlets; reprints. **Subscriptions:** 300 journals and other serials. **Services:** Library open to the public with director's permission. **Automated Operations:** Computerized serials. **Computerized Information Services:** PFDS Online, DIALOG Information Services, NLM, NEXIS, LEXIS, STN International, Chemical Information Systems, Inc. (CIS). **Networks/Consortia:** Member of New Jersey Library Network. **Special Catalogs:** Abstracts of related literature (card, microfiche). **Staff:** Rosemarie Parker, Unit Hd.; Andrea C. Holladay, Proprietary Rsrcs.; Vivian Carlson; Lisa A. Hayes; William G. Lampson; Alex F. Turfa.

★5528★
Exxon Chemical Americas - Information Services (Sci-Engr)
Box 4004 Phone: (713)425-5551
Baytown, TX 77522 Patsy B. Reid, Libn.
Founded: 1980. **Staff:** Prof 1; Other 5. **Subjects:** Engineering, business. **Holdings:** 1000 volumes; 4000 other cataloged items; industry standards; central files; maintenance and equipment records; safety and training films. **Subscriptions:** 125 journals and other serials. **Services:** Interlibrary loan; copying; SDI; services open to the public by appointment only. **Automated Operations:** Computerized cataloging and indexing. **Computerized Information Services:** DataTimes, DIALOG Information Services, Occupational Health Services, Inc. (OHS); internal databases. Performs searches on fee basis. **Publications:** Acquisitions List, bimonthly. **Special Indexes:** Safety and training films index (book). **Remarks:** FAX: (713)425-1017.

★5529★
Exxon Chemical Company - Energy Chemicals - Information Center (Sci-Engr)
8230 Stedman St. Phone: (713)671-8607
Houston, TX 77029 Richard L. Behling, Libn.
Founded: 1984. **Staff:** Prof 1. **Subjects:** Chemical technology, polymers, organic chemistry. **Holdings:** 1800 books. **Subscriptions:** 81 journals and other serials. **Services:** Interlibrary loan; copying. **Computerized Information Services:** DIALOG Information Services, STN International, PFDS Online; SprintMail (electronic mail service). **Remarks:** FAX: (713)671-8528.

★5530★
Exxon Company, U.S.A. - Exploration Library (Sci-Engr)
Box 4279 Phone: (713)591-5257
Houston, TX 77210-4279 Roza Ekimov, Sr.Libn.
Founded: 1971. **Staff:** 1. **Subjects:** Geology, geophysics. **Special Collections:** Alaska; Arctic. **Holdings:** 9370 volumes; 6680 other cataloged items. **Subscriptions:** 93 journals and other serials. **Services:** Interlibrary loan; library open to the public for reference use only by appointment. **Automated Operations:** Computerized cataloging. **Publications:** Library Bulletin, 4/year. **Remarks:** FAX: (713)591-5501.

★5531★
Exxon Company, U.S.A. - Exxon Research & Development Laboratories Library (Sci-Engr)
Box 2226 Phone: (504)359-7681
Baton Rouge, LA 70821 Barbara R. Biggs, Libn.
Founded: 1944. **Subjects:** Chemical engineering, chemical refining, petroleum, petrochemicals. **Holdings:** 7500 volumes. **Services:** Library not open to the public. **Automated Operations:** Computerized cataloging, acquisitions, and circulation. **Computerized Information Services:** DIALOG Information Services, PFDS Online, STN International.

★5532★
Exxon Company, U.S.A. - Law Library (Law)
Box 2180 Phone: (713)656-4383
Houston, TX 77252 Paula Howe Pence, Law Libn.
Staff: Prof 1; Other 3. **Subjects:** Law. **Holdings:** 30,000 volumes. **Services:** Library not open to the public. **Computerized Information Services:** LEXIS, WESTLAW, DIALOG Information Services, VU/TEXT Information Services, Dow Jones News/Retrieval. **Remarks:** FAX: (713)656-2329.

★5533★
Exxon Company, U.S.A. - Refinery Information Center (Sci-Engr)
2800 Decker Dr.
Box 3950 Phone: (713)425-4487
Baytown, TX 77520-2020 Martha C. Ramirez, Coord.
Staff: 2. **Subjects:** Engineering - civil, mechanical, electrical, chemical; instrumentation; mathematics; computing; systems. **Holdings:** 10,000 books; 75 bound periodical volumes; 30,000 manufacturers' catalogs on microfilm. **Subscriptions:** 150 journals and other serials. **Services:** Interlibrary loan; copying; library open to the public by special arrangement. **Computerized Information Services:** DIALOG Information Services. **Publications:** Periodical holdings, annual; Acquisition List, quarterly. **Remarks:** FAX: (713)425-3056.

★5534★
Exxon Corporation - Law-Tax Library (Law, Bus-Fin)
225 E. John W. Carpenter Fwy. Phone: (214)444-1601
Irving, TX 75062 Celia Garcia, Law-Tax Libn.
Staff: Prof 1; Other 1. **Subjects:** Corporate law, taxation. **Holdings:** 30,000 books; 250 bound periodical volumes. **Subscriptions:** 44 journals and other serials. **Services:** Library not open to the public. **Formerly:** Located in New York, NY.

★5535★
Exxon Research and Engineering Company - Florham Park Information Center - Library (Sci-Engr)
Box 101 Phone: (201)765-6704
Florham Park, NJ 07932 Marie Latino, Info.Spec.
Founded: 1961. **Staff:** Prof 1; Other 3. **Subjects:** Engineering - petroleum, chemical, mechanical, civil; materials science; environment; metallurgy; energy; business. **Holdings:** 12,000 books; 8000 bound periodical volumes; 1500 reels of microfilm; 281 microfiche. **Subscriptions:** 200 journals and other serials. **Services:** Center not open to the public. **Automated Operations:** Computerized cataloging, acquisitions, serials, and circulation. **Computerized Information Services:** DIALOG Information Services, PFDS Online, NEXIS, WILSONLINE, Dow Jones News/Retrieval, BRS Information Technologies.

★5536★
Exxon Research and Engineering Company - Research & Engineering Information Support (Sci-Engr, Energy)
Clinton Township
Rte. 22 E. Phone: (908)730-2924
Annandale, NJ 08801 Mary Jo Barnello, Info.Spec.
Founded: 1983. **Staff:** Prof 1; Other 4. **Subjects:** Petroleum refining processes and products, petrochemical processes and products, chemistry, physics, metallurgy, mathematics, industrial safety. **Special Collections:** U.S. patents, 1966 to present; Beilstein & Gmelin; chemical abstracts. **Holdings:** 35,000 volumes and microforms; patent holdings. **Subscriptions:** 550 journals and other serials. **Services:** Services not open to the public. **Automated Operations:** Computerized cataloging, acquisitions, serials, and circulation. **Computerized Information Services:** DIALOG Information Services, STN International, NEXIS, Dun & Bradstreet Business Credit Services, OAG Electronic Edition Travel Service. **Remarks:** FAX: (908)730-3021.

★5537★
Eye and Ear Institute Pavilion - Blair-Lippincott Library/LRC (Med)
230 Lothrop St. Phone: (412)647-2287
Pittsburgh, PA 15213 Bruce Johnston, Dir.
Founded: 1922. **Staff:** Prof 1; Other 1. **Subjects:** Ophthalmology, otolaryngology, audiology, head and neck surgery, speech pathology. **Holdings:** 5700 books; 6000 bound periodical volumes; 1800 microfiche; 250 video cassettes; 1600 audio cassettes; 5000 35mm slides. **Subscriptions:** 175 journals and other serials. **Services:** Interlibrary loan; copying; SDI; library open to the public for reference use only. **Automated Operations:** Computerized public access catalog, acquisitions, and serials (NOTIS). **Computerized Information Services:** MEDLARS, DIALOG Information Services, WILSONLINE; CD-ROM (Medline). **Publications:** Acquisitions newsletter, quarterly. **Remarks:** FAX: (412)647-8025. Library located at The Eye and Ear Institute, Suite 312.

★5538★
Eye Foundation Hospital - John E. Meyer Eye Foundation Library (Med)
1720 University Blvd. Phone: (205)325-8505
Birmingham, AL 35233-1895 Hugh Thomas, Med.Libn.
Founded: 1977. **Staff:** Prof 1. **Subjects:** Ophthalmology, otolaryngology, medicine, plastic surgery, hospital administration. **Holdings:** 1000 books; 1100 bound periodical volumes; 500 slides and cassettes. **Subscriptions:** 81 journals and other serials. **Services:** Interlibrary loan; copying; library open to medical professionals.

★5539★
Eye Research Institute/Boston Biomedical Research Institute - Library (Med)
20 Staniford St. Phone: (617)742-3140
Boston, MA 02114 Phyllis Ansel, Libn.
Founded: 1962. **Staff:** Prof 1. **Subjects:** Eye research and basic research. **Special Collections:** Institute publications. **Holdings:** 200 books; 1500 bound periodical volumes. **Subscriptions:** 132 journals and other serials. **Services:** Interlibrary loan; SDI; library open to the public by appointment. **Computerized Information Services:** BRS Information Technologies; internal databases. **Networks/Consortia:** Member of Massachusetts Health Sciences Libraries Network (MaHSLiN), Association of Visual Science Librarians (AVSL). **Publications:** ERI Publications List, annual. **Remarks:** FAX: (617)720-1069; (617)523-6649. **Formerly:** Eye Research Institute of Retina Foundation - Library.

F

F.B.I. Academy
See: **U.S. Federal Bureau of Investigation** (17488)

FAA
See: **U.S. Federal Aviation Administration** (17485)

★5540★
Fabricators & Manufacturers Association, International - Technical Information Center (Sci-Engr)
5411 State St. Phone: (815)399-8700
Rockford, IL 61108 Nancy Olson, Info.Spec.
Founded: 1980. **Staff:** 1.5. **Subjects:** Metal fabricating. **Holdings:** 400 volumes; AV programs. **Subscriptions:** 100 journals and other serials. **Services:** Interlibrary loan; copying; center open to the public by appointment. **Computerized Information Services:** DIALOG Information Services; DIALMAIL (electronic mail service). **Remarks:** FAX: (815)399-7279.

★5541★
Fachbibliothek fur Erwachsenenbildung (Educ)
Mentergasse 11 Phone: 222 5262091
A-1070 Vienna, Austria Dr. Christine Hinterhofer
Staff: Prof 2. **Subjects:** Adult education, social science. **Holdings:** 22,000 books; 10,000 bound periodical volumes; 100 microfiche; 4 reels of microfilm; videotapes; audiotapes. **Subscriptions:** 100 journals and other serials. **Services:** Interlibrary loan; copying; library open to the public. **Computerized Information Services:** BIBOS - Biblotheksorganisationssystem (national). Contact Person: Mrs. Birgit Jaindl. **Publications:** Documentation of articles; online documentation of adult education.

★5542★
Fachhochschulbibliothek Hannover - Fachbereichsbibliothek Elektrotechnik und Maschinenbau (Sci-Engr)
Ricklinger Stadtweg 118 Phone: 511 4503159
W-3000 Hannover 91, Germany H. Ferber
Founded: 1971. **Staff:** Prof 4; Other 2. **Subjects:** Engineering - electrical, mechanical. **Holdings:** 35,000 books; 3000 bound periodical volumes; 8000 microfiche. **Subscriptions:** 134 journals and other serials; 7 newspapers. **Services:** Interlibrary loan; library open to the public. **Computerized Information Services:** STN International, BRS Information Technologies, DIMDI, Data-Star, FIZ Technik, DIALOG Information Services, ESA/IRS. Contact Person: Margit Fassbender, Hd. of Info.Dept. **Remarks:** FAX: 511 4503111.

★5543★
Fachhochschule Braunschweig Wolfenbuttel - Bibliothek (Sci-Engr, Soc Sci)
Salzdahlumer Str 46-48 Phone: 5331 3010
W-3340 Wolfenbuttel, Germany Brigitte Waltes, Dipl.-Bibl.
Founded: 1974. **Staff:** Prof 5.5; Other 1. **Subjects:** Engineering, economics, social work. **Holdings:** 60,000 books; microfiche. **Subscriptions:** 230 journals and other serials; 5 newspapers. **Services:** Library not open to the public. **Computerized Information Services:** CD-ROMs.

★5544★
Fachhochschule fur Finanzen Nordrhein-Westfalen - Bibliothek (Bus-Fin)
Schloss.
W-4717 Nordkirchen 1, Germany Phone: 2596 1001
Founded: 1957. **Staff:** 3. **Subjects:** Taxation. **Services:** Library open to the public with restrictions.

★5545★
Fachhochschule Osnabruck - Bereichsbibliothek - Elektrotechnik, Maschinenbau, Werkstofftechnik, Wirtschaft (Sci-Engr, Soc Sci)
Albrechtstr. 30
W-4500 Osnabruck, Germany Phone: 541 9692211
Founded: 1970. **Subjects:** Engineering - electrical, mechanical, materials; economics. **Holdings:** 74,000 books; 2500 microfiche; 128 reels of microfilm. **Subscriptions:** 405 journals and other serials.

★5546★
Fachinformationszentrum Karlsruhe - Library (Sci-Engr, Energy)
W-7514 Eggenstein-Leopoldshafen Phone: 7247 808-333
2, Germany Dr. Werner Rittberger, Dir.
Founded: 1957. **Subjects:** Energy, nuclear research and technology, astronautics, aeronautics, space research, physics, mathematics and informatics, astronomy and astrophysics. **Holdings:** 92,000 monographs; 1.86 million reports. **Subscriptions:** 2120 journals and other serials. **Services:** Copying; SDI; library open to the public on a fee basis. **Computerized Information Services:** STN International. Performs searches on fee basis. **Remarks:** FAX: 7247 808-666. Telex: 17724710. **Also Known As:** FIZ Karlsruhe. **Staff:** Mrs. U. Keil, Hd., Lib.Div.

★5547★
Factory Mutual Research Corporation - Technical Information Center (Sci-Engr)
1151 Boston-Providence Tpke. Phone: (617)762-4300
Norwood, MA 02062 Janet B. Green, Libn.
Staff: Prof 2; Other 3. **Subjects:** Engineering with emphasis on fire research and loss prevention. **Holdings:** 5000 books; 500 bound periodical volumes; 2000 technical reports. **Subscriptions:** 150 journals and other serials. **Services:** Interlibrary loan; library open to the public by appointment. **Computerized Information Services:** DIALOG Information Services. **Remarks:** FAX: (617)762-9375. **Formerly:** Factory Mutual System. **Staff:** Janice T. Conroy, Asst.Libn.

★5548★
Facultad de Ciencias Economicas - Biblioteca Estanislao S. Zeballos (Bus-Fin)
Av Orono 1261 Phone: 41 212287
2000 Rosario, Argentina Ms. Clides Carolina Gajate
Founded: 1910. **Staff:** Prof 1; Other 12. **Subjects:** Accountancy, economics, administration, statistics. **Holdings:** 58,240 books; 17,646 bound periodical volumes; 84 microfiche; 1446 reels of microfilm; 42 maps. **Subscriptions:** 35 journals and other serials; 3 newspapers. **Services:** Interlibrary loan; copying; library open to the public. **Publications:** Revista de la Facultad de Ciencias Economicas; Sintesis Bibliograficas de Publicaciones Periodicas; Aportes Bibliograficos; Boletin de Obras.

Faculte St-Jean
See: **University of Alberta** (18193)

Facultes Universitaires Notre-Dame de la Paix - Institut d'Informatique
See: **Notre Dame de la Paix University Faculties - Informatics Institute** (12126)

★5549★
Faegre & Benson - Law Library (Law)
2200 Norwest Center
90 S. 7th St. Phone: (612)336-3724
Minneapolis, MN 55402-3901 Mary Schuman, Dir., Lib.Serv.
Staff: Prof 3; Other 3. **Subjects:** Law. **Holdings:** 25,000 books; 1350 bound periodical volumes. **Subscriptions:** 90 journals and other serials; 7 newspapers. **Services:** Library open to other law librarians and firms with special permission. **Computerized Information Services:** LEXIS, WESTLAW, DIALOG Information Services, DataTimes, VU/TEXT Information Services, LEGI-SLATE, NewsNet, Inc., PROFILE Information, InvesText. **Remarks:** FAX: (612)336-3026. Telex: 425131. **Staff:** Susan Rafter, Assoc.Libn., Ref.; JoAnn Altermatt, Assoc.Libn., Tech.Serv.

★5550★
Faeroe Islands - Foroya Landsbokasavn (Area-Ethnic)
P.O. Box 61 Phone: 11626
Torshavn, Faroe Islands Martin Naes, Dir.
Founded: 1828. **Staff:** Prof 9; Other 9. **Subjects:** Faeroe Islands - history and culture. **Holdings:** 111,000 books; 480 bound periodical volumes; 360 reels of microfilm; 800 manuscripts; microfiche. **Subscriptions:** 9 newspapers. **Services:** Interlibrary loan; copying; library open to the public. **Also Known As:** National Library of the Faeroe Islands.

★5551★
King Fahd University of Petroleum and Minerals - Research Institute - Technical Information Center (Energy)
Dhahran 31261, Saudi Arabia Phone: 8603319
Subjects: Petroleum and gas, energy resources, geology, minerals, water resources, environment, metrology, standards, materials, economic and industrial research. **Holdings:** 200,000 volumes and microfiche. **Subscriptions:** 83 journals and other serials. **Services:** Interlibrary loan; center not open to the public. **Computerized Information Services:** ORBIT Search Service, DIALOG Information Services, KACST (King Abdulaziz City of Science and Technology Database), DOBIS Canadian Online Library System; electronic mail service. **Remarks:** FAX: 8602266. Telex: 801913 KFUPMI SJ. **Formerly:** University of Petroleum and Minerals.

Robert J. Fahey Library
See: **Lawrence Memorial Hospital of Medford** (9010)

★5552★
Fair Acres Center - Medical Library (Med)
Rte. 352 Phone: (215)891-5717
Glen Riddle-Lima, PA 19037 Lisa A. Maffei, Dir., Med.Rec.
Staff: 1. **Subjects:** Medicine, nursing, geriatrics, allied health sciences. **Holdings:** 124 books; 60 unbound periodicals. **Subscriptions:** 10 journals and other serials. **Services:** Interlibrary loan; copying; library open to the public with restrictions. **Networks/Consortia:** Member of Consortium for Health Information & Library Services (CHI). **Formerly:** Fair Acres Geriatric Center.

★5553★
Fair Oaks Hospital - Medical Library (Med)
19 Prospect St. Phone: (908)277-9171
Summit, NJ 07901 JoAn Petersen, Libn.
Founded: 1977. **Staff:** Prof 1; Other 1. **Subjects:** Psychiatry, substance abuse. **Holdings:** 500 books; 200 bound periodical volumes. **Subscriptions:** 90 journals and other serials. **Services:** Interlibrary loan; copying; library open to the public by appointment. **Computerized Information Services:** MEDLARS, BRS Information Technologies. Performs searches on fee basis. **Networks/Consortia:** Member of Cosmopolitan Biomedical Library Consortium (CBLC), Health Sciences Library Association of New Jersey (HSLANJ), BHSL, New Jersey Library Network. **Remarks:** FAX: (908)522-9271.

John K. Fairbank Center for East Asian Research
See: **Harvard University** (6978)

★5554★
Fairbanks Daily News-Miner Newsroom - Library (Publ)
P.O. Box 70710 Phone: (907)456-6661
Fairbanks, AK 99707 Mary Beth Smetzer
Founded: 1983. **Staff:** Prof 1. **Subjects:** Alaska - history and people. **Special Collections:** Local and state photography files; Fairbanks Daily News-Miner (microfilm from early 1900's to present). **Holdings:** 1500 books; 20,000 photographs. **Subscriptions:** 5 journals and other serials; 20 newspapers. **Services:** Library open to the public on a limited basis when time allows; provides local and university libaries with index. **Special Indexes:** Fairbanks Daily News-Miner, June 1983 to present. **Remarks:** FAX: (907)452-5054.

Douglas Fairbanks Collection
See: **Museum of Modern Art - Film Stills Archive** (10908)

★5555★
Fairbanks Museum and Planetarium - Library (Biol Sci)
Main and Prospect Sts. Phone: (802)748-2372
St. Johnsbury, VT 05819 Howard B. Reed, Co-Dir.
Founded: 1890. **Staff:** Prof 1; Other 1. **Subjects:** Natural history, physical science, history, energy technology. **Holdings:** 2200 books; 550 bound periodical volumes; 5 boxes of unbound reports; 5 boxes of historical archival materials. **Subscriptions:** 15 journals and other serials. **Services:** Interlibrary loan; copying; library open to the public for reference use only.

★5556★
Fairbanks Native Association - Library (Area-Ethnic)
201 First Ave., 2nd Fl. Phone: (907)452-1648
Fairbanks, AK 99701 Jane Pollard Demment
Founded: 1984. **Staff:** Prof 1. **Subjects:** Native Alaskan issues and culture, North American Indian issues and culture, social issues, Alaskan history, federal programs. **Holdings:** Figures not available. **Services:** Library open to the public for reference use only. **Remarks:** FAX: (907)456-4148.

Fairchild Aerial Photography Collection
See: **Whittier College - Department of Geology** (20398)

★5557★
Fairchild Space & Defense Corporation - Technical Information Services (Sci-Engr)
Technical Information & Resource Center D-3
Fairchild Space
20301 Century Blvd. Phone: (301)428-6415
Germantown, MD 20874-1181 Ann Vlachos, Tech.Libn.
Staff: Prof 1; Other 1. **Subjects:** Electronics, aerospace science, communications. **Special Collections:** Collection of the National Advisory Committee for Aeronautics (NACA) Tech Memos (on microfiche). **Holdings:** 5000 books; 2000 bound periodical volumes; 96 drawers of microfiche; 11,000 hard copy reports. **Subscriptions:** 250 journals and other serials. **Services:** Library not open to the public. **Computerized Information Services:** DIALOG Information Services, OCLC, NASA/RECON, DTIC. **Networks/Consortia:** Member of Interlibrary Users Association (IUA), CAPCON Library Network.

★5558★
Fairchild Tropical Garden - Montgomery Library (Biol Sci)
11935 Old Cutler Rd. Phone: (305)665-2844
Miami, FL 33156 William Klein, Jr., Dir.
Founded: 1940. **Subjects:** Botany, horticulture. **Special Collections:** Manuscripts and correspondence of Dr. David Fairchild (4 filing cabinets). **Holdings:** 7000 volumes. **Subscriptions:** 150 journals and other serials. **Services:** Library open to the public by appointment. **Remarks:** FAX: (305)665-8032.

★5559★
Fairfax County Office of Comprehensive Planning - Library (Plan)
4050 Legato Rd., Suite 700 Phone: (703)246-1200
Fairfax, VA 22033 Ahmed Malek-Mohamadi, Pub.Info.Off.
Founded: 1970. **Staff:** Prof 1. **Subjects:** Land use planning, zoning, environment. **Special Collections:** Fairfax County Planning (1000 items). **Holdings:** 500 books; 500 periodical volumes; 500 reports/studies. **Subscriptions:** 30 journals and other serials; 5 newspapers. **Services:** Library not open to the public. **Networks/Consortia:** Member of Council of Planning Libraries. **Publications:** Planning Issues.

★5560★
Fairfax County Public Library - Fairfax City Regional Library - Business Specialty (Bus-Fin)
3915 Chain Bridge Rd. Phone: (703)246-2741
Fairfax, VA 22030 Sussanne Rehden, Br.Mgr.
Founded: 1972. **Staff:** Prof 2; Other 1. **Subjects:** Business, management, economics, investments, finance, computer technology. **Holdings:** 15,000 books; 350 telephone directories; annual reports, 1978 to present, on microfiche; Dun & Bradstreet Account Identification file on microfiche. **Subscriptions:** 300 journals and other serials. **Services:** Interlibrary loan; copying; library open to the public. **Automated Operations:** Computerized cataloging and circulation. **Computerized Information Services:** DIALOG Information Services, VU/TEXT Information Services. Performs searches on fee basis. **Remarks:** FAX: (703)385-6977. **Staff:** Vera Finberg, Bus.Spec.

★5561★
Fairfax County Public Library - Fairfax City Regional Library - Virginia Room (Hist)
3915 Chain Bridge Rd. Phone: (703)246-2123
Fairfax, VA 22030 Suzanne S. Levy, Libn.
Founded: 1940. **Staff:** Prof 1.5; Other 2.5. **Subjects:** Virginia - history, government, genealogy. **Special Collections:** Fairfax County History; Virginia Legislative Information; Fairfax County Photographic Archives; microfilm collection; map collection; Virginia and Fairfax city and county documents. **Holdings:** 23,650 books; 1225 bound periodical volumes; 9 VF drawers of Historic Landmarks Files; 1800 reels of microfilm; 149 boxes of manuscripts and scrapbooks; 15,000 photographs; 70,000 photographic negatives; 10,000 microfiche; 461 microcards; 45 VF drawers of clippings and pamphlets related to Virginia and local history. **Subscriptions:** 250 journals and other serials; 26 newspapers. **Services:** Interlibrary loan; copying; room open to the public. **Automated Operations:** Computerized cataloging and circulation. **Computerized Information Services:** Virginia State Division of Legislative Automated Systems, LOGIN. **Publications:** Fairfax County Public Library Guide to the Virginia General Assembly, annual. **Special Indexes:** Fairfax County History Index; Fairfax County Cemetery Index; Fairfax Herald Index; Local Newspaper Index; Local and State Periodical Index. **Staff:** Marjorie Schoenberg.

★5562★
Fairfax County Public Schools - Professional Library in Education (Educ)
3500 Old Lee Hwy. Phone: (703)591-4514
Fairfax, VA 22030 Betty H. Chilton, Staff Lib.Spec.
Staff: Prof 1; Other 1. **Subjects:** Education. **Holdings:** 17,000 books; ERIC microfiche collection. **Subscriptions:** 220 journals and other serials. **Services:** Copying; library open to the public for reference use only. **Computerized Information Services:** DIALOG Information Services. **Remarks:** FAX: (703)385-2743.

★5563★
Fairfax Hospital - Jacob D. Zylman Memorial Library (Med)
3300 Gallows Rd. Phone: (703)698-3234
Falls Church, VA 22046 Alice J. Sheridan, Lib.Dir.
Staff: Prof 3; Other 5. **Subjects:** Medicine, nursing, hospital management. **Holdings:** 8000 books; 9000 bound periodical volumes. **Subscriptions:** 450 journals and other serials. **Services:** Interlibrary loan; copying; library open to the public for reference use only. **Computerized Information Services:** MEDLARS, DIALOG Information Services, BRS Information Technologies.

★5564★
Fairfax Law Library (Law)
4110 Chain Bridge Rd. Phone: (703)246-2170
Fairfax, VA 22030 Jerilyn H. Polson, Law Libn.
Founded: 1978. **Staff:** Prof 1; Other 2. **Subjects:** U.S. Law. **Special Collections:** Virginia law. **Holdings:** 30,000 volumes; 800 other cataloged items; 3000 microfiche. **Subscriptions:** 30 journals and other serials. **Services:** Interlibrary loan; copying; library open to the public. **Computerized Information Services:** DIALOG Information Services, WESTLAW, Virginia State Division of Legislative Automated Systems, OCLC. Performs searches on fee basis. **Remarks:** FAX: (703)359-6004.

★5565★
Fairfield Hills Hospital - Health Sciences Library (Med)
Box 5525 Phone: (203)270-3083
Newtown, CT 06470 Mark J. Sosnowski, Libn.
Founded: 1933. **Staff:** Prof 1. **Subjects:** Psychiatry, psychology, social service, rehabilitation. **Holdings:** 6000 books; 2000 bound periodical volumes; 150 cataloged reference materials; 350 pamphlets and periodicals; AV programs. **Subscriptions:** 149 journals and other serials. **Services:** Interlibrary loan; copying; SDI; library open to the public for reference use only. **Computerized Information Services:** OCLC. **Networks/Consortia:** Member of Connecticut Association of Health Science Libraries (CAHSL), Southwestern Connecticut Library Council (SWLC), North Atlantic Health Science Libraries (NAHSL), BHSL, Northwestern Connecticut Health Science Library Consortium (NW-CT-HSL). **Remarks:** FAX: (203)270-3008.

★5566★
Fairfield Historical Society - Library (Hist)
636 Old Post Rd. Phone: (203)259-1598
Fairfield, CT 06430 Linda M. Mulford, Hd.Libn.
Founded: 1903. **Staff:** Prof 1; Other 4. **Subjects:** Local and regional history, genealogy, decorative arts. **Special Collections:** Cameron Clark architectural drawings (microfiche internal database); Restoration Resource Center. **Holdings:** 8200 books; 760 bound periodical volumes; 400 linear feet of manuscript material, including 17th-20th century family, court, cemetery, church, school, town, and shipping records, personal diaries, scrapbooks, account books and records of merchants, craftsmen, professional men and organizations, local ephemera; maps; photographs; 28 VF drawers of local history and genealogy; almanacs; city directories; tapes and transcripts of oral history. **Subscriptions:** 22 journals and other serials. **Services:** Copying; genealogical research on fee basis; library open to the public for reference use only. **Automated Operations:** Computerized cataloging. **Computerized Information Services:** Deeds (internal database). **Networks/Consortia:** Member of Southwestern Connecticut Library Council (SWLC). **Publications:** Fairfield in Connecticut, 1776-1976; Naval History of Fairfield County Men in the Revolution; Walking Through History - The Seaports of Black Rock and Southport; Newsletter, quarterly; Fairfield: a biography of a community, 1639-1989. **Special Indexes:** Indexes to selected manuscript collections and diaries.

Fairfield Nature Center
See: **Connecticut Audubon Society** (4177)

Fairlawn Museum Library
See: **Douglas County Historical Society - Archives** (4969)

★5567★
Fairleigh Dickinson University - Florham - Madison Campus Library - Special Collections (Bus-Fin, Art)
285 Madison Ave. Phone: (201)593-8515
Madison, NJ 07940 Dr. James F. Fraser, Dir.
Founded: 1956. **Staff:** Prof 5; Other 9. **Subjects:** Outdoor advertising, printing, graphic art, graphic satire, business, communism, socialism, secular Judaica. **Special Collections:** Outdoor Advertising Association Collection; Chesler Collection of Comic Art and Illustration; Lloyd Haberly Book Arts Collection; Rushmore Collection of History of Print and Paper Making; Czech Book Design, 1919-1939; Malik Verlag; William Weinstone Collection and Archive; Poster History. **Services:** Interlibrary loan; copying; collections open to the public by appointment. **Computerized Information Services:** DIALOG Information Services. Contact Person: Dr. Michael Adams, Asst.Dir., Pub.Serv. **Publications:** Malik Verlag Berlin-Prague-New York, 1984. **Special Catalogs:** Exhibition catalogs. **Remarks:** FAX: (201)593-8525.

★5568★
Fairleigh Dickinson University - Messler Library - New Jersey Room (Hist)
Montross Ave. Phone: (201)933-5000
Rutherford, NJ 07070 Richard A. Goerner, NJ Libn.
Staff: Prof 1; Other 1. **Subjects:** New Jersey - state and local history, social and economic conditions, politics and government, law. **Special Collections:** New Jersey state documents depository. **Holdings:** 6549 books; 713 bound periodical volumes; 5771 documents; 620 pamphlets; 733 maps; 14 feet of manuscripts; 381 reels of microfilm; 263 microcards; 183 microfiche. **Subscriptions:** 193 journals and other serials. **Services:** Interlibrary loan; copying; room open to the public on request. **Automated Operations:** Computerized cataloging. **Computerized Information Services:** DIALOG Information Services. **Networks/Consortia:** Member of PALINET, New York Metropolitan Reference and Research Library Agency. **Publications:** Documents of New Jersey Local Governments (1969); A Guide to Manuscripts on Microfilm (pamphlet; 1976).

★5569★
Fairleigh Dickinson University - Weiner Library - Reference/ Government Documents Department (Info Sci)
1000 River Rd. Phone: (201)692-2290
Teaneck, NJ 07666 Edward Grosek, Hd., Govt.Docs.
Founded: 1963. **Staff:** Prof 1; Other 1. **Subjects:** Census, environment, energy, foreign affairs, education, business, health, labor and fair

employment information. **Special Collections:** Depository for selected U.S. Government documents. **Holdings:** 823,958 printed documents; 70,988 documents on microfiche. **Subscriptions:** 1493 journals and other serials; 10 newspapers. **Services:** Interlibrary loan; copying; department open to the public. **Automated Operations:** Computerized cataloging. **Computerized Information Services:** BRS Information Technologies; CD-ROMs. **Networks/Consortia:** Member of PALINET. **Remarks:** FAX: (201)692-9815.

★5570★
Fairmont Early Childhood Family Education - Toy Lending Library (Educ)
115 S. Park Phone: (507)235-6205
Fairmont, MN 56031 Elayne Hested, Libn.
Staff: Prof 4. **Subjects:** Toys, books, records for infants, toddlers, preschoolers (birth to 5 years of age); parenting. **Holdings:** 450 toys. **Services:** Library open to the public on fee basis. **Remarks:** Maintains a Parent Resource Library of 253 volumes on parenting.

★5571★
Fairmount Temple - Arthur J. Lelyveld Center for Jewish Learning (Rel-Phil)
23737 Fairmount Blvd. Phone: (216)464-1330
Cleveland, OH 44122 Julie A. Moss, Libn.
Founded: 1927. **Staff:** Prof 1; Other 2. **Subjects:** Judaica. **Holdings:** 23,000 books; 20 bound periodical volumes. **Subscriptions:** 90 journals and other serials; 6 newspapers. **Services:** Interlibrary loan; center open to the public. **Automated Operations:** Computerized cataloging. **Staff:** Ronna Fox, Asst.Libn.; Rae Herman, Asst.Libn.

★5572★
Fairview College - Learning Resources Centre (Educ)
Box 3000 Phone: (403)835-6641
Fairview, AB, Canada T0H 1L0 Beverley A. Peterson, Mgr., LRC
Founded: 1951. **Staff:** Prof 1; Other 9. **Subjects:** Agriculture, animal health, beekeeping, trades technology, turfgrass, business, local history, adult upgrading. **Holdings:** 51,655 books; 372 bound periodical volumes; 5802 AV programs; 3957 microforms; 2766 software programs. **Subscriptions:** 37 journals and other serials; 35 newspapers. **Services:** Interlibrary loan; center open to the public. **Automated Operations:** Computerized circulation. **Remarks:** FAX: (403)835-6698. **Staff:** Kevin Davies, AV Supv.

★5573★
Fairview Developmental Center - Staff Library (Med)
2501 Harbor Blvd. Phone: (714)957-5394
Costa Mesa, CA 92626 Barbara Rycroft, Sr.Libn.
Founded: 1960. **Staff:** Prof 1; Other 1. **Subjects:** Mental retardation, developmental disabilities, psychology, special education, medicine. **Holdings:** 2801 books; 3120 bound periodical volumes; 45 staff research reports; 5 VF drawers of pamphlets. **Subscriptions:** 103 journals and other serials. **Services:** Interlibrary loan; copying; SDI; library open to the public for reference use only. **Automated Operations:** Computerized cataloging, serials, and circulation. **Computerized Information Services:** MEDLARS, DIALOG Information Services. **Networks/Consortia:** Member of National Network of Libraries of Medicine - Pacific Southwest Region.

★5574★
Fairview General Hospital - Medical Library (Med)
18101 Lorain Ave. Phone: (216)476-7118
Cleveland, OH 44111 Susan L. Favorite, Dir.
Staff: Prof 1; Other 4. **Subjects:** Internal medicine, obstetrics, gynecology, surgery, pediatrics, nursing. **Holdings:** 8700 books; 3520 bound periodical volumes. **Subscriptions:** 442 journals and other serials. **Services:** Interlibrary loan (limited); center not open to the public. **Computerized Information Services:** MEDLINE. **Remarks:** Includes the holdings of the School of Nursing Library.

★5575★
Fairview-Ridges Hospital - Medical Staff Library (Med)
201 E. Nicollet Blvd. Phone: (612)892-3013
Burnsville, MN 55337 Mary B. Carlson, Med.Libn.
Founded: 1984. **Staff:** Prof 1. **Subjects:** Medicine, nursing, and allied health sciences. **Holdings:** 350 books. **Subscriptions:** 61 journals and other serials. **Services:** Library not open to the public. **Computerized Information Services:** NLM, BRS Information Technologies.

★5576★
Fairview Southdale Hospital - Mary Ann King Health Sciences Library (Med)
6401 France Ave., S. Phone: (612)924-5005
Edina, MN 55435 Mary B. Carlson, Med.Libn.
Founded: 1965. **Staff:** Prof 1; Other 1. **Subjects:** Medicine, nursing, allied health sciences, hospital administration and management. **Special Collections:** Audio-visual collection. **Holdings:** 2000 books; 200 bound and unbound periodicals; vertical files. **Subscriptions:** 160 journals and other serials. **Services:** Interlibrary loan; copying; SDI; library open to the public with restrictions. **Computerized Information Services:** BRS Information Technologies, MEDLINE, DIALOG Information Services. **Networks/Consortia:** Member of Twin Cities Biomedical Consortium (TCBC), National Network of Libraries of Medicine - Greater Midwest Region.

★5577★
Fairview Veterinary Laboratory - Branch Library (Biol Sci)
P.O. Box 197 Phone: (403)835-2238
Fairview, AB, Canada T0H 1L0 Carol Kaip, Libn.
Subjects: Veterinary medicine. **Services:** Library not open to the public.

★5578★
King Faisal Specialist Hospital and Research Centre - Medical Library (Med)
P.O. Box 3354 Phone: 1 4647272
Riyadh 11211, Saudi Arabia Elizabeth Connor, Chf.Libn.
Staff: 6. **Subjects:** Clinical medicine, nursing, health administration, computers. **Special Collections:** Falconry. **Holdings:** 15,000 books; 45,000 bound periodical volumes; 2000 AV programs; 1000 microforms. **Subscriptions:** 1500 journals and other serials. **Services:** Interlibrary loan; clinical librarianship. **Computerized Information Services:** DIALOG Information Services, CD-ROM (Compact Cambridge). **Remarks:** FAX: 1 4427237. Telex: 401050 RYSPEC SJ. Cable: SPECIALIST.

Faith Evangelical Lutheran Seminary
See: **World Confessional Lutheran Association** (20611)

★5579★
Faith Presbyterian Church - Faith Library (Rel-Phil)
720 Marsh Rd. Phone: (302)764-8615
Wilmington, DE 19803 Dorothy V. Copper, Libn.
Founded: 1968. **Staff:** Prof 1; Other 4. **Subjects:** Religion. **Holdings:** 2730 books; 1635 cassette tapes; 60 videotapes. **Services:** Library not open to the public. **Publications:** Newsletter - for internal distribution only.

★5580★
Faith Presbyterian Church - Library (Rel-Phil)
5003 Whitesburg Dr. Phone: (205)881-4811
Huntsville, AL 35802 Pam McElhaney, Libn.
Staff: 1. **Subjects:** Bible study, children's literature, spiritual growth. **Holdings:** 2000 books; 50 magnetic tapes; 56 filmstrips; 38 phonograph records; 150 teaching pictures; 10 games and puzzles. **Services:** Library open to the public with restrictions.

Falconer Biology Library
See: **Stanford University** (15648)

Fales Library
See: **New York University** (11723)

Falk Library of the Health Sciences
See: **University of Pittsburgh** (19211)

★5581★
Maurice Falk Institute for Economic Research in Israel - Library (Bus-Fin)
Mount Scopus Campus Phone: 2 883124
91905 Jerusalem, Israel Mimi Feigelson, Libn.
Subjects: Economics. **Holdings:** Figures not available. **Services:** Copying; library open to the public.

★5582★
Fall River Historical Society - Museum/Library (Hist)
451 Rock St. Phone: (508)679-1071
Fall River, MA 02720 Michael Martins, Cur.
Founded: 1921. **Staff:** Prof 2. **Subjects:** Fall River Line, cotton textile industry, local history and genealogy. **Special Collections:** Lizzie Borden Collection. **Holdings:** 3000 books; 200 bound periodical volumes; 5000 manuscripts; reports. **Services:** Library open to the public by appointment for research. **Publications:** Museum newsletters, quarterly.

★5583★
Fall River Law Library (Law)
Superior Court House
441 N. Main St.
Fall River, MA 02720 Phone: (508)676-8971
Founded: 1894. **Staff:** Prof 2. **Subjects:** Law. **Special Collections:** Massachusetts reports, papers, briefs. **Holdings:** 18,283 volumes; 10,500 microfiche. **Services:** Library open to the public. **Computerized Information Services:** WESTLAW, LEXIS, OCLC; CD-ROMs. **Remarks:** Part of the Massachusetts State Trial Court; Marnie Warner, Law Library Coordinator. **Staff:** Lois B. Kane, Libn.; Madlyn Correa.

★5584★
Falls Village-Canaan Historical Society - Library (Hist)
Main St. Phone: (203)824-0707
Falls Village, CT 06031 Marion L. Stock, Cur.
Founded: 1953. **Staff:** 1. **Subjects:** Local history, ledgers and account books, Connecticut history, geneology. **Holdings:** 250 books. **Services:** Library open to the public for reference use only on limited schedule.

★5585★
Fallsview Psychiatric Hospital - Staff Library (Med)
330 Broadway, E. Phone: (216)929-8301
Cuyahoga Falls, OH 44221 Joy Prichard, Libn.
Staff: Prof 1. **Subjects:** Psychology, psychiatry, psychiatric nursing. **Holdings:** 3000 books. **Subscriptions:** 40 journals and other serials. **Services:** Interlibrary loan. **Automated Operations:** Computerized cataloging. **Networks/Consortia:** Member of NEOUCOM Council Associated Hospital Librarians. **Remarks:** FAX: (216)929-6659.

★5586★
Falmouth Historical Society - Resources Center - History & Genealogy Archives (Hist)
Palmer Ave. at the Village Green
Box 174 Phone: (508)548-4857
Falmouth, MA 02541 Dorothy Svenning, Archv.
Founded: 1901. **Staff:** 4. **Subjects:** Local history, genealogy. **Special Collections:** Old deeds, wills, and photographs. **Holdings:** 500 books; 30 ships logs, 1820 to present; 135 boxes of archival materials. **Services:** Archives open to the public.

★5587★
Family Foundation - Consumer Information Centre (Bus-Fin)
1871 Smith St. Phone: (306)787-3897
Regina, SK, Canada S4P 3V7 Rosanne Glass, Mgr., Educ.
Founded: 1973. **Subjects:** Consumer education and information, family matters, credit, advertising and marketing, money management. **Special Collections:** Consumer education resources (AV programs). **Holdings:** 1000 books; 400 AV programs. **Subscriptions:** 25 journals and other serials; 5 newspapers. **Services:** Interlibrary loan; copying; center open to the public with restrictions. **Publications:** Acquisition List, irregular; special bibliographies. **Remarks:** FAX: (306)787-8999.

★5588★
Family Health International - Library (Med)
P.O. Box 13950 Phone: (919)544-7040
Research Triangle Park, NC 27709 William Barrows, Info.Serv.Mgr.
Founded: 1971. **Staff:** Prof 2; Other 3. **Subjects:** Reproductive medicine, family planning, contraception, population, developing countries. **Special Collections:** AIDS; breast cancer. **Holdings:** 5500 books; 800 unbound periodical volumes; 9000 reprints and unpublished documents; 330 patents. **Subscriptions:** 425 journals and other serials; 280 newsletters. **Services:** Interlibrary loan; copying; SDI; library open to the public with prior approval. **Automated Operations:** Computerized cataloging and serials. **Computerized Information Services:** MEDLARS, DIALOG Information Services, BRS Information Technologies; internal databases. Performs searches free of charge. **Networks/Consortia:** Member of APLIC International Census Network. **Publications:** network (newsletter), quarterly; Magdelene Messenger, 2/year; Annual List of FHI Publications and Reprints. **Remarks:** FAX: (919)544-7261. Telex: 579442.

★5589★
The Family Institute - Crowley Library (Soc Sci)
680 N. Lake Shore Dr., Suite 1306 Phone: (312)908-7854
Chicago, IL 60611 Phyllis Anne Miller, Libn.
Founded: 1972. **Staff:** Prof 1. **Subjects:** Therapy - family, marital, divorce, step-family, adolescent; adoption issues; death and mourning; anorexia; schizophrenia; dysfunctional families; ethnic issues. **Special Collections:** Family therapy. **Holdings:** 2500 books; 5000 reprints; 60 videotapes; 200 audiocassettes. **Subscriptions:** 25 journals and other serials. **Services:** Interlibrary loan; copying; library open to the public (annual membership fee required for borrowing). **Special Indexes:** Indexes of Family Therapy Journals.

★5590★
Family Life Information Exchange (Med)
P.O. Box 37299 Phone: (301)585-6636
Washington, DC 20013-7299 Florence Lehr, Proj.Mgr.
Founded: 1976. **Subjects:** Family planning, sexually transmitted diseases, adolescent pregnancy, adoption, contraception, reproductive health. **Holdings:** 5000 monographs. **Subscriptions:** 60 journals and other serials. **Remarks:** The exchange was created to serve federally supported service agencies. It provides information to family-planning workers, educators, and trainers. FAX: (301)907-8906. **Staff:** Alyce Ortuzar, Ref.Spec.

★5591★
Family Resource Coalition - National Resource Center for Family Support Programs
200 S. Michigan Ave., No. 1520
Chicago, IL 60604
Founded: 1981. **Subjects:** Parent education and support; family resource programs, including teen parenting programs. **Holdings:** Files on 2000 family resource and parenting programs. **Remarks:** Currently inactive. **Formerly:** Its Clearinghouse on Family Resource and Support Programs.

★5592★
Family Service America - Severson National Information Center (Soc Sci)
11700 W. Lake Park Dr. Phone: (414)359-1040
Milwaukee, WI 53224 Susan Hornung, Dir.
Founded: 1911. **Staff:** Prof 2; Other 2. **Subjects:** Counseling, social work, social services for families, nonprofit administration, family trends, employee assistance programs. **Special Collections:** Unpublished materials on the programming and administration of local family service agencies. **Holdings:** 2000 books; 30 VF drawers of ephemera. **Subscriptions:** 120 journals and other serials. **Services:** Interlibrary loan; copying; center open to the public with restrictions for reference use only. **Automated Operations:** Computerized public access catalog. **Computerized Information Services:** DIALOG Information Services, BRS Information Technologies; internal database. **Networks/Consortia:** Member of Library Council of Metropolitan Milwaukee, Inc. (LCOMM), Southeastern Wisconsin Health Science Library Consortium (SWHSL). **Publications:** Directory of FSA Member Agencies, annual - for sale. **Remarks:** FAX: (414)359-1074. **Staff:** Debra Conlin, Libn.

★5593★
Fanshawe College of Applied Arts and Technology - Main Library (Educ)
P.O. Box 4005 Phone: (519)452-4240
London, ON, Canada N5W 5H1 Annette K. Frost, Mgr., Lib.Serv.
Founded: 1967. **Staff:** Prof 5; Other 18. **Subjects:** Business, mathematics, science, electrical technology, electronics, civil technology, health sciences and nursing, social sciences, fine arts, communication arts, design, psychology, library science, law, secretarial science, mechanical technology, motive power, human services, marketing, hospitality studies. **Special Collections:** Statistics Canada material; annual reports of business corporations. **Holdings:** 59,970 books; 5984 bound periodical volumes; 6788 pamphlets; 719 films; 230 cassettes; 2611 videotapes; 441 slide/tapes; 3 kits; 14 transparencies. **Subscriptions:** 683 journals and other serials; 13 newspapers. **Services:** Interlibrary loan; copying; library open to the public for reference use only. **Automated Operations:** Computerized acquisitions and circulation. **Computerized Information Services:** DOBIS Canadian Online Library System. **Networks/Consortia:** Member of The Bibliocentre. **Remarks:** FAX: (519)452-3570. **Staff:** Suzanne O'Neill, Pub.Serv.Libn.; Vicky Mok, Tech.Serv.Libn.; Elaine Vitali, Non-Print Coll.Libn.; Jennifer Morrissey, Print Coll.Libn.

FAPA - Information Center
See: **Future Aviation Professionals of America** (6220)

Far Eastern Library
See: **Royal Ontario Museum - H.H. Mu Library** (14130)

★5594★
Far Eastern Research Library (Area-Ethnic)
5812 Knox Ave., S.
Box 19324 Phone: (612)926-6887
Minneapolis, MN 55419 Dr. Jerome Cavanaugh, Dir.
Founded: 1969. **Staff:** Prof 3. **Subjects:** China - language, literature, history; Japan; Indonesia; Southeast Asia. **Special Collections:** Chinese dialects (2500 items). **Holdings:** 64,384 books; 2450 bound periodical volumes; 3000 Chinese serial titles. **Subscriptions:** 439 journals and other serials. **Services:** Interlibrary loan; copying; library open to the public for validated research projects. **Automated Operations:** Computerized public access catalog and serials. **Computerized Information Services:** NOTEBOOK, Western language catalog, Chinese and Japanese language catalog (internal databases). Performs searches on fee basis. **Special Indexes:** An Index to Four Collections of Chinese Book Collectors' Biographies (1977) - for sale. **Remarks:** Majority of library holdings are written in Chinese and Japanese.

Faraday Library
See: **Northern Illinois University** (11996)

Farallones Institute - Center for Sustainable Agriculture
See: **Center for Sustainable Agriculture** (3309)

Jean Farb Memorial Medical Library
See: **Mercy Hospital and Medical Center** (10147)

★5595★
Faribault Regional Center - Library (Med)
Faribault, MN 55021 Phone: (507)332-3274
Mary K. Heltsley, Libn.
Staff: Prof 1. **Subjects:** Mental retardation. **Holdings:** 2550 books; 285 bound periodical volumes; 11 VF drawers of pamphlets; 275 pamphlet boxes of unbound periodicals. **Subscriptions:** 50 journals and other serials. **Services:** Interlibrary loan; library open to the public. **Networks/Consortia:** Member of Minnesota Department of Human Services Library Consortium, Southeast Library System (SELS).

Farlow Reference Library
See: **Harvard University - Botany Libraries** (6950)

★5596★
The Farm Community - Farm School Library - Special Collections (Area-Ethnic)
50 The Farm Phone: (615)964-2325
Summertown, TN 38483 Mary Ellen Bowe
Founded: 1978. **Staff:** 1. **Subjects:** Classics, Native American lore, alternative energy, art, music, dance, world studies, history. **Holdings:** 3000 books; 100 maps. **Services:** Interlibrary loan; library open to the public with restrictions. **Remarks:** Alternate telephone number(s): 964-3670.

★5597★
Farm Credit Administration - Library (Bus-Fin, Law)
1501 Farm Credit Dr. Phone: (703)883-4296
McLean, VA 22102-5090 Laura M. Macqueen, Libn.
Staff: Prof 2; Other 1. **Subjects:** Federal law, business, banking and finance, agricultural credit, auditing. **Holdings:** 10,000 books. **Subscriptions:** 250 journals and other serials; 5 newspapers. **Services:** Interlibrary loan; copying; SDI; library open to the public by appointment. **Computerized Information Services:** DIALOG Information Services, NEXIS, LEXIS, Washington Alert Service, AgriData Network. **Networks/Consortia:** Member of FEDLINK. **Publications:** Newsletter, weekly; library brochure; bibliographies. **Remarks:** FAX: (703)734-5784. **Staff:** Steven Spector, Asst.Libn.; Dorothy Whitehead, Techn.

★5598★
Farm Journal, Inc. - Marketing Library (Agri, Publ)
230 W. Washington Sq. Phone: (215)829-4734
Philadelphia, PA 19106 Kandace Herzog, Mktg./Info.Mgr.
Founded: 1945. **Staff:** Prof 1; Other 3. **Subjects:** Farm markets, U.S. agriculture, advertising and media, marketing. **Holdings:** 962 books; 400 bound periodical volumes; 148 VF drawers of clippings, U.S. Government periodicals in farm field, Farm Journal statistical materials. **Subscriptions:** 209 journals and other serials. **Services:** Interlibrary loan; library open to the public on a limited schedule.

Farm Survival Project
See: **Rural Advancement Fund of the National Sharecroppers Fund Inc.** (14146)

★5599★
Farm Worker Law, Inc.
P.O. Box 310
La Paz
Keene, CA 93531
Defunct.

★5600★
Farmers Insurance Group, Inc. - Library (Bus-Fin)
Box 2478, Terminal Annex Phone: (213)932-3615
Los Angeles, CA 90051 Lucille L. Garber, Libn.
Founded: 1945. **Staff:** 1. **Subjects:** Insurance, business and business methods, finance, traffic safety. **Special Collections:** Company archives (35 VF drawers). **Holdings:** 5500 books; 10 VF drawers. **Subscriptions:** 200 journals and other serials. **Services:** Interlibrary loan; library not open to the public. **Remarks:** Library located at 4680 Wilshire Blvd., Los Angeles, CA 90010.

★5601★
Farmingdale Public Schools - Professional Library (Educ)
E. Memorial at Mill Lane School, Rm. 120
Mill Ln. Phone: (516)752-6553
Farmingdale, NY 11735 Barbara Pandolfo, Dir.
Founded: 1957. **Staff:** Prof 1; Other 2. **Subjects:** Education. **Holdings:** 1000 books; unbound periodicals; pamphlets. **Subscriptions:** 46 journals and other serials. **Services:** Library open to the public on a limited schedule.

Farmington Community Library - Oakland County Library for the Blind & Physically Handicapped
See: **Oakland County Library for the Blind & Physically Handicapped** (12198)

★5602★
Farmland Industries, Inc. - J.W. Cummins Memorial Library (Agri, Bus-Fin)
3315 N. Oak Trafficway
Box 7305 Phone: (816)459-6606
Kansas City, MO 64116 Rosetta Boyd, Info.Spec.
Founded: 1950. **Staff:** 1. **Subjects:** Cooperatives, agriculture, economics. **Special Collections:** Farmland News, December 1933 to present; American Cooperation, 1926 to present (proceedings of annual summer institutes of American Institute of Cooperation). **Holdings:** 2085 volumes; Teammates and Inside Farmland (employee publication), 1950 to present; microfilm. **Subscriptions:** 200 journals and other serials; 6 newspapers. **Services:** Interlibrary loan; copying; library open to the public by appointment. **Automated Operations:** Computerized cataloging. **Computerized Information Services:** DIALOG Information Services, WESTLAW, EBSCONET. **Networks/Consortia:** Member of Kansas City Metropolitan Library Network (KCMLN). **Remarks:** FAX: (816)459-5927.

Christine Dunlap Farnham Archives
See: **Brown University** (2277)

★5603★
Frank C. Farnham Company, Inc. - Library (Sci-Engr)
1932 Chestnut St., Suite 1203 Phone: (215)567-1500
Philadelphia, PA 19103 Connie Devlin, Gen.Mgr.
Staff: Prof 3; Other 5. **Subjects:** Medicine, chemistry, electronics, metallurgy, mining, plastics, pharmaceutics, history and art of translation. **Special Collections:** Bilingual and multilingual dictionaries (350). **Holdings:** 1100 books; 25,000 translations from patent and periodical literature. **Subscriptions:** 10 journals and other serials. **Services:** Library not open to the public. **Publications:** Guidelines for Translation Buyers. **Special Indexes:** Word and phrase indexes for internal use.

★5604★
William A. Farnsworth Library and Art Museum (Art)
Rockland, ME 04841 Phone: (207)596-6457
Barbara Watson, Libn.
Founded: 1948. **Staff:** Prof 7; Other 6. **Subjects:** Art - decorative, American, European, Oriental. **Special Collections:** Rare and illustrated books; Louise Nevelson Archives; N.C. Wyeth Collection; Maine artists archives (includes Robert Indiana, George Bellows, Waldo Peirce, Andrew Wyeth, Jonathan Fisher, Jamie Wyeth, William Barrett); Farnsworth Family Archives; Farnsworth Museum Archives; artist clipping files. **Holdings:** 4000 books; 100 early Maine imprints. **Subscriptions:** 15 journals and other serials. **Services:** Interlibrary loan; copying; library open to the public for reference use only. **Publications:** Annual Report; newsletter, quarterly. **Special Catalogs:** Catalogs of special exhibitions.

Grover C. Farquhar Library
See: **Missouri School for the Deaf** (10541)

C.D. Farquharson Health Sciences Library
See: **Centenary Hospital** (3201)

Farrar Library
See: **Clarke Institute of Psychiatry** (3777)

Farrell Library
See: **Kansas State University** (8563)

★5605★
Farris, Vaughan, Wills & Murphy - Library (Law)
700 W. Georgia St.
Box 10026 Phone: (604)684-9151
Vancouver, BC, Canada V7Y 1B3 L. Johanna Sigurdson, Libn.
Staff: Prof 1; Other 1. **Subjects:** Law - corporate/commercial, municipal, labor; intellectual property; litigation. **Holdings:** 3500 volumes. **Subscriptions:** 103 journals and other serials. **Services:** Interlibrary loan (limited); library not open to the public. **Computerized Information Services:** DIALOG Information Services, Infomart Online, QL Systems, WESTLAW, Info Globe, STM Systems Corporation, LEXIS, Infomart Online; QUICKMAIL, CBAMAIL (electronic mail services). **Remarks:** FAX: (604)661-9349. Telex: 04-507819.

Fashion Group of Detroit
See: **Tavy Stone Fashion Library** (15809)

★5606★
Fashion Institute of Design & Merchandising - Cyril Magnin Resource and Research Center (Art)
55 Stockton St., 5th Fl. Phone: (415)433-6691
San Francisco, CA 94108-5805 Carol M. Block, Libn.
Founded: 1977. **Staff:** Prof 1; Other 1. **Subjects:** Fashion design and merchandising, interior design, apparel manufacturing, advertising, merchandising, marketing. **Special Collections:** Designer Files (1000 international designers); Costume Library (200 garments); Rudi Gernreich Collection (45 garments); Joseph Magnin Advertising Art (1400 slicks and scrapbooks); Fashion Files (500); Retail Files (200); Manufacturers Files (200). **Holdings:** 4500 books; 300 AV programs; 900 newspaper clipping files. **Subscriptions:** 115 journals and other serials. **Services:** Copying; center open to the public for reference use only.

★5607★
Fashion Institute of Design & Merchandising - Resource and Research Center (Art)
3420 Bristol Phone: (714)546-0930
Costa Mesa, CA 92626 Kim Eldien, Coord.
Founded: 1980. **Staff:** Prof 2. **Subjects:** Fashion design and merchandising, costume history, interior design, apparel manufacturing, textile design, graphic arts, advertising, visual presentation. **Special Collections:** Designer files (260). **Holdings:** 2000 books; 230 bound periodical volumes; 1025 pamphlets; 1690 clippings files; 370 videotapes; 6000 slides; 215 retail catalogs; 80 annual reports. **Subscriptions:** 37 journals and other serials; 8 newspapers. **Services:** Copying; center open to the public for reference use only. **Remarks:** Maintains an interior design work room. **Staff:** Marcy Dillon, Asst.Coord.

★5608★
Fashion Institute of Design & Merchandising - Resource and Research Center (Art)
919 S. Grand Ave. Phone: (213)624-1200
Los Angeles, CA 90015-1421 Kaycee Hale, Exec.Dir.
Founded: 1972. **Staff:** Prof 3; Other 10. **Subjects:** Fashion design and merchandising, interior design, apparel manufacturing, textile design, graphic arts, cosmetics and fragrance advertising, theatrical costume design, visual presentation. **Special Collections:** Costume collection, 1785 to present (3500 garments and accessories); International Fashion Designers File (5000 files, biographies, pictures, and press releases); rare books; textiles. **Holdings:** 7700 books; 519 bound periodical volumes; 430 slide sets; 835 videotapes; 9800 newspaper clipping files; 130 retail catalogs. **Subscriptions:** 220 journals and other serials; 10 trade papers and newspapers. **Services:** Copying; center open to the public. **Networks/Consortia:** Member of State of California Answering Network (SCAN). **Publications:** Acquisitions list; Resource & Research Center Newsletter, quarterly - both for internal distribution only. **Special Indexes:** Index to textile and fabric periodicals (card). **Remarks:** Branch locations in California: San Francisco, Costa Mesa, and San Diego. FAX: (213)6 24-4777. **Staff:** Bonnie Rothbart Stark, Sr.Libn.; Gayle Williamson, Coll.Dev.Libn.

★5609★
Fashion Institute of Design & Merchandising - Resource and Research Center (Art)
1010 2nd Ave., 2nd Fl. Phone: (619)235-4515
San Diego, CA 92101 Kathryn Harris, Coord.
Founded: 1985. **Staff:** Prof 2. **Subjects:** Fashion design, merchandise marketing, visual presentation, interior design, manufacturing management, textile design, theater costume design. **Holdings:** 1200 books; 65 bound periodical volumes; AV programs. **Subscriptions:** 75 journals and other serials. **Services:** Copying; center open to the public for reference use only. **Remarks:** FAX: (619)238-8838.

★5610★
Fashion Institute of Design & Merchandising - Resource and Research Center (Art)
13701 Riverside Dr.
Sherman Oaks, CA 91423 Phone: (818)990-2133
Staff: Prof 1. **Subjects:** Fashion design, costume history, interior design, merchandising, visual merchandising, marketing, textiles, art, architecture. **Special Collections:** Vogue Magazine, 1956 to present (170 bound periodical volumes); American Fabrics & Fashions, 1946-1985. **Holdings:** 2350 books; 205 videotapes; 27 retail mail orders catalogs; fashion designer and subject clipping files. **Subscriptions:** 69 journals and other serials; 11 newspapers. **Services:** Copying; center open to the public for reference use only.

★5611★
Fashion Institute of Technology - Library (Art, Bus-Fin)
7th Ave. at 27th St. Phone: (212)760-7884
New York, NY 10001-5992 Rochelle Sager
Founded: 1952. **Staff:** Prof 18; Other 43. **Subjects:** Costume, fashion, interior design, management engineering technology, fashion buying and merchandising, textiles, advertising. **Special Collections:** Lady Duff-Gordon Collection (sketches and photographs); Max Meyer Collection (sketches); Haft-Swansdown Collection (sketches); Fredrick Milton Collection (sketches); Berley Collection (sketches); Gazette Du Bon Ton; Harper's Bazaar; Millinery Trade Review; Du Barry Fashion Studios Sketchbooks (55 volumes); Bergdorf Goodman Collection (sketches); Davidow Collection (sketches); Muriel King Collection (sketches). **Holdings:** 107,000 books; 4025 bound periodical volumes; 125 VF drawers of clippings and pamphlets on art and design; 120 VF drawers of clippings and pamphlets on business and technology; 46 titles on microfilm; 110,000 fashion slides. **Subscriptions:** 716 journals and other serials; 35 newspapers. **Services:** Interlibrary loan; copying; library open to the public for reference use only by appointment. **Automated Operations:** Computerized cataloging, acquisitions, and serials. **Computerized Information Services:** DIALOG Information Services, RLIN, ArtQuest, Sales Catalog Index Project Input On-line (SCIPIO); internal database. Contact Person: Beryl Rentof, Hd. of Ref., 760-7590. **Networks/Consortia:** Member of New York Metropolitan Reference and Research Library Agency, Research Libraries Information Network (RLIN). **Publications:** Library/Media Services Faculty Handbook; Newsletter, quarterly - for internal distribution only; bibliographies in subject areas including management engineering, clothing and home sewing, fashion, costume accessories, production, advertising, cosmetics, fashion buying, direct marketing, international trade, textile science. **Remarks:** FAX: (212)594-9206. **Staff:** Beryl Rentof, Hd. of Ref.; Marjorie Miller, Ref.Libn.; Judy Wood, Acq.Libn.; Janette Rozene, Cat.Libn.; Lionel White, Instr. Media Spec.; Lorraine Weberg, Ref.Libn.; Stephen Rosenberger, Ref.Circ.Libn.; Joshua Waller, Evening Ref.Libn.

★5612★
Fasken, Campbell, Godfrey - Library (Law)
Toronto Dominion Centre
P.O. Box 20 Phone: (416)865-5143
Toronto, ON, Canada M5K 1N6 Michele L. Miles, Libn.
Staff: Prof 1; Other 5. **Subjects:** Law - corporate, administrative, real estate, estate; taxation; litigation. **Holdings:** 10,500 books; 150 bound periodical volumes; federal and provincial legislation. **Subscriptions:** 300 journals and other serials. **Services:** Interlibrary loan; library open to the public with librarian's permission. **Automated Operations:** Computerized cataloging and serials. **Computerized Information Services:** Info Globe, QL Systems, WESTLAW, LEXIS, NEXIS, DIALOG Information Services, Infomart Online, INSIGHT, TradeRef. **Special Indexes:** Index to current federal and provincial legislation; index to legal memoranda. **Remarks:** FAX: (416)362-2381.

Jack Fatz Memorial Information Center
See: **Honeywell, Inc.** (7369)

★5613★
Jack Faucett Associates - Library (Bus-Fin, Energy)
4550 Montgomery Ave., Suite 300 N. Phone: (301)961-8800
Bethesda, MD 20814 Carolyn Diaz, Libn.
Founded: 1963. **Staff:** Prof 1; Other 2. **Subjects:** Economics, energy, transportation, environment, capital investment. **Holdings:** 16,000 books, technical reports, statistical series in hardcopy and microform. **Subscriptions:** 150 journals and other serials. **Services:** Interlibrary loan; library not open to the public. **Computerized Information Services:** DIALOG Information Services. **Publications:** Library Bulletin - for internal distribution only; JFA Technical Reports List, annual. **Remarks:** FAX: (301)469-3001.

★5614★
Faulkner Hospital - Ingersoll Bowditch Library (Med)
Allandale at Centre St. Phone: (617)983-7443
Boston, MA 02130 Barbara P. Pastan, Dir., Lib.Serv.
Founded: 1940. **Staff:** Prof 2. **Subjects:** Medicine, surgery, nursing, administration. **Holdings:** 800 books; 4000 bound periodical volumes; 350 audiotapes; 50 videotapes; 25 slide/tape sets; hospital reports; microfiche. **Subscriptions:** 195 journals and other serials. **Services:** Interlibrary loan; copying; SDI; library open to health professionals. **Automated Operations:** Computerized ILL (DOCLINE). **Computerized Information Services:** NLM, BRS Information Technologies. Performs searches on fee basis. **Networks/Consortia:** Member of National Network of Libraries of Medicine - New England Region, Boston Biomedical Library Consortium. **Remarks:** FAX: (617)524-8663. **Staff:** Patricia Johnson.

★5615★
Faulkner University - Jones School of Law - Library (Law)
5345 Atlanta Hwy. Phone: (205)272-5820
Montgomery, AL 36193 Judy Hughes, Dir.
Founded: 1928. **Staff:** Prof 3; Other 4. **Subjects:** Law. **Holdings:** 32,000 books. **Subscriptions:** 100 journals and other serials. **Services:** Library open to law students and local attorneys only. **Computerized Information Services:** WESTLAW, OCLC, DIALOG Information Services. **Networks/Consortia:** Member of SOLINET. **Staff:** Kay Newman, Cat.Libn.; Roianne Frith, Ref.Libn.; George Cameron, III, Ref.Libn.

★5616★
Fauquier County Public Schools - Teacher Resource Center - Library (Educ)
244 Waterloo St. Phone: (703)347-6170
Warrenton, VA 22186 Tamara Bannister
Founded: 1982. **Staff:** Prof 1; Other 2.5. **Subjects:** Education. **Holdings:** Books, periodicals, and audiovisual software. **Subscriptions:** 50 journals and other serials; 3 newspapers. **Services:** Interlibrary loan; library open to the public with restrictions. **Automated Operations:** Computerized public access catalog. **Remarks:** FAX: (703)347-6173.

★5617★
Faxton-Children's Hospital - Medical Library (Med)
1676 Sunset Ave. Phone: (315)738-6253
Utica, NY 13502 Halyna Liszczynskyj, Dir. of Lib.Serv.
Staff: Prof 1. **Subjects:** Oncology, chemotherapy, surgery, internal medicine, nursing, emergency medicine, orthopedics. **Holdings:** 815 books. **Subscriptions:** 132 journals and other serials. **Services:** Interlibrary loan; copying; SDI; library open to health professionals and students for reference use. **Automated Operations:** Computerized acquisitions. **Computerized Information Services:** OCLC, NLM; CD-ROMs (MEDLINE, CancerLit). **Networks/Consortia:** Member of Central New York Library Resources Council (CENTRO).

Oliver J. Fay Library
See: **Iowa Methodist Medical Center** (8229)

★5618★
Fayette County Historical Society - Library (Hist)
195 Lee St.
P.O. Box 421 Phone: (404)461-8493
Fayetteville, GA 30214 Carolyn Cary, County Hist.
Founded: 1972. **Subjects:** Fayette County genealogy, the Civil War and Georgia. **Special Collections:** War of the Rebellion collection (complete); Confederate Veteran collection (complete). **Holdings:** 300 books; 100 bound periodical volumes; 20 manuscripts. **Services:** Library open to the public.

★5619★
Fayette County Historical Society - Library (Hist)
100 N. Walnut Phone: (319)422-5797
West Union, IA 52175 Frances R. Graham
Subjects: Genealogy, history. **Holdings:** 500 books; 40 land record documents; 56 VF drawers of family files; 30 reels of microfilm; school records; photographs. **Services:** Copying; library open to the public. **Special Indexes:** Indexes to nearby county censuses; Index to Clayton County 1984 history.

★5620★
Fayette County Law Library (Law)
Court House
Uniontown, PA 15401 Elnora E. Mullooly, Law Libn.
Subjects: Law. **Holdings:** 20,000 volumes. **Services:** Library open to the public.

★5621★
Fayette County Law Library Association (Law)
Fayette County Court House Phone: (614)335-3608
Washington Court House, OH 43160 Steven H. Eckstein, Ch.
Founded: 1975. **Staff:** Prof 1. **Subjects:** Case and tax law. **Holdings:** 20,000 volumes. **Services:** Copying; library open to the public on a limited schedule. **Computerized Information Services:** Access to Veralex 2, LEXIS. **Staff:** Cindy Reeves, Asst. Law Libn.

Fayette County Urban Planning Commission
See: **Lexington-Fayette County Urban Planning Commission** (9089)

★5622★
Fayetteville Area Health Education Center - Library/Information Services (Med)
1601 Owen Dr. Phone: (919)678-7276
Fayetteville, NC 28304 Barbara A. Wright, Dir.
Founded: 1977. **Staff:** Prof 4; Other 3. **Subjects:** Medicine, nursing, mental health, allied health sciences. **Holdings:** 5000 books; 2000 bound periodical volumes; 1500 AV programs; 3 drawers of clippings and pamphlets. **Subscriptions:** 302 journals and other serials. **Services:** Interlibrary loan; copying; SDI; library open to the public with restrictions. **Automated Operations:** Computerized cataloging and acquisitions. **Computerized Information Services:** NLM, BRS Information Technologies, DIALOG Information Services; CD-ROMs (MEDLINE, CINAHL, AIDSLINE, MEDLINE PROFESSIONAL); EasyLink (electronic mail service). Performs searches on fee basis. **Networks/Consortia:** Member of Cape Fear Health Sciences Information Consortium (CFHSIC), North Carolina Area Health Education Centers Program Library and Information Services Network, National Network of Libraries of Medicine - Southeastern/Atlantic Region. **Publications:** Continuing Education Calendar and acquisitions list, monthly. **Special Catalogs:** Subject listings of AV programs. **Remarks:** FAX: (919)323-4007. Electronic mail address(es): 62918423 (EasyLink). **Staff:** Rebecca Johnston, Hd., Tech.Serv.; Marja Snyder, Outreach Libn.; Pamela Jackson, Libn.

★5623★
Fayetteville Publishing Company - Newspaper Library (Publ)
458 Whitefield Rd. Phone: (919)323-4848
Fayetteville, NC 28302 Daisy D. Maxwell, Libn.
Founded: 1969. **Staff:** Prof 1; Other 2. **Subjects:** Newspaper reference topics. **Holdings:** 1000 books; 260,000 pictures; 110 drawers of newspaper clippings; 831 reels of microfilm. **Subscriptions:** 53 journals and other serials; 60 newspapers. **Services:** Copying; library not open to the public. **Computerized Information Services:** VU/TEXT Information Services. Performs searches on fee basis. **Special Indexes:** The Fayetteville Observer Index, 1913-1919; 1947-1954; 1960-1964. **Remarks:** FAX: (919)486-3531. Publishes the Fayetteville Observer-Times.

FCC
See: **U.S. Federal Communications Commission** (17489)

FDA
See: **U.S. Food & Drug Administration** (17508)

FDIC
See: **U.S. Federal Deposit Insurance Corporation** (17490)

Federal Acquisition Institute Library
See: **General Services Administration - GSA Library** (6349)

Federal Aviation Administration
See: **U.S. Federal Aviation Administration** (17485)

★5624★
Federal Bar Foundation - Library (Law)
1815 H St., N.W. Phone: (202)638-1956
Washington, DC 20006 Lilian J. Weber, Libn.
Founded: 1960. **Staff:** Prof 3; Other 1 . **Subjects:** Law - federal, labor, administrative, tax, trade regulation, government procurement, condominium. **Holdings:** 35,000 volumes. **Subscriptions:** 343 journals and other serials. **Services:** Copying; library open to members of the legal profession. **Automated Operations:** Computerized cataloging and serials. **Computerized Information Services:** WESTLAW. Performs searches on fee basis. **Staff:** Hugh W. Walthall, Asst.Libn.

★5625★
Federal Business Development Bank - Corporate Research Centre (Bus-Fin)
800 Victoria Square, Suite 900 Phone: (514)283-7632
Montreal, PQ, Canada H4Z 1L4 Elise Rettinger, Libn.
Founded: 1977. **Staff:** Prof 1; Other 1. **Subjects:** Small business, management, Canadian business and industry, banking and finance, development banking. **Special Collections:** Statistics Canada collection. **Holdings:** 6000 books. **Subscriptions:** 300 journals and other serials; 15 newspapers. **Services:** Interlibrary loan; library not open to the public. **Automated Operations:** Computerized cataloging, acquisitions, and serials. **Computerized Information Services:** DOBIS Canadian Online Library System, Tourism Research and Data Centre Database (TRDC), Infomart Online, DIALOG Information Services, Info Globe, Business Opportunity Sourcing System (BOSS). **Networks/Consortia:** Member of Council of Federal Libraries (CFL). **Publications:** Library Acquisitions List, bimonthly - for internal distribution only. **Remarks:** FAX: (514)283-9718. Telex: 055-60707. **Staff:** Maria Szulhan, Lib.Techn.

Federal Communications Commission
See: **U.S. Federal Communications Commission** (17489)

Federal Court of Canada
See: **Canada - Federal Court of Canada** (2725)

Federal Deposit Insurance Corporation
See: **U.S. Federal Deposit Insurance Corporation** (17490)

Federal Election Commission
See: **U.S. Federal Election Commission** (17491)

★5626★
Federal Emergency Management Agency - National Emergency Training Center - Learning Resource Center (Sci-Engr)
16825 S. Seton Ave. Phone: (301)447-1032
Emmitsburg, MD 21727 Adele M. Chiesa, Chf.
Founded: 1976. **Staff:** Prof 5; Other 7. **Subjects:** Emergency management, fire science, civil defense, natural hazards, hazardous materials, arson, disasters, emergency medical services. **Special Collections:** Arson Resource Center; Emergency Management Information Center. **Holdings:** 20,000 books; 1500 bound periodical volumes; 17,000 research reports; 3100 AV programs; 3500 titles in microform; 55 VF drawers. **Subscriptions:** 400 journals and other serials; 5 newspapers. **Services:** Interlibrary loan; center open to the public for reference use only. **Automated Operations:** Computerized public access catalog, cataloging, and indexing. **Computerized Information Services:** OCLC, DIALOG Information Services. **Networks/Consortia:** Member of FEDLINK. **Special Indexes:** Index of emergency management journals. **Remarks:** Toll-free telephone number(s): is (800)638-1821.

Federal Employment Institute - Institute of Employment Research
See: **Germany - Federal Employment Institute - Institute of Employment Research - Information and Documentation Department** (6442)

★5627★
Federal Energy Regulatory Commission - Library (Energy)
825 N. Capitol St., N.E., Rm. 8502 Phone: (202)208-0200
Washington, DC 20426 Robert F. Kimberlin, III, Chf.
Founded: 1920. **Staff:** Prof 1; Other 2. **Subjects:** Energy, electric power, natural gas, oil pipelines, utility regulation, law. **Special Collections:** Federal Power Commission and Federal Energy Regulatory Commission publications, reports, case materials. **Holdings:** 40,000 books; U.S. Government documents. **Subscriptions:** 500 journals and other serials. **Services:** Interlibrary loan; library open to the public by appointment. **Automated Operations:** Computerized cataloging, acquisitions, serials, and circulation. **Computerized Information Services:** DIALOG Information Services, LEXIS, NEXIS, OCLC. **Networks/Consortia:** Member of FEDLINK. **Staff:** Lottie Davis, Tech.Proc.; Irene Barlow, ILL.

Federal Highway Administration
See: **U.S. Federal Highway Administration** (17492)

Federal Highway Research Insititute
See: **Germany - Federal Highway Research Institute - Documentation and Information Systems** (6444)

★5628★
Federal Home Loan Bank of Atlanta - Library Services (Bus-Fin)
Box 105565
Atlanta, GA 30348 Phone: (404)888-8000
Founded: 1970. **Staff:** 1. **Subjects:** Mortgage banking, housing, thrift industry, economics, finance. **Holdings:** 850 books. **Subscriptions:** 600 journals and other serials. **Services:** Interlibrary loan; copying. **Automated Operations:** Computerized acquisitions and serials. **Computerized Information Services:** DIALOG Information Services, LEXIS, NEXIS, WESTLAW, Dow Jones News/Retrieval, BRS Information Technologies. **Remarks:** FAX: (404)888-5648. Library located at 1475 Peachtree St., N.E., Atlanta, GA 30309.

★5629★
Federal Home Loan Bank of San Francisco - Library (Bus-Fin)
Box 7948 Phone: (415)616-2701
San Francisco, CA 94120 Inga Govaars, Mgr., Lib.Serv.
Staff: Prof 1. **Subjects:** Housing, savings and loan industry, economics, finance. **Holdings:** 2000 books. **Subscriptions:** 811 journals and other serials. **Services:** Interlibrary loan; library open to the public with restrictions. **Automated Operations:** Computerized public access catalog and serials. **Computerized Information Services:** LEXIS, NEXIS, U.S. Department of Commerce, DIALOG Information Services, Dow Jones News/Retrieval, WESTLAW, VU/TEXT Information Services, DataTimes, RLIN; DIALMAIL (electronic mail service). **Remarks:** FAX: (415)616-2626. Electronic mail address(es): 16018 (DIALMAIL).

★5630★
Federal Institute for East European and International Studies - Library (Area-Ethnic, Soc Sci)
Lindenbornstrasse 22 Phone: 221-57-470
W-5000 Cologne 30, Germany Dr. Joerg Streiter, Libn.
Founded: 1961. **Subjects:** International politics, international relations, Communism, Eastern Europe, Soviet Union, China. **Holdings:** 240,000 volumes. **Subscriptions:** 1200 journals and other serials; 180 newspapers. **Services:** Copying; library open to scientifically interested users. **Computerized Information Services:** Internal database. **Also Known As:** Bundesinstitut fuer Ostwissenschaftliche und Internationale Studien (BIOst).

Federal Institute for Snow and Avalanche Research
See: **Switzerland - Federal Research Institute for Forest, Snow and Landscape - Federal Institute for Snow and Avalanche Research** (15940)

★5631★
Federal Institute for Sports Science - Documentation and Information Division - Library (Rec)
Carl-Diem-Weg 4 Phone: 221 4979172
W-5000 Cologne 41, Germany Cornelia Wiese-Robrecht
Staff: 1.5. **Subjects:** Sports and sport science - sporting events, individual athletic performances, sports medicine, research; allied subjects. **Holdings:** 24,000 volumes; 35,000 reprints of journal articles. **Subscriptions:** 495 journals and other serials. **Services:** Library open to researchers and to those involved in sports sciences. **Computerized Information Services:** SPOLIT, SPOFOR. Performs searches on fee basis. **Publications:** List of new acquisitions, monthly. **Remarks:** FAX: 221 495164. Telex: 888U78 BISPD. **Also Known As:** Bundesinstitut fur Sportwissenschaft - Fachbereich Dokumentation und Information. **Staff:** Marion B. Biuher.

Federal Judicial Center
See: **U.S. Federal Judicial Center** (17493)

Federal Maritime Commission
See: **U.S. Federal Maritime Commission** (17494)

Federal Research Center for Agriculture and Forestry - Documentation Center for Phytomedicine
See: **Germany - Federal Research Center for Agriculture and Forestry - Documentation Center for Phytomedicine** (6446)

Federal Research Center for Fisheries
See: **Germany - Federal Research Center for Fisheries - Information and Documentation Center** (6447)

★5632★
Federal Reserve Bank of Atlanta - Research Library (Bus-Fin)
104 Marietta St., N.W. Phone: (404)521-8830
Atlanta, GA 30303 Barbara F. Hanes, Info.Serv.Coord.
Founded: 1938. **Staff:** Prof 3; Other 4. **Subjects:** Banking, finance, economics, statistics, agriculture, industry, foreign trade, domestic trade. **Special Collections:** Publications of the Federal Reserve Board and Federal Reserve Banks. **Holdings:** 15,000 volumes; 16 legal file drawers. **Subscriptions:** 1217 journals and other serials; 40 newspapers. **Services:** Interlibrary loan; copying; library open to the public by appointment. **Automated Operations:** Computerized cataloging, acquisitions, serials, and ILL. **Computerized Information Services:** DIALOG Information Services, NEXIS, OCLC; internal database. **Networks/Consortia:** Member of SOLINET, Georgia Online Database (GOLD). **Publications:** Morning News Update, daily; newsletters; acquisitions lists - all for internal distribution only. **Special Catalogs:** Federal Reserve System Union List. **Remarks:** (404)521-8830. **Staff:** Jerry Donovan, Res.Libn.; Steve Whigham, Tech.Serv.; David Barros, ILL.

★5633★
Federal Reserve Bank of Boston - Law Library (Law)
600 Atlantic Ave.
P.O. Box 2076 Phone: (617)973-3000
Boston, MA 02106-2076 Mary Vlantikas, Hd.Libn.
Subjects: Banking law, finance. **Holdings:** Figures not available. **Services:** Library not open to the public.

★5634★
Federal Reserve Bank of Boston - Research Library (Bus-Fin)
600 Atlantic Ave.
P.O. Box 2076 - T-9 Phone: (617)973-3393
Boston, MA 02106-2076 Mary C. Vlantikas, Lib.Dir.
Founded: 1921. **Staff:** Prof 2; Other 5. **Subjects:** Economics, money and banking, international economics, regional economics, public finance, business conditions. **Special Collections:** Federal Reserve System material. **Holdings:** 55,300 books and cataloged serials; 1200 bound periodical volumes; 7160 microforms. **Subscriptions:** 750 journals and other serials; 9 newspapers. **Services:** Interlibrary loan; library open to members of financial institutions, graduate students, research workers, and government personnel. **Computerized Information Services:** BRS Information Technologies, OCLC. **Networks/Consortia:** Member of NELINET, Inc. **Publications:** Book News, biweekly. **Remarks:** FAX: (617)973-3957. **Staff:** Sandra T. Cram, Asst.Libn.; Joyce Hannan, Cat.; Anita Denault, ILL Libn.

★5635★
Federal Reserve Bank of Chicago - Library (Bus-Fin)
230 S. LaSalle
Box 834 Phone: (312)322-5828
Chicago, IL 60690-0834 Elizabeth Maynard, Lib.Adm.
Founded: 1920. **Staff:** Prof 4; Other 4. **Subjects:** Banking, finance, agriculture, business conditions, central banking, statistics, economics. **Holdings:** 29,000 books and annual reports; 3000 bound periodical volumes; 350 VF drawers of pamphlets and statistical releases. **Subscriptions:** 1000 journals and other serials. **Services:** Interlibrary loan; library open to the public for use of Federal Reserve publications. **Automated Operations:** Computerized cataloging and serials. **Computerized Information Services:** DIALOG Information Services, WILSONLINE, Dow Jones News/Retrieval. **Networks/Consortia:** Member of Chicago Library System, ILLINET. **Staff:** Ruth Kobylecky Humphrey, Res.Libn.; Roberta Berkowitz, Res.Libn.; Melanie Ehrhart, Res.Libn.

★5636★
Federal Reserve Bank of Cleveland - Research Library (Bus-Fin)
Box 6387 Phone: (216)579-2961
Cleveland, OH 44101 Lee D. Faulhaber, Supv.Info.Serv.
Founded: 1918. **Staff:** Prof 4; Other 2. **Subjects:** Banking, finance, business, economics. **Holdings:** 20,000 volumes; 175 VF drawers of pamphlets. **Subscriptions:** 550 journals and other serials; 25 newspapers. **Services:** Interlibrary loan; library not open to the public. **Automated Operations:** Computerized cataloging, acquisitions, serials, and circulation. **Computerized Information Services:** OCLC, WILSONLINE, LEXIS, NEXIS, DIALOG Information Services; Dow Jones News/Retrieval; internal database; DIALMAIL (electronic mail service). **Networks/Consortia:** Member of FEDLINK. **Remarks:** Alternate telephone number(s): 579-2053. FAX: (216)579-3050. **Staff:** Lynn Sniderman, Assoc.Libn.; Diane Mogren, Assoc.Libn.; Lucia Green, Assoc.Libn.

★5637★
Federal Reserve Bank of Dallas - Research Library (Bus-Fin)
Sta. K Phone: (214)220-5135
Dallas, TX 75222 Michael C. Zimmerman, Lib.Adm.
Founded: 1943. **Staff:** Prof 2; Other 2. **Subjects:** Banking, finance, economics. **Special Collections:** Foreign central bank publications from 40 countries. **Holdings:** 8500 books; Federal Reserve publications. **Subscriptions:** 900 journals and other serials; 10 newspapers. **Services:** Interlibrary loan; SDI; library open to the public by appointment. **Automated Operations:** Computerized cataloging and serials. **Computerized Information Services:** DIALOG Information Services, OCLC, BRS Information Technologies, Dow Jones News/Retrieval. **Networks/Consortia:** Member of AMIGOS Bibliographic Council, Inc. **Publications:** Recent Additions to the Research Library. **Remarks:** FAX: (214)220-5192. **Staff:** Roselyn R. Boateng, Res.Libn.

★5638★
Federal Reserve Bank of Kansas City - Research Library (Bus-Fin)
Box 419560 Phone: (816)881-2676
Kansas City, MO 64141-6560 Ellen M. Johnson, Libn.
Founded: 1920. **Staff:** Prof 2; Other 2. **Subjects:** Economics, agriculture, statistics, banking. **Holdings:** 14,000 volumes. **Subscriptions:** 757 journals and other serials. **Services:** Interlibrary loan; library open to the public for reference use only. **Remarks:** FAX: (816)881-2199.

★5639★
Federal Reserve Bank of Minneapolis - Law Library (Law)
250 Marquette Ave. Phone: (612)340-2413
Minneapolis, MN 55480 Sheldon Azine, Dir.
Staff: Prof 4; Other 2. **Subjects:** Law. **Holdings:** 5000 volumes. **Services:** Library not open to the public. **Automated Operations:** Computerized acquisitions. **Remarks:** FAX: (612)344-2796. **Staff:** Joan Offendahl, Law Libn.

★5640★
Federal Reserve Bank of Minneapolis - Library (Bus-Fin)
250 Marquette Ave., S. Phone: (612)340-2292
Minneapolis, MN 55480 Janet Swan, Lib.Mgr.
Staff: Prof 3; Other 2. **Subjects:** Economic conditions, economics, financial services industry. **Special Collections:** Federal Reserve System publications. **Holdings:** 20,000 books; 2000 bound periodical volumes; 3500 pamphlets; 87 VF drawers of government documents and releases. **Subscriptions:** 2000 journals and other serials; 19 newspapers. **Services:** Interlibrary loan (limited); copying; library open to the public by appointment for reference use. **Automated Operations:** Integrated library system. **Computerized Information Services:** OCLC. **Networks/Consortia:** Member of MINITEX Library Information Network. **Publications:** Library Record, bimonthly - for internal distribution only. **Special Catalogs:** Periodical holdings catalog, semiannual. **Staff:** Karen Hovermale, Anl.; Joanne Farley, Libn./Archv.

★5641★
Federal Reserve Bank of New York - Computer Sciences Library (Comp Sci)
59 Maiden Ln., 24th Fl. Phone: (212)720-5766
New York, NY 10045 Thomas O'Keefe, Sr.Comp.Sci.Libn.
Staff: Prof 2. **Subjects:** Data processing and communication, system development, microcomputers, database management. **Holdings:** 1000 books; 400 reels of microfilm of periodicals; 1000 technical manuals. **Subscriptions:** 200 journals and other serials. **Services:** Library not open to the public. **Computerized Information Services:** DIALOG Information Services, LEXIS, NEXIS, OCLC. **Remarks:** FAX: (212)720-1298.

★5642★
Federal Reserve Bank of New York - Law Library Division (Law)
33 Liberty St. Phone: (212)720-5012
New York, NY 10045 Roberta Laskowitz, Chf. Law Libn.
Founded: 1930. **Staff:** Prof 6; Other 3. **Subjects:** Banking law. **Special Collections:** Legislative histories regarding Federal Reserve System. **Holdings:** 32,000 volumes; 300 VF drawers of legal precedent, legislative, and litigation files; 1100 reels of microfilm. **Subscriptions:** 182 journals and other serials. **Services:** Interlibrary loan. **Automated Operations:** Computerized cataloging, acquisitions, and serials. **Computerized Information Services:** LEXIS, WESTLAW, DIALOG Information Services, Dow Jones News/Retrieval, LEGI-SLATE, NYS Retrieval Service. **Remarks:** FAX: (212)720-1746. **Staff:** Myra Van Vactor, Asst.Chf. Law Libn.; Sherry Chachkin, Sr. Law Libn.; Jeannette A. Lawton, Law Libn.; Madelyn A. Robbins, Law Libn.

★5643★
Federal Reserve Bank of New York - Research Library (Bus-Fin)
33 Liberty St. Phone: (212)720-5670
New York, NY 10045 Emily Trueblood, Chf.Libn.
Founded: 1918. **Staff:** Prof 6; Other 6. **Subjects:** Economics, finance, business conditions, balance of international payments, international finance, monetary policy, central banking, foreign area economic and financial conditions. **Holdings:** 60,000 volumes; 3600 reels of microfilm; 1400 microfiche; 180 VF drawers of pamphlet material. **Subscriptions:** 1500 journals and other serials. **Services:** Library open to public for certain Federal Reserve publications. **Automated Operations:** Computerized public access catalog, acquisitions, and serials. **Computerized Information Services:** DIALOG Information Services, NEXIS, Dow Jones News/Retrieval, VU/TEXT Information Services, OCLC. **Publications:** Library News of Recent Acquisitions, biweekly - internal and external distribution. **Remarks:** FAX: (212)720-1372. **Staff:** Jean Wooten, Asst.Chf.Libn.; Kathleen McKiernan, Sr.Libn.; Amy Farber, Sr.Libn.; Matthew Ottenstein, Libn.; Angela Bird, Libn.

★5644★
Federal Reserve Bank of Philadelphia - Library (Bus-Fin)
10 Independence Mall Phone: (215)574-6540
Philadelphia, PA 19105 Deborah Naulty, Mgr.
Founded: 1922. **Staff:** Prof 4; Other 3. **Subjects:** Money, banking, economics. **Special Collections:** Central banking. **Holdings:** 35,000 books; 200 VF drawers. **Subscriptions:** 300 journals and other serials. **Services:** Interlibrary loan; SDI; library open to the public for reference use only. **Computerized Information Services:** DIALOG Information Services, Dow Jones News/Retrieval, VU/TEXT Information Services, OCLC, DataTimes, WILSONLINE. **Networks/Consortia:** Member of PALINET. **Publications:** FED in Print (cumulative index to publications of Federal Reserve banks and board), biennial - free upon request. **Remarks:** FAX: (215)574-3847. **Staff:** Barbara Turnbull, Supv., Tech.Proc.

★5645★
Federal Reserve Bank of Richmond - Research Library (Bus-Fin)
701 E. Byrd St.
Box 27622 Phone: (804)697-8131
Richmond, VA 23261 Susan R. Cash, Libn.
Founded: 1920. **Staff:** Prof 4; Other 4. **Subjects:** Banking, money, statistics, finance, agriculture, economics, business and industry. **Holdings:** 18,000 books; 1500 bound periodical volumes; 144 VF drawers of pamphlets, statistical releases, clippings, reference material. **Subscriptions:** 950 journals and other serials; 18 newspapers. **Services:** Interlibrary loan; library open to the public by appointment. **Automated Operations:** Computerized cataloging, acquisitions, and serials. **Computerized Information Services:** DIALOG Information Services, OCLC, VU/TEXT Information Services. **Networks/Consortia:** Member of FEDLINK. **Publications:** Library Bulletin. **Staff:** Veronica Cummings, Cat.; Gudrun Meyer, Ref.Libn.; Dorothy Ingram, Ser. & Automation Libn.

★5646★
Federal Reserve Bank of St. Louis - Research Library (Bus-Fin)
Box 442 Phone: (314)444-8552
St. Louis, MO 63166 Carol J. Thaxton, Asst.Mgr., Lib. Unit
Founded: 1922. **Staff:** Prof 2; Other 2. **Subjects:** Federal Reserve, money, banking, finance, economics, agriculture. **Holdings:** 15,000 books; 2170 bound periodical volumes; 136 VF drawers of pamphlets. **Subscriptions:** 800 journals and other serials; 15 newspapers. **Services:** Interlibrary loan; library open to the public with restrictions. **Automated Operations:** Computerized cataloging. **Computerized Information Services:** OCLC, DIALOG Information Services. **Networks/Consortia:** Member of Missouri Library Network Corp. (MLNC). **Remarks:** FAX: (314)444-8731. **Staff:** Charlene Fagyal, Libn. A.

★5647★
Federal Reserve Bank of San Francisco - Research Library (Bus-Fin)
Box 7702 Phone: (415)974-3216
San Francisco, CA 94120 Miriam Ciochon, Mgr.
Founded: 1919. **Staff:** Prof 4; Other 3. **Subjects:** Central banking, banking and finance, economics, Pacific Basin countries. **Holdings:** 20,000 books. **Subscriptions:** 1600 journals and other serials. **Services:** Interlibrary loan; library open to the public by appointment for reference use only. **Computerized Information Services:** DIALOG Information Services, DataTimes, VU/TEXT Information Services, NEXIS, OCLC, Dow Jones News/Retrieval. **Remarks:** FAX: (415)974-3429. **Staff:** Nyra Krstovich, Ref.Libn.; Patricia Rea, Ref.Libn.; Sandra Dye, Tech.Serv.; Diane Rosenberger, Sys.

★5648★
Federal Reserve System - Board of Governors - Law Library (Law)
20th & Constitution Ave., N.W. Phone: (202)452-3284
Washington, DC 20551 Julia Schaeffer, Law Libn.
Founded: 1975. **Staff:** Prof 2; Other 1. **Subjects:** Banking law, general federal law, state codes. **Special Collections:** Legislative histories on banking, monetary policy, and economic affairs (600 titles). **Holdings:** 26,000 volumes; 100 journal and newsletter titles. **Subscriptions:** 1000 serials. **Services:** Interlibrary loan; SDI; library open to the public by appointment. **Computerized Information Services:** DIALOG Information Services, WESTLAW, LEGI-SLATE, LEXIS, Dow Jones News/Retrieval. **Publications:** Legislative newsletter, weekly; Law Library Bulletin, monthly - both for internal distribution only. **Remarks:** FAX: (202)452-3101. **Staff:** Richard McKinney, Leg.Libn.

★5649★
Federal Reserve System - Board of Governors - Research Library (Bus-Fin)
20th & Constitution Ave., N.W. Phone: (202)452-3332
Washington, DC 20551 Ann Roane Clary, Chf.Libn.
Founded: 1914. **Staff:** Prof 6; Other 5. **Subjects:** Banking; money; finance; U.S. and foreign economic conditions; economic theory; credit, monetary and fiscal policy. **Special Collections:** Federal Reserve System; Foreign Central Banking. **Holdings:** 53,100 books; 11,400 bound periodical volumes. **Subscriptions:** 1850 journals and other serials; 33 newspapers. **Services:** Interlibrary loan (limited to special libraries in Washington); library open to the public with restrictions. **Automated Operations:** Computerized public access catalog, cataloging, acquisitions, serials, circulation, and accounting. **Computerized Information Services:** DIALOG Information Services, OCLC, NEXIS, Dow Jones News/Retrieval. **Networks/Consortia:** Member of FEDLINK. **Publications:** Research Library-Recent Acquisitions, monthly - free upon request. **Remarks:** FAX: (202)452-3819. Telex: 197-668. **Staff:** Julia G. Back, Asst.Chf.Libn./Rd.Serv.; Jean Rhodes, Govt.Doc.Libn.; Ioana Ratesh, Tech.Proc./Cat.; Susan Vincent, Ref.Libn.; Bernice Coles, Per.Libn.

Federal Statistical Office of Germany
See: **Germany - Federal Statistical Office** (6448)

Federal Trade Commission
See: **U.S. Federal Trade Commission** (17495)

★5650★
Federated Conservationists of Westchester County - FCWC Office Resource Library (Env-Cons)
Natural Science Bldg., Rm. 1002
SUNY
Purchase, NY 10577 Phone: (914)251-6888
Staff: 1. **Subjects:** Wetland legislation, water supply and quality, air pollution, historic preservation, land use, nuclear power. **Special Collections:** Environmental issues in Westchester County. **Holdings:** Government reports; environmental impact statements; legal cases; 15 file drawers of resource materials. **Subscriptions:** 10 journals and other serials. **Services:** Library open to the public for reference use only. **Publications:** Westchester Environment, quarterly.

★5651★
Federation of American Scientists - Library (Soc Sci)
307 Massachusetts Ave., N.E. Phone: (202)546-3300
Washington, DC 20002 Lora Lumpe, Act.Libn.
Staff: 1. **Subjects:** Arms control, Indochina, foreign policy, nuclear issues, defense, Soviet Union, Indochina chemical weapons, space policy. **Holdings:** 2000 books. **Subscriptions:** 58 journals and other serials. **Services:** SDI; library open to the public by appointment. **Computerized Information Services:** PeaceNet (electronic mail service). **Remarks:** FAX: (202)675-1010. Telex: 9102509251 FAS DC UQ. Electronic mail address(es): JStone (PeaceNet).

Federation Canadienne des Enseignants
See: **Canadian Teachers' Federation** (2993)

★5652★
Federation of Egalitarian Communities - Library (Soc Sci)
Route 3, Box 6B2
East Wind Community, Inc.
Tecumseh, MO 65760 Phone: (417)679-4682
Subjects: Cooperation, equality, nonviolence, egalitarian societies. **Holdings:** 35,000 volumes. **Services:** Library not open to the public.

★5653★
Federation Employment & Guidance Service - Richard J. Bernhard Memorial Library
114 5th Ave.
New York, NY 10011
Defunct.

★5654★
Federation of Flyfishers - International Fly Fishing Center (Rec)
Box 1088 Phone: (406)646-9541
West Yellowstone, MT 59758 Ralph W. Moon, Cur.
Subjects: Flyfishing. **Holdings:** 300 books; 55 bound periodical volumes; 125 AV programs. **Services:** Center open to the public with restrictions. **Remarks:** FAX: (406)646-9728.

★5655★
Federation of Islamic Associations in the United States and Canada - Library (Area-Ethnic)
25351 5 Mile Rd.
Redford, MI 48259 Phone: (313)535-0014
Subjects: Middle East - religion, politics, arts. **Holdings:** 10,000 volumes. **Computerized Information Services:** Internal database.

★5656★
Federation of Korean Trade Unions - Library (Bus-Fin)
FKTU Bldg.
35, Yoido-dong
Yoidodongpo-ku
Seoul, Republic of Korea Phone: 2 782-3884
Subjects: Korean trade unions, industrial relations. **Holdings:** 5000 volumes. **Remarks:** FAX: 2 784-6396. Telex: 29682 K. **Also Known As:** Hankuk Nodhong Johap Chongyeonmaeng.

★5657★
Federation des Medecins Omnipracticiens du Quebec - Documentation Centre (Med)
1440 Ouest Ste-Catherine, Suite 1100 Phone: (514)878-1911
Montreal, PQ, Canada H3G 1R8 Ghislaine Lincourt, Adm.
Founded: 1966. **Staff:** Prof 1. **Subjects:** Medicine - social aspects, unions, law, teaching. **Holdings:** 4000 books; 600 bound periodical volumes; government publications; reports. **Subscriptions:** 192 journals and other serials; 8 newspapers. **Services:** Interlibrary loan; center not open to the public. **Publications:** Liste d'acquisition; Bulletin signaletique. **Remarks:** FAX: (514)878-4455.

★5658★
Federation des Medecins Specialistes du Quebec - Bibliotheque (Med)
2 Complexe Desjardins
Tour de l'Est, Porte 3000 Phone: (514)288-7277
Montreal, PQ, Canada H5B 1G8 Ghislaine Lussier, Dir., Archv. & Doc.
Founded: 1976. **Staff:** 3. **Subjects:** Legal aspects of health management. **Holdings:** 5000 books; 800 bound periodical volumes; 20,000 archival items; 800 microfiche; statistical reports. **Subscriptions:** 196 journals and other serials; 8 newspapers. **Services:** Interlibrary loan; library not open to the public.

★5659★
Federation for Unified Science Education - FUSE Center Library (Educ)
231 Battelle Hall of Science
Capital University Phone: (614)236-6816
Columbus, OH 43209 Dr. Victor M. Showalter, Dir.
Founded: 1972. **Subjects:** Unified science education, philosophy of science, scientific and technologic literacy, science teaching materials and media. **Holdings:** 800 books; 280 program descriptions; 24 VF drawers. **Services:** Copying; library open to the public for reference use only.

Feed Research Library
See: **Central Soya Company, Inc.** (3363)

Feehan Memorial Library
See: **University of St. Mary of the Lake - Mundelein Seminary** (19287)

★5660★
Fred Fehl Photographer - Information Center (Aud-Vis)
415 W. 115th St.
New York, NY 10025 Phone: (212)662-2253
Staff: Prof 2. **Subjects:** Performance photographs of Broadway and Off-Broadway productions, 1940-1970; ballet and dance in America, 1940 to present; New York City opera, all productions, 1944-1980; orchestra conductors and musicians; color slides of U.S. National Parks, historic monuments, art treasures, scenic views of Europe. **Services:** Photographs are available for publication on a fee basis.

Benjamin F. Feinberg Library
See: **State University College at Plattsburgh** (15712)

Harry and Anna Feinberg Library
See: **Congregation Mishkan Tefila** (4163)

Sol Feinstone Library
See: **American Security Council Foundation** (738)

Sol Feinstone Library
See: **Bishop's Mill Historical Institute** (1867)

Feldberg Library
See: **Dartmouth College** (4609)

Norman F. Feldheym Library
See: **St. Bernardine Medical Center** (14251)

Dorothy G. Feldman Library
See: **Congregation Beth Am** (4149)

Felician Sisters - St. Mary Hospital
See: **St. Mary Hospital** (14503)

Fellowship of Friends - Asian Art Institute Library
See: **Museum of Classical Chinese Furniture** (10893)

★5661★
Fellowship of Reconciliation - Library (Soc Sci)
Box 271 Phone: (914)358-4601
Nyack, NY 10960 Paul Peabody, Libn.
Subjects: Peace movements, disarmament, human rights, racial and economic justice. **Special Collections:** Manuscripts by A.J. Muste. **Holdings:** 1800 books; 55 bound periodical volumes. **Subscriptions:** 208 journals and other serials. **Services:** SDI; library open to the public with restrictions. **Special Indexes:** Index of pamphlets from Institute for World Order (card). **Remarks:** FAX: (914)358-4924.

★5662★
Fellowship of Religious Humanists - Archives
P.O. Box 278 Phone: (513)767-1668
Yellow Springs, OH 45387-0278 Vianna Biehl, Off./Circ.Mgr.
Founded: 1963. **Staff:** 1. **Subjects:** Humanism, religious humanism, separation of church and state, positivism, philosophy, religion, history. **Holdings:** 200 books; 20 bound periodical volumes. **Services:** Archives not open to the public. **Publications:** Journal of Religious Humanism; Religious Humanism, quarterly. **Special Indexes:** Index for Religious Humanism.

Charlotte Ashley Felton Memorial Library
See: **Stanford University - Special Collections** (15658)

Fenerty, Robertson, Fraser & Hatch - Library
See: **Milner Fenerty** (10413)

★5663★
Fenton Historical Society - Library (Hist)
67 Washington St. Phone: (716)483-7521
Jamestown, NY 14701 Karen Livsey, Cur./Mss.
Founded: 1964. **Staff:** Prof 1; Other 4. **Subjects:** Genealogy, local history, Civil War. **Special Collections:** Early local photographs. **Holdings:** 4500 books; 100 bound periodical volumes; local daybooks, account books, town and school district records; 8 drawers of clippings and pamphlets; 15 shelves and 5 drawers of manuscripts. **Subscriptions:** 20 journals and other serials. **Services:** Copying; library open to the public on fee basis. **Publications:** Jamestown & Chautauqua County Trolleys; Chautauqua Lake Steamboats; History of Post Offices of Jamestown, N.Y.; Saga from the Hills: A History of the Swedes in Jamestown. **Special Indexes:** Newspaper deaths and marriages (card); Index to Biographical Cyclopedia of Chautauqua County (book); Index to Early History of Ellicott (book); A Complete Index to More Than 10,000 Personal Names Mentioned in Andrew W. Young's History of Chautauqua County, New York (book); Chautauqua County Census 1855; index to library's family surname folders.

Fenwick Library
See: **George Mason University - Fenwick Library - Special Collections and Archives** (9773)

Fenwick Music Library
See: **College of the Holy Cross - Fenwick Music Library** (3894)

Fer et Titane du Quebec, Inc.
See: **Q.I.T. - Fer et Titane Inc.** (13560)

★5664★
Ferenczy Museum - Library (Art, Hist)
Fo ter 6
Pf. 49.2001 Phone: 26 10244
H-2000 Szentendre, Hungary Edit G. Sin, Ph.D.
Founded: 1951. **Staff:** 1. **Subjects:** Art history, ethnography, archeology, local history. **Holdings:** 16,500 books; 6800 bound periodical volumes. **Subscriptions:** 30 journals and other serials; 104 subscriptions on an exchange basis. **Services:** Interlibrary loan; copying; library open for academic research only. **Remarks:** FAX: 26 10790.

★5665★
Fergus Falls Regional Treatment Center - Library
Corner of Fir & Union
Box 157
Fergus Falls, MN 56537
Defunct.

★5666★
Ferguson Baptist Church - Library (Rel-Phil)
Murphy Ave. Phone: (606)679-1690
Ferguson, KY 42533 Dorothy Hughes, Libn.
Staff: Prof 3. **Subjects:** Religion, biography, history, missions. **Special Collections:** Devotionals. **Holdings:** 4000 books; 3 VF drawers; 1 missionary tape; 1 set of Bible cassettes. **Services:** Library open to church families. **Staff:** Stelma Haynes, Libn.; Sue Poynter, Treas.

Charles Ferguson Medical Library
See: **Bayley Seton Hospital - Charles Ferguson Medical Library** (1599)

★5667★
Ferguson Gifford - Law Library (Law)
Park Place
666 Burrard St., Suite 500 Phone: (604)687-3216
Vancouver, BC, Canada V6C 3H3 Gillian Crabtree, Law Libn.
Founded: 1980. **Staff:** Prof 1; Other 1. **Subjects:** Law - corporate, commercial, insurance, securities, bankruptcy and insolvency, labor, family, intellectual property, tax; litigation. **Holdings:** 5000 books. **Services:** Library not open to the public. **Automated Operations:** Computerized cataloging. **Computerized Information Services:** QL Systems, WESTLAW, VU/TEXT Information Services, CAN/LAW, Canada Systems Group (CSG), Infomart Online, WISDOM Information Services, Chemical Abstracts Service (CAS); QUICKMAIL (electronic mail service). **Remarks:** FAX: (604)683-2780. Member of Goodman, LaPointe, Ferguson.

★5668★
Ferguson Library - Adult Services Department (Sci-Engr, Bus-Fin)
1 Public Library Plaza Phone: (203)964-1000
Stamford, CT 06904 Ernest A. DiMattia, Jr., Pres.
Staff: 9. **Subjects:** Business, technology. **Special Collections:** Local business file. **Holdings:** 16,000 books; annual reports; government documents. **Subscriptions:** 300 journals and other serials. **Services:** Interlibrary loan; photocopying; department open to the public. **Automated Operations:** Computerized public access catalog, cataloging, and circulation. **Computerized Information Services:** OCLC, DIALOG Information Services, ABI/INFORM, COMPACT DISCLOSURE, GPO Monthly Catalog, Academic American Encyclopedia. **Networks/Consortia:** Member of NELINET, Inc., Southwestern Connecticut Library Council (SWLC). **Publications:** Booklists; newsletters; flyers. **Remarks:** FAX: (203)357-0660. **Staff:** William Miller, Bus.Spec.

Lawrence Ferlinghetti Archives
See: **University of Southern California - Library - Department of Special Collections - American Literature Collection** (19338)

Enrico Fermi Cultural Center
See: **New York Public Library - Belmont Regional Library** (11597)

Fermi National Accelerator Laboratory
See: **Universities Research Association - Fermi National Accelerator Laboratory** (18144)

★5669★
Fernbank Science Center - Library (Sci-Engr, Biol Sci)
156 Heaton Park Dr., N.E. Phone: (404)378-4311
Atlanta, GA 30307 Mary Larsen, Libn.
Founded: 1979. **Staff:** Prof 1; Other 1. **Subjects:** Astronomy, biology, geology, meteorology, horticulture, forestry. **Holdings:** 15,580 books; 4300 bound periodical volumes; 10,000 slides; microfilm; 5 VF drawers of pamphlets and maps. **Subscriptions:** 355 journals and other serials; 7 newspapers. **Services:** Interlibrary loan; copying; library open to the public for reference use only. **Automated Operations:** Computerized cataloging and ILL. **Computerized Information Services:** DIALOG Information Services, OCLC, WILSONLINE. **Networks/Consortia:** Member of Atlanta Health Science Libraries Consortium (AHSLC), SOLINET, Georgia Online Database (GOLD). **Remarks:** FAX: (404)370-1336. Maintained by the DeKalb County Board of Education.

Ben Ferrel Platte County Museum/Library
See: **Platte County Historical Society - Ben Ferrel Platte County Museum/Library** (13140)

Carl R. Ferris, M.D. Medical Library
See: **Research Medical Center** (13842)

★5670★
Ferris State University - Abigail Smith Timme Library (Med)
901 S. State St. Phone: (616)592-3602
Big Rapids, MI 49307 Dr. Lawrence J. McCrank, Dean
Founded: 1884. **Staff:** Prof 19; Other 27. **Subjects:** Pharmacy, optometry, allied health sciences, business, occupational education, criminal justice, engineering technology. **Special Collections:** Woodbridge N. Ferris letters and materials relative to founding of the college (12,000 items); university archives (814 linear feet); regional studies of northwestern Michigan. **Holdings:** 213,352 volumes; 190,000 titles; 96,350 periodicals; 56,198 pamphlets and documents; 39,597 titles in microform; 13,270 phonograph records, tapes, and slides; 135 films. **Subscriptions:** 3502 journals and other serials; 22 newspapers. **Services:** Interlibrary loan; copying; library open to the public. **Automated Operations:** PALS Electronic Library System. **Computerized Information Services:** DIALOG Information Services, BRS Information Technologies, OCLC; CD-ROMs. Performs searches on fee basis. Contact Person: Richard Perrin, Ref.Libn., 592-3696. **Networks/Consortia:** Member of Michigan Library Consortium (MLC). **Publications:** LIStener (Library and Instructional Services), quarterly; FSU Library Resources: A Self-paced Workbook (1988), annual . **Remarks:** Maintains Individualized Learning Center (ILC) for media and computing; related Instructional Resource Center (IRC) consists of Media Production, television, Media Distribution, Academic Computing. FAX: (616)592-2662. **Formerly:** Library and Instructional Services. **Staff:** Felix Unaeze, Hd., Ref. & Instr.Serv.; Geraldine Hurt, Hd., Coll.Mgt. & Serv.; Edwin Harris, Hd., Lib.Sys. & Oper.

★5671★
Ferris State University - School of Pharmacy - Pharmacy Reading Room (Med)
901 S. State St.
Big Rapids, MI 49307 Phone: (616)592-2338
Founded: 1972. **Staff:** Prof 1; Other 3. **Subjects:** Pharmacy, pharmaceutical sciences. **Special Collections:** Catalog of faculty publications. **Holdings:** 1700 books; pamphlets; reprints; 150 tapes, slides, filmstrips; Iowa Drug Information Service, 1966 to present, on microfiche; DRUGDEX. **Subscriptions:** 160 journals and other serials. **Services:** Interlibrary loan; copying; room open to the public for reference use only by request. **Special Catalogs:** Periodical Holdings; Non-Print materials (both mimeographed lists).

★5672★
Ferro Corporation - Library (Sci-Engr)
7500 E. Pleasant Valley Rd. Phone: (216)641-8580
Independence, OH 44131 Deborah K. Oberlander, Supv., Info.Serv.
Founded: 1943. **Staff:** Prof 1; Other 1.5. **Subjects:** Polymer chemistry, plastics, ceramics, glazes, coatings, porcelain enamels. **Holdings:** 10,000 books; 1260 bound periodical volumes; 3500 microfiche of government documents; 24 VF drawers of research and laboratory notebooks. **Subscriptions:** 225 journals and other serials. **Services:** Interlibrary loan; library not open to the public. **Automated Operations:** Computerized circulation. **Computerized Information Services:** DIALOG Information Services, ORBIT Search Service, MEDLINE, Dow Jones News/Retrieval, DataTimes, STN International, Data-Star. **Networks/Consortia:** Member of OHIONET. **Publications:** Current Awareness Bulletin; Competitor Reports - for internal distribution only. **Remarks:** FAX: (216)524-0518.

★5673★
Ferrum College - Blue Ridge Heritage Archive (Hist)
Ferrum, VA 24088 Phone: (703)365-4416
Vaughan Webb, Folklorist
Subjects: Folk culture, legends, crafts, music, and customs of Virginia, especially the Blue Ridge Mountain area, 1780 to present. **Special Collections:** Elmer Smith Collection of Shenandoah Valley Folklore; Earl Palmer Collection of Appalachian Photographs; Virginia Commercial Recordings, 1902-1943. **Holdings:** 7000 videotapes, phonograph records, photographs, slides, 16mm films, books, reel-to-reel and cassette tapes of oral history and traditional music, correspondence, transcripts. **Services:** Copying; archive open to the public by appointment. **Remarks:** FAX: (703)365-4203.

★5674★
Fertilizer Institute (Agri)
501 Second St., N.E. Phone: (202)675-8250
Washington, DC 20002 Ron Phillips, V.P., Pub.Aff.
Founded: 1883. **Staff:** 22. **Subjects:** Agriculture with emphasis on fertilizers and soils. **Remarks:** Although the library holdings have been dispersed, the institute still serves as a source for fertilizer and soil fertility information. FAX: (202)544-8123.

★5675★
FES Information Center - Library (Med)
10524 Euclid Ave. Phone: (216)231-3257
Cleveland, OH 44106 Jeanne O'Malley Teeter, Dir.
Founded: 1988. **Staff:** 2. **Subjects:** Electrical stimulation, rehabilitation. **Special Collections:** Functional electrical stimulation (rehabilitation engineering; citations and reprints). **Holdings:** 18 books; 24 bound periodical volumes; 20 reports. **Subscriptions:** 2 journals and other serials. **Services:** Center open to the public with restrictions. **Computerized Information Services:** BRS Information Technologies; internal databases. Performs searches on fee basis. **Publications:** F.E.S. Directories Update (newsletter). **Remarks:** FAX: (216)231-3258. Toll-free telephone number(s): (800)666-2353. TDD: (216)231-3257. The FES Information Center is affiliated with Case Western Reserve University and Services for Independent Living, Inc. Supported by the National Institute on Disability and Rehabilitation Research. **Staff:** Kathy A. Stockmaster, MLS.

Feuchtwanger Memorial Library
See: **University of Southern California - Library - Department of Special Collections - Feuchtwanger Memorial Library** (19339)

Jordan E. Feuer Library
See: **Congregation Kins of West Rogers Park** (4160)

Barbara Fewell Memorial Library
See: **Northern Virginia Association of Realtors Inc.** (12017)

★5676★
Fiber Materials, Inc. - Technical Library (Sci-Engr)
Biddeford Industrial Park Phone: (207)282-5911
Biddeford, ME 04005 Judith A. Hall, Libn.
Staff: Prof 1. **Subjects:** Materials science, composites, ablation, carbon. **Holdings:** 2400 volumes; 7000 technical reports. **Subscriptions:** 124 journals and other serials. **Services:** Interlibrary loan; library not open to the public. **Remarks:** FAX: (207)282-7529.

Ficke-Laird Library
See: **University of Dubuque Theological Seminary - Library** (18555)

★5677★
Fidelity & Deposit Company of Maryland - Law Library (Law, Bus-Fin)
210 N. Charles St.
Box 1227 Phone: (301)659-3358
Baltimore, MD 21201-4098 Janice L. Wihlborg, Law Libn.
Founded: 1922. **Staff:** Prof 1. **Subjects:** Insurance, law. **Holdings:** 30,000 volumes. **Subscriptions:** 35 journals and other serials; 2 newspapers. **Services:** Library open to building tenants. **Computerized Information Services:** WESTLAW. **Remarks:** FAX: (301)659-3205.

★5678★
Fidelity Management & Research Company - Equity Research InfoCenter (Bus-Fin)
82 Devonshire St., F7J
Boston, MA 02109 Phone: (617)570-7574
Founded: 1973. **Staff:** Prof 8; Other 13. **Subjects:** Investment and securities, stock market behavior. **Special Collections:** Corporate Files Collection; International Investment Collection. **Holdings:** 500 books; 5 VF drawers of mutual fund literature. **Subscriptions:** 200 journals and other serials. **Services:** Services not open to the public. **Automated Operations:** Computerized cataloging, serials, reports, and indexing. **Computerized Information Services:** DIALOG Information Services, Dow Jones News/Retrieval, Bridge Information System, FactSet Data Systems, Inc., Tradecenter, First Call Corporation, NEXIS. **Networks/Consortia:** Member of NELINET, Inc. **Formerly:** Its Information/Research Services. **Staff:** Jane Curtis, Market Data Serv.Mgr.; Jack Cahill, Sr. Equity Ref.Libn.; Mary Melaugh, Equity Ref.Libn.; Liz Peoples, High Yield Ref.Libn.; Bonnie Lawton, Tech.Serv.Libn.

★5679★
Fidelity Management & Research Company - Fixed Income Research Center (Bus-Fin)
82 Devonshire St., I40A Phone: (617)570-2650
Boston, MA 02109 Susan L. Johnson, Mgr.
Founded: 1985. **Staff:** Prof 4; Other 4. **Subjects:** Investments and securities, economics and business conditions. **Special Collections:** Municipal Finance Collection; Corporate Files Collection. **Holdings:** 100 books; 200 journals. **Services:** Center not open to the public. **Automated Operations:** Computerized indexing. **Computerized Information Services:** DIALOG Information Services, NEXIS, Dow Jones News/Retrieval, Lotus One Source, Bloomberg Financial Markets, Tradecenter, First Call. **Staff:** Paula Kienert, Ref.Libn.; Cathy Tuohy, Market Data Serv.Mgr.

★5680★
Fiduciary International - Library (Bus-Fin)
1750 Pennsylvania Ave., N.W. Phone: (202)393-7900
Washington, DC 20006 Fran Rossiter, Libn.
Subjects: Stock market. **Holdings:** 3000 corporate files.

★5681★
Fiduciary Trust Company of New York - Research Library (Bus-Fin)
2 World Trade Center, 94th Fl. Phone: (212)466-4100
New York, NY 10048 Susan Reed, Res.Lib.Mgr.
Founded: 1933. **Staff:** 2. **Subjects:** Corporate records, banks and finance, investment, international trade, economics. **Special Collections:** Moody's manuals, 1945 to present. **Holdings:** 2500 books; 200 bound periodical volumes; 30 VF drawers of Extra annuals; 19 VF drawers of corporate records; 16 VF drawers of industry information; corporation files on 4000 companies; 10K, 10Q, reports and prospectuses for 226 companies; Wall Street Journal, January 1979 to present (microfilm). **Subscriptions:** 26 journals and other serials. **Services:** Interlibrary loan; copying; library open to clients and SLA members. **Computerized Information Services:** Internal databases. **Publications:** Research Library Bulletin. **Special Indexes:** Index to company economic and financial review. **Remarks:** FAX: (212)313-2551.

Arthur Fiedler Collection
See: **Boston University - Music Library** (2015)

Field Corporation - Field Publications - Library
See: **Weekly Reader Corporation** (20136)

★5682★
Eugene Field House and Toy Museum - Library (Hum)
634 S. Broadway
St. Louis, MO 63102 Phone: (314)421-4689
Subjects: Eugene Field. **Special Collections:** The works of Eugene Field (225 volumes). **Holdings:** 17 manuscripts of Eugene Field; 3 feet of clippings; 2 VF drawers of photographs; 6 VF drawers of correspondence and memorabilia. **Services:** Library open to the public with restrictions.

★5683★
Field & Field Perraton Masuch - Library (Law)
10235 101st St., Suite 2000 Phone: (403)423-3003
Edmonton, AB, Canada T5J 3G1 Linda Statt, Libn.
Staff: 1. **Subjects:** Law. **Services:** Library not open to the public. **Remarks:** FAX: (403)428-9329. **Formed by the merger of:** Field & Field and Perraton Masuch.

★5684★
Field Museum of Natural History - Library (Biol Sci, Sci-Engr)
Roosevelt Rd. & Lake Shore Dr. Phone: (312)922-9410
Chicago, IL 60605 W. Peyton Fawcett, Hd.Libn.
Founded: 1893. **Staff:** Prof 5; Other 6. **Subjects:** Anthropology, botany, geology, paleontology, zoology. **Special Collections:** Ayer Ornithology Library; Laufer Collection of Far Eastern Studies; Schmidt Herpetology Library. **Holdings:** 235,000 volumes. **Subscriptions:** 4000 journals and other serials. **Services:** Interlibrary loan; copying; library open to the public. **Automated Operations:** Computerized cataloging. **Computerized Information Services:** OCLC. **Networks/Consortia:** Member of ILLINET, Chicago Library System. **Remarks:** FAX: (312)427-7269. **Staff:** Benjamin Williams, Assoc.Libn.; Chi-Wei Pan, Cat.; Michele Calhoun, Ref.Libn.; Roger Buelow, Pubns.Mgr.

★5685★
Field Museum of Natural History - Webber Resource Center: Native Cultures of the Americas (Area-Ethnic)
Roosevelt Rd. & Lakeshore Dr. Phone: (312)922-9410
Chicago, IL 60605 Alexia Trzyna, Div.Hd.
Founded: 1987. **Staff:** 1. **Subjects:** Native North and South American culture and history; archaeology; contemporary Native American issues. **Special Collections:** Department of Anthropology archival photograph collection (6 albums); artifacts. **Holdings:** 1000 books; 35 periodical titles; 86 videotapes; 23 audiotapes; 45 maps; 140 teacher resources; activity boxes. **Subscriptions:** 10 newspapers. **Services:** Copying; library open to the public.

Barbara Fields Memorial Library
See: **Midstate College** (10372)

★5686★
Fifth Avenue Hospital - Medical Library (Med)
10560 5th, N.E.
Seattle, WA 98125 Phone: (206)364-2050
Founded: 1967. **Subjects:** Medicine, osteopathy, podiatry, surgery. **Holdings:** 525 books. **Subscriptions:** 55 journals and other serials. **Services:** Library not open to the public. **Remarks:** FAX: (206)361-5722.

★5687★
Figgie International - Interstate Electronics Corporation - Library (Sci-Engr)
1001 E. Ball Rd., Dept. 4543
Box 3117 Phone: (714)758-0500
Anaheim, CA 92803 Judy A. Baldwin, Libn.
Founded: 1956. **Staff:** Prof 1. **Subjects:** Electronics. **Holdings:** 1200 books; 12,000 reports and reprints; 2500 Armed Services Technical Information Agency (ASTIA) documents; 2000 military specifications. **Subscriptions:** 250 journals and other serials. **Services:** Interlibrary loan; copying; library open to the public with restrictions. **Computerized Information Services:** NERAC. **Remarks:** FAX: (714)758-3052.

★5688★
Fiji National Training Council - Library (Bus-Fin)
P.O. Box 6890
Nasinu, Fiji Phone: 392000
Subjects: Employee training. **Holdings:** 3000 volumes. **Remarks:** FAX: 392984. **Staff:** Mrs. Ranjana Nair.

★5689★
Fiji School of Medicine - Central Medical Research Library (Med)
Tamavua Phone: 311700
Suva, Fiji Mr. Chandraiya
Founded: 1888. **Staff:** Prof 1; Other 4. **Subjects:** Internal medicine, surgery, preclinical medicine, clinical medicine, nutrition, dietetics, environmental health. **Special Collections:** Pacific medicine collection; WHO collection. **Holdings:** 12,000 books; 5,000 bound periodical volumes; 200 reports; 50 archival items; 50 microfiche; 1000 audio tapes; 100 videotapes. **Services:** Interlibrary loan; copying; SDI; library open to the public for reference use only. **Computerized Information Services:** CD-ROM (MEDLINE).

★5690★
Fiji Trades Union Congress - Library (Bus-Fin)
32 Des Voeux Rd.
G.P.O. Box 1418
Suva, Fiji Phone: 315377
Staff: 1. **Subjects:** Trade unions, industrial relations. **Holdings:** 1000 volumes. **Remarks:** FAX: 300306.

Fikes Hall of Special Collections
See: **Southern Methodist University - De Golyer Library** (15499)

★5691★
Fillmore County Historical Society - Historical Center (Hist)
R.R. 1
Box 81 D Phone: (507)268-4449
Fountain, MN 55935 Jerry Henke, Exec.Dir.
Founded: 1934. **Staff:** 2. **Subjects:** History - Southeastern Minnesota, Southeastern Minnesota immigrants, agrarian history, agrarian machinery, Native American, rural lifestyles. **Special Collections:** Matthew Bue Photography Collection (5000 original glass negatives and photographs documenting life in Southeastern Minnesota, 1915-1950); Senator M. Anderson Collection (notes and documents on Minnesota government, 1927-1963). **Holdings:** 3700 books; 2200 bound periodical volumes; 1100 documents; 2800 nonbook items; 67 manuscripts. **Services:** Copying; library open to the public for reference use only.

★5692★
Millard Fillmore Hospitals - Kideney Health Sciences Library (Med)
3 Gates Circle Phone: (716)887-4848
Buffalo, NY 14209 Susan Grossman, Corp.Lib.Dir.
Founded: 1977. **Staff:** Prof 2; Other 2.7. **Subjects:** Clinical medicine, nursing, surgery, health care administration, management. **Special Collections:** Hand Center Library (hand surgery and rehabilitation); Bernard Smith Collection (neurology, neurosurgery, neuropharmacology). **Holdings:** 3970 books; 4861 bound periodical volumes; 4 VF drawers of pamphlets and articles; 1007 video cassettes. **Subscriptions:** 404 journals and other serials. **Services:** ILL; copying; SDI; library open to the public with restrictions. **Computerized Information Services:** BRS Information Technologies, DIALOG Information Services, MEDLARS, miniMEDLINE, Current Contents Search; CD-ROM (MEDLINE, Health Planning and Administration, Nursing and Allied Health Database). Performs searches on fee basis. **Networks/Consortia:** Member of Library Consortium of Health Institutions in Buffalo (LCHIB), Western New York Library Resources Council (WNYLRC). **Remarks:** FAX: (716)887-5084. **Staff:** Adrienne Doepp, Asst.Dir.

★5693★
Fillmore & Riley - Law Library (Law)
360 Main St., No. 1700 Phone: (204)956-2970
Winnipeg, MB, Canada R3C 3Z3 Christine Stewart, Libn.
Staff: Prof 1; Other 1. **Subjects:** Law. **Holdings:** 4000 books. **Services:** Library open to the public at librarian's discretion. **Computerized Information Services:** QL Systems, WESTLAW, DIALOG Information Services, CAN/LAW, Canada Systems Group (CSG), CBANet, VU/TEXT Information Services. **Remarks:** FAX: (204)957-0516.

Film Art Fund Inc.
See: **Anthology Film Archives - Library** (891)

Film Culture Non-Profit Corporation
See: **Anthology Film Archives - Library** (891)

★5694★
Filson Club - Library (Hist)
1310 S. 3rd St. Phone: (502)635-5083
Louisville, KY 40208 Dorothy C. Rush, Libn.
Founded: 1884. **Staff:** Prof 8; Other 10. **Subjects:** Kentucky and Virginia history, genealogy. **Holdings:** 50,000 volumes; 1 million manuscripts and private papers; 20,000 pictures; clippings on Kentucky; 1500 maps of Kentucky and the U.S.; ephemera. **Subscriptions:** 100 journals and other serials. **Services:** Copying (limited); library open to the public (fee required for nonmembers). **Special Catalogs:** Chronological catalog to manuscripts and newspapers (card). **Staff:** James R. Bentley, Dir.; James Holmberg, Mss.Cur.; Katherine House, Tech.Serv.Libn.; Mary Jean Kinsman, Cur., Photo. & Prints.

★5695★
Financial Accounting Foundation (FAF) - Library (Bus-Fin)
401 Merritt 7
Box 5116 Phone: (203)847-0700
Norwalk, CT 06856-5116 Charry D. Boris, Libn.
Founded: 1973. **Staff:** Prof 2; Other 1. **Subjects:** Accounting, finance. **Holdings:** 4000 volumes; 2000 other cataloged items. **Subscriptions:** 250 journals and other serials. **Services:** Interlibrary loan; library not open to the public. **Computerized Information Services:** PFDS Online, LEXIS, NEXIS, DIALOG Information Services, Dow Jones News/Retrieval, LEGI-SLATE. **Remarks:** FAX: (203)849-9714. **Staff:** Miriam Solomon, Asst.Libn.

★5696★
Financial Executives Research Foundation - Library (Bus-Fin)
10 Madison Ave.
Box 1938 Phone: (201)898-4600
Morristown, NJ 07960 Susan L. Ticker, Libn.
Founded: 1944. **Staff:** Prof 1. **Subjects:** Financial management and controllership on executive level, accounting, banking and finance. **Special Collections:** FEI and FERF published materials dating back to association beginnings. **Holdings:** 2000 books. **Subscriptions:** 70 journals and other serials. **Services:** Library not open to the public. **Computerized Information Services:** DIALOG Information Services, ORBIT Search Service.

★5697★
Financial Planning Information - Library (Bus-Fin)
Riverbend Office Park
9 Galend St.
Watertown, MA 02172 Phone: (617)876-9688
Subjects: Business, investment management, product development, marketing, consumerism. **Holdings:** 4000 volumes. **Formerly:** Located in Cambridge, MA.

★5698★
The Financial Post - Library (Bus-Fin, Publ)
333 King St. E. Phone: (416)350-6690
Toronto, ON, Canada M5A 4N2 Theresa M. Butcher, Lib.Mgr.
Founded: 1938. **Staff:** Prof 2; Other 4. **Subjects:** Canadian business, finance, and investment. **Special Collections:** Maclean Hunter publications. **Holdings:** 10,000 current Canadian corporation files; government and economic research studies. **Services:** Library not open to the public. **Remarks:** FAX: (416)350-6301.

★5699★
Financial Times of Canada - Library (Publ)
440 Front St., W. Phone: (416)585-5514
Toronto, ON, Canada M5V 3E6 Jennifer Osther, Libn.
Founded: 1962. **Staff:** 2. **Subjects:** Canadian corporations, finance, federal government, investments, business. **Holdings:** 1000 volumes; 150 VF drawers; Financial Times on microfilm. **Subscriptions:** 100 journals and other serials; 10 newspapers. **Services:** Interlibrary loan; library open to the public by special appointment. **Computerized Information Services:** Infomart Online, Info Globe, DIALOG Information Services, NEXIS, Reuters. **Remarks:** FAX: (416)585-5549. The Times is published by Thomson Newspaper Group.

★5700★
Financial World Partners - Editorial Library (Bus-Fin)
47 W. 34th St., 3rd Fl. Phone: (212)594-5030
New York, NY 10001 Laura Harris
Founded: 1935. **Staff:** 1. **Subjects:** Business, economics, company data, financial services, investment analysis, international relations. **Holdings:** 3000 books; 30 VF drawers; 200 reels of microfilm; U.S. and foreign company annual reports. **Subscriptions:** 25 journals and other serials; 10 newspapers. **Services:** Library not open to the public. **Computerized Information Services:** NEXIS, LEXIS, Dow Jones News/Retrieval.

★5701★
FIND/SVP - Library (Bus-Fin, Comp Sci)
625 Avenue of the Americas Phone: (212)645-4500
New York, NY 10011 Anne Dennis, V.P. Info.Res.
Founded: 1969. **Staff:** Prof 85; Other 10. **Subjects:** Business, health care, food, advertising, chemistry, transportation, energy, metals. **Holdings:** 2500 books; 10,000 subject files including pamphlets, statistics, government material; annual reports, 10K reports, proxies of 10,000 companies; 1600 U.S. and foreign telephone directories; 20,000 microfiche of U.S. and foreign 10K reports, census, New York Times, Wall Street Journal; 100 periodical titles on microfiche. **Subscriptions:** 2000 journals and other serials. **Services:** Interlibrary loan; library not open to the public. **Computerized Information Services:** DIALOG Information Services, BRS Information Technologies, CDA Investment Technologies, Inc., CompuServe Information Service, Data-Star, DataTimes, Dow Jones News/Retrieval, Info Globe, InvesText, LEXIS, NEXIS, NewsNet, Inc., MEDLARS, OCLC EPIC, ORBIT Search Service, FT PROFILE, Reuter TEXTLINE, Vickers Stock Research Corporation, VU/TEXT Information Services, WILSONLINE, Spectrum Ownership Profiles Online, Compu-Mark US, BASELINE, STSC. **Special Catalogs:** Information Catalog, quarterly - for sale. **Remarks:** This organization offers a complete package of information gathering, fact-finding, and research services.

★5702★
Fine Arts Museum of the South at Mobile - FAMOS Library (Art)
Langan Park
4850 Museum Dr.
Box 8426 Phone: (205)343-2667
Mobile, AL 36608 Melissa Thomas, Cur. of Educ.
Subjects: Fine arts. **Holdings:** 2200 books, exhibition catalogs, periodicals. **Subscriptions:** 17 journals and other serials. **Services:** Library open to the public for reference use only.

★5703★
Fine Arts Museums of San Francisco - Library (Art)
M.H. de Young Memorial Museum
Golden Gate Park Phone: (415)750-3600
San Francisco, CA 94118 Gerald Smith, Musm.Libn.
Founded: 1972. **Staff:** Prof 1. **Subjects:** Art - French, American, African, Oceania; art history. **Special Collections:** Achenbach Foundation for Graphic Arts Reference Library (3500 volumes); Bothin American Art Library Collection. **Holdings:** 32,000 books; 15,100 bound periodical volumes; auction sales catalogs; exhibition catalogs. **Subscriptions:** 170 journals and other serials. **Services:** Copying; library open to museum staff only. **Special Catalogs:** Catalogs of museum collections and exhibitions. **Remarks:** Library combines California Legion of Honor Library (founded 1930) and M.H. de Young Memorial Museum Library (founded 1955).

★5704★
Fine Hardwood Veneer Association/American Walnut Manufacturers Association - Library
5603 W. Raymond, Suite O
Indianapolis, IN 46241
Subjects: Wood technology, furniture design and construction, forestry production. **Holdings:** 240 volumes. **Remarks:** Currently inactive.

Barbara and Eli Fink Memorial Children's Library
See: **North Shore Congregation Israel - Romanek Cultural Center - Oscar Hillel Plotkin Adult Library** (11947)

Harold Fink Memorial Library
See: **Coney Island Hospital** (4133)

Finkelstein Library
See: **St. Mary's Hospital** (14513)

Finland - Central Medical Library
See: **Finland - National Library of Health Sciences** (5710)

★5705★
Finland - Central Statistical Office of Finland - Library (Bus-Fin)
P.O. Box 504 Phone: 0 9017341
SF-00101 Helsinki 10, Finland Hellevi Yrjola, Chf.Libn.
Founded: 1867. **Staff:** 17. **Subjects:** Statistics on Finnish society - population, housing, law enforcement, courts, elections, education, living conditions, prices, wages, economic conditions, industry, foreign trade, construction, enterprises, labor force, agriculture, financing, transport, communication. **Special Collections:** Central Statistical Office of Finland Archives (depository for unpublished data sets in table, microfiche, and microfilm forms; primary data, including questionnaire forms). **Holdings:** 240,000 books; 78,000 microcards; microfiche; microforms. **Subscriptions:** 750 journals and other serials. **Services:** Interlibrary loan; copying; SDI; library open to the public. **Computerized Information Services:** Searches more than 1000 databases; produces Finregion, Finseries, Finfarming, Finhousing; Dialcom, Inc. (electronic mail service). Performs searches on fee basis. **Publications:** Statistical publications; asscessions of the Library of Statistics. **Remarks:** Library located at Annankata 44, SF-00101 Helsinki 10, Finland. FAX: 0 9017342279; 0 9017342474. Telex: 1002111 TILASTO SF. Electronic mail address(es): 12762:BOX739 (Dialcom, Inc.). **Staff:** Kaisa Wolski, Info.Spec.; Taina Koivula, Info.Spec.; Mikko Makinen, Info.Spec.; Marketta Lukkari, Info.Spec.; Eini Karhulahti, Libn.

Finland - Geological Survey of Finland
See: **Geological Survey of Finland** (6366)

Finland - Ministry of Agriculture and Forestry - Finnish Forest Research Institute
See: **Finnish Forest Research Institute** (5716)

Finland - Ministry of Agriculture and Forestry - Finnish Geodetic Institute
See: **Finnish Geodetic Institute** (5717)

Finland - Ministry of Commerce and Industry - Geological Survey of Finland
See: **Geological Survey of Finland** (6366)

★5706★
Finland - Ministry of Justice - Library (Law)
Etelaesplanadi 10
P.O. Box 1 Phone: 0 1825238
SF-00130 Helsinki, Finland Marjo Tolvanen, Info.Spec.
Founded: 1884. **Staff:** Prof 1; Other 1. **Subjects:** Law - criminal, civil, procedural, public, drafting. **Holdings:** 40,000 books. **Subscriptions:** 60 journals and other serials; 9 newspapers. **Services:** Interlibrary loan; library not open to the public. **Computerized Information Services:** CELEX, Rattsbanken, Retsinfo, LOU Data, FINLEX; internal database. **Remarks:** 0 1825358.

★5707★
Finland - Ministry of Social Affairs and Health - Finnish Center for Radiation and Nuclear Safety - Library (Sci-Engr)
P.O. Box 268 Phone: 0 70821
SF-00101 Helsinki, Finland Armi Lankelin, Chf.Libn.
Founded: 1958. **Staff:** 3. **Subjects:** Radiation protection, nuclear safety. **Holdings:** 30,000 volumes. **Subscriptions:** 500 journals and other serials. **Services:** Interlibrary loan; copying; library open to the public. **Computerized Information Services:** ESA/IRS, KDOK, DIALOG Information Services, STN International; electronic mail service. **Remarks:** FAX: 0 7082215. **Also Known As:** Sateilyturvakeskus. **Staff:** Leena Innanen, Acq.; Hannu Arra, Intl. Loans.

★5708★
Finland - National Archives (Hist)
Rauhankatu 17
SF-00170 Helsinki 17, Finland Phone: 0 90176911
Founded: 1869. **Staff:** Prof 2. **Subjects:** History, Finnish history, archives management, archival sciences, heraldry, genealogy. **Holdings:** 70,000 volumes; 240 bound periodical volumes; source and official publications. **Services:** Copying; archives open to the public. **Remarks:** FAX: 0 176302.

★5709★
Finland - National Board of Patents and Registration - Library and Information Services (Law, Sci-Engr)
Albertinkatu 25 Phone: 0 69531
SF-00180 Helsinki, Finland Ritva Sundquist, Hd., Lib. & Info.Serv.
Founded: 1942. **Staff:** Prof 5; Other 30. **Subjects:** Patents, technology, science. **Special Collections:** Patent documents (23.5 million). **Holdings:** 12,500 books; 15,000 bound periodical volumes; 2.8 million reels of microfilm. **Subscriptions:** 380 journals and other serials; 5 newspapers. **Services:** Interlibrary loan; copying; SDI; library open to the public. **Computerized Information Services:** DIALOG Information Services, ESA/IRS, STN International, INPADOC, FIZ Technik, Questel, Pergamon Financial Data Services, FT PROFILE, KDOK/MINTTU, TENTTU, PATRE. Contact Person: Riitta Viikari, Info.Off. **Remarks:** FAX: 0 6953601.

Finland - National Library of Finland
See: **University of Helsinki - Library** (18635)

★5710★
Finland - National Library of Health Sciences (Med)
Haartmaninkatu 4 Phone: 0 90 43461
SF-00290 Helsinki, Finland Ritva Sievanen-Allen, Libn.
Subjects: Medicine. **Holdings:** 160,000 books and other bound volumes. **Subscriptions:** 2700 journals and other serials. **Computerized Information Services:** Produces MEDIC database. Performs searches on fee basis. **Publications:** FINMED, quarterly. **Remarks:** FAX: 90 410385. Telex: 12 1498 LKK SF. **Formerly:** Finland - Central Medical Library; Laaketieteellinen Keskuskirjasto. **Also Known As:** Terveystieteiden Keskuskirjasto. **Staff:** Irja-Liisa Oberg, Dep.Libn.

★5711★
Finland - National Ministry of Education - National Board of Antiquities - Library (Soc Sci, Art)
Box 913 Phone: 0 40501
SF-00101 Helsinki, Finland Kerttu Itkonen
Founded: 1893. **Staff:** 3. **Subjects:** Archeology, ethnology, art history, museology. **Holdings:** 130,000 volumes. **Subscriptions:** 1500 journals and other serials. **Services:** Interlibrary loan; copying; library open to the public. **Remarks:** FAX: 4050300. **Also Known As:** Museovirasto.

★5712★
Finland - Supreme Court - Library (Law)
Helenankatu 3
P.O. Box 301 Phone: 0 12381
SF-00171 Helsinki, Finland Pirjo Dahlbom, Libn.
Founded: 1918. **Staff:** Prof 1. **Subjects:** Law. **Holdings:** 11,500 books; 450 bound periodical volumes. **Subscriptions:** 45 journals and other serials; 8 newspapers. **Services:** Library not open to the public. **Computerized Information Services:** Finlex, Rattsbaken, LOU Data, Rattsinfo, Celex. **Remarks:** FAX: 0 1238354.

Finland - Technical Research Centre of Finland
See: **Technical Research Centre of Finland** (16030)

★5713★
Finland - Youth Policy Library and Information Service (Soc Sci)
Kasarmik 23A Phone: 0 7015883
SF-00130 Helsinki, Finland Vappu Turunen, Info.
Founded: 1974. **Subjects:** Concept of youth. **Special Collections:** Youth Psychiatric Society Collection. **Holdings:** 11,000 books; 200 bound periodical volumes. **Subscriptions:** 200 journals and other serials; 4 newspapers. **Services:** Interlibrary loan; copying; library open to the public. **Computerized Information Services:** KDV, MINTTV; MIKRO, MINTTU (internal database). **Publications:** Nuoriso Suomessa - Bibliografia (Youth in Finland). **Remarks:** FAX: 0 7017156.

C.J. Finlay Library
See: **Cuban Academy of Sciences - Center for the Study of the History and Organization of Science** (4465)

Finney Memorial Library
See: **St. Mary-Corwin Hospital** (14501)

Theodore M. Finney Music Library
See: **University of Pittsburgh** (19226)

Finnish-American Historical Archives
See: **Suomi College** (15880)

★5714★
Finnish American Historical Society of Michigan - Archives (Area-Ethnic)
19885 Melrose Phone: (313)354-1994
Southfield, MI 48075 Felix V. Jackonen, Pres.
Founded: 1945. **Subjects:** Finnish history, culture, religion; books in Finnish. **Holdings:** 200 books; archival materials; clippings; pamphlets. **Services:** Archives not open to the public.

★5715★
Finnish Broadcasting Company - Library and Information Services Ltd. (Info Sci)
POB 10, JA 76 Phone: 0 14801
SF-00241 Helsinki, Finland Ritva Valiaho
Founded: 1954. **Staff:** Prof 7; Other 2. **Subjects:** Broadcasting. **Special Collections:** Mass Media Collection (2000 items). **Holdings:** 60,000 books. **Services:** Interlibrary loan; library not open to the public. **Computerized Information Services:** DIALOG Information Services, FT PROFILE, Reuters, HELECON; Who's Who in Finland, Encyclopedia of Otawa (internal databases). Contact Person: Janta Ranta, Info.Spec. **Remarks:** FAX: 0 14805616. Telex: 124375 radio st. **Also Known As:** Oy Yleisradio Ab: n Kirjastotietopalvelu.

Finnish Center for Radiation and Nuclear Safety
See: **Finland - Ministry of Social Affairs and Health - Finnish Center for Radiation and Nuclear Safety** (5707)

★5716★
Finnish Forest Research Institute - Library (Biol Sci)
P.O. Box 18 (Rillitie 8) Phone: 0 857051
SF-01301 Vantaa, Finland Liisa Ikavalko-Ahvonen, Libn.
Founded: 1918. **Staff:** 3. **Subjects:** Forests and forest resources. **Holdings:** 45,000 volumes. **Subscriptions:** 3 journals and other serials. **Services:** Interlibrary loan; copying; library open to the public. **Computerized Information Services:** DIALOG Information Services. **Remarks:** FAX: 0 85705582. Telex: 121298 metlisf. Maintained by Finland - Ministry of Agriculture and Forestry. **Formerly:** Located in Helsinki, Finland. **Also Known As:** Metsantutkimuslaitos.

★5717★
Finnish Geodetic Institute - Library (Sci-Engr)
Ilmalankatu 1A Phone: 0 90410433
SF-00240 Helsinki, Finland Helena Vilenius, Libn.
Subjects: Geodesy, gravimetry, photogrammetry, cartography. **Holdings:** 35,000 volumes. **Services:** Interlibrary loan; library open to the public. **Publications:** Publications and reports of the Finnish Geodetic Institute. **Remarks:** Maintained by Finland - Ministry of Agriculture and Forestry. FAX: 0 90414946. **Also Known As:** Suomen Geodeettinen Laitos.

★5718★
Finnish Institute for International Affairs - Library (Soc Sci)
Pursimiehenkatu 17 Phone: 0 170434
SF-00150 Helsinki, Finland Jouko Rajakiili, Info.Spec.
Founded: 1968. **Staff:** Prof 2. **Subjects:** Finnish foreign policy, international relations, global environmental affairs, disarmament. **Holdings:** 13,000 books. **Subscriptions:** 200 journals and other serials; 30 newspapers. **Services:** Interlibrary loan; copying; library open to the public. **Computerized Information Services:** DIALOG Information Services, FT PROFILE, ECHO, KDOK; internal database. **Remarks:** 0 669375.

★5719★
Finnish Population and Family Welfare Federation - Library (Soc Sci)
Kalevankatu 16 Phone: 0 640235
SF-00100 Helsinki 10, Finland Ulla-Maija Mattila
Founded: 1946. **Staff:** 1. **Subjects:** Finnish family and population policy. **Holdings:** 12,500 volumes. **Subscriptions:** 200 journals and other serials; 7 newspapers. **Services:** Interlibrary loan; copying; library open to the public. **Computerized Information Services:** DIALOG Information Services, BLAISE-LINE, BLAISE-LINK; internal databases. **Publications:** Bibliography of Finnish Population Research. **Remarks:** FAX: 0 6121211. Telex: 123682 FAM SF. **Also Known As:** Vaestoliitto.

★5720★
Finnish Pulp and Paper Research Institute - Technical Information Management (Sci-Engr)
P.O. Box 70 Phone: 0 43711
SF-02151 Espoo, Finland Jorma Paakko, Res.Mgr.
Staff: Prof 7; Other 12. **Subjects:** Pulp, paper, board, packaging. **Holdings:** 40,000 volumes. **Subscriptions:** 420 journals and other serials. **Services:** Interlibrary loan; copying; SDI; open to the public. **Automated Operations:** Computerized public access catalog and cataloging. **Computerized Information Services:** DIALOG Information Services, PFDS Online, STN International; internal database. Performs searches on fee basis. Contact Person: Birgitta af Forselles, Info.Spec., 4371268. **Publications:** Weekly Survey of Periodicals; List of Accessions; List of Meetings. **Remarks:** FAX: 0 4371302. Teletex: 1001522 KCL SF. **Formerly:** Located in Helsinki, Finland. **Also Known As:** Oy Keskuslaboratorio - Centrallaboratorium Ab. **Staff:** Eija Ilveskorpi, Info.Spec.; Aimo Kaiku, Info.Spec.

★5721★
Finnish Standards Association SFS - Information Service (Sci-Engr)
Bulevardi 5 A 7
P.O. Box 205 Phone: 0 645 601
SF-00121 Helsinki, Finland Susanna Vahtila, Info.Spec.
Subjects: Finnish, international, and foreign standards. **Holdings:** 220,000 standards and documents. **Services:** Service open to the public. **Computerized Information Services:** Produces SFS-STAR Data Base. Performs searches on fee basis. **Publications:** SFS Tiedotus (list of new standards, drafts and draft technical regulations), bimonthly. **Special Catalogs:** SFS Catalogue (bilingual list of Finnish Standards Association Standards), annual with supplements. **Remarks:** Telex: 122303 stand sf. FAX: 358 0 643 147. **Also Known As:** Suomen Standardisoimisliitto SFS.

★5722★
Fire & Accident Reconstruction - Library (Mil)
17524 Colima Rd., Suite 360
Rowland Heights, CA 91748 Phone: (714)598-8919
Founded: 1978. **Staff:** 1. **Subjects:** Firearms, military accoutrements. **Holdings:** 178 books; 22 technical reports. **Subscriptions:** 10 journals and other serials. **Services:** Library not open to the public.

Fire Island National Seashore
See: **U.S. Natl. Park Service** (17705)

Fire Research Information Services
See: **U.S. Natl. Institute of Standards and Technology** (17616)

Firearms Litigation Clearinghouse
See: **Educational Fund to End Handgun Violence** (5257)

★5723★
Firefighters' Museum of Nova Scotia - Library & Information Center (Sci-Engr)
451 Main St. Phone: (902)742-5525
Yarmouth, NS, Canada B5A 1G9 David S. LeBlanc, Cur.
Founded: 1965. **Staff:** Prof 2. **Subjects:** Fires, firefighting. **Holdings:** 300 books; 750 magazines. **Subscriptions:** 15 journals and other serials. **Services:** Copying; library open to the public for reference use only. **Remarks:** FAX: (902)742-5525. **Staff:** Eleanor Atkins, Asst.Cur.

★5724★
Fireman's Fund Insurance Company - Insurance Library (Bus-Fin)
777 San Marin Dr. Phone: (415)899-2871
Novato, CA 94998 Linda L. Ghilotti, Lib.Dir.
Staff: Prof 2; Other 1. **Subjects:** Insurance, business, finance, management, accounting, marketing. **Holdings:** 5000 books. **Subscriptions:** 225 journals and other serials; 9 newspapers. **Services:** Interlibrary loan; SDI; center open to the public by appointment. **Computerized Information Services:** DIALOG Information Services, DataTimes, RLIN, Dow Jones News/Retrieval. **Networks/Consortia:** Member of CLASS. **Publications:** Recent Acquisitions, monthly. **Remarks:** FAX: (415)899-2852. **Staff:** Linda Aldrich, Libn.

Idabelle Firestone Audio Library
See: **New England Conservatory of Music** (11469)

★5725★
First Alabama Bank of Mobile - Ernest G. Cleverdon Library (Bus-Fin)
106 St. Francis St.
Box 2527 Phone: (205)690-1139
Mobile, AL 36622 Pat Looney, Libn.
Staff: Prof 1. **Subjects:** Banking, fiction and nonfiction, children's books. **Holdings:** 5000 books; 150 bound periodical volumes. **Services:** Interlibrary loan; library not open to the public.

★5726★
First Assembly of God - Church Library (Rel-Phil)
4501 Burrow Dr. Phone: (501)758-8553
North Little Rock, AR 72116-7040 Joye Murry, Chf.Libn.
Founded: 1952. **Staff:** 14. **Subjects:** Religion, fiction. **Holdings:** 4200 books; 3 VF drawers of pamphlets; 90 filmstrips; 120 slides; 210 AV programs. **Subscriptions:** 4 journals and other serials. **Services:** Library open to the public with recommendation from pastor or educational director.

First Baptist Academy
See: **First Baptist Church of Dallas - First Baptist Academy** (5749)

★5727★
First Baptist Church - E.F. Walker Memorial Library (Rel-Phil)
218 N. Magnolia
Box 90 Phone: (512)875-2227
Luling, TX 78648 Lucille Matthews, Libn.
Founded: 1957. **Staff:** 3. **Subjects:** Theology, missions, biography. **Holdings:** 1818 books; 1200 slides; 3 VF drawers; 130 filmstrips; 45 magnetic tapes; 45 phonograph records. **Services:** Library open to the public.

★5728★
First Baptist Church - I.C. Anderson Memorial Library & Media Center (Rel-Phil)
500 Webster St. Phone: (817)752-3000
Waco, TX 76706 Victor Cooper, Dir. of Lib.Serv.
Founded: 1952. **Staff:** Prof 1; Other 5. **Subjects:** Religion, philosophy, Christian life, Bible, social sciences, children's books, biography. **Special Collections:** First Baptist Church history (100 books, pamphlets, bulletins, pictures, yearbooks); rare books. **Holdings:** 20,000 books; 80 bound periodical volumes; 930 filmstrips; 450 cassette tapes. **Subscriptions:** 30 journals and other serials. **Services:** Library open to researchers and personnel from other churches. **Publications:** Media Directory (loose-leaf); list of videotapes on PC computer. **Staff:** Esther Davis, Libn.

★5729★
First Baptist Church - John L. Whorton Media-Library (Rel-Phil)
209 E. South St. Phone: (903)758-0681
Longview, TX 75601 Sandra Kay Trippett, Dir.
Founded: 1942. **Staff:** Prof 2; Other 13. **Subjects:** Religion, Bible, children. **Special Collections:** First Baptist Church historical collection. **Holdings:** 10,000 books; 703 AV programs; 2000 audio cassettes; 45 video cassettes. **Services:** Library open to members.

★5730★
First Baptist Church - Library (Rel-Phil)
Drawer I Phone: (205)886-2200
Slocomb, AL 36375 Gwen Ball, Libn.
Founded: 1963. **Staff:** Prof 1; Other 9. **Subjects:** Religion, philosophy, biography, history. **Holdings:** 4135 books; 143 filmstrips; 172 sound recordings; 2 vertical files; 189 slides; 20 cassette tapes; 86 video recordings. **Subscriptions:** 13 journals and other serials. **Services:** Library open to the public. **Special Catalogs:** Catalog of First Baptist Church History (local).

★5731★
First Baptist Church - Library (Rel-Phil)
561 Main St.
Melrose, MA 02176 Phone: (617)665-4470
Staff: Prof 1. **Subjects:** Religion. **Holdings:** 1000 volumes. **Services:** Library open to the public with restrictions.

★5732★
First Baptist Church - Library (Rel-Phil)
499 Wacouta St. Phone: (612)222-0718
St. Paul, MN 55101 Sumi Teramoto, Libn.
Staff: Prof 1; Other 3. **Subjects:** Religion, Christian education, biography, social concerns, psychology. **Holdings:** 3000 books. **Services:** Library not open to the public.

★5733★
First Baptist Church - Library (Rel-Phil)
401 W. Church Phone: (601)728-6272
Booneville, MS 38829 Sue K. Honeycutt, Libn.
Founded: 1937. **Staff:** Prof 1. **Subjects:** Religion. **Holdings:** 2378 volumes. **Staff:** Lee Barron, Asst.Libn.

★5734★
First Baptist Church - Library (Rel-Phil)
2105 14th St.
Box 70 Phone: (601)863-8501
Gulfport, MS 39501 Mrs. John K. Savell, Libn.
Staff: Prof 6; Other 2. **Subjects:** Religion, Christian life. **Holdings:** 6000 books; Bible in braille. **Services:** Copying; library open to the public.

★5735★
First Baptist Church - Library (Rel-Phil)
300 St. Francis St.
Kennett, MO 63857 Phone: (314)888-4689
Founded: 1946. **Staff:** Prof 1. **Subjects:** Bible, children's literature, holidays, crafts. **Holdings:** 3976 books. **Services:** Library open to the public with restrictions. **Staff:** David LaGore, Libn.; Sara LaGore, Libn.

★5736★
First Baptist Church - Library (Rel-Phil)
2205 Iron St. Phone: (816)842-1175
North Kansas City, MO 64116 Esther L. St. John, Hd.Libn.
Founded: 1950. **Staff:** 9. **Subjects:** Bible study, Christian education, Christian ethics, children's books, biography. **Holdings:** 2000 books; AV programs; video cassettes. **Services:** Library open to local residents.

★5737★
First Baptist Church - Library (Rel-Phil)
Box 26446 Phone: (505)247-3611
Albuquerque, NM 87125 Linnie B. Hyde, Libn.
Founded: 1937. **Staff:** 7. **Subjects:** Religion, biography, missions. **Holdings:** 9000 books; 100 bound periodical volumes; children's books; 200 other cataloged items. **Subscriptions:** 5 journals and other serials. **Services:** Library open to attendees at church activities.

★5738★
First Baptist Church - Library (Rel-Phil)
1000 W. Friendly
Box 5443 Phone: (919)274-3286
Greensboro, NC 27403 Jane Perkins-Rolnick, Dir., Media Serv.
Founded: 1947. **Staff:** Prof 1; Other 30. **Subjects:** Religion, biography, children's literature, art, history, social sciences, juvenile and young adult literature. **Holdings:** 16,000 books; 44 bound periodical volumes; 4 VF drawers; 1600 cassette tapes; 200 videocassettes; 33 8mm films; 600 filmstrips. **Subscriptions:** 31 journals and other serials. **Services:** Copying (limited); library open to the public. **Automated Operations:** Computerized cataloging and acquisitions. **Remarks:** FAX: (919)274-3288.

★5739★
First Baptist Church - Library (Rel-Phil)
612 N. Duke St. Phone: (717)392-8818
Lancaster, PA 17602 Loulette Simons, Chm., Commun.Comm.
Staff: 5. **Subjects:** Religion. **Special Collections:** First Baptist Church Archives, 1879 to present. **Holdings:** 1207 books. **Services:** Library open to church members only.

★5740★
First Baptist Church - Library (Rel-Phil)
1401 S. Covell Phone: (605)336-0966
Sioux Falls, SD 57105 Chris Carstensen, Libn.
Staff: 1. **Subjects:** Religion, theology. **Holdings:** 3500 books. **Subscriptions:** 18 journals and other serials. **Services:** Library open to the public.

★5741★
First Baptist Church - Library (Rel-Phil)
1200 Beech St. Phone: (512)686-7418
McAllen, TX 78501 Mrs. Hans Wells, Dir.
Founded: 1960. **Staff:** 6. **Subjects:** Religion, Bible, sociology, literature. **Holdings:** 5726 books; 207 filmstrips; 74 phonograph records. **Services:** Library open to the public with restrictions.

★5742★
First Baptist Church - Library (Rel-Phil)
515 McCullough Ave. Phone: (512)226-0363
San Antonio, TX 78215 Virginia Patterson, Libn.
Founded: 1939. **Staff:** Prof 1; Other 5. **Subjects:** Baptist history and doctrines, Bible, family religious life. **Holdings:** 25,000 books; 300 bound periodical volumes; 10 VF drawers of archival materials; 1400 filmstrips; 1000 tapes. **Subscriptions:** 35 journals and other serials. **Services:** Interlibrary loan; copying; library open to the public for reference use only. **Automated Operations:** Computerized cataloging and circulation.

★5743★
First Baptist Church - Mattie D. Hall Library (Rel-Phil)
Front St.
Box 459 Phone: (601)759-6378
Rosedale, MS 38769 Beulah R. Lane, Media Dir.
Staff: 7. **Subjects:** Theology, Christian living. **Holdings:** 3919 books. **Services:** Library open to the public with restrictions.

★5744★
First Baptist Church - Media Center (Rel-Phil)
425 W. University Ave. Phone: (904)376-4681
Gainesville, FL 32601 Dorothy S. Hammond, Media Lib.Dir.
Founded: 1953. **Staff:** Prof 2; Other 5. **Subjects:** Religion, Christian living, missionary biography, fiction, children's books, cookery, arts and crafts, music, parenting, biography. **Holdings:** 9000 books; 490 filmstrips; 200 phonograph records; 4 VF drawers of pamphlets; 335 slides; flipcharts and maps; 210 cassettes; church archives. **Subscriptions:** 20 journals and other serials. **Services:** Interlibrary loan; use of AV programs and equipment available to county Baptist churches; center open to the public. **Special Catalogs:** Catalog of filmstrip holdings (pamphlet), biennial. **Staff:** Doris Y. Hyatt, Asst.

★5745★
First Baptist Church - Media Center (Rel-Phil)
122 Gaston St. Phone: (704)883-8251
Brevard, NC 28712 Doris Harron, Chm., Media Ctr.
Staff: 5. **Subjects:** Religion, children's books, fiction. **Holdings:** 5000 books. **Services:** Center open to the public.

★5746★
First Baptist Church - Media Library (Rel-Phil)
Box 85 Phone: (915)673-5031
Abilene, TX 79604 Karin Richardson, Lib.Dir.
Founded: 1948. **Staff:** Prof 3; Other 11. **Subjects:** Religion, biography, history, travel, fiction, fine arts, philosophy, family life, children's literature. **Holdings:** 18,000 books; 650 cassette recordings; 30 phonograph records; 400 filmstrips; 4 VF drawers; 185 slides. **Subscriptions:** 12 journals and other serials. **Services:** Library open to the public with restrictions.

★5747★
First Baptist Church - Stinceon Ivey Memorial Library (Rel-Phil)
Box 663 Phone: (919)628-0626
Fairmont, NC 28340 Alice Johnson, Lib.Asst.
Staff: 5. **Subjects:** Religion. **Holdings:** 4369 books. **Services:** Library open to the public.

★5748★
First Baptist Church of Blanchard - FBC Media Center (Rel-Phil)
201 Attaway
PO Box 65 Phone: (318)929-4707
Blanchard, LA 71009 Kevin Sandifer, Dir.
Founded: 1963. **Staff:** 5. **Subjects:** Religion, family, biography, psychology, hobbies and recreation, missions, fiction, history, geography, pure and applied science. **Special Collections:** College texts and music of the J.S. Peck Family. **Holdings:** 2500 books; 150 bound periodical volumes; 4050 documents; 400 AV programs; 190 nonbook items; 5 manuscripts; 2000 photographs. **Services:** Interlibrary loan; copying; library open to church members and their relatives; archives open to the public. **Publications:** Media Informer; Mediagraphy, both quarterly. **Staff:** Charlotte Withrow; James Peck, III.

★5749★
First Baptist Church of Dallas - First Baptist Academy - George W. Truett Memorial Library (Rel-Phil)
1707 San Jacinto Phone: (214)969-2442
Dallas, TX 75201 Mary Anne Schmidt, Dir. of Lib.Serv.
Founded: 1936. **Staff:** Prof 4; Other 5. **Subjects:** Religion, Christian education, theology. **Special Collections:** Hymnals. **Holdings:** 35,000 books; 3600 magnetic tapes; archival materials and dissertations; VF materials; 76 other cataloged items; AV programs and equipment. **Subscriptions:** 260 journals and other serials. **Services:** Copying; library open to the public for reference use only. **Automated Operations:** Computerized public access catalog, cataloging, and circulation. **Computerized Information Services:** CD-ROM (Books in Print Plus); Godspeed - Bible references (internal database). **Remarks:** FAX: (214)969-7720. **Staff:** Grace Wilson, Spec.; Dianne Taylor, Dir., FBA Elementary; Janice Shanks, Dir., FBA Secondary; Betty Criswell, Libn.

★5750★
First Baptist Church of Lakewood - Church/School Library (Rel-Phil)
5336 Arbor Rd.
Long Beach, CA 90808 Phone: (213)420-1471
Founded: 1955. **Staff:** Prof 2; Other 8. **Subjects:** Bible study, devotions, Christian living, missions, biography, children's literature, children's non-fiction. **Holdings:** 8000 books; 1200 cassette tapes of the pastor's sermons; 100 cassette albums; pamphlet file; mission fields information. **Services:** Library open to the public with restrictions. **Automated Operations:** Computerized cataloging and circulation. **Special Catalogs:** Cassette catalog of sermons, 1975-1989 (pamphlet). **Remarks:** Includes the holdings of the School Library, grades K-6.

★5751★
First Baptist Church of Richmond - Library (Rel-Phil)
Monument & Boulevard
Richmond, VA 23220 Phone: (804)355-8637
Staff: Prof 10; Other 5. **Subjects:** Bible and Bible study, theology, Christian life, prayer, devotional literature, biography. **Holdings:** 9000 books; 500 filmstrips and recordings; 2 VF drawers of clippings, articles, folders, and pamphlets; 600 slides; 50 cassette tapes and phonograph records. **Subscriptions:** 35 journals and other serials. **Services:** Library open to the public. **Publications:** Current Book List and Memorials, monthly.

★5752★
First Baptist Church & Satsuma Christian School - Satsuma Library (Rel-Phil)
Old Hwy. 43
Box 557 Phone: (205)675-1280
Satsuma, AL 36572 Emily Peterson, Asst.Libn.
Remarks: No further information was supplied by respondent.

★5753★
First Boston Corporation - Information Center (Bus-Fin)
55 E. 52nd St. Phone: (212)909-4000
New York, NY 10055 Pamela C. Rollo, Mgr.
Founded: 1963. **Staff:** Prof 5; Other 2. **Subjects:** Finance, corporations, business, industries, investment and securities. **Special Collections:** U.S. and foreign corporation records; Securities and Exchange Commission files (microfiche). **Holdings:** 5000 books; 350,000 microfiche; 1500 reels of microfilm. **Subscriptions:** 500 journals and other serials; 22 newspapers. **Services:** Interlibrary loan; center not open to the public. **Automated Operations:** Computerized cataloging, acquisitions, and serials. **Computerized Information Services:** Dow Jones News/Retrieval, Mead Data Central, DIALOG Information Services, Info Globe, CDC, Spectrum Ownership Profiles Online, Dun & Bradstreet Business Credit Services, TEXTLINE, Reuters, DRI/McGraw-Hill, IDC, MAID. **Publications:** New Acquisitions, bimonthly; periodicals listing. **Remarks:** FAX: (212)752-4408. **Staff:** Angela Lynch, Tech.Serv.Libn.

★5754★
First Call For Help - Milwaukee (Soc Sci)
231 W. Wisconsin Ave.
Milwaukee, WI 53203 Phone: (414)272-5600
Founded: 1988. **Staff:** Prof 4; Other 4. **Subjects:** Human services, especially health, social work, and older adults. **Holdings:** Files on 1500 Milwaukee area human service agencies. **Services:** Service open to the public by appointment. **Publications:** FCFH data reports, monthly. **Special Indexes:** Alphabetical and numerical lists of agencies. **Staff:** Judith H. Cohen, Dir.; Alice C. Henry, Asst.Dir.; Joyce C. Reiss, Older Adult Serv.Coord.

★5755★
First Catholic Slovak Union of U.S.A. and Canada (Area-Ethnic)
6611 Rockslide Rd. Phone: (216)642-9406
Independence, OH 44131 Margaret M. Bacho, Exec.Sec.
Subjects: Slovakia. **Special Collections:** Books by Slovak authors. **Holdings:** Figures not available. **Remarks:** FAX: (216)642-4310. Publications for this organization are handled by Joseph C. Krajsa, Editor, Jednota Press, Box 350, Middletown, PA 17057, telephone: (717)944-0461.

★5756★
First-Centenary United Methodist Church - Library (Rel-Phil)
419 McCallie Ave. Phone: (615)756-2021
Chattanooga, TN 37401 Mrs. Donald L. Jones, Libn.
Staff: 7. **Subjects:** Bible, Christian life and education, church history and celebration. **Holdings:** 2000 books; 60 phonograph records and cassettes; 220 filmstrips; 30 video cassettes. **Services:** Library not open to the public.

★5757★
First and Central Presbyterian Church - Library (Rel-Phil)
11th & Market Sts. Phone: (302)654-5371
Wilmington, DE 19801 Helen D. Scott, Libn.
Remarks: No further information was supplied by respondent.

★5758★
First Christian Church - Library (Rel-Phil)
101 N. 10th St. Phone: (314)449-7265
Columbia, MO 65201 Moray Loring, Libn.
Staff: 8. **Subjects:** Bible, theology, philosophy, religious education, ecumenical church, missions, socioeconomic problems, Christian life and worship. **Holdings:** 4000 books; AV programs. **Services:** Library open to the public with restrictions.

★5759★
First Christian Church - Library (Rel-Phil)
10th & Faraon Sts.
St. Joseph, MO 64501 Phone: (816)233-2556
Founded: 1957. **Staff:** 3. **Subjects:** Religion, social problems. **Holdings:** 2300 books. **Services:** Interlibrary loan; library open to the public with restrictions.

★5760★
First Christian Church - Library (Rel-Phil)
6630 Dodge St.
Omaha, NE 68132-2794 Phone: (402)558-1939
Founded: 1870. **Staff:** 1. **Subjects:** Christian living, devotions, Bible, children's literature. **Holdings:** 1000 books. **Subscriptions:** 10 journals and other serials. **Services:** Library not open to the public.

★5761★
First Christian Church - Library (Rel-Phil)
On The Diamond Phone: (412)654-2529
New Castle, PA 16101 Eileen McEwen, Libn.
Founded: 1959. **Staff:** 4. **Subjects:** Religion. **Holdings:** 5000 books; 13 boxes of historical materials. **Subscriptions:** 2 journals and other serials. **Services:** Interlibrary loan; library open to the public.

★5762★
First Christian Church of Alexandria - Library (Rel-Phil)
2723 King St. Phone: (703)549-3911
Alexandria, VA 22302 Rev. Ronald J. Degges, Hd.Libn.
Founded: 1954. **Staff:** Prof 1; Other 1. **Subjects:** Bible, theology, philosophy, biblical archeology, history, biography. **Special Collections:** Robin June Gustafson Memorial Collection of Children's Books; commentaries on the Bible. **Holdings:** 3641 books; 449 sermons and pamphlets; 650 unbound periodicals and reports; 100 slides and filmstrips. **Subscriptions:** 12 journals and other serials. **Services:** Interlibrary loan; copying; library open to the public with permission of head librarian. **Publications:** Selected Current Acquisitions Lists, irregular.

★5763★
First Christian Church (Disciples of Christ) - Winona Roehl Library (Rel-Phil)
211 W. 5th Ave. Phone: (615)522-0545
Knoxville, TN 37917 Lenore A. McClain, Libn.
Founded: 1953. **Staff:** Prof 2; Other 3. **Subjects:** Religion, teaching aids, biography, children's books. **Special Collections:** E. Stanley Jones; Jane Merchant. **Holdings:** 3600 books; 20 bound periodical volumes; AV programs. **Subscriptions:** 4 journals and other serials. **Services:** Library open to the public.

★5764★
First Christian Reformed Church - Library (Rel-Phil)
15 S. Church St.
Zeeland, MI 49464 Betty G. Shoemaker, Church Libn.
Founded: 1928. **Staff:** 5. **Subjects:** Religion. **Holdings:** 5000 books; 60 bound periodical volumes. **Subscriptions:** 10 journals and other serials. **Services:** Library open to the public.

★5765★
First Church in Albany (Reformed) - Library (Rel-Phil)
N. Pearl & Clinton Sq. Phone: (518)463-4449
Albany, NY 12210 Marey L. Bailey
Founded: 1958. **Staff:** Prof 1; Other 1. **Subjects:** Religion, Albany history. **Holdings:** 1500 volumes; 1700 church records. **Services:** Library open to the public upon application.

★5766★
First Church of Christ Congregational - John P. Webster Library (Rel-Phil)
12 S. Main St. Phone: (203)232-3893
West Hartford, CT 06107 Rev. Lee K. Ellenwood, Lib.Dir.
Founded: 1978. **Staff:** Prof 1; Other 2. **Subjects:** Religion, psychology, social issues. **Holdings:** 12,000 items. **Subscriptions:** 62 journals and other serials. **Services:** Interlibrary loan; library open to the public.

★5767★
First Church of Christ Scientist - Archives and Library (Rel-Phil)
175 Huntington Ave. Phone: (617)450-3500
Boston, MA 02115 Mary M. Trammell, Mgr.
Founded: 1932. **Staff:** Prof 8. **Subjects:** Christian Science; Church of Christ, Scientist; Mary Baker Eddy; Christian healing. **Special Collections:** Bible collection. **Holdings:** 6000 books; 250 bound volumes of Christian Science periodicals; manuscript material; photographs; newspaper clippings, 1850-1912. **Subscriptions:** 48 journals and other serials. **Services:** Copying; library open to the public with restrictions. **Computerized Information Services:** MINARET (internal database). **Staff:** C.J. Wilson, Libn. 0 0

★5768★
First Church of Christ Scientist - Christian Science Reading Room - Library (Rel-Phil)
901 S. Walnut St.
Milford, DE 19963 Phone: (302)422-3475
Founded: 1941. **Subjects:** Bible, authorized Christian Science literature. **Holdings:** Figures not available. **Subscriptions:** 5 journals and other serials. **Services:** Library open to the public.

★5769★
First Church of Christ Scientist - Christian Science Reading Room - Library (Rel-Phil)
Delaware Ave. at Haines St. Phone: (302)999-0346
Newark, DE 19711 Winnie Russo
Founded: 1965. **Staff:** 8. **Subjects:** The Bible, Mary Baker Eddy, children's Bible stories. **Special Collections:** Mary Baker Eddy biography collection; Christian Science Journal collection; Christian Science Sentinel collection. **Holdings:** 50 books; 60 bound periodical volumes. **Services:** Library open to the public.

★5770★
First Congregational Church - Library (Rel-Phil)
Walton Place Phone: (203)323-0200
Stamford, CT 06901 Margaret Thomas
Founded: 1961. **Subjects:** Children's literature, religion, biography, children's religious literature, reference. **Holdings:** 2500 books; 50 reports; 8 archival items. **Subscriptions:** 4 journals and other serials. **Services:** Library open to the public.

★5771★
First Congregational Church - Library (Rel-Phil)
2001 Niles Ave. Phone: (616)983-5519
St. Joseph, MI 49085 Judy Whittier, Church Libn.
Founded: 1957. **Staff:** 1. **Subjects:** Religion, social science, fine arts, ethics, family life, children's literature. **Holdings:** 4657 books. **Services:** Library not open to the public.

★5772★
First Congregational Church of Auburn - Library (Rel-Phil)
128 Central St. Phone: (508)832-2845
Auburn, MA 01501 Florence LaPlante, Chm.
Founded: 1959. **Staff:** 5. **Subjects:** Bible commentary and history, religion, missions, education, current issues, family life, juvenile literature. **Holdings:** 3500 books; 8 VF drawers of unbound materials. **Services:** Library open to the public with restrictions.

★5773★
First Congregational Church of Cheshire - Library (Rel-Phil)
111 Church Dr.
Cheshire, CT 06410 Phone: (203)272-5323
Staff: 9. **Subjects:** Religion. **Holdings:** 2500 books. **Services:** Library not open to the public.

★5774★
First Congregational Church of Wellesley Hills - Church Library (Rel-Phil)
Washington St. at Chapel Pl. Phone: (617)235-4424
Wellesley Hills, MA 02181 Dr. Lorraine E. Tolman, Libn.
Founded: 1956. **Staff:** Prof 1. **Subjects:** Religion, Bible study, Christian education, current issues. **Holdings:** 4000 books; teachers' and audiovisual resource centers. **Subscriptions:** 5 journals and other serials. **Services:** Library open to the public with restrictions.

★5775★
First Division Museum & Library (Mil)
Cantigny
1 S 151 Winfield Rd. Phone: (708)668-5185
Wheaton, IL 60187 Dr. John F. Votaw, Dir.
Founded: 1960. **Staff:** Prof 5; Other 1. **Subjects:** History of the First Division, World Wars I and II, Vietnam, military history. **Special Collections:** Official First Division records of World War I and II (includes 200 reels of microfilm); Vietnam Conflict. **Holdings:** 10,000 books; 4000 photographs; 30,000 documents. **Subscriptions:** 75 journals and other serials. **Services:** Copying; library open to the public for reference use only. **Computerized Information Services:** OCLC. **Networks/Consortia:** Member of DuPage Library System, ILLINET. **Remarks:** FAX: (708)668-5332. The First Division Museum is operated by the Cantigny First Division Foundation on the grounds of Cantigny, the Robert R. McCormick estate. **Staff:** Eric Gillespie, Archv./Libn.; Andrew Woods, Ref.Libn.; Roberta Craig, Lib.Tech.Asst.

★5776★
First Hawaiian Inc. - First Hawaiian Bank Research Library (Bus-Fin)
Box 3200 Phone: (808)525-6353
Honolulu, HI 96847 Linda L. Uchida, Res.Libn.
Founded: 1959. **Staff:** Prof 1. **Subjects:** Economics, banking, business. **Holdings:** 5465 books; 40 bound periodical volumes; 20 VF drawers of news clippings; 20 VF drawers of newsletters; telephone books for major U.S. cities on microfiche; 68 VF drawers of government documents. **Subscriptions:** 350 journals and other serials; 23 newspapers. **Services:** Interlibrary loan; copying; library open to the public for reference use only. **Computerized Information Services:** NEXIS. **Publications:** Economic Indicators, bimonthly. **Special Indexes:** Indexes to Hawaii Business Magazine and Hawaii Investor (card). **Remarks:** FAX: (808)525-6204.

First Interstate Bank of Arizona Archives
See: **Northern Arizona University - Cline Library - Special Collections and Archives Department** (11992)

★5777★
First Interstate Bank of California - Research Center W21-12
707 Wilshire Blvd., 21st Fl.
Los Angeles, CA 90017
Defunct.

Joseph M. First Library
See: **Akiba Hebrew Academy** (164)

★5778★
First Lutheran Church - Adult Library (Rel-Phil)
1000 3rd Ave., S.E. Phone: (319)365-1494
Cedar Rapids, IA 52403 Ortha R. Harstad, Libn.
Founded: 1959. **Staff:** 1. **Subjects:** Religion, works of Luther, family, Bible. **Holdings:** 2500 books; 75 audio cassettes; 80 large print books; 104 art prints; 34 sculptures. **Services:** Library open to the public.

★5779★
First Lutheran Church - Parish Library (Rel-Phil)
415 Vine St. Phone: (814)536-7521
Johnstown, PA 15905 Elizabeth J. Will, Act.Libn.
Founded: 1954. **Staff:** 2. **Subjects:** Religion, church history, children's and young adults' reference topics. **Special Collections:** Complete collection of the history of Martin Luther (56 volumes). **Holdings:** 5000 books; 2 VF drawers of pamphlets; video cassettes; phonograph records. **Services:** Library open to the public with restrictions. **Staff:** Donna Oaks, Asst.Libn.; Melody Jacoby, Asst.Libn.

★5780★
First Lutheran Church of the Lutheran Church in America - Schendel Memorial Library (Rel-Phil)
615 5th St. Phone: (612)388-9311
Red Wing, MN 55066 Mrs. Delma Rigelman, Libn.
Founded: 1951. **Subjects:** Bible, Christian life, prayer. **Special Collections:** Luther's complete works; 20th century theology (50 titles). **Holdings:** 4000 books; 2 VF drawers of clippings, pamphlets, maps. **Subscriptions:** 10 journals and other serials. **Services:** Library open to Lutheran congregations in the area.

★5781★
First Meridian Heights Presbyterian Church - Hudelson Library (Rel-Phil)
4701 N. Central Ave. Phone: (317)283-1305
Indianapolis, IN 46205 Beverly R. Wolfarth, Chm., Lib.Comm.
Staff: 5. **Subjects:** Religion, children's literature. **Holdings:** 3500 books; 150 tape recordings; 200 photograph albums. **Services:** Library open to the public. **Networks/Consortia:** Member of INCOLSA.

★5782★
First Methodist Church - Bliss Memorial Library (Rel-Phil)
Head of Texas St.
Drawer 1567 Phone: (318)424-7771
Shreveport, LA 71165-1567 Dorothy Hanks, Chm., Libn.
Founded: 1946. **Staff:** Prof 3; Other 8. **Subjects:** Religion, social studies. **Special Collections:** Articles for Worship Centers; religious maps; church archives. **Holdings:** 10,300 books; 92 bound periodical volumes; 150 tapes; Methodist Conference proceedings. **Services:** Library not open to the public. **Staff:** Harriet Towery, Libn.; Marcia Alexander, Libn.

★5783★
First National Bank of Boston - Library 01-5M-09 (Bus-Fin)
Box 1896 Phone: (617)434-8440
Boston, MA 02105 Jane E. Gutowski-Connell, Mgr., Lib.Rsrcs.
Founded: 1920. **Staff:** Prof 2; Other 2. **Subjects:** Banking and business. **Special Collections:** Archives and bank history (8 VF drawers). **Holdings:** 12,000 volumes. **Subscriptions:** 600 journals and other serials. **Services:** Interlibrary loan; copying (limited); library open to clients, students, and other librarians with restrictions. **Computerized Information Services:** DIALOG Information Services, NEXIS, NewsNet, Inc., TEXTLINE, VU/TEXT Information Services, Dow Jones News/Retrieval, Info Globe, Lotus One Source. **Staff:** Michael Carr, Res.Libn.

★5784★
First National Bank of Chicago - Corporate Information Center (Bus-Fin)
One First National Plaza
Bldg. 1, Suite 0477 Phone: (312)732-4000
Chicago, IL 60670-0477 Betty Bonner, Mgr.
Founded: 1931. **Staff:** Prof 2; Other 4. **Subjects:** Banking, economics, finance, industries. **Holdings:** 11,000 books; 500 bound periodical volumes. **Subscriptions:** 980 journals and other serials; 20 newspapers. **Services:** Interlibrary loan; copying; SDI; center open to the public with restrictions. **Automated Operations:** Computerized cataloging and serials. **Computerized Information Services:** DIALOG Information Services, Dow Jones News/Retrieval, VU/TEXT Information Services, NEXIS; internal database. **Networks/Consortia:** Member of ILLINET. **Publications:** Corporate Information Center News, bimonthly - limited distribution. **Remarks:** Contains the holdings of the former Information Technology Library. **Staff:** Virginia Probst, Asst.Mgr.

★5785★
First Pennsylvania Bank, N.A. - Marketing Information Center
Center Square Tower, 42nd Fl.
1500 Market St.
Philadelphia, PA 19101
Defunct. Merged with CoreSTATES to form CoreSTATES Bank, N.A.

★5786★
First Presbyterian Church - Ewing Memorial Library (Rel-Phil)
5300 Main St. Phone: (713)526-2525
Houston, TX 77004 Mary Carter, Libn.
Subjects: Theology, Bible history, pastoral counseling, children's religious instruction. **Holdings:** 10,500 books; 450 tapes of sermons; 40 tapes of the Bible; 6 VF drawers. **Services:** Library open to members and their relatives and friends.

★5787★
First Presbyterian Church - Fern Young Memorial Library (Rel-Phil)
215 Locust St., N.E. Phone: (505)247-9594
Albuquerque, NM 87102 Beth Busick, Dir., Ch. Ministries
Staff: Prof 3; Other 9. **Subjects:** Religion, Bible, philosophy, geography, the arts, history, fiction, Southwest. **Holdings:** 7800 books. **Subscriptions:** 17 journals and other serials. **Services:** Interlibrary loan; library open to the public.

★5788★
First Presbyterian Church - John C. Gardner Memorial Library (Rel-Phil)
219 E. Bijou Phone: (719)471-3763
Colorado Springs, CO 80903 Elouise Young, Libn.
Founded: 1945. **Staff:** 1. **Subjects:** Religion. **Holdings:** 4400 books. **Subscriptions:** 14 journals and other serials. **Services:** Library open to the public with restrictions.

★5789★
First Presbyterian Church - Library (Rel-Phil)
500 Farragut Circle
El Cajon, CA 92020 Phone: (619)442-2583
Founded: 1980. **Subjects:** Bible, religion, congregational life, Christian life, biography. **Holdings:** 2000 books; 12 audiocassettes. **Subscriptions:** 4 journals and other serials. **Services:** Library open to the public with the permission of a pastor or librarian. **Staff:** Elva Colbeth, Libn.; Michelle Blackman, Libn.

★5790★
First Presbyterian Church - Library (Rel-Phil)
101 E. Foothill
Monrovia, CA 91016 Phone: (818)359-9371
Founded: 1960. **Staff:** 1. **Subjects:** Bible study, history, family, biography, missions, church-related literature. **Holdings:** 2000 books; audiocassettes. **Services:** Library not open to the public.

★5791★
First Presbyterian Church - Library (Rel-Phil)
869 N. Euclid Ave. Phone: (714)982-8811
Upland, CA 91786 Lucy Moore, Libn.
Founded: 1966. **Staff:** Prof 1; Other 3. **Subjects:** Religion and theology, missions, social concerns, children's and young adult books. **Special Collections:** Comfort Corner. **Holdings:** 2500 volumes; audio cassettes of sermons. **Services:** Library open to the public with restrictions.

★5792★
First Presbyterian Church - Library (Rel-Phil)
724 N. Woodland Blvd. Phone: (904)734-6212
De Land, FL 32720 Dorthea Beiler, Libn.
Founded: 1955. **Staff:** 1. **Subjects:** Religion, devotions, Christian education, family life, Bible, church history, theology, social problems. **Holdings:** 5400 books. **Subscriptions:** 4 journals and other serials. **Services:** Library open to the public.

★5793★
First Presbyterian Church - Library (Rel-Phil)
225 W. Maple Ave.
Box P
Libertyville, IL 60048 Phone: (708)362-2174
Subjects: Bible, religion, biography, children's books. **Holdings:** 1800 books. **Services:** Library open to parishioners of church.

★5794★
First Presbyterian Church - Library (Rel-Phil)
1432 Washtenaw Ave. Phone: (313)662-4466
Ann Arbor, MI 48104-3199 Anna Marie Austin, Dir., Christian Educ.
Staff: Prof 1. **Subjects:** Church history, theology, Christian education, missions, family life. **Holdings:** 3200 books. **Subscriptions:** 10 journals and other serials. **Services:** Library open to the public.

★5795★
First Presbyterian Church - Library (Rel-Phil)
321 W. South St. Phone: (616)344-0119
Kalamazoo, MI 49007 Lillian B. Auducon
Founded: 1956. **Staff:** Prof 6. **Subjects:** Religion. **Holdings:** 2500 books. **Services:** Library not open to the public.

★5796★
First Presbyterian Church - Library (Rel-Phil)
7th at Lincoln Ave. Phone: (402)462-5147
Hastings, NE 68901 Susan Nedderman, Libn.
Founded: 1950. **Staff:** Prof 1; Other 5. **Subjects:** Christian religion, philosophy, sociology, art, music. **Holdings:** 7000 books. **Subscriptions:** 12 journals and other serials. **Services:** Library open to the public. **Networks/Consortia:** Member of Hastings Area Librarians.

★5797★
First Presbyterian Church - Memorial Library (Rel-Phil)
143 Main St. Phone: (215)933-8816
Phoenixville, PA 19460 Marian Mercer, Chm., Lib.Committee
Subjects: Religion, Bible study, family life. **Holdings:** 4050 books. **Services:** Library open to the public with restrictions. **Automated Operations:** Computerized cataloging, acquisitions, and circulation. **Computerized Information Services:** Online systems. Performs searches free of charge.

★5798★
First Presbyterian Church - Thomas E. Boswell Memorial Library (Rel-Phil)
1427 Chicago Ave. Phone: (708)864-1472
Evanston, IL 60201 Judith Akers, Lib.Ch.
Founded: 1962. **Staff:** Prof 2; Other 4. **Subjects:** Religion, family life, biography, personal growth, children's literature, teenagers. **Holdings:** 3000 books. **Subscriptions:** 15 journals and other serials. **Services:** Library open to the public. **Publications:** Book Shelf (newsletter), monthly - for internal distribution only. **Staff:** Laurie Oh, Asst.Libn.

★5799★
First Presbyterian Church of Charleston - Library (Rel-Phil)
16 Broad St. Phone: (304)343-8961
Charleston, WV 25314 Joan Steven, Libn.
Founded: 1941. **Staff:** Prof 1; Other 10. **Subjects:** Religion. **Holdings:** 10,000 books; 200 phonograph records; 100 videotapes; 100 audiotapes; 460 filmstrips; pictures. **Subscriptions:** 12 journals and other serials; 5 newspapers. **Services:** Copying; library open to the public with restrictions. **Automated Operations:** Computerized cataloging.

★5800★
First Presbyterian Church of El Paso - Library (Rel-Phil)
1340 Murchison Dr.
El Paso, TX 79902 Phone: (915)533-7551
Founded: 1955. **Staff:** Prof 1. **Subjects:** Theology, history, family living. **Holdings:** 3700 volumes; 175 cassette tapes. **Subscriptions:** 3 journals and other serials. **Services:** Library open to the public.

★5801★
First Presbyterian Church of Flint - Peirce Memorial Library (Rel-Phil)
746 S. Saginaw St. Phone: (313)234-8673
Flint, MI 48502 Steven Hill, Libn.
Staff: 8. **Subjects:** Christian living and healing, church history, ancient history, Bible, biography, prayers, theology, Jesus Christ. **Special Collections:** Lay pastors; new members; Women's Guild; Bethel Bible Series. **Holdings:** 3000 books; magazines; papers; videotapes; audiotapes. **Services:** Library open to members and friends.

★5802★
First Presbyterian Church of Gadsden - Library (Rel-Phil)
530 Chestnut St.
Box 676 Phone: (205)547-5747
Gadsden, AL 35902 Margaret Smith, Libn.
Founded: 1959. **Staff:** 4. **Subjects:** Religion. **Holdings:** 3000 books. **Subscriptions:** 10 journals and other serials. **Services:** Library not open to the public.

★5803★
First Presbyterian Church, Milpitas - Library (Rel-Phil)
1435 Clear Lake Ave. Phone: (408)262-3353
Milpitas, CA 95035 Dottie Lowe, Libn.
Founded: 1980. **Staff:** Prof 1; Other 1. **Subjects:** Bible, children's literature, films, Christian literature, local church history, senior citizens' issues, local community, Christian colleges in U.S. **Special Collections:** Grace Livingston Hill Collection (35 books); Bible Collection (30 editions); History of Presbyterian Church collection. **Holdings:** 4800 books; videotapes. **Subscriptions:** 7 journals and other serials. **Services:** Interlibrary loan.

★5804★
First Presbyterian Church of San Diego - Christian Education Department - Library (Rel-Phil)
320 Date St. Phone: (619)232-7513
San Diego, CA 92101 Peggy Sparks, Libn.
Staff: 1. **Subjects:** Religion, Christian biography and autobiography. **Holdings:** 2700 books; 100 tapes. **Subscriptions:** 51 journals and other serials. **Services:** Library open to the public with restrictions. **Computerized Information Services:** Internal database. Performs searches free of charge.

★5805★
First Reformed Church - Johnson Library (Rel-Phil)
8 N. Church St. Phone: (518)377-2201
Schenectady, NY 12305 Joan W. Ipsen, Libn.
Founded: 1938. **Staff:** Prof 1; Other 2. **Subjects:** Religion, art, music, history, biography, personal development, literature. **Special Collections:** Children's Collection (800 books); Christmas Collection (150 books). **Holdings:** 5500 books. **Subscriptions:** 7 journals and other serials. **Services:** Library open to the public with restrictions on a limited schedule.

★5806★
First Southern Baptist Church - Library (Rel-Phil)
445 E. Speedway Phone: (602)623-5858
Tucson, AZ 85705 Joy English, Dir.
Founded: 1957. **Staff:** Prof 1; Other 6. **Subjects:** Religion, evangelical Christianity, Christian education. **Holdings:** 5890 books. **Services:** Library not open to the public. **Publications:** Messenger,

★5807★
First Unitarian Church - John G. MacKinnon Memorial Library (Rel-Phil)
730 Halsted Rd.
Wilmington, DE 19803 Phone: (302)478-2384
Services: Library open to church attendees only. **Remarks:** No further information was supplied by respondent.

★5808★
First United Methodist Church - Allen Library (Rel-Phil)
Bronson Park
212 S. Park St. Phone: (616)381-6340
Kalamazoo, MI 49007 Mildred S. Hedrick, Libn.
Founded: 1952. **Staff:** Prof 4; Other 10. **Subjects:** Religion, family and home, Christian ethics, biography, history, devotional and children's literature, race relations. **Holdings:** 7800 books; pictures; maps; pamphlets; 150 AV programs; 221 filmstrips; 75 phonograph records; 14 tapes; 14 kits. **Services:** Interlibrary loan; copying; library open to the public with restrictions. **Staff:** Mary Lou Robinson, Asst.Libn.; Christine Clark; Maxine Painter, Cat.

★5809★
First United Methodist Church - Broadhurst Library (Rel-Phil)
1115 S. Boulder Phone: (918)587-9481
Tulsa, OK 74119 Sally Shelton, Hd.Libn.
Founded: 1946. **Staff:** Prof 1; Other 13. **Subjects:** Religion, Bible history, church history, Christian life, Christian psychology, family life. **Special Collections:** Methodist history (200 items, including rare books); John Wesley Collection (150 historical materials and rare books). **Holdings:** 14,957 volumes; 1620 cassettes; 22 prints; 146 phonograph records; 2 VF drawers; large print books. **Subscriptions:** 22 journals and other serials. **Services:** Copying; library open to Methodist ministers.

★5810★
First United Methodist Church - Gertrude Callihan Memorial Library (Rel-Phil)
129 W. Hutchinson Phone: (512)392-6001
San Marcos, TX 78666 Lou Moloney, Lib.Chm.
Founded: 1955. **Staff:** Prof 1; Other 3. **Subjects:** Religion. **Holdings:** 4000 books. **Subscriptions:** 6 journals and other serials. **Services:** Library open to the public on a limited schedule.

★5811★
First United Methodist Church - Jennie E. Weaver Memorial Library (Rel-Phil)
7 Elm St. Phone: (518)725-9313
Gloversville, NY 12078 Nancy E. Naish, Libn.
Founded: 1954. **Staff:** 1. **Subjects:** Religion, general collection. **Holdings:** 2476 volumes. **Services:** Library open to the public with restrictions.

★5812★
First United Methodist Church - Library (Rel-Phil)
500 E. Colorado Blvd.
Pasadena, CA 91101 Phone: (818)796-0157
Founded: 1877. **Subjects:** Religion. **Holdings:** 7000 books. **Services:** Library open to the public. **Remarks:** Alternate telephone number(s): (818)796-0157. Library affiliated with First United Methodist Pasadena Commission on Education Program.

★5813★
First United Methodist Church - Library (Rel-Phil)
411 Turner St. Phone: (813)446-5955
Clearwater, FL 34616 Marjorie A. Kann, Libn.
Founded: 1970. **Staff:** Prof 2; Other 3. **Subjects:** Religion, literature, biography. **Special Collections:** Old Bibles Collection. **Holdings:** 4000 books; audio- and videotapes. **Services:** Library open to the public at librarian's discretion. **Staff:** Penny Nugeot.

★5814★
First United Methodist Church - Library (Rel-Phil)
424 Forest Ave. Phone: (708)469-3510
Glen Ellyn, IL 60137 Kathryn Collord, Libn.
Founded: 1959. **Subjects:** Religion, religious education, devotional materials, adults and children. **Holdings:** 3000 books; AV programs. **Services:** Interlibrary loan; library open to the public by appointment on a limited schedule.

★5815★
First United Methodist Church - Library (Rel-Phil)
211 N. School St. Phone: (309)452-2096
Normal, IL 61761 Catharine W. Knight, Libn.
Founded: 1959. **Staff:** 1. **Subjects:** Christian faith, United Methodist Church. **Special Collections:** Bible collection (27 versions). **Holdings:** 6000 books; filmstrips; sound recordings; pictures; maps; video cassettes. **Subscriptions:** 20 journals and other serials. **Services:** Library open to the public with restrictions.

★5816★
First United Methodist Church - Library (Rel-Phil)
1020 S. Granite Phone: (505)546-6460
Deming, NM 88030 Elizabeth K. Gottschalk, Libn.
Subjects: Religion, biography, fiction. **Holdings:** 2200 books; 12 AV programs; 1 vertical file of nonbook items; audiocassettes; videotapes; games; maps; phonograph records. **Subscriptions:** 2 journals and other serials. **Services:** Library open to members and friends only.

★5817★
First United Methodist Church - Library (Rel-Phil)
715 Diamond Dr. Phone: (505)662-6277
Los Alamos, NM 87544 Lora Belle Cole, Libn.
Subjects: Religion, Christian education, children's literature. **Holdings:** 2000 books; 30 AV programs. **Subscriptions:** 6 journals and other serials. **Services:** Interlibrary loan; library open to the public.

★5818★
First United Methodist Church - Library (Rel-Phil)
12th & Lavaca Sts.
Box 1666 Phone: (512)478-5684
Austin, TX 78767 Sharon Doss, Lib.Comm. Chair
Staff: Prof 4; Other 20. **Subjects:** Christian living. **Holdings:** 3000 books. **Services:** Library not open to the public.

★5819★
First United Methodist Church - Library (Rel-Phil)
805 E. Denman Ave. Phone: (409)639-3141
Lufkin, TX 75901 Zelma Cook, Hd.Libn.
Staff: 4. **Subjects:** Theology, children's literature, Christian education, sociology, psychology, history, biography, fiction. **Holdings:** 7000 books; filmstrips; cassettes; videotapes; phonograph records; pictures; games. **Services:** Library open to the public; circulation services provided for students and faculty.

★5820★
First United Methodist Church - Library (Rel-Phil)
534 W. Belt Line Rd.
Richardson, TX 75080 Bonnie Borrello, Libn.
Staff: 15. **Subjects:** Religion. **Holdings:** 4510 books. **Services:** Library open to the public with restrictions.

★5821★
First United Methodist Church - Memorial Library (Rel-Phil)
305 E. Anapamu St. Phone: (805)963-3579
Santa Barbara, CA 93101 Homer W. Freeman, Church Libn.
Founded: 1958. **Staff:** Prof 1. **Subjects:** Religion, biography, literature, arts and crafts, children's literature, history. **Holdings:** 2000 volumes; 2 VF drawers; 300 children's books; 32 videotapes. **Services:** Interlibrary loan; copying; library open to the public at librarian's discretion.

★5822★
First United Methodist Church of Sylvania, Ohio - Library (Rel-Phil)
7000 Erie St.
Sylvania, OH 43560 Phone: (419)882-2205
Staff: 2. **Subjects:** Religion, psychology, church history. **Holdings:** 1000 books. **Subscriptions:** 10 journals and other serials. **Services:** Library open to church members.

★5823★
First United Presbyterian Church of the Covenant - Brittain Library (Rel-Phil)
250 W. 7th St. Phone: (814)456-4243
Erie, PA 16501 Betty Robins, Libn.
Founded: 1930. **Staff:** Prof 1; Other 4. **Subjects:** Religion, philosophy, science, art, biography, children's books. **Holdings:** 7000 books. **Services:** Library open to the public with restrictions.

★5824★
Harry Fischel Institute for Research in Talmud and Jewish Law - Library (Law, Rel-Phil)
5 Hapisga St.
P.O. Box 16002 Phone: 2 416166
91160 Jerusalem, Israel Mr. S. Weinfeld
Subjects: Jewish law, ancient and medieval rabbinical works, codification of Jewish law, Jewish law as applied in Rabbinical Courts of Israel. **Holdings:** 40,000 volumes. **Services:** Library open to the public on a limited schedule. **Remarks:** FAX: 2 432955. Maintained by Israel - Ministry of Religious Affairs.

George W. Fischer Agricultural Sciences Branch Library
See: **Washington State University - Owen Science and Engineering Library** (20048)

★5825★
Fischer & Porter Co. - Corporate Engineering Library (Sci-Engr)
125 E. County Line Rd. Phone: (215)674-6000
Warminster, PA 18974 Sheryl Cherry, Contact
Staff: Prof 1. **Subjects:** Process control, software development, engineering. **Holdings:** 2500 books; 250 reels of microfilm; 23 VF drawers of technical reports and standards. **Subscriptions:** 100 journals and other serials. **Services:** Interlibrary loan; SDI; library open to the public by appointment. **Computerized Information Services:** DIALOG Information Services. **Publications:** Engineering Library Bulletin - for internal distribution only.

Hamilton Fish Collection
See: **Alice Curtis Desmond & Hamilton Fish - Library** (4799)

★5826★
Fish Memorial Hospital - Medical Library (Med)
245 E. New York Ave.
Box 167 Phone: (904)734-2323
De Land, FL 32721-0167 Carolyn E. Creeron, Med.Libn.
Founded: 1952. **Staff:** Prof 1; Other 1. **Subjects:** Medicine, nursing, and allied health sciences. **Holdings:** 100 books; 20 unbound periodicals. **Subscriptions:** 10 journals and other serials. **Services:** Interlibrary loan; library open to the public for reference use only. **Computerized Information Services:** MEDLINE. **Networks/Consortia:** Member of Tampa Bay Library Consortium, Inc. (TBLC).

★5827★
Fish and Neave - Library (Law)
875 3rd Ave. Phone: (212)715-0672
New York, NY 10022 Janet M. Stark, Hd.Libn.
Founded: 1900. **Staff:** Prof 5; Other 2. **Subjects:** Law - patent, trademark, unfair competition. **Holdings:** 26,000 books; 34 bound periodical titles. **Subscriptions:** 75 journals and other serials. **Services:** Interlibrary loan; library not open to the public. **Computerized Information Services:** LEXIS, DIALOG Information Services, WESTLAW. **Remarks:** FAX: (212)715-0673; (212)715-0674; (212)715-0678. **Staff:** Louise E. Studer, Ref.Libn.; Pamela E. Tunnell, ILL Libn.; Francesca Occhiogrosso, Asst.Libn.; Carol Hoffman, Asst.Libn.

★5828★
Fish and Wildlife Reference Service (Env-Cons)
5430 Grosvenor Ln., Suite 110 Phone: (301)492-6403
Bethesda, MD 20814 Mary J. Nickum, Proj.Mgr.
Founded: 1965. **Staff:** Prof 4; Other 2. **Subjects:** Wildlife management, fisheries management, endangered species. **Special Collections:** Selected Federal Aid in Fish and Wildlife Restoration Reports; selected Anadromous (sport) Fish Conservation Reports; Cooperative Fish and Wildlife Research Units Reports; Endangered Species Act Reports/Recovery Plans. **Holdings:** 22,000 Federal Aid reports on paper and microfiche (indexed). **Services:** Copying; SDI; service open to the public. **Computerized Information Services:** Internal database. **Publications:** Fish and Wildlife Reference Service Newsletter, quarterly - free upon request. **Special Indexes:** Indexes to computer-based system holdings for each state and territory of the U.S. **Remarks:** Primary function is to provide custom literature searches of computer files on fish and wildlife management research reports from state game and fish agencies. Toll-free telephone number(s): (800)582-3421. **Staff:** Geoffrey Yeadon; Paul E. Wilson.

Harris M. Fishbon Memorial Library
See: **University of California, San Francisco - Mount Zion Medical Center - Harris M. Fishbon Memorial Library** (18425)

B.L. Fisher Library
See: **Asbury Theological Seminary** (1102)

Fisher Controls Company
See: **Monsanto Company** (10634)

Fisher Library
See: **U.S. Army - TRADOC - Chemical School** (17009)

Fisher Scientific Group, Inc. - Instrumentation Laboratory Division
See: **Instrumentation Laboratory** (8007)

Thomas Fisher Rare Book Library
See: **University of Toronto** (19460)

Fishkill Historical Society, Inc. - Van Wyck Homestead Museum
See: **Van Wyck Homestead Museum** (19750)

Pliny Fisk Library of Economics and Finance
See: **Princeton University** (13383)

★5829★
Fisk University - Molecular Spectroscopy Research Laboratory - Library (Sci-Engr)
Box 15 Phone: (615)329-8620
Nashville, TN 37208 E. Silberman, Prof./Dir.
Founded: 1930. **Staff:** 4. **Subjects:** Spectroscopy - infrared, Raman, molecular. **Holdings:** 400 books. **Subscriptions:** 10 journals and other serials. **Services:** Library open to the public by appointment. **Computerized Information Services:** DIALOG Information Services, STN International. **Remarks:** FAX: (615)329-8634.

★5830★
Fisk University - Special Collections Department (Hum, Area-Ethnic)
17th at Jackson St. Phone: (615)329-8646
Nashville, TN 37203 Ann Allen Shockley, Assoc.Libn./Archv.
Founded: 1866. **Staff:** Prof 2. **Subjects:** African-American history and culture. **Special Collections:** Negro Collection; Fiskiana Collection (9 VF drawers); Yorkshire Collection; George Gershwin Collection; Langston Hughes Phonograph Collection; Black Oral History Collection (750 tapes); audiotape collection (200 tapes). **Holdings:** 64,000 books; 1565 bound periodical volumes; 3050 reels of microfilm of information by and about blacks; 2300 phonograph records; 4 VF drawers of pictures; 2 VF drawers of newspaper clippings; 4 VF drawers of biographical information by or about blacks; 878 Fisk University masters' theses; 100 archival and manuscript collections. **Subscriptions:** 48 journals and other serials; 7 newspapers. **Services:** Copying; department open to the public with restrictions. **Publications:** Banc! An Annotated Bibliography of the Fisk University Library's Black Oral History Collection. **Special Catalogs:** catalog to Oral History Collection; shelf lists for archives and manuscripts collections; Dictionary Catalog of the Negro Collection, 6 vols. (1974). **Remarks:** Alternate telephone number(s): (615)329-8580. **Staff:** Beth M. Howse, Spec.Coll.Libn.

Fiske Icelandic Collection
See: **Cornell University - Fiske Icelandic Collection** (4310)

★5831★
Fisons Pharmaceuticals - Library and Information Services (Med)
755 Jefferson Rd.
Box 1710 Phone: (716)274-5939
Rochester, NY 14603 Angela M. Scarfia, Mgr., Lib. & Info.Serv.
Staff: Prof 3; Other 1. **Subjects:** Pharmacology, pharmacy, chemistry, bioscience, medicine. **Holdings:** 3500 books; 4750 bound periodical volumes. **Subscriptions:** 400 journals and other serials. **Services:** Interlibrary loan. **Automated Operations:** Computerized ILL. **Computerized Information Services:** MEDLARS, DIALOG Information Services, PFDS Online, BRS Information Technologies, Chemical Abstracts Service (CAS), Questel, Data-Star. **Networks/Consortia:** Member of Rochester Regional Library Council (RRLC). **Remarks:** FAX: (716)272-3947.

Albert Fitch Memorial Library
See: **Pennsylvania College of Optometry** (12838)

★5832★
Fitchburg Historical Society - Library (Hist)
50 Grove St.
P.O. Box 953 Phone: (508)345-1157
Fitchburg, MA 01420 Eleanora F. West, Exec.Dir.
Founded: 1892. **Staff:** 1. **Subjects:** Fitchburg history, genealogy, Civil War, Fitchburg authors. **Holdings:** Books; bound periodical volumes; documents; 15 AV programs; manuscripts; city directories and reports; town histories. **Services:** Copying; library open to the public.

★5833★
Fitchburg Law Library (Law)
Superior Court House
84 Elm St. Phone: (508)345-6726
Fitchburg, MA 01420 Lyn Dee Lambert, Law Libn.
Founded: 1871. **Staff:** Prof 1. **Subjects:** Law, taxation. **Holdings:** 12,000 books; 275 bound periodical volumes. **Subscriptions:** 350 journals and other serials. **Services:** Interlibrary loan; copying; library open to the public. **Automated Operations:** Computerized public access catalog and ILL. **Computerized Information Services:** LEXIS, WESTLAW, OCLC; internal database; CD-ROM; electronic bulletin board. **Publications:** Fitchburg Law Library Guide; Fitchburg Law Library Newsletter.

★5834★
Fitchburg State College - Library (Educ)
160 Pearl St. Phone: (508)345-2151
Fitchburg, MA 01420 Robert Foley, Dir.
Founded: 1894. **Staff:** Prof 8; Other 7. **Subjects:** Education, special education, nursing, industrial technology, liberal arts, business administration, computer science. **Special Collections:** Finnish Collection; Robert Cormier Collection. **Holdings:** 146,000 books, 43,147 on microfiche; 30,251 bound periodical volumes; 10,561 pamphlets; 327,170 ERIC microfiche. **Subscriptions:** 1370 journals; 11 newspapers. **Services:** Interlibrary loan; library open to the public. **Automated Operations:** Computerized cataloging, serials, circulation, and ILL. **Computerized Information Services:** DIALOG Information Services, OCLC, InfoTrac, ERIC; CD-ROMs (ABI/INFORM, PsycLIT). **Networks/Consortia:** Member of Central Massachusetts Consortium of Health Related Libraries (CMCHRL), Worcester Area Cooperating Libraries (WACL). **Remarks:** FAX: (508)345-4270. **Staff:** Jeremiah Greene, Ref.Libn.; Faith Anttila, Per.Libn.; Lillian Gerecke, Ref.Libn.; Richard Griffin, Circ.Libn.; Linda Cone, ILL; Janice Ouellette, Per.Libn.; Bruce McSheehy, Hd., Tech.Proc.; Simone Blake, Cat.Libn.

★5835★
Fitzgerald, Abbott and Beardsley - Law Library (Law)
1221 Broadway, 21st Fl. Phone: (510)451-3300
Oakland, CA 94612 Betty J. Orvell, Att.
Subjects: Law. **Holdings:** 10,000 volumes. **Services:** Library not open to the public. **Automated Operations:** Computerized cataloging. **Computerized Information Services:** Internal database. **Remarks:** FAX: (510)451-1527.

★5836★
Fitzgerald Mercy Hospital - Health Sciences Library (Med)
Lansdowne Ave. & Baily Rd. Phone: (215)237-4150
Darby, PA 19023 Janet C. Clinton, Mgr.
Founded: 1933. **Staff:** Prof 1; Other 3. **Subjects:** Medicine, nursing, surgery and allied health sciences, psychiatry, religion and medical ethics. **Holdings:** 2900 books; 2500 bound periodical volumes; pamphlets; microforms; videocassettes; audiocassettes; slides. **Subscriptions:** 292 journals and other serials; 4 newspapers. **Services:** Interlibrary loan; copying; library open to the public for reference use only. **Computerized Information Services:** MEDLINE, DIALOG Information Services. **Networks/Consortia:** Member of Consortium for Health Information & Library Services (CHI), National Network of Libraries of Medicine - Middle Atlantic Region, BHSL. **Remarks:** FAX: (215)237-4830. **Formerly:** Mercy Catholic Medical Center - Fitzgerald Mercy Division.

★5837★
James A. FitzPatrick Library (Env-Cons, Biol Sci)
Miner Institute Phone: (518)846-7144
Chazy, NY 12921 Linda J. Masters, Libn.
Founded: 1972. **Subjects:** Ecology, environmental sciences, wildlife ecology, acid rain, in vitro cell biology, biotechnology, plant cell culture, tissue culture, agriculture. **Holdings:** 5400 books. **Subscriptions:** 145 journals and other serials. **Services:** Interlibrary loan; copying; library open to the public for reference use only. **Formerly:** Miner Center Library.

Fitzsimons Army Medical Center
See: **U.S. Army Hospitals** (17041)

Fitzwilliam Museum - Department of Manuscripts & Printed Books
See: **University of Cambridge - Fitzwilliam Museum - Department of Manuscripts & Printed Books** (18440)

★5838★
Five Civilized Tribes Museum - Library
Agency Hill on Honor Heights Dr.
Muskogee, OK 74401
Subjects: Cherokee, Chocktaw, Creek, Chickasaw, and Seminole Indians - history, current history, fiction, non-fiction. **Holdings:** Figures not available. **Remarks:** Currently inactive.

FIZ Karlsruhe
See: **Fachinformationszentrum Karlsruhe** (5546)

★5839★
Flag Research Center - Library (Hist)
3 Edgehill Rd. Phone: (617)729-9410
Winchester, MA 01890 Whitney Smith, Dir.
Founded: 1962. **Staff:** Prof 1. **Subjects:** Flags, heraldry, symbolism. **Special Collections:** Old flag charts; U.S. flag histories; Argentine and Dutch flag books. **Holdings:** 10,000 books; 90 bound periodical volumes; 130 cubic feet of correspondence, news clippings, pictures, pamphlets; 1000 charts; 1800 unbound periodicals; 20,000 cards of flag information; 2000 flags. **Subscriptions:** 50 journals and other serials. **Services:** Copying; consultation; rental artwork; translation provided to organizations; library open to those stating purpose of research by prior application. **Publications:** The Flag Bulletin, bimonthly; News from the Vexillarium, quarterly; Current National Flags; chart of flags of the world; occasional pamphlets; books; flag bibliography (partially published and on cards). **Special Indexes:** List of vexillologists (flag historians) and flag manufacturers. **Remarks:** The Flag Research Center is in touch with numerous private flag book collectors around the world and is familiar with the holdings of public and university libraries; its library will answer questions relating to this subject. FAX: (617)721-4817.

Kirsten Flagstad Collection
See: **San Francisco Performing Arts Library and Museum - Library** (14737)

★5840★
Father Flanagan's Boys' Home - Library Services (Soc Sci)
Boys Town Center
14100 Crawford St. Phone: (402)498-1426
Boys Town, NE 68010 Betty J. Otto, Lib.Serv.Mgr.
Founded: 1983. **Staff:** 3. **Subjects:** Children and youth, development. **Holdings:** 3500 books; 2800 other cataloged items. **Subscriptions:** 62 journals and other serials. **Services:** Interlibrary loan; copying; SDI; services open to the public. **Automated Operations:** Computerized cataloging. **Computerized Information Services:** DIALOG Information Services, PFDS Online, BRS Information Technologies, NewsNet, Inc., Dow Jones News/Retrieval, OCLC; internal database. **Networks/Consortia:** Member of Bibliographical Center for Research, Rocky Mountain Region, Inc. (BCR).

Flaschner Disabilities Library
See: **Mental Health Legal Advisors Committee** (10098)

John M. Flaxman Library
See: **Art Institute of Chicago - School of the Art Institute of Chicago** (1083)

G. Allen Fleece Library
See: **Columbia Bible College - G. Allen Fleece Library** (3978)

Max C. Fleischmann Medical Library
See: **St. Mary's Regional Medical Center** (14535)

Edwin A. Fleisher Collection of Orchestral Music
See: **Free Library of Philadelphia** (6114)

★5841★
Sir Sandford Fleming College of Applied Arts & Technology - Educational Resource Center (Educ)
Sutherland Campus
Brealey Bldg. Phone: (705)743-5610
Peterborough, ON, Canada K9J 7B1 Janice Coughlin, Dir.
Founded: 1968. **Staff:** Prof 1; Other 12. **Subjects:** Business, electromechanical technology, fine arts, psychology, sociology, nursing. **Holdings:** 35,000 books; 500 bound periodical volumes; 2000 nonprint materials; 500 vertical files. **Subscriptions:** 550 journals and other serials; 10 newspapers. **Services:** Interlibrary loan; copying; center open to the public. **Automated Operations:** Computerized cataloging and acquisitions. **Computerized Information Services:** DIALOG Information Services, Info Globe; CD-ROM. **Networks/Consortia:** Member of The Bibliocentre. **Remarks:** Above data includes the holdings of the Brealey and Daniel campus libraries. FAX: (705)749-5540.

Flemish Ministry of Education - Library
See: **Belgium - Flemish Ministry of Education - Library** (1666)

Fletcher School of Law & Diplomacy
See: **Tufts University - Fletcher School of Law & Diplomacy - Edwin Ginn Library** (16548)

★5842★
Flickinger Foundation for American Studies, Inc. - Library
300 St. Dunstan's Rd.
Baltimore, MD 21212
Defunct.

★5843★
Flinders University of South Australia - Medical Library (Med)
GPO Box 2100 Phone: 8 2045460
Adelaide, SA 5001, Australia Susan Jones, Med.Libn.
Founded: 1975. **Staff:** Prof 2; Other 6. **Subjects:** Medicine, nursing. **Holdings:** 18,500 books; 36,000 bound periodical volumes; 700 videotapes. **Services:** Interlibrary loan; copying; SDI; library open to the public at librarian's discretion. **Computerized Information Services:** DIALOG Information Services, OZLINE: Australian Information Network; CD-ROM (MEDLINE). **Remarks:** FAX: 8 2773721.

Lewis B. Flinn Library
See: **Delaware Academy of Medicine, Inc.** (4713)

Robert S. Flinn Medical Library
See: **Maricopa County Medical Society** (9661)

★5844★
Flint Genealogical Society - Genealogical Society Collection (Hist)
P.O. Box 1217
Flint, MI 48501-1213 Phone: (313)760-1169
Subjects: Genealogy. **Special Collections:** Merle Perry Collection (Genessee County, Michigan families). **Holdings:** 300 volumes; 250 notebooks. **Services:** Copying; collection open to the public.

★5845★
Flint Hills Area Vocational-Technical School - Library (Educ)
3301 W. 18th Ave. Phone: (316)342-6404
Emporia, KS 66801 Peggy Torrens, Lib. & Media Spec.
Founded: 1966. **Staff:** Prof 1. **Subjects:** Automotive mechanics, electronics, building trades, building and industrial maintenance, food preparation and management, practical nursing, welding, dental assisting, machine tooling, marketing and retailing, office occupations, graphic arts, data processing. **Holdings:** 2425 volumes. **Subscriptions:** 45 journals and other serials. **Services:** Interlibrary loan; copying; library open to the public for reference use only.

★5846★
Flint Institute of Arts - Library (Art)
1120 E. Kearsley St. Phone: (313)234-1695
Flint, MI 48503 Christopher Young, Cur.
Founded: 1969. **Subjects:** Art - North American Indian, African, decorative, Oriental, contemporary; glass paperweights; painting; sculpture; photography. **Holdings:** 3500 books; catalogs of museums' collections; exhibition catalogs; prints; drawings. **Subscriptions:** 19 journals and other serials. **Services:** Library open to the public with permission.

★5847★
Flint Journal - Editorial Library (Publ)
200 E. 1st St. Phone: (313)766-6192
Flint, MI 48502 David W. Larzelere, Chf.Libn.
Founded: 1935. **Staff:** Prof 1; Other 3. **Subjects:** Newspaper reference topics, journalism, local history, news events. **Holdings:** 2000 books; 1200 pamphlets; 2100 maps; 350,000 photographs; 4400 reels of microfilm of newspapers; 1 million newspaper clippings; 38,000 microfiche jackets of clippings. **Subscriptions:** 42 journals and other serials. **Services:** Library not open to the public. **Computerized Information Services:** VU/TEXT Information Services.

★5848★
Flint Newman Center - Library and Catholic Information Center (Rel-Phil)
609 E. 5th Ave. Phone: (313)239-9391
Flint, MI 48503 Rev. James B. Bettendorf, Dir.
Founded: 1967. **Staff:** 1. **Subjects:** Theology, philosophy, ethics, scripture, church history, aesthetics, sociology. **Special Collections:** Orestes Brownson's works. **Holdings:** 2390 books. **Subscriptions:** 45 journals and other serials. **Services:** Library open to the public.

★5849★
Flint Osteopathic Hospital - Dr. E. Herzog Memorial Medical Library (Med)
3921 Beecher Rd. Phone: (313)762-4587
Flint, MI 48532-3699 Doris M. Blauet, Dir.
Staff: Prof 1; Other 1. **Subjects:** Clinical medicine. **Holdings:** 2000 books; 7000 bound periodical volumes. **Subscriptions:** 394 journals and other serials. **Services:** Interlibrary loan; copying; SDI; library open to the public at librarian's discretion. **Automated Operations:** Computerized serials and circulation. **Computerized Information Services:** MEDLARS; CD-ROM (MEDLARS); internal database. Performs searches on fee basis. **Networks/Consortia:** Member of Flint Area Health Science Library Network (FAHSLN), National Network of Libraries of Medicine - Greater Midwest Region. **Remarks:** FAX: (313)762-3533. Alternate telephone number(s): 263-6364.

★5850★
Flint Public Library - Art, Music & Drama Department (Art, Mus)
1026 E. Kearsley St. Phone: (313)232-7111
Flint, MI 48502 Debra Rubey, Hd.
Staff: Prof 4; Other 3. **Subjects:** Art, drama, music, antiques, theater, architecture, film. **Holdings:** 52,094 books; 86 VF drawers of pictures; 20 VF drawers of mounted reproductions; 2375 posters; 3127 pieces of sheet music; 412 anthem titles (5 to 100 copies per title); 10,220 phonograph records; 750 compact discs; 1983 videotapes. **Services:** Interlibrary loan; copying; department open to the public with annual borrowing fee for nonresidents. **Automated Operations:** Computerized public access catalog, cataloging, and circulation. **Computerized Information Services:** DIALOG Information Services. **Networks/Consortia:** Member of Michigan Library Consortium (MLC). **Special Indexes:** Indexes to plays, Tune-Dex, portraits, biographies, Roland Scott Joke File, film reviews, songs, Flint Symphony and Ann Arbor May Festival program notes (all on cards). **Remarks:** FAX: (313)767-6740. **Staff:** Patricia A. Legg, First Asst.; Lloris Frounfelder, Asst.; Jo Ann Kingston, Asst.

★5851★
Flint Public Library - Automotive History Collection (Trans)
1026 E. Kearsley St. Phone: (313)232-7111
Flint, MI 48502 Margaret E. Williams, Dept.Hd.
Founded: 1958. **Staff:** Prof 4. **Subjects:** History of automotive industry. **Special Collections:** American Motors, Chrysler, Ford, and General Motors shop manuals (emphasis on Buick and Chevrolet manuals). **Holdings:** 2100 books; 15 VF drawers of clippings, pamphlets, owners' manuals. **Services:** Interlibrary loan; collection open to the public. **Computerized Information Services:** DIALOG Information Services, VU/TEXT Information Services. **Networks/Consortia:** Member of Mideastern Michigan Region of Cooperation. **Special Indexes:** Index to biographical information about pioneers of the U.S. automotive industry (card); periodical index to early General Motors history and histories of other Flint vehicle manufacturers (card). **Remarks:** FAX: (313)767-6740. Housed in the Business, Industry & Organized Labor Department. **Staff:** Linda Buell; Elizabeth Chambers; Carol Cole.

★5852★
Flint Public Library - Business, Industry & Organized Labor Department (Bus-Fin, Sci-Engr)
1026 E. Kearsley St. Phone: (313)232-7111
Flint, MI 48502 Margaret E. Williams, Dept.Hd.
Founded: 1958. **Staff:** Prof 4; Other 1. **Subjects:** Economics, labor, investments, management, real estate, insurance, physical sciences, technology. **Special Collections:** Telephone directories (475); trade directories (200). **Holdings:** 39,980 books; 2000 corporation annual reports; 48 VF drawers of pamphlets and clippings. **Services:** Interlibrary loan; copying; department open to the public with annual borrowing fee for nonresidents. **Computerized Information Services:** DIALOG Information Services, VU/TEXT Information Services. Performs searches on fee basis. **Networks/Consortia:** Member of Mideastern Michigan Region of Cooperation. **Remarks:** FAX: (313)767-6740. **Staff:** Linda Buell; Elizabeth Chambers; Carol Cole.

★5853★
Flint Public Library - Children's & Young Adult Department (Hum)
1026 E. Kearsley St. Phone: (313)232-7111
Flint, MI 48502 Cate Robarts, Dept.Hd.
Staff: Prof 2. **Subjects:** Pre-kindergarten through 10th grade level fiction and nonfiction. **Special Collections:** History and criticism of children's literature. **Holdings:** 56,433. **Services:** Department open to the public. **Networks/Consortia:** Member of Mideastern Michigan Region of Cooperation. **Remarks:** FAX: (313)767-6740. Jointly maintained by Flint Board of Education. Provides computer instruction for kindergarten through eighth grade children. **Staff:** Janet Bamberger; Rachel Swatzell.

★5854★
Flint Public Library - Michigan Room (Hist)
1026 E. Kearsley St.
Flint, MI 48502 Phone: (313)232-7111
Founded: 1972. **Staff:** Prof 1. **Subjects:** Local history, Michigan history, genealogy. **Special Collections:** Genesee Biography File; Flint directories, 1860 to present; Flint newspapers, 1839 to present; oral history tapes (43); local pictures and postcards (401); Michigan Histories (88 reels of microfilm). **Holdings:** 18,000 books; 67 VF drawers; 875 microcards; 3062

microfiche; 1670 reels of microfilm of census material; 318 drawers of surname/obituary indexes; Michigan document depository. **Subscriptions:** 140 journals. **Services:** Interlibrary loan; copying; mail inquiries answered; room open to the public. **Automated Operations:** Computerized public access catalog, cataloging, acquisitions, serials, and circulation. **Computerized Information Services:** DIALOG Information Services, VU/TEXT Information Services, Hannah Legislative Service, EPIC. Performs searches on fee basis. **Networks/Consortia:** Member of Mideastern Michigan Region of Cooperation. **Special Catalogs:** Local history and genealogy booklist (book). **Special Indexes:** Name index to Genesee county obituaries in local newspapers, 1850-1876, 1898 to present. **Remarks:** FAX: (313)767-6740.

★5855★
Florence City Planning and Development Library (Plan)
City-County Complex, Drawer FF Phone: (803)665-3141
Florence, SC 29501 Allen Burns, Dir.
Subjects: City and rural planning, state and federal administration, housing, finance, taxation. **Special Collections:** City plans (150); city maps (50; microfilm); multi-family studies (30). **Holdings:** 1500 books; 40 bound periodical volumes; 20 departmental reports. **Services:** Library not open to the public.

★5856★
Florence City Schools - Central Resource Center (Educ)
541 Riverview Dr. Phone: (205)766-3234
Florence, AL 35630 Charlotte Carr, Lib.Supv.
Staff: Prof 1. **Subjects:** Curriculum, social studies, language arts, science, school administration, arts. **Holdings:** 5000 books; 490 16mm films; 500 video cassettes; 500 multimedia kits. **Subscriptions:** 35 journals and other serials; 5 newspapers. **Services:** Interlibrary loan; copying; center open to staff.

★5857★
Florence-Darlington Technical College - Library (Educ)
Drawer 8000 Phone: (803)661-8032
Florence, SC 29501 Dr. Theodosia Shields
Staff: Prof 1; Other 2. **Subjects:** Health, business, data processing, secretarial science, engineering, fashion merchandising. **Special Collections:** Technology (7500 volumes). **Holdings:** 28,364 books; 747 bound periodical volumes; 1273 pamphlets; 10,338 microforms. **Subscriptions:** 385 journals and other serials; 20 newspapers. **Services:** Interlibrary loan; copying; library open to the public with restrictions. **Automated Operations:** Computerized cataloging. **Computerized Information Services:** DIALOG Information Services. Performs searches on fee basis. **Networks/Consortia:** Member of SOLINET, South Carolina Library Network. **Remarks:** FAX: (803)661-8041. **Staff:** Linda Coe.

★5858★
Florence-Lauderdale Public Library - Genealogy, Local History, & Civil War Collection (Hist)
218 N. Wood Ave. Phone: (205)764-6563
Florence, AL 35630 Penelope Blankenship, Libn.
Subjects: Genealogy, local history, Civil War. **Holdings:** 1700 books; 450 bound periodical volumes; 700 reels of microfilm; 9000 microfiche; 18 linear feet of manuscripts. **Services:** Copying; collection open to the public. **Remarks:** FAX: (205)764-6629.

Arturo Taracena Flores Library
See: **University of Texas at Austin - Benson Latin American Collection** (19380)

★5859★
Nieves M. Flores Memorial Library (Area-Ethnic)
254 Martyr St. Phone: (671)472-6417
Agana, GU 96910 Frank R. San Agustin, Territorial Libn.
Founded: 1949. **Staff:** Prof 5; Other 33. **Subjects:** Western Pacific, World War II. **Special Collections:** Guam documents and archives. **Holdings:** 194,098 books; 1931 bound periodical volumes; 7600 U.S. documents; 2716 pamphlets; 859 kits; 413 cassettes; 1665 videocassettes; 1190 phonograph records; 86 tapes; 1549 films and filmstrips; 2500 local documents; 3600 microforms. **Subscriptions:** 550 journals and other serials; 30 newspapers. **Services:** Interlibrary loan; copying; library open to the public. **Automated Operations:** Computerized public access catalog, cataloging, acquisitions, and serials. **Computerized Information Services:** Internal databases. **Publications:** Guam Newsletter; Life of San Vitores; 1898 Census. **Special Catalogs:** Union List of Serials, annual - to contributors and by request; Union Catalog of Guam & Pacific Area Materials (1979). **Special Indexes:** Index to Vital Statistics; Index to the Guam Recorder; Index to Pacific Daily News. **Remarks:** Library is a subregional library for the blind and physically handicapped. Maintains four branch libraries. Alternate telephone number(s): 472-8264. FAX: (671)477-9777. **Staff:** Carmen Kaneshi, Cat.; Alvina M. Quan, Ser.Supv.

★5860★
Florida A&M University - College of Education - Curriculum Laboratory (Educ)
203-C Gore Education Center Phone: (904)599-3366
Tallahassee, FL 32307 Cornelia Akins Taylor, Libn.
Founded: 1954. **Staff:** Prof 2; Other 3. **Subjects:** Education. **Holdings:** 15,008 volumes; children's books; teaching aids; curriculum guides; state of Florida school reports, guidelines, textbooks; AV programs. **Subscriptions:** 60 journals and other serials. **Services:** Interlibrary loan; copying; laboratory open to the public with restrictions. **Automated Operations:** Computerized public access catalog, circulation, and serials. **Staff:** Dr. Elinor V. Ellis, Coord.

★5861★
Florida A&M University - Pharmacy Library (Med)
Box 367 Phone: (904)599-3753
Tallahassee, FL 32307 Pauline E. Hicks, Univ.Libn.
Founded: 1957. **Staff:** Prof 3; Other 1. **Subjects:** Pharmacy, pharmaceutical chemistry, pharmacology, pharmacognosy, clinical pharmacy, environmental toxicology, medicinal chemistry. **Holdings:** 9935 books; 6800 bound periodical volumes; AV programs. **Subscriptions:** 625 journals and other serials. **Services:** Interlibrary loan (fee); copying; SDI; library open to the public with restrictions; CD-ROM (Drugdex). **Computerized Information Services:** DIALOG Information Services, MEDLINE, TOXLINE. **Publications:** New Acquisitions List; How to Find it Out in Pharmacy Library. **Remarks:** FAX: (904)599-3347. **Staff:** Ella Woodbury; Brenda Wright.

★5862★
Florida A&M University - School of Business & Industry - Coleman Library (Bus-Fin)
1 SBI Plaza Phone: (904)561-2326
Tallahassee, FL 32307 Bessyee G. Washington, Libn.
Founded: 1971. **Staff:** Prof 1; Other 1. **Subjects:** Management, finance, accounting, marketing, economics, labor relations. **Special Collections:** Robert Trueblood Collection; SBA Collection (2 VF drawers). **Holdings:** 10,015 books; 2367 bound periodical volumes; 8 VF drawers of career materials; 8 VF drawers of annual reports; 8 VF drawers of information files. **Subscriptions:** 260 journals and other serials; 22 newspapers. **Services:** Interlibrary loan; copying; library open to the public for reference use only. **Automated Operations:** Computerized cataloging, acquisitions, serials, and circulation. **Computerized Information Services:** CD-ROMs. **Publications:** Acquisitions list - for internal distribution only. **Remarks:** FAX: (904)599-3533.

★5863★
Florida A&M University - School of Journalism, Media & Graphic Arts - Resources Center (Info Sci)
Tallahassee, FL 32307 Phone: (904)599-3704
Gloria T. Woody, Dir./Libn.
Founded: 1976. **Staff:** Prof 1; Other 2. **Subjects:** Newspaper and broadcast journalism, public relations, photography, graphic design, magazine production, printing, production technology, printing management and supervision. **Holdings:** 1300 books; 447 volumes on microfilm; 26 volumes on microfiche; 119 video cassettes; 17 filmstrips and cassettes; 40 slide shows; 28 audio cassettes. **Subscriptions:** 75 journals and other serials; 8 newspapers. **Services:** Interlibrary loan (through main library); copying; center open to the public. **Automated Operations:** Computerized public access catalog, serials, acquisitions, and circulation (LUIS).

★5864★
Florida A&M University - Schools of Nursing/Allied Health Sciences Library (Med)
Box 136
Florida A&M University Phone: (904)599-3872
Tallahassee, FL 32307 Julita C. Awkard, Libn.
Staff: Prof 1; Other 2. **Subjects:** Nursing, allied health sciences, respiratory therapy, physical therapy, health care management, medical records administration. **Holdings:** 6000 books; 5194 software and hardware programs; 400 microfilm; 3000 microfiche; 150 films and AV materials. **Subscriptions:** 235 journals and other serials. **Services:** Interlibrary loan copying; SDI; library open to the public. **Automated Operations:** Computerized public access catalog, cataloging, acquisitions, serials, and circulation. **Computerized Information Services:** MEDLINE, NurseSearch. Performs searches on fee basis. **Publications:** Library handbook; newsletter. **Remarks:** Alternate telephone number(s): 599-3900.

★5865★
Florida A&M University - Technology Library (Sci-Engr)
B.B. Tech Center, A-301
Box 164 Phone: (904)599-3050
Tallahassee, FL 32307 Margaret F. Wilson, Univ.Libn.
Staff: Prof 1; Other 1. **Subjects:** Civil engineering, computer science, architecture, engineering, electronics, graphic arts, industrial education. **Holdings:** 11,000 books; 3500 bound periodical volumes; 823 reels of microfilm; 165 filmstrips; 75 films; 1000 microfiche; 210 other cataloged items. **Subscriptions:** 200 journals and other serials. **Services:** Interlibrary loan; copying; library open to the public for reference use only. **Automated Operations:** Computerized cataloging, acquisitions, serials, and circulation. **Computerized Information Services:** DIALOG Information Services, RLIN, OCLC; LUIS (internal database). **Networks/Consortia:** Member of Florida Library Network (FLN).

★5866★
Florida Atlantic University - South Atlantic Regional Resource Center (Educ)
1236 N. University Dr. Phone: (305)473-6106
Plantation, FL 33322 Isa Polansky, Libn.
Founded: 1980. **Staff:** Prof 1; Other 2. **Subjects:** Special education. **Special Collections:** Special Education Legislation and the Law. **Holdings:** 750 volumes. **Subscriptions:** 20 journals and other serials. **Services:** Center open to faculty and students. **Computerized Information Services:** NASA-Southern Technology Applications Center (STAC); internal database; SpecialNet (electronic mail service). **Publications:** LRE Topical Update, semiannual. **Remarks:** FAX: (305)424-4309. Electronic mail address(es): SARRC (SpecialNet).

★5867★
Florida Audubon Society - Information Center (Env-Cons)
460 Hwy. 436, Suite 200
Casselberry, FL 32707 Phone: (407)260-8300
Staff: 1. **Subjects:** Energy, environment, pollution, land use, endangered species, water resources, regional planning. **Holdings:** 1000 books; 1000 reports and documents; source materials on microfilm. **Services:** Library not open to the public. **Formerly:** Located in Maitland, FL.

★5868★
Florida Bankers Association - Library (Bus-Fin)
341 N. Mills Ave.
Box 538847
Orlando, FL 32853-8847 Phone: (407)896-6511
Founded: 1967. **Subjects:** Banking, finance, association operation. **Holdings:** 650 books; 12 bound periodical volumes; 8 VF drawers of clippings and pamphlets. **Subscriptions:** 40 journals and other serials. **Services:** Copying; library open to the public. **Remarks:** FAX: (407)896-9720.

★5869★
Florida Baptist Schools, Inc. - Copeland Memorial Library (Rel-Phil)
P.O. Box 2758 Phone: (813)684-1389
Brandon, FL 33509-2748 Joy E. Williams, Libn.
Staff: Prof 1. **Subjects:** Bible, theology, missions, Christian education, Biblical languages, music. **Holdings:** 20,000 books; 500 bound periodical volumes; 35 dissertations; 30 tapes; 158 cassette tapes. **Subscriptions:** 37 journals and other serials; 13 newspapers. **Services:** Interlibrary loan; copying; library open to the public with restrictions.

★5870★
Florida Baptist Theological College - Ida J. McMillan Library (Rel-Phil)
1306 College Dr. Phone: (904)263-3261
Graceville, FL 32440 Dr. Irvin H. Murrell, Jr., Libn.
Founded: 1943. **Staff:** Prof 1; Other 11. **Subjects:** Theology, Christian education, Baptist studies, church music, marriage, ethics, philosophy. **Special Collections:** College archives. **Holdings:** 47,324 books; 4293 bound periodical volumes. **Subscriptions:** 391 journals and other serials. **Services:** Interlibrary loan; copying; library open to the public. **Automated Operations:** Computerized public access catalog and cataloging. **Computerized Information Services:** BIBLIOFILE.

★5871★
Florida Conservation Foundation, Inc. - Environmental Information Center (Env-Cons)
1251-B Miller Ave. Phone: (407)644-5377
Winter Park, FL 32789-4827 Marcia Ramsdell, Dir.
Staff: Prof 2. **Subjects:** Environment, conservation, solar heating, natural areas. **Special Collections:** Above subjects as they relate to Florida. **Holdings:** 6000 environmental documents. **Services:** Copying; center open to the public for reference use only. **Publications:** List of publications - available on request. **Staff:** Mary D. Carmichael, Libn.

★5872★
Florida Diagnostic & Learning Resources System - Media Center (Educ)
100 S. Andrews Ave. Phone: (305)357-7444
Ft. Lauderdale, FL 33301 Merrill M. Murray, Media Spec.
Founded: 1978. **Staff:** Prof 1; Other 4. **Subjects:** Special education, teaching techniques, learning strategies, personal growth, handicapped awareness. **Holdings:** 10,000 books; 10,000 AV materials; instructional software; ERIC microfiche. **Subscriptions:** 350 journals and other serials. **Services:** Interlibrary loan; copying; center open to teachers, parents, and professionals who work with exceptional children. **Computerized Information Services:** DIALOG Information Services; internal database; SpecialNet (electronic mail service). **Publications:** FDLRS newsletter, quarterly. **Special Catalogs:** FDLRS Materials Catalog and supplements, annual. **Remarks:** Maintained by Broward County School Board. **Formerly:** Located in Pompano Beach, FL.

Florida Educational Information Service
See: **Florida State University - Center for Instructional Development and Services** (5911)

★5873★
Florida Historical Society - Library (Hist)
P.O. Box 290197 Phone: (813)974-3815
Tampa, FL 33687-0197 Dr. Lewis N. Wynne
Founded: 1856. **Staff:** Prof 1; Other 1. **Subjects:** Florida history. **Holdings:** Figures not available. **Subscriptions:** 73 journals and other serials. **Services:** Copying; library open to the public. **Automated Operations:** Computerized public access catalog, cataloging, acquisitions, and serials. **Publications:** Florida Historical Quarterly; Florida History Society Report (newsletter) - to members. **Remarks:** Library located at University of South Florida Library, Tampa, FL 33620.

★5874★
Florida Hospital - Medical Library (Med)
601 E. Rollins St. Phone: (407)897-1860
Orlando, FL 32803 Barbara Beckner, Libn.
Founded: 1950. **Staff:** Prof 2; Other 2. **Subjects:** Medicine, surgery. **Special Collections:** Nursing (350 books; 150 bound periodical volumes). **Holdings:** 1500 books; 7000 bound periodical volumes; 1 VF drawer; 25 titles on microfiche. **Subscriptions:** 320 journals and other serials. **Services:** Interlibrary loan; copying; library open to the public by telephone request. **Computerized Information Services:** MEDLARS. **Networks/Consortia:** Member of Central Florida Library Consortium (CFLC). **Remarks:** FAX: (407)897-1786. **Staff:** Dorothy Stoneback.

★5875★
Florida Institute of Phosphate Research - Library and Information Clearinghouse (Env-Cons)
1855 W. Main St. Phone: (813)534-7160
Bartow, FL 33830 Betty Faye Stidham, Libn.
Founded: 1980. **Staff:** Prof 1; Other 2. **Subjects:** Reclamation, ecology, phosphates, phosphate mining, minerals processing, radiation, fertilizers, environment. **Holdings:** 4700 books; 500 bound periodical volumes; 185 technical reports on microfiche; 260 maps. **Subscriptions:** 85 journals and other serials. **Services:** Interlibrary loan; copying; SDI; library open to the public. **Automated Operations:** Computerized cataloging. **Computerized Information Services:** DIALOG Information Services, Chemical Abstracts Service (CAS), OCLC. Performs searches on fee basis. **Networks/Consortia:** Member of Florida Library Network (FLN), Tampa Bay Library Consortium, Inc. (TBLC), SOLINET. **Publications:** Library and Information Clearinghouse Newsletter, quarterly. **Remarks:** FIPR is a state-supported research organization. FAX: (813)534-7165.

★5876★
Florida Institute of Technology - Evans Library (Sci-Engr)
150 W. University Blvd. Phone: (407)768-8000
Melbourne, FL 32901 Llewellyn L. Henson, Dir. of Libs.
Staff: Prof 7; Other 16. **Subjects:** Engineering - electrical, mechanical, computer, civil, aerospace, ocean; aeronautics; biology; chemistry; mathematics; management; psychology; space sciences; oceanography; physics; science education. **Special Collections:** General (Ret.) John Bruce Medaris Collection (personal papers and memorabilia); Edwin A. Link Collection (ocean-related personal papers); Botanical Collection; Indian River Lagoon Collection. **Holdings:** 225,661 books; 17,000 bound periodical volumes; 160 feet of archival materials and masters' theses; 20 linear feet of technical reports; 40 VF drawers of pamphlets and clippings; U.S. Government document depository. **Subscriptions:** 2055 journals and other serials. **Services:** Interlibrary loan; copying; library open to the public on fee basis. **Automated Operations:** Computerized public access catalog, cataloging, acquisitions, circulation, and serials (NOTIS). **Computerized Information Services:** DIALOG Information Services, STN International, NASA/RECON, OCLC. Performs searches on fee basis. **Networks/Consortia:** Member of SOLINET, Florida Library Network (FLN), Central Florida Library Consortium (CFLC). **Publications:** A Bibliography of the Edwin A. Link Collection of the Evans Library at F.I.T. **Remarks:** FAX: (407)724-2559. **Staff:** Thomas A. McFarland, Hd., Tech.Serv.; Deborah Anderson, Hd., Ref.Serv.; Jean C. Sparks, Hd., Govt.Docs.; Rosemary F. Kean, Hd., Circ.; Kathy Sales, Sys.Libn.

Florida Marine Research Institute
See: **Florida (State) Department of Natural Resources - Florida Marine Research Institute** (5896)

Florida Mental Health Institute
See: **University of South Florida** (19320)

Florida Museum of Natural History
See: **University of Florida - Florida Museum of Natural History** (18570)

★5877★
Florida Ophthalmic Institute - Library (Med)
7106 N.W. 11th Pl. Phone: (904)331-2020
Gainesville, FL 32605-3140 Norman S. Levy
Founded: 1977. **Subjects:** Ophthalmology, visual sciences. **Holdings:** 104 books; 14 bound periodical volumes. **Subscriptions:** 14 journals and other serials. **Services:** Library not open to the public. **Computerized Information Services:** Internal database. **Remarks:** FAX: (904)331-2019.

Florida Photographic Collection
See: **Florida (State) Division of Libraries & Information Services - Bureau of Archives & Records Management** (5898)

★5878★
Florida Power Corporation - Corporate Library (Energy)
Library A3
3201 34th St., S. Phone: (813)866-5304
St. Petersburg, FL 33711-3828 Douglas W. Cornwell, Corp.Libn.
Founded: 1972. **Staff:** Prof 1; Other 2. **Subjects:** Electric utilities, electric power and power resources, environmental engineering, ecology, atomic power plants, electrical engineering, manpower, personnel management, mechanical and civil engineering. **Special Collections:** Florida Power Corporation publications and archives; Electric Power Research Institute (EPRI) reports; nuclear regulations; multimedia materials (including videotape training materials, audiotapes, software tutorials). **Holdings:** 12,000 books; 3000 bound periodical volumes; 1000 technical reports; 9 drawers microfiche; 200 audio cassettes; 45 software tutorials; videotapes. **Subscriptions:** 425 journals and other serials; 10 newspapers. **Services:** Interlibrary loan; copying; SDI; library open to the public for reference use only and by appointment. **Automated Operations:** Computerized cataloging, acquisitions, circulation, and serials. **Computerized Information Services:** DIALOG Information Services, Integrated Technical Information System (ITIS), BRS Information Technologies, ORBIT Search Service, CompuServe Information Service, NewsNet, Inc., WILSONLINE, OCLC, Dow Jones News/Retrieval; DIALMAIL, CompuServe Information Service (electronic mail services). **Networks/Consortia:** Member of Tampa Bay Library Consortium, Inc. (TBLC), SOLINET, Florida Library Network (FLN). **Publications:** Directory of Library Services; periodicals holdings list, both irregular. **Remarks:** FAX: (813)866-4992. Electronic mail address(es): 10981 (DIALMAIL); 73367,3063 (CompuServe Information Service). **Staff:** Jo Ann Skrodenis, Lib.Spec.

★5879★
Florida Power & Light Company - Corporate Library (Energy)
9250 W. Flagler St.
Box 029100 Phone: (305)552-3210
Miami, FL 33102 Caryl Congleton, Libn.
Founded: 1975. **Staff:** Prof 1; Other 5. **Subjects:** Public utilities, nuclear science, mechanical and nuclear engineering, management and business, mathematics and statistics, safety engineering, energy, environment, materials technology, quality improvement, total quality control. **Special Collections:** VSMF industry and military standards; product catalogs. **Holdings:** 5000 books; 3200 technical reports (uncataloged). **Subscriptions:** 600 periodicals; 15 newspapers. **Services:** Interlibrary loan; library not open to the public. **Automated Operations:** Computerized public access catalog, acquisitions, serials, and circulation. **Computerized Information Services:** NEXIS, DIALOG Information Services, DunsPrint. **Publications:** Books 'N Stacks, Fiche 'N Facts, quarterly - to personnel. **Remarks:** Alternate telephone numbers are 552-3232, 552-3206, and 552-3211. FAX: (305)552-4181 and 552-4183.

★5880★
Florida Public Service Commission - Library (Energy)
Fletcher Bldg., Rm. 245
101 E. Gaines St. Phone: (904)488-0733
Tallahassee, FL 32399-0850 Brenda B. Monroe, Libn.
Founded: 1968. **Staff:** Prof 1. **Subjects:** Public and electric utilities, energy, telephone. **Holdings:** 8800 volumes. **Subscriptions:** 119 journals and other serials. **Services:** Interlibrary loan; library open to the public for reference use only. **Computerized Information Services:** WESTLAW. Performs searches on fee basis. **Remarks:** FAX: (904)487-0509.

★5881★
Florida Publishing Co. - Editorial Library (Publ)
1 Riverside Ave. Phone: (904)359-4237
Jacksonville, FL 32202 Maryann P. Sterzel, Dir.
Founded: 1967. **Staff:** Prof 4; Other 2. **Subjects:** Newspaper reference topics. **Holdings:** 2000 books; 2400 reports, pamphlets, studies; 4 million clippings; 750,000 photographs. **Subscriptions:** 15 journals and other serials; 30 newspapers. **Services:** Library not open to the public. **Computerized Information Services:** VU/TEXT Information Services, NEXIS, DataTimes. **Remarks:** FAX: (904)359-4478.

★5882★
Florida School for the Deaf and Blind - Library for the Deaf (Educ)
207 San Marco Ave. Phone: (904)823-4361
St. Augustine, FL 32084 Linda L. Zimmerman, Hd.Libn.
Founded: 1885. **Staff:** Prof 1; Other 1. **Subjects:** Education of the deaf (pre-kindergarden through high school), sign language and the deaf, fiction and

nonfiction (low level, high interest). **Special Collections:** Education professional collection (audiology, sign language, speech pathology); professional library; Gore Hall Preschool Library; Florida School for the Deaf and Blind Archives; media collection. **Holdings:** 13,500 books; 5 bound periodical volumes; pamphlets; filmstrips; captioned films; film loops. **Subscriptions:** 68 journals and other serials. **Services:** Library open to the public for reference use only. **Networks/Consortia:** Member of Florida Library Network (FLN). **Staff:** Lou Greco, Hd. Media Spec.; Bob Graham, Dir., Instr.Tech.

★5883★
Florida Solar Energy Center - Library (Energy)
300 State Rd. 401 Phone: (407)783-0300
Cape Canaveral, FL 32920 Iraida B. Rickling, Univ.Libn.
Founded: 1975. **Staff:** Prof 2; Other 3. **Subjects:** Solar and alternative sources of energy, science, technology. **Holdings:** 7876 books; 1654 bound periodical volumes; 14,271 technical documents; 6798 vertical files; 7398 slides; 56,292 microfiche; 11 films; 51 videotapes. **Subscriptions:** 321 journals and other serials. **Services:** Interlibrary loan; copying; library open to the public with restrictions. **Computerized Information Services:** DIALOG Information Services. **Networks/Consortia:** Member of SOLINET, Central Florida Library Consortium (CFLC). **Publications:** Acquisitions bulletin, monthly - for internal distribution only; Solar Alert, a Current Awareness Bulletin. **Remarks:** The Florida Solar Energy Center is part of the Florida State University System and is affiliated with the University of Central Florida. An additional telephone line called SUNCOM is 364-1120. FAX: (407)783-2571. **Staff:** Judy Hansen, Asst.Univ.Libn.

Florida State Archives
See: **Florida (State) Division of Libraries & Information Services - Bureau of Archives & Records Management** (5898)

★5884★
Florida State Board of Regents - Records and Archives (Educ)
325 W. Gaines St., Rm. 1626 FEC Phone: (904)488-6826
Tallahassee, FL 32399-1950 Jack Richardson, Rec.Adm.
Founded: 1963. **Staff:** Prof 1; Other 3. **Subjects:** Higher education - finance, planning, administration, students, faculty, manpower. **Holdings:** 3100 books; 2600 microforms; 8 VF drawers of pamphlets; 20 VF drawers of archival materials. **Subscriptions:** 70 journals and other serials; 12 newspapers. **Services:** Interlibrary loan; open to the public by appointment. **Publications:** List of current library acquisitions, quarterly. **Special Catalogs:** Catalog of archival records and records management (card). **Remarks:** FAX: (904)487-4568.

★5885★
Florida State Court of Appeal - 2nd District - Law Library (Law)
1005 E. Memorial Blvd.
Box 327 Phone: (813)499-2290
Lakeland, FL 33802 Jack Schoonover, Chf. Judge
Staff: 1. **Subjects:** Law. **Holdings:** 20,000 books. **Subscriptions:** 14 journals and other serials. **Services:** Library open to the public for reference use only. **Remarks:** FAX: (813)499-2277. **Staff:** Lori Holmes.

★5886★
Florida State Court of Appeal - 3rd District - Law Library (Law)
2001 S.W. 117th Ave. Phone: (305)221-1200
Miami, FL 33175 Joanne Sargent, Libn./Staff Att.
Founded: 1960. **Staff:** Prof 1. **Subjects:** Law. **Holdings:** 20,000 books. **Subscriptions:** 67 journals and other serials. **Services:** Library open to the public with restrictions. **Networks/Consortia:** Member of Florida Library Network (FLN).

★5887★
Florida (State) Department of Agriculture and Consumer Services - Division of Plant Industry - Library (Biol Sci)
Box 147100 Phone: (904)372-3505
Gainesville, FL 32614-7100 Beverly Pope, Libn.
Founded: 1915. **Staff:** Prof 1; Other 1. **Subjects:** Entomology, apiary, plant pathology, plant inspection, nematology. **Special Collections:** Taxonomic Entomology Collection; Division of Plant Industry Historical Archives and Entomology Museum. **Holdings:** 14,000 volumes; 124 microfiche. **Subscriptions:** 500 journals and other serials. **Services:** Interlibrary loan; copying; library open to the public for reference use only. **Computerized Information Services:** DIALOG Information Services; InterNet, BITNET (electronic mail services). **Publications:** List of publications - available on request. **Remarks:** FAX: (904)372-2501. Electronic mail address(es): dpilib.nervm (BITNET); dpilib.nervm.nerdc.ufl.edu (InterNet).

★5888★
Florida (State) Department of Commerce - Research Library (Bus-Fin)
301 Collins Bldg.
107 West Gaines St. Phone: (904)487-2971
Tallahassee, FL 32399-2000 Martha Morrison, Libn.
Staff: Prof 1. **Subjects:** Florida - economic and industrial development, census, cities, counties, history, description; employment and unemployment; income; international trade; tourism statistics. **Holdings:** 3000 books; 4500 government documents; 2200 subject folders in 100 VF drawers. **Subscriptions:** 100 journals and other serials. **Services:** Copying (limited); library open to the public for reference use only.

★5889★
Florida (State) Department of Education - Florida Division of Blind Services - Bureau of Library Services for the Blind and Physically Handicapped (Aud-Vis)
420 Platt St. Phone: (904)254-3824
Daytona Beach, FL 32114-2804 Donald John Weber, Dir.
Founded: 1950. **Staff:** Prof 6; Other 25. **Subjects:** Recreational reading material for the print handicapped, blindness, physical handicaps, rehabilitation. **Special Collections:** Braille and recorded books about Florida and the South. **Holdings:** 850,000 books recorded on disc and cassette; 60,000 books in braille. **Subscriptions:** 250 journals and other serials. **Services:** Interlibrary loan; copying; library open to the public; serves all visually and physically handicapped residents of Florida. **Automated Operations:** Computerized circulation. **Computerized Information Services:** DIALOG Information Services, BRS Information Technologies, BIBLIOFILE. **Networks/Consortia:** Member of National Library Service for the Blind & Physically Handicapped (NLS). **Publications:** Newsletter, quarterly - to the public; Hooked on Books (children's newsletter); El Noticorio (Spanish newsletter). **Remarks:** The library maintains ten subregional libraries in public libraries in Fort Lauderdale, Jacksonville, Miami, Orlando, West Palm Beach, Fort Myers, Bradenton, Pensacola, Cocoa, and Tampa. Toll-free telephone number(s): (800)342-5627 (in Florida). **Remarks:** FAX: (904)238-3160. **Staff:** Michael Gunde, Assoc.Dir. ; Mary Ann Sumner, Tech.Serv. & Ref.Libn.; Diane Schultz, Volunteer Coord.; Dorothy Minor, Rd./Fld.Serv.Sect.; Richard Temple, Comp.Prog.

★5890★
Florida (State) Department of Environmental Regulation - Library (Env-Cons)
2600 Blair Stone Rd. Phone: (904)488-0890
Tallahassee, FL 32301 Jacqueline W. McGorty, Libn.
Founded: 1973. **Staff:** Prof 1; Other 1. **Subjects:** Water quality and quantity, air pollution, toxicology, hazardous waste, solid waste. **Special Collections:** National Oceanic and Atmospheric Administration climatic data; HURD aerial photographs; Environmental Protection Agency, U.S. Geological Survey, and Florida Bureau of Geology reports. **Holdings:** 20,000 books and technical reports; 1 VF drawer; 1500 maps. **Subscriptions:** 200 journals and other serials. **Services:** Interlibrary loan; copying; library open to the public for reference use only. **Computerized Information Services:** DIALOG Information Services, NLM, Chemical Information Systems, Inc. (CIS); Dialcom Inc. (electronic mail service). **Networks/Consortia:** Member of Panhandle Library Access Network (PLAN). **Remarks:** FAX: (904)487-4938.

★5891★
Florida (State) Department of Insurance and State Treasurer - Department of Insurance - Law Library (Law)
Larson Bldg., Rm. 412
200 E. Gaines St. Phone: (904)488-4540
Tallahassee, FL 32399-0300 Pat Milam, Libn.
Founded: 1960. **Staff:** 2. **Subjects:** Insurance and administrative law, civil procedure. **Holdings:** 2100 volumes. **Subscriptions:** 10 journals and other serials. **Services:** Library not open to the public. **Remarks:** FAX: (904)488-0697.

★5892★
Florida (State) Department of Law Enforcement - Law Library (Law)
2331 Phillips Rd.
Box 1489 Phone: (904)488-8323
Tallahassee, FL 32308 Betty C. James, Exec.Sec./Libn.
Staff: 1. **Subjects:** Law enforcement. **Holdings:** 1225 volumes. **Subscriptions:** 30 journals and other serials. **Services:** Library not open to the public. **Computerized Information Services:** WESTLAW. **Remarks:** FAX: (904)488-2189.

★5893★
Florida (State) Department of Legal Affairs - Attorney General's Library (Law)
Capitol Bldg., Rm. 1604 Phone: (904)488-6040
Tallahassee, FL 32399-1050 Donna F. Mills, Libn.
Staff: Prof 1; Other 1. **Subjects:** Law. **Special Collections:** Old Florida legal materials. **Holdings:** 50,000 volumes. **Subscriptions:** 100 journals and other serials. **Services:** Copying; library open to the public. **Computerized Information Services:** WESTLAW. **Remarks:** FAX: (904)922-6425.

★5894★
Florida (State) Department of Natural Resources - Bureau of Geology Library (Sci-Engr)
903 W. Tennessee St. Phone: (904)488-9380
Tallahassee, FL 32304 Alice N. Jordan, Libn.
Founded: 1908. **Staff:** Prof 1; Other 1. **Subjects:** Geology, hydrology, mineral commodities, mining and reclamation, stratigraphy, micropaleontology, petroleum engineering, water resources, hydrology. **Special Collections:** Robert Burns Campbell Collection of geology (1400 general and geological works); rare books in geology (150 volumes); photographic archives (2500 slides and prints); H.S. Puri micropaleontology collection. **Holdings:** 2300 books; 3000 bound journal volumes; 10,000 bound federal and state documents; 190 pamphlets; 500 reports and journal article reprints; 200 reels of microfilm; 1500 aerial photographs; 9000 maps. **Subscriptions:** 35 journals and other serials. **Services:** Interlibrary loan; copying; library open to researchers by appointment. **Computerized Information Services:** DIALOG Information Services. **Networks/Consortia:** Member of Florida Library Network (FLN). **Publications:** Subject bibliographies (unpublished). **Special Indexes:** Index to bureau publications. **Remarks:** FAX: (904)488-8086.

Florida (State) Department of Natural Resources - Division of State Lands - Bureau of State Land Management
See: **Florida (State) Department of Natural Resources - Division of State Lands - Bureau of Survey and Mapping** (5895)

★5895★
Florida (State) Department of Natural Resources - Division of State Lands - Bureau of Survey and Mapping - Title Section (Plan)
3900 Commonwealth Blvd. Phone: (904)488-8123
Tallahassee, FL 32303 F.R. Williams, Planner IV
Founded: 1908. **Staff:** 2. **Subjects:** Land matters involving the title and description of the public domain. **Special Collections:** Spanish Archives (dealing with land matters). **Holdings:** 750 volumes; surveys; plats; maps; field notes; patents. **Services:** Copying; collection open to the public.

★5896★
Florida (State) Department of Natural Resources - Florida Marine Research Institute - Library (Biol Sci)
100 8th Ave., S.E. Phone: (813)896-8626
St. Petersburg, FL 33701-5095 Sandra J. Metzger, Lib.Hd.
Founded: 1955. **Staff:** Prof 1. **Subjects:** Marine biology, ichthyology, invertebrata, algology, mariculture, ecology. **Holdings:** 6000 books; 40,000 reprints. **Subscriptions:** 1700 journal titles and other serials. **Services:** Interlibrary loan; library open to the public for reference use only. **Computerized Information Services:** DIALOG Information Services, Current Contents. **Publications:** Florida Marine Research Publications, irregular; Memoirs of the Hourglass Cruises, irregular. **Remarks:** FAX: (813)823-0166. **Staff:** James M. Thomas, CIS; Rose Prince, ILL.

Florida (State) Department of State - Division of Historical Resources - Historic Pensacola Preservation Board
See: **Historic Pensacola Preservation Board** (7249)

Florida (State) Department of State - Division of Library and Information Services - State Library of Florida
See: **State Library of Florida** (15686)

★5897★
Florida (State) Department of Transportation - Transportation Research Center Library (Trans)
Haydon Burns Bldg.
605 Suwannee St., MS 30 Phone: (904)488-8572
Tallahassee, FL 32301 Sandy Porras, Adm.Asst.
Founded: 1969. **Staff:** 1. **Subjects:** Transportation - engineering, planning, administration, public transportation operations, construction, maintenance, general management. **Special Collections:** Transportation research. **Holdings:** Figures not available. **Services:** Interlibrary loan. **Computerized Information Services:** DIALOG Information Services. **Networks/Consortia:** Member of Florida Library Network (FLN). **Remarks:** FAX: (904)487-3403.

★5898★
Florida (State) Division of Libraries & Information Services - Bureau of Archives & Records Management - Florida State Archives (Hist)
R.A. Gray Bldg.
500 S. Bronough St. Phone: (904)487-2073
Tallahassee, FL 32399-0250 Jim Berberich, Chf.
Staff: Prof 12; Other 6. **Subjects:** Florida history. **Special Collections:** Florida Photographic Collection (history and culture of Florida; 750,000 photographic images); Florida Genealogical Collection (6000 volumes; 5000 reels of microfilm). **Holdings:** 25,000 cubic feet of state historical records, 1822 to present; 1250 cubic feet of manuscripts. **Services:** Copying; archives open to the public. **Computerized Information Services:** Internal database. **Remarks:** Contains the holdings of the former Florida Photographic Collection. FAX: (904)488-4894. **Staff:** Larry LaFollette, Presrv.Supv.; David Coles, Ref.Supv.; Susan Potts McDonald, Arrangement Supv.; Joan Morris, Photo.Supv.

★5899★
Florida (State) Division of Libraries & Information Services - Bureau of Florida Folklife Programs - Archives (Hist)
Box 265 Phone: (904)397-2192
White Springs, FL 32096 David Reddy, Folklife Prog.Adm.
Staff: Prof 1; Other 1. **Subjects:** Folklife - arts and crafts, storytelling, music, foodways, architecture; ethnic music; occupations. **Special Collections:** Florida Folk Festival recordings (600 audiotapes); Thelma Boltin papers (3 linear feet); folklore and folklife field recordings (200 audiotapes and cassettes); slides and photographs (4000); WPA files and recordings on Florida; Guy Miles Collection (700 reel-to-reel tapes); Stetson Kennedy WPA Collection on Florida folklife. **Holdings:** 800 books; 6 VF drawers of clippings, newsletters, pamphlets; 14 boxes of sound recordings. **Subscriptions:** 37 journals and other serials. **Services:** Copying; archives open to the public with restrictions. **Publications:** Festival Programs, annual; Florida Folk Arts Directory (1989). **Special Indexes:** Accession Register (notebook); indexes and work sheets for reel-to-reel tapes and cassettes.

★5900★
Florida State Energy Office - Department of Community Affairs - Library (Energy)
2740 Centerview Dr. Phone: (904)488-6764
Tallahassee, FL 32399-2100 Vera M. Tucker, Adm.Asst.
Staff: 1. **Subjects:** Energy, renewable resources, solar energy, cogeneration, data analysis, transportation. **Holdings:** Energy Information Administration (EIA) documents; Federal Energy Regulatory Commission statutes and regulations. **Subscriptions:** 20 journals and other serials. **Services:** Library open to the public with restrictions. **Remarks:** FAX: (904)488-7688. **Formed by the merger of:** Florida State Office of the Governor - Governor's Energy Office - Library and Florida Department of Community Affairs.

★5901★
Florida State Hospital - Health Science Library (Med)
Chattahoochee, FL 32324 Phone: (904)663-7205
Linda R. Hatcher, Lib.Asst.
Staff: 2. **Subjects:** Psychiatry, medicine, psychology, nursing, social service. **Holdings:** 2000 books; 75 bound periodical volumes. **Subscriptions:** 50 journals and other serials; 5 newspapers. **Services:** Library not open to the public.

★5902★
Florida State Hospital - Library Services (Med)
Chattahoochee, FL 32324 Phone: (904)663-7671
Jane Marie Hamilton, Dir.
Founded: 1945. **Staff:** Prof 3; Other 4. **Subjects:** General and mental health topics. **Special Collections:** Career planning; Florida; self help. **Holdings:** 15,000 volumes; 1200 films and filmstrips; 600 compact discs; photographs; toys; games; models. **Subscriptions:** 108 journals and other serials; 5 newspapers. **Services:** Interlibrary loan; library open to hospital staff, patients, and other libraries in the area. **Remarks:** Library Services includes the Patient/Staff Library, Central Forensic Library, Forensic Admission and Evaluation Library, and Correction Mental Health Institution. **Staff:** Rodney R. Hughes; Daniel Weine.

★5903★
Florida State Legislature - Joint Legislative Management Committee - Division of Legislative Library Services (Soc Sci, Law)
The Capitol, Suite 701 Phone: (904)488-2812
Tallahassee, FL 32399-1400 B. Gene Baker, Dir.
Founded: 1949. **Staff:** Prof 5; Other 1. **Subjects:** Law; public administration, finance, welfare, transportation; natural resources. **Special Collections:** Journals of House and Senate, 1901 to present; Laws of Florida, 1822 to present; Florida Statutes, 1847 to present. **Holdings:** 24,042 classified books, general reference works, state and federal documents; 92 VF drawers of committee reports and subject files; 972 reels of microfilm; 10,200 microfiche of federal documents, state session laws, periodicals. **Subscriptions:** 800 journals and other serials; 15 newspapers. **Services:** Interlibrary loan; copying; division open to the public on a limited schedule. **Automated Operations:** Computerized public access catalog, cataloging, serials, and circulation (LUIS). **Computerized Information Services:** LEXIS, NEXIS, WESTLAW, State Net 50, DIALOG Information Services; internal databases. **Publications:** Summary of General Legislation, annual; User's Manual, irregular - free upon request; checklist of recent acquisitions, monthly; Checklist of Recent Legislative Publications, quarterly. **Remarks:** FAX: (904)488-9879. **Staff:** Janet M. Lanigan, Ass.Dir.; Jo An Mahaffey, Libn.; Pamela Bagby, Libn.; Delbra McGriff, Archv.

(Florida) State Library of Florida
See: **State Library of Florida** (15686)

★5904★
Florida (State) Medical Entomology Laboratory Library (Biol Sci)
IFAS, University of Florida
200 9th St., S.E. Phone: (407)778-7200
Vero Beach, FL 32962 Carolee Zimmerman, Libn.
Founded: 1949. **Staff:** 1. **Subjects:** Biology, biochemistry, ecology, entomology, physiology, virology. **Holdings:** 5500 volumes. **Subscriptions:** 131 journals and other serials. **Services:** Library not open to the public. **Remarks:** FAX: (407)778-7205.

Florida State Museum
See: **University of Florida - Florida Museum of Natural History** (18570)

★5905★
Florida State Office of the Comptroller - Department of Banking & Finance - Legal Library (Bus-Fin, Law)
The Capitol, Suite 1302 Phone: (904)488-9896
Tallahassee, FL 32399-0350 Maggie Reschard, Libn.
Staff: Prof 1; Other 2. **Subjects:** Administrative law, securities, banking, finance, accounting and auditing. **Holdings:** 2250 books; 200 bound periodical volumes; 15 Continuing Legal Education materials; 30 Florida Attorney General's Reports. **Services:** Interlibrary loan; library not open to the public.

★5906★
Florida State Office of the Governor - Governor's Energy Office - Library
The Capitol
Tallahassee, FL 32399-0001
Defunct. Merged with Florida State Department of Community Affairs to form Florida State Energy Office - Department of Community Affairs - Library.

★5907★
(Florida State) South Florida Water Management District - Reference Center (Env-Cons)
Box 24680 Phone: (407)686-8800
West Palm Beach, FL 33416-4680 Cynthia H. Plockelman, Dir.
Founded: 1951. **Staff:** 2. **Subjects:** Flood control, hydrology, conservation of natural resources, land and water economics, water rights and legislation, land use, recreation, Florida agriculture, Florida environmental history, environmental engineering, limnology, wetland and coastal ecology. **Holdings:** 400 shelves of pamphlets, documents, reports, statistics. **Subscriptions:** 200 journals and other serials. **Services:** Interlibrary loan; center open to the public for reference use only with restrictions. **Computerized Information Services:** DIALOG Information Services. **Remarks:** FAX: (407)687-6442.

★5908★
Florida State Supreme Court Library (Law)
Supreme Court Bldg. Phone: (904)488-8919
Tallahassee, FL 32399-1926 Joan D. Cannon, Supreme Ct.Libn.
Founded: 1845. **Staff:** Prof 4.5; Other 2. **Subjects:** Law, history of law, history. **Special Collections:** Constitutional Convention files, 1966-1968; Florida Supreme Court Historical Society Archives. **Holdings:** 110,853 books; 12,453 bound periodical volumes. **Subscriptions:** 610 journals and other serials; 6 newspapers. **Services:** Copying; library open to the public for reference use only. **Computerized Information Services:** WESTLAW, DIALOG Information Services, LEXIS, NEXIS. **Remarks:** FAX: (904)922-5219. **Staff:** Jo Dowling, Asst. Supreme Ct.Libn.; Jo Smyly, Ser.Libn.; Joyce Elder, Ref.Libn.; Linda Cole, Tech.Serv.Libn.

★5909★
Florida State University - Beaches and Shores Resource Center - Library (Env-Cons)
2035 E. Paul Dirac Dr.
203 Morgan Bldg., Box 5 Phone: (904)644-2847
Tallahassee, FL 32304 Virginia Williams, Sec.
Founded: 1982. **Staff:** 6. **Subjects:** Coastal engineering, hydrodynamics, coastal processes. **Holdings:** 700 volumes. **Services:** Library not open to the public. **Remarks:** FAX: (904)644-6293.

★5910★
Florida State University - Career Center Library (Educ)
220 Bryan Hall Phone: (904)644-6431
Tallahassee, FL 32306-1035 Carol Chenoweth, Libn.
Founded: 1975. **Staff:** Prof 1; Other 15. **Subjects:** Career planning, occupational information, education and training, work experience, job hunting, employer information. **Special Collections:** Files on 500 companies that hire college graduates. **Holdings:** 600 books; 36 VF drawers; 175 audio- and videotapes. **Subscriptions:** 35 journals and other serials. **Services:** Library open to the public. **Computerized Information Services:** Career Key. 3 (internal database). **Remarks:** FAX: (904)644-3273.

★5911★
Florida State University - Center for Instructional Development and Services - Florida Educational Information Service (Educ)
2003 Apalachee Pkwy., Suite 301 Phone: (904)487-2054
Tallahassee, FL 32301 Rebecca Augustyniak, Coord.
Staff: 7. **Subjects:** Education - vocational, technical, education theory; instructional design and innovative programs. **Holdings:** 3000 volumes; 8 cabinets of publisher's listings for instructional materials; archival materials; ERIC microfiche collection. **Subscriptions:** 20 journals and other serials. **Services:** Interlibrary loan; copying; SDI; service open to the public. **Computerized Information Services:** DIALOG Information Services, BRS Information Technologies; internal databases. **Publications:** F.E.I.S. Information Series, irregular. **Special Indexes:** Subject index to publisher's listings of instructional materials; thesaurus of vocational subject headings. **Remarks:** FAX: (904)487-3656.

★5912★
Florida State University - Center for the Study of Population (Soc Sci)
659 Bellamy Phone: (904)644-1762
Tallahassee, FL 32306-4063 Robert McCann, Libn.
Founded: 1973. **Staff:** Prof 1. **Subjects:** Migration, urbanization, fertility, mortality, population education, family planning. **Special Collections:**

World Fertility Survey Comparitive Studies, Scientific Reports and Occasional Papers (200); Acquired Immune Deficiency Syndrome; U.S. Population & Housing Census, 1950-1990 (2100 volumes); Galina Selegen Collection of Soviet Population Materials (50 volumes). **Holdings:** 9700 books; 3500 bound periodical volumes; 3200 vertical files. **Subscriptions:** 100 journals and other serials. **Services:** Copying; SDI; center open to the public for reference use only. **Computerized Information Services:** CENSYS online (internal database). **Publications:** Working Papers series, irregular - by subscription. **Remarks:** FAX (904)644-8818.

★5913★
Florida State University - Communication Research Center - Library (Info Sci)
College of Communication
402 Diffenbaugh Bldg. Phone: (904)644-8774
Tallahassee, FL 32306-4021 Barry S. Sapolsky, Dir.
Founded: 1980. **Staff:** Prof 1; Other 2. **Subjects:** Communications, education, broadcasting, telecommunications, research methodology, social psychology, advertising, computers. **Special Collections:** Unpublished communication papers (500). **Holdings:** 2000 books; 5000 unbound periodicals; 250 indices. **Subscriptions:** 5 journals and other serials. **Services:** Library open to the public. **Automated Operations:** LUIS. **Computerized Information Services:** DIALOG Information Services; CD-ROMs. **Publications:** Communication Research Center Research Reports series; CRC Bulletin.

Florida State University - Florida Solar Energy Center
See: **Florida Solar Energy Center** (5883)

★5914★
Florida State University - Harold Goldstein Library Science Library (Info Sci)
Tallahassee, FL 32306-2048 Phone: (904)644-1803
Marva Carter, LSL Libn.
Founded: 1947. **Staff:** Prof 1; Other 1. **Subjects:** Library and information science, library architecture. **Special Collections:** Picture and children's books; personal papers of Joseph Wheeler and Paul Howard. **Holdings:** Figures not available. **Services:** Interlibrary loan; copying; library open to the public for reference use only. **Remarks:** FAX: (904)644-4702.

★5915★
Florida State University - Instructional Support Center - Film/Video Library (Aud-Vis)
Tallahassee, FL 32306-1019 Phone: (904)644-2820
Dr. John W. McLanahan, Dir.
Staff: Prof 2; Other 5. **Subjects:** Language arts, literature, humanities, social sciences, science, mathematics, art, music, history, social studies, guidance, character development. **Holdings:** 4000 16mm educational films and videotapes. **Services:** Rental and referral services; center open to the public. **Networks/Consortia:** Member of Consortium of College and University Media Centers (CCUMC). **Publications:** Florida State University Films, annual - available upon request. **Staff:** Peggy Stewart, AV Libn.

★5916★
Florida State University - Law Library (Law)
Tallahassee, FL 32306-1043 Phone: (904)644-4578
Edwin M. Schroeder, Dir.
Founded: 1966. **Staff:** Prof 8; Other 10. **Subjects:** Law. **Special Collections:** Florida Supreme Court Briefs, 1961 to present (microfiche); Florida Supreme Court Oral Arguments, 1985 to present (videotapes); selective U.S. Government document depository. **Holdings:** 190,000 volumes; 6200 reels of microfilm; 640,000 microfiche; 850 audiotapes; 1700 videotapes; 280 computer programs. **Subscriptions:** 5400 journals and other serials; 10 newspapers. **Services:** Interlibrary loan; copying; library open to the public. **Automated Operations:** Computerized cataloging, acquisitions, serials, and circulation. **Computerized Information Services:** LEXIS, OCLC, WESTLAW, RLIN. Performs searches on fee basis. Contact Person: Betsy L. Stupski, Ref.Libn., 644-4095. **Networks/Consortia:** Member of Research Libraries Information Network (RLIN), SOLINET. **Publications:** Acquisitions List; special releases. **Special Catalogs:** COM Catalog of Law Library holdings. **Remarks:** Alternate telephone number(s): (904)644-4578 (administration); 644-4095 (reference); 644-3405 (circulation); 644-1004 (tech.svcs.). FAX: (904)644-5216. **Staff:** Robin R. Gault, Assoc.Dir.; Betsy L. Stupski, Hd., Pub.Serv.; Mark S. Evans, Comp./AV Serv.Libn.; Anne D. Bardolph, Acq.Libn.; Alva T. Stone, Cat.Lib.; Janice Ross, Ser.Libn.

★5917★
Florida State University - Paul Dirac Science Library (Biol Sci, Sci-Engr)
Tallahassee, FL 32306-4070 Phone: (904)644-3079
Sharon Schwerzel, Hd.
Staff: Prof 1; Other 8. **Subjects:** Science, mathematics, astronomy, physics, chemistry, geology, biology, botany, zoology, technology, engineering, medicine, home economics, photography. **Holdings:** Figures not available. **Services:** Interlibrary loan; copying; department open to the public for reference use only. **Automated Operations:** Computerized cataloging, acquisitions, serials, and circulation. **Computerized Information Services:** DIALOG Information Services, NLM. Performs searches on fee basis. **Remarks:** FAX: (904)644-0025.

★5918★
Florida State University - School of Nursing - Learning Resource Center (Med)
310 School of Nursing Phone: (904)644-1291
Tallahassee, FL 32306 Leonard N. Barnes, Sr., Lrng.Rsrcs.Spec.
Staff: Prof 1; Other 8. **Subjects:** Community health, mental health, maternal and child care, surgery, pediatrics, anatomy, physiology. **Holdings:** 6838 books; 153 bound periodical volumes; 108 nursing films; 459 slides; 378 videotapes; 103 filmstrips; 30 anatomical models; federal and state documents; newsletters. **Subscriptions:** 76 journals and other serials. **Services:** Copying; center open to the public. **Remarks:** FAX: (904)644-7660.

Florida State University - Science-Technology Department
See: **Florida State University - Paul Dirac Science Library** (5917)

★5919★
Florida State University - Special Collections (Hum)
Robert Manning Strozier Library Phone: (904)644-3271
Tallahassee, FL 32306-2047 Gay Dixon, HD.
Staff: Prof 3; Other 2. **Subjects:** Florida, Florida State University, early Americana, Confederate imprints, book arts, herbals, poetry, Napoleon, history of area business. **Special Collections:** Florida Collection; Childhood in Poetry; Rare Books; Florida State University Archives; Napoleon Collection; Scottish Collection; Blue Ridge Institute for Southern Community Service Executives; McGregor Collection; Lois Lenski Collection; Night Before Christmas Collection; Christmas Greetings; Fuller Warren Papers; Richard Ervin Papers; Allen Morris Papers; William S. Rosasco Papers; George R. Fairbanks Papers; Claude Pepper Papers. **Holdings:** Figures not available. **Services:** Copying; collections open to the public. **Special Catalogs:** The Lois Lenski Collection in the Florida State University Library (1966); Childhood in Poetry (1968); Supplement 1 (1972), Supplement 2 (1976; 2 volumes); The Parodies of Lewis Carroll and Their Originals: Catalog of an Exhibition with Notes by John MacKay Shaw (1960); St. Nicholas Poetry Index, 1873-1943 (1965); What the Poets Have to Say About Childhood: An Exhibition of One Hundred Books, John MacKay Shaw (1966); The Poetry of Sacred Song; A Short-Title List Supplementing Childhood in Poetry - A Catalog (1972); A Sketch of the Fuller Warren Papers in the Special Collections Division of the Florida State University Library (1974); A Sketch of the Doak Campbell Papers in the Special Collections Division of the Florida State University Library (1974); A List of the Records of the Blue Ridge Institute for Southern Community Service Executives, 1927-1977 , on deposit in the Florida State University Library. **Remarks:** FAX: (904)644-4702.

★5920★
Florida State University - Warren D. Allen Music Library (Mus)
Tallahassee, FL 32306-2098 Phone: (904)644-5028
Dale L. Hudson, Mus.Libn.
Staff: Prof 1; Other 3. **Subjects:** Music. **Services:** Interlibrary loan; library open to the public for reference use only. **Automated Operations:** Computerized acquisitions, cataloging, and circulation. **Special Indexes:** Song Index of recordings and song collections in library (card). **Remarks:** FAX: (904)644-4702.

★5921★
Florida Today Newspaper - Library (Publ)
Gannett Plaza
Box 363000 Phone: (407)242-3582
Melbourne, FL 32936 Belinda Kehoe, Libn.
Founded: 1966. **Staff:** Prof 1; Other 2. **Subjects:** Newspaper reference topics. **Special Collections:** Cocoa Tribune, 1917 to present (microfilm); Today, 1966 to present (microfilm). **Holdings:** 150 books; microfilm. **Subscriptions:** 8 newspapers. **Services:** Interlibrary loan; library not open to the public. **Computerized Information Services:** DataTimes. **Publications:** Library Clips; Newsletter; Editorial Staff, all quarterly. **Special Indexes:** Index to Today articles, May 1, 1980 to present. **Remarks:** Published by Gannett Company, Inc.

Florissant Fossil Beds National Monument
See: **U.S. Natl. Park Service** (17706)

Fr. Georges Florovsky Library
See: **St. Vladimir's Orthodox Theological Seminary** (14625)

Flower Veterinary Library
See: **Cornell University - Flower Veterinary Library** (4311)

Carolyn Floyd Library
See: **Kodiak College** (8779)

★5922★
Floyd County Historical Society Museum - Library (Hist)
500 Gilbert St. Phone: (515)228-1099
Charles City, IA 50616 Mary Ann Townsend, Musm.Dir.
Subjects: History - Floyd County, family, Charles City. **Special Collections:** Hart-Parr history; Oliver White Farm "AG" history (15,000 items). **Holdings:** 500 books; 100 bound periodical volumes; manuscripts. **Services:** Copying; library open to the public with restrictions.

★5923★
Floyd Medical Center - Medical Library (Med)
Turner McCall Blvd.
Box 233 Phone: (404)295-5500
Rome, GA 30162 Dee Anna Ward, Libn.
Founded: 1960. **Staff:** Prof 1. **Subjects:** Medicine, nursing, hospital administration. **Holdings:** 1115 books; 3000 bound periodical volumes. **Subscriptions:** 100 journals and other serials. **Services:** Interlibrary loan; copying; library open to hospital personnel only. **Computerized Information Services:** MEDLARS, MEDLINE; DOCLINE (electronic mail service). **Remarks:** FAX: (404)295-3920.

★5924★
Fluid Power Consultants International - Library (Sci-Engr)
Russ Henke Associates
Elm Grove Phone: (414)782-0410
Milwaukee, WI 53122 Russell W. Henke, Pres.
Founded: 1970. **Subjects:** Fluitronics technology (a technology based on the principles of fluid mechanics). **Holdings:** 200 volumes. **Services:** open to the public for reference use only.

★5925★
Fluidyne Engineering Corporation - Technical Library (Sci-Engr)
5900 Olson Memorial Hwy. Phone: (612)544-2721
Minneapolis, MN 55422 Marlys J. Johnson, Tech.Libn.
Founded: 1952. **Staff:** Prof 1; Other 1. **Subjects:** Fluidized bed combustion, wind tunnel design and testing, aerospace, swim flume design. **Holdings:** 2000 books; 50 bound periodical volumes; 35,000 documents. **Subscriptions:** 120 journals and other serials. **Services:** Interlibrary loan; copying; library open to the public with restrictions. **Computerized Information Services:** DIALOG Information Services, RLIN, NASA/RECON. **Networks/Consortia:** Member of Twin Cities Standards Cooperators, Metronet. **Remarks:** FAX: (612)546-5617. **Remarks:** FAX: (612)546-5617. Telex: 290518.

★5926★
John Fluke Manufacturing Co., Inc. - Corporate Library (Sci-Engr)
P.O. Box 9090, MS 249C Phone: (206)356-5718
Everett, WA 98206-9090 Joan E. Collins, Corp.Libn.
Founded: 1965. **Staff:** Prof 1; Other 1. **Subjects:** Electronics, business, computers. **Holdings:** Books; microfilm; vendor catalogs; military/industry specifications and standards. **Subscriptions:** 700 journals and other serials; 5 newspapers. **Services:** Interlibrary loan; copying. **Automated Operations:** Computerized cataloging. **Computerized Information Services:** DIALOG Information Services, ORBIT Search Service, OCLC, WILSONLINE; OnTyme Electronic Message Network Service, InterNet (electronic mail services). **Networks/Consortia:** Member of CLASS. **Remarks:** FAX: (206)356-5116; 356-5174. Electronic mail address(es): jcollins@tc.fluke.com (InterNet).

★5927★
Fluor Daniel - Chicago Division Library (Sci-Engr)
200 W. Monroe Phone: (312)368-3719
Chicago, IL 60606 M. Thayer Jabin, Mgr. & Info.Spec.
Founded: 1912. **Staff:** Prof 1. **Subjects:** Engineering - civil, mechanical, electrical, nuclear, environmental; nuclear power. **Holdings:** 4500 books; 118 bound periodical volumes; engineering standards. **Subscriptions:** 40 journals and other serials. **Services:** Interlibrary loan; library open to other libraries. **Remarks:** FAX: (312)368-3746.

★5928★
Fluor Daniel - Houston Engineering Center - Library & Information Services (Sci-Engr)
Box 5014 Phone: (713)263-2244
Sugar Land, TX 77487-5014 Doris V. Brooks, Libn.
Founded: 1967. **Staff:** Prof 2. **Subjects:** Engineering - petroleum, chemical, design, environmental; occupational safety; construction; offshore engineering; pipelines. **Special Collections:** Coal and oil shale technologies. **Holdings:** 6000 volumes; 10,000 descriptive job books. **Subscriptions:** 80 journals and other serials. **Services:** Interlibrary loan; copying; SDI; library open to the public by appointment. **Computerized Information Services:** DIALOG Information Services, PFDS Online, NEXIS, LEXIS, VU/TEXT Information Services. **Publications:** Library Highlights. **Remarks:** FAX: (713)263-3276. Telex: 77 5319.

★5929★
Fluor Daniel - Technical Information Center (Sci-Engr)
100 Fluor Daniel Dr. Phone: (803)281-5362
Greenville, SC 29607-2762 Nancy Taylor, Mgr.
Founded: 1980. **Staff:** Prof 2; Other 1. **Subjects:** Engineering, construction, technology, business. **Holdings:** 2000 books; 6000 periodical volumes; industry standards; building codes; manufacturers' catalogs; microfilm. **Subscriptions:** 125 journals and other serials; 6 newspapers. **Services:** Interlibrary loan; copying; library open to the public with management approval. **Automated Operations:** Computerized public access catalog. **Computerized Information Services:** DIALOG Information Services, VU/TEXT Information Services; CD-ROMs (COMPACT DISCLOSURE, Books in Print Plus, ASME Boiler and Pressure Vessel Code, COMPENDEX PLUS, World Atlas, OHS MSDS on Disc, Electronic Sweet's, Grolier Electronic Encyclopedia, Thomas Register, U.S. Atlas GEOdisc, Magazine Article Summaries, WORLDSCOPE, ASTM Standards). Performs searches on fee basis. **Networks/Consortia:** Member of South Carolina Library Network. **Publications:** Newsletter, bimonthly. **Remarks:** FAX: (803)281-5115. **Formerly:** Its Library/Resource Center. **Staff:** Cheryl Martin, Asst.Libn.

★5930★
Fluor Daniel - Technical Information Center-CNQ (Sci-Engr)
3333 Michelson Dr. Phone: (714)975-5532
Irvine, CA 92730 Fia Vitar, Lib.Supv.
Founded: 1965. **Staff:** Prof 3; Other 1. **Subjects:** Engineering, construction, environmental engineering, nuclear engineering, synthetic fuels, business, chemical engineering, human resources. **Holdings:** 10,300 books; 8050 bound periodical volumes; 14,000 other cataloged items; VSMF subscription to military specifications; vendor catalogs; NRC documents; 35 Industry Standards; federal construction regulations through Information Handling Services (IHS). **Subscriptions:** 100 journals and other serials. **Services:** Interlibrary loan. **Automated Operations:** Computerized cataloging and circulation. **Computerized Information Services:** DIALOG Information Services, NEXIS, LEXIS, DataTimes, ORBIT Search Service, STN

International, MEDLARS, RECON; CD-ROMs. **Networks/Consortia:** Member of Orange County Libraries Association (OCLA). **Publications:** Technical Information Center Newsletter - all for internal distribution only. **Formerly:** Its Irvine Technical Library. **Staff:** Janet Beal, Info.Rec.Spec. III; Cathy Peck, Info.Spec. III; Sharon Delenoy; Laurie Graff, Info.Rec.Spec. I.

★5931★
Fluor Daniel Canada Inc. - Technical Information Centre (Sci-Engr)
P.O. Box 8799, Sta. F Phone: (403)259-1110
Calgary, AB, Canada T2J 4B4 Nancy Topper, Prin.Info./Rec.Spec.
Founded: 1978. **Staff:** 2. **Subjects:** Engineering. **Holdings:** 7000 books. **Subscriptions:** 52 journals and other serials. **Services:** Interlibrary loan; library not open to the public. **Computerized Information Services:** DIALOG Information Services, Infomart Online; Envoy 100 (electronic mail service). **Publications:** Newsletter - for internal distribution only. **Remarks:** FAX: (403)259-1222. Electronic mail address(es): FLUOR.LIB (Envoy 100). **Staff:** Linda Chambers.

★5932★
Flushing Hospital and Medical Center - Medical Library (Med)
4500 Parsons Blvd. & 45th Ave. Phone: (718)670-5653
Flushing, NY 11355-9980 Vincent C. Notarstefano, Dir.
Founded: 1940. **Staff:** Prof 1; Other 2. **Subjects:** Medicine and allied health sciences. **Special Collections:** Obstetrics/gynecology; pediatrics; surgery; internal medicine. **Holdings:** 3000 books; 2000 bound periodical volumes; 8 VF drawers of pamphlets and clippings; Audio-Digest tapes. **Subscriptions:** 190 journals and other serials. **Services:** Interlibrary loan; library not open to the public. **Computerized Information Services:** MEDLARS; DOCLINE (electronic mail service). **Networks/Consortia:** Member of New York Metropolitan Reference and Research Library Agency, BHSL, Brooklyn-Queens-Staten Island Health Sciences Librarians (BQSI). **Publications:** Library Guide; Periodical Guide. **Remarks:** FAX: (718)670-3188.

Henry N. Flynt Library
See: **Historic Deerfield, Inc./Pocumtuck Valley Memorial Association - Memorial Libraries** (7242)

Roy A. Flynt Memorial Library
See: **Georgia (State) Department of Transportation** (6406)

★5933★
FMC Corporation - Chemical Research & Development Center - Technical Information Services (Sci-Engr)
Box 8 Phone: (609)520-3636
Princeton, NJ 08543 June C. Mayer, Mgr.
Founded: 1956. **Staff:** Prof 5; Other 3. **Subjects:** Chemistry, chemical engineering, agricultural chemicals. **Holdings:** 30,000 books; 20,000 bound periodical volumes; reports; U.S. chemical patents, 1955 to present, in microform. **Subscriptions:** 350 journals and other serials. **Services:** Interlibrary loan; library not open to the public to the public. **Automated Operations:** Computerized cataloging. **Computerized Information Services:** STN International, DIALOG Information Services, NLM, ORBIT Search Service, Chemical Information Systems, Inc. (CIS). **Remarks:** FAX: (609)520-3003. **Staff:** Barbara F. Mendel, Sr.Libn.; Dr. Thadeus L. Kowalewski, Sr.Info.Chem.; Deirdre C. LaMarche, Sr.Info.Chem.

★5934★
FMC Corporation - Corporate Library (Bus-Fin)
200 E. Randolph Phone: (312)861-5708
Chicago, IL 60601 Gwen Adams, Corp.Libn.
Founded: 1979. **Staff:** Prof 1. **Subjects:** Business, management, law, taxation. **Holdings:** 3000 books. **Subscriptions:** 200 journals and other serials; 5 newspapers. **Services:** Interlibrary loan; copying; SDI. **Automated Operations:** Computerized cataloging. **Computerized Information Services:** DIALOG Information Services, Dow Jones News/Retrieval, PFDS Online, LEXIS, NEXIS, NewsNet, Inc., VU/TEXT Information Services, OCLC; DIALMAIL (electronic mail service). **Networks/Consortia:** Member of Chicago Library System.

★5935★
FMC Corporation - Corporate Technology Center - Information Services (Sci-Engr)
1205 Coleman Ave.
Box 580 Phone: (408)289-2529
Santa Clara, CA 95052 Keye L. Luke, Supv.
Founded: 1960. **Staff:** Prof 2. **Subjects:** Electronics, mechanical engineering, robotics, artificial intelligence, materials testing. **Holdings:** 6000 books; 2000 industrial standards; 12,000 technical reports. **Subscriptions:** 274 journals and other serials. **Services:** Interlibrary loan; copying; SDI; services open to the public for reference use only. **Automated Operations:** Computerized cataloging, acquisitions, serials, and circulation. **Computerized Information Services:** DIALOG Information Services, ORBIT Search Service, RLIN, STN International; OnTyme Electronic Message Network Service (electronic mail service). **Networks/Consortia:** Member of CLASS. **Publications:** Library Acquisitions Bulletin, monthly - to employees; Periodicals Received, annual. **Remarks:** FAX: (408)289-2732. Electronic mail address(es): FMCCEL (OnTyme Electronic Message Network Service). **Staff:** Bonnie Hometchko, Info.Spec.

★5936★
FMC Corporation - Ground Systems Division Library (Sci-Engr, Mil)
2890 De La Cruz Blvd.
Box 58123, PO5 Phone: (408)289-3490
Santa Clara, CA 95052 Sheila Smokey, Mgr., Lib.Serv.
Staff: Prof 3; Other 3. **Subjects:** Armored military vehicles; ordnance; weapon systems; mechanical and electrical engineering; human factors; defense business. **Holdings:** 5300 books; 42,000 specifications and technical reports, hardcopy and microfiche; 3100 military technical manuals; 4800 internal test reports; vendor catalogs; military, federal, industrial specifications and standards on microfilm. **Subscriptions:** 525 journals and other serials; 6 newspapers. **Services:** Interlibrary loan; copying; SDI; library open to the public by appointment for reference use only. **Automated Operations:** Computerized cataloging, acquisitions, serials, circulation, and membership statistics. **Computerized Information Services:** DIALOG Information Services, BRS Information Technologies, PFDS Online, VU/TEXT Information Services, DTIC, WILSONLINE, BASIS TECHLIB (internal database); OnTyme Electronic Message Network Service (electronic mail service). **Networks/Consortia:** Member of South Bay Cooperative Library System (SBCLS), CLASS. **Publications:** Newsletter. **Remarks:** FAX: (408)289-2868. Electronic mail address(es): FMCGSD (OnTyme Electronic Message Network Service). **Staff:** Michael Dines, Info.Spec.- Ref.; Leila Geronimo, Info.Spec.- Cat.

★5937★
FMC Corporation - Library/Information Center (Sci-Engr)
4800 E. River Rd. Phone: (612)572-7900
Minneapolis, MN 55421-1498 C.A. Clift, Lib.Mgr.
Staff: Prof 2; Other 2. **Subjects:** Ordnance, engineering, business. **Holdings:** 4500 books; 20,000 other cataloged items. **Subscriptions:** 350 journals and other serials. **Services:** Interlibrary loan; journal routing; library not open to the public. **Automated Operations:** Computerized cataloging. **Computerized Information Services:** DIALOG Information Services, DROLS, NewsNet, Inc., VU/TEXT Information Services, DataTimes, NEXIS, Data Resources (DRI), USNI Military Database, Aerospace Online. **Publications:** Newsletter; acquisitions list. **Remarks:** FAX: (612)572-9826. Telex: 170371. **Staff:** Donna Harnden, Sr.Info.Spec.

★5938★
FMC Corporation - Lithium Division - Research Library (Sci-Engr)
Box 795 Phone: (704)868-5536
Bessemer City, NC 28016 JoAnn Trull, Libn.
Founded: 1958. **Staff:** Prof 1. **Subjects:** Lithium, chemistry, chemical engineering, metallurgy. **Holdings:** 2500 books; 800 bound periodical volumes; 600 government reports; 7 VF drawers of patents; 75 drawers of technical abstracts on cards; 500 reels of microfilm. **Subscriptions:** 63 journals and other serials. **Services:** Library not open to the public. **Computerized Information Services:** DIALOG Information Services, STN International. **Publications:** Annotated bibliography, monthly - for internal distribution only. **Remarks:** FAX: (704)868-5496. **Formerly:** Its Lithium Corporation of America, Inc.

★5939★
FMC Corporation - Marine Colloids Division - Library (Sci-Engr)
191 Thomaston St. Phone: (207)594-3478
Rockland, ME 04841 Dee Kopesky, Info.Spec.
Staff: Prof 1. **Subjects:** Colloid science, chemistry, biochemistry, clinical chemistry, seaweeds, food science. **Holdings:** 2500 books; 250 bound periodical volumes; 10,000 reprints. **Subscriptions:** 90 journals and other serials. **Services:** Interlibrary loan; library open to the public with restrictions. **Computerized Information Services:** DIALOG Information Services, STN International, GenBank. **Publications:** Newsletter, biweekly - to library users. **Remarks:** FAX: (207)594-3426.

★5940★
FOG - Software Library (Comp Sci)
P.O. Box 1030 Phone: (916)678-7353
Dixon, CA 95620 Mike Kaufman, Exec.Dir.
Founded: 1981. **Staff:** 2. **Subjects:** MS-DOS and CP/M computer software. **Holdings:** (500 disks). **Services:** Library not open to the public. **Computerized Information Services:** CD-ROM (RBBS). **Publications:** Foghorn Quarterly - to members. **Also Known As:** Fog International Computer Users Group.

Raymond Fogelman Library
See: **New School for Social Research** (11548)

James Lemont Fogg Memorial Library
See: **Art Center College of Design** (1073)

Raymond H. Fogler Library
See: **University of Maine** (18780)

Fohrman Library
See: **Condell Memorial Hospital** (4128)

★5941★
FOI Services, Inc. - Library (Info Sci)
12315 Wilkins Ave. Phone: (301)881-0410
Rockville, MD 20852 John E. Carey, CEO
Founded: 1975. **Staff:** Prof 7; Other 5. **Subjects:** U.S. Food and Drug Administration documents. **Holdings:** 80,000 documents. **Services:** Copying; library open to clients only. **Computerized Information Services:** DIOGENES. Performs searches on fee basis. **Publications:** Regi Fax; FDA Freedom of Information Log; Index of FDA Regulatory Letters; FDA Drug and Device Product Approvals - all by subscription. **Remarks:** FAX: (301)881-0415. **Also Known As:** Freedom of Information Services, Inc. **Staff:** Marlene S. Bobka, Mktg.Dir.; Sue Eckel, Sr.Info.Spec.; Patrick Small, Sr.Info.Spec.; Larry Fuller, Oper.Mgr.; Brett McCoy, Sr.Info.Spec.

Howard Lane Foland Library
See: **Society for Promoting and Encouraging Arts & Knowledge of the Church** (15339)

★5942★
Foley & Lardner - Library (Law)
777 E. Wisconsin Ave. Phone: (414)271-2400
Milwaukee, WI 53202 Susan O'Toole, Hd.Libn.
Staff: Prof 2; Other 5. **Subjects:** Law - general, corporate, banking, antitrust, real estate, securities, intellectual property, employment, health, environmental, taxation, insurance; litigation; employee benefits. **Holdings:** 24,000 books; 25 bound periodical volumes; 550 pamphlets; 20 series in microform. **Subscriptions:** 580 journals and other serials. **Services:** Interlibrary loan; library not open to the public. **Computerized Information Services:** LEXIS, WESTLAW, DIALOG Information Services, Dow Jones News/Retrieval, LEGI-SLATE, Information America, Dun & Bradstreet Business Credit Services, VU/TEXT Information Services, DataTimes. **Networks/Consortia:** Member of Library Council of Metropolitan Milwaukee, Inc. (LCOMM). **Publications:** Information Bulletin; Summary of Wisconsin Legislation - both for internal distribution only. **Remarks:** FAX: (414)271-3791. Telex: 26819 Foley Lard Mil. **Staff:** Mariann Storck, Ref.Libn.

★5943★
Folger Shakespeare Library (Hum, Theater)
201 E. Capitol St. Phone: (202)544-4600
Washington, DC 20003 Dr. Werner Gundersheimer, Dir.
Founded: 1932. **Staff:** Prof 44; Other 38. **Subjects:** Shakespeare; history of English and Western civilization in the 16th and 17th centuries; history of the theater in England especially in the 16th to 18th centuries; Renaissance drama, history, literature. **Holdings:** 230,000 volumes; 50,000 manuscripts; 1000 reels of microfilm. **Subscriptions:** 198 journals and other serials. **Services:** Copying; library open to the public with restrictions. **Networks/ Consortia:** Member of Research Libraries Information Network (RLIN). **Publications:** Folger Library Newsletter, 3/year; series of publications in paper and hard cover editions; Shakespeare Quarterly. **Special Catalogs:** Catalog of Folger Books and Catalog of Folger Manuscripts (published); Catalog of Prints, Engravings, Photographs and Original Art Materials (published). **Remarks:** FAX: (202)544-4623. Largest collection of Shakespeariana in the world. **Staff:** Dr. Philip A. Knachel, Assoc.Dir.; Dr. Barbara Mowat, Dir. of Academic Prog.; Thomas McCance, Jr.,Dir., Dev.; Joan Morrison, Hd.Cat.; Dr. Nati H. Krivatsy, Ref.Libn.; Elizabeth Niemyer, Acq.Cur.; Janet Griffin, Dir., Pub.Prog.; Rachel Doggett, Cur. of Rare Book Exhibitions

Homer Folks Archives
See: **Columbia University - Whitney M. Young, Jr. Memorial Library of Social Work** (4028)

★5944★
Fond du Lac County Historical Society - Historic Galloway House and Village - Archives (Hist)
P.O. Box 1284 Phone: (414)922-6390
Fond du Lac, WI 54935 Jean Rentmeister, Hist.
Founded: 1989. **Staff:** Prof 1; Other 2. **Subjects:** Wisconsin and Fond du Lac area history, 1836 to present. **Special Collections:** Civil War through World War II (for Fond du Lac County). **Holdings:** Diaries; correspondence; photographs; genealogical records; vital statistics; land transfers; newspaper files; county histories; cemetery inscriptions; poll taxes; tax records. **Services:** Archives open to the public on a limited schedule and by appointment (for appointment call 414-921-4620). **Remarks:** All research materials are housed at the Adams House, which is open to the public for reference use only.

★5945★
Fond du Lac County Law Library (Law)
City-County Government Ctr., 2nd Fl.
160 S. Macy St. Phone: (414)929-3072
Fond du Lac, WI 54935 Bonnie M. Verges, Libn.
Staff: 1. **Subjects:** Law. **Holdings:** 10,000 volumes. **Services:** Library open to the public with restrictions.

★5946★
Fondation Martin Bodmer - Bibliotheca Bodmeriana (Hum, Art, Rare Book)
19-21, route du Guignard Phone: 22 7362370
CH-1223 Cologny-Geneve, Switzerland Dr. Hans E. Braun
Founded: 1971. **Staff:** Prof 3; Other 3. **Subjects:** World literature, fine arts. **Special Collections:** Rare book collection (papyri, manuscripts, first editions). **Holdings:** 160,000 volumes; 500 reels of microfilm. **Subscriptions:** 60 journals and other serials. **Services:** Copying; library open to the public with restrictions. **Publications:** Series Papyrus Bodmer.

Fondation Nationale des Sciences Politiques - Centre de Hautes Etudes sur l'Afrique et l'Asie Modernes
See: **Center for Advanced Studies on Modern Africa and Asia** (3205)

Fondo Colombiano de Investigaciones Cientificas y Proyectos Especiales Francisco Jose de Caldas
See: **Colombian Fund for Scientific Research and Special Projects of Francisco Jose de Caldas** (3927)

Fonds Mondial pour la Conservation de la Nature
See: **World Wide Fund for Nature** (20635)

Fonds Quetelet Library
See: **Belgium - Ministry of Economic Affairs** (1668)

★5947★
Fontenelle Forest Nature Center - Reference Library (Biol Sci)
1111 Bellevue Blvd., N. Phone: (402)731-3140
Bellevue, NE 68005 Donald H. Gilbert, Exec.Dir.
Founded: 1974. **Staff:** 17. **Subjects:** Natural history and ecology, Missouri Valley history. **Special Collections:** Rare books on natural history. **Holdings:** 900 books; 32 bound periodical volumes; 1000 pamphlets; extensive clipping file of nature magazines. **Subscriptions:** 20 journals and other serials. **Services:** Library open to the public for reference use only. **Remarks:** Maintained by Fontenelle Forest Association. **Remarks:** FAX: (402)731-2403.

Food and Agriculture Organization of the United Nations
See: **United Nations - Food and Agriculture Organization - David Lublin Memorial Library** (16752)

★5948★
Food Marketing Institute - Information Service (Food-Bev)
1750 K St., N.W. Phone: (202)452-8444
Washington, DC 20006 Barbara L. McBride, Dir., Info.Serv.
Founded: 1952. **Staff:** 6. **Subjects:** Food distribution. **Holdings:** 7000 volumes. **Subscriptions:** 700 journals and other serials. **Services:** Interlibrary loan; copying; service open to the public by appointment. **Publications:** Reference Point, Food Industry Abstracts, monthly; Weekly Card Service. **Remarks:** FAX: (202)429-4529.

★5949★
Foote Cone & Belding - Corporate Information Center (Bus-Fin)
101 E. Erie Phone: (312)751-7000
Chicago, IL 60611 John Kok, Dir.
Founded: 1977. **Staff:** Prof 9; Other 5. **Subjects:** Advertising and marketing. **Holdings:** 3000 books; 2000 subject files; 250 company files. **Subscriptions:** 400 journals and other serials; 6 newspapers. **Services:** Library not open to the public. **Computerized Information Services:** DIALOG Information Services, Reuter TEXTLINE, VU/TEXT Information Services, NEXIS, Dow Jones News/Retrieval, Info Globe, DataTimes, InvesText. **Networks/Consortia:** Member of Chicago Library System. **Remarks:** FAX: (312)751-1039. **Staff:** Mary Beth Markus, Mgr., Info.Serv.; Joanne Humphreville, Sr.Libn.; Mary Blankenheim, Libn.; Dwayne Nelson, Sr.Libn.; Abigail Cummings, Libn.; Marsha Smisko, Sr.Info.Anl.; Quinn Weller, Libn.

★5950★
Foote Cone & Belding - Information Center - SF (Bus-Fin)
1255 Battery St. Phone: (415)772-8116
San Francisco, CA 94111 Angela Moore-Evans
Founded: 1988. **Subjects:** Advertising. **Holdings:** Figures not available. **Services:** Interlibrary loan; center not open to the public. **Computerized Information Services:** DIALOG Information Services, NEXIS, Dow Jones News/Retrieval, DataTimes, VU/TEXT Information Services. **Remarks:** FAX: (415)398-2187. **Staff:** Julie Griffith, Info.Spec.

★5951★
W.A. Foote Memorial Hospital - Medical Library (Med)
205 N. East Ave. Phone: (517)788-4705
Jackson, MI 49201 Janet Zimmerman
Founded: 1987. **Staff:** Prof 1. **Subjects:** Medicine, nursing, and allied health sciences. **Holdings:** 1200 books. **Subscriptions:** 250 journals and other serials. **Services:** Interlibrary loan; library open to the public. **Computerized Information Services:** BRS Information Technologies, NLM. **Remarks:** FAX: (517)788-4706.

★5952★
Foothills Hospital - Library Services (Med)
1403 29th St., N.W. Phone: (403)270-4848
Calgary, AB, Canada T2N 2T9 Ruth MacRae, Lib.Coord.
Founded: 1965. **Staff:** 7. **Subjects:** Nursing and allied health. **Holdings:** 5000 volumes; 1000 AV programs. **Subscriptions:** 150 journals and other serials. **Services:** Interlibrary loan; open to the public with restrictions. **Computerized Information Services:** MEDLINE, DIALOG Information Services; Envoy 100 (electronic mail service). **Remarks:** FAX: (403)270-2400. Electronic mail address(es): ED.RES/FHPH (Envoy 100). **Formerly:** Its Educational Resources.

★5953★
Foothills Pipe Lines Ltd. - Library
707 8th Ave., S.W., Suite 3100 Phone: (403)294-4526
Calgary, AB, Canada T2P 3W8 Xenia Stanford, Supv., Lib.Serv.
Founded: 1974. **Staff:** 3. **Subjects:** Energy, engineering. **Holdings:** 10,000 books; 4000 reports; 100 microfiche; 100 reels of microfilm. **Subscriptions:** 500 journals and other serials; 25 newspapers. **Services:** Interlibrary loan; library open to the public by appointment. **Computerized Information Services:** DIALOG Information Services, LEXIS, NEXIS, QL Systems, Info Globe, GasNet; internal database. **Remarks:** FAX: (403)265-0137.

Footscray Institute of Technology
See: **Victoria University of Technology - Library** (19831)

★5954★
Footwear Industries of America, Inc. - Library (Sci-Engr)
1420 K St., N.W., Suite 600 Phone: (202)789-1420
Washington, DC 20005 Sarah Olson, Info.Rsrcs.Coord.
Staff: Prof 1; Other 1. **Subjects:** Shoemaking technology, footwear industry. **Holdings:** Figures not available. **Subscriptions:** 43 journals and other serials. **Services:** Library open to local students. **Computerized Information Services:** DIALOG Information Services. **Publications:** List of publications - available upon request. **Remarks:** FAX: (202)789-4058.

★5955★
Forbes Health System - Corporate Office Library (Med)
500 Finley St. Phone: (412)665-3553
Pittsburgh, PA 15206 Susan V. Reber, Libn.
Founded: 1976. **Staff:** Prof 1; Other 1. **Subjects:** Health care administration, medicine, law. **Holdings:** 1381 books; 26 bound periodical volumes; 69 tapes; 3 VF drawers of pamphlets and clippings. **Subscriptions:** 40 journals and other serials. **Services:** Interlibrary loan; copying; SDI; library open to the public with restrictions. **Computerized Information Services:** MEDLARS, BRS Information Technologies. **Networks/Consortia:** Member of Pittsburgh-East Hospital Library Cooperative.

★5956★
Forbes Health System - Forbes Center for Gerontology - Library (Med)
Frankstown Ave. & Washington Blvd. Phone: (412)665-3050
Pittsburgh, PA 15206 Susan V. Reber, Libn.
Staff: Prof 1; Other 1. **Subjects:** Medicine, nursing, geriatrics. **Holdings:** 843 books; 121 bound periodical volumes; reprints; clippings. **Subscriptions:** 75 journals and other serials. **Services:** Interlibrary loan; copying; library open to the public with restrictions. **Computerized Information Services:** MEDLARS, BRS Information Technologies. **Networks/Consortia:** Member of Pittsburgh-East Hospital Library Cooperative. **Publications:** Forbes Libraries Booktales, biennial.

★5957★
Forbes Health System - Forbes Metropolitan Health Center Library (Med)
225 Penn Ave. Phone: (412)247-2424
Pittsburgh, PA 15221 Susan V. Reber, Libn.
Founded: 1941. **Staff:** Prof 1; Other 1. **Subjects:** Health sciences, administration. **Holdings:** 2471 books; 1252 bound periodical volumes; 4 VF drawers. **Subscriptions:** 126 journals and other serials. **Services:** Interlibrary loan; copying; SDI; library open to hospital personnel. **Computerized Information Services:** MEDLARS, BRS Information Technologies. **Networks/Consortia:** Member of Pittsburgh-East Hospital Library Cooperative. **Publications:** Forbes Libraries Booktales, quarterly.

★5958★
Forbes Health System - Forbes Regional Health Center - Medical Library (Med)
2570 Haymaker Rd. Phone: (412)858-2422
Monroeville, PA 15146 Elena Hartmann, Med.Libn.
Founded: 1978. **Staff:** Prof 1. **Subjects:** Medicine, nursing, family practice, obstetrics, gynecology, pediatrics, oncology. **Holdings:** 1614 books; 462 bound periodical volumes; Audio-Digest tapes. **Subscriptions:** 111 journals and other serials. **Services:** Interlibrary loan; library not open to the public. **Computerized Information Services:** MEDLARS, BRS Information Technologies, DOCLINE. **Networks/Consortia:** Member of Pittsburgh-East Hospital Library Cooperative, National Network of Libraries of Medicine - Middle Atlantic Region. **Publications:** Forbes Libraries Booktales, irregular.

★5959★
Forbes, Inc. - Library (Bus-Fin, Publ)
60 5th Ave. Phone: (212)620-2200
New York, NY 10011 Anne P. Mintz, Dir., Info.Serv.
Founded: 1960. **Staff:** Prof 7; Other 6. **Subjects:** Business, corporate histories, current affairs, finance. **Holdings:** 2500 volumes; 200 bound periodical volumes; 3000 corporation records and subject files; 25,000 microfiche. **Subscriptions:** 1500 journals and other serials; 15 newspapers. **Services:** Interlibrary loan; library not open to the public. **Automated Operations:** Computerized cataloging and serials. **Computerized Information Services:** DIALOG Information Services, VU/TEXT Information Services, Info Globe, TEXTLINE, RLIN, NEXIS, DataTimes, Dow Jones News/Retrieval; DIALMAIL (electronic mail service). **Special Indexes:** Index to Forbes Magazine, 1917-1985 (card), 1986 to present (online). **Remarks:** FAX: (212)620-1811. Library will not take subscriber questions.

★5960★
Forbes Library (Hist)
20 West St. Phone: (413)584-8550
Northampton, MA 01060 Blaise Bisaillon, Dir.
Founded: 1895. **Staff:** Prof 5; Other 37. **Special Collections:** Calvin Coolidge Memorial Room Collection; Kingsley Room Collection (Northampton history); genealogical collection; Connecticut Valley History; World Wars I and II posters. **Holdings:** 270,000 volumes; scores. **Subscriptions:** 300 journals and other serials; 12 newspapers. **Services:** Interlibrary loan; copying; library open to the public. **Computerized Information Services:** InfoTrac, MAS. **Special Indexes:** Index to local news in Daily Hampshire Gazette. **Staff:** Faith Kaufmann, Art & Mus.Libn.; Elise Feeley, Ref.Libn.; Kerry Buckley, Coolidge Rm.Archv.

Forbes Medical Library
See: **Children's Hospital** (3566)

Ford Aerospace Corporation - Aeronutronic Division
See: **Loral Aeronutronic** (9305)

Ford Forestry Center
See: **Michigan Technological University** (10343)

★5961★
Ford Foundation - Investment Research Library (Bus-Fin)
320 E. 43rd St., 9th Fl. Phone: (212)573-4798
New York, NY 10017 Nick Sayward, Investment Serv.Libn.
Founded: 1971. **Staff:** Prof 1; Other 1. **Subjects:** U.S. and international investments, endowment and pension funds, U.S. and international business conditions, statistics. **Holdings:** 1000 books; 1700 corporate files; 95 industry and subject files. **Subscriptions:** 230 journals and other serials. **Services:** Interlibrary loan; library not open to the public. **Computerized Information Services:** DIALOG Information Services, NEXIS, Dow Jones News/Retrieval, NewsNet, Inc., VU/TEXT Information Services, InvesText, DataTimes. **Networks/Consortia:** Member of Consortium of Foundation Libraries (CFL). **Remarks:** FAX: (212)986-0414.

★5962★
Ford Foundation - Library (Soc Sci, Bus-Fin)
320 E. 43rd St. Phone: (212)573-5155
New York, NY 10017 Victoria A. Dawson, Libn.
Founded: 1953. **Staff:** Prof 3; Other 4. **Subjects:** Economic and technical assistance, urban affairs, human rights, education, philanthropy. **Holdings:** 25,000 volumes; 1630 reels of microfilm. **Subscriptions:** 987 journals and other serials. **Services:** Interlibrary loan; copying; library open to the public if material not available elsewhere. **Computerized Information Services:** DIALOG Information Services, NEXIS, OCLC, WILSONLINE, WESTLAW, DataTimes. **Networks/Consortia:** Member of New York Metropolitan Reference and Research Library Agency, Consortium of Foundation Libraries (CFL). **Remarks:** FAX: (212)599-4584. Telex: RCA: 224048. **Staff:** Mary Jane Ballou, Ref.Libn.; Martha Lazarevic, Tech.Serv.Libn.

Gerald R. Ford Library
See: **U.S. Presidential Libraries** (17923)

★5963★
Henry Ford Hospital - Frank J. Sladen Library (Med)
2799 W. Grand Blvd. Phone: (313)876-2550
Detroit, MI 48202 Nardina Nameth Mein, Dir., Lib.Serv.
Founded: 1918. **Staff:** Prof 4; Other 10. **Subjects:** Medicine, nursing, administration and management, allied health and basic sciences. **Special Collections:** History of medicine and nursing. **Holdings:** 18,000 books; 70,000 bound periodical volumes. **Subscriptions:** 1100 journals and other serials. **Services:** Interlibrary loan; library not open to the public. **Automated Operations:** Integrated library system. **Computerized Information Services:** MEDLARS, DIALOG Information Services, BRS Information Technologies; CD-ROM (MEDLINE). Performs searches free of charge. **Networks/Consortia:** Member of National Network of Libraries of Medicine - Greater Midwest Region. **Remarks:** FAX: (313)874-4730. **Staff:** Sylvia Graham, Asst.Libn.; Sheryl Stevens, Asst.Libn.; Valerie L. Reid, Assoc.Libn.

★5964★
Henry Ford Museum and Greenfield Village - Research Center (Hist)
20900 Oakwood Blvd.
Box 1970 Phone: (313)271-1620
Dearborn, MI 48121-1970 Judith E. Endelman, Spec.Coll.Cur./Lib.Hd
Founded: 1929. **Staff:** Prof 10; Other 4. **Subjects:** History of American technology and American material culture, including agriculture, community and domestic life, entertainment and leisure, trades and manufactures, transportation and communication, Henry Ford, Ford Motor Company, advertising and marketing, the automobile. **Special Collections:** Edison Institute Archives; Edsel B. Ford Automotive Design History Collection; Ford Motor Company Historical Records (includes Henry Ford Papers, Stout Metal Airplane Company, Ford Motor Company Production, public relations, sales and advertising, finance, subsidiary companies, international operations, engineering and purchasing records, 1903-1950 (350,000 images), Ford Motor Company Photographic Archives, 1910-1950, Ford Oral History Program, 400 interviews); Henry Austin Clark, Jr. Collection of automotive history; graphics collection including Detroit Publishing Company, Enterprise Chair Company, Autocar Company Photographic Archives, Lincoln Motor Company Photographic Archives, cased, card and mounted photograph collection, Decorative Art Print Collections and Detroit, Toledo & Ironton Railroad photographs (50,000 items); manuscripts of Thomas A. Edison, Boston & Sandwich Glass Company, D.S. Morgan Company, and Stickley Furniture Company; Trade Literature Collection; Almanacs; Automotive Literature Collection, 1896 to present; music sheets, 1786-1960; McGuffey Readers. **Holdings:** 34,500 monographs; 133,000 periodicals; 13,700 trade catalogs; 23,000 linear feet of archival materials. **Subscriptions:** 300 journals and other serials. **Services:** Interlibrary loan; copying; library open to researchers. **Computerized Information Services:** OCLC, DIALOG Information Services, Conservation Information Network. **Networks/Consortia:** Member of Michigan Library Consortium (MLC). **Publications:** Guide to the Archives & Research Library, 1983; Guide to the Ford Archives Photograph Print Collection, 1981; Henry Ford, A Personal History, revised edition, 1980. **Special Indexes:** Finding guides to collections. **Remarks:** FAX: (313)271-8013. **Formerly:** Its Archives & Library. **Also Known As:** Edison Institute. **Staff:** Jennifer M. Heymoss, Libn.; Jeanine Head, Archv.; Cynthia Read-Miller, Cur., Photos. & Film; Robert Casey, Automotive Hist.Cur.

James B. Ford Library
See: **Explorers Club** (5521)

★ **5965** ★
Ford Motor Company - Ford Communications Network - Video Library (Bus-Fin)
World Headquarters, Rm. E-18 Phone: (313)845-8570
Dearborn, MI 48121-1899 Jim Munsie, Res.Info.Spec.
Staff: Prof 3. **Subjects:** Ford - training programs, special events, history; employee comunication; Ford Company orientation. **Holdings:** 4000 edited master tapes; 10,000 element reels; 200 16mm films. **Services:** Library not open to the public. **Computerized Information Services:** Revelation (internal database). **Remarks:** FAX: (313)390-7241.

★ **5966** ★
Ford Motor Company - Technical Information Section (Sci-Engr, Trans)
20000 Rotunda Dr.
Box 1602 Phone: (313)323-1059
Dearborn, MI 48121 Donna Seiler Estry, Supv., Tech.Info.Sect.
Founded: 1920. **Staff:** Prof 6; Other 2. **Subjects:** Engineering - automotive, electrical, metallurgical, mechanical; chemistry; mathematics; physics; electronics; engineering mechanics; statistics; energy; materials; pollution; environmental health; transportation. **Holdings:** 23,000 books. **Subscriptions:** 700 journals and other serials. **Services:** Interlibrary loan; library open to the public for reference use only by request. **Automated Operations:** Computerized public access catalog, cataloging, acquisitions, serials, and circulation. **Computerized Information Services:** BRS Information Technologies, NLM, DIALOG Information Services, PFDS Online. **Remarks:** FAX: (313)323-7936.

★ **5967** ★
Ford New Holland - Engineering Library (Sci-Engr)
500 Diller Ave., P.O. Box 1895
Mail Sta. 638 Phone: (717)355-1358
New Holland, PA 17557 Judith E. Summers, Engr.Libn.
Staff: Prof 1. **Subjects:** Agricultural and mechanical engineering, agriculture. **Holdings:** 625 volumes. **Subscriptions:** 50 journals and other serials. **Services:** Interlibrary loan; copying; library open to the public with permission. **Remarks:** Affiliated with New Holland Inc. **Remarks:** FAX: (717)355-1939.

Perry T. Ford Memorial Library
See: **Tri-State University** (16495)

Fordham Health Sciences Library
See: **Wright State University - School of Medicine - Fordham Health Sciences Library** (20645)

★ **5968** ★
Fordham University - Library at Lincoln Center (Educ, Soc Sci)
W. 60th St. and Columbus Ave. Phone: (212)636-6056
New York, NY 10023 Linda LoSchiavo, Libn.
Founded: 1969. **Staff:** Prof 6; Other 8. **Subjects:** Education, educational testing and measurement, educational psychology, guidance, mental health, business, liberal arts, social work and casework, community organization, government and social welfare, delinquency and crime. **Special Collections:** SCAN documents depository. **Holdings:** 350,000 volumes; Alcohol Abstracts; ERIC microfiche. **Subscriptions:** 1500 journals and other serials. **Services:** Interlibrary loan; copying; library open to the public for reference use only with letter of introduction required. **Computerized Information Services:** DIALOG Information Services, Dow Jones News/Retrieval, BRS Information Technologies; CD-ROMs. **Networks/Consortia:** Member of New York Metropolitan Reference and Research Library Agency. **Staff:** Zoe Salem, Bus.Libn.; Susan Baer, Soc.Serv.Libn.; Kathleen Clancy, Circ.Libn.; Patricia LiButti, Ed.Libn.; Allan Halpern, Ref./Tech.Serv.

★ **5969** ★
Fordham University - Mulcahy Science Library (Biol Sci, Sci-Engr)
Mulcahy Hall, Rm. 420 Phone: (212)579-2590
Bronx, NY 10458 Peter Mix, Sci.Ref.Libn.
Founded: 1979. **Staff:** Prof 1; Other 1. **Subjects:** Chemistry and chemical industry, seismology, spectroscopy, electronics, atomic and nuclear physics, pure mathematics, mathematical statistics, bacteriology, cytology, embryology, genetics, entomology, physiology. **Holdings:** 83,000 volumes. **Subscriptions:** 500 journals and other serials. **Services:** Interlibrary loan; copying; library open to the public for reference use only with letter of introduction. **Computerized Information Services:** CD-ROM (General Science Index).

★ **5970** ★
Fordham University - School of Law - Leo T. Kissam Memorial Law Library (Law)
140 W. 62nd St. Phone: (212)636-6900
New York, NY 10023-7476 Janet Tracy, Prof. of Res. & Lib.Serv.
Founded: 1906. **Staff:** Prof 11; Other 30. **Subjects:** Law. **Special Collections:** Law of the European Economic Community. **Holdings:** 402,000 volumes. **Subscriptions:** 4400 journals and other serials; 5 newspapers. **Services:** Interlibrary loan; library open to the public for reference use only upon request. **Automated Operations:** Computerized cataloging, serials, and acquisitions. **Computerized Information Services:** LEXIS, WESTLAW, OCLC, RLIN; internal database. **Networks/Consortia:** Member of SUNY/OCLC Library Network. **Publications:** Fordham Law Library guide, biannual; F.U.L.L. Story (newsletter), irregular - both available upon request. **Remarks:** FAX: (212)977-2662. **Staff:** Kristine Kreilick, Assoc. Law Libn.; Janice Greer, Ref.Libn.; Yvette Le Roy, Ref.Libn.; Carol Shapiro, Hd.Cat.; Evelyn Ma, Cat.; Victor Essien, Foreign & Intl. Law Libn.; Joyce Dindayal, Circ.Libn.; Mary McKee, Acq.Libn.; Jorene Frankl Robbie, Ref.Libn.

★ **5971** ★
Fordham University - Special Collections (Hum)
Duane Library Phone: (212)579-2417
Bronx, NY 10458 Joseph A. LoSchiazo, Chf.Ref.Libn.
Founded: 1841. **Staff:** Prof 1. **Subjects:** Literature, history, Jesuitica, philosophy, theology. **Special Collections:** Charles Allen Munn Collection of Revolutionary and Early Federal Americana (98 volumes); Joseph Givernaud Collection on the French Revolution (5200 volumes); Zema Memorial Collection on Monastic History of the Middle Ages (600 volumes); McGarry Collection on Criminology (450 volumes); McGuire-McLees Collection of Gaelic Language and Literature (700 volumes); William Cobbett Collection (80 monographs and 20 manuscript letters); Jesuitica Collection (431 volumes). **Services:** Collections open to the public with restrictions. **Automated Operations:** Computerized cataloging. **Networks/Consortia:** Member of New York Metropolitan Reference and Research Library Agency.

★ **5972** ★
Forecasting International, Ltd. - Library (Sci-Engr)
1001 N. Highland St.
P.O. Box 1650
Arlington, VA 22210 Phone: (703)527-1311
Subjects: Technological forecasting, technology assessment, policy analysis, resource allocation. **Holdings:** 2000 bound volumes. **Subscriptions:** 30 journals and other serials. **Computerized Information Services:** DIALOG Information Services; internal database. Performs searches on fee basis.

★ **5973** ★
Foreign Claims Settlement Commission of the United States - Library (Law)
601 D St., N.W., Rm. 10430 Phone: (202)653-5883
Washington, DC 20579 David Bradley, Chf.Couns.
Staff: Prof 1. **Subjects:** Commission decisions, international law, federal regulations, U.S. code and statutes. **Holdings:** 2000 books. **Services:** Library open to the public by appointment. **Remarks:** Commission is part of the U.S. Department of Justice.

★ **5974** ★
Foreign Missions Society of Quebec - Library (Rel-Phil)
180, place Juge-Desnoyers
Pont Viau Phone: (514)667-4190
Laval, PQ, Canada H7G 1A4 Claude Dubois, Lib.Dir.
Founded: 1924. **Staff:** Prof 1; Other 1. **Subjects:** Theology, missiology, Holy Scripture, social sciences, biography, languages. **Holdings:** 25,000 volumes. **Subscriptions:** 121 journals and other serials. **Services:** Interlibrary loan; library not open to the public. **Also Known As:** Societe des Missions-Etrangeres.

★ **5975** ★
Foreign Policy Research Institute - Library (Soc Sci)
3615 Chestnut St. Phone: (215)382-0685
Philadelphia, PA 19104 Alan H. Luxenberg, Lib.Dir.
Founded: 1955. **Staff:** Prof 1; Other 1. **Subjects:** American foreign policy, regional studies, international relations, strategic and military studies.

Special Collections: Congressional hearings collection (400). **Holdings:** Foreign Broadcast Information Service Daily Reports, 1962-1972, on microfilm, and 1979 to present, in unbound volumes; Foreign Policy Research Institute publications, 1955 to present; ORBIS archives, 1957 to present. **Subscriptions:** 250 journals and other serials. **Services:** Copying; library open to the public for reference use only. **Remarks:** FAX: (215)382-0131.

Dr. Robert C. Foreman Health Sciences Library
See: **Scottsdale Memorial Hospital** (14970)

Foremost Dairies Company - Research Department Library
See: **National Food Processors Association - National Food Laboratory - Library** (11168)

★ 5976 ★
Forest Association of Hungary - Library (Env-Cons)
Anker-koz 1
H-1061 Budapest VI, Hungary — Phone: 1 225683
Subjects: Hungarian national forest policy, forest-related industry, agricultural-forest cooperatives. **Holdings:** 20,000 volumes; biographical archives. **Computerized Information Services:** Internal database. **Remarks:** Telex: 225369. **Also Known As:** Orszagos Erdeszeti Egyesulet.

★ 5977 ★
Forest County Law Library (Law)
c/o Steven Guillford
Court House — Phone: (814)755-3581
Tionesta, PA 16353 — Steven Guillford, Lib.Dir.
Subjects: Law. **Remarks:** No further information was supplied by respondent.

★ 5978 ★
Forest Engineering Research Institute of Canada - Information Resources (Biol Sci)
143, Place Frontenac — Phone: (514)694-1140
Pointe Claire, PQ, Canada H9R 4Z7 — Christel Mukhopadhyay, Hd., Info.Rsrcs.
Founded: 1976. **Staff:** Prof 1; Other 2. **Subjects:** Forest engineering, mechanization of silviculture, woodlot technology, transport of wood, forest biomass energy. **Special Collections:** Forest machinery patents (36 linear feet). **Holdings:** 4700 monographs; 160 bound periodical volumes; 9800 reports in series; 4 VF drawers of annual reports; 25 linear feet of pamphlets and reprints. **Subscriptions:** 125 journals. **Services:** Interlibrary loan; copying; SDI; library open to the public with restrictions. **Automated Operations:** Computerized public access catalog and cataloging. **Computerized Information Services:** DIALOG Information Services, Infomart Online, CAN/OLE, ORBIT Search Service; FERLIB, PERWATCH (internal databases). Performs searches on fee basis for member companies. **Publications:** Serials list, biennial; Information Resources-Communication, quarterly; Periodical Watch, 2/month - all to staff, member companies, selected libraries, and research centers. **Remarks:** FAX: (514)694-4351.

★ 5979 ★
Forest History Society, Inc. - Library and Archives (Env-Cons, Biol Sci)
701 Vickers Ave. — Phone: (919)682-9319
Durham, NC 27701 — Cheryl Oakes, Libn.
Founded: 1946. **Staff:** Prof 1; Other 2. **Subjects:** History of forestry, conservation of natural resources, environmental policy, lumber industry, land use. **Special Collections:** Oral history interviews with leaders of forestry and forest products industries (693 tapes); historical photo collection (50 VF drawers); archival collections of American Forest Institute, American Forestry Association, National Forest Products Association, and Society of American Foresters; papers of foresters. **Holdings:** 5500 books; 500 bound periodical volumes; 900 archives boxes of manuscripts; 195 VF drawers of pamphlets and documents; 50 VF drawers of photograph collections; 100 reels of microfilm of records. **Subscriptions:** 240 journals and other serials. **Services:** Interlibrary loan; copying; library open to the public for reference use only. **Computerized Information Services:** DIALOG Information Services; internal database. **Publications:** Forest and Conservation History, quarterly - available by subscription; North American Forest and Conservation History: A Bibliography; North American Forest History: A Guide to Archives and Manuscripts in the United States and Canada. **Remarks:** The Forest History Society refers the great bulk of all forest history source materials which it finds to repositories in the U.S. and Canada which are focal points for research in forest history.

★ 5980 ★
Forest Institute of Professional Psychology - Library (Med)
200 Glendale St. — Phone: (708)215-7870
Wheeling, IL 60090 — Janan Lundgren, Dir., Lib.Serv.
Founded: 1979. **Staff:** Prof 1; Other 1. **Subjects:** Psychology, psychiatry, family therapy, substance abuse, aging. **Holdings:** 9500 books; 2200 bound periodical volumes; 400 pamphlets and reprints; 2400 unbound periodicals; 5 drawers of microfiche; 160 dissertations. **Subscriptions:** 201 journals and other serials. **Services:** Interlibrary loan; library open to the public with restrictions. **Computerized Information Services:** DIALOG Information Services; CD-ROM (PsycLIT). **Networks/Consortia:** Member of North Suburban Library System (NSLS).

★ 5981 ★
Forest Lambton Museum Ltd. - Archives (Hist)
59 Broadway St. — Phone: (519)786-5884
Forest, ON, Canada N0N 1J0 — Ms. E.M. Powell, Cur. of Musm.
Founded: 1962. **Staff:** Prof 1. **Subjects:** Genealogy; town histories; area businesses, schools, churches. **Special Collections:** Private genealogical and archeological collections; doll collection. **Holdings:** Historical records. **Subscriptions:** 3 journals and other serials. **Services:** Archives open to the public with permission. **Publications:** Brochures on collections.

★ 5982 ★
Forest Products Accident Prevention Association - Library (Sci-Engr)
Box 270 — Phone: (705)472-4120
North Bay, ON, Canada P1B 8H2 — V. Jones, Libn.
Staff: 1. **Subjects:** Occupational safety and health, accident prevention, industrial and occupational diseases, forests and forestry, management, total loss control. **Holdings:** 600 books; 21 16mm films; 80 videotapes. **Subscriptions:** 30 journals and other serials. **Services:** Interlibrary loan; library not open to the public. **Publications:** Tallyboard, bimonthly - to members. **Special Catalogs:** Video catalog; educational materials catalog. **Remarks:** FAX: (705)472-0207.

★ 5983 ★
Forest Products Research Society - FOREST Information Retrieval System (Sci-Engr, Info Sci)
2801 Marshall Ct. — Phone: (608)231-1361
Madison, WI 53705 — Mary Gordon, Data Base Mgr.
Founded: 1974. **Staff:** Prof 1; Other 1. **Subjects:** Timber resources and harvesting; wood - machining, mechanical properties, energy; plywood and particleboard. **Holdings:** Magnetic tape database of 20,000 citations. **Subscriptions:** 100 journals and other serials. **Services:** Interlibrary loan; copying; system open to the public. **Computerized Information Services:** PFDS Online; internal database. **Publications:** 1981 Energy Bibliography; Keyword Thesaurus - for sale. **Special Indexes:** Author, subject, keyword, and species index to database (microfiche). **Remarks:** The FOREST or FOREST PRODUCTS database can be accessed online via PFDS Online. Worldwide references abstracted include periodicals and government, education, and trade association publications. Copies of all English articles in the FOREST database are available in hardcopy. FAX: (608)231-2152.

Forest Service Information Network Northwest
See: **U.S. Forest Service** (17515)

★ 5984 ★
Foresta Institute for Ocean and Mountain Studies - Environmental Studies Center (Env-Cons)
6205 Franktown Rd.
Carson City, NV 89704
Founded: 1960. **Staff:** 1. **Subjects:** Ichthyology, plant and animal ecology, Western American and Nevada environment and ecology. **Special Collections:** Antarctica (2500 books, reprints, maps); rare and endangered species (2000 books and reprints). **Holdings:** 7000 books; 100 bound periodical volumes; 3000 reprints and pamphlets; 2000 color slides; 200 maps. **Subscriptions:** 8 journals and other serials. **Services:** Library not open to the public.

Forestry Canada
See: **Canada - Forestry Canada** (2738)

★5985★
Forintek Canada Corp. - Eastern Laboratory - Information Resource Unit (Sci-Engr)
800 Montreal Rd. Phone: (613)744-0963
Ottawa, ON, Canada K1G 3Z5 Doreen Liberty, Libn.
Founded: 1913. **Staff:** 2; Other 2. **Subjects:** Wood - research, chemistry, biotechnology, engineering; forest products and technology; mycology. **Holdings:** 12,000 volumes. **Subscriptions:** 400 journals and other serials. **Services:** Interlibrary loan; copying (limited); SDI; library delivery service; center open to the public with restrictions. **Automated Operations:** Computerized cataloging, serials, circulation, and ILL. **Computerized Information Services:** DIALOG Information Services, CAN/OLE. **Publications:** Accessions list, monthly; subscriptions list, annual; library services booklet. **Remarks:** Parent organization located in Vancouver, BC, Canada. FAX: (613)744-0903. Telex: 053-0605. **Staff:** Cathy Cuzner.

★5986★
Forintek Canada Corp. - Western Laboratory - Library (Sci-Engr)
University of British Columbia
2665 E. Mall Phone: (604)224-3221
Vancouver, BC, Canada V6T 1W5 Barbara Holder, Libn.
Founded: 1927. **Staff:** Prof 1; Other 1. **Subjects:** Wood chemistry and identification, timber engineering, wood protection and preservation, sawmilling and wood seasoning, wood machining, glues and gluing. **Holdings:** 6000 books; 3200 bound periodical volumes; 500 microfiche; 160 VF drawers of pamphlets, reprints, internal publications; films; videotapes. **Subscriptions:** 350 journals and other serials. **Services:** Interlibrary loan; copying (limited); SDI; library open to the public by referral. **Automated Operations:** Computerized cataloging. **Computerized Information Services:** DIALOG Information Services, CAN/OLE, Infomart Online; BAT (Best Available Technology in Sawmilling; internal database); Envoy 100 (electronic mail service). Performs searches on fee basis. **Publications:** Occasional bibliographies; technical reports. **Remarks:** FAX: (604)222-5690. Telex: 04-508552. Electronic mail address(es): FORINTEK (Envoy 100).

★5987★
FORM, s.p. - Technicka Knihovna (Sci-Engr)
Cechynska 16 Phone: 5 334411
CS-657 01 Brno, Czechoslovakia Miroslava Gregrova
Founded: 1953. **Staff:** Prof 2. **Subjects:** Metallurgy. **Holdings:** 10,100 books; 190 bound periodical volumes; 1900 reports; catalogs; patents; research reports. **Subscriptions:** 36 journals and other serials; 4 newspapers. **Services:** Interlibrary loan; copying; SDI; library open to the public. **Computerized Information Services:** UNIX, INFORMIX; internal database. Performs searches. Contact Person: Ing. Milan Zamazal. **Publications:** Periodical survey of additions. **Remarks:** FAX: 5 334097. Telex: 62600 FORMC.

★5988★
Forney - Library (Art)
Hotel de Sens
1 rue du Figuier Phone: 1 42781460
F-69005 Paris, France Mlle. Lelieur, Chf.Cur.
Founded: 1886. **Subjects:** Arts, crafts, decorative arts. **Holdings:** 300,000 books; 2200 periodicals; 15,000 posters; 2000 wallpapers; 1 million postcards. **Subscriptions:** 2200 journals and other serials. **Services:** Interlibrary loan; copying; library open to the public. **Publications:** Bibliography, annual; Bulletins, quarterly. **Special Catalogs:** Exhibition catalogs, quarterly. **Remarks:** FAX: 1 42782253. **Also Known As:** Bibliotheque Forney.

★5989★
Forrest General Hospital - Medical Library (Med)
Drawer 16389 Phone: (601)288-4260
Hattiesburg, MS 39402 Bettye M. Duncan, Med.Libn.
Founded: 1976. **Staff:** Prof 1; Other 1. **Subjects:** Medicine, renal medicine, gynecology and obstetrics, gastroenterology, surgery. **Holdings:** 500 books; 1000 bound periodical volumes. **Subscriptions:** 31 journals and other serials. **Services:** Interlibrary loan; library not open to the public. **Computerized Information Services:** NLM, BRS Information Technologies. **Networks/Consortia:** Member of National Network of Libraries of Medicine (NN/LM), Mississippi Biomedical Library Consortium (MBLC).

Forschungsinstitut fuer Absatz und Handel
See: **Swiss Research Institute for Marketing and Distribution** (15939)

Forschungsinstitut fuer Internationale Politik und Sicherheit
See: **Research Institute for International Politics and Security** (13839)

★5990★
Forsyth Dental Center - Percy Howe Memorial Library (Med)
140 The Fenway Phone: (617)262-5200
Boston, MA 02115 Roberta Oppenheim, Lib.Dir.
Founded: 1914. **Staff:** Prof 2; Other 3. **Subjects:** Dentistry, dental hygiene, biochemistry, microbiology, molecular biology, anthropology, anatomy, immunology. **Special Collections:** History of the Forsyth Dental Center (photographs); archives (photographs and memorabilia; rare books; antique dental instruments). **Holdings:** 6200 books; 14,575 bound periodical volumes; pamphlets; photographs; staff reprints. **Subscriptions:** 230 journals and other serials. **Services:** Interlibrary loan (fee); library open to the public with restrictions. **Computerized Information Services:** DIALOG Information Services, NLM, BRS Information Technologies, STN International; CD-ROM; DOCLINE (electronic mail service). Performs searches on fee basis. **Networks/Consortia:** Member of National Network of Libraries of Medicine - New England Region. **Publications:** Acquisitions list, quarterly; newsletter, bimonthly. **Remarks:** FAX: (617)262-4021. **Staff:** Susan Abusch, Libn.

Forsyth Library
See: **Fort Hays University** (5999)

★5991★
Forsyth Memorial Hospital - John C. Whitaker Library (Med)
3333 Silas Creek Pkwy. Phone: (919)760-5995
Winston-Salem, NC 27103-3090 Margaret L. Cobb, Med.Libn.
Founded: 1964. **Staff:** Prof 1; Other 1. **Subjects:** Medicine, allied health sciences. **Holdings:** 1000 books; 5330 bound periodical volumes; 300 videotapes. **Subscriptions:** 124 journals and other serials. **Services:** Interlibrary loan; library not open to the public. **Automated Operations:** Computerized cataloging. **Computerized Information Services:** BRS Information Technologies; CD-ROM. Performs searches on fee basis.

★5992★
Forsyth Technical Community College - Library (Educ)
2100 Silas Creek Pkwy. Phone: (919)723-0371
Winston-Salem, NC 27103 Audrey B. Zablocki, Dir.
Founded: 1964. **Staff:** Prof 2; Other 4. **Subjects:** Technology, health, law, business, psychology, art. **Holdings:** 32,000 books; 1317 bound periodical volumes. **Subscriptions:** 303 journals and other serials; 6 newspapers. **Services:** Interlibrary loan; copying; library open to the public. **Remarks:** FAX: (919)761-2399. **Staff:** Tom Gordon, Rd.Serv.Libn.

★5993★
Fort Belknap Archives, Inc. - Library (Hist)
Route 1, Box 27 Phone: (817)549-1856
Newcastle, TX 76374 K.F. Neighbours, Ph.D., Archv.
Founded: 1961. **Staff:** Prof 2; Other 4. **Subjects:** History - local, Texas, Southwest, frontier; genealogy; Texana and Americana. **Holdings:** 3000 books; 500 bound periodical volumes; 500 manuscripts; 100,000 clippings; 500 documents; 10 reels of microfilm of U.S. Archives documents. **Subscriptions:** 15 journals and other serials; 10 newspapers. **Services:** Copying; library open to the public for reference use only. **Publications:** Report, annual; Fort Belknap Archives, Inc.; A Tour Through Fort Belknap and its Archives; Fort Belknap Frontier Saga, 1790-1980. **Remarks:** Maintained by the Board of Directors of Fort Belknap Archives, Inc. and Young County Commissioners. **Staff:** Barbara A. Ledbetter, Asst.Archv.

Fort Burgwin Research Center
See: **Southern Methodist University** (15500)

★5994★
Fort Clark Historical Society - The Old Guardhouse Museum - Library (Hist)
Fort Clark Springs
Box 1061 Phone: (512)563-2709
Brackettville, TX 78832 Donald A. Swanson, Dir./Cur.
Founded: 1976. **Staff:** 2. **Subjects:** Fort Clark history, U.S. Army units, U.S. Cavalry. **Special Collections:** Secretary of War annual reports, 1908-1912; Surgeon General reports; Inspector General reports on Fort Clark. **Holdings:** 220 volumes; 9 reels of microfilm; manuscripts; Fort Clark Post Returns, 1852-1916. **Services:** Library open to the public.

★5995★
Fort Collins Public Library - Local History Collection (Hist)
201 Peterson St. Phone: (303)221-6688
Fort Collins, CO 80524 Karen McWilliams, Local Hist.Coord.
Staff: Prof 1. **Subjects:** Fort Collins and Larimer County history. **Holdings:** 130,000 photographs; 400 oral history interview tapes and transcripts; maps; clipping and pamphlet files. **Subscriptions:** 10 journals and other serials; 4 newspapers. **Services:** Interlibrary loan; copying; collection open to the public. **Automated Operations:** Computerized circulation. **Computerized Information Services:** Knowledge Index. **Networks/Consortia:** Member of High Plains Regional Library Service System, Colorado Alliance of Research Libraries (CARL). **Special Indexes:** Index to Fort Collins newspapers (card); indexes to area history books (card and book); index to oral history collection (book); historical photographs index (multimedia hypercard database). **Remarks:** FAX: (303)221-6398.

★5996★
Fort Concho Museum Library (Hist)
213 E. Ave. D Phone: (915)657-4441
San Angelo, TX 76903 John C. Neilson, Hist./Archv.
Founded: 1969. **Staff:** Prof 1. **Subjects:** Local and regional civilian and military history; Indian Wars, 1865-1891. **Special Collections:** M.C. Ragsdale Photographic Collection (over 500 photographs of early West Texas); Oscar Ruffini Papers (drawings and specifications by pioneer architect); Papers of Captain George Gibson Huntt, 4th Cavalry. **Holdings:** 5000 books; 8000 photographs; 300 maps; military records (125 reels of microfilm); 300 cubic feet of archival material; 1500 file folders of research material. **Subscriptions:** 20 journals and other serials. **Services:** Interlibrary loan; copying; library open to the public by appointment for reference use only. **Publications:** Fort Concho and the South Plains Journal, quarterly. **Remarks:** Maintained by the city of San Angelo.

Fort Davis National Historic Site
See: **U.S. Natl. Park Service** (17707)

★5997★
Fort Frederica National Monument - Library (Hist)
Rt. 9, Box 286-C Phone: (912)638-3639
St. Simons Island, GA 31522 Ray Morris, Chf. Ranger
Founded: 1944. **Staff:** 2. **Subjects:** Colonial times - history, archeology, military history; Georgia history; regional natural history. **Special Collections:** Margaret Davis Cate Collection (colonial and regional history; 10,000 books, papers, photographs, microfilm, and other historical memorabilia); Fort Frederica vertical files. **Holdings:** 700 books; 50 bound periodical volumes; 25 AV programs. **Subscriptions:** 4 journals and other serials. **Services:** Copying; library open to the public by appointment. **Special Indexes:** Margaret Davis Cate Collection Inventory. **Remarks:** The photographs from the Margaret Davis Cate Collection are permanently on loan to and available through the Georgia Historical Society. **Remarks:** FAX: (912) 638-3639. **Staff:** Valerie Hunter, Libn.

★5998★
Fort Hamilton-Hughes Memorial Hospital Center - Sohn Memorial Health Services Library (Med)
630 Eaton Ave. Phone: (513)867-2310
Hamilton, OH 45013 Judy Leeds, Libn.
Founded: 1959. **Staff:** Prof 1. **Subjects:** Medicine. **Holdings:** 1000 books; 467 periodical volumes. **Subscriptions:** 50 journals and other serials. **Services:** Interlibrary loan; library not open to the public. **Remarks:** FAX: (513)867-2620.

★5999★
Fort Hays University - Forsyth Library - Special Collections (Hist)
600 Park St. Phone: (913)628-5901
Hays, KS 67601-4099 Esta Lou Riley, Archv./Spec.Coll.Libn.
Staff: Prof 2. **Special Collections:** Center fo Ethnic Studies Collection; Western Collection; University Archives (including Kansas Oral History Project and Historian-in-Residence Oral History Project cassettes, reel-to-reel tapes, transcriptions); Folklore Collection; Consortium for Children's and Young Adult's Books Collection (10,000 volumes of children's and juvenile literature). **Holdings:** 13,300 books; 58 boxes of university records and faculty papers; 60 tapes of university events, lectures, speeches; 640 oral history tapes and transcriptions; 87 tapes of folk songs, poems, stories, reminiscences; 25 video cassettes. **Subscriptions:** 6 journals and other serials; 2 newspapers. **Services:** Interlibrary loan; copying; collections open to the public with restrictions. **Automated Operations:** Computerized public access catalog, cataloging, acquisitions, circulation, and serials (NOTIS). **Computerized Information Services:** BRS Information Technologies, OCLC, DIALOG Information Services; BITNET (electronic mail service). Performs searches on fee basis. Contact Person: Phyllis Schmidt, 628-4338. **Special Catalogs:** Catalog for Center for Ethnic Studies Collection . **Special Indexes:** Index to Oral History Collection by interviewer/interviewee and brief subject guide; index to songs and superstitions in the Folklore Collection (card). **Remarks:** Telephone number for the Consortium for Children's and Young Adult's Books Collection is (913)628-4339. FAX: (913)628-4096. **Staff:** Martha Dirks.

★6000★
Fort Hays University - Instructional Resource Center (Educ)
Rarick Hall
600 Park St. Phone: (913)628-4339
Hays, KS 67601-4099 Robert R. Kilman, Supv./Asst.Prof.
Founded: 1981. **Staff:** Prof 1; Other 1. **Subjects:** Textbooks, reading services, computer laboratory, nonprint educational materials. **Holdings:** 10,761 books; 413 nonbook materials. **Services:** Center open to the public for reference use only. **Automated Operations:** Computerized cataloging.

★6001★
Fort Hays University - Sternberg Memorial Museum - Library (Biol Sci)
Hays, KS 67601 Phone: (913)628-4286
Dr. Richard J. Zakrzewski, Musm.Dir.
Founded: 1953. **Staff:** 1. **Subjects:** Paleontology, geology, archeology, history, museology. **Holdings:** 300 books; 1350 unbound periodicals; 19 boxes of pamphlets. **Subscriptions:** 2 journals and other serials. **Services:** Library open to qualified researchers.

★6002★
Fort Huachuca Historical Museum - Library (Hist)
ATZS-PTP-M Phone: (602)533-3638
Fort Huachuca, AZ 85613-6000 David A. Huet, Ck.
Subjects: History - U.S. military, Southwest, world. **Holdings:** 5000 books; 500 bound periodical volumes. **Services:** Copying; library open to the public by appointment.

Fort King George Library
See: **Georgia (State) Department of Natural Resources** (6404)

Fort Laramie National Historic Site
See: **U.S. Natl. Park Service** (17708)

★6003★
Fort Larned Historical Society, Inc. - Santa Fe Trail Center Library (Hist)
Rte. 3 Phone: (316)285-2054
Larned, KS 67550 Alan Hitz, Archv./Educ.Dir.
Staff: 1. **Subjects:** History of Santa Fe Trail and Kansas. **Special Collections:** R.R. Smith Glass Magic Lantern Slide Collection (2300 slides); Grand Army of the Republic records, B.F. Larned Post (30 boxes); Santa Fe Trail Association Archives. **Holdings:** 3500 books; 100 bound periodical volumes; 11 boxes of W.P.A. county histories; 2 boxes of maps of the Santa Fe Trail; 100 pieces of historical sheet music; Pawnee County Archives; photographic collection; Civil War official records. **Subscriptions:** 15 journals and other serials. **Services:** Copying; library open to the public with restrictions.

Fort Larned National Historic Site
See: **U.S. Natl. Park Service** (17709)

★6004★
Fort Lauderdale Historical Society - Library & Archives (Hist)
219 S.W. 2nd Ave. Phone: (305)463-4431
Fort Lauderdale, FL 33301 Daniel T. Hobby, Exec.Dir.
Founded: 1962. **Staff:** Prof 4; Other 3. **Subjects:** Local and state history, historic preservation. **Holdings:** 2500 books; 450 bound periodical volumes; 120 feet of manuscripts; 250 oral history cassettes; 200,000 photographs and slides. **Subscriptions:** 25 journals and other serials. **Services:** Copying; library open to the public by appointment. **Publications:** New River News. **Remarks:** FAX: (305)463-4434. **Staff:** Susan Gillis, Cur. of Coll.

★6005★
Fort Lee Public Library - Silent Film Photo Collection (Theater)
320 Main St. Phone: (201)592-3614
Fort Lee, NJ 07024 Rita Altomara, Dir.
Founded: 1971. **Staff:** Prof 1; Other 1. **Subjects:** Silent films, actors and actresses, Fort Lee film studios. **Special Collections:** Silent Film Photo Collection (1000 photographs); videotaped history of Fort Lee films. **Holdings:** 500 books; periodicals on microfilm; 10 interviews on tape; 41 silent films, most made in Fort Lee. **Subscriptions:** 2 journals and other serials. **Services:** Interlibrary loan (books only); copying; collection open to the public. **Networks/Consortia:** Member of Bergen County Cooperative Library System (BCCLS). **Remarks:** FAX: (201)585-0375.

★6006★
Fort Lewis College - Center of Southwest Studies (Area-Ethnic)
Fort Lewis College Library Phone: (303)247-7456
Durango, CO 81301 Richard N. Ellis, Dir.
Founded: 1964. **Staff:** Prof 4; Other 8. **Subjects:** Southwestern U.S. history, American Indians, railroads, mining, energy, water. **Special Collections:** Spanish exploration and colonization; Indians of the Southwest; records of geological surveys; mining; military; newspapers; narrow gauge railroads; politics and government. **Holdings:** 9800 books; 500 bound periodical volumes; 2000 reels of microfilm; maps and photographs; manuscripts; college archives; personal papers; artifacts. **Services:** Interlibrary loan; copying; center open to the public. **Automated Operations:** Computerized public access catalog and circulation. **Networks/Consortia:** Member of Southwest Regional Library Service System (SWRLSS), Colorado Alliance of Research Libraries (CARL). **Publications:** Occasional papers. **Special Catalogs:** Opportunities for Research. **Remarks:** FAX: (303)247-7588. **Staff:** Todd Ellison, Archv.; Dr. Duane A. Smith, Prof., Hist.; Dr. Mary Jean Moseley, Prof. Southwest Stud.

★6007★
Fort Ligonier Association - Henry Bouquet Room (Hist)
S. Market St. Phone: (412)238-9701
Ligonier, PA 15658 J. Martin West, Dir.
Founded: 1974. **Staff:** 1. **Subjects:** Fort Ligonier; French and Indian War; historical archeology; Arthur St. Clair; Ligonier Valley, 1758-1790; fortifications. **Holdings:** 400 books; 25 notebooks of archeological field records; 10 unpublished reports manuscripts; 650 pages of correspondence on historical archeology; 800 unbound periodicals and pamphlets. **Subscriptions:** 13 journals and other serials. **Services:** Copying; room open to the public by appointment. **Remarks:** The Henry Bouquet Room is a research facility dedicated to historical archeology. Fort Ligonier is a restored English frontier fort and museum.

Fort Logan Mental Health Center
See: **Colorado Mental Health Center at Fort Logan** (3942)

★6008★
Fort Malden National Historic Park - Resource Centre (Hist, Mil)
100 Laird Ave.
Box 38 Phone: (519)736-5416
Amherstburg, ON, Canada N9V 2Z2 Bob Garcia, Rsrc.Ctr.Spec.
Founded: 1941. **Staff:** Prof 1. **Subjects:** Fort Malden, War of 1812, Rebellion of 1837, Essex County history (original material and secondary sources), British and American military before 1860, weapons, British Indian Department. **Holdings:** 3100 books; 170 reels of microfilm; 65 sheets of microfiche; 20 linear feet of information files; 50 feet of manuscripts and archival materials; 20 feet of historic and contemporary photographic prints and negatives. **Subscriptions:** 25 journals and other serials. **Services:** Interlibrary loan; copying; center open to the public by appointment only. **Remarks:** FAX: (519)736-6603. Maintained by Canada - Environment Canada, Canadian Parks Service.

★6009★
Fort Massac Historic Site - Library (Hist)
1308 E. 5th St. Phone: (618)524-9321
Metropolis, IL 62960 Terry Johnson, Site Supt.
Founded: 1973. **Staff:** 1. **Subjects:** U.S. military history (1750-1830), weapons of early America, guides to collections in U.S. archives, plant life of Illinois. **Special Collections:** Typed copies of original Fort Massac documents, 1794-1835 (22 volumes); Anthony Wayne papers (21 reels of microfilm); Isaac Craig papers, 1787-1809 (5 reels of microfilm). **Holdings:** 60 books; 15 bound periodical volumes; 35 maps of North America, 1700-1900; 6 Fort Massac archeological reports. **Services:** Library open to the public for reference use only. **Special Catalogs:** Catalogue of Fort Massac Museum acquisitions - for internal distribution only. **Remarks:** Maintained by Illinois State Department of Conservation.

Fort Matanzas National Monument
See: **U.S. Natl. Park Service - Castillo de San Marcos Natl. Monument & Fort Matanzas Natl. Monument** (17685)

Fort McHenry National Monument & Historic Shrine - Library
See: **U.S. Natl. Park Service** (17710)

★6010★
Fort McMurray Regional Hospital - Learning Resource Center (Med)
7 Hospital St. Phone: (403)791-6084
Fort McMurray, AB, Canada T9H 1P2 Marianne E. Bruce, Libn.
Founded: 1980. **Staff:** 2. **Subjects:** Medicine, nursing, and allied health. **Holdings:** 3000 books. **Subscriptions:** 165 journals and other serials. **Services:** Interlibrary loan; library not open to the public. **Computerized Information Services:** MEDLARS. **Remarks:** FAX: (403)791-6042.

Fort Meade Museum
See: **U.S. Army - Forces Command - Fort Meade Museum** (16973)

Fort Necessity National Battlefield
See: **U.S. Natl. Park Service** (17711)

Fort Ontario State Historic Site
See: **New York (State) Office of Parks, Recreation & Historic Preservation** (11680)

Fort Pitt Museum
See: **Pennsylvania (State) Historical & Museum Commission** (12878)

★6011★
Fort Polk Military Museum - Library (Mil)
P.O. Box 3916 Phone: (318)531-7905
Fort Polk, LA 71459-0916 Dr. David S. Bingham, Musm.Dir./Cur.
Founded: 1975. **Staff:** 1. **Subjects:** U.S. military history. **Holdings:** 5000 books; 100 bound periodical volumes; training and field manuals; 5000 photographs. **Services:** Library not open to the public.

Fort Pulaski National Monument
See: **U.S. Natl. Park Service** (17712)

Fort Robinson Museum
See: **Nebraska State Historical Society** (11379)

★6012★
Fort Sanders Regional Medical Center - Medical/Nursing Library (Med)
1915 White Ave. Phone: (615)541-1293
Knoxville, TN 37916-2399 Nedra Cook, Libn.
Founded: 1949. **Staff:** Prof 1; Other 1. **Subjects:** Nursing and nursing education, medicine. **Special Collections:** National League for Nursing Collection. **Holdings:** 8000 books; 890 bound periodical volumes; 16 VF drawers. **Subscriptions:** 173 journals and other serials. **Services:** Interlibrary loan; copying. **Automated Operations:** Computerized cataloging and acquisitions. **Computerized Information Services:** CD-ROM (MEDLINE); DOCLINE (electronic mail service). Performs searches on fee basis. **Networks/Consortia:** Member of Knoxville Area Health Sciences Library Consortium (KAHSLC), National Network of Libraries of Medicine - Southeastern/Atlantic Region, Tennessee Health Science Library Association (THeSLA).

Fort Steele Heritage Town - Research Library
See: **British Columbia Ministry of Tourism & Culture** (2170)

Fort Sumter National Monument
See: **U.S. Natl. Park Service** (17713)

★6013★
Fort Ticonderoga Association, Inc. - Thompson-Pell Research Center (Hist)
Box 390 Phone: (518)585-2821
Ticonderoga, NY 12883 Nicholas Westbrook, Dir.
Founded: 1908. **Staff:** 7. **Subjects:** Champlain Valley history, United States and Canadian colonial history, fortifications, early United States military history. **Special Collections:** Colonial and Revolutionary history. **Holdings:** 8000 books; 1500 bound periodical volumes; 2500 manuscripts of early history of Fort Ticonderoga and Champlain Valley. **Subscriptions:** 20 journals and other serials. **Services:** Copying (limited); library open to the public open to the public by appointment. **Remarks:** FAX: (518)585-2210.

Fort Union National Monument
See: **U.S. Natl. Park Service** (17714)

★6014★
Fort Valley State College - Henry Alexander Hunt Memorial Learning Resources Center (Agri, Educ)
805 State College Dr. Phone: (912)825-6342
Fort Valley, GA 31030 Dr. Carole R. Taylor, Dir.
Staff: Prof 5; Other 8. **Subjects:** Education, agriculture, business and economics, arts and science, home economics. **Special Collections:** Fort Valley State College Collection; Ethnic Heritage Collection (7100 volumes); Experiment Station Collection (3831 items). **Holdings:** 188,287 books; 36,000 bound periodical volumes; 4654 phonograph records; 190,062 microforms; 6338 reels of microfilm; 690 other cataloged items. **Subscriptions:** 1213 journals and other serials; 50 newspapers. **Services:** Interlibrary loan; copying; center open to the public for reference use only. **Automated Operations:** Computerized cataloging. **Computerized Information Services:** OCLC. **Networks/Consortia:** Member of SOLINET, Central Georgia Associated Libraries (CGAL). **Publications:** The Info: New Acquisitions; Student Library Handbook; Collection Development Policy; Annual Report of the Librarian. **Special Catalogs:** Ethnic heritage; microprint. **Remarks:** FAX: (912)825-6916. **Staff:** Doris Gosier, Hd., Pub.Serv.; Bernice Eaton, Hd., Tech.Serv.; Alma Simmons, Curric.Mtls.Ctr.Libn.; Connie Smith, Ref.Libn.; Ida McCrary, Circ.; Betty Jones, Heritage Coll.; Robert Ross, Media Serv.

Fort Vancouver National Historic Site
See: **U.S. Natl. Park Service - Fort Vancouver Natl. Historic Site - Library** (17715)

★6015★
Fort Ward Museum - Dorothy C.S. Starr Civil War Research Library (Hist)
4301 W. Braddock Rd. Phone: (703)838-4848
Alexandria, VA 22304 Wanda S. Dowell, Dir.
Founded: 1972. **Staff:** 2. **Subjects:** Civil War. **Holdings:** 2000 books; 100 unbound publications on the Civil War. **Services:** Library open to the public by appointment. **Remarks:** Maintained by City of Alexandria.

Fort Wayne Bible College
See: **Summit Christian College** (15860)

★6016★
Fort Wayne Department of Community Development & Planning - Planning Library (Plan)
City-County Bldg.
1 Main St., Rm. 800 Phone: (219)427-1140
Fort Wayne, IN 46802 Gary Stair, Sr.Plan.
Staff: Prof 1. **Subjects:** Land use and zoning, neighborhood planning, community development, housing rehabilitation. **Special Collections:** Fort Wayne City departmental publications. **Holdings:** 3000 books; U.S. Department of Housing and Urban Development (HUD) publications; U.S. Bureau of Census Standard Metropolitan Statistical Area (SMSA) census data. **Subscriptions:** 22 journals and other serials. **Services:** Copying; library not open to the public.

Fort Wayne Historical Society
See: **Allen County-Fort Wayne Historical Society** (371)

★6017★
Fort Wayne Journal-Gazette - Newspaper Library (Publ)
600 W. Main St. Phone: (219)461-8377
Fort Wayne, IN 46802 T.C. Shane, Jr., Chf.Libn.
Founded: 1978. **Staff:** Prof 1; Other 6. **Subjects:** Newspaper reference topics. **Holdings:** 1076 books; 100 bound periodical volumes; 760,000 clippings; 140,000 photographs; 1010 reels of microfilm. **Subscriptions:** 40 journals and other serials; 12 newspapers. **Services:** Library open to the public on a fee basis. **Computerized Information Services:** VU/TEXT Information Services, DIALOG Information Services, LEXIS, NewsNet, Inc., DataTimes. **Networks/Consortia:** Member of Tri-ALSA. **Remarks:** FAX: (219)461-8648.

★6018★
Fort Wayne Museum of Art - Edward Daniel Auer Library (Art)
311 E. Main St. Phone: (219)422-6467
Fort Wayne, IN 46802 Joyce L. Leckrone, Libn.
Founded: 1984. **Staff:** Prof 1. **Subjects:** Art history, American and European painting, prints and printmaking, sculpture, crafts. **Holdings:** 3454 books; 1386 exhibition catalogs. **Subscriptions:** 49 journals and other serials. **Services:** Library not open to the public.

★6019★
Fort Wayne News-Sentinel - Library (Publ)
600 W. Main St. Phone: (219)461-8468
Fort Wayne, IN 46802 Jody Habayeb
Founded: 1930. **Staff:** Prof 1; Other 1. **Subjects:** News. **Special Collections:** News coverage of Dan Qualye, 1976 to present. **Holdings:** 1916 reels of microfilm. **Services:** Library open to the public for reference use only. **Computerized Information Services:** VU/TEXT Information Services. Performs searches on a limited basis. **Remarks:** FAX: (219)461-8649.

★6020★
Fort Worth Museum of Science & History - Library (Hist)
1501 Montgomery St. Phone: (817)732-1631
Fort Worth, TX 76107 C. Jane Dees, Libn.
Staff: 1. **Subjects:** Material culture, Texas history, anthropology, archeology, natural history, astronomy. **Special Collections:** Instituitional Archives, 1939 to present. **Holdings:** 5700 books; 130 bound periodical volumes; Federal Writer's Project (Fort Worth and Tarrant County) on microfiche. **Subscriptions:** 19 journals and other serials. **Services:** Library open to researchers by appointment only. **Remarks:** FAX: (817)732-7635.

★6021★
Fort Worth Public Library - Arts Department
300 Taylor St. Phone: (817)871-7339
Fort Worth, TX 76102 Thelma Stone, Hum. Unit Mgr.
Staff: Prof 3. **Subjects:** Drawing, painting, sculpture, music and dance, entertainment, theater, movies, bullfight and rodeo, handicrafts and hobbies, architecture and city planning, antiques and interior decorating, photography, games and sports. **Special Collections:** Sheet music and scores; picture file; Mrs. John F. Lyons Collection (autographed performing artists' photographs); Hal Coffman Collection (original cartoon art); Nancy Taylor Collection (bookplates); collection of rare books. **Holdings:** 85,000 books; 6700 bound periodical volumes; 22,500 pieces of sheet music, scores, tune cards; 10,000 picture postcards, pamphlets, programs. **Subscriptions:** 140 journals and other serials. **Services:** Interlibrary loan; copying; department open to the public. **Publications:** Bibliographies, irregular. **Special Indexes:** Sheet Music Index. **Remarks:** FAX: (817)870-7734. **Staff:** Shakuntala Gokhale, Libn.; Tom Threatt, Asst.Libn.

★6022★
Fort Worth Public Library - Business, Science, Technology Units (Bus-Fin, Sci-Engr)
300 Taylor St. Phone: (817)871-7727
Fort Worth, TX 76102 Sally McCoy, Bus., Sci. & Tech. Unit Mgr.
Founded: 1900. **Staff:** Prof 3.5.; Other 2. **Subjects:** Business, economics, natural science, applied science, earth science, popular medicine,

management, cooking. **Holdings:** 110,000 books; 18 VF drawers of pamphlets and clippings. **Subscriptions:** 458 journals and other serials. **Services:** Interlibrary loan; copying; units open to the public. **Automated Operations:** Computerized public access catalog, cataloging, acquisitions, and circulation. **Computerized Information Services:** DIALOG Information Services, Dow Jones News/Retrieval, DataTimes, Disclosure Incorporated; internal database. Performs searches on fee basis. Contact Person: Sally McCoy, Online Serv.Libn. **Networks/Consortia:** Member of Northeast Texas Library System (NETLS). **Publications:** Bibliographies and booklists, irregular. **Special Indexes:** Map index; VF index; Tarrant Business index. **Staff:** Roberta Schenewerk, Libn.; Viola Easley, Asst.Libn.

★6023★
Fort Worth Public Library - Business, Science, Technology Units - Earth Science Division (Sci-Engr, Geog-Map)
300 Taylor St. Phone: (817)871-7727
Fort Worth, TX 76102 Sally McCoy, Bus., Sci. & Tech. Unit Mgr.
Founded: 1957. **Staff:** 1. **Subjects:** Geology, petroleum, mineralogy, paleontology, geophysics, surveying. **Special Collections:** Geological maps; topographic maps; state bulletins. **Holdings:** 6400 volumes; 18,500 bound periodical volumes; 19,500 U.S. and state documents on geology and petroleum; 2300 maps; 4 VF drawers of pamphlets. **Subscriptions:** 58 journals and other serials. **Services:** Interlibrary loan; copying; faxing; division open to the public. **Automated Operations:** Computerized public access catalog, cataloging, acquisitions, and circulation. **Computerized Information Services:** DIALOG Information Services, Dow Jones News/Retrieval; internal database. Performs searches on fee basis. Contact Person: Sally McCoy, Online Serv.Libn. **Networks/Consortia:** Member of Northeast Texas Library System (NETLS). **Publications:** Bibliographies, irregular. **Special Indexes:** Map index. **Remarks:** FAX: (817)870-7734. **Staff:** Viola Easley, Asst.Libn.

★6024★
Fort Worth Public Library - Genealogy and Local History Department - Heritage Center (Hist)
300 Taylor St. Phone: (817)871-7740
Fort Worth, TX 76102 Kenneth N. Hopkins, Unit Mgr.
Founded: 1956. **Staff:** Prof 3; Other 2. **Subjects:** Local history, genealogy. **Special Collections:** Mary Daggett Lake Collection; WPA Tarrant County, Texas Writers Project; Fort Worth and Tarrant County local history; M. M. Moseley Architectural Papers; Ante-bellum Southern plantation papers; early American imprints (1639-1819); Carlin Art Galleries Records; Casa Manana scrapbooks; Texas maps; Bible records; Fort Worth Boys' Council records; Index to Texas Death Certificates, 1903-1973; Index to Texas Birth Certificates, 1903-1977; Van Zandt Smith Papers; Library Archives; Tarrant County Historical Society Papers; Abner Taylor Papers; First Methodist Church records; Hazel Kingsley Rucidlo Collection; Indiana WPA vital records; Texas Federation of Music Clubs; Tarrant County Community of Churches records; Fort Worth Aviations scrapbooks; Hal Hoffman Cartoon Collection. **Holdings:** 30,000 books; 8500 bound periodical volumes; 5600 reels of microfilm; 106,100 microcards; 6200 titles on microfiche; 50 lateral file drawers of pamphlets and clippings on local history; 135 linear feet of miscellaneous manuscript material; 1000 photographs. **Subscriptions:** 245 journals and other serials. **Services:** Copying. **Automated Operations:** Computerized public access catalog. **Computerized Information Services:** DIALOG Information Services. **Remarks:** FAX: (817)870-7734. **Staff:** Kathy Tims, Libn.

Fort Worth Star-Telegram - Archive
See: **University of Texas at Arlington - Libraries - Division of Special Collections** (19375)

★6025★
Fort Worth Star-Telegram - Library (Publ)
400 W. 7th St. Phone: (817)390-7741
Fort Worth, TX 76102 Kristin Sandefur, Hd.Libn.
Founded: 1909. **Staff:** Prof 3; Other 5. **Subjects:** Newspaper reference topics. **Holdings:** 1000 books; newspaper, 1877 to present, on microfilm; clippings, photographs, negatives, 1960 to present. **Subscriptions:** 10 journals and other serials; 10 newspapers. **Services:** Library not open to the public. **Computerized Information Services:** DataTimes. **Staff:** Julia Wilson; Susanne Stutheit.

★6026★
(Fortaleza) Instituto Brasil-Estados Unidos - USIS Collection (Educ)
Rua Solon Pinheiro, 58 Phone: 85 2213599
60000 Fortaleza, Ceara, Brazil Terezinha Fontenelle, Libn.
Founded: 1943. **Staff:** 2. **Special Collections:** English and Portuguese publications. **Holdings:** 7000 books. **Subscriptions:** 3 newspapers. **Services:** Library open to the public for reference use only. **Computerized Information Services:** Internal databases. **Remarks:** FAX: 85 2521567. Maintains a branch library located at Rua Nogueira Acioly, 891, 60110 Fortaleza, CD, Brazil. Maintained or supported by the U.S. Information Agency. Focus is on materials that will assist peoples outside the United States to learn about the United States, its people, history, culture, political processes, and social milieux.

Fortier Memorial Library
See: **Manistee County Historical Museum** (9596)

★6027★
Fortress of Louisbourg National Historic Park - Resource Center (Hist)
P.O. Box 160 Phone: (902)733-2280
Louisbourg, NS, Canada B0A 1M0 Judith-Marie Romard, Archv./Lib.Techn.
Founded: 1962. **Staff:** Prof 2. **Subjects:** 18th century European and Canadian history. **Special Collections:** Rare Book Collection (18th and early 19th century, including Diderot's "Encyclopedie"); 18th century picture file. **Holdings:** 16,000 books; 3000 bound periodical volumes; 180 unpublished reports; 750,000 frames of manuscripts (copies and microfilm); 500 maps, drawings, plans, views. **Subscriptions:** 40 journals and other serials. **Services:** Interlibrary loan (no rare books); copying; center open to serious researchers only. **Automated Operations:** Computerized acquisitions, serials, and circulation. **Computerized Information Services:** DOBIS Canadian Online Library System, DIALOG Information Services; internal database. **Remarks:** Maintained by Canada - Environment Canada, Parks. FAX: (902)733-2362. **Staff:** Eric Krause, Hist.Rec.Supv.

Fortunoff Video Archive for Holocaust Testimonies
See: **Yale University** (20713)

★6028★
Forum Publishing Co. - Library (Publ)
Box 2020 Phone: (701)235-7311
Fargo, ND 58102 Andrea H. Halgrimson, Hd.Libn.
Founded: 1922. **Staff:** Prof 1; Other 2. **Subjects:** Newspaper reference topics. **Holdings:** 100,000 biographical and subject files; newspapers on microfilm. **Services:** Library not open to the public. **Remarks:** FAX: (701)241-5487.

Edwin Foscue Map Library
See: **Southern Methodist University - Science/Engineering Library** (15504)

The Fossils, Inc.
See: **American Private Press Association - Library** (721)

★6029★
Fossils Quarterly - Archives (Biol Sci)
3616 Garden Club Lane Phone: (704)365-4346
Charlotte, NC 28210 Myra J. Davis, Chf.Libn.
Founded: 1982. **Staff:** Prof 2. **Subjects:** Paleontology, stratigraphy. **Holdings:** 3000 books; reprint files; maps. **Subscriptions:** 40 journals and other serials. **Services:** Archives not open to the public. **Publications:** Geological guide books; historical geology texts; Fossils Quarterly (magazine). **Remarks:** Currently researching Pliocene and Pleistocene marine invertebrate mollusca in the Atlantic Coastal region. **Formerly:** Geotech Ltd. **Staff:** Mrs. Richard L. Casanova, Libn.

★6030★
Foster Associates, Inc. - Library (Energy, Info Sci)
1015 15th St., N.W. Phone: (202)408-7710
Washington, DC 20005 Ann Blandamer, Libn.
Founded: 1956. **Staff:** Prof 2; Other 1. **Subjects:** Energy analysis and forecasts, public utilities regulations, telecommunications, postal service, economics. **Holdings:** 20,000 books; 35 VF drawers; 8 drawers of microfiche. **Subscriptions:** 130 journals and other serials; 5 newspapers. **Services:** Interlibrary loan; library not open to the public. **Computerized Information Services:** LEXIS, NEXIS. **Remarks:** FAX: (202)408-7723. **Staff:** Marsha Rabb, Asst.Libn.

Charles R. Foster Technical Library
See: **National Asphalt Pavement Association** (11048)

Foster Hall Collection
See: **University of Pittsburgh** (19212)

★6031★
Foster Higgins - Employee Benefit Documentation Centre (Bus-Fin)
800 Place Victoria, Suite 2624 Phone: (514)878-1780
Montreal, PQ, Canada H4Z 1C3 Claire Gendreau, Coord., Doc.Ctr.
Founded: 1972. **Staff:** Prof 1. **Subjects:** Employee benefits; insurance - life, health, dental; pensions. **Holdings:** 500 books; 60 government reports; 150 internal reports; 300 single and gazetted laws; 30 volumes of loose-leaf information services; 1000 clippings. **Subscriptions:** 40 journals and other serials; 10 newspapers. **Services:** Interlibrary loan; copying; library open to the public by appointment. **Publications:** Actualites, quarterly - for internal distribution and clients. **Remarks:** FAX: (514)878-4708. Telex: 05 24276. **Formerly:** Johnson & Higgins Willis Faber Inc.

L.A. Foster Library
See: **Hannibal-LaGrange College** (6891)

★6032★
Foster, Pepper & Shefelman - Law Library (Law)
1111 3rd Ave. Bldg. Phone: (206)447-4400
Seattle, WA 98101 Lisa L. Satterland, Lib.Mgr.
Staff: Prof 2; Other 4. **Subjects:** Law - tax, securities, banking, business, real estate; litigation. **Holdings:** 15,000 volumes. **Subscriptions:** 126 journals and other serials; 6 newspapers. **Services:** Interlibrary loan; library not open to the public. **Computerized Information Services:** LEXIS, WESTLAW, DIALOG Information Services, LEGI-SLATE, VU/TEXT Information Services, DataTimes, Dow Jones News/Retrieval, Compu-Mark; internal database. **Networks/Consortia:** Member of Western Library Network (WLN). **Remarks:** FAX: (206)447-9700. **Staff:** Donna Willis, Asst.Libn.

Ralph Foster Museum
See: **College of the Ozarks - Ralph Foster Museum** (3901)

Sumner & Laura Foster Library
See: **University of Michigan - Sumner & Laura Foster Library** (18886)

★6033★
Foster Wheeler Development Corporation - John Blizard Research Center - Research Information Center and Library (Sci-Engr)
12 Peach Tree Hill Rd. Phone: (201)535-2343
Livingston, NJ 07039 Susan E. Himsl, Mgr.
Founded: 1944. **Staff:** Prof 1. **Subjects:** Material testing and evaluation; applied thermodynamics; metallurgy; engineering - mechanical, chemical, nuclear; air pollution control; steam generating equipment; process plants; hazardous waste treatment. **Holdings:** 4750 volumes; 18,500 technical reports; 7500 microfiche. **Subscriptions:** 180 journals and other serials. **Services:** Interlibrary loan; copying; library open to members of American Society for Information Science, SLA, and to college students for reference use. **Automated Operations:** Computerized cataloging and circulation. **Computerized Information Services:** DIALOG Information Services. **Publications:** Current Technical Papers, bimonthly. **Remarks:** FAX: (201)535-2242. Telex 4992447 rewop ui.

★6034★
Foth & Van Dyke - Library (Sci-Engr)
2737 S. Ridge Rd.
Box 19012 Phone: (414)497-2500
Green Bay, WI 54307-9012 Nancy L. Jobelius, Libn.
Founded: 1980. **Staff:** Prof 1; Other 1. **Subjects:** Engineering, architecture, planning. **Holdings:** 2000 books. **Subscriptions:** 200 journals and other serials; 35 newspapers. **Services:** Interlibrary loan; copying; library open to the public by appointment. **Computerized Information Services:** DIALOG Information Services, TOXNET, WILSONLINE. **Networks/Consortia:** Member of Northeast Wisconsin Intertype Libraries (NEWIL). **Publications:** Focus (newsletter), quarterly - to the public; Plan & Profile (newsletter), monthly - for internal distribution only. **Remarks:** FAX: (414)497-8516.

★6035★
Foundation for Blind Children - Arizona Instructional Resource Center (Educ, Aud-Vis)
1201 N. 85th Place Phone: (602)947-3744
Scottsdale, AZ 85257 Pamela M. Brotherton, Dir.
Founded: 1959. **Staff:** Prof 1; Other 4. **Subjects:** Educational material for visually impaired students. **Special Collections:** Professional material pertaining to visual impairment and allied handicaps (200 books; tapes; journals). **Holdings:** 28,828 large-type textbooks, braille books, supplemental reading materials (10,719 titles). **Subscriptions:** 12 journals and other serials. **Services:** Interlibrary loan; library open to the public. **Remarks:** FAX: (602)949-7814.

★6036★
Foundation for Blood Research - Library (Med)
Box 190 Phone: (207)883-4131
Scarborough, ME 04070-0190 Dawn E. Adams, Mgr., Lib.Serv.
Staff: Prof 1. **Subjects:** Immunology, genetics, pediatrics, rheumatology, prenatal diagnosis. **Holdings:** 550 books; 1030 bound periodical volumes. **Subscriptions:** 64 journals and other serials. **Services:** Interlibrary loan; copying; library open to medical professionals. **Computerized Information Services:** NLM, BRS Information Technologies. Performs searches on fee basis. **Networks/Consortia:** Member of Health Science Library and Information Cooperative of Maine (HSLIC). **Publications:** Genetics Education, bimonthly during the academic year - to mailing list. **Remarks:** FAX: (207)883-1527.

★6037★
Foundation Center - Cleveland - Kent H. Smith Library (Bus-Fin)
1422 Euclid Ave., Suite 1356 Phone: (216)861-1934
Cleveland, OH 44115-2001 Patricia Pasqual, Dir.
Founded: 1977. **Staff:** 2. **Subjects:** Reports by and of foundations; government grants; corporate philanthropy; grantsmanship; proposal writing. **Special Collections:** Tax returns for foundations in Ohio, Illinois, Indiana, Kentucky, Michigan, Missouri, Pennsylvania, Wisconsin (microform); fundraising. **Holdings:** 1000 volumes; 500 pamphlets; 400 current annual reports of foundations; clippings on philanthropic foundations. **Subscriptions:** 12 journals and other serials. **Services:** Instructional sessions in the use of specialized materials on grants; library open to the public. **Networks/Consortia:** Member of Cleveland Area Metropolitan Library System (CAMLS). **Publications:** Library brochure; worksheets for grantseekers. **Remarks:** FAX: (216)861-1729.

★6038★
Foundation Center - New York - Library (Bus-Fin)
79 Fifth Ave., 8th Fl. Phone: (212)620-4230
New York, NY 10003 Sarah Collins, Dir.
Founded: 1956. **Staff:** Prof 4; Other 4. **Subjects:** Foundations, philanthropy. **Special Collections:** Computer Data Bases - Foundation Directory, Foundation Grants Index, National; foundation annual reports and IRS information returns. **Holdings:** 3000 books; 4000 pamphlets; 800 American and foreign foundation annual reports and retrospective collection; 250,000 aperture cards of foundation information returns, 1972 to present. **Subscriptions:** 100 journals and other serials. **Services:** Microfiche copying; copying; library open to the public. **Computerized Information Services:** DIALOG Information Services, Dialcom Inc. **Networks/Consortia:** Member of Consortium of Foundation Libraries (CFL). **Publications:** Foundation Directory; Foundation Center Source Book Profiles; Foundation Center National Data Book of Foundations; Foundation Grants to Individuals; Grant Guides; Foundation Fundamentals; special series in

philanthropy. **Special Indexes:** Foundation Grants Index. **Remarks:** Maintains libraries in New York, Washington, DC, Cleveland, and San Francisco; coordinates a network of 185 regional cooperating collections in all 50 states, England, the Virgin Islands, Mexico, Canada, Puerto Rico, Japan, and Australia. All libraries open to the public without charge. Center-operated libraries offer free biweekly orientations on funding research; special services for annual fee include toll-free telephone reference and fee-based custom computer search service. To locate your nearest Foundation Center regional or cooperating collection call toll-free (800)424-9386. **Staff:** Charlotte Dion; Mare Valgamae; Elizabeth McKenty.

★ 6039 ★
Foundation Center - San Francisco Office - Library (Bus-Fin)
312 Sutter St., 3rd Fl. Phone: (415)397-0902
San Francisco, CA 94108 Roberta Steiner, Dir.
Founded: 1977. **Staff:** Prof 3. **Subjects:** Philanthropic foundations, fund raising, corporate philanthropy, nonprofit organization management. **Holdings:** 1100 books; 1100 foundation annual reports; 75,000 aperture cards of foundation tax returns; 22 VF drawers of clippings; 1700 subject articles. **Subscriptions:** 50 journals and other serials. **Services:** Copying; library open to the public. **Computerized Information Services:** DIALOG Information Services. **Remarks:** FAX (415)397-7670. **Staff:** Susan Sheinfeld-Smith, Libn.; Debbie Sommer, Asst.Libn.

★ 6040 ★
Foundation Center - Washington Library (Bus-Fin)
1001 Connecticut Ave., N.W., Suite 938
Washington, DC 20036 Phone: (202)331-1400
Founded: 1964. **Staff:** Prof 5; Other 2. **Subjects:** Private philanthropic giving, corporations, foundations. **Special Collections:** Private foundation information returns; printed annual reports issued by private foundations; books and articles on private foundations and corporate giving, philanthropy and philanthropists, establishing and managing nonprofit organizations, fund raising, grants for individuals. **Holdings:** 3000 volumes. **Subscriptions:** 70 journals and other serials. **Services:** Copying; library open to the public. **Computerized Information Services:** DIALOG Information Services; internal database. **Remarks:** FAX: (202)331-1739. **Staff:** Mary Resnik, Libn.; James Mohan, Libn.; Mark Foley, Assoc.; Charlotte Reischauer, Assoc.

★ 6041 ★
The Foundation of the Charlotte Jewish Community - Speizman Jewish Library at Shalom Park (Rel-Phil)
5007 Providence Rd.
Box 13369 Phone: (704)366-5007
Charlotte, NC 28270 Amalia Warshenbrot, Libn.
Founded: 1987. **Staff:** Prof 1. **Subjects:** Judaica. **Holdings:** 5000 books. **Subscriptions:** 25 journals and other serials; 4 newspapers. **Services:** Library is accessible on a restricted basis. **Remarks:** FAX: (704)365-4507.

★ 6042 ★
Foundation for Citizen Education - Anna Lord Strauss Library (Soc Sci)
35 Maiden Ln. Phone: (518)465-4162
Albany, NY 12207 Rita Lashway, Exec.Dir.
Founded: 1972. **Staff:** Prof 1. **Subjects:** Woman's suffrage, government, politics, international relations. **Holdings:** 500 books; other cataloged items. **Services:** Library open to the public for reference use only. **Remarks:** FAX: (518)465-0812. Affiliated with the League of Women Voters of New York State. **Staff:** Margaret Watrous, Leg.Info.Coord.

★ 6043 ★
Foundation for Economic Education - Library (Bus-Fin)
30 S. Broadway Phone: (914)591-7230
Irvington, NY 10533 Bettina Bien Greaves, Libn.
Founded: 1946. **Staff:** Prof 2. **Subjects:** Economics, philosophy, political science, political theory. **Special Collections:** Henry Hazlitt Collection (2000 volumes); Austrian School of Economics; works of Ludwig von Mises. **Holdings:** 7500 books; 3000 pamphlets. **Subscriptions:** 102 journals and other serials. **Services:** Copying; library open to the public by appointment.

★ 6044 ★
Foundation Historical Association - Seward House (Hist)
33 South St. Phone: (315)252-1283
Auburn, NY 13021 Betty Mae Lewis, Cur.
Founded: 1955. **Subjects:** Civil War, Alaska, local history. **Holdings:** 10,000 volumes. **Services:** Library open to the public for reference use only.

★ 6045 ★
Foundation for Latin American Anthropological Research - Library (Soc Sci, Area-Ethnic)
Rollins College Art Dept.
Campus Box 2675 Phone: (407)646-2188
Winter Park, FL 32789 Nicholas M. Hellmuth, Pres.
Founded: 1969. **Subjects:** Archeology - Teotihuacan, Olmec, Aztec, Mixtec, Zapotec, Veracruz, Maya, Peru, Bolivia; architecture - pyramid-temple, palace; hieroglyphic inscriptions; codices; tropical flora and fauna; ethnohistory. **Special Collections:** Facsimiles of 16th century Aztec, Mixtec, and Maya codices; Hellmuth Photographic Archive of Maya Art (4th-9th century Maya art, architecture, and iconography). **Holdings:** 2000 volumes; 30,000 photographs and slides. **Services:** Library open to Rollins College students and community members with special interest in pre-Columbian research. **Remarks:** The Hellmuth Photographic Archive of Maya Art is said to be one of the largest such research collections in the world. Portions of the archive are housed at Dumbarton Oaks, Harvard University, and at the New York Metropolitan Museum of Art's Robert Goldwater Library of Primitive Art. Foundation maintains branch offices in Guatemala City, Guatemala, at the Museo Popol Vuh, and in Graz, Austria. FAX: (407)646-2600.

★ 6046 ★
Foundation for Public Affairs (Soc Sci)
1019 19th St., N.W., Suite 200 Phone: (202)872-1750
Washington, DC 20036 Leslie Swift-Rosenzweig, Exec.Dir.
Founded: 1976. **Staff:** Prof 3; Other 1. **Subjects:** Public interest groups, corporate public affairs programs. **Special Collections:** Files on 1700 public interest groups; corporate public affairs program materials. **Holdings:** 500 books; 75 VF drawers of clippings, program materials, and newsletters; 50 corporate public affairs manuals. **Subscriptions:** 100 journals and other serials. **Services:** Library open to the public by appointment only. **Publications:** Public Interest Profiles, triennial; Washington Office Salary Survey, biennial; Compensation Survey of Public Affairs Positions, biennial. **Remarks:** FAX: (202)835-8343. **Staff:** David Kinsman, Mgr., Prog.Sup. & Dev.; Mimi Koumanelis, Res.Assoc.

Foundation of Record Education (FORE)
See: **American Health Information Management Association** (605)

Foundation for Research on Eastern Europe - East European Institute, Munich
See: **East European Institute, Munich** (5119)

★ 6047 ★
Foundation for Research on the Nature of Man - Library/Archives (Rel-Phil)
402 Buchanan Blvd.
College Sta., Box 6847
Durham, NC 27708 Phone: (919)688-8241
Founded: 1962. **Staff:** Prof 4. **Subjects:** Parapsychology, psychical research, psychology, extrasensory perception, psychokinesis, experimental parapsychology. **Special Collections:** The J.B. and L.E. Rhine Archives; original records of published experiments. **Holdings:** 3500 books; 500 bound periodical volumes; 2600 unbound reports and manuscripts; 50 dissertations and theses; photograph file. **Subscriptions:** 60 journals and other serials. **Services:** Copying; library open to the public for reference use only. **Computerized Information Services:** Internal database. **Publications:** Journal of Parapsychology; FRNM Bulletin; Brief Introduction to Parapsychology. **Remarks:** FAX: (919)683-4338. **Staff:** Richard Broughton; Iris Oliver; Anne Carroll; John Palmer; H. Kanthamani; K.R. Rao, Dir.

★6048★
The Foundation for San Francisco's Architectural Heritage - Library (Art)
2007 Franklin St. Phone: (415)441-3000
San Francisco, CA 94109 Don Andreini
Founded: 1979. **Staff:** 1. **Subjects:** San Francisco and California architecture; architects; architectural history. **Special Collections:** Survey files on San Francisco buildings (10,000). **Holdings:** Archival items. **Services:** Library open to the public with restrictions. **Publications:** Newsletter; Splendid Survivors. **Remarks:** FAX: (415)441-3015.

★6049★
Foundation of Socio-Cultural Services - Library (Soc Sci)
Dambulla Rd. 55/4
Kurunegala, Sri Lanka
Subjects: Sri Lanka cultural advancement, socioeconomic development. **Holdings:** 1500 volumes. **Computerized Information Services:** Internal database.

★6050★
Foundation for the Study of Cycles Inc. - Library (Sci-Engr)
2600 Michelson Dr., Suite 1570 Phone: (714)261-7261
Irvine, CA 92715 Glennis Espinoza
Founded: 1941. **Staff:** 5. **Subjects:** Rhythmic and periodic phenomena. **Holdings:** 2750 volumes; 10,000 papers. **Subscriptions:** 15 journals and other serials. **Services:** Copying; library open to members. **Remarks:** FAX: (714)261-1708.

★6051★
Foundation of the Wall & Ceiling Industry - John H. Hampshire Memorial Reference & Research Library (Plan)
1600 Cameron St. Phone: (703)684-2924
Alexandria, VA 22314 Kathy B. Sedgwick, Exec.Dir.
Founded: 1981. **SStaff:** Prof 1. **Subjects:** Construction - specifications and standards, management, and law; asbestos removal; fire standards; insulation. **Special Collections:** Decorative plastering methods; hazard communications. **Holdings:** 1000 books; 500 unbound reports; manufacturers catalogs. **Subscriptions:** 100 journals and other serials. **Services:** Interlibrary loan; copying; library open to the public. **Automated Operations:** Computerized cataloging. **Computerized Information Services:** DIALOG Information Services. **Special Catalogs:** Materials on Asbestos Abatement (book). **Remarks:** Provides Information Kits: Lead-Based Paint Abatement Information. Information Hotline: (703)584-0374. FAX: (703)684-2935.

Foundry School Museum
See: **Putnam County Historical Society** (13556)

William E. Fountain Health Sciences Library
See: **Merced Community Medical Center** (10102)

★6052★
Four-One-One - Library (Soc Sci)
7304 Beverly St.
Annandale, VA 22003 Phone: (703)354-6270
Founded: 1969. **Staff:** 6. **Subjects:** Community/volunteer programs - planning, designing, managing. **Holdings:** 3000 volumes. **Subscriptions:** 2 journals and other serials **Services:** Library not open to the public. **Publications:** Federal Funding Forum; Volunteerism. **Remarks:** FAX: (703)941-4360. **Also Known As:** 411. **Staff:** Harriet Clyde Kipps; Mary Grubbs; Barbara Rodriguez.

★6053★
Fourth Middlesex Law Library (Law)
District Court
30 Pleasant St. Phone: (617)935-4000
Woburn, MA 01801 Barbara E. Curran, Law Libn.
Founded: 1967. **Staff:** Prof 1. **Subjects:** Massachusetts and federal statutes and cases, legal reference, practice materials. **Holdings:** 10,000 cataloged materials. **Subscriptions:** 10 journals and other serials. **Services:** Interlibrary loan; copying; library open to the public. **Publications:** Newsletter; Acquisitions List, both irregular.

Helen Fowler Library
See: **Denver Botanic Gardens** (4775)

Richard S. Fowler Memorial Library
See: **Hall of Flame** (6845)

Herbert Fox Memorial Library
See: **Pennsylvania (State) Department of Health - Bureau of Laboratories** (12861)

Raymond W. Fox Memorial Library
See: **Kalamazoo County Law Library** (8529)

★6054★
Fox, Rothschild, O'Brien and Frankel - Library (Law)
2000 Market St., 9th Fl. Phone: (215)299-2140
Philadelphia, PA 19103 Patricia La Pierre, Law Libn.
Staff: Prof 2; Other 2. **Subjects:** Law - corporate, business, labor, tax, real estate; litigation. **Holdings:** 12,500 books. **Subscriptions:** 145 journals and other serials; 10 newspapers. **Services:** Interlibrary loan; copying; library open to the public by appointment. **Computerized Information Services:** LEXIS, NEXIS, WESTLAW, DIALOG Information Services, Information America, DataTimes, VU/TEXT Information Services. **Remarks:** FAX: (215)299-2150.

★6055★
The Foxfire Fund, Inc. - Archives (Hist)
Rabun Gap, GA 30568 Phone: (404)746-5828
George Reynolds, Folklore/Mus.Dir.
Founded: 1977. **Subjects:** Cultural traditions in southern Appalachia (primarily northern Georgia and western North Carolina). **Holdings:** 1323 hours of taped interviews and oral histories; 30,000 black/white negatives. **Services:** Archives open to the public. **Remarks:** Alternate telephone number(s): 746-5318.

★6056★
FPG International Corporation (Aud-Vis)
32 Union Sq., E. Phone: (212)777-4210
New York, NY 10003 Patrick Bunyan, Photo.Lib.Dir.
Founded: 1937. **Staff:** 6. **Subjects:** Photography - scenery, industry, sports, human interest, science, travel, medicine; still life; special effects. **Special Collections:** Historical black and white and color collection; Gallery Black and White; travel; medicine; still life; special effects. **Holdings:** 5 million transparencies and black and white prints. **Services:** Library open to the public with reproduction fee. **Computerized Information Services:** Internal database. **Publications:** Newsletter of new submissions to the files, bimonthly; color file guide - available on request. **Remarks:** FAX: (212)995-9652. Library located between 15th and 16th Sts.

★6057★
Framingham Public Library - Framingham Room (Hist)
49 Lexington St. Phone: (508)879-3570
Framingham, MA 01701 James C. Flaherty, Dir.
Subjects: Framingham history and genealogy, Massachusetts town histories, genealogical methodologies. **Special Collections:** Wallace Nutting Collection (Nutting photographs, books, papers, memorabilia, club newsletters). **Holdings:** Maps; VF drawers of memorabilia, clippings, pamphlets, illustrations, photographs, uncataloged items; microfilm; annual town reports (1838 to present); vital records dating to 1850; New England Historical and Genealogical Register, 1847 to present; military records; 1790 Census. **Services:** Copying (limited); library open to the public for reference use only. **Remarks:** FAX: (508)820-7210. **Staff:** Melinda Place, Ref.Libn.

★6058★
Framingham Union Hospital - Tedeschi Library and Information Center (Med)
115 Lincoln St. Phone: (508)626-3595
Framingham, MA 01701 Sandra Clevesy, Dir.
Founded: 1960. **Staff:** Prof 1; Other 2. **Subjects:** Medicine, nursing, nursing education, health care delivery. **Special Collections:** Framingham Union Hospital Archives (1500 photographs; 9 linear feet of documents). **Holdings:** 5596 books; 5900 bound periodical volumes; 9 VF drawers of pamphlets. **Subscriptions:** 275 journals and other serials. **Services:** Interlibrary loan; copying; SDI; LATCH; library open to the public. **Automated Operations:** Computerized cataloging. **Computerized Information Services:** NLM, OCLC. **Networks/Consortia:** Member of Consortium for Information Resources (CIR). **Publications:** Books Added, quarterly - to staff, consortium members, and others on request. **Remarks:** FAX: (508)879-0471.

★ 6059 ★
France - Archives Nationales - Centre des Archives d'Outre Mer - Bibliotheque (Hist, Geog-Map)
29 Chemin du Moulin Detesta Phone: 42264321
F-13090 Aix-en-Provence, France Elisabeth Rabut, Lib.Hd.
Staff: Prof 4; Other 1.5. **Subjects:** History and geography of French colonies. **Special Collections:** Collection of the Colonial Ministry (80,000 titles). **Holdings:** 58,000 books; 4900 bound periodical volumes; 42,000 archival items. **Subscriptions:** 83 journals and other serials; 2 newspapers. **Services:** Interlibrary loan; copying; library open to the public for reference use only. **Remarks:** FAX: 42268459.

★ 6060 ★
France - Atomic Energy Commission - Saclay Research Center - MIST (Energy, Sci-Engr)
F-91191 Gif-sur-Yvette Cedex, France Phone: 1 69082208
Annick van Craeynest, Hd., Doc.Serv.
Founded: 1952. **Staff:** Prof 28. **Subjects:** Physics - high energy, nuclear, plasma; nuclear engineering; nuclear materials - chemistry, metallurgy; isotope technology; nuclear safety and health physics; radiobiology; nuclear medicine; energy - nuclear, fossil, renewable, conversion, storage, and conservation; electricity - production, distribution; scientific and technical meetings and conferences. **Holdings:** 56,000 books; 118,600 bound periodical volumes; 31,600 conference proceedings; 600,000 reports on microfiche. **Subscriptions:** 1650 journals and other serials. **Services:** Interlibrary loan; copying; SDI; center open primarily to the French nuclear community. **Automated Operations:** Computerized public access catalog. **Computerized Information Services:** INIS, ETDE; produces Meeting Agenda, Energirap, and LIBISAC. Performs searches on fee basis. **Remarks:** FAX: 1 69087695. Telex: 604641 ENERG X F. **Formerly:** Its Saclay Nuclear Research Center - Documentation Center. **Also Known As:** Commissariat a l'Energie Atomique - Centre d'Etudes de Saclay - Mission Information Scientifique et Technique (MIST). **Staff:** Phillipe Le Poac, Hd., Doc./Multimedia Publ.Dept.; Denise Lohner, Hd., Spec. Database Dept.

★ 6061 ★
France - Bibliotheque de l'Arsenal (Area-Ethnic, Hist, Hum)
1, rue de Sully Phone: 1 42774421
F-75004 Paris, France Jean-Claude Garreta, Cons. en chef
Founded: 1756. **Staff:** 20. **Subjects:** 17th and 18th century France, French literature, history of books, heraldry. **Special Collections:** Archives de la Bastille (18th century; 2700 documents); Enfantin Collection (19th century socialism; 800 volumes); Lambert Collection (J.-K. Huysmans; 95 manuscripts). **Holdings:** 1 million books; 100 microforms; 15,000 manuscripts; 100,000 engravings; 3000 maps. **Subscriptions:** 900 journals and other serials; 20 newspapers. **Services:** Interlibrary loan; copying; library open to the public with restrictions. **Computerized Information Services:** Opale (internal database). **Special Catalogs:** Catalogue des manuscrits de la bibliotheque de l'Arsenal Paris 1885-1892 (9 volumes). **Remarks:** FAX: 1 42770490. **Staff:** Daniele Muzerelle, Mss.; Martine LeFevre, Ancient Bks.; Sabine Coron.

France - Bibliotheque Nationale - Bibliotheque de l'Arsenal
See: **France - Bibliotheque de l'Arsenal** (6061)

★ 6062 ★
France - Bibliotheque Nationale - Departement de la Phonotheque Nationale et de l'Audiovisuel (Aud-Vis)
2, rue de Louvois Phone: 1 47 03 88 20
F-75002 Paris, France Monique Refouil, Chf., Pub.Serv.
Subjects: General collection. **Special Collections:** Romanian Collection, 1928; G. Massignon Ethnographic Collection, 1941-1966; Ch. Delaunay Collection, 1977; Nadia Boulanger Collection; Musee Charles Cros (350 old phonographs). **Holdings:** 4000 books; 500 serial titles; 1 million phonograph records, magnetic tapes, videotapes; 5000 AV programs. **Subscriptions:** 250 journals and other serials; 50 newspapers. **Services:** Copying; department open to the public with restrictions. **Computerized Information Services:** Internal database. Performs searches free of charge. **Publications:** Phonographies: Faure, Poulenc, Milhaud. **Remarks:** FAX: 42 96 84 47. **Staff:** Marie France Calas, Dir.

★ 6063 ★
France - Bibliotheque Nationale - Musee de l'Opera - Bibliotheque (Mus, Theater)
8 rue Scribe Phone: 1 47420702
F-75009 Paris, France Martine Kahane, Cons.
Staff: 13. **Subjects:** Opera, ballet, music. **Special Collections:** Russian ballet; Taglioni; Rouche; Saint Leon; Garnier. **Holdings:** 85,000 books; 1500 serial titles; 130,000 drawings and prints. **Services:** Interlibrary loan; copying; library open to the public. **Special Catalogs:** Catalogs to archives, circus collection, illustrated posters, and 19th century scenery drawings. **Remarks:** 1 42651016. **Staff:** Nicole Wild, Iconography; Aline Dardel, Iconography/ Cultural Serv.; Marie-Jose Kerhoas, Pub.Serv.; Patricia Damour, Photo.Serv.; Philippe Cousin, Bldg. & Tech.Serv.; Raymond Vaillant, Mus.Coll.

★ 6064 ★
France - Bureau de Recherches Geologiques et Minieres - Bibliotheque Centrale (Sci-Engr)
B.P. 6009 Phone: 38 643434
F-45060 Orleans Cedex 2, France Marie-Odile Bongrand, Libn.
Founded: 1945. **Staff:** 16. **Subjects:** Earth sciences - mineralogy, geochemistry, extraterrestrial geology, mineral deposits, economic geology, sedimentary and crystalline petrology, marine geology, stratigraphy, paleontology, hydrogeology, geomorphology, soil sciences, engineering geology. **Holdings:** 22,000 volumes; 55,000 maps. **Subscriptions:** 1600 journals and other serials. **Services:** SDI; department open to geologists. **Computerized Information Services:** Produces GEOBANQUE, ECOMINE, and PASCAL-GEODE databases. Performs searches on fee basis. **Publications:** Bibliographic bulletin, 10/year. **Remarks:** FAX: 38 643950. Telex: BRGM 780258 F. **Formerly:** Its Service Geologique National - Departement Service Public.

France - Centre National de la Recherche Scientifique - Bibliotheque de Sociologie du CNRS
See: **Centre National de la Recherche Scientifique - Bibliotheque de Sociologie du CNRS** (3273)

France - Embassy of France
See: **Embassy of France - Press and Information Service - Documentation Center** (5322)

France - Fondation Nationale des Sciences Politiques - Centre de Hautes Etudes sur l'Afrique et l'Asie Modernes
See: **Center for Advanced Studies on Modern Africa and Asia** (3205)

★ 6065 ★
France - Institut de l'Information Scientifique et Technique - Bibliotheque (Sci-Engr)
2, Alle du Parc de Brabois
F-54514 Vandoeuvre-les-Nancy Cedex, France Phone: 33 83504600
Nathalie Dusoulier, Inst.Hd.
Founded: 1939. **Subjects:** Physics, chemistry, biology, medicine, psychology, earth sciences, engineering, energy, food and agriculture, zoology, metallurgy, welding, building construction, mathematics. **Special Collections:** Periodiques (serials). **Holdings:** 6500 books; 26,000 bound periodical volumes; 34,000 French scientific reports; 60,000 French scientific dissertations; 45,000 conference proceedings. **Subscriptions:** 20,500 journals and other serials. **Services:** Copying; SDI; translation; center not open to the public. **Automated Operations:** Computerized cataloging. **Computerized Information Services:** ESA/IRS, Questel, DIALOG Information Services; produces PASCAL; FRANCIS. Performs searches on fee basis. **Publications:** Bibliographic publications from PASCAL and FRANCIS (Aides: Lexicons, Thesauri, PASCAL, FRANCIS user manuals). **Special Catalogs:** Liste des titres de periodiques, 1991; Catalogue des rapports de fin de contrat DGRST (1968-1981, supplements); Catalogue des rapports scientifiques et techniques FRT (1982 -1983); Catalogue des rapports de recherche sur l'environnement, annual. **Special Indexes:** Index permute des periodiques recus (1982, supplement); Liste des periodiques traduits (1980); Inventaire des theses soutenues devant les universites francaises, annual. **Remarks:** FAX: 33 83504650. PASCAL is an acronym for Programme Applique a la Selection et a la Compilation Automatiques de la Litterature. **Also Known As:** France - National Center for Scientific Research - Institute of Scientific and Technical Information.

France - Institut National de Recherche en Informatique et en Automatique
See: **Institut National de Recherche en Informatique et en Automatique** (7877)

France - Institute of Scientific and Technical Information
See: **France - Institut de l'Information Scientifique et Technique - Bibliotheque** (6065)

★6066★
France - Ministere de l'Education - Velazquez House - Library (Hum, Area-Ethnic)
Ciudad Universitaria Phone: 1 5433605
E-28040 Madrid, Spain Laurence Camous, Cons.
Subjects: Spain and Latin America - literature, arts, humanities, including history, geography, economy, art, hispanic anthropology, painting, sculpture, engraving, architecture, music, cinema. **Holdings:** 90,000 volumes; 1200 periodicals. **Subscriptions:** 900 journals and other serials. **Services:** Library open to those working on doctoral theses and with the authorization of the director. **Remarks:** FAX: 1 5446870. **Also Known As:** Casa de Velazquez.

★6067★
France - Ministere de l'Education Nationale - Bibliotheque de Documentation Internationale Contemporaine (Soc Sci, Hist, Mil)
6 allee de l'Universite Phone: 47 214022
F-92001 Nanterre Cedex, France Joseph Hue
Founded: 1914. **Staff:** 55. **Subjects:** World Wars, international relations, labor movement, political oppositions and emigrations, nationalities and minorities, East Europe, Latin America, CADIST. **Holdings:** 3 million documents, books, periodicals, posters, photographs. **Subscriptions:** 4000 journals and other serials. **Services:** Interlibrary loan; copying; library open to the public. **Publications:** List of publications - available on request. **Remarks:** Telex: 40 97 79 40. Maintains the Musee d'Histoire Contemporaine - BDIC, an iconographic section located at Hotel des Invalides, F-75007 Paris, France.

France - Ministere de l'Education Nationale - Bibliotheque Nationale et Universitaire de Strasbourg
See: **Bibliotheque Nationale et Universitaire de Strasbourg** (1833)

★6068★
France - Ministry of Culture - Department of Art Conservation - Office of French Museums - General Inventory of Monuments and Artistic Riches of France - Documentation Center (Art)
Palais du Louvre
34, Quai du Louvre Phone: 1 40209406
F-75058 Paris, France Bernard Centlivze, Dir.
Founded: 1964. **Subjects:** French architectural heritage - general, furniture, religious objects, stained glass. **Holdings:** 2500 volumes; 10 videotapes; 3500 microforms. **Subscriptions:** 150 journals and other serials. **Services:** Center open to the public. **Computerized Information Services:** Produces I-ARCHI and I-OBJET databases. Performs searches on fee basis. **Also Known As:** Conservation des Objets d'Art - Direction des Musees de France.

France - Ministry of Education - French Institute of Eastern Archeology
See: **French Institute of Eastern Archeology** (6148)

★6069★
France - National Assembly - Library (Law, Hist, Soc Sci, Hum)
126 rue de l'Universite Phone: 1 40636474
F-75355 Paris, France Michel Mopin, Chf.Libn.
Staff: Prof 21. **Subjects:** Law, history, economics, human sciences, literature. **Special Collections:** Manuscripts collection (1500); old newspaper collection; official government papers. **Holdings:** 700,000 books; microfiche; microfilm. **Subscriptions:** 500 newspapers. **Services:** Interlibrary loan; library open when Assembly is active. **Publications:** List of books; lists of periodical titles, 6/year. **Remarks:** FAX: 1 40635253.

France - National Foundation of Political Sciences - Center for Advanced Studies on Modern Africa and Asia
See: **Center for Advanced Studies on Modern Africa and Asia** (3205)

★6070★
France - National Institute of Demographic Studies - Library (Soc Sci)
27, rue du Commandeur Phone: 43 201345
F-75675 Paris 14, France M. Todd, Hd., Lib.Serv.
Founded: 1945. **Staff:** 7. **Subjects:** Demography. **Holdings:** 50,000 volumes. **Services:** Interlibrary loan; library open to the public. **Remarks:** FAX: 43 277240. **Also Known As:** Institut National d'Etudes Demographiques.

★6071★
France - National Telecommunications Research Center - Interministerial Documentation Service (Info Sci)
38-40, rue du General Leclerc
F-92131 Issy-les-Moulineaux, France Phone: 1 45294444
Staff: Prof 20. **Subjects:** Telecommunications hardware and software - telephony, telegraphy, facsimile, data communications, office automation, information technology and telematics, microwave and satellites, radio and television broadcasting and distribution, video communication, fiber optics, acoustics, automation, data and information processing, electronics, mathematics, optics, physics, documentation science, economics, law and legislation, management. **Holdings:** 25,000 bound volumes. **Subscriptions:** 900 journals and other serials. **Services:** SDI. **Computerized Information Services:** Produces Teledoc (available online through Questel). Performs searches on fee basis. Contact Person: Sylvie Hubert. **Publications:** Bulletin Signaletique des Telecommunications, monthly - by subscription. **Remarks:** Telex: 250317 F. Center is an external service of the Secretary of State for Posts and Telecommunications. **Also Known As:** Centre National d'Etudes des Telecommunications - Service de Documentation Interministerielle.

(France) National Conservatory of Arts and Crafts - National Institute for Information Science
See: **National Conservatory of Arts and Crafts - National Institute for Information Science** (11133)

Frances-Henry Library
See: **Hebrew Union College - Jewish Institute of Religion - Frances-Henry Library** (7097)

Franciscan Biblical Institute
See: **Studium Biblicum Franciscanum** (15838)

★6072★
Franciscan Children's Hospital & Rehabilitation Center - Medical Library (Med)
30 Warren St. Phone: (617)254-3800
Brighton, MA 02135 Marybeth Edwards, Med.Libn.
Staff: 1. **Subjects:** Pediatrics, child development, developmental disorders, nursing, therapies, handicapped children, rehabilitation, birth defects. **Special Collections:** Charities Research Collection on Autism (44 books, journals, proceedings); Human Ethics Collection (59 books, journals, proceedings). **Holdings:** 900 books; 1600 unbound and bound periodical volumes; 13 annuals. **Subscriptions:** 100 journals and other serials. **Services:** Interlibrary loan; copying; library open to the public with permission. **Networks/Consortia:** Member of Massachusetts Health Sciences Libraries Network (MaHSLiN), Boston Biomedical Library Consortium, North Atlantic Health Science Libraries (NAHSL). **Remarks:** Maintains a Patient Library.

Franciscan Custody of the Holy Land - Studium Biblicum Franciscanum
See: **Studium Biblicum Franciscanum** (15838)

Franciscan Fathers of California - Santa Barbara Mission Archive-Library
See: **Santa Barbara Mission Archive-Library** (14800)

★6073★
Franciscan Friars of the Atonement - Atonement Seminary Library (Rel-Phil)
145 Taylor St., N.E. Phone: (202)529-1114
Washington, DC 20017-1098 Bro. Edward Rankey, S.A., Libn.
Founded: 1948. **Staff:** Prof 3. **Subjects:** Theological and historical development of ecumenism, 19th century church history in Great Britain. **Special Collections:** Anglican Reformation History. **Holdings:** 46,500 books; 6000 bound periodical volumes; 300 reels of microfilm of periodicals. **Subscriptions:** 69 journals and other serials; 5 newspapers. **Services:** Copying; library open to the public for reference use only by appointment. **Staff:** Bernard Fortier, Cat.

★6074★
Franciscan Institute - Library (Rel-Phil)
Friedsam Memorial Library
St. Bonaventure University Phone: (716)375-2105
St. Bonaventure, NY 14778 Paul J. Spaeth, Libn.
Founded: 1940. **Staff:** Prof 2. **Subjects:** Franciscan theology, philosophy, history; Scholasticism; medieval studies; Catholicism. **Special Collections:** Rare books (including manuscripts and incunabula); Holy Name College Collection (Franciscana and rare books); Duns Scotus College Collection (Franciscana and rare books); microfilms and photostats of medieval philosophical manuscripts, including all known philosophical and theological works of William of Ockham; transcriptions of St. John Capistran's works; Juniper B. Carol Mariology Collection. **Holdings:** 20,000 books; 6000 bound periodical volumes; 6000 rare books (imprints 1501-1850); 95 manuscripts; 500 reels of microfilm; 221 incunabula. **Subscriptions:** 170 journals and other serials. **Services:** Interlibrary loan; copying; library open to researchers. **Automated Operations:** Computerized cataloging. **Computerized Information Services:** OCLC. **Publications:** Franciscan Studies, annual; The Cord, monthly; monographs on Franciscan subjects. **Staff:** Anthony LoGalbo, O.F.M., Asst.Libn.

Franciscan Medical Center - Jordan Library
See: **Illini-Franciscan Healthcare Information Service** (7667)

★6075★
Franciscan Medical Center - Jordan Library (Med)
2701 17th St. Phone: (309)793-2069
Rock Island, IL 61201 Priscilla Swatos, Coord., Hea.Info.Serv.
Founded: 1977. **Staff:** 1.5. **Subjects:** Clinical medicine, mental health. **Special Collections:** Burn care therapy collection (20 titles); mental health and counseling collection (50 titles); Hospital Satellite Network collection (700 videotapes). **Holdings:** 957 books. **Subscriptions:** 321 journals and other serials; 4 newspapers. **Services:** Interlibrary loan; copying; SDI; library open to the public. **Computerized Information Services:** DIALOG Information Services, WILSONLINE, MEDLARS, OCLC; DOCLINE (electronic mail service). Performs searches. Contact Person: Joan Sulser, Lib.Spec. **Remarks:** FAX: (309)793-2262. Affiliated with Illini Hospital in Silvis, Illinois.

★6076★
Franciscan Monastery Library
1400 Quincy St., N.E.
Washington, DC 20017
Founded: 1900. **Subjects:** Theology and religion, Franciscan studies, Holy Land. **Special Collections:** Montgomery Carmichael (300 volumes); Franciscana (3000 volumes); Near East, Palestine, and the Holy Land and religion (3500 volumes). **Holdings:** 30,000 books; 4000 bound periodical volumes; 1000 other bound volumes; 50 maps. **Remarks:** Currently inactive.

Franciscan School of Theology
See: **Graduate Theological Union** (6613)

★6077★
Franciscans of the Lithuanian Viceprovince - Franciscan Friary Library
Box 980
Kennebunkport, ME 04046
Founded: 1947. **Subjects:** Theology, philosophy. **Special Collections:** Franciscan literature (200 volumes); Lithuanian collection (most in Lithuanian; 3225 volumes). **Holdings:** 5575 books; 194 bound periodical volumes; 87 volumes of photographed archival material. **Remarks:** Currently inactive.

★6078★
Frank, Bernstein, Conaway & Goldman - Library (Law)
300 E. Lombard St. Phone: (301)625-3503
Baltimore, MD 21202 Carol B. Mundorf, Law Libn.
Staff: Prof 1; Other 3. **Subjects:** Law. **Holdings:** 20,000 books; 400 bound periodical volumes; 50 tapes; microfiche. **Subscriptions:** 55 journals and other serials. **Services:** Interlibrary loan; SDI; library open to the public with prior permission. **Computerized Information Services:** LEXIS, NEXIS, WESTLAW, Dow Jones News/Retrieval, DIALOG Information Services, OCLC EPIC, VU/TEXT Information Services, Performs searches on fee basis.

★6079★
Robert L. Frank Radio-Navigation Library (Trans)
30795 River Crossing
Birmingham, MI 48025 Phone: (313)645-9848
Founded: 1974. **Subjects:** Radio positioning and navigation systems, electronic instrumentation. **Holdings:** Figures not available. **Services:** Library open to the public by appointment.

Samuel Frank Medical Library
See: **Sinai Hospital of Detroit** (15186)

★6080★
Frankel & Company - Information Center (Bus-Fin)
111 E. Wacker Dr. Phone: (312)938-3434
Chicago, IL 60601 Nancy R. Kovitz, Mgr.
Founded: 1980. **Staff:** Prof 3. **Subjects:** Marketing research, sales promotion. **Holdings:** 1000 books; 25 lateral file drawers of subject files. **Subscriptions:** 200 journals and other serials; 15 newspapers. **Services:** Interlibrary loan; copying; center open to the public by appointment. **Computerized Information Services:** DIALOG Information Services, BRS Information Technologies, NEXIS, Dow Jones News/Retrieval. Performs searches on fee basis. **Networks/Consortia:** Member of Chicago Library System, ILLINET. **Publications:** Marketing Services Review, quarterly - internal distribution and to mailing list. **Special Indexes:** Marketing periodicals index; company research reports index. **Remarks:** FAX: (312)938-1901. **Staff:** Lynn Leinartas, Asst.Libn.; Bill Russell, Managerial Asst.

★6081★
Frankenmuth Historical Association Museum - Library (Hist)
613 S. Main St. Phone: (517)652-9701
Frankenmuth, MI 48734 Mary Nuechterlein, Reg.
Founded: 1972. **Staff:** Prof 2. **Subjects:** Local history; Saginaw valley; development of Frankenmuth as a Lutheran missionary colony. **Holdings:** 5455 diaries, letters, unpublished dissertations, research papers, photographs, other records; 23 reels of microfilm of local church records; newspapers, 1906-1927. **Services:** Copying; library open to the public. **Computerized Information Services:** Internal database (photographs).

Frankford Arsenal Archive
See: **U.S. Army - Armament, Munitions & Chemical Command - Armament Research, Development & Engineering Center - Scientific & Tech.Info. Branch - Information Center** (16918)

★6082★
Frankford Hospital - Hospital Libraries (Med)
Frankford Ave. & Wakeling St. Phone: (215)831-2182
Philadelphia, PA 19124 Dianne E. Rose, Med.Libn.
Founded: 1950. **Staff:** Prof 2; Other 2. **Subjects:** Medicine, surgery, nursing, nursing education, health care administration. **Holdings:** 6400 books. **Subscriptions:** 240 journals and other serials. **Services:** Interlibrary loan; copying; library open to the public with restrictions. **Computerized Information Services:** MEDLINE, BRS Information Technologies. Performs searches on fee basis. **Networks/Consortia:** Member of National Network of Libraries of Medicine - Middle Atlantic Region, Delaware Valley Information Consortium (DEVIC), BHSL. **Remarks:** Alternate telephone numbers are: 934-4135 and 831-2372. FAX: (215)934-4946. Holdings and services include the Torresdale Campus Library at Red Lion and Knight's Rd., Philadelphia, PA 19114. **Staff:** Ruth Games, Sch. of Nurs.Libn.

★6083★
Frankford Hospital - School of Nursing - Student Library (Med)
4918 Penn St. Phone: (215)831-2372
Philadelphia, PA 19124 Dianne Rose, Dir., Lib.Serv.
Staff: Prof 2. **Subjects:** Nursing, sciences, medicine. **Holdings:** 6200 volumes; videotapes; filmstrips. **Subscriptions:** 121 journals and other serials. **Services:** Interlibrary loan; copying; library open to the public with restrictions. **Computerized Information Services:** MEDLARS. **Networks/ Consortia:** Member of Delaware Valley Information Consortium (DEVIC), BHSL. **Remarks:** FAX: (215)831-2332. **Staff:** Ruth Games, Sch. of Nurs.Libn.; Elizabeth Tepper.

Benjamin Franklin Collection
See: **Yale University** (20704)

Benjamin Franklin Library Anahuac
See: **(San Nicolas de Los Garza) Instituto Mexicano-Norteamericano de Relaciones Culturales Anahuac, A.C.** (14773)

★6084★
Franklin College - Library - Special Collections (Hist, Rel-Phil)
501 E. Monroe Phone: (317)738-8164
Franklin, IN 46131 Mary Alice Medlicott, Archv.
Founded: 1960. **Staff:** 1. **Subjects:** Indiana - history, Baptist Church, literature; Northwest Territory; Franklin College. **Special Collections:** David Demaree Banta Collection of Indiana history and literature (11,200 volumes); Indiana Baptist Collection (400 volumes); Roger D. Branigin personal papers. **Holdings:** 4000 books; 200 bound periodical volumes; 60 boxes of manuscripts. **Subscriptions:** 6 journals and other serials; 3 newspapers. **Services:** Interlibrary loan; copying; collections open to the public for reference use only. **Automated Operations:** Computerized cataloging. **Computerized Information Services:** OCLC. **Networks/ Consortia:** Member of INCOLSA, Central Indiana Area Library Services Authority (CIALSA). **Special Catalogs:** Catalog of the David Demaree Banta Indiana Collection (1965). **Special Indexes:** Biographical index of Indiana Baptist manuscripts (book); analytical index of Franklin College manuscripts (book); biographical index of Baptist minutes. **Remarks:** FAX: (317)736-6030.

★6085★
Franklin County Historical Society - Research Center (Hist)
586 E. Town St. Phone: (614)621-0441
Columbus, OH 43215 Denny L. Jay, Off.Mgr.
Founded: 1988. **Staff:** 1. **Subjects:** History - Columbus, Franklin County, American, world. **Holdings:** 300 books. **Services:** Center open to the public with restrictions.

★6086★
Franklin County Law Library (Law)
Court House Phone: (717)263-4809
Chambersburg, PA 17201 Paula S. Rabinowitz, Libn.
Staff: 1. **Subjects:** Law. **Holdings:** 22,000 volumes. **Subscriptions:** 50 journals and other serials. **Services:** Copying; library open to the public with restrictions. **Computerized Information Services:** WESTLAW.

★6087★
Franklin County Library - Gertrude C. Mann Local History Room (Hist)
138 E. Court St. Phone: (703)483-3098
Rocky Mount, VA 24151 David Bass, Dir.
Subjects: Local history and genealogy. **Holdings:** 550 books; 70 tape recordings; 1000 photographs; 200 maps and charts; vertical file; clippings; newspapers. **Subscriptions:** 12 journals and other serials. **Services:** Copying; room open to the public with restrictions.

★6088★
Franklin Furnace Archive, Inc. - Library (Art)
112 Franklin St. Phone: (212)925-4671
New York, NY 10013-0920 Martha Wilson, Dir.
Founded: 1976. **Staff:** 3. **Subjects:** Artists' books and other ephemeral published artworks, performance art. **Holdings:** 20,000 books; 24 VF drawers of reference materials on artists' books; periodicals; postcards; records; cassette tapes; posters; pamphlets. **Subscriptions:** 100 journals and other serials. **Services:** library open to the public by appointment; limited lending for exhibition to qualified institutions. **Special Catalogs:** Catalogs of exhibitions. **Remarks:** Organization is dedicated to the preservation of printed edition books by artists. **Staff:** Michael Katchen, Dir. of Coll.; Julie Zelman, Prin.Cat.

★6089★
H.H. Franklin Club, Inc. - Library (Rec)
Cazenovia College Phone: (315)655-8283
Cazenovia, NY 13035 Stanley Kozaczka, Libn.
Founded: 1951. **Staff:** 1. **Subjects:** Franklin automobile company - history, advertising, technical information; Franklin Club publications. **Holdings:** Figures not available. **Services:** Library not open to the public but will answer inquiries by mail. **Remarks:** H.H. Franklin Club located at Cazenovia Colege.

★6090★
Franklin Hospital Medical Center - Medical Library (Med)
900 Franklin Ave. Phone: (516)825-8800
Valley Stream, NY 11582 Kathryn A. Boccieri, Libn.
Founded: 1964. **Staff:** Prof 1. **Subjects:** Medicine. **Holdings:** 1500 books; 3000 bound periodical volumes; Audio-Digest tapes; slides. **Subscriptions:** 55 journals and other serials. **Services:** Interlibrary loan; copying; library open to medical students. **Networks/Consortia:** Member of Medical & Scientific Libraries of Long Island (MEDLI).

★6091★
Franklin Institute of Boston - Library (Sci-Engr)
41 Berkeley St. Phone: (617)423-4630
Boston, MA 02116 Mary A. Steigner, Lib.Dir.
Staff: 1. **Subjects:** Architecture; drafting; engineering - civil, electrical, automotive, computer, electronic, mechanical; mathematics; physics. **Special Collections:** Ravich Collection in photographic science. **Holdings:** 10,000 volumes. **Subscriptions:** 133 journals and other serials. **Services:** Interlibrary loan; copying; library open to the public by appointment. **Computerized Information Services:** DIALOG Information Services.

★6092★
Franklin Institute Science Museum - Library (Sci-Engr)
20th & The Parkway Phone: (215)448-1239
Philadelphia, PA 19103-1194 Irene D. Coffey, Libn.
Founded: 1824. **Staff:** 1.7. **Subjects:** Astronomy, physics, computer science, mathematics, history of science, science education, geology, environment, chemistry, engineering, energy, metallurgy, underwater man. **Special Collections:** Ware Reference Collection on Sugar; Wright Brothers Aeronautical Engineering Collection; Underwater Man Library Section. **Holdings:** 15,000 books; 30,000 bound periodical volumes; 700 reels of microfilm; manuscripts; archives. **Subscriptions:** 115 journals and other serials. **Services:** Interlibrary loan; copying; library open to the public by appointment. **Remarks:** FAX: (215)448-1235.

★6093★
Franklin Law Library (Law)
Court House
Main St. Phone: (413)772-6580
Greenfield, MA 01301 Marilyn M. Lee, Libn. I
Founded: 1816. **Staff:** Prof 1; Other 1. **Subjects:** Law. **Special Collections:** Legal history; Massachusetts statute law, 1692 to present. **Holdings:** 35,000 volumes; 18 tapes; microfiche. **Subscriptions:** 25 journals and other serials. **Services:** Interlibrary loan; copying; library open to the public. **Automated Operations:** Computerized cataloging. **Computerized Information Services:** LEXIS, WESTLAW, OCLC. **Special Indexes:** Index to legal periodicals. **Remarks:** Part of the Massachusetts State Trial Court.

★6094★
Franklin and Marshall College - Martin Library of the Sciences (Sci-Engr)
P.O. Box 3003 Phone: (717)291-3843
Lancaster, PA 17604-3003 Charles J. Myers, Libn.
Founded: 1990. **Staff:** Prof 1; Other 2. **Subjects:** Geology, biology, psychology, chemistry, physics, math, astronomy. **Special Collections:** Landmarks of Science. **Holdings:** 40,000 books; 26,000 bound periodical volumes; 2000 reels of microfilm. **Subscriptions:** 394 journals and other serials. **Services:** Interlibrary loan; copying; library open to the public. **Automated Operations:** Computerized public access catalog. **Computerized Information Services:** DIALOG Information Services; BITNET (electronic mail service). **Remarks:** FAX: (717)291-4088. Electronic mail address(es): C–MYERS@FANDMLIB (BITNET).

★6095★
Franklin and Marshall College - Shadek-Fackenthal Library - Special Collections (Hum)
Lancaster, PA 17604 Phone: (717)291-4225
Charlotte B. Brown, Archv./Spec.Coll.Libn.
Founded: 1787. **Staff:** 1.5. **Special Collections:** Alexander Corbett Collection of Theatre Memorabilia (600 photographs); German American Imprint Collection (2500 volumes; 800 broadsides; 350 fraktur); W.W. Griest Collection of Lincolniana (300 photographs, engravings, etchings); Napoleana Collection (1900 volumes); Franklin J. Schaffner Collection (American television and film director); European imprints, 16th-18th century (3000 volumes); Reynolds Family Papers, 1765-1934. **Holdings:** 7600 books; 150 bound periodical volumes; 100 linear feet of manuscripts; 500 linear feet of archival material; photographs. **Services:** Interlibrary loan; copying; collections open to the public with restrictions. **Automated Operations:** Computerized public access catalog, cataloging, circulation, and acquisitions. **Computerized Information Services:** OCLC, DIALOG Information Services, Chemical Abstracts Service (CAS), RLIN, VU/TEXT Information Services, WILSONLINE; BITNET (electronic mail service). **Networks/Consortia:** Member of PALINET, Associated College Libraries of Central Pennsylvania (ACLCP), Central Pennsylvania Consortium (CPC). **Publications:** Library Letter, irregular - to friends of the library. **Remarks:** Alternate telephone number(s): 291-4224. FAX: (717)291-4160. Electronic mail address(es): C-BROWN@FANDMLIB (BITNET).

★6096★
Franklin Memorial Hospital - Turner Memorial Library (Med)
One Hospital Dr. Phone: (207)778-6031
Farmington, ME 04938 Betty Gensel, Lib.Mgr.
Staff: Prof 2. **Subjects:** Medicine. **Holdings:** 450 books. **Subscriptions:** 45 journals and other serials. **Services:** Interlibrary loan; copying; library open to the public with restrictions. **Computerized Information Services:** MEDLINE, BRS Information Technologies, MAINECAT; internal database; DOCLINE (electronic mail service). **Networks/Consortia:** Member of Health Science Library and Information Cooperative of Maine (HSLIC). **Staff:** Emily Scribner.

★6097★
Franklin Mint - Information Research Services (Hist)
Franklin Center, PA 19091 Phone: (215)459-6373
Ruth Powell, Dir.
Staff: Prof 6; Other 8. **Subjects:** Antiques, American history, art, decorative arts, travel, numismatics, natural history, philatelics, direct mail, collectibles, home decor, dolls. **Holdings:** 20,000 volumes; 100 VF drawers of pictures and slides. **Subscriptions:** 500 journals and other serials; 6 newspapers. **Services:** Interlibrary loan; services not open to the public. **Automated Operations:** Computerized public access catalog and serials. **Computerized Information Services:** DIALOG Information Services, DataTimes, WILSONLINE, NEXIS, Dow Jones News/Retrieval, VU/TEXT Information Services, Dun & Bradstreet Business Credit Services; internal databases; DIALMAIL (electronic mail service). **Publications:** What's Hot, What's Not (current awareness), weekly; Events Calendar, monthly; New Book List, monthly - for internal distribution only. **Remarks:** FAX: (215)459-6880.

★6098★
Franklin Regional Medical Center - Medical Library (Med)
1 Spruce St. Phone: (814)437-7000
Franklin, PA 16323 Mr. L.P. Gilliland, Libn.
Founded: 1977. **Subjects:** Medicine, nursing. **Holdings:** 600 books; 700 unbound periodical volumes. **Subscriptions:** 85 journals and other serials. **Services:** Interlibrary loan; copying; SDI; library open to the public by appointment. **Computerized Information Services:** MEDLARS. Performs searches on fee basis. **Networks/Consortia:** Member of Erie Area Health Information Library Cooperative (EAHILC), National Network of Libraries of Medicine - Middle Atlantic Region, Northwest Interlibrary Cooperative of Pennsylvania (NICOP).

★6099★
Franklin University - Library (Bus-Fin, Soc Sci)
201 S. Grant Ave. Phone: (614)341-6252
Columbus, OH 43215 Mr. Allyn Ehrhardt, Libn.
Founded: 1966. **Staff:** Prof 8; Other 2. **Subjects:** Economics, business, social sciences. **Holdings:** 72,000 books; 10,000 bound periodical volumes; 488 tapes; 10K reports: New York Stock Exchange (NYSE), American Stock Exchange (AMEX), Ohio; 25 drawers of annual reports; 12 drawers of pamphlets; 18,000 reels of microfilm; 122,000 microfiche. **Subscriptions:** 1200 journals and other serials; 9 newspapers. **Services:** Interlibrary loan; copying; faxing; library open to the public. **Computerized Information Services:** DIALOG Information Services, BRS Information Technologies, PFDS Online, VU/TEXT Information Services, Info Globe, TEXTLINE, OCLC; CD-ROMs (Compact Disclosure, ABI/INFORM, Business Dateline). Performs searches on fee basis. **Networks/Consortia:** Member of Columbus Area Libraries Information Council of Ohio (CALICO), OHIONET. **Remarks:** FAX: (614)461-0957. **Staff:** Fred Helser, Assoc.Libn.; Mr. Beauford McCall, Ser.Libn.

★6100★
Ivan Franko Museum & Library Society, Inc. - Ukrainian Public Library of Ivan Franko (Area-Ethnic)
200 McGregor St. Phone: (204)589-4397
Winnipeg, MB, Canada R2W 5L6 Anthony Bilecki, Dir.
Founded: 1956. **Staff:** 3. **Subjects:** Ukrainian literature. **Holdings:** 15,025 volumes. **Subscriptions:** 15 journals and other serials; 5 newspapers. **Services:** Interlibrary loan; library open to the public.

Virginia L. Franks Memorial Library
See: **University of Wisconsin--Madison - School of Social Work** (19617)

★6101★
Fraser and Beatty - Library (Law)
1 First Canadian Place
P.O. Box 100 Phone: (416)863-4527
Toronto, ON, Canada M5X 1B2 Joan Hudson, Sr. Law Libn.
Staff: Prof 2; Other 2. **Subjects:** Law. **Holdings:** 7800 volumes; government documents; law reports; statutes. **Subscriptions:** 80 journals and other serials; 5 newspapers. **Services:** Interlibrary loan; library not open to the public. **Computerized Information Services:** WESTLAW, Info Globe, QL Systems, Canada Systems Group (CSG). **Special Indexes:** Legal Memoranda of Law Collection (by subject, author, and statutes). **Remarks:** FAX: (416)863-4592. Telex: 06-219825. **Staff:** Jan Barrett, Libn.

Fraser-Burrard Hospital Society - Royal Columbian Hospital
See: **Royal Columbian Hospital** (14116)

★6102★
Fraser-Hickson Institute, Montreal - Free Library - Special Collections (Hist)
4855 Kensington Ave. Phone: (514)489-5301
Montreal, PQ, Canada H3X 3S6 Frances W. Ackerman, Chf.Libn.
Founded: 1885. **Staff:** Prof 4; Other 17. **Subjects:** Canadiana, art, biography. **Special Collections:** Archives and book collection of the Institut Canadien of Montreal; Archives of the Mercantile Library Association of Montreal; 19th century newspapers. **Holdings:** 160,000 books; 400 audiotapes; 300 videotapes. **Subscriptions:** 135 journals and other serials; 7 newspapers. **Services:** Interlibrary loan; copying; collections open to the public. **Automated Operations:** Computerized public access catalog, cataloging, acquisitions, and circulation. **Staff:** Jane Toward, Hd., Ch.Lib.; Isabel Randall, Hd., Circ.; Fernando Montserrat, Hd., Ref.

★6103★
Fraser Inc. - Central Technical Department Library (Sci-Engr)
27 Rice St. Phone: (506)735-5551
Edmundston, NB, Canada E3V 1S9 Cheryl Fetterly, Libn.
Founded: 1940. **Staff:** 2. **Subjects:** Pulp and paper, chemistry, mathematics. **Holdings:** 1494 books; 1497 bound periodical volumes. **Subscriptions:** 60 journals and other serials. **Services:** Library not open to the public. **Remarks:** FAX: (506)739-5604. **Staff:** D.L. Bishop.

★6104★
Fraser Institute - Library (Bus-Fin)
626 Bute St., 2nd Fl.
Vancouver, BC, Canada V6E 3M1 Phone: (604)688-0221
Founded: 1974. **Staff:** Prof 1. **Subjects:** Economics, free enterprise, privatization, taxation, Canadian statistics. **Holdings:** 6000 books. **Subscriptions:** 69 journals and other serials; 7 newspapers. **Services:** Interlibrary loan; copying; library open to the public with restrictions. **Publications:** List of publications - available on request. **Remarks:** FAX: (604)688-8539.

James Fraser Library
See: **Canadian Gay Archives** (2933)

Fraser Library
See: **State University College at Geneseo - College Libraries** (15707)

★6105★
Simon Fraser University - W.A.C. Bennett Library - Special Collections (Hum)
Burnaby, BC, Canada V5A 1S6 Phone: (604)291-4626
Gene Bridwell, Spec.Coll.Libn.
Founded: 1965. **Staff:** 1.5. **Special Collections:** Contemporary Literature Collection (Canadian and American avant-garde poetry and prose, 1945 to present; books, manuscripts, tapes, little magazines, ephemera related to Ezra Pound, Charles Olson, Gary Snyder, Michael McClure, H.D. (Hilda Doolittle), Gertrude Stein, over thirty others); Wordsworth Collection; William Blake facsimiles. **Holdings:** 16,000 books; 1600 periodical titles; 700 broadsides; 800 tape recordings; 330 linear feet of manuscripts. **Subscriptions:** 185 journals and other serials. **Services:** Copying; collections open to the public. **Computerized Information Services:** DIALOG Information Services, BRS Information Technologies; UNIX (electronic mail service). **Special Catalogs:** Manuscript catalog in MARC format. **Remarks:** FAX: (604)291-4908. Electronic mail address(es): bridwell@whistler.sfu.ca (UNIX).

★6106★
Fraunhofer Society - Information Centre for Regional Planning and Building Construction (Plan)
Nobelstrasse 12 Phone: 711 9702500
W-7000 Stuttgart 80, Germany Mr. H. Kreutz
Staff: 4. **Subjects:** Regional and city planning, housing, civil engineering, building development, spatial structure, regulations, urban renewal, conservation, economics, regional policy, building politics and economics, standards, architecture, horticulture and landscaping, construction. **Holdings:** 96,000 volumes; 2 million references in card files. **Subscriptions:** 1750 journals and other serials. **Services:** Copying; library open to the public for reference use only. **Computerized Information Services:** STN International, ORBIT Search Service, FIZ Technik. **Remarks:** FAX: 711 9702507. Telex: 7255167 irbd. **Also Known As:** Fraunhofer-Gesellschaft - Informationszentrum Raum und Bau.

Frazier Library of Afro-American Books
See: **State University of New York - Syracuse Educational Opportunity Center - Paul Robeson Library** (15725)

Frech Health Sciences Library
See: **Harrison Memorial Hospital** (6929)

★6107★
Frederick County Law Library (Law)
Court House Phone: (301)694-2563
Frederick, MD 21701 Janet D. Rippeon, Law Libn.
Subjects: Law. **Holdings:** 25,000 volumes. **Services:** Library open to the public.

★6108★
Frederick Memorial Hospital - Walter F. Prior Medical Library (Med)
Park Place & W. 7th St. Phone: (301)698-3459
Frederick, MD 21701 Linda A. Collenberg Bisaccia, Med.Libn.
Staff: Prof 1. **Subjects:** Clinical medicine. **Holdings:** 1500 volumes. **Subscriptions:** 75 journals and other serials. **Services:** Interlibrary loan; copying; library open to authorized persons and students for reference use on request. **Computerized Information Services:** MEDLARS.

Fredericksburg & Spotsylvania National Military Park
See: **U.S. Natl. Park Service** (17718)

★6109★
Free Library of Philadelphia - Art Department (Art)
Logan Square Phone: (215)686-5403
Philadelphia, PA 19103 William F. Lang, Hd.
Staff: Prof 5; Other 1. **Subjects:** Art history, architecture, painting, sculpture, costume history, drawing, decorative arts, ceramics, cartoons, crafts, design, commercial art, photography, graphic arts, antiques, numismatics, interior decorating. **Special Collections:** 18th and 19th century architectural pattern books; American Institute of Architects (original measured drawings of colonial Philadelphia buildings); John Frederick Lewis Collection of books on fine prints and printmaking (2645 volumes); Lawrence B. Saint formulas and cartoons for stained glasswork. **Holdings:** 150,000 volumes; 35,000 pamphlets and clippings; 735 periodical titles; card index of 15,700 artists; 10,000 name card index of exhibition catalogs of Pennsylvania Academy of the Fine Arts. **Subscriptions:** 175 journals and other serials. **Services:** Interlibrary loan; copying. **Remarks:** FAX: (215)563-3628.

★6110★
Free Library of Philadelphia - Business, Science and Industry Department (Bus-Fin, Sci-Engr)
Logan Square Phone: (215)686-5394
Philadelphia, PA 19103 Alex S. Weinbaum, Hd.
Founded: 1953. **Staff:** Prof 7; Other 4. **Subjects:** Business, economics, investment and banking, insurance, pure and applied sciences, automotive literature, technology, philately. **Special Collections:** Automobile Reference Collection; Klein-Deats Philatelic Literature Collection. **Holdings:** Books; periodicals; 165 VF drawers of pamphlets; 39,000 microcards; 43,500 microfiche; 21,000 reels of microfilm. **Subscriptions:** 1200 journals and other serials. **Services:** Interlibrary loan (limited); copying; will answer questions by mail, especially in special collections areas. **Remarks:** FAX: (215)563-3628.

★6111★
Free Library of Philadelphia - Central Children's Department - Special Collections (Hum)
Logan Square Phone: (215)686-5369
Philadelphia, PA 19103 Michele M. Gendron, Hd., Spec.Coll.
Staff: Prof 1. **Subjects:** Children's literature, 1837 to present; books about children's literature; biography; bibliography; folklore. **Special Collections:** Illustrator's Collection; Pennsylvania authors and illustrators of children's books; original materials from Marguerite de Angeli, Katherine Milhous, Carolyn Haywood, Tomi Ungerer, and others. **Holdings:** 33,235 books; 200 bound periodical volumes; 526 framed illustrations. **Services:** Copying; collections open to the public for reference use only. **Automated Operations:** Computerized cataloging. **Special Indexes:** Checklist of Children's Books, 1837-1876 (book); index to illustrators' collection (card); index to all collections by author (card). **Remarks:** FAX: (215)563-3628

★6112★
Free Library of Philadelphia - Database and Newspaper Center (Info Sci)
Logan Square
Philadelphia, PA 19103 Bernard F. Pasqualini, Hd.
Founded: 1987. **Staff:** Prof 6; Other 9. **Subjects:** Philadelphia area newspapers, colonial era to present; major current national, foreign, and local newspapers. **Holdings:** Over 16,000 reels of microfilm of local and regional newspapers; partial indexing for the Philadelphia Press and the Public Ledger/Evening Ledger; indexing for the Philadelphia Inquirer/ Daily News (online); over 65,000 reels of microfilm of periodicals; Philadelphia city directories; Philadelphia telephone directories. **Services:** Photocopies from newspapers; positive prints from microforms. **Computerized Information Services:** Online systems. **Remarks:** The telephone number for the Newspaper Center is (215)686-5431; for the Database Center: 686-2860. FAX: (215)563-3628.

★6113★
Free Library of Philadelphia - Education, Philosophy, Religion Department (Educ, Rel-Phil)
Logan Square
Philadelphia, PA 19103 Phone: (215)686-5392
Founded: 1954. **Staff:** Prof 6; Other 3. **Subjects:** Education, philosophy, psychology, religion, library science. **Special Collections:** College and school catalogs (hardcopy, microfiche); The Workplace (job and career education information; hardcopy, AV programs); Judaica (primarily history and religion); Bibles (various languages). **Holdings:** Books; periodicals; 50 VF drawers of clippings and pamphlets; 78 file boxes of library annual reports; 3120 reels of microfilm; 10,006 microfiche. **Subscriptions:** 655 journals and other serials. **Services:** Copying. **Computerized Information Services:** InfoTrac. **Remarks:** FAX: (215)563-3628.

★6114★
Free Library of Philadelphia - Edwin A. Fleisher Collection of Orchestral Music (Mus)
Logan Square Phone: (215)686-5313
Philadelphia, PA 19103 Frederick J. Kent, Cur.
Founded: 1929. **Staff:** Prof 3; Other 4. **Subjects:** Conductors' scores, orchestral parts, program information, American composers. **Holdings:** 15,000 sets of performance materials (scores and parts); 1500 reference scores; 520 audiotape recordings (primarily the Recording Guarantee Project of the American International Music Fund); 210 phonograph records; 177 reels of microfilm; composer, publisher, agent files; complete orchestral works of Isadore Freed, Harrison Kerr, Nicolai Lopatnikoff, Karl Weigl, Louis Gruenberg, Robert Casadesus, Edward Steuermann, Franz Bornschein, Frederick Jacobi, LaSalle Spier, David Van Vactor. **Services:** Collection available to public for reference use only; materials are lent only to organizations for performance, although copyrighted works must be cleared in advance. **Special Catalogs:** Edwin A. Fleisher Collection of Orchestral Music in the Free Library of Philadelphia, A Cumulative Catalog, 1929-1977; master catalog of Fleisher Collection holdings (card); union card catalog of orchestral music, scores, and theater arrangements. **Special Indexes:** Special subject indices and complete title index available by consulting collection. **Remarks:** FAX: (215)563-3628.

★6115★
Free Library of Philadelphia - Government Publications Department (Info Sci)
Logan Square Phone: (215)686-5330
Philadelphia, PA 19103 William A. Felker, Hd.
Founded: 1900. **Staff:** Prof 7; Other 4. **Subjects:** Publications of municipal, state, federal, and official international agencies. **Special Collections:** U.S. Patent Collection. **Holdings:** 77,494 bound volumes; 1.05 million unbound documents; 401,710 microprint cards; 9481 reels of microfilm; 621,858 microfiche. **Subscriptions:** 3000 journals and other serials. **Services:** Interlibrary loan; telephone and mail service; department open to the public with restrictions on circulation. **Remarks:** FAX: (215)563-3628.

★6116★
Free Library of Philadelphia - Library for the Blind and Physically Handicapped (Aud-Vis)
919 Walnut St. Phone: (215)925-3213
Philadelphia, PA 19107 Vickie L. Collins
Staff: Prof 6; Other 22. **Subjects:** General collection. **Holdings:** 9000 braille books; 21,000 talking book titles; 25,000 cassette tapes; 10,000 large print books. **Networks/Consortia:** Member of National Library Service for the Blind & Physically Handicapped (NLS). **Remarks:** Toll-free telephone number(s): in Pennsylvania is (800)222-1754.

★6117★
Free Library of Philadelphia - Literature Department (Hum)
Logan Square Phone: (215)686-5402
Philadelphia, PA 19103 Susan T. Horn, Hd.
Staff: Prof 5; Other 2. **Subjects:** Literature, criticism, theater, language, folklore, journalism. **Special Collections:** Theater Collection; Granger Collection of Poetry Anthologies; Ottemiller Collection of Play Anthologies; fiction reference collection. **Holdings:** 130,000 books; 35,000 bound periodical volumes; 11 VF drawers of pamphlets; 9800 reels of microfilm. **Subscriptions:** 275 journals and other serials. **Services:** Interlibrary loan; copying. **Remarks:** FAX: (215)563-3628.

★6118★
Free Library of Philadelphia - Mercantile Library
1021 Chestnut St.
Philadelphia, PA 19107
Defunct.

★6119★
Free Library of Philadelphia - Music Department (Mus)
Logan Square Phone: (215)686-5316
Philadelphia, PA 19103 Mary E. VandenBerge, Hd.
Founded: 1927. **Staff:** Prof 5; Other 3. **Subjects:** Music, dance. **Special Collections:** Edward I. Keffer Collection of Early American musical imprints; Harvey Husten Jazz Library (recordings); library of the Musical Fund Society of Philadelphia; chamber music; historical collection of records (RCA Victor Masterworks before LP). **Holdings:** 100,000 volumes; 4000 bound periodical volumes; 45,000 phonograph records; 190,000 pieces of sheet music; librettos; pamphlets; clippings. **Subscriptions:** 220 serials. **Services:** Interlibrary loan; copying. **Remarks:** FAX: (215)563-3628.

★6120★
Free Library of Philadelphia - Music Department - Drinker Library of Choral Music (Mus)
Logan Square Phone: (215)686-5364
Philadelphia, PA 19103 Judith A. Harvey, Hd.
Staff: Prof 1; Other 2. **Subjects:** Choral music - men's, women's, mixed voices; liturgical music for chorus - chorales, music, texts. **Special Collections:** Bach cantatas; Brahms solo songs; English translations of the texts of the vocal works of Bach, Brahms, Schumann, Schutz, Schubert (edited, arranged, translated by Henry S. Drinker); Library of American Choral Foundation (primarily 20th century works). **Holdings:** 348,000 unbound choral parts; 25,000 unbound instrumental parts for accompaniment to choral parts; 3000 unbound texts of vocal works; 10,000 solo songs. **Services:** Library open to the public for reference use only; circulation restricted to subscribers. **Publications:** Bach 389 Chorales. **Special Catalogs:** Catalog of the Drinker Library of Choral Music. **Remarks:** FAX: (215)563-3628.

★6121★
Free Library of Philadelphia - Print and Picture Department (Art)
Logan Square Phone: (215)686-5405
Philadelphia, PA 19103 J.B. Post, Hd.
Founded: 1953. **Staff:** Prof 3; Other 2. **Subjects:** Loan collection of pictures on all subjects; reference collection of fine prints. **Special Collections:** John Frederick Lewis Portrait Collection (220,000); Philadelphiana Collection (10,000 items); Americana (1194 items); John Gibb Smith Collection of Philadelphia Streetcars (906 items); WPA Collection of Prints (1415 items); Napoleonic Prints (3379); Rosenthal and Bendiner collections of American drawings of the 19th and 20th centuries (1000); American photographs of the 19th and 20th centuries (1200). **Holdings:** 1500 original graphics, 1491 to present; loan collection pictures; 800,000 photographs and art reproductions; postcards; greeting cards; travel posters. **Services:** Copying; exhibitions and displays. **Remarks:** Alternate telephone number(s): 686-5415. FAX: (215)563-3628.

★6122★
Free Library of Philadelphia - Rare Book Department (Rare Book)
Logan Square Phone: (215)686-5416
Philadelphia, PA 19103 Edwin J. Saeger, Hd.
Founded: 1949. **Staff:** Prof 4; Other 2. **Special Collections:** Cuneiform tablets (2800); European and Oriental illuminated manuscripts; Bibles; British common law; British and American legal autographs and prints; Horace; incunabula; Americana (discovery and exploration); early American children's books (including American Sunday-School Union collection); Oliver Goldsmith; Charles Dickens; Edgar Allan Poe; Pennsylvania German Fraktur and imprints (1100 items); 18th-19th century Irish and American pamphlets; Wing and Short Title Catalogue books; calligraphy; English and American library and auction catalogs; 19th century English and American literature; letters of British engravers; giftbooks; letters of the presidents of the United States; angling prints; printed views of Philadelphia; Arthur Rackham; Kate Greenaway; Beatrix Potter; A.B. Frost; Howard Pyle; Palmer Cox; Robert Lawson; Munro Leaf; Joseph Conrad; Rudyard Kipling; Robert Louis Stevenson; James Branch Cabell; Bret Harte; Mark Twain; Agnes Repplier; William Cowper; A. Edward Newton. **Holdings:** 41,120 books; 6725 pamphlets; 168 horn books; 22,352 prints and broadsides; 1350 Oriental miniatures; 2200 illuminated European miniatures and leaves; 17,225 manuscripts, letters, documents. **Services:** Microfilming (positive only supplied); photographs; department open to the public to view exhibitions; use of materials restricted to qualified research workers.

★6123★
Free Library of Philadelphia - Social Science & History Department (Soc Sci, Hist)
Logan Square Phone: (215)686-5396
Philadelphia, PA 19103 William Handley, Hd.
Founded: 1953. **Staff:** Prof 7; Other 4. **Subjects:** History, biography, social sciences, books and printing, law, travels and geography, archeology, anthropology, bibliography, sports and games. **Special Collections:** American Indians (Wilberforce Eames); chess (Charles Willing); Confederate imprints (Simon Gratz); Regional Foundation Collection. **Holdings:** 167,500 volumes; 47,500 pamphlets; 19 VF drawers of clippings; 370 boxes of microcards; 4000 annual reports. **Subscriptions:** 715 journals and other serials. **Services:** Interlibrary loan. **Remarks:** FAX: (215)563-3628.

★6124★
Free Library of Philadelphia - Social Science & History Department - Map Collection (Geog-Map)
Logan Square Phone: (215)686-5397
Philadelphia, PA 19103 Richard C. Boardman, Map Libn.
Staff: Prof 2. **Subjects:** General map collection with emphasis on local area. **Special Collections:** Kelso Collection of Jansson-Visscher maps of America (20 sheets); fire insurance and ward atlases of Philadelphia (500 volumes); Pennsylvania county atlases. **Holdings:** 15,000 atlases, gazetteers, cartobibliographies; 130,000 maps; 200 aerial photographs; 8000 microfiche. **Remarks:** FAX: (215)563-3628.

★6125★
Free Library of Philadelphia - Theatre Collection (Theater)
Logan Square Phone: (215)686-5427
Philadelphia, PA 19103 Geraldine Duclow, Hd.
Founded: 1951. **Staff:** Prof 1; Other 2. **Subjects:** Theater, film, television, radio, circus, minstrels. **Special Collections:** 19th century playbills; Lubin Film Company archives; Philadelphia playbills, 1803 to present. **Holdings:** 5000 books; 125 periodical titles; over 1 million programs, playbills, scrapbooks, posters, biographical newspaper clippings, reviews of movies and plays, pictures of productions, film stills, microfilm. **Services:** Copying. **Special Indexes:** Philadelphia Theatre Index (card index of productions since 1855). **Remarks:** FAX: (215)563-3628.

★6126★
Free Library of Philadelphia - Video and Film Center (Aud-Vis)
Logan Square Phone: (215)686-5367
Philadelphia, PA 19103 Elizabeth C. Orsburn, Hd.
Founded: 1958. **Staff:** Prof 2; Other 5. **Subjects:** Literature, intercultural relations, social problems, science, travel. **Special Collections:** Collection of films for children, preschool-age 13. **Holdings:** 2750 16mm sound films; 1300 video cassettes. **Services:** Center open to the public. **Special Catalogs:** Annotated Catalog of 16mm Films; Video Cassette for Children and American International Films on Video Cassette. **Remarks:** FAX: (215)563-3628.

★6127★
Free Methodist Church of North America - Marston Memorial Historical Library (Rel-Phil)
770 North High School Rd.
P.O. Box 535002 Phone: (317)244-3660
Indianapolis, IN 46253-5002 Frances Haslam, Exec.Sec.
Staff: Prof 1. **Subjects:** Free Methodist and Methodist history, Wesleyana, Holiness literature. **Holdings:** 12,000 books; 500 bound periodical volumes; manuscripts; journals; letters; photographs; pamphlets; microfilm; cassette tapes. **Subscriptions:** 10 journals and other serials. **Services:** Interlibrary loan; copying; library open to the public. **Publications:** The Free Methodist Church: A Bibliography - for sale. **Remarks:** FAX: (317)244-1247.

★6128★
Free Public Library of Elizabeth, NJ - Art and Music Department (Art, Mus)
11 S. Broad St. Phone: (201)354-6060
Elizabeth, NJ 07202 Roman A. Sawycky, Asst.Dir.
Staff: Prof 2; Other 4. **Subjects:** Painting, sculpture, art and music education, history of art and music, art and music biography, music appreciation. **Special Collections:** Japanese prints from Primitive Period through Revival (250 items); wooden carvings by Thomas H. Smith, 1825-1907 (50). **Holdings:** 30,000 books; 1000 pamphlets; scores; 13,600 phonograph records; 400 35mm filmstrips; 400 16mm motion picture films; 200,000 mounted pictures; 800 study art prints; 1000 audio cassettes; 2500 video cassettes. **Subscriptions:** 58 journals and other serials. **Services:** Interlibrary loan; copying; Slavonic language capability; audiovisual programs assistance; department open to the public. **Automated Operations:** Computerized cataloging and ILL. **Publications:** Calendar of Events. **Special Catalogs:** Separate printed catalogs for the filmstrip collection and motion pictures (annotated); videotape list. **Staff:** Sheila Braun, Music Libn.

Free Will Baptist Historical Collection
See: **Mount Olive College** (10806)

★6129★
Freeborn County Historical Society - Library (Hist)
1031 N. Bridge St.
Box 105
Albert Lea, MN 56007 Phone: (507)373-8003
Founded: 1980. **Staff:** Prof 1. **Subjects:** History - Albert Lea, Freeborn County, Minnesota. **Special Collections:** Freeborn County history and genealogy. **Holdings:** 500 books; 20 bound periodical volumes; 100 boxes of manuscripts; 2000 slides and photographs; 200 reels of microfilm. **Subscriptions:** 4 newspapers. **Services:** Copying; library open to the public for reference use only.

★6130★
Freedom House, Inc. (Soc Sci)
48 E. 21st St., 5th Fl. Phone: (212)473-9691
New York, NY 10010-7223 R. Bruce McColm, Exec.Dir.
Founded: 1941. **Staff:** 25. **Subjects:** Foreign affairs, problems of higher education, international communication, American heritage, international and domestic human rights, political rights, civil liberties. **Holdings:** Books; reports; manuscripts; archival material. **Services:** Library not open to the public. **Computerized Information Services:** InterNet, PeaceNet (electronic mail services). **Publications:** Freedom Review, bimonthly; Freedom Monitor (newsletter), quarterly; Freedom in the World: Political Rights and Civil Liberties, a yearbook; Perspective on Freedom, including titles on Nicaragua, The Helsinki Accords, El Salvador, Cuba, Press Licensing, Czechoslovakia, Ireland, developing countries around the world; Afghanistan Reader; Human Rights. **Remarks:** FAX: (212)477-4126. Toll-free telephone number(s): (800)289-8880. Telex: 429439-FREEDOM. Electronic mail address(es): freehouse@igc.org (InterNet).

★6131★
Freedom from Hunger Foundation - Library
Box 2000
Davis, CA 95617
Founded: 1967. **Subjects:** International agriculture, health, nurtrition, and development. **Holdings:** 1600 books; 12 VF drawers of reports and articles; 4 VF drawers of annual reports and pamphlets. **Remarks:** Currently inactive.

Freedom of Information Services, Inc.
See: **FOI Services, Inc.** (5941)

Freedom Newspapers - Colorado Springs Gazette Telegraph
See: **Colorado Springs Gazette Telegraph** (3950)

Freedom Newspapers - Odessa American
See: **(Odessa) American** (12248)

★6132★
Freedoms Foundation at Valley Forge - Library (Hist, Soc Sci)
Rte. 23 Phone: (215)933-8825
Valley Forge, PA 19481 Harold Badger, Libn.
Founded: 1965. **Staff:** 1. **Subjects:** U.S. history - social, political, economic, foreign policy; 20th century totalitarianism; modern economic and political systems; current events and public policy issues. **Special Collections:** U.S. Radical Movements Collection. **Holdings:** 30,000 books; 6000 bound periodical volumes; 1000 linear feet of unbound serials; pamphlets; posters; fugitive literature. **Subscriptions:** 125 journals and other serials. **Services:** Interlibrary loan; copying; library open to the public.

★6133★
The Freedonia Gazette - Marx Brothers Library & Archives (Theater)
Darien 28 Phone: (215)862-9734
New Hope, PA 18938-1224 Paul G. Wesolowski, Dir.
Founded: 1978. **Subjects:** Lives and careers of the Marx Brothers. **Special Collections:** Gloria Teasdale Collection, 1905 to present (850 items documenting the effect of the Marx Brothers on contemporary culture). **Holdings:** 250 books; 150 phonograph records; 3000 movie stills and photographs; 530 theatrical, movie, contemporary posters from the U.S. and 13 foreign countries; 42,000 magazine and newspaper articles. **Subscriptions:** 2 journals and other serials. **Services:** Reference questions answered by mail or Fax; library open to qualified researchers by special arrangement. **Publications:** The Freedonia Gazette, semiannual - by subscription; chronological bibliography of magazine and newspaper articles (13,000 entries; printout). **Special Indexes:** Index to names mentioned in articles (card). **Remarks:** FAX: (215)654-0408.

Eugene L. Freel Library
See: **North Adams State College** (11854)

A.B. Freeman School of Business
See: **Tulane University - A.B. Freeman School of Business Administration - Turchin Library** (16555)

★6134★
Daniel Freeman Hospitals Inc. - Health Sciences Library (Med)
333 N. Prairie Ave. Phone: (213)674-7050
Inglewood, CA 90301 Tracie Thomas, Lib.Asst.
Staff: 1; Other 1. **Subjects:** Medicine, nursing, hospital administration. **Holdings:** 2012 books; 4305 bound periodical volumes; 998 cassette tapes; 8 audiotape titles; 15 videotape titles; 25 video cassettes. **Subscriptions:** 420 journals and other serials. **Services:** Interlibrary loan; library open to the public with permission. **Automated Operations:** Computerized cataloging, acquisitions, serials, and circulation. **Computerized Information Services:** DIALOG Information Services, MEDLARS; DOCLINE (electronic mail service). Performs searches on fee basis. **Networks/Consortia:** Member of National Network of Libraries of Medicine - Pacific Southwest Region. **Publications:** Medical Library Update, irregular - for internal distribution only. **Remarks:** FAX: (213)419-8275.

★6135★
Daniel Freeman (Marina) Hospital - Medical Library & Resource Center
4650 Lincoln Blvd.
Marina Del Rey, CA 90292
Subjects: Medicine, nursing, allied health sciences. **Holdings:** 154 books; 198 audiotapes. **Remarks:** Currently inactive.

George E. Freeman Library
See: **State Technical Institute at Memphis** (15701)

Larry Freeman Decorative Arts Library
See: **American Life Foundation and Study Institute - Americana Research Library** (670)

Thomas Oscar Freeman Memorial Library
See: **Lake Forest College** (8892)

★6136★
Freeport Memorial Hospital - Medical Library (Med)
1045 W. Stephenson St. Phone: (815)235-0132
Freeport, IL 61032 Jan Stilson, MLS
Founded: 1964. **Staff:** Prof 1. **Subjects:** Medicine, immediate care, surgery, rehabilitation. **Holdings:** 600 books; 1500 bound periodical volumes; 200 videotapes. **Subscriptions:** 75 journals and other serials; 3 newspapers. **Services:** Interlibrary loan; copying; library open to nonmedical patrons referred by public and college libraries. **Computerized Information Services:** MEDLINE, MEDLARS; DOCLINE (electronic mail service). **Networks/Consortia:** Member of Northern Illinois Library System (NILS), Upstate Illinois Consortium. **Remarks:** FAX: (815)235-0544.

★6137★
Freer Gallery of Art - Arthur M. Sackler Gallery Library (Art)
1050 Independence Ave. Phone: (202)357-2091
Washington, DC 20560 Lily Kecskes, Hd.Libn.
Founded: 1923. **Staff:** Prof 4; Other 4. **Subjects:** Arts and cultures of the Far East, Near East, South Asia, and Southeast Asia; history and civilization; art and art history; archeology; pottery; painting. **Special Collections:** Washington Biblical manuscript facsimiles; C.L. Freer Letter Books (30 volumes); letters of Whistler, Tryon, Dewing, Thayer, Freer acquaintances, dealers, and business associates (2500-3000). **Holdings:** 53,000 books and bound periodical volumes (both Western and Oriental languages); 250 reels of microfilm; 6383 microfiche; 4 VF drawers of maps; 140,000 photographic images; 55,000 slides. **Subscriptions:** 400 journals. **Services:** Library reading room open to the public; slides loaned to public. **Automated Operations:** Computerized cataloging. **Computerized Information Services:** RLIN. **Networks/Consortia:** Member of Research Libraries Information Network (RLIN). **Special Indexes:** Index to KOKKA; index to Chinese calligraphers. **Remarks:** Affiliated with the Smithsonian Institution. FAX: (202)357-4911. **Staff:** Reiho Yoshimura, Asst.Libn.; Kathryn Phillips, Asst.Libn.; Colleen Hennessey, Arch.

★6138★
(Freetown) American Cultural Center - USIS Library (Educ)
8 Walpole St. Phone: 22 226481
Freetown, Sierra Leone Florence Lewis-Coker
Staff: 2. **Special Collections:** Gullah and Africa collection. **Holdings:** 3500 books. **Subscriptions:** 65 journals and other serials; 4 newspapers. **Services:** Copying; SDI; library open to the public with restrictions. **Remarks:** FAX: 22 225471. Telex: 3509 USEMBSL. Maintained or supported by the U.S. Information Agency. Focus is on materials that will assist peoples outside the United States to learn about the United States, its people, history, culture, political processes, and social milieux.

★6139★
(Freiburg) German-American Institute - USIS Collection (Educ)
Kaiser Joseph Strasse 266 Phone: 761 31646
W-7800 Freiburg, Germany Duncan Cummins, Lib.Hd.
Founded: 1952. **Staff:** 2.5. **Subjects:** American literature, American biographies, American travel and guidebooks, German-American relations, United States. **Holdings:** 12,500 books; 1000 microfiche; 750 audiocassettes; 380 videotapes; unbound periodicals. **Subscriptions:** 60 journals and other serials; 4 newspapers. **Services:** Interlibrary loan; copying; library open to the public. **Computerized Information Services:** Internal databases. **Publications:** Bibliographies based on holdings. **Remarks:** FAX: 761 39827. Maintained or supported by the U.S. Information Agency. Focus is on materials that will assist peoples outside the United States to learn about the United States, its people, history, culture, political processes, and social milieux. **Staff:** Petra Schelle; Gisela Hoppner.

★6140★
Freie Universitat Berlin - Institut fur Englische Philologie - Bibliothek (Hum)
Gosslerstr 2-4
W-1000 Berlin 33, Germany Phone: 30 83872326
Founded: 1949. **Staff:** Prof 1; Other 3. **Subjects:** English language and literature. **Holdings:** 69,000 books; 7527 reels of microfilm. **Subscriptions:** 172 journals and other serials; 3 newspapers. **Services:** Copying; library open to the public.

★6141★
Freie Universitat Berlin - John F. Kennedy Institut fur Nordamerikastudien - Bibliothek (Soc Sci, Area-Ethnic)
Lansstr 5-9 Phone: 30 8382858
W-1000 Berlin 33, Germany Ingeborg Schwalbe, Dir. of Lib.
Founded: 1963. **Staff:** Prof 10; Other 7. **Subjects:** American studies, United States, Canada. **Special Collections:** American popular culture collection; ethnic groups and minorities collection. **Holdings:** 160,000 books and bound periodical volumes; 360,000 microfiche; 34,600 reels of microfilm. **Subscriptions:** 1500 journals and other serials; 100 newspapers. **Services:** Interlibrary loan; copying; SDI; library open to the public. **Automated Operations:** Computerized public access catalog. **Computerized Information Services:** DIALOG Information Services. **Publications:** Accession lists; information brochure. **Remarks:** FAX: 30 8382882. Alternate telephone number(s): 30 8382860.

J.A. Freitas Library
See: **U.P.E.C. Cultural Center** (16608)

★6142★
French American Cultural Services and Educational Aid (FACSEA) (Area-Ethnic)
972 Fifth Ave. Phone: (212)439-1449
New York, NY 10021 Pascal Chrobocinski, Exec.Dir.
Founded: 1955. **Staff:** 5. **Subjects:** French history, geography, culture; French documentary, feature, geography, art, literature films. **Holdings:** 6500 films; 800 scientific and medical films; videocassettes. **Services:** Offers 16mm films for rent and videocassettes for sale. **Special Catalogs:** Catalogs - available upon request. **Remarks:** FAX: (212)439-1455. **Staff:** Katharine Branning.

★6143★
French-Canadian Genealogical Society of Connecticut, Inc. - French-Canadian Genealogical Library (Hist)
53 Tolland Green
Box 45 Phone: (203)872-0138
Tolland, CT 06084 Rod Wilscam, Lib.Hd.
Founded: 1981. **Staff:** Prof 9; Other 3. **Subjects:** French-Canadian genealogy and history. **Special Collections:** Hebert Collection of Acadian Genealogy; Repertoire Alphabetique Des Mariages Des Canadiens-Francais, 1730-1935 by Claude Drouin (49 volumes). **Holdings:** 800 books; 500 bound periodical volumes; 550 other cataloged items; 10,000 index cards on Acadians; index to 10,000 births, deaths, and marriages of Franco-Americans in Connecticut; 5000 index cards on Worcester County, Massachusetts, area. **Subscriptions:** 11 journals and other publications. **Services:** Cpoying; library open to the public with restrictions. **Publications:** The Connecticut Maple Leaf, semiannual. **Staff:** Susan Paquette, Ed.; Rollande Clark, Libn.; Charles Pelletier, Libn.; Paul Keroack. Libn.

★6144★
French-Canadian Heritage Society of Michigan - Library
P.O. Box 10028
Lansing, MI 48901-0028
Founded: 1980. **Subjects:** French-Canadian history, genealogy. **Holdings:** 400 books; birth, death, marriage records; family genealogies. **Remarks:** Currently inactive. Collection on loan until 2001 to the Mt. Clemens Public Library, 150 Cass Ave., Mt. Clemens, MI 48043-2296.

Harley E. French Library of the Health Sciences
See: **University of North Dakota - School of Medicine** (19103)

★6145★
French Institute/Alliance Francaise - Library (Area-Ethnic)
22 E. 60th St. Phone: (212)355-6100
New York, NY 10022-1077 Fred J. Gitner, Lib.Dir.
Founded: 1911. **Staff:** Prof 3; Other 3. **Subjects:** French literature, art, history, civilization; Paris. **Holdings:** 40,000 books; 750 bound periodical volumes; readers for students; 1350 phonograph records; 800 audiotapes. **Subscriptions:** 110 journals and other serials. **Services:** Interlibrary loan; copying; library open to the public with restrictions on circulation. **Automated Operations:** Computerized cataloging. **Computerized Information Services:** UTLAS. **Networks/Consortia:** Member of New York Metropolitan Reference and Research Library Agency. **Publications:** List of new acquisitions, quarterly - free upon request. **Remarks:** FAX: (212)935-4119. **Staff:** Michael Laird, Asst.Libn.; Eva Goldschmidt, Cat.

★6146★
French Institute of Andean Studies - Library (Area-Ethnic)
Casilla 18-1217 Phone: 14 476070
Lima 18, Peru Zaida Lanning de Sanchez, Libn.
Subjects: Andes - geology, anthropology, history, sociology, ethnology, geography. **Holdings:** 35,000 volumes. **Remarks:** Maintained by French Foreign Affairs Office. **Also Known As:** Institut Francais d'Etudes Andines.

★6147★
French Institute for Archaeology in the Near East - Library (Soc Sci, Area-Ethnic)
P.O. Box 11-1424 Phone: 917-511
Beirut, Lebanon Dr. Frank Braemer, Libn.
Subjects: Archeology and history of the Near East, fourth millenium B.C. to seventh century A.D. **Holdings:** 40,000 volumes. **Publications:** Bibliotheque Archeologique, 4-5/year (in French, German, English, Arabic). **Also Known As:** Institut Francais d'Archeologie du Proche-Orient.

★6148★
French Institute of Eastern Archeology - Library (Soc Sci, Area-Ethnic)
37 Sh. el Cheikh Aly Youssef (Mounira)
B.P. Qasr el Ainy 11562 Phone: 2 3 557142
Cairo, Egypt J.P. Corteggiani, Libn.
Subjects: Archeology, Egyptology, Coptology, Greek and Arabic languages, papyrology, Islam. **Holdings:** 60,000 volumes. **Remarks:** Maintained by France - Ministry of Education. **Also Known As:** Institut Francais d'Archeologie Orientale.

★6149★
French Library in Boston, Inc. (Area-Ethnic)
53 Marlborough St. Phone: (617)266-4351
Boston, MA 02114 Phyllis Dohanian, Exec.Dir.
Founded: 1945. **Staff:** Prof 3; Other 1. **Subjects:** Classical and contemporary French literature including criticism; French history, politics, social life; language and art; cinema; biography; sociology; children's books. **Special Collections:** Marcel Carne Film Archive (films; photographs; posters; books; letters; memorabilia). **Holdings:** 40,000 books; major lender for French film classics including Renoir, Truffaut, Rene Clair. **Subscriptions:** 40 journals and other serials; 5 newspapers. **Services:** Interlibrary loan; copying; library open to the public. **Publications:** Le Bibliophile (newsletter), quarterly; Cine Club Newsletter, 5/year. **Special Catalogs:** Printed catalog (1989) of 85 feature and documentary films and videotapes available for rental by institutions; AV Catalog, biennial. **Remarks:** Salles Carne (Marcel Carne) is said to be the only archive on a French filmmaker in the United States. FAX: (617)266-1780. **Staff:** Jane Stahl, Libn.

★6150★
French National Shipowners Association - Library (Trans)
73, blvd. Haussmann
F-75008 Paris, France Phone: 1 42653604
Subjects: French shipping industry. **Holdings:** 2000 volumes. **Remarks:** Telex: 660532 F. **Also Known As:** Comite Central des Armateurs de France.

★6151★
French Petroleum Institute - Board of Economics and Documentation - Library (Energy)
1-4, ave. de Bois-Preau Phone: 1 47490214
F-92506 Rueil-Malmaison, France Mr. Boy de la Tour, Dir.
Founded: 1945. **Staff:** Prof 12. **Subjects:** Petroleum, natural gas, and petrochemical industries - science, technology, engineering, economics, onshore and offshore drilling; alternative energy sources; thermodynamics. **Holdings:** 250,000 volumes. **Subscriptions:** 3434 journals and other serials. **Services:** Interlibrary loan; copying; SDI. **Computerized Information Services:** DIALOG Information Services, ESA/IRS, ORBIT Search Service, BRS Information Technologies, Questel; produces Principal Offshore Oil Spill and Tanker Casualties Data Bank, Principal Offshore-Platform Accidents. Performs searches on fee basis. **Remarks:** FAX: 1 47526429. Alternate telephone number(s): 1 47526676. Telex: IFP A 203050. **Staff:** Anne Girard, Hd., Sci. & Econ.Doc.Dept.

★6152★
French Textile Institute - Library (Bus-Fin)
B.P. 141 Phone: 1 46641540
F-92223 Bagneux Cedex, France Jacques Mesny, Dir.
Subjects: Textile industry - production and structure of textile fibers, processes, machines, treatment for manufactured goods. **Holdings:** 7500 volumes. **Subscriptions:** 350 journals and other serials. **Services:** Library open to the public. **Computerized Information Services:** Produces TITUS database (available online through STN International). **Publications:** INFOTEX, 11/year. **Remarks:** FAX: 1 46643245. Telex: 632659 F.

Freshwater Institute Library
See: **Canada - Fisheries & Oceans** (2731)

★6153★
Fresno Bee - Library (Publ)
1626 E St. Phone: (209)441-6128
Fresno, CA 93786 Mabel Wilson, Res.Libn.
Founded: 1922. **Staff:** Prof 1; Other 4. **Subjects:** Newspaper reference topics. **Holdings:** 200 books; bound volumes of Fresno Bee (1922 to present); microfilm. **Services:** Library open to the public on a limited schedule by appointment only. **Computerized Information Services:** VU/TEXT Information Services, LEXIS, NEXIS, DataTimes, DataQuick; LASR Retrieval System (internal database). **Remarks:** FAX: (209)441-6436.

★6154★
Fresno City and County Historical Society - Archives (Hist)
7160 W. Kearney Blvd. Phone: (209)441-0862
Fresno, CA 93706 John Panter, Archv.
Founded: 1919. **Staff:** Prof 1; Other 4. **Subjects:** Fresno County history, city and county records. **Special Collections:** A.W. Peters glass negative plates

(833 showing the history of Fresno County); Paul Hutchinson glass negative plates (250 showing the history of Fowler); subject and portrait photographs (8000); Ben Walker file (250,000 newspaper clippings); M. Theo Kearney Collection. **Holdings:** 500 books; 800 bound periodical volumes; 400 pamphlets; 150 manuscript collections of individuals, families, and businesses; 2100 bound city and county records; 30,000 unbound city and county records. **Subscriptions:** 30 journals and other serials. **Services:** Photograph reproduction, copying; archives open to the public by appointment. **Computerized Information Services:** Internal database. **Publications:** Fresno Past & Present, quarterly. **Remarks:** FAX: (209)441-1372.

★6155★
Fresno County Free Library - Californiana Collection (Hist)
2420 Mariposa St. Phone: (209)488-3195
Fresno, CA 93721 John K. Kallenberg
Founded: 1910. **Subjects:** California. **Special Collections:** Fresno County voter registration rolls (120 years); California county census rolls (140 reels of microfilm). **Holdings:** 39,000 books; 12 reels of microfilm; 1200 photographs. **Subscriptions:** 4 journals and other serials. **Services:** Collection open to the public with restrictions. **Remarks:** FAX: (209)488-1971.

★6156★
Fresno County Free Library - Foreign Language Collection (Hum)
2420 Mariposa St. Phone: (209)488-3209
Fresno, CA 93721 John K. Kallenberg, Dir.
Founded: 1910. **Subjects:** Languages - Spanish, Japanese, Armenian. **Special Collections:** Spanish fiction collection (3000 books); Spanish nonfiction collection (3600 books); Japanese language collection (1600 books); Armenian fiction collection (200 books); copies of the United States Constitution in Simple English, Hmong, Cambodian, Vietnamese, Spanish, and Laotian. **Subscriptions:** 6 journals and other serials; 8 newspapers. **Services:** Copying; library open to the public. **Remarks:** FAX: (209)488-1971.

★6157★
Fresno County Free Library - Special Collections (Hist, Hum)
2420 Mariposa St. Phone: (209)488-3195
Fresno, CA 93721 John K. Kallenberg, Libn.
Founded: 1910. **Subjects:** Fresno County - local history, architecture; American Indians - Mono, Miwok, Yokut. **Special Collections:** William Saroyan Collection (1550 books, 432 periodicals, 4 linear feet of manuscripts, photographs); Leo Politi Collection; architectural photographs; Local History Collection (15 linear feet of oral history manuscripts, vertical files of ephemera, biographical sketches, broadsides, maps, pamphlets); Ta-Kwa-Teu-Nee-Ya-Y Collection (200 books); South East Asian Acculturation Collection (300 books); Nell Strother Mother Goose and Nursery Rhyme Collection (200 books, 1900 to present). **Holdings:** 122 bound periodical volumes; 15 linear feet of archival materials; 15,000 microfiche; Fresno newspapers on microfilm (1840 to present). **Subscriptions:** 4 journals and other serials; 5 newspapers. **Services:** Copying; library open to the public with restrictions on the Saroyan Collection. **Computerized Information Services:** VU/TEXT Information Services; internal database. Performs searches. Contact Person: Linda Sitterding, Local Hist.Libn. **Networks/Consortia:** Member of San Joaquin Valley Library System (SJVLS). **Publications:** Ta-Kwa-Teu-Nee-Ya-Y Bibliography; South East Asian Cultural Materials Bibliography; Nell Strother Mother Goose and Nursery Rhyme Collection Bibliography. **Special Indexes:** Historical Landmarks and Records Commission Index; Fresno papers index (1851 to present); Photograph Index; Oral History Index. **Remarks:** FAX: (209)488-1971.

★6158★
Fresno County Law Library (Law)
1100 Van Ness Ave., Rm. 600 Phone: (209)237-2227
Fresno, CA 93721 James G. Sherman, Dir.
Founded: 1891. **Staff:** Prof 2; Other 1. **Subjects:** Law, legal medicine. **Holdings:** 59,631 volumes. **Subscriptions:** 237 journals. **Services:** Copying; library open to the public for reference use only.

★6159★
Fresno County Office of Education - IMS-Library (Educ)
111 Van Ness Blvd. Phone: (209)265-3092
Fresno, CA 93727 Ellis Vance, IMS Dir.
Founded: 1945. **Staff:** Prof 3; Other 18. **Subjects:** Education, curriculum, children's literature. **Special Collections:** Curriculum guides for California schools (2700 volumes); Adult Basic Education/English as a Second Language collection; educational software collection. **Holdings:** 8500 professional books; 23,500 elementary books; 7 VF drawers of pamphlets; 4 drawers of microfiche; 346 bilingual books, kits, games; 325 affective education books and kits; 5500 videocassettes; 5000 16mm films; 11,000 nonprint materials; 2500 revolving publisher's review copies; 150 video discs. **Subscriptions:** 152 journals and other serials. **Services:** Interlibrary loan; copying; library open only to educators whose schools have a service contract with the IMS-Library; public may use curriculum guides, publishers' samples, State Department of Education materials. Maintains teachers' center for school teachers in Fresno County. **Networks/Consortia:** Member of Area Wide Library Network (AWLNET). **Special Catalogs:** Catalog of 16mm films and videocassettes; catalog of building level materials; catalogue of literature sets (circulating K-8 library sets). **Remarks:** FAX: (209)237-3525. Library is a textbook display center for California textbook adoption. **Staff:** Dr. Donald Gregory, AV Coord.; Ronda Stuart, Ref.Libn.

★6160★
Fresno Diocesan Library
Box 1668
Fresno, CA 93717
Founded: 1933. **Subjects:** Roman Catholicism, Californiana. **Special Collections:** Central California materials. **Holdings:** 20,000 books; 500 bound periodical volumes; 75 VF drawers of unbound material, microfilm, pictures, maps of Central California Catholic churches. **Remarks:** Library located at 1550 N. Fresno St., Fresno, CA 93707. Currently inactive.

★6161★
Fresno Genealogical Society - Library (Hist)
Box 1429
Fresno, CA 93716 Virginia Dill, Libn.
Founded: 1965. **Staff:** 5. **Subjects:** Genealogy. **Holdings:** 900 books; 500 bound periodical volumes; 25 unbound periodicals; 8 reels of microfilm. **Subscriptions:** 80 journals and other serials. **Services:** Library open to the public with restrictions. **Publications:** Ash Tree Echo, biennial; Jotted Line, monthly.

★6162★
Fresno Pacific College & Mennonite Brethren Biblical Seminary - Hiebert Library (Rel-Phil)
1717 S. Chestnut Ave. Phone: (209)453-2090
Fresno, CA 93702 Steven Brandt, Dir.
Founded: 1944. **Staff:** Prof 4; Other 1. **Subjects:** Religion, history. **Special Collections:** Center for Mennonite Brethren Studies (Mennonite Brethren history and archives; Mennonitica). **Holdings:** 137,583 bound volumes; 153,917 microforms. **Subscriptions:** 874 journals and other serials; 20 newspapers. **Services:** Interlibrary loan; copying; library open to the public. **Computerized Information Services:** BRS Information Technologies, OCLC.

★6163★
Sigmund Freud-Gesellschaft - Sigmund Freud Haus Bibliothek (Med)
Berggasse 19 Phone: 222 3199177
A-1090 Vienna, Austria Dr. Hans Lobner
Staff: 1. **Subjects:** Psychoanalysis; psychotherapy; history of psychoanalysis; Sigmund Freud - life and work; applied psychoanalysis. **Special Collections:** Early psychoanalytic writings (1300 volumes). **Holdings:** 8000 books; 1500 bound periodical volumes; 15,000 journal articles (offprints). **Subscriptions:** 45 journals and other serials. **Services:** Copying; library open to the public with restrictions. **Remarks:** FAX: 222 340279. **Staff:** Mag. Doris Fritsche.

Sigmund Freud Library
See: **Columbia University - Augustus C. Long Health Sciences Library** (4001)

Freund Law Library
See: **Washington University - School of Law** (20068)

Carol J. Frey Library
See: **Kentucky School for the Blind** (8663)

★6164★
Friars of the Atonement - Graymoor Friary Library (Rel-Phil)
Graymoor, Rte. 9 Phone: (914)424-3671
Garrison, NY 10524 Peter Taran, S.A., Dir.
Founded: 1952. **Staff:** Prof 2; Other 1. **Subjects:** Ecumenical theology, church history, ecclesiology. **Special Collections:** Archives of the Franciscan Friars of the Atonement (documents and books about the history of the Graymoor Friars). **Holdings:** 50,000 books; 140 bound periodical volumes; 450 reels of microfilm of Library of Church Unity periodicals. **Subscriptions:** 76 journals and other serials; 12 newspapers. **Services:** Interlibrary loan; copying; library open to the public. **Staff:** Mary Resi, Libn.

★6165★
Frick Art Reference Library (Art)
10 E. 71st St. Phone: (212)288-8700
New York, NY 10021 Helen Sanger, Libn.
Founded: 1920. **Staff:** Prof 9; Other 56. **Subjects:** Art. **Special Collections:** American and European painting, drawing, sculpture (books; photographs); illuminated manuscripts and enamels from the early Christian era to 1930. **Holdings:** 177,624 volumes; 64,354 sales catalogs; 421,490 study photographs. **Subscriptions:** 250 journals and other serials. **Services:** Copying; print orders can be filled from collection of 58,003 negatives with the permission of the owner of the original work of art; library open to graduate level students of history of art. **Automated Operations:** Computerized cataloging and acquisitions. **Publications:** The Story of the Frick Art Reference Library: The Early Years (1979) - for sale. **Remarks:** The Frick Art Reference Library is a division of, but not maintained by, The Frick Collection, 1 E. 70th St., New York, NY 10021. **Staff:** Marie C. Keith, Assoc.Libn.

Frick Collection
See: **Frick Art Reference Library** (6165)

★6166★
Frick Community Health Center - Joseph F. Bucci Health Sciences Library (Med)
S. Church St. Phone: (412)547-1352
Mount Pleasant, PA 15666 Rosemary C. Panichella, Libn.
Founded: 1980. **Staff:** Prof 1; Other 1. **Subjects:** Medicine, nursing, hospital administration, allied health sciences. **Holdings:** 640 books. **Subscriptions:** 109 journals and other serials. **Services:** Interlibrary loan; copying; library open to the public for reference use only. **Computerized Information Services:** MEDLARS. Performs searches on fee basis. **Networks/Consortia:** Member of National Network of Libraries of Medicine - Middle Atlantic Region, BHSL. **Publications:** The Next Chapter, semiannual - for internal distribution only. **Remarks:** FAX: (412)547-1266.

Henry Clay Frick Fine Arts Library
See: **University of Pittsburgh** (19214)

★6167★
Fried Frank Harris Shriver & Jacobson - Library (Law)
1001 Pennsylvania Ave., N.W., Suite 800 Phone: (202)639-7102
Washington, DC 20004-2505 G. Diane Sandford, Mgr., Lib.Serv.
Staff: Prof 3; Other 3. **Subjects:** Law - securities, banking, government contracts; international trade; business. **Holdings:** 35,000 volumes. **Subscriptions:** 165 journals and other serials. **Services:** Interlibrary loan; copying; library open to the public by appointment. **Computerized Information Services:** DIALOG Information Services, NEXIS, LEXIS, Dow Jones News/Retrieval, Dun & Bradstreet Business Credit Services, Spectrum Ownership Profiles Online, LEGI-SLATE, WESTLAW, VU/TEXT Information Services, DataTimes, Information America, SEC/EXPRESS; internal database. **Remarks:** FAX: (202)639-7003. Telex: 892406. **Staff:** Mari Ann Buckwalter, Asst.Libn.; Margot Gee, Leg.Libn.

★6168★
Fried Frank Harris Shriver & Jacobson - Library & Information Center (Law)
1 New York Plaza Phone: (212)820-8000
New York, NY 10004 Warren Gordon, Hd.Libn.
Staff: 15. **Subjects:** Law - securities, Anglo-American, real estate, corporate, tax. **Holdings:** 35,000 books; 10,000 bound periodical volumes; 200 microforms; 50 VF drawers of pamphlets. **Subscriptions:** 175 journals and other serials. **Services:** Interlibrary loan; library not open to the public. **Computerized Information Services:** Online systems. **Special Catalogs:** Catalog of office legal memoranda. **Remarks:** FAX: (212)747-1526. **Staff:** Dolores Canning, Asst.Libn.; Michael Sharrow, Tax Libn.

Henry B. Fried Library
See: **American Watchmakers Institute** (785)

Jonas S. Friedenwald Library
See: **Johns Hopkins Hospital - Wilmer Ophthalmological Institute** (8414)

Arthur Friedheim Library
See: **Johns Hopkins University** (8424)

Eric Friedheim Library
See: **National Press Club** (11253)

★6169★
Friends Committee on National Legislation - Legislative Library (Soc Sci)
245 2nd St., N.E. Phone: (202)547-6000
Washington, DC 20002 Allison Oldham, Coord.
Founded: 1943. **Staff:** 18. **Subjects:** Disarmament, basic human needs, world institutions, Middle East, American Indians. **Holdings:** 300 boxes of reports and congressional documents. **Subscriptions:** 50 journals and other serials. **Services:** Copying; library open to the public by appointment. **Remarks:** Archival materials housed in Swarthmore College - Friends Historical Library - Peace Collection.

★6170★
Friends of the Earth - Library (Env-Cons)
Apdo. Postal 1891
Cuenca, Ecuador Phone: 7 824621
Subjects: Environmental protection, pollution, environmental law. **Holdings:** 1000 volumes. **Computerized Information Services:** Internal database. **Remarks:** Telex: 48570. **Also Known As:** Tierra Viva.

★6171★
Friends of the Earth-Holland - Library (Env-Cons)
Damrak 26
Postbus 19199 Phone: 20 6206401
NL-1000 GD Amsterdam, Netherlands L. Taekema, Dir.
Founded: 1979. **Staff:** 2. **Subjects:** Environmental protection, alternatives to governmental policies. **Holdings:** 8000 volumes. **Subscriptions:** 150 journals and other serials; 3 newspapers. **Services:** Interlibrary loan; copying; SDI; library open to the public by appointment. **Computerized Information Services:** Internal databases. **Remarks:** FAX: 20 6275287.

Friends Free Library
See: **Germantown Friends Meeting** (6436)

★6172★
Friends of Historic Boonville - Archival Collection (Hist)
614 E. Morgan Phone: (816)882-7977
Boonville, MO 65233 Judy Shields, Adm.
Staff: 1. **Subjects:** Boonville and Cooper County - history and genealogy. **Special Collections:** Historic photographs; early land surveys and maps (15). **Holdings:** 125 books; 110 newspapers; letters; personal papers. **Services:** Copying; collection open to the public. **Remarks:** Collection housed in the Old Cooper County Jail and Sheriffs Residence.

★6173★
Friends of Historic Meridian - Historical Collection (Hist)
Box 155 Phone: (517)349-1993
Okemos, MI 48805 Elaine C. Davis, Pres.
Subjects: Local history and genealogy. **Holdings:** 5 cubic feet of census, tax, cemetery records; 600 photographs. **Subscriptions:** 4 journals and other serials. **Services:** Collection open to the public by appointment; answers mail enquiries.

Friends Historical Library
See: **Swarthmore College** (15902)

★6174★
Friends Hospital - Norman D. Weiner Professional Library (Med)
4641 Roosevelt Blvd. Phone: (215)831-4763
Philadelphia, PA 19124-2399 Donna M. Zoccola Soultoukis, Dir., Lib.Serv.
Founded: 1974. **Staff:** Prof 1. **Subjects:** Psychoanalysis, psychiatry, psychology, behavioral sciences, human life cycle, psychiatric nursing. **Holdings:** 5000 books; 5000 bound periodical volumes; VF drawers; 275 audiotapes, 75 videocassettes. **Subscriptions:** 105 journals and other serials. **Services:** Interlibrary loan; library not open to the public. **Computerized Information Services:** DIALOG Information Services, Lithium Information Center. **Networks/Consortia:** Member of National Network of Libraries of Medicine - Middle Atlantic Region. **Remarks:** FAX: (215)289-9260.

Friends House Library
See: **Society of Friends** (15320)

★6175★
Friends of the Third World Inc. - Whole World Books (Soc Sci)
611 W. Wayne St. Phone: (219)422-6821
Fort Wayne, IN 46802 Marian R. Waltz, Rsrc.Coord.
Staff: Prof 1; Other 2. **Subjects:** Hunger, population, international politics and economics, U.S. minorities, food and nutrition, international and national poverty issues, American lifestyles and the environment. **Special Collections:** Alternative periodicals and newsletters; research files on Third World Handicraft production (600). **Holdings:** 800 books; 2000 pamphlets and periodicals; 24 VF drawers. **Subscriptions:** 30 journals and other serials. **Services:** Copying; open to the public for reference use only; requests for information or referral are answered by mail. **Computerized Information Services:** Internal database; Dialcom Inc. (electronic mail service). **Publications:** Alternative Trading News, quarterly - for sale. **Remarks:** Telex: 4900005862. Electronic mail address(es): TCN 225 (Dialcom, Inc.); FOTW (PEACENET).

★6176★
Friends University - Edmund Stanley Library - Special Collections (Rel-Phil)
2100 University Ave. Phone: (316)261-5880
Wichita, KS 67213 Jonathan Sparks, Dir.
Founded: 1898. **Staff:** Prof 2; Other 5. **Special Collections:** Quaker heritage and work; Noble Cain Collection of Music and Memorabilia; Friends University; Mid-America Yearly Meeting of Friends Archives; Pennington Collection (Midwest history and culture). **Subscriptions:** 603 journals and other serials. **Services:** Interlibrary loan; copying; collections open to the public for reference use only. **Automated Operations:** Computerized public access catalog, acquisitions, and serials. **Computerized Information Services:** OCLC, DIALOG Information Services; CD-ROMs. Performs searches on fee basis. Contact Person: Kathy Gaynor, Asst.Dir/Pub.Serv., 261-5880. **Networks/Consortia:** Member of Kansas Library Network. **Remarks:** FAX: (316)263-1092. **Staff:** Elaine Maack, Cur., Quaker Coll.

★6177★
Friends of the Western Philatelic Library (Rec)
Box 2219 Phone: (408)245-9171
Sunnyvale, CA 94087 Stuart Leven, Pres.
Founded: 1968. **Staff:** 1. **Subjects:** Stamp collecting. **Holdings:** 2000 books; 3000 bound periodical volumes; 10 cabinets of pamphlets and files. **Subscriptions:** 150 journals and other serials. **Services:** Interlibrary loan; copying; library open to the public. **Automated Operations:** Computerized circulation. **Publications:** Monthly newsletter. **Remarks:** Housed in the Sunnyvale Public Library, 665 W. Olive, Sunnyvale, CA 94087.

Hollis Burke Frissell Library-Archives
See: **Tuskegee University** (16592)

★6178★
Frito-Lay, Inc. - Corporate Library (Sci-Engr)
7701 Legacy Dr. Phone: (214)353-4737
Plano, TX 75024 Suzanne M. Ogden, Mgr., Lib.Serv.
Founded: 1980. **Staff:** Prof 1; Other 1. **Subjects:** Engineering, computer science, food science, marketing. **Special Collections:** Vendor catalogs of required products (2500); Tax Looseleaf Services. **Holdings:** 2400 books; 150 phone directories and maps of plant sites; standards on microfilm for American Society for Testing and Materials (ASTM), American National Standards Institute (ANSI), American Society of Mechanical Engineers (ASME), Institute of Electrical and Electronics Engineers (IEEE), Underwriters Laboratories (UL). **Subscriptions:** 500 journals and other serials. **Services:** Interlibrary loan; copying; SDI; library open to other librarians. **Automated Operations:** Computerized public access catalog and serials. **Computerized Information Services:** DIALOG Information Services, Dun & Bradstreet Business Credit Services, Dow Jones News/Retrieval, Disclosure Incorporated, InvesText. **Publications:** Descriptive brochure of services; Corporate Library Policy Manual, both updated as needed. **Special Catalogs:** Catalog of vendor catalogs; catalog to processing manuals (online).

★6179★
Frito-Lay, Inc. - Research & Development - Research Library (Food-Bev)
Box 152231 Phone: (214)579-2271
Irving, TX 75015 Pat Arnold, Mgr., Tech.Info.
Founded: 1980. **Staff:** 1.5. **Subjects:** Food science, nutrition, agriculture, chemical engineering, electronics, management. **Special Collections:** Project files, research notebooks, sensory files. **Holdings:** 4000 books; 1000 bound periodical volumes; 5000 patents and documents; 100 AV programs. **Subscriptions:** 350 journals and other serials. **Services:** Interlibrary loan; copying. **Computerized Information Services:** DIALOG Information Services, Dow Jones News/Retrieval; DIALMAIL (electronic mail service). **Remarks:** Library located at 900 N. Loop 12, Irving TX 75061. Alternate telephone number(s): (214)579-2326. FAX: (214)579-2848. Electronic mail address(es): 15416 (DIALMAIL).

Fritz Engineering Laboratory Library
See: **Lehigh University** (9058)

John Fritz Collection
See: **Hugh Moore Historical Park and Museums - Canal Museum - Research Library/Archives** (10711)

★6180★
Fritzsche, Dodge and Olcott - Research Library
76 Ninth Ave.
New York, NY 10011
Defunct. Merged with Givaudan Corporation to form Givaudan-Roure U.S.A.

Paul Fritzsche Library
See: **Johnson & Wales College** (8461)

Morris Fromkin Memorial Collection
See: **University of Wisconsin--Milwaukee** (19642)

Alfred Fromm Rare Wine Books Library
See: **Seagram Museum - Library** (14981)

Front de l'Independence
See: **Musee National de la Resistance** (10879)

★6181★
Frontenac County Board of Education - James F. Tennant Teachers' Centre (Educ)
164 Van Order Dr. Phone: (613)546-7446
Kingston, ON, Canada K7M 1C1 Joan E. Medd, Chf. Libn.
Founded: 1970. **Staff:** Prof 2; Other 7. **Subjects:** Teacher resources, curriculum support, video and film media. **Holdings:** 30,000 books; 1000 documents; 100 16mm films; 1523 videotapes; 200 software programs; 500 kits; reports. **Subscriptions:** 51 journals and other serials. **Services:** Interlibrary loan; copying; Preview library; AV production facilities; laminating; dubbing; AV and computer repair; center open to the public with restrictions. **Computerized Information Services:** Internal database. **Special Catalogs:** Media catalog (printout). **Remarks:** FAX: (613)544-6804. **Staff:** Sharon Wholgemut, Ctr.Coord.

★6182★
Frontier Community College - Learning Resource Center - Special Collections (Med)
2 Frontier Dr. Phone: (618)842-3711
Fairfield, IL 62837 Ted Davis, Dir. of LRC
Founded: 1978. **Staff:** Prof 1; Other 1. **Subjects:** Nursing. **Holdings:** 8000 books; 20,000 microfiche; 6 reels of microfilm. **Subscriptions:** 125 journals and other serials; 12 newspapers. **Services:** Interlibrary loan; copying; library open to the public. **Automated Operations:** LS/2. **Remarks:** FAX: (618)842-3711, ext. 4496.

★6183★
Frontier Gateway Museum - Library (Hist)
Belle Prairie Frontage Rd.
Box 1181 Phone: (406)365-8168
Glendive, MT 59330 Louise Cross, Cur.
Subjects: Homesteading in Montana, Indians of eastern Montana, prehistoric fossils, ranching, rural education, early businesses. **Special Collections:** Senator George McCone collection (40 items); M.E. Sutton Memorial Indian display (156 items); fossil collection. **Holdings:** 430 books; 290 unbound research items; 60 maps; 7 VF drawers of pictures; 14 VF drawers of clippings. **Services:** Interlibrary loan (limited); library open to the public from mid-May to mid-September only.

Frost Entomological Museum
See: **Pennsylvania State University** (12905)

★6184★
Frost & Jacobs - Library (Law)
2500 Central Trust Center
201 E. 5th St. Phone: (513)651-6810
Cincinnati, OH 45202 Yvonne M. Davis, Law Libn.
Staff: Prof 1; Other 2. **Subjects:** Law. **Special Collections:** Intellectual property. **Holdings:** 25,500 books; 800 bound periodical volumes; 15,000 microfiche. **Subscriptions:** 250 journals and other serials; 8 newspapers. **Services:** Library not open to the public. **Automated Operations:** Computerized public access catalog, cataloging, and serials. **Computerized Information Services:** LEXIS, NEXIS, DIALOG Information Services, Hannah Information Systems, UCLID, DataTimes, EPIC, PRISM, CITE. **Networks/Consortia:** Member of OHIONET. **Remarks:** FAX: (513)651-6981.

Robert Frost Collection
See: **Plymouth State College** (13154)

Robert Frost Library
See: **New York University** (11723)

★6185★
Frostburg State University - Lewis J. Ort Library (Educ)
Frostburg, MD 21532 Phone: (301)689-4395
David Gillespie, Dir.
Founded: 1902. **Staff:** Prof 12; Other 19. **Subjects:** Biology, wildlife management, business, teacher education, liberal arts. **Special Collections:** Depository for selected U.S. Government documents, Appalachian Regional Commission, and U.S. Defense Mapping Agency, Topographic Center (108,939 government documents). **Holdings:** 182,915 books; 26,867 bound periodical volumes; 31,738 AV programs; 39,694 microforms. **Subscriptions:** 1287 journals; 43 newspapers. **Services:** Interlibrary loan; copying; library open to the public. **Automated Operations:** Computerized cataloging and acquisitions. **Computerized Information Services:** OCLC, WILSONDISC, DIALOG Information Services, ACADEMIC INDEX, Grolier Encyclopedia. Performs searches on fee basis. Contact Person: Pam Williams, Hd.Ref., 689-4887. **Networks/Consortia:** Member of Pittsburgh Regional Library Center (PRLC), Colorado Alliance of Research Libraries (CARL). **Publications:** Handbooks; class bibliographies; subject bibliographies. **Remarks:** FAX: (301)689-4737. **Staff:** P. June Ketterman; Eleanor Messman-Mandicott; LaVern Pitman; Mary Jo Price; Sarah Sheehan; Charlie Spencer Lackey; Dorothy Van Scoy; Patricia Ward; Pamela Williams; Patricia Wilson; Larry Glotfelty.

★6186★
Fruehauf Corporation - Engineering Library (Trans)
26999 Central Park Blvd. Phone: (313)267-1000
Southfield, MI 48076-4178 Dave Barnowski, Mgr.
Subjects: Trailers, mechanical engineering, metallurgy, containers, freight transportation, welding. **Holdings:** 600 books; 1000 manufacturers' catalogs; 1200 technical reports; 500 internal projects and reports. **Formerly:** Located in Detroit, MI.

Fruehauf Corporation - Kelsey-Hayes Company
See: **Kelsey-Hayes Company - Research & Development Center Library** (8609)

★6187★
Fruitlands Museums - Library (Hist)
102 Prospect Hill Rd. Phone: (508)456-3924
Harvard, MA 01451 Maggie Stier, Cur.
Founded: 1914. **Staff:** 1. **Subjects:** American Indians, 19th century American paintings, Transcendentalist history, Shaker history. **Special Collections:** Shaker and Transcendentalist manuscripts. **Holdings:** 5000 books, bound periodical volumes, and manuscripts; 200 unbound reports. **Subscriptions:** 25 journals and other serials. **Services:** Library open to the public to qualified scholars.

★6188★
Fry Consultants Incorporated - Library (Bus-Fin)
1 Park Place, Suite 450
1900 Emery St., N.W. Phone: (404)352-2293
Atlanta, GA 30318 Lana S. Bueno, Bus.Libn.
Founded: 1942. **Staff:** Prof 3. **Subjects:** Management consulting, marketing, executive search, general business reference, industrial marketing, international marketing. **Special Collections:** Business Environment Risk Intelligence (BERI). **Holdings:** 1000 books; 500 bound periodical volumes; articles, speeches, and books on management consultancy; 1000 client reports, 1942 to present. **Subscriptions:** 25 journals and other serials; 5 newspapers. **Services:** Interlibrary loan; copying; center open to clients and potential clients. **Computerized Information Services:** DIALOG Information Services. Performs searches on fee basis. **Publications:** List of publications - available on request. **Remarks:** FAX: (404)352-2299. Telex: 4611041 COMTEL ATL. **Formerly:** Fry Consultants Incorporated - MacFarlane & Company, Inc. - Management Centre, Inc. **Staff:** Judy Cone, Libn.

Fry Jazz Archives
See: **West Virginia University - College of Creative Arts - Music Library** (20220)

★6189★
Charles and Emma Frye Art Museum - Library (Art)
Box 3005 Phone: (206)622-9250
Seattle, WA 98114 Mrs. W.S. Greathouse, Pres.
Subjects: European and American art of late 19th century and 20th century. **Holdings:** Figures not available. **Services:** Library not open to the public. **Remarks:** FAX: (206)223-1707.

FTC
See: **U.S. Federal Trade Commission** (17495)

Jacob D. Fuchsberg Law Center - Touro Law Center Library
See: **Touro College** (16433)

Fudger Medical Library
See: **Toronto General Hospital** (16412)

★6190★
Fugro-McClelland (USA) Inc. - Corporate Library (Sci-Engr)
6100 Hillcroft
Box 740010 Phone: (713)778-5500
Houston, TX 77274 Jane Vovk, Libn.
Founded: 1966. **Staff:** Prof 1. **Subjects:** Geotechnical engineering, geology, marine geotechnology, marine geophysics, civil engineering, marketing, management, waste management. **Holdings:** 7000 books; 500 bound periodical volumes; 20,000 company reports, 1946-1988, in 900 volumes; 3000 technical documents; 2000 issues of unbound serials; 250 microfilm cartridges; 1500 aerial photographs; 500 maps; microfiche. **Subscriptions:** 70 journals and other serials. **Services:** Interlibrary loan; copying; library open to the public by appointment with permission of librarian. **Automated Operations:** Computerized cataloging and ILL. **Computerized Information Services:** OCLC, DIALOG Information Services; MEI INDEX (internal database). **Networks/Consortia:** Member of AMIGOS Bibliographic Council, Inc. **Publications:** New in the Library, monthly - for internal distribution only. **Special Catalogs:** List of Holdings (in microform). **Remarks:** Library serves 11 company divisions and subsidiaries in the U.S., Canada, Europe, Saudi Arabia, and Southeast Asia. FAX: (713)778-5518.

★6191★
Fujian Institute of Oceanology - Library (Biol Sci)
34 Haishan Rd.
Dongdu
Xiamen 361012, Fujian, People's Republic of China Phone: 623168
Mr. Jiang Zhao-qi, Assoc.Res.Libn.
Founded: 1980. **Staff:** 7. **Subjects:** Marine sciences - biology, chemistry, geology, hydrometerology (Taiwan Strait and adjacent waters). **Holdings:** 9500 books; 3000 bound periodical volumes. **Subscriptions:** 120 journals and other serials; 24 newspapers. **Services:** Interlibrary loan; copying; library open to the public. **Publications:** Works of Fujian Institute of Oceanology.

★6192★
Fukuoka American Center - USIS Library (Educ)
1-3-36 Tenjin
Chuo-ku
Fukuoka 810, Japan Phone: 92 7616663
Holdings: 3681 books; 90 bound periodical volumes; microfiche; audio recordings; video recordings. **Services:** Copying; library open to the public with restrictions. **Remarks:** FAX: 92 7210109. Maintained or supported by the U.S. Information Agency. Focus is on materials that will assist peoples outside the United States to learn about the United States, its people, history, culture, political processes, and social milieux.

★6193★
Fukushima Medical College - Library (Med)
1
Hikarigaoka Phone: 245 482111
Fukushima 960-12, Japan Hideo Kochi
Founded: 1944. **Staff:** Prof 6; Other 4. **Subjects:** Medical sciences. **Holdings:** 130,170 books and bound periodical volumes. **Subscriptions:** 1810 journals and other serials; 6 newspapers. **Services:** Interlibrary loan; copying; SDI; library open to the public with restrictions. **Computerized Information Services:** DIALOG Information Services, JOIS. Contact Person: Hiroshi Sakuma, Libn. **Remarks:** FAX: 245 482535. Telex: 245 882234. **Also Known As:** Fukushima Kenritsu Ika Daigaku-Fuzoku Toshokan.

★6194★
Fulbright & Jaworski - Law Library (Law)
666 Fifth Ave., 32nd Fl. Phone: (212)318-3000
New York, NY 10103 Gayle Lynn-Nelson, Lib.Mgr.
Staff: Prof 2; Other 3. **Subjects:** Law, securities, corporate law. **Holdings:** 20,000 books; 1000 bound periodical volumes; 4 drawers of microfiche; 36 reels of microfilm. **Subscriptions:** 80 journals and other serials; 10 newspapers. **Services:** Interlibrary loan; copying; library open to SLA members by appointment. **Computerized Information Services:** DIALOG Information Services, LEXIS, NEXIS, WESTLAW, Dow Jones News/Retrieval, Dun & Bradstreet Business Credit Services, VU/TEXT Information Services, Information America, DataTimes, NewsNet, Inc., RLIN. Performs searches on fee basis. **Special Indexes:** Prospectus and tender offer file (card). **Remarks:** FAX: (212)752-5958. **Staff:** Paula Zieselman, Asst.Libn.; Glenn Li, ILL Coord.

★6195★
Fulbright & Jaworski - Library (Law)
1301 McKinney, Suite 5100 Phone: (713)651-5151
Houston, TX 77010-3095 Jane D. Holland, Dir. of Lib.Serv.
Founded: 1919. **Staff:** Prof 2; Other 8. **Subjects:** Law. **Holdings:** 50,000 volumes. **Subscriptions:** 1500 journals and other serials; 15 newspapers. **Services:** Interlibrary loan; copying; library open to other attorneys by invitation. **Computerized Information Services:** LEXIS, WESTLAW, DIALOG Information Services, Information America, DataTimes, VU/TEXT Information Services. **Staff:** Violanda Fabugais, Asst.Dir.

Helene Fuld Audio-Visual Center
See: **Lawrence Memorial Hospital of Medford** (9010)

Helene Fuld Learning Resource Center
See: **St. Joseph's Hospital** (14401)

★6196★
Helene Fuld Medical Center - Health Sciences Library (Med)
750 Brunswick Ave. Phone: (609)394-6065
Trenton, NJ 08638 Mary Anne Toner, Lib.Dir.
Staff: Prof 2; Other 1. **Subjects:** Medicine, nursing, allied health sciences. **Holdings:** 3500 books; 2800 bound periodical volumes; 750 reels of microfilm of journals; 350 videotapes; 5000 slides; 850 audiocassettes. **Subscriptions:** 245 journals and other serials. **Services:** Interlibrary loan; copying; SDI; library open to the public for reference use only. **Computerized Information Services:** MEDLARS, DIALOG Information Services, NLM. **Networks/Consortia:** Member of Health Sciences Library Association of New Jersey (HSLANJ), Central Jersey Health Science Libraries Association (CJHSLA), BHSL. **Publications:** HFMC Quarterly Acquisitions. **Remarks:** FAX: (609)394-3985. **Staff:** Jill Cook, Asst.Libn.

Helene Fuld Memorial Learning Resource Center
See: **Bryan Memorial Hospital - School of Nursing - Helene Fuld Memorial Learning Resource Center** (2298)

★6197★
Helene Fuld School of Nursing in Camden County - Library (Med)
Mt. Ephraim & Atlantic Aves. Phone: (609)342-4599
Camden, NJ 08104 David A. Cohen, Libn.
Staff: Prof 1; Other 1.5. **Subjects:** Nursing. **Special Collections:** Archives. **Holdings:** 2527 books; 500 bound periodical volumes; microfiche. **Subscriptions:** 117 journals and other serials. **Services:** Interlibrary loan; copying; library open to the public by appointment. **Automated Operations:** Computerized public access catalog, cataloging, and serials. **Computerized Information Services:** OCLC, BRS Information Technologies; CD-ROM (CINAHL). **Networks/Consortia:** Member of Southwest New Jersey Consortium for Health Information Services. **Special Catalogs:** Impact catalog (online). **Remarks:** FAX: (609)342-4349.

George F. Fuller Library
See: **Worcester Foundation for Experimental Biology** (20594)

★6198★
Fuller & Henry - Library (Law)
One Seagate, 17th Fl.
Box 2088 Phone: (419)247-2891
Toledo, OH 43603 Melvia A. Scott, Libn.
Founded: 1895. **Staff:** Prof 1; Other 1. **Subjects:** Law. **Holdings:** 23,000 volumes; loose-leaf services; periodicals; government reports. **Subscriptions:** 290 journals and other serials; 10 newspapers. **Services:** Library not open to the public. **Computerized Information Services:** LEXIS, NEXIS, WESTLAW. **Publications:** Internal newsletter.

★6199★
Fuller Museum of Art - Library
Oak St. on Upper Porters Pond
Brockton, MA 02401
Subjects: American art, art history and techniques. **Holdings:** 1800 books; 8 VF drawers of annual reports, pamphlets, clippings, artist files. **Remarks:** Currently inactive.

P.T. Fuller Staff Library
See: **Dorothea Dix Hospital** (4925)

Ralph Fuller Medical Library
See: **St. Mary's Hospital & Health Center** (14528)

★6200★
Fuller Theological Seminary - McAlister Library (Rel-Phil)
135 N. Oakland Ave. Phone: (818)584-5218
Pasadena, CA 91182 John Dickason, Dir.
Founded: 1948. **Staff:** Prof 4; Other 16. **Subjects:** Biblical studies, theology, religion, missiology, philosophy, psychology. **Holdings:** 183,000 volumes. **Subscriptions:** 826 journals and other serials. **Services:** Interlibrary loan; copying; library open to the public with borrowing restricted to students, faculty, and alumni. **Computerized Information Services:** OCLC, BRS Information Technologies, DIALOG Information Services, OCLC EPIC, RLIN; CD-ROM (PsycLIT). **Staff:** E. Yeung, Tech.Serv.; Shien-yu Hwang, Ref.; Olive Brown, Ref.; Anita Hutches, Circ.Libn.; Steve Magnuson, Per.Libn.; David Holifield, ILL.

★6201★
Fullerton Arboretum - Heritage House Library - Victoriana/Local History Collection (Hist)
California State University, Fullerton Phone: (714)773-3579
Fullerton, CA 92634 Celia Kutcher, Hd.Libn.
Founded: 1976. **Subjects:** Victoriana, local history. **Holdings:** 200 books, bound periodical volumes, and pamphlets. **Subscriptions:** 2 journals and other serials. **Services:** Copying; collection open to authorized researchers by appointment.

★6202★
Fullerton Arboretum - Library - Horticulture/Botany Collection (Biol Sci)
University of California, Fullerton Phone: (714)773-3579
Fullerton, CA 92634 Celia Kutcher, Hd.Libn.
Founded: 1977. **Subjects:** Horticulture, botany, natural history, allied topics. **Special Collections:** Seed catalogs, 1880-1920 (1227); pre-1930 horticulture and botany books (100 titles). **Holdings:** 2000 books, bound periodical volumes, and pamphlets. **Subscriptions:** 12 journals and other serials. **Services:** Copying; collection open to the public with restrictions on a limited schedule.

★6203★
Fullerton College - William T. Boyce Library (Hist)
321 E. Chapman Ave. Phone: (714)992-7061
Fullerton, CA 92634 John L. Ayala, Dean, Lrng.Rscrs.
Founded: 1913. **Staff:** Prof 7; Other 11.5. **Subjects:** History of Fullerton College and the Fullerton community, 1900 to present. **Special Collections:** Archives of Fullerton College; Fullerton College Oral History Program; Orange County history; United States Geographic Survey Topographical maps of California. **Holdings:** 95,622 books; 569 dissertations; 83,495 microforms; 19,303 pamphlets; 4332 maps; 145 linear feet of papers, oral history tapes, transcripts; 3125 photographs; 1135 slides. **Subscriptions:** 505 journals and other serials; 9 newspapers. **Services:** Interlibrary loan; copying; library open to the public. **Automated Operations:** Computerized public access catalog, cataloging, and circulation. **Computerized Information Services:** DIALOG Information Services; InfoTrac. **Networks/Consortia:** Member of OCLC Pacific Network. **Staff:** Godelieve Eggers, Acq./Ref.Libn.; Jacqueline Boll, Circ./Ref.Libn.; Michele Fitzsimmons, Ref.Libn.; Jacquelyn R. Malone, Bibliog.Instr./Ref.Libn.; Elvon L. Pearson, Lib.Tech.Prog.Coord.; Sandra Smith, Cat.Libn.

★6204★
Fulton County - Law Library (Law)
709 Courthouse
136 Pryor St., S.W. Phone: (404)730-4544
Atlanta, GA 30303 Sandra Howell, Law Libn.
Founded: 1913. **Staff:** Prof 1; Other 1. **Subjects:** Law - local, county, state, federal. **Holdings:** 18,000 volumes. **Services:** Copying; library open to the public. **Computerized Information Services:** LEXIS, WESTLAW. **Remarks:** FAX: (404)730-4565.

★6205★
Fulton County Historical and Genealogical Society - Parlin-Ingersoll Library (Hist)
45 N. Park Dr. Phone: (309)647-0771
Canton, IL 61520 Dr. Marjorie R. Bordner, Pres.
Founded: 1967. **Subjects:** Fulton County history, genealogy, and literature. **Holdings:** 600 books; cemetery inscriptions; marriage records; scrapbooks; local newspapers on microfilm. **Subscriptions:** 10 journals and other serials; 4 newspapers. **Services:** Copying; library open to the public.

★6206★
Fulton County Historical Society - Library (Hist)
R. 3
Box 89 Phone: (219)223-4436
Rochester, IN 46975 Shirley Willard, Pres.
Founded: 1963. **Staff:** 10. **Subjects:** Local history and genealogy, Elmo Lincoln (first movie Tarzan), Potawatomi Indians. **Special Collections:** Trail of Death removal of Potawatomi Indians from Indiana to Kansas in 1838; 40 volumes of newspapers, 1862-1921. **Holdings:** 4000 books; 15 file cabinets of clippings; 5 file cabinets of documents; 4 films; 25 rooms of archival materials. **Subscriptions:** 66 journals and other serials. **Services:** Copying; library open to the public for reference use only. **Publications:** Fulton County Historical Society Quarterly, 1964-1990 - to members; Fulton County Folks (volumes 1 and 2); Fulton County Images (magazine), annual. **Special Catalogs:** Card file of objects, books, donors; catalog of accession sheets.

★6207★
Fulton County Historical Society - Library (Hist)
Box 115 Phone: (717)485-3207
McConnellsburg, PA 17233 Hazel Harr, Libn.
Founded: 1976. **Subjects:** Local history and genealogy. **Special Collections:** Fulton Republican newspaper, 1865-1900; Fulton Democrat newspaper, 1866-1983; old school photographs; local family histories; county histories; church records. **Holdings:** 300 books; microfilm collection; 100 volumes of Pennsylvania Archives. **Services:** Copying; library open to the public with restrictions. **Special Indexes:** Cemetery file (card); Index to 1850 Fulton County census (book).

★6208★
Fulton County Law Library (Law)
Court House Phone: (717)485-4212
McConnellsburg, PA 17233 Travis L. Kendell, Lib.Dir.
Subjects: Law. **Remarks:** No further information was supplied by respondent.

★6209★
Fulton County Law Library Association - Law Library (Law)
Court House
210 S. Fulton Phone: (419)337-9260
Wauseon, OH 43567 Lynne E. Long, Libn.
Staff: Prof 1; Other 1. **Subjects:** Law. **Holdings:** 10,000 volumes; 50 audio cassettes. **Subscriptions:** 2 newspapers. **Services:** Copying; library open to the public with restrictions. **Computerized Information Services:** WESTLAW. Performs searches on fee basis.

Fulton-Hayden Memorial Library
See: **Amerind Foundation, Inc. - Fulton-Hayden Memorial Library** (800)

★6210★
Fulton State Hospital - Professional Library (Med)
600 E. 5th St., No. 102 Phone: (314)592-2262
Fulton, MO 65251 Berneice Deloney, Libn.
Staff: Prof 1; Other 1. **Subjects:** Psychiatry, pyschotherapy, medicine, nursing, social work, psychology. **Holdings:** 700 books; 20 bound periodical volumes. **Subscriptions:** 60 journals and other serials. **Services:** Interlibrary loan (limited); copying; SDI; library open to the public for reference use only. **Computerized Information Services:** Online systems (through Missouri Institute of Psychiatry Library).

★6211★
Fund for Modern Courts - Library (Law)
36 W. 44th St., Rm. 310 Phone: (212)575-1577
New York, NY 10036 Dr. M.L. Henry, Jr., Exec.Dir.
Staff: 1. **Subjects:** Judicial selection, court unification and administration, criminal justice, citizen participation in New York State. **Special Collections:** Court Monitoring; Citizen's Court Projects Manual; Family & Criminal Court Handbook. **Holdings:** 1000 volumes; 8 VF drawers of clippings and newsletters. **Services:** Interlibrary loan; library open to the public with restrictions. **Special Indexes:** Clipping index. **Remarks:** FAX: (212)869-1133.

★6212★
Fundacao Casa de Rui Barbosa - Biblioteca (Area-Ethnic, Law, Hum)
Rua Sao Clemente, 134 Phone: 21 2861297
22260 Rio de Janeiro, RJ, Brazil Maria Amelia Bianchini, Libn.
Founded: 1930. **Staff:** 8. **Subjects:** History of Brazil, law, literature, philology. **Special Collections:** Cordel collection (popular literature originating in northeast Brazil; 6000 pamphlets). **Holdings:** 60,000 books; 2200 periodical titles. **Subscriptions:** 8 journals and other serials. **Services:** Interlibrary loan; copying; library open to the public for reference use only. **Computerized Information Services:** Internal database. **Publications:** Bibliographies. **Remarks:** FAX: 21 5371114. Telex: 2137232. **Staff:** Beatriz Amaral de Salles Coelho, Hd.Libn.

Fundacao Getulio Vargas - Biblioteca Central
See: **Getulio Vargas Foundation - Library** (19781)

★6213★
Fundacao Instituto Brasileiro de Geografia e Estatistica - Departamento de Documentacao e Biblioteca (Geog-Map, Soc Sci)
Rua General Canabarro, 666 Phone: 21 2207243
20271 Rio de Janeiro, RJ, Brazil Maria Gomes, Hd.Libn.
Founded: 1977. **Staff:** 75. **Subjects:** Statistics, geography, economics, demography, cartography, natural resources. **Special Collections:** Rare books (early censuses); atlases; Brasiliana. **Holdings:** 43,629 books; 2550 bound periodical volumes; 9334 microfiche; 97 reels of microfilm. **Subscriptions:** 241 journals and other serials. **Services:** Interlibrary loan; copying; library open to the public. **Computerized Information Services:** Internal database. Performs searches free of charge. **Publications:** Publicacoes editadas pelo IBGE (Volume 1: Periodicals; Volume 2: Monographs); Boletim Bibliografico; Lista de Novas Aquisicoes; Sumarios de Periodicos Correntes; Serie Obras de Referencia da Biblioteca do IBGE; Divisao Territorial do Brasil; Periodicos Correntes na Biblioteca Central do IBGE; Mapas e Outros Materiais Cartograficos na Biblioteca Central do IBGE. v.1: Editados Pelo IBGE; Levantamentos e Pesquisas em Andamento no IBGE; Bibliographis das Biliografias Existenies na Biblioteca do IBGE; Fontes de Informcao em Geodesia, Cartografia e Sensoriamento Remoto; Publicacoes Editadas Pelo IBGE; Documentacao Censitaria Existente na Biblioteca Central do IBGE, 1851-1980; Obras Raras da Biblioteca do IBGE Bibliografia Brasileira de Geografia. **Special Catalogs:** Catalogo do IBGE 1986, 2nd edition; Catalogo de Publicacoes do IBGE. **Special Indexes:** Cumulated Index of Revista Brasileira de Estatistica, 1940-1979; Index Herbariorum Brasiliensium; Cumulated Index of Revista Brasileira de Estatistica, 1980-1990; Cumulated Index of Revista Brasileira de Geografia, 1939 -1983. **Remarks:** FAX: 21 2289575. Telex: 21 39 128. **Staff:** Ana Maria Raeder Ramos, Libn.; Antonio Silva Rego Filho, Libn.; Clea Nogueira Addor, Libn.; Debora Moscoso Pereira, Libn.; Edna Maria desa Moraes, Libn.; Elza Tristao Ferreira, Libn.; Isis Soares da Silva, Libn.; Joao Luiz Cazarotto Pereira, Libn.; Maria Celia Dos Santos B. Maroun, Libn.; Maria das Gracas Bueno Brandao, Libn.; Maria de Fatima Marques de Matos, Libn.; Maria de Lourdes T. Pacheco Neves, Libn.; Maria de Nazare Ferreira Pingarilho, Libn.; Maria Marlene de Oliveira, Libn.; Regina de Almedia Sa, Libn.; Regina Maria Fucci, Libn.; Sonia Maria Rezende Cardoso, Libn.; Sonia Regina Allevato, Libn.; Icleia Thiesen Magalhaes Costa, Libn.

★6214★
Fundacao Universidade de Brasilia - Biblioteca Central (Educ, Soc Sci, Med)
Campus Universitario
Asa Norte
C.P. 15-2951 Phone: 61 2742412
70910 Brasilia, DF, Brazil Murilo Bastos da Cunha, Dir.
Subjects: Mathematics, education, economics, social sciences, medicine, literature. **Special Collections:** Rare books (6000); classical studies (5000 volumes). **Holdings:** 513,775 books; 13,400 microforms; 275 AV programs; 5 rare manuscripts. **Subscriptions:** 7080 journals and other serials. **Services:** Interlibrary loan; copying; library open to the public with restrictions. **Computerized Information Services:** DIALOG Information Services, Questel, STN International, BIREME (Regional Library of Medicine), CIN/CNEN (Nuclear Information Center/Natl. Commission on Nuclear Energy), PRODASEN, IBICT (Institute of Scientific and Technological Information), IBGE (Natl. Institute of Geography and Statistics). **Remarks:** Telex: 61 1083.

Fundacion Lisandro Alvarado - Biblioteca Dr. Antonio Requena
See: **Lisandro Alvarado Foundation - Biblioteca Dr. Antonio Requena** (435)

★6215★
Fundacion Miguel Lillo - Centro de Informacion Geo-Biologica, NOA (Biol Sci)
Miguel Lillo, 251
4000 San Miguel de Tucuman, Argentina Prof. Natalia Schechaj, Dir.
Founded: 1931. **Staff:** Prof 3; Other 8. **Subjects:** Botany, geology, zoology. **Special Collections:** A. Humboldt and A. Bonpland "Voyage aux Regions Equinoxiales". **Holdings:** 130,000 volumes. **Subscriptions:** 400 journals and other serials. **Services:** Interlibrary loan; copying; center open to the public for reference use only. **Publications:** Lilloa; Aeta Zoologica Lilloana; Aeta Geologica Lilloana; Opera Lilloana; miscelanae; Serie Conservacion de Naturalija. **Special Catalogs:** Publicaciones Periodicas Biblioteca Fundacion Miguel Lillo. **Remarks:** Maintained by Argentina - Ministry of Education and Justice. **Also Known As:** Miguel Lillo Foundation. **Staff:** Herminia A. Caro de Prieto; Maria Angela Prieto de Basco; Rosalina Corroto.

Fundamental Constants Data Center
See: **U.S. Natl. Institute of Standards and Technology** (17618)

★6216★
Funding Information Center of Texas, Inc. (Bus-Fin)
507 Brooklyn Phone: (512)227-4333
San Antonio, TX 78215 Romelia Escamilla, Exec.Dir.
Founded: 1974. **Staff:** Prof 9. **Subjects:** Foundations, grantsmanship, federal and corporate funding, nonprofit management and fundraising. **Holdings:** 1300 volumes; 95 directories; 13,000 microfiche; 8 VF drawers of clippings and reports. **Subscriptions:** 63 journals and other serials; 6 newspapers. **Services:** Copying; center open to the public. **Computerized Information Services:** DIALOG Information Services. **Publications:** Directory of Texas Foundations; Texas Connection (digest newsletter); Grant Profile; Trustee Listings. **Special Catalogs:** Tax returns of 1900 Texas Foundations, 1973 to present. **Remarks:** FAX: (512)225-1961. **Staff:** Jan Travis.

Fuqua International Communications Center
See: **Hampden-Sydney College** (6878)

★6217★
Furman University Library - Special Collections (Hist)
Greenville, SC 29613 Phone: (803)294-2194
Lisa Pruitt, Cur.
Founded: 1826. **Staff:** Prof 1; Other 1. **Subjects:** South Carolina Baptist history. **Special Collections:** Furman University Collection (150 books; 325 theses and projects); Furman archives; Rare Books (1500); Baptist Historical Collection (2500 books; 150,000 pages on microfilm; 12,000 manuscripts). **Holdings:** 3500 books; 500 bound periodical volumes; 12,000 manuscripts; 500 linear feet of archives; 600 reels of microfilm. **Subscriptions:** 12 journals and other serials; 2 newspapers. **Services:** Interlibrary loan of microfilm; collections open to the public for reference use only. **Computerized Information Services:** BITNET (electronic mail service). **Publications:** Journal of South Carolina Baptist Historical Society, annual - to members and by subscription. **Remarks:** FAX: (803)294-3004. Electronic mail address(es): LPRUITT@FRMNVAX1 (BITNET).

★6218★
Furnas County Law Library (Law)
Courthouse Phone: (308)268-4015
Beaver City, NE 68926 Judy Beins
Founded: 1973. **Subjects:** State statutes. **Holdings:** 300 books; reports. **Services:** Library open to the public for reference use only.

Horace Howard Furness Memorial Library
See: **University of Pennsylvania** (19184)

★6219★
Furniture Library Association - Library (Art)
1009 N. Main St. Phone: (919)883-4011
High Point, NC 27262 Carl Vuncannon, Cur.
Founded: 1970. **Staff:** Prof 3. **Subjects:** Early architecture; design - interior, furniture, fabric; furniture styles, 1600 to present. **Special Collections:** Original complete volumes of Chippendale, Hepplewhite, Sheraton, and other 18th century designers (unique to this library). **Holdings:** 7000 books; bound periodical volumes, including over 100 years of furniture catalogs; Furniture World; trade journals. **Subscriptions:** 10 journals and other serials. **Services:** Photographing; library open to the public. **Remarks:** FAX: (919)883-6579. **Formerly:** Its Bernice Bienenstock Furniture Library. **Staff:** Melva Teague, Libn.; Karla Webb.

Furschungszentrum Juelich
See: **Germany - Juelich Research Center** (6449)

★6220★
Future Aviation Professionals of America - Information Center (Trans)
4959 Massachusetts Blvd. Phone: (404)997-8097
Atlanta, GA 30337 W. Louis Smith, Pres.
Founded: 1975. **Staff:** 40. **Subjects:** Professional pilot, maintenance, and flight attendant careers. **Special Collections:** Airline limited edition prints by artist Doug Nelson. **Holdings:** 120 volumes. **Subscriptions:** 51 journals and other serials. **Services:** Personal career counseling to pilot members; statistics provided to airline industry; employment information for professional air crews and database job assistance for air crew applicants; computerized selection of pilot applicants supplied to airlines, commuter lines, corporate and FBO employers. **Computerized Information Services:** CompuServe Information Service; Aviation Job Bank (internal database). **Publications:** Career Pilot (magazine); Job Report (newsletters for pilots, maintenance personnel, and flight attendants), monthly; employment guides for aviation personnel; directories of flight operations, aviation maintenance employers, and airlines; salary surveys; airline testing kits; aviation resumes. **Remarks:** Toll-free telephone number(s): (800)538-5627. FAX: (404)997-8111. **Also Known As:** FAPA Information Center. **Staff:** David Lasley, Dir., Mktg. 0 0

★6221★
Futures Group, Inc. - Library (Sci-Engr)
80 Glastonbury Blvd. Phone: (203)633-3501
Glastonbury, CT 06033-4409 Katherine H. Willson, Mgr., Info.Serv.
Founded: 1971. **Staff:** Prof 2; Other 1. **Subjects:** Futures research, technology assessment, business forecasting, competitive intelligence, international development, population. **Special Collections:** Social Marketing of Contraceptives (SOMARC). **Holdings:** 10,000 books; 2000 bound periodical volumes; 3500 other cataloged items; 3500 clippings and unbound reports. **Subscriptions:** 300 journals and other serials. **Services:** Interlibrary loan; library not open to the public. **Computerized Information Services:** DIALOG Information Services, PFDS Online, BRS Information Technologies, Mead Data Central, NewsNet, Inc., VU/TEXT Information Services, WILSONLINE; Social Marketing of Contraceptives (SOMARC) (internal database). **Staff:** Kellie O'Donnell, Info.Spec.

★6222★
Futuribles International - Library (Bus-Fin)
55, rue de Varenne
F-75341 Paris 7, France Phone: 1 42 22 63 10
Staff: Prof 2. **Subjects:** Futures studies, forecasting, planning. **Holdings:** 10,000 books. **Subscriptions:** 100 journals and other serials. **Services:** Interlibrary loan; library not open to the public. **Also Known As:** Association Internationale Futuribles.

G

Julia Meek Gaar Wayne County Historical Museum
See: **Wayne County Historical Museum** (20109)

Dennis Gabor Archives
See: **Leo Beiser Inc.** (1661)

★6223★
(Gaborone) American Library (Educ)
Embassy Dr.
P.O. Box 90
Gaborone, Botswana Phone: 31 353398
Founded: 1984. **Staff:** 2. **Subscriptions:** 60 journals and other serials; 5 newspapers. **Services:** SDI; library open to the public with restrictions. **Remarks:** FAX: 31 353385. Maintained or supported by the U.S. Information Agency. Focus is on materials that will assist peoples outside the United States to learn about the United States, its people, history, culture, political processes, and social milieux.

Annie Gabriel Library
See: **California Baptist College - Annie Gabriel Library** (2472)

★6224★
Gadjah Mada University - Fakultas Kedokteran - Perpustakaan (Med)
Jl Farmako Sekip
Yogyakarta, Indonesia Phone: 274 88688
Founded: 1949. **Staff:** Prof 4; Other 15. **Subjects:** Medical science, life sciences, allied health sciences, chemistry, physics. **Holdings:** 16,399 books; 275 bound periodical volumes; 1901 reports; 2016 archival items; 20,028 microfiche; audiocassettes; videocassettes; slides; slide sets; article reprints. **Subscriptions:** 12 journals and other serials; 3 newspapers. **Services:** Copying; SDI; library open to the public. **Automated Operations:** CDS/ISIS. Performs searches. Contact Person: Dr. Tri Septiyantono. **Publications:** Berita Tambahan Pustaka; Bulletin Fakultas Kedokteran.

GAF Corporation
See: **ISP Management Company, Inc.** (8261)

★6225★
GAF Corporation - Legal Department Library (Law)
1361 Alps Rd., Bldg. 10 Phone: (201)628-3000
Wayne, NJ 07470 Cathy Swatt, Libn.
Subjects: Business, law. **Holdings:** 2000 volumes.

★6226★
Gage & Tucker - Library (Law)
P.O. Box 418200 Phone: (816)474-6460
Kansas City, MO 64141 Joe Custer, Dir., Info.Serv.
Staff: Prof 1; Other 2. **Subjects:** Law - trial practice, appellate, administrative, business, corporate, estate planning, insurance, labor, municipal finance, partnership, probate, public contract, real estate, securities, taxation. **Holdings:** 16,725 volumes; 2500 titles; 74 periodical titles. **Subscriptions:** 8 newspapers; 200 loose-leaf services. **Services:** Interlibrary loan; library not open to the public. **Computerized Information Services:** LEXIS, WESTLAW, DIALOG Information Services, MEDLINE, LEGI-SLATE, Information America; MCI Mail (electronic mail service). **Networks/Consortia:** Member of Kansas City Law Libraries Network. **Publications:** Gage & Tucker Library Newsletter, monthly - to personnel and clients. **Special Indexes:** Index to legal brief and memorandum bank (online). **Remarks:** FAX: (816)471-2120. Library located at 2345 Grand Ave., 28th Fl., Kansas City, MO 64108.

★6227★
GAI Consultants, Inc. - Library (Env-Cons)
570 Beatty Rd. Phone: (412)856-6400
Monroeville, PA 15146 Barbara Reid, Libn.
Subjects: Geotechnology, environment, transportation, geology. **Holdings:** 8000 books; 1000 patents and documents. **Services:** Interlibrary loan; copying; library open to the public with restrictions. **Remarks:** FAX: (412)856-4970.

★6228★
Gainesville Sun - Library (Publ)
Drawer A Phone: (904)338-3109
Gainesville, FL 32602 Robert Ivey, Libn.
Staff: Prof 1; Other 1. **Subjects:** Newspaper reference topics. **Holdings:** 500 books; 16,000 photographs; 336 reels of microfilm of newspapers; 600 maps; 280 VF drawers of tearsheets. **Services:** Library not open to the public. **Computerized Information Services:** Internal database. **Remarks:** FAX: (904)338-3128.

★6229★
Galesburg Cottage Hospital - Health Sciences Library (Med)
695 N. Kellogg St. Phone: (309)345-4237
Galesburg, IL 61401 Michael Wold, Hea.Sci.Libn.
Founded: 1950. **Staff:** Prof 1. **Subjects:** Medicine, nursing, allied health sciences. **Holdings:** 1200 books. **Subscriptions:** 175 journals and other serials. **Services:** Interlibrary loan; copying; library open to the public with restrictions. **Computerized Information Services:** MEDLARS. **Networks/Consortia:** Member of National Network of Libraries of Medicine - Greater Midwest Region, Heart of Illinois Library Consortium (HILC), B.C. Post-Secondary Interlibrary Loan Network (NET). **Publications:** Recent acquisitions list, quarterly - to medical staff and hospital employees.

★6230★
Galesburg Public Library - Special Collections (Hist)
40 E. Simmons St. Phone: (309)343-6118
Galesburg, IL 61401 Marcia Heise, Spec.Coll.Libn.
Staff: Prof 1. **Subjects:** History - Illinois, Knox County, Galesburg; genealogy; local authors including Carl Sandburg. **Special Collections:** Mother Bickerdyke Collection. **Holdings:** 6889 books and pamphlets; 247 manuscripts; 4205 photographs, slides, negatives; 79 maps; 30 oral history tapes; 15 phonograph records; 14 videotapes; 9 newspapers on microfilm. **Subscriptions:** 11 journals and other serials. **Services:** Copying; SDI; collections open to the public with restrictions. **Publications:** Videotapes on local history and personalities. **Remarks:** FAX: (309)343-4877.

Gallagher Library of Geology & Geophysics
See: **University of Calgary** (18289)

Marian Gould Gallagher Law Library
See: **University of Washington** (19534)

★6231★
Gallatin County Historical Society - Library (Hist)
R.R. 1 Phone: (618)272-7092
Ridgway, IL 62979 Lucille Lawler, Sec.
Founded: 1966. **Subjects:** Illinois and Gallatin County history, genealogy. **Holdings:** Books; county censuses; cemetery records. **Services:** Library will answer written inquiries; open to the public by appointment.

★6232★
Gallaudet University - Library - Special Collection on Deafness (Educ)
800 Florida Ave., N.E. Phone: (202)651-5220
Washington, DC 20002-3695 John Day, Univ.Libn.
Founded: 1864. **Staff:** Prof 14; Other 16. **Subjects:** Deafness and the deaf, audiology and hearing. **Special Collections:** Baker Collection (528 items). **Holdings:** 37,956 books; 232 AV programs; 95 VF drawers; 4900 linear feet of archival materials; 3366 theses and dissertations on microfilm; 90 linear feet of photographs; ERIC microfiche; films. **Subscriptions:** 577 journals and other serials. **Services:** Interlibrary loan; copying; collection open to the public for reference use only. **Automated Operations:** Computerized public access catalog. **Computerized Information Services:** OCLC, DIALOG Information Services, BRS Information Technologies. **Networks/Consortia:** Member of FEDLINK, Washington Research Library Consortium. **Remarks:** FAX: (202)651-5213. **Staff:** Theresa Chang, Hd., Tech.Serv.; Sarah Hamrich, Hd., Pub.Serv.; Thomas Harrington, Hd., Media; Ulf Hedberg, Hd., Archv.; Carolyn Jones, Res./Bibliog.Libn.

★6233★
Gallery/Stratford - John Martin Library (Art)
54 Romeo St.
P.O. Box 129 Phone: (519)271-5271
Stratford, ON, Canada N5A 4S9 Robert C. Freeman, Dir.
Founded: 1968. **Subjects:** Fine arts. **Holdings:** 900 books; 3000 Canadian, U.S., and European exhibition catalogs. **Services:** Library open to gallery members, educators, students, and researchers by appointment.

★6234★
Gallier House Museum - Research Library (Hist)
1118-32 Royal St. Phone: (504)523-6722
New Orleans, LA 70116 Daisy Tarver, Cur.
Founded: 1971. **Subjects:** 19th century - lifestyle, decorative arts, architecture, art; 19th century New Orleans. **Holdings:** 1000 books; 10 AV programs. **Services:** Copying; library open to the public for reference use only by appointment.

★6235★
E. & J. Gallo Winery - Library (Food-Bev)
Box 1130 Phone: (209)579-3230
Modesto, CA 95353 Rebecca Vaille, Libn.
Founded: 1969. **Staff:** Prof 2. **Subjects:** Wine technology, chemical and biological research, statistics, packaging, beverage marketing. **Holdings:** 9000 books; 750 bound periodical volumes; 3800 VF materials; 400 catalogs; 8 VF drawers of trade literature. **Subscriptions:** 450 journals and other serials. **Services:** Library not open to the public. **Computerized Information Services:** DIALOG Information Services, STN International. **Networks/Consortia:** Member of 49-99 Cooperative Library System. **Publications:** New Material Received, weekly - for internal distribution only. **Remarks:** FAX: (209)579-4541.

Charles William Galloupe Library
See: **Beverly Historical Society & Museum - Library and Archives** (1801)

★6236★
Gallup Indian Medical Center - Medical Library (Med)
E. Nizhoni Blvd.
Box 1337 Phone: (505)722-1119
Gallup, NM 87301 Patricia V. Bradley, Med.Libn.
Founded: 1961. **Staff:** Prof 1. **Subjects:** Medicine, nursing, surgery, dentistry. **Special Collections:** Navajo Indian health. **Holdings:** 2000 books. **Subscriptions:** 114 journals and other serials. **Services:** Interlibrary loan; library open to the public with restrictions. **Computerized Information Services:** MEDLARS. **Networks/Consortia:** Member of New Mexico Consortium of Biomedical and Hospital Libraries. **Remarks:** Maintained by U.S. Public Health Service - Navajo Area Indian Health Service.

★6237★
Gallup-McKinley County Schools - Media Center (Educ)
1100 E. Aztec Ave. Phone: (505)863-6098
Gallup, NM 87301 Carol A. Sarath, Lib. Media Spec.
Staff: Prof 1; Other 2. **Subjects:** Education. **Holdings:** 2200 books; 4000 AV programs; K-12 curriculum guides. **Subscriptions:** 75 journals and other serials. **Services:** Center open to McKinley County community organizations. **Automated Operations:** Computerized film scheduling. **Computerized Information Services:** CD-ROM (ERIC). **Special Catalogs:** Media Collection Catalog; Professional Library Catalog.

★6238★
Galson Corporation - Galson Information Center (Med)
6601 Kirkville Rd. Phone: (315)434-9692
East Syracuse, NY 13057 Mary Y. Nasikan, Info.Serv.Mgr.
Founded: 1980. **Staff:** Prof 2; Other 1. **Subjects:** Industrial hygiene, air pollution, meteorology, dispersion modeling, hazardous waste, engineering design. **Holdings:** 5000 books and government reports; regulations and supplementary material from Occupational Safety and Health Administration (OSHA), Environmental Protection Agency (EPA), New York State Department of Environmental Conservation, and National Institute of Occupational Safety and Health (NIOSH); audio and video cassettes; U.S.G.S. topographic maps; MSDS (Material Safety Data Sheets). **Subscriptions:** 100 journals and other serials. **Services:** Interlibrary loan; literature searching (online); current awareness. **Computerized Information Services:** DIALOG Information Services, NLM, Occupational Health Services, Inc. (OHS); internal database. Performs searches on fee basis. **Networks/Consortia:** Member of Central New York Library Resources Council (CENTRO). **Special Indexes:** Indexes to equipment manufacturers' catalogs. **Remarks:** FAX: (315)437-0509. **Formerly:** Galson Technical Services - Information Center. **Staff:** Fred Lont.

Sir Alexander Galt Museum - Archives
See: **Lethbridge City Archives** (9071)

Galter Health Sciences Library
See: **Northwestern University** (12081)

Bryant L. Galusha, M.D. LRC of Charlotte AHEC
See: **Medical Library of Mecklenburg County** (10008)

Galveston Bay Information Center
See: **Texas A&M University at Galveston** (16203)

Paul V. Galvin Library
See: **Illinois Institute of Technology** (7675)

Thomas J. Galvin Memorial Medical Library
See: **Wichita Falls State Hospital** (20407)

★6239★
Gambia Family Planning Association - Library (Soc Sci)
P.O. Box 325 Phone: 91743
Banjul, Gambia J. Tunde Taylor-Thomas, Exec.Dir.
Founded: 1969. **Subjects:** Maternal and child health care, family planning, population, development. **Holdings:** 1500 volumes. **Services:** Library open to the public.

Elizabeth Gamble Deaconess Home Association
See: **James N. Gamble Institute of Medical Research - Library** (6240)

Gamble House
See: **University of Southern California - School of Architecture - Gamble House - Greene and Greene Library** (19345)

★6240★
James N. Gamble Institute of Medical Research - Library (Med)
2141 Auburn Ave. Phone: (513)369-2737
Cincinnati, OH 45219 Lisa L. McCormick, Lib.Dir.
Founded: 1932. **Staff:** Prof 1; Other 2. **Subjects:** Virology, oncology, immunology, cardiology, clinical medicine. **Holdings:** 5000 books; 8000 bound periodical volumes. **Subscriptions:** 282 journals and other serials. **Services:** Interlibrary loan; SDI; library open to the public by appointment. **Computerized Information Services:** NLM, BRS Information Technologies, PDQ (Physician Data Query). Performs searches on fee basis. **Networks/Consortia:** Member of National Network of Libraries of Medicine - Greater Midwest Region. **Remarks:** FAX: (513)241-3899. **Formerly:** Elizabeth Gamble Deaconess Home Association.

Gaming Resource Center
See: **University of Nevada--Las Vegas** (19011)

★6241★
Mahatma Gandhi Institute - Library (Area-Ethnic)
Mahatma Gandhi Inst. Ave. Phone: 4-8021
Moka, Mauritius Yves Chan Kam Lon, Libn.
Subjects: History and multiculturalism of Mauritius, oriental languages, oral traditions, demography, Indian immigration. **Holdings:** 30,500 volumes. **Remarks:** Maintained by Mauritius - Ministry of Education, Arts and Culture.

★6242★
Mahatma Gandhi Institute of Medical Science - Library (Med)
Sevagram
Phone: 2701
Wardha 442 102, Maharashtra, India Mr. D.N. Taksande, Libn.
Founded: 1969. **Staff:** Prof 3; Other 8. **Subjects:** Medical science. **Special Collections:** Gandhian thought and Vinobaji collection. **Holdings:** 12,863 books; 7761 bound periodical volumes; 694 reports; video cassettes. **Subscriptions:** 291 journals and other serials; 7 newspapers. **Services:** Copying; library open to the public at librarian's discretion. **Staff:** Kusun G. Raole, Asst.Libn.

★6243★
Gandhi Peace Center - Audio Library (Rel-Phil)
Box 254 Phone: (602)889-3100
Tucson, AZ 85702 Job Matusow
Founded: 1983. **Subjects:** World religions, faith. **Holdings:** 900 audiotapes. **Services:** Library open to the public by appointment. **Remarks:** FAX: (602)889-8535.

★6244★
Gannet Suburban Newspapers - Editorial Library (Publ)
One Gannett Dr. Phone: (914)694-5225
White Plains, NY 10604 Frances Henry Riley, Chf.Libn.
Founded: 1987. **Staff:** Prof 4; Other 8. **Subjects:** Newspaper reference topics. **Special Collections:** Westchester County history. **Holdings:** Figures not available. **Services:** Interlibrary loan; library not open to the public. **Computerized Information Services:** DIALOG Information Services, NEXIS, VU/TEXT Information Services, DataTimes; BASIS (internal database). **Staff:** Maureen Dwyer-Hirten.

Gannett Co. - USA Today
See: **USA Today** (19698)

Gannett Company, Inc. - Florida Today Newspaper
See: **Florida Today Newspaper** (5921)

Gannett-Estes Library
See: **Southeastern Bible College** (15448)

★6245★
Guy Gannett Publishing Company - Portland Press Herald-Maine Sunday Telegram - Library (Publ)
390 Congress St.
Box 1460 Phone: (207)780-9000
Portland, ME 04104 Marcia A. MacVane, Libn.
Founded: 1912. **Staff:** Prof 1; Other 5. **Subjects:** Newspaper reference topics. **Special Collections:** City directories, 1856 to present; state registers, 1872 to present. **Holdings:** 1000 books; 400,000 clipping files; 200,000 photographs; 27 VF drawers of pamphlets and newspapers, 1824 to present, on microfilm. **Services:** Library not open to the public; courtesy service to librarians. **Remarks:** FAX: (207)780-9499. **Formerly:** Guy Gannett Publishing Company - Portland Press Herald-Evening Express-Maine Sunday Telegram - Library.

Gannett Newspapers - Battle Creek Enquirer
See: **Battle Creek Enquirer** (1579)

Gannett Newspapers - Binghamton Press and Sun-Bulletin
See: **(Binghamton) Press and Sun-Bulletin** (1842)

Gannett Newspapers - Bridgewater Courier-News
See: **Bridgewater Courier-News** (2121)

Gannett Newspapers - Green Bay Press-Gazette
See: **Green Bay Press-Gazette** (6718)

Gannett Newspapers - Idaho Statesman
See: **Idaho Statesman** (7655)

Gannett Newspapers - Lafayette Journal and Courier
See: **Lafayette Journal and Courier** (8876)

Gannett Newspapers - Marin Independent Journal
See: **Marin Independent Journal** (9667)

Gannett Newspapers - The Shreveport Times
See: **The (Shreveport) Times** (15144)

Gannon Museum of Wagons
See: **Yakima Valley Museum and Historical Association - Archives** (20693)

Ganong Library
See: **New Brunswick Museum - Library and Archives Department** (11451)

Helen A. Ganser Library
See: **Millersville University** (10403)

★6246★
Gansu Provincial Academy of Social Sciences - Library and Information Department (Soc Sci)
Dajiazhuang
Shilidian
Lanzhou, Gansu Province, People's Republic of China Wu Mingde, Libn.
Founded: 1978. **Staff:** 7. **Subjects:** Philosophy, economics, history, scientific socialism, literature, Marxism, Leninism, Maoism, population. **Special Collections:** Chinese ancient books; politics, economy, history, and culture of Lanzhou district. **Holdings:** 70,000 volumes; 350 periodicals; 100 AV programs and microforms. **Services:** Interlibrary loan (limited). **Publications:** Social Sciences.

Evelyn & John R. Gant Library
See: **Wisconsin School for the Deaf** (20514)

Aaron Garber Library
See: **Cleveland College of Jewish Studies** (3801)

Garber Research Center Library
See: **Harbison-Walker Refractories Company** (6897)

Donald L. Garbrecht Law Library
See: **University of Maine School of Law** (18782)

Garceau Library
See: **St. Vincent's Hospital** (14618)

★6247★
Garden Center of Greater Cleveland - Eleanor Squire Library (Biol Sci, Agri)
11030 East Blvd. Phone: (216)721-1600
Cleveland, OH 44106 Joanna C. Bristol, Libn.
Founded: 1930. **Staff:** Prof 1. **Subjects:** Gardening, horticulture, landscape architecture, herbs, flower arranging, botany. **Special Collections:** Warren H. Corning Collection of Horticultural Classics. **Holdings:** 14,000 books; 500 bound periodical volumes; 1000 seed and nursery catalogs; clippings; pamphlets; illustrations; photographs; slides; botanical prints. **Subscriptions:** 250 journals and other serials. **Services:** Interlibrary loan; copying; personal consultations on gardening problems and program planning; library open to the public for reference use only. **Publications:** Garden Center of Greater Cleveland Bulletin. **Special Indexes:** Index of colored botanical illustrations (online); Flowering Plant Index (online, book). **Staff:** Elaine Averman, Asst.Libn.

★ 6248 ★
Garden Center of Rochester - Library (Biol Sci)
5 Castle Park Phone: (716)473-5130
Rochester, NY 14620 Regina P. Campbell, Libn.
Founded: 1945. **Staff:** 7. **Subjects:** Horticulture, landscaping, plant identification, garden history, nature study, flower arrangement. **Holdings:** 3000 books; 1000 bound periodical volumes; 12 VF drawers of clippings. **Subscriptions:** 34 journals and other serials. **Services:** Interlibrary loan; library open to members only on limited schedule.

★ 6249 ★
Garden City Osteopathic Hospital - Medical/Staff Library (Med)
6245 Inkster Rd. Phone: (313)458-4311
Garden City, MI 48135 C.J. Hunt
Founded: 1960. **Staff:** Prof 1; Other 1. **Subjects:** Medicine, surgery, nursing, orthopedics, pathology, laboratory sciences. **Holdings:** 2100 books; 5000 bound periodical volumes; journals on microfiche; AV items. **Subscriptions:** 181 journals and other serials; 6 newspapers. **Services:** Interlibrary loan; copying; library open to the public by appointment. **Computerized Information Services:** MEDLARS; DOCLINE (electronic mail service). Performs searches on fee basis. **Remarks:** Alternate telephone number(s): (313)458-4312. FAX: (313)421-3530. **Staff:** C. Grainger.

★ 6250 ★
Garden Grove Historical Society - E.G. Ware Library (Hist)
12174 Euclid Ave. Phone: (714)530-8871
Garden Grove, CA 92640 Denis Witcher, Pres.
Founded: 1971. **Staff:** 4. **Subjects:** Local history. **Special Collections:** Garden Grove photographs (750); fire department records from founding by volunteers to formal incorporation of city of Garden Grove. **Holdings:** 500 books. **Services:** Library open to the public by appointment.

★ 6251 ★
Gardenview Horticulture Park - Library (Agri)
16711 Pearl Rd. Phone: (216)238-6653
Strongsville, OH 44136 Henry A. Ross, Libn.
Founded: 1949. **Subjects:** Horticulture, birds and animals, crafts, self-sufficiency, do-it-yourself. **Holdings:** 4000 books. **Services:** Library open to members for reference use only.

★ 6252 ★
Gardiner Public Library - Children's Literature Collection (Hum)
152 Water St. Phone: (207)582-3312
Gardiner, ME 04345 Glenna Nowell, Dir.
Founded: 1881. **Staff:** Prof 3; Other 3. **Subjects:** Children's literature. **Special Collections:** Laura Richards Collection; E.A. Robinson Collection. **Services:** Interlibrary loan; copying; collection open to the public.

Charles B. Gardner Library
See: **Wheaton Cultural Alliance, Inc. - Museum of American Glass Research Library** (20373)

★ 6253 ★
Isabella Stewart Gardner Museum, Inc. - Archives and Rare Books Collection (Art)
2 Palace Rd. Phone: (617)566-1401
Boston, MA 02115 Susan Sinclair, Archv.
Founded: 1903. **Staff:** Prof 1. **Subjects:** Art - history, criticism, technique, conservation; artists; art museums; galleries; exhibition catalogs. **Special Collections:** Isabella Stewart Gardner Papers - correspondence and papers (6000 letters from 1000 correspondents; 1879-1924); travel scrapbooks (27 volumes, 2740 photographs; 1867-1895); travel diaries (3 volumes; 1874-1875; 1883-1884); guestbooks (15 volumes; 1893-1919); photographs (400; 1850-1924); news clippings (Isabella Stewart Gardner, 1880-1924; museum 1924 to present); Rare Book collection (1000 volumes, including rare books, fine bindings, literary and historical manuscripts, French horae, 17th and 18th century illustrated works, novels, memoirs, American first editions of 19th and early 20th century). **Holdings:** 2000 books; archival materials; memorabilia; clippings; photographs. **Subscriptions:** 10 journals and other serials. **Services:** Archiv es open to the public by appointment. **Publications:** List of publications - available on request. **Remarks:** FAX: (617)232-8039.

John Gardner Archive
See: **University of Rochester - Department of Rare Books and Special Collections** (19278)

John C. Gardner Memorial Library
See: **First Presbyterian Church** (5788)

Gardner Memorial Library
See: **St. Thomas Episcopal Church** (14595)

Yvelin Gardner Alcoholism Library
See: **Rutgers University - Rutgers Center of Alcohol Studies** (14172)

★ 6254 ★
Garland County Historical Society - Archives (Hist)
914 Summer Phone: (501)623-5875
Hot Springs, AR 71913 Inez E. Cline, City/County Hist./Dir.
Founded: 1960. **Staff:** 2. **Subjects:** Local history, genealogy. **Special Collections:** Chamber of Commerce Collection (35 cubic feet); Dr. Francis J. Scully Collection (3 cubic feet; artifacts); Floyd Housley Collection (8 scrapbooks); John Lonsdale Collection (5 scrapbooks); Garden Club Collection (3 cubic feet); Arkansas State Fair Association Collection (2 cubic feet); death record books, 1896-1923; local jail register, 1890s. **Holdings:** 150 books; 58 bound periodical volumes; 30 file drawers of subject files; 2000 local newspapers, 1887 to present; ledgers and account books; city and township maps; 10,000 photographs; city directories, 1885 to present; telephone directories, 1903 to present; Sentinel-Record, 1909-1949, on microfilm. **Subscriptions:** 20 journals and other serials. **Services:** Copying; archives open to the public on a limited schedule or by appointment. **Publications:** The Record, annual. **Remarks:** Located at Old Armory Building, 210 Woodbine St., Hot Springs, AR 71901. **Staff:** Wendy Richter, Ed. & Archv.; Bobbie J. McLane, Ed. & Archv.

Garnett Library
See: **University of Virginia - Special Collections Department** (19510)

Bruce A. Garrett Memorial Library & Media Center
See: **Baptist Memorial Hospital System** (1516)

Garrett Canada
See: **Allied-Signal Aerospace Canada** (397)

Eileen J. Garrett Library
See: **Parapsychology Foundation Inc.** (12737)

Garrett-Evangelical Seminary
See: **United Library of Garrett-Evangelical and Seabury-Western Theological Seminaries** (16723)

Jenkins Garrett Library
See: **University of Texas at Arlington - Libraries - Division of Special Collections** (19375)

John Work Garrett Library
See: **Johns Hopkins University** (8419)

★ 6255 ★
Gartner Group, Inc. - Information Resource Center (Comp Sci)
56 Top Gallant Rd. Phone: (203)967-6749
Stamford, CT 06904 Judith M. Weller
Founded: 1979. **Staff:** 7.5. **Subjects:** Information technology, computers, system design, telecommunications. **Holdings:** 3000 items. **Subscriptions:** 1200 journals and other serials. **Services:** Document delivery; SDI; center not open to the public. **Computerized Information Services:** DIALOG Information Services, NEXIS, Reuter TEXTLINE, NewsNet, Inc., Dow Jones News/Retrieval, Computer Intelligence (CI); Gartner Online ((internal database)). **Remarks:** FAX: (203)975-6480. Telex: 643528. **Staff:** Maureen A. Rossi.

★6256★
Gartner Lee Limited - Information Centre (Sci-Engr)
140 Renfrew Dr. Phone: (416)477-8400
Markham, ON, Canada L3R 8B6 Beverly Foss, Libn.
Founded: 1973. **Staff:** 1. **Subjects:** Geology, hydrology, biology. **Holdings:** Figures not available. **Services:** Library not open to the public.

Garwood Baptist Historical Collection
See: **Stetson University - Du Pont-Ball Library** (15784)

★6257★
Gas Research Institute - Library Services (Energy)
8600 W. Bryn Mawr Ave. Phone: (312)399-8386
Chicago, IL 60631 Ann B. Michael, Mgr., Lib.Serv.
Founded: 1982. **Staff:** Prof 7; Other 1. **Subjects:** Natural gas, energy, engineering. **Holdings:** 5500 books; 4000 internal reports; 2000 DOE and Electric Power Research Institute (EPRI) reports; 130,000 reports on microfiche; 10 VF drawers. **Subscriptions:** 790 journals and other serials. **Services:** Interlibrary loan; copying; SDI; services open to the public by appointment. **Automated Operations:** Computerized cataloging, acquisitions, and serials. **Computerized Information Services:** DIALOG Information Services, BRS Information Technologies, ORBIT Search Service, OCLC, Dow Jones News/Retrieval, NEXIS, DataTimes, NewsNet, Inc., LEXIS, gasLine, NGV Information Centre, A.G.A. GasNet, VU/TEXT Information Services, STN International, EPIC; internal database; DIALMAIL, A.G.A. GasNet (electronic mail services). **Networks/Consortia:** Member of Chicago Library System. **Publications:** New GRI Publications, monthly. **Remarks:** FAX: (312)399-8170. Telex: 253812. Electronic mail address(es): 9862 (DIALMAIL); II2009 (A.G.A. GasNet). **Staff:** Elizabeth N. Hindmarch, Sys.Supv.; Carol Ann Irons, Info.Serv.Supv.; Joyce M. Styler, Info.Anl.

Ismail Gaspirali Library
See: **American Association of Crimean Turks** (480)

★6258★
Gaston & Snow
1 Federal St.
Boston, MA 02110
Defunct.

Gate Collection on the Black Experience
See: **Lower Merion Library Association - Ardmore Library** (9413)

★6259★
Gates Rubber Co. - Information Center (Sci-Engr)
900 S. Broadway
Box 5887 Phone: (303)744-4150
Denver, CO 80217 Kathleen Rainwater, Mgr.
Founded: 1945. **Staff:** Prof 1; Other 1. **Subjects:** Rubber, chemistry, physics, management, plastics, textiles. **Holdings:** 4000 books; 40 VF drawers of research reports; 5 VF drawers of catalogs and bulletins. **Subscriptions:** 200 journals and other serials; 10 newspapers. **Services:** Interlibrary loan; copying; center open to the public by appointment. **Automated Operations:** Computerized public access catalog and cataloging. **Remarks:** FAX: (303)744-4000.

★6260★
Gateway Community College - Library (Educ)
108 N. 40th St. Phone: (602)392-5147
Phoenix, AZ 85034 Peg Smith, Dir.
Founded: 1969. **Staff:** Prof 2; Other 5. **Subjects:** Business, graphic communications, computer technology, pharmacy technology, nursing, electronics, robotics, respiratory therapy, radiography, ultrasound, nuclear medicine, surgical technology, RV maintenance. **Holdings:** 42,000 books; 7000 programmed materials and media kits; 6873 microfiche; 395 reels of microfilm; 1393 titles on cassette tapes; 864 titles of filmstrips and film loops; computer software. **Subscriptions:** 350 journals and other serials; 10 newspapers. **Services:** Interlibrary loan. **Automated Operations:** Computerized public access catalog, cataloging, and acquisitions. **Computerized Information Services:** DIALOG Information Services. **Publications:** Acquisitions List, monthly - for internal distribution only; bibliographies. **Remarks:** FAX: (602)392-5300. Gateway Community College is part of the Maricopa Community College District. **Staff:** Josefa Garcia, Ref.Libn.

★6261★
Gateway to the Panhandle - Gateway Library (Hum, Hist)
Box 27 Phone: (405)934-2004
Gate, OK 73844 Florence Whisenhunt, Libn.
Founded: 1976. **Staff:** 4. **Subjects:** Children's literature, history. **Special Collections:** Reader's Digest. **Holdings:** 8000 books. **Services:** Interlibrary loan; library open to the public.

★6262★
Gateway Technical College - Learning Resources Center (Educ)
3520 30th Ave. Phone: (414)656-6924
Kenosha, WI 53144 Gerald F. Perona, Dist.Libn.
Founded: 1964. **Staff:** Prof 3.5; Other 7. **Subjects:** Office education, law enforcement, nursing and allied health sciences, horticulture, aeronautics, electronics, data processing. **Special Collections:** Fire technology (300 items); career education (1000 items); vocational education (1500 items); hearing impaired (500 items). **Holdings:** 41,000 books; 5000 periodical volumes, hardcopy and microfilm; 360 bound theses; 5200 pamphlets; 400 16mm films; 10,000 video cassettes; 4000 microcomputer programs; 5000 other AV programs. **Subscriptions:** 377 journals and other serials; 30 newspapers. **Services:** Interlibrary loan; copying; center open to the public with restrictions. **Automated Operations:** Computerized public access catalog and circulation (PALS). **Computerized Information Services:** DIALOG Information Services, BRS Information Technologies, OCLC; internal database; MACC (electronic mail service). **Networks/Consortia:** Member of National Network of Libraries of Medicine - Greater Midwest Region, Library Council of Metropolitan Milwaukee, Inc. (LCOMM), Tri-County Library Consortium. **Special Catalogs:** Gateway Film and Videotape Catalog, annual; Hearing Impaired Film and Videotape Catalog. **Remarks:** FAX: (414)656-8966. Electronic mail address(es): Gateway (MACC). Maintains branch libraries at Kenosha, Racine, and Elkhorn. **Staff:** Kathy Orth, Racine Libn.; Araxie Kalvonjian, Tech.Proc./Acq.Libn.; Ann Sheehy, Elkhorn Lib.Techn.

★6263★
Gateways Hospital and Community Mental Health Center - Professional Library (Med)
1891 Effie St. Phone: (213)666-0171
Los Angeles, CA 90026 Ken Yabuki, Libn.
Founded: 1965. **Staff:** Prof 1. **Subjects:** Psychiatry, community mental health, penology. **Special Collections:** Karpf Collection (social psychology; 100 titles); hyperkinesis (500 titles). **Holdings:** 1000 books; 100 unbound periodical volumes; 500 pamphlets and government documents; 200 tape cassettes. **Subscriptions:** 25 journals and other serials. **Services:** Interlibrary loan; copying; library open to the public with permission.

★6264★
Gay Alliance of the Genesee Valley Inc. - Library (Soc Sci)
179 Atlantic Ave. Phone: (716)244-8640
Rochester, NY 14607 Tom Krolak, Libn.
Founded: 1974. **Staff:** 1. **Subjects:** Gay and lesbian literature, history, male and female fiction, feminism, sex, religion and philosophy. **Holdings:** 1400 books; periodicals; newspapers. **Subscriptions:** 5 journals and other serials; 6 newspapers. **Services:** Library open to the public. **Publications:** Empty Closet, monthly. **Staff:** Horace Lethbridge, Pres.

Gay Community News
See: **Bromfield Street Educational Foundation** (2208)

Gay Task Force of ALA
See: **ALA Gay & Lesbian Task Force** (179)

★6265★
Gaylord Hospital - Medical Library (Med)
Box 400 Phone: (203)284-2800
Wallingford, CT 06492 Meada G. Ebinger, Med.Libn.
Founded: 1962. **Staff:** Prof 1. **Subjects:** Rehabilitation, psychology, social service, medicine, nursing. **Special Collections:** Historic tuberculosis collection. **Holdings:** 1450 books; 100 video cassettes on rehabilitation. **Subscriptions:** 110 journals and other serials. **Services:** Interlibrary loan; copying; library open to the public with restrictions. **Computerized Information Services:** MEDLARS. **Networks/Consortia:** Member of Connecticut Association of Health Science Libraries (CAHSL), BHSL. **Publications:** Newsletter, monthly - for internal distribution only. **Remarks:** FAX: (203)284-2894.

Gaylord Music Library
See: **Washington University** (20062)

★6266★
Gazette International Networking Institute - Library (Soc Sci)
4502 Maryland Ave.
St. Louis, MO 63108 Phone: (314)361-0475
Subjects: Disabled - education, employment, equipment, family, hobbies and sports, housing, independent living; ventilator-assisted living. **Holdings:** 3000 research monographs, reports, proceedings, case histories, and other volumes; 300 bound periodical volumes; archival items.

★6267★
Gazoduc TQM - Centre de Documentation (Energy)
1, Place Ville Marie
Bureau 2220 Phone: (514)874-8800
Montreal, PQ, Canada H3B 3M4 Chantale Dion, Doc.
Founded: 1980. **Staff:** Prof 1; Other 1. **Subjects:** Pipeline construction, regulation, natural gas. **Holdings:** 5000 books; 1500 boxes of archival material. **Subscriptions:** 70 journals and other serials; 10 newspapers. **Services:** Interlibrary loan; copying; center open to the public by appointment. **Automated Operations:** Computerized cataloging. **Remarks:** FAX: (514)874-8888.

★6268★
GCG Dillon Consulting Ltd. - Library (Trans)
10239 178th St.
Edmonton, AB, Canada T5S 1M3 Phone: (403)483-8094
Subjects: Transportation, highways, mass transit. **Holdings:** 4000 books. **Subscriptions:** 75 journals and other serials. **Services:** Library open to the public by permission.

★6269★
GE Aerospace - Automated Systems - Engineering Library (Sci-Engr)
Box 588 Phone: (617)229-5000
Burlington, MA 01803 Dave Barber, Adm., Lib.Rsrcs.
Founded: 1955. **Staff:** Prof 1; Other 1. **Subjects:** Electronics, electrical engineering, mathematics, computer technology, management. **Holdings:** 5000 books; 500 bound periodical volumes; 1000 technical reports. **Subscriptions:** 150 journals and other serials. **Services:** Interlibrary loan; library not open to the public. **Computerized Information Services:** DIALOG Information Services, OCLC, DTIC. **Remarks:** An alternate telephone number is 229-5000.

★6270★
GE Aerospace - Communications & Strategic Systems Division - Government Communications Systems Department - Library (Sci-Engr)
Delaware Ave. & Cooper St., Bldg. 10-6-5 Phone: (609)338-4044
Camden, NJ 08102 Carol DeRooy, Contact
Founded: 1988. **Staff:** Prof 1. **Subjects:** Electronics, mathematics, physics, computers, telecommunications. **Holdings:** 14,000 books; 3500 bound periodical volumes; 375 VF drawers of reports, reprints, conference proceedings. **Subscriptions:** 200 journals and other serials. **Services:** Interlibrary loan; library open to the public by appointment. **Publications:** Library News. **Special Catalogs:** Catalog of reports (card).

★6271★
GE Aerospace - Government Electronic Systems Division - Engineering Library (Sci-Engr, Comp Sci)
101-222
Borton Landing Rd. Phone: (609)722-3394
Moorestown, NJ 08057 Natalie J. Mamchur, Mgr.
Founded: 1953. **Staff:** Prof 2; Other 1. **Subjects:** Radar and associated electronics, electrical engineering, computer science, technology, science and mathematics, military science, business. **Holdings:** 39,500 books; 2500 bound periodical volumes; 17,500 reports. **Subscriptions:** 625 journals and other serials; 15 newspapers. **Services:** Interlibrary loan; copying; library open to the public by appointment. **Computerized Information Services:** DIALOG Information Services, DTIC, Information Handling Services (IHS), USNI Military Database, PERISCOPE. **Special Catalogs:** Holdings list of periodicals and conference and symposia proceedings (online).

★6272★
GE Fanuc Automation N.A., Inc. - Industrial Electronics Information Center (Sci-Engr)
Box 8106 Phone: (804)978-5427
Charlottesville, VA 22906 Yolanda Burnside
Founded: 1980. **Staff:** 1. **Subjects:** Electrical and mechanical engineering, computer sciences. **Special Collections:** Robotics materials. **Holdings:** 2000 books. **Subscriptions:** 104 journals and other serials. **Services:** Interlibrary loan; copying; SDI; center open to the public with restrictions. **Automated Operations:** Computerized cataloging and circulation. **Computerized Information Services:** DIALOG Information Services, NEXIS, Dun & Bradstreet Business Credit Services. Performs searches free of charge. **Remarks:** FAX: (804)978-5102.

★6273★
GE Plastics - Technology Center - Library (Sci-Engr)
Box 68 Phone: (304)863-7335
Washington, WV 26181 Jo Ellen Butcher, Lib.Coord.
Founded: 1960. **Staff:** Prof 1; Other 2. **Subjects:** Polymers, organic chemistry, personnel, business, plastics, rubber, adhesives, chemical engineering, petrochemicals, management, sales, marketing. **Special Collections:** 350 safety films; 400 audiocassettes; video collection; company reports; lab notebooks; toxicity studies; agreements; patent/invention disclosures. **Holdings:** 25,000 volumes; 6 VF drawers of pamphlets; 13 drawers of U.S. patents on microfiche; 20 drawers of U.S. patents on microfilm. **Subscriptions:** 250 journals and other serials. **Services:** Interlibrary loan; library not open to the public. **Automated Operations:** Computerized serials and circulation. **Computerized Information Services:** DIALOG Information Services, PFDS Online, NLM, Dow Jones News/Retrieval, Chemical Abstracts Service (CAS), The Source Information Network, NLM, WILSONLINE, Chemical Information Systems, Inc. (CIS), NTIS, Occupational Health Services, Inc. (OHS), Superindex Inc., SEC Online, Corrosion Data Base; internal database. **Publications:** New Library Materials, monthly; Current Content Bulletins, weekly. **Remarks:** FAX: (304)863-7108. **Staff:** Wilma Breedlove, Sr.Lib.Asst.; Pamela Sadler, Ret.Spec.

Helen V. Gearn Library
See: **Historical Society of Newburgh Bay and the Highlands** (7276)

★6274★
Geauga County Historical Society - Shanower Memorial Library (Hist)
14653 E. Park St.
Box 153 Phone: (216)834-4012
Burton, OH 44021 Marlene F. Collins, Off.Mgr.
Founded: 1938. **Staff:** 1. **Subjects:** Local history. **Special Collections:** Early land grants and township records; diaries; genealogy. **Special Collections:** Personal papers of Hitchcock and Hickox families. **Holdings:** 1000 books. **Services:** Library open to the public by appointment.

★6275★
Geauga County Law Library (Law)
Court House Phone: (216)285-2222
Chardon, OH 44024 Audrey Moseley, Law Libn.
Founded: 1968. **Staff:** 1. **Subjects:** Law. **Holdings:** 19,000 volumes; Ohio Court of Appeals unreported decisions for the 1st-12th districts; 11th District Court of Appeals decisions, 1969 to present. **Services:** Copying; library open to authorized persons. **Computerized Information Services:** WESTLAW; LEXIS. **Remarks:** FAX: (216)285-3603.

James Gilliam Gee Library
See: **East Texas State University** (5131)

★6276★
Gee & Jenson Engineers, Architects, Planners, Inc. - Library/Records Center (Plan)
One Harvard Circle
Box 24600 Phone: (407)683-3301
West Palm Beach, FL 33416-4600 John F. Day, Mgr.
Founded: 1953. **Staff:** 1. **Subjects:** Florida water resources and land development; wastewater plants; Florida ports, paving, drainage. **Special**

Collections: Development of Disney World; Development of Port Canaveral; Florida weather data, 1950 to present. **Holdings:** 8200 books; 141 bound periodical volumes; 3000 drawings; 3 VF drawers of Florida city and county rules and regulations; 2 VF drawers of Florida maps; 2 drawers of microforms; Corps of Engineers design memorandum; American Society of Civil Engineers Transactions and Journals, 1936 to present; Florida Soil Conservation Service Surveys, 1930 to present; specifications; reports of Gee & Jenson, 1953 to present; file hearings and plans of the Cross Florida Barge Canal. **Subscriptions:** 315 journals and other serials; 10 newspapers. **Services:** Interlibrary loan; copying; SDI; library open to the public with referral from other libraries. **Computerized Information Services:** DIALOG Information Services, Civil Engineering Database; internal database. **Publications:** New book and periodical listings, monthly. **Special Indexes:** Gee & Jenson drawings, reports, and specifications (card). **Remarks:** FAX: (407)686-7446.

Karl W. Gehrkens Music Education Library
See: **Oberlin College - Conservatory of Music Library** (12218)

Helen Palmer Geisel Library
See: **San Diego Museum of Contemporary Art** (14700)

Geisel Library
See: **St. Anselm College** (14232)

★6277★
Geisinger Medical Center - Medical Library (Med)
100 N. Academy Ave. Phone: (717)271-6463
Danville, PA 17822-2101 Britain G. Roth, Dir., Lrng.Rsrcs.
Founded: 1927. **Staff:** Prof 3; Other 6. **Subjects:** Medicine, paramedical sciences. **Holdings:** 33,000 volumes; 1322 audiovisual items. **Subscriptions:** 1130 journals and other serials. **Services:** Interlibrary loan; copying; SDI; library open to the public. **Computerized Information Services:** MEDLARS, DIALOG Information Services, BRS Information Technologies, OCLC, PaperChase; CD-ROM. Performs searches on fee basis. Contact Person: Denise Forbare-De Ponio, Ref.Libn., 271-8198. **Networks/Consortia:** Member of Susquehanna Library Cooperative, Central Pennsylvania Health Sciences Library Association (CPHSLA). **Publications:** Library Bulletin, quarterly. **Special Catalogs:** Serials catalog; AV catalog.

★6278★
Geisinger Medical Center - School of Nursing Library (Med)
Danville, PA 17822 Phone: (717)271-6288
Claire A. Huntington, Lrng.Rsrcs.Coord.
Founded: 1938. **Staff:** Prof 1. **Subjects:** Nursing, allied health sciences. **Holdings:** 4401 books; 851 bound periodical volumes; 2 VF drawers of pamphlet material. **Subscriptions:** 91 journals and other serials; 4 newspapers. **Services:** Interlibrary loan; copying; library open to the public for reference use only. **Automated Operations:** Computerized cataloging. **Computerized Information Services:** OCLC.

★6279★
Gellman Research Associates, Inc. - GRA Library (Trans, Bus-Fin)
One Jenkintown Sta.
115 West Ave., Suite 201 Phone: (215)884-7500
Jenkintown, PA 19046 Dorothy K. Finn, Libn.
Staff: Prof 1. **Subjects:** Transportation, economics, technology transfer, antitrust, statistical models. **Holdings:** 8000 books; 500 other cataloged items. **Subscriptions:** 130 journals and other serials. **Services:** Interlibrary loan; library open to the public by appointment. **Automated Operations:** Computerized cataloging. **Computerized Information Services:** DIALOG Information Services, NASA/RECON. Performs searches on fee basis. Contact Person: Joseph E. Phillips, Sr.Sys.Anl. **Publications:** Monthly list of New Additions. **Remarks:** FAX: (215)884-1385. Telex: 834653.

Melvin Gelman Library
See: **George Washington University - Melvin Gelman Library** (20008)

★6280★
Gelman Sciences, Inc. - Technical Information Center (Sci-Engr)
600 S. Wagner Rd.
Ann Arbor, MI 48106 Phone: (313)665-0651
Founded: 1972. **Staff:** Prof 1; Other 1. **Subjects:** Microfiltration, polymer chemistry, electrophoresis, ultrafiltration, chemical engineering, medical device manufacturing. **Holdings:** 1250 books; 10,000 technical reprints; 6 VF drawers of patents; vertical file on filtration topics; standards. **Subscriptions:** 60 journals and other serials. **Services:** Center not open to the public. **Computerized Information Services:** DIALOG Information Services, STN International; internal database. **Networks/Consortia:** Member of National Network of Libraries of Medicine - Greater Midwest Region. **Publications:** Library Newsletter, monthly - for internal distribution only. **Special Indexes:** List of articles with abstracts that cite the use of Gelman products in a specific applications area (printout). **Remarks:** FAX: (313)761-1114. **Staff:** Leena N. Lalwani.

Gembloux Faculty of Agricultural Sciences - Library
See: **Belgium - Ministry of Education - Gembloux Faculty of Agricultural Sciences - Library** (1669)

★6281★
Gemological Institute of America - Research Library (Sci-Engr)
1660 Stewart St. Phone: (213)829-2991
Santa Monica, CA 90404 Dona Mary Dirlam, Libn.
Founded: 1931. **Staff:** Prof 5. **Subjects:** Gemology; mineralogy; jewelry - retailing, design, history. **Special Collections:** John and Marjorie Sinkankas Gemology & Mineralogy Library; rare book room. **Holdings:** 14,000 volumes. **Subscriptions:** 125 journals and other serials. **Services:** Copying; library open to the public with restrictions. **Computerized Information Services:** PFDS Online; GIA-NET (internal online system). **Publications:** Gems and Gemology, quarterly - by subscription. **Remarks:** FAX: (213)828-4866. **Staff:** Elise Misiorowski; Rose Tozer; Karen Stark; JoEllen Cole.

Gen Corp Aerojet
See: **Aerojet Propulsion Division - Library** (105)

★6282★
Genaire Limited - Library
P.O. Box 84 Phone: (416)684-1165
St. Catharines, ON, Canada L2R 6R4 Angela Perri, Libn.
Remarks: FAX: (416)684-2412. No further information was supplied by respondent.

★6283★
Genaway & Associates, Inc. - Library (Info Sci)
P.O. Box 477
530 W. Regency Circle
Canfield, OH 44406 Phone: (216)533-2194
Founded: 1970. **Staff:** 1. **Subjects:** Library and information systems. **Holdings:** 1500 bound volumes. **Subscriptions:** 51 journals and other serials. **Services:** Library not open to the public. **Computerized Information Services:** DIALOG Information Services. Performs searches on fee basis.

★6284★
GenCorp - Research Division Information Center (Sci-Engr)
2990 Gilchrist Rd. Phone: (216)794-6384
Akron, OH 44305 William F. Hollis, Hd., Info.Ctr.
Founded: 1946. **Staff:** Prof 1; Other 1. **Subjects:** Rubber and plastics; chemistry - inorganic, organic, analytical; composites; research management. **Holdings:** Figures not available. **Subscriptions:** 350 journals and other serials. **Services:** Interlibrary loan; center not open to the public. **Automated Operations:** Computerized cataloging, acquisitions, serials, and circulation. **Computerized Information Services:** DIALOG Information Services, ORBIT Search Service, STN International; DIALMAIL (electronic mail service).

Gendarmerie Royale du Canada
See: **Royal Canadian Mounted Police - Canadian Police College - Law Enforcement Reference Centre** (14108)

★6285★
Genealogical Association of Southwestern Michigan - Library (Hist)
Box 573 Phone: (616)983-7002
St. Joseph, MI 49085 Harold Atwood, Libn.
Founded: 1971. **Staff:** 1; Other 1. **Subjects:** Genealogy, local history. **Holdings:** 300 books; 500 bound periodical volumes; 4 VF drawers; card file of cemetery monuments in Berrien County, MI (100,000 names). **Subscriptions:** 50 journals and other serials. **Services:** Library open to the public. **Publications:** The Pastfinder, quarterly - to association members; Cemetery Records of Bainbridge, Baroda, Bertrand, Chikaming, Coloma, Hagar, Galien, Lake, Lincoln, and New Buffalo Townships, Berrien County, MI, early 1800s to 1985. **Special Indexes:** Ancestor Charts Index (book). **Remarks:** Library is housed in the Maud Preston Palenske Memorial (St. Joseph) Public Library, 500 Market St., St. Joseph, MI 49085. The Genealogical Association is affiliated with the Fort Miami Heritage Society, 708 State St., St. Joseph, MI. **Staff:** Robert Hatch, Asst.Libn.

★6286★
Genealogical Center Library (Hist)
P.O. Box 71343
Marietta, GA 30007-1343 Barbara A. Geisert, Dir.
Founded: 1975. **Staff:** 1. **Subjects:** Genealogy. **Holdings:** 6000 regular print books; 9,000 regular print genealogical magazines. **Subscriptions:** 25 journals and other serials. **Services:** Library lends books by mail to the public on fee basis. **Automated Operations:** Computerized cataloging. **Special Catalogs:** Catalog Updates, quarterly - to library members; catalog of 45,000 surnames. **Remarks:** (404)971-5058.

★6287★
Genealogical Forum of Oregon, Inc. - Library (Hist)
1410 S.W. Morrison St., Suite 812 Phone: (503)227-2398
Portland, OR 97205 Mary Lou Stroup, Dir.
Founded: 1957. **Subjects:** Genealogy, history, vital records, census. **Special Collections:** Records of Civil War Veterans who lived in Oregon (7 index drawers); Willis Corbitt's research material (4 VF drawers; 45 notebooks); Nellie (Mrs. Harry I.) Hiday's research material (2 VF drawers). **Holdings:** 13,000 books; 5000 vertical files; unbound periodicals. **Subscriptions:** 140 genealogical journals. **Services:** Copying; library open to the public (fee for non-members). **Publications:** List of publications - available on request. **Special Indexes:** Index to Surnames on members' lineage charts (card); Index to members' Oregon pioneer ancestors (card).

★6288★
Genealogical Society of Butler County - Poplar Bluff Library (Hist)
320 N. Main
P.O. Box 426
Poplar Bluff, MO 63901 Dewayne Beck Meir
Subjects: Butler County, Southeast Missouri, multi-state exchanges. **Holdings:** 400 books; family histories; city directories and phone books; newspapers, 1893 to present, on microfilm. **Services:** Copying; library open to the public with restrictions.

Genealogical Society of the Church of Jesus Christ of Latter-Day Saints
See: **Church of Jesus Christ of Latter-Day Saints** (3651)

★6289★
Genealogical Society of Flemish Americans - Library (Hist)
18740 13 Mile Rd.
Roseville, MI 48066 Phone: (313)776-7579
Founded: 1980. **Staff:** 2. **Subjects:** Belgium - history, art, geography; Flemish and Dutch ancestry and genealogy. **Special Collections:** Census Records of Flemish Towns (1814-15). **Holdings:** 200 volumes. **Subscriptions:** 200 journals and other serials. **Services:** Genealogical research; translation (Flemish, French, Latin). **Remarks:** Seeks to promote interest in and preserve Belgian culture and history.

★6290★
Genealogical Society of New Jersey - Manuscript Collections (Hist)
Special Collections and Archives
Alexander Library
Rutgers University Phone: (908)932-7510
New Brunswick, NJ 08903 Ronald Becker, Hd., Spec.Coll
Founded: 1921. **Subjects:** Genealogical records and information pertaining to New Jersey families. **Special Collections:** Bible records (4900); gravestone records (750 cemeteries); family notes; John P. Dornan Collection; Warren P. Coon Collection; Chester Jones Revolutionary Soldier file; Drake/Rankin Collection; Eleanor Bloomfield papers; Helen P. Alleman Collection; Mead/Dey Collection; Esther Serviss Papers. **Services:** Copying; collections open to the public for reference use only. **Publications:** Genealogical Magazine of N.J., 3/year - to members; GSNJ newsletter, 2/year. **Special Indexes:** Bible records; New Jersey family files; gravestone records; John P. Dornan and Coon Collections (all on cards); finding aids.

★6291★
General Accident Group - Library
436 Walnut St., 3rd Fl. Phone: (215)625-1382
Philadelphia, PA 19105 Micheko L. Enoch, Lib.Dir.
Remarks: No further information was supplied by respondent.

★6292★
General Agreement on Tariffs and Trade - GATT Library (Bus-Fin)
Centre William Rappard
154, rue de Lausanne Phone: 22 395295
CH-1121 Geneva 21, Switzerland Jany Grandjean, Libn.
Staff: 9. **Subjects:** International trade, service industry and trade, economics, monetary and trade policy, statistics. **Special Collections:** Complete collection of GATT documents and publications. **Holdings:** 19,000 books; 1800 statistical titles; 35 titles on microfiche. **Subscriptions:** 800 journals and other serials. **Services:** Interlibrary loan; copying; SDI; library open to the public with restrictions. **Publications:** List of publications received in the GATT Library, monthly; list of periodicals; current awareness bulletin, weekly. **Remarks:** FAX: 22 7314206. Telex: 412324 GATT CH. **Staff:** John Dickson; Evelyne Lattes.

★6293★
General American Investors Co., Inc. - Library (Bus-Fin)
330 Madison Ave. Phone: (212)916-8430
New York, NY 10017 Jennifer R. Jones, Dir., Info.
Founded: 1929. **Staff:** Prof 1; Other 2. **Subjects:** Investments, finance, economics. **Special Collections:** Corporation material (including annual and quarterly reports; 3000 corporation files). **Holdings:** 750 books; 1000 subject files. **Subscriptions:** 400 journals and other serials; 10 newspapers. **Services:** Library not open to the public. **Automated Operations:** Computerized public access catalog, cataloging, and serials. **Computerized Information Services:** DIALOG Information Services, NEXIS, Dow Jones News/Retrieval; internal database.

★6294★
General Cable Company - Research Center Library (Info Sci)
160 Fieldcrest Ave. Phone: (908)225-1040
Edison, NJ 08837 Roberta Zimmerman, Libn.
Founded: 1951. **Staff:** 1. **Subjects:** Telecommunications, fiber optics, electronics, polymers and plastics, materials science. **Special Collections:** Fiber optics patents; standards and specifications. **Holdings:** 2000 books; 100 bound periodical volumes; 10,000 reprints and special subject files. **Subscriptions:** 202 journals and other serials. **Services:** Interlibrary loan; library not open to the public. **Remarks:** FAX: (201)225-1090.

★6295★
General Datacomm, Inc. - Engineering Library (Sci-Engr)
Technical Center Phone: (203)574-1118
Middlebury, CT 06762-1299 John Wiehn, Libn.
Founded: 1976. **Staff:** Prof 1. **Subjects:** Electrical engineering, data communications, telecommunications, computers. **Holdings:** 1100 books; 15 volumes of Datapro reports; 3 volumes of Federal Communications Commission rules and regulations; 35 volumes of Bell technical references; regulations and specifications. **Subscriptions:** 80 journals and other serials. **Services:** Interlibrary loan; library open to the public with permission. **Automated Operations:** Computerized cataloging and circulation. **Computerized Information Services:** DIALOG Information Services; InterNet (electronic mail service). **Networks/Consortia:** Member of Southwestern Connecticut Library Council (SWLC). **Publications:** Monthly Acquisitions List. **Remarks:** FAX: (203)755-0896. Telex: 7104740027. Electronic mail address(es): WIEHN@GDC.PORTAL.COM (InterNet).

★6296★
General Drafting Co., Inc. - Map Library
Canfield Rd.
Convent Station, NJ 07961-0109
Founded: 1909. **Subjects:** Travel, geography, cartography, maps, atlases. **Special Collections:** Exxon Road Maps (U.S. and foreign); historical material and antique items pertaining primarily to oil company maps. **Holdings:** 1500 books; 100,000 U.S. and foreign maps. **Remarks:** Currently inactive.

★6297★
General Dynamics Corporation - Air Defense Systems Division - Library Mz 4-20 (Sci-Engr, Mil)
P.O. Box 2507 Phone: (714)868-1000
Pomona, CA 91769 D.J. Patterson, Sr.Libn.
Founded: 1952. **Staff:** Prof 1. **Subjects:** Tactical missiles, electronics, optoelectronics. **Holdings:** 17,000 books; 2000 bound periodical volumes; 90,000 technical documents. **Subscriptions:** 300 journals and other serials. **Services:** Interlibrary loan; library not open to the public. **Automated Operations:** Computerized cataloging. **Computerized Information Services:** DIALOG Information Services, DTIC; STAIRS (internal database).

★6298★
General Dynamics Corporation - Convair Division - Research Library (Sci-Engr)
Box 85386 Phone: (619)547-4876
San Diego, CA 92186-5386 Robert E. Arndal, Chf.Libn.
Founded: 1956. **Staff:** Prof 3; Other 3. **Subjects:** Aerospace, aircraft, electronics, missiles, spacecraft, computer technology. **Special Collections:** NACA/NASA reports; U.S. Department of Defense report collections; American Institute of Aeronautics and Astronautics (AIAA) papers; Jane's Annual series; NATO/AGARD reports. **Holdings:** 50,000 books; 15,000 bound periodical volumes; 1.25 million microfiche. **Subscriptions:** 500 journals and other serials. **Services:** Interlibrary loan; copying; SDI; library open to the public by appointment. **Automated Operations:** Computerized cataloging. **Computerized Information Services:** DIALOG Information Services, NASA/RECON, DROLS, DTIC; STAIRS (internal database). Perform searches. **Publications:** Periodicals holding list. **Remarks:** FAX: (619)547-4000. Telex: 182751. **Staff:** Lydia M. Curry, Engr.Libn.; Linda Riley, Engr.Libn.

★6299★
General Dynamics Corporation - Electric Boat Division - Division Library (Sci-Engr)
Inter-Library Loan, Dept. 633
75 Eastern Point Rd. Phone: (203)433-3481
Groton, CT 06340-4989 Charles E. Giles, Chf.Libn.
Founded: 1955. **Staff:** Prof 1; Other 2. **Subjects:** Electrical and marine engineering, underwater sciences, naval architecture, oceanography, submarine construction, metal and metal joining, underwater acoustics. **Holdings:** 10,000 books; 3000 bound periodical volumes; 23,000 technical reports. **Subscriptions:** 650 journals and other serials. **Services:** Interlibrary loan; library not open to the public. **Computerized Information Services:** Data Trek.

★6300★
General Dynamics Corporation - Fort Worth Division Research Library (Sci-Engr)
Grant's Ln., MZ2246
Box 901022 Phone: (817)763-1792
Fort Worth, TX 76101 Maxine Merriman, Lib.Chf.
Founded: 1949. **Staff:** Prof 3; Other 2. **Subjects:** Aerospace technology, electronics, mathematics, materials technology, TQM, market analysis, competitive analysis. **Special Collections:** Technical documents (775,000 microforms). **Holdings:** 50,000 books; 10,000 bound periodical volumes; 250,000 technical reports. **Subscriptions:** 1000 journals, newspapers, and other serials. **Services:** Interlibrary loan; copying; SDI; translation; library open to the public by appointment. **Automated Operations:** Computerized public access catalog and circulation. **Computerized Information Services:** BRS Information Technologies, Aerospace Online, DIALOG Information Services, DTIC, NASA/RECON, USNI (United States Naval Institute) Military Database, WILSONLINE, STAIRS, Navy Lessons Learned, Air Force Lessons Learned, NewsNet, Inc., VU/TEXT Information Services, Data-Star, Dow Jones News/Retrieval, STN International, NEXIS, EPIC; CD-ROMs, (Applied Science & Technology Index, Business Periodicals Index, PAIS, Computer Select, DIALOG Bluesheets, Faulkner Technical Reports Infodisks, DoD Hazardous Materials Information System, International Station Meteorological Climate Summary). Performs searches on fee basis. **Publications:** Guides; accessions lists; special reports; newsletter (online). **Remarks:** FAX: (817)777-2115. Telex: 758231. **Staff:** Gale Harris; David Thurston; Linda Brown; Debra Johnson.

★6301★
General Dynamics Corporation - Public Affairs Library (Sci-Engr)
3190 Fairview Park Dr. Phone: (703)876-3183
Falls Church, VA 22042 Victoria Mueller, Lib.Supv.
Staff: Prof 2. **Subjects:** Aerospace, shipping, electronics, resources and building materials. **Holdings:** Figures not available. **Services:** Library not open to the public. **Computerized Information Services:** Mead Data Central, NEXIS, CompuServe Information Service. **Remarks:** FAX: (703)876-3125. **Formerly:** Its Infocenter located in St. Louis, MO. **Staff:** Monika Taylor.

★6302★
General Dynamics Land Systems - Technical & Administrative Information Services (Mil)
Box 1901 Phone: (313)825-4402
Warren, MI 48090 Shirley E. Maguire, Supv.
Founded: 1954. **Staff:** Prof 3; Other 2. **Subjects:** Military and special purpose vehicles, ordnance systems, robotics, electronics, manufacturing methods, materials. **Holdings:** 9000 books; 65,000 scientific and technical reports and papers; technical reference services include military and federal specifications and standards, vendor catalogs, selected industrial and international standards (microfilm and CD-ROM). **Subscriptions:** 700 journals and other serials. **Services:** Interlibrary loan; services not open to the public. **Computerized Information Services:** DIALOG Information Services, NLM, DTIC, LEXIS, NEXIS. **Publications:** Monthly accession report - to division personnel. **Remarks:** FAX: (313)825-4013. Telex: 4320117. Consists of the holdings of four branch libraries: Central Office Complex Library, P.O. Box 1901, Warren, MI 48090. Contact Person: Michaelene Iwanyckyj, (313)825-4402; Lillian Wozniak, (313)825-4405. Sterling Technology Center Library, P.O. Box 2094, Warren, MI 48090. Contact Person: Lorraine Simon, (313)978-5741. **Staff:** Michaelene Iwanyckyj. Lima Army Tank Plant Library, 1161 Buckeye Rd., Lima, OH 45804. Contact Person: Carol Andrade, (419)221-8272.

★6303★
General Dynamics Services Company - Detroit Operations - Technical Library (Mil)
P.O. Box 760 Phone: (313)244-7233
Troy, MI 48099 Elaine Arnold Rusnak, Libn.
Founded: 1985. **Staff:** Prof 1. **Subjects:** Combat tanks, logistics, management, engineering, production and quality control, materials handling, manufacturing. **Special Collections:** Army technical manuals (1500). **Holdings:** 1000 books; 350,000 engineering drawings; 30 VF drawers; military and industry standards and specifications on microfilm; 350,000 documents on microfiche. **Subscriptions:** 31 journals and other serials. **Services:** Interlibrary loan; library not open to the public. **Automated Operations:** Computerized cataloging. **Computerized Information Services:** Haystack; CD-ROM. **Networks/Consortia:** Member of Macomb Region of Cooperation. **Remarks:** FAX: (313)244-7036. **Staff:** Joylyn Evans, Tech. Data Asst.; Patrice Gillette, Rec.Mgt.Coord.

General Electric Company - Aerospace Electronic Systems Department - Engineering Library
See: **General Electric Company - AESD Engineering Library** (6304)

★6304★
General Electric Company - AESD Engineering Library (Sci-Engr)
901 Broad St. Phone: (315)793-5170
Utica, NY 13503 Lori Scoones, Libn.
Founded: 1955. **Staff:** Prof 1. **Subjects:** Aerospace electronics, radar, optics, communication, management, reliability. **Special Collections:** Institute of Electrical and Electronics Engineering (IEEE) proceedings and transactions. **Holdings:** 5000 books; 300 bound periodical volumes; 100 cassettes; 9000 technical reports. **Subscriptions:** 193 journals and other serials. **Services:** Interlibrary loan; copying; center open to the public by appointment. **Automated Operations:** Computerized cataloging, serials, and circulation. **Computerized Information Services:** DIALOG Information Services; General Electric Company Libraries (internal database). **Networks/Consortia:** Member of Central New York Library Resources Council (CENTRO). **Publications:** Library News Quarterly. **Also Known As:** Its Aerospace Electronic Systems Department - Engineering Library.

★6305★
General Electric Company - Aircraft Engine Business Group - Law Library (Law)
Mail Drop F-17
1 Neumann Way Phone: (513)243-2298
Cincinnati, OH 45215 Connie Rigsby
Founded: 1950. **Subjects:** Government contracts, labor law, patents, antitrust laws, product liability. **Holdings:** 6498 volumes; patents. **Services:** Library not open to the public.

★6306★
General Electric Company - Aircraft Engine Business Group - Technical Information Center (Sci-Engr)
Bldg. 700, N-32 Phone: (513)243-4582
Cincinnati, OH 45215-6301 L. Kozerski, Mgr.
Founded: 1950. **Staff:** Prof 1; Other 3. **Subjects:** Aerospace materials, aeronautical engineering, physical sciences, mathematics, computer science. **Special Collections:** Aircraft Engine Group Technical Information Series Reports and Technical Memoranda (50,000). **Holdings:** 20,000 books; 14,000 bound periodical volumes; 4500 pamphlets; 180,000 technical reports; 13,000 technical society papers; 5000 U.S. and foreign patents; 785,000 reports on microfiche. **Subscriptions:** 100 journals and other serials. **Services:** Center not open to the public. **Automated Operations:** Computerized circulation. **Computerized Information Services:** NERAC. **Publications:** Technical Information Preview Series (TIPS), monthly; bibliographies; biblioabstracts; special reports, all as required. **Remarks:** Alternate telephone number(s): (513)243-2132. **Staff:** P.L. Sewell, Hd.Libn.

★6307★
General Electric Company - Aircraft Engines - Dr. C.W. Smith Technical Information Center, 24001 (Sci-Engr)
1000 Western Ave. Phone: (617)594-5363
Lynn, MA 01910 Sandra S. Moltz, Supv.
Founded: 1953. **Staff:** Prof 2. **Subjects:** Aeronautics, aircraft gas turbine engines, thermodynamics, aeronautical engineering, materials science, engine noise control. **Special Collections:** C.W. Smith Collection of Gas-turbine Literature. **Holdings:** 12,000 books; 4550 bound periodical volumes; 110,000 technical reports; 15,000 microforms. **Subscriptions:** 200 journals and other serials. **Services:** Interlibrary loan; center not open to the public. **Automated Operations:** TECHLIBplus. **Computerized Information Services:** NERAC; internal databases. **Publications:** Acquisitions list, biweekly; List of Journal Holdings, annual; brochure of services. **Formerly:** Its Aircraft Engine Business Group. **Staff:** Helen G. Brown, Tech.Info.Anl.

★6308★
General Electric Company - Astro-Space Division - Libraries, Valley Forge (Sci-Engr)
Box 8555 Phone: (215)354-2110
Philadelphia, PA 19101 R. Russo, Mgr.
Founded: 1945. **Staff:** Prof 4; Other 1. **Subjects:** Aerospace technology, energy, chemistry, ocean systems, physics, sensor physics, computer technology. **Holdings:** 80,000 books; 750 bound periodical volumes; 300 audio- and videotapes; complete NASA collection on microfiche. **Subscriptions:** 495 journals and other serials. **Services:** Interlibrary loan; SDI. **Automated Operations:** Computerized cataloging and circulation. **Computerized Information Services:** DIALOG Information Services, NEXIS, WILSONLINE, Integrated Technical Information System (ITIS), NASA/RECON, DTIC, Dow Jones News/Retrieval; TISCATE (internal database). Performs searches on fee basis. **Remarks:** FAX: (215)354-2020. A branch library is maintained in East Windsor, NJ. **Staff:** M.R. Thomas, Info.Spec.; E.V Sowicz, East Windsor Libn.

★6309★
General Electric Company - Astro-Space Division - Library, East Windsor (Sci-Engr)
Box 800 Phone: (609)426-2247
Princeton, NJ 08543-0800 R. Russo, Mgr.
Founded: 1958. **Staff:** Prof 1.5. **Subjects:** Electronics, astronautics, telecommunications, computers, mechanics, remote sensing. **Special Collections:** NASA formal report series. **Holdings:** 5700 books; 400 bound periodical volumes; unbound reports and pamphlets. **Subscriptions:** 160 journals and other serials. **Services:** Interlibrary loan; copying (both limited); library open to the public with restrictions. **Computerized Information Services:** DIALOG Information Services. **Remarks:** FAX: (609)490-6121.

★6310★
General Electric Company - Corporate Information Resource Center
3135 Easton Tpke.
Fairfield, CT 06431 Denise O. Lipkvich, Mgr.
Subjects: Computers, microprocessors, software, data communications, telecommunications. **Holdings:** 1000 books; 500 reports. **Subscriptions:** 225 journals and other serials. **Services:** Interlibrary loan; library not open to the public. **Automated Operations:** Computerized acquisitions and circulation. **Computerized Information Services:** DIALOG Information Services, NewsNet, Inc., VU/TEXT Information Services, NEXIS. **Networks/Consortia:** Member of Southwestern Connecticut Library Council (SWLC). **Formerly:** Its Corporate Information Technology Library located in Bridgeport, CT.

★6311★
General Electric Company - Corporate Research & Development - Whitney Library (Sci-Engr, Energy)
Box 8
KWF 116 Phone: (518)387-6162
Schenectady, NY 12301 James M. Lommel, Mgr., Sup.Serv.
Founded: 1900. **Staff:** Prof 6; Other 4. **Subjects:** Energy, physics, chemistry, electronics, metallurgy, ceramics, mathematics. **Holdings:** 25,000 books; 35,000 bound periodical volumes; 5000 microforms. **Subscriptions:** 800 journals and other serials. **Services:** Interlibrary loan; services not open to the public. **Automated Operations:** Computerized cataloging, acquisitions, serials, and circulation. **Computerized Information Services:** DIALOG Information Services, ORBIT Search Service, BRS Information Technologies, OCLC, STN International, Dun & Bradstreet Business Credit Services, Chemical Information Systems, Inc. (CIS), NLM, Mead Data Central, NewsNet, Inc., VU/TEXT Information Services, TOXNET; CRDLib, TISCAT (internal databases). **Networks/Consortia:** Member of Capital District Library Council for Reference & Research Resources (CDLC). **Remarks:** FAX: (518)387-7593. **Staff:** David Bates, Info.Sys.Libn.; Diane Glock, Cat. & Ser.; Louise Macuirles, Ref. & ILL; Marian Smith, Lead Libn.; Carolyn Warden, Online Serv.

★6312★
General Electric Company - Defense Systems Division - Armament Systems Department - Engineering Library (Mil)
Lakeside Ave., Rm. 1320 Phone: (802)657-6886
Burlington, VT 05401-4985 Sandy Goddard, Libn.
Founded: 1949. **Staff:** Prof 1. **Subjects:** Armament and weapon systems, electronics, mathematics, integrated circuits, ammunition, ground support equipment, feed systems, fuses. **Holdings:** 5000 books; 20,000 technical reports; military, commercial, federal specifications and standards. **Subscriptions:** 300 journals and other serials. **Services:** Interlibrary loan; library not open to the public. **Remarks:** FAX: (802)657-6411.

★6313★
General Electric Company - Defense Systems Division - Engineering Library (Sci-Engr)
100 Plastics Ave., Bldg. 2, Rm. 2465 Phone: (413)494-4207
Pittsfield, MA 01201 Eileen M. O'Connor, Libn.
Founded: 1958. **Staff:** Prof 1; Other 1. **Subjects:** Electronics, inertial guidance, weapon control, ordnance equipment, metallurgy, computer science. **Holdings:** 9250 books; 2000 bound periodical volumes; 8 file cabinets of documents. **Subscriptions:** 212 journals and other serials. **Services:** Interlibrary loan; library not open to the public. **Automated Operations:** Computerized circulation. **Computerized Information Services:** DIALOG Information Services.

★6314★
General Electric Company - G.E. Lighting - Advanced Technology Library No. 5430 (Sci-Engr)
Nela Park Phone: (216)266-3216
Cleveland, OH 44112 Sandra M. Cobb, Libn.
Founded: 1914. **Staff:** Prof 1. **Subjects:** Lighting technology, ceramics, refractory metals, physical and inorganic chemistry, plasma physics, optics. **Holdings:** 10,000 books; 9500 bound periodical volumes; 250 linear feet of internal reports, manuscripts, clippings, pamphlets, dissertations, documents. **Subscriptions:** 50 journals and other serials. **Services:** Interlibrary loan; copying (both limited); SDI; library open to the public by previous arrangement. **Computerized Information Services:** DIALOG Information Services, STN International; internal database. **Publications:** Internal publications. **Remarks:** FAX: (216)266-2063.

★6315★
General Electric Company - G.E. Plastics - Information Resource Center (Sci-Engr)
1 Plastics Ave. Phone: (413)448-7345
Pittsfield, MA 01201 Nancy J. Kane, Adm.
Founded: 1978. **Staff:** Prof 1.5; Other 1. **Subjects:** Plastics technology and marketing, organic chemistry, market research and planning. **Holdings:** 4900 books; 500 technical reports, annual report files, 10K reports. **Subscriptions:** 200 journals and other serials. **Services:** Interlibrary loan; copying; SDI; center open to the public by appointment. **Automated Operations:** public access catalog, cataloging, and circulation. **Computerized Information Services:** DIALOG Information Services, ORBIT Search Service, NEXIS, Data Resources (DRI), STN International, Dow Jones News/Retrieval. **Publications:** Resource Update, quarterly - for internal distribution only. **Remarks:** FAX: (413)448-7625. **Staff:** Wayne R. Cardillo, Info.Spec.

★6316★
General Electric Company - G.E. Silicones - Library and Information Center (Sci-Engr)
Waterford, NY 12188 Phone: (518)233-2264
Marianne K. Pouliott, Libn.
Services: Library not open to the public. **Remarks:** No further information was supplied by respondent.

★6317★
General Electric Company - Information Resources Center (Sci-Engr)
Electronics Park, Bldg. 3, Rm. 154 Phone: (315)456-2023
Syracuse, NY 13221 C.S. Webb, Mgr., Info. & Engr.Rsrcs.
Founded: 1948. **Staff:** Prof 2; Other 2. **Subjects:** Electronics, microwave engineering, physics, mathematics, business, computers. **Holdings:** 13,000 books; 2000 bound periodical volumes. **Subscriptions:** 300 journals and other serials. **Services:** Interlibrary loan; center not open to the public. **Automated Operations:** Computerized cataloging and circulation. **Computerized Information Services:** DIALOG Information Services, NEXIS, Dun & Bradstreet Business Credit Services, DMS/ONLINE, VU/TEXT Information Services, NewsNet, Inc., Aerospace Online. **Networks/Consortia:** Member of Central New York Library Resources Council (CENTRO). **Publications:** Current Awareness Bulletins (30 topics), semimonthly - for internal distribution only. **Remarks:** Center serves all General Electric departments in Syracuse and various components at other GE locations. **Staff:** Gerry Radway, Info.Spec.

General Electric Company - Knolls Atomic Power Laboratory
See: **Knolls Atomic Power Laboratory** (8768)

★6318★
General Electric Company - Library (Energy)
Box 530954 Phone: (408)365-6366
San Jose, CA 95153-5354 Dorothy Hutson, Mgr., Info. & Tech.Serv.
Founded: 1968. **Staff:** Prof 1. **Subjects:** Liquid metal fast breeder reactors, nuclear energy. **Holdings:** 2500 books; 40,000 technical reports; 30,000 reports on microfiche. **Subscriptions:** 203 journals and other serials. **Services:** Interlibrary loan; library open to the public by appointment. **Automated Operations:** Computerized cataloging and serials. **Computerized Information Services:** DIALOG Information Services, Integrated Technical Information System (ITIS), OCLC, NEXIS, Dow Jones News/Retrieval; OnTyme Electronic Message Network Service (electronic mail service). **Networks/Consortia:** Member of CLASS. **Special Catalogs:** Computer produced book and report catalogs. **Remarks:** FAX: (408)365-6498. Electronic mail address(es): GES (OnTyme Electronic Message Network Service).

★6319★
General Electric Company - Nuclear Energy Group - Library (Energy)
175 Curtner Ave., M/C 728 Phone: (408)925-3522
San Jose, CA 95125 Gordon T. Stiles, Mgr., Lib.
Founded: 1955. **Staff:** 2. **Subjects:** Nuclear energy and reactors. **Holdings:** 4000 books; 60,000 documents. **Subscriptions:** 201 journals and other serials. **Services:** Interlibrary loan; copying; SDI; library open to the public by appointment. **Computerized Information Services:** DIALOG Information Services, Dow Jones News/Retrieval, OCLC; Tymnet (electronic mail service). **Remarks:** FAX: (408)925-3536. **Staff:** Mary Larson, Acq.; Audrey Crosby, Doc.

★6320★
General Electric Company - Technical Information Center (Sci-Engr)
Dept. of Energy (DOE)
Box 2908 Phone: (813)545-6797
Largo, FL 34649-2908 Patricia A. Owen, Mgr.
Founded: 1956. **Staff:** Prof 1; Other 1. **Subjects:** Engineering, physics, chemistry. **Special Collections:** Military specifications and standards. **Holdings:** 7800 books; 1000 unbound reports. **Subscriptions:** 400 journals and other serials. **Services:** Interlibrary loan; center not open to the public. **Automated Operations:** Computerized cataloging, acquisitions, serials, circulation. **Computerized Information Services:** DIALOG Information Services, STN International, LEXIS, MEDLARS, OCLC; internal databases; DIALMAIL (electronic mail service). **Networks/Consortia:** Member of SOLINET. **Remarks:** FAX: (813)545-6816.

★6321★
General Electric Company - Transportation Technology Center - Technical Information Center
42-3
2901 E. Lake Rd.
Erie, PA 16531
Defunct.

★6322★
General Electrodynamics Corporation - Library (Sci-Engr)
8000 Calendar Rd.
Arlington, TX 76017 Phone: (817)572-0366
Staff: 2. **Subjects:** Chemistry, physics, electronics, optics. **Holdings:** 500 volumes; 400 government research reports; 2 VF drawers of patents. **Subscriptions:** 20 journals and other serials. **Services:** Interlibrary loan; library not open to the public.

★6323★
General Federation of Women's Clubs - Women's History and Resource Center (Soc Sci)
1734 N St., N.W. Phone: (202)347-3168
Washington, DC 20036 Cynthia N. Swanson, Dir.
Founded: 1984. **Staff:** 2. **Subjects:** Women's history, women's issues, women's clubs, public affairs, the arts, home life. **Special Collections:** Archives of the General Federation of Women's Clubs (1890 to present; 850 linear feet); Good Housekeeping "Women in Passage" Collection on the UN Decade for Women (1975-1985; 25 linear feet). **Holdings:** 1000 volumes; 68 bound periodical volumes; 100 AV programs; 1 reel of microfilm; VF drawers; manuscripts. **Services:** Copying; center open to the public by appointment. **Computerized Information Services:** OCLC. **Publications:** Brochure. **Remarks:** Center is dedicated to women's history, with emphasis on women in volunteerism. FAX: (202)835-0246.

★6324★
General Foods Corporation - General Foods Information Services (Food-Bev, Sci-Engr)
250 North St. Phone: (914)335-6785
White Plains, NY 10625 Judy Shaw, Mgr.
Founded: 1939. **Staff:** Prof 9; Other 1. **Subjects:** Food - marketing research, business, technology, science, microbiology; organic chemistry; chemical engineering; consumers. **Holdings:** 5000 books; 3000 bound periodical volumes; 10,000 reels of microfilm. **Subscriptions:** 300 journals and other serials. **Services:** SDI; center open to SLA members. **Automated Operations:** Computerized cataloging, acquisitions, and circulation. **Computerized Information Services:** OCLC, DIALOG Information Services, STN International, NEXIS, Dow Jones News/Retrieval, Data-Star, NewsNet, Inc., PRODUCTSCAN. **Networks/Consortia:** Member of SUNY/OCLC Library Network. **Remarks:** General Foods Information Services is comprised of the Technical Information Center located at 555 S. Broadway, Tarrytown, NY 10591 and the Marketing Information Center located at the above address. **Staff:** Sara McGarty; Paul Cloutier; Susan Cronizer; Eileen Donnelly; Anne Marie Civinskas; Nancy Bobrek; Phyllis Troger; Mary Ann Swanson.

General Foods Corporation - Marketing Information Center
See: **General Foods Corporation** (6324)

General Foods Corporation - Tarrytown Technical Information Center
See: **General Foods Corporation** (6324)

General Hospital, Everett - Health Information Network Services
See: **Health Information Network Services** (7077)

★6325★
The General Hospital (Grey Nuns) of Edmonton - Health Sciences Library (Med)
11111 Jasper Ave. Phone: (403)450-7300
Edmonton, AB, Canada T6L 5X8 Jake VandeBrink
NR**Founded:** 1970. **Staff:** Prof 1; Other 4. **Subjects:** Geriatrics, medicine, nursing. **Holdings:** 5000 books; 1200 bound periodical volumes. **Subscriptions:** 425 journals and other serials. **Services:** Interlibrary loan; copying; library open to health care professionals. **Automated Operations:** Computerized public access catalog, cataloging, acquisitions, and serials. **Computerized Information Services:** MEDLINE; Envoy 100 (electronic mail service). **Publications:** Current Awareness. **Remarks:** (403)482-3702. Electronic mail address(es): GREY.NUNS (Envoy 100). **Staff:** Sheila Fynn, Lib.Techn.; Susan Gamble, Lib.Techn.

★6326★
The General Hospital (Grey Nuns) of Edmonton - Health Sciences Library (Med)
3015 62nd St. Phone: (403)450-7300
Edmonton, AB, Canada T6L 5X8 Jake VandeBrink, Lib.Mgr.
Founded: 1970. **Staff:** Prof 1; Other 5. **Subjects:** Medicine and nursing. **Special Collections:** Geriatrics. **Holdings:** 5500 books; 1900 bound periodical volumes. **Subscriptions:** 398 journals and other serials. **Services:** Interlibrary loan; copying; library open to health care professionals. **Computerized Information Services:** MEDLINE; Envoy 100 (electronic mail service). **Publications:** Medical and Nursing Update, monthly. **Remarks:** FAX: (403)482-3702. Electronic mail address(es): GREY.NUNS (Envoy 100). **Staff:** Sheila Fynn, Lib.Techn.; Sue Gamble, Lib.Techn.

General Instrument Corporation - Government Systems Division - Engineering Library
See: **Litton Applied Technology** (9220)

General Inventory of Monuments and Artistic Riches of France - Documentation Center
See: **France - Ministry of Culture - Department of Art Conservation - Office of French Museums - General Inventory of Monuments and Artistic Riches of France - Documentation Center** (6068)

General Microfilm Company
See: **OmniSys Corporation** (12416)

★6327★
General Mills, Inc. - Betty Crocker Food & Publications Information Center (Food-Bev)
P.O. Box 1113 Phone: (612)540-3595
Minneapolis, MN 55440 Judith A. Galt, Info.Spec.
Staff: 1. **Subjects:** Cookery, nutrition. **Holdings:** 2200 books. **Subscriptions:** 81 journals and other serials. **Services:** Center not open to the public. **Automated Operations:** Computerized cataloging. **Computerized Information Services:** DIALOG Information Services; internal database. **Networks/Consortia:** Member of MINITEX Library Information Network. **Remarks:** Library located at 1 General Mills Blvd., Minneapolis, MN.

★6328★
General Mills, Inc. - Business Information Center (Bus-Fin)
Box 1113 Phone: (612)540-3536
Minneapolis, MN 55440-1113 Patricia Schumacher, Mgr., Bus.Info.Ctr.
Founded: 1947. **Staff:** Prof 3; Other 3. **Subjects:** Business, marketing research, food industry. **Holdings:** 1000 books; 17,000 internal marketing research reports, hardcopy and microfiche. **Subscriptions:** 180 journals and other serials; 7 newspapers. **Services:** Interlibrary loan; center not open to the public. **Automated Operations:** Computerized cataloging. **Computerized Information Services:** DIALOG Information Services, DunsPrint, VU/TEXT Information Services, PRODUCTSCAN, DataTimes, Reuters, Dow Jones News/Retrieval, NEXIS, Data-Star, Questel; internal databases. Performs searches. **Networks/Consortia:** Member of MINITEX Library Information Network, Metronet. **Remarks:** Library located at Number One General Mills Blvd., Minneapolis, MN 55426. FAX: (612)540-4742.

★6329★
General Mills, Inc. - James Ford Bell Technical Center - Technical Information Services (Sci-Engr, Food-Bev)
9000 Plymouth Ave., N. Phone: (612)540-3464
Minneapolis, MN 55427 Jacqueline A. Angus, Supv.
Founded: 1961. **Staff:** Prof 5; Other 5. **Subjects:** Food and chemical research. **Holdings:** 8000 books; 4000 bound periodical volumes; 3000 unbound periodical volumes; 50 VF drawers of patents; 8 VF drawers of annual reports; 1300 reels of microfilm of periodicals; 1060 reels of microfilm of patents. **Subscriptions:** 900 journals and other serials. **Services:** Interlibrary loan; services not open to the public. **Automated Operations:** Computerized public access catalog, cataloging, acquisitions, and serials. **Computerized Information Services:** DIALOG Information Services, BRS Information Technologies, Info Globe, Questel, PFDS Online, Reuters, Infomart Online, STN International, Dow Jones News/Retrieval, WILSONLINE, NEXIS, LFRA FOODLINE, OCLC, NLM; internal database. **Publications:** New in Library, semimonthly; Foods Adlibra, semimonthly - by subscription. **Remarks:** FAX: (612)540-3166.

★6330★
General Mills, Inc. - Law Library (Law)
Box 1113 Phone: (612)540-2047
Minneapolis, MN 55440 Gretchen Beede, Mgr., Lib.Serv.
Staff: Prof 1; Other 1. **Subjects:** Law. **Holdings:** 10,000 volumes. **Subscriptions:** 100 journals and other serials. **Services:** Interlibrary loan; library not open to the public. **Computerized Information Services:** DIALOG Information Services, WESTLAW, LEXIS. **Remarks:** FAX: (612)540-2268.

★6331★
General Motors Corporation - AC Rochester Division - Library (Sci-Engr)
1300 N. Dort Hwy. Phone: (313)257-8183
Flint, MI 48556 Eileen L. Lane, Mgr., Lib.Serv.
Staff: Prof 1; Other 1. **Subjects:** Ceramics, engineering, automotive technology, management, computer technology. **Special Collections:** Ceramics (books and bound journals of the American Ceramic Society Bulletin, 1922 to present). **Holdings:** 6000 books; 80 bound periodical volumes; 7 VF drawers of engineering reports; 600 theses; VSMF specifications. **Subscriptions:** 700 journals and other serials. **Services:** Interlibrary loan; library not open to the public. **Computerized Information Services:** DIALOG Information Services. **Networks/Consortia:** Member of Michigan Library Consortium (MLC). **Publications:** Newsletter, 4/year - to management. **Publications:** New acquisitions list, monthly. **Remarks:** FAX: (313)257-5573.

★6332★
General Motors Corporation - Advanced Engineering Staff - MFG Library (Sci-Engr)
General Motors Technical Center, A/MD-04
30300 Mound Rd. Phone: (313)947-0778
Warren, MI 48090-9040 Jean E. Schlage, Libn.
Founded: 1973. **Staff:** Prof 1. **Subjects:** Materials science, robotics, automation, manufacturing. **Special Collections:** Machine Tool & Design Research Conference Proceedings; North American Metalworking/Manufacturing Research Conference Proceedings (NAMRC). **Holdings:** 2428 books. **Subscriptions:** 154 journals and other serials. **Services:** Interlibrary loan; library not open to the public. **Computerized Information Services:** DIALOG Information Services; internal database. **Remarks:** FAX: (313)947-2320.

★6333★
General Motors Corporation - Allison Gas Turbine Library (Sci-Engr)
Mail Code S5
Box 420 Phone: (317)230-5651
Indianapolis, IN 46206-0420 Melanie S. Johnson, Sr.Libn.
Founded: 1941. **Staff:** Prof 1; Other 3. **Subjects:** Gas turbine engines, metallurgy, fluid mechanics, heat transfer, combustion. **Special Collections:** NASA reports. **Holdings:** 10,000 books; 600 bound periodical volumes; 2000 periodicals on microfilm; 50,000 technical reports. **Subscriptions:** 400 journals and other serials. **Services:** Interlibrary loan; copying; SDI; library open to the public with restrictions. **Automated Operations:** Computerized circulation. **Computerized Information Services:** DIALOG Information Services, DROLS (Defense RTD & E Online System). **Networks/Consortia:** Member of INCOLSA. **Remarks:** FAX: (317)230-5100.

★ 6334 ★
General Motors Corporation - Current Product Engineering - Engineering Research Technology Center (Sci-Engr)
WO-ERTC
GM Engineering Bldg.
30200 Mound Rd. Phone: (313)986-6439
Warren, MI 48090-9012 Kirk E. Nims, Hd.
Founded: 1959. **Staff:** Prof 1; Other 2. **Subjects:** Automotive engineering and design, engineering, science and technology, business and management. **Holdings:** 13,155 books; 5700 periodicals, bound and on microfiche; 500 unrestricted internal reports; corporate reports; pamphlets; government documents; Society of Automotive Engineering (SAE) papers; translations; 90,000 reports, project files, documents on microfiche. **Subscriptions:** 1094 journals and other serials. **Services:** Interlibrary loan; copying; library open to the public by appointment. **Automated Operations:** Computerized cataloging, acquisitions, serials, and circulation. **Computerized Information Services:** DIALOG Information Services, PFDS Online, ESA/IRS; DIALMAIL (electronic mail service). **Remarks:** FAX: (313)986-6828. **Formerly:** Its Engineering Library & Information Services.

★ 6335 ★
General Motors Corporation - Delco Chassis Market Research Department (Bus-Fin)
2000 Forrer Blvd. Phone: (513)455-9182
Dayton, OH 45420 Tara L. Carncross, Libn.
Founded: 1908 **Staff:** Prof 1. **Subjects:** Manufacturing, management, marketing, design materials, assembly and testing. **Special Collections:** ASTM references; ASM references; SAE publications. **Holdings:** 700 books. **Subscriptions:** 110 journals and other serials. **Automated Operations:** Computerized acquisitions and serials. **Computerized Information Services:** DIALOG Information Services, NEXIS, NERAC, Inc., PRS Corporate Information Services. Performs searches. **Remarks:** FAX: (513)455-7686. **Formerly:** Its Delco Products Information Resource Center.

General Motors Corporation - Delco Products Information Resource Center
See: **General Motors Corporation - Delco Chassis Market Research Department** (6335)

★ 6336 ★
General Motors Corporation - Design Staff Library (Art, Trans)
General Motors Technical Center
30100 Mound Rd. Phone: (313)986-4675
Warren, MI 48090-9030 Richard E. Stoey, Libn.
Founded: 1945. **Staff:** Prof 1. **Subjects:** Industrial and automotive design, art. **Special Collections:** General Motors, American, and foreign automobile brochures and advertisements (80 VF drawers). **Holdings:** 2100 books; 470 bound periodical volumes; 24 VF drawers. **Subscriptions:** 123 journals and other serials. **Services:** Interlibrary loan; library not open to the public. **Computerized Information Services:** DIALOG Information Services. **Special Indexes:** Road Test Index.

★ 6337 ★
General Motors Corporation - Economic Information Center - Detroit (Bus-Fin)
15-248-A General Motors Bldg.
3044 W. Grand Blvd. Phone: (313)556-3008
Detroit, MI 48202 Karen L. Stephens, Sr.Libn.
Founded: 1950. **Staff:** Prof 2; Other 1. **Subjects:** U.S. and international economics, motor vehicle industry. **Holdings:** 2500 books; 20 VF drawers of motor vehicle industry studies; government documents. **Subscriptions:** 100 journals and other serials; 5 newspapers. **Services:** Center not open to the public. **Automated Operations:** Computerized cataloging and circulation. **Computerized Information Services:** DIALOG Information Services, LEXIS, NEXIS, Reuters, DataTimes. **Remarks:** FAX: (313)974-7165. Telex: 425543.

★ 6338 ★
General Motors Corporation - Economics Information Center - New York
767 Fifth Ave., 26th Fl.
New York, NY 10153
Defunct.

★ 6339 ★
General Motors Corporation - Electro-Motive Division - Engineering Library (Sci-Engr)
9301 55th St. Phone: (708)387-6706
La Grange, IL 60525 Vicky Arcabos, Libn.
Founded: 1935. **Staff:** Prof 1. **Subjects:** Diesel engines, gas turbines, locomotives, industrial and marine engines, power plants. **Holdings:** 4000 books; 23 bound periodical titles; 3000 reports. **Subscriptions:** 70 journals and other serials. **Services:** Library not open to the public. **Remarks:** FAX: (312)387-3530.

★ 6340 ★
General Motors Corporation - Legal Staff Library (Law)
New Center One Bldg., 8th Fl.
3031 W. Grand Blvd.
Box 33121 Phone: (313)974-1900
Detroit, MI 48232 Marianne E. Maher, Legal Staff Libn.
Founded: 1941. **Staff:** Prof 1; Other 4. **Subjects:** Law - Anglo-American, foreign, international. **Special Collections:** Selected legislative histories; statutes for 50 states; state administrative regulations. **Holdings:** 70,000 volumes; U.S. Hearings and Reports. **Subscriptions:** 300 journals and other serials; 15 newspapers. **Services:** Interlibrary loan; library not open to the public. **Computerized Information Services:** LEXIS, NEXIS, WESTLAW, Dow Jones News/Retrieval, NewsNet, Inc., VU/TEXT Information Services, DIALOG Information Services, OCLC, FLIS (Franchise Law Information System); EasyLink (electronic mail service). **Networks/Consortia:** Member of Michigan Library Consortium (MLC). **Publications:** New books list, monthly; videotapes list, semiannual. **Remarks:** FAX: (313)974-1484.

★ 6341 ★
General Motors Corporation - Public Affairs Information Services (Bus-Fin)
General Motors Bldg., Rm. 11-235
3044 W. Grand Blvd. Phone: (313)556-2051
Detroit, MI 48202 Suzanne M. Petre, Coord.
Founded: 1946. **Staff:** Prof 3; Other 3. **Subjects:** Automotive industry (nontechnical material), business, economics, public relations, labor relations, government affairs. **Special Collections:** Publications by and about General Motors Corporation and its divisions. **Holdings:** 7500 books; 350 bound periodical volumes; 10,000 pamphlets. **Subscriptions:** 200 journals and other serials; 10 newspapers. **Services:** Services not open to the public. **Computerized Information Services:** DIALOG Information Services, DunsPrint, VU/TEXT Information Services, NEXIS, DataTimes, NewsNet, Inc., Dow Jones News/Retrieval, Reuters, Data-Star. **Staff:** Catherine F. Cochran, Supv.; Kathleen Presnail, Libn.

★ 6342 ★
General Motors Corporation - Research Laboratories Library (Sci-Engr)
30500 Mound Rd.
Box 9059 Phone: (313)986-3314
Warren, MI 48090-9059 Helene A. Brown, Chf.Libn.
Founded: 1920. **Staff:** Prof 8; Other 8. **Subjects:** Automotive engineering, physical sciences, mechanical engineering, chemistry, biomedicine, electronics, manufacturing safety, environment. **Special Collections:** Automotive catalogs; SAE publications. **Holdings:** 47,000 books; 50,000 bound periodical volumes. **Subscriptions:** 800 journals. **Computerized Information Services:** DIALOG Information Services, PFDS Online, STN International, OCLC, MEDLARS, Dow Jones News/Retrieval, LEXIS, NEXIS, BRS Information Technologies, EPIC, WILSONLINE, Data-Star, CompuServe Information Service, NewsNet, Inc. **Remarks:** FAX: (313)986-9378. **Staff:** Ernest L. Horne, Sr.Libn.; Diane P. Landsiedel, Sr.Libn.; Margaret E. Shepard, Sr.Libn.; Patricia R. Bristor, Sr.Libn.; Jean E. Schlage, Libn.; Lourdes P. Lim, Libn.; Mary L. Dalzell, Libn.

★ 6343 ★
General Motors Corporation - Tax Staff Library (Law)
3044 W. Grand Blvd., Rm. 14262 Phone: (313)556-1567
Detroit, MI 48202 Kathryn Wagnitz, Libn.
Founded: 1966. **Staff:** 1. **Subjects:** Foreign and domestic tax law, employee benefits. **Special Collections:** Canadian income tax law (250 volumes). **Holdings:** 4100 books; 270 bound periodical volumes; 1600 loose-leaf services; 4500 United States and Canadian bills of importance; 400 reels of microfilm. **Subscriptions:** 200 journals and other serials. **Services:** Interlibrary loan; library not open to the public. **Computerized Information Services:** LEXIS. **Publications:** Acquisition and selected reading list, bimonthly - for internal distribution only. **Remarks:** FAX: (313)556-7616.

General Radio Company
See: **GenRad, Inc.** (6359)

★6344★
General Railway Signal Co. - Technical Library (Sci-Engr)
Box 20600 Phone: (716)783-2106
Rochester, NY 14602-0600 Sandra E. Erickson, Tech.Libn.
Founded: 1967. **Staff:** Prof 1. **Subjects:** Electrical and systems engineering, electronics, railroads, rapid transit. **Special Collections:** Railroads/ Railroading (historical collection of early journals and proceedings). **Holdings:** 1800 books; 2000 technical reports; archival materials. **Subscriptions:** 237 journals and other serials. **Services:** Interlibrary loan; copying; SDI; library open to the public by appointment. **Computerized Information Services:** OCLC, DIALOG Information Services, PFDS Online, WILSONLINE, INVESTEXT. **Networks/Consortia:** Member of Rochester Regional Library Council (RRLC). **Publications:** SDI Journal Publication, weekly. **Remarks:** Library located at 801 West Ave., Rochester, NY 14611. FAX: (716)783-2080. Telex: 978317.

★6345★
General Refractories Company - U.S. Refractories Division - Research & Development Center Library (Sci-Engr)
400 Refractory Dr., N.W.
Warren, OH 44483 Phone: (216)847-9333
Staff: 1. **Subjects:** Refractories, ceramics, mineralogy, chemical and metallurgical engineering, petrography, chemistry, spectroscopy. **Holdings:** 300 books; 400 bound periodical volumes; 130 U.S. Bureau of Mines reports; 4 boxes of technical papers; 11 boxes of technical reports from U.S. and technical societies. **Subscriptions:** 30 journals and other serials. **Services:** Library not open to the public. **Remarks:** FAX: (216)847-8184.

★6346★
General Research Corporation - Library (Sci-Engr)
Box 6770 Phone: (805)964-7724
Santa Barbara, CA 93160 William Morlan, Supv., Acq.
Founded: 1961. **Staff:** Prof 2. **Subjects:** Aerospace technology, radar and systems analysis, data processing, computer science, transportation, mathematics. **Holdings:** 7000 volumes. **Subscriptions:** 165 journals and other serials; 8 newspapers. **Services:** Interlibrary loan; library not open to the public.

★6347★
General Research Corporation - Library (Sci-Engr, Mil)
1900 Gallows Rd. Phone: (703)506-5000
Vienna, VA 22182 Luci Bugg, Dir., Fac.Serv.
Founded: 1948. **Staff:** Prof 1; Other 1. **Subjects:** Research and development, biomedical sciences, military history, economics, mathematics, statistics, operations research. **Special Collections:** World War II history; operations research history. **Holdings:** 27,500 books; 400 bound periodical volumes. **Subscriptions:** 250 journals and other serials. **Services:** Interlibrary loan; copying; library open to the public with restrictions. **Computerized Information Services:** DIALOG Information Services. **Special Catalogs:** Index to operations research literature (card). **Remarks:** FAX: (703)356-4289. Contains the holdings of its former SWL library. **Staff:** Cathy Gordon, SWL.

★6348★
General Services Administration - Consumer Information Center (Soc Sci)
18th & F St., N.W., Rm. G-142 Phone: (202)501-1794
Washington, DC 20405 Teresa Nasif, Dir.
Founded: 1970. **Staff:** 20. **Subjects:** Federal programs, money, children, careers, education, health, food and nutrition, travel, housing. **Holdings:** 200 pamphlets. **Services:** News release and script service available to the media and interested educators; center not open to the public. **Special Catalogs:** Consumer Information Catalog, quarterly - free upon request. **Remarks:** The mailing address for publications is Consumer Information Center, Pueblo, CO 81009. FAX: (202)501-4281. **Also Known As:** GSA. **Staff:** Teresa Nasif, Dir., Pubn./Media Div.; Gerald A. Young, Dir., Prog.Sup.Div.; Sara Niccum, Ed.

★6349★
General Services Administration - GSA Library (Sci-Engr)
General Services Bldg., Rm. 1033
18th & F Sts., N.W. Phone: (202)501-0788
Washington, DC 20405 Gail L. Kohlhorst, Chf.
Founded: 1961. **Staff:** Prof 5; Other 3. **Subjects:** Building technology, telecommunications, procurement, real property, information resources management, architecture, management. **Special Collections:** Legislative histories of public laws of interest to General Services Administration; historic and official documents dealing with U.S. public buildings; Federal Acquisition Institute Library (historic and current materials on federal procurement). **Holdings:** 130,000 books; 3000 bound periodical volumes; 15,000 government documents; 4000 microforms; 9000 unbound reports, theses, handbooks, periodicals. **Subscriptions:** 303 journals and other serials. **Services:** Interlibrary loan; copying; SDI; library open to the public for reference use only. **Automated Operations:** Computerized cataloging. **Computerized Information Services:** DIALOG Information Services, NEXIS, WESTLAW, OCLC. **Networks/Consortia:** Member of FEDLINK. **Publications:** Current Literature, quarterly - for internal distribution only. **Special Catalogs:** Catalog of federal procurement and contracting (card). **Staff:** Helen Bradley, Asst.Chf.; Darwin Koester, Gen.Ref.Libn.; Jess Hawkins, Law Libn.; Barbara Cortina, Sys.Libn.

★6350★
General Society of Mayflower Descendants - Mayflower Descendant Library (Hist)
4 Winslow St.
Box 3297 Phone: (508)746-3188
Plymouth, MA 02361 Caroline Lewis Kardell, Hist. General
Subjects: Descendants of Mayflower passengers, family genealogy. **Special Collections:** Pilgrims collection. **Holdings:** 2500 books; bound periodical volumes. **Services:** Copying; library open to the public with restrictions.

★6351★
General Society of Mechanics and Tradesmen - Library (Hum)
20 W. 44th St. Phone: (212)921-1767
New York, NY 10036 Margery Peters, Libn.
Founded: 1820. **Staff:** Prof 1; Other 3. **Subjects:** History, biography, fiction. **Special Collections:** Gilbert and Sullivan. **Holdings:** 140,000 volumes. **Subscriptions:** 35 journals and other serials. **Services:** Library open to the public with fee for borrowing. **Networks/Consortia:** Member of New York Metropolitan Reference and Research Library Agency.

General Steel Wares Archive
See: **McMaster University - The William Ready Division of Archives and Research Collections** (9954)

General Synod of the Church of England - Council for the Care of Churches
See: **Council for the Care of Churches** (4360)

General Theological Center of Maine
See: **Bangor Theological Seminary** (1471)

★6352★
General Theological Seminary - St. Mark's Library (Rel-Phil)
175 Ninth Ave. Phone: (212)243-5150
New York, NY 10011 David Green, Lib.Dir.
Founded: 1817. **Staff:** Prof 3; Other 4. **Subjects:** Biblical studies, theology, patristics, church history, ecumenical movement, liturgics, English theology. **Special Collections:** Latin Bible (800 editions); Early English Theology Collection (Church of England; 6600 titles printed before 1701); Protestant Episcopal Church in the U.S.A. materials (printed and manuscript). **Holdings:** 220,000 books; manuscripts; clippings; microforms. **Subscriptions:** 1100 journals and other serials. **Services:** Interlibrary loan; library open to the public with a letter of introduction from Episcopal clergy, or from university or college faculty. **Automated Operations:** Computerized cataloging and circulation. **Computerized Information Services:** DIALOG Information Services. **Publications:** Annual report; accessions list, monthly. **Remarks:** FAX: (212)727-3907. **Staff:** William Watson, Hd., Tech.Serv.; Matthew Grande, Hd., Pub.Serv.

★6353★
Genesee County Circuit Court - Law Library (Law)
401 County Court House
900 S. Saginaw St. Phone: (313)257-3253
Flint, MI 48502 Janet E. Patsy, Law Libn.
Staff: 1. **Subjects:** Law. **Special Collections:** Michigan Supreme Court records and briefs, 1977 to present. **Holdings:** 21,000 books; 200 bound periodical volumes. **Subscriptions:** 75 journals and other serials. **Services:** Copying; library open to the public.

★6354★
Genesee County History Department - Research Library (Hist)
131 W. Main St. Phone: (716)343-1164
Batavia, NY 14020 Susan L. Conklin, County Hist.
Founded: 1977. **Staff:** Prof 2. **Subjects:** History - local, area (original Genesee County), state; western New York land grants and genealogy records; famous people of the area. **Special Collections:** Captain Charles Rand; General Emory Upton; General Ely Parker; William Morgan; Genesee County early railroads; area industries and architecture; Staples Genealogy of the Town of Elba; Cooley's genealogy file; Saulsbury Notes; tax rolls, 1838-1905. **Holdings:** 1663 books; 400 bound periodical volumes; 32 bound atlases; 28 reels of microfilm; 50 reels of microfilm of Federal Census of Genesee County, 1810-1880; 11 bound volumes of Genesee County Federal Census Records, 1820-1880; daily newspapers, 1823-1974; VF drawers of people, places, things, organizations, churches, schools, local history; historical society newsletters; genealogical queries and answers; early tax rolls, 1850-1905. **Services:** Copying; library open to the public on a limited sc hedule. **Publications:** Bridges - A Resource for 4th Grade Study of Local History; brochures on local history. **Staff:** Lois Brockway, Ck., Hist.Dept.

★6355★
Genesee County Metropolitan Planning Commission - Library (Plan)
1101 Beach St., Rm. 223 Phone: (313)257-3010
Flint, MI 48502-1470 Kimberly A. Shields, Data Mgr.
Staff: 1. **Subjects:** Water quality, transportation, housing, land use. **Special Collections:** Census data (1970, 1980, 1990). **Holdings:** 4000 volumes; 2 VF drawers of newspaper clippings; 2 VF drawers of agency newsletters. **Subscriptions:** 13 journals and other serials. **Services:** Copying; library open to the public with restrictions. **Networks/Consortia:** Member of Michigan Information Center (MIC). **Publications:** New Publications in the GLS Library (newsletter) - by request. **Remarks:** FAX: (313)257-3185. **Formerly:** Genesee-Lapeer-Shiawassee Region V Planning & Development Commission - Library.

★6356★
Genesee Hospital - Samuel J. Stabins, M.D. Medical Library (Med)
224 Alexander St. Phone: (716)263-6305
Rochester, NY 14607 Sally M. Gerling, Chf.Libn.
Staff: Prof 1; Other 4. **Subjects:** Medicine, nursing, allied health sciences. **Holdings:** 4000 books; 4700 bound periodical volumes; slide/tape sets; audio- and videotapes. **Subscriptions:** 250 journals and other serials. **Services:** Interlibrary loan; SDI; library open to health professionals only. **Computerized Information Services:** BRS Information Technologies, OCLC, MEDLINE; CD-ROM (MEDLINE); DOCLINE (electronic mail service). **Networks/Consortia:** Member of Rochester Regional Library Council (RRLC). **Remarks:** FAX: (716)263-2925.

Genesee-Lapeer-Shiawassee Region V Planning & Development Commission - Library
See: **Genesee County Metropolitan Planning Commission** (6355)

★6357★
Genetics Institute - Information Center (Biol Sci)
87 Cambridge Park Dr. Phone: (617)876-1170
Cambridge, MA 02140 Beth E. Smith, Info.Ctr.Mgr.
Founded: 1981. **Staff:** Prof 2; Other 6. **Subjects:** Biotechnology, genetics, pharmaceuticals. **Holdings:** 4000 books; 5500 bound periodical volumes; 6000 patents. **Subscriptions:** 425 journals and other serials. **Services:** Center not open to the public. **Automated Operations:** Computerized public access catalog. **Computerized Information Services:** DIALOG Information Services, BRS Information Technologies, Data-Star, ORBIT Search Service, NLM, STN International, LEXIS, NEXIS, Dow Jones News/Retrieval; internal database. **Networks/Consortia:** Member of NELINET, Inc. **Remarks:** FAX: (617)876-1504.

★6358★
Geneva Historical Society - James D. Luckett Memorial Archives (Hist)
543 S. Main St. Phone: (315)789-5151
Geneva, NY 14456 Eleanore R. Clise, Archv.
Founded: 1960. **Staff:** 3. **Subjects:** Local history, architecture, genealogy. **Special Collections:** James G. Vail collection of photographic plates of Geneva scenes and genre, 1862-1880 (900 subjects); Dr. G.J. Hucker slide collection of Geneva, events, scenes, and buildings, 1945-1987 (17,000 slides). **Holdings:** 5500 books; 50,000 photographs; 185 boxes and 20 VF drawers of clippings, manuscripts, pamphlets, documents, diaries; 39 reels of microfilm of 19th century Geneva newspapers; 27 reels of microfilm of federal and state census for Ontario County, NY, 1820-1925; 7 reels of microfilm of early Geneva church records; 64 cassette tapes of local oral history. **Services:** Copying; genealogical research; archives open to the public for reference use only. **Also Known As:** Prouty-Chew Museum and Library.

Geneva Medical College Library
See: **State University of New York Health Science Center at Syracuse - Library** (15745)

Gennadius Library
See: **American School of Classical Studies at Athens** (735)

★6359★
GenRad, Inc. - Information Center (Comp Sci)
300 Baker Ave., 3rd Fl. Phone: (508)369-4400
Concord, MA 01742-2174 Bonnie Duffy, Libn.
Founded: 1983. **Staff:** Prof 1. **Subjects:** Software engineering, marketing, electronics, management, business, new technologies. **Holdings:** 800 books; 2000 issues of trade journals; 250 reels of microfilm; internal training materials. **Subscriptions:** 73 journals and other serials. **Services:** Interlibrary loan; center not open to the public. **Computerized Information Services:** DIALOG Information Services, BRS Information Technologies, VU/TEXT Information Services, EdVENT. **Networks/Consortia:** Member of Northeast Consortium of Colleges and Universities in Massachusetts (NECCUM). **Publications:** Book News, monthly; Journal List, semiannual; Bibliography on Quality. **Also Known As:** General Radio Company.

★6360★
Genzyme Corp. - Information Services (Biol Sci)
1 Mountain Rd. Phone: (508)872-8400
Framingham, MA 01701 Dawn Renear, Dir.
Founded: 1982. **Staff:** 5.5. **Subjects:** Recombinant DNA, molecular biology, research biologicals, diagnostics. **Holdings:** 2000 books; 825 bound periodical volumes; 1600 documents; 1500 slides. **Subscriptions:** 333 journals and other serials. **Services:** Interlibrary loan; services not open to the public. **Computerized Information Services:** BRS Information Technologies, Data-Star, DIALOG Information Services, MEDLARS, STN International; internal databases. **Networks/Consortia:** Member of NELINET, Inc. **Remarks:** FAX: (508)872-9080. Telex: 928105 US25. **Staff:** Joseph LoRusso; Elizabeth Hesse Burton.

★6361★
Geographic Society of Lima - Geographic Library (Geog-Map, Plan)
Casilla 100-1176
Lima, Peru Phone: 14 273723
Founded: 1888. **Subjects:** Peruvian geography and land use. **Holdings:** 16,000 volumes. **Services:** Copying; library open to researchers and members only. **Computerized Information Services:** Internal database. **Special Indexes:** Indice Analitico del Boletin 1891-1989. **Remarks:** FAX: 14 369204. **Also Known As:** Sociedad Geografica de Lima. **Staff:** Dr. Elsa Camayo Vivario.

★6362★
Geographical Society of Philadelphia - Library
21 S. 12th St., Rm. 909
Philadelphia, PA 19107
Founded: 1891. **Subjects:** Travel and exploration. **Holdings:** 2000 books. **Remarks:** Currently inactive but its resources can be made available to researchers in the fields of geography, exploration, and travel, especially on subjects involving the Arctic and Antarctic.

Geologian Tutkimuskeskus
See: **Geological Survey of Finland** (6366)

★6363★
Geological Survey of Alabama - Library (Energy, Sci-Engr)
P.O. Box O Phone: (205)349-2852
Tuscaloosa, AL 35486 Marcia A. Irvin, Dir./Geol.
Founded: 1873. **Staff:** Prof 2. **Subjects:** Geology, paleontology, hydrology, oil and gas, geophysics, energy resources research, economic geology. **Special Collections:** Earth Science Information Center (ESIC-Federal) Air Photos, Maps, and Landsats. **Holdings:** 100,000 monographs, government documents, and state materials; 22 films; 6 VF drawers of manuscripts; 325 theses. **Subscriptions:** 100 journals and other serials. **Services:** Copying; library open to the public for reference use only. **Computerized Information Services:** CD-ROM (Geological Reference File). **Publications:** Bibliographies. **Remarks:** FAX: (205)349-2852, ext. 294. **Formerly:** Its Information Services Section & Library. **Also Known As:** Alabama Geological Survey. **Staff:** Dorothy L. Brady, Libn.

★6364★
Geological Survey of Austria - Library (Sci-Engr)
Rasumofskygasse 23
P.O. Box 154 Phone: 222 71256740
A-1031 Vienna, Austria Dr. Tillfried Cernajsek, Hd.
Founded: 1849. **Staff:** Prof 3; Other 3. **Subjects:** Geological mapping, exploration for mineral resources, engineering geology, hydrogeology. **Special Collections:** Geoscientific maps (38,000); science archives. **Holdings:** 55,000 books; 170,000 bound periodical volumes; 10,000 microforms; 8000 other cataloged items. **Subscriptions:** 1260 journals and other serials. **Services:** Interlibrary loan; copying; library open to the public. **Computerized Information Services:** GEOKART, GEOLIT (internal databases). Performs searches free of charge. **Remarks:** Maintained by Austria - Ministry of Science and Research. FAX: 222 712567456. Telex: 13 29 27. **Also Known As:** Bundesministerium fur Wissenschaft und Forschung - Bibliothek der Geologischen Bundesanstalt. **Staff:** Johanna Findl; Dr. Froud Haydari; Martina Steinboch.

Geological Survey of Canada
See: **Canada - Geological Survey of Canada** (2747)

★6365★
Geological Survey of Denmark - Library (Sci-Engr)
Thoravej 8 Phone: 31 106600
DK-2400 Copenhagen NV, Denmark Dorrit Korinth Jeppesen
Subjects: Geology, geochemistry, raw materials, groundwater, oil and gas, geothermal energy. **Special Collections:** Geological maps. **Holdings:** 35,000 items. **Subscriptions:** 170 journals and other serials. **Services:** Interlibrary loan; copying; library open to the public. **Computerized Information Services:** DIALOG Information Services, ESA/IRS, FIZ Technik. **Remarks:** FAX: 31 196868. Telex: 19999 dangeo dk. Survey is a research and advisory institution of Denmark - Ministry of Environment. **Also Known As:** Danmarks Geologiske Undersogelse.

★6366★
Geological Survey of Finland - Library (Sci-Engr)
Betonimiehenkuja 4 Phone: 0 46931
SF-02150 Espoo 15, Finland Helka Lauerma, Libn.
Founded: 1885. **Staff:** Prof 4; Other 2. **Subjects:** Geology, petrology, mineral resources, geophysics, geochemistry. **Holdings:** 128,000 volumes; 18,000 maps. **Subscriptions:** 930 journals and other serials. **Services:** Interlibrary loan; copying; SDI; library open to the public. **Computerized Information Services:** ORBIT Search Service; CD-ROM (GeoRef); FINGEO (internal database). Performs searches on fee basis. Contact Person: Lahja Voutilainen, Hd. **Remarks:** FAX: 90 462 205. Telex: 123185 geolo st. Maintained by Finland - Ministry of Commerce and Industry. **Also Known As:** Geologian Tutkimuskeskus. **Staff:** Jani Hurstinen, Fingeo; Liisa Vuorela, ILL; Kristiina Alho, Maps.

★6367★
Geological Survey of South Africa - Library (Sci-Engr)
280 Pretoria St.
Silverton
Private Bag X112 Phone: 12 8411000
Pretoria 0001, Republic of South Africa Mrs. L. Niebuhr, Sr.Libn.
Staff: 6. **Subjects:** Geology - general, structural, petrographic, stratigraphic, paleontologic, sedimentologic; geophysics; mineral resources; fossil fuels; mineralogy; petrology; geochemistry; engineering geology. **Special Collections:** Map Library (10,000). **Holdings:** 100,000 volumes. **Subscriptions:** 538 journals and other serials. **Services:** Interlibrary loan; copying; library open to the public. **Computerized Information Services:** SABINET, SLS Information Services; CD-ROM (GeoRef); SAGEOLIT (internal database). **Publications:** Bibliography and Subject Index of South African Geological Literature, annual. **Remarks:** FAX: 12 8411203. Alternate telephone number(s): 12 8411001; 12 841-1002; 12 8411045 (map library). Maintained by South Africa - Department of Mineral and Energy Affairs. **Staff:** Michelle Humphris, Libn.; Mrs. E.E. Vermeulen, Hd., Map Lib.

★6368★
Geological Survey of Wyoming - Public Records Section (Sci-Engr)
Box 3008, University Sta. Phone: (307)766-2286
Laramie, WY 82071 Gary B. Glass, State Geol.
Founded: 1933. **Staff:** 1. **Subjects:** Mineral resources, environment, oil and gas, geology. **Holdings:** 100 books; 1000 unbound reports and periodicals; 20,000 oil and gas records; 2000 mineral files; 3000 maps and miscellanea. **Subscriptions:** 60 journals and other serials. **Services:** Copying; section open to the public for reference use only. **Publications:** List of publications - available on request. **Special Indexes:** Oil and Gas (card); USGS open-file reports (card); index to geologic maps of Wyoming; indexes to theses and dissertations on Wyoming geology. **Remarks:** FAX: (307)766-2605. **Also Known As:** Wyoming (State) Geological Survey.

★6369★
Geomet Technologies Inc. - Information Center (Med)
20251 Century Blvd. Phone: (301)428-9898
Germantown, MD 20874 Kris Hinkley, Libn.
Founded: 1967. **Staff:** Prof 1; Other 2. **Subjects:** Toxicology, environmental health, hazardous waste, ventilation systems, atmospheric environment, indoor air quality, electromagnetic fields, weatherization techniques. **Holdings:** 400 books. **Subscriptions:** 30 journals and other serials; 3 newspapers. **Services:** Interlibrary loan; center not open to the public. **Computerized Information Services:** DIALOG Information Services, PFDS Online, NLM. **Remarks:** FAX: (301)428-9482.

Geon Vinyl Division
See: **B.F. Goodrich Company - Geon Vinyl Division - ALTC Information Center** (6566)

★6370★
Henry George Foundation of America - Center for the Study of Economics (Bus-Fin)
2000 Century Plaza, Suite 238 Phone: (301)740-1177
Columbia, MD 21044 Sharon Reynolds, Libn.
Founded: 1926. **Staff:** 3. **Subjects:** Economics, property taxation, land value taxation, urban growth. **Special Collections:** Henry George's philosophy and economics. **Holdings:** 205 volumes; newsletters; pamphlets. **Services:** Interlibrary loan; copying; SDI; center open to the public. **Publications:** Incentive Taxation, 8/year - by subscription and on request.

★6371★
Henry George Research Library (Bus-Fin)
121 E. 30th St. Phone: (212)689-0075
New York, NY 10016 Mark A. Sullivan, Libn.
Founded: 1932. **Subjects:** Henry George Sr., single tax, land value tax, economics. **Holdings:** 6000 books; 300 bound periodical volumes; 100 manuscripts. **Remarks:** Alternate telephone number(s): (212)889-8020.

★6372★
Henry George School of Los Angeles - Research Library (Bus-Fin)
10242 Mahogany Trail
Box 655 Phone: (818)352-4141
Tujunga, CA 91042 Mrs. G.E. Pollard, Libn.
Founded: 1949. **Staff:** 3. **Subjects:** Henry George, land-value taxation, single tax history, political economy theory, tax practices, property tax analysis. **Holdings:** 2000 books. **Subscriptions:** 12 journals and other serials. **Services:** Copying; library open to the public by appointment. **Computerized Information Services:** Internal database. **Publications:** The Good Society, quarterly. **Remarks:** FAX: (818)353-2242

★6373★
Henry George School of Social Science - Research Library
1568 Shrader St.
San Francisco, CA 95124
Founded: 1949. **Subjects:** Land economics, economics, tax, land value taxation, social justice. **Holdings:** 450 volumes; 3 VF drawers of news clippings; 300 pamphlets. **Remarks:** Currently inactive.

★6374★
Georgetown Public Library (Hist)
10 W. Pine St. Phone: (302)856-7958
Georgetown, DE 19947 Kelly Jowett
Staff: Prof 2; Other 3. **Special Collections:** History of Delaware and Georgetown. **Services:** Interlibrary loan; copying; library open to the public.

★6375★
Georgetown University - Blommer Science Library (Sci-Engr)
Reiss Science Bldg., 3rd Fl. Phone: (202)687-5651
Washington, DC 20057-1006 Margaret O'Rourke, Sci.Libn.
Founded: 1962. **Staff:** Prof 2; Other 2. **Subjects:** Chemistry, physics, biology, mathematics, computer science, general science. **Holdings:** 66,500 volumes; 160 motion picture loop cassettes. **Subscriptions:** 1500 journals and other serials. **Services:** Interlibrary loan; copying; library open to the public. **Automated Operations:** Computerized public access catalog, cataloging, and acquisitions. **Computerized Information Services:** OCLC, DIALOG Information Services, BRS Information Technologies, STN International. **Networks/Consortia:** Member of CAPCON Library Network. **Remarks:** FAX: (202)687-5897. **Staff:** Susan Makar, Asst.Sci.Libn.

★6376★
Georgetown University - Edward Bennett Williams Law Library (Law)
111 G St., N.W. Phone: (202)662-9140
Washington, DC 20001 Robert L. Oakley, Law Libn.
Founded: 1887. **Staff:** Prof 20; Other 45. **Subjects:** Law, international law. **Special Collections:** Environmental Resources; Federal Legislative Histories; United Nations documents. **Holdings:** 339,920 volumes; 1.4 million microforms. **Subscriptions:** 9243 journals and other serials. **Services:** Interlibrary loan; copying; library open to alumni and attorneys with restrictions. **Automated Operations:** Computerized public access catalog, cataloging, acquisitions, circulation, and serials. **Computerized Information Services:** LEXIS, NEXIS, WESTLAW, DIALOG Information Services, WILSONLINE, VU/TEXT Information Services, QL Systems. **Networks/Consortia:** Member of Consortium of Universities of the Washington Metropolitan Area. **Publications:** Headnotes; Library Guide; Title Page (acquisitions list and periodical tables of contents); bibliographies and reference aides, irregular. **Remarks:** FAX: (202)662-9202. **Staff:** Bruce Kennedy, Hd., Ref.Dept.; Gary Bravy, Media & Ref.Libn.; Laura Bedard, Spec.Coll.Libn.; Margaret Fry, Assoc.Libn., Adm.; Ellen Schaffer, Intl. Law Libn.; Bill Maxon, Sr.Ref.Libn.; Linda Davis, Cat.Libn.; Janice Anderson, Assoc.Libn., Tech.Serv.; Vivian L. Campbell, Assoc.Libn., Coll.Dev.; E. Gordon VanPielt, Asst.Cat.; Marilyn Schroeder, Acq.Libn.; Adeen Postar, Ext.Serv.Libn.; Ruth Bridges, Ref.Libn.; Barbara Rainwater, Coll.Mgt. & Ref.Libn.; Celeste Feather, Circ.Libn.; Annette Morris, Presrv.Libn.; Darcy Kirk, Assoc.Libn., Pub.Serv.; Margaret Maher, Search Serv.Libn.

★6377★
Georgetown University - Kennedy Institute of Ethics - National Reference Center for Bioethics Literature (Soc Sci)
Washington, DC 20057 Phone: (202)687-3885
Doris Goldstein, Dir., Lib. & Info.Serv.
Founded: 1973. **Staff:** Prof 10; Other 3. **Subjects:** Ethics, bioethics, medical ethics, human experimentation, death and dying, physician-patient relationship, genetic intervention, other areas of applied ethics. **Special Collections:** Kampelman Collection of Jewish Ethics; Shriver Collection of Christian Ethics; archival documents of federal commissions in bioethics. **Holdings:** 17,000 books; 85,000 articles; 1 file of organizations in the field. **Subscriptions:** 226 journals and other serials. **Services:** Interlibrary loan (photocopies only); copying; SDI; curriculum clearinghouse/syllabus exchange; document delivery service; center open to the public. **Automated Operations:** Computerized cataloging. **Computerized Information Services:** BIOETHICSLINE, Bioethics Information Retrieval System, OCLC; internal databases. Performs searches free of charge. **Networks/Consortia:** Member of CAPCON Library Network. **Publications:** Bibliography of Bioethics, annual; Bioethics Thesaurus, annual; New Titles in Bioethics (current awareness service), monthly - by subscription; Scope Note Series (overviews of current bioethical issues); Searching BIOETHICSLINE; International Directory of Bioethics Organizations. **Special Catalogs:** Syllabus Exchange Catalog. **Remarks:** Toll-free telephone number(s): (800)MED-ETHX (633-3849). FAX: (202)687-6770. **Staff:** Pat McCarrick, Ref.Libn.; Mary Carrington Coutts, Ref.Libn.; Joy Kahn, Sr.Biblog.

★6378★
Georgetown University - Medical Center - Dahlgren Memorial Library (Med)
3900 Reservoir Rd., N.W. Phone: (202)687-1176
Washington, DC 20007 Naomi C. Broering, Dir./Med.Ctr.Libn.
Founded: 1912. **Staff:** Prof 18; Other 26. **Subjects:** Medicine, dentistry, nursing, basic sciences, hospital management, health care administration. **Special Collections:** Rare books (1146); historical collection (2915 volumes). **Holdings:** 42,742 books; 95,520 bound periodical volumes; 747 archival materials; 1257 dissertations; 2936 AV programs; 441 microcomputer software programs; 6602 microforms. **Subscriptions:** 1739 journals and other serials. **Services:** Interlibrary loan (fee); copying; SDI; library open to the public for reference use only. **Automated Operations:** Computerized cataloging, acquisitions, serials, circulation, and bibliographic management. **Computerized Information Services:** NLM, BRS Information Technologies, DIALOG Information Services, miniMEDLINE, Physicians Data Query (PDQ), BIOETHICSLINE, Current Contents, CCIS, GenBank; Micromedex, Current Contents, RECONSIDER, Dxplain (internal databases); InterNet (electronic mail service). Performs searches on fee basis. Contact Person: Helen E. Bagdoyan, Assoc.Libn., Pub.Serv., 687-1666. **Networks/Consortia:** Member of CAPCON Library Network, District of Columbia Health Sciences Information Network (DOCHSIN), Health Sciences Consortium. **Publications:** LOG-IN (newsletter), 5/year - for internal distribution only; Faculty Publications Bulletin, annual; Library Guide, annual; Decade of Growth; Computers and Libraries: Management Seminar; Computers in Health Care; Strategic Planning: An Integrated Academic Information Management System (IAIMS). **Remarks:** FAX: (202)687-1862. Electronic mail address(es): broerinn@gumedlib.georgetown.edu (InterNet). **Staff:** Betsey King, Libn.; Anne Seymour, BIRC Libn.; Jane Banks, Asst.Libn., Databases; Janet Foote, Access Ser.Libn.; Nancy Key, Asst.Ref.Libn.; Wilma E. Bass, Coord., Cat.Sys.; Martha C. Ziessman, Acq./Ser.Libn.; Terrance Tobias, Instr.Libn.; Ashfin Nili, Ref.Libn.

Georgetown University - Medical School - National Biomedical Research Foundation
See: **National Biomedical Research Foundation** (11089)

★6379★
Georgetown University - Special Collections Division - Lauinger Memorial Library (Hist, Rare Book)
37th and O Sts., N.W. Phone: (202)687-7444
Washington, DC 20057 George M. Barringer, Hd., Spec.Coll.Div.
Founded: 1789. **Staff:** Prof 4; Other 3. **Subjects:** U.S. political science, history, Catholic and Jesuit history, diplomacy and foreign affairs, intelligence, English and American literature, linguistics, bibliography and fine printing, American graphic arts. **Special Collections:** Archives of Maryland Province, Society of Jesus; Archives of Woodstock College; Archives of the American Political Science Association; Shea Collection (Americana); Parsons Collection (early Catholic Americana); Endicott Collection (Panama and the Canall); Bowen Collection on Intelligence and Covert Activities; major author/artist collectioas: Charles Dickens, A.C. Swinburne, Cardinal Newman, Hilaire Belloc, G.K. Cherston, Edgar Lee Masters, C.S. Forester, Graham Greene, Evelyn Waugh, Elizabeth Jennings, Desmond Egan, Fulton Oursler, Anthony Powell, Arthur Ransome, Bruce Marshall, Theodore Maynard, Christopher Sykes, Sir Arnold Lunn, Barbara Ward, Lynd Ward, Grant Wood, Thomas Hart

Benton, Eric Smith, Isac Friedlander, Charles Quest. **Holdings:** 85,000 books; 1250 bound periodical volumes; 7000 linear feet of manuscripts in 650 separate collections; 2750 linear feet of university archives; 275,000 photographs, including 55,000 on motion picture history in the Quigley Photographic Archive; 11,000 maps, prints, drawings, original editorial cartoons. **Services:** Copying; library open to the public. **Automated Operations:** Computerized public access catalog. **Computerized Information Services:** OCLC; University Archives and manuscripts department (internal database). **Networks/Consortia:** Member of Washington Research Library Consortium. **Special Catalogs:** Exhibit catalogs and ephemera, irregular - distributed on item-by-item basis; Special Collections at Georgetown: A Descriptive Catalog (1989); finding aids for manuscript collections, University Archives. **Remarks:** FAX: (202)687-7501. **Staff:** Jon K. Reynolds, Univ.Archv.; Louis J. Reith, Rare Bks.Cat.; Nicholas B. Scheetz, Mss.Libn.

(Georgetown) USIS Library
See: **John F. Kennedy Library** (8627)

★ 6380 ★
Georgia Baptist Historical Society - Library (Hist, Rel-Phil)
Mercer Main Library
Mercer University — Phone: (912)744-2960
Macon, GA 31207 — Mary E. Overby, Spec.Coll.Archv.
Staff: 1. **Subjects:** History - Georgia Baptist, Mercer University, local. **Special Collections:** Georgia Baptist Convention minutes, 1822 to present; Georgia Baptist Associations; Southern Baptist Convention annuals. **Holdings:** Figures not available. **Services:** Copying; library open to the public on limited schedule. **Automated Operations:** Computerized public access catalog and cataloging. **Computerized Information Services:** DIALOG Information Services.

★ 6381 ★
Georgia Baptist Medical Center - Medical Library (Med)
300 Boulevard, N.E.
Box 415 — Phone: (404)653-4603
Atlanta, GA 30312 — Fay E. Evatt, Dir.
Staff: Prof 1; Other 2. **Subjects:** Medicine, allied health sciences. **Holdings:** 4000 books; 15,000 bound periodical volumes. **Subscriptions:** 279 journals and other serials; 15 newspapers; 12 AV subscriptions. **Services:** Interlibrary loan; copying; research; library open to medical and paramedical personnel. **Computerized Information Services:** MEDLINE. **Networks/Consortia:** Member of Atlanta Health Science Libraries Consortium (AHSLC). **Special Catalogs:** Reprint file; bibliography file; periodical holdings catalog (book). **Remarks:** FAX: (404)653-3894.

Georgia Center for Continuing Education
See: **University of Georgia** (18597)

★ 6382 ★
Georgia College - Ina Dillard Russell Library - Special Collections (Hum)
231 W. Hancock — Phone: (912)453-4047
Milledgeville, GA 31061 — Dr. Janice C. Fennell, Dir. of Libs.
Founded: 1889. **Holdings:** Flannery O'Connor Collection (original manuscripts; publications; personal library); horology collection (100 examples of antique timepieces); Bonner Collection; Middle Georgia Collection (state and local history; first editions; maps; manuscripts); Sibley papers. **Services:** Interlibrary loan; copying; collections open to the public with restrictions. **Automated Operations:** Computerized cataloging. **Computerized Information Services:** DIALOG Information Services. Performs searches on fee basis. Contact Person: Jeremy Sayles. **Networks/ Consortia:** Member of SOLINET, East Georgia Library Triangle, Central Georgia Associated Libraries (CGAL), Health Science Libraries Consortium of Central Georgia (HSLCG). **Special Indexes:** Flannery O'Connor Manuscript Collection Index; Southern Recorder (Union Recorder) Index. **Remarks:** FAX: (912)453-6847. **Staff:** Nancy Bray, Spec.Coll.Assoc.

★ 6383 ★
Georgia College - Media Services (Educ, Aud-Vis)
Box 079 — Phone: (912)453-4714
Milledgeville, GA 31061 — Rommie Johnson, Act.Coord.
Founded: 1972. **Staff:** Prof 1; Other 5. **Subjects:** College-wide media services, elementary education. **Special Collections:** Textbooks on the Georgia State Department of Education approved textbook list. **Holdings:** 6594 books; 754 audio cassettes; 326 records; 263 cards; 851 filmstrips; 25 games; 52 motion pictures; 166 realia; 6456 slides; 10 video recordings; 36 transparencies; microtext. **Services:** Interlibrary loan; photography laboratories; television studios; services open to the public. **Automated Operations:** Computerized cataloging. **Computerized Information Services:** OCLC. **Networks/Consortia:** Member of SOLINET, East Georgia Library Triangle, Central Georgia Associated Libraries (CGAL).

★ 6384 ★
Georgia Conservancy, Inc. - Library (Env-Cons)
781 Marietta St., N.W., Suite B100
Atlanta, GA 30318 — Phone: (404)876-2900
Subjects: Conservation, ecology, and pollution with special emphasis on the state of Georgia. **Holdings:** 425 books; 300 other cataloged items. **Services:** Copying; library open to the public. **Remarks:** FAX: (404)872-9229.

Georgia Experiment Station Library
See: **University of Georgia** (18598)

Georgia Geologic Survey
See: **Georgia (State) Department of Natural Resources - Environmental Protection Division** (6403)

★ 6385 ★
Georgia Historical Society - Library (Hist)
501 Whitaker St. — Phone: (912)651-2128
Savannah, GA 31499 — Anne P. Smith, Lib.Dir.
Founded: 1839. **Staff:** Prof 4; Other 1. **Subjects:** Savannah history, Georgia history, genealogy. **Special Collections:** Central of Georgia Railroad Collection; Walter C. Hartridge, Jr. Genealogical Records (records of over 2000 coastal families, including refugees from St. Domingo). **Holdings:** 20,000 books; 1385 feet of manuscripts and private papers; 216 feet of noncurrent Chatham County naturalization and courts records; 966 feet of noncurrent City of Savannah records; Savannah newspapers, 1763 to present, on microfilm; maps of Savannah, Georgia, U.S.; collection of photographs and prints of Savannah and Georgia; federal censuses of Georgia, 1820-1860, on microfilm. **Subscriptions:** 82 journals and other serials. **Services:** Copying; library open to the public. **Computerized Information Services:** RLIN. **Publications:** Georgia Historical Quarterly; Collections of the Georgia Historical Society, irregular; G.H.S. Footnotes, quarterly. **Special Indexes:** Index to manuscript collections. **Remarks:** FAX: (912)651-2831. **Staff:** A. Jan Flores, Archv.; Eileen A. Ielmini, Archv.

★ 6386 ★
Georgia Humanities Council - Georgia Humanities Resource Center (Hum)
Emory University
1556 Clifton Rd., N.E. — Phone: (404)727-7500
Atlanta, GA 30322 — Evelyn E. Garlington, Prog.Dev.Spec.
Founded: 1982. **Staff:** Prof 1; Other 1. **Subjects:** Georgia history, Southern literature and culture, American Indian history and culture, black history and culture, arts. **Holdings:** 58 film and videotape titles; 6 resource guides; 3 slide sets; 10 exhibits; 5 audiotapes. **Services:** Center open to the public. **Automated Operations:** Computerized cataloging. **Computerized Information Services:** Database of Georgia's Humanities Scholars (internal database). **Special Catalogs:** Resoruce Center catalog. **Remarks:** FAX: (404)727-0206.

★ 6387 ★
Georgia Institute of Technology - Library and Information Center (Sci-Engr, Geog-Map)
Atlanta, GA 30332-0900 — Phone: (404)894-4501
Miriam A. Drake, Dean & Dir. of Libs.
Founded: 1900. **Staff:** Prof 42; Other 62. **Subjects:** Engineering - aerospace, ceramic, chemical, civil, electrical, industrial, systems, mechanical, textile;

city planning; architecture; biology; chemistry; science and mechanics; geophysical science; information and computer sciences; mathematics; physics; psychology. **Special Collections:** Maps (162,000); patents (4.8 million); technical reports (2.2 million); government documents (750,000). **Holdings:** 2.5 million volumes; 25,000 photographs; 52,000 pamphlets; 2400 films; 3 million microforms. **Subscriptions:** 15,000 serials. **Services:** Interlibrary loan; copying; SDI; library open to the public with fee charged to noncampus users. **Automated Operations:** Computerized cataloging, acquisitions, serials, and circulation. **Computerized Information Services:** DIALOG Information Services, PFDS Online, BRS Information Technologies, OCLC; internal databases; BITNET, InterNet, ALANET (electronic mail services). Performs searches on fee basis. Contact Person: Kathy Tomajko, (404)894-8190. **Networks/Consortia:** Member of University Center in Georgia, Inc. **Remarks:** FAX: (404)894-6084. Electronic mail address(es): MDRAKE@GTRI01 (BITNET). **Staff:** Dr. Helen Citron Wiltse, Assoc.Dir.; Julia Zimmerman, Asst.Dir., Sys./Info.Serv.; C. Crit Stuart, Asst.Dir., Pub.Serv.; Amy Dykeman, Asst.Dir., Tech.Serv.

★6388★
Georgia Institute of Technology - Price Gilbert Memorial Library - Architecture Library (Art, Plan)
225 North Ave., N.W. Phone: (404)894-4877
Atlanta, GA 30332-0900 Kathryn S. Brackney, Arch.Libn.
Staff: Prof 1; Other 11. **Subjects:** Architecture, architectural history, art history, industrial design, urban planning, building construction. **Special Collections:** Rare books (1000); a select group of drawings and blueprints of the work of architect Neel Reid (2400). **Holdings:** 23,000 volumes; 50,000 slides; 6000 pamphlets. **Subscriptions:** 150 journals and other serials. **Services:** Interlibrary loan; copying; library open to the public with fee for noncampus users. **Automated Operations:** Computerized public access catalog, cataloging, and circulation. **Computerized Information Services:** DIALOG Information Services, STN International, WILSONLINE, BRS Information Technologies, RLIN. **Special Catalogs:** Catalog of slides (online). **Special Indexes:** Index to Neel Reid drawings collection (online).

★6389★
Georgia Institute of Technology - Systems Engineering Laboratory - Technical Information Center (Sci-Engr, Mil)
400 Tenth St., 510 CRB Phone: (404)894-3519
Atlanta, GA 30332 Deborah W. Thomas, Res.Assoc.
Founded: 1981. **Staff:** Prof 1; Other 1. **Subjects:** Electronics - warfare, countermeasures, support measures; radar systems; systems and concepts analysis. **Holdings:** 7000 research and reference documents; 19 security vaults. **Services:** Interlibrary loan; center not open to the public. **Automated Operations:** Computerized cataloging, acquisitions, serials, circulation, and document indexing. **Computerized Information Services:** Datatrieve (internal database). **Publications:** New acquisitions, monthly - for internal distribution only.

Georgia Mental Health Institute
See: **Georgia (State) Department of Human Resources - Georgia Mental Health Institute** (6399)

★6390★
Georgia-Pacific Corporation - Technical Information Center (Sci-Engr)
Box 105605 Phone: (404)521-4659
Atlanta, GA 30348-5605 Deanna Morrow Hall, Mgr., Tech.Info.Rsrcs.
Founded: 1969. **Staff:** Prof 6; Other 1.5. **Subjects:** Pulp and paper, solid wood products, chemicals. **Holdings:** 2300 books; 3400 reports; 1272 cartridges and 129 reels of microfilm. **Subscriptions:** 150 journals and other serials. **Services:** Interlibrary loan; center not open to the public. **Computerized Information Services:** DIALOG Information Services, PFDS Online, STN International; internal database. **Remarks:** Center located at 133 Peachtree St., 9th Fl., Atlanta, GA 30303. FAX: (404)521-5093. **Staff:** Gail L. Pansini, Tech.Info.Sci.; Pam L. Pudgett, Tech.Info.Sci.; Lynne S. Scott, Tech.Info.Sci.; W. Tony Coursey, Libn.; J. Dee Douglas, Asst.Libn.

★6391★
Georgia Power Company - Research Library (Energy)
333 Piedmont Ave.
Box 4545 Phone: (404)526-6855
Atlanta, GA 30302 Debora Mack, Libn.
Founded: 1957. **Staff:** Prof 1; Other 2. **Subjects:** Energy, technology, management, business, computer science, social sciences. **Special Collections:** Engineering publications; government documents; public utility annual reports; company history; Electric Power Research Institute (EPRI) documents. **Holdings:** 8000 books; 500 bound periodical volumes; 5200 titles in microform. **Subscriptions:** 450 journals and other serials. **Services:** Interlibrary loan; library not open to the public. **Automated Operations:** Computerized cataloging, acquisitions, serials, and circulation. **Computerized Information Services:** DIALOG Information Services, BRS Information Technologies, PFDS Online, Dow Jones News/Retrieval, Utility Data Institute, VU/TEXT Information Services, Novell NetWire; DIALMAIL, Evans Economics, Inc. (electronic mail services). **Publications:** New Professional Materials, monthly - for internal distribution only. **Remarks:** FAX: (404)526-6856. **Staff:** Melissa Wright; Darren Crowell.

★6392★
Georgia Regional Hospital at Augusta - Hospital Library (Med)
3405 Old Savannah Rd. Phone: (404)790-2699
Augusta, GA 30906 Joyce Fears, Libn.
Founded: 1970. **Staff:** Prof 1. **Subjects:** Psychiatry, nursing, psychology, social work, chaplaincy, recreation. **Holdings:** 2961 books; 925 cassettes; 28 games; 3 VF drawers; 103 phonograph records; 55 maps; 63 slides; 2 filmstrips. **Subscriptions:** 102 journals and other serials. **Services:** Interlibrary loan; copying; library open to the public for reference use only. **Special Catalogs:** Cassette catalog.

Georgia Retardation Center
See: **Georgia (State) Department of Human Resources** (6398)

★6393★
Georgia (State) Department of Archives and History - Land Records Office (Hist, Geog-Map)
Archives & Records Bldg.
330 Capitol Ave. Phone: (404)656-2393
Atlanta, GA 30334 Brenda S. Banks, Dir., Ref./Preservation
Staff: Prof 1. **Subjects:** Georgia history, geography, cartography. **Special Collections:** John H. Goff Collection of Georgia History. **Holdings:** 2000 manuscript volumes containing 1.5 million grants and plats of survey for Georgia; 10,000 maps; 200 papers, theses, dissertations. **Services:** Copying; library open to the public. **Computerized Information Services:** Disclosure Incorporated, OCLC, RLIN. **Networks/Consortia:** Member of SOLINET. **Publications:** Occasional publications from original holdings. **Staff:** Ingrid Shields, Sr.Archv.

★6394★
Georgia (State) Department of Archives and History - Reference Services (Hist)
330 Capitol Ave., S.E. Phone: (404)656-2393
Atlanta, GA 30334 Brenda S. Banks, Dir., Ref./Preservation
Founded: 1918. **Staff:** Prof 9; Other 4. **Subjects:** Georgia, southeastern U.S., genealogy. **Special Collections:** Georgia state records (82,000 cubic feet); county records (7500 cubic feet; 20,000 reels of microfilm); private papers (2500 cubic feet). **Holdings:** 20,000 volumes; 2000 reels of microfilm of newspapers; 10,500 maps; 20,000 prints and photographs. **Subscriptions:** 425 journals and other serials; 91 newspapers. **Services:** Copying; services open to the public. **Automated Operations:** Computerized cataloging. **Computerized Information Services:** RLIN; BITNET (electronic mail service). **Networks/Consortia:** Member of SOLINET, University Center in Georgia, Inc., Research Libraries Information Network (RLIN). **Publications:** List of publications of the Georgia State Department of Archives and History - free upon request. **Special Catalogs:** Civil War Pension Index (microfilm); Family Surname File; descriptive inventories for individual official record groups and of manuscript collections. **Remarks:** FAX: (404)651-9270. Electronic mail address(es): GSP@RLG (BITNET). **Staff:** Luanne Smalley, Ref.Mgr.; Sandy Boling, Ref.Mgr.; Alice James, Mail Ref.Coord.

★6395★
Georgia (State) Department of Corrections - Office of Library Services (Law)
10 Park Place S., 6th Fl., Rm. 658 Phone: (404)656-6020
Atlanta, GA 30303 Al Wheeler, Act. State Lib.Dir.
Founded: 1974. **Staff:** Prof 1; Other 1. **Subjects:** Corrections, criminal justice, counseling, rehabilitation, management. **Special Collections:** Project reports (200); female offenders (150 items). **Holdings:** 2500 books. **Subscriptions:** 50 journals and newsletters. **Services:** Interlibrary loan; copying; center open to the public for reference use only. **Computerized Information Services:** DIALOG Information Services. **Networks/Consortia:** Member of Georgia Online Database (GOLD), Criminal Justice Information Exchange Group. **Publications:** R/RC Alert; bibliographies. **Remarks:** FAX: (404)651-6819. **Formerly:** Its Reference/Resource Center.

★6396★
Georgia (State) Department of Education - Division of Public Library Services (Educ)
156 Trinity Ave., S.W. Phone: (404)656-2461
Atlanta, GA 30303-3692 Joe B. Forsee, Dir.
Founded: 1897. **Staff:** Prof 19; Other 26. **Subjects:** Education, Georgia. **Holdings:** 159,076 books; 613,499 microfiche; 21,506 reels of microfilm; 30 VF drawers of pamphlets. **Subscriptions:** 1768 journals and other serials. **Services:** Interlibrary loan; copying; bibliographic verification; library open to Georgia state employees. **Automated Operations:** Computerized cataloging, circulation, acquisitions, and serials. **Computerized Information Services:** DIALOG Information Services, OCLC, Georgia Online Database (GOLD); internal database; ALANET (electronic mail service). **Networks/Consortia:** Member of Georgia Online Database (GOLD), SOLINET. **Publications:** Fiche Union list of serials for Georgia, annual; Georgia Public Library Statistics, annual - all available upon request. **Remarks:** FAX: (404)656-7297. **Staff:** Diana Ray Tope, Dp.Dir.; Thomas Ploeg, Coord., Bldg.; JoEllen Ostendorf, Cons., Lib.; Linda Springer, Cons., Lib.Dev.; Robyn Hollar, Hd., Circ.; Rosemary Dyer, Hd., Cat.; Sharon Joseph, Hd., Acq.; Miriam Martin, Hd., Ref.

★6397★
Georgia (State) Department of Education - Library for the Blind & Physically Handicapped (Aud-Vis)
1150 Murphy Ave., S.W. Phone: (404)756-4619
Atlanta, GA 30310 Dale S. Snair, Dir.
Staff: Prof 4; Other 4. **Special Collections:** History of Georgia, books written by Georgians, blindiana. **Holdings:** 180,000 talking books; books in braille and large print; tapes and cassettes. **Subscriptions:** 4 journals and other serials. **Services:** Interlibrary loan; copying; tape duplication. **Computerized Information Services:** NLSNET (electronic mail service). **Networks/Consortia:** Member of National Library Service for the Blind & Physically Handicapped (NLS). **Remarks:** FAX: (404)756-4618. For access to NLSNET electronic mail, dial (404)756-4617. Coordinates talking book centers in Albany, Athens, Augusta, Bainbridge, Brunswick, Columbus, Dublin, Gainseville, LaFayette, Macon, Savannah, Rome, and Valdosta. **Staff:** Shirley Asare, Rd.Adv.; Cora Cofield, Rd.Adv.; Sharon Joseph, Equipment/New Patrons; Emily Yeh, Equipment/New Patrons.

★6398★
Georgia (State) Department of Human Resources - Brook Run - Professional Library (Educ, Med)
4770 N. Peachtree Rd. Phone: (404)551-7076
Dunwoody, GA 30338-5899 Jane F. Clark, Sr.Libn.
Founded: 1969. **Staff:** Prof 1. **Subjects:** Mental retardation, behavior therapy, education of the mentally retarded, special education. **Holdings:** 9000 books; 500 bound periodical volumes; 3 VF drawers of pamphlets. **Subscriptions:** 202 journals and other serials. **Services:** Interlibrary loan; copying; library open to the public. **Computerized Information Services:** BRS Information Technologies. **Networks/Consortia:** Member of Atlanta Health Science Libraries Consortium (AHSLC). **Remarks:** FAX: (404)551-7040. **Formerly:** Its Georgia Retardation Center.

★6399★
Georgia (State) Department of Human Resources - Georgia Mental Health Institute - Addison M. Duval Library (Med)
1256 Briarcliff Rd., N.E. Phone: (404)894-5663
Atlanta, GA 30306-2694 Rosalind Lett, Lib.Dir.
Founded: 1966. **Staff:** Prof 2; Other 7. **Subjects:** Psychiatry, nursing, social work, chaplaincy, activities therapy, psychology, substance abuse, forensic psychiatry. **Special Collections:** Department of Human Genetics Collection (600 books; 35 subscriptions); Department of Biological Psychiatry Collection (100 books; 11 subscriptions). **Holdings:** 20,000 books; 3500 bound periodical volumes. **Subscriptions:** 152 journals and other serials. **Services:** Interlibrary loan; clinical librarian service; document delivery; SDI; library open to the public on fee basis. **Automated Operations:** Computerized ILL (DOCLINE). **Computerized Information Services:** MEDLARS, BRS Information Technologies, DOBIS Canadian Online Library System, DIALOG Information Services. **Networks/Consortia:** Member of Atlanta Health Science Libraries Consortium (AHSLC), Georgia Health Sciences Library Association (GHSLA). **Publications:** Acquisition List, bimonthly; bibliographies; brochures; News Notes (newsletter). **Remarks:** FAX: (404)894-8502. The Grady Jackson Memorial Library, a patient library containing 1000 volumes, a Consumer Health Collection, and general reading materials is also located at the above address. **Staff:** Stephen M. Koplan, Libn.

★6400★
Georgia (State) Department of Human Resources - Public Health Division - Library
878 Peachtree St., N.E., Rm. 115
Atlanta, GA 30309
Defunct.

★6401★
Georgia (State) Department of Law - Georgia State Law Library (Info Sci)
40 Capitol Square, Suite 301 Phone: (404)656-3468
Atlanta, GA 30334 Carroll T. Parker, State Law Libn.
Founded: 1831. **Staff:** Prof 3; Other 2. **Subjects:** Law. **Holdings:** 80,000 books; 300 bound periodical volumes; 32,000 microfiche; federal documents. **Subscriptions:** 6 newspapers. **Services:** Interlibrary loan (limited); copying; library open to the public with restrictions. **Automated Operations:** Computerized public access catalog and cataloging. **Computerized Information Services:** LEXIS, WESTLAW, OLLI (Online Catalog of Georgia State University Law Library). **Remarks:** FAX: (404)651-9148, (404)651-5822. **Staff:** Martha M. Lappe, Ref./Rd.Serv.Libn.; F. Pamela Graham, Doc./Tech.Serv.Libn.

★6402★
Georgia (State) Department of Natural Resources - Coastal Resources Division - Anderson Library (Biol Sci)
1 Conservation Way Phone: (912)264-7218
Brunswick, GA 31523-8600 Karen Sloan, Act.Libn.
Staff: Prof 1; Other 1. **Subjects:** Shellfish, sport fishing, fish, estuarine ecology. **Holdings:** 1000 books; 600 bound periodical volumes; 7000 reprints. **Services:** Interlibrary loan; copying; SDI; library open to the public for reference use only. **Remarks:** FAX: (912)262-3143. Library contains the library of William W. Anderson, Senior Scientist (retired) for the U.S. Government and the state of Georgia.

★6403★
Georgia (State) Department of Natural Resources - Environmental Protection Division - Georgia Geologic Survey - Library (Sci-Engr)
19 Martin Luther King Jr. Dr., S.W., Rm. 400 Phone: (404)656-3214
Atlanta, GA 30334 Michael K. Laney, Info.Geol.
Founded: 1978. **Staff:** Prof 1. **Subjects:** Geology, hydrology. **Holdings:** 4000 volumes. **Subscriptions:** 23 journals and other serials. **Services:** Copying; library open to the public.

★6404★
Georgia (State) Department of Natural Resources - Fort King George Library (Hist)
P.O. Box 711 Phone: (912)437-4770
Darien, GA 31305 Ken Akins, Supt.
Founded: 1975. **Staff:** 2. **Subjects:** Fort King George, Spanish missions, archeology, Coastal Indians, timbering and sawmilling on the Altamaha River. **Special Collections:** Fort King George record and map collection (1720s). **Holdings:** 150 books; 1 AV program; 100 maps. **Services:** Copying; library open to the public by appointment. **Publications:** Ft. King George: Step One to Statehood (book). **Staff:** Andy Dominy, Int. Ranger.

★6405★
Georgia (State) Department of Natural Resources - Little White House Historic Site - Archives (Hist)
Drawer 68 Phone: (404)655-3511
Warm Springs, GA 31830 Gretchen Terry, Adm.Ck.
Staff: 1. **Subjects:** The career of President Franklin D. Roosevelt, especially his life as part-time resident of Georgia and originator and developer of Georgia Warm Springs Foundation. **Holdings:** 200 books; archives; documents. **Services:** Archives open to scholars by appointment. **Staff:** Mary Thrash, Interp. Ranger.

★6406★
Georgia (State) Department of Transportation - Roy A. Flynt Memorial Library (Trans)
15 Kennedy Dr. Phone: (404)363-7540
Forest Park, GA 30050 Stardina L. Wyche, Libn.
Founded: 1974. **Staff:** Prof 1. **Subjects:** Transportation, statistics. **Special Collections:** Transportation Research Board publications. **Holdings:** 20,000

volumes; 25 bound periodical volumes; 10,000 state Department of Transportation research reports; 6000 U.S. Department of Transportation documents; materials and testing standards and specifications. **Subscriptions:** 94 journals and other serials. **Services:** Interlibrary loan; copying; library open to the public for reference use only on request. **Computerized Information Services:** DIALOG Information Services; internal database. **Publications:** Annotated Research Bibliography, irregular - available upon request. **Remarks:** FAX: (404)363-7684.

★6407★
Georgia State Forestry Commission - Library (Biol Sci)
Box 819 Phone: (912)744-3211
Macon, GA 31298-4599 F. Carr, Act.Libn.
Founded: 1956. **Subjects:** Forestry, entomology. **Holdings:** Books; 100 bound periodical volumes; 21 shelves of pamphlets; 5 VF drawers of reference files. **Services:** Interlibrary loan; library open to the public. **Remarks:** Library is currently being renovated, but is still in use.

★6408★
Georgia State Health Planning Agency - Library (Med)
4 Executive Park Dr., N.E., Suite 2100 Phone: (404)679-4829
Atlanta, GA 30329 Karen Butler, Libn.
Founded: 1983. **Staff:** Prof 1. **Subjects:** Health planning, health and medical service delivery, health administration. **Holdings:** 3250 volumes; Federal Register, 1982-1983, on microfiche. **Subscriptions:** 72 journals, newsletters, and other serials. **Services:** Interlibrary loan; copying; library open to the public when librarian is present. **Networks/Consortia:** Member of Atlanta Health Science Libraries Consortium (AHSLC). **Remarks:** FAX: (404)679-4914.

Georgia State Law Library
See: **Georgia (State) Department of Law** (6401)

★6409★
Georgia (State) Office of Planning and Budget - Demographic and Statistical Services (Soc Sci)
254 Washington St., S.W., Rm. 640 Phone: (404)656-0911
Atlanta, GA 30334 Marty Sik, Coord.
Founded: 1970. **Staff:** Prof 3; Other 1. **Subjects:** Population, housing, income, labor, education, economics. **Special Collections:** Georgia County Population Estimates and Projections. **Holdings:** 1500 books; 300 U.S. Government publications; 100,000 pages of computer printouts; 175 reels of computer tapes; 300 primary data files; 2500 maps. **Subscriptions:** 15 journals and other serials. **Services:** Copying; center open to the public but some files are confidential. **Automated Operations:** Computerized acquisitions. **Publications:** Georgia County Population Estimates and Projections, annual; Georgia Descriptions in Data, annual. **Remarks:** Inventory includes all census data relevant to the state of Georgia. FAX: (404)656-3828.

★6410★
Georgia State Supreme Court Library (Law)
Judicial Bldg., 5th Fl.
40 Capitol Square, S.W. Phone: (404)656-4212
Atlanta, GA 30334 Laura M. Murphy, Libn.
Staff: Prof 1. **Subjects:** Law. **Holdings:** 10,000 volumes. **Subscriptions:** 10 journals and other serials. **Services:** Library not open to the public.

★6411★
Georgia State University - College of Law Library (Law)
University Plaza Phone: (404)651-2479
Atlanta, GA 30303 Nancy P. Johnson, Law Libn.
Founded: 1982. **Staff:** Prof 6; Other 11. **Subjects:** Law. **Holdings:** 216,134 volumes; Supreme Court records and briefs. **Subscriptions:** 4000 journals and other serials. **Services:** Interlibrary loan; library not open to the public. **Automated Operations:** Computerized cataloging and circulation. **Computerized Information Services:** WESTLAW, LEXIS, OCLC. **Networks/Consortia:** Member of SOLINET. **Remarks:** FAX: (404)651-2092. **Staff:** Ladd Brown; Nancy Deel; Barbara James; Rhea Ballard.

★6412★
Georgia State University - Small Business Development Center (Bus-Fin)
1 Park Place, S., Suite 1056 Phone: (404)651-3550
Atlanta, GA 30303 Peter Rassel, Res.Dir.
Founded: 1979. **Staff:** 7. **Subjects:** Small business, marketing, finance, international business, government procurement. **Holdings:** Business directories; government publications and journals, periodicals, training manuals and videotapes. **Subscriptions:** 11 journals and other serials. **Services:** Counseling; center open to the public for reference use only. **Computerized Information Services:** DIALOG Information Services. Performs searches on fee basis. **Remarks:** FAX: (404)651-2804.

★6413★
Georgia State University - Special Collections Department (Hist)
University Library Phone: (404)651-2477
Atlanta, GA 30303 Leslie S. Hough, Dir.
Founded: 1969. **Staff:** Prof 6; Other 15. **Special Collections:** Records of the International Association of Machinists and Aerospace Workers, United Textile Workers of America, Furniture Workers Division, International Union of Electronic Workers, Professional Air Traffic Controllers Organization, University and College Labor Education Association, personal papers of trade unionists, numerous collections from regional and local union offices, records of various professional organizations, and other research materials related to labor management relations; Johnny Mercer papers and popular music materials; university records; Georgia photographs; Georgia government materials; rare books; Media Center. **Holdings:** 2500 books; 100 bound periodical volumes; manuscripts; media materials. **Subscriptions:** 110 journals and other serials; 110 newspapers. **Services:** Interlibrary loan; copying; department open to the public with restrictions on selected collections. **Remarks:** FAX: (404)651-2508. **Staff:** Robert Dinwiddie, Archv./Asst.Dir.; Chris Paton, Archv.; Laurel Bowen, Archv.; Cliff Kuhn, Archv.; Peter Roberts, Archv.; Beneta Coburn, Media Ctr.

★6414★
Geoscience, Ltd. - Library (Sci-Engr)
410 S. Cedros Ave.
Solana Beach, CA 92075 Phone: (619)755-9396
Founded: 1961. **Staff:** Prof 1. **Subjects:** Mathematics, physics, medicine. **Holdings:** 700 volumes. **Services:** Library not open to the public.

★6415★
Geoscience Services - Technical Library (Sci-Engr)
25 Claremont Rd.
Bernardsville, NJ 07924
Founded: 1979. **Subjects:** Geological engineering, seismology. **Holdings:** 2000 volumes. **Subscriptions:** 5 journals and other serials. **Services:** Library not open to the public.

GeoStat
See: **Governors State University - GeoStat - Information Center** (6586)

Geotech Ltd.
See: **Fossils Quarterly - Archives** (6029)

★6416★
Geothermal Resources Council - Business Library (Energy)
2121 2nd St., Suite 101A Phone: (916)758-2360
Davis, CA 95616-5472 Cherri Martin, Sec.
Founded: 1980. **Staff:** 1. **Subjects:** Geothermal energy, geology, geophysics, exploration. **Holdings:** 3000 items. **Services:** Copying; library open to the public by appointment. **Publications:** List of publications - available on request. **Remarks:** FAX: (916)758-2839. Telex: 882410.

★6417★
Geotronics Laboratories, Inc. - Library (Sci-Engr)
115 W. Greenbriar Ln.
Dallas, TX 75208 Phone: (214)946-7573
Subjects: Engineering, research and development. **Holdings:** Figures not available.

Geraghty & Miller, Inc., Environmental Services - Water Information Center, Inc.
See: **Water Information Center, Inc.** (20079)

★ 6418 ★
Gerber Products Company - Corporate Library (Food-Bev)
445 State St. Phone: (616)928-2631
Fremont, MI 49413 Sherrie Harris, Corp.Libn.
Founded: 1946. **Staff:** Prof 1; Other 1. **Subjects:** Food processing, infant nutrition and development, pediatrics, business administration, international marketing, chemistry, microbiology, agriculture, quality control. **Special Collections:** Company archives; annual reports. **Holdings:** 6500 books; 2800 bound periodical volumes; 125 AV programs; 10,000 photoprints and pamphlets in hardcopy and on microfiche. **Subscriptions:** 750 journals and other serials; 20 newspapers. **Services:** Interlibrary loan; copying. **Computerized Information Services:** Online systems. **Publications:** Library Newsletter, monthly - for internal distribution only. **Remarks:** FAX: (616)928-2723.

Walter W. Gerboth Music Library
See: **Brooklyn College of City University of New York** (2234)

Gerhardt Library of Musical Information
See: **Towson State University** (16440)

Gerhardt Marimba & Xylophone Collection
See: **Towson State University** (16441)

★ 6419 ★
German Archaeological Institute - Athens Division - Library (Soc Sci)
Fidiou 1
GR-10678 Athens, Greece Phone: 1 3620-270
Subjects: Archeological studies of Greece, prehistoric to Byzantine period. **Holdings:** 60,000 volumes; photographs. **Services:** Library open to the public with restrictions. **Also Known As:** Deutsches Archaeologisches Institut - Abteilung Athen. **Staff:** Margit Heiber, Libn.

★ 6420 ★
German Archaeological Institute - Commission for Ancient History and Epigraphy (Hist)
Amalienstrasse 736 Phone: 89 28 43 51
W-8000 Munich 40, Germany Dr. K. Dietz, Libn.
Subjects: Ancient history, numismatics, epigraphy. **Holdings:** 19,000 volumes. **Also Known As:** Kommission fur Alte Geschichte und Epigraphik.

★ 6421 ★
German Archaeological Institute - Library (Soc Sci)
Podbielskiallee 69 Phone: 30 830080
W-1000 Berlin 33, Germany Dr. Anneliese Peschlow
Staff: Prof 2; Other 1. **Subjects:** Classical archeology. **Holdings:** 60,000 volumes. **Subscriptions:** 580 journals. **Services:** Library open to the public. **Remarks:** FAX: 30 83008168. Maintained by Federal Republic of Germany - Foreign Ministry. **Also Known As:** Deutsches Archaeologisches Institut. **Staff:** Helga Skottke, Libn.

★ 6422 ★
German Archaeological Institute - Madrid Division - Library (Soc Sci)
Serrano, 159 Phone: 1 5610904
E-28002 Madrid, Spain Uta Jarick, Libn.
Founded: 1943. **Staff:** 3. **Subjects:** Archeology and ancient history of the Iberian Peninsula. **Holdings:** 50,000 volumes. **Subscriptions:** 700 journals and other serials. **Services:** Library open to researchers. **Publications:** Zugangsverzeichnis der Bibliothek Madrid von Veroffentlichungen zur Archaologie der Iberischen Halbinsel. **Remarks:** FAX: 1 5640054. **Also Known As:** Deutsches Archaeologisches Institut - Abteilung Madrid.

★ 6423 ★
German Cement Works Association - Library (Sci-Engr)
Tannenstrasse 2
Postfach 301063 Phone: 211 45781
W-4000 Dusseldorf 30, Germany Prof. G. Wischers, Dr.-Ing.
Staff: 2. **Subjects:** Cement and concrete technology. **Holdings:** 30,900 volumes. **Subscriptions:** 160 journals and other serials. **Services:** Library not open to the public. **Publications:** Tatigkeitsbericht; Schriftenreihe der Zementindustrie; Betontechnische Berichte; Zement-Taschenbuch. **Remarks:** FAX: 211 4578296. Telex: 8584867. **Also Known As:** Verein Deutscher Zementwerke. **Staff:** Svenja Lawonn, Dipl.-Bibl.; Karin Klingen.

German Cultural Institute - Goethe House New York
See: **Goethe House New York** (6520)

★ 6424 ★
German Design Council - Library (Art)
Ludwig-Erhard-Anlage 1
Messegelande
Postfach 970287 Phone: 69 747919
W-6000 Frankfurt 1, Germany Helge Aszmoneit
Founded: 1960. **Staff:** 1. **Subjects:** Design and allied subjects. **Holdings:** 8000 volumes. **Publications:** Literatur Hinweise. **Remarks:** FAX: 69 7410911. **Also Known As:** Rat fuer Formgebung.

★ 6425 ★
German Electron-Synchrotron - DESY Scientific Documentation and Information Service (Sci-Engr)
Notkestr. 85 Phone: 40 89983602
W-2000 Hamburg 52, Germany Dietmar Schmidt, Dipl.-Phys.
Founded: 1962. **Staff:** Prof 1. **Subjects:** High energy technology, quantum field theory, elementary particle physics, and allied subjects. **Holdings:** 33,500 volumes; 45,000 preprints and reports; standards. **Subscriptions:** 338 journals and other serials. **Services:** SDI; service open to the public with restrictions. **Automated Operations:** Computerized public access catalog. **Computerized Information Services:** DESY-HEP (internal database). Performs searches free for subscribers active in pure research. **Publications:** High Energy Physics Index, biweekly - available by subscription. **Remarks:** Telex: 215 124 DESY D. **Also Known As:** Deutsches Elektronen-Synchrotron.

German Exile Archives
See: **Germany - Deutsche Bibliothek** (6440)

★ 6426 ★
German Foundation for International Development - Documentation Center (Soc Sci)
Hans-Bockler-Strasse 5 Phone: 228 40010
W-5300 Bonn 3, Germany Dietrich Steinert, Hd. of Info.Ctr.
Subjects: Developing countries - aid, development policy of national and international organizations, socioeconomic and cultural change. **Holdings:** 45,000 books; 420,000 clippings. **Subscriptions:** 850 journals and other serials. **Services:** Copying; SDI; center open to the public. **Computerized Information Services:** Internal database. Performs searches free of charge. **Publications:** Recent Acquisitions, 2/year; Kalendar, quarterly; Institutions of Development Cooperation/Institutionen der Entwicklungszusammenarbeit, irregular; State-of-the-Art Reports/Themendienst, irregular - all free upon request; Bibliography of German Research on Developing Countries, annual - for sale. **Remarks:** FAX: 228 4001 111. Telex: 886710. **Also Known As:** Deutsche Stiftung fur Internationale Entwicklung.

★ 6427 ★
German Genealogical Society of America - Library (Hist)
P.O. Box 291818
Los Angeles, CA 90029 Phone: (714)621-7399
Founded: 1986. **Staff:** Prof. 2. **Subjects:** German genealogy and ethnic history. **Holdings:** 2000 volumes; manuscripts; maps; foreign telephone directories; 4,500 family and surname files. **Subscriptions:** 103 journals and other serials. **Services:** Translation; research. **Special Indexes:** Surname index. **Staff:** Beatrice Beck, Libn.; Michael Palmer, Res.Dir.

German Hydrographic Institute
See: **Bundesamt fur Seeschiffahrt und Hydrographie** (2360)

★ 6428 ★
German Information Center - Federal Republic of Germany Collection (Area-Ethnic)
950 Third Ave.
New York, NY 10022 Phone: (212)888-9840
Subjects: General information on the Federal Republic of Germany. **Holdings:** Figures not available. **Services:** Center open to the public with restrictions. **Remarks:** FAX: (212)752-6691.

★ 6429 ★
German Institute for International Educational Research - Library and Documentation (Educ)
Schloss-Strasse 29-31
Postfach 900280 Phone: 69 770245
W-6000 Frankfurt am Main 90, Germany Hartmut Muller, Libn.
Founded: 1951. **Staff:** Prof 10. **Subjects:** Education - general, comparative, vocational, technical; law; psychology; economics. **Special Collections:** Textbooks (19,000). **Holdings:** 170,000 books; 1070 bound periodical volumes. **Subscriptions:** 1010 journals and other serials. **Services:** Copying; SDI; library open to the public. **Automated Operations:** Computerized public access catalog. **Computerized Information Services:** DBI (Deutsches Bibliotheksinstitut), DIMDI, ECHO (European Commission Host Organization), INKADATA (Informationssystem Karlsruhe), PFDS Online, Questel; PEDI, NEUTECH, INTERLIMES, TEST, ZEITDOK (internal databases). Performs searches on fee basis. Contact Person: Peter Birke. **Publications:** Zeitungsdokumentation Bildungswesen, semimonthly; Internationale Bibliographie zur Bildungsforschung - both by subscription. **Special Catalogs:** Catalog of countries; catalog of corporate sources (both on cards and computerized). **Remarks:** 69 708228. Telex: 4170331. **Also Known As:** Deutsches Institut fur Internationale Padagogische Forschung.

★ 6430 ★
German Iron and Steel Institute - Steel Information Centre and Library (Sci-Engr)
Sohnstrasse 65 Phone: 211 6707 460
W-4000 Dusseldorf 1, Germany Manfred Toncourt, Lib.Hd.
Founded: 1905. **Subjects:** Engineering and physical properties of iron and steel. **Special Collections:** Iron and steel metallurgy, from raw materials to finished products (books, serials, journals); techniques, materials, and application from 16th century to present. **Holdings:** 110,000 volumes; standards. **Subscriptions:** 500 journals and other serials. **Services:** Library open to the public. **Computerized Information Services:** PLANTFACTS (internal database). **Publications:** Literaturschau stahl und eisen. **Remarks:** Alternate telephone number(s): 211 6707464; 211 6707466; 211 6707468. FAX: 211 6707-310. Telex: 8582512. **Formerly:** German Iron and Steel Engineers Association. **Also Known As:** Verein Deutscher Eisenhuttenleute - VDEh. **Staff:** B. Deyk, Lib.; D. Gagg, Info.Serv.Lit.; R. Ewers, Info.Serv. Data.

German Music Archives
See: **Germany - Deutsche Bibliothek** (6440)

★ 6431 ★
German National Research Center for Computer Science - GMD Information Center for Information Science and Information Work (Info Sci, Comp Sci)
P.O. Box 710363
Herriotstrasse 5 Phone: 69 6687360
W-6000 Frankfurt am Main 71, Germany Dr. Peter Budinger, Hd.
Founded: 1977. **Staff:** Prof 14; Other 9. **Subjects:** Methodology of information and documentation; information processing, systems, networks; computational linguistics. **Holdings:** 40,000 monographs, reports, standards. **Subscriptions:** 630 journals and other serials. **Services:** SDI; center open to the public on fee basis. **Computerized Information Services:** Produces INFODATA. Performs searches on fee basis. **Publications:** Directory of Journals Held by the GMD Information Center, biennial; additional publications available. **Remarks:** FAX: 69 6687290. Telex: 4-14-351. **Formerly:** Society for Information and Documentation/ Gesellschaft fur Information und Dokumentation (GID) - GID-Informationszentrum fur Informationswissenschaft und -Praxis. **Also Known As:** Gesellschaft fur Mathematik und Datenverarbeitung mbH (GMD) - GMD-Informationszentrum fur Informationswissenschaft und -Praxis.

★ 6432 ★
German Plastics Institute - Information and Documentation Services (Sci-Engr)
Schlossgartenstr. 6 Phone: 6151 162105
W-6100 Darmstadt, Germany Jutta Wierer, Chem.
Founded: 1955. **Subjects:** Chemistry; physics; science and technology of polymers - general, plastics, rubbers, and fiber materials. **Holdings:** 11,000 bound volumes. **Subscriptions:** 110 journals and other serials. **Services:** SDI; Services open to the public. **Computerized Information Services:** Produces DKI, KKF, and POLYMAT databases (available online through FIZ Technik and STN International). Performs searches on fee basis. **Publications:** Literatur-Schnelldienst Kunststoffe Kautschuk Fasern, monthly - available by subscription; DKI Thesaurus - for sale. **Remarks:** FAX: 6151 292855. **Also Known As:** Deutsches Kunststoff-Institut - Dienstleistungen Information und Dokumentation.

★ 6433 ★
German Society of Pennsylvania - Joseph Horner Memorial Library (Area-Ethnic)
611 Spring Garden St.
Philadelphia, PA 19123 Phone: (215)627-4365
Founded: 1817. **Staff:** Prof 1; Other 1. **Subjects:** All subjects with special emphasis on history, biography, literature (85% in German language); juvenile literature in German. **Special Collections:** Americana-Germanica (12,000 volumes). **Holdings:** 75,000 books, including 12,000 archival materials. **Subscriptions:** 10 journals. **Services:** Interlibrary loan (fee); copying; library open to the public for reference use only. **Remarks:** FAX: (215)627-5297. **Staff:** Dr. Margarete Castrogiovanni; Amy Johnston, Libn.

★ 6434 ★
German Society of Winnipeg - Library (Area-Ethnic)
285 Flora Ave. Phone: (204)589-7724
Winnipeg, MB, Canada R2W 2R2 Liz Kolbe, Libn.
Founded: 1958. **Subjects:** General topics in the German language. **Holdings:** 1200 books. **Services:** Library open to the public on special request to president.

Germania Judaica - Kolner Bibliothek zur Geschichte des Deutschen Judentums e.V.
See: **Cologne Library on German-Jewish History** (3922)

★ 6435 ★
Germanisches Nationalmuseum - Bibliothek (Art, Hist, Area-Ethnic)
Kornmarkt 1
Postfach 9580 Phone: 911 13310
W-8500 Nuremberg 11, Germany Eberhard Slenczka, Lib.Dir.
Founded: 1852. **Subjects:** Germany - art, history, culture; musical instruments. **Holdings:** 491,449 books. **Subscriptions:** 1566 journals and other serials. **Services:** Interlibrary loan; copying; library open to the public with restrictions. **Remarks:** FAX: 911 1331200.

Germans from Russia Project Library
See: **Colorado State University** (3970)

★ 6436 ★
Germantown Friends Meeting - Friends Free Library (Rel-Phil)
5418 Germantown Ave. Phone: (215)951-2355
Philadelphia, PA 19144 Helen M. Eigabroadt, Dir.
Founded: 1848. **Staff:** Prof 2; Other 3. **Special Collections:** Quaker Collection; Germantown history; Irvin C. Poley Theater History of Philadelphia, 1904-1975 (250 scrapbooks). **Holdings:** 58,000 books. **Subscriptions:** 196 journals and other serials; 10 newspapers. **Services:** Interlibrary loan; copying; library open to the public. **Computerized Information Services:** DIALOG Information Services. **Remarks:** FAX: (215)951-2697. **Staff:** Rebekah L. Ray, Children's Libn.

★ 6437 ★
Germantown Historical Society - Library (Hist)
5501 Germantown Ave. Phone: (215)844-8428
Philadelphia, PA 19144-2291 Lisabeth M. Holloway, Act.Libn./Archv.
Founded: 1908. **Staff:** 1. **Subjects:** History of Germantown, Mt. Airy, Chestnut Hill, and Wissahickon sections of Philadelphia. **Special Collections:** Books and Bibles printed in Germantown; archives (7500 manuscripts, letters; 12,000 photographs). **Holdings:** 3200 books; scrapbooks; newspapers published in Germantown, 1830 to present; deeds and briefs of title; local genealogies. **Subscriptions:** 12 journals and other serials. **Services:** Copying; research on fee basis; library open to the public on fee basis. **Publications:** Germantown Crier, quarterly.

★6438★
Germantown Hospital and Medical Center - Professional Library (Med)
One Penn Blvd. Phone: (215)951-8291
Philadelphia, PA 19144 Alice Gilbert, Lib.Dir.
Founded: 1982. **Staff:** Prof 1. **Subjects:** Medicine, nursing, health administration. **Holdings:** 4000 books; 1500 bound periodical volumes; 9 VF drawers; 378 audio cassettes; 28 videotapes. **Subscriptions:** 215 journals and other serials. **Services:** Interlibrary loan; library open to medical and hospital personnel, nursing staff, allied health staff, and students. **Computerized Information Services:** BRS Information Technologies, DIALOG Information Services, NLM. Performs searches. **Networks/ Consortia:** Member of National Network of Libraries of Medicine - Middle Atlantic Region, Delaware Valley Information Consortium (DEVIC).

★6439★
Germany - Bundesminister des Innern - Bibliothek (Law, Soc Sci)
Graurheindorfer Str 198 Phone: 228 6813573
W-5300 Bonn, Germany Sundermann, OAR
Founded: 1949. **Staff:** Prof 8; Other 4. **Subjects:** Law, administration, politics, culture. **Special Collections:** East German Refugees (20,000 items). **Holdings:** 250,000 books; 100 microfiche. **Subscriptions:** 820 journals; 50 newspapers. **Services:** Interlibrary loan; library not open to the public. **Remarks:** FAX: 228 6814120.

★6440★
Germany - Deutsche Bibliothek (Area-Ethnic, Hum, Info Sci)
Zeppelinallee 4-8 Phone: 69 75 661
W-6000 Frankfurt am Main, Germany Klaus-Dieter Lehmann, Prof.
Founded: 1947. **Staff:** 798.5. **Subjects:** German publications and foreign German language publications, 1913 to present; foreign publications of translations of German works; foreign language publications about Germany. **Special Collections:** German Music Archives; German Exile Archives (works written by German-speaking emigrants, 1933-1945). **Holdings:** 8.89 million books and bound periodical volumes; 478,739 microforms; 805,913 music materials. **Subscriptions:** 66,628 journals and other serials; 431 newspapers. **Services:** Interlibrary loan; copying; SDI; magnetic tape and card services; library open to the public for reference use only. **Computerized Information Services:** BIBLIO-DATA; CD-ROMs. Performs searches on fee basis. Contact person in Frankfurt: Kristina Knull-Schlomann, 7566478. **Publications:** Deutsche bibliographie. **Remarks:** FAX: 69 7566476 (Frankfurt); 41 2271444 (Leipzig). Telex: 51562 dbuech dd. The information above reflects the holdings for both the Leipzig and Frankfurt locations. **Formed by the merger of:** Deutsche Bucherei Leipzig and Deutsche Bibliothek Frankfurt a.M.

★6441★
Germany - Deutsche Staatsbibliothek (Hum)
Postfach 1312
Unter den Linden 8 Phone: 2 03780
W-1086 Berlin, Germany Prof. Dr. Dieter Schmidmaier, Gen.Dir.
Founded: 1661. **Staff:** 520. **Subjects:** Literature, music, general. **Special Collections:** Children's literature collection (120,000 books); music collection (428,310 scores); literary autograph and manuscript collection (23,853 items). **Holdings:** 5.4 million books and bound periodical volumes; 168,661 microfiche and reels of microfilm. **Subscriptions:** 9173 journals and other serials; 164 newspapers. **Services:** Interlibrary loan; copying; SDI; library open to the public. **Computerized Information Services:** Internal database. Performs searches. Contact Person: Dr. Zeller, Dir. **Publications:** Kartographische Bestandsverzeichnisse; Handschrifteninventare; Fontaneblatter. **Remarks:** FAX: 2 0378717. Telex: 0112757.

★6442★
Germany - Federal Employment Institute - Institute of Employment Research - Information and Documentation Department (Bus-Fin)
Regensburger Str. 104 Phone: 911 1793016
W-8500 Nuremberg 30, Germany Gerd Peters, Hd.
Founded: 1967. **Staff:** Prof 2. **Subjects:** Labor market theory and practice, market projections, business and regional research, vocational research and sociology, statistics. **Holdings:** 51,000 volumes; monographs; grey literature; research reports. **Subscriptions:** 700 journals and other serials. **Services:** SDI; department open to the public. **Computerized Information Services:** Internal databases documenting literature, research projects, and institutions and personnel. Performs searches on fee basis. **Publications:** Literaturdokumentation zur Arbeitsmarkt- und Berufsforchung/ LitDokAB, annual; Forschungsdokumentation zur Arbeitsmarkt- und Berufsforchung/ FoDok AB, 3/year. **Remarks:** Department is the central German establishment for documentation of literature and research in relation to the labor market. FAX: 911 172123. Telex: 622348. **Also Known As:** Bundesanstalt fur Arbeit - Institut fur Arbeitsmarkt- und Berufsforschung - Informations- und Dokumentationsstelle.

★6443★
Germany - Federal Environmental Agency - Environmental Information and Documentation System - Central Environmental Library (Env-Cons)
Bismarckplatz 1 Phone: 30 89032305
W-1000 Berlin 33, Germany Dr. Klaus Luedcke
Founded: 1974. **Staff:** Prof 7; Other 13. **Subjects:** Environment, pollution, solid wastes, environmental chemicals and wastes, noise, environmental research, air pollution, water pollution, nature conservation, allied subjects. **Special Collections:** Sammlung Erhard (archives of solid waste, 1900 to present; 2000 books, journals, reports, photographs). **Holdings:** 150,000 volumes; 150,000 microforms. **Subscriptions:** 850 journals and other serials. **Services:** Interlibrary loan; copying; SDI; library open to the public. **Automated Operations:** Computerized public access catalog. **Computerized Information Services:** Data-Star, STN International, FIZ Technik; produces ULIDAT, UFORDAT; internal database. **Special Catalogs:** Environmental Research Catalogue (UFOKAT); Buecher zum Unweltschutz. **Remarks:** FAX: 30 89032285. Telex: 183 756. **Also Known As:** Umweltbundesamt - Informations- und Dokumentationssystem Umwelt - Zentrale Fachbibliothekumwelt.

★6444★
Germany - Federal Highway Research Institute - Documentation and Information Systems (Trans)
Bruederstr. 53 Phone: 2204 43351
W-5060 Bergisch Gladbach 1, Germany M. Koenig, Dir.
Founded: 1972. **Staff:** 4. **Subjects:** Highway construction, traffic safety, accident research, bridge construction, civil engineering, traffic medicine, traffic education, traffic engineering, geotechnics, and allied subjects. **Holdings:** 30,000 bound volumes; reports; standards; statistics. **Subscriptions:** 200 journals and other serials. **Services:** Library open to the public. **Computerized Information Services:** International Road Research Documentation, TRANSDOC, and other national and international online databases. Performs searches on fee basis. **Remarks:** FAX: 2204 43833. **Also Known As:** Bundesanstalt fur Strassenwesen.

Germany - Federal Institute for East European and International Studies
See: **Federal Institute for East European and International Studies** (5630)

★6445★
Germany - Federal Institute for Occupational Safety - Information and Documentation Center for Occupational Safety (Bus-Fin)
Postfach 17 02 02
Vogelpothsweg 50-52 Phone: 231 1763341
W-4600 Dortmund 1, Germany Ulrich Trapp, Libn.
Founded: 1972. **Staff:** Prof 4. **Subjects:** Occupational safety and health, humanization of work, ergonomics. **Holdings:** 60,000 bound volumes; 20,000 other cataloged items. **Subscriptions:** 530 journals and other serials. **Services:** SDI; copying; center open to the public. **Computerized Information Services:** Produces LITDOK database (available online through FIZ Technik). **Remarks:** FAX: 231 1763454. Telex: 822 153. **Also Known As:** Bundesanstalt fur Arbeitsschutz - Informations - und Dokumenttationzentr.

Germany - Federal Institute for Sports Science
See: **Federal Institute for Sports Science - Documentation and Information Division** (5631)

★6446★
Germany - Federal Research Center for Agriculture and Forestry - Documentation Center for Phytomedicine - Library (Biol Sci)
Konigin Luise Str. 19 Phone: 30 8304215
W-1000 Berlin 33, Germany Prof. Dr. Wolfrudolf Laux, Hd.
Founded: 1964. **Staff:** Prof 4. **Subjects:** Phytomedicine - plant protection, phytopathology, and allied topics in agriculture, biology, and chemistry. **Holdings:** 60,000 bound volumes. **Subscriptions:** 1500 journals and other serials. **Services:** Center open to the public. **Computerized Information Services:** Searches online vendors; produces PHYTOMED (available online on DIMDI and STN International). Performs searches on fee basis. **Publications:** Bibliography of Plant Protection, 4/year - available by subscription; PHYTOMED Thesaurus - contents in German and English. **Remarks:** FAX: 30 8304284. Center works cooperatively with the Federal Biological Research Center Library, the Information Center for Tropical Plant Protection, and several agricultural documentation centers in Germany.

★6447★
Germany - Federal Research Center for Fisheries - Information and Documentation Center (Agri, Biol Sci)
Palmaille 9 Phone: 40 38905113
W-2000 Hamburg 50, Germany Dr. Wulf P. Kirchner, Hd.
Founded: 1968. **Staff:** Prof 4; Other 5. **Subjects:** Fisheries, marine biology, limnology, aquaculture, ichthyology, and allied subjects. **Holdings:** 60,000 bound volumes. **Subscriptions:** 950 journals and other serials. **Services:** SDI; copying; microfiche duplication; center open to the public. **Automated Operations:** Computerized cataloging. **Computerized Information Services:** Online systems; participates in Aquatic Sciences and Fisheries Information System; SCIENCEnet (electronic mail service). **Publications:** Archiv fur Fischereiwissenschaft; Informationen fur die Fischwirtschaft; Informationen uber die Fischwirtschaft der Auslandes. **Remarks:** FAX: 40 38905129. Telex: 2157 16 BFAFI. Electronic mail address(es): W.Kirchner (SCIENCEnet). **Also Known As:** Bundesforschungsanstalt fur Fischerei - Informations- und Dokumentationsstelle.

★6448★
Germany - Federal Statistical Office - Library (Sci-Engr)
Gustav-Stresemann-Ring 11 Phone: 061217 51
W-6200 Wiesbaden, Germany Sibylle Engelke
Founded: 1948. **Staff:** Prof 9; Other 18. **Subjects:** Statistics, statistical methods, economics, demography, ecology, social sciences. **Special Collections:** International statistical publications. **Holdings:** 405,388 statistical publications; 5968 microfiche; 4000 clippings. **Subscriptions:** 1635 journals; 31 newspapers. **Services:** Interlibrary loan; copying; SDI; library open to the public. **Automated Operations:** Computerized public access catalog, cataloging, and serials. **Computerized Information Services:** STALIS (internal database). Performs searches free of charge. **Publications:** Current contents; SDI; accession list, all monthly; list of periodicals. **Also Known As:** Statistisches Bundesamt.

Germany - Foreign Ministry - German Archaelogical Institute
See: **German Archaeological Institute** (6421)

★6449★
Germany - Juelich Research Center - Central Library (Energy, Sci-Engr)
Postfach 1913 Phone: 2461 613013
W-5170 Juelich 1, Germany Dr. W. Neubauer, Libn.
Founded: 1956. **Staff:** 50. **Subjects:** Energy technology, materials research, nuclear research, nuclear fusion, physics, environmental research, chemistry. **Holdings:** 600,000 books; 280,000 reports. **Subscriptions:** 2000 journals; 50 newspapers. **Services:** Interlibrary loan; copying; SDI; library open to the public. **Automated Operations:** Computerized public access catalog, cataloging, acquisitions, circulation, and ILL. **Computerized Information Services:** DIALOG Information Services, ESA/IRS, STN International. **Publications:** List of recent acquisitions; bibliography of KFA publications. **Special Indexes:** Index to Juelich Research Reports. **Remarks:** FAX: 2461 616103. **Also Known As:** Furschungszentrum Juelich. **Staff:** Dr. Eramute Lapp, Hd., User Serv.; Monika Kallfass; Friedrich Grawenz.

★6450★
Germany - Ministry of Economics - Federal Office of Foreign Trade Information - Library (Bus-Fin)
Postfach 108007
Blaubach 13 Phone: 221 20571
W-5000 Cologne, Germany Mr. Dammann, Dir.
Subjects: Economic situations and development of markets abroad; projects, tenders, and trade opportunities in foreign markets; nontarrif barriers as they influence international trade; business and investment laws and acts; regulation and administrative acts regarding importing and exporting; fiscal and customs regulations and laws. **Special Collections:** Microfilm archive. **Holdings:** Reports; other cataloged items. **Subscriptions:** 2000 economic newspapers. **Services:** SDI; library open to the public. **Automated Operations:** Computerized SDI. **Computerized Information Services:** Produces database of documents on foreign markets, projects, tenders, and foreign trade inquiries (available online through GENIOS); GEO-Net (electronic mail service). **Remarks:** FAX: 221 2057212. Telex: 08 882 735 BFAK D. Electronic mail address(es): GEO3:BfAiKOELN (GEO-Net). **Also Known As:** Bundesministerium fur Wirshaft - Bundesstelle fur Aussenhandelsinformation.

Germany - Ministry of Research and Technology - Institute of Contemporary History
See: **Institute of Contemporary History** (7920)

Germany - Ministry of Transport - German Hydrographic Institute
See: **Bundesamt fur Seeschiffahrt und Hydrographie** (2360)

★6451★
Germany - National Library of Economics in Germany (Soc Sci)
Dusternbrooker Weg 120 Phone: 431 8841
W-2300 Kiel 1, Germany Dr. Erwin Heidemann, Dir.
Founded: 1914. **Founded:** 95. **Subjects:** Economics, political economics, allied social sciences. **Special Collections:** Erich-Schneider-Bibliothek. **Holdings:** 2.1 million volumes; yearbooks; newspapers. **Subscriptions:** 19,000 journals and other serials. **Services:** SDI; information retrieval; faxing; document delivery; library open to the public. **Computerized Information Services:** ECONIS (Economics Information System); CD-ROM. **Publications:** Thesaurus der ZBW, irregular; Bibliographie der Wirtschaftswissenschaften, semiannual; Kieler Schrifttumskunden zu Wirtschaft und Gesellschaft, irregular; Kieler Schnellbibliographien zu aktuellen Wirtschaftsthemen, irregular. **Remarks:** FAX: 431 85853. Telex: 292 479 WELTW D. **Also Known As:** Zentralbibliothek der Wirtschaftswissenschaften in der Bundesrepublik Deutschland.

★6452★
Germany - Rhenish Regional Library (Hist)
Hohenfelder Str 16 Phone: 261 31100
W-5400 Koblenz, Germany Ernst-Ludwig Berz, Ltd.Bibl.Dir.
Founded: 1987. **Staff:** Prof 32; Other 2. **Subjects:** Regional history (middle-Rhine). **Special Collections:** Manuscript and printed material about the middle-Rhine area; regional administrative publications (district of Koblenz). **Holdings:** 145,000 books and bound periodical volumes; 500 archives; 60,000 microfiche; 500 reels of microfilm; 5000 German Standard Papers (DIN). **Subscriptions:** 2000 journals and other serials; 110 newspapers. **Services:** Interlibrary loan; copying; SDI; library open to the public. **Computerized Information Services:** DIMDI, FIZ Technik, GBI International, STN International. Contact Person: Dr. Helmut Fruhauf, Lib.Dir. **Publications:** Schriften der Rheinischen Landesbibliothek. **Remarks:** FAX: 261 37635. **Also Known As:** Rheinische Landesbibliothek.

M.J. Gerrie, Sr., Medical Library
See: **Waterville Osteopathic Hospital** (20094)

George and Ira Gershwin Collection
See: **Museum of the City of New York - Theatre Collection** (10892)

Gerstein/Tiffany Library
See: **Canadian Jewellers Institute** (2946)

Gerstenzang Science Library
See: **Brandeis University** (2071)

★6453★
Gesamthochschule Kasser Universitat - Bereichsbibliothek Landwirtschaft - Internationale Agrarwirtschaft (Agri)
Norbahnhofstr 1a
Postfach 101380 Phone: 5542 503539
W-3430 Witzenhausen, Germany Silvia Henze-Schwartz
Subjects: Agricultural science, agricultural economics, biological agriculture developmental policy, rural sociology. **Holdings:** 30,000 books; 12,000 bound periodical volumes. **Subscriptions:** 520 journals and other serials; 10 newspapers. **Services:** Interlibrary loan; copying; library open to the public.

Gesellschaft fur Mathematik und Datenverarbeitung - GMD-Informationszentrum fur Informationswissenschaft und -Praxis
See: **German National Research Center for Computer Science - GMD Information Center for Information Science and Information Work** (6431)

John Marshall Gest Memorial Library
See: **Theodore F. Jenkins Memorial Law Library** (8362)

Gest Oriental Library and East Asian Collections
See: **Princeton University** (13374)

★6454★
Get Oil Out - Library (Energy)
1114 State St., No.301
Santa Barbara, CA 93101-2716 Phone: (805)965-1519
Founded: 1969. **Subjects:** Offshore oil and gas operations in the Santa Barbara Channel, allied state and federal legislation. **Holdings:** Figures not available. **Also Known As:** GOO.

★6455★
Gethsemani Abbey - Library (Rel-Phil)
Trappist, KY 40051 Phone: (502)549-3117
Fr. Hilarion Schmock, O.C.S.O., Libn.
Founded: 1848. **Staff:** 2. **Subjects:** Scripture, Christian and monastic writers, Benedictine/Cistercian monasticism, religious life, non-Christian religions, theology, liturgy, prayer, mysticism. **Special Collections:** Thomas Merton Collection; printed editions of the Rule of St. Benedict, 1500 to present (300). **Holdings:** 30,000 books; 1000 bound periodical volumes; 30 manuscripts and 60 incunabula on microfilm. **Subscriptions:** 90 journals and other serials; 10 newspapers. **Services:** Interlibrary loan; copying; library open to the public for specific research. **Remarks:** Rare books on Cisterian history and St. Bernard, manuscripts, and incunabula on permanent loan to Institute of Cistercian Studies at Western Michigan University. **Staff:** Fr. Bede Kok, O.C.S.O., Libn.

★6456★
Getty Center for the History of Art and the Humanities - Resource Collections (Art)
401 Wilshire Blvd., Suite 400 Phone: (310)458-9811
Santa Monica, CA 90401 Donald Anderle, Dir.
Founded: 1983. **Staff:** Prof 26; Other 53. **Subjects:** Art history, architecture, archeology, photography, decorative arts. **Special Collections:** Rare illustrated source books (15,000); auction catalogs (85,000). **Holdings:** 400,000 books; 130,000 bound periodical volumes; 2 million photographs; manuscripts; archival materials. **Subscriptions:** 3500 journals and other serials. **Services:** Interlibrary loan; copying; library open to the public by appointment. **Automated Operations:** Computerized public access catalog, cataloging, acquisitions, circulation, and serials (ORION). **Computerized Information Services:** DIALOG Information Services, BRS Information Technologies, NEXIS, Questel, ArtQuest. **Networks/Consortia:** Member of Research Libraries Information Network (RLIN), CLASS. **Remarks:** FAX: (310)458-6487. The Resource Collections comprise the book, photo, and archival collections of the Getty Center. **Staff:** Anne-Mieke Halbrook, Hd., Res.Serv./Coll.Mgt.; Bethany Mendenhall, Hd., Tech.Serv.; Kathleen Salomon, Hd., Ref.

★6457★
Gettysburg College - Musselman Library - Special Collections (Hist, Rare Book)
Gettysburg, PA 17325 Phone: (717)373-7011
David Hedrick, Spec.Coll.Libn.
Special Collections: Civil War (2500 books and newspapers); H.L. Mencken/F. Scott Fitzgerald (625 volumes); Coci Organ Music Collection (2400 volumes); letters (700); rare books (4900); rare documents (585); rare maps (500); college archives. **Holdings:** 8610 books; 72 VF drawers. **Services:** Interlibrary loan; copying; collections open to the public for reference use and consultation. **Automated Operations:** Computerized public access catalog, cataloging, and acquisitions. **Computerized Information Services:** Internal database; BITNET (electronic mail service). **Networks/Consortia:** Member of PALINET, Central Pennsylvania Consortium (CPC), Associated College Libraries of Central Pennsylvania (ACLCP). **Remarks:** FAX: (717)337-7029 (Attn: Hedrick). Electronic mail address(es): dhedrick@gettysburg.edu (BITNET).

★6458★
Gettysburg College - Sloat Chemistry Library (Sci-Engr)
Breidenbaugh Hall Phone: (717)337-6260
Gettysburg, PA 17325 Dr. Alex T. Rowland, Prof., Chem.
Subjects: Chemistry. **Holdings:** 2000 books. **Subscriptions:** 23 journals and other serials. **Computerized Information Services:** DIALOG Information Services. **Remarks:** FAX: (717) 337-6260

Gettysburg National Military Park
See: **U.S. Natl. Park Service** (17720)

★6459★
Oscar Getz Museum of Whiskey History - Library (Food-Bev)
114 N. 5th St. Phone: (502)348-2999
Bardstown, KY 40004 Flaget M. Nally, Cur.
Founded: 1957. **Staff:** 2. **Subjects:** History of whiskey prior to 1919. **Special Collections:** Medicinal whiskies collection (1913-1933). **Holdings:** Books; catalogs; memorabilia; advertisements; photographs. **Services:** Library not open to the public; may be consulted by liquor industry representatives, writers, and researchers.

George and Margaret Gey Library
See: **W. Alton Jones Cell Science Center** (8478)

★6460★
Ghana - Ministry of Agriculture - Reference Library (Agri)
PO Box 299 Phone: 664329
Accra, Ghana Evelyn M. Atsodibuor
Founded: 1890. **Staff:** Prof 1; Other 3. **Subjects:** Crops production, livestock, food, nutrition, forestry, agroforestry, fisheries, aquaculture, agricultural extension. **Holdings:** 2000 books; 500 bound periodical volumes; 2000 reports; 1000 archival items. **Subscriptions:** 5 journals and other serials; 3 newspapers. **Services:** Interlibrary loan; copying; SDI; library open to the public. **Automated Operations:** CDS/ISIS.

★6461★
Ghana Library Board - Research Library on African Affairs (Area-Ethnic, Soc Sci)
P.O. Box 2970 Phone: 228402
Accra, Ghana Christina D.T. Kwei, Libn.
Founded: 1961. **Staff:** 27. **Subjects:** Anthropology, social studies, history, literature, economics, geography. **Special Collections:** Ghana National Collection; Monia Collection (1026 volumes). **Holdings:** 35,000 books; 550 bound periodical volumes; 3000 microforms. **Subscriptions:** 130 journals and other serials; 50 newspapers. **Services:** Interlibrary loan; copying; library open to the public with restrictions. **Publications:** Special subject lists on African affairs; Ghana National Bibliography. **Remarks:** Library acts as the National Bibliographic Agency and the National ISDS Centre for Ghana. Additional services include the allocation of ISBNs (International Standard Book Numbers) and ISSNs (International Standard Serial Numbers) to publishers. **Staff:** Sarah Kamda; Faustina Oppong-Peprah.

★6462★
Ghost Club - Library (Soc Sci)
1 Whitehall Pl.
London SW1A 2HO, England
Subjects: Spontaneous and induced psychic phenomena. **Special Collections:** Biographical archives. **Holdings:** 4000 volumes. **Services:** Library not open to the public. **Remarks:** Club investigates and researches all subjects not yet fully understood or accepted by science.

★6463★
Ghost Ranch Conference Center - Ghost Ranch Library (Rel-Phil)
Ghost Ranch Phone: (505)685-4333
Abiquiu, NM 87510 Lidie Miller, Libn.
Founded: 1955. **Staff:** Prof 1. **Subjects:** Theology, religion, Bible study, Christian education, Southwest, children's literature, ecology, archeology, paleontology, fine arts. **Holdings:** 14,525 books; 3 VF drawers of pamphlets; uncataloged items. **Subscriptions:** 40 journals and other serials. **Services:** Copying; library open to ranch guests for reference use only. **Publications:** Ghost Ranch Journal. **Remarks:** Maintained by Presbyterian Church (U.S.A.).

Giannini Foundation of Agricultural Economics
See: **University of California, Berkeley** (18323)

Gibbes Museum of Art
See: **Carolina Art Association** (3088)

★6464★
Gibbs and Cox, Inc. - Technical Information Center (Sci-Engr)
50 W. 23rd St. Phone: (212)366-3900
New York, NY 10010 J.W. Hoffman, Jr., Mgr.
Founded: 1930. **Staff:** Prof 2; Other 3. **Subjects:** Naval architecture, marine engineering. **Holdings:** 6000 books; 50,000 engineering drawings; 4000 vendor catalogs; 10,000 reports. **Subscriptions:** 100 journals and other serials. **Services:** Center not open to the public. **Computerized Information Services:** Complete microfilm service; company documents on internal database with search capabilities.

★6465★
Gibbs & Hill, Inc. - Library (Sci-Engr)
11 Penn Plaza
New York, NY 10001 Phone: (212)216-6939
Staff: Prof 1; Other 2. **Subjects:** Nuclear engineering; nuclear safety; fossil power plants; alternative energy technology; environmental science and technology; engineering - electrical, civil, mechanical. **Special Collections:** Nuclear Safety Library; environmental library; standards and specifications (4000). **Holdings:** 3500 books; 200 bound periodical volumes; 1500 company reports; 2000 technical reports; 1500 vendor catalogs; 45,000 reports on microfiche; 500 cassettes of vendor information and standards. **Subscriptions:** 250 journals and other serials. **Services:** Interlibrary loan; library not open to the public. **Publications:** Current Awareness Microfiche Bulletin, monthly; Library Bulletin, monthly - to management and professionals. **Remarks:** FAX: (212)216-6476. Telex: 177199.

★6466★
Katharine Gibbs School, Boston - Library (Educ)
126 Newbury St. Phone: (617)578-7177
Boston, MA 02116 Cynthia W. Alcorn, Libn.
Founded: 1982. **Staff:** Prof 1.5. **Subjects:** Business careers including travel, hotel/restaurant, secretarial; women in the workplace; American woman. **Holdings:** 4000 books; 800 cassette tapes. **Subscriptions:** 72 journals and other serials; 5 newspapers. **Services:** SDI. **Remarks:** FAX: (617)262-2010.

★6467★
Gibraltar - Gibraltar Garrison - Library (Hist)
Gibraltar, Gibraltar Phone: 35077418
Founded: 1795. **Staff:** Prof 1. **Subjects:** Gibraltar and region. **Special Collections:** Gibraltar collection (19th and 20th centuries). **Holdings:** 40,000 books; 300 bound periodical volumes; 50 reports. **Services:** Copying; library open to the public by appointment. **Staff:** Jon Searle.

Gibraltar Research Library
See: **Crompton & Knowles Corporation - Dyes and Chemicals Division** (4436)

★6468★
Gibson City United Methodist Church - Library (Rel-Phil)
Church at 10th St. Phone: (217)784-5452
Gibson City, IL 60936 Christine L. Hazen, Libn.
Staff: 1. **Subjects:** Religion, children's literature. **Holdings:** 1200 books. **Subscriptions:** 2 journals and other serials. **Services:** Library open to the public.

★6469★
Gibson, Dunn & Crutcher - Law Library (Law)
333 S. Grand Ave. Phone: (213)229-7216
Los Angeles, CA 90071 Pamela R. Soreide, Chf.Libn.
Staff: Prof 4; Other 8. **Subjects:** Law. **Holdings:** 33,000 books; 1600 bound periodical volumes; 210 law memoranda; 600 pamphlets; 600 tape cassettes; 10,000 microfiche. **Subscriptions:** 170 journals and other serials; 8 newspapers. **Services:** Library not open to the public. **Computerized Information Services:** LEXIS, WESTLAW, Dow Jones News/Retrieval, DIALOG Information Services. **Special Catalogs:** Catalog to collection of bound Memoranda of Law, 1976 to present (online). **Remarks:** Alternate telephone number(s): 229-7217. **Staff:** Robert Creamer, Libn.; Susan I-Man Wu, Cat.; Shirley Proctor, Ref.; Betty Jo Page, Ref.; Dena Hollingsworth, Online Info.Spec.; Susan Jenks, Ref.

Gibson Library
See: **Kentucky Mountain Bible College** (8662)

Gibson Medical Resource Centre
See: **St. Mary's of the Lake Hospital** (14530)

R.E. Gibson Library and Information Center
See: **Johns Hopkins University - Applied Physics Laboratory** (8415)

Harry D. Gideonse Library
See: **Brooklyn College of City University of New York** (2232)

★6470★
Giffels Associates, Inc. - Library (Sci-Engr)
Box 5025 Phone: (313)355-4600
Southfield, MI 48086 Helen Kott, Libn.
Staff: 1. **Subjects:** Engineering, architecture. **Holdings:** 1100 books. **Subscriptions:** 80 journals and other serials. **Services:** Interlibrary loan; copying; library open to the public with restrictions. **Computerized Information Services:** DIALOG Information Services. **Networks/Consortia:** Member of Oakland Wayne Interlibrary Network (OWIN). **Remarks:** Library located at 25200 Telegraph Rd., Southfield, MI 48034. **Remarks:** FAX: (313)357-2710

John H. Gifford Memorial Library & Information Center
See: **American Chemical Society - Rubber Division** (524)

★6471★
Gifford Memorial Hospital - Health Information Center (Med)
44 S. Main St. Phone: (802)728-4441
Randolph, VT 05060 Linda Minsinger, Inservice Dir.
Staff: 1. **Subjects:** Medicine, nursing. **Holdings:** 532 books; 45 bound periodical volumes; 1 VF drawer of pamphlets; 4 drawers of journals on microfiche; 150 government publications; 50 tapes and filmstrips. **Subscriptions:** 42 journals and other serials. **Services:** Interlibrary loan; copying; center open to the public with restrictions. **Networks/Consortia:** Member of North Atlantic Health Science Libraries (NAHSL).

★6472★
GIFRIC Inc. - Centre de Documentation (Soc Sci)
342, Blvd. St-Cyrille, W. Phone: (418)687-4350
Quebec, PQ, Canada G1S 1R9 Urgel Fortin, Resp.
Founded: 1978. **Staff:** 20. **Subjects:** Clinical psychoanalysis; social and cultural change and their effects. **Special Collections:** Noeud Collection; Reseau Simplexe Collection. **Holdings:** Figures not available. **Remarks:** FAX: (418)683-1935.

Gila Cliff Dwellings National Monument
See: **U.S. Natl. Park Service - Gila Cliff Dwellings Natl. Monument** (17721)

★6473★
Gila County Superior Court - Law Library (Law)
1400 E. Ash St. Phone: (602)425-3231
Globe, AZ 85501 Dave Crossett, Libn.
Staff: 2. **Subjects:** Law. **Holdings:** 16,000 books; 8000 bound periodical volumes. **Services:** Interlibrary loan; copying; library open to the public. **Automated Operations:** Computerized public access catalog and cataloging. **Remarks:** FAX: (602)425-7714.

★6474★
Gilbert Commonwealth, Inc. - Library and Information Services (Sci-Engr, Energy)
P.O. Box 1498 Phone: (215)775-2600
Reading, PA 19603-1498 Deborah M. Bosler, Supv., Lib.Serv.
Founded: 1956. **Staff:** Prof 2; Other 3. **Subjects:** Engineering and management for power industry, energy research, environmental

engineering. **Special Collections:** Coal conversion (6000 reports); Electric Power Research Institute (EPRI) reports; Nuclear Regulatory Commission (NUREG) reports. **Holdings:** 20,000 books; 60,000 technical reports; plant engineering vendor catalogs and voluntary and military standards on 16mm microfilm; engineering standards. **Subscriptions:** 725 journals and other serials. **Services:** SDI; library open to the public by appointment. **Automated Operations:** Computerized cataloging, serials, circulation, and periodicals routing. **Computerized Information Services:** DTIC, DataTimes, DIALOG Information Services, Integrated Technical Information System (ITIS), DunsPrint, NRC; Spindex (internal database). **Networks/Consortia:** Member of Berks County Library Association (BCLA). **Publications:** Library Bulletin (list of new materials received in company), monthly; How to find company information; Library Services, Videotape: G/C Library and Information Services. **Special Catalogs:** Union List of Serials. **Remarks:** FAX: (215)775-2670. Telex: 173241. **Staff:** Frances Calvaresi, Tech.Libn.

Margaret Clark Gilbreath Memorial Library
See: **Baptist Medical Center** (1507)

Frank and Lillian Gilbreth Archives
See: **Hive Publishing Company - John Franklin Mee Memorial Library** (7294)

Frank & Lillian Gilbreth Memorial Library
See: **Institute of Industrial Engineers, Inc.** (7944)

★6475★
Thomas Gilcrease Institute of American History and Art - Library (Hist)
1400 Gilcrease Museum Rd. Phone: (918)582-3122
Tulsa, OK 74127 Sarah Erwin, Cur., Archv.Coll.
Founded: 1955. **Staff:** Prof 1. **Subjects:** History - Colonial, Western, Spanish Southwest, Indian. **Special Collections:** Hispanic documents, 1500-1800; John Ross papers (Chief of Cherokees, 1814-1870); Peter P. Pitchlynn papers (Chief of Choctaws); Grant Foreman Collection. **Holdings:** 50,000 books; 50 VF drawers of historic photographs and manuscripts; broadsides; maps; photostats. **Subscriptions:** 10 journals and other serials. **Services:** Copying (limited); library open to the public by appointment. **Networks/Consortia:** Member of Tulsa Area Library Cooperative (TALC). **Publications:** Guide to Manuscripts. **Special Catalogs:** Gilcrease-Hargrett Catalog; Hispanic Documents Catalog (out of print).

Gilfillan Engineering Library
See: **ITT Corporation** (8286)

★6476★
Gillette Children's Hospital - Professional Library (Med)
200 E. University Phone: (612)229-3835
St. Paul, MN 55101 Patricia Anderson, Med. Staff Asst.
Staff: Prof 1. **Subjects:** Orthopedics, pediatrics. **Holdings:** 2584 books; 54 bound periodical volumes. **Subscriptions:** 48 journals and other serials. **Services:** Library open to health professionals. **Remarks:** FAX: (612)229-3999.

★6477★
Gillette Company - Corporate R&D Library (Sci-Engr)
Gillette Park - 5GA-4 Phone: (617)463-3178
Boston, MA 02127-1096 Susan R. Fox, Sr.Info.Spec.
Founded: 1968. **Staff:** Prof 1. **Subjects:** Chemistry, hair, skin, cosmetics, materials, polymers, plastics, management. **Holdings:** 5000 books. **Subscriptions:** 200 journals and other serials. **Services:** Interlibrary loan; center not open to the public. **Computerized Information Services:** DIALOG Information Services, STN International, Data-Star, EPIC, WILSONLINE; internal database. **Remarks:** FAX: (617)463-2527. Contains the holdings of the former Gillette Company - Personal Care Division - Information Center.

★6478★
Gillette Company - Personal Care Division - Information Center
Box 2131
Boston, MA 02106
Defunct. Holdings absorbed by Gillette Company - R&D Library.

★6479★
Gillette Medical Evaluation Laboratories - Information Center (Sci-Engr, Med)
401 Professional Dr. Phone: (301)590-1551
Gaithersburg, MD 20879 Colleen A. Pritchard, Info.Ctr.Supv.
Founded: 1974. **Staff:** Prof 2. **Subjects:** Toxicology, cosmetics, dermatology, organic and surface chemistry, biology. **Special Collections:** Reprints dealing with cosmetics and dermatology (10,000). **Holdings:** 6500 books; 4200 bound periodical volumes; 1100 government documents; 13,000 reprints; 30 notebooks of OTC meeting minutes. **Subscriptions:** 312 journals and other serials. **Services:** Interlibrary loan; SDI; center open to the public by appointment. **Computerized Information Services:** DIALOG Information Services, Chemical Information Systems, Inc. (CIS), Occupational Health Services, Inc. (OHS), Questel, Chemical Abstracts Service (CAS), Data-Star, ELSS (Electronic Legislative Search System), NEXIS, NLM. **Networks/Consortia:** Member of Interlibrary Users Association (IUA). **Special Catalogs:** Catalog of Gillette corporate reports. **Special Indexes:** Index to Gillette Company Research Reports. **Remarks:** FAX: (301)590-1535. **Staff:** Diane Levitt.

Ray Gilmore Archives
See: **San Diego Society of Natural History** (14712)

Etienne Gilson Archive
See: **University of Toronto - St. Michael's College - John M. Kelly Library** (19459)

Adam and Sophie Gimbel Design Library
See: **Parsons School of Design** (12768)

Colonel Richard Gimbel Aeronautics History Library
See: **U.S. Air Force Academy - Library** (16822)

Edwin Ginn Library
See: **Tufts University - Fletcher School of Law & Diplomacy - Edwin Ginn Library** (16548)

★6480★
Ginsburg, Feldman & Bress - Law Library (Law)
1250 Connecticut Ave., N.W., Suite 800 Phone: (202)637-9108
Washington, DC 20036 Laura Speer, Libn.
Staff: Prof 1; Other 2. **Subjects:** Law - tax, aviation, communications, corporate, antitrust, banking, bankruptcy, international, real estate; litigation. **Holdings:** 15,000 books; 15 VF drawers. **Services:** Interlibrary loan; library open to the public by appointment. **Computerized Information Services:** WESTLAW, LEXIS, DIALOG Information Services, Dun & Bradstreet Business Credit Services, Dow Jones News/Retrieval, Information America, DataTimes, LEGI-SLATE, ATA; CD-ROM (DataWorld Infodisk).

★6481★
Girard College - Stephen Girard Papers and Effects (Hist)
Girard & Corinthian Aves. Phone: (215)787-2600
Philadelphia, PA 19121 Phyllis R. Abrams, Cur.
Founded: 1831. **Subjects:** Stephen Girard, real estate, ships, shipping, banking, commerce. **Special Collections:** Correspondence of Stephen Girard, including among the correspondents U.S. Presidents, statesmen, naval officers, diplomats, Simon Bolivar, Toussaint L'Ouverture, and members of the Bonaparte family; material on yellow fever epidemics. **Holdings:** 1 million documents, business papers, memoranda, law proceedings. **Services:** Papers are available to the public with the permission of the college president. **Special Catalogs:** Stephen Girard Collection catalog; A Catalogue of the Personal Library of Stephen Girard. **Remarks:** 663 reels of microfilm are housed at the American Philosophical Society in Philadelphia for scholarly use.

★6482★
Girl Scouts of the USA - Juliette Gordon Low Girl Scout National Center (Rec)
142 Bull St. Phone: (912)233-4501
Savannah, GA 31401 Katherine Keena, Prog.Spec.
Founded: 1953. **Staff:** Prof 5. **Subjects:** Juliette Gordon Low, early Girl Scout history, 19th century decorative arts, women's history. **Special Collections:** Gordon family book collection, 1820-1927. **Holdings:** 500 books; 2 boxes of manuscripts; 2 lateral file drawers of archival material; 1000 historical photographs; 1000 stereoviews. **Services:** Copying; limited research by staff; center open to the public by appointment. **Remarks:** FAX: (912)233-4659. **Staff:** Stephen Bohlin-Davis.

★6483★
Girl Scouts of the USA - Library (Rec)
830 3rd Ave. & 51st St. Phone: (212)940-7396
New York, NY 10022 Juana Alers-Quinones, Adm., Lib.
Staff: Prof 1. **Subjects:** Education, child development, management, Girl Scouts. **Holdings:** 7000 books; 35 shelves of publications. **Subscriptions:** 400 journals and other serials; 3 newspapers. **Services:** Copying; SDI (both limited); library open to the public by special arrangement. **Publications:** Acquisitions Notices, monthly - for internal distribution only. **Special Catalogs:** Memorabilia catalog (card); inventory list of archives records (loose-leaf). **Remarks:** FAX: (212)940-7859.

★6484★
Girl Scouts of the USA - National Historic Preservation Center (Rec)
830 3rd Ave. & 51st St. Phone: (212)940-7662
New York, NY 10022 Mary E. Levey, Dir.
Founded: 1988. **Staff:** Prof 2; Other 3. **Subjects:** Girl Scout history. **Special Collections:** Girl Scout publications (4000 titles). **Holdings:** 12,600 linear feet of records and archives; 5000 photographs; 300 historic uniforms; memorabilia. **Services:** Reference; research; center open to the public by appointment. **Remarks:** FAX: (212)940-7859. **Staff:** Martha Foley, Archv.

Girls Clubs of America
See: **Girls Incorporated - National Resource Center** (6485)

★6485★
Girls Incorporated - National Resource Center (Soc Sci)
441 W. Michigan St. Phone: (317)634-7546
Indianapolis, IN 46202 Mary Maschino, Libn.
Founded: 1981. **Staff:** Prof 1. **Subjects:** Girls' issues, including development, single sex environments, girls in math and science, health and sexuality, preventing adolescent pregnancy, sports, career education, nontraditional jobs, gender roles and relationships. **Holdings:** 3000 books; 25 filmstrips and slide sets; 240 vertical files; 650 dissertations on microfiche; 55 posters; 30 video cassettes; 120 program models. **Subscriptions:** 150 journals and other serials. **Services:** Copying; SDI; center open to the public for reference use only. **Networks/Consortia:** Member of Central Indiana Area Library Services Authority (CIALSA), INCOLSA. **Publications:** Choices: Teen Woman's Journal for Self-awareness and Personal Planning; What Do We Know About Girls; Facts and Reflections on Female Adolescent Sexuality; Facts and Reflections on Careers for Today's Girls; monographs; specialized bibliographies; Facts and Reflections on Girls and Substance Use. **Formerly:** Girls Clubs of America.

Maxwell Gitelson Film Library
See: **Chicago Institute for Psychoanalysis - McLean Library** (3523)

★6486★
Givaudan-Roure U.S.A. - Library (Sci-Engr)
125 Delawanna Ave.
Clifton, NJ 07015-5034 Phone: (201)365-8563
Founded: 1952. **Staff:** Prof 1; Other 1. **Subjects:** Fragrances, aroma chemicals, flavors. **Holdings:** 10,000 volumes; 17 VF drawers of U.S. and foreign patents; Chemical Abstracts on microfilm; 36 VF drawers of reprints and pamphlets. **Subscriptions:** 129 journals and other serials. **Services:** Interlibrary loan; library not open to the public. **Computerized Information Services:** Chemical Abstracts Service, STN International. **Remarks:** Library is part of the Research Department. FAX: (201)473-1508. **Formed by the merger of:** Fritzsche, Dodge and Olcott - Research Library and Givaudan Corporation - Library. **Staff:** Elaine Lembeck; Helen Cimera; Glen Fredericks, Mgr., Comp. and Info.Serv.

Glacier Inventory Photo Library
See: **U.S. Geological Survey - Ice and Climate Project - Glacier Inventory Photo Library** (17535)

Glacier National Park
See: **U.S. Natl. Park Service - Glacier Natl. Park** (17722)

Edward A. Glad Memorial Library
See: **Red Cross of Constantine - United Grand Imperial Council** (13759)

★6487★
Everett A. Gladman Memorial Hospital - Medical Library (Med)
2633 E. 27th St. Phone: (510)536-8111
Oakland, CA 94601 Lee Vares, Dir.Med.Rec.
Staff: Prof 1. **Subjects:** Psychiatry, psychology, medicine. **Holdings:** 500 books. **Subscriptions:** 50 journals and other serials. **Services:** Library not open to the public.

E. Gordon Glass, M.D., Memorial Library
See: **Muhlenberg Regional Medical Center** (10844)

Glass Memorial Library
See: **Johnson Bible College** (8434)

★6488★
Glassboro State College - Music Branch Library (Mus)
Wilson Bldg. 216200 Phone: (609)863-7306
Glassboro, NJ 08028 Marjorie Travaline, Libn.
Staff: Prof 1; Other 11. **Subjects:** Music - classical, jazz, theater, popular. **Holdings:** 15,000 books and scores; 8000 phonograph records and compact discs; videocassettes. **Services:** Interlibrary loan; library open to the public. **Automated Operations:** Computerized cataloging. **Computerized Information Services:** DIALOG Information Services, BRS Information Technologies, OCLC. **Networks/Consortia:** Member of PALINET. **Special Indexes:** Song index for score anthologies (card).

★6489★
Glassboro State College - Savitz Library - Stewart Room (Hist)
Glassboro, NJ 08028 Phone: (609)863-6303
Clara M. Kirner, Spec.Coll.Libn.
Founded: 1948. **Staff:** Prof 1; Other 1. **Subjects:** New Jersey history, early religious history, genealogy, Indians of North America, Revolutionary War, War of 1812, Grinnell Arctic expedition. **Special Collections:** Family papers: Howell, Inskeep, Haines, Lippincott; Frank H. Stewart Collection (8000 volumes); Charles A. Wolverton Papers (10 boxes); Summit Conference Papers (4 boxes); Satterthwaite Genealogical Collection (24 VF drawers). **Holdings:** 15,900 books; 422 bound periodical volumes; 5000 manuscripts; 13 VF drawers of college archives; 4070 volumes of masters' theses; rare books; deeds; surveys; marriage licenses; acts of assembly. **Subscriptions:** 28 journals and other serials. **Services:** Copying (limited); room open to the public for reference use only. **Publications:** Guide to the Special Collections - available on request. **Remarks:** FAX: (609)863-6313.

★6490★
P.H. Glatfelter Company - Ecusta Division - Technical Library (Sci-Engr)
Box 200 Phone: (704)877-2211
Pisgah Forest, NC 28768 Naia Parker, Tech.Libn.
Founded: 1939. **Staff:** Prof 1. **Subjects:** Cellulose chemistry, polymers and plastics, pulp and paper manufacture, water and air pollution control. **Holdings:** 4333 books; 5561 bound periodical volumes; 550 catalogs; 650 brochures; 22,966 literature separates and patents. **Subscriptions:** 111 journals and other serials. **Services:** Library open to the public for reference use only. **Computerized Information Services:** PFDS Online, DataTimes.

★6491★
P.H. Glatfelter Company - Research Library (Sci-Engr)
Spring Grove, PA 17362 Phone: (717)225-4711
Donna M. Myers, Res.Libn.
Staff: 1. **Subjects:** Pulp and paper, organic and inorganic chemistry, management, statistics, environment. **Holdings:** 2100 books; 107 bound periodical volumes; 5 VF drawers of patents; 12 VF drawers of information retrieval materials; 16 periodicals on microfilm. **Subscriptions:** 100 journals and other serials. **Services:** Library not open to the public. **Computerized Information Services:** PFDS Online, DIALOG Information Services.

Irma Glatty Library
See: **Mahaska County Historical Society - Irma Glatty Library** (9544)

Irene Glaus Memorial Library
See: **United Paperworkers International Union - Irene Glaus Memorial Library** (16778)

★6492★
Glaxo Canada, Ltd. - Library Information Centre (Med)
7333 Mississauga Rd., N. Phone: (416)819-3000
Mississauga, ON, Canada L5N 6L4 Helen Kornuta, Info.Ctr.Coord.
Founded: 1988. **Staff:** Prof 1; Other 2. **Subjects:** Pharmacology, medicine, pharmacy, chemistry, microbiology, business. **Holdings:** 900 books. **Subscriptions:** 300 journals and other serials. **Services:** Interlibrary loan; library not open to the public. **Automated Operations:** Computerized cataloging, serials, and acquisitions. **Computerized Information Services:** DIALOG Information Services, STN International, Data-Star, CAN/OLE, Info Globe, Infomart Online, DOBIS Canadian Online Library System; Glaxoline (internal database); Envoy 100 (electronic mail service). **Networks/Consortia:** Member of Sheridan Park Association. **Remarks:** FAX: (416)259-5659. Electronic mail address(es): SHI (Envoy 100). **Formerly:** Located in Toronto, ON.

★6493★
Glaxo Inc. - Library (Med)
Five Moore Dr. Phone: (919)990-5382
Research Triangle Park, NC 27709 Peggy F. Hull, Hd., Lib. & Info.Serv.
Founded: 1983. **Staff:** 21. **Subjects:** Medicine, pharmacy and pharmacology, chemistry, biology, business, computer science. **Holdings:** 11,500 books; 7200 bound periodical volumes; 379 annual reports. **Subscriptions:** 1500 journals and other serials; 6 newspapers. **Services:** Interlibrary loan; copying; SDI; library open to the public by appointment. **Computerized Information Services:** DIALOG Information Services, BRS Information Technologies, ORBIT Search Service, NLM, STN International, NewsNet, Inc., InvesText, Dow Jones News/Retrieval, VU/TEXT Information Services, Reuter TEXTLINE, Chemical Information Systems, Inc. (CIS), Questel, Mead Data Central, Computerized AIDS Information Network (CAIN), IMSMARQ, Data-Star, Human Resource Information Network (HRIN), BIOSIS Connection, GenBank, Citicorp Global Report, DataTimes, IMSWorld; Glaxoline (internal database). **Networks/Consortia:** Member of SOLINET. **Remarks:** FAX: (919)990-5328. Telex: 802813. **Staff:** Cindy Crawford; Elaine Francis; Michael Gelinne; Ann McLain; Cam Morrison; Kathleen Lucisano; Julie Roach; Dayna Scarborough; Sandra Chambers; Wadad Giles.

GLAZA
See: **Greater Los Angeles Zoo Association** (6706)

Ellen Gleason Library
See: **Santa Ynez Valley Historical Society** (14820)

Madeline Gleason Poetry Archive and Collection of San Francisco Poets
See: **University of San Francisco - Special Collections Department/ Donohue Rare Book Room** (19290)

★6494★
Glebe House Museum - Library (Hist)
P.O. Box 245
Hollow Rd.
Woodbury, CT 06798 Phone: (203)263-2855
Subjects: History, archaeology, decorative arts, 18th century, Woodbury history, Gertrude Jekyll. **Special Collections:** 18th century books. **Holdings:** 300 books. **Services:** Library open to the public.

Gledhill Library
See: **Santa Barbara Historical Society** (14799)

★6495★
Glen Helen Association - Library (Env-Cons)
Glen Helen Bldg.
405 Corry St. Phone: (513)767-7375
Yellow Springs, OH 45387 Mrs. George Asakawa, Libn.
Founded: 1973. **Staff:** 1. **Subjects:** Environmental protection, resource management, natural area preservation, forestry, outdoor recreation and education, wildlife. **Holdings:** 630 books; 14 VF drawers of pamphlets; 7 VF drawers of maps; 6 reels of film; 30 tapes; 10 volumes of U.S. Department of Interior Third Nationwide Outdoor Recreation Plan; 1 set color reproductions of John James Audubon's The Birds of America with text; 6 carousel trays of slides; 9 games; 11 filmstrip/audiotape kits; 17 microfiche; 15 video cassette recordings. **Subscriptions:** 50 journals and other serials. **Services:** Library open to the public. **Remarks:** Maintains a small reference library at the Trailside Museum for staff and junior naturalists. Library is affiliated with Antioch University.

★6496★
Glenbow-Alberta Institute - Library & Archives (Hist)
130 9th Ave., S.E. Phone: (403)264-8300
Calgary, AB, Canada T2G 0P3 Leonard J. Gottselig, Chf.Libn.
Founded: 1955. **Staff:** Prof 9; Other 9. **Subjects:** Western Canada, Canadian Arctic, Indians of North America, fur trade, missionaries, local history, Canadian art. **Special Collections:** Dewdney papers; J.J. Bowlen papers; George Coote papers; Sir F.W.G. Haultain papers. **Holdings:** 80,000 books; 3000 bound periodical volumes; 12 million pages of manuscripts; 4000 reels of microfilm; 48 VF drawers of newspapers clippings; 30 VF drawers of trade catalogs; 2000 Western Canadian political pamphlets and leaflets; 100 motion picture films; 500,000 photographs; 4000 tape recordings. **Subscriptions:** 450 journals and other serials; 20 newspapers. **Services:** Interlibrary loan (limited); copying; library open to the public for reference use only. **Computerized Information Services:** Envoy 100 (electronic mail service). **Publications:** List of publications - available on request. **Special Catalogs:** Catalog of Glenbow Historical Library (book). **Remarks:** FAX: (403)265-9769. Electronic mail address(es): GLENBOW.LIB (Envoy 100). **Staff:** Lindsay Moir, Asst.Libn.; Anthony L. Rees, Chf.Archv.; Douglas Cass, Asst.Chf.Archv.; Lynette Walton, Asst.Chf.Archv.; Susan Kooyman, Archv.; Janet Pieschel, Archv.; Andrea Garnier, Archv.

★6497★
Glencoe Publishing Company - Library (Publ)
936 Eastwind Dr. Phone: (614)890-1111
Westerville, OH 43081 Darlene Yeager, Libn.
Staff: 1. **Subjects:** Textbooks, state and local curriculum guides. **Holdings:** 7500 books; 4 VF drawers of information files; 3 VF drawers of state and country files; 1 VF drawer of newsletters; 2 VF drawers of photo source files; 3 VF drawers of publishers' catalogs. **Subscriptions:** 200 journals and other serials; 9 newspapers. **Services:** Library not open to the public. **Remarks:** Toll-free telephone number(s): is (800)848-6205.

★6498★
Glendale Adventist Medical Center - Library (Med)
1509 Wilson Terr. Phone: (818)409-8034
Glendale, CA 91206 June Levy, Lib.Dir.
Staff: Prof 2; Other 1. **Subjects:** Medicine, nursing, paramedical sciences, health education. **Holdings:** 6724 books; 9400 bound periodical volumes; 1126 AV programs; 50 microcomputer software programs; Cumulative Index to Nursing and Allied Health Literature. **Subscriptions:** 600 journals and other serials. **Services:** Interlibrary loan; copying. **Automated Operations:** Computerized public access catalog, cataloging, serials, and circulation. **Computerized Information Services:** DIALOG Information Services, MEDLARS, BRS Information Technologies, WILSONLINE, PaperChase; CD-ROM (MEDBASE); internal database; OnTyme Electronic Message Network Service (electronic mail service). **Remarks:** FAX: (818)546-5633.

★6499★
Glendale City Planning Division - Technical Library (Plan)
633 E. Broadway Phone: (818)548-2144
Glendale, CA 91206-9386 John W. McKenna, Dir., Plan.
Founded: 1957. **Staff:** 1. **Subjects:** Planning, urban development, zoning law, organization, legal codes and requirements, public administration, population and housing data, land use data. **Special Collections:** Historic Preservation; Glendale data (Planning Division publications; hill development proposals; tract developments; zoning information; related material). **Holdings:** 820 books; 126 bound periodical volumes; 400 unbound items. **Subscriptions:** 15 journals and other serials; 2 newspapers.**Services:** Interlibrary loan (limited); library open to the public with approval of the planning director. **Remarks:** FAX: (818)240-7913.

★6500★
Glendale Public Library - Brand Library (Art, Mus)
1601 W. Mountain St. Phone: (818)548-2051
Glendale, CA 91201 Cynthia Cleary, Sr.Lib.Supv.
Founded: 1955. **Staff:** Prof 3; Other 6. **Subjects:** Fine arts, music of all countries, architecture, photography, sculpture. **Special Collections:** Dieterle Collection (mounted art prints); harp music collection; classical scores collection. **Holdings:** 40,004 books; 3000 bound periodical volumes; 10,000 pieces of sheet music; 30,068 phonograph records; 2968 cassettes; 8000 compact discs; 197 piano rolls, 1895-1924. **Subscriptions:** 102 journals and other serials. **Services:** Interlibrary loan; copying; research for motion pictures and television studios; framed prints, videos, and slides for loan; library open to the public. **Automated Operations:** Computerized public access catalog, cataloging, acquisitions, and circulation. **Computerized Information Services:** DIALOG Information Services, OCLC. **Networks/Consortia:** Member of Metropolitan Cooperative Library System (MCLS). **Publications:** Events of the Month. **Special Indexes:** Song Index (card). **Remarks:** Brand Library is the art and music department of the Glendale Public Library, a Division of the City of Glendale. It contains a gallery and recital hall. FAX: (818)548-5079. **Staff:** Alline Merchant, Lib.Supv.

★6501★
Glendale Public Library - Special Collections Room (Hist, Biol Sci)
222 E. Harvard St. Phone: (818)548-2037
Glendale, CA 91205 Susan Curzon, Lib.Dir.
Founded: 1906. **Staff:** 1. **Subjects:** Glendale and area history, California history, cats and cat genealogy. **Special Collections:** Cat genealogy, 1904 to present (stud books); histories of all breeds; cat anatomy and pathology; Glendale and California history (15,000 historic photographs and slides; oral history tapes; 5000 other cataloged items). **Holdings:** 400 bound periodical volumes; city departmental reports; archives; 20 microfiche; microfilm. **Services:** Copying; room open to the public for reference use only. **Automated Operations:** Computerized public access catalog and ILL. **Computerized Information Services:** OCLC, DIALOG Information Services. **Networks/Consortia:** Member of Metropolitan Cooperative Library System (MCLS). **Special Indexes:** Index to Glendale News Press, 1988 to present. **Remarks:** Alternate telephone number(s): 548-2027. FAX: (818)241-5082. **Staff:** Barbara R. Boyd, Spec.Coll.Libn.

★6502★
Glendale University - College of Law Library (Law)
220 N. Glendale Ave. Phone: (818)247-0770
Glendale, CA 91206 Judy Greitzer, Libn.
Founded: 1969. **Staff:** Prof 2; Other 12. **Subjects:** Tax and accounting law. **Special Collections:** English law; early English and American law books. **Holdings:** 85,000 volumes. **Subscriptions:** 376 journals and other serials. **Services:** Library not open to the public. **Computerized Information Services:** LEXIS, NEXIS.

★6503★
Glengarry Genealogical Society - Highland Heritage Research Library (Hist)
Arlington Rd., R.R. 1 Phone: (613)347-2363
Lancaster, ON, Canada K0C 1N0 Alex W. Fraser, Mgr.
Founded: 1974. **Staff:** 2. **Subjects:** Genealogy, church records, history, gravestone inscriptions. **Special Collections:** Roots Glengarry (church records and index). **Holdings:** 400 volumes; 59 reels of microfilm of St. Raphael's and St. Andrew's church records, Glengarry News; 35 manuscripts on gravestones; 5 binders of clippings of birth, death, marriage records; 18 binders of local church records; 70 binders of family genealogies. **Subscriptions:** 3 journals and other serials. **Services:** Library open to the public by appointment on a fee basis. **Computerized Information Services:** Internal database. **Publications:** Highland Heritage, 1979-1989; Family Genealogies, 1981-1986, both irregular; Title Guide of Local Histories; Bridging the Gap, bimonthly (newsletter). **Special Indexes:** 100,000 names from local church, cemetery, and newspaper records (card); 24,000 local names (book). **Remarks:** Appointments can be made by mailing to the above address, or by telephoning Rhoda Ross at (613)347-3180.

★6504★
Glenmary Research Center - Library (Rel-Phil)
750 Piedmont Ave., N.E.
Atlanta, GA 30308 Phone: (404)876-6518
Subjects: Catholic church in rural America, evangelization, social ministry, ecumenism. **Holdings:** 6000 volumes.

★6505★
Glenrose Rehabilitation Hospital - Library (Med)
Glen East 613
10230-111 Ave. Phone: (403)471-2262
Edmonton, AB, Canada T5G 0B7 Peter Schoenberg
Staff: Prof 1; Other 1. **Subjects:** Rehabilitation, child development, occupational therapy, physical therapy, speech disorders. **Holdings:** 5000 books; 3500 bound periodical volumes; 200 reports; 40 boxes of archives; 200 videotapes. **Subscriptions:** 200 journals and other serials. **Services:** Interlibrary loan; copying; library open to the public. **Computerized Information Services:** CD-ROMs (BRS Information Technologies, CAN/OLE, MEDLARS); Envoy 100 (electronic mail service). **Remarks:** FAX: (403)471-7976. Electronic mail address(es): Glenrose.rehab (Envoy 100).

Glens Falls Queensbury Historical Association, Inc.
See: **Chapman Historical Museum** (3433)

★6506★
Glenview Area Historical Society - Hibbard Library (Hist)
1121 Waukegan Rd. Phone: (708)724-2235
Glenview, IL 60025 George Amidon, Lib.Comm.Chm.
Founded: 1965. **Subjects:** Area history - families, buildings, town functions, service clubs, businesses. **Holdings:** Obituaries; bicentennial collection; photographs; property deeds for early settlers; Northfield township record books, 1850-1910. **Services:** Copying; library open to the public by appointment. **Publications:** Glenview 1899 to present.

★6507★
Glenwood State Hospital-School - Staff Library (Med)
711 S. Vine
Glenwood, IA 51534 Phone: (712)527-4811
Staff: Prof 1. **Subjects:** Mental retardation, psychiatry, psychology, social work, medicine, nursing, special education. **Holdings:** 3540 books; 500 bound periodical volumes. **Subscriptions:** 155 journals and other serials; 5 newspapers. **Services:** Interlibrary loan; copying; library open to families of employees.

★6508★
The Glidden Company - Technical Information Services (Sci-Engr)
Glidden Research Center
16651 Sprague Rd. Phone: (216)826-5260
Strongsville, OH 44136 Dr. L. Violet Forgach, Mgr.
Founded: 1962. **Staff:** Prof 2; Other 4. **Subjects:** Coatings and resins, polymer chemistry, chemistry and allied subjects. **Holdings:** 5000 books. **Subscriptions:** 250 journals and other serials. **Services:** Interlibrary loan; copying; SDI; services open to the public with restrictions. **Computerized Information Services:** DIALOG Information Services, ORBIT Search Service, NLM, STN International. **Publications:** Newsletters. **Remarks:** The Glidden Company is a subsidiary of ICI Americas Inc. **Remarks:** FAX: (216)826-5555. **Staff:** Pat Starrett, Tech.Libn.

★6509★
Global Community Centre - Library (Soc Sci)
89-91 King St., N. Phone: (519)746-4090
Kitchener, ON, Canada N2J 2X3 Patricia McCaffrey, Rsrc.Coord.
Staff: Prof 1. **Subjects:** Development, aid, trade, food and agriculture, Latin and Central America, disarmament, Christianity and justice, technology, environment, Africa, Asia. **Holdings:** 400 volumes; clippings; AV materials. **Subscriptions:** 130 journals and other serials. **Services:** Library open to Waterloo County residents. **Computerized Information Services:** Microisis (internal database). **Publications:** Newsletter, 5/year. **Special Catalogs:** AV catalog. **Remarks:** FAX: (519)746-4096.

★6510★
Global Education Associates - Resource Library (Soc Sci)
475 Riverside Dr., Rm. 456 Phone: (212)870-3290
New York, NY 10115-0122 Harriet Zullo, Staff Coord.
Founded: 1973. **Subjects:** Global education, world order, alternative futures, conflict management, values, environment, world religions. **Special Collections:** Curricula resource lists; United Nations documents. **Holdings:** 3000 volumes; clippings; pamphlets; manuscripts. **Services:** Library open to the public by appointment. **Remarks:** FAX: (212)870-2055.

★6511★
Global Engineering Documents - Library (Sci-Engr)
2805 McGaw Ave. Phone: (714)261-1455
Santa Ana, CA 92713-9539 Dottie Schnug
Founded: 1968. **Staff:** Prof 10; Other 40. **Special Collections:** Quality control systems and services program; Mil-Spec collections for the aerospace and electronic industries. **Holdings:** 1 million specifications, standards, manuals, codes, publications from 3000 government, industry, military, and trade organizations. **Subscriptions:** 1000 journals and other serials. **Services:** Copying; technical manual preparation; spares provisioning. **Computerized Information Services:** Spec-Tree Reports, FarFinder, National Stock Number Research Service (internal databases). **Publications:** Drawing Requirements Manual; Qualified Products List and Sources, biannual; Instructions for Technical Manual Preparation; Plating Manual; Printed Circuit Manual; Quality Assurance Procedures; Source of Supply; list of additional publications - available upon request. **Remarks:** Telex: 692-373. FAX: (714)241 -1307. Global Engineering Documents is a division of Information Handling Services which is owned by Thyssen-Bornemisza, Inc. **Formerly:** Global Engineering Documentation.

★6512★
Global Learning - Library (Educ)
1018 Stuyvesant Ave. Phone: (908)964-1114
Union, NJ 07083 Jeffrey Brown, Exec.Dir.
Founded: 1974. **Subjects:** Elementary, secondary, and college curricula; global education; teacher-education materials. **Special Collections:** New Jersey in the World (college learning modules, databases). **Holdings:** 1000 volumes; AV programs. **Services:** Library open to the public for reference use only. **Computerized Information Services:** Internal databases. **Publications:** Gleanings (newsletter), quarterly; Sustainable Devlopment Curriculum Framework for World History/Cultures; New Jersey and the World (30 undergraduate modules and database) - all for sale; A Directory of Human Resources for Global Studies in New Jersey. **Remarks:** FAX: (908)964-6335.

★6513★
Globe Photos, Inc. - Library (Aud-Vis)
275 7th Ave. Phone: (212)689-1340
New York, NY 10001 Ray Whelan, Sr., Libn.
Subjects: Current events, personalities, features. **Holdings:** 10 million original color transparencies and black/white photos. **Remarks:** Firm provides images of subjects of interest to advertising agencies and publishers of magazines, books, encyclopedias. FAX: (212)627-8932. Contains the holdings of the former Photo Trends.

★6514★
Gloucester County Historical Society - Library (Hist)
17 Hunter St.
Box 409 Phone: (609)845-4771
Woodbury, NJ 08096 Edith E. Hoelle, Libn.
Founded: 1903. **Staff:** 5. **Subjects:** Genealogy, New Jersey and U.S. history. **Special Collections:** Richard Somers Collection (180 original documents pertaining to Richard Somers and the U.S. Navy in early 1800s); Howell Collection (3800 items concerning the Howell family, 1739-1890). **Holdings:** 7000 books; 1140 reels of microfilm of documents; 114 bound volumes of newspapers; 80,000 county manuscripts, 1686-1870; 55 VF drawers of files of genealogy and history, photographs, typescripts, clippings. **Subscriptions:** 35 journals and other serials. **Services:** Copying; library open to the public. **Publications:** List of publications - available on request.

★6515★
Gloucester County Times - Library (Publ)
309 S. Broad St. Phone: (609)845-3300
Woodbury, NJ 08096 Sally J. Ethier
Staff: Prof 1. **Subjects:** Newspaper reference topics. **Holdings:** 375 reels of microfilm (1819 to present). **Services:** Copying; library open to the public with restrictions. **Remarks:** (609)845-4318.

★6516★
Glover Memorial Hospital - Medical Library (Med)
148 Chestnut St. Phone: (617)444-5600
Needham, MA 02192 Louisa Tseng, Dir., Med.Lib.
Founded: 1977. **Staff:** Prof 1. **Subjects:** Medicine, nursing, health care administration. **Holdings:** 650 books; 586 bound periodical volumes. **Subscriptions:** 75 journals and other serials. **Services:** Interlibrary loan; copying; library open to Needham residents only. **Automated Operations:** Computerized cataloging. **Computerized Information Services:** DIALOG Information Services, MEDLINE. Performs searches on fee basis. **Networks/Consortia:** Member of Consortium for Information Resources (CIR), Massachusetts Health Sciences Libraries Network (MaHSLiN). **Remarks:** FAX: (617)449-6727.

Glover Memorial Library
See: **Altoona Hospital** (427)

Glynne Library
See: **St. Deiniol's Residential - Library** (14272)

★6517★
GMI Engineering & Management Institute - Library (Sci-Engr, Bus-Fin)
1700 W. 3rd Ave. Phone: (313)762-7818
Flint, MI 48504-4898 Brenda Meadows, Dir.
Founded: 1927. **Staff:** Prof 3; Other 5. **Subjects:** Engineering, business. **Special Collections:** Undergraduate theses; SAE and SME Technical Papers. **Holdings:** 53,698 books; 19,765 bound periodical volumes; 25,600 other cataloged items. **Subscriptions:** 740 journals and other serials; 13 newspapers. **Services:** Interlibrary loan; library open to the public with permission. **Automated Operations:** DYNIX. **Computerized Information Services:** DIALOG Information Services, Knowledge Index, OCLC, ABI/INFORM; CD-ROM (Business Periodicals Ondisc). **Networks/Consortia:** Member of Michigan Library Consortium (MLC). **Remarks:** FAX: (313)762-9744. **Staff:** Frank E. Elliott, Pub.Serv.Libn.

Goddard Institute for Space Studies
See: **NASA** (10982)

Goddard Library
See: **Gordon-Conwell Theological Seminary** (6575)

Goddard Memorial Library
See: **Oroville Hospital** (12573)

Robert F. Goddard Memorial Library
See: **Alaska (State) Department of Natural Resources** (217)

Goddard Space Flight Center
See: **NASA** (10983)

★6518★
Godfrey Memorial Library (Hist)
134 Newfield St. Phone: (203)346-4375
Middletown, CT 06457 Doris Post, Dir.
Founded: 1947. **Staff:** 2. **Subjects:** Genealogy, local history, biography. **Holdings:** 16,000 books; 7 million items in genealogical reference file. **Subscriptions:** 12 journals and other serials. **Services:** Interlibrary loan (limited); copying; genealogical research; library open to the public. **Publications:** Microfiche in the fields of genealogy and local history. **Special Indexes:** American Genealogical-Biographical Index, 5/year.

Morton R. Godine Library
See: **Massachusetts College of Art - Morton R. Godine Library** (9789)

Anne & Winfred Godwin Library
See: **Southern Regional Education Board** (15515)

★6519★
Emilio Goeldi Museum - Library (Biol Sci, Soc Sci)
Campus de Pesquisa
Av. Perimetral
C.P. 399 Phone: 91 228-2341
66000 Belem, Para, Brazil Helena Andrade da Silveira
Subjects: Amazon region - anthropology, zoology, archeology, botany, earth sciences, linguistics, ecology. **Special Collections:** Rare and special books. **Holdings:** 150,000 volumes. **Services:** Interlibrary loan; copying; library open to adults. **Computerized Information Services:** Internal database. **Remarks:** FAX: 91 2291412. Telex: 91 1419. Maintained by the National Council of Scientific and Technological Development. **Also Known As:** Museu Paraense Emilio Goeldi.

★6520★
Goethe House New York - Library (Area-Ethnic)
1014 5th Ave. Phone: (212)439-8688
New York, NY 10028 Elisabeth Pyroth, Hd.Libn.
Founded: 1957. **Staff:** Prof 2; Other 1. **Subjects:** Germany - literature, the arts, history, politics; social sciences. **Holdings:** 11,000 books; 20 reports on Germany and German affairs; 400 audio cassettes; 250 video cassettes. **Subscriptions:** 126 journals and other serials; 17 newspapers. **Services:** Interlibrary loan; library open to the public. **Publications:** Magazines and Newspapers at the Goethe-Institute Libraries in the United States and Canada. **Remarks:** Branch of German Cultural Institute/Goethe-Institute Munich. FAX: (212)439-8705.

★6521★
Goethe-Institute Atlanta - German Cultural Center - Library (Area-Ethnic)
400 Colony Square Phone: (404)892-2226
Atlanta, GA 30361 Luise Von Loew, Libn.
Founded: 1977. **Staff:** Prof 2. **Subjects:** Germany - contemporary literature, politics, language, children's literature, art, history, geography. **Holdings:** 9500 books; 150 documentary videotapes; 3500 tapes; 600 slides; 5 VF drawers of movie review clippings. **Subscriptions:** 50 journals and other serials; 5 newspapers. **Services:** Interlibrary loan; copying; library open to the public. **Special Catalogs:** Tape catalog (book); slide catalog (book). **Remarks:** FAX: (404)892-3832. Institute is the German Cultural Center for the southeastern United States. It is a branch of the German Cultural Institute/Goethe-Institute Munich. **Staff:** Susanne Tiedtke, Lib.Asst.

★6522★
Goethe-Institute Boston - Library (Area-Ethnic)
170 Beacon St. Phone: (617)262-6050
Boston, MA 02116 Hans Ulrich Kaup, Libn.
Founded: 1966. **Staff:** Prof 1. **Subjects:** Germany - history and politics, sociology, literature, arts. **Holdings:** 8500 books; 120 videotapes; 170 cassettes. **Subscriptions:** 50 journals; 23 newspapers. **Services:** Interlibrary loan; copying; library open to the public. **Publications:** List of new acquisitions. **Remarks:** FAX: (617)262-2615. The Goethe-Institut Boston is the German Cultural Center for New England. The holdings are in German, with approximately 20% English translation. It is a branch of the Goethe-Institute Munich.

★6523★
Goethe-Institute Chicago - German Cultural Center - Library (Area-Ethnic)
401 N. Michigan Ave., 1st Fl. Phone: (312)329-0074
Chicago, IL 60611 Elisabeth Angele, Libn.
Founded: 1978. **Staff:** Prof 1. **Subjects:** Contemporary German culture - language, literature, arts. **Special Collections:** AV materials for teaching German as a second language. **Holdings:** 7000 books; 1300 audio cassettes; 400 slide series; 800 videotapes; 800 phonograph records. **Subscriptions:** 100 journals and other serials; 12 newspapers. **Services:** Interlibrary loan; copying; library open to the public. **Computerized Information Services:** OCLC; Zeitschriften-dienst (German Periodical Articles Info Service ,internal database); MCI Mail (electronic mail service). **Networks/Consortia:** Member of ILLINET, Chicago Library System. **Publications:** Cultural Events, 2/year; selected and annotated new acquisitions listings, irregular; information guides on German genealogy reference sources; Where to Obtain German Videos, Books, and Periodicals in the U.S. **Special Catalogs:** Catalog of AV materials. **Remarks:** FAX: (312)329-2487. Telex: 494-6142 UW. Electronic mail address(es): 342-5013 (MCI Mail). Branch of the German Cultural Institute/Goethe-Institute Munich.

★6524★
Goethe Institute Houston - Library (Hum)
3120 Southwest Fwy., Suite 100 Phone: (713)523-0966
Houston, TX 77098 Brigitte Herzog, Libn.
Founded: 1983. **Staff:** Prof 1. **Subjects:** German language, German literature. **Holdings:** 6000 books; videotapes; audiocassettes; slide sets. **Subscriptions:** 25 journals and other serials; 5 newspapers. **Services:** Interlibrary loan; copying; library open to the public. **Remarks:** FAX: (713)528-4023.

★6525★
Goethe-Institute London - Library (Area-Ethnic)
50 Princes Gate/Exhibition Rd. Phone: 71 5815123
London SW7 2PH, England Regine Friederici, Hd.Libn.
Founded: 1956. **Staff:** 5. **Subjects:** Germany - literature, arts, philosophy, psychology, social sciences, history, language. **Special Collections:** German as a foreign language. **Holdings:** 32,000 books; 8000 microforms; AV programs. **Subscriptions:** 180 journals and other serials; 18 newspapers. **Services:** Interlibrary loan; copying; library open to the public. **Publications:** New acquisitions list; New Acquisitions from the British Market; German plays in English translation; video-list. **Remarks:** FAX: 71 5843180. **Staff:** Simone Muhlen.

★6526★
Goethe Institute Los Angeles - Library (Hum)
8501 Wilshire Blvd., Suite 205 Phone: (213)854-0301
Beverly Hills, CA 90211 John Schroeder
Founded: 1985. **Staff:** Prof 1. **Subjects:** Germany - cinema, language instruction, history, literature. **Holdings:** 3000 books; 80 reports; 625 videocassettes. **Subscriptions:** 35 journals and other serials; 12 newspapers. **Services:** Interlibrary loan; copying; library open to the public. **Publications:** Serials List of Goethe Institute Libraries in North America. **Remarks:** Approximately 90 percent of material is in German language. FAX: (213)854-6087. Telex: 6503148068. Alternate telephone number(s): 854-0993.

★6527★
Goethe-Institute Montreal - German Cultural Centre - Library (Area-Ethnic)
418, rue Sherbrooke, E. Phone: (514)499-0921
Montreal, PQ, Canada H2L 1J6 Marie-Elisabeth Morf, Libn.
Staff: Prof 1. **Subjects:** German literature and history, contemporary Germany. **Special Collections:** German language textbooks; English and French translations of German authors. **Holdings:** 6000 books; 450 phonograph records; 150 slide series; 340 cassettes; 155 viseo cassettes; 40 films. **Subscriptions:** 41 journals and other serials; 5 newspapers. **Services:** Interlibrary loan; copying; library open to the public. **Remarks:** FAX: (514)499-0905.

★6528★
Goethe-Institute San Francisco - Library (Area-Ethnic)
530 Bush St. Phone: (415)391-0428
San Francisco, CA 94108-3689 Dr. Barbara Bernhart, Libn.
Founded: 1970. **Staff:** Prof 1; Other 1. **Subjects:** Germany - contemporary literature, language, history, social sciences, arts, philosophy, psychology, children and young adults. **Special Collections:** Teacher's Reference Collection (German language). **Holdings:** 5000 books; 119 slide sets; 592 cassette tapes; 467 videotapes. **Subscriptions:** 63 journals; 15 newspapers. **Services:** Interlibrary loan; copying; library open to residents of Alaska, California, Colorado, Hawaii, Nevada, Utah, and Washington. **Networks/Consortia:** Member of OCLC Pacific Network, Bay Area Library and Information Network. **Publications:** Acquisitions list, 2/year - available on request; library guide; periodicals list; tracing American-German family roots (bibliography); Sources for Video Rental (German) in the U.S. (leaflet). **Special Catalogs:** Tape catalog; slide catalog; video catalog. **Remarks:** 90% of books are in German; 10% are in English. FAX: (415)391-0428. Institute is a branch of the German Cultural Institute/Goethe-Institute Munich.

★6529★
Goethe-Institute Toronto - German Cultural Centre (Area-Ethnic)
1067 Yonge St. Phone: (416)924-3327
Toronto, ON, Canada M4W 2L2 Ulla Habekost, Libn.
Founded: 1962. **Staff:** Prof 1. **Subjects:** Modern German literature, German literary history, language and linguistics, visual and performing arts in Germany, children's literature. **Holdings:** 7000 books (German and English translations); 478 phonograph records; 575 tapes; 332 slides; 118 German language films; 200 videos. **Subscriptions:** 49 journals and other serials; 5 newspapers. **Services:** Library open to the public on limited schedule. **Remarks:** FAX: (416)924-0589.

J. W. Goethe-Universitat - Fachbereich Biologie - Arbeitsbibliothek
See: **University of Frankfurt - Department of Biology - Library for Biological Sciences** (18592)

★6530★
Johann Wolfgang Goethe University - Senckenberg Library (Biol Sci, Sci-Engr)
Bockenheimer Landstrasse 134-138 Phone: 69 7982365
W-6000 Frankfurt am Main 1, Germany Helmut Burkhardt, Lib.Hd.
Founded: 1763. **Staff:** 36.5. **Subjects:** Mathematics, physics, chemistry, biochemistry, biophysics, natural sciences, pharmacy, geosciences, medicine (to 1920), history of above subjects. **Special Collections:** 16th-19th century stock (70,000 volumes); collection of scientifically relevant literature, published worldwide since 1949, on all fields of biology, botany, zoology, and allied subjects. **Holdings:** 1.05 million volumes. **Subscriptions:** 7000 journals and other serials. **Services:** Interlibrary loan; copying; library open to the public. **Automated Operations:** Computerized cataloging. **Remarks:** FAX: 69 7983147. **Also Known As:** Senckenbergische Bibliothek.

★6531★
Gokhale Institute of Politics and Economics - Library (Soc Sci, Bus-Fin)
Deccan Gymkhana Phone: 344287
Poone 411 004, Maharashtra, India Mrs. A. Ogale, Doc.Off.
Founded: 1905. **Staff:** 18. **Subjects:** Economic and social problems of India - agricultural economics, regional development, urban studies, sociology, industrial research, demography, education, economic policy and planning, monetary economics and finance, foreign trade, economic history; economics of Eastern Europe. **Holdings:** 229,595 volumes. **Subscriptions:** 200 journals and other serials. **Services:** Interlibrary loan; copying; library open to graduates. **Publications:** List of Periodical Holdings, 1984; List of Serial Holdings, 1967; List of Committees and Commissions on India; Fortnightly List of Additions; Fortnightly List of Articles on India. **Remarks:** Affiliated with University of Poona. **Staff:** Mrs. N. Gokhale; Miss N. Utgikar; Miss R. Joag; Mrs. V. Patwardhan; Mr. D. Pardesai; Mr. N. Chaudhari.

David Goldberg Memorial Medical Library
See: **Pascack Valley Hospital** (12776)

Herbert Goldberg Memorial Library
See: **Temple Beth Sholom** (16091)

Norman L. and Roselea J. Goldberg Research Library
See: **Vanderbilt University - Jean and Alexander Heard Library - Arts Collection** (19768)

★6532★
Golden Age Radio - The Best of Old Time Radio Collection (Hist)
Box 25215
Portland, OR 97225 Rex E. Bills, Owner
Founded: 1971. **Staff:** 1. **Subjects:** Vintage radio shows, 1940s-1960s. **Holdings:** 10,000 shows on reel-to-reel and cassette tapes. **Services:** Library not open to the public. **Special Catalogs:** Mini catalog - free upon request.

★6533★
Golden Ball Tavern Museum - Library (Hist)
P.O. Box 223 Phone: (617)894-1751
Weston, MA 02193 Dorothea Waterbury, Hd.Archv.
Subjects: History - colonial, American Revolution; decorative arts. **Special Collections:** Isaac Jones Family Archives (1750s to present). **Holdings:** 600 books and periodicals. **Services:** Library open to the public.

Golden Care Resource Center
See: **St. Michael Hospital - Regner Health Sciences Library** (14544)

★6534★
Golden and District Historical Society - Archives (Hist)
Box 992 Phone: (604)344-5169
Golden, BC, Canada V0A 1H0 Colleen Torrence, Musm.Cur.
Founded: 1981. **Staff:** Prof 1; Other 3. **Subjects:** Local history. **Holdings:** Golden Star newspapers; 4 reels of microfilm of Donald Truth newspaper; tax assessment rolls; early police diaries. **Subscriptions:** 3 journals and other serials. **Services:** Archives open to the public with restrictions. **Publications:** Golden Memories Revised (1982). **Special Indexes:** Index to Golden Star newspapers.

★6535★
Golden Gate Baptist Theological Seminary - Library (Rel-Phil)
Strawberry Point Phone: (415)388-8080
Mill Valley, CA 94941 William B. Hair, III, Dir.
Founded: 1944. **Staff:** Prof 2; Other 8. **Subjects:** Bible texts and commentaries, church history, philosophy, Christian ethics, Bible archeology, comparative religion, preaching, patristics, missions, systematic theology, religious education. **Special Collections:** Old and rare hymnals (115). **Holdings:** 131,353 books; 17,671 periodical volumes; 12 VF drawers of pamphlets; 4433 microforms; 670 videotapes; 6760 audiotapes; 1566 phonograph records. **Subscriptions:** 833 journals and other serials; 8 newspapers. **Services:** Interlibrary loan; library open to the public. **Computerized Information Services:** OCLC, DIALOG Information Services. **Networks/Consortia:** Member of Marin Library Network (MLN). **Remarks:** FAX: (415)381-2453. **Staff:** Jenny Sheldon, Rd.Serv.Libn.

★6536★
Golden Gate University - Libraries (Bus-Fin, Info Sci)
536 Mission St. Phone: (415)442-7000
San Francisco, CA 94105-2968 Catriona Wendroff, Dir.
Founded: 1901. **Staff:** Prof 8.5; Other 7. **Subjects:** Business, public administration, information systems, telecommunications. **Holdings:** 267,000 volumes. **Subscriptions:** 4405 journals and other serials. **Services:** Interlibrary loan; copying; libraries open to the public on fee basis. **Computerized Information Services:** DIALOG Information Services, RLIN; The Golden Retriever II (internal database). **Networks/Consortia:** Member of Bay Area Library and Information Network, CLASS. **Remarks:** FAX: (415)495-2671. **Staff:** Annemarie Walteke, Asst.Dir.; Joshua Adarkwa, Pub.Serv.Hd.; David Brown, Tech.Ser.Hd.; Janice Carter, Ref.; Nancy Cunningham, Ref.; Steven Dunlap, Ref.; Shirley Mack, Off-Campus Serv.Libn.

★6537★
Golden Gate University - School of Law Library (Law)
536 Mission St. Phone: (415)442-7260
San Francisco, CA 94105 Nancy Hoebelheinrich, Act.Dir.
Founded: 1901. **Staff:** Prof 4; Other 6. **Subjects:** Law. **Special Collections:** Taxation; land use; legal periodicals. **Holdings:** 202,657 volumes. **Subscriptions:** 3095 journals and other serials; 10 newspapers. **Services:** Interlibrary loan; copying; library open to the public for use of documents only. **Automated Operations:** Computerized cataloging. **Computerized Information Services:** LEXIS, RLIN, DIALOG Information Services, WESTLAW. **Networks/Consortia:** Member of CLASS, Research Libraries Information Network (RLIN). **Special Catalogs:** Periodical holdings (book). **Remarks:** FAX: (415)512-9395. **Staff:** Catherine Hardy, Docs./Media Libn.

Golden Library
See: **Eastern New Mexico University - Golden Library - Special Collections** (5163)

★6538★
Golden Radio Buffs of Maryland, Inc. - Tape Library (Hist)
301 Jeanwood Ct. Phone: (301)477-2550
Baltimore, MD 21222 Gene Leitner, Co-Founder
Staff: 2. **Subjects:** Old time radio shows, radio memorabilia, artifacts. **Holdings:** 10,000 tapes and other cataloged items. **Publications:** On the Air (newsletter), bimonthly - to members.

★6539★
Golden Valley Health Center - Medical Library & Research Center (Med)
4101 Golden Valley Rd. Phone: (612)588-2771
Golden Valley, MN 55422 Dawn Deibele, Clin.Spec.
Founded: 1973. **Subjects:** Medicine, nursing, psychiatry. **Holdings:** 700 books; 65 bound periodical volumes; 200 cassette tapes. **Subscriptions:** 85 journals and other serials. **Services:** Center not open to the public. **Remarks:** FAX: (612)520-1120.

★6540★
Golder Associates - Library (Sci-Engr)
2180 Meadowvale Blvd. Phone: (416)567-4444
Mississauga, ON, Canada L5N 5S3 Mira Wrezel, Libn.
Staff: Prof 1. **Subjects:** Mining engineering, hydrogeology, geophysics, engineering geology. **Holdings:** 2500 books. **Subscriptions:** 75 journals and other serials. **Services:** Interlibrary loan; library not open to the public. **Computerized Information Services:** DIALOG Information Services, CAN/OLE. **Remarks:** FAX: (416)567-6561.

★6541★
Golder Associates, Inc. - Library (Sci-Engr)
4104 148th Ave., N.E. Phone: (206)883-0777
Redmond, WA 98052 Susan Eipert, Lib.Mgr.
Founded: 1976. **Staff:** Prof 1.5; Other .5. **Subjects:** Geotechnical engineering, hazardous waste site characterization and remediation, radioactive and hazardous waste disposal, groundwater hydrology, geology and hydrology of Northwest. **Holdings:** 600 books; 300 technical reports on microfiche; 5000 technical reports; 1000 reprints. **Subscriptions:** 150 journals and other serials; 4 newspapers. **Services:** Library not open to the public. **Automated Operations:** Computerized cataloging. **Computerized Information Services:** DIALOG Information Services, MEDLARS, PFDS Online, STN International, Data-Star, BRS Information Technologies; internal database. **Remarks:** FAX: (206)882-5498. **Staff:** Laurie McLeod; Alison Keyes.

★6542★
Goldey Beacom College - J. Wilbur Hirons Library (Educ)
4701 Limestone Rd. Phone: (302)998-8814
Wilmington, DE 19808 Gloria M. Coe, Dir.
Founded: 1965. **Staff:** Prof 2; Other 2. **Subjects:** Business, management, accounting, business administration, marketing, computer science, secretarial studies. **Holdings:** 17,400 books; 5852 bound periodical volumes; transparencies; maps; 833 AV programs; 1024 reels of microfilm; 12,885 microfiche; 629 corporation annual reports. **Subscriptions:** 310 journals and other serials. **Services:** Interlibrary loan; copying; library open to the public for reference use only. **Automated Operations:** Computerized cataloging. **Computerized Information Services:** OCLC; InfoTrac. **Networks/Consortia:** Member of Libraries in the New Castle County System (LINCS), Independent Library Consortium (ILC). **Remarks:** FAX: (302)998-3467. **Staff:** Joyce Roe, Per. & Ref.Libn.

Leon Goldman, M.D. Archives
See: **University of Cincinnati - Medical Center Information and Communications - Cincinnati Medical Heritage Center** (18475)

★6543★
Goldman, Sachs & Co. - Library (Bus-Fin)
85 Broad St. Phone: (212)902-6655
New York, NY 10004-2456 Katherine Cray, V.P.
Founded: 1933. **Staff:** Prof 4; Other 19. **Subjects:** Corporate records, banking, finance. **Special Collections:** U.S. and foreign corporation records (10,000). **Holdings:** 7500 books; microfiche of annual, 10K, 10Q, 8K reports, proxies. **Subscriptions:** 950 journals and other serials. **Services:** Interlibrary loan; copying; SDI; library not open to the public. **Automated Operations:** Computerized cataloging, acquisitions, serials, and corporate file check-in. **Computerized Information Services:** DIALOG Information Services, Dow Jones News/Retrieval, NEXIS, Reuters, CompuServe Information Service, Info Globe; CD-ROMs. **Publications:** User manual; newsletter; select bibliographies. **Remarks:** FAX: (212)902-0600. **Staff:** Mary Elizabeth Poje, V.P./Hd., Ref.; Elizabeth Mason, Ref.Libn.; Frances Remini, Hd., Pubns./Subscriptions; Barbara Jeanneret, Hd., Corp. Files; Dorothy Nelsen-Gille, Ref.Libn.; Martha Ciaschini, Ref.Libn.

Goldsmith Civic Garden Center
See: **Memphis Botanic Garden Foundation, Inc. - Goldsmith Civic Garden Center** (10059)

Harold Goldstein Library Science Library
See: **Florida State University** (5914)

Goldthwait Polar Library
See: **Ohio State University - Byrd Polar Research Center** (12298)

Goldwater Memorial Hospital
See: **New York University - Medical Center - Goldwater Memorial Hospital - Health Sciences Library** (11728)

Robert Goldwater Library
See: **Metropolitan Museum of Art** (10214)

Golf House Museum & Library
See: **United States Golf Association** (17553)

★6544★
Gonzaga University - Crosby Library (Hum)
502 E. Boone Ave. Phone: (509)328-4220
Spokane, WA 99258 Robert L. Burr, Dean., Lib.Serv.
Founded: 1887. **Staff:** Prof 11; Other 12. **Special Collections:** Gerard Manley Hopkins Collection (4900 items); Crosby Memorabilia; Biology-Chemistry Library in Hughes Hall. **Holdings:** 215,500 books; 61,014 bound periodical volumes; 332,278 microforms. **Subscriptions:** 1950 journals and other serials. **Services:** Interlibrary loan; copying; library open to the public with restrictions. **Automated Operations:** Computerized cataloging and acquisitions. **Computerized Information Services:** DIALOG Information Services. **Networks/Consortia:** Member of Western Library Network (WLN). **Publications:** Crosby News & Notes. **Special Catalogs:** Hopkins Collected at Gonzaga (1970; book). **Remarks:** FAX: (509)484-2804. **Staff:** Paula Grenell, Hd., Pub.Serv.; Eileen Bell-Garrison, Hd., Tech.Serv.; Lewis R. Miller, Assoc.Dir.; David Buxton, Asst.Dir., Automated Serv.

★6545★
Gonzaga University - School of Law Library (Law)
E. 600 Sharp Ave.
Box 3528 Phone: (509)484-6092
Spokane, WA 99220 Arturo L. Torres, Dir.
Founded: 1912. **Staff:** Prof 5; Other 5.5. **Subjects:** Law. **Holdings:** 23,025 titles for 130,715 books and bound periodical volumes; 59,508 volumes in microform; 336 AV programs. **Subscriptions:** 2309 journals and other serials. **Services:** Interlibrary loan; copying; library open to the public. **Automated Operations:** Computerized cataloging, serials, and acquisitions. **Computerized Information Services:** WESTLAW, LEXIS, DIALOG Information Services; internal database; WLN IMAIL, OnTyme Electronic Message Network Service (electronic mail services). **Networks/Consortia:** Member of Western Library Network (WLN), Northwest Consortium of Law Libraries. **Publications:** User's Guide, annual; Self Guided Tour, annual; Computer Lab Manual, annual; newsletter, quarterly - to library patrons. **Special Indexes:** Index to student writing requirement (online). **Remarks:** FAX: (509)484-2833. Electronic mail address(es): CLASS.GONZALL (OnTyme Electronic Message Network Service). **Staff:** Elizabeth Thweatt, Tech.Serv.Libn.; June Stewart, Rd.Serv.Libn.; James Quinn, Ref.Libn.; Randall M. Manion, Automation Sys.Anl.; Lynn Robinson, Cat.Libn.

Frank Good Library
See: **Botanica, The Wichita Gardens** (2024)

Harold and Wilma Good Library
See: **Goshen College - Harold and Wilma Good Library** (6581)

★6546★
The Good Hope School - Ward M. Canaday Library - Special Collections (Biol Sci, Rare Book)
Frederiksted, VI 00840 Phone: (809)772-0022
Cynthia J. Mault, Libn.
Founded: 1970. **Staff:** 1. **Special Collections:** Marine science; Caribbeana; Dewitt Wallace Collection (rare books). **Services:** Collections open to the public with restrictions. **Automated Operations:** Computerized cataloging and acquisitions. **Staff:** Margaret Waniewski.

★6547★
Good Samaritan Church - Adult Resource Center (Rel-Phil)
6085 Park Blvd. Phone: (813)544-8558
Pinellas Park, FL 33565 Virginia M. Jones, Dir.
Founded: 1983. **Staff:** Prof 1; Other 5. **Subjects:** Bible study, social and personal problems. **Special Collections:** Homecoming, 1987; Diamond Jubilee, Socibles, 75th Jubilee (7 videotapes); stress (2 cassette tapes); 50th anniversary of the church (audiotapes). **Holdings:** 1087 books. **Services:** Copying; center open to the public.

Good Samaritan Health Systems, Inc. - Richard S. Beinecke Medical Library
See: **Good Samaritan Medical Center** (6556)

★6548★
Good Samaritan Hospital - Dr. Thomas Clark Health Services Library (Med)
407 14th Ave., S.E. Phone: (206)848-6661
Puyallup, WA 98371 Jade Trevere, Asst.Libn.
Subjects: Medicine, nursing, management. **Holdings:** 303 volumes. **Subscriptions:** 72 journals and other serials. **Services:** Interlibrary loan; library open to hospital personnel and students in health-related programs. **Computerized Information Services:** MEDLARS. **Networks/Consortia:** Member of Pierce County Medical Library Consortium. **Remarks:** FAX: (206)845-5966.

★6549★
Good Samaritan Hospital - Health Sciences Library (Med)
3217 Clifton Ave. Phone: (513)872-2433
Cincinnati, OH 45220-2489 Rosalie V. Zajac, Mgr.
Founded: 1915. **Staff:** Prof 1.5; Other 4. **Subjects:** Clinical medicine, clinical surgery, nursing, neurosurgery, obstetrics, gynecology. **Holdings:** 7172 books; 13,747 bound periodical volumes; 120 AV programs; 1371 audio cassettes; 271 videotapes; 266 slide/tape sets. **Subscriptions:** 606 journals and other serials. **Services:** Interlibrary loan; copying; SDI; library open to the public by special arrangement with the librarian. **Computerized Information Services:** MEDLINE, MEDLARS, BRS Information Technologies, DIALOG Information Services. **Networks/Consortia:** Member of National Network of Libraries of Medicine - Greater Midwest Region. **Publications:** Library News. **Special Catalogs:** Cincinnati Union List of Monographs (CULM; card). **Staff:** Suellen Fortine, Libn.

★6550★
Good Samaritan Hospital - Health Sciences Library (Med)
3600 N.W. Samaritan Dr. Phone: (503)757-5007
Corvallis, OR 97330 Anne Fraser, Libn.
Subjects: Medicine, nursing, and allied health sciences. **Services:** Interlibrary loan; copying; SDI; library open to the public with physician approval. **Automated Operations:** Computerized ILL (DOCLINE). **Computerized Information Services:** NLM, BRS Information Technologies, DIALOG Information Services; OnTyme Electronic Message Network Service (electronic mail service). **Remarks:** FAX: (503)757-8656. Electronic mail address(es): GDSAMOR (OnTyme Electronic Message Network Service).

★6551★
Good Samaritan Hospital - Krohn Memorial Library (Med)
4th & Walnut Sts. Phone: (717)270-7826
Lebanon, PA 17042 Deborah G. Lovett, Med.Libn.
Founded: 1955. **Staff:** Prof 1. **Subjects:** Medicine, surgery, pediatrics. **Holdings:** 500 books. **Subscriptions:** 75 journals and other serials. **Services:** Interlibrary loan; library not open to the public. **Computerized Information Services:** DIALOG Information Services, MEDLARS, BRS Information Technologies. **Networks/Consortia:** Member of Central Pennsylvania Health Sciences Library Association (CPHSLA), BHSL. **Remarks:** FAX: (717)270-7840.

Good Samaritan Hospital - Medical Library
See: **Good Samaritan Regional Medical Center/ - Health Science Library** (6558)

★6552★
Good Samaritan Hospital - Medical Library (Med)
310 S. Limestone Phone: (606)252-6612
Lexington, KY 40508 John Calk, M.D., MSLS, Knowledge Spec.
Staff: Prof 1. **Subjects:** Medicine, allied health sciences. **Holdings:** 250 books; 105 bound periodical volumes; 20 pamphlets; 80 cassettes. **Subscriptions:** 45 journals and other serials. **Services:** Interlibrary loan; copying; library open to the public with restrictions. **Computerized Information Services:** BRS/COLLEAGUE, MEDLARS.

★6553★
Good Samaritan Hospital - Medical Library (Med)
1000 Montauk Hwy. Phone: (516)661-3000
West Islip, NY 11795 Mary Ann Emsig, Med.Libn.
Founded: 1960. **Staff:** Prof 1. **Subjects:** Medicine, surgery, obstetrics, pediatrics. **Holdings:** 500 books; 4000 bound periodical volumes; yearbooks. **Subscriptions:** 80 journals. **Services:** Interlibrary loan; copying; library open to the public with restrictions. **Computerized Information Services:** MEDLARS, BRS Information Technologies. **Networks/Consortia:** Member of Medical & Scientific Libraries of Long Island (MEDLI), Long Island Library Resources Council. **Remarks:** FAX: (516)957-4166.

★6554★
Good Samaritan Hospital - Shank Memorial Library (Med)
2222 Philadelphia Dr. Phone: (513)278-2612
Dayton, OH 45406 Elizabeth A. Robinson, Libn.
Founded: 1966. **Staff:** Prof 2. **Subjects:** Medicine. **Holdings:** 6000 books; 14,000 bound periodical volumes; 1026 Audio-Digest tapes; 120 videotapes; 8 VF drawers of pamphlets. **Subscriptions:** 420 journals and other serials. **Services:** Interlibrary loan; copying; library open to the public with restrictions. **Automated Operations:** Computerized public access catalog, cataloging, and circulation. **Computerized Information Services:** MEDLINE, BRS Information Technologies. Performs searches on fee basis. **Remarks:** FAX: (513)277-2207. **Staff:** Kelly K. Griffin, MLS.

★6555★
Good Samaritan Hospital and Medical Center - Library (Med)
1015 N.W. 22nd Ave. Phone: (503)229-7336
Portland, OR 97210 Madelyn G. Hall, Dir.
Founded: 1941. **Staff:** Prof 3; Other 3. **Subjects:** Medicine, nursing. **Special Collections:** Ophthalmology Collection (975 items). **Holdings:** 8900 books; 5600 bound periodical volumes; 8 VF drawers of pamphlets; 505 AV cassettes, filmstrips, slide sets. **Subscriptions:** 530 journals and other serials. **Services:** Interlibrary loan; copying; SDI; library open to the public for reference use only. **Automated Operations:** Computerized cataloging and serials. **Computerized Information Services:** DIALOG Information Services, OCLC, BRS Information Technologies; CD-ROM (MEDLINE). Performs searches on fee basis. **Networks/Consortia:** Member of Oregon Health Information Online (ORHION). **Remarks:** FAX: (503)229-8016.

★6556★
Good Samaritan Medical Center - Library (Med)
P.O. Box 3166 Phone: (407)650-6315
West Palm Beach, FL 33402 Linda Kressal, Dir.
Founded: 1968. **Staff:** Prof 1; Other 2. **Subjects:** Clinical medicine, nursing, hospital management, management. **Special Collections:** Orthopedic

videotapes. **Holdings:** 2500 books; 7690 bound periodical volumes; 150 rare books; 971 videotapes; 139 audiotapes; 92 slides. **Subscriptions:** 232 journals and other serials. **Services:** Interlibrary loan; library not open to the public. **Computerized Information Services:** MEDLARS, BRS Information Technologies; internal database. **Networks/Consortia:** Member of National Network of Libraries of Medicine - Southeastern/Atlantic Region, Palm Beach Health Sciences Library Consortium (PBHSLC), Miami Health Sciences Library Consortium (MHSLC). **Special Catalogs:** Palm Beach County Orthopedic Videotape Collection Catalog. **Remarks:** FAX: (407)650-6239. **Formerly:** Good Samaritan Health Systems, Inc. - Richard S. Beinecke Medical Library.

★6557★
Good Samaritan Regional Health Center - Health Science Library (Med)
605 N. 12th St. Phone: (618)242-4600
Mt. Vernon, IL 62864 Brenda Clark, Libn.
Staff: Prof 1. **Subjects:** Hospital administration, medicine, nursing. **Holdings:** 900 books; 500 periodical volumes. **Subscriptions:** 200 journals and other serials. **Services:** Interlibrary loan; copying; SDI; library open to medical staff and hospital employees. **Computerized Information Services:** MEDLINE. **Networks/Consortia:** Member of Areawide Hospital Library Consortium of Southwestern Illinois (AHLC), Cumberland Trail Library System, National Network of Libraries of Medicine - Greater Midwest Region. **Remarks:** FAX: (618)242-3196.

★6558★
Good Samaritan Regional Medical Center/ - Health Science Library (Med)
700 E. Norwegian St. Phone: (717)621-4466
Pottsville, PA 17901 Velma L. Sippie, Libn.
Staff: Prof 1. **Subjects:** Health science. **Holdings:** 1200 books. **Subscriptions:** 104 journals and other serials. **Services:** Library not open to the public. **Computerized Information Services:** MEDLINE. **Networks/Consortia:** Member of Central Pennsylvania Health Sciences Library Association (CPHSLA). **Remarks:** FAX: (717)622-7950. **Formerly:** Good Samaritan Hospital - Medical Library.

★6559★
Good Samaritan Regional Medical Center - Health Science Library (Med)
1111 E. McDowell St.
Box 2989 Phone: (602)239-4353
Phoenix, AZ 85062 Jacqueline D. Doyle, Dir.
Founded: 1950. **Staff:** Prof 1; Other 4. **Subjects:** Medicine, nursing, health administration. **Special Collections:** GSMC Heritage Society Collection. **Holdings:** 7500 books; 9000 bound periodical volumes; 8 drawers of pamphlets; 200 AV programs. **Subscriptions:** 600 journals and other serials. **Services:** Interlibrary loan; library not open to the public. **Automated Operations:** Computerized serials. **Computerized Information Services:** NLM, BRS Information Technologies, DIALOG Information Services; OnTyme Electronic Message Network Service (electronic mail service). Performs searches on fee basis. **Networks/Consortia:** Member of Central Arizona Biomedical Libraries (CABL), National Network of Libraries of Medicine (NN/LM). **Publications:** New Books List, quarterly. **Remarks:** Electronic mail address(es): GDSAMPHX (OnTyme Electronic Message Network Service). **Remarks:** FAX: (602)239-3493.

★6560★
Good Samaritan Society - Library (Med)
Good Samaritan Auxiliary Hospital
9649 71st Ave. Phone: (403)439-6381
Edmonton, AB, Canada T6E 5J2 Julia L. Lubi, Libn.
Founded: 1975. **Staff:** Prof 1. **Subjects:** Geriatrics, long-term care, nursing, rehabilitation, pastoral care; home and community services. **Holdings:** 2060 books; 5 16mm films; 23 filmstrip/cassette sets; 300 cassette tapes; 600 slides; 110 video cassettes. **Subscriptions:** 102 journals and other serials. **Services:** Copying; library open to the public for reference use only. **Automated Operations:** Computerized cataloging. **Remarks:** FAX: (403)433-8098.

★6561★
Good Shepherd Medical Center - Medical Library (Med)
621 N. 5th St. Phone: (903)236-2165
Longview, TX 75601 Gail B. . Corr, Med.Libn.
Subjects: Medicine, nursing, and allied health sciences. **Holdings:** Figures not available. **Services:** Library not open to the public. **Remarks:** FAX: (903)236-4736.

★6562★
Good Shepherd Rehabilitation Hospital - Library (Med)
6th & St. John Sts. Phone: (215)776-3294
Allentown, PA 18103 Cynthia Smith, Coord., Lib.Serv.
Subjects: Medicine, nursing, and allied health sciences. **Services:** Interlibrary loan; library not open to the public. **Remarks:** FAX: (215)776-3368.

★6563★
Goodhue County Historical Society - Library (Hist)
1166 Oak St.
Red Wing, MN 55066 Phone: (612)388-6024
Staff: 6. **Subjects:** Goodhue County, local and state history. **Special Collections:** Rare books which belonged to early settlers. **Holdings:** 500 books; 3000 clippings and manuscripts; 8000 photographs; school census, 1917 to present; record books for local area organizations and businesses. **Services:** Copying; library open to the public.

Caroline Meriwether Goodlett Library
See: **United Daughters of the Confederacy** (16704)

★6564★
Goodman and Carr - Library (Law)
200 King St., W., Suite 2300 Phone: (416)595-2300
Toronto, ON, Canada M5H 3W5 Jane Simpson, Libn.
Staff: Prof 1; Other 2. **Subjects:** Taxation, corporate and commercial law, real estate, estate planning, leasing, litigation. **Holdings:** 10,000 books; 350 bound periodical volumes. **Subscriptions:** 150 journals and other serials. **Services:** Interlibrary loan; library not open to the public. **Computerized Information Services:** Info Globe, WESTLAW, DIALOG Information Services, Canada Systems Group (CSG), LEXIS, Infomart Online, VU/TEXT Information Services, CAN/LAW; Memoranda of Law (internal database). **Remarks:** FAX: (416)595-0567.

★6565★
Goodman and Goodman - Library (Law)
250 Yonge St., 25th Fl. Phone: (416)979-2211
Toronto, ON, Canada M5B 1N8 Mary Saulig, Libn.
Staff: Prof 2; Other 1. **Subjects:** Law - commercial, corporate, securities, bankruptcy, entertainment, family, planning, administrative; litigation; real estate; estates and trusts; taxation. **Holdings:** 12,000 volumes. **Subscriptions:** 250 journals and other serials. **Services:** Interlibrary loan; library open to the public by appointment. **Computerized Information Services:** QL Systems, WESTLAW, LEXIS, NEXIS, Info Globe, Canada Systems Group (CSG), Infomart Online, DIALOG Information Services; internal database. **Remarks:** FAX: (416)979-1234. **Staff:** Cathy Georgieff, Asst.Libn.; Janet Cheng, Lib.Techn.

Goodman, LaPointe, Ferguson - Ferguson Gifford
See: **Ferguson Gifford** (5667)

Leo Goodman Memorial Collection - Nuclear Energy
See: **Environmental Coalition on Nuclear Power - Library** (5376)

Louis E. Goodman Memorial Library
See: **U.S. District Court - Northern California District** (17453)

★6566★
B.F. Goodrich Company - Geon Vinyl Division - ALTC Information Center (Sci-Engr)
Box 122 Phone: (216)933-0524
Avon Lake, OH 44012 Peter W. Bowler, Supv., Info.Ctr.
Founded: 1959. **Staff:** Prof 2; Other 4. **Subjects:** Polymerization technology, plastics applications, rubber applications, specialty polymers, urethane technology, hydrophilics technology. **Holdings:** 10,000 volumes; 100,000 company technical reports on microfilm; U.S. and foreign patents, 1964 to present, with translations. **Subscriptions:** 200 journals and other serials. **Services:** Center open to the public with restrictions. **Automated Operations:** Computerized cataloging and serials. **Computerized Information Services:** PFDS Online, OCLC, DIALOG Information Services, STN International, WILSONLINE, Chemical Information Systems, Inc. (CIS), BiblioTech; internal databases; DIALMAIL, STN MAIL (electronic mail services). **Networks/Consortia:** Member of OHIONET. **Remarks:** FAX: (216)933-1648. **Formerly:** B.F. Goodrich Chemical Company - Avon Lake Technical Center. **Staff:** Patricia Hanlon.

★6567★
B.F. Goodrich Company - Research and Development Center - Charle Cross Goodrich Information Center (Sci-Engr)
9921 Brecksville Rd. Phone: (216)447-5299
Brecksville, OH 44141 Lillian DeVault, Supv.
Founded: 1914. **Staff:** Prof 4. **Subjects:** Plastics, polymer chemistry, aerospace. **Holdings:** 8000 books; 15,000 bound periodical volumes; 120,000 internal reports; 1800 reels of microfilm of journals; U.S. patents, 1952 to present, on microfilm; OG Patent (CD-ROM); Chemical Abstracts, 1907 to present, hardcopy and microfilm. **Subscriptions:** 480 journals and other serials. **Services:** Interlibrary loan; SDI; center open to the public with restrictions. **Automated Operations:** Computerized cataloging, serials, and circulation. **Computerized Information Services:** DIALOG Information Services, PFDS Online, STN International, NLM, OCLC; internal database. **Publications:** Information Center Newsletter, quarterly; current awareness bulletins - both for internal distribution only. **Special Catalogs:** Internal Database Thesaurus. **Remarks:** FAX: (216)447-5249. **Staff:** Sharon L. Butcher, Sr.Info.Spec.; Suzanne W. Marcy, Sr.Info.Spec.; Connie Bennett, Tech.Libn.; Yvonne Deyling, Sr.Info.Asst.

★6568★
Goodwin, Carlton & Maxwell, P.C. - Law Library (Law)
901 Main, No. 3300 Phone: (214)939-4400
Dallas, TX 75202-3714 Lynn Collins, Hd.Libn.
Founded: 1980. **Staff:** 2. **Subjects:** Law. **Holdings:** 10,000 books. **Subscriptions:** 45 journals and other serials; 5 newspapers. **Services:** Interlibrary loan; copying; library not open to the public. **Computerized Information Services:** WESTLAW; LEXIS; Information America. **Staff:** L. Chad Barlow, Asst.Libn.

Goodwin Family Library
See: **Congregation Beth Jacob-Beth Israel** (4153)

★6569★
Goodwin, Procter & Hoar - Law Library (Law)
Exchange Place Phone: (617)523-1333
Boston, MA 02109 Mary Jo Poburko, Dir., Lib.Serv.
Staff: Prof 2; Other 4. **Subjects:** Law - taxation, labor, securities, litigation, real estate, probate. **Holdings:** 30,000 books; 500 bound periodical volumes. **Subscriptions:** 500 journals and other serials. **Services:** Interlibrary loan; library not open to the public. **Computerized Information Services:** LEXIS, NEXIS, VU/TEXT Information Services, DIALOG Information Services.

★6570★
Goodyear Tire and Rubber Company - Research Information Center (Sci-Engr)
142 Goodyear Blvd. Phone: (216)796-4089
Akron, OH 44305 G.M. Heineking, Lib.Rsrcs.
Founded: 1942. **Staff:** Prof 8; Other 4. **Subjects:** Rubber, plastics, environment, organic chemistry, fibers. **Special Collections:** Government Rubber Reserve Reports. **Holdings:** 6000 books; 4465 bound periodical volumes. **Subscriptions:** 554 journals and other serials. **Services:** Center not open to the public. **Automated Operations:** Computerized serials. **Computerized Information Services:** DIALOG Information Services, ORBIT Search Service, NLM, STN International, Human Resource Information Network (HRIN), Mead Data Central.

★6571★
Goodyear Tire and Rubber Company - Tech Center Library (Sci-Engr)
P.O. Box 3531 Phone: (216)796-4089
Akron, OH 44309-3531 G.M. Heineking, Lib.Rsrcs.
Founded: 1983. **Staff:** Prof 3; Other 1. **Subjects:** Engineering, computer science, computer applications, tire technology, business, quality control. **Holdings:** 3500 books. **Subscriptions:** 150 journals and other serials. **Services:** Center not open to the public. **Automated Operations:** Computerized serials. **Computerized Information Services:** DIALOG Information Services, ORBIT Search Service, NLM, STN International, Human Resource Information Network (HRIN), Mead Data Central. **Networks/Consortia:** Member of OCLC Pacific Network.

★6572★
Gookin Engineers - Library (Sci-Engr)
4203 N. Brown Ave. Phone: (602)947-3741
Scottsdale, AZ 85251 W.S. Gookin, Pres.
Founded: 1960. **Subjects:** Hydrology. **Holdings:** Figures not available. **Remarks:** FAX: (602)947-0262.

★6573★
A.D. Gordon Agriculture and Nature Study Institute - Library (Biol Sci, Agri)
Deganya A Phone: 6 750040
15120 Emek Ha Yarden, Israel S. Lulav
Founded: 1935. **Staff:** Prof 4; Other 2. **Subjects:** Life sciences, meteorology, agriculture, astronomy. **Special Collections:** history of science; folklore in sciences. **Holdings:** 57,165 books and bound periodical volumes; 200 microfiche; 600 reels of microfilm; 577 maps. **Subscriptions:** 82 journals and other serials. **Services:** Interlibrary loan; copying; library open to the public.

Albert H. Gordon Library
See: **New York Road Runners Club - Albert H. Gordon Library** (11639)

Bruce Gordon Memorial Library
See: **Beth Emet, The Free Synagogue** (1767)

★6574★
Gordon College - Jenks Learning Resource Center (Hum)
255 Grapevine Rd. Phone: (508)927-2300
Wenham, MA 01984 John Beauregard, Dir.
Founded: 1889. **Staff:** Prof 4; Other 6. **Subjects:** Liberal arts, humanities, North American ethnology, Shakespeare, linguistics. **Special Collections:** Edward Payson Vining Collection. **Holdings:** 218,636 books; 10,080 bound periodical volumes; 37,569 other cataloged items. **Subscriptions:** 694 journals and other serials. **Services:** Interlibrary loan; copying; library open to the public with restrictions. **Automated Operations:** Computerized public access catalog, cataloging, and circulation. **Computerized Information Services:** DIALOG Information Services. **Networks/Consortia:** Member of Northeast Consortium of Colleges and Universities in Massachusetts (NECCUM), North of Boston Library Exchange, Inc. (NOBLE). **Remarks:** FAX: (508)921-1398. **Staff:** Randall M. Gowman, Pub.Serv.Libn.; Sherri S. Dietrich, Tech.Serv.Libn.; Elizabeth Moulton, Per.Supv.; Martha Crain, Cat./ILL Libn.

★6575★
Gordon-Conwell Theological Seminary - Goddard Library (Rel-Phil)
130 Essex St., No. 583 Phone: (508)468-7111
South Hamilton, MA 01982-2361 Addie Pearson, Lib.Asst./Tech.Serv.
Founded: 1945. **Staff:** Prof 3; Other 4. **Subjects:** Theology, Biblical studies, church history, church ministry, Christian education, world missions, evangelism, Christianity and society. **Special Collections:** Mercer Collection of Assyrio-Babylonian materials; Roger Babson Collection of rare Bibles (especially early English Bibles). **Holdings:** 101,693 books; 16,346 bound periodical volumes; 2872 cassettes; 893 reels of microfilm; 3000 microfiche; 152 sermon tapes; 4733 microcards; 279 phonograph records. **Subscriptions:** 835 journals and other serials; 10 newspapers. **Services:** Interlibrary loan; copying; library open to the public. **Automated Operations:** Computerized cataloging. **Computerized Information Services:** OCLC, DIALOG Information Services. **Networks/Consortia:** Member of Boston Theological Institute Libraries, NELINET, Inc. **Staff:** Kenneth Umenhofer, Assoc.Libn.; Norman E. Anderson, Assoc.Libn.

Donald B. Gordon Memorial Library
See: **Morikami Museum of Japanese Culture** (10741)

George C. Gordon Library
See: **Worcester Polytechnic Institute** (20597)

J. Roy Gordon Research Laboratory
See: **Inco Limited** (7729)

Gore Hall Preschool Library
See: **Florida School for the Deaf and Blind - Library for the Deaf** (5882)

★6576★
Gore Place Society, Inc. - Library (Hum)
52 Gore St. Phone: (617)894-2798
Waltham, MA 02154 Stephen A. Wilbur, Cur.
Founded: 1935. **Staff:** Prof 1. **Subjects:** 18th century English and American literature, law, history, philosophy, landscape and horticulture, works of Christopher Gore. **Holdings:** 2000 books; 100 manuscripts. **Services:** Library open to the public.

★6577★
Gore and Storrie Limited - Library (Sci-Engr)
255 Consumers Rd. Phone: (416)499-9000
North York, ON, Canada M2J 5B6 Dianne Sawh, Libn.
Founded: 1984. **Staff:** 2. **Subjects:** Environmental engineering. **Services:** Library not open to the public. **Computerized Information Services:** Envoy 100 (electronic mail service). **Remarks:** FAX: (416)499-4687. Electronic mail address(es): Gore.Storrie (Envoy 100).

★6578★
W.L. Gore & Associates, Inc. - Information Services (Sci-Engr)
551 Paper Mill Rd.
Newark, DE 19714-9206 Phone: (302)738-4880
Founded: 1979. **Staff:** Prof 3. **Subjects:** Polymers, chemistry, business, engineering. **Holdings:** 3500 books; archival materials; patents. **Subscriptions:** 500 journals and other serials. **Services:** Interlibrary loan; center not open to the public. **Automated Operations:** Computerized cataloging, serials, and acquisitions. **Computerized Information Services:** DIALOG Information Services, BRS Information Technologies, ORBIT Search Service, NLM, STN International, Occupational Health Services, Inc. (OHS). **Networks/Consortia:** Member of Libraries in the New Castle County System (LINCS). **Remarks:** FAX: (302)292-4159. **Staff:** Mr. Jamie Zingaro; Marilyn McAleck; Panna Sunecha.

★6579★
Gorgas Army Community Hospital - Samuel Taylor Darling Memorial Library (Med)
USA MEDDAC Panama
APO Miami, FL 34004 Fawn Walker, Libn.
Founded: 1918. **Staff:** Prof 1; Other 1. **Subjects:** Medicine, allied health sciences. **Holdings:** 3000 books; 20,000 bound periodical volumes; 1000 videotapes; 300 AV programs. **Subscriptions:** 195 journals and other serials. **Services:** Copying; library open to the medical community. **Remarks:** Maintained by the U.S. Army MEDDAC (Panama); located in Ancon, Panama. Telephone number is 82-5319.

★6580★
Gorgas Memorial Laboratory - Biomedical Research Library (Med)
Apartado 6991 Phone: 274111
Panama 5, Panama Nora E. Osses
Founded: 1928. **Staff:** 1. **Subjects:** Arboviruses, malaria, leishmaniasis, trypanosomiasis, vertebrate zoology, parasitology, bacteriology, entomology, ecology, yellow fever, microbiology, epidemiology, tissue culture, cytology, pathology, virology, veterinary medicine. **Special Collections:** Tropical Medicine; Gorgas Memorial Laboratory Publications (1029 reprints). **Holdings:** 10,000 volumes; 100 boxes of reprints and miscellanea; 20 VF drawers of pamphlets. **Subscriptions:** 507 journals and other serials. **Services:** Interlibrary loan; copying; library open for the use of physicians, medical students, scientists, nurses, and laboratory technicians. **Publications:** Annual Report; Bibliography of Publications of the Gorgas Memorial Laboratory; Evaluacion Ambiental y Efectos del Proyecto Hidroelectrico Fortuna; El Laboratorio Conmemorativo Gorgas: Su Historia y Su Labor - all free upon request. **Remarks:** FAX: 254366. Library located at Justo Arosemena Ave., No. 35-30, Panama City, Republic of Panama. **Also Known As:** Laboratorio Conmemorativo Gorgas - Biblioteca-Biomedica.

Gorno Memorial Music Library
See: **University of Cincinnati - College Conservatory of Music** (18465)

Thomas Gorton Music Library
See: **University of Kansas** (18739)

★6581★
Goshen College - Harold and Wilma Good Library - Hartzler Music Collection (Mus)
1700 S. Main Phone: (219)535-7431
Goshen, IN 46526 Devon J. Yoder, Libn.
Staff: Prof 3. **Subjects:** Early American music, American hymnody. **Holdings:** 3100 books. **Services:** Interlibrary loan; copying; collection open to the public. **Computerized Information Services:** DIALOG Information Services. **Networks/Consortia:** Member of INCOLSA. **Staff:** Sally Jo Milne, Assoc.Libn.; Kathy Kauffman, Assoc.Libn.

★6582★
Goshen Historical Society - Library (Hist)
c/o Mrs. Ellsworth D. Wood, Pres.
27 Kimberly Rd. Phone: (203)491-2665
Goshen, CT 06756 Hazel Wadhams, Cur.
Founded: 1955. **Staff:** 5. **Subjects:** Local history, genealogy. **Holdings:** Figures not available. **Services:** Genealogical research; library open to the public with restrictions. **Remarks:** Library located at Old Middle Rd., RD 1, Goshen, CT 06756.

Goss History of Engineering Library
See: **Purdue University - Engineering Library** (13540)

D. Samuel Gottesman Library
See: **Yeshiva University - Albert Einstein College of Medicine** (20751)

Mendel Gottesman Library of Hebraica and Judaica
See: **Yeshiva University** (20756)

★6583★
Gottlieb Memorial Hospital - Medical Library (Med)
701 W. North Ave. Phone: (708)450-4526
Melrose Park, IL 60160 Julie Mueller
Staff: Prof 1; Other 2. **Subjects:** Clinical medicine, patient information. **Holdings:** 300 books; 200 bound periodical volumes; pamphlets. **Subscriptions:** 200 journals and other serials; 2 newspapers. **Services:** Interlibrary loan; copying; SDI; library open to the public. **Computerized Information Services:** DIALOG Information Services, NLM, BRS Information Technologies. **Remarks:** FAX: (708)450-5058.

Gottlieb Memorial Library
See: **Congregation Adath Jeshurun** (4145)

Gottscho Packaging Information Center
See: **Rutgers University** (14164)

★6584★
Gould/AMI - Technical Library (Sci-Engr)
2300 Buckskin Rd. Phone: (208)233-4690
Pocatello, ID 83201 Karalee Holubar, Libn.
Founded: 1987. **Staff:** Prof 1. **Subjects:** Semiconductors, electronics, microelectronics, computers, business, management. **Holdings:** 1500 books; 120 bound periodical volumes. **Subscriptions:** 115 journals and other serials. **Services:** Interlibrary loan; copying; library open to the public with permission. **Automated Operations:** Computerized cataloging and circulation. **Computerized Information Services:** DIALOG Information Services. **Remarks:** FAX: (208)234-6795.

★6585★
Gould Inc. - Technical Information Center (Sci-Engr)
35129 Curtis Blvd. Phone: (216)953-5117
Eastlake, OH 44095 Martha C. Walunis, Info.Spec.
Founded: 1981. **Staff:** Prof 1. **Subjects:** Printed circuit board technology, electrochemistry, electrochemical engineering, electronic materials, thinfilms and coatings, materials characterization. **Holdings:** 4000 books; 540 bound periodical volumes; 5 VF drawers of technical reports; 8 VF drawers of patents. **Subscriptions:** 225 journals and other serials. **Services:** Interlibrary loan. **Computerized Information Services:** DIALOG Information Services, OCLC, EPIC, NEXIS, LEXIS. **Remarks:** FAX: (216)953-5050.

Governmental Refuse Collection and Disposal Association - Library
See: **Solid Waste Information Clearinghouse** (15357)

★6586★
Governors State University - GeoStat - Information Center (Energy)
c/o Dr. Elizabeth Hagens Phone: (708)534-5000
University Park, IL 60466 Dr. Elizabeth Hagens, Ph.D., Dir.
Founded: 1976. **Staff:** Prof 2; Other 3. **Subjects:** Geo-political, physical, and cultural resources mapping; solar and alternative energy, appropriate technology, community and international development, environmental planning. **Holdings:** 3000 books; 1000 bound periodical volumes; 4000 other cataloged items. **Subscriptions:** 300 journals and other serials; 5 newspapers. **Services:** Interlibrary loan; center open to the public. **Publications:** Research update, annual. **Remarks:** Alternate telephone number(s): (708)534-2455.

★6587★
Gowanda Psychiatric Center - A. Stephen Dubois Library (Med)
Rte. 62 Phone: (716)532-3311
Helmuth, NY 14079 Mark Wudyka, Libn.
Founded: 1961. **Staff:** Prof 1. **Subjects:** Psychiatry, psychology. **Holdings:** 4398 volumes. **Subscriptions:** 47 journals and other serials. **Services:** Interlibrary loan; copying; library open to the public by appointment. **Networks/Consortia:** Member of Western New York Library Resources Council (WNYLRC).

★6588★
Gowling, Strathy & Henderson - Law Library (Law)
3800 Commerce Court, W.
Box 438 Phone: (416)862-7525
Toronto, ON, Canada M5L 1J3 Paula Carroll, Libn.
Staff: Prof 3; Other 1. **Subjects:** Law. **Holdings:** 5500 volumes. **Subscriptions:** 500 journals and other serials; 4 newspapers. **Services:** Interlibrary loan (limited); library not open to the public. **Remarks:** FAX: (416)862-7661. **Staff:** Joanne Allen, Asst.Libn.

★6589★
Gowling, Strathy & Henderson - Library (Law)
160 Elgin St. Phone: (613)232-1781
Ottawa, ON, Canada K1N 8S3 Linda Marchand, Libn.
Founded: 1930. **Staff:** 4. **Subjects:** Law. **Holdings:** 3000 books. **Subscriptions:** 260 journals and other serials. **Services:** Interlibrary loan; copying; SDI; library open to the public. **Automated Operations:** Computerized cataloging. **Computerized Information Services:** QL Systems, LEXIS, WESTLAW, DIALOG Information Services, Info Globe, Infomart Online, STM Systems Corporation, Canadian Tax Online. **Remarks:** FAX: (613)563-9869.

GPT Stromberg-Carlson
See: **SIEMENS Stromberg-Carlson** (15158)

GPU Corporation - Metropolitan Edison Company
See: **Metropolitan Edison Company** (10200)

★6590★
GPU Nuclear - Corporate Library (Energy)
1 Upper Pond Rd. Phone: (201)316-7159
Parsippany, NJ 07054 Karen Gramberg
Founded: 1974. **Staff:** 1. **Subjects:** Nuclear power, utility-based engineering. **Special Collections:** Nuclear Regulatory Commission Reports (7300); Electric Power Research Institute Reports (3300). **Holdings:** 2700 books; 3100 engineering standards; 4500 technical reports. **Subscriptions:** 250 journals and other serials. **Services:** Interlibrary loan; library not open to the public. **Automated Operations:** Computerized acquisitions, circulation, and routing (Data Trek). **Computerized Information Services:** DIALOG Information Services, NEXIS; CARIRS (internal database). **Remarks:** FAX: (201)316-7296.

★6591★
GPU Nuclear - Oyster Creek Technical Library (Sci-Engr)
Oyster Creek Nuclear Generating Sta.
Box 388 Phone: (609)971-4616
Forked River, NJ 08731 Jon von Briesen, Staff Asst., Sr.
Founded: 1981. **Staff:** Prof 1. **Subjects:** Nuclear power and engineering. **Special Collections:** Engineering and nuclear industry standards (hardcopy, microfiche). **Holdings:** 1700 books; 2900 technical reports. **Subscriptions:** 140 journals and other serials. **Services:** Interlibrary loan; library not open to the public. **Computerized Information Services:** DIALOG Information Services, Institute of Nuclear Power Operations (INPO), NEXIS; CARIRS (internal database). **Remarks:** FAX: (609)971-4103.

★6592★
GPU Nuclear - TMI Technical Library (Energy)
Three Mile Island Nuclear Generating Sta.
Box 480 Phone: (717)948-8105
Middletown, PA 17057 Joan H. Slavin, Libn.
Staff: Prof 1; Other 1. **Subjects:** Nuclear and electric power, effects of radiation on health. **Holdings:** 1800 books; 1100 standards; 8000 technical reports. **Subscriptions:** 219 journals and other serials. **Services:** Interlibrary loan; library not open to the public. **Automated Operations:** Computerized cataloging, serials, and circulation. **Computerized Information Services:** DIALOG Information Services; STAIRS (internal database). **Publications:** New Titles List, monthly. **Remarks:** FAX: (717)948-8823.

★6593★
GPU Service Corporation - HQ Library (Bus-Fin)
100 Interpace Pkwy. Phone: (201)263-6185
Parsippany, NJ 07054 Anna Marie Deri
Staff: 2. **Subjects:** Electrical utility business, management, finance. **Holdings:** 1900 books; 7500 technical reports. **Services:** Interlibrary loan; library not open to the public. **Automated Operations:** Computerized acquisitions, circulation, and periodicals routing. **Computerized Information Services:** DIALOG Information Services; CARIRS (internal database). **Publications:** Library Bulletin, quarterly - for internal distribution. **Remarks:** FAX: (201)263-6822. **Staff:** Franzliska Fink.

★6594★
GPU Service Corporation - Library (Bus-Fin)
Rte. 183 & Van Reed Rd.
Reading, PA 19603 Phone: (215)375-5000
Staff: 1. **Subjects:** Electric utility business, electrical and mechanical engineering. **Holdings:** 925 books; 850 technical reports. **Subscriptions:** 266 journals and other serials. **Services:** Interlibrary loan; copying; library open to the public with restrictions. **Computerized Information Services:** Online systems. **Staff:** Joanna Rocktashel.

Victor Grabel/John Philip Sousa Music Library
See: **U.S. Marine Corps - Marine Band Library** (17602)

Dr. Charles F. Grabske, Sr. Library
See: **Independence Regional Health Center** (7733)

★6595★
Grace Bible College - Bultema Memorial Library (Rel-Phil)
1011 Aldon St., S.W.
Box 910 Phone: (616)538-2332
Grand Rapids, MI 49509 Guni Olson, Dir.
Staff: Prof 1; Other 6. **Subjects:** Theology, Biblical studies, missions, Christian education, practical theology. **Special Collections:** Dispensational Theology. **Holdings:** 35,002 books; 1800 bound periodical volumes; 707 microforms. **Subscriptions:** 180 journals and other serials. **Services:** Interlibrary loan; copying; library open to the public for reference use only. **Automated Operations:** Computerized cataloging and acquisitions. **Networks/Consortia:** Member of Lakeland Area Library Network (LAKENET), Michigan Library Consortium (MLC).

★6596★
Grace College of the Bible - Library (Rel-Phil, Educ)
1515 S. 10th St. Phone: (402)449-2893
Omaha, NE 68108 Stanley V. Udd, Hd.Libn.
Founded: 1943. **Staff:** Prof 1; Other 1. **Subjects:** Bible and theology, history, literature. **Special Collections:** Elementary/juvenile books for Elementary Education program (3100). **Holdings:** 55,562 books; 4370 bound periodical volumes; 900 phonograph records; 130 filmstrips and kits; clippings; films; maps; microfiche; pamphlets; tapes; video cassettes. **Subscriptions:** 130 journals and other serials. **Services:** Interlibrary loan; copying; library open to the public from metropolitan area. **Staff:** David Gorman, Asst.Libn.

Grace Community Church Archives
See: **Master's College and Seminary** (9840)

★6597★
Grace Energy Corporation - Document Control Department (Sci-Engr, Energy)
13455 Noel Rd., Suite 1500 Phone: (214)770-0200
Dallas, TX 75240-5003 Kimberly Hamilton, Mgr.-GIS
Founded: 1975. **Staff:** Prof 2; Other 2. **Subjects:** Petroleum, mining, paper, and energy industries. **Special Collections:** Energy industry annual reports file (2000 reports). **Holdings:** 1500 books; 4000 microforms; 50 boxes of pamphlets. **Subscriptions:** 200 journals and other serials; 10 newspapers. **Services:** Interlibrary loan; copying; open to other special librarians. **Computerized Information Services:** DIALOG Information Services, NEXIS, Dow Jones News/Retrieval, Dun & Bradstreet Business Credit Services. **Publications:** Periodicals list; publications list - both for internal distribution only. **Remarks:** FAX: (214)770-0252. **Staff:** Pat G. Terrell, Sr.Rec. & Info.Ck.; Janis A. Jelnick, Rec. & Retention Anl.; Karen Hubbard, Libn.

★6598★
Grace General Hospital - School of Nursing Library (Med)
241 LeMarchant Rd. Phone: (709)778-66425
St. John's, NF, Canada A1E 1P9 Debbie O'Reilly, Libn.
Founded: 1964. **Staff:** 1. **Subjects:** Nursing. **Holdings:** 2700 books; 130 bound periodical volumes; 20 boxes of pamphlets. **Subscriptions:** 32 journals and other serials. **Services:** Interlibrary loan; library open to the public for reference use only.

★6599★
Grace Lutheran Church - Library (Rel-Phil)
Box 174 Phone: (602)537-4817
Show Low, AZ 85924 Irene Scheider, Libn.
Founded: 1984. **Staff:** Prof 1. **Subjects:** Healing, Holy Spirit, Bible, theology, psychology, philosophy, Christian education, church history. **Special Collections:** Works of Martin Luther. **Holdings:** 5336 books; 384 cassette albums; 941 cassette tapes; 172 videotapes; 36 multi-media kits. **Subscriptions:** 14 journals and other serials. **Services:** Library open to the public. **Publications:** Living Stones, monthly - for internal distribution only.

★6600★
Grace Lutheran Church - Library (Rel-Phil)
18360 Minnetonka Blvd. Phone: (612)473-2362
Wayzata, MN 55391 Jeanne E. Fraley
Founded: 1958. **Staff:** 4. **Subjects:** Religion, social problems. **Holdings:** 4000 books; 3 VF drawers of pictures, clippings, pamphlets; 8 drawers of cassette tapes. **Subscriptions:** 12 journals and other serials. **Services:** Library open to the public.

★6601★
Grace Maternity Hospital - Medical Library (Med)
5821 University Ave. Phone: (902)420-6600
Halifax, NS, Canada B3H 1W3 Darlene A. Chapman, Libn.
Subjects: Obstetrics and gynecology, pediatrics, surgery, medicine. **Holdings:** 400 books. **Subscriptions:** 15 journals and other serials. **Services:** Interlibrary loan; library open to the public with restrictions.

Grace Specialty Chemical Company
See: **W.R. Grace and Company** (6604)

★6602★
Grace Theological Seminary - Morgan Library (Rel-Phil)
200 Seminary Dr. Phone: (219)372-5177
Winona Lake, IN 46590 William Darr, Dir.
Founded: 1939. **Staff:** Prof 3. **Subjects:** Bible, archeology, missions, Christian education. **Special Collections:** Billy Sunday Papers (28 cubic feet); Grace Brethren denominational archives. **Holdings:** 68,000 books; 7500 bound periodical volumes. **Subscriptions:** 300 journals and other serials. **Services:** Interlibrary loan; copying; library open to the public. **Automated Operations:** Computerized cataloging. **Networks/Consortia:** Member of INCOLSA. **Staff:** Jerry Lincoln, Assoc.Dir.

★6603★
W.R. Grace and Company - Dearborn Division Library (Env-Cons)
300 Genesee St.
Lake Zurich, IL 60047 Phone: (708)438-1800
Founded: 1940. **Staff:** Prof 1; Other 1. **Subjects:** Water treatment, corrosion, inorganic chemistry, organic chemistry, polymers, environmental engineering, pollution control, water bacteriology, spectroscopy. **Holdings:** 4000 books; 2100 bound periodical volumes; 900 research notebooks; 6000 U.S. and foreign patents; 5300 research reports. **Subscriptions:** 150 journals and other serials. **Services:** Interlibrary loan; copying; library open to the public by appointment. **Computerized Information Services:** DIALOG Information Services, STN International, National Pesticide Information Retrieval System (NPIRS). **Networks/Consortia:** Member of North Suburban Library System (NSLS). **Publications:** Literature Index and Recent Book Acquisitions - for internal distribution only. **Remarks:** FAX: (708)540-1566. **Staff:** Thea R. Sostrin, Libn.

★6604★
W.R. Grace and Company - Grace Specialty Chemical Company - Library (Sci-Engr)
62 Whittemore Ave. Phone: (617)876-1400
Cambridge, MA 02140 Marjorie Metcalf, Libn.
Founded: 1955. **Staff:** Prof 1; Other 2. **Subjects:** Chemistry - organic, colloidal, inorganic, analytical, polymer; rheology; rubber; cement; concrete. **Holdings:** 7000 books; 1000 bound periodical volumes. **Subscriptions:** 350 journals and other serials. **Services:** Interlibrary loan; copying; library open to the public by appointment. **Computerized Information Services:** DIALOG Information Services, STN International, ORBIT Search Service, Questel, NLM, DataTimes, Dow Jones News/Retrieval; DIALMAIL (electronic mail service). **Remarks:** FAX: (617)864-7198. **Staff:** Jennifer DeLeeuw, Asst.Libn.

★6605★
W.R. Grace and Company - Research Division - Library
1 Ledgemont Ctr.
128 Spring St.
Lexington, MA 02173
Subjects: Membranes, separation technology. **Holdings:** 500 books. **Remarks:** Currently inactive.

★6606★
W.R. Grace & Co.-Conn. - Cryovac Division - Technical Library (Sci-Engr)
Box 464 Phone: (803)433-2584
Duncan, SC 29334-0464 Harriet B. Oglesbee, Tech.Libn.
Founded: 1960. **Staff:** Prof 1; Other 1. **Subjects:** Plastic film, packaging, food packaging, polymer chemistry. **Special Collections:** Proprietary documents (lab reports, technical reports). **Holdings:** 7300 books; 220 bound volumes of proprietary documents; 30 VF drawers of technical reports and miscellanea; 1500 microforms. **Subscriptions:** 200 journals and other serials; 2 newspapers. **Services:** Interlibrary loan; copying; SDI; library open to the public at librarian's discretion. **Computerized Information Services:** DIALOG Information Services, OCLC EPIC, TOXNET, STN International, BRS Information Technologies. **Networks/Consortia:** Member of SOLINET. **Publications:** ACCESS, monthly - for internal distribution only. **Special Catalogs:** Cryovac Document Retrieval System. **Remarks:** Alternate telephone number is 433-2313. FAX: (803)433-2689.

★6607★
W.R. Grace & Co.-Conn. - Information Center (Sci-Engr)
7379 Rte. 32 Phone: (301)531-4268
Columbia, MD 21044 Jeanette S. Hamilton, Supv./Res.Info.Spec.
Founded: 1953. **Staff:** Prof 3; Other 3. **Subjects:** Biochemistry; chemical engineering; chemistry - inorganic, organic, analytical. **Holdings:** 15,000 books; 2500 bound periodical volumes; 12,000 internal reports; microforms; audio and videocassettes; patents; annual reports; market research studies; laboratory notebooks; material safety data sheets (MSDS). **Subscriptions:** 300 journals and other serials. **Services:** Interlibrary loan; copying; SDI; library open to the public with permission. **Automated Operations:** Computerized public access catalog, cataloging, acquisitions, serials, and circulation. **Computerized Information Services:** DIALOG Information Services, ORBIT Search Service, STN International, Questel, Data-Star, BRS Information Technologies, MEDLARS, Dow Jones News/Retrieval, Dun & Bradstreet Business Credit Services, LEXIS, LEXPAT, NEXIS, Teltech, OCLC, EPIC, Chemical Information Systems, Inc. (CIS); DIALMAIL (electronic mail service). **Publications:** InfoLine (newsletter), monthly. **Special Indexes:** Research reports index. **Remarks:** FAX: (301)531-4367. **Staff:** Michael McCulley, Sr.Info.Spec.; Ann Razgunas, Sr.Info.Spec./Online Coord.

★6608★
Graceland College - Frederick Madison Smith Library (Hum)
Lamoni, IA 50140 Phone: (515)784-5306
Diane E. Shelton, Lib.Dir.
Founded: 1895. **Staff:** Prof 2; Other 5. **Subjects:** Religion, literature, psychology, history, philosophy, education, art, economics, music, social and behavioral sciences. **Special Collections:** Mormonism; 20th century American literature. **Holdings:** 86,534 books; 20,697 bound periodical volumes; 48,936 microforms; 3500 pamphlets; 75,692 government documents. **Subscriptions:** 644 journals and other serials; 12 newspapers. **Services:** Interlibrary loan; copying; language laboratory; media laboratory; library open to the public. **Automated Operations:** Computerized public access catalog, cataloging, circulation, acquisitions, and serials. **Computerized Information Services:** ERIC, Academic Index. **Networks/ Consortia:** Member of Iowa Computer Assisted Network (ICAN), Bibliographical Center for Research, Rocky Mountain Region, Inc. (BCR). **Special Catalogs:** Mormonism (card). **Remarks:** FAX: (515)784-5497. **Staff:** Francis Acland, Assoc.Libn.

Graceland Library
See: **Audrain County Historical Society** (1289)

★6609★
Gracewood State School and Hospital - Library (Med)
Gracewood, GA 30812-1299 Phone: (404)790-2183
Linda D. Lawal, Libn.
Founded: 1963. **Staff:** Prof 1. **Subjects:** Mental retardation, pediatrics, psychology, medicine, dentistry, nursing. **Special Collections:** Pediatric tape collection (800 reels and cassettes); Mental Retardation and Reinforcement Therapy (4 films). **Holdings:** 3600 books; 810 bound periodical volumes; 2100 cassette tapes; 2333 reprints; 703 pamphlets; 3 films. **Subscriptions:** 62 journals and other serials. **Services:** Interlibrary loan; copying; library open to the public with restrictions. **Networks/Consortia:** Member of Georgia Health Sciences Library Association (GHSLA). **Special Catalogs:** Tapes catalog. **Special Indexes:** Reprint index.

★6610★
Gradient Corporation - Technical Reference Center (Env-Cons)
44 Brattle St. Phone: (617)576-1555
Cambridge, MA 02138 Marcia A. Olson, Mgr., Info.Rsrc.
Founded: 1986. **Staff:** Prof 2. **Subjects:** Environmental protection, pollution, environmental chemistry, toxicology. **Holdings:** 2000 books. **Subscriptions:** 50 journals and other serials. **Services:** Interlibrary loan; center not open to the public. **Automated Operations:** Computerized cataloging and circulation. **Computerized Information Services:** DIALOG Information Services, NLM, MEDLARS, STN International, Chemical Information Systems, Inc. (CIS). Performs searches on fee basis. **Publications:** New Library Additions, monthly - for internal distribution only. **Remarks:** FAX: (617)864-8469. **Staff:** Melody Norman-Camp.

★6611★
Graduate Hospital - Library (Med)
One Graduate Plaza Phone: (215)893-2401
Philadelphia, PA 19146 Diane M. Farny, Dir. of Lib.Serv.
Founded: 1977. **Staff:** Prof 2; Other 1. **Subjects:** Medicine, nursing, patient health education. **Special Collections:** M. Harris Samitz Dermatology Collection. **Holdings:** 1000 books; 6000 bound periodical volumes. **Subscriptions:** 330 journals and other serials. **Services:** Interlibrary loan (fee); copying; SDI; library open to the public by appointment. **Computerized Information Services:** DIALOG Information Services; CD-ROM (DIALOG OnDISC). Performs searches on fee basis. **Networks/ Consortia:** Member of National Network of Libraries of Medicine - Middle Atlantic Region, Delaware Valley Information Consortium (DEVIC), BHSL. **Remarks:** FAX: (215)893-2065.

★6612★
Graduate School and University Center of the City University of New York - Mina Rees Library (Soc Sci)
33 W. 42nd St. Phone: (212)642-2875
New York, NY 10036 Susan Newman, Chf.Libn.
Founded: 1964. **Staff:** Prof 12; Other 8. **Subjects:** Humanities, social sciences, mathematics. **Special Collections:** U.S. Presidential Papers (microfilm); Human Relations Area Files (paper set); CUNY doctoral dissertations. **Holdings:** 208,809 volumes; 385,790 microforms; 177,383 art slides; 1400 scores. **Subscriptions:** 1692 journals and other serials. **Services:** Interlibrary loan; copying; library open to faculty and students of other educational institutions. **Automated Operations:** Computerized ILL; cataloging, acquisitions, and serials (NOTIS). **Computerized Information Services:** OCLC. **Networks/Consortia:** Member of New York Metropolitan Reference and Research Library Agency. **Publications:** Acquisition Policy of the Graduate School and University Center Library; Library Handbook, annual. **Remarks:** FAX: (212)642-2896. **Staff:** Men-Sze Butt, Music Cat.Libn.; Helga Feder, Hum.Ref. & ILL Libn.; Carol Fitzgerald, Soc.Sci.Ref. & Circ.Libn.; Lois Hacker, Chf.Tech.Serv.Libn.; Susan Levkovitz, Chf.Cat.Libn.; Ofelia Rabassa, Book Acq.; Minna C. Saxe, Chf.Ser.Libn.; William Shank, Mus.Ref.Libn.; George Simor, Gifts Libn.; Faith Yoman, Cat.Libn.

★6613★
Graduate Theological Union - Flora Lamson Hewlett Library (Rel-Phil)
2400 Ridge Rd. Phone: (510)649-2400
Berkeley, CA 94709 Mary Williams, Dir.
Founded: 1969. **Staff:** Prof 10; Other 15. **Subjects:** Bible, denominations, theology, practical theology, church history, religion, new American religious movements. **Special Collections:** New Religious Movements. **Holdings:** 314,118 books; 48,289 bound periodical volumes; 6286 audiotapes, discs, cassettes; 226,366 microforms; 800 cubic feet of archival material; 11,356 pieces of miscellanea. **Subscriptions:** 2472 journals and other serials. **Services:** Interlibrary loan; copying; library open to the public with restrictions. **Automated Operations:** Computerized cataloging, acquisitions, and serials. **Computerized Information Services:** BRS Information Technologies, RLIN. Performs searches on fee basis. Contact Person: Diane Choquette, Hd., Ref. **Networks/Consortia:** Member of CLASS, Research Libraries Information Network (RLIN). **Remarks:** FAX: (510)649-1417. A consortium library uniting the holdings of nine seminaries: American Baptist Seminary of the West; Church Divinity School of the Pacific; Franciscan School of Theology; Pacific Lutheran Theological Seminary; Jesuit School of Theology at Berkeley; Dominican School of Philosophy and Theology; San Francisco Theological Seminary; Pacific School of Religion; Starr King School for the Ministry. Library works cooperatively with the library of the University of California, Berkeley and the Canon Law Collection of the University of California Law School. **Staff:** Catherine Sanborn, Hd., Tech.Serv.; Oscar Burdick, Hd., Coll.Dev.; Michael Peterson, Br.Libn.

Graff Medical and Scientific Library
See: **City of Hope National Medical Center** (3739)

★6614★
Grafton Historical Museum - Library (Hist)
Main St. Phone: (802)843-2584
Grafton, VT 05146 Jean L. Whitnack, Reg.
Founded: 1962. **Subjects:** Grafton history, genealogy. **Special Collections:** Photographs of old-time Grafton (1000); historical artifacts. **Holdings:** Original documents on Grafton history, 1754 to present; genealogical files. **Services:** Library open to the public for reference use only by arrangement. **Publications:** Grafton History, 1754-1985; Innkeeping 100 Years Ago; Barrett Store, 1815-1830; Grafton Cornet Band; Nine Historical Grafton Walks; Life of a Vermont Farmer - Diary, 1864-1933, The Grafton Quiet Coloring Book. **Remarks:** Alternate telephone number(s): (802)843-2344.

Billy Graham Center
See: **Wheaton College** (20367)

★6615★
Billy Graham Evangelistic Association - Library (Rel-Phil)
1300 Harmon Pl. Phone: (612)338-0500
Minneapolis, MN 55403 Rev. Roger C. Palms, Ed.
Staff: 1. **Subjects:** Religion, biography, history. **Special Collections:** Billy Graham articles; magazine and newspaper clippings concerning Billy Graham. **Holdings:** 8000 books; 2000 bound periodical volumes; 1000 other cataloged items; 82 reels of microfilm. **Subscriptions:** 200 journals and other serials. **Services:** Library not open to the public.

Billy Graham Room
See: **Southern Baptist Theological Seminary** (15463)

Dr. H. Carson Graham Memorial Library
See: **Lions Gate Hospital** (9201)

Fred J. Graham Library
See: **Trinity Bible College** (16500)

Graham Historical Society
See: **Nodaway County Genealogical Society** (11826)

★6616★
Graham Hospital - Medical Staff Library (Med)
210 W. Walnut St. Phone: (309)647-5240
Canton, IL 61520 Mrs. Moneta Bedwell, Dir.Lib.Serv.
Staff: Prof 1. **Subjects:** Surgery, internal medicine. **Holdings:** 500 books. **Subscriptions:** 25 journals and other serials. **Services:** Interlibrary loan; library not open to the public. **Networks/Consortia:** Member of Heart of Illinois Library Consortium (HILC), Illinois Valley Library System.

★6617★
Graham Hospital - School of Nursing Library (Med)
210 W. Walnut St. Phone: (309)647-5240
Canton, IL 61520 Mrs. Moneta Bedwell, Dir.Lib.Serv.
Founded: 1930. **Staff:** Prof 1. **Subjects:** Nursing and medicine. **Special Collections:** Historical textbooks; dolls costumed as historical nursing persons. **Holdings:** 3000 books; 170 bound periodical volumes; 3 VF drawers of pamphlets and clippings; 400 AV program titles. **Subscriptions:** 60 journals and other serials. **Services:** Interlibrary loan; copying; library open to the public for reference use only. **Computerized Information Services:** DIALOG Information Services; DOCLINE (electronic mail service). **Networks/Consortia:** Member of Heart of Illinois Library Consortium (HILC), Illinois Valley Library System. **Remarks:** FAX: (309)647-5986.

★6618★
Grain Processing Corporation - Technical Information Center (Sci-Engr)
1600 Oregon St.
Box 349 Phone: (319)264-4389
Muscatine, IA 52761 Rosemary A. Hollatz, Libn.
Founded: 1951. **Staff:** 1. **Subjects:** Paper technology, animal nutrition, antibiotics, protein, vitamins. **Holdings:** 2000 books; 1300 bound periodical volumes; 68 VF drawers of technical reports, patents, reprints. **Subscriptions:** 200 journals and other serials. **Services:** Interlibrary loan; copying; center open to the public by request. **Computerized Information Services:** DIALOG Information Services, NERAC, Inc. **Publications:** Bulletin, monthly - for internal distribution only. **Remarks:** FAX: (319)264-4216. Telex: 46 8497.

Rafael Garcia Granados Library
See: **Universidad Nacional Autonoma de Mexico - Instituto de Investigaciones Historicas** (17993)

Grand Army of the Republic Memorial Hall Museum - Archives and Library
See: **Wisconsin Veterans Museum - Archives and Library Division** (20534)

★6619★
Grand Army of the Republic Museum and Library (Mil)
4278 Griscom St. Phone: (215)289-6484
Philadelphia, PA 19124-3954 Elmer Atkinson, Pres.
Founded: 1926. **Staff:** 3. **Subjects:** Civil War, Grand Army of the Republic. **Special Collections:** Philadelphia Inquirer newspapers from Civil War era (originals, complete set); Harpers publications from Civil War era; Sons Union Veterans camp records; official Civil War records, 1861-1865 (complete set). **Holdings:** 1600 books; 30 bound periodical volumes; 1000 documents; 50 AV programs; Grand Army of the Republic records. **Services:** Copying; library open to the public by appointment. **Computerized Information Services:** Internal database. Performs searches on fee basis. **Remarks:** Alternate telephone numbers are 338-7558 and 673-1688.

Grand Canyon Natl. Park
See: **U.S. Natl. Park Service** (17723)

★6620★
Grand County Historical Association - Museum Library (Hist)
110 Byers Ave.
P.O. Box 165 Phone: (303)725-3939
Hot Sulphur Springs, CO 80451 Betty Kilsdonk, Musm.Dir.
Subjects: Winter sports, ranching, logging, government, guest ranching, pioneer life. **Special Collections:** William H. Jackson Collection (survey photographs of Grand County); Daisy Button Collection (pioneer life). **Holdings:** 550 books; 31 record groups; 408 manuscript collections; 100 oral history interviews; 90 maps; 5235 photographs. **Services:** Copying; library open to the public for reference use only.

★6621★
Grand Encampment Museum, Inc. - Library (Hist)
Box 395 Phone: (307)327-5310
Encampment, WY 82325 Vera Oldman, Pres.
Founded: 1966. **Subjects:** Local history. **Special Collections:** Library of W.T. Peryam, a pioneer settler. **Holdings:** 100 books; 100 pamphlets; 5 reels of microfilm of old area newspapers; pioneer oral history tapes; 1000 historical pictures; 100 historical manuscripts; file of Saratoga Lyre, 1888; file of Grand Encampment Herald, 1898-1912; maps; city record books; school record books; funeral records; cemetery records; mining account books; business account books. **Services:** Library open to the public by appointment.

★6622★
Grand Forks Herald - Library (Publ)
Box 6008 Phone: (701)780-1133
Grand Forks, ND 58206-6008 Cynthia Valtierra, Libn.
Staff: 1. **Subjects:** Newspaper reference topics, state and local history, Minnesota, agriculture. **Holdings:** 520 books; 72 VF drawers of clippings; Grand Forks Herald, 1879 to present, on microfilm; 50 VF drawers of photographs. **Subscriptions:** 48 journals and other serials; 70 newspapers. **Services:** Copying; library open to the public for reference use only. **Remarks:** FAX: (701)780-1123.

★6623★
Grand Haven Area Historical Society - Tri-Cities Museum - Archives/ Library (Hist)
1 N. Harbor Dr.
P.O. Box 234 Phone: (616)842-0700
Grand Haven, MI 49417 John Sanford, Musm.Dir.
Founded: 1959. **Staff:** Prof 3. **Subjects:** Local history - Grand Haven, Spring Lake, Ferrysburg, and North Ottawa County, Michigan. **Special Collections:** Photograph collection. **Holdings:** 100 books; 10 AV programs; manuscripts. **Subscriptions:** 3 journals and other serials. **Services:** Copying; library open to the public by appointment. **Publications:** Packet (newsletter), quarterly - available by subscription; indexes - for sale.

★6624★
Grand Lodge of Ancient Free and Accepted Masons of Kansas - Grand Lodge Masonic Library (Rec)
320 W. 8th St. Phone: (913)234-5518
Topeka, KS 66603 Albert O. Arnold, Jr., Grand Sec.
Staff: 2. **Subjects:** Masonic history. **Special Collections:** McFarland Library of Classics, History, & Novels. **Holdings:** 13,000 books. **Subscriptions:** 69 newspapers. **Services:** Library open to the public with restrictions. **Computerized Information Services:** Internal database.

★6625★
Grand Lodge of Ancient Free and Accepted Masons of Wyoming - Grand Lodge Library (Rec)
1820 Capitol Ave. Phone: (307)635-5666
Cheyenne, WY 82001 Fred B. Sellin, Grand Libn.
Subjects: Masonic history, Grand Lodge proceedings. **Holdings:** 2000 books. **Services:** Copying; library open to the public with restrictions.

★6626★
Grand Lodge of Free and Accepted Masons of California - Library and Museum (Rec)
1111 California St. Phone: (415)776-7000
San Francisco, CA 94108 D. Larry West, Dir.
Founded: 1958. **Staff:** 4. **Subjects:** Freemasonry, freemasonry in California, philosophy, religion, history. **Special Collections:** Papers of Charles Albert Adams, founder of Public Schools Week; archives, clippings, photographs, documents of Masonic historical significance (200 volumes). **Holdings:** 10,000 books; 250 bound periodical volumes; proceedings of worldwide Masonic bodies. **Subscriptions:** 15 journals and other serials; 20 newspapers. **Services:** Copying; library open to the public for reference use only; scholars may use by special request; borrowing privileges reserved for members in good standing only. **Publications:** Books list; cassette tape list; slide, photograph, and film list.

Grand Lodge of Free and Accepted Masons of Indiana
See: **Masonic Library & Museum of Indiana, Inc. - Masonic Library** (9780)

Grand Lodge of Free and Accepted Masons of Pennsylvania - Masonic Temple Library and Museum
See: **Masonic Library and Museum of Pennsylvania** (9781)

★6627★
Grand Lodge of Iowa, A.F. and A.M. - Iowa Masonic Library (Rec)
813 1st Ave., S.E.
Box 279 Phone: (319)365-1438
Cedar Rapids, IA 52406 Paul Wieck, Grand Sec./Libn.
Founded: 1845. **Staff:** Prof 2. **Subjects:** Freemasonry, literature, history, Iowa, biography, religion. **Special Collections:** Robert Burns; Abraham Lincoln; A.E. Waite. **Holdings:** 105,000 books; 7000 bound periodical volumes; pamphlets; clippings; autographs; certificates; documents; microfilm. **Subscriptions:** 250 journals and other serials. **Services:** Interlibrary loan; copying; research assistance for those who request it; library open to the public. **Special Indexes:** Indes Rerum (card). **Remarks:** FAX: (319)365-1439. **Staff:** Keith Arrington, Libn.

★6628★
Grand Lodge of Manitoba, A.F. and A.M. - Masonic Library (Rec)
Masonic Memorial Temple
420 Corydon Ave. Phone: (204)453-7410
Winnipeg, MB, Canada R3L 0N8 Charles A. Merrick, Grand Libn.
Founded: 1896. **Staff:** 6. **Subjects:** Freemasonry. **Holdings:** 2870 books; 58 bound periodical volumes; 86 tape recordings. **Services:** Interlibrary loan; copying; library open to the public.

★6629★
Grand Lodge of Massachusetts, A.F. and A.M. - Library (Rec)
Masonic Temple
186 Tremont St.
Boston, MA 02111 Phone: (617)426-6040
Staff: Prof 1; Other 1. **Subjects:** Freemasonry. **Holdings:** 65,000 volumes; 60 drawers of clippings and pamphlet material. **Subscriptions:** 100 journals and other serials. **Services:** Interlibrary loan; copying; library open to the public for research only. **Publications:** Short list of books on Freemasonry. **Remarks:** FAX: (617)426-6115.

★6630★
Grand Lodge of New York, F. and A.M. - Robert R. Livingston Library (Rec)
71 W. 23rd St. Phone: (212)741-4505
New York, NY 10010 Allan Boudreau, Dir.
Founded: 1781. **Staff:** Prof 3; Other 3. **Subjects:** Freemasonry, New York history. **Special Collections:** Haywood Memorial (1000 items on religion); Abraham Felt Memorial (New York City history); local history; New York State county histories. **Holdings:** 60,000 books; 5000 bound periodical volumes; 100 VF drawers; 500,000 manuscripts; photographs; slides; sound recordings; microfilm; videotapes. **Subscriptions:** 120 journals and other serials. **Services:** Interlibrary loan; copying; library open to the public for scholarly reference use. **Computerized Information Services:** Internal database. **Publications:** Empire State Mason, quarterly; Masonic Philatelist, quarterly; Transactions of the American Lodge of Research, annual. **Special Indexes:** Lodges in New York State; Freemasons in the American Revolution. **Remarks:** A branch library is maintained at 2150 Bleecker St., Utica, NY 13503. FAX: (212)633-2639. **Staff:** William Marquardt, Tours & Visitors Prog.; Aydin Y. Turkmen, Ref.Libn.; Helene Drum, Circ.; Robert C. Wilson, Proc.

★6631★
Grand Lodge of Virginia A.F. & A.M. - Library & Museum (Rec)
P.O. Box 27345 Phone: (804)222-3110
Richmond, VA 23261 Marie M. Barnett, Libn.
Founded: 1797. **Staff:** Prof 1. **Subjects:** Freemasonry - U.S., Virginia, foreign; Masonic proceedings, history, philosophy, art, architecture, customs, law, music, literature. **Special Collections:** Original proceedings of Grand Lodge of Virginia; early proceedings of Grand Lodges in the U.S.; local lodge histories; archives; transactions of AQC, ALR, Norcalore and Miscellanea (137 volumes); rare books (200). **Holdings:** 7600 books; 332 bound periodical volumes; 55 boxes of reports, letters, manuscripts, by-laws; 50 reels of microfilm; documents; photographs. **Subscriptions:** 45 journals and other serials. **Services:** Copying; library open to Masons and persons doing approved research. **Publications:** The Virginia Masonic Herald (newsletter), quarterly - for internal distribution only.

Grand Portage National Monument
See: **U.S. Natl. Park Service** (17724)

★6632★
Grand Rapids Art Museum - McBride Library (Art)
155 N. Division Phone: (616)459-4677
Grand Rapids, MI 49503 Luci King, Lib.Chm.
Founded: 1969. **Subjects:** Art and art history. **Special Collections:** Publicity scrapbooks, 1911-1988. **Holdings:** 5500 volumes; brochures; catalogs; periodicals. **Subscriptions:** 27 journals and other serials. **Services:** Copying; library open to the public for reference use only. **Remarks:** FAX: (616)459-8491.

★6633★
Grand Rapids Baptist College & Seminary - Miller Library (Rel-Phil)
1001 E. Beltline, N.E. Phone: (616)949-5300
Grand Rapids, MI 49505 David S. Slusher
Founded: 1941. **Staff:** Prof 4; Other 4. **Subjects:** Baptist church, religious education, theology. **Holdings:** 91,021 books; 7291 bound periodical volumes; 847 titles on 61,672 microfiche; 1293 films; 627 vertical files; 10 maps; 244 titles on microfilm. **Subscriptions:** 718 journals and other serials; 10 newspapers. **Services:** Interlibrary loan; copying; library open to the public. **Automated Operations:** Computerized acquisitions. **Computerized Information Services:** BRS Information Technologies, OCLC. **Networks/Consortia:** Member of Lakeland Area Library Network (LAKENET), Michigan Library Consortium (MLC). **Remarks:** FAX: (616)949-1883. **Staff:** Lynne Funtik; Gail Atwood; Ray Doerksen.

★6634★
Grand Rapids Junior College - Arthur Andrews Memorial Library - Special Collections (Hist)
140 Ransom, N.E. Phone: (616)771-3870
Grand Rapids, MI 49503 Bernice Whitley, Dir.
Staff: Prof 4; Other 5. **Special Collections:** Lincoln Collection. **Holdings:** 545 books; 315 pamphlets. **Services:** Interlibrary loan; copying; library open to the public. **Computerized Information Services:** DIALOG Information Services, OCLC. **Remarks:** FAX: (616)771-3878.

★6635★
Grand Rapids Law Library (Law)
200 Monroe, N.W., Suite 400 Phone: (616)454-5550
Grand Rapids, MI 49503 Julie K. Gotch, Law Libn.
Founded: 1886. **Staff:** 3. **Subjects:** Law. **Holdings:** 40,000 volumes; 2700 microfiche of 1st Reporter Series; 760 Internal Revenue Service Letter Rulings. **Subscriptions:** 120 journals and other serials. **Services:** Interlibrary loan; library not open to the public. **Computerized Information Services:** WESTLAW, DIALOG Information Services, LEXIS, Hannah Information Systems, VU/TEXT Information Services, Dow Jones News/Retrieval. **Publications:** Newsletter, monthly. **Remarks:** FAX: (616)454-7681.

★6636★
Grand Rapids Press - Reference Library (Publ)
155 Michigan St., N.W. Phone: (616)459-1475
Grand Rapids, MI 49503 Ruth Dryer, Libn.
Founded: 1963. **Staff:** Prof 1; Other 7. **Subjects:** Newspaper reference topics. **Holdings:** 800,000 files of clippings, pictures, veloxes. **Services:** Library open to the public for reference use only. **Remarks:** FAX: (616)459-1502.

★6637★
Grand Rapids Public Library - Foundation Center Regional Collection (Bus-Fin)
60 Library Plaza, N.E. Phone: (616)456-3600
Grand Rapids, MI 49503 Mary Lou Riley
Founded: 1973. **Subjects:** Private foundations. **Holdings:** IRS forms 990PF and 990AR for Michigan foundations on film; all publications of the Foundation Center, New York; Foundation Grants Index: Subjects, on film; complete set of Comsearch printouts (grant records by subject). **Subscriptions:** 3 journals and other serials. **Services:** Collection open to the public for reference use only. **Computerized Information Services:** DIALOG Information Services, BRS Information Technologies. **Publications:** Bibliography. **Remarks:** FAX: (616)456-3602.

★6638★
Grand Rapids Public Library - Furniture Design Collection (Art)
60 Library Plaza, N.E. Phone: (616)456-3600
Grand Rapids, MI 49503 Mary Lou Riley
Founded: 1913. **Subjects:** Furniture history and design - all periods and styles. **Holdings:** 1657 books; 980 bound periodical volumes.**Subscriptions:** 5 journals and other serials. **Services:** Copying; collection open to scholars and furniture designers. **Publications:** Grand Rapids Public Library List of Books on Furniture (1927), supplement (1954). **Remarks:** The collection of furniture books (housed in a separate room) is under the supervision of the Reference Department. Since the city has been commonly recognized as the "Furniture Capital of America," the library has always taken a great interest in books on furniture. FAX: (616)456-3602.

★6639★
Grand Rapids Public Library - May G. Quigley Collection (Hum)
60 Library Plaza, N.E. Phone: (616)456-3603
Grand Rapids, MI 49503 Diantha McBride, Youth Serv.Coord.
Founded: 1954. **Subjects:** Old and rare children's books - American imprints, early 1800s-mid 1900s. **Holdings:** 4000 books; 280 periodicals. **Services:** Collection open to the public for reference use only. **Remarks:** FAX: (616)456-3602.

★6640★
Grand Rapids Public Library - Michigan and Family History Collection (Hist)
60 Library Plaza, N.E. Phone: (616)456-3640
Grand Rapids, MI 49503 Gordon Olson, Hd.
Staff: Prof 3; Other 3. **Subjects:** Grand Rapids, Michigan, and Old Northwest history, genealogy. **Special Collections:** Historical photographs (1 million); manuscripts (400 cubic feet). **Holdings:** 30,000 books. **Subscriptions:** 100 journals and other serials. **Services:** Copying; collection open to the public for reference use only. **Computerized Information Services:** Internal database (historic photographs). **Special Indexes:** Grand Rapids Press newspaper index (online). **Remarks:** FAX: (616)456-3602.

★6641★
Grand Rapids Public Museum - Pictorial Materials Collection (Aud-Vis)
54 Jefferson St., S.E. Phone: (616)456-3966
Grand Rapids, MI 49503 Marilyn Merdzinski, Coll.Mgr.
Subjects: Grand Rapids street scenes, workplaces. **Holdings:** 30,000 photographs, 1850 to present. **Services:** Copying; collection open to the public by appointment. **Remarks:** Alternate telephone number(s): 456-3977. FAX: (616)456-3926.

★6642★
Grand Seminaire de Montreal - Bibliotheque (Rel-Phil)
2065 Sherbrooke, W. Phone: (514)935-1169
Montreal, PQ, Canada H3H 1G6 Paul A. Martin, C.S.C. Libn.
Founded: 1840. **Staff:** Prof 1; Other 4. **Subjects:** Religion, Bible, church law and history, religious biographies, philosophy. **Special Collections:** Migne's Patrologies (378 volumes, in Greek and Latin). **Holdings:** 111,000 books; 18,000 bound periodical volumes. **Subscriptions:** 155 journals and other serials. **Services:** Copying; library open to the public for reference use only. **Special Indexes:** Fichier Liturgique, Mont-Cesar Abbey (card). **Remarks:** FAX: (514)935-5497.

★6643★
Grand Seminaire des Saints Apotres - Bibliotheque (Rel-Phil)
130 Cathedrale
C.P. 430 Phone: (819)563-9934
Sherbrooke, PQ, Canada J1H 5K1 Sr. Therese Roy
Staff: 3. **Subjects:** Theology, religion, pastoral literature. **Special Collections:** J.P. Migne (412 volumes). **Holdings:** 28,000 books; archival materials; manuscripts. **Subscriptions:** 162 journals and other serials. **Services:** Interlibrary loan; copying; library open to the public.

Grand Teton National Park
See: **U.S. Natl. Park Service** (17725)

★6644★
Grand Traverse Pioneer & Historical Society - Library (Hist)
Box 1108 Phone: (616)946-3151
Traverse City, MI 49684 Steve Harold, Archv.
Founded: 1973. **Staff:** Prof 1; Other 1. **Subjects:** History - homesteading, transportation, Cherry Festival; local family history; local lumbering; historical buildings. **Special Collections:** Rare books (30); Campbell-Hobbs Collection (family books; pictures; albums); Roy Steffans Collection; Hannah Rifles (pictures; papers; letters); Spanish American War collection. **Holdings:** 100 books; 15 diaries; 2000 photographs; 300 biographies; 1500 negatives; 1500 clippings; 60 oral history tapes; 20 maps. **Services:** Copying; center open to the public. **Remarks:** Alternate telephone number(s): 723-5531.

★6645★
Grand View College - Archives (Area-Ethnic)
1351 Grandview Phone: (515)263-2951
Des Moines, IA 50316 Rudolf Jensen, Archv.
Founded: 1896. **Staff:** Prof 1. **Subjects:** Danish-American church life, 1871-1962; Danish-American culture; Danish literature, 18th to 20th century. **Holdings:** 3250 volumes. **Subscriptions:** 15 journals and other serials. **Services:** Interlibrary loan; copying; archives open to the public. **Automated Operations:** Computerized cataloging. **Remarks:** FAX: (515)263-2998.

★6646★
Grand View Hospital - Edward F. Burrow Memorial Library (Med)
700 Lawn Ave. Phone: (215)453-4632
Sellersville, PA 18960 Evelyn H. Kuserk, Med.Libn.
Staff: Prof 1. **Subjects:** Medicine, nursing, administration. **Holdings:** 500 volumes; 1000 bound periodical volumes; 2 VF drawers of pamphlets. **Subscriptions:** 80 journals and other serials. **Services:** Interlibrary loan; copying; library open to persons with referrals from medical and professional staff members. **Computerized Information Services:** BRS Information Technologies; electric mail service. Performs searches on fee basis. **Networks/Consortia:** Member of Delaware Valley Information Consortium (DEVIC), BHSL. **Remarks:** FAX: (215)257-2392.

★6647★
Grandview Hospital - Medical Library (Med)
405 Grand Ave. Phone: (513)226-3379
Dayton, OH 45405 Candy Winteregg, Dir.
Founded: 1969. Prof 3; Other 2. **Subjects:** Osteopathy, anesthesia, ophthalmology, orthopedics. **Special Collections:** Osteopathy. **Holdings:** 4500 books; 3500 bound periodical volumes. **Subscriptions:** 406 journals and other serials. **Services:** Interlibrary loan; library not open to the public. **Computerized Information Services:** DIALOG Information Services, BRS Information Technologies. **Networks/Consortia:** Member of National Network of Libraries of Medicine - Greater Midwest Region. **Remarks:** FAX: (513)226-3609. **Staff:** Elaine Olson, Asst.Libn.; Willie Nicholas, Media Asst.; Cynthia Dixon, Proj.Spec.

★6648★
The Granger Collection (Aud-Vis)
381 Park Ave., S. Phone: (212)447-1789
New York, NY 10016 William Glover, Mng. Dir.
Founded: 1964. **Staff:** Prof 6; Other 3. **Subjects:** People, places, things, and events of the past in pictures. **Holdings:** 2000 books; 1000 bound periodical volumes; 6 million prints, photographs, printed ephemera, color transparencies, woodcuts, engravings, movie stills, graphics. **Subscriptions:** 40 journals and other serials. **Services:** Copying; illustrations available to publishers and other professional users of illustrations on a fee basis; open to professional users of illustrations. **Remarks:** FAX: (212)447-1492. **Staff:** Johanna Glover, Mng.Dir.

★6649★
Grant County Historical Society - Library (Hist)
Elbow Lake, MN 56531 Phone: (218)685-4864
Patricia Olson, Cur.
Subjects: Local and state history; archeology. **Holdings:** 1000 books; Grant County, MN newspapers on microfilm; biographies; 100 tape recordings of local people and events. **Subscriptions:** 3 newspapers. **Services:** Copying; library open to the public.

David Grant Medical Center
See: **U.S. Air Force Hospital** (16899)

★6650★
Grant Hospital - Medical Library (Med)
111 S. Grant Ave. Phone: (614)461-3467
Columbus, OH 43215 Nancy E. Cohen, Libn.
Founded: 1961. **Staff:** Prof 1; Other 1. **Subjects:** Medicine, nursing, allied health sciences. **Holdings:** 5500 books; 6500 bound periodical volumes; audiotapes; 9 VF drawers. **Subscriptions:** 250 journals and other serials. **Services:** Interlibrary loan; library not open to the public. **Computerized Information Services:** MEDLINE. **Networks/Consortia:** Member of Central Ohio Hospital Library Consortium. **Remarks:** FAX: (614)224-2960.

★6651★
Grant Hospital of Chicago - Lindon Seed Library (Med)
550 W. Webster Ave. Phone: (312)883-3580
Chicago, IL 60614 Donna Foley, Lib.Dir.
Staff: Prof 1. **Subjects:** Medicine, nursing, hospital administration. **Holdings:** 2400 books; 3600 bound periodical volumes. **Subscriptions:** 388 journals and other serials. **Services:** Interlibrary loan; copying; SDI; library open to the public by special permission. **Computerized Information Services:** MEDLINE, BRS Information Technologies. Performs searches on fee basis. **Networks/Consortia:** Member of Metropolitan Consortium of Chicago, National Network of Libraries of Medicine - Greater Midwest Region, Chicago Library System. **Publications:** Newsletter, quarterly; serial list, annual. **Remarks:** FAX: (312)528-4960.

★6652★
Grant/Jacoby, Inc. - Information Services (Bus-Fin)
737 N. Michigan Ave. Phone: (312)664-2055
Chicago, IL 60611-2606 Carol Gates, Mgr., Info.Serv.
Founded: 1986. **Staff:** Prof 1; Other 1. **Subjects:** Advertising, marketing. **Holdings:** 500 books. **Subscriptions:** 200 journals and other serials; 5 newspapers. **Services:** Interlibrary loan; library not open to the public. **Computerized Information Services:** DIALOG Information Services, NEXIS, DataTimes, VU/TEXT Information Services, Dow Jones News/Retrieval. **Remarks:** FAX: (312)664-3596.

Grant-Kohrs Ranch National Historic Site
See: **U.S. Natl. Park Service** (17726)

Grant Law Library
See: **Scott County Bar Association** (14956)

Grant Library
See: **U.S. Army Post - Fort Carson** (17061)

★6653★
Grant Thornton - Information Center (Bus-Fin)
130 E. Randolph Dr., Suite 700 Phone: (312)856-0200
Chicago, IL 60601 Glory Tenny Kosmatka, Hd.Libn.
Staff: Prof 1; Other 1. **Subjects:** Accounting and auditing, domestic and international tax, consulting. **Holdings:** 1640 monographs. **Subscriptions:** 100 journals and other serials. **Services:** Interlibrary loan; library not open to the public. **Computerized Information Services:** LEXIS, NEXIS, VU/TEXT Information Services, Dow Jones News/Retrieval, InvesText, DataTimes, DIALOG Information Services, MAX. **Remarks:** FAX: (312)565-4719.

U.S. Grant's Home State Historic Site
See: **Illinois (State) Historic Preservation Agency - Galena State Historic Sites** (7697)

★6654★
Graphic Arts Technical Foundation - E.H. Wadewitz Memorial Library (Sci-Engr)
4615 Forbes Ave. Phone: (412)621-6941
Pittsburgh, PA 15213 Timothy D. Rozgonyi, Libn.
Founded: 1944. **Staff:** Prof 1; Other .5. **Subjects:** Printing processes, lithography, paper, ink, graphic design, desktop publishing, packaging, chemistry, physics, environmental control, safety and health, photography. **Special Collections:** Lee Augustine Collection (history of printing; 500 rare volumes). **Holdings:** 4000 books; 3500 bound periodical volumes; 16 VF drawers of pamphlets and trade catalogs; 3 drawers of patents; 31,000 abstracts; 120 videocassettes. **Subscriptions:** 260 journals and other serials; 5 newspapers. **Services:** Copying; document delivery; library open to the public. **Computerized Information Services:** DIALOG Information Services, ORBIT Search Service, WILSONLINE; Graphic Arts Abstracts (internal database). Performs searches on fee basis. **Publications:** Graphic Arts Abstracts, New Books in Review - both sections of GATFWORLD Magazine; Hot Topics (information packets). **Special Indexes:** Indexes to Graphic Arts Abstracts 1972-1987, annual. **Remarks:** FAX: (412)621-3049.

★6655★
Graphic Communications World - Library (Sci-Engr)
P.O. Box 727 Phone: (914)472-3051
Hartsdale, NY 10530-0727 John R. Werner, Pres.
Founded: 1968. **Staff:** Prof 4; Other 5. **Subjects:** Printing and graphic communications technology. **Holdings:** Figures not available. **Subscriptions:** 150 journals and other serials. **Services:** Library open to subscribers. **Publications:** Graphic Communications World.

★6656★
Graphic-Design Austria - Library (Art)
Schonbrunner Strasse 38/8
A-1050 Vienna, Austria Phone: 222 587 6501
Subjects: Graphic design, illustration, photographics, typography, video graphics. **Holdings:** 1000 volumes. **Remarks:** FAX: 222 587-6501. **Also Known As:** Grafik-Design Austria.

★6657★
Gratz College - Tuttleman Library (Area-Ethnic)
Old York Rd. & Melrose Ave. Phone: (215)635-7300
Melrose Park, PA 19126 Sara Spiegel, Dir.
Founded: 1895. **Staff:** Prof 4; Other 4. **Subjects:** Hebraica, Judaica, education, Jewish music, Holocaust. **Special Collections:** Holocaust Oral Archive; Jewish music; rare books in Judaica. **Holdings:** 78,000 books; 2000 bound periodical volumes; 1500 pamphlets; 120 videotapes; 20,000 scores. **Subscriptions:** 45 journals and other serials; 15 newspapers. **Services:** Interlibrary loan; copying; library open to the public. **Automated Operations:** Computerized cataloging and circulation. **Computerized Information Services:** OCLC, RLIN, ALEPH. **Networks/Consortia:** Member of PALINET. **Publications:** New acquisition list. **Remarks:** FAX: (215)635-7320. **Staff:** Marcia Goldberg, Hd.Cat.; Dr. Hayim Sheynin, Cat.; Robin Dichter, Mus.Libn.

Henry S. Graves Memorial Library
See: **Yale University - Yale Forestry Library** (20739)

L.M. Graves Memorial Library
See: **Harding Graduate School of Religion** (6902)

Robert Graves Archives
See: **University of Victoria - McPherson Library - Special Collections** (19489)

★6658★
Gravure Association of America - Library (Art)
1200-A Scottsville Rd. Phone: (716)436-2150
Rochester, NY 14624 Sherry Kasunich, Dir.,
Subjects: Graphic arts technology, gravure processes and equipment, environmental control. **Holdings:** Figures not available. **Services:** Library not open to public.

Bowman Gray School of Medicine
See: **Wake Forest University - Bowman Gray School of Medicine** (19940)

★6659★
Gray, Cary, Ames & Frye - Law Library (Law)
401 B St., Suite 1700 Phone: (619)699-2770
San Diego, CA 92101 June F. Mac Leod, Mgr., Lib.Serv.
Founded: 1927. **Staff:** 6. **Subjects:** Litigation, labor, taxation, trusts and estates, commerce, real estate, immigration, environment, admiralty law, government contracts, business. **Holdings:** 50,000 books; 250 bound periodical volumes. **Subscriptions:** 400 journals and other serials; 7 newspapers. **Services:** Copying; library open to the public by appointment at librarian's discretion. **Automated Operations:** Computerized circulation and inventory. **Computerized Information Services:** LEXIS, NEXIS, DIALOG Information Services, DataTimes, Information America, Legi-Tech, LEGI-SLATE, CompuServe Information Service, DataQuick, Compu-Mark. **Publications:** Law Library Manual; Law Library Newsletter, monthly - for internal distribution only. **Remarks:** FAX: (619)236-1048. Telex: 910-335-1273 G-CAF SDG.

Garland Gray Research Center & Library
See: **Historic Lexington Foundation** (7245)

Gray Herbarium Library
See: **Harvard University - Botany Libraries** (6950)

Joseph and Mae Gray Cultural Learning Center
See: **North Suburban Synagogue Beth El - Joseph and Mae Gray Cultural Learning Center** (11954)

★6660★
Gray Panthers - National Office Library (Soc Sci)
1424 16th St., N.W., No.602 Phone: (202)387-3111
Washington, DC 20036 Charlotte Flynn, Jr., Info.Spec., Natl.Ch.
Staff: Prof 1. **Subjects:** Aging - housing, health care, retirement and alternative work patterns, education, consciousness-raising; intergenerational programs in housing and education. **Holdings:** 15 VF drawers of clippings, pamphlets, and government publications; 100 tapes and cassettes. **Subscriptions:** 100 journals and other serials. **Services:** Copying; library open to the public for reference use only.

★6661★
Gray, Plant, Mooty, Mooty, and Bennett - Law Library (Law)
3400 City Ctr.
33 S. 6th St. Phone: (612)343-2955
Minneapolis, MN 55402 Jill Sonnesyn, Libn.
Staff: 1;Other 2. **Subjects:** Law. **Holdings:** 14,000 books; 300 bound periodical volumes; 35 loose-leaf services; internal brief and memoranda file. **Services:** Interlibrary loan; library not open to the public. **Computerized Information Services:** LEXIS, WESTLAW, NEXIS, DataTimes, DIALOG Information Services. **Remarks:** FAX: (612)333-0066. Telex: 9105762778.

Graymoor Friary Library
See: **Friars of the Atonement** (6164)

★6662★
Grays Harbor County Law Library (Law)
Courthouse, 2nd Fl. Phone: (206)249-5311
Montesano, WA 98563 E. Urquhart, Libn.
Staff: Prof 1; Other 1. **Subjects:** Law. **Holdings:** 15,000 volumes. **Services:** Library open to the public for reference use only.

John A. Graziano Memorial Library
See: **Merritt Peralta Medical Center** (10166)

★6663★
Great Britain - Atomic Energy Authority - AEA Technology - Culham/Harwell Library (Sci-Engr)
Abingdon, Oxfordshire OX14 3DB, England Phone: 235 21840
P.J. Jones, Libn.
Founded: 1962. **Staff:** Prof 3; Other 6. **Subjects:** Plasma physics, nuclear fusion, nuclear research and development, chemistry, chemical technology, computer science and systems, energy, engineering, environmental and mechanical sciences, instrumentation, materials, heat transfer and fluid flow, nondestructive testing, industrial waste and hazardous materials, separation processes, biotechnolgy. **Holdings:** 50,000 bound volumes; 70,000 reports; 265,000 reports in hard copy; 400,000 reports on microfiche; International Nuclear Information System and Energy Database data on magnetic tape. **Subscriptions:** 450 journals and other serials. **Services:** SDI; services available to the public by subscription. **Computerized Information Services:** BULLETIN, RECAP, LIBRIS (internal databases). **Publications:** Culham Laboratory Library Bulletin, weekly - available by subscription; Harwell Information Bulletin, weekly; Information Bulletin of Radioactive Waste, semimonthly; Irradiation of Medical Products Abstract Bulletin, quarterly; UKAEA List of Publications, monthly. **Remarks:** FAX: 235 463682. Telex: 83189 FUSION G. **Formed by the merger of:** Its Culham Laboratory - Plasma Physics Library and Information Service and its Harwell Laboratory - Harwell Library and Information Service to form Culham/Harwell Library.

★6664★
Great Britain - British Library - Humanities and Social Sciences Division - Department of Western Manuscripts (Hum)
Great Russell St. Phone: 71 636-1544
London WC1B 3DG, England Mrs. S.J. Tyacke, Dir. of Spec.Coll.
Subjects: Western manuscripts. **Special Collections:** Music; maps; topographical drawings; seals; ostraca. **Holdings:** 272,826 manuscripts; 4132 microforms. **Services:** Copying; department open to the public with restrictions. **Special Catalogs:** Catalogs of additional manuscripts published to 1955; catalogs of Arundel, Burney, Cotton, Harleian, Hargrave, Lansdowne, Royal, and Stowe Manuscripts. **Special Indexes:** Amalgamated index.

★6665★
Great Britain - British Library - Humanities and Social Sciences Division - Oriental & India Office Collections (Area-Ethnic)
14 Store St.
London WC1E 7DG, England Phone: 71 4127873
Staff: Prof 24; Other 31. **Subjects:** Humanities and social sciences in the languages of Asia and North and Northeast Africa (350 languages or language groups represented). **Special Collections:** Early imprints; rare manuscripts. **Holdings:** 660,000 books; 7500 serial titles; 1100 newspapers; 5000 microforms; 42,000 manuscripts. **Services:** Interlibrary loan; copying; collections open to the public with readers' pass. **Computerized Information Services:** BLAISE Online Services. **Publications:** Newsletter, semiannual; annual report. **Remarks:** FAX: 71 4127858. Department houses the national collections of books and manuscripts from Asia and North and Northeast Africa. **Staff:** G.W. Shaw, Dp.Dir.; A.J. Farrington, Dp.Dir.

★6666★
Great Britain - British Library - Newspaper Library (Publ)
Colindale Avenue Phone: 71 3237353
London NW9 5HE, England Geoffrey Hamilton
Founded: 1903. **Staff:** Prof 4; Other 90. **Subjects:** Newspaper reference topics. **Special Collections:** Burney Collection of early English newspapers (on microfilm); Royal Institute of International Affairs press clippings, 1939 to 1971. **Holdings:** 650,000 bound periodical volumes; 250,000 reels of microfilm. **Subscriptions:** 700 journals and other serials; 2300 newspapers. **Services:** Copying; library open to the public with restrictions. **Publications:** Newsletter, semiannual. **Remarks:** FAX: 71 3237379.

★ 6667 ★
Great Britain - British Library - Philatelic Collections (Rec)
Great Russell St. Phone: 71 3237635
London WC1B 3DG, England David Beech, Hd., Philatelic Coll.
Founded: 1973. **Staff:** Prof 2; Other 1. **Subjects:** Philately, postal history, history of philately. **Special Collections:** Tapling Collection; Supplementary Collection; Campbell-Johnston Collection; Crown Agents Collection; Crown Agents, Philatelic and Security Printing Archive; Board of Inland Revenue Stamping Department Archive; Harrison Collection; Kay Collection; Mosely Collection; Turner Collection; Universal Postal Union Collection; Wilson-Todd Collection; Fitzgerald Collection; Monks Collection of South African airmails; Scott Collection of Great Britain inland airmails; Chinchen Collection of Lundy Island; Ewen Collection of railway letter stamps; Sherborn Collection; Turner Collection of railway letter stamps; Walker Collection of Channel Islands, World War II German Occupation issues; Fletcher Collection; Bojanowicz Collection of Polish postal history 1938-1949; Foreign Office Collection; Model Collection of Germany 1945-1946 provisional issues; Murray Collection; Row Collection of Siam; Postal Authority Pre-issue Publicity Collection; Photograph Collection; A.H. Brunett Hyderabad collection; Libyan Revenue Stamp Collection; Peter Langmead Collection of Private and Post Office Telegraph Stamps of Great Britain and Ireland, 1854-1881. **Holdings:** 20,000 books; 8 million philatelic items. **Services:** Library open to holders of British Library pass. **Special Catalogs:** Catalogue of the Crawford Library of Philatelic Literature at the British Library. **Remarks:** FAX: 71 3237745. Telex: 21462.

★ 6668 ★
Great Britain - British Library - Science Reference and Information Service (Sci-Engr)
25 Southhampton Bldgs.
Chancery Ln. Phone: 71 3237494
London WC2A 1AW, England Alan Gomersall, Dir.
Founded: 1855. **Staff:** Prof 5. **Subjects:** Science, technology, business, patents, and allied subjects. **Holdings:** 32 million patents; 67,000 serial titles; 235,000 monographs. **Subscriptions:** 27,000 journals and other serials. **Services:** Copying; SDI; service open to the public with restrictions. **Computerized Information Services:** Performs searches on fee basis through most major European and U.S. vendors. Contact Person: Chris Baile. **Remarks:** FAX: 71 3237495. Telex: 266959 SCI REF G. Alternate telephone number(s): 71 3237496.

★ 6669 ★
Great Britain - British Library - Science Reference and Information Service (SRIS) - Reading Room
Kean Street Phone: 71 3237288
London WC2B 4AT, England Andrea Reid
Founded: 1973. **Staff:** Prof 4; Other 20. **Subjects:** Medicine, biological sciences, agriculture, geology, astronomy, mathematics. **Holdings:** 100,000 books. **Subscriptions:** 14,000 journals and other serials. **Services:** Copying; library open to the public. **Computerized Information Services:** CD-ROMs. **Publications:** Guide to Libraries and Information Units. **Special Catalogs:** SCICAT catalog (microfiche). **Remarks:** FAX: 71 3237217.

★ 6670 ★
Great Britain - C.A.B. International - Library Services Centre (Agri, Med)
Silwood Park
Buckhurst Rd.
Ascot, Berks. SL5 7TA, England Phone: 344 872747
Founded: 1913. **Staff:** Prof 7; Other 3.5. **Subjects:** Agricultural science, crop protection, pest management, veterinary science. **Holdings:** 30,000 books; 200,000 bound periodical volumes; 10,000 microfiche; 200,000 reels of microfilm. **Subscriptions:** 10,000 journals and other serials. **Services:** Copying; SDI; center not open to the public but services are available by mail on a fee basis. **Computerized Information Services:** DIALOG Information Services, ESA/IRS, CAB Abstracts, DIMDI; Dialcom, Inc., CGNET (electronic mail services). **Publications:** Pest Management: A Directory of Information Sources (3 volumes). **Remarks:** FAX: 344 872901. Telex: 9312102256. Electronic mail address(es): 157:CGI 167 (CGNET); 84CAU016 (Dialcom, Inc.).

★ 6671 ★
Great Britain - Countryside Commission - Library (Env-Cons, Agri)
John Dower House
Crescent Place Phone: 242 521381
Cheltenham GL50 3RA, England J.V. Bacon, Libn.
Founded: 1970. **Staff:** Prof 1.5; Other 2. **Subjects:** Countryside conservation and recreation, agriculture, forestry, town and country planning, tourism, transport. **Holdings:** 18,000 books and reports. **Subscriptions:** 300 journals and other serials; 20 newspapers. **Services:** Interlibrary loan; copying; SDI; library open to the public by appointment for reference use only.

★ 6672 ★
Great Britain - Department of Employment - Careers Service Branch - Careers and Occupational Information Centre (Educ)
Moorfoot Phone: 742 594575
Sheffield S1 4PQ, England Mel Dean, Gen.Mgr.
Subjects: Careers, occupations, professions, training, work conditions, adult career changes, and allied subjects. **Holdings:** 2000 bound volumes; professional literature; university prospectuses. **Subscriptions:** 24 journals and other serials. **Computerized Information Services:** Prestel; produces microDOORS, openDOORS. **Remarks:** FAX: 742 752035. Telex: 547885.

★ 6673 ★
Great Britain - Department of the Environment - Services Headquarters (Env-Cons, Trans)
2 Marsham St. Phone: 071 2764401
London SW1P 3EB, England P. Kirwan, Chf.Libn.
Founded: 1970. **Staff:** Prof 30; Other 36. **Subjects:** Environmental protection, transport, housing, planning, local government. **Special Collections:** Structure plans; Environmental Impact Assessments statements. **Holdings:** 1 million books. **Subscriptions:** 1500 journals and other serials; 15 newspapers. **Services:** Interlibrary loan; library open to the public with restrictions. **Publications:** List of publications - available on request. **Remarks:** FAX: 71 2765713. Library also serves Great Britain - Department of Transport.

★ 6674 ★
Great Britain - Department of Health and Social Security - Library (Soc Sci, Med)
Hannibal House
Elephant and Castle Phone: 71 403 4298
London SE1 6TE, England J.H. Wormald, Prin.Libn.
Founded: 1948. **Staff:** Prof 27; Other 26. **Subjects:** Health services, social security, social services, social policy, safety of medicines, health service buildings. **Holdings:** 200,000 volumes. **Subscriptions:** 2900 journals and other serials; 5 newspapers. **Services:** Interlibrary loan; copying; SDI; library open to research workers on application to librarian. **Automated Operations:** Computerized cataloging, acquisitions, serials, and routing. **Computerized Information Services:** Data-Star, DIALOG Information Services, PFDS Online, Scicon Ltd.; produces DHSS-DATA. **Publications:** Health Service Abstracts, monthly; Social Service Abstracts, monthly; Nursing Research Abstracts, quarterly; Quality Assurance Abstracts, quarterly; Social Security Library Bulletin, monthly; Current Literature on Occupational Pensions, monthly; Health Buildings Library Bulletin, monthly; Selected Abstracts on Occupational Diseases, quarterly; DHSS-DATA Thesaurus - for sale.

★ 6675 ★
Great Britain - Department of Trade and Industry - Export Market Information Centre (Bus-Fin)
Ashdown House
123 Victoria St. Phone: 71 2155444
London SW1E 6RB, England Andrew Lapworth
Staff: Prof 4; Other 5. **Subjects:** Export markets. **Holdings:** Statistical publications; directories; overseas mail order catalogs. **Services:** Copying; library open to the public by appointment. **Computerized Information Services:** TRADSTAT (World Trade Statistics), Data-Star; British Overseas Trade Information Service (BOTIS; internal database). Contact Person: Tass Montgomery, Asst.Libn. **Publications:** DTI Produce Country Profiles; Hints to Exporters; Sector Reports. **Remarks:** Alternate telephone number(s): 71 2155445. FAX: 71 2154231. Telex: 8813148 DIHQG.

Great Britain - Department of Transport - Library
See: **Great Britain - Department of the Environment** (6673)

★6676★
Great Britain - Department of Transport - Transport and Road Research Laboratory - Technical Information and Library Services (Trans)
Old Wokingham Rd. Phone: 344 773131
Crowthorne, Berkshire RG11 6AU, England Mrs. B.A. Crofts, Hd.
Founded: 1933. **Staff:** Prof 8. **Subjects:** Roads - structures, design, and construction; road safety; traffic control; road research; road transportation; transport planning; sociological and environmental effects. **Holdings:** 70,000 volumes. **Subscriptions:** 600 journals and other serials. **Services:** SDI; current awareness; some services restricted to the United Kingdom transportation and road community. **Automated Operations:** Computerized cataloging. **Computerized Information Services:** Produces International Road Research Documentation (IRRD) database; Telecom Gold (electronic mail service). **Publications:** Accessions List; library leaflet. **Special Catalogs:** Film and video catalogue. **Remarks:** FAX: 344 770193. Telex: 848272 TRUCR G. Electronic mail address(es): 72:MAG100078 (Telecom Gold).

★6677★
Great Britain - Driver and Vehicle Licensing Centre - DULA Library (Trans)
Longview Road Phone: 792782712
Swansea, Morriston SA6 7JL, England Julie Stevenson
Founded: 1973. **Staff:** Prof 1; Other 1. **Subjects:** Transport, management, road safety. **Holdings:** 5000 books; microfiche. **Subscriptions:** 100 journals and other serials; 2 newspapers. **Services:** Interlibrary loan; library not open to the public. **Computerized Information Services:** POLIS, TRANSDOC, MEDLINE, IRRD. Contact Person: Jan Gore. **Publications:** Library Bulletin.

★6678★
Great Britain - Home Office Forensic Science Service - Central Research and Support Establishment - Information Services Division (Sci-Engr)
Aldermaston
Reading, Berkshire RG7 4PN, Phone: 734 814100
England Dr. L.A. King, Hd., Info.Serv.Div.
Founded: 1967. **Staff:** Prof 8. **Subjects:** Forensic science - explosives, paint, glass, plastics, firearms, pathology, body fluids, fingerprints, plant materials, hairs, fibers, drugs of abuse, serology, immunology, electrophoresis, toxicology, document examination, and allied subjects. **Holdings:** 4000 volumes; reports. **Subscriptions:** 250 journals and other serials. **Services:** Current awareness; division open on a limited basis to forensic community. **Computerized Information Services:** Forensic Science Database (FORS; internal database). **Remarks:** FAX: 734 815490. The Division provides information services in the area of forensic sciences to six Home Office forensic laboratories and to the Metropolitan Police Laboratory, as well as to laboratories in Northern Ireland and Scotland.

★6679★
Great Britain - House of Commons - Department of the Library (Law, Soc Sci)
1 Derby Gate, Westminster
London SW1A 2DG, England Phone: 71 2194272
Founded: 1818. **Staff:** 192. **Subjects:** United Kingdom - politics, government, administration, trade, and foreign relations. **Holdings:** 150,000 bound volumes; United Kingdom, EEC, and UN official publications. **Subscriptions:** 1500 journals and other serials. **Services:** Library open to Members of Parliament only; Public Information Office offers telephone and postal reference service to the public. **Computerized Information Services:** Produces Parliamentary On-Line Information System (POLIS); Telecom Gold, Dialcom, Inc. (electronic mail services). **Publications:** House of Commons Library Documents, irregular; House of Commons Weekly Information Bulletin, produced when Parliament is in session. **Remarks:** Telex: 916318. Electronic mail address(es): 76:LRF001 (Telecom Gold); 76:LRF001 (Dialcom, Inc.). **Staff:** Miss J.B. Tanfield, Dp.Libn.; Dr. C.C. Pond, Hd. of Pub.Info.Off.; D.J.T. Englefield, Libn.

★6680★
Great Britain - House of Lords - Library and Information Centre (Law)
London SW1A OPW, England Phone: 71 219 5242
Roger Morgan, Libn.
Founded: 1826. **Staff:** 17. **Subjects:** British Parliament, law, and allied subjects. **Holdings:** 100,000 bound volumes; private files and press clippings in microform. **Subscriptions:** 600 journals and other serials. **Services:** Library not open to the public. **Computerized Information Services:** BLAISE, DIALOG Information Services, Reuter TEXTLINE, NEXIS, LEXIS, FT PROFILE, Prestel, CEEFAX, ORACLE; produces Parliamentary On-line Information System (POLIS). **Remarks:** The Library and Information Centre provides the House of Lords with library and information services that include maintenance of a joint Parliamentary computer-readable index to the library's holdings and Parliamentary proceedings.

★6681★
Great Britain - Ministry of Agriculture, Fisheries and Food - Central Science Laboratory Harpenden - Fisheries and Food Library (Agri)
Hatching Green Phone: 582 715241
Harpenden, Hertfordshire AL5 2BD, England Ms. J.M. Bailey
Founded: 1916. **Staff:** Prof 2; Other 2. **Subjects:** Plant health, agriculture - pesticides, entomology, plant pathology. **Holdings:** 15,000 books; 60,000 bound periodical volumes; 8000 reports; microfiche; microfilm; 20,000 photographs. **Subscriptions:** 750 journals and other serials; 5 newspapers. **Services:** Interlibrary loan; copying; SDI; library open to the public by appointment. **Computerized Information Services:** DIALOG Information Services, ESA/IRS, DIMDI; STATUS (internal database). **Remarks:** FAX: 582 762178. Telex: 826363.

★6682★
Great Britain - Ministry of Agriculture, Fisheries and Food - Fisheries Laboratory - Library (Agri)
Pakefield Rd Phone: 502 562244
Lowestoft, Suffolk NR33 OHT, England Derek Bate
Staff: Prof 1; Other 4. **Subjects:** Fisheries research, aquatic pollution. **Holdings:** 5000 books; 2000 microfiche; bound periodical volumes; reports; slide sets; videotapes. **Subscriptions:** 1000 journals and other serials. **Services:** Interlibrary loan; copying; library open to the public with restrictions. **Computerized Information Services:** DIALOG Information Services, DialTech; FISHLAB (internal database); SCIENCEnet (electronic mail service). **Publications:** Lists of staff publications, quarterly. **Remarks:** FAX: 502 513865. Telex: 97470. Electronic mail address(es): MAFF.LOWESTOFT (SCIENCEnet).

★6683★
Great Britain - Ministry of Defence - Whitehall Library (Mil)
3-5 Great Scotland Yard
London SW1A 2HW, England Phone: 71 2184445
Founded: 1700. **Staff:** Prof 21; Other 30. **Subjects:** Defense, management, technology, military and naval history, public administration, politics. **Special Collections:** Historical collections on the three services: Army, including a collection of material on the history of its regiments (12,000 volumes); Navy (20,000 volumes); RAF (5000 volumes). **Holdings:** 850,000 books; 200 bound periodical volumes; 50,000 reports; 70 microfiche and reels of microfilm. **Subscriptions:** 2000 journals and other serials; 7 newspapers. **Services:** Interlibrary loan; copying; library open to the public upon prior written application. **Computerized Information Services:** DIALOG Information Services, ESA/IRS, FT PROFILE, POLIS (Parliamentary On-Line Information System); CD-ROMs. **Publications:** Library Bulletin; New Books and Articles (limited distribution). **Remarks:** FAX: 71 2185413.

★6684★
Great Britain - Ministry of Defence (Navy) - Hydrographic Office - Library (Trans, Sci-Engr, Geog-Map)
Taunton, Somerset TA1 2DN, Phone: 283 337900
England David Dixey, Hd., Hydrographic Data Ctr.
Founded: 1950. **Staff:** Prof 1.5; Other 1. **Subjects:** Cartography, sea surveying, oceanography, navigation, geodesy. **Holdings:** 12,000 books; 1000 bound periodical volumes. **Subscriptions:** 220 journals and other serials; 3 newspapers. **Services:** Interlibrary loan; copying; library open to the public by appointment. **Publications:** Accessions Lists, 4/year. **Remarks:** FAX: 283 284077. Telex: 46274.

★6685★
Great Britain - National Library for the Blind (Aud-Vis)
Cromwell Rd.
Bredbury Phone: 61 4941531
Stockport, Cheshire SK6 2SG, England Allan Leach, Dir.-Gen.
Founded: 1882. **Staff:** 55. **Subjects:** General collection. **Special Collections:** Early tactile books (100); braille music (6000 pieces). **Holdings:** 400,000 volumes in braille, moon type, and large print. **Subscriptions:** 18 braille journals; 4 moon type journals. **Services:** Free and postage-free lending service to those who need materials (available through U.K. public libraries). **Publications:** NLB Bulletin; annual report; Braille Made Easy - as Pye; Braille Music: an International Survey. **Remarks:** FAX: 61 4066728. **Staff:** Jean Shepherd; Audrey Bramwell; Ann Shaw; Rosamund Willis-Fear.

★6686★
Great Britain - National Maritime Museum - Library (Hist)
Greenwich Phone: 81 8584422
London SE10 9NF, England Mary Shephard, B.A.
Founded: 1934. **Staff:** Prof 4; Other 5. **Subjects:** Naval and mercantile history, war- and mechant ships, shipwrecks, voyages, geneology. **Special Collections:** Gosse Piracy collection. **Holdings:** 100,000 books; 20,000 bound periodical volumes; 5280 feet of archive shelving; 2500 reels of microfilm; 5000 rare books. **Subscriptions:** 500 journals and other serials; 5 newspapers. **Services:** Copying; library open to the public. **Automated Operations:** Computerized cataloging. **Special Catalogs:** Printed library catalogue and guide to manuscripts. **Remarks:** FAX: 81 3126632.

★6687★
Great Britain - National Meteorological Library & Archive (Sci-Engr)
London Rd. Phone: 344 856694
Bracknell, Berkshire RG12 2SZ, England Maurice E. Crewe, Libn.
Founded: 1855. **Staff:** Prof 9; Other 6. **Subjects:** Meteorology, climatology, hydrometeorology, oceanology, fluid dynamics, allied atmospheric sciences. **Special Collections:** Rare and historic meteorological literature. **Holdings:** 150,000 books; 50,000 pamphlets; 30,000 photographs; 30,000 microfiche. **Subscriptions:** 450 journals and other serials; 9 newspapers. **Services:** Interlibrary loan; copying (both limited); library open to the public. **Automated Operations:** Computerized public access catalog, cataloging, and acquisitions. **Computerized Information Services:** ESA/IRS; MOLARS (Meteorological Office Library Accessions Retrieval System; internal database). **Publications:** Accessions List, monthly. **Special Catalogs:** Library Union Catalogue of Rare Books (published with the Royal Meteorological Society). **Remarks:** FAX: 344 854840. Telex: 849801. **Staff:** R. Anderson-Jones, Classifier; N.S. Harrison, Classifier.

★6688★
Great Britain - National Radiological Protection Board - Library (Sci-Engr)
Chilton Phone: 235 831600
Oxfordshire OX11 0RQ, England David Perry
Founded: 1970. **Staff:** Prof 1; Other 2. **Subjects:** Radiological protection, dosimetry, environmental modelling, non-ionizing radiation, hazard assessment. **Special Collections:** ICRP Publications; Safety Series collection. **Holdings:** 30,000 books; 20,000 reports. **Subscriptions:** 300 journals and other serials; 5 newspapers. **Services:** Interlibrary loan; copying; SDI; library open to the public by appointment. **Computerized Information Services:** DIALOG Information Services, ESA/IRS; internal database. **Publications:** List of publications - available on request. **Remarks:** FAX: 235 833891. Telex: 837124.

★6689★
Great Britain - Office of Population Censuses and Surveys - Library (Soc Sci)
St. Catherines House
10 Kingsway Phone: 71 2420262
London WC2B 6JP, England Sarah Whiting, Libn.
Staff: Prof 3; Other 3. **Subjects:** Vital statistics, census data, demography, social sciences. **Special Collections:** Foreign Statistical Publications collection. **Holdings:** 50,000 books; 10,000 microfiche; 1000 reels of microfilm. **Subscriptions:** 300 journals and other serials. **Services:** Interlibrary loan; library open to the public by appointment. **Computerized Information Services:** CAIRS (internal database). **Remarks:** FAX: 71 4301779.

★6690★
Great Britain - Overseas Development Administration - Abercrombie House - Library (Soc Sci)
Eaglesham Road
East Kilbride Phone: 41 0355843246
Glasgow G75 8EA, Scotland Richard Lewis
Founded: 1960. **Staff:** Prof 6.5; Other 5.5. **Subjects:** Economic development, social development, third-world countries. **Special Collections:** Statistics collection. **Holdings:** 40,000 books; 40,000 reports; 30,000 microfiche. **Subscriptions:** 450 journals and other serials; 20 newspapers. **Services:** Interlibrary loan; copying; SDI; library open to the public by appointment. **Publications:** New books lists; statistical publications lists. **Special Indexes:** Development Index (online). **Remarks:** 41 0355844099.

★6691★
Great Britain - Overseas Development Administration - Natural Resources Institute - NRI Library (Agri)
Central Ave.
Chatham Maritime Phone: 634 880088
Chatham, Kent ME4 4TE, England J.A. Wright, Chf.Libn.
Founded: 1895. **Staff:** 19. **Subjects:** Tropical agriculture. **Holdings:** 40,000 books; 90,000 annual reports and technical reports. **Subscriptions:** 2500 journals and other serials. **Services:** SDI; current awareness; library responds to overseas enquiries. **Automated Operations:** Computerized cataloging, acquisitions, circulation, indexing, and SDI. **Computerized Information Services:** Produces TRAIS (Tropical Agriculture Information Services). **Publications:** Library Accessions Bulletin, monthly. **Remarks:** FAX: 634 880066; 634 880077. Telex: 634 263907; 634 263908. Institute assists developing countries in deriving greater benefit from their plant and animal resources; library staff advises overseas libraries in the improvement of facilities and services. **Formerly:** Overseas Development Natural Resources Institute.

Great Britain - Royal Aeronautical Society
See: **Royal Aeronautical Society** (14093)

Great Britain - Royal Botanic Gardens
See: **Royal Botanic Gardens** (14103)

Great Britain - Science Engineering Research Council - Royal Greenwich Observatory
See: **Royal Greenwich Observatory - Library** (14119)

Great Britain - Science Museum
See: **Science Museum** (14939)

★6692★
Great Falls Clinic - Library
1400 29th St., S.
Great Falls, MT 59405
Defunct. Holdings absorbed by Montana Deaconess Medical Center/ Montana State University - Health Science Library.

★6693★
Great Falls Genealogy Society - Library (Hist)
1400 1st Ave., N., Rm. 30
Great Falls, MT 59401 Ann Fox, Libn.
Founded: 1975. **Staff:** 30. **Subjects:** Family and local history. **Special Collections:** Census (258 reels of microfilm); War of the Rebellion (official army and navy records); Boxeman and Billings, MT newspapers (75 bound volumes); city directories, 1906 to present; official records of Army and Navy for the War of the Rebellion. **Holdings:** 2700 books; 500 unbound periodicals; Great Falls, MT obituary file, late 1800s to present; Cascade County marriage file, 1887-1910. **Subscriptions:** 98 genealogy society exchanges. **Services:** Library open to the public for reference use only. **Publications:** Treasure State Lines, quarterly - to members and on exchange. **Special Indexes:** Obituary file index; cemetery indexes; marriages index.

Great Lakes Basin Commission - Great Lakes Basin Library
See: **International Joint Commission - Great Lakes Regional Office Library** (8137)

★6694★
Great Lakes Bible College - Louis M. Detro Memorial Library (Rel-Phil)
6211 W. Wilson Hwy. Phone: (517)321-0242
Lansing, MI 48917 Arthur L. Grove, Libn.
Founded: 1949. **Staff:** Prof 1; Other 9. **Subjects:** Religion, Bible, music, history. **Special Collections:** C.S. Lewis. **Holdings:** 27,151 books; 3252 periodical volumes; 6278 other cataloged items. **Subscriptions:** 234 journals and other serials. **Services:** Interlibrary loan; library open to the public on a fee basis. **Computerized Information Services:** OCLC. **Networks/Consortia:** Member of Michigan Library Consortium (MLC). **Remarks:** FAX: (517)321-5902.

Great Lakes Cartographic Resource Centre
See: **University of Western Ontario - Department of Geography** (19557)

★6695★
Great Lakes Colleges Association - Philadelphia Center (Plan)
1227-29 Walnut St., 3rd/4th Fl.
Philadelphia, PA 19107 Phone: (215)574-9490
Founded: 1969. **Staff:** Prof 1; Other 2. **Subjects:** Urban studies, experiential education, Philadelphia studies, art, religion and philosophy, economics, finance, literature. **Special Collections:** Philadelphia Files. **Holdings:** 3200 books. **Subscriptions:** 29 journals and other serials. **Services:** Interlibrary loan; library not open to the public. **Computerized Information Services:** CompuServe Information Service, DIALOG Information Services. **Formerly:** Its Emma B. Fisher Memorial Library.

★6696★
Great Lakes Commission - Library (Env-Cons)
The Argus II Bldg.
400 S. 4th St.
Ann Arbor, MI 48103 Phone: (313)665-9135
Subjects: Water and related land resources of the Great Lakes Basin - development, use, protection. **Holdings:** 4000 volumes; reports; journals; articles; statistics. **Computerized Information Services:** Great Lakes Regional Water Use Data Base and Repository. **Remarks:** FAX: (313)665-4370.

★6697★
Great Lakes Historical Society - Clarence Metcalf Research Library (Hist)
480 Main St. Phone: (216)967-3467
Vermilion, OH 44089 A.B. Cook, III
Founded: 1953. **Staff:** 8. **Subjects:** Great Lakes - history, shipbuilding, shipwrecks, shipping records, battle of Lake Erie in 1812, lighthouses, lifesaving service, ship logbooks. **Special Collections:** Great Lakes Historical Society Photo Collection; St. Clair Collection; Beeson's, Greens, Red Book, Merchant Vessels of the U.S., and Lloyd's Registers Marine Directories. **Holdings:** 2500 books; 10,000 photographs; records of shipping firms; logbooks. **Services:** Library open to members only. **Publications:** Inland Seas (journal), quarterly - to society members; Chadburn Society newsletter. **Remarks:** FAX: (216)967-1519.

Great Lakes Information Service
See: **Center for the Great Lakes** (3243)

★6698★
Great Lakes Maritime Institute - Dossin Great Lakes Museum Information Center (Hist)
Belle Isle Phone: (313)267-6440
Detroit, MI 48207 John F. Polacsek, Cur.
Founded: 1960. **Staff:** Prof 2. **Subjects:** Great Lakes history, ship history, records and plans. **Holdings:** Logs, corporate records, clippings, advertising, lithographs, paintings of Great Lakes maritime subjects; 200 linear feet of miscellanea; 50,000 prints and negatives. **Services:** Inquiries answered if accompanied by self-addressed stamped envelope; center open to the public by appointment. **Publications:** Telescope Magazine (Great Lakes history and current events), bimonthly - by subscription.

★6699★
Great Lakes Research Corporation - Research Library (Sci-Engr)
Box 1031 Phone: (615)543-3111
Elizabethton, TN 37643 Loretta Colbaugh, Libn.
Founded: 1962. **Staff:** Prof 1. **Subjects:** Carbon and graphite technology. **Holdings:** 5250 books; 7000 bound periodical volumes; 4860 government publications; 42 VF drawers of reports, reprints, pamphlets. **Subscriptions:** 300 journals and other serials. **Services:** Interlibrary loan; library not open to the public. **Remarks:** FAX: (615)542-1717.

★6700★
Great Plains Black Museum - Library (Area-Ethnic)
2213 Lake St. Phone: (402)345-2212
Omaha, NE 68110 Bertha Calloway, Founder/Dir.
Founded: 1976. **Staff:** Prof 2; Other 10. **Subjects:** Blacks in Nebraska and the Great Plains. **Special Collections:** Black women; cowboys; Homesteaders Room. **Holdings:** 2000 books; photographs; archival materials; quilts; military items; rare books. **Subscriptions:** 12 journals and other serials. **Services:** Library open to the public for reference use only. **Staff:** Alice Station, Geneal.; Vickie Parks, Libn.; Dr. Jennie Rucker, Cons.

Great Plains Research Library and Archives
See: **Museum of the Great Plains** (10901)

★6701★
Great Plains Zoo & Museum - Reference Library (Biol Sci)
805 S. Kiwanis Ave. Phone: (605)339-7059
Sioux Falls, SD 57104-3714 Edward Asper, Exec.Dir.
Founded: 1963. **Staff:** 1. **Subjects:** Natural history, mammals, management of wild animals in captivity. **Special Collections:** The Royal Natural History; International Zoo Yearbooks (25 volumes); Grizimek's Animal Life Encyclopedia (14 volumes). **Holdings:** 200 books. **Subscriptions:** 5 journals and other serials. **Services:** Library open to the public for reference use only. **Remarks:** Library located at 805 S. Kiwanis Ave., Sioux Falls, SD. FAX: (605)338-8340.

Great Smoky Mountains National Park
See: **U.S. Natl. Park Service - Great Smoky Mountains Natl. Park** (17727)

★6702★
Great-West Life Assurance Company - Research and Reference Library (Bus-Fin)
60 Osborne St., N. Phone: (204)946-8906
Winnipeg, MB, Canada R3C 3A5 Dale W. Nelson, Corp.Libn.
Founded: 1928. **Staff:** 3. **Subjects:** Life and health insurance, insurance law, economics, business management, accounting, taxation. **Holdings:** 7,000 volumes. **Subscriptions:** 75 journals and other serials. **Services:** Interlibrary loan; library open to the public with restrictions. **Computerized Information Services:** Info Globe, Infomart Online, DIALOG Information Services, Dun & Bradstreet Business Credit Services, GIN International Database, CAN/OLE, DOBIS Canadian Online Library System; Envoy 100 (electronic mail service). **Remarks:** FAX: (204)946-7838. Electronic mail address(es): D.NELSON (Envoy 100).

★6703★
Greater Baltimore Medical Center - John E. Savage Medical Library (Med)
6701 N. Charles St. Phone: (301)828-2530
Baltimore, MD 21204 Deborah Thomas-Peters, Lib. & AV Serv.Mgr.
Founded: 1968. **Staff:** Prof 1; Other 1.75. **Subjects:** Medicine, nursing. **Holdings:** 1500 books; 12,000 bound periodical volumes; 200 AV programs. **Subscriptions:** 165 journals and other serials. **Services:** Interlibrary loan; library not open to the public. **Computerized Information Services:** MEDLARS, BRS/COLLEAGUE; CD-ROM (MEDLINE Knowledge Finder). **Networks/Consortia:** Member of National Network of Libraries of Medicine - Southeastern/Atlantic Region. **Staff:** Lisa Michael, AV Spec.; Joan Meo, AV Spec.

★6704★
Greater Cincinnati Chamber of Commerce - Research Data Center (Bus-Fin)
300 Carew Tower
441 Vine St. Phone: (513)579-3181
Cincinnati, OH 45202 Marge Rotte, Mgr.
Staff: Prof 4. **Subjects:** Economics, marketing, census, labor. **Special Collections:** Cinfax (200 fact sheets on Cincinnati). **Holdings:** 500 books; 300 bound periodical volumes; 400 files. **Subscriptions:** 18 journals and other serials. **Services:** Library not open to the public. **Computerized Information Services:** Internal databases. **Special Indexes:** Cinfax Index (index of available demographic materials), annual. **Remarks:** FAX: (513)579-3102. Alternate telephone number(s): (513)579-3136. **Staff:** Marge Limke, Asst.Mgr.; Judy Sinnard, Info.Spec.; Mary Jo Hren, Info.Spec.

Greater Cleveland Hospital Association Library
See: **Center for Health Affairs** (3244)

★6705★
Greater Egypt Regional Planning and Development Commission - Library-Research Center (Plan)
P.O. Box 3160
Carbondale, IL 62902 Phone: (618)549-3306
Founded: 1961. **Subjects:** Regional planning, social-economic development, criminal justice planning, water resources, zoning, housing. **Special Collections:** Local government and regional planning (64 VF drawers); commission's publications collection (700 reports and special studies); federal government publications. **Holdings:** 3500 volumes; 322 other cataloged items; 1500 county, municipality, and regional maps; 377 documents on microfiche; 193 sets of slides, filmstrips, videotapes. **Subscriptions:** 12 journals and other serials; 6 newspapers. **Services:** Center open to the public at librarian's discretion for reference use only. **Remarks:** FAX: (618)549-3309.

★6706★
Greater Los Angeles Zoo Association - Library (Biol Sci)
Andrew Norman Education Center
5333 Zoo Dr. Phone: (213)664-1100
Los Angeles, CA 90027-1498 Barbara McKinzie-Slater, Libn.
Founded: 1964. **Staff:** Prof 1; Other 5. **Subjects:** Mammals, birds, reptiles, amphibians, zoology, animal behavior. **Holdings:** 3000 books. **Subscriptions:** 85 journals and other serials. **Services:** Library open to zoo staff. **Computerized Information Services:** Internal database. **Remarks:** FAX: (213)662-6879. **Also Known As:** GLAZA.

★6707★
Greater Madison Chamber of Commerce - Materials Reference Library (Bus-Fin)
Box 71 Phone: (608)256-8348
Madison, WI 53701 Robert Brennan, Pres.
Staff: 10. **Subjects:** Madison and Dane County. **Holdings:** Telephone and city directories of selected major U.S. cities; census tract data; city and county demographic data; small business operation information. **Services:** Copying; library open to the public. **Publications:** Greater Madison, monthly; Statistical Bulletin, semimonthly; Issues & Viewpoint (legislative information), monthly.

★6708★
Greater Niagara General Hospital - Health Sciences Library (Med)
P.O. Box 1018 Phone: (416)358-0171
Niagara Falls, ON, Canada L2E 6X2 John Dunn, Lib.Techn.
Staff: 1. **Subjects:** Medicine, nursing, and allied health sciences. **Holdings:** 1000 books. **Subscriptions:** 176 journals and other serials. **Services:** Interlibrary loan; library not open to the public. **Computerized Information Services:** MEDLARS; internal databases. **Remarks:** FAX: (416)358-8435.

★6709★
Greater Portland Landmarks, Inc. - Frances W. Peabody Research Library (Hist)
165 State St. Phone: (207)744-5561
Portland, ME 04101 Martha B. Deprez, Exec.Dir.
Founded: 1971. **Subjects:** Architecture - American, Maine, New England, interior; preservation - historic, techniques, history; Portland area historic buildings. **Special Collections:** Architecture notebooks (depicting architectural style details of Maine homes as compared with homes in other northeast areas); Scientific American Building Monthly (20 volumes; 1885-1905); Biography of Architects in Maine. **Holdings:** 2000 books; maps; photographs; prints; slides. **Subscriptions:** 20 journals and other serials. **Services:** Copying; library open to the public for reference use only on limited schedule. **Publications:** Brochure. **Remarks:** Is said to be the largest such collection north of Boston.

★6710★
Greater Southeast Community Hospital - Lura Health Sciences Library (Med)
1310 Southern Ave., S.E. Phone: (202)574-6793
Washington, DC 20032 Sally F. Reyes, Libn.
Staff: Prof 1. **Subjects:** Medicine, nursing, and allied health sciences; general management. **Special Collections:** Patient Education Center (100 pamphlet and booklet titles on various diseases). **Holdings:** 2335 books; AV tapes (756 titles). **Subscriptions:** 197 journals and other serials. **Services:** Interlibrary loan; copying; library open to the public for reference use only. **Computerized Information Services:** MEDLINE. Performs searches. **Networks/Consortia:** Member of Maryland and D.C. Consortium of Resource Sharing (MADCORS), District of Columbia Health Sciences Information Network (DOCHSIN).

★6711★
Greater Vancouver Regional District - Library (Plan)
4330 Kingsway, 19th Fl. Phone: (604)432-6335
Burnaby, BC, Canada V5H 4G8 Frances Christopherson, Libn.
Founded: 1970. **Staff:** Prof 1; Other 1. **Subjects:** Regional and urban development. **Holdings:** 15,000 books; 120 feet of unbound periodicals; 60 feet of statistics; 12 VF drawers of pamphlets; 4 shelves of legislative material; 26 VF drawers of publications of the district and its predecessor; annual reports. **Subscriptions:** 500 journals and other serials; 40 newspapers. **Services:** Interlibrary loan; copying; library open to the public with restrictions on loans. **Automated Operations:** Computerized public access catalog, acquisitions, serials, and circulation. **Computerized Information Services:** DIALOG Information Services, CAN/OLE. **Publications:** Accessions list, monthly; list of member municipality planning reports, quarterly; inventory of major GVRD publications; bibliographies - available on request. **Remarks:** FAX: (604)432-6399.

★6712★
Greater Victoria Hospital Society - Victoria Medical & Hospital Libraries (Med)
1900 Fort St. Phone: (604)595-9723
Victoria, BC, Canada V8R 1J8 Cliff Cornish, Mgr.
Founded: 1986. **Staff:** Prof 1.7; Other 3. **Subjects:** Clinical medicine, nursing, rehabilitation, long term care, hospital administration. **Special Collections:** History of medicine. **Holdings:** 10,000 books; 10,000 bound periodical volumes; 800 AV programs. **Subscriptions:** 553 journals and other serials. **Services:** Interlibrary loan; copying; SDI; libraries open to the public with restrictions. **Automated Operations:** Computerized cataloging. **Computerized Information Services:** DIALOG Information Services, MEDLARS; Envoy 100 (electronic mail service). Performs searches on fee basis. **Publications:** G.V.H.S. Library Newsletter, quarterly - to physicians and hospital staff. **Special Catalogs:** Rare book list. **Remarks:** Alternate telephone number(s): 595-9612. FAX: (604)595-1525. Electronic mail address(es): ROY.JUB (Envoy 100). Maintains branch libraries at Royal Jubilee Hospital, Victoria General Hospital, Gorge Road Hospital, and Fairfield Health Centre Gerontology Library. **Staff:** Wendy Evanoff, Libn.

★6713★
Greater West Bloomfield Historical Society - Museum Library (Hist)
3951 Orchard Lake Rd.
P.O. Box 240514 Phone: (313)851-1440
Orchard Lake, MI 48324 J.D. Laarman, Pres.
Founded: 1986. **Subjects:** Local history - West Bloomfield Township, Orchard Lake, Apple Island; Chief Pontiac. **Special Collections:** Lakeland Newspaper; Michigan Pioneer Collection; agricultural encyclopedia; school year books. **Holdings:** 150 books; 30 linear feet of documents; 70 AV programs; 100 manuscripts. **Subscriptions:** 3 journals and other serials. **Services:** Library open to the public with restrictions. **Publications:** Newsletters.

★6714★
Conrad Grebel College - Library/Archives (Rel-Phil)
Waterloo, ON, Canada N2L 3G6 Phone: (519)885-0220
Samuel Steiner, Libn. & Archv.
Founded: 1964. **Staff:** Prof 1; Other 3. **Subjects:** Anabaptist/Mennonite history, peace studies. **Special Collections:** Mennonite Archives of Ontario (300 linear feet; 6600 feet on microfilm). **Holdings:** 30,000 books; 2000 bound periodical volumes; 5500 microforms; 10 linear feet of clipping files; 400 oral history cassettes. **Subscriptions:** 200 journals and other serials; 10 newspapers. **Services:** Interlibrary loan; copying; library open to the public; archives open to the public by appointment. **Automated Operations:** Computerized public access catalog and circulation. **Remarks:** FAX: (519)885-0014.

Greco-Romain Museum
See: **Organization of Egyptian Antiquities - Greco-Romain Museum** (12562)

Greece - Ministry of Justice - Hellenic Institute of International and Foreign Law
See: **Hellenic Institute of International and Foreign Law** (7118)

★6715★
Greece - National Library of Greece (Area-Ethnic, Hist)
Odos Venizelou 32 Phone: 1 3614413
GR-106 79 Athens, Greece Dr. Panayotis G. Nicolopoulos, Gen.Dir.
Founded: 1829. **Staff:** Prof 28; Other 50. **Subjects:** Greece - culture, history, general. **Special Collections:** 18th century and Revolution of 1821 (200,000 items); book manuscripts (5300); 16th century book collection (2500); incunabula (130 items). **Holdings:** 1 million books; 1.5 million bound periodical volumes; 200,000 archival documents; 5000 reels of microfilm. **Subscriptions:** 400 journals and other serials. **Services:** Copying; library open to the public. **Publications:** National Bibliography. **Remarks:** FAX: 1 3608495.

★6716★
Greeley and Hansen - Library (Env-Cons)
100 S. Wacker Dr., Suite 1400 Phone: (312)558-9000
Chicago, IL 60606-4003 Marilyn T. Cichon
Founded: 1914. **Staff:** Prof 1; Other 1. **Subjects:** Wastewater and water treatment, solid waste disposal, sewerage, flood control, hydraulics. **Holdings:** 8000 books; 300 bound periodical volumes; 14,000 internal reports and drawings; 30,000 microforms; 700 municipal annual reports. **Subscriptions:** 275 journals and other serials. **Services:** Interlibrary loan; copying; SDI; library open to the public with restrictions. **Automated Operations:** Computerized cataloging. **Computerized Information Services:** DIALOG Information Services, VU/TEXT Information Services, DataTimes, Civil Engineering Database. **Networks/Consortia:** Member of ILLINET. **Remarks:** FAX: (312)648-5658.

★6717★
Greeley Municipal Museum - Library (Hist)
919 7th St. Phone: (303)350-9220
Greeley, CO 80631 Peggy A. Ford, Musm.Coord., Res. & Educ.
Founded: 1968. **Staff:** 2. **Subjects:** Greeley and Weld County history, biographies of early pioneers, Colorado history. **Special Collections:** Record books of the Union Colony (founding colony of Greeley); Colorado History Collection. **Holdings:** 3000 books; 100 bound periodical volumes; Nunn newspaper for 29 years on microfilm; 39 scrapbooks of clippings; 45 VF drawers of manuscripts, clippings, maps, photographs. **Subscriptions:** 6 journals and other serials. **Services:** Copying; library open to the public with restrictions. **Special Catalogs:** R.A. Moorman catalog of Colorado railroad materials. **Remarks:** Colorado History Collection formerly housed at the Greeley Public Library.

Greeley Public Library - Colorado History Collection
See: **Greeley Municipal Museum - Library** (6717)

General A.W. Greely's Polar Library
See: **National Geographic Society** (11186)

Adolph Green Collection
See: **Museum of the City of New York - Theatre Collection** (10892)

★6718★
Green Bay Press-Gazette - Library (Publ)
Box 19430 Phone: (414)435-4411
Green Bay, WI 54307-9430 Diane L. Laes, Libn.
Founded: 1957. **Staff:** Prof 2. **Subjects:** Biography, newspaper reference topics. **Holdings:** 500 books; 8000 subject files; 15,000 biography files; 650 reels of microfilm; 18,000 negative files. **Subscriptions:** 20 newspapers. **Services:** Library not open to the public. **Remarks:** Published by Gannett Newspapers. **Staff:** Jean Eggert, Photo.Libn.

★6719★
Green Clinic - Library (Med)
1200 S. Farmerville St. Phone: (318)255-3690
Ruston, LA 71270 Sara Sharp, Libn.
Founded: 1955. **Staff:** Prof 1. **Subjects:** Internal medicine, surgery, pediatrics, obstetrics and gynecology, ophthalmology, orthopaedics, otolaryngology, adolescent medicine, urology, family practice. **Holdings:** 850 books; 1500 bound periodical volumes; 500 bound single issues of medical journals and yearbooks; 50 volumes of unbound medical journals; 4 VF drawers. **Subscriptions:** 110 journals and other serials. **Services:** Copying; library open to the public for reference use only.

David W. Green Medical Library
See: **Memorial Hospital of Salem County** (10042)

Francis Harvey Green Library
See: **West Chester University - Francis Harvey Green Library** (20186)

★6720★
Green Mountain College - Griswold Library - Special Collections (Art)
Poultney, VT 05764 Phone: (802)287-9313
Katharine Reichert
Founded: 1834. **Staff:** Prof 3; Other 3. **Subjects:** Decoration. **Special Collections:** Welsh Collection (2000 books and artifacts); Ramsey Collection of Early American Decoration (1000 books and decorated artifacts). **Services:** Interlibrary loan; copying; library open to the public with restrictions. **Computerized Information Services:** DIALOG Information Services.

★6721★
Green Mountain Power Corporation - Information Resources (Energy)
Box 850 Phone: (802)864-5731
South Burlington, VT 05402-0850 Tamara Durfee Smith, Adm.
Founded: 1983. **Staff:** Prof 1. **Subjects:** Electric power research, business, records management. **Special Collections:** Green Mountain Power corporate history archives (100 diaries; 1000 photographs). **Holdings:** 200 books. **Subscriptions:** 150 periodicals; 4 newspapers. **Services:** Resources open to the public by appointment. **Automated Operations:** Computerized cataloging, acquisitions, serials, and circulation. **Computerized Information Services:** DIALOG Information Services, CompuServe Information Service, VU/TEXT Information Services, Dow Jones News/Retrieval, NewsNet, Inc. **Remarks:** FAX: (802)865-9974. **Staff:** Nora L. Roberts, Info.Rec.Coord.

Kate Greenaway Collection
See: **Butler University - Irwin Library - Hugh Thomas Miller Rare Book Room** (2416)

★6722★
Greenbaum, Rowe, Smith, Ravin, Davis & Bergstein - Law Library (Law)
Metro Corporate Campus One
99 Wood Ave., S. Phone: (908)549-5600
Iselin, NJ 08830 Leigh DeProspo, Hd.Libn.
Staff: Prof 1; Other 3. **Subjects:** Law - real estate, construction, corporate, bankruptcy, environmental, estate planning, elder. **Holdings:** 10,000 books. **Subscriptions:** 70 journals and other serials; 2 newspapers. **Services:** Interlibrary loan; library not open to the public. **Automated Operations:** INMAGIC. **Computerized Information Services:** WESTLAW, LEXIS, DIALOG Information Services; internal databses. **Remarks:** FAX: (908)549-1881.

★6723★
Greenberg, Glusker, Fields Claman & Machtinger - Library (Law)
1900 Avenue of the Stars Phone: (213)553-3610
Los Angeles, CA 90067 Lisa Winslow, Libn.
Founded: 1973. **Staff:** Prof 2; Other 3. **Subjects:** Law. **Holdings:** 40,000 books. **Subscriptions:** 200 journals and other serials. **Services:** Interlibrary loan; copying; library open to other law firms. **Computerized Information Services:** LEXIS, DIALOG Information Services, WESTLAW, Information America. **Remarks:** FAX: (213)553-0687.

Robert B. Greenblatt, MD Library
See: **Medical College of Georgia - Robert B. Greenblatt, MD Library** (9995)

★6724★
Greenbrier Historical Society - Archives (Hist)
North House, Church St.
P.O. Box 884 Phone: (304)645-3503
Lewisburg, WV 24901 Frances A. Swope, Archv.
Founded: 1963. **Subjects:** History of Greenbrier Valley area. **Special Collections:** Mrs. Alex McVeigh Miller Collection (dime novelist of the 1890s); original illustrations by Ashton Reniers and Naomi Hosterman for books by Ruth Woods Dayton. **Holdings:** 658 titles; 19 periodicals; 9 VF drawers of manuscripts, clippings, pamphlets; 1 VF drawer of pictures; facsimiles of Harrison-Handley Map of Greenbrier County (1887); Map of Lewisburg (1880); Bicentennial Map of Greenbrier County (1978); annual journals remaining in print for the years 1969-1973, 1975-1978, 1980-1991; History of Greenbrier County (1986). **Services:** Archives open to the public on a limited schedule. **Publications:** Journal, annual - for sale. **Remarks:** Society Headquarters telephone number is (304)645-3398.

★6725★
Greene County Historical Society - Library and Museum (Hist)
Box 127 Phone: (412)627-3204
Waynesburg, PA 15370 David Donley, Libn.
Staff: 2. **Subjects:** Greene County and Western Pennsylvania history and genealogy; Union and Confederate armies. **Special Collections:** Greene County Cemetery Records; Shaker Material; War of the Rebellion; Greene County obituaries. **Holdings:** 2000 books. **Services:** Copying; library open to the public for reference use only on fee basis and on limited schedule.

★6726★
Greene County Historical Society - Vedder Memorial Library (Hist)
R.D. 1, Box 10A Phone: (518)731-6822
Coxsackie, NY 12051 Raymond Beecher, Libn.
Founded: 1964. **Staff:** Prof 1; Other 8. **Subjects:** Greene County, The Catskills, mid-Hudson River Valley region. **Special Collections:** Greene county archives, 1801-1900. **Holdings:** 1303 manuscript volumes; 29 VF drawers and 135 boxes of manuscripts; county newspapers, 1792 to present; pictorial file. **Services:** Library open to the public on a limited schedule. **Also Known As:** Bronck Museum Library.

★6727★
Greene County Law Library (Law)
Court House, Rm. 309 Phone: (513)376-5115
Xenia, OH 45385 Jill Montgomery, Libn.
Subjects: Law. **Holdings:** 24,000 volumes. **Remarks:** Alternate telephone number(s): 376-5290.

★6728★
Greene County Law Library (Law)
Court House Phone: (412)852-1171
Waynesburg, PA 15370 Audrey Szoyka, Libn.
Founded: 1924. **Staff:** Prof 1. **Subjects:** Law. **Holdings:** 10,000 books; 10,000 bound periodical volumes; 4 other cataloged items. **Services:** Library open to the public for reference use only. **Automated Operations:** Computerized cataloging. **Publications:** Greene County Reports, weekly. **Remarks:** FAX: (412)627-4716.

★6729★
Greene County Public Library - Greene County Room (Hist)
76 E. Market St.
Box 520 Phone: (513)376-4952
Xenia, OH 45385 Julie M. Overton, Coord., Local Hist.
Founded: 1973. **Staff:** Prof 1; Other 26. **Subjects:** Genealogy, with emphasis on Ohio and mid-Atlantic states; local history. **Special Collections:** William Galloway papers (4 feet); Fred C. Kelly papers (1 foot); Raymond Higgins papers (1 foot); tornado materials (1974; 6 feet); books by Greene County authors (250 bound volumes); Mountain Laurel Collection of southeastern Kentucky, western Virginia, and eastern Tennessee (2 linear feet of books and manuscripts). **Holdings:** 4500 books; 115 bound periodical volumes; 2500 reels of microfilm; 80 cassette tapes of local history interviews. **Subscriptions:** 72 journals and other serials. **Services:** Copying; room open to the public. **Automated Operations:** Computerized cataloging. **Computerized Information Services:** OCLC. **Special Indexes:** Greene County Biographies; index to obituaries; index to local history topics; index to census records, 1820-1890. **Remarks:** FAX: (513)372-4673. **Formerly:** Greene County District Library.

Greene and Greene Library
See: **University of Southern California - School of Architecture - Gamble House - Greene and Greene Library** (19345)

Greene Memorial Museum
See: **University of Wisconsin--Milwaukee** (19640)

Stephen Greene Memorial Library of the Association of American Publishers
See: **American Booksellers Association (ABA) - Information Center** (504)

★6730★
Greenfield Community College - Pioneer Valley Resource Center (Hist)
1 College Dr. Phone: (413)774-3131
Greenfield, MA 01301 Carol G. Letson, Act.Dir.
Founded: 1981. **Staff:** Prof 2. **Subjects:** Pioneer Valley of Western Massachusetts. **Special Collections:** State Data Center Affiliate (75 books on federal and state census); Howes Photographic Collection, 1882-1907 (29 reels of microfilm; 200 prints); oral history (58 cassettes). **Holdings:** 2757 books; 387 nonprint materials. **Subscriptions:** 9 journals and other serials. **Services:** Interlibrary loan; copying; center open to the public.

★6731★
Greenfield Community College Foundation - Archibald MacLeish Collection (Hum)
1 College Dr. Phone: (413)774-3131
Greenfield, MA 01301 Margaret E.C. Howland, Cur.
Founded: 1974. **Staff:** Prof 2. **Subjects:** Archibald MacLeish. **Special Collections:** Interviews with Archibald MacLeish, 1976-1981 (41 cassettes). **Holdings:** 2485 books; 76 artifacts; 556 manuscripts; 9273 nonprint materials. **Services:** Copying; collection open to the public by appointment. **Computerized Information Services:** OCLC; internal database. **Networks/Consortia:** Member of NELINET, Inc. **Publications:** Bibliography of works by and about Archibald MacLeish; Descriptive Catalog, volume I - MacLeish's Library.

Frederick William Greenfield Young People's Library
See: **92nd Street Young Men's and Young Women's Hebrew Association - Buttenwieser Library** (11815)

Greenfield Village
See: **Henry Ford Museum and Greenfield Village** (5964)

★6732★
Greenforest Baptist Church - Library (Rel-Phil)
3250 Rainbow Dr. Phone: (404)286-0479
Decatur, GA 30034 Dorothy T. Lassiter, Cur.
Staff: Prof 3; Other 17. **Subjects:** Bible, Christian education and life, missions. **Holdings:** 4000 books; 4 drawers of filmstrips; 500 pictures; 2 drawer vertical file; sound recordings; videocassettes; transparencies. **Subscriptions:** 30 journals and other serials. **Services:** Copying; library open to the public. **Staff:** Evelyn Smith; Cora Lima.

Greenhoe Library
See: **Memorial Presbyterian Church - Greenhoe Library** (10047)

★6733★
Simon Greenleaf School of Law - Simon Greenleaf Library (Law)
3855 E. La Palma Ave. Phone: (714)998-2888
Anaheim, CA 92807 Samuel Casey, Dir.
Staff: Prof 2; Other 1. **Subjects:** Law, theology, human rights. **Special Collections:** English and Continental Legal History, especially 16th-17th centuries; Protestant Theology of the Reformation and Post-Reformation Period; English Law Reporters of the 16th-19th centuries; Law and the Occult/Witchcraft Trials (2000 items total); rare books (15th-18th century classical literature; 500 volumes). **Holdings:** 30,000 books; 100 bound periodical volumes; 60 vertical files; 20 dissertations; 100 cassette tapes. **Subscriptions:** 30 journals and other serials. **Services:** Interlibrary loan; copying; library open to the public with restrictions. **Publications:** The Simon Greenleaf Law Review, annual - by subscription. **Staff:** Gilbert Feliciano, Law Libn.; Jim Hanley, M.A. Libn.

Thomas D. Greenley Library
See: **State University of New York** (15719)

★6734★
Greenpeace U.S.A., Inc. - Library (Env-Cons)
1436 U St., N.W.
Washington, DC 20009 Phone: (202)462-1177
Subjects: Save the Whales, Greenpeace III, dolphins, The Comprehensive Test Ban, wildlife, toxic substances, disarmament, ocean ecology, atmosphere and energy, tropical forests. **Holdings:** Videotapes; films; pamphlets. **Services:** Interlibrary loan; copying. **Automated Operations:** Computerized circulation. **Publications:** Greenpeace, bimonthly.

★6735★
Greensboro Historical Museum - Archives (Hist)
130 Summit Ave. Phone: (919)373-2043
Greensboro, NC 27401 J. Stephen Catlett, Archv.
Founded: 1924. **Staff:** Prof 1. **Subjects:** O. Henry, Dolley Madison, decorative arts, Greensboro and Guilford County history, military. **Holdings:** 150 linear feet of rare books; 100 linear feet of manuscripts; 10,000 photographs and negatives; 300 state and local maps and architectural drawings. **Services:** Copying; archives open to the public by appointment.

★6736★
Greensboro Masonic Museum Library (Rec)
426 W. Market St.
Box 466 Phone: (919)273-8502
Greensboro, NC 27402 Joan Miller
Founded: 1932. **Staff:** 1. **Subjects:** Masonic history, ancient Egyptian history. **Special Collections:** Masonic papers published by the Grand Lodge of A.F. & A.M. of North Carolina, 1931 to present. **Holdings:** 500 volumes. **Services:** Library not open to the public.

★6737★
Greensboro News and Record - Library (Publ)
Box 20848 Phone: (919)373-7044
Greensboro, NC 27420 Robert L. Beall, Dir.
Founded: 1969. **Staff:** Prof 3. **Subjects:** Newspaper reference topics. **Holdings:** Reference books; clippings; photographic prints; microfilm. **Subscriptions:** 38 newspapers. **Services:** Library not open to the public. **Computerized Information Services:** VU/TEXT Information Services. **Remarks:** FAX: (919)373-7382. **Staff:** Gail Scullion; Patricia Callahan.

★6738★
Greensboro Planning & Community Development Department - Library (Plan)
Drawer W-2 Phone: (919)373-2761
Greensboro, NC 27402 Arthur Davis, III, Sr.Plan.
Staff: Prof 2. **Subjects:** Municipal planning and development. **Holdings:** 225 books; 100 bound periodical volumes; special subject files. **Subscriptions:** 100 journals and other serials; 5 newspapers. **Services:** Copying; library open to the public with restrictions. **Remarks:** FAX: (919)373-2138. **Staff:** Gwen Torain, CD Plan.

★6739★
Greensboro Public Library - Business Library (Bus-Fin)
201 N. Greene St. Phone: (919)373-2471
Greensboro, NC 27402 Mary Alice Watkins, Bus.Libn.
Founded: 1952. **Staff:** Prof 1. **Subjects:** Management, investment, automation, salesmanship, marketing, economics, real estate, taxes, accounting. **Holdings:** 20,000 books; 300 pamphlets; 2 VF drawers. **Subscriptions:** 400 journals and other serials. **Services:** Interlibrary loan; copying; library open to the public. **Automated Operations:** Computerized cataloging, acquisitions, and circulation. **Computerized Information Services:** CD-ROMs (ABI/INFORM, Newsbank). **Publications:** Bibliographies, irregular. **Remarks:** FAX: (919)333-6781. **Staff:** Reid G. Newnam, Bus.Libn.

★6740★
Greensfelder, Hemker & Gale - Library (Law)
1800 Equitable Bldg.
10 S. Broadway Phone: (314)241-9090
St. Louis, MO 63102 Helen R. Gibson, Libn.
Staff: Prof 1; Other 1. **Subjects:** Law - Missouri, Illinois, federal, corporate, tax, construction, labor, health and hospital. **Holdings:** 10,000 books; 100 bound periodical volumes. **Subscriptions:** 500 journals and other serials. **Services:** Interlibrary loan; copying; library open to the public by recommendation of firm member. **Computerized Information Services:** LEXIS, NEXIS, Information America. **Remarks:** FAX: (314)241-8624. Telex: 910-761-0410.

Greenville-Butler County Library
See: **Butler County Historical Society - Greenville-Butler County Library** (2409)

★6741★
Greenville County Museum of Art - Slide Library (Art, Aud-Vis)
420 College St. Phone: (803)271-7570
Greenville, SC 29601 Carol J. White, Proj.Coord./Educ. & Prog.
Founded: 1980. **Staff:** Prof 1. **Subjects:** Art history. **Special Collections:** Art historical slides. **Holdings:** 8000 slides. **Services:** Library open to area art faculty and organizations with advance permission.

★6742★
Greenville County Planning Commission - Planning Technical Library
301 University Ridge, Suite 400
Greenville, SC 29601-3660 Phone: (803)240-7270
Founded: 1964. **Subjects:** Urban planning, land use, housing, zoning, statistical and economic analysis, transportation, education, culture, historic preservation, Greenville, South Carolina. **Holdings:** 2300 volumes; maps; aerial photographs; census data. **Remarks:** Currently inactive.

★6743★
Greenville Hospital System - Health Sciences Library (Med)
701 Grove Rd. Phone: (803)455-7176
Greenville, SC 29605 Fay Towell, Dir.
Staff: Prof 2; Other 2. **Subjects:** Medicine, nursing, allied health sciences, hospital administration, management. **Holdings:** 5000 books; 10,000 bound periodical volumes; AV programs. **Subscriptions:** 400 serials. **Services:** Interlibrary loan; copying; library open to the public for reference use only. **Computerized Information Services:** NLM; CD-ROM (MEDLINE). Performs searches on fee basis. **Networks/Consortia:** Member of Area Health Education Consortium of South Carolina (AHEC). **Remarks:** Maintains branch libraries at Roger C. Peace Institute of Rehabilitative Medicine and Marshall I. Pickens Psychiatric Hospital. FAX: (803)242-8404. **Staff:** Ora Bechtler, Asst.Dir.; Debbie Porter, ILL; Theresa Head, Circ./Ser.

★6744★
Greenville Law Library (Law)
Court House Phone: (513)547-7329
Greenville, OH 45331 Eileen N. Litchfield, Libn.
Staff: 1. **Subjects:** Law. **Holdings:** 14,000 books. **Services:** Copying; library open to the public for reference use only. **Computerized Information Services:** LEXIS.

★6745★
Greenville Mental Health Center - Library (Med)
715 Grove Rd. Phone: (803)241-1040
Greenville, SC 29605-4280 Bo Hedrick, Libn.
Founded: 1969. **Staff:** Prof 1. **Subjects:** Mental health, psychiatry, psychology, counseling and therapy, social work. **Special Collections:** Pastoral Care Section - Psychiatry and Religion (75 volumes); Crisis Intervention. **Holdings:** 3000 books; 337 bound periodical volumes; 250 pamphlets and unbound periodicals; 8 VF drawers of pamphlet material. **Subscriptions:** 69 journals and other serials. **Services:** Interlibrary loan; copying; library open to the public for research only by prior arrangement with librarian. **Networks/Consortia:** Member of National Network of Libraries of Medicine - Southeastern/Atlantic Region. **Remarks:** Maintained by South Carolina State Department of Mental Health.

★6746★
Greenville News Piedmont Company - News Piedmont Library
P.O. Box 1688 Phone: (803)298-4323
Greenville, SC 29602 Cindy Harris, Libn.
Subjects: Newspaper reference topics. **Holdings:** Figures not available. **Remarks:** Library located at 305 S. Main St., Greenville, SC 29601.

★6747★
Greenville Technical College - Learning Resources Center/Library (Educ)
Box 5539 Phone: (803)250-8319
Greenville, SC 29606 Dr. L. Gene Elliott, Dir., Lib.Serv.
Founded: 1962. **Staff:** Prof 4; Other 5. **Subjects:** Technical, scientific, and business education; engineering; technology; nursing arts and sciences. **Holdings:** 44,000 books; 1174 bound periodical volumes; 1958 government documents; 198 state documents; 1581 pamphlets; 12,443 microforms. **Subscriptions:** 541 journals and other serials; 10 newspapers. **Services:** Interlibrary loan; copying; library open to the public. **Automated Operations:** Computerized public access catalog (Data Research Associates, Inc.), cataloging, circulation, acquisitions, and serials. **Computerized Information Services:** DIALOG Information Services. Performs searches on fee basis. Contact Person: Rosa Eisenstadt, Ref.Libn. **Networks/Consortia:** Member of SOLINET. **Remarks:** FAX: (803)250-8506. **Staff:** Don Massey, Dir., Instr. Media Tech.; Jane Mason, Tech.Serv.Libn.; Doris Jones, Pub.Serv.Libn.

★6748★
Greenwich Hospital Association - Gray Carter Library (Med)
Perryridge Rd. Phone: (203)863-3284
Greenwich, CT 06830 Carmel Fedors, Lib.Dir.
Staff: Prof 1; Other 1. **Subjects:** Medicine, allied health sciences, nursing, hospital administration. **Holdings:** 1617 books; 1949 bound periodical volumes. **Subscriptions:** 150 journals and other serials. **Services:** Interlibrary loan; library open to the public with restrictions. **Computerized Information Services:** MEDLARS, MEDLINE, BRS Information Technologies, NORD Services/Rare Disease Database, REPROTOX. **Networks/Consortia:** Member of Southwestern Connecticut Library Council (SWLC), Connecticut Association of Health Science Libraries (CAHSL). **Remarks:** FAX: (203)863-3427.

★6749★
Greenwich Library - Oral History Project (Hist)
101 W. Putnam Ave. Phone: (203)622-7900
Greenwich, CT 06830 Richard Hart, Ref.Libn.
Founded: 1973. **Subjects:** Local history. **Special Collections:** Transcriptions of oral history interviews (521); published edited transcriptions (114). **Holdings:** 798 oral history cassettes; 355 microfiche of transcriptions. **Services:** Interlibrary loan (limited); copying; project open to the public with restrictions. **Automated Operations:** Computerized cataloging, acquisitions, serials, and circulation. **Special Indexes:** Composite index of all transcriptions; Greenwich publications index.

Greenwich Time Library
See: **Southern Connecticut Newspapers Inc.** (15481)

★6750★
Greenwood County Historical Society - Library (Hist)
117 N. Main Phone: (316)583-6682
Eureka, KS 67045 Nancy Beitz
Founded: 1975. **Staff:** 1. **Subjects:** Greenwood County and Eureka town history and genealogy. **Holdings:** Greenwood County newspapers, from 1868; old census records on microfilm; family histories. **Services:** Copying; library open to the public. **Publications:** History of Greenwood County, Kansas (2 volumes).

★6751★
Greenwood Genetic Center - Library (Biol Sci)
1 Gregor Mendel Circle Phone: (803)223-9411
Greenwood, SC 29646 Michelle Bennett, Libn.
Holdings: 600 books; 1500 bound periodical volumes. **Services:** Copying. **Remarks:** FAX: (803)227-1614.

Greenwood Press, Inc.
See: **Greenwood Publishing Group, Inc. - Library** (6752)

★6752★
Greenwood Publishing Group, Inc. - Library (Publ)
88 Post Rd., W.
Box 5007 Phone: (203)226-3571
Westport, CT 06881-9990 Laura Kaminsky, Ed.
Subjects: Urban affairs. **Special Collections:** Urban Documents Microfiche Collection (45,000 local government documents from the United States and Canada). **Holdings:** 84,000 microfiche. **Services:** Library not open to the public. **Computerized Information Services:** LOGIN. **Special Indexes:** Index to Current Urban Documents, quarterly with annual cumulation (online). **Remarks:** FAX: (203)222-1502. **Formerly:** Greenwood Press, Inc. **Staff:** Jane Lerner, Customer Serv.

Greer Music Library
See: **Connecticut College** (4179)

★6753★
Greiner, Inc. - Library (Sci-Engr)
P.O. BOX 31646 Phone: (813)286-1711
Tampa, FL 33631-3416 Lexie W. Schwabel, Libn.
Founded: 1984. **Staff:** Prof 1; Other 2. **Subjects:** Civil engineering, transportation, planning, environmental studies. **Holdings:** 1500 books; 3200 internal reports. **Subscriptions:** 371 journals and other serials; 6 newspapers. **Services:** Interlibrary loan; library not open to the public. **Automated Operations:** Computerized public access catalog (LUIS). **Computerized Information Services:** DIALOG Information Services. **Publications:** Information Management News, 6/year - for internal distribution only. **Remarks:** FAX: (813)287-8591.

★6754★
Grenada Chamber of Industry and Commerce - Library (Bus-Fin)
c/o Ms. Daphne Brown
DeCaul Bldg.
Mount Gay
St. George's, Grenada Phone: 4402937
Founded: 1921. **Staff:** 5. **Subjects:** National economic policy, investment, business ethics and standards. **Holdings:** 500 volumes. **Services:** Interlibrary loan; copying; library open to members and business persons. **Computerized Information Services:** Internal database. **Remarks:** Alternate telephone number(s): 4404485. FAX: 4406627.

Newton Gresham Library
See: **Sam Houston State University** (7465)

Gressette Learning Resource Center
See: **Orangeburg-Calhoun Technical College** (12516)

★6755★
Grey Advertising, Inc. - Information Center (Bus-Fin)
777 3rd Ave. Phone: (212)546-2511
New York, NY 10017 Tesse Santoro, Mgr.
Founded: 1948. **Staff:** Prof 3; Other 1. **Subjects:** Advertising, marketing. **Holdings:** 200 books; 300 directories; 300 VF drawers of reports and documents. **Subscriptions:** 250 journals and other serials; 5 newspapers. **Services:** Interlibrary loan (limited to SLA members). **Computerized Information Services:** DIALOG Information Services. NEXIS, VU/TEXT, DataTimes, PRODUCTSCAN. **Remarks:** FAX: (212)546-1495. **Staff:** Ellen Spross, Res.; Sallie Doerfler, Res.

Greyhound Corporation
See: **Dial Corporation** (4849)

★6756★
Greystone Park Psychiatric Hospital - Health Science Library (Med)
Box A Phone: (201)538-1800
Greystone Park, NJ 07950 Brian C. Hamilton, Libn.
Founded: 1930. **Staff:** Prof 1. **Subjects:** Psychiatry, psychiatric nursing, psychology, medicine. **Holdings:** 1570 books; 60 bound periodical volumes. **Subscriptions:** 50 journals and other serials. **Services:** Interlibrary loan (fee); library open to the public with permission.

Ellen Griep Memorial Library
See: **Pacific Medical Center** (12673)

Gries Library
See: **Suburban Temple** (15844)

Lucile Dauby Gries Memorial Library
See: **Cleveland Hearing and Speech Center** (3808)

★6757★
Griffin Hospital - Health Sciences - Library (Med)
130 Division St. Phone: (203)732-7399
Derby, CT 06418 Katerini Giotsas, Libn./Mgr.
Staff: Prof 1. **Subjects:** Medicine, nursing, and allied health sciences. **Holdings:** 800 journals and other serials; 2000 bound periodical volumes. **Subscriptions:** 225 journals and other serials; 4 newspapers. **Services:** Interlibrary loan; copying; SDI; library open to the public. **Computerized Information Services:** MEDLINE; CD-ROM (SilverPlatter).

★6758★
Griffin Memorial Hospital - Professional Library (Med)
Box 151 Phone: (405)321-4880
Norman, OK 73070 Shirley M. Pierce, Med.Libn.
Staff: Prof 1. **Subjects:** Psychiatry, psychology, medicine, nursing. **Special Collections:** Child psychiatry; historical medical book collection, 1800s-1915 (85 books). **Holdings:** 7800 books; 140 bound periodical volumes; 4 VF drawers of clippings and dissertations; 3 shelves of government documents; 3 VF drawers of newsletters and nursing statements; 115 tapes; 20 films; 2 video cassettes; 200 filmstrips. **Subscriptions:** 106 journals and other serials. **Services:** Interlibrary loan; copying; library open to the public. **Publications:** Bookends, irregular - to hospital staff. **Formerly:** Central State Hospital - Professional Library.

D.W. Griffith Collection
See: **Museum of Modern Art - Film Stills Archive** (10908)

Griffith Memorial Library
See: **Sheridan College** (15124)

★6759★
Griffith Observatory - Library (Sci-Engr)
2800 E. Observatory Rd. Phone: (213)664-1181
Los Angeles, CA 90027 Dr. E.C. Krupp, Dir.
Founded: 1935. **Staff:** 1. **Subjects:** Astronomy, astrophysics, earth sciences, physical sciences. **Holdings:** 5500 books; 200 bound periodical volumes. **Subscriptions:** 20 journals and other serials. **Services:** Library not open to the public. **Automated Operations:** Computerized cataloging. **Computerized Information Services:** Internal database. **Publications:** Griffith Observer, monthly - by subscription. **Remarks:** FAX: (213)663-4323. Maintained by City of Los Angeles. **Staff:** Laura Williams, Libn.

Griffith Resource Library
See: **American College of Cardiology** (533)

★6760★
Sherman Grinberg Film Libraries, Inc. (Aud-Vis)
630 Ninth Ave. Phone: (212)765-5170
New York, NY 10036-3787 Bernard Chertok, Pres.
Staff: Prof 29; Other 2. **Subjects:** News on film and videotapes. **Special Collections:** Pathe and Paramount newsreels; American Broadcasting Corporation's National News Outtakes; Nature Footage; other private film libraries, including major Hollywood and major motion picture studios' outtakes. **Holdings:** 150 million feet of film; 500,000 videocassettes. **Subscriptions:** 11 journals and other serials. **Services:** Library open by appointment to researchers and filmmakers. **Remarks:** FAX: (212)262-1532. Telex: 269950 SGFL. A branch library is located at 1040 N. McCadden Place, Hollywood, CA 90038, telephone: (213)464-7491; FAX: (213)462-5352; Telex: 265823 SFLG. **Staff:** Linda Grinberg, V.P.; Nancy Casey, Chf.Libn.; William Hennessy, Supv.; Andrew Noren, Res.Libn.; Mike Miller, Res.Libn.

★6761★
Grindstone Bluff Museum - Library (Soc Sci)
875 Cotton St. Phone: (318)425-5646
Shreveport, LA 71101 J. Ashley Sibley, Jr., Dir.
Founded: 1958. **Subjects:** Archeology, anthropology, regional American Indians, arts and crafts, geology, physical geography, nature. **Special Collections:** Caddo Indians; Arkansas-Louisiana-Texas archeological society journals (20 file drawers). **Holdings:** 5700 books; 2000 bound periodical volumes; 50 maps; 2500 slides; 50 original tape recordings; 2000 sound recordings. **Subscriptions:** 25 journals and other serials. **Services:** Library open to the public for reference use only by appointment. **Publications:** Periodical curriculum materials for workshops.

Griswold Library
See: **Green Mountain College** (6720)

★6762★
Grolier Club of New York - Library (Info Sci, Publ)
47 E. 60th St. Phone: (212)838-6690
New York, NY 10022 Martin Antonetti, Libn.
Founded: 1884. **Staff:** Prof 2. **Subjects:** Bibliography, history of printing, book-collecting, bookselling, arts of the book. **Special Collections:** Early printing; book bindings; private library, auction, and bookseller catalogs. **Holdings:** 70,000 volumes; 5000 prints and portraits; bookplates. **Subscriptions:** 30 journals and other serials. **Services:** Library open to the public with restrictions. **Computerized Information Services:** RLIN. **Special Catalogs:** Occasional exhibition catalogs. **Remarks:** FAX: (212)838-2445. **Staff:** Kimball Higgs, Cat.

★6763★
Grolier Incorporated - Library (Publ)
Sherman Tpke. Phone: (203)797-3848
Danbury, CT 06816 Charles Chang, Chf.Libn.
Staff: Prof 1; Other 1. **Subjects:** General reference. **Holdings:** 15,000 books. **Subscriptions:** 160 journals and other serials. **Services:** Library not open to the public. **Remarks:** FAX: (203)797-3197.

Jenny Gross Memorial Library
See: **Adath Jeshurun Congregation** (68)

Jacob and Rose Grossman Library
See: **Hebrew College** (7092)

★6764★
Group 243 Inc. - Library (Bus-Fin)
1410 Woodridge Ave. Phone: (313)761-3585
Ann Arbor, MI 48105 Cathy Powell, Corp.Libn.
Founded: 1982. **Staff:** Prof 1. **Subjects:** Advertising, marketing, graphic design. **Holdings:** 313 books; slides; pamphlets; photographs; tapes; transparencies; negatives; artwork. **Subscriptions:** 100 journals and other serials; 7 newspapers. **Services:** Library not open to the public. **Computerized Information Services:** DIALOG Information Services. **Remarks:** FAX: (313)995-0866.

★6765★
Group for Advanced Analytical Sciences - Spectroscopic Information Center (Sci-Engr)
28 rue St. Dominique Phone: 1 45559236
F-75007 Paris, France Mme. D. Sandino, Adjunct Dir.
Founded: 1955. **Staff:** 1. **Subjects:** Spectroscopic data - infrared, ultraviolet, nuclear magnetic resonance, Raman, mass spectra. **Holdings:** 41,404 mass spectra; 276,009 infrared spectra; 44,549 ultraviolet spectra; 1194 Raman spectra; 66,457 nuclear magnetic resonance spectra. **Services:** Center open to members only. **Computerized Information Services:** Internal database. **Remarks:** FAX: 1 45559249. **Formerly:** Groupement pour l'Avancement des Methodes Spectroscopiques et Physicochimique d'Analyse. **Also Known As:** Groupe pour L'Avancement des Sciences Analytiques - Centre d'Information Spectroscopiques.

★6766★
Group Health Association of America, Inc. - Gertrude Sturges Memorial Library (Bus-Fin)
1129 20th St., N.W. Phone: (202)778-3200
Washington, DC 20036 Nina M. Lane, Lib.Dir.
Founded: 1972. **Staff:** Prof 2; Other 1. **Subjects:** Health maintenance organizations, health insurance and administration, medical economics. **Special Collections:** Prepaid health care and managed health care systems (articles; presentations; dissertations; monographs). **Holdings:** 3000 books. **Subscriptions:** 200 journals and other serials. **Services:** Interlibrary loan; copying; SDI; library open to the public by appointment. **Computerized Information Services:** MEDLARS; internal database. Performs searches on fee basis. Telephone: (202)778-3268. **Networks/Consortia:** Member of District of Columbia Health Sciences Information Network (DOCHSIN). **Publications:** Selected Annotated Bibliography on Health Maintenance Organizations, 1974-1978 - for sale. **Remarks:** FAX: (202)331-7487. **Staff:** Erin Carlson, Res.Libn.; Susan Fong, Lib.Techn. for Doc. Delivery & ILL.

★6767★
Group Health Cooperative of Puget Sound - Medical Library (Med)
200 15th Ave., E. Phone: (206)326-3393
Seattle, WA 98112 Jackie Gagne, Dir., Med.Libs.
Founded: 1969. **Staff:** Prof 2; Other 3. **Subjects:** Clinical medicine, group medical plans, family practice, nursing, pharmacy. **Holdings:** 1800 books; 2500 bound periodical volumes; 4000 audiotape cassettes; Audio-Digest tapes. **Subscriptions:** 410 journals and other serials. **Services:** Interlibrary loan; copying; SDI; library occasionally open to public by permission. **Automated Operations:** Computerized serials and circulation. **Computerized Information Services:** DIALOG Information Services, NLM, BRS Information Technologies; OnTyme Electronic Message Network Service (electronic mail service). **Networks/Consortia:** Member of Seattle Area Hospital Library Consortium (SAHLC). **Publications:** Shelf-Life, monthly - for internal distribution only. **Remarks:** Electronic mail address(es): GHCCEN (OnTyme Electronic Message Network Service). A branch library is maintained at Eastside Hospital, 2700 152nd N.E., Redmond, WA 98052.

★6768★
Group Technologies Corp. - Division Library (Sci-Engr)
10901 Malcolm McKinley Dr.
Tampa, FL 33612 Phone: (813)972-6000
Founded: 1981. **Staff:** Prof 1. **Subjects:** Electronics, engineering, quality, production. **Holdings:** 800 books; 100 bound periodical volumes. **Subscriptions:** 80 journals and other serials. **Services:** Library not open to the public. **Remarks:** FAX: (813)972-6704.

Groupe pour L'Avancement des Sciences Analytiques - Centre d'Information Spectroscopiques
See: **Group for Advanced Analytical Sciences - Spectroscopic Information Center** (6765)

Groupement pour l'Avancement des Methodes Spectroscopiques et Physicochimique d'Analyse
See: **Group for Advanced Analytical Sciences - Spectroscopic Information Center** (6765)

★6769★
Grout Museum of History and Science - Genealogy, Archives and Reference Library (Hist)
503 South St. Phone: (319)234-6357
Waterloo, IA 50701 Janice M. Taylor, Archv.
Founded: 1956. **Staff:** Prof 1; Other 1. **Subjects:** Genealogy, area histories. **Special Collections:** Rare books on area history, Indians, Civil War; books by Iowa authors; Iowa school book collection. **Holdings:** 1800 books; 3000 clippings; 1500 archival materials; 950 photographs. **Services:** Copying; library open to the public for reference use only.

V.G. Grove Research Library of Mathematics-Statistics
See: **Michigan State University** (10339)

Malcolm Grow Medical Center
See: **U.S. Air Force Hospital** (16901)

★6770★
Grumman Aerospace Corporation - Corporate Information Center (Sci-Engr)
L01-35 Phone: (516)575-3912
Bethpage, NY 11714 Harold B. Smith, Mgr.
Founded: 1955. **Staff:** Prof 5; Other 6. **Subjects:** Aerodynamics, avionics, electronics, physics, materials, mathematics, business management. **Holdings:** 20,000 books; 11,500 bound periodical volumes; 100,000 hardcopy technical reports; 800,000 technical reports on microfiche. **Subscriptions:** 520 journals and other serials. **Services:** Interlibrary loan; center not open to the public. **Automated Operations:** Computerized serials and circulation. **Computerized Information Services:** BRS Information Technologies, Dun & Bradstreet Business Credit Services, DIALOG Information Services, LEXIS, NEXIS, NASA/RECON, Dow Jones News/Retrieval, PFDS Online, Occupational Health Services, Inc. (OHS), Data Resources (DRI), DMS/ONLINE, DTIC, NewsNet, Inc., USNI Military Database, Aerospace Online, VU/TEXT Information Services. **Networks/Consortia:** Member of Long Island Library Resources Council. **Special Indexes:** Periodical listing. **Remarks:** FAX: (516)575-7428. **Staff:** Mary Westerling, Asst.Chf.Libn.; John Burden, Tech.Libn.; Thomas Rees, Jr., Tech.Libn.; Royal Scheiman, Tech.Libn.

Heinz Gruner Library
See: **American Society for Photogrammetry and Remote Sensing** (756)

Grupo de Trabajo para los Pueblos Indigenas
See: **Working Group Indigenous Peoples** (20603)

★6771★
H.J. Gruy & Co. - Library (Energy)
711 Louisiana
1600 Penoil
Houston, TX 77002 Phone: (713)228-7000
Staff: 1. **Subjects:** Petroleum engineering, geology, energy, economics. **Holdings:** 7000 books. **Subscriptions:** 200 journals and other serials. **Automated Operations:** Computerized acquisitions, serials, and map cataloging. **Computerized Information Services:** DIALOG Information Services. **Formerly:** H.J. Gruy & Associates, Inc.

★6772★
GS Club of America - Library (Rec)
1213 Gornto Rd. Phone: (912)244-0577
Valdosta, GA 31602 Dr. Lance Marlette, Libn.
Founded: 1984. **Staff:** Prof 2; Other 2. **Subjects:** Buick Gran Sport automobile - original road testing, performance engine rebuilding. **Holdings:** 88 books; 64 bound periodical volumes; 7 manuscripts. **Services:** Library not open to the public. **Staff:** Starke Miller, Asst.Libn.

★6773★
GSC Associates, Inc. - Library (Comp Sci)
2304 Artesia Blvd., Suite 201
Redondo Beach, CA 90278 Phone: (310)379-2113
Founded: 1975. **Staff:** 1. **Subjects:** Computer science, information science, mathematics, electrical engineering, exploratory development, artificial intelligence, computer communications. **Holdings:** 3000 volumes; 15,000 periodicals; 20,000 standards documents. **Subscriptions:** 60 journals and other serials; 2 newspapers. **Services:** Library not open to the public. **Remarks:** FAX: (310)379-1649.

★6774★
GTE Corporation - Government Systems - Library (Info Sci, Sci-Engr)
1 Research Dr. Phone: (508)870-4700
Westborough, MA 01581 Charles A. Thornhill, Libn.
Founded: 1981. **Staff:** 3. **Subjects:** Antennas, communications, computer technology, electronics, command and control systems, fiber optics, mathematics. **Special Collections:** U.S. federal and military standards and specifications. **Holdings:** 7000 books; 2400 reports; 200 journal titles on microfiche. **Subscriptions:** 300 journals and other serials. **Services:** Interlibrary loan; SDI; library open to the public by appointment. **Computerized Information Services:** DIALOG Information Services, Government and Industry Data Exchange Program (GIDEP). Performs searches on fee basis. **Networks/Consortia:** Member of GTE LIBNET. **Publications:** Library newsletter; periodical listing, bimonthly. **Remarks:** FAX: (508)870-5278. **Staff:** Mary Fortin; Laurel King.

★6775★
GTE Corporation - Government Systems - Library Research Center (Sci-Engr, Info Sci)
77 A St. Phone: (617)455-4462
Needham Heights, MA 02194 Harriet T. Randall, Mgr., Lib.Serv.
Founded: 1952. **Staff:** 5. **Subjects:** Electronics, electronic devices, communications, antennas, detection systems, countermeasures, command and control systems, computer and data processing systems, physics, mathematics. **Special Collections:** U.S. federal and military standards and specifications. **Holdings:** 12,000 books; 3500 bound periodical volumes; 2000 reels of microfilm of periodicals; vendor catalogs; Jane's and IEEE (Institute of Electrical and Electronics Engineers) publications; industry standards. **Subscriptions:** 350 journals and other serials. **Services:** Interlibrary loan; SDI; library open to the public by appointment. **Automated Operations:** Computerized public access catalog. **Computerized Information Services:** NEXIS, LEXIS, Haystack, DIALOG Information Services, DTIC; CD-ROM. Performs searches on fee basis. **Networks/Consortia:** Member of GTE LIBNET. **Publications:** Library newsletter; periodical listing, bimonthly. **Remarks:** FAX: (617)455-4460. **Staff:** Lisa Righini; Tod McMahon; Cristina Malinn; Laurel King.

★6776★
GTE Government Systems - Technical Library (Info Sci, Comp Sci)
15000 Conference Center Dr. Phone: (703)818-5224
Chantilly, VA 22021 Bonnie Witlin, Libn.
Founded: 1955. **Staff:** Prof 1. **Subjects:** Communications, computer networks, software engineering, artificial intelligence. **Holdings:** 3500 books; 1000 bound periodical volumes; military standards; specifications; government reports and documents. **Subscriptions:** 200 journals and other serials; 50 newspapers. **Services:** Interlibrary loan; services not open to the public. **Automated Operations:** Computerized cataloging. **Computerized Information Services:** DIALOG Information Services, DRI/McGraw-Hill, Dun & Bradstreet Business Credit Services, NEXIS, GIDEP (Government-Industry Data Exchange Program). **Networks/Consortia:** Member of Interlibrary Users Association (IUA). **Remarks:** FAX: (703)359-7765. Telex: 824079. **Formerly:** Contel Technology Center.

★6777★
GTE Government Systems Corporation - Electronic Defense Information Resource Center (Sci-Engr, Info Sci)
MC3G01
PO Box 7188 Phone: (415)966-3082
Mountain View, CA 94039 Julie B. Del Fierro, Supv., Lib.Serv.
Founded: 1952. **Staff:** Prof 2; Other 3. **Subjects:** Communications, physics, electronics, mathematics. **Holdings:** 15,000 books; 5000 bound periodical volumes; 25,000 technical reports. **Subscriptions:** 450 journals and other serials; 5 newspapers. **Services:** Interlibrary loan; copying; library open to the public with restrictions. **Computerized Information Services:** DIALOG Information Services, PFDS Online, DTIC. **Networks/Consortia:** Member of GTE LIBNET, CLASS. **Publications:** Accessions Bulletin. **Remarks:** FAX: (415)966-3401. **Staff:** Susan Giammona, Asst.Libn.

★6778★
GTE Laboratories - Library (Sci-Engr, Info Sci)
40 Sylvan Rd. Phone: (617)466-4214
Waltham, MA 02254 Sue Wolfman, Mgr.
Founded: 1971. **Staff:** Prof 4; Other 3. **Subjects:** Telecommunications, computer sciences, materials sciences, chemistry, physics, microelectronics. **Special Collections:** Consultive Committee on International Telegraphy and Telephony (CCITT) Standards; Bellcore publications. **Holdings:** 18,000 volumes. **Subscriptions:** 500 journals and other serials; 12 newspapers. **Services:** Interlibrary loan; SDI; library open to the public upon request. **Automated Operations:** Computerized retrieval system, table of contents routing, cataloging, serials, and circulation. **Computerized Information Services:** DIALOG Information Services, STN International, OCLC, Chemical Abstracts Service (CAS), Mead Data Central, BRS After Dark; GTE TELENET (internal database); TELENET (electronic mail services). Performs searches on fee basis. Katherine Graham, Info.Spec., 466-2472. **Publications:** Internal Library Bulletin, monthly; GTE Union List of Serials, annual. **Remarks:** FAX: (617)890-5790. Electronic mail address(es): SLW1@BUNNY.GTE.COM (TELENET). **Staff:** David Jelley, Tech.Libn.

GTE Service Corporation - Technical Information Resource Center - Library
See: **GTE Telephone Operations Headquarters - Market Research Library** (6782)

★6779★
GTE Spacenet Corporation - Library (Info Sci)
1700 Old Meadow Rd. Phone: (703)848-0119
McLean, VA 22102 Terri Brooks, Libn.
Founded: 1985. **Staff:** Prof 1; Other 1. **Subjects:** Communication satellites, telecommunications, business management, electrical engineering, science and technology. **Holdings:** 2000 books; technical reports; conference proceedings; vendor catalogs on microfilm; government and industry standards on microfilm. **Subscriptions:** 200 journals and other serials. **Services:** Interlibrary loan; SDI; library open to the public by appointment. **Automated Operations:** Computerized cataloging, acquisitions, serials, and circulation. **Computerized Information Services:** DIALOG Information Services, NEXIS, Dow Jones News/Retrieval; internal database; SprintMail (electronic mail service). **Networks/Consortia:** Member of GTE LIBNET. **Remarks:** FAX: (703)848-0004. Electronic mail address(es): T.BROOKS (SprintMail).

★6780★
GTE Sylvania - Engineering Library (Sci-Engr)
100 Endicott St. Phone: (508)750-2349
Danvers, MA 01923 Mildred A. McKenna, Libn./Mgr.
Staff: Prof 1. **Subjects:** Engineering, chemistry, physics. **Holdings:** 8000 volumes; 1976 journals on microfilm. **Subscriptions:** 175 journals and other serials. **Services:** Library not open to the public. **Computerized Information Services:** DIALOG Information Services.

★6781★
GTE Telephone Operations - Southwest Area - E.H. Danner Library of Telephony
M.C. 8101
2701 S. Johnson St.
Box 1001
San Angelo, TX 76904-1001
Defunct.

★6782★
GTE Telephone Operations Headquarters - Market Research Library (Sci-Engr)
4500 Fuller Dr.
MCF04P01 Phone: (214)718-5549
Irving, TX 75038 Charlotte Wixx Clark, Lib.Hd.
Founded: 1987. **Staff:** 3. **Subjects:** Market research, telecommunications, technology, business telecommunication related products. **Holdings:** 450 books; 5000 studies; reports; manuscripts. **Subscriptions:** 152 journals and other serials. **Services:** Interlibrary loan; library not open to the public. **Computerized Information Services:** DIALOG Information Services, NewsNet, Inc., Gartner; internal database. **Remarks:** FAX: (214)718-5276. **Formerly:** GTE Service Corporation - Technical Information Resource Center - Library.

★6783★
(Guadalajara) Instituto Cultural Mexicano-Norteamericano de Jalisco, A.C. - USIS Collection (Educ)
Tolsa 300
44100 Guadalajara, Jalisco, Mexico
Remarks: Maintained or supported by the U.S. Information Agency. Focus is on materials that will assist peoples outside the United States to learn about the United States, its people, history, culture, political processes, and social milieux.

(Guadalajara) USIS Library
See: **Biblioteca Benjamin Franklin - (Guadalajara) USIS Library** (1819)

★6784★
Guadalupe Medical Center - Medical Staff Library (Med)
2430 W. Pierce St. Phone: (505)887-6633
Carlsbad, NM 88220 Lee Weeks, Med. Staff Libn.
Staff: Prof 1; Other 1. **Subjects:** Medicine and allied health sciences. **Holdings:** 562 books; 212 bound periodical volumes; 5 VF drawers of Pediatric Notes; 51 VF drawers of medical journals. **Subscriptions:** 17 journals and other serials. **Services:** Interlibrary loan (fee); library not open to the public. **Special Indexes:** Attrition book and card indexes by title and author.

★6785★
Guale Historical Society - Bryan-Lang Historical Library (Hist)
P.O. Box 725 Phone: (912)576-5601
Woodbine, GA 31569 John H. Christian, Libn.
Founded: 1984. **Staff:** 1. **Subjects:** History, genealogy, Camden County, coastal Georgia. **Special Collections:** Bryan-Lang Collection (1100 volumes, 600 folders); Berrie Collection (300 volumes); Coastal Highway Collection (300 folders). **Holdings:** 2000 books; 100 documents; 300 nonbook items. **Subscriptions:** 7 journals and other serials; 3 newspapers. **Services:** Copying; library open to the public.

★6786★
Guam Bureau of Planning - Library (Plan)
Box 2950 Phone: (671)472-4201
Agana, GU 96910 Susan Ham, Plan. IV
Founded: 1975. **Staff:** Prof 4. **Subjects:** Guam - people, insular resources, economic development, government, history. **Holdings:** 3359 volumes; 1200 bound periodical volumes; 5000 other cataloged items; reports and studies about the island, people, and government of Guam. **Subscriptions:** 9 journals and other serials. **Services:** Interlibrary loan; library open to the public with restrictions. **Computerized Information Services:** Internal database. **Special Catalogs:** Guam Inventory of Planning Information. **Remarks:** FAX: (671)477-1812. **Staff:** Monica Guerrero, Plan. II; Janet Unsiog, Plan. II.

★6787★
Guam Memorial Hospital Authority - Medical Library (Med)
850 Gov. Carlos Camacho Rd. Phone: (671)646-5801
Tamuning, GU 96911 Juliana S. Torres, Med.Libn.
Staff: Prof 1. **Subjects:** Medicine, nursing, hospital administration. **Special Collections:** Health and Medicine in Guam and Micronesia (4 VF drawers). **Holdings:** 1519 books. **Subscriptions:** 75 journals and other serials. **Services:** Interlibrary loan; copying; library open to the public for reference use only. **Networks/Consortia:** Member of National Network of Libraries of Medicine - Pacific Southwest Region. **Special Indexes:** Health & Medicine in Guam & Micronesia (list and cards). **Remarks:** FAX: (671)649-5506.

★6788★
Guam Territorial Law Library (Law)
141 San Ramon Rd. Phone: (671)477-7623
Agana, GU 96910 David Gaarder, Territorial Law Libn.
Founded: 1978. **Staff:** Prof 1; Other 3. **Subjects:** Law. **Holdings:** 25,000 books; 100 bound periodical volumes. **Subscriptions:** 485 journals and other serials. **Services:** Interlibrary loan; copying; library open to the public. **Computerized Information Services:** WESTLAW, LEXIS; MCI Mail (electronic mail service). Performs searches on fee basis. **Remarks:** FAX: (671)472-1246.

Guangdong Entomological Institute
See: **Academy of Science of Guangdong Province** (38)

★6789★
Guangzhou Academy of Fine Arts - Library (Art, Hum)
Xiaogang Xincun
Guangzhou, Guangdong Province, People's Republic of China Phone: 51626
Wang Yilun, Libn.
Founded: 1951. **Staff:** 10. **Subjects:** Fine arts, social sciences, literature. **Special Collections:** Original Chinese traditional paintings and stamps; albums of foreign paintings. **Holdings:** 141,096 volumes; 4213 periodicals. **Publications:** Fine Arts Bulletin.

★6790★
Guangzhou Institute of Energy Conversion - Library (Energy)
81 Central Xianlie Lu
P.O. Box 1254
Guangzhou 510070, People's Republic of China Phone: 775600
Zhang Huan-fen, Div.Chf.
Subjects: Energy conversion; biomass, solar, geothermal energy; waste heat recovery; fluidized bed combustion; electrical generators; heat storage; heat pumps; wave/ocean energy utilization. **Holdings:** 50,000 volumes. **Remarks:** Affiliated with the Chinese Academy of Sciences.

★6791★
Guatemala - Ministerio de Cultura y Deportes - Instituto de Antropologia e Historia - Library (Area-Ethnic, Soc Sci)
12 Avenida 11-65, Zona 1 Phone: 25948-25571
Guatemala City, Guatemala Maria Elena de Allara
Subjects: Central America - archeology, ethnology, linguistics, anthropology, arts, history. **Holdings:** 35,000 volumes. **Services:** Library open to the public for reference use only. **Also Known As:** Guatemala - Ministry of Culture and Sports - Institute of Anthropology and History.

(Guatemala City) Instituto Guatemalteco Americano
See: **Walt Whitman Library** (20394)

★6792★
(Guayaquil) Centro Ecuatoriano Norteamericano - USIS Collection (Educ)
L. Urdaneta y Cordova Esquina
P.O. Box 5717
Guayaquil, Ecuador
Remarks: Maintained or supported by the U.S. Information Agency. Focus is on materials that will assist peoples outside the United States to learn about the United States, its people, history, culture, political processes, and social milieux.

★ 6793 ★
Guedel Memorial Anesthesia Center - Library (Med)
2395 Sacramento St.
Box 7999 Phone: (415)923-3240
San Francisco, CA 94120 Peggy Tahir, Libn.
Staff: Prof 1. **Subjects:** Anesthesiology. **Holdings:** 1278 books; 988 bound periodical volumes; 813 cassette tapes; 36 videotapes; exhibits; artifacts. **Subscriptions:** 53 journals and other serials. **Services:** Interlibrary loan; copying; library open to members. **Computerized Information Services:** DIALOG Information Services, MEDLARS. **Special Catalogs:** Guedal Memorial Anesthesia Center Catalog. **Remarks:** (415)923-6597.

★ 6794 ★
Guelph General Hospital - Dr. William Howitt Memorial Library (Med)
115 Delhi St. Phone: (519)822-5350
Guelph, ON, Canada N1E 4J4 Brenda Vegso, Libn.
Remarks: No further information was supplied by respondent.

★ 6795 ★
Guernsey County Law Library (Law)
Guernsey County Court House Phone: (614)432-9258
Cambridge, OH 43725 Richard A. Baker, Law Libn.
Staff: Prof 1; Other 1. **Subjects:** Law. **Holdings:** 8000 books; 500 bound periodical volumes; 1500 microfiche. **Services:** Copying; library open to the public with restrictions. **Computerized Information Services:** WESTLAW. **Remarks:** FAX: (614)432-9257.

★ 6796 ★
Solomon R. Guggenheim Museum - Library (Art)
1071 Fifth Ave. Phone: (212)360-3538
New York, NY 10128 Sonja Bay, Libn.
Founded: 1953. **Staff:** 2. **Subjects:** Painting and sculpture of the 20th century. **Holdings:** 20,000 books; 1600 bound periodical volumes; 50,000 file folders of pamphlets; 2500 slides; 300 tapes. **Subscriptions:** 50 journals and other serials. **Services:** Copying; library open to graduate students and qualified scholars. **Staff:** Tara Massarsky, Asst.Libn.

★ 6797 ★
Pat Guida Associates - Library (Sci-Engr)
24 Spielman Rd. Phone: (201)227-7418
Fairfield, NJ 07004-3412 Pat Guida, Pres.
Founded: 1980. **Staff:** Prof 1; Other 1. **Subjects:** Food chemistry, chemistry, medicine, pharmacology, technology, nutrition, toxicology, environmental sciences. **Holdings:** 1400 books; 1000 bound periodical volumes; unbound periodicals. **Subscriptions:** 55 journals and other serials. **Services:** Interlibrary loan; library not open to the public. **Computerized Information Services:** MEDLARS, DIALOG Information Services, Knowledge Index. Performs searches on fee basis.

Guidance and Control Information Analysis Center
See: **IIT Research Institute** (7661)

Guided Study Programs/Communications Office of the Diocese of London - Library
See: **St. Stephen Centre Library** (14590)

★ 6798 ★
Guild of Book Workers - Library (Publ)
Main Library
University of Iowa Phone: (319)335-5908
Iowa City, IA 52242 Pamela Spitzmueller, Univ.Consrv.
Staff: Prof 1. **Subjects:** Bookbinding, history of the book, calligraphy, printing, paper making. **Holdings:** 500 books. **Services:** Library open to members only. **Computerized Information Services:** BITNET (electronic mail service). **Remarks:** FAX: (319)335-5830. Electronic mail address(es): CADPAMTS@UIAMVS (BITNET).

★ 6799 ★
Guild of Carillonneurs in North America - Archives (Mus)
Grosse Pointe Memorial Church
16 Lakeshore Dr. Phone: (313)882-5330
Grosse Pointe, MI 48236 William De Turk, Archv.
Founded: 1936. **Staff:** Prof 1. **Subjects:** Carillons, chimes, campanology. **Holdings:** 15 VF drawers of archives, tapes, records, books. **Services:** Archives not open to the public but information can be obtained by contacting archivist.

John E. Guilday Library
See: **Carnegie Museum of Natural History - Library** (3085)

★ 6800 ★
Guilford College - Hege Library - Special Collections (Hist)
5800 W. Friendly Ave. Phone: (919)316-2000
Greensboro, NC 27410 Dr. Herbert Poole, Lib.Dir.
Founded: 1837. **Staff:** Prof 7; Other 6. **Subjects:** American Revolution, North Caroliniana, Civil War; science fiction. **Special Collections:** Friends Historical Collection (original records and minutes of the Society of Friends in North Carolina). **Holdings:** 167,439 books; 17,897 bound periodical volumes; 21,153 microforms; 12,653 AV programs. **Subscriptions:** 1051 journals and other serials; 21 newspapers. **Services:** Interlibrary loan; copying; SDI; media production; collections open to the public with restrictions. **Automated Operations:** Computerized cataloging. **Computerized Information Services:** DIALOG Information Services, EPIC. **Networks/Consortia:** Member of SOLINET. **Publications:** Occasional papers; The Southern Friend: Journal of the North Carolina Friends Historical Society. **Remarks:** FAX: (919)316-2951; (919)316-2952. **Staff:** Carole Treadway, Spec.Coll.Libn.; Nancy Scism, Hd., Tech.Serv.; Elizabeth Place-Beary, Ref.Libn.; Malone Stinson, Ref.Libn.; Karen Behm, Circ.Libn.; Carol Cothern, Acq.Libn.; Stan Gilliam, Media Libn.

★ 6801 ★
Guilford Technical Community College - Learning Resource Center (Educ)
High Point Rd.
Box 309 Phone: (919)334-4822
Jamestown, NC 27282 Beverley Gass, Dean, Lrng.Rsrc.Ctr.
Founded: 1963. **Staff:** Prof 5; Other 15. **Subjects:** Technology, vocational education, nursing, dental technology, commercial art, electronics. **Holdings:** 63,246 books; 1050 bound periodical volumes; 12 VF drawers of clippings and pamphlets; 12 VF drawers of archives; 8333 films, filmstrips, videotapes, recordings, other AV programs; 25,732 microforms. **Subscriptions:** 505 journals and other serials; 17 newspapers. **Services:** Interlibrary loan; copying; media production; computers and typewriter for student use; tutorial assistance; library open to the public. **Automated Operations:** Computerized public access catalog (LaserGuide). **Computerized Information Services:** DIALOG Information Services, WESTLAW, InfoTrac, ERIC, CINAHL, Electronic Newsbank. Performs searches on fee basis. Contact Person: Randy Candelaria, Pub. & Info.Serv.Libn., 334-4822, ext. 2232. **Publications:** Faculty Guide, annual; List of AV Materials, annual; Periodicals List, annual - all to faculty. **Remarks:** FAX: (919)841-4350. **Staff:** Martha Davis, Tech.Serv.; Betty Lipford, Circ.; Gloria Pitts, Greensboro Campus Lib.; Scott Burnette, AV Supv.; Belinda Daniels, Ref./ILL; Robin Brewington, Lrng.Ctr.

Guilford Township Historical Collection
See: **Plainfield Public Library** (13094)

★ 6802 ★
Guitar Foundation of America - Archive (Mus)
c/o Music Library
Wisconsin Conservatory of Music
1584 N. Prospect Ave. Phone: (414)276-5760
Milwaukee, WI 53202 George Lindquist, Archv.
Staff: 3. **Subjects:** Guitar music. **Holdings:** 36 volumes; 2500 scores; 7 dissertations on the guitar; 1 VF drawer of information on guitarists and the guitar; 4 VF drawers of modern guitar music. **Services:** Copying; archive open to the public by appointment. **Automated Operations:** Computerized cataloging. **Special Catalogs:** Catalog of guitar music - for sale. **Remarks:** Mail orders are handled at Wisconsin Conservatory of Music. The Reference Library of Modern Editions is located at the Music Resource Center, University of Akron, School of Music, Akron, OH; contact Nancy L. Stokes. Acquisitions and cataloging are handled at Music Library, Sullivant Hall, Ohio State University, Columbus, OH 43210; contact Thomas A. Heck, (614)292-2310. Club headquarters located at P.O. Box 878, Claremont, CA 91711.

★ 6803 ★
Gujarat Agriculture University - Library (Agri)
Sadar Krushinagar 385 506, India Phone: 65
K.H. Bhatt
Founded: 1976. **Staff:** Prof 3; Other 5. **Subjects:** Agriculture, biological science, veterinary science. **Holdings:** 12,894 books; 3278 bound periodical volumes; 2640 reports; theses. **Services:** Interlibrary loan; library open to the public for reference use only.

★ 6804 ★
Gujarat Vidya Sabha - Sheth Bholabhai Jeshingbhai Institute of Learning and Research - Library (Area-Ethnic, Hum)
R.C. Marg Phone: 408862
Ahmedabad 380 009, Gujarat, India Vidula T. Mistry, Libn.
Subjects: Indian culture, history, archeology; iconography and painting; Sanskrit and Gujarati literature. **Holdings:** 65,900 volumes. **Services:** Interlibrary loan; library open to research students and to students working toward their M.A. in culture.

★ 6805 ★
Gujarat Vidyapith - Peace Research Center, Ahmedabad - Library (Soc Sci)
Ashram Rd. Phone: 447292
Ahmedabad 380 014, Gujarat, India Mr. Kanubhai Shah, Libn.
Subjects: Peace, peace education, science and nonviolence, Gandhian thought, impact of war. **Holdings:** 10,000 volumes. **Subscriptions:** 30 journals and other serials. **Services:** Interlibrary loan; copying; SDI; library open to the public for reference use only. **Computerized Information Services:** Internal database. **Remarks:** Gujarat Vidyapith was founded in 1920 by Mohandas Gandhi to work towards the establishment of a society based on truth and nonviolence. Telex: 121 6254 GUVI IN.

★ 6806 ★
Gulf Arab States Educational Research Center - Library (Educ)
P.O. Box 25566 Phone: 4835203
Safat 13116, Kuwait Mohei A. Hak, Libn.
Founded: 1978. **Subjects:** Education in Arab countries - kindergarten through higher education, teacher training, teaching methods, educational objectives, special education, curriculum development, educational evaluation. **Holdings:** 15,000 volumes. **Remarks:** Affiliated with Regional Arab Bureau of Education. FAX: 4830571. Telex: 44118.

★ 6807 ★
Gulf Canada Resources Ltd. - Library (Energy)
P.O. Box 130, Sta. M Phone: (403)233-3804
Calgary, AB, Canada T2P 2H7 Susan Lowe, Sr.Libn.
Founded: 1959. **Staff:** Prof 1; Other 2. **Subjects:** Petroleum industry, petroleum engineering, geology, exploration, production, marketing, business. **Holdings:** 15,000 volumes; 6000 reports; 6000 maps. **Subscriptions:** 475 journals and other serials. **Services:** Interlibrary loan; copying; library open to the public with approval from management. **Automated Operations:** Computerized cataloging. **Computerized Information Services:** PFDS Online, Info Globe, DIALOG Information Services, Dow Jones News/Retrieval, QL Systems, CAN/OLE; Envoy 100 (electronic mail service). **Publications:** Acquisition list, monthly. **Remarks:** FAX: (403)233-3070. Telex: 038-24551. Electronic mail address(es): ILL.GULF (Envoy 100). **Staff:** Betty Erickson, Ref.Techn.; Debbie Mann, Ref.Techn.

★ 6808 ★
Gulf Coast Research Laboratory - Gunter Library (Biol Sci)
Box 7000 Phone: (601)872-4253
Ocean Springs, MS 39564-7000 Malcolm S. Ware, Sr.Libn.
Founded: 1947. **Staff:** Prof 1. **Subjects:** Marine sciences, including biology, microbiology, physiology, parasitology, geology, chemistry, botany, ecology, oceanography, zoology, toxicology; fisheries research and management. **Special Collections:** Piatt Collection/Embryology (3775 papers); Gunter Collection/Marine Biology (2700 papers); Bennett Collection/Marine Invertebrates (4000 papers). **Holdings:** 15,000 books; 5000 periodical volumes; 14 journal titles on microfilm; 45 journal titles on microcard; 30,000 reprints. **Subscriptions:** 156 journals and other serials. **Services:** Interlibrary loan; copying (limited); library open to the public for reference use only. **Networks/Consortia:** Member of Mississippi Biomedical Library Consortium (MBLC). **Publications:** Gulf Research Reports, irregular - by exchange. **Remarks:** Alternate telephone number(s): (601)872-4213. FAX: (601)872-4204.

★ 6809 ★
Gulf Publishing Co., Inc. - Biloxi Sun Herald - Editorial Library (Publ)
Debuys Rd.
Box 4567 Phone: (601)896-2308
Biloxi, MS 39535-4567 Marilyn Pustay, Libn.
Founded: 1974. **Staff:** 2. **Subjects:** Newspaper reference topics. **Holdings:** 120 VF drawers of Biloxi Sun and Herald clippings; 300 reports of state and local agencies; Daily Herald, 1888 to present, on microfilm; Biloxi Sun, 1973 to present, on microfilm; Biloxi Sun Herald, 1985 to present, on microfilm. **Subscriptions:** 16 journals and other serials. **Services:** Copying; library open to the public with restrictions. **Remarks:** Alternate telephone number(s): 896-2108. FAX: (601)896-2104. Part of the Knight Ridder Newspaper Group. **Staff:** Rhonda Cockrell.

Gulf States Information Documentation Center
See: **Arab Gulf States Information Documentation Center** (933)

★ 6810 ★
Gulf States Utilities Company - Corporate Library (Energy)
Box 2951 Phone: (409)838-6631
Beaumont, TX 77704 Gloria H. Smith, Libn.
Founded: 1956. **Staff:** Prof 1; Other 1. **Subjects:** Public utility industry and regulations; electrical engineering; nuclear power, engineering, licensing; management; government; business; accounting. **Holdings:** 6000 volumes; 160 films; Energyfiche; U.S. Federal Register and Code of Federal Regulations, 1936 to present, on microfiche. **Subscriptions:** 700 journals and other serials. **Services:** Interlibrary loan; copying; library open to the public with restrictions. **Automated Operations:** Computerized cataloging and acquisitions. **Computerized Information Services:** DIALOG Information Services, PFDS Online, OCLC, DataTimes, NEXIS, WESTLAW, Dow Jones News/Retrieval. **Networks/Consortia:** Member of AMIGOS Bibliographic Council, Inc. **Remarks:** Library located at 350 Pine St., Beaumont, TX 77701. FAX: (409)839-3077.

★ 6811 ★
Gulf States Utilities Company - Law Library (Law)
Box 2951 Phone: (409)838-6631
Beaumont, TX 77704 Barbara J. Penry, Legal Asst.
Subjects: Texas, Louisiana, federal statutes; public utility law; labor relations; federal regulations. **Holdings:** 2175 books; bound periodical volumes. **Subscriptions:** 11 journals and other serials. **Services:** Library open to other attorneys for reference use. **Remarks:** FAX: (409)839-3016.

★ 6812 ★
Gulf States Utilities Company - River Bend Station - Technical Resource/Reference Center (Energy, Law)
Box 220 Phone: (504)381-4361
St. Francisville, LA 70775 P.S. Jones
Founded: 1979. **Staff:** 1. **Subjects:** Nuclear regulation. **Special Collections:** Nuclear power plants licensing regulations. **Holdings:** 3000 titles of Nuclear Regulatory Commission publications; 650 federal reports; 500 utility safety analysis documents; 600 River Bend Nuclear Station materials; 900 corporation and regulatory documents; 200 National Laboratory documents. **Subscriptions:** 7 journals and other serials. **Services:** Interlibrary loan. **Computerized Information Services:** OCLC. **Remarks:** FAX: (504)381-4873.

Mirza Abu'l-Fadl Gulpaygani Library
See: **Baha'i World Centre** (1407)

Jessica R. Gund Memorial Library
See: **Cleveland Institute of Art** (3809)

★ 6813 ★
Gundersen/Lutheran Medical Center - Health Sciences Library (Med)
1910 South Ave. Phone: (608)785-0530
La Crosse, WI 54601 Kathleen Cimpl Wagner, Dir.
Founded: 1961. **Staff:** Prof 1; Other 5. **Subjects:** Medicine, nursing, allied health sciences, administration, pastoral care. **Holdings:** 7000 books; 14,000 bound periodical volumes. **Subscriptions:** 670 journals and other serials. **Services:** Interlibrary loan; copying; SDI; library open to the public with restrictions. **Automated Operations:** Computerized acquisitions, serials, and ILL (DOCLINE). **Computerized Information Services:** MEDLINE, BRS Information Technologies. Performs searches on fee basis. **Networks/Consortia:** Member of Northwestern Wisconsin Health Science Library Consortium, National Network of Libraries of Medicine - Greater Midwest Region. **Publications:** Medical staff and nursing bulletins. **Remarks:** FAX: (608)785-2181.

L.P. Gundry Health Sciences Library
See: **St. Agnes Hospital** (14221)

Emery A. Gunnin Architectural Library
See: **Clemson University** (3793)

Morgan A. and Aline D. Gunst Memorial Library of the Book Arts
See: **Stanford University - Special Collections** (15658)

★6814★
Gunston Hall - Library (Hist, Rare Book)
10709 Gunston Rd. Phone: (703)550-9220
Lorton, VA 22079-3901 Anne Baker, Libn.
Founded: 1974. **Staff:** 1. **Subjects:** George Mason and Mason family, John Mercer, law and government, architecture, colonial American and Virginia history, fine and decorative arts, cooking, gardening. **Special Collections:** Mason-Mercer Rare Book Collection (2000 volumes representing library holdings of 18th century gentleman); Pamela C. Copeland Collection (500 volumes on Virginiana and genealogy); Robert Carter of Nomini Hall Collection (170 volumes); Elizabeth L. Frelinghuysen Collection (1000 volumes). **Holdings:** 7500 books; 500 bound periodical volumes; 35 papers and letters of George Mason; photostats of 5000 Mason Family papers; 200 maps; 100 reels of microfilm. **Subscriptions:** 20 journals. **Services:** Copying; library open to the public by appointment. **Remarks:** FAX: (703)550-9480. Maintained by the Commonwealth of Virginia.

Gunter Library
See: **Gulf Coast Research Laboratory** (6808)

Raymond Gustafson Archives
See: **Iron County Museum** (8249)

★6815★
Gustavus Adolphus College - Lund Music Library (Mus)
St. Peter, MN 56082 Phone: (507)931-7365
Jan Jensen, Mus.Lib.Asst.
Founded: 1971. **Staff:** 1. **Subjects:** Music. **Special Collections:** Mettetal Record Collection (14,000 phonograph records). **Holdings:** 5000 books; 4000 scores. **Services:** Interlibrary loan; library open to the public with restrictions. **Automated Operations:** Computerized public access catalog and cataloging. **Computerized Information Services:** OCLC, DIALOG Information Services. **Networks/Consortia:** Member of MINITEX Library Information Network. **Special Indexes:** Index of Swedish music in the library (notebook).

Emil & Lilly Gutheil Memorial Library
See: **Postgraduate Center for Mental Health** (13270)

★6816★
Guthrie Medical Center - William C. Beck Health Science Library and Resource Center (Med)
Guthrie Square Phone: (717)882-4700
Sayre, PA 18840 Robert V. Pezdek, Dir.
Founded: 1929. **Staff:** Prof 4; Other 4. **Subjects:** Medicine, surgery, ophthalmology, anesthesia, nursing, oncology. **Holdings:** 4300 books; 5000 bound periodical volumes. **Subscriptions:** 550 journals and other serials. **Services:** Interlibrary loan; library not open to the public. **Automated Operations:** Computerized acquisitions. **Computerized Information Services:** MEDLINE; CD-ROMs (CINAHL, HealthPLAN-CD). Performs searches on fee basis. **Networks/Consortia:** Member of Susquehanna Library Cooperative, Central Pennsylvania Health Sciences Library Association (CPHSLA). **Remarks:** FAX: (717)882-4703. **Formerly:** Its Robert Packer Hospital Health Sciences Library. **Staff:** Richard D. Reilly, Circuit Libn.; David Lester, Circuit Libn.

★6817★
Guthrie Theater Foundation - Guthrie Theater Staff Reference Library (Theater)
725 Vineland Pl. Phone: (612)347-1133
Minneapolis, MN 55403 Sheila J. O'Brien, Libn.
Founded: 1972. **Staff:** Prof 1. **Subjects:** Costume design and history, decorative arts, architecture, history of theater, actors and acting, stage lighting and design, technical production, dramatic literature and critical works, poetry, music, general history and geography. **Special Collections:** Ladies Home Companion, The Designer, Delineator, 1908-1950; complete collection of programs from past productions. **Holdings:** 3000 books; 1900 plays; 8 VF drawers of slides; 12 VF drawers of photographs of past productions; 8 VF drawers of scripts from past productions. **Subscriptions:** 6 journals and other serials. **Services:** Library not open to the public. **Special Indexes:** Play index (card). **Remarks:** FAX: (612)347-1188.

Monroe C. Gutman Library
See: **Harvard University - Graduate School of Education** (6968)

Guttman Library and Information Center
See: **Sacramento-El Dorado Medical Society** (14195)

James Samuel Guy Library
See: **Emory University** (5332)

★6818★
Gwynedd-Mercy College - Lourdes Library (Med, Rel-Phil)
Gwynedd Valley, PA 19437 Phone: (215)646-7300
Sr. Berenice Marie Appel, Lib.Dir.
Founded: 1948. **Staff:** Prof 4.5; Other 6. **Subjects:** Health, religious studies. **Special Collections:** Irish Collection; Children's Collection. **Holdings:** 90,000 books; 738 bound periodical volumes; 29,000 microfiche; 3000 reels of microfilm; media programs. **Subscriptions:** 745 journals and other serials; 6 newspapers. **Services:** Interlibrary loan; copying; library open to the public by appointment and with restrictions. **Automated Operations:** Computerized acquisitions. **Computerized Information Services:** BRS Information Technologies. Performs searches. **Networks/Consortia:** Member of Tri-State College Library Cooperative (TCLC), PALINET. **Publications:** Library Guide; Acquisitions List. **Remarks:** FAX: (215)641-5596. **Staff:** Purnima Bagga, Cat.; Constance Davis, Ref.Libn.; Linda Jones, Ser.Libn.; Evey Udall, Cat.

Gyogyszerkutato Intezet Kv.
See: **Institute for Drug Research** (7928)

H

★6819★
H.M.S. Bounty Society, International - Research Library and Depository (Hist)
Box 5121 Phone: (415)345-2899
San Mateo, CA 94402-5121 A. Munro Christian, Dir.
Founded: 1971. **Staff:** Prof 1; Other 5. **Subjects:** H.M.S. Bounty history, H.M.S. Pandora, H.M.S. Sirius, genealogy, Christian heraldry, Pitcairn/ Norfolk Island history. **Special Collections:** Christian family pedigree, 13th-20th centuries; H.M.S. Bounty historical documents; H.M.S. Bounty crew genealogy. **Holdings:** 1000 books; 5 bound periodical volumes; 150 manuscripts. **Subscriptions:** 4 journals and other serials; 2 newspapers. **Services:** Copying; library open to the public for research use only. **Remarks:** FAX: (415)345-2899. Affiliated with the Norfolk Island Historical Society & Museum Trust, Norfolk Island 2899, South Pacific Ocean and the Pitcairn Island Museum and Library.

Ha Hevre ha Historit ha Israelit
See: **Historical Society of Israel** (7270)

John A.W. Haas Library
See: **Cedar Crest and Muhlenberg College Libraries** (3183)

Ruth A. Haas Library
See: **Western Connecticut State University** (20240)

Habitat
See: **United Nations - Centre for Human Settlements (Habitat)** (16750)

★6820★
Habitat Institute for the Environment - Natural History Library (Biol Sci)
10 Juniper Rd.
Box 136 Phone: (617)489-5050
Belmont, MA 02178 Barbara B. Herzstein, Libn.
Founded: 1970. **Staff:** 1. **Subjects:** Natural history, environmental education, horticulture, ecology. **Holdings:** 1700 books. **Subscriptions:** 10 journals and other serials. **Services:** Copying; library open to the public with restrictions.

★6821★
Hacettepe University - Libraries (Med, Sci-Engr, Soc Sci)
Ankara, Turkey Phone: 41-3117998
Mrs. Z. Sezen Tan
Subjects: Medicine, engineering, social sciences, physical therapy, dentistry, nursing, pharmacy, conservation. **Holdings:** 125,000 books; 200,000 bound periodical volumes; 22,000 AV programs; 200 manuscripts. **Subscriptions:** 700 journals and other serials. **Services:** Interlibrary loan; copying; SDI; library open to the public with restrictions. **Computerized Information Services:** DIALOG Information Services, MEDLINE; BIBLIOFILE (internal database). **Special Catalogs:** Hacettepe University Periodicals Catalog. **Remarks:** Includes the holdings of the Medical Center Library and the Beytepe Campus Library. Telex: 42237 htk tr.

★6822★
Hackensack Medical Center - Medical Library (Med)
30 Prospect Ave. Phone: (201)996-2326
Hackensack, NJ 07601 Duressa Pujat, Libn.
Founded: 1951. **Staff:** Prof 2; Other 2. **Subjects:** Medicine, surgery, nursing, hospital administration. **Special Collections:** Hospital archives. **Holdings:** 5200 books; 15,000 bound periodical volumes; vertical files; pamphlets; 500 tapes. **Subscriptions:** 272 journals and other serials. **Services:** Interlibrary loan; copying; library open to the public. **Automated Operations:** Computerized serials. **Computerized Information Services:** NLM. Performs searches on fee basis. **Networks/Consortia:** Member of Bergen Passaic Regional Library Cooperative. **Publications:** Accessions List, quarterly - for internal distribution only. **Remarks:** FAX: (201)996-2467. **Staff:** Cynthia Schutzer, Assoc.Libn.

★6823★
Hackettstown Community Hospital - Medical Staff Library (Med)
651 Willow Grove St. Phone: (908)852-5100
Hackettstown, NJ 07840 Ruth E. Scarborough, Libn.
Founded: 1971. **Subjects:** Medicine, nursing. **Holdings:** 1000 books; 300 bound periodical volumes; 95 reports. **Subscriptions:** 106 journals and other serials. **Services:** Interlibrary loan; copying; library open to the public on a limited schedule. **Remarks:** FAX: (908)850-6804.

★6824★
Hackettstown Historical Society - Museum (Hist)
106 Church St. Phone: (201)852-8797
Hackettstown, NJ 07840 Helen G. Montfort, Archv., Cur.
Founded: 1975. **Subjects:** Local history and genealogy. **Holdings:** 540 books; 700 newspapers, 1874-1975; 325 documents; 96 genealogies; 30 volumes of Warren County cemetery records; 35 oral histories; 2 volumes of historical buildings in Hackettstown; 5 histories of Hackettstown by local historians; 50 scrapbooks and 25 volumes of photographs of historical materials; 158 slides; 10 maps; 12 cuneiform tablets; 17 quilts, 1870-1930; 14,600 archival materials; 18 VF drawers. **Subscriptions:** 8 journals and other serials; 2 newspapers. **Services:** Copying; museum open to the public for reference use only. **Networks/Consortia:** Member of New Jersey Library Network, Northwest Regional Library Cooperative. **Staff:** Warren Page, Pres.; Ruth E. Scarborough, Libn., Archv., Cur.

★6825★
Hackley Hospital - Library (Med)
1700 Clinton St.
P.O. Box 3302 Phone: (616)728-4766
Muskegon, MI 49443-3302 Betty Marshall, Libn.
Founded: 1962. **Staff:** 1. **Subjects:** Medicine, nursing, allied health sciences. **Holdings:** 1500 books; 3296 bound periodical volumes. **Subscriptions:** 155 journals and other serials. **Services:** Interlibrary loan; copying; library open to area health care personnel. **Computerized Information Services:** BRS Information Technologies. **Networks/Consortia:** Member of National Network of Libraries of Medicine - Greater Midwest Region, Lakeland Area Library Network (LAKENET).

★6826★
Hadassah Mt. Scopus Medical Center - Medical Library (Med)
Mt. Scopus
POB 24035 Phone: 2 818111
91240 Jerusalem, Israel Mrs. Yaffa Weingarten
Founded: 1979. **Staff:** Prof 1; Other 1. **Subjects:** Medicine. **Holdings:** 2000 books; 5800 bound periodical volumes. **Subscriptions:** 50 journals and other serials. **Services:** Interlibrary loan; copying; SDI; library open to the public. **Computerized Information Services:** MEDLINE. **Remarks:** FAX: 2 823515. Alternate telephone number(s): 2 822411; 2 814644.

Hadley Library
See: **Earlham College - Joseph Moore Museum** (5095)

Hadley Memorial Library
See: **Washington Psychoanalytic Society** (20021)

Helen Hagan Rare Book Room
See: **University of North Carolina at Wilmington - William Madison Randall Library** (19093)

Alice Hagar Curriculum Resource Center
See: **University of Wisconsin--La Crosse** (19573)

W.W. Hagerty Library
See: **Drexel University** (5005)

Haggard Memorial Library
See: **East Dallas Christian Church** (5118)

★6827★
The Haggin Museum - Almeda May Castle Petzinger Library (Hist, Art)
1201 N. Pershing Ave. Phone: (209)462-1404
Stockton, CA 95203 Tod Ruhstaller, Act.Libn.
Founded: 1948. **Staff:** Prof 1. **Subjects:** California history, local biography, agricultural technology of San Joaquin Valley, Caterpillar tractors, local business and industry. **Special Collections:** Ralph Yardley drawings of early Stockton history; Bert Whitman's editorial cartoons; Stockton Iron Works business records; V. Covert Martin Photo Collection; Holt Manufacturing Company archives; Stephens Bros. Boat Works archives. **Holdings:** 7000 books; 280 bound periodical volumes; 60,000 manuscripts, maps, business records, diaries, documents, photographs. **Subscriptions:** 14 journals and other serials. **Services:** Copying; library open to the public for reference use only on a fee basis. **Remarks:** FAX: (209)462-1404.

★6828★
Hagley Museum and Library (Hist)
Box 3630 Phone: (302)658-2400
Wilmington, DE 19807 Dr. Glenn Porter, Dir.
Founded: 1953. **Staff:** Prof 11; Other 4.5. **Subjects:** History - business, industrial, technological, naval, computer; French Revolution; explosives; aeronautics. **Special Collections:** Papers of du Pont Family, 1760-1954, and Du Pont Company, 1802-1975; business and industrial records of over 500 companies in the Mid-Atlantic states. **Holdings:** 185,000 books, bound periodical volumes, pamphlets, trade catalogs; 20 million manuscripts and archival materials; 12,000 microforms; 500,000 photographs, prints, engineering drawings. **Subscriptions:** 220 journals and other serials. **Services:** Interlibrary loan; copying; library open to the public. **Automated Operations:** Computerized cataloging and acquisitions. **Computerized Information Services:** RLIN. **Publications:** Occasional guides to collections and other bibliographical aids; Guide to Manuscripts (1970; 1978 supplement); Pictorial Collections brochure. **Remarks:** FAX: (302)658-0568. **Staff:** Susan Hengel, Hd. Imprints Libn.; Marian Matyn, Ref.Libn.; Michael H. Nash, Cur., Mss.; Jon Williams, Cur., Pictorial Coll.

★6829★
(The Hague) American Documentation Center - USIS Library (Educ)
2 Korte Voorhout 2
NL-2511 EK The Hague, Netherlands
Remarks: Maintained or supported by the U.S. Information Agency. Focus is on materials that will assist peoples outside the United States to learn about the United States, its people, history, culture, political processes, and social milieux.

Otto Hahn Bibliothek
See: **Max Planck Institute for Biophysical Chemistry** (13099)

★6830★
Hahnemann University - Library (Med)
245 N. 15th St, M.S. 449 Phone: (215)448-7631
Philadelphia, PA 19102-1192 Carol Hansen Fenichel, Ph.D., Dir.
Founded: 1868. **Staff:** Prof 8; Other 13. **Subjects:** Medicine, allied health professions, nursing, mental health. **Special Collections:** Constantine Hering Collection on Paracelsus (200 items); homeopathy (350 volumes); history of medicine (1000 volumes). **Holdings:** 42,000 books; 46,000 bound periodical volumes; 1300 theses; 1000 government and miscellaneous reports; 26 VF drawers; 450 reels of microfilm; 307 audiotapes; 755 videotapes; 132 slide sets; 52 films and filmstrips; 550 linear feet of archives, manuscripts, photographs, memorabilia. **Subscriptions:** 1311 journals and other serials. **Services:** Interlibrary loan; copying; SDI; library open to the public on a fee basis. **Automated Operations:** Computerized public access catalog, cataloging, circulation, and serials. **Computerized Information Services:** NLM, DIALOG Information Services, OCLC, BRS Information Technologies, WILSONLINE, VU/TEXT Information Services, STN International, EasyNet; CD-ROMs (MEDLINE, PSYCLIT, SCI, Nursing & Allied Health (CINAHL)-CD, MICROMEDEX); InterNet (electronic mail service). Performs searches on fee basis. Contact Person: Judith Baker, Assoc.Dir., Pub.Serv., (215)448-7632. **Networks/Consortia:** Member of National Network of Libraries of Medicine - Middle Atlantic Region, Interlibrary Delivery Service of Pennsylvania (IDS), PALINET, Health Sciences Libraries Consortium (HSLC). **Publications:** Library Newsletter, monthly - for internal distribution only. **Special Catalogs:** Serials holdings; audiovisual catalog. **Remarks:** FAX: (215)448-8180. Electronic mail address(es): FENICHEL@SHRSYS.HSLC.ORG (InterNet). **Staff:** Geraldine Eisenberg, Assoc.Dir., Tech.Serv.; Paul Keenan, Hd., Lrng.Rsrc.Ctr.; Judith Donovan, Ref.Libn.; Howard Silver, Hd., Access Serv.; Tamara Georgick, Ref.Libn.; Lori Joffe, AV Libn.

★6831★
Haifa National Maritime Museum - Library (Hist)
198 Allenby Rd.
POB 44855 Phone: 4 536622
31447 Haifa, Israel Dalia Argov
Founded: 1972. **Staff:** Prof 1. **Subjects:** Maritime history, nautical archeology, cartography, naval history, explorations, scientific instruments. **Special Collections:** Ancient Books collection (150 volumes). **Holdings:** 5500 books; 1200 bound periodical volumes. **Subscriptions:** 30 journals and other serials.

★6832★
Haight, Gardner, Poor and Havens - Library (Law)
195 Broadway Phone: (212)341-7380
New York, NY 10007 Amy R. Comeau, Libn.
Staff: Prof 1; Other 4. **Subjects:** Admiralty and aviation law. **Holdings:** 25,000 books; 800 bound periodical volumes; 7 VF drawers of maps and charts; 15 VF drawers of pamphlets; 5 VF drawers of legal forms. **Subscriptions:** 50 journals and other serials; 14 newspapers. **Services:** Interlibrary loan. **Automated Operations:** Computerized cataloging and serials. **Computerized Information Services:** LEXIS, DIALOG Information Services, WESTLAW. **Remarks:** FAX: (212)385-9010.

★6833★
Haileybury Northern School of Mines - Library (Sci-Engr)
Latchford St. Phone: (705)672-3376
Haileybury, ON, Canada P0J 1K0 Carol Cameron, Libn.
Founded: 1959. **Staff:** Prof 1. **Subjects:** Mining, geophysics, geology, physiography, mineralogy, surveying, metallurgy, mineral dressing, qualitative and quantitative analysis, drafting, assaying, electricity, magnetism, ventilation, ground control, hydraulics, technical communications. **Special Collections:** Publications and maps of the Ontario Department of Mines and Geological Survey of Canada; Mining Institutes Transactions. **Holdings:** 10,000 books; 9000 bound periodical volumes; 3113 government reports; 6698 maps. **Subscriptions:** 30 journals and other serials; 10 newspapers. **Services:** Interlibrary loan; copying; library open to the public.

Richard D. Haines Medical Library
See: **Scott & White Memorial Hospital** (14964)

★6834★
Haiti - Archives Nationales d'Haiti (Hist)
Angle rues Geffrard et Borgella Phone: 1 20227
Port-au-Prince, Haiti Jean Wilfrid Bertrand, Dir.-Gen.
Founded: 1960. **Staff:** Prof 20; Other 55. **Subjects:** Haiti - history, official documents, periodicals, archives, documentation. **Special Collections:** Moreau de St. Mery Library on Microfilm (collection focused on colonial period). **Holdings:** 3000 books; 500 bound periodical volumes; 2152 archival items; 1160 microfiche; 114 reels of microfilm; 165 other cataloged items. **Subscriptions:** 12 journals and other serials; 5 newspapers. **Services:** Archives open to the public.

Hajji Baba Society Library
See: **Macculloch Hall Historical Museum - Macculloch Hall Archives** (9492)

★6835★
Hale and Dorr - Library (Law)
60 State St. Phone: (617)742-9100
Boston, MA 02109 Jane Huston, Dir., Lib.Serv.
Founded: 1960. **Staff:** Prof 3; Other 6. **Subjects:** Law. **Holdings:** 20,000 volumes. **Subscriptions:** 200 journals and other serials. **Services:** Interlibrary loan; library not open to the public. **Computerized Information Services:** DIALOG Information Services, LEXIS, VU/TEXT Information Services, WESTLAW, Information America, Dow Jones News/Retrieval, NewsNet, Inc., Dun & Bradstreet Business Credit Services, Securities Data Company, Venture Economics. **Staff:** Patricia Michalowskij, Hd., Ref.; Lynn Chickering, Asst.Libn./Adm.

Hale Hospital
See: **Haverhill Municipal (Hale) Hospital** (7018)

Haleakala, Inc.
See: **The Kitchen** (8746)

Haleakala National Park
See: **U.S. Natl. Park Service** (17728)

★6836★
Haley & Aldrich, Inc. - Library (Sci-Engr)
58 Charles St. Phone: (617)494-4910
Cambridge, MA 02141 Anne C. Hughes, Libn.
Staff: Prof 1. **Subjects:** Engineering - geotechnical, environmental; geology. **Holdings:** 7000 books; maps. **Subscriptions:** 80 journals and other serials. **Services:** Interlibrary loan; copying; SDI; library open to the public with restrictions. **Automated Operations:** Computerized cataloging (INMAGIC). **Computerized Information Services:** DIALOG Information Services, NLM, EPIC, Ground Water On-Line.

★6837★
Halifax City Development and Planning Department - Library (Plan)
P.O. Box 1749 Phone: (902)421-7652
Halifax, NS, Canada B3J 3A5 Deborah Chambers, Info.Coord.
Services: Library not open to the public; material available by appointment. **Remarks:** FAX: (902)421-2659. **Formerly:** Halifax City Planning Information Office - Library.

★6838★
Halifax City Regional Library - Special Collections (Hist)
5381 Spring Garden Rd. Phone: (902)421-6980
Halifax, NS, Canada B3J 1E9 Diane MacQuarrie, Chf.Libn.
Founded: 1951. **Special Collections:** Halifax reference collection; Canadian and Nova Scotia Government document depository. **Services:** Interlibrary loan; copying; collections open to the public. **Automated Operations:** Computerized cataloging. **Computerized Information Services:** UTLAS. **Publications:** Serials directory, annual; bibliographies; resource lists; community directories. **Remarks:** FAX: (902)421-2791.

★6839★
Halifax Herald Ltd. - Library (Publ)
1650 Argyle St. Phone: (902)426-3080
Halifax, NS, Canada B3J 2T2 Alberta Dube, Libn.
Staff: 3. **Subjects:** Newspaper reference topics. **Holdings:** Newspaper files; microfilm; reference materials. **Services:** Library not open to the public. **Remarks:** FAX: (902)426-1158.

★6840★
Halifax Historical Society, Inc. - Library (Hist)
252 S. Beach St. Phone: (904)255-6976
Daytona Beach, FL 32114-4407 Dr. William Doremus, Pres.
Staff: 2. **Subjects:** Florida history, automobiles, history, educational institutions. **Holdings:** 1000 books; 170 bound periodical volumes; 30 VF drawers of photographs, scrapbooks, postcards, maps, clippings, slides. **Services:** Copying; photo reproduction; library open to the public for reference use only by appointment. **Staff:** Elizabeth B. Baker, Act.Dir.

★6841★
Halifax Infirmary - Health Services Library (Med)
1335 Queen St. Phone: (902)428-3058
Halifax, NS, Canada B3J 2H6 Dr. Anitra Laycock, Libn.
Founded: 1963. **Staff:** Prof 1; Other 1. **Subjects:** Medicine, nursing, allied health sciences, administration. **Holdings:** 1500 books; 5000 slides, archives, and videotapes. **Subscriptions:** 350 journals and other serials. **Services:** Interlibrary loan; copying; SDI; library open to the public with restrictions. **Automated Operations:** Computerized serials. **Computerized Information Services:** Online systems.

★6842★
Halifax Medical Center - Medical Library (Med)
Box 2830 Phone: (904)254-4051
Daytona Beach, FL 32115 Addajane L. Wallace, Med.Libn.
Founded: 1963. **Staff:** Prof 1. **Subjects:** Medicine, nursing, hospital administration, consumer health information. **Holdings:** 2788 books; 2312 bound periodical volumes; 6 subscriptions for cassette tapes. **Subscriptions:** 200 journals and other serials. **Services:** Interlibrary loan; copying; research; library open to the public. **Computerized Information Services:** MEDLARS.

★6843★
Hall-Brooke Hospital - Professional Library (Med)
47 Long Lots Rd. Phone: (203)227-1251
Westport, CT 06880 Sharon Rerak, Coord., Educ.
Founded: 1960. **Staff:** 2. **Subjects:** Psychiatry, psychology, mental health, psychiatric nursing, family therapy. **Holdings:** 1800 books; 500 bound periodical volumes. **Subscriptions:** 120 journals and other serials. **Services:** Interlibrary loan; library not open to the public. **Computerized Information Services:** BRS Information Technologies. **Networks/Consortia:** Member of Connecticut Association of Health Science Libraries (CAHSL), Southwestern Connecticut Library Council (SWLC).

★6844★
Hall County Museum - Stuhr Museum - Reynolds Research Center (Hist)
3133 W. Hwy. 34 Phone: (308)381-5316
Grand Island, NE 68801 Steve Adams, Dir. of Res.
Founded: 1961. **Staff:** 2. **Subjects:** Local and state history; building and community development, 1850-1900; German and Danish ethnic groups. **Holdings:** 3000 books; U.S. federal census records, 1860-1900; Nebraska state census records, 1885; Grand Island newspaper, 1870-1925; 50 cubic feet and 100 boxes of documents, diaries, letters, manuscripts, and business ledgers; 22,000 photographs; 28,000 glass plates; land records on microfilm. **Subscriptions:** 12 journals and other serials. **Services:** Copying; center open to the public. **Publications:** Sand-Krog-German Resort on the Platte; Town Building - Nebraska 1850-1900; Bartenbach Opera House; Robert Taylor-"Sheep King"; Edgar Reynolds Diary, 1852 - Overland Route to California from Red Oak, IA. **Special Catalogs:** Catalog to Solomon D. Butcher Collection; catalog to Paine-Bentley Collection. **Staff:** Tom Anderson, Hist., Photo-Archv.

Edward T. Hall Library
See: **University of Arizona - Environmental Psychology Program - Library** (18216)

★6845★
Hall of Flame - Richard S. Fowler Memorial Library (Sci-Engr)
6101 E. Van Buren Phone: (602)275-3473
Phoenix, AZ 85008 George F. Getz, Jr., Pres.
Founded: 1979. **Staff:** 2. **Subjects:** Disasters, fires, fire departments and salvage corps, fire prevention, and fire services. **Special Collections:** Catalogs of fire apparatus manufacturers; histories of major fires; photographs of fires; service manuals and other materials relating to fire departments and the fire service. **Holdings:** 4000 books; 300 bound periodical volumes; company reports; newspaper clippings. **Subscriptions:** 2 newspapers. **Services:** Library open to the public for reference use only. **Remarks:** The telephone number above is designed to read ASK FIRE. Library is operated by the National Historical Fire Foundation. **Staff:** Sheila A. Milan, Libn.

George Talbott Hall Library
See: **Bloomfield College** (1902)

J.B. Hall Memorial Library
See: **Nova Scotia Department of Advanced Education and Job Training - College of Geographic Sciences** (12134)

James Hall Library
See: **Vandalia Historical Society** (19763)

★6846★
Hall of Justice Library (Law)
850 Bryant St., Rm. 305 Phone: (415)553-1763
San Francisco, CA 94103 Tyrene L. Labutan, Legal Asst./Libn.
Founded: 1979. **Staff:** Prof 1. **Subjects:** Law. **Holdings:** 6000 volumes; 1000 bound and unbound serials; 500 microforms. **Subscriptions:** 2 newspapers. **Services:** Library open to attorneys. **Computerized Information Services:** WESTLAW. **Remarks:** Library serves the San Francisco District Attorney and the San Francisco Public Defender offices. **Remarks:** FAX: (415)553-9054.

★6847★
Linda Hall Library (Sci-Engr)
5109 Cherry St. Phone: (816)363-4600
Kansas City, MO 64110 Louis E. Martin, Dir.
Founded: 1946. **Staff:** Prof 19; Other 41. **Subjects:** Mathematics, astronomy, physics, chemistry, geology, biology, pharmacy, pharmacology, engineering, agriculture. **Special Collections:** History of Science; standards and specifications of over 300 governmental and professional organizations (over 100,000); U.S. Patents (PDL). **Holdings:** 633,000 volumes; U.S. patent specifications, July 1946 to present; 1.02 million microforms; technical reports; maps. **Subscriptions:** 16,500 journals and other serials. **Services:** Interlibrary loan; copying; library open to the public. **Automated Operations:** Computerized cataloging. **Computerized Information Services:** DIALOG Information Services, OCLC. **Networks/Consortia:** Member of Bibliographical Center for Research, Rocky Mountain Region, Inc. (BCR), Kansas City Library Network, Inc. (KCLN). **Publications:** Serials Holdings in the Linda Hall Library. **Remarks:** FAX: (816)363-5020 (Adm.); (816)444-9076 (ILL). **Staff:** Paul Peterson, Asst. to Dir.; Siegfried Ruschin, Libn., Coll.Dev.; Wilma L. Hartman, Libn., Pub.Serv.; Nancy K. Day, Libn., Proc.Serv. ; Bruce Bradley, Libn., Hist. of Sci.; James Huesmann, Libn., Automated Sys.

Mattie D. Hall Library
See: **First Baptist Church** (5743)

Paul Hall Library and Maritime Museum
See: **Seafarer's Harry Lundeberg Maryland Seamanship School** (9439)

Hall School of Nursing
See: **Northeast Georgia Medical Center & Hall School of Nursing/ Brenau College** (11968)

Senator Kenneth Hall Learning Resources Center - Special Collections
See: **State Community College** (15677)

Thomas Lee Hall Post Library
See: **U.S. Army Post - Training Command & Fort Jackson** (17077)

Virginia B. Hall Pharmacy Library
See: **Ohio State University - Pharmacy Library** (12324)

Wilford Hall U.S.A.F. Medical Center
See: **U.S. Air Force Hospital** (16909)

William Hammond Hall Archives
See: **Strybing Arboretum Society - Helen Crocker Russell Library of Horticulture** (15833)

★6848★
William S. Hall Psychiatric Institute - Professional Library (Med)
P.O. Box 202 Phone: (803)734-7136
Columbia, SC 29202 Ms. Neeta N. Shah, Chf.Med.Libn.
Founded: 1964. **Staff:** Prof 3; Other 2. **Subjects:** Psychiatry, psychology, sociology, neurology, pastoral counseling, genetics, psychopharmacology, nursing, occupational therapy. **Special Collections:** Historical collection; Asylum reports, 1836 to present; Transactions of the American Medico-Psychological Association, 1901 to present; annual reports of the South Carolina State Hospital, 1853 to present. **Holdings:** 12,800 books; 8500 bound periodical volumes; 64 videotapes; 550 cassettes; 12 VF drawers of pamphlets and reprints. **Subscriptions:** 340 journals and other serials. **Services:** Interlibrary loan; copying; library open to the public for reference use only. **Computerized Information Services:** MEDLARS, DIALOG Information Services; CD-ROM (PsycLIT). **Networks/Consortia:** Member of Columbia Area Medical Librarians' Association (CAMLA), South Carolina Health Information Network (SCHIN). **Publications:** Psychiatric Forum, 3/year - to selected institutions. **Remarks:** FAX: (803)734-7087.

George Hallauer Memorial Library
See: **Western Evangelical Seminary** (20244)

Dessie M. Hallett Library
See: **Mount Vernon Place United Methodist Church** (10824)

★6849★
Halliburton Logging Services - Engineering Library (Energy)
Box 1936 Phone: (817)293-1300
Fort Worth, TX 76101 Julie Watson, Tech.Libn.
Staff: Prof 1. **Subjects:** Oil well logging, petroleum engineering, physics, geosciences, engineering. **Holdings:** 1200 books; 2000 patents; 25,000 technical papers, reprints, reports, standards, specifications; 5000 data books in microform. **Subscriptions:** 40 journals and other serials. **Services:** Interlibrary loan; copying; SDI. **Automated Operations:** Computerized cataloging and acquisitions. **Computerized Information Services:** DIALOG Information Services, PFDS Online; internal databases.

★6850★
Halliburton Logging Services - Engineering Library (Sci-Engr)
2135 Highway 6, S. Phone: (713)596-5495
Houston, TX 77077 Pat Farnell, Libn.
Founded: 1981. **Staff:** Prof 1. **Subjects:** Applied mathematics, nuclear science, computer software, electronics, geophysics, geology. **Holdings:** 1500 books. **Subscriptions:** 82 journals and other serials. **Services:** Interlibrary loan; library not open to the public. **Automated Operations:** Computerized acquisitions. **Computerized Information Services:** DIALOG Information Services. **Special Indexes:** Technical papers and reports index (card). **Remarks:** FAX: (713)496-8344. **Formerly:** Welex Halliburton Company.

★6851★
Halliburton NUS Environmental Corporation - Library (Env-Cons)
910 Clopper Rd. Phone: (301)258-1841
Gaithersburg, MD 20877 Geraldine M. Fry, Libn.
Founded: 1960. **Staff:** Prof: 1; Other: 1. **Subjects:** Nuclear engineering, waste management, environmental science, energy. **Special Collections:** NTIS reports, 1973 to present (900,000 on microfiche); U.S. Nuclear Regulatory Commission docketed reports. **Holdings:** 10,000 books; 250 bound periodical volumes; 3500 internal reports. **Subscriptions:** 250 journals and other serials. **Services:** Interlibrary loan; library not open to the public. **Automated Operations:** Computerized public access catalog and cataloging. **Computerized Information Services:** DIALOG Information Services. **Networks/Consortia:** Member of Interlibrary Users Association (IUA). **Publications:** NUS Library Bulletin. **Formerly:** NUS Corporation.

★6852★
Halliburton NUS Environmental Corporation - Technical Library (Env-Cons)
Foster Plaza VII
661 Andersen Dr. Phone: (412)921-7090
Pittsburgh, PA 15220 Melanie S. Goga, Libn.
Founded: 1964. **Staff:** Prof 1. **Subjects:** Hazardous waste/waste treatment, environmental health and safety, toxicology, chemistry, geology. **Holdings:** 6000 books and reports; microfiche technical report file; EPA reports; USATHAMA reports; USGS maps and reports. **Subscriptions:** 110 journals. **Services:** Interlibrary loan; library not open to the public. **Computerized Information Services:** DIALOG Information Services, Integrated Technical Information System (ITIS), NLM, CIS, Dow Jones News/Retrieval. **Remarks:** Alternate telephone number(s): (412)921-8628. FAX: (412)921-4040. **Formerly:** NUS Corporation.

★6853★
Halliburton Services - Research Center Library (Sci-Engr)
Box 1431 Phone: (405)251-3516
Duncan, OK 73536-0400 Sammy Croy, Res.Libn.
Subjects: Engineering, chemistry, computer science, petroleum industry. **Holdings:** 2900 books; bound periodical volumes; reports; patents; catalogs; telephone books; conference papers. **Subscriptions:** 114 journals and other serials. **Services:** Interlibrary loan; library not open to the public. **Computerized Information Services:** ORBIT Search Service, STN International; TECHLIT (conference papers; internal database); ORBIT Mail (electronic mail service). **Remarks:** FAX: (405)251-3218.

★6854★
Hallmark Cards, Inc. - Business Research Library (Bus-Fin)
2501 McGee, No. 203
Box 419580 Phone: (816)274-4648
Kansas City, MO 64141-6580 Isidro de la Herran, Bus.Res.Lib.Mgr.
Founded: 1980. **Staff:** Prof 2; Other 1. **Subjects:** Marketing, business forecasting, demographics, operations research. **Holdings:** 800 books. **Subscriptions:** 100 journals and other serials. **Services:** Library not open to the public. **Computerized Information Services:** DIALOG Information Services, VU/TEXT Information Services, DataTimes, NEXIS, Dow Jones News/Retrieval. **Special Indexes:** Index to market research reports (online). **Remarks:** FAX: (816)274-7397. **Staff:** Ruth Hemingson, Bus.Res.Libn.

★6855★
Hallmark Cards, Inc. - Creative Research Library (Art)
25th & McGee St. Phone: (816)274-5525
Kansas City, MO 64108 Jon M. Henderson, Mgr., Creative Rsrc.Ctr.
Founded: 1930. **Staff:** Prof 2; Other 2. **Subjects:** Fine art, lettering, advertising, graphic art, design, illustration, pictures. **Special Collections:** Old and rare books collection. **Holdings:** 16,500 books; 60 bound periodical volumes; 100,000 pictures and clippings in 32 VF drawers. **Subscriptions:** 150 journals and other serials; 5 newspapers. **Services:** Interlibrary loan; library not open to the public. **Special Catalogs:** Cross-index file for clippings. **Staff:** Carol Carr, Creative Res.Libn.

Hallock Medical Library
See: **Connecticut Valley Hospital** (4207)

Hallstrom Pacific Library
See: **Centre for Pacific Development and Training** (3277)

Rabbi Mordecai S. Halpern Memorial Library
See: **Congregation Beth Shalom** (4154)

Halpin Memorial Library
See: **University of Wisconsin--Madison - Poultry Science Department** (19614)

★6856★
HALT - An Organization of Americans for Legal Reform - Library (Law)
1319 F St., N.W., Suite 300 Phone: (202)347-9600
Washington, DC 20004 Theresa Meekan Reedy
Founded: 1985. **Staff:** Prof 1. **Subjects:** Law - reform, self help. **Holdings:** 1000 books; 40 bound periodical volumes. **Subscriptions:** 30 journals and other serials; 10 newspapers. **Services:** Library open to the public.

Hamady Health Sciences Library
See: **Hurley Medical Center** (7583)

Eric W. Hamber Memorial Library
See: **University of British Columbia** (18267)

★6857★
Hamburg Center for the Mentally Retarded - Staff Training Library (Med)
Hamburg Ctr., Old Rte. 22 Phone: (215)562-6051
Hamburg, PA 19526 Frederick Herman, Dir., Staff Dev. & Trng.
Founded: 1960. **Staff:** Prof 2; Other 1. **Subjects:** Mental retardation, medicine, nursing, psychiatry, diagnosis, nutrition, habilitation, behavior management, anatomy, management development. **Holdings:** 755 books. **Subscriptions:** 4 journals and other serials. **Services:** Interlibrary loan; copying. **Remarks:** Maintained by Pennsylvania State Department of Public Welfare. Operates a small client library. **Staff:** Joseph Taglieri, Sp.Educ. Teacher.

Ferdinand Hamburger, Jr. Archives
See: **Johns Hopkins University - Milton S. Eisenhower Library - Special Collections Department - Ferdinand Hamburger, Jr. Archives** (8423)

★6858★
Hamburger Kunsthalle - Bibliothek
Glockengiesserwall Phone: 40 248252606
W-2000 Hamburg 1, Germany Eckhard Schaar, Sr.Cur.
Founded: 1869. **Staff:** Prof 3. **Subjects:** Painting, printing, drawing, sculpture, coins, medals. **Holdings:** 130,000 books; archival materials; prints; drawings. **Subscriptions:** 330 journals and other serials. **Services:** Interlibrary loan; copying (limited); library open to the public. **Remarks:** FAX: 40 24862482. **Staff:** Annette Stewner, Libn.

★6859★
Hamilton Board of Education - Dr. Harry Paikin Library (Educ)
100 Main St., W. Phone: (416)527-5092
Hamilton, ON, Canada L8N 3L1 Ingrid Scott, Hd.Libn.
Founded: 1967. **Staff:** Prof 2; Other 2. **Subjects:** Teaching methods, educational philosophy, educational psychology, history of education, special education, guidance, child psychology. **Holdings:** 20,000 books; ERIC microfiche, 1974 to present; supplementary classroom resource material. **Subscriptions:** 450 journals and other serials. **Services:** Interlibrary loan; copying; library open to the public for reference use only. **Computerized Information Services:** DIALOG Information Services, BRS Information Technologies, UTLAS, WILSONLINE; CD-ROM (ERIC). Performs searches on fee basis. **Publications:** Subject Bibliographies, irregular; Periodical Content Listing, 8/year - both for internal distribution only; Just Arrived, bimonthly. **Remarks:** FAX: (416)521-2540. **Staff:** Karyn Hogan, Res.Libn.; Leslie Ferguson, Lib.Tech.

★6860★
Hamilton General Division - Library (Med)
286 Victoria Ave. N. Phone: (416)527-0271
Hamilton, ON, Canada L8L 5G4 Candace A. Thacker, MLS, HG Div.Lib.
Founded: 1931. **Staff:** Prof 1; Other 2. **Subjects:** Medicine, allied health, nursing. **Holdings:** 3500 books; 10,000 bound periodical volumes. **Subscriptions:** 140 journals and other serials. **Services:** Interlibrary loan; library not open to the public. **Computerized Information Services:** MEDLINE, MEDLARS; CD-ROM (MEDLINE, CINAHL). **Networks/Consortia:** Member of Hamilton/Wentworth District Health Library Network. **Remarks:** FAX: (416)527-1941.

★6861★
Hamilton Hospital - Medical Library (Med)
1881 Whitehorse-Hamilton Square Rd.
Box H Phone: (609)584-6473
Trenton, NJ 08690 Patricia Kowalski, Coord.
Staff: 1. **Subjects:** Medicine, sports medicine. **Holdings:** 330 books; 200 bound periodical volumes; 3500 other cataloged items. **Subscriptions:** 67 journals and other serials. **Services:** Interlibrary loan; copying; SDI; library open to the public. **Computerized Information Services:** MEDLARS, BRS Information Technologies. Performs searches on fee basis. **Networks/Consortia:** Member of Central Jersey Health Science Libraries Association (CJHSLA). **Publications:** Medical Library Bulletin, quarterly - to hospital and medical staff and others by request. **Remarks:** FAX: (609)586-6723.

John Hamilton Library
See: **Carnegie Museum of Natural History - Library** (3085)

Kathryn Hamilton Library
See: **Anniston Museum of Natural History** (879)

★6862★
Hamilton/KSA - Library (Med, Bus-Fin)
2021 E. Hennepin, Suite 450
Minneapolis, MN 55413 Phone: (612)378-1700
Staff: Prof 1. **Subjects:** Hospital and health care planning and administration; nursing administration; hospital financial management; hospitals - architecture, design, engineering, and construction. **Holdings:** 846 volumes; 14 shelves of documents and reports; 5 VF drawers; 2 VF drawers of maps; 20 shelves of government publications. **Subscriptions:** 61 journals and other serials. **Services:** Interlibrary loan; copying; library open to the public with restrictions. **Publications:** Acquisitions list, quarterly - for internal distribution only. **Remarks:** FAX: (612)378-0071. Branch offices with small resource centers are located in San Francisco, and Washington, DC.

★6863★
Hamilton Law Association - Anthony Pepe Memorial Law Library (Law)
50 Main St., E. Phone: (416)522-1563
Hamilton, ON, Canada L8N 1E9 Wendy Hearder-Moan, Hd.Libn.
Founded: 1879. **Staff:** Prof 1; Other 2. **Subjects:** Law. **Holdings:** 24,000 volumes. **Services:** Interlibrary loan; copying; library open to the public with permission. **Computerized Information Services:** QL Systems, Info Globe, WESTLAW; QUICKMAIL (electronic mail service). Performs searches on fee basis. **Publications:** Newsletter, monthly - to members; Member's Handbook and Legal Directory - for sale. **Special Indexes:** Index of Unified Family Court Decisions (book). **Remarks:** FAX: (416)572-1188. Electronic mail address(es): Box 1029 (QUICKMAIL).

Hamilton Library
See: **Cumberland County Historical Society & Hamilton Library** (4475)

★6864★
Hamilton Medical Center - Medical Library (Med)
Memorial Drive
P.O. Box 1168 Phone: (404)272-6056
Dalton, GA 30720 Susan Seay, Med.Libn.
Staff: Prof 1. **Subjects:** Medicine, nursing, and allied health sciences. **Holdings:** 500 books; 1200 bound periodical volumes. **Subscriptions:** 79 journals and other serials. **Services:** Interlibrary loan; copying; SDI; library open to the public by appointment. **Computerized Information Services:** BRS Information Technologies, NLM. Performs searches. **Remarks:** FAX: (404)272-6094.

Hamilton Memorial Library
See: **Essex County Hospital Center** (5446)

★6865★
Hamilton Psychiatric Hospital - Library Resource Centre (Med)
P.O. Box 585 Phone: (416)388-2511
Hamilton, ON, Canada L8N 3K7 Anne Devries, Libn.
Staff: Prof 2. **Subjects:** Psychiatry, social work, psychiatric nursing, psychology, psychogeriatrics, occupational therapy, rehabilitation services, pastoral services. **Holdings:** 6000 books; 1000 bound periodical volumes; 60 slide/tape sets; 225 tapes; 9 VF drawers. **Subscriptions:** 175 journals and other serials. **Services:** Interlibrary loan; copying; center open to hospital staff. **Computerized Information Services:** NLM, MEDLINE. **Networks/Consortia:** Member of Hamilton/Wentworth District Health Library Network, Ontario Psychiatric Hospital Group. **Publications:** Library brochure. **Special Catalogs:** Audiovisual catalog, annual - to libraries within the consortia. **Remarks:** Maintained by Ontario Ministry of Health - Mental Health Division. **Remarks:** FAX: (416)575-5509. **Staff:** Joanne Morgan, Media Libn.

★6866★
Hamilton Public Library - Special Collections (Hist)
55 York Blvd. Phone: (416)529-8111
Hamilton, ON, Canada L8R 3K1 J. Brian Henley, Hd.
Founded: 1974. **Staff:** Prof 2; Other 3. **Subjects:** Canadiana. **Special Collections:** Local history and archives; Canadian Association in Support of the Native Peoples material (12 VF drawers, update on microfiche); War of 1812; Arctic exploration; government documents (full depository - federal/provincial/municipal). **Holdings:** 40,000 books; 780 linear feet of other cataloged items. **Subscriptions:** 72 journals and other serials; 8 newspapers. **Services:** Interlibrary loan; copying; collections open to the public with restrictions. **Automated Operations:** Computerized cataloging, serials, and circulation. **Computerized Information Services:** DIALOG Information Services, PFDS Online, QL Systems, CAN/OLE, UTLAS, DOBIS Canadian Online Library System. **Networks/Consortia:** Member of Southern Ontario Library Service. **Publications:** Bibliography of War of 1812 holdings. **Special Indexes:** Extensive index to local history material (card). **Remarks:** FAX: (416)529-5326. **Staff:** Margaret Houghton, Archv.

★6867★
Hamilton Public Library - Urban/Municipal Collection (Plan)
55 York Blvd. Phone: (416)529-8111
Hamilton, ON, Canada L8R 3K1 Kathryn Deiter, Urban/Municipal Libn.
Founded: 1980. **Staff:** Prof 1. **Subjects:** Local government and concerns. **Special Collections:** Hamilton City and Hamilton-Wentworth Regional Municipality documents depository collection; Hamilton and Hamilton-Wentworth Region Council and committee agendas and meeting minutes; Hamilton Board of Education meeting minutes and committee agendas; government and agency documents pertaining to Hamilton and Hamilton-Wentworth. **Holdings:** 2000 documents; 2 VF drawers of clippings. **Services:** Copying; collection open to the public. **Computerized Information Services:** Internal database. **Publications:** Urban/Municipal Acquisitions List, quarterly. **Remarks:** FAX: (416)529-5326.

★6868★
Hamilton Spectator - Information Services Centre (Publ)
44 Frid St. Phone: (416)526-3315
Hamilton, ON, Canada L8N 3G3 John Lawrence, Chf.Libn.
Founded: 1935. **Staff:** Prof 1; Other 4. **Subjects:** Newspaper reference topics. **Holdings:** 3000 books; clippings on 30,000 subjects; Spectator, 1847 to present, on microfilm. **Subscriptions:** 15 journals and other serials; 6 newspapers. **Services:** Library open to the public. **Computerized Information Services:** Infomart Online, Info Globe. **Remarks:** FAX: (416)521-8986.

★6869★
Hamilton-Wentworth Roman Catholic Separate School Board - Dr. Nicholas Mancini Center - Professional Library (Educ)
690 Barton St. E. Phone: (416)525-2930
Hamilton, ON, Canada L8L 3A6 Phillip Jeffrey, Libn.
Founded: 1970. **Staff:** Prof 3; Other 5. **Subjects:** Education, library science, Catholicism, social science, religion. **Special Collections:** Literature and Primary Loan Services (400 items); textbooks (500). **Holdings:** 1000 books; 20 drawers of microfilm of periodicals; 5000 AV titles. **Subscriptions:** 165 journals and other serials. **Services:** Interlibrary loan; center open to the public with permission of Superintendent of Curriculum. **Automated Operations:** Computerized public access catalog and cataloging. **Computerized Information Services:** Internal databases; CD-ROMs (DIALOG Information Services, WILSONDISC). **Publications:** Catalogue of Learning Materials; Professional Books List; New from the Professional Library; Books reviewed by teacher-librarians; selected subject bibliographies. **Remarks:** FAX: (416)574-2118. Center located at 690 Barton St., E., Hamilton, ON L8L 3A6. **Staff:** Gerry Ferguson, Coord., Lrng.Mtls.

Hamiltonian Library
See: **National Hamiltonian Party** (11191)

Elizabeth W. Hamlin Oriental Library of Art and Archaeology
See: **Buffalo Society of Natural Sciences - Research Library** (2340)

★6870★
Hamline University - Bush Memorial Library - Special Collections (Area-Ethnic, Hist)
1536 Hewitt Ave. Phone: (612)641-2373
St. Paul, MN 55104 Jack King, Dir.
Special Collections: South Asian Collection, 1947 to present (2100 volumes; 500 notebooks); Monumental Brass Rubbing Collection (1000 rubbings from 14th-20th centuries with emphasis on the 14th-17th centuries; 20 volumes); Jewish Studies Slide Archive (history and culture of Judaism and the nation of Israel; 2000 slides). **Services:** Collections open to the public with restrictions. **Computerized Information Services:** Electronic mail. **Networks/Consortia:** Member of MINITEX Library Information Network. **Remarks:** FAX: (612)641-2956. For use of the collections, please contact the following: South Asian Collection - M. Diane Clayton, 641-2046; Brass Rubbing Collection - Dr. Jack King, 641-2048; Jewish Studies Slide Archive - Dr. Steven Derfler, 641-2392; Reference - 641-2375.

★6871★
Hamline University - School of Law - Library (Law)
1536 Hewitt Ave. Phone: (612)641-2125
St. Paul, MN 55104 Susan Kiefer, Dir.
Founded: 1973. **Staff:** Prof 5; Other 5. **Subjects:** Law. **Holdings:** 34,250 book titles; 67,240 microform titles; 160 non-book titles; 121,730 paper volumes; 74,380 microform volumes; Congressional Information Services, 1970-1980, in microform; U.S. Supreme Court Record and Briefs, 1940 to present; Codes of Federal Regulations; Federal Register. **Subscriptions:** 2800 journals and other serials. **Services:** Interlibrary loan; copying; library open to the public. **Automated Operations:** Computerized public access catalog (DYNIX) and cataloging. **Computerized Information Services:** OCLC, LEXIS, DIALOG Information Services, WESTLAW; CD-ROMs; InterNet (electronic mail service). **Networks/Consortia:** Member of MINITEX Library Information Network, Cooperating Libraries in Consortium (CLIC). **Remarks:** Alternate telephone number(s): (612)641-2119. FAX: (612)641-2435. Public access catalog: (612)690-3003. **Staff:** John Tessner, Hd. of Pub.Serv.; Mary Ann Van Cura, Hd. of Tech.Serv.; Miki Scholl, Asst.Libn., Cat.; Leslie Loar, Asst.Libn., Govt.Doc.

Hamma Library
See: **Trinity Lutheran Seminary** (16514)

Dag Hammarskjold Library
See: **United Nations Headquarters - Dag Hammarskjold Library** (16772)

Roy Hammer Library
See: **Ambassador College** (451)

★6872★
Hammer, Siler, George Associates - Library (Plan)
1111 Bonifant St. Phone: (301)565-5200
Silver Spring, MD 20910 Susan Bishop, Libn.
Founded: 1954. **Staff:** Prof 1. **Subjects:** Economic development, development management, housing, land use, planning, transportation, historic preservation, commercial revitalization. **Special Collections:** Census Collection (Census of Population, Housing, Business, Manufacturing, Census Tract, 1950 to present; 55 shelves); Geographic Collection (data on states arranged by area and subject; 2500 items). **Holdings:** 7000 volumes; 2000 HSGA company reports; 8 shelves of state employment statistics. **Subscriptions:** 138 journals and other serials; 8 newspapers. **Services:** Library not open to the public. **Special Catalogs:** Geographic catalog for internal company reports. **Remarks:** FAX: (301)588-0942.

Hammermill Library
See: **Mercyhurst College** (10157)

★6873★
Hammond Historical Society - Calumet Room (Hist)
564 State St. Phone: (219)931-5100
Hammond, IN 46320 Kathryn Thegze, Libn.
Founded: 1967. **Staff:** Prof 1. **Subjects:** History of Hammond and the Calumet Region. **Holdings:** 700 books; 18 VF drawers of pamphlets and clippings; 96 VF drawers of newspaper negatives; 45 personal scrapbooks; 165 tapes (Historical Society programs, community events, personal interviews); 6 video cassettes of interviews. **Services:** Interlibrary loan; copying; room open to the public with restrictions, for reference use only, and on a limited schedule. **Remarks:** Maintained by Hammond Public Library.

Horace Hammond Memorial Library
See: **Birmingham Botanical Gardens** (1850)

★6874★
Hammond, Inc. - Editorial Division Library (Geog-Map, Publ)
515 Valley St. Phone: (201)763-6000
Maplewood, NJ 07040 Ernest J. Dupuy, Dir.
Founded: 1945. **Staff:** Prof 2. **Subjects:** Geography, cartography, astronomy, anthropology, history, archeology. **Special Collections:** U.S. and foreign census publications. **Holdings:** 10,000 books; 50 VF drawers of pamphlets and clippings; 25,000 maps; 1100 atlases. **Subscriptions:** 160 journals and other serials. **Services:** Library not open to the public. **Networks/Consortia:** Member of APLIC International Census Network. **Remarks:** FAX: (201)763-7658. Telex: 13-6585. Toll-free telephone number(s): (800)526-4953. **Staff:** David D. Crouthers, Assoc.Libn.

Hammond Library
See: **Chicago Theological Seminary** (3547)

Jake and Nancy Hamon Arts Library
See: **Southern Methodist University** (15502)

★6875★
Hamot Medical Center - Library Services (Med)
201 State St. Phone: (814)870-6000
Erie, PA 16550 Jean A. Tauber, Dir.
Founded: 1963. **Staff:** Prof 2; Other 2. **Subjects:** Medicine, hospital administration, nursing. **Holdings:** 2200 books; 4500 bound periodical volumes. **Subscriptions:** 378 journals and other serials. **Services:** Interlibrary loan; copying; library open to health care professionals and students. **Computerized Information Services:** DIALOG Information Services, MEDLARS. **Networks/Consortia:** Member of Erie Area Health Information Library Cooperative (EAHILC), Northwest Interlibrary Cooperative of Pennsylvania (NICOP). **Remarks:** FAX: (814)870-6188.

★6876★
Hampden-Booth Theatre Library (Theater)
The Players
16 Gramercy Park Phone: (212)228-7610
New York, NY 10003 Raymond Wemmlinger, Cur. & Libn.
Founded: 1957. **Staff:** Prof 2. **Subjects:** American and English theater. **Special Collections:** Edwin Booth; Walter Hampden; Union Square Theatre; 18th-19th century playbills (4000); Players Pipe Nights; Maurice Evans; Robert B. Mantell; Charles Coburn; Edward Hugh Sothern & Julia Marlowe. **Holdings:** 8000 volumes; 500 playscripts and promptbooks; 15 VF drawers of letters and documents; 30,000 photographs; 30 VF drawers of playbills; 30 VF drawers of clippings. **Services:** Copying; library open to writers and scholars for research use on request.

★6877★
Hampden Law Library (Law)
50 State St.
Box 559 Phone: (413)781-8100
Springfield, MA 01101 Kathleen M. Flynn, Law Libn.
Founded: 1860. **Staff:** Prof 1; Other 3. **Subjects:** Law. **Special Collections:** Massachusetts law. **Holdings:** 72,000 books; 2880 bound periodical volumes. **Subscriptions:** 200 journals and other serials. **Services:** Interlibrary loan; copying; library open to the public. **Computerized Information Services:** OCLC, LEXIS, WESTLAW, VU/TEXT Information Services. **Networks/Consortia:** Member of Cooperating Libraries of Greater Springfield, A CCGS Agency (CLGS). **Publications:** Union list. **Remarks:** Part of the Massachusetts State Trial Court; Marnie Warner, Law Library Coordinator.

★6878★
Hampden-Sydney College - Fuqua International Communications Center (Aud-Vis)
Eggleston Library
Box 7 Phone: (804)223-6293
Hampden-Sydney, VA 23943 Sandra Heinemann, Act.Dir.
Founded: 1986. **Staff:** Prof 1; Other 1. **Subjects:** International studies, foreign languages. **Holdings:** 300 European videotapes titles; 500 compact disc titles; 415 video disc titles; 2460 phonodiscs. **Subscriptions:** 20 journals and other serials. **Services:** Interlibrary loan; copying; center open to the public. **Automated Operations:** Computerized cataloging. **Computerized Information Services:** DIALOG Information Services; Film and Video Title Holdings (internal database). Performs searches on fee basis. Contact Person: Catherine Pollari, Ref.Libn. **Networks/Consortia:** Member of SOLINET, Southside Virginia Library Network. **Special Catalogs:** Compact disc catalog (card). **Special Indexes:** Index to film and video titles (online); index to computer software (brochure); Checklist of Cooney Phonodisc Collection. **Remarks:** FAX: (804)223-6351. **Staff:** John Norris, Media Libn.

John H. Hampshire Memorial Reference & Research Library
See: **Foundation of the Wall & Ceiling Industry** (6051)

★6879★
Hampshire Law Library (Law)
Court House
99 Main St. Phone: (413)586-2297
Northampton, MA 01060 Barbara Fell-Johnson, Law Libn.
Founded: 1908. **Staff:** Prof 1; Other 1. **Subjects:** Law. **Special Collections:** New England statutes; English cases. **Holdings:** 24,000 volumes. **Subscriptions:** 60 journals. **Services:** Interlibrary loan; copying; library open to the public. **Computerized Information Services:** WESTLAW, LEXIS, Veralex 2. **Remarks:** Part of the Massachusetts State Trial Court; Marnie Warner, Law Library Coordinator.

Hampton Historical Society
See: **Meeting House Green Memorial and Historical Association, Inc.** (10020)

★6880★
Hampton Institute - William R. & Norma B. Harvey Library (Hist, Area-Ethnic)
Hampton University
30 Tyler St. Phone: (804)727-5371
Hampton, VA 23668 Dr. Earl Bean, Dir.
Founded: 1904. **Special Collections:** George Foster Peabody Collection of Negro Literature and History; Hampton University Archives (4 million items); U.S. Government documents (partial depository). **Holdings:** 31,748 volumes. **Services:** Interlibrary loan; copying; collections open to the public with restrictions on circulation. **Automated Operations:** Computerized cataloging. **Computerized Information Services:** DIALOG Information Services, OCLC. Performs searches on fee basis. Contact Person: Mary Marks, Acq. **Networks/Consortia:** Member of SOLINET, Council on Botanical Horticultural Libraries. **Special Catalogs:** Dictionary Catalog of the George Foster Peabody Collection of Negro Literature and History, 1972. **Formerly:** Its Collis P. Huntington Memorial Library. **Staff:** Fritz Malval, Archv.

★6881★
Hampton Roads Agricultural Experiment Station - Library (Agri)
1444 Diamond Springs Rd. Phone: (804)363-3900
Virginia Beach, VA 23455 Suzanne H. Thurman, Ck.
Founded: 1920. **Staff:** 1. **Subjects:** Horticulture, soils, entomology, pesticides, farming. **Holdings:** 5450 volumes. **Subscriptions:** 62 journals and other serials. **Services:** Library open to the public for reference use only.

★6882★
Hancock County Law Library Association (Law)
Hancock County Courthouse Phone: (419)424-7077
Findlay, OH 45840 Deborah L. Ward, Law Libn.
Staff: 2. **Subjects:** Law. **Holdings:** 24,000 volumes; 4511 microfiche; 13 filing boxes. **Services:** Library for use of bar members, members of the courts, local attorneys, county officials, and the public. **Computerized Information Services:** WESTLAW. **Remarks:** FAX: (419)425-4136.

★6883★
Hancock County Law Library, Inc. (Law)
60 State St.
Ellsworth, ME 04605 Phone: (207)667-7176
Founded: 1907. **Staff:** 1. **Subjects:** Law. **Holdings:** 6000 books. **Services:** Public must register at office of Clerk of Courts to use library.

★6884★
Hancock & Estabrook - Law Library (Law)
Mony Tower I
P.O. Box 4976 Phone: (315)471-3151
Syracuse, NY 13221-4976 Barbara Briggs, Law Libn.
Founded: 1889. **Staff:** Prof 1. **Subjects:** New York state and federal law; labor relations; taxes; securities; estates and trusts; negligence; products liability; malpractice; municipalities; real property. **Holdings:** 10,500 books. **Subscriptions:** 92 journals and other serials. **Services:** Interlibrary loan; library open to the public with restrictions. **Computerized Information Services:** LEXIS, NEXIS. **Remarks:** FAX: (315)471-3167.

★6885★
John Hancock Mutual Life Insurance Company - Corporate Library (Bus-Fin)
John Hancock Place
Box 111 Phone: (617)572-7676
Boston, MA 02117 Amy C. Wang, Mgr.
Founded: 1949. **Staff:** Prof 3; Other 1. **Subjects:** Business, life and health insurance, financial services, employee benefits, management. **Special Collections:** Company archives. **Holdings:** 17,000 books; 105 VF drawers of unbound material; microfilm. **Subscriptions:** 250 journals and other serials. **Services:** Resource not open to the public. **Automated Operations:** Computerized cataloging, indexing, and periodicals routing. **Computerized Information Services:** DIALOG Information Services, NEXIS, DataTimes, Dun & Bradstreet Business Credit Services; internal database; CD-ROM. Performs searches on fee basis. **Special Indexes:** Index of pertinent articles from publications received. **Remarks:** FAX: (617)572-7642. **Staff:** Joann Huddleston, Coord.; Jo-Anne Breiner, Res.Cons.

★6886★
Hancock Shaker Village, Inc. - Library (Rel-Phil)
Box 898 Phone: (413)443-0188
Pittsfield, MA 01202 Robert F.W. Meader, Libn.
Founded: 1960. **Staff:** Prof 2. **Subjects:** Shakeriana. **Holdings:** 389 books; 45 bound periodical volumes; 5515 broadsides, drawings, manuscripts, ancillary research materials; 9661 photographs, microforms, and other cataloged items. **Subscriptions:** 2 journals and other serials. **Services:** Copying; library open to the public by appointment. **Computerized Information Services:** Internal database. **Staff:** Dr. Magda Gabor-Hotchkiss, Cur. of Photo.

Hand Center Library
See: **Millard Fillmore Hospitals - Kideney Health Sciences Library** (5692)

Daniel Hand Library
See: **Madison Historical Society, Inc. - Library** (9523)

Wayland D. Hand Library of Folklore and Mythology
See: **University of California, Los Angeles - Wayland D. Hand Library of Folklore and Mythology** (18401)

★6887★
Handels og Sofartsmuseet - Bibliotek (Trans)
Kronborg slot Phone: 49 210685
DK-3000 Helsingor, Denmark Bert Blom, Libn.
Founded: 1915. **Staff:** Prof 1. **Subjects:** Danish merchant shipping, naval architecture, marine technology, navigation, transportation and traffic, underwater archeology. **Special Collections:** Logbooks and ship's journals (520); Danish merchant ships photograph collection; Handels og Sofarsmuseet yearbooks, 1942 to present. **Holdings:** 25,500 books; reports; archival material. **Subscriptions:** 120 journals and other serials; 5 newspapers. **Services:** Copying; library open to the public. **Publications:** Sohistoriske Skrifter; Maritema; Sohistorisk billedbog. **Remarks:** FAX: 945 49213440.

Handleman Institute of Recorded Sound Archives
See: **University of Miami - School of Music - Albert Pick Music Library** (18850)

★6888★
Handwriting Analysis Research Library (Soc Sci)
91 Washington St. Phone: (413)774-4667
Greenfield, MA 01301 Robert E. Backman, Cur.
Founded: 1949. **Staff:** Prof 1. **Subjects:** Graphology, handwriting, handwriting analysis, penmanship, questioned documents. **Special Collections:** Phyllis Grossberg Memorial Collection (12,215 classified handwriting samples); Anna Aab Memorial Collection (1160 penmanship copy books, booklets, copy slips); Kathleen S. Dunn Memorial Collection (4460 books, booklets, handbooks, textbooks). **Holdings:** 164 bound periodical volumes; 706 research reports; 57,909 manuscripts, clippings, photocopies; 731 translated items; 4669 abstracts; archival records of 9 defunct handwriting analysis organizations (closed reserve). **Subscriptions:** 24 journals and other serials. **Services:** Interlibrary loan; copying; library open to the public for reference use only. **Publications:** Schools, Teachers and Penmanship; reprints of historical items on graphology, handwriting, handwriting analysis, and penmanship; Graphological Abstracts (book); Graphomancy Revisited. **Special Indexes:** Bibliographic card file; abstracts card file; special subject and topic index (card).

★6889★
Handy HRM Corporation - Research Library (Bus-Fin)
250 Park Ave. Phone: (212)557-0400
New York, NY 10177 Kari Sheehan, Libn.
Founded: 1955. **Subjects:** Business, economics, management, personnel administration, executive compensation and benefits. **Holdings:** 1500 books; 50 VF drawers of company annual reports, proxies, clippings. **Formerly:** Handy Associates, Inc.

★6890★
Hanford Environmental Health Foundation - Resource Center (Med)
Box 100 Phone: (509)376-6125
Richland, WA 99352 Athena Bradham, Libn.
Staff: Prof 2. **Subjects:** Occupational health, employee assistance and health promotion, industrial hygiene, applied research, environmental monitoring and analysis. **Holdings:** 3675 volumes; 2500 other cataloged items. **Subscriptions:** 216 journals and other serials. **Services:** Center not open to the public. **Computerized Information Services:** BRS Information Technologies, MEDLINE, WLN. **Remarks:** FAX: (509)376-9818. **Staff:** Judi Nellis, Libn.

Hankuk Nodhong Johap Chongyeonmaeng
See: **Federation of Korean Trade Unions** (5656)

Wilson C. Hanna Library/Research Library
See: **San Bernardino County Museum** (14683)

★6891★
Hannibal-LaGrange College - L.A. Foster Library - Special Collections (Rare Book)
2800 Palmyra Rd. Phone: (314)221-3675
Hannibal, MO 63401 Julie Dothager, Lib.Dir.
Founded: 1858. **Staff:** Prof 1; Other 2. **Special Collections:** Rare books; Missouri Collection; HLG Archives. **Services:** Interlibrary loan; copying; library open to the public. **Computerized Information Services:** DIALOG Information Services; BIBLIOFILE (internal database). Performs searches.

★6892★
Hanoi - Institute of Mathematics - Library (Sci-Engr)
Bo Ho POB 631 Phone: 2 43303
Hanoi, Vietnam Mrs. Vo Thi Gai
Founded: 1970. **Staff:** Prof 2. **Subjects:** Mathematics, management science, informatics, mechanics. **Holdings:** 10,000 books; 200 bound periodical volumes; 50 reports. **Services:** Copying; library open to the public. **Remarks:** FAX: 2 52483. Telex: 411525 NCSR VT.

★6893★
Hanover General Hospital - Newkirk Medical Library (Med)
Hanover, PA 17331 Phone: (717)637-3711
Diane Milcoff, Lib.Dir.
Remarks: No further information was supplied by respondent.

Clarence B. Hanson, Jr. Library
See: **Birmingham Museum of Art** (1851)

★6894★
Hanson Engineers, Inc. - Technical Library (Sci-Engr)
1525 S. 6th St. Phone: (217)788-2450
Springfield, IL 62703 Betty Lou Hicks, Supv., Info.Rsrc.
Staff: 2. **Subjects:** Civil engineering, Illinois geology, soil mechanics, geotechnical engineering, structural engineering, environmental engineering. **Special Collections:** Illinois geology. **Holdings:** 6500 volumes. **Subscriptions:** 280 journals and other serials. **Services:** Library not open to the public. **Computerized Information Services:** DIALOG Information Services, OCLC, EPIC, NLM, STN International, CIS (Chemical Information Systems, Inc.). **Networks/Consortia:** Member of Rolling Prairie Library System (RPLS). **Remarks:** FAX: (217)788-2503.

Hanson Industries - SCM Chemicals
See: **SCM Chemicals** (14950)

Hanson Materials Engineering
See: **Canspec Group Inc.** (3012)

Hanson Materials Engineering - Main Office Library
See: **Canspec Group Inc. - Library** (3013)

★6895★
Har Zion Temple - Ida and Matthew Rudofker Library (Rel-Phil)
Hagys Ford & Hollow Rds. Phone: (215)667-9190
Penn Valley, PA 19072 Jessie Rubenstone, Libn.
Founded: 1924. **Staff:** Prof 1; Other 1. **Subjects:** Judaica. **Special Collections:** Holocaust; children's, juvenile, young adult literature; Jewish music; Hebrew. **Holdings:** 6000 books. **Subscriptions:** 34 journals and other serials. **Services:** Copying (limited); SDI; library open to members of congregation, affiliated organizations, and the community.

★6896★
(Harare) American Cultural Center - USIS Library (Educ)
Century House E.
38 Baker Ave.
P.O. Box 4010 Phone: 4 728957
Harare, Zimbabwe Stephen B. Mushonga, Libn.
Founded: 1983. **Staff:** 4. **Holdings:** 5400 books. **Subscriptions:** 107 journals and other serials; 5 newspapers. **Services:** Copying; SDI; library open to the public with restrictions. **Remarks:** FAX: 4 729965. Alternate telephone number(s): 4 728958; 4 728959. Maintained or supported by the U.S. Information Agency. Focus is on materials that will assist peoples outside the United States to learn about the United States, its people, history, culture, political processes, and social milieux.

★6897★
Harbison-Walker Refractories Company - Garber Research Center Library (Sci-Engr)
1001 Pittsburgh-McKeesport Blvd. Phone: (412)469-3880
West Mifflin, PA 15122 Donna Hizer, Contact
Founded: 1925. **Staff:** Prof 1; Other 1. **Subjects:** Refractories, ceramics, geology, metallurgy. **Holdings:** 2500 books; 3000 bound periodical volumes. **Subscriptions:** 320 journals and other serials. **Services:** Interlibrary loan; library open to the public.

★6898★
Harbor Branch Oceanographic Institution, Inc. - Library (Biol Sci)
5600 Old Dixie Hwy. Phone: (407)465-2400
Fort Pierce, FL 34946 Kristen L. Metzger, Libn.
Founded: 1975. **Staff:** Prof 1; Other 1. **Subjects:** Marine sciences, marine engineering, marine ecology, biological oceanography, fisheries science. **Holdings:** 5000 books; 10,000 bound periodical volumes; 720 reels of microfilm of periodicals. **Subscriptions:** 250 journals and other serials. **Services:** Interlibrary loan; copying; library open to the public by appointment. **Automated Operations:** Computerized serials and circulation. **Computerized Information Services:** DIALOG Information Services; SCIENCEnet, OnTyme Electronic Message Network Service (electronic mail services). **Remarks:** FAX: (407)465-2446. Electronic mail address(es): HBOI.LIBRARY (SCN); HARBORBRANCH (OnTyme Electronic Message Network Service).

★6899★
Harbor Hospital Center - Medical Library (Med)
3001 S. Hanover St. Phone: (301)347-3419
Baltimore, MD 21230 Shirley Lay, Libn.
Founded: 1770. **Staff:** Prof 1; Other 1. **Subjects:** Internal medicine, nursing. **Special Collections:** Ciba Collection of Medical Illustrations. **Holdings:** 1558 books; 3717 bound periodical volumes; 250 Network for Continuing Medical Education programs; 545 other AV programs. **Subscriptions:** 150 journals and other serials. **Services:** Interlibrary loan; library not open to the public. **Automated Operations:** Computerized cataloging. **Computerized Information Services:** MEDLARS, DIALOG Information Services; internal database. **Networks/Consortia:** Member of Maryland Association of Health Science Librarians (MAHSL). **Publications:** Library Newsletter.

Harbor-UCLA Medical Center
See: **Los Angeles County/Harbor-UCLA Medical Center** (9330)

★6900★
Harbridge House, Inc. - Information Resource Center (Bus-Fin)
12 Arlington St. Phone: (617)267-6410
Boston, MA 02116 Monica Reuss, Dir.
Founded: 1970. **Staff:** Prof 2; Other 2. **Subjects:** Business and management, management training and development. **Holdings:** 1000 books; 3500 internal reports; 400 reels of microfilm; 6 VF drawers of company and industry topic files. **Subscriptions:** 60 journals and other serials; 6 newspapers. **Services:** Copying; copyright administration; center open to the public by appointment only. **Computerized Information Services:** DIALOG Information Services, NewsNet, Inc., InvesText, NEXIS, Dow Jones News/Retrieval, DataTimes, VU/TEXT Information Services; internal database. **Publications:** Current Contents, monthly - for internal distribution only; Guide to the IRC. **Special Catalogs:** Harbridge House studies and reports catalog (card). **Remarks:** FAX: (617)267-5836. **Staff:** P. Berens, Int.Info.

★6901★
Harcros Pigments Canada - Technical Library (Sci-Engr)
36 Towns Rd. Phone: (416)251-1161
Toronto, ON, Canada M8Z 1A3 Peter Duncker, Tech.Dir.
Founded: 1968. **Staff:** 2. **Subjects:** Magnetism, physical and inorganic chemistry, ferrite processing and properties, electron microscopy, iron oxide pigments. **Special Collections:** Ferrite and electronic ceramics collection; American Society for Testing and Materials X-ray diffraction file inorganic sets 1-20. **Holdings:** 386 volumes; 100 patents. **Subscriptions:** 20 journals and other serials. **Services:** Library not open to the public. **Remarks:** FAX: (416)251-4774. Harcros Pigments Canada is a division of Harcros Pigments, Inc. **Formerly:** Northern Pigment.

George Hardie Aerospace Collection
See: **University of Wisconsin--Milwaukee - Golda Meir Library** (19633)

Grace Hardie Collection of Children's Books
See: **Birmingham Public and Jefferson County Free Library - Linn-Henley Library for Southern Historical Research** (1857)

James Hardie Library of Australian Fine Arts
See: **State Library of Queensland** (15692)

★6902★
Harding Graduate School of Religion - L.M. Graves Memorial Library (Rel-Phil)
1000 Cherry Rd. Phone: (901)761-1354
Memphis, TN 38117 Don L. Meredith, Libn.
Founded: 1958. **Staff:** Prof 2; Other 2. **Subjects:** Bible and religion, philosophy, church history, missions, counseling. **Special Collections:** Restoration history; religious education curriculum library. **Holdings:** 93,126 volumes. **Subscriptions:** 682 journals and other serials. **Services:** Interlibrary loan; copying; library open to the public with restrictions. **Computerized Information Services:** BRS Information Technologies, OCLC. **Staff:** Bonnie Baker, Asst.Libn.

Harding Library
See: **San Diego Space & Science Foundation** (14713)

★6903★
Hardinge Brothers, Inc. - Library
3575 Upper Oakwood Ave. Phone: (607)734-2281
Horseheads, NY 14845 Nancy Comspock, Libn.
Remarks: No further information was supplied by respondent.

★6904★
Hardwood Plywood Manufacturers Association - Library (Sci-Engr)
1825 Michael Faraday Dr.
Box 2789
Reston, VA 22090 Phone: (703)435-2900
Founded: 1921. **Staff:** 1. **Subjects:** Hardwood plywood; veneer; laminated hardwood flooring; prefinished hardwood paneling; testing - flamespread, formaldehyde, adhesive, structural; building codes. **Holdings:** 325 volumes. **Subscriptions:** 50 journals and other serials; 5 newspapers. **Services:** Interlibrary loan; copying; library open to the public with restrictions. **Publications:** Hardwood Plywood & Veneer Newsletter, monthly; Laboratory Price List; Literature Price List; Literature Survey. **Remarks:** FAX: (703)435-2537.

Hardy BBT Limited
See: **HBT AGRA Limited** (7072)

Thomas Hardy Wine Library
See: **State Library of South Australia - Special Collections** (15695)

Philip B. Hardymon Library
See: **St. Anthony Medical Center** (14239)

Hargrett Rare Book and Manuscript Library
See: **University of Georgia** (18600)

★6905★
Edward S. Harkness Eye Institute - John M. Wheeler Library (Med)
635 W. 165th St. Phone: (212)305-2916
New York, NY 10032 Ilse B. Philleo, Dir.
Founded: 1933. **Staff:** Prof 1; Other 1. **Subjects:** Ophthalmology. **Special Collections:** Early ophthalmic instruments; memorabilia. **Holdings:** 13,628 books; 4641 bound periodical volumes; 4250 reprints; 485 audiotapes. **Subscriptions:** 93 journals and other serials. **Services:** Interlibrary loan (photocopies only); library open to the public with restrictions. **Networks/Consortia:** Member of Research Libraries Information Network (RLIN), Medical Library Center of New York (MLCNY), National Network of Libraries of Medicine - Middle Atlantic Region. **Remarks:** Maintained by Columbia-Presbyterian Medical Center of New York. **Remarks:** FAX: (212)305-3173.

★6906★
Harlem Hospital Medical Center - Health Sciences Library (Med)
506 Lenox Ave., KP 6108 Phone: (212)491-8264
New York, NY 10037 Vernon Bruette, Chf.Libn.
Staff: Prof 2; Other 4. **Subjects:** Medicine, dentistry, nursing, allied health sciences. **Holdings:** 3500 books; 9000 bound periodical volumes. **Subscriptions:** 400 journals and other serials. **Services:** Interlibrary loan; copying; library open to the public for reference use only on request. **Automated Operations:** Computerized cataloging. **Computerized Information Services:** BRS Information Technologies, OCLC; DOCLINE (electronic mail service). **Networks/Consortia:** Member of Medical Library Center of New York (MLCNY), New York Metropolitan Reference and Research Library Agency, Manhattan-Bronx Health Sciences Library Consortia. **Publications:** Annual reports; Library Guide; Serials Lists.

★6907★
Harlem Valley Psychiatric Center - E.W. Wimble Memorial Library (Med)
Sta. A Phone: (914)832-6611
Wingdale, NY 12594-0330 Virginia Lewandowski, Sr.Libn.
Founded: 1973. **Staff:** Prof 1; Other 1. **Subjects:** Psychology, psychiatry, medicine, nursing, social work. **Special Collections:** History of New York State Department of Mental Hygiene. **Holdings:** 3500 books; 800 bound periodical volumes; AV programs. **Subscriptions:** 60 journals and other serials. **Services:** Interlibrary loan; copying; library open to the public. **Networks/Consortia:** Member of National Network of Libraries of Medicine - Middle Atlantic Region, Southeastern New York Library Resources Council (SENYLRC). **Publications:** Library Services at Harlem Valley, annual - for internal distribution only. **Remarks:** FAX: (914)832-3516.

★6908★
Harley-Davidson, Inc. - Engineering Library
3700 W. Juneau Ave.
Box 653
Milwaukee, WI 53208
Founded: 1978. **Subjects:** Motorcycles, motor vehicles, engineering. **Holdings:** 385 volumes; SAE technical reports. **Remarks:** Currently inactive.

Harman Library
See: **United Cooperatives of Ontario** (16702)

★6909★
Harmarville Rehabilitation Center - Staff Library (Med)
Guys Run Rd.
Box 11460 Phone: (412)826-2741
Pittsburgh, PA 15238-0460 Susan L. Wertz, Dir.
Staff: Prof 1; Other 1. **Subjects:** Rehabilitation of the physically handicapped adult, spinal cord injuries, hemiplegia, paraplegia, architectural accessibility, sexual aspects of disability, oncology rehabilitation. **Holdings:** 2600 books; bound periodical volumes; 525 nonprint materials; 410 videotapes; 325 audiocassettes; 54 slide/sound sets. **Subscriptions:** 188 journals and other serials. **Services:** Interlibrary loan; copying; SDI; library open to the public for reference use only. **Computerized Information Services:** DIALOG Information Services, BRS Information Technologies, NLM; DOCLINE (electronic mail service). **Networks/Consortia:** Member of National Network of Libraries of Medicine - Middle Atlantic Region, Pittsburgh-East Hospital Library Cooperative, BHSL. **Publications:** Medical Update, Therapy Update, Nursing Update, Administrative Update - all monthly current awareness publications. **Remarks:** FAX: (412)828-6955.

Harmony Foundation
See: **Society for the Preservation and Encouragement of Barber Shop Quartet Singing in America** (15337)

Harmony Society Library
See: **Pennsylvania (State) Historical & Museum Commission - Old Economy Village** (12880)

★6910★
Harper-Grace Hospitals - Grace Hospital Division - Oscar Le Seure Professional Library (Med)
18700 Meyers Rd. Phone: (313)966-3276
Detroit, MI 48235 Frances M. Phillips, Dir., Lib. & AV Serv.
Founded: 1914. **Staff:** Prof 1. **Subjects:** Medicine, medical specialties, nursing. **Special Collections:** Transcultural Healthcare Index (10 books, vertical file). **Holdings:** 3500 books; 6500 bound periodical volumes; 391 AV programs. **Subscriptions:** 251 journals and other serials. **Services:** Interlibrary loan; copying; SDI; AV production; library open to students in hospital for medical training. **Automated Operations:** Computerized cataloging, acquisitions, and circulation. **Computerized Information Services:** MEDLINE, BRS Information Technologies, OCLC; Nursesearch (internal database); DOCLINE (electronic mail service). **Networks/Consortia:** Member of Michigan Library Consortium (MLC). **Remarks:** FAX: (313)966-4089. **Staff:** Mary A. Dery, Asst.Libn.

★6911★
Harper Hospital - Department of Libraries (Med)
3990 John R St. Phone: (313)745-1443
Detroit, MI 48201-2097 Sandra I. Martin, Supv., Lib./AV Serv.
Founded: 1890. **Staff:** Prof 2; Other 1. **Subjects:** Medicine, nursing, allied health sciences, hospital and business administration. **Special Collections:** Lay health collection (2500 volumes); hospital and corporate archives; professional library. **Holdings:** 9000 book titles; 19,000 bound periodical volumes; 8 VF drawers of pamphlets; audio- and videotapes; AV programs. **Subscriptions:** 720 journals and other serials. **Services:** Interlibrary loan; copying; professional library open to community professionals on application to librarian. **Automated Operations:** Computerized cataloging, acquisitions, circulation, and ILL (NOTIS). **Computerized Information Services:** MEDLARS, DIALOG Information Services, BRS Information Technologies, OCLC, Hannah Information Systems, WILSONLINE. **Networks/Consortia:** Member of Michigan Library Consortium (MLC), Detroit Associated Libraries. **Remarks:** FAX: (313)993-0239. **Staff:** Karen J. Fulwood, Asst.Libn.

Harpers Ferry National Historical Park
See: **U.S. Natl. Park Service** (17730)

★6912★
William F. Harrah Foundation - National Automobile Museum - Library (Trans)
10 Lake St., S. Phone: (702)333-9300
Reno, NV 89501 Janet Ross, Libn.
Founded: 1961. **Staff:** 1. **Subjects:** Automotive literature, automobile restoration. **Special Collections:** Meurisse/Wilson/Finn Auto Racing negatives; Thomas Flyer round-the-world race memorabilia; automotive periodicals, 1900 to present; restoration manuals for vehicles in the Museum's collection. **Holdings:** Books; sales brochures; owners manuals; shop manuals; technical data; supply catalogs; parts lists; wiring diagrams; AMA and AEA data; photographs. **Services:** Library not open to the public; research allowed for fee. **Special Indexes:** Periodicals index by auto manufacturer and year, 1900 to 1960. **Remarks:** FAX: (702)333-9309.

George T. Harrell Library
See: **Pennsylvania State University - College of Medicine** (12900)

Harrington California Indian Archives
See: **Santa Barbara Museum of Natural History - Library** (14802)

★6913★
Harrington Institute of Interior Design - Design Library (Art)
410 S. Michigan Ave. Phone: (312)939-4975
Chicago, IL 60605 Adeline Schuster, MLS, Hd.Libn.
Founded: 1974. **Staff:** Prof 2; Other 4. **Subjects:** Architecture, design, building materials, furniture, 20th century design. **Special Collections:** Current catalogs from manufacturers of contemporary furnishings; paint color catalogs; plastic laminate samples of currently available colors and patterns. **Holdings:** 15,000 books; 900 bound periodical volumes; 15,000 slides. **Subscriptions:** 100 journals and other serials. **Services:** Interlibrary loan; copying; library open to the public by appointment for reference use only with referral from another library. **Automated Operations:** Computerized cataloging and ILL. **Computerized Information Services:** OCLC. **Networks/Consortia:** Member of Chicago Library System, ILLINET. **Publications:** Subject bibliographies, irregular; accessions lists. **Remarks:** FAX: (312)939-8005. **Staff:** Craig Davis, Circ.Spec.; Elaine Lowenthal, Cat. & Hd., Tech.Serv.

Harrington Meeting House
See: **Pemaquid Historical Association** (12817)

Al Harris Library
See: **Southwestern Oklahoma State University** (15542)

★6914★
Harris Catalog Library - Catalog World: America's Mail Order Theater (Bus-Fin)
4555 Auburn Blvd., Suite 11 Phone: (916)487-6964
Sacramento, CA 95841 Warren D. Harris, Pres.
Founded: 1982. **Staff:** 1. **Subjects:** Catalogs - clothing, gift, sports/recreation, food, home furnishings, craft, children's, toys/games, business, art, books/videos, animals, science/nature, hobbies, food/drink. **Special Collections:** Depository of mail-order catalogs. **Holdings:** 1800 catalogs. **Services:** Catalog World open to the public. **Computerized Information Services:** Performs searches free of charge.

Chancellor R.V. Harris Memorial Library
See: **Anglican Church of Canada - Church House Library** (867)

★6915★
Harris Corporation - Government Support Systems Division - Information Center (Sci-Engr)
6801 Jericho Tpke. Phone: (516)677-2000
Syosset, NY 11791 Eleanor Pienitz, Chf., Lib.Serv.
Staff: Prof 1. **Subjects:** Electronics, electrical engineering, computer science. **Holdings:** 1290 books; 653 bound periodical volumes. **Subscriptions:** 93 journals and other serials; 12 newspapers. **Services:** Interlibrary loan; center not open to the public. **Computerized Information Services:** DIALOG Information Services. **Networks/Consortia:** Member of Long Island Library Resources Council.

★6916★
Harris County Heritage Society - Library (Hist, Art)
1100 Bagby Phone: (713)655-1912
Houston, TX 77002 Valerie Olsen
Founded: 1954. **Staff:** Prof 2. **Subjects:** 19th century decorative arts, history of Houston, Texas and Southwest, art and artists, architecture, restoration. **Special Collections:** 19th century photographs, fire equipment, toys, costumes. **Holdings:** 1200 books; 120 bound periodical volumes; newspaper articles; 1 VF drawer of pamphlets; maps; slides of 19th century decorative arts, homes, and history. **Services:** Copying; library open to the public with restrictions.

★6917★
Harris County Law Library (Law)
Congress Plaza
1019 Congress, 17th Fl. Phone: (713)755-5183
Houston, TX 77002 John R. Eichstadt, Dir.
Founded: 1913. **Staff:** Prof 2; Other 9. **Subjects:** Law. **Holdings:** 100,000 volumes.

Harris County Medical Archive
See: **Houston Academy of Medicine - Texas Medical Center Library** (7445)

★6918★
Harris Electronic Systems Sector - Library (Sci-Engr)
Box 37
MS 3A-8544 Phone: (407)727-4677
Melbourne, FL 32902 Mary B. Briand, Lib.Serv.Adm.
Staff: Prof 1; Other 1. **Subjects:** Electrical and electronic engineering, communication systems. **Holdings:** 10,000 books; periodicals of the Institute of Electrical and Electronics Engineers (IEEE). **Subscriptions:** 160 journals and other serials. **Services:** Center not open to the public. **Automated Operations:** Computerized circulation. **Computerized Information Services:** DIALOG Information Services, DTIC. **Publications:** Library bulletin, monthly - for internal distribution only. **Remarks:** FAX: (407)729-3363. **Staff:** Selma Reed, Assoc.Adm.; Stephanie McKinnon, Assoc.Adm.

★6919★
Frederic R. Harris, Inc. - Technical Library (Sci-Engr, Trans)
300 E. 42nd St. Phone: (212)973-3064
New York, NY 10017 Karyn Wickers, Libn.
Founded: 1960. **Staff:** Prof 1. **Subjects:** Engineering - civil, electrical, mechanical, structural; ports and harbors; transportation planning. **Holdings:** 5000 books; 2500 nautical charts; 2000 company project reports. **Subscriptions:** 130 journals and other serials. **Services:** Interlibrary loan; copying; library open to SLA members. **Remarks:** FAX: (212)557-5079; (212)953-0399.

Lillian and Milford Harris Library
See: **Case Western Reserve University** (3126)

★6920★
Louis Harris & Associates, Inc. - Information Services (Soc Sci)
630 Fifth Ave. Phone: (212)698-9697
New York, NY 10111 Jean E. Castle, Libn.
Staff: Prof 1; Other 1. **Subjects:** Public opinion. **Holdings:** 100 books; 100 unbound periodicals; Harris Surveys; internal reports. **Subscriptions:** 104 journals and other serials. **Services:** Interlibrary loan; service not open to the public but telephone reference requests accepted. **Computerized Information Services:** DIALOG Information Services, NEXIS, Public Opinion Location Library (POLL), University of North Carolina Louis Harris Data Center. **Publications:** Bibliography of Published Reports, irregular - free upon request; The Harris Poll, 2/week - by subscription. **Special Indexes:** Index to the Harris Poll, 1963 to present.

Louis Harris Data Center
See: **University of North Carolina at Chapel Hill - Institute for Research in Social Science - Data Library** (19066)

★6921★
Harris Methodist Fort Worth - Medical Library (Med)
1301 Pennsylvania Ave. Phone: (817)882-2118
Fort Worth, TX 76104 Vaida Durham, Libn.
Founded: 1949. **Staff:** 1. **Subjects:** Medicine, surgery. **Holdings:** 1800 books; 3500 bound periodical volumes; 2266 tapes and cassettes. **Subscriptions:** 161 journals and other serials. **Services:** Interlibrary loan; copying; library open to the public for reference use only.

★6922★
Harris Publishing Company - Library (Info Sci)
2057-2 Aurora Rd.
Twinsburg, OH 44087 Phone: (216)425-9000
Subjects: Electronics, manufacturing, and service firms; company and marketing data. **Holdings:** 500 volumes; census demographic reports. **Subscriptions:** 25 journals and other serials. **Computerized Information Services:** Produces Selectories (databases of industrial information for selected states). Performs custom data searches and printouts on fee basis. **Publications:** Industrial Directories (print and ondisc) - available for purchase. **Remarks:** FAX: (800)643-5997; (216)425-7150. Toll-free telephone number(s): 800-888-5900. **Formerly:** Harris Information Services.

★6923★
Harris-Stowe State College Library (Educ)
3026 Laclede Ave. Phone: (314)533-3366
St. Louis, MO 63103 Martin Knorr, Dir.
Founded: 1857. **Staff:** Prof 3; Other 4. **Subjects:** Education. **Special Collections:** Elementary education; Education of Exceptional Children; Black Studies; Juvenile Literature; Civil Rights. **Holdings:** 90,000 books; 2400 reels of microfilm of periodicals. **Subscriptions:** 325 journals and other serials; 9 newspapers. **Services:** Interlibrary loan; library open to teachers and education professionals with courtesy card. **Automated Operations:** Computerized circulation. **Computerized Information Services:** DIALOG Information Services. **Networks/Consortia:** Member of St. Louis Regional Library Network. **Remarks:** FAX: (314)533-0916. **Staff:** Marion Shapiro, Tech.Serv.Libn.; Joe Roger, Pub.Serv.Libn.; Linda Orzel, Ser.Libn.

★6924★
Harrisburg Hospital-Capital Health System - Library Services (Med)
S. Front St. Phone: (717)782-5510
Harrisburg, PA 17101-2099 Cheryl A. Capitani, Mgr.
Founded: 1936. **Staff:** Prof 2; Other 3. **Subjects:** Clinical medicine, nursing, hospital management, consumer health information. **Holdings:** 3452 monographs; 5219 bound periodical volumes; 875 AV programs; journals on microfilm. **Subscriptions:** 519 journals. **Services:** Interlibrary loan; copying; library open to the public for reference use only with permission of manager. **Automated Operations:** Computerized cataloging. **Computerized Information Services:** DIALOG Information Services, OCLC, BRS Information Technologies, NLM. **Networks/Consortia:** Member of Central Pennsylvania Health Sciences Library Association (CPHSLA), National Network of Libraries of Medicine - Middle Atlantic Region, PALINET. **Publications:** Library Newsletter, bimonthly. **Remarks:** FAX: (717)782-5512. **Staff:** Elizabeth E. Coldsmith, Asst.Libn.

★6925★
Harrisburg State Hospital - Library Services (Med)
Cameron & Maclay Sts.
Pouch A Phone: (717)257-7615
Harrisburg, PA 17105-1300 Martha E. Ruff, Libn.
Founded: 1851. **Staff:** Prof 1; Other 1. **Subjects:** Psychiatry, psychology, nursing, social work, rehabilitation, hospital administration. **Special Collections:** Patient Audio-Visual Collection. **Holdings:** 2500 books; Dorothea Dix Library and Museum (housed in Building 09); 1977 Audio-Digest tapes on psychiatry. **Subscriptions:** 90 journals and other serials; 10 newspapers. **Services:** Interlibrary loan; copying; library open to the public with restrictions. **Automated Operations:** Computerized cataloging. **Computerized Information Services:** DIALOG Information Services (through State Library of Pennsylvania). **Networks/Consortia:** Member of Central Pennsylvania Health Sciences Library Association (CPHSLA), Health Sciences Libraries Consortium (HSLC). **Publications:** The Bookmark (newsletter) , bimonthly - for internal distribution only. **Remarks:** FAX: (717)257-7653.

★6926★
Benjamin Harrison Memorial Home - Research Library (Hist)
1230 N. Delaware St. Phone: (317)631-1898
Indianapolis, IN 46202 Ann Moore, Libn.
Founded: 1985. **Staff:** 1. **Subjects:** Political history, government reports. **Special Collections:** Personal papers of Benjamin Harrison and family members. **Holdings:** 1500 books; 200 pamphlets; 20 reels of microfilm of microfilm of Harrison papers from Library of Congress; 3 reels of microfilm of newspapers; 4 boxes of nonbook items. **Services:** Copying, library open to the public for research on premises. **Remarks:** Maintained by the President Benjamin Harrison Foundation.

★6927★
Harrison County Historical Museum - Inez Hatley Hughes Research Center - Library (Hist)
Peter Whetstone Square Phone: (903)938-2680
Marshall, TX 75670 Inez H. Hughes, Dir.
Founded: 1965. **Staff:** 7. **Subjects:** History - Civil War, local, Texas, United States, world; genealogy; railroads; music. **Special Collections:** Judaism (200 books); sheet music (100); secular and sacred songbooks (25); textbooks (30); historical and genealogical periodicals; telephones. **Holdings:** 500 books; 26 VF drawers of clippings; 143 scrapbooks; 100 maps; 300 genealogy books; 50 telephone directories; 25 Marshall City directories; 1000 other cataloged items. **Services:** Copying; center open to the public for reference use only.

★6928★
Harrison County Law Library (Law)
1801 23rd Ave. Phone: (601)865-4004
Gulfport, MS 39501 Francine Jackson Perry, Libn.
Staff: Prof 1; Other 2. **Subjects:** Mississippi law, law. **Holdings:** 20,000 books. **Services:** Copying; library open to the public. **Computerized Information Services:** WESTLAW. Performs searches on fee basis.

Francis M. Harrison Memorial Library
See: **Easter Seal Rehabilitation Center of Southwestern Connecticut** (5140)

Harold E. Harrison Library
See: **Francis Scott Key Medical Center** (8697)

Mel Harrison Memorial Library
See: **Temple Judea** (16116)

★6929★
Harrison Memorial Hospital - Frech Health Sciences Library (Med)
2520 Cherry Ave. Phone: (206)377-3911
Bremerton, WA 98310 Pia Fish, Dir., Lib.Serv.
Founded: 1980. **Staff:** Prof 1. **Subjects:** Clinical sciences, nursing, hospital administration. **Holdings:** 750 books; 1200 unbound periodical volumes; microfiche. **Subscriptions:** 140 journals and other serials. **Services:** Interlibrary loan; library not open to the public. **Computerized Information Services:** MEDLARS, BRS Information Technologies; OnTyme Electronic Message Network Service (electronic mail service).

Harrison Memorial Library
See: **Valley View Centre** (19739)

Michael and Margaret B. Harrison Western Research Center
See: **University of California, Davis** (18355)

★6930★
Harrisonburg-Rockingham Historical Society and Museum - Library (Hist)
115 Bowman Rd.
Box 716 Phone: (703)879-2616
Dayton, VA 22821 Faye A. Witters, Adm.
Subjects: History and genealogy of Rockingham County and Harrisonburg. **Special Collections:** Writings and printed works of Joseph Funk and other family members who were music publishers in the county (150); Henkel Press publications and family correspondence (200 items). **Holdings:** 600 books; 3 VF drawers of genealogical materials; 6 VF drawers of local newspaper obituaries; 3 VF drawers of miscellany. **Services:** Copying; library open to the public for reference use only. **Publications:** Rockingham Recorder, biennial.

Tom Harrisson Mass-observation Archive
See: **University of Sussex - University Library** (19360)

★6931★
Harrodsburg Historical Society - Morgan Row Library (Hist)
220 S. Chiles St.
Harrodsburg, KY 40330 James H. Miller, Pres.
Founded: 1960. **Subjects:** Mercer County and Kentucky history; family and land history. **Special Collections:** Pleasant Hill, Kentucky Shaker History (journals and papers). **Holdings:** 1467 books; 17 bound periodical volumes; 52 bound newspapers; archives; microfiche; microfilm. **Subscriptions:** 6 journals and other serials. **Services:** Library open to the public by appointment on fee basis. **Computerized Information Services:** Performs genealogical searches on fee basis.

Vivian G. Harsh Collection of Afro-American History & Literature
See: **Chicago Public Library - Carter G. Woodson Regional Library - Vivian G. Harsh Research Collection of Afro-American History & Literature** (3527)

Donn V. Hart Southeast Asian Collection
See: **Northern Illinois University** (11994)

Hart Nautical Collections
See: **Massachusetts Institute of Technology - M.I.T. Museum and Historical Collections - Hart Nautical Collections** (9809)

Stephen H. Hart Library
See: **Colorado Historical Society** (3941)

★6932★
Harte-Hanks Communications, Inc. - San Angelo Standard-Times - Library (Publ)
34 W. Harris
Box 5111 Phone: (915)653-1221
San Angelo, TX 76902 Edna A. Ramirez, Lib.Hd.
Founded: 1948. **Staff:** Prof 1. **Subjects:** Newspaper reference topics. **Holdings:** 300 books; newspaper on microfilm, 1884 to present; 26 filing cabinets of newspaper clippings; 9 filing cabinets of local photographs. **Subscriptions:** 20 journals and other serials; 16 newspapers. **Services:** Copying; library open to the public with restrictions. **Computerized Information Services:** DataTimes. **Remarks:** FAX: (915)658-7341.

★6933★
Hartford Courant - News Library (Publ)
285 Broad St. Phone: (203)241-6470
Hartford, CT 06115 Kathleen McKula, News Libn.
Staff: Prof 1; Other 8. **Subjects:** Newspaper reference topics. **Holdings:** Figures not available. **Remarks:** FAX: (203)520-6906.

★6934★
Hartford Hospital - Health Science Libraries (Med)
80 Seymour St. Phone: (203)524-2971
Hartford, CT 06115-0729 Gertrude Lamb, Ph.D., Dir.
Founded: 1900. **Staff:** Prof 9; Other 9. **Subjects:** Clinical medicine, nursing, education, administration, gerontology, allied health specialties. **Special Collections:** Foley Collection (early books on nursing). **Holdings:** 10,586 books; 15,109 bound periodical volumes; 30 VF drawers of pamphlets; 11 audiocassettes; 400 videocassettes; 450 slide sets and kits; 20 16mm films. **Subscriptions:** 817 journals and other serials. **Services:** Interlibrary loan; copying; SDI; library open to the public for reference use only. **Computerized Information Services:** DIALOG Information Services, NLM, BRS Information Technologies, OCLC; CD-ROMs. **Networks/Consortia:** Member of Connecticut Association of Health Science Libraries (CAHSL), BHSL. **Remarks:** Includes the holdings of the Robinson Library, Medical Library, and the Gerontology Resource Center. FAX: (203)524-2415. **Staff:** Janice J. Kaplan, Asst.Dir./Med.Libn.; Virginia Corcoran, Asst.Dir./Div. of Info.Serv.; Steve Lytle, Archv.; Sherry Morgan, Sr.Libn., Robinson Library; Linda Kaczmarczyk, Clin.Libn., Pediatrics; Robert Veenstra, Clin.Libn., Med.

★ 6935 ★
Hartford Hospital - Jefferson House-Gerontology Resource Center (Med)
One John H. Stewart Dr. Phone: (203)667-4453
Newington, CT 06111 Virginia H. Corcoran, Gerontologist Libn.
Founded: 1981. **Staff:** Prof 1; Other 1. **Subjects:** Geriatrics, gerontology. **Holdings:** 500 books; 360 bound periodical volumes; unpublished reports and news clippings (online). **Subscriptions:** 46 journals and other serials. **Services:** Interlibrary loan; copying; SDI; center open to the public by appointment. **Computerized Information Services:** NLM, BRS Information Technologies; GRCDB (internal database). Performs searches on fee basis. **Networks/Consortia:** Member of Capital Area Consortium (CAC). **Publications:** Geri-Source (newsletter), 3/year - to mailing list.

★ 6936 ★
Hartford Medical Society - Walter Steiner Memorial Library (Med)
230 Scarborough St. Phone: (203)236-5613
Hartford, CT 06105 H. David Crombie, M.D., Libn.
Founded: 1873. **Staff:** Prof 1. **Subjects:** Medicine, history of medicine, anesthesiology. **Special Collections:** Gershom Bulkeley manuscripts; Hartford imprints; medical and dental tools and artifacts. **Holdings:** 34,342 volumes. **Subscriptions:** 50 journals and other serials. **Services:** Interlibrary loan; copying; library open to the public for reference use only. **Networks/Consortia:** Member of Capital Region Library Council (CRLC). **Special Catalogs:** A Catalogue of Selected Objects from The Historical Museum of Medicine and Dentistry. **Staff:** Diane G. Neumann, Asst.Libn.

★ 6937 ★
Hartford Public Library - Art, Music and Recreation Department (Art, Mus, Aud-Vis)
500 Main St. Phone: (203)293-6000
Hartford, CT 06103 Vernon Martin, Hd.
Founded: 1774. **Staff:** 5. **Subjects:** Art, music, recreation. **Special Collections:** Helen A. Rice Memorial Collection (chamber music parts). **Holdings:** 330,000 pictures; 15,000 pamphlets; 400 films; 200 video cassettes; 15,000 phonograph records. **Subscriptions:** 80 journals and other serials. **Services:** Interlibrary loan; copying. **Special Catalogs:** Catalog of Helen A. Rice Memorial Collection. **Special Indexes:** Song index. **Staff:** J. Porter; E. Raynor; K. Brophy.

★ 6938 ★
Hartford Public Library - Business, Science & Technology Department (Bus-Fin, Sci-Engr)
500 Main St. Phone: (203)293-6000
Hartford, CT 06103 Charles S. Griffen, Hd.
Founded: 1929. **Staff:** Prof 5; Other 6. **Subjects:** Commerce, economics, statistics, applied science, science and technology, mathematics, natural sciences. **Special Collections:** Corporate annual reports; radio and television service manuals; mail order catalogs. **Holdings:** 50,400 volumes; 38 VF drawers of pamphlets; 120,000 government documents; 1250 reels of microfilm. **Subscriptions:** 375 journals and other serials. **Services:** Interlibrary loan; copying. **Computerized Information Services:** CD-ROMs (Government Publications Index, Moody's 5000 plus). **Special Indexes:** Automobile evaluations index; automobile index (card). **Staff:** Mary Albro, Govt.Docs.Libn.; Marlene Melcher; Evelyn Ball; Janice Hadley; Susan Kaehrle.

★ 6939 ★
Hartford Public Library - Reference and General Reading Department (Soc Sci, Hist)
500 Main St. Phone: (203)293-6000
Hartford, CT 06103 Rafael Moreno, Hd.
Founded: 1774. **Staff:** 9. **Subjects:** History; biography; travel; literature; social sciences; philosophy; psychology; religion; political science; performing arts - theater, motion pictures, radio, television; education. **Special Collections:** Hartford Collection (36,000 cataloged items, 3000 pictures); Grant Information Collection; Municipal Reference Collection. **Holdings:** 100,000 books; 44 VF drawers; 50,000 maps; depository for U.S. government documents (72,000 items) and Connecticut government documents (1500 items); 2250 reels of microfilm; 1700 microfiche; 3000 pictures; 500 recordings. **Subscriptions:** 340 journals and other serials; 45 newspapers. **Services:** Interlibrary loan; copying. **Automated Operations:** Computerized cataloging, acquisitions, circulation and indexing. **Computerized Information Services:** InfoTrac. **Networks/Consortia:** Member of Capital Region Library Council (CRLC), NELINET, Inc. **Special Indexes:** Index to Hartford Courant, 1945 to present; Hartford Times, 1945 to 1976. **Staff:** Beverly Loughlin, Asst.Hd.; Mary Billings; Dorothy Brickett; Carol Fitting; Janice Hadley; Shirley Kiefer; Judith King; Fernando Labault; Susan Kaehrle.

★ 6940 ★
Hartford Seminary - Library (Rel-Phil)
77 Sherman St. Phone: (203)232-4451
Hartford, CT 06105 Edna Madden, Libn.
Founded: 1834. **Staff:** Prof 1; Other 2. **Subjects:** Theology, Christian-Muslim relations, church history, missions, sociology, contemporary church. **Special Collections:** Duncan Black Macdonald Collection of Arabian Nights (1000 volumes); Arabic manuscripts (1200); illuminated Qu'rans (50); Armenian gospels (50); manuscript sermons and letters of 18th and 19th century theologians (10,000). **Holdings:** 61,415 volumes; 6698 bound periodical volumes; 100,000 archival materials; 6463 microforms; 600 dissertations; 175 audiotapes. **Subscriptions:** 315 journals and other serials. **Services:** Interlibrary loan; copying; library open to the public. **Automated Operations:** Computerized cataloging. **Computerized Information Services:** OCLC. **Networks/Consortia:** Member of Hartford Consortium for Higher Education. **Remarks:** FAX: (203)236-8570.

★ 6941 ★
Hartford State Technical College - Grom Hayes Library (Sci-Engr)
401 Flatbush Ave. Phone: (203)527-4111
Hartford, CT 06106 Dr. Larry W. Yother, Lib.Dir.
Founded: 1963. **Staff:** Prof 1. **Subjects:** Engineering - civil, mechanical, manufacturing; computer and electronic technology. **Special Collections:** Architecture history. **Holdings:** 15,000 books. **Subscriptions:** 78 journals and other serials. **Services:** Interlibrary loan; copying; library open to state residents. **Automated Operations:** Computerized cataloging, serials, and circulation. **Computerized Information Services:** Grom Hayes Systems (internal database). **Publications:** Automation systems manual, semiannual.

Hartman Library
See: **Robert Wood Johnson Pharmaceutical Research Institute** (8458)

★ 6942 ★
Hartnell College - Library - O.P. Silliman Memorial Library (Biol Sci)
156 Homestead Ave. Phone: (408)755-6872
Salinas, CA 93901 Beverly Braun
Founded: 1920. **Staff:** 10.5. **Subjects:** Ornithology. **Special Collections:** O.P. Silliman collection. **Holdings:** 5000 volumes. **Services:** Interlibrary loan; copying; library open to the public. **Automated Operations:** Computerized cataloging and circulation. **Computerized Information Services:** DIALOG Information Services, WILSONLINE, OCLC; OnTyme Electronic Message Network Service (electronic mail service). Performs searches on fee basis. Contact Person: Esta Lee Albright, Pub.Serv.Libn. **Networks/Consortia:** Member of Monterey Bay Area Cooperative Library System (MOBAC). **Remarks:** FAX: (408)755-6751. Electronic mail address(es): HART (OnTyme Electronic Message Network Service). **Staff:** Ms.Sze Soo.

Hartness Library
See: **Vermont Technical College** (19811)

★ 6943 ★
Hartshorn Family Association - Clearinghouse (Hist)
1204 4th Street Dr., S.E. Phone: (704)464-4981
Conover, NC 28613 Derick S. Hartshorn, Pres.
Founded: 1985. **Subjects:** Genealogy. **Holdings:** 400 books; vital records. **Services:** Library open to the public by appointment. **Computerized Information Services:** Internal database. **Publications:** The Hartshorn Family; The Hartshorns of Ohio. **Remarks:** Serves as a clearinghouse for biographical and genealogical information on the name Hartshorn/Hartshorne/Hartson.

Hartt School of Music
See: **University of Hartford - Hartt School of Music** (18614)

★ 6944 ★
Hartwick College - Stevens-German Library - Special Collections (Area-Ethnic)
Oneonta, NY 13820 Phone: (607)431-4440
Robert E. Danford, Dir.
Founded: 1928. **Staff:** Prof 8; Other 11. **Subjects:** Indians of North America, especially Eastern Woodland Indians. **Special Collections:** Yager Collection

of Rare Books; Congressman James Hanley papers concerned with Native Americans (2 cubic feet); Hatrwick Seminary records (40 cubic feet); Judge William Cooper papers (15 cubic feet); Willard E. Yager Manuscript Collection (15 cubic feet); John Christopher Hartwick Library (290 titles). **Holdings:** 6200 books; 200 bound periodical volumes; 200 folders of clippings; 1000 reels of microfilm; 3000 microfiche. **Subscriptions:** 1202 journals and other serials; 17 newspapers. **Services:** Interlibrary loan; copying; collection open to the public. **Automated Operations:** Computerized cataloging. **Computerized Information Services:** DIALOG Information Services; InterNet, ALANET (electronic mail services). **Publications:** Indians of North and South America, a bibliography based on the collection of the Willard E. Yager Library Museum, 1977; supplement, 1987. **Remarks:** FAX: (607)431-4457. Electronic mail address(es): DANFORDR@HARTWICK.EDU (InterNet); HARTWICK (ALANET). **Staff:** Eric Von Brockdorff; Carol Wolf; Susan Stevens; Nancy Chiang; Carolyn N. France; Shelley Wallace; Barbara Niederhoff.

Hartzler Music Collection
See: **Goshen College - Harold and Wilma Good Library** (6581)

Armenak and Nunia Harutunian Library
See: **Armenian Society of Los Angeles** (1053)

Harvard Business School
See: **Harvard University - Harvard Business School - Baker Library** (6969)

Harvard Forest Library
See: **Harvard University** (6970)

★6945★
Harvard Library in New York (Educ)
27 W. 44th St. Phone: (212)827-1246
New York, NY 10036 Adrienne G. Fischier, Libn.
Founded: 1978. **Staff:** 2. **Special Collections:** Harvardiana. **Holdings:** 25,000 books; 600 bound periodical volumes. **Subscriptions:** 150 journals and other serials; 10 newspapers. **Services:** Interlibrary loan (limited); library open to the public by appointment on a limited schedule. **Computerized Information Services:** Internal database. **Remarks:** Maintained by Harvard Club of New York City. **Remarks:** FAX: (212)827-1250.

★6946★
Harvard Musical Association - Library (Mus)
57A Chestnut St. Phone: (617)523-2897
Boston, MA 02108 Natalie Palme, Libn.
Founded: 1837. **Staff:** Prof 1; Other 1. **Subjects:** Music. **Holdings:** 2130 books; 325 bound periodical volumes; 7512 musical items. **Services:** Interlibrary loan; library open to the public.

Harvard Theatre Collection
See: **Harvard University** (6972)

Harvard Ukrainian Research Institute
See: **Harvard University** (6973)

★6947★
Harvard University - Archives (Hist)
Pusey Library Phone: (617)495-2461
Cambridge, MA 02138 Harley P. Holden, Cur.
Founded: 1636. **Staff:** Prof 9; Other 7. **Subjects:** Harvard University (archives, publications, books about); Harvard graduates (biography and clippings); Harvard professors. **Special Collections:** Harvard University theses and dissertations; personal and professional papers of Harvard professors. **Holdings:** 94,102 volumes and pamphlets. **Services:** Copying; reference service on Harvard University and Harvard people; archives open to the public. **Computerized Information Services:** OCLC. **Networks/Consortia:** Member of NELINET, Inc., Center for Research Libraries (CRL). **Publications:** Descriptive Guide (1974); Visual Collections Manual (1982). **Staff:** Clark A. Elliott, Assoc.Cur.; Mark J. Duffy, Assoc.Cur.

★6948★
Harvard University - Bernhard Kummel Library of the Geological Sciences (Sci-Engr)
24 Oxford St. Phone: (617)495-2029
Cambridge, MA 02138 Constance S. Wick, Libn.
Founded: 1960. **Staff:** Prof 1; Other 3. **Subjects:** Mineralogy, petrology, economic geology, stratigraphy, geophysics. **Holdings:** 60,000 volumes; 21,000 geological maps. **Subscriptions:** 912 journals and other serials. **Services:** Interlibrary loan; copying. **Automated Operations:** Computerized acquisitions, cataloging, and serials. **Computerized Information Services:** DIALOG Information Services; CD-ROMs. Performs searches on fee basis. **Networks/Consortia:** Member of NELINET, Inc., Center for Research Libraries (CRL).

★6949★
Harvard University - Biological Laboratories Library (Biol Sci)
16 Divinity Ave. Phone: (617)495-3944
Cambridge, MA 02138 Dorothy J. Solbrig, Libn.
Staff: Prof 1; Other 1. **Subjects:** Cell and developmental biology, biochemistry and molecular biology, plant and animal physiology, genetics. **Holdings:** 27,000 volumes. **Subscriptions:** 260 journals and other serials. **Services:** Interlibrary loan; library open to the public. **Automated Operations:** Computerized public access catalog, cataloging, and acquisitions. **Computerized Information Services:** BRS Information Technologies, OCLC; DIALMAIL (electronic mail service). **Networks/Consortia:** Member of NELINET, Inc., Center for Research Libraries (CRL). **Remarks:** FAX: (617)495-9300. Telex: 921496.

★6950★
Harvard University - Botany Libraries (Biol Sci)
22 Divinity Ave. Phone: (617)495-2366
Cambridge, MA 02138 Judith Warnement, Libn.
Founded: 1890. **Staff:** Prof 4; Other 4. **Subjects:** Botany and horticulture. **Special Collections:** Manuscript letters from botanists. **Holdings:** 269,000 volumes and pamphlets; archives; manuscripts; portraits; photographs. **Subscriptions:** 1500 journals and other serials. **Services:** Copying; library open to the public for reference use only. **Computerized Information Services:** OCLC EPIC, BRS Information Technologies. **Networks/Consortia:** Member of NELINET, Inc., Center for Research Libraries (CRL). **Special Indexes:** Gray Herbarium Index (reproduction of 259,000 cards with names and literature citations of newly described or established vascular plants of the Western Hemisphere). **Remarks:** FAX: (617)495-9484. Botany Libraries include Arnold Arboretum Library, Gray Herbarium Library, Economic Botany Library, Oakes Ames Orchid Library, and Farlow Reference Library (previously listed separately). **Staff:** Jill Thomas, Tech.Serv.Libn.; Jean Cargill, Ref.Libn.

Harvard University - Botany Libraries - Arnold Arboretum & Gray Herbarium Library
See: **Harvard University - Botany Libraries** (6950)

Harvard University - Botany Libraries - Economic Botany Library
See: **Harvard University - Botany Libraries** (6950)

Harvard University - Botany Libraries - Farlow Reference Library
See: **Harvard University - Botany Libraries** (6950)

★6951★
Harvard University - Carpenter Center for the Visual Arts - Photography Collection (Art)
Cambridge, MA 02138 Phone: (617)495-3251
Barbara P. Norfleet, Cur./Sr. Lecturer
Founded: 1972. **Staff:** Prof 1. **Subjects:** Social history and social reform in America; art photography. **Special Collections:** Social ethics; studio photographers. **Holdings:** 10,000 negatives; 30,000 photographs. **Services:** Collection open to the public by appointment. **Publications:** Wedding; The Champion Pig; Killing Time. **Special Catalogs:** The Social Question.

★6952★
Harvard University - Center for European Studies - Library (Area-Ethnic)
27 Kirkland St. Phone: (617)495-4303
Cambridge, MA 02138 Loren Goldner, Libn.
Founded: 1969. **Staff:** Prof 1. **Subjects:** Contemporary European domestic politics, history, sociology, economics, and labor relations. **Special Collections:** German domestic politics and history; sources for Laurence Wylie's Bibliography on France: the events of May-June, 1968 (books; pamphlets; journals; newspapers). **Holdings:** 6000 books; 300 papers on European politics; 20 dissertations. **Subscriptions:** 82 journals and other serials; 18 newspapers. **Services:** Interlibrary loan; copying; library open to the public. **Computerized Information Services:** OCLC. **Networks/Consortia:** Member of NELINET, Inc., Center for Research Libraries (CRL). **Remarks:** FAX: (617)495-8509.

★6953★
Harvard University - Center for Hellenic Studies - Library (Hum, Area-Ethnic)
3100 Whitehaven St., N.W. Phone: (202)234-3738
Washington, DC 20008 Ellen C. Roth, Libn.
Founded: 1961. **Staff:** Prof 1; Other 2. **Subjects:** Ancient Greek history and civilization, literature, philosophy, religion. **Holdings:** 42,000 books, bound periodical volumes, pamphlets. **Subscriptions:** 208 journals and other serials. **Services:** Copying; library open to qualified scholars. **Computerized Information Services:** OCLC; Thesarus Linguae Graecae. **Networks/Consortia:** Member of CAPCON Library Network, Center for Research Libraries (CRL).

★6954★
Harvard University - Center for International Affairs - Library (Soc Sci)
Coolidge Hall
1737 Cambridge St. Phone: (617)495-2173
Cambridge, MA 02138 Malcolm White, Hd.Libn.
Founded: 1958. **Staff:** Prof 1. **Subjects:** International relations, diplomacy, strategic studies, national security. **Holdings:** 20,000 books. **Subscriptions:** 100 journals and other serials. **Services:** Interlibrary loan; copying; library open to the public with restrictions. **Automated Operations:** Computerized public access catalog. **Computerized Information Services:** InterNet (electronic mail service). **Remarks:** FAX: (617)495-8292. Electronic mail address(es): WHITEZ@HUSCH.HARVARD.EDU (InterNet).

★6955★
Harvard University - Center for Middle Eastern Studies - Library (Area-Ethnic)
Coolidge Hall
1737 Cambridge St. Phone: (617)495-2173
Cambridge, MA 02138 Malcolm D. White, Libn.
Founded: 1959. **Staff:** 1. **Subjects:** History of Islam; ancient and modern Middle East - Turkey, Iran, Egypt, Syria, Jordan, Israel, Libya, North Africa; current political and economic issues. **Holdings:** 5005 volumes. **Subscriptions:** 20 journals and other serials. **Services:** Interlibrary loan; copying; library open to the public with restrictions. **Computerized Information Services:** InterNet (electronic mail service). **Remarks:** FAX: (617)495-8292. Electronic mail address(es): WHITEZ@HUSCH.HARVARD.EDU (InterNet).

★6956★
Harvard University - Center for Science and International Affairs - Library (Soc Sci)
John F. Kennedy School of Government
79 Kennedy St., Rms. 369 and 371 Phone: (617)495-1408
Cambridge, MA 02138 Stephen J. Stillwell, Jr., Libn.
Founded: 1973. **Staff:** 1. **Subjects:** Arms control, international affairs, international security. **Holdings:** 5000 volumes. **Subscriptions:** 100 journals and other serials. **Services:** Copying; library open to the public on a limited schedule. **Automated Operations:** Computerized public access catalog, cataloging, acquisitions, and serials. **Publications:** International Security, quarterly - by subscription. **Remarks:** FAX: (617)495-8963.

★6957★
Harvard University - Chemistry Library (Sci-Engr)
Converse Memorial Laboratory
12 Oxford St. Phone: (617)495-4079
Cambridge, MA 02138 Dr. Ludmila Birladeanu, Supv.
Staff: Prof 1; Other 1. **Subjects:** Chemistry. **Holdings:** 51,000 books, bound periodical volumes. pamphlets. **Subscriptions:** 411 journals and other serials. **Services:** Interlibrary loan (fee); copying; library open to the public with restrictions.

★6958★
Harvard University - Divinity School - Andover-Harvard Theological Library (Rel-Phil)
45 Francis Ave. Phone: (617)495-5788
Cambridge, MA 02138 Louis Charles Willard, Libn.
SFounded: 1812. **Staff:** Prof 7; Other 8. **Subjects:** Theology, Bible, Protestantism, allied subjects. **Special Collections:** American Congregational, Unitarian, and Universalist materials. **Holdings:** 405,375 volumes; 2400 filing boxes of manuscripts; 51,597 microforms. **Subscriptions:** 2400 journals and other serials. **Services:** Interlibrary loan; copying; library open to the public on special application. **Automated Operations:** Computerized cataloging and acquisitions. **Computerized Information Services:** OCLC. **Networks/Consortia:** Member of NELINET, Inc., Center for Research Libraries (CRL), Boston Theological Institute Libraries. **Publications:** Guide. **Staff:** Laura Whitney, Circ.; Russell Pollard, Tech.Serv.; Alan Seaburg, Mss. and Archv.; Doris Freitag, Consrv.; Clifford Wunderlich, Cat.; Allan Junik, Cat.; Susan Yoon, Recon.Cat.

★6959★
Harvard University - Division of Applied Sciences - Department of Earth & Planetary Sciences - Blue Hill Meteorological Observatory Library (Sci-Engr)
Pierce Hall
29 Oxford St. Phone: (617)495-2836
Cambridge, MA 02138 Martha F. Wooster, Libn.
Founded: 1885. **Staff:** Prof 1; Other 3. **Subjects:** Atmosphere, climatology, earth sciences, meteorology, oceanography, weather. **Special Collections:** Center publications. **Holdings:** 6817 volumes. **Subscriptions:** 100 journals and other serials. **Services:** Interlibrary loan (fee); copying; library open to the public for reference use only. **Automated Operations:** Computerized public access catalog, cataloging, acquisitions, and serials. **Computerized Information Services:** OCLC; HOLLIS (internal database). **Networks/Consortia:** Member of NELINET, Inc., Center for Research Libraries (CRL). **Remarks:** FAX: (617)495-9837.

★6960★
Harvard University - Division of Applied Sciences - Gordon McKay Library (Sci-Engr, Comp Sci)
Pierce Hall
29 Oxford St. Phone: (617)495-2836
Cambridge, MA 02138 Martha F. Wooster, Libn.
Founded: 1919. **Staff:** Prof 1; Other 3. **Subjects:** Applied mathematics and physics, computers, environment, mechanics, electronics. **Special Collections:** Divisional publications. **Holdings:** 96,557 volumes; 75,465 microcards of technical reports; 117,156 microfiche of technical reports. **Subscriptions:** 754 journals and other serials. **Services:** Interlibrary loan (fee); copying; library open to the public for reference use only. **Automated Operations:** Computerized public access catalog, cataloging, acquisitions, and serials. **Computerized Information Services:** OCLC; HOLLIS (internal database). **Networks/Consortia:** Member of NELINET, Inc., Center for Research Libraries (CRL). **Remarks:** FAX: (617)495-9837.

★6961★
Harvard University - Dumbarton Oaks - Pre-Columbian Studies Library (Area-Ethnic, Hist)
1703 32nd St., N.W. Phone: (202)342-3265
Washington, DC 20007 Bridget Toledo, Libn.
Founded: 1963. **Staff:** 1.5. **Subjects:** Pre-Columbian anthropology and art history; Latin American linguistics and ethnology. **Special Collections:** Maya ceramic archive. **Holdings:** 18,800 volumes; photographs; slides. **Subscriptions:** 134 journals. **Services:** Copying; library open to qualified scholars by appointment. **Publications:** List of publications - available upon request.

★6962★
Harvard University - Dumbarton Oaks Garden Library - Program for Studies in Landscape Architecture (Agri, Art)
1703 32nd St., N.W. Phone: (202)342-3280
Washington, DC 20007 Dr. Joachim Wolschke-Bulmahn, Act.Dir.
Founded: 1963. **Staff:** Prof 2. **Subjects:** History - gardens and garden design, landscape architecture, garden ornaments, horticulture. **Special Collections:** Rare books; drawings; prints; botanical and floral illustrations. **Holdings:** 13,910 volumes; 103 periodical titles; VF drawers of pamphlet materials; photographs; slides; microfiche. **Subscriptions:** 39 journals and other serials. **Services:** Interlibrary loan; copying; library open to scholars and professionals by appointment. **Networks/Consortia:** Member of CAPCON Library Network. **Publications:** Colloquium on the History of Landscape Architecture, annual - for sale. **Remarks:** FAX: (202)342-3207. **Staff:** Linda Lott, Libn.; Annie Thacher, Assoc.Libn.

★6963★
Harvard University - Dumbarton Oaks Research Library and Collection - Byzantine Library (Hist)
1703 32nd St., N.W. Phone: (202)342-3241
Washington, DC 20007 Dr. Irene Vaslef, Libn.
Founded: 1940. **Staff:** Prof 2; Other 6. **Subjects:** Early Christian, Byzantine, and medieval civilization - art, archeology, religion, history, source material. **Holdings:** 110,000 volumes. **Subscriptions:** 1155 journals and other serials. **Services:** Interlibrary loan; copying; library open to research scholars only and by appointment. **Automated Operations:** Computerized cataloging. **Computerized Information Services:** OCLC. **Networks/Consortia:** Member of CAPCON Library Network. **Publications:** Byzantine Library Serials List. **Staff:** Dr. Virgil Crisafulli, Chf.Cat.

★6964★
Harvard University - Eda Kuhn Loeb Music Library (Mus)
Cambridge, MA 02138 Phone: (617)495-2794
Michael Ochs, Libn.
Founded: 1956. **Staff:** Prof 6; Other 13. **Subjects:** Music. **Special Collections:** Isham Memorial Library (rare materials and microfilm of early music prints and manuscripts). **Holdings:** 110,000 books and scores; 45,000 recordings; 20,000 reels of microfilm. **Subscriptions:** 700 journals and other serials. **Services:** Interlibrary loan (fee); library use may require a letter of introduction; fee for extended use. **Automated Operations:** Computerized public access catalog. **Computerized Information Services:** Hollis (internal database). **Staff:** John B. Howard, Assoc.Libn.; Robert J. Dennis, Recordings Libn.; Florence Lynch, Cat.; Millard Irion, Pub.Serv.Libn.

★6965★
Harvard University - Fine Arts Library (Art)
Werner Otto Hall Phone: (617)495-3373
Cambridge, MA 02138 Richard Wendorf, Act.Libn.
Founded: 1962. **Staff:** Prof 12; Other 20. **Subjects:** History of art. **Special Collections:** Exhibition catalogs; auction sale catalogs; classical art and archeology; Islamic architecture; Italian Renaissance painting; German Expressionism; Wendell Portrait Collection. **Holdings:** 243,031 volumes; 282 boxes of pamphlets and catalogs; 122 linear feet of archival materials and manuscripts; 1.4 million slides and photographs; 38,000 microforms. **Subscriptions:** 1364 journals and other serials. **Services:** Copying; library open to members of the university. **Computerized Information Services:** RLIN; RLG, InterNet (electronic mail services). **Networks/Consortia:** Member of Research Libraries Information Network (RLIN), Center for Research Libraries (CRL). **Publications:** Guide to the Fine Arts Library; Harvard List of Books on Art; New Acquisitions Newsletter; Art Periodical Contents; Guide to Special Collections in the Visual Collections. **Special Indexes:** Iconographic Index to Old Testament Themes in the Visual Collections. **Remarks:** Library maintains the Rubel Asiatic Research Collection , housed separately in the A.M. Sackler Museum (tel. (617)495-0570) and the Documentation Center for the Aga Khan Program in Islamic Architecture. FAX: (617)495-9936. Electronic mail address(es): BM.FAL (RLG); FOGREF@HARVARDA.HARVARD.EDU (InterNet). **Staff:** Patricia Rogers, Assoc.Libn., Bk.Coll.; Helene Roberts, Cur., Vis.Coll.; Mrs. Yen-shew Lynn Chao, Cur., Rubel Coll.; Andras Riedlmayer, Bibliog., Islamic Arch.

★6966★
Harvard University - Godfrey Lowell Cabot Science Library (Sci-Engr)
Science Center
1 Oxford St. Phone: (617)495-5351
Cambridge, MA 02138 Alan E. Erickson, Libn./Sci.Spec.
Founded: 1973. **Staff:** Prof 4; Other 12. **Subjects:** General science, pure mathematics, theoretical statistics. **Holdings:** 150,283 volumes. **Subscriptions:** 866 journals and other serials. **Services:** Interlibrary loan; copying; library open to members of Harvard. **Automated Operations:** Computerized public access catalog, cataloging, acquisitions, circulation, and serials. **Computerized Information Services:** DIALOG Information Services, BRS Information Technologies, BRS/After Dark, Knowledge Index, OCLC, STN International; InterNet (electronic mail service). **Networks/Consortia:** Member of NELINET, Inc., Center for Research Libraries (CRL). **Remarks:** FAX: (617)495-0403. Electronic mail address(es): CABREF@HARVARDA.HARVARD.EDU (InterNet). **Staff:** William A. Bourque, Libn., Bibliog. Control; Patricia Blount, Hd., Circ.; Michael A. Blake, Hd., Ref.; Jon Kinnamon, Ref.Libn.

★6967★
Harvard University - Graduate School of Design - Frances Loeb Library (Plan)
Gund Hall Phone: (617)495-2574
Cambridge, MA 02138 Hinda F. Sklar, Libn.
Founded: 1902. **Staff:** Prof 7; Other 9. **Subjects:** Architecture, landscape architecture, urban design. **Special Collections:** Charles Mulford Robinson Collection; Charles Eliot Collection; Warren Manning Collection; Cluny Collections; Le Corbusier Collection; Hugh Stubbins Archives; Sert Collection. **Holdings:** 250,000 books, bound periodical volumes, pamphlets; 20,010 maps; 5000 architectural drawings; 130,000 slides; plans. **Subscriptions:** 1635 journals and other serials. **Services:** Interlibrary loan; copying; library open to the public for reference use only. **Automated Operations:** Computerized cataloging and acquisitions. **Computerized Information Services:** OCLC. **Networks/Consortia:** Member of NELINET, Inc., Center for Research Libraries (CRL). **Remarks:** FAX: (617)496-5929. Library also maintains an AV work station. **Staff:** Hugh Wilburn, Hd. of Pub.Serv.; Judith Auerbach, Acq.Libn.; Ruth Rosenbloom, Hd., Tech.Serv.; Martha Mahard, Vis.Coll.Libn.; Mary Daniels, Spec.Coll.Libn.

★6968★
Harvard University - Graduate School of Education - Monroe C. Gutman Library (Educ)
6 Appian Way Phone: (617)495-4225
Cambridge, MA 02138 John W. Collins, III, Libn.
Founded: 1920. **Staff:** Prof 13; Other 22. **Subjects:** Education, psychology, related social sciences, emphasis on social and public policy relating to education. **Special Collections:** 18th and 19th century textbooks (38,000); reading collection; children and television; U.S. public school reports and private school catalogs; educational software. **Holdings:** 160,000 books; 300,000 microforms. **Subscriptions:** 1200 journals and other serials. **Services:** Interlibrary loan; copying; library open to the public with restrictions. **Automated Operations:** Computerized public access catalog, acquisitions, and serials. **Computerized Information Services:** BRS Information Technologies, DIALOG Information Services, OCLC, CompuServe Information Service; Educational Technologies Database (internal database). Performs searches on fee basis. **Networks/Consortia:** Member of NELINET, Inc., Northeast Consortium of Colleges and Universities in Massachusetts (NECCUM). **Publications:** Current Awareness; Recent Acquisitions: A Selected List of Books; Journals List. **Special Catalogs:** Test Collection Catalog; Educational Textbooks, 18th and 19th century. **Remarks:** FAX: (617)495-0540. **Staff:** Deborah Garson, Ref.; Jospph Gabriel, Tech.Serv.; Gladys Dratch, Coll.Dev.; Suzanne Teuteberg, Media; Vera Meyer, Adm.; Doris H. Christo, Spec.Proj.Coord.

★6969★
Harvard University - Harvard Business School - Baker Library (Bus-Fin)
Soldiers Field Phone: (617)495-6044
Boston, MA 02163 Mary Chatfield, Libn.
Founded: 1908. **Staff:** Prof 18; Other 19. **Subjects:** Business and economics. **Special Collections:** Kress Library of Business and Economics (publications before 1850; 37,000 volumes); corporate reports on 19,340 companies; manuscripts and archives (80,000 volumes). **Holdings:** 540,000 books, bound periodical volumes, pamphlets; 600,000 microfiche; 15,200 reels of microfilm. **Subscriptions:** 6500 journals and other serials. **Services:** Interlibrary loan; copying; library open to qualified persons for reference.

Automated Operations: Computerized cataloging and serials. **Computerized Information Services:** OCLC, DIALOG Information Services, BRS Information Technologies, Dun & Bradstreet Business Credit Services, VU/TEXT Information Services, Info Globe, Dow Jones News/Retrieval, NEXIS, LEXIS, InvesText. **Networks/Consortia:** Member of NELINET, Inc. **Publications:** Recent Additions to Baker Library, monthly; Working Papers in Baker Library: A Quarterly Checklist. **Remarks:** FAX: (617)495-6001. **Staff:** Gwendolyn Weaver, Dir., Info.Rsrcs.; Michele Marram, Dir., Res.Serv.; Michael Stevenson, Bus.Info.Anl.; Sarah Collins, Bus.Info.Anl.; Chris Allen, Bus.Info.Anl.; Claire Abernathy, Circ.; Sue Marsh, Dir.of Current Coll.; Florence Lathrop, Dir., Spec.Coll.; Becky Smith, Ref.; Erika McCaffrey, Hd., Ref.; Nanu Dixon, Ref.; Sophia Wang, Ser.Cat.; Charlene Cunniffe, Ref.; Philip Hamilton, Stat.Res.Serv.Coord.; Sarah Woolverton, Res. Database Anl.

★6970★
Harvard University - Harvard Forest Library (Biol Sci)
Shaler Hall
N. Main St.
PO Box 68 Phone: (508)724-3302
Petersham, MA 01366 B. Flye, Libn.
Founded: 1908. **Subjects:** Forestry - ecology, economics, management; tree physiology; forest soils; forestry research. **Special Collections:** U.S. government publications, with emphasis on USDA Forest Service; international forestry journals. **Holdings:** 24,500 volumes. **Subscriptions:** 150 journals and other serials. **Services:** Interlibrary loan; library not open to the public. **Computerized Information Services:** Internal database. **Remarks:** FAX: (508)724-3595.

★6971★
Harvard University - Harvard-Smithsonian Center for Astrophysics (CFA) - Library (Sci-Engr)
60 Garden St. Phone: (617)495-7289
Cambridge, MA 02138 Donna J. Coletti, Hd.
Founded: 1959. **Subjects:** Astrophysics, astronomy, space sciences. **Holdings:** 36,000 books; 20,000 bound periodical volumes; 12,000 unbound reports; 40,000 microfiche; 500,000 astronomical photographic plates. **Subscriptions:** 600 journals and other serials. **Services:** Interlibrary loan; copying; library open to the public by arrangement. **Automated Operations:** Computerized cataloging. **Computerized Information Services:** DIALOG Information Services, STN International, SIMBAD; BITNET, SPAN (electronic mail services). **Publications:** Quarterly Acquisitions List. **Remarks:** Alternate telephone number(s): 495-5488. FAX: (617)495-7199. Electronic mail address(es): LIBRARY@CFA (BITNET). Library is maintained by Harvard University and the Smithsonian Institution. **Also Known As:** John G. Wolbach Library; Phillips Library. **Staff:** John Carper, Asst.Libn.; Joyce Watson, Tech.Info.Spec.

★6972★
Harvard University - Harvard Theatre Collection (Theater)
Pusey Library Phone: (617)495-2445
Cambridge, MA 02138 Jeanne T. Newlin, Cur., Theater Coll.
Founded: 1901. **Staff:** Prof 3; Other 1. **Subjects:** Performing arts - theater, dance, circus, minstrels, popular entertainment. **Special Collections:** Angus McBean Collection; Alix Jeffry Collection; H.W.L. Dana Collection; William Como Collection on Twentieth Century Dance; John and Rita Russell Viennese Collection; George Pierce Baker Collection; Rose Winter and Marian Hannah Winter Memorial Collection; George Chaffee Ballet Collection; Robert Gould Shaw Collection; Edward B. Sheldon Collection; E.J. Wendell Collection; Otis Skinner Collection; Edwin Binney 3rd Collection on Ballet; Melvin R. Seiden Collection of Hirschfeld Drawings. **Holdings:** 25,000 books; 3 million playbills and programs; over 650,000 photographs; 250,000 engraved portraits and scenes; 15,000 scenery and costume designs; manuscripts; documents; prompt books; posters; clippings. **Subscriptions:** 125 journals and other serials. **Services:** Copying (limited); Sheldon Exhibition Rooms open to the public; library open to the public with restrictions. **Computerized Information Services:** OCLC. **Networks/Consortia:** Member of NELINET, Inc., Center for Research Libraries (CRL). **Special Catalogs:** Catalog of Dramatic Portraits in the Theatre Collection of the Harvard College Library (4 volumes). **Staff:** Catherine Johnson, Asst.Cur.

★6973★
Harvard University - Harvard Ukrainian Research Institute - Reference Library (Area-Ethnic)
1583 Massachusetts Ave. Phone: (617)496-5891
Cambridge, MA 02138 Ksenya Kiebuzinski, Archv./Bibliog.
Founded: 1973. **Staff:** Prof 1. **Subjects:** Ukraine - history, culture, linguistics, literature, religion, social sciences, societies, institutions; ancillary historical disciplines - textology, historiography, filangrology. **Special Collections:** Specialized bibliographies of monographs and serials; works of major Ukrainian authors (including translations of scholarly and literary importance); classic textbooks in history, literature, linguistics, religion, theology, social sciences; Western languages (Ukrainica; 190 volumes); translations to Ukrainian (350 titles); offprints of articles of Ukrainian scholars (all disciplines) and those relating to Ukraine; national bibliography. **Holdings:** 8571 books; periodicals; atlases; classic textbooks; offprints. **Subscriptions:** 168 journals and other serials; 35 newspapers. **Services:** Library open to the public for reference use only. **Publications:** Harvard Ukrainian Studies, 4/year; Ukrainica in the Harvard University Library, 1975 to present; Harvard Series in Ukrainian Studies volumes. **Remarks:** (617)495-8097.

★6974★
Harvard University - Harvard-Yenching Library (Area-Ethnic)
2 Divinity Ave. Phone: (617)495-3327
Cambridge, MA 02138 Eugene Wu, Libn.
Founded: 1928. **Staff:** Prof 15; Other 17. **Subjects:** Humanities and social sciences relating to China, Japan, and Korea. **Special Collections:** Rare Chinese books and manuscripts; Chinese rubbings; Tibetan and Mongolian Tripitaka; Manchu publications; Nakhi manuscripts; Vietnamese publications; Tiananmen Archives. **Holdings:** 774,897 volumes; 43,271 reels of microfilm; 5431 microfiche; 12,605 journals; 560 newspapers; personal papers; photographs. **Subscriptions:** 3958 journals and other serials; 194 newspapers. **Services:** Interlibrary loan; copying; library open to those with identification, with a fee for borrowing. **Automated Operations:** Computerized public access catalog (HOLLIS), cataloging, acquisitions, and serials. **Computerized Information Services:** BITNET (electronic mail service). **Networks/Consortia:** Member of Center for Research Libraries (CRL). **Publications:** Occasional Reference Notes; Harvard-Yenching Library Bibliographical Series. **Special Catalogs:** Japanese and Chinese Book Catalogs; Korean Catalog; Catalog of Protestant Missionary Works in Chinese. **Remarks:** FAX: (617)496-6008. Electronic mail address(es): WU2@HUSC4 (BITNET). **Staff:** Timothy Connor, Pub.Serv.Libn.; John Yung-Hsiang Lai, Assoc.Libn./Cat.; Chia-Yaung Hu, Asst Libn./Chinese Sect.; Toshiyuki Aoki, Asst.Libn./Japanese Sect.; Choong Nam Yoon, Asst.Libn./Korean Sect.; Sidney Tai, Supv., Rare Bks.Rm.; Raymond D. Lum, Asst.Libn./Western Sect.

★6975★
Harvard University - History of Science Library (Sci-Engr)
Widener Library, Rm. 91 Phone: (617)496-2647
Cambridge, MA 02138 Everett Mendelsohn, Prof.
Subjects: History of science. **Holdings:** 24,312 volumes and pamphlets. **Subscriptions:** 32 journals and other serials. **Services:** Library open to research scholars on a limited basis. **Computerized Information Services:** OCLC. **Networks/Consortia:** Member of NELINET, Inc., Center for Research Libraries (CRL).

★6976★
Harvard University - Houghton Library (Rare Book)
Cambridge, MA 02138 Phone: (617)495-2441
Richard Wendorf, Libn.
Founded: 1942. **Staff:** 40. **Subjects:** Major historical collection of rare books and manuscripts in all fields, with particular emphasis on history, literature, history of science, philosophy, music, illustrated books, and theater and dance. **Holdings:** 360,000 volumes; 28,000 linear feet of manuscripts. **Services:** Copying (including microfilms, photographs, and slides); library open to the public. **Automated Operations:** Computerized cataloging and acquisitions. **Computerized Information Services:** OCLC. **Networks/Consortia:** Member of NELINET, Inc., Center for Research Libraries (CRL). **Remarks:** FAX: (617)495-1376. **Staff:** Roger E. Stoddard, Cur., Rare Bks.; Rodney G. Dennis, Cur., Mss.; Anne Anninger, Cur., Printing & Graphic Arts; Jeanne Newlin, Cur., Theatre Coll.; James E. Walsh, Kpr., Printed Bks.; James Lewis, Cur., Reading Rm.; Mollie Della Terza, Hd., Tech.Serv.

★6977★
Harvard University - John F. Kennedy School of Government - Library (Soc Sci)
79 John F. Kennedy St. Phone: (617)496-1776
Cambridge, MA 02138 Malcolm C. Hamilton, Libn.
Founded: 1978. **Staff:** Prof 5; Other 8. **Subjects:** Public policy, public administration, government. **Special Collections:** Center for Science and International Affairs (4000 volumes). **Holdings:** 44,800 books; 4000 working papers. **Subscriptions:** 1521 journals and other serials; 22 newspapers. **Services:** Interlibrary loan; copying; library open to the public for reference use only. **Automated Operations:** Computerized public access catalog, cataloging, acquisitions, and serials. **Computerized Information Services:** DIALOG Information Services, BRS Information Technologies, NEXIS, WILSONLINE, VU/TEXT Information Services, OCLC; internal database. Performs searches on fee basis. Contact Person: Ellen Isenstein, Assoc.Libn., Ref. & Coll.Dev. **Publications:** Journals List, annual; table of contents (6 series). **Special Indexes:** Index to working papers; index to directories in the reference collection. **Remarks:** FAX: (617)495-1972. **Staff:** Beata Panagopoulos, Hd. of Tech.Serv.; Paula Ebbitt, Hd., Circ. & Reserves; Leslie A. Donnell, Cat.

★6978★
Harvard University - John K. Fairbank Center for East Asian Research - Library (Area-Ethnic)
1737 Cambridge St. Phone: (617)495-5753
Cambridge, MA 02138 Nancy Hearst, Libn.
Founded: 1963. **Staff:** Prof 1. **Subjects:** China, 1949 to present. **Holdings:** 10,000 volumes. **Subscriptions:** 150 journals and other serials. **Services:** Copying; library open to the public with restrictions. **Remarks:** FAX: (617)495-9976.

★6979★
Harvard University - Law School - Program on Negotiation - Specialized Collection in Dispute Resolution and Negotiation (Soc Sci)
Pound Hall 500
1563 Massachusetts Ave. Phone: (617)495-1684
Cambridge, MA 02138 J. William Breslin, Dir. of Pubs.
Founded: 1985. **Subjects:** Negotiation theory and technique, international negotiations, public policy negotiation, labor-management relations. **Holdings:** 600 books. **Subscriptions:** 10 journals and other serials. **Services:** Collection open to the public for reference use and with permission only. **Remarks:** FAX: (617)495-7818.

★6980★
Harvard University - Law School Library (Law)
Langdell Hall Phone: (617)495-3174
Cambridge, MA 02138 Harry S. Martin, III, Dir.
Founded: 1817. **Staff:** Prof 36; Other 75. **Subjects:** Law. **Special Collections:** International law; historical American, foreign, and comparative law; Treasure Room (collection of rare books, manuscripts, incunabula); legal art (paintings; prints; photographs; realia). **Holdings:** 1.49 million volumes; 500,000 microforms. **Subscriptions:** 15,000 journals and other serials. **Services:** Interlibrary loan; copying; library open for legal research to those requiring these resources. **Automated Operations:** Computerized public access catalog, cataloging, acquisitions, and serials. **Computerized Information Services:** WESTLAW, NEXIS, LEXIS, DIALOG Information Services, VU/TEXT Information Services, RLIN. **Networks/Consortia:** Member of Center for Research Libraries (CRL), Research Libraries Information Network (RLIN), New England Law Library Consortium (NELLCO). **Publications:** List of publications - available on request. **Special Catalogs:** Harvard Law Catalogs through 1981 (microfiche). **Remarks:** FAX: (617)495-4449. **Staff:** Robert Buckwalter, Assoc.Libn., Coll.Serv.; Marian F. Parker, Assoc.Libn. Res.Serv.; Jeanette Yachle, Hd.ILS Ref.Serv.; Ann Sitkin, Cat.Serv.; David Warrington, Libn., Spec.Coll.; Joan Duckett, Hd., Anglo Amer.Ref.; Susan Parker, Circ.Libn.; Willis Meredith, Presrv.Libn.; Harold Moren, Acq.Libn.; Cathy Conroy, Ser.Libn.

★6981★
Harvard University - Littauer Library (Soc Sci)
Cambridge, MA 02138 Phone: (617)495-2106
Arlyne A. Jackson, Hd.Libn.
Founded: 1938. **Staff:** Prof 6; Other 9. **Subjects:** Economics, statistics, government, manpower and industrial relations. **Holdings:** 451,588 volumes, including 120,000 state and city documents. **Subscriptions:** 3460 journals and other serials, including 2000 labor newspapers. **Services:** Interlibrary loan (fee); copying; library open to qualified users. **Automated Operations:** Computerized cataloging and acquisitions. **Computerized Information Services:** OCLC; InterNet (electronic mail service). Performs searches on fee basis. **Networks/Consortia:** Member of NELINET, Inc., Center for Research Libraries (CRL). **Remarks:** Electronic mail address(es): LITREF@HARVARDA.HARVARD.EDU (InterNet). **Staff:** Maryellen McCarthy, Hd. of Pub.Serv. & Ref.Libn.; Catherine B. Carpenter, Hd. of Cat.; Steven McGinty, Hd. of Acq.; Claire L. Brown, Libn., Slichter Indus.Rel.Coll.; Danila Terpanjian, Monographs Cat.

★6982★
Harvard University - Map Collection (Geog-Map)
Pusey Library Phone: (617)495-2417
Cambridge, MA 02138 David A. Cobb, Hd., Map Coll.
Founded: 1818. **Staff:** Prof 1; Other 2. **Subjects:** Atlases and maps. **Special Collections:** U.S. Defense Mapping Agency; Hydrographic/Topographic Center; U.S. National Oceanic and Atmospheric Administration; U.S. Geological Survey. **Holdings:** 10,000 volumes; 500,000 maps. **Services:** Collection for U.S. Government depository use only.

★6983★
Harvard University - Mathematical Library (Sci-Engr)
Science Center
1 Oxford St. Phone: (617)495-2147
Cambridge, MA 02138 Yum Tong Siu
Subjects: Mathematics. **Holdings:** 11,440 books, bound periodical volumes, pamphlets; 1050 reports. **Subscriptions:** 76 journals and other serials. **Services:** Interlibrary loan; copying; library open to the public for reference use only. **Computerized Information Services:** OCLC. **Networks/Consortia:** Member of NELINET, Inc., Center for Research Libraries (CRL). **Also Known As:** George David Birkhoff Library.

★6984★
Harvard University - Museum of Comparative Zoology - Library (Sci-Engr, Biol Sci)
Oxford St. Phone: (617)495-2475
Cambridge, MA 02138 Eva Jonas, Libn.
Founded: 1861. **Staff:** Prof 4; Other 6. **Subjects:** Zoology, paleontology, evolution, oceanography. **Special Collections:** Rare books; original drawings; manuscripts; archives. **Holdings:** 244,640 volumes. **Subscriptions:** 1630 journals and other serials. **Services:** Interlibrary loan; copying; library open to the public for reference use only. **Computerized Information Services:** BRS Information Technologies. **Networks/Consortia:** Member of NELINET, Inc., Center for Research Libraries (CRL).

★6985★
Harvard University - New England Regional Primate Research Center - Henry Coe Meadow Library (Biol Sci)
1 Pine Hill Dr.
PO Box 9102 Phone: (508)624-8028
Southborough, MA 01772-9102 Sydney Ann Fingold, Libn.
Founded: 1966. **Staff:** 1. **Subjects:** Primatology, veterinary research, cardiophysiology, reproductive technology, pharmacology, immunology, pathology, behavioral biology, neurogenetics, microbiology. **Holdings:** 8500 books; 7000 bound periodical volumes. **Subscriptions:** 160 journals and other serials. **Services:** Interlibrary loan; library open to qualified scientific researchers by appointment. **Automated Operations:** Computerized public access catalog (HOLLIS). **Computerized Information Services:** BRS Information Technologies, DIALOG Information Services; DOCLINE, BITNET, InterNet (electronic mail services). **Networks/Consortia:** Member of Central Massachusetts Consortium of Health Related Libraries (CMCHRL), Massachusetts Health Sciences Libraries Network (MaHSLiN), North Atlantic Health Science Libraries (NAHSL). **Publications:** Psychological Well-Being of Captive Nonhuman Primates. **Remarks:** FAX: (508)460-1209. Electronic mail address(es): fingold@husc4 (BITNET); fingold@husc4.harvard.edu (InterNet).

Harvard University - Oakes Ames Orchid Library
See: **Harvard University - Botany Libraries** (6950)

★6986★
Harvard University - Physics Research Library (Sci-Engr)
450 Jefferson Library
17 Oxford St. Phone: (617)495-2878
Cambridge, MA 02138 Michael R. Leach, Libn.
Founded: 1931. **Staff:** Prof 1; Other 1. **Subjects:** Physics. **Holdings:** 19,500 volumes. **Subscriptions:** 190 journals and other serials. **Services:** Interlibrary loan; copying; library open to the public for reference use only. **Automated Operations:** Computerized public access catalog, cataloging, acquisitions, and serials. **Computerized Information Services:** OCLC, DIALOG Information Services, STN International; BITNET (electronic mail service). **Networks/Consortia:** Member of NELINET, Inc., Center for Research Libraries (CRL). **Remarks:** FAX: (617)495-0416. Electronic mail address(es): LIBRARY@HUHEPL (BITNET).

★6987★
Harvard University - Psychology Research Library (Soc Sci)
33 Kirkland St. Phone: (617)495-3858
Cambridge, MA 02138 Richard E. Kaufman, Libn.
Staff: Prof 1. **Subjects:** Experimental psychology, history of psychology, cognitive processes, physiological psychology, animal behavior, psychology of motivation and learning, psychological aspects of language and communication, biological and experimental aspects of developmental and abnormal psychology, psychophysics. **Holdings:** 14,530 books, bound periodical volumes, theses. **Subscriptions:** 149 journals and other serials. **Services:** Copying; library open for research and graduate work only. **Automated Operations:** Computerized cataloging. **Computerized Information Services:** OCLC. **Networks/Consortia:** Member of NELINET, Inc., Center for Research Libraries (CRL).

★6988★
Harvard University - Radcliffe College - Morse Music Library (Mus)
59 Shepard St. Phone: (617)495-8730
Cambridge, MA 02138 Martin Max Schreiner, Mus.Libn.
Founded: 1927. **Staff:** Prof 1. **Subjects:** Music. **Special Collections:** The Shakespeare Plays (BBC Productions; 199 videotapes). **Holdings:** 3968 books; 500 bound periodical volumes; 5300 phonograph records; 5600 scores; 710 compact discs; 380 cassette tapes. **Subscriptions:** 17 journals and other serials. **Services:** Library open to students of Radcliffe College and Harvard University and registered guests. **Computerized Information Services:** OCLC. **Networks/Consortia:** Member of NELINET, Inc., Center for Research Libraries (CRL).

★6989★
Harvard University - Reischauer Institute - Documentation Center on Contemporary Japan (Soc Sci)
Coolidge Hall
1737 Cambridge St. Phone: (617)495-8386
Cambridge, MA 02138 Kuniko Yamada, Dir.
Founded: 1988. **Subjects:** Contemporary Japan. **Holdings:** 2000 books. **Subscriptions:** 200 journals and other serials. **Services:** Copying; center open to the public with restrictions. **Automated Operations:** Computerized public access catalog. **Computerized Information Services:** Japan Information Vendor (host computer located in Tokyo, Japan). **Remarks:** FAX: (617)496-8083.

★6990★
Harvard University - Robbins Library (Rel-Phil)
Emerson Hall Phone: (617)495-2193
Cambridge, MA 02138 Steven Affeldt, Hd.Libn.
Staff: 5. **Subjects:** Philosophy, mathematical logic. **Special Collections:** Kierkegaard Collection (220 volumes); Bechtel Collection (455 volumes). **Holdings:** 10,000 volumes. **Subscriptions:** 69 journals and other serials. **Services:** Copying; library open to the public. **Computerized Information Services:** OCLC. **Networks/Consortia:** Member of NELINET, Inc., Center for Research Libraries (CRL).

★6991★
Harvard University - Russian Research Center - Library (Area-Ethnic)
Coolidge Hall Library
1737 Cambridge St. Phone: (617)495-4030
Cambridge, MA 02138 Susan Jo Gardos, Libn.
Founded: 1948. **Staff:** Prof 1; Other 1. **Subjects:** Soviet Union and post-World War II Eastern Europe - political science, history, economics, sociology, military. **Special Collections:** Harvard Project on the Soviet Social System, Schedule A (38 volumes). **Holdings:** 16,000 volumes. **Subscriptions:** 175 journals and other serials; 30 newspapers. **Services:** Library open to scholars. **Computerized Information Services:** OCLC. **Networks/Consortia:** Member of NELINET, Inc., Center for Research Libraries (CRL). **Publications:** New Books Bulletin, monthly - for internal distribution only. **Remarks:** FAX: (617)495-8319.

★6992★
Harvard University - School of Medicine - The Libraries of the Massachusetts Eye and Ear Infirmary (Med)
243 Charles St. Phone: (617)573-3196
Boston, MA 02114 Chris Nims, Lib.Dir.
Founded: 1928. **Staff:** Prof 4; Other 3. **Subjects:** Ophthalmology, otolaryngology. **Special Collections:** Medical instruments (2000). **Holdings:** 16,000 books, bound periodical volumes, pamphlets; 300 stereophotographs of diseases of the eye; 130 cubic feet of archival materials; 40 cubic feet of manuscripts; 1500 rare books. **Subscriptions:** 212 journals and other serials. **Services:** Interlibrary loan; copying; library open to the public for reference use only. **Computerized Information Services:** MEDLINE, PaperChase, BRS/COLLEAGUE; CD-ROM (MEDLINE). Performs searches on fee basis. **Networks/Consortia:** Member of National Network of Libraries of Medicine - New England Region, Center for Research Libraries (CRL). **Remarks:** FAX: (617)573-3370. **Staff:** Kathleen Kennedy.

★6993★
Harvard University - School of Medicine - Schering Foundation Library of Health Care (Med)
643 Huntington Ave. Phone: (617)432-2103
Boston, MA 02115 Anne L. Alach, Libn.
Founded: 1970. **Staff:** Prof 1. **Subjects:** Preventive and social medicine, health economics, medical ethics. **Holdings:** 5000 volumes. **Subscriptions:** 38 journals and other serials. **Services:** Interlibrary loan; library open to Harvard community for reference use only. **Computerized Information Services:** MEDLARS.

★6994★
Harvard University - School of Public Health - Center for Population Library (Soc Sci)
665 Huntington Ave., Rm. 1-1111 Phone: (617)432-1234
Boston, MA 02115 Hannah Doress, Lib.Coord.
Founded: 1965. **Staff:** 2. **Subjects:** Population studies and international health. **Holdings:** 22,000 volumes. **Subscriptions:** 235 journals and other serials. **Services:** Library open to the public with restrictions. **Computerized Information Services:** POPLINE, MEDLINE.

★6995★
Harvard University - School of Public Health - Kresge Center Library (Med)
665 Huntington Ave., Rm. 1306 Phone: (617)432-3488
Boston, MA 02115 Betty Hauser, Libn.
Staff: Prof 1. **Subjects:** Physiology of the lung, environmental health. **Special Collections:** Library and publications of Dr. Philip Drinker. **Holdings:** 225 books; 225 bound periodical volumes; 120 dissertations. **Subscriptions:** 34 journals and other serials. **Services:** Library open to the public upon written request for permission. **Remarks:** FAX: (617)432-4710.

★6996★
Harvard University - Schools of Medicine, Dental Medicine & Public Health - Boston Medical Library - Francis A. Countway Library (Med, Biol Sci)
10 Shattuck St. Phone: (617)432-2142
Boston, MA 02115 Judith Messerle
Founded: 1964. **Staff:** Prof 20; Other 41. **Subjects:** Anatomy, biochemistry, dentistry, history of medicine, legal medicine, microbiology, parasitology, physiology, public health. **Special Collections:** History of medicine (810 incunabula); European books printed 16th-19th centuries; English books published 1475-1800; American books, 1668-1870, especially New England imprints and Bostoniana; 14th century medical Hebraica and Judaica; manuscripts and archives, especially of New England origin; national archive of medical illustration; Warren Collection of early books in the history of medicine; world famous collection of medical medals and portraits. **Holdings:** 545,464 volumes. **Subscriptions:** 5346 journals and

other serials. **Services:** Interlibrary loan; copying; SDI; library open to the public on fee basis. **Automated Operations:** Computerized public access catalog, cataloging, acquisitions, and serials. **Computerized Information Services:** OCLC, MEDLARS, DIALOG Information Services, BRS Information Technologies; CD-ROMs (MEDLINE, CANCERLIT, Healthline). Performs searches on fee basis. **Networks/Consortia:** Member of NELINET, Inc., Center for Research Libraries (CRL). **Publications:** Library Guide. **Special Catalogs:** Countway serials online titles. **Remarks:** FAX: (617)432-0693. **Staff:** Ellen Westling, Assoc.Libn.; Elaine Alligood, Asst.Libn., User Serv.; Susan E. Whitehead, Asst.Libn., Info.Serv.; Richard Tremblay, Hd. of Copy Serv.; Richard J. Wolfe, Cur., Rare Bks. & Mss.

★6997★
Harvard University - Social Relations/Sociology Library (Soc Sci)
33 Kirkland St. Phone: (617)495-3838
Cambridge, MA 02138 Richard E. Kaufman, Libn.
Staff: Prof 1. **Subjects:** Sociology, social psychology, personality, abnormal psychology. **Holdings:** 21,880 volumes. **Subscriptions:** 157 journals and other serials. **Services:** Library open to the public with restrictions. **Automated Operations:** Computerized cataloging. **Computerized Information Services:** OCLC. **Networks/Consortia:** Member of NELINET, Inc., Center for Research Libraries (CRL).

★6998★
Harvard University - Statistics Library (Sci-Engr)
Science Center, 6th Fl.
1 Oxford St. Phone: (617)495-5496
Cambridge, MA 02138 Dale Rinkel, Staff Asst.
Founded: 1959. **Subjects:** Statistical theory and applied statistics. **Holdings:** 2331 volumes; reprints; dissertations. **Subscriptions:** 26 journals and other serials. **Services:** Library open to the public with permission only.

★6999★
Harvard University - Tozzer Library (Soc Sci)
21 Divinity Ave. Phone: (617)495-2253
Cambridge, MA 02138 Lynne M. Schmelz-Keil, Libn.
Founded: 1866. **Staff:** Prof 6; Other 9. **Subjects:** Biological anthropology, cultural anthropology, linguistics, prehistoric archeology. **Special Collections:** Latin American archeology, ethnology, and linguistics. **Holdings:** 185,000 volumes. **Subscriptions:** 2000 journals and other serials. **Services:** Interlibrary loan; copying; library open to the public for reference use only. **Computerized Information Services:** OCLC; InterNet (electronic mail service). **Networks/Consortia:** Member of NELINET, Inc., Center for Research Libraries (CRL). **Publications:** Anthropological Literature, quarterly. **Special Catalogs:** Author and subject catalogs of the Tozzer Library, 1988 (on microfiche); Bibliographic Guide to Anthropology and Archaeology, annual (1987 to present). **Remarks:** Electronic mail address(es): DIXON@HARVARDA (InterNet). **Staff:** Maija Lutz, Hd., Tech.Serv.; Fred Hay, Ref.Libn.; Isabel Quintana, Cat.; Julia Hendon, Indexer; Gene De Vita, Hd., Circ.Serv.

★7000★
Harvard University - Woodberry Poetry Room (Hum)
Harvard College Library Phone: (617)495-2454
Cambridge, MA 02138 Stratis Haviaras, Cur.
Founded: 1931. **Staff:** Prof 1; Other 2. **Subjects:** 20th century Engllish language poetry and poetics. **Holdings:** 11,000 books; 115 unbound periodicals; 3850 phonograph records; 1800 open-reel audiotapes; 555 audio cassettes; 30 videotapes. **Subscriptions:** 115 journals and other serials. **Services:** Interlibrary loan; copying; room open to poets and qualified scholars for reference use. **Automated Operations:** Computerized public access catalog, cataloging, and acquisitions. **Computerized Information Services:** OCLC; HOLLIS 1 (internal database). Performs searches on fee basis. Contact Person: Jennie Faries, Asst. to Cur. **Networks/Consortia:** Member of NELINET, Inc., Center for Research Libraries (CRL). **Publications:** Harvard Book Review, 3/year - by subscription; The Poet's Voice (cassette recordings); Vladimir Nabokov at Harvard (cassette recordings); Seamus Heaney at Harvard (cassette recordings).

Harvard-Yenching Library
See: **Harvard University** (6974)

★7001★
Harvey, Pennington, Herting, & Renneisen, Ltd. - Library
11 Penn Ctr.
1835 Market St., 28th Fl. Phone: (215)563-4470
Philadelphia, PA 19103 Charlotte Braunstein, Lib.Dir.
Founded: 1971. **Staff:** Prof 1. **Subjects:** Law. **Holdings:** 850 books. **Subscriptions:** 50 journals and other serials. **Services:** Interlibrary loan; library not open to the public. **Computerized Information Services:** LEXIS, NEXIS, WESTLAW, DIALOG Information Services. **Remarks:** FAX: (215)568-1044. Telex: 325324 (HPHR PHA).

William R. & Norma B. Harvey Library
See: **Hampton Institute** (6880)

H.L. "Red" Harvill Memorial Library
See: **North American Die Casting Association** (11858)

Rudolph Harwich Library
See: **California School of Professional Psychology - Berkeley/Alameda Campus** (2505)

E.C. Harwood Library
See: **American Institute for Economic Research** (636)

★7002★
Haryana Agricultural University - Library (Agri)
Hissar 125 004, Haryana, India Phone: 4166
Prem Singh, Univ.Libn.
Staff: Prof 13; Other 69. **Subjects:** Agricultural sciences, veterinary sciences, basic sciences, humanities. **Holdings:** 151,750 books; 71,529 bound periodical volumes; 3709 theses. **Subscriptions:** 10 newspapers. **Services:** Interlibrary loan; copying; library open to the public at librarian's discretion, upon enrollment as special members.

★7003★
Harza Engineering Company - Library (Env-Cons)
Sears Tower
233 S. Wacker Dr. Phone: (312)831-3000
Chicago, IL 60606 Lorraine A. Potrykus, Lb.Svcs.Coord.
Founded: 1920. **Subjects:** Development of water, land, and energy resources. **Holdings:** 10,000 titles. **Subscriptions:** 288 journals and other serials. **Services:** Interlibrary loan; library open to the public by appointment. **Automated Operations:** Computerized cataloging. **Computerized Information Services:** DIALOG Information Services, OCLC, ASCE Civil Engineering Database; internal database. **Networks/Consortia:** Member of ILLINET, Chicago Library System. **Publications:** Acquisition list, monthly - for internal distribution only. **Special Indexes:** Index to internally produced reports. **Remarks:** FAX: (312)831-3999. Telex: 25 3527; 25 3540.

Haseloff Archive
See: **Columbia University - Department of Art History & Archaeology** (4013)

Haskell Laboratory for Toxicology & Industrial Medicine
See: **E.I. Du Pont de Nemours & Company, Inc.** (5022)

★7004★
Haskins Laboratories - Library (Med)
270 Crown St. Phone: (203)865-6163
New Haven, CT 06511 Fawn Zefang Wang, Lib.Dir.
Founded: 1939. **Staff:** 1. **Subjects:** Speech communication, linguistics, experimental psychology, speech physiology, computers and programming. **Special Collections:** Acoustics; speech perception; speech physiology. **Holdings:** 2800 books; 145 bound periodical volumes; 410 file boxes of irregular serials and occasional papers from other research groups and organizations; 45 file boxes of Haskins Laboratories publications, 1939 to present. **Subscriptions:** 175 journals and other serials. **Services:** Interlibrary loan; copying; library open to the public on written request; loans are made only by special permission. **Computerized Information Services:** BRS Information Technologies; BITNET (electronic mail service). **Publications:** Haskins Laboratories Status Report on Speech Research, quarterly - to libraries serving research colleagues. **Remarks:** FAX: (203)865-8963. Alternate telephone number(s): 432-0890. Electronic mail address(es): HASKINS@YALEHASK (BITNET).

★7005★
Hassard Bonnington Rogers & Huber - Library (Law)
50 Fremont St., Suite 3400 Phone: (415)543-8405
San Francisco, CA 94105 Jeanne Shea
Founded: 1910. **Staff:** Prof 1; Other 2. **Subjects:** Law, medical law. **Holdings:** 7000 books; 700 other cataloged items. **Subscriptions:** 209 journals and other serials. **Services:** Interlibrary loan; library not open to the public. **Computerized Information Services:** DIALOG Information Services, LEXIS, VU/TEXT Information Services, WESTLAW, Information America, DataTimes. **Remarks:** FAX: (415)979-0378.

★7006★
The Hastings Center - Library (Soc Sci, Med)
255 Elm Rd. Phone: (914)762-8500
Briarcliff Manor, NY 10510 Marna Howarth, Libn.
Founded: 1969. **Staff:** Prof 1. **Subjects:** Medical ethics, ethics, ethics in life and social sciences, reproductive technologies, teaching of ethics, abortion, death/dying, AIDS, genetics, public policy, health policy. **Holdings:** 6000 books; 40 VF drawers. **Subscriptions:** 120 journals and other serials. **Services:** Library not open to the public. **Computerized Information Services:** DIALOG Information Services, LEXIS, NEXIS. **Publications:** IRB: A Review of Human Subjects Research, bimonthly; Hastings Center Report, bimonthly. **Remarks:** FAX: (914)762-2124.

Hastings College of the Law
See: **University of California, San Francisco** (18422)

★7007★
Hastings Regional Center - Medical Library (Med)
Box 579 Phone: (402)463-2471
Hastings, NE 68902 Ruth Swingle, Libn.
Staff: Prof 1. **Subjects:** Psychiatry, psychiatric nursing, psychiatric social work, medicine, patient education, mental health. **Holdings:** 4000 books; 500 bound periodical volumes; 12 VF drawers of pamphlets and reprints. **Subscriptions:** 47 journals and other serials. **Services:** Interlibrary loan; copying; library open to the public with restrictions. **Computerized Information Services:** BRS Information Technologies. **Remarks:** FAX: (402)463-6136.

★7008★
Hastings & Sons Publishers - Daily Evening Item - Newspaper Morgue (Publ)
38 Exchange St. Phone: (617)593-7700
Lynn, MA 01903 Judith Johnson, Res.Libn.
Founded: 1933. **Staff:** Prof 1. **Subjects:** Newspaper reference topics. **Special Collections:** Historical photographs and clippings. **Holdings:** 76 VF drawers of clippings, photographs, and other items; newspapers, 1877 to present, on microfilm. **Services:** Copying; morgue open to the public with restrictions. **Remarks:** FAX: (617)581-3178.

★7009★
Hatboro Baptist Church - Library (Rel-Phil)
32 N. York Ave. Phone: (215)675-8400
Hatboro, PA 19040 Carolyn A. Zimmerman, Libn.
Founded: 1950. **Staff:** Prof 1. **Subjects:** Bible commentaries and histories, missions, church organization, church history, inspiration, Christian education and ethics, theology and doctrine. **Holdings:** 6328 books.

★7010★
Hatch Associates Ltd. - Library (Sci-Engr)
2800 Speakman Dr. Phone: (416)855-7600
Mississauga, ON, Canada L5K 2R7 Racquel L. Fineza, Info.Off.
Staff: Prof 1; Other 1. **Subjects:** Metallurgy, mining, environment. **Holdings:** Figures not available. **Subscriptions:** 85 journals and other serials. **Services:** Interlibrary loan; library not open to the public. **Automated Operations:** Computerized cataloging and acquisitions. **Computerized Information Services:** DIALOG Information Services; Hatch Infocentre (internal database). Performs searches on fee basis. **Remarks:** FAX: (416)962-0622. **Formerly:** Located in Toronto, ON. **Staff:** Theresa Salari.

★7011★
Hatch-Billops Collection, Inc. (Area-Ethnic)
491 Broadway, 7th Fl. Phone: (212)966-3231
New York, NY 10012 Camille Billops, Pres.
Founded: 1975. **Staff:** Prof 1. **Subjects:** African Americana, theater, visual arts. **Special Collections:** Oral history interviews (1210); art slides (14,000); Owen and Edith Dodson Memorial Collection (plays, manuscripts, photos, and letters); Charles and Ellyce Weir Griffin Collection (400 black and white film stills; lobby cards); Theodore Ward plays; Arthur Smith Collection (jewelry designs, photographs, patterns, and business communications). **Holdings:** 4000 books; 1000 black/white photographs; 300 posters; 1200 playbills; 300 art catalogs. **Subscriptions:** 12 journals and other serials. **Services:** Copying; collection open to the public by appointment. **Computerized Information Services:** Internal database (playbills, manuscripts, theater articles). **Publications:** Artist and Influence. **Special Catalogs:** Catalog of oral history holdings with abstracts; catalog of African American theater history; catalog of African American playbills. **Staff:** James V. Hatch, Sec.

Hatch Library
See: **Willard Psychiatric Center** (20442)

★7012★
Evelyn Payne Hatcher Museum of Anthropology - Library (Soc Sci)
Stewart Hall, Rm. 113
St. Cloud State University Phone: (612)255-3021
St. Cloud, MN 56301 Julie Broyles, Musm.Dir.
Founded: 1973. **Staff:** 1. **Subjects:** Anthropology, archeology. **Special Collections:** Festival Research Project Archives, 1973-1988; Archaeology Field School Archives. **Holdings:** 500 books; 500 bound periodical volumes; slides; tapes; documentation. **Services:** Library open to the public with restrictions. **Publications:** List of publications - available upon request.

Hatfield Marine Science Center
See: **Oregon State University - Hatfield Marine Science Center - Library** (12551)

Harry S. Hathaway Library of Natural History and Conservation
See: **Audubon Society of Rhode Island** (1291)

Hatheway Environmental Resource Library
See: **Massachusetts Audubon Society** (9788)

★7013★
Hattiesburg American - Library (Publ)
825 N. Main St.
P.O. Box 111 Phone: (601)582-4321
Hattiesburg, MS 39401 John A. Tuggle
Founded: 1979. **Staff:** Prof 1; Other 2. **Subjects:** Newspaper reference topics. **Holdings:** 200 books; 70 bound newspaper volumes; 396 rolls of microfilm; 42 feet of vertical files. **Subscriptions:** 2 journals and other serials; 7 newspapers. **Services:** Library not open to the public.

Peter D. Haughton Memorial Library
See: **Trotting Horse Museum** (16525)

Haunt Hunters
See: **Psychic Science Institute** (13466)

Eric V. Hauser Memorial Library
See: **Reed College** (13769)

William A. Hausman Medical Library
See: **Sacred Heart Hospital** (14202)

Havas Children's Library
See: **Bureau of Jewish Education - Jewish Community Library** (2369)

★7014★
Haven Scott Associates - Business Library for Job Seekers (Bus-Fin)
145 Oak Hill Plaza Phone: (215)265-1714
King of Prussia, PA 19406-2884 Judy Lupinski, Libn.
Founded: 1983. **Staff:** Prof 1; Other 1. **Subjects:** Business, career planning. **Special Collections:** Complete works of Isabelle Briggs. **Holdings:** 1846 books; 212 bound periodical volumes; 284 diskettes; 5 cases of magazines; 4 reports. **Subscriptions:** 16 journals and other serials. **Services:** Library not open to the public. **Automated Operations:** Computerized acquisitions. **Computerized Information Services:** CompuServe Information Service, Dun & Bradstreet Business Credit Services; internal database. **Remarks:** Haven Scott Associates is supported through its membership to the National Association of Career Development Consultants.

Havens House Museum
See: **Shelter Island Historical Society** (15118)

★7015★
Haverford College - Quaker and Special Collections (Rel-Phil)
Haverford College Library Phone: (215)896-1161
Haverford, PA 19041 Emma Jones Lapsansky, Cur.
Founded: 1833. **Staff:** Prof 3; Other 2. **Subjects:** History, religious thought, biography, fiction, and other subjects relating to Society of Friends throughout the world; rare books and manuscripts; mysticism. **Special Collections:** William H. Jenks Collection (1600 17th century Quaker tracts); Dictionary of Quaker Biography (typescript containing 20,000 biographical sketches); Charles Roberts Autograph Letter Collection (20,000); Haverfordiana; Rufus M. Jones Collection on Mysticism (1400 books and pamphlets); William Pyle Philips Collection (rare books and manuscripts, mostly of Renaissance period); Photography Collection (3000 items); Harris Collection of ancient and Oriental manuscripts (75); Lockwood Collection of Italian Humanists; Christopher Morley Collection (420 volumes; 2000 letters; memorabilia). **Holdings:** 32,000 Quaker volumes; 250,000 Quaker manuscripts; 20,000 other manuscripts; 3000 rare books; pictures; maps; microfilm. **Subscriptions:** 200 journals and other serials. **Services:** Interlibrary loan (limited); copying; permission to use collection may be requested. **Automated Operations:** Computerized cataloging, acquisitions, and serials. **Computerized Information Services:** DIALOG Information Services, BRS Information Technologies. **Networks/Consortia:** Member of PALINET. **Publications:** Guide to the Records of Philadelphia Yearly Meetings. **Special Catalogs:** Quaker fiction (card); Quaker necrology (card); pamphlet collection (card); all manuscript collections; historical maps, especially Pennsylvania (card); graphics (card). **Remarks:** Contains partial holdings of the Society of Friends - Philadelphia Yearly Meeting. **Staff:** Elisabeth Potts Brown, Quaker Bibliog.; Sheila Hallowell, Spec.Coll.Asst. & Off.Mgr.; Eva Walker Myer, Sec. & Geneal.; Diana Franzusoff Peterson, Mss.Cat.

★7016★
Haverford State Hospital - Medical Library (Med)
3500 Darby Rd. Phone: (215)525-9620
Haverford, PA 19041-1098 Diane K. Smith, Libn. I
Founded: 1963. **Staff:** Prof 1. **Subjects:** Psychiatry, psychiatric nursing, medicine, psychology, pharmacology, geriatrics, gerontology. **Holdings:** 2000 books; 214 bound periodical volumes; 800 unbound periodicals; 200 cassette tapes. **Subscriptions:** 118 journals and other serials. **Services:** Interlibrary loan; copying; library open to the public. **Networks/Consortia:** Member of Health Sciences Libraries Consortium (HSLC). **Remarks:** FAX: (215)526-2615. Maintained by Pennsylvania State Department of Public Welfare.

★7017★
Haverford Township Historical Society - Library (Hist)
Box 825 Phone: (215)353-1213
Havertown, PA 19083 Margaret E. Johnston, Cur.
Subjects: History of Haverford Township, Delaware County, and Pennsylvania. **Special Collections:** Collections on 1810 Nitre Hall Powder Mills and Philadelphia/West Chester Transit Line. **Holdings:** Figures not available. **Services:** Library open to the public with restrictions. **Publications:** Newsletter, semiannual.

★7018★
Haverhill Municipal (Hale) Hospital - Medical Library (Med)
140 Lincoln Ave. Phone: (508)374-2000
Haverhill, MA 01830 Eleanor Howard, Libn.
Staff: Prof 1. **Subjects:** Medicine, nursing, allied health sciences. **Holdings:** 1200 books; 2000 bound periodical volumes; 300 unbound journals; 4 VF drawers of pamphlets. **Subscriptions:** 76 journals and other serials. **Services:** Interlibrary loan; copying; library open to the public with permission. **Networks/Consortia:** Member of Northeastern Consortium for Health Information (NECHI).

★7019★
Haverhill Public Library - Special Collections Division (Hist)
99 Main St. Phone: (508)373-1586
Haverhill, MA 01830-5092 Howard W. Curtis, Dir.
Founded: 1874. **Staff:** Prof 2; Other 5. **Subjects:** Genealogy and local history, John Greenleaf Whittier, art, early children's books. **Special Collections:** John Greenleaf Whittier Collection (2500); Gale Art Collection (5300); Haverhill History Collection (4000); Pecker Local History and Genealogy Collection (7600). **Holdings:** 22,000 books; 700 bound periodical volumes; 800 pamphlets; 4000 manuscripts; 400 broadsides; 250 maps; 1000 reels of microfilm; city documents in manuscript; 10,000 Haverhill photographs; 375 volumes of bound Haverhill newspapers; 200 volumes of clippings; genealogical microfiche. **Subscriptions:** 18 journals and other serials. **Services:** Interlibrary loan (microfilm only; fee); copying; division open to the public. **Networks/Consortia:** Member of Merrimack Valley Library Consortium. **Publications:** Annual Report; Architectural Heritage of Haverhill; John Greenleaf Whittier: A Biography (1985); The Whittier Newsletter, annual. **Special Catalogs:** Whittier Collection Holdings (book); Haverhill History (card). **Staff:** Gregory H. Laing, Cur./Spec.Coll.

Walter Havighurst Special Collections Library
See: **Miami University** (10270)

Haviland Records Room
See: **Society of Friends** (15323)

★7020★
Hawaii Bottle Museum - Business Library (Art)
Box 1635 Phone: (808)396-6441
Honokaa, HI 96727 Doreen W. Grant
Founded: 1976. **Staff:** Prof 2; Other 2. **Subjects:** Historical and modern bottles; glass - historical, modern, collectible; glass art. **Special Collections:** Hawaiian bottles of the 1800s. **Holdings:** 320 books; 210 bound periodical volumes; 52 other cataloged items. **Subscriptions:** 14 journals and other serials. **Services:** Library not open to the public. **Automated Operations:** Computerized cataloging, acquisitions, and serials. **Formerly:** Located in Honolulu, HI.

★7021★
Hawaii Chinese History Center - Library (Area-Ethnic)
111 N. King St., Suite 410 Phone: (808)521-5948
Honolulu, HI 96817-4703 Chow Loy Tom, Libn.
Founded: 1970. **Staff:** Prof 1. **Subjects:** History of Chinese in Hawaii - genealogy, traditions, historic sites, biographies of early and contemporary leaders. **Holdings:** Books; 16 VF drawers; tape recordings of early Chinese residents; information on Chinese societies in Hawaii; maps of the Kwangtung/Guangdong Province of China, with emphasis on the Chungshan and Zhongshan districts; genealogies and family histories of Hawaiian Chinese families. **Services:** Library open to the public by appointment on a limited schedule; provides genealogical reference and referral to national, state, and other historical or genealogical centers or archives. **Publications:** Books; newsletters; publications on the history of Chinese in Hawaii. **Staff:** Margaret A. Wong, Asst.

★7022★
Hawaii Employers Council - Library (Bus-Fin)
P.O. Box 29699 Phone: (808)836-1511
Honolulu, HI 96820 Sonja Tyau, Libn.
Founded: 1943. **Staff:** Prof 1; Other 2. **Subjects:** Labor relations, labor law, management, compensation and benefits, personnel administration,

employment systems and development, industrial psychology, labor economics and living costs, employment and unemployment statistics. **Special Collections:** Local collective bargaining agreements; industrial films; company employee publications; employers' association publications; newspaper clippings concerning labor history and development in Hawaii. **Holdings:** 6000 books; 150 bound periodical volumes; 50 council research publications; 600 current local collective bargaining agreements and allied documents; 120 local collective bargaining agreements and allied documents, 1944-1966, on microfilm; 115 industrial films and tapes; federal and local government documents; local newspaper clippings. **Subscriptions:** 336 journals and other serials; 17 newspapers. **Services:** Interlibrary loan; copying; library open to council staff, member companies, and students. **Remarks:** Library located at 2682 Waiwai Loop, Honolulu, HI 96819.

★7023★
Hawaii Institute of Geophysics - School of Ocean and Earth Science and Technology Library (Sci-Engr)
University of Hawaii
2525 Correa Rd. Phone: (808)956-7040
Honolulu, HI 96822 Marilyn Moore, Rsrc.Coll.Spec.
Founded: 1963. **Staff:** Prof 1; Other 1. **Subjects:** Geology, geophysics, oceanography, meteorology, ocean engineering. **Holdings:** 3250 books; 5300 bound periodical volumes; 15,100 unbound serial volumes; 8350 maps and charts; 2000 reprints; 4550 reports. **Subscriptions:** 159 journals and other serials. **Services:** Interlibrary loan; copying; library open to the public. **Computerized Information Services:** DIALOG Information Services; CD-ROM (GeoRef). Performs searches on fee basis. **Remarks:** FAX: (808)956-2538.

★7024★
Hawaii Medical Library, Inc. (Med)
1221 Punchbowl St. Phone: (808)536-9302
Honolulu, HI 96813 John A. Breinich, Exec.Dir.
Founded: 1913. **Staff:** Prof 6; Other 8. **Subjects:** Medicine, nursing, tropical diseases. **Holdings:** 25,000 books; 60,000 bound periodical volumes; 500 pamphlets; 500 audio cassettes. **Subscriptions:** 2100 journals and other serials. **Services:** Interlibrary loan; copying; library open to the public. **Automated Operations:** Computerized cataloging. **Computerized Information Services:** MEDLINE, OCLC; BITNET (electronic mail service). **Remarks:** FAX: (808)524-6956. Electronic mail address(es): BREINICH@UHUNIX (BITNET).

★7025★
Hawaii Newspaper Agency - Library (Publ)
605 Kapiolani Blvd. Phone: (808)525-7669
Honolulu, HI 96813 Beatrice S. Kaya, Hd.Libn.
Founded: 1935. **Staff:** 10. **Subjects:** Newspaper reference topics. **Special Collections:** Hawaiiana. **Holdings:** 2000 books and pamphlets; 4000 reels of microfilm; dissertations; reports. **Subscriptions:** 4 newspapers. **Services:** Library open to public with editors' authorization. **Computerized Information Services:** NEXIS. **Staff:** Margaret Iwamoto, Asst.Libn.

★7026★
Hawaii Research Center for Futures Studies - Resource Room (Soc Sci)
2424 Maile Way, Rm. 721 A Phone: (808)956-6601
Honolulu, HI 96822 James Dator, Dir.
Founded: 1983. **Staff:** Prof 1; Other 1. **Subjects:** Education, communication and the media, science and technology, law and politics. **Holdings:** 500 books; 15 bound periodical volumes; 100 monographs; 5 file cabinets of reports and manuscripts; 1 file cabinet of research from the Commission on the Year 2000. **Subscriptions:** 12 journals and other serials. **Services:** Room open to the public by appointment. **Computerized Information Services:** BITNET (electronic mail service). **Remarks:** FAX: (808)956-2889. Telex: 7238962 WFSF HR. Electronic mail address(es): DATOR@UHCCVX.UHCC.HAWAII.EDU (BITNET).

★7027★
Hawaii State Circuit Court - 2nd Circuit - Law Library (Law)
2145 Main St. Phone: (808)244-2245
Wailuku, HI 96793 Morris Haoli, Libn.
Founded: 1907. **Staff:** 1. **Subjects:** Real property, criminal law, juveniles, personal injury, local government, federal laws. **Holdings:** 13,200 volumes. **Subscriptions:** 35 journals and other serials. **Services:** Interlibrary loan; library open to the public. **Automated Operations:** Computerized public access catalog.

★7028★
Hawaii State Circuit Court - 3rd Circuit - Kona Branch Law Library (Law)
P.O. Box 1970 Phone: (808)322-6550
Kealakekua, HI 96750 Benjamin Heloca, Lib.Techn.
Staff: 1. **Subjects:** Law. **Holdings:** 12,000 books. **Services:** Library open to the public for reference use only.

★7029★
Hawaii State Circuit Court - 3rd Circuit - Law Library (Law)
State Bldg.
75 Aupini St.
Box 1007 Phone: (808)933-1338
Hilo, HI 96721 Margie Hanselman, Libn.
Staff: 1. **Subjects:** Law. **Holdings:** 30,000 books. **Services:** Copying; library open to the public for reference use only.

★7030★
Hawaii (State) Department of Accounting and General Services - State Archives (Hist)
Iolani Palace Grounds Phone: (808)586-0329
Honolulu, HI 96813 Jolyn G. Tamura, State Archv.
Founded: 1906. **Staff:** Prof 10; Other 4. **Subjects:** Hawaiian history and government. **Special Collections:** Captain Cook Collection (Cook and discovery of the Hawaiian Islands); historic photograph collection (Hawaiian monarchs, major towns, Waikiki, sugar and pineapple industries, and historic events, 1800s-1980s; 107,000 photographs and negatives). **Holdings:** 2683 books; 160 bound periodical volumes; 575 cubic feet of private manuscript collections; 9000 cubic feet of official archives; 5553 microforms; 11,000 aerial photographs; 2700 maps. **Services:** Copying; archives open to the public. **Remarks:** FAX: (808)586-0330. **Staff:** Richard Thompson, Libn.

★7031★
Hawaii (State) Department of Business, Economic, and Tourism Development - Library (Plan, Soc Sci)
P.O. Box 2359 Phone: (808)548-3059
Honolulu, HI 96804 Debra N. Miyashiro, Libn.
Founded: 1967. **Staff:** Prof 3; Other 3. **Subjects:** Economics, statistics, land use, energy, economic development, agriculture, international trade, science and technology policy, tourism, public administration. **Holdings:** 11,000 titles; 500 microfiche. **Subscriptions:** 254 journals and other serials; 10 newspapers. **Services:** Interlibrary loan; copying; library open to the public. **Automated Operations:** Computerized cataloging. **Computerized Information Services:** DIALOG Information Services, LEXIS, NEXIS. **Remarks:** FAX: (808)548-8156. **Staff:** Michelle Pommer, Libn.; Patrick McNally, Libn.

★7032★
Hawaii (State) Department of Commerce and Consumer Affairs - Consumer Advocacy Division - Library (Bus-Fin)
P.O. Box 541 Phone: (808)586-2800
Honolulu, HI 96809 Sandra Yonesaki, Sec.
Founded: 1976. **Subjects:** Public utilities, finance, engineering. **Holdings:** 2000 volumes. **Remarks:** Library located at 1010 Richards St., Honolulu, HI 96813.

Hawaii (State) Department of Education - Hawaii State Public Library System - Hawaii State Library
See: **Hawaii State Public Library System - Hawaii State Library** (7039)

★7033★
Hawaii (State) Department of Education - Visual Technology and Services (Educ, Aud-Vis)
641 18th Ave. Phone: (808)732-2824
Honolulu, HI 96816 Paul Kodama, Act.Adm.
Founded: 1946. **Staff:** Prof 1; Other 8. **Subjects:** Language arts; social sciences; mathematics; science; music; health; art; education - physical, career, environmental, business; guidance; industrial arts; home economics; Hawaiian studies; Asian and European languages; computers; nutrition; agriculture. **Holdings:** 44,565 videotape prints; 4575 titles of audiotape masters. **Services:** Services not open to the public. **Automated Operations:** Computerized circulation. **Computerized Information Services:** PARADOX (internal database). **Special Catalogs:** Videotape and 16mm Catalog. **Remarks:** FAX: (808)737-5217. Maintained by the Office of Instructional Services, Multimedia Services Branch, Technical Assistance Center Section.

★7034★
Hawaii (State) Department of Health - Hastings H. Walker Medical Library (Med)
3675 Kilauea Ave. Phone: (808)734-0221
Honolulu, HI 96816 Barbara Kodama, Sec. of Adm.
Founded: 1944. **Staff:** 1. **Subjects:** Clinical medicine, tuberculosis and respiratory diseases, tropical medicine, psychiatry, nursing, leprosy, hospital administration. **Holdings:** 6053 books; 1500 bound periodical volumes; 57 pamphlets. **Subscriptions:** 194 journals and other serials. **Services:** Interlibrary loan; library open to the public for reference use only. **Remarks:** FAX: (808)732-8505.

★7035★
Hawaii (State) Department of Land and Natural Resources - State Parks, Outdoor Recreation and Historic Sites Division - Library (Rec)
P.O. Box 621 Phone: (808)587-0300
Honolulu, HI 96809 William Paty, Dir./Chm.
Subjects: Archeology, recreation, historic preservation. **Holdings:** 1500 recreation planning and study reports; 1000 unpublished archeological surveys. **Remarks:** Library located at 1151 Punchbowl St., Honolulu, HI 96813.

★7036★
Hawaii State Hospital - Medical Library (Med)
45-710 Keaahala Rd. Phone: (808)247-2191
Kaneohe, HI 96744 Sandra L. Okubo, Med.Libn.
Founded: 1950. **Staff:** Prof 1. **Subjects:** Behavioral sciences, psychiatry, psychology, neuropsychology, psychiatric nursing, mental health. **Holdings:** 5000 books; 1400 bound periodical volumes; 8 VF drawers of unbound materials; 200 magnetic tapes; 100 cassette tapes; current and historic collection of Hawaii State Mental Health Division publications. **Subscriptions:** 98 journals and other serials. **Services:** Interlibrary loan; library open to the public by permission. **Computerized Information Services:** DIALOG Information Services, MEDLINE. **Publications:** HSH Medical Library Bulletin, bimonthly - for internal distribution only. **Remarks:** FAX: (808)235-5038.

★7037★
Hawaii State Legislative Reference Bureau - Library (Soc Sci)
State Capitol Phone: (808)587-0690
Honolulu, HI 96813 Frances F. Enos, Hd.Res.Libn.
Founded: 1943. **Staff:** Prof 3; Other 2. **Subjects:** State government, state legislatures, public policy, finance, administration, legislation, law. **Special Collections:** Hawaiian codes and statutes, from period of Hawaiian Kingdom to present; session laws; journals. **Holdings:** 71,500 books and pamphlets. **Subscriptions:** 270 journals and other serials. **Services:** Interlibrary loan; copying; faxing; library open to the public. **Automated Operations:** Computerized public access catalog, cataloging, acquisitions, and circulation. **Computerized Information Services:** DIALOG Information Services, LEGISNET, WESTLAW, ISIS; bill status databases (internal database). **Publications:** Guide to Government in Hawaii, 1991; Directory of State, County, and Federal Officials, annual; Serials List, semiannual; First Reading (newsletter to the Hawaii State Legislature). **Remarks:** FAX: (808)587-0699. **Staff:** Jean Imamoto, Res.Libn.; Claire Marumoto, Res.Libn.

Hawaii State Library
See: **Hawaii State Public Library System - Hawaii State Library** (7039)

★7038★
Hawaii State Public Library System - Hawaii State Library - Art, Music & Recreation - Audiovisual Section (Aud-Vis)
478 S. King St.
Honolulu, HI 96813 Phone: (808)586-3520
Staff: Prof 6; Other 6. **Subjects:** Art, theater, music, motion pictures, dance, sports, Hawaiian music. **Holdings:** 45,691 books; 3363 reels of film; 1198 videocassettes; 915 pieces of sheet music; 11,542 scores; 19,353 phonograph records; 60,005 pictures; 3489 audiocassettes; 923 compact discs. **Subscriptions:** 363 journals and other serials. **Services:** Interlibrary loan; section open to the public. **Remarks:** FAX: (808)586-3584. **Formerly:** Its Fine Arts and Audiovisual Section. **Staff:** Vernon H.Q. Tam, Sect.Hd./Mus.Spec.; Norma C. Hirota, Libn./Art & Arch.Spec.; Haesun K. Morse, Libn./Entertainment Arts Spec.; Sarah Preble, Libn./Applied Arts Spec.; Sally Walstrum, Libn. & Unit Hd./AV; Ivy Lin, Libn./Video Mtls.

★7039★
Hawaii State Public Library System - Hawaii State Library - Business, Science, Technology Unit (Bus-Fin, Sci-Engr)
478 S. King St. Phone: (808)586-3481
Honolulu, HI 96813 JoAnn M. Schindler, Hd.
Staff: Prof 5; Other 2. **Subjects:** Economics, commerce, management, transportation, natural sciences, medicine, engineering, agriculture, nutrition, technology. **Special Collections:** Telephone books. **Holdings:** 57,000 books; 15,000 pamphlets. **Subscriptions:** 435 journals and other serials. **Services:** Interlibrary loan; unit open to the public. **Automated Operations:** Computerized public access catalog. **Computerized Information Services:** DIALOG Information Services; CD-ROM (NTIS, Business File, Health Reference Center). Performs searches free of charge for government agencies. **Publications:** Count on the Library for Business Information; Guide to Investment Information in the Hawaii State Library. **Remarks:** FAX: (808)586-3584. **Staff:** Joyce Kidani, Sci. Selector; Samuel Wagatsuma, Bus. Selector

★7040★
Hawaii State Public Library System - Hawaii State Library - Edna Allyn Room (Area-Ethnic)
478 S. King St. Phone: (808)586-3510
Honolulu, HI 96813 Shirley S. Naito, Oahu Ch.Coord.
Staff: Prof 3; Other 2. **Subjects:** Children's books, Hawaiiana, foreign books for children. **Special Collections:** Historical collection of out-of-print and rare children's books; alphabet books; counting books; autographed Nene Award books. **Holdings:** 72,356 books; 394 book/cassette kits. **Subscriptions:** 44 journals and other serials. **Services:** Interlibrary loan; copying; room open to the public. **Automated Operations:** Computerized public access catalog, acquisitions, and circulation. **Remarks:** FAX: (808)586-3584. **Staff:** Hewitt Reynolds, Libn.; Lucy Ann A. Taniguchi.

★7041★
Hawaii State Public Library System - Hawaii State Library - Federal Documents Section (Info Sci)
478 S. King St. Phone: (808)586-3477
Honolulu, HI 96813 Ellen K. Stempel, Hd.
Staff: Prof 2; Other 2. **Subjects:** U.S. Government documents. **Special Collections:** Popular collection for inventors; U.S. Patent and Trademark Depository Library. **Holdings:** 142,870 documents; 600,240 documents in microform; international and state documents; U.S. Patents (1985 to present). **Services:** Interlibrary loan; copying; section open to the public. **Computerized Information Services:** DIALOG Information Services, U.S. Patent Classification System. **Remarks:** FAX: (808)586-3584. **Staff:** Jan Y. Tawarahara, Libn.

★7042★
Hawaii State Public Library System - Hawaii State Library - Hawaii and Pacific Section I (Area-Ethnic, Hist)
478 S. King St. Phone: (808)586-3535
Honolulu, HI 96813 Joyce Miyamoto, Hd.
Founded: 1913. **Staff:** Prof 4.5; Other 4.5. **Subjects:** Hawaiiana, Pacifica. **Special Collections:** Hawaii and the Pacific Collection (73,807 volumes); State Documents Collection (44,931); Admiral Thomas Papers (130); Phillips Collection (1705 items). **Holdings:** 75,788 books; 1179 bound periodical volumes; 69,829 pamphlets and newspaper clippings; 65,897 state documents on microfiche; 261 titles of periodicals on microfilm. **Subscriptions:** 1557 journals and other serials. **Services:** Interlibrary loan; copying; section open to the public. **Computerized Information Services:** DIALOG Information Services. **Publications:** Basic Hawaiiana; What to Read About Hawaii; bibliographies. **Special Indexes:** Index to Honolulu Advertiser and Honolulu Star-Bulletin; Hawaii Documents Cumulative Index, 1989-1990; Basic Hawaiiana; Hawaiian Legends Index. **Remarks:** FAX: (808)586-3584.

★7043★
Hawaii State Public Library System - Hawaii State Library - Language, Literature and History Section (Hum)
478 S. King St. Phone: (808)596-3499
Honolulu, HI 96813 Sandra Kolloge, Hd.
Staff: Prof 5; Other 2. **Subjects:** Language, literature, history, travel. **Special Collections:** Genealogy (10,000 items); Foreign Language (10,883 items). **Holdings:** 150,000 books; 2000 pamphlets; 3300 maps; 7500 titles on microfiche. **Subscriptions:** 318 journals and other serials. **Services:** Section open to the public. **Automated Operations:** Computerized cataloging. **Computerized Information Services:** Online systems. **Publications:** Bibliographies.

★7044★
Hawaii State Public Library System - Hawaii State Library - Library for the Blind and Physically Handicapped (Aud-Vis)
402 Kapahulu Ave. Phone: (808)732-7767
Honolulu, HI 96815 Sally W. Morgan, Dir.
Founded: 1931. **Staff:** Prof 3; Other 12. **Subjects:** General collection. **Holdings:** 16,814 braille books; 28,675 talking books; 75 open reel tapes; 5617 large-type books; 45,451 cassette books; 1760 phonograph records; 1908 inkprint books; 1370 pamphlets; 806 film loops; 65 filmstrips; 14 16mm films; 337 manipulatives; 661 multimedia kits; 22 video cassettes. **Subscriptions:** 160 journals in various media. **Services:** Interlibrary loan; duplicating; transcribing; circulation of talking books and other media; machine lending service; institutional library services; library open to students and researchers. **Computerized Information Services:** READS (internal database). **Publications:** News is Getting Around the Pacific, quarterly - available upon request to registered patrons and agencies working with the handicapped. **Remarks:** FAX: (808)732-4158. **Staff:** Sue Sugimura, Pub.Serv.Libn.; Fusako Miyashiro, Transcribing Serv.Libn.

★7045★
Hawaii State Public Library System - Hawaii State Library - Serials Section (Info Sci)
478 S. King St. Phone: (808)586-3494
Honolulu, HI 96813 Thomas P. Churma, Ser.Libn.
Staff: Prof 1; Other 6. **Subjects:** Business, science, fine arts and literature, sports, language, social sciences, history. **Special Collections:** Staff collection of library periodicals (99 titles). **Holdings:** 478 microfilm titles; 8883 bound periodical volumes; 19,411 reels of microfilm. **Subscriptions:** 2038 journals and other serials; 90 newspapers. **Services:** Interlibrary loan; copying; section open to the public. **Computerized Information Services:** Index to the Honolulu Advertiser and Honolulu Star-Bulletin (internal database); CD-ROMs (InfoTrac, General BusinessFile, Magazine Index/Plus, National Newspaper Index). **Special Catalogs:** Serials Holding List: magazines, newspapers, and microforms of the Hawaii State Public Library System, annual. **Remarks:** FAX: (808)586-3585.

★7046★
Hawaii State Public Library System - Hawaii State Library - Social Science and Philosophy Section (Soc Sci, Hum)
478 S. King St. Phone: (808)586-3529
Honolulu, HI 96813 Colette F.H. Young, Sect.Hd.
Founded: 1967. **Staff:** Prof 5; Other 2. **Subjects:** Social science, religion, philosophy, psychology, education, government, law, folklore. **Holdings:** 67,634 books; 7288 pamphlets; 7000 college catalogs (hardcopy and microfiche). **Subscriptions:** 409 journals and other serials; 5 indexes on CD-ROM. **Services:** Interlibrary loan; copying; section open to the public. **Automated Operations:** Computerized public access catalog. **Computerized Information Services:** DIALOG Information Services. **Remarks:** FAX: (808)586-3584. **Staff:** Miriam H. Sato, Libn.; Pamela Ho-Wong, Libn.; Ross Christensen, Libn.; Carol Takara, Techn.

★7047★
Hawaii State Public Library System - Hawaii State Library - Young Adult Section (Educ)
478 S. King St. Phone: (808)586-3490
Honolulu, HI 96813 Sylvia C. Mitchell, Oahu Young Adult Coord.
Founded: 1943. **Staff:** Prof 1.5. **Subjects:** Young adult books, Hawaiiana, occupational information, teen sexuality. **Holdings:** 21,000 titles; 5000 pamphlets; 500 uncataloged items. **Subscriptions:** 40 journals and other serials; 10 school newspapers. **Services:** Interlibrary loan; copying; booktalks for Oahu public schools, grades 8 and 10; section open to the public. **Computerized Information Services:** InfoTrac. **Publications:** Career Success: Include the Library When You Plan for the Future, annual; Love and Loving. **Staff:** Kathryn Suzuki, Libn.

★7048★
Hawaii State Supreme Court - Law Library (Law)
417 S. King St.
Box 779 Phone: (808)548-7432
Honolulu, HI 96808 Ann S. Koto, State Law Libn.
Founded: 1851. **Staff:** Prof 3; Other 5. **Subjects:** Law. **Holdings:** 81,000 volumes; 282,000 microfiche; 351 films; 580 tapes. **Subscriptions:** 290 journals and other serials. **Services:** Library open to the public for reference use only. **Computerized Information Services:** Ho'ike (internal database). **Staff:** Irene Wong, Pub.Serv.Libn.

Hawaii Volcanoes National Park
See: **U.S. Natl. Park Service** (17731)

Hawaii War Records Depository
See: **University of Hawaii - Special Collections** (18625)

★7049★
Hawaiian Electric Co., Inc. - Corporate Research Center (Energy)
Box 2750 Phone: (808)543-7366
Honolulu, HI 96840 Deborah Uchida, Corp.Res.Coord.
Founded: 1980. **Staff:** Prof 1. **Subjects:** Electric utility management. **Special Collections:** Corporate archives. **Holdings:** 350 books. **Subscriptions:** 19 journals and other serials. **Automated Operations:** Computerized cataloging. **Computerized Information Services:** DIALOG Information Services; internal databases; Knight-Ridder Unicom (electronic mail service). **Publications:** Library Highlights, monthly. **Remarks:** Library is located at 900 Richards St., Honolulu, HI 96813. FAX: (808)543-7790.

★7050★
Hawaiian Electric Co., Inc. - Engineering Library (Sci-Engr)
820 Ward Ave.
Box 2750 Phone: (808)543-7915
Honolulu, HI 96840 Deborah Uchida, Corp.Res.Coord.
Founded: 1965. **Subjects:** Electrical and mechanical engineering, energy, civil engineering, alternate energy. **Holdings:** 4000 books; 5000 pamphlets. **Subscriptions:** 50 journals and other serials. **Services:** Library open to college and university students by appointment only. **Automated Operations:** Computerized cataloging. **Computerized Information Services:** DIALOG Information Services; internal databases; Knight-Ridder Unicom (electronic mail service). **Publications:** Library Highlights, monthly - to engineering personnel. **Special Indexes:** Technical file index (online). **Remarks:** FAX: (808)543-7519.

★7051★
Hawaiian Historical Society - Mission-Historical Library (Hist)
560 Kawaiahao St. Phone: (808)537-6271
Honolulu, HI 96813 Barbara E. Dunn, Adm.Dir.
Founded: 1893. **Staff:** Prof 1. **Subjects:** Pacific and round the world voyages, history of Hawaiian Islands and Polynesia, local biography. **Special Collections:** Newspapers printed in Hawaiian Islands, 1836-1900; Hawaiian language imprints, 1822-1900 (600 volumes). **Holdings:** 10,000 volumes; 2808 pamphlets; 5 VF drawers of manuscripts; 10 VF drawers of clippings; 5 VF drawers of photographs; early newspapers on microfilm; 3 VF drawers of maps; 1 VF drawer of broadsides; 50 photograph albums and scrapbooks. **Subscriptions:** 28 journals and other serials. **Services:** Copying; library open to the public, but it is primarily for researchers. **Publications:** The Hawaiian Historical Society, A Guide to the Library Collections.

★7052★
Hawaiian Mission Children's Society - The Mission Houses Museum Library Collections (Hist)
553 S. King St. Phone: (808)531-0481
Honolulu, HI 96813 Marilyn L. Reppun, Hd.Libn.
Founded: 1908. **Staff:** Prof 2. **Subjects:** 19th century Hawaiian history, history of Protestant missionaries in Hawaii, voyages to Hawaii. **Special Collections:** Manuscripts of American Protestant missionaries, 1820-1900 (includes unpublished letters, journals, reports); Hawaiian language materials; early Hawaiian newspapers and magazines; archives of the Congregational Church in Hawaii, Micronesia, and the Marquesas. **Holdings:** 12,000 books; 400 bound periodical volumes; 6 drawers of microfilm; 245 linear feet of manuscript material; engravings; drawings; daguerreotypes; photographs. **Subscriptions:** 15 journals and other serials. **Services:** Copying (very limited); qualified researchers may use manuscript material; library open to the public. **Publications:** Guide to Manuscript Collections (pamphlet); The Hawaii Journals of the New England Missionaries, 1813-1894: A Guide to the Holdings of the Mission Houses Museum Library, Collections of the Hawaiian Mission Children's Society; Hawaiian Language Imprints Bibliography, 1822-1899. **Remarks:** FAX: (808)545-2280. **Staff:** Lela Goodell, Asst.Libn./Cat.

★7053★
Hawaiian Sugar Planters' Association Experiment Station - Library (Food-Bev, Biol Sci)
99-193 Aiea Heights Dr.
Box 1057 Phone: (808)487-5561
Aiea, HI 96701 Ann L. Marsteller, Libn.
Founded: 1907. **Staff:** Prof 1; Other 2. **Subjects:** Sugar technology, plant breeding and physiology, entomology, chemistry, plant pathology, agriculture. **Special Collections:** Project files of experiment station (5000 folders). **Holdings:** 85,000 volumes. **Subscriptions:** 300 journals and other serials. **Services:** Interlibrary loan; library open to researchers with permission from director or librarian. **Computerized Information Services:** DIALOG Information Services, STN International. **Remarks:** FAX: (808)486-5020.

★7054★
Hawk Mountain Sanctuary Association - Library (Biol Sci)
Rte. 2, Box 191 Phone: (215)756-6961
Kempton, PA 19529 Laurie Goodrich, Libn.
Founded: 1934. **Subjects:** Ornithology, raptors, Appalachian ecology. **Holdings:** 1000 volumes. **Services:** Library not open to the public. **Computerized Information Services:** Internal database on raptor fall migration counts, 1934 to present.

★7055★
Hawker Siddeley Canada Inc. - Orenda Division - Engineering Library
3160 Dery Rd. E.
Mississauga, ON, Canada L4T 1A9
Founded: 1960. **Subjects:** Engines, space aircraft. **Holdings:** 7000 volumes. **Remarks:** Currently inactive.

Hawkesbury Library
See: **University of Western Sydney** (19565)

★7056★
Hawkins, Delafield & Wood - Library (Law)
67 Wall St. Phone: (212)820-9447
New York, NY 10005 Susan van Beek, Dir., Lib.Serv.
Founded: 1896. **Staff:** Prof 2. **Subjects:** Law. **Special Collections:** Municipal bond law. **Holdings:** 40,000 volumes. **Subscriptions:** 100 journals and other serials. **Services:** Interlibrary loan; library not open to the public. **Computerized Information Services:** LEXIS, DIALOG Information Services, WESTLAW, LEGI-SLATE, Securities Data Company, Inc. **Special Indexes:** Bond memoranda of law index. **Remarks:** FAX: (212)344-6258. **Staff:** Lynda Sayer.

Rose Hawley Museum and Historical Library
See: **Mason County Historical Society** (9772)

Nathaniel Hawthorne Collection
See: **Bowdoin College - Library - Special Collections** (2033)

Clarence L. Hay Library
See: **Cape Cod Museum of Natural History** (3024)

★7057★
The Hay Group - Corporate Library (Bus-Fin)
229 S. 18th St. Phone: (215)875-2300
Philadelphia, PA 19103 Mary Lou Troy, Corp.Libn.
Founded: 1978. **Staff:** Prof 1. **Subjects:** Management, compensation, personnel, pensions and benefits. **Holdings:** 2000 books. **Subscriptions:** 150 journals and other serials. **Services:** Interlibrary loan; library not open to the public. **Automated Operations:** Computerized serials. **Computerized Information Services:** DIALOG Information Services, Dow Jones News/Retrieval, VU/TEXT Information Services, NEXIS; DIALMAIL (electronic mail service).

Hayden Planetarium
See: **American Museum of Natural History - Hayden Planetarium** (688)

Grom Hayes Library
See: **Hartford State Technical College** (6941)

★7058★
Helen Hayes Hospital - Library (Med)
Route 9W Phone: (914)947-3000
West Haverstraw, NY 10993 Kathleen Fiola, Lib.Dir.
Staff: Prof 1; Other 2. **Subjects:** Orthopedics, rehabilitation medicine, neurology, physical therapy, occupational therapy, biomedical engineering, rehabilitation technology, psychology, psychiatry, speech and hearing. **Holdings:** 5000 books; 5000 bound periodical volumes. **Subscriptions:** 200 journals and other serials. **Services:** Interlibrary loan; library open to health professionals. **Computerized Information Services:** BRS Information Technologies, MEDLARS. **Networks/Consortia:** Member of National Network of Libraries of Medicine - Middle Atlantic Region, Southeastern New York Library Resources Council (SENYLRC), Health Information Libraries of Westchester (HILOW), Ramapo Catskill Library System, BHSL. **Publications:** Library newsletter - for internal distribution only. **Remarks:** A fax number, available for emergency use only, can be obtained by telephoning the library.

★7059★
Max S. Hayes Vocational School - Library (Educ)
4600 Detroit Ave. Phone: (216)634-8683
Cleveland, OH 44102 Robert Stephen, Libn.
Founded: 1958. **Staff:** Prof 1; Other 1. **Subjects:** Automotive trades, metalwork, machine shop work, vocational education, construction, textile fabrication. **Holdings:** 12,000 volumes; U.S. and foreign car shop manuals, 1965 to present. **Subscriptions:** 85 journals and other serials. **Services:** Interlibrary loan; copying; library open to the public by appointment. **Remarks:** Maintained by the Cleveland Board of Education.

★7060★
Rutherford B. Hayes Presidential Center - Library (Hist)
Spiegel Grove Phone: (419)332-2081
Fremont, OH 43420-2796 Roger D. Bridges, Dir.
Founded: 1911. **Staff:** Prof 4; Other 3. **Subjects:** Rutherford B. Hayes library and papers; Hayes family papers and papers of many of the President's contemporaries, including William M. Evarts; Civil War and Reconstruction in the South; American railroads; the American presidency and its development; U.S. political and economic history; American biography; American letters; Ohio history; Sandusky River Valley history; genealogy. **Special Collections:** Charles E. Frohman Local History Collection (Erie County, Ohio; 100 linear feet); Frank E. Hamilton Collection (Great Lakes; 54 linear feet); Great Lakes marine collection; genealogy. **Holdings:** 75,000 volumes; 1 million manuscripts; 70,000 photographs; 6200 reels of microfilm of census, manuscripts, newspapers; 6100 bound newspaper volumes. **Subscriptions:** 200 journals and other serials; 3 newspapers. **Services:** Interlibrary loan; copying; library open to the public. **Publications:** Hayes Historical Journal, quarterly - for sale; The Statesman (newsletter), quarterly - available on request; Papers of Rutherford B. Hayes (microfilm) - for sale; guide to microfilm edition of Rutherford B. Hayes Papers (book); First Lady: The Life of Lucy Webb Hayes (book) - for sale; Presidency of Rutherford B. Hayes (book) - for sale. **Special Indexes:** Index to Rutherford B. Hayes Papers (card); index to obituaries in Sandusky County newspapers (card and online). **Remarks:** Affilated with the Ohio Historical Society. **Staff:** Thomas A. Smith, Hd. of Res.; Barbara Paff, Libn.; Rebecca Hill, Libn.; Gilbert Gonzalez, Hd., Photo.Rsrcs.; Thomas J. Culbertson, Archv.

Samuel P. Hayes Research Library
See: **Perkins School for the Blind** (12946)

★7061★
Hayes, Seay, Mattern & Mattern Inc. - Corporate Library (Sci-Engr, Plan)
1315 Franklin Rd., S.W.
Box 13446 Phone: (703)857-3140
Roanoke, VA 24034 Alfred T. Whitelock, Corp.Libn.
Founded: 1958. **Staff:** Prof 1. **Subjects:** Architecture; engineering - civil, electrical, mechanical, structural; planning; construction. **Holdings:** 9500 books; college catalogs; microfiche; maps; cassettes; videotapes; standards and specifications; military documents. **Subscriptions:** 296 journals and periodicals. **Services:** Interlibrary loan; library not open to the public. **Publications:** Monthly library newsletter and accessions list (online). **Remarks:** FAX: (703)857-3180.

★7062★
Stanley W. Hayes Research Foundation - Library (Env-Cons)
801 Elks Rd.
Box 1404 Phone: (317)962-3745
Richmond, IN 47374 Randall P. Kirk, Arboretum Dir.
Subjects: Ecology, entomology, ornithology, geology, biology, botany. **Holdings:** 1300 volumes. **Remarks:** Library located on grounds of Hayes Regional Arboretum.

Haynes Collection
See: **Montana State University - Libraries** (10654)

★7063★
Haynes International, Inc. - Technical Information Center (Sci-Engr, Bus-Fin)
1020 W. Park Ave.
Box 9013 Phone: (317)456-6142
Kokomo, IN 46904-9013 Betty S. Baranow, Supv., Info.Comm.
Founded: 1952. **Staff:** Prof 2; Other 1. **Subjects:** Metallurgy, inorganic chemistry, marketing, business. **Holdings:** 11,000 volumes; 15,000 technical reports; 10,000 technical reports on microfilm; slides; tapes. **Subscriptions:** 200 journals and other serials. **Services:** Interlibrary loan; copying; center open to the public by special arrangement. **Automated Operations:** Computerized cataloging. **Computerized Information Services:** OCLC, DIALOG Information Services. **Networks/Consortia:** Member of INCOLSA. **Remarks:** FAX: (317)456-6905. **Staff:** Amy J. Russell, Libn.

Haynes Memorial Library
See: **The Living Desert** (9230)

Commander Silas B. Hays Army Community Hospital
See: **U.S. Army Hospitals** (17036)

George H. Hays Memorial Library
See: **Mount Sinai Medical Center of Cleveland** (10817)

★7064★
Haystack Mountain School of Crafts - Library (Art)
Deer Isle, ME 04627-0518 Phone: (207)348-2306
Subjects: Fine arts, ceramics, weaving, glassblowing, flat glass, jewelry, surface and textile design, wood, blacksmithing, printmaking, papermaking, weaving. **Holdings:** 500 books. **Subscriptions:** 20 journals and other serials. **Services:** Interlibrary loan; library open to the public.

Lillian R. Hayt Memorial Library
See: **Hospital Association of New York (State) - Hospital Educational and Research Fund** (7416)

Earl W. Hayter Regional History Center
See: **Northern Illinois University** (11995)

★7065★
Hayward Daily Review - Library (Publ)
116 W. Winton Ave. Phone: (510)783-6111
Hayward, CA 94540 Ruth Day
Founded: 1952. **Staff:** Prof 1. **Subjects:** Newspaper reference topics. **Special Collections:** Photographs of city and local persons. **Holdings:** Microfilm (1975 to present); clippings files. **Services:** Interlibrary loan; library not open to the public. **Remarks:** FAX: (510)293-2490.

★7066★
Hazardous Materials Control Research Institute - Library (Env-Cons)
7237 Hanover Pkwy. Phone: (301)982-9500
Greenbelt, MD 20770-3602 Harold Bernard, Exec.Dir.
Founded: 1976. **Subjects:** Hazardous waste, hazardous materials, superfund legislation, environment. **Holdings:** 500 volumes. **Subscriptions:** 14 journals and other serials. **Services:** Interlibrary loan; copying; library open to institute members. **Remarks:** FAX: (301)220-3870.

★7067★
Hazardous Waste Research and Information Center - Library (Env-Cons)
1 E. Hazelwood Dr. Phone: (217)333-8957
Champaign, IL 61820 Sara Tompson, Libn.
Founded: 1986. **Staff:** Prof 1; Other 2. **Subjects:** Hazardous waste, pollution prevention, industrial audits. **Special Collections:** Waste reduction; small quantity generators; household hazardous waste. **Holdings:** 3000 books; 500 microfiche; 20 videotapes. **Subscriptions:** 190 journals and other serials; 3 newspapers. **Services:** Interlibrary loan; library open to the public for reference use only. **Automated Operations:** Computerized serials and cataloging. **Computerized Information Services:** DIALOG Information Services, NLM, TOXNET. **Networks/Consortia:** Member of Lincoln Trail Libraries System (LTLS), ILLINET. **Publications:** Acquisitions list, monthly - available on request; waste reduction bibliography, quarterly. **Remarks:** FAX: (217)333-8944.

★7068★
Hazelden Foundation - Staff Library (Med)
Box 11 Phone: (612)257-4010
Center City, MN 55012 Barbara S. Weiner, MLS, Staff Libn.
Founded: 1966. **Staff:** Prof 1. **Subjects:** Chemical dependency, rehabilitation, addictions. **Special Collections:** Alcohol archives. **Holdings:** 7000 books; 300 cassette tapes. **Subscriptions:** 100 journals and other serials. **Services:** Library not open to the public. **Computerized Information Services:** BRS Information Technologies; internal database; DOCLINE (electronic mail service). **Networks/Consortia:** Member of Twin Cities Biomedical Consortium (TCBC), Substance Abuse Librarians and Information Specialists (SALIS), Central Minnesota Libraries Exchange (CMLE). **Remarks:** FAX: (612)257-4449.

★7069★
Hazeltine Corporation - Technical Information Center (Sci-Engr)
Cuba Hill Rd. Phone: (516)261-7000
Greenlawn, NY 11740 Connie Muscolino, Hd.Libn.
Staff: 1. **Subjects:** Antennas, electronics, computers. **Holdings:** Figures not available. **Services:** Interlibrary loan (limited); copying; center not open to the public; loans through LILRC. **Computerized Information Services:** DIALOG Information Services, DTIC. **Remarks:** FAX: (516)262-8020.

★7070★
Hazleton General Hospital - Medical Library (Med)
E. Broad St. Phone: (717)450-4257
Hazleton, PA 18201 Elaine M. Curry, Libn.
Staff: Prof 1. **Subjects:** Medicine, nursing, and allied health sciences. **Holdings:** 1300 books; 1521 bound periodical volumes. **Subscriptions:** 248 journals and other serials. **Services:** Interlibrary loan; document delivery; library open to the public when librarian is on duty. **Computerized Information Services:** MEDLARS, CINAHL. **Networks/Consortia:** Member of Health Information Library Network of Northeastern Pennsylvania (HILNNEP). **Remarks:** Alternate telephone number(s): 450-4257. FAX: (717)450-4280.

★7071★
Hazleton Wisconsin - Information Services (Sci-Engr)
Box 7545 Phone: (608)242-2712
Madison, WI 53707 Sandra L. Thompson, Libn.
Founded: 1945. **Staff:** Prof 2. **Subjects:** Food science, chemistry, toxicology, drugs, laboratory animals. **Holdings:** 2000 books; 3000 bound periodical volumes. **Subscriptions:** 500 journals and other serials. **Services:** Interlibrary loan; copying; SDI; library open to the public with restrictions. **Computerized Information Services:** DIALOG Information Services, NLM, STN International, BRS Information Technologies, Data-Star, InvesText, Dow Jones News/Retrieval, Chemical Information Systems, Inc. (CIS). **Networks/Consortia:** Member of National Network of Libraries of Medicine - Greater Midwest Region, Multitype Advisory Library Committee (MALC). **Remarks:** FAX: (608)241-7227. Parent company is Corning Glass Works.

Henry Hazlitt Collection
See: **Foundation for Economic Education - Library** (6043)

★7072★
HBT AGRA Limited - Library (Sci-Engr)
4810 93rd St. Phone: (403)436-2152
Edmonton, AB, Canada T6E 5M4 Janice Huggan, Libn.
Subjects: Engineering - geotechnical, materials; analytical chemistry; environment. **Holdings:** 5000 books; 200 bound periodical volumes; 1000 maps; 8 VF drawers. **Services:** Library not open to the public. **Remarks:** FAX: (403)435-8425. **Formerly:** Hardy BBT Limited.

★7073★
HCA/Lewis-Gale Hospital - Medical Library (Med)
1900 Electric Rd. Phone: (703)989-4261
Salem, VA 24153 Roberta L. Miller, Med.Lib.Cons.
Subjects: Medicine, surgery. **Holdings:** 500 books; bound periodical volumes. **Subscriptions:** 150 journals and other serials. **Services:** Interlibrary loan; library not open to the public. **Publications:** Bibliographies.

★7074★
HDR Engineering - Library (Sci-Engr)
11225 S.E. 6th St.
Bldg. C, Suite 200 Phone: (206)453-1523
Bellevue, WA 98004-6441 Karen Baker
Founded: 1978. **Staff:** Prof 1. **Subjects:** Water resources and quality, meteorological data for the western United States, hydropower development, transportation. **Holdings:** 3000 books; 1000 other cataloged items. **Subscriptions:** 72 journals and other serials. **Services:** Interlibrary loan; copying; library not open to the public. **Automated Operations:** Computerized cataloging. **Computerized Information Services:** Internal databases. **Remarks:** FAX: (206)453-7107.

Louis S. Headley Memorial Library
See: **Science Museum of Minnesota** (14940)

★7075★
Headley-Whitney Museum - Library (Art)
4435 Old Frankfort Pike Phone: (606)255-6653
Lexington, KY 40510 Susan B. Thompson, Exec.Dir.
Staff: 1. **Subjects:** Art, jewels and minerals, natural history. **Holdings:** 1300 books. **Services:** Library open to the public for reference use only.

Heafey Law Library
See: **Santa Clara University** (14809)

★7076★
Heald College - Library (Sci-Engr, Comp Sci)
684 El Paseo de Saratoga Phone: (408)295-8000
San Jose, CA 95130 Marilyn May Kanemura, Libn.
Founded: 1980. **Staff:** Prof 1; Other 2. **Subjects:** Electronics, microcomputers, microprocessors, computer programming, business, accounting, telecommunications, mathematics. **Special Collections:** Electronic and computer product databook collection (500); career education collection (121 books and pamphlets). **Holdings:** 2700 books; 25 college catalogs; 2 VF drawers of reprints and clippings; 59 AV programs. **Subscriptions:** 38 journals and other serials. **Services:** Interlibrary loan; copying; library open to the public for reference use only with staff approval. **Networks/Consortia:** Member of SOUTHNET. **Publications:** Subject bibliographies, quarterly - to students; Writing a Research Paper: Helpful Hints, quarterly - to technical communications students.

Joseph P. Healey Library
See: **University of Massachusetts at Boston, Harbor Campus** (18832)

Health Alliance Plan
See: **Metro Medical Group - Detroit Northwest** (10192)

Health Dimensions Inc. - San Jose Medical Center
See: **San Jose Medical Center** (14754)

★7077★
Health Information Network Services (Med)
Pacific & Nassau
Box 1067 Phone: (206)258-7558
Everett, WA 98206 Cheryl M. Goodwin, Dir.
Founded: 1974. **Staff:** Prof 1; Other 2. **Subjects:** Medicine, nursing, hospital management. **Holdings:** 2000 books. **Subscriptions:** 500 journals and other serials. **Services:** Interlibrary loan; copying; SDI; services open to the public with restrictions. **Automated Operations:** Computerized cataloging, acquisitions, serials, and circulation. **Computerized Information Services:** MEDLARS, BRS Information Technologies, DIALOG Information Services, Western Library Network (WLN); DOCLINE, OnTyme Electronic Message Network Service (electronic mail services). Performs searches on fee basis. **Networks/Consortia:** Member of Seattle Area Hospital Library Consortium (SAHLC). **Publications:** Network (newsletter), monthly - for internal distribution only. **Remarks:** The Health Information Network Services is a joint service of Providence Hospital, Everett and the General Hospital of Everett. FAX: (206)258-7266.

★7078★
Health Law Institute - Library (Med, Law)
461 Law Centre
University of Alberta Phone: (403)432-8342
Edmonton, AB, Canada T6G 2H5 Patricia L. James, Exec.Dir.
Founded: 1977. **Staff:** 1. **Subjects:** Health law, medicolegal issues, medical malpractice. **Holdings:** Reported and unreported Canadian common law court cases dealing with health law, 1950 to present; a selection of Quebec cases; English and Commonwealth health law cases, 1975 to present; United States health law court cases; Canadian, Commonwealth, and American journals and articles on medicolegal issues; Law Reform Commission of Canada reports. **Computerized Information Services:** CANCASE, COMCASE, USCASE, ART (internal databases). **Publications:** Health Law Review, 3/year. **Remarks:** FAX: (403)492-4924. The Health Law Institute is funded by the Alberta Law Foundation, University of Alberta.

★7079★
Health Occupations Center - Library (Med)
8756 Mast Blvd. Phone: (619)579-4793
Santee, CA 92071 Kathleen A. Johnson
Staff: Prof 1. **Subjects:** Nursing, medicine, dentistry. **Special Collections:** Nursing collection (700 filmstrips, 120 videotapes). **Holdings:** 2100 books. **Subscriptions:** 40 journals and other serials. **Services:** Copying; library open to the public for reference use only.

★7080★
Health Research and Educational Trust of New Jersey - Corporate Information Center (Med)
760 Alexander Rd. (CN-1) Phone: (609)275-4230
Princeton, NJ 08543-0001 Michelle Volesko, Dir.
Founded: 1966. **Staff:** Prof 1; Other 3. **Subjects:** Hospital and health care administration, consumer health education, hospital and in-service education, business and management. **Special Collections:** New Jersey Hospital Long Range Plans (500 titles); New Jersey Patient Origin and Market Share Reports (25 titles); corporate archive. **Holdings:** 2300 books; 720 bound periodical volumes; 2500 serial volumes; 1900 vertical files; 200 videotape and film titles; 200 audio cassettes; 4 drawers of microfiche; 26 internal newsletters. **Subscriptions:** 400 journals and other serials; 5 newspapers. **Services:** Interlibrary loan; center open to the public by appointment. **Automated Operations:** Computerized cataloging, serials, ILL (DOCLINE). **Computerized Information Services:** BRS Information Technologies, DIALOG Information Services, OCLC, OCLC EPIC, Human Resource Information Network (HRIN). Performs searches on fee basis. **Networks/Consortia:** Member of MEDCORE, New Jersey Library Network. **Publications:** Selected Recent Acquisitions, monthly - to New Jersey hospital libraries and by subscription; Total Quality Management in Health Care; Semi Annual Bibliography. **Special Catalogs:** AV catalog; periodical holdings and subject catalog. **Remarks:** The Health Research and Educational Trust of New Jersey is a non profit affiliate of the New Jersey Hospital Association at the Center for Health Affairs. FAX: (609)275-4107.

★7081★
Health Services and Promotion Information Network
Jeanne Mance Bldg, Rm. 500
Tunney's Pasture
Ottawa, ON, Canada K1A 1B4
Defunct. Merged with Canada - Health and Welfare Canada - Policy, Planning & Information Branch - Library to form Canada - Health and Welfare Canada - Departmental Library.

Health and Welfare Canada
See: **Canada - Health and Welfare Canada** (2750)

★7082★
Health and Welfare Council, Inc. - Staff Reference Library
22 Light St.
Baltimore, MD 21202-1075
Defunct.

HealthEast - The Allentown Hospital
See: **The Allentown Hospital** (384)

HealthEast - Bethesda Lutheran Hospital
See: **Bethesda Lutheran Hospital - Library** (1789)

HealthEast - Midway Hospital
See: **Midway Hospital** (10374)

HealthEast - St. John's Northeast Hospital
See: **St. John's Northeast Hospital - Medical Library** (14343)

★7083★
HealthSouth Medical Hospital - Medical Library
1127 S. 12th St.
Birmingham, AL 35205
Founded: 1910. **Subjects:** Medicine, surgery, orthopedic surgery, otolaryngology. **Holdings:** 500 books; 450 bound periodical volumes. **Remarks:** Currently inactive. **Formerly:** South Highlands Hospital - Medical Library.

★7084★
Healthtrust - Riverton Memorial Hospital - Medical Library (Med)
2100 W. Sunset Phone: (307)856-4161
Riverton, WY 82501 Connie Krause, RN, Educ.Dir.
Staff: Prof 2; Other 2. **Subjects:** Medicine, nursing, management. **Holdings:** 200 books; 220 bound periodical volumes. **Subscriptions:** 34 journals and other serials. **Services:** Interlibrary loan; copying; library open to the public. **Computerized Information Services:** MEDLINE, DOCLINE. **Networks/Consortia:** Member of Health Sciences Information Network (HSIN). **Remarks:** FAX: (307)856-7664. **Staff:** Roberta Cassity, RN.

Jean and Alexander Heard Library
See: **Vanderbilt University - Jean and Alexander Heard Library - Arts Collection** (19768)

Jean and Alexander Heard Library - Anne Potter Wilson Music Library
See: **Vanderbilt University - Jean and Alexander Heard Library** (19767)

★7085★
Heard Museum - Library and Archives (Art, Area-Ethnic)
22 E. Monte Vista Rd. Phone: (602)252-8840
Phoenix, AZ 85004-1480 Mario Nick Klimiades, Libn./Archv.
Founded: 1929. **Staff:** Prof 1. **Subjects:** American Indians, Native American art, ethnology, material culture, archeology, primitive art, Southwest travel, history, and exploration. **Special Collections:** Native American Artists Resource Collection (information on 8200 Native American artists); Fred Harvey Company papers and photographs. **Holdings:** 40,000 volumes; 300 films and videotapes; 10,000 photographs; slides; pamphlet file; clippings; museum archives; sound recordings; manuscripts. **Subscriptions:** 110 journals and other serials. **Services:** Copying; duplication of nonprint material; library open to the public by appointment and for reference use only. **Computerized Information Services:** Internal database. **Remarks:** FAX: (602)252-9757.

Hearst Castle Staff Library
See: **California (State) Department of Parks and Recreation - Hearst San Simeon State Historical Monument** (2534)

★7086★
Hearst Corporation - Hearst Metrotone News Library (Aud-Vis)
235 E. 45th St. Phone: (212)455-4000
New York, NY 10017 Ted Troll, Chf.Libn.
Staff: Prof 1. **Subjects:** Special documentary and film projects on news and sports. **Holdings:** Screen News Digest; Perspective on Greatness Series (26 1-hour documentaries on people and topics of the 20th century); Time Capsule Series (2000 1-minute vignettes of people, places, events of our time); educational films for schools; Almanac Newsreel; Years in Review. **Services:** Library open to the public. **Remarks:** FAX: (212)687-8673.

Hearst Corporation - House Beautiful
See: **House Beautiful** (7438)

Hearst Corporation - San Francisco Examiner
See: **San Francisco Examiner** (14732)

Hearst Newsreel Library
See: **University of California, Los Angeles - UCLA Film and Television Archive - Research and Study Center** (18399)

★7087★
Phoebe Apperson Hearst Historical Society, Inc. - Museum Center (Hist)
850 Walton Phone: (314)629-3186
St. Clair, MO 63077 Mabel Reed, Sec.
Founded: 1961. **Staff:** 1. **Subjects:** Archeology, history, radio programs. **Holdings:** Historical books; Congressional Records; clippings; tapes; slides; photographs; phonograph records; manuscripts. **Services:** Interlibrary loan; center open to the public. **Publications:** Newsletter.

★7088★
Heart of America Genealogical Society & Library, Inc. (Hist)
Kansas City Public Library
311 E. 12th St. Phone: (816)221-2685
Kansas City, MO 64106 Gladys Deever, Libn.
Founded: 1955. **Subjects:** Genealogy. **Special Collections:** Alice Langton Collection (200 volumes of English and Irish records). **Holdings:** 9000 books; 1800 bound periodical volumes; 2500 family histories and genealogies; ancestor charts. **Subscriptions:** 140 journals and other serials. **Services:** Copying; library open to the public. **Publications:** The Kansas City Genealogist, quarterly - by subscription and on exchange. **Special Indexes:** Family Record Sheets (70,000 names). **Remarks:** The genealogy collection is housed in the Kansas City Public Library.

★7089★
Heart and Stroke Foundation of Alberta - Library (Med)
1825 Park Rd., S.E. Phone: (403)264-5549
Calgary, AB, Canada T2G 3Y6 Tracey Ginn, Lib.Serv.Coord.
Staff: Prof 2; Other 2. **Subjects:** Cardiovascular health and disease, treatment, prevention, rehabilitation, stress, smoking, high blood pressure, blood cholesterol, exercise, nutrition and heart health. **Holdings:** 600 volumes; 70 films; 12 slide/tape sets. **Services:** Library open to the public. **Publications:** Modern Concepts; Current Concepts; Cardiovascular Nursing. **Remarks:** FAX: (403)237-0803. **Staff:** Emily Alstad, Educ.Coord.

★7090★
Heartland Health Systems - Heartland Hospital East - Health Sciences Library (Med)
5325 Faraon St. Phone: (816)271-6075
St. Joseph, MO 64506 Joan Hughes, Hea.Sci.Libn.
Founded: 1981. **Staff:** Prof 1. **Subjects:** Medicine. **Holdings:** 350 books; 300 bound periodical volumes. **Subscriptions:** 64 journals and other serials. **Services:** Interlibrary loan; copying; library open to the public for reference use only when librarian is present. **Computerized Information Services:** MEDLARS. Performs searches on fee basis. **Networks/Consortia:** Member of National Network of Libraries of Medicine - Midcontinental Region.

★7091★
Heartland Institute (Bus-Fin)
634 S. Wabash, 2nd Fl.
Chicago, IL 60605 Phone: (312)427-3060
Subjects: Privatization, deregulation, libertarian thought, education reform, free market. **Holdings:** Figures not available. **Services:** Library open to the public. **Computerized Information Services:** CompuServe Information Service (electronic mail service). **Remarks:** Electronic mail address(es): 71257,3025 (CompuServe Information Service).

Heartman Collection
See: **Texas Southern University - Library - Heartman Collection** (16231)

Heberden Library of British Association of Rheumatology
See: **Royal College of Physicians of London** (14113)

★7092★
Hebrew College - Jacob and Rose Grossman Library (Rel-Phil, Area-Ethnic)
43 Hawes St. Phone: (617)232-8710
Brookline, MA 02146 Maurice S. Tuchman, Dir., Lib.Serv.
Founded: 1922. **Staff:** Prof 4; Other 1. **Subjects:** Education, Jewish history, Hebrew literature, Bible, Israel, children's literature, Rabbinic literature. **Special Collections:** Responsa literature; Kabbalah and Hassidic literature; Jewish education; large-print Judaica; Dr. Harry A. and Beatrice Savitz Jewish Medical History Collection; Russian Judaica; Japanese Judaica; women's studies collection. **Holdings:** 100,000 books; 2000 bound periodical volumes; 2 incunabula; 320 16th and 17th century rare books; 75 manuscripts; 1020 phonograph records; 60 maps and charts; 649 reels of microfilm; 100 slides; 134 audio cassettes. **Subscriptions:** 252 journals and other serials; 12 newspapers. **Services:** Interlibrary loan; copying; library open to the public. **Networks/Consortia:** Member of Fenway Library Consortium (FLC). **Special Catalogs:** Manuscript catalog (book); Russian Judaica; Microform Judaica; Japanese Judaica; Genealogical Resources in the Hebrew College Library; Jewish Reference Books, 1980-1990. **Staff:** Shalva Sieg el, Spec. Subjects Cat.; Judy Schiff, Ref.Libn.; Leon Taylor, Cat.

★7093★
Hebrew Educational Alliance - Library (Rel-Phil)
1555 Stuart St. Phone: (303)629-0410
Denver, CO 80204 Barbara A. Fine, Libn.
Founded: 1932. **Staff:** 1. **Subjects:** Judaica and Hebraica. **Holdings:** 2000 books. **Subscriptions:** 20 journals and other serials. **Services:** Library open to the public.

Hebrew Institute of Pittsburgh
See: **Jewish Education Institute** (8388)

★7094★
Hebrew Theological College - Saul Silber Memorial Library (Rel-Phil)
7135 N. Carpenter Rd. Phone: (312)267-9800
Skokie, IL 60077-3263 Nira Wolfe, Hd.Libn. & Cur.
Founded: 1922. **Staff:** Prof 2. **Subjects:** Judaica, philosophy, ethics, Hebraica, Rabbinics, Biblical literature, Jewish history, Zionism. **Special Collections:** J. Rapoport; R. Farber; Saul Silber; Max Shulman Zionist Library; Rev. Newman Hebrew Periodical Collection; Rabbi Simon H. Album Halakha Collection; Rabbi Leonard C. Mishkin Holocaust Collection; Women in Judaism. **Holdings:** 64,000 volumes; manuscripts; microfilm. **Subscriptions:** 170 journals and other serials. **Services:** Interlibrary loan; copying; library open to the public. **Networks/Consortia:** Member of North Suburban Library System (NSLS), Judaica Library Network of Chicago. **Remarks:** Alternate telephone number(s): (708)674-7750. FAX: (708)674-6381. **Staff:** Joseph Bachrach, Asst.Libn.

★7095★
Hebrew Union College - Jewish Institute of Religion - American Jewish Archives (Area-Ethnic, Rel-Phil)
3101 Clifton Ave. Phone: (513)221-1875
Cincinnati, OH 45220 Kevin Proffitt, Archv.
Founded: 1947. **Staff:** Prof 4; Other 13. **Subjects:** Western Hemisphere Jewish history and culture. **Holdings:** 8 million manuscript pages. **Subscriptions:** 5000 journals and other serials. **Services:** Interlibrary loan; copying; services available to all scholars and researchers in the field of Western Hemisphere Jewish history. **Publications:** American Jewish Archives, semiannual. **Special Catalogs:** Manuscript catalog of the American Jewish Archives, 5 volumes; Guide to the Holdings of the American Jewish Archives, 1979. **Remarks:** FAX: (513)221-7812. **Staff:** Dr. Abraham J. Peck, Adm.Dir.; Prof. Jacob R. Marcus, Dir.; Kathy Spray, Assoc.Archv.

★7096★
Hebrew Union College - Jewish Institute of Religion - American Jewish Periodical Center (Info Sci)
3101 Clifton Ave.
Cincinnati, OH 45220 Phone: (513)221-1875
Founded: 1956. **Staff:** Prof 2; Other 2. **Subjects:** American Jewish periodicals and newspapers. **Holdings:** 10,030 reels of microfilm. **Services:** Interlibrary loan; copying; center open to the public. **Publications:** Jewish Newspapers and Periodicals on Microfilm. **Remarks:** FAX: (513)221-0321. **Staff:** Herbert C. Zafren, Co-Dir.; Jacob R. Marcus, Co-Dir.

★7097★
Hebrew Union College - Jewish Institute of Religion - Frances-Henry Library (Rel-Phil)
3077 University Ave. Phone: (213)749-3424
Los Angeles, CA 90007 Harvey P. Horowitz, Libn.
Founded: 1958. **Staff:** Prof 1; Other 3. **Subjects:** Bible, Talmud, Rabbinics, Jewish history, Jewish education, philosophy, art, Jewish communal service, Hebrew literature, religion, Zionism. **Special Collections:** Rare Hebraica; Joseph H. Rosenberg American Jewish Archives. **Holdings:** 85,000 books; 2500 bound periodical volumes; 5000 reels of microfilm; 1000 phonograph records; 85 dissertations. **Subscriptions:** 350 journals and other serials; 25 newspapers. **Services:** Interlibrary loan; copying; library open to the public. **Computerized Information Services:** RLIN; RLG (electronic mail service). **Remarks:** FAX: (213)747-6128. Electronic mail address(es): BM.HIH (RLG).

★7098★
Hebrew Union College - Jewish Institute of Religion - Klau Library (Rel-Phil, Area-Ethnic)
1 W. Fourth St. Phone: (212)674-5300
New York, NY 10012 Philip E. Miller, Libn.
Founded: 1922. **Staff:** Prof 2; Other 4. **Subjects:** Jewish literature, history, sociology, music; Near Eastern languages, including Hebrew and Aramaic; philosophy; archeology; religious education. **Holdings:** 126,000 books. **Subscriptions:** 300 journals and other serials; 30 newspapers. **Services:** Interlibrary loan; copying; library open to the public for reference use only. **Computerized Information Services:** RLIN; BITNET (electronic mail service). **Publications:** Studies in Bibliography & Booklore. **Remarks:** Electronic mail address(es): BM.H2H@RLG (BITNET). **Staff:** Henry Resnick, Circ./ILL; Suzanne M. Stauffer, Ref.Serv.

★7099★
Hebrew Union College - Jewish Institute of Religion - Klau Library (Rel-Phil, Area-Ethnic)
3101 Clifton Ave. Phone: (513)221-1875
Cincinnati, OH 45220-2488 David J. Gilner, Libn.
Founded: 1875. **Staff:** Prof 10; Other 13. **Subjects:** Judaica, Hebraica, ancient Near East, Biblica, Rabbinics. **Special Collections:** Spinoza; Jewish music; rare books and manuscripts; anti-Semitism; maps and broadsides; Jewish Americana; Josephus; Judeo-Persian collection; Yiddish theater. **Holdings:** 374,808 volumes; 17,700 reels of microfilm; 18,810 microfiche; 3000 volumes of manuscripts. **Subscriptions:** 2057 journals and other serials. **Services:** Interlibrary loan; copying; library open to the public. **Automated Operations:** Computerized cataloging. **Computerized Information Services:** RLIN, BITNET (electronic mail services). **Publications:** Studies in Bibliography and Booklore, irregular - by subscription; Bibliographica Judaica (monograph series). **Remarks:** FAX: (513)221-0321. Electronic mail address(es): BM.HUC@RLG (BITNET). **Staff:** Herbert C. Zafren, Sr.Cons.; Ellen S. Kovacic, Hd., Tech.Serv.; Gloria Wolfson, Hd., Adm.Serv.; Bernard H. Rabenstein, Hebrew Acq.; Arnona Rudavsky, Loan Serv.Libn.; Ida Cohen Selavan, Ref.Libn.; Allan Satin, Judaica Libn.; Sarah Barnard, Ser.Libn.; Laurel Wolfson, Cons.Libn.

★7100★
Hebrew University of Jerusalem - Einstein Institute of Mathematics and Computer Science - Library (Sci-Engr)
Giv'at-Ram Campus Phone: 2 584379
91904 Jerusalem, Israel Gila Manusovich
Founded: 1925. **Staff:** Prof 3. **Subjects:** Mathematics, computer science. **Special Collections:** Nineteenth century and early twentieth century mathematics reprints (16,000); seventeenth and eighteenth century rare books; doctoral theses. **Holdings:** 35,000 books; 35,000 bound periodical volumes; microfiche. **Subscriptions:** 400 journals and other serials. **Services:** Interlibrary loan; copying; library open to the public for reference use only. **Computerized Information Services:** CD-ROM (MathSci). **Publications:** New Book List.

★7101★
Hebrew University of Jerusalem - Givat Ram Campus - Jewish Music Research Centre - Library (Mus, Area-Ethnic)
P.O. Box 503
91004 Jerusalem, Israel Phone: 2 585059
Subjects: Musical traditions and musical life of Jewish communities, ethnomusicology. **Special Collections:** Jacob Michael Collection of Jewish Music (2000 books; 6000 manuscripts and scores). **Holdings:** 15,000 volumes; 200,000 sound recordings and videotapes. **Remarks:** FAX: 2 527741. Telex: 25367. Center located next to the Music Department and National Sound Archive of the Jewish National and University Library.

★7102★
Hebrew University of Jerusalem - Harry S Truman Institute for the Advancement of Peace - Library and Documentation Centre (Soc Sci, Area-Ethnic)
Mount Scopus Phone: 2 882313
91905 Jerusalem, Israel Cecile Panzer, Dir.
Founded: 1970. **Staff:** 6. **Subjects:** Peace, Middle East, Asia, Africa, Latin America. **Special Collections:** Archives on Shanghai Jews; newspapers clippings on Israeli relations; reports written by Israeli experts serving in African developing countries. **Holdings:** 50,000 volumes; ephemera. **Subscriptions:** 1800 journals and other serials; 100 newspapers. **Services:** Interlibrary loan; copying; SDI; library open to the public for academic research only. **Computerized Information Services:** ALEPH (internal database); BITNET (electronic mail service). **Remarks:** Many of the holdings maintained are written in various languages, including European languages, English, Hebrew, Arabic, Chinese, and Japanese. Alternate telephone number(s): 2 882320. FAX: 2 322545. Telex: 26458 IL. Electronic mail address(es): WSRCP@HUJIVM1 (BITNET). **Staff:** Terza Margoliot; Avram Greenhaus; Ricardo Schwed; Amnon Ben-Areeh; Malka Pappo; Shulamit Korsch.

★7103★
Hebrew University of Jerusalem - Muriel and Philip Berman National Medical Library (Med)
Ein Karem Medical Center
POB 1172 Phone: 2 428795
Jerusalem, Israel Dafna Yudelevitch
Founded: 1919. **Staff:** Prof 14.5; Other 11.5. **Subjects:** Medicine, pharmacy, public health, dentistry, nursing. **Special Collections:** History of Medicine (includes the Dr. Morris Collection); Museum of Medical History (5495 volumes); Isakower Psychiatric Collection (2500 volumes). **Holdings:** 95,000 books; 405,000 bound periodical volumes. **Subscriptions:** 1400 journals and other serials; Interlibrary loan; copying; SDI; library open to the public with restrictions. **Computerized Information Services:** DIALOG Information Services, BRS Information Technologies, Data-Star, STN International; CD-ROMs (Medline, CINAHL, Health Planning). Contact Person: Esther Ermann, Ref.Libn. **Remarks:** FAX: 2 784010. Telex: 26132 NULMD IL.

★7104★
Hebrew University of Jerusalem - Society for Research on Jewish Communities - Center for Research and Documentation of East European Jewry - Library and Archives (Area-Ethnic)
Mount Scopus
91905 Jerusalem, Israel Phone: 2 584271
Subjects: History, culture, social aspects of East European Jewry, especially Soviet Jewry. **Special Collections:** Archives. **Holdings:** 50,000 volumes. **Remarks:** "Contains the largest collection of books, periodicals, and archival materials on Soviet and East European Jewry in the West."

Sigmund Hecht Library
See: **Wilshire Boulevard Temple** (20463)

★7105★
Heckscher Museum - Library (Art)
Prime Ave. Phone: (516)351-3250
Huntington, NY 11743 C. Shirley Brevda, Libn.
Founded: 1981. **Staff:** Prof 3; Other 2. **Subjects:** American and European art, art history. **Special Collections:** Exhibition catalogs; contemporary American artists clipping file. **Holdings:** 2000 books, catalogs and monographs; 53 audio- and videotapes; 500 slides; ephemera. **Subscriptions:** 20 journals and other serials. **Services:** Library open to the public for reference use only by appointment. **Special Catalogs:** Exhibition catalogs, irregular. **Remarks:** FAX: (516)423-2145.

Hege Library
See: **Guilford College - Hege Library** (6800)

Thomas Heggen Memorial Library
See: **University of Minnesota - Eric Sevareid Journalism Library** (18908)

★7106★
Heidelberg College - Water Quality Laboratory - Library (Env-Cons)
310 E. Market St.
Tiffin, OH 44883 Phone: (419)448-2201
Subjects: Water quality in the Great Lakes region. **Holdings:** Figures not available. **Services:** library not open to the public.

★7107★
(Heidelberg) German-American Institute - USIS Collection (Educ)
Sophienstrasse, 12
W-6900 Heidelberg 1, Germany
Remarks: Maintained or supported by the U.S. Information Agency. Focus is on materials that will assist peoples outside the United States to learn about the United States, its people, history, culture, political processes, and social milieux.

★7108★
Heidrick and Struggles, Inc. - Library Research Center (Bus-Fin)
125 S. Wacker Dr., Suite 2800 Phone: (312)372-8811
Chicago, IL 60606 Carol L. Dimer, Mgr.
Staff: Prof 1; Other 1. **Subjects:** Corporate information, compensation. **Special Collections:** Miscellaneous files on industry. **Holdings:** 4500 books; 2 VF drawers of clippings; industry and association directories. **Subscriptions:** 108 journals and other serials; 12 newspapers. **Services:** Interlibrary loan; copying; SDI; center open to businesses and special libraries. **Automated Operations:** Computerized cataloging, acquisitions, and circulation. **Computerized Information Services:** DIALOG Information Services, Dun & Bradstreet Business Credit Services, NEXIS, DataTimes, VU/TEXT Information Services, ORBIT Search Service, InvesText. **Networks/Consortia:** Member of Chicago Library System. **Remarks:** FAX: (312)372-1698.

★7109★
Heights Baptist Church - Media Library (Rel-Phil)
529 Jefferson St., N.E.
Albuquerque, NM 87108 Phone: (505)268-4531
Founded: 1950. **Staff:** 3. **Subjects:** Bible commentaries, Christian life, Baptist history, general and Baptist missionary biography, children's literature. **Holdings:** 5700 books. **Services:** Library not open to the public.

Heim Memorial Library
See: **Allentown State Hospital** (387)

★7110★
Heinrich Heine Institute - Library (Mus)
BilkerStrasse 12-14 Phone: 211 8995572
Dusseldorf, Germany Prof. J.A. Kruse
Founded: 1970. **Subjects:** Writers, musicians, artists, and scientists of the Rhine area from 16th-20th century. **Special Collections:** Heinrich Heine; Robert and Clara Schumann. **Holdings:** 35,000 books; 500 bound periodical volumes; 40,000 manuscripts; 140 archival materials; 200 reels of microfilm; autographs; photographs; memorabilia. **Services:** Interlibrary loan; copying; library open to the public. **Publications:** Heine-Jahrbuch; Heine-Studien; Veroffentlichungen des Heinrich-Heine-Instituts. **Remarks:** Alternate telephone number(s): 211 8995581. FAX: 211 8993645.

★7111★
H.J. Heinz Company - Technical Information Center (Food-Bev)
1062 Progress St. Phone: (412)237-5948
Pittsburgh, PA 15212 Nancy M. Wright, Libn.
Founded: 1903. **Staff:** Prof 1; Other 1. **Subjects:** Food processing and engineering, agriculture, nutrition, packaging, chemistry, bacteriology. **Special Collections:** Company archives. **Holdings:** 5800 books; 2000 bound periodical volumes; 16,000 pamphlets; 40 drawers of microfilm; food patents; clippings; house organs; road maps. **Subscriptions:** 300 journals and other serials; 6 newspapers. **Services:** Interlibrary loan; center not open to the public. **Automated Operations:** Computerized cataloging, acquisitions, and serials. **Computerized Information Services:** DIALOG Information Services, Chemical Abstracts Service (CAS), STN International, Dow Jones News/Retrieval, PFDS Online, LEXIS, NEXIS, Leatherhead Food Research Association Information Group; internal databases. **Publications:** Abstracts from Current Magazines, weekly - for internal distribution only. **Remarks:** FAX: (412)237-5725. Telex: 199-104 HJH HO E PGH. **Staff:** Nancy Winstanley, Asst.Libn.

Werner Heisenberg Institute
See: **Max Planck Institute for Physics - Werner Heisenberg Institute - Library** (13111)

★7112★
Heisey Collectors of America, Inc. - HCA Library & Archives (Rec)
169 W. Church St. Phone: (614)345-2932
Newark, OH 43055 Katherine McCracken, Cur.
Founded: 1971. **Staff:** 5. **Special Collections:** Heisey glassware made in Newark, 1896-1957; original mold drawings, 1901-1957 (5000). **Holdings:** 280 volumes; 25 VF drawers; 70 microfiche. **Subscriptions:** 15 journals and other serials; 5 newspapers. **Services:** Copying (limited); library open to the public with restrictions. **Publications:** Heisey News (newsletter), monthly - to members; Heisey's Lariat & Athena Patterns; Heisey by Imperial, 2nd edition; Heisey Toothpick Holders; Heisey's Orchid Etching; Heisey Rose; Heisey's Classic Ridgeleigh; Heisey Candlesticks, Candelabra and Lamps; reprints of original catalogs. **Special Catalogs:** Heisey Glassware - The Color Era, 1925-1938.

Andrew Heiskell Library for the Blind and Physically Handicapped
See: **New York Public Library** (11592)

★7113★
Held-Poage Memorial Home & Research Library (Hist)
603 W. Perkins St. Phone: (707)462-6969
Ukiah, CA 95482-4726 Lila J. Lee, Libn.
Founded: 1970. **Staff:** 2. **Subjects:** History - Mendocino County, California, U.S., Civil War; Pomo and other Indians. **Special Collections:** Writings of Edith Van Allen Murphey, Dr. John Whiz Hudson, Helen Carpenter. **Holdings:** 5000 books; 15,000 negatives; photographs; maps; bound county records; clippings; genealogies. **Subscriptions:** 13 journals and other serials. **Services:** Interlibrary loan; copying; library open to the public on a limited schedule for reference use only, by appointment. **Remarks:** Maintained by Mendocino County Historical Society.

★7114★
Helicon Foundation - Library (Med)
4622 Santa Fe St. Phone: (619)272-3884
San Diego, CA 92109 Dr. Charles A. Thomas, Jr.
Subjects: Health promotion, human defense/repair systems assessment, nutritional/neural enhancement. **Holdings:** 25 contemporary scientific journals on biochemistry and molecular biology. **Services:** Library not open to the public. **Remarks:** FAX: (619)272-1137.

★7115★
Helicopter Foundation International - Archive (Trans, Hist)
1619 Duke St. Phone: (703)683-4646
Alexandria, VA 22314-3406 John M. Slattery, Cur.
Founded: 1983. **Staff:** 1 **Subjects:** Helicopters - international, domestic, military, commercial, history, industry, role in society. **Special Collections:** Twirly Birds. **Holdings:** 20,000 documents, rare books, and other memorabilia; 900 helicopter models. **Subscriptions:** 30 journals and other serials. **Services:** Copying; archive open to the public.

★7116★
Hellenic College - Library (Rel-Phil, Area-Ethnic)
50 Goddard Ave. Phone: (617)731-3500
Brookline, MA 02146 Rev.Dr. George C. Papademetriou, Dir.
Founded: 1937. **Staff:** Prof 3; Other 1. **Subjects:** Greek Orthodox theology, modern Greek studies, Byzantine studies and art, church history, patristics. **Holdings:** 100,000 volumes; 500 microforms; 300 videotapes. **Subscriptions:** 450 journals and other serials; 30 newspapers. **Services:** Interlibrary loan; copying; computer workstation; library open to the public for reference use only. **Automated Operations:** Computerized cataloging. **Computerized Information Services:** OCLC; internal database. Contact Person: Athanasia Papademetriou, Assoc.Dir./Cat. **Networks/Consortia:** Member of Boston Theological Institute Libraries. **Publications:** Guide to the Library; accessions list, quarterly; Photian Studies. **Remarks:** FAX: (617)738-9169. **Staff:** Hilary Rogler, Circ.; Steven Gromatzky, Acq.

★7117★
Hellenic Folklore Research Center - Library (Area-Ethnic)
1 Dipla St. and 129 Syngrou Ave., 117 45 Phone: 1 9344 811
Athens, Greece Dr. Anna Papamichael, Dir.
Subjects: Greek folklore and anthropology. **Special Collections:** Hellenic folk songs, singing and dancing, popular music, social life and activities of the people, sound recordings, popular musical instruments, manuscripts, photographs, and films. **Holdings:** 5800 volumes. **Services:** Library open to scholars, researchers, and students at librarian's discretion. **Computerized Information Services:** Internal database. **Remarks:** Maintained by Academy of Athens. **Also Known As:** Kentron Erevnis Ellinikis Laographias.

★7118★
Hellenic Institute of International and Foreign Law - Library (Law)
73 Solonos St. Phone: 1 3615646
GR-10679 Athens, Greece Dr. Cloure Spirou, Atty.
Founded: 1949. **Staff:** 8. **Subjects:** Law - foreign, civil, commercial, international; European Community; civil procedure. **Holdings:** 25,000 volumes. **Subscriptions:** 300 journals and other serials. **Services:** Library open to lawyers, public organizations, and students. **Publications:** Revue Hellenique de droit international. **Remarks:** FAX: 1 3619777. Supervised by Greece - Ministry of Justice. **Staff:** Mrs. S. Aggellaki.

★7119★
Heller, Ehrman, White & McAuliffe - Law Library (Law)
333 Bush St., 31st Fl. Phone: (415)772-6105
San Francisco, CA 94104-2878 Loretta Mak, Libn.
Founded: 1921. **Staff:** Prof 4; Other 6.5. **Subjects:** Law. **Holdings:** 25,000 volumes. **Services:** Interlibrary loan; library not open to the public. **Computerized Information Services:** LEXIS, DIALOG Information Services, WESTLAW, Information America, Dow Jones News/Retrieval, Dun & Bradstreet Business Credit Services, IRIS. **Remarks:** FAX: (415)772-6268. **Staff:** Justin Villa, Asst.Libn.; Don Whitton, Ref.Libn.; Kate Alderman, Ref.Libn.

★7120★
Hellmuth, Obata & Kassabaum, Inc. - HOK Library (Plan)
1831 Chestnut St. Phone: (314)421-2000
St. Louis, MO 63103 Susan Baerwald, Libn.
Staff: Prof 2.5. **Subjects:** Building types, contemporary architects, architectural history, planning, interiors, graphics. **Special Collections:** Slides of HOK work (125,000). **Holdings:** 3000 books; 250 bound periodical volumes; 30,600 black/white photographs of HOK work; 750 HOK reports; 8000 unbound periodicals; 200 codes and standards; 10 VF drawers of clippings, pamphlets, maps. **Subscriptions:** 240 journals and other serials. **Services:** Interlibrary loan; copying; library open to the public by appointment. **Remarks:** FAX: (314)421-6073. Telex: 44 7192. **Staff:** Blythe Cermak, Photography Libn.

★7121★
Hellmuth, Obata & Kassabaum, Inc. - Library (Plan)
6688 N. Central Expy., Suite 700 Phone: (214)739-6688
Dallas, TX 75206 Cindy A. Davis, Libn. & Mktg.Coord.
Founded: 1970. **Staff:** Prof 1; Other 1. **Subjects:** Architecture, planning, interior and landscape design, facility programming, mechanical and electrical engineering, graphic design. **Special Collections:** Soil Surveys of Texas; Building Codes, Slide Library of HOK Projects. **Holdings:** 560 books; 151 bound periodical volumes. **Subscriptions:** 43 journals and other serials. **Services:** Interlibrary loan; copying; SDI; library open to the public by appointment. **Computerized Information Services:** Internal databases. **Publications:** Project Case Studies.

★7122★
Hellmuth, Obata & Kassabaum, Inc. - Library/Archives (Plan)
1 Harrison St. Phone: (415)243-0555
San Francisco, CA 94105 Mark G. Maloy, Info.Mgr.
Staff: Prof 1; Other 3. **Subjects:** Architecture, interior design, landscape architecture. **Special Collections:** Construction products and interior design materials catalogs (2000); slides of completed projects (10,000). **Holdings:** 1200 books; 225 bound periodical volumes; 50 shelves of construction and interior design product samples; 12 VF drawers of product literature; 500 reports; 3 VF drawers of clippings; 1675 rolls of drawings; 545 file boxes and 7 file drawers of microfiche of construction documents and specifications. **Subscriptions:** 92 journals and other serials. **Services:** Interlibrary loan; library not open to the public. **Automated Operations:** Computerized serials and circulation. **Publications:** Recent acquisitions, quarterly. **Special Indexes:** Indexes to catalogs and product literature, product representatives, slide collection (all on cards); index to reprint collection (binder).

Hellmuth Photographic Archive of Maya Art
See: **Foundation for Latin American Anthropological Research - Library** (6045)

Milton Helpern Library of Legal Medicine
See: **New York City Office of Chief Medical Examiner** (11564)

★7123★
Helsingin Yliopisto - Maatalouskirjasto (Agri)
Vikki Phone: 0 70851
SF-00710 Helsinki 71, Finland Heli Myllys
Founded: 1930. **Subjects:** Agriculture, home economics, nutrition, food, environment. **Holdings:** 320,000 books, bound periodical volumes, and reports. **Subscriptions:** 3754 journals and other serials. **Services:** Interlibrary loan; copying; SDI; library open to the public. **Computerized Information Services:** HELKA (internal database). Contact Person: Kristiina Hormia-Poutanen. **Publications:** Finagri. **Remarks:** FAX: 90 7085011. Telex: 122352 hymk st.

Helsingin Yliopisto - Matematiikan Laitoksen Kirjasto.
See: **University of Helsinki - Department of Mathematics - Library** (18634)

★7124★
Helsingor Tekniske - Bibliotek (Sci-Engr)
Rasmus Knudsensvej 50 Phone: 49 216126
DK-3000 Helsingor, Denmark Denis C. Jolly, Hd. of Lib.
Founded: 1966. **Staff:** Prof 1; Other 2. **Subjects:** Engineering, plastics engineering, transport engineering, ship architecture. **Holdings:** 10,000 books; 14,000 bound periodical volumes; 1000 reports; 9000 microfiche. **Subscriptions:** 200 journals and other serials; 8 newspapers. **Services:** Interlibrary loan; copying; library open to the public. **Automated Operations:** Computerized public access catalog, cataloging, and circulation. **Computerized Information Services:** ESA/IRS, BMT Abstracts Online (BOATS), ALIS, ALBA. **Remarks:** FAX: 49 213324.

★7125★
(Helsinki) American Center Library - USIS Library (Educ)
Kaivokatu 10A Phone: 0 176630
SF-00100 Helsinki, Finland Liisa Kujanpaa, Hd.Libn.
Founded: 1946. **Staff:** 3. **Holdings:** 9000 books; 140 videotapes. **Subscriptions:** 120 journals and other serials; 3 newspapers. **Services:** Interlibrary loan; copying; library open to the public. **Computerized Information Services:** DIALOG Information Services, LEGI-SLATE; PDQ (internal database). **Remarks:** FAX: 0 652940. Maintained or supported by the U.S. Information Agency. Focus is on materials that will assist peoples outside the United States to learn about the United States, its people, history, culture, political processes, and social milieux.

★7126★
Helsinki University of Technology - University Library and National Resource Library (Sci-Engr)
Otaniementie 9 Phone: 0 4514124
SF-02150 Espoo, Finland Dr. Sinikka Koskiala, Dir.
Founded: 1849. **Staff:** Prof 25; Other 50. **Subjects:** Engineering - electrical, mechanical, civil, chemical; information technology; mining and metallurgy; chemistry; physics; mathematics; geology; industrial economy; architecture. **Special Collections:** Collection of reports on energy, environmental protection. **Holdings:** 500,000 books; 15,000 serial publications; 500,000 items on microfiche. **Subscriptions:** 5000 journals; 10 newspapers. **Services:** Interlibrary loan; copying; SDI; library open to the public. **Automated Operations:** Computerized public access catalog and cataloging. **Computerized Information Services:** DIALOG Information Services, STN International, PFDS Online, ESA/IRS, Questel; produces TALI, TENTTU, INSSI, NORDRES; InterNet (electronic mail service). Performs searches on fee basis. Contact Person: Irma Pasanen-Tuomainen, Info.Spec., 4514124. **Publications:** Monograph Series OTA-kirjasto, irregular; accession lists, monthly. **Special Catalogs:** List of current journals received; directory of master's theses. **Special Indexes:** Tekniikan Aikakauslenti Indeksi-TALI (articles in Finnish periodicals; online). **Remarks:** FAX: 0 4514132. Telex: 121591 TKK SF. Electronic mail address(es): SINIKKA.KOSKIALA@HUT.FI (InterNet).

★7127★
Hemet Valley Hospital District - Dr. Leslie J. Clark Memorial Library (Med)
1116 E. Latham Ave. Phone: (714)652-2811
Hemet, CA 92343 Dixie Cirocco, Med.Libn.
Founded: 1980. **Staff:** Prof 1; Other 1. **Subjects:** Clinical medicine, nursing, psychiatry. **Holdings:** 1136 books; 918 bound periodical volumes. **Subscriptions:** 106 journals and other serials. **Services:** Interlibrary loan; copying; library open to the public by appointment. **Computerized Information Services:** MEDLINE. **Networks/Consortia:** Member of Inland Empire Medical Library Cooperative (IEMLC), San Bernardino, Inyo, Riverside Counties United Library Services (SIRCULS).

Heminger Health Sciences Library
See: **Central Washington Hospital** (3380)

★7128★
Hemlock Society - Library (Soc Sci)
Box 11830 Phone: (503)342-5748
Eugene, OR 97440 Diana Smith, Libn.
Founded: 1980. **Staff:** 1. **Subjects:** Voluntary euthanasia. **Holdings:** 200 volumes. **Services:** Library not open to the public. **Publications:** Euthanasia statistics. **Remarks:** FAX: (503)345-2751.

★7129★
Hempstead Public Library - Special Collections (Hum, Hist)
115 Nichols Ct. Phone: (516)481-6990
Hempstead, NY 11550 Irene A. Duszkiewicz, Dir.
Founded: 1898. **Special Collections:** Walt Whitman; Long Island Collection; Foreign Language Collection for Children and Adults; New York State History; Job and Education Information Center; Career Counseling; New York State Documents Reference Center; Black studies; Adult Learning Center; ESL Classes. **Holdings:** 190,000 books. **Subscriptions:** 400 journals and other serials; 75 newspapers. **Services:** Interlibrary loan; copying; collections open to the public. **Automated Operations:** Computerized cataloging, acquisitions, and circulation. **Computerized Information Services:** DIALOG Information Services. Performs searches free of charge for village residents only. **Networks/Consortia:** Member of Nassau Library System. **Remarks:** FAX: (516)481-6719.

★7130★
Henan Academy of Sciences - Geography Research Institute - Library (Sci-Engr)
West Longhai Lu
Zhengzhou, Henan Province, People's Republic of China Phone: 9875
Founded: 1959. **Staff:** 4. **Subjects:** Earth sciences, meteorology, climatology, hydrography, hydrogeology, geomorphology, geology, soil science, economic geography, cartography, remote sensing, telemetering, environmental protection, paleogeography, historical geography. **Holdings:** 45,000 volumes; 5000 bound periodical volumes; 15,000 technical reports. **Publications:** Translations on Geography. **Special Catalogs:** Book Catalog; Reference Materials Catalog. **Remarks:** Alternate telephone number(s): 9487.

★7131★
Hendershot Bibliography & Consultants - Library
4114 Ridgewood Dr.
Bay City, MI 48706
Defunct.

★7132★
Henderson Advertising Inc. - Library (Bus-Fin)
60 Pointe Circle
Box 2247 Phone: (803)271-6000
Greenville, SC 29602 Connie Hart, Rsrc.Coord.
Remarks: No further information was supplied by respondent.

Charles W. Henderson Memorial Library
See: **U.S. Bureau of Mines** (17112)

★7133★
Henderson State University - Huie Library - Special Collections (Educ, Hist)
Arkadelphia, AR 71923 Phone: (501)246-5511
Marilyn J. Martin, Dir., Lrng.Rsrcs.
Staff: Prof 6; Other 14. **Special Collections:** Howard A. Dawson Rural Education Collection; Arkansas State Documents Collection; Southwest Arkansas History Collection. **Holdings:** 225,000 books; 25,000 bound periodical volumes. **Subscriptions:** 1800 journals and other serials. **Services:** Interlibrary loan; copying; collections open to the public. **Automated Operations:** Computerized cataloging and circulation. **Computerized Information Services:** DIALOG Information Services, BRS Information Technologies, OCLC; CLSI (internal database). Performs searches on fee basis. **Remarks:** FAX: (501)246-9113. **Staff:** Lea Ann Alexander; Vicki Baker; Harvey Peebles; John Ragni; Robert Yehl.

Virginia Henderson International Nursing Library
See: **Sigma Theta Tau International** (15164)

★7134★
Hendrick Medical Center - Sellers Library (Med)
1242 N. 19th St. Phone: (915)670-2375
Abilene, TX 79601 Jean Snodgrass
Staff: 1. **Subjects:** Medicine, health, nursing. **Holdings:** 1600 books; 150 microfilms. **Subscriptions:** 250 journals and other serials; 3 newspapers. **Services:** Interlibrary loan; copying; library open to the public. **Computerized Information Services:** DIALOG Information Services, MEDLINE. **Remarks:** FAX: (915)670-2422.

Hendrickson House
See: **Old Swedes Foundation, Inc.** (12393)

★7135★
Henkel Corporation - Emery Group - Research Library (Sci-Engr)
4900 Este Ave. Phone: (513)482-2157
Cincinnati, OH 45232-1491 E.J. Clendenen, Libn.
Staff: 1. **Subjects:** Organic chemistry, allied sciences. **Holdings:** Figures not available. **Services:** Interlibrary loan; copying; library open to the public by appointment. **Remarks:** FAX: (513)641-3666.

Henkel Corporation - PARKER & AMCHEM
See: **PARKER & AMCHEM** (12751)

★7136★
Henkel Corporation - Technical Library (Sci-Engr)
Bldg. 23
300 Brookside Ave. Phone: (215)628-1526
Ambler, PA 19002 Amy J. Meskin, Libn.
Founded: 1934. **Staff:** Prof 1. **Subjects:** Organic chemistry, surfactants, polymer, paper, leather, business, metal treatment. **Holdings:** 8000 volumes; U.S. Chemicals patents, 1959 to present, on microfilm. **Subscriptions:** 180 journals and other serials. **Services:** Library not open to the public. **Computerized Information Services:** DIALOG Information Services, STN International. **Publications:** Henkel Corporation Technical Library Newsletter.

Henkel Research Corporation - Library
See: **Cogins, Inc. - Technical Information Services** (3867)

Hennepin County History Museum
See: **Hennepin History Museum - Archives** (7139)

★7137★
Hennepin County Law Library (Law)
C2451 Government Center Phone: (612)348-3022
Minneapolis, MN 55487 Anne W. Grande, Dir.
Founded: 1883. **Staff:** Prof 6; Other 5. **Subjects:** Law. **Holdings:** 90,000 books; 10,000 bound periodical volumes; 40,000 microfiche; 6000 reels of microfilm. **Subscriptions:** 400 journals and other serials. **Services:** Interlibrary loan; copying; library open to the public. **Automated Operations:** Computerized public access catalog, cataloging, and circulation. **Computerized Information Services:** WESTLAW, LEXIS, DIALOG Information Services, DataTimes, VU/TEXT Information Services. **Publications:** Newsletter, bimonthly - local distribution. **Remarks:** FAX: (612)348-4230. **Staff:** Margaret Hall, Tech.Serv.; Judy Zetterberg, Pub.Serv.; Kathleen Kelly, Ref.; Lois Lenroot-Ernt, Ref.; Jane Rustad, Cat.

★7138★
Hennepin County Medical Center - Thomas Lowry Health Sciences Library (Med)
701 Park Ave. Phone: (612)347-2710
Minneapolis, MN 55415 Barbara Brian, Dir.
Staff: Prof 2; Other 5. **Subjects:** Clinical medicine, nursing, allied health sciences. **Holdings:** 60,000 books and bound periodical volumes; 900 video cassettes; AV programs. **Subscriptions:** 550 journals and other serials. **Services:** Interlibrary loan; copying; SDI; Current Awareness Service; library open to the public on fee basis for services. **Computerized Information Services:** MEDLINE, BRS Information Technologies, DIALOG Information Services. **Networks/Consortia:** Member of Twin Cities Biomedical Consortium (TCBC), National Network of Libraries of Medicine - Greater Midwest Region. **Publications:** Library Newsletter; Serial Title List. **Remarks:** FAX: (612)347-6292. **Staff:** Anne Mackereth, Libn.

★7139★
Hennepin History Museum - Archives (Hist)
2303 3rd Ave., S. Phone: (612)870-1329
Minneapolis, MN 55404 Dorthea Guiney, Dir.
Staff: 1. **Subjects:** Local history, lumber and milling industries, genealogy, house history, transportation. **Special Collections:** St. Anthony Falls Water Power Company (5 boxes of photographs and maps); Photograph Collection. **Holdings:** 2000 books; 551 bound periodical volumes; 1800 photographs; 75 VF drawers of clippings and ephemera; 30 boxes and 20 VF drawers of archives, maps, atlases; 19 volumes of Sanborn Insurance Maps. **Subscriptions:** 67 newsletters; 17 newspapers. **Services:** Copying; archives open to the public for reference use only. **Publications:** Hennepin County History, quarterly; Newsletter, bimonthly. **Special Indexes:** Index of archival holdings and maps; index of clipping and ephemera files; index of biographies (all on cards). **Formerly:** Hennepin County History Museum.

★7140★
Henry County Historical Society - Library (Hist)
Henry County Historical Bldg.
606 S. 14th St. Phone: (317)529-4028
New Castle, IN 47362 Richard McKnight, Pres.
Staff: 4. **Subjects:** Henry County and Indiana history. **Holdings:** Manuscripts; letters; photographs; paintings; scrapbooks; county histories; atlases. **Services:** Library open to the public on a limited schedule. **Publications:** Newsletter, 2/year. **Remarks:** The library does genealogical research on a fee basis for people living outside the county. **Staff:** Joan Paul, Cur.

★7141★
Henry County Law Library (Law)
Court House Phone: (419)592-6801
Napoleon, OH 43545 John Donovan, Law Libn.
Subjects: Law. **Holdings:** 5000 volumes. **Services:** Library not open to the public. **Computerized Information Services:** Veralex 2, LEXIS.

O. Henry Collection
See: **Austin Public Library - Austin History Center** (1315)

★7142★
A. Barton Hepburn Hospital - Medical Library (Med)
214 King St. Phone: (315)393-3600
Ogdensburg, NY 13669 Ellen J. Darabaner, Circuit Rider Libn.
Founded: 1960. **Staff:** Prof 2. **Subjects:** Medicine, nursing, allied health sciences. **Holdings:** 300 books. **Subscriptions:** 32 journals and other serials. **Services:** Interlibrary loan; copying; SDI; library open to the public with permission. **Computerized Information Services:** BRS Information Technologies, MEDLINE, CINAHL Corporation. Performs searches on fee basis. **Networks/Consortia:** Member of North Country Reference and Research Resources Council (NCRRRC). **Remarks:** Affiliated with the Hospital Library Program, Mercy Hospital, Watertown, NY. **Staff:** Mark Uebler, Circuit Rider Libn.

★7143★
Herald Publishing Company - Herald Library (Publ)
One Herald Square Phone: (203)225-4601
New Britain, CT 06050 Virginia Leipold, Libn.
Staff: Prof 1. **Subjects:** Newspaper reference topics. **Special Collections:** New Britain Herald history (1 VF drawer). **Holdings:** 200 books; bound newspapers, 1880 to present; 12 VF drawers of photographs and negatives; newspapers, 1921 to present, on microfilm; 9 VF drawers of clippings and pamphlets. **Services:** Library open to the public. **Special Indexes:** Herald index, 1954 to present (card).

★7144★
The Herb Society of America, Inc. - Library (Biol Sci)
9019 Kirtland-Chardon Rd.
Mentor, OH 44060 Phone: (216)256-0514
Founded: 1933. **Subjects:** Herbs, botany, horticulture. **Holdings:** 650 volumes.

George Herbert Collection
See: **University of North Carolina at Greensboro** (19082)

★7145★
T.A. Herbert and Associates, Inc. - Library (Env-Cons)
Box 10129 Phone: (904)222-4634
Tallahassee, FL 32302 Jaime Petrin, Libn.
Staff: 1. **Subjects:** Natural resources development, anthropology, social science, environmental science, marine biology, geology. **Special Collections:** Dales S. Beaumariage Fisheries Collection. **Holdings:** 2500 books and reprints. **Computerized Information Services:** DIALOG Information Services, BRS Information Technologies, VU/TEXT Information Services. **Remarks:** FAX: (904)224-9952. Subsidiaries are Computer Liaison, Inc., and Polomar Aquatics, Inc. **Staff:** Donna L. Foster.

★7146★
Hercules Aerospace Company - Bacchus Works Library (Sci-Engr)
Mail Stop H, Box 98 Phone: (801)251-2544
Magna, UT 84044 Mary Marquez, Supv.
Founded: 1959. **Staff:** Prof 2; Other 6. **Subjects:** Chemical propulsion, rocketry, explosives, space technology, graphite fiber, ammunition, composite materials. **Holdings:** 5000 books; 200,000 technical reports; 170,000 microfiche. **Subscriptions:** 150 journals and other serials. **Services:** Interlibrary loan; library not open to the public. **Automated Operations:** Computerized cataloging. **Computerized Information Services:** DIALOG Information Services, ORBIT Search Service, STN International, WILSONLINE, NASA/RECON, DTIC, NLM, OCLC; AIRES (internal database). **Networks/Consortia:** Member of Bibliographical Center for Research, Rocky Mountain Region, Inc. (BCR). **Publications:** AIRES Current Awareness Bulletin - for internal distribution only. **Staff:** Dorothy H. Alley, Info.Res.Spec.

★7147★
Hercules Defense Electronics Systems, Inc. - Engineering Library (Sci-Engr)
Box 4648 Phone: (813)572-3504
Clearwater, FL 34618 Richard Smith, Pubn.Engr.
Founded: 1959. **Staff:** 2. **Subjects:** Electronic engineering, physics, mathematics, mechanical engineering, logistics, manufacturing. **Special Collections:** Program specific contract technical data. **Holdings:** 3000 books. **Subscriptions:** 45 journals and other serials. **Services:** Interlibrary loan; center not open to the public. **Computerized Information Services:** DIALOG Information Services. **Remarks:** Center located at 13133 34th St., Clearwater, FL 34622. FAX: (813)572-2395. **Staff:** A. Barry; J. Scarberry; R. Milione.

★7148★
Hercules, Inc. - Aerospace Division - McGregor Technical Information Center (Sci-Engr)
P.O. Box 548 Phone: (817)840-2811
McGregor, TX 76657 Sandra Quicksall, Pubns.Coord.
Founded: 1952. **Staff:** Prof 1. **Subjects:** Solid rocketry, engineering, chemistry, mathematics, physics, management. **Holdings:** 23,000 technical reports in computerized data retrieval system. **Subscriptions:** 20 journals and other serials. **Services:** Center not open to the public. **Networks/Consortia:** Member of Hercules Aerospace Division Group Information System. **Publications:** Library Bulletins; Library Accession List.

★7149★
Hercules, Inc. - Hattiesburg Plant Laboratory - Library (Sci-Engr)
613 W. 7th St.
Box 1937 Phone: (601)545-3450
Hattiesburg, MS 39401 Nell Buckley, Adm.Serv.Supv.
Staff: 1. **Subjects:** Chemistry, chemical engineering. **Holdings:** 3000 books; 300 bound periodical volumes; 2000 reprints; 6000 Hercules Research Investigation files; 200 Naval Stores translations. **Subscriptions:** 45 journals and other serials. **Services:** Library not open to the public. **Publications:** New listings, semiannual.

★7150★
Hercules, Inc. - Jefferson Plant - Library (Sci-Engr)
State Hwy. 837 Phone: (412)384-2520
West Elizabeth, PA 15088 Norman E. Daughenbaugh, Res.Chem.
Staff: 1. **Subjects:** Chemistry; engineering. **Holdings:** 400 books; 700 bound periodical volumes. **Services:** Library open to the public with restrictions.

★7151★
Hercules, Inc. - Law Department Library (Law)
Hercules Plaza, 8200 S.W.
1313 N. Market St. Phone: (302)594-5678
Wilmington, DE 19894 Margaret C. Carlson, Law Libn.
Staff: 1. **Subjects:** Law, business. **Holdings:** 20,000 books. **Subscriptions:** 20 journals and other serials. **Services:** Library not open to the public. **Computerized Information Services:** LEXIS. **Remarks:** FAX: (302)594-7252. Telex: 499 4538 HERCL.

★7152★
Hercules, Inc. - Research Center - Technical Information Division - Library (Sci-Engr)
Wilmington, DE 19894 Phone: (302)995-3484
JoAnn McArthur, Libn.
Founded: 1928. **Staff:** Prof 7; Other 8. **Subjects:** Chemistry, engineering, physics, business, management. **Holdings:** 13,000 books; 25,500 bound periodical volumes; research reports; patents; correspondence. **Subscriptions:** 600 journals and other serials. **Services:** Interlibrary loan; copying; division open to the public on request. **Automated Operations:** Computerized cataloging, serials, and circulation. **Computerized Information Services:** DIALOG Information Services, PFDS Online, BRS Information Technologies, NLM. **Publications:** Journal Literature Bulletin, biweekly; Technical Information Bulletin, quarterly. **Remarks:** FAX: (302)995-4101. Contains the holdings of its former Home Office Library. **Staff:** Joanne Henderson, Libn.; Dr. Wayne Messer, Gp.Ldr.; Lucille Golt, Abstractor/Indexer; Barbara Chapman, Abstractor/Indexer; Ruth E. Curtiss, Online Search; H. Wagner, Transl.

★7153★
Johann Gottfried Herder Institute - Library (Area-Ethnic)
Gisonenweg 7 Phone: 2 50 44
W-3550 Marburg, Germany Dr. Horst von Chmielewski, Libn.
Founded: 1950. **Staff:** 13. **Subjects:** Eastern Central Europe - geography, ethnography, and political, legal, economic, cultural history. **Holdings:** 280,000 volumes. **Subscriptions:** 1400 journals and other serials; 200 newspapers. **Services:** Interlibrary loan; copying; library open to the public. **Also Known As:** Johann-Gottfried-Herder-Institut.

★7154★
Heriot-Watt University - Offshore Engineering Information Service (Sci-Engr)
Riccarton Campus Phone: 31 4495111
Edinburgh EH14 4AS, Scotland Arnold Myers, Info.Sci.
Founded: 1973. **Staff:** Prof 1. **Subjects:** Marine technology - offshore oil, offshore engineering, environmental protection, seabed resources, underwater operations, diving, pipelines, oil spills, modeling, seaweed, aquaculture. **Special Collections:** Offshore Engineering Collection. **Holdings:** 150,000 bound volumes. **Subscriptions:** 1800 journals and other serials. **Services:** SDI; current awareness. **Computerized Information Services:** Electronic mail. Performs searches on fee basis. **Publications:** New publications and forthcoming meetings bulletin, monthly. **Remarks:** FAX: 31 4513164. **Formerly:** Its Institute of Offshore Engineering - Library and Information Service.

Heritage House Library - Victoriana/Local History Collection
See: **Fullerton Arboretum - Heritage House Library - Victoriana/Local History Collection** (6201)

★7155★
Heritage Museum - Library (Hist)
510 Scurry St. Phone: (915)267-8255
Big Spring, TX 79720 Angela Way, Dir.
Staff: 2. **Subjects:** Western ranching, settlement, oil industry. **Special Collections:** Howard Co. genealogies. **Holdings:** 200 books. **Services:** Library open to the public. **Publications:** Howard Co. Historian (newsletter), quarterly.

★7156★
Heritage Park - Pinellas County Historical Museum - Library (Hist)
11909 125th St., N. Phone: (813)588-8123
Largo, FL 34644 Dr. Bob Harris, Cur. of Coll.
Founded: 1981. **Staff:** 9. **Subjects:** History - Florida, Pinellas County; genealogy; museology; antiques. **Special Collections:** Rare books (200). **Holdings:** 2000 books; 700 periodical volumes; 500 documents; 200 AV programs; 100 manuscripts; 4000 photographs; 1000 maps;40 genealogical notebooks. **Services:** Copying; library open to the public.

★7157★
Heritage Presbyterian Church - Library (Rel-Phil)
140 Airport Rd. Phone: (302)322-8067
New Castle, DE 19720 Nina Latimer
Founded: 1960. **Subjects:** Religion, Bible, biography, church history. **Special Collections:** Minutes of the Presbyterian Church in America; Minutes of the Delaware Presbytery, PCA; Minutes of the Heritage Presbytery, PCA. **Holdings:** 2000 books. **Services:** Interlibrary loan; library open to the public.

Heritage Press Archives
See: **Chicago Public Library - Carter G. Woodson Regional Library - Vivian G. Harsh Research Collection of Afro-American History & Literature** (3527)

★7158★
Herkimer County Law Library (Law)
Court House
Main St. Phone: (315)867-1172
Herkimer, NY 13350 Deborah E. Melnick, Law Lib.Ck.
Staff: 1. **Subjects:** Law. **Holdings:** 11,882 volumes; Federal Reporter, Federal Supplement, Code of Federal Regulations and government publications on microfiche (21,800). **Subscriptions:** 42 journals and other serials. **Services:** Interlibrary loan; copying; library open to the public with restrictions. **Automated Operations:** Computerized ILL. **Computerized Information Services:** WESTLAW, CCH (Commerce Clearing House, Inc.). **Networks/Consortia:** Member of Central New York Library Resources Council (CENTRO). **Remarks:** FAX: (315)866-7991.

★7159★
Herkimer-Oneida Counties Comprehensive Planning Program - Library (Plan)
800 Park Ave. Phone: (315)798-5710
Utica, NY 13501 Michael Gapin, Prog.Dir.
Founded: 1964. **Staff:** 1. **Subjects:** Regional planning, zoning. **Holdings:** 800 volumes; 1950, 1970, 1980, and 1990 local and New York state census data; microfiche. **Subscriptions:** 3 journals and other serials. **Services:** Copying; library open to the public for reference use only. **Computerized Information Services:** New York State Data Center. **Remarks:** FAX: (315)798-4042.

Herman Memorial Library
See: **U.S. Army - Letterman Army Institute of Research** (16984)

★7160★
Hermann-Grima House - Library (Hist)
820 St. Louis St. Phone: (504)525-5661
New Orleans, LA 70112 Harriet P. Bos, Dir.
Subjects: New Orleans, 1830-1860. **Holdings:** 670 books. **Services:** Copying; library open to the public with restrictions. **Remarks:** Sponsored by Christian Women's Exchange. **Staff:** Emelie Willkomm, Libn.

Grover M. Hermann Engineering Library
See: **Manhattan College** (9592)

★7161★
Hermes Electronics Ltd. - Research Library (Sci-Engr)
Box 1005 Phone: (902)466-7491
Dartmouth, NS, Canada B2Y 4A1 Betty Kemp, Libn
Staff: Prof 1. **Subjects:** Electronics, mechanical engineering, oceanography, acoustical engineering. **Special Collections:** Dr. Hans Castelliz Collection of general interest engineering. **Holdings:** 3900 books; 43 VF drawers of company technical documents; 1500 product catalogs; 100 microfiche. **Services:** Interlibrary loan; copying; library open to the public with restrictions. **Special Indexes:** KWIC index for company technical documents.

Hermes Library
See: **Theosophical Society** (16298)

★7162★
(Hermosillo) Instituto Mexicano de Relaciones Culturales - USIS Collection (Educ)
Blvd. Navarrete y Monteverde
83000 Hermosillo, SON, Mexico
Remarks: Maintained or supported by the U.S. Information Agency. Focus is on materials that will assist peoples outside the United States to learn about the United States, its people, history, culture, political processes, and social milieux.

★7163★
Herner and Company - Library (Info Sci)
1110 N. Glebe Rd., Suite 550 Phone: (703)558-8200
Arlington, VA 22201 Marianne Moerman, Libn.
Founded: 1955. **Staff:** Prof 1; Other 1. **Subjects:** Information science, library science, biomedicine. **Holdings:** 1300 books; 226 company technical reports; 3000 reports in microform. **Subscriptions:** 87 journals and other serials. **Services:** Interlibrary loan; copying; SDI; library open to the public by appointment. **Computerized Information Services:** DIALOG Information Services, BRS Information Technologies, PFDS Online, MEDLINE. **Networks/Consortia:** Member of Interlibrary Users Association (IUA). **Remarks:** Herner and Company is a library and information science consulting and service firm. FAX: (703)558-4979.

Felipe Herrera Library
See: **Inter-American Development Bank** (8027)

Herrick Health Sciences Library
See: **Alta Bates-Herrick Hospitals** (419)

Margaret Herrick Library
See: **Academy of Motion Picture Arts and Sciences - Margaret Herrick Library** (35)

Herrick Memorial Library
See: **Alfred University - Herrick Memorial Library** (347)

Herron School of Art
See: **Indiana University-Purdue University at Indianapolis - University Libraries/Herron School of Art** (7814)

Herschler Building Information Center
See: **Wyoming State Library - State Government Information Services Division - Herschler Building Information Center** (20672)

★7164★
Hershey Foods Corporation - Information Analysis Center (Food-Bev)
1025 Reese Ave.
P.O. Box 805 Phone: (717)534-5106
Hershey, PA 17033 William M. Woodruff, Mgr.
Founded: 1979. **Staff:** Prof 4; Other 2. **Subjects:** Confectionery, chocolate, food science, nutrition, chemistry, engineering, business, marketing, finance. **Holdings:** 4000 books; 350 journal titles in microform; 6 VF drawers of unbound material, including patents and reports; 200 titles on microfilm. **Subscriptions:** 350 journals and other serials; 7 newspapers. **Services:** Interlibrary loan; copying; SDI; center open to the public by appointment. **Automated Operations:** Computerized cataloging, acquisitions, and serials. **Computerized Information Services:** DIALOG Information Services, BRS Information Technologies, TEXTLINE, Chemical Information Systems, Inc. (CIS), Data-Star, Dow Jones News/Retrieval; internal database. **Networks/Consortia:** Member of PALINET. **Publications:** IAC NewFacts, monthly; Weekly Facts; Resource Announcements; Resource Selections. **Remarks:** FAX: (717)534-5069. **Formerly:** Its Communications Center. **Staff:** Peg Salvaggio, Sr.Info.Spec.; Michal Stefannacci, Info.Anl.

General Lewis B. Hershey Museum
See: **Tri-State University** (16494)

Melville J. Herskovits Library of African Studies
See: **Northwestern University** (12085)

★7165★
Herty Pulp & Paper Development Center - Library
Brampton Rd.
Box 7798
Savannah, GA 31418
Subjects: Pulp, paper, chemistry, chemical engineering, forest products. **Holdings:** 2500 volumes. **Remarks:** Currently inactive.

Hertzberg Circus Collection and Museum
See: **San Antonio Public Library and Information Center** (14672)

★7166★
Hertzler Research Foundation - Library (Med)
4th & Chestnut Phone: (316)835-2241
Halstead, KS 67056 Teresa R. Coady, Med.Libn.
Founded: 1907. **Staff:** Prof 1. **Subjects:** Cardiology, oncology, thoracic and cardiovascular surgery, orthopaedics, pathology, gastroenterology. **Special Collections:** History of medicine; Arthur Hertzler, M.D. Collection. **Holdings:** 4000 books; 6662 periodical volumes. **Subscriptions:** 150 journals and other serials. **Services:** Interlibrary loan; copying; library open to medical researchers and doctors. **Computerized Information Services:** BRS/COLLEAGUE, MEDLARS. **Remarks:** FAX: (316)835-2138.

Dr. E. Herzog Memorial Medical Library
See: **Flint Osteopathic Hospital** (5849)

★7167★
Hessisches Staatsarchiv und Archivschule - Bibliothek (Hist)
Friedrichspl 15
Postfach 540
W-3550 Marburg, Germany Phone: 6421 25078
Founded: 1870. **Staff:** 2. **Subjects:** Archives, history. **Holdings:** 100,000 books. **Subscriptions:** 267 journals and other serials. **Services:** Library open to the public with restrictions. **Remarks:** FAX: 6421 161125.

★7168★
Hetrick, Zaleski, Ernico & Pierce, P.C. - Library
Box 1265 Phone: (717)236-9581
Harrisburg, PA 17108 Linda Sites, Off.Adm.
Remarks: FAX: (717)232-0817. No further information was supplied by respondent.

Frederic Heutte Memorial Library
See: **Norfolk Botanical Garden Society** (11844)

Rabbi Simon Hevesi Jewish Heritage Library
See: **Queens College of City University of New York - Ethnic Studies Project** (13641)

★7169★
Hewitt Associates - Library (Bus-Fin)
100 Half Day Phone: (708)295-5000
Lincolnshire, IL 60069 Maureen Theobald, Libn.
Founded: 1948. **Staff:** Prof 4. **Subjects:** Compensation, employee benefits, wage and salary administration, actuarial science, insurance, business, finance, general management, personnel. **Holdings:** 6500 volumes; 8000 proxy statements (annually). **Subscriptions:** 800 journals and other serials. **Services:** Library open to clients. **Automated Operations:** Computerized public access catalog, serials, and circulation. **Computerized Information Services:** LEXIS, NEXIS, DIALOG Information Services; DataTimes; CD-ROM (COMPUSTAT PC PLUS: Corporate Text). **Publications:** What's New, monthly. **Staff:** Dawn Braun; Deborah Reeber.

Flora Lamson Hewlett Library
See: **Graduate Theological Union** (6613)

★7170★
Hewlett-Packard Company - Andover Site Library (Sci-Engr)
3000 Minuteman Rd. Phone: (508)681-2344
Andover, MA 01810-1099 Carol Miller, Info.Res.Anl.Supv.
Founded: 1977. **Staff:** Prof 1; Other 1.5. **Subjects:** Electronic design, marketing, cardiology, general business, software development. **Holdings:** 3500 books; 150 bound periodical volumes; 300 videotapes; government reports. **Subscriptions:** 300 journals and other serials. **Services:** Interlibrary loan; SDI; library open to the public with permission. **Automated Operations:** Computerized cataloging. **Computerized Information Services:** RLIN, BRS Information Technologies, DIALOG Information Services, OCLC; OnTyme Electronic Message Network Service (electronic mail service). **Networks/Consortia:** Member of WELEXACOL, Hewlett-Packard Library/Information Network. **Remarks:** FAX: (508)686-7262.

★7171★
Hewlett-Packard Company - Avondale Site Library (Sci-Engr)
Route 41, Box 900 Phone: (215)268-5644
Avondale, PA 19311 Bev Maniatakes, Lib.Ck.
Founded: 1970. **Staff:** 1. **Subjects:** Gas and liquid chromatography. **Holdings:** 1500 books; 200 bound periodical volumes. **Subscriptions:** 100 journals and other serials. **Services:** Interlibrary loan; library not open to the public. **Computerized Information Services:** RLIN. **Remarks:** FAX: (215)268-5396. **Formerly:** Its Avondale Division Library.

★7172★
Hewlett-Packard Company - Boise Site Learning Resource Center (Comp Sci)
11311 Chinden Blvd. Phone: (208)323-2911
Boise, ID 83707 Gail Lester, Dir.
Founded: 1979. **Staff:** Prof 1; Other 1. **Subjects:** Computers, electronics, engineering, physics. **Holdings:** 3000 books. **Subscriptions:** 120 journals and other serials; 5 newspapers. **Services:** Interlibrary loan; library not open to the public. **Computerized Information Services:** DIALOG Information Services; CD-ROM; InterNet (electronic mail service). **Networks/Consortia:** Member of Research Libraries Information Network (RLIN), CLASS, Western Library Network (WLN). **Remarks:** FAX: (208)323-2049; (208)323-2896. Electronic mail address(es): gaill@hpdmd48.boi.hp.com (InterNet).

★7173★
Hewlett-Packard Company - Fort Collins Site Library (Comp Sci)
3404 E. Harmony Rd. Phone: (303)229-3830
Fort Collins, CO 80525 Jane St. Germain, Libn.
Founded: 1978. **Staff:** Prof 2; Other 5. **Subjects:** Computers, electronics. **Holdings:** 4500 books; 200 audiotape sets; 100 videotapes. **Subscriptions:** 325 journals and other serials; 24 newspapers. **Services:** Interlibrary loan; copying; library open to the public by appointment. **Automated Operations:** Computerized cataloging, acquisitions, serials, and circulation. **Computerized Information Services:** DIALOG Information Services, RLIN, OCLC, Dow Jones News/Retrieval, Dun & Bradstreet Business Credit Services, NewsNet, Inc., NEXIS, OCLC EPIC. **Publications:** Library News. **Staff:** Susan K. Charles, Info.Res.Anl.; Robyn J. Hutson, Info.Res.Anl.

★7174★
Hewlett-Packard Company - HP Labs - Deer Creek Branch Library (Sci-Engr)
3500 Deer Creek Rd. Phone: (415)857-5205
Palo Alto, CA 94304 Eugenie Prime
Founded: 1975. **Staff:** 1. **Subjects:** Solid state physics, electronics, physics, science technology. **Holdings:** 5000 books; 650 bound periodical volumes. **Subscriptions:** 100 journals and other serials; 7 newspapers. **Services:** Interlibrary loan; copying; SDI; library open to the public by appointment. **Automated Operations:** Computerized public access catalog (SOCRATES) and cataloging. **Computerized Information Services:** DIALOG Information Services, RLIN, VU/TEXT Information Services, NEXIS, NewsNet, Inc., Dow Jones News/Retrieval, Data-Star; internal databases; OnTyme Electronic Message Network Service (electronic mail service). **Networks/Consortia:** Member of CLASS, Research Libraries Information Network (RLIN), SOUTHNET. **Remarks:** FAX: (415)857-5206. Electronic mail address(es): CLASSHP (OnTyme Electronic Message Network Service). **Staff:** Lorene Hall.

★7175★
Hewlett-Packard Company - HP Labs - Research Library (Sci-Engr, Comp Sci)
1501 Page Mill Rd. Phone: (415)857-3091
Palo Alto, CA 94304 Eugenie Prime, Mgr.
Founded: 1052. **Staff:** Prof 9; Other 10. **Subjects:** Computers, electronics, solid state physics, instrumentation, medical electronics, chemistry, business and management, physics. **Holdings:** 49,000 books and reports; 30,000 bound periodical volumes; 6000 Hewlett-Packard instrument manuals on microfiche; 1738 videotapes and training films; 10K reports on microfiche. **Subscriptions:** 800 journals and other serials; 10 newspapers. **Services:** Interlibrary loan; copying; SDI; library open to the public by appointment. **Automated Operations:** Computerized public access catalog (SOCRATES) and cataloging. **Computerized Information Services:** DIALOG Information Services, Data-Star, NEXIS, VU/TEXT Information Services, NewsNet, Inc., RLIN, Dow Jones News/Retrieval, Compact Disclosure; internal database; diskette (CORPTECH, Institution of Electrical Engineers); OnTyme Electronic Message Network Service (electronic mail service). **Networks/Consortia:** Member of CLASS, Research Libraries Information Network (RLIN), SOUTHNET. **Publications:** Library Line, weekly - for internal distribution only. **Special Catalogs:** Computer-produced union list of Hewlett-Packard libraries periodical holdings (book); Union Catalog of Hewlett-Packard Library Network (online). **Remarks:** FAX: (415)852-8187. Electronic mail address(es): CLASS HP (OnTyme Electronic Message Network Service). **Staff:** Kathe Gust Sr. Info. Anl.; Euni Bae; Inge Formenti; Laurel Stushek; Celeste Welch; Liz Vugrinecz; Ellen Warneke.

★7176★
Hewlett-Packard Company - Information Center (Sci-Engr, Comp Sci)
1000 N.E. Circle Blvd. Phone: (503)750-2535
Corvallis, OR 97330 Susan Dyer-Preston, Mgr.
Founded: 1980. **Staff:** Prof 2; Other 4. **Subjects:** Electrical and mechanical engineering, computer science, chemistry, physics, business, management, semiconductor technology. **Special Collections:** Technical memoranda; annual reports. **Holdings:** 15,000 volumes. **Subscriptions:** 435 journals and other serials. **Services:** Interlibrary loan; center not open to the public. **Automated Operations:** Computerized cataloging, acquisitions, serials, and circulation. **Computerized Information Services:** DIALOG Information Services, BRS Information Technologies, STN International, RLIN, OCLC, Dow Jones News/Retrieval; OnTyme Electronic Message Network Service (electronic mail service). **Remarks:** FAX: (503)750-4015. **Staff:** Sharon O. Williams, Res./Coll.Dev.; Margie Johnson, ILL; Maggie Trolard, Acq.; Kay Rosenau, Ser.; Linda Watson, Mtls.Proc.

★7177★
Hewlett-Packard Company - Lake Stevens Instrument Division - Library (Sci-Engr)
MS-220
8600 Soper Hill Rd. Phone: (206)335-2406
Everett, WA 98205-1298 Ruth L. Van Dyke, Lib.Mgr.
Founded: 1984. **Staff:** Prof 2; Other 1. **Subjects:** Electrical engineering. **Holdings:** 2000 books. **Subscriptions:** 250 journals and other serials. **Services:** Interlibrary loan; copying; SDI; library open to the public by appointment. **Automated Operations:** Computerized serials and acquisitions. **Computerized Information Services:** DIALOG Information Services, Dow Jones News/Retrieval, OCLC, Reuters; DIALMAIL, InterNet (electronic mail services). **Networks/Consortia:** Member of OCLC Pacific Network. FAX: (206)335-2828. Electronic mail address(es): 10584 (DIALMAIL); ruthv@lsid.hp.com (InterNet).

★7178★
Hewlett-Packard Company - Library (Med, Sci-Engr)
175 Wyman St. Phone: (617)890-6300
Waltham, MA 02254 Susan Saraidaridis, Hd. Libn.
Founded: 1957. **Staff:** Prof 1; Other 3. **Subjects:** Medicine, engineering, business. **Holdings:** 6500 books; 4000 bound periodical volumes. **Subscriptions:** 350 journals and other serials. **Services:** Interlibrary loan (limited); SDI; collection accessible to the public by appointment. **Automated Operations:** Computerized public access catalog and circulation. **Computerized Information Services:** DIALOG Information Services, InvesText; internal database. **Networks/Consortia:** Member of WELEXACOL, Hewlett-Packard Library/Information Network. **Publications:** Acqusitions list, monthly.

★7179★
Hewlett-Packard Company - Loveland Facility Library (Sci-Engr, Comp Sci)
Box 301 Phone: (303)679-2460
Loveland, CO 80539 Rose Finch, Libn.
Staff: Prof 1; Other 2. **Subjects:** Electronics, electrical engineering, computers, business. **Holdings:** 10,000 books; 1000 bound periodical volumes. **Subscriptions:** 345 journals and other serials. **Services:** Interlibrary loan; copying; library open to the public with restrictions. **Automated Operations:** Computerized cataloging. **Computerized Information Services:** BRS Information Technologies, DIALOG Information Services, Dow Jones News/Retrieval; OnTyme Electronic Message Network Service (electronic mail service). **Networks/Consortia:** Member of Research Libraries Information Network (RLIN), CLASS. **Remarks:** FAX: (303)679-5954.

★7180★
Hewlett-Packard Company - San Diego Division - Resource and Technical Service Library (Sci-Engr)
16399 W. Bernardo Dr. Phone: (619)592-4687
San Diego, CA 92127 MaryAnn Savercool, Libn.
Founded: 1979. **Staff:** 2. **Subjects:** Engineering - mechanical, electronic, chemical; computer science. **Holdings:** 2000 books. **Subscriptions:** 200 journals and other serials. **Services:** Interlibrary loan (limited to photocopies of articles only); library not open to the public. **Computerized Information Services:** DIALOG Information Services. **Networks/Consortia:** Member of Hewlett-Packard Library/Information Network. **Remarks:** FAX: (619)592-4587.

★7181★
Hewlett-Packard Company - Santa Clara Division Library (Sci-Engr)
5301 Stevens Creek Blvd., MS 27 Phone: (408)553-2593
Santa Clara, CA 95051 Diana Robba, Lib.Br.Mgr.
Staff: 1. **Subjects:** Technology, engineering, electrical engineering and industries, physics. **Holdings:** 3000 books; 100 bound periodical volumes. **Subscriptions:** 200 journals and other serials. **Services:** Interlibrary loan; library not open to the public. **Computerized Information Services:** DIALOG Information Services, RLIN. **Remarks:** FAX: (408)553-7755.

★7182★
Hewlett-Packard Company - Southern Colorado Regional Library (Comp Sci)
Box 2197 Phone: (719)590-2314
Colorado Springs, CO 80901-2197 June Fritz, Libn.
Founded: 1970. **Staff:** Prof 1; Other 2. **Subjects:** Electronics, computer sciences, chemistry, management. **Holdings:** 1400 books; back issues for 200

periodicals. **Subscriptions:** 134 journals and other serials. **Services:** Interlibrary loan; center open to the public by appointment. **Automated Operations:** Computerized serials. **Computerized Information Services:** RLIN. **Networks/Consortia:** Member of Colorado Alliance of Research Libraries (CARL), Hewlett-Packard Library/Information Network. **Remarks:** Center located at 1900 Garden of the Gods Rd., Colorado Springs, CO 80907. FAX: (719)590-3104.

★7183★
Hewlett-Packard Company - Technical Information Center (Comp Sci)
19483 Pruneridge Ave., MS 48NC — Phone: (408)447-4042
Cupertino, CA 95014-9974 — Shirley Roth, Info.Res.Anl.Mgr.
Founded: 1969. **Staff:** Prof 1; Other 1. **Subjects:** Computers, programming, programming languages, electronics, databases, operating systems, software. **Holdings:** 5000 volumes. **Subscriptions:** 206 journals and other serials; 25 newspapers. **Automated Operations:** Computerized cataloging. **Computerized Information Services:** DIALOG Information Services, BRS Information Technologies, PFDS Online; OnTyme Electronic Message Network Service (electronic mail service). **Networks/Consortia:** Member of Hewlett-Packard Library/Information Network. **Remarks:** Alternate telephone number(s): (408)447-4974. FAX: (408)447-5809.

★7184★
Hewlett-Packard Company - Workstation Systems Division - Technical Information Center (Comp Sci)
300 Apollo Dr. — Phone: (508)256-6600
Chelmsford, MA 01824 — Charles Matthews, Mgr.
Founded: 1984. **Staff:** 2. **Subjects:** Computer science, operating systems, workstations, distributed computing. **Holdings:** 2500 books; 1500 bound periodical volumes; 2500 patents and documents; 1000 AV programs. **Subscriptions:** 350 journals and other serials; 25 newspapers. **Services:** Interlibrary loan; center not open to the public. **Computerized Information Services:** DIALOG Information Services, OCLC; InterNet (electronic mail service). **Networks/Consortia:** Member of NELINET, Inc. **Remarks:** FAX: (508)256-2178. Electronic mail address(es): MATTHEWS@APOLLO.HP.COM (InterNet). **Formerly:** Its Apollo Systems Division.

Hi-Tek Polymers, Inc. - Technical Information Center
See: **Rhone-Poulenc, Inc.** (13887)

★7185★
Hialeah Hospital - George H. Wessel Memorial Library (Med)
651 E. 25th St. — Phone: (305)835-4635
Hialeah, FL 33013 — Yvonne Barkman, Libn.
Founded: 1969. **Staff:** Prof 1. **Subjects:** Medicine, nursing, paramedical sciences, hospital administration. **Holdings:** 1300 books; 600 bound periodical volumes; 3 VF drawers of pamphlets and clippings; AV programs. **Subscriptions:** 105 journals and other serials. **Services:** Interlibrary loan; copying; library open to the public with restrictions. **Computerized Information Services:** MEDLINE. **Networks/Consortia:** Member of Miami Health Sciences Library Consortium (MHSLC). **Publications:** Health Sciences Update, quarterly - for internal distribution only.

Hibbard Library
See: **Glenview Area Historical Society** (6506)

★7186★
Hickory Museum of Art, Inc. - Fine Arts Library (Art)
Box 2572 — Phone: (704)327-8576
Hickory, NC 28601 — Thomas R. Perryman, Asst.Dir.
Founded: 1982. **Staff:** 4. **Subjects:** Visual art history, American art history. **Holdings:** 750 books; 550 bound periodical volumes. **Subscriptions:** 12 journals and other serials; 4 newspapers. **Services:** Library open to the public. **Computerized Information Services:** Internal database. **Staff:** Ellen Schwarzbek; John Post; Angela Chapman.

Edward J. and Gena G. Hickox Library
See: **Naismith Memorial Basketball Hall of Fame** (10957)

Gerald Hicks Memorial Library
See: **Lorain County Historical Society** (9302)

★7187★
Hidalgo County Law Library (Law)
Courthouse
100 Closner — Phone: (512)318-2155
Edinburg, TX 78539 — Joy Eaves, Law Libn.
Founded: 1954. **Staff:** Prof 1. **Subjects:** Law, Texas statutes. **Special Collections:** Notable Trials Library. **Holdings:** 12,804 books; 49 bound periodical volumes; reports; microfiche; microfilm. **Subscriptions:** 10 journals and other serials; 4 newspapers. **Services:** Copying; library open to the public. **Remarks:** FAX: (512)381-4269.

Hiebert Library
See: **Fresno Pacific College & Mennonite Brethren Biblical Seminary - Hiebert Library** (6162)

★7188★
A. Foster Higgins & Company, Inc. - Research Library (Bus-Fin)
125 Broad St., 4th Fl. — Phone: (212)574-9022
New York, NY 10004 — Patrick Sweeney, Libn.
Staff: Prof 1; Other 3. **Subjects:** Health care, pensions, Social Security, group insurance. **Holdings:** 3000 books; 15 VF drawers of annual reports; 32 VF drawers of clippings. **Subscriptions:** 200 journals and other serials. **Services:** Interlibrary loan. **Remarks:** FAX: (212)574-9122.

★7189★
Higgins Armory Museum - Memorial Library (Hist)
100 Barber Ave. — Phone: (508)853-6015
Worcester, MA 01606-2434 — Walter J. Karcheski, Jr., Cur.
Founded: 1966. **Staff:** Prof 1; Other 1. **Subjects:** Arms and armor, history, art, military history. **Holdings:** 2500 books, auction catalogs, bound periodical volumes. **Subscriptions:** 5 journals and other serials. **Services:** Library open to the public for reference use only by appointment and on a limited schedule. **Special Catalogs:** Catalogue of Armor (out of print); Catalogue of Books (out of print); Medieval and Renaissance Splendor (exhibition catalog).

★7190★
Higgs, Fletcher & Mack - Law Library (Law)
401 West A St., Suite 2000 — Phone: (619)236-1551
San Diego, CA 92101 — Diane Garcia, Libn.
Staff: Prof 1; Other 1. **Subjects:** Law - aviation, bankruptcy, corporate, securities, tax. **Holdings:** 12,000 volumes. **Subscriptions:** 70 journals and other serials; 10 newspapers. **Services:** Library not open to the public. **Computerized Information Services:** LEXIS, WESTLAW, Dow Jones News/Retrieval, Information America, DataTimes. **Remarks:** FAX: (619)696-1410.

The High Library
See: **Elizabethtown College** (5300)

High Blood Pressure Information Center
See: **National Heart, Lung, and Blood Institute - Education Programs' Information Center** (11193)

★7191★
High Museum of Art - Library (Art)
1280 Peachtree St. — Phone: (404)892-3600
Atlanta, GA 30309 — Dr. Jack Miller, Musm.Libn.
Founded: 1926. **Staff:** 1. **Subjects:** American painting and art; art - decorative, contemporary, European, African; photography. **Special Collections:** Pendley Collection (decorative arts). **Holdings:** 9500 books; 16,000 slides; 3000 auction catalogs; 5000 artist files. **Subscriptions:** 50 journals and other serials; 5 newspapers. **Services:** Interlibrary loan; copying; library open to the public by appointment for research only. **Computerized Information Services:** OCLC. **Networks/Consortia:** Member of CCLC. **Remarks:** FAX: (404)898-9578.

★7192★
High Street Christian Church - H.A. Valentine Memorial Library (Rel-Phil)
131 S. High St. Phone: (216)434-1039
Akron, OH 44308 Evelyn R. Ling, Libn.
Founded: 1965. **Staff:** Prof 1; Other 11. **Subjects:** Religion, Christian education. **Special Collections:** Church Archives. **Holdings:** 8000 books. **Services:** Library open to the public by special permission.

Highland Botanical Park
See: **Monroe County Parks Department - Highland Botanical Park** (10625)

★7193★
Highland Community College - Library - Special Collections (Hist)
Pearl City Rd. Phone: (815)235-6121
Freeport, IL 61032 Eric C. Welch, Dir. of Lrng.Rsrcs.
Founded: 1963. **Staff:** Prof 1; Other 2. **Special Collections:** Stephenson County (Illinois) Collection, local authors. **Holdings:** 40,000 books. **Subscriptions:** 250 journals and other serials; 12 newspapers. **Services:** Interlibrary loan; copying; SDI; collections open to the public. **Computerized Information Services:** DIALOG Information Services, BRS Information Technologies. **Networks/Consortia:** Member of Northern Illinois Library System (NILS). **Remarks:** FAX: (815)235-6130.

★7194★
Highland County Law Library (Law)
Court House
High & Main Sts. Phone: (513)393-4863
Hillsboro, OH 45133 Michelle Vanzant-Salyer, Law Libn.
Founded: 1936. **Staff:** Prof 1. **Subjects:** Law. **Holdings:** 7029 books; 90 bound periodical volumes; 2150 microfiche. **Services:** Interlibrary loan; copying; library open to the public for reference use only. **Automated Operations:** Computerized cataloging. **Computerized Information Services:** WESTLAW. **Remarks:** FAX: (513)393-6878.

Highland Heritage Research Library
See: **Glengarry Genealogical Society** (6503)

Highland Hospital
See: **Alameda-Contra Costa Medical Association & Highland Hospital** (196)

★7195★
Highland Hospital - John R. Williams, Sr. Health Sciences Library (Med)
1000 South Ave. Phone: (716)461-6761
Rochester, NY 14620 Diane Dayton Robbins, Lib.Dir.
Founded: 1956. **Staff:** Prof 1. **Subjects:** Medicine, surgery, family medicine, nursing, hematology/oncology, radiation therapy, obstetrics, gynecology. **Holdings:** 6000 books and bound periodical volumes; 7 VF drawers of archives; AV programs. **Subscriptions:** 200 journals and other serials. **Services:** Interlibrary loan; copying; library open to the public by appointment. **Computerized Information Services:** NLM, BRS Information Technologies, DIALOG Information Services; CD-ROMs. **Networks/Consortia:** Member of Rochester Regional Library Council (RRLC). **Remarks:** FAX: (716)473-1613.

★7196★
Highland Hospital, Inc. - Medical Library (Med)
2412 50th St. Phone: (806)795-8251
Lubbock, TX 79412 Jo Nell Wischkaemper, Dir.
Staff: 1. **Subjects:** Medicine, allied health sciences. **Holdings:** 475 books; 250 bound periodical volumes; 324 audio cassettes. **Subscriptions:** 28 journals and other serials. **Services:** Interlibrary loan; library not open to the public.

★7197★
Highland Park Historical Society - Library (Hist)
326 Central Ave.
Box 56 Phone: (708)432-7090
Highland Park, IL 60035 Betty M. Mills, Exec.Dir.
Founded: 1969. **Subjects:** Local history. **Holdings:** 500 books; 1000 photographs; 2500 35mm slides. **Services:** Library open to the public.

★7198★
Highland Park Hospital - Medical Library (Med)
718 Glenview Ave. Phone: (708)432-8000
Highland Park, IL 60035 Joy Kennedy, Med.Libn.
Staff: Prof 1. **Subjects:** Medicine. **Holdings:** 1400 books; microfiche. **Subscriptions:** 154 journals and other serials. **Services:** Interlibrary loan; copying; library open to the public at librarian's discretion. **Computerized Information Services:** NLM; CD-ROMs. **Networks/Consortia:** Member of Northeastern Illinois Library Consortium. **Remarks:** FAX: (708)480-3944.

★7199★
Highland Park Presbyterian Church - Madeline Roach Meyercord Library (Rel-Phil)
3821 University Blvd. Phone: (214)526-7457
Dallas, TX 75205 Louise White, Chm.
Founded: 1953. **Staff:** 30. **Subjects:** Religion, children, birds. **Holdings:** 18,500 books. **Subscriptions:** 15 journals and other serials. **Services:** Library open to the public with restrictions. **Staff:** Martha Green.

★7200★
Highland Park United Methodist Church - Library (Rel-Phil)
3300 Mockingbird Ln. Phone: (214)521-3111
Dallas, TX 75205 Sarah Wood, Libn.
Staff: Prof 1; Other 18. **Subjects:** Religion, biography, fiction, poetry, drama, children's literature, history, travel, art, crafts, cookbooks, retirement, health, nature. **Special Collections:** Texas Library; Large Type Books; National Geographic, 1911-1985. **Holdings:** 18,000 books; 780 sermon tapes; maps. **Subscriptions:** 14 journals and other serials. **Services:** Library open to church members and visitors with restrictions.

★7201★
Highland Presbyterian Church - Elizabeth Milholland Library (Rel-Phil)
708 Highland Ave. Phone: (412)654-7391
New Castle, PA 16101 Anne M. Graham, Libn.
Founded: 1967. **Staff:** Prof 2. **Subjects:** Bible, Christian life. **Holdings:** 2200 books; 40 videotapes; 57 audiocassettes; church history and annual reports. **Services:** Library open to the public.

★7202★
Highlands and Islands Enterprise - Library (Agri)
Bridge House
20 Bridge St. Phone: 463 244293
Inverness 1V1 1QR, Scotland R.J. Ardern
Founded: 1969. **Staff:** Prof 2; Other 1. **Subjects:** Economic development, agriculture, fish and fisheries, tourism, training, environment. **Holdings:** 15,000 books; 50 bound periodical volumes. **Subscriptions:** 200 journals and other serials; 40 newspapers. **Services:** Interlibrary loan; copying; library open to the public for reference use only. **Computerized Information Services:** DIALOG Information Services, BLAISE, FT PROFILE. **Remarks:** FAX: 463 244469.

★7203★
Highsmith Company, Inc. - Corporate Library (Bus-Fin)
W5527 Hwy. 106
Box 800 Phone: (414)563-9571
Fort Atkinson, WI 53538-0800 Lisa Guedea, Corp.Libn.
Founded: 1986. **Staff:** Prof 1; Other 1. **Subjects:** Business - management, marketing, strategic planning and human resources; education; library and information science; information technology. **Special Collections:** Internal policies; Highsmith catalog archives; corporate history; general consumer mail order collection. **Holdings:** 1200 books; 40 AV programs. **Subscriptions:** 425 journals and other serials. **Services:** Interlibrary loan; copying; SDI; library open to the public at librarian's discretion. **Automated Operations:** Computerized cataloging, acquisitions, and serials. **Computerized Information Services:** DIALOG Information Services, WILSONLINE, OCLC, VU/TEXT Information Services; DIALMAIL (electronic mail service). **Networks/Consortia:** Member of Wisconsin Interlibrary Services (WILS). **Publications:** Inhouse acquisitions list. **Remarks:** FAX: (414)563-7395. Telex: 467 916 HIGHSMITH CI. Electronic mail address(es): 25701 (DIALMAIL).

★7204★
Sara Hightower Regional Library - Library (Bus-Fin)
205 Riverside Pkwy. Phone: (404)236-4600
Rome, GA 30161 Jim L. Doyle, Ref.Libn.
Founded: 1967. **Staff:** Prof 1; Other 1. **Subjects:** Investment, management, consumer information, small business information, company information. **Holdings:** 1700 volumes; 12 VF drawers of clippings and pamphlets; 18 magazines on microfiche; 104 reels of microfilm. **Subscriptions:** 126 journals and other serials; 8 newspapers. **Services:** Interlibrary loan; copying; library open to the public. **Publications:** Brochures on offerings of Business Library, irregular. **Special Catalogs:** Union List of Periodicals maintained by all the libraries in the area (card).

★7205★
Sara Hightower Regional Library - Special Collections (Hist, Area-Ethnic)
205 Riverside Pkwy. Phone: (404)236-4607
Rome, GA 30161 Jacqueline D. Kinzer, Cur.
Founded: 1911. **Staff:** 2. **Subjects:** Cherokee Indians, Georgia and local history, genealogy, Southern history, Civil War. **Special Collections:** J.F. Brooks Cherokeeana Collection (401 books); Ellen Louise Axson Wilson Collection; John L. Harris Papers (3 VF drawers); George M. Battey, III, Papers (5 VF drawers); Civil War collection; Yancey Lipscomb Collection (4 VF Drawers). **Holdings:** 12,000 books; 30 VF drawers; 350 maps; 7000 microforms; 450 unbound periodicals. **Subscriptions:** 71 journals and other serials. **Services:** Interlibrary loan; copying; collections open to the public with restrictions. **Automated Operations:** Computerized public access catalog, cataloging, and circulation. **Remarks:** FAX: (404)236-4605.

Highway Safety Research Center
See: **University of North Carolina at Chapel Hill** (19062)

The Hihn Archive
See: **University of California, Santa Cruz - Map Collection** (18436)

★7206★
Hilbert College - McGrath Library - Special Collections (Area-Ethnic)
5200 S. Park Ave. Phone: (716)649-7900
Hamburg, NY 14075 Thaddeus J. Ciambor, Dir.
Founded: 1957. **Staff:** Prof 4. **Subjects:** Polish language and culture. **Special Collections:** Weiss Polish Culture Collection. **Holdings:** 1673 books. **Services:** Interlibrary loan; copying; collections open to the public. **Automated Operations:** Computerized public access catalog. **Computerized Information Services:** OCLC EPIC, LEXIS, NEXIS. **Networks/Consortia:** Member of Western New York Library Resources Council (WNYLRC). **Remarks:** FAX: (716)648-6530. **Staff:** Sue Stanley, Ref.Libn.; Barbara Bonanno, Ser./Cat.Libn.; Matthew Bartle, Comp./AV Libn.

Hilding Medical Library
See: **St. Luke's Hospital** (14477)

★7207★
Hill and Barlow - Library (Law)
1 International Place
100 Oliver St. Phone: (617)439-3555
Boston, MA 02110 Julia E. Snyder, Libn.
Staff: Prof 1; Other 2. **Subjects:** Law. **Holdings:** 15,000 volumes. **Services:** Interlibrary loan; library not open to the public. **Computerized Information Services:** LEXIS, NEXIS, DIALOG Information Services, WESTLAW, VU/TEXT Information Services. **Remarks:** FAX: (617)439-3580.

★7208★
Hill, Betts & Nash - Law Library (Law)
1 World Trade Center, Suite 5215 Phone: (212)839-7160
New York, NY 10048 Lynn Tofte, Libn.
Staff: Prof 1; Other 1. **Subjects:** Law - maritime, shipping, banking, aviation. **Special Collections:** Japanese Collection. **Holdings:** 15,000 books; 2 VF drawers. **Subscriptions:** 125 journals and other serials; 9 newspapers. **Services:** Interlibrary loan; copying; library open to the public through ILL. **Computerized Information Services:** LEXIS, NEXIS, DIALOG Information Services, Dow Jones News/Retrieval, DunsPRINT. **Publications:** Library Bulletin. **Remarks:** FAX: (212)466-1896.

Hill Center for the Mathematical Sciences
See: **Rutgers University** (14165)

★7209★
Hill College - Harold B. Simpson Confederate Research Center and Audie L. Murphy Gun Museum (Hist, Mil)
Hillsboro, TX 76645 Phone: (817)582-2555
Dr. B.D. Patterson, Dir.
Founded: 1964. **Staff:** Prof 1; Other 1. **Subjects:** Civil War, military history, Texas history, guns and ammunition, artillery. **Special Collections:** Hood's Texas Brigade, Army of Northern Virginia; special library on guns, edged weapons, artillery, and ammunition (300 volumes); capsule histories of 3300 Confederate regiments and special units; listing of Confederate soldiers (on microfilm). **Holdings:** 3000 books; 500 bound periodical volumes; 200 booklets; 2 VF drawers of unpublished manuscripts, diaries, letters; 3 VF drawers of photographs, muster roll compilations, Civil War miscellanea; 4 VF drawers of newspaper and magazine articles; 3 VF drawers of microfilm of Texas forts, 1848-1861; service records for Hood's Texas Brigade; Texas newspapers, 1846-1861. **Subscriptions:** 49 journals and other serials. **Services:** Interlibrary loan; copying; center open to the public.

D.H. Hill Library
See: **North Carolina State University - D.H. Hill Library** (11899)

★7210★
Hill, Farrer & Burrill - Law Library (Law)
Union Bank Bldg., 35th Fl.
445 S. Figueroa St. Phone: (213)620-0460
Los Angeles, CA 90071 Nina A. Hall
Staff: Prof 1; Other 1. **Subjects:** Law. **Holdings:** 17,000 books; 400 bound periodical volumes; 2100 legal memoranda; 300 audio cassettes. **Subscriptions:** 350 journals and other serials. **Services:** Library not open to the public. **Computerized Information Services:** LEXIS, Information America, CDB. **Remarks:** FAX: (213)624-4840.

★7211★
Hill International, Inc. - Library (Bus-Fin)
Garden Plaza Bldg.
Box 397 Phone: (609)871-5800
Willingboro, NJ 08046 Roz Richman, Res.
Founded: 1976. **Subjects:** Construction claims avoidance and resolution. **Holdings:** Comprehensive case histories of claims. **Services:** Interlibrary loan; library not open to the public. **Remarks:** FAX: (609)871-5714. Toll-free telephone number(s): (800)222-0127.

★7212★
James Jerome Hill Reference Library (Bus-Fin, Trans)
80 W. 4th St. Phone: (612)227-9531
St. Paul, MN 55102 Sheila A. Meyer, Exec.Dir.
Founded: 1921. **Staff:** Prof 16; Other 17. **Subjects:** Applied business, commerce, transportation, business history with an emphasis on transportation. **Special Collections:** James Jerome Hill's personal library of local history books covering Minnesota, the Greater Northwest, and Western Canada; Frank P. Donovan, Jr. Collection on Railroads in Literature (3200 volumes); James Jerome Hill papers (450 linear feet of personal and business records related to railroads, agriculture, banking and finance, lumbering, mining, philanthropy, and politics in Minnesota, Upper Midwest, Pacific Northwest, Western Canada, and the New York/Boston financial community, 1856-1916); Louis Warren Hill papers (1000 linear feet of personal and business records related to railroading, Glacier National Park, agriculture, politics, banking and finance, mining, lumbering, fossil fuels, tourism, philanthropy, Indian-white relations, and general economic development in Minnesota, the Greater Northwest, and the Southwestern United States, 1887-1948). **Holdings:** 170,000 volumes; 10K and proxy reports for 12 states; regional, national, and international business information. **Subscriptions:** 3600 journals and other serials; 11 newspapers. **Services:** Interlibrary loan; copying; library open to the public. **Automated Operations:** Computerized public access catalog, cataloging, acquisitions, serials, and circulation (PALS). **Computerized Information Services:** DIALOG Information Services, Dow Jones News/Retrieval, OCLC; Datanet. Performs searches on fee basis. Contact Person: Steve Jarzyna, Ref.Libn. **Networks/Consortia:** Member of Cooperating Libraries in Consortium (CLIC), MINITEX Library Information Network, Metropolitan Library Service Agency (MELSA). **Publications:** Directory of Minnesota Business and Professional Associations (book). **Special Indexes:** Index of Minnesota Business Periodicals. **Remarks:** FAX: (612)222-4139.

★7213★
Hill and Knowlton, Inc. - Information Center (Bus-Fin)
111 E. Wacker Dr., Suite 1700 Phone: (312)565-1200
Chicago, IL 60601 Barbara Allamian, Mgr., Res.
Subjects: Public relations, general business. **Holdings:** 500 books; 750 annual reports. **Subscriptions:** 300 journals and other serials; 10 newspapers. **Services:** Center not open to the public. **Computerized Information Services:** CDA Investment Technologies, Inc., DIALOG Information Services, LEXIS, NEXIS, DataTimes, VU/TEXT Information Services, Dow Jones News/Retrieval, Reuter TEXTLINE, Burrelle's Broadcast Database; internal database. Performs searches. Contact Person: Barbara Allamian, Mgr. of Res. **Remarks:** FAX: (312)565-4360.

Leslie Pinckney Hill Library
See: **Cheyney University of Pennsylvania** (3509)

★7214★
Hill Lewis - Library (Law)
100 Renaissance Ctr., 32nd Fl. Phone: (313)259-3232
Detroit, MI 48243 Kathleen A. Nagrant, Libn.
Founded: 1890. **Staff:** Prof 1; Other 1. **Subjects:** Law. **Holdings:** 10,000 books; 133 bound periodical volumes. **Subscriptions:** 155 journals and other serials; 8 newspapers. **Services:** Interlibrary loan; library open to the public with approval of Library Committee. **Computerized Information Services:** VU/TEXT Information Services, WESTLAW, LEXIS; internal databases. **Remarks:** FAX: (313)259-7616.

Lister Hill Library of the Health Sciences
See: **University of Alabama at Birmingham - Lister Hill Library of the Health Sciences** (18171)

Hill Monastic Manuscript Library
See: **St. John's Abbey and University - Hill Monastic Manuscript Library** (14334)

★7215★
Hillcrest Christian College - Library (Rel-Phil)
2801 13th Ave., S.E. Phone: (403)526-6951
Medicine Hat, AB, Canada T1A 3R1 Agatha Heinrichs, Libn., M.L.S.
Founded: 1941. **Staff:** Prof 1; Other 1. **Subjects:** Christian religion. **Special Collections:** Evangelical Church. **Holdings:** 15,579 books; 82 bound periodical volumes; 817 microforms; 621 AV items. **Subscriptions:** 139 journals and other serials. **Services:** Copying; library open to the public.

★7216★
Hillcrest Medical Center - Library (Med)
1120 S. Utica Phone: (918)587-1300
Tulsa, OK 74104 Peggy Cook, Libn.
Founded: 1976. **Staff:** Prof 1. **Subjects:** Medicine, nursing, aging and health. **Special Collections:** Patient Education Resources Collection (1 LF drawer); Management Self-Directed Learning Center (200 books, AV programs, and journals); Aging and Health Collection (300 books; 15 journal titles); National League for Nursing publications. **Holdings:** 2691 books; 4765 bound periodical volumes; 1023 AV programs; 3 lateral file drawers drawers of pamphlets; 1 lateral file drawer of bibliographies; 1 lateral file drawer of newsletters. **Subscriptions:** 236 journals and other serials. **Services:** Interlibrary loan; copying; library open to the public for reference use only. **Computerized Information Services:** MEDLINE, BRS/COLLEAGUE; DOCLINE, OCLC (electronic mail services). **Networks/Consortia:** Member of Tulsa Area Library Cooperative (TALC), Oklahoma Health Sciences Library Association (OHSLA), National Network of Libraries of Medicine - South Central Region. **Publications:** List of Recent Acquisitions for the Medical Profession, monthly; List of Recent Acquisitions for the Nursing Profession, monthly. **Remarks:** FAX: (918)584-6636.

Hillerud Memorial Library
See: **Northwest Bible College - J.C. Cooke Library** (12042)

Florence Bayard Hilles Library
See: **National Woman's Party** (11327)

★7217★
Hilleshog Mono-Hy Inc. - Research Library (Biol Sci)
11939 Sugarmill Rd.
Longmont, CO 80501 Phone: (303)776-1802
Founded: 1910. **Subjects:** Plant breeding, plant physiology, agronomy, horticulture, nematology, weed control, organic chemistry. **Holdings:** 650 volumes; 5100 slides; 600 photographs; 4500 reprints and separates. **Subscriptions:** 25 journals and other serials. **Services:** Interlibrary loan; copying; library open to the public with prior approval of librarian or director of operations. **Remarks:** FAX: (303)776-0392.

James Frazer Hillman Health Sciences Library
See: **Shadyside Hospital** (15066)

Hillman Library
See: **Niles Township Jewish Congregation** (11811)

★7218★
Hillsborough County Historical Commission - Library (Hist)
County Court House, Rm. 250 Phone: (813)272-5919
Tampa, FL 33602 R. Randy Stevens, Chm.
Founded: 1949. **Staff:** Prof 1. **Subjects:** History of Florida and other southern states; genealogy. **Holdings:** 2000 books; Florida, Georgia, North Carolina, and South Carolina census records; Florida Confederate records; county records. **Services:** Library open to the public for reference use only. **Staff:** Mrs. G.B. Jones, Libn.

★7219★
Hillsborough County Law Library (Law)
725 E. Kennedy Blvd., 1st Fl. Phone: (813)272-5818
Tampa, FL 33602-5027 William M. Bailey, Dir.
Staff: Prof 2; Other 2. **Subjects:** Law. **Holdings:** 45,000 volumes. **Subscriptions:** 100 journals and other serials. **Services:** Copying; library open to the public with restrictions. **Computerized Information Services:** WESTLAW, CompuServe Information Service. **Remarks:** FAX: (813)272-5226.

Hillside Hospital
See: **Long Island Jewish Medical Center** (9290)

Hillyer Art Library
See: **Smith College** (15234)

★7220★
Hilo Hospital - Medical Library (Med)
1190 Waianuenue Ave. Phone: (808)969-4125
Hilo, HI 96720 Lorna Nekoba, Libn.
Founded: 1920. **Staff:** Prof 1. **Subjects:** Medicine, allied health sciences. **Holdings:** 700 books; 1296 cassettes. **Subscriptions:** 60 journals and other serials. **Services:** Interlibrary loan; copying; library not open to the public. **Computerized Information Services:** MEDLARS, DIALOG Information Services. **Networks/Consortia:** Member of National Network of Libraries of Medicine - Pacific Southwest Region, Medical Library Group of Hawaii. **Remarks:** FAX: (808)935-2009.

★7221★
Hilton-Davis Chemical Company - Library (Sci-Engr)
2235 Langdon Farm Rd. Phone: (513)841-4074
Cincinnati, OH 45237 Joe Kern, Libn.
Staff: Prof 1. **Subjects:** Pigments, chemical intermediates, dyes, chromogenic compounds. **Holdings:** 4800 books; 4000 bound periodical volumes; 7 VF drawers; 675 reports; 219 reels of microfilm; 340 microfiche; 19 audiotapes. **Subscriptions:** 175 journals and other serials. **Remarks:** FAX: (513)841-4841. Alternate telephone number(s): 841-4000.

Mae Hilty Memorial Library
See: **Texas Chiropractic College** (16207)

★7222★
Himachal Pradesh Agricultural University - Library (Agri)
H.P. Krisbi Vishva Vidyalaya Phone: 2644
Palanpur 176 062, Gujarat, India C.D. Handa, Libn.
Founded: 1966. **Staff:** Prof 4; Other 31. **Subjects:** Agriculture and allied sciences, veterinary science, home science, basic sciences, social sciences, languages. **Special Collections:** FAO Collection; Himachal Section collection (books on hilly areas of Himachal Pradesh). **Holdings:** 29,080 books; 16,707 bound periodical volumes and reports; 1091 theses; 501 pamphlets. **Subscriptions:** 374 journals and other serials; 8 newspapers. **Services:** Interlibrary loan; copying; library open to the public at librarian's discretion. **Remarks:** Library serves as a FAO depository library.

★7223★
Himalayan International Institute of Yoga Science and Philosophy of the U.S.A. - Library (Rel-Phil)
R.R. 1, Box 400
Honesdale, PA 18431 Phone: (717)253-5551
Subjects: Meditation, philosophy, holistic health care, yoga. **Holdings:** 10,000 volumes. **Remarks:** Toll-free telephone number(s): (800)444-5772. Telex: 5106001805. Electronic mail address(es): C001350 (EasyLink).

Paul Himmelfarb Health Sciences Library
See: **George Washington University - Medical Center** (20007)

★7224★
Himont USA, Inc. - R&D Center Library (Sci-Engr)
800 Greenbank Rd. Phone: (302)996-5177
Wilmington, DE 19808 Marlene A. Rossing
Founded: 1989. **Staff:** Prof 1; Other 1. **Subjects:** Polymers, chemicals. **Holdings:** 1900 books. **Subscriptions:** 150 journals and other serials. **Services:** Interlibrary loan; library not open to the public. **Computerized Information Services:** DIALOG Information Services, ORBIT Search Service, STN International; Proprietary Report (internal database). **Remarks:** FAX: (302)996-9387.

★7225★
Hinckley, Allen, Snyder & Comen - Law Library (Law)
1500 Fleet Ctr. Phone: (401)274-2000
Providence, RI 02903 Dawn F. Oliveri, Hd.Libn.
Staff: Prof 2; Other 5. **Subjects:** Tax; litigation; law - corporate, labor, medical, trusts, estate. **Special Collections:** Rhode Island Administrative Law Collection (2 vertical file drawers); Rhode Island City and Town Ordinances (45 volumes). **Holdings:** 12,000 books. **Subscriptions:** 100 journals and other serials. **Services:** Interlibrary loan (limited); library not open to the public. **Computerized Information Services:** LEXIS, NEXIS, DIALOG Information Services, WESTLAW, Dow Jones News/Retrieval, VU/TEXT Information Services, Information Access Company. **Special Indexes:** Index to internal legal memoranda, briefs, and opinion letters (card); RI Legislative Tracking Database. **Remarks:** FAX: (401)277-9600. Telex: 952039. Maintains a satellite library in Boston. **Staff:** Monica Elder, Asst.Libn.

★7226★
Hinckley Foundation Museum - Library (Hist)
410 E. Seneca St. Phone: (607)273-7053
Ithaca, NY 14850 Lori Abbott-Herrick, Dir.
Founded: 1972. **Staff:** Prof 2. **Subjects:** Local history. **Special Collections:** Ithaca imprints; Hinckley family papers; Celia Smith papers. **Holdings:** 1000 books; 10 boxes of papers. **Services:** Library open to the public for reference use only.

★7227★
C.M. Hincks Treatment Center - C.M. Hincks Institute - Jackman Library (Med)
440 Jarvis St. Phone: (416)972-1935
Toronto, ON, Canada M4Y 2H4 Mary W. Smith, Libn.
Founded: 1967. **Staff:** Prof 1. **Subjects:** Child and adolescent psychiatry and psychology, child development and care, social work, family therapy. **Holdings:** 1600 books; 700 bound periodical volumes; VF drawers; reprints; bibliographies. **Subscriptions:** 69 journals and other serials. **Services:** Interlibrary loan; copying. **Computerized Information Services:** Internal database. **Publications:** Acquisitions list, quarterly - for internal distribution only. **Special Indexes:** Index to journals (online). **Remarks:** Alternate telephone number(s): 924-1164. FAX: (416)924-8208.

★7228★
Hinds General Hospital - William M. Suttle Medical Library (Med)
1850 Chadwick Dr. Phone: (601)376-1148
Jackson, MS 39204 Wanda W. King, Med.Libn.
Founded: 1977. **Staff:** Prof 1. **Subjects:** Medicine, nursing, dentistry, hospital administration. **Holdings:** 1500 books; 2500 bound periodical volumes. **Subscriptions:** 148 journals and other serials. **Services:** Interlibrary loan; library not open to the public. **Computerized Information Services:** MEDLARS. Performs searches on fee basis. **Networks/Consortia:** Member of Central Mississippi Consortium of Medical Libraries, Central Mississippi Library Council, Mississippi Biomedical Library Consortium (MBLC). **Remarks:** FAX: (601)376-2841.

Walter C. Hinkle Memorial Library
See: **State University College of Technology at Alfred** (15715)

★7229★
Hinomoto Bunko - Library
129 N. Saratoga St. Phone: (213)264-7147
Los Angeles, CA 90033 Masayo Keyaki, Libn.
Remarks: No further information was supplied by respondent.

William A. Hinrichs Medical Library
See: **Converse County Memorial Hospital** (4262)

★7230★
Hinsdale Hospital - Health Sciences Library (Med)
120 N. Oak St. Phone: (708)887-2868
Hinsdale, IL 60521 Hilda J. Smith, MLS, Libn.
Founded: 1990. **Staff:** Prof 1; Other 2. **Subjects:** Nursing, religion, medicine, clinical medicine. **Special Collections:** Ellen G. White Collection (200 volumes). **Holdings:** 7000 books; 1000 bound periodical volumes; 19 VF drawers of pamphlets; 5 films; 200 pieces of miscellanea. **Subscriptions:** 246 journals and other serials. **Services:** Interlibrary loan; copying; library open to the public for reference use only. **Computerized Information Services:** MEDLINE, BRS Information Technologies. Performs searches on fee basis. **Networks/Consortia:** Member of Chicago and South Consortium, Suburban Library System (SLS), ILLINET. **Publications:** Library newsletter, quarterly - available to members of the medical and nursing administration.

★7231★
Hiram College - Teachout-Price Memorial Library - Archives and Special Collections (Hist)
Hiram, OH 44234 Phone: (216)569-5361
Joanne M. Sawyer, Archv.
Staff: Prof 1. **Subjects:** Hiram history, regional studies, Disciples of Christ history, juvenile literature, Hiram authors, World War I. **Special Collections:** Regional studies collection (57 volumes; 25 document cases); institutional history (200 linear feet); local history collection (6 linear feet); personal papers of James A. Garfield, Burke A. Hinsdale, N. Vachel Lindsay, John S. Kenyon, Edmund B. Wakefield, the Henry Family (58 linear feet); Maurice and Ethlynn Fox Collection (87 antique regional maps; 87 volumes; geographies; atlases; journals); church history (100 volumes; 1 storage carton; 11 document cases); early textbook collection (570 volumes); juvenile literature (223 volumes; 10 document cases); Hiram authors (33 linear feet); World War I pamphlets (6 linear feet); rare books (69 volumes). **Holdings:** 1019 books; 402 linear feet of other cataloged items. **Services:** Interlibrary loan; copying; collections open to the public by appointment. **Automated Operations:** Computerized cataloging and acquisitions. **Computerized Information Services:** DIALOG Information Services, OCLC. **Special Catalogs:** Catalogs to regional studies, church history, textbooks, juvenile literature, and Hiram authors (all on cards). **Remarks:** FAX: (216)569-5491.

J. Wilbur Hirons Library
See: **Goldey Beacom College** (6542)

Hiroshima/Nagasaki Memorial Collection
See: **Wilmington College of Ohio - Peace Resource Center** (20461)

Emil G. Hirsch Library
See: **Chicago Sinai Congregation** (3543)

Hirsch Library
See: **Museum of Fine Arts, Houston** (10899)

Jack Hirschman Archives
See: **University of Southern California - Library - Department of Special Collections - American Literature Collection** (19338)

Hirshhorn Museum and Sculpture Garden
See: **Smithsonian Institution** (15261)

Hirst Free Law Library
See: **Temple University - Law Library** (16148)

L. Hirszfeld Institute of Immunology and Experimental Therapy
See: **Poland - Polish Academy of Sciences - L. Hirszfeld Institute of Immunology and Experimental Therapy** (13172)

Ira V. Hiscock Epidemiology and Public Health Library
See: **Yale University** (20716)

★7232★
Hispanic Baptist Theological Seminary - Library (Rel-Phil)
8019 S. Pan Am Expy. Phone: (512)924-4338
San Antonio, TX 78224-1397 James O. Wallace, Dir.
Founded: 1956. **Staff:** Prof 1; Other 3. **Subjects:** Theology, Baptist history. **Holdings:** 16,836 books; 1813 bound periodical volumes; 155 microforms; 1907 AV items. **Subscriptions:** 202 journals and other serials. **Services:** Interlibrary loan; copying; fax services; library open to seminary students. **Automated Operations:** Computerized cataloging and ILL. **Remarks:** 34 percent of holdings are in Spanish. FAX: (512)924-0888.

★7233★
Hispanic Institute in the United States - Library (Hum)
Columbia University
Casa Hispanica
612 W. 116th St. Phone: (212)854-8292
New York, NY 10027 Prof. Susana Redondo De Feldman, Dir.
Subjects: Spanish and Portuguese literature and linguistics. **Special Collections:** Magazine and newspaper clipping archives, 1934-1969 (authors from Spain, Portugal, Spanish America, and Brazil). **Holdings:** 10,000 books. **Subscriptions:** 103 journals and other serials. **Services:** Library open to students and literary researchers by permission. **Remarks:** Alternate telephone number(s): 854-4187.

★7234★
Hispanic Society of America - Department of Iconography - General Reference File (Area-Ethnic)
613 155th St. Phone: (212)926-2234
New York, NY 10032 Anita Andreasian, Hd. of Dept. of Iconography
Subjects: Spanish and Portuguese art (fine and decorative); cities and buildings in Spain and Portugal and their former possessions; costumes and customs of Spain and Portugal. **Holdings:** 170,000 photographs; prints; maps; globes; slides. **Services:** Photographs available for study; file open to the public by appointment.

★7235★
Hispanic Society of America - Library (Area-Ethnic)
Broadway & 155th St. Phone: (212)926-2234
New York, NY 10032 Dr. Gerald J. Mac Donald, Cur., Modern Lib.
Founded: 1904. **Staff:** Prof 3; Other 6. **Subjects:** Art, history, literature, and general culture of Spain, Portugal, and colonial Hispanic America. **Special Collections:** Books printed before 1701; manuscripts. **Holdings:** 250,000 volumes; 200,000 manuscripts; 113 VF drawers of clippings; 200 manuscript maps; periodicals. **Subscriptions:** 123 journals and other serials; 5 newspapers. **Services:** Microfiliming (rare books only); library open to the public on a limited schedule; appointments are recommended for rare books, and required for manuscripts. **Publications:** List of publications - available on request. **Special Catalogs:** Catalog of the library through 1972 (10 volumes with 4 volume supplement); catalog of printed books, 1468-1700 (book). **Special Indexes:** Spanish Drama of the Golden Age; medieval manuscripts. **Staff:** Dr. Sandra Sider, Mss./Rare Bks.Cur.; Jose Marzol, Per.

★7236★
Hispano-American Astronomical Society - Library (Sci-Engr)
Ave. Diagonal 377, 2
E-08008 Barcelona, Spain Phone: 3 218-7880
Subjects: Astronomy, geology, and allied subjects. **Holdings:** 1500 volumes; biographical archives. **Also Known As:** Sociedad Astronomica de Espana y America.

★7237★
Historic Annapolis Foundation - Library (Plan)
194 Prince George St. Phone: (301)267-7619
Annapolis, MD 21401 Mary M. Vittek, Libn.
Founded: 1952. **Staff:** Prof 1; Other 1. **Subjects:** Preservation, urban planning, state and local history, genealogy, decorative arts. **Special Collections:** 1983 architectural survey of Annapolis' Historic District. **Holdings:** 1210 books; 30 volumes of clippings; Annapolis and Anne Arundel County history records; extensive 19th and 20th century photographic files; computer file of 17th and 18th century Anne Arundel County probate records; architectural databank; maps. **Subscriptions:** 13 journals and other serials. **Services:** Interlibrary loan; copying; library open to serious scholars only.

★7238★
Historic Annapolis, Inc. - William Paca Garden Conservation Center (Biol Sci)
3 Martin St. Phone: (301)269-0601
Annapolis, MD 21401 Lucy Dos Passos Coggin, Prog.Coord.
Founded: 1984. **Staff:** Prof 1; Other 2. **Subjects:** Horticulture, conservation, historic landscape and flora. **Special Collections:** Historic roses (51 volumes). **Holdings:** 385 books; 700 bound periodical volumes; 125 pieces of general horticultural and conservation material; 400 national and international garden files; 5200 color slides of plants and historic gardens. **Subscriptions:** 300 nursery catalogs. **Services:** Center open to the public by appointment. **Computerized Information Services:** WPG plant inventory (internal database). **Special Indexes:** Index to color slide files of 18th century plants; index to native mid-Atlantic plants; index to plant sources.

★7239★
Historic Bethabara Park - Library (Hist)
2147 Bethabara Rd. Phone: (919)924-8191
Winston-Salem, NC 27106 J. Rodney Meyer, Dir.
Founded: 1966. **Staff:** Prof 2; Other 20. **Subjects:** History - Moravian, Winston-Salem/Forsyth County, North Carolina; colonial crafts; museology; wild flowers. **Holdings:** 800 books; 100 manuscripts. **Services:** Library open to the public for reference use only. **Remarks:** Historic Bethabara Park (the first Moravian settlement in the state) is an 80-acre historic site and is administered by the city of Winston-Salem, NC. **Staff:** Gena Elias.

★7240★
Historic Bethlehem Inc. - Library/Archives (Hist)
459 Old York Rd. Phone: (215)868-6311
Bethlehem, PA 18018 Charles LeCount, Cur.
Founded: 1957. **Staff:** 1. **Subjects:** Bethlehem history, early American tools and trades, museum administration. **Special Collections:** Photograph collection of Bethlehem. **Holdings:** 1500 books. **Subscriptions:** 12 journals and other serials. **Services:** Library not open to the public. **Publications:** HBI Member's Newsletter.

Historic Camden Revolutionary War Park
See: **Camden Historical Commission** (2610)

★7241★
Historic Cherry Hill - Library (Hist)
523 1/2 S. Pearl St.
Albany, NY 12202 Phone: (518)434-4791
Founded: 1964. **Staff:** 5. **Subjects:** Albany history; devotional literature; law; medicine, 1850-1900; gardening; travel. **Special Collections:** Philip Van Rensselaer Family Collection (5000 books). **Services:** Library open to the public with restrictions. **Special Catalogs:** Selections from a Van Rensselaer Family Library, 1536-1799.

★7242★
Historic Deerfield, Inc./Pocumtuck Valley Memorial Association - Memorial Libraries (Hist)
Memorial St.
P.O. Box 53 Phone: (413)774-5581
Deerfield, MA 01342 David R. Proper, Libn.
Founded: 1870. **Staff:** Prof 2; Other 1. **Subjects:** History of Deerfield and Western Massachusetts; American decorative arts; museology; genealogy; Connecticut Valley studies; architecture. **Special Collections:** Works by local authors; manuscripts and account books of local persons; Western Massachusetts imprints; photographs by Mary and Frances Allen. **Holdings:** 38,000 books; 225 bound periodical volumes; 250 boxes of family manuscripts, diaries, letters; 400 account books; 110 boxes of town, business, miscellaneous papers; 15 boxes of photographs; 250 reels of microfilm; travel accounts; hymnals. **Subscriptions:** 35 journals and other serials. **Services:** Copying; library open to the public for reference use only. **Computerized Information Services:** OCLC. **Publications:** Research at Deerfield. **Remarks:** FAX: (413)773-7415. The Memorial Libraries consist of the 25,000-volume Pocumtuck Valley Memorial Association Library and the 13,000-volume Historic Deerfield, Inc. Henry N. Flynt Library. **Staff:** Sharman E. Prouty, Asst.Libn.

Historic Galloway House and Village
See: **Fond du Lac County Historical Society** (5944)

★7243★
Historic Hudson Valley - Special Library & Archives (Art, Hist)
150 White Plains Rd.
Tarrytown, NY 10591 Phone: (914)631-8200
Founded: 1951. **Staff:** Prof 1. **Subjects:** 17th, 18th, and 19th century Hudson River Valley history; decorative arts and architecture; Washington Irving. **Special Collections:** Manuscript holdings of Van Cortlandt and Philipse families; Washington Irving manuscripts. **Holdings:** 25,000 volumes; pamphlets; 49 VF drawers of maps, plans, graphics; 19 microfilm files; unpublished reports; archives; plans and blueprints of Historic Hudson Valley restored buildings. **Subscriptions:** 160 journals and other serials. **Services:** Copying (limited); library open to scholars, authors, and researchers by appointment. **Networks/Consortia:** Member of New York Metropolitan Reference and Research Library Agency. **Remarks:** Toll-free telephone number(s): (800)HHV-4007. FAX: (914)631-0089. **Staff:** Kathleen Eagen Johnson, Libn.

★7244★
Historic Landmarks Foundation of Indiana, Inc. - Information Center (Plan)
340 W. Michigan St. Phone: (317)639-4534
Indianapolis, IN 46202 Marsh Davis, Dir. of Commun.Serv.
Founded: 1960. **Staff:** Prof 1. **Subjects:** State architectural surveys, architecture, history, adaptive use, historic preservation, restoration techniques, neighborhood preservation, art, antiques. **Holdings:** 1200 books; 15,000 color slides; 24 slide/tape programs; 5 16mm films; 1400 black/white photographs; 250 unbound reports; 580 pamphlets; 5000 black/white negatives; clippings. **Subscriptions:** 75 journals and other serials. **Services:** Copying; center open to the public with restrictions. **Automated Operations:** Computerized cataloging. **Publications:** Properties brochures; The Indiana Preservationist, bimonthly; Preservation Bulletin, irregular; publications on preservation, irregular. **Special Indexes:** Indiana architects; Indiana historic structures, listed by county (both on cards). **Remarks:** FAX: (317)639-6734.

★7245★
Historic Lexington Foundation - Garland Gray Research Center & Library (Hist)
Stonewall Jackson House
8 E. Washington St. Phone: (703)463-2552
Lexington, VA 24450 Ms. Michael Anne Lynn, Dir.
Founded: 1954. **Staff:** 1. **Subjects:** Thomas J. "Stonewall" Jackson, Civil War, historic preservation, museum practices, decorative arts. **Special Collections:** T.M. Wade Collection. **Holdings:** 1592 books. **Services:** Copying; library open to the public by appointment for reference use. **Publications:** The Genealogies of the Jackson, Junkin and Morrison Families, 1981; Stonewall Jackson and the Virginia Military Institute: The Lexington Years, 1982; Stonewall Jackson in Lexington: The Christian Soldier, 1984.

★7246★
Historic Mobile Preservation Society - Mitchell Archives (Hist)
300 Oakleigh Pl. Phone: (205)432-6161
Mobile, AL 36608 Jean T. Getchell, Archv.Chm.
Founded: 1940. **Staff:** 3. **Subjects:** Mobile history, Mardi Gras, Mobiliana. **Special Collections:** William E. Wilson Photographic Collection of Mobile scenes and people, 1895-1910 (2000 glass negatives); worldwide architectural books (500). **Holdings:** 500 books; 15 VF drawers of clippings; 4 VF drawers of documents; 4 VF drawers of photographs; 5 VF drawers of maps and prints. **Subscriptions:** 16 journals and other serials. **Services:** Copying; research on premises; fee for use of photographic prints; send stamped envelope with out-of-town inquiries.

★7247★
Historic New Orleans Collection - Library (Hist)
533 Royal St. Phone: (504)523-4662
New Orleans, LA 70130 Florence M. Jumonville, Hd.Libn.
Founded: 1966. **Staff:** Prof 3; Other 1. **Subjects:** History - New Orleans, Louisiana, Gulf South, Louisiana Purchase territory; New Orleans architecture. **Special Collections:** Vieux Carre Survey (New Orleans architecture and the French Quarter; 150 binders); New Orleans City Directories; New Orleans imprints; sheet music (2000 items). **Holdings:** 15,000 books; 100 bound periodical volumes; 8000 pamphlets. **Subscriptions:** 30 journals and other serials. **Services:** Copying; library open to the public. **Computerized Information Services:** FACETS (internal database). **Networks/Consortia:** Member of SOLINET. **Publications:** Bibliography of New Orleans Imprints, 1764-1864 (monograph) - available for purchase. **Special Catalogs:** Bound to Please: Fifty Rare Books About Louisiana; Guide to the Vieux Carre Survey. **Remarks:** Collection is administered by The Kemper and Leila Williams Foundation. **Staff:** Pamela D. Arceneaux, Ref.Libn.; Jessica Travis, Ref.Libn.

★7248★
Historic Northampton - Historical Collection (Hist)
46 Bridge St. Phone: (413)584-6011
Northampton, MA 01060 Pamela Toma, Dir.
Founded: 1905. **Staff:** 2. **Subjects:** Local history and biography. **Special Collections:** Brewster Civil War letters. **Holdings:** Documents; letters; diaries; manuscripts; account books; ephemera; photographs; clippings; oral histories. **Services:** Copying.

★7249★
Historic Pensacola Preservation Board - Library (Hist)
120 Church St. Phone: (904)444-8905
Pensacola, FL 32501 John Daniels, Dir.
Founded: 1967. **Subjects:** Historic preservation, Florida and regional history, museum administration, architectural history, antiques. **Holdings:** 1800 books; 3 scrapbooks; 30 oral history tapes; slide library. **Services:** Library open to the public for reference use only by written request. **Remarks:** Maintained by Florida State Department of State - Division of Historical Resources.

★7250★
Historic Preservation Association of Bourbon County - Old Congregation Church - Resource Library (Hist)
117 S. Main Phone: (316)223-5443
Fort Scott, KS 66701 Kathryn A. Reed, Exec.Dir.
Founded: 1973. **Staff:** 1. **Subjects:** Bourbon County history. **Special Collections:** 19th century Bible collection. **Holdings:** Books; periodicals; papers; photographs; other cataloged items. **Services:** library open to the public.

★7251★
Historic Preservation League of Oregon - Library (Plan)
26 N.W. 2nd Ave., 2nd Fl.
Box 40053 Phone: (503)243-1923
Portland, OR 97240 Eric Eisemann, Exec.Dir.
Subjects: Historic preservation, cultural resources management. **Holdings:** Figures not available. **Services:** Library open to the public for reference use only.

Historic Rugby, Inc. - Thomas Hughes Library
See: **Thomas Hughes Library** (7519)

★7252★
Historic St. Augustine Preservation Board - Hispanic Research Library (Hist)
Box 1987
St. Augustine, FL 32085 Phone: (904)825-5033
Founded: 1959. **Staff:** 1. **Subjects:** Hispanic and Southeastern ethnography, archeology, and history of Florida, St. Augustine, and the Caribbean. **Special Collections:** 16th-18th century Spanish documents (transcripts and translations); St. Augustine preservation project files; historical maps. **Holdings:** 3000 books; 60 bound periodical volumes; 4500 slides; 800 maps; 3500 negatives; 100 reels of microfilm; 45 VF drawers of research materials; 350 architectural drawings. **Subscriptions:** 10 journals and other serials. **Services:** Copying; library open to the public by appointment. **Remarks:** FAX: (904)825-5096.

★7253★
Historic St. Mary's City - Research Library (Hist)
Box 39 Phone: (301)862-0974
St. Mary's City, MD 20686 Dr. Henry M. Miller, Dir., Dept. of Res.
Staff: 1. **Subjects:** Historic sites archeology, material culture, folk architecture, Maryland history and architecture. **Special Collections:** Transcripts of colonial real estate valuations and probate inventories, 1638-1750 (2 VF drawers); abstracts from colonial documents on material culture (2 card files); records and research on 17th century Maryland; research files on Maryland's 17th century capital; land records; archeological records. **Holdings:** 400 volumes; 150 bound periodical volumes; 3000 transcripts; 300 manuscripts; 20 VF drawers; 30 linear feet of excavation notes and artifact catalogs. **Services:** Copying; library open to the public for reference use only by appointment. **Staff:** Peggy L. Lewis, Res.Libn.

★7254★
Historic Schaefferstown, Inc. - Thomas R. Brendle Memorial Library & Museum (Hist)
N. Market St. Phone: (717)949-3795
Schaefferstown, PA 17088 Violet Webber
Staff: 1. **Subjects:** Local history, Pennsylvania German folklore. **Special Collections:** Thomas R. Brendle Collection of Pennsylvania German Folklore; Dialect program (radio broadcasts, Jan. 29, 1966 - Feb. 10, 1971; 262 tapes). **Holdings:** 1000 books; Brendle family manuscripts. **Services:** Library open to the public on request.

★7255★
Historic Tallahassee Preservation Board - Library (Plan)
329 N. Meridian St. Phone: (904)488-3901
Tallahassee, FL 32301 Vivian Young, Commun.Asst.Cons.
Subjects: Tallahassee and Leon County architecture and history; historic preservation. **Special Collections:** Historic photographs. **Holdings:** Figures not available. **Services:** Library open to the public by appointment.

★7256★
Historical Association of Southern Florida - Charlton W. Tebeau Library of Florida History (Hist)
101 W. Flagler St. Phone: (305)375-1492
Miami, FL 33130 Rebecca A. Smith, Cur., Res.Mtls.
Founded: 1940. **Staff:** Prof 1; Other 1. **Subjects:** Florida history, especially South Florida; Caribbean; Dade County history; Bahamas. **Special Collections:** Early telephone and business directories; photographs, including the works of Claude Matlack, Richard B. Hoit, Ralph Munroe, Annette and Rudi Rada; manuscripts, including the papers of Carl Fisher, George Merrick, James Jaudon, Gilpin Family, Julia Tuttle, Reginald V. Waters; Miami Beach Visitor & Convention Authority; Miami News; family scrapbooks. **Holdings:** 4000 books; 300 bound periodical volumes; 1600 maps; 146 reels of microfilm; 40 VF drawers of pamphlets and clippings; 900,000 photographs; 400 linear feet of archival materials and manuscripts; 200 oral history tapes and transcripts; 300 sets of architectural drawings. **Subscriptions:** 60 journals and other serials. **Services:** Copying; SDI; library open to the public for research use only. **Computerized Information Services:** Internal databases. **Publications:** Tequesta, annual; South Florida History Magazine, quarterly; Currents, quarterly. **Remarks:** FAX: (305)375-1609.

★7257★
Historical Committee of the Mennonite Church - Archives of the Mennonite Church (Rel-Phil, Hist)
Goshen College Phone: (219)535-7477
Goshen, IN 46526 Dennis Stoesz, Archv.
Founded: 1911. **Staff:** Prof 2; Other 3. **Subjects:** Official records of the Mennonite Church, its boards, committees, agencies, and institutions; peace collections; archives collection of the Mennonite Central Committee; private papers of 1100 church leaders. **Special Collections:** J.F. Funk and H.S. Bender Collections of manuscripts and papers; Doug Hostetter manuscripts and artifacts of Vietnam War. **Holdings:** 12 million items. **Services:** Copying; archives open to the public. **Publications:** Mennonite Historical Bulletin, quarterly - for sale. **Special Catalogs:** Inventory listings of major collections. **Remarks:** FAX: (219)535-7660.

★7258★
Historical and Genealogical Society of Indiana County - Library and Archives (Hist)
200 S. 6th St.
Indiana, PA 15701-2999 Phone: (412)463-9600
Founded: 1938. **Staff:** Prof 2; Other 1. **Subjects:** Local history, Western Pennsylvania history and genealogy, Pennsylvania regimental histories, historic preservation, antiques. **Special Collections:** Genealogical files; Frances Strong Helman Collection; Cecil Smith Bequest; Published Pennsylvania Archives. **Holdings:** 10,000 books; 150 volumes of newspapers on microfilm; manuscripts; surname vertical files of Indiana County birth and marriage announcements and obituaries; selected federal census schedules on microfilm. **Subscriptions:** 50 journals and other serials. **Services:** Copying; library open to the public during specified hours. **Publications:** Newsletter, monthly; Indiana County Heritage; The Quarterly - all free to members and by subscription.

★7259★
Historical and Genealogical Society of Somerset County - County Historical Library and Research Center (Hist)
Somerset Historical Center
R.F.D. 2, Box 238 Phone: (814)445-6077
Somerset, PA 15501 James A. Bochy, Pres.
Founded: 1960. **Staff:** 2. **Subjects:** Somerset County history, genealogy. **Holdings:** 300 books; 5 drawers of source materials on local history and genealogy; films of documents and source material; 200 reels of microfilm. **Subscriptions:** 25 journals and other serials. **Services:** Copying; microfilm printing; library open to the public. **Automated Operations:** Computerized indexing. **Publications:** Laurel Messenger, quarterly. **Staff:** Bernice Sarver; Bernadette Gardosik.

Historical Library of Missions
See: **Yale University - Divinity School Library** (20708)

Historical Museum of the Wabash Valley
See: **Vigo County Historical Society** (19840)

★7260★
Historical Pictures Service, Inc. (Aud-Vis, Hist)
921 W. Van Buren St., Rm. 201 Phone: (312)733-3239
Chicago, IL 60607 Shirley Neiman, Sales/Res.
Founded: 1900. **Staff:** Prof 3. **Subjects:** Documentary history - political, military, economic, technological, social. **Special Collections:** Harris and Ewing collection of news events photographs, 1900-1955, and photographs of prominent persons; Americana; portraits. **Holdings:** 250,000 prints and photographs. **Services:** Pictures available on a fee basis; collection not open to the public. **Remarks:** FAX: (312)733-2844.

★7261★
Historical Research Repository, Inc. - Library (Area-Ethnic)
P.O. Box 15364
Fox Creek Sta. Phone: (313)822-9027
Detroit, MI 48215-0364 John M. Green, Archv.
Founded: 1968. **Staff:** Prof 1. **Subjects:** Black history, Michigan black history. **Special Collections:** Pre-1940 postcards of blacks (115); African American U.S. postal stamps (complete set). **Holdings:** 85 books. **Services:** Library not open to the public. **Publications:** Black Nobel Prize Winners (poster); Michigan Black History Review. **Remarks:** Library has access to International Afro-American Sports Hall of Fame and Gallery newspapers, photographs, and films.

★7262★
Historical Society of Alpine County - Alpine County Museum - Library (Hist)
P.O. Box 24 Phone: (916)694-2317
Markleeville, CA 96120 Nancy C. Thornburg, Musm.Dir.
Founded: 1964. **Staff:** 1. **Subjects:** Alpine County history. **Holdings:** 400 books; 200 documents; photographs; manuscripts. **Services:** Copying (limited); research facility open to the public by appointment. **Computerized Information Services:** Internal database. **Publications:** Alpine Heritage; Alpine County (U.S.) Census, 1870, 1880, 1900, 1910.

★7263★
Historical Society of Berks County - Library (Hist)
940 Centre Ave. Phone: (215)375-4375
Reading, PA 19601 Barbara Gill, Dir.
Staff: Prof 1; Other 1. **Subjects:** Local history, genealogy, German Americans in Pennsylvania. **Special Collections:** Early newspapers; church records; county archives; slide collection of barn signs; original account books of early forges and furnaces of Berks County. **Holdings:** 9000 books; 400 bound periodical volumes; 504 maps; 300 reels of microfilm; documents; letters; diaries; muster rolls. **Subscriptions:** 14 journals and other serials. **Services:** Copying; library open to the public.

★7264★
Historical Society of Carroll County - Research Library (Hist)
210 E. Main St. Phone: (301)848-6494
Westminster, MD 21157 Jay A. Graybead, Cur.
Founded: 1939. **Staff:** 2. **Subjects:** Family and local history. **Special Collections:** Dr. Arthur G. Tracey Collection (land patents and setlement patterns in Western Maryland; file cards, drawings, surveyors' books, maps); Leland Jordan Collection of Carroll County Newspapers (The Democratic Advocate, 1842-1972; The Carrolltonian, 1833-1844; Union Bridge Pilot, 1899-1972; American Sentinel, 1855-1928; Carroll County Times, 1911 to present). **Holdings:** 2500 books; 100 bound periodical volumes; 100 AV programs; 10,000 manuscripts; 25 nonbook items. **Subscriptions:** 10 journals and other serials; 2 newspapers. **Services:** Copying (limited); library open to the public on a fee basis. Appointments are recommended for Manuscript Room. **Publications:** Library Guide.

★7265★
Historical Society of the Cocalico Valley - Museum and Library (Hist)
249 W. Main St.
Box 193 Phone: (717)733-1616
Ephrata, PA 17522 Cynthia Marquet, Libn.
Staff: Prof 1. **Subjects:** Local history, genealogy, Pennsylvania German culture and art. **Special Collections:** Milton H. Heinecke Collection of manuscript notebooks on local history (52); Col. George Sallade Howard Collection (first conductor of the U.S. Air Force Band; manuscripts and photographs). **Holdings:** 3310 books; 3532 manuscripts and typescripts; 6700 photographs; 183 tapes and reels of microfilm. **Subscriptions:** 14 journals and other serials. **Services:** Copying; library open to the public. **Publications:** Book of photographs, semiannual; annual journal.

★7266★
Historical Society of Delaware - Library (Hist)
505 Market Street Mall
Wilmington, DE 19801 Phone: (302)655-7161
Founded: 1864. **Staff:** Prof 3; Other 2. **Subjects:** Delaware - history, business, industry; politics and diplomacy; law; religion; genealogy. **Special Collections:** Delaware newspapers; rare books, pamphlets, and Delaware imprints; photographs (150,000); maps (1000); business, organization, and personal papers. **Holdings:** 50,000 books; 10,000 pamphlets; 53 cubic feet of ephemera; 12 VF drawers and 60 catalog drawers of reference and genealogical files. **Subscriptions:** 80 journals and other serials; 5 newspapers. **Services:** Interlibrary loan (limited); copying; photograph reproduction; library open to the public. **Publications:** Delaware History, semiannual. **Special Catalogs:** Imprints, photographs, maps, newspapers (card); manuscript catalog (card and inventory); manuscript books catalog (printed); special subjects catalog (card). **Staff:** Constance Cooper, Mss.Libn.; L. Ellen Peterson, Cur. of Bks. and Photo.; Kevin Kennard, Ref.Libn.

★7267★
Historical Society of Douglas County - Library/Archives Center (Hist)
Box 11398 Phone: (402)451-1013
Omaha, NE 68110-0398 Roger L. Reeves, Cur./Lib.Dir.
Founded: 1981. **Staff:** Prof 3; Other 1. **Subjects:** History - Douglas County, Omaha; Department of the Platte/Fort Omaha; Douglas County authors, overland trails, Missouri Valley exploration and fur trade. **Special Collections:** Records of the National Association of American Balloon Corps Veterans; Omaha World Herald Newspaper clipping files (5 million); Tuesday Musical Club; Omaha Marine Dads' Association; Omaha Magic Theatre; Barker Family Letters (1860-1871); N.P. Dodge Letters (1854-1901). **Holdings:** 1800 books; 850 letters; 6000 photographs; 7500 collected items; diaries; memoirs; scrapbooks; oral history interviews and transcripts; legal documents and business records; documents; artifacts; art work; maps. **Subscriptions:** 10 journals and other serials; 5 newspapers. **Services:** Copying; photograph duplication; library open to the public for reference use only. **Computerized Information Services:** DataTimes; Index to Omaha World-Herald Clippings Files (internal database). **Publications:** Transcripts of Society Lecture Series and the River City Roundup Oral History Interviews. **Remarks:** FAX: (402)451-1394. **Staff:** Ann B. Haller, Libn.; John K. Brudney, Cat.

Historical Society of the Eastern Pennsylvania Conference
See: **United Methodist Church - Historical Society of the Eastern Pennsylvania Conference** (16734)

★7268★
Historical Society of Frederick County - Library (Hist)
24 E. Church St. Phone: (301)663-1188
Frederick, MD 21701 Angie F. Brosius, Libn.
Founded: 1985. **Subjects:** History, genealogy, religion, literature, Frederick County. **Holdings:** 1500 books; 500 photographs; 70 historic maps; glass negatives; manuscripts. **Subscriptions:** 3 journals and other serials. **Services:** Copying; library open to the public for reference use only. **Staff:** Mary S. Cramer, Asst.Libn.

★7269★
Historical Society of Haddonfield - Library (Hist)
343 King's Hwy., E. Phone: (609)429-7375
Haddonfield, NJ 08033 Katherine M. Tassini, Libn.
Founded: 1914. **Staff:** Prof 2; Other 4. **Subjects:** Local and state history, genealogy. **Holdings:** 1500 volumes; 3 VF drawers of maps; 15 VF drawers of manuscripts; pamphlets collection; newspapers on microfilm; history recordings. **Services:** Library open to the public on limited schedule. **Publications:** Bulletin, 4/year - to members and other historical societies.

★7270★
Historical Society of Israel - Library (Hist)
22 Rashba St.
P.O. Box 4179 Phone: 2 637171
91041 Jerusalem, Israel Zivia Florsheim
Founded: 1973. **Subjects:** Jewish history, Judaica, Judaism. **Special Collections:** President Zalman Shazar collection. **Holdings:** 7000 volumes. **Subscriptions:** 40 journals and other serials. **Services:** Library open to academic researchers only. **Publications:** ZION, quarterly. **Remarks:** FAX: 2 662135. Alternate telephone number(s): 2 669464. **Also Known As:** Ha Hevre ha Historit ha Israelit.

★7271★
Historical Society of Long Beach - Archives (Hist, Aud-Vis)
Senior Center
1150 E. 4th St.
Box 1869 Phone: (213)435-7511
Long Beach, CA 90801 Zona Gale Forbes, Photo.Archv.
Founded: 1962. **Staff:** 5. **Subjects:** Local history. **Special Collections:** Photograph collection (25,000 negatives and contact prints). **Holdings:** 2000 slides; 20 scrapbooks; 16 VF drawers of newspaper clippings; 10 VF drawers of pamphlets and ephemera. **Services:** Copying; archives open to the public. **Publications:** Photograph Journals, irregular; Newsletter, monthly. **Special Indexes:** Index to Los Fierros Quarterly.

★7272★
Historical Society of Marshall County - Research Library (Hist)
P.O. Box 304 Phone: (515)752-6664
Marshalltown, IA 50158 Jeff Quam, Adm.
Subjects: Marshall County history. **Special Collections:** War of Rebellion Collection (official records of the Union and Confederate Armies and Navies); works of E.P. Roe; Law Library, Putney. **Holdings:** City directories; periodicals; agriculture yearbook; early newspapers. **Services:** Copying; library open to the public for reference use only.

★7273★
Historical Society of Michigan - Center for the Teaching of Michigan History (Hist)
2117 Washtenaw Ave. Phone: (313)769-1828
Ann Arbor, MI 48104 Thomas L. Jones, Exec.Dir.
Founded: 1990. **Staff:** 1. **Subjects:** Michigan history, teaching. **Special Collections:** Teaching resources (published and unpublished); in-state and out-of-state historical society publications and related materials. **Holdings:** 300 books; 50 bound periodical volumes. **Services:** 50 journals and other serials. **Services:** Copying; library open to the public. **Remarks:** FAX: (313)769-4267.

★7274★
Historical Society of the Militia and National Guard - Library of the National Guard (Mil)
1 Massachusetts Ave., N.W. Phone: (202)789-0031
Washington, DC 20001 Maj. Thomas M. Weaver, Dir.
Staff: Prof 2. **Holdings:** Military histories, including the National Guard and state militia archives; Adjutants General Reports. **Subscriptions:** 30 journals and other serials; 20 newspapers. **Services:** Copying; library open to the public. **Automated Operations:** Computerized cataloging. **Computerized Information Services:** DIALOG Information Services, Washington Alert Service, OCLC; Dialcom (electronic mail service). **Special Indexes:** Index to the National Guard Magazine (1988 to present). **Remarks:** FAX: (202)682-9358. Electronic mail address(es): NGX 9999 (Dialcom). **Staff:** Chris Anderson, Asst.Libn.

★7275★
Historical Society of Moorestown - Library (Hist)
12 High St.
Box 477 Phone: (609)235-0353
Moorestown, NJ 08057 Mary B. Bamber
Founded: 1969. **Subjects:** Local history, historic clothing, local genealogy. **Holdings:** 350 books. **Services:** Library open to the public on a limited schedule.

★7276★
Historical Society of Newburgh Bay and the Highlands - Helen V. Gearn Library (Hist)
189 Montgomery St. Phone: (914)561-2585
Newburgh, NY 12550 Mary McTamaney, Chm. of Lib.Comm.
Founded: 1951. **Staff:** 2. **Subjects:** Local history. **Holdings:** 3000 books; maps; pictures; city directories; scrapbooks. **Services:** Library open to the public by appointment. **Networks/Consortia:** Member of Southeastern New York Library Resources Council (SENYLRC). **Staff:** Patricia T. Favata.

★7277★
Historical Society of Ocean Grove, New Jersey - Library/Archives (Hist)
Box 446 Phone: (201)774-1869
Ocean Grove, NJ 07756 Elsalyn Palmisano-Drucker, Libn.Archv.
Staff: Prof 2. **Subjects:** Ocean Grove and Victoriana. **Holdings:** 250 books. **Subscriptions:** 10 journals and other serials. **Services:** Library open to the public. **Publications:** Newsletter of the Historical Society of Ocean Grove. **Staff:** Frederic C. Pachman, Libn./Archv.

★7278★
Historical Society of Okaloosa & Walton Counties, Inc. - Museum Library (Hist)
115 Westview Ave. Phone: (904)678-2615
Valparaiso, FL 32580 Nancy Williams, Libn.
Founded: 1971. **Staff:** Prof 1. **Subjects:** Local and Florida history, Civil War, antiques, folk crafts, genealogy. **Special Collections:** Okaloosa County official records (80 volumes). **Holdings:** 2500 volumes; 125 bound periodical volumes; 58 boxes of letters, clippings, brochures; 49 linear feet of newspapers; 70 oral history tapes; 20 folders of maps. **Subscriptions:** 16 journals and other serials. **Services:** Library open to the public.

★7279★
Historical Society of Old Newbury - Library (Hist)
Cushing House Museum
98 High St. Phone: (508)462-2681
Newburyport, MA 01950 Suzanne Simon, Cur.
Founded: 1877. **Staff:** 2. **Subjects:** History of Old Newbury, genealogy. **Special Collections:** Mary Adams Rolfe Genealogical Collection (handwritten); photograph archives. **Holdings:** 1500 books; 50 bound periodical volumes; 10,000 manuscripts. **Services:** Library open to the public on fee basis on limited schedule.

★7280★
Historical Society of Old Yarmouth - Library (Hist)
P.O. Box 11 Phone: (508)362-3021
Yarmouth Port, MA 02675 Grace T. Hudson, Libn.
Subjects: History - Yarmouth, Cape Cod, Massachusetts; Cape Cod genealogy and literature. **Special Collections:** Joseph C. Lincoln Collection. **Holdings:** 1000 books; 100 manuscripts; archival material. **Services:** Copying; library open to the public for reference use only.

★7281★
Historical Society of Palm Beach County - Library (Hist)
3650 Summit Blvd. Phone: (407)471-1492
West Palm Beach, FL 33406 Nan Dennison, Ph.D., Dir.
Founded: 1937. **Staff:** Prof 1; Other 10. **Subjects:** History of Palm Beach County, local authors, Florida history. **Special Collections:** Tropical Sun, 1891-1921 (not complete); Palm Beach Post-Times, 1916-1932 (microfilm); Palm Beach Post Times, 1933-1953 (microfilm); Addison Mizner, Gustav Maass, Treanor, and Fatio architectural drawings. **Holdings:** 3000 books; 160 bound periodical volumes; 5000 photographs; early slides of Palm Beach County; 25 VF drawers of pamphlets, documents, reports; 9 files of postcards of Florida; 4000 slides of Florida; 2 hurricane films. **Services:** Copying; library open to the public. **Publications:** Selected Reading List on Florida History.

★7282★
Historical Society of Pennsylvania - Library (Hist)
1300 Locust St. Phone: (215)732-6201
Philadelphia, PA 19107 Thomas Jay Kemp, Lib.Dir.
Founded: 1824. **Staff:** Prof 16. **Subjects:** History - U.S., 1783-1865, Colonial, Revolutionary, Pennsylvania; genealogy; Afro-Americana. **Holdings:** 564,000 volumes; 16 million manuscripts; 2800 microcards; 17,200 microfiche; 14,700 reels of microfilm; maps; prints; drawings; paintings; newspapers; ephemera. **Subscriptions:** 4000 journals and other serials. **Services:** Copying; library open to the public on fee basis. **Automated Operations:** Computerized cataloging. **Computerized Information Services:** OCLC, RLIN. **Networks/Consortia:** Member of PALINET, Research Libraries Information Network (RLIN), Area Consortium of Special Collections Libraries. **Publications:** The Pennsylvania Magazine of History and Biography, quarterly; The Pennsylvania Correspondent (newsletter), 5/year - to members. **Remarks:** FAX: (215)732-2680. **Staff:** Linda Stanley, Mss.Cur.; Marion Egge, Assoc.Libn.; Daniel Rolph, Ref.Libn.

★7283★
Historical Society of Porter County - Old Jail Museum Library (Hist)
153 Franklin St.
Valparaiso, IN 46383 Phone: (219)465-3595
Staff: Prof 1. **Subjects:** Porter County and Indiana history. **Special Collections:** The War of the Rebellion; Official Records of Union Army, series 1-4; applications for Grand Army of the Republic (G.A.R.) membership of Porter County Civil War veterans and naturalization records, 1854-1955. **Holdings:** Books; reports; manuscripts. **Services:** Copying; library open to the public for reference use only on limited schedule.

★7284★
Historical Society of Princeton - Library (Hist)
158 Nassau St.
Princeton, NJ 08542 Phone: (609)921-6748
Founded: 1938. **Staff:** 1. **Subjects:** Princeton and New Jersey history and genealogy. **Holdings:** 2000 volumes; 500 manuscript collections; 10,000 glass plate negatives; photographs; maps; microfilm; post cards. **Services:** Copying (limited); library open to the public for reference use only on limited schedule. **Publications:** Princeton History, annual; News and Notes (newsletter), quarterly; A Guide to the Manuscript Collections in the Historical Society of Princeton, New Jersey. **Special Indexes:** Index to Hageman's History of Princeton.

★7285★
Historical Society of Quincy and Adams County - Library (Hist)
425 S. 12th St. Phone: (217)222-1835
Quincy, IL 62301 Caroline Sexauer
Founded: 1896. **Staff:** 1. **Subjects:** History and biography of Illinois, Quincy, and Adams County; history of dolls. **Special Collections:** Papers of Gen. John D. Morgan; books by Quincy authors. **Holdings:** 1075 volumes; 25 bound periodical volumes; manuscripts. **Subscriptions:** 4 journals and other serials. **Services:** Copying; library open to the public for reference use only.

★7286★
Historical Society of Rockland County - Library (Hist)
20 Zukor Rd. Phone: (914)634-9629
New City, NY 10956 Debra Walker, Ph.D., Dir.
Founded: 1959. **Staff:** 4. **Subjects:** Local history, genealogy. **Holdings:** 500 books; 50 manuscripts; 12 VF drawers; 10 boxes of archival material; 20 boxes of family papers; photographs. **Services:** Copying; library open to the public by appointment. **Staff:** Frances Yonke, Libn.

★7287★
Historical Society of Saratoga Springs - Beatrice S. Sweeney Archive (Hist)
Casino, Congress Park
Box 216 Phone: (518)584-6920
Saratoga Springs, NY 12866 Heidi A. Fuge, Dir.
Founded: 1883. **Staff:** 2. **Subjects:** Historical Saratoga Springs, including Saratoga's mineral springs and Saratoga as a 19th century resort. **Special Collections:** George S. Batcheller and James A. Andrews families (letters and memorabilia); Reuben Hyde Walworth (last Chancellor of New York State; documents; letters; partial law library); Ellen Hardin Walworth (founding member of Daughters of the American Revolution; letters; journals; diaries); Rev. Clarence A. Walworth (founding member of Paulist Order; letters; partial library); Frank Sullivan Collection (correspondence of Algonquin Roundtable members; letters and manuscripts of Frank Sullivan). **Holdings:** 1800 books; 80 bound periodical volumes; 16 VF drawers of documents, letters, clippings, pamphlets, unbound reports; 70 18th-20th century local maps; 19th and 20th century handbills, advertisements, posters; 20 World War I posters; local architectural plans; 75 19th century historical engravings and lithographs; 60,000 photographs of local architecture and people, 1860 to present; 300 local post cards, 1870-1950; local newspapers, 1819-1890; city directories, 1868 to present. **Services:** Copying; library open to researchers by appointment. **Computerized Information Services:** Internal database (photograph collection). **Publications:** Newsletter, monthly - to members. **Special Indexes:** Walworth Collection (card).

★7288★
Historical Society of Seattle & King County - Sophie Frye Bass Library of Northwest Americana (Hist)
Museum of History & Industry
2700 24th Ave., E. Phone: (206)324-1125
Seattle, WA 98112 Rick Caldwell, Libn.
Founded: 1952. **Staff:** Prof 3; Other 1. **Subjects:** History - Seattle, King County, Pacific Northwest, maritime. **Special Collections:** Joe Williamson Maritime Photograph Collection (68,000 images); Webster and Stevens Photograph Collection (58,000 images); Seattle Historical Society Photograph Collection (20,000 images); Seattle Post-Intelligencer Photograph Collection (290,000 images); glass lantern slides (4000). **Holdings:** 10,000 books; 200 bound periodical volumes; 450,000 photographs; 1200 maps and charts; 250 linear feet of manuscripts; 250 linear feet of ephemera and clippings. **Subscriptions:** 150 journals, newsletters, and other serials. **Services:** Copying; library open to the public by appointment. **Computerized Information Services:** DIALOG Information Services. **Remarks:** FAX: (206)324-1346. Includes the holdings of the Puget Sound Maritime Historical Society. **Staff:** Carolyn Marr, Asst.Libn.; Carolina Veenstra, Cons.Spec.

★7289★
Historical Society of the Tarrytowns - Headquarters Library (Hist)
1 Grove St. Phone: (914)631-8374
Tarrytown, NY 10591 Ruth Neuendorffer, Libn.
Founded: 1889. **Staff:** Prof 1. **Subjects:** General history of the communities and the region; capture of Major John Andre at Tarrytown, September 23, 1780, and allied events; Westchester County and New York State history; local genealogy. **Special Collections:** Ward B. Burnett Post, G.A.R., records; Captain Charles H. Rockwell Civil War papers; local school district records. **Holdings:** 3000 books; 100 bound periodical volumes; 36 VF drawers of clippings, letters, documents, pictures; 715 cataloged maps, 1785 to present; Civil War manuscripts and records; local weekly newspapers, 1875-1946, on microfilm; bound volumes of The Daily News, 1916-1937, 1943, 1953. **Services:** Copying; library open to the public on limited schedule.

★7290★
The Historical Society of the Town of Greenwich, Inc. - Bush-Holley House - Library (Hist)
William E. Finch, Jr. Archives Bldg.
39 Strickland Rd.
Cos Cob, CT 06807 Phone: (203)869-6899
O'**Founded:** 1931. **Staff:** Prof 3. **Subjects:** Local history, genealogy, 19th century American impressionist art, American decorative art. **Holdings:** 500 books; 20 VF drawers of other cataloged items; manuscripts; deeds; documents; photographs; post cards. **Services:** Library open to the public by appointment on a limited schedule. **Staff:** Susan Tritschler, Dir.; Barbara H. Freeman, Prog.Coord.

★7291★
Historical Society of Washington, D.C. - Library (Hist)
1307 New Hampshire Ave., N.W. Phone: (202)785-2068
Washington, DC 20036 Cheryl Miller, Cur.
Founded: 1955. **Staff:** Prof 1. **Subjects:** Washington, DC - history, art, architecture, planning, neighborhoods. **Special Collections:** Proctor family papers; James Goode papers; Machen Collection (700 rare historical prints of the City of Washington). **Holdings:** 14,000 volumes; manuscript collections; 30 VF drawers of newspaper clippings; 70,000 photographs; scrapbooks of the history of the District of Columbia and its immediate environs; maps. **Services:** Copying; library open to the public. **Computerized Information Services:** Internal databases. **Remarks:** FAX: (202)331-1979.

★7292★
Historical Society of Western Pennsylvania - Library & Archives (Hist)
4338 Bigelow Blvd. Phone: (412)681-5533
Pittsburgh, PA 15213 Dr. Carolyn S. Schumacher, Dir., Lib. & Archv.
Founded: 1879. **Staff:** 5.5. **Subjects:** History of Pittsburgh and Western Pennsylvania, genealogy, iron and steel, glass manufacturing, French & Indian War. **Special Collections:** Papers of John and William Thaw, William J. Holland, Jacob D. Mathiot, Isaac and Neville Craig, Denny family, James O'Hara, Max Henrici, John Covode; Pittsburgh city records; business ledger collections (200 cubic feet); Jewish Archives; Western Pennsylvania Genealogical Society (1200 volumes); African American Archives. **Holdings:** 35,000 books; 1000 bound periodical volumes; 265 reels of microfilm; 70,000 photographs; 90 boxes of unbound newspapers; 28 VF drawers of pamphlets and clippings; 1000 linear feet and 888 bound volumes of manuscripts. **Subscriptions:** 100 journals and other serials; 10 newspapers. **Services:** Interlibrary loan; copying; library open to the public. **Networks/Consortia:** Member of Pittsburgh Regional Library Center (PRLC). **Publications:** Pittsburgh History (magazine); Chrysalis: Willa Cather in Pittsburgh; The Jewish Experience in Western Pennsylvania: A History, 1755-1945; 1876 Atlas of Allegheny County, PA (reprint). **Special Indexes:** Cumulative Index and Supplement to Western Pennsylvania Historical Magazine, volumes 1-53; index to lineage charts, members of the Western Pennsylvania Genealogical Society; index to obituaries of persons born in Pennsylvania who have died in other areas, 1982 to present; biography index. **Remarks:** FAX: (412)681-3029. **Staff:** Audrey Iacone, Libn.; Helen M. Wilson, Asst.Libn.; Denise Dyni, Archv.Spec.

★7293★
Historical Society of York County - Library and Archives (Hist)
250 E. Market St. Phone: (717)848-1587
York, PA 17403 June Lloyd, Libn./Archv.
Founded: 1895. **Staff:** Prof 2; Other 1. **Subjects:** York County and city history, York County genealogy, Pennsylvania and American history, fine and decorative arts. **Special Collections:** Lewis Miller Collection of Folk Art; Shettle Collection of Theatre and Circusiana; General Jacob Devers Collection. **Holdings:** 20,000 books; 1400 bound periodical volumes; 15,000 York County land records; 18,000 York County tax records, 1762-1900; 450 linear feet of York County manuscripts; 50,000 photographs and negatives of York County; 1075 reels of microfilm of York County newspapers and manuscripts; Dempwolf Architectural Firm architectural drawings (1880-1930). **Subscriptions:** 36 journals and other serials. **Services:** Copying; limited research by mail; library open to the public on fee basis. **Computerized Information Services:** Paradox (internal database). **Special Indexes:** Inventories of manuscript collections (pamphlets). **Staff:** Donna Shermeyer, Asst.Libn.

Ethan Allen Hitchcock Collection
See: **St. Louis Mercantile Library Association** (14444)

Allen R. Hite Art Institute
See: **University of Louisville - Allen R. Hite Art Institute** (18767)

Walter Hitschfeld Environmental Earth Sciences Library
See: **McGill University - Walter Hitschfeld Environmental Earth Sciences Library** (9912)

★7294★
Hive Publishing Company - John Franklin Mee Memorial Library (Bus-Fin)
Box 1004 Phone: (215)258-6663
Easton, PA 18044 Jill Simpson, Libn.
Founded: 1972. **Staff:** 2. **Subjects:** History of management thought, historical figures in management, efficiency and scientific management movements. **Special Collections:** Frank and Lillian Gilbreth Archives; Frederick W. Taylor Archives. **Holdings:** 5000 volumes; 600 other cataloged items. **Subscriptions:** 6 journals and other serials. **Services:** Copying; library open to the public by appointment. **Publications:** HQ (Hive Quarterly Journal of Management History). **Special Catalogs:** The Father of Scientific Management, Frederick W. Taylor; The Scientific Management & Efficiency Movements, 1909-1929; Management and Financial Controls, 1850-1950; Labor Views Scientific Management; Efficiency Redux, 1940-1946 (1989); Motion Study, 1845-1945. **Remarks:** FAX: (215)258-6663.

Norman E. Hjorth Memorial Library
See: **Trinity Presbyterian Church** (16517)

★7295★
HKM Associates Engineers/Planners - Library (Sci-Engr)
2727 Central Ave.
Box 31318 Phone: (406)656-6399
Billings, MT 59107 Irene Nelson, Libn.
Staff: Water resources development; engineering - sanitary, transportation, structural; geology. **Special Collections:** U.S. Geological Survey quadrangle maps (2300). **Holdings:** 7000 books; 100 reports on microfiche. **Subscriptions:** 73 journals and other serials. **Services:** Library not open to the public. **Computerized Information Services:** DIALOG Information Services. **Remarks:** FAX: (406)656-6398.

Ho Samut Haeng Chat
See: **Thailand - National Library of Thailand** (16293)

★7296★
Hoag Memorial Hospital-Presbyterian - Medical Library (Med)
301 Newport Blvd.
Box Y Phone: (714)760-2308
Newport Beach, CA 92658 Mrs. Ute Schultz, Med.Libn.
Staff: Prof 2; Other 2. **Subjects:** Medicine, nursing, psychiatry. **Holdings:** 5000 books; 9000 bound periodical volumes; 1500 audio cassettes and other AV programs. **Subscriptions:** 300 journals and other serials. **Services:** Interlibrary loan; copying; SDI; library open to the public with restrictions. **Computerized Information Services:** MEDLINE, DIALOG Information Services; DOCLINE (electronic mail service). Performs searches on fee basis. **Remarks:** FAX: (714)760-5729.

Hoagland Medical Library
See: **Long Island College Hospital** (9287)

★7297★
Hoard Historical Museum - Library (Hist)
407 Merchant Ave. Phone: (414)563-7769
Fort Atkinson, WI 53538 Helmut Knies, Cur.
Founded: 1933. **Staff:** Prof 2. **Subjects:** Black Hawk War, 1800-1840; local Indians and history; birds; quilts; furniture. **Special Collections:** Rare books on Black Hawk War, local history, and regional birds; Indian artifacts, 7000 B.C. to present; National Dairy Shrine Museum. **Holdings:** 5108 books; 4813 local pictures. **Services:** Copying; library open to the public. **Publications:** Bibliography (Jefferson County); History of Jefferson County, WI; History of Fort Atkinson, WI.

★7298★
Hobart Historical Society, Inc. - Mariam J. Pleak Memorial Library and Archive (Hist)
706 E. 4th St.
Box 24
Hobart, IN 46342 Elin B. Christianson, Cur.
Staff: Prof 1. **Subjects:** Local history and genealogy. **Holdings:** 1200 books; 36 VF drawers of archival materials; 50 reels of microfilm of Hobart newspapers. **Subscriptions:** 6 journals and other serials. **Services:** Interlibrary loan; copying; library open to the public. **Special Indexes:** Index to families listed in 1850-1910 federal censuses for Hobart Township.

★7299★
Hobart Institute of Welding Technology - John H. Blankenbuehler Memorial Library (Sci-Engr)
400 Trade Square East Phone: (513)332-5603
Troy, OH 45373 Martha A. Baker, Libn.
Founded: 1964. **Staff:** Prof 1. **Subjects:** Welding, metallurgy. **Special Collections:** Current files of the American Welding Society, American Society of Mechanical Engineers, military specifications, American Society for Testing and Materials, and foreign standards and specifications related to welding procedures and processes. **Holdings:** 4000 books; 500 bound periodical volumes; 25 VF drawers of educational materials and government publications; 1 drawer of microfiche; 50 volumes of government documents; 20 volumes of International Institute of Welding documents. **Subscriptions:** 100 journals and other serials. **Services:** Interlibrary loan; copying; library open to the public with permission of director. **Computerized Information Services:** DIALOG Information Services, ORBIT Search Service. Performs searches on fee basis. **Remarks:** FAX: (513)332-5200. Telex: 288265 HOBROCO TRYO. **Staff:** Ray W. Shook, Pres.

★7300★
Hobe Sound Bible College - Library (Rel-Phil, Educ)
Box 1065 Phone: (407)546-5534
Hobe Sound, FL 33455 Estaline Allison, Hd.Libn.
Founded: 1960. **Staff:** Prof 1. **Subjects:** Religion, education, literature, music, math, business. **Holdings:** 31,500 books; 1300 bound periodical volumes; 3500 AV programs; 770 microfiche; 12 VF drawers. **Subscriptions:** 240 journals and other serials. **Services:** Interlibrary loan; copying; library open to the public with restrictions. **Remarks:** FAX: (407)546-9379. **Staff:** Frances Fuller, Asst.Libn.; Sherilyn Marshall, Asst.Libn.

★7301★
Hochschule der Kunste Berlin - Bildende Kunste und Architektur - Hochschulbibliothek H5B 1 (Art)
Hardenbergstr 33
Postfach 126720 Phone: 30 31852695
W-1000 Berlin 12, Germany Dr. Barbara Tiemann
Founded: 1975. **Staff:** Prof 8; Other 4. **Subjects:** 20th century art, modern architecture. **Holdings:** 73,700 books. **Subscriptions:** 105 journals and other serials. **Services:** Library open to the public. **Remarks:** FAX: 30 31852679. **Staff:** Dr. Claudia Muller.

★7302★
Hochschule der Kunste Berlin - Musik m - Barstellende Kunst - Hochschulbibliothek H5B 2 (Art)
Postfach 126720 Phone: 30 31852405
W-1000 Berlin 12, Germany Dr. Wolfgang Rathert
Founded: 1975. **Staff:** Prof 12; Other 5. **Subjects:** Music history (18th and 19th centuries), performing arts, historical dance. **Special Collections:** Estates of Joseph Joachim and Philipp Spitta (music prints, books on music); Karl Heinz Taubert Collection (historical dance); Parlor music; rare music prints (16th to 19th centuries). **Holdings:** 50,000 books and bound periodical volumes; 1164 reels of microfilm. **Subscriptions:** 80 journals and other serials. **Services:** Library open to the public. **Special Catalogs:** Catalog of rare music prints. **Remarks:** FAX: 30 31852707.

★7303★
Hochschule fuer Musik und Darstellende Kunst in Wien - Hochschulbibliothek (Mus, Art)
Lothringerstrasse 18 Phone: 222 58806
A-1030 Vienna 3, Austria Dr. Helga Scholz, Dir.
Founded: 1909. **Subjects:** Music, theater, film, television, dance, pedagogy, fine arts, cultural history, history of literature. **Holdings:** 133,000 books and music volumes; 169 bound periodical volumes; 33,300 AV programs; 70 nonbook items. **Services:** Interlibrary loan; copying; library open to the public. **Publications:** Acquisitions list. **Staff:** Dr. Susanne Eschwe, Mgr.

★7304★
Hockey Hall of Fame and Museum - Library (Rec)
Exhibition Place Phone: (416)595-1345
Toronto, ON, Canada M6K 3C3 Phil Pritchard, Dir./Info. & Acq.
Staff: Prof 1; Other 2. **Subjects:** Hockey history and statistics. **Special Collections:** Turofsky, Prazek, and Nadel Collections. **Holdings:** 1100 books; 300 bound periodical volumes; 40,000 photographs; 6000 35mm slides of players; microfilm; scrapbooks. **Subscriptions:** 15 journals and other serials. **Services:** Library open to the public by appointment. **Automated Operations:** Computerized cataloging. **Remarks:** FAX: (416)971-5828.

★7305★
Hocking College - Library (Educ)
Rte. 1 Phone: (614)753-3591
Nelsonville, OH 45764 Margy L. Kramer, Dir.
Founded: 1969. **Staff:** Prof 1; Other 1. **Subjects:** Wildlife, parks and recreation, forestry, police science, corrections, nursing, hotel/motel administration, ceramic engineering. **Holdings:** 18,000 books; 450 bound periodical volumes; 18 VF drawers of pamphlets. **Subscriptions:** 270 journals and other serials; 7 newspapers. **Services:** Interlibrary loan; copying; library open to the public. **Automated Operations:** Computerized public access catalog and circulation. **Computerized Information Services:** BRS Information Technologies. **Remarks:** FAX: (614)753-3034.

★7306★
Bernard Hodes Advertising - Information Center (Bus-Fin)
555 Madison Ave., 15th Fl. Phone: (212)758-2600
New York, NY 10022 David Mott, V.P./Dir. of Corp.Commun.
Staff: Prof 4; Other 1. **Subjects:** Recruitment advertising, human resources/ personnel, employment. **Holdings:** 1000 books; 900 media kits; 300 subject files; 100 unbound periodical titles; 130 VF drawers. **Subscriptions:** 150 journals and other serials. **Services:** Interlibrary loan; center open to information professionals. **Computerized Information Services:** DIALOG Information Services, LEXIS, NEXIS, Human Resource Information Network (HRIN). **Publications:** Personnel Forum; Media Monitor; Labor Force Monitor. **Staff:** Donna Diemen, Corp.Commun.Spec.; Sio Gong, Info.Spec.; Anne Yarema, Res.Supv.

★7307★
Hodge Computer Research Corporation - Library (Comp Sci)
1588 N. Batavia
Orange, CA 92667 Phone: (714)998-7750
Founded: 1972. **Staff:** 1. **Subjects:** Computer technology - image processing, computer architecture, telecommunications, switching systems, database management, automated tool control. **Holdings:** 4000 volumes. **Subscriptions:** 100 journals and other serials; 4 newspapers. **Services:** Library not open to the public. **Remarks:** FAX: (714)921-8038. Telex: 1509508 (MCI). **Staff:** Alan H. Nise.

Clara Hodgkins Memorial Health Sciences Library
See: **Mid-Maine Medical Center** (10348)

Edith M. Hodgson Memorial Library
See: **Bryant College of Business Administration** (2299)

Keith Hodson Memorial Library
See: **Canada - National Defence - Canadian Forces College** (2779)

★7308★
Hoechst Celanese Corporation - Engineering Plastics Division - Information Center (Sci-Engr)
26 Main St. Phone: (201)635-4244
Chatham, NJ 07928 Genevieve Sparicin, Sr.Info.Spec.
Founded: 1952. **Staff:** Prof 1; Other 2. **Subjects:** Marketing material on plastics, business. **Holdings:** 1000 books; 800 market reports; 100 reels of microfilm; 400 microfiche; 25 file drawers. **Subscriptions:** 180 journals and other serials; 5 newspapers. **Services:** Interlibrary loan; center open to the public by appointment. **Computerized Information Services:** DIALOG Information Services, PFDS Online, PIERS (Port Import/Export Reporting Service). **Publications:** Information Center Newsletter; Metals Newsletter. **Remarks:** FAX: (201)635-3341.

★7309★
Hoechst Celanese Corporation - Fibers and Films Group - Library (Sci-Engr)
P.O. Box 32414 Phone: (704)554-2000
Charlotte, NC 28232 Margaret Greer, Libn.
Staff: 14. **Subjects:** Textiles. **Holdings:** 10,000 books. **Subscriptions:** 200 journals and other serials. **Services:** Library open to the public for reference use only by permission. **Remarks:** Contains the holdings of its former Specialty Chemicals Group - Library.

★7310★
Hoechst Celanese Corporation - R.L. Mitchell Technical Center - Technical Information Center (Sci-Engr)
86 Morris Ave. Phone: (908)522-7939
Summit, NJ 07901 Karen Rappaport, Mgr., Info. & Comp.Sci.
Staff: Prof 3; Other 3. **Subjects:** Polymers; plastics; fibers; chemicals; coatings; chemistry - organic, physical, analytical, inorganic. **Holdings:** 20,000 books; 20,000 bound and microform periodical volumes; 35,000 internal reports in hardcopy and microform; 1.5 million patents in microform. **Subscriptions:** 403 journals and other serials. **Services:** Interlibrary loan; center open to the public for reference use only by permission. **Automated Operations:** Computerized cataloging, acquisitions, serials, and circulation. **Computerized Information Services:** DIALOG Information Services, PFDS Online, Chemical Abstracts Service (CAS), BRS Information Technologies, Dun & Bradstreet Business Credit Services, Questel, NLM; internal database. **Remarks:** FAX: (908)522-3902. **Staff:** Jean Shepley, Info.Sci.; Jana Volavka, Info.Sci.; Dessie Mauldin, Pub.Info.

★7311★
Hoechst Celanese Corporation - Technical Information Center (Sci-Engr)
1901 Clarkwood Rd.
Box 9077 Phone: (512)242-4231
Corpus Christi, TX 78469-9077 Marsha J. Saylor, Tech.Info.Ctr.Coor.
Founded: 1947. **Staff:** Prof 2; Other 2. **Subjects:** Organic aliphatic chemistry and derived technologies, physical chemistry of combustion, production of petroleum chemicals via direct oxidation. **Holdings:** 17,000 books; 9000 bound periodical volumes; 225,000 U.S. and foreign patents; internal and government technical reports. **Subscriptions:** 300 journals and other serials. **Services:** Interlibrary loan. **Computerized Information Services:** Online systems; CD-ROMs. **Publications:** TICkler Newsletter, monthly; TOPIC of Interest, monthly. **Remarks:** FAX: (512)242-4251. **Formerly:** Its Technical Center - Library.

Hoechst Celanese Corporation - Technical Information Center - IZIP 750
See: **Hoechst Diafoil Company** (7312)

★7312★
Hoechst Diafoil Company - Technical Information Center - IZIP 750 (Sci-Engr)
Hood Rd.
P.O. Box 1400
Greer, SC 29652 Phone: (803)879-5000
Founded: 1970. **Staff:** Prof 1; Other 1. **Subjects:** Polymer chemistry, food and drug regulations, plastics patents. **Holdings:** 900 books; 100 bound periodical volumes; 290 reels of microfilm; 1200 reports. **Subscriptions:** 153 journals and other serials. **Services:** Interlibrary loan; copying; center open to the public with restrictions. **Automated Operations:** Computerized serials and circulation. **Special Indexes:** Index to Patents; index to internal documents (online). **Remarks:** FAX: (803)879-5940. **Formerly:** Hoechst Celanese Corporation - Technical Information Center.

★7313★
Hoechst-Roussel Pharmaceuticals, Inc. - Library (Med)
Route 202-206, N. Phone: (908)231-2394
Somerville, NJ 08876 Loretta F. Stangs, Gp.Mgr.
Staff: Prof 9; Other 4. **Subjects:** Chemistry, pharmacology, toxicology, medicine, pharmaceutical marketing, pesticides, psychopharmacology, industrial management. **Holdings:** 72,000 books; 7500 bound periodical volumes; 5000 reels of microfilm of journals and patents; 1000 AV programs. **Subscriptions:** 1000 journals and other serials. **Services:** Interlibrary loan; copying; translation; SDI; library open to the public by request. **Automated Operations:** Computerized cataloging, serials, circulation, and product

information. **Computerized Information Services:** DIALOG Information Services, PFDS Online, U.S. Patents Files, MEDLINE, BRS Information Technologies, Chemical Abstracts Service (CAS). **Publications:** HRPI Drugs, monthly; Book Acquisitions List, monthly; Library Quarterly. **Remarks:** FAX: (201)231-2704; 231-2802. **Staff:** Ann Van Dine, Mgr.; June Strupczewski, Sr.Info.Sci.; Alina Lysiuk, Libn.; Irmhild Oehme, Transl.Coord.; Janet Waas, Info.Sci.; Margaret Hill, Info.Sci.; Janet Drong, Asst.Info.Sci.

Charles A. Hoffman Library of the History of Medical Sciences
See: **Marshall University - James E. Morrow Library** (9724)

J.S. Hoffman Memorial Library
See: **Congregation Rodfei Zedek** (4165)

Malvina Hoffman Archives
See: **Cedar Rapids Museum of Art - Herbert S. Stamats Art Library** (3186)

★7314★
Hoffmann-La Roche, Inc. - Library (Med, Bus-Fin)
340 Kingsland St. Phone: (201)235-3091
Nutley, NJ 07110-1199 Phyllis Deline, Mgr.
Founded: 1930. **Staff:** Prof 5; Other 6. **Subjects:** Pharmaceutical industry, medicinal chemistry, business, vitamins, pharmacology, marketing. **Holdings:** 19,000 books; 20,000 bound periodical volumes; 417 pamphlets; 350 annual reports; 3552 reels of microfilm of journals. **Subscriptions:** 519 journals and other serials; 4 newspapers. **Services:** Interlibrary loan; copying; library open to Special Libraries Association members with permission. **Automated Operations:** Computerized acquisitions and serials. **Computerized Information Services:** DIALOG Information Services, STN International, Data-Star, MEDLARS, OCLC. **Networks/Consortia:** Member of PALINET. **Publications:** Current Events, weekly; Periodicals/Serials List, annual. **Remarks:** FAX: (201)235-3617. **Staff:** Janet Czarnecki, Tech.Ref.Libn.; Irma Smith, ILL Libn.; Marian Koob, Tech.Serv.Libn.; Patricia Williams, Bus.Ref.Libn.

★7315★
Hoffmann-La Roche, Ltd. - Corporate Library (Med)
2455 Meadowpine Blvd. Phone: (416)542-5542
Mississauga, ON, Canada L5N 6L7 Colin G.D. Hoare, Mgr.
Founded: 1956. **Staff:** Prof 2. **Subjects:** Medicine, clinical pharmacology, toxicology, analytical chemistry, pharmaceutical technology, marketing. **Holdings:** 1200 books; 30 periodical titles on microfiche; 18 VF drawers of product literature catalogs; 25 drawers of microfiche; pamphlets; brochures. **Subscriptions:** 264 journals and other serials. **Services:** Interlibrary loan; copying; library open to the public by appointment. **Computerized Information Services:** DIALOG Information Services, MEDLINE, CAN/OLE, Info Globe, Infomart Online; internal database. **Remarks:** FAX: (416)542-7130. Telex: 0621-8087. **Staff:** Nancy Millwood, Libn.

★7316★
Hofstra University - Library - Special Collections (Hist, Hum)
1000 Fulton Ave. Phone: (516)463-5097
Hempstead, NY 11550 Barbara M. Kelly, Cur.
Staff: Prof 1; Other 3. **Subjects:** History, humanities, social sciences. **Special Collections:** Author collections; Bloomsbury group; Georgian poets; New York State/Long Island History; Long Island Studies Institute Collection; Howard L. and Muriel Weingrow Collection of Avant-Garde Art and Literature; Nila Banton Smith Reading; Private Presses (Golden Cockerel, Hogarth, Mosher, Nonesuch & Overbrook); Utopian communities (Shakers, Oneida, Quakers); history of the book (fine printing, illustration, fine binding). **Holdings:** 15,883 books. **Subscriptions:** 6 journals and other serials; 2 newspapers .**Services:** Copying (limited); collections open to the public for reference use only. **Automated Operations:** Computerized cataloging. **Computerized Information Services:** Internal database. **Networks/Consortia:** Member of SUNY/OCLC Library Network, Long Island Library Resources Council. **Remarks:** FAX: (516)560-7679. Long Island Studies Institute Collection is jointly maintained by Hofstra University and Nassau County Museum Reference Library. **Staff:** Richard A. Winsche, Hist.; Gary Hammond, Libn.

★7317★
Hofstra University - School of Law Library (Law)
Hempstead, NY 11550 Phone: (516)463-5900
Eugene M. Wypyski, Dir.
Staff: Prof 9; Other 8. **Subjects:** Law. **Holdings:** 285,000 volumes. **Services:** Library not open to the public.

★7318★
Charles V. Hogan Regional Center - Staff Library (Med)
Box A Phone: (508)774-5000
Hathorne, MA 01937-9998 Bonnie Stecher, Libn.
Staff: Prof 1. **Subjects:** Mental retardation, special education, medicine, rehabilitation, behavioral psychology, psychiatry, psychology, community mental health services. **Holdings:** 2000 books; 19 VF drawers of pamphlets, articles, booklets. **Subscriptions:** 100 journals and other serials. **Services:** Interlibrary loan; library open to the public with restrictions. **Networks/Consortia:** Member of Massachusetts Mental Health Librarians, Northeastern Consortium for Health Information (NECHI). **Publications:** Extensive subject bibliographies. **Remarks:** FAX: (508)727-9550, ext. 217. Maintained by Massachusetts State Department of Mental Health.

★7319★
Hogan & Hartson - Library (Law)
555 13th St., N.W. Phone: (202)637-8700
Washington, DC 20004 R. Austin Doherty, Lib.Dir.
Founded: 1967. **Staff:** Prof 9; Other 14. **Subjects:** Law. **Holdings:** 65,000 books; 2000 bound periodical volumes. **Subscriptions:** 400 journals and other serials. **Services:** Interlibrary loan; library open to the public with restrictions. **Computerized Information Services:** LEXIS, DIALOG Information Services, ORBIT Search Service, LEGI-SLATE, Dow Jones News/Retrieval, WESTLAW, Reuters. **Remarks:** FAX: (202)637-5910. **Staff:** Carol Blessing, Res.Libn.; Margaret Mona, Res.Libn.; Ed Fishpaw, Res.Libn.; Jeff Mang, Res.Libn.; Hannah Bucholz, Res.Libn.; Susan Herrick, Res.Libn.; Alem Tesfaye, Cat.; John Duvall, Adm.Libn.

William Ransom Hogan Jazz Archive
See: **Tulane University** (16567)

★7320★
Hogarth Westmount Hospital - Staff Library (Med)
300 N. Lillie St. Phone: (807)625-1110
Thunder Bay, ON, Canada P7C 4Y7 Kathy Deguns, Libn.
Founded: 1984. **Staff:** Prof 1. **Subjects:** Long term care, geriatrics, rehabilitation. **Holdings:** 1100 books. **Subscriptions:** 180 journals and other serials. **Services:** Interlibrary loan; copying; library open to the public for reference use only. **Networks/Consortia:** Member of Northern Outreach Library Service (NOLS). **Remarks:** FAX: (807)622-1173.

★7321★
Hogeschool Alkmaar Sector Techniek - Bibliotheek (Sci-Engr)
Postbus 403 Phone: 72 183400
NL-1800 AK Alkmaar, Netherlands Mr. J. Baas, Libn.
Founded: 1972. **Staff:** Prof 1. **Subjects:** Engineering - electrical, industrial, mechanical, civil. **Holdings:** 13,186 books; 350 reports. **Services:** Interlibrary loan; copying; library open to the public with restrictions. **Computerized Information Services:** Internal database. **Remarks:** FAX: (072)183495.

Hogg Foundation for Mental Health
See: **University of Texas at Austin** (19394)

Philip J. Hohlweck Civil War Collection
See: **University of Wisconsin--Milwaukee - Golda Meir Library** (19636)

★7322★
Hokkaido Nogyo Shikenjo Kikaku Renrakushitsu Johoshiryoka (Agri)
1 Hitsuigaoka
Toyohira-ku Phone: 11 8519141
Sapporo 062, Hokkaido, Japan Mrs. Yoriko Takahata
Founded: 1925. **Staff:** Prof 4; Other 2. **Subjects:** Rural development, crop production, field crop science, animal breeding, grasslands, agro-environmental management. **Holdings:** 7300 books; 75,400 bound periodical volumes; 51,000 reports; 7105 microfiche; 21 reels of microfilm. **Subscriptions:** 347 journals and other serials; 7 newspapers. **Services:** Library not open to the public. **Remarks:** FAX: 11 8535916. **Also Known As:** Hokkaido National Agricultural Experiment Station.

T.L. Holcomb Library
See: **American Baptist Theological Seminary** (499)

★7323★
Holden Arboretum - Warren H. Corning Library (Biol Sci)
9500 Sperry Rd. Phone: (216)946-4400
Mentor, OH 44060 Paul C. Spector, Dir. of Educ.
Founded: 1963. **Staff:** 2. **Subjects:** Horticulture, botany, environmental education, natural history. **Special Collections:** Warren H. Corning Collection of Horticultural Classics (1800 volumes). **Holdings:** 7000 books; 10 VF drawers; 10,000 slides; 55 videocassettes. **Subscriptions:** 125 journals and other serials. **Services:** Library open to the public for reference use only. **Networks/Consortia:** Member of Cleveland Area Metropolitan Library System (CAMLS). **Publications:** Arbor Day: A Bibliography of Materials Available for Use at the Corning Library. **Remarks:** FAX: (216)256-1655. **Staff:** Nadia Aufderheide, Hd.Libn.; Stanley Johnston, Cur., Rare Bks.

★7324★
Holden Day Wilson - Law Library (Law)
Toronto Dominion Bank Tower
P.O. Box 52 Phone: (416)361-1444
Toronto, ON, Canada M5K 1E7 Patricia Raible, Libn.
Staff: 3. **Subjects:** Law. **Remarks:** FAX: (416)361-1258.

Thomas F. Holgate Library
See: **Bennett College** (1721)

★7325★
Holladay Park Medical Center - Library (Med)
1225 N.E. 2nd Ave. Phone: (503)233-3242
Portland, OR 97232 Carolyn T. Olson, Libn.
Founded: 1981. **Staff:** Prof 1. **Subjects:** Medicine, psychiatry. **Holdings:** 600 books. **Subscriptions:** 125 journals and other serials. **Services:** Interlibrary loan; copying; SDI; library open to the public with restrictions. **Computerized Information Services:** NLM, BRS Information Technologies; OnTyme Electronic Message Network Service, DOCLINE (electronic mail services). Performs searches on fee basis. **Networks/Consortia:** Member of Oregon Health Sciences Libraries Association (OHSLA), Portland Area Health Sciences Librarians, National Network of Libraries of Medicine - Pacific Northwest Region. **Remarks:** FAX: (503)234-3342

★7326★
Holland Community Hospital - Hospital and Medical Staff Library (Med)
602 Michigan Ave. Phone: (616)394-3107
Holland, MI 49423 Eleanor Lopez, Libn.
Founded: 1968. **Staff:** Prof 1; Other 1. **Subjects:** Medicine, hospital administration, nursing. **Holdings:** 1600 books; 1500 bound periodical volumes. **Subscriptions:** 220 journals and other serials. **Services:** Interlibrary loan; copying; library open to the public with restrictions. **Automated Operations:** Computerized cataloging. **Computerized Information Services:** MEDLINE, DIALOG Information Services. **Remarks:** FAX: (616)392-8448.

★7327★
Holland & Hart - Library (Law)
Box 8749 Phone: (303)295-8096
Denver, CO 80201 Merrie Jo McNally, Mgr., Lib. & File Serv.
Staff: Prof 3; Other 3. **Subjects:** Law. **Holdings:** 23,000 volumes. **Services:** Library not open to the public. **Automated Operations:** Computerized cataloging. **Computerized Information Services:** LEXIS, DIALOG Information Services, BRS Information Technologies, WESTLAW. **Networks/Consortia:** Member of Bibliographical Center for Research, Rocky Mountain Region, Inc. (BCR).

★7328★
(Holland) Joint Archives of Holland (Area-Ethnic)
Hope College Campus Phone: (616)394-7798
Holland, MI 49423 Larry J. Wagenaar, Archv.
Staff: 6. **Subjects:** Dutch in Western Michigan and the United States, local history, Hope College, Reformed Church in America. **Holdings:** 500 books; Dutch newspapers; manuscripts; records; photographs; vertical files; biographical and pamphlet collections; AV materials. **Services:** Copying; library open to the public on a limited schedule. **Computerized Information Services:** Internal database; BITNET (electronic mail service). **Publications:** Guide to the Collections of the Joint Archives of Holland, 1989; Supplement ot the Guide to the Collections, 1991; The Joint Archives Quarterly. **Remarks:** FAX: (616)394-7965. Electronic mail address(es): Wagenaar@Hope (BITNET). **Formed by the merger of:** Netherlands Museum - Archives, Hope College - Archives, and Western Theological Seminary - Archives. **Staff:** Craig G. Wright, Assoc.Archv.

Mailande W. Holland Library
See: **Pinellas County Juvenile Welfare Board** (13066)

★7329★
Holland Society of New York - Library (Hist)
122 E. 58th St. Phone: (212)758-1871
New York, NY 10022-1939 Margaret Hutchinson, Libn.
Founded: 1885. **Staff:** Prof 2; Other 2. **Subjects:** Colonial history of the New Netherland Area (New York, New Jersey, Delaware) with emphasis on genealogical sources and cultural history; genealogies of families which settled there prior to 1675. **Special Collections:** Unpublished manuscript genealogies and Reformed Dutch Church records of New York and New Jersey. **Holdings:** 5000 volumes; 300 reels of microfilm. **Subscriptions:** 20 journals and other serials. **Services:** Copying; library open to the public on a limited schedule. **Publications:** de Halve Maen, quarterly - to members, libraries, and the interested public.

W. J. Holland Library
See: **Carnegie Museum of Natural History - Library** (3085)

★7330★
A.G. Holley State Hospital - Benjamin L. Brock Medical Library (Med)
Box 3084 Phone: (407)582-5666
Lantana, FL 33462 Andree D. Sweek, Dir., Med.Rec.
Staff: 1. **Subjects:** Medicine. **Holdings:** 1325 books; 2100 bound periodical volumes. **Subscriptions:** 27 journals and other serials. **Services:** Interlibrary loan; copying; library open to health professionals.

★7331★
John D. Hollingsworth on Wheels, Inc. - Information Services (Sci-Engr)
Box 516 Phone: (803)297-1000
Greenville, SC 29602 Sandra Blackwell, Info.Spec.
Staff: Prof 1. **Subjects:** Textiles, engineering. **Holdings:** Figures not available. **Services:** Interlibrary loan; services not open to the public. **Computerized Information Services:** Online systems.

★7332★
Hollins College - Music Department - Erich Rath Music Library & Listening Center (Mus)
Box 9641 Phone: (703)362-6511
Roanoke, VA 24020 Shari Barbour, Mus.Libn.
Founded: 1842. **Subjects:** Music. **Holdings:** 4200 scores; 4400 phonograph records; 200 tapes; 19th-20th century American songs; piano and symphony scores; music textbooks; jazz record collection. **Services:** Center open to the public for reference use with permission of chairman or librarian. **Staff:** Oscar McCullough, Chm.

Hollis Health Sciences Library
See: **Winthrop-University Hospital** (20505)

★7333★
Hollister Incorporated - Corporate Library (Law)
2000 Hollister Dr. Phone: (708)680-1000
Libertyville, IL 60048 Elizabeth A. Cunningham, Corp.Libn.
Founded: 1983. **Staff:** Prof 1; Other 1. **Subjects:** Medicine, technology, science, social sciences, law. **Special Collections:** Care of ostomy patients. **Holdings:** 1400 books; 500 bound periodical volumes; 10 VF drawers of patents. **Subscriptions:** 237 journals and other serials. **Services:** Interlibrary loan; library not open to the public. **Automated Operations:** Computerized public access catalog (ILLINET). **Computerized Information Services:** DIALOG Information Services. **Networks/Consortia:** Member of Northeastern Illinois Library Consortium, North Suburban Library System (NSLS), ILLINET. **Remarks:** FAX: (708)680-2123. Telex: 910-684-3268.

★7334★
Hollywood Community Hospital - Medical Staff Library (Med)
6245 DeLongpre Ave. Phone: (213)462-2271
Hollywood, CA 90028 Betsey Beamish, Med.Lib.Cons.
Staff: Prof 1. **Subjects:** Clinical medicine, nursing. **Special Collections:** College of Osteopathic Medicine of the Pacific (COMP) student collection (50 books). **Holdings:** 320 books; 80 Audio-Digest tapes; 188 NCME video cassettes. **Subscriptions:** 58 journals and other serials. **Services:** Interlibrary loan; copying; SDI; library open to the public with restrictions. **Automated Operations:** Computerized cataloging. **Computerized Information Services:** NLM; DOCLINE (electronic mail service). **Networks/Consortia:** Member of National Network of Libraries of Medicine - Pacific Southwest Region. **Staff:** Beverly Gardner.

★7335★
Hollywood Film Archive - Library (Aud-Vis)
8344 Melrose Ave. Phone: (213)933-3345
Hollywood, CA 90069 D. Richard Baer, Dir.
Founded: 1972. **Staff:** 5. **Subjects:** Motion pictures, television, video. **Special Collections:** Original synopses of 12,000 movies. **Holdings:** 2300 volumes; 5700 motion picture stills; Monthly Film Bulletin, 1938 to present; Motion Picture Exhibitor, 1931-1972; Motion Picture Herald, 1932-1970; Boxoffice, 1960 to present. **Services:** Library open to the public by appointment only. **Computerized Information Services:** Hollywood Film Archive Reference Catalog (internal database); BITNET (electronic mail service). **Publications:** Movie World Almanac, biennial; film series list; Film Superlist of Motion Pictures in the Public Domain, 1894-1959; Harrison's Reports and Film Reviews, 1919-1962.

Hollywood Presbyterian Medical Center
See: **Queen of Angels - Hollywood Presbyterian Medical Center** (13620)

Irene Holm Memorial Library
See: **Ottawa Research Corporation** (12603)

Holman Print Shop Archives
See: **Boston Public Library - Fine Arts Department** (1992)

★7336★
Holme Roberts & Owen - Library (Law)
1700 Lincoln, No. 4100 Phone: (303)861-7000
Denver, CO 80203 Mark E. Estes, Libn.
Staff: Prof 3; Other 3. **Subjects:** Law. **Holdings:** 30,000 volumes. **Subscriptions:** 600 journals and other serials. **Services:** Library not open to the public. **Automated Operations:** Computerized cataloging and serials. **Computerized Information Services:** DIALOG Information Services, LEXIS, WESTLAW, Dow Jones News/Retrieval; Memo of Law (internal database). **Publications:** News from the Library - to attorneys and paralegal personnel. **Remarks:** FAX: (303)866-0200. **Staff:** Lou Ellen Runyan, Asst.Libn., Ref.; Jean Tarbel, Asst.Libn., Tech.Serv.

★7337★
Holmes County Law Library (Law)
Court House Phone: (216)674-5086
Millersburg, OH 44654 Judge Thomas D. White, Law Libn.
Staff: Prof 1; Other 1. **Subjects:** Law. **Holdings:** 4600 volumes. **Services:** Library open to the public. **Staff:** Eleanor Teisher, Asst.Libn.

Ernest Holmes College Library
See: **United Church of Religious Science** (16701)

John Holmes Collection
See: **Tufts University - Nils Yngve Wessell Library** (16552)

John H. Holmes Library
See: **Westminster Presbyterian Church** (20331)

★7338★
Mary Holmes College - Barr Library - Oral History Collection (Hist)
Hwy. 50, W.
Box 1257 Phone: (601)494-6820
West Point, MS 39773 Gail Davis-Peyton
Founded: 1967. **Staff:** 6. **Subjects:** History, sociology, folklore. **Special Collections:** Taped interviews and transcriptions of conversations with rural black Mississippians 70 years of age and older (600); African American Collection (1000 titles). **Holdings:** 14 volumes. **Subscriptions:** 115 journals and other serials; 13 newspapers. **Services:** Interlibrary loan; copying; collection open to the public for reference use only. **Computerized Information Services:** InfoTrac. **Remarks:** FAX: (601)494-5319. **Staff:** Rose Parkman Davis, Ref. & Tech.Serv.Libn.; David Faulkner, Media Spec.

Oliver Wendell Holmes Library
See: **Library of Congress - Rare Book & Special Collections Division** (9135)

Oliver Wendell Holmes Library
See: **Phillips Academy** (13005)

Oliver Wendell Holmes Stereoscopic Research Library
See: **National Stereoscopic Association** (11306)

★7339★
Holnam Inc. - Library (Sci-Engr)
Box 1468 Phone: (303)482-5600
LaPorte, CO 80535 Leo M. Meyer
Founded: 1953. **Subjects:** Portland cement, concrete, inorganic chemistry, mineralogy. **Holdings:** 1600 books; 4 VF drawers of U.S., British, and Canadian patents; 1300 bulletins, reports, translations. **Subscriptions:** 100 journals and other serials. **Services:** Interlibrary loan; library open to the public by appointment. **Remarks:** FAX: (303)482-5608.

★7340★
Holocaust Center of Northern California (Hist)
639 14th Ave. Phone: (415)751-6040
San Francisco, CA 94118 Joel Neuberg, Exec.Dir.
Founded: 1978. **Staff:** Prof 1; Other 1. **Subjects:** Holocaust, Nazi Germany, modern Europe, World War II, Jews in Europe and North Africa, survivors of concentration camps. **Special Collections:** Memorial books on destroyed Jewish communities of Europe (400). **Holdings:** 10,000 books; 2000 photographs; 300 oral history tapes and transcripts; 400 videotapes; 200 audiotapes of programs on the Holocaust; 50 artifacts of the period. **Subscriptions:** 5 journals and other serials. **Services:** Copying; center open to the public for reference use only. **Automated Operations:** Computerized public access catalog. **Computerized Information Services:** Internal databases. **Networks/Consortia:** Member of Bay Area Library and Information Network. **Publications:** Brochure; monthly newsletter. **Remarks:** FAX: (415)751-6735. Library located at 601 14th Ave., San Francisco, CA. **Staff:** Elizabeth Houdek.

Holocaust Education and Resource Center
See: **Jewish Community Relations Council - Anti-Defamation League of Minnesota-Dakotas - Library** (8386)

Holocaust Martyrs' and Heroes' Remembrance Authority
See: **Yad Vashem** (20689)

Holocaust Oral Archive
See: **Gratz College - Tuttleman Library** (6657)

★7341★
Holston Valley Hospital and Medical Center - The Robert D. Doty Health Sciences Library (Med)
W. Ravine St.
Box 238 Phone: (615)229-7063
Kingsport, TN 37662 Patsy S. Ellis, Libn.
Founded: 1953. **Staff:** Prof 1. **Subjects:** Medicine, nursing, and allied health sciences. **Holdings:** 5191 books; 2681 bound periodical volumes. **Subscriptions:** 179 journals and other serials. **Services:** Interlibrary loan; document delivery; library open to the public for reference use only. **Computerized Information Services:** MEDLARS; CD-ROMs (MEDLINE, CINAHL); DOCLINE (electronic mail service). Performs searches. **Networks/Consortia:** Member of Tri-Cities Area Health Sciences Libraries Consortium, Tennessee Health Science Library Association (THeSLA). **Remarks:** Affiliated with the James H. Quillen College of Medicine, East Tennessee State University.

Holt Manufacturing Company Archives
See: **The Haggin Museum - Almeda May Castle Petzinger Library** (6827)

Ruth Holt Library
See: **Mount Paran Church of God** (10808)

★7342★
Holy Apostles College - Library (Rel-Phil)
33 Prospect Hill Rd. Phone: (203)632-3009
Cromwell, CT 06416-0903 Lucille S. Halfpenny, Hd.Libn.
Founded: 1957. **Staff:** 3. **Subjects:** Religious studies, science, theology, sociology, philosophy, English literature, and art. **Holdings:** 50,500 books; 400 bound periodical volumes. **Subscriptions:** 154 journals and other serials. **Services:** Interlibrary loan; library open to the public.

★7343★
Holy Cross Catholic Church - Parish Library (Rel-Phil)
3175 Hathaway Court, N.E. Phone: (404)939-3501
Atlanta, GA 30341 Ray Fager, Libn.
Founded: 1964. **Staff:** 3. **Subjects:** Philosophy, theology, holy scripture, hagiography, Church history. **Holdings:** 1000 books; Theological Dictionary of the New Testament; New Catholic Encyclopedia. **Services:** Library open to the public. **Automated Operations:** Computerized cataloging.

★7344★
Holy Cross Hospital - Health Sciences Library (Med)
2701 W. 68th St. Phone: (312)471-5643
Chicago, IL 60629 Warren Albert, Med.Libn.
Founded: 1962. **Staff:** Prof 1; Other 2. **Subjects:** Medicine, nursing, management, hospital administration. **Holdings:** 2500 books; 4600 bound periodical volumes; 7 audiotape title series; 7 VF drawers; 2 video cassette title series, 1987 to present; CIM microfiche, 1980 to present. **Subscriptions:** 170 journals and serials; 10 newspapers. **Services:** Interlibrary loan; library not open to the public. **Computerized Information Services:** MEDLINE. **Networks/Consortia:** Member of ILLINET, Chicago Library System, National Network of Libraries of Medicine - Greater Midwest Region, Chicago and South Consortium. **Publications:** Occasional Memorandum (series). **Remarks:** FAX: (312)471-5646.

★7345★
Holy Cross Hospital - Medical Library (Med)
1050 E. South Temple Phone: (801)350-4060
Salt Lake City, UT 84102 Lynda Van Wagoner, Med.Libn.
Founded: 1961. **Staff:** Prof 1. **Subjects:** Medicine, surgery, nursing, allied health sciences. **Holdings:** 1000 books; 200 Audio-Digest tapes. **Subscriptions:** 125 journals and serials. **Services:** Interlibrary loan (fee); copying; SDI; library open to hospital physicians, staff, and medical and nursing students. **Computerized Information Services:** MEDLINE; DOCLINE (electronic mail service). **Networks/Consortia:** Member of Utah Health Sciences Library Consortium (UHSLC).

★7346★
Holy Cross Hospital of Calgary - Library Services (Med)
2210 2nd St., S.W. Phone: (403)541-2142
Calgary, AB, Canada T2S 1S6 Mumtaz Jivraj, Libn.
Founded: 1976. **Staff:** Prof 1; Other 1. **Subjects:** Medicine, nursing, hospitals, allied health sciences. **Holdings:** 3300 books; 1200 bound periodical volumes; 700 cassette tapes; 275 video cassettes; 40 slide/tape programs. **Subscriptions:** 250 journals and other serials. **Services:** Interlibrary loan; services. **Remarks:** FAX: (403)541-2595.

★7347★
Holy Cross Hospital of Silver Spring - Medical Library (Med)
1500 Forest Glen Rd. Phone: (301)905-1211
Silver Spring, MD 20910 Bernetta Payne, Libn.
Founded: 1963. **Staff:** Prof 1. **Subjects:** Medicine, allied health sciences. **Holdings:** 1400 books; 750 bound periodical volumes; 500 Audio-Digest tapes. **Subscriptions:** 185 journals and other serials. **Services:** Interlibrary loan; copying; library open to the public on request. **Computerized Information Services:** NLM; CD-ROM (CD-Plus). **Networks/Consortia:** Member of Maryland and D.C. Consortium of Resource Sharing (MADCORS). **Remarks:** FAX: (301)905-1045.

★7348★
Holy Cross Medical Center - Health Sciences Library (Med)
15031 Rinaldi St. Phone: (818)898-4545
Mission Hills, CA 91345-9986 Lucille R. Moss, Mgr.
Founded: 1973. **Staff:** Prof 1; Other 1. **Subjects:** Clinical medicine, nursing, hospital administration. **Holdings:** 1200 books; 3200 bound periodical volumes. **Subscriptions:** 250 journals and other serials. **Services:** Interlibrary loan; copying; library open to the public with restrictions. **Automated Operations:** Computerized cataloging and serials. **Computerized Information Services:** MEDLARS. Performs searches on fee basis. **Remarks:** FAX: (818)898-4621; 898-4607.

★7349★
Holy Family College - Library - Special Collections (Area-Ethnic)
Grant & Frankford Aves. Phone: (215)637-5828
Philadelphia, PA 19114 Kathleen Mulroy, Dir.
Founded: 1954. **Staff:** 10. **Special Collections:** Collection of Polish literature and cultural history (3375 items). **Services:** Interlibrary loan; copying; collection open to the public for reference use only. **Automated Operations:** Computerized cataloging, acquisitions, and ILL. **Computerized Information Services:** BRS Information Technologies, OCLC. **Networks/Consortia:** Member of Tri-State College Library Cooperative (TCLC), Interlibrary Delivery Service of Pennsylvania (IDS), PALINET, Consortium for Health Information & Library Services (CHI). **Remarks:** FAX: (215)632-8067. **Staff:** Robert Ellermeyer, Ref.Libn.; Charles Seeburger, Ref.Libn.; Florence Hogan, ILL; Florence Tilsner, Per.; Patricia Wagner, Acq.; Florence Dolan, Circ.

★7350★
Holy Family Convent - Library (Rel-Phil)
Benet Lake, WI 53102 Phone: (414)862-2010
Founded: 1949. **Subjects:** Theology, scripture, spiritual reading, biography, history, English, science. **Special Collections:** Benedictine collection (150 books). **Holdings:** 7000 books; 58 pamphlets; 500 cassette tapes; 50 reel-to-reel tapes.

★7351★
Holy Family Hospital - Health Sciences Library (Med)
100 N. River Rd. Phone: (708)297-1800
Des Plaines, IL 60016 Val Baker, Libn.
Staff: Prof 1; Other 1. **Subjects:** Medicine, nursing, hospital administration. **Holdings:** 5000 books. **Subscriptions:** 364 journals and other serials; 2 newspapers. **Services:** Interlibrary loan; copying; SDI; library open to the public when librarian is present. **Computerized Information Services:** MEDLARS, BRS Information Technologies, DIALOG Information Services, LEXIS, NEXIS. Performs searches free of charge for physicians and hospital employees. **Networks/Consortia:** Member of North Suburban Library System (NSLS), National Network of Libraries of Medicine - Greater Midwest Region. **Publications:** New acquisitions list, bimonthly. **Staff:** Sister Eleanore.

★7352★
Holy Family Hospital and Medical Center - Health Science Library (Med)
70 East St. Phone: (508)687-0151
Methuen, MA 01844 Chin-Soon Han, Med.Libn.
Founded: 1950. **Staff:** Prof 1; Other 2. **Subjects:** Medicine, nursing, hospital administration. **Special Collections:** Oncology. **Holdings:** 1000 books; 1400 bound periodical volumes; 10 volumes of archival materials; 7 VF drawers on specific diseases. **Subscriptions:** 100 journals and other serials. **Services:** Interlibrary loan; library not open to the public. **Computerized Information Services:** MEDLARS. Performs searches. **Networks/Consortia:** Member of Northeastern Consortium for Health Information (NECHI), North Atlantic Health Science Libraries (NAHSL). **Remarks:** FAX: (508)688-7689.

★7353★
Holy Family Medical Center - Health Sciences Library (Med)
2300 Western Ave.
P.O. Box 1450 Phone: (414)684-2260
Manitowoc, WI 54221-1450 Dan Eckert, Libn.
Founded: 1976. **Staff:** 1. **Subjects:** Medicine and nursing. **Holdings:** 1500 books. **Subscriptions:** 128 journals and other serials. **Services:** Interlibrary loan; copying; library open to the public with restrictions. **Computerized Information Services:** MEDLINE, DIALOG Information Services; CD-ROMs (MEDLINE, CINAHL, HealthPLAN); DOCLINE (electronic mail service). **Networks/Consortia:** Member of Fox River Valley Area Library Consortium (FRVALC). **Remarks:** FAX: (414)684-2522.

★7354★
Holy Name Hospital - Library (Med)
Teaneck Rd. Phone: (201)833-3395
Teaneck, NJ 07666 Ronald Rizio, Dir., Lib.Serv.
Founded: 1925. **Staff:** Prof 1; Other 2. **Subjects:** Medicine, nursing, and allied health sciences. **Holdings:** 6000 books; 3000 bound periodical volumes; 250 video cassettes; 500 cassette tapes. **Subscriptions:** 200 journals and other serials; 3 newspapers. **Services:** Interlibrary loan; copying; library open to the public with restrictions. **Automated Operations:** Computerized circulation. **Computerized Information Services:** BRS Information Technologies, MEDLARS, DIALOG Information Services; DOCLINE (electronic mail service). Performs searches on fee basis. **Networks/Consortia:** Member of Bergen Passaic Regional Library Cooperative, Health Sciences Library Association of New Jersey (HSLANJ), BHSL, National Network of Libraries of Medicine - Middle Atlantic Region. **Publications:** Medical Dialogue; physician's newsletter. **Remarks:** FAX: (201)833-3006.

★7355★
Holy Name of Jesus Hospital - Library (Med)
Box 268 Phone: (205)547-4911
Gadsden, AL 35902 Jean F. Bonds, Supv.
Founded: 1965. **Staff:** Prof 1; Other 1. **Subjects:** Medicine, medical specialties, surgery, surgical specialties. **Holdings:** 615 books; 586 bound periodical volumes. **Subscriptions:** 60 journals and other serials. **Services:** Interlibrary loan; copying; library open to the public with restrictions.

Holy Spirit Research Center
See: **Oral Roberts University - Graduate Theology Library - John Messick Learning Resource Center** (13967)

Holy Spirit Research Center
See: **Oral Roberts University - Library** (13968)

★7356★
Holy Trinity Lutheran Church - Library (Rel-Phil)
2730 E. 31st St.
Minneapolis, MN 55406 Phone: (612)729-8358
Founded: 1952. **Holdings:** 4000 books; 40 bound periodical volumes. **Services:** Library open to church members.

★7357★
Holzer Medical Center - Medical Library (Med)
385 Jackson Pike Phone: (614)446-5057
Gallipolis, OH 45631 Beverly J. Jackson, Libn.
Staff: 1. **Subjects:** Medicine, surgery, urology, pediatrics, diseases of the eye, ear, nose and throat, oncology, cardiology, radiation oncology. **Special Collections:** Nursing and Medical Archives. **Holdings:** 2500 books; 70 periodical titles. **Services:** Interlibrary loan; copying; library open to the public with restrictions. **Computerized Information Services:** Online systems. **Networks/Consortia:** Member of National Network of Libraries of Medicine - Greater Midwest Region. **Publications:** Newsletter, quarterly. **Special Indexes:** Serials list. **Remarks:** FAX: (614)446-5068.

★7358★
Holzmacher, McLendon & Murrell, P.C. - H2M Group Library (Sci-Engr, Env-Cons)
575 Broad Hollow Rd. Phone: (516)756-8000
Melville, NY 11747 Beatrice Uzzo, Libn.
Founded: 1960. **Staff:** 1. **Subjects:** Civil engineering, sanitary engineering, environmental science, architecture, water and waste treatment, industrial waste, water supply, environmental engineering. **Holdings:** 12,000 books; 1050 reports; 5 years of Federal Registers on microfiche; maps. **Subscriptions:** 170 journals and other serials; 30 newspapers. **Services:** Interlibrary loan; copying; library open to the public by appointment. **Remarks:** FAX: (516)694-4122.

★7359★
Home Life Insurance Company - Library (Bus-Fin)
75 Wall St. Phone: (212)428-2142
New York, NY 10005 Jennie Del Vecchio, Libn.
Founded: 1934. **Staff:** Prof 1. **Subjects:** Life insurance, health insurance, tax, securities. **Holdings:** 1350 volumes; 58 VF drawers of unbound materials. **Subscriptions:** 130 journals and other serials. **Services:** Interlibrary loan (Special Libraries Association members only); library not open to the public. **Computerized Information Services:** LEXIS, NEXIS. **Remarks:** FAX: (212)428-2155.

Home News Publishing Company
See: **Central New Jersey Home News** (3352)

Home Office Forensic Science Service
See: **Great Britain - Home Office Forensic Science Service** (6678)

★7360★
Home Oil Company, Ltd. - Information and Records Department (Energy, Sci-Engr)
1600 Home Oil Tower
324 8th Ave., S.W. Phone: (403)232-5020
Calgary, AB, Canada T2P 2Z5 Gail L. Fraser, Coord.
Staff: Prof 1; Other 3. **Subjects:** Geology, business, petroleum technology, computer science, energy resources. **Holdings:** 8000 books; company technical records. **Subscriptions:** 400 journals and other serials. **Services:** Interlibrary loan; center not open to the public. **Automated Operations:** Computerized cataloging, acquisitions, serials, and circulation. **Computerized Information Services:** DIALOG Information Services, Reuters, Info Globe, Infomart Online. **Remarks:** FAX: (403)232-7044. **Formerly:** Its Information and Graphics Centre.

Winslow Homer's Library
See: **The Strong Museum - Library** (15832)

Homestead National Monument
See: **U.S. Natl. Park Service** (17732)

★7361★
Homewood Hospital Center - Library Services
2724 N. Charles St.
Baltimore, MD 21218
Defunct.

★7362★
O. Hommel Company - Research Library
235 Hope St.
Carnegie, PA 15106-3696 Phone: (412)279-0700
Remarks: No further information was supplied by respondent.

Homolovi Ruins State Park Library
See: **Arizona State Parks** (1007)

★7363★
Homosexual Information Center - Library (Soc Sci)
115 Monroe St. Phone: (318)742-4709
Bossier City, LA 71111 Leslie Colfax, Libn.
Founded: 1952. **Staff:** Prof 1; Other 2. **Subjects:** Homosexuality, civil liberties, censorship, sexual freedom, lesbiana, prostitution, abortion. **Special Collections:** Homosexual Movement Collection (papers from 1948 to present). **Holdings:** 9800 books and bound periodical volumes; 32 VF drawers of manuscripts, clippings, pamphlets, documents; 86 legal briefs and court opinions; 30 boxes. **Subscriptions:** 32 journals and other serials; 21 newspapers. **Services:** Interlibrary loan; copying; center open to the public. **Publications:** Directory of Homosexual Organizations; Seeds of the American Sexual Revolution; Prostitution is Legal; HIC Newsletter; Selected Bibliography of Homosexuality; selected bibliographies; reading lists; subject heading guides; list of other publications - available upon request. **Remarks:** Provides information and referral services at Homosexual Information Center, Box 8252, Universal City, CA 91608. **Also Known As:** The Tangent Group. **Staff:** Don Slater, Chm.

★7364★
Honduras - National Archives (Hum, Soc Sci)
6a Avda No. 408 Phone: 228338
Tegucigalpa, Honduras Pablo H.R. Rosales, Dir.
Subjects: History, social sciences, literature. **Special Collections:** Honduran books and periodicals. **Holdings:** 200 books; 1000 bound periodical volumes; 10,000 archival items; 300 reels of microfilm. **Subscriptions:** 5 journals and other serials; 5 newspapers. **Services:** Library not open to the public. **Publications:** Anales del Archivo Nacional, updated 1991. **Special Indexes:** Indice de Titulos de Tierra. **Also Known As:** Archivo Nacional de Honduras.

★7365★
Honey Creek Church Preservation Group - Honey Creek Friends Meetinghouse - Library (Hist)
Rte. 1, Box 18 Phone: (515)497-5458
New Providence, IA 50206 Vera Cutler
Founded: 1973. **Subjects:** Society of Friends history, community history, New Providence history, New Providence Academy history. **Holdings:** 150 books; 75 bound periodical volumes; 25 manuscripts; 300 nonbook items; cemetery, church, and academy records. **Services:** Library open to the public for reference use only. **Publications:** Newsletters.

★7366★
Honeywell, Inc. - Air Transport Systems - Engineering Library (Sci-Engr)
Box 21111 Phone: (602)869-6414
Phoenix, AZ 85036 Pat DeVillier, Libn.
Founded: 1960. **Staff:** Prof 1. **Subjects:** Electronic engineering, computer sciences, flight instrumentation. **Holdings:** 3000 books; 1000 technical reports. **Subscriptions:** 150 journals and other serials. **Services:** Interlibrary loan; copying; library open to the public by appointment. **Computerized Information Services:** DIALOG Information Services. Performs searches on fee basis.

★7367★
Honeywell, Inc. - Commercial Bldg. Group - Library (Sci-Engr)
1500 W. Dundee
Arlington Heights, IL 60004 Phone: (708)394-4000
Founded: 1972. **Subjects:** Electrical engineering, computer programming, management. **Special Collections:** Energy management (500 unbound reports). **Holdings:** 500 books; 1000 internal documents. **Subscriptions:** 20 journals and other serials. **Services:** Interlibrary loan; copying; library not open to the public. **Automated Operations:** Computerized serials. **Computerized Information Services:** DIALOG Information Services; Honeywell Computerized Library Catalog (HCLC) (internal database). **Networks/Consortia:** Member of Honeywell Information Network (HIN). **Publications:** Honeywell Union List of Serials, annual - for internal distribution only. **Special Catalogs:** Union list of serials and conference proceedings for Honeywell Information Network. **Remarks:** FAX: (708)870-5490.

★7368★
Honeywell, Inc. - Government Systems Field Marketing - MRA Information Center
7900 Westpark Dr., Suite 530
McLean, VA 22102
Defunct.

★7369★
Honeywell, Inc. - Jack Fatz Memorial Information Center (Sci-Engr)
13350 U.S. Hwy. 19, N. Phone: (813)531-4611
Clearwater, FL 34624-7290 V. Hopkins, Libn.
Founded: 1959. **Staff:** Prof 2. **Subjects:** Aeronautics, navigation, electrical engineering. **Holdings:** 3000 books; 200 bound periodical volumes; 1000 reports. **Subscriptions:** 200 journals and other serials. **Services:** Center not open to the public. **Computerized Information Services:** DIALOG Information Services, WILSONLINE, NASA/RECON.

★7370★
Honeywell, Inc. - Micro Switch - Business and Technical Information Center (Sci-Engr)
11 W. Spring St. Phone: (815)235-5609
Freeport, IL 61032 Mary C. Schneider, Res.Libn.
Founded: 1960. **Staff:** Prof 2. **Subjects:** Electrical engineering, business administration, competitive intelligence. **Holdings:** 2600 books. **Subscriptions:** 300 journals and other serials; 2 newspapers. **Services:** Interlibrary loan; copying; SDI; center open to the public. **Automated Operations:** Computerized public access catalog and circulation. **Computerized Information Services:** WILSONLINE, DIALOG Information Services, DataTimes, Dun & Bradstreet Business Credit Services, Reuter TEXTLINE; DIALMAIL (electronic mail service). **Networks/Consortia:** Member of Honeywell Information Network (HIN), Northern Illinois Library System (NILS). **Remarks:** FAX: (815)235-5623. **Staff:** Pat Vorwald, Res.Libn.

★7371★
Honeywell, Inc. - Process Controls Division - Information Center
1100 Virginia Dr.
Fort Washington, PA 19034
Defunct.

★7372★
Honeywell, Inc. - Residential & Building Controls Divisions - Library Information Services (Sci-Engr)
MN10-1459
1985 Douglas Dr., N. Phone: (612)542-6828
Golden Valley, MN 55422 Mary K. Swanson, Lib.Info.Cons.
Founded: 1944. **Staff:** Prof 1; Other 1. **Subjects:** Engineering, business, HVAC, indoor air quality. **Holdings:** 3500 books; 2500 periodical volumes. **Subscriptions:** 100 journals and other serials. **Services:** Interlibrary loan; SDI; center open to the public with restrictions. **Automated Operations:** Computerized cataloging, acquisitions, serials, and circulation. **Computerized Information Services:** DIALOG Information Services, DataTimes, VU/TEXT Information Services, Reuters Information Services, NEXIS; DIALMAIL (electronic mail service). **Networks/Consortia:** Member of Honeywell Information Network (HIN). **Remarks:** FAX: (612)542-6887.

★7373★
Honeywell, Inc. - Sensors & Signal Processing Laboratory Library (Sci-Engr)
10701 Lyndale Ave., S. Phone: (612)887-4321
Bloomington, MN 55420 Michael McClellan, Libn.
Founded: 1956. **Staff:** Prof 1. **Subjects:** Physics, chemistry, electrical engineering. **Holdings:** 7000 books; 8000 bound periodical volumes. **Subscriptions:** 250 journals and other serials. **Services:** Library not open to the public. **Automated Operations:** Computerized cataloging. **Computerized Information Services:** DIALOG Information Services, Dow Jones News/Retrieval, Mead Data Central, BRS Information Technologies, OCLC. **Remarks:** FAX: (612)887-4517.

★7374★
Honeywell, Inc. - Solid State Electronics Center Library (Sci-Engr)
MN14-4B50
12001 Hwy. 55 Phone: (612)541-2075
Plymouth, MN 55441 Sandra Bennett, Libn.
Founded: 1979. **Staff:** Prof 1. **Subjects:** Integrated circuits, semiconductors, electronics. **Holdings:** 800 books; 600 bound periodical volumes; 100 reports. **Subscriptions:** 100 journals and other serials. **Services:** Interlibrary loan; library not open to the public. **Automated Operations:** Computerized cataloging (SYDNEY). **Computerized Information Services:** DIALOG Information Services, OCLC; DIALMAIL (electronic mail service). **Networks/Consortia:** Member of Honeywell Information Network (HIN).

★7375★
Honeywell, Inc. - Systems & Research Center - Sensor & System Development Center - Library & Information Center (Sci-Engr, Comp Sci)
3660 Technology Dr. Phone: (612)782-7690
Minneapolis, MN 55418 Maro Theologides, Mgr., Lib.Info.Serv.
Founded: 1951. **Staff:** Prof 5; Other 3. **Subjects:** Aerospace technology, computer sciences, control systems technology, information systems, advanced sensors and displays, microsystems and circuits, systems and artificial intelligence, home automation. **Holdings:** 8000 books; 7500 bound periodical volumes; 15,000 internal reports; 70,000 technical documents. **Subscriptions:** 425 journals and other serials; 5 newspapers. **Services:** Interlibrary loan; SDI; library open to the public with restrictions. **Automated Operations:** Computerized cataloging and circulation. **Computerized Information Services:** DIALOG Information Services, Aerospace Online, NASA/RECON, NewsNet, Inc., DTIC, OCLC; GCOS (internal database); DIALMAIL (electronic mail service). **Networks/Consortia:** Member of Honeywell Information Network (HIN). **Publications:** Recent Acquisitions Bulletin, monthly; Infobriefs, monthly - both for internal distribution only. **Remarks:** Alternate telephone number(s): 782-7400. FAX: (612)782-7438. Electronic mail address(es): 10493 (DIALMAIL). **Staff:** Sue Landgraff, Libn.; Nancy Dunlavy, Libn.; Vern Bartlett, Info.Spec.; Jane Kaufenberg, Libn.; Peggy Perschbacher, Asst.Libn.

Honeywell, Inc. - Test Instruments Division
See: **Metrum Information Storage** (10236)

Howard and Edna Hong Kierkegaard Library
See: **St. Olaf College** (14552)

Hong Kong - Royal Observatory, Hong Kong
See: **Royal Observatory, Hong Kong** (14128)

(Hong Kong) American Library - USIS Library
See: **American Library in Hong Kong** (666)

★7376★
Honigman Miller Schwartz & Cohn - Law Library (Law)
2290 First National Bldg. Phone: (313)256-7513
Detroit, MI 48226 Patricia A. McKanna, Lib.Mgr.
Staff: Prof 4; Other 3. **Subjects:** Law - real estate, bankruptcy, corporate, environmental, hospital, tax. **Holdings:** 10,000 books; 500 bound periodical volumes; 500 loose-leaf binders and reports. **Subscriptions:** 200 journals and other serials; 7 newspapers. **Services:** Interlibrary loan; library not open to the public. **Computerized Information Services:** LEXIS, WESTLAW, DIALOG Information Services, Dow Jones News/Retrieval. **Remarks:** FAX: (313)962-2447. **Staff:** Margi Heinen, Libn.; Jean Kawata, Libn.; Alexia Repella, Libn.

Bengt E. Honning Memorial Library
See: **Self Winding Clock Society - Bengt E. Honning Memorial Library** (15019)

Honnold/Mudd Library
See: **The Claremont Colleges - Honnold/Mudd Library** (3753)

★7377★
Honolulu Academy of Arts - Robert Allerton Library (Art)
900 S. Beretania St. Phone: (808)538-3693
Honolulu, HI 96814 Anne T. Seaman, Libn.
Founded: 1927. **Staff:** Prof 1; Other 1. **Subjects:** Art history, especially Chinese and Japanese art. **Special Collections:** Michigan archives of the Palace Museum, Taiwan (8000 mounted black/white photographs; 2000 2x2 color slides). **Holdings:** 40,000 books; 12,000 bound periodical volumes; 4000 pamphlets; 36 VF drawers of clippings and announcements; 15 reels of microfilm. **Subscriptions:** 220 journals and other serials. **Services:** Interlibrary loan; copying; library open to members.

★7378★
Honolulu Academy of Arts - Slide Collection (Art, Aud-Vis)
900 S. Beretania St. Phone: (808)532-8700
Honolulu, HI 96814 Gwen Harada, Kpr.
Founded: 1972. **Staff:** Prof 1. **Subjects:** Art, architecture, crafts. **Special Collections:** Chinese painting. **Holdings:** 45,000 slides. **Services:** Collection open to the public with restrictions. **Remarks:** FAX: (808)521-6591.

★7379★
Honolulu (City and County) Municipal Reference and Records Center (Soc Sci, Plan)
558 S. King St. Phone: (808)523-4577
Honolulu, HI 96813 Proserfina A. Strona, Dir.
Founded: 1929. **Staff:** Prof 3; Other 3. **Subjects:** Municipal government; urban planning, development, and renewal; engineering and public works; traffic and transportation; public administration. **Special Collections:** Honolulu Ordinances File. **Holdings:** 43,440 volumes; 150 VF drawers of newspaper clippings. **Subscriptions:** 376 journals and other serials. **Services:** Interlibrary loan to Oahu libraries; copying; center open to the public. **Automated Operations:** Computerized cataloging. **Computerized Information Services:** LOGIN, DIALOG Information Services. Performs searches on fee basis. **Publications:** Bookshelf: A Selected Bibliography of Library Acquisitions, bimonthly - to local libraries and government agencies. **Remarks:** FAX: (808)523-4576. **Staff:** Kathleen S. Kudo, Libn.; Verna K. Miura, Libn.

★7380★
Hood Theological Seminary - Library (Rel-Phil)
Livingstone College
W.J. Walls Center
800 W. Thomas St. Phone: (704)638-5645
Salisbury, NC 28144 Ella M. Hargett, Lib.Dir.
Founded: 1880. **Staff:** Prof 2; Other 1. **Subjects:** Philosophy, logic, ethics, natural and Bible religion, doctrine, devotions, pastoral concerns, Christian church history, language. **Special Collections:** W.C. Brown Ecumenical Collection; Bible Collection; Jones and Spottswood Collection. **Holdings:** 30,000 books; 1890 bound periodical volumes; 625 reels of microfilm; 325 microfiche; 240 tapes and filmstrips; 300 other cataloged items; archival materials. **Subscriptions:** 156 journals and other serials; 15 newspapers. **Services:** Interlibrary loan; copying; library open to the public. **Publications:** Student handbook; Accessions. **Special Catalogs:** Tape catalog; AV catalog. **Remarks:** Alternate telephone number(s): (704)638-5648. **Staff:** Donald Heidt, Cat.Libn.

Ruth H. Hooker Research Library and Technical Information Center
See: **U.S. Navy - Naval Research Laboratory** (17869)

David Wayne Hooks Memorial Library
See: **Psychical Research Foundation** (13468)

William Stanley Hoole Special Collections Library
See: **University of Alabama** (18169)

Dorothy H. Hoover Library
See: **Ontario College of Art** (12432)

Herbert Hoover Library
See: **U.S. Presidential Libraries** (17925)

Hoover Institution on War, Revolution and Peace
See: **Stanford University** (15650)

John Edgar Hoover Collection
See: **Scottish Rite Supreme Council - Library** (14969)

Hoover Natural Science Library
See: **Palm Springs Desert Museum - Toor Library & Hoover Natural Science Library** (12704)

Philip A. Hoover, M.D. Library
See: **York Hospital - Philip A. Hoover, M.D. Library** (20773)

Hope College - Archives
See: **(Holland) Joint Archives of Holland** (7328)

★7381★
Hope College - Van Wylen Library - Special Collections (Sci-Engr)
Holland, MI 49423-3698 Phone: (616)394-7790
David Jensen, Dir.
Founded: 1866. **Staff:** Prof 5.5; Other 9. **Subjects:** Chemistry, biology, art history, American history before 1877. **Special Collections:** Dutch in America; Immigration; Census documents (11,000). **Services:** Interlibrary loan; copying; library open to the public. **Automated Operations:** Computerized public access catalog, cataloging, acquisitions, serials, and circulation. **Computerized Information Services:** DIALOG Information Services, BRS Information Technologies, OCLC; BITNET (electronic mail service). Performs searches. Contact Person: Kelly Jacobsma, Hd. of Pub.Serv. **Networks/Consortia:** Member of Michigan Library Consortium (MLC). **Publications:** Bookbytes (newsletter). **Remarks:** FAX: (616)394-7965. Electronic mail address(es): DJENSEN@HOPE (BITNET). **Staff:** Collen Conway; Gloria Slaughter; David O'Brien; Carol Juth.

★7382★
Hope Lutheran Church - Library (Rel-Phil)
1115 N. 35th St. Phone: (414)342-0471
Milwaukee, WI 53208 Esther Damkoehler, Libn.
Staff: 4. **Subjects:** Religion, sociology, history, psychology, children's literature. **Holdings:** 2930 volumes; records; tapes. **Subscriptions:** 10 journals and other serials. **Services:** Library

★7383★
Hope Reformed Church - Blanche Cathcart Memorial Library (Rel-Phil)
77 W. 11th St. Phone: (616)399-9533
Holland, MI 49423 Anne E. Dirkse, Libn.
Founded: 1960. **Subjects:** Church resources, children. **Holdings:** 5800 books. **Services:** Library open to the public with restrictions.

★7384★
Hopedale Medical Complex - Medical Library (Med)
Hopedale, IL 61747 Phone: (309)449-3321
Mrs. Bobby Murphy, Libn.
Subjects: Geriatrics, substance abuse, rehabilitation. **Holdings:** 200 books; 200 bound periodical volumes. **Subscriptions:** 25 journals and other serials. **Services:** Interlibrary loan; copying; library open to the patients and medical students. **Remarks:** FAX: (309)449-5441.

Grace Hoper Press Archive
See: **University of San Francisco - Special Collections Department/ Donohue Rare Book Room** (19290)

Hopewell Furnace National Historic Site
See: **U.S. Natl. Park Service** (17733)

★7385★
Hopewell Museum - Library (Hist)
28 E. Broad St. Phone: (609)466-0103
Hopewell, NJ 08525 Beverly Weidl, Cur.
Staff: 2. **Subjects:** Local history, genealogy. **Holdings:** 300 books. **Services:** Library open to the public with restrictions. **Publications:** Pioneers of Old Hopewell, 1963 reprint; Hopewell Valley Heritage, 1974; Medical Records of Benjamin VanKirk, 1768-1815; John Hart - The Biography of a Signer of the Declaration of Independence.

Fred A. Hopf Library
See: **University of Arizona - Optical Sciences Center - Fred A. Hopf Library** (18226)

★7386★
Hopital de Chicoutimi Inc. - Bibliotheque (Med)
305, rue St-Vallier
C.P. 5006 Phone: (418)509-2195
Chicoutimi, PQ, Canada G7H 5H6 Angele Tremblay, Biblio.
Staff: Prof 2; Other 3. **Subjects:** Medicine, public health. **Holdings:** 6300 books; 9100 bound periodical volumes; 15,000 slides and cassettes. **Subscriptions:** 100 journals and other serials. **Services:** Interlibrary loan; copying; library open to the public. **Staff:** Rodrigue Girard, Biblio.

★7387★
Hopital de l'Enfant-Jesus - Bibliotheque Scientifique Charles-Auguste Gauthier (Med)
1401 18ieme Rue Phone: (418)649-5686
Quebec, PQ, Canada G1J 1Z4 Madeleine Dumais, Resp.
Founded: 1964. **Staff:** Prof 1; Other 1. **Subjects:** Medicine. **Holdings:** 1600 books; 4775 bound periodical volumes. **Subscriptions:** 220 journals and other serials. **Services:** Interlibrary loan; library not open to the public. **Computerized Information Services:** MEDLINE; Envoy 100 (electronic mail service). **Remarks:** FAX: (418)649-5920. Electronic mail address(es): QQHEJ (Envoy 100).

★7388★
Hopital General du Lakeshore - Bibliotheque medicale (Med)
160 Stillview Rd. Phone: (514)630-2101
Pointe Claire, PQ, Canada H9R 2Y2 Guylaine Marion, Libn.
Founded: 1965. **Staff:** Prof 1. **Subjects:** Medicine, surgery, obstetrics, gynecology, pathology, psychiatry, nursing. **Holdings:** 1000 books; bound periodical volumes; magnetic tapes; microfiche. **Subscriptions:** 125 journals and other serials. **Services:** Interlibrary loan; library open to the public for reference use only. **Networks/Consortia:** Member of McGill Medical and Health Libraries Association (MMHLA). **Publications:** Liste des nouveautes. **Remarks:** FAX: (514)630-3302. **Also Known As:** Lakeshore General Hospital - Medical Library.

Hopital General d'Ottawa
See: **Ottawa General Hospital** (12600)

★7389★
Hopital du Haut-Richelieu - Bibliotheque Medicale (Med)
920, Blvd. du Seminaire Phone: (514)359-5055
St. Jean, PQ, Canada J3A 1B7 Helene Heroux-Bouchard, Biblio.
Staff: Prof 1. **Subjects:** Medicine, psychiatry, pediatrics, obstetrics and gynecology, surgery. **Holdings:** 1900 books; 850 bound periodical volumes. **Subscriptions:** 85 journals and other serials. **Services:** Interlibrary loan; library not open to the public.

★7390★
Hopital l'Hotel-Dieu de Quebec - Bibliotheque Medicale (Med)
11, Cote du Palais Phone: (418)691-5073
Quebec, PQ, Canada G1R 2J6 Lizette Germain, Libn.
Founded: 1959. **Staff:** Prof 1; Other 2. **Subjects:** Cancer, nephrology. **Holdings:** 3432 books. **Subscriptions:** 359 journals and other serials. **Services:** Interlibrary loan; library open to the public. **Computerized Information Services:** CD-ROM (MEDLINE).

★7391★
Hopital Jean-Talon - Bibliotheque Medicale (Med)
1385 E. Jean-Talon Phone: (514)495-6767
Montreal, PQ, Canada H2E 1S6 Pierrette Galarneau, Med.Libn.
Founded: 1961. **Staff:** Prof 1. **Subjects:** Medicine. **Special Collections:** CIBA Collection (slides). **Holdings:** 1800 books. **Subscriptions:** 160 journals and other serials. **Services:** Interlibrary loan; copying; library open to the public for consultation only. **Remarks:** FAX: (514)495-6734. **Also Known As:** Jean-Talon Hospital.

Hopital Juif de Readaptation
See: **Jewish Rehabilitation Hospital** (8404)

★7392★
Hopital Louis H. Lafontaine - Bibliotheque (Med)
7401, rue Hochelaga Phone: (514)251-4000
Montreal, PQ, Canada H1N 3M5 Camil Lemire, Biblio.
Founded: 1950. **Staff:** Prof 1; Other 3. **Subjects:** Psychology, psychiatry, psychoanalysis. **Holdings:** 6400 books; 3000 bound periodical volumes. **Subscriptions:** 150 journals and other serials. **Services:** Interlibrary loan; copying; library open to the public with restrictions. **Computerized Information Services:** MEDLINE, DIALOG Information Services. **Networks/Consortia:** Member of Association des Bibliotheques de la Sante Affiliees a l'Universite de Montreal (ABSAUM).

★7393★
Hopital Maisonneuve-Rosemont - Service des Bibliotheques (Med)
5415 de l'Assomption Blvd. Phone: (514)252-3463
Montreal, PQ, Canada H1T 2M4 Helene Lauzon, Chf.Libn.
Staff: Prof 4; Other 1. **Subjects:** Medicine, surgery, psychiatry, pneumology, gynecology, pediatrics, hospital administration, nursing, medical technology, immunology, obstetrics, neurology, cardiology. **Holdings:** 3000 books; 15,000 bound periodical volumes; 153 other cataloged items. **Subscriptions:** 374 journals and other serials. **Services:** Interlibrary loan; copying; library open to the public with restrictions. **Automated Operations:** Computerized public access catalog, cataloging, acquisitions, serials, and circulation. **Computerized Information Services:** DIALOG Information Services, MEDLINE; CD-ROM (Medline); Envoy 100 (electronic mail service). Performs searches on fee basis. **Special Catalogs:** Periodical lists and basic volumes, annual. **Remarks:** FAX: (514)252-3589 (Medical Library). Electronic mail address(es): QMHMR (Envoy 100).

★7394★
Hopital de Mont-Joli, Inc. - Bibliotheque (Med)
800 Sanatorium Phone: (418)775-7261
Mont-Joli, PQ, Canada G5H 3L6 Helene Jean, Biblio.
Founded: 1974. **Staff:** Prof 1. **Subjects:** Psychiatry, psychology, medicine, health care, long-term care, physical and geriatric rehabilitation. **Special Collections:** Psychiatry (150 volumes); medicine (300 volumes). **Holdings:** 5350 books; 88 periodical volumes. **Services:** Interlibrary loan; library not open to the public. **Remarks:** FAX: (418)775-8607.

★7395★
Hopital Notre Dame - Medical Library (Med)
C.P. 1560, Succ. C. Phone: (514)876-6862
Montreal, PQ, Canada H2L 4K8 Andre Allard, Chf.Libn.
Founded: 1935. **Staff:** Prof 1; Other 4. **Subjects:** Medicine, allied health sciences. **Holdings:** 10,000 books; 40,000 bound periodical volumes. **Subscriptions:** 600 journals and other serials. **Services:** Interlibrary loan; copying; library open to the public for reference use only. **Automated Operations:** Computerized ILL. **Computerized Information Services:** MEDLARS; CD-ROM; Envoy 100 (electronic mail service). Performs searches on fee basis. **Networks/Consortia:** Member of Association des Bibliotheques de la Sante Affiliees a l'Universite de Montreal (ABSAUM). **Special Catalogs:** Catalogue collectif des periodiques regulierement recus dans les bibliotheques de la sante affiliees a l'Universite de Montreal. **Also Known As:** Notre Dame Hospital.

★7396★
Hopital Reine Elizabeth - A. Hollis Marden Bibliotheque (Med)
2100 Marlowe Ave. Phone: (514)488-2311
Montreal, PQ, Canada H4A 3L6 Ms. S.L. Mullan, Lib.Techn.
Founded: 1937. **Staff:** 2. **Subjects:** Medicine, nursing. **Holdings:** 13,009 volumes. **Subscriptions:** 199 journals and other serials. **Services:** Interlibrary loan; library not open to the public. **Remarks:** FAX: (514)485-3276.

★7397★
Hopital Riviere-des-Prairies - Bibliotheque du Personnel (Med)
7070, blvd. Perras Phone: (514)323-7260
Montreal, PQ, Canada H1E 1A4 Robert Aubin, Hd.
Founded: 1966. **Staff:** Prof 1; Other 1.5. **Subjects:** Child psychiatry, mental retardation. **Holdings:** 9000 books; 3000 bound periodical volumes; 1800 reprints; 100 videotapes; 800 cassettes; 1500 microfiche. **Subscriptions:** 200 journals and other serials. **Services:** Interlibrary loan; copying; SDI; library open to the public for reference use only. **Computerized Information Services:** MEDLARS, DIALOG Information Services, CAN/OLE; Envoy 100 (electronic mail service). Performs searches on fee basis. **Networks/Consortia:** Member of Association des Bibliotheques de la Sante Affiliees a l'Universite de Montreal (ABSAUM). **Publications:** Monthly list of new books; annual report; bibliographies. **Remarks:** FAX: (514)323-8622. Electronic mail address(es): QMHRP (Envoy 100).

★7398★
Hopital du Sacre Coeur de Montreal - Bibliotheque Albert-Prevost (Med)
6555 Gouin Blvd., W.
Montreal, PQ, Canada H4K 1B3 Phone: (514)338-4284
Founded: 1962. **Staff:** Prof 1. **Subjects:** Psychiatry, psychoanalysis, child psychiatry, psychology. **Holdings:** 7748 books; 361 Audio-Digest tapes on psychiatry; 136 videocassettes. **Subscriptions:** 105 journals and other serials. **Services:** Interlibrary loan; copying. **Computerized Information Services:** DIALOG Information Services; Envoy 100 (electronic mail service). **Networks/Consortia:** Member of Association des Bibliotheques de la Sante Affiliees a l'Universite de Montreal (ABSAUM). **Formerly:** Its Pavillon Albert-Prevost.

★7399★
Hopital Ste. Jeanne d'Arc - Bibliotheque Medicale (Med)
3570, rue St. Urbain Phone: (514)282-6951
Montreal, PQ, Canada H2X 2N8 Louise Lemay, Biblio.
Founded: 1957. **Staff:** Prof 1. **Subjects:** Medicine, surgery, psychology, psychiatry. **Holdings:** 1800 books; 1000 bound periodical volumes; 1300 cassettes. **Subscriptions:** 98 journals and other serials; 6 newspapers. **Services:** Interlibrary loan; copying; library open to the public for reference use only.

★7400★
Hopital Santa Cabrini - Centre de Documentation (Med)
5655 E. St-Zotique St. Phone: (514)252-6488
Montreal, PQ, Canada H1T 1P7 Diane Seguin, Lib.Techn.
Staff: Prof 1. **Subjects:** Medicine, pathology, surgery, nursing, urology, cardiology. **Holdings:** 2800 books; 1955 bound periodical volumes. **Subscriptions:** 198 journals and other serials. **Services:** Interlibrary loan; library not open to the public. **Publications:** Acquisitions list, annual; periodical holdings list, annual. **Remarks:** FAX: (514)252-6535.

★7401★
Hopital Ste-Francois d'Assise - Bibliotheque Medicale et Administrative (Med)
10, rue de l'Espinay Phone: (418)525-4408
Quebec, PQ, Canada G1L 3L5 Ulric Lefebvre, Chief
Founded: 1959. **Staff:** Prof 3. **Subjects:** Obstetrics, neonatology, pediatrics, gynecology, internal medicine, surgery, perinatology. **Holdings:** 5200 books; 4650 bound periodical volumes; annual reports; documents. **Subscriptions:** 360 journals and other serials. **Services:** Interlibrary loan; library not open to the public. **Computerized Information Services:** MEDLINE. **Publications:** Liste de volume, periodiques, rapports. **Also Known As:** Hopital Generale.

★7402★
Hopital Ste-Justine - Centre d'Information sur la Sante de l'Enfant (Med)
3175, chemin Cote Ste-Catherine Phone: (514)345-4680
Montreal, PQ, Canada H3T 1C5 Louis-Luc Lecompte, Hd.
Founded: 1962. **Staff:** Prof 2; Other 7. **Subjects:** Pediatrics, obstetrics and gynecology, pediatric nursing, child psychiatry, adolescence. **Holdings:** 11,000 books; 6200 reports, videotapes, other cataloged items. **Subscriptions:** 750 journals and other serials. **Services:** Interlibrary loan; copying; SDI; center open to the public with restrictions. **Automated Operations:** Computerized public access catalog, cataloging, acquisitions, serials, and circulation. **Computerized Information Services:** DIALOG Information Services, MEDLINE; CD-ROM (CD Plus/MEDLINE); Envoy 100 (electronic mail service). Performs searches on fee basis. Contact Person: Louise Jolin, Libn., 345-4679. **Special Catalogs:** Catalog of Quebec hospital videotape productions on child and maternal health. **Remarks:** FAX: (514)345-4806.

★7403★
Hopital Ste-Luc - Bibliotheque Medicale (Med)
1058 St. Denis St. Phone: (514)281-6167
Montreal, PQ, Canada H2X 3J4 Pierre Duchesneau, Hd.
Staff: Prof 3; Other 2. **Subjects:** Medicine, paramedical sciences, surgery, hospital administration, nursing. **Holdings:** 9500 books; 4600 bound periodical volumes. **Subscriptions:** 450 journals and other serials. **Services:** Interlibrary loan; copying; SDI; library open to medical and paramedical personnel. **Computerized Information Services:** DIALOG Information Services, MEDLARS; Envoy 100, QMHSL (electronic mail services). Performs searches on fee basis. **Networks/Consortia:** Member of Association des Bibliotheques de la Sante Affiliees a l'Universite de Montreal (ABSAUM). **Remarks:** Alternate telephone number(s): 281-6166. FAX: (514)281-2486. **Also Known As:** St. Luc Hospital

★7404★
Hopital du Ste-Sacrement - Bibliotheque Medicale (Med)
1050, chemin Ste-Foy Phone: (418)682-7730
Quebec, PQ, Canada G1S 4L8 Diane St-Pierre, Biblio.Techn.
Founded: 1935. **Staff:** Prof 2; Other 1. **Subjects:** Medicine. **Holdings:** 1120 books. **Subscriptions:** 220 journals and other serials. **Services:** Interlibrary loan; copying; library open to the public for reference use only. **Computerized Information Services:** CD-ROM (MEDLINE). **Remarks:** FAX: (418)682-6835.

★7405★
Hopkins & Carley - Library (Law)
150 Almaden Blvd., 15th Fl. Phone: (408)286-9800
San Jose, CA 95113 Paul Reavis, Libn.
Subjects: Prof 1; Other 1. **Subjects:** Law. **Special Collections:** Legislative histories of major tax bills enacted since 1970. **Holdings:** 3000 books. **Subscriptions:** 25 journals and other serials; 6 newspapers. **Services:** Library not open to the public. **Computerized Information Services:** LEXIS. **Remarks:** FAX: (408)998-4790.

★7406★
Hopkins Historical Society - Library (Hist)
1010 1st St., S. Phone: (612)938-7315
Hopkins, MN 55343 Clint Blomquist, Archv.
Subjects: Local history. **Special Collections:** Hopkins Women's Club records, 1908-1974 (1 cubic foot); materials concerning the Bohemian ethnic background of residents; complete official Hopkins school records, 1869 to early 1900s. **Holdings:** 700 books (150 in Bohemian language); 2500 pictures; 3700 documents; 5650 newspapers; 935 artifacts; 1675 magazines; 300 maps; 100 city directories; 37 scrapbooks. **Services:** Library open to the public by appointment. **Remarks:** Library located at 33 14th Ave. N., Hopkins, MN.

James Roy Hopkins Archives
See: **Springfield Museum of Art - Library** (15608)

Hopkins Marine Station
See: **Stanford University - Hopkins Marine Station** (15651)

★7407★
Hopkins & Sutter - Library (Law)
888 16th St., N.W. Phone: (202)835-8000
Washington, DC 20006 Janice A. Hammond, Libn.
Staff: Prof 1; Other 4. **Subjects:** Law. **Holdings:** 30,000 books. **Services:** Interlibrary loan; copying; SDI. **Computerized Information Services:** DIALOG Information Services, LEXIS, NEXIS, Dun & Bradstreet Business Credit Services, LEGI-SLATE, Dow Jones News/Retrieval, WESTLAW, NewsNet, Inc., Information America, DataTimes, CQ Weekly Alert. **Remarks:** FAX: (202)835-8136.

★7408★
Hopkins & Sutter - Library (Law)
3 First National Plaza, 43rd Fl. Phone: (312)558-6732
Chicago, IL 60603 Denise Mahaney, Hd.Libn.
Founded: 1921. **Staff:** Prof 2; Other 5. **Subjects:** Law. **Holdings:** 30,000 books; 1000 bound periodical volumes; 3000 microfiche. **Subscriptions:** 500 journals and other serials; 8 newspapers. **Services:** Interlibrary loan; library not open to the public. **Computerized Information Services:** DIALOG Information Services, LEXIS, NEXIS, WESTLAW, Illinois State Legislature - Legislative Information System (LIS). **Networks/Consortia:** Member of ILLINET. **Remarks:** FAX: (312)558-7713.

★7409★
Hopland Field Station - Library (Agri)
4070 Univ. Rd. Phone: (707)744-1424
Hopland, CA 95449 Robert M. Timm
Founded: 1951. **Subjects:** Animal science, agronomy, range management, soil science, wildlife management. **Special Collections:** Complete collection of reprints of publications resulting from research conducted on the Hopland Field Station, 1951 to present (800 publications). **Holdings:** 200 books; 125 bound periodical volumes; 500 reports. **Subscriptions:** 20 journals and other serials. **Services:** Copying; library open to the public with restrictions. **Remarks:** FAX: (707) 744-1040.

Hopper Resource Library
See: **Butler Institute of American Art - Hopper Resource Library** (2414)

Hopwood Room
See: **University of Michigan** (18866)

Paul Horgan Library
See: **New Mexico Military Institute - J. Penrod Toles Learning Center** (11522)

★7410★
Horizons (The Illinois Career Information System) (Educ)
217 E. Monroe, Suite 203 Phone: (217)785-0789
Springfield, IL 62706 Jan Staggs, Exec.Dir.
Founded: 1977. **Staff:** Prof 12; Other 3. **Subjects:** Career and occupational information, labor market, government procurement. **Holdings:** Figures not available. **Services:** Copying; open to the public. **Computerized Information Services:** Career Resources Information; Occupational Information System (internal database). Performs searches on fee basis. **Publications:** Occupational Information; Programs of Study and Training; School Information; Occupational Information Sources in Illinois. **Remarks:** FAX: (217)785-6184. System is maintained by Eastern Illinois University and is a project of Illinois Occupational Information Coordinating Committee.

Hormel Institute
See: **University of Minnesota** (18911)

Horn Library
See: **Babson College** (1396)

Horn Point Environmental Lab
See: **University of Maryland, Cambridge** (18802)

Hornbake Library
See: **University of Maryland, College Park Libraries** (18814)

Marilyn Horne Archives
See: **Long Beach Public Library - Performing Arts Department** (9281)

★7411★
Frank W. Horner, Inc. - Research Library (Med)
P.O. Box 959 Phone: (514)731-3931
Montreal, PQ, Canada H3C 2W6 Mr. Yvon Dugas, Libn.
Staff: 1. **Subjects:** Medical sciences, analytical chemistry, biochemistry, pharmacology, sales. **Holdings:** 2000 books; 5000 bound periodical volumes. **Subscriptions:** 125 journals and other serials. **Services:** Interlibrary loan; library not open to the public. **Computerized Information Services:** DIALOG Information Services, CAN/OLE. **Remarks:** Library located at 5485 Ferrier St., Montreal, PQ. **Remarks:** FAX: (514)738-5509. Telex: 05-25219.

Joseph Horner Memorial Library
See: **German Society of Pennsylvania** (6433)

Karen Horney Psychoanalytic Institute and Center - Muriel Ivimey Library
See: **Muriel Ivimey Library** (8293)

Horrax Library
See: **New England Deaconess Hospital** (11470)

Horrmann Library
See: **Wagner College** (19933)

Horseshoe Bend National Military Park
See: **U.S. Natl. Park Service** (17734)

J. William Horsey Library
See: **Ontario Bible College/Ontario Theological Seminary** (12428)

★7412★
Horsham Clinic - Angelo Zosa Memorial Library
722 E. Butler Pike
Ambler, PA 19002-2398
Defunct.

★7413★
Horticultural Art Society of Colorado Springs - Helen H. Smith Memorial Library
1438 N. Hancock Ave.
Colorado Springs, CO 80903
Defunct. Holdings absorbed by Pikes Peak Library District.

Horticultural Research Institute of Ontario
See: **Ontario Ministry of Agriculture and Food** (12450)

★7414★
Horticultural Society of New York - Library (Biol Sci)
128 W. 58th St. Phone: (212)757-0915
New York, NY 10019 Katherine Powis, Libn.
Founded: 1924. **Staff:** Prof 1; Other 1. **Subjects:** Horticulture; landscape design; garden history; botany; herbs; international floras; flower arrangement. **Special Collections:** Enid A. Haupt Young Peoples Collection of books in horticulture and gardening (100 volumes). **Holdings:** 6000 books; 2000 bound periodical volumes; biographical file on 400 botanists and horticulturists; VF material on 1800 subjects. **Subscriptions:** 147 journals and other serials. **Services:** Library open to the public for reference use only. **Computerized Information Services:** AGRICOLA. **Networks/Consortia:** Member of New York Metropolitan Reference and Research Library Agency, Council on Botanical Horticultural Libraries. **Publications:** Members newsletter, quarterly. **Special Indexes:** Gardener's Index. **Remarks:** FAX: (212)246-1207.

Horton Health Sciences Library
See: **Providence Medical Center** (13450)

★7415★
Horton Memorial Hospital - Medical Library (Med)
60 Prospect Ave. Phone: (914)343-2424
Middletown, NY 10940 Laura Leese, Med.Libn.
Founded: 1970. **Staff:** Prof 1. **Subjects:** Medicine, surgery, nursing, allied health sciences. **Holdings:** 1500 books; 2000 bound periodical volumes; 50 pamphlets; 25 pamphlets (uncataloged); vertical file of 1900 research topics; 200 audiotapes. **Subscriptions:** 100 journals and other serials. **Services:** Interlibrary loan; library open to allied medical professionals and law enforcement personnel. **Computerized Information Services:** MEDLINE. **Networks/Consortia:** Member of New York State Interlibrary Loan Network (NYSILL), Southeastern New York Library Resources Council (SENYLRC), Health Information Libraries of Westchester (HILOW).

Hosier Library
See: **Royal Agricultural College** (14094)

★7416★
Hospital Association of New York (State) - Hospital Educational and Research Fund - Lillian R. Hayt Memorial Library (Med)
74 N. Pearl St. Phone: (518)434-7600
Albany, NY 12207 Elaine C. Rotman, Dir., Lib.Serv.
Staff: Prof 1. **Subjects:** Hospital and health care administration, management, health economics. **Holdings:** 3000 books; 18 VF drawers of pamphlets and reports. **Subscriptions:** 400 journals and other serials. **Services:** Interlibrary loan; copying; library open to the public by appointment. **Computerized Information Services:** DIALOG Information Services, BRS Information Technologies, EPIC. **Networks/Consortia:** Member of Capital District Library Council for Reference & Research Resources (CDLC). **Remarks:** FAX: (518)434-7812.

★7417★
Hospital Association of Pennsylvania - Library Services (Med)
4750 Lindle Rd.
P.O. Box 8600 Phone: (717)564-9200
Harrisburg, PA 17105-8600 Fran Cohen, Libn.
Staff: Prof 1; Other 1. **Subjects:** Hospital administration; health regulation, legislation, economics; hospital data. **Special Collections:** History of Pennsylvania Hospitals. **Holdings:** 4000 volumes. **Subscriptions:** 183 journals and other serials. **Services:** Interlibrary loan; copying; library open to the public for research by appointment only. **Computerized Information Services:** MEDLARS, DIALOG Information Services. **Networks/Consortia:** Member of Central Pennsylvania Health Sciences Library Association (CPHSLA), National Network of Libraries of Medicine - Middle Atlantic Region. **Remarks:** FAX: (717)561-5333.

★7418★
Hospital Center at Orange - William Pierson Medical Library (Med)
188 S. Essex Ave. Phone: (201)266-2000
Orange, NJ 07051-3421 Jeanette Merkl, Libn.
Staff: Prof 1. **Subjects:** Medicine. **Holdings:** 1016 books; 1120 bound periodical volumes. **Subscriptions:** 78 journals and other serials. **Services:** Interlibrary loan; library not open to the public. **Networks/Consortia:** Member of Cosmopolitan Biomedical Library Consortium (CBLC), BHSL, Health Sciences Library Association of New Jersey (HSLANJ).

Hospital Corporation of America - Woodview-Calabasas Psychiatric Hospital
See: **Woodview-Calabasas Psychiatric Hospital** (20582)

Hospital Corporation of America - Worcester City Hospital
See: **Worcester City Hospital** (20591)

Hospital Engineering Logistics & Planning, Inc.
See: **American Tekdyne, Inc.** (774)

Hospital General de Montreal
See: **Montreal General Hospital** (10698)

★7419★
Hospital of the Good Samaritan - Medical Library (Med)
616 S. Witmer St. Phone: (213)977-2326
Los Angeles, CA 90017-2395 Susan Efteland, Lib.Dir.
Staff: Prof 1. **Subjects:** Preclinical and clinical medicine, nursing, hospital administration. **Special Collections:** Historical collection (250 volumes). **Holdings:** 3000 books; 5300 bound periodical volumes. **Subscriptions:** 170 journals and other serials. **Services:** Interlibrary loan; library not open to the public. **Automated Operations:** Computerized cataloging, acquisitions, and serials. **Computerized Information Services:** MEDLARS, DIALOG Information Services; DOCLINE (electronic mail service). Performs searches on fee basis.

Hospital for Joint Diseases Orthopaedic Institute
See: **Beth Israel Medical Center** (1771)

★7420★
Hospital of St. Raphael - Health Sciences Library (Med)
1450 Chapel St. Phone: (203)789-3330
New Haven, CT 06511 Patricia L. Wales, Dir., Lib.Serv.
Founded: 1942. **Staff:** Prof 2. **Subjects:** Medicine, nursing, allied health sciences, health management. **Holdings:** 3000 books; 4000 bound periodical volumes; 4 VF drawers. **Subscriptions:** 460 journals and other serials. **Services:** Interlibrary loan; copying; library open to the public for reference use only. **Computerized Information Services:** NLM, BRS Information Technologies, PaperChase, OCLC, MEDLARS. Performs searches on fee basis. **Networks/Consortia:** Member of Connecticut Association of Health Science Libraries (CAHSL), BHSL, North Atlantic Health Science Libraries (NAHSL). **Staff:** Nancy P. Crandall, Asst.Libn.

★7421★
Hospital for Sick Children - Hospital Library (Med)
555 University Ave. Phone: (416)598-6693
Toronto, ON, Canada M5G 1X8 Deirdre Green, Libn.
Founded: 1919. **Staff:** Prof 2; Other 9. **Subjects:** Pediatrics. **Special Collections:** Pediatric journals published in English from their inception. **Holdings:** 7500 books; 25,000 periodical volumes. **Subscriptions:** 626 journals and other serials. **Services:** Interlibrary loan; library open to the public. **Computerized Information Services:** MEDLARS, BRS Information Technologies, DIALOG Information Services; CD-ROM (MEDLINE); Envoy 100 (electronic mail service). **Publications:** Library Bulletin (listing contents of some journals received). **Remarks:** FAX: (416)598-7523. Electronic mail address(es): HSC.LIB (Envoy 100).

★7422★
Hospital Sisters of Third Order of St. Francis - Community Archives (Hist, Rel-Phil)
St. Francis Convent
Sangamon Ave. Rd. Phone: (217)522-3386
Springfield, IL 62794-9431 Sr. Dominica McGuire, Archv.
Founded: 1950. **Staff:** 1. **Subjects:** History of the order in Germany and its founding in America in 1875 as well as its 13 hospitals; work of the order in China, Taiwan, Japan, Poland, India, Haiti, and American Indian missions; apostolic works. **Special Collections:** Heritage Room (memorabilia of members); Medical Equipment Display Room (equipment used from turn of the century to circa 1950); artifacts and art objects from Taiwan, Japan, China, India, Germany, Haiti, and Poland; Navajo Indian artifacts. **Holdings:** 40 books; 50 bound periodical volumes; 48 theses; 300 hospital publications; 100 manuscripts; 2000 slides; 25 tapes; committee reports; photographs; 20 file cabinets and 232 boxes of manuscripts, photographs, records; 60 pamphlets. **Subscriptions:** 2 newspapers. **Services:** Copying; archives open to serious researchers.

★7423★
Hospital for Special Surgery - Kim Barrett Memorial Library (Med)
535 E. 70th St., Rm. 212 Phone: (212)606-1210
New York, NY 10021 Marshall J. Giannotti, Med.Libn.
Founded: 1934. **Staff:** Prof 1. **Subjects:** Orthopedic surgery and rheumatic diseases. **Holdings:** 3117 books; 2918 bound periodical volumes; 2924 reprints; 335 video cassettes, slide programs, films. **Subscriptions:** 94 journals and other serials. **Services:** Library open to affiliated institutions for reference use and to researchers with restrictions. **Computerized Information Services:** MEDLARS. **Publications:** Library News; List of Journals.

★7424★
Hospital of the University of Pennsylvania - Robert Dunning Dripps Library of Anesthesia (Med)
Department of Anesthesia
3400 Spruce St. Phone: (215)662-3784
Philadelphia, PA 19104 Janet Stokes, M.A.
Founded: 1980. **Staff:** 2. **Subjects:** Anesthesia. **Special Collections:** History of anesthesia (150 texts and transcripts). **Holdings:** 600 books; 40 bound periodical volumes; 70 videotape teaching cassettes. **Subscriptions:** 40 journals and other serials. **Services:** Copying; library open to area anesthesiologists only. **Networks/Consortia:** Member of National Network of Libraries of Medicine - Middle Atlantic Region.

★7425★
Hotel-Dieu d'Arthabaska - Medical Library-Documentation Service (Med)
5 des Hospitalieres Phone: (819)357-1151
Arthabaska, PQ, Canada G6P 6N2 Micheline LeClair, Lib.Techn.
Founded: 1960. **Staff:** Prof 1. **Subjects:** Health sciences, nursing. **Holdings:** 1800 books; 3366 bound periodical volumes. **Subscriptions:** 115 journals and other serials. **Services:** Interlibrary loan; copying; SDI; library open to the public. **Computerized Information Services:** MEDLINE. **Remarks:** FAX: (819)357-7406.

★7426★
Hotel Dieu Hospital - Library (Med)
Box 61262 Phone: (504)588-3470
New Orleans, LA 70161 Sr. Agnes Caffarel, Hea.Sci.Libn.
Founded: 1972. **Staff:** Prof 1. **Subjects:** Medicine, surgery, hospital administration, nursing. **Holdings:** 1082 books; 510 bound periodical volumes; 42 volumes of hospital archives. **Subscriptions:** 144 journals and other serials. **Services:** Interlibrary loan; library not open to the public. **Automated Operations:** Computerized cataloging and serials. **Computerized Information Services:** MEDLINE; internal databases. Performs searches on fee basis. **Networks/Consortia:** Member of Health Sciences Library Association of Louisiana. **Remarks:** FAX: (504)524-7584. Library located at 2021 Perdido St., New Orleans, LA 70112.

★7427★
Hotel-Dieu Hospital - Staff Library (Med)
166 Brock St. Phone: (613)544-3310
Kingston, ON, Canada K7L 5G2 Lynda Silver, Dir., Staff Lib.
Remarks: No further information was supplied by respondent.

★7428★
Hotel-Dieu de Levis - Bibliotheque (Med)
143, rue Wolfe Phone: (418)835-7121
Levis, PQ, Canada G6V 3Z1 Jocelyne Dufour
Founded: 1950. **Staff:** 1. **Subjects:** Medicine. **Holdings:** 5394 books. **Subscriptions:** 278 journals and other serials. **Services:** Interlibrary loan; library not open to the public. **Remarks:** FAX: (418)835-7183.

★7429★
Hotel-Dieu de Montreal - Service de Documentation (Med)
3840 Rue St-Urbain Phone: (514)843-2638
Montreal, PQ, Canada H2W 1T8 Ginette Boyer, Chf.Libn.
Founded: 1947. **Staff:** Prof 1; Other 3. **Subjects:** Medicine, nursing. **Holdings:** 3000 books; 26,500 bound periodical volumes; 58,271 slides. **Subscriptions:** 250 journals and other serials. **Services:** Interlibrary loan; copying; service open to the public for reference use only. **Computerized Information Services:** MEDLINE; Envoy 100 (electronic mail service). Performs searches on fee basis. **Networks/Consortia:** Member of Association des Bibliotheques de la Sante Affiliees a l'Universite de Montreal (ABSAUM). **Remarks:** FAX: (514)843-2707. Electronic mail address(es): QMHD (Envoy 100).

★7430★
Hotel-Dieu du Sacre-Coeur de Jesus de Quebec - Bibliotheque Medicale (Med)
1, Ave. du Sacre-Coeur Phone: (418)529-6851
Quebec, PQ, Canada G1N 2W1 Christian Martel, Lib.Techn.
Founded: 1968. **Staff:** Prof 1; Other 1. **Subjects:** Child psychiatry, neurology. **Holdings:** 4200 books. **Subscriptions:** 100 journals and other serials. **Services:** Interlibrary loan; copying; library open to the public for reference use only. **Remarks:** FAX: (418)529-2971.

★7431★
Hotel-Dieu of St. Joseph Hospital - Medical Library (Med)
1030 Ouellette Ave. Phone: (519)973-4444
Windsor, ON, Canada N9A 1E1 Toni Janik, Libn.
Staff: Prof 1. **Subjects:** Medicine and allied health sciences. **Holdings:** 400 books; 2000 bound periodical volumes; 15 slide/tape programs; 30 video cassettes; 100 vertical files. **Subscriptions:** 300 journals and other serials. **Services:** Interlibrary loan; copying; library open to other librarians. **Computerized Information Services:** MEDLARS, BRS Information Technologies, Canadian Centre for Occupational Health & Safety, CAN/OLE. **Remarks:** FAX: (519)973-0642.

★7432★
Hotel Sales and Marketing Association International - Sales Research Library (Bus-Fin)
1300 L St., N.W., Suite 800 Phone: (202)789-0089
Washington, DC 20005 Leonard H. Hoyle, Jr., Exec. V.P.
Subjects: Hotels - sales promotion, merchandising, public relations, marketing, direct mail, publicity, advertising, sales education. **Special Collections:** Compilation of hotel sales promotion material covering 30 years. **Holdings:** 200 volumes. **Subscriptions:** 22 journals and other serials. **Services:** Library may be visited only by special arrangement. **Publications:** List of publications - available on request.

Harry Houdini Library
See: **Library of Congress - Rare Book & Special Collections Division** (9135)

★7433★
Houghton College - Buffalo Extension Campus - Ada M. Kidder Memorial Library (Rel-Phil, Educ)
910 Union Rd. Phone: (716)674-6363
West Seneca, NY 14224 George E. Bennett, Libn.
Founded: 1938. **Staff:** Prof 1; Other 3. **Subjects:** Theology, missions, Christian education, early childhood education. **Holdings:** 35,500 books; 1220 bound periodical volumes; 550 phonograph records; 275 cassettes; 150 filmstrips; 95 reels of microfilm. **Subscriptions:** 119 journals and other serials. **Services:** Interlibrary loan; copying; library open to the public for reference use only. **Computerized Information Services:** BRS/After Dark. **Networks/Consortia:** Member of SUNY/OCLC Library Network, Western New York Library Resources Council (WNYLRC).

★7434★
Houghton County Historical Society - Museum (Hist)
Highway M-26, Lock Box D Phone: (906)296-4121
Lake Linden, MI 49945 Flora O. Graham, Cur.
Staff: 2. **Subjects:** Mining, transportation, engineering, forestry, industry, local history. **Special Collections:** Engineering and mining journals; copper handbooks; Lake Superior books. **Holdings:** Figures not available. **Services:** Museum open to the public with approval of Board of Directors.

★7435★
E.F. Houghton & Co. - Technical Center Library (Sci-Engr)
P.O. Box 930 Phone: (215)666-4146
Valley Forge, PA 19482-0930 Margaret C. Schweitzer, Libn.
Staff: Prof 1. **Subjects:** Industrial oils and chemicals, metallurgy, organic chemistry, lubricants, hydraulics, paper and textiles. **Holdings:** 6000 books; 300 bound periodical volumes; 8 VF drawers of research reports; 10 VF drawers of patents; 8 VF drawers of catalogs and pamphlets. **Subscriptions:** 75 journals and other serials. **Services:** Interlibrary loan; library not open to the public. **Computerized Information Services:** DIALOG Information Services, MEDLINE. **Remarks:** FAX: (215)666-7354.

Houghton Library
See: **Harvard University** (6976)

Houghton Memorial Library
See: **Huntingdon College** (7569)

★7436★
Houghton Mifflin Company - Library (Publ, Educ)
1 Beacon St. Phone: (617)725-5270
Boston, MA 02108 Guest Perry, Dir., Corp.Lib.
Founded: 1966. **Staff:** Prof 4; Other 3. **Subjects:** Publishing, education, textbooks. **Holdings:** 15,000 books; 15 VF drawers of pamphlets. **Subscriptions:** 600 journals and other serials. **Services:** Interlibrary loan; research. **Automated Operations:** Computerized public access catalog and JLL. **Computerized Information Services:** DIALOG Information Services, Dow Jones News/Retrieval, OCLC, Dun & Bradstreet Business Credit Services, Data-Star, NEXIS. **Publications:** Guide to the library; Newsletter. **Remarks:** FAX: (617)227-5409. **Staff:** Terry Moran, Res.Libn.; Amy Cohen-Rose, Res.Libn.; Karen Holtzman, Asst.Libn.

★7437★
Houlton Regional Hospital - Library (Med)
20 Hartford St. Phone: (207)532-9471
Houlton, ME 04730 Elizabeth Petrocelli, Med.Libn.
Staff: 1. **Subjects:** Medicine, nursing. **Holdings:** 150 books. **Subscriptions:** 40 journals and other serials. **Services:** Interlibrary loan; copying; SDI; library open to the public for reference use only. **Networks/Consortia:** Member of Health Science Library and Information Cooperative of Maine (HSLIC). **Remarks:** FAX: (207)532-7934.

★7438★
House Beautiful - Staff Library (Art, Publ)
1700 Broadway, 29th Fl.
New York, NY 10019 Phone: (212)903-5212
Staff: 1. **Subjects:** Architecture, interior design, decorative arts. **Holdings:** 2000 books. **Subscriptions:** 100 journals and other serials. **Services:** Library not open to the public. **Remarks:** House Beautiful is published by Hearst Corporation.

House of the Book
See: **Brandeis-Bardin Institute** (2069)

House of Commons (of Great Britain)
See: **Great Britain - House of Commons** (6679)

★7439★
House Ear Institute - George Kelemen Library (Med)
2100 W. 3rd St., 5th Fl. Phone: (213)483-4431
Los Angeles, CA 90057 Liz Gnerre, Libn.
Founded: 1975. **Staff:** Prof 1; Other 1. **Subjects:** Otology, otolaryngology, psychoacoustics, audiology, hearing rehabilitation, neurosurgery, biomedical engineering. **Special Collections:** Otology teaching seminars (273 video cassettes); rare books (100 volumes). **Holdings:** 2200 books; 1615 bound periodical volumes; 3700 reprints; 20 dissertations; 200 audio cassettes; 500 slides. **Subscriptions:** 180 journals and other serials. **Services:** Interlibrary loan; library open to the public with restrictions. **Computerized Information Services:** DIALOG Information Services, MEDLARS. **Special Catalogs:** Author/subject reprint catalog (notebook); AV Catalog. **Remarks:** FAX: (213)413-6739.

★7440★
House Ear Institute - Sam and Rose Stein Children's Center - Parent Resource Library (Soc Sci)
2100 W. 3rd St., 5th FL. Phone: (213)483-4431
Los Angeles, CA 90057 Liz Gnerre, Libn.
Founded: 1980. **Staff:** Prof 1; Other 1. **Subjects:** Deafness - social problems, special education, sign language, communication, child rearing. **Holdings:** 550 books; 9 VF drawers of reprints, manuscripts, reports, graduate projects, clippings, brochures, special studies, documents pertaining to hearing-impaired children and adults and family relationships. **Services:** Interlibrary loan; copying; library open to the public. **Computerized Information Services:** DIALOG Information Services. Performs searches on fee basis. **Special Catalogs:** Parent Resource Catalog; annotated catalog (printout). **Remarks:** FAX: (213)413-6739.

House of Lords (of Great Britain)
See: **Great Britain - House of Lords** (6680)

★7441★
Household International - Corporate Library (Bus-Fin)
2700 Sanders Rd. Phone: (708)564-6211
Prospect Heights, IL 60070 Mollie R. Brumbaugh
Founded: 1930. **Staff:** Prof 1; Other 1. **Subjects:** Finance, business, management, statistics. **Holdings:** 1000 books. **Subscriptions:** 150 journals and other serials. **Services:** Interlibrary loan; library open to the public by appointment. **Automated Operations:** Computerized cataloging, acquisitions, and serials. **Computerized Information Services:** DIALOG Information Services, LEXIS, NEXIS, Dow Jones News/Retrieval, VU/TEXT Information Services. **Networks/Consortia:** Member of North Suburban Library System (NSLS). **Publications:** Corporate Library Review. **Remarks:** FAX: (708)205-7526.

★7442★
Houser Henry - Library (Law)
145 King St., W., Suite 2000 Phone: (416)362-3411
Toronto, ON, Canada M5H 2B6 Sandra Findlay, Libn.
Founded: 1934. **Staff:** 1. **Subjects:** Law. **Holdings:** 500 books. **Subscriptions:** 150 journals and other serials; 5 newspapers. **Services:** Library not open to the public. **Remarks:** FAX: (416)362-3757.

★7443★
Housing Advocates - Law and Consumer Affairs Library (Soc Sci)
3214 Prospect Ave., E. Phone: (216)391-5444
Cleveland, OH 44115-2600 Edward G. Kramer, Dir.
Staff: Prof 1. **Subjects:** Housing, law, consumer affairs. **Special Collections:** Mobile homes, zoning. **Holdings:** 2633 books; 41 bound periodical volumes; 2 VF drawers of clippings on housing and community development; 2 vertical files of investigatory material on General Revenue Sharing; 9 VF drawers plus 6 feet of legal brief files. **Subscriptions:** 55 journals and other serials. **Services:** Copying; SDI; library open for in-house use. **Remarks:** FAX: (216)431-6149. Library offers consumer service to Ohio libraries, foundations, and government agencies.

★7444★
Housing Association of Delaware Valley - Library (Plan)
1314 Chestnut St., Suite 900 Phone: (215)545-6010
Philadelphia, PA 19107 James Berry, Commun.Rel.Spec.
Founded: 1909. **Subjects:** Housing, urban development, city/regional planning, zoning, law, local government. **Special Collections:** HADV publications, 1909 to present. **Holdings:** 1000 books; 2000 pamphlets. **Subscriptions:** 50 journals and other serials; 8 newspapers. **Services:** Copying; library open to the public. **Remarks:** Most of collection is housed in the Temple University - Central Library System - Urban Archives.

★7445★
Houston Academy of Medicine - Texas Medical Center Library (Med, Biol Sci)
1133 M.D. Anderson Blvd. Phone: (713)795-4200
Houston, TX 77030 Richard Lyders, Exec.Dir.
Founded: 1915. **Staff:** Prof 24.5; Other 55. **Subjects:** Medicine, nursing, psychology, psychiatry, biological sciences, pharmacology. **Special Collections:** Harris County Medical Archive; NASA Space Life Sciences Archive; papers from members of the Atomic Bomb Casualty Commission; papers of Philip S. Hench; papers of R. Lee Clark; the Burbank/Fraser Collection on Arthritis, Rheumatism and Gout. **Holdings:** 237,800 volumes. **Subscriptions:** 2817 journals; 1579 other serials. **Services:** Interlibrary loan; copying; SDI; library open to the public with restrictions. **Automated Operations:** Computerized public access catalog, cataloging, acquisitions, serials, and circulation. **Computerized Information Services:** DIALOG Information Services, NLM, OCLC, BRS Information Technologies, STN International, WILSONLINE; TexSearch (internal database); DOCLINE (electronic mail service). **Networks/Consortia:** Member of Houston Area Research Library Consortium (HARLIC), National Network of Libraries of Medicine - South Central Region, South Central Academic Medical Libraries Consortium (SCAMEL). **Publications:** Library Lines - to mailing list; Annual Statistics of Medical School Libraries in the United States and Canada. **Remarks:** FAX: (713)790-7052. **Staff:** Nancy Bierschenk, Assoc.Exec.Dir.

★7446★
Houston Area Research Center (HARC) - Texas Accelerator Center - Library (Sci-Engr)
4802 Research Forest Dr., Bldg. 2 Phone: (713)363-0121
The Woodlands, TX 77381 Brenda Harris, Tech.Libn.
Founded: 1983. **Staff:** Prof 1. **Subjects:** Accelerators, high energy physics, mathematics, technical design. **Holdings:** 200 volumes. **Services:** Library not open to the public.

★7447★
Houston Baptist University - Moody Library (Hist)
7502 Fondren Rd. Phone: (713)995-3435
Houston, TX 77074-3298 Dr. Jon M. Suter, Dir.
Founded: 1962. **Staff:** Prof 6; Other 5. **Subjects:** Baptist history, Civil War, military and Texas history, Victorian fiction, Matthew Arnold. **Special Collections:** J.E. Hicks Memorial Collection (Texas history; 1500 volumes); Palmer Bradley and Robert Bradley collections (4000 volumes); Albert Sidney Johnston Confederate Collection (1100 volumes). **Holdings:** 168,581 books; 21,855 bound periodical volumes; 3678 sound recordings. **Subscriptions:** 883 journals and other serials. **Services:** Interlibrary loan; copying; library open to students and faculty. **Automated Operations:** Computerized cataloging and acquisitions. **Computerized Information Services:** DIALOG Information Services, ProQuest. **Networks/Consortia:** Member of AMIGOS Bibliographic Council, Inc. **Remarks:** FAX: (713)995-3489. **Staff:** Virginia An, ILL; Dorothy Allen, Pub. Serv.; Ann Noble, Tech.Serv.; Tina Hou, Act.Ref.

★7448★
Houston Chronicle - Editorial Library (Publ)
Box 4260 Phone: (713)220-7313
Houston, TX 77210 Sherry Adams, Libn.
Founded: 1960. **Staff:** Prof 2; Other 17. **Subjects:** Newspaper reference topics, Texana, Houstoniana. **Holdings:** 2500 books; 2 million clippings; 300,000 photographs; pamphlets; 1300 reels of microfilm; 55,000 microfiche. **Subscriptions:** 20 journals and other serials; 15 newspapers. **Services:** Library not open to the public. **Computerized Information Services:** DataTimes. **Remarks:** Located at 801 Texas Ave., Houston, TX 77002. FAX: (713)220-7275. **Staff:** Melissa Mantel, Asst.Libn.

★7449★
Houston City Aviation Department - Library (Trans)
Box 60106
Houston, TX 77205 Phone: (713)443-1714
Founded: 1976. **Staff:** 2. **Subjects:** Aviation. **Holdings:** Aviation Daily/Airport Operators Council International (AOCI) reports; slides of airports; technical reports. **Subscriptions:** 18 journals and other serials. **Services:** Interlibrary loan; copying; library open to the public by appointment. **Remarks:** FAX: (713)230-2874.

★7450★
Houston City Legal Department - Law Library (Law)
City Hall, 4th Fl.
P.O. Box 1562 Phone: (713)247-2000
Houston, TX 77251 Evangeline Bell, Law Libn.
Founded: 1910. **Staff:** Prof 1. **Subjects:** Municipal law and jurisprudence. **Holdings:** 22,000 volumes. **Services:** Interlibrary loan; library not open to the public.

★7451★
Houston Community College - Eastwood Campus Nursing School Library (Med)
3100 Shenandoah Phone: (713)746-5308
Houston, TX 77021 Oraida Padron Starr, Libn.
Founded: 1976. **Staff:** 3. **Subjects:** Nursing, emergency medical technology, radiologic technology, respiratory therapy, animal health management, surgical technology, physical and occupational therapy, and other allied health occupation fields. **Holdings:** 13,500 books; 261 unbound titles; 2000 AV programs; 50,000 microform and nonbook items. **Subscriptions:** 78 journals and other serials. **Services:** Interlibrary loan (restricted), copying; library open to local fee-paying members. **Computerized Information Services:** DIALOG Information Services (at Main branch). **Remarks:** FAX: (713)746-5370. A branch of the Houston community college system of 23 libraries. **Staff:** John Hunter; Claude Parker.

★7452★
Houston County Historical Commission - Archives (Hist)
Houston County Courthouse, 1st Fl. Phone: (409)544-3255
Crockett, TX 75835 Eliza H. Bishop, Libn.
Founded: 1978. **Staff:** 1. **Subjects:** History - local, county, state. **Holdings:** 215 books; tapes; microfilm; county and city records; genealogical records; county maps; newspapers; photographs; cemetery publication surveys. **Subscriptions:** 23 journals and other serials. **Services:** Copying; archives open to the public on a limited schedule. **Publications:** Mini-history - available on request.

Houston Engineering Library Project
See: **Access Information Associates, Inc.** (45)

★7453★
Houston Lighting & Power Company - Library (Energy)
Box 1700, 5GWP1349 Phone: (713)623-3126
Houston, TX 77251 Alicia B. Quinn, Supv.
Founded: 1969. **Staff:** Prof 1; Other 2. **Subjects:** Power systems, business management, energy, engineering. **Holdings:** 3000 books; 100 bound periodical volumes. **Subscriptions:** 154 journals and other serials. **Services:** Interlibrary loan; library not open to the public. **Computerized Information Services:** DIALOG Information Services, Dun & Bradstreet Business Credit Services. **Remarks:** FAX: (713)623-3127.

★7454★
Houston Love Memorial Library - Division for the Blind & Physically Handicapped
212 W. Burdeshaw St.
Box 1369 Phone: (205)793-9767
Dothan, AL 36302 Betty Forbus, Libn.
Remarks: No further information was supplied by respondent.

★7455★
Houston Museum of Decorative Arts - Library (Art)
201 High St. Phone: (615)267-7176
Chattanooga, TN 37403 Sybil Chadwick, Art.Dir.
Founded: 1961. **Staff:** Prof 2. **Subjects:** Hand-blown antique glass, porcelain, pottery, ceramics, early American furniture, decorative art. **Special Collections:** Antique guns (12); antique music boxes (15); handwoven coverlets and old quilts. **Holdings:** 250 books; 750 unbound reports; unbound periodical volumes; archival files of articles pertaining to the collection. **Services:** Library open to the public with restrictions.

★7456★
Houston Museum of Natural Science - Reference Library (Biol Sci)
1 Hermann Circle Dr.
Houston, TX 77030 Phone: (713)639-4600
Founded: 1970. **Subjects:** Natural science and allied subjects. **Holdings:** 10,000 volumes; slides; motion pictures. **Services:** Library not open to the public. **Remarks:** FAX: (713)523-4125.

★7457★
Houston Post - Editorial Library (Publ)
4747 S.W. Fwy.
Box 4747 Phone: (713)840-5614
Houston, TX 77210 Margaret Walker, Chf.Libn.
Founded: 1955. **Staff:** Prof 1; Other 7. **Subjects:** Newspaper reference topics, local and state history, biography. **Special Collections:** Texana (340 volumes); Houston City Directories, 1887 to present. **Holdings:** 3600 books; 3.5 million pictures; 5.5 million clippings; 160 pamphlets; 3600 reels of microfilm. **Subscriptions:** 100 journals and other serials; 25 newspapers. **Services:** Interlibrary loan; library not open to the public. **Computerized Information Services:** DIALOG Information Services, NEXIS, VU/TEXT Information Services, DataTimes. **Remarks:** FAX: (713)840-6722.

★7458★
Houston Public Library - Business, Science & Technology Department (Bus-Fin, Sci-Engr)
500 McKinney Ave. Phone: (713)236-1313
Houston, TX 77002 Phyllis Harvison, Dept.Mgr.
Founded: 1961. **Staff:** Prof 15; Other 12. **Subjects:** Geology, business, engineering, mathematics, labor and economics, science, commerce, public services and utilities, manufactures. **Special Collections:** Barton, Dumble, and Dewolf collections (petroleum geology). **Holdings:** 222,272 volumes; 657,000 government documents; industrial, federal, military standards and specifications; corporate annual, 10K, proxy reports; Texas Drillers Logs; Electric Well Logs (Gulf Coast area); Texas Railroad Commission District 3 Production Records (oil, gas, and distillate). **Subscriptions:** 1200 journals and other serials. **Services:** Interlibrary loan; copying. **Automated Operations:** Computerized cataloging, acquisitions, and circulation. **Computerized Information Services:** DIALOG Information Services, VU/TEXT Information Services, WILSONLINE, DataTimes; CD-ROMs (Compact Disclosure, American Business Disk, Impact). **Networks/Consortia:** Member of Houston Area Library System (HALS), Houston Area Research Library Consortium (HARLIC). **Staff:** Karen Henry, Asst.Mgr.

★7459★
Houston Public Library - Clayton Library - Center for Genealogical Research (Hist)
5300 Caroline St. Phone: (713)524-0101
Houston, TX 77004-6896 Maxine Alcorn, Mgr.
Founded: 1921. **Staff:** Prof 8; Other 10. **Subjects:** Genealogy. **Special Collections:** Federal census, 1790-1900 (complete), 1910 (complete); 1900 Soundex (complete); 1910 Soundex (partial); military records; state and colonial records; county records; family histories. **Holdings:** 40,000 books; 2000 bound periodical volumes; 35,000 reels of microfilm; 50,000 microfiche; VF material. **Subscriptions:** 285 journals and other serials. **Services:** Copying; center open to the public. **Automated Operations:** Computerized public access catalog. **Networks/Consortia:** Member of AMIGOS Bibliographic Council, Inc. **Publications:** In-house Finding Aids. **Staff:** Margaret J. Harris, Asst.Mgr.

★7460★
Houston Public Library - Film Collection Department (Aud-Vis)
500 McKinney Ave. Phone: (713)247-1657
Houston, TX 77002 Syma Zerkow, Dept.Mgr.
Founded: 1975. **Staff:** Prof 2; Other 8. **Holdings:** 5000 16mm films; 3150 popular videocassettes; 3525 educational videocassettes. **Services:** Department open to the public. **Networks/Consortia:** Member of Houston Area Library System (HALS), Houston Area Research Library Consortium (HARLIC). **Remarks:** FAX: (713)247-3531. **Staff:** Rob Safley, Asst.Mgr.

★7461★
Houston Public Library - Fine Arts & Recreation Department (Art, Rec, Mus)
500 McKinney Ave. Phone: (713)236-1313
Houston, TX 77002 John Harvath, Dept.Mgr.
Staff: Prof 6; Other 5. **Subjects:** Art, Oriental art, decorative and minor arts, architecture, landscaping, sculpture, drawing, handicrafts, costumes, antiques, furniture, painting, photography, music, entertainment, theater, dance, sports. **Special Collections:** Current and retrospective sheet music (12,400 pieces); auction and exhibition catalogs (5700); artist information file (25,704 items). **Holdings:** 205,000 books; 515 framed reproductions; 2500 slides; 27,833 VF materials; 30 sculpture replicas; 12,000 phonograph records; 6000 compact discs. **Subscriptions:** 406 journals and other serials. **Services:** Interlibrary loan; copying; department open to the public. **Automated Operations:** Computerized cataloging, acquisitions, and circulation. **Networks/Consortia:** Member of Houston Area Library System (HALS), Houston Area Research Library Consortium (HARLIC). **Remarks:** FAX: (713)247-3531. **Staff:** Scott Skelton, Asst.Mgr.

★7462★
Houston Public Library - Houston Metropolitan Research Center (Area-Ethnic)
500 McKinney Ave. Phone: (713)247-1661
Houston, TX 77002 Louis J. Marchiafava, Ph.D., Archv.
Founded: 1975. **Staff:** Prof 5; Other 1. **Subjects:** Houston - business, politics, architecture, church records, city and county government, agencies. **Special Collections:** John Milsaps Collection (Salvation Army); panoramic

photograph collection (500); local photographs (1.8 million); county records for two-county area; Houston African-American Collection; Mexican-American Collection; Oral History Collection; Architectural collection; Texas State Archives regional depository; Texas Jazz Archive. **Holdings:** 18,000 linear feet of archival material. **Services:** Copying; center open to the public. **Networks/Consortia:** Member of Houston Area Library System (HALS), Houston Area Research Library Consortium (HARLIC). **Publications:** The Houston Review, 3/year - by subscription; guide books to the collection. **Remarks:** Alternate telephone number(s): 247-3562. FAX: (713)247-3531. **Staff:** Nancy Hadley, Asst.Mgr.

★7463★
Houston Public Library - Special Collections Department (Hum)
500 McKinney Ave.
Houston, TX 77002 Phone: (713)236-1313
Subjects: U.S. slavery and Civil War, Salvation Army, religious history, 19th century travel. **Special Collections:** Milsaps Collection (8642 titles; 3000 pamphlets; 900 18th century book titles); Annette Finnigan Collection (fine press books; 60 volumes); Mark Twain, Alice Books, limited editions; Historical Juvenile Literature Collection: Reynolds Room (700 rare books) and Julia Ideson Stacks (1527 historical books); St. Nicholas Magazine collection; British and American Chapbooks of the 18th and 19th Century (500); New England Primers, late 18th-early 19th century (73); American Dictionary Collection, 1780 to present (emphasis on slang); manuscripts and early printing, 1100-1800. **Holdings:** 22,091 books. **Services:** Library open to the public by appointment - contact Texas & Local History Department. **Networks/Consortia:** Member of Houston Area Research Library Consortium (HARLIC).

★7464★
Houston Public Library - Texas and Local History Department (Hist)
500 McKinney Ave. Phone: (713)236-1313
Houston, TX 77002 Carol Johnson, Dept.Mgr.
Staff: Prof 3; Other 3. **Subjects:** Houstonia, Texana. **Special Collections:** Sheet music (200 pieces); Texas city directories (1500); high school and organization yearbooks; Maresh Files (typescript of original research done for Federal Writers Project; materials used in Texas and Houston Writers Projects). **Holdings:** 24,000 volumes; 28,200 Texas state government documents; 3000 municipal documents; newspaper clippings on microfiche; scrapbooks; maps; pamphlets; photographs; 19th century Texas newspapers on microfilm. **Services:** Copying; department open to the public. **Networks/Consortia:** Member of Project TexNet Interlibrary Loan Network (TexNet). **Remarks:** FAX: (713)247-3531. **Staff:** Will Howard, Asst.Mgr.

Sam Houston Regional Library and Research Center
See: **Texas State Library - Local Records Division** (16262)

★7465★
Sam Houston State University - Newton Gresham Library - Special Collections (Hist)
Huntsville, TX 77341 Phone: (409)294-1619
Paul M. Culp, Jr., Spec.Coll.Libn.
Founded: 1879. **Staff:** 2.5. **Special Collections:** S. Bangs; Black Sparrow Press; Criminal Justice Collections: Eliasberg, Bennett, Bates, MacCormick; Confederate and Texana Collection (Clark, Goree, Porter, Shettles); S. Houston; G. Stein; Thomason; Twain; H.G. Wells; WILD DOG (a 60s little magazine) archives. **Holdings:** 11,000 books; 1000 bound periodical volumes; 300 feet of archival material and manuscripts. **Subscriptions:** 5 journals and other serials. **Services:** Interlibrary loan; copying; collections open to the public for reference use only. **Automated Operations:** Computerized public access catalog, cataloging, acquisitions, serials, and circulation. **Computerized Information Services:** DIALOG Information Services, BRS Information Technologies, OCLC. **Networks/Consortia:** Member of AMIGOS Bibliographic Council, Inc. **Special Catalogs:** Catalog of periodical/newspaper holdings (printout). **Remarks:** FAX: (409)294-1597. **Staff:** Linda Fowler, Archv.

★7466★
Howard Career Center - Instructional Media Center - Library (Educ)
401 E. 12th St. Phone: (302)571-5437
Newark, DE 19801 Theresa V. Kough
Staff: Prof 1. **Subjects:** Vocational and technical careers. **Holdings:** 3400 books. **Services:** Interlibrary loan; library not open to the public. **Computerized Information Services:** DIALOG Information Services; CD-ROMs (Books in Print, Grolier Encyclopedia, Infotrac, Facts on File). **Remarks:** FAX: (302)571-5437

★7467★
Howard County General Hospital - Health Sciences Library (Med)
5755 Cedar Ln. Phone: (301)740-7860
Columbia, MD 21044 Marian G. Czajkowski, Med.Libn.
Founded: 1976. **Staff:** Prof 1. **Subjects:** Medicine. **Holdings:** 632 books; 1021 bound periodical volumes. **Subscriptions:** 140 journals and other serials. **Services:** Interlibrary loan; copying; library open to professionals and students. **Networks/Consortia:** Member of Maryland Association of Health Science Librarians (MAHSL).

★7468★
Howard, Mackie Law Firm - Library (Law)
1000 Canterra Tower
400 3rd Ave., S.W. Phone: (403)232-9402
Calgary, AB, Canada T2P 4H2 Joan Scilley, Libn.
Staff: Prof 2; Other 1. **Subjects:** Law. **Holdings:** 8000 books. **Subscriptions:** 300 journals and other serials. **Services:** Interlibrary loan; SDI. **Computerized Information Services:** WESTLAW, QL Systems, Info Globe, CAN/LAW. **Remarks:** FAX: (403)266-1395.

★7469★
Howard Rice Nemerovski Canady Robertson & Falk - Library (Law)
3 Embarcadero Center, Suite 700 Phone: (415)399-3043
San Francisco, CA 94111 Joan Loftus, Libn.
Founded: 1978. **Staff:** Prof 2; Other 2. **Subjects:** Law. **Holdings:** 15,000 volumes. **Subscriptions:** 350 journals and other serials. **Services:** Interlibrary loan. **Automated Operations:** Computerized cataloging. **Computerized Information Services:** Mead Data Central, DIALOG Information Services, Dow Jones News/Retrieval, RLIN, WESTLAW, VU/TEXT Information Services, NewsNet, Inc, DataTimes, Dun & Bradstreet Business Credit Services. **Remarks:** FAX: (415)399-3041. **Staff:** Marlowe Griffiths.

Howard-Tilton Memorial Library
See: **Tulane University** (16557)

★7470★
Howard University - African-American Resource Center (Area-Ethnic, Soc Sci)
2400 6th St., N.W.
Box 746 Phone: (202)806-7242
Washington, DC 20059 Mr. E. Ethelbert Miller, Dir.
Founded: 1969. **Staff:** Prof 1. **Subjects:** Black studies, economics, history, political science, literature, international relations. **Holdings:** 20,000 books. **Subscriptions:** 50 journals and other serials; 10 newspapers. **Services:** Copying; center open to the public. **Remarks:** Library located at Founders Library, 500 Howard Place, 3rd Fl., Rm. 300, Washington D.C.

★7471★
Howard University - Allen Mercer Daniel Law Library (Law)
2900 Van Ness St., N.W. Phone: (202)806-8045
Washington, DC 20008 DiAnne T. Moore, Act.Dir.
Founded: 1867. **Staff:** Prof 5; Other 6. **Subjects:** Law. **Special Collections:** Civil rights. **Holdings:** 190,000 volumes; 59,269 microforms; 44 motion pictures; 269 audio cassettes; 126 video cassettes. **Subscriptions:** 1426 journals and other serials. **Services:** Interlibrary loan; copying; library open to the public. **Automated Operations:** Computerized public access catalog and cataloging. **Computerized Information Services:** LEXIS, WESTLAW, DIALOG Information Services; internal databases. **Networks/Consortia:** Member of CAPCON Library Network, Consortium of Universities of the Washington Metropolitan Area. **Publications:** Acquisitions list, monthly. **Special Indexes:** Index of microform holdings; Checklist of U.S. Congress Committee Hearings & Committee Prints; Checklist of United Nations Documents; Legislative Research Documents: state; Subject List of Legal Lectures on Tape (all pamphlets). **Remarks:** FAX: (202)686-0740. **Staff:** Meera Kashyap, Asst.Libn., Tech.Serv.; Felicia Ayanbiola, Ref.Libn.; Mamie Moore, Circ.; Aurora Herrera, Ser.; Kwei-Yuei Hung, Proc.

★7472★
Howard University - Architecture & Planning Library (Plan)
6th St. & Howard Place, N.W. Phone: (202)806-7773
Washington, DC 20059 Gertis Fenuku, Libn.
Staff: Prof 1; Other 2. **Subjects:** Architectural history, construction and design, city planning, environmental design. **Holdings:** 24,260 books; 4705

bound periodical volumes; 33,921 slides, filmstrips, lantern frames; 1666 reels of microfilm; 428 maps. **Subscriptions:** 425 journals and other serials. **Services:** Interlibrary loan; library open to the public. **Automated Operations:** Computerized cataloging, acquisitions, and serials. **Computerized Information Services:** DIALOG Information Services. Performs searches on fee basis. **Networks/Consortia:** Member of CAPCON Library Network, Consortium of Universities of the Washington Metropolitan Area. **Publications:** SLIDEX (a system for indexing, filing, and retrieving slides); About the A & P Library; Resources for Architects and Planners in Washington, DC and Metropolitan Area; recent acquisitions.

★7473★

Howard University - Center for Economic Education - Library (Bus-Fin)
Department of Economics — Phone: (202)806-6733
Washington, DC 20059 — Charles L. Betsey, Chm.
Subjects: Macro- and microeconomics, economics education, economic development, labor markets, urban economics, international economics. **Holdings:** 800 volumes. **Subscriptions:** 38 journals and other serials. **Services:** Library not open to the public. **Publications:** Reports. **Staff:** Dr. K.K. Dompere, Libn.

★7474★

Howard University - Channing Pollock Theatre Collection (Theater)
500 Howard Pl., NW
Founders Library Bldg., Rm. 213 — Phone: (202)806-7259
Washington, DC 20059 — Jean Church, Cur.
Founded: 1950. **Staff:** Prof 2; Other 1. **Subjects:** Theater, drama, performing arts. **Special Collections:** William Warren I journals, 1796-1831; William Warren II diaries, dramatic scrapbooks, letters, and promptbooks (the American Stage and the Boston Museum, 1847-1888; 4 diaries; 2 scrapbooks). **Holdings:** 16,334 books; 2695 bound periodical volumes; 1904 other cataloged items; 90,548 clippings; 38,651 articles; 1923 autograph letters; autograph letter signatures, card autographs, and archive autographs; 12,377 Carte de visite/Cabinet photographs; 6603 photographs; 260 manuscripts; 1493 pieces of sheet music; 2240 prints; 12,594 playbills; 485 rare programs; 516 souvenir programs; 1137 reels of microfilm; 5571 microcards; 5067 microfiche. **Subscriptions:** 382 journals and other serials; 5 newspapers. **Services:** Copying; collection open to the public with identification. **Automated Operations:** Computerized cataloging, acquisitions, and serials. **Networks/Consortia:** Member of CAPCON Library Network, Consortium of Universities of the Washington Metropolitan Area. **Special Indexes:** Indexes to scrapbooks - Olga Nethersole Collection (9 volumes of scrapbooks), Percy G. Williams Collection (Novelty Theatre, Brooklyn, programs), Alfred H. Woods Collection (theatrical contracts), Roland Reed Collection (playbills), Albert Berkowitz Collection (photographs of the Old Vic Company), Channing Pollock Collection (complete library and his writings), Harvard/Radcliff Program Collection.

★7475★

Howard University - Health Sciences Library (Med)
600 W St., N.W. — Phone: (202)806-6433
Washington, DC 20059 — Salvador Waller, Assoc.Dir.
Founded: 1927. **Staff:** Prof 7; Other 11. **Subjects:** Medicine, dentistry, nursing, and allied health sciences. **Special Collections:** Sickle cell anemia (2 drawers of clippings and pamphlets); Negroes in medicine, dentistry, and psychiatry (2 drawers; 20 boxes). **Holdings:** 198,813 books; 79,257 bound periodical volumes; 515 bibliographies; 121 shelves of AV programs; 20 VF drawers of disease, health, medicine files; 6 VF drawers of biographical files; 115 drawers of microfilm. **Subscriptions:** 5026 journals and other serials. **Services:** Interlibrary loan; copying; SDI; library open to the public for reference use only. **Automated Operations:** Computerized cataloging, acquisitions, serials, and circulation. **Computerized Information Services:** MEDLARS, DIALOG Information Services. Performs searches on fee basis. Contact Person: Howertine Farrell-Duncan, Libn./Supv., Ref. **Networks/Consortia:** Member of CAPCON Library Network, Consortium of Universities of the Washington Metropolitan Area, Consortium of Academic Health Science Libraries of the District of Columbia, District of Columbia Health Sciences Information Network (DOCHSIN). **Special Catalogs:** Sickle cell anemia; hypertension among Negroes (both card).

★7476★

Howard University - Health Sciences Library - Annex (Pharmacy) (Med, Biol Sci)
2300 4th St. — Phone: (202)806-6545
Washington, DC 20059 — Salvador Waller, Act.Libn.
Staff: Prof 1; Other 2. **Subjects:** Pharmacy, pharmacology, pharmacognosy, biomedicinal chemistry. **Holdings:** 15,261 books; 4943 bound periodical volumes; 974 reels of microfilm; 415 cassettes; 4001 slides; 31,480 microfiche. **Subscriptions:** 448 journals and other serials. **Services:** Interlibrary loan; copying; library open to the public with restrictions. **Automated Operations:** Computerized cataloging, acquisitions, serials, and circulation. **Computerized Information Services:** DIALOG Information Services, NLM. Performs searches on fee basis. **Networks/Consortia:** Member of CAPCON Library Network, Consortium of Universities of the Washington Metropolitan Area.

★7477★

Howard University - Moorland-Spingarn Research Center - Library Division (Area-Ethnic)
500 Howard Place, N.W. — Phone: (202)806-7260
Washington, DC 20059 — Thomas C. Battle, Dir.
Founded: 1914. **Staff:** Prof 10. **Subjects:** Afro-Americana, Africana, Caribbean, Latin Americana. **Holdings:** 150,000 books; 9564 bound periodical volumes; 10,852 microforms; 563 dissertations. **Subscriptions:** 531 journals and other serials; 130 newspapers. **Services:** Copying; division open to the public. **Networks/Consortia:** Member of CAPCON Library Network, Consortium of Universities of the Washington Metropolitan Area. **Remarks:** FAX: (202)806-6405. **Staff:** Janet Sims-Wood, Hd., Ref. & Rd.Serv.; Malik Abdul Azeez, Ref.Libn.; Kathy K. Jenkins, Acq.Libn.; Bessie Fowler, Cat.

★7478★

Howard University - Moorland-Spingarn Research Center - Manuscript Division (Area-Ethnic)
500 Howard Place, N.W. — Phone: (202)806-7480
Washington, DC 20059 — Karen L. Jefferson, Cur.
Founded: 1914. **Staff:** Prof 5; Other 2. **Subjects:** Afro-Americana, Africana, Caribbeana. **Special Collections:** Ralph J. Bunche Oral History Collection (individuals involved in 1960s civil rights activities; 700 tapes and transcripts); Music Collection (4000 pieces of sheet music); Prints and Photographs (24,000, including Rose McClendon Collection of Photographs of Celebrated Negroes by Carl Van Vechten, Mary O.H. Williamson Collection, Griffith Davis Collection). **Holdings:** 2000 linear feet of processed manuscripts; 4800 linear feet of unprocessed manuscripts. **Services:** Copying; division open to qualified researchers. **Publications:** Guide to Processed Collections in the Manuscript Division of the Moorland-Spingarn Research Center. **Remarks:** FAX: (202)806-6405. **Staff:** Esme E. Bhan, Mss.Res.Assoc.; Joellen ElBashir, Sr.Mss.Libn.; Avril Madison, Oral Hist.Libn.; Helen Rutt, Mss.Libn.

★7479★

Howard University - School of Business and Public Administration - Library (Bus-Fin)
2600 6th St., N.W., Rm. 120 — Phone: (202)806-1561
Washington, DC 20059 — Lucille B. Smiley, Libn.
Staff: Prof 2; Other 5. **Subjects:** Business administration, public administration, health services administration, management, accounting, real estate, insurance, marketing, finance, computer-based management information systems, hotel/motel management, international business. **Holdings:** 55,260 books; 5780 bound periodical volumes; 82 technical assistance reports; 17,633 reels of microfilm; 308,814 10K reports on microfiche. **Subscriptions:** 3139 journals and other serials; 75 newspapers. **Services:** Interlibrary loan; copying; library open to the public for reference use only. **Automated Operations:** Computerized cataloging, acquisitions, serials, and circulation. **Computerized Information Services:** DIALOG Information Services, Dow Jones News/Retrieval, Dun & Bradstreet Business Credit Services, LEXIS, NEXIS. Performs searches on fee basis. **Networks/Consortia:** Member of CAPCON Library Network, Consortium of Universities of the Washington Metropolitan Area. **Publications:** Accessions, 10/year; The Negro in the Field of Business, an annotated bibliography.

★7480★
Howard University - School of Divinity Library (Rel-Phil)
1400 Shepherd St., N.E. Phone: (202)806-0760
Washington, DC 20018 Arthuree M. Wright, Act.Libn.
Founded: 1932. **Staff:** Prof 1; Other 2. **Subjects:** Theology. **Special Collections:** Afro-American religious studies. **Holdings:** 104,967 books; 11,247 bound periodical volumes. **Subscriptions:** 492 journals and other serials. **Services:** Interlibrary loan; copying; library open to the public with restrictions on circulation. **Automated Operations:** Computerized cataloging, acquisitions, serials, and circulation. **Networks/Consortia:** Member of CAPCON Library Network, Consortium of Universities of the Washington Metropolitan Area, Washington Theological Consortium. **Publications:** Biographical Directory of Negro Ministers; Afro-American Religious Studies and supplements; The Howard University Bibliography of African and Afro-American Religious Studies. **Special Indexes:** Alphabetical name index of 1800 Negro ministers with addresses.

★7481★
Howard University - Social Work Library (Soc Sci)
6th St. & Howard Place, N.W. Phone: (202)806-7316
Washington, DC 20059 Julia C. Player, Libn.
Founded: 1971. **Staff:** Prof 1; Other 2. **Subjects:** Social work theory and practice; social policy, planning, administration; social welfare problems of black community; urban-oriented problems; human development; women's issues; gerontology. **Holdings:** 37,881 books; 8880 bound periodical volumes. **Subscriptions:** 804 journals and other serials. **Services:** Interlibrary loan; copying; library open to the public for reference use only. **Automated Operations:** Computerized cataloging, acquisitions, serials, and circulation. **Computerized Information Services:** DIALOG Information Services, OCLC. Performs searches on fee basis. **Networks/Consortia:** Member of CAPCON Library Network, Consortium of Universities of the Washington Metropolitan Area.

★7482★
C.D. Howe Institute - Library (Bus-Fin)
125 Adelaide St., E. Phone: (416)865-1866
Toronto, ON, Canada M5C 1L7 Susan Knapp, Libn.
Founded: 1973. **Staff:** 2. **Subjects:** Economics, energy, business, industrial relations, international trade. **Holdings:** 8000 books; 16 VF drawers of clippings; 4 VF drawers of annual reports. **Subscriptions:** 600 journals and other serials; 5 newspapers. **Services:** Interlibrary loan; copying; library open to the public by appointment. **Publications:** Periodicals Contents, monthly; Publications Received, monthly - both for internal distribution only. **Remarks:** FAX: (416)865-1866.

Percy Howe Memorial Library
See: **Forsyth Dental Center** (5990)

Mary A. Hower Medical Library
See: **Children's Hospital Medical Center** (3576)

Dr. William Howitt Memorial Library
See: **Guelph General Hospital** (6794)

Howorth Library
See: **Mississippi Museum of Art** (10515)

★7483★
Howrey & Simon - Library (Law)
1730 Pennsylvania Ave., N.W. Phone: (202)783-0800
Washington, DC 20006-4793 Marie Coleman Kaddell, Dir.
Staff: Prof 5; Other 6. **Subjects:** Law - antitrust, patent, copyright and trademark, government contracts, international trade, insurance; trade regulation. **Holdings:** 45,000 books. **Subscriptions:** 1500 journals and other serials. **Services:** Interlibrary loan; SDI; library open to the public by appointment. **Computerized Information Services:** DIALOG Information Services, LEXIS, NEXIS, NewsNet, Inc., VU/TEXT Information Services, DataTimes, Dun & Bradstreet Business Credit Services, LEGI-SLATE, Information America, Current USC, EPIC, WESTLAW, Dow Jones News/Retrieval, Data-Star, State Net; internal database. **Remarks:** FAX: (202)383-6610. Telex: 753472. **Staff:** Joan Marshman, Asst.Lib.Dir.; Elizabeth Conte, Online Serv.Libn.; Irene Xanthos, Ref.Libn.

★7484★
The Hoyt Library - Brewster Memorial Library (Hist)
284 Wyoming Ave. Phone: (717)287-2013
Kingston, PA 18704 William Frederick, Dir.
Founded: 1963. **Staff:** Prof 2; Other 17. **Subjects:** Local, state, and American history; local authors. **Holdings:** 466 books; maps. **Services:** Copying; library open to the public. **Staff:** Diane M. Rebar, Ref.Libn.

★7485★
Hoyt Public Library - Eddy Genealogical and Historical Collection (Hist)
505 Janes Ave. Phone: (517)755-0904
Saginaw, MI 48605 Kate Tesdell, Br.Hd.
Founded: 1964. **Staff:** 1. **Subjects:** Saginaw and Michigan history, genealogy. **Special Collections:** Michigan Government Document Collection; Buena Vista, Saginaw, and Richland township records; St. Charles records; Saginaw Fire Department records; Brand & Hardin Family business papers (Grist Mill, farmlands, lumbering); Barnard Family papers; Fordney Family papers; Mershon papers; Hoyt Public Library and Hoyt Family history (manuscripts); William L. Webber Collection (attorney for Pere Marquette Railroad; personal/railroad scrapbooks, photo album); Stroebel Family papers; Mitts & Merrill Company ledgers and blueprints; Goll Family business papers (oil); Rathbone Family genealogy papers; Henry Northrup papers (1880s postmaster); Tittabawasse Boom Company ledgers and minutes (logging company); Polish Falcons records books; United Polish Societies ledgers; Zorn Co llection of Saginaw & Michigan genealogical materials; cemetery readings; land records; Saginaw Chapter-Daughters of the American Revolution scrapbooks; organizational scrapbooks and ledger records (11 organizations); Military Collection; Saginaw maps, photographs, postcards; Saginaw newspapers, 1853 to present (microfilm); Saginaw German language newspapers, 1887-1917; Gladwin newspapers, 1877-1928 (microfilm); Bridgeport newspapers, 1897-1906 and 1939-1987 (microfilm); Saginaw composers (sheet music); Stanley Schubert Pageants; Saginaw High School Distinguished Alumni scrapbooks; Arthur Hill High School collection; obituary, biography, local history files (240 drawers of 3x5 cards); newspaper clipping file (38 VF drawers). **Holdings:** 10,000 books; 1500 bound periodical volumes; 100 feet of manuscripts; 4500 nonbook items. **Subscriptions:** 80 journals and other serials. **Services:** Interlibrary loan (limited); copying; collections open to the public with limited borrowing privileges. **Publications:** Guides to the Eddy Historical Collection (by topic); Genealogy Materials in the Eddy Historical Collection, 1975 and 1979. **Staff:** Anna Mae Maday, Mgr., Eddy Coll.

★7486★
HRN - The Information Center (Soc Sci)
1926 Arch St. Phone: (215)299-2900
Philadelphia, PA 19103 J.K. Bucsko, Mgr.
Founded: 1971. **Staff:** Prof 1; Other 4. **Subjects:** Corporate public policy and strategic planning, special interest groups, public policy issues and legislation. **Special Collections:** Organization files (1000); corporate social reports (100). **Holdings:** 5500 volumes; 1600 clipping files; 250 foundation files; 100 research organizations files. **Subscriptions:** 200 journals and other serials; 10 newspapers. **Services:** Center not open to the public. **Automated Operations:** Computerized serials. **Computerized Information Services:** Internal databases. Performs searches on fee basis for clients only. **Special Indexes:** Client Projects Index; HRN Bound Client Reports Index. **Remarks:** FAX: (215)496-0251.

Roman L. Hruska U.S. Meat Animal Research Center
See: **U.S.D.A. - Agricultural Research Service - Meat Animal Research Center** (17187)

★7487★
Hsi Lai University - Library (Rel-Phil, Area-Ethnic)
3456 S. Glenmark Dr. Phone: (818)369-0017
Hacienda Heights, CA 91745 Frances Wong
Founded: 1991. **Staff:** 1. **Subjects:** Buddhist literature; Far Eastern languages; East and West - philosophy, psychology, history, literature. **Special Collections:** Buddhism (holdings in Chinese, Japanese, Pali, Sanskrit, and Tibetan languages). **Holdings:** 50,000 books. **Services:** Library open to scholars with qualifications. **Remarks:** FAX: (818)369-1944.

★7488★
HTB, Inc. - Technical Information Center (Plan)
Box 1845 Phone: (405)239-4765
Oklahoma City, OK 73101 Marilyn Schumacher, Libn.
Staff: Prof 1. **Subjects:** Architecture, engineering, planning. **Holdings:** 400 books; 50 bound periodical volumes; 200 government documents; 15,000 photographs; 15,000 slides; 750 unbound reports. **Subscriptions:** 175 journals and other serials; 10 newspapers. **Services:** Interlibrary loan; center not open to the public. **Networks/Consortia:** Member of Metronet. **Publications:** TIC Communicator, bimonthly - for internal distribution only. **Remarks:** FAX: (405)239-4750.

★7489★
The Hub - Physically Disabled Service Centre - Information Centre (Med)
21 Merrymeeting Rd.
P.O. Box 13788 Phone: (709)754-0352
St. John's, NF, Canada A1B 4G3 Maureen Broderick, Info.Ctr.Coord.
Founded: 1976. **Staff:** Prof 1; Other 1. **Subjects:** Physical disabilities, rehabilitation. **Holdings:** Figures not available. **Subscriptions:** 100 journals and other serials; 25 newspapers. **Services:** Interlibrary loan; copying; center open to the public. **Publications:** Information Update, irregular - available to the public. **Remarks:** FAX: (709)754-2110.

Elbert Hubbard Home - Library and Museum
See: **Aurora Historical Society - ScheideMantel House** (1305)

★7490★
Hubbs-Sea World Research Institute - Library (Biol Sci)
1700 S. Shores Rd. Phone: (619)226-3870
San Diego, CA 92109 Suzanne I. Bond, Res.Asst.
Founded: 1978. **Staff:** 1. **Subjects:** Marine mammals, acoustics, aquatic animal behavior, population biology, mariculture. **Holdings:** 550 books; 50 bound periodical volumes. **Subscriptions:** 30 journals and other serials. **Services:** Copying; center open to the public for reference use only. **Publications:** Currents, 4/year - free upon request. **Remarks:** FAX: (619)226-3944.

★7491★
Hubei Provincial Institute for Drug Control - Library (Med)
275 Ziyang Lu Phone: 871249
Wuhan 430064, Hubei Province, People's Republic of China Hong Belen
Founded: 1973. **Staff:** 2. **Subjects:** Pharmacy, medicament analysis for traditional Chinese medicine and western medicine, instrumental analysis, traditional Chinese medicine, biology, chemistry, toxicology, biochemistry, pharmacology, clinical pharmacology, genetic toxicology. **Holdings:** 26,492 volumes; 357 periodicals. **Services:** Interlibrary loan; copying. **Publications:** Hubei Chinese Herbal Medicine (2 volumes). **Remarks:** Alternate telephone number(s): 871961.

★7492★
J.M. Huber Corporation - Research Library (Sci-Engr)
Box 2831 Phone: (806)274-6331
Borger, TX 79007 Linda Kittell
Subjects: Chemistry, engineering. **Holdings:** 1600 books; 2000 bound periodical volumes. **Subscriptions:** 50 journals and other serials. **Services:** Library not open to the public. **Remarks:** FAX: (806)274-2471.

Hubrecht Laboratory Library
See: **Royal Academy of Sciences - Netherlands Institute for Developmental Biology** (14092)

Hudelson Library
See: **First Meridian Heights Presbyterian Church** (5781)

★7493★
Hudson County Law Library (Law)
Hudson County Administration Bldg.
595 Newark Ave. Phone: (201)795-6629
Jersey City, NJ 07306 Theresa Banks, Law Libn.
Staff: Prof 1. **Subjects:** Law. **Holdings:** 19,000 volumes; 100 bound periodical volumes. **Services:** SDI; library open to the public with restrictions. **Computerized Information Services:** Internal database. **Networks/Consortia:** Member of Essex Hudson Regional Library Cooperative. **Remarks:** FAX: (201)795-6603.

★7494★
Hudson Essex Terraplane Club - Library (Rec)
5765 Munger Rd. Phone: (313)434-3289
Ypsilanti, MI 48197 Charles Liskow, Libn.
Founded: 1965. **Staff:** Prof 1; Other 1. **Subjects:** History and detail specifications of Hudson, Essex, and Terraplane cars; Hudson Motor Car Company. **Special Collections:** Original factory photographs of Hudson Motor Car Company (2000); White Triangle News (1960s to present). **Holdings:** 5 books; 100 bound periodical volumes; 100 other cataloged items (owners manuals, shop manuals, parts books, service and sales literature for Hudson, Essex, and Terraplane cars, 1909-1957); 6 linear feet of AV programs; films; audio- and videotapes. **Services:** Copying; library open to the public by appointment. **Publications:** Newsletter. **Special Indexes:** Index of holdings relating to cars by model year.

★7495★
Hudson Institute - Library (Soc Sci)
5395 Emerson Way
Box 26-919 Phone: (317)545-1000
Indianapolis, IN 46226-0919 Joan Kolias, Lib.Dir.
Founded: 1962. **Staff:** Prof 2; Other 1. **Subjects:** Future studies - social, economic, political; public policy; military affairs; arms control; country studies. **Holdings:** 10,000 books; 4000 reports; 700 reels of microfilm; 2 drawers of microfiche. **Subscriptions:** 300 journals and other serials; 10 newspapers. **Services:** Interlibrary loan; copying; library access by special arrangement only. **Computerized Information Services:** DIALOG Information Services, OCLC, WILSONLINE, EPIC. **Networks/Consortia:** Member of INCOLSA, Central Indiana Area Library Services Authority (CIALSA). **Remarks:** FAX: (317)545-9639. Telex: 855477. **Staff:** Ann S. Minde, Asst.Libn.

★7496★
Hudson Library and Historical Society (Hist)
22 Aurora St. Phone: (216)653-6658
Hudson, OH 44236 Thomas L. Vince, Libn.
Founded: 1910. **Staff:** Prof 4; Other 6. **Subjects:** Hudson and Summit County history, Ohio history and genealogy, John Brown. **Special Collections:** Grace Goulder Izant Ohioana Collection; Clarence Gee Collection and Clark-Brown Collection (John Brown material). **Holdings:** 62,052 volumes; 9030 phonograph records; 760 reels of microfilm; 2234 microfiche; 1809 slides; 182 boxes of manuscripts. **Subscriptions:** 185 journals and other serials; 8 newspapers. **Services:** Interlibrary loan; copying; library open to the public. **Automated Operations:** Computerized public access catalog, cataloging, and circulation (CLEVNET). **Computerized Information Services:** InfoTrac. **Publications:** Annual Report; Ex Libris, quarterly. **Remarks:** FAX: (216)650-4693. **Staff:** Gail E. Dowell, Cat. & Mus.Libn.; Marjorie Origlio, Ch.Libn.; James F. Caccamo, Archv.

Lorne Philip Hudson Memorial Library
See: **Western Pentecostal Bible College - Lorne Philip Hudson Memorial Library** (20288)

Mary Elizabeth Hudson Library
See: **Planned Parenthood of Houston & Southeast Texas, Inc.** (13125)

★7497★
Hudson River Environmental Society - Richard W. Barnett Memorial Library (Env-Cons)
P.O. Box 535
New Paltz, NY 12561 Phone: (914)255-1647
Founded: 1978. **Staff:** Prof 1. **Subjects:** Marine biology, regional planning, waste treatment, toxicology. **Special Collections:** Hudson River Ecology (7 symposia). **Holdings:** 2500 publications. **Services:** Library open to the public.

★7498★
Hudson River Psychiatric Center - Staff Library (Med)
Cheney Bldg. - H.R.P.C. Branch B Phone: (914)452-8000
Poughkeepsie, NY 12601 Norma Parkinson, Asst.
Founded: 1976. **Staff:** 1. **Subjects:** Psychiatry, medicine, psychology, social services, mental health administration. **Special Collections:** Complete Psychological Works of Sigmund Freud; International Encyclopedia of Psychology, Psychiatry, Psychoanalysis & Neurology. **Holdings:** 4000 books; 12,000 bound periodical volumes; 65 computer searches; 80 tapes. **Subscriptions:** 101 journals and other serials. **Services:** Interlibrary loan; copying; library open to the public by appointment. **Networks/Consortia:** Member of Southeastern New York Library Resources Council (SENYLRC).

★7499★
Hudson Valley Community College - Dwight Marvin Learning Resources Center - Special Collections (Educ)
80 Vandenburgh Ave. Phone: (518)270-7330
Troy, NY 12180 Brenda Twiggs, Dir., LRC
Founded: 1953. **Special Collections:** Automotive technology; Microbook Library of American Civilization; allied health sciences; local history (limited); 20th Century video encyclopedia. **Services:** Interlibrary loan; copying; center open to the public with restrictions. **Automated Operations:** Computerized cataloging, acquisitions, and ILL. **Computerized Information Services:** BRS Information Technologies, WILSONLINE, LEXIS; CD-ROMs; internal database. Performs searches free of charge. **Networks/Consortia:** Member of Capital District Library Council for Reference & Research Resources (CDLC). **Publications:** Kaleidoscope (newsletter), semiannual; faculty handbook; new acquisitions. **Remarks:** Maintains Instructional Media Center and Learning Assistance Center. FAX: (518)270-7509. **Staff:** Marjorie Allen, Assoc.Dir.; Susan Blandy, Per.Libn.; Maureen Coughlin, Circ. & Bibliog.Instr.; Sue Grayson, LEXIS; Mary Kirsch, Bk. Selection; Marybeth McCartin, Archv.; Christine Root, Ref. & Law Coll.; Lindsey Watson, Sr. Media Spec.; Ed Wightman, Coord., Lrng. Assistance Ctr.; Mary Blake, Lrng. Disabilities Spec.; Michael Thayer, Tech.Serv. & Acq.Libn.

Hudson's Bay Company Archives
See: **(Manitoba) Provincial Archives of Manitoba** (9625)

★7500★
Hudson's Bay Company Archives (Hist)
Provincial Archives of Manitoba
Manitoba Archives Bldg.
200 Vaughan St.
Winnipeg, MB, Canada R3C 1T5 Phone: (204)945-4949
Founded: 1920. **Staff:** Prof 5; Other 2. **Subjects:** History - Canadian Arctic, Canadian West, northwestern United States, Hudson's Bay Company, fur trade, Indian and Inuit. **Holdings:** 2500 books; 2000 rare books; 7500 linear feet of classified documents; 20,000 maps; 150,000 photographs. **Services:** Interlibrary loan; copying (both limited); archives open to the public; responds to written or telephone inquiries. **Computerized Information Services:** Envoy 100 (electronic mail service). **Special Indexes:** Index to the George Simpson Inward Correspondence, 1821-1860. **Remarks:** FAX: (204)948-2008. Telex: 07 587881. Electronic mail address(es): HBCA.PAM (Envoy 100). **Staff:** Judith Beattie; Anne Morton; David Arthurs; Debra Moore; Maureen Dolyniuk.

Solomon S. Huebner Archives
See: **American College - Vane B. Lucas Memorial Library - Oral History Center & Archives** (532)

Hufeland Library
See: **Thomas Paine National Historical Association (of New Rochelle)** (12690)

Huff Memorial Library
See: **Bradford Hospital** (2056)

Huffington Library
See: **American Academy of Family Physicians** (459)

★7501★
Huffman Memorial United Methodist Church - Library (Rel-Phil)
2802 Renick Phone: (816)233-0239
St. Joseph, MO 64507 Dorothy Thomann, Libn.
Founded: 1958. **Subjects:** Religion. **Holdings:** 4335 books; 400 filmstrips, tapes, phonograph records. **Services:** Library not open to the public.

★7502★
Hufstedler, Kaus & Ettinger - Library (Law, Bus-Fin)
355 S. Grand Ave. Phone: (213)617-6614
Los Angeles, CA 90071 Mary Anne T. Donaldson, Libn.
Founded: 1966. **Staff:** Prof 2; Other 2. **Subjects:** Law, business. **Holdings:** 45,000 books; 125 bound periodical volumes. **Subscriptions:** 230 journals and other serials; 6 newspapers. **Services:** Interlibrary loan; copying; SDI; library open to the public with restrictions. **Automated Operations:** Computerized cataloging, acquisitions, and serials. **Computerized Information Services:** DIALOG Information Services, Information America, LEGI-SLATE, WILSONLINE, RLIN, WESTLAW, NEXIS, LEXIS, Dow Jones News/Retrieval, DataTimes, Dun & Bradstreet Business Credit Services, Legi-Tech; internal database. **Remarks:** FAX: (213)621-2959. **Formerly:** Hufstedler, Kaus & Beardsley.

★7503★
Hughes Aircraft Company - Corporate Business Information Center (Bus-Fin)
Bldg. C1, M/S A154
7200 Hughes Terr. Phone: (213)568-6641
Los Angeles, CA 90080-0028 Alice J. Taylor, Hd.
Founded: 1982. **Staff:** Prof 2; Other 1. **Subjects:** Foreign industry, international marketing, countertrade, foreign governments. **Special Collections:** Company files for over 2000 foreign high technology companies; overseas guidebooks and maps (35 countries). **Holdings:** 600 books; 700 vugraphs; brochures for 200 Hughes products. **Subscriptions:** 85 journals and other serials. **Services:** Interlibrary loan; library not open to the public. **Computerized Information Services:** DIALOG Information Services, Reuters, LEXIS, NEXIS, Dow Jones News/Retrieval; IOSS, ITRANS, VUGRAPH (internal databases); MCI Mail, InterNet (electronic mail services). **Remarks:** FAX: (213)568-6942. TELEX: 9103286566 HACCORP LSA. Electronic mail address(es): 3449590 (MCI Mail); LABREA:ALICET@AP433101.EMIS.HAC.COM (InterNet). **Formerly:** Its Offshore Trade Development Library.

★7504★
Hughes Aircraft Company - Electro-Optical & Data Systems Group - Company Technical Document Center (Sci-Engr)
2000 E. El Segundo Blvd.
Bldg. E1, Mail Sta. E110
Box 902 Phone: (310)616-0414
El Segundo, CA 90245-0902 Dorothy Webb, Hd.
Founded: 1958. **Staff:** Prof 4; Other 6. **Subjects:** Aeronautics, electronics, engineering, missile technology, mathematics, physics, weapon systems. **Holdings:** 109,000 documents; 350,000 documents on microfiche. **Services:** Center open to the public by appointment only. **Computerized Information Services:** Hughes Document Information Retrieval System (internal database). **Publications:** Library Information Bulletin, monthly - for internal distribution only. **Special Catalogs:** Hughes Document Catalog. **Remarks:** FAX: (310)616-7029. Center is part of the EDSG Information Services Department. **Staff:** Stephanie K. Tiffany, Ref.Libn; Mary Minshall, Cat.Libn.; Carol Petrowski, Cat.Libn.

★7505★
Hughes Aircraft Company - Electro-Optical & Data Systems Group - Information Services Department (Sci-Engr)
2000 E. El Segundo Blvd.
Bldg. E1, Mail Sta. E117
Box 902 Phone: (310)616-0404
El Segundo, CA 90245-0902 Jeffrey A. Sevier, Mgr.
Founded: 1956. **Staff:** Prof 9; Other 16. **Subjects:** Electronics, aeronautics, missile technology, weapons systems, space sciences, physics, chemistry, mathematics, management. **Publications:** Library Research Guide; Library Information Guide - for internal distribution only. **Remarks:** The Information Services Department is composed of two sections: the Company Technical Document Center, and the Technical Library. FAX: (310)616-7029.

★7506★
Hughes Aircraft Company - Electro-Optical & Data Systems Group - Technical Library (Sci-Engr)
2000 E. El Segundo Blvd.
Bldg. E1, Mail Sta. E117
Box 902 Phone: (310)616-3333
El Segundo, CA 90245-0902 Rajeana Jensen, Hd.
Founded: 1950. **Staff:** Prof 4; Other 9. **Subjects:** Electronics, physics, aerospace technology, computers, mathematics, chemistry, management. **Holdings:** 26,500 books; 22,000 bound periodical volumes; 20,000 microfiche. **Subscriptions:** 525 journals and other serials. **Services:** Interlibrary loan; copying; library open to the public by appointment only. **Automated Operations:** Computerized circulation. **Computerized Information Services:** Aerospace Online, BRS Information Technologies, DIALOG Information Services, DTIC, LEXIS, NEXIS, NASA/RECON, PFDS Online, STN International; Hughes Document Information Retrieval System (internal database). **Networks/Consortia:** Member of Metronet. **Publications:** Computer Bibliography; Laser Bibliography; Microelectronics Bibliography; Radar Abstracts - all monthly and for internal distribution only. **Remarks:** FAX: (310)616-7029. Library is part of the EDSG Information Services Department. **Staff:** Darryl Banton, Info.Spec.; Eileen Walraven, Info.Spec.; Pamela Wolf, Info.Spec.

★7507★
Hughes Aircraft Company - Engineering Library (Sci-Engr)
500 Superior Ave. Phone: (714)759-2492
Newport Beach, CA 92663 Barbara L. Squyres, Engr.Libn.
Founded: 1957. **Staff:** 1. **Subjects:** Solid state electronics, semiconductors, microelectronics, physics, crystallography, transistors, chemistry. **Holdings:** 4050 books; 2650 bound periodical volumes; 393 microfiche; 55 reels of microfilm. **Subscriptions:** 127 journals and other serials. **Services:** Library not open to the public. **Automated Operations:** Computerized public access catalog and circulation. **Computerized Information Services:** DIALOG Information Services. **Remarks:** FAX: (714)759-6521.

★7508★
Hughes Aircraft Company - Ground Systems Group - Technical Library (Sci-Engr)
Bldg. 600, M.S. C-222
Box 34005 Phone: (714)732-3506
Fullerton, CA 92634-3310 Don H. Matsumiya, Lib.Supv.
Founded: 1957. **Staff:** Prof 1; Other 4. **Subjects:** Radar, antennas, communications systems, computer science, sonar. **Holdings:** 11,000 books; 7000 bound periodical volumes; 53,000 technical reports on microfiche; 1000 maps; 500 standards. **Subscriptions:** 375 journals and other serials; 10 newspapers. **Services:** Interlibrary loan; library open to the public by appointment. **Automated Operations:** Computerized public access catalog (MELVYL). **Computerized Information Services:** DIALOG Information Services, DTIC. **Publications:** Accessions List, monthly. **Remarks:** FAX: (714)732-0995.

★7509★
Hughes Aircraft Company - Hughes Research Laboratories Library (Sci-Engr)
3011 Malibu Canyon Rd., M/S RL84 Phone: (213)317-5115
Malibu, CA 90265 Larry Markworth, Supv.
Founded: 1959. **Staff:** Prof 2. **Subjects:** Physics, electronics, optics, semiconductors, superconductors, lasers, artificial intelligence. **Holdings:** 10,000 books; 4500 bound periodical volumes. **Subscriptions:** 425 journals and other serials. **Services:** Interlibrary loan; copying; library open by appointment to qualified users. **Computerized Information Services:** DIALOG Information Services, STN International, EBSCO Subscription Services, OCLC; internal database; InterNet (electronic mail service). **Networks/Consortia:** Member of CLASS, OCLC Pacific Network. **Publications:** List of acquisitions, quarterly. **Remarks:** FAX: (213)317-5483. Electronic mail address(es): MARKWORTH@CSFVAX.HRL.HAC.COM (InterNet). **Staff:** Carolyn Morgan, Libn.

★7510★
Hughes Aircraft Company - Missile Systems Group - Library (Sci-Engr)
Bldg. 277, Mail Sta. T-10
8433 Fallbrook Ave. Phone: (818)702-2222
Canoga Park, CA 91304-0445 Hazel H. Wetts, Libn.
Founded: 1966. **Staff:** Prof 2. **Subjects:** Electronics, physics, mathematics, missiles and rockets. **Holdings:** 12,206 books; 325 bound periodical volumes; 58,000 reports on microfiche; 996 government research reports. **Subscriptions:** 317 journals and other serials. **Services:** Interlibrary loan; library not open to the public. **Computerized Information Services:** DIALOG Information Services, NASA/RECON, DTIC, WILSONLINE, PFDS Online. **Networks/Consortia:** Member of CLASS. **Remarks:** FAX: (818)702-1888. **Staff:** Patricia Alpine, Libn.

Hughes Aircraft Company - Offshore Trade Development Library
See: **Hughes Aircraft Company - Corporate Business Information Center** (7503)

★7511★
Hughes Aircraft Company - Santa Barbara Research Center - Technical Library (Sci-Engr)
75 Coromar Dr. Phone: (805)562-2542
Goleta, CA 93117 Susan K. Gentry, Sr.Tech.Libn.
Founded: 1960. **Staff:** Prof 1; Other 2. **Subjects:** Infrared technology, solid state electronics, electro-optics, space science and technology, solid state physics, astronomy. **Holdings:** 5000 books; 150 bound periodical volumes; 13,440 unbound volumes; 3000 reports on microfiche. **Subscriptions:** 161 journals and other serials. **Services:** Interlibrary loan; library not open to the public. **Automated Operations:** Computerized cataloging, acquisitions, serials, and circulation. **Computerized Information Services:** NASA/RECON, DIALOG Information Services, Chemical Abstracts Service (CAS), DTIC. **Publications:** Library Bulletin, quarterly; Infrared Abstracts, monthly. **Remarks:** FAX: (805)562-4591.

★7512★
Hughes Aircraft Company - SCG/RSG Research Libraries (Sci-Engr, Comp Sci)
Box 92919 Phone: (310)648-4668
Los Angeles, CA 90009 Susan G. Clifford, Mgr.
Founded: 1963. **Staff:** Prof 7; Other 4. **Subjects:** Space sciences, electronics, computer sciences, telecommunications, radar, optics, physics. **Special Collections:** Satellite communications specifications and standards. **Holdings:** 20,000 books; 25,000 reports on microfiche; 200,300 other cataloged items. **Subscriptions:** 950 journals and other serials. **Services:** Interlibrary loan; copying; SDI; library open to the public with company approval. **Automated Operations:** Computerized public access catalog, cataloging, acquisitions, serials, and circulation. **Computerized Information Services:** DIALOG Information Services, DTI Data Trek, Inc., WILSONLINE, PFDS Online, DTIC, NASA/RECON, NEXIS, Electronic Materials Information Service (EMIS), Dow Jones News/Retrieval; internal database; OnTyme Electronic Message Network Service (electronic mail service). **Networks/Consortia:** Member of CLASS, OCLC Pacific Network. **Publications:** New books list. **Remarks:** Library located at 1950 E. Imperial Hwy., Los Angeles, CA 90245. FAX: (310)648-8965. Maintains four branch libraries. **Staff:** Margaret Deeds, Sr.Libn.; Linda Morris, Sr.Libn.; Gita Srivastava, Supv.Libn.; Dorothy Tompkins, Sr.Libn.; Blair Hinz, Sr.Libn.; Sherril Hisaw-Johnson, Market Res.Anl.

★7513★
Hughes Aircraft Company - Space and Communications Group - Research Information Center (Bus-Fin)
Box 80002 Phone: (310)364-5593
Los Angeles, CA 90009 Joanna Sutton, Supv.
Founded: 1983. **Staff:** Prof 2; Other 3. **Subjects:** Communication satellites; telecommunications; broadcasting and cable television industries;

telecommunication industry regulation; international satellite markets. **Special Collections:** Federal Communications Commission dockets, tariffs, and applications. **Holdings:** 600 books; 200 market research reports. **Subscriptions:** 125 journals and other serials. **Services:** Center not open to the public. **Automated Operations:** Computerized cataloging, acquisitions, serials, and circulation. **Computerized Information Services:** DIALOG Information Services, NEXIS, NewsNet, Inc., Dow Jones News/Retrieval, Reuter TEXTLINE, Telebase EASYNET. **Remarks:** Center is located at 200 N. Sepulveda Blvd., El Segundo, CA. **Staff:** Linda G. Harris, Sr.Bus.Info.Spec.

★7514★
Hughes Aircraft Company - Technical Library 231/2029 (Sci-Engr)
3100 W. Lomita Blvd.
Box 2999 Phone: (310)517-5490
Torrance, CA 90509 Marcia W. Spaid, Lib.Mgr.
Founded: 1976. **Staff:** Prof 1; Other 1. **Subjects:** Microelectronics, traveling wave tubes, microwaves, semiconductors. **Holdings:** 10,000 books; 2600 bound periodical volumes; 700 other cataloged items. **Subscriptions:** 150 journals and other serials. **Services:** Interlibrary loan; library not open to the public. **Automated Operations:** Computerized public access catalog, cataloging, acquisitions, serials, and circulation. **Computerized Information Services:** DIALOG Information Services, DTIC. **Publications:** Newsletter, monthly - for internal distribution only. **Remarks:** FAX: (310)517-5657.

G.M. Hughes Electronics - Delco Electronics
See: **Delco Electronics** (4741)

★7515★
Howard Hughes Medical Institute - Library (Med)
6701 Rockledge Dr. Phone: (301)571-0217
Bethesda, MD 20817 Cathy Harbert, Libn.
Founded: 1986. **Staff:** Prof 1; Other 1.5. **Subjects:** Investments; medical research - genetics, immunology, cellular biology, structural biology, neurosciences. **Holdings:** 300 books. **Subscriptions:** 250 journals and other serials; 8 newspapers. **Services:** Interlibrary loan; library not open to the public. **Automated Operations:** Computerized cataloging and circulation. **Computerized Information Services:** DIALOG Information Services, LEXIS, NEXIS, ORBIT Search Service. **Publications:** Weekly Journals Contents Service. **Remarks:** FAX: (301)571-0218.

★7516★
Hughes Hubbard and Reed - Library (Law)
1300 I St., N.W., Suite 900W Phone: (202)408-3705
Washington, DC 20005-3306 Tina Ramoy, Libn.
Founded: 1972. **Staff:** 1. **Subjects:** Law - commercial, litigation, international trade, banking. **Holdings:** 5000 books. **Subscriptions:** 30 journals and other serials. **Services:** Interlibrary loan; SDI; library open to members of Law Librarians Society of D.C. **Computerized Information Services:** LEXIS, NEXIS, LEGI-SLATE, WESTLAW, Dun & Bradstreet Business Credit Services. **Remarks:** FAX: (202)408-3636. Telex: 892674.

★7517★
Hughes Hubbard and Reed - Library (Law)
1 Battery Park Plaza Phone: (212)837-6666
New York, NY 10004 Jennifer G. Rish, Dir., Lib.Serv.
Staff: Prof 4; Other 6. **Subjects:** Litigation; law - corporate, securities, banking, taxation, bankruptcy, labor, insurance, intellectual property. **Holdings:** 45,000 books. **Subscriptions:** 300 journals and other serials; 10 newspapers. **Services:** Interlibrary loan; library not open to the public. **Automated Operations:** Computerized cataloging. **Computerized Information Services:** LEXIS, NEXIS, WESTLAW, DIALOG Information Services, Dow Jones News/Retrieval, Dun & Bradstreet Business Credit Services, VU/TEXT Information Services, Information America, RLIN, LEGI-SLATE, State Net 50, Reuters, Prentice Hall Online, CCH Access. **Remarks:** FAX: (212)422-4726. Telex: 427120. **Staff:** Robert Harned, Hd.Ref.Libn.; Katherine Ewing, Ref.Libn.; Veera Williamson, Cat.

Inez Hatley Hughes Research Center
See: **Harrison County Historical Museum** (6927)

Langston Hughes Collection
See: **University of West Florida** (19550)

Langston Hughes Community Library and Cultural Center
See: **Queens Borough Public Library - Library Action Committee of Corona-East Elmhurst, Inc.** (13630)

Langston Hughes Memorial Library
See: **Inner City Cultural Center** (7857)

Langston Hughes Memorial Library
See: **Lincoln University** (9190)

★7518★
Hughes & Luce, L.L.P. - Library (Law)
1717 Main St., Suite 2800 Phone: (214)939-5510
Dallas, TX 75201 Valarie J. Rodawalt, Mgr., Lib.Serv.
Staff: Prof 2; Other 3.5. **Subjects:** Law. **Holdings:** 40,000 volumes. **Subscriptions:** 290 journals and other serials; 12 newspapers. **Services:** Interlibrary loan; copying; SDI; library open to the public by appointment. **Computerized Information Services:** LEXIS, DIALOG Information Services, WESTLAW, Dow Jones News/Retrieval, VU/TEXT Information Services, Information America, LEGI-SLATE, Prentice Hall Online; Accu Search (internal database). Performs searches on fee basis. **Networks/Consortia:** Member of Dallas Association of Law Librarians (DALL). **Special Indexes:** Corporate Documents Index; Memo or Brief Bank. **Remarks:** FAX: (214)939-6100. **Staff:** Nancy Lawrence, Asst.Libn.; Thomas Austin, Asst.Libn.

Thomas Hughes Children's Library
See: **Chicago Public Library Cultural Center** (3538)

★7519★
Thomas Hughes Library (Rare Book, Hum)
Box 8 Phone: (615)628-2441
Rugby, TN 37733 Barbara Stagg, Exec.Dir.
Founded: 1882. **Subjects:** Victorian literature - novels, poetry, children's literature. **Holdings:** 7000 books. **Services:** Library open to public for research by request. **Remarks:** Library contains original 7000 books and equipment unchanged since it was built in 1882; maintained by Historic Rugby, Inc.

★7520★
Hughes Training Inc. - Technical Library
1200 E. San Bernardino Rd.
West Covina, CA 91791
Defunct.

Huguenot and Historical Association - Library
See: **Thomas Paine National Historical Association (of New Rochelle)** (12690)

★7521★
Huguenot Historical Society - Library (Hist)
88 Huguenot St.
Box 339 Phone: (914)255-1660
New Paltz, NY 12561 Kenneth E. Hasbrouck, Dir.
Founded: 1894. **Staff:** Prof 4; Other 15. **Subjects:** History and genealogy of Ulster and Orange counties, history of New York State, Huguenot culture, Civil War. **Holdings:** 4000 books and manuscripts; 40 reports; 2500 documents. **Subscriptions:** 10 journals and other serials. **Services:** Copying; library open to the public for reference use only by appointment.

★7522★
Huguenot Society of America - Library (Hist)
122 E. 58th St. Phone: (212)755-0592
New York, NY 10022 Beverly M. Christy, Exec.Sec.
Staff: 1. **Subjects:** French Huguenot migration to America, Huguenot history in France and elsewhere, biography, genealogy. **Holdings:** 2035 volumes; 30 manuscripts; 20 autograph letters. **Services:** Copying; library open on a limited schedule.

★7523★
Huguenot Society of South Carolina - Library (Hist)
138 Logan St. Phone: (803)723-3235
Charleston, SC 29401 Melissa W. Ballentine, Libn.
Founded: 1885. **Staff:** 3. **Subjects:** Genealogical data on Huguenots and allied families. **Special Collections:** Publications of the Huguenot Society of London (England). **Holdings:** 2000 volumes; 8 VF drawers of genealogical data. **Services:** Library open to the public. **Publications:** Transactions, annual.

Huie Library
See: **Henderson State University** (7133)

Cordell Hull Law Library
See: **Samford University - Cumberland School of Law** (14661)

★7524★
Huls America - Library (Sci-Engr)
Box 365 Phone: (908)981-5253
Piscataway, NJ 08854 Joan A. Carnahan, Mgr., Lib./Info.Ctr.
Founded: 1935. **Staff:** Prof 1. **Subjects:** Polymers, coatings, organic chemistry. **Holdings:** 5000 books; 6500 bound periodical volumes; 70 VF drawers of patents. **Subscriptions:** 100 journals and other serials. **Services:** Copying. **Computerized Information Services:** DIALOG Information Services, TOXLINE, Chemical Abstracts Service (CAS), PFDS Online. **Remarks:** FAX: (908)981-5057.

★7525★
Human Factor Programs (HFP) - Library (Med)
1125 E. 17th St., Suite E-209 Phone: (714)972-0117
Santa Ana, CA 92701 Linda Garcia, Dir. of Res.
Founded: 1977. **Subjects:** Behavioral medicine, biofeedback, forensic psychology, hypnosis, medical psychology, stress, behavior crisis development issues, allied health sciences. **Holdings:** 10,000 books, reprints, bound journals. **Services:** Library not open to the public. **Publications:** Behavior Crisis Development Report; Behavior Crisis Development Newsletter; Behavior Crisis Development Newsnote.

Human Genome and Toxicology Information Program - Environmental Teratology Information Center (ETIC)
See: **Oak Ridge National Laboratory - Environmental Teratology Information Center (ETIC)** (12187)

★7526★
Human Lactation Center, Ltd. - Library (Soc Sci, Med)
666 Sturges Hwy. Phone: (203)259-5995
Westport, CT 06880 Dana Raphael, Ph.D., Dir.
Founded: 1975. **Staff:** 5. **Subjects:** Breastfeeding, maternal and infant nutrition, social science, demography, childbirth, women in development, supportive behavior, mammalian reproduction, incest and child sexual abuse. **Holdings:** 4000 volumes; 7 VF drawers of reports, manuscripts, dissertations; 40 tapes; 4 films. **Subscriptions:** 70 journals and other serials; 5 newspapers. **Services:** Library open to the public by appointment. **Publications:** Only Mothers Know: Patterns of Infant Feeding in Traditional Cultures; Being Female: Reproduction, Power and Change; Breastfeeding and Food Policy in a Hungry World; The Tender Gift: Breastfeeding. **Remarks:** FAX: (203)259-7667. **Staff:** Pamela Syz; Diane Wikse.

★7527★
Human Life Center - Library (Soc Sci)
University of Steubenville Phone: (614)282-9953
Steubenville, OH 43952 Dr. Mark Reznick
Subjects: Abortion, euthanasia, and allied "sanctity of human life" issues; sexuality corresponding to Christian moral values; Catholic moral and social teachings; natural family planning; pro-life organizations. **Holdings:** 4000 volumes. **Remarks:** FAX: (614)282-0769.

★7528★
Human Life International - Library (Soc Sci)
7845 E. Airpark Rd. Phone: (301)670-7884
Gaithersburg, MD 20879 Vernon L. Kirby, Dir., Pubns.
Founded: 1981. **Staff:** 2. **Subjects:** Abortion, contraception, post-abortion stress, euthanasia, population control, chastity. **Holdings:** 1000 books; 3 bound periodical volumes; 30 reports. **Subscriptions:** 50 journals and other serials; 20 newspapers. **Services:** Copying; library open to the public with restrictions (material available via mail). **Special Catalogs:** Human Life International's Pro-life/Family Catalog. **Remarks:** FAX: (301)869-7363. **Staff:** William Marshner, Dir., Res.

★7529★
Human Relations Area Files, Inc. - Library (Soc Sci)
755 Prospect St. Phone: (203)777-2334
New Haven, CT 06511 Marlene Martin, Libn.
Founded: 1949. **Staff:** 1. **Subjects:** Anthropology, sociology, geography, psychology. **Special Collections:** Human Relations Area Files Archive (7000 printed and microfiche documents). **Holdings:** 5000 books; 25 bound periodical volumes; 3 million file slips; 1000 other cataloged items. **Subscriptions:** 25 journals and other serials; 5 newspapers. **Services:** Copying; files open to the public. **Computerized Information Services:** CD-ROM (Cross-Cultural CD); produces Ethnographic Bibliography of North America; BITNET (electronic mail service). **Publications:** Behavior Science Research, quarterly; HRAF monographs. **Special Indexes:** Index to HRAF Archive (microfiche). **Remarks:** FAX: (203)777-2337. Electronic mail address(es): HRAFSIR@YALEVM (BITNET).

★7530★
Human Resources Research Organization - Van Evera Library (Soc Sci)
66 Canal Ctr. Plaza, Suite 400 Phone: (703)549-3611
Alexandria, VA 22314 Josephine R. Hunter, Libn.
Founded: 1951. **Staff:** Prof 1. **Subjects:** Psychology, human engineering, education, computer-assisted instruction. **Holdings:** 1500 books; 220 bound periodical volumes; 5000 technical reports. **Subscriptions:** 25 journals and other serials. **Services:** Interlibrary loan; copying (limited); library open to the public by appointment. **Publications:** HumRRO Bibliography; HumRRO Reports.

★7531★
Human Resources School - Rehabilitation Research Library (Soc Sci)
201 I.U. Willets Rd., W. Phone: (516)747-5400
Albertson, NY 11507 Gary Kishanuk, Lib.Hd.
Founded: 1962. **Staff:** Prof 1; Other 1. **Subjects:** Rehabilitation, vocational rehabilitation of disabled, job placements, attitudes, career education, self sufficiency, recreation, special education. **Holdings:** 2000 books; 45 VF drawers of pamphlets; 300 periodical volumes on microfilm. **Subscriptions:** 250 journals and other serials. **Services:** Interlibrary loan; copying; library open to the public by appointment. **Computerized Information Services:** BRS Information Technologies. **Networks/Consortia:** Member of Long Island Library Resources Council. **Remarks:** FAX: (516)746-3298.

★7532★
Human Rights Documentation Centre (Soc Sci)
c/o Human Rights Centre
University of Ottawa
57 Louis Pasteur Phone: (613)564-3492
Ottawa, ON, Canada K1N 6N5 Ivana Caccia, Hd., Doc.
Founded: 1975. **Staff:** PROF 3. **Subjects:** International human rights. **Special Collections:** Canadiana civil rights. **Holdings:** 20,000 books; 50 VF drawers of pamphlets, clippings, documents; newsletters; reports; periodicals. **Subscriptions:** 700 journals and other serials. **Services:** Copying; library open to the public. **Automated Operations:** Computerized cataloging, acquisitions, and serials. **Computerized Information Services:** Internal

databases. Performs searches on fee basis. **Publications:** Human Rights Internet Reporter, 4/year - to contributors and by subscription; Human Rights Directory: Latin America, Africa, Asia; North American Human Rights Directory; Human Rights Directory: Western Europe; Human Rights Directory: Eastern Europe and the USSR; Africa: Human Rights Directory & Bibliography; Teaching Human Rights (a collection of course outlines and bibliographies); Human Rights Directory: Latin American and the Caribbean; Human Rights Research and Education Bulletin, quarterly - available by subscription. **Remarks:** FAX: (613)564-4054. Telex: 5106014536. A joint project of Human Rights Internet and the Human Rights Centre, University of Ottawa. **Staff:** Lucie Bernier.

★7533★
Humana Hospital Audubon - Medical Library (Med)
1 Audubon Plaza — Phone: (502)636-7296
Louisville, KY 40217 — Elizabeth Fischer, Libn.
Staff: Prof 1. **Subjects:** Medicine and nursing. **Holdings:** 450 books; 1300 bound periodical volumes; 400 Audio-Digest tapes. **Subscriptions:** 59 journals and other serials. **Services:** Interlibrary loan; copying; library open to students. **Computerized Information Services:** MEDLARS, MEDLINE.

★7534★
Humana Hospital-Michael Reese - Department of Library & Media Resources (Med)
2908 S. Ellis Ave. — Phone: (312)791-2474
Chicago, IL 60616 — Dr. George Mozes, Dir.
Founded: 1935. **Staff:** Prof 2; Other 2. **Subjects:** Medicine, dentistry, nursing. **Holdings:** 5725 books; 12,785 bound periodical volumes; 800 audio- and videotapes. **Subscriptions:** 331 journals and other serials. **Services:** Interlibrary loan; computer assisted instruction; library open to the public for reference use only. **Automated Operations:** Computerized cataloging. **Computerized Information Services:** NLM, BRS Information Technologies; CD-ROM. **Formerly:** Michael Reese Hospital & Medical Center. **Staff:** Lourdes Aquino, Mgr., Lib.Rsrcs.

★7535★
Humana Hospital Sunrise - Medical Library (Med)
3186 Maryland Pkwy.
Las Vegas, NV 89108 — Phone: (702)731-8210
Founded: 1976. **Staff:** Prof 1. **Subjects:** Medicine, allied health sciences. **Holdings:** 1600 books; 2500 bound periodical volumes; 400 reels of microfilm; 100 videotapes. **Subscriptions:** 160 journals. **Services:** Interlibrary loan; SDI; library open to health professionals only. **Computerized Information Services:** MEDLARS. **Networks/Consortia:** Member of National Network of Libraries of Medicine - Pacific Southwest Region.

★7536★
Humana Hospital University - Gradie R. Rowntree Medical Library (Med)
530 S. Jackson St. — Phone: (502)562-3947
Louisville, KY 40202 — Jody Branson, Med.Libn.
Subjects: Medicine, surgery, allied health sciences, nursing. **Special Collections:** Ophthalmology. **Holdings:** 1000 books; 1000 bound periodical volumes. **Subscriptions:** 160 journals and other serials. **Services:** Interlibrary loan; copying; library open to the public for reference use only. **Computerized Information Services:** MEDLINE; CD-ROM. **Networks/Consortia:** Member of Kentucky Health Sciences Library Consortium.

Humanistic Psychology Archive
See: **University of California, Santa Barbara - Library - Humanistic Psychology Archive** (18432)

★7537★
Humber College - Library - Special Collections (Educ)
205 Humber College Blvd. — Phone: (416)675-3111
Rexdale, ON, Canada M9W 5L7 — K.R. (Vihari) Hivale, Dir.
Founded: 1967. **Subjects:** Horsemanship, mortuary science, Canadiana, horticulture. **Holdings:** 134,650 volumes; 6231 AV items. **Subscriptions:** 1000 journals and other serials; 13 newspapers. **Services:** Interlibrary loan; copying; collections open to the public with restrictions on borrowing. **Networks/Consortia:** Member of The Bibliocentre. **Remarks:** Alternate telephone number(s): (416)675-5059. FAX: (416)675-1483. **Staff:** Maggie Trott, Campus Libn.; Cheryl Salkey, Sr.Ref.Libn.; Karina Fong, Coll.Dev.Libn.; Lynne Bentley, Sys.Libn.; Margie Zekulin, Per.Libn.; Janice Rouse, Libn.

★7538★
Humber Memorial Hospital - Health Sciences Library (Med)
200 Church St. — Phone: (416)243-4597
Weston, ON, Canada M9N 1N8 — M. Dorbolo, Libn.
Subjects: Medicine, nursing, and allied health sciences. **Holdings:** Figures not available. **Services:** Interlibrary loan; library not open to the public. **Computerized Information Services:** MEDLINE. **Remarks:** FAX: (416)249-1312.

★7539★
Humboldt County Law Library (Law)
Court House
825 5th St., Rm. 223 — Phone: (707)445-7201
Eureka, CA 95501 — Nancy A. Guy, Law Libn.
Founded: 1897. **Staff:** Prof 1. **Subjects:** Law. **Holdings:** 18,206 volumes. **Subscriptions:** 20 journals and other serials. **Services:** Interlibrary loan; copying; library open to the public.

Humboldt Museum
See: **North Central Nevada Historical Society** (11914)

H.H. Humphrey Memorial Staff Library
See: **Brown County Mental Health Center** (2266)

Humphreys Engineer Center
See: **U.S. Army - Corps of Engineers** (16942)

★7540★
Hunan Teachers College - Library (Educ)
Yuelushan
Changsha, Hunan Province, — Phone: 82911
People's Republic of China — Wang Ziyun, Dp.Libn.
Founded: 1953. **Staff:** 61. **Subjects:** Teaching of politics, history, physical education, linguistics, foreign languages, mathematics, physics, chemistry, biology, earth sciences; education; philology. **Special Collections:** Chinese ancient books (487 titles; 5316 volumes); district histories of places of historical significance; Confucian classics and histories. **Holdings:** 1.09 million volumes. **Subscriptions:** 1216 journals and other serials. **Services:** Copying.

★7541★
Hungarian Academy of Fine Arts - Library (Art)
Andrassy ut 69-71 — Phone: 1 1421738
H-1062 Budapest, Hungary — Katalin Blaskone Wajko, Dir.
Founded: 1871. **Staff:** Prof 5. **Subjects:** Fine arts, art theory and history, costume and stage design, architecture, applied arts. **Holdings:** 53,170 books; 25 bound periodical volumes; translated articles. **Subscriptions:** 61 journals and other serials; 4 newspapers. **Services:** Interlibrary loan; copying; library open to the public for reference use only. **Remarks:** FAX: 1 1421563. **Also Known As:** Magyar Kepzomuveszeti Foiskola - Konyvtar. **Staff:** Anelia Velkova, Libn.

★7542★
Hungarian Academy of Sciences - Archaeological Institute - Library (Soc Sci)
Uri utca 49
Postafiok 14 — Phone: 1 759011501
H-1250 Budapest, Hungary — Judit Solti, Libn.
Founded: 1951. **Staff:** 3. **Subjects:** Archeology - prehistory, classical, Roman, Middle Ages. **Holdings:** 37,100 volumes. **Subscriptions:** 16 journals and other serials. **Services:** Interlibrary loan; copying; library open to the public. **Computerized Information Services:** Internal database. **Remarks:** FAX: 1 564567. **Also Known As:** Magyar Tudomanyos Akademia - Regeszeti Intezet.

★7543★
Hungarian Academy of Sciences - Ethnographical Institute - Library (Area-Ethnic)
Orszaghaz utca 30 Phone: 1 759011
H-1251 Budapest I, Hungary Katalin Angyal
Founded: 1968. **Subjects:** Hungarian and general ethnography, folklore, and social and cultural anthropology. **Holdings:** 70,000 volumes. **Subscriptions:** 30 journals and other serials. **Services:** Interlibrary loan; copying; library open to the public. **Remarks:** Alternate telephone number(s): 1 556665. **Also Known As:** Magyar Tudomanyos Akademia - Neprajzi Kutato Intezete.

★7544★
Hungarian Academy of Sciences - Institute of Economics (Bus-Fin)
Budaorsi utca 45 Phone: 1 1851527
H-1112 Budapest XI, Hungary Peter Devai, Chf.Libn.
Founded: 1954. **Staff:** 7. **Subjects:** Economics, international trade and finance, socioeconomic problems. **Holdings:** 50,000 bound volumes. **Subscriptions:** 1000 journals and other serials. **Services:** Library open to Hungarian government personnel, scientists, businesses, and other authorized persons. **Computerized Information Services:** Internal databases. **Remarks:** FAX: 1 1851120. Telex: ECNAT 227030. **Also Known As:** Magyar Tudomanyos Akademia - Kozgazdasagtudomanyi Intezete. **Staff:** Tatjana Lengyel, Libn.; Agnes Poor, Libn.; Eva Laszlo, Libn.; Andras Szego, Econ.; Katalin Tiboldi, Libn.

★7545★
Hungarian Academy of Sciences - Institute of Economics - Economic Information Unit (Bus-Fin)
Budaorsi utca 45 Phone: 1 850 878
H-1112 Budapest, Hungary Dr. Tamas Foldi, Dir.
Founded: 1973. **Subjects:** Socio-economic problems, international trade and finance, economic policies. **Holdings:** 500 bound volumes; book review file; research papers. **Subscriptions:** 60 journals and other serials. **Services:** Unit open to Hungarian government personnel, scientists, businesses, and other authorized persons. **Publications:** Information Bulletin, 6-10/year - distributed to all users; Occasional Bulletins - available to specialists by request. **Remarks:** FAX: 1851 158. Telex: ECNAT 227030. **Also Known As:** Magyar Tudomanyos Akademia - Kozgazdasagtudomanyi Intezete - Kozgazdasagi Informacios Szolgalat. **Staff:** I. Fabo, Libn.

★7546★
Hungarian Academy of Sciences - Institute of History - Library (Hist)
Uri utca 53 Phone: 1 75 9011
H-1014 Budapest, Hungary Angela Borsos, Hd. of Lib.
Founded: 1949. **Staff:** Prof 7; Other 1. **Subjects:** Hungarian and world history - economics, politics, society, civilization, culture, ideologies. **Holdings:** 90,060 books; 10,002 bound periodical volumes; 3000 items on microfilm; 3010 other cataloged items. **Subscriptions:** 290 journals and other serials; 15 newspapers. **Services:** Interlibrary loan; copying; SDI; library open to researchers and students. **Computerized Information Services:** ABACUS, SCI (internal databases). **Publications:** Annual bibliography of Hungarian historical books. **Also Known As:** Magyar Tudomanyos Akademia - Tornettudomanyi Intezete.

★7547★
Hungarian Academy of Sciences - Institute of Linguistics - Library (Hum)
I. Szentharomsag utca 2 Phone: 1 75 8285
H-1014 Budapest, Hungary Mrs. G. Szathury, Libn.
Founded: 1949. **Subjects:** History and descriptive analysis of Hungarian language, general and applied linguistics. **Holdings:** 40,000 volumes. **Subscriptions:** 120 journals and other serials; 3 newspapers. **Services:** Copying; library not open to the public. **Also Known As:** Magyar Tudomanyos Akademia - Nyelvtudomanyi Intezete.

★7548★
Hungarian Academy of Sciences - Institute of Literary Studies - Library (Hum)
Menesi ut 11-13 Phone: 1 665861
H-1118 Budapest, Hungary Dr. Katalin S. Nemeth, Dir.
Founded: 1895. **Staff:** 6. **Subjects:** Hungarian literature, literary history, literary criticism, comparative literature. **Holdings:** 150,000 volumes. **Subscriptions:** 250 journals and other serials; 20 newspapers. **Services:** Interlibrary loan; library open to the public for reference use only. **Publications:** National Bibliography of Hungarian Literary History. **Also Known As:** Magyar Tudomanyos Akademia - Irodalomtudomanyi Intezet. **Staff:** Dr. Z. Hejjas Eszter, Dp.Dir.

★7549★
Hungarian Academy of Sciences - Konkoly Observatory - Library (Sci-Engr)
Konkoly Thege U. 13-17
Postafiok 67 Phone: 1 1754122
H-1525 Budapest, Hungary Jozsef Marton
Founded: 1899. **Staff:** Prof 2. **Subjects:** Astronomy. **Special Collections:** Astronomy, mathematics, and physics books printed before 1848 (1000). **Holdings:** 12,503 books; 19,671 bound periodical volumes. **Subscriptions:** 56 journals and other serials. **Services:** Interlibrary loan; copying; library open by director's permission. **Computerized Information Services:** SINBAD (internal database); UUCP (electronic mail service). Contact Person: Andras Holl. **Remarks:** FAX: 1 1569640. Telex: (61)227460 KONOB H. Electronic mail address(es): H697KON@ELLA.HU (UUCP).

★7550★
Hungarian Academy of Sciences - Library (Sci-Engr)
Arany Janos u.1. Phone: 1 382344
H-1361 Budapest, Hungary Gyorgy Rozsa, Dir.Gen.
Founded: 1826. **Staff:** 162. **Subjects:** Social sciences, humanities, science, basic research. **Special Collections:** Department of Manuscripts; Collection of Old Books; Oriental Collections; Archives. **Holdings:** 2 million volumes. **Subscriptions:** 5500 journals and other serials. **Services:** Library open to the public with restrictions. **Computerized Information Services:** CD-ROMs; internal databases. **Remarks:** FAX: 1 1316954. Telex: 224139 aktar H. **Also Known As:** Magyar Tudomanyos Akademia - Konyvtara. **Staff:** Dr. Tibor Braun, Dp.Dir.Gen.; Dr. Alojzia Domsa, Act.Dp.Dir.Gen.

Hungarian Research Library
See: **Kossuth Foundation** (8799)

★7551★
Hungary - Central Research and Design Institute for the Silicate Industry - Library (Sci-Engr)
Becsi utca 126 Phone: 1 1804311
H-1034 Budapest, Hungary Agnes Domotor, Libn.
Founded: 1953. **Staff:** Prof 2; Other 1. **Subjects:** Hungarian silicate industry, silicate chemistry, geology, mineralogy, chemistry, new technology, power engineering methods and systems, industrial sanitary engineering and environmental protection, new building materials, marketing, market research. **Holdings:** 25,000 volumes. **Subscriptions:** 140 journals and other serials. **Services:** Interlibrary loan; copying; library open to the public. **Remarks:** FAX: 1 1687626. Telex: 226827. **Also Known As:** Szilikatipari Kozponti Kutato es Tervezo Intezet.

★7552★
Hungary - Central Statistical Office - Library and Documentation Service (Soc Sci)
Keleti Karoly utca 5
Postafiok 10 Phone: 1 2018206
H-1024 Budapest, Hungary Dr. Istvan Csahok, Gen.Dir.
Founded: 1867. **Staff:** 80. **Subjects:** Hungarian economic and social statistics, demography, data analysis and methods. **Special Collections:** Hungarian and international official statistical publications (155,000 volumes). **Holdings:** 600,000 volumes; 10,000 maps; 800 scientific manuscripts. **Subscriptions:** 3400 Hungarian and foreign journals and other serials. **Services:** Copying; library open to the public. **Computerized Information Services:** Internal databases. **Publications:** Statistical Methods; Papers in Historical Statistics; Studies on Historical Statistics; Special Bibliographies. **Remarks:** FAX: 1 159085. Telex: 224308. **Also Known As:** Magyar - Kozponti Statisztikai Hivatal.

★7553★
Hungary - Karolyi Mihaly National Agricultural Library (Agri, Food-Bev)
Attila utca 93 Phone: 1 568 211
H-1012 Budapest, Hungary Sandor Szabo, Act.Gen.Dir.
Founded: 1946. **Staff:** Prof 55; Other 69. **Subjects:** Agriculture, food industry, forestry and timber industries. **Holdings:** 336,800 bound volumes; 128,700 translations, reports, standards, and patents; CAB Abstracts. **Subscriptions:** 3100 journals and other serials. **Services:** SDI; library open to the public. **Computerized Information Services:** DIALOG Information Services, International Atomic Energy Agency (IAEA), DIMDI, Data-Star; CD-ROMs (CABCD, FSTA, AGRIS, AGRICOLA, CRIS/ICAR); internal databases. **Publications:** Hungarian Agricultural Bibliography, quarterly; Hungarian Agricultural Review, quarterly; Agricultural Review, monthly; Information Bulletin for Agriculture and Food Industry Libraries, quarterly; Information on Food Science and Technology Literature, bimonthly. **Remarks:** FAX: 1568846. Telex: 224717 AGINF H. **Also Known As:** Karolyi Mihaly Orszagos Mezogazdasagi Konyvtar.

Hungary - Ministry of Building and Urban Development
See: **Hungary - Ministry for Transport, Communication and Construction** (7554)

★7554★
Hungary - Ministry for Transport, Communication and Construction - Information Centre of Building - Library (Plan)
P.O. Box 83 Phone: 111-7317
H-1400 Budapest, Hungary Dr. Peter Hamvay, Dir.
Subjects: Building and construction in Hungary and worldwide. **Holdings:** 40,000 volumes; 22,500 product information documents; 21,000 translations; 11,500 study-tour reports; research reports; 49,000 documents, standards, patents, other cataloged items. **Subscriptions:** 264 journals and other serials. **Services:** SDI; library open to government officials, planning and building firms, research organizations, private builders, and architects and engineers in building, civil engineering, and building materials industries. **Computerized Information Services:** Produces KGST-CMEA, STN-ICONDA. Performs searches on fee basis. **Publications:** Accession lists. **Remarks:** Telex: 226564. **Formerly:** Hungary - Ministry of Building and Urban Development/Epitesugyi es Varosfejlesztesi Miniszterium. **Also Known As:** Hungary - Kozlekedesi, Hirkozlesi es Epitesugyi Miniszterium - Epitesugyi Tajekoztatasi Kozpont.

Hungary - National Agriculture Library
See: **Hungary - Karolyi Mihaly National Agricultural Library** (7553)

★7555★
Hungary - National Educational Library and Museum (Educ)
Honved utca 19 Phone: 1 126-862
H-1363 Budapest, Hungary Dr. Mayerne Zsadon Eva, Dept.Hd.
Founded: 1873. **Staff:** 75. **Subjects:** Education - general, history, comparative; sociology; psychology. **Special Collections:** Textbooks; school annuals; foreign and Hungarian juvenile literature. **Holdings:** 321,700 books; 98,588 bound periodical volumes; 7174 manuscripts; microforms. **Subscriptions:** 657 journals and other serials. **Services:** Interlibrary loan; copying; SDI; library open to the public. **Publications:** Hungarian Educational Literature; International Educational Information; International Education; Educational News from Abroad; School Systems; Books and Education; Comparative Education Studies; Studies in History of Education; additional publications available. **Also Known As:** Orszagos Pedagogiai Konyvtar es Muzeum. **Staff:** Dr. Kelemen Elemer, Dir.-Gen.

★7556★
Hungary - National Institute for Medical Information and Library of Medicine (Med)
PO Box 278 Phone: 1 1176352
H-1444 Budapest, Hungary Alexander B. Fedinecz, M.D., M.P.H.
Founded: 1949. **Staff:** Prof 77; Other 28. **Subjects:** Medical science, public health. **Holdings:** 35,000 books; 22,300 bound periodical volumes. **Services:** 850 journals and other serials. **Services:** Interlibrary loan; copying; library open to the public. **Computerized Information Services:** Data-Star, DIMDI, DIALOG Information Services. Contact Person: T. Borsy, Hd., Dept. for Comp.Lit.Serv. **Publications:** Hungarian Medical Bibliography Abstracts; Magyar Orvosi Bibliografia; Health Information and Libraries; Az Orvosi Konyvtaros; Nover; Gondozas. **Remarks:** FAX: 1 1176352. **Also Known As:** Orszagos Orvostudomanyi Informacios Intezet Es Konyvtar.

★7557★
Hungary - National Szechenyi Library - Centre for Library Science and Methodology (Info Sci)
Budavari Palota, F epulet Phone: 1 75 9984
H-1827 Budapest, Hungary Emoke Kovacs, Hd., Lib.Sci.Lib.
Founded: 1959. **Staff:** 58. **Subjects:** Library and information science. **Holdings:** 57,000 volumes; 9500 study-tour reports, dissertations, translations, prospectuses; International Federation of Library Associations (IFLA) papers and publications; photographs; prints. **Subscriptions:** 574 journals and other serials. **Services:** Interlibrary loan; copying; center open to Hungarian and foreign experts in librarianship and information science and students. **Computerized Information Services:** Internal databases; electronic mail. **Publications:** Konyvtari Figyuelo (Library Review), quarterly; Magyar Konyvtari Szakirodalom Bibliografiaja (Hungarian Library of Literature), quarterly; Uj Kouyvek (New Books), 30/year; Hungarian Library and Information Science Abstracts (in English), semiannual; additional publications available. **Remarks:** FAX: 1 1751721. Telex: 224226 bibln.h. **Also Known As:** Orszagos Szechenyi Konyvtar - Konyvtartudomanyi es Modszertani Kozpont.

★7558★
Hungary - National Technical Information Centre and Library (Sci-Engr)
P.O. Box 12
Muzeum utca 17 Phone: 1 1382300
H-1428 Budapest, Hungary Dr. Peter Horvath, Dir.Gen.
Founded: 1883. **Staff:** 355. **Subjects:** Science, technology, applied economics. **Holdings:** 540,000 bound volumes; 347,000 bound periodical volumes; 150,000 research reports; 510,000 translations; 7000 records of licenses sold or purchased in Hungary; magnetic tapes. **Subscriptions:** 4400 journals and other serials. **Services:** Copying; SDI; library open to the public. **Computerized Information Services:** DIALOG Information Services, PFDS Online, CAS ONLINE, Data-Star, IAEA/INIS, Tenders Electronic Daily (TED); CD-ROMs; internal database. Performs searches on fee basis. **Publications:** Hungarian R and D Abstracts: Science and Technology (in English), quarterly; Abstract Journals (21 subject sections); Technical Digest Journals (18 subject sections); Technical-Economic Digest Journals (5 subject sections); Technical Information Journals for Managers; Primary Journals in Science and Technology; other publications available - all in Hungarian. **Remarks:** FAX: 1 1382414. Telex: 22-4944 omikk h. **Also Known As:** Orszagos Muszaki Informacios Kozpont es Konyvtar. **Staff:** Peter Szanto, Dir.

★7559★
The Hunger Project - Library (Soc Sci)
1 Madison Ave., 8A
New York, NY 10010 Phone: (212)532-4255
Subjects: Hunger, starvation, elimination of both. **Holdings:** 1200 volumes. **Publications:** Newspaper, newsletters.

Henry Alexander Hunt Memorial Learning Resources Center
See: **Fort Valley State College** (6014)

Hunt Institute for Botanical Documentation
See: **Carnegie Mellon University** (3083)

Jack R. Hunt Memorial Library
See: **Embry Riddle Aeronautical University** (5327)

The Reed O. Hunt Archive of President Nixon's Commission on Financial Structure & Regulation
See: **University of San Francisco - Special Collections Department/ Donohue Rare Book Room** (19290)

★7560★
Hunt-Wesson - Technical Library (Food-Bev)
1645 W. Valencia Dr., M.S. 506 Phone: (714)680-2158
Fullerton, CA 92633-3899 Joy Hastings, Mgr.
Founded: 1967. **Staff:** Prof 1. **Subjects:** Food science, technology, and packaging. **Holdings:** 5000 books; 1000 bound periodical volumes; 8 VF drawers of patents; 1300 government documents; 25 VF drawers of technical reports; 4 VF drawers of annual reports. **Subscriptions:** 278 journals and other serials. **Services:** Interlibrary loan; library not open to the public. **Computerized Information Services:** DIALOG Information Services, ORBIT Search Service, DataTimes. **Remarks:** FAX: (714)449-5166; 449-5101. **Formerly:** Beatrice/ Hunt-Wesson - Technical Library.

William Morris Hunt Memorial Library
See: **Museum of Fine Arts** (10898)

★7561★
Hunter College of City University of New York - Centro de Estudios Puertorriquenos (Area-Ethnic)
695 Park Ave. Phone: (212)772-5685
New York, NY 10021 Nelida Perez, Libn.
Staff: Prof 3; Other 1. **Subjects:** Puerto Rico - history, culture, literature; Puerto Ricans in the U.S., especially New York City. **Special Collections:** Jesus Colon Collection (manuscripts); Justo A. Marti Photographic Collection. **Holdings:** 8000 books; 150 bound periodical volumes; 1184 theses; 24 VF drawers of reports and pamphlets; 108 drawers of microfilm of 19th and 20th century Puerto Rican papers, rare pamphlets, literary journals, historical documents; 40 films; 200 art prints and posters; video cassettes. **Subscriptions:** 550 journals and other serials. **Services:** Copying; center open to the public. **Automated Operations:** Computerized public access catalog and cataloging. **Computerized Information Services:** OCLC. **Networks/Consortia:** Member of New York Metropolitan Reference and Research Library Agency. **Publications:** Bibliography series; Library Essay Series. **Remarks:** Alternate telephone number(s): (212)772-4197, 772-4000. **Staff:** Amilcar Tirado, Libn.; Felix Rivera, Tech.Serv.

★7562★
Hunter College of City University of New York - Health Professions Library (Med)
425 E. 25th St. Phone: (212)481-5117
New York, NY 10010 Barbara Charton, Assoc.Prof.
Founded: 1909. **Staff:** Prof 2; Other 2. **Subjects:** Nursing, medicine, speech and hearing pathology, physical therapy, dance therapy, medical laboratory sciences, environmental health sciences, allied health services administration, community health education, nutrition, occupational health. **Holdings:** 20,000 books; 7000 bound periodical volumes; 1500 federal and state environmental reports on microfiche. **Subscriptions:** 380 journals and other serials. **Services:** Interlibrary loan. **Computerized Information Services:** DIALOG Information Services, MEDLINE; CD-ROM. **Publications:** Recent Acquisitions List, quarterly. **Remarks:** FAX: (212)481-5116.

★7563★
Hunter College of City University of New York - Hunter College School of Social Work - Library (Soc Sci)
129 E. 79th St. Phone: (212)452-7076
New York, NY 10021 Judith Segal, Hd.Libn.
Founded: 1969. **Staff:** Prof 2; Other 5. **Subjects:** Social work, psychology, sociology, public administration, urban affairs, ethnology, education, law, health. **Special Collections:** Paul Schreiber Collection: History of Social Welfare, U.S. and Europe. **Holdings:** 37,000 books; 6000 bound periodical volumes; 480 volumes of masters' theses; 60 dissertations; 13 VF drawers; 2214 reels of microfilm; 1100 microfiche. **Subscriptions:** 276 journals and other serials. **Services:** Interlibrary loan; library not open to the public. **Automated Operations:** Computerized cataloging, acquisitions, serials, and circulation. **Computerized Information Services:** BRS Information Technologies. **Networks/Consortia:** Member of New York Metropolitan Reference and Research Library Agency. **Publications:** New Acquisitions. **Special Catalogs:** Theses and Dissertations Catalog (card). **Remarks:** FAX: (212)517-2499. **Staff:** Tanya Kalinin, Asst.Libn.

Hunter Library
See: **Western Carolina University** (20237)

Hunter Memorial Pediatric Library
See: **Rockford Memorial Hospital - Health Science Library** (14004)

★7564★
Hunter Museum of Art - Library (Art)
10 Bluff View Phone: (615)267-0968
Chattanooga, TN 37403 Ellen Simak, Cur. of Coll.
Founded: 1958. **Staff:** Prof 1. **Subjects:** American art, antiques, architecture, biography, abstract art, arts and crafts. **Holdings:** 2500 books; 13 VF drawers of sales and auction catalogs; 17 VF drawers of museum and exhibition catalogs. **Subscriptions:** 38 journals and other serials. **Services:** Copying; library open to the public for reference use only. **Staff:** Elizabeth Donahue, Assoc.Cur. of Educ.

Reverend Andrew Hunter Library
See: **Valley Forge Historical Society - Washington Memorial Library** (19731)

★7565★
Hunterdon County Historical Society - Hiram E. Deats Memorial Library (Hist)
114 Main St. Phone: (201)782-1091
Flemington, NJ 08822 Roxanne K. Carkhuff, Lib.Chm.
Founded: 1885. **Staff:** 2. **Subjects:** Hunterdon County and New Jersey history and genealogy. **Special Collections:** Hiram E. Deats Genealogical Collection; Emley-Race manuscripts; Capner Family manuscripts; county newspaper files, 1825 to present. **Holdings:** 5000 books. **Services:** Copying; genealogical queries answered by mail; library open to the public for reference use only. **Special Indexes:** Index of manuscript groups (card).

★7566★
Hunterdon County Law Library (Law)
Court House
Main St. Phone: (908)788-1240
Flemington, NJ 08822 Nona E. Spooner, Law Libn.
Staff: Prof 1. **Subjects:** State and federal law, criminal law, taxation. **Special Collections:** Lindbergh Trial collection (State of New Jersey v. Richard Hauptmann). **Holdings:** 9216 volumes. **Subscriptions:** 20 journals and other serials. **Services:** Library open to the public.

★7567★
Hunterdon Developmental Center - Adaptive Learning Center - Library (Med)
Pittstown Rd.
CN 4220 Phone: (201)735-4031
Clinton, NJ 08809 Roger Schumacher, Dir.
Staff: Prof 3; Other 2. **Subjects:** Mental retardation, psychology, psychiatry, nursing, education. **Holdings:** 1700 professional books; 2000 children's books; AV programs and adapted materials for children. **Subscriptions:** 70 journals and other serials. **Services:** Library not open to the public. **Staff:** Anne Thornton, Teacher/Libn.

★7568★
Hunterdon Medical Center - Medical Library (Med)
2100 Wescott Dr. Phone: (908)788-6100
Flemington, NJ 08822-9237 Jeanne L. Dutka, Med.Libn.
Founded: 1953. **Staff:** Prof 1. **Subjects:** Medicine, family practice. **Holdings:** 2000 books; 1500 bound periodical volumes; 200 Audio-Digest tapes. **Subscriptions:** 66 journals and other serials. **Services:** Interlibrary loan; copying; library open to students only. **Computerized Information Services:** NLM, DIALOG Information Services. **Networks/Consortia:** Member of MEDCORE, Health Sciences Library Association of New Jersey (HSLANJ), Northwest Regional Library Cooperative.

★7569★
Huntingdon College - Houghton Memorial Library - Archives and Special Collections (Rel-Phil, Hist)
1500 E. Fairview Ave. Phone: (205)265-0511
Montgomery, AL 36106-2148 Eric Kidwell, Dir.
Founded: 1976. **Staff:** Prof 1. **Subjects:** Huntingdon College, Methodism, Civil War, political cartoons. **Special Collections:** War of the Rebellion: Official Records of the Union and Confederate Armies (130 volumes); 19th century and rare books (650); original cartoons by Spang (25). **Holdings:** 1050 Methodist historical books; 100 bound Methodist periodical volumes; 45 college-related books; 100 bound college periodical volumes; 200 linear feet of paper records and photographs; 70 reels of microfilm; 58 artifacts; college archives and manuscripts; Methodist archival records, manuscripts, personal papers. **Subscriptions:** 14 journals and other serials. **Services:** Copying; collections open to the public. **Computerized Information Services:** Internal database. **Special Indexes:** Accession Registers (indexed by subject). **Staff:** Mary Ann Pickard, Archv.

★7570★
Huntingdon County Bar Law Library (Law)
Court House, 2nd Fl. Phone: (814)643-4510
Huntingdon, PA 16652 John Peters, Lib.Dir.
Subjects: Law. **Remarks:** No further information was supplied by respondent.

Collis P. Huntington Memorial Library
See: **Hampton Institute** (6880)

★7571★
Huntington Free Library - Museum of the American Indian - Library (Area-Ethnic)
9 Westchester Sq. Phone: (212)829-7770
Bronx, NY 10461 Mary B. Davis, Libn.
Founded: 1930. **Staff:** Prof 1; Other 3. **Subjects:** Archeology and ethnology of Indians of the Western Hemisphere; linguistics; anthropology; history; current affairs. **Special Collections:** American Indian newspapers. **Holdings:** 17,000 volumes; 100 VF drawers; 50 manuscripts. **Subscriptions:** 200 journals and other serials; 140 Indian newspapers. **Services:** Copying; library open to the public by appointment. **Networks/Consortia:** Member of New York Metropolitan Reference and Research Library Agency. **Remarks:** Museum also maintains archives.

★7572★
Henry E. Huntington Library, Art Collections and Botanical Gardens (Rare Book)
1151 Oxford Rd. Phone: (818)405-2191
San Marino, CA 91108 Robert A. Skotheim, Pres.
Founded: 1919. **Staff:** Prof 25; Other 25. **Subjects:** Incunabula, early English and American printed books, English and American literature, medieval English manuscripts, English history to 1837, American history to 1900, California history, history and philosophy of early science. **Holdings:** 356,707 rare books; 317,184 reference books; 2.5 million manuscripts; microforms. **Subscriptions:** 600 journals and other serials. **Services:** Interlibrary loan (photoduplications only); copying; library open to qualified scholars. **Networks/Consortia:** Member of Research Libraries Information Network (RLIN). **Publications:** Program Brochure; Huntington Library Press Publications; People and Progress; Huntington Library Quarterly; Calendar of Exhibitions. **Remarks:** FAX: (818)405-0225. **Staff:** Alan Jutzi, Cur., Rare Bks.; Mary Robertson, Cur., Mss.; Kathleen Martin, Cat.Libn.; Virginia J. Renner, Rd.Serv.Libn.; William A. Moffett, Dir.

★7573★
Huntington Historical Society - Library (Hist)
209 Main St. Phone: (516)427-7045
Huntington, NY 11743 Irene Sniffin, Lib.Reg.
Founded: 1909. **Staff:** 2. **Subjects:** Local history, genealogy, New York history, American crafts and decorative arts. **Special Collections:** Nellie Ritch Scudder Collection of Long Island Genealogical Records; Scudder (family) Association Genealogical Records; W. Wilton Wood Collection (business records and family papers, late 18th century through 1960s; 20 linear feet); Crossman Brickyard Records (19th century; 2 linear feet); The Long Islander (newspaper), 1839 to present; Domesday Book: A Survey of the Counties of England (40 volumes). **Holdings:** 4500 books; 128 bound periodical volumes; 325 linear feet of manuscripts and archival materials; 8 clipping files; 30,000 photographs; 7000 slides. **Subscriptions:** 30 journals and other serials. **Services:** Copying; library open to the public for research only. **Networks/Consortia:** Member of Long Island Library Resources Council. **Publications:** Huntington-Babylon Town History; Eaton's Neck; Huntington at the Turn of the Century; Huntingto n in Our Time; John Sloss Hobart, Forgotten Patriot. **Special Indexes:** Index to the Long Islander, 1839-1842, 1843-1849, and 1850-1857; Index to the Long Islander, Marriages and Deaths 1839-1864 and 1865-1881.

★7574★
Huntington Hospital - Medical Library (Med)
270 Park Ave. Phone: (516)351-2283
Huntington, NY 11743 Ruth I. Glick, Dir.
Founded: 1961. **Staff:** Prof 2. **Subjects:** Medicine and surgery, nursing, pathology, radiology, nuclear medicine, sonography. **Holdings:** 900 books; 5325 bound periodical volumes; audiotapes. **Subscriptions:** 261 journals and other serials. **Services:** Interlibrary loan; copying; library open to qualified students only. **Networks/Consortia:** Member of Medical & Scientific Libraries of Long Island (MEDLI). **Publications:** Acquisitions list, quarterly. **Staff:** Angela Governale, Med.Libn.

★7575★
Huntington Memorial Hospital - Health Sciences Library (Med)
100 W. California Blvd.
Box 7013 Phone: (818)397-5161
Pasadena, CA 91109-7013 Samir Maurice Zeind, Mgr.
Staff: Prof 3; Other 3. **Subjects:** Medicine, surgery, nursing, radiology, psychiatry, hospital administration, patient information and resources. **Holdings:** 5000 books; 20,000 bound periodical volumes; 1000 audiotapes. **Subscriptions:** 617 journals and other serials. **Services:** Interlibrary loan; copying; SDI; library open to the public. **Computerized Information Services:** DIALOG Information Services, MEDLARS; CD-ROM (MEDLINE); DOCLINE (electronic mail service). Performs searches on fee basis. Contact Person: Suzanne Huddleson, Ref.Libn. **Networks/Consortia:** Member of National Network of Libraries of Medicine - Pacific Southwest Region. **Publications:** List of Periodicals; New Books List; Patient Education List; Computer Software List. **Remarks:** FAX: (818)397-8009.

★7576★
Huntington Museum of Art - Library (Art)
Park Hills Phone: (304)529-2701
Huntington, WV 25701 Christopher Hatten, Libn.
Staff: Prof 1. **Subjects:** Historic and contemporary glass, American painting, prints, photography. **Special Collections:** Glass manufacturers trade catalogs; exhibition catalogs. **Holdings:** 8000 books; 4000 slides; 1 drawer of microfiche. **Subscriptions:** 60 journals and other serials. **Services:** Copying; library open to the public for reference use only. **Remarks:** FAX: (304)529-7447.

Huntington Wildlife Forest Library
See: **State University of New York - College of Environmental Science & Forestry** (15723)

★7577★
Hunton & Williams - Law Library (Law)
Riverfront Plaza, East Tower
951 E. Byrd St. Phone: (804)788-8272
Richmond, VA 23219 Frosty Owen, Dir.
Staff: 8. **Subjects:** Law - corporate, real estate, antitrust, tax, labor, environmental, health care, international; litigation. **Holdings:** 60,000 volumes. **Subscriptions:** 500 journals and other serials; 6 newspapers. **Services:** Library not open to the public. **Computerized Information Services:** WESTLAW, LEXIS, LEGI-SLATE, DIALOG Information Services, Dun & Bradstreet Business Credit Services, VU/TEXT Information Services, DataTimes, Information America. **Remarks:** FAX: (804)788-8218. **Staff:** Mary Kofrm, Tech.Serv.Libn.; Gail Zwirner, Ref.Libn.; Duane Schrock, Ref.Libn.; Debbie Piercy, Ref.Libn.

★7578★
Huntsman Chemical Corporation - Technical Information Center (Sci-Engr)
5100 Bainbridge Rd. Phone: (804)494-2650
Chesapeake, VA 23320 Janet Coe Mitchell, Libn.
Staff: Prof 1. **Subjects:** Chemistry - polymer, organic, analytical; materials flammability; packaging; marketing and business. **Holdings:** 4000 books; 5000 bound periodical volumes; 1000 unbound reports; Chemical Abstracts, 1907-1983, in hardcopy and, 1984-1985, on microfiche. **Subscriptions:** 84 journals and other serials. **Services:** Interlibrary loan; copying; SDI; center open to the public with restrictions. **Computerized Information Services:** DIALOG Information Services, STN International. **Remarks:** FAX: (804)494-2774.

★7579★
Huntsville Memorial Hospital - Medical Library (Med)
3000 Interstate 45
P.O. Box 4001 Phone: (409)291-4545
Huntsville, TX 77342-4001 Darlene Burris, Libn.
Founded: 1966. **Staff:** Prof 2; Other 1. **Subjects:** Professional and vocational nursing, medicine. **Special Collections:** Ciba Collection; reconstructive plastic surgery. **Holdings:** 900 books; 290 bound periodical volumes; 200 filmstrips; 1600 videotapes. **Subscriptions:** 20 journals and other serials. **Services:** Interlibrary loan; copying; library open to the public with restrictions. **Computerized Information Services:** MEDLARS; DOCLINE (electronic mail service). **Networks/Consortia:** Member of AMIGOS Bibliographic Council, Inc., South Central Academic Medical Libraries Consortium (SCAMEL). **Remarks:** FAX: (409)295-9316. **Staff:** Barbara Bohanon, RN, Dept. of Educ.Dir.

★7580★
Huntsville Museum of Art - Library (Art)
700 Monroe St. Phone: (205)535-4350
Huntsville, AL 35801 Janet Saczawa, Libn.
Staff: 1. **Subjects:** Art. **Holdings:** 800 books; 130 bound periodical volumes; 2400 exhibition catalogs. **Subscriptions:** 48 journals and other serials. **Services:** Copying; library open to the public.

★7581★
The Huntsville Times - Library (Publ)
2317 S. Memorial Pkwy. Phone: (205)532-4414
Huntsville, AL 35801 Rebecca L. Moore
Staff: 2.5. **Subjects:** Newspaper reference topics. **Special Collections:** Historic Huntsville Times Newspapers. **Holdings:** 1500 books; 750 reels of microfilm; 250,000 photos. **Subscriptions:** 50 journals and other serials; 30 newspapers. **Services:** Library not open to the public. **Computerized Information Services:** Local and Regional News Stories (internal database). Contact Person: Emily McKay, Asst.Libn. **Remarks:** (205)532-4420.

Hupp Medical Library
See: **Ohio Valley Medical Center** (12336)

Captain Charles H. Hurley Library
See: **Massachusetts Maritime Academy** (9822)

Donald J. Hurley Library
See: **National Center for State Courts - Northeastern Regional Office** (11108)

★7582★
Hurley Medical Center - Community Health Information Library (Med)
1 Hurley Plaza — Phone: (313)257-9000
Flint, MI 48502 — Martha Studaker, Dir.
Founded: 1981. **Subjects:** Health. **Holdings:** 1200 books. **Services:** Library open to patients, their families, and community members with health concerns.

★7583★
Hurley Medical Center - Hamady Health Sciences Library (Med)
1 Hurley Plaza — Phone: (313)257-9427
Flint, MI 48502 — Martha Studaker, Dir.
Founded: 1976. **Staff:** Prof 2; Other 3. **Subjects:** Medicine, nursing, hospital administration, health. **Holdings:** 8000 books; 1065 AV programs; pamphlet files. **Subscriptions:** 650 journals and other serials. **Services:** Interlibrary loan; copying; SDI. **Automated Operations:** Computerized public access catalog, cataloging, serials, and circulation. **Computerized Information Services:** MEDLARS, DIALOG Information Services, NTIS, WILSONLINE. Performs searches on fee basis. **Networks/Consortia:** Member of Flint Area Health Science Library Network (FAHSLN). **Publications:** Booklist; Newsletter - for internal distribution only. **Remarks:** FAX: (313)762-7107. **Staff:** Nancy Winslow, Pub.Serv.Libn.; Sharon Williams, Tech.Serv.Libn.; Gloria Stoudamire, Pub.Serv.Libn.; Phyllis Reams, Tech.Serv.Libn.

★7584★
Huron City Museum - Library (Hist)
7930 Huron City Rd. — Phone: (517)428-4123
Port Austin, MI 48467 — C.A. Scheffner, Dir., Musms.
Subjects: Literature. **Special Collections:** Library of William Lyon Phelps. **Holdings:** 10,400 books; bound periodical volumes. **Services:** Interlibrary loan (limited); library open to the public for reference use only. **Remarks:** FAX: (517)428-4473.

★7585★
Huron College - Silcox Memorial Library (Rel-Phil, Hum)
1349 Western Rd. — Phone: (519)438-7224
London, ON, Canada N6G 1H3 — Pamela MacKay, Chf.Libn.
FO 1863. **Staff:** Prof 2; Other 4. **Subjects:** Theology, English and French literature, history, philosophy, psychology. **Holdings:** 130,000 volumes; 8 linear feet of archival materials; 5 linear feet of manuscripts. **Subscriptions:** 302 journals and other serials. **Services:** Interlibrary loan; copying.

★7586★
Huron County Law Library (Law)
Huron County Courthouse, 3rd Fl.
The Square — Phone: (519)524-7962
Goderich, ON, Canada N7A 1M2 — Gail Bettger, Libn.
Staff: Prof 1. **Subjects:** Law. **Holdings:** 6162 books. **Services:** Library open to the public with restrictions. **Remarks:** FAX: (519)524-1065. Maintained by Huron County Law Association.

Huron Road Hospital
See: **Meridia Huron Hospital** (10158)

★7587★
Huronia Historical Parks - Resource Centre (Hist)
P.O. Box 160 — Phone: (705)526-7838
Midland, ON, Canada L4R 4K8 — Sandra Saddy, Libn.
Founded: 1971. **Staff:** Prof 1; Other 1. **Subjects:** New France to 1660; Jesuit missions in North America; Huron Indians in the 17th century; British naval and military establishments in Penetanguishene; archeology. **Holdings:** 7000 books; 50 bound periodical volumes; 2500 photocopied articles; 4 drawers of manuscripts; 10 boxes of archival records; 1000 maps; 3200 pictures; 3000 slides; 250 microforms. **Subscriptions:** 75 journals and other serials. **Services:** Interlibrary loan; copying; SDI; Center open to the public. **Computerized Information Services:** DIALOG Information Services; Envoy 100 (electronic mail service). **Publications:** Recent Acquisitions, irregular - for internal distribution only. **Special Indexes:** Manuscript file (cards). **Remarks:** FAX: (705)526-9193. Electronic mail address(es): HURONIA.HIST.PARKS (Envoy 100). Maintained by Ontario Ministry of Tourism and Recreation. **Formerly:** Its Information Services Department.

★7588★
Huronia Regional Centre - Library (Med)
Box 1000 — Phone: (705)326-7361
Orillia, ON, Canada L3V 6L2 — Maureen Maguire, Libn.
Founded: 1974. **Staff:** Prof 1. **Subjects:** Developmental disabilities. **Special Collections:** Huronia Regional Centre archives/museum (photos, documents, and artifacts that illustrate history of care of and policy relating to developmentally disabled in Ontario, 1876 to present). **Holdings:** 2500 books; 200 reports; 14 VF drawers of reports, pamphlets, articles. **Subscriptions:** 125 journals and other serials. **Services:** Interlibrary loan; copying; library open to the public. **Networks/Consortia:** Member of Central Ontario Health Libraries Association (COHLA), Ontario Hospital Libraries Association (OHLA). **Publications:** Periodical Holdings List, annual - to other libraries. **Remarks:** FAX: (705)326-5269. Maintained by Ontario Ministry of Community and Social Services.

Hurst Library
See: **Northwest College of the Assemblies of God** (12044)

Hurst Memorial Library
See: **Pacific Christian College** (12661)

Nathaniel J. Hurst Library
See: **Park Ridge Hospital** (12749)

R.O. Hurst Library
See: **University of Toronto - Faculty of Pharmacy** (19448)

★7589★
Hurty-Peck Library of Beverage Literature (Food-Bev)
5600 W. Raymond St. — Phone: (317)243-3521
Indianapolis, IN 46241 — Ben Wilson
Founded: 1959. **Staff:** 1. **Subjects:** Beer and brewing, cider, cocktails and mixed drinks, coffee, drinks and drinking, flavorings, food and drink, inns, liquors, mineral waters, soft drinks, tea, temperance, wine and winemaking. **Holdings:** 6000 books; files on soft drinks and alcoholic beverages. **Subscriptions:** 15 journals and other serials. **Services:** Interlibrary loan; library open to the public by appointment. **Publications:** Beverage Literature: A Bibliography (catalog of books in library), 1971. **Remarks:** FAX: (317)240-1524. Maintained by Universal Flavor Corporation, a division of Universal Foods.

Hurwitz Memorial Library
See: **Sinai Samaritan Medical Center** (15187)

★7590★
Husky Oil Operations Ltd. - Corporate Library (Energy)
Sta. D, Box 6525 — Phone: (403)298-7066
Calgary, AB, Canada T2P 3G7 — Jane Orr, Lib.Coord.
Staff: Prof 2; Other 1.5. **Subjects:** Earth sciences, petroleum engineering, petroleum industry. **Holdings:** 15,000 books and government documents. **Subscriptions:** 600 journals and other serials; 5 newspapers. **Services:** Interlibrary loan; library not open to the public. **Automated Operations:** Computerized cataloging, circulation, serials, and ILL. **Computerized Information Services:** DIALOG Information Services, ORBIT Search Service, Info Globe, Reuters Information Services (Canada), Infomart Online, Dun & Bradstreet Business Credit Services, CAN/OLE; Envoy 100 (electronic mail service). **Remarks:** FAX: (403)298-7464. Electronic mail address(es): ILL.Husky (Envoy 100).

Hobart Huson's Dawgwood Research Library
See: **Dawgwood Research Library** (4653)

Harvey Husten Jazz Library
See: **Free Library of Philadelphia - Music Department** (6119)

Dr. John A. Hutch Library
See: **John Muir Medical Center - Medical Library** (10845)

★7591★
Hutcheson & Grundy - Law Library
3300 Citicorp Ctr.
1200 Smith St. Phone: (713)951-2855
Houston, TX 77002 Alsa Cotner, Hd.Libn.
Remarks: No further information was supplied by respondent.

Hutchins Library
See: **Berea College - Hutchins Library - Special Collections** (1727)

★7592★
Fred Hutchinson Cancer Research Center - Library (Med)
1124 Columbia St. Phone: (206)667-4314
Seattle, WA 98104 Eve Ruff, M.S.
Founded: 1975. **Staff:** 3.5; Other 2.5. **Subjects:** Leukemia, immunology, molecular biology, cancer research, genetics, cancer prevention. **Special Collections:** Bone marrow transplantation collection. **Holdings:** 2000 books; 11,000 bound periodical volumes. **Subscriptions:** 250 journals and other serials; 2 newspapers. **Services:** Interlibrary loan; copying; SDI; library open to the public. **Computerized Information Services:** DIALOG Information Services, OCLC, BRS Information Technologies; CD-ROM (MEDLINE). **Publications:** Line-Up (newsletter). **Remarks:** FAX: (206)667-4737.

Huttner Abolition & Anti-Slavery Collection
See: **Minneapolis Public Library & Information Center - Special Collections Department** (10454)

★7593★
E.F. Hutton & Company, Inc. - Research Library
American Express Tower C
World Finance Center, 15th Fl.
New York, NY 10285
Defunct. Holdings absorbed by Lehman Brothers - Corporate Library.

★7594★
Hutzel Hospital - Medical Library (Med)
4707 St. Antoine Blvd. Phone: (313)745-7178
Detroit, MI 48201 Jean M. Brennan, Dir., Lib.Serv.
Founded: 1936. **Staff:** Prof 2; Other 1. **Subjects:** Obstetrics and gynecology, orthopedics, ophthalmology, substance abuse, arthritis/rheumatology. **Holdings:** 2500 books; 10,000 bound periodical volumes; 6 VF drawers; Audio-Digest tapes in surgery, internal medicine, obstetrics, gynecology; state medical association journals. **Subscriptions:** 450 journals and other serials. **Services:** Interlibrary loan; copying; SDI; library open to the public with restrictions. **Automated Operations:** Computerized serials and circulation. **Computerized Information Services:** BRS Information Technologies, DIALOG Information Services, NLM; CD-ROM (MEDLINE). **Networks/Consortia:** Member of Michigan Health Sciences Libraries Association (MHSLA). **Remarks:** FAX: (313)993-0152.

★7595★
Huxford Genealogical Society, Inc. - Genealogical Library (Hist)
Corner of Dame & College Sts.
P.O. Box 595 Phone: (912)487-2310
Homerville, GA 31634 Mary Day, Libn.
Founded: 1972. **Staff:** 2. **Subjects:** Genealogy. **Special Collections:** Judge Folks Huxford, F.A.S.G. Collection (12 VF drawers); International Genealogical Indexes for U.S., England, Scotland, and Wales. **Holdings:** 2617 volumes (including microfilm); 79 boxes of magazines; 155 boxes of microfilm. **Services:** Copying; library open to nonmembers on a fee basis. **Publications:** Huxford Genealogical Society Magazine, quarterly.

★7596★
Huxley College of Environmental Studies - Environmental Resource Library (Env-Cons)
ESC 535, Huxley College Phone: (206)676-3520
Bellingham, WA 98225 Amy Dearbom, Coord.
Founded: 1970. **Staff:** Prof 2; Other 5. **Subjects:** Environmental education; human ecology; social science; environmental philosophy and ethics; environmental planning; terrestrial, fresh water, marine ecology; environmental health and toxicology; agriculture, nutrition, food supply; environmental technology and recycling; energy alternatives. **Holdings:** 2000 books; 3 files of pamphlets and clippings; 50 newsletters; 600 student reports; 12 tapes; Environmental Protection Agency documents. **Subscriptions:** 32 journals and other serials. **Services:** Library open to the public. **Publications:** The Monthly Planet. **Remarks:** Huxley College is a division of Western Washington University. The Environmental Resource Library is jointly maintained by Western Washington University and its Associated Students Environmental Center.

Huxley Institute for Biosocial Research
See: **American Schizophrenia Association** (734)

★7597★
Alice Hyde Hospital Association - Medical/Nursing Library (Med)
Malone, NY 12953 Phone: (518)483-3000
Dorothy Gonyea, Libn.
Founded: 1980. **Staff:** 1. **Subjects:** Medicine, nursing. **Holdings:** 250 books. **Subscriptions:** 20 journals and other serials. **Services:** Interlibrary loan; copying; SDI; library open to the public with restrictions. **Computerized Information Services:** BRS Information Technologies. **Networks/Consortia:** Member of North Country Reference and Research Resources Council (NCRRRC). **Remarks:** FAX: (518)483-5056.

★7598★
Hyde Collection (Hum)
161 Warren St. Phone: (518)792-1761
Glens Falls, NY 12801 Cecilia Esposito, Dir.
Founded: 1952. **Staff:** 15. **Subjects:** Art, local history, British poetry, old travel books. **Special Collections:** Nuremberg Chronicle; Augsberg Chronicle; Book of Hours. **Holdings:** 2600 volumes. **Subscriptions:** 10 journals and other serials. **Services:** Collection open for scholarly research only.

Inez L. Hyde Memorial Collection
See: **Tulare Public Library** (16570)

★7599★
Hyde Park Historical Society - Archives (Hist)
30 Ayles Rd. Phone: (617)361-4398
Hyde Park, MA 02136 Nancy H. Hannan, Pres.
Founded: 1887. **Subjects:** Hyde Park history, Civil War era. **Special Collections:** Scrapbooks of Hyde Park newspapers and mementos (10); town papers, directories, and reports; People & Places Hyde Park (photographs); works of Hyde Park authors; genealogy records from Hyde Park, Massachusetts, and New England. **Holdings:** 2000 books; 200 bound periodical volumes; 100 AV programs; 50 nonbook items. **Services:** Archives open to the public by appointment. **Remarks:** FAX: (617)361-4398. Appointment may be made by contacting Elizabeth Freeman, Sec., at (617)364-0082.

★7600★
(Hyderabad) American Center - USIS Library (Educ)
Hospital Rd.
Hyderabad, Pakistan
Remarks: Maintained or supported by the U.S. Information Agency. Focus is on materials that will assist peoples outside the United States to learn about the United States, its people, history, culture, political processes, and social milieux.

Hydraulic Engineering Information Analysis Center
See: **U.S. Army - Engineer Waterways Experiment Station** (16968)

★7601★
Hydro-Quebec - Bibliotheque (Sci-Engr, Energy)
75 Rene Levesque Blvd., W., Mezzanine Fl. Phone: (514)289-2145
Montreal, PQ, Canada H2Z 1A4 Claude-Andre Bonin, Mgr.
Founded: 1962. **Staff:** Prof 7; Other 4. **Subjects:** Electrical engineering, hydraulics, energy, management. **Holdings:** 20,000 books; 10 VF drawers of unbound documents and pamphlets; 60 VF drawers of electrical and international standards; 6000 microfiche of technical reports. **Subscriptions:** 1100 journals and other serials. **Services:** Interlibrary loan; copying; SDI; library open to the public with restrictions. **Automated Operations:** Computerized cataloging, acquisitions, and serials. **Computerized Information Services:** CAN/OLE, DIALOG Information Services, PFDS Online, QL Systems, MEDLINE, Info Globe, Questel; RIDAQ (internal database). **Publications:** Au Courant (library list of accessions), monthly - free upon request; SURVOL (library list of accessions), monthly - for internal distribution only. **Special Catalogs:** COM Union catalog. **Remarks:** FAX: (514)849-9898.

★7602★
Hydro-Quebec - Institut de Recherche - Bibliotheque (Sci-Engr)
1800, montee Ste-Julie
C.P. 1000 Phone: (514)652-8398
Varennes, PQ, Canada J3X 1S1 Mr. Daniel Auguet, Hd.
Founded: 1967. **Staff:** Prof 2; Other 4. **Subjects:** Electricity, electrochemistry, energy. **Holdings:** 20,000 books; 70,000 bound periodical volumes; 5500 reports. **Subscriptions:** 550 journals and other serials. **Services:** Interlibrary loan; copying; SDI; library open to the public by appointment. **Automated Operations:** Computerized cataloging and acquisitions. **Computerized Information Services:** DIALOG Information Services, Questel, CAN/OLE; internal database. **Remarks:** FAX: (514)652-8040. Telex: 05 267486. **Staff:** Pierre Adant, Ref.Libn.

★7603★
Hydro-Quebec - Planification Generale - Centre de Documentation (Bus-Fin)
75 Rene Levesque Blvd., W., 8th Fl. Phone: (514)289-4627
Montreal, PQ, Canada H2Z 1A4 Celine Bellerose, Doc.Coord.
Founded: 1969. **Staff:** Prof 1; Other 2. **Subjects:** Strategic planning, energy, economics. **Special Collections:** Statistics Canada publications. **Holdings:** 4500 books; 600 bound periodical volumes; 3000 other cataloged items. **Subscriptions:** 500 journals and other serials; 30 newspapers. **Services:** Interlibrary loan; copying; SDI; center open to the public by appointment. **Automated Operations:** Computerized cataloging, acquisitions, serials, and circulation. **Computerized Information Services:** RIDAQ (internal database). Performs searches free of charge. **Publications:** Dossier de presse (abstracts); Revue d'actualite; Nouveautes. **Special Catalogs:** Catalogue VPPG. **Remarks:** FAX: (514)987-2960. **Staff:** Paul Fillion, Lib.Techn.

★7604★
Hydro Research Science - Library (Sci-Engr)
3334 Victor Ct. Phone: (408)988-1027
Santa Clara, CA 95054 Dr. Alexander Rudavsky
Staff: Prof 1. **Subjects:** Fluid mechanics, experimental hydraulics, model studies in hydrology. **Special Collections:** Delft Hydraulics Laboratory Reports, 1967 to present. **Holdings:** 425 books; 82 bound periodical volumes; 1100 technical reports. **Subscriptions:** 49 journals and other serials. **Services:** Interlibrary loan; library not open to the public. **Computerized Information Services:** DIALOG Information Services; DIALMAIL (electronic mail service). **Publications:** Acquisitions list. **Remarks:** FAX: (408)988-8634.

★7605★
Hydrosource Associates/ - Library (Sci-Engr)
26 Winter St.
P.O. Box 609 Phone: (603)968-3733
Ashland, NH 03217 Rosemarie De Mars, Libn.
Founded: 1982. **Staff:** Prof 1. **Subjects:** Hydrology, geology, remote sensing, groundwater exploration and protection, hazardous waste. **Special Collections:** U.S. Geological Survey and state geologic and hydrologic reports (New England, Southeastern and Southwestern United States, some overseas locations); geologic maps. **Holdings:** 100 books; 1000 reports and maps; 200 microfiche. **Subscriptions:** 25 journals and other serials. **Services:** Interlibrary loan; library not open to the public. **Computerized Information Services:** EROS Data Center. **Remarks:** FAX: (603)968-7605. **Formerly:** BCI Geonetics, Inc. - Library located in Laconia, NH.

★7606★
Hymn Society in the United States and Canada, Inc. - National Headquarters - Library (Rel-Phil)
Texas Christian University
Box 30854 Phone: (817)921-7608
Fort Worth, TX 76129 W. Thomas Smith, Exec.Dir.
Founded: 1922. **Staff:** 2. **Subjects:** Hymns and hymnology. **Holdings:** 3000 books. **Services:** Library open to the public for reference use only. **Publications:** The Hymn (magazine), quarterly - to members; The Stanza (newsletter), semiannual. **Remarks:** FAX: (817)921-7333. Part of the library is housed and accessible at the Union Theological Seminary, New York.

★7607★
J. Allen Hynek Center for UFO Studies - Information Center (Sci-Engr)
2457 W. Peterson Ave. Phone: (312)271-3611
Chicago, IL 60659 George M. Eberhart, Archv. & Ctr.Libn.
Founded: 1973. **Subjects:** Unidentified flying objects (UFOs), extraterrestrial life, space exploration and travel. **Special Collections:** UFO Reports and Photographs, 1900 to present; aerial and terrestrial phenomena; special files on investigations and evaluations. **Holdings:** 3000 volume equivalents; 10 file cabinets of unbound periodicals, news clippings, technical reports, articles and papers, private correspondence, tape recordings. **Subscriptions:** 50 journals and other serials. **Services:** Center open to qualified researchers on fee basis; telephone or write for further information.

★7608★
Hyster Company - Engineering Library (Sci-Engr)
2701 N.W. Vaughn, Suite 900 Phone: (503)721-6238
Portland, OR 97210 Jeanine Braaksma, Engr.Libn.
Founded: 1961. **Staff:** 1. **Subjects:** Material handling, metallurgy and welding, safety and design standards, automotive engineering. **Special Collections:** Manufacturers catalogs (1851); legal publications. **Holdings:** 2500 books; Society of Automotive Engineers papers; 20,500 engineering test reports; 6 shelves of archives. **Subscriptions:** 90 journals and other serials. **Services:** Interlibrary loan; library open to the public with restrictions. **Publications:** Library Bulletin, irregular. **Special Indexes:** Test reports (card). **Remarks:** FAX: (503)721-6001. Telex: 18-5999; 18-5904 Hyster.

I

★7609★
I.D. Group Inc. - Library (Sci-Engr)
905 Waverley St. Phone: (204)489-5900
Winnipeg, MB, Canada R3T 5P4 Mark Allen
Founded: 1955. **Staff:** Prof 1. **Subjects:** Civil and geotechnical engineering, environmental research. **Holdings:** 9000 titles. **Subscriptions:** 200 journals and other serials. **Services:** Interlibrary loan; copying; library open to the public with restrictions. **Computerized Information Services:** CAN/OLE. Performs searches on fee basis. **Remarks:** FAX: (204)453-9012.

★7610★
I Love a Clean San Diego County, Inc. - Environmental Resource Library (Env-Cons)
4901 Morena Blvd., Suite 703 Phone: (619)270-8393
San Diego, CA 92117 Kellie Deane, Env.Libn.
Founded: 1978. **Staff:** 1. **Subjects:** Environmental quality, legislation, energy, land use, solid and liquid waste management, recycling, conservation, resource recovery, bio-degradation, packaging and consumer issues, water quality and supply, air quality, wildlife, population, noise, gardening. **Holdings:** 600 books; 2000 handbooks, pamphlets; 44 VF drawers of reports, guidebooks, teaching materials; 50 videocassettes. **Subscriptions:** 30 journals and other serials; 60 newsletters. **Services:** Library open to the public. **Publications:** Eco-Logic (newsletter), quarterly - to members and elected officials. **Remarks:** FAX: (619)270-8449.

I Tatti Archive
See: **New York University - Institute of Fine Arts - Slide and Photographic Collection** (11724)

★7611★
IAO Research Centre Inc. - Research Library of Divine Sciences & the Healing Arts
P.O. Box 5265, Sta.A
Toronto, ON, Canada M5W 1N5
Founded: 1973. **Subjects:** Astrology, astronomy, metaphysical systems, divinatory sciences, myth and magic, healing, parapsychology. **Special Collections:** Astrology (240 linear feet); magic (24 linear feet); healing (24 linear feet); UFOs (24 linear feet); religions (50 linear feet); yoga (24 linear feet); metaphysics (50 linear feet); I Ching (8 linear feet); Qaballah (6 linear feet); birth data and diaries (24 linear feet); calendars and almanacs (24 linear feet). **Holdings:** 12,000 books; 5000 bound periodical volumes; 2000 slides and charts. **Remarks:** Currently inactive.

★7612★
(Ibadan) American Cultural Center - USIS Library (Educ)
DGC Enconsult House
Bodija
Private Mail Bag 5089
Ibadan, Nigeria
Remarks: Maintained or supported by the U.S. Information Agency. Focus is on materials that will assist peoples outside the United States to learn about the United States, its people, history, culture, political processes, and social milieux.

Ibero-Amerikanisches Institut
See: **Stiftung Preussischer Kulturbesitz** (15795)

★7613★
IBM Canada, Ltd. - Headquarters Library (Comp Sci)
31/917
3500 Steeles Ave., E. Phone: (416)946-2512
Markham, ON, Canada L3R 2Z1 Anne F. Martin, Libn.
Founded: 1982. **Staff:** Prof 1; Other 2. **Subjects:** General business management, computer science, office automation, information technology, personal computing. **Holdings:** Books; magazines; annual reports; IBM product literature; videotapes; slides; photographs; clipping files. **Subscriptions:** 100 journals and other serials; 5 newspapers. **Services:** Interlibrary loan; library not open to the public. **Computerized Information Services:** DIALOG Information Services, The Financial Post DataGroup, Infomart Online, Info Globe, NEXIS; CD-ROM; internal databases. **Publications:** Newsletter. **Remarks:** FAX: (416)474-2790.

★7614★
IBM Canada, Ltd. - Marketing Library (Comp Sci, Bus-Fin)
844 Don Mills Rd. Phone: (416)946-9000
North York, ON, Canada M3C 1V7 Marjorie Lauer, Mktg.Libn.
Founded: 1978. **Staff:** Prof 1; Other 1. **Subjects:** Computers, business, management. **Special Collections:** IBM documentation. **Holdings:** 2000 books; IBM product literature; videotapes; slide sets; clippings; audiocassettes; annual reports. **Subscriptions:** 135 journals and other serials. **Services:** Interlibrary loan; library not open to the public. **Computerized Information Services:** DIALOG Information Services, Info Globe, Infomart Online, The Financial Post DataGroup. **Publications:** Library Newsletter. **Remarks:** FAX: (416)443-4746. **Formerly:** Located in Don Mills, ON.

★7615★
IBM Canada, Ltd. - M&D Information Resource Centre (Comp Sci)
1150 Eglinton Ave., E. Phone: (416)448-3418
North York, ON, Canada M3C 1H7 Barbara Wallace, Libn.
Founded: 1969. **Staff:** Prof 1; Other 2. **Subjects:** Computer technology, management, programming, data communications. **Holdings:** 4000 books; IBM reports, standards, external reports on microfiche. **Subscriptions:** 150 journals and other serials; 10 newspapers. **Services:** Interlibrary loan; library not open to the public. **Automated Operations:** Computerized public access catalog. **Computerized Information Services:** DIALOG Information Services, BRS Information Technologies, Info Globe; internal databases. **Remarks:** FAX: (416)448-3545. **Formerly:** Its Lab Information Resource Centre.

★7616★
IBM Corporation - Almaden Research Center - Research Library (Sci-Engr, Comp Sci)
Dept. K74/802
650 Harry Rd. Phone: (408)927-1580
San Jose, CA 95120-6099 Vilia Ma, Mgr.
Founded: 1952. **Staff:** Prof 2; Other 2. **Subjects:** Chemistry, physics, computer science. **Holdings:** 23,000 books; 23,500 bound periodical volumes; 30,000 microfiche; 5400 uncatalogued IBM reorts. **Subscriptions:** 500 journals and other serials; 7 newspapers. **Services:** Interlibrary loan; library not open to the public. **Automated Operations:** Computerized cataloging, serials, and circulation. **Computerized Information Services:** DIALOG Information Services, BRS Information Technologies, STN International, Chemical Abstracts Service (CAS); IBM Technical Information Retrieval Center System (internal database). **Staff:** Beverley Clarke, Sr.Assoc.Info.Anl.; Lois Nakamura, Sr.Assoc.Info.Anl.

★7617★
IBM Corporation - Boulder Library (Sci-Engr, Comp Sci)
Dept. 419/022L
6300 Diagonal Hwy. Phone: (303)924-5064
Boulder, CO 80301 Judy O'Neill, Libn.
Founded: 1967. **Staff:** Prof 2. **Subjects:** Software development, programming, management. **Holdings:** 10,000 volumes; 100,000 microfiche. **Subscriptions:** 400 journals and other serials. **Services:** Interlibrary loan; SDI. **Automated Operations:** Computerized cataloging, acquisitions, serials, and circulation. **Computerized Information Services:** DIALOG Information Services, BRS Information Technologies; ITIRC (internal database); electronic mail service. **Publications:** Periodical Subscription Holdings; Library Guide to IBM Boulder. **Staff:** Barbara Landgren, Libn.

★7618★
IBM Corporation - Data Systems Division - MVH Kingston Technical Library Learning Center (Comp Sci)
Dept. 65P/687
Neighborhood Rd. Phone: (914)385-3698
Kingston, NY 12401 Joy G. Wofse, Contract Lib.Mgr.
Founded: 1956. **Staff:** Prof 1; Other 3. **Subjects:** Computer graphics, display technology, software/hardware development, electronics, physics, mathematics, chemistry. **Special Collections:** Self-study and computer-aided instruction course materials. **Holdings:** 13,000 books; 14,000 bound periodical volumes; 4000 technical reports; 124,000 microfiche. **Subscriptions:** 450 journals and other serials. **Services:** Interlibrary loan; copying; visitors may consult books and periodicals by appointment. **Automated Operations:** Computerized cataloging, acquisitions, serials, and circulation. **Computerized Information Services:** BRS Information Technologies, DIALOG Information Services, NEXIS, STN International, Dow Jones News/Retrieval; ITIRC (internal database). **Networks/Consortia:** Member of Southeastern New York Library Resources Council (SENYLRC). **Remarks:** Alternate telephone number(s): (914)385-3705. FAX: (914)385-1963. **Staff:** G. Michael Birzenieks, Libn.; Stephanie Morgan, Lrng.Ctr.

★ 7619 ★
IBM Corporation - Federal Systems Division - Avionics Systems - Library/Information Resource Center (Sci-Engr, Comp Sci)
Owego, NY 13827 Phone: (607)751-2725
J.T. Williams, Mgr.
Founded: 1951. **Staff:** Prof 1; Other 3. **Subjects:** Aeronautics and astronautics, computers, electronics and electronic equipment, mathematics, nuclear sciences, physics, psychology and human engineering, space sciences, management and administration, documentation and information retrieval. **Special Collections:** Clippings on plant history. **Holdings:** 10,000 books; 4500 bound periodical volumes; 45,000 technical reports; 3000 slides; 16 VF drawers of pamphlets; 225 videotapes; 55 computer diskettes. **Subscriptions:** 350 journals and other serials; 5 newspapers. **Services:** Interlibrary loan. **Automated Operations:** Computerized cataloging and circulation. **Computerized Information Services:** Online systems. **Publications:** Library Readings. **Special Indexes:** Cumulated KWIC indexes. **Remarks:** FAX: (607)751-5208. **Staff:** Patricia Haskins, Libn.

★ 7620 ★
IBM Corporation - General Technology Division - East Fishkill Facility - Library (Sci-Engr, Comp Sci)
Rte. 52 Phone: (914)892-0578
Hopewell Junction, NY 12533-6531 Karen A. Murley, Prog.Adm./Lib.Serv.
Founded: 1964. **Staff:** 2. **Subjects:** Electronics, computers, semiconductor technology and manufacturing. **Holdings:** 19,000 books; 8000 bound periodical volumes; 75,000 microforms. **Subscriptions:** 400 journals and other serials. **Services:** Interlibrary loan; library not open to the public. **Automated Operations:** Computerized cataloging. **Computerized Information Services:** DIALOG Information Services, BRS Information Technologies; ITIRC (internal database). **Publications:** Library News, monthly - for internal distribution only. **Remarks:** FAX: (914)894-7361.

★ 7621 ★
IBM Corporation - Information Resource Center/Library (Comp Sci, Sci-Engr)
Dept. 205, Hwy. 52 & 37th St., N.W. Phone: (507)253-0767
Rochester, MN 55901 Polly Frierson, Libn.
Staff: Prof 1; Other 3. **Subjects:** Programming, engineering, business, materials. **Special Collections:** Manufacturers' catalogs on microfilm (10,000). **Holdings:** 17,000 books; 1000 bound periodical volumes. **Subscriptions:** 550 journals and other serials. **Services:** Interlibrary loan. **Automated Operations:** Computerized cataloging, acquisitions, and circulation. **Computerized Information Services:** BRS Information Technologies, DIALOG Information Services, NewsNet, Inc., NEXIS, Dow Jones News/Retrieval; ITIRC (internal database). **Remarks:** FAX: (507)253-9362.

IBM Corporation - IP Technical Library
See: **Lexmark International, Inc. - Technical Library** (9095)

★ 7622 ★
IBM Corporation - Library/Information Center (Comp Sci, Sci-Engr)
Dept. 425, Bldg. 861
1000 River St. Phone: (802)769-0111
Essex Junction, VT 05452-4299 Donna Ovitt, Mgr.
Founded: 1965. **Staff:** Prof 3. **Subjects:** Computer science, chemistry, solid-state electronics, physics, programming, management science, mathematics. **Holdings:** 12,000 books; 1900 bound periodical volumes; 800 audio cassettes; 250,000 microfiche; 100 reels of microfilm; 25,000 IBM technical reports; 380 video cassettes. **Subscriptions:** 435 journals and other serials; 9 newspapers. **Services:** Interlibrary loan; center open to the public with restrictions. **Automated Operations:** Computerized cataloging, serials, and circulation. **Computerized Information Services:** BRS Information Technologies, Dow Jones News/Retrieval. **Special Catalogs:** Audio Cassette Listing. **Remarks:** FAX: (802)769-3726. **Staff:** Ron Gagner; Bob Pontbriand; Donna Ovitt.

★ 7623 ★
IBM Corporation - Library/Information Resource Center (Sci-Engr, Comp Sci)
Dept. 80L, B/908 Z/9819
11400 Burnet Rd. Phone: (512)838-1067
Austin, TX 78758 Pat Knudsen, Mgr.
Founded: 1967. **Staff:** Prof 1; Other 3. **Subjects:** Electrotechnology, computer science, telecommunications, management, human factors, communications. **Special Collections:** Information retrieval; technical education. **Holdings:** 11,000 books; 500 bound periodical volumes; 400 videotapes; 200 audio cassettes; 250,000 microfiche; 2000 reels of microfilm. **Subscriptions:** 400 journals, newsletters, and other serials; 15 newspapers. **Services:** Interlibrary loan; library not open to the public. **Automated Operations:** Computerized cataloging and acquisitions. **Computerized Information Services:** BRS Information Technologies, DIALOG Information Services, Dow Jones News/Retrieval; ITIRC (internal database); electronic mail service. **Special Catalogs:** Audiovisual catalog; periodical holdings. **Staff:** Ed Gillen, Tech.Libn.

★ 7624 ★
IBM Corporation - Manassas Technical Information Center (Comp Sci)
259/039
9500 Godwin Dr. Phone: (703)367-4922
Manassas, VA 22110 Michael Sheridan, Mgr.
Staff: Prof 1; Other 2. **Subjects:** Computer systems and technology; programming languages; signal processing; VLSI; electronics; sonar. **Holdings:** 3000 books; 2000 bound periodical volumes; 100 reports. **Subscriptions:** 375 journals and other serials; 10 newspapers. **Services:** Interlibrary loan; center not open to the public. **Automated Operations:** Computerized cataloging, acquisitions, serials, and circulation. **Computerized Information Services:** DIALOG Information Services, ORBIT Search Service, BRS Information Technologies; ITIRC (internal database). **Publications:** New acquisitions, monthly; Periodicals List, annual. **Staff:** Kay Paff, Staff Libn.

★ 7625 ★
IBM Corporation - MVH Library/Learning Center (Comp Sci)
Dept. A15/701
Box 950 Phone: (914)435-1024
Poughkeepsie, NY 12602 Joy G. Wofse, Contract Lib.Mgr.
Founded: 1957. **Staff:** Prof 2; Other 4. **Subjects:** Computer software and hardware technology, engineering. **Holdings:** 35,000 books; 15,000 bound periodical volumes. **Subscriptions:** 400 journals and other serials. **Services:** Interlibrary loan; library open to researchers with written permission of library manager. **Automated Operations:** Computerized cataloging, acquisitions, serials, and circulation. **Computerized Information Services:** BRS Information Technologies, DIALOG Information Services, Chemical Abstracts Service (CAS), NEXIS, STN International, Dow Jones News/Retrieval; ITIRC (internal database). **Remarks:** FAX: (914)435-1024. **Staff:** Quentin Packard, Libn.; Sarah Browne, Libn.

★ 7626 ★
IBM Corporation - Networking Systems - Library (Comp Sci, Info Sci)
Dept. 609/Bldg. 062
Box 12195 Phone: (919)543-1299
Research Triangle Park, NC 27709 Dorothy L. Huey, Tech.Libn.
Founded: 1965. **Staff:** 5. **Subjects:** Communications, telecommunications, computer science. **Holdings:** 11,500 books. **Subscriptions:** 425 journals and other serials. **Services:** Interlibrary loan; library not open to the public. **Formerly:** Its Communication Systems Division.

★ 7627 ★
IBM Corporation - Product Laboratory Library (Sci-Engr)
Dept. 192
Rte. 17C & Glendale Dr.
Box 225 Phone: (607)752-1456
Endicott, NY 13760 Eileen M. Deemie, Lib.Info.Ctr.Spec.
Founded: 1933. **Staff:** Prof 2; Other 3. **Subjects:** Mathematics, mechanics, electrical engineering, electronics, chemistry, computers, data processing, physics. **Holdings:** 15,000 books; 5000 bound periodical volumes. **Subscriptions:** 600 journals and other serials. **Services:** Interlibrary loan; library not open to the public. **Automated Operations:** Computerized serials and circulation. **Remarks:** FAX: (607)752-1506. **Formerly:** Its Systems Development Library. **Staff:** Joseph T. Dobransky, Libn.

★7628★
IBM Corporation - Programming Services Division - Santa Teresa Laboratory Library (Comp Sci)
555 Bailey Ave. Phone: (408)463-4050
San Jose, CA 95141 Nilene T. Finn, Libn.
Founded: 1975. **Staff:** Prof 1; Other 2. **Subjects:** Programming languages, software engineering, management, database systems, artificial intelligence, systems. **Holdings:** 6300 books; 1524 bound periodical volumes. **Subscriptions:** 274 journals and other serials; 13 newspapers; CD-ROM full-image journals. **Automated Operations:** Computerized public access catalog, cataloging, acquisitions, serials, and circulation. **Computerized Information Services:** DIALOG Information Services, BRS Information Technologies, Dow Jones News/Retrieval. **Remarks:** FAX: (408)463-3261.

★7629★
IBM Corporation - Storage Systems Products Division - Technical Library (Comp Sci)
Dept. 275, Bldg. 281
5600 Cottle Rd. Phone: (408)256-2908
San Jose, CA 95193 Ray Harding, Mgr.
Founded: 1961. **Staff:** Prof 1; Other 3. **Subjects:** Data processing, electronics, computers, chemistry, physics, mathematics, electrical engineering. **Holdings:** 15,000 books; 3000 bound periodical volumes. **Subscriptions:** 310 journals and other serials; 8 newspapers. **Services:** Library not open to the public. **Automated Operations:** Computerized cataloging, acquisitions, and circulation. **Computerized Information Services:** DIALOG Information Services, BRS Information Technologies, Information Handling Services (IHS), MEDLARS, STN International; ITIRC (internal database). **Networks/Consortia:** Member of CLASS. **Formerly:** Its General Products Division - Technical Library/Learning Center.

★7630★
IBM Corporation - T.J. Watson Research Center Library (Sci-Engr, Comp Sci)
Box 218 Phone: (914)945-1415
Yorktown Heights, NY 10598 Alice Lean, Mgr.
Founded: 1952. **Staff:** Prof 5; Other 5. **Subjects:** Physics, computer science, mathematics, engineering, chemistry. **Holdings:** 49,200 books; 33,000 bound periodical volumes; 5000 journals on microfilm. **Subscriptions:** 1750 journals and other serials. **Services:** Interlibrary loan; library open to the public by appointment. **Automated Operations:** Computerized public access catalog, serials, and circulation. **Computerized Information Services:** DIALOG Information Services, BRS Information Technologies, STN International; ITIRC (internal database). Telephone: 945-1289. **Networks/Consortia:** Member of SUNY/OCLC Library Network.

★7631★
IBM Corporation - Thornwood Information Resource Center (Comp Sci, Sci-Engr)
500 Columbus Ave. Phone: (914)742-5508
Thornwood, NY 10594 Scott Kostenbander, Mgr.
Founded: 1985. **Staff:** 3. **Subjects:** Computer science, telecommunications, manufacturing, quality. **Holdings:** 12,340 books; 612 bound periodical volumes; 1408 AV programs. **Subscriptions:** 545 journals and other serials. **Services:** Interlibrary loan; copying; SDI; library not open to the public. **Computerized Information Services:** BRS Information Technologies, DIALOG Information Services, Dow Jones News/Retrieval, Mead Data Central, STN International; ITIRC (internal database). **Publications:** Newsletter; guide to services. **Special Catalogs:** Video catalog; periodical holdings catalog. **Remarks:** FAX: (914)742-6016. **Staff:** Roberta Ferguson, Libn.

★7632★
IBM Corporation - United States Marketing & Services - Communications Library (Comp Sci)
1133 Westchester Ave.
White Plains, NY 10604 Phone: (914)642-6437
Staff: Prof 2; Other 1. **Subjects:** Automation, computers, data processing, information retrieval, business management, marketing. **Special Collections:** Complete file of IBM annual reports; complete library of IBM product publications. **Holdings:** 4000 books; films; product photographs and slides. **Subscriptions:** 450 journals and other serials. **Services:** Library not open to the public. **Computerized Information Services:** Online systems. **Special Indexes:** Chronological listing of IBM product announcements.

★7633★
IBM Corporation - U.S. Marketing & Services - Library (Comp Sci)
2 Riverway Phone: (713)940-2554
Houston, TX 77056 Rosie De La Cruz, Libn.
Founded: 1971. **Staff:** 1. **Subjects:** Electronic data processing, marketing, systems engineering. **Holdings:** 20,000 cataloged materials; 350 35mm slide sets; 150 video cassettes; 65 audiotapes. **Subscriptions:** 10 journals and other serials. **Services:** Library not open to the public. **Automated Operations:** Computerized circulation.

★7634★
Iceland - Building Research Institute - Library (Sci-Engr)
Keldnaholti Phone: 1 676000
IS-112 Reykjavik, Iceland Svanlaug Baldursdottir, Libn.
Founded: 1977. **Staff:** Prof 1. **Subjects:** Construction industry, concrete and cement, geology and geotechnology, roads, acoustics, ventilation. **Holdings:** 12,000 books. **Subscriptions:** 150 journals and other serials; 10 newspapers. **Services:** Interlibrary loan; copying; SDI; library open to the public. **Publications:** Acquisition list, monthly; Bibliography in the Annual Report of the Institute. **Remarks:** FAX: 1 678811.

★7635★
Iceland - The Library of Althingi (Bus-Fin, Soc Sci)
Althingi Phone: 1 11560
IS-150 Reykjavik, Iceland Larus Blondal
Founded: 1974. **Staff:** Prof 1. Other 2. **Subjects:** Public administration, economics, politics. **Holdings:** 28,500 books and bound periodical volumes. **Subscriptions:** 150 journals and other serials; 10 newspapers. **Services:** Library open to the public with restrictions. **Remarks:** FAX: 1 22274. **Staff:** Viggo Gislason.

Iceland - National Archives
See: **Thjodskjalasafn Islands** (16311)

★7636★
Iceland - National Energy Authority - Library (Sci-Engr)
Grensasvegi 9 Phone: 1 696000
IS-108 Reykjavik, Iceland Erla Sigthorsdottir, Libn.
Founded: 1967. **Staff:** Prof 1; Other 1. **Subjects:** Energy resources, geology, hydrology, geochemistry, geophysics, engineering geology. **Special Collections:** Research reports and reprints. **Holdings:** 11,000 books; 50 bound periodical volumes. **Subscriptions:** 200 journals and other serials. **Services:** Interlibrary loan; copying; SDI; library open to the public. **Remarks:** FAX: 1 688896. Telex: 2339 orkust is.

★7637★
Iceland - National Gallery of Iceland - Library (Art)
Frikirkjuvegi 7
P.O. Box 668 Phone: 1 62100
IS-121 Reykjavik, Iceland Audur Sigurdardottir, Libn.
Founded: 1950. **Staff:** Prof 1. **Subjects:** Icelandic art, art history, sculpture, pictorial arts. **Special Collections:** Icelandic art exhibition catalogs and newspaper clippings. **Holdings:** 2500 books; 36 meters of newspaper clippings; 11.25 meters of exhibition catalogs. **Subscriptions:** 60 journals and other serials; 5 newspapers. **Services:** Interlibrary loan; copying; library open to the public for reference use only. **Remarks:** FAX: 1 621312.

★7638★
Iceland - Technological Institute of Iceland - Library (Sci-Engr)
Keldnaholti Phone: 1 687000
IS-112 Reykjavik, Iceland Eydis Arnvidardottir, Libn.
Staff: Prof 1. **Subjects:** Materials technology, management, biotechnology, environmental science. **Holdings:** 6000 books; 4000 reports. **Subscriptions:** 150 journals and other serials; 2 newspapers. **Services:** Interlibrary loan; copying; library open to the public. **Remarks:** FAX: 1 687409.

★7639★
ICF Inc. - Library (Env-Cons)
9300 Lee Hwy. Phone: (703)934-3831
Fairfax, VA 22031-1207 Susan G. Press, Mgr., Lib.Serv.
Founded: 1969. **Staff:** Prof 3; Other 3. **Subjects:** Environment, health policy, energy, defense, economics, engineering. **Holdings:** 3000 books.

Subscriptions: 350 journals and other serials. **Services:** Interlibrary loan; copying; SDI; library open to the public by appointment. **Automated Operations:** Computerized cataloging. **Computerized Information Services:** DIALOG Information Services, MEDLARS, Dun & Bradstreet Business Credit Services, CIS, LEXIS, NEXIS, DataTimes, Ground Water On-Line, ORBIT Search Service, Numerica, National Pesticide Information Retrieval System (NPIRS), WESTLAW, BRS Information Technologies, STN International, Haver Analytics. Performs searches on fee basis. Contact Person: Mary D. Clark, Online Libn., (202)862-1161. **Networks/Consortia:** Member of CAPCON Library Network. **Remarks:** FAX: (703)934-9740.

★7640★
ICF Kaiser Engineers, Inc. - Engineering Library (Sci-Engr)
Box 23210 Phone: (510)419-5086
Oakland, CA 94623 Elaine Zacher, Tech.Libn.
Founded: 1951. **Staff:** Prof 1. **Subjects:** Engineering - civil, hydraulic, mechanical, mining and metallurgy, sanitary, structural. **Holdings:** 3500 books; 300 reports; 500 microfiche; 200 reels of microfilm. **Subscriptions:** 152 journals and other serials. **Services:** Interlibrary loan; copying; library open to the public by appointment. **Automated Operations:** Computerized serials. **Computerized Information Services:** DIALOG Information Services. **Remarks:** Library located at 1800 Harrison St., Oakland, CA 94612. FAX: (510)419-5355. Telex: 335326.

★7641★
ICI Americas Inc. - Atlas Library (Biol Sci, Sci-Engr)
P.O. Box 15365 Phone: (302)886-8232
Wilmington, DE 19897 Frieda S. Mecray, Libn.
Founded: 1913. **Staff:** Prof 4; Other 7. **Subjects:** Biomedicine, chemistry, chemical technology, business economics, pharmaceuticals. **Holdings:** 20,000 volumes; 25 VF drawers of trade catalogs; U.S. patents, 1964 to present, on microfilm; 108 titles on microfilm. **Subscriptions:** 1400 journals and other serials; 6 newspapers. **Services:** Interlibrary loan; copying; SDI; library open to local public on limited basis. **Automated Operations:** Computerized public access catalog, acquisitions, serials, and circulation. **Computerized Information Services:** DIALOG Information Services, ORBIT Search Service, STN International, NEXIS, Disclosure Incorporated, BRS Information Technologies, Data-Star. **Remarks:** FAX: (302)886-5369. **Staff:** Cathy Hornberger, Ref.Libn.; Sally Ledger; Linda Gabriel, Tech.Serv.

★7642★
ICI Americas Inc. - Process Technology Department Library (Sci-Engr)
333 Main St. Phone: (508)669-6731
Dighton, MA 02715 Mary Washburn
Staff: 1. **Subjects:** Organics, dyes, general chemistry. **Holdings:** 300 books; 280 bound periodical volumes. **Services:** Library open to the public by permission.

★7643★
ICI Americas Inc. - Western Research Center - Libraries (Sci-Engr)
1200 S. 47th St. Phone: (510)231-1020
Richmond, CA 94804 Linda Saylor, Supv., Info.Serv.
Staff: Prof 6; Other 4. **Subjects:** Chemistry, chemical engineering, agriculture, biological sciences, entomology, weed science. **Holdings:** 20,000 volumes; microforms; AV programs; patents. **Subscriptions:** 700 journals and other serials. **Services:** Library not open to the public. **Automated Operations:** Computerized cataloging and serials. **Computerized Information Services:** DIALOG Information Services, STN International, Questel, MEDLINE, Chemical Information Systems, Inc. (CIS), Occupational Health Services, Inc., NEXIS, National Pesticide Information Retrieval System (NPIRS). **Remarks:** Contains the holdings of its former Mountain View Research Center - Library. **Staff:** Insoo Chu, Sr.Tech.Info.Spec.; Joan Hishida, Sr.Tech.Info.Spec.; Ginger Guthrie, Tech.Rec.Spec.; Lynne Apostle, Libn.; Judy Warrick, Sr.Libn.

★7644★
ICI Autocolor - Research Laboratory - Technical Information Centre
1330 Castlefield Ave.
Toronto, ON, Canada M6B 4B3
Defunct.

★7645★
ICI Canada Inc. - Business Information Services (Sci-Engr)
90 Sheppard Ave., E.
P.O. Box 200, Sta. A Phone: (416)229-8047
North York, ON, Canada M2N 6H2 Jillian L. Ayres, Bus.Libn.
Founded: 1928. **Staff:** Prof 1; Other 1. **Subjects:** Chemical industry, management. **Holdings:** 2500 books; 1500 annual reports. **Subscriptions:** 200 journals and other serials; 6 newspapers. **Services:** Interlibrary loan; copying; SDI; services open to the public by appointment. **Computerized Information Services:** PFDS Online, DIALOG Information Services, Info Globe, STM Systems Corporation, Infomart Online, WILSONLINE, CAN/OLE. **Remarks:** FAX: (416)229-7752.

★7646★
ICI Canada Inc. - Sheridan Park Research Centre - Library (Sci-Engr)
2101 Hadwen Rd. Phone: (416)823-7160
Mississauga, ON, Canada L5K 2L3 Helen E. Marschall, Lib.Serv.Coord.
Founded: 1945. **Staff:** Prof 1; Other 1. **Subjects:** Chemistry, chemical engineering, agriculture, biotechnology, pulping and bleaching. **Holdings:** 3000 books; 4000 bound periodical volumes; 4 VF drawers of government reports; 25,000 Canadian, U.S., foreign patents; 1500 internal reports. **Subscriptions:** 150 journals and other serials. **Services:** Interlibrary loan; SDI. **Automated Operations:** Computerized public access catalog and cataloging. **Computerized Information Services:** PFDS Online, DIALOG Information Services, CAN/OLE, STN International, Canada Systems Group (CSG), Data-Star. **Networks/Consortia:** Member of Sheridan Park Association. **Remarks:** FAX: (416)823-0044. **Staff:** Tracy Morgan, Lib.Techn.

Idaho Geological Survey
See: **University of Idaho** (18650)

Idaho Health Information Retrieval Center
See: **St. Luke's Regional Medical Center - Medical Library** (14491)

Idaho Museum of Natural History
See: **Idaho State University - Idaho Museum of Natural History** (7654)

Idaho National Engineering Laboratory
See: **EG&G Idaho, Inc. - Idaho National Engineering Laboratory** (5268)

★7647★
Idaho (State) Historical Society - Genealogical Library (Hist)
450 N. 4th St. Phone: (208)334-2305
Boise, ID 83702 Gene Williams, Libn.
Founded: 1956. **Staff:** Prof 1; Other 2. **Subjects:** Genealogy. **Holdings:** 10,000 books; 600 bound periodical volumes; 2000 microfiche; 5000 microfilm. **Subscriptions:** 160 journals and other serials. **Services:** Copying; library open to the public for reference use only. **Automated Operations:** Computerized cataloging and acquisitions. **Computerized Information Services:** WLN LaserCat. **Special Indexes:** 1910 Idaho Census index; Ada County Cemetery records; Social Security Death Index; Idaho Death Certificates, 1911-1932. **Remarks:** Library located at 325 W. State St., Boise, ID 83702.

★7648★
Idaho (State) Historical Society - Library and Archives (Hist)
450 N. 4th St. Phone: (208)334-3356
Boise, ID 83702 Elizabeth P. Jacox, Libn.
Founded: 1907. **Staff:** Prof 5; Other 2. **Subjects:** Idaho - state government, irrigation, law, architecture, labor; genealogy; Pacific Northwest history. **Special Collections:** W.E. Borah manuscripts; J.H. Hawley manuscripts; Henry Dworshak manuscripts; Twin Falls Carey Act irrigation records; State Federation of Labor records; Boise-Cascade Lumber Company records; R.E. Smylie manuscripts; Orval Hansen manuscripts; Idaho Oral History Collection (700 hours of taped interviews). **Holdings:** 5000 books; 3200 bound periodical volumes; 1520 cubic feet of manuscripts; 4800 maps; 9600 cubic feet of Idaho State archives; 75,000 photographs; 7000 reels of microfilm; 60 cubic feet of vertical file material. **Subscriptions:** 100 journals and other serials; 68 newspapers. **Services:** Interlibrary loan (limited to microfilm); copying; library and archives open to the public. **Publications:** Idaho Yesterdays, quarterly - to members and by subscription; Reference Series, irregular; Idaho Historical Series, irregular; Mountain Light (newsletter), quarterly. **Special Catalogs:** Manuscripts and pictures (card); Oral History (card); Idaho Folklore Archives (card). **Staff:** William Tydeman, State Archv.; Thomas Jaehn, Archv.; Larry Jones, Hist.; M. Gary Bettis, Archv.

★7649★
Idaho State Law Library (Law, Hist)
Supreme Court Bldg.
451 W. State St. Phone: (208)334-3316
Boise, ID 83720 Laura M. Pershing, State Law Libn.
Founded: 1870. **Staff:** Prof 4; Other 6. **Subjects:** Law, Idaho history. **Holdings:** 112,000 volumes; 4 VF drawers of pamphlets; 37 drawers of microfiche; unbound periodicals; loose-leaf services. **Subscriptions:** 540 journals and other serials. **Services:** Copying; library open to the public. **Automated Operations:** Computerized cataloging. **Computerized Information Services:** LEXIS, WESTLAW; CD-ROM. Performs searches on fee basis. **Networks/Consortia:** Member of Western Library Network (WLN). **Remarks:** FAX: (208)334-4019. Maintained by Idaho State Supreme Court. **Staff:** Greg Ewing; Kristin Everson; Andrea Murray.

★7650★
Idaho State Library (Info Sci)
325 W. State St. Phone: (208)334-2150
Boise, ID 83702 Charles Bolles, State Libn.
Founded: 1901. **Staff:** Prof 20; Other 30. **Subjects:** Idaho and Pacific Northwest, library science, public administration. **Holdings:** 125,000 books; 5200 phonograph records and cassettes; 2500 films and videotapes; federal and state document depository. **Subscriptions:** 1100 journals and other serials. **Services:** Interlibrary loan; copying; library open to the public. **Automated Operations:** Computerized public access catalog, circulation, acquisitions, and ILL. **Computerized Information Services:** DIALOG Information Services, BRS Information Technologies; OnTyme Electronic Message Network Service, ALANET (electronic mail services). **Networks/Consortia:** Member of CLASS, Western Library Network (WLN), OCLC Pacific Network. **Publications:** Newsletter, monthly - to Idaho librarians and trustees; Idaho Library Directory; Idaho Library Laws; State Documents Checklist. **Special Catalogs:** Film and video catalog, biennial - to Idaho librarians. **Remarks:** FAX: (208)334-4016.

★7651★
Idaho State Library - Regional Library for the Blind and Physically Handicapped (Aud-Vis)
325 W. State St. Phone: (208)334-2117
Boise, ID 83702 Kay Salmon, Reg.Libn.
Founded: 1973. **Staff:** Prof 1; Other 12. **Special Collections:** Books by Idaho authors and books about Idaho recorded on cassette (420). **Holdings:** 184,000 talking books. **Subscriptions:** 43 journals and other serials; 3 newspapers. **Services:** Interlibrary loan; copying; library open to the public. **Automated Operations:** Computerized circulation. **Computerized Information Services:** READS (Reader Enrollment and Delivery System; internal database). **Networks/Consortia:** Member of National Library Service for the Blind & Physically Handicapped (NLS). **Special Catalogs:** Large Print Catalog (book); Volunteer Recorded Books Catalog (book). **Remarks:** FAX: (208)334-4016. An alternate telephone number is 334-2150.

Idaho State Supreme Court - Idaho State Law Library
See: **Idaho State Law Library** (7649)

★7652★
Idaho (State) Transportation Department - Library (Trans)
Box 7129 Phone: (208)334-8021
Boise, ID 83707-1129 Pat Marler
Founded: 1975. **Staff:** 1. **Subjects:** Transportation. **Holdings:** 3000 volumes. **Services:** Library not open to the public. **Remarks:** Library is located at 3311 W. State St., Boise, ID 83703. FAX: (208)334-3858.

★7653★
Idaho State University - College of Education - Instructional Materials Center (Educ)
Pocatello, ID 83209 Phone: (208)236-2652
Joan K. Downing, Dir.
Founded: 1953. **Staff:** Prof 1; Other 1. **Subjects:** Textbooks in all subjects, kindergarten through grade 12; professional books; children's literature; curriculum guides; vendor catalogs. **Special Collections:** Multicultural collections. **Holdings:** 18,800 books; service bulletins; AV programs; media reference materials. **Subscriptions:** 18 journals and other serials. **Services:** Instructional materials production area and teaching simulation laboratory for student teachers, education students, and other professional educators; center open to the public. **Automated Operations:** Computerized public access catalog. **Computerized Information Services:** DIALOG Information Services. **Remarks:** FAX: (208)236-4300.

★7654★
Idaho State University - Idaho Museum of Natural History - Stirton-Kelson Library (Sci-Engr, Biol Sci)
Box 8096 Phone: (208)236-3317
Pocatello, ID 83209-0009 Regina Szymansky, Pubns.Mgr.
Founded: 1960. **Staff:** Prof 1; Other 1. **Subjects:** Paleontology, anthropology, biology, geology, herbitology. **Special Collections:** Stirton collection of paleontological publications; Kelson collection of anthropological and paleontological publications. **Holdings:** 750 books; 2150 bound periodical volumes; 600 other cataloged items. **Subscriptions:** 34 journals and other serials; 5 newspapers. **Services:** Interlibrary loan; library not open to the public. **Publications:** Tebiwa (journal), irregular; occasional papers of the Idaho Museum of Natural History; special publications, irregular. **Remarks:** FAX: (208)236-4000.

★7655★
Idaho Statesman - Library (Publ)
1200 N. Curtis Rd.
Box 40 Phone: (208)377-6435
Boise, ID 83707 Karen Reynolds, Chf.Libn.
Founded: 1972. **Staff:** Prof 1; Other 3. **Subjects:** Newspaper reference topics. **Holdings:** 500 books; 300,000 newspaper clippings; 150,000 negatives; 25,000 photographs. **Subscriptions:** 10 journals and other serials; 30 newspapers. **Services:** Library not open to the public; performs research services on a limited basis. **Computerized Information Services:** DIALOG Information Services, VU/TEXT Information Services, Gannett News Service. **Remarks:** FAX: (208)377-6449. Telex: 377-6449. Maintained by Gannett Newspapers. **Staff:** Peter Jacobson; Torra Fort; Michelle Jensen.

Idaho Water Resources Research Institute
See: **University of Idaho** (18651)

★7656★
Ideamatics, Inc. - Library (Energy)
1806 T St., N.W. Phone: (202)667-9495
Washington, DC 20009 Will Skowronski
Founded: 1975. **Subjects:** Energy, telecommunications. **Holdings:** 150 books; 1000 bound periodical volumes; 200 reports. **Services:** Interlibrary loan; library not open to the public. **Remarks:** FAX: (202)667-9498.

Ides Law and Reference Library
See: **Illinois (State) Department of Employment Security** (7688)

★7657★
IDS Financial Services - Investment Library (Bus-Fin)
IDS Tower - 10 Phone: (612)671-3429
Minneapolis, MN 55440 Ann Becker
Founded: 1940. **Staff:** 7. **Subjects:** Investments. **Holdings:** 800 titles; corporation files on 3500 companies. **Subscriptions:** 300 journals and other serials; 6 newspapers. **Services:** Library open to the public for reference use only by appointment. **Computerized Information Services:** Dow Jones News/Retrieval, DIALOG Information Services. **Remarks:** FAX: (612)671-2262.

★7658★
IFI/Plenum Data Company - Library (Sci-Engr)
302 Swann Ave. Phone: (703)683-1085
Alexandria, VA 22301 Harry M. Allcock, V.P.
Founded: 1955. **Staff:** Prof 23; Other 10. **Subjects:** Chemistry, mechanics, electronics. **Special Collections:** U.S. Chemical Patent Index, 1950 to present; U.S. Mechanical and Electrical Patent Bibliographic Data Collection, 1963. **Holdings:** Figures not available. **Subscriptions:** 24 journals and other serials. **Services:** Copying; SDI; library open to the public with restrictions. **Automated Operations:** Computerized indexing. **Computerized Information Services:** Online systems. **Special Indexes:** Uniterm Index to U.S. Chemical Patents-Magnetic Tape. **Remarks:** FAX: (703)683-0246. Telex: 901 834. Maintained by IFI/Plenum Publishing Corporation. **Staff:** Rick Myrick, Gen.Mgr.; Darlene Slaughter, Tech.Supv.; David Young, Mgr., Comp.Sys.

★7659★
IIMI - Information Center (Soc Sci)
4205 K St.
Philadelphia, PA 19124 Albert C. Vara, Libn.
Founded: 1970. **Staff:** Prof 1; Other 1. **Subjects:** Marketing; food research; job location for ex-convicts, parolees, and former addicts; natural family planning; parenteral nutrition; population studies. **Special Collections:** Cocaine use in persons on methadone maintenance. **Holdings:** 2005 books; 50 bound periodical volumes; 1115 reports; 6 VF drawers of documents and reports. **Subscriptions:** 14 journals and other serials. **Services:** Center not open to the public. **Computerized Information Services:** DIALOG Information Services, OCLC, RLIN, ABI/INFORM, ERIC. Performs searches on fee basis. **Publications:** Current Contents (newsletter) - for internal distribution only. **Special Indexes:** Inquirer Index; AIDS-related bibliographies. **Staff:** Trieste Sbraqua, Asst.Libn.

★7660★
IIT Research Institute - Electromagnetic Compatibility Analysis Center (Sci-Engr, Comp Sci)
185 Admiral Cochrane Dr. Phone: (410)573-7075
Annapolis, MD 21401-7388 Katherine E. A. Sorci, Mgr.
Founded: 1961. **Subjects:** Electromagnetic compatibility, radio frequency interference, RF communications systems, optical communication systems, radar systems, spectrum engineering, wave propagation, communications systems modeling. **Special Collections:** Complete library of spectrum signatures; all Department of Defense frequency allocation applications. **Holdings:** 7000 books; 45,000 technical reports; 12,000 military and commercial equipment manuals; 30,000 microfiche of research and development reports; 10,000 standards and specifications; back issues of periodicals, bound and in microform. **Subscriptions:** 400 journals and other serials. **Services:** Interlibrary loan; other services not open to the public. **Automated Operations:** Computerized public access catalog, cataloging, serials, acquisitions, and circulation. **Computerized Information Services:** DTIC, DIALOG Information Services, OCLC, NASA/RECON, FAR Online, PERISCOPE, U.S. Bureau of Labor Statistics (BLS); internal database. **Networks/Consortia:** Member of Interlibrary Users Association (IUA), FEDLINK. **Publications:** ECAC Info Center Bulletin, monthly - for internal distribution only; ECAC Quarterly Report Bulletin - for Department of Defense distribution only. **Remarks:** FAX: (410)573-7296. **Also Known As:** U.S. Electromagnetic Compatibility Analysis Center.

★7661★
IIT Research Institute - Guidance and Control Information Analysis Center (GACIAC) (Sci-Engr)
10 W. 35th St. Phone: (312)567-4519
Chicago, IL 60616 Dr. Robert J. Heaston, Dir.
Founded: 1977. **Staff:** Prof 4; Other 2. **Subjects:** Tactical weapons, guidance and control systems for missiles, rockets, projectiles, and bombs. **Special Collections:** Tactical Weapons Guidance and Control Collection (10,000 technical reports, conference proceedings, journal articles). **Holdings:** 10,000 hardcopy and microfiche items. **Services:** Center not open to the public. **Computerized Information Services:** GACIAC (internal database of over 35,000 citations). Performs searches on fee basis. **Publications:** GACIAC Bulletin, bimonthly; handbooks; proceedings; special reports; state of the art reviews; technology assessments; GACIAC Bibliography; Annual Demand Bibliographies. **Remarks:** FAX: (312)567-4889. **Staff:** Vakare K. Valaitis, Info.Sci.

★7662★
IIT Research Institute - Library & Information Center
10 W. 35th St.
Chicago, IL 60616
Defunct.

★7663★
IIT Research Institute - Manufacturing Technology Information Analysis Center (Sci-Engr, Comp Sci)
10 W. 35th St. Phone: (800)421-0586
Chicago, IL 60616 Michal Safar, Dir.
Founded: 1984. **Staff:** Prof 4; Other 2. **Subjects:** Electronics, computer-aided design/computer-aided manufacture (CAD/CAM), metals, nonmetals, inspection and testing, munitions. **Holdings:** 10,000 technical reports. **Subscriptions:** 81 journals and other serials. **Services:** Center open to the public by appointment on a fee basis. **Automated Operations:** Computerized acquisitions. **Computerized Information Services:** DIALOG Information Services, BRS Information Technologies, PFDS Online; SIMON, Mantech Data Base, Manufacturing Technology Bibliographic Data Base (internal databases); electronic mail. Performs searches on fee basis. **Publications:** MTIAC Current Awareness Bulletin, quarterly; technology assessments; handbooks; state-of-the-art reviews; Directory of Manufacturing Research Centers. **Remarks:** MTIAC's objective is to collect, analyze, and disseminate information on the characteristics and utilization of manufacturing technology for the production of defense materials. FAX: (312)567-4736. **Staff:** Bruce McGregor, Info.Spec.; Joel Pacheco, Tech.Coord.; Dr. Keith McKee, Tech.Adv.

★7664★
IIT Research Institute - Reliability Analysis Center (Sci-Engr)
P.O. Box 4700 Phone: (315)337-0900
Rome, NY 13440-8200 Debbie Canning, Libn.
Founded: 1968. **Staff:** Prof 15; Other 20. **Subjects:** Microcircuit, discrete semiconductor, electronic systems, and nonelectric part reliability, maintainability, and technology. **Holdings:** 400 books; 5000 bound periodical volumes; 15,000 other cataloged items; reliability data; 3 drawers of Government Industry Data Exchange Program microfilm files. **Services:** Consulting services and search services; center open to the public on fee basis. **Computerized Information Services:** Internal databases. **Publications:** List of publications - available on request. **Remarks:** The Reliability Analysis Center has been established as a U.S. Department of Defense Information Analysis Center for the collection, analysis, and dissemination of reliability and experience information. It features an analysis capability, producing output engineering information from raw input data.

★7665★
Ikebana International - Library (Art)
1-6 Kanda Surugadai, Chiyoda-ku Phone: 33 293-8188
Tokyo 101, Japan Keiko Ohta
Founded: 1956. **Subjects:** Ikebana (Japanese flower arranging). **Holdings:** Figures not available.

★7666★
Iliff School of Theology - Ira J. Taylor Library (Rel-Phil)
2233 S. University Blvd. Phone: (303)744-1287
Denver, CO 80210-4796 Sara J. Myers, Dir.
Founded: 1892. **Staff:** Prof 3; Other 5. **Subjects:** Bible, Christian history and missions, philosophy of religion, Christian theology and ethics, religious education, parish ministry, sociology of religion, psychology of religion, counseling, women and religion. **Special Collections:** Hymnals (750, covering many denominations); church histories of the Methodist Rocky Mountain Conference; denominational histories of the Rocky Mountain area. **Holdings:** 166,400 volumes; 380 linear feet of archival materials; 37,000 microforms; 2270 cassette tapes; 218 reel-to-reel tapes of sermons. **Subscriptions:** 900 journals and other serials; 7 newspapers. **Services:** Interlibrary loan; copying; library open to the public. **Automated Operations:** computerized cataloging and ILL. **Computerized Information Services:** OCLC. **Networks/Consortia:** Member of Bibliographical Center for Research, Rocky Mountain Region, Inc. (BCR), Colorado Alliance of Research Libraries (CARL). **Remarks:** FAX: (303)777-3387. **Staff:** Alice Runis, Tech.Serv.Libn.; Paul Millette, Cat. & Archv.Libn.

Mary Illick Memorial Library
See: **Northampton County Historical and Genealogical Society** (11963)

★7667★
Illini-Franciscan Healthcare Information Service - Library (Med)
801 Hospital Rd. Phone: (309)792-4360
Silvis, IL 61282-1804 Priscilla Swatos, Coord., Hea.Info.Serv.
Founded: 1980. **Staff:** Prof 1; Other 2. **Subjects:** Clinical medicine, health care management. **Special Collections:** Medical liabilities and malpractice; burn care; psychiatry and mental health services collection; geriatric mental health and elder abuse; health care quality assurance. **Holdings:** 3000 books. **Subscriptions:** 225 journals and other serials; 3 newspapers. **Services:** Interlibrary loan; copying; SDI; library open to the public. **Computerized Information Services:** DIALOG Information Services, WILSONLINE, MEDLARS, OCLC; DOCLINE (electronic mail service). Performs searches. Contact Person: Barb Tharp, Lib.Asst. **Networks/Consortia:** Member of Quad City Area Biomedical Consortium. **Remarks:** FAX: (309)792-4362. Electronic mail address(es): LIBID 61282A (DOCLINE); VCF, FM2 (OCLC). **Formed by the merger of:** Illini Hosptal - Health Sciences Library and Franciscan Medical Center - Jordan Library.

Illini Hospital - Health Sciences Library
See: **Illini-Franciscan Healthcare Information Service** (7667)

★7668★
Illinois Agricultural Association - Illinois Farm Bureau Library (Agri)
1701 Towanda Ave.
Box 2901 Phone: (309)557-2552
Bloomington, IL 61701 Rue E. Olson, Dir. of Lib.Serv.
Founded: 1957. **Staff:** Prof 2; Other 4. **Subjects:** Agriculture - economics, marketing, cooperatives, management, insurance. **Special Collections:** Alternative sources of energy. **Holdings:** 14,000 volumes; 900 reels of microfilm; 20,000 microfiche. **Subscriptions:** 500 journals and other serials; 8 newspapers. **Services:** Interlibrary loan; copying; abstracting; library open to the public for reference use only. **Automated Operations:** Computerized cataloging and serials. **Computerized Information Services:** DIALOG Information Services, VU/TEXT Information Services, WILSONLINE, NEXIS, OCLC; CD-ROMs. Performs searches on fee basis. Contact Person: Vince Sampson, Ref./Res.Mgr., 557-2551. **Networks/Consortia:** Member of ILLINET. **Publications:** New Publications List, monthly - for internal distribution only. **Special Indexes:** Thesaurus covering collection's subject matter (typed list). **Remarks:** FAX: (309)557-3185.

★7669★
Illinois Bell Telephone Company - Reference Library (Bus-Fin, Info Sci)
225 W. Randolph St., HQ 20-D Phone: (312)727-9411
Chicago, IL 60606 Ruby Cooper
Founded: 1927. **Staff:** Prof 1. **Subjects:** Business management, technology, telephone industry and history. **Special Collections:** Microfilm collection of documents and photographs on the history of the telephone and Illinois Bell Telephone Company; telephone journals. **Holdings:** 18,000 volumes. **Subscriptions:** 63 journals and other serials. **Services:** Interlibrary loan; copying; library open to employees only.

★7670★
Illinois Benedictine College - Theodore Lownik Library (Rel-Phil)
5700 College Rd. Phone: (708)960-1500
Lisle, IL 60532-0900 Bert A. Thompson, Dir., Lib.Serv.
Founded: 1887. **Staff:** Prof 4; Other 12. **Subjects:** Theology, science. **Special Collections:** Lincolniana; rare book collection; Czech Heritage collection; college archives. **Holdings:** 152,080 volumes; 10,513 AV programs; 40 linear feet of corporate annual reports; 35,000 government documents; 14,196 microforms; 32 VF drawers. **Subscriptions:** 903 journals. **Services:** Interlibrary loan; copying; library open to the public with restrictions. **Automated Operations:** Computerized cataloging and circulation. **Computerized Information Services:** DIALOG Information Services. Performs searches on fee basis. Contact Person: Bert A. Thompson, Dir. **Networks/Consortia:** Member of LIBRAS Inc., Suburban Library System (SLS), ILLINET. **Special Catalogs:** SLS/LIBRAS Union List of Serials (printout); catalog of AV sources. **Remarks:** FAX: (708)960-1126. **Staff:** Mark A. Kroll, Tech.Serv.Libn.; Joan M. Hopkins, Coll.Dev.Libn.; Anton W. Schragel, AV Spec.; Marg L. Caron, Circ.

The Illinois Career Information System
See: **Horizons (The Illinois Career Information System)** (7410)

★7671★
Illinois College of Optometry - Carl F. Shepard Memorial Library (Med)
3241 S. Michigan Ave. Phone: (312)225-1700
Chicago, IL 60616 Gerald Dujsik, Dir., Lrng.Rsrcs.
Founded: 1955. **Staff:** Prof 6; Other 2. **Subjects:** Optometry, vision, vision malfunctions, optics, perception, eye diseases. **Special Collections:** Senior Research Projects. **Holdings:** 19,377 books; 4617 bound periodical volumes; 2129 pamphlets and theses; 748 AV programs; 750 microforms. **Subscriptions:** 245 journals and other serials. **Services:** Interlibrary loan; copying; library open to the public for reference use only. **Automated Operations:** Computerized public access catalog, cataloging, serials, and circulation. **Computerized Information Services:** DIALOG Information Services, NLM, OCLC. **Networks/Consortia:** Member of National Network of Libraries of Medicine - Greater Midwest Region, Metropolitan Consortium of Chicago. **Publications:** Acquisitions list, quarterly. **Special Indexes:** VAL (Vision Articles Online). **Remarks:** FAX: (312)791-1970. **Staff:** Peter E. Weil, Tech.Serv.Libn.; Sandra Engram, Pub.Serv.Libn.; Laurie Curtis, Pub.Serv.Libn.; Al Pouch, Media Prod.Mgr.; Tom Brady, Media Spec.

★7672★
Illinois Commerce Commission - Technical Information Center (Energy)
527 E. Capitol
P.O. Box 19280 Phone: (217)524-5054
Springfield, IL 62794-9280 Christine Westerlund, Libn.
Founded: 1981. **Staff:** Prof 1. **Subjects:** Public utilities, transportation, economics, finance, regulation. **Holdings:** 1200 books; 150 reports. **Subscriptions:** 180 journals and other serials; 25 newspapers. **Services:** Interlibrary loan; copying; center open to the public by appointment. **Computerized Information Services:** LEXIS, NEXIS; CrossTalk Forum (electronic mail service). **Remarks:** FAX: (217)524-0674.

★7673★
Illinois Early Childhood Intervention Clearinghouse (Med)
830 S. Spring St. Phone: (217)785-1364
Springfield, IL 62704 Chet Brandt, Proj.Dir.
Founded: 1986. **Staff:** Prof 1; Other 1.5. **Subjects:** Early childhood, at-risk children, developmental disabilities. **Holdings:** 2500 books; 200 videocassettes. **Subscriptions:** 200 journals and other serials. **Services:** Interlibrary loan; copying; clearinghouse open to Illinois residents. **Automated Operations:** PRO-CITE. **Networks/Consortia:** Member of Rolling Prairie Library System (RPLS), ILLINET, Capital Area Consortium (CAC). **Publications:** Early Intervention (newsletter), quarterly - free upon request; Clearinghouse Bibliography Series. **Remarks:** Toll-free telephone number(s): (800)852-4302 (Illinois only). FAX: (217)524-5339. Sponsored by the Illinois Public Health Association and affiliated with the Illinois State Board of Education.

Illinois Historical Survey
See: **University of Illinois** (18678)

★7674★
Illinois Institute of Technology - Chicago Kent Law School - Library (Law)
565 W. Adams Phone: (312)906-5600
Chicago, IL 60661 Prof. Mickie Voges Piatt, Dir., Leg.Info.Ctr.
Staff: Prof 7; Other 11. **Subjects:** Federal and Illinois law; law and aging; international relations law. **Holdings:** 309,000 books; 90,000 bound periodical volumes; 200,000 Congressional Information Service hearings and reports; 6500 state session laws; Library of International Relations materials; U.S. Government documents. **Subscriptions:** 6300 journals and other serials; 7 newspapers. **Services:** Interlibrary loan; copying; faxing; library open to the public. **Automated Operations:** Computerized cataloging. **Computerized Information Services:** LEXIS, NEXIS, WESTLAW, DIALOG Information Services; BITNET (electronic mail service). **Remarks:** FAX: (312)906-5685. **Staff:** Richard Gibson, Assoc.Dir. of Law Lib.; Helmut Reiter, Hd.Cat.; Yoon Park, Asst.Cat.; Lenore Glanz, Ref.; John Strzynski, Intl. Law Libn.; Lucy Moss, Ref.

★7675★
Illinois Institute of Technology - Paul V. Galvin Library (Plan, Sci-Engr)
35 W. 33rd St. Phone: (312)567-6844
Chicago, IL 60616 Sohair Elaz, Act.Dir. of Libs.
Founded: 1892. **Staff:** Prof 11; Other 19. **Subjects:** Architecture, design, engineering, computer science, science, technology. **Special Collections:** Fire protection engineering. **Holdings:** 200,000 books; 300,000 bound periodical volumes; annual reports; dissertations; 100,000 depository documents; Defense Mapping Agency depository; Government Printing Office depository. **Subscriptions:** 2500 journals and other serials; 16 newspapers. **Services:** Interlibrary loan; library open to the public. **Automated Operations:** Computerized cataloging, acquisitions, serials, circulation, and ILL. **Computerized Information Services:** DIALOG Information Services, OCLC, Illinois State Library; internal database; Faxon Courier (electronic mail service). **Networks/Consortia:** Member of ILLINET, Chicago Library System. **Publications:** Library Handbook; Serial Publications Held in IIT Libraries. **Remarks:** FAX: (312)567-3955. **Staff:** Anita Anderson, Ref.; Helen Gbala, Monographs; Nancy Roberts, Docs.; Linda Jayes, Ser.

★7676★
Illinois Institute of Technology - Pritzker Institute of Medical Engineering - Library (Med, Sci-Engr)
10 W. 32nd St. Phone: (312)567-5324
Chicago, IL 60616 Cathie D'Amico, Dept.Adm.
Founded: 1981. **Subjects:** Engineering, physiology, medicine. **Holdings:** 500 volumes. **Remarks:** FAX: (312)567-5707.

★7677★
Illinois Masonic Medical Center - Medical Library (Med)
836 W. Wellington Ave., Rm. 7501 Phone: (312)296-5083
Chicago, IL 60657 Ann Markham, Mgr., Lib.Serv.
Founded: 1963. **Staff:** Prof 1; Other 3. **Subjects:** Health sciences. **Holdings:** 4500 books; bound periodical volumes. **Subscriptions:** 300 journals and other serials. **Services:** Interlibrary loan; copying; library open to the public for reference use only. **Computerized Information Services:** NLM, OCLC, BRS Information Technologies, MEDLARS; DOCLINE (electronic mail service). Performs searches free of charge for in-house users only. **Networks/Consortia:** Member of Metropolitan Consortium of Chicago, ILLINET, National Network of Libraries of Medicine - Greater Midwest Region, Chicago Library System. **Publications:** Update, quarterly - for internal distribution only. **Remarks:** FAX: (312)296-7421.

Illinois Occupational Information Coordinating Committee - Horizons
See: **Horizons (The Illinois Career Information System)** (7410)

Illinois Oral History Clearinghouse
See: **Sangamon State University - Archives - Oral History Collection** (14791)

Illinois Public Health Association - Illinois Early Childhood Intervention Clearinghouse
See: **Illinois Early Childhood Intervention Clearinghouse** (7673)

★7678★
Illinois Railway Museum - Technical Library (Hist, Trans)
Box 431 Phone: (815)923-4391
Union, IL 60180 James E. Kehrein, Libn.
Founded: 1974. **Staff:** 2. **Subjects:** Railroad technology and history, steam locomotive technology, electric railroads, diesel locomotives. **Special Collections:** Pullman Company Collection (75,000 blueprints and linen tracings); Railway Educational Bureau Collection (1000 books; 100 blueprints); T-Z Railway Equipment Company Collection (2000 blueprints); Brewster Company Blueprint Collection (500 blueprints). **Holdings:** 2500 books; 3500 blueprints; bound periodical volumes; pamphlets; maps; photographs. **Services:** Library open to the public with restrictions. **Automated Operations:** Computerized cataloging.

★7679★
Illinois Resource Center/Adult Resource Center Library - Library (Educ)
1855 Mt. Prospect Rd. Phone: (708)803-3535
Des Plaines, IL 60018 Richard H. Peiser, Cat./Libn.
Founded: 1972. **Staff:** Prof 1; Other 1. **Subjects:** English as a second language; bilingual, vocational, literacy, and citizenship education; refugee assistance; cross-cultural studies. **Holdings:** 25,000 volumes. **Subscriptions:** 50 journals and other serials. **Services:** Interlibrary loan; copying; library open to the public with restrictions. **Computerized Information Services:** Internal database. Performs searches free of charge. **Networks/Consortia:** Member of North Suburban Library System (NSLS). **Publications:** Recommended Adult ESL Bibliography; specialized bibliographies (computer-generated) - for sale. **Remarks:** FAX: (708)803-3231. **Formerly:** Northwest Educational Cooperative - Library.

★7680★
Illinois School for the Deaf - Media Center (Educ, Aud-Vis)
125 Webster Phone: (217)245-5141
Jacksonville, IL 62650 Randy Burge, Media Ctr.Dir.
Staff: Prof 5; Other 4. **Subjects:** Deafness and deaf education, curriculum supporting AV programs, high interest/low vocabulary materials, audiology, children's and adult books. **Special Collections:** Captioned films (1700); ISD Historical Picture File (700 photographs). **Holdings:** 15,000 books; 560 bound periodical volumes; 21,500 nonprint materials; 42 boxes of pamphlets. **Subscriptions:** 51 journals and other serials; 8 newspapers. **Services:** Interlibrary loan; center open to the public with restrictions. **Networks/Consortia:** Member of Great River Library System (GRLS). **Publications:** Sights and Sounds, 3/year - for internal distribution only; Captioned Films Region 4 Newsletter, monthly - to regional and film library managers; HINOTES (newsletter), quarterly. **Staff:** Mary Metcalf, Lib.Serv.Mgr.; Dave Adams, TV Coord.; Carole Hack, AV Serv.Mgr.; Lana Shea, Comp.Spec.; Georgia Elias, Captioned Film Coord.

★7681★
Illinois School for the Visually Impaired - Library (Educ, Aud-Vis)
658 E. State St. Phone: (217)245-4101
Jacksonville, IL 62650 Barbara J. Jenkins, Libn.Assoc.
Staff: Prof 1; Other 2. **Subjects:** Blindness, education, child psychology, exceptional children, medicine, social work. **Holdings:** 15,290 books; 166 bound periodical volumes; 192 filmstrips; 96 videocassettes; 450 tactile items; pamphlets; unbound periodicals; tapes; scrapbooks; braille, talking, large print, cassette books; phonograph records. **Subscriptions:** 96 journals and other serials. **Services:** Interlibrary loan; copying; library open to the visually handicapped.

★7682★
Illinois State Appellate Court, 3rd District - Library (Law)
1004 Columbus St. Phone: (815)434-5050
Ottawa, IL 61350 Sharon Smith, Libn.
Staff: 1. **Subjects:** Law. **Holdings:** 15,000 volumes, including journals of 7 Chicago area law schools. **Subscriptions:** 3 newspapers. **Services:** Copying; library open to the public for reference use only.

★7683★
Illinois State Appellate Court, 5th District - Library (Law)
14th & Main Sts. Phone: (618)242-6414
Mt. Vernon, IL 62864 James Sanders, Res.Dir.
Subjects: Law and government. **Holdings:** 11,553 volumes. **Services:** Interlibrary loan; library open to the public. **Staff:** Janet Aydt, Libn.

Illinois State Archives
See: **Illinois (State) Office of the Secretary of State** (7703)

Illinois (State) Board of Education - East Central Network for Curriculum Coordination
See: **Sangamon State University - East Central Network for Curriculum Coordination** (14793)

Illinois State Board of Education - Illinois Early Childhood Intervention Clearinghouse
See: **Illinois Early Childhood Intervention Clearinghouse** (7673)

Illinois State Bureau of the Budget
See: **Illinois State Data Center** (7685)

★7684★
Illinois (State) Criminal Justice Information Authority - Library (Law)
120 S. Riverside Plaza, Ste. 1016 Phone: (312)793-8901
Chicago, IL 60606 Jeff Travis, Res.Anl./Libn.
Founded: 1986. **Staff:** Prof 1. **Subjects:** Criminal justice, technical information. **Holdings:** 5750 volumes; 184 bound periodical volumes; 400 reports; 42 videotapes. **Subscriptions:** 86 journals and other serials; 10 newspapers. **Services:** Library not open to the public. **Automated Operations:** Computerized cataloging. **Remarks:** FAX: (312)793-8422.

★7685★
Illinois State Data Center (Soc Sci)
Illinois Bureau of the Budget
605 Stratton Bldg. Phone: (217)782-1381
Springfield, IL 62706 Sue Ebetsch, Coord.
Founded: 1980. **Staff:** 1. **Subjects:** U.S. Census Bureau information. **Holdings:** 1000 books; census maps, 1970-1990; computer tapes; microfiche. **Subscriptions:** 2 journals and other serials. **Services:** Copying; center open to the public. **Computerized Information Services:** CD-ROMs. **Networks/ Consortia:** Member of Illinois State Data Center Cooperative (ISDCC). **Remarks:** FAX: (217)524-4876. Maintained by the U.S. Census Bureau and the Illinois Bureau of the Budget.

★7686★
Illinois (State) Department of Commerce & Community Affairs - DCCA Library (Bus-Fin)
620 E. Adams St. Phone: (217)785-6107
Springfield, IL 62701 Janet Noecker, Libn.
Founded: 1976. **Staff:** Prof 1. **Subjects:** Economic development in Illinois, Job Training Partner Act. **Holdings:** 3210 volumes; 762 annual reports. **Subscriptions:** 177 journals and other serials. **Services:** Interlibrary loan; copying (both limited); library open to the public for reference use only. **Automated Operations:** Computerized public access catalog (ILLINET Online).

Illinois (State) Department of Conservation - Fort Massac Historic Site
See: **Fort Massac Historic Site** (6009)

★7687★
Illinois (State) Department of Corrections - Training Academy - Library (Law)
1301 Concordia Ct. Phone: (217)522-2666
Springfield, IL 62702 Muriel Nellis, Libn.
Founded: 1975. **Staff:** Prof 1. **Subjects:** Corrections, management. **Special Collections:** Training Academy curriculum (500 books). **Holdings:** 950 books; 20 bound periodical volumes; 1000 microfiche. **Subscriptions:** 51 journals and other serials; 3 newspapers. **Services:** Interlibrary loan; copying; library open to the public. **Publications:** Library Newsletter, semimonthly.

★7688★
Illinois (State) Department of Employment Security - Ides Law and Reference Library (Bus-Fin)
401 S. State St., Rm. 310 Phone: (312)793-6202
Chicago, IL 60605 Eunice Choi, Libn.
Founded: 1976. **Staff:** Prof 1. **Subjects:** Law, unemployment insurance, labor market information, employment services, occupations, statistics, economics. **Special Collections:** Illinois labor market information reports; labor market information reports from other states. **Holdings:** 2500 books. **Subscriptions:** 70 journals and other serials. **Services:** Interlibrary loan; library not open to the public. **Computerized Information Services:** LEXIS, OCLC, WESTLAW, DIALOG Information Services. **Networks/Consortia:** Member of ILLINET, Chicago Library System. **Remarks:** FAX: (312)793-6292.

★7689★
Illinois (State) Department of Energy and Natural Resources - Chicago Energy Operations Library (Energy)
State of Illinois Center
100 W. Randolph, Suite 11-600 Phone: (312)814-3895
Chicago, IL 60601 Alice I. Lane, Lib.Assoc.
Founded: 1983. **Staff:** Prof 1. **Subjects:** Energy conservation - residential, religious/places of worship, transportation. **Special Collections:** Audiovisual collection. **Holdings:** 200 books; 6 VF drawers of leaflets, brochures, pamphlets; films; filmstrips; slides; video cassettes. **Services:** Interlibrary loan; copying; library open to the public for reference use only. **Automated Operations:** Computerized cataloging. **Computerized Information Services:** OCLC, Integrated Technical Information System (ITIS), DIALOG Information Services (through Springfield library). **Networks/Consortia:** Member of ILLINET. **Publications:** Energy Conservation Publication List (listing of materials available to staff and public).

★7690★
Illinois (State) Department of Energy and Natural Resources - Library (Energy)
325 W. Adams St., Rm. 300 Phone: (217)785-2388
Springfield, IL 62704-1892 Pat Poehlman Burg, Libn.
Founded: 1977. **Staff:** Prof 1; Other 2. **Subjects:** Energy conservation, biomass energy, coal, electric utilities, energy and environmental policy, natural resources, petroleum and power resources, solar and alternative energy. **Special Collections:** Agency archives; Energy Information Center (EIC) Envirofiche and Acid Rain Fiche. **Holdings:** 11,000 books and documents. **Subscriptions:** 275 journals and other serials. **Services:** Interlibrary loan; copying; library open to the public for reference use only. **Computerized Information Services:** DIALOG Information Services, OCLC. **Networks/Consortia:** Member of Rolling Prairie Library System (RPLS). **Publications:** Acquisition list, monthly. **Remarks:** FAX: (217)785-2618 (Attn.: Library).

Illinois (State) Department of Mental Health and Development Disabilities - H. Douglas Singer Mental Health and Development Center.
See: **H. Douglas Singer Mental Health and Developmental Center** (15192)

Illinois (State) Department of Mental Health and Developmental Disabilities - Elgin Mental Health Center
See: **Elgin Mental Health Center** (5298)

Illinois (State) Department of Mental Health and Developmental Disabilities - George A. Zeller Mental Health Center
See: **George A. Zeller Mental Health Center** (20838)

Illinois (State) Department of Mental Health and Developmental Disabilities - Jack Mabley Development Center
See: **Jack Mabley Development Center** (9487)

Illinois (State) Department of Mental Health and Developmental Disabilities - John J. Madden Mental Health Center
See: **John J. Madden Mental Health Center** (9513)

Illinois (State) Department of Mental Health & Developmental Disabilities - McFarland Mental Health Center
See: **McFarland Mental Health Center** (9889)

★7691★
Illinois (State) Department of Mines & Minerals - Land Reclamation Division - Library (Sci-Engr)
300 W. Jefferson, Suite 300
Box 10197 Phone: (217)782-4970
Springfield, IL 62791-0197 Paul J. Ehret, Supv.
Founded: 1971. **Subjects:** Surface and underground coal mining, land reclamation and restoration. **Holdings:** 1900 volumes. **Services:** Library open to the public with special permission. **Remarks:** FAX: (217)524-4819.

★7692★
Illinois (State) Department of Rehabilitation Services - Resource Center - Library (Med)
623 E. Adam St. Phone: (217)524-0706
Springfield, IL 62794-9429 Jan Perone, Libn.
Founded: 1990. **Staff:** Prof 1; Other 2. **Subjects:** Rehabilitation. **Holdings:** 600 books; 200 microfiche. **Subscriptions:** 200 journals and other serials; 10 newspapers. **Services:** Interlibrary loan; copying; library open to residents of Illinois. **Computerized Information Services:** DIALOG Information Services, OCLC, OCLC EPIC, ILLINET Online; internal database. **Remarks:** FAX: (217)524-0707. TDD: (217)524-0818.

★7693★
Illinois (State) Department of Transportation - Technical Reference Library (Trans)
025 Administration Bldg.
2300 S. Dirksen Pkwy. Phone: (217)782-6680
Springfield, IL 62764 Gisela Motzkus, Libn.
Founded: 1963. **Staff:** Prof 1; Other 1. **Subjects:** Transportation - planning, economics, administration; traffic control and operations; urban transportation administration and systems; maintenance; law. **Special Collections:** Complete law library. **Holdings:** 1027 textbooks; 260 bound periodical volumes; 5000 other cataloged items; 20 VF drawers of pamphlets, conference reports, speeches; 15 shelves of Illinois documents; 3800 titles of U.S. Department of Transportation documents on microfiche. **Subscriptions:** 282 journals and other serials. **Services:** Interlibrary loan; library not open to the public. **Computerized Information Services:** DIALOG Information Services, OCLC. **Networks/Consortia:** Member of ILLINET, Rolling Prairie Library System (RPLS). **Publications:** Acquisitions List bimonthly. **Remarks:** FAX: (217)782-1927 (Library).

★7694★
Illinois (State) Environmental Protection Agency - Library (Env-Cons)
2200 Churchill Rd. Phone: (217)782-9691
Springfield, IL 62794-9276 Nancy Simpson, Libn.
Staff: Prof 1; Other 1.5. **Subjects:** Environmental pollution and protection, environmental law, environmental health. **Holdings:** 25,000 books; 300 bound periodical volumes; 1500 legal documents; 30,000 EPA technical reports on microfiche. **Subscriptions:** 350 journals and other serials. **Services:** Interlibrary loan; library open to the public for reference use only. **Automated Operations:** Computerized cataloging. **Computerized Information Services:** DIALOG Information Services, MEDLARS. **Networks/Consortia:** Member of ILLINET, National Network of Libraries of Medicine - Greater Midwest Region. **Publications:** Acquisitions list, monthly - for internal distribution only. **Remarks:** FAX: (217)524-4916.

★7695★
Illinois (State) General Assembly - Legislative Research Unit - Library (Law)
222 S. College, 3rd Fl. Phone: (217)782-6851
Springfield, IL 62704 Dorothy Nadasdy, Adm.
Founded: 1937. **Staff:** Prof 2; Other 1. **Subjects:** Law, legislative research, public affairs. **Holdings:** 1000 books; 500 bound periodical volumes; 4000 titles of Illinois documents; 2000 research reports; videotapes; microfilm; historical Illinois information files; maps. **Subscriptions:** 150 journals and other serials; 10 newspapers. **Services:** Library not open to the public. **Automated Operations:** Computerized cataloging, acquisitions, and serials. **Computerized Information Services:** DIALOG Information Services, CompuServe Information Service, Bill Track, LEXIS, NEXIS, LEGISNET; internal databases. **Publications:** Acquisitions list, bimonthly - for internal distribution only. **Remarks:** FAX: (217)785-7572. **Also Known As:** Illinois Legislative Research Unit. **Staff:** Bernadine Gretzer.

★7696★
Illinois State Geological Survey - Library (Sci-Engr, Energy)
615 E. Peabody Phone: (217)333-5110
Champaign, IL 61820 Mary Krick, Libn.
Staff: Prof 2; Other 1. **Subjects:** Geology, stratigraphy, mineral economics, fuel technology, paleontology, geochemistry, coal chemistry, analytical chemistry, hydrogeology, environmental geology, mining and mineral resources of Illinois. **Special Collections:** State geological survey publications; Illinios Superconducting Super Collider Project Archives (2000 items). **Holdings:** 4000 books; 6100 bound periodical volumes; 23,000 documents; 25,000 maps; 1800 unpublished manuscripts; 2 VF drawers; 6300 photographs and slides; 7500 aerial photographs; 350 microfiche; 2300 U.S. and State documents. **Subscriptions:** 330 journals and other serials. **Services:** Interlibrary loan; library open to the public for reference use only. **Automated Operations:** Computerized serials, cataloging, and map circulation. **Computerized Information Services:** DIALOG Information Services, BRS Information Technologies, GeoRef (Geological Reference File), Illinois Legislative Data Base; BITNET (electronic mail service). **Networks/Consortia:** Member of ILLINET. **Publications:** Acquisition list, monthly - for internal distribution only. **Special Catalogs:** Illinios State Geological Survey List of Publications. **Remarks:** FAX: (217)244-7004. Electronic mail address(es): KRICK@UIUCVMD (BITNET). **Staff:** Kristi Mercer, Asst.Libn.; Patricia Wasson, Asst.Libn.

Illinois (State) Historic Preservation Agency - Division of Historic Sites
See: **Illinois (State) Historic Preservation Agency - Galena State Historic Sites** (7697)

★7697★
Illinois (State) Historic Preservation Agency - Galena State Historic Sites - Library (Hist)
908 3rd St. Phone: (815)777-3310
Galena, IL 61036 Thomas A. Campbell, Jr., Site Mgr.
Founded: 1971. **Staff:** 1. **Subjects:** Ulysses S. Grant, Elihu B. Washburne, Old Market House, Galena and lead mine region history, museum studies, historic preservation, Elihu B. Washburne. **Special Collections:** Alfred W. Mueller Historic Photographic Collection (3000 images). **Holdings:** 500 books; 51 unbound periodical volumes; 12 drawers of research files; local newspaper, 1828-1931, on microfilm; 2500 documents; 25 AV programs; 200 nonbook items; reports; historic periodicals. **Subscriptions:** 24 journals and other serials. **Services:** Copying; library open to the public when staff member is present. **Publications:** Historic Illinois (newsletter), bimonthly - to the public. **Remarks:** Library serves the three Galena State Historic Sites: U.S. Grant's Home State Historic Site, located at 500 Bouthiller St., telephone 777-0248; Old Market House State Historic Site, located at Market Square, telephone 777-2570; E.B. Washburne House State Historic Site, located at 908 Third St., telephone 777-3310. The E.B. Washburne House is not open to the public.

Illinois (State) Historic Preservation Agency - Illinois State Historical Library
See: **Illinois State Historical Library** (7698)

★7698★
Illinois State Historical Library (Hist)
Old State Capitol Phone: (217)782-4836
Springfield, IL 62701 Janice A. Petterchak, Hd.
Founded: 1889. **Staff:** Prof 15; Other 7. **Subjects:** Illinois history, Lincolniana, Civil War history, Midwest Americana, Mormon history, Indian history, genealogy. **Special Collections:** Abraham Lincoln Collection (1425 manuscripts; 8000 books and pamphlets); Picture and Print Collection (250,000). **Holdings:** 166,000 volumes; 9 million manuscripts; 70,000 reels of newspapers on microfilm; 2000 maps; 3500 broadsides. **Subscriptions:** 600 journals and other serials; 300 newspapers. **Services:** Interlibrary loan (limited); copying; library open to the public. **Automated Operations:** Computerized cataloging. **Computerized Information Services:** OCLC. **Networks/Consortia:** Member of ILLINET. **Remarks:** Maintained by Illinois (State) Historic Preservation Agency. **Staff:** Cheryl Schnirring, Mss.Cur.; Thomas F. Schwartz, Cur., Lincoln Coll.; Gary Stockton, Acq.; Sandra Stark, Sr.Libn.; Mary Michals, Iconographer; Gloria Gibbons, Supv., Tech.Serv.; Jill Blessman, Ser.; Joseph Adams, Repro.Serv.; Bonnie E. Parr, Cons.Libn.; Kathryn Harris, Supv., Ref. & Tech.Serv.; Robert Salata, Supv., Spec.Coll.; George Heerman, Ref.Libn.

★7699★
Illinois State Legislative Reference Bureau (Law)
State House, Rm. 112 Phone: (217)782-6625
Springfield, IL 62706 Patricia A. Coughlin, Law Libn.
Founded: 1913. **Staff:** Prof 1. **Subjects:** Law and legislation. **Special Collections:** Illinois statutes and reports; statutes of all other states. **Holdings:** 14,000 books; House and Senate Bills, 1877-1982, on microfilm. **Subscriptions:** 15 journals and other serials. **Services:** Bureau open to the public. **Publications:** Legislative Synopsis and Digest, weekly when General Assembly is in session - for sale.

Illinois State Legislative Research Unit
See: **Illinois (State) General Assembly - Legislative Research Unit** (7695)

★7700★
Illinois State Library (Info Sci)
300 S. 2nd St. Phone: (217)782-2994
Springfield, IL 62701-1796 Bridget L. Lamont, Dir.
Founded: 1839. **Staff:** Prof 60; Other 66. **Subjects:** U.S. and Illinois state government, business. **Special Collections:** State documents (475,000); federal documents (1.6 million); U.S. patents; maps (140,000). **Holdings:** 4.5

million items. **Subscriptions:** 2250 journals and other serials; 27 newspapers. **Services:** Interlibrary loan; copying; current awareness; library open to the public. **Automated Operations:** Computerized cataloging, acquisitions, serials, and circulation. **Computerized Information Services:** BRS Information Technologies, DIALOG Information Services, LEXIS, Chemical Abstracts Service (CAS), OCLC, U.S. Patent Classification System, WILSONDISC; CLSI (internal database); ALANET (electronic mail service). **Networks/Consortia:** Member of National Network of Libraries of Medicine - Greater Midwest Region, ILLINET. **Publications:** Illinois Libraries, 10/year; Insight, 12/year. **Remarks:** FAX: (217)785-4326. Headquarters of the network ILLINET. **Staff:** Marlene Deuel, Chf.Dp.Dir.; Kathleen Bloomberg, Assoc.Dir., Lib.Dev.; Thomas J. Dorst, Assoc.Dir., Coll., Access, & T.S.

Illinois State Museum - Dickson Mounds Museum
See: **Dickson Mounds Museum** (4857)

★7701★
Illinois (State) Museum of Natural History and Art - Technical Library (Art, Sci-Engr)
Springfield, IL 62706 Phone: (217)782-6623
Orvetta Robinson, Libn.
Staff: 2. **Subjects:** Anthropology, archeology, art, botany, geology, zoology. **Special Collections:** R.M. Barnes Collection (ornithology); Benjamin S. Hunter Collection (art); Raymond Janssen Collection (geology); Thorne Deuel Collection (anthropology). **Holdings:** 21,000 volumes; 9 VF drawers of pamphlets; 1000 maps. **Subscriptions:** 200 journals and other serials. **Services:** Interlibrary loan; copying; library open to the public for reference use only. **Publications:** Living Museum, quarterly - free upon request.

Illinois State Natural History Survey
See: **University of Illinois** (18679)

★7702★
Illinois (State) Office of the Auditor General - Library (Law)
509 S. 6th St., 1st Fl. Phone: (217)782-1055
Springfield, IL 62701 Barbara Gossrow, Libn.
Founded: 1974. **Staff:** Prof 1; Other 1. **Subjects:** Auditing and accounting, Illinois state government, public administration, evaluation. **Special Collections:** Illinois state government auditing documents (4350 volumes; 130 cartridges of microfilm of older audits); out-of-state auditing documents (700 volumes). **Holdings:** 4800 books; 140 periodical volumes; 120 cartridges of microfilm; 25 microfiche series titles; 4000 uncataloged Illinois auditing documents. **Subscriptions:** 74 journals and other serials; 5 newspapers. **Services:** Interlibrary loan; copying; library open to the public for reference use only. **Computerized Information Services:** LEGISNET, ISIS. **Networks/Consortia:** Member of ILLINET, Rolling Prairie Library System (RPLS). **Publications:** Annual report. **Remarks:** FAX: (217)785-8222.

★7703★
Illinois (State) Office of the Secretary of State - Illinois State Archives (Hist)
Archives Bldg. Phone: (217)782-4682
Springfield, IL 62756 John Daly, Dir.
Founded: 1921. **Staff:** Prof 31; Other 16. **Subjects:** Illinois history and official records. **Holdings:** 52,000 cubic feet of state agency reports, land patents, manuscript records, county and state agency records. **Subscriptions:** 3 journals and other serials. **Services:** Copying; genealogical, war records, historical, and land record research; archives open to the public, mental health records closed by law. **Computerized Information Services:** Internal databases. **Publications:** A Descriptive Inventory of the Archives of the State of Illinois; A Guide to Management of State Records and Services of the Archives-Records Management Division; A Guide to County Records in the Illinois Regional Archives; Chicago City Council Proceedings Files, 1833-1871: An Inventory. **Special Indexes:** Name Index of individuals found in records prior to 1850; indexes to records of Illinois' participation in wars to 1900; listing of all public domain land sales in Illinois (online); Chicago City Council Proceedings Files, 1833-1871: An Index.

★7704★
Illinois State Psychiatric Institute - Jack Weinberg Library (Med)
1153 N. LaVergne Ave. Phone: (312)854-6565
Chicago, IL 60651 Margo McClelland, Hd.Libn.
Founded: 1959. **Staff:** Prof 1; Other 1. **Subjects:** Psychiatry, psychology, psychopharmacology. **Holdings:** 15,500 books; 380 audio cassettes; 294 videotapes. **Subscriptions:** 170 journals and other serials. **Services:** Interlibrary loan; copying; SDI; library open to the public by appointment for reference use only. **Networks/Consortia:** Member of National Network of Libraries of Medicine - Greater Midwest Region, Illinois Department of Mental Health and Developmental Disabilities Library Services Network (LISN). **Publications:** Newsletter, bimonthly - for internal distribution only; subject bibliographies. **Remarks:** FAX: (312)854-6567.

★7705★
Illinois (State) Supreme Court Library (Law)
Supreme Court Bldg. Phone: (217)782-2424
Springfield, IL 62701-1791 Brenda I. Larison
Staff: Prof 3; Other 2.5. **Subjects:** Law. **Special Collections:** Early English reports in folio; British materials. **Holdings:** 91,000 volumes; reports; statutes. **Subscriptions:** 340 journals and other serials. **Services:** Library open to the public. **Computerized Information Services:** OCLC. **Networks/Consortia:** Member of Rolling Prairie Library System (RPLS). **Remarks:** FAX: (217)782-5287.

★7706★
Illinois State University - Census and Data Users Services - Library (Soc Sci)
Dept. 4690
Research Services Bldg., Suite A Phone: (309)438-5946
Normal, IL 61761-6901 Roy C. Treadway, Dir.
Founded: 1977. **Staff:** 4. **Subjects:** U.S. Census data. **Holdings:** 400 volumes; 100 computer tapes; 400 computer cartridges; 1970, 1980, and 1990 census data and recent economic censuses for Illinois and surrounding states. **Services:** Library open to the public. **Computerized Information Services:** BITNET (electronic mail service). **Remarks:** FAX: (309)438-2488. Electronic mail address(es): TREADWAY@ILSTU (BITNET).

★7707★
Illinois State University - Milner Library - Special Collections (Hum)
Normal, IL 61761 Phone: (309)438-2871
Laura E. Gowdy, Spec.Coll.Libn./Univ.Archv.
Staff: Prof 1; Other 1. **Subjects:** Children's literature, American and English authors of the 19th and 20th centuries, private presses, 19th century textbooks, university archives. **Special Collections:** Circus and related arts (5300 books; 100,000 posters, photographs, slides, correspondence); Sage Lincoln Collection (1500 books; 1800 pamphlets); Lois Lenski (125 books; manuscripts; correspondence; scrapbooks); Maurice Gnesin Collection (English language plays of the modern period, 1920s-1950s). **Holdings:** 33,000 books; 1000 cubic feet of university archives. **Subscriptions:** 8 journals and other serials. **Services:** Interlibrary loan; copying; collections open to the public. **Automated Operations:** Computerized cataloging and acquisitions. **Networks/Consortia:** Member of ILLINET. **Publications:** A Bibliography of the D.H. Lawrence Collection at Illinois State University (Bloomington, ILL.: Scarlet Ibis Press, 1979). **Special Catalogs:** A Descriptive and Bibliographic Catalog of the Circus & Related Arts Collection at Illinois State University, Normal, Illinois; A Bibliography of the D.H. Lawrence Collection at Illinois State University. **Remarks:** FAX: (309)438-3250.

★7708★
Illinois State Water Survey - Library (Sci-Engr)
208 Water Survey Research Center
2204 Griffith Dr. Phone: (217)333-4956
Champaign, IL 61820-7495 Frances L. Drone-Silvers, Libn.
Founded: 1950. **Staff:** Prof 1; Other 1. **Subjects:** Hydrology, water resources, atmospheric and aquatic chemistry, water quality, meteorology, atmospheric sciences, global climate change. **Special Collections:** State Water Survey Archives; Water Supply Papers of U.S. Geological Survey (entire set); U.S. climatic data; HIPLEX reports. **Holdings:** 29,272 volumes; 1200 bound periodical volumes; 400 microfiche titles. **Subscriptions:** 300 journals and other serials. **Services:** Interlibrary loan; SDI; library open to the public. **Automated Operations:** Computerized cataloging, serials, circulation, and journal routing (INMAGIC). **Computerized Information Services:** DIALOG Information Services; InterNet (electronic mail service).

Performs searches on fee basis. **Networks/Consortia:** Member of Lincoln Trail Libraries System (LTLS), ILLINET. **Publications:** Acquisitions list, monthly - to researchers; newsletter, bimonthly. **Special Indexes:** Illinois County Index to State Water Survey Publications (online). **Remarks:** FAX: (217)333-6540. Electronic mail address(es): Frances@sun.sws.uiuc.edu (InterNet).

★7709★
Illinois Wesleyan University - Thorpe Music Library (Mus)
303 E. University Phone: (309)556-3003
Bloomington, IL 61701 Robert C. Delvin, Fine Arts Libn.
Staff: Prof 1; Other 10. **Subjects:** Music, music education. **Holdings:** 15,000 books; 250 bound periodical volumes; 6000 sound recordings; 145 masters' theses; 150 reels of microfilm. **Subscriptions:** 50 journals and other serials. **Services:** Interlibrary loan; copying; library open to the public with restrictions. **Automated Operations:** Computerized cataloging and circulation. **Computerized Information Services:** DIALOG Information Services, OCLC. Performs searches free of charge. **Networks/Consortia:** Member of ILLINET. **Publications:** Monthly lists of new acquisitions - to faculty.

Illinois Youth Service Resource Center
See: **Youth Network Council of Chicago, Inc.** (20823)

The Image Bank
See: **Stockphotos - Library** (15802)

Imaginative Representations of the Vietnam War Collection
See: **La Salle University - Connelly Library - Special Collections Department** (8856)

★7710★
IMD International - Library (Bus-Fin)
Chemin de Bellerive 23 Phone: 21 267112
CH-1007 Lausanne, Switzerland Linda Stoddart, Dir., Info.Serv.
Staff: Prof 4. **Subjects:** Management, business, economics. **Special Collections:** Company reports (1200); IMD case studies (1700). **Holdings:** 10,000 books; 2250 bound periodical volumes; 850 microfiche; 60 reels of microfilm; 210 videotapes. **Subscriptions:** 600 journals and other serials; 30 newspapers. **Services:** Library open to the public by appointment. **Computerized Information Services:** Data-Star, Mead Data Central, G-CAM, DIALOG Information Services, ECHO, Eurobase, Reuter TEXTLINE, O.R. Telematique; internal database. **Publications:** IMD Library's Current Contents for Managers, biweekly; Additions to IMD Case Collection, quarterly and annual; Recent Additions to IMD Library, monthly; bibliography (online). **Remarks:** Alternate telephone number(s): 21 6180111. FAX: 21 266725. Telex: 455 871. **Staff:** Catherine Theissens; Lynda Allen; Eliane Barthlome; Valerie Juif.

★7711★
Imed Corporation - Library (Sci-Engr)
9775 Businesspark Ave. Phone: (619)566-9000
San Diego, CA 92131 Sue R. Albright, Libn.
Founded: 1981. **Staff:** 1. **Subjects:** Medicine, electronics, thermoplastics, assembly, engineering, medical instrumentation, clinical medicine. **Holdings:** 1200 books; 7 VF drawers of patents; 4 VF drawers of manuals. **Subscriptions:** 200 journals and other serials. **Services:** Interlibrary loan; library not open to the public. **Automated Operations:** Computerized cataloging and serials. **Computerized Information Services:** DIALOG Information Services, ORBIT Search Service, BRS Information Technologies; DIALMAIL (electronic mail service). **Publications:** Subject bibliographies for infusion therapy, and company business information. **Remarks:** FAX: (619)695-8796. Electronic mail address(es): ALBRIGHT (DIALMAIL).

★7712★
Immaculate Heart of Mary - Parish Library (Rel-Phil)
3700 Canyon Rd.
Los Alamos, NM 87544 Phone: (505)662-6193
Founded: 1961. **Staff:** 20. **Subjects:** Religion, religious education, theology, philosophy, marriage and family, psychology, socioeconomic concerns. **Holdings:** 5000 books; 45 records and record/book sets; 25 reel-to-reel tapes; 500 cassette tapes; 80 video cassettes. **Subscriptions:** 15 journals and other serials. **Services:** Interlibrary loan; library open to the public on request. **Staff:** Marcella Backsen, Libn.

★7713★
Immanuel Medical Center - Professional Library (Med)
6901 N. 72nd St. Phone: (402)572-2345
Omaha, NE 68122-1799 Joy A. Winkler, Libn.
Staff: 1. **Subjects:** Medicine, nursing, and allied health sciences. **Holdings:** 500 books; 189 bound periodical volumes. **Subscriptions:** 225 journals and other serials. **Services:** Interlibrary loan; library not open to the public.

Richard P. Immerman Memorial Library
See: **Potomac Hospital** (13273)

Immigration History Research Center
See: **University of Minnesota** (18913)

★7714★
Imo Industries Inc. - De Laval Turbine Division - Technical Library (Sci-Engr)
P.O. Box 8788 Phone: (609)890-5000
Trenton, NJ 08650 Barbara Moyer, Lib.Supv.
Founded: 1943. **Staff:** 1. **Subjects:** Mechanical and marine engineering, compressors, gears, pumps, turbines, cogeneration turbines. **Holdings:** 2500 books; 1000 reports; 10 VF drawers of pamphlets and clippings; 6 VF drawers of archival materials. **Subscriptions:** 100 journals and other serials. **Services:** Interlibrary loan; copying; library open to the public by referral. **Automated Operations:** Computerized cataloging, acquisitions, and serials. **Remarks:** FAX: (609)890-5085.

★7715★
Imodco - Business Library (Energy)
23901 Calabasas Rd., Suite 2090
Calabasas, CA 91302-1542 Phone: (818)591-2090
Staff: Prof 1. **Subjects:** Engineering, offshore oil industry. **Holdings:** 500 books; Offshore Technology Conference (OTC) proceedings; 460 catalogs; 400 files of technical reports. **Subscriptions:** 65 journals and other serials. **Services:** Library not open to the public.

★7716★
Imperial College of Science, Technology and Medicine - Mathematics Department Library (Sci-Engr)
Huxley Bldg.
180, Queens Gate Phone: 71 5895111
London SW7 2BZ, England Adrian M. Clark
Staff: Prof 1; Other .5. **Subjects:** Pure mathematics, applied mathematics, statistics, numerical analysis, mathematical physics. **Holdings:** 16,000 books; 9000 bound periodical volumes; 2500 reports; 10,000 reprints. **Subscriptions:** 130 journals and other serials. **Services:** Interlibrary loan; copying; SDI; library open to the public for reference use only. **Computerized Information Services:** CD-ROM (MathSci).

★7717★
Imperial County Law Library (Law)
Court House
939 Main St. Phone: (619)339-4374
El Centro, CA 92243 Judy Birt, Law Libn.
Subjects: Law. **Holdings:** 10,700 volumes. **Services:** Copying; library open to the public.

★7718★
Imperial Life Assurance Company - Library (Bus-Fin)
95 St. Clair Ave., W. Phone: (416)926-2857
Toronto, ON, Canada M4V 1N7 Mr. Robert Bingham, Coord.
Founded: 1896. **Staff:** 1. **Subjects:** Insurance - proceedings, law, history; general and actuarial mathematics; life insurance and statistics; office management; investment; marketing; economics. **Holdings:** Figures not available. **Services:** Library not open to the public. **Remarks:** FAX: (416)923-1599.

★7719★
Imperial Oil, Ltd. - Audio-Visual Resource Centre (Energy, Aud-Vis)
111 St. Clair Ave., W. Phone: (416)968-4920
Toronto, ON, Canada M5W 1K3 Linda Scott, Lib.Techn.
Staff: 1. **Subjects:** Petroleum industry, offshore exploration, refineries, service stations, laboratories. **Holdings:** 6000 slides; 2500 black/white photographs; 350 videotapes; 17 films. **Services:** Interlibrary loan; copying; center open to the public. **Automated Operations:** Computerized cataloging. **Remarks:** FAX: (416)968-5228.

Imperial Oil, Ltd. - Esso Resources Canada Limited
See: **Esso Resources Canada Limited** (5458)

★7720★
Imperial Oil, Ltd. - Information Centres (Bus-Fin)
111 St. Clair Ave., W.
Toronto, ON, Canada M5W 1K3 Phone: (416)968-4866
Founded: 1945. **Staff:** Prof 7; Other 6. **Subjects:** Petroleum industry, industrial relations, marketing, management, economics, public relations. **Holdings:** 7000 books; 20 shelf feet of annual reports; 70 VF drawers of pamphlets and reports; 10,000 shelf feet of archival records; 450 corporate videos; 5500 shelf feet of corporate slides, photographs and films. **Subscriptions:** 200 journals and other serials. **Services:** Interlibrary loan; copying; SDI; current awareness services. **Automated Operations:** Computerized cataloging, acquisitions, serials, and circulation. **Computerized Information Services:** DIALOG Information Services, PFDS Online, CAN/OLE, Info Globe, LEXIS, NEXIS, Infomart Online, Dow Jones News/Retrieval, WILSONLINE, STM Systems Corporation. **Remarks:** FAX: (416)968-5228.

★7721★
Imperial Tobacco Ltd. - Corporate Library (Bus-Fin, Agri)
P.O. Box 6500 Phone: (514)932-6161
Montreal, PQ, Canada H3C 3L6 Yolande Mukherjee, Corp.Libn.
Founded: 1938. **Staff:** 4. **Subjects:** Tobacco, management. **Special Collections:** Tobacco nostalgia (20,000 ads, packages, paintings, other memorabilia). **Holdings:** 6000 books; 10,000 pamphlets; 20 VF drawers of photographs. **Subscriptions:** 1200 journals and other serials. **Services:** Interlibrary loan; library open to the public. **Automated Operations:** Computerized cataloging, serials, and circulation. **Computerized Information Services:** DIALOG Information Services, REUTERS, Infomart Online, Envoy 100 (electronic mail service). **Publications:** Selection, monthly - available on request; What's New/Nouveautes - for internal distribution only. **Special Catalogs:** About Tobacco: Books and Periodicals on Tobacco (book). **Special Indexes:** Canadian Cigar and Tobacco Journal, 1898 to 1951. **Remarks:** FAX: (514)939-0432. Electronic mail address(es): QMIT.ILL (Envoy 100).

★7722★
Imperial Tobacco Ltd. - Research Library (Agri)
P.O. Box 6500 Phone: (514)932-6161
Montreal, PQ, Canada H3C 3L6 Miss R.A. Ayoung, Supv.
Founded: 1954. **Staff:** Prof 1; Other 2. **Subjects:** Tobacco, chemistry of natural products, agricultural chemistry, biochemistry. **Holdings:** 2150 books; 1000 bound periodical volumes; 2 drawers of reports; 18 drawers of reprints and photocopies; 4 drawers and 25 boxes of pamphlets. **Subscriptions:** 142 journals and other serials. **Services:** Interlibrary loan; library not open to the public. **Computerized Information Services:** CAN/OLE. **Remarks:** Library located at 734 Bourget St., Montreal, PQ H4C 2M7. FAX: (514)934-5928.

★7723★
Importers and Exporters Association of Taipei - Library (Bus-Fin)
5F, 350 Sungkiang Rd. Phone: 2 5813521
Taipei 10477, Taiwan Shirley Lin
Founded: 1965. **Staff:** 3. **Subjects:** Taiwan - exporting, importing, manufacturing. **Holdings:** 3000 volumes of domestic and foreign trade directories and periodicals. **Subscriptions:** 297 journals and other serials; 17 newspapers. **Computerized Information Services:** Videotex; Taiopei Traders Information System (internal database). **Remarks:** FAX: 2 5363328. Telex: 23339 IMEXTAI. **Staff:** Sophia Lin; Sophie Chang, Libn.

★7724★
In-Fact - Research and Information Service (Law)
Righter Rd.
Rural Delivery Box 35D Phone: (518)797-5154
Rensselaerville, NY 12147 Kate Storms, Pres.
Founded: 1976. **Subjects:** Government; legislative intent; law; social sciences. **Holdings:** 2000 volumes. **Services:** Service not open to the public. **Computerized Information Services:** Access to DIALOG Information Services, WESTLAW, New York Legislative Retrieval System (LRS). **Networks/Consortia:** Member of Capital District Library Council for Reference & Research Resources (CDLC). **Remarks:** FAX: (518)797-3692.

★7725★
IN-SIGHT - Technical Information Center (Med)
43 Jefferson Blvd. Phone: (401)941-3322
Warwick, RI 02888 Connie Worthington, Coord., Volunteer Serv.
Founded: 1925. **Staff:** Prof 1; Other 1. **Subjects:** Blindness, vision, education and rehabilitation of the blind, aging, diabetes. **Holdings:** 250 books. **Subscriptions:** 10 journals and other serials. **Services:** Center open to the public by appointment. **Publications:** IN-SIGHT News, 4 per year. **Remarks:** Center has a braille to braille copy (thermoform) machine and the capability to produce braille.

INADES-Documentation
See: **Institut Africain pour le Developpement Economique et Social** (7862)

★7726★
Incarnate Word Hospital - Medical Library (Med)
3545 Lafayette Ave. Phone: (314)664-6500
St. Louis, MO 63104 Karen L. Launsby, Med.Libn.
Founded: 1960. **Staff:** Prof 1; Other 4. **Subjects:** Medicine, allied health sciences, staff development. **Holdings:** 1000 books; 1000 bound periodical volumes; 50 pamphlets; reports and medical papers. **Subscriptions:** 70 journals and other serials. **Services:** Interlibrary loan; copying; library open to medical and nursing students. **Computerized Information Services:** MEDLARS; DOCLINE (electronic mail service).

★7727★
Inco Alloys International, Inc. - Technology Information Services (Sci-Engr)
3200 Riverside Dr.
Box 1958 Phone: (304)526-5433
Huntington, WV 25720 Connie E. Back, Info.Serv.Adm.
Staff: 2. **Subjects:** Nonferrous and nickel alloys, metallurgical engineering, analytical chemistry, environment. **Holdings:** 4500 books; 3500 bound periodical volumes; 2500 government reports; 300 translations; 20 VF drawers of reports. **Subscriptions:** 150 journals and other serials. **Services:** Interlibrary loan; copying; library open to the public by appointment. **Computerized Information Services:** DIALOG Information Services, OCLC. **Remarks:** FAX: (304)526-5973. **Staff:** Joyce A. Ward, Info.Serv.Techn.

★7728★
Inco Limited - Exploration Library
Royal Trust Tower, Box 44
Toronto Dominion Centre
Toronto, ON, Canada M5K 1N4
Defunct. Holdings merged with Inco Limited - Records & Information Management.

★7729★
Inco Limited - J. Roy Gordon Research Laboratory - Library (Energy)
2060 Flavelle Blvd. Phone: (416)822-3322
Mississauga, ON, Canada L5K 1Z9 L. Green, Supv., Info. and Off.Serv.
Founded: 1966. **Staff:** Prof 2; Other 2. **Subjects:** Extractive metallurgy, electrochemistry, mining, pollution control, chemical analysis. **Holdings:** 4000 books; 8000 bound periodical volumes; 6000 patents; government documents. **Subscriptions:** 190 journals and other serials. **Services:** Interlibrary loan; copying; SDI; library open to the public by appointment. **Automated Operations:** Computerized cataloging. **Computerized Information Services:** DIALOG Information Services, CAN/OLE, QL Systems, Info Globe, STN International; internal database. **Networks/Consortia:** Member of Sheridan Park Association. **Publications:** Extramet Digest, semimonthly - for internal distribution only. **Special Indexes:** Index to Inco staff publications (book). **Remarks:** FAX: (416)822-3922. Telex: 06982263. **Staff:** Janet MacLachlan.

★7730★
Inco Limited - Records & Information Management (Sci-Engr, Bus-Fin)
Royal Trust Tower, Box 44
Toronto Dominion Centre Phone: (416)361-7750
Toronto, ON, Canada M5K 1N4 Neftalie Abrenica, Supv.
Staff: Prof 2; Other 5. **Subjects:** Mining; mineral commodities; geology; exploration; mining processes and technology; business; finance; economics; investments. **Special Collections:** Annual reports (13,500); geological surveys; map collection (geological, topographical, worldwide). **Holdings:** 10,000 books; 100 bound periodical volumes; 2 VF drawers of pamphlets and clippings. **Subscriptions:** 280 journals and other serials; 12 newspapers. **Services:** Interlibrary loan; copying; library open to the public by appointment only. **Automated Operations:** Computerized cataloging, serials, and circulation. **Computerized Information Services:** DIALOG Information Services, Info Globe; internal database. **Remarks:** FAX: (416)361-7782. **Staff:** Maria Mendoza, Info.Spec.; Ben Bergla, Info.Spec.; Tracy Kit, Info.Spec.; Christina Wu, Acq.Libn.

★7731★
Independence Blue Cross - Corporate Research Center (Bus-Fin)
1901 Market St., 25th Fl. Phone: (215)241-3300
Philadelphia, PA 19103-1480 Denise M. Dodd, Res.Cons.
Founded: 1965. **Staff:** Prof 1; Other 1. **Subjects:** Health care, insurance, management, business. **Special Collections:** Blue Cross Historical Collection. **Holdings:** 1700 volumes. **Subscriptions:** 135 journals and other serials; 7 newspapers. **Services:** Interlibrary loan; copying; library open to the public by appointment. **Computerized Information Services:** DIALOG Information Services, NEXIS. **Remarks:** FAX: (215)241-3237.

★7732★
Independence Mental Health Institute - Medical Library (Med)
Box 111 Phone: (319)334-2583
Independence, IA 50644 Lois J. Samek, Med.Libn.
Founded: 1880. **Staff:** Prof 1. **Subjects:** Psychiatry, medicine, psychiatric nursing. **Holdings:** 2400 books; 650 bound periodical volumes; 250 cassette tapes. **Subscriptions:** 30 journals and other serials. **Services:** Interlibrary loan; library open to the public with restrictions.

Independence National Historical Park
See: **U.S. Natl. Park Service** (17735)

★7733★
Independence Regional Health Center - Dr. Charles F. Grabske, Sr. Library (Med)
1509 W. Truman Rd. Phone: (816)836-6639
Independence, MO 64050 Katie Voss, Libn.
Founded: 1967. **Staff:** Prof 1; Other 2. **Subjects:** Nursing. **Holdings:** 8500 books; 100 bound periodical volumes. **Subscriptions:** 200 journals and other serials. **Services:** Interlibrary loan; library not open to the public. **Automated Operations:** Computerized cataloging and acquisitions. **Computerized Information Services:** NLM, BRS Information Technologies; DOCLINE (electronic mail service). Performs searches on fee basis. **Networks/Consortia:** Member of Kansas City Library Network, Inc. (KCLN). **Publications:** The Pager (newsletter), weekly - for internal distribution only. **Remarks:** FAX: (816)836-6649.

★7734★
Independent Community Consultants - Library (Soc Sci)
Planning and Training Office
P.O. Box 141
Hampton, AR 71744 Phone: (501)798-4510
Subjects: Nonprofit organizations - organizational and community problems; statistics on corporate philanthropy, population, and social trends. **Holdings:** 9000 books, tapes, and microfiche; statistics.

★7735★
Independent Energy - Library (Energy)
620 Central Ave., N.
Milaca, MN 56353 Phone: (612)983-6892
Founded: 1971. **Subjects:** Energy - wind, hydropower, waste-to-energy, geothermal, photovoltaic, cogeneration; district heating. **Holdings:** 1200 books; files of 26,000 energy companies and organizations. **Subscriptions:** 3500 journals and other serials. **Services:** Library not open to the public. **Remarks:** FAX: (612)983-6893.

★7736★
The Independent Institute - Library (Soc Sci)
134 98th Ave.
Oakland, CA 94603 Phone: (510)632-1366
Founded: 1986. **Staff:** 1. **Subjects:** Political economy of social and economic problems; public policy; government reform; national and international affairs. **Holdings:** 6000 volumes. **Subscriptions:** 54 journals and other serials. **Services:** Library not open to the public. **Publications:** LibertyTree; Independent Studies in Political Economy. **Remarks:** FAX: (510)568-6040.

★7737★
Independent Presbyterian Church - John N. Lukens Library (Rel-Phil)
3100 Highland Ave., S. Phone: (205)933-1830
Birmingham, AL 35256 Gaynelle Tatum
Staff: 6. **Subjects:** Theology, family, Bible commentaries, seasons of the church, biography, philosophy, fine arts. **Special Collections:** Bible collection; children's library. **Holdings:** 3400 books. **Subscriptions:** 8 journals and other serials. **Services:** Library open to the public on a limited basis. **Remarks:** Church archival material is located in the Birmingham Public Library Archives.

Index of American Design
See: **National Gallery of Art** (11178)

Index of Christian Art
See: **Princeton University - Department of Art & Archaeology** (13371)

India - Board of Education - Silk and Art Silk Mills' Research Association
See: **Silk and Art Silk Mills' Research Association - SASMIRA Library** (15165)

★7738★
India - Council of Scientific and Industrial Research - Indian National Scientific Documentation Centre - INSDOC Library (Sci-Engr)
14, Satsang Vihar Marg
New Delhi 110 067, Delhi, India Phone: 665837
Subjects: All aspects of science and technology. **Holdings:** 124,068 volumes; 2500 reports; 1000 microforms. **Subscriptions:** 4610 journals and other serials. **Services:** SDI; library open to scientists and technologists in industry, government, universities, and research institutes. **Computerized Information Services:** Internal databases. Performs searches on fee basis. **Publications:** Bibliographies; Annals of Library Science and Documentation, quarterly; Russian Scientific & Technical Publications - An Accession List, bimonthly.

★7739★
India - Department of Agriculture - Library (Agri)
Seshadri Rd. Phone: 812 215093
Bangalore 560-001, Karnataka, India D.B. Gadagkar, Sr.Libn.
Founded: 1913. **Staff:** Prof 3; Other 3. **Subjects:** Agriculture, soil science, agronomy, plant protection, irrigation. **Holdings:** 6000 books; 3000 bound periodical volumes. **Subscriptions:** 150 journals and other serials; 9 newspapers. **Services:** Library open to the public for reference use only. **Publications:** Quarterly Bulletin of New Arrivals.

India - Embassy of India
See: **Embassy of India** (5323)

★7740★
India - Ministry of Agriculture - Department of Rural Development - National Institute of Rural Development - Centre on Rural Documentation (Agri, Soc Sci)
Rajendranagar Phone: 842 245766
Hyderabad 500 030, Andhra Pradesh, India K.A. Raju, Dir.
Founded: 1965. **Staff:** 25. **Subjects:** Social sciences, rural development. **Holdings:** 70,000 volumes. **Subscriptions:** 750 journals and other serials; 19 newspapers. **Services:** Interlibrary loan; copying; SDI; center open to participants, staff, and research scholars. **Computerized Information Services:** Internal database. **Publications:** CORD Abstracts; CORD Accessions. **Special Indexes:** CORD Index. **Remarks:** FAX: 842 245277. Telex: 0425-6510. Institute is a center for research, training, consultancy, and documentation on rural development in India. **Staff:** Mr. Amin Ahmad Khan, Dp.Dir.; Mr. Anil Takalkar, Doc.Off.; Mr. U. Haranath, Sr.Libn.; Mr. D.J. Dange, Asst.Libn.; Mr. I.B. Gajghate, Doc.Asst.; Ms. Laxmi Murthy, Asst.Libn.; Ms. T. Rama Devi, Asst.Libn.

★7741★
India - Ministry of Education - Central Institute of Indian Languages - Library (Hum)
Manasagnangotri Phone: 23820
Mysore 570 006, Karnataka, India C.R. Sulochana, Libn.
Subjects: Linguistics, Indian languages. **Holdings:** 50,000 volumes.

★7742★
India - Ministry of Food - Library (Agri)
45, Krishi Bhawan Phone: 11 384349
New Delhi 110 001, Delhi, India Mrs. Raj Grover, Sr.Lib. and Info.Asst.
Founded: 1952. **Staff:** Prof 3; Other 2. **Subjects:** Agriculture, food, nutrition, food preservation. **Holdings:** 16,100 books; 7340 bound periodical volumes; 128 reports; 45 archival items. **Subscriptions:** 92 journals and other serials; 16 newspapers. **Services:** Interlibrary loan; copying; SDI; library open to researchers who receive permission from department head. **Publications:** Bibliography of nutrition publications.

★7743★
India - Ministry of Health and Family Welfare - All India Institute of Hygiene and Public Health - Library (Med)
110 Chittaranjan Ave. Phone: 345271
Calcutta 700 073, West Bengal, India Mr. A.K. Biswas, Libn.
Subjects: Public health, allied health sciences. **Holdings:** 51,610 volumes.

India - Ministry of Textiles - Silk and Art Silk Mills' Research Association
See: **Silk and Art Silk Mills' Research Association - SASMIRA Library** (15165)

★7744★
India - National Archives of India - Library (Hist, Area-Ethnic)
Janpath Phone: 383436
New Delhi 110 001, Delhi, India Dr. R.K. Perti, Dir.
Subjects: India - history, political science, social sciences, education. **Special Collections:** Fort William College Collection; proscribed publications relating to freedom struggle; rare books. **Holdings:** 200,000 volumes; official gazettes and gazetteers; blue books; statutes; census reports; survey and settlement reports; travel accounts, civil lists; parliamentary papers relating to Indian affairs. **Services:** Interlibrary loan; library not open to the public. **Publications:** Patriotic poetry banned by the Raj; Patriotic writings banned by the Raj; Azadi Ke Tarane; Desh Bhakti Ke Geet. **Staff:** Sh.R.C. Puri, Libn.

★7745★
India - National Institute of Health and Family Welfare - National Documentation Centre (Med)
New Mehrauli Rd.
Munirka Phone: 11 667773
New Delhi 110 067, India Ms. R. Chobra, Sr.Doc.Off.
Founded: 1977. **Staff:** Prof 8; Other 10. **Subjects:** Health and family welfare - health care and administration, public health genetics, population, education and training, biomedicine, communication, environmental problems, and allied subjects. **Holdings:** 30,000 bound volumes; 5000 reports; microfiche; microfilm; AV materials. **Subscriptions:** 500 journals and other serials. **Services:** Center open to faculty of the institute, related organizations, and to those working in the family welfare areas in India. **Computerized Information Services:** Internal database. **Publications:** Bibliographies; current titles listings, quarterly; Abstracting Journals, bimonthly. **Special Indexes:** Press Clippings Index, monthly. **Remarks:** Alternate telephone number(s): 11 669872. **Staff:** Mr. B.K. Singh, Libn.; Ms. A. Maintani, Libn.; Mr. Madan Gobal, STA; Mr. Hansraj, STA; Mr. Ramkumar, STA; Mrs. N.U. Singh, STA; Ms. S.P. Bhalla, Asst.Libn.

★7746★
India - National Institute of Oceanography - Library (Sci-Engr)
Dona Paula 403004, Goa Daman and Diu, India Phone: 46253
M.P. Tapaswi, Doc.Off.
Founded: 1966. **Staff:** Prof 4. **Subjects:** Oceanography and marine sciences - physical sciences, chemistry, biology, and geology; ocean engineering and instrumentation; and allied subjects. **Holdings:** 20,000 bound volumes; 6000 technical reports. **Subscriptions:** 100 journals and other serials. **Services:** Interlibrary loan; copying; SDI; library open to the public for reference use only. **Computerized Information Services:** ASFA, Current Contents on Diskette/Agriculture, Biology & Environmental Sciences; Oceanographic Data Base, Computer Aided Directory Information Service, Computer Aided Bibliographic Information Service (internal databases). **Remarks:** FAX: 8324612. Telex: 0194-216 NIO IN; 0194-316 MGG IN. Institute is an affiliate of the Council of Scientific and Industrial Research. **Staff:** Mrs. S.H. Oka; Mr. G.H. Sainekar; Mr. A.K. Gawas.

India - National Social Science Documentation Centre
See: **Indian Council of Social Science Research - National Social Science Documentation Centre - Library** (7749)

India - University of Agricultural Sciences
See: **University of Agricultural Sciences - Library** (18148)

★7747★
Indian Agricultural Research Institute - Pusa Library (Agri, Sci-Engr)
New Delhi 110 012, India Phone: 587438
Chhotey Lal, Hd., Lib.Serv.
Founded: 1905. **Staff:** Prof 52; Other 41. **Subjects:** Crop improvement - genetics, horticulture and fruit technology, vegetable crops, floriculture and landscaping, seed science and technology; crop production - agronomy, soil science and agricultural chemistry, agricultural physics and engineering; crop protection - mycology and plant pathology, entomology and insect pests, nematology and nematode pest, agricultural chemicals; basic sciences - biochemistry, plant physiology, microbiology; nuclear research in agrobiology; water technology; biotechnology; molecular biology; agro-energy; seed testing; bio-fertilizer. **Special Collections:** Plant sciences collection, 1597 to present; Research Bulletin Collection (45,000 field reports from agricultural experiment station). **Holdings:** 150,000 books; 300,000 bound periodical volumes; 12,000 dissertations; 45,000 field reports. **Subscriptions:** 5100 journals and other serials; 12 newspapers. **Services:** Interlibrary loan; copying; SDI; current awareness services; library open to the public with letter of introduction from parent organization. **Publications:** Bibliography of Indian Agriculture; Developmental News in Agriculture; Futuristic Agriculture, all quarterly; monthly list of additions. **Special Catalogs:** Catalogue of IARI Library Serials (1967); Bibliography of IARI Contributions, 1905-1963; Bibliography of IARI Theses, 1936-1973; Guide to Information Sources in IARI Library; revised edition of IARI Library serials, to 1987. **Special Indexes:** Index to classified part of IARI Library catalog; Index to classification numbers of species of insects, fungi, weeds, medicinal plants.

Indian Arts and Crafts Board
See: **U.S. Dept. of the Interior** (17246)

Indian Claims Commission Archives
See: **University of Tulsa - McFarlin Library** (19466)

★7748★
Indian and Colonial Research Center, Inc. - Eva Butler Library (Hist, Area-Ethnic)
Box 525 Phone: (203)536-9771
Old Mystic, CT 06372 Kathleen Greenhalgh, Libn.
Founded: 1965. **Staff:** Prof 2; Other 15. **Subjects:** Indians, genealogy, colonial history. **Special Collections:** Elmer Waite collection of glass plate negatives of the area; rare American school books, 1700-1850 (300). **Holdings:** 2000 books; 954 manuscripts; 90 maps and atlases; 2000 early American notebooks; 69 boxes of bulletins and pamphlets; 2000 photographs. **Subscriptions:** 2 journals and other serials. **Services:** Copying; library open to the public. **Publications:** Our Woodland Indians (coloring book). **Remarks:** Also maintains a museum.

★7749★
Indian Council of Social Science Research - National Social Science Documentation Centre - Library (Soc Sci)
35, Ferozeshah Rd. Phone: 384353
New Delhi 110 001, Delhi, India Dr. K.G. Tyagi, Dir.
Founded: 1970. **Subjects:** Anthropology, commerce, demography, economics, education, geography, history, law, management studies, political science, public administration, psychology, sociology, town and country planning. **Special Collections:** Doctoral theses. **Holdings:** 25,000 books; 2500 research project reports and working papers. **Subscriptions:** 2000 journals and other serials. **Services:** Interlibrary loan; copying; translation; consultation; library open to social scientists. **Computerized Information Services:** Internal databases. **Publications:** Bibliographies - by request. **Remarks:** Alternate telephone number(s): 385959. Telex: 31 61083 ISSR IN.

Indian National Scientific Documentation Centre
See: **India - Council of Scientific and Industrial Research** (7738)

Indian & Northern Affairs Canada
See: **Canada - Indian & Northern Affairs Canada** (2756)

★7750★
Indian River Memorial Hospital - J.C. Robertson Memorial Library (Med)
1000 36th St. Phone: (407)567-4311
Vero Beach, FL 32960 E.W. Knowles, Aux.Libn.
Founded: 1967. **Staff:** Prof 4. **Subjects:** Medicine; medical specialties; surgery - abdominal, thorcic, vascular. **Holdings:** 616 books; 512 bound periodical volumes. **Subscriptions:** 62 journals and other serials. **Services:** Copying; library open to the public by appointment. **Automated Operations:** Computerized cataloging and acquisitions. **Networks/Consortia:** Member of Florida Health Sciences Library Association (FHSLA). **Staff:** J. Kirkpatrick; B. Flynn; C. Griffith; M. Menzies; C. Peterson.

★7751★
Indian Temple Mound Museum - Library (Soc Sci)
139 Miracle Strip Pkwy.
P.O. Box 4009 Phone: (904)243-6521
Fort Walton Beach, FL 32548 Steve Tuthill, Musm.Dir.
Subjects: Archaeology and prehistoric people, anthropology, Native Americans, museum management, archaeological sites, Florida history. **Holdings:** 3500 books; 500 bound periodical volumes; 1500 slides and photographs. **Services:** Copying (limited); library open to the public for reference use only. **Staff:** Anna Peele, Cur., Educ.

★7752★
Indiana Academy of Science - John Shepard Wright Memorial Library (Sci-Engr)
State Library
140 N. Senate Ave. Phone: (317)232-3686
Indianapolis, IN 46204-2296 J. Holly Oster, Libn.
Founded: 1896. **Subjects:** Science and technology. **Holdings:** 11,000 volumes. **Services:** Interlibrary loan; copying; library open to the public. **Automated Operations:** Computerized cataloging and circulation. **Computerized Information Services:** OCLC. **Networks/Consortia:** Member of INCOLSA. **Remarks:** FAX: (317)232-3728.

★7753★
Indiana County Law Library (Law)
Court House
Eighth & Philadelphia Phone: (412)465-3956
Indiana, PA 15701 Bonnie Brady, Law Libn.
Staff: Prof 1. **Subjects:** Law. **Holdings:** 18,000 volumes. **Subscriptions:** 2 journals and other serials. **Services:** Copying; library open to county residents for reference use only.

★7754★
Indiana Hand Center - Library (Med)
PO Box 80434
Indianapolis, IN 46280-0434 Phone: (317)875-9105
Founded: 1973. **Staff:** Prof 1. **Subjects:** Surgery - hand, plastic, micro; general orthopedics. **Holdings:** 700 books; 100 videotapes. **Subscriptions:** 11 journals and other serials. **Services:** Interlibrary loan; copying; library open to the public by appointment. **Computerized Information Services:** DIALOG Information Services, BRS Information Technologies, NLM. **Remarks:** FAX: (317)875-8638.

★7755★
Indiana Historical Society - William Henry Smith Memorial Library (Hist)
315 W. Ohio St. Phone: (317)232-1879
Indianapolis, IN 46202-3299 Bruce L. Johnson, Dir.
Founded: 1934. **Staff:** Prof 14; Other 6. **Subjects:** History of Indiana and Old Northwest. **Special Collections:** Architectural history (including Burns & Burns, Bohlen Meyer & Gibson, Russ and Harrison, James & Associates, Rubush and Hunter, and Fenstermaker collections; 161,356 items); black history (including Mme. C.J. Walker, Elijah Roberts, and Herbert Heller manuscript collections, Emmett Brown photograph collection; 6000 items); railroads (including Kauffman Photograph Collection, Preston Collection; 6000 items); Indiana in the Civil War (including Lew Wallace, D.E. Beem, and Jefferson C. Davis manuscript collections; 15,000 items); 19th century Indiana politics (including Charles Fairbanks, William H. English, and John G. Davis manuscript collections; 10,000 items); Old Northwest Territory history (600 manuscripts); William Henry Harrison and Indiana Territory history (500 manuscripts); charitable organizations (including Family Service Association, Pleasant Run Children's Home, and Jewish Welfare Federation manuscript collections; 85,000 items). **Holdings:** 65,000 books; 150 bound periodical volumes; 4 million manuscripts; 1000 maps; 1600 reels of microfilm; 1.5 million pictures. **Subscriptions:** 360 journals and other serials. **Services:** Copying; library open to the public. **Computerized Information Services:** OCLC; ARCHIE (internal database). Performs searches free of charge. **Networks/Consortia:** Member of INCOLSA. **Publications:** Indiana Historical Society annual report (accessions); Black History News and Notes, quarterly. **Special Catalogs:** Manuscript catalog. **Remarks:** FAX: (317)233-3109. **Staff:** Eric Mundell, Hd., Rdr.Serv.; Leigh Darbee, Cur., Printed Coll.; Ramona Duncan-Huse, Hd., Cons.; Wilma Gibbs, Prog.Archv.; Paul Brockman, Archv.; Deborah McAnallen, Hd., Lib. Access Sys.; Sally Childs-Helton, Mss.Libn.; Stephen Fletcher, Cur., Vis.Coll.

★7756★
Indiana Humanities Council - Resource Center (Hum)
1500 N. Delaware St. Phone: (317)638-1500
Indianapolis, IN 46208 David Hoppe, Prog.Dir.
Founded: 1976. **Staff:** Prof 1; Other 2. **Subjects:** Humanities, history, literature, philosophy, Indiana. **Special Collections:** Grant projects of the Indiana Committee for the Humanities; Indiana. **Holdings:** 375 books; 50 films; 600 videotapes; 6 exhibits; 200 audiotapes. **Services:** Center open to the public with restrictions. **Networks/Consortia:** Member of Central Indiana Area Library Services Authority (CIALSA). **Special Catalogs:** Biennial catalog of center materials published and available to the public.

★7757★
Indiana Institute of Technology - McMillen Library (Sci-Engr)
1600 E. Washington Blvd. Phone: (219)422-5561
Fort Wayne, IN 46803 Gene Knoch, Dir.
Founded: 1932. **Staff:** Prof 2. **Subjects:** Engineering, technology, business. **Holdings:** 26,825 books; 10,424 bound periodical volumes; 2000 Society of Automotive Engineers papers; 1300 student seminar reports; microfiche. **Subscriptions:** 200 journals and other serials; 5 newspapers. **Services:** Interlibrary loan; copying; library open to the public. **Computerized Information Services:** DIALOG Information Services. Performs searches on fee basis. **Networks/Consortia:** Member of Tri-ALSA. **Remarks:** FAX: (219)422-7696 (administration building). **Staff:** Margareta L. Slogar, Asst.Libn.

★7758★
Indiana Jewish Historical Society - Library (Hist, Area-Ethnic)
203 W. Wayne St. Phone: (219)423-3862
Fort Wayne, IN 46802 Joseph Levine, Exec.Sec.
Staff: Prof 1; Other 1. **Subjects:** History of Jewish communities, congregations, organizations in Indiana; family and oral histories. **Holdings:** 5000 items. **Publications:** Quarterly newsletter; Indiana Jewish History, 1-2/year.

★7759★
Indiana Law Enforcement Academy - David F. Allen Memorial Learning Resources Center (Law)
Box 313 Phone: (317)839-5191
Plainfield, IN 46168 Donna K. Zimmerman, Libn.
Staff: Prof 1. **Subjects:** Police science, law enforcement, criminology, weapons, drugs. **Special Collections:** Law - U.S. Code Annotated; Supreme Court Reporter; Federal Reporter; Federal Supplement, Burn's Indiana Statutes Annotated; Indiana Code, NE2 - Indiana Cases; law dictionaries and encyclopedias. **Holdings:** 5000 books; 36 bound periodical volumes; 200 pamphlets; 500 16mm films; 125 slide/tape series; 18 filmstrips, 200 videotapes. **Subscriptions:** 70 journals and other serials. **Services:** Interlibrary loan; copying; center open to the public by appointment. **Networks/Consortia:** Member of Central Indiana Area Library Services Authority (CIALSA), Criminal Justice Information Exchange Group. **Publications:** Subject bibliographies (loose-leaf). **Special Catalogs:** AV Catalog (bound). **Remarks:** FAX: (317)839-9741.

★7760★
Indiana Limestone Institute of America, Inc. - Library and Information Center (Sci-Engr)
Stone City Bank Bldg., Suite 400 Phone: (812)275-4426
Bedford, IN 47421 Donna Johnson, Sec.
Subjects: Indiana limestone, building stone, construction, architectural styles. **Holdings:** 300 books. **Subscriptions:** 10 journals and other serials. **Services:** Library not open to the public.

Indiana Masonic Library & Museum
See: **Masonic Library & Museum of Indiana, Inc. - Masonic Library** (9780)

★7761★
Indiana Medical History Museum - Library (Med)
3000 W. Washington St. Phone: (317)635-7329
Indianapolis, IN 46222-4055 Oren S. Cooley, Dir.
Founded: 1896. **Staff:** 1.5. **Subjects:** Historical medicine; late 19th to early 20th century medicine, pathology, psychiatry, neurology. **Special Collections:** Walter Breutsch, M.D. papers. **Holdings:** 3000 books; 3 boxes of manuscripts. **Subscriptions:** 3 journals and other serials. **Services:** Copying; library open to the public. **Publications:** Snakeroot Extract (newsletter). **Staff:** Ann Blunk, Musm.Asst.

★7762★
Indiana School for the Deaf - Library (Educ)
1200 E. 42nd St. Phone: (317)924-4374
Indianapolis, IN 46205 Linda Canty
Founded: 1935. **Staff:** Prof 1; Other .5. **Subjects:** Audiology, psychology of deafness, multiple-handicapped, special education. **Holdings:** 25,455 volumes; 1000 other cataloged items. **Subscriptions:** 140 journals and other serials. **Services:** Interlibrary loan; copying; library open to Members of Central Indiana Area Library Services Authority. **Remarks:** Library is a depository for Captioned Education Films for the Deaf.

Indiana State Archives
See: **Indiana (State) Commission on Public Records - Indiana State Archives** (7765)

★7763★
Indiana (State) Board of Health - Jacob T. Oliphant Library (Med)
P.O. Box 1964
1330 W Michigan St. Phone: (317)633-8585
Indianapolis, IN 46206-1964 Billy Smith, Libn.
Founded: 1950. **Staff:** Prof 1; Other 1. **Subjects:** Communicable disease, chronic disease, nursing, public health, health education, sanitation, pollution, drugs. **Holdings:** 3000 books; 3000 bound periodical volumes; 2 VF drawers of Board of Health archives. **Subscriptions:** 150 journals and other serials. **Services:** Interlibrary loan; copying; library open to the public for reference use only. **Networks/Consortia:** Member of Central Indiana Area Library Services Authority (CIALSA). **Publications:** Annual Report; Monthly Bulletin.

★7764★
Indiana (State) Chamber of Commerce Library (Bus-Fin)
One N. Capitol Ave., Suite 200 Phone: (317)264-6870
Indianapolis, IN 46204-2248 Linda Lee Horvath, Libn.
Founded: 1987. **Staff:** Prof 1. **Subjects:** Business, state government. **Special Collections:** Indiana State Chamber of Commerce publications archives (14 linear feet); Indiana business/institution files (20 linear feet). **Holdings:** 500 books. **Subscriptions:** 368 magazines, newspapers, and newsletters. **Services:** Library open to members of Indiana State Chamber of Commerce. **Computerized Information Services:** DIALOG Information Services, Economic, Development Information Network (EDIN), DataTimes, InvesText. Performs searches on fee basis. **Publications:** Indiana Map Collection (booklet). **Special Indexes:** City index to Indiana phone books. **Remarks:** FAX: (317)264-6855.

★7765★
Indiana (State) Commission on Public Records - Indiana State Archives (Hist)
State Library Bldg., Rm. 117
140 N. Senate Ave. Phone: (317)232-3660
Indianapolis, IN 46204 F. Gerald Handfield, Jr., State Archv./Dir.
Founded: 1913. **Staff:** Prof 6; Other 3. **Subjects:** Indiana government; Indiana civil and military records; natural resources; education; public utilities; taxation; finance; state institutional records; internal improvements; corrections. **Special Collections:** Aerial photographs; incorporations; military records, War of 1812 through Korea; public land records. **Holdings:** 25,000 cubic feet of state archival records; 5000 cubic feet of county and municipal records; 70,000 reels of microfilm of archival materials. **Subscriptions:** 15 journals and other serials. **Services:** Copying; division open to the public. **Computerized Information Services:** Internal database. **Publications:** Archive inventories; genealogical resources; aerial photographs. **Remarks:** Alternate telephone number(s): 232-3656. FAX: (317)233-3744. **Staff:** Dr. Justin Walsh, Hd., Archv.Div.; Lawrie Meldrum, Rec.Anl. IV; Dr. Alan January, Rec.Anl. III; Stephen E. Towne, Rec.Anl. III; Robert Horton, Rec.Anl. III; Eugene Smith, Rec.Anl. IV.

★7766★
Indiana (State) Department of Commerce - Office of Engery Policy - Energy Resource Center-Library (Energy)
1 N. Capitol, 6th Fl. Phone: (317)232-7578
Indianapolis, IN 46204-2288 Edward Hoy, Contact
Founded: 1977. **Staff:** 2. **Subjects:** Energy - conservation, alternative sources, resource development, consumption and production. **Holdings:** Figures not available. **Subscriptions:** 72 journals and other serials. **Services:** Interlibrary loan; SDI; library open to the public. **Computerized Information Services:** Access to DIALOG Information Services. **Networks/Consortia:** Member of Central Indiana Area Library Services Authority (CIALSA). **Remarks:** FAX: (317)232-8995.

★7767★
Indiana (State) Department of Education - Professional Library (Educ)
229 State House Phone: (317)232-9129
Indianapolis, IN 46204 Dorothy M. Everett, Libn.
Founded: 1965. **Staff:** Prof 1; Other 1. **Subjects:** Teacher education. **Holdings:** 3500 books; 4 VF drawers. **Subscriptions:** 215 journals and other serials. **Services:** Interlibrary loan; copying; library open to the public with restrictions. **Computerized Information Services:** Online systems. **Remarks:** FAX: (317)232-9121.

Indiana State Geological Survey - Indiana State University - Geology Library
See: **Indiana University - Geology Library** (7788)

★7768★
Indiana State Library (Info Sci, Aud-Vis)
140 N. Senate Ave. Phone: (317)232-3675
Indianapolis, IN 46204 C. Ray Ewick, Dir.
Founded: 1825. **Staff:** Prof 43; Other 39. **Subjects:** Genealogy, Indiana history, federal and state documents, library science. **Special Collections:** Indiana Academy of Science Library; braille and talking books; Indiana Manuscript Collection. **Holdings:** 1.5 million items; regional depository for federal documents; state documents. **Subscriptions:** 15,792 journals and other serials. **Services:** Interlibrary loan; copying; library open to the public. **Automated Operations:** Computerized cataloging and circulation. **Computerized Information Services:** DIALOG Information Services, OCLC, STATIS, Library of Congress Information System. **Networks/Consortia:** Member of INCOLSA. **Publications:** Indiana Libraries, quarterly; Focus on Indiana Libraries, monthly; Hoosier Highlights. **Special Indexes:** Index of Indianapolis newspapers since 1898 (card); genealogical indexes; newspaper, biographical, picture, and map holdings index (card). **Remarks:** The Indiana State Library is the regional library for the blind and physically handicapped. FAX: (317)232-3728. **Staff:** Martha Roblee, Assoc.Dir., Network Coord.; Marilyn Hite, Assoc.Dir., Lib.Dev.; Robert Logsdon, Assoc.Dir., Pub.Serv.; Barney McEwen, Assoc.Dir., Ctrl.Sup.Serv.; Mary Hartzler, Hd., Cat.Div.; Diane Sharp, Coord., Geneal.Serv.; Lissa Shanahan, Hd., Div. for Blind; Gail Winsmore, Hd., Ref. & Loan; Peggy Morlan, Bus.Mgr.; John Presnell, Hd., MIS Div.

★7769★
Indiana State Library - Indiana Division (Hist)
140 N. Senate Ave. Phone: (317)232-3668
Indianapolis, IN 46204-2296 Cynthia Faunce, Div.Hd.
Founded: 1825. **Staff:** Prof 8; Other 4. **Subjects:** Indiana - history, authors, biography, music and composers; local history. **Special Collections:** Indiana newspapers. **Holdings:** 55,000 volumes; depository for state documents; 8644 maps; 50,135 pamphlets; 3.25 million manuscripts; 34 VF drawers of pictures; 40 VF drawers of programs; 2320 broadsides; 1758 reels of microfilm; 395 oral history tapes; 148 VF drawers of clippings. **Subscriptions:** 295 newspapers. **Services:** Interlibrary loan; copying (both limited); division open to the public. **Automated Operations:** Computerized cataloging. **Networks/Consortia:** Member of INCOLSA, Central Indiana Area Library Services Authority (CIALSA). **Publications:** Checklist of Indiana State Documents, quarterly - available on request. **Special Indexes:** Newspaper index (200,000 cards); biographical index (140,000 cards). **Remarks:** FAX: (317)232-3728. **Staff:** Martha Wright, Ref.Libn.; John Selch, Newspaper Libn.; David Lewis, Ref.Libn.; Barney Thompson, Ref.Libn.; Laurence Hathaway, Ref.Libn.; Pamela Wasmer, Ms.Libn.

★7770★
Indiana State Supreme Court - Law Library (Law)
316 State House Phone: (317)232-2557
Indianapolis, IN 46204 Constance Matts, Law Libn.
Founded: 1867. **Staff:** Prof 1; Other 2. **Subjects:** Law. **Special Collections:** Official state reports; early volumes of Indiana law; selective government depository; State Justice Institute depository. **Holdings:** 71,000 volumes. **Subscriptions:** 187 journals and other serials. **Services:** Interlibrary loan; copying; library open to the public. **Automated Operations:** Computerized cataloging. **Computerized Information Services:** LEXIS, WESTLAW, DIALOG Information Services. **Networks/Consortia:** Member of INCOLSA. **Remarks:** FAX: (317)232-8372.

★7771★
Indiana State University - Center for Governmental Services (Educ)
HH 201 Phone: (812)237-2436
Terre Haute, IN 47809 Dr. Manindra K. Mohapatra, Dir.
Founded: 1966. **Staff:** Prof 1; Other 2. **Subjects:** Education, careers, internships, research methods, state governments, public personnel management, survey research, content analysis. **Holdings:** 3000 books; 50 periodicals and newsletters; 49 journals; employment guides. **Subscriptions:** 105 journals and other serials. **Services:** Center open to the public. **Publications:** Bibliography on Public Administration in Indiana. **Remarks:** FAX: (812)237-2567. **Staff:** Mary Richmond, Libn.

★7772★
Indiana State University - Department of Rare Books and Special Collections (Rare Book)
Cunningham Memorial Library
6 1/2 & Sycamore Sts. Phone: (812)237-2610
Terre Haute, IN 47809 David E. Vancil, Hd.
Staff: Prof 3; Other 1. **Subjects:** Lexicography and lexicology in English and Western European languages; Eugene V. Debs, labor, and socioeconomic history; Indiana education, history, and literature; Indiana Federal Writers' Project/Program; American education; travel, discovery, and geography; great works of literature; fine printing and bindings; early illustrated works. **Special Collections:** Warren N. and Suzanne B. Cordell Collection of Dictionaries (pre-1901, 11,000; 20th century, 4300); Eugene V. Debs Collection (1500 books; 3875 letters; 3600 pamphlets; 6000 articles and speeches; scrapbooks; clippings; memorabilia); Indiana Collection (4650 books); WPA Indiana Writers Project (135 cubic feet of manuscripts); Cunningham Collection (1300 books); Floyd Family Collection (1400 books); Walker Collection (800 books); Faculty Publications (625 books; 1000 offprints); rare books (6300); Kirk Collection (14,000 scores); Manuscripts Collection (65 cubic feet); Brotherhood Locomotive Magazine, 1878-1894; Brotherhood of Locomotive Firemen and Enginemen Convention Proceedings, 1873-1960; Appeal to Reason (Girard, KS; 1907-1914) files. **Holdings:** 40,000 volumes; 225 cubic feet of manuscripts; educational and other organizational publications/archival materials. **Subscriptions:** 3 journals and other serials. **Services:** Interlibrary loan; copying; library open to the public. **Automated Operations:** Computerized public access catalog, cataloging, acquisitions, and serials. **Computerized Information Services:** DIALOG Information Services, WILSONLINE, BRS Information Technologies, OCLC; internal databases; ALANET, BITNET, InterNet (electronic mail services). Performs searches on fee basis. Contact Person: Ms. Pat Ensor, 237-2580. **Networks/Consortia:** Member of Stone Hills Area Library Services Authority. **Special Catalogs:** A Short-Title Catalogue of the Warren N. and Suzanne B. Cordell Collection of Dictionaries, 1475-1900 (1975); English Dictionaries from 1604 Through 1900: The Warren N. and Suzanne B. Cordell Collection of Dictionaries (1988). **Remarks:** FAX: (812)237-2567. **Staff:** Robert L. Carter, Ref.Libn.; Kathyrn Wright, Cat.

★7773★
Indiana State University - Science Library (Sci-Engr, Biol Sci)
Science Bldg., Rm. 70 Phone: (812)237-2060
Terre Haute, IN 47809 Susan J. Thompson, Hd.
Founded: 1968. **Staff:** Prof 1; Other 2. **Subjects:** Chemistry, physics, life sciences, geology. **Holdings:** 17,228 books; 37,513 bound periodical volumes (9543 in remote storage); 175 reels of microfilm; 13,137 microfiche. **Subscriptions:** 581 journals and other serials. **Services:** Interlibrary loan; copying; library open to the public. **Automated Operations:** Computerized public access catalog, cataloging, acquisitions, serials, and circulation. **Computerized Information Services:** DIALOG Information Services, BRS Information Technologies, OCLC; CD-ROMs; internal databases; BITNET (electronic mail service). Performs searches on fee basis (limited). **Remarks:** FAX: (812)237-2567. Electronic mail address(es): LIBSJT@INDST (BITNET).

★7774★
Indiana State University - Teaching Materials, Microforms and Media (Educ)
Cunningham Memorial Library
6 1/2 & Sycamore Sts. Phone: (812)237-2617
Terre Haute, IN 47809 Rolland H. McGiverin, Hd.
Staff: Prof 2; Other 3. **Subjects:** Education and curricula, music, literature, history, instructional media, children's literature. **Holdings:** 35,263 books; 622,014 microforms; 1064 curriculum guides; 1340 mental tests; 508 publishers' catalogs; 23,686 AV programs. **Subscriptions:** 34 journals and other serials. **Services:** Interlibrary loan; copying; open to the public. **Automated Operations:** Computerized public access catalog, serials, acquisitions, serials, and circulation. **Computerized Information Services:** ERIC, A-V Online, Education Library. **Remarks:** FAX: (812)237-2567. **Staff:** Virginia Anderson, Libn.

★7775★
Indiana Transportation Museum - Library (Trans)
P.O. Box 83 Phone: (317)773-6000
Noblesville, IN 46060-0083 Jerry Marlette
Founded: 1962. **Staff:** Prof 1. **Subjects:** Railroads, aviation. **Holdings:** 500 books; 150,000 Conrail predecessor railroad drawings; railroad public timetables; railroad employee timetables; railroad annual reports and periodicals; aviation periodicals. **Services:** Copying; library not open to the public. **Publications:** Indiana Transportation Museum News - for internal distribution only. **Remarks:** Alternate telephone number(s): 773-6000.

Indiana University - Aerospace Research Application Center (ARAC) - NASA Technical Information Center
See: **Technology Transfer Society** (16047)

★7776★
Indiana University - Archives of Traditional Music (Mus)
Morrison Hall Phone: (812)855-4679
Bloomington, IN 47405 Ruth M. Stone, Dir.
Founded: 1936. **Staff:** Prof 3; Other 7. **Subjects:** Ethnic music, folk music, oral data, ethnomusicology, discography, early jazz. **Special Collections:** Hoagy Carmichael Collection (manuscripts; recordings; photographs; memorabilia). **Holdings:** 35,000 tape recordings; 6300 cylinder recordings; 36,600 disc recordings; 209 wire recordings. **Subscriptions:** 5 journals and other serials. **Services:** Copying; archives open to the public. **Automated Operations:** Computerized cataloging. **Computerized Information Services:** OCLC; internal database. **Networks/Consortia:** Member of INCOLSA. **Publications:** Resound, quarterly - by subscription. **Special Catalogs:** A Catalog of Phonorecordings of Music and Oral Data Held by the Archives of Traditional Music; African Music and Oral Data, 1902-1975; Native North American Music and Oral Data, A Catalogue of Sound Recordings, 1893-1976; Early Field Recordings (1987). **Special Indexes:** Indiana Folk Music and Oral Data (typescript). **Remarks:** Includes the Center for African Oral Data and Archives of Languages of th e World. **Staff:** Mary Russell, Lib. & Assoc.Dir.; Marilyn Graf, Archv.Coord.

★7777★
Indiana University - Biology Library (Biol Sci)
Jordan Hall Phone: (812)855-9791
Bloomington, IN 47405 Steven Sowell, Hd.
Staff: Prof 2; Other 3. **Subjects:** Microbiology, botany, zoology. **Holdings:** 103,000 volumes; 21,000 microforms. **Subscriptions:** 880 journals and other serials. **Services:** Interlibrary loan; copying; library open to the public. **Computerized Information Services:** DIALOG Information Services; BITNET (electronic mail service). **Remarks:** FAX: (812)855-6612. Electronic mail address(es): SOWELL@IUBACS (BITNET). **Staff:** Carol Tullis.

★7778★
Indiana University - Black Culture Center - Library (Area-Ethnic)
109 N. Jordan Ave. Phone: (812)855-3237
Bloomington, IN 47405 Grace Jackson-Brown, Hd.Libn.
Founded: 1972. **Staff:** Prof 1; Other 3. **Subjects:** Blacks - history, reference works, music, literature, drama; black-oriented novels. **Special Collections:** The Arno Press Collection (250 titles). **Holdings:** 3000 books; 75 bound periodical volumes; 100 cassette tapes; 170 titles on 285 tapes; pamphlet files. **Subscriptions:** 22 journals and other serials; 12 newspapers. **Services:** Library open to the public. **Publications:** Shelf list of additions to the Afro-American Collections, 1985-1986; Selected Acquisitions List, 1989-1990; Selected Reference Tools in African American Subject Areas; bibliographies, irregular.

★7779★
Indiana University - Business/SPEA Library (Bus-Fin, Env-Cons)
Business Bldg. Phone: (812)855-1957
Bloomington, IN 47405 Michael Parrish, Hd.
Founded: 1926. **Staff:** Prof 3; Other 8. **Subjects:** Accounting, environment, energy, ecology, finance, insurance, management, marketing, public administration, social problems, urban affairs. **Special Collections:** History of management thought. **Holdings:** 158,000 volumes; 99,000 microforms. **Subscriptions:** 1450 journals and other serials. **Services:** Interlibrary loan; copying; library open to the public. **Computerized Information Services:** BITNET (electronic mail service). **Remarks:** FAX: (812)855-3398. Electronic mail address(es): PARRISH1@IUBACS (BITNET). **Staff:** Nels Gunderson.

★7780★
Indiana University - Chemistry Library (Sci-Engr)
Chemistry Bldg. Phone: (812)855-9452
Bloomington, IN 47405 Gary Wiggins, Hd.
Founded: 1941. **Staff:** Prof 2; Other 2. **Subjects:** Chemistry, allied sciences. **Holdings:** 59,000 volumes; 21,000 microforms. **Subscriptions:** 395 journals and other serials. **Services:** Interlibrary loan; copying; SDI; microfilming; table of contents service; library open to the public. **Computerized Information Services:** Chemical Information Systems, Inc. (CIS), DIALOG Information Services, PFDS Online, Cambridge Structural Database (CSD); BITNET (electronic mail service). **Publications:** International Standard Interest Profiles on: Crystal Structure, biweekly; Charge, Spin and Momentum Density, every six weeks; Isotope Effects, Gas Phase Molecular Structure, monthly - all by subscription. **Remarks:** FAX: (812)855-6611. Electronic mail address(es): WIGGINS@IUBACS (BITNET). **Staff:** Roger Beckman.

★7781★
Indiana University - East Asian Collection (Area-Ethnic)
Indiana University Library, E860 Phone: (812)855-9695
Bloomington, IN 47405 Thomas H. Lee, East Asian Libn.
Founded: 1961. **Staff:** Prof 4; Other 2. **Subjects:** Literature and languages, history and government, culture and social sciences, religion and philosophy, art, law. **Special Collections:** Chinese classics collection; rare book collection; East Asian reference collection. **Holdings:** 134,343 books (94,383 in Chinese, 33,011 in Japanese, 6949 in Korean); 1099 reels of microfilm. **Subscriptions:** 791 journals and other serials. **Services:** Interlibrary loan; copying; library open to qualified users. **Automated Operations:** Computerized cataloging and serials. **Computerized Information Services:** BRS Information Technologies, DIALOG Information Services, WILSONLINE, OCLC, RLIN; electronic mail service. Performs searches on fee basis. **Publications:** I.U. Library News - for internal distribution only. **Special Catalogs:** Chinese, Japanese, and Korean serials (lists). **Remarks:** Alternate telephone number(s): (812)855-8028. FAX: (812)855-8229. **Staff:** Taemin Park, Ser.Cat.; Wen-ling Liu, Chinese Cat.; Mayumi Koide, Japanese Cat.; Lisa Hsi-chu Huang, Chinese Cat.

★7782★
Indiana University - Education Library (Educ)
Bloomington, IN 47405 Phone: (812)855-1798
Pat Steele, Hd.
Founded: 1955. **Staff:** Prof 1; Other 5. **Subjects:** Education theory, practice, and history; child development; guidance; educational psychology. **Special Collections:** Curriculum materials. **Holdings:** 47,000 volumes; 426,000 ERIC microfiche and other microforms. **Subscriptions:** 345 journals and other serials. **Services:** Interlibrary loan; copying; library open to the public. **Computerized Information Services:** DIALOG Information Services, PFDS Online; BITNET (electronic mail service). **Remarks:** FAX: (812)855-9978. Electronic mail address(es): STEELE@IUBACS (BITNET). **Staff:** Gwen Pershing.

★7783★
Indiana University - Fine Arts Library (Art)
Fine Arts Center Phone: (812)855-5743
Bloomington, IN 47405 Betty Jo Irvine, Hd.
Staff: Prof 3; Other 8. **Subjects:** Art, history of arts and crafts, photography. **Holdings:** 73,000 volumes; 21,000 microforms; 58,000 photographs. **Subscriptions:** 354 journals and other serials. **Services:** Interlibrary loan; copying; library open to the public with limited circulation. **Computerized Information Services:** BITNET (electronic mail service). **Remarks:** FAX: (812)855-3443. Electronic mail address(es): IRVINE@IUBACS (BITNET). **Staff:** Rosann Auchstetter.

★7784★
Indiana University - Fine Arts Slide Library (Art)
Fine Arts 415 Phone: (812)855-6717
Bloomington, IN 47405 Eileen Fry, Slide Libn.
Staff: Prof 1; Other 3. **Subjects:** Art history. **Special Collections:** Sieber African Slide Collection (11,000 slides of African and Third World art). **Holdings:** 291,300 slides. **Services:** Library not open to the public. **Computerized Information Services:** BITNET (electronic mail service). **Remarks:** FAX: (812)855-3443. Electronic mail address(es): FRYP@IUBACS (BITNET).

★7785★
Indiana University - Folklore Archives
Morrison Hall, Rm. 103
Bloomington, IN 47405
Subjects: Folklore, folksong, material culture. **Special Collections:** Joseph T. Hall Limerick Collection (5000); Roger Mitchell Collection of Micronesian Folktales (300). **Holdings:** 100 books; 40 bound periodical volumes; 200 dissertations; 40,000 folklore items; 500 cassettes; 80 tapes; 1000 slides. **Remarks:** Currently inactive. Holdings temporarily housed at Indiana University - Archives of Traditional Music.

★7786★
Indiana University - Folklore Collection (Hist, Area-Ethnic)
10th and Jordan Sts. Phone: (812)855-1550
Bloomington, IN 47405 Polly S. Grimshaw, Libn./Cur.
Staff: Prof 1; Other 1. **Subjects:** Folk literature; ethnomusicology; material culture; ethnic, regional, and urban folklore; folk ritual. **Special Collections:** Stith Thompson Collection (8000 items); Henri Gaidoz Collection (6500 items). **Services:** Interlibrary loan; copying; SDI; collection open to the public. **Publications:** Acquisitions Lists, irregular - for internal distribution and to researchers on request; list of journals and monograph series in the Folklore Collection; Annotated Bibliography of Indiana Folklore, revised annually. **Special Catalogs:** Subject catalog of the Gaidoz Collection.

★7787★
Indiana University - Geography and Map Library (Geog-Map)
301 Kirkwood Hall Phone: (812)855-1108
Bloomington, IN 47405 Daniel Seldin, Hd.
Founded: 1946. **Staff:** Prof 1; Other 2. **Subjects:** Geography, cartography. **Special Collections:** Sanborn Fire Insurance maps of Indiana cities. **Holdings:** 14,500 volumes and atlases; 19,000 microforms; 244,400 maps and charts. **Subscriptions:** 210 journals and other serials. **Services:** Interlibrary loan; copying; library open to the public with limited circulation. **Computerized Information Services:** BITNET (electronic mail service). **Remarks:** FAX: (812)855-4919. Electronic mail address(es): DIN@IUBACS (BITNET).

★7788★
Indiana University - Geology Library (Sci-Engr)
Geology Bldg.
1005 E. 10th St. Phone: (812)855-7170
Bloomington, IN 47405 Lois Heiser, Hd.
Founded: 1894. **Staff:** Prof 1; Other 2. **Subjects:** Geochemistry, geology, geomorphology, geophysics, mineral resources, mineralogy, paleontology, petrology, stratigraphy. **Holdings:** 93,200 volumes; 23,400 microforms; 283,700 maps and charts. **Subscriptions:** 1445 journals and other serials. **Services:** Interlibrary loan; copying; SDI; library open to the public. **Computerized Information Services:** DIALOG Information Services, PFDS Online; BITNET (electronic mail service). **Remarks:** FAX: (812)855-6614. Electronic mail address(es): HEISER@IUBACS (BITNET). Also serves the Indiana State Geological Survey.

★7789★
Indiana University - Health, Physical Education & Recreation Library (Educ)
HPER Bldg. 031 Phone: (812)855-4420
Bloomington, IN 47401 Julie Bobay, Hd.
Founded: 1978. **Staff:** 6. **Subjects:** Physical education, recreation and park administration, health and safety, coaching, adapted physical education and therapeutic recreation, sports medicine and psychology. **Holdings:** 15,300 volumes; 8600 microforms. **Subscriptions:** 200 journals and other serials. **Services:** Interlibrary loan; copying; library open to the public. **Automated Operations:** Computerized cataloging. **Computerized Information Services:** Association of Research Libraries (ARL), DIALOG Information Services, PFDS Online, BRS Information Technologies, OCLC; BITNET (electronic mail service). **Networks/Consortia:** Member of INCOLSA. **Remarks:** FAX: (812)855-6615. Electronic mail address(es): BOBAY@IUBACS (BITNET).

★7790★
Indiana University - Institute for the Study of Developmental Disabilities - Library (Educ)
2853 E. 10th St. Phone: (812)855-9396
Bloomington, IN 47405 Marilyn Irwin, Dir., Lib./Info. Dissem.Spec.
Founded: 1979. **Staff:** Prof 2; Other 3. **Subjects:** Developmental disabilities; curriculum materials for the developmentally disabled; early childhood intervention programs; assistance for parents of the developmentally disabled; parenting; community integration of handicapped persons. **Holdings:** 6000 books; 10 VF drawers of information files; 2 drawers of bibliographies; 3 drawers of test files; 2 drawers of organization files; 15 drawers of periodical files; 10 drawers of publishers' catalogs. **Subscriptions:** 25 journals and other serials. **Services:** Interlibrary loan; copying; library open to the public. **Computerized Information Services:** SpecialNet, SCAN (electronic mail services). **Networks/Consortia:** Member of Stone Hills Area Library Services Authority. **Publications:** Information Packet, annual. **Special Catalogs:** Publications Catalog, annual. **Remarks:** FAX: (812)855-9630. **Staff:** Christopher Lewis, Lib. Media Spec.

★7791★
Indiana University - Institute for Urban Transportation - Resource Center (Trans)
825 E. 8th St.
Bloomington, IN 47408 Phone: (812)855-8143
Founded: 1969. **Subjects:** Urban transportation. **Holdings:** 250 books; 7600 technical reports; 2000 microfiche; 36 VF drawers of maps, schedules, annual reports, reprints; 15 slide shows, video cassettes, films. **Subscriptions:** 25 journals and other serials. **Services:** Library not open to the public. **Remarks:** FAX: (812)855-8022.

★7792★
Indiana University - Journalism Library (Info Sci)
Ernie Pyle Hall
7th St. Phone: (812)855-3517
Bloomington, IN 47405 Frances Wilhoit, Hd.
Staff: Prof 1; Other 1. **Subjects:** Journalism, mass communication. **Special Collections:** Ernie Pyle. **Holdings:** 18,400 volumes; 600 microforms. **Subscriptions:** 286 journals and other serials. **Services:** Interlibrary loan; copying; library open to the public. **Computerized Information Services:** BITNET (electronic mail service). **Publications:** Mass Media Periodicals: an annotated bibliography (monograph). **Remarks:** FAX: (812)855-3393. Electronic mail address(es): WILHOIT@IUBACS (BITNET).

★7793★
Indiana University - Law Library (Law)
School of Law Phone: (812)855-9666
Bloomington, IN 47405 Colleen K. Pauwels, Dir.
Founded: 1925. **Staff:** Prof 10; Other 10. **Subjects:** Law. **Special Collections:** U.S. Government documents depository; U.S., 7th Circuit, Indiana Supreme Court, and Indiana Court of Appeals records and briefs depository. **Holdings:** 304,414 volumes; 761,594 microforms. **Subscriptions:** 5534 journals and other serials. **Services:** Interlibrary loan; copying; library open to the public. **Computerized Information Services:** LEXIS, OCLC, NEXIS, WESTLAW, DIALOG Information Services. **Networks/Consortia:** Member of INCOLSA. **Publications:** Res Ipsa Loquitur (newsletter). **Remarks:** FAX: (812)855-7099. **Staff:** Linda K. Fariss, Assoc.Dir.; Keith Buckley, Ref.Libn.; Nona Watt, Hd., Tech.Serv.; Marianne Mason, Docs.Libn.; Michael Maben, Cat.; Will Sadler, Sys.Coord.; Richard Vaughan, Ser.Libn.; Ralph Gaebler, Foreign/Intl. Law Libn.; Mitchell Counts, Comp.Serv.Libn.

★7794★
Indiana University - Lilly Library (Hist, Hum)
Bloomington, IN 47405 Phone: (812)855-2452
William R. Cagle, Libn.
Founded: 1960. **Staff:** Prof 7; Other 10. **Subjects:** British literature, especially Milton, Defoe, Wordsworth, 19th century British drama, modern literary manuscripts; American literature, especially Poe, Riley, Sinclair, Plath, and the files of several American publishers and literary magazines; American history, especially discovery, American Revolution, U.S. Constitution, War of 1812, Lincoln, Indiana, and Western expansion; European expansion, especially Spanish, Portuguese, and Dutch colonial empires; history of science and medicine. **Special Collections:** Mendel Latin American Collection; Ellison Far West Collection; Elisabeth Ball Children's Literature Collection; Oakleaf Lincoln Collection; J.K. Lilly Collection; Wendell Willkie papers; Orson Welles papers. **Holdings:** 355,500 volumes; 6.4 million manuscripts; 435 microforms. **Services:** Copying; library open to the public. **Computerized Information Services:** BITNET (electronic mail service). **Publications:** Lilly Library Publications Series, irregular - to Friends of the Lilly Library. **Special Catalogs:** Exhibition catalogs. **Remarks:** FAX: (812)855-3143. Electronic mail address(es): CAGLE@IUBACS (BITNET). **Staff:** Joel Silver, Hd., Reader Serv.; Elizabeth Johnson, Hd., Tech.Serv.; Becky Cape, Asst.Cur. of Ms.; Stephen Cape, Cat.; Erla Heyns, Ref. & Reader Serv.; Saundra Taylor, Cur. of Ms.

★7795★
Indiana University - Medical Sciences Library (Med)
251 Myers Hall Phone: (812)855-3347
Bloomington, IN 47405 Doug Freeman, Hd.
Staff: Prof 1; Other 1. **Subjects:** Anatomy, physiology, pharmacology, pathology, medicine, biomedical computer science, biochemistry, immunology. **Holdings:** 27,200 bound volumes; 3100 microforms. **Subscriptions:** 184 journals and other serials. **Services:** Interlibrary loan; copying; library open to the public. **Computerized Information Services:** BITNET (electronic mail service). **Remarks:** FAX: (812)855-5816. Electronic mail address(es): FREEMAN@IUBACS (BITNET).

★7796★
Indiana University - Music Library (Mus)
School of Music Phone: (812)855-8541
Bloomington, IN 47405 Dr. David Fenske, Hd.
Founded: 1939. **Staff:** Prof 5; Other 9. **Subjects:** Music. **Special Collections:** Apel Collection (photocopies of early keyboard music compiled by Professor Willi Apel; 200 volumes); black music; Latin American music; opera; piano pedagogy. **Holdings:** 338,200 volumes; 82,000 scores; 15,000 microforms; 68,300 phonograph records; 50,000 audiotapes; 1100 compact discs. **Subscriptions:** 543 journals and other serials. **Services:** Interlibrary loan; copying; library open to the public. **Automated Operations:** Computerized cataloging. **Computerized Information Services:** OCLC; BITNET (electronic mail service). **Networks/Consortia:** Member of INCOLSA. **Remarks:** FAX: (812)855-3843. Electronic mail address(es): FENSKE@IUBACS (BITNET). **Staff:** Michael Fling, Acq.; David Lasocki, Pub.Serv.; Ralph Papakhian, Hd., Tech.Serv.; Sue Stancu, Sound Recordings Cat.

★7797★
Indiana University - Optometry Library (Med)
Optometry Bldg. Phone: (812)855-8629
Bloomington, IN 47405 Doug Freeman, Hd.
Founded: 1968. **Staff:** Prof 1; Other 1. **Subjects:** Vision. **Holdings:** 16,000 volumes; 4100 microforms. **Subscriptions:** 265 journals and other serials. **Services:** Interlibrary loan; copying; library open to the public. **Computerized Information Services:** BITNET (electronic mail service). **Networks/Consortia:** Member of National Network of Libraries of Medicine - Greater Midwest Region, Association of Visual Science Librarians (AVSL). **Publications:** List of acquisitions, monthly. **Remarks:** FAX: (812)855-6616. Electronic mail address(es): FREEMAN@IUBACS (BITNET).

★7798★
Indiana University - Oral History Research Center (Hist)
Memorial Hall West, Rm. 401 Phone: (812)855-2856
Bloomington, IN 47405 John Bodnar, Dir.
Founded: 1968. **Staff:** Prof 2; Other 4. **Subjects:** Indiana - history, industry, agriculture, politics. **Special Collections:** History of the Kinsey Institute for Sex Research (27 interviews); Biography of Melvyn Douglas (26 interviews); History of the Theater in the Twentieth Century (10 interviews); Auto workers of Indiana (60 interviews); History of Paoli (50 interviews); History of Philanthropy in the U.S. (3 projects, 80 interviews). **Holdings:** 50 books; 1200 oral histories; 1 VF drawer; clippings. **Subscriptions:** 4 journals and other serials. **Services:** Copying (limited); library open to the public for reference use only. **Publications:** Newsletter, annual.

★7799★
Indiana University - Research Institute for Inner Asian Studies - Library (Area-Ethnic)
Goodbody Hall 344 Phone: (812)855-1605
Bloomington, IN 47405 Prof. Yuri Bregel, Dir.
Founded: 1967. **Subjects:** Inner Asia - history, civilization, linguistic studies. **Holdings:** 8500 books; 250 Tibetan blockprints and manuscripts; 400,000 pages on microfiche; Central Asian manuscripts on microfilm. **Subscriptions:** 25 journals and other serials. **Services:** Library open to the public for reference use only. **Remarks:** FAX: (812)855-7500.

★7800★
Indiana University - School of Dentistry Library (Med)
1121 W. Michigan St. Phone: (317)274-7204
Indianapolis, IN 46202 Sara Hook-Shelton, Lib.Dir.
Founded: 1929. **Staff:** Prof 2; Other 10. **Subjects:** Dentistry and allied health sciences, basic sciences, education. **Holdings:** 53,169 volumes; 5172 other cataloged items; 12,963 uncataloged items. **Subscriptions:** 581 journals and other serials. **Services:** Interlibrary loan; SDI; library open to the public. **Automated Operations:** Computerized public access catalog (NOTIS). **Computerized Information Services:** DIALOG Information Services, BRS Information Technologies, NLM, OCLC; CD-ROM (MEDLINE). Performs searches on fee basis. **Networks/Consortia:** Member of INCOLSA, Central Indiana Health Science Library Consortium, Central Indiana Area Library Services Authority (CIALSA). **Publications:** New Book List; The Library Tipster News; The Library Tipster: Guide to Policies, Services, and Resources. **Remarks:** FAX: (317)274-2419. **Staff:** Elizabeth Halpin, Tech.Serv.Libn.

★7801★
Indiana University - School of Law - Library (Law)
735 W. New York St. Phone: (317)274-4027
Indianapolis, IN 46202-5194 Prof. James F. Bailey, III, Dir., Law Lib.
Founded: 1893. **Staff:** Prof 6; Other 11. **Subjects:** Law - U.S., Commonwealth, international, comparative; jurisprudence; legal history. **Special Collections:** U.S. Government publications depository, 1967 to present; United Nations publications depository, 1977 to present; Organization of American States records, 1977 to present; law and law-related publications of European community. **Holdings:** 375,000 volumes. **Subscriptions:** 5456 journals and other serials; 24 newspapers. **Services:** Interlibrary loan; copying; library open to the public for reference use only. **Automated Operations:** Computerized public access catalog and cataloging. **Computerized Information Services:** LEXIS, Veralex 2, OCLC, NEXIS, VU/TEXT Information Services, DIALOG Information Services, WESTLAW. **Networks/Consortia:** Member of INCOLSA, Central Indiana Area Library Services Authority (CIALSA). **Publications:** Recent Acquisitions List, monthly - for internal distribution only. **Remarks:** Alternate telephone number(s): (317)274-4028. FAX: (317)274-8825. **Staff:** Wendell Johnting, Asst.Dir., Tech.Serv.; Merlin Whiteman, Asst.Dir., Rdr.Serv.; Mahnaz Moshfegh, Acq.; Minde Glenn, Ref.; Kiyoshi Otsu, Cat.

★7802★
Indiana University - School of Library and Information Science Library (Info Sci)
10th & Jordan Sts. Phone: (812)855-5968
Bloomington, IN 47405 Judith Dye, Hd.
Founded: 1947. **Staff:** Prof 1; Other 1. **Subjects:** Library and information science. **Special Collections:** Children's collection. **Holdings:** 34,300 volumes; 1400 microforms. **Subscriptions:** 383 journals and other serials. **Services:** Interlibrary loan; library open to the public. **Computerized Information Services:** DIALOG Information Services; BITNET (electronic mail service). **Publications:** Acquisitions list, bimonthly; bibliographies. **Remarks:** FAX: (812)855-3386. Alternate telephone number(s): 335-1619. Electronic mail address(es): JDYE@IUBACS (BITNET).

★7803★
Indiana University - Swain Hall Library (Sci-Engr, Comp Sci)
Bloomington, IN 47405 Phone: (812)855-2758
Carol Hutchins, Hd.
Founded: 1940. **Staff:** Prof 1; Other 3. **Subjects:** Physics, mathematics, astronomy, computer science. **Special Collections:** Astronomy Chart Room (300 volumes); Goethe Link Observatory (900 volumes); Cyclotron Facility (1500 volumes). **Holdings:** 95,000 volumes; 3700 microforms. **Subscriptions:** 1079 journals and other serials. **Services:** Interlibrary loan; copying; SDI; library open to the public. **Computerized Information Services:** DIALOG Information Services; BITNET (electronic mail service). **Publications:** Acquisition List, monthly; Annual Report - both free upon request. **Remarks:** FAX: (812)855-6613. Electronic mail address(es): HUTCHINS@IUBACS (BITNET).

★7804★
Indiana University - William Hammond Mathers Museum - Museum Library
601 E. 8th St.
Bloomington, IN 47405
Defunct.

★7805★
Indiana University - Workshop in Political Theory & Policy Analysis - Workshop Library (Soc Sci)
513 N. Park St. Phone: (812)855-0441
Bloomington, IN 47405 Charlotte Hess, Libn.
Staff: 1. **Subjects:** Institutional analysis - macro-organization, intermediate organization, micro-organization; common pool resources; game theory; urban public services; decentralization; local governance in developing countries; indigenous institutions; self-governance. **Holdings:** 3000 books; 12,000 papers, journal articles, dissertations, recent and bound periodicals, subject files, and other items. **Services:** Copying; library open to the public with restrictions. **Computerized Information Services:** BITNET (electronic mail service). **Publications:** Bibliographies; reprints; monographs. **Remarks:** FAX: (812)855-3150. Telex: 272279 INDIANA UBLOM. Electronic mail address(es): HESS@IUBACS (BITNET).

★7806★
Indiana University - Zooarcheology Laboratory - Library (Biol Sci)
407 Rawles Hall Phone: (812)855-6755
Bloomington, IN 47405 William R. Adams
Founded: 1945. **Staff:** 1. **Subjects:** Zoology, anthropology, biology, archeology, forensics. **Special Collections:** National Geographic Magazine, 1919 to present. **Holdings:** 500 books; 1000 bound periodical volumes; 2000 reports. **Services:** Library open to the public by appointment. **Remarks:** FAX: (812)855-4358. Telex: 272279.

Indiana University, Indianapolis - School of Law Library
See: **Indiana University - School of Law** (7801)

★7807★
Indiana University, Indianapolis - School of Medicine Library (Med)
975 W. Walnut Phone: (317)274-7182
Indianapolis, IN 46202 Dana McDonald, Hd.
Founded: 1917. **Staff:** Prof 13; Other 18. **Subjects:** Medicine, nursing, allied health sciences. **Special Collections:** History of medicine. **Holdings:** 174,759

volumes. **Subscriptions:** 2067 journals and other serials; 6 newspapers. **Services:** Interlibrary loan; library open to the public. **Automated Operations:** Computerized cataloging and ILL. **Computerized Information Services:** MEDLINE, BRS Information Technologies, DIALOG Information Services, PFDS Online, OCLC; DOCLINE, OnTyme Electronic Message Network Service (electronic mail services). Performs searches on fee basis. Contact Person: Fran Brahmi, Dir., Info.Serv. **Networks/Consortia:** Member of National Network of Libraries of Medicine - Greater Midwest Region, INCOLSA. **Remarks:** FAX: (317)274-2088. Electronic mail address(es): ICOLSA4 (OnTyme Electronic Message Network Service). **Staff:** Janine Orr, Ref.Libn.; Julia Tyler, Ref.Libn.; Carole Francq, Dir., Coll.Mgt.; Kathy Schmidt, Ser.Libn.; James Morgan, Automation Libn.; Julie Fore, Asst. Automation Libn.; Peggy Richwine, Coll. Database Mgr.; JoAnn Switzer, Ref.Libn.; Nancy Eckerman, Spec.Coll.Libn.

★7808★
Indiana University--Northwest - Calumet Regional Archives (Hist) Library
3400 Broadway — Phone: (219)980-6628
Gary, IN 46408 — Stephen McShane, Archv./Cur.
Founded: 1973. **Staff:** Prof 4. **Subjects:** Calumet Region - urban history, labor history, ethnic history, industrialization, education history, women's history, environmental history. **Special Collections:** International Institute of Northwest Indiana (100 linear feet); United States Steel photographs (2 file cabinets and 10 boxes); Hammond Oil, Chemical, and Atomic Workers' Union (7 linear feet); Gary Historical Society papers (6 linear feet); Bailly Alliance papers (10 linear feet); Community Action to Reverse Pollution papers (2 linear feet); Gary YWCA records (19 linear feet); Lake County local government records, 1858-1961 (350 volumes); Adam Benjamin Papers; United Steelworkers of America (USWA) Local records; Anderson Company records; Save-the-Dunes Council records. **Holdings:** 150 books; 1000 linear feet of manuscript materials. **Services:** Copying; archives open to the public. **Publications:** Newsletter, semiannual - to donors, academic institutions, and other interested parties; Skinning Cats; Latinos in Northwest Indiana. **Remarks:** FAX: (219)980-6558. The Calumet Regional Archives collects most types of archival materials relating to the history of the Calumet Region, Indiana, 1900 to present. **Staff:** Ronald D. Cohen, Co-Dir.; James B. Lane, Co-Dir.; Robert Moran, Co-Dir.

★7809★
Indiana University of Pennsylvania - American Language Institute - Library (Hum)
212 Eicher Hall
Indiana, PA 15705 — Phone: (412)357-2402
Founded: 1982. **Subjects:** Linguistics, language acquisition, English as a second language. **Holdings:** 2000 volumes. **Remarks:** FAX: (412)357-5640. Telex: 5106017797IUP-UD.

★7810★
Indiana University of Pennsylvania - Cogswell Music Library (Mus)
Cogswell Hall — Phone: (412)357-2892
Indiana, PA 15705-1070 — Carl Rahkonen, Mus.Libn.
Founded: 1965. **Staff:** Prof 1; Other 14. **Subjects:** Music. **Holdings:** 10,000 books; 16,000 scores; 11,000 sound recordings. **Services:** Interlibrary loan; library open to the public with restrictions. **Automated Operations:** Computerized public access catalog, cataloging, and acquisitions. **Computerized Information Services:** OCLC; IUPTOMUS, Carlyle Ststems Inc. (internal databases). **Networks/Consortia:** Member of Pittsburgh Regional Library Center (PRLC). **Publications:** Elliker, Calvin Monumentae: A Union List of Music Monuments in Pennsylvania Chapter (Music Library Association, 1987; book).

★7811★
Indiana University of Pennsylvania - Patrick J. Stapleton, Jr. Library (Hum)
Indiana, PA 15705-1096 — Phone: (412)357-2330
Larry A. Kroah, Dir., Libs./Media Rsrcs.
Founded: 1875. **Staff:** Prof 22; Other 26. **Subjects:** U.S. public education; Pennsylvania history; home economics; American and English literature; music; labor and industrial relations; social studies; fine arts. **Special Collections:** Curriculum materials; University School Library (6000 volumes); Charles Darwin; Herman Melville; Mark Twain; Edgar Allan Poe, John Greenleaf Whittier; Norman Mailer; Washington Irving; Districts 2, 4, and 5 of the United Mine Workers Union; Rochester and Pittsburgh Coal Company Papers. **Holdings:** 620,000 books; 100,000 bound periodical volumes; select U.S. and Pennsylvania Government document depository; pamphlets; clippings; pictures; 1.7 million microforms; slides; phonograph records. **Subscriptions:** 3900 journals and other serials; 15 newspapers. **Services:** Interlibrary loan; copying; faxing; library open to the public. **Automated Operations:** Computerized public access catalog, cataloging, acquisitions, serials, and circulation. **Computerized Information Services:** DIALOG Information Services; CD-ROMs (ABI/INFORM Ondisc, Disertation Abstracts Ondisc, ERIC, PsychLit, Disclosure Incorporated, Compustat PC Plus). Performs searches on fee basis. **Networks/Consortia:** Member of Pittsburgh Regional Library Center (PRLC). **Special Catalogs:** Monumentae: A Union List of Music Monuments in Pennsylvania Chapter--Music Library Association Member Libraries. **Remarks:** FAX: (412)357-6213. Public access catalog dial-up access number: 357-7700. **Staff:** Ronald Steiner, Assoc.Libn.; Carol Connell, Asst.Libn.; Sandra Janicki, Asst.Libn.; James Hooks, Libn.; Rosa Jen, Asst.Libn.; David Kaufman, Assoc.Libn.; Robert Kirby, Asst.Libn.; Lynne Lucas, Asst.Libn.; Theresa McDevitt, Asst.Libn.; Blaine Knupp, Asst.Libn.; Daniel Shively, Assoc.Libn.; Karen Brown, Assoc.Libn.; Walter Laude, Assoc.Libn.; Phillip Zorich, Asst.Libn.; Carl Rahkonen, Asst.Libn.; John Grassinger.

★7812★
Indiana University-Purdue University at Indianapolis - Archives and Special Collections (Hist)
815 W. Michigan St. — Phone: (317)274-0464
Indianapolis, IN 46202 — Eric Pumroy, Hd.
Staff: 3. **Subjects:** History of Indiana University/Purdue University at Indianapolis and its predecessor schools; German-Americana; sports history; history of philanthropy. **Special Collections:** Records of the American Turners national office, 1855-1988 (30 linear feet); records of the Athenaeum Turners of Indianapolis, including records of the Normal College of the American Gymnastic Union, the Free-Thinkers' Society, the Indianapolis Maennerchor, and other German-American organizations in Indianapolis, 1850s-1970s (74 linear feet); music library of the Indianapolis Maennerchor, 1857-1938 (325 pieces); records of PAX/Indianapolis (organizing committee for the 1987 Pan American Games in Indianapolis; 141 linear feet); records of the John Herron School of Art, 1902-1967 (30 linear feet); records of Dr. Leslie Freeman's paraplegia, 1943-1967 (84 linear feet); records of Indiana University/Purdue University at Indianapolis and predecessor schools, 1900-1990 (2000 linear feet); Philanthropy collection (papers of fund raisers Harold L. Oram and the Oram group, Maurice Gurin, and George Brakeley, Jr.); records of the Natural Society of Fund Raising Executives, and CASE (Council for Advancement and Support of Education). **Services:** Copying; library open to the public during business hours. **Computerized Information Services:** BITNET (electronic mail service). **Remarks:** Electronic mail address(es): IMXJ100@INDYCMS (BITNET).

★7813★
Indiana University-Purdue University at Indianapolis - Science and Engineering Library (Sci-Engr, Biol Sci, Comp Sci)
1201 E. 38th St. — Phone: (317)274-0497
Indianapolis, IN 46205 — Marie Wright, Act.Hd., Pub.Serv.
Founded: 1962. **Staff:** Prof 3; Other 3. **Subjects:** Biology, chemistry, computer science and technology, engineering, mathematics, physics, psychology. **Special Collections:** NASA microfiche. **Holdings:** 34,178 books; 33,813 bound periodical volumes; 538,217 microfiche. **Subscriptions:** 976 journals and other serials; 9 newspapers. **Services:** Interlibrary loan; copying; library open to the public. **Automated Operations:** Computerized public access catalog and circulation. **Computerized Information Services:** BRS Information Technologies, DIALOG Information Services, OCLC; CD-ROMs (PsycLit, Compendex-Plus, Computer-Select, MathSci, NTIS, Biological Abstracts, SuperTech Abstracts Plus, Electronic Sweets); BITNET (electronic mail service). Performs searches on fee basis. Contact Person: Randi L. Stocker, Ref.Libn. **Networks/Consortia:** Member of INCOLSA, Central Indiana Area Library Services Authority (CIALSA). **Remarks:** FAX: (317)274-2950. Electronic mail address(es): ITHLIOO@INDYCMS (BITNET). **Staff:** Ann Koopman, Ref.Libn.

★7814★
Indiana University-Purdue University at Indianapolis - University Libraries/Herron School of Art (Art)
1701 N. Pennsylvania — Phone: (317)923-3651
Indianapolis, IN 46202 — Jennifer L. Hehman, Act.Hd.Libn.
Founded: 1970. **Staff:** Prof 1; Other 3. **Subjects:** Visual arts. **Holdings:** 20,000 books; 3430 bound periodical volumes; 114,800 35mm slides; 11,000

lantern slides; 16 VF drawers of clippings, exhibition catalogs, pictures. **Subscriptions:** 136 journals and other serials. **Services:** Interlibrary loan; copying; library open to the public. **Automated Operations:** Computerized public access catalog and cataloging. **Computerized Information Services:** DIALOG Information Services; electronic mail service. Performs searches on fee basis. **Networks/Consortia:** Member of INCOLSA. **Remarks:** FAX: (317)924-4472.

★7815★
Indiana University-Purdue University at Indianapolis - University Library (Soc Sci)
815 W. Michigan St. Phone: (317)274-8278
Indianapolis, IN 46202 Barbara B. Fischler, Dir. of Libs.
Founded: 1928. **Staff:** Prof 15; Other 21. **Subjects:** Social work, business, child welfare, community organization, criminology, public welfare, the aged, education, philanthropy and fund raising. **Holdings:** 283,032 volumes; 193,361 microforms. **Subscriptions:** 3236 journals and other serials; 30 newspapers. **Services:** Interlibrary loan; copying; library open to the public. **Automated Operations:** Computerized public access catalog, cataloging, and acquisitions. **Computerized Information Services:** DIALOG Information Services, BRS Information Technologies, OCLC, Economic Development Information Network (EDIN), ERIC. **Networks/Consortia:** Member of INCOLSA, Central Indiana Area Library Services Authority (CIALSA). **Publications:** Staff newsletter, irregular - for internal distribution only. **Remarks:** FAX: (317)274-0492. **Staff:** Jean Gnat, Assoc.Dir.; Dolores Hoyt, Hd., Tech.Serv.; Eric Pumroy, Archv.; Ann Griffin, Adm.Asst.; Steven Schmidt, Circ./ILL; Marie Wright, Hd., Pub.Serv.; Shirley Yegerlehner, Online Searching Coord.; Janet Huettner, Bibliog., Ctr. on Philanthropy.

★7816★
Indiana Vocational Technical College - Learning Resource Center (Educ)
1440 E. 35th Ave. Phone: (219)981-1111
Gary, IN 46409 John M. Niemann, Dir.
Founded: 1974. **Staff:** Prof 2; Other 1. **Subjects:** Health occupations, industrial maintenance, fire science, business science, electronics, drafting. **Holdings:** 5000 books; 2000 other cataloged items; transparencies; slides; filmstrips; programmed materials; videotapes. **Subscriptions:** 103 journals and other serials. **Services:** Interlibrary loan; copying; instructional material developing; center open to the public for reference use only. **Computerized Information Services:** InfoTrac. **Networks/Consortia:** Member of Northwest Indiana Area Library Services Authority (NIALSA). **Staff:** Nick P. Vasil, Tech.Serv.Supv.

★7817★
Indianapolis Bar Association - Library (Law)
10 W. Market St., Suite 440
Indianapolis, IN 46204 Phone: (317)269-2000
Founded: 1878. **Subjects:** Law - tax, bankruptcy, business organizations, Indiana, labor. **Holdings:** 20,000 volumes; reporters. **Services:** Interlibrary loan; library not open to the public. **Remarks:** FAX: (317)464-8118.

★7818★
Indianapolis-Marion County Public Library - Arts Division (Art, Hum)
40 E. St. Clair St. Phone: (317)269-1764
Indianapolis, IN 46204 Daniel Gann, Hd.
Founded: 1924. **Staff:** Prof 11. **Subjects:** Art, language, drama, sports, literature, music. **Special Collections:** Julia Conner Thompson Collection (books on the finer arts of homemaking); James Whitcomb Riley Collection (1st editions and memorabilia); Philharmonic Symphony programs; choral music; music scores and parts; framed art collection. **Holdings:** 100,000 titles; 70 VF drawers of pamphlets, clippings, mounted pictures; 30,000 phonograph records; 10,000 pieces of sheet music; New York Times Index on microfilm. **Subscriptions:** 280 journals and other serials. **Services:** Interlibrary loan; copying; listening facilities; concert series. **Special Indexes:** Index to symphony program notes (card); index to sheet music. **Remarks:** FAX: (317)269-1768. **Staff:** Penny Cannon; Joe Cehovin; C. Sue Chapman; Deborah Colter; Lora Crain; Val Elliott; Nancy Gootee; Glen Halberstadt; Marilyn Martin; Caroline Smerk.

★7819★
Indianapolis-Marion County Public Library - Business, Science and Technology Division (Bus-Fin, Sci-Engr)
Box 211 Phone: (317)269-1741
Indianapolis, IN 46206 Mark Leggett, Mgr.
Founded: 1921. **Staff:** Prof 10. **Subjects:** Science, engineering, space science, agriculture, electronics, computer science, building, health, cookery, television, accounting, advertising, economics, business, insurance, investment management. **Special Collections:** Wright Marble Collection of rare cookbooks; Arthur Stumpf Collection of old menus; U.S. patent depository. **Holdings:** 65,000 titles; 90 VF drawers. **Subscriptions:** 950 journals and other serials. **Services:** Interlibrary loan; copying. **Computerized Information Services:** Access to DIALOG Information Services, NEXIS, U.S. Patent Classification System (CASSIS), Statistical Information System (STATIS). **Remarks:** FAX: (317)269-1768. **Staff:** Rob Rutledge; Margaret Glesing; Matt Hannigan; Phyllis Karrh; Betty Tomeo; James Cannon; Karen Cohen; Maureen Duncan; Mike Williams.

★7820★
Indianapolis-Marion County Public Library - Newspaper and Periodical Division (Info Sci)
40 E. St. Clair St. Phone: (317)269-1728
Indianapolis, IN 46204 Harriet Cohen, Mgr.
Founded: 1981. **Staff:** Prof 1; Other 7. **Subjects:** Newspapers, periodicals, government documents. **Holdings:** 63,700 bound periodical volumes; 17,000 government documents. **Subscriptions:** 1200 journals; 70 newspapers. **Services:** Interlibrary loan; copying; division open to the public. **Computerized Information Services:** DIALOG Information Services, NEXIS, Statistical Information System (STATIS), WILSONLINE, BRS Information Technologies, DataTimes, OCLC-EPIC; internal database; ALANET (electronic mail service). **Publications:** Periodical, newspaper and microfilm list, annual. **Remarks:** FAX: (317)269-1768.

★7821★
Indianapolis-Marion County Public Library - Social Science Division (Soc Sci, Rel-Phil)
Box 211 Phone: (317)269-1733
Indianapolis, IN 46206 Lois Laube, Mgr.
Founded: 1960. **Staff:** Prof 8. **Subjects:** Bibliography, philosophy, religion, sociology, law, folklore, political science, education, travel, history, biography. **Special Collections:** Indiana and Indianapolis (90 VF drawers); Indiana county histories; Foundation Center Collection; financial aid; college catalogs on microfiche; adult education information files; club and organization file; nonprofit newsletter file. **Holdings:** 125,000 titles; 25 VF drawers of subject files; 49 VF drawers of miscellaneous place, costume, portrait, career, foundation files; microforms. **Subscriptions:** 400 journals and other serials; 70 newspapers. **Services:** Interlibrary loan; copying. **Computerized Information Services:** DIALOG Information Services, NEXIS, Indiana Chamber of Commerce Legislative Database, DataTimes, WILSONLINE, NewsBank, Infotrac, EDIN. **Networks/Consortia:** Member of Central Indiana Area Library Services Authority (CIALSA), INCOLSA. **Publications:** Foundation newsletter; bibliographies. **Remarks:** FAX: (317)269-1768. **Staff:** Randall Ayers; Georgia Cravey; Nancy Dubin; Linda Herreman; Kathy Barnard; Martha McKnight; James Simon.

★7822★
Indianapolis-Marion County Public Library - Visual Arts Division (Aud-Vis)
1435 N. Illinois St. Phone: (317)269-1821
Indianapolis, IN 46202 Randall O. Starks, Mgr.
Founded: 1948. **Staff:** Prof 2; Other 9. **Holdings:** 1200 framed art prints; 20,000 videotapes. **Services:** Library open to the public.

★7823★
Indianapolis Museum of Art - Reference Library (Art)
1200 W. 38th St. Phone: (317)923-1331
Indianapolis, IN 46208 Carolyn J. Metz, Dir., Educ.Rsrcs.
Founded: 1907. **Staff:** Prof 2; Other 1. **Subjects:** Fine arts. **Special Collections:** Indiana artists (6 VF drawers of clippings and catalogs). **Holdings:** 30,000 volumes; auction, sales, and exhibition catalogs; 78 VF drawers of clippings and pamphlets. **Subscriptions:** 102 journals and other serials. **Services:** Copying; library open to the public for reference use only. **Automated Operations:** Computerized cataloging. **Computerized Information Services:** OCLC. **Networks/Consortia:** Member of INCOLSA, Central Indiana Area Library Services Authority (CIALSA). **Remarks:** FAX: (317)926-8931. **Staff:** Janice Meyers, Cat.

★7824★
Indianapolis Museum of Art - Slide Collection (Art)
1200 W. 38th St. Phone: (317)923-1331
Indianapolis, IN 46208 Carolyn J. Metz, Dir., Educ.Rsrcs.
Staff: Prof 2; Other 1. **Subjects:** Art history, painting, sculpture, minor arts, decorative arts, architecture. **Holdings:** 150,000 slides. **Services:** Collection open to the public on a limited schedule. **Special Indexes:** Artist name card file; theme and subject guides. **Remarks:** FAX: (317)926-8931. **Staff:** Joni Marie Back, Slide Coord.

★7825★
Indianapolis Newspapers, Inc. - Indianapolis Star and Indianapolis News - Reference Library (Publ)
307 N. Pennsylvania St.
Box 145 Phone: (317)633-9293
Indianapolis, IN 46206-0145 Sandra E. Fitzgerald, Hd.Libn.
Founded: 1912. **Staff:** Prof 4; Other 11. **Subjects:** Newspaper reference topics, especially Indiana and Indianapolis news. **Special Collections:** Star and News, 1912 to present. **Holdings:** 1600 books. **Services:** Copying (limited); library open to the public on a limited schedule. **Computerized Information Services:** DIALOG Information Services, NEXIS, VU/TEXT Information Services, Statistical Information System (STATIS), DataTimes. **Special Indexes:** Index to Star and News. **Staff:** M. Cathern Hess, Asst.Hd.Libn./Day Supv.; Barbara Hoffman, Night Supv.

★7826★
Indianapolis Power & Light Company - Corporate Communications Reference Center (Energy)
25 Monument Circle
Box 1595 Phone: (317)261-8387
Indianapolis, IN 46206-1595 Christopher Feeney, Hd.
Founded: 1980. **Staff:** Prof 1; Other 1. **Subjects:** Electric power. **Holdings:** Figures not available. **Services:** Interlibrary loan; center not open to the public. **Networks/Consortia:** Member of INCOLSA, Central Indiana Area Library Services Authority (CIALSA).

★7827★
Indianapolis Public Schools - Karl R. Kalp Teachers Library (Educ)
120 E. Walnut St. Phone: (317)226-4499
Indianapolis, IN 46204 Dorothy R. Crenshaw, Supv.
Founded: 1921. **Staff:** 1. **Subjects:** Education. **Special Collections:** Human relations; state adopted textbooks. **Holdings:** 10,000 books; 1400 bound periodical volumes; 52 shelves of pamphlets and courses of study; microfilm; 2500 microfiche. **Subscriptions:** 120 journals and other serials. **Services:** Interlibrary loan; copying; research services for administrators and teachers in school system; library open to the public but circulation only to Indianapolis Public Schools personnel and nonteaching students in Indianapolis colleges. **Computerized Information Services:** CD-ROM (Education Index). Performs searches free of charge. **Publications:** Bookmark, 4/school year - to administrators and teachers in the school system; bibliographies.

★7828★
Indianapolis Zoological Society, Inc. - Indianapolis Zoo Library (Biol Sci)
1200 W. Washington St. Phone: (317)630-2040
Indianapolis, IN 46222 Suzanne K. Braun, Libn.
Founded: 1988. **Staff:** Prof 1. **Subjects:** Animal behavior, management of animals in captivity, wildlife conservation, animal nutrition, veterinary medicine, zoo horticulture. **Special Collections:** Zoo Archives. **Holdings:** 2000 books; 10,000 slides. **Subscriptions:** 100 journals and other serials. **Services:** Copying; SDI; library open to the public by appointment. **Automated Operations:** Computerized cataloging. **Computerized Information Services:** DIALOG Information Services, OCLC. **Networks/Consortia:** Member of INCOLSA, Central Indiana Area Library Services Authority (CIALSA). **Remarks:** FAX: (317)630-5153.

Indianhead Technical College
See: **Wisconsin Indianhead Technical College, New Richmond Campus** (20511)

★7829★
Indochina Project - Library (Area-Ethnic)
2001 S St., N.W., Suite 740 Phone: (202)483-9222
Washington, DC 20009 Bill Herod, Dir.
Founded: 1979. **Staff:** Prof 12. **Subjects:** U.S.-Indochinese relations, human rights and humanitarian affairs in Indochina. **Holdings:** 75 bound periodical volumes. **Subscriptions:** 54 journals and other serials. **Services:** Library open to the public by permission. **Computerized Information Services:** CompuServe Information Service; MCI Mail (electronic mail service). **Publications:** Weekly Indochina Digest - by subscription. **Remarks:** FAX: (202)483-9314. Electronic mail address(es): Indochina (MCI Mail).

Indonesia - Department of Industry - Institute for Research and Development of Handicraft and Batik Industries
See: **Institute for Research and Development of Handicraft and Batik Industries** (7971)

★7830★
Indonesian Institute of Sciences - Centre for Scientific Documentation and Information (Sci-Engr)
Jalan Jenderal Gatot Subroto Kav. 10
P.O. Box 269/JKSMG/88 Phone: 21 583465
Jakarta 12790, Indonesia Miss Luwarsih Pringgoadisurjo, Hd.
Founded: 1965. **Staff:** Prof 90; Other 146. **Subjects:** Science, technology, industry, social sciences, humanities. **Special Collections:** Women for Development (2435 titles); standards (11,444 titles). **Holdings:** 136,862 volumes; 15,713 report titles; 1517 patents; 3100 dissertations; 49,547 microforms. **Subscriptions:** 1092 journals and other serials. **Services:** Interlibrary loan; copying; SDI; center open to Indonesians without restrictions. **Automated Operations:** Computerized cataloging and acquisitions. **Computerized Information Services:** DIALOG Information Services, BISTINFOS Information Service; internal databases. Performs searches on fee basis. Contact Person: B. Sudarsono. **Publications:** Accessions list (books and microforms); BACA (brief communication); Annual Report; Directory of Special Libraries and Information Sources in Indonesia; bibliographies on various technical topics; additional publications available. **Special Catalogs:** Union List of Serials; Union List of Indonesian Dissertations; catalog of microform holdings held by the centre. **Special Indexes:** Index of Indonesian Learned Periodicals; Index of Research and Survey Reports; Index of papers submitted to seminars, conferences, workshops, and meetings held in Indonesia. **Remarks:** Alternate telephone number(s): 510719; 511065. Telex: 62875 IA. **Also Known As:** Lembaga Ilmu Pengetahuan Indonesia - Pusat Dokumentasi dan Informasi Ilmiah.

★7831★
Industrial Accident Prevention Association - Information Centre (Sci-Engr)
2 Bloor St., W., 31st Fl. Phone: (416)965-8888
Toronto, ON, Canada M4W 3N8 Dolores Harms Penner, Mgr.
Founded: 1977. **Staff:** Prof 2; Other 5. **Subjects:** Accident prevention, occupational health and safety. **Holdings:** 8000 books and reports. **Subscriptions:** 400 journals and other serials. **Services:** Interlibrary loan; library open to the public for reference use only. **Automated Operations:** Computerized cataloging and acquisitions. **Computerized Information Services:** DIALOG Information Services, CAN/OLE, MEDLARS, CCINFO, QL Systems, ORBIT Search Service. **Publications:** Info. News, 6/year. **Remarks:** FAX: (416)963-1189. **Staff:** Saul Kaufman.

★7832★
Industrial-Alliance Life Insurance Company - Library (Bus-Fin)
1080 St. Louis Rd.
Box 1907 Phone: (418)684-5282
Quebec, PQ, Canada G1K 7M3 Martine Robichaud, Sec.
Founded: 1961. **Staff:** 1. **Subjects:** Insurance, accounting, finance, salesmanship, psychology of selling, mathematics, office management, personnel management, economics, investments. **Holdings:** 5500 books; 1000 pamphlets. **Subscriptions:** 47 journals and other serials. **Services:** Copying; library open to qualified users. **Remarks:** FAX: (418)683-4449.

★7833★
Industrial Health Foundation, Inc. - Library (Med)
34 Penn Circle, W. Phone: (412)363-6600
Pittsburgh, PA 15206 Marianne C. Kaschak, Dir., Info.Serv.
Founded: 1969. **Staff:** Prof 1; Other 1. **Subjects:** Industrial hygiene, occupational safety and health, toxicology, environmental issues. **Holdings:**

2000 books; 100 bound periodical volumes; 60,000 abstracts; 20 VF drawers of pamphlets and reprints. **Subscriptions:** 60 journals and other serials. **Services:** Interlibrary loan; library not open to the public. **Computerized Information Services:** DIALOG Information Services, NLM. **Publications:** Industrial Hygiene Digest (abstract service), monthly - by subscription; Memos to Members (newsletter), quarterly; technical bulletins; subject bibliographies; symposia proceedings, all irregular - all for sale. **Special Catalogs:** Publications Catalog (pamphlet) - free upon request. **Special Indexes:** Yearly and decennial indexes to Industrial Hygiene Digest. **Remarks:** FAX: (412)363-6605.

★7834★
Industrial Indemnity Company - Library (Bus-Fin)
255 California St.
Box 94120 Phone: (415)627-5329
San Francisco, CA 94111 Judy Kogan, Libn.
Founded: 1956. **Staff:** 1. **Subjects:** Californiana, insurance, insurance history, business, biography, political science. **Holdings:** 17,000 books. **Subscriptions:** 30 journals and other serials. **Services:** Library not open to the public.

Industrial Research Center of Quebec
See: **Centre de Recherche Industrielle du Quebec** (3284)

★7835★
Industrial Risk Insurers - Library (Sci-Engr)
85 Woodland St. Phone: (203)520-7412
Hartford, CT 06102 Patricia Sasso, Libn.
Founded: 1952. **Staff:** Prof 1. **Subjects:** Fire protection, engineering. **Holdings:** 2000 books; specialized periodicals; company catalogs; Underwriter Laboratories standards and reports; 450 other cataloged items. **Subscriptions:** 100 journals and other serials. **Services:** Interlibrary loan; copying; library open to the public by appointment. **Publications:** Sentinel, quarterly - free to persons interested in fire and loss prevention. **Special Indexes:** IRI Index (lists slide show titles, film and videotape titles, placards, available publications). **Remarks:** FAX: (203)527-3160; 549-5780.

★7836★
Industrial Technology Institute - Information Resources Center (Comp Sci)
2901 Hubbard
Box 1485 Phone: (313)769-4290
Ann Arbor, MI 48106 Janet L. Smith, Mgr., Info.Serv.
Founded: 1983. **Staff:** Prof 2; Other 1. **Subjects:** Computerized integrated manufacturing, automation of factory floor, software development, manufacturing engineering, training. **Holdings:** 3500 books. **Subscriptions:** 300 journals and other serials; 6 newspapers. **Services:** Interlibrary loan; center not open to the public. **Automated Operations:** Computerized cataloging, acquisitions, serials, and circulation. **Computerized Information Services:** DIALOG Information Services, BRS Information Technologies, PFDS Online, NEXIS, ESA/IRS, WILSONLINE, VU/TEXT Information Services, STN International; UNIX (electronic mail service). Performs searches on fee basis. **Networks/Consortia:** Member of Michigan Library Consortium (MLC). **Publications:** Inside Information, bimonthly. **Remarks:** Alternate telephone number(s): 769-4000. FAX: (313)769-4064. Electronic mail address(es): JLS@HELA.ITI.ORG (UNIX).

★7837★
Industrial Technology Research Institute - Union Chemical Laboratories - Library (Sci-Engr)
321 Kuang-Fu Rd., Section 2 Phone: 72-1321
Hsinchu 30042, Taiwan Ms. A. Du, Libn.
Subjects: Chemistry, chemical engineering, polymers, biotechnology. **Holdings:** 40,000 volumes. **Remarks:** Telex: 31478 UCL ITRI.

★7838★
Industrial Workers of the World - Library (Bus-Fin)
1095 Market St. No. 204
San Francisco, CA 94103 Phone: (415)863-9627
Founded: 1905. **Staff:** 1. **Subjects:** Labor history, economics, political science. **Holdings:** 20 books; 15 bound periodical volumes; IWW publications on microfilm (1925 to present); foreign language publications. **Subscriptions:** 30 journals and other serials; 50 newspapers. **Services:** Library open to the public by appointment for reference use only; material stored in boxes. **Publications:** Industrial Worker, monthly - by subscription. **Remarks:** FAX: (415)626-2685. Primary material is located at Wayne State University - Archives of Labor and Urban Affairs/University Archives.

★7839★
Infocom Ltd. - Library (Sci-Engr)
P.O. Box 78
East Grinstead, West Sussex RH19 Phone: 342 323382
2YW, England Dr. Gordon Wilkinson, Mng.Dir.
Subjects: Science and technology, laboratory equipment and analytical instrumentation. **Holdings:** 500 bound volumes; reports; patents. **Computerized Information Services:** Online systems. Performs searches on fee basis. **Remarks:** FAX: 342 315939. Telex: 94070150 AIIR G.

★7840★
InfoCorp - Library (Comp Sci)
2880 Lakeside Dr., Suite 300 Phone: (408)980-4300
Santa Clara, CA 95054 Sara Lake, Lib.Mgr.
Founded: 1982. **Staff:** Prof 1; Other 2. **Subjects:** Computer industry, business, market research. **Holdings:** 40 books; 20 loose-leaf services; 120 VF drawers; brochures; press releases. **Subscriptions:** 65 journals and other serials; 8 newspapers. **Services:** Library not open to the public. **Automated Operations:** Computerized serials. **Computerized Information Services:** DIALOG Information Services, CompuServe Information Service, NEXIS, LEXIS, COMLINE, Computer Select, Computer Intelligence, IBM Link, Electronic Store; internal database. **Publications:** Dealer Channel Tracking Service (newsletter), 4/month; Industry Update Services, 8/month - both to clients. **Remarks:** FAX: (408)980-4350.

★7841★
Infomark - Chartered Institute of Marketing - Library (Bus-Fin)
Moor Hall
Cookham Phone: 628 524922
Maidenhead, Berks. SL6 9QH, England Meriel Riseley, Info.Serv.Mgr.
Founded: 1970. **Staff:** 8. **Subjects:** Marketing principles and practices. **Holdings:** 5000 volumes. **Subscriptions:** 100 journals and other serials. **Services:** Copying; library open to members and Infomark subscribers only. **Computerized Information Services:** Internal database. **Remarks:** FAX: 628 850079. Telex: 849462 TELFAC G. **Formerly:** Institute of Marketing.

INFORM
See: **University of Minnesota - ESTIS/INFORM** (18909)

Informatics Institute
See: **Notre Dame de la Paix University Faculties - Informatics Institute** (12126)

★7842★
Information Consulting, Inc. - Library
P.O. Box 21865
Columbus, OH 43221-0865
Founded: 1975. **Subjects:** Information retrieval, business, online databases, library science, chemistry, patents. **Holdings:** 400 books. **Remarks:** Currently inactive.

Information Handling Services - Global Engineering Documentation
See: **Global Engineering Documents** (6511)

★7843★
Information Handling Services - Library (Info Sci)
15 Inverness Way, E. Phone: (303)790-0600
Englewood, CO 80150 Terrie O'Rourke, Info.Spec.
Staff: Prof 1. **Subjects:** Information science, marketing, publishing. **Holdings:** 500 books. **Subscriptions:** 230 journals and other serials; 7 newspapers. **Services:** Library not open to the public.

Information Service of India Library
See: **Consulate General of India** (4237)

★7844★
Information Services Library (Bus-Fin)
3825 Ridgewood Rd. Phone: (601)982-6313
Jackson, MS 39211 Sherrill Toney, Libn.
Founded: 1960. **Staff:** Prof 2; Other 3. **Subjects:** Economics, statistics, Mississippi economic data, technology, management, community planning, industrial development, community appearance, engineering. **Special Collections:** Collection of audiovisual aids available on loan in fields of supervisory training, management, community planning, merchandising, salesmanship, technology (160). **Holdings:** 30,000 books; Data Bank of pamphlets and unbound reports; printouts and publications of census data; telephone directories; archives of internal publications; maps. **Subscriptions:** 460 journals. **Services:** Interlibrary loan; copying; telephone inquiries; library open to the public with restrictions. **Automated Operations:** Computerized public access catalog, and audiovisual aids scheduler, shipper, and management reports. **Computerized Information Services:** DIALOG Information Services, OCLC. Performs searches on fee basis for local area residents (DIALOG only). **Networks/Consortia:** Member of SOLINET. **Publications:** Handbook of Selected Data, irregular. **Special Catalogs:** Catalog of Audiovisual Aids Available on Loan, irregular. **Remarks:** FAX: (601)982-6144. Affiliated with Jackson State University.

★7845★
The Information Store, Inc. (Info Sci)
500 Sansome St., Suite 400 Phone: (415)433-5500
San Francisco, CA 94111-3219 Georgia L. Finnigan, Pres.
Founded: 1979. **Subjects:** Information services, document retrieval, translation. **Holdings:** 500 proceedings. **Subscriptions:** 20 journals and other serials. **Services:** Library not open to the public. **Computerized Information Services:** OCLC, BRS Information Technologies, Data-Star, DIMDI; AT&T Mail, CompuServe Information Service, DIALMAIL, EasyLink, MCI Mail, OnTyme Electronic Message Network Service (electronic mail services). **Remarks:** FAX: (415)433-0100. Electronic mail address(es): INFOSTOR (AT&T Mail); 76667,665 (CompuServe Information Service); 9987 (DIALMAIL); 62771978 (EasyLink); INFOSTORE (MCI Mail); INFORSTORE (OnTyme Electronic Message Network Service).

★7846★
Information Systems Consultants Inc. - Library (Comp Sci)
1711 P Street, N.W., No. B Phone: (202)745-1952
Washington, DC 20036 Sue Luensmann, Adm.Asst.
Founded: 1978. **Staff:** Prof 2; Other 2. **Subjects:** Automation, data communication, video and optical disks, telefacsimile, micrographics, library architecture. **Holdings:** 2000 books; 2500 other cataloged items. **Subscriptions:** 73 journals and other serials. **Services:** Library not open to the public. **Computerized Information Services:** DIALOG Information Services. **Publications:** Literary System Newsletter. **Remarks:** FAX: (202)745-2528.

★7847★
Information Ventures, Inc. - Library (Med)
1500 Locust, Suite 3216
Philadelphia, PA 19102 Phone: (215)732-9083
Subjects: Carcinogenesis, cancer biology, cancer diagnosis and therapy, occupational safety and health, toxicology, bioelectromagnetics, water resources, environment, medicine. **Holdings:** 1000 bound volumes. **Subscriptions:** 150 journals and other serials. **Services:** SDI; document delivery. **Computerized Information Services:** CANCERLIT, NIOSHTIC, and other databases; produces EMF Database. **Remarks:** FAX: (215)732-3754.

★7848★
Informetrica - Library (Bus-Fin)
130 Slater St., 11th Fl. Phone: (613)238-4831
Ottawa, ON, Canada K1P 5P9 Mary Daniel, Hd.
Staff: Prof 1. **Subjects:** Economics, Canadian economy and government, statistics, energy, business, computer science. **Special Collections:** Informetrica publications; Candide documents. **Holdings:** 800 books; 5000 Canadian and foreign official documents; 8000 unbound reports, manuscripts, clippings. **Subscriptions:** 280 journals and other serials; 5 newspapers. **Services:** Interlibrary loan; copying; library open to the public with restrictions. **Automated Operations:** Computerized cataloging and serials. **Remarks:** FAX: (613)238-7698.

★7849★
Inforonics, Inc. - Technical Library (Comp Sci)
550 Newtown Rd.
Box 458 Phone: (508)486-8976
Littleton, MA 01460 Merle Downing, Mgr., Spec.Lib.Serv.
Founded: 1962. **Staff:** Prof 4; Other 3. **Subjects:** Systems analysis, word and text processing, library automation, information retrieval, computer typesetting, law library cataloging. **Holdings:** 500 books; 1000 reports. **Subscriptions:** 50 journals and other serials. **Services:** Interlibrary loan; library not open to the public. **Automated Operations:** Computerized cataloging. **Computerized Information Services:** Online systems. **Remarks:** FAX: (508)486-0027.

Infoterm
See: **International Information Centre for Terminology** (8122)

Infrared Information and Analysis Center (IRIA)
See: **Environmental Research Institute of Michigan - Infrared Information Analysis Center (IRIA)** (5382)

Ingalls Library
See: **Cleveland Museum of Art - Ingalls Library** (3813)

★7850★
Ingalls Memorial Hospital - Medical Library (Med)
1 Ingalls Dr. Phone: (708)333-2300
Harvey, IL 60426 Donna L. Foley, Libn.
Founded: 1968. **Staff:** Prof 1; Other 1. **Subjects:** Medicine, nursing, health sciences. **Holdings:** 2000 books; 3000 bound periodical volumes; 1000 cassette tapes; 2000 slides, videotapes, films. **Subscriptions:** 200 journals and other serials; 5 newspapers. **Services:** Interlibrary loan; library not open to the public. **Computerized Information Services:** MEDLINE, BRS Information Technologies. **Networks/Consortia:** Member of Chicago and South Consortium, Suburban Library System (SLS). **Remarks:** FAX: (708)210-3109.

★7851★
Ingersoll-Rand Company - Engineering Library (Sci-Engr)
150 Burke St. Phone: (603)882-2711
Nashua, NH 03060 Mona D. Jewell, Mgr., Engr.Doc. & Cont.
Staff: Prof 1. **Subjects:** Engineering, pulp and paper industry, industrial process equipment, solid-liquid separation. **Special Collections:** Commercial trade catalogs (3000); Visual Search Microfilm File (VSMF) vendor catalog file; pulp and paper equipment patents (8000). **Holdings:** 2000 books. **Subscriptions:** 155 journals and other serials; 10 newspapers. **Services:** Interlibrary loan; library not open to the public. **Automated Operations:** Computerized serials. **Networks/Consortia:** Member of Nashua Area Materials Exchange (NAME). **Publications:** Library News, monthly. **Special Indexes:** Patent index (online); trade catalog index (card).

★7852★
Ingersoll-Rand Company - Ingersoll-Rand Corporate Technical Library (Sci-Engr)
942 Memorial Pkwy. Phone: (908)859-8288
Phillipsburg, NJ 08865 Sharon L. Shiner, Corp.Libn.
Founded: 1950. **Staff:** Prof 1; Other 1. **Subjects:** Engineering, mechanical metallurgy, business. **Holdings:** 5000 volumes; miscellaneous paper file; society paper file; military, foreign, and industrial standards. **Subscriptions:** 225 journals and other serials. **Services:** Interlibrary loan; library not open to the public. **Automated Operations:** Computerized public access catalog. **Computerized Information Services:** DIALOG Information Services; internal database. **Publications:** Library Bulletin; I-R Quality Bulletin. **Remarks:** Library is the central resource center for all standards and specifications used in Ingersoll-Rand. FAX: (908)859-7595.

★7853★
Ingham Medical Center Corporation - John W. Chi Memorial Medical Library (Med)
401 W. Greenlawn Ave. Phone: (517)334-2270
Lansing, MI 48910-2819 David G. Keddle, Dir.
Founded: 1960. **Staff:** Prof 1; Other 4. **Subjects:** Medicine, nursing, pharmacology, hospital administration, allied health management,

consumer health. **Special Collections:** Consumer Health (1800 volumes). **Holdings:** 10,500 books; 10,000 bound periodical volumes; 2000 audiocassettes. **Subscriptions:** 1005 journals and other serials; 7 newspapers. **Services:** Interlibrary loan; copying; SDI; library open to the public. **Automated Operations:** Computerized cataloging, serials, acquisitions, and circulation. **Computerized Information Services:** OCLC, EPIC, BRS Information Technologies, DIALOG Information Services, PFDS Online, WILSONLINE, MEDLARS; CD-ROMs (Cambridge Scientific Abstracts, Physician's Desk Reference, CONSULT, New England Journal of Medicine, Federal Register); Electronic Information Exchange System (electronic mail service). Performs searches on fee basis. **Networks/Consortia:** Member of National Network of Libraries of Medicine - Greater Midwest Region, Capital Area Library Network (Calnet), Michigan Health Sciences Libraries Association (MHSLA). **Publications:** Chi Medical Library Acquisitions. **Remarks:** FAX: (517)334-2551. **Staff:** Mary C. Andrick, Lib.Coord.

Ann Inglett Library
See: **University Presbyterian Church** (19231)

Edward Ingraham Library
See: **American Clock and Watch Museum** (529)

Ingraham Library
See: **Litchfield Historical Society** (9206)

Irvine Sullivan Ingram Library
See: **West Georgia College - Irvine Sullivan Ingram Library** (20192)

Inhalation Toxicology Research Institute
See: **Lovelace Biomedical & Environmental Research Institute, Inc. - Inhalation Toxicology Research Institute** (9404)

★7854★
Initiative Resource Center - Library (Law)
235 Douglass St. Phone: (415)431-4765
San Francisco, CA 94114 David D. Schmidt, Exec.Dir.
Founded: 1985. **Staff:** 1. **Subjects:** Initiative and referendum campaigns, procedure, and history. **Holdings:** 23 volumes; archives; clipping files. **Services:** Library open to the public by appointment. **Publications:** Initiative and Referendum: The Power of the People (newsletter), quarterly; Citizen Lawmakers (1989; book). **Remarks:** Alternate telephone number(s): (415)647-1462.

Inland Rivers Library
See: **Public Library of Cincinnati and Hamilton County - Department of Rare Books & Special Collections** (13479)

★7855★
Inland Steel Industries - Research Corporate Library (Sci-Engr)
3001 E. Columbus Dr. Phone: (219)399-6120
East Chicago, IN 46312 Barbara Minne Banek, Sr.Libn.
Staff: 1.5. **Subjects:** Metallurgy and allied sciences, technology, management, business. **Holdings:** 13,000 books; 9000 bound periodical volumes; 3600 government pamphlets, reports, and papers; 47 VF drawers of translations; 20 VF drawers of patents. **Subscriptions:** 325 journals and other serials. **Services:** Interlibrary loan; copying; library open to the public if authorized by the Vice President of Research. **Computerized Information Services:** DIALOG Information Services, STN International; internal database. **Networks/Consortia:** Member of INCOLSA. **Special Indexes:** Computerized index for company research and development reports. **Remarks:** Alternate telephone number(s): 399-6121. FAX: (219)399-6562.

★7856★
Inlow Clinic - Library (Med)
Box 370
Shelbyville, IN 46176 Phone: (317)392-3651
Founded: 1923. **Staff:** Prof 1. **Subjects:** History and philosophy of medicine, medicine, social sciences, history. **Special Collections:** Indiana history. **Holdings:** 3500 books; 2500 bound periodical volumes; 4 VF drawers of pamphlets. **Services:** Interlibrary loan; copying; library open to the public by appointment.

★7857★
Inner City Cultural Center - Langston Hughes Memorial Library (Area-Ethnic)
1308 S. New Hampshire Ave.
Los Angeles, CA 90006 Phone: (213)387-1161
Founded: 1967. **Staff:** Prof 2; Other 2. **Subjects:** Ethnic groups, performing and visual arts. **Holdings:** 6500 uncataloged books; 300 bound periodical volumes; 100 manuscripts; 100 sound recordings and tapes; 250 clippings; 175 reports; 200 photographs. **Subscriptions:** 10 journals and other serials. **Services:** Library not open to the public. **Remarks:** Center also maintains Inner City Press, which publishes Innerview (newsletter), books, and recordings.

★7858★
Innovative Media Services, Inc. (Aud-Vis, Sci-Engr)
2170 S. 116th St. Phone: (414)541-8008
West Allis, WI 53227 Michelle Adams, Info.Serv.Mgr.
Founded: 1891. **Staff:** 8. **Subjects:** Science, natural history, school curriculum. **Holdings:** 30 volumes; 16,000 16mm educational films; 3000 video cassettes; 65,000 color glass slides; 1500 museum specimens; miniature dioramas; Jonas miniature models; mounted plants and animals; museum artifacts. **Services:** Center open to the public. **Automated Operations:** Computerized cataloging, acquisitions, serials, and circulation. **Computerized Information Services:** Internal database. **Publications:** IMS News and Views (newsletter), quarterly. **Special Catalogs:** Audiovisual Resource Catalog. **Remarks:** FAX: (414)541-8123. Contains the holdings of the former Milwaukee Public Museum - Audiovisual Center.

★7859★
INRA Station d'Economie et Sociologie Ruales - Bibliotheque Pierre Bartoli (Agri)
Pl Viala Phone: 67 612209
F-34060 Montpellier Cedex, France Odile Bedu
Founded: 1858. **Staff:** Prof 4; Other 1. **Subjects:** Agricultural economy, rural sociology, management. **Holdings:** 15,000 books; 5000 reports; archival items; microfiche; theses. **Subscriptions:** 300 journals and other serials; 100 newspapers. **Services:** Interlibrary loan; copying; library open to the public with restrictions. **Computerized Information Services:** ESA/IRS - SUMMIST; internal databases. **Publications:** Lists of publications and acquisitions. **Remarks:** FAX: 67545805.

★7860★
Insect Control and Research, Inc. - Library (Biol Sci)
5819 N.W. 57th Way Phone: (904)373-7384
Gainesville, FL 32606-3227 Dr. Eugene J. Gerberg, Pres.
Founded: 1946. **Subjects:** Entomology, plant pathology, tropical diseases, pesticides, agriculture, food plant sanitation. **Holdings:** 1500 books; 600 bound periodical volumes; 7000 reprints. **Subscriptions:** 50 journals and other serials. **Services:** Library open to the public. **Remarks:** FAX: (904)373-7384. **Formerly:** Located in Baltimore, MD.

★7861★
Inspiration University - Library (Rel-Phil)
1 Campbell Hot Springs Rd. Phone: (916)994-3737
Sierraville, CA 96126-0234 Leonard Orr, Owner
Founded: 1975. **Staff:** Prof 4. **Subjects:** Physical immortality, rebirthing, prosperity, gentle childbirth, energy breathing. **Holdings:** 500 books; 20 cassette tapes; 3 videotapes; 33 other cataloged items. **Subscriptions:** 10 journals and other serials; 5 newspapers. **Services:** Interlibrary loan; copying; library open to the public with restrictions. **Automated Operations:** Computerized public access catalog. **Computerized Information Services:** Internal database. **Publications:** Consciousness Connection, monthly. **Remarks:** Alternate telephone number(s): (916)893-8643. **Also Known As:** Consciousness Village - Inspiration University.

Institucion Mila y Fontanals
See: **Spain - Council for Scientific Research - Mila and Fontanals Institution** (15561)

Institusi Jurutera, Malaysia
See: **Institution of Engineers, Malaysia** (7991)

Institut d'Administration Publique du Canada
See: **Institute of Public Administration of Canada** (7968)

★7862★
Institut Africain pour le Developpement Economique et Social - INADES-Documentation (Bus-Fin, Soc Sci)
B.P. 8 Phone: 441594
Abidjan 08, Cote d'Ivoire Yves Morel, Dir.
Founded: 1962. **Staff:** 9. **Subjects:** Africa - economy, development, agriculture, sociology, ethnology, politics, history, geography, religion. **Holdings:** 43,000 books; 300 bound periodical volumes; 400 titles in microform. **Subscriptions:** 270 journals and other serials. **Services:** Interlibrary loan; copying; SDI; open to the public. **Computerized Information Services:** Internal database. **Publications:** Fichier Afrique (abstracts of papers about African countries); Commented Bibliographies (development in Africa). **Remarks:** FAX: 440641. Telex: 202139 FRCINF. **Staff:** Marie-Paule Coing, Biblio.-Doc.

★7863★
Institut fur Afrika Kunde - Bibliothek (Soc Sci, Area-Ethnic)
Neuer Jungfernstieg 21 Phone: 40 3562526
W-2000 Hamburg 36, Germany Gertrud Wellmann-Hofmeier
Founded: 1966. **Staff:** 2.5. **Subjects:** Africa - south of Sahara; social sciences; economics; politics; legal sciences. **Holdings:** 37,000 books; unbound periodicals. other cataloged items. **Subscriptions:** 450 journals and other serials; 30 newspapers. **Services:** Interlibrary loan; copying; library open to the public. **Computerized Information Services:** ESA/IRS. Contact Person: Dr. Reinknecht. **Publications:** Neuerwerbungen der Bibliothek, semiannual. **Remarks:** FAX: 40 3562547.

★7864★
Institut Armand-Frappier - Applied Microbiology Research Centre - Library (Med, Biol Sci)
P.O. Box 100, LDR Station Phone: (514)687-5010
Laval, PQ, Canada H7N 4Z3 Monique St. Jean, Libn.
Founded: 1938. **Staff:** 4. **Subjects:** Microbiology, preventive medicine, biotechnology, biochemistry, immunology, virology, food sciences. **Holdings:** 13,000 books. **Subscriptions:** 512 journals and other serials. **Services:** Interlibrary loan; copying; SDI; library open to the public by appointment only. **Computerized Information Services:** BADADUQ, DIALOG Information Services, CAN/OLE, STN International. **Remarks:** FAX: (514)686-5501. Telex: 055-62171. Library located at 531 Blvd. des Prairies, Laval, PQ, Canada H7V 1B7. Maintained by Universite du Quebec. **Staff:** Diane Sauve, Libn.

★7865★
Institut Armand-Frappier - Medicine Research Centre - Library (Med)
C.P. 100 Phone: (514)687-5010
Laval, PQ, Canada H7N 4Z3 Monique St. Jean, Libn.
Founded: 1938. **Staff:** Prof 2; Other 2. **Subjects:** Bacteriology, immunology, virology, comparative medicine, veterinary medicine, epidemiology. **Holdings:** 35,000 volumes. **Subscriptions:** 375 journals and other serials. **Services:** Library open to the public by appointment. **Automated Operations:** Computerized public access catalog and cataloging. **Computerized Information Services:** DIALOG Information Services, MEDLARS, BADADUQ, STN International, CAN/OLE. Performs searches on fee basis. Contact Person: Diane Sauve, Hd., Ref. **Remarks:** FAX: (514)686-5501. Library located at 531 Blvd. des Praries, Laval, PQ, Canada, H7V 1B7.

Institut Biologii Juznych Morej im O O Kovalevskogo
See: **Institute of Biology of the Southern Seas - Biblioteka** (7906)

Institut Canadien Archives (Montreal)
See: **Fraser-Hickson Institute, Montreal - Free Library - Special Collections** (6102)

Institut Canadien pour les Aveugles (INCA)
See: **Canadian National Institute for the Blind - Library for the Blind** (2969)

Institut Canadien de Conservation
See: **Canada - Communications Canada - Canadian Conservation Institute** (2672)

Institut Canadien du Film
See: **Canadian Film Institute** (2929)

★7866★
Institut Canadien-Francais d'Ottawa - Library (Area-Ethnic)
316 Dalhousie St.
Ottawa, ON, Canada K1N 7E7 Phone: (613)234-1288
Staff: Prof 1. **Subjects:** History, biography, science. **Special Collections:** French (Paris) collection of l'Illustration, 1849-1940. **Holdings:** 4000 volumes. **Subscriptions:** 20 journals and other serials; 6 newspapers. **Services:** Library open to students, researchers, and historians. **Remarks:** Alternate telephone number(s): (613)234-3367.

Institut Canadien de l'Information Scientifique et Technique
See: **Canada - National Research Council - Canada Institute for Scientific and Technical Information (CISTI)** (2814)

Institut Canadien de Recherches sur les Pates et Papiers
See: **Pulp and Paper Research Institute of Canada** (13528)

Institut Canado-Americain
See: **Association Canado-Americaine** (1151)

Institut fur Deutsche Sprache
See: **Institute for German Language** (7942)

Institut fur Dokumentation und Information uber Sozialmedizin und Offentliches Gesundheitswesen
See: **Institute for Documentation and Information in Social Medicine and Public Health** (7927)

★7867★
Institut Drevnich Rukopisej - Matenadaran im Mastoca - Biblioteka (Soc Sci)
Mashots Ave., 111 Phone: 8852 583292
SU-375009 Yerevan 9, Armenia Prof. Sen Arevshatian, Dir.
Founded: 5th century. **Staff:** Prof 50; Other 70. **Subjects:** Codicology, religion, history, literature, philosophy, medicine. **Special Collections:** Collection of Armenian manuscripts; collection of foreign manuscripts. **Holdings:** 100,000 books; 25,000 bound periodical volumes; 110,000 archival items; 17,000 manuscripts; 8000 reels of microfilm. **Services:** Library open to the public. **Publications:** Banber Matenadarani (in Armenian; summaries in English and French). **Special Catalogs:** Catalogue of Armenian Manuscripts of Matenadaran (2 volumes); General Catalogue of Armenian Manuscripts of Matenadaran (1 volume). **Remarks:** Maintains a manuscript exhibition hall, open to visitors. **Staff:** B. Chookasizian, Dp.Dir.

Institut fur Entwicklungsforschung und Entwicklungspolitik
See: **Institute for Development Research and Development Policy** (7926)

Institut za Etnologiju i Folkloristiku
See: **Institute of Ethnology and Folklore Research - Library** (7936)

★7868★
Institut d'Etudes Medievales - Bibliotheque (Hist)
2715, chemin de la Cote Ste-Catherine Phone: (514)739-3597
Montreal, PQ, Canada H3T 1B6 Roger Blain, Dir.
Founded: 1942. **Staff:** Prof 1; Other 2. **Subjects:** Medieval civilization - philosophy, theology, literature, history, economic and political history; church history; classics; ancient philosophy and patristics (texts and studies); canon law; medieval art history; paleography; pastoral concerns. **Special Collections:** MGH. **Holdings:** 73,000 books; 20,000 bound periodical volumes; 300 reels of microfilm of manuscripts. **Subscriptions:** 450 journals and other serials. **Services:** Interlibrary loan; copying; library open for consultation only. **Staff:** Rosaire Rivard.

Institut de Formation Linguistique
See: **University of Regina** (19261)

Institut Francais d'Archeologie Orientale
See: **French Institute of Eastern Archeology** (6148)

Institut Francais d'Archeologie du Proche-Orient
See: **French Institute for Archaeology in the Near East** (6147)

Institut Francais d'Etudes Andines
See: **French Institute of Andean Studies** (6146)

★7869★
Institut Francais d'Etudes Arabes de Damas - Bibliotheque (Area-Ethnic)
B.P. 344 Phone: 330 214-331 962
Damascus, Syrian Arab Republic Gilbert Delanoue, Dir.
Founded: 1923. **Staff:** 3. **Subjects:** Arabic and Islamic studies. **Special Collections:** Bulletin d'Etudes Orientales, 1928 to present. **Holdings:** 50,000 books; 800 periodicals in Arabic and European languages. **Subscriptions:** 350 journals and other serials. **Services:** library open to the public by appointment open to the public for reference use only. **Publications:** Ahmed Sawqi, l'homme et l'oeuvre, 1977; Le personnage de RNla femme dans le roman et la nouvelle egyptiens de 1914 a 1960, 1979; Culture et education arabo-islamiques au Sam pendant les trois premiers siecles de l'Islam d'apres le Tarih Dimasq d'Ibn Asakir, 1981; list of additional publications available. **Staff:** Oliver Dubois, Libn.; Claude Salame, Libn.

Institut Francais du Petrole - Direction Economie et Documentation
See: **French Petroleum Institute - Board of Economics and Documentation - Library** (6151)

★7870★
Institut fur Geschichte der Medizin der Robert Bosch Stiftung - Bibliothek (Med)
StrauBweg 17 Phone: 711 483013
W-7000 Stuttgart 1, Germany Beate Schleh
Founded: 1980. **Staff:** Prof 1; Other 2. **Subjects:** History of homeopathy, social history of medicine. **Special Collections:** Samuel Hahnemann and Clemens von Bonninghausen collections. **Holdings:** 16,000 books; 9000 microfiche. **Subscriptions:** 70 journals and other serials. **Services:** Interlibrary loan; library open to the public. **Publications:** Medizin, Gasellschaft ud Geschichte: Jahrbuch des Institut fur Geschichte der Medizin. **Special Catalogs:** Katalog der Bibliothek des Homoopathie-Archivs: aus den Bestanden des Institut fur Geschichte der Medizin der Robert Bosch Stiftung. **Remarks:** FAX: 711 461755.

★7871★
Institut Interculturel de Montreal - Bibliotheque (Soc Sci)
4917 St-Urbain Phone: (514)288-7229
Montreal, PQ, Canada H2T 2W1 Real Bathalon, Libn.
Founded: 1963. **Staff:** Prof 1; Other 1. **Subjects:** Intercultural studies. **Special Collections:** Complete works of Raimundo Panikkar. **Holdings:** 5000 books; 250 maps; 400 illustrations; 500 files on ethnocultural organizations; records; slides; cassettes; tapes. **Subscriptions:** 120 journals and other serials; 70 newspapers. **Services:** Interlibrary loan; copying; library open to the public. **Computerized Information Services:** ETHNODOC (internal database). Performs searches free of charge. **Publications:** Ethnocultural Directory of Canada, 1990 - for sale; Horizons interculturels, quarterly; Interculture (available in French or English), quarterly - all by subscription. FAX: (514)844-6800. **Also Known As:** Intercultural Institute of Montreal.

Institut International du Froid
See: **International Institute of Refrigeration** (8133)

Institut International de Planification de l'Education
See: **International Institute for Educational Planning** (8127)

Institut International des Sciences Humaines Integrales
See: **International Institute of Integral Human Sciences** (8129)

Institut Jules Bordet
See: **Jules Bordet Institute** (1969)

Institut fur Kirchliche Zeitgeschichte
See: **Institute for Contemporary Ecclesiastical History** (7919)

★7872★
Institut fur Landwirtschaftliche Marktforschung Bundesforschungsanstalt fur Landwirtschaft Braunschweig Volkenrode (FAL) - Okonomische Bibliothek (Bus-Fin, Sci-Engr)
Brundesallee 50 Phone: 531 596566
W-3300 Brunswick, Germany Prof. H.E. Buchholz, Lib.Hd.
Founded: 1949. **Staff:** Prof 2; Other 4. **Subjects:** Agricultural economics, structural research, statistics, market research, mathematics. **Holdings:** 37,500 books; 25,000 bound periodical volumes; 5000 reports; 100 archival items; 1000 microfiche. **Subscriptions:** 500 journals and other serials; 5 newspapers. **Services:** Interlibrary loan; copying; library open to the public. **Computerized Information Services:** Allegro C (internal database). **Remarks:** FAX: 531 596367. **Also Known As:** Institutes of Agricultural Economic Research - Library of Agricultural Economics.

★7873★
Institut Matematiki im. V.I. Romanovskogo AN Respubliki Uzbekistan - Biblioteka (Sci-Engr, Hum)
ul. F. Rhodzhaeva, 29 Phone: 332820
700143 Taskent, Uzbekistan M.S. Stalbovskaja
Founded: 1947. **Staff:** Prof 2. **Subjects:** Mathematics, geophysics, mechanics, linguistics. **Special Collections:** Rare book collection; old mathematics textbooks; books signed by famous mathematicians. **Holdings:** 19,000 books; 13,000 bound periodical volumes; 800 reports; 1000 archival items; 4723 microfiche. **Subscriptions:** 150 journals and other serials; 50 newspapers. **Services:** Interlibrary loan; library open to the public with restrictions. **Publications:** Bio-bibliography of Soviet mathematicians, V.I. Romanovsky, N.N. Nazarov, T.A. Sazymsakov, J.S. Wczhanuch, S.H. Sizazhdinou.

★7874★
Institut Matematiki i Mechaniki AN Azerbajdzanskoj SSR - Biblioteka (Sci-Engr)
ul Kecchoveli
553 Kvartal Phone: 70005
Baku, Azerbaijan Khalida Asadulla Vagubova
Founded: 1977. **Staff:** Prof 2. **Subjects:** Mathematics, geometry, topology, mathematical analysis, number theory. **Holdings:** 14,026 books; 22,706 bound periodical volumes; 110 microfiche; 20,057 reels of microfilm. **Subscriptions:** 217 journals and other serials; 16 newspapers. **Services:** Interlibrary loan; library open to the public.

Institut Maurice-LaMontagne
See: **Canada - Fisheries & Oceans** (2733)

Institut National de l'Environment Industriel et des Risques (INERIS)
See: **National Insitute of Industrial Environment and Hazards** (11203)

★7875★
Institut National d'Etude du Travail et d'Orientation Professionnelle - Conservatoire National des Arts et Metiers - Bibliotheque (Educ, Soc Sci)
41 rue Gay-Lussac Phone: 1 66107831
F-75005 Paris, France Remi Guerrier
Founded: 1927. **Staff:** Prof 3; Other 1. **Subjects:** Psychology, career guidance, education, vocational training, job counseling, sociology. **Holdings:** 18,000 books; 550 bound periodical volumes. **Subscriptions:** 77 journals and other serials. **Services:** Interlibrary loan; copying; library open to the public. **Computerized Information Services:** DIALOG Information Services, Data-Star, Questel; internal database. **Publications:** Bulletin Documentaire. **Remarks:** FAX: 1 43541091.

Institut National d'Etudes Demographiques
See: **France - National Institute of Demographic Studies** (6070)

★7876★
Institut National de la Recherche Agronomique - Bibliotheque (Agri)
99 av de Tamara
Boite Postale 415 Phone: 7 74003
Rabat, Morocco Mr. Lakrimi
Founded: 1936. **Staff:** Prof 5; Other 6. **Subjects:** Agronomical research, food and alimentation, animal breeding, horticulture, soil science. **Holdings:** 30,000 books; 2000 bound periodical volumes; 3000 reports; 5000 microfiche; brochures; maps. **Subscriptions:** 120 journals and other serials; 16 newspapers. **Services:** Copying; SDI; library open to the public. **Computerized Information Services:** ESA/IRS, CND/CDSISIS; AGRIDOC (internal database). **Publications:** Al Awamia; Les Cahiers de la Recherche Agromomique; Fiches Techniques; Bulletin de Sommaires; Bulletin Agr doc. **Special Catalogs:** Catalogue des Publication de l'INRA. **Remarks:** Alternate telephone number(s): 775530. FAX: 774003.

★7877★
Institut National de Recherche en Informatique et en Automatique - Centre de Documentation (Comp Sci)
B.P. 105 Phone: 1 39635424
F-78153 Le Chesnay Cedex, France Mrs. Touzeau
Founded: 1967. **Staff:** Prof 8; Other 7. **Subjects:** Computer science, automation and control, applied mathematics. **Special Collections:** French theses in computer science; computer science proceedings; computer science research reports. **Holdings:** 22,900 monograph, thesis, and conference titles; 475 bound periodical volumes; 31,000 reports and theses. **Subscriptions:** 630 journals and other serials. **Services:** Interlibrary loan; copying; center open to the public. **Automated Operations:** Computerized public access catalog, cataloging, acquisitions, and circulation. **Computerized Information Services:** ESA/IRS, DIALOG Information Services; BIB, TRAP, PERI-CF (internal databases). Performs searches on fee basis. Contact Person: Nicole Szwarcbaum, Libn., 1 39635653. **Publications:** Bulletin de Liaison de la Recherche en Informatique et en Automatique, monthly; INRIATHEQUE (list of new acquisitions received), weekly; INRIA Information, monthly. **Special Catalogs:** Catalogue Collectif National des Publications en Serie. **Special Indexes:** Authors, titles, meetings (online). **Remarks:** FAX: 1 39635228.

Institut National de la Recherche Scientifique-Urbanisation
See: **Universite du Quebec a Montreal** (18118)

★7878★
Institut Nazareth et Louis-Braille - Bibliotheque (Aud-Vis)
1111 St. Charles, W. Phone: (514)463-1710
Longueuil, PQ, Canada J4K 5G4 Claire Dubois, Chf. of Info.Serv.
Founded: 1911. **Staff:** Prof 1; Other 7. **Subjects:** Humanities. **Holdings:** 45,000 braille books (15,000 titles); 15,000 musical Braille books; 1400 bound periodical volumes. **Subscriptions:** 25 journals and other serials in braille. **Services:** Interlibrary loan; library open to visually impaired persons. **Automated Operations:** Integrated library system (MULTILIS). **Computerized Information Services:** CANUC:H; CAMELIA (internal database). **Publications:** Le Carrefour Braille, monthly; Supplement de la Bibliotheque Braille, 2/year. **Special Catalogs:** Ink print catalog (card and book); braille catalog (card and book). **Remarks:** FAX: (514)463-0243.

★7879★
Institut Nazareth et Louis-Braille - Centre de Documentation (Aud-Vis)
1111 St. Charles, W. Phone: (514)463-1710
Longueuil, PQ, Canada J4K 5G4 Claire Dubois, Chf. of Info.Serv.
Founded: 1984. **Staff:** Prof 1; Other 1. **Subjects:** Visual impairment, low vision, rehabilitation. **Holdings:** 3500 books; 50 braille books; 10 talking books; 250 bound periodical volumes; 500 reports; 3000 diapositives; 50 video cassettes. **Subscriptions:** 100 journals and other serials (5 in braille; 5 on cassette). **Services:** Interlibrary loan; copying; center open to the public. **Automated Operations:** Integrated library system (MULTILIS). **Publications:** INFO-DOC, 4/year. **Remarks:** FAX: (514)463-0243.

Institut Pasteur
See: **Pasteur Institute** (12784)

Institut Pasteur d'Algerie
See: **Pasteur Institute of Algeria** (12785)

★7880★
Institut Philippe Pinel de Montreal - Centre de Documentation (Med)
10905 Henri-Bourassa Blvd., E. Phone: (514)648-8461
Montreal, PQ, Canada H1C 1H1 Marc Lamarre, Libn.
Founded: 1970. **Staff:** 1. **Subjects:** Forensic psychiatry, mentally ill offenders, criminology, clinical psychology. **Holdings:** 2500 books; 850 bound periodical volumes; 5 VF drawers of reprints and pamphlets. **Subscriptions:** 150 journals and other serials. **Services:** Interlibrary loan; library not open to the public. **Computerized Information Services:** DIALOG Information Services; Envoy 100 (electronic mail service). **Publications:** Pinel-Documentation, irregular - for internal distribution only. **Remarks:** FAX: (514)494-4406. Electronic mail address(es): QMIPP (Envoy 100).

★7881★
Institut de Police du Quebec - Bibliotheque (Law)
350, rue d'Youville
C.P. 1120 Phone: (819)293-8631
Nicolet, PQ, Canada J0G 1E0 Dominique Laganiere, Tech.Doc.
Founded: 1970. **Staff:** Prof 1. **Subjects:** Law and legislation, justice, police science, criminology. **Holdings:** 6000 books; AV material. **Subscriptions:** 120 periodicals. **Services:** Interlibrary loan; copying; library open to the public. **Remarks:** FAX: (819)293-8718.

★7882★
Institut Raymond-Dewar - Centre de Documentation (Med)
3600, rue Berri, Suite 034 Phone: (514)284-2581
Montreal, PQ, Canada H2L 4G9 Sylvie Laverdiere, Libn.
Founded: 1980. **Staff:** Prof 1; Other 1. **Subjects:** Hearing impairment, audiology, deaf-blindness, rehabilitation, psychology, social sciences. **Special Collections:** Sign Language Dictionaries (55 volumes). **Holdings:** 4000 books; 210 bound periodical volumes; 350 reprints and reports; 110 dissertations; 155 videotapes; 35 sign language courses on videotape. **Subscriptions:** 130 journals and other serials. **Services:** Interlibrary loan (excluding AV programs); copying; center open to the public. **Publications:** La Puce a l'Oeil, 3-4/year; List of Acquisitions, annual; List of AV Materials, annual; List of Periodicals, annual - all free upon request. **Remarks:** FAX: (514)284-0699.

★7883★
Institut de Readaptation de Montreal - Centre de Documentation (Med)
6300 Darlington Ave. Phone: (514)340-2085
Montreal, PQ, Canada H3S 2J4 Maryse Boyer, Lib.Techn.
Staff: Prof 1; Other 1. **Subjects:** Rehabilitation, physical medicine, occupational and physical therapy, orthopedics, neurology, prosthetics and orthotics, physically handicapped. **Holdings:** 2000 books; 500 bound periodical volumes. **Subscriptions:** 135 journals and other serials. **Services:** Interlibrary loan; copying; library open to the public. **Networks/Consortia:** Member of Association des Bibliotheques de la Sante Affiliees a l'Universite de Montreal (ABSAUM). **Publications:** Acquisitions list, quarterly; Holdings of Periodicals, annual. **Remarks:** FAX: (514)340-2149.

★7884★
Institut de Recherche en Sante et en Securite du Travail - Informatheque (Med)
505, blvd. de Maisonneuve, W., 11th Fl. Phone: (514)288-1551
Montreal, PQ, Canada H3A 3C2 Francois Lemay, Hd.
Founded: 1981. **Staff:** Prof 2; Other 2. **Subjects:** Industrial hygiene and safety, ergonomics. **Holdings:** 7000 books; 20,000 reprints; 700 standards; 120 microfiche; 20 AV programs. **Subscriptions:** 268 journals and other serials. **Services:** Interlibrary loan; copying; SDI; informatheque open to the public with restrictions. **Automated Operations:** Computerized cataloging and ILL. **Computerized Information Services:** CAN/OLE, DIALOG Information Services, Questel, Canadian Center for Occupational Health and Safety, OLF, PFDS Online, MEDLARS; CAS, ISST (internal databases); Envoy 100 (electronic mail service). **Remarks:** FAX: (514)288-6097. Telex: 055 61348. Electronic mail address(es): IRSST.INFO (Envoy 100). **Staff:** Jacques Blain, Libn.

Institut de Recherches Cliniques de Montreal - Centre de Documentation
See: **Clinical Research Institute of Montreal/ - Medical Library** (3836)

★7885★
Institut de Recherches et d'Etudes sur le Monde Arabe et Musulman - IREMAM - Bibliotheque (Area-Ethnic)
Maison de la Mediterranee
3-5, ave. Pasteur Phone: 42 215988
F-13100 Aix-en-Provence, France A. Raymond, Dir.
Subjects: Social, economic, political, geographic aspects of contemporary North Africa - Algeria, Libya, Morocco, Tunisia - and the Middle East. **Holdings:** 40,000 volumes. **Subscriptions:** 250 journals and other serials. **Services:** Library open to researchers and educators. **Computerized Information Services:** Produces Maghreb Data Base. Performs searches on fee basis. Contact Person: Jean-Jacques Regnier or V. Michel. **Formerly:** Centre de Recherche et d'Etudes sur les Societes Mediterraneennes. **Also Known As:** Institute for Research and Studies on the Arab and Muslim World.

Institut de Recherches sur les Fruits et Agrumes
See: **International Cooperation Center of Agricultural Research for Development - Institute of Research on Fruits and Citrus Fruits** (8087)

Institut des Relations Internationales du Cameroun
See: **Cameroon Institute of International Relations** (2616)

★7886★
Institut Roland-Saucier - Bibliotheque Medicale (Med)
150, rue Pinel
C.P. 2250 Phone: (418)549-5474
Chicoutimi, PQ, Canada G7G 3W4 Danielle Saucier, Biblio.
Founded: 1974. **Staff:** Prof 1. **Subjects:** Clinical psychiatry, mental health, psychopharmacology, psychology, psychiatric social work. **Holdings:** 4000 books; 500 bound periodical volumes. **Subscriptions:** 100 journals and other serials; 21 newspapers. **Services:** Interlibrary loan; copying; library open to the public with restrictions. **Special Indexes:** Abstracts index (card). **Remarks:** FAX: (418)549-8143.

Institut Royal Meteorologique de Belgique
See: **Royal Observatory of Belgium** (14127)

Institut Royal du Patrimoine Artistique - Bibliotheque
See: **Royal Institute for Cultural Heritage of Belgium - Library** (14121)

Institut fur Seeverkehrwirtschaft und Logistik
See: **Institute of Shipping Economics and Logistics - Library** (7976)

★7887★
Institut Superieur Industriel de l'Etat de Huy-Gembloux-Verviers - Bibliotheque (Agri)
rue Saint Victor 3 Phone: 85 214826
B-4500 Huy, Belgium J. Mertens
Staff: Prof 1.25; Other 1. **Subjects:** Agronomy, rural development, landscape architecture, horticulture, textiles. **Special Collections:** Sorgho collection (400 items); bionethane collection (100 items); urtica dioicae collection; in vitro culture collection; hydroponics collection. **Holdings:** 14,000 books; 200 microfiche. **Subscriptions:** 200 journals and other serials; 4 newspapers. **Services:** Interlibrary loan; copying; library open to the public with proper documentation. **Computerized Information Services:** BELINDASINDIS STAIRS/VS. Contact Person: L. Schoonbroodt, Libn. **Remarks:** FAX: 85 211541.

★7888★
Institut de Technologie Agro-Alimentaire - Centre de Documentation (Agri, Biol Sci)
401, rue Poire Phone: (418)856-1110
La Pocatiere, PQ, Canada G0R 1Z0 Denis Dumont
Founded: 1859. **Staff:** Prof 1; Other 2. **Subjects:** General agriculture, biochemistry, economics, botany, animal husbandry, field crops. **Holdings:** 13,000 books. **Subscriptions:** 257 journals and other serials. **Services:** Interlibrary loan; copying; center open to the public with restrictions. **Computerized Information Services:** DIALOG Information Services. **Remarks:** FAX: (418)856-1719. Telex: 051-3445.

Institut Textile de France
See: **French Textile Institute - Library** (6152)

★7889★
Institut de Tourisme et d'Hotellerie du Quebec - Mediatheque (Bus-Fin, Food-Bev)
401, rue de Rigaud Phone: (514)282-5114
Montreal, PQ, Canada H2L 4P3 Lyne Hebert, Chf.Libn.
Founded: 1975. **Staff:** Prof 2; Other 8. **Subjects:** Tourism, hotel and restaurant management, administration, cuisine, travel. **Special Collections:** Recipe collection (8000); menu collection (500). **Holdings:** 28,700 books; 2841 bound periodical volumes. **Subscriptions:** 150 journals and other serials. **Services:** Interlibrary loan; copying; library open to the public. **Automated Operations:** Computerized cataloging. **Computerized Information Services:** UTLAS. **Networks/Consortia:** Member of Quebec Province Government Library Network. **Publications:** Sommaire des Periodiques; Liste des Nouveau. **Staff:** Celine Beauchemin.

★7890★
Institut der Wirtschaftprufer in Deutschland - Informationsreferat - Bibliothek (Bus-Fin)
Tersteegenstr 14
Postfach 3020580 Phone: 211 45610
W-4000 Dusseldorf 30, Germany Dr. Helmut Ulaas
Founded: 1932. **Staff:** Prof 2. **Subjects:** Accounting, auditing, tax law, economic law. **Holdings:** 20,000 books; 10,000 bound periodical volumes; 400 microfiche. **Subscriptions:** 150 journals and other serials; 4 newspapers. **Services:** Copying; library open to students on Wednesdays and Thursdays. **Computerized Information Services:** Internal database. **Remarks:** FAX: 211 4541097.

Institut fur Zeitgeschichte - Bibliothek
See: **Institute of Contemporary History** (7920)

Institut fur Zeitungsforschung - Haus der Bibliotheken
See: **Institute of Press Research - Library** (7964)

★7891★
Institute for Advanced Business Studies - Library (Bus-Fin)
University of Navarra
Ave. Pearson 21 Phone: 3 2044000
E-08034 Barcelona, Spain Prof. Joaquim Vila, Libn.
Founded: 1960. **Staff:** 5. **Subjects:** Business, business administration, economics. **Holdings:** 32,000 volumes. **Subscriptions:** 400 journals and other serials; 8 newspapers. **Services:** Interlibrary loan; copying; SDI; library open to members, alumni, students, and faculty only. **Computerized Information Services:** DIALOG Information Services, ESA/IRS, Data-Star, ECHO, ICEX, IMPI. **Remarks:** FAX: 3 2801177. Telex: 50924 IESB-E. **Also Known As:** Instituto de Estudios Superiores de la Empresa (IESE). **Staff:** Ana Elizalde; Carina Huguet; Carmen Manzanares; Maria Marques; Mercedes Quintana.

★7892★
Institute of Advanced Manufacturing Sciences - Machinability Data Center (Sci-Engr)
1111 Edison Dr. Phone: (513)948-2000
Cincinnati, OH 45216 Susan M. Moehring, Mgr.
Founded: 1964. **Staff:** Prof 6; Other 5. **Subjects:** Machinability, material removal, surface integrity. **Holdings:** 1700 books; 41,000 documents. **Subscriptions:** 70 journals and other serials. **Services:** Interlibrary loan; center open to the public by appointment. **Computerized Information Services:** DIALOG Information Services; internal database. Fees for searches performed subject to individual quotation based on subject requested. **Publications:** Machining Data Handbook. **Special Indexes:** Machining and material removal document file. **Remarks:** FAX: (513)948-2109.

★7893★
Institute for Advanced Perception - Library (Rel-Phil)
P.O. Box 2856 Phone: (708)447-8372
Naperville, IL 60567-2856 Donna Schroeppel, Pres.
Founded: 1967. **Staff:** 2. **Subjects:** Occultism, yoga, extrasensory perception (ESP), astrology, psychology. **Holdings:** 1500 books; 3 VF drawers. **Subscriptions:** 2 journals and other serials. **Services:** Library not open to the public.

Institute for Advanced Safety Studies - Safety Information Center
See: **Triodyne Consulting Engineers and Scientists - Safety Information Center** (16522)

★7894★
Institute for Advanced Studies of World Religions - Library (Rel-Phil)
Rte. 301
R.D. 2 Phone: (914)225-1445
Carmel, NY 10512 Lena Lee Yang, Dir.
Founded: 1970. **Staff:** Prof 2; Other 5. **Subjects:** Buddhism, Hinduism and Indology, Islam, and other religions of Asian origin; Christian pastoral theology; allied subjects in history, philosophy, culture; comparative religious studies. **Special Collections:** Richard A. Gard Collection of Buddhist and Related Studies (24,000 volumes); Ngiam Hoo-pang Collection of Chinese Buddhist Texts (9700 volumes); collection of Tibetan books published in India since 1963 (10,300 volumes); Sanskrit Collection (5200 volumes); other South Asia collections (mainly on Hinduism and Islam; 8200 volumes); G.E. Sargent Collection of Asian Philosophy and Comparative Literature (4000 volumes); Garma C.C. Chang Tibetan Collection (microform); Richard Hu See-yee Chi Collection of Buddhist Philosophy and Chinese Art (1280 volumes); A. Crescenzo, J.P.Mitton, and D.B. Lefevere collections in Pastoral Theology (8000 volumes). **Holdings:** 70,500 books; 7632 bound periodical volumes; 183 reels of microfilm of Chinese manuscripts from Tun-huang; 53,000 microfiche of Sanskrit, Tibetan, Chinese texts; 1850 microfiche of Cambodian Tipitaka; 481 maps; 346 audiotapes; 11 videotapes; 11 VF drawers of correspondence from U.S. and foreign religious and educational organizations. **Subscriptions:** 361 journals and other serials. **Services:** Copying; SDI; library open to the public for reference use only. **Automated Operations:** Computerized cataloging. **Computerized Information Services:** OCLC. **Publications:** List of publications - available on request. **Special Catalogs:** A Classified Catalogue of Chinese Books in the Library of the IAWSR (book); Descriptive Catalog for IASWR Buddhist Sanskrit Manuscripts (microfiche); Descriptive Catalog of Microfiche of Indic Manuscripts Collection from the University of Pennsylvania (microfiche). **Remarks:** FAX: (914)225-0447. The institute aims to preserve religious literature which has not received adequate attention from scholars and translators. It seeks to provide bibliographic information, as well as publish important religious materials in various languages and the translation of selected texts into English. In addition, the institute seeks to strengthen contacts and cooperation among those concerned with the academic study and practical applications of world religions.

★7895★
Institute for Advanced Study - Libraries (Hum, Sci-Engr)
Princeton, NJ 08540 Phone: (609)734-8371
Founded: 1940. **Staff:** Prof 3; Other 6. **Subjects:** Archeology; art history; astrophysics; classical, medieval, and Renaissance studies; history; mathematics; theoretical physics; social sciences. **Special Collections:** History of science. **Holdings:** 110,000 volumes. **Subscriptions:** 1200 journals and other serials. **Services:** Library not open to the public. **Automated Operations:** Computerized cataloging and acquisitions. **Computerized Information Services:** DIALOG Information Services, WILSONLINE, Dow Jones News/Retrieval, RLIN; CD-ROM (Thesaurus Linguae Graecae Canon of Greek Authors and Works, Duke Data Bank of Documentary Papyri). **Remarks:** FAX: (609)924-8399. Alternate telephone number(s): (609)734-8181. **Staff:** Elliott Shore, Hist.Stud. & Soc.Sci.Libn.; Faridah Kassim, Assoc.Libn.; Momota Ganguli, Math/Natural Sci.Libn.

★7896★
Institute for Advanced Study of Human Sexuality - Exodus Trust Archives of Erotology - Research Library (Soc Sci)
1523 Franklin St. Phone: (415)928-1133
San Francisco, CA 94109 Dr. Ted McIlvenna, Dir.
Founded: 1976. **Staff:** Prof 10. **Subjects:** Human sexuality. **Special Collections:** Lyle Stuart Library of Sexual Science; Harry Mohne Collection. **Holdings:** 60,000 books; 12,000 bound periodical volumes; 189,000 films; 500 slides; 16,000 videotapes; 50,000 periodicals; 25,000 magazines, special photographs; videotapes of all lectures given at the institute; 10 unbound volumes of American and European journals on homosexuality. **Subscriptions:** 15 journals and other serials; 5 newspapers. **Services:** Library not open to the public. Researchers may submit a formal written request for access to the library. **Remarks:** FAX: (415)928-8061.

★7897★
Institute for Advanced Talmudic Study - Library (Rel-Phil)
515 Coldstream Ave. Phone: (416)789-1853
Toronto, ON, Canada M6B 2K7 Rabbi W. Shmuel Reich, Libn.
Founded: 1974. **Staff:** Prof 3; Other 5. **Subjects:** Theology, ethics, Talmudic research. **Holdings:** 6000 books. **Services:** Library open to the public with restrictions (will not answer queries over the phone). **Publications:** Hamayan (volumes 1-4); Kolel Newsletter, quarterly - to the public.

Institute of Aesthetics Research
See: **Universidad Nacional Autonoma de Mexico - Instituto de Investigaciones Esteticas** (17992)

Institute of African Studies
See: **University of Ghana - Institute of African Studies** (18608)

★7898★
Institute for Agricultural Research - Library (Agri)
Ahmadu Bello University
Private Mail Bag 1044
Samaru Phone: 50571-74
Zaria, Kaduna, Nigeria Rabiu Salami, Libn.
Staff: 21. **Subjects:** Cereals, oilseeds, fibers, grain legumes and horticultural crops, soil and crop improvement, agricultural mechanization, farming systems, irrigation, food science and technology. **Special Collections:** Publications on Nigerian agriculture. **Holdings:** 47,454 books and pamphlets. **Subscriptions:** 921 journals and other serials. **Services:** Interlibrary loan; copying; SDI; library open to researchers from other sectors and students from all sectors within and outside IAR/ABU. **Publications:** Abstract on Samaru Research Bulletin. **Remarks:** Affiliated with Ahmadu Bello University. **Staff:** Andrew D.K. Taivgsen; Mrs. R.A. Musa.

★7899★
Institute for Agriculture and Trade Policy - Library (Agri)
1313 5th St., S.E., Suite 303 Phone: (612)379-5980
Minneapolis, MN 55414 Mark Ritchie, Dir.
Founded: 1986. **Staff:** Prof 1. **Subjects:** Food, trade, agriculture, land, rural affairs, environment, sustainable development. **Holdings:** Books; 10 reports; articles. **Subscriptions:** 25 journals and other serials; 6 newspapers. **Services:** Interlibrary loan, copying, library open to the public with restrictions. **Computerized Information Services:** Internal database; EcoNet (electronic mail service). **Publications:** Monthly indexed clipping service on food, land, agriculture, and trade. **Remarks:** FAX: (612)379-5982. Electronic mail address(es): IATP (EcoNet).

★7900★
Institute for Alternative Futures - Library (Soc Sci)
108 N. Alfred St. Phone: (703)684-5880
Alexandria, VA 22314 Clement Bezold, Ph.D., Exec.Dir.
Founded: 1977. **Subjects:** Health issues, futures, political science. **Holdings:** 1000 volumes; files on citizen goals and futures projects in the U.S.

★7901★
Institute of American Indian and Alaska Native Culture and Arts Development - Library (Art, Area-Ethnic)
College of Santa Fe Campus
St. Michael's Dr.
Box 20007 Phone: (505)988-6670
Santa Fe, NM 87504 Mary L. Young, Dir. of Libs.
Founded: 1962. **Staff:** Prof 1; Other 1. **Subjects:** American Indian culture, history and technique of American Indian fine arts. **Special Collections:** Exhibition catalogs. **Holdings:** 18,000 books; 8 file drawers of archival materials; 9000 art slides; 4000 Indian slides; 24 file drawers of art catalogs; 27,826 Smithsonian Indian photographs; 8 file drawers of Indian newspapers; 60 tapes, 88 cassettes and 585 phonograph records of Indian music recordings; Indian newspapers. **Subscriptions:** 110 journals and other serials. **Services:** Interlibrary loan; library open to the public. **Remarks:** FAX: (505)988-6446. Institute is not affiliated with the College of Santa Fe.

Institute of American Indian Arts
See: **Institute of American Indian and Alaska Native Culture and Arts Development** (7901)

★7902★
The Institute of the American Musical, Inc. (Mus, Theater)
121 N. Detroit St. Phone: (213)934-1221
Los Angeles, CA 90036 Miles Kreuger, Pres./Cur.
Founded: 1972. **Subjects:** American musical theater and film, broadcasting, music, world's fairs and allied areas of showmanship. **Special Collections:** Record catalogs and supplements (1500); unpublished screenplays (200). **Holdings:** 6000 books; 100,000 phonograph records, tapes, cylinders, 1890 to present; theater and film playbills and programs; periodicals; sheet music; vocal scores, 1836 to present; silent filmed excerpts from performances of 175 Broadway musicals, 1931-1973; motion picture press books; 250,000 movie stills, 1914 to present; biographies; musical comedy scripts published in America (some in manuscript form); original or photocopied materials from the archives of movie studios and recording companies, including discographies of major Broadway and Hollywood stars. **Subscriptions:** 15 journals and other serials. **Services:** Library open to qualified scholars by appointment. Produces film retrospectives and exhibitions for the public.

Institute of Arctic & Alpine Research
See: **University of Colorado--Boulder** (18498)

★7903★
Institute of Arctic Biology - Library (Biol Sci)
311 Irving Bldg. Phone: (907)474-7174
Fairbanks, AK 99775 Carol J. Button, Lib.Asst.
Founded: 1962. **Subjects:** Physiology, cold adaption, biochemistry. **Holdings:** 1500 books. **Subscriptions:** 7 journals and other serials. **Services:** Interlibrary loan; copying; library open to the public. **Computerized Information Services:** Internal database. **Remarks:** FAX: (907)474-6967.

★7904★
Institute of Argentine Standards - Documentation Center (Sci-Engr)
Chile 1192 Phone: 1 37-3387
1098 Buenos Aires, Bs. As., Argentina Enzo Di Muro, Libn.
Founded: 1936. **Subjects:** Standards - electric, iron, construction, engineering. **Holdings:** 700,000 items. **Subscriptions:** 20 journals and other serials; 5 newspapers. **Services:** Interlibrary loan; copying; SDI; center open to the public. **Publications:** Dinamico, monthly - free by subscription. **Also Known As:** Instituto Argentino de Racionalizacion de Materiales - Centro de Documentacion.

Institute for Astronomical Computations
See: **Astronomisches Rechen-Institut** (1183)

★7905★
Institute for Balkan Studies - Library (Area-Ethnic)
Meg. Alexandru 31-A
P.O. Box 10611 Phone: 832-143
GR-54110 Thessaloniki, Greece Thomy Verrou-Karakostas, Libn.
Founded: 1954. **Staff:** 2. **Subjects:** Balkan region - history, culture, arts, language, folklore. **Special Collections:** Rare book collection. **Holdings:** 20,000 books. **Subscriptions:** 250 journals and other serials. **Services:** Copying; library open to the public with restrictions. **Special Indexes:** Index of Vol. 1-20, 21-30 of Balkan Studies. **Remarks:** FAX: 831429.

★7906★
Institute of Biology of the Southern Seas - Biblioteka (Biol Sci, Env-Cons)
prosp. Nachimova 2 Phone: 20550
SU-335011 Sevastopol, Ukraine Olga Akimova
Founded: 1871. **Staff:** Prof 6. **Subjects:** Marine biology; ecology - marine, environmental; ichthyology; oceanology; botany, zoology. **Special Collections:** A.L. Behning Collection; M. Hartmann Collection; V.M. Rilov Collection; S.A. Zernov Collection. **Holdings:** 53,123 books; 82,054 bound periodical volumes; 5551 reports; 1324 microfiche; 2522 microfilm. **Subscriptions:** 249 journals and other serials; 16 newspapers. **Services:** Interlibrary loan; library open to the public. **Computerized Information Services:** SCIENCEnet (electronic mail service). **Special Indexes:** Biology of Black and Azov Seas Indexes. **Remarks:** FAX: 592813. Telex: 187124 IBSS SU. Electronic mail address: IBSS.SEVASTOPOL (SCIENCEnet). **Also Known As:** Institut Biologii' Juznych Morej im O O Kovalevskogo.

Institute for Biomedical Communication (of South Africa)
See: **Medical Research Council Information Group - Library** (10011)

★7907★
Institute of Buddhist Studies - Library (Rel-Phil)
1900 Addison St. Phone: (510)849-2383
Berkeley, CA 94704 Margaret T. Yam, Hd.Libn.
Founded: 1966. **Staff:** Prof 1; Other 5. **Subjects:** Buddhism, Asian religions and philosophy. **Special Collections:** Shin Buddhism materials (1000 volumes); Pure Land Buddhism; Japanese contemporary writing in Jodoshinshu; instructional reference material in Buddhist education. **Holdings:** 10,300 books (7000 in Japanese); 647 periodical titles; 500 reports and manuscripts; 75 dissertations; 3500 clippings; 20 boxes of realia budistica. **Subscriptions:** 94 journals and other serials; 16 newspapers. **Services:** Copying; library open to the public at librarian's discretion. **Automated Operations:** MELVYL. **Publications:** Pacific World Journal. **Special Catalogs:** English listing of new titles and holdings. **Remarks:** FAX: (510)849-2158.

★7908★
Institute for Cancer and Blood Research - Library (Med)
150 N. Robertson Blvd., Suite 350 N. Phone: (213)655-4706
Beverly Hills, CA 90211-9951 Belle Gould, Libn.
Founded: 1967. **Staff:** 1. **Subjects:** Hematology, oncology. **Holdings:** 300 books; 30 bound periodical volumes. **Subscriptions:** 35 journals and other serials. **Services:** Library not open to the public. **Remarks:** FAX: (213)657-2185.

★7909★
Institute for Cancer Research - Talbot Research Library (Med)
Fox Chase Cancer Center Phone: (215)728-2710
Philadelphia, PA 19111 Karen M. Albert, Libn.
Founded: 1926. **Staff:** Prof 2; Other 4. **Subjects:** Biochemistry, cancer, cell biology, chemistry, clinical research, experimental pathology. **Special Collections:** A.L. Patterson Collection on crystallography and mathematics (1100 volumes). **Holdings:** 5000 books; 17,000 bound periodical volumes; 1350 reels of microfilm; 529 reports. **Subscriptions:** 422 journals and other serials. **Services:** Interlibrary loan; SDI; library open to the public by appointment. **Computerized Information Services:** DIALOG Information Services, MEDLARS, BRS Information Technologies, STN International, Mead Data Central, Data-Star, ORBIT Search Service. Performs searches on fee basis, telephone: 728-2711. **Networks/Consortia:** Member of Interlibrary Delivery Service of Pennsylvania (IDS), Health Sciences Libraries Consortium (HSLC). **Remarks:** FAX: (215)728-3655. **Staff:** Beth A. Lewis.

★7910★
Institute for Central European Research - Library (Area-Ethnic)
2910 Warrensville Center Rd. Phone: (216)752-9927
Shaker Heights, OH 44122 W.K. Von Uhlenhorst-Ziechmann, Dir.
Founded: 1945. **Staff:** 2. **Subjects:** Central Europe - history, literature, genealogy, horticulture, heraldry. **Holdings:** 800 books; 25 bound periodical volumes; 200 manuscripts and periodicals; 20 boxes and files of clippings and archival material. **Services:** Library not open to the public.

★7911★
Institute of Certified Travel Agents - Travel Reference Library (Bus-Fin)
148 Linden St.
Box 56 Phone: (617)237-0280
Wellesley, MA 02181-0503 Dawn Ringel, Mgr. Media Rel.
Founded: 1964. **Subjects:** Travel and tourism; travel agency history, education, administration; vintage travel. **Special Collections:** Travel Weekly and The Travel Agent (trade publications; complete set). **Holdings:** 3000 books; travel memorabilia. **Services:** Library open to the public by appointment. **Remarks:** FAX: (617)237-3860.

★7912★
Institute of Chartered Accountants - Library (Bus-Fin)
87-89 Pembroke Rd. Phone: 1 680400
Dublin 4, Dublin, Ireland Isabella Downes, Libn.
Founded: 1965. **Staff:** Prof 1; Other 1. **Subjects:** Accounting, taxation, corporate law, economics, management. **Special Collections:** Irish company annual reports; government publications, including acts of the Oireachtas (1922 to present). **Holdings:** 12,000 books; 200 bound periodical volumes; 40 audiocassettes; 10 videotapes. **Subscriptions:** 140 journals and other serials. **Services:** Copying; library open to members of accountancy bodies with whom special arrangements exist. **Publications:** Subject bibliographies. **Remarks:** FAX: 1 680842.

★7913★
Institute of Chartered Accountants in England and Wales - Library (Bus-Fin)
Moorgate Pt.
PO Box 433 Phone: 71 6287060
London EC2P 2BJ, England Ms. S.P. Moore
Founded: 1880. **Staff:** Prof 6; Other 4. **Subjects:** Accountancy, law, investment, finance, auditing, taxation, information technology. **Special Collections:** Historical accounting literature (2500 volumes). **Holdings:** 38,000 books. **Subscriptions:** 300 journals and other serials; 4 newspapers. **Services:** Interlibrary loan; copying; library open to the public with restrictions. **Automated Operations:** Computerized public access catalog. **Computerized Information Services:** Reuters, FT PROFILE; internal database. **Remarks:** FAX: 71 9200175. Telex: 88444 3.

★7914★
Institute of Chinese Studies - Library (Area-Ethnic)
1605 Elizabeth St. Phone: (818)398-2320
Pasadena, CA 91104 James A. Ziervogel, Dir.
Founded: 1977. **Staff:** 2. **Subjects:** Chinese peoples and cultures, including Han Chinese and minority peoples; Christian missions; China - travel, geography, history and culture, literature and language; minorities of China costumes. **Special Collections:** Periodicals Collection. **Holdings:** 1600 volumes; 4 VF drawers; 40 reports, manuscripts, and dissertations. **Subscriptions:** 100 journals and other serials; 2 newspapers. **Services:** Copying; library open to the public. **Publications:** Watchman on the Great Wall, irregular - free upon request; Extended Family, irregular; Bibliographies on China. **Remarks:** FAX: (818)398-2329.

Institute of Christian Oriental Research (ICOR) Library
See: **Catholic University of America - Semitics** (3165)

★7915★
Institute for Christian Studies - Library (Rel-Phil)
1909 University Ave. Phone: (512)476-2772
Austin, TX 78705 Gary Holloway, Libn.
Founded: 1975. **Staff:** Prof 1. **Subjects:** Religion, ethics, philosophy, theology, behavioral sciences, church history. **Special Collections:** G.H.P. Showalter Library (theology; 210 volumes). **Holdings:** 10,131 books; 213 bound periodical volumes; 557 cassette tapes. **Subscriptions:** 68 journals and other serials. **Services:** Copying; library open to the public with restrictions. **Publications:** ICS Report, quarterly; Christian Studies: Faculty Bulletin for the Institute for Christian Studies, semiannual. **Also Known As:** University Avenue Church of Christ Library and Institute for Christian Studies Library.

Institute of Cistercian Studies - Library
See: **Western Michigan University - Waldo Library - Rare Book Room** (20275)

★7916★
Institute for Clinical Social Work - Library (Soc Sci)
30 N. Michigan Ave., Suite 420 Phone: (312)726-8480
Chicago, IL 60602 Shirley Bennett, Libn.
Founded: 1981. **Subjects:** Clinical social work, psychiatry, psychology. **Holdings:** 4000 books; 300 professional articles. **Subscriptions:** 35 journals and other serials. **Services:** Interlibrary loan; library not open to the public. **Computerized Information Services:** DIALOG Information Services.

★7917★
Institute of Comparative Social and Cultural Studies - Information Center (Area-Ethnic)
6935 Wisconsin Ave., Suite 500 Phone: (301)656-7996
Chevy Chase, MD 20815 Shelly Vilov, Contact
Subjects: Perceptions and values of different cultural groups in the United States - Hispanics, Latin Americans, Far and Middle Eastern peoples. **Holdings:** Publications. Figures not available. **Computerized Information Services:** Internal database. **Remarks:** FAX: (301)652-9020.

★7918★
Institute of Contemporary Art - Library (Art)
955 Boylston St.
Boston, MA 02115 Phone: (617)266-5152
Founded: 1935. **Subjects:** Contemporary art, theater, video/film, architecture. **Holdings:** Books; catalogs from exhibitions. **Services:** Library open to the public by appointment; research requests accepted. **Remarks:** FAX: (617)266-4021.

★7919★
Institute for Contemporary Ecclesiastical History - Library (Rel-Phil, Hist)
Monchsberg 2a Phone: 84 25 21
A-5020 Salzburg, Austria Theodora Bogalin, Libn.
Subjects: Contemporary ecclesiastical history, Austrian history. **Holdings:** 7900 volumes. **Services:** Library open to the public. **Remarks:** Maintained by Internationales Forschungszentrum fur Grundfragen der Wissenschaften Salzburg. **Also Known As:** Institut fur Kirchliche Zeitgeschichte.

★7920★
Institute of Contemporary History - Library (Area-Ethnic, Hist)
Leonrodstrasse 46b Phone: 89 12 68 80
W-8000 Munich 19, Germany Dr. Christoph Weisz, Libn.
Subjects: Contemporary history of the German Reich, Third Reich, and Federal Republic of Germany; emigration of Germans during the years 1933-1945; national socialism; Bavarian contemporary history. **Holdings:** 125,000 volumes. **Subscriptions:** 300 journals and other serials. **Services:** Library open to the public. **Remarks:** FAX: 89 123 17 27. Affiliated with Federal Republic of Germany - Ministry of Research and Technology and Bavarian State Ministry for Science and Culture. **Also Known As:** Institut fur Zeitgeschichte - Bibliothek.

★7921★
Institute for Creation Research - Research Library (Rel-Phil)
Box 2667 Phone: (619)448-0900
El Cajon, CA 92021 James Stambaugh, Dir. of Lib.
Founded: 1970. **Staff:** Prof 1. **Subjects:** Evolution, creation, catastrophism, anti-evolution polemic. **Special Collections:** Harald F.J. Ellingsen Collection (theology); curriculum laboratory. **Holdings:** 6500 books; 250 bound periodical volumes; 4200 periodicals; 126 video cassettes; vertical file; clipping and photocopy file. **Subscriptions:** 200 journals and other serials. **Services:** Interlibrary loan; copying; library open to the public.

Institute for the Crippled and Disabled
See: **International Center for the Disabled (ICD)** (8070)

Institute of Culture and Communication - CCPC - Resource Materials Collection
See: **East-West Center - Institute of Culture and Communication - CCPC** (5133)

★7922★
Institute for Defense Analyses - Center for Communications Research - Library (Sci-Engr, Comp Sci)
Thanet Rd. Phone: (609)924-4600
Princeton, NJ 08540 Jane P. Ciosek, Supv., Info.Serv.
Founded: 1959. **Staff:** Prof 1; Other 2. **Subjects:** Mathematics, computer science, speech. **Holdings:** 10,000 books; 5000 bound periodical volumes; reprints; pamphlets. **Subscriptions:** 325 journals and other serials. **Services:** Library not open to the public. **Computerized Information Services:** DIALOG Information Services, Data-Star. **Formerly:** Its Communications Research Division.

★7923★
Institute for Defense Analyses - Technical Information Services (Sci-Engr)
1801 N. Beauregard St. Phone: (703)845-2043
Alexandria, VA 22311 Dr. Russell Fries, Mgr.
Founded: 1960. **Staff:** Prof 6; Other 7. **Subjects:** Aeronautical and chemical engineering, economics, mathematics, physics, political science, weapons

and operations research, policy analysis, systems analysis, social problems. **Holdings:** 12,000 volumes; 110,000 other cataloged items. **Subscriptions:** 400 journals and other serials; 10 newspapers. **Services:** Interlibrary loan; services not open to the public. **Automated Operations:** Computerized cataloging, acquisitions, and serials. **Computerized Information Services:** DIALOG Information Services, NEXIS, DTIC, WILSONLINE, NewsNet, Inc., Aerospace Online, Dow Jones News/Retrieval, NASA/RECON, CompuServe Information Service, BYTE Information Exchange (BIX); EasyLink; OCLC; (electronic mail service). **Networks/Consortia:** Member of CAPCON Library Network. **Publications:** Monthly Bulletin. **Remarks:** Alternate telephone number(s): 845-2058. FAX: (703)845-2588. Telex: 324 659 IDA ALX. **Staff:** Bettye Schubert, Ref.Libn.; Joan Sweeney, Res.Libn.; Jane Lehman, Ref.Libn.; Bettye Pringle, Cat.

★7924★
Institute for Defense and Disarmament Studies - Library (Mil)
675 Massachusetts Ave.
Cambridge, MA 02139 Phone: (617)354-4337
Founded: 1980. **Staff:** 6. **Subjects:** Alternative defense, arms control negotiations, conventional and nuclear arms reduction, weapons, military policy, peace and peace-related organizations. **Special Collections:** Alternative defense proposals. **Holdings:** 3000 books; government documents; documents from military and disarmament-related agencies. **Subscriptions:** 301 journals and other serials. **Services:** Copying; center open to the public for reference use only. **Automated Operations:** Computerized public access catalog, acquisitions, and serials. **Computerized Information Services:** Internal databases; electronic mail service. Performs searches on fee basis. Contact Person: Emily Kessler. **Publications:** Arms Control Reporter, monthly; ViennaFax, monthly; list of other publications - available on request. **Remarks:** FAX: (617)354-1450. **Staff:** Randall Watson Forsberg, Exec.Dir.

★7925★
Institute for Development Anthropology - Library (Soc Sci)
99 Collier St.
Box 2207 Phone: (607)772-6244
Binghamton, NY 13902 Cheryl T. Naslund, Libn.
Founded: 1976. **Staff:** Prof 2. **Subjects:** Social, economic, rural development; natural resource management; food production. **Special Collections:** Agricultural/Livestock Development (3200 items); African Development (4000 items); Economic Development (2200 items); Development Policy and Strategy (2700 items); Senegal Bibliography Documents (1000 items); Pastoral Bibliography Documents (1000 items). **Holdings:** 1450 books; 14,600 other cataloged items. **Subscriptions:** 28 journals and other serials. **Services:** Copying; library open to the public. **Computerized Information Services:** BITNET (electronic mail service). **Publications:** Development Anthropology Network, biennial - by subscription. **Remarks:** FAX: (607)773-8993. Telex: 932433. **Staff:** Stephanie R. Horowitz, Asst.Libn.

★7926★
Institute for Development Research and Development Policy - Library (Bus-Fin, Soc Sci)
Ruhr-Universitat Bochum
Postfach 102148 Phone: 234 7002302
W-4630 Bochum, Germany Dorothee Sensen, Libn.
Subjects: Development policy and strategy, economics of education, government and politics, economic and social geography, demography and sociology, agricultural policy, statistics and econometrics. **Special Collections:** Afghanistan Archive (3500 titles). **Holdings:** 28,500 volumes. **Subscriptions:** 71 journals and other serials. **Services:** Copying; library open to the public. **Remarks:** FAX: 234 7002001. Maintained by Ruhr-University. Telex: 08 25 860. **Also Known As:** Institut fur Entwicklungsforschung und Entwicklungspolitik.

★7927★
Institute for Documentation and Information in Social Medicine and Public Health - Library (Med)
Postfach 20 10 12
Westerfeldstrasse 35-37
W-4800 Bielefeld 1, Germany Phone: 521 86033
Founded: 1956. **Subjects:** Addiction and alcoholism; drug-induced diseases; environmental health and toxicology; epidemiology; medicine - industrial, legal, preventive, social, traffic; health education; occupational health; mental retardation; public health; medical sociology. **Special Collections:** German medical statistics. **Holdings:** 70,000 volumes; microfiche; AV programs. **Subscriptions:** 700 journals and other serials. **Services:** Library open to the public. **Computerized Information Services:** DIMDI; produces SOMED. **Remarks:** Maintained by the State Ministry of Labor, Health and Social Affairs of North Rhine-Westphalia. **Also Known As:** Institut fur Dokumentation und Information uber Sozialmedizin und Offentliches Gesundheitswesen.

★7928★
Institute for Drug Research - Library (Med, Sci-Engr)
Szabadsagharcosok utja 47-49
Postafiok 82 Phone: 1 1690 011
H-1325 Budapest, Hungary Dr. Judit Stverteczky, Hd. of Lib.
Founded: 1950. **Staff:** Prof 3; Other 3. **Subjects:** Organic chemistry, biochemistry, analytical chemistry, bioengineering, new drugs, medicine, pharmacy, pharmacology. **Holdings:** 15,765 books; 17,108 bound periodical volumes. **Subscriptions:** 109 journals and other serials; 9 newspapers. **Services:** Interlibrary loan; copying; SDI; library open to the public. **Computerized Information Services:** DIALOG Information Services, Data-Star, STN International. **Remarks:** FAX: 1693-229. Telex: 224219 gyoki h. **Also Known As:** Gyogyszerkutato Intezet Kv.

★7929★
Institute of Dunhuang Relics Study - Library (Hist)
Mogaoku
Dunhuang, Gansu Province,
People's Republic of China Feng zhi Wen, Prof.
Founded: 1960. **Staff:** 11. **Subjects:** Fine arts archeology, Chinese western regions archeology, Buddhism. **Special Collections:** Dunhuang Study Collection (articles; sutras; Chinese ancient books and paintings). **Holdings:** 85,221 volumes; 200 periodicals; 50 technical reports; 5 AV programs and microforms. **Services:** Interlibrary loan. **Computerized Information Services:** Internal database. **Publications:** Dunhuang Study (magazine); Dunhuang Painted Sculpture; Dunhuang Frescoes; Dunhuang Artistic Treasures; Dunhuang (5 volumes).

★7930★
Institute of Early American History and Culture - Kellock Library (Hist)
College of William and Mary
Box 220 Phone: (804)221-1126
Williamsburg, VA 23187 Patricia V. Higgs, Supv.
Staff: 2. **Subjects:** Early American history, book publishing. **Holdings:** 6950 books; 855 bound periodical volumes; 1975 reels of microfilm. **Subscriptions:** 54 journals and other serials. **Services:** Interlibrary loan; library open to outside users with permission of director. **Remarks:** Institute is sponsored by the College of William and Mary and the Colonial Williamsburg Foundation.

★7931★
Institute for East-West Security Studies - Pal Racz Memorial Library (Soc Sci)
360 Lexington Ave., 13th Fl. Phone: (212)557-2570
New York, NY 10017 Rosalinda M. Rupel, Libn.
Founded: 1982. **Staff:** Prof 1; Other 2. **Subjects:** International affairs, security affairs, East-West relations, arms control. **Special Collections:** Soviet and East Europe Security Affairs Collection (original and translated materials). **Holdings:** 5000 books; 256 bound periodical volumes. **Subscriptions:** 220 journals and other serials; 23 newspapers. **Services:** Interlibrary loan; library not open to the public. **Publications:** Recent Library Acquisition List, 10/year - to other libraries and institutes in Europe in the same field of study. **Remarks:** FAX: (212)949-8043. Telex: 760 8127 EWS.

Institute of Ecology Archives
See: **University of Georgia - Department of Records Management & University Archives** (18596)

★ 7932 ★
Institute for Economic, Market Research and Informatics Ltd. - Library (Bus-Fin)
Dorottya u 6
Pf 133-Bpest 62
POB 133 Phone: 1 1184307
H-1389 Budapest, Hungary Gyulane Trebits
Founded: 1964. **Staff:** Prof 3; Other 3. **Subjects:** Economics, marketing, finance, informatics. **Special Collections:** European Community collection; press documentation. **Holdings:** 22,000 books; 4000 reports; 500,000 archival items; 100 microfiche; 20 floppy disks. **Subscriptions:** 800 journals and other serials; 100 newspapers. **Services:** Interlibrary loan; copying; SDI; library open to the public. **Computerized Information Services:** DIALOG Information Services, Data-Star; internal databases. Contact Persons: Imrene Szabo; Eva Veres. **Publications:** Register of Papers and Publications, annual. **Remarks:** FAX: 1 1186483. Telex: 22-5646. **Also Known As:** Konjunktura-, Piackutato es Informatikai Intezet Rt. - Konyvtar.

Institute of Economics (of Hungary)
See: **Hungarian Academy of Sciences - Institute of Economics** (7544)

★ 7933 ★
Institute of Ecosystem Studies - Library (Biol Sci, Env-Cons)
Cary Arboretum
New York Botanical Garden
Box AB Phone: (914)677-5343
Millbrook, NY 12545 Annette R. Frank, Libn.
Founded: 1972. **Staff:** Prof 1; Other 1. **Subjects:** Ecology, botany, horticulture, environmental studies, wildlife management. **Special Collections:** Limnology. **Holdings:** 8000 books; 2000 bound periodical volumes; 450 maps. **Subscriptions:** 225 journals and other serials. **Services:** Interlibrary loan; copying; library open to the public. **Computerized Information Services:** BRS Information Technologies, DIALOG Information Services, OCLC EPIC; internal database. Performs searches on fee basis. **Networks/Consortia:** Member of Southeastern New York Library Resources Council (SENYLRC). **Remarks:** FAX: (914)677-5976.

★ 7934 ★
Institute of Electrical Research - Library (Sci-Engr)
Apdo. Postal 475 Phone: 73 182496
62000 Cuernavaca, Morelos, Mexico Dr. Jaime Pontigo, Tech.Info.Mgr.
Founded: 1975. **Staff:** 25. **Subjects:** Power generation, transmission, distribution, and automation. **Holdings:** 50,000 volumes. **Subscriptions:** 900 journals and other serials. **Services:** Interlibrary loan; copying; library open to graduate students. **Computerized Information Services:** DIALOG Information Services, BRS Information Technologies, ORBIT Search Service; REFERENCIAS IIE, SCPP, NORMAS, RIE, REMISM (internal databases). **Remarks:** FAX: 73 182461. Telex: 17-76352 IIEMME. **Also Known As:** Instituto de Investigaciones Electricas. **Staff:** Nohemi Sosa; Cecilia Culebra; Pedro Mondragon; Yumara Lugo; Maria del Carmen Soto; Eduardo Neri.

★ 7935 ★
Institute of Environmental Sciences - Library (Env-Cons)
940 E. Northwest Hwy. Phone: (708)255-1561
Mt. Prospect, IL 60056 Janet A. Ehmann, Exec.Dir.
Staff: 10. **Subjects:** Engineering, energy and environment, contamination control. **Holdings:** Figures not available. **Services:** Library not open to the public. **Publications:** List of publications - available on request. **Remarks:** FAX: (708)255-1699.

★ 7936 ★
Institute of Ethnology and Folklore Research - Library (Area-Ethnic)
Ulica Kralja Zvonimira 17/IV
PP 287
YU-41000 Zagreb, Croatia, Yugoslavia Phone: 41 417254
Anamarija Starcevic-Stambuk, Libn.
Founded: 1948. **Subjects:** Croatian folklore - oral and folk literature, popular literature, folk theater and dance, customs, urban folklore, ethnology and folkloristics, ethnomusicology. **Special Collections:** Folklore Archives (1378 unpublished manuscripts; 2353 tapes and cassettes; 364 phonograph records; 30,400 photographs and slides; 170 videocassettes). **Holdings:** 22,000 volumes. **Services:** Interlibrary loan; copying; SDI; library open to the public for reference use only. **Computerized Information Services:** Internal database. **Publications:** List of new publications in library, monthly. **Remarks:** Alternate telephone number(s): 41 410617. FAX: 41 440880. **Formerly:** Institute for Philology and Folkloristics - Institute for Folklore Research. **Also Known As:** Institut za Etnologiju i Folkloristiku.

★ 7937 ★
Institute of European Studies - Vienna Library (Area-Ethnic, Bus-Fin)
Palais Corbelli
Johannesgasse 7
A-1010 Vienna, Austria Phone: 222 51222601
Founded: 1955. **Staff:** Prof 3; Other 10. **Subjects:** Eastern European studies, arts, Austrian cultural studies, international business and economics, international relations, psychology. **Special Collections:** Scores; libretti. **Holdings:** 8500 books; students' term papers and essays; 170 audiotapes; 350 phonograph records. **Subscriptions:** 20 journals and other serials; 6 newspapers. **Services:** Interlibrary loan; library not open to the public. **Publications:** Annual Report. **Remarks:** Materials are in English. FAX: 222 51222601. **Staff:** Cele Cerne, Libn.; Anneliese Fischer, Libn.

★ 7938 ★
Institute of Family History & Genealogy - Library (Hist)
21 Hanson Ave. Phone: (617)666-0877
Somerville, MA 02143 Joseph M. Glynn, Jr., Dir./Libn.
Staff: 1. **Subjects:** Genealogy, history, surnames, heraldry. **Special Collections:** Peter Knight's index to Boston streets and wards, 1850-1870; biographical archives. **Holdings:** 200 books; 25 unbound periodicals; 8 drawers of subject files; 75 lecture tapes. **Subscriptions:** 25 journals and other serials. **Services:** Library open to the public by appointment. **Publications:** New England Genealogy (newsletter); Genealogical Observer (newsletter). **Remarks:** Alternate telephone number(s): 593-0364.

★ 7939 ★
Institute of Fiscal Studies - Library (Bus-Fin)
Casado del Alisal 6 Phone: 91 420 1477
E-28014 Madrid, Spain Antonio Pajuelo Macias, Libn.
Subjects: Public finance, taxation, economics. **Holdings:** 55,000 volumes. **Remarks:** Maintained by Spain - Ministry of Finance and Economy. **Also Known As:** Instituto de Estudios Fiscales.

★ 7940 ★
Institute of Fundamental Technological Research - Library (Sci-Engr)
ulica Swietokrzyska 21 Phone: 22 261281
PL-00-049 Warsaw, Poland Marta Dmitruk, Libn.
Founded: 1953. **Staff:** 10. **Subjects:** Applied mechanics, acoustics, electrodynamics, nondestructive testing, energy research, robotics. **Holdings:** 80,000 volumes. **Subscriptions:** 707 journals and other serials. **Services:** Interlibrary loan; copying; library open to the public. **Remarks:** FAX: 22 269815. Alternate telephone number(s): 22 260129. Telex: 825638 ippt pl. Affiliated with Polish Academy of Sciences. **Also Known As:** Instytut Podstawowych Problemow Techniki.

★ 7941 ★
Institute of Gas Technology - Technical Information Center (Energy)
3424 S. State St. Phone: (312)567-3963
Chicago, IL 60616 Carol Worster, Supv., Tech.Info.Ctr.
Founded: 1941. **Staff:** Prof 2; Other 1. **Subjects:** Natural gas technology, energy, coal, bioengineering, chemical engineering. **Special Collections:** American Chemical Society Division of Fuel Chemistry Preprints, 1957 to present; Pipeline Simulation Interest Group papers. **Holdings:** 17,200 books; 18,000 bound periodical volumes; 200,000 microfiche of technical reports; 94,000 industrial, organizational, governmental reports; 1000 dissertations; 1000 congressional hearings; 5050 patents. **Subscriptions:** 504 journals and other serials. **Services:** Interlibrary loan; copying; SDI; center open to the public for reference use only by appointment. **Automated Operations:** Computerized cataloging. **Computerized Information Services:** DIALOG Information Services, OCLC; gasLine (internal database); electronic mail. Performs searches on fee basis. **Networks/Consortia:** Member of Chicago Library System, ILLINET. **Remarks:** FAX: (312)567-5209. Telex: 312-25-6189.

★ 7942 ★
Institute for German Language - Library (Hum)
R5, 6-13
P.O. Box 10 16 21 Phone: 621 44010
W-6800 Mannheim 1, Germany Eva Teubert, Libn.
Founded: 1964. **Staff:** 3. **Subjects:** Contemporary German language, linguistics, and literature. **Special Collections:** Spoken German-language dialects (12,000 audiotape recordings). **Holdings:** 60,000 volumes. **Subscriptions:** 300 journals and other serials. **Services:** Library open to institutions and scholars of German language and linguistics. **Computerized Information Services:** Internal databases; Datex-P (electronic mail service). **Publications:** List of acquisitions of new books. **Remarks:** FAX: 621 4401200. Electronic mail address(es): 45621043161 (Datex-P). **Also Known As:** Institut fur Deutsche Sprache.

Institute for Great Lakes Research
See: **Bowling Green State University** (2037)

The Institute of Heraldry
See: **U.S. Army - Total Army Personnel Center - Personnel Service Support Directorate - The Institute of Heraldry** (17003)

Institute of Historical Research
See: **Universidad Nacional Autonoma de Mexico - Instituto de Investigaciones Historicas** (17993)

★7943★
Institute of Historical, Social, and Political Studies of the Central Committee of the Romanian Communist Party - Library (Soc Sci)
Strada Ministerului 4 Phone: 17 01 06
70000 Bucharest, Romania Dr. Nicolae Popescu
Subjects: Communist party, revolutionary and democratic movements in Romania and other countries. **Holdings:** 100,000 volumes. **Also Known As:** Institutul de Studii Istorice si Social-Politice de pe Linga Comitetul Central al Partidului Comunist Roman.

★7944★
Institute of Industrial Engineers, Inc. - Frank & Lillian Gilbreth Memorial Library (Sci-Engr)
25 Technology Park/Atlanta Phone: (404)449-0460
Norcross, GA 30092 Jerry Johnson
Staff: 2. **Subjects:** Industrial engineering, management, engineering technology. **Special Collections:** Complete bound sets of Industrial Engineering magazine (40 volumes), IIE Transactions (21 volumes), The Engineering Economist (33 volumes), Industrial Management (31 volumes). **Holdings:** 3000 books; 80 periodicals; 25 conference proceedings. **Subscriptions:** 200 journals and other serials. **Services:** Copying (limited); library open to the public by appointment. **Remarks:** FAX: (404)263-8532.

★7945★
Institute of International Education - Information Center (Educ)
809 United Nations Plaza, 1st Fl. Phone: (212)984-5413
New York, NY 10017 Marie Stapleton, Mgr., Info.Serv.
Founded: 1985. **Staff:** 3. **Subjects:** International educational exchanges/higher education in the United States and abroad - scholarships and grants, career opportunities, internships, volunteer programs. **Holdings:** 3600 U.S. and foreign university catalogs; 600 reference volumes. **Services:** Center open to the public. **Networks/Consortia:** Member of Consortium of Foundation Libraries (CFL). **Remarks:** Institute also maintains a Staff Library of 3000 volumes. FAX: (212)984-5452. Alternate telephone number(s): (212)984-5535 (recording). Telex: TRT 175977. **Staff:** W. Richard Heyer, Libn.

★7946★
Institute of International Finance - Library (Bus-Fin)
2000 Pennsylvania Ave., N.W., Suite 8500 Phone: (202)857-3642
Washington, DC 20006 Jean Frankel, Libn.
Founded: 1983. **Subjects:** International finance, banking, economics. **Holdings:** 1500 books. **Subscriptions:** 480 journals and other serials; 18 newspapers. **Services:** Interlibrary loan; library not open to the public. **Automated Operations:** Computerized cataloging and periodical circulation. **Remarks:** FAX: (202)775-1430. Telex: 64165 IIF.

Institute of Jazz Studies
See: **Rutgers University** (14166)

★7947★
Institute of Judicial Administration - Library
1 Washington Sq. Village
New York, NY 10012
Defunct. Holdings absorbed by New York University - School of Law Library.

★7948★
Institute for Juvenile Research - Research Library
907 S. Wolcott
Chicago, IL 60612
Founded: 1928. **Subjects:** Psychology, psychiatry, family therapy, sociology, organization and administration, psychotherapy and mental health. **Holdings:** 5000 books; 2000 bound periodical volumes; archival materials. **Remarks:** Currently inactive.

★7949★
Institute for Latin American Integration - Library (Bus-Fin)
Esmeralda 130, Piso 16 Phone: 1 3942260
1035 Buenos Aires, Argentina Lic. Graciela B. De Moyano
Founded: 1965. **Staff:** 4. **Subjects:** Economic integration in Latin America. **Holdings:** 50,000 books and documents; 900 periodicals. **Services:** Interlibrary loan; SDI; library open to the public. **Computerized Information Services:** Internal database. **Remarks:** FAX: 1 3942293. Telex: 21520 AR BIDBA. Holdings are in Spanish.

★7950★
Institute of Living - Medical Library (Med)
400 Washington St. Phone: (203)241-6824
Hartford, CT 06106 Harriet E. Rosenfeld, Dir.
Founded: 1822. **Staff:** Prof 4. **Subjects:** Neurology, psychiatry, psychoanalysis, social sciences. **Special Collections:** Norman Collection (development of psychiatry and mental hospitals; 300 volumes); Zilboorg Collection (290 rare books on medical psychology). **Holdings:** 24,000 books; 11,000 bound periodical volumes; 30 boxes of hospital archives; 500 audio cassettes; 40 video cassettes. **Subscriptions:** 200 journals and other serials. **Services:** Interlibrary loan; copying; SDI; library open to qualified professionals and college students for reference use only. **Computerized Information Services:** Online systems. **Networks/Consortia:** Member of Connecticut Association of Health Science Libraries (CAHSL). **Publications:** Digest of Neurology and Psychiatry, 6/year - free to doctors and librarians upon request. **Staff:** Patricia J. Reynolds, Libn.; Elizabeth A. Fishe, Assoc.Dir.; Joseph Pallis, Libn.

★7951★
Institute for Local Self-Reliance - Library (Env-Cons)
2425 18th St., N.W.
Washington, DC 20009 Phone: (202)232-4108
Founded: 1974. **Subjects:** Recycling and waste utilization, energy, alternative energy sources, cities and neighborhoods, ecology and environment, local economic development, materials policy. **Holdings:** 300 books. **Subscriptions:** 40 journals and other serials. **Services:** Library not open to the public. **Computerized Information Services:** EcoNet (electronic mail service). **Publications:** Facts to Act On. **Remarks:** FAX: (202)332-0463.

★7952★
Institute of Logistics and Distribution Management - Library (Bus-Fin)
Douglas House
Queens Sq. Phone: 536 205500
Corby, Northamptonshire NN 17, England R.C. Horsley, Dir.Gen.
Founded: 1981. **Subjects:** Physical distribution of goods, logistics. **Holdings:** 500 volumes. **Remarks:** FAX: 536 400979.

★7953★
Institute of Logopedics - Clyde C. Berger Resource Center (Med)
2400 Jardine Dr. Phone: (316)262-8271
Wichita, KS 67219 Valorie Thaw, Libn.
Founded: 1934. **Staff:** Prof 1. **Subjects:** Speech pathology, audiology, neurology, psychology, special education. **Special Collections:** Collections of rare books on speech pathology and audiology (100 volumes). **Holdings:** 3000 books; 20,000 reprints of scientific articles, government documents, pamphlets, other ephemera. **Subscriptions:** 20 journals and other serials. **Services:** Interlibrary loan; copying; library open to the public. **Computerized Information Services:** DIALOG Information Services. **Networks/Consortia:** Member of National Network of Libraries of Medicine - Midcontinental Region. **Publications:** Bibliographies - prepared on request; new acquisitions lists, irregular.

★7954★
Institute of Man and Resources - Centre for Information and Technical Assistance
P.O. Box 414
Charlottetown, PE, Canada C1A 7K7
Defunct.

★7955★
Institute of Management Accountants - Library (Bus-Fin)
10 Paragon Dr. Phone: (201)573-6235
Montvale, NJ 07645-1760 Elaine Goldman, Mgr.
Founded: 1920. **Staff:** Prof 1; Other 1. **Subjects:** Management and financial accounting, data processing, management and financial management. **Special Collections:** Trade association accounting manuals (150). **Holdings:** 10,000 books; 450 bound periodical volumes; 30 VF drawers. **Subscriptions:** 300 journals and other serials. **Services:** Interlibrary loan; copying (both limited); library open to the public for reference use only. **Computerized Information Services:** LEXIS, NEXIS, DIALOG Information Services; EasyLink (electronic mail service). **Publications:** Subject bibliographies, annual - free upon request. **Remarks:** Alternate telephone number(s): 573-6236. FAX: (201)573-0639. **Formerly:** National Association of Accountants.

Institute for Marine Environmental Research
See: **Plymouth Marine Laboratory and Marine Biological Association of the United Kingdom** (13152)

Institute of Marketing
See: **Infomark** (7841)

Institute for Medical Information - State Medical Library
See: **Czechoslovakia - National Library of Medicine** (4515)

★7956★
Institute of Mental Health - Staff Library (Med)
Adolph Meyer Bldg.
Box 8281 Phone: (401)464-2580
Cranston, RI 02920 Deirdre Donohue, Lib.Coord.
Remarks: No further information was supplied by respondent.

★7957★
Institute of Navigation - Library (Trans)
1026 16th St., N.W., Suite 104 Phone: (202)783-4121
Washington, DC 20036 Maxine Pusser, Pub.Spec.
Founded: 1945. **Subjects:** Navigation and allied subjects. **Holdings:** 200 books. **Subscriptions:** 50 journals and other serials. **Services:** Library open to the public by appointment. **Remarks:** FAX: (202)347-4698.

★7958★
Institute of Noetic Sciences - Library (Soc Sci)
475 Gate Five Rd., Suite 300 Phone: (415)331-5650
Sausalito, CA 94965 Nola D. Lewis, Res.Asst.
Founded: 1973. **Staff:** 4. **Subjects:** Psychology and cognitive sciences, health and biomedical sciences, neurosciences, social issues, futures studies, religion and philosophy, education and training. **Holdings:** 1200 books; 12 VF drawers of unbound reports, manuscripts, clippings, documents. **Subscriptions:** 50 journals and other serials. **Services:** Library not open to the public. **Computerized Information Services:** DIALOG Information Services.

★7959★
Institute of Nuclear Power Operations - Library (Energy)
1100 Circle 75 Pkwy., Suite 1500 Phone: (404)953-3600
Atlanta, GA 30339 Mary L. Watson, Tech.Libn.
Founded: 1979. **Staff:** 2. **Subjects:** Safety, reliability, and evaluation of nuclear power plants. **Holdings:** 20,000 volumes; reports. **Services:** Library not open to the public. **Computerized Information Services:** Nuclear Plant Reliability Database System (NPRDS; internal database).

Institute of Nutrition of Central America and Panama
See: **Pan American Health Organization - Institute of Nutrition of Central America and Panama** (12717)

★7960★
Institute of Ocean Sciences - Library (Sci-Engr)
9860 W. Saanich Rd.
Box 6000 Phone: (604)363-6392
Sidney, BC, Canada V8L 4B2 Sharon Thomson, Libn.
Founded: 1970. **Staff:** Prof 1; Other 1. **Subjects:** Physical and chemical oceanography, hydrographic surveying, oil pollution, remote sensing, applied and marine geophysics, marine geology, seismology. **Holdings:** 6000 books; 600 bound periodical volumes; 10,000 technical documents; 4320 microfiche; 520 microforms. **Subscriptions:** 430 journals and other serials. **Services:** Interlibrary loan; library open to the public for reference use only. **Automated Operations:** Computerized circulation. **Computerized Information Services:** DIALOG Information Services, CAN/OLE; Envoy 100, SCIENCEnet (electronic mail services). **Publications:** Canadian Reports of Hydrography and Ocean Sciences. **Remarks:** FAX: (604)363-6390. Telex: 636700764 MBX CA. Electronic mail address(es): 10SBC.LIBRARY (SCIENCEnet). Institute is funded by Canada - Fisheries and Oceans and Canada - Energy, Mines & Resources Canada.

Institute of Offshore Engineering
See: **Heriot-Watt University** (7154)

Institute of Outdoor Drama
See: **University of North Carolina at Chapel Hill** (19065)

★7961★
Institute for Palestine Studies - Library (Area-Ethnic)
Anis Nsouli St., Off Verdun
P.O. Box 11-7164 Phone: 312-512
Beirut, Lebanon Mona Nsouli, Libn.
Founded: 1963. **Staff:** Prof 3; Other 2. **Subjects:** Palestine problem, Arab-Israeli conflict, Judaica, Zionism, Jewish-Arab relations. **Special Collections:** Rare books (pertaining to Mandate period); private papers; photograph collection; official correspondence, records, and private collections of the Public Record Office, London; League of Arab States and United Nations documents. **Holdings:** 31,000 books; 11,600 bound periodical volumes; pamphlet files; 3850 reels of microfilm; 400 maps; 200 theses. **Subscriptions:** 380 journals and other serials; 40 newspapers. **Services:** Interlibrary loan; copying; library open to the public. **Publications:** Accessions list, bimonthly. **Special Indexes:** Periodicals index. **Remarks:** Alternate telephone number(s): 868387. FAX: 868387; 814193. Telex: MADAF 23317 LE. **Staff:** Leila Halawi, Asst.Libn., Cat.; Jeanette Seraphim, Asst.Libn., Doc.

★7962★
Institute of Paper Science and Technology - Library (Sci-Engr)
575 14th St., N.W. Phone: (404)853-9530
Atlanta, GA 30318 Hartley K. Phinney, Jr., Chf.Libn.
Founded: 1930. **Staff:** Prof 2; Other 4. **Subjects:** Pulp and paper technology, chemistry, engineering. **Special Collections:** Dard Hunter Collection on the history of papermaking (1300 books; 3000 documents). **Holdings:** 26,511 books; 21,214 bound periodical volumes; 195,000 patents on papermaking and allied processes; 1876 student reports; 7290 technical translations; 500,000 technical abstracts on 3x5 cards; 680 dissertations on microfilm; 82 VF drawers; 550 specialized bibliographies issued by the institute; 1800 government reports on microfiche; 25 journal titles on 1700 reels of microfilm. **Subscriptions:** 850 journals and other serials. **Services:** Copying; SDI; custom translating service; library open to the public for reference use only. **Automated Operations:** Computerized serials. **Computerized Information Services:** DIALOG Information Services, STN International, PFDS Online, Chemical Abstracts Service (CAS), OCLC; OnTyme Electronic Message Network Service (electronic mail service). Performs searches on fee basis. Contact Person: Gail Stahl, 853-9528. **Networks/Consortia:** Member of SOLINET, University Center in Georgia, Inc. **Publications:** Abstract Bulletin of the Institute of Paper Science and Technology (hardcopy, microform, online), monthly; bibliographies; Paper CLIPP; Forthcoming Meetings. **Remarks:** Toll-free telephone number(s): (800)-558-6611. FAX: (404)853-9510. **Staff:** Nancy Skifstad.

Institute of Papua New Guinea Studies
See: **Papua New Guinea - Department of Culture and Tourism** (12733)

★7963★
Institute of the Pennsylvania Hospital - Medical Library (Med)
111 N. 49th St. Phone: (215)471-2013
Philadelphia, PA 19139 June M. Strickland, Libn.
Founded: 1841. **Staff:** Prof 2. **Subjects:** Psychiatry, psychology, psychoanalysis, mental health, allied health sciences. **Special Collections:** Historical collection. **Holdings:** 8000 books; 6700 bound periodical volumes; 200 microfiche; 100 reels of microfilm; hospital reports; pamphlets. **Subscriptions:** 210 journals and other serials. **Services:** Interlibrary loan; copying; library not open to the public. **Computerized Information Services:** BRS/COLLEAGUE.

Institute for Philology and Folkloristics - Institute for Folklore Research
See: **Institute of Ethnology and Folklore Research - Library** (7936)

Institute for Phytomedicine
See: **Swiss Botanical Society - Library** (15936)

★7964★
Institute of Press Research - Library (Info Sci)
Hansaplatz Phone: 231 5023221
W-4600 Dortmund, Germany Hans Bohrmann, Ph.D.
Founded: 1926. **Staff:** Prof 9; Other 4. **Subjects:** Press history, mass media, media history. **Holdings:** 50,000 books; 55,000 bound periodical volumes; 6500 microfiche; 65,079 reels of microfilm; 5800 posters. **Subscriptions:** 195 journals and other serials; 76 newspapers. **Services:** Interlibrary loan; library open to the public. **Remarks:** 231 5023199. **Also Known As:** Institut fur Zeitungsforschung - Haus der Bibliotheken.

★7965★
Institute for the Protection of the Natural and Cultural Heritage of Slovenia - Library (Hist, Env-Cons)
Plecnikov trg 2
Postanski Fah 176 Phone: 213-022
Ljubljana, Yugoslavia Mrs. Alenka Prunk, Libn.
Subjects: Slovenia - monument preservation and nature conservation. **Holdings:** 20,000 volumes. **Subscriptions:** 230 journals and other serials; 11 newspapers. **Services:** Library open to the public. **Also Known As:** Zavod SR Slovenije za Varstvo Naravne in Kulturne Dediscine.

Institute for Psychoanalysis
See: **Chicago Institute for Psychoanalysis - McLean Library** (3523)

★7966★
Institute of Public Administration - General Directorate of Libraries (Soc Sci, Bus-Fin)
P.O. Box 205 Phone: 1 4792136
Riyadh 11141, Saudi Arabia Mostafa Sadhan, Dir.Gen.
Founded: 1961. **Subjects:** Public administration, management, law, financial administration, library and information sciences, computer science, economics, political science, Islamic law, education, sociology, accounting, statistics, office management, hotel management, marketing, English language. **Special Collections:** Rare books on Saudi Arabia, Islam, and the Arabian Gulf States; Saudi government documents. **Holdings:** 168,500 books; 15,772 bound periodical volumes; 45,106 documents; 200 AV programs; 19,014 microforms; maps; theses; films. **Subscriptions:** 669 journals and other serials; 19 newspapers. **Services:** Interlibrary loan; copying; current awareness service; library open to the public. **Computerized Information Services:** DIALOG Information Services; Ibn al-nadeem, Numuw (internal databases). **Publications:** Information Sources on Saudi Arabia, 3rd edition, 1989; periodicals holdings list, 1987 (in English); Bibliography of Saudi Government publications in IPA Document Center, 1984 (in Arabic); Bibliography of IPA publications, 2nd edition, 1989; List of Arabic Periodicals in the Library of the Institute of Public Administration, 1976; Maktabat Al-Idara: IPA Library and Documents Center, 1970-1988, quarterly (in Arabic); Bibliography of the Library's holdings of doctoral theses, 1983; Arabic Subject Headings List, 1985. **Special Indexes:** An Index of Arabic Periodicals in the Library of the Institute of Public Administration, 2 vols., 1988 (in Arabic); Cumulative Index to the General International Agreements of the United Nations Treaty Series, 1984; Subject Index to IPA journals, 1984 (in Arabic). **Remarks:** Library holdings are in Arabic, English, and French. Alternate telephone number(s): 1 4792127. FAX: 1 4792136. Telex: 401160; 404360. **Staff:** Ali S. Sowaine, Dir. of Info.Org.Dept.; Fahd I. Al-Askar, Dir. of Info.Serv.Dept.; Sorayye Al-Sorayye, Dir., Saudi Govt.Docs.Dept.; Saud A. Huzaimi, Dir., Coll.Dev.Dept.; Saad A. Al-Meflih, Dir., Info.Tech.Dept.; Abdulrahman Al-Arfaj, Dir. of Dammam Br.Lib.; Shakir Abdullah Khalil, Dir. of Jeddah Br.Lib.; Munira Al-Suneideh, Dir., Women Br.Lib.

★7967★
Institute of Public Administration - Library (Soc Sci, Plan)
55 W. 44th St. Phone: (212)730-5631
New York, NY 10036 Steven Unger, Lib.Dir.
Founded: 1906. **Staff:** Prof 1; Other 2. **Subjects:** Public administration, metropolitan area problems, civil service, local government, housing, urban transportation, public enterprises, public finance. **Special Collections:** International material on urbanization, regional planning, metropolitan government. **Holdings:** 50,000 volumes; 80 VF drawers. **Subscriptions:** 450 journals and other serials. **Services:** Interlibrary loan; copying; library open to researchers by appointment. **Automated Operations:** Computerized cataloging. **Computerized Information Services:** DIALOG Information Services; IPA Studies and Reports (internal database). **Networks/Consortia:** Member of SUNY/OCLC Library Network. **Publications:** Bibliographies, irregular. **Remarks:** FAX: (212)398-9305. Alternate telephone number(s): 730-5632.

★7968★
Institute of Public Administration of Canada - Library (Soc Sci)
897 Bay St. Phone: (416)923-7319
Toronto, ON, Canada M5S 1Z7 Rose McKenzie, Sec. to the Ed.
Staff: Prof 8. **Subjects:** Canadian public administration, history, law, social sciences, political science and economy. **Special Collections:** Canadian Public Administration Series (22 titles); Monograph Series (11 titles); Case Programs (60 titles); National Seminar Series (16 titles); International Seminar Series (3 titles). **Holdings:** 25 books; 20 bound periodical volumes; government reports. **Subscriptions:** 50 journals and other serials; 10 newspapers. **Services:** Copying; library open to the public. **Remarks:** FAX: (416)923-8994. **Also Known As:** Institut d'Administration Publique du Canada.

★7969★
Institute of Race Relations - Library (Soc Sci)
2-6 Leeke St.
King's Cross Rd. Phone: 71 8370041
London WC1X 9HS, England Hasel Waters, Dp.Libn.
Subjects: Civil rights, civil liberties; race relations. **Holdings:** 40,000 books, journals, and pamphlets. **Services:** Library open to the public at librarian's discretion. **Remarks:** FAX: 71 2780623.

★7970★
The Institute for Rehabilitation and Research (TIRR) - Information Services Center (Med)
1333 Moursund Ave. Phone: (713)797-5947
Houston, TX 77030 Dell M. Davis
Staff: 2. **Subjects:** Rehabilitation medicine. **Holdings:** 2000 books; 590 bound periodical volumes. **Subscriptions:** 40 journals and other serials. **Services:** Interlibrary loan; library open to the public for reference use only. **Remarks:** FAX: (713)799-7095.

★7971★
Institute for Research and Development of Handicraft and Batik Industries - IRDHBI Library (Art)
2 Jalan Kusumanegara 7 Phone: 2557
Yogyakarta, Indonesia Slamet Rahayu, Libn.
Subjects: Handicraft and batik industries, rattan, wood carving. **Holdings:** 12,260 volumes. **Remarks:** Maintained by Indonesia - Department of Industry. **Also Known As:** Balai Besar Penelitian dan Pengembangan Industri Kerajinan dan Batik.

Institute of Research on Fruits and Citrus Fruits
See: **International Cooperation Center of Agricultural Research for Development - Institute of Research on Fruits and Citrus Fruits** (8087)

★7972★
Institute for Research in Hypnosis - Bernard B. Raginsky Research Library (Med)
1991 Broadway, Suite 18B Phone: (212)874-5290
New York, NY 10023 Dr. Milton V. Kline, Dir.
Founded: 1965. **Staff:** 2. **Subjects:** Clinical and experimental applications of hypnosis, hypnoanalysis, and hypnotherapy. **Special Collections:** Tape recordings of the hypnotherapy of Bernard B. Raginsky. **Holdings:** 1000 books; 2000 reprints; 500 tapes. **Subscriptions:** 15 journals and other serials; 3 newspapers. **Services:** Library not open to the public. **Remarks:** FAX: (914)238-1422.

Institute for Research and Studies on the Arab and Muslim World
See: **Institut de Recherches et d'Etudes sur le Monde Arabe et Musulman** (7885)

Institute for Research on Teaching
See: **Michigan State University** (10325)

★7973★
Institute of Scientific Health Information - Slovak Medical Library (Med)
Cs Armady 24
Spitalska 10 Phone: 7 59829
CS-814 42 Bratislava, Czechoslovakia Dr. Jozef Ciffra, Ph.D.
Founded: 1951. **Staff:** Prof 44; Other 8. **Subjects:** Biomedicine. **Holdings:** 65,051 books; 55,388 bound periodical volumes; 14,050 other cataloged items. **Subscriptions:** 1061 journals and other serials. **Services:** Interlibrary loan; copying; SDI; library open to the public. **Computerized Information Services:** MEDLINE, Excerpta Medica, CHEM-BANK; Union Catalog of Biomedical Periodicals, Catalog of the Book Holdings of the SML, Union Catalog of New Biomedical Books in Slovakia. Contact Person: Maria Pracna. **Remarks:** Library is a depository library for the World Health Organization. **Also Known As:** Ustav Vedeckych Zdravotnickych Informacil - Slovenska Lekarska Kniznica.

★7974★
Institute for Scientific Information - Corporate Communications Department Library (Sci-Engr, Hum, Biol Sci)
3501 Market St. Phone: (215)386-0100
Philadelphia, PA 19104 Judith E. Schaeffer, Mgr., Bibliog.Res.Dept.
Founded: 1960. **Staff:** 2. **Subjects:** Life sciences; physical and chemical sciences; clinical medicine; engineering and technology; agriculture; environmental, social, behavioral sciences; arts and humanities. **Holdings:** Figures not available. **Subscriptions:** 8000 journals and other serials. **Services:** SDI, including Research Alert; The Genuine Article document delivery service; institute not open to the public. **Computerized Information Services:** Produces SCISEARCH, SOCIAL SCISEARCH, ISI/BIOMED, ISI/CompuMath; CD-ROMs (Current Contents Search, Arts and Humanities Search). **Publications:** Current Contents, weekly - 7 editions covering the life sciences, clinical medicine, physical, chemical and earth sciences, social and behavioral sciences, engineering, technology and applied sciences, agricultural, biological, and environmental sciences, and arts and humanities; Science Citation Index, bimonthly with annual cumulation; Science Citation Index (compact disc edition), quarterly and cumulated; Index Chemicus, weekly; Social Sciences Citation Index, 3/year with annual cumulation; Index to Scientific Reviews, semiannual; Arts and Humanities Citation Index, semiannual; Index to Scientific and Technical Proceedings, monthly with annual cumulation; Index to Social Sciences and Humanities Proceedings, quarterly with annual cumulation; Index to Scientific Book contents, quarterly with annual cumulation; Compumath Citation Index, 3/year with annual cumulation; Current Contents on Diskette, weekly. **Remarks:** ISI is said to be the world's largest independent, multidisciplinary retriever of information from the world's professional journals. FAX: (215)386-6362. **Staff:** Valerie Sowell.

★7975★
Institute for Scientific, Technical and Economic Information - Library (Info Sci)
ulica Jasna 14/16 Phone: 22 264073
PL-00-041 Warsaw, Poland Krystyna Belkowska, Lib.Hd.
Founded: 1971. **Staff:** 1. **Subjects:** Scientific, technical, and economic information services and systems; information science; documentation. **Special Collections:** Information sciences and documentation standards; translations; archives; materials of ISTEI (4120). **Holdings:** 45,000 volumes. **Subscriptions:** 70 journals and other serials. **Services:** Interlibrary loan; copying; library open to the public. **Computerized Information Services:** CDS/ISIS. **Remarks:** FAX: 22 264075. Maintained by Institute for Scientific, Technical and Economic Information - Central Planning Office. **Also Known As:** Institut Informacji Naukowej, Technicznej i Ekonomicznej (IINTE).

Institute of Scientific and Technical Information of China
See: **People's Republic of China - Institute of Scientific and Technical Information of China - Library** (12925)

Institute of Sedimentary & Petroleum Geology
See: **Canada - Geological Survey of Canada** (2746)

Institute for Sensory Research
See: **Syracuse University** (15963)

★7976★
Institute of Shipping Economics and Logistics - Library (Trans)
Universitatsallee GW 1, Block A
W-2800 Bremen 33, Germany Phone: 421 220960
Founded: 1954. **Staff:** 4. **Subjects:** Shipping, shipbuilding, ports, traffic, transport, logistics. **Special Collections:** Biographical archives; ship registers. **Holdings:** 70,000 volumes. **Subscriptions:** 360 journals and other serials; 10 newspapers. **Services:** Copying; SDI; library open to the public. **Computerized Information Services:** Internal databases. **Publications:** ISL Thesaurus - Shipping Economics and Logistics (in English and German); ISL List of Journals; Acquisitions List, quarterly - available by subscription. **Remarks:** FAX: 421 2209655. **Also Known As:** Institut fur Seeverkehrwirtschaft und Logistik (ISL). **Staff:** Brigitte Lang, Dipl.-Dok.

Institute of Sindhology
See: **University of Sind** (19301)

★7977★
Institute of Social Studies - Library (Soc Sci)
P.O. Box 90733
NL-2509 LS The Hague, Netherlands Phone: 70 510100
Founded: 1952. **Staff:** 14. **Subjects:** Social policy, including development policy and the state, rural development, international economic issues, international relations, labor and development, women and development, urban-rural relations. **Holdings:** 60,000 volumes. **Subscriptions:** 550 journals and other serials. **Services:** Interlibrary loan; copying; library open to the public. **Computerized Information Services:** DIALOG Information Services, ESA/IRS, FT PROFILE. **Remarks:** Library located at Badhuisweg 251, The Hague. FAX: 549851. Telex: 31491 ISS NL. Maintained by Netherlands - Ministry of Development/Ministry of Education.

★7978★
Institute for Socioeconomic Studies - Library (Soc Sci)
Airport Rd. Phone: (914)428-7400
White Plains, NY 10604 Allan T. Ostergren, Dir.
Subjects: Quality of life, economic development, social motivation, poverty, urban regeneration, problems of the elderly. **Holdings:** 5500 volumes.

★7979★
Institute of Southeast Asian Studies - Library (Area-Ethnic, Soc Sci)
Heng Mui Keng Terrace
Pasir Panjang Phone: 7780955
Singapore 0511, Singapore Miss Ch'ng Kim See, Libn.
Staff: 12. **Subjects:** Southeast Asia, international relations and strategic studies, economics, sociology and anthropology, history, demography. **Special Collections:** Photo archive (Southeast Asian ethnography). **Holdings:** 76,004 volumes; 6695 documents; 108,641 microforms; 464 maps; 77,642 multi-media resources. **Subscriptions:** 2070 journals and other serials; 31 newspapers. **Services:** Interlibrary loan; library open to affiliated scholars. **Computerized Information Services:** Southeast Asian Biography Database, ISEAS Conference Database (internal databases); BITNET (electronic mail service). **Publications:** ASEAN: a bibliography; ASEAN: a bibliography II; Malay World of Southeast Asia: a select cultural bibliography; Cambodia: a bibliography; Laos: a bibliography; additional publications available; Tan Cheng Lock papers, a descriptive list; Southeast Asian census publications; ISEAS current serials; Southeast Asian statistical publications. **Remarks:** FAX: 7756184. Telex: RS 37068 ISEAS. Electronic mail address(es): IHLISEAS@NUSVM (BITNET). Cable: ISEAS. **Staff:** Ms. Zaleha Tamby, Sr.Asst.Libn.; Ms. Lai Siew Yoong, Sr.Asst.Libn.; Ms. Pang Yin Wah, Asst.Libn.; Lawrence Chang, Asst.Libn.

★7980★
Institute for Southeast European Studies - Library (Area-Ethnic)
Blvd. Republicii 13
P.O. Box 22159 Phone: 0 14 49 96
Bucharest, Romania Corina Mihailescu, Libn.
Subjects: Southeast Europe - history, philology, linguistics, literary history, art history, law, ethnology. **Holdings:** 27,000 volumes. **Services:** Library open to the public. **Remarks:** Affiliated with Bucharest University. **Also Known As:** Institutul de Studii Sud-Est Europene.

Institute of Soviet and East European Studies - East-West Project
See: **Carleton University - Institute of Soviet and East European Studies - East-West Project** (3054)

★7981★
Institute of Space and Astronautical Science - ISAS Library (Sci-Engr)
3-1-1 Yoshinodai Phone: 427 513911
Sagamihara 229, Kanagawa, Japan Ryojiro Akiba, Dir.-Gen.
Subjects: Space sciences, astronautics, satellites, new spacecraft technology, planetary sciences. **Special Collections:** NASA Reports collection. **Holdings:** 90,650 volumes. **Subscriptions:** 897 journals and other serials; 8 newspapers. **Services:** Library open to the public. **Remarks:** FAX: 427 681297. **Also Known As:** Uchu-ken Tosjo. **Staff:** Akiko Maeyama; Kimiko Inoue.

★7982★
Institute for Strategic Studies on Terrorism - Library (Soc Sci)
Box 3372 Phone: (915)646-8674
Early, TX 76803 Arthur E. Gerringer, Dir.
Founded: 1980. **Staff:** 1. **Subjects:** Terrorism, counter-terrorism, executive protection. **Holdings:** 100 books. **Subscriptions:** 11 journals and other serials. **Services:** Library not open to the public. **Computerized Information Services:** Internal database. **Publications:** Treatise on Terrorism; copies of articles - for sale. **Remarks:** An alternate telephone number is 643-1433.

Institute for the Study of Earth and Man
See: **Southern Methodist University** (15501)

★7983★
Institute for the Study of Man, Inc. - Library (Soc Sci, Biol Sci)
6861 Elm St., Suite 4-H Phone: (703)442-8010
McLean, VA 22101 Dr. Roger Pearson, Exec.Dir.
Founded: 1975. **Subjects:** Anthropology, genetics and evolution, cultural history, anthropological linguistics. **Holdings:** 12,000 volumes; manuscripts. **Services:** Library not open to the public. **Remarks:** FAX: (202)789-0231. **Formerly:** Located in Washington, DC.

★7984★
Institute of Textile Technology - Textile Information Services - Roger Milliken Textile Library (Sci-Engr)
P.O. Box 391 Phone: (804)296-5511
Charlottesville, VA 22902 Terry L. Beckwith, Mgr.
Founded: 1944. **Staff:** Prof 1; Other 2. **Subjects:** Textile technology, dyeing, polymers, apparel manufacture. **Holdings:** 13,000 books; 15,000 bound periodical volumes; 4500 cataloged translations; 2500 technical reports; 66,000 patents; 25 shelves of reprints; 5 shelves of trade literature; 36 VF drawers; 900 microforms. **Subscriptions:** 700 journals and other serials; 25 newspapers. **Services:** Interlibrary loan; copying; library open to the public. **Computerized Information Services:** DIALOG Information Services; internal database. **Publications:** ITT Bibliography, irregular; New Additions to the Library, annual; Textile Library List - all free upon request; Textile Technology Digest, monthly - by subscription. **Special Indexes:** Keyterm Index. **Remarks:** FAX: (804)977-5400. Library located at Rte. 250 W., 22901.

★7985★
Institute of Transpersonal Psychology - Library (Soc Sci)
250 Oak Grove Ave. Phone: (415)326-1960
Menlo Park, CA 94025 Peter Hirose
Founded: 1981. **Staff:** Prof 1; Other 4. **Subjects:** Transpersonal psychology, psychology, spiritual discipline, body work. **Special Collections:** Classics of western spirituality; collected works of C.G. Jung; complete psychological works of Sigmund Freud. **Holdings:** 7000 books; 90 ITP dissertations; 650 cassettes. **Subscriptions:** 80 journals and other serials. **Services:** Interlibrary loan; copying; SDI; library open to the public with restrictions. **Automated Operations:** Computerized cataloging. **Computerized Information Services:** BRS Information Technologies. **Networks/Consortia:** Member of CLASS.

★7986★
Institute of Transportation Engineers - Library (Trans)
525 School St., S.W., Suite 410 Phone: (202)554-8050
Washington, DC 20024 Thomas W. Brahms, Exec.Dir.
Founded: 1930. **Staff:** 14. **Subjects:** Traffic and transportation engineering, transportation planning, highway safety. **Special Collections:** ITE Journal, ITE publications, and Institute of Transportation Engineers Technical Council Reports (complete file of back issues). **Holdings:** Figures not available. **Services:** Copying; library open to the public with restrictions. **Publications:** Publications list of Institute of Transportation Engineers. **Special Indexes:** Index to ITE Journal. **Remarks:** FAX: (202)863-5486. Telex: 467943 ITE WSHCI.

★7987★
Institute for University Cooperation - Library (Soc Sci)
viale B. Buozzi 60 Phone: 6 3221341
I-00197 Rome, Italy Pier G. Palla, Dir., Res.Dept.
Subjects: Third World development. **Holdings:** 1500 volumes. **Subscriptions:** 50 journals and other serials; 20 newspapers. **Services:** Copying; library not open to the public. **Remarks:** Institute seeks to promote Third World development through the international cooperation of universities and institutions of scientific research. FAX: 6 3221259. Telex: 621448 UNIV I. **Also Known As:** Istituto per la Cooperazione Universitaria.

★7988★
Institute of Water Conservancy and Hydroelectric Power - Library (Energy, Sci-Engr)
10 Chegongzhuang Xi Lu
P.O. Box 366 Phone: 1 890781
Beijing 1172, People's Republic of China Shen Conggang, Libn.
Founded: 1956. **Staff:** 7. **Subjects:** Science; applied mathematics; mechanics - fluid, hydraulic, soil, rock, structural, aerodynamic; geological geography; meteorology; geomorphology; hydrogeology; irrigation works; soil improvement; engineering - hydropower, electrical, civil, hydraulic; electrotechnics; automation. **Holdings:** 108,824 volumes; 2150 periodicals; 618 AV programs and microforms. **Services:** Interlibrary loan; copying. **Publications:** Journal of Water Conservancy; Silt Research; reports of research results - all on exchange.

★7989★
Institute for World Understanding of Peoples, Cultures and Languages - Library (Soc Sci)
939 Coast Blvd., 19DE
La Jolla, CA 92037 Phone: (619)454-0705
Subjects: Comparative study of populations, cultures, and languages. **Holdings:** 5000 volumes.

★7990★
Institutes of Religion and Health - Library (Med)
3 W. 29th St. Phone: (212)725-7850
New York, NY 10001 Rob S. Coleman
Founded: 1961. **Staff:** Prof 1; Other 2. **Subjects:** Psychiatry, psychology, pastoral counseling, marriage counseling, psychotherapy. **Holdings:** 5000 books; 4 VF drawers of reports, pamphlets, dissertations. **Subscriptions:** 23 journals and other serials. **Services:** Interlibrary loan; library not open to the public. **Remarks:** FAX: (212)689-3212.

Institutet for Byggdokumentation
See: **BYGGDOK/The Swedish Institute of Building Documentation** (2423)

★7991★
Institution of Engineers, Malaysia - Library (Sci-Engr)
Lots 60 & 62, Jalan 52/4
Peti Surat 223, Jalan Sultan
46720 Petaling Jaya, Selangor Darul Ehsan, Malaysia Phone: 3 7569173
Founded: 1958. **Staff:** 1. **Subjects:** Engineering - practice and ethics. **Holdings:** 6000 reference books; journals; seminar and conference proceedings. **Subscriptions:** 38 journals and other serials; 4 newspapers. **Services:** Library open to members only. **Remarks:** FAX: 3 7577678. **Also Known As:** Institusi Jurutera, Malaysia.

★7992★
Institution of Mechanical Engineers - Library (Sci-Engr)
1 Birdcage Walk Phone: 71 9731266
London SW1H 9JJ, England Jacqui Ollerton
Founded: 1847. **Staff:** Prof 5; Other 6. **Subjects:** Mechanical engineering, railway engineering, tribology, vibration, strength of materials. **Special Collections:** David Joy drawings collection. **Holdings:** 25,000 books; 20,000 bound periodical volumes; 50,000 reports; 1500 archival items. **Subscriptions:** 300 journals and other serials. **Services:** Interlibrary loan; copying; SDI; library open to the public for reference use only for a fee. **Computerized Information Services:** DIALOG Information Services, ESA/IRS, ORBIT Search Service, Data-Star, KOMPASS UK; internal database. Contact Person: Annette Watts, Sr.Info.Off. **Publications:** Series of information packets; sourcebooks; bibliographies; reading lists. **Remarks:** FAX: 71 2228762. Telex: 917944. Alternate telephone number(s): 71 9731267.

★7993★
Institution of Mining and Metallurgy - Library and Information Services (Sci-Engr)
44 Portland Pl. Phone: 71 580 3802
London W1N 4BR, England Michael McGarr, Hd.
Founded: 1894. **Staff:** Prof 5; Other 1. **Subjects:** Economic and exploration geology; mining technology and operations; processing of minerals other than coal; nonferrous extractive metallurgy; mining and metallurgy - economics, health and safety, environment, legislation, management, analysis, and instrumentation. **Holdings:** Books; reports; maps; conference proceedings. **Subscriptions:** 1200 journals and other serials. **Services:** SDI; copying; library open to the public. **Computerized Information Services:** Produces IMAGE database. Performs searches on fee basis. **Publications:** IMM Abstracts, bimonthly; catalog of IMM publications - available on request. **Special Indexes:** Subject and geographical indexes of IMM Abstracts (microfiche, 1894-1949; card, 1949 to present). **Remarks:** FAX: 71-436 5388. Telex: 261410.

★7994★
Institutional and Municipal Parking Congress - Library (Trans)
701 Kenmore Ave.
P.O. Box 7167 Phone: (703)371-7535
Fredericksburg, VA 22404-7167 Scott Williamson, Asst.Dir., Tech.Serv.
Founded: 1978. **Staff:** 8. **Subjects:** Parking industry, public parking statistics, construction. **Holdings:** 700 technical documents. **Subscriptions:** 12 journals and other serials. **Services:** Copying; library open to the public. **Computerized Information Services:** Internal databases. **Publications:** Statistical Guide to Parking. **Remarks:** FAX: (703)371-8022.

★7995★
Instituto Agronomico Campinas (Agri)
CP 28
91000 Sao Paulo, SP, Brazil Rogeria Aparecida Romualdo
Founded: 1887. **Staff:** Prof 4; Other 7. **Subjects:** Agriculture, soil science, crop science, plant diseases, agricultural engineering, plant/soil/climate relations. **Holdings:** 31,000 books; 160,000 bound periodical volumes. **Subscriptions:** 225 journals and other serials; 2 newspapers. **Services:** Interlibrary loan; copying; SDI; library open to the public. **Remarks:** FAX: 19 315422. Telex: 19 1059.

★7996★
Instituto Amatller de Arte Hispanico - Biblioteca (Art)
Paseo de Gracia 41 Phone: 3 2160175
E-08007 Barcelona, Spain Santiago Alcolea, Dir.
Founded: 1942. **Staff:** Prof 4. **Subjects:** Spanish art. **Special Collections:** Spanish art photograph collection (300,000). **Holdings:** 20,000 books. **Subscriptions:** 80 journals and other serials; 2 newspapers. **Services:** Library open to the public. **Remarks:** FAX: 3 4875827.

Instituto Antartico Argentino
See: **Argentine Antarctic Institute** (972)

Instituto de Antropologia e Historia
See: **Guatemala - Ministerio de Cultura y Deportes - Instituto de Antropologia e Historia** (6791)

Instituto Argentino de Racionalizacion de Materiales - Centro de Documentacion
See: **Institute of Argentine Standards - Documentation Center** (7904)

Instituto de Asuntos Nucleares - Centro de Documentacion e Informacion Nuclear
See: **Colombia - Ministry of Mines & Petroleum - Institute for Nuclear Affairs - Library** (3924)

★7997★
Instituto Boliviano de Tecnologia Agropecuaria - Centro de Documentacion e Informacion (Agri)
Casilla 5783
Plaza Espana esq. Mendex Arcos, No. 710 Phone: 2 374289
La Paz, Bolivia Elio Flores, Agri.Engr.
Founded: 1975. **Staff:** 1. **Subjects:** Oil-bearing plants, tropical and Andean crops, Quinua, minor cereals, legumes, cameloids, sheep, forage, plant and animal breeding, horticulture, maize, sorghum and beans, tuber crops, wheat, rural sociology. **Holdings:** 5000 volumes. **Subscriptions:** 8 journals and other serials. **Services:** Interlibrary loan; library open by special permission of the librarian; interactions with the library should be in the Spanish language. **Remarks:** Maintained by Bolivia - Ministry of Agriculture and Campesino Affairs. **Also Known As:** Bolivian Institute of Agricultural Technology - Information and Documentation Center.

Instituto de Botanica "Darwinion"
See: **Darwinian Institute of Botany** (4618)

Instituto Brasileiro de Informacao em Ciencia e Tecnologia
See: **Brazil - National Council of Scientific and Technological Development - Brazilian Institute for Information in Science and Technology** (2095)

Instituto Butantan
See: **Butantan Institute** (2406)

Instituto Centroamericano de Investigacion y Tecnologia Industrial - Biblioteca Manuel Noriega Morales
See: **Central American Research Institute for Industry** (3325)

Instituto Cubano de Investigaciones Azucareras
See: **Cuba - Ministerio del Azucar - Instituto Cubano de Investigaciones Azucareras - Departamento de Informacion Cientifica-Tecnica** (4463)

Instituto de Ecologia, A.C. - Biblioteca
See: **Ecological Institute, Civil Association - Library** (5210)

Instituto Ecuatoriano de Ciencias Naturales
See: **Ecuadorian Institute of Natural Sciences** (5222)

★7998★
Instituto de Estudios Islamicos - Biblioteca General (Rel-Phil, Area-Ethnic)
Calle Rey de Bahamonde, 121
Vista Alegre, Surco — Phone: 14 489720
Lima 33, Peru — Elva Zegarra Torreblanca, Prof.
Subjects: Cultural roots, Zionism, Islam in Latin America, colonialism in La Ummah. **Special Collections:** Libya; Iran; disinformation regarding pseudo-terrorism; luchas de liberacion; religion. **Holdings:** 15,000 volumes; 250 AV programs; 400 manuscripts. **Services:** Library not open to the public. **Computerized Information Services:** A database of the political, military, and other aspects of the Arab-Islamic world is under development.

Instituto de Estudios Superiores de la Empresa
See: **Institute for Advanced Business Studies** (7891)

★7999★
Instituto Franklin de Veracruz - USIS Collection (Educ)
Calle Jose Azueta No. 1229
Colonia Diaz Miron
91909 Veracruz, Mexico — Phone: 29 315737
Founded: 1955. **Staff:** 1. **Subjects:** Social sciences, fiction, history, arts, literature, language, pure sciences. **Holdings:** 3782 books; 1 bound periodical volume; 25 encyclopedias. **Subscriptions:** 2 journals and other serials. **Services:** Library open to the public. **Remarks:** Alternate telephone number(s): 29 315736. Maintained or supported by the U.S. Information Agency. Focus is on materials that will assist peoples outside the United States to learn about the United States, its people, history, culture, political processes, and social milieux. **Staff:** Sonia Navarro, Libn.; Narciso Ortiz.

★8000★
Instituto Franklin de Yucatan - (Merida) USIS Collection (Educ)
Calle 57, No. 474-A
97000 Merida, Yucatan, Mexico
Remarks: Maintained or supported by the U.S. Information Agency. Focus is on materials that will assist peoples outside the United States to learn about the United States, its people, history, culture, political processes, and social milieux.

Instituto de Informacion y Documentacion en Ciencia y Tecnologia
See: **Spain - Council for Scientific Research - Institute for Information and Documentation in Science and Technology** (15560)

Instituto Interamericano do Cooperacion para la Agricultura (IICA)
See: **Inter-American Institute for Cooperation on Agriculture (IICA) - Biblioteca Venezuela** (8029)

★8001★
Instituto de Investigaciones Agropecuarias - Biblioteca Central (Agri)
Casilla 439 Correo 3 — Phone: 2 5586061
Santiago, Chile — Sonia Elso Galano
Founded: 1964. **Staff:** Prof 5; Other 4. **Subjects:** Agriculture, veterinary medicine, animal husbandry, food science. **Special Collections:** Chilean university agronomy and veterinary science theses (7000). **Holdings:** 8000 books; 18,600 bound periodical volumes; 50,000 serial publication reports. **Subscriptions:** 6 newspapers. **Services:** Interlibrary loan; copying; SDI; library open to the public. **Computerized Information Services:** AGRICOLA, AGRIS; CD-ROM (CAB); BIBA (internal database). Contact Person: Veronica Bravo, Libn. **Publications:** Bibliografia Agricola Chilena. **Remarks:** FAX: 2 5586061 ext. 296. Telex: 242207 INIA CL.

Instituto de Investigaciones Electricas
See: **Institute of Electrical Research - Library** (7934)

Instituto de Investigaciones Esteticas
See: **Universidad Nacional Autonoma de Mexico - Instituto de Investigaciones Esteticas** (17992)

Instituto de Investigaciones Historicas
See: **Universidad Nacional Autonoma de Mexico - Instituto de Investigaciones Historicas** (17993)

★8002★
Instituto de Investigaciones Socio-Economicas de Honduras - Library (Soc Sci)
Apdo. Postal 20-057
Colonia San Angel
01000 Mexico City, DF, Mexico — Phone: 5 689-4829
Subjects: Honduran social and economic issues - effects of foreign intervention. **Special Collections:** Documentation center (Honduran journals). **Holdings:** 200 volumes. **Computerized Information Services:** Internal database.

Instituto Latinoamericano del Fierro y el Acero
See: **Latin American Iron and Steel Institute** (8969)

Instituto Nacional de Estudios del Teatro
See: **National Institute for the Study of the Theater** (11216)

Instituto Nacional de Investigacao Cientifica
See: **Portugal - National Institute for Scientific Research** (13262)

Instituto Nacional de Investigaciones Nucleares
See: **Mexico - National Institute of Nuclear Research - Nuclear Information and Documentation Center** (10242)

Instituto Nacional de Pesquisas da Amazonia
See: **National Institute of Amazon Research** (11206)

★8003★
Instituto National de Pesquisas Espaciais - Biblioteca Central (Comp Sci, Sci-Engr)
Av dos Astronautas 1758
CP 515 — Phone: 123 418977
12201 Sao Jose dos Campos, SP, Brazil — Maria do Carmo Nogueira, Hd.
Founded: 1966. **Staff:** Prof 7; Other 3. **Subjects:** Computer science, space science, atmospheric science, meteorology, remote sensing, engineering, space technology, physics, mathematics, astronautics. **Holdings:** 35,000 books; 1880 bound periodical volumes; 30,000 reports; 10,000 microfiche; military specification cartridges; standards. **Subscriptions:** 800 journals and other serials; 5 newspapers. **Services:** Interlibrary loan; copying; SDI; library open to the public. **Computerized Information Services:** SIRIUS (internal database). **Publications:** Bulletin Acquisition News Publications. **Remarks:** FAX: 123 218743; 123 229325; 123 229285. Telex: 123353OINPE BR.

Instituto de Nutricion de Centro America y Panama
See: **Pan American Health Organization - Institute of Nutrition of Central America and Panama** (12717)

Instituto Riva-Aguero
See: **Pontificia Universidad Catolica del Peru - Riva-Aguero Institute** (13215)

Instituto de Salud Publica de Chile
See: **Chile - Ministry of Public Health - Public Health Institute of Chile** (3596)

Instituto de Suelos de Cuba
See: **Cuba - Ministerio de la Agricultura - Instituto de Suelos de Cuba - Biblioteca** (4462)

★8004★
Instituto Tecnologico de Costa Rica - Biblioteca (Sci-Engr)
Apartado 159 - 7050 Phone: 51-53-33
Cartago, Costa Rica Aura Leticia Mata Picado, Lib.Hd.
Subjects: Engineering, science. **Holdings:** 46,000 books. **Services:** Interlibrary loan; library open to the public with restrictions. **Remarks:** FAX: 51-53-48. Telex: 8013 ITCR CR.

Instituto Universitario Orientale - Dipartimento di Studi Asiatici - Biblioteca
See: **Oriental University - Department of Asian Studies - Library** (12567)

Institutul Cantacuzino
See: **Romania - Ministry of Health - Cantacuzino Institute** (14048)

Institutul de Istoria Artei
See: **Academy of Social and Political Sciences - Art History Institute** (39)

Institutul National de Metrologie
See: **Romania - National Institute of Metrology** (14050)

Institutul de Studii Istorice si Social-Politice de pe Linga Comitetul Central al Partidului Comunist Roman
See: **Institute of Historical, Social, and Political Studies of the Central Committee of the Romanian Communist Party** (7943)

Institutul de Studii Sud-Est Europene
See: **Institute for Southeast European Studies** (7980)

★8005★
Instituut voor Bodemvruchtbaarheid - Bibliotheek (Agri)
Oosterweg 92
Postbus 30003 Phone: 50 337231
NL-9750 RA Haren, Netherlands H.A. Dykstra
Founded: 1939. **Staff:** Prof 2. **Subjects:** Soil - fertility, chemistry, physics, biology. **Holdings:** 6310 books; 14,707 bound periodical volumes; 5000 reports; 58 microfiche; 152 reels of microfilm. **Subscriptions:** 930 journals and other serials; 11 newspapers. **Services:** Interlibrary loan; copying; library open to the public. **Computerized Information Services:** Internal databases. **Publications:** List of publications; journal catalog; Publications Bulletin. **Remarks:** FAX: 50 337291. Telex: 53990 ibhrn nl.

★8006★
Instrument Society of America - Albert F. Sperry Library (Sci-Engr)
67 Alexander Dr. Phone: (919)549-8411
Box 12277 Quentin S. Clark, Jr.,
Research Triangle Park, NC 27709 Dir.,Standards&Tech.Serv.
Founded: 1964. **Staff:** Prof 1; Other 1. **Subjects:** Automatic control, automation, instrumentation. **Holdings:** 1000 books; 60 bound periodical volumes. **Subscriptions:** 100 journals and other serials. **Services:** Library not open to the public. **Computerized Information Services:** Internal database. **Remarks:** Library is primarily archival for Instrument Society of America's past journals, proceedings, and books. FAX: (919)549-8288. Telex: 802 540 (ISA DURM).

★8007★
Instrumentation Laboratory - Library-S-33 (Sci-Engr)
113 Hartwell Ave. Phone: (617)861-4328
Lexington, MA 02173 Janet R. Mierzykowski, Mgr., Lib.Serv.
Staff: 1. **Subjects:** Medicine, chemistry, biotechnology. **Holdings:** 6600 volumes; 400 technical reports, hardcopy and microfiche. **Subscriptions:** 200 journals and other serials. **Services:** Interlibrary loan; library not open to the public. **Automated Operations:** Computerized ILL. **Computerized Information Services:** DIALOG Information Services, OCLC. **Networks/Consortia:** Member of North Atlantic Health Science Libraries (NAHSL), Northeastern Consortium for Health Information (NECHI). **Publications:** New Books List, quarterly; Periodicals Holding List, annual. **Remarks:** FAX: (617)862-5830. **Formerly:** Fisher Scientific Group, Inc. - Instrumentation Laboratory Division - Library.

Instytut Immunologii i Terapii Doswiadczalnej im. Ludwika Hirszfelda
See: **Poland - Polish Academy of Sciences - L. Hirszfeld Institute of Immunology and Experimental Therapy** (13172)

Instytut Informacji Naukowej, Technicznej i Ekonomicznej
See: **Institute for Scientific, Technical and Economic Information** (7975)

★8008★
Instytut Lotnictwa - Branzowy Osrodek Informacji, Naukowej, Technicznej i Ekonomicznej - Biblioteka (Sci-Engr)
Al. Krakowska 110-114 Phone: 22 460011
PL-02-255 Warsaw, Poland Jerzy Grzegorzewski
Founded: 1926. **Staff:** Prof 3; Other 1. **Subjects:** Aeronautics. **Holdings:** 70,000 books; 5000 bound periodical volumes; 4000 reports; 6000 archives; 150 microfiche; 4000 reels of microfilm. **Subscriptions:** 200 journals and other serials. **Services:** Interlibrary loan; library open to the public. **Remarks:** Telex: 813-537.

Instytut Matki i Dziecka
See: **Poland - Ministry of Health and Social Welfare - National Research Institute of Mother and Child** (13166)

Instytut Podstawowych Problemow Techniki
See: **Institute of Fundamental Technological Research** (7940)

★8009★
Insurance Bureau of Canada - Library (Bus-Fin)
181 University Ave., 13th Fl. Phone: (416)362-2031
Toronto, ON, Canada M5H 3M7 Lynne Genova, Libn
Founded: 1968. **Staff:** Prof 2. **Subjects:** Insurance - automobile, property, casualty; Canadian insurance law. **Holdings:** 2500 books. **Subscriptions:** 200 journals and other serials; 12 newspapers. **Services:** Interlibrary loan; library open by appointment to members only. **Automated Operations:** Computerized cataloging, serials, and circulation. **Computerized Information Services:** Info Globe, Infomart Online, QL Systems; internal database. **Publications:** Periodical and acquisitions lists, irregular. **Remarks:** FAX: (416)361-5952. **Staff:** Russ Gilchrist, Lib.Techn.

★8010★
Insurance Corporation of British Columbia - Corporate Library (Law)
151 W. Esplanade, Rm. 505 Phone: (604)661-6960
North Vancouver, BC, Canada V7M 3H9 Grace Makarewicz, Mgr.
Staff: Prof 2; Other 3. **Subjects:** Law, traffic safety, insurance. **Special Collections:** Adjusters Research Library (liability research materials for claims adjusters). **Holdings:** 6000 volumes. **Computerized Information Services:** Envoy 100 (electronic mail service). **Special Catalogs:** ICBC Cases (list of judicial decisions based on legislation relating to the corporation). **Remarks:** FAX: (604)443-7304. Electronic mail address(es): ICBC.LIB (Envoy 100).

★8011★
Insurance Industry Meetings Association - Library (Bus-Fin)
2330 S. Brentwood Blvd.
St. Louis, MO 63144-2096 Phone: (314)961-2300
Subjects: Insurance claims cost containment. **Holdings:** 14,400 books; 672 bound periodical volumes; 26,830 documents; 430 microforms; 43 AV programs; 90 manuscripts. **Services:** Library not open to the public. **Remarks:** FAX: (314)961-9828.

★8012★
Insurance Information Institute - Library (Bus-Fin)
110 William St. Phone: (212)669-9200
New York, NY 10038 Madine Singer, Libn.
Founded: 1959. **Staff:** Prof 2. **Subjects:** Property and casualty insurance and allied subjects. **Holdings:** 2000 books. **Subscriptions:** 75 journals and other serials. **Services:** Library open to the public by appointment. **Computerized Information Services:** NEXIS. Contact Person: Marjorie Gorgon, Dir., Info.Serv. **Publications:** Information packages, demonstrations, and training publications. **Remarks:** FAX: (212)732-1916. **Staff:** Nancy Williamson.

Insurance Institute of America
See: **American Institute for Chartered Property Casualty Underwriters - Insurance Institute of America - Library** (634)

★8013★
Insurance Institute for Highway Safety - Library (Trans)
1005 N. Glebe Rd., Suite 800 Phone: (703)247-1500
Arlington, VA 22201 Christine A. Pruzin, Libn.
Staff: 3. **Subjects:** Highway safety research, transportation, automotive engineering and medicine, traffic laws and implementation. **Holdings:** 600 volumes; 5000 research reports; 600 institute publications; institute-produced 1/2" and 3/4" videotapes and 16mm films. **Subscriptions:** 200 journals and other serials; 20 newspapers. **Services:** Interlibrary loan; copying; library open to the public by appointment. **Computerized Information Services:** DIALOG Information Services, ORBIT Search Service, VU/TEXT Information Services, WESTLAW, CompuServe Information Service. **Publications:** Status Report, biweekly - upon request. **Special Indexes:** Status Report Index (book). **Remarks:** FAX: (703)247-1678.

★8014★
Insurance Institute of Southern Alberta - Library (Bus-Fin)
1015 4th St., S.W., No. 801 Phone: (403)266-3427
Calgary, AB, Canada T2R 1J4 Lisa Roach, Sec.
Founded: 1953. **Staff:** 2. **Subjects:** Insurance. **Holdings:** 209 volumes; 5 films and filmstrips. **Services:** Library open to the public for reference use only on limited schedule. **Remarks:** Part of the Insurance Institute of Canada.

★8015★
Insurance Library Association of Boston (Bus-Fin)
156 State St. Phone: (617)227-2087
Boston, MA 02109 Jean E. Lucey, Dir.
Founded: 1887. **Staff:** Prof 2. **Subjects:** Insurance - fire, casualty, property, life, health. **Special Collections:** Sanborn Map Collection (New England); Henry Belknap Collection (fire insurance, fire prevention, firemen). **Holdings:** 5000 books; 2700 bound periodical volumes; reports of insurance companies and insurance commissioners; pamphlets; pictures. **Subscriptions:** 203 journals and other serials. **Services:** Interlibrary loan; copying; library open to the public. **Computerized Information Services:** Internal database. **Publications:** Quarterly Newsletter - to members. **Remarks:** FAX: (617)723-8524. **Staff:** Phyllis Smithers, Asst.Dir.

Insurance Society of New York
See: **College of Insurance - Insurance Society of New York - Kathryn and Shelby Cullom Davis Library** (3897)

Integrated Genetics, Inc.
See: **Genzyme Corp.** (6360)

★8016★
Intel Corporation - Aloha Library & Information Services (Sci-Engr, Comp Sci)
AL 4-60
5200 N.E. Elam Young Pkwy. Phone: (503)642-6598
Hillsboro, OR 97214-6497 Florence Graham, Mgr.
Founded: 1978. **Staff:** Prof 1; Other 3. **Subjects:** Microelectronics, manufacturing automation, quality, semiconductors, physics, chemistry. **Holdings:** 3500 books; technical reports. **Subscriptions:** 200 journals and other serials. **Services:** Interlibrary loan; center not open to the public. **Automated Operations:** Computerized public access catalog, cataloging, circulation, acquisitions, and serials. **Computerized Information Services:** DIALOG Information Services, DataTimes; Semiconductor Research Corp., Dataquest, STN International; DIALMAIL (electronic mail service). **Networks/Consortia:** Member of CLASS, Research Libraries Information Network (RLIN), Washington County Cooperative Library Services (WCCLS). **Remarks:** FAX: (503)642-8108.

★8017★
Intel Corporation - Hawthorn Farm Library and Information Services (Comp Sci)
HF1-36
5200 N.E. Elam Young Pkwy. Phone: (503)696-5114
Hillsboro, OR 97124-6497 Anne Isbell, Mgr.
Founded: 1987. **Staff:** Prof 1; Other 2. **Subjects:** Computer science, business, marketing, engineering. **Special Collections:** Marketing services and reports; industrial and military standards and specifications. **Holdings:** 4000 book titles; technical reports; videotapes. **Subscriptions:** 200 journals and other serials. **Services:** Interlibrary loan; library not open to the public. **Automated Operations:** Computerized public access catalog, cataloging, and circulation (TECHLIB). **Computerized Information Services:** DIALOG Information Services, RLIN, DataTimes. **Networks/Consortia:** Member of CLASS, Research Libraries Information Network (RLIN), Washington County Cooperative Library Services (WCCLS). **Remarks:** FAX: (503)696-6996.

★8018★
Intel Corporation - Library & Information Services (Sci-Engr)
CH2-92
5000 W. Chandler Blvd. Phone: (602)554-8018
Chandler, AZ 85226 Jayne E. Roorda, Lib.Mgr.
Staff: Prof 2; Other 3. **Subjects:** Electronics, semiconductors, solid state physics, computer science, marketing, engineering, quality, manufacturing automation, artificial intelligence, management. **Special Collections:** Marketing services and reports; industrial and military standards and specifications; technical reports; technical documentation for electronic components. **Holdings:** 5000 books. **Subscriptions:** 300 journals and other serials. **Services:** Interlibrary loan; services not open to the public. **Automated Operations:** Computerized public access catalog, cataloging, and circulation. **Computerized Information Services:** DIALOG Information Services, BRS Information Technologies, NewsNet, Inc., INVESTEXT, DATAQUEST, STN International, DunsPrint; internal database; DIALMAIL (electronic mail service). **Networks/Consortia:** Member of CLASS. **Remarks:** FAX: (602)554-7181.

★8019★
Intel Corporation - Library & Information Services (Sci-Engr)
MS FM2-50
1900 Prairie City Rd. Phone: (916)351-5982
Folsom, CA 95630 Terry Fagan, Info.Spec.
Founded: 1985. **Staff:** Prof 1; Other 2. **Subjects:** Semiconductor industry, business, microcomputer components, telecommunications. **Holdings:** 1600 books. **Subscriptions:** 200 journals and other serials; 25 newspapers. **Services:** Interlibrary loan; services not open to the public. **Computerized Information Services:** DIALOG Information Services, Dow Jones News/Retrieval. **Networks/Consortia:** Member of CLASS. **Remarks:** Alternate telephone number(s): 351-5981.

★8020★
Intel Corporation - Library & Information Services (Comp Sci)
2250 Mission College Blvd., SC9-32
Box 58120 Phone: (408)765-9158
Santa Clara, CA 95052-8120 James H. Schwartz, Mgr.
Founded: 1978. **Staff:** Prof 1; Other 2. **Subjects:** Semiconductors, microprocessors, microcomputers, computer-aided design and manufacturing, management, thin films, integrated circuits. **Holdings:** 3000 books; 3000 technical reports; 180 annual reports; 150 volumes of market research reports; U.S. patents; industrial product catalog data. **Subscriptions:** 320 journals and other serials; 20 newspapers. **Services:** Interlibrary loan; library not open to the public. **Automated Operations:** Computerized cataloging, acquisitions, serials, and circulation. **Computerized Information Services:** BRS Information Technologies, Dataquest, Inc., Semiconductor Research Corp., DIALOG Information Services, PFDS Online, STN International; internal database; electronic mail. **Networks/Consortia:** Member of South Bay Cooperative Library System (SBCLS), CLASS. **Special Catalogs:** Techlib (book catalog; online).

Intelligent Computer Systems Research Institute
See: **University of Miami** (18843)

★8021★
Intelsat Library (Sci-Engr)
3400 International Dr., N.W. Phone: (202)944-6820
Washington, DC 20008 Rosa Liu, Sect.Mgr., Lib. & Rec.
Founded: 1979. **Staff:** Prof 2; Other 1. **Subjects:** Satellite communication, communication engineering, telecommunication policy, electrical engineering. **Special Collections:** International Telecommunications Union publications, 1976 to present. **Holdings:** 8000 books; 750 bound periodical volumes; technical reports. **Subscriptions:** 325 journals and other serials. **Services:** Interlibrary loan; library not open to the public. **Computerized Information Services:** DIALOG Information Services, NEXIS, NewsNet, Inc.; internal database. **Publications:** Bibliography of publications. **Special Indexes:** Index to articles by and about Intelsat. **Remarks:** FAX: (202)944-7115. Telex: 89-2707. Maintained by International Telecommunications Satellite Organization. **Staff:** Ann Marshall, Libn.

★8022★
Intensive Caring Unlimited - Library (Med)
910 Bent Lane
Philadelphia, PA 19118 Phone: (215)233-4723
Subjects: Premature and high-risk infants, children with medical or developmental problems, high-risk pregnancy, infant and neonatal death. **Holdings:** 1200 volumes. **Remarks:** The activities of this parent support organization are concentrated in Pennsylvania and southern New Jersey, but it disseminates information nationwide.

Inter-American Agricultural Documentation and Information Center - Biblioteca Venezuela
See: **Inter-American Institute for Cooperation on Agriculture (IICA) - Biblioteca Venezuela** (8029)

★8023★
Inter-American Center for Regional Development - D.F. Maza Zavala Library (Soc Sci)
Calle 69, No. 15 D-32
Apdo. Postal 1304 Phone: 61 517336
Maracaibo, Venezuela Lourdes Crespo De Cruz, Lib.Hd.
Founded: 1977. **Staff:** 1. **Subjects:** Latin American development. **Special Collections:** Regional development collection; Development projects; administration collection. **Holdings:** 5000 volumes. **Subscriptions:** 212 newspapers. **Services:** Copying; library open to the public. **Publications:** Publicaciones Seriadas; Hojo Informativa; Documentos Cursos Cinder. **Remarks:** FAX: 61 523554. Telex: 61101. **Also Known As:** Centro Interamericano para el Desarrollo Regional - Biblioteca D.F. Maza Zavala.

★8024★
Inter-American Center for Research and Documentation on Vocational Training - Library (Educ)
Avenida Uruguay 1238
Casilla de Correo 1761
Montevideo, Uruguay Phone: 986023
Subjects: Vocational training in Latin American and Caribbean countries. **Holdings:** 21,000 volumes. **Subscriptions:** 650 journals and other serials. **Services:** Copying; SDI; library open to the public with restrictions. **Computerized Information Services:** FORPRO, MADIC, PERFOR (internal databases). **Remarks:** Alternate telephone number(s): 920063. FAX: 921305. Telex: 22573 CINFOR UY. Maintained by Organizacion Interacional del Trabajo. **Also Known As:** Centro Interamericano de Investigacion y Documentacion sobre Formacion Profesional.

★8025★
Inter-American Commission on Human Rights - Library (Soc Sci)
1889 F St., N.W., Suite LL2
Washington, DC 20006 Phone: (202)458-6007
Subjects: Human rights law. **Holdings:** 5000 volumes.

★8026★
Inter-American Defense College - Library (Mil, Soc Sci)
Fort McNair, Bldg. 52 Phone: (202)646-1330
Washington, DC 20319-6100 Salvador Velez, Hd.Libn.
Founded: 1962. **Staff:** Prof 2; Other 3. **Subjects:** Social, economic, political, and military affairs of individual countries with emphasis on Latin America; Inter-American system. **Holdings:** 15,000 books; 11,000 documents and pamphlets. **Subscriptions:** 225 journals and other serials; 28 newspapers. **Services:** Interlibrary loan; library open to the public with restrictions. **Staff:** Gioconda Vallarino, Cat.

★8027★
Inter-American Development Bank - Felipe Herrera Library (Bus-Fin)
1300 New York Ave.
Stop W0102 Phone: (202)623-3213
Washington, DC 20577 Benita Weber Vassallo, Chf. of Lib.Serv.
Founded: 1960. **Staff:** Prof 3; Other 9. **Subjects:** Economic and social development with emphasis on Latin America; trade; agriculture; energy; industry; appropriate technology. **Special Collections:** Commodities; international agricultural centers. **Holdings:** 200,000 monographs, documents, periodicals, and economic reports. **Subscriptions:** 3500 journals and other serials. **Services:** Interlibrary loan; copying; center open to the public with restrictions. **Automated Operations:** Computerized circulation, cataloging, serials, and acquisitions. **Computerized Information Services:** OCLC, DIALOG Information Services, LEXIS, NEXIS. **Networks/Consortia:** Member of CAPCON Library Network. **Publications:** Calendar Future International Meetings and Seminars, quarterly; selected list of acquisitions. **Remarks:** FAX: (202)623-3183. **Staff:** Nelsa Doris Bentos, Cat.Libn.; Marina Schreiber, Pub.Serv./Ref.Libn.; Rolland Lamberton, ILL Asst.

Inter-American Indian Institute
See: **Organization of American States - Inter-American Indian Institute** (12559)

★8028★
Inter-American Institute for Cooperation on Agriculture - Tropical Agricultural Research and Training Center - Library (Agri)
7170 CATIE Phone: 561615
Turrialba, Costa Rica Laura Coto Royo, Chf.Libn.
Founded: 1943. **Staff:** 13. **Subjects:** Agriculture, farming systems, animal husbandry, agroforestry, genetic resources, pastures, watershed management, conservation, cocoa and coffee production. **Holdings:** 85,000 volumes. **Subscriptions:** 11,300 journals and other serials. **Services:** Interlibrary loan; copying; SDI; library open to the public. **Computerized Information Services:** Cafe, cacao, BCO, CIDIA, Banano y Platano (UPEB) (internal databases); CD-ROMs (AGRICOLA, CAB, AGRIS, SESAME); BITNET (electronic mail service). **Publications:** Redcafe; Cacao; Bibliografias especializadas; Nuevas adquisiciones; Canje y donacion. **Remarks:** Maintains field units in Latin America and the Caribbean. FAX: 561533. Telex: 8005 CATIE, CR. Electronic mail address(es): LCoto@UCRVM2 (BITNET). **Also Known As:** IICA/CATIE; Biblioteca Conmemorativa Orton. **Staff:** Martha Abarca Monge; Rigoberto Aguilar Martinez.

★8029★
Inter-American Institute for Cooperation on Agriculture (IICA) - Biblioteca Venezuela (Agri)
Apartado Postal 55-2200 Coronado Phone: 29-02-22
San Jose, Costa Rica Ghislaine Poitevien, Hd.Libn.
Subjects: Agricultural policy planning, technology generation and transfer, rural development, agricultural marketing, animal health, plant protection. **Holdings:** 10,000 books; 280 bound periodical volumes; 2000 microforms; IICA publications; statistical data collection. **Services:** Interlibrary loan; copying; SDI; library open to the public with restrictions. **Computerized Information Services:** DIALOG Information Services, AGRIS (International Information System for the Agricultural Sciences and Technology), CAB (Commonwealth Agriculture Bureaux) ABSTRACTS; EIES (electronic mail service). Performs searches on fee basis. Contact Person: Lina Roman, Bibliotecologa, 29-02-22, ext. 326. **Remarks:** Library is part of Inter-American Agricultural Documentation and Information Center. FAX: (506)294741. Telex: 2144-IICA. **Also Known As:** Instituto Interamericano do Cooperacion para la Agricultura (IICA) - Centro Interamericano de Documentacion e Informacion Agricola (CIDIA).

Inter-American Music Archive
See: **University of Miami - School of Music - Albert Pick Music Library** (18850)

★8030★
Inter-American Organization for Higher Education - Library (Educ)
3460, rue de la Perade, Suite 1.10
Ste. Foy, PQ, Canada G1X 3Y5 Phone: (418)644-6910
Subjects: Universities in the Americas. **Holdings:** 2000 volumes. **Remarks:** FAX: (418)646-3039. Telex: 051-31506. **Also Known As:** Organisation Universitaire Interamericaine.

Inter-American Tropical Tuna Commission Collection
See: **U.S. Natl. Marine Fisheries Service - Southwest Fisheries Science Center** (17643)

★8031★
Inter American University of Puerto Rico - School of Law - Domingo Toledo Alamo Law Library (Law)
1610 Fernandez Juncos Ave.
Box 8897 Phone: (809)727-1930
Santurce, PR 00910 Rigel Sabater-Sola, Lib.Dir.
Founded: 1961. **Staff:** Prof 5; Other 15. **Subjects:** Law - criminal, constitutional, civil, comparative, trial, administrative. **Special Collections:** Domingo Toledo Alamo Collection (rare books); Puerto Rico Law. **Holdings:** 114,736 books; 22,317 bound periodical volumes; 3931 reels of microfilm; 113,900 microfiche; 365 tapes and cassettes; 623 video cassettes. **Subscriptions:** 1339 journals and other serials; 7 newspapers. **Services:** Interlibrary loan; copying; library open to the public with restrictions. **Automated Operations:** Computerized cataloging, acquisitions, and circulation. **Computerized Information Services:** LEXIS, NEXIS, VERALEX. **Publications:** List of New Acquisitions; List of Subject Headings. **Remarks:** FAX: (809)728-3085. **Staff:** Odila Collazo, Acq.Libn.; Alberto Guzman, Ref.Libn.; Marisol Zapater, Cat.

Inter-University Consortium for Political and Social Research
See: **University of Michigan - Institute for Social Research** (18868)

Inter-University Consortium for Political and Social Research Archives
See: **Rutgers University - Computing Services** (14161)

★8032★
Inter/University Group for Research in Ethnopsychiatry and Medical Anthropology - Library (Med)
University of Montreal
P.O. Box 6128, Sta. A
Montreal, PQ, Canada H3C 3J7 Phone: (514)343-5832
Subjects: Ethnopsychiatry, medical anthropology. **Holdings:** Figures not available. **Remarks:** FAX: (514)343-2494.

Interagency Advanced Power Group
See: **U.S. Interagency Advanced Power Group** (17560)

★8033★
Intercollegiate Center for Nursing Education - Betty M. Anderson Library (Med)
W. 2917 Ft. George Wright Dr. Phone: (509)325-6139
Spokane, WA 99204-5290 Robert M. Pringle, Jr., Hd.Libn.
Founded: 1969. **Staff:** Prof 2; Other 4. **Subjects:** Nursing, allied health sciences. **Special Collections:** History of nursing. **Holdings:** 10,000 books; 500 bound periodical volumes; 25 VF drawers. **Subscriptions:** 300 journals and other serials. **Services:** Interlibrary loan; copying; library open to the public for reference use only. **Computerized Information Services:** DIALOG Information Services, BRS Information Technologies, MEDLINE; OnTyme Electronic Message Network Service (electronic mail service). Performs searches on fee basis. **Networks/Consortia:** Member of Western Library Network (WLN), Inland Northwest Health Sciences Libraries (INWHSL). **Special Indexes:** Indexes to publications of American Nurses Association and National League for Nursing. **Remarks:** FAX: (509)325-7163. Electronic mail address(es): ICFNE (OnTyme Electronic Message Network Service). Maintained by Washington State University. **Staff:** Mary L. Wood.

★8034★
Intercom Information Resources, Inc. (Info Sci)
1399 9th Ave., Suite 1519
San Diego, CA 92101 Carlos E. Ayala, Dir.
Founded: 1984. **Staff:** Prof 3; Other 5. **Subjects:** Business, international trade, scientific and technical information. **Holdings:** Figures not available. **Services:** Current awareness; document retrieval; custom research; translation. **Computerized Information Services:** DIALOG Information Services, BRS Information Technologies, Dow Jones News/Retrieval, PFDS Online, NewsNet, Inc.; internal databases; MCI Mail (electronic mail service). Performs searches on fee basis.

★8035★
InterConsult Inc. - Library (Info Sci)
366 Massachusetts Ave.
Arlington, MA 02174 Phone: (617)646-9600
Subjects: Electronic publishing, graphic arts automation, phototypesetting, electronic printing, office automation. **Holdings:** 5000 bound volumes. **Subscriptions:** 50 journals and other serials. **Computerized Information Services:** MCI Mail (electronic mail service). **Remarks:** FAX: (617)646-9615. Toll-free telephone number(s): (800)777-1647. Telex: 9109974669. Electronic mail address(es): ICIMA (MCI Mail).

★8036★
Intercultural Communication Institute - Intercultural Library (Info Sci)
8835 S.W. Canyon Lane, Suite 238 Phone: (503)297-4622
Portland, OR 97225 Beth Prins, Adm.
Founded: 1986. **Staff:** 4. **Subjects:** Intercultural communication, counseling, and training; international education. **Holdings:** 750 books; 2000 Society for Intercultural Education documents; 3000 fugitive materials. **Services:** Copying; library open to the public. **Remarks:** FAX: (503)297-4695.

★8037★
Intercultural Development Research Association (IDRA) - Library
5835 Callaghan Rd., Suite 350
San Antonio, TX 78228
Defunct.

Intercultural Institute of Montreal
See: **Institut Interculturel de Montreal - Bibliotheque** (7871)

★8038★
Interfaith Center on Corporate Responsibility (Soc Sci)
475 Riverside Dr., Rm. 566
New York, NY 10115-0050 Phone: (212)870-2293
Founded: 1970. **Staff:** 12. **Subjects:** Corporate responsibility, South Africa, investment in Latin America, infant formula abuse, space warfare, economic

conversion, nuclear weapons production, affirmative action and equal employment opportunity, alternate investments, energy and environment, pharmaceutical marketing, corporate governance. **Holdings:** 20 VF cabinets of corporate annual reports, research papers, newsletters of action groups on corporate responsibility issues, newspaper clippings on corporate social issues. **Subscriptions:** 50 journals and other serials. **Services:** Center not open to the public. **Publications:** Corporate Examiner, 10/year - by subscription, sample copy free upon request; studies and CE briefs; Directory of Alternative Investments; Subscriber Service, 10/year; packets for concerned investors - all for sale. **Remarks:** FAX: (212)870-2023. **Staff:** Diane Bratcher, Pubn.Mgr.; Timothy H. Smith, Exec.Dir.

★8039★
Interfaith Medical Center - Brooklyn Jewish Division - Medical & Nursing Library (Med)
555 Prospect Pl. Phone: (718)935-7085
Brooklyn, NY 11238 Sharon Ruth Peterson, Med.Libn.
Founded: 1896. **Staff:** Prof 1; Other 1. **Subjects:** Medicine, nursing, and allied health sciences. **Holdings:** 2500 books; 10,000 bound periodical volumes; 6 VF drawers. **Subscriptions:** 210 journals and other serials. **Services:** Interlibrary loan; library not open to the public. **Computerized Information Services:** MEDLARS; DOCLINE (electronic mail service). **Networks/Consortia:** Member of Medical Library Center of New York (MLCNY), Brooklyn-Queens-Staten Island Health Sciences Librarians (BQSI), New York Metropolitan Reference and Research Library Agency.

★8040★
Interfaith Medical Center - St. John's Episcopal Hospital - Nursing and Medical Library (Med)
1545 Atlantic Ave. Phone: (718)604-6030
Brooklyn, NY 11216 Dallas C. Hopson, Dir.
Founded: 1900. **Staff:** Prof 1. **Subjects:** Pediatrics, obstetrics/gynecology. **Holdings:** 2500 books; 200 bound periodical volumes. **Subscriptions:** 105 journals and other serials. **Services:** Interlibrary loan; library not open to the public. **Automated Operations:** Computerized serials and circulation. **Computerized Information Services:** BRS Information Technologies, MEDLARS; DOCLINE (electronic mail service). **Networks/Consortia:** Member of Brooklyn-Queens-Staten Island Health Sciences Librarians (BQSI), Medical Library Center of New York (MLCNY), New York Metropolitan Reference and Research Library Agency.

★8041★
Intergalactic Corp. - Library (Sci-Engr)
Box 7025 Phone: (801)262-2332
Salt Lake City, UT 84107 Douglas MacGregor, Dir.
Founded: 1937. **Staff:** Prof 3; Other 5. **Subjects:** Testing procedures, chemistry, nuclear sciences, engineering. **Special Collections:** Antique scientific works prior to 1850; product and test standards (120,000). **Holdings:** 18,500 books; 13,250 bound periodical volumes; 12,000 product data materials; 22,000 technical reports; 7300 material science studies. **Subscriptions:** 212 journals and other serials; 7 newspapers. **Services:** Interlibrary loan; copying; library open to the public with restrictions. **Automated Operations:** Computerized cataloging and circulation. **Publications:** Unilink Journal - by subscription. **Remarks:** Library located at 4030 S. 500 W., Bldg. 60, Salt Lake City, UT 84123. FAX: (801)262-2363. **Staff:** Pat Plese, Libn.

★8042★
Intergovernmental Committee on Urban and Regional Research (ICURR) - Information Exchange Service (Soc Sci, Plan)
150 Eglinton Ave., E., Suite 301 Phone: (416)973-5629
Toronto, ON, Canada M4P 1E8 Monica Hope, Info.Coord.
Founded: 1967. **Staff:** Prof 5; Other 5. **Subjects:** Housing and building, municipal and urban affairs, rural and regional development, environment, transportation, recreation. **Holdings:** 10,000 documents. **Subscriptions:** 254 journals and other serials. **Services:** Interlibrary loan; service open to Canadian government personnel; open to consultants and universities on fee basis. **Computerized Information Services:** Internal database. **Publications:** Liaison, bimonthly. **Remarks:** FAX: (416)973-1375. **Also Known As:** Comite intergouvernemental de recherches urbaines et regionales. **Staff:** Michael Afar, Doc.

★8043★
Intergovernmental Health Policy Project - Clearinghouse (Med)
2021 K St., N.W., Suite 800 Phone: (202)872-1445
Washington, DC 20006 Molly Stauffer
Staff: Prof 1; Other 1. **Subjects:** Medicaid, AIDS, longterm care, mental health, certificate of need, homelessness. **Special Collections:** Summaries of AIDS laws from legislative sessions, 1983 to present. **Holdings:** 10,000 books; 10,000 bound periodical volumes. **Subscriptions:** 30 journals and other serials. **Services:** Copying; Legislative Tracking Service; Clearinghouse open to the public on a fee basis. **Computerized Information Services:** Electronic Legislative Search System (ELSS). **Publications:** AIDS: A Public Health Challenge (3 volume report); Major Changes in State Medicaid, annual; Newsletters: State Health Notes, State ADM Reports, Intergovernmental AIDS Report; List of publications - available upon request. **Special Indexes:** State Health Policy Legislation. **Remarks:** FAX: (202)825-0114.

★8044★
Interlac - Library (Art, Rec)
97 Woodmere Rd. Phone: (203)975-1554
Stamford, CT 06905 Tom Burkert
Founded: 1976. **Staff:** 1. **Subjects:** Comic books, popular culture. **Holdings:** 20,000 volumes. **Subscriptions:** 20 journals and other serials. **Services:** Library not open to the public.

★8045★
Interlochen Center for the Arts - Music Library (Mus)
Interlochen, MI 49643 Phone: (616)276-9221
E. Delmer Weliver, Dir.
Staff: Prof 2; Other 20. **Subjects:** Music. **Holdings:** 10,000 orchestra titles; 5775 band titles; 3450 choir titles; 650 jazz band titles; 17,125 solo and small ensemble titles; 3300 recordings; 3000 study score titles. **Services:** Copying; library open to the public for reference use only. **Remarks:** FAX: (616)276-6321. **Staff:** Alice Freudigman; David Lake.

★8046★
Intermedics, Inc. - Library Information Services Department (Med)
240 W. 2nd St.
Box 617 Phone: (409)233-8611
Freeport, TX 77541 Charlene P. Kanter, Mgr.
Founded: 1979. **Staff:** Prof 1; Other 2. **Subjects:** Cardiology, biomedical engineering, electrical engineering. **Special Collections:** Pacemakers; biomaterials. **Holdings:** 1500 books. **Subscriptions:** 50 journals and other serials. **Services:** Interlibrary loan; copying; SDI; library open to the public with restrictions. **Automated Operations:** Computerized acquisitions and serials. **Computerized Information Services:** DIALOG Information Services, MEDLINE, Dow Jones News/Retrieval; PACERS (internal database). Performs searches free of charge for clients. **Publications:** Journal Holdings List; PACERS brochure. **Remarks:** FAX: (409)233-6474.

★8047★
Intermetrics Inc. - Library (Comp Sci)
733 Concord Ave. Phone: (617)661-1840
Cambridge, MA 02138 Willa MacAllen, Libn.
Staff: 1. **Subjects:** Computer science, mathematics, physics, aeronautics, astronautics, avionics. **Holdings:** 1000 books; 200 bound periodical volumes; 1500 technical reports. **Subscriptions:** 150 journals and other serials. **Services:** Library not open to the public. **Computerized Information Services:** DIALOG Information Services.

★8048★
Intermountain Cultural Center & Museum, Inc. - Genealogical Research Library (Hist)
2295 Paddock Ave.
P.O. Box 307 Phone: (208)549-0205
Weiser, ID 83627 Carol Odoms, Mgr.
Founded: 1962. **Subjects:** Washington County, Idaho, Intermountain Institute, local authors. **Holdings:** Figures not available. **Services:** Library open to the public during museum hours.

Intermountain Health Care, Inc. - L.D.S. Hospital
See: **L.D.S. Hospital** (8842)

Internal Revenue Service
See: **U.S. Internal Revenue Service** (17561)

Internationaal Belasting Documentatie Bureau
See: **International Bureau of Fiscal Documentation** (8069)

★8049★
International Academy at Santa Barbara - Library (Energy)
800 Garden St., Suite D Phone: (805)965-5010
Santa Barbara, CA 93101 Susan J. Shaffer, Off.Mgr.
Staff: 7. **Subjects:** Energy, environment, current world leaders, information management. **Holdings:** Figures not available. **Services:** Library open to the public. **Computerized Information Services:** DIALOG Information Services; CD-ROM (Environmental Periodicals Bibliography). **Publications:** Environmental Periodicals Bibliography, bimonthly; Energy Review, 3/year; Current World Leaders, 6/year; Almanac, 3/year; Biography & News/Speeches & Reports, 3/year; Education for Information Management; Energy Books Quarterly; Environmental Bibliography Search Guide; Annual Directory of World Leaders, annual; Alternative Energy Digests, monthly; Waste Information Digests, monthly. **Remarks:** FAX: (805)965-6071.

★8050★
International Academy of Sciences - Library (Sci-Engr)
Kleinberger Weg 16 B Phone: 05251 64200
W-4790 Paderborn, Germany Prof. Helmar Frank
Founded: 1985. **Subjects:** Scientific terminology and international academic standards in the fields of cybernetics, humanities, structural sciences, philosophy, natural sciences, and morphological sciences. **Holdings:** 300 volumes. **Also Known As:** Akademio Internacia de la Sciencoj.

★8051★
International Advertising Association - World Secretariat (Bus-Fin)
342 Madison Ave., Suite 2000
New York, NY 10017 Phone: (212)557-1133
Founded: 1938. **Staff:** 6. **Subjects:** Advertising and marketing. **Holdings:** General reference books; foreign advertising and marketing periodicals. **Subscriptions:** 50 journals and other serials; 10 newspapers. **Services:** Center open to members only. **Remarks:** FAX: (212)983-0455. Telex: 237969 IAA UR. **Staff:** Tracy Poltie.

★8052★
International Agency for Research on Cancer - Library (Med)
150, cours Albert-Thomas Phone: 72 73 84 85
F-69372 Lyon Cedex 8, France Helis Miido, Libn.
Founded: 1967. **Staff:** Prof 2; Other 2. **Subjects:** Cancer, chemical carcinogenesis, cancer epidemiology, environmental carcinogenesis, virology/genetics, biostatistics. **Holdings:** 8000 books; 7000 bound periodical volumes; annual reports; World Health Organization documents. **Subscriptions:** 280 journals and other serials. **Services:** Interlibrary loan; copying; library open to the public on a limited schedule. **Computerized Information Services:** NLM, DIALOG Information Services. **Publications:** Library Bulletin. **Remarks:** FAX: 72 73 85 75. Telex: 380 023. Agency is the autonomous cancer research arm of the World Health Organization.

International Archive of Women in Architecture
See: **Virginia Polytechnic Institute and State University** (19873)

International Archives for the Women's Movement
See: **International Information Center and Archives for the Women's Movement** (8121)

International Association of Assessing Officers
See: **Merriam Center Library** (10161)

★8053★
International Association of Assessing Officers - Research and Technical Services Department - Paul V. Corusy Memorial Library (Bus-Fin)
1313 E. 60th St. Phone: (312)947-2050
Chicago, IL 60637-9990 Mary Kay Siebert, Libn.
Staff: Prof 1; Other 1. **Subjects:** Property taxation, assessment administration, appraisal. **Special Collections:** Archive of IAAO publications. **Holdings:** 10,000 volumes; 25 linear feet of pamphlet and clipping files. **Subscriptions:** 650 journals and other serials. **Services:** Interlibrary loan; copying; library open to the public by application. **Computerized Information Services:** OCLC. **Networks/Consortia:** Member of ILLINET. **Publications:** Bibliographic Series, irregular; Research and Information Series, irregular. **Remarks:** Affiliated with the Charles E. Merriam Center Library.

★8054★
International Association of Chiefs of Police - Center for Law Enforcement Research
1110 N. Glebe Rd., Suite 200
Arlington, VA 22201
Subjects: Criminal justice, law enforcement. **Special Collections:** Police department manuals (40). **Holdings:** 6000 volumes; FBI uniform crime reports; Police Chief magazine, 1934 to present; Police Yearbook, 1893 to present. **Remarks:** Currently inactive.

★8055★
International Association of Correctional Officers - Library (Law)
1333 S. Wabash Ave.
Box 53 Phone: (312)996-9267
Chicago, IL 60605 Tonya Matz, Libn.
Founded: 1977. **Staff:** 2. **Subjects:** Criminal rehabilitation, law enforcement. **Special Collections:** Supreme Court decisions. **Holdings:** 205 volumes; 63 unbound reports; 54 manuscripts. **Subscriptions:** 10 journals and other serials. **Services:** Interlibrary loan; copying; library open to the public with restrictions. **Publications:** Library Guide. **Remarks:** FAX: (312)413-2713. Alternate telephone number(s): (312)996-5401. **Formerly:** Located in Marquette, MI.

★8056★
International Association of Cross-Reference Directory Publishers - Library (Publ)
Bresser Company
684 W. Baltimore
Detroit, MI 48202 Phone: (313)874-0570
Subjects: Cross-reference directory publishing. **Holdings:** 500 volumes.

★8057★
International Association of Educators for World Peace - IAEWP Center for Intercultural Information (Soc Sci)
Mastin Lake Sta.
P.O. Box 3282 Phone: (205)534-5501
Huntsville, AL 35810-0282 Dr. Charles Mercieca, Exec. V.P.
Founded: 1974. **Staff:** Prof 5. **Subjects:** Education, philosophy, sociology, history, literature, languages. **Holdings:** 150,000 volumes; 2200 slides and cassettes. **Subscriptions:** 30 journals and other serials. **Services:** Copying; center open to the public with restrictions. **Computerized Information Services:** Online systems. **Publications:** Education for Peace; Peace Progress Journal; Peace Education Journal; The Age of Trust; Mismanagement in Higher Education; Circulation Newsletter. **Special Catalogs:** Peace education literature. **Remarks:** The IAEWP is committed to promoting international understanding and world peace through education, to protect the environment from man-made air and water pollution, and to help implement the Universal Declaration of Human Rights. The IAEWP Center incorporates private libraries of IAEWP officials in 50 chapters worldwide. Center located at 2013 Orba Dr., N.E., Huntsville, AL 35811. FAX: (205)851-9157. Telex: 9102405482.

★8058★
International Association of Fire Chiefs - Management Information Center (Sci-Engr)
1329 18th St., N.W. Phone: (202)833-3420
Washington, DC 20036-6516 Ann Swing, Dir., MIC
Staff: 1. **Subjects:** Fire prevention, fire fighting, fire protection, safety, municipal and administrative topics, hazardous materials, labor relations. **Holdings:** 5000 volumes. **Subscriptions:** 175 journals and other serials. **Services:** Center not open to the public. **Remarks:** FAX: (202)452-0684.

★8059★
International Association for Identification - Library (Soc Sci)
P.O. Box 2423 Phone: (510)865-2174
Alameda, CA 94501-6370 Ashley R. Crooker, Jr., Sec./Treas.
Subjects: Forensic identification, criminalistics. **Holdings:** 500 volumes. **Services:** Interlibrary loan; library not open to the public. **Remarks:** Library collection housed at the F.B.I. Academy Learning Resource Center in Quantico, VA.

★8060★
International Association for Psychiatric Research - Library (Med)
P.O. Box 457 Phone: (516)862-6651
St. James, NY 11780 Max Fink, M.D.
Founded: 1967. **Staff:** Prof 1. **Subjects:** Electroconvulsive therapy. **Holdings:** 800 books; 600 bound periodical volumes. **Subscriptions:** 20 journals and other serials. **Services:** Library not open to the public. **Computerized Information Services:** ECT (internal database). Performs searches. **Remarks:** FAX: (516)862-8604.

★8061★
International Association of Pupil Personnel Workers Inc. - Archives (Law)
c/o William Chmela
2025 Joneway Dr. Phone: (219)872-4975
Long Beach, IN 46360 William Chmela, Dir.
Founded: 1911. **Subjects:** Truancy, juvenile delinquency. **Special Collections:** IAPPW journals, 1911 to present. **Holdings:** 1000 books. **Services:** Library not open to the public. **Computerized Information Services:** ERIC. **Formerly:** Located in Chicago, IL.

★8062★
International Association of Security Service - Library (Law)
Box 8202 Phone: (708)973-7712
Northfield, IL 60093 Howard W. Ross, Exec.Dir.
Founded: 1973. **Staff:** 6. **Subjects:** Security and guard services. **Holdings:** 600 volumes.

International Atomic Energy Agency - International Centre for Theoretical Physics
See: **International Centre for Theoretical Physics** (8077)

★8063★
International Bank Note Society - Library (Bus-Fin)
Box 1642 Phone: (414)554-6255
Racine, WI 53401 Angus E. Bruce, Libn.
Founded: 1961. **Staff:** 1. **Subjects:** Bank note printing and collection, monetary systems. **Holdings:** 423 books; 510 bound periodical volumes; 260 other cataloged items. **Services:** Interlibrary loan; copying; library open to society members. **Special Indexes:** Indexes to subjects, photographs, authors, and book reviews in the society's quarterly journal. **Staff:** Mike Turner, U.K. Libn.

International Baptist Theological Seminary
See: **European Baptist Federation** (5480)

★8064★
International Bee Research Association - Library (Agri)
18 North Rd. Phone: 222 372409
Cardiff CF1 3DY, Wales S. Zabaneh
Founded: 1949. **Staff:** 2. **Subjects:** Bee research; pollination, especially by bees. **Holdings:** 4000 books; 28,000 reprints and reports; 8000 photographs. **Subscriptions:** 250 journals and other serials. **Services:** Interlibrary loan; library not open to the public. **Remarks:** FAX: 222 665522. **Also Known As:** Association Internationale de Recherche Apicole; IBRA.

International Biographical Archive of Central European Emigres, 1933-1945
See: **Research Foundation for Jewish Immigration, Inc. - Archives** (13836)

★8065★
International Bird Rescue Research Center - Library (Biol Sci)
699 Potter St. Phone: (510)841-9086
Berkeley, CA 94710 Jay Holcomb, Dir.
Founded: 1971. **Subjects:** Avian physiology, pathology, and behavior; effects of pollutants; oiled bird rehabilitation; contingency plans. **Holdings:** 100 books; 450 reprints; 20 microforms; 200 pages of San Francisco Oil Spill records; 2500 IBM cards of veterinary records for birds. **Services:** Library not open to the public. **Publications:** Sea Otter Rehabilitation Program 1989 Exxon Valdez Oil Spill; Rehabilitating Oiled Sea-Birds - A Field Manual; Results of the Eagle Capture Health Assessment and Short-Term Rehabilitation Program Following the Valdez Oil Spill. **Remarks:** FAX: (510)841-9089.

★8066★
International Brotherhood of Old Bastards, Inc. - Sir Thomas Crapper Memorial Archives (Hist)
2330 S. Brentwood Blvd., Suite 666 Phone: (314)961-2300
St. Louis, MO 63144-2096 Bro. Maven A. Goniff, Sr., O.B., Chf., Archv./Kpr.
Founded: 1869. **Staff:** 13. **Subjects:** Bastardy, genealogy, politics, royalty. **Holdings:** 13,621 books; 872 bound periodical volumes; 511 archive reports; 1174 maps; 6 tons of archival material and many unopened boxes from predecessor organizations in Spain and England; miscellaneous information. **Subscriptions:** 52 journals and other serials; 16 newspapers. **Services:** Interlibrary loan; copying; archives open to scholarly research subject to approval of the Board of Presiding Archbastards. **Publications:** Ye Olde Bastards Bulletin, semiannual; Archives Report, irregular; Emergency Bulletins, as needed; Special Research Reports, semimonthly. **Special Indexes:** Punched card index. **Remarks:** FAX: (314)961-9828. **Staff:** Bro. Lewis N. Clarke; Bro. Cozen P. Bantling; Bro. Solomon Sciuridae, O.B.; Bro. Wiley Maven, Sr.

★8067★
International Brotherhood of Teamsters - Library (Bus-Fin)
25 Louisiana Ave., N.W. Phone: (202)624-6927
Washington, DC 20001 Saul E. Bronder, Dir.
Founded: 1955. **Staff:** Prof 3; Other 4. **Subjects:** Labor economics, transportation economics, labor law, business. **Special Collections:** Archives of IBT. **Holdings:** 30,000 books; microfilm of union serial publications; pamphlets; tapes; films; photographs. **Subscriptions:** 1000 journals and other serials. **Services:** Library not open to the public. **Automated Operations:** Computerized serials and circulation. **Computerized Information Services:** NEXIS, LEXIS, DIALOG Information Services, PFDS Online, BRS Information Technologies, DataTimes, VU/TEXT Information Services, Info Globe, NewsNet, Inc., WILSONLINE, Infomart Online, Information America, Aviation Online. **Remarks:** FAX: (202)624-6910. **Formerly:** International Brotherhood of Teamsters, Chauffeurs, Warehousemen and Helpers of America. **Staff:** Terri Fritz, Libn.; Janet Wamsley, Asst.Libn.; John Doenges, Asst.Libn.

International Brotherhood of Teamsters, Chauffeurs, Warehousemen and Helpers of America
See: **International Brotherhood of Teamsters - Library** (8067)

★8068★
International Bulb Society - Research Library (Biol Sci)
Box 985 Phone: (619)477-5333
National City, CA 92151 R. Mitchel Beauchamp
Founded: 1933. **Staff:** 1. **Subjects:** Amaryllidaceae and related bulbous plant families, botany, taxonomy, flowers. **Holdings:** 4000 volumes. **Subscriptions:** 120 journals and other serials. **Services:** Library not open to the public.

International Bureau of Education
See: **United Nations Educational, Scientific and Cultural Organization - International Bureau of Education** (16764)

★8069★
International Bureau of Fiscal Documentation - Library (Bus-Fin)
Muiderpoort-Sarphatistraat 124
Postbus 20237 Phone: 20 6267726
NL-1000 HE Amsterdam, Netherlands J. Booy, Libn.
Founded: 1938. **Subjects:** International taxation. **Holdings:** 25,000 volumes. **Subscriptions:** 400 journals and other serials. **Services:** Library open to the public. **Computerized Information Services:** Internal database. **Remarks:** Founded by International Fiscal Association. Telex: 13217 INTAX NL. FAX: 20 6209397. **Also Known As:** Internationaal Belasting Documentatie Bureau.

International Center for Aquaculture
See: **Auburn University** (1282)

★8070★
International Center for the Disabled (ICD) - Bruce Barton Memorial Library (Med)
340 E. 24th St. Phone: (212)679-0100
New York, NY 10010 Helen Stonehill, Dir., Lib./Info.Ctr.
Founded: 1917. **Staff:** Prof 1; Other 1. **Subjects:** Rehabilitation, physical medicine, vocational training, psychology, psychiatry, psychopharmacology, job placement, speech and hearing, gerontology, chemical dependency. **Holdings:** 6000 books; 2000 bound periodical volumes; 78 VF drawers; 50 boxes of occupational materials; 4000 research reports on microfiche. **Subscriptions:** 150 journals and other serials. **Services:** Interlibrary loan; copying; SDI; library open to the public. **Computerized Information Services:** BRS Information Technologies. **Networks/Consortia:** Member of New York Metropolitan Reference and Research Library Agency, Manhattan-Bronx Health Sciences Library Consortia. **Publications:** Acquisitions List, quarterly. **Also Known As:** Institute for the Crippled and Disabled. **Staff:** Helen Stonehill.

International Center for Holocaust Studies
See: **Braun Center for Holocaust Studies** (2089)

★8071★
International Centre of Insect Physiology and Ecology - Library (Biol Sci)
P.O. Box 30772 Phone: 2 802501
Nairobi, Kenya Mr. Noah Nsubuga, Lib.Hd.
Founded: 1973. **Staff:** Prof 3; Other 3. **Subjects:** Entomology; insect ecology. **Holdings:** 6000 books; 200 archival items. **Subscriptions:** 130 journals and other serials; 3 newspapers. **Services:** Interlibrary loan; copying; library open to the public by appointment. **Computerized Information Services:** CGIAR Union Serials; CD-ROM (CAB Abstracts). Performs searches. Contact Person: Dorothy Barasa, Doc. **Remarks:** Telex: 22053 ICIPE; 2506 DUDU. Electronic mail address(es): CGI063.

★8072★
International Center for Living Aquatic Resources Management - Ian R. Smith Memorial Library and Documentation Center (Biol Sci)
MC, P.O. Box 1501
Makati, Metro Manila 1299, Phone: 2 818-0466
Philippines Rosalinda M. Temprosa, Chf.Libn.
Founded: 1978. **Staff:** Prof 5; Other 1. **Subjects:** Fisheries, aquaculture, coastal resources management, biological research, economics. **Special Collections:** Newspaper clipping and reprint collection (fisheries and aquaculture; coastal resources management in tropical and developing countries). **Holdings:** 10,000 books, monographs, theses, dissertations, conference proceedings, papers; CD-ROM. **Subscriptions:** 600 serial titles. **Services:** Interlibrary loan; copying; library open to the public for reference use only to fisheries and aquaculture researchers. **Automated Operations:** Computerized cataloging and serials. **Computerized Information Services:** DIALOG Information Services; internal database; CGNET, SCIENCEnet (electronic mail services). **Publications:** Annual Book Catalog; Serials Holdings List - selective distribution; other publications available. **Remarks:** Alternate telephone number(s): 2 818-9283; 2 817-5255. FAX: 2 816-3183. Telex: ETPI 64794 ICLARM PN. Electronic mail address(es): ICLARM.MANILA (SCIENCEnet); IcLARM (CGNET). **Formerly:** Its ICLARM Library. **Staff:** Mrs. Norma I. Jhocson, Libn.; Mrs. Erlinda B. Gonzalez, Assoc.Libn.; Reynaldo Damalerio; Adelina Mendoza; Mationtiman Cruz.

International Center for Marine Resource Development
See: **University of Rhode Island** (19265)

★8073★
International Centre for Parliamentary Documentation - Library (Law)
Place du Petit-Saconnex
C.P. 438 Phone: 227 34 41 50
CH-1211 Geneva 19, Switzerland Peter St. J. Dawe
Founded: 1965. **Subjects:** Structure and working methods of all national parliaments. **Holdings:** 7000 volumes. **Services:** Library open to the public by appointment. **Remarks:** Telex: 28 97 84. **Also Known As:** Centre International de Documentation Parlementaire (CIDP).

★8074★
International Center of Photography - Archives and Collections (Art)
1133 Avenue of the Americas Phone: (212)768-4688
New York, NY 10036 Miles Barth, Cur., Archv. & Coll.
Founded: 1979. **Staff:** Prof 2. **Subjects:** Photography - 20th century, artistic, social, political, documentary, photojournalism. **Special Collections:** Photography in the Fine Arts, 1959-1968; Jacob Deschin Collection (original photographic prints; audiotapes of interviews with photographers and members of the photographic community; clipping books of copies of his reviews for the New York Times; personal correspondence); original manuscripts and letters of photographers. **Holdings:** 15,000 original photographic prints; 2500 hours of audiotape interviews and lectures; 250 hours of film and videotape; catalogs of auctions and other photography collections. **Services:** Open to the public by appointment. **Computerized Information Services:** Internal database. **Remarks:** FAX: (212)360-6490.

★8075★
International Center of Photography - Library Resource Center (Art)
1130 Fifth Ave. Phone: (212)860-1778
New York, NY 10128 Lucia Siskin, Libn.
Founded: 1975. **Staff:** Prof 2. **Subjects:** Photography, critical writing on photography. **Special Collections:** Literature of Photography series (58 volumes); Life Magazine collection (bound; complete set); archives; photograph collections (photographs by Lewis Hine, Weegee, Picture Post Magazine, Jacob Riis, Andreas Feininger, Aaron Siskind, Werner Bischof, Elliott, Lucien Aigner, Ernst Haas, Marc Riboud, Robert Capa, and Cornell Capa); Literature of Photography (complete set); Afterimage set; OCTOBER (complete set). **Holdings:** 6000 books; 15 bound periodical volumes; 10,000 unbound volumes of American photography periodicals and journals; 500 museum catalogs; 150 auction catalogs; 6000 clipping files on photographers with biographical data from primary materials; 10,000 slides; 7000 photographs; 700 hours of audiotapes; 50 videotapes; 15 AV programs; 40 16mm films; critical essays. **Subscriptions:** 75 journals and other serials. **Services:** Copying; center open to the public by appointment. **Publications:** Annual Reports - to patrons and donors. **Remarks:** FAX: (212)360-6490. **Staff:** Phil Block, Dir., Educ.

International Centre for Research on Language Planning
See: **Universite Laval** (18067)

★8076★
International Center for Research on Women - Resource Center (Soc Sci)
1717 Massachusetts Ave., N.W., Suite 302 Phone: (202)797-0007
Washington, DC 20036 Patricia Martin, Prog.Asst.
Staff: Prof 12; Other 8. **Subjects:** Women's issues - credit, income generation, development projects, access to agricultural extension services, survival strategies, heads of households, structural adjustment, recession, maternal health, child welfare, women's health. **Holdings:** 2000 books; 8500 other cataloged items. **Subscriptions:** 75 journals and other serials. **Services:** Interlibrary loan; library open to the public by appointment. **Automated Operations:** INMAGIC. **Remarks:** FAX: (202)797-0020.

★8077★
International Centre for Theoretical Physics - Library (Sci-Engr)
Strada Costiera 11
C.P. 586 Phone: 40 22401
I-34100 Trieste, Italy Maria Zingarelli, Libn.
Founded: 1964. **Subjects:** Physics - high energy, condensed matter, plasma, atomic, nuclear; applied mathematics; physics of the earth; atmosphere and oceans. **Holdings:** 80,000 volumes. **Subscriptions:** 1200 scientific journals; 20 newspapers. **Services:** Interlibrary loan; library not open to the public. **Computerized Information Services:** Electronic mail. **Remarks:** Jointly maintained by the International Atomic Energy Agency and UNESCO. FAX: 40 224163. Telex: 460392.

★8078★
International Center for Tropical Agriculture - Information Unit (Agri)
Apdo. Aereo 6713 Phone: 23 675050
Cali, Colombia Elizabeth Goldberg, Hd., Info. Unit
Founded: 1969. **Staff:** 29. **Subjects:** Agricultural technology, germplasm development on beans, cassava, rice, tropical pastures, management of natural resources on hillsides, forest margins, savannah ecosystems. **Special Collections:** CINFOS collection (literature on common beans, cassava, and tropical pastures). **Holdings:** 40,000 volumes. **Subscriptions:** 2165 journals and other serials; 8 newspapers. **Services:** Copying; SDI; library open to the public for reference use only. **Automated Operations:** Computerized cataloging and serials. **Computerized Information Services:** DIALOG Information Services, AGLINET, IAALD; CD-ROMs (AGRICOLA, AGRIS, CAB, FSTA, SESAME, TREECD, BIOSIS, TROPAG); DIALMAIL, BITNET (electronic mail services). **Remarks:** FAX: 23 647243. Telex: 05769 CIAT CO. Electronic mail address(es): 57:CGI302, CGI301 (DIALMAIL); UNIDINFO CIATCOL (BITNET). Member of the Consultative Group on International Agricultural Research. **Also Known As:** Centro Internacional de Agricultura Tropical. **Staff:** Piedad Montano; Hernan Poveda; Jorge Lopez; Marinao Mejia; Alicia Misas; Lynn Menendez; Zeneire Cadena; Nora Rizo; Gilma Moreno; Patricia Cruz; Marlene Cardenas; Marleny Saenz; LuzMarina Alvare.

★8079★
International Child Resource Institute - Information Clearinghouse (Soc Sci)
1810 Hopkins Phone: (510)644-1000
Berkeley, CA 94707 Susan Gordon, Off.Mgr.
Founded: 1981. **Subjects:** Children - health, abuse, care, advocacy. **Holdings:** 10,000 pieces of information. **Services:** Clearinghouse open to the public. **Computerized Information Services:** CRIB (internal database); PeaceNet (electronic mail service). Performs searches on fee basis for nonmembers. **Remarks:** FAX: (510)525-4106. Electronic mail address(es): icri@igc.org (PeaceNet).

★8080★
International Children's Centre - Documentation Department (Soc Sci)
Chateau de Longchamp
Bois de Boulogne Phone: 1 45207992
F-75016 Paris, France Daniel Baudin, Mgr., Doc.Dept.
Founded: 1950. **Staff:** Prof 8. **Subjects:** Childhood and adolescence - emotional, nutritional, health, educational, social, and allied topics, with emphasis on developing countries; mother and child health. **Holdings:** 16,000 items. **Subscriptions:** 400 journals and other serials. **Services:** Services open to the public. **Computerized Information Services:** Produces Robert Debre Information Base (BIRD) and corresponding CD-ROM. **Publications:** Children in the Tropics; Children and AIDS; Children and Television; specific bibliographic bulletins. **Remarks:** FAX: 1 45257367. Telex: CIENFAN 648 379. **Also Known As:** Centre International de l'Enfance; Centro Internacional de la Infancia.

★8081★
International City Management Association - Library (Soc Sci)
777 North Capitol St., N.E., Suite 500 Phone: (202)289-ICMA
Washington, DC 20002-4201 Elena O. Mina, Libn.
Founded: 1972. **Staff:** Prof 1; Other 1. **Subjects:** Municipal government and management, public administration. **Special Collections:** City budgets; annual reports and comprehensive plans; ICMA Archives; council-manager form of government. **Holdings:** 3000 books; 2000 monographs and reports; 60 VF drawers. **Subscriptions:** 250 journals and other serials. **Services:** Interlibrary loan; copying; library open to the public by appointment.

★8082★
International Civil Aviation Organization - Library (Trans)
1000 Sherbrooke St., W. Phone: (514)286-6232
Montreal, PQ, Canada H3A 2R2 Mrs. M.C. Tuduri
Founded: 1947. **Staff:** 4. **Subjects:** Aeronautics, aviation medicine, airports, air law, international law, international organizations, telecommunications, meteorology, maps and charts. **Special Collections:** Academie de Droit International Recueil, 1923 to present; Commission Internationale de Navigation Aerienne, 1922-1947; Institut du Transport Aerien (ITA) Collection; United Nations Treaty Series, 1946 to present; United Nations and Specialized Agencies Documents (2-5 years); International Organizations Documents (2-5 years); Member-States Governments, Civil Aviation Economic and Technical Publications. **Holdings:** 16,500 books. **Subscriptions:** 164 journals and other serials; 10 newspapers. **Services:** Interlibrary loan; library open to the public. **Publications:** Library Information - Recent Accessions and Selected Articles, bimonthly. **Special Indexes:** Index of ICAO publications (annual cumulation).

★8083★
International Civil Defence Organization - Documentation Center (Soc Sci)
10-12, Chemin de Surville
Petit-Lancy
CH-1213 Geneva, Switzerland Phone: 22 7934433
Founded: 1958. **Staff:** 1. **Subjects:** Civil defense - organization, training, equipment, protection, legislation. **Holdings:** 3000 books; 5000 bound periodical volumes; 7000 documents; 50 videotapes. **Subscriptions:** 200 journals and other serials. **Services:** Copying; SDI; library open to the public. **Computerized Information Services:** Internal database. **Remarks:** FAX: 22 7934428. Telex: 423 786 ch. **Also Known As:** Organizacion Internacional de Proteccion Civil; Organisation Internationale de Protection Civile.

International Clarinet Society Research Center
See: **University of Maryland, College Park Libraries - Music Library** (18821)

★8084★
International Coffee Organization - Library (Food-Bev, Bus-Fin)
22 Berners St. Phone: 71 5808591
London W1P 4DD, England C.P.R. Dubois, MA, MBCS
Founded: 1963. **Staff:** 3. **Subjects:** Coffee - production, price fluctuation, consumption, technology, physiological effects; economic development of coffee-producing countries. **Holdings:** 20,000 volumes; 10,000 slides. **Subscriptions:** 250 journals and other serials. **Services:** Copying; library open to the public by appointment. **Computerized Information Services:** DIALOG Information Services; produces COFFEELINE (26,000 bibliographic records). **Publications:** Library Monthly Entries. **Remarks:** FAX: 71 5806129. Telex: 267659 INTCAF G. **Also Known As:** Organisation Internationale du Cafe. **Staff:** Mrs. A.M. Tradnock.

★8085★
International Columbian Quincentenary Alliance, Ltd. - Christopher Columbus Library (Hist)
P.O. Box 1492 Phone: (609)859-3154
Columbus, NJ 08022 Joseph M. Laufer, Dir.
Founded: 1986. **Staff:** 1. **Subjects:** Christopher Columbus, discovery of America, Age of Discovery, Columbian Expo of 1893, Quincentenary of 1992, Spanish conquest. **Special Collections:** Earliest biographies of Christopher Columbus (25 books); Chicago Columbian Expo (10 books; memorabilia); periodicals dealing with 1992 Quincentenary. **Holdings:** 200 books; 6 bound periodical volumes; 6 documents; 10 AV programs; 30 nonbook items; 5 manuscripts. **Services:** Copying; library open to the public by appointment. **Publications:** Discovery Five Hundred (newsletter); leaflets. **Remarks:** Library was created in anticipation of the 500th anniversary of the discovery of America by Christopher Columbus, to be celebrated in 1992. **Remarks:** FAX: (609)859-1746.

★8086★
International Committee of the Red Cross - Library (Law)
19 Avenue de la Paix
CH-1202 Geneva, Switzerland Phone: 22 7346001
Founded: 1864. **Staff:** Prof 1.5; Other 1. **Subjects:** Red Cross and Red Crescent Movement, public interest laws, international humanitarian law. **Holdings:** 16,000 books. **Subscriptions:** 200 journals and other serials. **Services:** Interlibrary loan; copying; library open to the public. **Publications:** Acquisitions list.

International Cooperation Center of Agricultural Research for Development - Center for the Study and Experimentation of Tropical Agricultural Machinery
See: **Centre de Cooperation Internationale en Recherche Agronomique pour le Developpement - Centre d'Information et de Documentation en Agronomie des Regions Chaudes** (3224)

★8087★
International Cooperation Center of Agricultural Research for Development - Institute of Research on Fruits and Citrus Fruits - Documentation Center (Agri)
B.P. 5035 Phone: 67 615800
F-34032 Montpellier Cedex 1, France Bernard Moreau, Hd.
Founded: 1945. **Staff:** Prof 6; Other 1. **Subjects:** Tropical and subtropical fruits, temperate fruits under tropical climate - general, culture, transport, derivative products, economics, technology. **Holdings:** 5000 bound volumes; 4500 booklets; microfilm. **Subscriptions:** 250 journals and other serials. **Services:** Copying; SDI; library open to the public. **Publications:** Fruits, monthly. **Remarks:** FAX: 67 615871. Telex: 485631 IRFAMON or IRFAGRU 610992F. **Also Known As:** Centre de Cooperation Internationale en Recherche Agronomique pour le Developpement - Institut de Recherches sur les Fruits et Agrumes - Centre de Documentation. **Staff:** Arlette Champion; Chantal Cabot; Elinor Lipman

★8088★
International Copper Research Association, Inc. - Library (Sci-Engr)
708 Third Ave.
New York, NY 10017 Phone: (212)697-9355
Founded: 1960. **Subjects:** Metallurgy, chemistry, mining. **Special Collections:** Complete set of the association's project reports (300 volumes). **Holdings:** Figures not available. **Services:** Library not open to the public.

★8089★
International Copyright Information Center (Law)
c/o Association of American Publishers
1718 Connecticut Ave., N.W. Phone: (202)232-3335
Washington, DC 20009 Carol A. Risher, Dir.
Founded: 1971. **Subjects:** Copyright law. **Holdings:** Figures not available. **Services:** Center not open to the public. **Remarks:** Maintained by the Association of American Publishers. Center assists publishers in the U.S. and Third World countries with negotiations for reprint and translation rights and other copyright matters. FAX: (202)745-0694. Telex: 6975774. Electronic mail address(es): Carol Risher (MCI Mail).

★8090★
International Council for Bird Preservation - Library (Env-Cons)
32 Cambridge Rd.
Girton Phone: 223 277318
Cambridge CB3 0PJ, England Alison Stattersfield, Res.Off.
Founded: 1980. **Staff:** 1.25. **Subjects:** Ornithology, conservation, wildlife. **Special Collections:** Threatened birds reprint collection. **Holdings:** 1000 books. **Subscriptions:** 200 journals and other serials. **Services:** Library open to researchers by appointment only. **Special Catalogs:** Slide library catalog (online). **Remarks:** FAX: 223 277200. Telex: 818794 ICBPG.

★8091★
International Council of Environmental Law - Library (Law, Env-Cons)
Adenauerallee 214 Phone: 228 2692240
W-5300 Bonn 1, Germany Eric S. Howard, Info.Off.
Staff: 3. **Subjects:** Environmental law, environmental policy and administration. **Holdings:** 30,000 volumes. **Subscriptions:** 200 journals and other serials. **Services:** Library not open to the public. **Computerized Information Services:** Environmental Law Information System (ELIS) (internal database). **Publications:** References to Environmental Law and Policy Literature. **Remarks:** FAX: 228 2692250. **Also Known As:** Conseil International du Droit de l'Environnement.

★8092★
International Council for the Exploration of the Sea - Library (Biol Sci)
Palaegrade 2-4 Phone: 3 1154225
DK-1261 Copenhagen K, Denmark E.M. Thomasson
Founded: 1902. **Staff:** Prof 1. **Subjects:** Fisheries, oceanography, marine science, marine pollution. **Special Collections:** ICES Council Meeting papers (bound; 1964 to present). **Holdings:** 100 books; 15,000 periodical volumes; 100 reports; archives. **Subscriptions:** 250 journals and other serials. **Services:** Interlibrary loan; copying; library open to the public. **Publications:** List of Contributions; Annual Report. **Special Catalogs:** Publications Catalogue, annual.

International Council of Museums
See: **United Nations Educational, Scientific and Cultural Organization - International Council of Museums** (16765)

★8093★
International Council of Shopping Centers - Library/Information Center (Bus-Fin)
665 Fifth Ave. Phone: (212)421-8181
New York, NY 10022 Susan A. Pistilli, Res.Lib.Mgr.
Staff: Prof 1; Other 1. **Subjects:** Shopping centers - development, management, marketing, law, design. **Holdings:** 1500 books; AV programs. **Subscriptions:** 70 journals and other serials; 8 newspapers. **Services:** Copying; library open to members by appointment and open to the public by appointment for fee. **Computerized Information Services:** DIALOG Information Services.

★8094★
International Crane Foundation - Ron Savey Library for Bird Conservation (Biol Sci)
E-11376 Shady Lane Rd. Phone: (608)356-9462
Baraboo, WI 53913-9778 Scott Swengel, Asst.Cur. of Birds
Founded: 1973. **Subjects:** Cranes, bird conservation. **Holdings:** 5000 manuscripts; 1000 books, articles and clippings about crane research, captive propagation, habitat developments throughout the world. **Subscriptions:** 50 journals and other serials. **Services:** Library open to the public with permission of administrator. **Remarks:** FAX: (608)356-9465.

★8095★
International Crops Research Institute for the Semi-Arid Tropics - Semi-Arid Tropical Crops Information Service (Agri)
Patancheru 502324, Andhra Pradesh, India Phone: 224016
L.J. Haravu, Lib. & Doc.Serv.
Founded: 1987. **Staff:** Prof 5. **Subjects:** Sorghum, millets, chickpea, pigeonpea, groundnut, farming systems in the semi-arid tropics. **Holdings:** 12,700 bound volumes. **Subscriptions:** 525 journals and other serials. **Services:** SDI; service open to researchers in related subject areas. **Computerized Information Services:** AGRIS, CABI; AGRICOLA (CD-ROM); SATCRIS (internal database); Dialcom, Inc. (electronic mail service). **Publications:** Chickpeas and Pigeonpeas, quarterly; Groundnuts, quarterly; Surghum and Millet Abstracts, bimonthly. **Remarks:** FAX: 241239; 9198420. Telex: 422203 ICRI IN; 4256366 ICRI IN. Electronic mail address(es): 157:CGI505 (Dialcom, Inc.).

★8096★
International Data Corp. - Information Center (Comp Sci)
5 Speen St. Phone: (508)935-4253
Framingham, MA 01701 Merrill H. Walsh, Mgr.
Founded: 1970. **Staff:** Prof 1; Other 1. **Subjects:** Computer technology, finance. **Holdings:** 600 books; 300 annual reports; 3000 company files; 250 subject files. **Subscriptions:** 300 journals and other serials. **Services:** Interlibrary loan; center not open to the public. **Computerized Information Services:** DIALOG Information Services, Dow Jones News/Retrieval. **Publications:** Library News; Article Alert; Subject Alert; Reference Highlights; Focus. **Remarks:** FAX: (508)935-4015. Telex: 95 1168.

★8097★
International Development Research Centre - Library (Soc Sci)
P.O. Box 8500
Ottawa, ON, Canada K1G 3H9 Phone: (613)236-6163
Founded: 1971. **Staff:** Prof 8; Other 14. **Subjects:** International development, including agriculture, food, nutrition, population, health; information science; social sciences. **Holdings:** 45,000 books. **Subscriptions:** 4200 journals and other serials; 38 newspapers. **Services:** Interlibrary loan; copying; library open to the public with restrictions. **Automated Operations:** Computerized cataloging, acquisitions, and serials. **Computerized Information Services:** DIALOG Information Services, PFDS Online, QL Systems, MEDLINE, CAN/OLE, BRS Information Technologies, IST-Informatheque Inc., Info Globe, International Labour Office, United Nations Food and Agriculture Organization, United Nations Educational, Scientific and Cultural Organization, United Nations Industrial Development Organization (UNIDO); USAID, IDRIS (internal databases). **Publications:** Ex Libris (accessions list), monthly.

★8098★
International Diabetes Center - Library (Med)
5000 W. 39th St. Phone: (612)927-3393
Minneapolis, MN 55416 Helen R. Bowlin, Dir., Sys.Dev.
Subjects: Diabetes mellitus, patient education. **Holdings:** 500 books. **Subscriptions:** 15 journals and other serials. **Services:** Interlibrary loan; library not open to the public. **Publications:** List of publications - available on request.

★8099★
International District Heating and Cooling Association - Library (Sci-Engr)
1101 Connecticut Ave., N.W. Phone: (202)429-5111
Washington, DC 20006 David F. Hobson, Exec.Dir.
Subjects: District heating. **Holdings:** 600 volumes. **Services:** Library not open to the public. **Remarks:** FAX: (202)429-5113.

★8100★
International Documentation Center for Industries Using Agricultural Products (Food-Bev)
Ave. des Olympiades Phone: 1 69209738
F-91300 Massy Cedex, France Gisele Carra, Dir.
Founded: 1967. **Staff:** 10. **Subjects:** Food - science, technology, economics; industrial utilization of agricultural products and by-products. **Holdings:** 6000 bound volumes; 135,000 microfiche. **Subscriptions:** 800 journals and other serials. **Services:** SDI; current awareness; microfiche reproduction; document delivery. **Computerized Information Services:** Produces IALINE database (available online through Questel). Performs searches on fee basis. **Publications:** Abstracts journal. **Remarks:** FAX: 1 60117585. Center receives support from the French Ministry of Agriculture. **Also Known As:** Centre de Documentation Internationale des Industries Utilisatrices de Produits Agricoles.

★8101★
International Electrophoresis Society - Library (Sci-Engr)
P.O. Box 279 Phone: (301)898-3772
Walkersville, MD 21793 Janet Cunningham, Exec.Dir.
Founded: 1980. **Subjects:** Scientific advancement in electrophoretic theory and applications. **Holdings:** Historical and archival materials. **Subscriptions:** 400 journals and other serials. **Services:** Library not open to the public. **Publications:** Applied and Theoretical Electrophoresis (journal). **Remarks:** FAX: (301)898-5596.

★8102★
International Exchangors Association - Library (Bus-Fin)
Drawer L
Rancho Santa Fe, CA 92067 A.D. Kessler, Chm.
Founded: 1978. **Subjects:** Education, law, and tax aspects of real estate exchanging. **Holdings:** 168 volumes.

★8103★
International Fabricare Institute - Library (Sci-Engr)
12251 Tech Rd. Phone: (301)622-1900
Silver Spring, MD 20904 B. Leppin, Dir., Tech.Serv.
Staff: 1. **Subjects:** Chemistry, textiles, dry cleaning, laundering. **Special Collections:** Periodicals pertaining to dry cleaning and laundry industries. **Subscriptions:** 15 journals and other serials 5 newspapers. **Services:** Library open to the public by appointment only. **Remarks:** FAX: (301)236-9320.

★8104★
International Federation of Family Life Promotion - Library (Soc Sci)
1511 K St., N.W., Suite 326 Phone: (202)783-0137
Washington, DC 20005 Richard Sevigny
Founded: 1974. **Staff:** 1. **Subjects:** Natural family planning, sexuality. **Holdings:** 1000 books; 5 bound periodical volumes; 250 reports. **Subscriptions:** 20 journals and other serials; 4 newspapers. **Services:** Library open to the public by appointment. **Publications:** Listings of Natural Family Planning Centers (worldwide); NFP reports; Congress Proceedings. **Remarks:** FAX: (202)783-7351. Telex: 497-2704 FIDAF.

★8105★
International Federation of Petroleum and Chemical Workers - Library (Bus-Fin)
Box 6603 Phone: (303)388-9237
Denver, CO 80206 Curtis J. Hogan, Gen.Sec.
Founded: 1964. **Staff:** 1. **Subjects:** International trade unions, petroleum unions, industrial relations and International Labor Organization (ILO). **Special Collections:** ILO publications. **Holdings:** 1500 books. **Subscriptions:** 12 journals and other serials; 38 newspapers. **Services:** Interlibrary loan; copying; library open to the public by appointment.

★8106★
International Fertilizer Development Center - Library (Agri)
Wilson Dam Rd.
TVA Reservation
Box 2040 Phone: (205)381-6600
Muscle Shoals, AL 35662 Jean S. Riley, Libn.
Founded: 1977. **Staff:** Prof 1; Other 1. **Subjects:** Fertilizers, agricultural economics, nutrient management. **Special Collections:** Country file. **Holdings:** 4000 books; 1382 bound periodical volumes; 5919 pamphlets; 252 AV programs; 837 patents. **Subscriptions:** 262 journals and other serials. **Services:** Interlibrary loan; library not open to the public. **Automated Operations:** Computerized cataloging, acquisitions, circulation, and journal routing. **Computerized Information Services:** DIALOG Information Services, STN International, OCLC; internal databases. **Publications:** Library Bulletin, quarterly - for internal distribution only. **Remarks:** FAX: (205)381-7408. Telex: 810-731-3970 IFDEC MCHL.

★8107★
International Festivals Association - Library (Bus-Fin)
PO Box 2950 Phone: (206)457-3141
Port Angeles, WA 98362 Carolyn Pendergast, Asst.Exec.Dir.
Founded: 1960. **Staff:** Prof 4. **Subjects:** Management, civic and nonprofit festival organizations. **Special Collections:** Videotapes of major festival events. **Holdings:** 150 volumes. **Services:** Library open to members only. **Remarks:** FAX: (206)452-4695. **Formerly:** Located in Pasadena, CA.

★8108★
International Flavors and Fragrances, Inc. - Technical Information Center (Sci-Engr)
1515 Hwy. 36 Phone: (908)888-2435
Union Beach, NJ 07735 Bernard J. Mayers, Sr.Tech.Info.Sci.
Founded: 1952. **Staff:** Prof 2; Other 3. **Subjects:** Organic chemistry, essential oils, flavors, perfumery, spectroscopy. **Holdings:** 6000 volumes; 400 VF drawers of internal research reports; 5500 reels of microfilm. **Subscriptions:** 200 journals and other serials. **Services:** Center not open to the public. **Computerized Information Services:** DIALOG Information Services, PFDS Online, NLM, STN International. **Remarks:** FAX: (908)888-2657. **Staff:** Kenneth Di Fiore, Chem.Info.Spec.

International Fly Fishing Center
See: **Federation of Flyfishers** (5654)

★8109★
International Food Policy Research Institute - Library (Soc Sci)
1776 Massachusetts Ave., N.W. Phone: (202)862-5614
Washington, DC 20036 Patricia W. Klosky, Libn.
Founded: 1977. **Staff:** 1. **Subjects:** Food policy and research, developmental economics, international trade, agricultural economics and statistics. **Holdings:** 3000 books; 4000 research reports. **Subscriptions:** 160 journals and other serials. **Services:** Interlibrary loan; copying; library open to the public by appointment. **Computerized Information Services:** DIALOG Information Services; CGNET (electronic mail service). **Remarks:** FAX: (202)467-4439. Telex: 440054. Electronic mail address(es): CGI 701 (CGNET).

★8110★
International Foodservice Distributors Association - Library (Food-Bev)
201 Park Washington Ct. Phone: (703)532-9400
Falls Church, VA 22046 Gilbert L. Kretzer, V.P.
Subjects: Food distribution and food service operations. **Holdings:** 250 volumes. **Services:** Library not open to the public.

★8111★
International Fortean Organization - INFO Research Library (Sci-Engr)
P.O. Box 367 Phone: (703)522-9232
Arlington, VA 22210 Raymond D. Manners, Pres.
Founded: 1966. **Staff:** 1. **Subjects:** Philosophy of science, astronomy, archeology, geology, paleontology, medicine, vulcanology, geophysics, scientific anomalies. **Special Collections:** Newspaper clippings on science (1934 to present). **Holdings:** 2000 books; 400 bound periodical volumes. **Subscriptions:** 50 journals and other serials. **Services:** Library open to qualified researchers by appointment. **Computerized Information Services:** Internal database. **Publications:** INFO Journal, quarterly - for INFO members only. **Special Catalogs:** Index to INFO Journal.

★8112★
International Foundation of Employee Benefit Plans - Information Center (Bus-Fin)
18700 W. Bluemound Rd. Phone: (414)786-6700
Brookfield, WI 53005 Dee Birschel, Dir.
Founded: 1970. **Staff:** Prof 5; Other 4. **Subjects:** Employee benefits, insurance, investments, management, economics, collective bargaining. **Holdings:** 11,000 books; 600 bound periodical volumes; 100 VF drawers of documents, clippings; 45 VF drawers of archival materials. **Subscriptions:** 500 journals and other serials; 15 newspapers. **Services:** Copying; SDI; center open to members only. **Automated Operations:** Computerized cataloging, acquisitions, and serials. **Computerized Information Services:** DIALOG Information Services, WESTLAW, Electronic Legislative Search System (ELSS); Employee Benefits InfoSource (internal database). **Networks/Consortia:** Member of Library Council of Metropolitan Milwaukee, Inc. (LCOMM). **Publications:** List of publications - available on request. **Remarks:** FAX: (414)786-2990. **Staff:** Julia E. Miller, Mgr., Tech.Serv.; Patricia Krajnak, Mgr., Ref.Serv.; Kelli Kolsrud, Libn.; Julie Stich, Asst.Libn.

★8113★
International Franchise Association - IFA World Resource Center (Bus-Fin)
1350 New York Ave., N.W., Suite 900 Phone: (202)628-8000
Washington, DC 20005 Terrian C. Barnes, Dir., Res.
Staff: Prof 2. **Subjects:** Franchising. **Holdings:** 100 books; 3 shelves of legal reports and journal articles; 2 VF drawers of annual reports. **Subscriptions:** 50 journals and other serials. **Services:** Interlibrary loan; copying; center open to the public by appointment. **Publications:** List of publications - available on request. **Remarks:** FAX: (202)628-0812. Telex: 323175.

★8114★
International Frankenstein Society - Library (Rec)
Penthouse North
29 Washington Square, W. Phone: (212)982-6754
New York, NY 10011 Dr. Jeanne Youngson, Founder
Founded: 1980. **Staff:** 1. **Subjects:** Mary Wollstonecraft Shelley, Frankenstein, golem. **Holdings:** 250 volumes. **Services:** Library not open to the public.

★8115★
International Game Fish Association - International Library of Fishes (Rec)
3000 E. Las Olas Blvd.
Fort Lauderdale, FL 33316 Phone: (305)467-0161
Founded: 1973. **Staff:** Prof 1; Other 2. **Subjects:** Fish, sport fishing. **Special Collections:** Michael Lerner Collection (photos; papers; films; memorabilia); Joe Brooks Collection (photos; paper prepared for a history of angling; rare books). **Holdings:** 9500 books; fishing club yearbooks and newsletters; 650 fishing films, videos, stamps; photographs; angling artifacts. **Subscriptions:** 700 journals and other serials. **Services:** Library open to the public for reference use only. **Computerized Information Services:** Internal database. **Remarks:** FAX: (305)467-0331. **Staff:** Gail M. Morchower, Libn.

★8116★
International Health and Temperance Association - Library (Soc Sci)
12501 Old Columbia Pike
Silver Spring, MD 20904 Phone: (301)680-6719
Subjects: Social problems - alcohol, tobacco, narcotics; health and temperance - general, history. **Holdings:** 3200 volumes. **Remarks:** FAX: (301)680-6090. Telex: 440186.

★8117★
International Herb Growers and Marketers Association - Library (Biol Sci)
1202 Allanson Rd. Phone: (708)949-4372
Mundelein, IL 60060-3808 Maureen Buehrle, Exec.Dir.
Founded: 1987. **Subjects:** Herbs and allied subjects. **Holdings:** 500 books; 10 bound periodical volumes. **Subscriptions:** 20 journals and other serials. **Services:** Library open to the public by appointment. **Publications:** Herb Grower & Marketer, bimonthly.

★8118★
International Hibernation Society (Biol Sci)
P.O. Box 9059 Phone: (702)784-4874
Reno, NV 89507 Dr. Richard Simmons
Founded: 1960. **Staff:** Prof 1. **Subjects:** Mammalian hibernation. **Holdings:** Over 1200 references. **Services:** Open to public through mail requests. **Publications:** Newsletter, bimonthly - to members. **Formerly:** Located in Rockville, MD.

International Horn Society Archives
See: **Ball State University - Bracken Library - Archives & Special Collections** (1438)

★8119★
International Human Resources, Business and Legal Research Association - Library (Bus-Fin)
Box 9478 Phone: (301)948-5876
Washington, DC 20016 Dr. Maximillien De La Croix, Dir.
Founded: 1981. **Staff:** 12. **Subjects:** International business, human resources education, legal studies. **Holdings:** 21,571 volumes. **Subscriptions:** 210 newspapers. **Services:** Library not open to the public. **Computerized Information Services:** Internal database. **Publications:** List of publications - available on request. **Staff:** Dr. John H. Chen, Sr.Res.Libn.; Dr. Garo Kebabdjian, Media Anl.Libn.; Marna Roanne Wells, Info.Serv.Dir.

★8120★
International Human Rights Law Group - Library (Soc Sci)
1601 Connecticut Ave., N.W., Suite 700 Phone: (202)232-8500
Washington, DC 20009 Mindy Phillips, Adm.Asst.
Founded: 1978. **Staff:** 7. **Subjects:** International human rights law, election observing. **Special Collections:** United Nations Commission on Human Rights; European Commission on Human Rights; Inter-American Commission on Human Rights; Helsinki Accords information; international legal materials; International Election Observing Reports. **Holdings:** Books; newspaper clippings; reports; proceedings. **Services:** Interlibrary loan. **Remarks:** FAX: (202)232-6317.

★8121★
International Information Center and Archives for the Women's Movement (Soc Sci)
Postbus 19504
NL-1000 GM Amsterdam, Netherlands Phone: 20 6244268
Founded: 1935. **Staff:** 17. **Subjects:** Women, women's movement. **Special Collections:** Archives (100 linear meters); photograph collection. **Holdings:** 50,000 books. **Subscriptions:** 575 journals and other serials; 5 newspapers. **Services:** Interlibrary loan; copying; archives open to the public. **Computerized Information Services:** Adlib (internal database). **Remarks:** FAX: 20 6233855. Jointly maintained by Netherlands - Ministry of Social Affairs and University of Amsterdam. Located at Keizersgracht 10, NL-1015 CN Amsterdam. **Staff:** Claire C. Posthumus, Libn.

★8122★
International Information Centre for Terminology - Library (Info Sci)
Austrian Standards Institute
P.O. Box 130 Phone: 1 267535
A-1021 Vienna, Austria Christian Galinski, Dir.
Founded: 1971. **Staff:** 7. **Subjects:** Terminology of all subject fields in all languages. **Holdings:** 1500 bound volumes; magnetic tapes. **Subscriptions:** 100 journals and other serials. **Services:** Current awareness; library open to individuals active in the field of terminology. **Computerized Information Services:** Internal databases; TERMIUM (electronic mail service). **Publications:** Infoterm Newsletter, quarterly; BiblioTerm (current awareness bulletin), quarterly. **Remarks:** Library located at Heinestr. 38, A-1020 Vienna, Austria. FAX: 1 2163272. Telex: 115960 ONORM A. Electronic mail address(es): 8 wga (TERMIUM). **Also Known As:** Infoterm. **Staff:** G. Budin, Dep.Dir.

★8123★
International Information Service Ltd. - Library (Sci-Engr)
Wing On Plaza, Rm. 103
Tsimshatsui East Phone: 3 7391818
Kowloon, Hong Kong Mr. Chiu Nam Shum, Dp.Mng.Dir.
Founded: 1981. **Staff:** 6. **Subjects:** China - science and technology, trade, economics. **Holdings:** 300 bound volumes. **Subscriptions:** 160 journals and other serials. **Services:** FAXing; library open to the public. **Computerized Information Services:** China Economic Database (internal database). Performs searches on fee basis. **Publications:** China Database: Economics and Foreign Trade, monthly; World's New Technical Products, in Chinese; International, bimonthly. **Remarks:** FAX: 3 7213692. Telex: 30431 NTEDL HX.

International Institute of Agriculture Library
See: **United Nations - Food and Agriculture Organization - David Lublin Memorial Library** (16752)

★8124★
International Institute for Applied Systems Analysis - Library (Soc Sci)
Schloss Laxenburg
Schlossplatz 1
P.O. Box 40 Phone: 2236 71521
A-2361 Laxenburg, Austria Eduard Loeser, Hd.Libn.
Founded: 1973. **Staff:** 4.5. **Subjects:** Applied mathematics, systems analysis, policy studies on global and regional scales, environment, technology. **Holdings:** 40,000 volumes; 930 periodicals. **Subscriptions:** 430 periodicals. **Services:** Copying; library open to the public by appointment. **Automated Operations:** Computerized public access catalog. **Computerized Information Services:** DIALOG Information Services, ESA/IRS, Data-Star, STN International, Questel, FT PROFILE, ECHO, BLAISE, DBI, ECONIS, GMD, VINITI, ETHICS, KOALA, INION; BITNET, DIALMAIL (electronic mail services). **Remarks:** FAX: 2236 71521 ext.412. Telex: 079 137 iiasa a.

★8125★
International Institute of Communications - Library (Info Sci)
Tavistock House South
Tavistock Sq.
London WC1H 9LF, England Phone: 71 388 0671
Subjects: Contemporary communication technology - economics, social impact, law, politics; telecommunications; journalism. **Holdings:** 10,000 volumes. **Remarks:** FAX: 71 3800623. Telex: 245 78 IICLDN G.

★8126★
International Institute for Development, Cooperation and Labour Studies - Library (Soc Sci)
7 Neharde'a St.
P.O. Box 16201 Phone: 3 229195
64235 Tel Aviv, Israel Leah Simon Kornbluth, Libn.
Founded: 1958. **Staff:** 1.5. **Subjects:** Developing countries, socio-economic development, rural and community development, cooperation and cooperatives, labor and trade unions. **Holdings:** 17,600 books, pamphlets, and other cataloged items. **Subscriptions:** 300 journals and other serials. **Services:** Library open to the public for reference use only. **Remarks:** Alternate telephone number(s): 3 229196. FAX: 3 222714. Telex: 361480. **Also Known As:** Afro-Asian Institute for Cooperative and Labour Studies. **Staff:** Armand Cohen.

★8127★
International Institute for Educational Planning - Documentation Center (Educ)
7-9, rue Eugene-Delacroix Phone: 1 45037780
F-75116 Paris, France Francoise du Pouget, Libn.
Founded: 1965. **Staff:** 4. **Subjects:** Educational planning; social, economic and political dynamics of educational development. **Holdings:** 35,000 volumes. **Subscriptions:** 600 journals and other serials. **Services:** Library open to professors, specialists, and post-graduate students in education. **Computerized Information Services:** IIEPDOC, EPIDOC (internal databases). **Remarks:** FAX: 1 40728366. Telex: 640032. Institute is part of UNESCO. **Also Known As:** Institut International de Planification de l'Education.

★8128★
International Institute for Environment & Development - Library (Env-Cons)
3 Endsleigh St. Phone: 71 388-2117
London WC1H 0DD, England Rachel Weinstein
Subjects: Environment, development. **Holdings:** Figures not available. **Services:** Copying; library open to the public by appointment.

★8129★
International Institute of Integral Human Sciences - IIHS Library (Rel-Phil)
1974 de Maisonneuve, W. Phone: (514)937-8359
Montreal, PQ, Canada H3H 1K5 Rene Egli, Libn.
Founded: 1975. **Staff:** Prof 1. **Subjects:** Psychical research, world religions, yoga philosophy, healing, oriental medicine, esoteric traditions, comparative mysticism, ancient religions and cultures, consciousness studies. **Holdings:** 10,000 books. **Services:** Copying; library open to members and students. **Also Known As:** Institut International des Sciences Humaines Integrales.

★8130★
International Institute of Islamic Thought - Library (Area-Ethnic)
555 Grove St., Suite 101 Phone: (703)471-1133
Herndon, VA 22070 Yahya Monastra, Libn.
Founded: 1981. **Staff:** 1. **Subjects:** Islam - social sciences, history, jurisprudence; comparative religions; education. **Special Collections:** Hadith, Tafsir, education; Isma'il al-Faruqi's library. **Holdings:** 32,000 volumes. **Subscriptions:** 21 journals and other serials; 3 newspapers. **Services:** Interlibrary loan; library open to the public for reference use only. **Computerized Information Services:** RLIN. **Publications:** al-Nashrah al-Ikhbariyah (Information Bulletin). **Remarks:** FAX: (703)471-3922. Telex: 901153 IIIT WASH. The collection is two-thirds in Arabic and one-third in English.

International Institute for Land Reclamation and Improvement
See: **Netherlands - Ministry of Agriculture, Nature Management and Fisheries - International Institute for Land Reclamation and Improvement - Library** (11403)

★8131★
International Institute for Ligurian Studies - Library (Area-Ethnic)
Museo Bicknell
via Romana, 39 bis
I-18012 Bordighera, Italy Phone: 263601
Subjects: History and archeology of ancient Liguria. **Holdings:** 46,000 volumes. **Also Known As:** Istituto Internazionale di Studi Liguri.

★8132★
International Institute of Municipal Clerks - Management Information Center (Soc Sci)
160 N. Altadena Dr. Phone: (818)795-6153
Pasadena, CA 91107 John J. Hunnewell, Exec.Dir.
Staff: Prof 4; Other 4. **Subjects:** Municipal ordinances, records management. **Special Collections:** Examples of agendas, computers and software programs, minutes, filing systems, records, administration programs from U.S. and Canadian municipalities. **Holdings:** 650 books; 1200 file folders on sample ordinances. **Subscriptions:** 200 journals and other serials. **Services:** Center not open to the public. **Remarks:** FAX: (818)795-6153.

★8133★
International Institute of Refrigeration - Documentary Service (Sci-Engr)
177, Blvd. Malesherbes Phone: 1 42273235
F-75017 Paris, France Louis Lucas, Dir.
Founded: 1908. **Staff:** Prof 3. **Subjects:** Refrigeration, cryogenic systems, heat pumps, cryology, thermodynamics, heat and mass transfer, food science and technology, freeze-drying, cryobiology. **Holdings:** 4700 bound volumes; 60,000 documents. **Services:** Service open to members of the refrigeration and related industries. **Computerized Information Services:** FRIGINTER, FRIDOC (internal databases). Performs searches on fee basis. **Publications:** International Institute of Refrigeration Bulletin, bimonthly; FRIGINTER Consulting Manual; FRIGINTER Thesaurus. **Remarks:** FAX: 1 47631798. Telex: 643269 F. **Also Known As:** Institut International du Froid. **Staff:** Christine Maunier, Libn.

★8134★
International Institute of Social History - Library (Soc Sci)
Cruquiusweg 31 Phone: 20 6685866
NL-1019 AT Amsterdam, Netherlands J. Kloosterman
Founded: 1935. **Staff:** 63. **Subjects:** Social history, working class, labor history. **Holdings:** 1 million volumes; archival items. **Subscriptions:** 3500 journals and other serials. **Services:** Interlibrary loan; copying; library open to the public. **Computerized Information Services:** Geac. **Publications:** Working Papers (series); Guide to the International Archives of the IISH. **Remarks:** FAX: 20 6654181. **Staff:** Ms. M. Yzermans, Info.; Mr. H. Sanders, Pub.Serv.

International Institute for the Study of Human Reproduction - Center for Population & Family Health
See: **Columbia University - Center for Population & Family Health** (4008)

★8135★
International Institute of Tropical Agriculture - Library and Documentation Centre (Agri)
Oyo Rd.
Private Mail Bag 5320 Phone: 22 400300
Ibadan, Oyo, Nigeria Y.A. Adedigba, Hd.
Founded: 1969. **Staff:** Prof 12; Other 16. **Subjects:** Tropical regions - food crops, agricultural research, soil and crop management, farming methods. **Special Collections:** World Report; CGIAR Center's Publications. **Holdings:** 33,000 books and monographs; 33,450 bound periodical volumes; 14,865 microforms; 2655 slides; 30 audio tapes; 145 maps; 22 videocassettes. **Subscriptions:** 1250 journals and other serials. **Services:** Interlibrary loan; copying; SDI; library open to the public. **Automated Operations:** Computerized public access catalog, cataloging, acquisitions, serials, and circulation. **Computerized Information Services:** Automated Library Service for Tropical Agriculture (internal database); CD-ROMs; electronic mail. Performs searches on fee basis. **Publications:** A Guide to Library and Documentation Center; A guide to Library Database: What it does and how to use it; Library and Documentation Center Staff Manual; IITA Publications in Print (1986); A bibliography of yams and genus Dioscorea (2 volumes); Farming Systems in Africa: a working bibliography (book). **Special Catalogs:** Cowpeas (Vigna unguiculata L. Walp) Abstracts of World Literature, Volumes 1-5; IITA: Record of Publications (2 volumes). **Remarks:** Alternate telephone number(s): 22 400318. FAX: 1 611896. Telex: 31417 TROPIB NG. Maintained by the Consultative Group on International Agricultural Research. **Staff:** J.I. Adeyomoye, Prin.Libn., Users' Serv.; F.N. Ubogu, Prin.Libn., Tech.Serv.; O.R. Adeniran, Prin.Libn., Database Dev.; E.A. Adekanye, Cat./Indexer; T.A. Adigun, Cat./Indexer; M.I. Okoh, Acq.Libn.; O.O. Osaniyi, Assoc.Libn., Outreach & SDI; Y. Falua, Asst.Libn., Circ. & Gen.Ref.; A.N. Alimole, Asst.Libn., Bibliog.; S.O. Akinsola, Database Off.; M.A. Aluko, Bindery Supt.

★8136★
International Institute for the Unification of Private Law - Library (Law)
via Panisperna 28 Phone: 6 6841372
I-00184 Rome, Italy Walter Rodino
Founded: 1927. **Staff:** 5. **Subjects:** Unification and harmonization of law in the international community, comparative law, private law, private international law. **Holdings:** 220,000 volumes; 550 periodicals. **Subscriptions:** 550 journals and other serials. **Services:** Copying; library open to the public. **Remarks:** 6 6841394. Telex: 623166.

★8137★
International Joint Commission - Great Lakes Regional Office Library (Env-Cons)
100 Ouellette Ave., 7th Fl. Phone: (519)256-7821
Windsor, ON, Canada N9A 6T3 Patricia Murray, Libn.
Founded: 1975. **Staff:** Prof 1; Other 1. **Subjects:** Great Lakes water quality, resources management, land use, toxic substances, limnology, wastewater treatment. **Special Collections:** Pollution from Land Use Activities Research Group (PLUARG) reports (120); Pollution of Boundary Waters reports, 1951-1970. **Holdings:** 2500 books; 12 VF drawers of clippings and pamphlets; 40,000 technical reports; 70,000 microfiche. **Subscriptions:** 300 journals and other serials. **Services:** Interlibrary loan; copying; library open to the public by appointment. **Automated Operations:** Computerized cataloging. **Computerized Information Services:** Online systems. **Publications:** Reports issued under the Great Lakes Water Quality Agreement 1972/1978, a Bibliography, annual; PLUARG Bibliography, 1980. **Remarks:** Contains the holdings of the Great Lakes Basin Commission - Great Lakes Basin Library. FAX: (519)256-7791.

★8138★
International Joint Commission - Library (Sci-Engr)
100 Metcalfe St., 18th Fl.
Ottawa, ON, Canada K1P 5M1 Phone: (613)995-2984
Staff: 1. **Subjects:** Water resources, international relations involving shared natural resources. **Special Collections:** International Joint Commission reports. **Holdings:** 1500 volumes. **Subscriptions:** 28 journals and other serials. **Services:** Interlibrary loan; copying; library open to the public. **Computerized Information Services:** Envoy 100 (electronic mail service). **Remarks:** FAX: (613)993-5583. Electronic mail address(es): IJC.CMI (Envoy 100).

★8139★
International Labor Office - Washington Branch Library (Soc Sci)
1828 L St., N.W., Suite 801 Phone: (202)653-7652
Washington, DC 20036 James Tisdale, Adm.Asst.
Founded: 1919. **Staff:** 1. **Subjects:** Social and economic development, world employment program, labor statistics, labor-management relations, child labor, women at work, vocational training, occupational safety and health. **Special Collections:** ILO publications; Labor Law Documents, 1919 to present (laws and regulations on labor and social security of more than 100 nations in English translation); International Labor Review, 1919 to present; Labor and Society, 1976 to present; Social and Labor Bulletin, 1973 to present; International Social Security Review, 1963 to present; International Labour Documentation, 1957-1976; World Employment Program Research Working Papers, 1972 to present. **Holdings:** 2500 ILO documents (uncataloged). **Subscriptions:** 12 journals and other serials. **Services:** Copying; library open to the public by appointment. **Remarks:** FAX: (202)653-7687. The main International Labor Office Library, located in Geneva, Switzerland, contains a worldwide collection of 1 million publications and prepares publications and catalogs.

★8140★
International Labor Rights Educational Research Fund - International Labor Rights Clearinghouse (Bus-Fin, Law)
110 Maryland Ave., N.E.
Box 68 Phone: (202)544-7198
Washington, DC 20002 Pharis J. Harvey, Exec.Dir.
Founded: 1986. **Staff:** Prof 1; Other 3. **Subjects:** International labor law, labor rights, child labor practices, labor abuses in foreign countries. **Holdings:** Reports; Congressional hearings; government documents; petitions filed with U.S. Government; videotapes; newspaper reprints; economic studies; bibliographies. **Services:** Interlibrary loan; clearinghouse open to the public. **Computerized Information Services:** PEACENET (electronic mail service). **Publications:** Newsletter - by subscription. **Remarks:** FAX: (202)543-5999. Electronic mail address(es): CDP: LABORRIGHTS (PEACENET).

★8141★
International Laboratory for Research on Animal Diseases - ILRAD Library (Med)
P.O. Box 30709 Phone: 2 632311
Nairobi, Kenya William Umbima, Libn.
Founded: 1975. **Staff:** 5. **Subjects:** Immunology, parasitology, veterinary medicine. **Special Collections:** African tryanosomiasis; East Coast fever. **Holdings:** 3000 volumes. **Subscriptions:** 250 journals and other serials. **Services:** Library open to research workers from universities and research institutes. **Computerized Information Services:** DIALOG Information Services, DIMDI; internal database; BT GOLD (electronic mail service). **Publications:** List of scientific publications; Weekly Alert (current awareness). **Remarks:** Maintained by Consultative Group on International Agricultural Research. FAX: 2 631499. Telex: 22040. Electronic mail address(es): CGUO17 (BT GOLD). **Staff:** Bernard Arachi.

★8142★
International Labour Office - Central Library and Documentation Branch (Bus-Fin)
4, route des Morillons Phone: 22 7996092
CH-1211 Geneva 22, Switzerland Eleanor Frierson, Dir.
Founded: 1919. **Staff:** Prof 30. **Subjects:** Labor relations, labor law, employment, working conditions, vocational training, management, and labor-related aspects of economics, social and rural development, technological change. **Special Collections:** ILO publications, 1919 to present. **Holdings:** 1 million volumes; 47,000 microfiche; 1200 reels of microfilm. **Subscriptions:** 7000 journals and other serials. **Services:**

Interlibrary loan; copying; SDI; library open to persons engaged in policymaking, planning, or research in social and labor fields. **Computerized Information Services:** ESA/IRS, Human Resource Information Network (HRIN), PFDS Online; produces LABORDOC. Performs searches free of charge. Contact Person: Andy Jesse, Lib.Sys.Coord., 799 86 28. **Publications:** International Labour Documentation (abstracting journal), monthly; occasional bibliographies; ILO Thesaurus. **Special Catalogs:** Subject Guide to Publications of the International Labour Office, 1980-1985 (1987). **Special Indexes:** Register of Periodicals in the ILO Library, semiannual update (microfiche). **Remarks:** FAX: 22 7988685. Telex: 415647 ILO CH. **Staff:** Laura Alpern, Proc.Coord.; Liliana Canadas, External Info.Serv.Coord.; Laurel Dryden, Info.Serv.Coord.; Sue Luzy, Terminology Coord.; Andy Jesse, Lib.Sys.Coord.

★8143★
International Ladies' Garment Workers Union - Research Department Library (Bus-Fin)
1710 Broadway Phone: (212)265-7000
New York, NY 10019 Walter Mankoff, Assoc.Dir. of Res.
Founded: 1937. **Staff:** Prof 1. **Subjects:** Earnings and hours, employment and payrolls, fringe benefits, labor and labor statistics, old-age insurance, social insurance, trade unions, unemployment insurance, union agreements, wearing apparel industry, women's clothing industry. **Holdings:** 14,000 volumes; 75 VF drawers. **Subscriptions:** 155 journals and other serials; 6 newspapers. **Services:** Library open to the public with restrictions.

★8144★
International Law Students Association - Information Center (Law)
2223 Massachusetts Ave., N.W. Phone: (202)265-4375
Washington, DC 20008-2864 Brett Lorenzen, Exec.Dir.
Staff: 2. **Subjects:** International law and legal education. **Special Collections:** Philip C. Jessup International Law Moot Court Competition (past problems and judges' memoranda). **Holdings:** 22,000 items. **Subscriptions:** 250 journals and other serials. **Services:** Center open to the public for reference use only. **Remarks:** FAX: (202)797-7133.

★8145★
International Lead Zinc Research Organization - Library (Sci-Engr)
Box 12036 Phone: (919)361-4647
Research Triangle Park, NC 27709-2036 Eustace Reid, Mgr., Lib.Serv.
Subjects: Metals. **Holdings:** 1500 volumes. **Services:** Library not open to the public. **Remarks:** FAX: (919)361-1957. Telex: 261533.

International Library of African Music
See: **Wayne State University - Folklore Archive** (20120)

★8146★
International Library, Archives & Museum of Optometry (Med)
243 N. Lindbergh Blvd. Phone: (314)991-0324
St. Louis, MO 63141 Bridget Kowalczyk, Libn.
Founded: 1902. **Staff:** 6. **Subjects:** Vision, optometry, ophthalmology. **Special Collections:** Early optometric publications; Archives of the American Optometric Association; early eyeglasses and optical instruments. **Holdings:** 10,000 books; 400 feet of archives. **Subscriptions:** 450 journals and other serials. **Services:** Interlibrary loan; copying; library open to the public. **Automated Operations:** Computerized public access catalog. **Computerized Information Services:** BRS Information Technologies. **Networks/Consortia:** Member of Association of Visual Science Librarians (AVSL), National Network of Libraries of Medicine - Midcontinental Region. **Publications:** Visionlink (newsletter), monthly; Calendar of Meetings, quarterly - both by subscription. **Remarks:** FAX: (314)991-4101. **Staff:** Sandra Smith, Asst.Libn.; Linda Draper, Cat.Libn.: Helen Staehle, Coll.Dev.; Aileen Fish, Ser.Coord.; Joan Nohova, Circ.Coord.

International Library of Fishes
See: **International Game Fish Association** (8115)

★8147★
International Literary and Information Centre in Science Extension - Library (Publ)
P.O. Box 225
H-1476 Budapest, Hungary Phone: 1 1560498
Founded: 1987. **Staff:** 2. **Subjects:** Publishers of printed and videotaped works in science, the arts, and humanities. **Holdings:** 1500 bound volumes; 200 videotapes. **Services:** Library open to the public for reference use only. **Computerized Information Services:** Information in Science Extension (internal database). Performs searches on fee basis. **Publications:** Abstract Review in Science Extension, monthly. **Remarks:** FAX: 1 1553779. Telex: 227836.

★8148★
International Livestock Centre for Africa - Documentation Centre (Agri)
P.O. Box 5689 Phone: 1 183215
Addis Ababa, Ethiopia Azab Abraham, Libn.
Founded: 1977. **Staff:** Prof 9; Other 11. **Subjects:** Livestock production - forage plant production, ecology, economics, sociology. **Holdings:** 40,000 volumes; 25,000 microfiche. **Subscriptions:** 1200 journals and other serials. **Services:** SDI; center open to non-African users on fee basis. **Computerized Information Services:** Internal database. Performs searches on fee basis. **Publications:** Accessions bulletin, quarterly; bibliographies, irregular; photomap acquisitions, irregular. **Remarks:** FAX: 1 513284. Telex: 21207.

★8149★
International Longshoremen's and Warehousemen's Union - Anne Rand Research Library (Bus-Fin)
1188 Franklin St. Phone: (415)775-0533
San Francisco, CA 94109 Gene Vrana, Res.Libn.
Founded: 1946. **Staff:** Prof 1. **Subjects:** Trade unions, longshoremen, shipping, sugar, collective bargaining, pensions, welfare. **Special Collections:** Union archives. **Holdings:** 3000 books; 450 VF drawers; 300 boxes. **Subscriptions:** 100 journals and other serials; 65 newspapers. **Services:** Library open to the public with restrictions. **Remarks:** FAX: (415)775-1302.

★8150★
International Maledicta Society - Maledicta: International Research Center for Verbal Aggression - Archives (Soc Sci)
P.O. Box 14123 Phone: (707)523-4761
Santa Rosa, CA 95402-6123 Dr. Reinhold A. Aman, Pres.
Founded: 1965. **Staff:** Prof 1. **Subjects:** Verbal aggression, slurs, insults, name-calling, blasphemy, scatology, sexual terminology, value judgments, language. **Holdings:** 2000 books; 17,000 pages of book and article manuscripts; 6000 newspaper clippings; 15 theses and dissertations; 5500 bibliography cards. **Subscriptions:** 20 journals and other serials. **Services:** Archives not open to the public. **Computerized Information Services:** Dictionary of Regional Anatomical Terms (internal database). Performs searches on fee basis. **Publications:** Maledicta: The International Journal of Verbal Aggression, annual - by subscription; Maledicta Monitor (newsletter), quarterly; books; originals; reprints.

International Marine Archives
See: **Old Dartmouth Historical Society - Whaling Museum Library** (12383)

★8151★
International Maritime, Inc. - Library (Biol Sci)
839 S. Beacon St., No. 217
San Pedro, CA 90731 Phone: (310)514-8304
Founded: 1959. **Subjects:** Ocean science, technology, and resources development; underwater systems engineering. **Holdings:** 10,000 books, periodicals, and reports. **Subscriptions:** 20 journals and other serials. **Services:** Library not open to the public. **Computerized Information Services:** DIALOG Information Services; internal databases. **Remarks:** Provides technical advice for motion pictures. FAX: (310)514-8380. Telex: 501278 (IMI US). Subsidiaries are Parker Diving Service and Soyuz Marine Service (USSR).

★8152★
International Medical Information Center - Library (Med)
Shoei South Bldg.
4-22-8 Sendagaya
Shibuya-ku Phone: 3 33531358
Tokyo 151, Japan Yasuji Matsuo, Hd., Gen.Aff.Div.
Founded: 1972. **Staff:** 80. **Subjects:** Japan - biomedical and health sciences. **Holdings:** 22,000 books; 800 cassette tapes. **Subscriptions:** 2600 journals and other serials. **Services:** Interlibrary loan; copying; SDI; translation. **Computerized Information Services:** DIALOG Information Services, Japan Information Center for Science and Technology, BRS Information Technologies. Performs searches on fee basis. **Publications:** IMIC Journal, quarterly. **Remarks:** FAX: 3 33513452. Telex: 2323141 IMICJP J.

★8153★
International Microwave Power Institute - Reference Library (Sci-Engr)
13542 Union Village Circle Phone: (703)830-5588
Clifton, VA 22024 Robert C. LaGasse, Exec.Dir.
Founded: 1966. **Subjects:** Microwave power - industrial, scientific, medical, domestic; cooking. **Special Collections:** All publications of the IMPI. **Holdings:** 100 volumes. **Services:** Library not open to the public. **Remarks:** FAX: (703)830-0281.

★8154★
International Military Archives (Mil)
5613 Johnson Ave. Phone: (301)897-0083
Bethesda, MD 20817-3503 Helga K. Knoeppel, Libn.
Founded: 1965. **Staff:** Prof 2. **Subjects:** Paramilitary and military politics, propaganda, history and biography, uniforms and insignia, colors and standards, aircraft and armored vehicles, psychological warfare, weapons systems. **Special Collections:** Elebaut Collection on Adolf Hitler; German World War II military and political photographs. **Holdings:** 600 rare books in German, several hundred in English; negatives and color slides; prints and maps; postage stamp issues; miscellanea. **Services:** Historical research and searching service on a fee basis; picture editing; translation from German; archives not open to the public. **Special Catalogs:** Catalog of surplus books for sale; catalog of photographs available from archives. **Staff:** Lowell Anson Kenyon, Dir.

★8155★
International Minilab Association - Business Library
2627 Grimsley St.
Greensboro, NC 27403
Defunct.

★8156★
International Monetary Fund - Law Library (Law)
700 19th St., N.W.
Washington, DC 20431 Phone: (202)623-7707
Staff: Prof 1; Other 2. **Subjects:** Law - international, constitutional, commercial; conflict of laws; legislation and law reports of member countries. **Special Collections:** Central bank, banking, and monetary laws of member countries. **Holdings:** 55,000 volumes; 122 binders of central bank and banking laws; 123 binders of monetary laws. **Subscriptions:** 220 journals and other serials; 6 newspapers. **Services:** Interlibrary loan (limited); library not open to the public. **Automated Operations:** Computerized cataloging. **Computerized Information Services:** WESTLAW, PHINet FedTax Database, LEXIS; Minisis (internal database). **Publications:** The Digest of the IMF Law Library, monthly - available on request. **Special Catalogs:** Catalog of monographs, periodicals, and law reports (online). **Special Indexes:** Legal journals and annuals currently received (online); banking and monetary laws of member countries (arranged by country; card and binders). **Also Known As:** IMF.

★8157★
International Monetary Fund/World Bank - Joint Bank-Fund Library (Bus-Fin)
700 19th St., N.W. Phone: (202)623-7054
Washington, DC 20431 Peter Hegedus, Chf.Libn.
Founded: 1946. **Staff:** Prof 21.5. **Subjects:** Economic development, international economics, international finance, money and banking. **Holdings:** 200,000 volumes. **Subscriptions:** 4500 journals and other serials; 350 newspapers. **Services:** Interlibrary loan (limited); library open to the public for reference use only by appointment. **Automated Operations:** Computerized cataloging, acquisitions, circulation, indexing, and routing. **Computerized Information Services:** DIALOG Information Services, Dow Jones News/Retrieval, LEGI-SLATE, NEXIS, RLIN, Questel, NewsNet, Inc., OCLC, TEXTLINE, VU/TEXT Information Services, UNBIS; Minisis (internal database). **Networks/Consortia:** Member of CAPCON Library Network. **Publications:** List of Recent Periodical Articles, monthly; The Developing Areas, a Classified Bibliography of the Joint Bank-Fund Library (1975; 3 volumes); IMF Bibliography. **Special Indexes:** Economics and Finance: Index to Periodical Articles, 1947-1971 (1972; 4 volumes); First Supplement, 1972-1974; Second Supplement, 1975-1977. **Remarks:** FAX: (202)623-6417.

★8158★
International Museum of Photography at George Eastman House - Library (Art)
900 East Ave. Phone: (716)271-3361
Rochester, NY 14607 Rachel Stuhlman, Libn.
Founded: 1949. **Staff:** Prof 3. **Subjects:** Photography and cinematography - history, science, aesthetics. **Special Collections:** 19th century books illustrated with photographs (500 volumes); Sipley/3M Collection; Alvin Langdon Coburn Collection; Lewis W. Hine Collection. **Holdings:** 23,000 books; 12,000 bound periodical volumes; 25 VF drawers of history of photography and current activities; 8 taped interviews with photographers; letters and manuscripts. **Subscriptions:** 425 journals and other serials. **Services:** Interlibrary loan; copying; mail reference. **Automated Operations:** Computerized cataloging. **Computerized Information Services:** OCLC. **Publications:** IMAGE, quarterly - to members. **Remarks:** FAX: (716)271-3970. **Staff:** Barbara Schaefer, Cat.; Rebecca Simmons, Assoc.Libn.

★8159★
International Museum of Surgical Science - Library (Med)
1524 N. Lake Shore Dr. Phone: (312)642-6502
Chicago, IL 60610 Linda E. Schubert, Cur.
Founded: 1955. **Staff:** Prof 2. **Subjects:** History of medicine and surgery. **Holdings:** 7000 volumes; 250 manuscripts and letters. **Services:** Library open to the public by appointment for reference use only. **Remarks:** Includes the holdings of the Dr. Max Thorek Library and Manuscript Room. FAX: (312)787-1624.

International Nuclear Information System - Australian Nuclear Science and Technology Organisation
See: **Australia - Australian Nuclear Science and Technology Organisation** (1319)

★8160★
International Numismatic Society - Library (Rec)
1100 17th St., N.W.
Box 66555 Phone: (202)223-4496
Washington, DC 20035 Charles R. Hoskins, Dir.
Founded: 1976. **Staff:** Prof 2; Other 3. **Subjects:** Coins, currency, medals. **Holdings:** 800 books; 400 unbound numismatic publications, 1890-1990. **Subscriptions:** 12 journals and other serials; 3 newspapers. **Services:** Copying; library open to the public with restrictions. **Publications:** INSight, quarterly - to members.

International Nursing Library
See: **Sigma Theta Tau International** (15164)

International Ocean Disposal Symposium
See: **International Ocean Pollution Symposium** (8161)

★8161★
International Ocean Pollution Symposium (Env-Cons)
Department of Oceanography
Florida Institute of Technology Phone: (407)768-8000
Melbourne, FL 32901 Dr. Iver W. Duedall, Chm.
Founded: 1978. **Subjects:** Oceanic waste disposal. **Holdings:** 2300 rare documents and other cataloged items. **Publications:** GESAMP. **Remarks:** FAX: (407)984-8461. **Formerly:** International Ocean Disposal Symposium.

★8162★
International Oil Scouts Association - Library (Sci-Engr)
P.O. Box 272949 Phone: (713)652-5926
Houston, TX 77277-2949 Don Grimm, Treas.
Founded: 1924. **Subjects:** Petroleum. **Holdings:** Figures not available. **Services:** Library open to members, students, and nonprofit organizations. **Publications:** Yearbooks of Petroleum Exploration and Production Statistics, 1930 to present; Oil Scout Directory - both for sale; International Oil and Gas Development Yearbook (annual review); newsletter, quarterly.

★8163★
International Old Lacers, Inc. - Library (Art)
5409 157th Dr., N.E. Phone: (206)885-4876
Redmond, WA 98052 Barbara Larsen
Founded: 1982. **Staff:** 1. **Subjects:** History of lace, lace-making instruction. **Holdings:** 300 volumes. **Services:** Library not open to the public; provides mail service to members.

★8164★
International Olive Oil Council - Library (Food-Bev)
Juan Bravo, 10, Piso 2 Phone: 1 5774735
E-28006 Madrid, Spain Mr. Ferid Abassi
Founded: 1960. **Staff:** 3. **Subjects:** Olives, olive oil. **Special Collections:** Bibliographical archives. **Holdings:** 2500 volumes. **Subscriptions:** 2 journals and other serials. **Services:** Library open to the public upon request. **Computerized Information Services:** Internal database (in progress). **Publications:** Olive Pruning, Table Olive Processing, Olive Oil Quality Improvement & Treatise on Olive Entomology (technical handbooks). **Remarks:** FAX: 1 4316127. Telex: 48197 IOOC E. **Also Known As:** Conseil Oleicole International; Consejo Oleicola Internacional; Consiglio Oleicolo Internazionale.

★8165★
International Ombudsman Institute - I.O.I. Library (Soc Sci)
Faculty of Law
University of Alberta
Edmonton, AB, Canada T6G 2H5 Phone: (403)492-3196
Staff: 1. **Subjects:** Ombudsmanship, human rights, administrative law. **Holdings:** 3000 books; 100 pieces of legislation; 1500 annual reports. **Services:** Copying; library open to the public. **Automated Operations:** Computerized cataloging and serials. **Computerized Information Services:** Internal database. **Publications:** List of publications - available on request. **Remarks:** FAX: (403)492-4924.

★8166★
International Organization for Standardization - ISO Library (Sci-Engr)
1, rue de Varembe
Case Postale 56
CH-1211 Geneva 20, Switzerland Phone: 22 341240
Subjects: International standards - intellectual, scientific, technological, economic. **Holdings:** 100,000 reference works. **Remarks:** FAX: 22 333430. Telex: 412205 ISO CH. Cable: ISORGANIZ. ISO coordinates national standards bodies.

★8167★
International Orienteering Federation, Scientific Group - Library (Rec)
c/o Dr. Roland Seiler
Psychologisches Institut
Deutches Sporthoschule Koln
Carl-Diem-Weg Phone: 221 562480
W-5000 Cologne 41, Germany Dr. Helga Kolb
Founded: 1984. **Subjects:** Orienteering. **Holdings:** 400 volumes. **Also Known As:** Internationale Orientierungslauf Foderation, Wissenschaftliche Arbeitsgruppe.

★8168★
International Paper - Erie Research Center - Technical Library (Sci-Engr)
1540 East Lake Rd.
Box 10050 Phone: (814)870-6304
Erie, PA 16533 Rose Marie Mitchell, Tech.Libn.
Founded: 1966. **Staff:** 1. **Subjects:** Pulp and paper manufacture - natural resources, equipment, processes; chemical and wood by-product recovery; corrosion control; metallurgy; material sciences; air and water pollution control; pulp and paper/construction materials - analytical chemical methods, physical and chemical testing methods. **Special Collections:** American Society for Testing and Materials (ASTM) standards; Technical Association of the Pulp and Paper Industry (TAPPI) standards and test methods. **Holdings:** 1100 books; 6200 bound periodical volumes. **Subscriptions:** 50 journals and other serials. **Services:** Interlibrary loan; library open to the public. **Computerized Information Services:** DIALOG Information Services, PFDS Online. **Remarks:** FAX: (814)870-6367.

★8169★
International Paper - Technical Information Center (Sci-Engr)
Long Meadow Rd. Phone: (914)577-7262
Tuxedo, NY 10987 Bernadette Marasco, Mgr.
Founded: 1969. **Staff:** Prof 2; Other 2. **Subjects:** Pulp and paper, forestry, cellulose chemistry, environment, packaging. **Holdings:** 14,000 volumes; 1500 documents; dissertations. **Subscriptions:** 400 journals and other serials. **Services:** Interlibrary loan; SDI; center open to the public by appointment only. **Computerized Information Services:** DIALOG Information Services, PFDS Online, NLM, NEXIS, OCLC, STN International, OCLC EPIC. **Networks/Consortia:** Member of Southeastern New York Library Resources Council (SENYLRC). **Remarks:** FAX: (914)577-7307.

★8170★
International Paper Company - Corporate Information Center (Sci-Engr)
International Place I
6400 Poplar Ave. Phone: (901)763-6000
Memphis, TN 38197 Carl Mower, Dept.Hd.
Founded: 1962. **Staff:** Prof 1; Other 2. **Subjects:** Pulp, paper, and forest products; plastics; business; finance; marketing; data processing; economics; government; energy; communications; science and technology. **Special Collections:** History of Papermaking collection. **Holdings:** 5180 volumes; 115 VF drawers of annual reports, pamphlets, research materials; 639 reels of microfilm; 14,614 microfiche; 45 audio and video cassettes; maps. **Subscriptions:** 600 journals; 17 newspapers. **Services:** Interlibrary loan; center open to Special Libraries Association members and by appointment. **Automated Operations:** Computerized serials. **Computerized Information Services:** DIALOG Information Services, PFDS Online, Mead Data Central, Dow Jones News/Retrieval, NEXIS, LEXIS. **Networks/Consortia:** Member of New York Metropolitan Reference and Research Library Agency. **Publications:** Acquisitions List, quarterly; periodicals listing; Special Issues, quarterly; Directory of Services. **Remarks:** FAX: (518)654-3487.

★8171★
International Paper Company - Erling Riis Research Laboratory - ERRL Library (Sci-Engr)
Box 2787 Phone: (205)470-3245
Mobile, AL 36652 Eunice H. Torres, Mgr., Tech.Info. & Commun.
Staff: Prof 2. **Subjects:** Wood pulp, paper, cellulose, wood chemistry, forest products, chemical engineering, packaging, printing, pollution. **Special Collections:** National Council of Paper Industry for Air and Stream Improvement technical reports (600); Technical Association of Pulp and Paper Industry Proceedings, 1918 to present. **Holdings:** 8750 books; 3000 bound periodical volumes; 500 pamphlets and translations; 3000 U.S. patents; 1000 Canadian patents. **Subscriptions:** 200 journals and other serials. **Services:** Interlibrary loan; library not open to the public. **Computerized Information Services:** DIALOG Information Services, PFDS Online. **Publications:** Acquisitions list, monthly - for internal distribution only. **Special Indexes:** Internal research reports index and technical reports index (book), annual with 5-year cumulations - for internal distribution only. **Remarks:** FAX: (205)470-3280. **Staff:** Katherine D. Johns, Info.Spec.

International Percussion Reference Library
See: **Arizona State University - Music Library** (1017)

★8172★
International Personnel Management Association - Center for Personnel Research (Bus-Fin)
1617 Duke St. Phone: (703)549-7100
Alexandria, VA 22314 Ann L. Sanders, Coord.
Founded: 1973. **Staff:** Prof 1. **Subjects:** Public human resource management - classification, job analysis, policies and procedures, separation and retirement; wage and salary administration; employee relations; benefits; test development. **Holdings:** 5000 volumes. **Subscriptions:** 2 newsletters. **Services:** Center not open to the public. **Computerized Information Services:** askSam (internal database). **Publications:** IPMA Information Packets, 5/year - to member agencies. **Remarks:** FAX: (703)684-0948.

International Piano Archives at Maryland
See: **University of Maryland, College Park Libraries - Music Library** (18822)

★8173★
International Planned Parenthood Federation - Library (Soc Sci)
Regent's College
Inner Circle
Regent's Park Phone: 71 4860741
London NW1 4NS, England Rita Ward
Founded: 1964. **Staff:** 2. **Subjects:** Family planning, population, sex education, status of women. **Holdings:** 5000 volumes. **Subscriptions:** 70 journals and other serials. **Services:** Interlibrary loan; copying; SDI; library open to the public. **Computerized Information Services:** CD-ROMs (POPLINE, BIRD). **Networks/Consortia:** Member of APLIC International Census Network. **Remarks:** Cable: IPEPEE G LONDON. FAX: 71 4877950. Telex: 919573 IPEPEE G.

★8174★
International Planned Parenthood Federation - Western Hemisphere Region, Inc. - Library (Soc Sci)
902 Broadway, 10th Fl. Phone: (212)995-8800
New York, NY 10010 Abigail Hourwich, Libn.
Staff: Prof 1. **Subjects:** Family planning, population, demography, maternal-child health. **Special Collections:** Population and family planning in Latin America and the Caribbean. **Holdings:** 5000 books; AV programs. **Subscriptions:** 200 journals and other serials. **Services:** Interlibrary loan; copying; center open to the public by appointment. **Computerized Information Services:** MEDLARS. **Networks/Consortia:** Member of APLIC International Census Network, Consortium of Foundation Libraries (CFL), New York Metropolitan Reference and Research Library Agency. **Publications:** FORUM - to family planners in Latin America and the Caribbean; occasional essays and other publications. **Remarks:** FAX: (212)995-8853. Telex: 620661.

International Polar Motion Service - IPMS Library
See: **National Astronomical Observatory, Mizusawa** (11083)

★8175★
International Potato Center - Information Unit (Agri)
P.O. Box 5969 Phone: 14 366920
Lima 100, Peru Carmen Siri, Hd., Info.Sci.Dept.
Founded: 1972. **Staff:** Prof 6. **Subjects:** Potatoes, sweet potatoes. **Holdings:** 8000 bound volumes; 9000 reprints; 1000 annual reports. **Subscriptions:** 90 journals and other serials. **Services:** SDI; document delivery; unit open to potato researchers and others involved in the improvement of potato crops. **Computerized Information Services:** CABI, AGRIS, DIALOG Information Services; Publications Procedures Database, potato literature database (internal databases). Performs searches free of charge except DIALOG Information Services. **Publications:** Acquisitions lists; specialized bibliographies. **Special Catalogs:** Serial catalog. **Remarks:** FAX: 14 351570. Telex: 25672 PE CIPAPA. Center is supported by the Consultative Group on International Agricultural Research. **Also Known As:** Centro Internacional de la Papa. **Staff:** Carmen Podesta, Libn./Info.Off.

★8176★
International Railroad & Transportation Postcard Collectors Club - Library (Rec)
Box 6782
Providence, RI 02940 Robert J. Andrews, Pres.
Founded: 1976. **Staff:** 2. **Subjects:** Transportation vehicles, postcards. **Holdings:** 1000 volumes; bulletins. **Subscriptions:** 20 journals and other serials; 15 newspapers. **Services:** Copying; library open to the public with restrictions. **Special Indexes:** Checklist of transportation postcards.

★8177★
International Railway Union - Documentation Center (Trans)
14, rue Jean Rey Phone: 1 42730120
F-75015 Paris, France Juliette Engel, Chf., Doc.Ctr.
Founded: 1922. **Subjects:** Management and administration of railways - operation, commercial services and tariffs, finance and accounting, legal matters, mechanical and civil engineering; other modes of transport that compete with railways. **Holdings:** 3000 volumes; 800 reports. **Subscriptions:** 200 journals and other serials. **Services:** Bureau open to members of the International Railway Union. **Publications:** Rail International; International Railways Statistics, annual; International Railway Union Code Leaflets; bibliogarphies - publications issued in English, French, and German. **Remarks:** FAX: 1 42730140. Telex: 270835 UNINFER F. **Also Known As:** Union Internationale des Chemins de Fer; Internationaler Eisenbahnverband. **Staff:** Sylvette Langet, Doc.; Brigitte Boulle.

★8178★
International Reading Association - Ralph C. Staiger Library (Educ)
800 Barksdale Rd.
Box 8139 Phone: (302)731-1600
Newark, DE 19714-8139 Wendy Wei, Libn.
Founded: 1974. **Staff:** Prof 1; Other 1. **Subjects:** Reading, language arts, learning disabilities, children's literature, teaching and remedial teaching of reading. **Special Collections:** Nila Banton Smith Research Collection in Reading; Reading Test Collection; IRA Past President and Historical Readers Collection; William S. Gray Collection in Reading; Children's Choices Collection; Young Adult Choices Collection; Teacher's Choices Collection. **Holdings:** 15,000 volumes; 600 technical and annual reports; 4 VF drawers of clippings, pamphlets, brochures; 9000 microforms. **Subscriptions:** 214 journals and other serials. **Services:** Interlibrary loan; copying; library open to the public. **Automated Operations:** Computerized serials. **Networks/Consortia:** Member of Libraries in the New Castle County System (LINCS). **Special Indexes:** IRA Literature Retrieval Index. **Remarks:** FAX: (302)731-1057. **Also Known As:** IRAS.

★8179★
International Real Estate Institute - Library (Bus-Fin)
8383 E. Evans Rd. Phone: (602)998-8267
Scottsdale, AZ 85260-3614 Robert G. Johnson, Exec.Dir.
Founded: 1975. **Subjects:** Real estate - development, finance, investment, management, valuation. **Holdings:** 5000 volumes. **Services:** Library not open to the public. **Remarks:** FAX: (602)998-8022. Telex: 165092.

International Reference Centre for Avian Haematozoa
See: **Memorial University of Newfoundland** (10053)

★8180★
International Reference Organization in Forensic Medicine & Sciences - Library and Reference Center (Med, Law)
P.O. Box 8282 Phone: (316)685-7612
Wichita, KS 67208 Dr. William G. Eckert, Dir.
Founded: 1966. **Staff:** 2. **Subjects:** Abortion, accidents, alcohol, alcoholism, drugs and drug abuse, forensic sciences, medicolegal history, homicide, iatrogenic problems, legal medicine, pediatric medicine, poisoning, suicidology, sex problems, thanatology, toxicology, trauma, war crimes, war wounds. **Special Collections:** Texts in forensic medicine from 20 countries; journals in forensic and legal medicine from 20 countries; reference materials on forensic medical problems in 80 countries. **Holdings:** 1700 books; 1500 bound periodical volumes; 2000 papers; 2000 miscellaneous reports; 100 bibliographies; 500 hours of videotapes; 1000 hours of magnetic tapes; AV programs; microfilm. **Subscriptions:** 30 journals and other serials. **Services:** Copying; sale of slide lectures; library open to the public. **Automated Operations:** Computerized reference service. **Publications:** INFORM Newsletter, quarterly; list of other publications - available on request. **Special Indexes:** Special indexed compilations of subjects listed above; special indexed compilations of the table of contents for the following - Journal of Forensic Sciences, Medicine, Science and the Law, Journal of Forensic Medicine, Journal of Indian Academy of Forensic Sciences, American Journal of Clinical Pathology (volumes 1-56). **Remarks:** Center acts as the Secretariat for the Pan-American Association of Forensic Sciences. It is affiliated with the William G. Eckert Medico-Legal Institute, Sao Paulo, Brazil. **Also Known As:** INFORM.

International Register of Potentially Toxic Chemicals - Library
See: **United Nations Environment Programme** (16769)

International Rehabilitation and Research Center for Torture Victims
See: **Rehabilitation and Research Center for Torture Victims** (13804)

★8181★
International Research & Evaluation (IRE) - Information & Technology Transfer Resource Center (Sci-Engr, Env-Cons, Law)
21098 IRE Control Ctr. Phone: (612)888-9635
Eagan, MN 55121 Randall L. Voight, Info.Dir.
Founded: 1972. **Staff:** Prof 12; Other 39. **Subjects:** Waste management and resources recovery, energy and environmental engineering, law enforcement and criminal justice, robotics, fiber optics and lasers. **Holdings:** 715,401

books; 14,771 bound periodical volumes; 27 million microfiche; 501,722 ultrafiche; 12,942 videotapes and films; 3106 microforms. **Subscriptions:** 5150 journals and other serials; 321 newspapers. **Services:** Interlibrary loan; copying; SDI; center open to guest pass holders. **Automated Operations:** Computerized cataloging, acquisitions, and serials. **Computerized Information Services:** DIALOG Information Services, BRS Information Technologies, PFDS Online; Information & Technology Transfer Database (ITTD; internal database). Performs searches on fee basis. Contact Person: E. Goldes, Oper.Sup.Mgr. **Publications:** Information Age, monthly - by subscription. **Special Indexes:** KWIC index (printout). **Remarks:** FAX: (612)798-5574. **Staff:** George Franklin, Jr., Plan. & Dev.Dir.; Dr. R. Danford, Sr.Libn.; Valentina Voight, Coll.Dev.Dir.; D.N. Rice, Circ. & Cont.Mgr.

★8182★
International Rice Research Institute - Library (Agri)
P.O. Box 933 Phone: 2 8181926
Manila, Philippines Lina M. Vergara, Libn.
Staff: 16. **Subjects:** Rice, azolla. **Holdings:** 147,000 rice publications; 4184 serial titles. **Services:** Copying; library open to the public. **Computerized Information Services:** CD-ROMs (AGRICOLA, CAB Abstracts, Biological Abstracts); assists in production of CABI Rice Abstracts. **Publications:** International Bibliography of Rice Research; Rice Literature Update; Theses and Dissertations on Rice Available in the Library of the International Rice Research Institute; International Bibliography on Azolla. **Remarks:** FAX: 2 8178470. Telex: (ITT)45365 RICE PM; 40890 RICE PM. Maintained by the Consultative Group on International Agricultural Research.

★8183★
International Rock and Roll Music Association, Inc. - Library (Mus)
P.O. Box 158946 Phone: (615)297-9072
Nashville, TN 37215 Bernard G. Walters, Pres.
Founded: 1980. **Staff:** 3. **Subjects:** English and American rock and roll, Beatles, Rolling Stones. **Special Collections:** Early English rock periodicals, photographs, slides, and posters. **Holdings:** 40 books; 1200 unbound periodicals; 2100 rock concert slides; 5000 rock photographs; 900 phonograph records. **Services:** Library not open to the public.

★8184★
International Sanitary Supply Association - Library (Bus-Fin)
7373 N. Lincoln Ave. Phone: (708)982-0800
Lincolnwood, IL 60646 Joan Cooke, Oper. Data Proc.Mgr.
Founded: 1923. **Subjects:** Industrial and institutional cleaning, marketing, sales. **Holdings:** 250 volumes; 30 video cassettes. **Computerized Information Services:** Internal databases.

★8185★
International School of Theology - Library (Rel-Phil)
Arrowhead Springs
P.O. Box 50015 Phone: (714)886-7876
San Bernardino, CA 92414 Bernardine Smith, Lib.Mgr.
Founded: 1978. **Staff:** 3. **Subjects:** Theology, Bible, counseling, pastoral studies, communication, management. **Holdings:** 34,700 books; 1950 bound periodical volumes; 2000 audio and video cassettes; 2000 reels of microfilm. **Subscriptions:** 255 journals and other serials. **Services:** Interlibrary loan; library open to the public with permission. **Computerized Information Services:** OCLC.

★8186★
International Sericultural Commission - Library (Biol Sci)
25, quai Jean-Jacques Rousseau Phone: 78504198
F-69350 La Mulatiere, France Dr. G. Chavancy
Staff: 1. **Subjects:** Silk. **Special Collections:** Biographical archives. **Holdings:** 3,000 historical and scientific books. **Subscriptions:** 75 journals and other serials. **Services:** Library not open to the public. **Computerized Information Services:** Internal database. **Remarks:** FAX: 78860957. Sericulture is the production of raw silk by raising silk worms. Maintains documentation service. **Also Known As:** Commission Sericicole Internationale.

★8187★
International Soap Box Derby Inc. - Library (Rec)
Derby Downs
Box 7233 Phone: (216)733-8723
Akron, OH 44306 Jeff Iula, Gen.Mgr.
Founded: 1934. **Staff:** Prof 1. **Subjects:** Soap Box Derby. **Special Collections:** History of past races. **Holdings:** 100 books; 25 films; heat records; pictures. **Services:** Library open to the public with restrictions. **Computerized Information Services:** Online systems. Performs searches on fee basis. **Special Catalogs:** The Soap Box Derby Rule Book, annual. **Remarks:** FAX: (216)733-1370.

International Society for Music Education Archives
See: **University of Maryland, College Park Libraries - Music Library** (18821)

International Society for Optical Engineering
See: **SPIE** (15585)

★8188★
International Society of Parametric Analysts - ISPA Library (Bus-Fin)
3190 Fairview Park Dr. Phone: (703)876-3000
Falls Church, VA 22042 Clyde Perry, Libn.
Founded: 1979. **Staff:** Prof 1; Other 1. **Subjects:** Cost, schedule, performance, and risk analysis; cost benefit analysis; life cycle cost estimates; technology forecasting; international standardization; parametric modeling techniques. **Holdings:** 500 books; 200 reports; 32 video cassettes; 11 lateral file drawers. **Services:** Interlibrary loan; library not open to the public. **Publications:** Parametric World, monthly; Journal of Parametrics, quarterly. **Special Catalogs:** Annual proceedings. **Special Indexes:** ISPA index. **Remarks:** FAX: (314)889-8839. **Formerly:** Located in St. Louis, MO.

★8189★
International Society for Philosophical Enquiry - Archives (Educ)
c/o Betty Hansen
277 Washington Blvd. Phone: (518)828-1996
Hudson, NY 12534 Palmer McCurdy, Hist.
Founded: 1974. **Staff:** Prof 1. **Subjects:** IQ testing, science, philosophy. **Holdings:** TELICOM (journal of the International Society for Philosophical Enquiry; 500 unbound volumes). **Subscriptions:** 500 journals and other serials. **Services:** Archives not open to the public. **Publications:** Charter, History, Membership Roster.

★8190★
International Society for Rehabilitation of the Disabled/Rehabilitation International - Library (Med)
25 E. 21st St. Phone: (212)420-1500
New York, NY 10010 Barbara Duncan, Dir. of Info.
Subjects: International aspects of disability. **Special Collections:** Disabled children in developing countries; barrier free design; economics of disability. **Holdings:** 2500 books; 5000 documents. **Services:** Library open to scholars by appointment with restrictions. **Publications:** List of publications - available on request. **Remarks:** FAX: (212)505-0871.

★8191★
International Society for Vehicle Preservation - Library (Trans)
P.O. Box 50046 Phone: (602)741-2121
Tucson, AZ 85703 E.C. Hanson, Dir.
Subjects: Origin, development, and progress of self-propelled vehicles (cars, trucks, buses, fire engines, motorcycles). **Holdings:** 1000 volumes. **Remarks:** Society promotes the preservation of self-propelled vehicles, literature, artifacts, and allied products.

★8192★
International Stamp Collectors Society - Library (Rec)
Box 854 Phone: (818)997-6496
Van Nuys, CA 91408 Mrs. Israel Bick, Exec.Dir.
Staff: 1. **Subjects:** Philately. **Special Collections:** Philatelic magazines and reference books. **Holdings:** 200 books; 50 bound periodical volumes; other cataloged items. **Subscriptions:** 75 journals and other serials; 50 newspapers. **Services:** Library open to the public by appointment. **Publications:** Newsletter, irregular. **Remarks:** FAX: (818)988-4337.

★8193★
International Swimming Hall of Fame - Museum & Library (Rec)
One Hall of Fame Dr. Phone: (305)462-6536
Fort Lauderdale, FL 33316 Marion Washburn, Libn.
Founded: 1968. **Staff:** 1. **Subjects:** Swimming history and instruction, sports medicine and psychology, pool care and management, diving and water polo, swim officiating, synchronized swimming. **Special Collections:** Sports stamp collection; aquatic memorabilia; historical swimming and diving films and tapes; medals and trophies of major swimmers past and present. **Holdings:** 5200 books; 130 bound periodical volumes; 80 scrapbooks; 50 theses and dissertations; guidebooks; swimmers' biographies; games, charts, tables for swim officiating. **Subscriptions:** 20 journals and other serials. **Services:** Copying; library open to the public. **Publications:** Yearbooks, annual; newsletters, annual - both to contributors and honorees. **Remarks:** FAX: (305)525-4031.

★8194★
International Technical Publications, Ltd. - Library (Info Sci)
Rua Peixoto Gomide, 209 Phone: 11 2588442
01409 Sao Paulo, Brazil Rubens Pujol Yamamoto, Libn.
Founded: 1972. **Staff:** Prof 10. **Subjects:** Technical publications - science, technology, administration, marketing. **Holdings:** 2000 bound volumes; microfiche; publishers' catalogs. **Subscriptions:** 50 journals and other serials. **Services:** SDI. **Automated Operations:** Computerized SDI. **Publications:** Information Management, quarterly; BOOKALERT, monthly. **Remarks:** FAX: 11 2586990. Telex: 1135844 APTI BR. **Also Known As:** Publicacoes Tecnicas Internacionais.

★8195★
International Technology Corporation - Technical Library (Env-Cons)
11499 Chester Rd. Phone: (513)782-4700
Cincinnati, OH 45246 Penny Fraley, Tech.Libn.
Founded: 1973. **Staff:** Prof 1. **Subjects:** Environment; engineering - environmental, civil, mechanical; industrial hygiene; chemistry; air and water pollution; water treatment and hazardous waste. **Holdings:** 1500 books; 900 EPA reports and 25,000 government/contractor reports on microfiche; 1500 U.S. Government reports. **Subscriptions:** 125 journals and other serials. **Computerized Information Services:** DIALOG Information Services, Chemical Information Systems (CIS). **Remarks:** FAX: (513)782-4807. **Formerly:** PEI Associates, Inc.

★8196★
International Telecommunication Union - Central Library, Documentation, and Archives Section (Info Sci)
Place des Nations Phone: 22 7305111
CH-1211 Geneva 20, Switzerland A.G. El-Zanati, Chf.
Founded: 1965. **Subjects:** Telecommunications - history, technology, general, telegraphy, telephone, radio communications, television, space telecommunications, broadcasting, electronics, physics, mathematics, computer science and data processing, economics, legislation and regulation. **Holdings:** 25,000 bound volumes; documentation files of press clippings, articles, and photographs; films; microfiche; 1400 serial titles; 1000 periodicals; 370 annuals. **Services:** Library open to researchers, ITU member states, and staff. **Computerized Information Services:** Monitoring Information Data Bank, List of Ship Stations, International Frequency Register, List of Telegraph Offices, Coast Frequency Reference File, Address Bank (internal databases). **Publications:** Acquisitions lists. **Remarks:** Alternate telephone number(s): 22 995236. FAX: 22 337256. Telex: 421 000 UIT CH. The International Telecommunication Union is a specialized agency of the United Nations.

International Telecommunications Satellite Organization - Intelsat Library
See: **Intelsat Library** (8021)

★8197★
International Tennis Hall of Fame and Tennis Museum - Library (Rec)
Newport Casino
194 Bellevue Ave. Phone: (401)849-3990
Newport, RI 02840 Jan Armstrong, Musm.Dir.
Founded: 1954. **Staff:** Prof 1. **Subjects:** Lawn tennis, court tennis, other racquet games. **Holdings:** Books; periodicals; catalogs; photographs. **Services:** Copying. **Remarks:** Alternate telephone number(s): 849-6378.

★8198★
International Test and Evaluation Association - Library (Sci-Engr)
4400 Fair Lakes Ct. Phone: (703)631-6220
Fairfax, VA 22033-3899 Alan Plishker, Exec.Dir.
Founded: 1980. **Subjects:** Test and evaluation processes, technology, organization, management. **Holdings:** 100 volumes. **Subscriptions:** 2000 journals and other serials. **Services:** Library not open to the public. **Remarks:** FAX: (703)631-4693.

★8199★
International Theatre Institute of the United States, Inc. - International Theatre Collection (Theater)
220 W. 42nd St., Suite 1710 Phone: (212)944-1490
New York, NY 10036-7202 Louis A. Rachow, Dir.
Founded: 1970. **Staff:** Prof 1; Other 1. **Subjects:** Contemporary international theater. **Holdings:** 6100 books; 13,000 plays; 275 periodicals on performing arts; yearbooks, newsletters, programs, house organs, press releases, production schedules, brochures, reviews, photographs from theaters in 146 countries. **Subscriptions:** 200 journals and other serials. **Services:** Copying; collection open to the public by appointment. **Remarks:** FAX: (212)944-1506.

★8200★
International Tin Research Institute - Library (Sci-Engr)
Kingston Ln. Phone: 895 272406
Uxbridge, Middlesex UB8 3PJ, England Dr. L.A. Hobbs
Staff: 3. **Subjects:** Tin, tin alloys and compounds, industrial processes involving tin. **Holdings:** 40,000 papers; 43,000 abstracts; 2000 monographs. **Subscriptions:** 250 journals and other serials. **Services:** Interlibrary loan; copying; SDI; library open to the public by appointment. **Computerized Information Services:** Internal database; Dialcom, Inc. (electronic mail service). **Remarks:** FAX: 895 251841. Telex: 9312130315 SN G. Electronic mail address(es): 87:WQQ401 (DIALMAIL). **Formerly:** International Tin Research Council - ITRC Library.

International Trombone Association Resource Library
See: **University of Arizona - Music Collection** (18224)

International Trumpet Guild Archives
See: **Western Michigan University - Harper C. Maybee Music & Dance Library** (20271)

★8201★
International Tsunami Information Center (Sci-Engr)
Box 50027 Phone: (808)541-1658
Honolulu, HI 96850-4993 Dr. George Pararas-Carayannis, Dir.
Founded: 1964. **Staff:** Prof 2; Other 2. **Subjects:** Tsunamis, earthquakes, oceanography. **Holdings:** 2000 volumes. **Subscriptions:** 20 journals and other serials. **Services:** Interlibrary loan; copying; SDI; center open to the public. **Publications:** International Tsunami Information Center Newsletter, semiannual; Tsunami Reports, annual; Director's Report, biennial. **Remarks:** FAX: (808)541-1678. The Center is maintained by the U.S. National Weather Service, under international agreement with UNESCO - Intergovernmental Oceanographic Commission and member states which participate in the International Tsunami Warning System in the Pacific.

★8202★
International Union for Conservation of Nature and Natural Resources - Library (Env-Cons)
c/o World Conservation Centre
Avenue du Mont-Blanc Phone: 22 649114
CH-1196 Gland, Switzerland Kevin Grose, Hd.Libn.
Founded: 1948. **Staff:** 3. **Subjects:** Conservation of the natural environment, ecological processes necessary to life on earth, wildlife. **Holdings:** 10,000 books. **Subscriptions:** 125 journals and other serials; 5 newspapers. **Services:** Interlibrary loan; copying; library open to the public. **Computerized Information Services:** MIBIS (internal database). **Remarks:** FAX: 22 642926. Telex: 419605 iucn ch. Affiliated with World Wide Fund for Nature. **Also Known As:** Union Mondial pour la Nature. **Staff:** Cecilo Thiery.

International Union for Conservation of Nature and Natural Resources - World Wide Fund for Nature - Photographic Library
See: **World Wide Fund for Nature** (20635)

★8203★
International Union of Operating Engineers - Research Department - Library (Bus-Fin)
1125 17th St., N.W. Phone: (202)429-9100
Washington, DC 20036 David Treanor
Subjects: Union history, productivity of heavy equipment, industrial safety. **Holdings:** 2000 books; industrial surveys; slides; motion pictures; microfiche. **Services:** Library not open to the public. **Computerized Information Services:** Internal database.

★8204★
International Union of Operating Engineers - Training Center - Local 68, 68A, 68B - Library (Sci-Engr)
14 Fairfield Pl.
Box 534 Phone: (201)227-6426
West Caldwell, NJ 07006 Gail F. Longo, Libn.
Staff: Prof 1. **Subjects:** Refrigeration, welding, heating, ventilation, air conditioning, labor, occupational health and safety. **Holdings:** 700 books; 2000 VF materials; 15 operator's manuals; 40 equipment manuals; 80 AV programs. **Subscriptions:** 33 journals and other serials. **Services:** Copying; SDI; library open to the public by appointment.

International Union, United Automobile, Aerospace & Agricultural Implement Workers of America
See: **United Automobile, Aerospace & Agricultural Implement Workers of America - Research Library** (16687)

★8205★
The International University - International Relations Library and Research Center (Soc Sci)
1301 S. Noland Rd. Phone: (816)461-3633
Independence, MO 64055 Dr. John W. Johnston, Dir.
Founded: 1973. **Staff:** Prof 1; Other 2. **Subjects:** European studies, Latin American studies, international education, world community. **Special Collections:** Hibernian Collection (170 volumes). **Holdings:** 5325 books; 130 bound periodical volumes; 375 pamphlets; 2500 photocopies of documents; 100,000 clippings; 16 dissertations. **Subscriptions:** 16 journals and other serials. **Services:** Library open to selected researchers. **Remarks:** FAX: (816)461-3634. **Also Known As:** TIU.

★8206★
International Wild Waterfowl Association - Lee Ridge Aviaries - Reference Library (Biol Sci)
7 James Farm Rd. Phone: (603)659-5442
Durham, NH 03824 Walter B. Sturgeon, Owner
Founded: 1975. **Subjects:** Birds - waterfowl, gamebirds, general; mammals; Arctic exploration; natural history. **Holdings:** 500 books; 10,000 slides. **Subscriptions:** 5 journals and other serials. **Services:** Library open to the public. **Remarks:** A list of books is available upon request.

International Women Pilots Association
See: **Ninety-Nines, Inc.** (11813)

International Women's History Archives
See: **Women's History Research Center, Inc. - Women's History Library** (20559)

★8207★
International Women's Tribune Centre - Resource Centre (Soc Sci)
777 United Nations Plaza, 3rd Fl. Phone: (212)687-8633
New York, NY 10017 Alice Mastrangelo, Rsrc.Ctr.Hd.
Founded: 1978. **Staff:** 9. **Subjects:** Women in development, appropriate technology, community economic development, communication, media, training, funding, financial management, gender, small business. **Special Collections:** Violence Against Women; Women and Environment. **Services:** Library open to the public for reference use only. **Computerized Information Services:** Internal database. **Remarks:** FAX: (212)661-2704. **Staff:** Meera Singh.

★8208★
International Working Group for the Construction of Sports and Leisure Facilities - IAKS Library (Plan)
Carl-Diem-Weg 3
W-5000 Cologne 41, Germany Phone: 221 492991
Subjects: Planning, constructing, equipping, and maintaining recreation and sports facilities. **Holdings:** 8000 technical books, planning guidelines, research data. **Services:** Copying; library open to members. **Publications:** Literature Documentation, quarterly. **Remarks:** Maintains Documentation and Information Center of literature, films, photographs, slides, and a data bank. FAX: 221 4971280. Telex: 8881792. **Also Known As:** Internationaler Arbeitskreis Sport- und Freizeiteninrichtungen.

★8209★
International Youth Council - Library
8807 Colesville Rd.
Silver Spring, MD 20910
Defunct.

Internationale Orientierungslauf Foderation, Wissenschaftliche Arbeitsgruppe
See: **International Orienteering Federation, Scientific Group** (8167)

Internationaler Arbeitskreis Sport- und Freizeiteninrichtungen
See: **International Working Group for the Construction of Sports and Leisure Facilities** (8208)

Internationaler Eisenbahnverband
See: **International Railway Union - Documentation Center** (8177)

Internationales Esperanto Museum Sammlung fuer Plansprachen
See: **Austria - Oesterreichische Nationalbibliothek - Special Collections** (1354)

Internationales Forschungszentrum fur Grundfragen der Wissenschaften Salzburg - Institut fur Kirchliche Zeitgeschichte
See: **Institute for Contemporary Ecclesiastical History** (7919)

★8210★
Interpublic Group of Companies - Center for Advertising Services (Bus-Fin)
1271 Avenue of the Americas Phone: (212)399-8222
New York, NY 10020 Robin Feuerstein, Dir. of Info.
Staff: Prof 7; Other 4. **Subjects:** Advertising, marketing, packaged goods. **Holdings:** Figures not available. **Subscriptions:** 153 journals and other serials. **Services:** Center not open to the public. **Computerized Information Services:** DIALOG Information Services, Mead Data Central, Reuter TEXTLINE. **Remarks:** FAX: (212)399-8130. **Staff:** Joan Leake, Info.Spec.; Sharon Rennhack, Info.Spec.; Lee Ballou, Info.Spec.; Susan Lilly, Info.Spec.; Margie Braimon, Info.Spec.

★8211★
Interstate Commerce Commission - Library (Bus-Fin, Trans)
Twelfth & Constitution Ave., N.W., Rm. 3392 Phone: (202)275-7328
Washington, DC 20423 Albert G. West, Libn.
Founded: 1894. **Staff:** Prof 1. **Subjects:** Transportation, U.S. transportation history, finance, law, federal regulation, economics, valuation, administrative law, accounting, statistics. **Holdings:** 94,000 volumes; 18 files of pamphlets and unbound materials; 46 files of congressional materials. **Subscriptions:** 95 journals and other serials. **Services:** Interlibrary loan; library open to the public for reference use only.

Interstate Electronics Corporation
See: **Figgie International** (5687)

★8212★
Interstate Oil and Gas Compact Commission - Library (Env-Cons)
900 N.E. 23rd St.
Box 53127 Phone: (405)525-3556
Oklahoma City, OK 73152 W. Timothy Dowd, Exec.Dir.
Founded: 1935. **Staff:** 8. **Subjects:** Conservation of oil and gas. **Holdings:** 80 VF drawers; 10,000 file cards. **Subscriptions:** 50 journals and other serials. **Services:** Library open to the public. **Remarks:** FAX: (405)525-3592.

Inuvik Research Centre
See: **Canada - Science Institute of the Northwest Territories** (2846)

★8213★
Inventors Clubs of America - Library (Sci-Engr)
Box 450261 Phone: (800)336-0169
Atlanta, GA 30345 Alexander T. Marinaccio, Pres.
Founded: 1935. **Subjects:** Inventions - patenting, development, manufacturing, marketing, advertising. **Holdings:** 2000 volumes. **Services:** library not open to the public.

★8214★
Inventors Workshop - Library (Sci-Engr)
3201 Corte Malpaso, Suite 304-A Phone: (805)484-9786
Camarillo, CA 93012 Alan Tratner
Founded: 1971. **Staff:** Prof 1; Other 5. **Subjects:** Inventions, inventing, intellectual property, technology, energy, environment. **Special Collections:** Light Bulb Magazine (newsletter, complete set); Invent! Magazine (complete set); Renewable Energy News Digest (complete set). **Holdings:** 600 books; 18 bound periodical volumes. **Subscriptions:** 25 journals and other serials. **Services:** Library open to members and instructors only.

★8215★
Investigative Reporters and Editors, Inc. - Paul Williams Memorial Resource Center (Info Sci)
Box 838 Phone: (314)882-2042
Columbia, MO 65205 Andy Scott, Act.Exec.Dir.
Founded: 1978. **Staff:** 7. **Subjects:** Investigative reports in the U.S. and Canada published in newspapers and magazines or broadcast on radio and television. **Holdings:** 800 books; 7000 clippings. **Services:** Copying; center open to the public with restrictions. **Remarks:** FAX: (314)882-5431.

★8216★
Investment Canada - Information Center (Bus-Fin)
PO Box 2800, Sta. D Phone: (613)996-1921
Ottawa, ON, Canada K1P 6A5 Camrose Burdon, Mgr.
Founded: 1986. **Staff:** Prof 2; Other 3. **Subjects:** International business, finance, investment, multinationals, economic conditions. **Special Collections:** Investment company reports; international company reports; Canadian technology company profiles. **Holdings:** 1500 books; 3000 reports. **Subscriptions:** 1000 journals and other serials; 20 newspapers. **Services:** Interlibrary loan; SDI; center open to the public. **Automated Operations:** Computerized cataloging, acquisitions, serials, and circulation. **Computerized Information Services:** DIALOG Information Services, DOBIS Canadian Online Library System, STM Systems Corporation, CAN/OLE, Reuters, Info Globe, Infomart Online, NewsNet, Inc., QL Systems, WESTLAW; CD-ROMs (General BusinessFile, F & S Plus, Computer Select). **Publications:** Info!, Current Awareness Bulletin - for internal distribution only; Investing in Canada (newsletter), quarterly - available upon request. **Remarks:** FAX: (613)996-2515. **Staff:** Camrose Burdon; Diane Rudzevicius; Lisa McPhail.

★8217★
Investment Company Institute - Library (Bus-Fin)
1600 M St., N.W., Suite 600 Phone: (202)293-7700
Washington, DC 20036 Cut Parker, Libn.
Founded: 1970. **Staff:** Prof 1. **Subjects:** Investment, mutual funds, banking laws and regulations, economics. **Special Collections:** Investment materials. **Holdings:** 380 books; 200 bound periodical volumes; 150 other cataloged items; ICI historical data and publications. **Subscriptions:** 115 journals and other serials; 5 newspapers. **Services:** Library open to the public to members and others performing work for members. **Publications:** Mutual Funds News, quarterly. **Remarks:** FAX: (202)659-1519.

★8218★
Invisible Ministry - Library (Rel-Phil)
PO Box 4608 Phone: (503)362-9634
Salem, OR 97302-8608 A. Stuart Otto, Dir.
Founded: 1965. **Staff:** 3. **Subjects:** Religion, philosophy, metaphysics, science. **Holdings:** 800 books; 100 bound periodical volumes; 250 cassettes and recordings. **Services:** Library open by appointment only. **Publications:** Tidings, bimonthly; Theologia 21, quarterly; Master Thoughts, weekly - all to mailing list; list of other publications - available on request. **Remarks:** Invisible Ministry is an Oregon nonprofit religious corporation. It includes a publishing subsidiary, The Dominion Press. **Formerly:** Located in San Marcos, CA.

★8219★
Inyo County Law Library (Law)
168 N. Edwards
Drawer K Phone: (619)878-2411
Independence, CA 93526 Brad Yonge, Law Lib.Ck.
Staff: 1. **Subjects:** Law. **Holdings:** 2800 volumes. **Services:** Copying; library open to the public.

★8220★
Iolab Corporation - Research Information Services (Med)
500 Iolab Dr. Phone: (714)624-2020
Claremont, CA 91711 Ardis Weiss, Sr.Res.Info.Sci.
Founded: 1983. **Staff:** Prof 1. **Subjects:** Ophthalmology, pharmaceuticals, polymer chemistry. **Holdings:** 600 books; 561 periodical volumes. **Subscriptions:** 182 journals and other serials. **Services:** Interlibrary loan; SDI; center open to the public with restrictions. **Automated Operations:** Computerized public access catalog, cataloging, acquisitions, serials, and circulation. **Computerized Information Services:** DIALOG Information Services, STN International, OCLC. **Networks/Consortia:** Member of CLASS. **Remarks:** FAX: (714)399-1425. Corporation is a division of Johnson and Johnson.

Ion Kinetics and Energetics Data Center
See: **U.S. Natl. Institute of Standards and Technology** (17619)

★8221★
Ionics, Inc. - Research Department Library (Sci-Engr)
65 Grove St. Phone: (617)926-2500
Watertown, MA 02172 Catherine Zaremba, Act.Libn.
Staff: Prof 1. **Subjects:** Ion exchange membranes, electrodialysis, electrochemistry, membrane processes. **Holdings:** Figures not available. **Subscriptions:** 149 journals and other serials. **Services:** Interlibrary loan; library not open to the public. **Computerized Information Services:** DIALOG Information Services. **Remarks:** FAX: (617)926-4304. Telex: 922 473.

★8222★
Iowa Beef Processors, Inc. - Corporate Library (Food-Bev)
Box 515
Dakota City, NE 68731 Phone: (402)494-2061
Founded: 1976. **Subjects:** Meat industry and science, management, business. **Holdings:** 1600 books; 250 government and research reports; 10 drawers of clippings; 7 drawers of annual reports.

★8223★
Iowa Drug Information Service (Med)
University of Iowa
Oakdale Hall Phone: (319)335-4800
Iowa City, IA 52242 Hazel H. Seaba, R.Ph., Dir.
Founded: 1966. **Staff:** Prof 10; Other 8. **Subjects:** Drugs and human drug therapy. **Holdings:** 286,000 articles with descriptors on microfilm; Drug and Disease Indexes (1966 to present, on microfilm; 1985 to present, on CD-ROM; 1966 to present, online through database vendors). **Subscriptions:** 140 journals and other serials. **Services:** SDI; service open to subscribers. **Computerized Information Services:** Produces IDIS SYSTEM (available in CD-ROM format and online through BRS Information Technologies and Data-Star). **Publications:** IDIS SYSTEM (microfiche), monthly; Procedure Manuals, annual; World of Drugs (newsletter), quarterly. **Special Indexes:** Drug Cross Reference Index, quarterly; Disease Cross Reference Index, quarterly. **Remarks:** FAX: (319)335-4077.

★8224★
Iowa Genealogical Society - Library (Hist)
6000 Douglas
Box 7735 Phone: (515)276-0287
Des Moines, IA 50322 Sue Cochran, Libn.
Founded: 1966. **Subjects:** Genealogy, local history. **Special Collections:** Pioneer Certificate Collection; Iowa census records and obituaries; Iowa Federal Census through 1910 (complete; on microfilm); Federal Censuses for all states for 1800, 1810, 1820, 1830, 1840, 1850, and 1870 (on microfilm; partial sets for other years); Surname Index, 5 vols. **Holdings:** 166 volumes of D.A.R. lineage books; 69 volumes of Pennsylvania archives; U.S. and foreign genealogy books; 1000 genealogies; 400 rolls of Iowa courthouse records. **Services:** Copying; library open to the public on fee basis, free to members. **Publications:** Hawkeye Heritage, quarterly; newsletter, 6/year.

Iowa Genealogical Society - Linn County Genealogy Research Center
See: **Linn County Heritage Society - Linn County Genealogical Research Center** (9196)

★8225★
Iowa Hospital Association - Library (Med)
100 E. Grand Phone: (515)288-1955
Des Moines, IA 50309 Roxanna Tovrea, Lib.Dir.
Founded: 1974. **Staff:** Prof 1; Other 1. **Subjects:** Hospital administration, rural health, nursing, inservice training and education, standards and regulations. **Special Collections:** Health administration; rural health. **Holdings:** 3000 books; 180 AV programs; 5 lateral file drawers of pamphlet material, educational material, publications, bibliographies. **Subscriptions:** 200 journals and other serials. **Services:** Interlibrary loan; copying; library open to the public. **Automated Operations:** Computerized cataloging, acquisitions, and serials. **Computerized Information Services:** DIALOG Information Services. Performs searches on fee basis. **Networks/Consortia:** Member of Polk County Biomedical Consortium (PCBC). **Remarks:** FAX: (515)283-9366.

★8226★
Iowa Law Enforcement Academy - Library (Law)
Iowa Law Enforcement Academy
Camp Dodge
Box 130 Phone: (515)242-5357
Johnston, IA 50131 Jo Ellen Warne, Libn.
Founded: 1976. **Staff:** Prof 1. **Subjects:** Police, law enforcement, criminal justice, criminal law. **Holdings:** 2200 books; 500 documents and training materials; 321 films and slide programs; 3 VF drawers of clippings. **Subscriptions:** 57 journals and other serials. **Services:** Interlibrary loan; copying; SDI; library open to Iowa law enforcement personnel and to the public with permission. **Special Catalogs:** Film catalog (booklet).

★8227★
Iowa Lutheran Hospital - Levitt Health Sciences Library (Med)
University at Penn Phone: (515)263-5181
Des Moines, IA 50316 Molly H. Yapp, Dir.
Founded: 1971. **Staff:** Prof 2. **Subjects:** Medicine, nursing, health care administration, practice management, patient education. **Holdings:** 2125 books; periodicals; 6 16mm films; 250 video cassettes; 591 audiotapes; 25 slide/tape kits; 2 VF drawers of pamphlets. **Subscriptions:** 160 journals and other serials. **Services:** Interlibrary loan; copying; library open to the public for reference use only. **Computerized Information Services:** MEDLARS, DIALOG Information Services, BRS Information Technologies. **Networks/Consortia:** Member of Polk County Biomedical Consortium (PCBC), National Network of Libraries of Medicine - Greater Midwest Region. **Remarks:** FAX: (515)263-2214.

★8228★
Iowa Methodist Medical Center - Marjorie Gertrude Morrow Library (Med)
1117 Pleasant St. Phone: (515)241-6453
Des Moines, IA 50309 Nancy O'Brien, Libn.
Founded: 1901. **Staff:** Prof 1; Other 1. **Subjects:** Nursing, nutrition. **Holdings:** 2919 books; 272 bound periodical volumes; brochures; pamphlets. **Subscriptions:** 118 journals and other serials. **Services:** Interlibrary loan; library open to the public for reference use only. **Computerized Information Services:** DIALOG Information Services, NLM; DOCLINE (electronic mail service) . **Networks/Consortia:** Member of Polk County Biomedical Consortium (PCBC), National Network of Libraries of Medicine - Greater Midwest Region.

★8229★
Iowa Methodist Medical Center - Oliver J. Fay Library (Med)
1200 Pleasant St. Phone: (515)241-6490
Des Moines, IA 50309 Mary Wegner, Dir., Hea.Sci.Lib.
Founded: 1940. **Staff:** Prof 1; Other 1. **Subjects:** Medicine, allied health sciences. **Holdings:** 3800 books; 2900 bound periodical volumes; 650 cassette tapes. **Subscriptions:** 350 journals and other serials. **Services:** Interlibrary loan; copying; SDI; library open to hospital employees and medical staff. **Computerized Information Services:** MEDLARS, DIALOG Information Services, PaperChase. **Networks/Consortia:** Member of Polk County Biomedical Consortium (PCBC), National Network of Libraries of Medicine - Greater Midwest Region.

Iowa Social Science Institute
See: **University of Iowa - Iowa Social Science Institute** (18712)

★8230★
Iowa (State) Department for the Blind - Library for the Blind & Physically Handicapped (Aud-Vis)
524 4th St. Phone: (515)281-1333
Des Moines, IA 50309 Catherine Ford, Prog.Mgr./Libn.
Founded: 1960. **Staff:** Prof 6; Other 19. **Holdings:** 110,429 braille volumes; 143,564 cassettes; 116,197 talking books; 20,767 large type books; 4348 print reference books. **Services:** Interlibrary loan; library open to the public. **Computerized Information Services:** LEXIS, NEXIS; Central Blind Registry (internal database). **Networks/Consortia:** Member of National Library Service for the Blind & Physically Handicapped (NLS). **Publications:** Subject bibliographies. **Special Catalogs:** Book lists; catalog of volunteer-produced materials by media (cassette, braille) and genre. **Remarks:** Library also offers an instructional media center, volunteer production of braille and tape materials, thermoforming and tape duplication, computer-assisted braille production, and training for volunteer tapists and braillists. Provides services to eligible blind, physically handicapped, and reading-disabled Iowans. FAX: (515)281-1263. **Staff:** Karen Paloma, Libn.; Carol Eckey, Libn.; Karen Eis, Libn.; Lisa Davis, Supv., Prod.; Linda Rutz, Coord., Tape Prod.

Iowa (State) Department of Cultural Affairs - State Library of Iowa
See: **State Library of Iowa** (15687)

★8231★
Iowa (State) Department of Education - Information Resource Center (Educ)
Grimes State Office Bldg.
Des Moines, IA 50319 Phone: (515)281-5294
Founded: 1967. **Staff:** Prof 1. **Subjects:** Education. **Holdings:** 4253 books; 152 VF drawers of curriculum and educational materials; 6426 textbooks; ERIC documents. **Subscriptions:** 400 journals and other serials. **Services:** Interlibrary loan; copying; center open to the public with restrictions. **Computerized Information Services:** DIALOG Information Services. **Remarks:** FAX: (515)242-5988.

★8232★
Iowa (State) Department of Human Services - Library (Soc Sci)
Hoover Bldg. Phone: (515)281-6033
Des Moines, IA 50319 Kay M. Elliott, Chf.Libn.
Founded: 1968. **Staff:** Prof 1; Other 1. **Subjects:** Social casework, public assistance, mental health and retardation, child abuse, child support. **Holdings:** 8000 books; 100 bound periodical volumes; 1250 VF materials; 360 AV programs. **Subscriptions:** 127 journals and other serials. **Services:** Interlibrary loan; copying; SDI; library open to the public. **Automated Operations:** Computerized cataloging. **Networks/Consortia:** Member of Bibliographical Center for Research, Rocky Mountain Region, Inc. (BCR). **Publications:** New Books, quarterly - for internal distribution only.

Iowa (State) Department of Human Services - Mount Pleasant Mental Health Institute
See: **Mount Pleasant Mental Health Institute** (10809)

★8233★
Iowa (State) Department of Natural Resources - Technical Library (Env-Cons, Energy)
Henry A. Wallace Bldg. Phone: (515)281-8897
Des Moines, IA 50319 Cecilia Nelson, Rec.Ck.
Founded: 1973. **Staff:** 3. **Subjects:** Energy, air and water quality, hazardous waste, solid wastes, chemical technology, radiation, administration, conservation. **Holdings:** 3713 books; publications of Environmental Protection Agency. **Subscriptions:** 100 journals and other serials. **Services:** Library open to the public for reference use only. **Remarks:** FAX: (515)281-8895.

★8234★
Iowa (State) Department of Public Health - Statistical Services (Med)
Lucas State Office Bldg. Phone: (515)281-4945
Des Moines, IA 50319-0075 Mike Dare, Stat.Res.Anl.
Subjects: Vital statistics; statistical tabulations - Iowa births, marriages, divorces, deaths; health manpower statistics; statistical tabulations - location of Iowa dentists, dental hygienists, chiropractors, optometrists, physical therapists, physicians, podiatrists, nursing home administrators. **Services:** Center not open to the public. **Computerized Information Services:** Online systems. **Publications:** Annual Statistical Supplement to the Biennial Report of the Iowa State Department of Health - to agencies and individuals indicating sustained interest, exchange upon request. **Remarks:** FAX: (515)281-4958. Services include the provision of tabulated distributions, incidental consultation, and assistance.

★8235★
Iowa (State) Department of Transportation - Library (Trans)
800 Lincoln Way Phone: (515)239-1200
Ames, IA 50010 Hank Zaletel, Libn.
Staff: Prof 1; Other 1. **Subjects:** Highways and transportation, road construction and materials, aeronautics, public transit, motor vehicles, railroads, rivers. **Special Collections:** Historic roads and trail files of Iowa (80 folders); Rock Island Railroad newspaper clippings (1958-1970; 2 files); road picture collection (1913-1928). **Holdings:** 10,000 books; 800 bound periodical volumes and documents. **Subscriptions:** 220 journals and other serials; 10 newspapers. **Services:** Interlibrary loan; copying; SDI; library open to the public. **Automated Operations:** Computerized cataloging. **Computerized Information Services:** DIALOG Information Services, OCLC. **Publications:** Library Bulletin, semimonthly. **Remarks:** FAX: (515)239-1639.

★8236★
Iowa State Legislative Service Bureau - Library (Law)
State House Phone: (515)281-3312
Des Moines, IA 50319 Jonetta Y. Douglas, Libn.
Founded: 1962. **Staff:** Prof 1; Other 1. **Subjects:** Studies of other states, legislation introduced and enacted in Iowa. **Holdings:** 100 books; 100 bound periodical volumes; 7000 publications and documents. **Subscriptions:** 30 journals and other serials. **Services:** Interlibrary loan; copying (both limited); library open to the public with restrictions. **Remarks:** FAX: (515)281-8027.

(Iowa) State Library of Iowa
See: **State Library of Iowa** (15687)

★8237★
Iowa State Mental Health Institute - Clarinda Treatment Complex - Professional Library
Box 338
Clarinda, IA 51632
Founded: 1941. **Subjects:** Psychiatry, psychology, psychiatric nursing, social services education, pastoral counseling, maintenance and dietary services. **Holdings:** 2800 books; 3 VF drawers; 190 cassette tapes. **Remarks:** Currently inactive.

★8238★
Iowa State University - Institute for Physical Research and Technology - Rare-earth Information Center (Sci-Engr)
Ames, IA 50011-3020 Phone: (515)294-2272
Karl A. Gschneidner, Jr., Dir.
Founded: 1966. **Staff:** Prof 2; Other 1. **Subjects:** Rare earth metals, alloys, compounds; physical metallurgy; solid state physics; chemistry - analytical, inorganic, physical; toxicity; technology; geochemistry; ceramics. **Holdings:** 55,000 books and journal references; 3000 reports; 5000 abstracts. **Services:** Copying; inquiries, referrals, surveys, and in-depth analyses done on fee basis; center open to public with prior notice. **Computerized Information Services:** Internal database; BITNET (electronic mail service). **Publications:** RIC Newsletter, quarterly - free upon request; Reviews, irregular; RIC Insight, monthly - to supporters and subscribers. **Remarks:** FAX: (515)294-3709. Telex 269266. Electronic mail address(es): RIC@ALISUVAX (BITNET). **Staff:** Joel Calhoun, Prog.Asst.

★8239★
Iowa State University - Library - Department of Special Collections (Agri, Sci-Engr)
Ames, IA 50011-2140 Phone: (515)294-6672
Ivan Hanthorn, Hd.
Founded: 1969. **Staff:** Prof 3; Other 3. **Subjects:** Agriculture, business, veterinary medicine, natural history, history of science and technology, statistics, politics. **Special Collections:** American Archives of the Factual Film (24,155 items); Archives of American Agriculture; Archives of American Veterinary Medicine; Statistics Archives; University Archives; Little Blue Books (2210); Evolution/Creation Archive; Underground Comix (3396 items). **Holdings:** 27,535 rare book volumes; 3311 linear feet of other cataloged items. **Services:** Copying; collections open to the public for reference use only. **Automated Operations:** Computerized public access catalog. **Publications:** Guide to Manuscript Collections in the Iowa State University Library, irregular - limited distribution. **Special Indexes:** Index to Agriculture Related Collections. **Remarks:** FAX: (515)294-1885. **Staff:** Ann Kenne, Univ.Archv.; Cynthia Henderson, Spec.Coll.Libn.

★8240★
Iowa State University - Veterinary Medical Library (Med, Biol Sci)
Ames, IA 50011 Phone: (515)294-2225
Sally A. Fry, Vet.Med.Libn.
Staff: Prof 1; Other 3. **Subjects:** Veterinary and comparative medicine, anatomy, biomedical engineering, physiology, toxicology, clinical sciences, microbiology, preventive medicine, pathology, pharmacology. **Special Collections:** German theses (5515). **Holdings:** 14,000 books; 14,000 bound periodical volumes. **Subscriptions:** 652 journals and other serials. **Services:** Copying; SDI; library open to the public for reference use only. **Computerized Information Services:** DIALOG Information Services, MEDLARS. **Networks/Consortia:** Member of National Network of Libraries of Medicine - Greater Midwest Region, Polk County Biomedical Consortium (PCBC), Bibliographical Center for Research, Rocky Mountain Region, Inc. (BCR).

★8241★
Iowa State University - World Food Institute - Library (Food-Bev)
45 Kildee Hall Phone: (515)294-7699
Ames, IA 50011 Janet Olson
Subjects: Food. **Special Collections:** Women in Development; theses/dissertations/reports of projects funded through the World Food Institute. **Holdings:** 500 books. **Services:** Library open to the public, primarily intended for students at Iowa State University. **Remarks:** FAX: (515)294-0939. Telex: 283 359 IASU UR.

Iowa Urban Community Research Center
See: **University of Iowa** (18713)

Iparmuveszeti Muzeum - Konyvtar
See: **Budapest - Museum of Applied Arts - Library** (2321)

Iran - Children's Book Council of Iran
See: **Children's Book Council of Iran** (3565)

★8242★
Iran - Ministry of Culture and Higher Education - Iranian Documentation and Information Center - IRANDOC Library (Sci-Engr, Info Sci)
1188 Enqelab Ave.
P.O. Box 13185-1371 Phone: 21 662223
Tehran, Iran Ali Ajil-Froush, Dir.
Founded: 1970. **Staff:** Prof 54; Other 12. **Subjects:** Science, technology, social sciences, library and information science. **Holdings:** 28,000 books; 4000 periodicals; 22,000 goverment publications and nonbook materials; 10,000 theses and dissertations of graduates abroad. **Subscriptions:** 300 journals and other serials. **Services:** Interlibrary loan; copying; library open to researchers and professionals. **Computerized Information Services:** Internal database (information demands for research in Iran). **Remarks:** Alternate telephone number(s): 21 6409997. FAX: 21 662254. Telex: 214554 NCSR IR.

★8243★
Iran - National Library of the Islamic Republic of Iran (Area-Ethnic, Info Sci)
30 Tir St. Phone: 21 673315
Tehran 11364, Iran Mohammad Rajabi, Dir.
Founded: 1937. **Staff:** Prof 18; Other 60. **Subjects:** Iranology, Islamic studies, library and information science. **Special Collections:** Persian and Arabic manuscripts (12,000 volumes). **Holdings:** 500,000 books; 13,100 bound periodical volumes; 20,000 microforms. **Subscriptions:** 350 journals and other serials; 100 newspapers. **Services:** Copying; library open to the public with restrictions. **Computerized Information Services:** Internal databases. **Publications:** National Bibliography of Iran; Directory of Iranian Periodicals; Directory of Iranian Newspapers; The National Library of Iran, quarterly; additional publications available. **Special Catalogs:** Catalog of manuscripts. **Remarks:** FAX: 21 662040. **Staff:** Mrs. Poori Soltani, Hd. of Dept. of Lib.Res.; Mr. Kamran Fani; Mrs. Zohreh Alavi; Ms. Mandana Sadiq-Behzadi; Ms. Guiti Arian; Mr. Mehrdad Niknam-Vazifeh; Mrs. Shirin Ta'avoni; Ms. Mahvash Behnam; Ms. Monir-al-Sadat Molavi; Ashraf-al-Sadat Bozorgi.

★8244★
Ireland - Central Statistics Office - Department of the Taoiseach - Library (Sci-Engr)
Earlsfort Terrace Phone: 1 767531
Dublin 2, Ireland Anne Lacy, Asst.Prin.
Founded: 1949. **Staff:** 2. **Subjects:** Statistics. **Holdings:** 40,000 books; 500 bound periodical volumes. **Subscriptions:** 10 journals and other serials; 6 newspapers. **Services:** Interlibrary loan; copying; library open to the public for reference use only. **Publications:** Monthly acquisitions list. **Remarks:** FAX: 1 682221.

★8245★
Ireland - National Botanic Gardens - Library (Biol Sci, Agri)
Glasnevin Phone: 1 374388
Dublin 9, Ireland Valerie Ingram
Founded: 1799. **Subjects:** Botany, horticulture, history of botany, history of horticulture. **Special Collections:** Irish floristic works. **Holdings:** 40,000 books; 340 bound periodical volumes; reports; archival materials; microfiche; microfilm. **Subscriptions:** 50 journals and other serials. **Services:** Interlibrary loan; copying; library open to the public for reference use only at librarian's discretion. **Automated Operations:** Computerized cataloging.

Ireland - National Library of Ireland
See: **Republic of Ireland - Department of the Taoiseach** (13827)

Archbishop Ireland Memorial Library
See: **College of St. Thomas - School of Divinity - Archbishop Ireland Memorial Library** (3913)

★8246★
Irell & Manella - Library (Law)
1800 Avenue of the Stars, Suite 900 Phone: (213)277-1010
Los Angeles, CA 90067 Louise L. Lieb, Dir., Lib.Serv.
Founded: 1941. **Staff:** Prof 5; Other 7. **Subjects:** Law - tax, corporate, corporate securities, entertainment, antitrust, trusts and estates, probate; labor; federal and state litigation; real estate; insurance; computer law. **Special Collections:** Federal Trade Commission publications, 1979 to present; legal bibliographies. **Holdings:** 70,000 volumes; microfiche; audio- and videotapes. **Subscriptions:** 480 journals and other serials; 25 newspapers. **Services:** Interlibrary loan; library not open to the public. **Automated Operations:** Computerized serials. **Computerized Information Services:** LEXIS, DIALOG Information Services, WESTLAW, Dow Jones News/Retrieval, VU/TEXT Information Services, DataTimes, LEGI-SLATE, Legi-Tech, Current USC, Current CFR; MCI Mail (electronic mail service). **Publications:** Library Newsletter; Database Research Newsletter; Audio-Visual Newsletter. **Special Indexes:** Legal memo/opinion letter index. **Remarks:** FAX: (213)203-7199. **Staff:** Monica Hamor, Assoc.Dir.; Marilyn Wills; June Han; Carole Levitt.

IREMAM
See: **Institut de Recherches et d'Etudes sur le Monde Arabe et Musulman** (7885)

★8247★
Irish-American Cultural Association - Library (Hum)
10415 S. Western Phone: (312)239-6760
Chicago, IL 60643 Cynthia L. Buescher, Libn.
Founded: 1974. **Staff:** Prof 3; Other 5. **Subjects:** Literature, history, biography, art, music. **Holdings:** 3000 books. **Services:** Library not open to the public. **Staff:** Richard T. Crowe, Dir.; Thomas R. McCarthy, Asst.Dir.

★8248★
Irish Family Names Society - Library (Hist)
P.O. Box 2095 Phone: (619)466-8739
La Mesa, CA 91943-2095 William P. Durning, Dir.
Founded: 1978. **Staff:** 1. **Subjects:** Irish genealogy and history. **Holdings:** 500 volumes. **Services:** Library not open to the public.

★8249★
Iron County Museum - Raymond Gustafson Archives (Hist)
Box 272 Phone: (906)265-2617
Caspian, MI 49915 Marcia Bernhardt, Cur.
Founded: 1970. **Staff:** 1. **Subjects:** Local history, lumbering, mining. **Special Collections:** Letters of Carrie Jacobs Bond; manuscript of Iron County by Jack Hill; manuscript of Iron Country (Class of 44, paperback title) by Mary Jane Patterson. **Holdings:** 200 books; 1500 other cataloged items; 8200 underground mining maps; 7500 photographs; 40,000 obituaries. **Services:** Archives open to researchers by request. **Publications:** Past-Present Prints, annual - free upon request; list of other publications - available on request. **Remarks:** Maintained by Iron County Historical and Museum Society. The winter address for the archives is 233 Bernhardt Rd., Iron River, MI 49935.

Iron Range Resources & Rehabilitation Board - Minnesota Iron Range Research Center
See: **Minnesota (State) Iron Range Research Center - State Government Library** (10488)

★8250★
Irondequoit Town Historian - Photograph Collection (Hist, Aud-Vis)
c/o Historian
2180 Ridge Rd. Phone: (716)336-6065
Rochester, NY 14622 Patricia Wayne, Hist.
Subjects: Local history, 1600s to present. **Holdings:** 15,000 photographs. **Services:** Copying; collection open to the public on limited schedule and by appointment.

★8251★
Iroquois County Genealogical Society - Library (Hist)
Old Courthouse Museum
103 W. Cherry St. Phone: (815)432-2215
Watseka, IL 60970 Cheryl Gocken, Sec.
Founded: 1970. **Staff:** 1. **Subjects:** Local history and family genealogy. **Holdings:** 1250 books; 500 county records; 500 reels of microfilm of census reports and newspapers; 25 family Bibles; 100 volumes of school reports; 25 VF drawers of historical pamphlets and leaflets of local interest. **Subscriptions:** 35 journals and other serials. **Services:** Copying; library open to the public. **Publications:** Iroquois Stalker, quarterly; newsletter, bimonthly. **Special Catalogs:** Catalog of local county records (card). **Special Indexes:** Index of county cemeteries (card); pedigree charts (card). **Remarks:** Maintained by Iroquois County Historical Society.

IRS
See: **U.S. Internal Revenue Service** (17561)

Harriet Irving Library
See: **University of New Brunswick** (19025)

★8252★
Irving House Historic Centre and New Westminster Museum - Archives (Hist, Aud-Vis)
302 Royal Ave. Phone: (604)521-7656
New Westminster, BC, Canada V3L 1H7 Archie W. Miller, Cur.
Founded: 1950. **Staff:** Prof 2. **Subjects:** Local history. **Holdings:** Historical photograph collection. **Services:** Copying; archives open to the public by appointment. **Remarks:** Archives maintained by the City of New Westminster. **Staff:** Valerie Francis, Musm.Asst.

Irwin Army Hospital
See: **U.S. Army Hospitals** (17043)

Forrest A. Irwin Library
See: **Jersey City State College - Forrest A. Irwin Library - Special Collections** (8370)

Irwin Library
See: **Butler University - Irwin Library - Hugh Thomas Miller Rare Book Room** (2416)

★8253★
Isanti County Historical Society - Resource Center (Hist)
Box 525 Phone: (612)689-4229
Cambridge, MN 55008 Valorie Stavem Arrowsmith, Dir.
Staff: Prof 1. **Subjects:** Isanti County history, Swedish immigration. **Special Collections:** Isanti County archives. **Holdings:** 250 books; 400 photographs of rural life, 1890-1930; 3 VF drawers of documents; 30 oral history tapes. **Subscriptions:** 5 journals and other serials. **Services:** Interlibrary loan; copying; center open to the public on a limited schedule and by appointment for reference use. **Networks/Consortia:** Member of Central Minnesota Libraries Exchange (CMLE). **Publications:** Isanti Cuttings (newsletter), quarterly - to members. **Special Catalogs:** Inventory of Isanti County cemeteries with maps of gravestones (loose-leaf notebook); photograph, artifact, and document catalog (card). **Remarks:** Center located at 139 E. 1st St.

Isham Memorial Library
See: **Harvard University - Eda Kuhn Loeb Music Library** (6964)

★8254★
(Islamabad) American Center - USIS Library (Educ)
No. 60
Sector F-6/4
Jinnah Ave. Phone: 51 824051
Islamabad, Pakistan Syed Irshad Ali, Lib.Dir.
Founded: 1951. **Staff:** 7. **Subjects:** International relations, U.S. government and politics, public administration. **Holdings:** 9000 books; 30,000 microfiche; 2000 reports; 18,000 reels of microfilm. **Subscriptions:** 104 journals and other serials; 3 newspapers. **Services:** Interlibrary loan; copying; SDI; library open to the public. **Computerized Information Services:** ERIC, PDQ; INN (internal database). **Publications:** Annual Union List of Periodicals; Bimonthly Recent Additions. **Remarks:** FAX: 51 825514. Telex: 5864 AEISLPK. Maintained or supported by the U.S. Information Agency. Focus is on materials that will assist peoples outside the United States to learn about the United States, its people, history, culture, political processes, and social milieux. **Staff:** Manzur H. Soil, Dp.Lib.Dir.; Rafiq Ahmad, Ref.Libn.; M. Ishaq Naseem, Tech.Serv.Libn.

★8255★
Islamic Computing Centre - Library (Rel-Phil)
73 St. Thomas's Rd. Phone: 71 3596233
London N4 2QJ, England Mufti A.K. Barkatulla, Chm.
Founded: 1982. **Staff:** 2. **Subjects:** Islam - law, history, morality, teachings of Mohammad, Qur'anic interpretations; Christianity; Judaism. **Holdings:** 2000 bound volumes. **Subscriptions:** 20 journals and other serials. **Services:** Library open to the public by appointment. **Computerized Information Services:** Produces Al-Hadith databases, Al-Qur'an database, Islamic LAN Base. **Remarks:** FAX: 71 2262024. Telex: 21489 HILAL G. **Staff:** F. Khan.

★8256★
Islamic Development Bank - Library (Area-Ethnic)
P.O. Box 5925 Phone: 2 6361400
Jeddah 21432, Saudi Arabia Dr. Helmi M. Foudeh, Chf.Libn.
Founded: 1975. **Staff:** 19. **Subjects:** Economic and social development of African and Asian Muslim states and Muslim communities. **Holdings:** 22,950 volumes; 12,776 documents; 17,489 government publications; 920 periodicals; statistics. **Subscriptions:** 911 journals and other serials; 20 newspapers. **Services:** Interlibrary loan; copying; library open to researchers upon request. **Computerized Information Services:** DIALOG Information Services; MCFILE, IOFILE, ISLAMECO (internal databases); DIALMAIL (electronic mail service). **Publications:** Bibliographical lists, such as Islamic Economics and Banking. **Special Catalogs:** Special subject catalogs. **Remarks:** FAX: 2 6366871. Telex: 601137 ISDB SJ; 601407 ISDB SJ. Cable: BANKISLAMI - JEDDAH. Electronic mail address(es): 161624 (DIALMAIL). **Staff:** Ali Ali Al-Marwai; Sibte Raza Nadvi; Abdul Aziz Ben-Swaileh; Mohid Ben Mousa.

★8257★
Islamic Library Association - Library (Sci-Engr)
6304 Cory St. Phone: (805)526-3999
Simi Valley, CA 93063 Rasheed Moinuddin, Sec.
Founded: 1980. **Staff:** 1. **Subjects:** Medicine, engineering, technology, science, pure and applied sciences. **Holdings:** Figures not available. **Services:** Copying; library open to members only. **Staff:** Bader Shaheed Khan.

★8258★
Islamic Thought Foundation - Library (Rel-Phil)
P.O. Box 14155-3987
Tehran, Iran Phone: 21 844-0926
Subjects: Islam. **Holdings:** 2400 volumes.

★8259★
Island Resources Foundation - Library (Env-Cons)
Red Hook, Box 33
Charlotte Amalie Phone: (809)775-6225
St. Thomas, VI 00802 Sandra Tate, Libn.
Founded: 1971. **Subjects:** Caribbean environmental management, insular systems resource management, environmental impact mitigation strategies. **Holdings:** 200 linear feet of books, reports, and documents; 60 linear feet of unbound materials; 10 linear feet of VHS; 17 VF drawers of documents and legislative materials; 1500 nautical and topographic maps and charts; 150 rolled maps and charts; 25 atlases and oversized books; 4000 color slides and photographs; 1000 black and white prints, contact sheets, and negatives; 600 aerial photographs. **Services:** Copying; library open to the public by appointment. **Computerized Information Services:** Eastern Caribbean Non-governmental Organizations (internal database). **Publications:** Caribbean environmental management reference sources bibliography (online). **Remarks:** FAX: (809)775-3254. Maintains a branch library at 1718 P St., N.W., T-4, Washington, DC, 20036. Contact person: Jean Pierre Bacle, at (202)265-9712.

Islesford Historical Museum
See: **U.S. Natl. Park Service - Acadia Natl. Park** (17662)

ISO Library
See: **International Organization for Standardization - ISO Library** (8166)

★8260★
Isotta Fraschini Owners Association - Research Library (Rec)
4 River St. Phone: (508)744-4561
Salem, MA 01970 Paul R. Willis, Dir.
Founded: 1954. **Subjects:** History and technical information pertaining to Isotta Fraschini automobiles. **Holdings:** Books; bound periodical volumes; photographs; advertisements; catalogs; pamphlets. **Services:** Interlibrary loan; copying; material available by special request only.

★8261★
ISP Management Company, Inc. - Technical Information Services (Sci-Engr)
1361 Alps Rd. Phone: (201)628-3321
Wayne, NJ 07470 Ira Naznitsky, Mgr.
Founded: 1942. **Staff:** Prof 4; Other 1. **Subjects:** Chemistry, engineering, pulp and paper, petroleum, polymers, brighteners, chemical intermediates, textile assistants, organic chemistry. **Holdings:** 9500 books; 10,000 bound periodical volumes; 500 unbound journal volumes; 1 million U.S. patents; 3000 foreign patents; 10,000 reels of microfilm; 63 VF drawers of pamphlets. **Subscriptions:** 270 journals and other serials. **Services:** Interlibrary loan; copying; use of library for reference may be requested. **Computerized Information Services:** PFDS Online, NLM, BRS Information Technologies, DIALOG Information Services, Chemical Abstracts Service (CAS). **Publications:** Internal Reports; Searches; Translations. **Formerly:** GAF Corporation. **Staff:** Melanie C. Sze, Supv., Tech.Lib.; Ceil Garcia, Sr.Tech.Info.Spec.; Felisa Maliksi, Libn.

★8262★
Israel - Knesset - Library (Area-Ethnic, Soc Sci)
Kiryat Ben-Gurion
91950 Jerusalem, Israel Phone: 2 753333
Subjects: Israel, political science, law, journalism, Knesset, education, Judaism, literature. **Holdings:** 150,000 books. **Subscriptions:** 716 journals and other serials; 25 newspapers. **Services:** Interlibrary loan; library not open to the public. **Computerized Information Services:** Internal database (Knesset proceedings, 1949 to present). **Remarks:** Alternate telephone number(s): 2 753369. FAX: 2 662733.

★8263★
Israel - Ministry of Health - Asaf Ha-Rofe Medical Center - Medical Library (Med)
Be'er Ya'aqov
P.O. Phone: 8 449113
70350 Zerifin, Israel Rachel Goori
Founded: 1950. **Staff:** Prof 2.5. **Subjects:** Medicine. **Holdings:** 20,000 bound periodical volumes. **Subscriptions:** 200 journals and other serials. **Services:** Interlibrary loan; copying; library open to the public for reference use only. **Computerized Information Services:** CD-ROM (MEDLINE). **Remarks:** FAX: 8 449502.

Israel - Ministry of Religious Affairs - Harry Fischel Institute for Research in Talmud and Jewish Law
See: **Harry Fischel Institute for Research in Talmud and Jewish Law** (5824)

★8264★
Israel - National Center of Scientific and Technological Information - Library (Sci-Engr)
PO Box 43074
Atidim Scientific Park
Devorah-Haneviah St. Phone: 3 492040
61430 Tel Aviv, Israel Mr. Yaacov Lev, Dir.
Subjects: Scientific and technological information, library science, information science, computers. **Holdings:** 4000 volumes, including directories of information resources, technical reports, multilingual technical dictionaries, thesauri, and catalogs. **Subscriptions:** 200 journals and other serials. **Services:** SDI; center open to the public. **Computerized Information Services:** BRS Information Technologies, DIALOG Information Services, Commerce Business Daily, COMPENDEX, DOE, ERIC, Fairbase, INSPEC, ISI, Jerusalem Post Electronic Edition, KOMPASS ISRAEL, NTIS; Energy database, News and Press Releases of the Israeli Government Press Office, PCR (internal databases). **Remarks:** Alternate telephone number(s): 3 5614619. FAX: 3 492033. Telex: 03 2332. Center is a unit of the Israeli Ministry of Energy and Infrastructure. **Staff:** Mr. Hezzy Mena, Hd., Dept. of Doc.Acq.

★8265★
Israel - Prime Minister's Office - Israel State Archives - Library (Area-Ethnic)
Kiryat Ben-Gurion Phone: 2 639231
91000 Jerusalem, Israel Josepha Taslizky, Libn.
Subjects: Israel - history, economics, society; Middle East; Jews in Israel and abroad; Arab-Israeli conflicts. **Holdings:** Figures not available. **Remarks:** Alternate telephone number(s): 639231/205.

★8266★
Israel Aircraft Industries Ltd. - Technical Information Center (Sci-Engr)
B.G. INTL Airport
Dept. 2416 Phone: 3 935 8068
Lod, Israel David Elazar
Founded: 1955. **Subjects:** Aeronautics, avionics, aircraft maintenance, high technology. **Special Collections:** Aircraft Overhaul and Repair Manuals. **Holdings:** 100,000 books; 5000 bound periodical volumes; 50,000 reports; 40,000 microfiche. **Subscriptions:** 2000 journals and other serials. **Services:** Center not open to the public. **Computerized Information Services:** DIALOG Information Services, NewsNet, Inc., Aerospace Online; LMS - Library Management (internal database); DIALMAIL (electronic mail service). **Remarks:** FAX: 3 971 2336. Telex: 381014. Electronic mail address(es): 9345 (DIALMAIL).

★8267★
Israel-America Chamber of Commerce and Industry - Library (Bus-Fin)
35 Shaul Hamelech Blvd.
P.O. Box 33174
61331 Tel Aviv, Israel Phone: 3 6952341
Subjects: International trade, with emphasis on U.S.-Israeli trade. **Holdings:** 300 volumes. **Computerized Information Services:** Internal database. **Remarks:** FAX: 3 6951272. Telex: 32139.

★8268★
Israel Antiquities Authority - Library (Soc Sci)
Rockefeller Bldg.
POB 586 Phone: 2 292617
91004 Jerusalem, Israel Giovanna Barouch
Founded: 1937. **Staff:** Prof 3. **Subjects:** Archeology, numismatics, ancient art, epigraphy, ancient pottery, ancient travels. **Holdings:** 40,000 books; 20,000 bound periodical volumes. **Subscriptions:** 300 journals and other serials. **Services:** Copying; library open to the public. **Remarks:** FAX: 2 292628.

★8269★
Israel Atomic Energy Commission - Soreq Nuclear Research Center - Library and Technical Information Department (Energy, Sci-Engr)
70600 Yavne, Israel Phone: 8 434380
Mrs. E. Meisner, Hd.
Founded: 1952. **Staff:** Prof 5; Other 6. **Subjects:** Nuclear physics, chemistry, and engineering; lasers; electro-optics. **Holdings:** 75,000 volumes; 280,000 technical reports. **Subscriptions:** 300 journals and other serials. **Services:** Interlibrary loan; copying; SDI; library open to center staff and cooperating scientists. **Computerized Information Services:** DIALOG Information Services; internal database. **Publications:** Accession list of new books, quarterly; accession list of new reports, monthly; current journal subscriptions, annual. **Remarks:** FAX: 8 437364. Telex: 381455.

★8270★
Israel Export Institute - Library (Bus-Fin)
29 Ha Mared St.
P.O. Box 50084 Phone: 3 5142879
61500 Tel Aviv, Israel Amos Cohen, Hd. of Info.Dept.
Staff: Prof 2. **Subjects:** Foreign trade, marketing. **Special Collections:** European Community Journal on microfiche. **Holdings:** 4000 books; 100 bound periodical volumes. **Subscriptions:** 150 journals and other serials; 10 newspapers. **Services:** Library open to the public with restrictions. **Computerized Information Services:** DIALOG Information Services, Data-Star, LEXIS, ORBIT Search Service, MAID, TRADSTAT. Contact Person: Haim Schneider. **Remarks:** FAX: 3 5142902.

★8271★
Israel National Commission for UNESCO - Library
Ministry of Education and Culture
34 Shivety Yisrael St.
91911 Jerusalem, Israel
Defunct.

★8272★
Israeli Dance Institute Inc. - Resource Information Center (Area-Ethnic)
711 3rd Ave., 12th Fl.
New York, NY 10017 Phone: (212)983-4806
Founded: 1951. **Staff:** 2. **Subjects:** Israeli folk dance, history of Jewish dance, Israeli and Jewish music, Jewish dance costume. **Holdings:** Books; bound periodical volumes; education materials; teaching materials. **Subscriptions:** 500 journals and other serials. **Services:** Costume bank; center open to the public by appointment. **Publications:** Harikud; Chassidic Dance; Mechol Ha'am; 100 Israeli Folk Dances; Teacher's Guide - all for sale; Nirkoda (newsletter), 3/year - to the public. **Remarks:** FAX: (212)983-4084. Center offers professional guidance to teachers, community leaders, performing groups, and Israeli folk dance enthusiasts. **Staff:** Danny Uziel, Co-Dir.; Ruth Goodman Burger, Co-Dir.

★8273★
(Istanbul) Amerikan Kutuphanesi - USIS Library (Educ)
104-108 Mesrutiyet Caddesi
Tepebasi
Istanbul, Turkey
Remarks: Maintained or supported by the U.S. Information Agency. Focus is on materials that will assist peoples outside the United States to learn about the United States, its people, history, culture, political processes, and social milieux.

Istituto per la Cooperazione Universitaria
See: **Institute for University Cooperation** (7987)

Istituto Internazionale di Studi Liguri
See: **International Institute for Ligurian Studies** (8131)

Istituto Italiano di Cultura
See: **Italian Cultural Institute** (8277)

Istituto Nazionale di Studi Romani
See: **Italy - Ministry of Cultural Affairs - National Institute of Roman Studies** (8281)

★8274★
Istituto Sperimentale per le Colture Industriali - Sezione Operativa Periferica - Biblioteca (Agri, Food-Bev)
Via Amendola 82 Phone: 425 360113
I-45100 Rovigo, Italy E. Biancardi
Founded: 1914. **Staff:** 1. **Subjects:** Sugar beet - breeding, agronomy, and biology. **Holdings:** 10,000 books; 2000 bound periodical volumes. **Subscriptions:** 40 journals and other serials. **Services:** Library open to the public. **Remarks:** FAX: 425 34681.

Istvan Kiraly Muzeum - Konyvtar
See: **King Stephen Museum - Library** (8719)

★8275★
Italian Association of Saint Cecilia - Library (Mus)
piazza Agostino n. 20/A
I-00186 Rome, Italy Phone: 6 654-0461
Subjects: Sacred music. **Holdings:** 3000 volumes. **Remarks:** Association is named for Saint Cecilia, the patron saint of music. **Also Known As:** Associazione Italiana Santa Cecelia.

★8276★
Italian Association for Women in Development - Library (Soc Sci)
via Tagliamento 14
I-00298 Rome, Italy
Subjects: Third World - development, women's issues. **Holdings:** 1000 volumes; documents. **Also Known As:** Associazione Italiana Donne per la Sviluppo.

★8277★
Italian Cultural Institute - Library (Area-Ethnic)
686 Park Ave. Phone: (212)879-4242
New York, NY 10021 Dr. Franco Derlenga, Hd.Libn.
Founded: 1959. **Staff:** 3. **Subjects:** Italy and Italian culture. **Holdings:** 34,000 books; 103 VF drawers of clippings; 228 slide sets; 123 containers of photographs. **Subscriptions:** 100 journals and other serials. **Services:** Interlibrary loan; copying; library open to the public with card required for borrowing. **Publications:** Recent Italian Publications, annual; Books Translated from the Italian and Books of Italian Interest Published in the U.S., biennial - both free upon request. **Remarks:** FAX: (212)861-4018. This is a cultural agency of the Italian Government. **Also Known As:** Istituto Italiano di Cultura.

★8278★
Italian Cultural Service - Library (Area-Ethnic)
1200 Dr. Penfield Ave. Phone: (514)849-3473
Montreal, PQ, Canada H3A 1A9 Dr. Lucia Cenerini
Founded: 1962. **Staff:** Prof 3; Other 2. **Subjects:** Italian culture: art, theater, cinema, literature, history, philosophy, music, social sciences. **Holdings:** 9700 books. **Subscriptions:** 11 journals and other serials. **Services:** Interlibrary loan; library open to the public. **Remarks:** FAX: (514)849-2569. **Also Known As:** Istituto Italiano di Cultura. **Staff:** Dr. Roberta Maccagnani.

★8279★
Italian Library Association - Library (Info Sci)
Istituto Centrale per la Patalogia del Libro
via Milano 76
I-00184 Rome, Italy Phone: 6 493 532
Subjects: Library science. **Holdings:** 5000 volumes. **Also Known As:** Associazione Italiana Biblioteche.

★8280★
Italy - Ministero beni Cultrali - Biblioteca Nazionale Vittorio Emanuele III (Info Sci, Hum, Theater)
Piazza Plebiscito
Palazzo Reale Phone: 81 40 28 42
Naples, Italy Maria Rosaria Romano Vicenzo, Dir.
Subjects: General collection with emphasis on humanities. **Special Collections:** Papyrus manuscripts; Biblioteca Lucchesi Palli (theater and cinema); Zagazzi Collection; Americana Collection; Neapolitan Collection. **Holdings:** 2 million books; 7442 bound periodical volumes; 18,522 documents; 2030 reels of microfilm; 12,379 manuscripts. **Services:** Interlibrary loan; copying; library open to the public with restrictions. **Publications:** Quarterly newsletter.

★8281★
Italy - Ministry of Cultural Affairs - National Institute of Roman Studies - Library (Area-Ethnic)
Piazza dei Cavalieri di Malta 2 Phone: 6 5743442
I-00153 Rome, Italy Dr. Fernanda Roscetti, Dir.
Subjects: Ancient and modern Rome - archeology, sociology, language, literature, history, art history, allied subjects. **Holdings:** 20,800 books. **Subscriptions:** 1070 journals and other serials. **Services:** Library open to the public. **Also Known As:** Istituto Nazionale di Studi Romani.

★8282★
Italy - Ministry of Employment and Social Security - Library (Soc Sci, Bus-Fin)
Via Flavia 6 Phone: 6 4882555
I-00187 Rome, Italy Andrea Caruso, Lib.Mgr.
Founded: 1946. **Staff:** 11. **Subjects:** Labor, sociology, employment problems, social security, labor organization. **Special Collections:** General agreement on wages and conditions during the period of fascism. **Holdings:** 35,000 books; 15,000 bound periodical volumes; archival materials; audiovisual programs. **Subscriptions:** 230 journals and other serials. **Services:** Copying; library open to the public for reference use only. **Computerized Information Services:** Internal database. **Publications:** Periodicals purchasing bulletins. **Remarks:** 6 4880890. **Staff:** Josephine Soloperto; Josephine Mazzeschi.

★8283★
Italy - Ministry of Foreign Affairs - Library (Soc Sci)
Farnesina Phone: 6 3236347
I-00194 Rome, Italy Raffaelia Maimieri, Dir.
Founded: 1886. **Staff:** Prof 6; Other 10. **Subjects:** International relations, diplomacy, history. **Special Collections:** Fondo Armao (Atlanti Di Ve Coromelli, 17th-18th centuries). **Holdings:** 150,000 books; 300,000 bound periodical volumes; 50,000 reports. **Subscriptions:** 300 journals and other serials. **Services:** Copying; library open to the public. **Automated Operations:** Servizio Biblioteca Nazionale (SBN).

★8284★
Itasca County Historical Society - Museum and Library (Hist)
Central School
Pokegama Ave. at 4th St.
Box 664 Phone: (218)326-6431
Grand Rapids, MN 55744 John A. Kelsch, Exec.Dir.
Founded: 1972. **Staff:** 1. **Subjects:** Itasca County and Minnesota history. **Special Collections:** Judy Garland memorabilia. **Holdings:** Books; photographs; manuscripts. **Services:** Copying; library open to researchers by appointment. **Computerized Information Services:** Online systems. Performs searches on fee basis. **Publications:** Newsletter, quarterly - for internal distribution only.

★8285★
ITT Corporation - Aerospace/Communications Division - Information Services Center (Sci-Engr)
1919 W. Cook Rd.
Box 3700 Phone: (219)487-6298
Fort Wayne, IN 46801 Carol L. Hilkey, Info.Spec.
Founded: 1977. **Staff:** 2. **Subjects:** Electronics, communications. **Holdings:** 1000 volumes; military and industry specifications, standards and related documents. **Subscriptions:** 102 journals and other serials. **Services:** Interlibrary loan; center open to employees only. **Automated Operations:** Computerized cataloging. **Computerized Information Services:** DIALOG Information Services, DTIC, Teltech, NASA/RECON; TAIS, PARTSMASTER (internal databases); electronic mail service. **Networks/Consortia:** Member of Tri-ALSA. **Remarks:** FAX: (219)487-6269.

★8286★
ITT Corporation - Gilfillan Engineering Library (Sci-Engr)
7821 Orion Ave.
Box 7713 Phone: (818)988-2600
Van Nuys, CA 91409 Dawn N. Villere, Sr.Tech.Libn.
Staff: Prof 2. **Subjects:** Radars, electronics, electrical engineering, navigation/communication, microwaves/filters, optics. **Special Collections:** Radars. **Holdings:** 10,000 books; 20,000 bound periodical volumes; 30,000 documents; complete AD and NASA microfiche files; military specifications on microfilm. **Subscriptions:** 250 journals and other serials. **Services:** Interlibrary loan; library open to the public with restrictions. **Automated Operations:** Computerized acquisitions, serials, and circulation. **Computerized Information Services:** DIALOG Information Services. **Publications:** Library Accessions Listings, monthly; ITTG Current Contents. **Remarks:** Includes technical library of the Electro-Optical Products Division. **Staff:** Juanita Lopez, Asst.Libn.

★8287★
ITT Corporation - ITT Aerospace Communications Division - Technical Library (Sci-Engr)
100 Kingsland Rd., Dept. 43401 Phone: (201)284-3810
Clifton, NJ 07014 Rita C. Reisman, Tech.Libn.
Staff: Prof 1; Other 1. **Subjects:** Electronics, navigation, physics, data processing, astronautics. **Holdings:** 7000 volumes; 1000 technical reports; 103 microforms. **Subscriptions:** 200 journals and other serials. **Services:** Library not open to the public. **Computerized Information Services:** DIALOG Information Services. **Publications:** Recent Accessions - for internal distribution only. **Remarks:** FAX: (201)284-4838. **Formerly:** ITT Avionics/Aerospace Communications Division.

★8288★
ITT Corporation - Library (Bus-Fin)
1330 Avenue of the Americas Phone: (212)258-1223
New York, NY 10019 Susan D. Narciso, Mgr., Res. & Lib.Serv.
Founded: 1947. **Staff:** Prof 1. **Subjects:** Business, finance, public relations. **Holdings:** 1000 books. **Subscriptions:** 200 journals and other serials; 20 newspapers. **Services:** Interlibrary loan; library not open to the public. **Automated Operations:** Computerized acquisitions. **Computerized Information Services:** NEXIS. **Remarks:** Alternate telephone number(s): 258-1222; FAX: (212)489-5099; 489-5098.

★8289★
ITT Hartford - Corporate Library (Bus-Fin)
Hartford Plaza Phone: (203)547-5516
Hartford, CT 06115-2531 Bonnie Jean Woodworth, Corp.Libn.
Founded: 1968. **Staff:** Prof 1; Other 2. **Subjects:** Finance. **Special Collections:** Moody's Bank & Finance, 1928 to present; bank and quotation record, 1922 to 1986. **Holdings:** 3000 books; 166 legal file drawers of corporate and financial information. **Subscriptions:** 250 journals and other serials. **Services:** Interlibrary loan; copying; library open to the public by appointment. **Networks/Consortia:** Member of Capital Region Library Council (CRLC).

★8290★
ITT Hartford Insurance Group - Technical Research Services Unit and Loss Control Library (Sci-Engr)
Hartford Plaza Phone: (203)547-3099
Hartford, CT 06115 Sarah Hager Johnston, Dir., Tech.Res.Serv.
Founded: 1940. **Staff:** Prof 1; Other 1. **Subjects:** Safety engineering; toxicology; chemistry; fire protection; transportation; occupational safety and health; industrial hygiene; ergonomics; industry standards - American National Standards Institute (ANSI), Underwriters Laboratories (UL), American Standard of Testing Materials (ASTM). **Holdings:** 5000 books; VF drawers. **Subscriptions:** 200 journals and other serials. **Services:** Interlibrary loan; library open to the public by special arrangement only. **Computerized Information Services:** DIALOG Information Services, Mead Data Central, ORBIT Search Service, MEDLINE, Occupational Health Services, Inc. (OHS), OCLC. **Networks/Consortia:** Member of NELINET, Inc., Center for Research Libraries (CRL). **Publications:** Technical Bulletin; Focus; Library Bulletin. **Remarks:** FAX: (203)547-6004.

★8291★
ITT Rayonier, Inc. - Research Center - Library (Sci-Engr)
409 E. Harvard St. Phone: (206)426-4461
Shelton, WA 98584 Patricia A. Tostevin, Libn./Info. Spec.
Staff: Prof 1; Other 1. **Subjects:** Pulp and paper, natural products chemistry, forests and forestry, chemical engineering. **Holdings:** 8000 books; 7500 bound periodical volumes; 14,150 patents; 600 translations; 50 cassette tapes; reports on microfiche; videotapes. **Subscriptions:** 200 journals and other serials. **Services:** Library not open to the public. **Computerized Information Services:** DIALOG Information Services, PFDS Online, BRS Information Technologies, MEDLARS, Chemical Abstracts Service (CAS), WILSONLINE, STN International; CD-ROM; OnTyme Electronic Message Network Service (electronic mail service). **Networks/Consortia:** Member of CLASS, Western Library Network (WLN). **Remarks:** FAX: (206)426-7537.

★8292★
Ivanovskij Mezotraslevoj Territorialnyj Centr Naucno Techniceskoj Informacii i Propagandy - Centralnaja Naucno Techniceskaja Biblioteka (Sci-Engr, Bus-Fin)
pl. Revoljucii 2 Phone: 29520
Ivanovo 1, Russia A.A. Kaverin
Founded: 1963. **Staff:** Prof 10. **Subjects:** Economics, management, mechanical engineering, energy, textile industry, transportation, building. **Holdings:** 32,306 books; 21,308 bound periodical volumes; 619 reports; 36,770 reels of microfilm. **Services:** Interlibrary loan; copying; library open to the public. **Computerized Information Services:** Internal databases.

Stinceon Ivey Memorial Library
See: **First Baptist Church** (5747)

★8293★
Muriel Ivimey Library (Med)
329 E. 62nd St. Phone: (212)838-8044
New York, NY 10021 Frederick Burnett, CSW, Chm., Lib.Comm.
Founded: 1962. **Staff:** Prof 1; Other 1. **Subjects:** Psychoanalysis. **Holdings:** 4000 books; 500 bound periodical volumes. **Subscriptions:** 35 journals and other serials. **Services:** Library not open to the public. **Remarks:** Library formed by Association for the Advancement of Psychoanalysis, Karen Horney Psychoanalytic Institute and Center, and American Institute for Psychoanalysis.

★8294★
Ivinson Memorial Hospital - Medical Library (Med)
255 N. 30th St. Phone: (307)742-2141
Laramie, WY 82070 Connie Baker, Med.Libn.
Founded: 1973. **Staff:** Prof 1. **Subjects:** Medicine, patient care, nursing, health administration. **Holdings:** 350 books; 5 drawers of pamphlets. **Subscriptions:** 105 journals and other serials. **Services:** Interlibrary loan; copying; SDI; library open to the public for reference use only. **Computerized Information Services:** MEDLARS. Performs searches on fee basis. **Networks/Consortia:** Member of National Network of Libraries of Medicine - Midcontinental Region. **Remarks:** FAX: (307)742-2150.

Ivorydale Technical Center
See: **Procter & Gamble Company** (13396)

★8295★
(Izmir) Amerikan Kutuphanesi - USIS Library (Educ)
Sehit Nevres Bey Bulvari 23A
Post Box 404
Izmir, Turkey
Remarks: Maintained or supported by the U.S. Information Agency. Focus is on materials that will assist peoples outside the United States to learn about the United States, its people, history, culture, political processes, and social milieux.

J

★8296★
J-B Publishing Company - Research Library (Publ)
430 Ivy Ave. Phone: (402)826-3356
Crete, NE 68333 William F. Rapp, Mng.Ed.
Staff: 1. **Subjects:** Railway history, industrial archeology. **Holdings:** 700 books and bound periodical volumes; 5000 photographs. **Subscriptions:** 10 journals and other serials. **Services:** Copying; library open to the public by appointment. **Publications:** The Bulletin; Railroad Station Historical Society; Railway History Monographs.

★8297★
J.F.K. Memorial Hospital - Medical Library (Med)
S. Congress Ave.
Box 1489 Phone: (407)642-3511
Lake Worth, FL 33460 Nancy M. Adams, Dir.
Staff: Prof 1; Other 1. **Subjects:** Medicine. **Holdings:** 450 books; 300 bound periodical volumes. **Subscriptions:** 175 journals and other serials. **Services:** Interlibrary loan; copying; SDI. **Computerized Information Services:** DIALOG Information Services. **Networks/Consortia:** Member of Palm Beach Health Sciences Library Consortium (PBHSLC). **Remarks:** FAX: (407)642-3623.

★8298★
J & L Testing Company, Inc. - Library (Sci-Engr)
938 S. Central Ave.
Canonsburg, PA 15317 Phone: (412)746-4441
Subjects: Geotechnical and geosynthetic research, systems design. **Holdings:** 8000 volumes and periodicals. **Remarks:** FAX: (412)745-4261.

★8299★
J2CP Information Services (Soc Sci)
Box 184 Phone: (714)248-5843
San Juan Capistrano, CA 92693-0184 Sr. Mary Elizabeth, SSE, Dir.
Founded: 1986. **Staff:** Prof 2. **Subjects:** Transsexualism, gender dysphoria syndrome, HIV/AIDS. **Special Collections:** Law library (700 volumes). **Holdings:** 800 books. **Services:** Services not open to the public. **Computerized Information Services:** HIV/AIDS Information BBS (internal database). **Publications:** Information packet on transsexualism with bibliography - for sale. **Remarks:** Affiliated with the Sisters of St. Elizabeth of Hungary. Contains the holdings of the former Janus Information Facility, the Erickson Education Foundation, the John Augustus Foundation, Renaissance: Gender Identity Services, and the ACLU Transsexual Rights Committee.

★8300★
Jablon Computer Associates - Library (Sci-Engr)
2250 Monterey Rd. Phone: (805)466-3209
Atascadero, CA 93422 D. Hordeski
Founded: 1980. **Staff:** Prof 3. **Subjects:** Electrical engineering, personal computers, computer applications, local area networks. **Holdings:** 500 books; 500 bound periodical volumes; 1000 reports. **Subscriptions:** 10 journals and other serials. **Services:** Copying; library open to the public on a fee basis. **Publications:** Microcomputer Dictionary; Communications Networks; Computer Integrated Manufacturing; Local Area Networks; Control Systems; Tranducers; Computer Design.

Jackman Library
See: **C.M. Hincks Treatment Center - C.M. Hincks Institute - Jackman Library** (7227)

★8301★
Jackson County Court House - Law Library (Law)
239 Main St., 2nd Fl. Phone: (614)286-3601
Jackson, OH 45640 Joe Oths, Off.
Subjects: Law. **Holdings:** 5000 volumes. **Services:** Library open to the public.

★8302★
Jackson County Historical Society - Archives and Research Library (Hist)
Independence Square Courthouse, Rm.103 Phone: (816)252-7454
Independence, MO 64050 Jennifer Parker, Archv.
Founded: 1958. **Staff:** Prof 1; Other 6. **Subjects:** Local Civil War history, Jackson County history, California/Oregon Trail, William Quantrill, Jesse James. **Special Collections:** Strauss-Peyton glass negatives, 1901-1960 (50,000 images); photograph collection, 1850 to present (10,000 images). **Holdings:** 2000 books; 400 bound periodical volumes; 3000 cubic feet of manuscripts, letters, records; 40 VF drawers of abstracts; clipping file; maps. **Services:** Copying; center open to the public. **Special Catalogs:** Strauss-Peyton negatives (online). **Staff:** Kathleen Halcro, Site Dir.

★8303★
Jackson County Historical Society - Library (Hist)
307 N. Hwy. 86 Phone: (507)662-5505
Lakefield, MN 56150 Phyllis Nauerth, Exec.Dir.
Founded: 1974. **Staff:** 1. **Subjects:** County history. **Special Collections:** Biography of Inkpaduta; biographies of early settlers. **Holdings:** 200 books; 3 dissertations; plat books for county, 1874 to present; county newspapers on microfilm. **Services:** Library open to the public for reference use only. **Publications:** Jackson County History, volumes 1 and 2.

★8304★
Jackson County Law Library (Law)
1125 Grand Ave., Suite 1050 Phone: (816)221-2221
Kansas City, MO 64106 Ellen H. Bull, Libn.
Founded: 1872. **Staff:** Prof 1; Other 3. **Subjects:** Law. **Holdings:** 32,500 volumes; 16,600 microfiche; 1400 ultrafiche. **Subscriptions:** 130 journals and other serials. **Services:** Copying; library open to the public on fee basis. **Computerized Information Services:** WESTLAW, DIALOG Information Services. **Remarks:** FAX: (816)221-6607.

★8305★
Jackson County Law Library (Law)
Justice Bldg.
10 S. Oakdale Ave. Phone: (503)776-7214
Medford, OR 97501 Pamela Pfeil, Law Libn.
Founded: 1931. **Staff:** 1. **Subjects:** Oregon and case law. **Holdings:** 30,006 volumes; Court of Appeals and Supreme Court briefs; 38 drawers of microfilm; 4 drawers of microfiche. **Services:** Interlibrary loan; copying; library open to the public on a limited schedule. **Computerized Information Services:** WESTLAW. **Networks/Consortia:** Member of Southern Oregon Library Federation (SOLF). **Remarks:** Maintained by Jackson County Library System.

★8306★
Jackson/Hinds Library System - Eudora Welty Library - Special Collections (Hum)
300 N. State St. Phone: (601)968-5811
Jackson, MS 39201 Carolyn McCallum, Hd.Libn.
Founded: 1914. **Special Collections:** Mississippi Collection (15 VF drawers); Foundation Center; Regional Depository Library (IRS returns of state and national foundations on microfiche; Foundation Center publications and directories); genealogy collection (1000 volumes). **Services:** Interlibrary loan; copying; collections open to the public. **Automated Operations:** Computerized cataloging. **Networks/Consortia:** Member of Central Mississippi Library Council. **Staff:** Gordon Saucier, Ref.Coord.

The Jackson Homestead
See: **Newton City Museum: The Jackson Homestead** (11787)

★8307★
Jackson Hospital & Clinic, Inc. - Medical Library (Med)
1235 Forest Ave. Phone: (205)298-8898
Montgomery, AL 36106 Cindy Musso, Med.Libn.
Founded: 1955. **Staff:** Prof 1. **Subjects:** Medicine, surgery, pediatrics. **Holdings:** 100 books; 663 bound periodical volumes. **Subscriptions:** 42 journals and other serials. **Services:** Interlibrary loan; copying; library open to health care professionals and students.

J. Hugh Jackson Library
See: **Stanford University** (15652)

John Herrick Jackson Music Library
See: **Yale University** (20717)

★8308★
Jackson & Kelly - Library (Law)
1600 Laidley Tower
Box 553 Phone: (304)340-1000
Charleston, WV 25322 Richard Earl Boaz, Libn.
Staff: Prof 1; Other 2. **Subjects:** Law. **Holdings:** 25,000 books. **Subscriptions:** 42 journals and other serials; 8 newspapers. **Services:** Library open to attorneys. **Computerized Information Services:** DIALOG Information Services, Human Resource Information Network (HRIN), WESTLAW, LEXIS, VU/TEXT Information Services, West Virginia Online Legislative Services. **Remarks:** FAX: (304)340-1130; 340-1129 (backup number).

★8309★
Jackson Laboratory - Joan Staats Library (Biol Sci, Med)
600 Main St. Phone: (207)288-3371
Bar Harbor, ME 04609 Douglas T. Macbeth, Libn.
Founded: 1929. **Staff:** Prof 2; Other 2. **Subjects:** Inbred strains of mice, genetics, cancer, growth, animal health and husbandry, immunology, aging, cell biology, molecular genetics. **Holdings:** 3000 books; 20,000 bound periodical volumes; 46,000 reprints. **Subscriptions:** 350 journals and other serials. **Services:** Interlibrary loan; SDI; library open to scientists, students and visitors. **Automated Operations:** Computerized cataloging and serials. **Computerized Information Services:** NLM, DIALOG Information Services, BRS Information Technologies, OCLC, EPIC, WILSONLINE; CD-ROM; internal database; InterNet (electronic mail service). Performs searches. **Networks/Consortia:** Member of Health Science Library and Information Cooperative of Maine (HSLIC), Medical Library Center of New York (MLCNY), NELINET, Inc. **Remarks:** FAX: (207)288-5079. Electronic mail address(es): LIBRARY@ARETHA.JAX.ORG (InterNet). **Staff:** Ann L. Jordan, Info.Anl.; Suzanne Serreze, Ser.Spec.; Irene Pettengill, ILL Spec.

Lambert L. Jackson Memorial Library
See: **Mount Cuba Astronomical Observatory, Inc.** (10803)

★8310★
Jackson-Madison County General Hospital - Learning Center (Med)
708 W. Forest Ave. Phone: (901)425-6024
Jackson, TN 38301 Linda G. Farmer, Dir.
Founded: 1972. **Staff:** Prof 1. **Subjects:** Medicine, nursing, health. **Holdings:** 1500 books; 600 bound periodical volumes. **Subscriptions:** 202 journals and other serials. **Services:** Interlibrary loan; copying; center open to the public with restrictions. **Computerized Information Services:** BRS Information Technologies. **Networks/Consortia:** Member of Association of Memphis Area Health Science Libraries (AMAHSL), Tennessee Health Science Library Association (THeSLA). **Remarks:** FAX: (901)425-6983.

★8311★
Jackson Memorial Hospital - School of Nursing Library (Med)
1755 N.W. 12th Ave. Phone: (305)585-6833
Miami, FL 33136-1094 Lynn MacAuley, Libn.
Staff: Prof 1; Other 3. **Subjects:** Nursing, medicine, health. **Special Collections:** History of Nursing (50 books). **Holdings:** 2500 books; 150 bound periodical volumes; 230 National League for Nursing reports and pamphlets; 243 video cassettes. **Subscriptions:** 84 journals and other serials. **Services:** Interlibrary loan; copying; SDI; library open to the public for reference use only. **Networks/Consortia:** Member of Miami Health Sciences Library Consortium (MHSLC). **Remarks:** Alternate telephone number(s): (305)585-6641.

★8312★
Jackson Park Hospital - Medical Library (Med)
7531 S. Stony Island Ave. Phone: (312)947-7653
Chicago, IL 60649 Syed A. Maghrabi, Med.Ref.Libn.
Staff: Prof 1. **Subjects:** Medicine. **Holdings:** 2500 books. **Subscriptions:** 190 journals and other serials. **Services:** Interlibrary loan; copying; SDI; library open to the public with valid need. **Computerized Information Services:** MEDLARS, BRS/COLLEAGUE. **Networks/Consortia:** Member of Chicago and South Consortium.

R.W.B. Jackson Library
See: **Ontario Institute for Studies in Education (OISE)** (12444)

Jackson State University - Information Services Library
See: **Information Services Library** (7844)

★8313★
Jackson Sun - Library (Publ)
245 W. Lafayette
Box 1059 Phone: (901)427-3333
Jackson, TN 38302-1059 Ellen Henry, Libn.
Founded: 1974. **Staff:** 1. **Subjects:** Newspaper reference topics. **Holdings:** 651 reels of microfilm.

★8314★
Jacksonville Developmental Center - Library
1201 S. Main St. Phone: (217)479-2117
Jacksonville, IL 62650 Bell Curry, Staff Dev.Spec.
Subjects: Mental retardation, psychiatry, general psychology, developmental disabilities, psychological evaluation, behavior modification. **Holdings:** 100 books. **Services:** Library open to the public with restrictions.

★8315★
Jacksonville Public Libraries - Florida and Genealogy Collections (Hist)
122 N. Ocean St. Phone: (904)630-2410
Jacksonville, FL 32202 Judith L. Williams, Dir. of Libs.
Founded: 1914. **Staff:** Prof 3. **Subjects:** Genealogy, especially southeastern United States; Florida and Jacksonville - history, biography, description and travel, politics and government, plants and wildlife, fine arts, economics. **Special Collections:** Merritt Collection of Floridiana (500 rare books, maps, documents). **Holdings:** 19,170 books and cataloged pamphlets; 1096 bound periodical volumes; 7281 reels of microfilm; 11,070 checklisted Florida documents; 60 file boxes and 7144 checklisted copies of Jacksonville documents; 110 file boxes of Florida documents; 11 VF drawers of uncataloged pamphlets; 17 VF drawers of newspaper clippings; 2 VF drawers of photographs; 480 maps; 1807 microfiche. **Subscriptions:** 47 journals and other serials. **Services:** Copying; collection open to the public for serious research with restrictions. **Automated Operations:** Computerized cataloging. **Computerized Information Services:** OCLC. **Networks/Consortia:** Member of SOLINET. **Special Indexes:** Florida Times-Union Index, 1895-1925, 1929, 1938 to present (book, microfilm); PL News Index (online); Star Edition (black newspaper) Deaths Index, 1950-1963; Jacksonville Journal Index, 1925-1938 (book, microfilm). **Remarks:** The above telephone number is for Florida reference; the Genealogy reference telephone number is 630-2409. FAX: (904)630-2431. **Staff:** Mr. Carol Harris, FL Cur.; Ms. Arden Brugger, Geneal.Libn.

Lotte Jacobi Photo Archive
See: **University of New Hampshire - Department of Instructional Services - Film Library** (19031)

★8316★
The Jacobite Association - Athlone Court & Historiographer Royal Research Library (Hist)
White Rose House
Box 66
Greenwich, CT 06831 Neil Christopher Bennett, Libn.
Founded: 1976. **Staff:** Prof 16; Other 8. **Subjects:** Jacobites - biography, history, genealogy, peerages; British history and culture. **Holdings:** 4000 books; 6100 bound periodical volumes; manuscripts and archival papers. **Subscriptions:** 22 journals and other serials; 9 newspapers. **Services:** Answers questions submitted by mail. **Computerized Information Services:** Internal database. **Special Indexes:** Biographical, historical, and genealogical index concerning Jacobites and royal Stuart family and Loyalists since 1688; biographical and historiobiographic indices prepared upon request. **Staff:** Vere Patrick Gaydon, Asst.Libn.; Nicholas Raines, Archv.; Hon. Donald Armstrong, Geneal./Biogr.; Theodore Cole, Polit.Hist./Historiobiogr.; Lorenzo Scott, Mil.Hist.; Anne Grant, Acq.

★8317★
Jacobs Engineering Group - Information Center (Energy)
4848 Loop Central Dr., Suite 415 Phone: (713)699-2200
Houston, TX 77081 Sara Davis, Libn.
Founded: 1964. **Staff:** Prof 1. **Subjects:** Petroleum refining technology, petrochemical plant design, natural gas processing, environmental engineering, business statistics. **Holdings:** 6000 books; 800 bound periodical volumes; 300 company reports; 2500 microforms. **Subscriptions:** 100 journals and other serials. **Services:** Interlibrary loan; copying; services open to the public by appointment. **Automated Operations:** Data Trek. **Computerized Information Services:** DIALOG Information Services, ORBIT Search Service, STN International, DataTimes. **Remarks:** FAX: (713)669-0045.

Jacobson Library
See: **B'nai Jeshurun Temple on the Heights** (1921)

Jagiellonian University
See: **Uniwersytet Jagiellonski** (19665)

Janheinz Jahn Library
See: **Universitat Mainz - Institut fur Ethnologie und Afrika Studien - Bibliothek** (18047)

Jail Museum Genealogy Library
See: **Kosciusko County Historical Society - Genealogy Section** (8797)

Wilson C. Jainsen Library
See: **St. Francis Hospital and Medical Center** (14302)

★8318★
(Jakarta) American Cultural Center - USIS Library (Educ)
Wisma Metropolitan II, 3rd Fl.
Jalan Jendral Sudirman 29 Phone: 21 5711481
Jakarta, Indonesia Melling Simanjuntak
Founded: 1986. **Staff:** Prof 7. **Subjects:** United States - social sciences, political science, the arts, history. **Holdings:** 12,000 books; 37 microfiche; 3 reels of microfilm. **Subscriptions:** 176 journals and other serials. **Services:** Copying; SDI; library open to the public. **Automated Operations:** Computerized public access catalog. **Computerized Information Services:** DIALOG Information Services, LEGI-SLATE, PDQ; CD-ROMs. **Publications:** Alert. **Remarks:** FAX: 21 5711495. Maintained or supported by the U.S. Information Agency. Focus is on materials that will assist peoples outside the United States to learn about the United States, its people, history, culture, political processes, and social milieux. **Staff:** Ms. Wawa Rustini; Medi Soeyono.

★8319★
(Jakarta) Perhimpunan Persahabatan Indonesia-Amerika - USIS Collection (Educ)
Jalan Pramuka Kav. 30
P.O. Box 300
Jakarta, Indonesia
Remarks: Maintained or supported by the U.S. Information Agency. Focus is on materials that will assist peoples outside the United States to learn about the United States, its people, history, culture, political processes, and social milieux.

★8320★
Jamaica - Ministry of Agriculture and Fisheries - Library (Agri)
P.O. Box 480 Phone: (809)9273576
Kingston 6, Jamaica Trevor A. Wong, Act.Libn.
Founded: 1877. **Staff:** 6. **Subjects:** Agriculture. **Special Collections:** Jamaican and West Indian Collection. **Holdings:** 20,000 books; 15,000 bound periodical volumes; 300 microfiche; maps; manuscripts; clippings. **Subscriptions:** 5000 journals and other serials; 3 newspapers. **Services:** Interlibrary loan; library open to the public with restrictions. **Publications:** AGRIJAM (abstracts); AGRINDEX (abstracts); Union List of Serials.

★8321★
Jamaica - National Library of Jamaica (Area-Ethnic, Info Sci)
12 East St.
P.O. Box 823 Phone: (809)922-0620
Kingston, Jamaica Stephney Ferguson, Dir.
Founded: 1879. **Staff:** 89. **Subjects:** Jamaica, West Indies. **Special Collections:** Jamaicana and West Indiana collection. **Holdings:** 41,615 books; 31,212 AV programs; 23,575 microforms; 2060 manuscripts; 3119 newspapers; 20,364 photographs; 1286 prints; 25,000 maps. **Subscriptions:** 37,474 journals and other serials; 15 newspapers. **Services:** Interlibrary loan; copying; microfilming. **Computerized Information Services:** Internal databases. Performs searches. **Publications:** Jamaican National Bibliography; Occasional Bibliography Series; Freedom To Be: The Abolition of Slavery in Jamaica and Its Aftermath. **Special Indexes:** Index to the Daily Gleaner, 1975 to present. **Remarks:** FAX: (809)922-5567. **Staff:** John Aarons; June Vernon; Eppie Edwards; Horace Lewis; Fay Williams; Byron Palmer.

★8322★
Jamaica Hospital - Medical Library (Med)
89th Ave. & Van Wyck Expy. Phone: (718)262-6042
Jamaica, NY 11418 Carolyn Mansbach, Dir.
Founded: 1963. **Staff:** Prof 1; Other 1. **Subjects:** Medicine. **Holdings:** 4000 books; 4500 bound periodical volumes; Audio-Digest tapes. **Subscriptions:** 275 journals and other serials. **Services:** Interlibrary loan; copying; library open to students and visiting physicians with permission. **Computerized Information Services:** MEDLINE. **Networks/Consortia:** Member of Brooklyn-Queens-Staten Island Health Sciences Librarians (BQSI), Medical & Scientific Libraries of Long Island (MEDLI), BHSL, New York Metropolitan Reference and Research Library Agency. **Remarks:** FAX: (718)262-6495.

Henry James Collection of First Editions
See: **San Diego State University** (14718)

M. Lucia James Curriculum Laboratory
See: **University of Maryland, College Park** (18806)

★8323★
James River Corporation - Business Information Center (Bus-Fin)
300 Lakeside Dr., Rm. 1105 Phone: (510)874-3958
Oakland, CA 94612-3592 Linda Suzuki, Hd.
Founded: 1953. **Staff:** 2. **Subjects:** Marketing research, marketing, paper industry, business statistics. **Special Collections:** Trade journals of the pulp and paper industry. **Holdings:** 5900 books; 3500 pamphlets; 12 VF drawers of trade association material; 2 drawers of microforms. **Subscriptions:** 350 journals and other serials. **Services:** Interlibrary loan; center not open to the public. **Automated Operations:** Computerized periodical circulation. **Computerized Information Services:** DIALOG Information Services, PFDS Online, RLIN, NEXIS. **Networks/Consortia:** Member of Bay Area Library and Information Network, CLASS. **Remarks:** FAX: (510)874-3575.

★8324★
James River Corporation - Camas Technical Center (Sci-Engr)
349 N.W. 7th Ave. Phone: (206)834-8315
Camas, WA 98607 Dorothea Crawford, Info.Spec.
Founded: 1938. **Staff:** Prof 1; Other 1. **Subjects:** Paper technology, chemistry, textiles, engineering. **Holdings:** 8000 volumes. **Subscriptions:** 225 journals and other serials; 10 newspapers. **Services:** Interlibrary loan; copying; library open to the public by appointment. **Computerized Information Services:** DIALOG Information Services, ORBIT Search Service. **Remarks:** FAX: (206)834-8252.

★8325★
James River Corporation - Neenah Technical Center - Technical Information Center (Sci-Engr)
1915 Marathon Ave.
Box 899
Neenah, WI 54956 Phone: (414)729-8169
Founded: 1937. **Staff:** Prof 1; Other 2. **Subjects:** Pulp, paper, and paperboard chemistry and technology; plastics; packaging technology; food technology;

chemical engineering. **Special Collections:** All U.S. patents, 1978 to present (microfilm). **Holdings:** 10,000 books; 2500 bound periodical volumes; 20,000 technical documents. **Subscriptions:** 600 journals and other serials. **Services:** Interlibrary loan; copying; SDI; center open to the public with restrictions. **Automated Operations:** Computerized public access catalog and cataloging. **Computerized Information Services:** DIALOG Information Services, ORBIT Search Service, OCLC, STN International, WILSONLINE. **Networks/Consortia:** Member of Fox Valley Library Council, Wisconsin Interlibrary Services (WILS). **Publications:** Patent Alert; Information Update. **Remarks:** FAX: (414)729-8161.

★8326★
Jameson Memorial Hospital - School of Nursing Library (Med)
1211 Wilmington Ave. Phone: (412)656-4050
New Castle, PA 16105-2595 Cathy D. Clark, Libn.
Staff: Prof 1. **Subjects:** Medicine, surgery, nursing. **Holdings:** 4648 books; 341 bound periodical volumes. **Subscriptions:** 120 journals and other serials. **Services:** Interlibrary loan; copying; library open to the public with approval of librarian. **Computerized Information Services:** MEDLARS. **Remarks:** FAX: (412)656-4179.

Jamieson Memorial Library
See: **Washington County Historical Society** (19994)

Jamron Health Science Library
See: **Sinai Samaritan Medical Center - Jamron Health Science Library** (15188)

★8327★
Janacek Academy of Music and Dramatic Art - Library (Mus, Theater)
Gorkeho 11 Phone: 5 759841
CS-602 00 Brno, Czechoslovakia Marie Masickova, Ph.D.
Founded: 1948. **Staff:** 3. **Subjects:** Music, theater, plays. **Holdings:** 36,000 books; 4000 bound periodical volumes; 41,000 pieces of music; 12,000 phonograph records. **Subscriptions:** 75 journals and other serials. **Services:** Interlibrary loan; library open to the public with restrictions. **Publications:** Monthly list of additions in the library. **Also Known As:** Janackova Akademie Muzickych Umeni - Ustredni Knihovna JAMU. **Staff:** Bohuna Dofkova; Alexandra Lukasova.

Janackova Akademie Muzickych Umeni - Ustredni Knihovna JAMU
See: **Janacek Academy of Music and Dramatic Art - Library** (8327)

★8328★
Dr. Charles A. Janeway Child Health Centre - Library Services (Med)
Pleasantville Phone: (709)778-4344
St. John's, NF, Canada A1A 1R8 Shaila Mensinkai, Hosp.Libn.
Founded: 1966. **Staff:** 1. **Subjects:** Pediatrics, medicine, surgery. **Holdings:** 3000 books; 4500 bound periodical volumes; 857 Audio-Digest tapes; 390 pamphlets. **Subscriptions:** 170 journals and other serials. **Services:** Interlibrary loan; library not open to the public. **Computerized Information Services:** MEDLINE, Nursing & Allied Health Database. **Remarks:** FAX: (709)722-9605. **Formerly:** Its Janeway Medical Library.

Janus Information Facility - J2CP Information Services
See: **J2CP Information Services** (8299)

★8329★
Japan - Environment Agency - National Institute for Environmental Studies - Environmental Information Center (Env-Cons)
16-2 Onogawa
Tsukuba Phone: 298 516111
Ibaraki 305, Japan Mr. Tadaaki Watanabe, Dir.
Founded: 1990. **Staff:** Prof 4; Other 17. **Subjects:** Environment. **Holdings:** 28,400 bound volumes; 84,953 technical reports of local, national, and foreign governments. **Subscriptions:** 1962 journals and other serials. **Services:** Division open to Institute members and officials of the Environment Agency. **Computerized Information Services:** DIALOG Information Services, JICST On-line Information Service, INFOTERRA database, STN International; Environmental Numerical Data File (internal database). **Publications:** Annual Report of the NIES; Annual Report of Special Research Projects from the NIES; Annual Report of Global Environmental Research from the NIES; Report of Special Research from the NIES; Research Report from the NIES; Data Compendium; NIES News, bimonthly. **Remarks:** FAX: 298 514732. **Staff:** Ms. Sanae Furuta, Info.Mgt.Sect.

★8330★
Japan - Ministry of Agriculture, Forestry and Fisheries - Fruit Tree Research Station - Library (Agri)
2-1 Fujimoto Phone: 56-6416
Yatabe 305, Ibaraki, Japan Dr. Akira Yamaguchi, Dir.
Subjects: Agronomy; fruit trees - breeding techniques, pomology, plant protection. **Holdings:** 40,000 volumes.

★8331★
Japan - Ministry of Construction - Building Research Institute - Library (Plan)
1 Tatehara Phone: 64-2151
Tsukuba, Ibaraki, Japan Ms. K. Kimura, Libn.
Subjects: Housing and building economy, building materials, structural engineering, building production, environmental design and fire protection, urban planning, disaster prevention, new building techniques, energy, natural resources. **Holdings:** 35,000 volumes. **Subscriptions:** 250 journals and other serials. **Services:** Interlibrary loan; library open to research workers. **Computerized Information Services:** BRI Library System (internal database). **Remarks:** FAX: 64-2989. Telex: 72 3652560 BRIMOC J.

Japan - Ministry of Education, Science, and Culture
See: **Japan - National Language Research Institute** (8336)

Japan - Ministry of Education, Science, and Culture - National Astronomical Observatory, Mizusawa
See: **National Astronomical Observatory, Mizusawa** (11083)

★8332★
Japan - Ministry of Health and Welfare - Institute for Population Problems - Population Reference Center (Soc Sci)
2-2 1-Chome, Kasumigaseki
Chiyoda-ku Phone: 33 591-4816
Tokyo, Japan Kiichi Yamaguchi, Act.Chf.
Subjects: Population; demography; population problems and policies in Japan, Asia, the world. **Holdings:** 110,000 volumes.

★8333★
Japan - Ministry of Transport - Ship Research Institute - Library (Trans, Sci-Engr)
38-1 6-Chome, Shinkawa
Mitaka Phone: 33 45-5171
Tokyo, Japan Kaitsu Saegusa, Libn.
Subjects: Shipbuilding, engineering. **Holdings:** 51,000 volumes.

★8334★
Japan - National Diet Library (Info Sci)
10-1, Nagata-cho 1 chome
Chiyoda-ku Phone: 3 35812331
Tokyo 100, Japan Masakatsu Katogi, Libn.
Founded: 1948. **Staff:** 850. **Special Collections:** All publications published in Japan; books on Japan published abroad. **Holdings:** 5.6 million volumes; 122,000 journals and newspapers; 340,000 maps; 334,000 gramophone records; 182,000 reels of microfilm; other cataloged items. **Services:** Interlibrary loan; copying; library open to the public with restrictions. **Automated Operations:** Computerized cataloging and indexing. **Computerized Information Services:** Japan MARC M & S; CD-ROM (Japan MARC M). **Publications:** Japanese National Bibliography, weekly; Directory of Japanese Scientific Periodicals, irregular. **Special Indexes:** Japanese Periodicals Index, quarterly; General Index to the Debates at the Diet. **Remarks:** Provides library services for the Diet, government ministries and agencies, and the general public. Telex: 2225393 NADLIB.

★8335★
Japan - National Institute of Agro-Environmental Sciences - Library (Agri, Env-Cons)
3-1-1 Kannondai Phone: 298 388161
Tsukuba 305, Ibaraki, Japan Akira Hashimoto
Founded: 1983. **Staff:** Prof 6; Other 5. **Subjects:** Agriculture, environmental science. **Holdings:** 37,800 books; 41,000 bound periodical volumes; 33,000 reports. **Subscriptions:** 271 journals and other serials; 3 newspapers. **Computerized Information Services:** DIALOG Information Services. **Publications:** Bulletin; Annual Report. **Remarks:** FAX: 298 388199. **Also Known As:** Nogyo Kankyo Gijutsu Kenkyojo - Toshoka.

★8336★
Japan - National Language Research Institute - Library (Hum)
3-9-14 Nisigaoka
Kita-ku
Tokyo 115, Japan
Phone: 33 900-3111
Kikuo Nomoto, Dir.
Founded: 1948. **Staff:** Prof 2. **Subjects:** Modern Japanese language studies, linguistics. **Special Collections:** Books printed in the Meiji era; books on Japanese dialects; Japanese language dictionaries printed before the Meiji era. **Holdings:** 77,000 volumes; 871 reels of microfilm; 355 records; 565 open-reel and cassette tapes. **Subscriptions:** 801 journals and other serials; 5 newspapers. **Services:** SDI; library open to the public with restrictions. **Publications:** Library News, irregular; Acquisition list, quarterly - both for internal distribution only; Bibliography of bibliographies of Japanese Language Researchers. **Remarks:** FAX: 33 906-3530. Affiliated with Japan - Ministry of Education, Science, and Culture. **Also Known As:** Kokuritsu Kokugo Kenkyusho. **Staff:** Michiko Otsuko, Chf.Libn.

★8337★
Japan Atomic Energy Research Institute (JAERI) - Department of Technical Information (Energy)
2-2-2 Uchisaiwai-cho
Chiyoda-ku
Tokyo 100, Japan
Phone: 3 35922364
Mr. Akira Nakamo, Dir.
Founded: 1956. **Staff:** Prof 30; Other 5. **Subjects:** Nuclear science and technology. **Holdings:** 36,000 books; 38,000 bound periodical volumes; 660,000 technical reports. **Subscriptions:** 1200 journals and other serials. **Services:** Library open to Japanese nuclear community. **Computerized Information Services:** INIS (International Nuclear Information System). Performs searches on fee basis. **Remarks:** FAX: 3 35922349.

★8338★
Japan Center for International Exchange - Reference Library (Bus-Fin)
4-9-17, Minami Azabu
Minato-ku
Tokyo 106, Japan
Phone: 33 3446-7781
Staff: Prof 1. **Subjects:** International relations, United States-Japan relations, Asia-Pacific region, Europe-Japan relations, research institutions, philanthropic organizations. **Special Collections:** Publications of major policy-related research organizations in United States, Western Europe, Asia, and Japan. **Services:** Library is open primarily for staff use. **Remarks:** FAX: 33 3443-7580. Telex J23239 JAPANEX.

★8339★
Japan Economic Institute of America - Library (Bus-Fin)
1000 Connecticut Ave., N.W.
Washington, DC 20036
Phone: (202)296-5633
Sally Bryant, Staff Asst.
Founded: 1956. **Staff:** 1. **Subjects:** Japanese economy, U.S.-Japan economic relations. **Holdings:** 1800 books; Japanese language reference materials. **Subscriptions:** 131 journals and other serials; 8 newspapers. **Services:** Interlibrary loan; copying; library open to the public for reference use only. **Remarks:** FAX: (202)296-8333.

(Japan) National Council of YMCAs of Japan
See: **National Council of YMCAs of Japan** (11145)

★8340★
Japan Pharmaceutical Information Center - Library (Med)
3rd Fl., Nagai-kinenkan
2-12-15, Shibuya
Shibuya-ku
Tokyo 150, Japan
Phone: 33 54661811
Fuminae Kubo, Dir.
Founded: 1972. **Staff:** 3. **Subjects:** Drugs - general, regulation, safety in clinical use. **Special Collections:** Drug package inserts (30,000). **Holdings:** 3600 books; microfiche. **Subscriptions:** 600 journals and other serials. **Services:** Center open to the public with restrictions. **Computerized Information Services:** Produces JAPIDOC, Drugs Data Base. **Publications:** Japan Pharmaceutical Abstracts, monthly. **Remarks:** FAX: 33 2219137. Center is affiliated with the Ministry of Health and Welfare. **Also Known As:** Nihon Iyaku Joho Center.

★8341★
Japan Society, Inc. - Library (Area-Ethnic)
333 E. 47th St.
New York, NY 10017
Phone: (212)832-1155
Reiko Sassa, Dir., Lang., Educ. & Lib.
Founded: 1971. **Staff:** 2. **Subjects:** Japan - culture, customs, art, history, religion, travel, social sciences, foreign relations, economics, language. **Holdings:** 10,000 volumes; dictionaries; trade and commerce directories. **Subscriptions:** 75 journals and other serials; 13 newspapers. **Services:** Copying; library open to the public for reference use only by appointment. **Publications:** Bibliographies. **Remarks:** Library holdings are in English and Japanese.

★8342★
Japanese American National Library (Area-Ethnic)
1619 Sutter St.
P.O. Box 590598
San Francisco, CA 94159
Phone: (415)567-5006
Karl K. Matsushita, Dir.
Founded: 1969. **Staff:** 3. **Subjects:** Japanese in United States and Canada. **Special Collections:** National Repository of Japanese American Redress (50 boxes); Japanese American vernacular newspapers (27). **Holdings:** 10,000 books; 46 bound periodical volumes; 30 nonbook items. **Subscriptions:** 21 journals and other serials; 27 newspapers. **Services:** Copying; library open to the public for reference use only; phone inquiries accepted. **Publications:** Books-in-Print: Japanese in America, annual; bulletin, quarterly. **Special Indexes:** Abstract-Index of Japanese American Vernacular Newspapers, quarterly. **Remarks:** Library is said to collect all published materials relating to the Japanese in the U.S. and Canada, particularly in the fields of history, literature, art, social sciences, mental health, interracial marriage, medicine, and current events. **Formerly:** Japanese American Library.

Bertha Jaques Archives
See: **Cedar Rapids Museum of Art - Herbert S. Stamats Art Library** (3186)

★8343★
Jardin Botanique de Montreal - Bibliotheque (Biol Sci)
4101 Sherbrooke St., E.
Montreal, PQ, Canada H1X 2B2
Phone: (514)872-1824
Celine Arseneault, Botanist/Libn.
Founded: 1940. **Staff:** Prof 1; Other 4. **Subjects:** Botany, horticulture, urban horticulture, landscaping architecture. **Special Collections:** Botanical magazines, 18th century to present. **Holdings:** 14,000 books; 4000 bound periodical volumes; 12,000 unbound periodicals; 32,500 reprints and pamphlets; 110,000 slides. **Subscriptions:** 400 journals and other serials. **Services:** Interlibrary loan; copying; library open to the public. **Automated Operations:** Computerized public access catalog. **Publications:** Publications au Jardin Botanique de Montreal, annual - available on request. **Remarks:** FAX: (514)872-3765. **Also Known As:** Montreal Botanical Garden.

★8344★
Jardin Zoologique du Quebec - Bibliotheque (Biol Sci)
8191, ave. du Zoo
Charlesbourg, PQ, Canada G1G 4G4
Phone: (418)646-9239
Founded: 1942. **Subjects:** Zoology, mammalogy, ornithology, ichthyology, zoological gardens, horticulture, botany. **Holdings:** 3500 books; 80 bound periodical volumes. **Subscriptions:** 18 newspapers. **Services:** Copying. **Computerized Information Services:** Internal database. **Remarks:** FAX: (418)646-9239. **Also Known As:** Quebec Zoological Garden.

Randall Jarrell Collection
See: **University of North Carolina at Greensboro** (19088)

Mamye Jarrett Learning Center
See: **East Texas Baptist University** (5129)

William C. Jason Library
See: **Delaware State College** (4723)

★8345★
John Jay College of Criminal Justice of CUNY - Lloyd George Sealy Library (Law)
899 10th Ave. Phone: (212)237-8225
New York, NY 10019 Prof. Marilyn Lutzker, Chf.Libn.
Founded: 1965. **Staff:** Prof 11; Other 10. **Subjects:** Criminal justice, government, fire science, forensic science, forensic psychology, public administration, police science. **Special Collections:** John Howard Collection (prison reform; 100 volumes); Theater for the Forgotten Workshops (30 videotapes); New York City criminal courts trial transcripts, 1890-1920 (2500 volumes); Lewis E. Lawes (warden of Sing Sing Prison) papers, 1883-1947 (13 boxes); papers of Flora Rheta Schreiber. **Holdings:** 180,000 books; 21,000 bound periodical volumes. **Subscriptions:** 1419 journals and other serials. **Services:** Interlibrary loan; copying; library open to the public for reference use only. **Automated Operations:** Computerized public access catalog (NOTIS). **Computerized Information Services:** DIALOG Information Services, WESTLAW; CD-ROMs (faculty and student use only). **Networks/Consortia:** Member of New York Metropolitan Reference and Research Library Agency. **Publications:** Research guides; bibliographies. **Remarks:** FAX: (212)237-8221. **Staff:** Prof. M. Kandel, Hd., Tech.Serv.

John Jay Homestead State Historic Site
See: **New York (State) Office of Parks, Recreation & Historic Preservation** (11681)

★8346★
Jazz Composers Orchestra Association - New Music Distribution Service - Library
500 Broadway
New York, NY 10012
Subjects: Music industry. **Holdings:** 2000 recordings from 350 record companies. **Remarks:** Library specializes in independent label recordings of experimental music. Currently inactive.

Jean-Talon Hospital
See: **Hopital Jean-Talon** (7391)

Jefferson County Free Library
See: **Birmingham Public and Jefferson County Free Library** (1853)

★8347★
Jefferson County Historic Preservation and Archives (Hist)
Urban County Government Center
810 Barret Ave.
Louisville, KY 40204 Phone: (502)625-5761
Staff: Prof 4; Other 1. **Subjects:** Jefferson County government and historic sites. **Holdings:** 7500 cubic feet of official records. **Services:** Copying; office open to the public. **Formerly:** Jefferson County Office of Historic Preservation and Archives. **Staff:** Leslee F. Keys, Div.Dir.; David Morgan, Archv.Spec.; Donald Lee, Mgt.Asst.; Olivia Frederick, Cons.Archv.

★8348★
Jefferson County Historical Society - Library (Hist)
228 Washington St. Phone: (315)782-3491
Watertown, NY 13601 Persijs Kolberg, Ph.D, Dir.
Subjects: Watertown and Jefferson County history. **Special Collections:** Papers of Governor R.P. Flower. **Holdings:** 750 volumes; pamphlets, ledgers, daybooks, account books, journals of 19th century country stores; 19th century bank record books; boxes of archival materials; current museum periodicals and directories. **Services:** Copying; library open to the public for reference use only.

★8349★
Jefferson County Historical Society - Museum (Hist)
City Hall
210 Madison Phone: (206)385-1003
Port Townsend, WA 98368 Patricia J. Warren, Dir.
Founded: 1951. **Staff:** 2. **Subjects:** Jefferson County and regional history; biography; ships and shipping; early Pacific Northwest histories; historic preservation and restoration. **Holdings:** 162 volumes; 100 maps and nautical charts; 33 manuscript cases of family histories; 6000 historical photographs; Genealogical Society records; city, county, school records; bound volumes of the Port Townsend Leader, 1891 to present; Port Townsend Leader, 1896-1903, on microfilm; Oral History. **Services:** Copying; library open to the public for reference use only under supervision of research staff. **Staff:** Betty J. Pfouts, Res.Libn.; Marge Samuelson, Musm.Asst.

★8350★
Jefferson County Law Library (Law)
900 Jefferson County Court House Phone: (205)325-5628
Birmingham, AL 35263 Linda M. Hand, Law Libn.
Staff: Prof 2; Other 3. **Subjects:** Law. **Holdings:** 54,006 volumes. **Subscriptions:** 119 journals and other serials. **Services:** Interlibrary loan; copying and faxing of cases for members of the Bench and Bar of Alabama (fee for attorneys); library open to the public for reference use only. **Automated Operations:** Computerized cataloging. **Computerized Information Services:** WESTLAW. Performs searches on fee basis for Alabama Bar Association members only. **Remarks:** FAX: (205)322-5915. **Staff:** Patty P. Grissett, Asst. Law Libn.

★8351★
Jefferson County Law Library (Law)
Courthouse Phone: (614)283-8553
Steubenville, OH 43952 Jan Morley, Libn.
Founded: 1900. **Staff:** Prof 1; Other 1. **Subjects:** Law. **Holdings:** 16,500 volumes; 6800 volumes of microfiche reporters. **Subscriptions:** 31 journals and other serials. **Services:** Copying; library open to the public for research only. **Remarks:** Maintained by Jefferson County Law Library Association.

★8352★
Jefferson County Law Library (Law)
200 Main St. Phone: (814)849-1621
Brookville, PA 15825 June Kindel, Law Libn.
Subjects: Law. **Holdings:** 8875 books. **Services:** Library open to residents of Jefferson County. **Computerized Information Services:** Veralex 2, WESTLAW. **Remarks:** FAX: (814)849-1649.

Jefferson County Office of Historic Preservation and Archives
See: **Jefferson County Historic Preservation and Archives** (8347)

Jefferson County Planning Commission
See: **Louisville and Jefferson County Planning Commission** (9400)

★8353★
Jefferson County Public Law Library (Law)
Old Jail Bldg.
514 W. Liberty, Suite 240 Phone: (502)625-5943
Louisville, KY 40202-2806 Linda Miller Robbins, Dir.
Founded: 1839. **Staff:** Prof 5. **Subjects:** Law. **Special Collections:** Kentucky law. **Holdings:** 100,000 volumes; 150 bound periodical volumes. **Subscriptions:** 60 journals and other serials. **Services:** Interlibrary loan; copying; library open to the public for reference use only. **Remarks:** FAX: (502)625-3483.

★8354★
Jefferson County Public Schools R1 - Professional Library Media Center (Educ)
1829 Denver West Dr., No. 27 Phone: (303)273-6550
Golden, CO 80401 Shelley Shea
Founded: 1962. **Staff:** Prof 1; Other 2. **Subjects:** Education, art, music, special education, computer science. **Holdings:** 13,376 books; 4383 phonograph records; 6432 AV programs; 16,000 curriculum books; 604 computer software packages; 1967 titles of sheet music; publishers' catalogs and pamphlet file; microforms. **Subscriptions:** 254 journals and other serials. **Services:** Interlibrary loan; center open to Jefferson County taxpayers. **Computerized Information Services:** BRS Information Technologies, MEDLARS, DIALOG Information Services. Performs searches free of charge for district personnel. **Remarks:** FAX: (303)273-6749.

★8355★
Jefferson Foundation - Library (Hist)
1529 18th St., N.W. Phone: (202)466-2311
Washington, DC 20033 Mary E. Kennedy, Exec.Dir.
Subjects: Constitutional history, public policy, American intellectual history. **Holdings:** 250 books. **Publications:** Foundation publishes booklets on specific Constitutional reform issues including term limitations and the line item veto. **Remarks:** The Jefferson Foundation is a nonpartisan, nonprofit organization whose purposes are: to study historical trends and contemporary opinion on constitutional reforms which have been proposed in Congress as ways of improving the structure and functioning of government and to educate the public on these reform issues.

★8356★
Jefferson Historical Society and Museum - Archives (Hist)
223 Austin St.
Jefferson, TX 75657 Phone: (903)665-2775
Subjects: Local history, Civil War, genealogy. **Special Collections:** Carl Hertzog Collection (his typography, arranging, printing). **Holdings:** Books; bound periodical volumes; 35 manuscripts; 20 notebooks of clippings; several hundred documents; maps. **Services:** Archives open to the public with restrictions.

Jefferson House-Gerontology Resource Center
See: **Hartford Hospital** (6935)

Jefferson National Expansion Memorial
See: **U.S. Natl. Park Service** (17736)

★8357★
Thomas Jefferson Cultural Center - (Makati) USIS Library (Educ)
395 Sen. Gil J. Puyat Ave.
Makati, Metro Manila 3177, Philippines
Remarks: Maintained or supported by the U.S. Information Agency. Focus is on materials that will assist peoples outside the United States to learn about the United States, its people, history, culture, political processes, and social milieux.

Thomas Jefferson Law Library
See: **College of William and Mary - Marshall-Wythe Law Library** (3919)

Thomas Jefferson Learning Resource Center
See: **National College** (11121)

Thomas Jefferson Library
See: **Library of Congress - Rare Book & Special Collections Division** (9135)

Thomas Jefferson Library
See: **University of Missouri--St. Louis** (18982)

★8358★
Thomas Jefferson Memorial Foundation, Inc. - Research Library (Hist)
Box 316 Phone: (804)295-1832
Charlottesville, VA 22902 Lucia C. Stanton, Dir. of Res.
Subjects: Thomas Jefferson. **Special Collections:** Howard C. Rice Collection (18th century Paris and France, and Americans who spent time there; 400 books and pamphlets); Thomas Jefferson's Paris, 1976 and Chastellux's Travels, 1963 (14 boxes of Howard C. Rice's papers dealing with the preparation of these publications). **Holdings:** 1200 books; 100 reels of microfilm of Jefferson's papers; 6 drawers of research topics related to Jefferson. **Services:** Copying; library open to the public by appointment. **Remarks:** FAX: (804)977-7757. **Also Known As:** Monticello.

★8359★
Thomas Jefferson University - Cardeza Foundation - Tocantins Memorial Library (Med)
1015 Walnut St. Phone: (215)955-7714
Philadelphia, PA 19107 Sandor S. Shapiro, M.D., Dir.
Founded: 1962. **Staff:** Prof 1; Other 1. **Subjects:** Hematology and allied health sciences. **Holdings:** 200 books; 400 bound periodical volumes. **Subscriptions:** 28 journals and other serials. **Services:** Library open to staff only. **Remarks:** FAX: (215)923-3836.

★8360★
Thomas Jefferson University - Scott Memorial Library (Med)
1020 Walnut St. Phone: (215)955-6994
Philadelphia, PA 19107 Edward Tawyea, Dir.
Founded: 1896. **Staff:** Prof 16; Other 31. **Subjects:** Medicine and allied health sciences. **Special Collections:** Bland Collection (history of obstetrics and gynecology); University archives. **Holdings:** 72,230 monographs; 73,860 periodical volumes; 14,984 microforms containing 184 periodical titles; 608 audiotapes and cassettes; 1298 videocassettes, slide sets, multimedia kits. **Subscriptions:** 2595 journals and other serials. **Services:** Interlibrary loan; copying; SDI; library open to the public with restrictions. **Automated Operations:** Computerized cataloging, acquisitions, serials, and circulation. **Computerized Information Services:** BRS Information Technologies, DIALOG Information Services, PFDS Online, U.S. National Technical Information Service (NTIS), OCLC, MEDLINE. **Networks/Consortia:** Member of PALINET, Interlibrary Delivery Service of Pennsylvania (IDS), Health Sciences Libraries Consortium (HSLC). **Publications:** Monthly Booklist of Current Acquisitions - available upon request; Connections (newsletter). **Remarks:** FAX: (215)955-7642. **Staff:** Alice O. Mackov, Ref.Libn.; Henry T. Armistead, Hd., Coll.Dept.; Elaine Spyker, Sys.Libn.; Claire McCurdy, Archv.; Adrianne Loev, Hd., Ref.; Margaret Devlin, Assoc.Libn., Pub.Serv.; Elizabeth Mikita, Cat.Libn.; Nancy Calabretta, Ref.Libn.; Lillian Brazin, Res.Libn.; Elizabeth Warner, User Educ.Libn.; Steven Ifshin, Assoc.Libn., Sys.; Diana Zinatto, Assoc.Libn., Coll.Mgmt.; Valerie Bennett, Doc.Del.Libn.; Joanne Sparks, LRC Coord.; Judith Hesp, Mgr., Educ.Serv.

★8361★
Jekyll Island Authority - Jekyll Island Museum Archives (Hist)
375 Riverview Dr. Phone: (912)635-2119
Jekyll Island, GA 31527 Martha Teall
Subjects: Jekyll Island early history and state era. **Special Collections:** Jekyll Island Club records. **Holdings:** 1100 books; 1375 documents; 2000 photographs; 32 manuscripts. **Services:** Copying; archives open to the public by appointment with restrictions on some holdings. **Remarks:** FAX: (912)635-4004. **Staff:** Leslie Hicks, Cur. of Educ.

Arthur D. Jenkins Library
See: **Textile Museum** (16284)

Jenkins Research Library
See: **Southern Baptist Convention - Foreign Mission Board** (15458)

★8362★
Theodore F. Jenkins Memorial Law Library (Law)
841 Chestnut St., Suite 1220 Phone: (215)592-5690
Philadelphia, PA 19107 Regina A. Smith, Dir.
Founded: 1802. **Staff:** Prof 11; Other 20. **Subjects:** Law. **Special Collections:** John Marshall Gest Memorial Library (civil and canon law; 1900 volumes). **Holdings:** 270,000 volumes; 1991 reels of microfilm; Pennsylvania state legislative material. **Subscriptions:** 4080 journals and other serials; 8 newspapers. **Services:** Interlibrary loan; copying; faxing; library open to the public. **Automated Operations:** Computerized public access catalog, cataloging, serials, and acquisitions. **Computerized Information Services:** WESTLAW, DIALOG Information Services, NEXIS, LEXIS, Information America, MONTCO, VU/TEXT Information Services, WILSONLINE, Dow Jones News/Retrieval. Performs searches on fee basis. Contact Person: Ida Weingram, Hd., Pub.Serv., 592-5693. **Networks/Consortia:** Member of PALINET, Mid-Atlantic Law Library Cooperative (MALLCO). **Remarks:** FAX: (215)925-2105; (215)592-5694 or 592-5695 (reference). Public access catalog: (215)925-1874. **Staff:** Nancy Garner, Ref.; John Schaefer, Ref.; Christine Amadio, Ref./ILL; Katarzyna Piechnik, Cat.; Charlene Chou, Cat.; Kathy Coon, Assoc.Libn.; Constance Smith, Acq.; Ann Liivak, Ref.; Jennifer Hohenstein, Circ.; Peggy Mahan, Hd., Tech.Serv.

William R. Jenkins Architecture and Art Library
See: **University of Houston** (18646)

★8363★
Jenkintown Library - Pennsylvania Collection (Hist)
York & Vista Rds. Phone: (215)884-0593
Jenkintown, PA 19046 Joan Markham, Hd.Libn.
Founded: 1803. **Staff:** Prof 1; Other 3. **Subjects:** Local history. **Special Collections:** Pennsylvania Collection. **Holdings:** 40,000 volumes. **Subscriptions:** 105 journals and other serials. **Services:** Interlibrary loan; copying; collection open to the public. **Remarks:** Maintained by the Abington Library Society.

Jenks Learning Resource Center
See: **Gordon College** (6574)

Jenks Memorial Collection of Adventual Materials
See: **Aurora University** (1308)

★8364★
Jenner & Block - Law Library (Law)
One IBM Plaza Phone: (312)222-9350
Chicago, IL 60611 Marie M. Del Bene, Hd.Libn.
Staff: Prof 3; Other 5. **Subjects:** Law. **Holdings:** 37,000 books; 1000 bound periodical volumes. **Services:** Interlibrary loan; library not open to the public. **Automated Operations:** Computerized cataloging, serials, and acquisitions. **Computerized Information Services:** DIALOG Information Services, LEXIS, NEXIS, OCLC, Dow Jones News/Retrieval, Hannah Information Systems, LEGI-SLATE, VU/TEXT Information Services. **Publications:** Counsel Briefings, bimonthly - for internal distribution only; Professional Reading, bimonthly; Law Locators, irregular. **Remarks:** FAX: (312)644-4314. **Staff:** Samantha Whitney, Ref.Libn.; Sandra Jacobson, Ref.Libn.

Otto E. Jennings Library
See: **Carnegie Museum of Natural History - Library** (3085)

★8365★
Jensen Associates, Inc. - Library (Energy)
129 South St. Phone: (617)482-7700
Boston, MA 02111 Jean A. Malinasky, Libn.
Founded: 1975. **Staff:** Prof 2. **Subjects:** Energy economics, energy resources, petroleum, natural gas, electricity. **Holdings:** 2000 books. **Subscriptions:** 80 journals and other serials. **Services:** Library not open to the public. **Computerized Information Services:** DIALOG Information Services, Reuters Information Service. **Publications:** New in the Library, monthly - for internal distribution only. **Remarks:** FAX: (617)482-7078. **Staff:** Janet C. Dwyer, Libn.

Jens Jensen Archive
See: **Morton Arboretum - Sterling Morton Library** (10762)

Lillian Anderson Jensen Library for Historical Research
See: **Mondak Heritage Center** (10606)

★8366★
Rolf Jensen & Associates - Library (Sci-Engr)
1751 Lake Cook Rd., Suite 400 Phone: (708)948-0700
Deerfield, IL 60015 Andrea Kiene, Libn.
Staff: Prof 1. **Subjects:** Fire protection, fire safety, building research, architectural design. **Special Collections:** Fire protection; fire research. **Holdings:** 2000 books; 32 bound periodical volumes; 1500 product catalogs; 20 VF drawers of technical data; 500 volumes of standards and codes; 5000 technical reports; 300 reports on microfiche. **Subscriptions:** 120 journals and other serials. **Services:** Interlibrary loan; copying; library open to the public. **Computerized Information Services:** DIALOG Information Services. **Remarks:** FAX: (312)948-0866.

Henry G. Jepson Memorial Library
See: **Wheeling Hospital, Inc.** (20375)

★8367★
Andrew Jergens Co. - Research Library
2535 Spring Grove Ave. Phone: (513)421-1400
Cincinnati, OH 45214 Karla Gansmuller, Libn.
Remarks: No further information was supplied by respondent.

★8368★
John Jermain Memorial Library - Historical Research Room (Hist)
Main St. Phone: (516)725-0049
Sag Harbor, NY 11963 James C. Ashe, Dir.
Founded: 1910. **Staff:** Prof 1; Other 5. **Subjects:** Whaling, Sag Harbor history. **Holdings:** 23,231 books; 5 bound periodical volumes. **Subscriptions:** 100 journals and other serials; 6 newspapers. **Services:** Interlibrary loan; copying; room open to the public. **Automated Operations:** Computerized public access catalog and circulation. **Computerized Information Services:** CD Union List Suffolk County. **Networks/Consortia:** Member of Suffolk Cooperative Library System, Long Island Library Resources Council. **Remarks:** FAX: (516)725-0529.

Jerome Medical Library
See: **St. Joseph's Hospital** (14402)

★8369★
Jersey City Medical Center - Medical Library (Med)
50 Baldwin Ave. Phone: (201)915-2009
Jersey City, NJ 07304 Judith Wilkinson
Founded: 1966. **Staff:** Prof 1; Other 3.5. **Subjects:** Medicine. **Holdings:** 1000 books; 10,000 bound periodical volumes. **Subscriptions:** 200 journals and other serials; 3 newspapers. **Services:** Interlibrary loan; SDI; library open to the public at librarian's discretion. **Computerized Information Services:** DIALOG Information Services, BRS Information Technologies, NLM; CD-ROMs. **Networks/Consortia:** Member of Health Sciences Library Association of New Jersey (HSLANJ), BHSL. **Remarks:** FAX: (201)915-2006.

★8370★
Jersey City State College - Forrest A. Irwin Library - Special Collections (Educ)
2039 Kennedy Blvd. Phone: (201)200-3030
Jersey City, NJ 07305-1597 Robert S. Nugent, Dir., Irwin Lib.
Founded: 1927. **Staff:** 25. **Special Collections:** Juvenile Collection; Curriculum Materials Center; Library of American Civilization (20,000 items); Library of English Literature (4522 items); Human Relations Area File (79,086 items). **Holdings:** 232,225 books; 5021 bound periodical volumes; 550,947 microfiche; 13,894 reels of microfilm. **Subscriptions:** 1465 journals and other serials; 10 newspapers. **Services:** Interlibrary loan; copying; collection open to faculty and students. **Automated Operations:** Computerized cataloging, acquisitions, circulation, and ILL. **Computerized Information Services:** DIALOG Information Services; CD-ROM (WILSONDISC, InfoTrac Academic Index, ERIC Silver Platter). Performs searches on fee basis. Contact Person: Mrs. Epp Tsirk Hd.Ref.Libn., 200-3473. **Networks/Consortia:** Member of PALINET. **Remarks:** FAX: (201)200-2072. **Staff:** John Luchechko, Asst.Dir. of Rd.Serv.; Marta Sawczuk, Acq.Libn. I; James Davis, Hd.Cat.Libn.; Anne Trattner, Cat.Libn. II; Sandra Brown, Cat.Libn. III; Toby Heyman, Ref.Libn. II; Michele Hoban, Ref.Libn. III; Theresa Tsui, Gov.Doc.Libn.I; Fred Smith, Per.Libn.II; Lawrence Holland, Circ.Libn.I & Reserve; Min Zhou, Ref.Libn.III; Maryann R. Marino, Libn. III CMC.

★8371★
Jersey Shore Medical Center - Ann May School of Nursing Library & Media Center (Med)
1945 Rte. 33 Phone: (201)776-4195
Neptune, NJ 07754 Darlene Robertelli, Lib.Serv.Coord.
Staff: Prof 1; Other 4. **Subjects:** Nursing, women's health, consumer education and health, allied health sciences. **Holdings:** 4000 books; 650 bound periodical volumes; 20 VF drawers; computer programs; 500 AV programs; National League for Nurses' and American Nursing Association publications. **Subscriptions:** 175 journals and other serials. **Services:** Interlibrary loan; copying; library open to the public for reference use only. **Networks/Consortia:** Member of Monmouth-Ocean Biomedical Information Consortium (MOBIC), Health Sciences Library Association of New Jersey (HSLANJ), BHSL, Central Jersey Regional Library Cooperative. **Publications:** Bimonthly acquisitions lists; Library Handbook; vertical file subject headings list; periodical holdings list; subject bibliographies. **Special Catalogs:** Audiovisual software catalog.

★8372★
Jersey Shore Medical Center - Medical Library (Med)
1945 Rte. 33 Phone: (908)776-4265
Neptune, NJ 07753 Mr. Gian C. Hasija, Lib.Supv.
Staff: Prof 1. **Subjects:** Medicine. **Holdings:** 1200 books; 6500 bound periodical volumes; 1500 AV programs. **Subscriptions:** 205 journals. **Services:** Interlibrary loan; copying; library open to students. **Computerized Information Services:** Online systems (158 databases available through BRS Information Technologies); CD-ROM (MEDLINE Express). **Publications:** Newsletter, quarterly. **Remarks:** FAX: (908)776-4230.

★8373★
(Jerusalem) American Cultural Center - USIS Library (Educ)
19 Keren Hayesod St.
Post Box 920
94188 Jerusalem, Israel
Remarks: Maintained or supported by the U.S. Information Agency. Focus is on materials that will assist peoples outside the United States to learn about the United States, its people, history, culture, political processes, and social milieux.

★8374★
Jervis Public Library (Hist)
613 N. Washington St. Phone: (315)336-4570
Rome, NY 13440 Carole F. Fowler, Dir.
Founded: 1895. **Staff:** 24. **Holdings:** John Jervis Library (railroads, aqueducts, and canals; 2000 volumes; 900 reports, survey maps, engineering drawings; 30,000 broadly classified pages of correspondence); Huntington-Bright Collection of historical papers; letters and broadsides from French and Indian and Revolutionary periods; Washington, Lafayette, Declaration Signers, generals (250 items). **Subscriptions:** 350 journals and other serials; 15 newspapers. **Services:** Interlibrary loan; copying; collections open to the public with restrictions. **Computerized Information Services:** DIALOG Information Services; MYDAS (internal database); Easynet (electronic mail service). **Networks/Consortia:** Member of Mid-York Library System. **Special Indexes:** Index to Jervis Papers (book); Index to Selected Drawings (booklet).

Lloyd W. Jessen Health Science Library
See: **Silver Cross Hospital** (15170)

Jesuit Center Library
See: **California Province of the Society of Jesus - Jesuit Center Library** (2501)

★8375★
Jesuit-Krauss-McCormick Library (Rel-Phil)
1100 E. 55th St. Phone: (312)753-0739
Chicago, IL 60615 Mary Bischoff, Dir.
Founded: 1975. **Staff:** 12. **Subjects:** Biblical studies, Lutherana, Presbyteriana, Reformation in Europe, early Christian church history. **Special Collections:** Biblical manuscripts, 9th-14th centuries (16); church ministry resources (10,000 items). **Holdings:** 400,000 cataloged materials. **Subscriptions:** 1200 journals and other serials. **Services:** Interlibrary loan; copying; library open to the public with restrictions on circulation. **Automated Operations:** Computerized cataloging, acquisitions, serials, and ILL. **Computerized Information Services:** BRS Information Technologies, DIALOG Information Services, WILSONLINE. **Networks/Consortia:** Member of Association of Chicago Theological Schools Library Council, ILLINET. **Remarks:** Library primarily serves the students and faculty of the Lutheran School of Theology at Chicago and the McCormick Theological Seminary. **Staff:** William Beermann, Cat.; Kenneth Sawyer, Pub.Serv.Libn.; Tina Krause, Rsrc.Ctr.Supv.; Emilie G. Pulver, Tech.Serv.Libn.; Stase Vaskelis, Ser.; Lorraine Lazouskas, Circ.; Samantha Zhu, Circ.; Yi Xu, Acq.; Janet Russell, Ref./ILL; Pamela Huggins, Cat.; Lucille Craig, Admin.Asst.

Jesuit School of Theology at Berkeley
See: **Graduate Theological Union** (6613)

Jesuits Library and Archives
See: **Compagnie de Jesus** (4096)

★8376★
Jet Research Center, Inc. - Technical Information and Science Library (Sci-Engr)
Engineering Dept.
2001 S. I-35
Alvarado, TX 76009 Phone: (817)783-5111
Founded: 1958. **Staff:** 1. **Subjects:** Explosives, pyrotechnics. **Special Collections:** Patents and patent holdings (18 books). **Holdings:** 497 books; 83 bound periodical volumes; 804 vendor catalogs; 5 VF drawers of reports; military and federal specifications and standards; government documents. **Services:** Interlibrary loan; library not open to the public.

★8377★
Jewish Board of Family & Children Services - Mary & Louis Robinson Library (Soc Sci)
120 W. 57th St. Phone: (212)582-9100
New York, NY 10019 Sue Weiland, Libn.
Staff: Prof 1. **Subjects:** Child and adolescent psychology and psychiatry, social work, family therapy, psychoanalysis, psychiatry. **Special Collections:** The Charities (Hebrew charities), 1891-1907; Conference on Charities, 1896-1929, continued as National Conference of Social Work, 1930-1949, continued as Social Welfare Forum, 1950 to present. **Holdings:** 5000 books; 2000 bound periodical volumes; 8 VF drawers of manuscripts and dissertations. **Subscriptions:** 50 journals and other serials. **Services:** Interlibrary loan; library not open to the public.

★8378★
Jewish Braille Institute of America, Inc. - Library (Aud-Vis)
110 E. 30th St. Phone: (212)889-2525
New York, NY 10016 Cantor Mindy J. Fliegelman, Adm., Lib.Serv.
Founded: 1931. **Staff:** Prof 3; Other 8. **Subjects:** Judaica. **Special Collections:** English and Hebrew braille books; English, Yiddish, and Hebrew tapes; English and Hebrew large-type books. **Holdings:** 7000 books; 100,000 tapes. **Subscriptions:** 2 journals and other serials. **Services:** Library open to the public. **Publications:** Jewish Braille Review; English braille monthly; JBI Voice: English record, monthly; concert, lecture, and poetry series, quarterly. **Special Catalogs:** Catalogs based on subject, language, and medium. **Remarks:** Toll-free telephone number(s): (800)433-1531. FAX: (212)689-3692. **Staff:** Richard Borgersen, Dir., Spec.Lib.Serv.; Vivian Williams, Supv., Lib.Circ.

★8379★
Jewish Community Center - Library
525 14th St.
Sioux City, IA 51105
Founded: 1906. **Subjects:** Books of current interest in English, Hebrew, and Yiddish. **Holdings:** 1500 books. **Remarks:** Currently inactive.

★8380★
Jewish Community Center - Library (Area-Ethnic)
801 Percy Warner Blvd. Phone: (615)356-7170
Nashville, TN 37205 Annette Levy Ratkin, Libn.
Founded: 1902. **Staff:** Prof 1; Other 1. **Subjects:** Judaica; Israel; Holocaust; Hebrew, Russian, and Yiddish languages. **Holdings:** 6000 books; unbound periodicals. **Subscriptions:** 23 journals and other serials. **Services:** Interlibrary loan; copying; library open to the public. **Special Catalogs:** Joint catalog of books in West End Synagogue and Temple libraries. **Remarks:** FAX: (615)352-0056.

★8381★
Jewish Community Centre - Library (Area-Ethnic)
151 Chapel St. Phone: (613)232-7306
Ottawa, ON, Canada K1N 7Y2 Estelle Buckman
Founded: 1955. **Staff:** Prof 1. **Subjects:** Judaica. **Holdings:** 6000 books; pamphlets. **Subscriptions:** 15 journals and other serials; 10 newspapers. **Services:** Library open to the public.

Jewish Community Center - Samuel & Rebecca Astor Judaica Library
See: **East County Jewish Community Center** (5117)

★8382★
Jewish Community Center of Greater Minneapolis - Library (Area-Ethnic)
4330 S. Cedar Lake Rd. Phone: (612)377-8330
Minneapolis, MN 55416 Gerald Wesberg, Exe. Dir.
Founded: 1969. **Subjects:** Judaica, Israel, historical views of Jews and Christians, arts and sciences, American and European literature, Jewish reference material, Hebrew and Yiddish literature, social issues and ecology. **Holdings:** 3000 books; 200 unbound periodicals; 300 phonograph records. **Services:** Interlibrary loan; library open to the public. **Publications:** Identity Magazine, 2/year. **Remarks:** Library maintained by National Council of Jewish Women Volunteers.

★8383★
Jewish Community Center of Greater Washington - Kass Judaic Library (Area-Ethnic)
6125 Montrose Rd. Phone: (301)881-0100
Rockville, MD 20852 T.K. Feldman, Dir., Lit. Arts
Founded: 1969. **Staff:** Prof 1. **Subjects:** Bible, Israel, Zionism, religion, history, sociology, Holocaust, biography, fiction. **Special Collections:** American Jewry; Jews in other countries; Jewish holidays; archeology; masterworks of Yiddish literature. **Holdings:** 6000 books. **Subscriptions:** 24 journals and other serials. **Services:** Library open to the public. **Remarks:** FAX: (301)881-5512.

★8384★
Jewish Community Center of Metropolitan Detroit - Henry & Delia Meyers Memorial Library (Area-Ethnic)
6600 W. Maple Rd. Phone: (313)661-1000
West Bloomfield, MI 48322 Ann Parker, Libn.
Founded: 1959. **Staff:** Prof 1; Other 2. **Subjects:** Judaica, Jewish life. **Special Collections:** Judaica and non-Judaica for children; newspapers and periodicals in English, Yiddish, and Hebrew. **Holdings:** 11,000 volumes; 4 VF drawers; AV programs; videotapes. **Subscriptions:** 32 journals and other serials; 10 newspapers. **Services:** Interlibrary loan; library open to the public. **Remarks:** FAX: (313)661-3680.

★8385★
Jewish Community Center, Saskatoon - Library (Rel-Phil)
715 McKinnon Ave. Phone: (306)343-7023
Saskatoon, SK, Canada S7H 2G2 Rabbi Roger V. Pavey
Subjects: Judaism. **Holdings:** 2500 books. **Services:** Copying; library open to students and for research.

Jewish Community Library - Peter M. Kahn Memorial Library
See: **Bureau of Jewish Ecucation of Greater Los Angeles** (2368)

★8386★
Jewish Community Relations Council - Anti-Defamation League of Minnesota-Dakotas - Library (Soc Sci, Area-Ethnic)
1111 3rd Ave, S., No. 112 Phone: (612)338-7816
Minneapolis, MN 55404-1000 Brenda Barrie, Exec.Dir.
Founded: 1975. **Staff:** Prof 3; Other 3. **Subjects:** Anti-Semitism, prejudice and discrimination, Judaism, Soviet Jewry, Israel, teacher education in human relations, the Holocaust, minority studies. **Special Collections:** Holocaust Education and Resource Center (films; publications; oral history tapes; teaching resources); racism materials and videotapes. **Holdings:** 1000 books; 15 VF drawers; 85 films. **Subscriptions:** 10 journals and other serials. **Services:** Library open to the public. **Publications:** List of publications and films - available on request. **Remarks:** FAX: (612)349-6569.

★8387★
Jewish Defense Organization - Library (Hist)
134 W. 32nd St., Rm. 602 Phone: (212)239-0447
New York, NY 10001 Steuart Leben
Founded: 1982. **Staff:** 1. **Subjects:** Holocaust, Jewish resistance, Judaism, Torah. **Holdings:** 1000 volumes.

★8388★
Jewish Education Institute - Sol Rosenbloom Library (Rel-Phil)
6401 Forbes Ave. Phone: (412)521-1100
Pittsburgh, PA 15217 Irene Seiden, Libn.
Founded: 1916. **Staff:** Prof 2. **Subjects:** Juvenile literature, Bible, Bible commentary, religion, language, education, Jewish community reference, history of Israel. **Special Collections:** Gertrude Nachman Memorial Collection of Juvenile Books. **Holdings:** Figures not available. **Subscriptions:** 45 journals and other serials; 5 newspapers. **Services:** Interlibrary loan; copying; library open to the public. **Formerly:** Hebrew Institute of Pittsburgh.

★8389★
Jewish Federation of Delaware & Jewish Community Center - Halina Wind Preston Holocaust Education Resource Center (Hist)
101 Garden of Eden Rd. Phone: (302)478-6200
Wilmington, DE 19803 Constance Kreshtool, Coord.
Founded: 1986. **Staff:** 1. **Subjects:** Holocaust education and studies. **Holdings:** 190 volumes; 24 videotapes; 2 audiotapes. **Services:** Interlibrary loan; center open to the public. **Remarks:** FAX: (302)478-5364.

Jewish Federation of Greater Philadelphia
See: **Philadelphia Jewish Archives Center at the Balch Institute** (12988)

Jewish Federation of Greater Toronto
See: **Canadian Jewish Congress - Jewish Federation of Greater Toronto** (2947)

★8390★
Jewish Federation of Nashville and Middle Tennessee - Archives (Area-Ethnic)
801 Percy Warner Blvd. Phone: (615)356-7170
Nashville, TN 37205 Annette Levy Ratkin, Dir.
Founded: 1979. **Staff:** Prof 2. **Special Collections:** Archives of the Nashville Jewish community (95 linear feet); oral history collection (Holocaust and senior adults). **Holdings:** 3 record groups; 45 manuscript collections; 106 small collections; Jewish newspapers on microfilm. **Services:** Interlibrary loan; archives open to the public with restrictions. **Computerized Information Services:** Internal database. **Remarks:** FAX: (615)352-0056.

★8391★
Jewish Federation of Omaha - Library (Rel-Phil)
333 S. 132nd St. Phone: (402)334-8200
Omaha, NE 68154 Edythe Wolf, Dir.
Founded: 1928. **Staff:** Prof 1; Other 2. **Subjects:** Jewish religion and philosophy, Biblical commentary and research, history, Jewish literature and art, Israel, Holocaust, fiction. **Special Collections:** Marc Chagall; Rabbi Moses Maimonides; Saul Raskin; comparative religion. **Holdings:** 27,000 books; 1100 bound periodical volumes; 2600 records; 1000 pamphlets; 150 films; 1150 filmstrips; 60 audio-slide presentations; 200 videocassettes. **Subscriptions:** 75 journals and other serials. **Services:** Interlibrary loan; copying; library open to public. **Special Indexes:** Index to Omaha Jewish Press (book).

★8392★
Jewish Guild for the Blind - JGB Cassette Library International (Aud-Vis)
15 W. 65th St. Phone: (212)769-6331
New York, NY 10023 Bruce E. Massis, Dir.
Founded: 1974. **Staff:** Prof 1; Other 2. **Subjects:** Fiction, nonfiction, poetry. **Holdings:** 68,000 cassettes containing 1250 titles; periodicals. **Services:** Interlibrary loan; library open to the blind, physically handicapped, and print-impaired. **Special Catalogs:** Large Print Catalog (printed form and compact cassette), quarterly update. **Remarks:** Entire collection is on standard compact cassettes; books are circulated by mail without charge to blind persons in the United States and foreign countries. FAX: (212)769-6266.

★8393★
Jewish Historical Society of Maryland, Inc. - Archives (Hist, Area-Ethnic)
15 Lloyd St. Phone: (301)732-6400
Baltimore, MD 21202 Virginia R. North, Archv.
Founded: 1961. **Staff:** 1. **Subjects:** History of Jews in Maryland, 18th century to present; social welfare history. **Special Collections:** Maryland Jewish families and personalities, including Benjamin and Henrietta Szold, Harry Friedenwald, and Herman Seidel (110 cubic feet); oral history interviews with members of the Baltimore Jewish community (220 tapes); local Jewish organizations. **Holdings:** 1000 books; 110 cubic feet of manuscripts; genealogical works; listing of local Jewish organizations, members, birth and death records, immigration records, census records; microfiche and microfilm of local Jewish publications; Jewish Chronicle (Vol. 1-2, 1875), Jewish Comment (Vols. 12-43, October 19, 1900 to April 24, 1916), Jewish Exponent (November 25, 1887 to August 31, 1888), Hapisgah (1891-1892), Sinai (1856-1864), Jewish Times (September 24, 1919 to present). **Subscriptions:** 10 journals and other serials. **Services:** Copying; archives open to the public by appointment. **Publications:** Monographs. **Special Catalogs:** Exhibition catalogs.

★8394★
Jewish Historical Society of New York, Inc. - Library (Hist, Area-Ethnic)
8 W. 70th St. Phone: (212)415-5544
New York, NY 10023 Steven W. Siegel, Sec.
Founded: 1973. **Staff:** Prof 1. **Subjects:** American and New York Jewish history, Jewish genealogy. **Holdings:** Figures not available. **Services:** Provides telephone and mail reference service only.

Jewish Historical Society of Western Canada
See: **Canadian Jewish Congress** (2948)

★8395★
Jewish Hospital - Medical Library (Med)
217 E. Chestnut St. Phone: (502)587-4280
Louisville, KY 40202 Gene Haynes, Dir.
Founded: 1974. **Staff:** Prof 1; Other 1. **Subjects:** Medicine. **Holdings:** 1500 books; 700 bound periodical volumes. **Subscriptions:** 270 journals and other serials. **Services:** Interlibrary loan; library not open to the public. **Automated Operations:** Computerized cataloging. **Computerized Information Services:** MEDLINE, OCLC, BRS Information Technologies. **Networks/Consortia:** Member of SOLINET, Kentucky Health Sciences Library Consortium.

★8396★
Jewish Hospital - School of Nursing - Moses Shoenberg Memorial Library (Med)
306 S. Kingshighway Phone: (314)454-8474
St. Louis, MO 63110 Betsy Mueth, Libn.
Founded: 1920. **Staff:** Prof 1; Other 5. **Subjects:** Nursing, nursing education, medicine. **Special Collections:** NLN publications. **Holdings:** 2000 books; VF materials; AV collection; software; anatomical models. **Subscriptions:** 100 journals and other serials. **Services:** Interlibrary loan; library open to persons in the health sciences field for limited use. **Computerized Information Services:** CD-ROM (CINAHL).

★8397★
Jewish Hospital of Cincinnati - Medical Library (Med)
3200 Burnet Ave. Phone: (513)569-2014
Cincinnati, OH 45229 David Self, Med.Libn.
Founded: 1959. **Staff:** Prof 1; Other 2. **Subjects:** Medicine. **Special Collections:** History of medicine (1004 volumes); medical rare books (374); Robert C. Rothenberg shelf for leisurely medical reading (300 volumes). **Holdings:** 4000 books; 6000 bound periodical volumes; 280 video cassettes; 1000 audio cassettes. **Subscriptions:** 280 journals and other serials. **Services:** Interlibrary loan. **Computerized Information Services:** NLM, BRS Information Technologies, DIALOG Information Services. **Networks/Consortia:** Member of National Network of Libraries of Medicine - Greater Midwest Region. **Remarks:** FAX: (513)569-3235. Contains the holdings of its former School of Nursing - Library.

★8398★
Jewish Hospital at Washington University Medical Center - Rothschild Medical Library (Med)
216 S. Kingshighway Phone: (314)454-7208
St. Louis, MO 63110 Kathleen Mullen, Lib.Dir.
Founded: 1930. **Staff:** Prof 2. **Subjects:** Medicine. **Holdings:** 2262 books; 5634 bound periodical volumes. **Subscriptions:** 95 journals and other serials. **Services:** Interlibrary loan; copying; library open to medical personnel. **Computerized Information Services:** BRS Information Technologies, NLM.

Jewish Hospital at Washington University Medical Center - School of Nursing
See: **Jewish Hospital - School of Nursing** (8396)

Jewish Institute of Religion
See: **Hebrew Union College - Jewish Institute of Religion** (7095)

★8399★
Jewish Labor Bund - Bund Archives of the Jewish Labor Movement (Area-Ethnic, Hist)
25 E. 21st St. Phone: (212)473-5101
New York, NY 10010 Dr. Benjamin Nadel, Exec.Dir.
Staff: Prof 3; Other 1. **Subjects:** Jewish Labor Bund; labor Zionism; Jewish anarchists, communists, and socialists in the U.S.; Holocaust. **Holdings:** 30,000 books; 2500 bound periodical volumes; 10,000 photographs; 600 posters; 2000 handbills; 400 reels of microfilm; 100 tapes; 3000 linear feet of archival material; 1000 other cataloged items. **Subscriptions:** 65 journals and other serials; 5 newspapers. **Services:** Copying; SDI; archives open to researchers and college students. **Networks/Consortia:** Member of Council of Archives and Research Libraries in Jewish Studies (CARLJS). **Publications:** Di Groise Einzamlung, 1963; A Great Collection: The Archives of the Jewish Labor Movement, 1965; Bulletin of the Bund Archives, New Series, 1979 to present (in English and Yiddish); Guide to the European Collection of the Bund Archives (internal use). **Remarks:** The archives contain a collection of rare editions, journ als, and documentary material on the history of the Jewish Labor Movement, mid-nineteenth century to present, including underground papers from Tsarist Russia and Nazi-occupied Poland during World War II. **Staff:** Irving Glaser, Sec.

★8400★
The Jewish Museum - Library
1865 Broadway
New York, NY 10128
Founded: 1947. 1; Other 5. **Subjects:** Jewish art, architecture, ceremonial art, history, religion, archeology, coins. **Holdings:** 3000 books; 1000 other cataloged items. **Remarks:** Museum operates under the auspices of the Jewish Theological Seminary of America. Currently inactive.

★8401★
Jewish Museum - National Jewish Archive of Broadcasting (Area-Ethnic, Info Sci)
1865 Broadway, 4th Fl. Phone: (212)399-3382
New York, NY 10023 Wanda Bershen, Dir.
Founded: 1981. **Staff:** 5. **Subjects:** Jewish history, biographies, religion, culture; Holocaust; Israel; media studies. **Special Collections:** Television and radio collection on Jewish culture and history (2800 items, including 178 hours of the Eichmann Trial; 500,000 feet of 16mm film of outtakes from Heritage Civilization and the Jews); press releases and news clippings about Jewish-related broadcasts (12 VF drawers). **Services:** Viewing carrels; archive open to scholars and researchers by appointment. **Automated Operations:** Computerized cataloging and acquisitions. **Computerized Information Services:** Internal databases. **Publications:** A subject guide to the collection of the Jewish Museum's National Jewish Archive of Broadcasting. **Special Catalogs:** Annotated Catalogue of Selected Holdings of The Jewish Museum's National Jewish Archive of Broadcasting. **Remarks:** FAX: (212)399-3399. Above address is temporary; library will return to permanent address in January, 1993. Permanent address: 1109 Fifth Ave., New York, NY 10128. tel: (212)860-1886. **Staff:** Avina Weintraub, Archv.Coord.; Ralph McKay, Prog.Coord.; Alessandro Cavadini, AV Coord.; Michael Paley, Archv.Assoc.

★8402★
Jewish Public Library
1725 Main St. Phone: (204)338-4048
Winnipeg, MB, Canada R2V 1Z4 S. Pinsky, Libn.
Staff: 1. **Services:** Library open to the public.

★8403★
Jewish Public Library of Montreal (Area-Ethnic)
5151 Cote St. Catherine Rd. Phone: (514)345-2627
Montreal, PQ, Canada H3W 1M6 Zipporah Dunsky-Shnay, Dir.
Founded: 1914. **Staff:** Prof 5; Other 13. **Subjects:** Judaica and Hebraica. **Special Collections:** Jewish Canadiana; archives; photographs; vertical file on world Jewry; rare books; Holocaust Collection. **Holdings:** 105,000 books; 5000 bound periodical volumes; 1000 tapes; video collection; talking books; phonograph records. **Subscriptions:** 250 journals and other serials (in 4 languages). **Services:** Interlibrary loan; copying; library open to the public. **Publications:** Holocaust Bibliography. **Special Indexes:** Index to R. Branin's Hebrew and Yiddish correspondence. **Remarks:** FAX: (514)342-6477. Maintains a branch library in Laval and a children's library. **Staff:** Claire Stern, Hd., Pub.Serv.

★8404★
Jewish Rehabilitation Hospital - Health Sciences Information Centre (Med)
3205 Alton Goldbloom Phone: (514)688-9550
Laval, PQ, Canada H7V 1R2 Irene Deborah Shanefield, Med.Libn.
Founded: 1979. **Staff:** Prof 1. **Subjects:** Medicine, physical therapy, cognitive rehabilitation, occupational therapy, nuerology, therapeutics. **Special Collections:** Travel guides for the disabled (500). **Holdings:** 1300 books; 800 bound periodical volumes. **Subscriptions:** 90 journals and other serials. **Services:** Interlibrary loan; copying; center open to the public by appointment. **Automated Operations:** Computerized acquisitions. **Computerized Information Services:** MEDLINE. **Networks/Consortia:** Member of McGill Medical and Health Libraries Association (MMHLA). **Publications:** Information Package, quarterly. **Remarks:** FAX: (514)688-3673. **Also Known As:** Hopital Juif de Readaptation.

Jewish Studies Slide Archive
See: **Hamline University - Bush Memorial Library - Special Collections** (6870)

Jewish Theological Seminary of America - The Jewish Museum
See: **The Jewish Museum** (8400)

★8405★
Jewish Theological Seminary of America - Library (Rel-Phil)
3080 Broadway Phone: (212)678-8082
New York, NY 10027 Dr. Mayer E. Rabinowitz, Libn.
Founded: 1903. **Staff:** Prof 18; Other 10. **Subjects:** Bible, rabbinics, theology, Jewish history, liturgy, Hebrew literature, early Yiddish writings, science, medicine. **Special Collections:** Haggadot; Megillot (Esther scrolls); Ketuboth (marriage contracts); incunabula; L. Ginzberg microfilm collection (Hebrew manuscripts). **Holdings:** 280,000 volumes; 10,000 manuscripts. **Subscriptions:** 728 journals and other serials. **Services:** Interlibrary loan; copying; library open to the public. **Automated Operations:** Computerized cataloging. **Computerized Information Services:** DIALOG Information Services; BITNET, RLG (electronic mail services). **Networks/Consortia:** Member of SUNY/OCLC Library Network, New York Metropolitan Reference and Research Library Agency, Research Libraries Information Network (RLIN). **Publications:** Selected list of recent acquisitions, monthly. **Remarks:** FAX: (212)678-8998. Electronic mail address(es): BM.JTC@RLG (BITNET, RLG). **Staff:** Edith Degani, Asst.Libn.

Jewish Theological Seminary of America - Schocken Institute for Jewish Research
See: **Schocken Institute for Jewish Research** (14915)

★8406★
Jewish Vocational Service - Library (Soc Sci)
1 S. Franklin Phone: (312)346-6700
Chicago, IL 60606 Elisa F. Topper, Dir. of Info.Serv.
Founded: 1935. **Staff:** Prof 1. **Subjects:** Social services, vocational rehabilitation, career counseling, psychology. **Holdings:** 2500 books; 350 bound periodical volumes; 75 VF drawers of pamphlets. **Subscriptions:** 100 journals and other serials. **Services:** Interlibrary loan; library open to qualified users in social work and allied fields by appointment only. **Computerized Information Services:** DIALOG Information Services. **Publications:** INFOSOURCE; Pertinent Publications, both bimonthly - both for internal distribution only.

JGB Cassette Library International
See: **Jewish Guild for the Blind** (8392)

★8407★
JHK & Associates - Technical Library - East (Trans)
4660 Kenmore Ave. Phone: (703)370-2411
Alexandria, VA 22304 Kay E. Hathaway, Libn.
Founded: 1975. **Staff:** Prof 2; Other 1. **Subjects:** Traffic engineering, transportation, regional and environmental studies. **Holdings:** 7800 books; 1500 bound periodical volumes; 25,000 vertical file materials; 1800 slides and maps. **Subscriptions:** 150 journals and other serials. **Services:** Interlibrary loan; copying; library open to the public by appointment. **Computerized Information Services:** Transportation Research Information Services (TRIS). **Publications:** Acquisition list, quarterly; annual report. **Remarks:** FAX: (703)823-8347.

★8408★
JHK & Associates - Western Consulting Division - Library (Trans)
110 S. Church Ave., Suite 470 Phone: (602)624-2306
Tuscon, AZ 85701 William D. Pearson, Libn.
Founded: 1971. **Staff:** Prof 1; Other 1. **Subjects:** Traffic engineering, transportation, environmental studies, defense-crisis studies, management. **Holdings:** 10,500 books; 800 bound periodical volumes; 2000 company files. **Services:** Interlibrary loan; copying; library open to the public with restrictions. **Computerized Information Services:** DIALOG Information Services; internal databases. Performs searches. **Publications:** Annual report. **Remarks:** FAX: (602)624-5290.

Zenobia y Juan Ramon Jimenez Room
See: **University of Puerto Rico - Library System** (19252)

★8409★
JJH, Inc. - Engineering Library (Mil, Sci-Engr)
Cuthbert Blvd.
Route 70, P.O. Box 5031 Phone: (609)663-3020
Cherry Hill, NJ 08034 Evelyn Maldonado, Libn.
Staff: 5. **Subjects:** Marine engineering, naval architecture, Coast Guard. **Holdings:** 25,000 military specifications and standards; 8000 instructional materials; 6000 technical reports; 5000 Navy standard drawings; 4000 vendor catalogs; 2000 special reports and drawings on specific contracts; 1700 naval technical manuals; 360 Marine handbooks; 170 classified documents; 100 directories. **Subscriptions:** 154 journals and other serials; 5 newspapers. **Services:** Library not open to the public. **Remarks:** FAX: (609)663-9305.

★8410★
The Jockey Club - Library (Rec)
821 Corporate Dr. Phone: (606)224-2700
Lexington, KY 40503 Connie Brannen
Subjects: Thoroughbred breeding and racing. **Special Collections:** Stud books of many countries. **Holdings:** 2000 books; 500 bound periodical volumes. **Services:** Library not open to the public. **Remarks:** FAX: (606)224-2710. Telex: 856599.

★8411★
(Johannesburg) American Cultural Center - USIS Library (Educ)
African Life Center, 3rd Fl.
111 Commissioner St.
Johannesburg 2001, Republic of South Africa
Remarks: Maintained or supported by the U.S. Information Agency. Focus is on materials that will assist peoples outside the United States to learn about the United States, its people, history, culture, political processes, and social milieux.

★8412★
John XXII Centre for Adult Faith Development - Library (Rel-Phil)
2275 Wellesley St. Phone: (519)254-2090
Windsor, ON, Canada N8W 2G1 Joyce Rocheleau, Libn./Coord.
Founded: 1965. **Staff:** 5. **Subjects:** Religion, the Bible, spirituality, marriage and family, philosophy, theology, morality, ethics. **Holdings:** 4650 books; 275 videotapes; 58 films; 250 filmstrips; 400 audiocassettes; 200 slides. **Subscriptions:** 25 journals and other serials. **Services:** Copying; library open to the public. **Remarks:** FAX: (519)254-0330. **Formerly:** John XXII Catholic Formation Centre.

Harold E. Johns Library
See: **Saskatoon Cancer Centre** (14872)

★8413★
Johns Hopkins Hospital - Department of Radiology - Library (Med)
600 N. Wolfe St. Phone: (301)955-6029
Baltimore, MD 21205 Elaine Pinkney, Libn.
Staff: Prof 1; Other 1. **Subjects:** Radiology, sonography, computed tomography, nuclear medicine, magnetic resonance imaging. **Holdings:** 1700 books; 5000 bound periodical volumes; 10,000 X-ray films. **Subscriptions:** 54 journals and other serials. **Services:** Interlibrary loan; copying; library open to the public with restrictions.

★8414★
Johns Hopkins Hospital - Wilmer Ophthalmological Institute - Jonas S. Friedenwald Library (Med)
3/B 50 Woods Bldg.
601 N. Broadway Phone: (301)955-3127
Baltimore, MD 21205 Michael Piorunski, Dept.Libn.
Founded: 1925. **Staff:** Prof 1; Other 1. **Subjects:** Ophthalmology. **Special Collections:** Friedenwald Collection. **Holdings:** 9500 books; 12,000 bound periodical volumes; 1000 AV programs. **Subscriptions:** 143 journals and other serials. **Services:** Copying; library open to the public with restrictions. **Computerized Information Services:** BRS/COLLEAGUE; CD-ROM (CD-PLUS). **Special Catalogs:** Collected Wilmer Reprints Catalog (cards). **Remarks:** FAX: (301)955-0046.

★8415★
Johns Hopkins University - Applied Physics Laboratory - R.E. Gibson Library and Information Center (Sci-Engr)
Johns Hopkins Rd. Phone: (301)953-5151
Laurel, MD 20723 Robert S. Gresehover, Hd.Libn.
Founded: 1946. **Staff:** Prof 10; Other 18. **Subjects:** Physics, electronics, space research, mathematics, computing sciences, mechanical engineering, biophysics. **Holdings:** 60,000 books; 16,000 bound periodical volumes. **Subscriptions:** 600 journals and other serials. **Services:** Interlibrary loan; copying; current awareness; library open to the public with restrictions. **Automated Operations:** Computerized public access catalog, circulation, acquisitions, and serials. **Computerized Information Services:** DIALOG Information Services, ORBIT Search Service, DTIC, BRS Information Technologies, NASA/RECON, OCLC, EPIC, USNI Military Database; Current Contents. **Networks/Consortia:** Member of Interlibrary Users Association (IUA), Maryland Interlibrary Organization (MILO). **Publications:** Information Interface, quarterly - for internal distribution only. **Remarks:** FAX: (301)953-5353. **Staff:** DeAnna Jones, Acq.Sect.Supv.; Jacqueline Weitzel, Sup.Serv.Sect.Supv.; Linda Kosmin, Rd.Serv.Sect.Supv.; Philip Albert, Archv.Supv.

★8416★
Johns Hopkins University - Center of Canadian Studies - Library (Soc Sci)
1740 Massachusetts Ave., N.W. Phone: (202)663-5656
Washington, DC 20036 Elaine Ferat
Founded: 1969. **Subjects:** Canadian government, foreign policy, and economics. **Holdings:** 4000 monographs. **Subscriptions:** 30 journals and other serials. **Services:** Library not open to the public. **Remarks:** FAX: (202)663-5656.

★8417★
Johns Hopkins University - Chemical Propulsion Information Agency (Sci-Engr)
10630 Little Patupent Pkwy., Suite 202 Phone: (410)992-7300
Columbia, MD 21044-3200 Thomas W. Christian, Dir.
Founded: 1946. **Staff:** Prof 9; Other 10. **Subjects:** Chemical propellants, solid rocket motors, liquid rocket engines, ramjet engines, gun propellants. **Holdings:** 61,000 chemical propulsion research, development, test, and evaluation reports. **Subscriptions:** 12 journals and other serials. **Services:** Agency open only to outside users who are registered with DTIC and/or DLSC; payment of annual service charge required. **Computerized Information Services:** Internal databases. Performs searches on fee basis. Contact Person: Karen L. Brown, Bus.Mgr. **Publications:** List of publications - available on request. **Special Indexes:** Indexes to Chemical Propulsion Abstracts. **Remarks:** FAX: (410)730-4969. **Formerly:** Located in Laurel, MD. **Staff:** Thomas L. Reedy, Assoc.Dir.; Debra S. Eggleston, Group Adm.Asst.

★8418★
Johns Hopkins University - Department of Earth and Planetary Sciences - Singewald Reading Room (Sci-Engr)
Baltimore, MD 21218 Phone: (410)516-7135
Bruce D. Marsh, Chm.
Founded: 1966. **Staff:** Prof 1; Other 1. **Subjects:** Chemistry, mineralogy, economic geology, paleontology, sedimentology, structural geology, regional geology, petrology, geophysics. **Special Collections:** Geological theses. **Holdings:** 300 books; 850 bound periodical volumes; 200 dissertations. **Subscriptions:** 30 journals and other serials. **Services:** Interlibrary loan; room not open to the public. **Remarks:** FAX: (410)516-7933.

Johns Hopkins University - Ferdinand Hamburger, Jr. Archives
See: **Johns Hopkins University - Milton S. Eisenhower Library - Special Collections Department - Ferdinand Hamburger, Jr. Archives** (8423)

★8419★
Johns Hopkins University - John Work Garrett Library (Rare Book)
Evergreen House
4545 N. Charles St. Phone: (301)516-0341
Baltimore, MD 21210 Judy Gardner-Flint, Libn.
Founded: 1952. **Staff:** Prof 1. **Subjects:** 16th and 17th century English literature, 15th century books, early travel exploration, architecture, Bibles. **Special Collections:** Books printed before 1700 relating to Maryland; Lawrence H. Fowler Architectural Collection; Hofmann Bible Collection; Signers of the Constitution (75 pieces). **Holdings:** 20,000 books; 500 bound periodical volumes. **Services:** Copying (limited); library open to the public with restrictions. **Automated Operations:** Computerized cataloging. **Networks/Consortia:** Member of Research Libraries Information Network (RLIN). **Publications:** Seventeenth Century Maryland: A Bibliography compiled by Elizabeth Baer, 1949. **Special Catalogs:** The Fowler Architectural Catalog, compiled by Laurence Hall Fowler and Elizabeth Baer, 1961; Medals Relating to Medicine and Allied Sciences in the Numismatic Collection of the Johns Hopkins University, a catalog compiled by Sarah Elizabeth Freeman, 1964. **Remarks:** The John Work Garrett Library is a part of the Milton S. Eisenhower Library, Special Collections Division.

★8420★
Johns Hopkins University - Milton S. Eisenhower Library - George Peabody Collection (Hist, Hum)
Charles & 34 St. Phone: (301)516-8335
Baltimore, MD 21218 Scott Bennett, Libn.
Founded: 1857. **Staff:** Prof 2; Other 4. **Subjects:** English and American history, genealogy, languages and literature (especially English, Romance,

Classical), art and architecture, cartography/exploration and travel, natural history, history of science. **Holdings:** 250,000 books; 40,000 bound periodical volumes. **Subscriptions:** 140 journals and other serials. **Services:** Interlibrary loan; copying; collection open to the public for reference use only; responds to mail queries. **Networks/Consortia:** Member of Maryland Interlibrary Organization (MILO). **Special Catalogs:** Catalog of the Peabody Institute Library. **Remarks:** Administered by the Milton S. Eisenhower Library - Special Collections Department. Alternate telephone number(s): 659-8179. **Staff:** Gary E. Myer, Ref.Asst.

★8421★
Johns Hopkins University - Milton S. Eisenhower Library - Government Publications/Maps/Law Library (Info Sci, Geog-Map)
Charles & 34th Sts. Phone: (410)516-8360
Baltimore, MD 21218 James E. Gillispie, Hd.
Staff: Prof 2; Other 4. **Special Collections:** U.S. Government documents, 1882 to present; U.N. documents, 1945 to present; international documents; technical reports (Atomic Energy Commission); League of Nations documents; U.S. Geological Survey maps. **Holdings:** 432,137 government publications; 202,544 maps; 1383 atlases; 117,812 microfiche; 1217 reels of microfilm; state and federal legal materials. **Subscriptions:** 2428 journals and other serials. **Services:** Interlibrary loan; copying; department open to the public. **Automated Operations:** Computerized cataloging, acquisitions, serials, and circulation. **Computerized Information Services:** DIALOG Information Services, BRS Information Technologies, VU/TEXT Information Services, WILSONLINE, OCLC, RLIN; CD-ROMs. **Networks/Consortia:** Member of Research Libraries Information Network (RLIN), Maryland Interlibrary Organization (MILO). **Remarks:** FAX: (410)516-6029 **Staff:** Beth Ann Kremer, Rsrc.Serv.Libn.

★8422★
Johns Hopkins University - Milton S. Eisenhower Library - Special Collections Department (Hum)
3400 N. Charles St. Phone: (410)516-8348
Baltimore, MD 21218 Cynthia H. Requardt, Hd., Spec.Coll.
Founded: 1876. **Staff:** Prof 3; Other 4. **Subjects:** Economic history and thought, German literature, American sheet music, English and American literature, graduate education in the U.S., art history, history of science, French popular drama of the 18th and 19th centuries. **Special Collections:** Byron Collection (1000 volumes); Kurrelmeyer German Literature Collection; Abram G. Hutzler Collection of Economic Classics (5300 volumes); Levy Sheet Music Collection (33,000 items); Sidney Lanier Collection. **Holdings:** 43,000 books; 2600 linear feet of manuscripts from early presidents and faculty of the university. **Services:** Copying; division open to qualified researchers. **Automated Operations:** Computerized cataloging. **Computerized Information Services:** BITNET (electronic mail service). **Networks/Consortia:** Member of Research Libraries Information Network (RLIN). **Remarks:** FAX: (410)516-8596. Electronic mail address(es): SPCOLL@JHUVM (BITNET). **Staff:** Carolyn Smith, Rare Bk. & Coll.Dev.Libn.; Judy Gardner-Flint, Sr. Rare Bk.Cat.

★8423★
Johns Hopkins University - Milton S. Eisenhower Library - Special Collections Department - Ferdinand Hamburger, Jr. Archives (Hist)
3400 North Charles St. Phone: (410)516-8323
Baltimore, MD 21218 James Stimpert, Archv.
Founded: 1971. **Staff:** Prof 1; Other 2. **Subjects:** Johns Hopkins University. **Holdings:** 3000 linear feet of archives. **Subscriptions:** 10 journals and other serials. **Services:** Copying; archives open to the public by appointment. **Automated Operations:** Computerized cataloging. **Computerized Information Services:** MARCON (internal database). Contact Person: Brian Harrington, Archv.Techn. **Networks/Consortia:** Member of Research Libraries Information Network (RLIN). **Remarks:** FAX: (410)516-8596. This is the official archival repository for the nonmedical divisions of the university. Archives is a division of Johns Hopkins University - Milton S. Eisenhower Library Special Collections Department.

Johns Hopkins University - National Foreign Language Center
See: **National Foreign Language Center at Johns Hopkins University** (11170)

★8424★
Johns Hopkins University - Peabody Conservatory of Music - Arthur Friedheim Library (Mus)
21 E. Mt. Vernon Pl. Phone: (410)659-8255
Baltimore, MD 21202 Edwin A. Quist, Libn.
Founded: 1866. **Staff:** Prof 2; Other 3. **Subjects:** Music. **Special Collections:** Caruso Collection (62 volumes); John Charles Thomas Collection; manuscripts of Arthur Friedheim, Asger Hamerik, Timothy Spelman, Gustav Strube, Louis Cheslock, Howard Thatcher, Vladimir Padwa, Robert L. Paul, Theodore Hemberger, George Boyle. **Holdings:** 67,000 books and scores; 1500 bound periodical volumes; 21,000 recordings; 400 reels of microfilm; 2000 manuscripts; 8 VF drawers; 6 boxes of clippings. **Subscriptions:** 300 journals and other serials. **Services:** Interlibrary loan; copying (nonmusic materials only); library open to the public. **Automated Operations:** Computerized cataloging. **Computerized Information Services:** RLIN, DIALOG Information Services; BITNET (electronic mail service). Performs searches on fee basis. Contact Person: Ursula McLean, Asst.Libn./Rd.Serv. **Networks/Consortia:** Member of Maryland Interlibrary Organization (MILO), Research Libraries Information Network (RLIN). **Publications:** Cotage (newsletter), irregular. **Remarks:** FAX: (410)685-0657. Electronic mail address(es): QUIST–E@JHUVMS (BITNET). **Staff:** Christopher Lobingier, Sound Recordings Libn.; Rosalind Mann, Circ.Supv.

★8425★
Johns Hopkins University - Population Information Program (Soc Sci)
527 St. Paul Pl. Phone: (410)659-6300
Baltimore, MD 21202 Dr. Phyllis T. Piotrow, Dir.
Founded: 1972. **Staff:** Prof 14; Other 14. **Subjects:** Population, family planning, human fertility, contraception, related health, law, and policy issues. **Holdings:** 1000 books; 150,000 documents. **Subscriptions:** 500 journals and other serials. **Services:** Interlibrary loan; copying; SDI; program open to the public by appointment. **Computerized Information Services:** MEDLARS, DIALOG Information Services, BRS Information Technologies, POPLINE; CD-ROM (POPLINE); INPROS (internal database). Performs searches on fee basis. Contact Person: Edith Sonntag, Database Ed. **Networks/Consortia:** Member of APLIC International Census Network. **Publications:** Population Reports, bimonthly - to worldwide mailing list; User's Guide to POPLINE Keywords. **Remarks:** The purpose of the program is to provide accurate, continuing, systematic, and up-to-date information on new developments in population, family planning, and related health issues. The program is supported primarily by the United States Agency for International Development. FAX: (410)659-6266. Telex: 240430 JHUPES UR. **Staff:** Ward Rinehart, Dp.Dir.; Anne Compton, Assoc.Dir.

★8426★
Johns Hopkins University - Research & Development Center - Center for Social Organization of Schools (Educ)
3505 N. Charles St. Phone: (415)516-0370
Baltimore, MD 21218 John H. Hollifield, Assoc.Dir.
Founded: 1966. **Staff:** 25. **Subjects:** School organization, elementary and middle school research, at-risk students, parent involvement, microcomputers in schools. **Holdings:** 400 research reports. **Services:** Interlibrary loan; center open to the public by appointment. **Publications:** Annual publications; abstracts; research reports, newsletters. **Remarks:** FAX: (415)516-6370.

★8427★
Johns Hopkins University - School of Advanced International Studies - Sydney R. & Elsa W. Mason Library (Soc Sci)
1740 Massachusetts Ave., N.W. Phone: (202)663-5900
Washington, DC 20036 Peter J. Promen, Libn.
Founded: 1943. **Staff:** Prof 5; Other 10. **Subjects:** International affairs since 1945, international economics and law, history, politics, sociology. **Holdings:** 105,000 books; 10,000 bound periodical volumes; 5400 reels of microfilm; 31,000 microfiche. **Subscriptions:** 907 journals and other serials; 35 newspapers. **Services:** Interlibrary loan; copying; library open to the public with registration and fee. **Automated Operations:** Computerized cataloging. **Computerized Information Services:** OCLC, RLIN, DIALOG Information Services, WILSONLINE. **Networks/Consortia:** Member of PALINET. **Staff:** Linda Carlson, Rd.Serv.Libn.; Sabiha Famularo, Cat.Libn.

★8428★
Johns Hopkins University - School of Hygiene and Public Health - Abraham M. Lilienfeld Memorial Library (Med)
624 N. Broadway, 9th Fl. Phone: (301)955-3028
Baltimore, MD 21205-1901 Edward S. Terry, Dir.
Founded: 1963. **Staff:** Prof 3; Other 4. **Subjects:** Health policy and management, epidemiolgy, maternal and child health, mental hygiene, international health, behavioral sciences, sociology, environmental health sciences, immunology, infectious diseases. **Holdings:** 30,000 volumes. **Subscriptions:** 250 journals and other serials. **Services:** Library open to health professionals and researchers in the Baltimore area. **Computerized Information Services:** BRS Information Technologies, DIALOG Information Services; CD-ROM (SilverPlatter Information Inc.). **Publications:** List of selected acquisitions, monthly - for internal distribution only. **Staff:** Barbara L. Zelnik, Asst.Dir.; Mary Grace Flaherty, Ref.Libn.

★8429★
Johns Hopkins University - School of Hygiene and Public Health - Population Center Collection (Soc Sci, Med)
615 N. Wolfe St., Rm. 2300 Phone: (301)955-3573
Baltimore, MD 21205 L. Terri Singer, Libn.
Staff: Prof 1; Other 2. **Subjects:** Population dynamics, demography, family planning, physiology of reproduction, statistics. **Special Collections:** U.S. Census publications, 1790 to present; U.S. vital and health statistics, 1935 to present. **Holdings:** 16,000 books; 700 bound periodical volumes; 175 theses; 675 National Center for Health Statistics pamphlets; 600 Population Association of America documents. **Subscriptions:** 170 journals and other serials. **Services:** SDI; library open to the public. **Automated Operations:** Computerized cataloging. **Computerized Information Services:** MEDLARS, DIALOG Information Services, IDRC (International Development Research Centre), OCLC; PRO-CITE (internal database). Performs searches on fee basis. **Publications:** Current contents of journals received, bimonthly - to faculty and students; acquisitions list, monthly - to students, faculty, and university libraries; serials holdings list. **Special Catalogs:** Reprints and working papers catalog. **Remarks:** FAX: (301)955-1215.

★8430★
Johns Hopkins University - School of Medicine - Department of Pediatrics - Baetjer Memorial Library (Med)
CMSC 2-104 Johns Hopkins Hospital Phone: (301)955-3124
Baltimore, MD 21205 Sheila A. Kuhn, Libn.
Founded: 1963. **Staff:** Prof 1. **Subjects:** Pediatrics, general medicine. **Special Collections:** Transactions of the American Pediatric Society; Archives of Pediatrics, 1884-1922. **Holdings:** 450 books; 2500 bound periodical volumes. **Subscriptions:** 53 journals and other serials. **Services:** Library not open to the public. **Computerized Information Services:** BRS Information Technologies, MEDLARS; CD-ROM (MEDLINE). **Publications:** Department of Pediatrics Collected Reprints, annual.

★8431★
Johns Hopkins University - School of Medicine - Joseph L. Lilienthal Library (Med)
400 Halsted
600 N. Wolfe St. Phone: (301)955-7911
Baltimore, MD 21205 L. Robin Armstrong, Libn.
Staff: Prof 1. **Subjects:** Internal medicine. **Holdings:** 1000 books; 3000 bound periodical volumes; slide/tape Postgraduate Course in Internal Medicine. **Subscriptions:** 45 journals and other serials. **Services:** Copying; library open to the public with restrictions.

★8432★
Johns Hopkins University - William H. Welch Medical Library (Med, Biol Sci)
1900 E. Monument St. Phone: (301)955-3411
Baltimore, MD 21205 Nina W. Matheson, Dir./Libn.
Founded: 1929. **Staff:** Prof 22; Other 53. **Subjects:** Medicine, clinical medicine, history of medicine, life sciences, nursing, public health, psychiatry, neurology, neurosurgery. **Special Collections:** Institute of the History of Medicine (50,000 volumes); Henry Jacobs Collection (history of the diseases of the chest and vaccination); Florence Nightingale Collection (history of nursing). **Holdings:** 358,385 volumes; 2788 AV programs. **Subscriptions:** 2870 journals and other serials. **Services:** Interlibrary loan; copying; SDI; document delivery; library open to academic and education professionals. **Automated Operations:** Computerized public access catalog, cataloging, acquisitions, serials, and circulation. **Computerized Information Services:** MEDLINE, Current Contents Search, BRS Information Technologies, DIALOG Information Services, NLM, OCLC, PsycLIT; InterNet (electronic mail service). **Networks/Consortia:** Member of PALINET, Maryland Interlibrary Organization (MILO), National Network of Libraries of Medicine - Southeastern/Atlantic Region. **Publications:** Annual report; Welch Library Issues; GDB Forum. **Remarks:** FAX: (301)955-8020. Electronic mail address(es): FITZ@WELCHLAB.WELCH.JHU.EDU (InterNet). **Staff:** Karen Butter, Dp.Dir.; Robert Robbins, Assoc.Dir., Res. & Comp.Serv.; Patricia FitzGerald, Asst.Dir., Adm.Serv.

Addison B. Johnson Air Traffic Control Resource Center
See: **U.S. Federal Aviation Administration - Technical Center Library (ACM-651)** (17487)

Andrew Johnson National Historic Site
See: **U.S. Natl. Park Service** (17665)

★8433★
Bernard Johnson, Inc. - Technical Library (Sci-Engr)
5050 Westheimer Rd.
Houston, TX 77056 Phone: (713)622-1400
Founded: 1975. **Staff:** Prof 1. **Subjects:** Engineering, architecture, environment, land development. **Holdings:** 4000 books; 79 bound periodical volumes; 750 VF drawers of company archives; 4 VF drawers of clippings; 20 VF drawers of maps. **Subscriptions:** 302 journals and other serials. **Services:** Interlibrary loan; library open to the public by appointment only. **Automated Operations:** Computerized cataloging, serials, and circulation. **Computerized Information Services:** DIALOG Information Services; internal database. **Publications:** New at the Library, monthly - free upon request. **Remarks:** FAX: (713)961-1720.

★8434★
Johnson Bible College - Glass Memorial Library (Rel-Phil)
Knoxville, TN 37998 Phone: (615)573-4517
Helen E. Lemmon, Libn.
Founded: 1893. **Staff:** Prof 1; Other 20. **Subjects:** Theology, church history, literature. **Holdings:** 76,298 books; 5527 bound periodical volumes; 14 VF drawers of pamphlets; 6 VF drawers of mission letters; 349 reels of microfilm. **Subscriptions:** 313 journals and other serials; 5 newspapers. **Services:** Interlibrary loan; copying.

★8435★
Carol R. Johnson & Associates, Inc. - Library (Plan)
1100 Massachusetts Ave. Phone: (617)868-6115
Cambridge, MA 02138 Ruth G. Wolz, Res.Libn.
Staff: Prof 1. **Subjects:** Landscape architecture, architecture, horticulture, parks and recreation. **Special Collections:** Graphics collection (photographs, slides, drawings of company projects). **Holdings:** 1000 books; technical data; product literature. **Subscriptions:** 25 journals and other serials. **Services:** Copying; library open to the public by appointment. **Remarks:** FAX: (617)864-7890.

★8436★
Johnson City Press - Library (Publ)
204 W. Main St.
P.O. Box 1717 Phone: (615)929-3111
Johnson City, TN 37605 Phyllis J. Brown
Founded: 1950. **Staff:** Prof 1. **Subjects:** Newspaper reference topics. **Special Collections:** Newspaper clipping file. **Holdings:** 1500 books; 12 bound periodical volumes; 516 microfiche; 2000 reels of microfilm. **Subscriptions:** 10 journals and other serials; 15 newspapers. **Services:** Copying; library open on a limited basis. **Automated Operations:** Computerized indexing. **Remarks:** FAX: (615)929-7484.

★8437★
Johnson Controls, Inc. - Technical Information Center G2 (Sci-Engr)
5757 N. Green Bay Ave.
Box 591 Phone: (414)228-2381
Milwaukee, WI 53209 Julie Baldwin, Libn.
Founded: 1988. **Staff:** Prof 1; Other 1. **Subjects:** Chemistry, batteries, management, engineering, physics, materials science. **Holdings:** 7000 books. **Subscriptions:** 450 journals and other serials. **Services:** Interlibrary loan; library open to the public by appointment. **Automated Operations:** Computerized public access catalog, cataloging, acquisitions, serials, and circulation. **Computerized Information Services:** DIALOG Information Services, PFDS Online, DataTimes, OCLC. **Networks/Consortia:** Member of Wisconsin Interlibrary Services (WILS). **Publications:** Information Update, bimonthly - for internal distribution only. **Remarks:** FAX: (414)228-2008.

★8438★
Johnson Controls, Inc. - Technology and Business Information Center M47 (Sci-Engr)
507 E. Michigan St.
Box 423 Phone: (414)274-4446
Milwaukee, WI 53201 Mary F. Kaczmarek, Supv.
Founded: 1973. **Staff:** Prof 2; Other 1. **Subjects:** Electronics, building controls technology, artificial intelligence, business, management. **Holdings:** 8500 books; 130 bound periodical volumes; 8250 technical reports; 1000 standards and specifications. **Subscriptions:** 525 journals and other serials. **Services:** Interlibrary loan; library open to the public with restrictions. **Automated Operations:** Computerized public access catalog, cataloging, acquisitions, serials, and circulation. **Computerized Information Services:** DIALOG Information Services, ORBIT Search Service, OCLC, DataTimes, InvesText. **Networks/Consortia:** Member of Library Council of Metropolitan Milwaukee, Inc. (LCOMM), Wisconsin Interlibrary Services (WILS). **Publications:** Serials list. **Remarks:** FAX: (414)274-5810. **Staff:** Pat A. Riese, Info.Spec.; Martha J. Bollig, Info.Spec.

★8439★
Johnson County Historical Society - Mary Miller Smiser Heritage Library (Hist)
300 N. Main St. Phone: (816)747-6480
Warrensburg, MO 64093 Joy Young, Adm.
Founded: 1968. **Staff:** Prof 4. **Subjects:** History of townships, genealogy, business; transportation. **Special Collections:** U.S. Senator Cockrell papers (3 VF drawers); Smiser Collection; Warrensburg Standard Herald, 1865-1936 (bound volumes); Knobnoster Gem, 1920-1923 and 1945-1947 (4 volumes). **Holdings:** 500 volumes; directories; census records; diaries; cemetery records; documents; manuscripts; marriage records; 75 tapes. **Subscriptions:** 32 journals and other serials. **Services:** Copying; library open to the public on a limited schedule and for reference use only. **Publications:** The Bulletin, semiannual - to members. **Staff:** Dr. Roy Stubbs, Cur.; Helen Vogel, Ed.; Mildred Adams, Hist.

★8440★
Johnson County Law Library (Law)
Courthouse Phone: (913)782-5000
Olathe, KS 66061 J.W. Breyfogle, III, Libn.
Founded: 1953. **Staff:** Prof 1; Other 1. **Subjects:** Law. **Holdings:** 15,000 books; 100 bound periodical volumes; cassettes. **Subscriptions:** 75 journals and other serials; 5 newspapers. **Services:** Interlibrary loan; copying; library open to the public.

★8441★
Johnson County Memorial Hospital - Library (Med)
1125 W. Jefferson Phone: (317)736-3456
Franklin, IN 46131 Kathryn Jester, Libn.
Founded: 1973. **Staff:** Prof. 1. **Subjects:** Medicine, nursing. **Holdings:** 300 books. **Subscriptions:** 51 journals and other serials. **Services:** Interlibrary loan; library not open to the public. **Computerized Information Services:** BRS Information Technologies. **Remarks:** (317)736-2692.

★8442★
Johnson County Mental Health Center - John R. Keach Memorial Library (Med)
6000 Lamar Ave.
Mission, KS 66202 Phone: (913)831-2550
Founded: 1963. **Staff:** Prof 11. **Subjects:** Mental health, psychology, psychiatry, social work. **Special Collections:** The Complete Psychological Works of Sigmund Freud (Volumes 1-24). **Holdings:** 1722 books; 199 bound periodical volumes; 8 VF drawers. **Subscriptions:** 25 journals and other serials. **Services:** Interlibrary loan; copying; library open for staff and client use only. **Networks/Consortia:** Member of National Network of Libraries of Medicine - Midcontinental Region. **Staff:** Fred Kouri, Supv.; Bonnie Lancaster, Supv.

★8443★
Johnson Filtration System, Inc.
Box 64118
St. Paul, MN 55164-0118
Defunct.

★8444★
George Johnson Advertising - Library (Bus-Fin)
13823 Barrett Pkwy., No. 251 Phone: (314)822-0553
Ballwin, MO 63021 Gina Manzo, Libn.
Founded: 1965. **Staff:** Prof 1. **Subjects:** Advertising, management, marketing. **Holdings:** 349 volumes; 21 VF drawers of clippings. **Subscriptions:** 30 journals and other serials; 5 newspapers. **Services:** Interlibrary loan; copying; library open to the public with restrictions. **Automated Operations:** Computerized public access catalog. **Remarks:** (314)569-3443.

★8445★
Johnson & Gibbs - Library (Law)
1301 K. St., N.W., Suite 800 E. Phone: (202)682-4676
Washington, DC 20005 Georgia Chadwick, Br.Libn.
Founded: 1987. **Staff:** 2. **Subjects:** Taxation, labor. **Holdings:** 1500 volumes; 50 bound periodical volumes; 700 nonbook items. **Services:** Library open to attornies and law libraries. **Computerized Information Services:** LEXIS, WESTLAW. **Remarks:** FAX: (202)682-4674.

★8446★
Johnson & Gibbs - Library (Law, Bus-Fin)
100 Founders Square
900 Jackson St. Phone: (214)977-9701
Dallas, TX 75202-4499 Betty B. Dewberry, Dir., Libs.
Founded: 1970. **Staff:** Prof 4; Other 3. **Subjects:** Law - taxation, financial services, labor; multinational/public securities; oil and gas; litigation; intellectual property; real estate. **Holdings:** 54,000 books; 1850 bound periodical volumes; 40 volumes of bound transactions; 7800 volumes in microform; microfiche; collection of bills introduced during the most recent Texas legislative session. **Subscriptions:** 1600 journals and other serials; 14 newspapers. **Services:** Interlibrary loan. **Automated Operations:** Computerized public access catalog, cataloging, and serials. **Computerized Information Services:** LEXIS, DIALOG Information Services, WESTLAW, LEGI-SLATE, Dow Jones News/Retrieval, PHINet FedTax Database, VU/TEXT Information Services, RLIN, DataTimes, Dun & Bradstreet Business Credit Services, Information America, CCH Access. **Networks/Consortia:** Member of Dallas Association of Law Librarians (DALL), Research Libraries Information Network (RLIN). **Publications:** Library Newsletter (new acquisitions); Labor & International Law Watch Service. **Special Catalogs:** Catalog of internal opinions and memoranda (card); catalog for bound transactions (card). **Remarks:** FAX: (214)977-9004.Maintains branch libraries in: Austin, TX, Washington, DC, and Houston, TX. **Staff:** Ernestine Chipman, Sr.Ref.Libn.; Cheryl Butler, Asst.Libn.; Jane Reynolds, Supv., Tech.Serv.; Mary Coyne, Br.Libn.; Georgia Chadwick, Br.Libn.

Johnson Graduate School of Management
See: **Cornell University - Johnson Graduate School of Management** (4316)

Johnson Health Sciences Library
See: **Long Beach Community Hospital** (9274)

Herbert F. Johnson Museum of Art
See: **Cornell University - Herbert F. Johnson Museum of Art** (4312)

Johnson & Higgins Willis Faber Inc.
See: **Foster Higgins** (6031)

★8447★
Johnson and Johnson - COSAT Information Services (Sci-Engr)
410 George St. Phone: (908)524-2555
New Brunswick, NJ 08901-2021 Anne D. Stark, Info.Spec.
Founded: 1989. **Staff:** Prof 1. **Subjects:** Science, medicine, biotechnology. **Holdings:** 1000 books. **Subscriptions:** 100 journals and other serials. **Services:** Interlibrary loan; copying; SDI; library open to the public by appointment for reference use only. **Computerized Information Services:** DIALOG Information Services, Dow Jones News/Retrieval, Data-Star, NEXIS, Questel. **Publications:** Guide to Library Services. **Remarks:** FAX: (201)524-2549.

Johnson and Johnson - Critikon, Inc.
See: **Critikon, Inc.** (4434)

Johnson and Johnson - Iolab Corporation
See: **Iolab Corporation** (8220)

★8448★
Johnson and Johnson - Ortho Diagnostic Systems Inc. - Research Library Information Center
U.S. Hwy. Rte. 202
Raritan, NJ 08869 Phone: (908)218-8163
Services: Library not open to the public. **Remarks:** No further information was supplied by respondent.

Johnson and Johnson - Personal Products Company
See: **Personal Products Company** (12953)

★8449★
Johnson and Johnson - Research Information Center (Sci-Engr)
2351 Rte. 130
Box 940 Phone: (908)274-3126
Dayton, NJ 08810-0940 Bryan Young, Mgr., Res.Info.Ctr.
Founded: 1947. **Staff:** Prof 1; Other 1. **Subjects:** Textiles - medical, nonwoven, polymers. **Holdings:** 2000 books. **Subscriptions:** 102 journals and other serials. **Services:** Interlibrary loan; library not open to the public. **Automated Operations:** Computerized cataloging, acquisitions, serials, and circulation. **Computerized Information Services:** PFDS Online, DIALOG Information Services, STN International. **Publications:** Newsletter, monthly; Accessions List. **Remarks:** FAX: (201)274-3158. **Formerly:** Its Chicopee Research Library.

★8450★
Johnson and Johnson Consumer Products Inc. - Business & Technical Information Center (Sci-Engr)
Grandview Rd. Phone: (908)874-1439
Skillman, NJ 08558 Marilyn H. Faulkner, Mgr.
Staff: Prof 3. **Subjects:** Infant care, health and beauty aids, toiletries, chemistry, pharmaceuticals, oral care, wound care, skin care. **Holdings:** 2000 books; 1500 bound periodical volumes. **Subscriptions:** 400 journals and other serials. **Services:** Interlibrary loan; SDI; center open to the public by appointment for reference use only. **Automated Operations:** Computerized acquisitions, serials, and circulation. **Computerized Information Services:** DIALOG Information Services, MEDLARS, PFDS Online, Chemical Information Systems, Inc. (CIS), Occupational Health Services, Inc., Mead Data Central, Dow Jones News/Retrieval, VU/TEXT Information Services, NewsNet, Inc., Chemical Abstracts Service (CAS), Data-Star, MAID. **Remarks:** FAX: (908)874-1212. **Staff:** C. Christensen; A. Laplante.

★8451★
Johnson and Johnson, Inc. - Research Library (Sci-Engr)
7101 Notre Dame St., E.
Montreal, PQ, Canada H1N 2G4 Phone: (514)252-5029
Founded: 1954. **Staff:** 1. **Subjects:** Nonwovens, textiles, chemistry, pulp and paper, plastics, feminine hygiene products. **Holdings:** 1200 books; patents; reprints. **Subscriptions:** 87 journals and other serials. **Services:** Interlibrary loan; library not open to the public. **Remarks:** Alternate telephone number(s): 251-5151. FAX: (514)251-5132.

★8452★
Johnson and Johnson Medical Inc. - Library (Biol Sci, Sci-Engr)
2500 Arbrook Blvd.
Box 130 Phone: (817)784-4529
Arlington, TX 76004-0130 Carolyn Cohenour, Lib.Adm.
Founded: 1970. **Staff:** Prof 1. **Subjects:** Chemical and biological sciences. **Special Collections:** Antimicrobial chemistry (5000 reprints). **Holdings:** 2400 books. **Subscriptions:** 150 journals and other serials. **Services:** Interlibrary loan; copying. **Computerized Information Services:** DIALOG Information Services. **Networks/Consortia:** Member of Health Libraries Information Network (HealthLINE). **Publications:** Library information bulletin - for internal distribution only. **Formerly:** Johnson and Johnson Medical Corp. - Technical Information Center.

Johnson, Johnson and Roy, Inc. - Planning and Landscape Architectural Archives
See: **Michigan State University - C.W. Barr Planning and Design Library** (10317)

Juanita J. Johnson Memorial Library
See: **Westminster Presbyterian Church** (20332)

★8453★
Lawrence Johnson & Associates, Inc. - Library (Soc Sci)
13917 Crest Hill Ln. Phone: (301)236-4433
Silver Spring, MD 20905 Mrs. Tish Nearon, Libn.
Staff: Prof 4; Other 3. **Subjects:** Psychology, race relations, human relations development, child welfare, human factors, education. **Special Collections:** Race relations in the military services (50 volumes). **Holdings:** 2000 books; 2500 technical reports; 700 unbound periodicals; 150 boxes of unpublished manuscripts and dissertations; 200 vuegraphs, slides, audiotapes. **Subscriptions:** 50 journals and other serials; 5 newspapers. **Services:** Interlibrary loan; library not open to the public. **Remarks:** FAX: (301)236-4434. **Formerly:** Located in Washington, D.C.

Johnson Library
See: **Bergen County Historical Society** (1733)

Johnson Library
See: **First Reformed Church** (5805)

Lyndon B. Johnson Library and Museum
See: **U.S. Presidential Libraries** (17928)

Lyndon B. Johnson National Historical Park
See: **U.S. Natl. Park Service** (17746)

Lyndon B. Johnson Space Center
See: **NASA** (10988)

★8454★
Martin and Osa Johnson Safari Museum - Stott Explorers Library (Sci-Engr)
111 N. Lincoln Phone: (316)431-2730
Chanute, KS 66720 Conrad G. Froehlich, Musm.Dir.
Founded: 1980. **Subjects:** Natural history, exploration, photography. **Special Collections:** Complete set of materials by Martin and Osa Johnson, including some unpublished material; Martin and Osa Johnson Photographic Collection (several films and several thousand photographs). **Holdings:** 11,000 books; reprint file. **Subscriptions:** 15 journals and other serials. **Services:** Interlibrary loan (limited); copying; library open to scholars by appointment. **Publications:** Exploring with Osa and Martin Johnson (biography); Empty Masks - both for sale; The Johnson Safari Wait-a-bit News, quarterly - to members, museums, and libraries. **Special Catalogs:** The Cultural Heritage of Africa (museum catalog) - for sale. **Staff:** Barbara Henshall, Cur.

Johnson Memorial Library
See: **St. Paul's United Methodist Church** (14578)

Mildred Johnson Library
See: **North Dakota State College of Science** (11920)

Johnson Newspaper Corporation - Watertown Daily Times
See: **Watertown Daily Times** (20090)

★8455★
Johnson Publishing Company, Inc. - Library (Area-Ethnic, Publ)
820 S. Michigan Ave. Phone: (312)322-9320
Chicago, IL 60605 Pamela Cash Mensies, Libn.
Founded: 1949. **Staff:** Prof 2; Other 1. **Subjects:** Afro-Americana; black history, literature, biography; Africa. **Special Collections:** Newspaper clippings, 1940s to present; black newspapers, 1846 to present, on microfilm. **Holdings:** 10,000 books; 1000 bound periodical volumes; 300 drawers of newspaper clippings; pamphlets; company publications. **Subscriptions:** 150 journals and other serials; 50 newspapers. **Services:** Library not open to the public.

R.W. Johnson Pharmaceutical Research Insititute
See: **Ortho-McNeil Inc.** (12578)

★8456★
R.W. Johnson Pharmaceutical Research Institute - Library (Med)
Spring House, PA 19477 Phone: (215)628-5627
Diane C. Shaffer, Mgr., Lib. & Info.Serv.
Founded: 1966. **Staff:** Prof 4; Other 5. **Subjects:** Chemistry, pharmacology, biochemistry, clinical medicine, toxicology, technology. **Holdings:** 8000 books; 12,000 bound periodical volumes. **Subscriptions:** 900 journals and other serials. **Services:** Interlibrary loan; SDI; library open to the public by appointment only. **Automated Operations:** Integrated library system. **Computerized Information Services:** DIALOG Information Services, PFDS Online, NLM, BRS Information Technologies, STN International, Dow Jones News/Retrieval, Data-Star, TEXTLINE, VU/TEXT Information Services, NEXIS; internal databases. **Networks/Consortia:** Member of Delaware Valley Information Consortium (DEVIC). **Remarks:** FAX: (215)628-5984. **Staff:** Dr. Norman Schwartz, Sr.Info.Sci.; Jean M. Ellis, Lib.Info.Serv.Coord.; Pam Wicks, Assoc.Info.Sci.; Dr. Norman Santora, Sr.Info.Sci.

★8457★
Robert Wood Johnson Foundation - Library (Med)
Rte. 1 and College Rd.
Box 2316 Phone: (609)243-5897
Princeton, NJ 08543-2316 Philip J. Gallagher, Libn.
Founded: 1972. **Staff:** Prof 1; Other 1. **Subjects:** Health policy, health economics, health manpower, medical education, philanthropy. **Holdings:** 5500 books; 80 bound periodical volumes; 200 annual reports of foundations; 9 films; 105 cassettes; 170 health school catalogs. **Subscriptions:** 165 journals and other serials; 6 newspapers. **Services:** Interlibrary loan; copying; library open to the public. **Computerized Information Services:** DIALOG Information Services; DOCLINE (electronic mail service). **Networks/Consortia:** Member of Consortium of Foundation Libraries (CFL), Central Jersey Health Science Libraries Association (CJHSLA).

Robert Wood Johnson Library of the Health Sciences
See: **University of Medicine and Dentistry of New Jersey** (18838)

Robert Wood Johnson Medical School
See: **University of Medicine and Dentistry of New Jersey** (18839)

★8458★
Robert Wood Johnson Pharmaceutical Research Institute - Hartman Library (Med)
Rte. 202, Box 300 Phone: (908)704-4109
Raritan, NJ 08869-0602 June Bente, Mgr., Lib.Serv.
Founded: 1944. **Staff:** Prof 3; Other 2. **Subjects:** Medicine, pharmacy, endocrinology, biological sciences, chemistry. **Holdings:** 8000 books; 15,000 bound periodical volumes. **Subscriptions:** 1000 journals and other serials. **Services:** Interlibrary loan; library open to the public by appointment. **Automated Operations:** Computerized public access catalog, cataloging, acquisitions, serials, and circulation. **Computerized Information Services:** BRS Information Technologies, DIALOG Information Services, PFDS Online, MEDLINE, U.S. National Technical Information Service (NTIS). **Networks/Consortia:** Member of MEDCORE. **Remarks:** FAX: (908)707-9860. **Staff:** Barbara Boyajian, Assoc.Info.Sci.; Cynthia Cohrs, Assoc.Info.Sci.

★8459★
S.C. Johnson and Son, Inc. - Technical & Business Information Center (Sci-Engr)
M.S. 123
1525 Howe St. Phone: (414)631-2372
Racine, WI 53403 Mara Teranis, Sr.Res.Sci., Info.Ctr.
Staff: Prof 2; Other 3. **Subjects:** Chemistry, biology, physics, business. **Holdings:** 14,000 books; 7500 bound periodical volumes. **Subscriptions:** 350 journals and other serials. **Services:** Interlibrary loan; SDI. **Automated Operations:** Computerized serials. **Computerized Information Services:** DIALOG Information Services, NEXIS, BRS Information Technologies, National Pesticide Information Retrieval System (NPIRS), STN International, Dow Jones News/Retrieval, MEDLARS, DataTimes, VU/TEXT Information Services, Chemical Information Systems, Inc. (CIS). **Publications:** Activity and acquisitions list - for internal distribution only. **Remarks:** FAX: (414)631-2044. **Staff:** Luanne C. Frey, Res.Sci., Info.Ctr.; Connie A. Taagen, Sci., Info.Ctr.

Johnson Space Center History Archive
See: **Rice University - Woodson Research Center** (13897)

★8460★
Johnson Technical Institute - Library (Educ)
3427 N. Main Ave. Phone: (717)342-6404
Scranton, PA 18508-1495 Esther K. Friedmann, Lib.Dir.
Founded: 1969. **Staff:** 1.5. **Subjects:** Technologies - automotive, electronic, biomedical equipment; construction; carpentry; drafting and design; machine trades; tool and die making; welding. **Holdings:** 4598 books; 55 bound periodical volumes; 12 VF drawers; 140 AV items. **Subscriptions:** 93 journals and other serials; 9 newspapers. **Services:** Interlibrary loan; copying; library open to the public for reference use only. **Computerized Information Services:** DIALOG Information Services. Performs searches on fee basis.

Johnson Victrola Museum
See: **Delaware State Museums - Johnson Victrola Museum** (4736)

★8461★
Johnson & Wales College - Paul Fritzsche Library (Food-Bev)
8 Abbott Park Pl.
Providence, RI 02903 Phone: (401)456-1174
Founded: 1979. **Staff:** Prof 2; Other 2. **Subjects:** Cookbooks, food service, menu planning, nutrition, professional management, catering and banquets, household manuals, canning, preserving and freezing, hotel and motel management. **Special Collections:** Specialized culinary and food service video collection. **Holdings:** 8300 books; 45 bound periodical volumes; 100 menus. **Subscriptions:** 20 journals and other serials. **Services:** Copying; library open to the public. **Special Indexes:** Periodical index. **Staff:** Felicia Hokanson, Libn.; Nancy Toher, Supv.

Walter Johnson Library
See: **Nordic Heritage Museum** (11841)

Ben Johnston Archive
See: **Northwestern University - Music Library** (12086)

Johnston Memorial Library
See: **Virginia State University** (19895)

★8462★
E.R. Johnstone Training & Research Center - Professional Library (Med)
Burlington St. Phone: (609)298-2500
Bordentown, NJ 08505 William Holloway, Ph.D., Res.Sci.
Founded: 1956. **Subjects:** Mental retardation, psychology, developmental disabilities. **Holdings:** 3700 books; 1550 bound periodical volumes; 110 Johnstone bulletins; 85 research reports; 61 microfiche. **Subscriptions:** 50 journals and other serials. **Services:** Interlibrary loan; copying; library open to the public. **Networks/Consortia:** Member of South Jersey Regional Library Cooperative. **Remarks:** FAX: (609)298-6577.

Johnstown Flood National Memorial
See: **U.S. Natl. Park Service** (17663)

★8463★
Johnstown Historical Society - Library Reference Center (Hist)
17 N. William St. Phone: (518)762-7076
Johnstown, NY 12095 James F. Morrison, Archv.
Founded: 1892. **Staff:** 2. **Subjects:** Local history; historical persons associated with Johnstown - Sir William Johnson, Molly Brant, Major Nick Stoner, Captain Silas Talbot, Lafayette, Washington Irving, Aaron Burr, Elizabeth Cady Stanton, Judge Daniel Cady, Governor Enos Throop, E.L. Henry, Brigadier General Edgar S. Dudley, Grace Livingston Hill, Rose M. Knox. **Special Collections:** Keck Zouaves; Knox Gelatin; Talmadge Edwards and glove industry equipment; cooper's equipment for barrelmaking; genealogy. **Holdings:** 1600 books; 52 bound periodical volumes; 400 booklets and pamphlets; 2300 photographs; 1350 documents; 5 files of clippings; 43 old maps; 6 files of old documents; 2 files of genealogical materials; 1100 old newspapers; and 300 old periodicals. **Services:** Library open to the public. **Staff:** Mrs. Gaal Rathburn, Geneal.

Joint Archives of Holland
See: **(Holland) Joint Archives of Holland** (7328)

★8464★
Joint Astronomy Centre - Library (Sci-Engr)
665 Komohana St. Phone: (808)961-3756
Hilo, HI 96720 Kevin Krisciunas
Founded: 1979. **Staff:** Prof 1. **Subjects:** Astronomy, astrophysics, optics, computer science, cryogenics, physics. **Holdings:** 1000 books; 1200 bound periodical volumes. **Subscriptions:** 35 journals and other serials. **Services:** Library open to the public. **Computerized Information Services:** InterNet (electronic mail service). **Special Indexes:** Sky and Telescope (biographic index). **Remarks:** FAX: (808)961-6516. Electronic mail address(es):KEVIN@JACH.HAWAII.EDU (InterNet).

★8465★
Joint Center for Political and Economic Studies, Inc. - Office of Information Resources (Soc Sci)
1301 Pennsylvania Ave., N.W., Suite 400 Phone: (202)626-3530
Washington, DC 20004 Auriel J. Pilgrim, Dir.
Founded: 1979. **Staff:** Prof 1; Other 2. **Subjects:** Blacks - political participation, social and economic conditions, demographic studies; public, education, and economic policies concerning minorities. **Special Collections:** Black elected officials; blacks in the military; black voting and voter registration statistics. **Holdings:** 3606 volumes; 2700 unbound materials; 450 unpublished reports; 111 VF drawers of clippings and archival material; 5 drawers of AV programs. **Subscriptions:** 238 journals and other serials; 4 newspapers. **Services:** Interlibrary loan; copying; office open to the public by appointment for reference use only. **Automated Operations:** Computerized cataloging and acquisitions. **Computerized Information Services:** DIALOG Information Services, NEXIS. **Publications:** Periodical table of contents bulletin, weekly - for internal distribution only. **Remarks:** FAX: (202)626-3521.

★8466★
Joint Economic Commission - Library (Bus-Fin)
Plantation House, Third Fl.
Place d'Armes
Port Louis, Mauritius Phone: 23302
Subjects: Economics, sugar, Mauritian history. **Holdings:** 3000 volumes. **Remarks:** Telex: 4214 SUGMAUR IW.

Joint Institute for Laboratory Astrophysics (JILA)
See: **University of Colorado--Boulder - Joint Institute for Laboratory Astrophysics (JILA) - Atomic Collision Cross Section Data Center** (18500)

Oswald Jonas Memorial Archive
See: **University of California, Riverside - Music Library** (18411)

Bayard H. Jones Liturgical Library
See: **University of the South - School of Theology Library** (19303)

Bishop Jones Library
See: **St. Mark's Episcopal Church** (14495)

★8467★
Bob Jones University - Church Ministries Resource Lab (Rel-Phil)
Greenville, SC 29614 Phone: (803)242-5100
Mrs. James Berg, Supv.
Founded: 1957. **Staff:** Prof 4; Other 5. **Subjects:** Church ministries, denominational and nondenominational curriculums, youth programs, children's materials, adult materials. **Holdings:** 1700 books; 29 VF drawers of clippings and articles; 200 filmstrips and phonograph records; 45 tapes; 1650 cassettes; 110 video cassettes. **Subscriptions:** 30 journals and other serials. **Services:** Lab not open to the public. **Staff:** Mrs. Daniel Boone; Mrs. Nelson McGeoch; Mrs. Tony Miller.

★8468★
Bob Jones University - Music Library (Mus)
Greenville, SC 29614 Phone: (803)242-5100
Dr. Karen S. Wilson, Mus.Libn.
Staff: Prof 1; Other 2. **Subjects:** Music. **Holdings:** 3833 books; 463 copies of sheet music; 9536 music recordings; 87 librettos; 428 speech recordings; 503 cassette tapes; 26 masters' projects; 447 opera vocal scores; 4970 oratorio and opera chorus scores; 81 filmstrips; 130 videotapes; 278 compact discs; 1276 folders of choral music. **Subscriptions:** 65 journals and other serials. **Services:** Interlibrary loan; copying; library open to the public with restrictions. **Computerized Information Services:** DIALOG Information Services. **Networks/Consortia:** Member of SOLINET.

★8469★
Bob Jones University - School of Education - Media Center (Educ)
Greenville, SC 29614 Phone: (803)242-5100
Jonna T. Carper, Dir.
Founded: 1953. **Staff:** Prof 1; Other 6. **Subjects:** Education - general, Christian, elementary, special; audiovisual methods. **Special Collections:** Bob Jones University Press Publications. **Holdings:** 600 books; 16 bound periodical volumes; 400 media catalogs; masters' theses and prospectuses; doctoral dissertations; computer software. **Subscriptions:** 21 journals and other serials. **Services:** Center not open to the public.

★8470★
Jones, Day, Reavis & Pogue - Law Library (Law)
2300 Trammell Crow Ctr.
2001 Ross Ave. Phone: (214)969-4824
Dallas, TX 75201 Joan E. Jarosek, Hd.Libn.
Founded: 1981. **Staff:** Prof 2; Other 3. **Subjects:** Law - corporate, tax, labor, real estate, entertainment; environment; litigation; construction; banking; government regulations. **Special Collections:** Texas Attorney General general opinions, 1947 to present; Texas Session Laws, 1835 to present; Texas Register, Volume 1, No. 1 to present. **Holdings:** 30,000 volumes. **Subscriptions:** 350 journals and other serials. **Services:** Interlibrary loan. **Automated Operations:** Computerized cataloging. **Computerized Information Services:** LEXIS, WESTLAW, DIALOG Information Services, LEGI-SLATE, OCLC, Dow Jones News/Retrieval, DataTimes, VU/TEXT Information Services; internal database. **Special Catalogs:** Union list of titles (online); periodicals list (online). **Staff:** Anne Leather, Assoc.Libn.

★8471★
Jones, Day, Reavis & Pogue - Library (Law)
555 W. 5th St. Phone: (213)489-3939
Los Angeles, CA 90013-1025 Joan Schipper, Libn.
Founded: 1985. **Staff:** Prof 2; Other 2. **Subjects:** Law. **Holdings:** 38,000 books. **Subscriptions:** 400 journals and other serials. **Services:** Interlibrary loan; library not open to the public. **Automated Operations:** Computerized cataloging. **Computerized Information Services:** LEXIS, WESTLAW, Legi-Tech, Information America. Performs searches on fee basis. **Staff:** Valerie Julius, Tech.Serv.Libn.

★8472★
Jones, Day, Reavis & Pogue - Library (Law)
3300 First Atlanta Tower Phone: (404)581-8118
Atlanta, GA 30383-3101 Jane Crawford, Libn.
Staff: Prof 4; Other 1. **Subjects:** Law. **Holdings:** 30,000 books. **Services:** Library not open to the public.

★8473★
Jones, Day, Reavis & Pogue - Library - North Point (Law)
901 Lakeside Ave. Phone: (216)586-3939
Cleveland, OH 44114 Sharon R. McIntyre, Libn.
Staff: Prof 3; Other 5. **Subjects:** Law. **Holdings:** 35,000 books; 1500 bound periodical volumes. **Subscriptions:** 160 journals and other serials. **Services:** Interlibrary loan; library not open to the public. **Computerized Information Services:** DIALOG Information Services, PFDS Online, WESTLAW, LEXIS. **Staff:** Timothy Petty, Asst.Libn.; Lynda Green, Online Serv.Libn.

Gordon W. Jones Medical Library
See: **Mary Washington Hospital** (20015)

Jones Graduate School of Administration
See: **Rice University** (13895)

Isaac Jones Family Archives
See: **Golden Ball Tavern Museum - Library** (6533)

★8474★
Jones Library, Inc. - Special Collections (Hist, Hum)
43 Amity St. Phone: (413)256-4090
Amherst, MA 01002 Daniel J. Lombardo, Cur.
Founded: 1921. **Staff:** Prof 1; Other 3. **Subjects:** Local and regional history, Amherst authors, genealogy. **Special Collections:** Robert Frost Collection; Emily Dickinson Collection; Ray Stannard Baker Collection; Clifton Johnson Collection (1200 books; 2300 photographs; letters; notebooks). **Holdings:** 15,000 books; 50,000 historical photographs; 20,000 other cataloged items; 240 reels of microfilm. **Subscriptions:** 11 journals and other serials. **Services:** Copying; collections open to the public. **Publications:** Finding aids. **Special Indexes:** Index of local newspapers (online). **Remarks:** FAX: (413)256-4096.

Louis C. Jones Folklife Archives
See: **New York (State) Historical Association - Library** (11663)

★8475★
Jones Memorial Library (Hist)
2311 Memorial Avenue Phone: (804)846-0501
Lynchburg, VA 24501 Edward Gibson
Staff: Prof 4; Other 2. **Subjects:** Genealogy, architectural drawings, local history, family histories. **Special Collections:** Lynchburg Architectural Archives; Lynchburg Foundery Archives. **Holdings:** 40,000 books; 5000 bound periodical volumes; 500 boxes of archival items; 3500 reels of microfilm; 12,000 drawings. **Subscriptions:** 50 journals and other serials; 9 newspapers. **Services:** Interlibrary loan; copying; library open to the public. **Remarks:** Library performs genealogical research by mail on a fee basis.

O.W. Jones Medical Library
See: **Davies Medical Center** (4638)

Perrie Jones Memorial Room
See: **St. Paul Public Library - Highland Park Branch** (14564)

Jones School of Law
See: **Faulkner University** (5615)

Seby Jones Library
See: **Toccoa Falls College** (16383)

★8476★
Spike Jones International Fan Club - Spike Jones Archives (Rec)
129 E. Colorado Blvd., Suite 508 Phone: (818)357-4947
Monrovia, CA 91016 Scott Corbet, Pres.
Subjects: Spike Jones. **Special Collections:** 1000 records related to Spike Jones. **Holdings:** 15 volumes; 2000 documents; 10 AV programs; 5 manuscripts; toys; record lists; newsletters. **Services:** Copying; library open to the public with restrictions. **Computerized Information Services:** Internal database. Performs searches on fee basis. Contact Person: Steve Blankenship, Ed. **Publications:** Spike Jones Newsletter, quarterly; Illustrated Guide to Spike Jones Recordings and Collectibles. **Remarks:** Spike Jones (Lindsay Armstrong) was famous for satirizing popular songs from the 1940s through the 1960s. FAX: (818)358-6788. Telex: 4720635.

★8477★
Jones & Stokes Associates, Inc. - Library (Plan, Env-Cons)
2600 V St. Phone: (916)737-3000
Sacramento, CA 95818-1914 Cynthia Ervin, Acq.Libn.
Founded: 1972. **Staff:** Prof 2; Other 1. **Subjects:** Land use planning; natural resources; science - ecological, physical, atmospheric, life; water resources; socioeconomics. **Holdings:** 13,000 books; 1800 reports; 1000 microfiche. **Subscriptions:** 500 journals and other serials. **Services:** Library not open to the public. **Automated Operations:** Computerized cataloging, circulation, and acquisitions. **Computerized Information Services:** DIALOG Information Services, MELVYL. **Remarks:** FAX: (916)737-3030. **Staff:** Ruby Hampton, Ref.Libn.

T.J. Jones Memorial Library
See: **North Central Bible College** (11910)

★8478★
W. Alton Jones Cell Science Center - George and Margaret Gey Library (Biol Sci)
10 Old Barn Rd. Phone: (518)523-1267
Lake Placid, NY 12946 Teresa B. Wilmes, MLS
Staff: Prof 1. **Subjects:** Cell culture, organ culture, cytology, cancer research, virology, biochemistry, immunology. **Special Collections:** Tissue culture. **Holdings:** 5000 books; 4500 bound periodical volumes. **Subscriptions:** 125 journals and other serials. **Services:** Interlibrary loan; copying; library open to the public with permission. **Computerized Information Services:** MEDLINE, DIALOG Information Services. **Networks/Consortia:** Member of North Country Reference and Research Resources Council (NCRRRC). **Remarks:** FAX: (518)523-4385.

★8479★
Jones, Walker, Waechter, Poitevent, Carrere & Denegre - Law Library (Law)
201 St. Charles Ave. Phone: (504)582-8589
New Orleans, LA 70170 Tina Gambrell, Libn.
Staff: Prof 1; Other 7. **Subjects:** Law, Louisiana law. **Holdings:** 21,000 books; 1000 bound periodical volumes; 5000 other cataloged items. **Subscriptions:** 350 journals and other serials; 12 newspapers. **Services:** Interlibrary loan. **Automated Operations:** Computerized cataloging. **Computerized Information Services:** LEXIS, NEXIS, DIALOG Information Services. **Remarks:** FAX: (504)582-8583; (504)582-8549.

Raymond Jonson Archives
See: **University of New Mexico - Art Museum - Raymond Jonson Archives** (19038)

J. Erik Jonsson Central Library
See: **Dallas Public Library** (4559)

★8480★
Joong Ang Daily News - Library (Soc Sci)
7, Soonhwa-dong
Chung-gu
Seoul, Republic of Korea Phone: 2 7527741
Staff: Prof 6. **Subjects:** Newspaper reference topics, market opinion, business information. **Holdings:** 50,000 bound volumes. **Subscriptions:** 350 journals and other serials. **Remarks:** FAX: 2 7515521579. Telex: 25587 K. Library is affiliated with the SVP (S'il Vous Plait) network of worldwide independent information-on-demand companies.

Jordan - Royal Scientific Society
See: **Royal Scientific Society** (14134)

Alice M. Jordan Collection
See: **Boston Public Library** (1991)

Barbara Jordan Archives
See: **Texas Southern University - Library - Heartman Collection** (16231)

★8481★
Jordan College Energy Institute - Library (Energy)
155 7-Mile Rd., N.W. Phone: (616)784-7595
Comstock Park, MI 49321 Roger L. Sorensen, Libn.
Founded: 1976. **Staff:** Prof 1; Other 1. **Subjects:** Energy - renewable, solar, biomass, wind; energy-conscious construction and technology . **Holdings:** 2500 books; 1000 other cataloged items; 23 VF drawers of topical and manufacturer information; 1000 government documents. **Subscriptions:** 46 journals and other serials. **Services:** Interlibrary loan; copying; library open to the public with restrictions on borrowing. **Networks/Consortia:** Member of Lakeland Area Library Network (LAKENET). **Remarks:** FAX: (616)784-0998.

Jordan College of Fine Arts Music Library
See: **Butler University** (2417)

Jordan Library
See: **Franciscan Medical Center** (6075)

L.R. Jordon Library
See: **Baptist Medical Centers-Samford University - Ida V. Moffett School of Nursing** (1512)

★8482★
Josephine County Historical Society - Research Library (Hist)
508 S.W. 5th St. Phone: (503)479-7827
Grants Pass, OR 97526 Martha A. Murphy, Exec.Dir.
Founded: 1972. **Staff:** Prof 1; Other 8. **Subjects:** History - Josephine County, southern Oregon. **Special Collections:** Amos Voorhies Photograph Collection; newspaper collection (200 reels of microfilm); Anna Prag picture postcard collection (400 cards); Claus and Hannchen Schmidt family albums (9 boxes); original county tax records, 1856-1953. **Holdings:** 755 books; 156 bound periodical volumes; 10 VF drawers of clippings; 4 VF drawers of photographs; 2000 slides; 106 boxes of manuscripts; 21 oral history tapes; unbound periodicals; maps. **Subscriptions:** 6 journals and other serials. **Services:** Copying; library open to the public. **Automated Operations:** Computerized public access catalog. **Networks/Consortia:** Member of Southern Oregon Library Federation (SOLF). **Publications:** The Oldtimer, 6/year - to members.

★8483★
Josephine County Law Library (Law)
Courthouse Phone: (503)479-8445
Grants Pass, OR 97526 Lynda Kettler, Libn.
Founded: 1939. **Staff:** Prof 1; Other 1. **Subjects:** Law - state, federal, bankruptcy, criminal, real property, tort, business, general. **Holdings:** 200 books; 11,000 bound periodical volumes; 2050 microfiche. **Subscriptions:** 52 journals and other serials. **Services:** Copying; library open to the public for reference use only. **Remarks:** FAX: (503)474-5105.

Josey Memorial Health Sciences Library
See: **Richland Memorial Hospital** (13906)

Joshua Tree National Monument
See: **U.S. Natl. Park Service** (17738)

★8484★
Joslin Diabetes Center, Inc. - Dooley Library (Med)
1 Joslin Place Phone: (617)732-2573
Boston, MA 02215 Richard Kitch, Libn.
Staff: Prof 1. **Subjects:** Diabetes mellitus, physiology, pathology, biochemistry. **Special Collections:** Archives (490 volumes); reprint collection of papers by the staff of the Joslin Diabetes Center (1000). **Holdings:** 7000 volumes; 80 VF folders. **Subscriptions:** 108 journals and other serials. **Services:** Interlibrary loan; copying; library open to the public at librarian's discretion. **Computerized Information Services:** MEDLARS, DIALOG Information Services; MEDLINK (electronic mail service). **Networks/Consortia:** Member of Boston Library Consortium (BLC), Massachusetts Health Sciences Libraries Network (MaHSLiN), Northeast Consortium of Colleges and Universities in Massachusetts (NECCUM). **Publications:** Acquisitions list, monthly; bibliography of staff papers, annual. **Special Indexes:** Index to papers published by the staff of Joslin Diabetes Center.

★8485★
Joslyn Art Museum - Art Reference Library (Art)
2200 Dodge St.
Omaha, NE 68102 Phone: (402)342-3300
Founded: 1931. **Staff:** Prof 1; Other 2. **Subjects:** American and European art, with emphasis on 19th and 20th centuries; Western and Native American art and history. **Special Collections:** Joslyn Museum history files. **Holdings:** 20,000 books; 3000 bound periodical volumes; 100 VF drawers on artists and museums; 500 bound bulletins and annual reports; 20,000 slides; 700 art reproductions. **Subscriptions:** 200 journals and other serials. **Services:** Library open to the public. **Computerized Information Services:** OCLC. **Networks/Consortia:** Member of NEBASE. **Remarks:** FAX: (402)342-2376.

★8486★
Josselyn Center for Mental Health - Mental Health Library (Med)
405 Central Phone: (708)441-5600
Northfield, IL 60093 Jean M. Peterson, Libn.
Founded: 1967. **Staff:** 1. **Subjects:** Child development, adolescence, parenting, divorce, psychoanalysis, psychotheraphy. **Special Collections:** Films and videotapes on suicide. **Holdings:** Figures not available. **Services:** Library open to the public. **Remarks:** FAX: (708)441-7968. **Formerly:** Irene Josselyn Clinic.

Irene Josselyn Clinic
See: **Josselyn Center for Mental Health** (8486)

Werner Josten Library of the Performing Arts
See: **Smith College** (15238)

★8487★
The Journal of Commerce - Library/Information Center (Bus-Fin, Publ)
2 World Trade Center, 27th Fl. Phone: (212)837-7116
New York, NY 10048 Christine Karpevych, Info. & Lib.Mgr.
Founded: 1977. **Staff:** Prof 1; Other 2. **Subjects:** Transportation - air, truck, railroad; international business; maritime industry; foreign trade; international finance; energy; insurance; chemicals and plastics; commodities. **Holdings:** 500 books; statistical reports on trade and transportation; 1200 annual reports. **Subscriptions:** 79 journals and other serials; 12 newspapers. **Services:** Library open to SLA members by appointment. **Computerized Information Services:** VU/TEXT Information Services, DIALOG Information Services. **Publications:** Clues (newsletter), irregular - for internal distribution only.

★8488★
Journal/Sentinel, Inc. - News Information Center (Publ)
PO Box 661 Phone: (414)224-2376
Milwaukee, WI 53201 Jo Reitman, Mgr.
Founded: 1920. **Staff:** Prof 3; Other 35. **Subjects:** Newspaper reference topics, Milwaukee, state of Wisconsin. **Holdings:** 4500 books; periodicals; 3 million clippings; 2 million photographs. **Services:** Copying; answers mail inquiries (limited); center open to the public with restrictions. **Computerized Information Services:** DataTimes, VU/TEXT Information Services. **Remarks:** FAX: (414)224-2388. Library located at 333 W. State St., Milwaukee, WI 53203. Published by Journal Communications. Center serves the Milwaukee Journal and the Milwaukee Sentinel. **Staff:** Rosemary Arakelian Jensen; Sandra Krchmar.

Captain Vincent J. Joy, Jr. Memorial Library
See: **Alaska Bible College** (202)

Joyner Library
See: **East Carolina University** (5114)

★8489★
Jubilee Centre for Agricultural Research - Family Farm/Stewardship Library (Agri)
115 Woolwich St. Phone: (519)837-1620
Guelph, ON, Canada N1H 3V1 N. Van Donkersgoed, Lib.Coord.
Founded: 1988. **Staff:** 3; Other 1. **Subjects:** Agriculture, environment, rural families. **Special Collections:** Rural sociology, alternative agriculture, plant and animal biotechnology, stewardship, animal bioengineering, animal rights and welfare, soil and water conservation, acid rain, farm crisis, environment, pollution, recycling. **Holdings:** 3000 books; 500 unbound periodicals; 2000 file folders of agricultural policy development, agriculture, and energy. **Subscriptions:** 300 journals and other serials; 25 newspapers. **Services:** Copying; library open to the public with restrictions. **Automated Operations:** Computerized cataloging, acquisitions, serials, and circulation. **Computerized Information Services:** Interal database. **Special Indexes:** Agricultural index. **Remarks:** FAX: (519)824-1835. **Formerly:** Jubilee Foundation for Agricultural Research.

Judaica Music Library
See: **Temple Beth Israel - Library** (16089)

★8490★
Judson College - Benjamin P. Browne Library (Rel-Phil)
1151 N. State St. Phone: (708)695-2500
Elgin, IL 60123 Dennis Read, Lib.Dir.
Founded: 1964. **Staff:** Prof 5; Other 1. **Subjects:** Religion, music, art. **Special Collections:** Baptist history and missions. **Holdings:** 75,000 books; 9100 bound periodical volumes; 6000 phonograph records; 6300 dramatic plays; 8000 scores; 400 radio shows; 27,000 microforms. **Subscriptions:** 420 journals and other serials; 6 newspapers. **Services:** Interlibrary loan; copying; SDI; library open to the public. **Automated Operations:** Computerized public access catalog, cataloging, acquisitions, serials, and circulation. **Computerized Information Services:** DIALOG Information Services, BRS Information Technologies; internal database; BITNET (electronic mail service). Performs searches on fee basis. **Networks/Consortia:** Member of ILLINET, North Suburban Library System (NSLS), LIBRAS Inc. **Remarks:** FAX: (708)695-0407. Electronic mail address(es): AXUJUDR@UICVMC (BITNET). **Staff:** Cathy Zange, Ref. & Ser.Libn.; Lynn Hammerlund, Tech.Serv.; Jane Miller, Circ.

Juelich Research Center - Central Library
See: **Germany - Juelich Research Center** (6449)

Jugoslovenski Centar za Tehnicku i Naucnu Dokumentaciju
See: **Yugoslav Center for Technical and Scientific Documentation** (20826)

★8491★
Juilliard School - Lila Acheson Wallace Library (Mus)
Lincoln Center Plaza Phone: (212)799-5000
New York, NY 10023 Jane Gottlieb, Hd.Libn.
Founded: 1945. **Staff:** Prof 5.5; Other 7. **Subjects:** Music, drama, dance. **Special Collections:** 19th century opera scores and librettos; Liszt Early and First Editions; rare and unusual chamber music editions. **Holdings:** 18,000 books; 15,000 sound recordings; 47,000 scores; 460 choral scores. **Subscriptions:** 170 journals and other serials. **Services:** Interlibrary loan; library open to public for reference use by arrangement only. **Computerized Information Services:** OCLC. **Networks/Consortia:** Member of New York Metropolitan Reference and Research Library Agency. **Remarks:** FAX: (212)724-0263. **Staff:** Taras Pavlovsky, Asst.Libn.; Stephanie Cimino, Cat.; Sandra Czajkowski, Rec.Libn.

★8492★
Julien, Schlesinger & Finz, P.C., Attorneys-At-Law - Library (Law)
150 William St. Phone: (212)962-8020
New York, NY 10038 Bob Epstine, Libn.
Subjects: Law, products liability, malpractice, negligence tort. **Holdings:** 5000 volumes. **Subscriptions:** 30 journals and other serials. **Services:** Interlibrary loan; library not open to the public.

★8493★
C.G. Jung Institute of Boston - Jean D. Yeomans Memorial Library (Soc Sci)
283 Commonwealth Ave. Phone: (617)267-5984
Boston, MA 02115 Francine Figelman, Libn.
Founded: 1979. **Staff:** Prof 1. **Subjects:** Psychology, religion, mythology, folklore, anthropology, literature. **Holdings:** 3000 books; 50 bound periodical volumes. **Subscriptions:** 6 journals and other serials. **Services:** Copying; library open to the public for reference use only.

★8494★
C.G. Jung Institute of Chicago - Library (Soc Sci)
550 Callan Ave. Phone: (708)475-4848
Evanston, IL 60202 Mark Swanson, Rsrc.Coord.
Founded: 1976. **Staff:** 1. **Subjects:** Jungian psychology, psychoanalysis, fairy tales, mythology, dreams, women's studies, men's studies. **Special Collections:** Jung's unpublished seminar notes, 1923-1940. **Holdings:** 2300 books; 1700 bound periodical volumes; 350 audiocassettes. **Services:** Copying; library open to the public for reference use only. **Automated Operations:** Computerized cataloging. **Computerized Information Services:** Internal database. Performs searches on fee basis for extensive research. **Remarks:** (708)475-4970.

★8495★
C.G. Jung Institute of Los Angeles, Inc. - Max and Lore Zeller Library (Soc Sci)
10349 West Pico Blvd. Phone: (310)556-1196
Los Angeles, CA 90064-2694 Linda Weidlinger
Founded: 1948. **Staff:** Prof 1. **Subjects:** Analytical (Jungian) psychology, general and children's psychology, religion, mythology. **Special Collections:** ARAS (Archive for Research in Archetypal Symbolism) pictorial archive. **Holdings:** 6000 books, cassettes, theses, papers. **Subscriptions:** 12 journals and other serials. **Services:** Copying; library open to the public on fee basis. **Publications:** Psychological Perspectives, semiannual - by subscription. **Remarks:** FAX: (213)556-2290. **Staff:** Linda Martin Weidlinger, Libn.

★8496★
C.G. Jung Institute of San Francisco - Library (Soc Sci)
2040 Gough St. Phone: (415)771-8055
San Francisco, CA 94109 Joan Alpert
Staff: 1. **Subjects:** Jung-psychology, mythology, religion, symbolism, art. **Holdings:** 7000 books; 50 bound periodical volumes; 1000 manuscripts; 1200 cassettes; 25 videotapes. **Subscriptions:** 100 journals and other serials. **Services:** Library open to the public on a limited schedule and on a fee basis; annual subscription required for borrowing privileges. **Automated Operations:** Computerized public access catalog and acquisitions (INMAGIC). **Special Indexes:** Index of 10 major Jungian periodicals (online). **Staff:** Mary Webster; Shirley Berrgessa.

★8497★
C.G. Jung Institute of Zurich - Library (Soc Sci)
Hornweg 28 Phone: 1 9104761
CH-8700 Kusnacht, Switzerland Ellie Stillman, Libn.
Founded: 1948. **Staff:** Prof 2; Other 3. **Subjects:** Analytical psychology, religion, folklore and fairy tales, ethnology, mythology, psychiatry, psychology. **Special Collections:** Privately published and unpublished manuscripts, records, and works by C.G. Jung; development of analytical psychology; picture archive (photographs; reproductions; paintings and drawings by patients undergoing psychological treatment); diploma theses. **Holdings:** 12,000 books. **Subscriptions:** 20 journals and other serials. **Services:** Copying; library open to the public by application to librarian. **Publications:** New acquisitions list, semiannual; theses title lists. **Also Known As:** C.G. Jung-Institut Zurich. **Staff:** Helga Kopecky, Libn.

★8498★
Juniata County Law Library (Law)
Court House
P.O. Box 68
Mifflintown, PA 17059 Phone: (717)436-8991
Subjects: Law. **Services:** Library open to the public by appointment. **Remarks:** No further information was supplied by respondent.

Junta de Calidad Ambiental
See: **Puerto Rico** (13509)

Alfred Jurzykawski Memorial Library
See: **Polish Institute of Arts and Sciences of America, Inc.** (13179)

Justice for Children and Youth Resource Centre
See: **Canadian Foundation for Children, Youth and the Law** (2930)

★8499★
Justice Institute of British Columbia - Library (Law)
4198 W. 4th Ave. Phone: (604)222-7200
Vancouver, BC, Canada V6R 4K1 April Haddad, Libn.
Founded: 1978. **Staff:** Prof 2; Other 4. **Subjects:** Police science, criminology, fire science, corrections, emergency medicine, management, disasters, search and rescue. **Special Collections:** Justice Institute photographs. **Holdings:** 10,000 books; 2000 AV items. **Subscriptions:** 150 journals and other serials. **Services:** Interlibrary loan; copying; center open to the public for reference use only. **Automated Operations:** Computerized public access catalog. **Computerized Information Services:** DIALOG Information Services, Infomart Online; Envoy 100 (electronic mail service). **Publications:** Library newsletter, monthly - for internal distribution only; bibliographies. **Special Catalogs:** Audiovisual catalog (book). **Special Indexes:** Fire Index (fire science periodicals; online). **Remarks:** FAX: (604)660-9637. Electronic mail address(es): JI (Envoy 100). **Staff:** Christine Babec, Asst. Libn.

Justice and Peace Center (Milwaukee) Archives
See: **Marquette University - Department of Special Collections and University Archives - Manuscript Collections Memorial Library** (9709)

Justice-Query Instructional Materials Center
See: **Appalachian State University - Belk Library** (914)

K

★8500★
K.K. Bene Israel/Rockdale Temple - Sidney G. Rose Memorial Library (Rel-Phil)
8501 Ridge Rd. Phone: (513)891-9900
Cincinnati, OH 45236 Ellen Dunsker, Libn.
Staff: Prof 2. **Subjects:** Judaica. **Special Collections:** Judaica large print. **Holdings:** 6000 books. **Subscriptions:** 12 journals and other serials. **Services:** Library open to the public with restrictions. **Staff:** Judy Feintuch, Ch.Libn.

★8501★
K.T. Analytics, Inc. - Library (Trans)
885 Rosemount Rd.
Oakland, CA 04610 Phone: (510)839-7702
Staff: Prof 1. **Subjects:** Parking management, transportation systems management, transit planning, congestion pricing, road tolling, fleet management. **Holdings:** 200 reports; 50 manuscripts. **Subscriptions:** 10 journals and other serials. **Services:** Library not open to the public; **Computerized Information Services:** Internal database. **Remarks:** FAX: (510)839-9887.

★8502★
KABI Pharmacia Ophthalmics - Library (Med)
P.O. Box 5036
605 E. Huntington Dr.
Monrovia, CA 91017 Phone: (818)301-8500
Staff: Prof 1. **Subjects:** Ophthalmology, biomaterials, polymer science. **Holdings:** 500 books; 75 bound periodical volumes. **Subscriptions:** 71 journals and other serials. **Services:** Library not open to the public. **Computerized Information Services:** DIALOG Information Services, PFDS Online; DIALMAIL (electronic mail service). **Publications:** Newsletter - for internal distribution only. **Formerly:** Pharmacia Ophthalmics - Library.

★8503★
(Kaduna) American Cultural Center - USIS Library (Educ)
5, Ahmadu Bello Way
Private Mail Bag 2060 Phone: 62 201070
Kaduna, Nigeria Elizabeth Akinbulumo, Libn.
Staff: 2. **Holdings:** 3000 books; reports; vertical files. **Subscriptions:** 72 journals and other serials; 4 newspapers. **Services:** Interlibrary loan; copying; SDI; library open to the public with restrictions. **Publications:** Annotated Bibliography of books on special subjects. **Remarks:** Alternate telephone number(s): 62 217491. Maintained or supported by the U.S. Information Agency. Focus is on materials that will assist peoples outside the United States to learn about the United States, its people, history, culture, political processes, and social milieux.

Hugh Kahl Library
See: **Carnegie Museum of Natural History - Library** (3085)

Albert Kahn Architecture Library
See: **Detroit Institute of Arts - Research Library** (4809)

Peter M. Kahn Memorial Library
See: **Bureau of Jewish Ecucation of Greater Los Angeles** (2368)

★8504★
Kaiser Aluminum & Chemical Corporation - Technical Information Center (Sci-Engr)
Center for Technology
6177 Sunol Blvd.
Box 877 Phone: (510)847-4264
Pleasanton, CA 94566 Gertrude I. Rooshan, Mgr.
Founded: 1968. **Staff:** Prof 1; Other 2. **Subjects:** Aluminum, chemistry, metallurgy, nonferrous metals, aluminas, extractive metallurgy, ores. **Holdings:** 10,000 books; 15,000 bound periodical volumes; 30,000 reports and reprints. **Subscriptions:** 800 journals and other serials. **Services:** Interlibrary loan; center not open to the public. **Automated Operations:** Computerized public access catalog, cataloging, acquisitions, serials, and circulation. **Computerized Information Services:** DIALOG Information Services, PFDS Online, BRS Information Technologies, Chemical Abstracts Service (CAS), MEDLARS. **Networks/Consortia:** Member of CLASS. **Publications:** Library Accessions List, monthly. **Special Catalogs:** Computer-produced book catalogs of book and periodical holdings, documents, and KACC company reports. **Remarks:** FAX: (510)484-2472.

★8505★
Kaiser Engineers Hanford Company - Library (Sci-Engr, Mil)
1200 Jadwin, E6-13 Phone: (509)376-6941
Richland, WA 99352 Janice L. McMullin, Libn.
Founded: 1965. **Staff:** Prof 2. **Subjects:** Specifications and standards. **Holdings:** Industrial catalogs; federal, military, commercial specifications and standards; drawings; military handbooks. **Services:** Copying; library open to local business only. **Remarks:** Alternate telephone number(s): 376-6052. FAX: (509)376-9399. **Staff:** L. Barbara Marsh.

★8506★
Kaiser Foundation Hospital - Medical Library (Med)
9961 Sierra Ave.
Fontana, CA 92335 Phone: (714)829-5085
Staff: Prof 2; Other 2. **Subjects:** Orthopedics, dermatology, surgery, ophthalmology, pediatrics, internal medicine. **Holdings:** 3500 books; 4000 bound periodical volumes. **Subscriptions:** 400 journals and other serials. **Services:** Interlibrary loan; library not open to the public. **Automated Operations:** Computerized cataloging, acquisitions, serials, and circulation. **Computerized Information Services:** DIALOG Information Services, MEDLINE; KPLS (internal database). Performs searches on fee basis. **Networks/Consortia:** Member of Inland Empire Medical Library Cooperative (IEMLC), Kaiser Permanente Library System (KPLS) - Southern California Region. **Staff:** Shirley Younce, Chf.Libn.

★8507★
Kaiser Foundation Hospital - Medical Library (Med)
25825 S. Vermont Ave. Phone: (310)517-2090
Harbor City, CA 90710 L. A. Ravenswood, Mgr.Lib.Serv.
Founded: 1960. **Staff:** Prof 2; Other 2.5. **Subjects:** Health sciences. **Special Collections:** Medical and Nursing Textbooks collection. **Holdings:** 3840 books; 4560 bound periodical volumes. **Subscriptions:** 317 journals and other serials. **Services:** Interlibrary loan; library not open to the public. **Computerized Information Services:** BRS Information Technologies, NLM. **Networks/Consortia:** Member of Kaiser Permanente Library System (KPLS) - Southern California Region. **Staff:** Lily Yang.

★8508★
Kaiser Foundation Hospitals - Center for Health Research Library (Med)
3800 N. Kaiser Center Dr. Phone: (503)335-2400
Portland, OR 97227-1098 Mara Sani, Ph.D., Res.Libn.
Founded: 1964. **Staff:** Prof 2; Other 2. **Subjects:** Health maintenance organizations (HMO), quality of care, health care utilization, manpower, health behavior, group practice. **Holdings:** 3500 books; 27 VF drawers; 30,000 microfiche. **Subscriptions:** 175 journals and other serials. **Services:** Interlibrary loan; library open to the public. **Automated Operations:** Computerized cataloging. **Computerized Information Services:** DIALOG Information Services, BRS Information Technologies, MEDLARS; OnTyme Electronic Message Network Service (electronic mail service). **Networks/Consortia:** Member of Oregon Health Sciences Libraries Association (OHSLA). **Remarks:** FAX: (503)233-4328. Electronic mail address(es): KAISP (OnTyme Electronic Message Network Service). **Staff:** Nancy Brown.

★8509★
Kaiser Foundation Hospitals - Medical Library (Med)
12301 Snow Rd. Phone: (216)362-2086
Parma, OH 44130 Bonita Rosen, Med.Libn.
Staff: 1. **Subjects:** Medicine, nursing, ancillary health services. **Holdings:** 700 books. **Subscriptions:** 136 journals and other serials. **Services:** Interlibrary loan; library not open to the public. **Computerized Information Services:** MEDLARS, BRS Information Technologies.

★8510★
Kaiser Foundation Hospitals - Regional Offices - Management Effectiveness Library (Med)
393 E. Walnut St. Phone: (818)405-3089
Pasadena, CA 91188 Henri Mondschein, Mgr.
Founded: 1976. **Staff:** Prof 2; Other 1. **Subjects:** Hospital administration, management. **Holdings:** 4600 books; 1050 bound periodical volumes. **Subscriptions:** 200 journals and other serials. **Services:** Interlibrary loan; copying (limited); SDI; library open to the public with restrictions. **Automated Operations:** Computerized public access catalog, cataloging, acquisitions, serials, and circulation. **Computerized Information Services:** DIALOG Information Services, MEDLINE, BRS Information Technologies, DataTimes, California Union List of Periodicals (CULP). **Networks/Consortia:** Member of Kaiser Permanente Library System (KPLS) - Southern California Region. **Staff:** Edward Reaser, Asst.Libn.

Georg Kaiser Archive
See: **University of Alberta - Humanities and Social Sciences Library - Bruce Peel Special Collections Library** (18196)

★8511★
Kaiser-Permanente Medical Care Program - Health Sciences Library/ Media Center (Med)
9400 E. Rosecrans Ave. Phone: (310)920-4247
Bellflower, CA 90706 Geraldine N. Graves, Lib./Media Oper.
Founded: 1965. **Staff:** Prof 2; Other 4. **Subjects:** Medicine and medical specialties, nursing, hospital administration. **Holdings:** 4828 books; 5093 bound periodical volumes; 1350 Audio-Digest tapes; 2 VF drawers of pamphlets; 2471 AV programs; videotapes; 15 trays microfiche; 325 other cataloged items. **Subscriptions:** 325 journals and other serials. **Services:** Interlibrary loan; copying; SDI; library open to the public by appointment. **Automated Operations:** Computerized public access catalog, cataloging, acquisitions, serials, and circulation. **Computerized Information Services:** MEDLINE, DIALOG Information Services; KPLS (Kaiser Permanente Library System; internal database); DOCLINE (electronic mail service). Performs searches on fee basis. Contact Person: Mary E. White, Asst.Libn., 920-4247. **Networks/Consortia:** Member of National Network of Libraries of Medicine - Pacific Southwest Region. **Publications:** Union List of Serials (online); Library Newsletter - for internal distribution only. **Remarks:** FAX: (310)920-4948.

★8512★
Kaiser-Permanente Medical Center - Health Education Center (Med)
27400 Hesprian Blvd. Phone: (510)784-4531
Hayward, CA 94545 Marilyn Libresco, Hea.Educ.Dir.
Subjects: Health information for the layperson. **Holdings:** Medical reference texts; pamphlets; AV programs. **Services:** Center open to the public.

★8513★
Kaiser-Permanente Medical Center - Health Education Center (Med)
3772 Howe St.
Oakland, CA 94611 Phone: (510)596-6204
Founded: 1970. **Staff:** Prof 2; Other 2. **Subjects:** Health maintenance, prenatal care, nutrition, family planning, child care, cancer, medicine. **Holdings:** 1000 books; 226 pamphlet titles; 52 audio cassettes; 200 video cassettes; AV programs. **Subscriptions:** 12 journals and other serials. **Services:** Interlibrary loan (limited); copying; center open to the public. **Networks/Consortia:** Member of Kaiser Permanente Library System (KPLS) - Southern California Region. **Publications:** Book List, annual; Equipment, Sources & Software; Pamphlet List - both free upon request. **Staff:** Margaret Winslow, Co-Mgr.; Dianne Mathis, Co-Mgr.

★8514★
Kaiser-Permanente Medical Center - Health Science Library (Med)
4747 Sunset Blvd. Phone: (213)667-8568
Los Angeles, CA 90027 Judith A. Dowd, Adm.
Founded: 1956. **Staff:** Prof 2.25; Other 4. **Subjects:** Clinical medicine, nursing, health media. **Special Collections:** Media center (1116 AV programs). **Holdings:** 7000 books; 6000 bound periodical volumes; 1000 audiotapes. **Subscriptions:** 450 journals and other serials. **Services:** Interlibrary loan; library not open to the public. **Automated Operations:** Computerized circulation. **Computerized Information Services:** MEDLARS, DIALOG Information Services; internal database. **Networks/ Consortia:** Member of Kaiser Permanente Library System (KPLS) - Southern California Region. **Publications:** Acquisitions lists; wants lists; exchange lists. **Special Catalogs:** Local and regional catalogs of holdings (book). **Formerly:** Its Kaiser Foundation Hospital Medical Library. **Staff:** Kati Krei, Asst.Med.Libn.

★8515★
Kaiser-Permanente Medical Center - Health Sciences Library (Med)
27400 Hesperian Blvd. Phone: (510)784-4420
Hayward, CA 94545 Marsha Mielke, Med.Libn.
Founded: 1962. **Staff:** Prof 1. **Subjects:** Medicine and medical specialties, nursing, allied health sciences. **Holdings:** 1970 volumes. **Subscriptions:** 210 journals and other serials. **Services:** Interlibrary loan; copying; library open to the public for reference use only by referral. **Computerized Information Services:** DIALOG Information Services, MEDLARS.

★8516★
Kaiser-Permanente Medical Center - Health Sciences Library (Med)
2025 Morse Ave. Phone: (916)973-6944
Sacramento, CA 95825 Michael W. Bennett, Hea.Sci.Libn.
Staff: Prof 1; Other 1.5. **Subjects:** Medicine, nursing, allied health sciences, health care administration. **Holdings:** 3000 books; 3000 bound periodical volumes; 780 Audio-Digest tapes; 200 videotapes. **Subscriptions:** 305 journals and other serials. **Services:** Interlibrary loan; copying; library open to the public by appointment. **Automated Operations:** Computerized cataloging. **Computerized Information Services:** DIALOG Information Services, MEDLARS, BRS Information Technologies; DOCLINE, OnTyme Electronic Message Network Service (electronic mail services). **Networks/Consortia:** Member of National Network of Libraries of Medicine - Pacific Southwest Region, Northern California and Nevada Medical Library Group (NCNMLG), Sacramento Area Health Sciences Librarians (SAHSL). **Remarks:** FAX: (916)973-6943. Electronic mail address(es): KAISERSAC (OnTyme Electronic Message Network Service).

★8517★
Kaiser-Permanente Medical Center - Health Sciences Library (Med)
4647 Zion Ave. Phone: (619)528-READ
San Diego, CA 92120 Sheila E. Latus, Med.Libn.
Founded: 1967. **Staff:** Prof 2; Other 4. **Subjects:** Medicine, nursing, allied health professions. **Holdings:** 6300 books; 7900 bound periodical volumes; 2000 audiotapes. **Subscriptions:** 500 journals and other serials. **Services:** Interlibrary loan; copying; SDI; library open to the public with restrictions. **Automated Operations:** Computerized serials, cataloging, and circulation. **Computerized Information Services:** MEDLINE, BRS Information Technologies; KPLS (internal database); OnTyme Electronic Message Network Service, DOCLINE (electronic mail services). Performs searches on fee basis. **Networks/Consortia:** Member of Kaiser Permanente Library System (KPLS) - Southern California Region. **Remarks:** FAX: (619)528-3444. Electronic mail address(es): NETEX.KP/SD (OnTyme Electronic Message Network Service). **Staff:** Laurel Windrem, Med.Libn.

★8518★
Kaiser-Permanente Medical Center - Health Sciences Library (Med)
2425 Geary Blvd. Phone: (415)929-4101
San Francisco, CA 94115 Vincent Lagano, Med.Libn.
Founded: 1955. **Staff:** Prof 1; Other 1. **Subjects:** Clinical sciences. **Holdings:** 3800 books; 12,000 bound periodical volumes; 200 pamphlets; 2 file boxes of staff reprints. **Subscriptions:** 197 journals. **Services:** Interlibrary loan; library not open to the public. **Computerized Information Services:** MEDLINE; DOCLINE (electronic mail service). **Networks/Consortia:** Member of San Francisco Biomedical Library Network, Kaiser Permanente Library System (KPLS) - Southern California Region. **Publications:** Recent Acquisitions; Current Journals; Current Periodicals Holding Subject List. **Special Catalogs:** Staff Publications.

★8519★
Kaiser-Permanente Medical Center - Medical Library (Med)
280 W. MacArthur Blvd. Phone: (510)596-6158
Oakland, CA 94611 Ysabel R. Bertolucci, Libn.
Founded: 1946. **Staff:** Prof 2; Other 2. **Subjects:** Medicine, surgery. **Holdings:** 3400 books; 8000 bound periodical volumes. **Subscriptions:** 300 journals and other serials. **Services:** Interlibrary loan; library not open to the public. **Automated Operations:** Computerized serials and ILL. **Computerized Information Services:** MEDLARS, DIALOG Information Services, BRS Information Technologies; DOCLINE. **Networks/Consortia:** Member of National Network of Libraries of Medicine - Pacific Southwest Region, Northern California and Nevada Medical Library Group (NCNMLG), Kaiser Permanente Library System (KPLS) - Southern California Region.

★8520★
Kaiser-Permanente Medical Center - Medical Library (Med)
3288 Moanalua Rd. Phone: (808)834-9420
Honolulu, HI 96819 Georgia M. Howton, Libn.
Staff: Prof 1; Other 2. **Subjects:** Medicine, surgery, allied health sciences. **Special Collections:** Kaiser Archives; comference papers. **Holdings:** 806 books; audio- and videotapes. **Subscriptions:** 172 journals and other serials. **Services:** Interlibrary loan; library not open to the public. **Computerized Information Services:** MEDLARS, MEDLINE. **Remarks:** FAX: (808)834-3990.

★8521★
Kaiser-Permanente Medical Center - Medical Library (Med)
5055 N. Greeley Ave. Phone: (503)285-9321
Portland, OR 97217 Daphne Plaut, Med.Libn.
Staff: Prof 1. **Subjects:** Medicine. **Holdings:** 700 books; 400 bound periodical volumes. **Subscriptions:** 270 journals and other serials. **Services:** Interlibrary loan; library not open to the public. **Automated Operations:** Computerized ILL. **Computerized Information Services:** NLM, MEDLINE, DIALOG Information Services; OnTyme Electronic Message Network Service, DOCLINE (electronic mail services).

★8522★
Kaiser-Permanente Medical Center - Panorama City Health Science Library (Med)
13652 Cantara St. Phone: (818)908-2239
Panorama City, CA 91402 Winnie Yu, Hd.Libn.
Founded: 1962. **Staff:** 4. **Subjects:** Medicine. **Holdings:** 1800 books; 2500 bound periodical volumes; 200 cassettes. **Subscriptions:** 225 journals and other serials. **Services:** Interlibrary loan; library not open to the public. **Automated Operations:** Computerized cataloging, serials, and circulation. **Computerized Information Services:** MEDLINE. **Networks/Consortia:** Member of Kaiser Permanente Library System (KPLS) - Southern California Region. **Staff:** Susan Lichten, Asst.Libn.

★8523★
Kaiser-Permanente Medical Center - South San Francisco Health Sciences Library (Med)
1200 El Camino Real Phone: (415)742-2540
South San Francisco, CA 94080 Sara Pimental, Health Sci.Libn.
Staff: Prof 1; Other 1. **Subjects:** Medicine and nursing. **Holdings:** 1000 books; 2000 bound periodical volumes. **Subscriptions:** 160 journals and other serials. **Services:** Interlibrary loan; library not open to the public. **Computerized Information Services:** MEDLARS, DIALOG Information Services. **Networks/Consortia:** Member of Northern California and Nevada Medical Library Group (NCNMLG).

★8524★
Kaiser-Permanente Mental Health Center - Professional Library (Med)
765 College St. Phone: (213)580-7260
Los Angeles, CA 90012 Kaushika Vyas, MLIS, Libn.
Founded: 1978. **Staff:** Prof 1; Other 3. **Subjects:** Psychology, psychiatry, clinical social work, psychopharmacology, psychoanalysis, women's studies, body/mind interface. **Holdings:** 6000 books; 4500 bound periodical volumes. **Subscriptions:** 152 journals and other serials; 6 newspapers. **Services:** Interlibrary loan; copying; SDI; library open to the public by appointment for reference use. **Automated Operations:** Computerized cataloging, serials, and circulation. **Computerized Information Services:** BRS Information Technologies, DIALOG Information Services; KPLS (internal database). **Networks/Consortia:** Member of Kaiser Permanente Library System (KPLS) - Southern California Region. **Publications:** Newsletter, monthly. **Remarks:** FAX: (213)580-7220.

Kaiser-Ramaker Library
See: **North American Baptist Seminary** (11857)

★8525★
Kaiser Sunnyside Medical Center - Health Sciences Library (Med)
10180 S.E. Sunnyside Rd. Phone: (503)652-2880
Clackamas, OR 97015 Ann H. Haines, Dir. of the Hea.Sci.Lib.
Founded: 1975. **Staff:** Prof 1; Other 5. **Subjects:** Medicine, nursing. **Holdings:** 800 books. **Subscriptions:** 150 journals and other serials. **Services:** Interlibrary loan; copying; library open to the public with permission of librarian. **Computerized Information Services:** MEDLINE, DIALOG Information Services; OnTyme Electronic Message Network Service (electronic mail service). **Remarks:** FAX: (503)652-4291. Alternate telephone number(s): (503)652-4291. Electronic mail address(es): CLASS.KASMC (OnTyme Electronic Message Network Service).

★8526★
Kaiser Wilhelm Museum - Art Library (Art)
Karlspl 35 Phone: 02151 770044
W-4150 Krefeld, Germany Julian Heynen, Dir.
Founded: 1883. **Subjects:** Art - post-1945, modern, turn-of-the-century applied. **Holdings:** 25,000 books; 8000 bound periodical volumes. **Subscriptions:** 10 journals and other serials. **Services:** Library open to the public for reference use only. **Remarks:** FAX: 2151 770368.

★8527★
Kaivalyadhama SMYM Samiti - Library (Rel-Phil)
Yoga-Mimamsa Office
Lonavla
Poona 410 403, Maharashtra, India Manoj Kulkarni, Libn.
Founded: 1948. **Staff:** 3. **Subjects:** Yoga, philosophy, religion, medicine, psychology. **Special Collections:** Yoga manuscripts; Yoga theses. **Holdings:** 21,000 volumes. **Subscriptions:** 53 journals and other serials; 6 newspapers. **Services:** Copying; library open to the public for reference use only. **Staff:** B.D. Kute; Mrs. A. Sinha.

★8528★
Kalamazoo College - Upjohn Library - A.M. Todd Rare Book Room (Rare Book, Hist)
Thompson & Academy Sts. Phone: (616)383-8481
Kalamazoo, MI 49006 Eleanor H. Pinkham, Dir.
Founded: 1833. **Staff:** Prof 1; Other 1. **Subjects:** Illustrated bird books; history of books and printing; private presses; exploration and travel; history of science. **Holdings:** 3000 books. **Services:** Copying; room open to the public on a limited schedule and by appointment. **Networks/Consortia:** Member of Michigan Library Consortium (MLC).

★8529★
Kalamazoo County Law Library - Raymond W. Fox Memorial Library (Law)
227 W. Michigan Ave. Phone: (616)384-8258
Kalamazoo, MI 49007 Karen K. Lason, Law Libn.
Staff: Prof 1. **Subjects:** Law. **Holdings:** 15,000 books; federal and state statutes; reporters. **Services:** Copying; library open to the public. **Computerized Information Services:** WESTLAW. Performs searches for Bar Association members only.

★8530★
Kalamazoo Institute of Arts - Library (Art)
314 S. Park St. Phone: (616)349-7775
Kalamazoo, MI 49007 Rebecca D. Steel, Libn.
Founded: 1961. **Staff:** Prof 1; Other 1. **Subjects:** American art, photography, art history, painting, architecture, drawing, prints, sculpture. **Special Collections:** Kalamazoo Weavers Guild Collection. **Holdings:** 7000 books; 275 bound periodical volumes; 8500 slides; 36 VF drawers on artists and art-related subjects; exhibition and sales catalogs. **Subscriptions:** 65 journals and other serials. **Services:** Slide loans to schools and other established groups; collections circulate to members; library open to the public for reference use only during gallery hours. **Networks/Consortia:** Member of Southwest Michigan Library Cooperative (SMLC). **Publications:** Forum (newsletter); exhibit catalogs. **Remarks:** FAX: (616)349-9313.

★8531★
Kalamazoo Nature Center - Reference Library
7000 N. Westnedge Ave.
Kalamazoo, MI 49007
Founded: 1962. **Subjects:** Ornithology, natural history, pollution, environmental education, alternative energy, citizen action. **Holdings:** Figures not available. **Remarks:** Currently inactive.

Kalamazoo Spice Extraction Company
See: **Kalsec, Inc.** (8535)

★8532★
Kalba International, Inc. - Library (Info Sci)
23 Sandy Pond Rd. Phone: (617)259-9589
Lincoln, MA 01773 Beverly Hall Spencer, Libn./Info.Spec.
Founded: 1978. **Staff:** Prof 1. **Subjects:** Communications research and technology, information science and services, public policy. **Holdings:** 750 reports; clippings file. **Subscriptions:** 50 journals and other serials. **Services:** Library not open to the public. **Remarks:** FAX: (617)259-1460. **Formerly:** Kalba Bowen Associates.

Carl Kales Memorial Library
See: **Beth El Temple Center** (1766)

Sarkis & Meline Kalfayan Center for Armenian Studies
See: **California State University, Fresno - Armenian Studies Program** (2560)

★8533★
Kalispell Regional Hospital - Medical Library (Med)
310 Sunny View Ln. Phone: (406)752-5111
Kalispell, MT 59901 Susan Long, Med.Libn.
Founded: 1976. **Staff:** Prof 1. **Subjects:** Medicine, surgery, nursing. **Holdings:** 450 books; 742 bound periodical volumes; 400 video cassettes. **Subscriptions:** 100 journals and other serials. **Services:** Interlibrary loan; copying; library open to the public for reference use only by appointment. **Computerized Information Services:** MEDLARS; CD-ROM; OnTyme Electronic Message Network Service (electronic mail service). **Networks/Consortia:** Member of Western Library Network (WLN). **Remarks:** FAX: (406)752-8771. Electronic mail address(es): CLASS.KALIS (OnTyme Electronic Message Network Service).

★8534★
Kalmbach Publishing Company - David P. Morgan Memorial Library (Rec, Publ)
21027 Crossroads Circle
P.O. Box 1612 Phone: (414)796-8776
Waukesha, WI 53187 George H. Drury, Libn.
Founded: 1974. **Staff:** Prof 1. **Subjects:** Railroads, model railroading. **Holdings:** 7000 books; 2000 bound periodical volumes; documents; manuscripts; photographs. **Subscriptions:** 250 journals and other serials. **Services:** Library not open to the public. **Special Indexes:** Model Railroader All-Time Index of Prototype Plans, 1934-1990. **Remarks:** This is a research library used by the staffs of Model Railroader, Classic Toy Trains, Trains, and Trains Illustrated magazines, Kalmbach Miniatures, and Kalmbach Books.

Karl R. Kalp Teachers Library
See: **Indianapolis Public Schools** (7827)

★8535★
Kalsec, Inc. - Library (Food-Bev)
3713 W. Main
Box 511 Phone: (616)349-9711
Kalamazoo, MI 49005 Mary Sagar, Lib.Mgr.
Founded: 1972. **Staff:** Prof 1; Other 2. **Subjects:** Chemistry, food technology, business. **Holdings:** 3000 books; 800 bound periodical volumes; 3000 annual reports, patents, pamphlets, reprints, tapes, microfiche, clippings. **Subscriptions:** 70 journals and other serials. **Services:** Interlibrary loan; library open to employees only. **Automated Operations:** Computerized cataloging and serials. **Computerized Information Services:** DIALOG Information Services, Chemical Abstracts Service (CAS); internal database. **Networks/Consortia:** Member of Southwest Michigan Library Cooperative (SMLC). **Remarks:** FAX: (616)382-3060. Telex: 295181. **Also Known As:** Kalamazoo Spice Extraction Company.

★8536★
Kaman Sciences Corporation - Library (Sci-Engr)
1500 Garden of the Gods Rd.
Box 7463 Phone: (719)599-1777
Colorado Springs, CO 80933 Barbara A. Kinslow, Libn.
Founded: 1963. **Staff:** 1. **Subjects:** Chemistry, mechanical and nuclear engineering, electronics, instrumentation, materials, mathematics, meteorology, physics. **Holdings:** 7800 books; 17,600 technical reports; 1000 Kaman reports. **Subscriptions:** 250 journals and other serials. **Services:** Interlibrary loan; copying; library open to the public with restrictions. **Computerized Information Services:** DIALOG Information Services, NASA/RECON, DTIC. **Remarks:** FAX: (719)599-1942.

★8537★
Kaman Sciences Corporation - Metal Matrix Composites Information Analysis Center (Sci-Engr)
816 State St.
P.O. Box 1479 Phone: (805)963-6455
Santa Barbara, CA 93102-1479 Dr. William McNamara, Dir.
Founded: 1980. **Staff:** Prof 3. **Subjects:** Metal matrix composite materials and technology; composite materials; discontinuous and continuous fibers; defense systems applications; cost, test, and evaluation methods; properties; serviceability/repairs. **Special Collections:** Metal matrix composites. **Holdings:** 60 books; 4400 technical reports and articles; 200 patents and dissertations. **Subscriptions:** 20 journals and other serials; 15 newsletters. **Services:** Center open to the public with restrictions. **Automated Operations:** Computerized cataloging. **Computerized Information Services:** DIALOG Information Services, PFDS Online, ESA/IRS, DTIC, BRS Information Technologies, Circ II; MMC Base (internal database). Performs searches free of charge on DTIC only. Contact Person: Joan Champeny, Info.Spec., 963-6455. **Publications:** List of publications - available on request. **Special Catalogs:** Patents Catalog. **Special Indexes:** SiC/Al and Gr/Al data indexes. **Remarks:** FAX: (805)963-8420. The Metal Matrix Composites Information Analysis Center (MMCIAC) collects, reviews, analyzes, evaluates, summarizes, and stores information from Department of Defense technical reports, other government agencies, industry, academic institutions, and open literature, including foreign and unpublished sources. **Staff:** David Higa; Jacques Schoutens.

Max L. Kamiel Library
See: **Masonic Medical Research Laboratory** (9782)

Kammandale Library
See: **Orphan Voyage** (12574)

★8538★
Kanabec County Historical Society - Kanabec History Center (Hist)
W. Forest Ave.
P.O. Box 113 Phone: (612)679-1665
Mora, MN 55051 Edna Cole, Exec.Dir.
Staff: 2. **Subjects:** Kanabec County, Minnesota, Minnesota counties, Native Americans, farming, ethnic groups, local authors. **Holdings:** 196 books; 148 bound periodical volumes; 117 nonbook items. **Subscriptions:** 4 journals and other serials; 2 newspapers. **Services:** Copying; center open to the public for reference use only on a fee basis.

Kananaskis Centre for Environmental Research
See: **University of Calgary** (18290)

★8539★
Kandiyohi County Historical Society - Victor E. Lawson Research Library (Hist)
610 N.E. Hwy. 71 Phone: (612)235-1881
Willmar, MN 56201 Mona Nelson, Prog.Dir.
Subjects: History - local, state, U.S. **Holdings:** 1100 books; 500 bound periodical volumes; 297 volumes and 67 linear feet of archival material and manuscripts. **Subscriptions:** 30 journals and other serials; 5 newspapers. **Services:** Copying; library open to the public by appointment. **Publications:** Kandi Express (newsletter), quarterly. **Special Indexes:** Index to local newspapers (card); archives & manuscripts guide and index (card).

★8540★
(Kandy) American Center - USIS Library (Educ)
17 Malabar St.
Kandy, Sri Lanka
Remarks: Maintained or supported by the U.S. Information Agency. Focus is on materials that will assist peoples outside the United States to learn about the United States, its people, history, culture, political processes, and social milieux.

★8541★
Kankakee County Historical Society - Library (Hist)
8th Ave. at Water St. Phone: (815)932-5279
Kankakee, IL 60901 Carol A. Shidler, Dir.
Founded: 1906. **Staff:** Prof 1. **Subjects:** County and state history, Civil War. **Special Collections:** Indian artifact collection; photograph collection (6000); French-Canadian artifacts; newspaper collection, 1853-1987. **Holdings:** 4000 books; genealogies; city directories; manuscripts; documents; clippings; Civil War volumes. **Subscriptions:** 11 journals and other serials. **Services:** Copying; library open to the public with restrictions. **Staff:** Don Des Lauriers, Cur.

★8542★
Kankakee Daily Journal - Library (Publ)
8 Dearborn Sq. Phone: (815)937-3378
Kankakee, IL 60901 Glory Klasey, Hd.Libn.
Staff: Prof 2. **Subjects:** Newspaper reference topics. **Holdings:** Bound volumes of newspapers; newspapers, 1854 to present, on microfilm. **Services:** Library open to the public when staff member is present.

★8543★
(Kano) American Cultural Center - USIS Library
Post Office Rd.
Private Mail Bag 3059
Kano, Nigeria
Remarks: Maintained or supported by the U.S. Information Agency. Focus is on materials that will assist peoples outside the United States to learn about the United States, its people, history, culture, political processes, and social milieux.

★8544★
Kansas City Art Institute - Library (Art, Hum)
4415 Warwick Blvd. Phone: (816)561-4852
Kansas City, MO 64111 Allen Morrill, Dir.
Founded: 1885. **Staff:** Prof 2; Other 3. **Subjects:** Painting and printmaking, decorative arts, ceramics, craft, photography, Japanese literature. **Special Collections:** Artists books. **Holdings:** 35,000 books; 2000 bound periodical volumes. **Subscriptions:** 133 journals and other serials. **Services:** Interlibrary loan; copying; library open to the public for reference use only. **Networks/Consortia:** Member of Kansas City Regional Council for Higher Education (KCRCHE), Kansas City Metropolitan Library Network (KCMLN).

★8545★
Kansas City Development Department - Library (Plan)
City Hall
414 E. 12th St. Phone: (816)274-1972
Kansas City, MO 64106 Alma Lee, Libn.
Staff: Prof 2. **Subjects:** Area plans, master plans, housing, environmental quality, census materials. **Holdings:** 5000 books. **Subscriptions:** 100 journals and other serials. **Services:** Interlibrary loan; library open to the public. **Remarks:** Alternate telephone number(s): (816)274-1864.

★8546★
Kansas City Museum - Archives (Hist)
3200 Norledge Ave. Phone: (816)483-8300
Kansas City, MO 64123 Denise Morrison, Archv.
Founded: 1940. **Staff:** Prof 1. **Subjects:** History of Kansas City, Missouri. **Holdings:** 2000 books; 90 periodical titles; 1000 cubic feet of archives and manuscript collections; 50,000 photographs. **Subscriptions:** 25 journals and other serials. **Services:** Copying; archives open to the public by appointment. **Publications:** An Oral History Guide to the Economic Development of Kansas City (1990). **Special Catalogs:** Guide to the Archival Collections of the Kansas City Museum (1986). **Remarks:** FAX: (816)483-8300, ext. 232.

★8547★
Kansas City Public Library - Art and Music Collection (Art, Mus)
311 E. 12th St. Phone: (816)221-2685
Kansas City, MO 64106 Carol Wallace, Art & Mus.Spec.
Founded: 1873. **Staff:** 2. **Subjects:** Art, music. **Holdings:** 38,000 monographs; 15,000 scores; 8315 phonograph records; 2180 audio cassettes; 350 framed pictures; 150,000 picture clippings; 20,000 mounted pictures; 25,000 slides; 1500 compact discs. **Subscriptions:** 40 journals and other serials; 26 newspapers. **Services:** Interlibrary loan; copying; collection open to the public. **Computerized Information Services:** DIALOG Information Services; Community Organization DataBank (internal database). **Remarks:** FAX: (816)421-7484.

★8548★
Kansas City Public Library - Business and Technical Collection (Bus-Fin, Sci-Engr)
311 E. 12th St. Phone: (816)221-9650
Kansas City, MO 64106 Pamela K. Jenkins, Spec.
Subjects: Economics, business administration, insurance, commerce, investment, science, industrial technology. **Special Collections:** Government Documents Depository Library (federal and state); Foundation Center Cooperating Collection (1600 volumes); schematics for radio, television, stereo, and VCR repair (4500 volumes); directories (trade and telephone, U.S. and foreign); annual reports of companies; auto/truck repair manuals. **Holdings:** 50,300 books. **Subscriptions:** 347 journals and other serials; 26 newspapers. **Services:** Interlibrary loan; copying; collection open to the public. **Automated Operations:** Computerized public access catalog, cataloging, acquisitions, serials, and circulation. **Computerized Information Services:** DIALOG Information Services. **Networks/Consortia:** Member of Kansas City Metropolitan Library Network (KCMLN). **Remarks:** FAX: (816)842-6839. Collection is accessible through Central Reference.

Kansas City Public Library - Heart of America Genealogical Society & Library, Inc.
See: **Heart of America Genealogical Society & Library, Inc.** (7088)

★8549★
Kansas City Public Library - Missouri Valley Special Collections (Hist)
311 E. 12th St. Phone: (816)221-2698
Kansas City, MO 64106 Gloria Maxwell, Dept.Mgr.
Founded: 1873. **Staff:** Prof 4; Other 6. **Subjects:** Local history, genealogy, Oregon trail, Western history. **Special Collections:** Ramos/Black Experience (2500 titles; 15 rolls of microfilm; vertical file); local music and musicians. **Holdings:** 43,192 titles; 1000 bound periodical volumes; 2800 reels of microfilm; 10,000 photographs; advertising postcards; maps. **Subscriptions:** 187 journals and other serials; 10 newspapers. **Services:** Copying; room open to the public. **Automated Operations:** Computerized public access catalog, cataloging, acquisitions, and circulation. **Computerized Information Services:** DataTimes. **Networks/Consortia:** Member of Kansas City Metropolitan Library Network (KCMLN). **Special Indexes:** Index to Kansas City Star & Times Newspapers; Local History Electronic Index (online). **Remarks:** FAX: (816)842-6839.

★8550★
Kansas City Public Library - Periodical-Microfilm Collection (Aud-Vis)
311 E. 12th St. Phone: (816)221-2685
Kansas City, MO 64106 Ann Cahill
Staff: Prof 8. **Holdings:** 51,000 bound periodical volumes; 35,668 reels of microfilm. **Subscriptions:** 1950 journals and other serials; 31 newspapers. **Services:** Interlibrary loan; copying; collection open to the public with restrictions. **Computerized Information Services:** DRA (internal database). **Remarks:** Alternate telephone number(s): (816)474-0411. FAX: (816)842-6839.

★8551★
Kansas City Star Newspaper - Library (Publ)
1729 Grand Ave. Phone: (816)234-4141
Kansas City, MO 64108 Aurora E. Davis, Dir., Info.Serv.
Staff: Prof 1; Other 9. **Subjects:** Newspaper reference topics. **Holdings:** 5000 books; 1 million photographs; 20 million newspaper clippings files; records on microfilm. **Subscriptions:** 68 journals and other serials. **Services:** Library not open to the public. **Computerized Information Services:** NEXIS, VU/TEXT Information Services, DataTimes, DIALOG Information Services, CompuServe Information Service. **Publications:** Eyeopener (current awareness newsletter), weekly - for internal distribution only. **Remarks:** The Kansas City Star Newspaper is owned by Capital Cities/ABC, Inc.

Kansas College of Technology - Library/Resource Center
See: **Kansas State University, Salina** (8576)

★8552★
Kansas Energy Extension Service
133 Ward Hall
Kansas State University
Manhattan, KS 66506
Defunct.

★8553★
Kansas Heritage Center - Library (Hist)
Box 1275 Phone: (316)227-1616
Dodge City, KS 67801 Jeanie Covalt, Res.Libn.
Founded: 1966. **Staff:** 4. **Subjects:** Frontier and pioneer life, Kansas, the West, Indians of North America, cowboys, cattle trade, transportation, agricultural history, folklore. **Special Collections:** Historical collections from the states of Kansas, Oklahoma, Arizona, Missouri, Colorado, and New Mexico. **Holdings:** 10,000 volumes; clippings; pamphlets; microfilm; filmstrips; slides; tapes and phonograph records; 16mm films; videotapes. **Subscriptions:** 6 journals and other serials. **Services:** Interlibrary loan; copying; assembles mini-kits on various subjects; programs and workshops; library open to the public. **Publications:** Sentinel to the Cimarron; The Frontier Experience of Fort Dodge, Kansas (1970); Up From the Prairie (1974); The Process of Oral History (1976); Dodge City (1982); West by Southwest (1984); Indians in Kansas (1987); Adventures with the Santa Fe Trail (1989); bibliographies. **Special Catalogs:** Reference Materials and Resources (catalog; 1970, 1973, 1975, 1979, 1981, 1982, 1984, 1986, 1988, 1990).

Kansas Music Teachers' Association Archives
See: **Wichita State University - Thurlow Lieurance Memorial Music Library** (20413)

★8554★
Kansas (State) Board of Agriculture - Division of Water Resources - Library (Sci-Engr)
901 S. Kansas, 2nd Fl. Phone: (913)296-3717
Topeka, KS 66612-1283 Abdel Hakim Saadi, Civil Engr.
Staff: Prof 1. **Subjects:** Water resources, applied sciences. **Holdings:** 3000 volumes. **Services:** Copying; library open to the public. **Remarks:** Alternate telephone number(s): 296-6081. Maintains field offices in Topeka, Stafford, Stockton, and Garden City, KS.

Kansas State Data Center - Institute for Public Policy and Business Research
See: **University of Kansas - Institute for Public Policy and Business Research** (18727)

★8555★
Kansas (State) Department of Health and Environment - Library
Landon State Office Bldg., 10th Fl.
900 Jackson
Topeka, KS 66612
Defunct.

Kansas (State) Department of Social & Rehabilitation Services - Parsons State Hospital and Training Center
See: **Parsons State Hospital and Training Center** (12770)

★8556★
Kansas (State) Department of Social & Rehabilitation Services - Staff Development Training Center Library (Soc Sci)
300 S.W. Oakley St. Phone: (913)296-4327
Topeka, KS 66606 Jean Barton, Libn.
Founded: 1935. **Staff:** Prof 1. **Subjects:** Social service and welfare, personnel, staff development. **Holdings:** 2600 books; 295 bound periodical volumes; 8400 reports and pamphlets; films; tapes. **Subscriptions:** 39 journals and other serials. **Services:** Interlibrary loan; consultation services to librarians from other agency libraries.

★8557★
Kansas State Geological Survey - Moore Hall Library (Sci-Engr)
1930 Constant Ave. Phone: (913)864-3965
Lawrence, KS 66044 Janice H. Sorensen, Libn.
Founded: 1974. **Staff:** Prof 1. **Subjects:** Geology, Kansas geology, mineral resources, oil and gas, well logs, environmental geology, geochemistry, water resources, geomathematics, geologic research. **Holdings:** 25,000 books; 380 bound periodical volumes; 800 open-file reports; 200 reels of microfilm; 200 computer contributions; 1000 slides and photographs. **Subscriptions:** 40 journals and other serials. **Services:** Interlibrary loan; copying; library open to the public with restrictions. **Computerized Information Services:** Internal database. **Publications:** List of open-file reports published by Kansas Geological Survey.

★8558★
Kansas State Geological Survey - Wichita Well Sample Library (Sci-Engr)
4150 Monroe St. Phone: (316)943-2343
Wichita, KS 67209 Lawrence H. Skelton, Mgr.
Founded: 1938. **Staff:** Prof 1; Other 6. **Subjects:** Wellbore sample cuttings. **Holdings:** Drill cuttings from 130,000 wells, primarily from Kansas; 90,000 microfiche of wireline logs. **Services:** Copying; library open to the public. **Remarks:** Microscopes, U-V lights, and other resources can be provided for sample examination. All Kansas Geological Survey publications and maps are available for reference; in-print copies are for sale.

★8559★
Kansas State Historical Society - Library (Hist)
Historical Research Center
120 W. 10th St. Phone: (913)296-3251
Topeka, KS 66612-1291 David A. Haury, Act.Dir.
Founded: 1875. **Staff:** Prof 6; Other 11. **Subjects:** Kansas history, local history of other states, genealogy, American Indians, the West, American biography, Civil War. **Special Collections:** Kansas (20,974 books; 129,432 pamphlets); genealogy and local history (18,262 books; 7225 pamphlets); American Indians and the West (4721 books; 2115 pamphlets). **Holdings:** 132,973 books; 25,651 bound periodical volumes; 74,086 bound volumes of Kansas newspapers; 12,373 bound volumes of out-of-state newspapers; 1977 volumes of clippings; 51,706 reels of microfilm; 194 titles on microcard. **Subscriptions:** 300 journals and other serials. **Services:** Interlibrary loan; copying (both limited); library open to the public. **Special Catalogs:** Guide to the Microfilm Collections of Kansas State Historical Society (1991). **Remarks:** FAX: (913)296-1005. **Staff:** Margaret Knecht, Asst.Lib.Dir.; Susan Forbes, Western Hist.Cat.; Jane Kelsey, Geneal.Cat.

★8560★
Kansas State Library (Info Sci)
Statehouse, 3rd Fl. Phone: (913)296-3296
Topeka, KS 66612 Duane F. Johnson, State Libn.
Founded: 1855. **Staff:** Prof 11; Other 13. **Subjects:** Public administration, census, Kansas government and legislation. **Special Collections:** Federal and state documents depository. **Holdings:** 60,000 books; 10,000 bound periodical volumes; 60,000 other cataloged items. **Subscriptions:** 250 journals and other serials; 10 newspapers. **Services:** Interlibrary loan; copying; SDI; library open to the public. **Automated Operations:** Computerized cataloging. **Computerized Information Services:** DIALOG Information Services, BRS Information Technologies, WESTLAW, PFDS Online, Library Information Service (LIS); Kansas State legislative online data information (internal database). Performs searches on fee basis. **Networks/Consortia:** Member of Bibliographical Center for Research, Rocky Mountain Region, Inc. (BCR). **Publications:** Kansas Public Library Statistics, annual - to all public libraries and regional systems; State Data Center News, quarterly; Kansas Libraries, monthly; Kansas Library Automation News, bimonthly. **Special Catalogs:** Kansas Government Documents Catalog. **Special Indexes:** Index to Kansas Legislative Bills. **Remarks:** FAX: (913)296-6650. **Staff:** Ernestine Voss, Dir., Lib.Dev.; Tom Roth, ILL; Bruce Flanders, Lib. Automation/Rsrc. Sharing; Cindy Roupe, Asst.Dir., Ref; Bill Sowers, Hd., Tech.Info.Serv.; Marc Galbraith, Dir. of Ref.

★8561★
Kansas State Supreme Court - Law Library (Law)
Judicial Center
301 W. 10th Phone: (913)296-3257
Topeka, KS 66612-1598 Fred W. Knecht, Law Libn.
Founded: 1855. **Staff:** Prof 5; Other 2. **Subjects:** Law - federal, state, foreign. **Special Collections:** Rare Book Collection (400 titles of English materials).

Holdings: 289,664 books; 45,000 bound periodical volumes. **Subscriptions:** 3500 journals and other serials; 5 newspapers. **Services:** Interlibrary loan; copying; library open to the public. **Computerized Information Services:** WESTLAW. Performs searches on fee basis. Contact Person: Claire E. King, Asst. Law Libn. **Publications:** Recent Acquisitions List, quarterly - to law schools and Kansas Bar Association. **Staff:** Janice L. Cook, Tech.Serv.Libn.; Duane H. McCord, Legal Lit.Libn.; Donna Cobler, Ref.Libn.

★8562★
Kansas State University - Chemistry/Biochemistry Library (Biol Sci, Sci-Engr)
Willard Hall Phone: (913)532-6530
Manhattan, KS 66506 Ruth Nellis, Libn.
Founded: 1881. **Staff:** Prof 1; Other 2. **Subjects:** Chemistry, biochemistry. **Special Collections:** Sadtler Standard Spectra (200 volumes). **Holdings:** 18,000 volumes. **Subscriptions:** 500 journals and other serials. **Services:** Interlibrary loan; copying; library open to the public. **Automated Operations:** Computerized public access catalog, cataloging, acquisitions, and circulation. **Computerized Information Services:** STN International; BITNET (electronic mail service). **Remarks:** FAX: (913)532-6144. Electronic mail address(es): LIBRARY@KSUVM (BITNET).

★8563★
Kansas State University - Farrell Library (Agri, Sci-Engr, Educ)
Manhattan, KS 66506 Phone: (913)532-7400
Brice G. Hobrock, Dean of Libs.
Founded: 1863. **Staff:** Prof 38; Other 64. **Subjects:** Physical sciences, farming systems, agriculture, engineering, applied science and technology, natural sciences, veterinary medicine, home economics. **Special Collections:** Rare Books (33,935 volumes); University Archives (1200 volumes; 1300 linear feet; 20,000 photographs; dissertations and theses; ephemera); Department of Energy/Energy Research and Development Administration/Atomic Energy Commission Collection (26,000 paper titles; 92,000 microcards; 714,000 microfiche); ERIC Collection (complete); Juvenile Literature Collection (10,378 volumes); Curriculum Materials Collection; Physical Fitness Collection; Human Relations Area Files; Travels in the West and Southwest. **Holdings:** 1.2 million volumes; 680,000 government documents; 20,000 maps; 3.3 million microforms; 13,500 sound recordings; 29,500 slides; 650 tapes; 650 filmstrips; 350 films; 8662 scores; 2380 audiocassettes; 650 videocassettes. **Subscriptions:** 9170 journals and other serials; 195 newspapers. **Services:** Interlibrary loan; copying; library open to the public. **Automated Operations:** NOTIS. **Computerized Information Services:** DIALOG Information Services, BRS Information Technologies, OCLC, STN International, Chemical Abstracts Service (CAS); CD-ROMs; BITNET (electronic mail service). **Networks/Consortia:** Member of Bibliographical Center for Research, Rocky Mountain Region, Inc. (BCR), Center for Research Libraries (CRL), KIC Interlibrary Loan Network. **Publications:** Kansas State University Library Bibliography Series, irregular - by exchange and for sale. **Remarks:** FAX (913)532-6144. Electronic mail address(es): LIBRARY@KSUVM (BITNET). **Staff:** Ann Scott, Assoc. Dean, Info./Res.Serv.; John Johnson, Hd., Ref./Info.Serv.; Cherie Geiser, Hd., Gen. User Serv.; Nelda Elder, Coll.Dev.; Debora Madsen, Acq.; Charlene Grass, Assoc. Dean, Coll. & Tech.Serv.; Brenda Evans, ILL; Terry Ratliff, Circ.; Kevin Jones, Ref. & Online Search Serv.; Tony Crawford, Hd., Spec.Coll./Archv.; James Mason, Presrv.; John J. Vander Velde, Spec.Coll.Libn.

★8564★
Kansas State University - Farrell Library - Minority Resource Research Center (Area-Ethnic)
Manhattan, KS 66506 Phone: (913)532-7453
Founded: 1971. **Staff:** Prof 1; Other 1. **Subjects:** African-American history and literature, American ethnic studies, Kansas minority groups, Native American archeology, 20th century Native American sociology, Chicano studies. **Special Collections:** American Ethnic Studies (100 titles); Kansas State Minority Programs (125 titles). **Holdings:** 5000 volumes; 147 microfiche; 388 reels of microfilm; 15 VF drawers of reports; 4 VF drawers of archives; 732 AV programs. **Subscriptions:** 75 journals and other serials; 22 newspapers. **Services:** ILL; copying; library open to the public. **Automated Operations:** Computerized cataloging, acquisitions, and circulation. **Computerized Information Services:** DIALOG Information Services, BRS Information Technologies, OCLC, STN International, Chemical Abstracts Service (CAS); BITNET (electronic mail service). **Publications:** AV Guide; Minority Children's Bibliography; Minority Reference Collection Bibliography; annotated bibliography of KSU theses and dissertations by and about minorities. **Remarks:** FAX: (913)532-6144. Electronic mail address(es): LIBRARY@KSUVM (BITNET). Center provides consultation on minority-related programming. **Staff:** Charlene Grass, Assoc. Dean.

★8565★
Kansas State University - Food and Feed Grain Institute - Post-Harvest Documentation Service (Agri)
Farrell Library Phone: (913)532-7452
Manhattan, KS 66502 Donna Schenck-Hamlin, Coord.
Founded: 1979. **Staff:** 3. **Subjects:** Grain harvesting, post-harvest losses, stored-product pests, grain drying, storage facilities, cereals marketing, nutrition and utilization. **Holdings:** 20,000 articles, pamphlets, reports. **Services:** Document copying and delivery; service open to the public with restrictions. **Computerized Information Services:** Internal database; BITNET (electronic mail service). **Publications:** Bimonthly short catalog. **Special Indexes:** Author, title, and keyword indexes to stored citations and abstracts (online). **Remarks:** FAX: (913)532-6144. Electronic mail address(es): PHDS@KSUVM (BITNET).

★8566★
Kansas State University - Grain Science and Industry - Swanson Resource Room (Agri)
Shellenberger Hall Phone: (913)532-6161
Manhattan, KS 66506 Marion Rice, Libn.
Founded: 1950. **Staff:** Prof 1. **Subjects:** Milling, feed, and baking technology; grain handling and storage; cereal chemistry; nutrition. **Holdings:** 2500 books; 1800 bound periodical volumes; 200 pamphlets and bulletins; 1500 reprints. **Subscriptions:** 50 journals and other serials. **Services:** Copying; room open to the public. **Remarks:** FAX: (913)532-7010.

★8567★
Kansas State University - Herbarium Library (Biol Sci)
Bushnell Hall Phone: (913)532-6619
Manhattan, KS 66506 T.M. Barkley, Cur.
Founded: 1870. **Staff:** Prof 3; Other 1. **Subjects:** Flora of the Central Prairies and Plains, basic botany. **Holdings:** 1900 books; 2700 monographs and pamphlets. **Subscriptions:** 12 journals and other serials. **Services:** Interlibrary loan; copying; library open to the public.

★8568★
Kansas State University - Institute for Environmental Research - Library (Env-Cons)
Dept. of Mechanical Engineering Phone: (913)532-5620
Manhattan, KS 66506 Byron Jones, Dir.
Founded: 1963. **Staff:** 5. **Subjects:** Human thermal comfort, environmental ergonomics, heat stress, temperature-related product design and testing, protective clothing. **Holdings:** 1500 technical articles. **Services:** Library open to the public by appointment. **Computerized Information Services:** Internal database . **Publications:** List of reprints - available on request. **Remarks:** FAX: (913)532-6642.

★8569★
Kansas State University - International Agricultural Programs - Resources on Developing Countries (Agri)
Farrell Library Phone: (913)532-6516
Manhattan, KS 66506 Nancy Donohue, Libn.
Founded: 1979. **Staff:** Prof 1; Other 1. **Subjects:** Farming systems, rural development. **Special Collections:** Farming systems research; Rural Third World; Third World Women. **Holdings:** 5500 items. **Subscriptions:** 100 newsletters. **Services:** Interlibrary loan; copying; SDI; resources open to the public with restrictions. **Computerized Information Services:** DIALOG Information Services, BRS Information Technologies; Farming Systems Research (internal database); BITNET (electronic mail service). **Publications:** Farming Systems Research Bibliography. **Special Indexes:** Subject/location index to Rural Third World collection. **Remarks:** FAX: (913)532-6144. Electronic mail address(es): LIBRARY@KSUVM (BITNET).

★8570★
Kansas State University - Math/Physics Library (Sci-Engr)
Cardwell Hall Phone: (913)532-6827
Manhattan, KS 66506 Barbara Steward, Libn.
Founded: 1963. **Staff:** 1. **Subjects:** Mathematics; physics - atomic, molecular, nuclear, particle, general; condensed matter. **Special Collections:** World Meteorological Organization publications. **Holdings:** 24,000 volumes. **Subscriptions:** 440 journals and other serials. **Services:** Interlibrary loan; library open to the public. **Computerized Information Services:** BITNET (electronic mail service). **Remarks:** FAX: (913)532-6144. Electronic mail address(es): LIBRARY@KSUVM (BITNET).

★8571★
Kansas State University - Population Research Laboratory - Library (Soc Sci)
Manhattan, KS 66506 Phone: (913)532-5984
Donald J. Adamchak, Dir.
Founded: 1967. **Staff:** Prof 1. **Subjects:** Demography - community, rural, developing countries. **Holdings:** 600 books; 50 other cataloged items; Census of Population, 1920-1980; Census of Agriculture, 1930, 1950-1960, 1969, 1974, 1978, 1982. **Subscriptions:** 18 journals and other serials. **Services:** Library open to the public.

★8572★
Kansas State University - Special Collections Department (Hum, Food-Bev, Sci-Engr)
Farrell Library Phone: (913)532-7455
Manhattan, KS 66506 Tony Crawford, Ch., Spec.Coll.
Founded: 1966. **Staff:** Prof 1; Other 1. **Special Collections:** Abby Marlatt and Clementine Paddleford Cookery Collections (3225 volumes); Mackenzie Linnaeana (1389 volumes); Leonora Hering Memorial Poultry Collection (1116 volumes); Fred and Jeannette Higginson Robert Graves and James Joyce Collections (Graves, 925 volumes; Joyce, 416 volumes); Kansas Collection (1275 volumes); Rex and Lucille Anderson Abraham Lincoln Collection (4652 volumes); Historic Costume and Textile Collection (685 volumes); Objectivist Poetry Collection (135 volumes); Veterinary Medicine Collection (primarily on the horse and its diseases); History of American Agriculture Collection. **Holdings:** 36,500 volumes. **Services:** Collections open to the public. **Computerized Information Services:** BITNET (electronic mail service). **Special Catalogs:** Descriptive Catalog of Seventeenth Century Religious Literature (1966); Linnaeana (1970); The Kansas State University Receipt Book and Household Manual (1968). **Remarks:** FAX: (913)532-6144. Electronic mail address(es): LIBRARY@KSUVM (BITNET). **Staff:** John J. Vander Velde, Spec.Coll.Libn.

★8573★
Kansas State University - University Archives (Hist)
Farrell Library Phone: (913)532-7456
Manhattan, KS 66506 Anthony Crawford, Univ.Archv.
Founded: 1983. **Staff:** Prof 1; Other 1. **Subjects:** Kansas State University; Kansas; Manhattan, Kansas; agriculture; agricultural cooperatives; school lands in Kansas; education; Kansas politics and government; consumer education, organizations, protection; literature. **Special Collections:** Dan D. Casement papers (18 linear feet); Harold Fatzer Papers (12 linear feet); Kansas Extension Homemakers Council (18 linear feet); Wendell Lady papers (18 linear feet); Clementine Paddleford papers (105 linear feet); William R. Roy papers (135 linear feet); Arthur Capper Cooperative Research Collection, FAR-MAR-CO, Inc.; Richard L.D. Morse Papers (90 linear feet); Consumer Movement Archives; Alfred M. Landon Lecture Series; Velma Carson Collection (5 linear feet); Gordon Parks Collection (1 linear foot); William H. Avery Papers (3 linear feet); Alice C. Nichols Papers (3 linear feet); Isaac T. Goodnow Papers (1 linear foot); Martha Keys Papers (90 linear feet); Edna Worthy Underwood Papers (2 linear feet); Currin Shields Papers (2 linear feet); Gail Kubik Collection (20 linear feet); American Council on Consumer Interests (9 linear feet); Kansans for ERA (2 linear feet). **Holdings:** 7300 volumes; 4400 linear feet of university archival records and manuscript collections; 30,000 photographs; 6 file cabinets of ephemera; 575 reels of microfilm; 9300 dissertations, theses, masters reports; university newspapers, 1875 to present. **Subscriptions:** 85 journals and other serials. **Services:** Copying; archives open to the public. **Computerized Information Services:** Internal database; BITNET (electronic mail service). **Special Catalogs:** Photograph collection (card); typed inventories of university records; registers for manuscript collections. **Special Indexes:** KSU history index (card). **Remarks:** FAX: (913)532-6144. Electronic mail address(es): LIBRARY@KSUVM (BITNET).

★8574★
Kansas State University - Veterinary Medical Library (Med)
Manhattan, KS 66506 Phone: (913)532-6006
Gayle K. Willard, Vet.Med.Libn.
Founded: 1936. **Staff:** Prof 1; Other 2. **Subjects:** Veterinary medicine, comparative medicine, preclinical science, internal medicine, pharmacology, toxicology. **Special Collections:** Faculty reprints (2314); German dissertations from the Hanover School of Veterinary Medicine, 1969 to present (2574); Animal Nutrition Collection; Human-Animal Bond Collection. **Holdings:** 32,400 volumes; 1700 AV programs; 8 VF drawers of pamphlets. **Subscriptions:** 950 journals and other serials. **Services:** Interlibrary loan; copying; library open to the public; document delivery service (limited). **Automated Operations:** Computerized public access catalog, cataloging, acquisitions, and circulation. **Computerized Information Services:** MEDLINE, CAB Abstracts; BITNET (electronic mail service). **Networks/Consortia:** Member of National Network of Libraries of Medicine (NN/LM). **Publications:** Acquisitions List, semimonthly; selected bibliographies - available on request. **Remarks:** FAX: (913)532-5884. Electronic mail address(es): LIBRARY@KSUVM (BITNET).

★8575★
Kansas State University - Weigel Library of Architecture and Design (Plan)
323 Seaton Hall Phone: (913)532-5968
Manhattan, KS 66506 Patricia Weisenburger, Libn.
Founded: 1917. **Staff:** Prof 1; Other 3. **Subjects:** Architecture, regional and community planning, building construction, historic preservation, interior space design, landscape design. **Special Collections:** English and French architecture prior to World War I (illustrations of decorative motifs; Pironesi engravings; detailed sketches, photographs, design and structural features of cathedrals, opera houses, and city halls; 300 volumes) **Holdings:** 33,700 volumes. **Subscriptions:** 200 journals and other serials. **Services:** Interlibrary loan; copying; SDI; library open to the public. **Automated Operations:** Computerized acquisitions and circulation. **Computerized Information Services:** BITNET (electronic mail service). **Special Catalogs:** Accounts of Architecture (an annotated subject catalog of special books in the library). **Remarks:** FAX: (913)532-6144. Electronic mail address(es): LIBRARY@KSUVM (BITNET).

★8576★
Kansas State University, Salina - Tullis Library/Resource Center (Sci-Engr, Comp Sci)
2408 Scanlan Ave. Phone: (913)825-0275
Salina, KS 67401 Beverlee Kissick, Ph.D., Libn.
Founded: 1965. **Staff:** Prof 1; Other 2. **Subjects:** Computers, electronics, chemistry, aeronautics, civil and mechanical engineering. **Special Collections:** Computer programming; management; applied engineering. **Holdings:** 23,000 books; videotapes collection. **Subscriptions:** 300 journals and other serials; 9 newspapers. **Services:** Interlibrary loan; copying; library open to the public with restrictions. **Automated Operations:** Computerized public access catalog, cataloging, acquisitions, serials, and circulation (NOTIS). **Computerized Information Services:** CD-ROMs (WILSONDISC, Le Pac: Government Documents, Computer Select, Encyclopedia of Polymer Science and Engineering Online); CC Mail (electronic mail service). Contact Person: Marilou Wenthe. **Remarks:** Serves as an Aviation Education Resource Center for Kansas, Nebraska, Iowa, and Missouri. FAX: (913)825-8475. **Formed by the merger of:** Kansas College of Technology and Kansas State University. **Staff:** Karlene Propst.

Kansas Yearly Meeting of Friends Archives
See: **Friends University - Edmund Stanley Library - Special Collections** (6176)

MacKinlay Kantor Collection
See: **Kendall Young Library** (20814)

★8577★
Kaohsiung Private Medical College - Library (Med)
100 Shihch'uan Rd Phone: 7 3210564
Kaohsiung 80708, Taiwan Keh-Min Liou
Founded: 1954. **Staff:** Prof 11; Other 1. **Subjects:** Medicine, dentistry, pharmacy, nursing, medical technology, public health. **Holdings:** 55,575 books; 34,435 bound periodical volumes; 848 microfilm; 719 tapes. **Subscriptions:** 1782 journals and other serials; 24 newspapers. **Services:** Copying; SDI; library open to the public. **Computerized Information Services:** DIALOG Information Services; STICNET (internal database). Contact Person: Ms. Su-Sing Lo. **Publications:** Kaohsiung Journal of Medical Sciences. **Special Catalogs:** Kaohsiung Medical College Library Periodicals Catalog. **Remarks:** FAX: 7 3210564.

★8578★
Kapiolani Medical Center - KMC Library (Med)
1319 Punahou St. Phone: (808)973-8332
Honolulu, HI 96816 Ikuko Uesato, Libn.
Founded: 1978. **Staff:** Prof 1. **Subjects:** Obstetrics and gynecology, pediatrics, child psychiatry. **Holdings:** 1000 books; 600 bound periodical volumes. **Subscriptions:** 100 journals and other serials. **Services:** Interlibrary loan; copying; library open to the public for reference use only. **Computerized Information Services:** MEDLINE. Performs searches on fee basis. **Networks/Consortia:** Member of Medical Library Group of Hawaii. **Remarks:** Alternate telephone number(s): 973-8511.

Louis Kaplan Memorial Library
See: **Philadelphia Association for Psychoanalysis** (12974)

★8579★
Kaplan/McLaughlin/Diaz Architects & Planners - Library (Plan)
222 Vallejo Phone: (415)398-5191
San Francisco, CA 94111 Janice Vargo, Libn.
Staff: Prof 1; Other 1. **Subjects:** Architectural design, especially hospital design; San Francisco. **Holdings:** 4000 books; 175 bound periodical volumes; 1500 catalogs and 16 VF drawers of product technical information; 16 VF drawers of design information; 200 planning documents; 500 programming documents; 100 volumes of codes and standards; 1200 boxes of archives. **Subscriptions:** 104 journals and other serials. **Services:** Library open to the public with permission of librarian. **Automated Operations:** Computerized cataloging, acquisitions, circulation, and routing. **Computerized Information Services:** DIALOG Information Services. **Publications:** Library newsletter. **Remarks:** FAX: (415)394-7158.

Mordecai M. Kaplan Library
See: **Reconstructionist Rabbinical College** (13754)

Frederic T. Kapp Memorial Library
See: **Cincinnati Psychoanalytic Institute** (3708)

★8580★
(Karachi) American Center - USIS Library (Educ)
Collector's Lane
8 Abdullah Haroom Rd.
Karachi, Pakistan
Remarks: Maintained or supported by the U.S. Information Agency. Focus is on materials that will assist peoples outside the United States to learn about the United States, its people, history, culture, political processes, and social milieux.

Carl Kardatzke Memorial Library
See: **Park Place Church of God** (12748)

Coleman Karesh Law Library
See: **University of South Carolina** (19306)

Karnosh Medical Library
See: **Cleveland Psychiatric Institute** (3815)

Karolinska Institute
See: **Sweden - Karolinska Institute** (15906)

Karolyi Mihaly Orszagos Mezogazdasagi Konyvtar
See: **Hungary - Karolyi Mihaly National Agricultural Library** (7553)

★8581★
Karr Tuttle Campbell - Law Library (Law)
1201 3rd Ave., Suite 2900 Phone: (206)223-1313
Seattle, WA 98101-3028 Jane Stewart
Staff: Prof 2; Other 2. **Subjects:** Law. **Holdings:** 10,000 volumes; 270 expert witness depositions; microfiche. **Subscriptions:** 540 journals and other serials. **Services:** Interlibrary loan. **Computerized Information Services:** LEXIS, DIALOG Information Services, WESTLAW, DataTimes, Dow Jones News/Retrieval, VU/TEXT Information Services, LEGI-SLATE, OCLC. **Networks/Consortia:** Member of Western Library Network (WLN). **Remarks:** FAX: (206)682-7100. **Staff:** Barbara Arnett, Assoc.Libn.

Joseph E. Karth Research Center
See: **Ramsey County Historical Society** (13700)

Michael Kasak Library
See: **Milwaukee County Mental Health Complex** (10423)

Kass Judaic Library
See: **Jewish Community Center of Greater Washington** (8383)

★8582★
(Kathmandu) American Library (Educ)
New Road
P.O. Box 58
Kathmandu, Nepal
Remarks: Maintained or supported by the U.S. Information Agency. Focus is on materials that will assist peoples outside the United States to learn about the United States, its people, history, culture, political processes, and social milieux.

★8583★
Katholieke Universiteit Leuven - Faculteitsbibliotheek Landbouwwetenschappen (Agri)
Kardinaal Mercierlaan 92 Phone: 16 220931
B-3001 Leuven, Belgium Georges Mertens, Lib.Hd.
Founded: 1950. **Staff:** Prof 1. **Subjects:** Agriculture, botany, microbiology, soil science, forestry. **Holdings:** 20,000 books; 10,000 reports. **Subscriptions:** 500 journals and other serials. **Services:** Interlibrary loan; copying; library open to the public for reference use only. **Automated Operations:** Computerized public access catalog (LIBIS). **Remarks:** FAX: 16 205032.

Katholieke Universiteit Leuven - Faculteitsbibliotheek Letteren en Wijsbegeerte
See: **Catholic University of Leuven - Faculty Library of Letters and Philosophy** (3166)

★8584★
Katholieke Universiteit Leuven - Wiskunde/Computerwetenschappen - Bibliotheek (Sci-Engr)
Celestijnenlaan 200B Phone: 16 200656
B-3001 Leuven, Belgium Ria Vanhove
Staff: Prof 1.5. **Subjects:** Mathematics, astronomy, statistics, computer science, history of science. **Holdings:** 32,000 books; 50 microfiche; 80 reels of microfilm; 60 videotapes. **Subscriptions:** 380 journals and other serials. **Services:** Interlibrary loan; copying; SDI; library open to the public. **Computerized Information Services:** DIALOG Information Services, ESA/IRS, STN International, INFOLINE; LIBIS (internal database). Contact Person: Ludo Holans, Campus Libn. **Remarks:** FAX: 16 293545.

★8585★
Katholisch Theologische Hochschule Linz - Bibliothek (Rel-Phil)
Bethlehemstrasse 20 Phone: 732 784293
A-4020 Linz, Austria Johannes Lackinger, Mag.
Founded: 1794. **Staff:** Prof 15; Other 17. **Subjects:** Theology, philosophy, art, history, pedagogics. **Holdings:** 145,000 books; 20,000 bound periodical volumes; 50 microfiche; 20 reels of microfilm; manuscripts; AV materials; maps. **Subscriptions:** 400 journals and other serials; 30 newspapers. **Services:** Copying; library open to the public. **Remarks:** FAX: 732 784293, ext. 55.

Joseph Katkowsky Library
See: **Congregation Beth Achim** (4148)

★8586★
Katten Muchin & Zavis - Library (Law)
525 W. Monroe, Suite 1600 Phone: (312)902-5675
Chicago, IL 60661-3693 Susan P. Siebers, Dir., Lib. & Info.Serv.
Founded: 1974. **Staff:** Prof 4; Other 12. **Subjects:** Law, taxation, securities law, labor law. **Holdings:** 30,000 books; 315 bound periodical volumes. **Subscriptions:** 800 journals and other serials; 10 newspapers. **Services:** Interlibrary loan; library open to other law firm librarians. **Computerized Information Services:** LEXIS, DIALOG Information Services, Data-Star, Hannah Information Systems, InvesText, VU/TEXT Information Services, WILSONLINE, WESTLAW, OCLC, Dow Jones News/Retrieval, Legislative Information System (LIS), DataTimes, Information America, LEGI-SLATE, Spectrum Ownership Profiles Online, SEC/EXPRESS, Dun's Legal Services; Data-Star. **Networks/Consortia:** Member of Chicago Library System, ILLINET. **Remarks:** FAX: (312)902-1061. Telex: 298264 ATLAW UR. **Staff:** Carol J. Dawe, Tech.Serv.Libn.; Beth A. Mrkvicka, Ref.Libn.; Pamela M. LaMarca, Ref.Libn.

Joseph M. Katz Graduate School of Business
See: **University of Pittsburgh - Joseph M. Katz Graduate School of Business - Library** (19216)

★8587★
Raphael Katzen Associates International, Inc. - Library (Sci-Engr)
7162 Reading Rd., Suite 1200 Phone: (513)351-7500
Cincinnati, OH 45237 Dr. Raphael Kytren
Founded: 1953. **Staff:** 13. **Subjects:** Chemistry, engineering, pulp, sugar, pollution, energy, pilot plant design, hazardous processes operation. **Holdings:** 2000 volumes. **Subscriptions:** 20 journals and other serials. **Services:** ILL; library not open to the public. **Remarks:** FAX: (513)351-0810. **Staff:** Jane Wagner.

Ingeborg S. Kauffman Library
See: **California School of Professional Psychology** (2506)

★8588★
Henry J. Kaufman and Associates, Inc. - Information Center (Bus-Fin)
2233 Wisconsin Ave., N.W., Suite 500 Phone: (202)333-0700
Washington, DC 20007 Mary Filberg, Dir., Info.Serv.
Founded: 1979. **Staff:** Prof 2. **Subjects:** Advertising, marketing, and public relations industries. **Holdings:** 350 books; 2 VF drawers of pictures; 5000 slides; 7 VF drawers of clippings; 10 VF drawers of archival material; 1 VF drawer of annual reports; 2 VF drawers of competitive advertisements; 2 VF drawers of client information; 75 unbound periodicals. **Subscriptions:** 200 journals and other serials; 10 newspapers. **Services:** Interlibrary loan; copying; SDI; center open to the public by appointment. **Computerized Information Services:** DIALOG Information Services, Mead Data Central. **Remarks:** FAX: (202)337-0449.

★8589★
Kaweah Delta District Hospital - Library (Med)
400 W. Mineral King Ave. Phone: (209)625-7216
Visalia, CA 93291 Jeannine M. Hinkel, Lib.Dir.
Staff: Prof 1; Other 1. **Subjects:** Clinical medicine, nursing, hospital administration. **Holdings:** 2000 books. **Subscriptions:** 250 journals and other serials. **Services:** Interlibrary loan; copying; library open to the public by appointment. **Automated Operations:** Computerized public access catalog, serials, routing, and circulation. **Computerized Information Services:** DIALOG Information Services, MEDLARS; DOCLINE (electronic mail service). Performs searches on fee basis. **Networks/Consortia:** Member of Northern California and Nevada Medical Library Group (NCNMLG), San Joaquin Valley Library System (SJVLS). **Remarks:** FAX: (209)732-1022. Electronic mail address(es): LIBID: 93291A (DOCLINE).

Dr. Ken Kaye Memorial Library
See: **British Columbia Ministry of Health - Dr. Ken Kaye Memorial Library** (2164)

★8590★
Kaye, Scholer, Fierman, Hays & Handler - Law Library (Law)
425 Park Ave. Phone: (212)836-8312
New York, NY 10022 Gerald Goodhartz, Libn.
Staff: Prof 5; Other 8. **Subjects:** Law. **Special Collections:** Law - antitrust, tax, copyright, trademark, corporate, real estate, banking, bankruptcy, labor. **Holdings:** 65,000 books; 1100 bound periodical volumes; 5450 microfiche; 600 ultrafiche; 1600 reels of microfilm; 100 VF drawers. **Subscriptions:** 1500 journals and other serials; 20 newspapers. **Services:** Interlibrary loan; copying; SDI; library open to members of SLA and Law Library Association of Greater New York by appointment. **Computerized Information Services:** LEXIS, NEXIS, PFDS Online, DIALOG Information Services, Info Globe, WESTLAW, Dow Jones News/Retrieval, Information America. **Remarks:** FAX: (212)836-7153. Telex: 126921. **Staff:** Jeffrey Giles, Ref.Libn.; Susan Kane, Ref.Libn.; Carolyn Woods, Ref.Libn; John H. Williams, Tech.Serv.Libn.

Theodore Kazimiroff Research Library
See: **Bronx County Historical Society** (2212)

★8591★
KC Publishing, Inc. - Research Library (Publ)
4251 Pennsylvania Ave. Phone: (816)531-5730
Kansas City, MO 64111 Jeffrey S. Nightingale, Bk.Proj.Mgr.
Staff: 1. **Subjects:** Horticulture, needlework and home arts, wood working, health, nature, home improvement. **Holdings:** 2000 volumes. **Subscriptions:** 100 journals and other serials. **Services:** Library not open to the public. **Remarks:** FAX: (816)531-3873.

John R. Keach Memorial Library
See: **Johnson County Mental Health Center** (8442)

★8592★
Kean Archives (Art)
1320 Locust St. Phone: (215)735-1812
Philadelphia, PA 19107 Frances Kean, Owner
Founded: 1939. **Staff:** Prof 1; Other 1. **Subjects:** General pictorial scenes, popular American music. **Special Collections:** David Edwin, 1st American engraver; Alexander Anderson, 1st American wood engraver; Rosenthals, lithographers, artists, engravers; Sartains, engravers; history of photography; Bible illustrations; Civil War. **Holdings:** Books; 350 bound periodical volumes; over 3 million pictures; engravings; lithographs; portraits; woodcuts; photographs; sheet music. **Subscriptions:** 10 journals and other serials. **Services:** Copying; archives open to the public by appointment. **Special Indexes:** Authority index; birthday and date file; chronological and title popular music file.

★8593★
Kean College of New Jersey - Adult Advisory Services (Educ)
Union, NJ 07083 Phone: (908)527-2210
Barbara Lindeman, Dir.
Staff: 1. **Subjects:** Vocational information, careers, job hunting, education, employment references. **Holdings:** 300 books; 3 file drawers of vocational information; 3 drawers of general information files; 3 shelves of college catalogs. **Subscriptions:** 5 newspapers. **Services:** Library open to the public. **Publications:** Adult Advisory Services newsletter, semiannual - to mailing list.

★8594★
Kean College of New Jersey - Instructional Resource Center (Educ)
Morris Ave. Phone: (201)527-2073
Union, NJ 07083 Vincent V. Merlo, Dir., Media & Tech.
Founded: 1958. **Staff:** Prof 5; Other 8. **Special Collections:** Nonprint media representative of each of the major disciplines presented in the curriculum. **Holdings:** 354 books; 8000 nonprint materials. **Services:** Center provides instructional materials and media production facilities for use by faculty and students of the college. **Remarks:** FAX: (908)527-0320. **Staff:** Kevin Mulligan, Coord., Media/Tech.; Jean Mattson, Asst.Dir.; Geraldine Durden, Asst.Dir.; Maria Perez, Asst.Dir.

★8595★
Kean College of New Jersey - Nancy Thompson Library (Educ)
Morris Ave. Phone: (908)527-2017
Union, NJ 07083 Barbara Simpson, Dir.
Staff: Prof 12; Other 27. **Subjects:** Education, humanities, sciences. **Special Collections:** New Jersey collection; Dwyers Papers. **Holdings:** 265,000 books; 19,000 bound periodical volumes; 2010 reels of microfilm; 110 VF drawers. **Subscriptions:** 1300 journals. **Services:** Interlibrary loan; copying; library open to the public for reference use only. **Automated Operations:** Computerized cataloging, acquisitions, serials, and circulation. **Computerized Information Services:** DIALOG Information Services, PFDS Online, OCLC; internal database. **Networks/Consortia:** Member of PALINET. **Remarks:** FAX: (908)527-2365. **Staff:** Pamela Thornton, Asst.Dir.; Mark M. Ferrara, Assoc.Dir.; Tamara Avdzej, Acq.Libn.; Kevork Berberian, Cat.Libn.; Schi-Zhin Rhie, Coord., CD-ROM; Edwin Erbe, Per.Coord.; Eleanor McKnight, Coord., Access Serv.; Susan Sabatino, Evening/Weekend Pub.Serv.

★8596★
Kearfott Guidance & Navigation Corp. - Technical Information Center MS 12 B33 (Sci-Engr)
150 Totowa Rd. Phone: (201)785-6481
Wayne, NJ 07470 N.W. Patton, Mgr.
Founded: 1956. **Staff:** Prof 1. **Subjects:** Aerospace sciences, metallurgy, mathematics, electrical and electronic engineering, computer science. **Holdings:** 26,000 books; 23,000 bound serials; 23,000 reports, pamphlets, reprints; 4500 microforms. **Subscriptions:** 60 journals and other serials. **Services:** Interlibrary loan; center not open to the public. **Computerized Information Services:** DIALOG Information Services, DTIC. **Networks/Consortia:** Member of Bergen Passaic Regional Library Cooperative. **Remarks:** FAX: (201)785-6019.

★8597★
A.T. Kearney, Inc. - Corporate Information Center (Bus-Fin)
222 S. Riverside Plaza Phone: (312)993-8914
Chicago, IL 60606 Linda E. Larsen, Dir.
Staff: Prof 3. **Subjects:** Management systems, business, finance, marketing, organization, personnel administration, production and operations, transportation, environment, telecommunications, technology, international relations, management consulting. **Holdings:** 6000 books; 35 VF drawers of pamphlets; 40 VF drawers of annual reports; client reports on microfiche. **Subscriptions:** 230 journals and other serials. **Services:** Interlibrary loan; center not open to the public. **Computerized Information Services:** DIALOG Information Services, LEXIS, NEXIS, Dun & Bradstreet Business Credit Services, VU/TEXT Information Services, PFDS Online, Dow Jones News/Retrieval, Info Globe, Data-Star, TRADSTAT (World Trade Statistics), Global Scan, CompuServe Information Service, NAMNET; CD-ROM. **Networks/Consortia:** Member of ILLINET. **Publications:** Acquisition List, quarterly; Periodical List; Software List, both annual. **Remarks:** FAX: (312)648-5594. For telex, call (312)687-1155. **Staff:** Spencer Hall, Supv., Res.; Mary Pietryga, Res.Spec.; George Schlichter, Res.Asst.; Juanita Collins, Res.Asst.; Pat Porter, Supv., Rsrcs.; Arlene Arp, Rsrcs.Assoc.; Michael Jordan, Rsrcs.Spec.

Kearney Agricultural Center
See: **University of California** (18297)

Kearney State College
See: **University of Nebraska at Kearney** (19008)

Kenneth B. Keating Library
See: **Roberts Wesleyan College** (13969)

★8598★
Keck Mahin & Cate - Information Services (Law)
8300 Sears Tower Bldg. Phone: (312)876-3574
Chicago, IL 60606 Wendy Moorhead, Hd.Libn.
Staff: Prof 3.5; Other 5. **Subjects:** Law. **Holdings:** 27,000 books. **Subscriptions:** 1800 journals and other serials. **Services:** Interlibrary loan; library open to the public with restrictions. **Automated Operations:** Computerized routing. **Computerized Information Services:** LEXIS, DIALOG Information Services, WESTLAW, DataTimes, LEGI-SLATE, VU/TEXT Information Services, Dow Jones News/Retrieval, Information America. **Networks/Consortia:** Member of ILLINET. **Remarks:** FAX: (312)876-3582. **Staff:** Judith Foltin, Res.Libn.; Diann Erskine, Res.Libn.

★8599★
Keefer, Wood, Allen, Rahal - Library
P.O. Box 11963 Phone: (717)255-8031
Harrisburg, PA 17108-1963 Charles W. Rubendall, II, Lib.Dir.
Remarks: No further information was supplied by respondent.

Martin J. Keena Memorial Library
See: **American Stock Exchange** (769)

★8600★
Keene State College - Wallace E. Mason Library (Educ)
Appian Way Phone: (603)358-2723
Keene, NH 03431 C. Paul Vincent, Dir.
Founded: 1909. **Staff:** Prof 8; Other 10.5. **Subjects:** Teacher education, liberal arts. **Special Collections:** Preston Collection (New Hampshire; 2000 volumes). **Holdings:** 183,424 volumes; 60,347 microfiche titles of American civilization and English literature; 489,301 other microfiche; 12 VF drawers of pamphlets. **Subscriptions:** 1062 current periodicals; 40 newspapers. **Services:** Interlibrary loan; copying; library open to the public for reference use only. **Computerized Information Services:** DIALOG Information Services, OCLC; CD-ROMs (ABI/INFORM, MEDLINE, PsycLIT, ERIC); InterNet (electronic mail service). Performs searches on fee basis. Contact Person: Patrick O'Brien, Ref. **Networks/Consortia:** Member of New Hampshire College & University Council Library Policy Committee (NHCUC), NELINET, Inc. **Publications:** Check-it-Out (newsletter). **Remarks:** FAX: (603)358-2743. **Staff:** Robert J. Madden, Ref.; Nancy E. Butterfield, Tech.Serv.; Marilyn Hanley, Sys.; Peg Barrett, Ref.; Peggie Partello, Pub.Serv.; Judy Hildebrandt, LRC.

★8601★
Keeneland Association - Library (Rec)
Keeneland Race Course
Box 1690 Phone: (606)254-3412
Lexington, KY 40592-1690 Doris Jean Waren, Libn.
Founded: 1939. **Staff:** Prof 2. **Subjects:** Thoroughbred horse racing and breeding, horse sports. **Special Collections:** Photographic negatives of American racing (for publication purposes only). **Holdings:** 6000 books; 1000 bound periodical volumes; clippings; pamphlet file. **Subscriptions:** 35 journals and other serials. **Services:** Library open to the public for reference use only on limited schedule. **Special Catalogs:** The Keeneland Association Library, Guide to the Collection, (1958). **Remarks:** FAX: (606)288-4348. Telex: 21 8462. **Staff:** Cathy Schenck, Assoc.Libn.

Kegley Library
See: **Wytheville Community College** (20674)

Kegoayah Kozga Public Library
See: **Nome Library/Kegoayah Kozga Public Library** (11829)

Kegyesrendi Kozponti Konyvtar
See: **Piarist Central Library** (13035)

Robert A. Kehoe Archives
See: **University of Cincinnati - Medical Center Information and Communications - Cincinnati Medical Heritage Center** (18475)

★8602★
Keio Daigaku - Igaku Joho Senta - Medical Library and Information Center (Med)
35 Shinanomachi
Shinjuku-ku Phone: 3 3531211
Tokyo 160, Japan Yoshio Amano
Founded: 1937. **Staff:** Prof 12; Other 12. **Subjects:** Medicine, and allied subjects. **Holdings:** 69,633 books; 150,109 bound periodical volumes; 6 microfiche; 439 reels of microfilm. **Subscriptions:** 3027 journals and other serials; 7 newspapers. **Services:** Interlibrary loan; copying; SDI; library open to the public for reference use only. **Computerized Information Services:** BRS Information Technologies, DIALOG Information Services, MEDLINE, Japan Information Center of Science and Technology (JICST). Contact Person: Ms. Ichiko Midori, Ref.Libn. **Remarks:** FAX: 3 33572031. Telex: 3 32322198.

George Camp Keiser Library
See: **Middle East Institute - George Camp Keiser Library** (10351)

George Kelemen Library
See: **House Ear Institute** (7439)

Kellar Library
See: **Baptist Missionary Association Theological Seminary** (1517)

Keller Army Community Hospital
See: **U.S. Army Hospitals** (17044)

Helen Keller Archives
See: **American Foundation for the Blind** (590)

★8603★
Helen Keller Braille Library (Aud-Vis, Educ)
320 Fulton Ave. Phone: (516)485-1234
Hempstead, NY 11550 John Heller, Libn.
Founded: 1956. **Staff:** 5. **Subjects:** Elementary through high school textbooks, reading books in braille and large type. **Holdings:** 110,000 volumes. **Services:** Interlibrary loan; copying. **Remarks:** FAX: (516)538-6785. **Staff:** Edith Magee, Volunteer Assignments Mgr.

★8604★
J.J. Keller & Associates, Inc. - Research & Technical Library (Trans)
3003 W. Breezewood Ln.
PO Box 368 Phone: (414)722-2848
Neenah, WI 54957-0368 John K. Breese, Sr.Mgr.
Founded: 1958. **Staff:** Prof 5; Other 3. **Subjects:** Transportation, motor carrier regulations, occupational safety, hazardous materials, hazardous wastes, chemical processing industry. **Special Collections:** Transportation/motor carrier industry and regulations; hazardous materials/wastes handling and regulations. **Holdings:** 6500 books, AV programs, and documents (Department of Transportation, Environmental Protection Agency, Interstate Commerce Commission, and Department of Labor). **Subscriptions:** 406 journals and other serials. **Services:** Interlibrary loan; copying; library open to the public by referral. **Computerized Information Services:** DIALOG Information Services, WILSONLINE, CompuServe Information Service. **Networks/Consortia:** Member of Fox Valley Library Council. **Publications:** Library Bulletin, monthly. **Staff:** Marie E. Beede; Julie A. Nussbaum; Lisa A. Zwickey; Susan L. Mory.

★8605★
Kelley, Drye & Warren - Law Library (Law)
100 Chopin Plaza, Suite 2400 Phone: (305)372-2553
Miami, FL 33131 Sid Kaskey, Libn.
Staff: Prof 1; Other 1. **Subjects:** Law - general, civil practice, corporation, estate planning, taxation, probate, real estate, banking, international, maritime. **Holdings:** 17,000 volumes. **Subscriptions:** 300 journals and other serials. **Services:** Library open to attorneys only. **Computerized Information Services:** WESTLAW, LEXIS, Maxwell Macmillan Taxes Online, VU/TEXT Information Services, NEXIS. **Remarks:** FAX: (305)372-2490.

★8606★
Kelley, Drye & Warren - Law Library (Law)
101 Park Ave. Phone: (212)808-7800
New York, NY 10178 Patricia A. Renze, Hd.Libn.
Staff: Prof 5; Other 5. **Subjects:** Law - banking, corporate, securities, trusts and estates, labor, tax; employee benefits. **Holdings:** 40,000 books. **Subscriptions:** 110 journals and other serials; 10 newspapers. **Services:** Interlibrary loan (limited); library not open to the public. **Computerized Information Services:** NEXIS, LEXIS, DIALOG Information Services, WESTLAW. **Publications:** Library Bulletin, monthly - for internal distribution only. **Remarks:** FAX: (212)808-7897. **Staff:** Mary Eileen Maloney; Macia Stuart; Maureen Cleary; Ann Caufield.

Kellock Library
See: **Institute of Early American History and Culture** (7930)

★8607★
Kellogg Company - Science and Technology Information Center (Food-Bev)
235 Porter St.
Box 3423 Phone: (616)961-6949
Battle Creek, MI 49016-3423 Joann Beattie, Supv., Sci. & Tech.Info.Ctr.
Staff: Prof 2; Other 2. **Subjects:** Food technology, nutrition, engineering, analytical chemistry, management. **Special Collections:** Engineering drawings; vendor catalogs. **Holdings:** 2200 books. **Subscriptions:** 185 journals and other serials. **Services:** Interlibrary loan; center not open to the public. **Computerized Information Services:** DIALOG Information Services, ORBIT Search Service, PFDS Online, Dialcom Inc. **Publications:** Dietary Fiber Bibliography, quarterly - to fiber researchers. **Staff:** Emily Weingartz, Info.Spec.

J.L. and Helen Kellogg Cancer Care Center
See: **Evanston Hospital** (5507)

★8608★
M.W. Kellogg - Kellogg Library (Sci-Engr)
601 Jefferson Ave.
P.O. Box 4557 Phone: (713)753-4015
Houston, TX 77210-4557 John Galloway, Supv.
Founded: 1936. **Staff:** Prof 2; Other 2. **Subjects:** Engineering - petroleum, chemical, mechanical; chemistry. **Holdings:** 10,000 books; 20,000 bound periodical volumes; government reports; patents. **Subscriptions:** 150 journals and other serials. **Services:** Interlibrary loan; copying; division open to the public by appointment. **Computerized Information Services:** DIALOG Information Services, PFDS Online, LEXIS, NEXIS, Dow Jones News/Retrieval, DataTimes, Dun & Bradstreet Business Credit Services, MEDLARS, TOXNET. **Publications:** New Acquisitions, quarterly. **Remarks:** FAX: (713)753-5353. Telex: 166385 MWKHOC. **Staff:** Karen Weishaupt, Asst.Libn.

W.K. Kellogg Arabian Horse Library
See: **California State Polytechnic University - Library** (2551)

W.K. Kellogg Biological Station
See: **Michigan State University - W.K. Kellogg Biological Station** (10341)

W.K. Kellogg Health Sciences Library
See: **Dalhousie University - W.K. Kellogg Health Sciences Library** (4541)

John M. Kelly Library
See: **University of Toronto - St. Michael's College - John M. Kelly Library** (19459)

★8609★
Kelsey-Hayes Company - Research & Development Center Library (Sci-Engr)
2500 Green Rd.
Ann Arbor, MI 48105 Phone: (313)769-5890
Staff: Prof 1. **Subjects:** Engineering. **Holdings:** 200 books; 200 technical reports; 300 manufacturers' catalogs. **Subscriptions:** 45 journals and other serials. **Services:** Interlibrary loan; library not open to the public. **Computerized Information Services:** DIALOG Information Services. **Remarks:** Operated as a branch library of Fruehauf Corporation - Engineering Library.

Kelton Law Library
See: **University of West Los Angeles** (19552)

Kementerian Penerangan - Perpustakan Penyelidikan
See: **Malaysia - Ministry of Information - Research Library** (9568)

Kemp Library
See: **East Stroudsburg University - Kemp Library** (5124)

★8610★
C. Henry Kempe National Center for the Prevention and Treatment of Child Abuse and Neglect - Library (Soc Sci)
University of Colorado Health Sciences Center
Department of Pediatrics
1205 Oneida
Denver, CO 80220-2944 Phone: (303)321-3963
Founded: 1962. **Subjects:** Child abuse - diagnosis, prevention, treatment, intervention; sexual abuse; parenting. **Holdings:** Books; bound periodical volumes; reports; files. **Subscriptions:** 6 journals and other serials. **Services:** Library open to the public by appointment.

★8611★
Kemper National Insurance Companies - Human Resources Information Center (Bus-Fin, Law)
F-5 Phone: (708)540-2229
Long Grove, IL 60049 Rebecca Edmunds, Corp.Libn.
Founded: 1926. **Staff:** Prof 3; Other 2. **Subjects:** Insurance law, general law, insurance. **Holdings:** 25,000 books; 48 VF drawers of pamphlets. **Subscriptions:** 400 journals and other serials; 5 newspapers. **Services:** Interlibrary loan; copying; center open to the public for reference use only on request. **Computerized Information Services:** LEXIS, DIALOG Information Services, Dow Jones News/Retrieval, VU/TEXT Information Services, DataTimes. **Networks/Consortia:** Member of Northeastern Illinois Library Consortium, North Suburban Library System (NSLS).

★8612★
Kemptville College of Agricultural Technology - Purvis Library (Agri)
Kemptville, ON, Canada K0G 1J0 Phone: (613)258-8294
Jackie Mills, Libn.
Founded: 1946. **Staff:** Prof 1; Other 1. **Subjects:** Agriculture, home economics. **Holdings:** 9500 books. **Subscriptions:** 125 journals and other serials. **Services:** Interlibrary loan; copying; library open to the public.

★8613★
Kenai District Media Center - Library (Educ)
143 Park Avenue Phone: (907)262-1023
Soldotna, AK 99669 Kari Mohn, Dist. Media Coord.
Founded: 1977. **Staff:** Prof 1; Other 2. **Subjects:** K-12 school curriculum. **Holdings:** 1256 books; 1098 16mm film, 446 Apple computer discs, 369 books with cassettes, 125 audio cassettes, 1350 filmstrips with cassette; 472 kits; 171 manipulatives, 50 slides with cassettes, 97 study prints, 2219 videos. **Services:** Library not open to the public. **Computerized Information Services:** Internal database. **Special Catalogs:** Catalog of the District Media Center. **Remarks:** FAX: (907)262-7165.

Kenan Chemistry Library
See: **University of North Carolina at Chapel Hill** (19069)

★8614★
Kendall College - Library - Special Collections (Area-Ethnic, Food-Bev)
2408 Orrington Ave. Phone: (708)866-1322
Evanston, IL 60201 Iva M. Freeman, Dir.
Founded: 1934. **Staff:** Prof 2; Other 1. **Special Collections:** North American Collection (Indian museum); Culinary Collection. **Holdings:** 30,000 books. **Subscriptions:** 190 journals and other serials; 10 newspapers. **Services:** Interlibrary loan; copying; collections open to the public for reference use only. **Automated Operations:** Computerized cataloging. **Computerized Information Services:** DIALOG Information Services, OCLC. **Networks/Consortia:** Member of LIBRAS Inc., ILLINET, North Suburban Library System (NSLS). **Remarks:** FAX: (312)866-1320. Alternate telephone number(s): (708)866-1287. **Staff:** Andrea Leftwich, Tech.Serv.

★8615★
Kendall College - Mitchell Indian Museum - Library (Area-Ethnic)
2408 Orrington Ave. Phone: (708)866-1395
Evanston, IL 60201 Jane T. Edwards, Dir./Cur.
Founded: 1977. **Staff:** 2. **Subjects:** Native Americans - history, anthropology, art, literature, ethnography. **Special Collections:** Jesuit relations; Bureau of Ethnology reports. **Holdings:** 1100 books; 14 AV programs. **Subscriptions:** 5 journals and other serials; 3 newspapers. **Services:** Interlibrary loan; copying; SDI; library open to educators and members. **Remarks:** FAX: (708)866-1320. **Staff:** Iva Freeman, Kendall Coll.Libn.

★8616★
Kendall College of Art & Design - Van Steenberg Library (Art)
111 Division Ave., N. Phone: (616)451-2787
Grand Rapids, MI 49503 Ruth Hornbach, Hd.Libn.
Founded: 1929. **Staff:** Prof 2; Other 1. **Subjects:** Art history, furniture, interior design, advertising, illustration. **Special Collections:** Furniture collection. **Holdings:** 14,500 books; 1580 bound periodical volumes; 40,000 slides. **Subscriptions:** 95 journals; 10 newspapers. **Services:** Center open to the public. **Staff:** Halina Poplawska, Asst.Libn.

★8617★
Kendall Whaling Museum - Library (Hist)
27 Everett St.
Box 297 Phone: (617)784-5642
Sharon, MA 02067 Sarah E. Hays, Libn.
Founded: 1956. **Staff:** Prof 5; Other 3. **Subjects:** Whaling, art inspired by the whaling industry, seal hunting. **Special Collections:** Whaling manuscripts (voyage journals, logbooks, account books). **Holdings:** 8000 books; 900 logbooks; 60 cases of pamphlets; 300 account books; 15,000 photographs of whaleships and whaling; 5000 prints; 450 paintings; clippings. **Subscriptions:** 12 journals and other serials. **Services:** Interlibrary loan (limited); copying; library open to members and qualified scholars. **Publications:** Kendall Whaling Museum Monograph Series, 3/year; books; bibliographies; Newsletter. **Staff:** Stuart M. Frank, Ph.D, Dir.; Gare B. Reid, Dp.Dir.; Ellen Z. Hazen, Reg.

★8618★
Kenilworth Historical Society - Kilner Library (Hist)
415 Kenilworth Ave.
Box 181 Phone: (708)251-2565
Kenilworth, IL 60043 Mary H. Suker, Pres.
Staff: 1. **Subjects:** Local history; area authors. **Special Collections:** Diaries of Dorothy Sears. **Holdings:** 500 books; 200 bound periodical volumes; archives. **Services:** Copying; library open to the public for reference use only. **Publications:** Joseph Sears and his Kenilworth; Kenilworth Tree Stories; Kenilworth - The First Fifty Years (all books) - for sale or in-house use.

★8619★
Kenmore Association, Inc. - Archives (Hist)
1201 Washington Ave. Phone: (703)373-3381
Fredericksburg, VA 22401 Stacia G. Norman, Cur.
Subjects: Betty Washington Lewis, 1733-1797; Fielding Lewis, 1725-1781; Lewis children and descendants, 1750 to present; Fredericksburg, Virginia. **Holdings:** 550 manuscripts, letters, household accounts, deeds, bills. **Services:** Archives open to researchers with permission of the curator.

★8620★
Kenmore Mercy Hospital - Health Sciences Learning Resource Center (Med)
2950 Elmwood Ave. Phone: (716)879-6114
Kenmore, NY 14217 Brenda L. Cassoni, Libn.
Founded: 1971. **Staff:** Prof 1. **Subjects:** Medicine, nursing, allied health sciences. **Holdings:** 500 books; 10,000 unbound periodicals. **Subscriptions:** 115 journals and other serials. **Services:** Interlibrary loan; copying; SDI; center open to the public with approval of librarian. **Computerized Information Services:** MEDLINE. **Networks/Consortia:** Member of Western New York Library Resources Council (WNYLRC).

★8621★
Kennebec County Law Library
95 State St.
Augusta, ME 04330
Founded: 1915. **Subjects:** Law. **Holdings:** 11,000 volumes. **Remarks:** Currently inactive.

★8622★
Kennebec Valley Medical Center - Medical Library (Med)
6 E. Chestnut St. Phone: (207)626-1000
Augusta, ME 04330 Nancy Greenier, Med.Libn.
Founded: 1968. **Staff:** Prof 1; Other 1. **Subjects:** Medicine, surgery, nursing, health sciences. **Special Collections:** History and Biography of Medicine (300 volumes); death, dying, and hospice collection. **Holdings:** 3100 volumes; 6 VF drawers of reprints; 4 VF drawers of pamphlets; 2600 audiotapes; 320 filmstrips; 700 video cassettes; 350 slide sets; 64 16mm films. **Subscriptions:** 162 journals and other serials. **Services:** Interlibrary loan; copying. **Computerized Information Services:** BRS Information Technologies, MEDLARS. **Networks/Consortia:** Member of Health Science Library and Information Cooperative of Maine (HSLIC). **Publications:** LRC Bulletin, monthly - to library users. **Special Catalogs:** Audiovisual Holdings Catalog (book).

★8623★
Kennebunkport Historical Society - Library (Hist)
P.O. Box 1173 Phone: (207)967-2751
Kennebunkport, ME 04046 Joan Sullivan, Cur./Adm.
Subjects: Kennebunkport history. **Holdings:** Documents; manuscripts. **Services:** Copying; library open to the public.

★8624★
Kennedy Galleries Inc. - Library (Art)
40 W. 57th St., 5th Fl. Phone: (212)541-9600
New York, NY 10019-4044 Lillian Brenwasser, V.P.
Staff: Prof 1. **Subjects:** American painting and sculpture, fine prints. **Holdings:** 4000 books; 2 drawers of microfilm of early 20th century art periodicals; 1 drawer of microfilm of Ph.D. dissertations on American art; 10 VF drawers of clippings on American artists. **Services:** Library not open to the public. **Publications:** American Art Journal; Profiles of American artists (book). **Special Catalogs:** Exhibition catalogs; 18th, 19th, and 20th century American Masters catalogs; Marine and Western artists' catalogs; Fine Print catalog. **Remarks:** FAX: (212)333-7451.

★8625★
The Kennedy Institute - Training and Library Services (Med)
707 N. Broadway, Rm. 512 Phone: (410)550-9447
Baltimore, MD 21205 Bettea J. Hoofnagle, Asst.Dir.
Staff: Prof 1; Other 3. **Subjects:** Mental retardation, birth defects, cerebral palsy, epilepsy, developmental disabilities, special education, audiology, child psychology. **Special Collections:** Parent/family collection on developmental disabilities. **Holdings:** 3000 books; 1726 bound periodical volumes; 15 VF drawers; 300 videotapes; 370 audiocassettes; 15 teaching packages. **Subscriptions:** 102 journals and other serials. **Services:** Interlibrary loan; copying; SDI; library open to the public for reference use only. **Automated Operations:** Integrated library system. **Computerized Information Services:** BRS Information Technologies, DIALOG Information Services, MEDLARS; internal database. Performs searches on fee basis. **Networks/Consortia:** Member of Maryland Association of Health Science Librarians (MAHSL), Maryland Interlibrary Organization (MILO), CAPCON Library Network. **Publications:** Production of videocassettes and audiocassettes relating to developmental disabilities. **Remarks:** FAX: (410)550-9084. **Formerly:** Its Library/Media Center.

Kennedy Institute of Ethics
See: **Georgetown University - Kennedy Institute of Ethics** (6377)

J.F. Kennedy Memorial Collection
See: **Alabama A & M University - J.F. Drake Memorial Learning Resources Center** (180)

★8626★
Kennedy/Jenks Consultants - Library (Sci-Engr)
303 2nd St., 10th Fl. N. Phone: (415)243-2531
San Francisco, CA 94107 Alice Sullivan, Corp.Libn.
Founded: 1974. **Staff:** Prof 1; Other 1. **Subjects:** Engineering - civil, sanitary, environmental, hydraulic; hydrology; biological sciences. **Holdings:** 2000 books; 3000 technical reports; 2500 pamphlets, annual reports, reprints. **Subscriptions:** 80 journals and other serials. **Services:** Interlibrary loan; library not open to the public. **Computerized Information Services:** DIALOG Information Services, LEXIS, Ground Water On-Line. **Publications:** Library Bulletin, monthly - for internal distribution only. **Special Catalogs:** Technical Reports Catalog (online); Product Catalogs (online). **Remarks:** FAX: (415)896-0999. **Formerly:** Kennedy/Jenks/Chilton.

John F. Kennedy Center for the Performing Arts
See: **Library of Congress** (9120)

John F. Kennedy Institut fur Nordamerikastudien
See: **Freie Universitat Berlin** (6141)

John F. Kennedy Institut fur Nordamerikastudien
See: **New York University - Conservation Center - Library** (11721)

John F. Kennedy Library
See: **U.S. Presidential Libraries** (17927)

★8627★
John F. Kennedy Library - (Georgetown) USIS Library (Educ)
34A North & King Sts.
P.O. Box 10888
Lacytown
Georgetown, Guyana
Remarks: Maintained or supported by the U.S. Information Agency. Focus is on materials that will assist peoples outside the United States to learn about the United States, its people, history, culture, political processes, and social milieux.

★8628★
John F. Kennedy Medical Center - Medical Library (Med)
65 James St.
P.O. Box 3059 Phone: (201)321-7181
Edison, NJ 08818-3059 Lena Friedel, Med.Libn.
Founded: 1967. **Staff:** Prof 1; Other 1. **Subjects:** Internal medicine, family practice, rehabilitation. **Holdings:** 800 books; 1000 bound periodical volumes; Audio-Digest tapes; NCME videotapes. **Subscriptions:** 250 journals and other serials. **Services:** Interlibrary loan; copying; SDI. **Computerized Information Services:** DIALOG Information Services, BRS Information Technologies, MEDLARS, Physician Data Query (PDQ). **Networks/Consortia:** Member of MEDCORE, BHSL. **Publications:** Library Update.

★8629★
John F. Kennedy Memorial Hospital - Medical & Nursing Libraries (Med)
47-111 Monroe St. Phone: (619)347-6191
Indio, CA 92201 Dan Dickinson, Med.Libn.
Staff: Prof 1. **Subjects:** Medicine, nursing. **Holdings:** 1000 books; 100 bound periodical volumes; 100 pamphlets. **Subscriptions:** 130 journals. **Services:** Interlibrary loan; library not open to the public. **Computerized Information Services:** MEDLINE, NLM. **Networks/Consortia:** Member of Inland Empire Medical Library Cooperative (IEMLC), National Network of Libraries of Medicine - Pacific Southwest Region.

John F. Kennedy School of Government
See: **Harvard University - John F. Kennedy School of Government - Library** (6977)

John F. Kennedy Space Center
See: **NASA** (10985)

★8630★
John F. Kennedy University - Joy Feinberg Library
1500 16th St.
San Francisco, CA 94103
Defunct. Holdings absorbed by its main library.

★8631★
Kennedy-King College - Library (Area-Ethnic)
6800 S. Wentworth Ave. Phone: (312)962-3200
Chicago, IL 60621 Mary Jane Rudolph, Chm.
Founded: 1934. **Staff:** Prof 4; Other 5. **Subjects:** Black studies - history, sociology, current issues, nursing. **Holdings:** 42,000 volumes. **Subscriptions:** 400 journals and other serials; 12 newspapers. **Services:** Interlibrary loan; copying; library open to the public with restrictions. **Computerized Information Services:** OCLC. **Networks/Consortia:** Member of ILLINET. **Staff:** James B. Osgood, Cat.

★8632★
Kennedy Memorial Hospitals - Cherry Hill Division - Dr. Barney A. Slotkin Memorial Library (Med)
Chapel Ave. & Cooper Landing Rd.
Box 5009 Phone: (609)488-6865
Cherry Hill, NJ 08034 Sharon Sobel, Libn.
Founded: 1974. **Staff:** Prof 1. **Subjects:** Medicine, nursing, osteopathy. **Holdings:** 1148 books; 1710 bound periodical volumes. **Subscriptions:** 130 journals and other serials. **Services:** Interlibrary loan; copying; library open to the public on request. **Computerized Information Services:** NLM, BRS Information Technologies. **Networks/Consortia:** Member of Health Sciences Library Association of New Jersey (HSLANJ), Pinelands Consortium for Health Information. **Staff:** Kathleen Schwartz.

★8633★
Kennedy Memorial Hospitals/University Medical Center - Washington Township Division - Barsky Memorial Library (Med)
Hurffville and Cross Keys Rds. Phone: (609)582-2675
Turnersville, NJ 08012 William Dobkowski, Med.Libn.
Founded: 1980. **Staff:** Prof 1. **Subjects:** Medicine. **Holdings:** 500 books; 700 bound periodical volumes. **Subscriptions:** 105 journals and other serials. **Services:** Interlibrary loan; library open to the public by appointment for reference use only. **Computerized Information Services:** NLM. **Networks/ Consortia:** Member of BHSL, Health Sciences Library Association of New Jersey (HSLANJ), Pinelands Consortium for Health Information. **Remarks:** Alternate telephone number(s): (609)582-2500. FAX: (609)582-2807.

Robert E. Kennedy Library
See: **California Polytechnic State University** (2500)

Robert F. Kennedy Assassination Archive
See: **University of Massachusetts at Dartmouth - Library Communications Center** (18833)

Kenner Army Community Hospital
See: **U.S. Army Hospitals** (17045)

Kennesaw Mountain National Battlefield Park
See: **U.S. Natl. Park Service** (17739)

Sister Kenny Institute
See: **Abbott-Northwestern Hospital Corporation** (15)

★8634★
Kenora Board of Education - Learning Materials Resources (Educ)
100 First Ave., W. Phone: (807)468-5571
Kenora, ON, Canada P9N 3Z7 Mary Lindsey, Libn.
Remarks: FAX: (807)468-3857. No further information was supplied by respondent.

★8635★
Kenosha Achievement Center - Library (Med)
1218 79th St.
Kenosha, WI 53143 Phone: (414)658-1687
Subjects: Mental retardation, job placement, rehabilitation administration, developmental disabilities, counseling. **Holdings:** 200 books. **Services:** Library open to the public only on a restricted basis. **Remarks:** FAX: (414)658-1562.

★8636★
Kenosha County Historical Society & Museum - Historical Research Library (Hist)
6300 3rd Ave. Phone: (414)654-5770
Kenosha, WI 53143 Dane F. Pollei, Exec.Dir.
Founded: 1878. **Staff:** Prof 1. **Subjects:** Local, regional, state history; genealogy; iconography. **Holdings:** 2000 books; 250 bound periodical volumes; local newspapers; 9 VF drawers of documents and clippings; maps, 1837-1920s; 5000 photographic images; 100 manuscripts, diaries, ledgers; file of death notices. **Services:** Copying; library open to the public. **Publications:** Newsletters, quarterly; books and booklets on local history, irregular.

★8637★
Kenosha Hospital and Medical Center - Health Sciences Library (Med)
6308 8th Ave. Phone: (414)656-2120
Kenosha, WI 53143 Patty Westrich, Hea.Sci.Libn.
Founded: 1970. **Staff:** Prof 1; Other 1. **Subjects:** Medicine, nursing. **Holdings:** 2000 books; 100 audio cassettes; 200 video cassettes. **Subscriptions:** 135 journals and other serials. **Services:** Interlibrary loan; copying (limited); library open to staff, students, and persons referred by doctors. **Computerized Information Services:** MEDLINE; DOCLINE (electronic mail service). **Networks/Consortia:** Member of Southeastern Wisconsin Health Science Library Consortium (SWHSL), National Network of Libraries of Medicine - Greater Midwest Region. **Remarks:** FAX: (414)656-2124.

★8638★
Kenosha News - Newspaper Library (Publ)
715 58th St.
Box 190 Phone: (414)657-1000
Kenosha, WI 53141-0190 Bernice L. Nagy, Libn.
Staff: Prof 1. **Subjects:** Newspaper reference topics. **Holdings:** 200 books; 84 drawers of clippings and photographs; 320 reels of microfilm. **Subscriptions:** 19 newspapers. **Services:** Library open to the public for reference use only.

★8639★
Kenosha Public Museum - Library (Art)
Civic Center
5608 10th Ave. Phone: (414)656-8026
Kenosha, WI 53140 Paula Touhey, Dir.
Subjects: Art, natural history, ethnology. **Holdings:** 1875 books; 50 bound periodical volumes. **Subscriptions:** 10 journals and other serials. **Services:** Library open to the public for reference use only.

★8640★
Kenrick-Glennon Seminary - Charles L. Souvay Memorial Library (Rel-Phil)
5200 Glennon Dr. Phone: (314)644-0266
St. Louis, MO 63119 Mary Beth Gladieux, Libn.
Founded: 1893. **Staff:** Prof 1; Other 3. **Subjects:** Roman Catholic theology, scripture, patristics. **Special Collections:** Thomas Merton Collection; Official Catholic Directory; cuneiform tablets; rare books (2269); Pre-Vatican II Catechisms. **Holdings:** 56,374 books; 14,894 bound periodical volumes; 182 major papers; 1122 VF materials; 709 other cataloged items; 1529 cassettes; 304 reels of microfilm; 249 microforms; 88 video cassettes. **Subscriptions:** 296 journals and other serials; 17 newspapers. **Services:** Interlibrary loan; copying; library open to the public. **Automated Operations:** Computerized cataloging. **Computerized Information Services:** OCLC, BRS Information Technologies, WILSONLINE. **Publications:** Handbook, annual; Monthly New Books Listing - for internal distribution only. **Remarks:** FAX: (314)644-3079. **Also Known As:** St. Louis Roman Catholic Theological Seminary.

★8641★
Kent County Memorial Hospital - Health Sciences Library (Med)
455 Toll Gate Rd. Phone: (401)737-7010
Warwick, RI 02886 Jo-Anne M. Aspri, Libn.
Staff: Prof 1. **Subjects:** Surgery, medicine, nursing, drug therapy. **Holdings:** 1100 books; 1700 bound periodical volumes; 957 journal volumes in microform. **Subscriptions:** 180 journals and other serials. **Services:** Interlibrary loan; SDI; library open to area professionals and students in the health field by appointment. **Computerized Information Services:** MEDLINE; DOCLINE (electronic mail service). **Networks/Consortia:** Member of Association of Rhode Island Health Sciences Librarians (ARIHSL), BHSL. **Remarks:** Alternate telephone number(s): 737-7000 ext. 1309. FAX: (401)737-7010 ext. 2220.

★8642★
Kent General Hospital - Medical Library (Med)
640 S. State St. Phone: (302)674-7357
Dover, DE 19901 Jane Irving, Circuit Libn.
Remarks: No further information was supplied by respondent.

★8643★
Kent Historical Society - Library (Hist)
R.D. 1
Box 321 Phone: (203)927-3055
Kent, CT 06757 Emily Hopson, Info.Dir.
Founded: 1935. **Staff:** 3. **Subjects:** Local history, settlement, development; Scaticook Indians; iron industry; genealogy. **Special Collections:** Collection of the works of George Lawrence Nelson (paintings and lithographs); photographs of early Kent (1000). **Holdings:** 20 VF drawers; ledgers. **Services:** Library open to the public. **Networks/Consortia:** Member of Region One Cooperating Library Service Unit, Inc. **Remarks:**; Alternate telephone number(s): 927-3419; 927-3759.

★8644★
Kent Institute of Art and Design - Library (Art)
Oakwood Park Phone: 622 757286
Maidstone, Kent ME16 8AG, England Vanessa Crane, Inst.Libn.
Founded: 1987. **Staff:** Prof 8; Other 8. **Subjects:** Visual arts, architecture, three- and two-dimensional design, crafts. **Special Collections:** Herbert Read Collection. **Holdings:** 76,000 books; bound periodical volumes; microfiche; slides; videotapes. **Subscriptions:** 400 journals and other serials; 10 newspapers. **Services:** Interlibrary loan; copying; library open to the public by appointment. **Automated Operations:** Computerized public access catalog. **Computerized Information Services:** BCIS. **Remarks:** FAX: 622 692003.

Marguerite Kent Library/Information Center
See: **American Marketing Association** (676)

★8645★
Kent Memorial Library - Historical Room (Hist)
50 N. Main St.
Suffield, CT 06078 Phone: (203)668-2325
Founded: 1894. **Staff:** Prof 4; Other 6. **Subjects:** Local history, genealogy. **Holdings:** 1000 books; 50 bound periodical volumes; 100 diaries; 125 account books, 25 on microfilm; 35,000 manuscripts, letters; 1000 photographs; photograph albums; scrapbooks of clippings, 1898 to present; newspapers. **Services:** Copying; room open to the public by appointment. **Networks/Consortia:** Member of Capital Region Library Council (CRLC). **Staff:** Francine Aloisa, Co-Dir.; Anne Borg, Co-Dir.

★8646★
Kent State University - Audio Visual Services (Aud-Vis, Educ)
330 University Library Phone: (216)672-3456
Kent, OH 44242 John P. Kerstetter, Dir., AV Serv.
Founded: 1948. **Staff:** Prof 4; Other 23. **Subjects:** Elementary through higher education - general curriculum, foreign languages, music, English literature, business, management, training. **Special Collections:** Film and Video Collection; School of Music Recital tapes; Ohio history tapes. **Holdings:** 8112 films; 2600 videotapes; 200 AV reference tools; cassettes; slide/tape sets. **Services:** Interlibrary loan (limited to film and video); services open to the public on a fee basis. **Automated Operations:** NOTIS. **Computerized Information Services:** MediaMinder, XL-Time (internal databases). **Networks/Consortia:** Member of Consortium of College and University Media Centers (CCUMC). **Special Catalogs:** Educational Video & Film Rental Catalog, every 3 years with annual supplements; subject area catalogs - both to customers in continental U.S., schools and colleges of Ohio, and campus faculty. **Remarks:** FAX: (216)672-3463. Toll-free telephone number(s): (800)338-5718. **Staff:** Robert A. Yoder, Asst.Dir.; Larry Rubens, Hd., Instr. Graphics; Robert Minno, Hd., Campus Serv.; John Whyde, Hd., Media Libn.

★8647★
Kent State University - Center for the Study of Ethnic Publications and Cultural Institutions (Area-Ethnic)
University Library, Rm. 318 Phone: (216)672-2782
Kent, OH 44242 Dr. Lubomyr Wynar, Dir.
Staff: Prof 1. **Subjects:** Ethnic bibliography, history, education, and press; ethnic libraries, archives, and museums. **Special Collections:** Ethnic reference files. **Holdings:** 1000 books; 500 pamphlets. **Subscriptions:** 200 journals and other serials. **Services:** Center open to the public with permission. **Publications:** Ethnic Forum: Journal of Ethnic Studies and of Ethnic Bibliography, 2/year - by subscription; Ethnic, Nationality, and Foreign-Language Broadcasting and Telecasting in Ohio (1981); Slavic Ethnic Libraries, Museums and Archives in the United States: A Guide and Directory (1980); Guide to Ethnic Press (1986). **Remarks:** FAX: (216)672-7965.

★8648★
Kent State University - Chemistry/Physics Library (Sci-Engr, Biol Sci)
312 Williams Hall Phone: (216)672-2532
Kent, OH 44242 Raghini S. Suresh
Founded: 1942. **Staff:** 1. **Subjects:** Biochemistry, chemistry, physics, liquid crystal. **Holdings:** 40,000 volumes. **Subscriptions:** 450 journals and other serials. **Services:** Interlibrary loan; copying; library open to the public. **Computerized Information Services:** DIALOG Information Services, BRS Information Technologies, Chemical Abstracts Service (CAS), STN International; BITNET (electronic mail service). **Remarks:** FAX: (216)672-4702. Electronic mail address(es): BSURESH@KENTVM (BITNET).

★8649★
Kent State University - Department of Special Collections and Archives (Hum)
University Library Phone: (216)672-2270
Kent, OH 44242 Alex Gildzen, Cur., Spec.Coll. & Archv.
Founded: 1968. **Staff:** Prof 2. **Subjects:** American and English literature, American history, cryptography, history of printing, performing arts, true crime, campus unrest, university history. **Special Collections:** Open Theater Archives; Joseph Chaikin papers; Jean-Claude van Itallie papers; James Broughton papers; Robert Lewis papers; Virginia Hamilton papers; Cynthia Rylant papers; Saalfield Publishing Company Archives; May 4th collection; Cowles family papers; Fuller family papers; Arthur Trory photographs. **Holdings:** 80,000 books; 1500 boxes of manuscripts. **Services:** Copying; department open to the public. **Publications:** Occasional Papers Series, irregular. **Special Catalogs:** Exhibition catalogs. **Remarks:** FAX: (216)672-2265. **Formed by the merger of:** Its Rare Books and Manuscripts, Archives, and Regional History Collections.

★8650★
Kent State University - Government Documents Division (Info Sci)
Library, 10th Fl. Phone: (216)672-2388
Kent, OH 44242 Rosemary D. Harrick, Hd., Govt.Docs.
Founded: 1962. **Staff:** Prof 1; Other 2. **Subjects:** Government and political science, economics, business, geology, health and welfare, education, agriculture, science. **Special Collections:** Depository for (Ohio) state documents; geological publications of other states and Canada; Readex UN documents, 1965 to present; Readex government non-depository publications, 1965 to present; Department of Energy Technical Reports, 1977 to present (DOE fiche). **Holdings:** 375,000 documents; 332,000 microfiche; 212,113 microcards; 1789 reels of microfilm. **Services:** Interlibrary loan; copying; collection open to the public. **Automated Operations:** Computerized cataloging and serials. **Computerized Information Services:** CD-ROMs (IMPACT, Statistical Masterfile 1990, Congressional Masterfile, Electronic Index to United Nations Documents and Publications). **Networks/Consortia:** Member of NEOMARL, OHIONET. **Special Catalogs:** Union List of Northeast Ohio Depository Libraries (printout); Department of Energy Technical Report Number List (printout). **Remarks:** FAX: (216)672-2265.

★8651★
Kent State University - Joseph F. Morbito Architecture Library (Plan)
309 Taylor Hall Phone: (216)672-2876
Kent, OH 44242 Alfred Willis, Arch.Libn.
Founded: 1987. **Staff:** Prof 1; Other 8. **Subjects:** Architecture, city planning, landscape architecture, historic preservation. **Special Collections:** Archives of John Carr (architectural drawings , office records). **Holdings:** 11,000 books; 1000 bound periodical volumes. **Subscriptions:** 109 journals and other serials. **Services:** Interlibrary loan; copying; SDI; library open to the public. **Remarks:** FAX: (216)672-2265.

★8652★
Kent State University - Map Library (Geog-Map)
406-10 McGilvrey Hall Phone: (216)672-2017
Kent, OH 44242 Edward J. Hall, Map Libn.
Founded: 1968. **Staff:** Prof 1. **Subjects:** Topography, geology, geography, soils, climate, urban geography. **Special Collections:** Sanborn Insurance Map and Atlas Collection (116 volumes; 536 sheets); Nirenstein's Realty Map Company Real Estate Atlas Collection; depository for California Automobile Association Map Collection. **Holdings:** 223,054 maps; 27 VF drawers of U.S.G.S. publications; depository for U.S. Geological Survey topographic and geological maps. **Subscriptions:** 25 newsletters and other serials. **Services:** Interlibrary loan; copying; library open to the public with KSU courtesy card. **Automated Operations:** Computerized cataloging and acquisitions. **Computerized Information Services:** BITNET (electronic mail service). **Networks/Consortia:** Member of NEOMARL. **Publications:** GeoKent: Selected Acquisitions Newsletter, quarterly - on exchange. **Special Indexes:** Index to Sanborn Atlases and Maps of Ohio (card). **Remarks:** FAX: (216)672-GE0G. Electronic mail address(es): EHALL@KENTVM (BITNET).

★8653★
Kent State University - Mathematics Library (Sci-Engr)
Kent, OH 44242 Phone: (216)672-2532
O.P. Stachelbery
Founded: 1960. **Subjects:** Mathematics, computer science. **Holdings:** 10,000 bound periodical volumes. **Subscriptions:** 202 journals and other serials. **Services:** library open to the public with restrictions.

★8654★
Kent State University - Music Library (Mus)
D5 Music & Speech Bldg. Phone: (216)672-2004
Kent, OH 44242 Jack Scott, Mus.Libn.
Founded: 1967. **Staff:** 1. **Subjects:** Music. **Special Collections:** Choralist (11,500 items). **Holdings:** 41,243 volumes; 21,001 scores and sheet music, unbound and uncataloged; 23,786 tapes, cassettes, phonograph records; 602 reels of microfilm. **Subscriptions:** 150 journals and other serials. **Services:** Interlibrary loan; copying; library open to the public. **Special Indexes:** Song index; choral index; education song index. **Remarks:** FAX: (216)672-2265.

★8655★
Kent State University - Speech and Hearing Clinic - Library (Med)
Kent, OH 44242 Phone: (216)672-3150
Dr. Toliver
Founded: 1910. **Subjects:** Speech, language, communication disorders, psycholinguistics, audiology, language disorders, speech pathology. **Holdings:** Figures not available. **Services:** Interlibrary loan; copying; library open to the public. **Computerized Information Services:** CD-ROMs; BITNET (electronic mail service). **Remarks:** FAX: (216)672-2265. Electronic mail address(es): KENTVM (BITNET).

★8656★
Kenton County Public Library - Kentucky & Local History Collection (Hist)
5th & Scott Sts. Phone: (606)491-7610
Covington, KY 41011 Charles King, Local Hist.Libn.
Staff: Prof 1; Other 3. **Subjects:** Kentucky genealogy, local history. **Special Collections:** Northern Kentucky Photograph Collection (3000 prints, 1880-1920; 300 prints, 1921-1962; 12,000 prints, 1963-1983); Frank Duveneck Paintings (12 oil paintings). **Holdings:** 4200 books; 160 bound periodical volumes; 4751 reels of microfilm; 1500 local history files; 600 family files; 1200 maps. **Subscriptions:** 300 journals and other serials; 22 newspapers. **Services:** Interlibrary loan; copying; collection open to the public for reference use only. **Automated Operations:** Computerized public access catalog (DYNIX). **Computerized Information Services:** OCLC. **Networks/Consortia:** Member of SOLINET, Greater Cincinnati Library Consortium (GCLC). **Special Indexes:** Card index to Covington and Newport newspapers, 1835-1919, 1920-1925 (in process), 1984-1989 (in process).

Kentron Erevnis Ellinikis Laographias
See: **Hellenic Folklore Research Center** (7117)

Kentucky Business Industry Data Network
See: **University of Louisville - Urban Research Institute** (18776)

★8657★
Kentucky Christian College - Young Library (Rel-Phil)
617 N. Carol Malone Blvd. Phone: (606)474-6613
Grayson, KY 41143-1199 Lemuel W. Waite, Dir.
Founded: 1919. **Staff:** Prof 2; Other 5. **Subjects:** Religion, Restoration Movement history, philosophy, education, business, physical science, mathematics, computer technology and applications. **Special Collections:** Restoration Movement history books and writers, including first editions. **Holdings:** 87,000 books; 8900 bound periodical volumes; 205 journals on microfilm; 1801 cassette tapes; 431 filmstrips; 184 phonograph records. **Subscriptions:** 333 journals and other serials; 10 newspapers. **Services:** Interlibrary loan; copying; library open to the public. **Remarks:** FAX: (606)474-3502.

★8658★
Kentucky Covered Bridge Association - Library (Hist)
62 Miami Pkwy. Phone: (606)441-7000
Fort Thomas, KY 41075-1137 Dr. L.K. Patton, Exec.Dir.
Founded: 1964. **Staff:** 3. **Subjects:** Covered bridges in Kentucky and other states. **Special Collections:** Dr. J. Winston Coleman's covered bridge picture collection from his Kentuckiana Collection. **Holdings:** 400 volumes; 1000 newspaper clippings in scrapbooks; 50 archival records; 3000 photographs of covered bridges; 60 maps and blueprints; 10 state highway department reports. **Services:** Copying; library open to the public for reference use only. **Publications:** Timbered Tunnel Talk, monthly - free to members and through various Chambers of Commerce. **Special Indexes:** Index to 17 existing bridges and material pertaining to them (card).

★8659★
Kentucky Historical Society - Kentucky Military History Museum - Library (Hist)
Old State House
P.O. Box H Phone: (502)564-3265
Frankfort, KY 40602-2108 Thomas W. Fugate, Musm.Cur.
Founded: 1973. **Staff:** 4. **Subjects:** Military history - general and Kentucky. **Special Collections:** Civil War quarter master records (Kentucky). **Holdings:** 2500 books; 1500 bound periodical volumes; 10,000 documents; 20 manuscripts. **Subscriptions:** 12 journals and other serials. **Services:** Copying; library open to the public at librarian's discretion.

★8660★
Kentucky Historical Society - KHS Library (Hist)
Old Capitol Annex
300 W. Broadway
Box H Phone: (502)564-3016
Frankfort, KY 40602-2108 Anne McDonnell, Lib.Mgr.
Staff: Prof 6; Other 4. **Subjects:** Kentucky history, genealogy, history. **Holdings:** 80,000 books; 15,000 bound periodical volumes; 10,000 reels of microfilm; 1000 cubic feet of manuscripts; 125 cubic feet of maps; 75,000 photographs. **Subscriptions:** 300 journals and other serials; 5 newspapers. **Services:** Copying; library open to the public. **Staff:** Mary E. Winter, Photo./Map Archv.; Mary Margaret Bell, Archv.; Ron Bryant, Cur., Rare Bks.

★8661★
Kentucky Horse Park - Equine Research Library (Biol Sci)
4089 Iron Works Pike Phone: (606)233-4030
Lexington, KY 40511 Barbara Dietrich, Coord., Educ.
Subjects: Horses, history of man and horse, horse equipment and racing, horse breeds, horses in sport. **Holdings:** 2000 books; 600 bound periodical volumes; 55 AV programs; reference file. **Subscriptions:** 77 journals and other serials. **Services:** Library open to the public for reference use only. **Computerized Information Services:** Internal database. **Remarks:** FAX: (606)254-0253.

Kentucky Military History Museum
See: **Kentucky Historical Society - Kentucky Military History Museum** (8659)

★8662★
Kentucky Mountain Bible College - Gibson Library (Rel-Phil)
Box 10 Phone: (606)666-5000
Vancleve, KY 41385 Patricia A. Bowen, Libn.
Founded: 1939. **Staff:** Prof 1. **Subjects:** Bible, theology, Christian education, religious history, sacred music, Christian missions, history, religions, sermons. **Special Collections:** Christian Holiness. **Holdings:** 16,500 books; pamphlets; AV programs. **Subscriptions:** 183 journals and other serials. **Services:** Library open to the public. **Formerly:** Kentucky Mountain Bible Institute.

★8663★
Kentucky School for the Blind - Carol J. Frey Library (Aud-Vis, Educ)
1867 Frankfort Ave. Phone: (502)897-1583
Louisville, KY 40206 Cathy Hicks, Libn.
Staff: Prof 1; Other 1. **Subjects:** Blind and physically handicapped, adult and juvenile fiction, nonfiction. **Holdings:** 4100 books; 6903 recorded books; 5087 braille volumes; 600 recordings; 300 filmstrips; 1116 tapes. **Subscriptions:** 49 journals and other serials. **Services:** Library open to students and alumni of the school.

★8664★
Kentucky School for the Deaf - Learning Resource Center (Educ)
S. 2nd St. Phone: (606)236-5132
Danville, KY 40422-0027 Duane L. Belcher, Dir., Media Serv.
Staff: Prof 4; Other 3. **Subjects:** K-12 educational materials. **Special Collections:** Deafness/Deaf Education (1000 volumes). **Holdings:** 11,000 books; 75 bound periodical volumes; 5000 nonprint materials; Captioned Films for the Deaf depository. **Subscriptions:** 68 journals and other serials. **Services:** Copying; center open to the public with restrictions. **Networks/Consortia:** Member of Kentucky Library Network, Inc. (KLN). **Staff:** Gayle A. DeVille, Elementary Libn.; Nadene N. May, Secondary Libn.; Genivieve Lyman, Captioned Film Depository Mgr.

★8665★
Kentucky (State) Cabinet for Economic Development - Division of Research - Library (Bus-Fin)
133 Holmes St. Phone: (502)564-4715
Frankfort, KY 40601 Shirley Wood, Libn.
Founded: 1958. **Staff:** Prof 2. **Subjects:** Industry, population, labor, income, housing. **Holdings:** 12,000 books; 5680 bound periodical volumes; manufacturing directories. **Services:** Library not open to the public.

★8666★
Kentucky (State) Council on Higher Education - Information Services Center (Educ)
1050 U.S. 127 S. Phone: (502)564-3553
Frankfort, KY 40601-4395 Marilyn Peck, Interoffice Oper.
Staff: 1. **Subjects:** Higher and health education. **Holdings:** 1500 books. **Subscriptions:** 30 journals and other serials; 4 newspapers. **Services:** Library not open to the public. **Remarks:** FAX: (502)564-2063.

Kentucky (State) Court of Justice - Administrative Office of the Courts - Kentucky State Law Library
See: **Kentucky State Law Library** (8676)

Kentucky State Data Center
See: **University of Louisville - Urban Research Institute** (18776)

★8667★
Kentucky (State) Department of Economic Development - Research & Planning Division - Library (Bus-Fin)
Capitol Plaza Office Tower Phone: (502)564-4886
Frankfort, KY 40601 Shirley Wood, Libn.
Founded: 1966. **Staff:** Prof 1. **Subjects:** Government statistics, economic development, industrial geology. **Holdings:** 12,100 volumes; manufacturers' directories. **Subscriptions:** 250 journals and other serials; 6 newspapers. **Services:** Copying (limited); library open to the public for reference use only.

★8668★
Kentucky (State) Department for Environmental Protection - EPIC Library (Env-Cons)
18 Reilly Rd. Phone: (502)564-2150
Frankfort, KY 40601 Laura Doyle, Libn.
Founded: 1980. **Staff:** Prof 1. **Subjects:** Water quality, air pollution and quality, solid waste, hazardous waste. **Special Collections:** Environmental Protection Agency Water Treatment Materials (400 titles); University of Kentucky Water Resources Institute Publications (100 titles); U.S. Army Corps of Engineers Phase I Reports (200 titles); Kentucky Administrative Regulations; Environment Reporter; Air & Water Pollution Control; partial repository for Kentucky Natural Resources and Environmental Protection Cabinet (NREPC) documents. **Holdings:** 200 books; 5000 reports on paper and microfiche. **Subscriptions:** 275 journals and other serials. **Services:** Interlibrary loan; center not open to the public. **Computerized Information Services:** DIALOG Information Services. **Remarks:** FAX: (502)564-4245.

★8669★
Kentucky (State) Department for Human Resources - Library (Med, Soc Sci)
275 E. Main St. Phone: (502)564-4530
Frankfort, KY 40621 Douglas Raisor, Supv.
Founded: 1960. **Staff:** Prof 2; Other 2. **Subjects:** Public health, social welfare, social work, child welfare, mental health. **Holdings:** 27,500 books; 10,000 unbound periodicals; 3000 pamphlets. **Subscriptions:** 223 journals and other serials. **Services:** Interlibrary loan; copying; library open to the public for reference use only. **Computerized Information Services:** BRS Information Technologies. **Publications:** CHR Library Holdings List. **Remarks:** FAX: (502)564-3674.

★8670★
Kentucky (State) Department for Libraries & Archives - Kentucky Talking Book Library (Aud-Vis)
300 Coffee Tree Rd.
Box 818 Phone: (502)875-7000
Frankfort, KY 40602 Richard Feindel, Br.Mgr.
Staff: Prof 4; Other 9. **Subjects:** General collection. **Special Collections:** Kentucky Collection (600 volumes). **Holdings:** 160,000 volumes. **Subscriptions:** 75 journals and other serials. **Services:** Interlibrary loan; library open to eligible blind and physically handicapped persons. **Automated Operations:** Computerized cataloging, serials, and circulation. **Networks/Consortia:** Member of National Library Service for the Blind & Physically Handicapped (NLS). **Publications:** Newsletter, quarterly. **Staff:** Judy Baron, Sr.Libn.; Chris Payne, Sr.Libn.; Wendy Hatfield, Sr.Libn.

★8671★
Kentucky (State) Department for Libraries & Archives - Public Records Division - Archives (Hist)
300 Coffee Tree Rd.
Box 537 Phone: (502)875-7000
Frankfort, KY 40602 Richard N. Belding, Dir./State Archv.
Staff: Prof 20; Other 48. **Subjects:** Kentucky - history, genealogy, government, politics, health services. **Holdings:** 91,000 cubic feet of state and local documents; 26,000 reels of microfilm; 1000 microfiche; 100 videocassettes; 200 audiocassettes; 25,000 photographic negatives. **Services:** Copying; archives open to the public. **Computerized Information Services:** Internal database. **Publications:** List of publications - available on request. **Remarks:** FAX: (502)564-5773. **Staff:** Barbara Teague, Archv.Serv.Mgr.; Charles Robb, Tech.Anl. & Sup.Mgr.; Diana Moses, State Rec.Mgr.; Darrell Gabhart, Local Rec.Mgr.; Milton Matzke, Micrographics Mgr.; Mary B. Samples, Doc.Presrv.Supv.; James Prichard, Prin.Archv.; Diane Matzke, Archv.Prin.; Tim Tingle, Archv.Prin.; Glen McAninch, Network Dev.Spec.; Jane Minder, Prog.Coord.; Lesley Conniff, Sr.Archv.; Lee Forrest, Archv.; Martha Froias, Comp.Oper.Anl.; Cindy Hamilton, Comp.Oper.Anl.; Suzanne Durham, Cons.Sr.; Kathy Gilliland, Rec.Anl.Prin.; Jeff Duff, Reg.Adm.; Frank R. Levstik, Reg.Adm.; Lena Jones Turner, Reg.Adm.; Gerald Thompson, Reg.Adm.

★8672★
Kentucky (State) Department for Libraries & Archives - State Library Services Division (Info Sci)
300 Coffee Tree Rd.
Box 537 Phone: (502)875-7000
Frankfort, KY 40602 William E. Paplinski, Div.Dir.
Founded: 1957. **Staff:** Prof 17; Other 18. **Subjects:** Kentucky, arts, library science. **Holdings:** 120,000 books; 76,000 documents; 5900 16mm films and

videos. **Subscriptions:** 580 journals; 9 newspapers. **Services:** Interlibrary loan; copying; division open to the public. **Automated Operations:** Computerized cataloging. **Computerized Information Services:** DIALOG Information Services, INFO-KY, VU/TEXT Information Services, DataTimes, WILSONLINE, LOCIS. **Networks/Consortia:** Member of Kentucky Library Network, Inc. (KLN). **Remarks:** FAX: (502)564-5773. **Staff:** Charlene E. Davis, Br.Mgr., Tech.Sup.; Brenda Fuller, Prin.Libn., Docs.; Martha Gregory, Br.Mgr., Pub.Serv.; Ressie Johnson, Prin.Libn., Ref.; Linda L. Sherrow, Br.Mgr., Network Dev.; Ellen Dickerson, Prin.Libn., AV.

★8673★
Kentucky (State) Department of Public Advocacy - Library (Law)
1264 Louisville Rd.
Perimeter Park West — Phone: (502)564-8006
Frankfort, KY 40601 — Barbara J. Sutherland, Libn.
Staff: Prof 1; Other 1. **Subjects:** Criminal law, juvenile case law, death penalty, protection and advocacy. **Holdings:** 10,000 books. **Subscriptions:** 30 journals and other serials. **Services:** Interlibrary loan; copying; library open to the public. **Networks/Consortia:** Member of Kentucky Library Network, Inc. (KLN). **Special Catalogs:** Catalog of DPA training materials, handouts, audio- and videotapes (book).

★8674★
Kentucky (State) Finance and Administration Cabinet - Governmental Services Center Library (Bus-Fin)
Academic Services Bldg., No. 407
Kentucky State University — Phone: (502)564-8170
Frankfort, KY 40601 — Mary Jean Reece, Chf.Ck.
Staff: 2. **Subjects:** Management, training. **Special Collections:** Cassettes featuring Earl Nightingale on management and successful living. **Holdings:** 500 books. **Services:** Library not open to the public. **Special Catalogs:** Government Services Center Catalog of Courses, biennial. **Remarks:** FAX: (502)564-2732.

★8675★
Kentucky (State) Governor's Office for Policy and Management (Bus-Fin)
Capitol Annex, Rm. 284
Frankfort, KY 40601 — Phone: (502)564-7300
Founded: 1965. **Staff:** 1. **Subjects:** Budgeting, planning and development, grants information. **Special Collections:** Background information on budgeting. **Holdings:** 4500 volumes; 5 drawer information file. **Subscriptions:** 63 journals and other serials. **Services:** Interlibrary loan; copying; library open to the public. **Remarks:** FAX: (502)564-6684.

★8676★
Kentucky State Law Library (Law)
State Capitol, Rm. 200 — Phone: (502)564-4848
Frankfort, KY 40601-3489 — Sallie M. Howard, State Law Libn.
Founded: 1954. **Staff:** Prof 3; Other 5. **Subjects:** American law. **Special Collections:** Published legal material concerning past and present practice of law in Kentucky, 25,000 State Law Library, 90,000 Judges' Chambers' A.O.C., Circuit Clerks' Libraries. **Holdings:** 140,000 books; 8470 bound periodical volumes. **Subscriptions:** 304 journals. **Services:** Copying; library open to the public. **Computerized Information Services:** LEXIS. **Publications:** Guide to Kentucky Legal Research: A State Bibliography, 1985 (2nd edition) - for sale. **Special Indexes:** Index to the Kentucky Juvenile Code, 1989; Index to Kentucky Legal History, 1983 - for sale. **Remarks:** FAX: (502)564-5491 (Attn: St. Law Lib.). Maintained by the Kentucky Court of Justice, Adminstrative Office of the Courts. **Staff:** Evelyn M. Lockwood, Res. & Cat.Libn.; Jean Collier, Staff Att.; Marjorie H. Jones, Adm. & Res.Asst.

★8677★
Kentucky State Legislative Research Commission - Library (Law, Soc Sci)
State Capitol, 4th Fl. — Phone: (502)564-8100
Frankfort, KY 40601 — Peggy D. King, Leg.Libn.
Founded: 1950. **Staff:** Prof 1.25; Other 3. **Subjects:** Law, government, public administration. **Holdings:** 10,000 volumes; 300 pamphlet boxes of state publications; 800 audiotapes. **Subscriptions:** 276 journals and other serials. **Services:** Interlibrary loan; copying; SDI; library open to the public. **Computerized Information Services:** LEGISNET, State Net 50, ISIS, CQ Washington Alert Service, OCLC. **Networks/Consortia:** Member of Kentucky Library Network, Inc. (KLN). **Special Indexes:** Index of legislation since 1950 and legislators since 1908 (card). **Remarks:** FAX: (502)223-5094. **Staff:** Celeste Moore, Cat.

Kentucky Talking Book Library
See: **Kentucky (State) Department for Libraries & Archives** (8670)

★8678★
Kentucky Wesleyan College - Library Learning Center - Special Collections (Rel-Phil, Hist)
3000 Frederica St. — Phone: (502)926-3111
Owensboro, KY 42301 — Dudley V. Yates, Dir.
Founded: 1975. **Subjects:** Kentucky United Methodist Heritage Center Historical Materials of the Louisville Conference; Methodist Church history; Kentucky Wesleyan College Archives; Dr. and Mrs. M. David Orrahood Collection of First and Rare Editions; Matsumoto Memorial Library of Japanese Culture; Dan M. King Architecture Collection. **Holdings:** 3000 books; 30 bound periodical volumes; 4 videotapes; 235 audiotapes; 150 pieces of realia; 2000 photographs; 125 volumes of clippings; 223 archival containers. **Subscriptions:** 2 journals and other serials. **Services:** Interlibrary loan; copying; collections open to the public by appointment for reference use. **Publications:** Guide to the Dr. and Mrs. David Orrahood Collection, 1979. **Special Catalogs:** Catalog of the Dan M. King Architecture Collection, 1985. **Special Indexes:** Index to the Memoirs of the Kentucky Annual Conference, 1821 to present; Index to the Louisville Annual Conference, 1845 to presen t (both obituaries); Index to Obituaries in the Central Methodist Advocate, 1872-1902 and 1908-1929; Index of Names in Minutes of the Madison (Kentucky) Circuit, 1810-1845. **Remarks:** FAX: (502)926-3196. **Staff:** Dr. Richard A. Weiss, Lib.Bibliog. & Archv.

★8679★
Kenya - Ministry of Agriculture - Central Library (Agri)
P.O. Box 30028 — Phone: 2 718870
Nairobi, Kenya — Mr. D.N. Kinyanjui
Founded: 1900. **Staff:** Prof 3; Other 8. **Subjects:** Agriculture, economics, range management, animal husbandry. **Holdings:** 172,000 books; 359 bound periodical volumes. **Subscriptions:** 28 journals and other serials; 3 newspapers. **Services:** Interlibrary loan; copying; SDI; library open to the public for reference use only. **Publications:** Accession lists. **Special Indexes:** Index to newspaper articles.

Kenya - Ministry of Research, Science & Technology - Kenya Industrial Research and Development Institute
See: **Kenya Industrial Research and Development Institute** (8680)

★8680★
Kenya Industrial Research and Development Institute - Library (Sci-Engr)
P.O. Box 30650 — Phone: 557762
Nairobi, Kenya — Paul B. Imende, Libn.
Founded: 1942. **Subjects:** Agro-industrial research, food, engineering, building materials, weather. **Holdings:** 15,000 volumes. **Subscriptions:** 56 journals and other serials; 6 newspapers. **Services:** Interlibrary loan; copying; SDI; library open to industrialists, entrepreneurs, and researchers. **Computerized Information Services:** DIALOG Information Services, ESA/IRS, CDS, ISIS; internal database; electronic mail service. **Remarks:** FAX: 505546. Alternate telephone number(s): 557728; 504866; 504867. Telex: 24225. Maintained by Kenya - Ministry of Research, Science & Technology. **Staff:** Clement Kabiru; Lucy S. Mukum; Hamn O. Rapemo.

Kenya National Archives
See: **Michigan State University - Africana Library** (10312)

Roy C. Kepler Library for Nonviolence and Social Change
See: **Resource Center for Nonviolence - Roy C. Kepler Library for Nonviolence and Social Change** (13848)

★8681★
Kern County Law Library (Law)
Courts & Administration Bldg., Rm. 301 — Phone: (805)861-2379
Bakersfield, CA 93301 — Mary J. Gaede, Act. Law Libn.
Founded: 1891. **Staff:** Prof 1; Other 2. **Subjects:** Law. **Special Collections:** State depository (selective). **Holdings:** 27,000 books; Federal Register, 1945 to present; pamphlets. **Subscriptions:** 57 journals and other serials. **Services:** Interlibrary loan (limited); copying; library open to the public for reference use only. **Computerized Information Services:** WESTLAW.

★8682★
Kern County Library System - Beale Memorial Library (Sci-Engr, Hist)
701 Truxtun Ave. Phone: (805)861-2136
Bakersfield, CA 93301 Dee Mooneyham, Spec.Coll.Libn.
Founded: 1936. **Staff:** 2. **Special Collections:** Geology, Mining and Petroleum Collection (33,327 items); Kern County Historical Collection (21,263 items). **Holdings:** 250,000 books; 160 bound periodical volumes; 12 manuscripts; 4106 reels of microfilm; 900 VF drawers. **Subscriptions:** 65 journals and other serials. **Services:** Interlibrary loan; copying; library open to the public. **Automated Operations:** DYNIX Automated Library System. **Computerized Information Services:** DIALOG Information Services, NEXIS; OnTyme Electronic Message Network Service (electronic mail service). **Networks/Consortia:** Member of San Joaquin Valley Library System (SJVLS). SI Newspaper Index (card). **Remarks:** FAX: (805)631-9439. Electronic mail address(es): CLASS.KERN (OnTyme Electronic Message Network Service). **Staff:** John Walden, Hist.Libn.; David Fuller, Geol.Coll.Libn.

★8683★
Kern County Museum - Library (Hist)
3801 Chester Ave. Phone: (805)861-2132
Bakersfield, CA 93301 David McCauley, Asst.Dir.
Founded: 1940. **Staff:** Prof 2. **Subjects:** Local history. **Holdings:** 2000 volumes; photograph archive. **Subscriptions:** 6 journals and other serials. **Services:** Copying; library open to staff and researchers by appointment. **Special Catalogs:** Subject catalog of photograph archive. **Remarks:** FAX: (805)322-6415. **Staff:** Russell Czaplewski, Cur. of Coll.

★8684★
Kern County Superintendent of Schools Office - Professional Library - Instructional Resources Center (Educ)
5801 Sundale Ave. Phone: (805)398-3764
Bakersfield, CA 93309 Laurie Maclin, Instr. Materials Cons.
Founded: 1935. **Staff:** Prof 1; Other 1. **Subjects:** Education. **Special Collections:** History of Kern County; adopted textbooks of the State of California (IMDC); elementary library collection; curriculum guides on microfiche; Phi Delta Kappa Reavis Reading Area; grantsmanship; educational computer software. **Holdings:** 10,000 books; 5000 bound periodical volumes; 10,000 films and videos; 3 cabinets of microforms; 2000 curriculum guides. **Subscriptions:** 85 journals and other serials. **Services:** Interlibrary loan; copying; center open to the public. **Automated Operations:** Computerized cataloging. **Computerized Information Services:** DIALOG Information Services, ERIC. **Publications:** New acquisitions. **Remarks:** FAX: (805)398-3698.

★8685★
Kern Medical Center - Kern Health Sciences Library (Med)
1830 Flower St. Phone: (805)326-2227
Bakersfield, CA 93305-4197 Pat Hamlett, Lib.Techn.
Staff: Prof 1; Other 2. **Subjects:** Clinical medicine, nursing, allied health sciences, hospital administration. **Holdings:** 3000 books; 11,000 bound periodical volumes; 300 audiotapes; 3500 slides. **Subscriptions:** 325 journals and other serials. **Services:** Interlibrary loan; copying; SDI; library open to the public with restrictions. **Computerized Information Services:** MEDLINE, BRS Information Technologies; OnTyme Electronic Message Network Service, DOCLINE (electronic mail services).

★8686★
Kerr Manufacturing Company - Research Library (Sci-Engr)
28200 Wick Rd. Phone: (313)946-7800
Romulus, MI 48174-0908 Bob Wrona, Libn.
Founded: 1891. **Staff:** Prof 1. **Subjects:** Dental materials; dentistry; chemical research; polymers - silicon, composites; amalgam alloys. **Special Collections:** U.S. patents - dentistry (abstracted; 1930 to present). **Holdings:** 2000 books; 200 reports; 400 microfiche; 50 reels of microfilm; 20,000 unbound periodicals. **Subscriptions:** 20 journals and other serials; 2 newspapers. **Services:** Interlibrary loan; copying; library open to the public by appointment. **Automated Operations:** Computerized cataloging. **Computerized Information Services:** DIALOG Information Services, OCLC; internal databases. **Publications:** Kerr Patent Update. **Remarks:** FAX: (313)946-8316. Telex: 0230132.

★8687★
Kerr-McGee Corporation - McGee Library (Sci-Engr, Energy)
Box 25861 Phone: (405)270-3367
Oklahoma City, OK 73125 Virginia Phillips, Mgr.
Founded: 1948. **Staff:** Prof 3; Other 2. **Subjects:** Geology, energy, mineral deposits, petroleum technology, economics, business. **Holdings:** 13,000 books; 16,000 documents; 6000 maps. **Subscriptions:** 600 journals and other serials. **Services:** Interlibrary loan; library not open to the public. **Automated Operations:** Computerized cataloging. **Computerized Information Services:** DIALOG Information Services, ORBIT Search Service, STN International, Dow Jones News/Retrieval, NLM, RLIN, DRI/McGraw-Hill, Reuters Information Services (Canada), Data-Star, Info Globe; internal database. **Publications:** New Publications Received in the McGee Library, monthly - for internal distribution only. **Remarks:** Alternate telephone number(s): 270-3358. FAX: (405)270-3123. **Staff:** Vicki Vann, Libn.; Marilynn Rhone, Asst.Libn.

★8688★
Kerr-McGee Corporation - Technical Center Library (Bus-Fin)
Box 25861 Phone: (405)775-5619
Oklahoma City, OK 73125 Evelyn Du Bose, Info.Spec.
Founded: 1963. **Staff:** Prof 1; Other 2. **Subjects:** Chemical engineering. **Special Collections:** Chemical patents (500,000); Chemical Abstracts (Volume 1 to present). **Holdings:** 7500 books; 3500 bound periodical volumes; 5000 corporate reports. **Subscriptions:** 250 journals and other serials. **Services:** Library not open to the public. **Automated Operations:** Computerized cataloging, circulation, and serials. **Computerized Information Services:** DIALOG Information Services, PFDS Online, STN International; Datalib (internal database). **Remarks:** FAX: (405)775-5632. Library located at 3301 N.W. 150th, Oklahoma City, OK 73134.

Robert S. Kerr Environmental Research Laboratory
See: **U.S. Environmental Protection Agency** (17482)

William Jasper Kerr Library
See: **Oregon State University** (12553)

★8689★
Kerrville State Hospital - Professional Library (Med)
721 Thompson Dr. Phone: (512)896-2211
Kerrville, TX 78028 Dana L. White, Libn.
Staff: Prof 1. **Subjects:** Geriatrics, psychology, medicine, nursing, social studies. **Holdings:** 1800 books; audio cassettes. **Subscriptions:** 49 journals and other serials. **Services:** Interlibrary loan; library open to the public at librarian's discretion. **Computerized Information Services:** CD-ROM (MEDLINE). **Networks/Consortia:** Member of Health Oriented Libraries of San Antonio (HOLSA). **Remarks:** FAX: (512)792-4926. Telex: (512)825-6283.

Kersey Library
See: **University of Louisville** (18770)

★8690★
Kershaw County Applied Technology Education Campus - Vocational-Technical Library (Educ)
874 Vocational Ln. Phone: (803)425-8980
Camden, SC 29020 Mollye Robinson, Libn.
Founded: 1970. **Staff:** 2. **Special Collections:** Careers and Occupations; MECC (computer) software; High School Textbooks; V-TEC Catalogs. **Holdings:** 5000 books. **Subscriptions:** 80 journals and other serials; 2 newspapers. **Services:** Library open to the public. **Formerly:** Kershaw County Vocational Center.

★8691★
Kesher Zion Synagogue and Sisterhood - Library (Rel-Phil)
1245 Perkiomen Ave. Phone: (215)374-1763
Reading, PA 19602 Rachel Yaffee, Libn.
Staff: Prof 1. **Subjects:** Judaica. **Holdings:** 2500 books. **Services:** Library open to the public with restrictions.

Kesler Circulating Library
See: **Vanderbilt University - Jean and Alexander Heard Library - Divinity Library** (19770)

★8692★
Ketchum Communications Inc. - Ketchum Library Services (Bus-Fin)
Six PPG Place Phone: (412)456-3977
Pittsburgh, PA 15222 Florence V. Merkel, Lib.Supv.
Founded: 1949. **Staff:** Prof 1. **Subjects:** Advertising, marketing, general reference. **Holdings:** 1100 books; 40 VF drawers of marketing material; reference collection; annual reports. **Subscriptions:** 450 journals and other serials. **Services:** Interlibrary loan. **Computerized Information Services:** DIALOG Information Services, Mead Data Central, Dow Jones News/Retrieval, VU/TEXT Information Services. **Special Indexes:** KLS Users' Manual. **Remarks:** FAX: (412)456-3834.

M.B. Ketchum Memorial Library
See: **Southern California College of Optometry** (15466)

★8693★
Ketron, Inc. - Library
1700 N. Moore St.
Arlington, VA 22209
Defunct.

★8694★
Kettering College of Medical Arts - Learning Resources Center (Med)
3737 Southern Blvd. Phone: (513)296-7201
Kettering, OH 45429 Sheila Shellabarger, Dir.
Founded: 1967. **Staff:** Prof 2; Other 7. **Subjects:** Nursing, allied health sciences. **Holdings:** 53,513 volumes; 6289 AV programs. **Subscriptions:** 507 journals and other serials. **Services:** Interlibrary loan; copying; center open to the public. **Automated Operations:** Computerized cataloging and circulation. **Computerized Information Services:** Online systems; internal database. **Networks/Consortia:** Member of National Network of Libraries of Medicine - Greater Midwest Region, Southwestern Ohio Council for Higher Education (SOCHE).

★8695★
Kettering Medical Center Hospital - Medical Library (Med)
3535 Southern Blvd. Phone: (513)298-4331
Kettering, OH 45429 Dr. Joseph P. Stoia, Lib.Dir.
Founded: 1964. **Staff:** Prof 4; Other 1. **Subjects:** Medicine, allied health sciences. **Special Collections:** Consumer health education; health care administration. **Holdings:** 9000 books; 17,000 bound periodical volumes; 3776 AV programs; 47,000 microfiche. **Subscriptions:** 660 journals and other serials; 3 newspapers. **Services:** Interlibrary loan; copying; SDI. **Computerized Information Services:** DIALOG Information Services, MEDLINE, BRS Information Technologies, WILSONLINE, LEXIS, NEXIS. Performs searches on fee basis for non-primary clientel. **Special Catalogs:** Union list of serials; union list of audiovisuals. **Remarks:** Maintains 40 departmental collections and a branch library at Sycamore Medical Center. **Staff:** Lydia Chuang; Tony Gibbons; Jane Buch; Donna Lawrence.

Olive Kettering Library
See: **Antioch/New England Graduate School - Professional Resource Center** (898)

★8696★
Kewanee Historical Society - Library (Hist)
211 N. Chestnut St. Phone: (309)854-9701
Kewanee, IL 61443 Marcella Richards, Cur.
Founded: 1976. **Subjects:** Local history - Kewanee, factory, business, people. **Special Collections:** Corn Huskers Hall of Fame Collection (12 books). **Holdings:** 175 scrap books. **Services:** Library open to the public.

★8697★
Francis Scott Key Medical Center - Harold E. Harrison Library (Med)
4940 Eastern Ave. Phone: (301)955-0678
Baltimore, MD 21224 Rebecca A. Charton, Libn.
Founded: 1935. **Staff:** Prof 1; Other 3. **Subjects:** Medicine. **Holdings:** 3503 books; 16,750 bound periodical volumes. **Subscriptions:** 364 journals and other serials. **Services:** Interlibrary loan; copying; SDI; library open to medical, nursing, and paramedical personnel only.

Asa Keyes Medical Library
See: **Brattleboro Retreat** (2088)

★8698★
Keyes Associates - Library (Sci-Engr)
10 Lincoln Center Blvd. Phone: (401)333-0100
Lincoln, RI 02865 Abby Davis, Libn.
Staff: Prof 1. **Subjects:** Engineering - environmental, civil, structural, mechanical, electrical; architecture; landscape and interior design. **Holdings:** 3000 books; 650 specifications and reports; 300 VF drawers of project files. **Subscriptions:** 200 journals and other serials. **Services:** Interlibrary loan; library open to public by permission of librarian. **Publications:** Current Acquisitions List, bimonthly - for internal distribution only. **Remarks:** FAX: (401)333-4556.

★8699★
Keystone Carbon Company - Library
1935 State St. Phone: (814)781-4350
St. Marys, PA 15857 Mary Ann Fritz, Libn.
Holdings: 2000 books; bound periodical volumes; reports; patents. **Services:** Library not open to the public. **Remarks:** FAX: (814)781-3893. Telex: 91 4517.

★8700★
Keystone Custodian Funds, Inc. - Library (Bus-Fin)
99 High St. Phone: (617)338-3435
Boston, MA 02110 Kathleen Young, Libn.
Staff: 1. **Subjects:** Business and statistics. **Holdings:** 300 books. **Subscriptions:** 100 journals and other serials; 11 newspapers. **Services:** Library not open to the public.

Keystone Job Corps Center Research Facility
See: **RCA Service Company** (13738)

★8701★
Keystone Press Agency, Inc. - Picture Library (Aud-Vis)
202 E. 42nd St. Phone: (212)924-8123
New York, NY 10017 Satoko Alpert, Photo Libn.
Founded: 1914. **Staff:** Prof 1; Other 1. **Subjects:** Photographs of all aspects of life with worldwide coverage. **Special Collections:** Picture material for educational publications. **Holdings:** Several million black/white and color photographs. **Services:** Library not open to the public. **Remarks:** FAX: (212)924-8123.

★8702★
Keystone State Consultants - Library (Sci-Engr)
Box 5071 Phone: (215)742-5107
Philadelphia, PA 19111 R. Krauss, Cons.
Subjects: Firearms, ammunition, explosives, forensics. **Holdings:** 3500 volumes. **Remarks:** Telex: 4996139.

Keystone University Research Corporation - Northwest Institute of Research
See: **Northwest Institute of Research** (12053)

Aga Khan Program in Islamic Architecture - Documentation Center
See: **Harvard University - Fine Arts Library** (6965)

★8703★
(Khartoum) American Center - USIS Library (Educ)
Plot No. 2, 4G
Post Box 699
Khartoum East, Sudan
Remarks: Maintained or supported by the U.S. Information Agency. Focus is on materials that will assist peoples outside the United States to learn about the United States, its people, history, culture, political processes, and social milieux.

Ma Kiam Library
See: **University of Virginia - Special Collections Department** (19510)

Ada M. Kidder Memorial Library
See: **Houghton College - Buffalo Extension Campus** (7433)

★8704★
Kidder, Peabody & Co. Incorporated - Library (Bus-Fin)
10 Hanover Square, 4th Fl. Phone: (212)510-4250
New York, NY 10005 Nancy I. Cohen, Libn.
Founded: 1962. **Staff:** Prof 10; Other 8. **Subjects:** Finance, investments, business conditions, economics. **Holdings:** Figures not available. **Services:** Interlibrary loan (to SLA members only); library not open to the public. **Automated Operations:** Computerized cataloging and acquisitions. **Computerized Information Services:** DIALOG Information Services, NEXIS, Dow Jones News/Retrieval, MAID (Market Analysis and Information Database), VU/TEXT Information Services, InvesText, Reuter TEXTLINE, Info Globe, DataTimes; CD-ROMs (Compact Disclosure, Lotus One Source, LaserDisclosure, Dun's Million Dollar Disc, Moody's International). **Staff:** Cecelia Beekman, Res.Serv.Mgr.; Shawn Speller, Sr.Ref.Libn.; Eileen Holst-Grubbe, Doc.Serv.Mgr.; Robert DiFede, Ref.Libn.; Rebecca Caponi, Ref.Libn.; Frank Dell'Aquila, Ref.Libn.; Wendy Kleinberg, Ref.Libn.; Barbara Fiorillo, Tech.Serv.Libn.

Kideney Health Sciences Library
See: **Millard Fillmore Hospitals - Kideney Health Sciences Library** (5692)

Kiehle Library
See: **University of Minnesota, Crookston** (18938)

Kienbusch Library of Arms and Armour
See: **Philadelphia Museum of Art - Library** (12990)

★8705★
Kilborn, Ltd. - Library
2200 Lakeshore Blvd., W. Phone: (416)252-5311
Toronto, ON, Canada M8V 1A4 Terry Milley, Exec.Sec.
Remarks: No further information was supplied by respondent.

★8706★
Izaak Walton Killam Hospital for Children - Health Sciences Library (Med)
5850 University Ave. Phone: (902)428-8238
Halifax, NS, Canada B3J 3G9 Darlene Chapman, Libn.
Founded: 1970. **Staff:** Prof 1. **Subjects:** Medicine, allied health. **Holdings:** 900 books; 125 titles; 300 audiotapes. **Subscriptions:** 150 journals and other serials. **Services:** Interlibrary loan; copying; SDI; library open to the public with restrictions. **Automated Operations:** Computerized cataloging. **Computerized Information Services:** MEDLARS; Envoy 100 (electronic mail service). **Publications:** IWK Library News, monthly - for internal distribution only; union list of serials (Halifax hospitals), irregular.

Kilner Library
See: **Kenilworth Historical Society** (8618)

★8707★
Kilpatrick & Cody - Library (Law)
3100 Equitable Bldg.
100 Peachtree St. Phone: (404)572-6397
Atlanta, GA 30303 Claire Engel, Dir., Lib.Serv.
Founded: 1904. **Staff:** Prof 4; Other 4. **Subjects:** Law. **Holdings:** 45,000 books; 2000 bound periodical volumes; 10,000 microfiche; 300 reels of microfilm. **Subscriptions:** 240 journals and other serials; 10 newspapers. **Services:** Interlibrary loan; library not open to the public. **Computerized Information Services:** DIALOG Information Services, Information America, WESTLAW, LEXIS, IMSMARQ, DunsPrint, LEGI-SLATE, OCLC. Performs searches on fee basis. **Networks/Consortia:** Member of CCLC. **Publications:** Newsletter, monthly. **Remarks:** FAX: (404)572-6555. **Staff:** Louise Cherry, Ref.Libn.; Kathy Croslin, Ref.Libn.; Susan Jenks, Ref.Libn.

Fiske Kimball Fine Arts Library
See: **University of Virginia - Fiske Kimball Fine Arts Library** (19503)

★8708★
Kimbell Art Museum - Library (Art)
3333 Camp Bowie Blvd. Phone: (817)332-8451
Fort Worth, TX 76107 Chia-Chun Shih, Libn.
Founded: 1967. **Staff:** Prof 2; Other 1. **Subjects:** Artists, art history, art. **Holdings:** 31,700 books; 3000 bound periodical volumes; 2410 microfiche; auction catalogs. **Subscriptions:** 98 journals and other serials. **Services:** Interlibrary loan; copying; library open to the public by appointment. **Automated Operations:** Computerized cataloging. **Computerized Information Services:** DIALOG Information Services, RLIN. **Networks/Consortia:** Member of Research Libraries Information Network (RLIN). **Remarks:** FAX: (817)877-1264.

★8709★
Kimberly-Clark Corporation - Library (Sci-Engr)
2100 Winchester Rd.
P.O. Box 999 Phone: (414)721-5261
Neenah, WI 54957-0999 Mary E. Sutliff, Tech.Libn.
Staff: Prof 1; Other 3. **Subjects:** Paper technology and chemistry, engineering, biomedical sciences, business and management. **Holdings:** 6500 books; 3000 bound periodical volumes; 7500 pamphlets. **Subscriptions:** 450 journals and other serials; 10 newspapers. **Services:** Library not open to the public. **Computerized Information Services:** PFDS Online, Mead Data Central.

★8710★
Kimberly-Clark Corporation - Technical Library (Sci-Engr)
1400 Holcomb Bridge Rd. Phone: (404)587-7878
Roswell, GA 30201 Jaye Peklo, Tech.Libn.
Founded: 1981. **Staff:** Prof 2; Other 2. **Subjects:** Nonwoven textiles, polymers, pulp and paper, health care, engineering, chemistry. **Holdings:** 3000 books. **Subscriptions:** 400 journals. **Services:** Interlibrary loan; library not open to the public. **Computerized Information Services:** DIALOG Information Services, MEDLARS, STN International. **Networks/Consortia:** Member of Georgia Online Database (GOLD). **Remarks:** FAX: (404)587-7228.

★8711★
Kindel & Anderson - Library (Law)
555 S. Flower St., 29th Fl. Phone: (213)680-2222
Los Angeles, CA 90071-2498 Monica E. Hamor, Law Libn.
Staff: 3. **Subjects:** Law - corporate, probate, state and federal trial practice and tax, labor, securities. **Holdings:** 22,000 books; 400 bound periodical volumes. **Services:** Library not open to the public. **Automated Operations:** Computerized cataloging and serials. **Computerized Information Services:** LEXIS, WESTLAW, DIALOG Information Services, Dow Jones News/Retrieval, RLIN, VU/TEXT Information Services, AdvanceLine, LEGI-SLATE. **Remarks:** FAX: (213)688-7564. Telex: 67 7497.

★8712★
King County Law Library (Law)
W621 County Courthouse Phone: (206)296-0940
Seattle, WA 98104 James J. McArdle, Libn.
Founded: 1915. **Staff:** Prof 3; Other 2. **Subjects:** Law. **Holdings:** 85,000 books; 4700 bound periodical volumes. **Subscriptions:** 200 journals and other serials. **Services:** Copying; library open to the public. **Staff:** Alan B. Anderson, Asst.Libn.; Richard L. Stroup, Asst.Libn.

King/Drew Medical Center
See: **Los Angeles County/King/Drew Medical Center** (9332)

Emma B. King Library
See: **Shaker Museum and Library** (15067)

King George III Memorial Library
See: **Monarchist League of Canada - Centre for Monarchical Studies - King George III Memorial Library** (10601)

★8713★
King of Glory Lutheran Church - Library (Rel-Phil)
2201 E. 106th St.
Carmel, IN 46032 Phone: (317)846-1555
Founded: 1965. **Staff:** 1. **Subjects:** Bible, religions, personal fulfillment. **Holdings:** 3000 books. **Services:** Library not open to the public. **Publications:** Trumpet (newsletter), biweekly - for internal distribution only.

Margaret I. King Library
See: **University of Kentucky** (18752)

★8714★
Martin Luther King, Jr. Center for Nonviolent Social Change, Inc. - King Library and Archives (Soc Sci, Area-Ethnic)
449 Auburn Ave. Phone: (404)524-1956
Atlanta, GA 30312 Dr. Marshia Turner, Libn.
Founded: 1968. **Staff:** Prof 1; Other 2. **Subjects:** Dr. Martin Luther King, Jr., Civil Rights Movement, African-American history, nonviolence, African-American religion, African-American politics. **Special Collections:** Bilingual materials by Martin Luther King, Jr.; organizational records of the SCLC (1954-1970); SNCL (1959-1972); CORE (1944-1968); MFDP (1964-1965); Delta Ministry (1963-1971); National Lawyers Guild (1936-1968); ESCRU (1959-1970); CCCO (1964-1968); USNSA (1957-1969); Personal papers of Martin Luther King, Jr. (1954-1968), Fred Shuttleworth (1953-1969), Johnnie Carr (1956-1979) and Julian Bond (1964-1968). **Holdings:** 4000 books; over 1 million documents focusing primarily on the American civil rights movement. **Services:** Copying; library open to the public. **Publications:** Martin Luther King Center Newsletter, quarterly; library holdings and services brochures. **Remarks:** Archives are dedicated to the documentation of the post-1954 Civil Rights Movement with emphasis on the life and work of Martin Luther King, Jr. and the nonviolent movement which continues. **Staff:** Diane Ware, Ref.Archv.

★8715★
Martin Luther King, Jr. Library - (Accra) USIS Collection (Educ)
Independence Ave.
Post Box 2288 Phone: 21 229179
Accra, Ghana A.C.K. Akpalu, Libn.
Founded: 1957. **Staff:** 5. **Subjects:** United States - history, politics and government, literature, art. **Special Collections:** African-American Collection. **Holdings:** 6400 books; 62 bound periodical volumes. **Subscriptions:** 3 newspapers. **Services:** Interlibrary loan; copying; SDI; library open to the public. **Remarks:** FAX: 21 776008. Alternate telephone number(s): 21 229829; 21 229882. Telex: 2579 EBUSA GH. Maintained or supported by the U.S. Information Agency. Focus is on materials that will assist peoples outside the United States to learn about the United States, its people, history, culture, political processes, and social milieux. **Formerly:** (Accra) American Center - USIS Library. **Staff:** E.A. Hanson, Asst.Libn.

Martin Luther King, Jr. National Historic Site
See: **U.S. Natl. Park Service** (17748)

★8716★
Martin Luther King Library - American Cultural Center - (Lusaka) USIS Library (Educ)
Veritas House
Heroes Place
Post Box 32053
Lusaka, Zambia
Remarks: Maintained or supported by the U.S. Information Agency. Focus is on materials that will assist peoples outside the United States to learn about the United States, its people, history, culture, political processes, and social milieux.

Mary Ann King Health Sciences Library
See: **Fairview Southdale Hospital** (5576)

★8717★
King Research, Inc. - Library (Info Sci)
1010 Rockville Pike, Suite 501
Rockville, MD 20852 Phone: (301)738-1341
Subjects: Information and library science, and allied subjects. **Holdings:** 300 bound volumes; 1500 technical reports. **Subscriptions:** 20 journals and other serials. **Remarks:** FAX: (301)738-6857.

★8718★
King & Spalding - Law Library (Law)
191 Peachtree St. Phone: (404)572-4600
Atlanta, GA 30303 Mary Anne C. Fry, Dir., Info.Serv.
Staff: Prof 6; Other 4. **Subjects:** Law - corporate, antitrust, real estate, tax, banking, labor, international, general litigation. **Holdings:** 40,000 volumes. **Services:** Interlibrary loan; library not open to the public. **Automated Operations:** Computerized cataloging, acquisitions, and serials routing. **Computerized Information Services:** DIALOG Information Services, WESTLAW, LEXIS, Information America, VU/TEXT Information Services, Dun & Bradstreet Business Credit Services. **Staff:** Glenda Chastain, Hd.Libn.

★8719★
King Stephen Museum - Library (Soc Sci)
Orszagzaszlo ter 3
Pf. 78
H-8002 Szekesfehervar, Hungary Phone: 22 15583
Founded: 1873. **Staff:** 3. **Subjects:** Archeology, ethnography, art, local history. **Holdings:** 40,000 books; 20,000 bound periodical volumes. **Subscriptions:** 60 journals and other serials. **Services:** Interlibrary loan; copying; library open to the public for reference use only. **Publications:** Alba Regia yearbook. **Special Catalogs:** Exhibition catalogs. **Remarks:** Alternate telephone number(s): 22 29506. **Also Known As:** Istvan Kiraly Muzeum - Konyvtar. **Staff:** Jeno Fitz, Co-Dir. of Musm.; Peter Kovacs, Co-Dir. of Musm.

Kingdon Library
See: **University of King's College** (18760)

★8720★
Kingman Museum of Natural History - Library (Biol Sci)
W. Michigan Ave. at 20th St. Phone: (616)965-5117
Battle Creek, MI 49017 Debbie Smith, Cur. of Coll.
Staff: Prof 4. **Subjects:** Ecology, geology, astronomy, ethnology, botany, zoology, museum studies. **Holdings:** 1463 books. **Subscriptions:** 64 journals and other serials. **Services:** Library open to the public. **Staff:** D. Thomas Johnson, Cur. of Exhibits; Paul Rheaume, Cur./Prog.; Robert Learner, Dir.

Kingman Tavern Historical Museum
See: **Cummington Historical Commission - Kingman Tavern Historical Museum** (4481)

★8721★
King's College - D. Leonard Corgan Library (Hist)
14 W. Jackson St. Phone: (717)826-5641
Wilkes-Barre, PA 18711 Judith Tierney, Spec.Coll.Libn.
Founded: 1946. **Staff:** Prof 5; Other 8. **Subjects:** Folklore; Daniel J. Flood; coal mines and mining; Wyoming Valley, PA history. **Special Collections:** The George Korson Folklore Archive (books; records; 42 linear feet of personal papers; 107 reels of tape); Daniel J. Flood Collection (600 linear feet of public and private papers); collections on Wyoming Valley, PA. **Holdings:** Figures not available. **Services:** Library open to the public by appointment. **Publications:** A Description of the George Korson Folklore Archive; Daniel J. Flood, A Register of His Papers. **Remarks:** Headquarters of Northeastern Pennsylvania Bibliographic Center.

King's College Library
See: **University of King's College** (18760)

Kings County Hospital - Psychiatry Library
See: **State University Health Science Center at Brooklyn - Department of Psychiatry Library** (15717)

★8722★
Kings County Law Library (Law)
County Government Center
1400 W. Lacey Blvd. Phone: (209)582-3211
Hanford, CA 93230 Cheryll Lehn, Law Libn.
Founded: 1893. **Subjects:** Law. **Holdings:** 11,650 volumes. **Services:** Library open to the public for reference use only.

Kings Mountain National Military Park
See: **U.S. Natl. Park Service** (17740)

★8723★
Kings Park Psychiatric Center - KPPC Medical Library (Med)
Box 9000 Phone: (516)544-3207
Kings Park, NY 11754 Judith Sartori, Sr.Libn.
Founded: 1959. **Staff:** Prof 1. **Subjects:** Psychiatry, nursing, medicine, allied health sciences. **Special Collections:** Collection in psychiatry. **Holdings:** 7000 books; 1000 bound periodical volumes; 15 VF drawers of pamphlets; 1000 audiotapes. **Subscriptions:** 70 journals and other serials. **Services:** Interlibrary loan; library not open to the public. **Computerized Information Services:** CD-ROMs (DIALOG OnDisc, MEDLINE). **Networks/Consortia:** Member of Medical & Scientific Libraries of Long Island (MEDLI), Long Island Library Resources Council. **Remarks:** Alternate telephone number(s): (516)544-1076.

★8724★
Kingsboro Psychiatric Center - Health Sci Library (Med)
681 Clarkson Ave. Phone: (718)221-7273
Brooklyn, NY 11203-2199 Basheva Blokh, Dir., Hea.Sci.Lib.
Founded: 1895. **Staff:** Prof 1; Other 1. **Subjects:** Psychiatry, medicine, psychology, rehabilitation, social service, nursing. **Holdings:** 3000 books; 4 VF files of pamphlets and clippings; 258 tape cassettes. **Subscriptions:** 144 journals and other serials. **Services:** Interlibrary loan; copying; SDI; library open to the public for reference use only. **Computerized Information Services:** MEDLINE, BRS Information Technologies. Performs searches free of charge. **Networks/Consortia:** Member of Brooklyn-Queens-Staten Island Health Sciences Librarians (BQSI), BHSL. **Publications:** Library bulletins and bibliographies. **Remarks:** FAX: (718)221-7206.

★8725★
Kingsborough Community College of City University of New York - Kingsborough Historical Society - Library (Hist)
2001 Oriental Blvd. Phone: (718)368-5122
Brooklyn, NY 11235 John B. Manbeck, Archv.
Founded: 1970. **Staff:** Prof 2; Other 2. **Subjects:** Brooklyn, New York history. **Special Collections:** Old and new photographs of Coney Island and Manhattan Beach. **Holdings:** 100 books; photographs; clippings; newspapers; pamphlets; color slides; films music. **Subscriptions:** 18 journals and other serials. **Services:** Interlibrary loan; library open to the public. **Remarks:** Alternate telephone number(s): 368-5849; 368-5259. **Staff:** Lorraine Tondi, Dir./Res.

★8726★
Kingsbrook Jewish Medical Center - Medical Library (Med)
585 Schenectady Ave. Phone: (718)604-5689
Brooklyn, NY 11203-1891 Mary E. Buchheit, Dir., Med.Lib.
Founded: 1925. **Staff:** Prof 1; Other 3. **Subjects:** Pathology, neurology, orthopedics, rehabilitative medicine, clinical medicine. **Holdings:** 4900 books; 7200 bound periodical volumes. **Subscriptions:** 272 journals and other serials. **Services:** Interlibrary loan; library not open to the public. **Computerized Information Services:** NLM, MEDLARS; DOCLINE (electronic mail service).

★8727★
(Kingston) American Center - USIS Library (Educ)
2 Oxford Rd.
P.O. Box 541
Kingston 5, Jamaica
Remarks: Maintained or supported by the U.S. Information Agency. Focus is on materials that will assist peoples outside the United States to learn about the United States, its people, history, culture, political processes, and social milieux.

★8728★
Kingston General Hospital - Hospital Library (Med)
76 Stuart St. Phone: (613)548-3232
Kingston, ON, Canada K7L 2V7 Margaret Darling, Lib.Mgr.
Founded: 1961. **Staff:** Prof 1; Other 1. **Subjects:** Medicine, surgery, nursing, nutrition, laboratory technology, rehabilitative medicine, administration, respiratory technology. **Holdings:** 1400 books; 2000 bound periodical volumes. **Subscriptions:** 190 journals and other serials. **Services:** Interlibrary loan; copying; library open to hospital staff. **Computerized Information Services:** MEDLARS, DIALOG Information Services, INFOHEALTH; internal database. Performs searches on fee basis.

★8729★
Kingston Hospital - Library (Med)
396 Broadway Phone: (914)331-3131
Kingston, NY 12401 Ann Blish, Libn.
Staff: Prof 1. **Subjects:** Medicine, nursing. **Holdings:** 850 books; 4 VF drawers of articles and bibliographies. **Subscriptions:** 123 journals and other serials. **Services:** Interlibrary loan; copying; library open to the public with restrictions. **Computerized Information Services:** MEDLINE. Performs searches on fee basis. **Networks/Consortia:** Member of Southeastern New York Library Resources Council (SENYLRC), Health Information Libraries of Westchester (HILOW), BHSL. **Remarks:** FAX: (914)331-3238.

★8730★
Kingston Polytechnic - Canbury Park Centre Library (Sci-Engr)
Canbury Park Rd Phone: 1549 0151
Kingston upon Thames, Greater London KT2 6LA, England Rob James
Founded: 1969. **Subjects:** Engineering - aeronautical, civil, mechanical, production. **Holdings:** 35,000 books; 7500 bound periodical volumes; 5000 reports; 5000 microfiche; 160 reels of microfilm. **Subscriptions:** 80 journals and other serials; 5 newspapers. **Services:** Interlibrary loan; copying; library open to the public. **Computerized Information Services:** DIALOG Information Services, ESA/IRS; CD-ROMs (COMPENDEX, PERINORM).

★8731★
Kingston Polytechnic - Knights Park Centre - Library (Art)
Kingston-Upon-Thames Phone: 81 5477057
Surrey KT1 2OJ, England Alan Kent
Staff: Prof 3; Other 3. **Subjects:** Fine art, architecture, interior design, fashion, graphics, photography, film. **Special Collections:** Slide collection (300,000); illustrations (150,000); autographed book collection (4000); video collection (200); record collection (12,000); map collection (1000). **Holdings:** 45,000 books; 400 bound periodical volumes. **Subscriptions:** 200 journals and other serials; 4 newspapers. **Services:** Interlibrary loan; copying; library open to the public with restrictions. **Computerized Information Services:** CD-ROMs; JANET (electronic mail service). **Publications:** Various bibliographies. **Remarks:** FAX: 81 5477011. Electronic mail address(es): Library@Kingston (JANET).

★8732★
Kingston Psychiatric Hospital - Staff Library (Med)
Bag 603 Phone: (613)546-1101
Kingston, ON, Canada K7L 4X3 Karen Gagnon, Libn.
Staff: Prof 1.**Subjects:** Psychiatry, psychology, medicine, nursing, social work, occupational therapy. **Holdings:** 2741 books; 4639 bound periodical volumes; 3 VF drawers of clippings and pamphlets; 418 audiocassettes; 40 videos. **Subscriptions:** 110 journals and other serials. **Services:** Interlibrary loan; copying; library open to the public. **Computerized Information Services:** MEDLARS, DIALOG Information Services, CAN/OLE; Envoy 100 (electronic mail service). **Publications:** Recent Library Additions, 6/year - for internal distribution, university psychiatry department, and residents. **Remarks:** FAX: (613)548-5588. Electronic mail address(es): ILL.OKPH (Envoy 100). Maintained by Ontario Ministry of Health - Mental Health Division.

★8733★
Kingwood Center - Library (Biol Sci)
900 Park Ave., W. Phone: (419)522-0211
Mansfield, OH 44906 William W. Collins, Educ.Coord./Libn.
Founded: 1953. **Staff:** Prof 1. **Subjects:** Horticulture, natural history. **Special Collections:** Significant 17th-19th century herbals and gardening books; current literature. **Holdings:** 8200 books; 500 bound periodical volumes; 12 VF drawers of pamphlets, pictures, clippings; 600 current seed and nursery catalogs. **Subscriptions:** 100 journals and other serials. **Services:** Interlibrary loan; copying; library open to the public. **Publications:** Kingwood Center News.

★8734★
A.M. Kinney Inc. - Library (Sci-Engr)
2900 Vernon Place Phone: (513)281-2900
Cincinnati, OH 45219 Ann Guy, Libn.
Founded: 1929. **Staff:** Prof 1. **Subjects:** Chemistry, engineering, architecture. **Holdings:** 10,000 volumes. **Subscriptions:** 200 journals and other serials. **Services:** Interlibrary loan; library not open to the public. **Automated Operations:** Computerized circulation. **Remarks:** FAX: (513)281-1123.

★8735★
Kino Community Hospital - Library (Med)
2800 E. Ajo Way Phone: (602)294-4471
Tucson, AZ 85713 Barbara Edwards, Act.Libn.
Founded: 1959. **Staff:** 1. **Subjects:** Human anatomy, physiology, biochemistry, pharmacology, bacteriology and immunology, pathology, psychiatry, nursing, radiology, obstetrics/gynecology, geriatrics, gastrointerology. **Holdings:** 1344 books. **Subscriptions:** 55 journals and other serials. **Services:** Interlibrary loan; library not open to the public.

Kino Institute Library
See: **Diocese of Phoenix** (4881)

Harry L. Kinsel Library
See: **Metcalf & Eddy, Inc.** (10178)

★8736★
Kinsey Institute for Research in Sex, Gender & Reproduction, Inc. - Library and Information Service (Soc Sci, Med)
313 Morrison Hall
Indiana University
Bloomington, IN 47405 Phone: (812)855-7686
Founded: 1947. **Staff:** Prof 2. **Subjects:** Sexual behavior and attitudes, erotic literature and art, gender, reproduction. **Special Collections:** Multimedia/nonbook sex-related materials; unpublished behavioral data. **Holdings:** 75,000 books, reprints, bound periodical volumes; 39 VF drawers; 209 reels of microfilm; 105 tapes; 108 phonograph records; 3500 objects; 55,000 photographs; 5000 slides; 6500 films. **Subscriptions:** 100 journals and other serials. **Services:** Copying (limited); library open to qualified scholars. **Automated Operations:** Computerized public access catalog. **Computerized Information Services:** Internal reference databases; BITNET (electronic mail service). **Remarks:** FAX: (812)855-8277. Electronic mail address(es): harlerm@iubacs (BITNET). **Staff:** Maggie Harter, Hd. of Info.Serv.; Liana Zhou, Hd. of Tech.Serv.

★8737★
Kinsey's On The Move - Family Archives (Hist)
664 S. 1st Ave. Phone: (303)659-4232
Brighton, CO 80601 Janice R. Kinsey Dodd, Ed.
Founded: 1983. **Staff:** 1. **Subjects:** Genealogy. **Holdings:** 200 volumes; family group files; photographs; maps; journals; area histories. **Services:** Copying; library open by appointment only for genealogists. **Publications:** Kinsey's On The Move (newsletter), quarterly. **Remarks:** Provides information on families bearing the surname Kinsey. **Staff:** Judy K. Kinsey Brooks.

★8738★
(Kinshasa) Centre Culturel Americain - USIS Library (Educ)
Blvd. du Trente Juin
B.P. 8622
Kinshasa, Zaire
Remarks: Maintained or supported by the U.S. Information Agency. Focus is on materials that will assist peoples outside the United States to learn about the United States, its people, history, culture, political processes, and social milieux.

★8739★
Kinsmen Rehabilitation Foundation of British Columbia - Library Information Services (Med)
2256 W. 12th Ave. Phone: (604)736-8841
Vancouver, BC, Canada V6K 4L2 Katheleen M. Ellis, Libn.
Founded: 1980. **Staff:** Prof 1; Other 2. **Subjects:** Physical disabilities, independent living, equipment and services for people with disabilities, accessibility, attitudes. **Holdings:** 2300 books; 130 equipment catalogs; 1400 equipment/service brochures; 4000 computer records; 100 AV programs; 18 multimedia kits. **Subscriptions:** 130 journals and other serials. **Services:** Interlibrary loan; copying; library open to the public. **Automated Operations:** Computerized public access catalog, cataloging, and acquisitions. **Computerized Information Services:** KRIS (internal database); Envoy 100 (electronic mail services). Performs searches free of charge for people with disabilities. **Publications:** Image, quarterly - free upon request. **Remarks:** FAX: (604)738-0015. TDD: (604)738-0603. Electronic mail address(es): DLRC.ELLIS (Envoy 100).

Kipling Collection
See: **Dalhousie University - Special Collections** (4540)

Rudyard Kipling Collection
See: **Syracuse University - George Arents Research Library for Special Collections** (15961)

Kirby Library of Government and Law
See: **Lafayette College** (8874)

★8740★
Kirchenbibliothek (Rel-Phil)
Schlosspl. 1
Postfach 1320 Phone: 916 2213
W-8530 Neustadt an der Aisch, Germany Reinhold Ohlmann
Founded: 1525. **Staff:** 1. **Subjects:** Theology, history, classics, philosophy, geography, music. **Special Collections:** Incunabula (250 items); 250 manuscripts from the 9th through 18th centuries. **Holdings:** 15,000 books; 5500 bound periodical volumes. **Services:** Library open to the public by appointment.

★8741★
Kirkland & Ellis - Library (Law)
200 E. Randolph Dr. Phone: (312)861-2304
Chicago, IL 60601 Charles E. Kregel, Jr., Info.Serv.Mgr.
Staff: Prof 8.5; Other 7. **Subjects:** Law, business. **Holdings:** Figures not available. **Services:** Library not open to the public. **Networks/Consortia:** Member of ILLINET. **Remarks:** FAX: (312)861-2290. **Staff:** Mary Eggert, Res.Spec.; Nancy Kelly, Res.Spec.; Renita Miller, Res.Spec.; Mindy Parker, Res.Spec.; Janet Smith, Res.Serv.Coord.; Patricia Tegler, Lib.Oper.Coord.; Anne Waldron, Res.Spec.; Lisa Walling, Res.Spec.; Timothy Woodward, Res.Spec.

★8742★
Kirkpatrick & Lockhart - Library (Law)
1800 M St., N.W., Suite 900 S. Phone: (202)778-9160
Washington, DC 20036-5891 Patricia Keller, Libn.
Staff: Prof 1; Other 4. **Subjects:** Law - securities, banking, taxation, trade. **Holdings:** 13,500 books; 750 bound periodical volumes. **Subscriptions:** 166 journals and other serials; 11 newspapers. **Services:** Interlibrary loan; library open to other law firms. **Automated Operations:** Computerized cataloging and acquisitions. **Computerized Information Services:** OCLC, LEXIS, WESTLAW, DIALOG Information Services, LEGI-SLATE, Dow Jones News/Retrieval. **Remarks:** FAX: (202)778-9100; 778-9200. **Staff:** Kimberly Hurley, Asst.Libn.; Laura Turbe, Ref.Libn.

★8743★
Kirkpatrick & Lockhart - Library (Law)
1500 Oliver Bldg. Phone: (412)355-6718
Pittsburgh, PA 15222 Gwen Vargas, Hd.Libn.
Subjects: Law - business, tax, litigation. **Holdings:** Figures not available. **Services:** Library not open to the public. **Computerized Information Services:** LEXIS, WESTLAW, DIALOG Information Services, Dow Jones News/Retrieval, VU/TEXT Information Services; MCI Mail (electronic mail service). **Remarks:** FAX: (412)355-6501.

★8744★
Kirksville College of Osteopathic Medicine - A.T. Still Memorial Library (Med)
Kirksville, MO 63501 Phone: (816)626-2345
Lawrence W. Onsager, Dir. of Lib.
Founded: 1897. **Staff:** Prof 1; Other 11. **Subjects:** Osteopathic medicine, medicine, psychology, basic sciences. **Special Collections:** Osteopathic medicine. **Holdings:** 38,939 books; 32,661 bound periodical volumes; 8105 AV programs; 600 osteopathic materials; 8 VF drawers of osteopathic pamphlets; 120 reels of microfilm; 35 linear feet of archives and manuscripts. **Subscriptions:** 852 journals and other serials; 5 newspapers. **Services:** Interlibrary loan; copying; SDI; library open to the public with restrictions. **Computerized Information Services:** BRS Information Technologies, MEDLINE, DIALOG Information Services, OCLC; CD-ROM (MEDLINE); DOCLINE (electronic mail service). Performs searches on fee basis. **Networks/Consortia:** Member of National Network of Libraries of Medicine - Midcontinental Region, Missouri Library Network Corp. (MLNC). **Publications:** Library News & Notes, quarterly - to other osteopathic libraries; Audiovisual Materials, annual. **Remarks:** FAX: (816)626-2333. **Staff:** Jean Sidwell, Pub.Serv.Libn.; Karen Tannenbaum, Tech.Serv.Libn.; Kathy Davisson, Spec.Coll.Libn.

★8745★
Kirovskij Mezotraslevoj Territorialnyj Centr Naucno Techniceskoj Informacii i Propagandy - Centralnaja Naucno Techniceskaja Biblioteka (Sci-Engr)
ul. Engelsa 67 Phone: 833 0624563
SU-610601 Kirov, Russia Alevtina G. Menchikova, Hd., Info.Ref. Fund
Founded: 1957. **Staff:** Prof 10. **Subjects:** Power engineering, metallurgy, machinery, forestry and woodworking, food industry, light industry, construction, agriculture, transportation. **Special Collections:** Patent information (1.4 million titles); technical and standard documentation (161,711 titles); local industrial innovations collection (7273 titles). **Holdings:** 19,743 books; 14,687 bound periodical volumes; 269,935 microfiche; 133,831 reels of microfilm; 374,867 information booklets; 100,600 bibliographies. **Computerized Information Services:** RASISD, RASDPI; internal databases. Contact Person: N.N. Tretyakova, Hd. of Patent & Tech.Info.Div. **Publications:** List of newspapers, magazines, and information publications received by libraries of Kirov, annual.

Kirstein Business Branch
See: **Boston Public Library** (1995)

Leo T. Kissam Memorial Law Library
See: **Fordham University - School of Law** (5970)

Gertrude Kistler Memorial Library
See: **Rosemont College** (14067)

★8746★
The Kitchen - Video Archive (Art)
512 W. 19th St. Phone: (212)255-5793
New York, NY 10011 Steven Gallagher, Video Curr.
Founded: 1971. **Subjects:** Experimental performing arts - video, music, dance, performance, film. **Special Collections:** Collection of experimental video art. **Holdings:** 2000 videotapes. **Services:** Archive is open to those with appropriate credentials. **Remarks:** FAX: (212)645-4258. **Also Known As:** Haleakala, Inc.

Kitchener Public Library - Grace Schmidt Room of Local History
See: **Waterloo Historical Society - Grace Schmidt Room of Local History** (20087)

★8747★
Kitchener-Waterloo Art Gallery - Eleanor Calvert Memorial Library (Art)
101 Queen St., N. Phone: (519)579-5860
Kitchener, ON, Canada N2H 6P7 Brad Blain, Dir.
Founded: 1968. **Subjects:** Fine arts. **Holdings:** 3500 books; 4000 vertical files; 19 carousels of slide/sound lecture series; 3000 slides. **Subscriptions:** 26 journals and other serials. **Services:** Interlibrary loan; copying; library open to the public for reference use only. **Special Catalogs:** Slide catalogs. **Remarks:** FAX: (519)578-9230.

★8748★
Kitchener-Waterloo Hospital - Health Sciences Library (Med)
835 King St., W. Phone: (519)742-3611
Kitchener, ON, Canada N2G 1G3 Thelma Bisch, Libn.
Founded: 1954. **Staff:** Prof 1; Other 1. **Subjects:** Medicine, nursing, hospital administration, paramedical sciences. **Special Collections:** Chapel Committee Collection (ethics and religion; 650 books). **Holdings:** 2800 books; 4000 bound periodical volumes; 1000 AV programs. **Subscriptions:** 250 journals and other serials. **Services:** Interlibrary loan; library not open to the public.

★8749★
Kitchener-Waterloo Record - Library (Publ)
225 Fairway Rd., S. Phone: (519)894-2231
Kitchener, ON, Canada N2G 4E5 Penny Coates, Libn.
Founded: 1972. **Staff:** Prof 2; Other 3. **Subjects:** Newspaper reference topics, biography. **Special Collections:** Waterloo regional material. **Holdings:** 300 books; 1000 pamphlets; 6500 subject files; 40,000 personal biographies. **Subscriptions:** 20 newspapers. **Services:** Interlibrary loan; library not open to the public. **Computerized Information Services:** Infomart Online. **Remarks:** FAX: (519)894-3829.

★8750★
Kitimat Centennial Museum Association - Archives (Hist)
293 City Centre Phone: (604)632-7022
Kitimat, BC, Canada V8C 1T6 Montserrat Gonzalez, Cur.
Founded: 1969. **Staff:** Prof 1; Other 1. **Subjects:** History and natural history of Kitimat Valley and Northwestern British Columbia. **Special Collections:** Letters of early Kitimat pioneers; paper from Kitamaat Temple of Temperance, 1898; Na-Na-Kwa, 1898-1907 (missionary newsletter); Alcan Project publications, 1950-1959. **Holdings:** 200 books; 19,000 historical photographs; 18,000 artifacts; 15 linear meters of early survey reports, documents, biographies; clipping file. **Services:** Copying; archives open to the public with restrictions. **Publications:** Three Towns, 1983; Geology of the Northwest Mainland, 1985 (both books); Tseax Lava Beds, 1983 (pamphlet); archival guide. **Special Catalogs:** Subject catalog; photographic guide and catalog. **Special Indexes:** Indexes to newsletters (card).

★8751★
Kitsap County Historical Museum - Library (Hist)
3343 N.W. Byron St. Phone: (206)692-1949
Silverdale, WA 98383 Suzanne T. Anest, Musm.Dir.
Founded: 1948. **Staff:** 1. **Subjects:** Local history, agriculture, forestry. **Holdings:** 500 books and bound newspapers. **Services:** Library open to the public with restrictions. **Computerized Information Services:** Internal database. **Publications:** Kitsap County History: A History; The Year of the Child.

★8752★
Kitsap County Law Library (Law)
614 Division St. Phone: (206)876-7140
Port Orchard, WA 98366 Barbara Van Buskirk, Libn.
Founded: 1947. **Subjects:** Law. **Holdings:** 10,000 volumes. **Services:** Library open to the public for reference use only.

★8753★
Kitt Peak National Observatory - Library (Sci-Engr)
Box 26732 Phone: (602)325-9295
Tucson, AZ 85726 Cathaleen Van Atta, Libn.
Founded: 1959. **Staff:** Prof 1. **Subjects:** Astronomy, physics, mathematics. **Holdings:** 35,000 volumes. **Subscriptions:** 275 journals and other serials. **Services:** Interlibrary loan (limited); library open to the public with restrictions. **Automated Operations:** Computerized cataloging. **Computerized Information Services:** OCLC, DIALOG Information Services, STN International. **Networks/Consortia:** Member of FEDLINK. **Remarks:** Library located at 950 N. Cherry Ave., Tucson, AZ 85716. **Also Known As:** National Optical Astronomy Observatories (NOAO).

★8754★
Kittochtinny Historical Society - Library (Hist)
175 E. King St. Phone: (717)264-1667
Chambersburg, PA 17201 Lillian F. Colletta, Sec.
Founded: 1898. **Staff:** 8. **Subjects:** History, genealogy. **Special Collections:** Fendrick Collection (genealogical records); Pennsylvania census (1790-1850); Gabler Collection (genealogy); church histories. **Holdings:** Books; manuscripts; newspapers (microfilm, hard copy); cemetery records; funeral directors' records; abstracts of wills; family files; historical files; historical photographs. **Subscriptions:** 3 journals and other serials. **Services:** Library open to the public on a limited schedule.

★8755★
Klamath County Library - Loyd De Lap Law Library (Law)
Court House
316 Main St. Phone: (503)883-5128
Klamath Falls, OR 97601 Ruth Rice, Law Libn.
Founded: 1929. **Staff:** 2. **Subjects:** Law. **Holdings:** 15,000 volumes; 74 bound periodical volumes. **Subscriptions:** 18 journals and other serials. **Services:** Interlibrary loan; copying; library open to the public. **Computerized Information Services:** WESTLAW. **Remarks:** Fax: (503)882-6953.

★8756★
Klamath County Museum - Research Library (Hist)
1451 Main St. Phone: (503)883-4208
Klamath Falls, OR 97601 Patsy H. McMillan, Musm.Dir.
Founded: 1954. **Staff:** 1. **Subjects:** Oregon and local history, Modoc and Klamath Indians, Modoc Indian War. **Special Collections:** Modoc Indian War collection; oral history collection. **Holdings:** 1500 books; photo/document archives; microfilm. **Subscriptions:** 5 journals and other serials. **Services:** Copying; library open to the public for reference use only. **Publications:** Research books on local history; Guardhouse, Gallows, and Graves (Modoc Indian War information).

Klanwatch
See: **Southern Poverty Law Center** (15513)

Klau Library
See: **Hebrew Union College - Jewish Institute of Religion** (7098)

L. Klauber Herpetological Library
See: **San Diego Society of Natural History** (14712)

★8757★
KLD Associates, Inc. - Library (Trans)
300 Broadway
Huntington Station, NY 11746 Phone: (516)549-9803
Founded: 1971. **Staff:** 2. **Subjects:** Traffic engineering, transportation, computer programming. **Holdings:** 250 books; 2000 papers; 500 microfiche. **Subscriptions:** 45 journals and other serials. **Services:** Library not open to the public. **Networks/Consortia:** Member of Long Island Library Resources Council. **Remarks:** FAX: (516)351-7190.

★8758★
Klehr, Harrison, Harvey, Branzburg, Ellers, & Weir - Library
1401 Walnut St., 8th Fl. Phone: (215)568-0525
Philadelphia, PA 19102 Peggy Fallon, Lib.Dir.
Remarks: No further information was supplied by respondent.

★8759★
B. Klein Publications - Research Library (Publ)
P.O. Box 8503 Phone: (305)752-1708
Coral Springs, FL 33075 B. Stecher, Libn.
Founded: 1960. **Staff:** Prof 1. **Subjects:** Social studies, history, business, research. **Holdings:** 2000 books. **Services:** Library not open to the public. **Remarks:** FAX: (305)752-2547.

Edward Klein Memorial Library
See: **Stephen Wise Free Synagogue** (20537)

Leonard Ross Klein USIS Collection
See: **(Salvador) Associacao Cultural Brasil-Estados Unidos** (14650)

Rabbi Isaac Klein Library
See: **Temple Shaarey Zedek** (16121)

William Klenz Library & Music Collection
See: **State University of New York at Binghamton - Special Collections** (15731)

★8760★
Klett Lieber Rooney & Schorling - Library (Law)
One Oxford Center, 41st Fl. Phone: (412)392-2046
Pittsburgh, PA 15219 Ann P. Orsag, Lib.Dir.
Staff: 4. **Subjects:** Law. **Special Collections:** Commerce Clearing Housing Standard Federal Tax Reports (complete holdings); Pennsylvania Bar Institute Seminar Coursebooks. **Holdings:** 10,000 books. **Services:** Interlibrary loan. **Computerized Information Services:** LEXIS, NEXIS, WESTLAW, Information America, DIALOG Information Services, VU/TEXT Information Services. **Publications:** Subject bibliographies; Guide to Library Subject Pathfinders; Newsletter. **Remarks:** FAX: (412)392-2128; 392-2129. **Formerly:** Klett, Lieber-Library. **Staff:** Diane Braun, Libn.

Klinck Memorial Library
See: **Concordia University - Klinck Memorial Library** (4120)

Nathan S. Kline Institute for Psychiatric Research
See: **New York (State) Office of Mental Health** (11674)

Kline Science Library
See: **Yale University** (20718)

★8761★
Klinikum der Stadt Mannheim - Meolizinish Wissenschaftliche Bibliothek (Med)
Postfach 100023 Phone: 621 3832212
W-6800 Mannheim 1, Germany Dorothee Boeckh
Founded: 1951. **Staff:** Prof 7. **Subjects:** Medicine, life sciences, medical statistics. **Holdings:** 25,000 books; 60,000 bound periodical volumes. **Subscriptions:** 550 journals and other serials. **Services:** Interlibrary loan; library open to the public with restrictions. **Computerized Information Services:** CD-ROM (MEDLINE). **Remarks:** FAX: 621 3832705.

Margaret Klipple Memorial Archives of African Folktales
See: **Cleveland Public Library - Fine Arts and Special Collections Department - Special Collections Section - John G. White Collection and Rare Books** (3823)

★8762★
Klockner Stadler Hurter Ltd. - Library (Sci-Engr)
1400 rue du Fort, Suite 900 Phone: (514)932-4611
Montreal, PQ, Canada H3H 2T1 Terri Macpherson, Libn.
Founded: 1976. **Staff:** Prof 1. **Subjects:** Engineering, pulp and paper. **Holdings:** 5,000 books; technical reports; standards. **Subscriptions:** 85 journals and other serials. **Services:** Interlibrary loan; library not open to the public. **Computerized Information Services:** DIALOG Information Services. **Remarks:** FAX: (514)932-9700. Telex: 05 24838.

Klondike Gold Rush National Historical Park
See: **U.S. Natl. Park Service** (17741)

H.J. Klosterman Chemistry Library
See: **North Dakota State University - H.J. Klosterman Chemistry Library** (11928)

★8763★
Kmetijski Institut Slovenije - Knjiznica (Agri)
Hacquetova 2 Phone: 61 123111
YU-61109 Ljubljana, Yugoslavia Sabina Cesnik
Founded: 1964. **Staff:** Prof 3. **Subjects:** Animal husbandry, crop farming, agricultural economics, fruit and vine growing, plant protection, agricultural mechanizations. **Holdings:** 13,061 books; 10, 833 bound periodical volumes; 6200 archival items. **Subscriptions:** 106 journals and other serials; 2 newspapers. **Services:** Interlibrary loan; copying; SDI; library open to the public with restrictions. **Computerized Information Services:** Internal databases. **Publications:** List of newly acquired books, quarterly. **Remarks:** FAX: 61 323057.

★8764★
KMS Fusion, Inc. - Fusion Library
700 KMS Place
Ann Arbor, MI 48106
Defunct.

Knesset
See: **Israel - Knesset** (8262)

Allen Knight Maritime Museum
See: **Monterey History & Art Association, Ltd.** (10668)

Knight Publishing Company, Inc. - Charlotte Observer
See: **Charlotte Observer - Library** (3448)

Knight-Ridder, Inc. - Akron Beacon Journal
See: **Akron Beacon Journal** (168)

Knight Ridder Newspaper Group - Gulf publishing Co., Inc.
See: **Gulf Publishing Co., Inc.** (6809)

★8765★
Knights of Columbus - Supreme Council - Archives (Rec)
Columbus Plaza Phone: (203)772-2130
New Haven, CT 06507 Susan H. Brosnan, Archv./Libn.
Staff: 1. **Subjects:** Knights of Columbus, Christopher Columbus, history of the Catholic Church. **Holdings:** Figures not available. **Services:** Copying; library open to the public by appointment.

Knights of Columbus Vatican Film Library
See: **St. Louis University** (14464)

Knihovna Narodni Galerie u Praze
See: **Czechoslovakia - National Gallery of Prague** (4514)

Knihovna Narodniho Muzea
See: **Czechoslovakia - Knihovna Narodniho Muzea - Library** (4512)

Knipling-Bushland U.S. Livestock Insects Laboratory
See: **U.S.D.A. - Agricultural Research Service** (17186)

Knipp Physics Reading Room
See: **Tufts University** (16550)

★8766★
Knoedler Gallery - Art Reference Library (Art)
19 E. 70th St. Phone: (212)794-0567
New York, NY 10021 Melissa De Medeiros, Libn.
Founded: 1846. **Staff:** Prof 1. **Subjects:** 19th and 20th century European and American art. **Special Collections:** Exhibition and art auction catalogs; photograph collection; archives. **Holdings:** 50,000 volumes. **Subscriptions:** 21 journals and other serials. **Services:** Copying; library open to the public by appointment on fee basis. **Publications:** The Knoedler Library on (microfiche) - for sale. **Remarks:** FAX: (212)570-6616. **Formerly:** M. Knoedler & Co., Inc.

Knoedler Library
See: **Norton Simon Museum of Art at Pasadena - Library and Archives** (15180)

M. Knoedler & Co., Inc. - Library
See: **Amon Carter Museum - Library** (3109)

★8767★
Knoll Pharmaceuticals - Science Information Center (Med)
30 N. Jefferson Rd. Phone: (201)428-4199
Whippany, NJ 07981 Joanne Lustig, Mgr., Med./Sci.Info.
Founded: 1938. **Staff:** Prof 4; Other 1. **Subjects:** Cardiovascular medicine, drug information, pharmacology, pharmaceutical industry, consumer health, oncology, pain. **Holdings:** 1500 books; 3000 bound periodical volumes; foreign and domestic patents. **Subscriptions:** 350 journals and other serials; 10 newspapers. **Services:** SDI; document delivery; translations. **Automated Operations:** TECHLIBplus, BASISplus. **Computerized Information Services:** DIALOG Information Services, Data-Star, Chemical Abstracts Service (CAS), Pharmaceutical Literature Documentation (RINGDOC), MEDLARS; internal databases. **Networks/Consortia:** Member of MEDCORE, Health Sciences Library Association of New Jersey (HSLANJ), Northwest Regional Library Cooperative. **Publications:** Pharm-Alert (current awareness bulletin), semimonthly; To Your Health (consumer health information), bimonthly; The Winners' Circle, quarterly (newsletter) - to sales force; Quality in Action, quarterly. **Remarks:** FAX: (201)515-4535. Knoll Pharmaceuticals is a unit of BASF K & F Corporation. **Staff:** Susan Thompson, Sr.Info.Spec.; Diana Gowe, Info.Spec.; Anne Fagundus, Sr.Info.Spec.

★8768★
Knolls Atomic Power Laboratory - Libraries (Sci-Engr, Energy)
Box 1072 Phone: (518)395-4317
Schenectady, NY 12301 Mike Gerard, Mgr., Lib.Serv.
Founded: 1946. **Staff:** Prof 2; Other 5. **Subjects:** Nuclear science and engineering, chemistry, physics, mathematics, metallurgy. **Special Collections:** U.S. Navy specifications, standards, handbooks, manuals; naval nuclear propulsion engineering support documents (100,000). **Holdings:** 34,000 volumes; 5000 pamphlets; 300,000 research and development reports. **Subscriptions:** 500 journals and other serials. **Services:** Interlibrary loan; libraries not open to the public. **Computerized Information Services:** Integrated Technical Information System (ITIS); computerized information retrieval system for internal documentation (internal database). **Publications:** Book Shelf, bimonthly; Listing of New Reports, bimonthly; Latest Issue List of Specifications and Standards, monthly - all for internal distribution only. **Remarks:** Operated by General Electric Company under contract to the U.S. Department of Energy. **Staff:** Patricia A. Oliver, Prof.Libn.; Kathy Spetla, Libn., Manuals & Standards.

Alfred A. and Blanche Knopf Library and Publishing Archives
See: **University of Texas at Austin - Harry Ransom Humanities Research Center** (19392)

Knox College
See: **University of Toronto - Knox College** (19454)

★8769★
Knox College - Henry M. Seymour Library - Special Collections (Hist)
P.O. Box 500 Phone: (309)343-0112
Galesburg, IL 61401 Jeffrey Douglas
Founded: 1890. **Staff:** Prof 1; Other 2. **Subjects:** History - Midwestern, college, local. **Special Collections:** Finley Collection (history of the Northwest Territory); Ray D. Smith Collection (Civil War); Preston Player collection (Mississippi River Valley); Hughes collection (Ernest Hemingway and the Lost Generation). **Holdings:** Books; bound periodical volumes; archival materials; manuscripts; prints. **Services:** Copying; library open to the public. **Computerized Information Services:** Finding Aids (internal database). Performs searches. Contact Person: Carley R. Robison, Cur., Dept.Hd.

★8770★
Knox Community Hospital - Medical Library (Med)
1330 Coshocton Rd. Phone: (614)393-9000
Mount Vernon, OH 43050 Havilah Phelps, Libn.
Staff: Prof 1. **Subjects:** Medicine, surgery, nursing. **Holdings:** 1250 books; 300 bound periodical volumes. **Subscriptions:** 30 journals and other serials. **Services:** Interlibrary loan; library not open to the public. **Networks/Consortia:** Member of Central Ohio Hospital Library Consortium.

★8771★
Knox County Governmental Library (Law)
City-County Bldg., M-47
Main Ave. Phone: (615)521-2368
Knoxville, TN 37902 Meredith Douglas, Libn.
Founded: 1955. **Staff:** Prof 1. **Subjects:** Law. **Holdings:** 12,000 books; 66 bound periodical volumes. **Services:** Copying; library open to the public.

★8772★
Knox County Historical Society - Library (Hist)
Edina, MO 63537 Phone: (816)397-2346
Brenton Karhoff, Pres.
Founded: 1966. **Staff:** 1. **Subjects:** Local and state history, genealogy. **Holdings:** 120 books; 50 bound periodical volumes; 7 scrapbooks; clippings. **Services:** Copying; library open to the public with restrictions.

★8773★
Knox County Public Library System - McClung Historical Collection (Hist)
500 W. Church Ave. Phone: (615)544-5744
Knoxville, TN 37902-2505 Steve Cotham, Hd.
Founded: 1921. **Staff:** Prof 4; Other 5. **Subjects:** History and genealogy of Knoxville, Knox County, Tennessee, and other southeastern states. **Special Collections:** Knoxville and Tennessee newspapers, 1791 to present; 1982 World's Fair Archives (750,000 manuscripts); local architectural plans; Jim Thompson Photographic Collection. **Holdings:** 33,348 books; 4073 bound periodical volumes; 1 million manuscripts; 1341 maps; 8269 reels of microfilm; 33,854 microfiche; 135 VF drawers of photographs and clippings. **Subscriptions:** 240 journals and other serials; 10 newspapers. **Services:** Copying; collection open to the public for reference use only. **Networks/Consortia:** Member of SOLINET. **Publications:** Occasional publications; A Guide to the Manuscript Collections of the Calvin M. McClung Historical Collection (book); A Descriptive Guide to the Processed Manuscript Collections of the Calvin M. McClung Historical Collection of Knox County Public Library System (book). **Remarks:** Collection located in East Tennessee Historical Center, 314 W. Clinch Ave., Knoxville, TN 37902-2203. The East Tennessee Historical Society, organized in 1925, has its headquarters in the East Tennessee Historical Center as well; gifts to the society become part of the McClung Collection's holdings. **Staff:** Sue Klipsch, Tech.Serv./Ref.Libn.; Sally K. Ripatti, Spec.Mtls.Archv.; Barbara Cook, Pub.Serv.Libn.

Dudley Knox Library
See: **U.S. Navy - Naval Postgraduate School - Dudley Knox Library** (17868)

L. Jane Knox Resource Centre
See: **Saskatchewan Registered Nurses Association** (14865)

★8774★
Knoxville Business College - Library (Bus-Fin)
720 N. 5th Ave. Phone: (615)524-3043
Knoxville, TN 37917 Shelly W. Robinson, Dir., Lib.Serv.
Staff: Prof 1. **Subjects:** Business administration, small business, secretarial science, paralegal, hotel and restaurant management. **Special Collections:** Archival collection on the history of the college (1 file). **Holdings:** 4000 books; 8 VF drawers; 214 volumes on microfilm; 1 cabinet of microfiche. **Subscriptions:** 76 journals and other serials. **Services:** Interlibrary loan; copying; SDI. **Computerized Information Services:** WESTLAW. **Publications:** Subject bibliographies for specific courses - available on request. **Remarks:** FAX: (615)637-0127.

★8775★
Knoxville-Knox County Metropolitan Planning Commission - Library (Plan)
City-County Bldg., Suite 403
400 Main St. Phone: (615)521-2500
Knoxville, TN 37902 Gretchen F. Beal, Libn.
Founded: 1975. **Staff:** Prof 1. **Subjects:** Urban planning, economic development, transportation, housing, environment, land use/zoning. **Holdings:** 10,000 volumes; 2000 local documents; 4 VF drawers of clippings; dissertations; manuscripts; archives. **Subscriptions:** 92 journals and other serials. **Services:** Interlibrary loan; copying; library open to the public. **Publications:** Acquisitions List, monthly - for internal distribution only. **Special Catalogs:** Publications Catalog, annual.

★8776★
Kobenhavns Universitet - Engelsk Institut - Biblioteket (Hum)
84 Njalsgade Phone: 3 1542211
DK-2300 Copenhagen S, Denmark Gorm Schou-Rode
Founded: 1900. **Staff:** Prof 1; Other 1. **Subjects:** English language; English and American literature and social science. **Holdings:** 23,000 books; 1500 bound periodical volumes. **Subscriptions:** 91 journals and other serials. **Services:** Interlibrary loan; copying; library open to the public for reference use only.

★8777★
Kobenhavns Universitet - Medicinsk Historisk Museum - Biblioteket (Med)
Bredgade 62 Phone: 3 3152501
DK-1260 Copenhagen K, Denmark Anna-Elisabeth Brade
Founded: 1907. **Staff:** Prof 1; Other 1. **Subjects:** Medicine, pharmacy, medical laboratory, surgery, odontology. **Holdings:** 25,000 books. **Subscriptions:** 32 journals and other serials. **Services:** Interlibrary loan; copying; library open to the public. **Remarks:** FAX: 3 3152125.

★8778★
Koch Membrane Systems, Inc. - KMS Library
850 Main St.
Wilmington, MA 01887
Defunct.

★8779★
Kodiak College - Carolyn Floyd Library (Hist)
117 Benny Benson Dr. Phone: (907)486-4161
Kodiak, AK 99615 Charlotte Hatfield
Founded: 1972. **Staff:** Prof 1; Other 2.5. **Special Collections:** Koniag Collection of Alaskana (300 titles). **Holdings:** 18,000 books. **Subscriptions:** 185 journals and other serials; 5 newspapers. **Services:** Interlibrary loan; copying; library open to the public. **Computerized Information Services:** GNOSIS (internal database). **Networks/Consortia:** Member of Western Library Network (WLN).

Leon and Thea Koerner Foundation
See: **Victoria Conservatory of Music** (19827)

Kohler Art Library
See: **University of Wisconsin--Madison** (19601)

★8780★
John Michael Kohler Arts Center - Resource Center (Art)
608 New York Ave.
Box 489 Phone: (414)458-6144
Sheboygan, WI 53081 Eric Johnson
Founded: 1968. **Staff:** Prof 1. **Subjects:** Contemporary American crafts, nontraditional photography, art of naives and visionaries, folk art. **Special Collections:** Archive of Eugene Von Brunehenhien's paintings, photographs, writings; survey of Wisconsin folk art. **Holdings:** 4000 books; 80,000 slides and photographs of works included in exhibitions. **Subscriptions:** 50 journals and other serials. **Services:** Center open to the public by appointment. **Remarks:** FAX: (414)458-4473

Blanche Wolf Kohn Library
See: **Settlement Music School** (15053)

Harold Kohn Memorial Visual Science Library
See: **State University of New York - College of Optometry** (15724)

★8781★
Kokomo Tribune - Library (Publ)
300 N. Union Phone: (317)459-3121
Kokomo, IN 46901 Janice Johnson, Libn.
Founded: 1976. **Staff:** 1. **Subjects:** Newspaper reference topics. **Holdings:** 200 books; 8 VF drawers of pamphlets; 26 VF drawers of clippings; 4 VF drawers of historical photographs; photographic file, 1976 to present; negative file, 1958 to present; Tribune, 1868 to present, on microfilm; 4 VF drawers of backlog clippings, 1970-1976. **Subscriptions:** 30 journals and other serials. **Services:** Interlibrary loan; library not open to the public. **Remarks:** FAX: (317)456-3815.

Kokuritsu Kokugo Kenkyusho
See: **Japan - National Language Research Institute** (8336)

★8782★
Kollsman, Division of Sequa Corporation - Kollsman Library (Sci-Engr)
2-D15-1
220 Danil Webster Hwy. Phone: (603)886-2083
Merrimack, NH 03054 Mary Anfuso
Staff: Prof 1. **Subjects:** Aeronautics, optics, electronics, engineering, mathematics, management, marketing, accounting. **Holdings:** 2500 volumes; 5 volumes of patents. **Subscriptions:** 150 journals and other serials. **Services:** Interlibrary loan; library not open to the public. **Automated Operations:** Computerized cataloging, acquisitions, and circulation. **Computerized Information Services:** DIALOG Information Services, Government Industry Data Exchange Program (GIDEP), DROLS (Defense RDT & E OnLine System) Database. **Remarks:** FAX: (603)889-7966.

★8783★
Komatsu Dresser Co. - Haulpak Division - Engineering Technical Library (Sci-Engr)
2300 N.E. Adams St.
Box 240 Phone: (309)672-7132
Peoria, IL 61650-0240 Marilyn G. Kopp, Libn.
Founded: 1965. **Staff:** 1. **Subjects:** Engineering, welding, steel, metals and alloys. **Holdings:** 3500 books; 11 VF drawers of society papers. **Subscriptions:** 32 journals and other serials. **Services:** Interlibrary loan; library not open to the public. **Networks/Consortia:** Member of Illinois Valley Library System. **Remarks:** FAX: (309)672-7271.

Kommission fur Alte Geschichte und Epigraphik
See: **German Archaeological Institute - Commission for Ancient History and Epigraphy** (6420)

Kongelige Bibliotek
See: **Denmark - Royal Library** (4770)

★8784★
Koninklijk Instituut voor de Marine - Bibliotheek (Mil, Trans)
Het nieuwe Diep 8 Phone: 2230 56991
NL-1780 CA Den Helder, Netherlands S.D. Elphick, M.Sc.
Founded: 1828. **Staff:** Prof 6; Other 1. **Subjects:** Military sciences and technology, law, nautical sciences, management, international relations, shipbuilding and engineering. **Special Collections:** Antiquarian book collection dating from the beginning of 17th century (400 vols.); atlas collection. **Holdings:** 40,000 books; 20,000 bound periodical volumes; 30,000 reports; 3000 microfiche; 300 videotapes. **Subscriptions:** 440 journals and other serials; 3 newspapers. **Services:** Interlibrary loan; copying; SDI; library open to the public at librarian's discretion. **Computerized Information Services:** DIALOG Information Services, ESA/IRS. Contact Person: J.B.G. Taken, M.Sc. **Publications:** General library guide; Inlending bibliotheckgebruik en Literatuurondeuzoek. **Special Catalogs:** Catalogus van de Historische collectie. **Remarks:** FAX: 2230 57640.

★8785★
Koninklijk Museum voor Schone Kunsten - Bibliotheek (Art)
Plaatsnijdersstraat 2 Phone: 3 2387809
B-2000 Antwerp, Belgium Leo Wuyts, Sci.Libn.
Founded: 1948. **Staff:** 3. **Subjects:** Painting and sculpture of western Europe; art history. **Holdings:** 40,000 books; 120 bound periodical volumes. **Subscriptions:** 124 journals and other serials. **Services:** Copying; library open to the public by appointment. **Remarks:** FAX: 3 2480810. Maintained by the Ministry of Culture.

Koninklijke Bibliotheek Albert I
See: **Belgium - Ministry of National Education - Bibliotheque Royale de Belgique** (1671)

★8786★
Koninklijke Nederlandse Akademie van Wetenschappen - P.J. Meertens-Instituut - Bibliotheek (Hum)
Keizersgracht 569-571 Phone: 20 6234698
NL-1017 DR Amsterdam, Netherlands Gemma van der Spek, Hd.
Staff: 2. **Subjects:** Dialectology, onomastics, folklore. **Holdings:** 60,000 books. **Subscriptions:** 900 journals and other serials. **Services:** Interlibrary loan; copying; library open to the public by appointment. **Remarks:** FAX: 20 6240639. **Staff:** Jan Pieter Kunst; Bernadette Boom-Siching.

Konjunktura-, Piackutato es Informatikai Intezet Rt. - Konyvtar
See: **Institute for Economic, Market Research and Informatics Ltd.** (7932)

Konkoly Observatory - Library
See: **Hungarian Academy of Sciences - Konkoly Observatory** (7549)

W.S. Konold Memorial Library
See: **Doctors Hospital** (4935)

★8787★
Koochiching County Historical Society - Museum (Hist)
Smokey Bear Park
214 6th St.
Box 1147 Phone: (218)283-4316
International Falls, MN 56649 Sandra J. Boen, Exec.Dir.
Founded: 1958. **Staff:** 4. **Subjects:** History - Koochiching County, Boise Cascade, personal; logging. **Special Collections:** Mando photograph collection (10 VF drawers); International Lumber Company & Bussman papers; Harold Reich papers; S.F. Plummer diaries; early county records; post office records; Hadler Collection; women's clubs records. **Holdings:** 600 volumes; 21 VF drawers and 15 boxes of records and manuscripts; 15 VF drawers of photographs. **Subscriptions:** 3 newspapers. **Services:** Copying; museum open to the public. **Publications:** Koochiching Chronicle (newsletter), 8/year.

★8788★
Kootenay Lake Historical Society - Archives (Hist)
Box 537 Phone: (604)353-2525
Kaslo, BC, Canada V0G 1M0 Elizabeth Scarlett, Archv.
Founded: 1988. **Staff:** 4. **Subjects:** Local history, 1891 to present. **Special Collections:** History of sternwheeler transportation in the Kootenays. **Holdings:** Books; society records; journals; newspapers; photographs; personal papers; audiocassettes; videocassettes. **Services:** Copying; archives open to the public for reference use only. **Remarks:** Alternate telephone number(s): (604)353-2563.

★8789★
Kootenay Museum Association and Historical Society - Nelson Museum - Archives (Hist)
402 Anderson St. Phone: (604)352-9813
Nelson, BC, Canada V1L 3Y3 Alan R. Ramsden, Pres.
Founded: 1955. **Staff:** Prof 1; Other 2. **Subjects:** Local history, west Kootenays. **Special Collections:** 54th Kootenay Battalion Association during World War 1; Nelson newspapers, 1894-1970. **Holdings:** Photographs; West Koontenay archival material; assessment rolls. **Services:** Copying (limited); archives open to the public on a limited schedule when staff member is present. **Remarks:** FAX: (604)352-6355. **Staff:** Mrs. Shawn Lamb, Proj.Dir.

Kopolow Business Library
See: **Washington University** (20064)

Korea - Ministry of Agriculture and Fisheries - Rural Development Administration
See: **Republic of Korea - Rural Development Administration** (13829)

Korea - Ministry of Science and Technology - Electronics and Telecommunications Research Institute
See: **Electronics and Telecommunications Research Institute** (5293)

Korea - Ministry of Science and Technology - Korea Atomic Energy Research Institute
See: **Korea Atomic Energy Research Institute** (8790)

★8790★
Korea Atomic Energy Research Institute - KAERI Library (Energy)
P.O. Box 7, Daedukdanji Phone: 42 820-2000
Taejon 305-353, Republic of Korea Whan Tae Kim, Libn.
Founded: 1959. **Subjects:** Nuclear science. **Holdings:** 500,000 volumes. **Subscriptions:** 980 journals and other serials; 30 newspapers. **Services:** Library open to graduate students for reference use only. **Computerized Information Services:** DIALOG Information Services, BRS Information Technologies, INIS, JOIS, Nihon Keizai Shimbun, Inc. (NIKKEI), KIETLINE; TRRS (Technical Reports Retrieval System), KAERI-TIPS (Technical Information Processing System; internal databases). **Publications:** KAERI Journal; Annual Report. **Remarks:** FAX: 42 8202702. Telex: KAERI K45553. Maintained by Korea - Ministry of Science and Technology.

★8791★
Korea Institute for Economics & Technology - KIET Library (Sci-Engr, Bus-Fin)
P.O. Box 205
Cheong Ryang Phone: 2 965-6211
Seoul 131, Republic of Korea Sukyoung Kim, Dir., Info.Rsrcs.Div.
Subjects: Science and technology, industrial economics. **Holdings:** 50,000 volumes; 20,000 reports; 9000 noncurrent periodical titles. **Subscriptions:** 7500 journals and other serials. **Services:** SDI; publication service; document delivery service; library open to industry research and development institutes, academic institutions, government agencies. **Computerized Information Services:** Chemical Abstracts Service, COMPENDEX, INSPEC, Information Service in Mechanical Engineering (ISMEC), NTIS Bibliographic Data Base, METADEX, FSTAM Biotech Abstracts, World Patents Index (WPI); produces KIETLINE; internal databases. Performs searches on fee basis. **Publications:** Bibliographies. **Remarks:** Maintains six regional information services branches. FAX: 2 962-4702. Telex: 966 6506. **Formerly:** Korea Institute for Industrial Economics and Technology.

★8792★
Korea Trade Promotion Center - Library (Bus-Fin)
460 Park Ave., Rm. 402
New York, NY 10022 Phone: (212)826-0900
Subjects: Korean exports and imports, Korean business, international trade. **Holdings:** 35,000 volumes. **Remarks:** FAX: (212)888-4930.

Korea University - Asiatic Research Center
See: **Asiatic Research Center** (1124)

★8793★
Korea University - Medical Library (Med)
126-1, 5-ka, Anam-Dong
Sungbuk-ku Phone: 2 9275111
Seoul, Republic of Korea Young-Suk Suh
Founded: 1969. **Staff:** Prof 4; Other 3. **Subjects:** Medical science, nursing science, biological science. **Special Collections:** Index Medicus (1960 to present). **Holdings:** 25,100 books; 23,500 bound periodical volumes; 11,500 reports. **Subscriptions:** 600 journals and other serials; 25 newspapers. **Services:** Interlibrary loan; copying; library open to persons in the field of medical science. **Computerized Information Services:** CD-ROM (MEDLINE). **Remarks:** FAX: 2 9275594.

★8794★
Korean Cultural Center - Library (Area-Ethnic)
5505 Wilshire Blvd. Phone: (213)936-7141
Los Angeles, CA 90036 Song Ja Kim, Libn.
Founded: 1980. **Staff:** Prof 1; Other 1. **Subjects:** Korea - government, culture, arts, history, language, literature, philosophy, religions, sciences. **Special Collections:** Films on Korea. **Holdings:** 12,500 books (9700 in Korean, 2800 in English); 160 16mm films; 170 videotapes; 20 slide sets. **Subscriptions:** 52 journals and other serials; 7 newspapers. **Services:** Library open to the public. **Remarks:** FAX: (213)936-5712. **Formerly:** Korean Cultural Service.

★8795★
Korean Scientists and Engineers Association in America - Library (Sci-Engr)
6261 Executive Blvd.
Rockville, MD 20852 Phone: (301)984-7048
Founded: 1971. **Staff:** 2. **Subjects:** Scientific, technological, and cultural bonds between Korea and the United States. **Holdings:** 100 scientific handbooks and yearbooks in Korean. **Services:** Library not open to the public. **Computerized Information Services:** Internal database. **Remarks:** FAX: (301)984-1231.

★8796★
Korn/Ferry International - Research Library (Bus-Fin)
120 S. Riverside Plaza, Suite 918 Phone: (312)726-1841
Chicago, IL 60606 Pamela Frazier, Res.Dir.
Founded: 1979. **Staff:** Prof 3; Other 1. **Subjects:** Executive search, business reference. **Holdings:** 250 books. **Subscriptions:** 11 journals and other serials. **Services:** Library not open to the public. **Computerized Information Services:** Online systems. **Special Indexes:** Index to resumes. **Remarks:** FAX: (312)726-2836.

Kornhauser Health Sciences Library
See: **University of Louisville** (18771)

George Korson Folklore Archive
See: **King's College - D. Leonard Corgan Library** (8721)

★8797★
Kosciusko County Historical Society - Genealogy Section - Jail Museum Genealogy Library (Hist)
P.O. Box 1071
Warsaw, IN 46581 Phone: (219)269-1078
Subjects: Kosciusko County. **Holdings:** 1000 books; 200 reels of microfilm; 70 family histories; county courthouse records; cemetery and plat books; tax records, 1843-1969, on microfilm; censuses, 1840-1910; newspapers on microfilm. **Services:** Copying; library open to the public on a limited schedule. **Special Indexes:** Courthouse record indices. **Staff:** Douglas Mayer, Libn.; Max Fribley, Co-Chm.; Shirley Thompson, Co-Chm.; Mary Ettinger, Res.Chm.

★8798★
Kosciuszko Foundation - Reference Library (Area-Ethnic)
15 E. 65th St. Phone: (212)734-2130
New York, NY 10021 Mr. Metchie J.E. Budka, Lib.Cons.
Founded: 1925. **Subjects:** Polish history, art, music, literature; Polish-American history. **Holdings:** 10,000 books. **Services:** Library not open to the public. **Remarks:** FAX: (212)628-4552.

★8799★
Kossuth Foundation - Hungarian Research Library (Area-Ethnic)
Butler University Phone: (317)283-9532
Indianapolis, IN 46208 Dr. Janos Horvath, Pres.
Founded: 1957. **Staff:** Prof 1; Other 1. **Subjects:** Hungary, Hungarian culture, social sciences, American-Hungarian relations. **Special Collections:** Hungarica-Americana; the Hungarian Revolutions, 1848 and 1956; Hungarian scholars, scientists, artists in the United States. **Holdings:** 3000 books; 70 bound periodical volumes; 500 pamphlets; newspaper clippings; manuscripts; documents; photographs; maps; tapes. **Subscriptions:** 20 journals and other serials; 15 newspapers. **Services:** Interlibrary loan; library open to the public for reference use only.

Kozlekedesi, Hirkozlesi es Epitesugyi Miniszterium - Epitesugyi Tajekoztatasi
See: **Hungary - Ministry for Transport, Communication and Construction** (7554)

KPIX Film Library
See: **San Francisco State University - J. Paul Leonard Library - Special Collections/Archives** (14743)

★8800★
KPMG Peat Marwick - Information and Research Center (Bus-Fin)
Peat Marwick Plaza
303 E. Wacker Dr. Phone: (312)938-1000
Chicago, IL 60601 Mabel K. Wong, Supv., Info.Serv.
Staff: Prof 2; Other 1. **Subjects:** Accounting and auditing, business and management consulting. **Holdings:** 2000 books; 2000 unbound periodicals and newsletters; 30,000 public company annual reports on microfiche. **Subscriptions:** 280 journals and other serials; 4 newspapers. **Services:** Interlibrary loan. **Automated Operations:** Computerized cataloging and serials. **Computerized Information Services:** LEXIS, NEXIS, National Automated Accounting Research System (NAARS), DIALOG Information Services, Dow Jones News/Retrieval, VU/TEXT Information Services, DataTimes, Reuter TEXTLINE; Dialcom, Inc. (electronic mail service). **Remarks:** FAX: (312)938-0449. Telex: 206794 PEATMARCOCG. Electronic mail address(es): PMM053902 (Dialcom, Inc.). **Staff:** Terrance McHale, Sr.Info.Spec.

★8801★
KPMG Peat Marwick - Information and Research Center (Bus-Fin)
345 Park Ave. Phone: (212)872-6531
New York, NY 10154 George Mauter, Dir.
Founded: 1952. **Staff:** Prof 4; Other 2. **Subjects:** Accounting, auditing, management consulting. **Holdings:** 15,000 books; 500 periodical titles; 80 VF drawers of pamphlets. **Services:** Interlibrary loan; center not open to the public. **Automated Operations:** Computerized cataloging, acquisitions, and serials. **Computerized Information Services:** DIALOG Information Services, LEXIS, NEXIS, CompuServe Information Service, VU/TEXT Information Services, Dow Jones News/Retrieval, Reuters, Securities Data Company. **Publications:** Information Update, quarterly - for internal distribution only. **Remarks:** FAX: (212)758-9819. **Staff:** Karen Neuberg, Info.Spec.; Alison Donald, Info.Spec.; Marianne Carson, Info.Spec.

★8802★
KPMG Peat Marwick - Information Services (Bus-Fin)
725 S. Figueroa St. Phone: (213)972-4000
Los Angeles, CA 90017 Tom Schutter, Supv., Info.Serv.
Staff: Prof 1; Other 1. **Subjects:** Accounting, taxation, business management, auditing, economics. **Special Collections:** Peat Marwick client newsletters (4 shelves). **Holdings:** 2500 books; 100 bound periodical volumes; 1000 pamphlets; 7 drawers of microfilm; 2 boxes of microfiche. **Subscriptions:** 636 journals and other serials; 10 newspapers. **Services:** Interlibrary loan; copying; SDI; services open to the public with librarian approval. **Automated Operations:** Computerized cataloging, acquisitions, and serials. **Computerized Information Services:** Mead Data Central, DIALOG Information Services, Dow Jones News/Retrieval, Dun & Bradstreet Business Credit Services, VU/TEXT Information Services, DataTimes, NewsNet, Inc., Interactive Data Services, Inc., InvesText, Reuter TEXTLINE, Maxwell Online, Inc., CompuServe Information Service, COMPUSTAT, BASELINE, UMI Ondisc, Lotus One Source; internal databases; Dialcom Inc. (electronic mail service). **Publications:** Serials holdings list, monthly - free upon request. **Remarks:** FAX: (213)622-1217.

★8803★
KPMG Peat Marwick - Information Services (Bus-Fin)
4200 Norwest Ctr.
90 S. 7th St. Phone: (612)337-9437
Minneapolis, MN 55402 Susan C. Kopher, Mgr., Info.Serv.
Founded: 1973. **Staff:** Prof 1; Other 2. **Subjects:** Accounting; taxation - state, federal, foreign; industry statistics. **Special Collections:** KPMG publications. **Holdings:** 3000 books; annual reports. **Subscriptions:** 150 journals and other serials; 7 newspapers. **Services:** Interlibrary loan; copying; SDI; services open to the public by request. **Automated Operations:** Computerized acquisitions and serials. **Computerized Information Services:** DIALOG Information Services, LEXIS, NEXIS, Dow Jones News/Retrieval, DataTimes, InvesText, Estate Valuation Service, VU/TEXT Information Services, PFDS Online, Interactive Data Corporation; Dialcom Inc. (electronic mail service). **Special Catalogs:** Catalog of KPMG publications and annual reports. **Remarks:** FAX: (612)341-0202. **Staff:** Lisa Lehti, Info.Spec.

★8804★
KPMG Peat Marwick - Information Services (Bus-Fin)
1601 Elm St., Suite 1400 Phone: (214)754-2330
Dallas, TX 75201 Margaret R. McClure, Info.Serv.Dir.
Founded: 1978. **Staff:** Prof 2. **Subjects:** Taxation, accounting, auditing, oil and gas taxation, insurance taxation. **Holdings:** 2500 books; 500 bound periodical volumes; 1500 unbound periodicals; 500 volumes of loose-leaf services; 100 boxes of legislative history materials and government documents. **Subscriptions:** 250 journals and other serials; 5 newspapers. **Services:** Copying; SDI; services open to firm clients. **Automated Operations:** Computerized serials. **Computerized Information Services:** DIALOG Information Services, PFDS Online, Dow Jones News/Retrieval, DataTimes, LEXIS; internal database; Dialcom, Inc. (electronic mail service). Performs searches on fee basis. **Publications:** Research Notes, bimonthly - for internal distribution only. **Special Indexes:** Index to in-house research memoranda; Selected Peat Marwick Newsletters (online). **Remarks:** FAX: (214)754-2297. **Staff:** Jane Whittlesey, Asst.Supv.

★8805★
KPMG Peat Marwick - Library (Bus-Fin)
3 Embarcadero, 21st Fl. Phone: (415)951-0100
San Francisco, CA 94111 Tony Obregon, Libn.
Founded: 1970. **Staff:** 1. **Subjects:** Tax services, accounting, auditing, management advisory services. **Holdings:** 1000 books. 50 journals and other serials; 5 newspapers. **Services:** Interlibrary loan; copying; library open to the public at librarian's discretion. **Computerized Information Services:** LEXIS, NEXIS, Maxwell Macmillan Taxes Online, Estate Valuation Service. **Publications:** New books/materials list, irregular. **Remarks:** FAX: (415)296-0628. Telex: 703189; 62188300.

★8806★
KPMG Peat Marwick - Library (Plan)
P.O. Box 8007
San Francisco Intl. Airport Phone: (415)571-7722
San Francisco, CA 94128-8007 Karen A. Mayers, Libn.
Staff: Prof 1; Other 2. **Subjects:** Planning - airport, environmental, transportation. **Holdings:** 800 books; 41 VF drawers of reports. **Subscriptions:** 100 journals and other serials. **Services:** Interlibrary loan; library not open to the public. **Computerized Information Services:** Aviation Online, LEXIS, NEXIS, DIALOG Information Services, AIMS (American Association of Airport Executives); Dialcom, Inc. (electronic mail service). **Remarks:** FAX: (415)571-5220.

★8807★
KPMG Peat Marwick - Library (Bus-Fin)
2001 M St., N.W. Phone: (202)467-3000
Washington, DC 20036 Nancy J. Holland, Mgr., Info.Serv.
Staff: Prof 2; Other 1. **Subjects:** Accounting, taxation, transportation, business and finance. **Holdings:** 5000 books; 1000 technical reports. **Subscriptions:** 300 journals and other serials. **Services:** Interlibrary loan; copying; library open to the public by appointment. **Computerized Information Services:** DIALOG Information Services, Aerospace Online, LEXIS, NEXIS, Dow Jones News/Retrieval, DataTimes.

★8808★
KPMG Peat Marwick - Library (Bus-Fin)
P.O. Box 4545 Phone: (713)224-4262
Houston, TX 77210 Patricia Baron, Supv., Info.Serv.
Founded: 1968. **Staff:** Prof 2; Other 2. **Subjects:** Taxation, accounting, management consulting, employee benefits. **Holdings:** 6000 books; 400 bound periodical volumes; annual reports; prospectuses. **Subscriptions:** 300 journals and other serials. **Services:** Interlibrary loan; copying. **Computerized Information Services:** DIALOG Information Services, LEXIS, Dow Jones News/Retrieval. **Remarks:** FAX: (713)224-3607. **Staff:** Shelley Boltri, Libn.

★8809★
KPMG/Peat Marwick - Tax Library
345 Park Ave., 36th Fl. Phone: (212)872-6503
New York, NY 10154 Marlene Augustin, Libn.
Services: Library not open to the public. **Remarks:** No further information was supplied by respondent.

★8810★
KPMG Peat Marwick Thorne - Information Resources/Centre de Documentation (Bus-Fin)
1155 Boul. Rene Levesque, Suite 2000 Phone: (514)840-2245
Montreal, PQ, Canada H3B 2J9 Judy Macfarlane, Sr.Mgr.
Founded: 1980. **Staff:** Prof 3; Other 2. **Subjects:** Accounting, auditing, taxation, business, data processing. **Holdings:** 5000 books; 500 bound periodical volumes; 17 drawers of annual reports; 16 VF drawers of research files and clippings; 25 drawers of tax forms. **Subscriptions:** 325 journals and other serials; 10 newspapers. **Services:** Interlibrary loan; copying; SDI; center open to the public by appointment. **Automated Operations:** Computerized public access catalog, cataloging, and serials. **Computerized Information Services:** DIALOG Information Services, PFDS Online, Info Globe, Dow Jones News/Retrieval, Reuter TEXTLINE, Dun and Bradstreet Canada Limited, STM Systems Corporation, LEXIS, NEXIS, InvesText, Reuters; National Tax Research File, Contact Register System, ARRA (index of annual reports) (internal databases); Dialcom Inc. (electronic mail service). Performs searches on fee basis. **Publications:** Acquisition List, monthly; Information Update, irregular - both for internal distribution only. **Remarks:** Services are available in both English and French. Alternate telephone number(s): 840-2252; 840-2253. FAX: (514)840-2233. Telex: 05-268735. **Also Known As:** Peat Marwick Thorne. **Staff:** Karen Bleakley, Libn.; Linda Bleiziffer, Ser.; Nathalie Gauthier, Cat.

★8811★
KPMG Peat Marwick Thorne - John Walker Library (Bus-Fin)
1 Toronto St. Phone: (416)777-8515
Toronto, ON, Canada M5C 2V5 Cathy Gareau, Mgr.
Founded: 1959. **Staff:** 4. **Subjects:** Accounting, auditing, business and management, finance. **Special Collections:** Statistics Canada. **Holdings:** 5000 books; annual reports; microfiche. **Subscriptions:** 332 journals and other serials. **Services:** Interlibrary loan; center not open to the public. **Automated Operations:** Computerized cataloging. **Computerized Information Services:** DIALOG Information Services, Info Globe, Dun & Bradstreet Business Credit Services, STM Insight, QL Systems, WESTLAW, Marketscan, Infomart Online, CAN/OLE, VU/TEXT Information Services, FT PROFILE; internal database. **Publications:** Current Accounts (newsletter). **Remarks:** FAX: (416)777-8818. Telex: 6217692.

★8812★
KPMG Peat Marwick Thorne - Resource Centre (Bus-Fin)
Bow Valley Square 2
205 5th Ave., S.W., Suite 1200 Phone: (403)691-8470
Calgary, AB, Canada T2P 4B9 Roxie Buhler, Libn.
Staff: Prof 1; Other 1. **Subjects:** Canadian and U.S. taxation, accounting, auditing, oil, gas. **Holdings:** 704 volumes; annual reports; prospectuses. **Subscriptions:** 105 journals and other serials; 6 newspapers. **Services:** Interlibrary loan; library open to clients and other libraries. **Automated Operations:** Computerized cataloging and serials. **Computerized Information Services:** DIALOG Information Services, Dow Jones News/Retrieval, QL Systems, WESTLAW, Info Globe, FP OnLine. Performs searches on fee basis. **Publications:** InSearch (newletter), quarterly - for internal distribution only. **Special Catalogs:** Score File. **Remarks:** FAX: (403)691-8008. **Also Known As:** Peat Marwick Thorne.

★8813★
KPMG Peat Marwick Thorne - Resource Centre (Bus-Fin)
1200, 205-5th Ave., S.W. Phone: (403)691-8470
Calgary, AB, Canada T2P 4B9 Roxie Buhler, Libn.
Founded: 1982. **Staff:** Prof 1; Other 1. **Subjects:** Accounting, taxation, investment, oil and gas. **Special Collections:** Energy (national and international coverage; 2500 titles). **Holdings:** 1000 books; 75 bound periodical volumes; 700 reports; 100 manuscripts; 500 documents. **Subscriptions:** 100 journals and other serials; 6 newspapers. **Services:** Interlibrary loan; copying; services open to the public by appointment. **Automated Operations:** Computerized cataloging. **Computerized Information Services:** DIALOG Information Services, Infomart Online, Canadian Tax Online, QL Systems, LEXIS, NEXIS; internal database. Performs searches on fee basis. **Publications:** Acquisitions Update, monthly - for internal distribution only. **Remarks:** Alternate telephone number(s): 691-8268. FAX: (403)691-8008. **Also Known As:** Peat Marwick Thorne.

KQED Film Archives
See: **San Francisco State University - J. Paul Leonard Library - Special Collections/Archives** (14743)

★8814★
Kraft Food Ingredients Corporation - Technical Center Library (Food-Bev)
8000 Horizon Center Blvd. Phone: (901)385-6566
Memphis, TN 38133 Jan Davidson, Libn.
Founded: 1967. **Staff:** Prof 1. **Subjects:** Edible fats and oils, food processing, food chemistry, analytical chemistry, packaging, quality control. **Holdings:** 3100 books; 2250 bound periodical volumes; 250 pamphlets; technical reports. **Subscriptions:** 223 journals and other serials. **Services:** Interlibrary loan (limited); center not open to the public. **Remarks:** Alternate telephone number(s): (901)385-6500. FAX: (901)385-6510. Toll-free telephone number(s): (800)458-8324.

★8815★
Kraft General Foods, Inc. - Technical Information Research (Food-Bev)
801 Waukegan Rd. Phone: (708)998-3749
Glenview, IL 60025 Helen Pettway, Mgr., Tech.Info.Res.
Founded: 1938. **Staff:** Prof 2; Other 3. **Subjects:** Food technology, dairy science, nutrition, microbiology, packaging. **Holdings:** 7500 books; 800 bound periodical volumes; 17,000 patents; 7450 reels of microfilm; 21,500 research reports. **Subscriptions:** 370 journals and other serials. **Services:** Interlibrary loan; not open to the public. **Automated Operations:** Computerized cataloging and circulation. **Computerized Information Services:** DIALOG Information Services, ORBIT Search Service, BRS Information Technologies, STN International, LEXIS, NEXIS, VU/TEXT Information Services. **Networks/Consortia:** Member of North Suburban Library System (NSLS). **Remarks:** FAX: (708)998-5150. **Formerly:** Kraft USA. **Staff:** Marguerite Schutten, Supv.

Kraft USA
See: **Kraft General Foods, Inc. - Technical Information Research** (8815)

★8816★
(Krakow) Biblioteka Amerykanska - USIS Library (Educ)
Konsulat Stanow Zjednoczonych Ameryki
Ulica Stolarska 9 Phone: 12 216767
Cracow, Poland Janina Galas
Founded: 1976. **Staff:** 2. **Special Collections:** Management Core Collection. **Holdings:** 4600 books. **Subscriptions:** 70 journals and other serials; 2 newspapers. **Services:** Interlibrary loan; SDI; library open to the public. **Remarks:** Maintained or supported by the U.S. Information Agency. Focus is on materials that will assist peoples outside the United States to learn about the United States, its people, history, culture, political processes, and social milieux. FAX: 12 218212. **Staff:** Iwona Sadecka; Maria Brzostek.

★8817★
Kramer Chin and Mayo Inc. - Library (Sci-Engr)
1917 1st Ave. Phone: (206)443-5367
Seattle, WA 98101 Ruth J. Bell
Founded: 1960. **Staff:** Prof 1. **Subjects:** Engineering, water and sewer engineering, land planning and water resources, aquaculture and fisheries, transportation. **Special Collections:** Aquaculture and fisheries research. **Holdings:** 2200 books; 2000 reports; newsletter, pamphlet, trade catalog files. **Subscriptions:** 10 journals and other serials; 5 newspapers. **Services:** Interlibrary loan; library not open to the public. **Publications:** Accessions list, monthly - for internal distribution only. **Remarks:** FAX: (206)443-5372.

★8818★
Krames Communications - Library and Resource Center (Med)
1100 Grundy Ln. Phone: (415)742-0400
San Bruno, CA 94066-3030 Susan Prather, Libn.
Staff: Prof 1; Other 2. **Subjects:** Health, wellness, patient information. **Holdings:** Figures not available. **Subscriptions:** 300 journals and other serials. **Services:** Center not open to the public. **Automated Operations:** Computerized acquisitions and serials. **Computerized Information Services:** DIALOG Information Services, Dow Jones News/Retrieval, WILSONLINE, MEDLARS; internal databases; DIALMAIL (electronic mail service). **Staff:** James O'Grady, Lib.Coord.

Krasker Memorial Film/Video Library
See: **Boston University** (2012)

Kraus Curriculum Development Library
See: **University of Windsor - Faculty of Education Library** (19566)

Joseph Krauskopf Memorial Library
See: **Delaware Valley College of Science and Agriculture** (4737)

Charles E. Krausz Library
See: **Pennsylvania College of Podiatric Medicine** (12840)

Krauth Memorial Library
See: **Lutheran Theological Seminary** (9465)

Kravitz Memorial Library
See: **Park Synagogue Library** (12750)

Kresge Business Administration Library
See: **University of Michigan** (18870)

Kresge Center Library
See: **Harvard University - School of Public Health - Kresge Center Library** (6995)

Kresge Engineering Library
See: **University of California, Berkeley** (18330)

Kresge Medical Library
See: **Scripps Research Institute** (14973)

Kresge Physical Sciences Library
See: **Dartmouth College** (4610)

Kress Library of Business and Economics
See: **Harvard University - Harvard Business School - Baker Library** (6969)

Kretsch Brain Injury Resource Library
See: **A Chance to Grow - Kretsch Brain Injury Resource Library** (3427)

David B. Kriser Dental Center
See: **New York University - David B. Kriser Dental Center** (11722)

Hilda Kroeker Library
See: **Calvary Bible College** (2586)

Krohn Memorial Library
See: **Good Samaritan Hospital** (6551)

★8819★
Krotona Institute of Theosophy - Krotona Library - Betty Warrington Memorial (Rel-Phil)
Krotona 2 Phone: (805)646-2653
Ojai, CA 93023 Mary Kokochak, Libn.
Founded: 1912. **Staff:** 2. **Subjects:** Theosophy, philosophy, religions, philosophy of science, parapsychology, metaphysics, mysticism. **Holdings:** 8000 volumes. **Subscriptions:** 30 journals and other serials. **Services:** Copying (limited); library open to the public.

★8820★
Krymskaja Oblastnaja Naucno Medicinskaja - Biblioteka (Med, Biol Sci)
Gorkogo 5 Phone: 277778
SU-333000 Simferopol, Ukraine Larisa Aleksandrovna Yermolenko
Founded: 1946. **Staff:** Prof 21; Other 7. **Subjects:** Medicine, public health, pharmacology, biology, genetics, politics. **Special Collections:** Rare book collection, 18th and 19th centuries (851 volumes). **Holdings:** 315,078 books; 89,135 bound periodical volumes; 1000 reels of microfilm; 4160 theses. **Subscriptions:** 231 journals and other serials; 17 newspapers. **Services:** Interlibrary loan; library open to the public with restrictions. **Publications:** List of new books, monthly. **Special Catalogs:** Subject catalogs. **Special Indexes:** Indexes on health resort treatment.

★8821★
KSB Aktiengesellschaft - Fachbucherei und Technische Information (Sci-Engr)
Postfach 1725 Phone: 6233 862414
W-6710 Frankenthal, Germany Hans-Dieter Ahreus
Founded: 1954. **Staff:** Prof 4; Other 2. **Subjects:** Pumps, valves, power stations. **Special Collections:** Fluid flow and cavitation collections. **Holdings:** 12,000 books; 200 bound periodical volumes; 1000 reports; 27,000 microfiche. **Subscriptions:** 500 journals and other serials; 10 newspapers. **Services:** Interlibrary loan; copying; library open to the public with restrictions. **Computerized Information Services:** DIALOG Information Services, ESA/IRS, ORBIT Search Service, BRS Information Technologies, STN International, PFDS Online. Performs searches. Contact Person: Barbara Finke. **Remarks:** FAX: 6233 863400. Telex: 465211-0.

★8822★
KTA-Tator, Inc. - Library (Sci-Engr)
115 Technology Dr. Phone: (412)788-1300
Pittsburgh, PA 15275 Dwight Weldon, Lab.Dir.
Founded: 1947. **Staff:** Prof 35; Other 10. **Subjects:** Organic coatings, industrial paint performance, industrial color, industrial maintenance. **Holdings:** Case histories of paint performance in industrial exposures on 35,000 punched information cards keyed to original data sources in record and microfilm files. **Services:** Library open to clients; reviews or reports made by staff on fee basis. **Remarks:** FAX: (412)788-1306.

★8823★
Kuban State Agricultural University - Library (Agri)
ul. Kalinina 13 Phone: 502609
Krasnodar, Russia Ludmila Butko, Lib.Hd.
Founded: 1922. **Staff:** Prof 83. **Subjects:** Agriculture, crop science, animal breeding, economics, plant protection, veterinary science, agricultural engineering. **Special Collections:** Ancient book collection (1899 titles). **Holdings:** 629,110 books; 374,075 bound periodical volumes; 17,896 reports; 400 microfiche. **Subscriptions:** 433 journals and other serials; 90 newspapers. **Services:** Interlibrary loan; library open to the public. **Special Indexes:** Current Research Index on Agriculture: Publications of the University Staff. **Also Known As:** Kubanskij Selskochozjajstvennyj Institut - Biblioteka.

Kubanskij Selskochozjajstvennyj Institut - Biblioteka
See: **Kuban State Agricultural University - Library** (8823)

John M. Kuehne Physics-Mathematics-Astronomy Library
See: **University of Texas at Austin - Physics-Mathematics-Astronomy Library** (19402)

Kuehner Memorial Library
See: **Reformed Episcopal Church - Philadelphia Theological Seminary** (13779)

Kulas Music Library
See: **Case Western Reserve University** (3124)

Kultura Centro Esperantista
See: **Esperanto Cultural Centre** (5442)

Bernhard Kummel Library of the Geological Sciences
See: **Harvard University** (6948)

Kungl. Biblioteket
See: **Sweden - Royal Library - National Library of Sweden** (15911)

Kungliga Tekniska Hogskolans Bibliotek
See: **Sweden - Royal Institute of Technology** (15910)

★8824★
Kunstakademie Dusseldorf - Bibliothek (Art)
Eiskellerstr 1 Phone: 211 1396461
W-4000 Dusseldorf, Germany Helmut Kleinenbroich, Dipl.Bibl.
Founded: 1776. **Staff:** Prof 1; Other 3. **Subjects:** Fine arts, architecture, aesthetics. **Holdings:** 100,000 books and bound periodical volumes. **Subscriptions:** 5 newspapers. **Services:** Copying; library open to the public for reference use only. **Remarks:** FAX: 211 1396225.

★8825★
Kunsthalle zu Kiel - Fachbibliothek der Universitatsbibliothek Kiel - Bibliothek (Art)
Dusternbrooker Weg 1-7 Phone: 431 5973751
W-2300 Kiel, Germany Jens Kohler
Founded: 1958. **Staff:** 4. **Subjects:** Art - 19th century, 20th century, contemporary. **Holdings:** 35,000 books. **Subscriptions:** 73 journals and other serials. **Services:** Copying; library open to the public for reference use only. **Remarks:** FAX: 431 5973754.

★8826★
Kunsthistorische Musea - Rubenianum (Art)
Kolveniersstraat 20 Phone: 3 232-3920
B-2000 Antwerp, Belgium Nora De Poorter, Asst. Keeper
Founded: 1960. **Subjects:** Art history. **Special Collections:** Old Master Paintings (80,000 photographs). **Holdings:** 27,000 books. **Subscriptions:** 130 journals and other serials. **Services:** Copying; library open to the public. **Publications:** Corpus Rubenianum Ludwig Burchard (catalog of works of P.P. Rubens).

★8827★
The Kurdish Heritage Foundation of America, Inc. - The Kurdish Library (Area-Ethnic)
345 Park Pl. Phone: (718)783-7930
Brooklyn, NY 11238 Dr. Vera Beaudin Saeedpour, Dir.
Founded: 1986. **Staff:** 3. **Subjects:** Kurdish culture, language, history, literature, politics, contemporary affairs; Kurds in Turkey, Iran, Iraq, Syria, Soviet Union, and abroad. **Special Collections:** Archibald Roosevelt, Jr., publications from Mahabad; Ismetvanly Slide Collection (300); Dana Adams Schmidt photographic collection of Iraqi Kurdistan; Bahia Gulick Village Jewelry; Kurdish costume. **Holdings:** 1500 books; clip file; photographs; videotapes. **Services:** Copying; library open to the public by appointment. **Publications:** Kurdish Times (journal), semiannual - available by subscription, free to members; Kurdish Life, quarterly - free to members. **Remarks:** FAX: (718)398-4365.

The Kurdish Library
See: **The Kurdish Heritage Foundation of America, Inc.** (8827)

★8828★
George Kurian Reference Books - Editorial Library (Publ)
Box 519 Phone: (914)962-3287
Baldwin Place, NY 10505-0519 Sarah Claudine, Hd., Ref. & Res.
Founded: 1972. **Staff:** Prof 1; Other 1. **Subjects:** Reference, history, international affairs, statistics, scholarly books, bibliography. **Holdings:** 6500 books; 100 bound periodical volumes; 170 other cataloged items. **Subscriptions:** 47 journals and other serials.

★8829★
Kutak Rock & Campbell - Law Library (Law)
1650 Farnam St. Phone: (402)346-6000
Omaha, NE 68102 Avis B. Forsman, Libn.
Founded: 1965. **Staff:** 6. **Subjects:** Law. **Holdings:** 25,000 books; 550 bound periodical volumes; 3000 pamphlets. **Subscriptions:** 175 journals and other serials. **Services:** Library open to the public by appointment. **Computerized Information Services:** DIALOG Information Services, LEXIS, WESTLAW, Dow Jones News/Retrieval, WILSONLINE, DataTimes. **Remarks:** FAX: (402)346-1148.

★8830★
Kutak Rock & Campbell - Library (Law)
1101 Connecticut Ave., N.W. Phone: (202)828-2400
Washington, DC 20036 John H. Harbison, Dir., Info.Serv.
Founded: 1978. **Staff:** Prof 1; Other 1. **Subjects:** Litigation; law - corporate, international (municipal finance), securities, taxation, banking. **Special Collections:** Security and Exchange Commission microfiche. **Holdings:** 2500 books; 200 bound periodical volumes; Securities and Exchange Commission documents on microfiche; 1000 SEC prospectuses; pamphlets. **Subscriptions:** 250 journals and other serials; 5 newspapers. **Services:** Interlibrary loan; copying; SDI; library open to the public by appointment. **Automated Operations:** Computerized cataloging, serials, and circulation. **Computerized Information Services:** LEXIS, NEXIS, WESTLAW, DIALOG Information Services, Newsnet, Inc., VU/TEXT Information Services, Dow Jones News/Retrieval; MCI Mail (electronic mail service). **Remarks:** FAX: (202)828-2488.

★8831★
Kutak Rock & Campbell, Attorneys at Law - Law Library (Law)
4400 Georgia-Pacific Center
133 Peachtree St., N.E.
Atlanta, GA 30303 Phone: (404)222-4600
Staff: Prof 1. **Subjects:** Law. **Holdings:** 15,000 books; 500 bound periodical volumes; 5000 other cataloged items; 2000 volumes on microfiche. **Subscriptions:** 80 journals and other serials; 8 newspapers. **Services:** Interlibrary loan; copying; SDI; library open to the public with restrictions. **Computerized Information Services:** LEXIS, DIALOG Information Services, WESTLAW, Information America, WILSONLINE. Performs searches on fee basis. **Publications:** Library Newsletter, monthly - for internal distribution only. **Special Indexes:** Memorandums of Law. **Remarks:** FAX: (404)222-4654.

★8832★
Kutztown University - Rohrbach Library (Hum)
Kutztown, PA 19530 Phone: (215)683-4480
Margaret Devlin, Dir. of Lib.Serv.
Founded: 1866. **Staff:** Prof 12; Other 12. **Subjects:** Education, art, library science, literature, history. **Special Collections:** Russian Culture Center Collection; Curriculum Materials Center; Pennsylvania Collection. **Holdings:** 391,013 books; 54,963 bound periodical volumes; 1.1 million, microforms; 22,561 maps; 3607 pamphlets; 2130 college catalogs; 407 telephone directories; 1697 teaching aids. **Subscriptions:** 2052 periodicals and newspapers. **Services:** Interlibrary loan; copying; library open to the public. **Automated Operations:** Computerized public access catalog, cataloging and acquisitions. **Computerized Information Services:** DIALOG Information Services, OCLC; CD-ROMs; ALANET (electronic mail service). Performs searches on fee basis. **Networks/Consortia:** Member of PALINET, Associated College Libraries of Central Pennsylvania (ACLCP). **Remarks:** FAX: (215)683-4483. **Staff:** Margaret Apostolos, Microtext & Per.Libn.; Paul Apostolos, Evening Per.Libn.; Janet Bond, Ref.Coord.; Linda Woods, Ref.Libn.; Claire Andrews, Ref.Libn.; Janet Simone-Hohe, Evening Ref.Libn.; Mildred Reilley, Curriculum Materials Libn.; Anita Sprankle, Spec.Proj./Maps; Susan Czerny, Acq.Libn.; Sandra Allen, Cat.Coord.; Linda Halma, Cat.Libn.; Helen Berg, Access Serv.Libn.

★8833★
Kuwait Chamber of Commerce - Library (Bus-Fin)
P.O. Box 775
Safat 13008, Kuwait Phone: 2433854
Subjects: Business, Kuwaiti national economic policy. **Holdings:** 7000 volumes. **Remarks:** FAX: 2404110. Telex: 22198 GURFTIGARA.

★8834★
Kuwait Science Club - Library (Sci-Engr)
P.O. Box 23259
Safat 13093, Kuwait Phone: 4741908
Subjects: Science, agriculture, applied technology, astronomy, chemistry, computers, mechanics. **Holdings:** 1000 volumes. **Remarks:** FAX: 4716029. Telex: 31949.

★8835★
(Kwangju) American Cultural Center - USIS Library (Educ)
No. 80 Hwangkum-dong
Dong-ku, 500
Kwangju, Republic of Korea
Remarks: Maintained or supported by the U.S. Information Agency. Focus is on materials that will assist peoples outside the United States to learn about the United States, its people, history, culture, political processes, and social milieux.

★8836★
Kwasha Lipton - Library (Bus-Fin)
2100 N. Central Rd.
Box 1400 Phone: (201)592-1300
Fort Lee, NJ 07024 Mary Seaman, Lib.Mgr.
Staff: Prof 1; Other 1. **Subjects:** Employee benefits - taxation, demographics, policy formation, trends. **Special Collections:** Internal Revenue Service (IRS) private letter rulings on employee benefits (categorized by holding); special interest files (10 VF drawers). **Holdings:** 2000 books; 45 bound periodical volumes. **Subscriptions:** 140 journals and other serials; 10 newspapers. **Services:** Library not open to the public. **Computerized Information Services:** DIALOG Information Services, Dow Jones News/Retrieval, LEXIS, NEXIS, Maxwell Macmillan Taxes Online, Human Resource Information Network (HRIN), BNA (Bureau of National Affairs, Inc.) Online. Performs searches on fee basis. **Publications:** Internal Memo Finding List. **Special Indexes:** Index to Internal Memos (book). **Remarks:** FAX: (201)592-9012.

★8837★
Kyoto American Center - USIS Library (Educ)
Higashi Monzencho 657
Sokoku-ji, Kamigyo-ku
Kyoto 602, Japan
Remarks: Maintained or supported by the U.S. Information Agency. Focus is on materials that will assist peoples outside the United States to learn about the United States, its people, history, culture, political processes, and social milieux.

★8838★
Kyoto University - Institute for Research in Humanities - Library (Hum, Area-Ethnic)
Ushinomiya-cho
Yoshida, Sakyo-ku Phone: 75-753-6909
Kyoto 606, Japan Shigeo Yamamoto, Libn.
Staff: Prof 10; Other 11. **Subjects:** Humanities; Japan; China; Asia; Western civilization; history of fine arts, religions, science; social anthropology. **Holdings:** 443,000 books; 4416 bound periodical volumes. **Subscriptions:** 399 journals and other serials; 12 newspapers. **Services:** Interlibrary loan; library not open to the public. **Remarks:** FAX: 753-6903. **Also Known As:** Zinbun Kagaku Kenkyusho. **Staff:** T. Yoshikowa.

★8839★
Kyungnam University - Institute for Far Eastern Studies - IFES Library (Area-Ethnic)
28-42 Samchung-dong
Chongro-ku Phone: 2 7353202
Seoul, Republic of Korea Joomi Kim
Staff: 3. **Subjects:** North Korea, China and the Soviet Union, United States and Japan, third world, economics of Communist countries. **Special Collections:** Slavic Studies Library. **Holdings:** 30,000 volumes. **Subscriptions:** 220 journals and other serials; 15 newspapers. **Services:** Library open to scholars and students of Asian affairs. **Publications:** Monographs. **Special Indexes:** Index to journal articles. **Remarks:** FAX: 2 7354359. Telex: KIFES K26834.

★8840★
Kyushu University - Research Institute of Fundamental Information Science - Library (Info Sci)
10-1, Hakozaki 6-Chome
Higashi-ku, Fukuoka-shi Phone: 92 6412668
Fukuoka 812, Japan Setuo Arikawa, Dir.
Founded: 1967. **Staff:** 8. **Subjects:** Information science - cybernetics, bionics, computer science, data analysis, statistical program packages, software systems. **Holdings:** 2600 bound volumes. **Subscriptions:** 27 journals and other serials. **Computerized Information Services:** NISAN, Micro-NISAN (internal databases). **Remarks:** FAX: 92 6112668.

★8841★
KZF, Inc. - KZF Library (Sci-Engr)
655 Eden Park Dr. Phone: (513)621-6211
Cincinnati, OH 45202 Dennis O. Hamilton, Adm.Serv.Mgr.
Founded: 1974. **Staff:** Prof 1; Other 1. **Subjects:** Architecture; engineering - civil, mechanical, electrical, structural; environmental sciences; planning; interior design. **Holdings:** 2000 books; 2000 specifications; 200 company reports; 9 VF drawers of pamphlets; 40 cassettes. **Subscriptions:** 200 journals and other serials. **Services:** Interlibrary loan; copying; library open to the public by appointment. **Computerized Information Services:** DIALOG Information Services, WILSONLINE. **Remarks:** FAX: (513)621-6530.

L

★8842★
L.D.S. Hospital - Library (Med)
325 8th Ave. Phone: (801)321-1054
Salt Lake City, UT 84143 Mr. Terry L. Heyer, Lib.Dir.
Founded: 1957. **Staff:** Prof 1. **Subjects:** Medicine, nursing. **Holdings:** 3500 books; 7500 bound periodical volumes; 175 pamphlets; 900 audiotape cassettes. **Subscriptions:** 400 journals and other serials; 12 newspapers. **Services:** Interlibrary loan; copying; SDI; library open to the public. **Automated Operations:** Computerized cataloging and serials. **Computerized Information Services:** MEDLINE. Performs searches on fee basis. **Networks/Consortia:** Member of National Network of Libraries of Medicine - Midcontinental Region. **Remarks:** FAX: (801)321-5008. Maintained by Intermountain Health Care, Inc.

★8843★
L & F Products - Information Center (Sci-Engr)
1 Philips Pkwy. Phone: (201)573-6031
Montvale, NJ 07645-1810 Irene S. Frye, Libn.
Staff: Prof 1. **Subjects:** Business management, cosmetics, dermatology, microbiology, marketing, detergents, disinfectants, floor waxes. **Holdings:** 1000 books; 800 bound periodical volumes and reels of microfilm; 8 VF drawers of patents; 8 VF drawers of pamphlets and articles. **Subscriptions:** 250 journals and other serials. **Services:** Interlibrary loan; copying. **Computerized Information Services:** DIALOG Information Services; DIALMAIL (electronic mail service). **Remarks:** FAX: (201)573-6046. L & F Products is a unit of Eastman Kodak Company.

L.M. Media Marketing Services Ltd. - Canadian Film Institute
See: **Canadian Film Institute** (2929)

★8844★
La Grange College - William and Evelyn Banks Library - Special Collections (Hist)
601 Broad St. Phone: (404)882-2911
LaGrange, GA 30240 Frank R. Lewis, Dir.
Founded: 1831. **Staff:** Prof 3; Other 3. **Subjects:** LaGrange College history; LaGrange, Georgia history; Lafayette. **Special Collections:** Florence Grogan Collection (original manuscripts of short stories and plays; 50); Lafayette Collection (memorabilia and manuscripts; 250 items). **Holdings:** 101,000 books; 15,000 bound periodical volumes; 1500 reels of microfilm; 10 cabinets microfilm; 250 unbound reports and manuscripts. **Subscriptions:** 475 journals and other serials; 9 newspapers. **Services:** Interlibrary loan; copying; SDI; collections open to the public for reference use only. **Automated Operations:** Computerized cataloging. **Computerized Information Services:** OCLC, DIALOG Information Services. Performs searches on fee basis. Contact Person: Steve Weaver, Ref.Libn. **Networks/Consortia:** Member of SOLINET. **Remarks:** FAX: (404)884-6567. **Staff:** Charlene A. Baxter, Cat.

★8845★
La Grange Memorial Hospital - Zitek Medical Library (Med)
5101 Willow Springs Rd. Phone: (708)579-4040
La Grange, IL 60525 Patricia J. Grundke, Dir., Lib.Rsrcs.
Founded: 1955. **Staff:** Prof 1. **Subjects:** Medicine, nursing, and allied health sciences. **Holdings:** 1200 books; 3500 bound periodical volumes. **Subscriptions:** 160 journals and other serials. **Services:** Interlibrary loan; copying; SDI; library open to the public for reference use only by appointment. **Computerized Information Services:** MEDLARS, BRS Information Technologies; ALANET (electronic mail service). Performs searches on fee basis. **Networks/Consortia:** Member of National Network of Libraries of Medicine - Greater Midwest Region, Chicago and South Consortium, ILLINET, Suburban Library System (SLS). **Remarks:** FAX: (708)352-6072. **Staff:** Paul M. Martinez, Media Coord.

★8846★
La Guardia Hospital - Health Sciences Library (Med)
102-01 66 Rd. Phone: (718)830-4188
Forest Hills, NY 11366 Rosalyn Barth, Lib.Dir.
Founded: 1972. **Staff:** 1. **Subjects:** Medicine, surgery, nursing. **Holdings:** 1589 books; 2900 bound periodical volumes. **Subscriptions:** 165 journals and other serials. **Services:** Interlibrary loan; library not open to the public. **Computerized Information Services:** MEDLINE. **Networks/Consortia:** Member of BHSL, New York Metropolitan Reference and Research Library Agency. **Remarks:** FAX: (718)830-4344.

★8847★
La Laurentienne Compagnie Muturelle d'Assurance Generale - Library (Bus-Fin)
P.O. Box 1216 Phone: (418)647-5151
Quebec, PQ, Canada G1K 7E3 Louise Bedard, Tech.Libn.
Staff: Prof 1; Other 1. **Subjects:** Insurance, management, psychology, business, administration. **Holdings:** 5000 books; 180 bound periodical volumes. **Subscriptions:** 170 journals and other serials; 8 newspapers. **Services:** Interlibrary loan (fee); copying; library open to the public with restrictions. **Publications:** Biblio - for internal distribution only.

★8848★
La Leche League International - Center for Breastfeeding Information (Med)
9616 Minneapolis Ave.
P.O. Box 1209 Phone: (708)455-7730
Franklin Park, IL 60131 Betty L. Crase, Dir., CBI
Founded: 1956. **Staff:** 3. **Subjects:** Breast-feeding, parenting. **Holdings:** 200 books and monographs; 7500 published research studies and case reports. **Services:** Center open to the public on fee basis. **Computerized Information Services:** Center for Breastfeeding Information (internal database). **Remarks:** Toll-free telephone number(s): (800) LALECHE. FAX:(708)455-0125. **Staff:** Carol Huotari, Ref.Libn.

★8849★
La Mesa Presbyterian Church - Library (Rel-Phil)
7401 Copper, N.E. Phone: (505)255-8095
Albuquerque, NM 87108 Susan K. Smith, Christian Educ.Coord.
Subjects: Religion, children's literature. **Holdings:** 1600 books; 12 bound periodical volumes. **Services:** Library open to the public with restrictions.

★8850★
(La Paz) Centro Boliviano-Americano - USIS Collection (Educ)
Parque Zenon Iturralde
Ave. Arce 121
Casilla 20623 Phone: 20 366005
La Paz, Bolivia Violeta B. De Lavino, Hd.Libn.
Founded: 1946. **Staff:** 3. **Holdings:** 6000 books; 10 reports; 2 microfiche. **Subscriptions:** 121 journals and other serials. **Services:** Library open to the public. **Remarks:** FAX: 20 355081. Maintained or supported by the U.S. Information Agency. Focus is on materials that will assist peoples outside the United States to learn about the United States, its people, history, culture, political processes, and social milieux. **Staff:** Juan Fierro, Asst.Libn.

★8851★
La Porte Herald-Argus - Library (Publ)
701 State St. Phone: (219)362-2161
La Porte, IN 46350 Anita Purkal, Libn.
Founded: 1966. **Staff:** Prof 2. **Subjects:** Newspaper reference topics. **Special Collections:** Congressional Directories (10 volumes); Congressional Staff Directories (8 volumes); Historical Guide on Indiana. **Holdings:** 104 books; 66 bound periodical volumes; 30 reports; 40 maps; 35 directories. **Subscriptions:** 30 newspapers. **Services:** Copying; library open to the public with restrictions.

★8852★
La Presse, Ltee. - Centre de Documentation (Publ)
7, rue St-Jacques, W. Phone: (514)285-7007
Montreal, PQ, Canada H2Y 1K9 Gerard Monette, Spec.Adv.
Founded: 1969. **Staff:** 8. **Subjects:** Newspaper reference topics, statistics, political science, economics, public administration, technology, literature,

history. **Special Collections:** Le Nouveau Journal, 1961-1962 (complete collection); La Presse, 1884 to present (945 reels of microfilm); La Patrie, 1879 to present (662 reels of microfilm). **Holdings:** Clippings on 25,000 subjects, 1962-1978; 1.5 million photographs, 1900 to present. **Subscriptions:** 200 journals and other serials; 17 newspapers. **Services:** Interlibrary loan; center not open to the public. **Automated Operations:** Computerized indexing. **Computerized Information Services:** MINISIS. **Special Catalogs:** Catalogues des Dossiers; Catalogue des Photos. **Special Indexes:** Index du Journal La Presse.

★8853★
La Purisima Mission - Archives (Hist)
La Purisima Mission State Historic Park
2295 Purisima Rd. Phone: (805)733-3713
Lompoc, CA 93436 Joe McCummins, Ranger I
Founded: 1936. **Staff:** Prof 1; Other 2. **Subjects:** Spanish Colonial Period. **Special Collections:** Edith Webb Collection (personal papers pertaining to the mission); Harrington Collection. **Holdings:** 60 books; 300 blueprint drawings; artifacts; restoration material; 600 pieces of correspondence (indexed). **Services:** Archives open to the public through written application with a resume. **Remarks:** Maintained by State Parks System of California.

★8854★
La Que Center for Corrosion Technology, Inc. - Library (Sci-Engr)
P.O. Box 656 Phone: (919)256-2271
Wrightsville Beach, NC 28480 Margie Skipper, Libn.
Subjects: Corrosion, fracture mechanics. **Holdings:** 2000 volumes. **Services:** Library not open to the public. **Computerized Information Services:** Internal database (marine and industrial corrosion). **Remarks:** FAX: (919)256-9816.

★8855★
La Ramie Soils Service - Library (Sci-Engr)
209 Grand Ave., Suite 408-409
P.O. Box 255 Phone: (307)742-4185
Laramie, WY 82070 M. McFaul, Owner
Founded: 1980. **Subjects:** Soils and sediment, geomorphology, geoarcheology. **Special Collections:** Current research on the Pleistocene Era. **Holdings:** 400 volumes. **Subscriptions:** 4 journals and other serials. **Services:** Library open to the public for reference use only. **Networks/ Consortia:** Member of Colorado Alliance of Research Libraries (CARL).

★8856★
La Salle University - Connelly Library - Special Collections Department - Imaginative Representations of the Vietnam War Collection (Hist)
20th St. and Olney Ave. Phone: (215)951-1290
Philadelphia, PA 19141 John S. Baky, Dir., Lib.Serv.
Founded: 1863. **Staff:** Prof 10; Other 25. **Subjects:** Vietnam War - fiction, art, poetry, music. **Special Collections:** Imaginative Representations of the Vietnam War (4000); Japanese Tea Ceremony (400); Graham Greene (first editions and their international translations). **Holdings:** 4000 book; 500 videocassettes; 700 nonbook items; films; graphics, comics and cartoons; manuscripts; scripts, holograph copeis; poetry broadsides; dealer's catalogs; strategy games; software; curriculum guides; other ephemeral material. **Services:** Interlibrary loan; copying; SDI; collection open to scholars and professional researchers for reference use only (others need letter from a sponsoring institution). **Computerized Information Services:** OCLC, BRS Information Technologies, DIALOG Information Services, BIOSIS, Humanities Index; CD-ROM (WILSONDISC). Performs searches on fee basis. Contact Person: Eithne Bearden. **Remarks:** Collection seeks to demonstrate "how a complex event is interpreted through creative means" and "how creative treatments of an event use aesthetic values to reveal both the fact and emotional essence of traumatic cultural phenomena." This is the largest collection of its kind in the world. FAX: (215)951-1595.

★8857★
La Sierra University - Library (Rel-Phil, Educ)
4700 Pierce St. Phone: (714)785-2397
Riverside, CA 92515 H. Maynard Lowry
Founded: 1922. **Staff:** Prof 7; Other 5. **Subjects:** Adventist history, education, Reformation. **Services:** Interlibrary loan; copying; library open to the public. **Computerized Information Services:** DIALOG Information Services, BRS Information Technologies. Contact Person: Jon Hardt, Ref.Libn. **Remarks:** FAX: (714)785-2445.

La Sorbonne - Bibliotheque
See: **Universites de Paris I, III, IV, V, VII** (18134)

Laaketieteellinen Keskuskirjasto
See: **Finland - National Library of Health Sciences** (5710)

★8858★
Lab Chrysotile, Inc. - Quality Control/Research & Development Library (Sci-Engr)
P.O. Box 459 Phone: (418)338-7500
Thetford Mines, PQ, Canada G6G 5T5 Pierre Laroche, Q.C. Mgr.
Founded: 1986. **Staff:** Prof 1. **Subjects:** Chrysotile, fiber applications and processing, mining, legislation. **Holdings:** 600 volumes. **Subscriptions:** 10 journals and other serials; 4 newspapers. **Services:** Library not open to the public. **Remarks:** FAX: (418)338-7661. Telex: 05 833586.

★8859★
John Labatt Limited - Central Research Library (Sci-Engr)
150 Simcoe St.
Box 5050 Phone: (519)667-7355
London, ON, Canada N6A 4M3 Maryanne MacDonald, Mgr., Lib.Serv.
Founded: 1956. **Staff:** Prof 1; Other 1. **Subjects:** Chemistry - general, physical, inorganic, analytical; general science; microbiology; biotechnology; genetics. **Holdings:** 10,000 books; 3000 bound periodical volumes. **Subscriptions:** 250 journals and other serials; 5 newspapers. **Services:** Interlibrary loan; library not open to the public. **Automated Operations:** Computerized cataloging. **Computerized Information Services:** DIALOG Information Services, CAN/OLE; VT 100 (internal database). **Remarks:** FAX: (519)667-7473. Telex: 064 7244. **Staff:** Mrs. L. Eden, Lib.Techn.

★8860★
Labor Research Association - Library
145 W. 28th St., Suite 6R
New York, NY 10001-6191
Defunct.

Laboratorio Conmemorativo Gorgas Biblioteca-Biomedica
See: **Gorgas Memorial Laboratory** (6580)

Laboratorio Nacional de Engenharia Civil
See: **Portugal - Ministerio das Obras Publicas Transportes e Communicacoes** (13260)

★8861★
Laboratorios Nacionales de Fomento Industrial - Centro de Informacion Tecnologica Industrial (Sci-Engr)
Ave. Industria Militar 261
Lomas de Sotelo Phone: 91 5897103
53390 Naucalpan, DF, Mexico L. Rafael Sandoval Blanchet, Libn.
Founded: 1981. **Staff:** 8. **Subjects:** Industrial research and development in Mexico; chemistry; chemical engineering; food science and technology; biotechnology; packaging; product development; process development. **Holdings:** 6000 volumes. **Subscriptions:** 100 journals and other serials; 7 newspapers. **Services:** Interlibrary loan; copying; SDI; library open to the public. **Computerized Information Services:** Online services. **Publications:** Alerta (bulletin); SDI (bulletin). **Remarks:** FAX: 91 2943713. Telex: 017-71166 LNFIME CLAVE LANFIMEX. **Also Known As:** National Laboratories of Industrial Development. **Staff:** Jose Luis Vazquez Luna; Carlos Camacho Campos.

Labour Canada
See: **Canada - Labour Canada** (2760)

★8862★
The Labour Movement - Library and Archive (Bus-Fin, Soc Sci)
Rejsbygade 1 Phone: 331241522
DK-1759 Copenhagen V, Denmark Dr. Gerd Callesen
Founded: 1909. **Staff:** 14. **Subjects:** Labor movement; trade unions; socialdemocratic, socialist, communist organizations; Socialism; Marxism; cultural and educational associations of the labor movement. **Special Collections:** Labor organization archives (50,000 photographs; 3000 posters; 600 banners; 7000 unprinted protocols and minutebooks; 3000 linear meters of manuscripts; oral history tapes; videotapes; personal papers of members of labor movement). **Holdings:** 85,000 books; 6000 periodical titles. **Subscriptions:** 1100 journals and other serials; 4 newspapers. **Services:** Interlibrary loan; copying; library open to the public. **Computerized Information Services:** Internal database. **Publications:** ABAs bibliografiske serie; Tilvaekst liste; International arbejderbevaegelse; Under de rode faner; Et arkiv bliver til. **Special Indexes:** Index to periodicals found in the library. **Remarks:** FAX: 331243222. **Also Known As:** Arbejderbevaegelsens Bibliotek og Arkiv. **Staff:** Karen Pedersen; Dorte Ellesoe Hansen ; Marianne Bagge Hansen; Hannah Linden.

★8863★
Labrador Institute of Northern Studies - LINS Information Centre (Area-Ethnic)
P.O. Box 490, Sta. B Phone: (709)896-2978
Happy Valley, NF, Canada A0P 1E0 Sharon Langdon, Info.Ctr.Asst.
Founded: 1983. **Staff:** Prof 1. **Subjects:** Labrador history and culture, environmental issues. **Holdings:** 2947 books; 113 bound periodical volumes; 1550 reprints. **Subscriptions:** 125 journals and other serials. **Services:** Interlibrary loan; copying; center open to the public. **Computerized Information Services:** SPIRES (Stanford Public Information Retrieval System); Envoy 100 (electronic mail service). **Remarks:** FAX: (709)896-2970. Electronic mail address(es): LINS (Envoy 100).

★8864★
Labrum & Doak - Library (Law)
1700 Market St., Suite 700 Phone: (215)561-4400
Philadelphia, PA 19103 Ann Zemsky, Lib.Dir.
Founded: 1930. **Subjects:** Law. **Holdings:** 13,500 books; 4500 microfiche. **Subscriptions:** 135 journals and other serials. **Services:** Interlibrary loan; library not open to the public. **Computerized Information Services:** DIALOG Information Services, LEXIS, WESTLAW. **Remarks:** FAX: (215)563-1193.

★8865★
LAC/High Desert Medical Center - Richard E. Osgood, M.D. Medical Library (Med)
44900 N. 60th St., W. Phone: (805)945-8350
Lancaster, CA 93536 Dorothy Schoeppner, Lib.Asst. II
Founded: 1975. **Staff:** 1. **Subjects:** Medicine, nursing, administration, management. **Special Collections:** California Administrative Code; Los Angeles County Code; Health and Safety Code; Welfare and Institutions Code; Business and Professions Code. **Holdings:** 1150 books; 810 bound periodical volumes; 79 code books; 56 telephone directories. **Subscriptions:** 173 journals and other serials. **Services:** Interlibrary loan; copying; library open to student nurses by appointment. **Networks/Consortia:** Member of Los Angeles County Health Sciences Library Consortium, National Network of Libraries of Medicine - Pacific Southwest Region. **Remarks:** FAX: (805)945-8474. **Formerly:** Los Angeles County/ High Desert Hospital.

★8866★
LAC/Olive View Medical Health Center - Health Sciences Library (Med)
14445 Olive View Dr., 2C 160 Phone: (818)364-4241
Sylmar, CA 91342 Maria Rietdijk, Act.Libn.
Founded: 1920. **Staff:** 3. **Subjects:** Internal medicine, ophthalmology, emergency medicine, obstetrics/gynecology, pathology, pediatrics, psychiatry, perinatology, radiology/nuclear medicine, surgery, oncology, neonatology, forensic science. **Holdings:** 3000 books; 7000 bound periodical volumes. **Subscriptions:** 480 journals and other serials. **Services:** Interlibrary loan; library not open to the public. **Computerized Information Services:** MEDLINE. **Remarks:** FAX: (818)364-3011.

★8867★
Lac Qui Parle County Historical Society - Museum Library (Hist)
Box 124 Phone: (612)598-7678
Madison, MN 56256 Christian Schulstad, Libn.
Founded: 1972. **Staff:** Prof 1; Other 1. **Subjects:** State and local history, Indian history and artifacts, genealogy. **Special Collections:** N.F. Soderberg Bible Collection; Ethel Melum Hobby Books; Mel Wroolie Stamp Collection; Minnesota legislative manuals, 1895-1988; Torgils Utne Collection (157 books). **Holdings:** 1600 books; 100 bound periodical volumes; 50 old and rare books; 50 other cataloged items; 15 binders of obituaries, 1964-1989; newspaper file; scrapbooks; pioneer stories; city, county, territorial, statehood centennials. **Subscriptions:** 12 journals and other serials. **Services:** Library open to the public for reference use only. **Publications:** Annual Report. **Special Indexes:** Obituary index (card). **Staff:** Gerda Dolman, Asst.Libn.

Lacey Architecture Archives
See: **Broome County Historical Society - Josiah T. Newcomb Library** (2251)

★8868★
Lackawanna Bar Association - Law Library (Law)
Court House, 2nd Fl. Phone: (717)963-6712
Scranton, PA 18503 Marita E. Paparelli, Dir.
Staff: Prof 2. **Subjects:** Law. **Holdings:** 20,000 volumes. **Services:** Interlibrary loan; copying; Faxing; library open to the public. **Computerized Information Services:** WESTLAW, DIALOG Information Services. **Remarks:** FAX: (717)344-2944. **Staff:** Ann M. Kouacn, Asst. Law Libn.

★8869★
Lackawanna Historical Society - Catlin House Library and Archives (Hist)
232 Monroe Ave. Phone: (717)344-3841
Scranton, PA 18510 Maryellen Calemmo, Exec.Dir.
Founded: 1886. **Staff:** Prof 2; Other 2. **Subjects:** Local history and literature, genealogy, ethnic studies, architecture. **Special Collections:** George Scranton papers; Delaware, Lackawanna & Western Railroad Coal Company record books; Scranton Lace Company archives; photograph archives; ethnic studies; coal mining; railroads. **Holdings:** 3220 volumes; 54 VF drawers of manuscripts, maps, blueprints. **Subscriptions:** 15 journals and other serials. **Services:** Copying; library open to the public on fee basis. **Publications:** Lackawanna Historical Society Journal, quarterly - to members. **Special Catalogs:** Catalog of Scranton Lace Company archives and ethnic studies holdings (booklets).

Monsignor George Lacombe Archive of Medieval Philosophy
See: **University of San Francisco - Special Collections Department/ Donohue Rare Book Room** (19290)

★8870★
Laconia Congregational United Church of Christ - Library (Rel-Phil)
18 Veterans Sq. Phone: (603)524-0668
Laconia, NH 03246 Ruth Stuart
Founded: 1960. **Staff:** 1. **Subjects:** Religion in life, parenting, grief. **Holdings:** 800 books. **Subscriptions:** 3 journals and other serials. **Services:** Library open to the public.

★8871★
Laczko Dezso Museum - Library (Hist)
Erzsebet liget 1
Pf. 32 Phone: 80 24610
H-8201 Veszprem, Hungary Kophazi Ferencne
Founded: 1903. **Staff:** Prof 1. **Subjects:** Archeology, history, numismatics, ethnography, fine and industrial arts. **Holdings:** 21,000 books; 11,000 bound periodical volumes. **Subscriptions:** 31 journals and other serials; 5 newspapers. **Services:** Interlibrary loan; copying; library open to the public. **Remarks:** FAX: 80 26081. **Also Known As:** Laczko Dezso Muzeum - Konyvtar.

George and Helen Ladd Library
See: **Bates College** (1560)

★8872★
Ladish Co. - Technical Information Center (Sci-Engr)
5481 S. Packard Ave. Phone: (414)747-3011
Cudahy, WI 53110 A.F. Hayes, Mgr.
Founded: 1942. **Staff:** Prof 1. **Subjects:** Metalworking technology, chemical analysis, metal cleaning and testing, mechanical and physical properties, metallography, corrosion, industrial environment. **Holdings:** 2500 volumes; 10,000 unbound reports. **Subscriptions:** 30 journals and other serials. **Services:** Center not open to the public. **Computerized Information Services:** DIALOG Information Services.

★8873★
Lafayette Clinic - Library (Med)
951 E. Lafayette Phone: (313)256-9596
Detroit, MI 48207 Nancy E. Ward, Libn.
Founded: 1956. **Staff:** Prof 1; Other 1. **Subjects:** Psychiatry, psychology, psychopharmacology, geriatrics, neurology, movement disorders, affective disorders, Alzheimer's Disease, memory disorders, Parkinsonism. **Holdings:** 4897 books; 1473 bound periodical volumes; 10 years of unbound periodicals. **Subscriptions:** 146 journals and other serials. **Services:** Interlibrary loan; SDI; library open to the public for reference use only. **Computerized Information Services:** DIALOG Information Services, MEDLINE. **Networks/Consortia:** Member of Michigan Health Sciences Libraries Association (MHSLA), Detroit Associated Libraries Region of Cooperation (DALROC), National Network of Libraries of Medicine - Greater Midwest Region.

★8874★
Lafayette College - Kirby Library of Government and Law (Law)
Lafayette College
Kirby Hall Phone: (215)250-5399
Easton, PA 18042-1780 Mercedes Benitez Sharpless, Libn.
Founded: 1930. **Staff:** Prof 1; Other 5. **Subjects:** Political science, international law and relations, constitutional law, urban organization. **Special Collections:** British Parliamentary Debates, 1st through 5th series (1468 volumes). **Holdings:** 20,400 books; 2200 bound periodical volumes; 3 VF drawers of pamphlets. **Subscriptions:** 130 journals and other serials. **Services:** Interlibrary loan; library not open to the public. **Computerized Information Services:** OCLC. **Networks/Consortia:** Member of PALINET, Lehigh Valley Association of Independent Colleges, Inc. (LVAIC). **Remarks:** Includes the holdings of the Kirby Library of Civil Rights.

★8875★
Lafayette College - Special Collections and College Archives (Hist)
David Bishop Skillman Library Phone: (215)250-5148
Easton, PA 18042 Diane Windham Shaw, Spec.Coll.Libn. & Coll.Archv.
Staff: Prof 2. **Subjects:** Marquis de Lafayette, angling, American literature, Lafayette College history, history of printing. **Special Collections:** American Friends of Lafayette Collection (4000 books, manuscripts, prints); William E. Simon Collection (140 cubic feet); College Archives (6350 volumes; 500 cubic feet); Rare Books (4000 volumes); Stephen Crane Collection (500 books and articles). **Holdings:** 16,500 books; 750 cubic feet of manuscripts and archives. **Services:** Copying; collections and archives open to the public by appointment. **Computerized Information Services:** OCLC; BITNET (electronic mail service). **Networks/Consortia:** Member of PALINET, Lehigh Valley Association of Independent Colleges, Inc. (LVAIC). **Remarks:** FAX: (215)252-0370. Electronic mail address(es): SD O@LAFAYACS (BITNET).

★8876★
Lafayette Journal and Courier - Library (Publ)
217 N. 6th St. Phone: (317)423-5511
Lafayette, IN 47901 John R. Fisher, Libn.
Founded: 1964. **Staff:** Prof 1. **Subjects:** Newspaper reference topics. **Holdings:** The newspaper, 1950 to present, on microfilm; clipping file. **Services:** Library open to the public with restrictions. **Special Indexes:** Index to the newspaper (card). **Remarks:** Published by Gannett Newspapers. **Remarks:** FAX: (317)420-5246.

★8877★
Lafayette Natural History Museum - Research Library (Biol Sci)
637 Girard Park Dr. Phone: (318)268-5544
Lafayette, LA 70503 Dr. Heather C. Kelly, Libn.
Founded: 1969. **Subjects:** Natural history, astronomy, Southwest Louisiana culture, science education. **Special Collections:** Audubon Books (1st edition Octova set); Southwest Louisiana culture cassette presentations; vertical file material on Louisiana Indian Tribes. **Holdings:** 1644 books; 78 unbound periodical volumes. **Subscriptions:** 75 journals and other serials. **Services:** Interlibrary loan; copying; library open to the public with restrictions. **Publications:** Special publications are prepared for exhibits and other museum programs. **Staff:** Mary Ann Bernard, Cur., Educ.

Lafayette University - Library
See: **Notre Dame De Lafayette University** (12124)

★8878★
Lafleur, Brown, de Grandpre, Kronstom - Library (Law)
1 Place Ville Marie, Suite 3725 Phone: (514)878-9641
Montreal, PQ, Canada H3B 3P4 Linda Ramsay, Libn.
Founded: 1940. **Staff:** Prof 2; Other 1. **Subjects:** Law - civil, corporate, insurance, securities, labor, taxation. **Special Collections:** English Case Law. **Holdings:** 2000 books; 500 bound periodical volumes; 100 loose-leaf services; 3000 volumes of law reports; 300 volumes of federal and provincial statutes and regulations. **Subscriptions:** 400 journals and other serials; 5 newspapers. **Services:** Interlibrary loan; library not open to the public. **Computerized Information Services:** QL Systems, SOQUIJ, The Financial Post Information Service, CAN/LAW, Info Globe; iNet 2000, Envoy 100 (electronic mail services). **Remarks:** FAX: (514)878-1450.

Benoist LaForte Archives
See: **Cornell University - History of Science Collections** (4313)

★8879★
Lahey Clinic Medical Center - Richard B. Cattell Memorial Library (Med)
41 Mall Rd. Phone: (617)273-8253
Burlington, MA 01805 Carol Spencer, Libn.
Founded: 1965. **Staff:** Prof 1; Other 1. **Subjects:** Medicine. **Holdings:** 1500 books; 8500 bound periodical volumes. **Subscriptions:** 325 journals and other serials. **Services:** Interlibrary loan; copying; library open to the public with permission of librarian. **Computerized Information Services:** MEDLARS, MEDLINE. Performs searches on fee basis. **Networks/Consortia:** Member of National Network of Libraries of Medicine - New England Region, Boston Biomedical Library Consortium, Massachusetts Health Sciences Libraries Network (MaHSLiN).

★8880★
(Lahore) American Center - USIS Library (Educ)
20, Shahrah-e-Fatima Jinnah
Lahore, Pakistan
Remarks: Maintained or supported by the U.S. Information Agency. Focus is on materials that will assist peoples outside the United States to learn about the United States, its people, history, culture, political processes, and social milieux.

Kathleen Laidlaw Historical Center
See: **Scituate Historical Society** (14949)

R.C. Laird Health Sciences Library
See: **Toronto Western Hospital** (16424)

★8881★
Lake Circuit Court - Library
2293 N. Main St.
Crown Point, IN 46307
Defunct.

★8882★
Lake County Central Law Library (Law)
3400 Broadway Phone: (219)980-6797
Gary, IN 46408 Lee-Ann Weber-Hatch, Hd. Law Libn.
Founded: 1986. **Staff:** Prof 1. **Subjects:** Law, Indiana legislation. **Special Collections:** Pre-National Reporter System cases. **Holdings:** 20,500 books; 800 bound periodical volumes; 200 other cataloged items; 300 microcards; 54 volumes of microfiche. **Subscriptions:** 147 journals and other serials. **Services:** Interlibrary loan; copying; library open to the public.

★8883★
Lake County Department of Planning, Zoning & Environmental Quality - Research Library (Plan)
18 N. County St., Rm. A-803 Phone: (708)360-6350
Waukegan, IL 60085 Mrs. Bhagwant Kaur Sidhu, Res.Libn.
Founded: 1977. **Staff:** 1. **Subjects:** Land use planning, planning law, housing, natural environment, census, municipal information. **Special Collections:** 1990 Census Tiger files for Lake County (organized by municipalities, census tracts, census blocks). **Holdings:** 5000 books; 50 bound periodical volumes; 3000 pieces of census data, county map boundaries, addresses, properties (online). **Subscriptions:** 70 journals and other serials; 10 newspapers. **Services:** Copying; library open to the public for reference use only. **Automated Operations:** Computerized cataloging. **Computerized Information Services:** OCLC; internal database. Performs searches on fee basis. **Remarks:** FAX: (708)360-1538.

★8884★
Lake County Forest Preserve District - Ryerson Nature Library (Biol Sci)
2000 N. Milwaukee Ave. Phone: (708)948-7750
Libertyville, IL 60048 Nan Buckardt, Site Mgr.
Founded: 1976. **Subjects:** Botany, zoology, ecology, environmental education, agriculture, forestry. **Holdings:** 2200 books; 4 VF drawers of pamphlets and clippings. **Subscriptions:** 12 journals and other serials. **Services:** Interlibrary loan (limited); library open to the public for reference use only.

★8885★
Lake County Historical Society - Library (Hist)
Box 1011 Phone: (707)279-4466
Lakeport, CA 95453 Norma Wright, Pres.
Subjects: Lake County Historical Society and Genealogical Society, mid-1800s to present; Pomo Indian history and culture; early pioneers. **Holdings:** 2200 photographs; 8200 manuscript pages; genealogical data; oral history tapes. **Services:** Library open to the public by appointment.

★8886★
Lake County Historical Society - Research Library (Hist)
8610 King Memorial Rd. Phone: (216)255-8979
Mentor, OH 44060-8207 Carl Thomas Engel, Cur. of Hist.
Staff: Prof 1; Other 2. **Subjects:** Local history and genealogy, President James A. Garfield. **Holdings:** 2500 books; manuscripts; clippings; Painesville Telegraph on microfilm 1822-1924; 11 reels of microfilm of Federal Census, 1820-1910; Lake County and Geauga County marriages to 1900; Common Pleas, probate court, and deeds to 1840; obituaries to 1900. **Subscriptions:** 20 journals and other serials. **Services:** Copying; library open to older students and adults. **Publications:** Lake County Historical Society, annual; Here is Lake County, Ohio, 1964 (book). **Special Indexes:** Genealogy Index (70,000 names; card).

★8887★
Lake County Historical Society, Inc. - Library and Museum (Hist)
315 W. Main St. Phone: (904)343-9332
Tavares, FL 32778 Sue Nunes, Libn.
Founded: 1953. **Staff:** Prof 2; Other 2. **Subjects:** Local history and affairs. **Holdings:** Newspaper articles, 1953 to present; cassette tapes; survey maps; courthouse records; photographs; several volumes of Pioneers. **Services:** Copying; library open to the public. **Automated Operations:** Computerized circulation. **Publications:** Lake County - Then and Now; Tangelo (bulletin), quarterly.

★8888★
Lake County Law Library (Law)
Lake County Courthouse
315 W. Main St. Phone: (904)343-9786
Tavares, FL 32278 Faye Osebold, Libn.
Staff: Prof 1. **Subjects:** Law. **Holdings:** 15,000 volumes. **Services:** Copying; library open to the public for reference use only.

★8889★
Lake County Law Library (Law)
18 N. County St. Phone: (708)360-6654
Waukegan, IL 60085-4339 Joanne T. Baker, Law Libn.
Staff: Prof 1; Other 1. **Subjects:** Law, state legislative history. **Holdings:** 20,000 books; 7500 microfiche; Illinois Appellate Court Briefs, 2nd district, 1964 to present. **Subscriptions:** 132 journals and other serials. **Services:** Interlibrary loan; copying; library open to the public for reference use only. **Computerized Information Services:** WESTLAW. **Special Indexes:** Index to Illinois Institute for Continuing Legal Education Books.

★8890★
Lake County Museum - Library and Information Center (Hist)
Lakewood Forest Preserve
Rte. 176 & Fairfield Rd. Phone: (708)526-7878
Wauconda, IL 60084 Jan Gallimore-Smith, Dir.
Founded: 1957. **Staff:** 14. **Subjects:** History - Lake County, Chicago, Illinois, Civil War; United States popular culture. **Special Collections:** Curt Teich Postcard Archives, 1898-1975 (425,000 view and advertising postcards). **Holdings:** 1500 books; pamphlets; 14 VF cabinets; maps. **Subscriptions:** 25 journals and other serials. **Services:** Interlibrary loan; copying; photographic reproduction; library and postcard archives open to the public by appointment. **Computerized Information Services:** Mitinet, Foxbase (internal databases). **Publications:** Image File. **Special Indexes:** Index to postcard archives (online). **Remarks:** FAX: (708)526-0024. **Staff:** Katherine Hamilton-Smith, Cur. of Spec.Coll.; Christina Pyle, Asst.Cur. of Spec.Coll.; Elizabeth Marston, Cur. of Coll.; Diana Dretske, Archv.

★8891★
Lake County Public Library - Special Collections (Hist)
1115 Harrison Ave. Phone: (719)486-0569
Leadville, CO 80461 David R. Parry, Dir.
Founded: 1903. **Staff:** Prof 1; Other 4. **Subjects:** Colorado Mountain History, Leadville-Lake County history and genealogy, 10th Mountain Division, Camp Hale, Colorado. **Holdings:** 1250 volumes; 2500 historic local photographs; 162 reels of microfilm of Leadville newspapers and local census schedules. **Services:** Interlibrary loan; copying; collections open to the public for reference use only. **Automated Operations:** Computerized cataloging and ILL. **Networks/Consortia:** Member of Three Rivers Regional Library Service System. **Publications:** Special subject bibliographies. **Remarks:** FAX: (719)486-3544.

Lake Erie Programs Library
See: **Ohio State University - Lake Erie Programs Library** (12316)

★8892★
Lake Forest College - Thomas Oscar Freeman Memorial Library (Sci-Engr, Biol Sci)
Lake Forest, IL 60045 Phone: (708)234-3100
Vanaja Menon, Libn.
Founded: 1962. **Staff:** 2. **Subjects:** Chemistry, physics. **Holdings:** 2000 books; 2000 bound periodical volumes. **Subscriptions:** 30 journals and other serials. **Services:** Interlibrary loan; copying; library open to persons who cannot be served by their public library; letter of reference required. **Automated Operations:** Computerized cataloging and circulation. **Computerized Information Services:** DIALOG Information Services, PFDS Online, BRS Information Technologies. **Remarks:** FAX: (708)234-7170.

★8893★
Lake Forest Hospital - Medical Staff Library (Med)
660 N. Westmoreland Rd. Phone: (708)234-5600
Lake Forest, IL 60045 Judy Curtis, Med.Libn.
Staff: 1. **Subjects:** Medicine. **Holdings:** 1000 books; unbound periodicals. **Subscriptions:** 41 journals and other serials. **Services:** open to medical staff; limited access to other users. Interlibrary loan; copying; library open to medical staff; limited access to other users. **Computerized Information Services:** BRS/COLLEAGUE. **Networks/Consortia:** Member of Northeastern Illinois Library Consortium. **Remarks:** FAX: (312)234-6428.

★8894★
Lake Hospital System - Medical Libraries (East and West) (Med)
Washington at Liberty Phone: (216)354-2400
Painesville, OH 44077 Holly S. Kimborowicz, Hea.Sci.Libn.
Staff: Prof 1; Other 2. **Subjects:** Medicine, nursing, health administration. **Holdings:** 2185 books. **Subscriptions:** 270 journals and other serials. **Services:** Interlibrary loan; consumer health information services provided. **Computerized Information Services:** NLM, DIALOG Information Services. **Remarks:** FAX: (216)354-1916.

Lake Mead National Recreation Area
See: **U.S. Natl. Park Service** (17742)

★8895★
Lake Michigan Federation - Environmental Library (Env-Cons)
59 E. Van Buren, No. 2215 Phone: (312)939-0838
Chicago, IL 60605-1220 Glenda Daniels, Dp.Dir.
Founded: 1970. **Staff:** Prof 5; Other 20. **Subjects:** Lake Michigan, water quality, land disposal, erosion-shoreland management, contaminated sediment, wetlands. **Services:** Files open to the public for reference use only. **Networks/Consortia:** Member of ILLINET, Chicago Library System. **Publications:** Lake Michigan, quarterly - to members; Lake Michigan Monitor, quarterly; Wetlands and Water Quality; Waves Against the Shore; Shoreline Protection Kit; Great Lakes Toxic Hotspots: A Citizen Action Guide (1987); Citizen's Guide to Cleaning Up Contaminated Sediments; Restoring Lake Michigan's Ecosystem (poster/map) - all for sale. **Remarks:** FAX: (312)939-2708.

★8896★
Lake Shore Railway Historical Society - Museum Library (Hist)
Box 571 Phone: (814)825-2724
North East, PA 16428 James C. Caldwell, Dir.
Founded: 1967. **Subjects:** Railways, Pullman Company, Heisler Locomotive Works, General Electric Co. locomotives. **Special Collections:** Heisler Locomotive Works Builder's Negatives (400 glass plate negatives); General Electric Co. Locomotive & Car Equipment Department Negatives (10,000). **Holdings:** 500 books; 200 bound periodical volumes; 2000 reports, documents, specifications. **Subscriptions:** 40 journals and other serials. **Services:** Library open to the public by appointment. **Publications:** The Lake Shore Timetable (newsletter), monthly - for internal distribution only.

★8897★
Lake Superior Museum of Transportation - Library (Trans)
506 W. Michigan Phone: (218)727-0687
Duluth, MN 55802 Tom Gannon, Cur.
Founded: 1975. **Subjects:** Railroads. **Holdings:** 3000 books; 400 bound periodical volumes; 6000 documents; 25 AV programs; 2000 photographs. **Services:** Library open to the public by appointment.

★8898★
Lake Superior State University - Kenneth J. Shouldice Library - Michigan & Marine Collections (Hist)
Sault Ste. Marie, MI 49783 Phone: (906)635-2402
Dr. Frederick A. Michels, Dir.
Founded: 1946. **Staff:** Prof 5; Other 6. **Subjects:** History of Michigan's Upper Peninsula; Indians of Michigan's Upper Peninsula; local history of Sault Ste. Marie, Michigan. **Special Collections:** Special editions and sources of Longfellow's "Hiawatha"; Marine-Laker Collection. **Holdings:** 1400 books; Sault Evening News on microfilm; 16 VF drawers of pamphlets concerned with local and area history. **Subscriptions:** 1200 journals and other serials. **Services:** Interlibrary loan; copying; collections open to the public for reference use only. **Automated Operations:** Computerized public access catalog and cataloging. **Computerized Information Services:** DIALOG Information Services; CD-ROMs (Wilson Disc - BPI, RG, SSI, AST, CINAHL, Books In Print, Serials Directory, Computer Library). Performs searches on fee basis. Contact Person: Ruth Neveu, Pub.Serv.Libn. **Networks/Consortia:** Member of Michigan Library Consortium (MLC), Upper Peninsula Region of Library Cooperation (UPRLC). **Remarks:** FAX: (906)635-2193. **Staff:** Linda Cullum, Pub.Serv.Libn.; Maureen Delaney, Cat.; Mary June, Ref. & ILL Libn.

★8899★
Lake Tahoe Historical Society - Lake Tahoe Museum - Library (Hist)
3058 Hwy. 50
P.O. Box 404 Phone: (916)541-5458
South Lake Tahoe, CA 95705 Dr. Lyndall Landauer, Pres.
Subjects: Lake Tahoe and Sierra Nevada history, California and Nevada Indians. **Special Collections:** Oral history collection; Lake Tahoe area photographs. **Holdings:** 50 books; 100 bound periodical volumes; 150 documents; 4 AV programs; 15 nonbook items; 50 manuscripts. **Services:** Library open to the public for reference use only.

★8900★
Lake Wales Hospital - Medical Library (Med)
410 S. 11th St.
Box 3460 Phone: (813)676-1433
Lake Wales, FL 33853 Ada Leigh Byrd, Mgr.
Founded: 1983. **Staff:** Prof 1. **Subjects:** Medicine, pediatrics, obstetrics/gynecology, geriatrics. **Holdings:** 150 books; 15 bound periodical volumes. **Subscriptions:** 65 journals and other serials; 6 newspapers. **Services:** Interlibrary loan; copying; library open to the public.

★8901★
Lake of the Woods County Historical Society - Museum Library/Archives (Hist)
8th Ave., S.E. Phone: (218)634-1200
Baudette, MN 56623 Marlys Hirst, Cur.
Founded: 1978. **Staff:** 1. **Subjects:** County and state history, old textbooks, local natural history. **Special Collections:** Oral history transcripts (80). **Holdings:** 400 books; 15 manuscripts; 3 VF drawers of documents and reports; 60 reels of microfilm of local and regional newspapers, 1897-1985. **Subscriptions:** 5 journals and other serials. **Services:** Copying; library open to the public. **Special Indexes:** Index to Oral History Collection; index to society's newspaper column features, 1977-1982 (both online); Index to museum photographic collection (book); Index to County Cemeteries (1 volume).

★8902★
Lakehead University - Chancellor Paterson Library (Sci-Engr, Bus-Fin, Hum)
Oliver Rd. Phone: (807)343-8205
Thunder Bay, ON, Canada P7B 5E1 Fred McIntosh, Chf.Libn.
Founded: 1962. **Staff:** Prof 12; Other 32. **Subjects:** Arts and science, forestry, engineering, physical education, outdoor recreation, business administration, nursing, library technology, education. **Special Collections:** Northern and Regional Studies collection (Northwestern Ontario; database of 35,000 records). **Holdings:** 330,521 books; 95,341 bound periodical volumes; 2027 linear feet of documents; 60,500 volumes on microfiche; 576 linear feet of manuscripts and archives. **Subscriptions:** 5453 journals and other serials; 27 newspapers. **Services:** Interlibrary loan; copying; library open to the public. **Automated Operations:** Computerized public access catalog, cataloging, acquisitions, and circulation. **Computerized Information Services:** DIALOG Information Services, ORBIT Search Service, MEDLARS, QL Systems, CAN/OLE, BRS Information Technologies, Info Globe, WILSONLINE; Northern and Regional Studies (internal database). Contact Person: Valerie Gibbons. **Remarks:** FAX: (807)343-8007. **Staff:** Anne Deighton, Coll.Dev.; Shirley Boneca, Ref.Serv.; Ian Dew, Sys./Bibliog.Proc.

★8903★
Lakehead University - Education Library (Educ)
Oliver Road Phone: (807)343-8718
Thunder Bay, ON, Canada P7B 5E1 Mr. J. Arnot, Libn.
Founded: 1960. **Staff:** Prof 1; Other 7. **Subjects:** Education. **Special Collections:** Curriculum; educational administration. **Holdings:** 42,238 books; 1528 bound periodical volumes; 780 reels of microfilm; 75,051 microfiche; 195 audiotapes; 466 multimedia kits; 1086 filmstrips; 41 films; 119 slide sets; 8 VF drawers of pamphlets; 96 videotapes; 257 picture charts; 55 games; 174 phonograph records; 124 transparencies. **Subscriptions:** 352 journals and other serials; 2 newspapers. **Services:** Interlibrary loan; copying; library open to the public. **Automated Operations:** Computerized public access catalog and circulation. **Computerized Information Services:** CD-ROMs (ERIC, CD:Education). **Publications:** Student guides; bibliographies. **Remarks:** FAX: (807)344-6807.

★8904★
Lakehead University - Geography Department - Map Library (Geog-Map)
955 Oliver Rd. Phone: (807)343-8548
Thunder Bay, ON, Canada P7B 5E1 Cathy A. Chapin, Map Cur./Cartographer
Founded: 1970. **Staff:** Prof 1. **Special Collections:** Canada NTS Series; European travels slide collection. **Holdings:** Maps; AV programs; air photographs. **Services:** Library open to the public. **Special Indexes:** Index to teaching materials in collection (online); index to Geography Department undergraduate theses. **Remarks:** FAX: (807)343-8023. Telex: 073-4594.

Lakeland Hospital
See: **Lakeland Medical Center** (8905)

★8905★
Lakeland Medical Center - Medical Library (Med)
Hwy. NN
Box 1002 Phone: (414)741-2000
Elkhorn, WI 53121 Barbara Andry, Lib.Asst.
Founded: 1974. **Staff:** Prof 1. **Subjects:** Medicine, nursing. **Holdings:** 300 books. **Subscriptions:** 70 journals and other serials. **Services:** Interlibrary loan; library not open to the public. **Automated Operations:** Computerized ILL (DOCLINE). **Computerized Information Services:** MEDLARS. **Networks/Consortia:** Member of National Network of Libraries of Medicine - Greater Midwest Region, Southeastern Wisconsin Health Science Library Consortium (SWHSL). **Remarks:** FAX: (414)741-2175. **Formerly:** Lakeland Hospital.

★8906★
Lakeland Regional Medical Center - Medical Library (Med)
1324 Lakeland Hills Blvd.
Drawer 95448 Phone: (813)687-1176
Lakeland, FL 33804-0448 Jan Booker, Lib.Serv.Coord.
Founded: 1959. **Staff:** Prof 2; Other 3. **Subjects:** Medicine, nursing, medical administration. **Holdings:** 1000 books; 5000 bound periodical volumes; AV programs; 300 other cataloged items. **Subscriptions:** 166 journals and other serials. **Services:** Interlibrary loan; copying; SDI; library open to the public by doctor's permission. **Computerized Information Services:** MEDLINE, DIALOG Information Services; DOCLINE (electronic mail service).

Lakeland Village Branch Library
See: **Washington State Library** (20037)

Arthur Lakes Library
See: **Colorado School of Mines - Arthur Lakes Library** (3947)

Lakeshore General Hospital - Medical Library
See: **Hopital General du Lakeshore - Bibliotheque medicale** (7388)

★8907★
Lakeshore Technical College - Educational Resource Center (Educ)
1290 North Ave. Phone: (414)458-4183
Cleveland, WI 53015 Linda McCabe, Lib.Mgr.
Staff: Prof 2; Other 4. **Subjects:** Vocational education, business, allied health. **Special Collections:** Hazardous materials (150 volumes; 200 AV programs); Legal Collection (1720 volumes; 140 AV programs); Equine Collection (125 volumes; 68 AV programs); Women/Parenting (477 volumes; 115 AV programs). **Holdings:** 21,054 books; 4100 AV programs; 8 periodical titles on microfiche. **Subscriptions:** 300 journals and other serials; 16 newspapers. **Services:** Interlibrary loan (limited); copying; center open to residents of the district. **Automated Operations:** Computerized circulation. **Computerized Information Services:** OCLC, DIALOG Information Services. **Networks/Consortia:** Member of Fox River Valley Area Library Consortium (FRVALC). **Remarks:** FAX: (414)693-8966. **Staff:** Carol Shaffer, Info.Serv.Spec.

Lakeside Hospital Medical Library
See: **U.S. Dept. of Veterans Affairs (IL-Chicago)** (17325)

★8908★
Lakeview Center, Inc. - Library (Med)
1221 W. Lakeview Ave. Phone: (904)432-1222
Pensacola, FL 32501-1857 Dr. Susan Seabury Smith, Ctr.Libn.
Founded: 1982. **Staff:** Prof 1. **Subjects:** Psychiatry, psychology, alcoholism, drug addiction, children's and young adult's problems, management. **Special Collections:** Archives. **Holdings:** 1642 books; 242 audiocassettes; 104 videocassettes; 63 kits; 13 films; 227 government documents; 5 games. **Subscriptions:** 42 journals and other serials. **Services:** Interlibrary loan; copying; library open to adult practitioners and interns.

★8909★
Lakeville Hospital - Health Sciences Library (Med)
Main St. Phone: (508)947-1231
Lakeville, MA 02347 Anne S. Lima, Libn.
Founded: 1910. **Staff:** 1. **Subjects:** Medicine, nursing education, rehabilitation, orthopedics and orthopedic surgery, birth defects and crippling conditions. **Holdings:** 1500 books; 1520 bound periodical volumes; pamphlet file; 125 AV programs. **Subscriptions:** 103 journals and other serials. **Services:** Interlibrary loan; copying; library open to the public with restrictions. **Computerized Information Services:** Online systems. **Networks/Consortia:** Member of Southeastern Massachusetts Consortium of Health Science Libraries (SEMCO). **Publications:** Newsletter, semiannual - local distribution. **Remarks:** Maintained by Massachusetts State Department of Public Health.

★8910★
Lakewood Historical Society - Library (Hist)
14710 Lake Ave. Phone: (216)221-7343
Lakewood, OH 44107 Martha Folsom, Libn.
Founded: 1952. **Staff:** Prof 1. **Subjects:** Lakewood and Western Reserve history. **Special Collections:** Early school books; slides of people, places, events of Lakewood, Ohio (6000). **Holdings:** Figures not available. **Services:** Library open to the public by appointment. **Publications:** Romance of Lakewood Streets (newsletter), quarterly - to members.

★8911★
Lakewood Hospital - Medical Library (Med)
14519 Detroit Ave. Phone: (216)521-4200
Lakewood, OH 44107 Jo Ann Hudson, Dir.
Staff: Prof 1. **Subjects:** Medicine, nursing, hospital administration, sciences. **Holdings:** 6605 books; 4787 bound periodical volumes; pamphlet files. **Subscriptions:** 352 journals and other serials; 5 newspapers. **Services:** Interlibrary loan; copying; library open to the public by permission. **Automated Operations:** Computerized cataloging. **Computerized Information Services:** BRS Information Technologies. **Publications:** LibGuide; Acquisition List; Biomedical Serials List - all for internal distribution only; Special Bibliographies. **Remarks:** FAX: (216)529-7093.

★8912★
Lakewood's Historical Belmar Village - Archives (Hist)
797 S. Wadsworth Blvd. Phone: (303)987-7850
Lakewood, CO 80226 Jennifer M. Karber, Coll.Cur.
Founded: 1976. **Staff:** 6. **Subjects:** Antique collections history, Colorado and Western history, arts and crafts of the past, U.S. transportation history, farming history, Lakewood history. **Special Collections:** Vietnam War (letters, photographs); Historical Lakewood photographs and ephemera collections; Lakewood Sentinel newspapers; antique schoolbooks; historic preservation information; museum administration and collections sources. **Holdings:** 300 books; 5 AV programs; 1000 photographs; 200 manuscripts. **Services:** Archives open to the public at librarian's discretion.

David and Dorothy Lam Management Research Library
See: **University of British Columbia - Faculty of Commerce & Business Administration** (18268)

★8913★
LaMalie Associates, Inc. - Research Department (Bus-Fin)
13920 N. Dale Mabry Phone: (813)961-7494
Tampa, FL 33618 Nancy M. Clausen, Dir., Res.
Founded: 1976. **Staff:** Prof 8; Other 4. **Subjects:** Executive search, management consulting, business. **Holdings:** 1000 books; 1700 annual reports; 1000 other cataloged items. **Subscriptions:** 80 journals and other serials; 10 newspapers. **Services:** Interlibrary loan; copying; department open to the public with restrictions. **Computerized Information Services:** DIALOG Information Services, DataTimes; internal database; DIALMAIL (electronic mail service). **Remarks:** FAX: (813)962-2138. **Staff:** Susan E. Burke, Res.; Tamara J. Costello, Res.; Cindy G. Leydon, Res.; Cindy A. Oskroba, Res.; Edee Hammer, Res.; Dorothy K. Siani, Res.; Debbie Byrne, Res.

★8914★
Lambda, Inc. - Barnes Library (Soc Sci)
Box 55913 Phone: (205)326-8600
Birmingham, AL 35255 Ron Joullian, Coord.
Staff: 3. **Subjects:** Gay and lesbian literature. **Special Collections:** Alabama Gay Archives; Lady B.J. Memorial Collection (gay and lesbian books and records from the entertainment world). **Holdings:** 805 books; 150 folders of gay and lesbian information; 25 subject binders. **Subscriptions:** 30 newsletters; 15 newspapers. **Services:** Library open to the public with restrictions on a limited schedule. **Remarks:** Library located at 516 S. 27th St., Birmingham, AL 35233. Telex (205)326-8600.

★8915★
Harold M. Lambert Studios - Photo Library (Aud-Vis)
2801 W. Cheltenham Ave.
Box 27310 Phone: (215)885-3355
Philadelphia, PA 19150 Raymond Lambert, Owner
Founded: 1936. **Holdings:** 1 million color transparencies and black/white prints. **Services:** Stock photographs available on fee basis.

Lambs Club (NY) Archives
See: **New York Public Library for the Performing Arts** (11634)

Lamont-Doherty Geological Observatory
See: **Columbia University - Lamont-Doherty Geological Observatory** (4016)

★8916★
Lancaster Bible College - Stoll Memorial Library (Rel-Phil)
901 Eden Rd. Phone: (717)560-8250
Lancaster, PA 17601 Deborah R. Hunt, Lib.Dir.
Founded: 1933. **Staff:** Prof 2; Other 1.5. **Subjects:** Bible, theology, missions, Christian education, music, secretarial science, liberal arts, pastoral studies, computers in ministry, teacher education, counseling. **Special Collections:** Lloyd M. Perry Collection of pastoral theology. **Holdings:** 46,394 books; 3706 bound periodical volumes; 3457 AV volumes; 54 feet pamphlets, flannelgraphs, missions materials; 1383 microform books; 4177 volumes uncataloged collections. **Subscriptions:** 310 journals and other serials. **Services:** Interlibrary loan; copying; SDI; library open to the public. **Automated Operations:** Computerized cataloging. **Computerized Information Services:** OCLC; internal databases. **Networks/Consortia:** Member of PALINET. **Special Indexes:** Lloyd M. Perry Collection indexes; Curriculum Resource Center indexes. **Staff:** Margaret Storm, Cat.

★8917★
Lancaster County Historical Society - Library (Hist)
Willson Bldg.
230 N. President Ave. Phone: (717)392-4633
Lancaster, PA 17603 Salinda M. Matt, Hd.Libn.
Founded: 1886. **Staff:** Prof 3; Other 1. **Subjects:** History of Southeastern Pennsylvania and Lancaster County. **Special Collections:** Jasper Yeates Law Library Collection (1043 volumes on English law assembled by Judge Yeates in the 1760s and 1770s, being virtually every work on law published in England between 1600 and 1800); tax records for Lancaster County, 1750-1939. **Holdings:** 10,300 books; 1500 bound periodical volumes; 740 bound newspaper volumes; 37 cubic feet and 98 cases of manuscripts. **Subscriptions:** 27 journals and other serials. **Services:** Copying; library open to the public.

★8918★
Lancaster County Law Library (Law)
50 N. Duke St.
Box 3480 Phone: (717)299-8090
Lancaster, PA 17603 Eleanor Gerlott, Libn.
Staff: Prof 1; Other 1. **Subjects:** Law. **Holdings:** 22,700 volumes. **Subscriptions:** 24 journals and other serials. **Services:** Interlibrary loan; copying; SDI; library open to the public. **Computerized Information Services:** WESTLAW. Performs searches on fee basis. **Remarks:** FAX: (717)295-2509.

★8919★
Lancaster General Hospital - Mueller Health Sciences Library (Med)
555 N. Duke St.
Box 3555 Phone: (717)299-5511
Lancaster, PA 17603 Claudette Strohm, Libn.
Founded: 1967. **Staff:** Prof 1; Other 1. **Subjects:** Medicine, allied health sciences, hospital administration. **Holdings:** 5000 books; 2000 bound periodical volumes. **Subscriptions:** 361 journals and other serials. **Services:** Interlibrary loan; copying; library open to the public. **Computerized Information Services:** MEDLARS, BRS Information Technologies; CD-ROMs (MEDLINE, CINAHL). **Networks/Consortia:** Member of Central Pennsylvania Health Sciences Library Association (CPHSLA). **Publications:** Monthly book lists.

★8920★
Lancaster Historical Commission - Document Collection (Hist)
Town Hall, Thayer Dr.
Lancaster, MA 01523 Phone: (508)368-4855
Founded: 1964. **Subjects:** History of Lancaster and central Massachusetts. **Special Collections:** Alice Greene Chandler Photographic Collection (1860-1900); James Macdonald Photographic Collection (1900-1930); Lancaster iconographic collection; document collection. **Holdings:** 150 books; 45 reels of microfilm; 3 VF drawers of manuscripts; military history records; letters; and other archival materials. **Services:** Copying; library open to the public on a limited schedule.

★8921★
Lancaster Mennonite Historical Society - Library (Rel-Phil, Hist)
2215 Millstream Rd. Phone: (717)393-9745
Lancaster, PA 17602-1499 Carolyn C. Wenger, Dir.
Founded: 1958. **Staff:** Prof 2; Other 2. **Subjects:** Local, denominational, and reformation history; genealogy, especially Pennsylvania German names; theology; Pennsylvania German dialect; arts and culture. **Special Collections:** Mennonitica; Amishana; hymnody. **Holdings:** 24,922 titles; 3000 archive boxes; 220,000 vital statistics cards; 200 maps; 350 reels of microfilm. **Subscriptions:** 500 journals and other serials. **Services:** Translation; copying; library open to the public (fee for non-members). **Computerized Information Services:** Internal databases. **Networks/Consortia:** Member of Eastern Mennonite Associated Libraries & Archives (EMALA). **Publications:** Pennsylvania Mennonite Heritage, quarterly - by subscription; Mirror, bimonthly - to mailing list; Used, Out-of-Print, and Rare Book Sales (brochure) - by subscription. **Special Catalogs:** Genealogical catalog of abstracted vital statistics (card); cemetery files. **Special Indexes:** Pennsylvania Mennonite Heritage index (online). **Staff:** Lloyd Zeager, Libn.; David J. Rempel Smucker, Geneal.

★8922★
Lancaster Newspapers, Inc. - Newspaper Library (Publ)
8 W. King St. Phone: (717)291-8811
Lancaster, PA 17603 Edward Wilson, Lib.Mgr.
Founded: 1952. **Staff:** Prof 3; Other 5. **Subjects:** Newspaper reference topics; state, county, city government events and personalities; current events. **Special Collections:** Local newspapers, 1795 to present. **Holdings:** 500 books; Remington Rand Lektriever subject file; Linedex subject index with 15,500 subject headings; Remington Rand Lektriever biographical file; 7 filing cabinets of pictures, pamphlets, maps. **Services:** Copying. **Computerized Information Services:** DataTimes. **Remarks:** Library serves staffs of Lancaster Sunday News, Intelligencer-Journal, and Lancaster New Era. **Staff:** Bonnie Popdan, Lib. Database Mgr.; Susan Sweeney, Night Libn.

★8923★
Lancaster Theological Seminary of the United Church of Christ - Philip Schaff Library (Rel-Phil)
555 W. James St. Phone: (717)393-0654
Lancaster, PA 17603 Rev. Richard R. Berg, Dir., Lib.Serv.
Founded: 1825. **Staff:** Prof 1; Other 2. **Subjects:** Biblical studies, theology, pastoral counseling, church history, Christian education, church and society. **Special Collections:** Albright Collection (source materials in American church history; 7500 volumes). **Holdings:** 149,287 volumes. **Subscriptions:** 420 journals and other serials. **Services:** Interlibrary loan; copying; library open to the public. **Automated Operations:** Computerized cataloging. **Networks/Consortia:** Member of Southeastern Pennsylvania Theological Library Association (SEPTLA), PALINET.

★8924★
Land O'Lakes, Inc. - Library (Food-Bev)
Box 116 Phone: (612)481-2691
Minneapolis, MN 55440 Donna Koenig, Libn.
Staff: Prof 1. **Subjects:** Dairy products, agriculture. **Holdings:** 1000 books; pamphlet files. **Subscriptions:** 120 journals and other serials. **Services:** Interlibrary loan; library not open to the public. **Computerized Information Services:** DIALOG Information Services. **Remarks:** FAX: (612)481-2002.

★8925★
Land Registration & Information Service (LRIS) - Information Records Centre
P.O. Box 310
Amherst, NS, Canada B4H 3Z5
Defunct.

★8926★
Landauer Associates, Inc. - Landauer Information Center (Bus-Fin)
335 Madison Ave., 18th Fl. Phone: (212)687-2323
New York, NY 10017-4683 Beverly Fletcher, Dir., Info.Serv.
Founded: 1974. **Staff:** Prof 1; Other 3. **Subjects:** Real estate, finance, marketing, land use, development, property acquisition and management. **Holdings:** 375 books; 100 VF drawers of reports; 16,000 clippings, offerings, brochures, statistical data; 125 VF drawers of research materials; U.S. maps; annual reports; 1960, 1970, 1980 census publications; government documents. **Subscriptions:** 200 journals and other serials. **Services:** Center not open to the public. **Automated Operations:** Computerized cataloging, acquisitions, and serials. **Computerized Information Services:** DIALOG Information Services, Mead Data Central, Dow Jones News/Retrieval, Dun & Bradstreet Business Credit Services, Urban Decision Systems, Inc. (UDS), Marshall and Swift; internal database. **Publications:** Landauer Library Letter, bimonthly - to the public. **Remarks:** FAX: (212)687-3426.

★8927★
Landels, Ripley & Diamond - Library (Law)
350 Steuart St., No. 600 Phone: (415)788-5000
San Francisco, CA 94105-1250 Cella Mitchell, Mgr., Info.Rsrcs.
Staff: Prof 2; Other 2. **Subjects:** Law. **Holdings:** 20,000 books; 200 periodicals. **Subscriptions:** 170 journals and other serials; 5 newspapers. **Services:** Interlibrary loan; library not open to the public. **Computerized Information Services:** LEXIS, DIALOG Information Services, WESTLAW, Dow Jones News/Retrieval, Dun & Bradstreet Business Credit Services. **Remarks:** FAX: (415)392-3149.

Clara Lander Library
See: **Winnipeg Art Gallery** (20487)

★8928★
Lander Valley Medical Center - Medical Library (Med)
1320 Bishop Randall Dr. Phone: (307)332-4420
Lander, WY 82520 Jane Heuer, Med.Libn.
Founded: 1978. **Staff:** 1. **Subjects:** Medicine, nursing, and allied health sciences. **Holdings:** 800 books. **Subscriptions:** 10 journals and other serials. **Services:** Interlibrary loan; copying; library open to the public. **Computerized Information Services:** MEDLARS; DOCLINE (electronic mail service). Performs searches on fee basis. **Remarks:** FAX: (307)332-4420, ext. 368.

Ralph R. Landes Medical Library
See: **Memorial Hospital - Ralph R. Landes Medical Library** (10035)

Landesanstalt fur Immissionsschutz Nordrhein- Westfalen
See: **North Rhine-Westphalia State Agency for Air Pollution and Noise Abatement** (11944)

★8929★
Landis Valley Museum - Library (Hist)
2451 Kissel Hill Rd. Phone: (717)569-0401
Lancaster, PA 17601 Robert W. Johnson, Dir.
Founded: 1953. **Subjects:** History, Pennsylvania German culture, crafts, folklore, agriculture, cooking, decorative arts and crafts. **Special Collections:** Old manufacturers' catalogs; Fraktur broadsides; Anabaptist Collection (150 volumes); almanacs. **Holdings:** 7,000 volumes. **Subscriptions:** 8 journals and other serials. **Services:** Library open to the public by appointment. **Remarks:** FAX: (717)560-2147. **Staff:** Alice W. Hostetter.

★8930★
Landmark College - Library - Special Collections (Educ)
Putney, VT 05346 Phone: (802)387-4767
Robert H. Rhodes
Founded: 1985. **Staff:** Prof 2; Other 1. **Special Collections:** Dyslexia, Specific Learning Disabilities Collection (769 books); High/Low Collection (2150 books). **Holdings:** 26,000 books; 235 bound periodical volumes. **Subscriptions:** 124 journals and other serials; 8 newspapers. **Services:** Interlibrary loan; copying; library open to the public for reference use only. **Computerized Information Services:** DIALOG Information Services. Performs searches. Contact Person: Marilyn Graves. **Publications:** Bibliography of Learning Disabilities Collection.

★8931★
Landmark Conservators - Cabots Old Indian Pueblo Museum - Library (Hist, Area-Ethnic)
67-616 E. Desert View Ave. Phone: (619)329-7610
Desert Hot Springs, CA 92240 Colbert H. Eyraud, Pres./Cur.
Founded: 1969. **Staff:** 3. **Subjects:** Indians, history, art, earthquake and geothermal data, weather logs, business. **Special Collections:** City Council and Planning Commission agenda and actions, 1968-1985; Desert Sentinel newspaper, 1946-1981 (microfilm); Earthquake Watch newsletter, 1980-1982; photographs of Wintun Culture Indians in northern California (from original 1901 glass plates). **Holdings:** 3500 books; 50 bound periodical volumes; 20 VF drawers of clippings; 4 boxes of old newspapers; 1500 78rpm records; 100 Edison cylinders. **Subscriptions:** 21 journals and other serials. **Services:** Library open to the public with restrictions. **Publications:** Monthly 1980-85 Musings from the Pueblo by Shareese Von Strauss. **Remarks:** FAX: (619)329-1956.

★8932★
Landmark Society of Western New York - Wenrich Memorial Library (Plan)
133 S. Fitzhugh St. Phone: (716)546-7029
Rochester, NY 14608 Ann B. Parks, Dir. of Musm.
Founded: 1971. **Staff:** Prof 2. **Subjects:** Architecture, state and local history, historic preservation and restoration techniques, decorative arts, landscape architecture, planning. **Special Collections:** John Wenrich Collection (architectural and locomotive renderings); Walter Cassebeer Collection (lithographs of area buildings and historic scenes). **Holdings:** 5000 books; 70 bound periodical volumes; 7000 slides; 7500 photographs; 100 drawings. **Subscriptions:** 38 journals and other serials. **Services:** Interlibrary loan; copying; library open to the public with restrictions. **Networks/Consortia:** Member of Rochester Regional Library Council (RRLC). **Publications:** Newsletter; Landmark Exchange, both bimonthly - to members and the public on request; listing of area buildings for sale that are of architectural and/or historical interest. **Remarks:** FAX: (716)546-4788. **Staff:** Cynthia Howk, Cons.Coord.

★8933★
Landmarks Division of the (Kansas City) City Planning & Development Department - Archives (Plan)
City Hall Phone: (816)274-2555
Kansas City, MO 64106 Lisa Lassman Briscoe, Adm.
Staff: 2. **Subjects:** Historic preservation. **Holdings:** 10,000 survey inventories; 2000 slides; bound periodical volumes of National Roster Forms; AV program; building permits; photographs; atlases. **Subscriptions:** 7 journals and other serials. **Services:** Copying; archives open to the public with restrictions.

Landowne-Bloom Collection
See: **Yeshiva University - Pollack Library** (20758)

Landsmanshaft Archive
See: **Yivo Institute for Jewish Research - Library and Archives** (20759)

★8934★
Landwirtschaftlich Chemische Bundesanstalt - Bibliothek (Agri)
Trunnerstr 1 Phone: 222 21113
A-1020 Vienna, Austria Eva Krebs
Founded: 1869. **Staff:** Prof 1. **Subjects:** Agriculture, biology, nutrition, chemistry, veterinary science. **Holdings:** 6000 books; 9000 bound periodical volumes. **Services:** Interlibrary loan; copying; library open to the public at librarian's discretion. **Remarks:** FAX: 222 21113, ext. 350.

Bishop Lane Library
See: **St. Anthony College of Nursing** (14233)

★8935★
Lane Council of Governments - Library (Plan)
125 E. 8th Ave., 2nd Fl. Phone: (503)687-4283
Eugene, OR 97401 JoAnn McCauley
Subjects: Planning - city, regional, transportation, human services; population; census; zoning. **Holdings:** 6000 books. **Services:** Library open to the public for reference use only. **Automated Operations:** Computerized cataloging.

★8936★
Lane County Historical Museum - Special Collections & Archives (Hist)
740 W. 13th Ave. Phone: (503)687-4239
Eugene, OR 97402 Marty West, Cur., Spec.Coll.
Founded: 1971. **Staff:** Prof 1. **Subjects:** Lane County history and settlement. **Special Collections:** William Kyle and Sons (24 linear feet); Eugene Woolen Mills (10 linear feet); Central Lane League of Women Voters (20 linear feet); Oregon Repertory Theater (5 linear feet); American Rhododendron Society, Eugene Chapter (4 linear feet); H.H. Waechter (architect; 35 linear feet); Willamette Peoples Co-op (15 linear feet); Elizabeth Romane Portrait Photographer (14,000 images); New Mime Circus (9 linear feet). **Holdings:** 4000 books; 50,000 photographs; 75 linear feet of Lane County archives; 300 maps; 27 reels of microfilm; 22 VF drawers of ephemera and clippings; 97 architectural drawings; 301 maps; 139 oral history cassette tapes. **Services:** Copying; archives open to the public by appointment. **Special Catalogs:** Exhibit catalogs, irregular; Catalogue of Manuscript Collections (1980); A Piece of the Old Tent (artifact catalog). **Special Indexes:** Lane County Historians, 1959 to present.

★8937★
Lane County Law Library (Law)
Courthouse
125 E. 8th St. Phone: (503)687-4337
Eugene, OR 97401 R. Burdett Mafit, Law Libn.
Founded: 1948. **Staff:** Prof 1; Other 2. **Subjects:** Law. **Holdings:** 15,500 books; 500 bound periodical volumes; Oregon Supreme Court briefs, 1955 to present; Oregon Court of Appeals briefs, 1969 to present. **Subscriptions:** 25 journals. **Services:** Copying; library open to the public with restrictions. **Computerized Information Services:** DIALOG Information Services, WESTLAW, Oregon Legislative Information System; internal databases. Performs searches on fee basis. **Publications:** Lane County Law Library Newsletter, bimonthly - to members of the local bar. **Remarks:** FAX: (503)687-4315. Maintained by Lane County Department of Finance & Management Services.

Lane Hall Memorial Library
See: **Athol Murray College of Notre Dame** (10870)

Lane Library
See: **Armstrong State College** (1057)

Lane Medical Library
See: **Stanford University** (15653)

★8938★
Lane & Mittendorf - Law Library (Law)
99 Park Ave. Phone: (212)972-3000
New York, NY 10016 Candi McBride, Libn.
Founded: 1952. **Staff:** 1. **Subjects:** Law. **Holdings:** 9000 books. **Subscriptions:** 40 journals and other serials; 7 newspapers. **Services:** Interlibrary loan; library open to members of the Law Library Association of Greater New York. **Computerized Information Services:** LEXIS, WESTLAW, DIALOG Information Services, Prentice Hall Online, Dow Jones News/Retrieval, LEGI-SLATE, DataTimes, Current USC, Dun & Bradstreet Legal Search. **Remarks:** FAX: (212)972-5647.

★8939★
Lane Powell Spears Lubersky - Library (Law)
520 S.W. Yamhill St., Suite 800 Phone: (503)226-6151
Portland, OR 97204 Jerold W. Hilary, Law Libn.
Staff: Prof 1; Other 3. **Subjects:** Law. **Holdings:** 20,000 books; 2000 internal legal memoranda. **Subscriptions:** 400 journals and other serials. **Services:** Interlibrary loan; library not open to the public. **Computerized Information Services:** WESTLAW, LEXIS, NEXIS, DIALOG Information Services, LEGI-SLATE, DataTimes. **Remarks:** FAX: (503)224-0388.

★8940★
Lane Powell Spears Lubersky - Library (Law)
1420 5th Ave., Suite 1400 Phone: (206)223-6245
Seattle, WA 98101-2338 Denyse I. McFadden, Lib.Mgr.
Founded: 1889. **Staff:** Prof 3; Other 2.5. **Subjects:** Law. **Holdings:** 28,500 books. **Subscriptions:** 300 journals and other serials; 15 newspapers. **Services:** Interlibrary loan; library open to the public by appointment. **Automated Operations:** Computerized cataloging. **Computerized Information Services:** WESTLAW, LEXIS, DataTimes, Reuters, DIALOG Information Services, VU/TEXT Information Services, Dow Jones News/Retrieval, OCLC, Reuters; Brief Retrieval System (internal database). **Networks/Consortia:** Member of Western Library Network (WLN). **Remarks:** FAX: (206)223-7107. Telex: 32 8808. **Staff:** Charles Crawford, Libn.; Nancy McMurrer, Libn.

Lane Public Library - Smith Library of Regional History
See: **Smith Library of Regional History** (15247)

★8941★
Lang, Michener, Lawrence and Shaw - Library (Law)
BCE Place
181 Bay St., Suite 2500 Phone: (416)307-4140
Toronto, ON, Canada M5J 2T7 Margaret Szucs, Mgr., Lib.Serv.
Staff: 4. **Subjects:** Law. **Services:** Library not open to the public. **Remarks:** FAX: (416)365-1719. **Staff:** Nancy L. Urbankiewicz.

Norman McKee Lang Library
See: **Lester B. Pearson College of the Pacific** (12810)

Lange Library
See: **University of Wyoming - Family Practice Residency Program at Casper - Lange Memorial Library** (19656)

★8942★
Lange, Simpson, Robinson & Somerville - Library (Law)
1700 First Alabama Bank Bldg. Phone: (205)250-5000
Birmingham, AL 35203 Cherie D. Feenker, Libn.
Founded: 1919. **Staff:** Prof 1; Other 3. **Subjects:** Law - securities, corporate, banking, antitrust, labor, tax. **Holdings:** 30,000 books; 250 bound periodical volumes; 1600 briefs and memorandum; form files; expert witness files; pamphlets files. **Subscriptions:** 110 journals and other serials; 5 newspapers. **Services:** Interlibrary loan; copying; SDI; library open to the public with permission. **Computerized Information Services:** DIALOG Information Services, WESTLAW. **Remarks:** FAX: (205)250-5034.

Langley Research Center
See: **NASA - Langley Research Center** (10986)

★8943★
Langley School District - Milner Education Centre (Educ, Aud-Vis)
22259 48th Ave. Phone: (604)530-5151
Langley, BC, Canada V3A 3Z7 Susan Krantz, Supv.
Founded: 1963. **Staff:** Prof 2; Other 9. **Subjects:** Educational materials. **Holdings:** 314 books; 1262 16mm films; 151 picture sets; 305 transparencies; 404 filmstrips; 4679 programmed videotapes; 67 models; 284 media kits; 225 computer software programs; 53 audiocassettes; 58 slide sets; 1604 sound filmstrips; 14 science kits; 83 book kits. **Subscriptions:** 36 journals and other serials. **Services:** Center not open to the public. **Automated Operations:** Computerized cataloging, acquisitions, and circulation. **Publications:** Content, quarterly; Allspice, biweekly. **Special Catalogs:** Catalog of resources (book); list of periodical contents. **Remarks:** Alternate telephone number(s): 530-0301. FAX: (604)530-2906. **Staff:** Jean Gregson, Cat.Libn.

Langstaff Foundation
See: **Burlington County Lyceum of History and Natural Science** (2374)

★8944★
Langston University - Melvin B. Tolson Black Heritage Center (Area-Ethnic)
Langston, OK 73050 Phone: (405)466-3346
Ronald Keys, Act.Cur.
Founded: 1969. **Staff:** Prof 1. **Subjects:** Afro-American experience in the U.S., Afro-Americans in the humanities and arts since 1900, African history. **Special Collections:** African Art Collection (93 items); Langston University Archives (brochures; programs; yearbooks; presidential papers); Melvin B. Tolson Collection (books; personal items; pictures; awards). **Holdings:** 15,000 books; 1200 bound periodical volumes; 750 recordings; 600 audio cassettes; 150 video cassettes; 100 films; 10,000 VF materials. **Subscriptions:** 90 journals and other serials; 50 newspapers. **Services:** Interlibrary loan; copying; center open to the public. **Publications:** Acquisitions List, monthly; newsletter, quarterly. **Special Indexes:** Biography index; periodical articles index. **Remarks:** FAX: (405)466-3459. **Staff:** Edward Grady, Asst.Cur.

Wann Langston Memorial Library
See: **Baptist Medical Center** (1510)

Laning Humphrey Journalistic Archives
See: **Boston Public Library - Music Department** (1997)

★8945★
Lankenau Hospital - Medical Library (Med)
100 Lancaster Ave. Phone: (215)645-2698
Wynnewood, PA 19096 Kathleen A. Leigh, Dir., Med.Lib.
Founded: 1860. **Staff:** Prof 1. **Subjects:** Medicine, medical research. **Special Collections:** Collected papers of the Lankenau Hospital Department of Research. **Holdings:** 4400 books; 12,500 bound periodical volumes; 450 audio cassettes. **Subscriptions:** 400 journals and other serials. **Services:** Interlibrary loan; copying; library open to the public for reference use only. **Automated Operations:** Computerized ILL (DOCLINE). **Computerized Information Services:** MEDLARS, PDQ. **Networks/Consortia:** Member of National Network of Libraries of Medicine - Middle Atlantic Region. **Remarks:** FAX: (215)645-3425.

★8946★
Lankenau Hospital - School of Nursing Library (Med)
City Ave. & 64th St. Phone: (215)642-3931
Wynnewood, PA 19096 Maude H. Meyerend, Libn.
Founded: 1909. **Staff:** Prof 1. **Subjects:** Nursing and nursing history, medicine, public health, microbiology, chemistry, psychology, sociology. **Special Collections:** First editions of nursing textbooks; Lankenau historical collection. **Holdings:** 3600 volumes; 8 VF drawers of illustrations, clippings, pamphlets, reports, archival materials. **Subscriptions:** 75 journals and other serials. **Services:** Interlibrary loan; copying; library open to the public by appointment. **Networks/Consortia:** Member of Consortium for Health Information & Library Services (CHI). **Remarks:** FAX: (215)642-6915.

★8947★
Lansing General Hospital, Osteopathic - K.M. Baker Memorial Library (Med)
2727 S. Pennsylvania Phone: (517)377-8389
Lansing, MI 48910-3490 Judith A. Barnes, Med.Libn.
Founded: 1969. **Staff:** Prof 1; Other1. **Subjects:** Medicine, sports medicine, nursing, substance abuse, rehabilitation, osteopathy, orthodpedics, geriatric psychiatry. **Holdings:** 2800 books; 3500 bound periodical volumes; 1800 microfiche of journals; 800 Audio-Digest tapes; 300 audiovisuals. **Subscriptions:** 427 journals and other serials. **Services:** Interlibrary loan; copying; SDI; library open to the public. **Automated Operations:** Computerized public access catalog, cataloging, acquisitions, serials, circulation, ILL, and statistics. **Computerized Information Services:** MEDLARS, DIALOG Information Services, BRS Information Technologies, WILSONLINE; CD-ROM (MEDLINE). **Networks/Consortia:** Member of Michigan Health Sciences Libraries Association (MHSLA), Michigan Library Consortium (MLC), National Network of Libraries of Medicine - Greater Midwest Region. **Remarks:** FAX: (517)372-0341.

★8948★
Lansing State Journal - Library (Publ)
120 E. Lenawee St. Phone: (517)377-1008
Lansing, MI 48919 Pamela Gawronski
Founded: 1950. **Staff:** 1. **Subjects:** Newspaper reference topics. **Holdings:** Clipping files; photographs.

★8949★
Lanterman Developmental Center - Library (Med)
3530 W. Pomona Blvd.
Box 100 Phone: (714)595-1221
Pomona, CA 91769 Kathryn Pudlock, Libn.
Founded: 1954. **Staff:** Prof 1. **Subjects:** Mental retardation, child psychology, neurology, special education, medicine. **Holdings:** 12,000 volumes; 15 VF drawers of pamphlets. **Subscriptions:** 150 journals and other serials. **Services:** Interlibrary loan (fee); copying; library open to the public. **Computerized Information Services:** MEDLINE, DIALOG Information Services. Performs searches on fee basis. **Networks/Consortia:** Member of National Network of Libraries of Medicine - Pacific Southwest Region. **Remarks:** FAX: (714)595-1221, ext. 2524.

★8950★
Lanzhou Railway Institute - Library (Trans)
West Anning Lu
Lanzhou, Gansu Province, People's Phone: 66221
Republic of China Prof. Wei Ging Huai, Libn.
Founded: 1958. **Staff:** 63. **Subjects:** Railway construction and transport, locomotives, communication signals, water supply and drainage. **Holdings:** 459,921 volumes; 2972 periodicals. **Subscriptions:** 1919 journals and other serials; 180 newspapers. **Services:** Interlibrary loan; copying; library open to the public with restrictions. **Computerized Information Services:** Internal databases. **Publications:** Chinese and Foreign New Books Quarterly. **Staff:** Gao Jie Min; Wang Han Cheng.

★8951★
LaPalme Memorial Hospital - Library (Med)
320 Pomfret St. Phone: (203)928-6541
Putnam, CT 06260 Elaine Davis, Libn.
Founded: 1973. **Staff:** 1. **Subjects:** Medicine. **Holdings:** 500 books; 800 bound periodical volumes. **Subscriptions:** 56 journals and other serials; 3 newspapers. **Services:** Interlibrary loan; copying; library open to the public for reference use only. **Computerized Information Services:** OCLC, MEDLINE. **Remarks:** FAX: (203)928-1398.

Lapeer County Library System - Oakdale Regional Center
See: **Oakdale Regional Center** (12193)

★8952★
LaRabida Children's Hospital and Research Center - Lawrence Mercer Pick Memorial Library (Med)
E. 65th St. at Lake Michigan Phone: (312)363-6700
Chicago, IL 60649 Paula Jaudes, Chf. of Med. Staff
Founded: 1959. **Staff:** 1. **Subjects:** Biomedical research, medicine, dentistry, nursing. **Holdings:** 920 books; 508 bound periodical volumes. **Subscriptions:** 49 journals and other serials. **Services:** Library not open to the public.

★8953★
Laramie Plains Museum Association - Library (Hist)
603 Ivinson Phone: (307)742-4448
Laramie, WY 82070 Daniel A. Nelson, Dir.
Founded: 1972. **Staff:** 3. **Subjects:** History, American culture, local history. **Special Collections:** Wyoming history collection. **Holdings:** 1000 volumes; bound manuscripts; newspapers. **Services:** Library open to the public for reference use only.

★8954★
Larned State Hospital - J.T. Naramore Library (Med)
Route 3, Box 89 Phone: (316)285-2131
Larned, KS 67550-9365 Rita Renfrow, Off.Asst. III
Founded: 1964. **Staff:** Prof 1; Other 1. **Subjects:** Psychiatry, psychiatric nursing, psychology, mental health, medicine. **Special Collections:** J.T. Naramore Collection (525 books); Dr. D.H. "Homer" Davis Collection (48 books). **Holdings:** 6057 books; 80 journal titles, 1976-1991. **Subscriptions:** 68 journals and other serials. **Services:** Interlibrary loan.

Las Campanas Observatory
See: **Carnegie Institution of Washington - Observatories - Library** (3074)

★8955★
Las Vegas City Municipal Court - Library (Law)
400 E. Stewart Ave. Phone: (702)386-6509
Las Vegas, NV 89101 Diane Ortiz, Mgt.Anl./Court Rec.Libn.
Staff: Prof 1. **Subjects:** Judicial/court administration, traffic and criminal courts, criminal justice planning, court automation/information technology/records management, sentencing and judgements, statutory and legal materials, court counseling. **Holdings:** 1000 books. **Subscriptions:** 33 journals and other serials. **Services:** Interlibrary loan (limited); copying; library open to the public by appointment.

Las Vegas Medical Center
See: **New Mexico (State) Department of Hospitals** (11526)

★8956★
Las Vegas Review-Journal - Library (Hist)
Box 70 Phone: (702)383-0269
Las Vegas, NV 89125 Padmini P. Pai, Libn.
Founded: 1960. **Staff:** Prof 2; Other 2. **Subjects:** Nevada history, current history, newspaper reference topics. **Holdings:** 115 bound periodical volumes; newspaper, 1905 to present, on microfilm. **Services:** Library not open to the public. **Computerized Information Services:** DataTimes. **Remarks:** FAX: (702)383-0302. Library located at 1111 W. Bonanza, Las Vegas, NV 89106. **Staff:** Kathy McLaughlin, Asst.Libn.

Mauricio Lasansky Archives
See: **Cedar Rapids Museum of Art - Herbert S. Stamats Art Library** (3186)

★8957★
Lashly & Baer, P.C. - Law Library (Law)
714 Locust St. Phone: (314)621-2939
St. Louis, MO 63101 Carol R. Teaney, Libn.
Staff: Prof 1; Other 1. **Subjects:** Law. **Holdings:** Figures not available. **Services:** Interlibrary loan; library not open to the public. **Automated Operations:** Computerized cataloging. **Computerized Information Services:** LEXIS. **Remarks:** FAX: (314)621-6844.

Lasker Memorial Library
See: **Temple B'nai Israel** (16094)

Virginia Davis Laskey Library
See: **Scarritt-Bennett Center** (14897)

Lassiter Library
See: **Hezekiah Alexander Foundation** (340)

★8958★
Latah County Historical Society - Research Library (Hist)
110 S. Adams Phone: (208)882-1004
Moscow, ID 83843 Joann Jones
Founded: 1968. **Staff:** Prof 2; Other 5. **Subjects:** Latah County authors and history. **Special Collections:** Oral history collection (700 hours of tape; 150 transcripts); technical library on historic preservation (100 volumes); photo collection. **Holdings:** 350 books; 315 feet of boxes of manuscripts; 16 boxes of pamphlets; 4 reels of microfilm; 2 file drawers of clippings and ephemera; 5000 photographs. **Subscriptions:** 15 journals and other serials. **Services:** Copying; library open to the public for reference use only. **Publications:** Guide to The Latah County, Idaho, Oral History Collection (book); Guide to the Local History Library at the Latah County Historical Society (book); Guide to Historical & Genealogical Records in Latah County, Idaho; A Great Good Country: A Guide to Historic Moscow and Latah County. **Staff:** Mary Reed, Dir.

★8959★
The Latham Foundation - Human/Animal Bond Resource Library (Soc Sci)
Latham Plaza Bldg.
Clement and Schiller Phone: (510)521-0920
Alameda, CA 94501 Hugh H. Tebault, Pres.
Founded: 1918. **Staff:** 1. **Subjects:** Human/animal bond, pet-facilitated therapy. **Holdings:** Books; videotapes. **Subscriptions:** 10 journals and other serials. **Services:** Copying; library open to the public. **Computerized Information Services:** Internal database. **Remarks:** FAX: (510)521-9861. **Staff:** S. Nagy.

★8960★
Latham & Watkins - Law Library (Law)
650 Town Center, Suite 2000 Phone: (714)755-8273
Costa Mesa, CA 92626 Alice Chu, Info.Serv.Mgr.
Founded: 1975. **Staff:** Prof 2; Other 1. **Subjects:** Law. **Holdings:** Figures not available. **Services:** Interlibrary loan; library not open to the public. **Computerized Information Services:** DIALOG Information Services, Information America, CDB Infotek, DataQuick, Disclosure Orderline, LEXIS, NEXIS, WESTLAW, Dun & Bradstreet Business Credit Services, DataTimes, LEGI-SLATE, Legi-Tech, ELSS (Electronic Legislative Search System), Dow Jones News/Retrieval, Prentice Hall Online, VU/TEXT Information Services. **Networks/Consortia:** Member of OCLC Pacific Network. **Publications:** Library bulletin. **Remarks:** FAX: (714)755-8290. Telex: 590777. **Staff:** Sheila Kern.

★8961★
Latham & Watkins - Law Library (Law)
633 W. 5th St. Phone: (213)891-8295
Los Angeles, CA 90071 Patricia Adorno, Law Libn.
Founded: 1962. **Staff:** Prof 5; Other 6. **Subjects:** Law. **Holdings:** 35,000 volumes; microforms. **Subscriptions:** 450 journals and other serials; 20 newspapers. **Services:** Interlibrary loan; library not open to the public. **Computerized Information Services:** LEXIS, NEXIS, WESTLAW, DIALOG Information Services, Dow Jones News/Retrieval, VU/TEXT Information Services, DataTimes, BNA, RLIN, Human Resources Information Network (HRIN), Information America, QL Systems, ELSS (Electronic Legislative Search System), DataQuick, Chemical Information Systems, Inc. (CIS), OCLC; EasyLink (electronic mail service). **Publications:** Library Bulletin, monthly. **Remarks:** FAX: (213)891-8763.

★8962★
Latham & Watkins - Law Library (Law)
701 B St., Suite 2100 Phone: (619)236-1234
San Diego, CA 92101 Carolyn L. Vega, Law Libn.
Founded: 1982. **Staff:** Prof 2; Other 1. **Subjects:** Law. **Holdings:** 10,000 books. **Subscriptions:** 99 journals and other serials. **Services:** Interlibrary loan; library not open to the public. **Computerized Information Services:** DataQuick, DataTimes, DIALOG Information Services, Dow Jones News/Retrieval, ELSS, Information America, Legi-Tech, LEXIS, NEXIS, OCLC, VU/TEXT Information Services, WESTLAW, LEGI-SLATE; internal database. **Remarks:** FAX: (619)696-7419. **Staff:** Melinda Briggs.

★8963★
Latham & Watkins - Law Library (Law)
5800 Sears Tower Phone: (312)876-7700
Chicago, IL 60606 Janet Collins, Libn.
Staff: Prof 2; Other 2. **Subjects:** Law. **Holdings:** 10,000 books. **Subscriptions:** 200 journals and other serials; 5 newspapers. **Services:** Interlibrary loan; library not open to the public. **Automated Operations:** Computerized cataloging. **Computerized Information Services:** LEXIS, WESTLAW, DIALOG Information Services, OCLC, Dun & Bradstreet Business Credit Services, Dow Jones News/Retrieval. **Networks/Consortia:** Member of ILLINET. **Remarks:** FAX: (312)993-9767.

Vincent Lathbury Library
See: **Mid-Coast Mental Health Center** (10346)

★8964★
Norman Lathrop Enterprises - Library (Info Sci)
2342 Star Dr.
Box 198 Phone: (216)262-5587
Wooster, OH 44691 Norman Lathrop, Owner
Founded: 1963. **Staff:** Prof 2. **Subjects:** Newspaper and periodical indexing, arts and crafts. **Holdings:** 150 periodical titles in craft, hobby, modelmaking. **Subscriptions:** 103 journals and other serials. **Services:** Library not open to the public. **Publications:** Lathrop Reports on Newspaper Indexing. **Special Indexes:** Index to How to Do It Information, 1963 to present. **Staff:** Mary Lou Lathrop, Chf. Indexer.

★8965★
Lathrop Norquist & Miller - Library (Law)
2600 Mutual Benefit Life Bldg.
2345 Grand Ave.
Kansas City, MO 64108 Phone: (816)842-0820
Founded: 1890. **Staff:** Prof 1. **Subjects:** Law - corporate, real estate, tax, Securities and Exchange Commission, banking. **Holdings:** 15,000 volumes. **Subscriptions:** 10 journals and other serials. **Services:** Library not open to the public.

Lathrope Health Sciences Library
See: **Morristown Memorial Hospital** (10757)

★8966★
Latin American Economic System - Library (Bus-Fin)
Apartado Postal 17035
El Conde
Caracas 1010-A, Venezuela Phone: 2 9514233
Subjects: Latin America and the Caribbean - international relations, economic cooperation, technical and economic involvement in developing countries. **Holdings:** 400,000 volumes. **Remarks:** Telex: 23294 VC.

★8967★
Latin American Energy Organization - Department of Informatics and Communications - Document Center (Energy)
Edificio OLADE
Avenida Occidental, Sector San Carlos
Cassilla 6413 CCI Phone: 2 538122
Quito, Ecuador Antonio Carlos Tatit Holtz, Dir. of Info. & Commun.
Founded: 1981. **Staff:** 3. **Subjects:** Latin American energy - resources, market, technology. **Holdings:** 20,000 volumes. **Subscriptions:** 100 journals and other serials; 2 newspapers. **Services:** Interlibrary loan; copying; center open to the public. **Computerized Information Services:** Internal database. **Publications:** List of publications; CDD Report. **Special Indexes:** Index of articles published in Energy Magazine. **Remarks:** FAX: 2 539684. Telex: 2728 OLADE-ED. **Staff:** Maria Eugenia Lopez, Asst. de Doc.

★8968★
Latin American Institute for Cooperation and Development - Library (Soc Sci)
EDIF Fundacion UTAL
Apartado 4453
San Antonio de los Altos
Caracas 1010-A, Venezuela Phone: 2 710422
Subjects: Socioeconomic self-development in Latin America; cooperatives; women's and youth organizations; workers' social and cultural organizations. **Holdings:** 60,000 volumes (in Spanish). **Remarks:** Telex: 29873 LAWTU VC.

★8969★
Latin American Iron and Steel Institute - ILAFA Library (Sci-Engr)
Dario Urzua, No. 1994
Casilla 16065
Santiago 9, Chile Phone: 2 2237581
Subjects: Iron, steelmaking, allied subjects. **Holdings:** 1000 documents. **Remarks:** Telex: 340 348 ILAFA CK. **Also Known As:** Instituto Latinoamericano del Fierro y el Acero.

Latino Community Development Archive
See: **University of California, Los Angeles - Chicano Studies Research Library** (18376)

★8970★
Albert J. Latner Jewish Public Library (Area-Ethnic, Rel-Phil)
4600 Bathurst St. Phone: (416)635-2996
Willowdale, ON, Canada M2R 3V3 Rabbi Z. Wolkenstein, Exec.Dir. & Hd.Libn.
Founded: 1939. **Staff:** Prof 2; Other 3. **Subjects:** Bible and Talmud, Rabbinics and Hassidism, Holocaust, Israel and Zionism, history, language and literature. **Special Collections:** Judaica, Hebraica, and Russian. **Holdings:** 30,000 volumes. **Subscriptions:** 50 journals and other serials. **Services:** Interlibrary loan; copying; library open to the public. **Computerized Information Services:** Jewish history (internal databases). **Remarks:** Maintained by Toronto Jewish Congress. **Staff:** Anna Liberman, Libn.

Kenneth Scott Latourette Library
See: **William Carey International University** (3043)

★8971★
Latrobe Area Hospital - Medical & Nursing Libraries (Med)
W. Second Ave.
Latrobe, PA 15650 Phone: (412)537-1275
Staff: Prof 1; Other 1. **Subjects:** Medicine, nursing, medical technology. **Holdings:** 1600 books; 420 bound periodical volumes; 12 VF drawers of pamphlets and clippings; 2 VF drawers of patient education materials. **Subscriptions:** 147 journals and other serials. **Services:** Interlibrary loan; copying; libraries open to the public with permission. **Automated Operations:** Computerized cataloging. **Computerized Information Services:** MEDLINE. **Publications:** Library Newsletter, monthly; Current Contents of Journals, monthly - to health professionals.

★8972★
Latvian Studies Center - Library (Area-Ethnic)
1702 Fraternity Village Dr. Phone: (616)343-0254
Kalamazoo, MI 49007 Maira Bundza, Libn.
Founded: 1983. **Staff:** Prof 1. **Subjects:** Latvian literature, Latvia, Latvians, Baltic states. **Special Collections:** Archives (50 boxes). **Holdings:** 24,000 books; 350 bound periodical volumes; 15 videotapes; 700 sound recordings; 1000 slides; 270 reels of microfilm; 1800 pieces of sheet music; 20 manuscripts. **Subscriptions:** 50 journals and other serials; 10 newspapers. **Services:** Interlibrary loan; copying; library open to the public. **Publications:** Periodical holdings lists; book lists. **Remarks:** Co-sponsored by Western Michigan University.

★8973★
Laubach Literacy International, Inc. - Library (Educ)
1320 Jamesville Ave.
Box 131 Phone: (315)422-9121
Syracuse, NY 13210 Jenny L. Ryan, Lib.Mgr.
Founded: 1959. **Staff:** Prof 1; Other 1. **Subjects:** Adult basic education, literacy, illiteracy, reading, ESL, voluntarism, publishing for adult new readers, management. **Special Collections:** Literacy, adult basic education, and reading resource material for volunteer tutors; writings of Frank C. Laubach (101 volumes and 4 VF drawers); foreign language materials of historical value for adult beginning readers (141 languages). **Holdings:** 3535 books; 4923 documents (15 VF drawers) including pamphlets, unbound reports, clippings, dissertations, other documents; 83 slide/tape sets; 49 video cassettes; 164 microfiche. **Subscriptions:** 71 journals and newsletters. **Services:** Interlibrary loan; copying (limited); library open to researchers for reference use only. **Automated Operations:** Computerized public access catalog. **Publications:** Bibliographies; Literacy Collection Development in Libraries: A Bibliography, 2nd ed., 1989; fact sheets. **Special Catalogs:** Catalog of the LLA Loan Collection. **Special Indexes:** Index of the Laubach Archival Collection at Bird Library, Syracuse University; foreign language collection index. **Remarks:** FAX: (315)422-6369. Includes publications of Laubach Literacy International, Laubach Literacy Action, New Readers Press, and Frank C. Laubach.

★8974★
Estee Lauder Inc. - Information Center (Sci-Engr)
125 Pine Lawn Rd. Phone: (516)531-1174
Melville, NY 11747 Dr. Dorothy A. Kramer, Mgr. & Info.Sci.
Founded: 1983. **Staff:** Prof 2; Other 2. **Subjects:** Cosmetics, dermatology, biochemistry, chemistry, computer science, engineering. **Special Collections:** U.S. and foreign patents (2000). **Holdings:** 4500 books; 1500 bound periodical volumes; supplier literature. **Subscriptions:** 250 journals and other serials; 6 newspapers. **Services:** Interlibrary loan; center not open to the public. **Computerized Information Services:** DIALOG Information Services, PFDS Online, STN International, Chemical Abstracts Service (CAS), Questel, Data-Star, LEXIS, NEXIS, MEDLARS, CompuServe Information Service, VU/TEXT Information Services, DataTimes, OCLC. Performs searches free of charge. **Networks/Consortia:** Member of Long Island Library Resources Council. **Publications:** Patents Bulletins; U.S. and Foreign New Books; Serials List; Cosmetics Abstract Bulletin; Patent Abstract Bulletin. **Special Indexes:** Japanese Cosmetic Ingredient Index (online). **Remarks:** FAX: (516)454-7662. **Staff:** Jeanne Oppenheimer, Libn.

Matthew Laughlin Memorial Library
See: **Chicago Academy of Sciences** (3512)

Lauinger Memorial Library
See: **Georgetown University - Special Collections Division - Lauinger Memorial Library** (6379)

Laurel Grove Hospital
See: **Eden Hospital Medical Center** (5227)

★8975★
Laurelton Center - Library (Med)
Laurelton, PA 17835 Phone: (717)922-5266
Jane G. Slack, Libn.
Founded: 1913. **Staff:** Prof 1. **Subjects:** Mental retardation, psychology, special education, social service. **Special Collections:** Freud's books on mental retardation. **Holdings:** 5241 volumes. **Subscriptions:** 84 journals and other serials. **Services:** Interlibrary loan; library not open to the public. **Remarks:** Alternate telephone number(s): 922-5267.

★8976★
Laurelwood Hosptial - Library (Med)
35900 Euclid Ave. Phone: (216)421-5615
Willoughby, OH 44094 Pamela Alderman, Dir.
Subjects: Psychiatry, substance abuse, geriatrics, adolescent health. **Holdings:** 200 books. **Subscriptions:** 26 journals and other serials. **Services:** Library not open to the public. **Computerized Information Services:** NLM, DIALOG Information Services, BRS Information Technologies, Data-Star, STN International. **Remarks:** FAX: (216)421-6198. Affiliated with Mt. Sinai Medical Center - Medical Library.

★8977★
Laurentian Hospital - Medical Library (Med)
41 Ramsey Lake Rd. Phone: (705)522-2200
Sudbury, ON, Canada P3E 5J1 Rannah Brosseau, Libn.
Founded: 1945. **Staff:** 1. **Subjects:** Medicine, allied health sciences. **Holdings:** 1000 books; 5000 bound periodical volumes; 250 cassettes; 35 video cassettes. **Subscriptions:** 120 journals and other serials. **Services:** Interlibrary loan; copying. **Computerized Information Services:** MEDLINE. Performs searches. **Remarks:** FAX: (705)523-7017.

★8978★
Laurentian University - J.N. Desmarais Library - Special Collections, Rare Books, and Archives (Area-Ethnic)
Ramsey Lake Rd. Phone: (705)675-1151
Sudbury, ON, Canada P3E 2C6 Joyce Garnett, Dir. of Libs.
Founded: 1991. **Special Collections:** Rare books; University Archives. **Holdings:** Figures not available. **Formed by the merger of:** Its Main Library, School of Education Library, and Science and Engineering Library.

Blanche and Irving Laurie Music Library
See: **Rutgers University** (14157)

★8979★
Wilfrid Laurier University - Library (Hum, Bus-Fin)
75 University Ave., W. Phone: (519)884-1970
Waterloo, ON, Canada N2L 3C5 Erich R.W. Schultz, Univ.Libn.
Founded: 1911. **Staff:** Prof 13; Other 41. **Subjects:** Humanities, business and economics, social work, religion, music. **Holdings:** 550,000 books; 10,025 serial titles; 112,000 government documents; 110 VF drawers of annual reports, pamphlets, clippings; 23,750 reels of microfilm; 59,500 microcards; 510,000 microfiche; 8100 recordings; 250 cassettes; 1900 compact discs; 54,500 slides. **Subscriptions:** 4550 journals and other serials; 31 newspapers. **Services:** Interlibrary loan; copying; library open to the public on payment of user fee. **Automated Operations:** Computerized public access catalog, cataloging, acquisitions, serials, and circulation. **Computerized Information Services:** DIALOG Information Services, BRS Information Technologies, CAN/OLE, Info Globe, The Financial Post DataGroup, International Development Research Centre (IDRC); Envoy 100 (electronic mail service). Performs searches on fee basis. Contact Person: John Arndt, Ref./Coll.Libn., 884-1970, ext. 2417. **Networks/Consortia:** Member of Ontario Council of University Libraries (OCUL). **Publications:** Bibliographies; Handbooks; Annual Report; Serials List; CODOC. **Special Catalogs:** WLU Extension Catalogue. **Remarks:** FAX: (519)884-8023. Electronic mail address(es): ER.SCHULTZ (Envoy 100). **Staff:** Mrs. Brooke Skelton, Cat.; Brian Flood, Cat.; Vera Fesnak, Cat.; Howard Parkinson, Circ.Libn.; Diane Wilkins, Ser.Libn.; Richard Woeller, Govt.Doc.Libn.; Joan Mitchell, Bibliog./Acq.Depts.; John McCallum, Ref./Coll.Libn.; Diane Peters, Ref./Coll.Libn.; Herbert Schwartz, Sys.; Michael Skelton, Ref./Coll.Libn; Lois Clifford, Cat./Ref.Libn.; John Warren, Ref./Coll.Libn.

★8980★
Wilfrid Laurier University - Research Centre for Management of Advanced Technology/Operations (Sci-Engr)
University Ave. Phone: (519)884-1970
Waterloo, ON, Canada N2L 3C5 Carole Litwiller, Coord.
Subjects: Cost effectiveness of implementation and acquisition of new technology, including computerization, robotics, flexible manufacturing systems, and global manufacturing. **Holdings:** Figures not available. **Computerized Information Services:** IMPLEMENTECH (internal database). Performs searches on fee basis. **Remarks:** FAX: (519)884-8853. **Formerly:** Its REMAT (Research Centre for Management of New Technology).

Charles C. Lauritsen Library
See: **Aerospace Corporation** (109)

Lauterman Library of Art
See: **McGill University - Blackader Library of Architecture/Lauterman Library of Art** (9892)

Lava Beds National Monument
See: **U.S. Natl. Park Service** (17743)

Lavalin Engineers, Inc.
See: **S.N.C. Lavalin Inc.** (14187)

★8981★
Lavalin Environnement Inc. - Documentation (Plan)
1100, blvd. Rene Levesque ouest
Montreal, PQ, Canada H3B 4P3 Phone: (514)393-1000
Founded: 1975. **Staff:** Prof 1. **Subjects:** Environment. **Holdings:** 7500 books; 100 bound periodical volumes; 360 maps; 550 internal reports. **Subscriptions:** 80 journals and other serials. **Services:** Interlibrary loan; copying; documentation open to the public by appointment. **Computerized Information Services:** DIALOG Information Services, CAN/OLE, DOBIS. **Remarks:** FAX: (514)876-9273.

Lavalin Inc.
See: **SNC Partec Inc.** (15291)

★8982★
Lavalin Inc. - Bibliotheque Lavalin (Sci-Engr)
1100, blvd. Rene Levesque ouest Phone: (514)393-1000
Montreal, PQ, Canada H3B 4P3 Marcel Marcotte, Hd.Libn.
Founded: 1946. **Staff:** Prof 1; Other 3. **Subjects:** Engineering, transportation, electricity, water resources, construction, metallurgy. **Holdings:** 12,000 books; 3500 standards and specifications; Transportation Research Board documents. **Subscriptions:** 350 journals and other serials; 15 newspapers. **Services:** Interlibrary loan; copying; library open to the public by appointment. **Computerized Information Services:** DIALOG Information Services, CAN/OLE, Prima Telematic Inc., DOBIS Canadian Online Library System. **Remarks:** FAX: (514)876-9273. Telex: 055-61250.

★8983★
Laventhol and Horwath - National Information Center
1845 Walnut St.
Philadelphia, PA 19103
Defunct.

★8984★
Law Engineering Consulting, Inc. - Library (Sci-Engr)
605 E. Robinson St., Suite 230
Orlando, FL 32801 Phone: (407)246-0066
Subjects: Construction materials engineering, roof and pavement materials, computer applications in engineering. **Holdings:** 1000 volumes. **Remarks:** FAX: (407)332-9440.

★8985★
Law Environmental - Library (Sci-Engr)
7375 Boston Blvd., Suite 200
Springfield, VA 22153 Phone: (703)912-9400
Founded: 1979. **Staff:** Prof 1; Other 1. **Subjects:** Water, wastewater, sanitary engineering, solid and hazardous wastes and their effects on health, environmental engineering. **Holdings:** 2000 books. **Subscriptions:** 39 journals and other serials. **Services:** Interlibrary loan; copying; library open to the public at librarian's discretion. **Computerized Information Services:** DIALOG Information Services, STN International. Performs searches on fee basis. **Special Indexes:** Pro-Lit (files of current product literature), semiannual.

★8986★
Law Library Association of St. Louis (Law)
1300 Civil Courts Bldg. Phone: (314)622-4386
St. Louis, MO 63101 Rosa Gahn Wright, Libn.
Founded: 1838. **Staff:** Prof 1; Other 6. **Subjects:** Law. **Holdings:** 96,431 volumes; 3495 microforms. **Subscriptions:** 213 journals and other serials. **Services:** Library not open to the public. **Computerized Information Services:** DIALOG Information Services, WESTLAW, WILSONLINE.

Law Library in Brooklyn
See: **New York State Supreme Court - 2nd Judicial District - Law Library** (11686)

★8987★
Law Library of Louisiana (Law)
100 Supreme Court Bldg.
301 Loyola Ave. Phone: (504)568-5705
New Orleans, LA 70112 Carol D. Billings, Dir.
Staff: Prof 4; Other 4. **Subjects:** Law. **Holdings:** 135,000 volumes. **Services:** Interlibrary loan; copying; faxing; library open to the public. **Automated Operations:** Computerized cataloging. **Computerized Information Services:** OCLC, WESTLAW, DataTimes, LegalTrac. Performs searches on fee basis. Contact Person: Tina McLellan, Ref. & ILL. **Networks/Consortia:** Member of SOLINET. **Publications:** Newsletter of the Friends of the Law Library of Louisiana. **Remarks:** FAX: (504)568-5069. **Staff:** Janice Shull, Cat.; Betty Kern, Acq. & Ser.

Law Reform Commission of Canada
See: **Canada - Law Reform Commission of Canada** (2763)

★8988★
Law Society of Alberta - Calgary Library (Law)
Court House
611 4th St., S.W. Phone: (403)297-6148
Calgary, AB, Canada T2P 1T5 Robert Leigh, Reg.Libn.
Founded: 1910. **Staff:** Prof 2; Other 3. **Subjects:** Law. **Holdings:** 58,000 books; 2 VF drawers of pamphlets; 2 cabinets of unreported Alberta judgements. **Subscriptions:** 800 journals and other serials. **Services:** Interlibrary loan; copying; library open to the public for reference use only. **Automated Operations:** Computerized cataloging. **Computerized Information Services:** QL Systems. Performs searches on fee basis. Contact Person: Susan McManus, 297-2415. **Special Indexes:** Index and Biographies of all Alberta Federally Appointed Judiciary (book; card). **Remarks:** FAX: (403)297-5171. Housed with the Alberta Attorney General - Court of Queen's Bench Law Library. **Staff:** Sandra Engelhardt, Pub.Serv.Libn.

★8989★
Law Society of Alberta - Drumheller Library (Law)
Court House
511 3rd Ave., W. Phone: (403)823-1721
Drumheller, AB, Canada T0J 0Y0 Elizabeth Braybrook, Libn.
Subjects: Law. **Services:** Library open to the public with restrictions. **Remarks:** FAX: (403)823-6013. No further information was supplied by respondent.

★8990★
Law Society of Alberta - Fort Macleod Library (Law)
Box 1360 Phone: (403)553-5000
Fort Macleod, AB, Canada T0L 0Z0 Pamela Young, Libn.
Subjects: Law. **Remarks:** No further information was supplied by respondent. **Remarks:** FAX: (403)553-5043

★8991★
Law Society of Alberta - Law Society Library (Law)
Law Courts Bldg.
1A Sir Winston Churchill Square, 2nd Fl. Phone: (403)422-2345
Edmonton, AB, Canada T5J 0R2 Shih-Sheng Hu, Chf.Prov. Law Libn.
Founded: 1908. **Staff:** Prof 2; Other 5. **Subjects:** Law. **Holdings:** 41,000 volumes; reports; statutes; government documents. **Subscriptions:** 300 journals and other serials. **Services:** Library open to the public for reference use only. **Remarks:** A branch of the Alberta Attorney General; housed with the Judges' Law Library. FAX: (403)427-0397.

★8992★
Law Society of Alberta - Library (Law)
320 4th St., S.
Bag 3014 Phone: (403)381-5639
Lethbridge, AB, Canada T1J 4C7 Grant Janzen, Libn.
Staff: Prof 1; Other 3. **Subjects:** Law. **Holdings:** 12,000 books; 1750 bound periodical volumes. **Subscriptions:** 65 journals and other serials. **Services:** Interlibrary loan; copying; library open to the public for reference use only. **Remarks:** FAX: (403)381-5703.

★8993★
Law Society of Alberta - Peace River Library (Law)
Box 34 - Bag 900 Phone: (403)624-6418
Peace River, AB, Canada T8S 1T4 Laura Gloor, Libn.
Founded: 1952. **Staff:** 1. **Subjects:** Law. **Holdings:** 7800 books; 9 bound periodical volumes; 28 reports; 14 digests; 4 statutes. **Subscriptions:** 70 journals and other serials. **Services:** Interlibrary loan; copying; library open to the public for reference use only. **Remarks:** FAX: (403)624-6563.

★8994★
Law Society of British Columbia - Library (Law)
Court House
1600 3rd Ave. Phone: (604)565-6357
Prince George, BC, Canada V2L 3G6 Julie Loerkie, Libn.
Subjects: Law. **Remarks:** No further information was supplied by respondent.

★8995★
Law Society of New Brunswick - Library (Law)
Justice Bldg., Rm. 305
P.O. Box 6000 Phone: (506)453-2500
Fredericton, NB, Canada E3B 5H1 Diane H. Hanson, Law Libn.
Founded: 1846. **Staff:** Prof 1; Other 1. **Subjects:** Law. **Holdings:** 25,000 volumes. **Subscriptions:** 180 journals and other serials. **Services:** Interlibrary loan; copying; library open to the public for reference use only. **Computerized Information Services:** QL Systems, CAN/LAW. **Special Indexes:** Index to Maritime Provinces Reports cases. **Remarks:** FAX: (506)453-9438. The Law Society of New Brunswick also administers law libraries in Bathurst, Edmundston, Newcastle, Campbellton, St. Stephen, and Woodstock.

★8996★
Law Society of Newfoundland - Library (Law)
Court House
Duckworth St.
P.O. Box 1028 Phone: (709)753-7770
St. John's, NF, Canada A1C 5M3 Gail Hogan, M.L.S, Libn.
Founded: 1836. **Staff:** Prof 1; Other 1. **Subjects:** Law. **Holdings:** 10,000 volumes. **Subscriptions:** 110 journals and other serials. **Services:** Interlibrary loan; library not open to the public. **Remarks:** FAX: (709)753-0054.

★8997★
Law Society of Saskatchewan - Barristers Library (Law)
Court House
520 Spadina Crescent, E. Phone: (306)933-5141
Saskatoon, SK, Canada S7K 3G7 Peta Bates, Libn.
Staff: Prof 1; Other 1. **Subjects:** Law. **Holdings:** 15,000 books; 150 bound periodical volumes. **Services:** Interlibrary loan; SDI; library open to the public with referral from another library. **Automated Operations:** Computerized serials control. **Computerized Information Services:** QL Systems, CAN/LAW, WESTLAW. **Special Indexes:** Saskatchewan regulation index. **Remarks:** FAX: (306)933-5166.

★8998★
Law Society of Saskatchewan - Library (Law)
2425 Victoria Ave.
P.O. Box 5032 Phone: (306)569-8020
Regina, SK, Canada S4P 3M3 Michael J. McGuire, Dir.
Founded: 1907. **Staff:** Prof 3; Other 6. **Subjects:** Law. **Holdings:** 30,000 volumes. **Services:** Interlibrary loan; copying; reference assistance provided to public libraries. **Automated Operations:** Computerized acquisitions and circulation. **Computerized Information Services:** QL Systems, Info Globe, WESTLAW, CAN/LAW; LSLIN (internal database). **Publications:** This Week's Law (online) - by subscription. **Special Indexes:** Index to the statutes of Saskatchewan. **Remarks:** FAX: (306)569-0155. Alternate telephone number(s): 569-8047. The Law Society of Saskatchewan maintains branches in the courthouses of Saskatoon, Moose Jaw, Prince Albert, Battleford, Estevan, Yorkton, Swift Current, Melville, Melfort, Weyburn, Humboldt, Lloydminster, Kerrobert, Meadow Lake, La Ronge, Wynyard, Gravelbourg, Assiniboia, Moosomin, Shaunavon, and Nipawin, SK. Holdings in the entire system comprise 85,000 volumes. **Staff:** Sheila Dowling, Leg.Res.; Maxine Seely, Ref.Libn.

★8999★
Law Society of Upper Canada - Great Library (Law)
Osgoode Hall
130 Queen St., W. Phone: (416)947-3400
Toronto, ON, Canada M5H 2N6 Glen Howell, Chf.Libn.
Founded: 1827. **Staff:** Prof 10; Other 19. **Subjects:** Canadian, British, Commonwealth, and American law. **Special Collections:** Riddell Collection of Canadiana (6000 volumes). **Holdings:** 140,000 volumes; 4500 government documents; 1500 rare books. **Subscriptions:** 1170 journals and other serials. **Services:** Copying; research assistance for lawyers; library open to the public by appointment. **Computerized Information Services:** QL Systems, CAN/LAW, WESTLAW, LEXIS. **Publications:** CLE Research Guide; Index to CLE Publications of the Law Society of Upper Canada, annual; Monthly List of Books Catalogued; Acquisition List, 9/year; Index to Applications Disposed of by the Ontario Municipal Board, monthly. **Special Indexes:** Index to Private Statutes (Canada and Ontario), 1916 to present; Indexes to Current Legislation (all provinces and Canada); Index to Supreme Court of Canada Proceedings and Decisions. **Remarks:** FAX: (416)869-0331. **Staff:** Theresa Roth, Hd., Ref.Dept.; Dana Dvorak, Hd., Cat.Dept.; Maureen Hyland, Hd., Acq.Dept.; Karen Teasdale, Ref.Libn.; Franklin Ng, Cat.; Jeanette Bowley, Ref.Libn.; Mary Pigott, Mgr., Search Law; Margaret Truesdale, Search Law.

Lawler, Felix & Hall
See: **Artcher, Haeden, Lawler, Felix & Hall** (1089)

★9000★
Lawler Matusky & Skelly Engineers - Library (Env-Cons, Biol Sci)
1 Blue Hill Plaza Phone: (914)735-8300
Pearl River, NY 10965-3104 Aileen P. McGuire, Info.Sci.
Staff: Prof 1; Other 1. **Subjects:** Environment, water supply, wastewater treatment, hazardous materials, hydrogeology, water quality, environmental impact assessment, ecology, aquatic biology, limnology. **Special Collections:** LMSE reports (800). **Holdings:** 6500 books; 7000 other cataloged items; 50,000 documents on microfiche; 82 reels of microfilm. **Subscriptions:** 155 journals and other serials; 6 newspapers. **Services:** Interlibrary loan; copying; library open to the public with restrictions. **Computerized Information Services:** DIALOG Information Services, PFDS Online, STORET, Chemical Information Systems, Inc. (CIS). **Networks/Consortia:** Member of Southeastern New York Library Resources Council (SENYLRC). **Special Indexes:** LMSE Reports Index (online). **Remarks:** FAX: (914)735-7466.

★9001★
Lawrence Berkeley Laboratory - Library (Sci-Engr)
Bldg. 50B-4206
University of California Phone: (510)486-5621
Berkeley, CA 94720 Hillis L. Griffin, Lib.Dir.
Founded: 1946. **Staff:** Prof 7; Other 4. **Subjects:** Physics, chemistry, materials science, biological physics, radiation biology, nonnuclear energy. **Holdings:** 22,000 books; 21,863 bound periodical volumes; 202,543 reports and preprints. **Subscriptions:** 1200 journals and other serials. **Services:** Interlibrary loan; library not open to the public. **Automated Operations:** Computerized cataloging, acquisitions, and serials. **Computerized Information Services:** DIALOG Information Services, PFDS Online, BRS Information Technologies, MEDLINE, SPIRES, STN International, RLIN; InterNet (electronic mail service). **Publications:** Berkeley New Titles, quarterly - for internal distribution only. **Remarks:** The Lawrence Berkeley Laboratory is operated by the University of California under contract to the U.S. Department of Energy. **Remarks:** FAX: (510)486-6404. Electronic mail address(es): LIBRARY@LBL.GOV (InterNet). **Staff:** Carol Backhus, Hd., User Serv.; Richard Robinson, ILL.

★9002★
C.J. Lawrence, Morgan Grenfell Inc. - Research Library (Bus-Fin)
1290 Avenue of the Americas Phone: (212)468-5071
New York, NY 10104 Mitch Highfill, Res.Libn.
Founded: 1965. **Staff:** Prof 1; Other 1. **Subjects:** Business, finance, investments. **Special Collections:** Company reports. **Holdings:** 100 bound periodical volumes; 121 VF drawers of corporate records. **Subscriptions:** 200 journals and other serials; 5 newspapers. **Services:** Interlibrary loan; library open to SLA members by appointment. **Computerized Information Services:** NEXIS. **Remarks:** FAX: (212)468-5490.

★9003★
Lawrence County Law Library (Law)
4th Floor Annex
County Court House Phone: (614)533-0582
Ironton, OH 45638-1586 Sharon Bradshaw, Dir., Lib.Serv.
Founded: 1911. **Staff:** Prof 1; Other 1. **Subjects:** Law. **Special Collections:** Ruling Cases of Scotland and England in the 1800s (60 volumes). **Holdings:** 15,000 books; 5000 bound periodical volumes; cases; videotapes. **Subscriptions:** 12 journals and other serials. **Services:** Library not open to the public. **Computerized Information Services:** WESTLAW, DIALOG Information Services; internal databases. **Remarks:** Maintained by the Lawrence County Bar and Law Library Association. FAX: (614)533-4387.

★9004★
Lawrence County Law Library (Law)
New Castle, PA 16101 Phone: (412)658-2541
Margaret J. Ross, Law Libn.
Subjects: Law. **Holdings:** 15,000 books. **Services:** Interlibrary loan; copying; library open to the public. **Computerized Information Services:** WESTLAW. **Remarks:** FAX: (412)658-4489.

★9005★
Lawrence Electronics Company - Library (Sci-Engr)
14636 Ambaum S.W.
P.O. Box 66556
Seattle, WA 98166 Phone: (202)243-7310
Founded: 1963. **Subjects:** Hydrogen measurement - experimentation, systems design, new product development. **Holdings:** 2000 volumes.

★9006★
Lawrence General Hospital - Health Science Library (Med)
1 General St. Phone: (508)683-4000
Lawrence, MA 01842 Carmel M. Gram, Libn. Consultant
Staff: Prof 1. **Subjects:** Clinical medicine, nursing. **Holdings:** 1500 books; 156 bound periodical volumes. **Subscriptions:** 113 journals and other serials. **Services:** Interlibrary loan; copying; SDI; library open to the public with permission. **Computerized Information Services:** MEDLINE, DIALOG Information Services. **Networks/Consortia:** Member of Northeastern Consortium for Health Information (NECHI).

Lawrence Hall of Science
See: **University of California, Berkeley - Lawrence Hall of Science** (18332)

★9007★
Lawrence Hospital - Ashley Baker Morrill Library (Med)
55 Palmer Ave. Phone: (914)337-7300
Bronxville, NY 10708 Virgil C. Larkin, Libn.
Staff: Prof 1; Other 1. **Subjects:** Medicine, nursing, hospital administration. **Special Collections:** Health information for laymen. **Holdings:** 2220 books; 2184 bound periodical volumes; 9 VF drawers. **Subscriptions:** 210 journals and other serials. **Services:** Interlibrary loan; copying; library open to the public. **Computerized Information Services:** MEDLINE. **Networks/Consortia:** Member of Health Information Libraries of Westchester (HILOW), BHSL, New York Metropolitan Reference and Research Library Agency.

Jerome Lawrence Theatre Research Institute
See: **Ohio State University - Jerome Lawrence & Robert E. Lee Theatre Research Institute - Library** (12313)

★9008★
Lawrence Law Library (Law)
78 Amesbury St. Phone: (508)687-7608
Lawrence, MA 01840 Jane (Charlie) Colokathis, Libn.
Founded: 1904. **Staff:** 2. **Subjects:** Law. **Holdings:** 30,000 books; 29 bound periodical volumes. **Subscriptions:** 52 journals and other serials. **Services:** Interlibrary loan; copying; library open to the public. **Computerized Information Services:** WESTLAW, LEXIS. **Remarks:** Part of the Massachusetts State Trial Court; Marnie Warner, Law Library Coordinator.

★9009★
Lawrence Livermore National Laboratory - Technical Information Department Library (Sci-Engr, Energy)
Box 5500 Phone: (510)422-5277
Livermore, CA 94550 Isom Harrison, Lib.Mgr.
Founded: 1952. **Staff:** Prof 19; Other 38. **Subjects:** Nuclear science, physics, chemistry, mathematics, electronics, engineering, biology, medicine, materials, energy. **Holdings:** 67,637 books; 122,000 bound periodical volumes; 261,282 technical reports; 643,000 microfiche. **Subscriptions:** 7200 journals and other serials. **Services:** Interlibrary loan; library not open to the public. **Automated Operations:** Computerized public access catalog, cataloging, acquisitions, serials, and circulation. **Computerized Information Services:** DIALOG Information Services, ORBIT Search Service, MEDLINE, RLIN, NASA/RECON, BRS Information Technologies, NEXIS, NewsNet, Inc., STN International; DIALMAIL, MCI Mail (electronic mail services). **Remarks:** Lawrence Livermore National Laboratory operates under contract to the U.S. Department of Energy. **Staff:** H. Leonard Fisher, Hd., Branches; Thomas Smith, Hd., Tech.Serv.; Richard K. Hunt, Hd., Res.Info. Group; Barbara Ingram, Hd., Circ.; Jerry R. Byrnes, Hd., Sys.

★9010★
Lawrence Memorial Hospital of Medford - Robert J. Fahey Library (Med)
170 Governors Ave. Phone: (617)396-9250
Medford, MA 02155 Terri K. Niland, Hd.Libn.
Staff: Prof 1; Other 1. **Subjects:** Nursing, medicine, hospital administration. **Special Collections:** Helene Fuld Audio-Visual Center. **Holdings:** 4000 books; 1200 bound periodical volumes; 800 filmstrip cassettes and videotapes; 200 subject pamphlet file. **Subscriptions:** 161 journals and other serials. **Services:** Interlibrary loan; copying; SDI; library open to the public with restrictions. **Computerized Information Services:** BRS Information Technologies, NLM, MEDLARS; MESSAGES (electronic mail service). Performs searches on fee basis. **Networks/Consortia:** Member of Northeastern Consortium for Health Information (NECHI), Libraries and Information for Nursing Consortium (LINC). **Remarks:** FAX: (617)391-2235.

★9011★
Lawrence Technological University - Library (Sci-Engr)
21000 W. 10 Mile Rd. Phone: (313)356-0200
Southfield, MI 48075 Gary R. Cocozzoli, Dir.
Founded: 1932. **Staff:** Prof 6; Other 4. **Subjects:** Engineering - electrical, mechanical, construction; architecture; management; physical sciences; mathematics; literature. **Special Collections:** The Albert Kahn Architecture Collection (3000 volumes); Society of Automotive Engineers (SAE) Papers, 1965 to present (on microfiche). **Holdings:** 40,000 books; 40,000 bound periodical volumes; 9000 boxes of microfilm. **Subscriptions:** 650 journals and other serials; 5 newspapers. **Services:** Interlibrary loan; copying; library open to the public. **Automated Operations:** Computerized cataloging. **Computerized Information Services:** DIALOG Information Services, WILSONLINE, VU/TEXT Information Services; internal database; BITNET (electronic mail service). Performs searches on fee basis. **Networks/Consortia:** Member of Michigan Library Consortium (MLC), Smaller Libraries Information Consortium (SLIC). **Remarks:** FAX: (313)562-0200, ext. 3005. Electronic mail address(es): LTU-LIBRARY@LTUVAX (BITNET). **Staff:** Marianne Hipp, Cat.; Sandra Tolbert, ILL/Ser.; Caroline McCollom, Bibliog.Inst.; Kay Van Buskirk, Databases; Mary Wilson, Circ.; Carole Burke, Ref.

Walter Lawrence Memorial Library
See: **West Suburban Hospital Medical Center** (20199)

★9012★
Laws Railroad Museum and Historical Site - Library (Hist)
Library & Arts Bldg.
Silver Canyon Rd.
P.O. Box 363 Phone: (619)873-5950
Bishop, CA 93514 Mary H. Coles, Libn.
Founded: 1966. **Staff:** 1. **Subjects:** History - California, Western, U.S.; railroads; technology; science; poetry; prose; art. **Special Collections:** Californiana; Owens Valley history; Chalfant and Cashbaugh collections. **Holdings:** 3800 books; 200 bound periodical volumes; antique books. **Services:** Copying; library open to the public for reference use only. **Remarks:** Library located in Laws, California.

Roberta Campbell Lawson Indian Library
See: **Philbrook Museum of Art** (12997)

Victor E. Lawson Research Library
See: **Kandiyohi County Historical Society** (8539)

George Lawton Memorial Library
See: **National Psychological Association for Psychoanalysis** (11254)

★9013★
Lawyers' Joint Law Library (Law)
3930 IDS Tower Phone: (612)338-4320
Minneapolis, MN 55402 Pat Petersen, Libn.
Founded: 1973. **Staff:** Prof 1; Other 2. **Subjects:** Law. **Holdings:** 22,000 books; 400 bound periodical volumes; 4 VF drawers of pamphlets; 5 plat books of maps. **Subscriptions:** 45 journals and other serials; 7 newspapers. **Services:** Library not open to the public. **Publications:** Lawyers' Joint Law Library Associates.

★9014★
Layland Museum - Research Archives (Hist)
201 N. Caddo St. Phone: (817)641-3321
Cleburne, TX 76031 Mildred Padon, Cur.
Founded: 1979. **Staff:** Prof 2. **Subjects:** Local and state history, Civil War, Indians. **Special Collections:** Genealogy; cartography; Santa Fe Railroad. **Holdings:** 160 books; 10 reels of microfilm; 30 scrapbooks; 900 slides; photographs. **Subscriptions:** 3 journals and other serials. **Services:** Copying; archives open to the public. **Remarks:** Museum maintained by the city of Cleburne. **Staff:** Mabel McCall.

★9015★
Layne Texas Division - Library
5931 Britmore Rd. Phone: (713)928-5741
Houston, TX 77041 John F. Waldron, Libn.
Remarks: The company is a division of Layne Western, Inc. No further information was supplied by respondent.

★9016★
Lazard Freres & Company - Financial Library (Bus-Fin)
One Rockefeller Plaza Phone: (212)632-6333
New York, NY 10020 Nicola J. Brown, Mgr.
Staff: Prof 5; Other 6. **Subjects:** Finance, investment, corporate records. **Holdings:** 500 volumes; 50,000 microfiche; 40 VF drawers. **Subscriptions:** 500 journals and other serials. **Services:** Interlibrary loan; library not open to the public. **Automated Operations:** Computerized cataloging, serials, and acquisitions. **Computerized Information Services:** DIALOG Information Services, Dow Jones News/Retrieval, NEXIS, TEXTLINE, Info Globe, Dun & Bradstreet Business Credit Services, VU/TEXT Information Services, Data-Star, InvesText, CDA Investment Technologies, Inc. **Remarks:** FAX: (212)632-6051. **Staff:** Joan Morris, Hd., Ref.; Lori Krevoruck, Ref.Libn.; Jean Trapani, Ref.Libn.; Beth Adus, Ref.Libn.

Paula K. Lazrus Library of Intergroup Relations
See: **National Conference of Christians and Jews** (11129)

★9017★
Le Bonheur Children's Medical Center - Health Sciences Library (Med)
1 Children's Plaza Phone: (901)522-3167
Memphis, TN 38103 Jan LaBeause, Libn.
Staff: Prof 1. **Subjects:** Pediatrics. **Holdings:** 1200 books; 1500 bound periodical volumes; 1 shelf of faculty reprints. **Subscriptions:** 150 journals and other serials. **Services:** Interlibrary loan; copying; library open to health professionals. **Computerized Information Services:** MEDLARS. Performs searches on fee basis. **Networks/Consortia:** Member of Association of Memphis Area Health Science Libraries (AMAHSL), CLASS. **Publications:** Guide for Users, Newsletter, both monthly - both free upon request. **Special Catalogs:** References from Morning Report, Grand Rounds, Nursing Grand Rounds, and Journal Club (card).

Le Brun Library
See: **Montclair Art Museum** (10656)

★9018★
Le Devoir - Centre de Documentation (Publ)
211, rue du St-Sacrement Phone: (514)844-3361
Montreal, PQ, Canada H2Y 1X1 Gilles Pare, Libn.
Founded: 1972. **Staff:** Prof 1; Other 2. **Subjects:** Newspaper reference topics, politics, economy, social problems. **Holdings:** 2000 books; 150 bound periodical volumes; 10,000 files of clippings; 40,000 files of photographs; 235 reels of microfilm. **Subscriptions:** 120 journals and other serials; 30 newspapers. **Services:** Interlibrary loan; center not open to the public. **Remarks:** FAX: (514)286-9255.

★9019★
Le Droit - Centre de Documentation (Publ)
47 Clarence St., Suite 222 Phone: (613)560-2500
Ottawa, ON, Canada K1N 9K1 Francine Parent
Founded: 1971. **Staff:** Prof 1; Other 1. **Subjects:** Newspaper reference topics; local, regional, and international news. **Holdings:** 500 books; 100,000 clippings; 15,000 documents; 1000 color slides. **Subscriptions:** 20 journals and other serials; 30 newspapers. **Services:** Copying; center open to the public. **Automated Operations:** Computerized cataloging and acquisitions. **Special Catalogs:** Subject catalog for clipping collection and color slides (card).

★9020★
Le Moyne College - Library - Special Collections (Hum, Rel-Phil)
Syracuse, NY 13214-1399 Phone: (315)445-4330
James J. Simonis, Dir. of the Lib.
Founded: 1946. **Staff:** 12. **Subjects:** Modern Irish literature, James Joyce, W.B. Yeats, Jesuit history, Catholic Church history. **Special Collections:** McGrath Music Collection; Irish literature (300 books); Jesuitica (110 books); rare books (3150). **Holdings:** 3560 books; archives. **Subscriptions:** 1619 journals and other serials. **Services:** Interlibrary loan; copying; collections open to the public with restrictions. **Automated Operations:** Computerized cataloging, acquisitions, and ILL. **Computerized Information Services:** OCLC, DIALOG Information Services, NLM, WILSONLINE, LEXIS, NEXIS, STN International, OCLC EPIC; CD-ROMs (ERIC, Newspaper Abstracts, Business Index, General Science Index, Humanities Index, Readers Guide to Periodical Literature, Social Sciences Index). Performs searches on fee basis. **Networks/Consortia:** Member of Central New York Library Resources Council (CENTRO), SUNY/OCLC Library Network. **Publications:** Bibliography of Le Moyne Authors; library guides; alphaBYTES. **Special Catalogs:** Periodical holdings (complete aphabetical list by title). **Remarks:** FAX: (315)445-4642. **Staff:** Inga H. Barnello, Social Sci.Ref.Libn.; Gretchen E. Pearson, Pub.Serv.Libn.; Tanya Popovic, Cat./Ref.Libn.; Peter Tagtmeyer, Sci./Ser.Libn.; Jeannine Soucy, Sci./Ser.Libn.

Le Moyne House Museum
See: **Washington County Historical Society and Le Moyne House Museum** (19997)

★9021★
Le Roy House Museum and Historical Society - Library (Hist)
23 E. Main St.
Box 176
Le Roy, NY 14482 Phone: (716)768-7433
Founded: 1940. **Staff:** Prof 1; Other 1. **Subjects:** Local history and genealogy. **Special Collections:** Morganville Pottery; Le Roy Family; Daniel Webster material; Jell-O; Ingham University; works of local artists; Henry Wyckoff papers; Miles P. Lampson papers. **Holdings:** 900 books; 10 bound periodical volumes; 20 VF drawers of reports, clippings, and scrapbooks; family photographs; local family manuscripts; local photographs and newspapers, 1826 to present. **Services:** Copying; library open to the public on a limited schedule. **Publications:** Annual Report; newsletter, quarterly.

★9022★
Le Sault de Sainte Marie Historical Sites - Museum Ship VALLEY CAMP Maritime Library (Hist)
P.O. Box 1668 Phone: (906)632-3658
Sault Ste. Marie, MI 49783 Phyllis Weaver, Hd.Libn.
Founded: 1988. **Staff:** 1. **Subjects:** Great Lakes shipping, 1900 to present; Upper Peninsula of Michigan. **Special Collections:** U.S. Steel logbooks of shipping information on Great Lakes, 1893-1968 (58 volumes); logbooks from Wilson Marine Transit Fleet's steam-powered vessels. **Holdings:** 600 volumes. **Services:** Copying; library open to the public by appointment.

Oscar Le Seure Professional Library
See: **Harper-Grace Hospitals - Grace Hospital Division** (6910)

★9023★
Le Sueur County Historical Society Museum - Library (Hist)
Box 240 Phone: (507)267-4620
Elysian, MN 56028 Caroline Roessler, Genealogist
Founded: 1967. **Staff:** 3. **Subjects:** Local and state history. **Special Collections:** Books, sketches, works of artist Adolf Dehn; books, articles, works of wildlife artist Roger Preuss; works of artist Albert Christ-Janer; articles and works of wildlife artist David Maass; artifacts and works of artist Lloyd Herfendahl; silhouettes and works of Earle Swaine. **Holdings:** 1405 volumes; 60 interview tapes of older citizens; 700 reels of microfilm of newspapers; 20 volumes of obituary clippings; county church records; state laws and statistics; county cemetery records; local store ledgers; county tax receipts. **Subscriptions:** 5 newspapers. **Services:** Library open to the public for reference use only by request from May through October. **Staff:** Dorothy Hruska, Dir. & Cur.

Henry Charles Lea Library
See: **University of Pennsylvania** (19183)

★9024★
Stephen Leacock Museum - Library (Hum)
Old Brewery Bay
P.O. Box 625 Phone: (705)326-9357
Orillia, ON, Canada L3V 6K5 Jay Cody, Dir./Cur.
Founded: 1957. **Staff:** Prof 1; Other 6. **Subjects:** Stephen Leacock. **Holdings:** 5000 books; 15,000 letters; 311 manuscripts; 500 contemporary review clippings of Leacock's books; 200 documents. **Services:** Research inquiries answered; library open to scholars with credentials for reference use. **Remarks:** FAX: (705)325-5178. **Formerly:** Stephen Leacock Memorial Home.

League of Arab Countries - Arab Center for the Study of Arid Zones and Dry Lands
See: **Arab Center for the Study of Arid Zones and Dry Lands** (932)

★9025★
League of Arab States - Documentation and Information Center (ALDOC) (Area-Ethnic)
37 Khereddine Pacha St. Phone: 1 890100
Tunis, Tunisia Mrs. Faria Zahawi, Dir.Gen.
Founded: 1981. **Staff:** 68. **Subjects:** Arab region - politics, economics, law, military and social concerns; international affairs; communication; environment. **Special Collections:** Arab League documents; documents from other international organizations. **Holdings:** 26,000 volumes; 150 magnetic tapes; 14,000 microforms; 4000 clipping files. **Subscriptions:** 1700 journals and other serials. **Services:** Interlibrary loan; copying; SDI; center open to the public. **Automated Operations:** Computerized cataloging, acquisitions, serials, circulation, and indexing. **Computerized Information Services:** Online systems; internal databases. **Publications:** Accessions List, bimonthly; Current Contents Bulletin, bimonthly; Fahras, quarterly; bibliographies; Aris-Net Newsletter, monthly; Info-Packs; manuals; directories. **Remarks:** FAX: 1 781801. Telex: 14411 JAMIA TN.

★9026★
League of Canadian Poets - Library (Hum)
24 Ryerson Ave. Phone: (416)363-5047
Toronto, ON, Canada M5T 2P3 Dolores Ricketts
Founded: 1966. **Staff:** 2. **Subjects:** Canadian poetry. **Special Collections:** Signed editions. **Holdings:** 1300 volumes of members' books. **Subscriptions:** 10 journals and other serials. **Services:** Library open to the public by appointment. **Remarks:** FAX: (418)860-0826.

★9027★
League for International Food Foundation - Library
1126 16th St., N.W., Suite 404
Washington, DC 20036
Defunct.

★9028★
League of Iowa Municipalities - Library (Soc Sci)
100 Court Ave., Suite 209 Phone: (515)244-7282
Des Moines, IA 50309-2200 Peter B. King, Exec.Dir.
Subjects: Municipal government. **Special Collections:** Codes of Iowa cities. **Holdings:** 1150 volumes; informational booklets and fact sheets; model ordinances. **Services:** Copying; library open to city officials and member cities with consent of director. **Special Catalogs:** Listing of municipal officials of Iowa. **Remarks:** FAX: (515)244-0740.

★9029★
League of Minnesota Cities - Library (Law)
183 University Ave., E. Phone: (612)227-5600
St. Paul, MN 55101 Peter Tritz, Res.Dir.
Founded: 1913. **Staff:** Prof 2; Other 6. **Subjects:** Ordinance codes of many cities, Minnesota Statutes and Session laws, municipal government. **Special Collections:** City charters of all 108 home rule cities. **Holdings:** 1000 books; 300 bound periodical volumes; 150 memoranda. **Subscriptions:** 150 journals and other serials; 12 newspapers. **Services:** Interlibrary loan; copying; library open to the public with restrictions. **Computerized Information Services:** RES (internal database). Performs searches on fee basis. **Publications:** Minnesota Cities, monthly - to members and by subscription; Cities Bulletin, weekly during session (20 issues) and biweekly during the interim; City Handbook, annual; Directory of Minnesota City Officials, annual; Local and Regional Planning in Minnesota; Model Ordinance Code; research memoranda, irregular. **Remarks:** FAX: (612)221-0986. **Staff:** Jeannette Bach, Libn.

League of United Latin American Citizens Archive
See: **University of Texas at Austin - Benson Latin American Collection** (19380)

League of Women Voters of New York State - Foundation for Citizen Education
See: **Foundation for Citizen Education** (6042)

★9030★
League for Yiddish - Library (Area-Ethnic)
200 W. 72nd St., Suite 40 Phone: (212)787-6675
New York, NY 10023 Leybl Kahn, Libn.
Subjects: Yiddish culture, Judaica. **Holdings:** 1500 books; documents; correspondence. **Subscriptions:** 50 journals and other serials. **Services:** Library open to the public.

★9031★
Lear Astronics Corp. - Technical Library (Sci-Engr)
3400 Airport Ave. Phone: (213)452-6726
Santa Monica, CA 90406 Margaret Ann Mathews, Supv.
Founded: 1981. **Staff:** Prof 1; Other 1. **Subjects:** Flight control, avionics, computer science, electronics. **Holdings:** 1150 books; 3860 technical reports. **Subscriptions:** 115 journals and other serials. **Services:** Interlibrary loan; library not open to the public. **Automated Operations:** Computerized cataloging.

Learning Center for Lung Health
See: **American Lung Association of Hawaii** (672)

★9032★
Learning Incorporated - Library (Educ)
Learning Place Phone: (207)244-5015
Manset-Seawall, ME 04656 A.L. Welles, Dir.
Subjects: Learning handicaps, teaching spelling and reading, teaching those with learning disabilities and dyslexia. **Holdings:** 15,000 volumes. **Services:** Library open to the public by appointment. **Publications:** Learning Incorporated Dictionary of Learning Handicaps - for sale.

★9033★
Leatherhead Food Research Association - Information Group (Food-Bev)
Randalls Rd.
Leatherhead, Surrey KT22 7RY, England Phone: 372 376761
Mr. R.J.D. Saunders, Group Mgr.
Subjects: Food and food industry - general, technology, processing, marketing, trade, companies, packaging, new products, process control, storage, legislation, and allied subjects. **Holdings:** 12,000 bound volumes; standards; pamphlets. **Subscriptions:** 900 journals and other serials. **Automated Operations:** CAIRS LMS. **Computerized Information Services:** Online systems; produces Food Equipment and Additives Suppliers and Traders, Food Launch Awareness in the Retail Sector, Food Market Awareness Databank, Food Regulation Inquiries, Food News Scanning Database, Food RA Online Scientific and Technical Information. Performs searches on fee basis. **Remarks:** FAX: 0372 386228. Telex: 929846 FOODRA G. **Also Known As:** British Food Manufacturing Industries Research Association.

★9034★
Clyde Leavitt Incorporated - Library (Trans)
13901 Puerto Dr. Phone: (601)875-5711
Ocean Springs, MS 39564-2019 Clyde M. Leavitt, Pres.
Founded: 1955. **Subjects:** Naval architecture, ship construction, maritime history, marine surveying, ship model construction, marine safety. **Holdings:** Figures not available. **Services:** Library not open to the public. **Remarks:** Alternate telephone number(s): 875-9802.

★9035★
Lebanon County Historical Society - Library (Area-Ethnic)
924 Cumberland St. Phone: (717)272-1473
Lebanon, PA 17042 Christine L. Mason, Asst.Coord./Libn.
Founded: 1898. **Staff:** 3. **Subjects:** History of Lebanon County and Pennsylvania, local genealogy, Germans in Pennsylvania. **Special Collections:** Bibles; hymn books; school books; Coleman Collection (housed at the Pennsylvania Historical and Museum Commission). **Holdings:** 3000 books; 3000 pictures; 1000 files; 1000 deeds; 700 reels of microfilm; archives. **Subscriptions:** 14 journals and other serials. **Services:** Copying; genealogical searching (fee); library open to the public with restrictions. **Publications:** Papers of the Lebanon County Historical Society - free to members, for sale to others; reprint of 1875 Lebanon County Atlas (index separate). **Special Indexes:** Papers of the Lebanon County Historical Society (card); 1904 Biographical Annals of Lebanon County (book).

★9036★
Lebanon County Law Library (Law)
400 S. 8 St., Rm. 305 Phone: (717)274-2801
Lebanon, PA 17042 Luz Rosario, Lib.Dir.
Subjects: Law. **Holdings:** Microfiche. **Services:** Interlibrary loan; library open to the public for reference use only.

★9037★
Leberco Testing, Inc. - Library (Sci-Engr)
123 Hawthorne St. Phone: (908)245-1933
Roselle Park, NJ 07204 Anthony Lo Pinto
Founded: 1939. **Staff:** 1. **Subjects:** Toxicology, microbiology, analytic chemistry, in regard to pharmaceutical and medical devices, cosmetics, toiletries, household products, food, industrial chemicals, and drinking and waste water. **Holdings:** 3500 volumes. **Subscriptions:** 37 journals and other serials; 2 newspapers. **Services:** Library not open to the public. **Computerized Information Services:** DIALOG Information Services. **Remarks:** FAX: (908)245-6253. Toll-free telephone number(s): (800)523-LABS.

★9038★
Lebhar-Friedman, Inc. - Chain Store Age - Reader Service Research Library (Publ)
425 Park Ave. Phone: (212)371-9400
New York, NY 10022 Ruth Weselteer, Libn.
Founded: 1925. **Staff:** 1. **Subjects:** Chain stores - retailing, personnel, sales promotion, merchandising, store location, construction and equipment, warehousing, public relations, shopping centers, discount houses, home centers, restaurants, drugstores. **Holdings:** 300 books; 200 bound periodical volumes; 1500 pamphlets; 11 VF drawers. **Subscriptions:** 97 journals and other serials. **Services:** Interlibrary loan; copying (both limited); library open to the public. **Remarks:** FAX: (212)838-9487.

★9039★
Leboeuf, Lamb, Leiby & MacRae - Library (Law)
520 Madison Ave. Phone: (212)715-8000
New York, NY 10022 Eleanor A. Sabo
Founded: 1929. **Staff:** Prof 6; Other 2. **Subjects:** Law - general, public utilities, taxation, energy, insurance, securities, municipal bonds, banking, environment. **Holdings:** 30,000 books; 29 VF drawers. **Subscriptions:** 500 journals and other serials; 15 newspapers. **Services:** Interlibrary loan; copying; library open to clients. **Automated Operations:** Computerized cataloging, acquisitions, serials, and circulation. **Computerized Information Services:** LEXIS, WESTLAW, DIALOG Information Services, LEGI-SLATE, VU/TEXT Information Services. **Remarks:** FAX: (212)715-8500.

Lederle Laboratories
See: **American Cyanamid Company - Lederle Laboratories Division** (559)

★9040★
Lee County Iowa Historical Society - Samuel F. Miller House Museum - Library (Hist)
318 N. 5th St. Phone: (319)524-7283
Keokuk, IA 52632 Douglas Atterberg, Pres.
Subjects: Lee County - economic development, early city government, local authors. **Special Collections:** Hydro-electric development on the Mississippi; College of Physicians & Surgeons, 1850-1908. **Holdings:** 200 books; 1000 manuscripts. **Services:** Copying; library open to the public with restrictions. **Publications:** Samuel Freeman Miller - A Home In Keokuk, A Place in History (narrative, photos, and facsimiles) - for sale.

★9041★
Lee County Law Library (Law)
Justice Center
1700 Monroe St. Phone: (813)335-2230
Fort Myers, FL 33901 Owen Grant, Libn.
Founded: 1957. **Staff:** Prof 1. **Subjects:** Law. **Holdings:** 14,000 books. **Services:** Copying; library open to the public.

Lee Enterprises, Inc. - Billings Gazette
See: **Billings Gazette** (1838)

Harold B. Lee Library
See: **Brigham Young University - Science and Technology Department Library** (20807)

Jeremiah Lee Mansion
See: **Marblehead Historical Society** (9654)

Joseph Lee Memorial Library and Information Center
See: **National Recreation and Park Association** (11263)

Lawrence R. Lee Memorial Library
See: **National Railway Historical Society - Mohawk and Hudson Chapter** (11262)

Lee Library
See: **Don Bosco Technical Institute** (1974)

★9042★
Lee Pharmaceuticals - Library (Sci-Engr)
1444 Santa Anita Ave.
South El Monte, CA 91733 Phone: (818)442-3141
Subjects: Polymer chemistry, biomedical polymers, dentistry. **Holdings:** 2000 books. **Services:** Library not open to the public.

Lee Ridge Aviaries
See: **International Wild Waterfowl Association** (8206)

Robert E. Lee Memorial
See: **U.S. Natl. Park Service - Arlington House, the Robert E. Lee Memorial** (17669)

Robert E. Lee Theatre Research Institute
See: **Ohio State University - Jerome Lawrence & Robert E. Lee Theatre Research Institute - Library** (12313)

★9043★
Leeds and Northrup Company - Technical Center Library
Sumneytown Pike
North Wales, PA 19454
Founded: 1920. **Subjects:** Instrumentation and control systems. **Holdings:** 5000 books; 5500 bound periodical volumes; 36 VF drawers of trade catalogs. **Remarks:** Currently inactive.

★9044★
Leedshill-Herkenhoff, Inc. - Library (Sci-Engr)
500 Copper N.W. Phone: (505)247-0294
Albuquerque, NM 87102 Anne Barnes, Info.Mgr.
Staff: Prof 1. **Subjects:** Engineering - civil, water, environmental, structural, electrical, mechanical, controls; water resources; hydraulics; environmental sciences; geology. **Special Collections:** Collection of documents on the history of New Mexico highway and water system development. **Holdings:** Product catalogs; professional papers; company reports; miscellaneous standards and specifications. **Services:** Interlibrary loan; copying; library open to the public on request. **Computerized Information Services:** DIALOG Information Services, TECH-NET. **Remarks:** FAX: (505)242-4845.

★9045★
Leelanau Historical Museum - Archives (Hist)
203 E. Cedar St. Phone: (616)256-7475
Leland, MI 49654 Laura Quackenbush, Cur.
Staff: 1. **Subjects:** Leelanau County history. **Special Collections:** 19th and 20th century textbooks (25); Norwegian, German, Bohemian religious books; Township and County records; historic photographs; local business records; local history. **Holdings:** 500 books. **Services:** Copying; archives open to the public by appointment. **Special Catalogs:** Hans Anderson: His Life and Works, 1988.

★9046★
Leeward Community College Library - Special Collections (Area-Ethnic)
96-045 Ala Ike Phone: (808)455-0209
Pearl City, HI 96782-3393 Christine Tomoyasu, Hd.Libn.
Founded: 1968. **Subjects:** Asia, Asian Americans. **Special Collections:** Hawaiian/Pacific Collection; selected regional federal government depository. **Services:** Interlibrary loan; copying; collections open to the public. **Automated Operations:** Computerized public access catalog, cataloging, and circulation.

Leffingwell Inn Library
See: **Society of the Founders of Norwich, Connecticut** (15318)

Robert A. Leflar Law Center
See: **University of Arkansas, Fayetteville - School of Law** (18235)

★9047★
Al Paul Lefton Company, Inc. - Research Library
Rohm & Haas Bldg.
Independence Mall W. Phone: (215)923-9600
Philadelphia, PA 19106 Bea Russ, Libn.
Remarks: No further information was supplied by respondent.

★9048★
Legal Aid Society - Libraries (Law)
15 Park Row, 14th Fl. Phone: (212)577-3333
New York, NY 10038 Deonna L. Taylor, Dir.
Staff: Prof 3; Other 38. **Subjects:** Law - criminal, civil, juvenile rights; social services. **Special Collections:** English Common Law collection. **Holdings:** Figures not available. **Services:** Libraries not open to the public. **Automated Operations:** Computerized cataloging and acquisitions. **Computerized Information Services:** WESTLAW, DIALOG Information Services, LEXIS, NEXIS, VU/TEXT Information Services, Legislative Retrieval Service. **Remarks:** "The Legal Aid Society has no central library. The collection is in 38 offices throughout the 5 boroughs." FAX: (212)964-1584. **Staff:** Mary Matuszak, Libn., Criminal Appeals; Peter Shao, Asst.Libn.

★9049★
Legal Aid Society of Hawaii - Library (Law)
1108 Nuuanu Ave. Phone: (808)536-4302
Honolulu, HI 96817 Mr. Kelly R. Madraisao, Lib.Techn.
Staff: 1. **Subjects:** Law - public assistance, family, health, employment, housing, education, consumer. **Holdings:** Figures not available. **Services:** Library not open to the public.

★9050★
Legal Aid Society of Westchester - Library (Law)
1 North Broadway Phone: (914)682-3400
White Plains, NY 10601 Mina Pease, Dir.
Staff: Prof 2; Other 1. **Subjects:** Law - criminal, matrimonial, administrative. **Holdings:** 4000 volumes; 10 audio cassettes. **Subscriptions:** 10 journals and other serials; 6 newspapers. **Services:** Library not open to the public. **Special Indexes:** Local newspaper morgue clipping file index (MorClip).

★9051★
Legal Assistance Foundation of Chicago - Library (Law)
343 S. Dearborn Phone: (312)341-1070
Chicago, IL 60604 John Ryden, Libn.
Staff: Prof 1. **Subjects:** Welfare law. **Holdings:** 12,000 books; 300 other cataloged items; 200 legal documents. **Subscriptions:** 91 journals and other serials. **Services:** Library not open to the public. **Networks/Consortia:** Member of ILLINET, Chicago Library System.

Legal Services Corporation - Center on Social Welfare Policy and Law
See: **Center on Social Welfare Policy and Law** (3298)

★9052★
Legal Services of Eastern Missouri, Inc. - Library (Law)
625 N. Euclid Ave. Phone: (314)367-1700
St. Louis, MO 63108 Marsha Griffin, Asst.Libn.
Staff: Prof 1. **Subjects:** Federal and Missouri law, poverty law. **Holdings:** 6000 volumes. **Subscriptions:** 90 journals and other serials. **Services:** Interlibrary loan; copying; library not open to the public. **Remarks:** FAX: (914)331-3238.

★9053★
Legal Services Organization of Indiana, Inc. - Library (Law)
101 Court St., Suite 101 Phone: (812)426-1295
Evansville, IN 47708 Tim Sanders, Staff Att.
Founded: 1978. **Staff:** 1. **Subjects:** Law. **Holdings:** 2509 books; 41 bound periodical volumes. **Subscriptions:** 59 journals and other serials. **Services:** Interlibrary loan; library not open to the public. **Networks/Consortia:** Member of Four Rivers Area Library Services Authority (ALSA).

★9054★
Legal Services Organization of Indiana, Inc. - Library (Law)
151 N. Delaware, 18th Fl. Phone: (317)631-9410
Indianapolis, IN 46204 Gwendolyn Wilson, Libn.
Founded: 1973. **Staff:** Prof 1. **Subjects:** Law - federal, state, welfare, consumer. **Holdings:** 8000 books; 4 VF drawers of periodicals; 6 VF drawers of briefs; 1 VF drawer of hearings, government documents. **Subscriptions:** 67 journals and other serials. **Services:** Library not open to the public. **Publications:** You and the Law, annual. **Special Catalogs:** Brief bank (internal briefs by attorneys; cataloged by subject, client, and author). **Remarks:** FAX: (317)631-9775.

Legislative Assembly of Alberta
See: **(Alberta) Legislative Assembly of Alberta** (288)

★9055★
Lehigh County Historical Society - Scott Andrew Trexler II Memorial Library (Hist)
Old Court House
5th & Hamilton Sts.
Box 1548 Phone: (215)435-1072
Allentown, PA 18105 June B. Griffiths, Libn./Archv.
Founded: 1904. **Staff:** Prof 2. **Subjects:** Pennsylvania and Lehigh County history, genealogy. **Special Collections:** Allentown Newspapers, 1810-1916; family genealogies; photographs; Civil War; Allentown imprints; native Indians. **Holdings:** 8000 books; 200 newspaper volumes; 2000 pamphlets; 200 manuscripts, archives, records of local families and businesses; deeds; maps; church records. **Subscriptions:** 12 journals and other serials. **Services:** Copying; library open to the public on fee basis. **Publications:** Proceedings, biennial; quarterly newsletter; Allentown 1762-1987: A 225-Year History (2 volumes); occasional papers. **Remarks:** Alternate telephone number(s): 435-4664. **Staff:** Carol M. Herrity, Asst.Libn.

★9056★
Lehigh County Law Library (Law)
County Court House
5th & Hamilton Sts.
Box 1548 Phone: (215)820-3308
Allentown, PA 18105 Lorelei A. Nebinger, Law Libn.
Founded: 1869. **Staff:** Prof 1; Other 3. **Subjects:** Law, Pennsylvania history and statutes. **Holdings:** 20,000 books; 1900 bound periodical volumes; 2 VF drawers of local municipal ordinances; 4000 microform volumes. **Subscriptions:** 60 journals and other serials. **Services:** Interlibrary loan; copying; library open to the public. **Automated Operations:** Computerized public access catalog, circulation, cataloging, and acquisitions. **Publications:** Acquisitions. **Remarks:** FAX: (215)820-3311.

★9057★
Lehigh-Northampton Counties Joint Planning Commission - Library (Plan)
Allentown-Bethlehem-Easton Airport
3411 Airport Rd.
Government Bldg.
Allentown, PA 18103-1098 Phone: (215)264-4544
Founded: 1961. **Staff:** 1. **Subjects:** Architecture, engineering and design, census and statistics, economics and finance, governmental legislation, housing, transportation, urban analysis, planning theory, land use, recreation. **Special Collections:** Joint Planning Commission Reports on various municipalities in Lehigh-Northampton Counties; initial housing element, recreation reports. **Holdings:** 2000 volumes; slides; pictures; maps. **Subscriptions:** 25 journals and other serials; 6 newspapers. **Services:** Library open to the public for reference use only.

★9058★
Lehigh University - Fritz Engineering Laboratory Library (Sci-Engr)
Dept. of Civil Engineering
Bldg. 13, Rm. 601 Phone: (215)758-3520
Bethlehem, PA 18015 Eleanor S. Nothelfer, Info.Spec.
Staff: 1. **Subjects:** Structural engineering, fatigue and fracture of bridges, hydraulics, environmental engineering, geotechnics. **Special Collections:** Fritz Engineering Laboratory Research Project reports (12,000). **Holdings:** 2000 books; 360 bound periodical volumes; 5000 other cataloged items. **Subscriptions:** 35 journals and other serials. **Services:** Interlibrary loan; copying; library open to the public for reference use only. **Publications:** Fritz Engineering Laboratory List of Publications. **Remarks:** FAX: (215)758-4522.

★9059★
Lehigh Valley Committee Against Health Fraud, Inc. - Library (Med)
Box 1747 Phone: (215)437-1795
Allentown, PA 18105 Dr. Stephen Barrett, Chm.
Staff: 1. **Subjects:** Quackery and health frauds, consumer health, chiropractic, nutrition, health food industry, consumer protection, medical care. **Holdings:** 1600 books; 6000 unbound magazines, journals and newsletters; 100 VF drawers of documents and clippings; 350 cassette tapes; 80 reprints. **Subscriptions:** 130 journals and other serials. **Services:** Copying; library open to the public with restrictions. **Publications:** Nutrition Forum (newsletter), bimonthly - by subscription for a fee.

★9060★
Lehigh Valley Hospital Center - Health Sciences Library (Med)
1200 S. Cedar Crest Blvd. Phone: (215)776-8410
Allentown, PA 18103 Barbara J. Iobst
Founded: 1974. **Staff:** Prof 1; Other 3.5. **Subjects:** Medicine - general, trauma, surgery, burns. **Holdings:** 2000 books; 8000 bound periodical volumes. **Subscriptions:** 350 journals and other serials; 3 newspapers. **Services:** Interlibrary loan; copying; library open to the public on fee basis. **Computerized Information Services:** DIALOG Information Services, NLM, BRS Information Technologies; CD-ROM (MEDLINE). Performs searches. Contact Person: Sherry Giardiniere. **Remarks:** FAX: (215)776-8409.

Lehigh Valley Transportation Research Center
See: **Railways to Yesterday, Inc.** (13696)

★9061★
Lehman Brothers - Corporate Library (Bus-Fin)
American Express Tower, 15th Fl.
200 Vesey St. Phone: (212)298-2783
New York, NY 10285-1500 Richard Willner, First V.P.
Founded: 1930. **Staff:** Prof 15; Other 27. **Subjects:** Finance. **Special Collections:** Annual reports; Securities and Exchange Commission (SEC) filings and pricings. **Holdings:** 10,000 volumes; 900 VF drawers of pamphlets. **Subscriptions:** 800 journals and other serials; 20 newspapers. **Services:** Interlibrary loan; library not open to the public. **Automated Operations:** Computerized cataloging, acquisitions, and serials. **Computerized Information Services:** DIALOG Information Services, NEXIS, Dow Jones News/Retrieval, International Data Corporation (IDC), Vickers Stock Research Corporation, Dun & Bradstreet Business Credit Services, Disclosure Information Group, InvesText, Reuters, Info Globe, MAID; internal databases. **Remarks:** FAX: (212)619-9457. **Staff:** Sreekumar Menon, AVP Ref.; Lynn Reynolds, Libn.; Cheryl Wacher, Libn.; Harriet Wisher, Libn.; Lauren Lawrence, AVP Pricing; Martha Keller, AVP Corp.Doc.; Tom Learon, AVP Tech.Serv. and Sys.

Ezra Lehman Memorial Library
See: **Shippensburg University** (15136)

Herbert H. Lehman Library
See: **Columbia University - Herbert H. Lehman Library** (4015)

Mme. Lotte Lehman Archive
See: **University of California, Santa Barbara - Department of Special Collections** (18428)

Robert Lehman Collection
See: **Metropolitan Museum of Art** (10215)

S.A. Lehman Memorial Library
See: **Summit Christian College** (15860)

★9062★
Ernest K. Lehmann & Associates, Inc. - Library (Sci-Engr)
Kickernick Bldg., Suite 790
430 1st Ave., N.
Minneapolis, MN 55401 Phone: (612)338-5584
Staff: Prof 1. **Subjects:** Geology, mining, mineral economics, mineral exploration. **Holdings:** 5000 books. **Subscriptions:** 50 journals and other serials. **Computerized Information Services:** DIALOG Information Services. Performs searches on fee basis. **Remarks:** FAX: (612)338-5457. Telex: 283091 ELA UR.

Leiden State University - National Herbarium of the Netherlands
See: **Netherlands - National Herbarium of the Netherlands** (11409)

Ethel Traphagen Leigh Memorial Library
See: **Traphagen School of Fashion** (16465)

George M. Lein Information Center
See: **Mohawk Valley Psychiatric Center** (10592)

★9063★
Leipzig Museum of Arts and Crafts - Library
Johannispl Phone: 41 291543
O-7010 Leipzig, Germany Eberhard Patzig, Sci.Libn.
Founded: 1874. **Staff:** Prof 4. **Subjects:** Arts and crafts, decorative arts, architecture, modern design, cultural history, topography of arts, art history and theory. **Special Collections:** Graphic collection related to ornaments (20,000 prints); Japanese woodcut collection; Persian miniatures collection. **Holdings:** 35,000 books; archives; 25,000 photographs, negatives, and slides. **Subscriptions:** 200 journals and other serials. **Services:** Copying; library open to the public. **Also Known As:** Museum des Kunsthandwerks Leipzig - Grassimuseum - Bibliothek.

Arthur J. Lelyveld Center for Jewish Learning
See: **Fairmount Temple** (5571)

Lembaga Ilmu Pengetahuan Indonesia - Pusat Dokumentasi dan Informasi Ilmiah
See: **Indonesian Institute of Sciences - Centre for Scientific Documentation and Information** (7830)

Lemos Library
See: **Mendocino Historical Research, Inc.** (10082)

★9064★
Lenawee County Historical Museum - Library (Hist)
110 E. Church
Box 511 Phone: (517)265-6071
Adrian, MI 49221 Charles N. Lindquist, Cur.
Staff: 1. **Subjects:** County history. **Special Collections:** Elmer D. Smith Collection (500 glass negatives); complete holdings of Official Records of Civil War. **Holdings:** County tax records, 1845-1920; portraits; photographs; tintypes; early deeds; miscellaneous artifacts. **Subscriptions:** 13 journals and other serials. **Services:** Library open to the public with restrictions.

Lenke Insurance Library
See: **Public Library of Cincinnati and Hamilton County - Government and Business Department** (13483)

★9065★
Lennox and Addington County Museum - Library & Archives (Hist)
97 Thomas St., E.
Postal Bag 1000 Phone: (613)354-3027
Napanee, ON, Canada K7R 3S9 Jane Foster, Mgr.
Founded: 1907. **Staff:** Prof 1; Other 1. **Subjects:** Local history and genealogy. **Holdings:** 300 linear feet of bound volumes; 300 linear feet of manuscripts and miscellanea; 75 linear feet of newspapers; 20 linear feet of photographs. **Services:** Genealogical research; copying; library open to the public. **Special Indexes:** Cemetery Index for Lennox and Addington (card); Birth/Marriage/Death newspaper index (card); Preliminary Inventory of Collections of Lennox and Addington Historical Society, 1959 (book); index to photographic collection; indexes to the collections of the Lennox and Addington Historical Society (supplement to the 1959 inventory).

★9066★
Lenox Hill Hospital - Jerome S. Leopold Health Sciences Library (Med)
100 E. 77th St. Phone: (212)439-2075
New York, NY 10021 Shirley E. Dansker, Dir.
Founded: 1925. **Staff:** Prof 2; Other 3. **Subjects:** Medicine and medical specialties, surgery, nursing, history of medicine. **Holdings:** 4500 books; 10,000 bound periodical volumes. **Subscriptions:** 380 journals and other serials. **Services:** Interlibrary loan; copying; library open to the public with permission of hospital administrator. **Computerized Information Services:** BRS Information Technologies, MEDLINE; DOCLINE (electronic mail service). **Networks/Consortia:** Member of National Network of Libraries of Medicine - Middle Atlantic Region, Manhattan-Bronx Health Sciences Library Consortia, Medical Library Center of New York (MLCNY), New York Metropolitan Reference and Research Library Agency. **Remarks:** Alternate telephone number(s): 439-2076. FAX: (212)439-2074. **Staff:** Julia Chai, Asst.Libn.

Lois Lenski Collection
See: **University of North Carolina at Greensboro** (19084)

Lentz Health Center Library
See: **Nashville Metropolitan Department of Public Health** (11001)

Sanford V. Lenz Library
See: **Cornell University - New York State School of Industrial and Labor Relations** (4327)

Ada I. Leonard Memorial Library
See: **Middletown Regional Hospital** (10363)

J. Paul Leonard Library
See: **San Francisco State University - J. Paul Leonard Library - Special Collections/Archives** (14743)

Leonard Library
See: **University of Toronto - Wycliffe College - Leonard Library** (19464)

Jerome S. Leopold Health Sciences Library
See: **Lenox Hill Hospital** (9066)

Lepidopterists' Society Library
See: **Natural History Museum of Los Angeles County - Research Library** (11341)

Leprosy Archives
See: **U.S. Public Health Service Hospital - Gillis W. Long Hansen's Disease Center - Medical Library** (17934)

Penny Lernoux Memorial Library on Latin America
See: **Central America Resource Center - Penny Lernoux Memorial Library on Latin America** (3324)

Richard Lert Library
See: **Rice University - Alice Pratt Brown Library** (13893)

★9067★
Les Entreprises Videoway Ltd. - Library (Info Sci)
2021 Union Ave., 10th Fl.
Montreal, PQ, Canada H3A 2C1 Phone: (514)285-5700
Founded: 1984. **Staff:** Prof 1. **Subjects:** Videotex, business, computers, cable television, telecommunications, electrical engineering. **Holdings:** 400 books. **Subscriptions:** 50 journals and other serials. **Services:** Interlibrary loan; library not open to the public.

Lesbian and Gay Archives
See: **Naiad Press, Inc.** (10954)

★9068★
Lesbian Herstory Educational Foundation, Inc. - Archives (Soc Sci)
Box 1258
New York, NY 10116 Phone: (212)874-7232
Founded: 1974. **Subjects:** Lesbian history and culture, women's history. **Special Collections:** Manuscript collection; oral history collection; international lesbian collection; lesbian organizations (files on 400 groups); biographical collection (files on 1000 individuals); art and music collection; button, T-shirt, and photography collections. **Holdings:** 8500 books; 30 bound periodical volumes; 350 unbound periodical volumes; 700 tapes; 500 subject files; dissertations. **Subscriptions:** 200 journals and other serials; 50 newspapers. **Services:** Copying; archives open to the public by appointment. **Publications:** L.H.A. Newsletter, irregular - to mailing list; occasional bibliographies. **Special Indexes:** Index of periodical holdings; (card and typed list); index of organization holdings.

Lesher Communications - Contra Costa Times - Library
See: **Contra Costa Times - Library** (4256)

★9069★
Lesotho - National Library Service (Area-Ethnic)
P.O. Box MS 985 Phone: 322592
Maseru 100, Lesotho F. Mongoaela, Sr.Libn.
Founded: 1976. **Staff:** 11. **Subjects:** Lesotho - English-language literature, social sciences, history, geography, science, arts. **Special Collections:** Lesotho Collection (3000 volumes). **Holdings:** 24,000 books. **Subscriptions:** 4 newspapers. **Services:** Interlibrary loan; library open to the public. **Remarks:** FAX: 310194. Telex: 4228.

★9070★
Letchworth Developmental Diabilities Services - Isaac N. Wolfson Library (Med)
Thiells, NY 10984 Phone: (914)947-1000
Eleanor Flaherty, Sr.Ck./Lib.Asst.
Staff: 1. **Subjects:** Mental retardation, developmental disabilities, special education, psychology. **Special Collections:** Developmental disabilities, aging. **Holdings:** 5000 books; 60 reports on microfiche; 160 cassettes and videotapes; 10 VF drawers of pamphlets. **Subscriptions:** 50 journals and other serials. **Services:** Interlibrary loan; copying; library open to the public. **Computerized Information Services:** Searches performed through New York State Library. **Networks/Consortia:** Member of Southeastern New York Library Resources Council (SENYLRC), Health Information Libraries of Westchester (HILOW), Ramapo Catskill Library System. **Remarks:** FAX: (914)942-2812.

★9071★
Lethbridge City Archives (Hist)
Community Services Dept.
910 4th Ave., S. Phone: (403)329-7302
Lethbridge, AB, Canada T1J 0P6 Greg Ellis, City Archv.
Founded: 1980. **Staff:** Prof 2; Other 4. **Subjects:** History of Lethbridge and southern Alberta. **Special Collections:** Lethbridge Herald Photographic Collection (50,000); Regional History Library (400 volumes); Lethbridge Northern Irrigation District Collection (35 linear feet). **Holdings:** 500 books; 750 linear feet of manuscripts; 110,000 photographs and negatives. **Services:** Copying; archives open to the public. **Automated Operations:** Computerized cataloging. **Computerized Information Services:** Internal database. **Publications:** Study papers, irregular. **Remarks:** FAX: (403)329-4958. **Formerly:** Sir Alexander Galt Museum - Archives. **Staff:** Pat Marshall, Archv.Ck.

★9072★
LeTourneau University - Margaret Estes Library (Sci-Engr, Hum)
2100 S. Mobberly
Box 7001 Phone: (903)753-0231
Longview, TX 75607 Lois Braymer, Dir.
Founded: 1946. **Staff:** Prof 3.5; Other 5.25. **Subjects:** Engineering, technology, aviation, humanities, Biblical studies, business. **Special Collections:** Robert G. LeTourneau Memorabilia; Billy Sunday Collection; Harmon General Hospital Collection; Rare Afro Art & Native Antiques Exhibit; Rare Book Collection. **Holdings:** 90,699 books; 12,773 bound periodical volumes; 82,418 microform titles; 4657 AV programs; 23,954 clippings, pictures, and VF materials. **Subscriptions:** 420 journals and other serials; 12 newspapers. **Services:** Interlibrary loan; copying. **Computerized Information Services:** DIALOG Information Services, OCLC, InfoTrac; internal databases. Performs searches on fee basis. **Remarks:** FAX: (903)237-2730. **Also Known As:** Longview Citizens' Resource Center. **Staff:** Mary Sue Beaty, Asst. Dir. & Acq.; Christy Henegar, Asst.Dir.; Wynona Prince, Ref./Circ.; Ron Glass, Ref./Circ.Supv.; Hilda Fyock, Dir., Media Serv.; Gladyne Hluchan, Tech.Proc.; Marjorie Heath, Cat.; Betty Sterrett, Cat.

Letterman Army Institute of Research
See: **U.S. Army - Letterman Army Institute of Research** (16984)

Letterman U.S. Army Hospital
See: **U.S. Army Hospitals** (17046)

★9073★
Leukemia Society of America, Inc. - Library (Med)
733 3rd Ave. Phone: (212)573-8484
New York, NY 10017 Mariana Jordan, Pub.Info.Spec.
Founded: 1984. **Staff:** Prof 1; Other 1. **Subjects:** Leukemia, lymphomas, multiple myeloma, Hodgkin's Disease, psychosocial aspects of leukemia and allied diseases, cancer. **Holdings:** 300 books; 3 drawers of clippings, unbound reports, resource organization materials. **Subscriptions:** 20 journals and other serials. **Services:** Interlibrary loan; copying; library open to qualified researchers by appointment. **Networks/Consortia:** Member of Manhattan-Bronx Health Sciences Library Consortia. **Remarks:** FAX: (212)972-5776. **Staff:** Doris Jaeger, Lib.Cons.

★9074★
Kenneth Leventhal & Company - Library (Bus-Fin)
2049 Century Park, E., 16th Fl. Phone: (213)277-0880
Los Angeles, CA 90067 Ellyn Hasama, Dir. of Lib.Serv.
Founded: 1972. **Staff:** Prof 2; Other 3. **Subjects:** Accounting, auditing, taxation. **Special Collections:** Housing and real estate. **Holdings:** 4000 books. **Subscriptions:** 400 journals and other serials. **Services:** Library not open to the public. **Automated Operations:** Computerized cataloging. **Computerized Information Services:** NAARS, LEXIS, DIALOG Information Services, NEXIS, PHINet FedTax Database, ORION, OCLC. **Remarks:** FAX: (213)284-7970.

Levere Memorial Temple Library
See: **Sigma Alpha Epsilon Foundation** (15163)

Levi Memorial Library
See: **University of Cincinnati - Medical Center Information and Communications - Nursing Educational Resources** (18477)

Wendell Mitchell Levi Library & Archives
See: **College of Charleston - Robert Scott Small Library - Special Collections** (3887)

Louis R. Levin Memorial Library
See: **Curry College** (4488)

★9075★
Levine, Huntley, Vick & Beaver - Library (Bus-Fin)
355 Park Ave., S. Phone: (212)545-3618
New York, NY 10010 John Lovari, Dir., Info.Serv.
Founded: 1983. **Staff:** 1. **Subjects:** Advertising and marketing. **Holdings:** Figures not available. **Computerized Information Services:** NEXIS, DIALOG Information Services, DataTimes, InvesText, MRI, QL Systems. **Formerly:** Levine, Huntley & Beaver.

Levitt Health Sciences Library
See: **Iowa Lutheran Hospital** (8227)

Levitt Library
See: **York College** (20767)

Levitt Medical Library
See: **Mercy Hospital Medical Center** (10148)

Austin T. and June Rockwell Levy Library
See: **Emma Pendleton Bradley Hospital - Austin T. and June Rockwell Levy Library** (2057)

Gustave L. & Janet W. Levy Library
See: **Mount Sinai School of Medicine of City University of New York** (10819)

Leon Levy Library
See: **University of Pennsylvania - School of Dental Medicine** (19192)

Elizabeth Lewin Business Library & Information Center
See: **National Chamber of Commerce for Women, Inc.** (11112)

Byron R. Lewis Historical Library
See: **Vincennes University** (19850)

★9076★
Lewis and Clark Law School - Northwestern School of Law - Paul L. Boley Law Library (Law)
10015 S.W. Terwilliger Blvd. Phone: (503)244-1181
Portland, OR 97219 Prof. Peter S. Nycum, Law Libn.
Founded: 1884. **Staff:** Prof 7; Other 10. **Subjects:** Law. **Special Collections:** Milton A. Pearl Environmental Law Library (3500 volumes); Samuel S. Johnson Public Land Law Review Commission Collection (50,000 pages). **Holdings:** 37,093 books; 126,892 serial volumes; 145,357 microforms. **Subscriptions:** 3136 journals and other serials. **Services:** Interlibrary loan; copying; library open to the public with restrictions. **Automated Operations:** Computerized cataloging. **Computerized Information Services:** LEXIS, WESTLAW, DIALOG Information Services, Oregon Legislative Information System, ELSS (Electronic Legislative Search System); MCI Mail (electronic mail service). Performs searches on fee basis for attorneys. Contact Person: Dean Taylor, Dir., Serv., 245-7878. **Networks/Consortia:** Member of Northwest Consortium of Law Libraries. **Publications:** Handbook, annual; subject bibliographies: estate planning and taxation, admiralty, environmental law. **Remarks:** FAX: (503)246-8542. **Staff:** Lynn Williams, Rd.Serv.Libn.; Kathy Faust, Asst.Libn./Tech.Serv.; D.R. Jones, Ref.Libn.; Barbara Arnett, Ref.Libn.; George Pike, Asst. Law Libn.; Tedy Mercier, Circ.Libn.

★9077★
Lewis County Historical Museum - Library (Hist)
599 N.W. Front St. Phone: (206)748-0831
Chehalis, WA 98532 Brenda A. O'Connor, Dir.
Founded: 1978. **Staff:** Prof 2; Other 4. **Subjects:** History of Lewis County, Chehalis Indians, genealogy. **Special Collections:** St. Helens Club (minutes and scrapbooks); Chehalis Bee-Nuggett, 1883-1930; Lewis County cemetery history; Chehalis Indian Archival Files; genealogy research books and records; Ernst Bechley History Collection; Lewis County voting records, 1870-1930; Daily Chronicle newspapers, 1930-1964; restoration and preservation of artifacts: textiles, photographs, furniture, glassware. **Holdings:** 12,000 photographs; 400 oral history cassette tapes; 36 feet of archival papers and newspaper clippings; 3 feet of family histories; 200 maps. **Subscriptions:** 400 journals and other serials. **Services:** Family research upon request; copies and transcripts of oral history tapes; library open to the public - must have staff present. **Publications:** Periodical Genealogy & History books; Lewis County Log, quarterly - to members. **Special Indexes:** Photograph index by subject; index of oral histories by subject (both card); index to obituary files.

★9078★
Lewis County Superior Court - Law Library (Law)
351 N.W. North St.
Box 357 Phone: (206)748-9121
Chehalis, WA 98532 Josephine S. Dagnie, Act.Libn.
Subjects: Law. **Holdings:** 6000 volumes. **Services:** Copying; library open to the public. **Remarks:** FAX: (206)748-2199, ext. 252.

★9079★
Elma Lewis School of Fine Arts - Library
122 Elmhill Ave.
Dorchester, MA 02121
Defunct.

Frederic Lewis Stock Photos - Photographic Library
See: **Archive Photos - Library** (957)

G. Pillow Lewis Memorial Library
See: **Memphis College of Art** (10061)

Julia Deal Lewis Library
See: **Loyola University of Chicago** (9421)

Logan Lewis Library
See: **Carrier Corporation** (3096)

Nolan D.C. Lewis Library
See: **Carrier Foundation** (3097)

Lewis Research Center
See: **NASA** (10987)

★9080★
Lewis, Rice & Fingersh - Law Library (Law)
611 Olive St., Suite 1400 Phone: (314)444-7681
St. Louis, MO 63101 Helen Capdevielle
Staff: Prof 1. **Subjects:** Litigation, banking, taxation, corporate law, labor law, estate planning, bankruptcy, environmental law. **Holdings:** 25,000 volumes; 25 bound periodical volumes; 215 other cataloged items. **Subscriptions:** 260 journals and other serials; 10 newspapers. **Services:** Interlibrary loan; library open to the public at librarian's discretion. **Computerized Information Services:** LEXIS, WESTLAW, Information America; MCI (electronic mail service). **Publications:** Accessions list, monthly - to attorneys and paralegals. **Remarks:** FAX: (314)241-6056.

★9081★
Lewis and Roca - Library (Law)
40 N. Central Ave. Phone: (602)262-5303
Phoenix, AZ 85004 Victoria K. Trotta, Law Libn.
Founded: 1950. **Staff:** Prof 2; Other 2. **Subjects:** Law - general, corporate, insurance. **Holdings:** 40,000 volumes. **Subscriptions:** 250 journals and other serials. **Services:** Interlibrary loan; library not open to the public. **Computerized Information Services:** WESTLAW, DIALOG Information Services, LEXIS. **Networks/Consortia:** Member of AMIGOS Bibliographic Council, Inc. **Remarks:** FAX: (602)262-5747. **Staff:** Nancy Nelson, Ref.Libn

★9082★
Sinclair Lewis Information Interpretive Centre/Museum (Hum)
Box 222
Sauk Centre, MN 56378 Phone: (612)352-5201
Founded: 1978. **Subjects:** Sinclair Lewis - life, books, literary criticism of his works. **Special Collections:** Foreign editions (30 copies); letters (8 originals); memorabilia (Boyhood Home). **Holdings:** Reports; manuscripts. **Services:** Open to outside users with restrictions. **Remarks:** Maintained by the Sinclair Lewis Foundation, Inc. The Boyhood Home is a state historic site and a National Historic Landmark.

★9083★
Lewis University - Canal Archives and Special Collection of History (Hist)
Rte. 53 Phone: (815)838-0500
Romeoville, IL 60441 John M. Lamb, Info.Dir.
Founded: 1977. **Staff:** Prof 2; Other 4. **Subjects:** Canals - Illinois, U.S., English; Illinois and Michigan canal; history of canal area. **Special Collections:** Materials relating to towns on the Illinois and Michigan Canal National Heritages Corridor (1000 maps, manuscripts, bound volumes). **Holdings:** 400 volumes; 200 pamphlets; 5 boxes of manuscript materials; 2000 photographs; 150 maps; 50 plans. **Subscriptions:** 7 journals and other serials. **Services:** Archives open to the public. **Publications:** Illinois Canal Society annual publication on canals. **Remarks:** FAX: (815)838-9456. **Staff:** Joseph O'Malley, F.S.C.; Fredrika Moskel.

★9084★
Lewis University - Library (Bus-Fin, Hum, Soc Sci)
Rte. 53 Phone: (815)838-0500
Romeoville, IL 60441 Ms. F.A. Moskal, Lib.Dir.
Founded: 1952. **Staff:** Prof 5; Other 5. **Subjects:** Business and economics, political science, mathematics, nursing, English and American literature. **Holdings:** 113,000 books; 21,333 bound periodical volumes; 50,000 federal government documents; 1252 records; 24,708 books on microfiche; 7000 microfiche; 5483 boxes of periodicals and newspapers on microfilm. **Subscriptions:** 550 journals and other serials; 5 newspapers. **Services:** Interlibrary loan; copying; library open to the public for reference use only. **Automated Operations:** Computerized cataloging. **Computerized Information Services:** OCLC, DIALOG Information Services, Knowledge Index, GENERAL PERIODICALS INDEX-Academic Library Edition. **Networks/Consortia:** Member of ILLINET, LIBRAS Inc., Chicago and South Consortium. **Remarks:** FAX: (815)838-9456. **Staff:** Laura Patterson, Hd., Pub.Serv.; Joseph O'Malley, Ref.Libn.

Irene Lewisohn Costume Reference Library
See: **Metropolitan Museum of Art** (10212)

Irene Lewisohn Library
See: **Neighborhood Playhouse School of the Theatre** (11386)

Lewison Memorial Library
See: **Mount Sinai Hospital Medical Center** (10816)

★9085★
Lewiston Tribune - Library (Publ)
505 C St.
Box 957 Phone: (208)743-9411
Lewiston, ID 83501 Phyllis Collins, Libn.
Founded: 1950. **Staff:** Prof 1. **Subjects:** Newspaper reference topics, area events and history. **Holdings:** Newspaper, 1892 to present, on microfilm. **Subscriptions:** 10 newspapers. **Services:** Interlibrary loan; copying; library open to the public for reference use only. **Special Catalogs:** Key to pictures (book); organizations and historical files (card); obituary file, 1962 to present; newspaper clipping file; biography file; business file. **Remarks:** FAX: (208)746-7341.

★9086★
Lewistown Genealogy Society - Library (Hist)
701 W. Main St. Phone: (406)538-5212
Lewistown, MT 59457 Lily Zwolle, Libn.
Founded: 1978. **Staff:** 2. **Subjects:** Genealogy, local history. **Holdings:** 424 books. **Services:** Interlibrary loan; copying; library open to the public on fee basis.

★9087★
Lewistown Hospital - Medical Library (Med)
400 Highland Ave. Phone: (717)242-7242
Lewistown, PA 17044-1198 Susan J. Smith, Med.Lib.Ck.
Staff: Prof 1; Other 1. **Subjects:** Medicine, nursing, hospital administration. **Holdings:** 1200 books. **Subscriptions:** 110 journals and other serials; 7 newspapers. **Services:** Interlibrary loan; copying; SDI; library open to the public for reference use only. **Computerized Information Services:** DIALOG Information Services, MEDLARS. Performs searches on fee basis. **Networks/Consortia:** Member of National Network of Libraries of Medicine - Middle Atlantic Region, Central Pennsylvania Health Sciences Library Association (CPHSLA). **Remarks:** FAX: (717)242-7245.

★9088★
Lexington Community College - Library (Educ)
Oswald Bldg.
Cooper Dr. Phone: (606)257-4919
Lexington, KY 40506-0235 Martha J. Birchfield, Hd.Libn.
Staff: Prof 4; Other 3. **Subjects:** Associated health technologies, engineering, data processing, business technology, statistical process control. **Holdings:** 20,000 volumes. **Subscriptions:** 180 journals and other serials. **Services:** Interlibrary loan; copying; library open to the public. **Automated Operations:** Computerized public access catalog and cataloging. **Computerized Information Services:** DIALOG Information Services, OCLC. **Networks/Consortia:** Member of SOLINET, Kentucky Library Network, Inc. (KLN). **Remarks:** FAX: (606)257-4339. **Staff:** Brenda Turner, Pub.Serv.; Kathleen Richardson, Tech.Serv.; Charles James, Media; Rick Rydz, Media.

★9089★
Lexington-Fayette County Urban Planning Commission - Technical Information Library (Plan)
200 E. Main St. Phone: (606)258-3160
Lexington, KY 40507 Dale B. Thoma, Dir.
Founded: 1961. **Subjects:** Community planning - administration, theory, practice. **Holdings:** 400 books; 1500 reports. **Subscriptions:** 13 journals and other serials. **Services:** Interlibrary loan; copying; library open to the public. **Publications:** Agency reports, monthly.

★9090★
Lexington Herald-Leader - Library (Publ)
100 Midland Ave. Phone: (606)231-3335
Lexington, KY 40508 Lu-Ann Dunn Farrar, Chf.Libn.
Founded: 1946. **Staff:** Prof 3. **Subjects:** Newspaper reference topics. **Holdings:** 800 books; 92,000 subject clips (indexed); 58,000 photographs; microfilm; biographical and news clippings. **Subscriptions:** 46 journals and other serials. **Services:** Library not open to the public. **Computerized Information Services:** VU/TEXT Information Services, DIALOG Information Services, DataTimes, NEXIS, WILSONLINE, Dow Jones News/Retrieval. Performs searches on fee basis. **Networks/Consortia:** Member of Kentucky Library Network, Inc. (KLN). **Remarks:** Offers Herald-Leader Research Service an information broker service, for a fee. **Staff:** Linda Smith Niemi, Libn.; Robin Luger, Libn.

★9091★
Lexington Historical Society, Inc. - Library (Hist)
Box 514 Phone: (617)861-0928
Lexington, MA 02173 Sarah Brophy, Dir.
Staff: 1. **Subjects:** Lexington history. **Holdings:** 500 books; 50 hours of oral history tapes; documents; manuscripts; photographs. **Services:** Library open to the public by appointment. **Publications:** Newsletter.

★9092★
Lexington Public Schools - Curriculum Resource Center
1557 Massachusetts Ave.
Lexington, MA 02173
Defunct.

★9093★
Lexington School for the Deaf - Library Media Center (Educ)
30th Ave. & 25th St. Phone: (718)899-8800
Jackson Heights, NY 11370 Marie-Ann Marchese, Coord., Lib.Serv.
Staff: Prof 2; Other 1. **Subjects:** Audiology, behavior modification, deafness, education, language, child study, exceptional children, psychology, reading, speech, parenting. **Special Collections:** Professional collection (2158 books, including additional archival materials related to the history of the deaf and deaf education in the U.S.). **Holdings:** 16,788 books. **Subscriptions:** 59 journals and other serials; 6 newspapers. **Services:** Center open to the public for reference use only. **Remarks:** FAX: (718)899-9846. **Staff:** Mary Kielbus, Media.

★9094★
Lexington Theological Seminary - Bosworth Memorial Library (Rel-Phil)
631 S. Limestone Phone: (606)252-0361
Lexington, KY 40508 Philip N. Dare, Hd.Libn.
Founded: 1865. **Staff:** Prof 2; Other 4. **Subjects:** Christian theology, American church history, Disciples of Christ, Biblical studies, Southern states, Biblical archeology. **Special Collections:** John Mason Neale. **Holdings:** 110,000 volumes; 150 volumes of manuscripts of missionaries and ministers; 90 VF drawers of pamphlets; 500 reels of microfilm. **Subscriptions:** 1119 journals and other serials. **Services:** Interlibrary loan; copying; library open to those engaged in scholarly research. **Automated Operations:** Computerized cataloging. **Networks/Consortia:** Member of Team-A Librarians, SOLINET. **Publications:** Occasional studies, irregular. **Staff:** Marcia Freyman, Asst.Libn.

★9095★
Lexmark International, Inc. - Technical Library (Sci-Engr)
Dept. 990, Bldg. 032-2
740 New Circle Rd., N.W. Phone: (606)232-6044
Lexington, KY 40511 Joanne Goode, Hd.Libn.
Founded: 1959. **Staff:** 1. **Subjects:** Electronics, mechanics, chemistry, physics, mathematics, programming, management. **Special Collections:** Trade literature; product manuals; personal and technical vitality (books; audio cassettes). **Holdings:** 10,000 books; 2500 bound periodical volumes; 1000 unbound reports; microfilm; microfiche; 2 files of archival materials; 150 cassettes. **Subscriptions:** 350 journals and other serials. **Services:** Interlibrary loan; copying; library open to the public by appointment. **Automated Operations:** Computerized cataloging. **Computerized Information Services:** DIALOG Information Services, Dow Jones News/Retrieval, STN International; internal database; BITNET, InterNet (electronic mail services). **Networks/Consortia:** Member of SOLINET. **Remarks:** FAX: (606)232-5728. Electronic mail address(es): JMGOODE@UKCC.UKY.EDU (BITNET); KLIDSH@UKCC.UKY.EDU (InterNet). **Formerly:** IBM Corporation - IP Technical Library. **Staff:** Deborah S. Hatfield, Tech.Serv.Libn.

★9096★
Libbey-Owens-Ford Company - Library (Sci-Engr)
1701 E. Broadway
Toledo, OH 43605 Phone: (419)247-4367
Founded: 1946. **Staff:** Prof 1; Other 1. **Subjects:** Glass, optics, engineering, automotives. **Holdings:** 10,000 books; 12,000 bound periodical volumes; 75 VF drawers of manufacturers' catalogs. **Subscriptions:** 250 journals and other serials. **Services:** Interlibrary loan; copying; library open to the public with special permission. **Computerized Information Services:** DIALOG Information Services, STN International; CD-ROMs. **Remarks:** FAX: (419)247-4224. Telex: 286437. **Staff:** Don Boring, Asst.Libn.

Liberation News Service Archive
See: **Temple University - Central Library System - Contemporary Culture Collection** (16133)

★9097★
Liberty Medical Center, Inc. - Reigner Medical Library (Med)
2600 Liberty Heights Ave. Phone: (410)383-4351
Baltimore, MD 21215 Bettie S. Holmes, Dir., Lib.Serv.
Founded: 1948. **Staff:** Prof 1. **Subjects:** Internal medicine, surgery, gynecology, podiatry, hospital administration. **Holdings:** 1500 books; 3800 bound periodical volumes. **Subscriptions:** 170 journals and other serials. **Services:** Interlibrary loan; copying; SDI; library open to health professionals. **Computerized Information Services:** DIALOG Information Services, NLM. **Networks/Consortia:** Member of Maryland Association of Health Science Librarians (MAHSL). **Remarks:** FAX: (410)669-4769.

★9098★
Liberty Memorial Museum and Archives (Hist)
100 W. 26th St. Phone: (816)221-1918
Kansas City, MO 64108 Cynthia Rogers, Archv.
Founded: 1926. **Staff:** Prof 1. **Subjects:** World War I. **Special Collections:** World War I posters (900); archives of Women's Overseas Service League; World War I archival material (50 square feet of maps, letters, films, photographs); Liberty Memorial Archives (40 square feet; 35 volumes). **Holdings:** 2000 books; 900 stereograph slides; 250 pieces of sheet music. **Subscriptions:** 20 journals and other serials. **Services:** Copying; archives open to the public by appointment. **Publications:** Brochure - available on request. **Special Catalogs:** Catalogs of posters, sheet music, certificates and citations, and World War I camp and unit newspapers (all card). **Special Indexes:** Shelf lists for diaries, manuscripts, and manuscript collections.

★9099★
Liberty Mutual Insurance Company - Business Reference Library (Bus-Fin)
One PPG Place, Suite 2700 Phone: (412)391-6555
Pittsburgh, PA 15222-5409 Dorothy Fornof, Supv., Lib.Serv.
Founded: 1980. **Staff:** Prof 1. **Subjects:** Insurance, management. **Holdings:** 2000 books. **Subscriptions:** 78 journals and other serials. **Services:** Interlibrary loan; copying. **Computerized Information Services:** DIALOG Information Services. **Publications:** Book Shelf, biweekly - for internal distribution only. **Remarks:** FAX: (412)281-5860.

★9100★
Liberty Mutual Insurance Company - Education/Information Resources (Bus-Fin)
175 Berkeley St. Phone: (617)357-9500
Boston, MA 02117 Ann M. McDonald, Mgr.
Founded: 1965. **Staff:** Prof 4; Other 3. **Subjects:** Insurance, management, business, training, information systems. **Holdings:** 20,000 books; 1000 periodical volumes; 10 VF drawers of pamphlets (uncataloged). **Subscriptions:** 250 journals and other serials. **Services:** Interlibrary loan. **Computerized Information Services:** DIALOG Information Services; CD-ROM (Business Periodicals Online). **Publications:** Info Track, monthly - available upon request. **Remarks:** FAX: (617)338-1950. **Staff:** Linda E. Peterson, Dir., Lib.Serv.; Ruth D. Haugen, Tech.Serv.Supv.

★9101★
Liberty Mutual Insurance Company - Education/Information Resources (Bus-Fin)
Riverside Office Park
13 Riverside Rd. Phone: (617)891-8900
Weston, MA 02193 Joan Callahan, Dir.
Founded: 1981. **Staff:** Prof 1. **Subjects:** Insurance, management, business, training, data processing. **Holdings:** 5000 books. **Subscriptions:** 53 journals and other serials. **Services:** Interlibrary loan; SDI; resources open to the public by appointment. **Computerized Information Services:** DIALOG Information Services. **Publications:** In Search, monthly. **Remarks:** FAX: (617)891-0926.

★9102★
Liberty Mutual Insurance Company - Law Library (Law)
175 Berkeley St. Phone: (617)357-9500
Boston, MA 02117 W. Leslie Peat, Dir. of Law Libs.
Founded: 1912. **Staff:** Prof 2; Other 2. **Subjects:** Insurance, law, medicine. **Holdings:** 30,000 volumes. **Subscriptions:** 108 journals and other serials. **Services:** Library not open to the public. **Computerized Information Services:** WESTLAW, DIALOG Information Services. **Remarks:** FAX: (617)426-7125. Company has 46 branch law libraries with a total of 125,000 volumes. **Staff:** Cecelia D. Russell, Cat.

★9103★
Libra Laboratories, Inc. - Library (Food-Bev)
44 Stelton Rd.
Piscataway, NJ 08854 Phone: (908)968-5200
Subjects: Food science technology, quality control, processed and snack foods, deep-fat frying. **Holdings:** 500 volumes and serial publications. **Computerized Information Services:** Internal database (frying oil analytical data). Contact Person: Nancy Berkenfeld, Res. **Remarks:** FAX: (908)968-9552. Telex: 9102501168.

Library Action Committee of Corona-East Elmhurst, Inc.
See: **Queens Borough Public Library - Library Action Committee of Corona-East Elmhurst, Inc.** (13630)

Library of American Civilization
See: **Jersey City State College - Forrest A. Irwin Library - Special Collections** (8370)

Library of American Civilization
See: **U.S. Navy - U.S. Marine Corps Air Station (MCAS El Toro) - Station Library** (17909)

Library of American Transportation
See: **National Railway Historical Society** (11261)

★9104★
Library Association of La Jolla - Athenaeum Music and Arts Library (Art, Mus)
1008 Wall St. Phone: (714)454-5872
La Jolla, CA 92037 Erika Torri, Libn.
Staff: Prof 2; Other 3. **Subjects:** Fine arts, music, drama. **Special Collections:** Bach Gesellschaft (47 volumes). **Holdings:** 8400 volumes; 10,000 phonograph records; 4000 cassettes; 2000 CD's; 900 videos. **Subscriptions:** 70 journals and other serials. **Services:** Library open to the public for reference use only.

Library of the Boston Authors Club
See: **Boston Public Library - Rare Books and Manuscripts** (1999)

Library of the Botanic Gardens of Adelaide and State Herbarium
See: **Botanic Gardens of Adelaide and State Herbarium - Library** (2023)

Library of the Browning Society
See: **Boston Public Library - Rare Books and Manuscripts** (1999)

★9105★
Library Company of the Baltimore Bar (Law)
618 Mitchell Courthouse Phone: (410)727-0280
Baltimore, MD 21202-1783 Kai-Yun Chiu, Libn.
Founded: 1840. **Staff:** Prof 3; Other 12. **Subjects:** Law. **Special Collections:** Federal and state statutory and case law; treatises; British and Canadian case law and statutes. **Holdings:** 180,000 volumes; 80 videocassettes; 30 drawers of microfiche; 4 drawers of microfilm; 12 drawers of audiocassettes. **Subscriptions:** 350 journals and other serials; 5 newspapers. **Services:** Interlibrary loan (limited); library not open to the public. **Computerized Information Services:** WESTLAW, LEXIS. **Publications:** Bar Library Advance Sheet, quarterly - to members. **Remarks:** FAX: (410)685-4791. **Staff:** Joseph W. Bennett, Asst.Libn.; Rhea L. Wilson, Tech.Serv.Libn

★9106★
Library Company of Philadelphia (Hist)
1314 Locust St. Phone: (215)546-3181
Philadelphia, PA 19107 John C. VanHorne, Libn.
Founded: 1731. **Staff:** Prof 6; Other 7. **Subjects:** Pre-1860 Americana, Philadelphia and Pennsylvania, pre-1820 medical material, black history before 1906. **Special Collections:** Early printed books from Girard College and Christ Church (on deposit). **Holdings:** 450,000 books; 50,000 prints and photographs; 160,000 manuscripts. **Subscriptions:** 130 journals and other serials. **Services:** Interlibrary loan; copying; library open to the public for research. **Computerized Information Services:** RLIN. **Networks/Consortia:** Member of Research Libraries Information Network (RLIN). **Publications:** Annual reports; newsletters - both free to libraries and individuals on request. **Special Catalogs:** Afro-Americana, 1553-1906 in collections of the Library Company and the Historical Society of Pennsylvania; The Library of James Logan; Quarter of a Millennium: The Library Company of Philadelphia, 1731-1981; occasional catalogs of special exhibitions; American Education, 1622-1860; Agriculture in America, 1622-1860; Natural History in America, 1609-1860; American Philanthropy, 1731-1860 (4 volume set covering the collections of the Library Company, Historical Society of Pennsylvania, and the American Philosophical Society). **Remarks:** FAX: (215)546-5167. **Staff:** Gordon M. Marshall, Asst.Libn.; Mary Anne Hines, Chf. of Ref.; Kenneth Finkel, Cur., Prints/Photo.; James N. Green, Cur., Printed Books; Jennifer Woods, Bindery/Cons.

★9107★
Library of Congress - African & Middle Eastern Division (Area-Ethnic)
John Adams Bldg., Rm. 1015 Phone: (202)707-7937
Washington, DC 20540 Dr. George Atiyeh, Act.Chf.
Remarks: The Library of Congress has extensive holdings of books, newspapers, manuscripts, periodicals, and other material relating to nations of Africa and the Middle East. Detailed reference services on the 650,000 western-language volumes relating to this area in the library's general collections are provided by the division's African, Hebraic, and Near East sections. In addition, the Hebraic Section has custody of over 131,000 volumes in Hebrew, Yiddish, and cognate languages covering such topics as the Bible, ancient Middle East, and Jews and Judaism throughout the world. The Near East Section has holdings of more than 148,000 volumes in Arabic, Turkish, Persian, and other languages of an area of responsibility that extends from Afghanistan to Morocco, excluding Israel. The African Section, with primary responsibility for Africa south of the Sahara, has a small reference collection and extensive pamphlet files. Both the Hebraic and Near East sections maintain union catalogs relating to their respective areas of responsibility, while the African Section has a card index of citations to Africana periodical literature. The phone numbers for the 3 sections of this Division are as follows: African Section 707-5528; Hebraic Section 707-5422; Near East Section 707-5421. **Staff:** Beverly A. Gray, Hd., African Sect.; Michael Grunberger, Hd., Hebraic Sect.

★9108★
Library of Congress - American Folklife Center (Hist)
Thomas Jefferson Bldg. Phone: (202)707-6590
Washington, DC 20540 Alan Jabbour, Dir.
Founded: 1976. **Staff:** Prof 13; Other 5. **Subjects:** American folklife with emphasis on research, public programs, and technical assistance; folksong; folk music; folklife; ethnomusicology; oral history. **Special Collections:** Archive of Folk Culture. **Holdings:** 4000 books; 1300 serial titles; 40,000 hours of unpublished field recordings; manuscript collection (600,000 pages); results of current research projects including fieldnotes, sound recordings, photographs, and videotapes; 200,000 ephemera; 170,000 photographs. **Services:** Copying (limited); reading room open to the public; listening by appointment; correspondence and telephone inquiries; an intern program for interested students. **Automated Operations:** Computerized public access catalog. **Computerized Information Services:** Internal databases. **Publications:** Folklife Center News, quarterly; mailing list composed of folklife organizations, institutions, and individuals - additions made upon request; Folklife Sourcebook: A Directory of Folklife Resources in the United States and Canada - for sale; Folklife and Fieldwork (English and Spanish editions); American Folk Music and Folklore Recordings: A Selected List; LC recordings of folk music and lore; 200 reference and finding aids - available upon request; Federal Cylinder Project Catalogs; list of publications - available upon request. **Special Catalogs:** Catalog of issued LPs/cassettes (pamphlet); catalog of recorded collections (card); catalog of individual titles on some recordings (card); catalog of manuscript and microform collections (card). Alternate telephone number(s): 707-5510 (Ref.) **Staff:** Ray Dockstader, Dp.Dir.; Timothy Lloyd, Asst. to the Dir.; Joseph C. Hickerson, Acq.; Gerald Parsons, Ref.; David Taylor, Folklife Spec.; Mary Hufford, Folklife Spec.; Peter Bartis, Folklife Res.; James Hardin, Ed.; Judith Gray, Ethnomusicologist; Stephanie Hall, Proc.Archv.; Jennifer Cutting, Prog.Asst.; Catherine Kerst, Cat. - Amer. Memory Proj.; Elaine Bradtke, Cat. - Amer. Memory Proj.

★9109★
Library of Congress - Asian Division (Area-Ethnic)
John Adams Bldg., LA 130 Phone: (202)707-5426
Washington, DC 20540 Warren Tsuneishi, Chf.
Staff: Prof 20; Other 10. **Holdings:** Asian Division contains 1.6 million volumes in Asian languages. Chinese: 570,000 volumes, with emphasis on local histories, rare books, and materials of the Ch'ing period, 1644-1911, and post-1949 periodical publications. Japanese: 716,000 volumes, with emphasis on social sciences and modern history. Korean: 95,000 volumes, with emphasis on historical works and current publications. Southern Asia: 216,000 volumes of research literature from Pakistan to Philippines, especially Bengali, Punjabi, Gujarati, Marathi, Hindi, Tamil, Telugu, Malayalam, Oriya, Kannada, Urdu, Sindhi, Nepali, Newari, Assamese, Indonesian, Vietnamese, Thai, Malaysian, and Burmese; 29,300 reels of microfilm; 144,000 microfiche. **Subscriptions:** 12,000 titles. **Services:** Interlibrary loan; division open to the public. **Computerized Information Services:** RLIN, Multiple Use MARC System (MUMS). **Special Catalogs:** Far Eastern Languages Catalog (Chinese, Japanese, and Korean dictionary catalog); Japanese National Union Catalog; Korean National Union Catalog; Chinese National Union Catalog (all on cards). **Staff:** Richard C. Howard, Asst.Chf.; Chi Wang, Hd., Chinese/Korean Sect.; Hisao Matsumoto, Hd., Japanese Sect.; Louis A. Jacob, Hd., Southern Asia Sect.

★9110★
Library of Congress - Children's Literature Center (Hum)
Thomas Jefferson Bldg., Rm. 140H Phone: (202)707-5535
Washington, DC 20540 Sybille A. Jagusch, Chf.
Founded: 1963. **Staff:** 3. **Automated Operations:** MUMS, SCORPIO. **Computerized Information Services:** OCLC; LCCC (internal database).

Remarks: The Library of Congress has approximately 200,000 children's books in numerous foreign languages, and approximately 20,000 rare books. The Children's Literature Center is a reference and referral division and deals with questions concerning all aspects of children's books. It further acts as a consultant to the library concerning collection development, exhibitions, or other special events. In its office, the Center houses a modest collection of reference books, periodicals, and pamphlets. The Center organizes symposia, special programs, and celebrations (supported by private funds), and promotes children's books and reading. It publishes the annual, selective bibliography of Books for Children, as well as other items. List of publications - available on request. Users of the Children's Literature Center can request all Library of Congress services such as interlibrary loans, copying services, photoduplication, and assistance in automatic searches. **Staff:** Margaret Coughlan, Ref.Spec.

★9111★

Library of Congress - Congressional Research Service (Soc Sci)
James Madison Memorial Bldg., LM213 Phone: (202)707-5700
Washington, DC 20540 Joseph E. Ross, Dir.
Founded: 1914. **Staff:** 860. **Services:** Service not open to the public. **Remarks:** The Congressional Research Service provides research and analytical, consultative, and informational services exclusively to the members and committees of Congress in connection with their official business. In addition, it publishes, at regular intervals, the Digest of Public General Bills and Resolutions, Major Legislation of Congress, CRS Review, and the Constitution of the United States of America - Analysis and Interpretation (published decennially with biennial supplements). The service is organized into divisions, established along broad subject field lines, as follows: (1) an American Law Division, which provides research in the fields of federal, state, county, and municipal law and prepares for publication the Digest of Public General Bills; (2) an Economics Divisio n covering the fields of money and banking, housing and community development, transportation and communications, labor, industrial organization and corporate finance, international trade, and economic geography; (3) an Environment and Natural Resources Policy Division, covering agriculture, mineral economics, forestry and lumber, energy resources, environmental protection, pollution, and the fields of water, irrigation, reclamation, and land use; (4) a Foreign Affairs and National Defense Division, covering international relations, regional affairs, and national defense; (5) an Education and Public Welfare Division, covering education, health, social security, retirement systems, problems of the aging, and immigration; (6) a Government Division, covering political science and public administration, the general field of history, civil rights, governmental organization and operations, governmental procedures, some areas of criminology, and Indian Affairs; and (7) a Science Policy Research Division, covering public policy and legislative problems relating to science and technology. The service also has an Office of Senior Specialists, providing authoritative, consultative, and analytical research services, primarily to congressional committees. A Congressional Reference Division, which responds to general reference questions, conducts literature searches of books, magazines, newspapers, government documents, and congressional publications, and provides a rush telephone response service, also operates reference centers in the House and Senate office buildings and maintains two Information Distribution Centers as well as two Congressional Reading Rooms for the exclusive use of Members of Congress, their families, and official staff. A Library Services Division is responsible for the acquisition, processing, and servicing of research materials for the research and reference staff of the service as well as the provision of bibliographies and SDI services and the distribution of CRS reports to congressional staff members. In addition to publications and other research products, the service provides numerous seminars, workshops, and institutes for members and staff of Congress on topics of current legislative concern and maintains extensive automated data resources for congressional use. FAX: (202)707-6745.

★9112★

Library of Congress - Copyright Public Information Office (Law)
James Madison Memorial Bldg., LM-401 Phone: (202)479-0700
Washington, DC 20559 Joan Doherty, Chf., Info. & Ref.Div.
Staff: Prof 16. **Subjects:** Copyright. **Holdings:** Copyright Card Catalog (40 million cards). **Services:** Office supplies general information about copyright in response to telephone and mail requests. **Computerized Information Services:** COPICS (internal database). **Publications:** Circulars, application forms - free upon request. **Special Catalogs:** Catalog of Copyright Entries (microfiche). **Remarks:** The Forms Hotline number, to order copyright registration application forms, is (202)707-9100. **Staff:** Joseph G. Ross, Jr., Hd., Pubn.; Stephen Soderberg, Hd., Info.Sect.

★9113★

Library of Congress - European Division (Area-Ethnic)
Thomas Jefferson Bldg., Rm. 204 Phone: (202)707-5414
Washington, DC 20540 David H. Kraus, Chf.
Founded: 1951. **Staff:** 16. **Subjects:** Europe (except Spain, Portugal, and Britain) - social sciences, humanities. **Services:** Interlibrary loan; division open to the public. **Automated Operations:** MUMS, SCORPIO. **Remarks:** The European Division provides specialized reference and bibliographic services, is responsible for the development of the collections within its area and subject specialization, and maintains liaison with governmental and academic specialists in the field. A staff of area specialists and librarians, supported by pertinent reference files and tools, render these services with respect to the past and present of the following areas, countries, and peoples: Albania, Austria, Belgium, Bulgaria, Cyprus, Czechoslovakia, Denmark, Estonia, Finland, France, Germany, Greece, Hungary, Iceland, Italy, Latvia, Lithuania, Luxembourg, Monaco, Netherlands, Norway, Poland, Romania, San Marino, Sweden, Switzerland, the USSR, Vatican City, and Yugoslavia. Reading, study, and reference facilities, the lat ter including a reference collection of more than 10,000 volumes on European countries, are available in the division's European Reading Room. The division has custody of current Slavic and Baltic periodicals and newspapers. The general collection of the Library of Congress includes close to 4.5 million volumes of monographs and several tens of thousands of periodical and newspaper titles in the languages of or pertaining to the countries covered by the division. FAX: (202)707-8482. **Staff:** Carol Ambruster, France & Italy Coll.; Ronald Bachman, Poland & Eastern Europe Coll.; Albert E. Graham, Mil.Aff., Soviet Union & Eastern Europe Coll.; Margrit B. Krewson, German & Dutch Coll.; Harold M. Leich, Russia & Soviet Union Coll. ; Kenneth E. Nyirady, Hungary Coll.; Paul P. Pajic, Bulgaria & Yugoslavia Coll.; Bohdan Yasinsky, Byelorussia & Ukraine Coll.

★9114★

Library of Congress - General Reading Rooms Division - Business Reference Service (Soc Sci, Bus-Fin, Educ)
John Adams Bldg. Phone: (202)707-5522
Washington, DC 20540 James Stewart, Hd.
Staff: 8. **Remarks:** Reference collections in the Business Reference Service comprise more than 10,000 volumes covering business and economics. Librarians provide reference service in these areas, prepare reference aids, and assist readers in using SCORPIO and MUMS, the library's automated bibliographic systems. The reading room is open to persons above high school age. **Formerly:** Its Social Science Reading Room Section.

★9115★

Library of Congress - General Reading Rooms Division - Local History & Genealogy Reading Room Section (Hist)
Thomas Jefferson Bldg., Rm. LJ244 Phone: (202)707-5537
Washington, DC 20540 Judith P. Austin, Hd.
Staff: 9. **Remarks:** The Library of Congress has more than 400,000 volumes of U.S. and European genealogy, heraldry, and U.S. local history, including compiled genealogies, city directories, published vital statistics, military records, and church registers. Local History and Genealogy Room has a 10,000 volume reference collection, 40 current periodicals, and several card catalogs, including a 200,000 entry index to biographical histories from 50 states. The section offers its services to persons over high school age.

★9116★

Library of Congress - General Reading Rooms Division - Main Reading Room Section (Info Sci)
Thomas Jefferson Bldg. - GRR 122C Phone: (202)707-5522
Washington, DC 20540 Larry Boyer, Hd.
Founded: 1897. **Staff:** 26. **Services:** Section open to adults only. **Computerized Information Services:** LOCIS (internal database). **Remarks:** Reference librarians in the Main Reading Room, with its extensive collection of 70,000 reference volumes, provide orientation to the library, reference service in a broad range of subjects (especially humanities and social sciences), and guidance in using the library's catalogs. The staff helps readers select materials from the library's collections, prepares reference aids, and assists readers in using SCORPIO and MUMS, the library's automated bibliographic systems.

★9117★
Library of Congress - General Reading Rooms Division - Microform Reading Room Section (Hum, Hist)
Thomas Jefferson Bldg. - LJ-140B Phone: (202)707-5471
Washington, DC 20540 Betty Culpepper, Hd.
Staff: 11. **Subjects:** Early state records; early English and American periodicals; American fiction to 1905; dime novels; American and British black journals; underground newspapers; oral histories; U.S. nondepository documents; U.S. Department of Education ERIC Reports; copyright records of the U.S. District Courts, 1790-1870; Barbour Collection of Connecticut vital records; State labor reports, 1865-1900; American labor union constitutions and proceedings; English books to 1700; architectural books, 15th-19th centuries; English and American plays, 1516-1830; Western Americana; pre-1900 Canadiana; papers of select British prime ministers; cabinet reports by British foreign ministers, 1837-1916; Journals and Sessional Papers of the British Parliament; papers of the Parliament of Northern Ireland, 1921-1972; manuscripts of American interest filmed by the American Council of Learned Societies; English parish registers, 16th to 19th centuries; Irish genealogical records; British radical periodicals; Modern Language Association reproductions of manuscripts and rare books; manuscripts in St. Catherine's Monastery on Mt. Sinai, in the libraries of the Greek and Armenian Patriarchates in Jerusalem, and in the monasteries of Mt. Athos; early editions of Petrarch and Ronsard; pandects of the Notaries of Genoa to 1300; minutes of the Senate of the Venetian Republic; inventories from the Archives Nationales (Paris) and of numerous German, Austrian, and Italian archives and libraries; Archives of the Austrian Foreign Office, 1848-1918; Spanish drama; early Latin American imprints; papers of Simon Bolivar; Mexican provincial and local archives from Jalisco, Oaxaca, Parral, Pueblo, and other cities; 16th and 17th century Russian imprints; 19th and 20th century Russian history and culture; archives of the Japanese Ministry of the Foreign Affairs and other ministries, 1868-1945; ULTRA intelligence messages, 1939-1945; summaries and translations of world broadcasts since World War II; press summaries and translations from Mainland China, Japan, Indonesia, and Yugoslavia; economic literature prior to 1830; social and economic plans of developing countries; League of Nations documents; United Nations documents; Human Relations Area Files; doctoral dissertations; books from the library's general collections copied for preservation purposes; Early American imprints to 1819; international censuses of population to 1967; contemporary statistics (ASI, IIS, & SRI); women's history and history of U.S. and British woman suffrage; auction and art exhibition catalogs; biographical archives for Great Britain, Germany, and the Soviet Union; photographic archives of art and architecture in France and Germany; Schomburg clipping file on black history; Spanish Civil War pamphlets; inventories of Latin manuscripts published before 1600 A.D.; Organization of American States documents; early science fiction; history and sources for Vietnam War; sources on ecumenical movement; sources on church in Russia and Soviet bloc; records of the Fabian Society; Dutch underground press; publications of Solidarity movement; archives and files relating to Germany in World War II; records of the Oneida community, of Millerites, and of early Adventists and Shakers; Portugese pamphlets, 1610-1921; history of nursing and pharmacy; early Texas imprints; BBC broadcasts during World War II; U.S. Department of State and Central Intelligence Agency reports. **Holdings:** 3.5 million reels and strips of microfilm, microfiche, and micro-opaques. **Services:** Reading room is open to persons above high school age. **Remarks:** A guide to selected microform sets is available on request. **Staff:** Robert Costenbader, Asst.Hd.

Library of Congress - General Reading Rooms Division - Social Science Reading Room Section
See: **Library of Congress - General Reading Rooms Division - Business Reference Service** (9114)

★9118★
Library of Congress - Geography & Map Division (Geog-Map)
James Madison Memorial Bldg., LMBO2 Phone: (202)707-8530
Washington, DC 20540 Ralph E. Ehrenberg, Chf.
Founded: 1897. **Staff:** Prof 25; Other 10. **Subjects:** Cartography, geography. **Holdings:** 50,000 atlases, 4 million maps, charts, globes, models, other cartographic forms covering more than 700 subjects; LANDSAT browse file. **Subscriptions:** 200 journals and other serials. **Services:** Interlibrary loan; copying. **Computerized Information Services:** MUMS (internal database). **Publications:** Bibliographies, irregular. **Special Indexes:** Indexes to satellite and aerial photographs (approximately 7 million items). **Staff:** David K. Carrington, Hd., Tech.Serv.; Ronald E. Grim, Hd., Ref. & Bibliog.Sect.

★9119★
Library of Congress - Hispanic Division (Area-Ethnic)
Thomas Jefferson Bldg., Rm. 239 Phone: (202)707-5400
Washington, DC 20540 Cole Blasier, Chf.
Founded: 1939. **Staff:** Prof 10; Other 4. **Remarks:** This center for the pursuit of studies in Spanish, Portuguese, Brazilian, Spanish-American, and Caribbean cultures was established in 1939 with the cooperation of the Hispanic Society of America. The library's Hispanic and Portuguese collections are among the finest in the world and represent resources that have been increasing for nearly two centuries. Primary and secondary source materials are available for the study of all periods, from pre-Columbian and medieval Iberian to the present. All major subject areas are represented; the collections are especially strong in history, literature, and the social sciences. Of the 21 million volumes in the general book collections of the library, 2.1 million volumes are concerned with Hispanic, Portuguese, and Caribbean cultures. The reference collection includes 90,000 pamphlets; 8000 Spanish plays; tapes of the Archive of Hispanic Literature, representing 600 authors; 4500 volumes and clippings files of reference material. The division's primary roles are to develop the library's collections relating to Latin America, Spain, and Portugal; to assist scholars, officials, and the general public in the use of these materials; and to describe and interpret Hispanic library resources through published guides and bibliographies. The division compiles the annual Handbook of Latin American Studies, which contains 6000 annotated entries on publications in the major world languages. FAX: (202)707-2005. **Staff:** Georgette M. Dorn, Spec.; Everette E. Larson, Hd., Ref.Sect.; Dolores M. Martin, Ed.

★9120★
Library of Congress - John F. Kennedy Center for the Performing Arts - The Performing Arts Library (Art, Mus, Theater)
John F. Kennedy Ctr. Phone: (202)707-5507
Washington, DC 20566 Jim Pruett, Chf.
Staff: Prof 3; Other 1. **Subjects:** Music, film, theater, dance, broadcasting, performing arts. **Special Collections:** The White House Record Library (duplicates; donated by the Recording Industry Association of America). **Holdings:** 5000 books; 6000 sound recordings and video cassettes; 40 VF drawers of clippings. **Subscriptions:** 450 magazines and trade publications; 10 newspapers. **Services:** Emphasis on current information; remote playback of sound recordings housed in the Madison Building of the Library of Congress - by appointment. **Automated Operations:** Computerized public access catalog. **Computerized Information Services:** OCLC. **Remarks:** Maintained by Library of Congress - Music Division. **Staff:** Vicky J. Wulff, Ref.Libn./Dance; Walter Zvonchenko, Ref.Libn./Theater.

★9121★
Library of Congress - Law Library (Law)
James Madison Memorial Bldg., Rm. 240 Phone: (202)707-5065
Washington, DC 20540 M. Kathleen Price, Law Libn.
Founded: 1832. **Staff:** 103. **Subjects:** All legal systems - secular, religious, historic - as well as international law, comparative law, general law, jurisprudence, philosophy of law and legal history. **Special Collections:** Primary and secondary American and foreign legal sources (40,000 reels of microfilm; 660,000 microfiche); rare law books (25,000). **Holdings:** 2 million volumes. **Remarks:** Figures include holdings of all divisions of the Law Library.

★9122★
Library of Congress - Law Library - American-British Law Division (Law)
James Madison Memorial Bldg., Rm. 235 Phone: (202)707-5077
Washington, DC 20540 Robert Nay, Chf.
Subjects: American federal and state law, British Commonwealth law. **Special Collections:** American colonial and early state law; U.S. court records and briefs; early British law; American and English trials; U.S. legislative publications and congressional documents. **Remarks:** This division administers the Law Library Reading Room.

★9123★
Library of Congress - Law Library - European Law Division (Law)
James Madison Memorial Bldg., Rm. 240 Phone: (202)707-5088
Washington, DC 20540 Ivan Sipkov, Chf.
Subjects: Legal materials on all subjects covering the nations of continental Europe and their possessions, excluding Portugal, Spain, Iceland, and the United Kingdom. **Special Collections:** European country collections; ancient law; feudal law; Germanic law; incunabula; manuscripts; medieval law; consilia; customary law; law of the European Communities.

★9124★
Library of Congress - Law Library - Far Eastern Law Division (Law)
James Madison Memorial Bldg., Rm. 235 Phone: (202)707-5085
Washington, DC 20540 Tao-Tai Hsia, Chf.
Subjects: Legal materials on all subjects covering the nations of East and Southeast Asia, including China, Taiwan, Indonesia, Japan, Korea, and Thailand.

★9125★
Library of Congress - Law Library - Hispanic Law Division (Law)
James Madison Memorial Bldg., Rm. 235 Phone: (202)707-5070
Washington, DC 20540 Rubens Medina, Chf.
Subjects: Legal materials on all subjects covering Latin America, Spain, Portugal, Spanish- and Portuguese-language states of Africa, Philippines, and Puerto Rico. **Special Collections:** Roman Law; canon law; comprehensive collections of national and state materials for Mexico, Argentina, and Brazil. **Special Indexes:** Index to Latin American Legislation, including abstracts from the official gazettes of 25 countries (online).

★9126★
Library of Congress - Law Library - Near Eastern and African Law Division (Law)
James Madison Memorial Bldg., Rm. 240 Phone: (202)707-5073
Washington, DC 20540 Anton Wekerle, Act.Chf.
Subjects: Legal materials on all subjects covering the African and Middle Eastern countries excluding Spanish and Portuguese language states; Roman-Dutch African law; religious law (Jewish, Christian, and Islamic); tribal and customary African law.

★9127★
Library of Congress - Loan Division (Info Sci)
Thomas Jefferson Bldg. - G15
Washington, DC 20540 Phone: (202)707-5444
Remarks: The Loan Division provides bibliographic searching, verifying, and document delivery to Congress, federal agencies, and to scholars nationally and internationally through interlibrary loan. This service is available through academic, public, or special libraries in the U.S. and major libraries throughout the world under the guidelines of the 1980 (U.S.) Interlibrary Loan Code and the International Federation of Library Associations. This service is intended to supplement the resources of other libraries by making available unusual materials not readily accessible elsewhere and by providing location for materials not found through standard bibliographic sources. Local, state, and regional libraries are expected to serve as the primary sources of research materials, while the Library of Congress serves as a library of last resort. Normally, requests are submitted by mail on regular interlibrary loan forms, but requests are also accepted by special arrangement via OCLC, RLIN, ALANET (electronic mail service) mail, and telefacsimile. FAX: (202)707-5986.

★9128★
Library of Congress - Machine-Readable Collections Reading Room (Comp Sci)
Thomas Jefferson Bldg. LJG 140 Phone: (202)707-5278
Washington, DC 20540 John W. Kimball, Jr., Hd., Automation & Ref.
Founded: 1988. **Staff:** Prof 3; Other 1. **Subjects:** Microcomputers and software, CD-ROM reference publications, video disc reference publications. **Holdings:** 325 volumes; 1430 software programs, CD-ROMs, videodiscs, and books with discs; 25 compact discs and video discs. **Subscriptions:** 25 journals and other serials. **Services:** Room open to adults only. **Automated Operations:** Computerized public access catalog and cataloging. **Computerized Information Services:** DIALOG Information Services, RLIN, OCLC; internal databases.

★9129★
Library of Congress - Manuscript Division (Hist)
James Madison Memorial Bldg., LM 101-102 Phone: (202)707-5383
Washington, DC 20540 James H. Hutson, Chf.
Subjects: Collections of the papers of most of the Presidents, from George Washington through Calvin Coolidge, other political, military, scientific, and literary leaders, and records of numerous enterprises and institutions, totaling more than 45 million pieces. Among them: Records of the Virginia Company of London, the American Colonization Society, National American Woman Suffrage Association, National Association for the Advancement of Colored People, National Urban League, National Women's Party, the League of Women Voters, Russian Orthodox Greek Church in Alaska, Kraus Collection (Latin America), Harkness Collection (Mexico and Peru), Herndon-Weik Collection (Lincolniana); WPA Collection (Federal Writer's Project and Historical Records Survey); papers of Henry H. Arnold, Newton D. Baker, Nathaniel P. Banks, Clara Barton, Alexander Graham Bell, Albert J. Beveridge, Nicholas Biddle, Hugo Black, the Blackwell family, James G. Blaine, Gutzon Borglum, Huntington Cairns, Andrew Carnegie, Carrie Chapman Catt, Thomas Corcoran, Charlotte S. Cushman, Jo Davidson, William O. Douglas, Frederick Douglass, Ira C. Eaker, James A. Farley, Hamilton Fish Family, Felix Frankfurter, Benjamin Franklin, Daniel Chester French, Sigmund Freud, Lillian Gish, Alexander Hamilton, W. Averell Harriman, Patricia Roberts Harris, Roy Howard, B.W. Huebsch, Charles Evans Hughes, Cordell Hull, Harold Ickes, John Paul Jones, Ernest J. King, Frank Knox, Robert M. La Follette Family, Jacques Loeb, Raymond Loewy, Henry R. and Clare Boothe Luce, Archibald MacLeish, William McAdoo, Margaret Mead, Edna St. Vincent Millay, Ogden Mills, William (Billy) Mitchell, Samuel F.B. Morse, Reinhold Niebuhr, Frederick Law Olmsted and the records of the Olmsted Associates, Inc., J. Robert Oppenheimer, George S. Patton, Jr., John J. Pershing, Gifford Pinchot, A. Philip Randolph, Joseph L. Rauh, Jr., Whitelaw Reid Family, Abraham Ribicoff, Elliot Richardson, William T. Sherman, Carl Spaatz, Arthur Spingarn, Harlan Fiske Stone, William Styron, Robert A. Taft, Joseph M. Toner, Earl Warren, Booker T. Washington, Daniel Webster, Casper W. Weinberger, James A. McNeill Whistler, Walt Whitman, Roy Wilkins, Owen Wister, Wilbur and Orville Wright; reproductions of manuscripts in foreign archives that relate to American history. **Services:** Reading room is open to adults; open to high school students with a letter of introduction from faculty advisors.

★9130★
Library of Congress - Motion Picture, Broadcasting & Recorded Sound Division (Aud-Vis)
James Madison Memorial Bldg., LM-338 Phone: (202)707-5840
Washington, DC 20540 David Francis, Chf.
Subjects: International archival collection of 125,000 motion picture titles and 65,408 video titles, including films made from earliest paper prints deposited for copyright; 1.6 million sound recordings on disc, tape, wire, and cylinder, including radio programs, 1920s to present; television programs on tape and film, 1948 to present. **Services:** Holdings are not for loan, but many items are available for individual study on library premises by advanced researchers. Viewing reservations must be made in advance. Copies may be ordered, subject to considerations of copyright and other restrictions. **Publications:** Film and Television; Sound Recordings; information brochures - free upon request. **Remarks:** FAX: (202)707-2371. The telephone number of the Recorded Sound Reference Center is 707-7833; the number for the Motion Picture and Television Reading Room is 707-1000.

★9131★
Library of Congress - Music Division (Mus)
James Madison Memorial Bldg., LM-113 Phone: (202)707-5503
Washington, DC 20540 James W. Pruett, Chf.
Subjects: Music and music literature of the world, emphasizing Western civilization, American music, opera and librettos, and chamber music; music organizations; literature about music in various languages (excepting Hebraic and Asiatic). **Special Collections:** Copyright deposits of music and books; holograph manuscripts of music 17th century to present; autographed letters from musicians; Dayton C. Miller Collection (flute and flute-type instruments); collection of string instruments (including five by Antonio Stradivari). **Holdings:** 6 million cataloged items; manuscripts, scores, correspondence, and collected papers of musicians; microforms. **Subscriptions:** 1000 journals. **Services:** Interlibrary loan (limited); listening and video viewing facilities in the Performing Arts Reading Room. **Automated Operations:** Computerized cataloging. **Computerized Information Services:** OCLC, DIALOG Information Services. **Publications:** The Music Division: A Guide to Its Collections and Services; The Dayton C. Miller Flute Collection in the Library of Congress - both brochures; Resources in American Music History; Special Collections in the Library of Congress: A Selective Guide - both bibliographies. **Remarks:** The Music Division commissions new works through endowments established for that purpose. Numerous special collections are bibliographically accessible only in the Music Division. The telephone number for the Reading Room is 707-5507. Maintains John F. Kennedy Center for Performing Arts - Performing Arts Library. This branch library's reference collection emphasizes current events and activities, and contains 5000 volumes, 450 journals and newspapers, clippings, sound recordings, and videotapes. Contact Person: Peter J. Fay, Hd. Telephone: 707-6245. **Staff:** Jon W. Newsom, Asst.Chf.; Elizabeth H. Auman, Hd., Acq. & Proc.Sect./Coord., Pub. Events; Geraldine E. Ostrove, Hd., Rd.Serv.

★9132★
Library of Congress - National Library Service for the Blind and Physically Handicapped (Aud-Vis)
1291 Taylor St., N.W. Phone: (202)707-5100
Washington, DC 20542 Frank Kurt Cylke, Dir.
Automated Operations: Computerized cataloging. **Computerized Information Services:** DIALOG Information Services, SCORPIO, BRS Information Technologies; BLND (internal database). **Publications:** News, quarterly; Update, quarterly; Talking Book Topics, bimonthly; Braille Book Review, bimonthly - all free upon request. **Special Catalogs:** Reading Materials for Blind and Physically Handicapped Individuals (COM). **Remarks:** The National Library Service for the Blind and Physically Handicapped administers a library program that provides recorded and braille books and magazines through 146 regional and subregional libraries located in all parts of the United States. The collection of approximately 35,000 titles in recorded form (disc and cassette) and 23,000 titles in braille may be borrowed from any network library by persons who are unable to read standard printed material because of visual or physical impairment. Special playback equipment for recorded discs and cassettes is also part of this free library service. A collection of over 30,000 music scores, textbooks, and instructional materials in braille, large type, and recorded form is available on loan directly from the National Library Service for the Blind and Physically Handicapped. Through the efforts of volunteer braille transcribers and tape narrators additional titles are provided in limited copies. Reference and information services on all aspects of handicapping conditions are available to libraries, organizations, and the public by telephone, mail, or in person. FAX: (202)707-0712. Telex: 710 822 1969.

★9133★
Library of Congress - Photoduplication Service (Info Sci)
John Adams Bldg., LA 120
Washington, DC 20540 Phone: (202)707-5640
Holdings: 375,000 reels of master negative microfilm; 194,000 master microfiche; 100,000 scientific and technical reports released through the Publication Board of the U.S. Department of Commerce, Office of Technical Services prior to June 1, 1961; Auxiliary Publications through document number 10.073. **Services:** Copying (limited); service open to the public. **Remarks:** FAX: (202)707-1771.

★9134★
Library of Congress - Prints & Photographs Division (Art, Aud-Vis)
James Madison Memorial Bldg., LM 339 Phone: (202)707-5836
Washington, DC 20540 Stephen Edward Ostrow, Chf.
Founded: 1897. **Staff:** Prof 22; Other 8. **Subjects:** Architecture, design, engineering, popular and applied graphic art, documentary photographs, fine prints, master photographs, posters. **Special Collections:** J. and E.R. Pennell Collection (modern and contemporary fine prints, Pennelliana, Whistleriana); Gardiner Greene Hubbard Collection (fine prints, 15th-19th century); 19th century American lithographs by Currier and Ives and other printmakers; Cabinet of American Illustration (original drawings); Civil War drawings by Edwin Forbes, A.R. Waud, and others (originals); American political cartoons; American and British satirical prints from the 18th and 19th centuries; the Yanker Collection (political propaganda, mainly posters, 1965-1980); the Carnegie Survey of the Architecture of the South (pictorial archives of early American architecture); stereoscopic photoprints; documentary photographs, mainly American scenes; photographic collections; U.S. and international geographic collections; Mathew B. Brady and the Brady-Handy Collection (Civil War, portraits, the American scene); portrait collections; documentary photographers: Frances Benjamin Johnston, Lewis Hine, Roger Fenton, Carleton Watkins, William Henry Jackson; George Grantham Bain (news photographs, 1898-1926); Detroit Publishing Company (archive of views, events, and Americana, 1898-1914); Alexander Graham Bell Collection; Herbert E. French (news photographs, Washingtoniana, 1910-1935); American Red Cross (1900-1930s); Erwin Evans Smith Collection (cowboys and the western ranges); photographic survey of America made by the Farm Security Administration and the Office of War Information (1935-1945); Historic American Buildings Survey, Historic American Engineering Record (measured drawings, photographs, data, negatives); Archive of Hispanic Culture (photographs of Latin American art and architecture); Matson Collection (Near East, 1898-1946); Seagram County Court House Collection (1100 buildings in 48 states); Washingtoniana (800 lots consisting of 750,000 photographs); U.S. News and World Report (1.25 million photographs). **Holdings:** 190,000 prints and drawings; 80,000 posters; 12 million photographic prints and negatives, daguerreotypes, slides; 1.8 million architectural drawings and related materials; 50,000 images on video disc. **Services:** Photoduplication service; division open to the public. **Computerized Information Services:** Multiple Use MARC System (MUMS), SCORPIO. **Publications:** List of publications - available on request. **Remarks:** The division houses 15 million images of all sorts other than painting and sculpture. FAX: (202)707-5844. **Staff:** Renata V. Shaw, Asst.Chf.; Mary Ison, Hd., Ref.Sect.; Bernard Reilly, Hd., Cur.Sect.; Elisabeth Betz Parker, Hd., Proc.Sect.

★9135★
Library of Congress - Rare Book & Special Collections Division (Rare Book)
Thomas Jefferson Bldg., Deck B
200 Independence Ave., S.E. Phone: (202)707-5434
Washington, DC 20547 Larry E. Sullivan, Chf.
Subjects: Aeronautics and ballooning, almanacs, Americana, anarchism, early American architecture, Bibles, book arts, children's literature, dime novels, English printing (1478-1640), early French literature, gastronomy, genealogy, illustrated books, incunabula, magic and the occult, Medieval and Renaissance manuscripts, miniature books, Anglo-American 18th and 19th century pamphlets, playbills, Presidents' books, private press books, radicalism, Shakers, Slavic studies, Spanish-American printing (1543-1820), woman's suffrage, World War II. **Special Collections:** American Almanacs, 17th-19th centuries; American Imprints, 1640-1800; Susan B. Anthony; Armed Services Editions; Artists' Books; Paul Avrich (anarchism); Charles Edward Banks Genealogical Manuscripts; John Davis Batchelder; Big Little Book; Katherine Golden Bitting (gastronomy); Bollingen Foundation; Broadsides; Early Bulgarian Imprints, 1806-1877 (Plotchev); Carrie Chapman Catt; Cervantes; Confederate States of America; Congressional Speeches; Dell Paperback; Early Copyright Records, 1790-1870; Copyright Titlepages, 1790-1897; Documents of the First Fourteen Congresses; Harrison Elliott (history of papermaking); George Fabyan (Bacon-Shakespeare controversy and cryptography); Herman Finkelstein (20th century first editions); Benjamin Franklin; Sigmund Freud; Frederic W. Goudy; Gryphius Imprints; Henry Harrisse; Hawaiian; Jean Hersholt (Hans Christian Andersen, Hugh Walpole, Sinclair Lewis); Oliver Wendell Holmes Library; Harry Houdini Library; House Committee on Un-American Activities Pamphlets; Henry James; Thomas Jefferson Library; Leonard Kebler (Don Quixote); Rudyard Kipling (William M. Carpenter, Adm. Lloyd H. Chandler, H. Dunscombe Colt); Hans and Hanni Kraus (Sir Francis Drake); Francis Longe (English drama, 1607-1812); Martin Luther; McManus-Young (magic/occult); Manuscript Plays; Daniel Murray (pamphlets by Afro-American authors); National American Woman Suffrage Association; Elizabeth Robins Pennell (cookery); Reformation; Bruce Rogers; Theodore Roosevelt Hunting Library; Lessing J. Rosenwald (incunabula and illustrated books); Russian Imperial; Alfred Whital Stern Collection of Lincolniana; John Boyd Thacher (incunabula, early discovery of the Americas, French Revolution autographs); Third Reich; Jesse Stuart; Joseph Meredith Toner (medicine, 19th century American local history); Jules Verne; Otto Vollbehr (incunabula); Wagner-Camp (Western Americana); Fredric Wertham; Walt Whitman (Charles Feinberg, Carolyn Wells Houghton); Woodrow Wilson Library; World War II Propaganda; Yudin (18th and 19th century Russian history and literature). **Holdings:** 619,000 items, including the largest collection of incunabula (more than 5600) in the Western Hemisphere.

★9136★
Library of Congress - Science & Technology Division (Sci-Engr)
John Adams Bldg., Rm. 5204 Phone: (202)707-5664
Washington, DC 20540 Joseph W. Price, Chf.
Staff: 35. **Publications:** Bibliographies; LC Science Tracer Bullet series; chronologies. **Remarks:** Within the Library of Congress, the Science and Technology Division has acquisition-recommending responsibility for the science and technology collections; provides reference and bibliographic services on these collections to the scientific community, other government agencies, and the general public; prepares and issues various special bibliographies and other documents; and carries on a limited number of special bibliographic projects under transfer-of-funds arrangements with other agencies. Its services are based on the library's collections in science and technology, which include 3.5 million books, 60,000 journal and serial titles, and 4.5 million unclassified (as to security) technical reports. The last-named category includes comprehensive holdings of the unclassified outputs of the Department of Energy, the National Aeronautics and Space Administration, and the Department of Defense and its contractors (mainly in microform). Collections of American National Standards Institute (ANSI) standards, U.S.S.R. state standards, Chinese standards, U.S. federal military and society specifications and standards, and International Science Organization (ISO) standards are available. Computer terminals in Science Reading Room provide online bibliographic access to the emerging Library of Congress machine-readable catalogs. FAX: (202)707-1925.

★9137★
Library of Congress - Serial and Government Publications Division (Info Sci)
James Madison Memorial Bldg., LM-133 Phone: (202)707-5647
Washington, DC 20540 Karen Renninger, Chf.
Staff: 76. **Subjects:** Unbound serial publications, including periodicals, journals of learned societies, and government serials (approximately 85,000 titles); depository for U.N. and U.S. government publications, 1979 to present; bound volumes, and microfilm of domestic and foreign newspapers in Western and Cyrillic alphabets, current and retrospective from the 17th century (approximately 34,000 titles, including over 1600 domestic and foreign titles received currently). **Holdings:** 450,000 reels of microfilm; 85,000 comic books; 100,000 pamphlets. **Subscriptions:** 85,000 journals and other serials; 1656 newspapers. **Services:** Interlibrary loan; copying; division open to the public with restrictions. **Computerized Information Services:** Bill Digest, Magazine Index; internal database; CD-ROMs (Business Periodicals OnDisc, General Periodicals OnDisc, ABI/INFORM, Newspaper Abstracts, MARCIVE, CD NewsBank); InterNet (electronic mail service). **Publications:** Newspapers Received Currently in the Libra ry of Congress. **Remarks:** FAX: (202)707-6128. Electronic mail address(es): ghig@seg1.loc.gov Attn. Georgia Higley (InterNet). **Staff:** George Caldwell; Robert Schaaf; Lyle Minter; Frank Carroll; Irene Schubert.

Library of English Literature
See: **Jersey City State College - Forrest A. Irwin Library - Special Collections** (8370)

★9138★
Library of Henry J. Grund (Hist)
4897 Corduroy Rd.
Mentor Headlands
Mentor, OH 44060-1216 Henry J. Grund, II, Dir.
Founded: 1958. **Staff:** Prof 1; Other 1. **Subjects:** Ohio history, railroads, agriculture, outdoor life, North American history, art, literature. **Special Collections:** Ohio Collection (1150 volumes); Railroads Collection (1850 volumes); Rare Book Collection (2465 volumes). **Holdings:** 14,201 books; 60 volumes of Pennsylvania County histories; 20 volumes of New York State county histories. **Services:** Interlibrary loan (limited); library open to the public with written approval.

Library of the Immaculate Heart of Mary
See: **Carmelite Monastery** (3066)

★9139★
Library of Inner Mongolia Autonomous Region (Area-Ethnic)
People's Park Phone: Huhhot 4948
Huhhot, Inner Mongolia, People's Republic of China Liang Jixiao, Libn.
Founded: 1950. **Staff:** 83. **Subjects:** General collection. **Special Collections:** Mongolian nationality and regional history. **Holdings:** 1.15 million volumes. **Subscriptions:** 2050 journals and other serials. **Services:** Copying. **Publications:** Library Work Newsletter, irregular.

Library for Lasallian Studies
See: **St. Mary's College of California - Library - Special Collections** (14511)

★9140★
Library Management Services, Ltd. (Law)
766 Hickory Lane Phone: (215)296-3430
Berwyn, PA 19312 Eileen M. Macbeth, Law Libn./Pres.
Staff: 6. **Subjects:** Law. **Remarks:** Firm provides part-time service to law libraries and does consulting work. **Staff:** Lynne Schammahorn; Ellen Bodenheimer; Wendy Glazer; Barbara Felicetti.

Library of Marquis of Dorchester
See: **Royal College of Physicians of London** (14113)

★9141★
Library of Michigan (Info Sci, Law)
717 W. Allegan
P.O. Box 30007 Phone: (517)373-1580
Lansing, MI 48909 James W. Fry, State Libn.
Founded: 1828. **Staff:** Prof 38; Other 70. **Subjects:** Public policy and management, politics and government, automation. **Special Collections:** Public policy and management law; Michigan newspapers; special Michigan collection; regional depository for federal documents; official depository for State of Michigan documents; Michigan law; library science; genealogy. **Holdings:** 700,000 books; 40,000 bound periodical volumes; 3.5 million microforms; 350 AV items; 2 million pieces of ephemera. **Subscriptions:** 2500 journals and other serials; 57 newspapers. **Services:** Interlibrary loan; copying; library open to the public. **Automated Operations:** Computerized public access catalog, cataloging, acquisitions, circulation. **Computerized Information Services:** DIALOG Information Services, BRS Information Technologies, OCLC; internal databases. **Networks/Consortia:** Member of Michigan Library Consortium (MLC). **Publications:** Access, bimonthly; Michigan Library Directory, annual; Michigan Library Statistics, annual; Library Link, bimonthly; LSCA Dissemination Report, annual; Michigan State Laws Relating to Michigan Libraries, irregular; SBPH Perspective, quarterly. **Special Indexes:** Michigan Documents, quarterly (microfiche). **Remarks:** FAX: (517)373-3381; (517)373-8933. **Staff:** Jeffrey P. Johnson, Dp. State Libn.; Kathleen Menanteaux, Tech.Serv.Div.; Susan Nearing, Pub.Serv.Div.; Stephen James, Statewide Lib.Prog. Div.; Sue Adamczak, Law Div.

★9142★
Library of Michigan - Law Library (Law)
Law Bldg.
Box 30012 Phone: (517)373-0630
Lansing, MI 48909 Susan Adamczak, Dir.
Founded: 1828. **Staff:** Prof 3; Other 2. **Subjects:** Law. **Special Collections:** Michigan Records and Briefs, 1874 to present; United States Records and Briefs, 1870 to present. **Holdings:** 145,000 volumes. **Subscriptions:** 800 journals. **Services:** Interlibrary loan; copying. **Computerized Information Services:** WESTLAW, LEXIS, Project Hermes, CITE; Questor, Michigan Bill Status (internal databases). **Remarks:** FAX: (517)373-3915; (517)373-7130. Statistics given are also included in entry for Library of Michigan (see above). **Staff:** Mary Karpinski; Nancy Whitmer; Richard Lucas.

★9143★
Library of Michigan - Service for the Blind and Physically Handicapped (Aud-Vis)
717 W. Allegan
Box 30007 Phone: (517)373-1590
Lansing, MI 48909 Margaret Wolfe, Reg.Libn.
Founded: 1932. **Staff:** Prof 3; Other 9. **Holdings:** 12,667 disc recordings of books; 21,965 cassettes of books; 9467 braille books. **Subscriptions:** 87 journals and other serials. **Services:** Service open to qualified individuals. **Automated Operations:** Computerized cataloging and circulation. **Computerized Information Services:** BRS Information Technologies. **Networks/Consortia:** Member of National Library Service for the Blind & Physically Handicapped (NLS). **Publications:** Perspective, quarterly - available upon request, in large print, braille, or cassette. **Remarks:** Reader advisory, reference, and referral services are available by telephone and mail. Catalogs and bibliographies are provided to qualified individuals and to institutions which have eligible members. Materials are mailed postage free to and from the borrower. Educational materials supplied through the Media Center for the Visually Impaired. Toll-free telephone number(s): (800)992-9012. FAX: 800/726-7323; (517)335-1483.

Library of the National Guard
See: **Historical Society of the Militia and National Guard** (7274)

Library of Natural Sounds
See: **Cornell University - Laboratory of Ornithology** (4318)

Library of the Presidents
See: **U.S. Presidential Museum** (17930)

Library of Shoghi Effendi
See: **Baha'i World Centre** (1407)

★9144★
Library Store, Ltd. - Library (Info Sci)
7720 Wisconsin Ave. Phone: (301)652-8811
Bethesda, MD 20814-3529 Betty Doudnikoff, Pres.
Founded: 1980. **Staff:** Prof 14; Other 9. **Subjects:** Computers, library science, micrographics. **Holdings:** Figures not available. **Services:** Copying; library open to the public. **Automated Operations:** Computerized cataloging. **Publications:** Newsletter - available on request. **Remarks:** FAX: (301)654-4960. **Staff:** Pat Nichols, V.P.; Tim Doudnikoff, Micrographics; Bill McDowell, Lib. Layouts; Bill Doudnikoff, Trng. & Cons.; Jim Ratino, Computer Software.

Library of William Lyon Phelps
See: **Huron City Museum - Library** (7584)

Library of World Peace Studies
See: **University of Akron - Center for Peace Studies - Library** (18154)

★9145★
Librascope Corporation - Technical Information Center (Sci-Engr, Comp Sci)
833 Sonora Ave. Phone: (818)502-7751
Glendale, CA 91201 Evelyn Matzat, Supv.
Founded: 1954. **Staff:** Prof 1; Other 1. **Subjects:** Computers; engineering - systems, electronic, mechanical, electrical; data processing; military electronics; electro-optics; instruments; mathematics. **Holdings:** 2000 books; 1000 bound periodical volumes; 6000 reports; VSMF microfilm files; 25,000 microfiche; 65 VF cabinets of technical and contract-related reports. **Subscriptions:** 250 journals and other serials. **Services:** Interlibrary loan; copying; project data bank management. **Automated Operations:** Computerized cataloging. **Computerized Information Services:** DIALOG Information Services, NewsNet, Inc.; internal database; CD-ROMs (DODISS, QPL). **Publications:** Computer-generated data bank lists; specification and standards lists; acquisitions list. **Remarks:** FAX: (818)502-8248.

★9146★
(Libreville) Centre Culturel Americain - USIS Library (Educ)
16 Ave. du Col. Parant
Post Box 2237
Libreville, Gabon
Remarks: Maintained or supported by the U.S. Information Agency. Focus is on materials that will assist peoples outside the United States to learn about the United States, its people, history, culture, political processes, and social milieux.

Lick Observatory Library
See: **University of California, Santa Cruz - Science Library** (18438)

★9147★
Licking County Genealogical Society - Library (Hist)
743 E. Main St.
Box 4037 Phone: (614)345-3571
Newark, OH 43055 Mrs. G.R. Rose, Libn.
Founded: 1972. **Staff:** 20. **Subjects:** Genealogy. **Holdings:** 3000 books; bound periodical volumes; 400 reels of microfilm; family histories. **Subscriptions:** 100 journals and other serials. **Services:** Copying; library open to the public for reference use only. **Publications:** Licking Lantern, quarterly - to members.

★9148★
Licking County Law Library Association (Law)
22 1/2 N. Second St.
Newark, OH 43055 James Pyle, Libn.
Founded: 1896. **Subjects:** Law. **Holdings:** 30,000 books; 350 bound periodical volumes. **Services:** Library not open to the public.

★9149★
Licking Memorial Hospital - Ralph E. Pickett Medical Library (Med)
1320 W. Main St. Phone: (614)344-0331
Newark, OH 43055 Lindsay J. Freytag, Libn.
Founded: 1966. **Staff:** Prof 1; Other 2. **Subjects:** Clinical medicine. **Holdings:** 300 books; tapes. **Subscriptions:** 25 journals. **Services:** Interlibrary loan; library not open to the public. **Computerized Information Services:** BRS Information Technologies. **Networks/Consortia:** Member of Central Ohio Hospital Library Consortium.

Lieb Library of Leonardo Da Vinci
See: **Stevens Institute of Technology - Samuel C. Williams Library** (15788)

Elias Lieberman Higher Education Contract Library
See: **National Center for the Study of Collective Bargaining in Higher Education and the Professions** (11109)

★9150★
Liebert, Short, & Hirshland - Library (Law)
1901 Market St., 31st Fl. Phone: (215)557-4124
Philadelphia, PA 19103 Michelle A. Ayers, Law Libn.
Founded: 1972. **Staff:** Prof 1. **Subjects:** Law. **Holdings:** 12,000 books. **Subscriptions:** 16 journals and other serials; 8 newspapers. **Services:** Interlibrary loan; copying; library open to the public by appointment. **Computerized Information Services:** DIALOG Information Services, LEXIS, NEXIS, WESTLAW, VU/TEXT Information Services, Information America. **Publications:** Newsletter, monthly - for internal distribution only. **Remarks:** FAX: (215)564-3311.

Liechtenstein Music Archive
See: **Syracuse University - E.S. Bird Library - Fine Arts Department** (15958)

★9151★
Liechtensteinische Landesbibliothek (Hum)
FL-9490 Vaduz, Liechtenstein Phone: 75 66362
Dr. Alois Ospelt, Libn.
Founded: 1961. **Staff:** Prof 3; Other 4. **Special Collections:** Liechtenstein literature. **Holdings:** 16,600 books; 520 reels of microfilm; 1200 videotapes. **Subscriptions:** 600 journals and other serials; 20 newspapers. **Services:** Interlibrary loan; copying; library open to the public. **Publications:** Liechtenstein bibliography. **Remarks:** FAX: 75 81419.

Thurlow Lieurance Memorial Music Library
See: **Wichita State University - Thurlow Lieurance Memorial Music Library** (20413)

★9152★
Life Chiropractic College West - Library (Med)
2005 Via Barrett Phone: (510)276-9345
San Lorenzo, CA 94580 Marda Woodbury, Lib.Dir.
Founded: 1980. **Staff:** Prof 3; Other 4. **Subjects:** Chiropractic, basic sciences, roentgenology, manipulative and physical therapy, medicine, health, musculoskeletal system. **Special Collections:** Chiropractic history archive (300 items). **Holdings:** 10,500 books; 2366 bound periodical volumes; 800 AV programs; 6000 vertical files. **Subscriptions:** 280 journals and other serials. **Services:** Interlibrary loan; copying; SDI; library open to the public. **Automated Operations:** Computerized circulation. **Computerized Information Services:** MEDLINE, OCLC; CD-ROM (Core MEDLINE); Article Database (internal database); OnTyme Electronic Message Network Service (electronic mail service). Performs searches on fee basis. Contact Person: Barbara Palka, Pub.Serv.Libn. **Networks/Consortia:** Member of Chiropractic Library Consortium (CLIBCON), Northern California and Nevada Medical Library Group (NCNMLG), CLASS, Bay Area Library and Information Network. **Publications:** What's New in the Library, irregular; Library Handbook; Pathfinders (research guides), 12/year - for internal distribution only. **Remarks:** FAX: (510)276-4893. **Staff:** Annette Osenga, Media Libn.

★9153★
Life Insurance Marketing and Research Association - William J. Mortimer Library (Bus-Fin)
Box 208 Phone: (203)677-0033
Hartford, CT 06141 Gail W. Buchholz, Dir.
Founded: 1926. **Staff:** Prof 6. **Subjects:** Life insurance, industrial psychology, statistical methods. **Holdings:** 10,000 books; 215 VF drawers of clippings, pamphlets, documents. **Subscriptions:** 300 journals and other serials. **Services:** Interlibrary loan; library open to members and to others upon application. **Computerized Information Services:** DIALOG Information Services. **Special Indexes:** LIMRA publication index (book), annual. **Remarks:** Library located at 8 Farm Springs, Farmington, CT 06032. FAX: (203)678-0187. Telex: 643 952. **Staff:** Rita C. Butkus, Sr. Info.Spec.

★9154★
Life Office Management Association - Information Center (Bus-Fin)
5770 Powers Ferry Rd. Phone: (404)951-1770
Atlanta, GA 30327 Patricia A. Toups, Libn.
Founded: 1924. **Staff:** Prof 1; Other 3. **Subjects:** Life insurance, office management, statistics, life insurance company history, finance, personnel management, accounting. **Holdings:** 500 books; 15,000 reports; 15 VF drawers of reports. **Subscriptions:** 100 journals and other serials. **Services:** Interlibrary loan (to member companies); center open to the public for reference use only by request. **Computerized Information Services:** NEXIS. **Special Indexes:** Index to Information, annual. **Also Known As:** LOMA.

★9155★
Lifespan Resources, Inc. - Library (Soc Sci)
1212 Roosevelt Phone: (313)663-9891
Ann Arbor, MI 48104 Carol H. Tice, Pres.
Founded: 1979. **Subjects:** Intergenerational issues and programs; prevention programs for youth at risk of school dropout. **Holdings:** Guides; reports; videotapes. **Services:** Library open to the public by appointment. **Remarks:** Alternate telephone number(s): (313)994-4715.

★9156★
The Lifwynn Foundation - Library (Soc Sci)
72 Hillandale Rd.
Westport, CT 06880 Phone: (203)227-4139
Founded: 1927. **Staff:** Prof 4. **Subjects:** Psychiatry, sociology, psychology, anthropology, neurophysiology. **Holdings:** 3000 books; 500 bound periodical volumes; microfilm. **Subscriptions:** 10 journals and other serials. **Services:** Copying; library open to the public by appointment.

★9157★
Liggett & Myers Tobacco Co. - Information Services (Biol Sci)
Research Department
Box 1572 Phone: (919)683-8985
Durham, NC 27702 Sandra S. Harris, Info.Serv.Coord.
Founded: 1950. **Subjects:** Tobacco technology, chemistry, engineering, medicine. **Holdings:** 1550 books; 600 bound periodical volumes. **Subscriptions:** 60 journals and other serials. **Services:** Library not open to the public. **Computerized Information Services:** DIALOG Information Services, Chemical Information System (CIS); internal databases (patent and chemical information). **Special Indexes:** Indexes to Registry Systems.

★9158★
Lighthouse for the Blind and Visually Impaired - Library (Aud-Vis)
20 10th St. Phone: (415)431-1481
San Francisco, CA 94103 Dorothy M. Allen
Founded: 1940. **Staff:** 1. **Subjects:** General collection. **Holdings:** 2200 braille volumes. **Services:** Library open to the public. **Remarks:** FAX: (415)863-7568.

Lighthouse Library
See: **New York Association for the Blind** (11553)

★9159★
Lightnin - R&D Library (Env-Cons)
135 Mt. Read Blvd. Phone: (716)436-5550
Rochester, NY 14611 Ginny Stover, Libn.
Staff: 1. **Subjects:** Mixing technology; chemical and mechanical engineering; waste and water treatment; product, plant, and machine design; marketing; sales. **Holdings:** 950 books; bound periodical volumes, 1940 to present; 55 VF drawers of R&D reports; 30 VF drawers of articles; 5 VF drawers of patents; 100 theses. **Subscriptions:** 40 journals and other serials. **Services:** Interlibrary loan; library not open to the public. **Computerized Information Services:** OCLC, DIALOG Information Services. **Remarks:** FAX: (716)235-8750. **Formerly:** Mixing Equipment Company, Inc. - Mixco R&D Library.

★9160★
Lightning Technologies, Inc. - Library (Sci-Engr)
10 Downing Pkwy.
Pittsfield, MA 01201 Phone: (413)499-2135
Subjects: Lightning - effects, protection design for aircraft and ground-based facilities, systems, and structures. **Holdings:** 500 reports and papers.

★9161★
Lignotech (U.S.) Inc. - Research Library (Sci-Engr)
100 Hwy. 51, S. Phone: (715)359-6544
Rothschild, WI 54474-1198 Tina Nickel, R & D Serv.Ck.
Founded: 1949. **Subjects:** Lignins. **Holdings:** 2100 volumes; 850 bound periodical volumes. **Subscriptions:** 70 journals and other serials. **Services:** Library open to the public with permission. **Remarks:** FAX: (715)355-3648. **Formerly:** Daishowa Chemicals Inc.

Ligue de Securite du Quebec
See: **Quebec Safety League** (13618)

Abraham M. Lilienfeld Memorial Library
See: **Johns Hopkins University - School of Hygiene and Public Health** (8428)

Joseph L. Lilienthal Library
See: **Johns Hopkins University - School of Medicine** (8431)

Lillick & McHose
See: **Pillsbury Madison & Sutro** (13052)

Miguel Lillo Foundation
See: **Fundacion Miguel Lillo - Centro de Informacion Geo-Biologica, NOA** (6215)

★9162★
Eli Lilly and Company - Business/Law Library (Bus-Fin, Law)
Lilly Corporate Center Phone: (317)276-3241
Indianapolis, IN 46285 Delores E. Wright-Wood, Libn.
Founded: 1950. **Staff:** Prof 2; Other 5. **Subjects:** Management, marketing, law, finance, advertising, engineering. **Holdings:** 10,000 books; 65 VF drawers of pamphlets and clippings; annual reports. **Subscriptions:** 900 journals and other serials. **Services:** Interlibrary loan; copying; library open to the public with restrictions. **Automated Operations:** Computerized cataloging and circulation. **Computerized Information Services:** DIALOG Information Services, OCLC, Dow Jones News/Retrieval, PFDS Online, WESTLAW, NEXIS, LEXIS, DataTimes, Nihon Keizai Shimbun, Inc. (NIKKEI). **Networks/Consortia:** Member of INCOLSA, Central Indiana Area Library Services Authority (CIALSA). **Special Catalogs:** Business information abstract file (card). **Remarks:** FAX: (317)276-9607. **Staff:** Magdaline Engle.

★9163★
Eli Lilly and Company - Greenfield Laboratories - Library Agricultural Service (Agri)
Box 708 Phone: (317)277-4000
Greenfield, IN 46140 Marta White, Sr.Libn.
Founded: 1957. **Staff:** Prof 2; Other 3. **Subjects:** Plant science, animal nutrition, veterinary medicine, toxicology, chemistry. **Holdings:** 5500 books; 6300 bound periodical volumes. **Subscriptions:** 650 journals and other serials. **Services:** Interlibrary loan; library open to the public by appointment. **Computerized Information Services:** DIALOG Information Services, PFDS Online, BRS Information Technologies. **Networks/Consortia:** Member of INCOLSA.

★9164★
Eli Lilly and Company - Lilly Archives (Bus-Fin)
Lilly Corporate Center Phone: (317)261-2173
Indianapolis, IN 46285 Anita Martin, Archv.
Founded: 1956. **Staff:** Prof 1. **Subjects:** Lilly family; Eli Lilly and Company - company administration, engineering, finance, industrial relations, marketing, production, research, foreign operations, subsidiary companies. **Special Collections:** Company publications (indexed). **Holdings:** 250 volumes; 40,000 pictures; 15,000 35mm slides; 300 reels of 16mm movies. **Services:** Archives not open to the public.

★9165★
Eli Lilly and Company - Scientific Library (Sci-Engr, Med)
Lilly Corporate Center Phone: (317)276-1017
Indianapolis, IN 46285 Lee Ann Bertram, Info.Sci.
Founded: 1890. **Staff:** 8. **Subjects:** Chemistry, medicine, biological sciences, pharmacy. **Special Collections:** Drug product compendia and encyclopedias (foreign and domestic); worldwide Pharmacopoeias; history of pharmacy. **Holdings:** 35,000 volumes; 1.7 million drug product information cards. **Subscriptions:** 1600 journals and other serials. **Services:** Interlibrary loan; copying; translation arrangements; SDI; library open to the public with advance approval. **Automated Operations:** Computerized cataloging and serials. **Computerized Information Services:** InterNet (electronic mail service). **Networks/Consortia:** Member of INCOLSA. **Publications:** Scientific Library Bulletin, semiweekly - for internal distribution only. **Special Catalogs:** Lilly Serial Periodical Holdings (loose-leaf); drug product information (card); bound volumes of publications from research and scientific divisions of Eli Lilly and Company. **Remarks:** FAX: (317)276-4127. Electronic mail address(es): BERTRAM-LEE-ANN@LILLY.COM (InterNet). Maintains a branch library, Bldg. 88 Library, whose holdings are included here.

Lilly Library
See: **Indiana University** (7794)

★9166★
(Lilongwe) American Cultural Center - USIS Library (Educ)
Old Mutual Bldg.
Robert Mugabe Crescent
City Ctr. 3
Post Box 30373
Lilongwe, Malawi
Remarks: Maintained or supported by the U.S. Information Agency. Focus is on materials that will assist peoples outside the United States to learn about the United States, its people, history, culture, political processes, and social milieux.

LILRC
See: **Long Island Library Resources Council, Inc.** (9292)

★9167★
Lima Memorial Hospital - Health Sciences Library (Med)
Linden & Mobel Sts. Phone: (419)228-3335
Lima, OH 45804 Michelle M. Pohlman, Hea.Sci.Libn.
Founded: 1972. **Staff:** Prof 1. **Subjects:** Medicine, nursing, pharmacology, hospital administration. **Holdings:** 1400 books; 682 bound periodical volumes; 1 drawer of clippings, pamphlets, documents. **Subscriptions:** 50 journals and other serials. **Services:** Interlibrary loan; copying; library open to the public with restrictions. **Computerized Information Services:** MEDLARS. **Remarks:** FAX: (419)220-5061.

Oliveira Lima Library
See: **Catholic University of America** (3161)

★9168★
Lima State Hospital - Oakwood Forensic Center (Soc Sci)
3200 N. West St. Phone: (419)225-8052
Lima, OH 45801 Mary Bice, Libn.
Founded: 1961. **Staff:** Prof 1; Other 2. **Subjects:** Philosophy and psychology, religion, social service, science, psychiatry. **Holdings:** 14,000 books; 78 bound periodical volumes; 2500 tapes. **Subscriptions:** 32 journals and other serials; 14 newspapers. **Services:** Interlibrary loan; copying; center open to the public with restrictions. **Computerized Information Services:** OCLC. **Networks/Consortia:** Member of Western Ohio Regional Library Development System (WORLDS). **Publications:** Habilitator; Bridgebuilder. **Special Catalogs:** Catalog of cassette tapes.

★9169★
(Lima) USIS Outreach/Reference Service (Educ)
Jiron Washington 1592
Lima 1, Peru
Remarks: Maintained or supported by the U.S. Information Agency. Focus is on materials that will assist peoples outside the United States to learn about the United States, its people, history, culture, political processes, and social milieux.

★9170★
Limestone County Archives (Hist)
310 W. Washington St. Phone: (205)233-6404
Athens, AL 35611 Philip W. Reyer, Archv.
Founded: 1980. **Staff:** 1.5. **Subjects:** Limestone County. **Special Collections:** Law Library (450 volumes); Robert Walker Collection; Malvania Moore Collection; Limestone County Historical Society Collection; church records; photograph collection (2000 prints); Robert Donnell Collection; Alabama collection (90 volumes); annuals; cemeteries; Athens College Annuals, 1908-1980; Limestone Authors collection (23 volumes); Board of Education Records; census collection (26 rolls); Circuit Clerk Records; County Commission Records; Maps and blueprints; Family Histories collection (60 volumes); Probate Court Records; Board of Registrars; Tax Assessment Sources (75 volumes). **Holdings:** 200 books; 50 bound periodical volumes; 200 reels of microfilm; 1000 manuscripts; tax records; documents. **Subscriptions:** 5 journals and other serials. **Services:** Copying; archives open to the public. **Computerized Information Services:** Internal database. **Staff:** Susan Bzdell, Res.

Abraham Lincoln Birthplace National Historic Site
See: **U.S. Natl. Park Service** (17661)

Abraham Lincoln Collection
See: **Boston University - Department of Special Collections** (2008)

Abraham Lincoln Museum
See: **Lincoln Memorial University - Abraham Lincoln Museum** (9185)

Lincoln Boyhood National Memorial
See: **U.S. Natl. Park Service** (17744)

★9171★
Lincoln Cathedral - Library (Rel-Phil, Rare Book)
Lincoln LN2 1PZ, England Phone: 522 544544
Dr. Nicholas Bennett, Cathedral Libn.
Founded: 1092. **Staff:** Prof 1. **Subjects:** Lincoln Cathedral, ecclesiastical history, liturgy. **Special Collections:** Early printed books. **Holdings:** 12,000 books; 400 bound periodical volumes; 300 manuscripts. **Subscriptions:** 6 journals and other serials. **Services:** Library open to the public with letter of recommendation. **Special Catalogs:** Catalogue of the Wren Library of Lincoln Cathedral, 1982; Catalogue of the Manuscripts of Lincoln Cathedral Chapter Library, 1989.

★9172★
Lincoln Center - (Buenos Aires) USIS Library (Educ)
Florida 935
1005 Buenos Aires, Argentina
Remarks: Maintained or supported by the U.S. Information Agency. Focus is on materials that will assist peoples outside the United States to learn about the United States, its people, history, culture, political processes, and social milieux.

★9173★
Lincoln Christian College & Seminary - Jessie C. Eury Library (Rel-Phil)
100 Campus View Dr. Phone: (217)732-3168
Lincoln, IL 62656 Thomas M. Tanner, Lib.Dir.
Founded: 1944. **Staff:** Prof 2; Other 3. **Subjects:** Biblical studies, Restoration movement, religion, philosophy, ministry. **Special Collections:** Enos E. Dowling Rare Book Room (2000 hymnbooks); Chi Lambda Cult/Occult Research Center. **Holdings:** 77,800 books; 5800 bound periodical volumes; 5200 volumes in microform; 23,600 AV programs. **Subscriptions:** 455 journals and other serials; 9 newspapers. **Services:** Interlibrary loan; copying; library open to the public. **Automated Operations:** Computerized cataloging. **Computerized Information Services:** DIALOG Information Services. **Networks/Consortia:** Member of Sangamon Valley Academic Library Consortium (SVALC), Rolling Prairie Library System (RPLS). **Staff:** Nancy J. Olson, Asst.Libn.; Ann Spellman, Media Ctr.Libn.; Phyllis Bussman, ILL.

Lincoln Collection
See: **Bridgewater State College** (2122)

★9174★
Lincoln County Board of Education - Educational Resource Library (Educ)
191 Carlton St. Phone: (416)641-1550
St. Catharines, ON, Canada L2R 1S1 Dennis Munn, Cons.Info. & Media Serv.
Founded: 1963. **Staff:** Prof 1. **Subjects:** Education - general, special. **Holdings:** 4000 books. **Subscriptions:** 100 journals and other serials. **Services:** Interlibrary loan; copying. **Automated Operations:** Computerized cataloging and circulation. **Computerized Information Services:** Info Globe, BRS Information Technologies; CD-ROMs (ERIC, Grolier, Bibliophile, Bookshelf, McGraw-Hill Science & Tech, Readers Guide, Books in Print, SPORT Discus, Toronto Sun, Library of the Future). Performs searches on fee basis. Contact Person: Corrine McKernan, Lib.Techn., ext. 2305. **Publications:** Newsletter, irregular - to schools. **Remarks:** FAX: (416)685-8511.

★9175★
Lincoln County Historical Society - Library (Hist)
545 S.W. 9th Phone: (503)265-7509
Newport, OR 97365 Marilen Pool, Dir./Cur.
Founded: 1949. **Staff:** Prof 2. **Subjects:** Lincoln County and Oregon history, local Indian reference material. **Special Collections:** Crawford Collection on Siletz Tribal legislation. **Holdings:** 165 volumes. **Services:** Copying; library open to the public for reference use only. **Publications:** List of publications - available on request.

★9176★
Lincoln County Law Library (Law)
Lincoln County Courthouse
High St.
Wiscasset, ME 04578 Phone: (207)882-7517
Subjects: Law. **Holdings:** 10,200 volumes. **Services:** Library open to the public with permission.

★9177★
Lincoln Cultural Center - USIS Library (Educ)
181, Jalan Ampang
P.O. Box 35
Kuala Lumpur 01-02, Malaysia
Remarks:. Maintained or supported by the U.S. Information Agency. Focus is on materials that will assist peoples outside the United States to learn about the United States, its people, history, culture, political processes, and social milieux.

★9178★
Lincoln General Hospital - Hospital Library (Med)
2300 S. 16th St. Phone: (402)473-5637
Lincoln, NE 68502 Lucille Rosenberg, Hosp.Libn.
Founded: 1976. **Staff:** Prof 1. **Subjects:** Medicine, oncology, orthopedics, psychiatry, nursing, trauma, allied health sciences and professions. **Special Collections:** Winett Orr orthopedic books. **Holdings:** 1000 books; 90 periodical volumes. **Subscriptions:** 100 journals and other serials. **Services:** Interlibrary loan; copying; library open to the public with restrictions. **Computerized Information Services:** MEDLINE. **Networks/Consortia:** Member of Lincoln Health Science Library Group (LHSLG). **Special Catalogs:** Union List of Serials, 4th edition (ring bound book); Nebraska Union List of Serials (microfiche). **Special Indexes:** National Library of Medicine Serials, Serials Indexed for Online Users (microfiche). **Remarks:** FAX: (402)473-5707. **Staff:** Carmen Jirovec.

★9179★
John C. Lincoln Hospital - Library (Med)
205 E. Dunlap St. Phone: (602)870-6328
Phoenix, AZ 85020 Edith M. Hart, Med.Libn.
Staff: Prof 1; Other 1. **Subjects:** Medicine, nursing. **Special Collections:** Sports medicine collection. **Holdings:** 1000 books. **Subscriptions:** 125 journals and other serials. **Services:** Interlibrary loan; copying; SDI; library open to the public. **Computerized Information Services:** MEDLINE, DIALOG Information Services. **Special Indexes:** Patient Education Index (in progress). **Remarks:** FAX: (602)997-9325.

Joseph C. Lincoln Memorial Library
See: **National Soaring Museum** (11288)

★9180★
Lincoln Journal-Star - Library (Publ)
926 P St.
Box 81709 Phone: (402)473-7298
Lincoln, NE 68501 Patricia R. Loos, Hd.Libn.
Founded: 1951. **Staff:** Prof 3; Other 3. **Subjects:** Newspaper reference topics. **Special Collections:** Newspaper clippings of Starkweather-Fugate murder spree and follow-up, 1957-1973 (on microfilm). **Holdings:** 2500 books; 1430 reels of microfilm of Journal-Star newspapers and other subjects; 500,000 pictures; clipping files on microfiche. **Subscriptions:** 25 journals and other serials; 20 newspapers. **Services:** Copying; library open to the public on fee basis. **Automated Operations:** Computerized cataloging and acquisitions. **Remarks:** FAX: (402)473-7291. **Staff:** Joanne Fettinger, Asst.Libn.

Lincoln Laboratory Library and Information Services
See: **Massachusetts Institute of Technology** (9806)

★9181★
Lincoln Library - (Quito) USIS Library (Educ)
American Embassy
Ave. Patria
No. 120 y 12 de Octubre
P.O. Box 538 Phone: 2 549570
Quito, Ecuador Theresa S.P. Molineros, Hd.Libn.
Founded: 1975. **Staff:** 4. **Subjects:** Economics, business administration, political science, American studies, science and technology. **Holdings:** 6000 books; 20,000 microfiche; 300 AV items. **Subscriptions:** 149 journals and other serials; 5 newspapers. **Services:** Interlibrary loan; copying; SDI; library open to the public. **Computerized Information Services:** CD-ROMs; internal databases. **Publications:** Annotated bibliographies. **Remarks:** FAX: 2 569072. Maintained or supported by the U.S. Information Agency. Focus is on materials that will assist peoples outside the United States to learn about the United States, its people, history, culture, political processes, and social milieux. **Staff:** Jorge O. Sosa, Outreach Libn.

★9182★
Lincoln Library - Sangamon Valley Collection (Hist)
326 S. 7th St. Phone: (217)753-4910
Springfield, IL 62701 Edward J. Russo, Hd.
Founded: 1972. **Staff:** Prof 2; Other 2. **Subjects:** Local history, genealogy, current area information. **Special Collections:** Vachel Lindsay Collection (4 VF drawers); city documents depository. **Holdings:** 8000 books; 200 bound periodical volumes; 30,000 local photographs. **Subscriptions:** 159 journals and other serials. **Services:** Interlibrary loan; copying; collection open to the public. **Publications:** Bulletin, monthly. **Special Indexes:** Local obituary index; current index to Illinois State Journal-Register and Illinois Times. **Staff:** Karen Graff; Linda Garvert; Millicent Harper.

★9183★
Lincoln Medical Center - Health Sciences Library (Med)
234 E. 149th St. Phone: (212)579-5745
Bronx, NY 10451 Miss Milagros M. Paredes, Med.Libn.
Staff: Prof 1; Other 3. **Subjects:** Medicine, surgery, pediatrics, obstetrics and gynecology, nursing. **Holdings:** 2265 books; 7677 bound periodical volumes. **Subscriptions:** 300 journals and other serials. **Services:** Interlibrary loan; library not open to the public.

Lincoln Memorial Library
See: **Veterans Home of California** (19819)

★9184★
Lincoln Memorial Shrine - Library (Hist)
125 W. Vine St. Phone: (714)798-7632
Redlands, CA 92373 Donald McCue, Archv.
Founded: 1932. **Staff:** Prof 2; Other 1. **Subjects:** Abraham Lincoln, Civil War. **Special Collections:** Rare pamphlet collection of Civil War and Lincoln (4000); Gideon Welles manuscript collection (120). **Holdings:** 4200 books; 800 unbound periodicals; 2100 manuscripts; 4000 pamphlets; 1100 photographs; 3000 clippings. **Subscriptions:** 12 journals and other serials. **Services:** Copying; library open to the public. **Automated Operations:** Computerized cataloging. **Publications:** Annual Lincoln Dinner speeches; Lincoln Memorial Association Newsletter, quarterly; postcards - all for sale; A Selective Bibliography of the Holdings of the Lincoln Memorial Shrine; keepsake publications. **Remarks:** FAX: (714)798-7566. Maintained by A.K. Smiley Public Library. **Staff:** Christie J. Hammond.

★9185★
Lincoln Memorial University - Abraham Lincoln Museum (Hist)
Hwy. 25 E. Phone: (615)869-3611
Harrogate, TN 37752 Tina Buis, Act.Dir.
Staff: Prof 1; Other 4. **Subjects:** Abraham Lincoln, Civil War, Cumberland Gap, Lincoln Memorial University. **Special Collections:** Presidential Signatures Collection. **Holdings:** 8500 books; 15,000 pamphlets; 20,000 clippings; 25,000 artifacts, archival and manuscript materials; Civil War States sheet music; Lincoln sheet music; manuscripts of Abraham Lincoln, Civil War, Cassius M. Clay, O.O. Howard; microfilm; scrapbooks. **Subscriptions:** 49 journals and other serials. **Services:** Copying; museum open to the public for reference use only by appointment. **Publications:** Lincoln Herald, quarterly - by subscription. **Remarks:** FAX: (615)869-6235.

Lincoln Museum
See: **Lincoln National Life Insurance Company** (9187)

★9186★
Lincoln National Corporation - Law Library (Law, Bus-Fin)
1300 S. Clinton St., 7th Fl.
Box 1110 Phone: (219)427-3870
Fort Wayne, IN 46801 Marcyle Voigt, Asst., Info.Serv.
Staff: Prof 1; Other 1. **Subjects:** Law, insurance. **Holdings:** 19,000 volumes. **Subscriptions:** 359 journals and other serials. **Services:** Interlibrary loan; copying; SDI; library open to in-house professionals for research use only. **Automated Operations:** Computerized cataloging, acquisitions, and serials. **Computerized Information Services:** NEXIS, LEXIS, Dow Jones News/Retrieval, DIALOG Information Services; internal database; MCI Mail, (electronic mail service). Performs searches on fee basis. **Networks/Consortia:** Member of Tri-ALSA, INCOLSA. **Remarks:** FAX: (219)455-5135.

★9187★
Lincoln National Life Insurance Company - Lincoln Museum - Library (Hist)
1300 S. Clinton St. Phone: (219)455-3031
Fort Wayne, IN 46801 Dr. Mark E. Neely, Jr., Dir.
Founded: 1928. **Staff:** Prof 3; Other 1. **Subjects:** Lincolniana; 19th century American history, biography, and politics; Civil War; slavery; reconstruction. **Special Collections:** Association books (books similar to those Lincoln read; 400); manuscripts; philatelic Lincolniana; metallic Lincolniana; pictorial Lincolniana (original paints, rare lithographs, engravings, original photographs, and prints). **Holdings:** 20,000 volumes; 10,000 pieces of Lincolniana; 9600 collateral books. **Subscriptions:** 36 journals and other serials. **Services:** Interlibrary loan (by special request); copying; library open to researchers and students. **Publications:** Lincoln Lore, monthly; R. Gerald McMurty Lecture, annual - available on request. **Remarks:** FAX: (219)455-6922. **Formerly:** Its Louis A. Warren Lincoln Library and Museum. **Staff:** Ruth E. Cook, Asst. to Dir.; Marilyn K. Tolbert, Proj.Spec.

★9188★
Lincoln Park Zoological Gardens - Library (Biol Sci)
2200 N. Cannon Dr. Phone: (312)294-4640
Chicago, IL 60614-3895 Joyce M. Shaw, Libn.
Founded: 1979. **Staff:** Prof 1; Other 2. **Subjects:** Zoology, animal behavior and care, wildlife conservation, management of captive wild animals, endangered species, zoos. **Special Collections:** Zoo & Aquarium Reference Collection (ZARC; information on 190 national and international zoos and aquariums); Zoo Poster Collection (from 70 zoos); zoo archives; Marlin Perkins Zoo Parade videotapes (200). **Holdings:** 2200 books; 200 bound periodical volumes; 450 newsletters, inventories; 77 organization files; studbooks. **Subscriptions:** 110 journals and other serials; 75 newsletters. **Services:** Interlibrary loan; copying; library open to the public by appointment. **Computerized Information Services:** OCLC, DIALOG Information Services. **Networks/Consortia:** Member of Chicago Library System, ILLINET, American Association of Zoological Parks & Aquariums, Consortium of Museum Libraries in the Chicago Area. **Publications:** Subject Bibliographies. **Remarks:** FAX: (312)935-2249.

★9189★
Lincoln University - Inman E. Page Library (Educ)
Jefferson City, MO 65101 Phone: (314)681-5512
Elizabeth A. Wilson, Dir.
Founded: 1866. **Staff:** Prof 6; Other 6. **Subjects:** Liberal arts; elementary and secondary education; nursing; corrections and law enforcement. **Special Collections:** Pro-slavery and antislavery tracts; pre- and post-Civil War period; black and ethnic collections (7000 books). **Holdings:** 134,169 books; 9000 bound periodical volumes; 74,670 government documents; 230 theses and dissertations; 30 VF drawers; 4 VF drawers of pictures; 91,945 titles in microform. **Subscriptions:** 705 journals and other serials; 53 newspapers. **Services:** Interlibrary loan; faxing; copying; SDI; library open to the public with restrictions. **Computerized Information Services:** BRS Information Technologies; ALANET (electronic mail service). Performs online searches on fee basis; performs CD-ROM searches at no charge. Contact Person: Oi-Chi Hui, Ref., 681-5512. **Networks/Consortia:** Member of Missouri Library Network Corp. (MLNC). **Publications:** Lincoln's Page, irregular; Bibliography of Books By and About Blacks, annual supplement; Monthly Checklist (selected); newsletter; students handbook; annual report; Library Manual. **Remarks:** FAX: (314)681-5511. Electronic mail address(es): ALA 2931 (ALANET). **Staff:** Connie May, Per./Govt.Doc.Libn.; Cynthia S. Cotner, Asst.Libn./Coord., Pub.Serv.; Sam Schnieders, Media Coord.; Tesuk Im, Asst.Libn./Coord., Tech.Serv.

★9190★
Lincoln University - Langston Hughes Memorial Library - Special Collections (Area-Ethnic)
Lincoln University, PA 19352-0999 Phone: (215)932-8300
Staff: Prof 1; Other 2. **Subjects:** Black studies - fine arts, history, civil rights, education; African studies - economics, history, political science, language, literature; antislavery. **Special Collections:** Personal library of Langston Hughes (3300 items); manuscripts of Pennsylvania Colonization Society and Young Men's Colonization Society (6 volumes); rare books (850); rare antislavery pamphlets (200); personal library of Dr. Therman B. O'Daniel (4000 items). **Holdings:** 18,350 books; 1060 bound periodical volumes; 772 reels of microfilm; 100 phonograph records; 250 historical pictures of black performers; 6000 unbound periodicals; 1595 microfiche; 1300 African Government documents; 2500 VF materials; 6000 archival materials and miscellanea. **Subscriptions:** 180 journals and other serials; 7 newspapers. **Services:** Interlibrary loan; copying; collections open to the public for reference use only. **Automated Operations:** Computerized cataloging and ILL. **Computerized Information Services:** OCLC. **Networks/Consortia:** Member of PALINET, Tri-State College Library Cooperative (TCLC). **Publications:** Selected bibliography on Malcolm X; bimonthly accessions lists - both free upon request. **Special Catalogs:** Catalog of the Special Negro and African Collection (2 volumes and supplement, 1970); Computer Output Microfilm Catalog, July 1970 - June 1977; A Survey of the Special Negro Collections; Reference Handbook of Special Collections - all for sale; mimeographed list of periodicals in the African collection; mimeographed reference handbook. **Remarks:** FAX: (215)932-8317. **Staff:** Emery Wimbish, Jr., Hd.Libn.

★9191★
Lincoln University - Law Library (Law)
2160 Lundy Ave. Phone: (408)434-0727
San Jose, CA 95131 Myrna Brookman
Staff: Prof 1; Other 1. **Subjects:** Law. **Holdings:** 18,000 books; 700 bound periodical volumes. **Subscriptions:** 20 journals and other serials. **Services:** Copying; library open to the public with restrictions.

★9192★
Erich Lindemann Mental Health Center - Library (Med)
Government Center
25 Staniford St. Phone: (617)727-7100
Boston, MA 02114 Vishakha Menta, Lib.Dir.
Staff: Prof 1. **Subjects:** Psychology, psychiatry, community mental health, mental retardation, drug rehabilitation. **Special Collections:** Documents and archives of Massachusetts Department of Mental Health (1000 items). **Holdings:** 3000 books; 300 bound periodical volumes; 500 documents; 16 VF drawers of pamphlets. **Subscriptions:** 20 journals and other serials. **Services:** Interlibrary loan; copying; library open to the public for reference use only. **Networks/Consortia:** Member of Massachusetts Health Sciences Libraries Network (MaHSLiN), Boston Library Consortium (BLC). **Remarks:** Maintained by Massachusetts State Department of Mental Health.

Lindgren Library
See: **Massachusetts Institute of Technology** (9807)

Luke Lindoe Library
See: **Alberta College of Art** (257)

Lindsay Law Library
See: **Widener University** (20418)

★9193★
Lindsay Law Library (Law)
Wolfgram Memorial Library
Widener University
14th St.
Chester, PA 19013-5792 Phone: (215)499-4031
Staff: Prof 1. **Subjects:** Law. **Holdings:** 9000 volumes. **Subscriptions:** 19 journals and other serials. **Services:** Copying; library open to the public.

Lineberger Memorial Library
See: **Lutheran Theological Southern Seminary** (9467)

★9194★
Linen Hall Library (Area-Ethnic, Hist)
17 Donegall Sq., N. Phone: 232 321707
Belfast BT1 5GD, Northern Ireland John Gray, Dp.Libn.
Founded: 1788. **Staff:** Prof 3; Other 10. **Subjects:** Irish and British history, biography, travel, topography. **Special Collections:** Northern Ireland Political Literature Collection; Belfast Printed Books Collection. **Holdings:** 200,000 books; 1000 microforms; 500 manuscripts. **Services:** Interlibrary loan; copying; library open to the public. **Remarks:** FAX: 232 438586.

Leslie R. Lingeman Memorial Medical Library
See: **Blount Memorial Hospital** (1905)

★9195★
Link Flight Simulation Corp. - Technical Library (Comp Sci)
1077 E. Arques Ave. Phone: (408)720-5656
Sunnyvale, CA 94088-3484 Toula New, Lib.Hd.
Staff: Prof 1; Other 1. **Subjects:** Computer science, electrical engineering, computer graphics, simulation, Link trainers, flight simulation, flight trainers, radar, electronics. **Holdings:** 1600 volumes; 500 technical reports. **Subscriptions:** 90 journals and other serials. **Services:** Interlibrary loan; library not open to the public. **Publications:** Information from the Technical Library, monthly - for internal distribution only. **Remarks:** Alternate telephone number(s): 720-5880. FAX: (408)733-9484.

★9196★
Linn County Heritage Society - Linn County Genealogical Research Center (Hist)
101 8th Ave., S.E. Phone: (319)362-1501
Cedar Rapids, IA 52406 Marilyn Walsh, Pres.
Founded: 1965. **Subjects:** Linn County and Iowa genealogy. **Special Collections:** Linn County Cemetery and Court House records. **Holdings:** 3000 books; 208 reels of microfilm of marriage, birth and death records, probates, land deeds for Linn County; some microfilm for Benton County family history; complete 1790 Federal Census Index; 1925 Linn County census. **Subscriptions:** 20 journals and other serials. **Services:** Copying; library open to the public. **Publications:** Heritage Hunter, quarterly. **Formerly:** Iowa Genealogical Society - Linn County Genealogy Research Center.

★9197★
Linn County Historical Society - Library (Hist)
Box 137 Phone: (913)352-8739
Pleasanton, KS 66075 Ola May Earnest, Pres.
Founded: 1968. **Staff:** 3. **Subjects:** Local history and genealogy, county history. **Special Collections:** Linn County photographs. **Holdings:** 600 books; 30 manuscripts; 8 drawers; newspapers and census on microfilm. **Subscriptions:** 35 journals and other serials. **Services:** Copying; genealogical research; library open to the public for reference use only. **Publications:** Linn County Historical News; Kin In Linn, both quarterly; list of additional publications - available upon request.

★9198★
Linn County Law Library (Law)
Linn County Court House Phone: (319)398-3449
Cedar Rapids, IA 52401 Betty Dye, Law Libn.
Founded: 1907. **Staff:** 1. **Subjects:** Law. **Holdings:** 15,000 volumes. **Subscriptions:** 3 journals and other serials. **Services:** Copying; library open to the public for reference use only. **Remarks:** Operates under the auspices of the Linn County Board of Supervisors.

Linn-Henley Library for Southern Historical Research
See: **Birmingham Public and Jefferson County Free Library - Linn-Henley Library for Southern Historical Research - Department of Archives and Manuscripts** (1856)

Otto F. Linn Library
See: **Warner-Pacific College** (19972)

★9199★
Linnean Society of London - Library (Biol Sci)
Burlington House
Piccadilly Phone: 71 4344479
London W1V 0LQ, England Gina Douglas, Libn./Archv.
Founded: 1788. **Staff:** 1. **Subjects:** Natural history, taxonomy, flora, fauna, evolutionary theory, history of biology. **Special Collections:** Linnean Collections (books, manuscripts, and specimens belonging to C. von Linne); manuscript collections. **Holdings:** 25,000 books; 75,000 bound periodical volumes; 1000 manuscripts. **Subscriptions:** 10 journals and other serials. **Services:** Library open to the public by appointment. **Special Catalogs:** Catalogue of Manuscripts in the Library of the Linnean Society of London (4 volumes). **Remarks:** FAX: (71)2879364.

★9200★
Lintas Campbell-Ewald Company - Reference Center (Bus-Fin)
30400 Van Dyke Phone: (313)574-3400
Warren, MI 48093 Susan B. Stepek, Sr. V.P. & Mgr.
Founded: 1925. **Staff:** Prof 6; Other 4. **Subjects:** Advertising, marketing, automotive industry, general business and reference. **Special Collections:** Automobilia; descriptive state file; art library; clips of advertisements. **Holdings:** 3200 books; 3100 bound periodical volumes; 2600 subject folders; 1200 reports, documents, bulletins, maps, client and company archives, government documents, services. **Subscriptions:** 500 regular journals and other serials; 1800 sample journals and other serials. **Services:** Center open to the public on fee basis. **Computerized Information Services:** DIALOG Information Services, NEXIS, Dow Jones News/Retrieval. **Publications:** Social Change Briefs, bimonthly; Monthly Headline Services.

★9201★
Lions Gate Hospital - Dr. H. Carson Graham Memorial Library (Med)
231 E. 15th St. Phone: (604)988-3131
North Vancouver, BC, Canada V7L 2L7 Sharon M. Lyons, Libn.
Founded: 1961. **Staff:** 2. **Subjects:** Medicine. **Holdings:** 2500 books. **Subscriptions:** 120 journals and other serials. **Services:** Interlibrary loan; library not open to the public.

★9202★
Lipkin, Marshall, Bohorad & Thornbeurg - Library
One Norwegian Plaza
P.O. Drawer K Phone: (717)622-1811
Pottsville, PA 17901 Rose Lipsett, Lib.Dir.
Remarks: FAX: (717)622-4850. No further information was supplied by respondent.

★9203★
Liposome Company - Research Library (Biol Sci)
Princeton Forrestal Ctr.
1 Research Way
Princeton, NJ 08540 Phone: (609)452-7060
Founded: 1982. **Staff:** 1. **Subjects:** Biochemistry, biology, liposomes, medicine. **Holdings:** 100 books; 20 reports. **Subscriptions:** 100 journals and other serials; 2 newspapers. **Services:** Library not open to the public. **Remarks:** FAX: (609)520-8920.

Lippincott Library
See: **University of Pennsylvania** (19186)

Lawrence Lipton Archives
See: **University of Southern California - Library - Department of Special Collections - American Literature Collection** (19338)

★9204★
Thomas J. Lipton, Co. - Library/Information Center (Food-Bev)
800 Sylvan Ave. Phone: (201)894-7568
Englewood Cliffs, NJ 07632 Teris W. Binder, Mgr.
Founded: 1942. **Staff:** Prof 2; Other 1. **Subjects:** Tea, food technology. **Holdings:** 9000 books; 3500 bound periodical volumes; U.S. chemical patents, 1970 to present, on microfilm. **Subscriptions:** 250 journals and other serials. **Services:** Interlibrary loan; library not open to the public. **Computerized Information Services:** DIALOG Information Services, NEXIS, STN International, MEDLINE; Database of Tea Technology (internal database). **Networks/Consortia:** Member of Bergen Passaic Regional Library Cooperative, New Jersey Library Network. **Publications:** Bulletin, monthly. **Remarks:** FAX: (201)871-8149. **Staff:** Diane Y. Cassatly, Tech.Info.Spec.

★9205★
Liquid Air Engineering Corporation - E & C Library (Sci-Engr)
1155 Sherbrooke St., W. Phone: (514)842-5431
Montreal, PQ, Canada H3A 1H8 Collette Tremblay, Libn.
Founded: 1946. **Staff:** 1. **Subjects:** Chemical engineering, welding, metallurgy, cryogenics, industrial gases. **Holdings:** 1700 books; 200 bound periodical volumes; 10 cases of patents; 1 drawer of archival materials. **Subscriptions:** 37 journals and other serials. **Services:** Interlibrary loan; library not open to the public.

Sidney Liswood Library
See: **Mount Sinai Hospital** (10815)

Franz Liszt Collection
See: **Boston University - Music Library** (2015)

★9206★
Litchfield Historical Society - Ingraham Library (Hist)
Box 385 Phone: (203)567-4501
Litchfield, CT 06759 Catherine Keene, Dir.
Founded: 1856. **Staff:** Prof 1; Other 2. **Subjects:** Local history, genealogy, local authors, early American law. **Special Collections:** Manuscript collections; graphic archives. **Holdings:** 12,000 volumes; 40,000 manuscripts; 300 account books; 20 cartons of almanacs; 70 volumes of Ransom autograph materials; 40 cartons of pamphlets. **Subscriptions:** 15 journals and other serials. **Services:** Copying; genealogical research; library open to the public. **Special Catalogs:** Manuscript card catalog. **Remarks:** Alternate telephone number(s): 567-4502. FAX: (203)567-3565.

★9207★
Literacy Council of Alaska - Library (Educ)
823 3rd Ave. Phone: (907)456-6212
Fairbanks, AK 99701 Tom Murphy, Dir.
Staff: Prof 3; Other 1. **Subjects:** Adult beginning reading, English as a second language, GED preparation. **Holdings:** 1000 books. **Subscriptions:** 3 newspapers. **Services:** Library open to Literacy Council tutors and students only.

★9208★
Literacy Volunteers of America - Library (Educ)
5795 Widewaters Pkwy. Phone: (315)445-8000
Syracuse, NY 13214 Frances J. Farnsworth, Libn.
Founded: 1962. **Staff:** 1. **Subjects:** Teaching reading to adults, teaching English as a second language, program management. **Special Collections:** Humanistic reading for grades 1-5 (300 titles); reference materials for teaching basic reading and English as a second language (400 titles). **Holdings:** 2000 books; clippings; picture file. **Subscriptions:** 15 journals and other serials. **Services:** Copying; library open to the public with restrictions. **Publications:** The Reader (newsletter), quarterly. **Remarks:** FAX: (315)445-8006.

★9209★
Literary and Historical Society of Quebec - Library (Hist)
44 St. Stanislas St. Phone: (418)694-9147
Quebec, PQ, Canada G1R 4H3 Cynthia Dooley, Libn.
Staff: Prof 1; Other 2. **Subjects:** Quebec history. **Holdings:** 25,000 books. **Services:** Library open to the public with restrictions.

Literary History of the United States Archives
See: **University of Pennsylvania - Special Collections** (19197)

Lithium Corporation of America, Inc.
See: **FMC Corporation** (5938)

Lithium Information Center
See: **University of Wisconsin--Madison - Department of Psychiatry** (19593)

★9210★
Lithuanian Catholic Library (Area-Ethnic)
351 Highland Blvd. Phone: (718)647-2434
Brooklyn, NY 11207 Rev. Casimir Pugevicius, Eec.Dir.
Founded: 1979. **Staff:** Prof 1. **Subjects:** Lithuania - current events. **Holdings:** 500 bound volumes. **Subscriptions:** 50 journals and other serials. **Services:** Library open to the public with restrictions. **Computerized Information Services:** Internal database. Performs searches on fee basis. **Remarks:** FAX: (718)827-6696. Telex: 5101013171. **Formerly:** Lithuanian Information Center.

Lithuanian Marian Fathers Library
See: **Lithuanian Research and Studies Center, Inc. - Libraries** (9211)

Lithuanian Museum of Medicine
See: **Lithuanian Research and Studies Center, Inc. - Libraries** (9211)

★9211★
Lithuanian Research and Studies Center, Inc. - Libraries (Area-Ethnic)
5620 S. Claremont Ave. Phone: (312)434-4545
Chicago, IL 60636 Dr. Robert A. Vitas, V.P./Dir., Libs.
Founded: 1982. **Staff:** Prof 6; Other 3. **Subjects:** Literature, history, language, music, art, geography. **Special Collections:** Zilevicius-Kreivenas Lithuanian Music Archive (15,000 items); World Lithuanian Archives; Lithuanian Historical Society; Lithuanian Institute of Education; Lithuanian Youth Association; Casimer Baltramaitis Collection; Professor Juozas Brazaitis Collection; Lithuanian Journalists Association; Lithuanian Government Gazette (Vyriausybes Zinios); Sruoga Collection; Antanas

Skema Collection; Voice of America; Radio Liberty; Jonas Dainauskas History Library; Lithuanian Museum of Medicine; Lithuanian Displaced Persons (Germany and Austria) Collection; Dauzvardis Consular Collection; Lithuanian Writers Association; Institute of Lithuanian Studies; Lithuanian Relief Fund of America; Lithuanian World Community; Lithuanian American Community; Pakstas & Krupavicius Collections; Stasys Barzdukas Collection; Lithuanian Educational Council; Lithuanian youth orgazizations (Scouts, Ateitis); General Stasys Dirmantas Collection; Alicija Rugyte Collection; Lithuanian Research and Studies Center Museum; Lithuanian Marian Fathers Library. **Holdings:** 100,000 books; 1500 periodical titles; 1000 manuscripts; 1200 government documents; 2000 scores; 100 maps; 1000 sound recordings; 200 videotapes; 1000 archival and vertical file categories; 20 flags; 90 AV programs; 2000 letters; 200 posters; 200 archive boxes. **Subscriptions:** 50 journals and other serials; 20 newspapers. **Services:** Copying; libraries open to the public. **Automated Operations:** Computerized cataloging. **Publications:** User's Manual, annual; subject catalog, annual. **Remarks:** FAX: (312)434-9363. .**Staff:** Kazys Skaisgirys, Dir., Mus.; Ceslovas Grincevicius, Dir., Archv.; Rimantas Zemaitaitis, Dir., Cart.; Dr. John A. Rackauskas, Pres.; Nijole Mackevicius, Dir., Musms.; Dr. Milda Budrys, Dir., Med.Musm.; Arunas Zailskas, Dir.Res.Serv.; Lindas Kairys, Dir.Per.; Dalia Peciulis, Dir.Cat.

★9212★
Lithuanian Research and Studies Center, Inc. - Lithuanian World Archives, Inc. (Area-Ethnic)
5620 S. Claremont Ave. Phone: (312)434-4545
Chicago, IL 60636 Ceslovas V. Grincevicius, Dir.
Founded: 1946. **Staff:** Prof 2; Other 4. **Subjects:** Lithuania. **Special Collections:** Krupavicius Collection; Pakstas Collection; Dauzvardis Consular Archive; official document repository of the Lithuanian World Community, Inc. **Holdings:** 60,000 books; 1100 periodical titles; 150 boxes of archives; manuscripts; documents; flags; badges; buttons; products; posters; audiotapes; maps; photographs; uniforms; medals. **Subscriptions:** 50 journals and other serials; 12 newspapers. **Services:** Copying; archives open to the public. **Automated Operations:** Computerized cataloging. **Computerized Information Services:** Internal database. **Publications:** Book of Deported Lithuanians. **Remarks:** FAX: (312)434-9363. **Staff:** Lindas Kairys, Dir.Per.

Lithuanian World Archives, Inc.
See: **Lithuanian Research and Studies Center, Inc. - Lithuanian World Archives, Inc.** (9212)

★9213★
Litman, Litman, Harris, Brown & Watzman - Library (Law)
3600 One Oxford Center Phone: (412)456-2000
Pittsburgh, PA 15219 Jean Weir, Leg.Asst.
Subjects: Law. **Remarks:** No further information was supplied by respondent.

Littauer Library
See: **Harvard University** (6981)

★9214★
Arthur D. Little, Inc. - Cambridge Information Center (Bus-Fin, Sci-Engr)
15 Acorn Park Phone: (617)864-5770
Cambridge, MA 02140-2390 Ann J. Wolpert, Hd.Libn.
Founded: 1886. **Staff:** Prof 13; Other 9. **Subjects:** Engineering, chemistry, energy, industry, safety, information, science, business, management, food environment. **Special Collections:** Annual reports and 10Ks (domestic and foreign); Vendor Catalogs; Management Education Institute Learning Resources; Life Sciences Collection. **Holdings:** 6000 books; 7000 company annual reports. **Subscriptions:** 2100 journals and other serials. **Services:** Interlibrary loan; center not open to the public. **Automated Operations:** Computerized public access catalog, ILL, and cataloging. **Computerized Information Services:** 30 database vendor systems; CD-ROMs; SprintMail (electronic mail service). **Networks/Consortia:** Member of NELINET, Inc. **Publications:** Union list of serials; various brochures. **Remarks:** FAX: (617)864-6041; (617)661-8024. Electronic mail address(es): ADLITTLE.INFOCTR (SprintMail). Telex: 921436. Contains the holdings of the former Arthur D. Little, Inc. - Life Sciences Library. **Staff:** Cynthia Hibberd, Mgr., Info.Sys.; Jinny Nathans, Mgr., Tech.Serv.; Beverly Colby, Sr.Info.Spec./Sci.-Tech.; Judy Uhrig, Sr.Info.Spec./Bus.

★9215★
Arthur D. Little, Inc. - Life Sciences Library
25 Acorn Park
Cambridge, MA 02140
Defunct. Holdings absorbed by Arthur D. Little, Inc. - Cambridge Information Center.

★9216★
Arthur D. Little, Inc. - Research Library (Sci-Engr)
25 Acorn Park Phone: (617)864-5770
Cambridge, MA 02140-2390 Ann Wilpert
Founded: 1886. **Staff:** Prof 2; Other 3. **Subjects:** Chemistry, physics, electrical and mechanical engineering, electronics, food and agriculture, science and technology, research administration. **Holdings:** 31,000 books; 3000 bound periodical volumes; 3 file cabinets of microfiche reports. **Subscriptions:** 1275 journals and other serials. **Services:** Interlibrary loan; copying; SDI; library open to the public by appointment. **Automated Operations:** Computerized cataloging and serials. **Computerized Information Services:** DIALOG Information Services, BRS Information Technologies, NLM, Chemical Information Systems, Inc. (CIS), PFDS Online, OCLC, NASA/RECON, STN International, LEXIS, NEXIS. **Networks/Consortia:** Member of NELINET, Inc. **Special Catalogs:** Union List of Serials, annual with quarterly supplement - to section heads, foreign offices, and area libraries. **Remarks:** FAX: (617)661-8024. **Staff:** Beverly Colby, Info.Spec.

★9217★
Arthur D. Little, Inc. - Systems Library (Comp Sci)
25 Acorn Park Phone: (617)864-5770
Cambridge, MA 02140 Joanne C. Adamowicz, Libn.
Founded: 1979. **Staff:** Prof 1; Other 1. **Subjects:** Information systems, telecommunications, computer engineering, computer application. **Holdings:** 2250 books. **Subscriptions:** 175 journals and other serials. **Services:** Interlibrary loan; library not open to the public. **Automated Operations:** Computerized cataloging. **Computerized Information Services:** DIALOG Information Services, NEXIS, NewsNet, Inc., VU/TEXT Information Services, Dow Jones News/Retrieval. **Networks/Consortia:** Member of NELINET, Inc. **Publications:** Periodicals currently received, 2/year - for internal distribution only. **Remarks:** FAX: (617)864-6041.

Little Flower Society
See: **Society of the Little Flower** (15330)

Little Museum
See: **Cameron County Historical Society** (2613)

Little White House Historic Site
See: **Georgia (State) Department of Natural Resources** (6405)

Littlejohn Rare Book Room
See: **Wofford College - Sandor Teszler Library** (20548)

★9218★
Littleton Historical Museum - Library (Hist)
6028 S. Gallup Phone: (303)795-3950
Littleton, CO 80120 Robert J. McQuarie, Dir.
Founded: 1970. **Staff:** Prof 10; Other 9. **Subjects:** Local history including agriculture and railroad. **Special Collections:** Photograph collection of local subjects (4000 pictures). **Holdings:** 500 books; 175 bound periodical volumes; 25,000 museum artifacts; 60 boxes of public records and city council data; 50 reels of microfilm of newspapers; 60 maps. **Subscriptions:** 12 journals and other serials. **Services:** Copying; library open to the public with restrictions. **Remarks:** FAX: (303)795-3819.

★9219★
Littleton Research and Engineering Corporation - Library (Sci-Engr)
95 Russell St.
P.O. Box 128
Littleton, MA 01460 Phone: (508)486-3526
Founded: 1963. **Subjects:** Engineering - mechanical, electrical, structural, naval, marine; ship hull vibration. **Holdings:** 2000 volumes; 4500 pamphlets; technical books. **Subscriptions:** 12 journals and other serials.

★9220★
Litton Applied Technology - Government Systems - Library (Sci-Engr)
600 W. John St. Phone: (516)933-3443
Hicksville, NY 11802-0710 Irene Meier, Libn.
Subjects: Electronics and engineering, electronic warfare. **Holdings:** 3000 books; 500 bound periodical volumes; 10,000 other cataloged items; military specifications; technical publications. **Subscriptions:** 200 journals and other serials; 10 newspapers. **Services:** Library open to the public with restrictions. **Formerly:** General Instrument Corporation - Government Systems Division - Engineering Library.

★9221★
Litton Computer Services - Technical Library (Comp Sci)
4747 Hellyer Ave.
P.O. Box 210059 Phone: (408)363-2624
San Jose, CA 95151-0059 Jeannette N. Helfrich, Mgr.
Founded: 1987. **Staff:** Prof 1. **Subjects:** Computer software and hardware, aerospace, business, automation. **Holdings:** 500 books; military standards. **Subscriptions:** 35 journals and other serials; 5 newspapers. **Services:** Interlibrary loan; library not open to the public. **Automated Operations:** Computerized public access catalog. **Computerized Information Services:** DIALOG Information Services; CD-ROM. **Publications:** Acquisitions bulletin, irregular. **Special Indexes:** Online indexes to internal programs and all documents. **Remarks:** FAX: (408)363-2401. Telex: 910-339-9264. **Formerly:** Located in Mountain View, CA.

★9222★
Litton Industries - Corporate and Law Library (Law)
360 N. Crescent Dr. Phone: (213)859-5141
Beverly Hills, CA 90210 Judith Runyon, Corp. & Law Libn.
Staff: Prof 3; Other 3. **Subjects:** Law, business, finance. **Special Collections:** Intellectual property; government contracts; taxation. **Holdings:** 10,000 volumes. **Subscriptions:** 500 journals and other serials; 30 newspapers. **Services:** Interlibrary loan; library not open to the public. **Computerized Information Services:** LEXIS, WESTLAW, Data-Star, DataTimes, DIALOG Information Services, Dow Jones News/Retrieval, NEXIS, ORBIT Search Service, Reuters, Aviation Online, Global Scan; IBM Information Network. **Remarks:** FAX: (213)859-5940. **Staff:** Merrill Lishan, Asst.Corp. & Law Libn.; Suzann Sporing, Tech.Serv.Libn.; Ramona Sliva, Acq. & Paralegal; Keith Webster, Rec.Ctr.Adm.

★9223★
Litton Industries - Data Systems Division - Technical Engineering Library (Sci-Engr)
8000 Woodley Ave. Phone: (818)902-5903
Van Nuys, CA 91409 Tallulah Moore, Mgr., Tech.Engr.Lib.
Founded: 1956. **Staff:** Prof 1. **Subjects:** Electronics, engineering, computer technology, communications, management. **Holdings:** 11,000 books; 1200 bound periodical volumes. **Subscriptions:** 83 journals and other serials; 1 newspapers. **Services:** Interlibrary loan; copying; library open to the public. **Remarks:** FAX: (818)912-5052.

★9224★
Litton Industries - Electron Devices Division - Library (Sci-Engr)
960 Industrial Rd. Phone: (415)591-8411
San Carlos, CA 94070 Carol Rominger, Libn.
Founded: 1942. **Staff:** Prof 1. **Subjects:** Electronics, physics. **Holdings:** 4398 books; 473 bound periodical volumes. **Subscriptions:** 39 journals and other serials. **Services:** Interlibrary loan; library not open to the public. **Automated Operations:** Computerized cataloging, acquisitions, serials, and circulation. **Computerized Information Services:** DIALOG Information Services; internal database. **Publications:** Monthly bulletin. **Remarks:** FAX: (415)591-5623.

★9225★
Litton Industries - Guidance and Control Systems Technical Information Center - Library (Sci-Engr, Comp Sci)
5500 Canoga Ave. Phone: (818)719-7550
Woodland Hills, CA 91367 Elsbeth Mason, Supv., Lib.Serv.
Founded: 1954. **Staff:** Prof 2. **Subjects:** Computer technology, electrical and mechanical engineering, electronics, inertial guidance, management, mathematics, physics. **Holdings:** 40,000 books; 3500 bound periodical volumes; 5000 reports; pamphlets. **Subscriptions:** 520 journals and other serials. **Services:** Interlibrary loan; center not open to the public. **Computerized Information Services:** OCLC; DIALOG Information Services; internal databases. **Remarks:** FAX: (818)712-7151. **Staff:** Manuela Wood.

★9226★
Litton Industries - Itek Optical Systems Library (Sci-Engr)
10 Maguire Rd. Phone: (617)276-2643
Lexington, MA 02173 Mary R. Latham, Sr.Libn.
Staff: Prof 1. **Subjects:** Physics, optics, electronics, photography, business. **Holdings:** 7000 books; 500 bound periodical volumes; 1700 Itek reports; documents. **Subscriptions:** 200 journals and other serials. **Services:** Interlibrary loan; copying; library not open to the public. **Computerized Information Services:** DIALOG Information Services, Dun & Bradstreet Business Credit Services, NASA/RECON. **Publications:** Newsletter, monthly; holdings list, annual. **Remarks:** FAX: (617)276-3306.

★9227★
Litton Industries - Technical Library (Sci-Engr)
4747 Hellyer Ave., MS 211
Box 7012 Phone: (408)365-4756
San Jose, CA 95150-7012 Lee F. Perkins, Sr.Tech.Libn.
Founded: 1964. **Subjects:** Electronics; millimeter wave technology; radar, electro-optics, and electronic countermeasures. **Holdings:** 5000 books; 528 bound periodical volumes; 540 pamphlets; 4000 technical reports; 772 microfilm cartridges of vendor catalogs; 450 microfilm cartridges of military specifications and standards; 8 VF drawers of instruction manuals. **Subscriptions:** 210 journals and other serials. **Services:** Interlibrary loan; library not open to the public. **Automated Operations:** Computerized circulation. **Computerized Information Services:** DIALOG Information Services. **Networks/Consortia:** Member of CLASS, SOUTHNET. **Remarks:** FAX: (408)224-1354.

★9228★
Liturgy Library (Rel-Phil)
8000 Hickory Ln.
P.O. Box 30221 Phone: (402)488-1668
Lincoln, NE 68503-0221 Judy H. Barrick, Dir.
Founded: 1975. **Staff:** 1. **Subjects:** History, theology, and practice of worship in the Judeo-Christian traditions. **Special Collections:** Special needs and contributions of Asian, Black, Hispanic, Native American, aging, disabled, single, and women worshippers. **Holdings:** 5000 books; 125 audio cassettes, filmstrips, kits; 125 sets of choir music; unbound periodicals. **Subscriptions:** 20 journals and other serials. **Services:** Interlibrary loan; copying (limited); library open to the public on fee basis. **Publications:** Informational brochure; price list; acquisitions list - available on request. **Formerly:** Ecumenical Music & Liturgy Resource Library. **Also Known As:** EMLR Library.

Litzenberg-Lund Library
See: **University of Minnesota - Department of Obstetrics and Gynecology** (18903)

Livability Clearinghouse
See: **Partners for Livable Places** (12771)

Charles H. Livengood, Jr. Memorial Labor Law Library
See: **North Carolina (State) Department of Labor** (11891)

★9229★
Livestock Feed Board of Canada - Library (Agri)
P.O. Box 177
Snowdon Station Phone: (514)283-8710
Montreal, PQ, Canada H3X 3T4 A. Douglas Mutch, Dir., Econ.Res.
Staff: Prof 2. **Subjects:** Canadian and U.S. agriculture, economic policy, farm produce, marketing, grain, transportation, government information. **Holdings:** 2030 books. **Subscriptions:** 420 journals and other serials; 20 newspapers. **Services:** Interlibrary loan; copying; SDI; library open to the public. **Remarks:** Library located at 5180 Queen Mary Rd., Suite 400, Montreal, PQ H3W 3E7. FAX: (514)283-2754.

★9230★
The Living Desert - Haynes Memorial Library (Biol Sci)
47-900 Portola Ave. Phone: (619)346-5694
Palm Desert, CA 92260 Karen Sausman, Exec.Dir.
Founded: 1973. **Subjects:** Desert ecology, herpetology, mammalogy, birds, invertebrates, North American ecology, botany, Indian history, local history. **Holdings:** 740 books; 10 bound periodical volumes; 23 manuscripts; 8 dissertations; 1 VF drawer of clippings; 4 VF drawers of unbound periodicals. **Subscriptions:** 16 journals and other serials. **Services:** Library open to the public with restrictions.

★9231★
A Living Memorial to the Holocaust - Museum of Jewish Heritage - Documentation & Research Library
342 Madison Ave., Suite 706 Phone: (212)687-9141
New York, NY 10173 Bonnie Gurewitsch, Res.Libn./Archv.
Staff: Prof 6; Other 6. **Subjects:** Holocaust, World War II, anti-Semitism, Jewish history. **Special Collections:** Memorial books of European Jewish communities. **Holdings:** 2500 books; 185 linear feet of archival photographs, manuscripts, artifacts, diaries, documents, oral histories; reference files; AV programs. **Subscriptions:** 15 journals and other serials. **Services:** Interlibrary loan; library open to the public. **Publications:** Newsletter, irregular; Bibliography Series, irregular; Oral History Series, irregular. **Remarks:** FAX: (212)573-9847.

A.E. Livingston Health Sciences Library
See: **BroMenn Healthcare** (2207)

★9232★
Livingston County Law Library (Law)
2 Court St. Phone: (716)243-7000
Geneseo, NY 14454 Marge Davis, Sec.
Staff: 1. **Subjects:** Law. **Holdings:** 5000 volumes. **Services:** Library open to the public with restrictions.

Livingston Library
See: **Webb Institute of Naval Architecture** (20130)

Robert R. Livingston Library
See: **Grand Lodge of New York, F. and A.M.** (6630)

★9233★
Livingstone College - American Black and African Studies Collection (Hist, Area-Ethnic)
Andrew Carnegie Library
701 W. Monroe St.
Salisbury, NC 28144 Phone: (704)638-5629
Founded: 1908. **Staff:** Prof 5; Other 2. **Special Collections:** Africans and American Blacks; African Methodist Episcopal Zion Church; Ecumenical Methodist Conference, 1881-1956; Livingstone College. **Holdings:** 75,000 books; 4415 bound periodical volumes; 37,226 microfiche; 2752 reels of microfilm. **Subscriptions:** 258 journals and other serials; 28 newspapers. **Services:** Interlibrary loan; copying; collection open to the public. **Computerized Information Services:** DIALOG Information Services. **Remarks:** FAX: (704)638-5646. **Staff:** Walter Mitchell; Michael Robbian.

Livingstone College - Hood Theological Seminary
See: **Hood Theological Seminary - Library** (7380)

★9234★
Lizzadro Museum of Lapidary Art - Library (Art)
220 Cottage Hill Ave.
Elmhurst, IL 60126 Phone: (708)833-1616
Founded: 1962. **Subjects:** Gemology, geology, Chinese jade, jewelry, lapidary, mineralogy, engraved stones, paleontology. **Holdings:** 750 volumes. **Subscriptions:** 6 journals and other serials. **Services:** Library open to members for reference use only. **Publications:** Lizzadro Museum, semiannual - free to members, for sale to others; Lizzadro Collection (book).

★9235★
(Ljubljana) Americki Centar - USIS Library (Educ)
Cankarjeva 11
Post Box 287
YU-61000 Ljubljana, Yugoslavia
Remarks: Maintained or supported by the U.S. Information Agency. Focus is on materials that will assist peoples outside the United States to learn about the United States, its people, history, culture, political processes, and social milieux.

Llewellyn Publications - Carl L. Weschcke Library
See: **Carl L. Weschcke Library** (20170)

★9236★
Alice Lloyd College - Appalachian Oral History Project
Pippa Passes, KY 41844
Special Collections: Oral history interviews concerning Appalachian life and culture, folklore, history, music, coal mining, the Depression. **Holdings:** 650 transcripts; 1000 audiocassettes; reel-to-reel recordings of music and lectures. **Remarks:** Currently inactive.

★9237★
Lloyd Center for Environmental Studies, Inc. - Resource Center (Biol Sci)
430 Potomska Rd.
Box 87037 Phone: (508)990-0505
South Dartmouth, MA 02748 Cynthia J. Marks, Libn.
Founded: 1981. **Staff:** Prof 1. **Subjects:** Coastal resources, coastal resources ecology, environmental education, oceanography, ecology, zoology. **Holdings:** 1500 books. **Subscriptions:** 20 journals and other serials. **Services:** Copying; library open to the public.

Lloyd House
See: **Alexandria Library** (344)

★9238★
Lloyd Library and Museum (Biol Sci, Med)
917 Plum St. Phone: (513)721-3707
Cincinnati, OH 45202 Rebecca A. Perry, Libn.
Founded: 1864. **Staff:** Prof 3; Other 2. **Subjects:** Botany, pharmacy, biology, chemistry, natural science, zoology, entomology, mycology. **Special Collections:** Pharmacopoeias; dispensatories; formularies; eclectic medicine; herbals. **Holdings:** 70,000 books; 120,000 bound periodical volumes; 100,000 pamphlets. **Subscriptions:** 500 journals and other serials. **Services:** Interlibrary loan; copying; library open to the public with restrictions. **Automated Operations:** Computerized cataloging. **Computerized Information Services:** OCLC. **Networks/Consortia:** Member of Council on Botanical Horticultural Libraries, OHIONET. **Publications:** The Journal of Natural Products (LLOYDIA), bimonthly - by subscription. **Staff:** William C. Black, Archv. & Cons.

★9239★
LM Architectural Group - Library (Art)
290 Vaughan St., Suite 300 Phone: (204)942-0681
Winnipeg, MB, Canada R3B 2L9 W.T. Shibata, Tech.Info.Off.
Remarks: No further information was supplied by respondent.

★9240★
Loan Brokers Association - Information Services (Bus-Fin)
PO Box 1553
Owosso, MI 48867 Ben Campbell, Dir.
Subjects: Loan brokers, loan consulting, credit repair, lending, credit cards, venture capital. **Services:** Copying; SDI; library to members or by permission. **Publications:** Loan Broker (newsletter); Directory of Loan Brokers; Guide to Grants & Gifts; Directory of Credit Repair Services; Index to Private Lending Services.

★9241★
Lock Haven University - George B. Stevenson Library - Archives (Educ)
Lock Haven, PA 17745 Phone: (717)893-2371
Robert S. Bravard
Founded: 1870. **Staff:** 14. **Special Collections:** Eden Phillpotts Works (266 volumes); Orrin B. Good lumber industry records, 1900-1955; T. Eyk comic book collection; college archives. **Services:** Interlibrary loan; copying; archives open to the public with restrictions. **Automated Operations:** Computerized cataloging. **Computerized Information Services:** DIALOG Information Services, OCLC. **Networks/Consortia:** Member of PALINET, State System of Higher Education Libraries Council (SSHELCO), Susquehanna Library Cooperative. **Remarks:** FAX: (717)893-2506. **Staff:** Caryn J. Carr, Archv.

★9242★
Lock Museum of America Inc. - Library (Sci-Engr)
PO Box 104 Phone: (203)589-6359
Terryville, CT 06786 Thomas F. Hennessy, Cur.
Founded: 1972. **Staff:** 2. **Subjects:** Locks, keys, ornate hardware. **Special Collections:** Financial and sales records of The Eagle Lock Company, 1900-1930; company catalogs; lock patents, 1830-1930 (1000). **Holdings:** 1000 books; 500 bound periodical volumes. **Services:** Copying; library open to the public. **Staff:** Sharon Moran, Libn.

★9243★
Lockheed Aeronautical Systems Company - Georgia Division - Technical Information Center (Sci-Engr)
86 S. Cobb Dr.
Dept. 82-13, Zone 0680
Marietta, GA 30063-0680 Phone: (404)494-2522
Founded: 1951. **Staff:** Prof 2; Other 3. **Subjects:** Aeronautics, operations research, engineering, human factors, electronics, marketing, management, materials. **Holdings:** 38,000 books; 4500 bound periodical volumes; 150,000 technical reports; 10 VF drawers of pamphlets; 1100 maps; 360,000 microfiche; 50,000 specifications and standards; cassettes; annual reports. **Subscriptions:** 500 journals and other serials; 25 newspapers. **Services:** Interlibrary loan; center open to the public by appointment. **Automated Operations:** Computerized cataloging, acquisitions, circulation, and correspondence log. **Computerized Information Services:** DIALOG Information Services, DTIC, NASA/RECON, Lockheed Information Network System (LINKS). **Networks/Consortia:** Member of SOLINET. **Publications:** Accession List (computer-prepared), bimonthly; bibliographies; journal subscription lists; News Bulletin, irregular - for internal distribution only; Abbreviations/Acronyms; Style Manual. **Special Indexes:** Computer-prepared indexes to all material added to the collection since 1963. **Remarks:** Alternate telephone number(s): (404)494-6046. FAX: (404)494-0732. **Staff:** L.W. Kimbro, Tech.Libn.

★9244★
Lockheed Missiles & Space Company, Inc. - Technical Information Center (Sci-Engr)
3251 Hanover St. Phone: (415)424-2802
Palo Alto, CA 94304-1187 Ralph W. Lewis, Mgr.
Founded: 1954. **Staff:** Prof 14; Other 11. **Subjects:** Aerospace sciences, missile and space vehicles, electronics, materials and structures, data processing, information sciences, laser systems, energy systems, physics, chemistry, engineering. **Special Collections:** Archives of company documents. **Holdings:** 38,000 books; 27,500 bound periodical volumes; 125,000 technical reports; 2400 periodical volumes on microfilm; 65,000 reports on microfiche; 175,000 pieces of technical data. **Subscriptions:** 700 journals and other serials. **Services:** Interlibrary loan; center not open to the public. **Automated Operations:** Computerized cataloging and circulation. **Computerized Information Services:** DIALOG Information Services, NASA/RECON, DTIC, PFDS Online, Chemical Abstracts Service (CAS), Integrated Technical Information System (ITIS), Chemical Information Systems, Inc. (CIS), DMS/ONLINE, Data Resources (DRI); internal databases. **Networks/Consortia:** Member of SOUTHNET. **Remarks:** FAX: (415)424-3124. Maintains 3 branch libraries in Sunnyvale, CA. **Staff:** E.B. Leong, Palo Alto Libn.; R. Woo, Tech. Data Libn.; J. Thomas Conahan, Acq.Libn; S. Stanek, Sunnyvale Libn.; D. Robinson, Sunnyvale Libn.; H.A. Abbott, Lit. Search; A. Bryant, Palo Alto Ref.Lib.

★9245★
Lockheed Sanders, Inc. - Technical Information Center (Mil, Comp Sci)
95 Canal St., NCA 1-1342
P.O. Box 868 Phone: (603)885-4144
Nashua, NH 03061 Gibson Kennedy, Mgr., Media Serv.
Founded: 1955. **Staff:** Prof 2; Other 2. **Subjects:** Defense electronics, computer graphics, electrical engineering. **Holdings:** 10,000 books; 2000 bound periodical volumes; 20,000 microfiche. **Subscriptions:** 601 journals and other serials. **Services:** Interlibrary loan; center open to industrial community by appointment only. **Computerized Information Services:** DIALOG Information Services, BRS Information Technologies, DTIC, LINKS; DIALMAIL (electronic mail service). **Remarks:** FAX: (603)885-4143. **Staff:** David Morrison, Tech.Libn.; Diane Belland, Tech.Libn.

★9246★
Lockwood, Andrews & Newnam, Inc. - Information Center (Sci-Engr)
1500 City West Blvd., Suite 100
Houston, TX 77042-3088 Phone: (713)266-6900
Founded: 1977. **Staff:** Prof 1; Other 2. **Subjects:** Engineering - civil, mechanical, electrical; architecture; energy. **Holdings:** 1820 volumes; 2400 reels of microfilm; 1000 company records and manuscripts; 3200 archival records and books. **Subscriptions:** 200 journals and other serials; 5 newspapers. **Services:** Interlibrary loan; center not open to the public. **Automated Operations:** Computerized cataloging and acquisitions. **Computerized Information Services:** Internal database. **Remarks:** FAX: (713)266-2089.

Lockwood Memorial Library - Polish Collection
See: **State University of New York at Buffalo - Lockwood Memorial Library - Polish Collection** (15739)

★9247★
Loctite Corporation - Research and Development Library (Sci-Engr)
705 N. Mountain Rd. Phone: (203)278-1280
Newington, CT 06111 Kathryn Leritz, Sr.Libn.
Staff: Prof 1; Other 2. **Subjects:** Adhesives and sealants, polymer chemistry, organic chemistry, management. **Special Collections:** Patent files for adhesives and sealants. **Holdings:** 10,000 volumes; 4 VF drawers of technical reports. **Subscriptions:** 150 journals and other serials; 8 newspapers. **Services:** Interlibrary loan; library not open to the public. **Computerized Information Services:** DIALOG Information Services, STN International, LEXIS, NEXIS; Technical Report Index (internal database). **Publications:** R & D Newsletter, monthly - for internal distribution only. **Remarks:** FAX: (203)280-3558.

Miriam Lodge Professional Library
See: **Rosewood Center** (14076)

Eda Kuhn Loeb Music Library
See: **Harvard University - Eda Kuhn Loeb Music Library** (6964)

Frances Loeb Library
See: **Harvard University - Graduate School of Design** (6967)

★9248★
Loeb and Loeb - Law Library (Law)
1000 Wilshire Blvd., 18th Fl. Phone: (213)688-3565
Los Angeles, CA 90017 Nella L. Jarett, Libn.
Founded: 1909. **Staff:** Prof 2; Other 2.5. **Subjects:** Law - taxation, bankruptcy. **Holdings:** 34,000 volumes. **Subscriptions:** 200 journals and other serials; 6 newspapers. **Services:** Library not open to the public. **Automated Operations:** Computerized serials. **Computerized Information Services:** LEXIS, DIALOG Information Services, WESTLAW, Dow Jones News/Retrieval, INFOtek, LEGI-SLATE, DataTimes, DAMAR, Information America, Prentice Hall Online; internal database. **Publications:** Monthly Memo. **Special Catalogs:** Union list of periodicals. **Remarks:** FAX: (213)688-3460. **Staff:** Lan Dang, Asst.Libn.

Loews Inc. - Lorillard Research Center Library
See: **Lorillard Research Center Library** (9319)

LOEX National Library Instruction Clearinghouse
See: **Eastern Michigan University** (5158)

★9249★
Logan College of Chiropractic - Learning Resources Center (Med)
1851 Schoettler Rd.
Box 1065 Phone: (314)227-2100
Chesterfield, MO 63006-1065 Rosemary E. Buhr, Dir.
Founded: 1935. **Staff:** Prof 3; Other 3.4. **Subjects:** Chiropractic, orthopedics, body mechanics, radiology, anatomy, nutrition, neurology, sports medicine, physical therapy. **Special Collections:** Osseous material (full skeletons, spines, individual bones); anatomical models; current information on chiropractic legislation from state legislatures, chiropractic associations, other chiropractic organizations (vertical file). **Holdings:** 10,000 books; 950 slide/tape programs; videotapes. **Subscriptions:** 220 journals and other serials. **Services:** Interlibrary loan; copying; center open to the public with restrictions. **Automated Operations:** Integrated library system (DYNIX). **Computerized Information Services:** MEDLINE, BRS Information Technologies; OnTyme Electronic Message Network Service (electronic mail service). Performs searches on fee basis. Contact Person: Bob Snyders, Pub.Serv./Ref.Libn. **Networks/Consortia:** Member of Chiropractic Library Consortium (CLIBCON), St. Louis Regional Library Network. **Remarks:** FAX: (314)227-8503. **Staff:** Jean Rose, Tech.Serv.Libn./Sys.Coord.

John A. Logan Library
See: **Rose-Hulman Institute of Technology** (14063)

★9250★
Logansport State Hospital - Staff Library (Med)
R.R. 2 Phone: (219)722-4141
Logansport, IN 46947 Pam Kindem, Rehabilitation Supv.
Founded: 1938. **Staff:** Prof 1. **Subjects:** Medicine, psychiatry, psychology, social service, drug abuse, nursing, alcoholism, geriatrics. **Holdings:** 1500 books. **Subscriptions:** 70 journals and other serials. **Services:** Interlibrary loan; library open to the public for reference use only. **Networks/Consortia:** Member of Wabash Valley Library Network. **Remarks:** FAX: (219)735-3414.

★9251★
Logicon, Inc. - Information Center (Comp Sci)
222 W. 6th St.
Box 471 Phone: (213)831-0611
San Pedro, CA 90733-0471 Constance B. Davenport, Info.Serv.Mgr.
Founded: 1972. **Staff:** Prof 2; Other 3. **Subjects:** Computer science, software testing, programming languages, weapons systems. **Special Collections:** Logicon technical reports; military standards. **Holdings:** 4000 books; 920 boxes of periodicals; 5000 documents; 750 standards and specifications; 10,000 microfiche. **Subscriptions:** 241 journals and other serials; 9 newspapers. **Services:** Interlibrary loan; center not open to the public. **Automated Operations:** Computerized cataloging and circulation. **Computerized Information Services:** DIALOG Information Services, DTIC, NASA/RECON, DataTimes, NewsNet, Inc., Aerospace Online; internal databases. **Remarks:** FAX: (213)548-4870. Lowri Lee Sprung, Sr.Libn.

★9252★
Logicon, Inc. - Tactical & Training Systems Division Library (Sci-Engr, Comp Sci)
Box 85158 Phone: (619)455-1330
San Diego, CA 92138-5158 Paula Oquita
Staff: Prof 1; Other 2. **Subjects:** Tactical systems; command, control, and communications systems; training systems; simulated training; simulation and simulators; system engineering; database management. **Holdings:** 2500 books; 20,000 reports; 250 VF drawers of company reports; military specifications and standards. **Subscriptions:** 250 journals and other serials. **Services:** Interlibrary loan; copying; library open to the public with restrictions. **Computerized Information Services:** DIALOG Information Services, internal databases. **Publications:** Accessions list, monthly; subject bibliographies, irregular. **Remarks:** Library located at 4010 Sorrento Valley Blvd., San Diego, CA 92121. FAX: (619)552-1021.

★9253★
Logicon R & D Associates - Information Services (Sci-Engr)
6053 W. Century Blvd.
P.O. Box 92500 Phone: (213)645-1122
Los Angeles, CA 90009 Shirley Lee Tanaka, Mgr.
Staff: Prof 2; Other 1. **Subjects:** Defense systems, nuclear physics, electronics, energy systems, systems engineering, weapon systems, computer science, national security. **Holdings:** 6,000 books; 30,000 reports. **Subscriptions:** 200 journals and other serials. **Services:** Interlibrary loan; library not open to the public. **Automated Operations:** Computerized cataloging and circulation. **Computerized Information Services:** DIALOG Information Services, RLIN; OnTyme Electronic Message Network Service (electronic mail service). **Networks/Consortia:** Member of CLASS. **Remarks:** FAX: (213)645-2553. Electronic mail address(es): RDA (OnTyme Electronic Message Network Service). **Formerly:** R & D Associates. **Staff:** Janet Katz, Sr.Libn.; Gail Adams, Sr.Lib.Asst.

★9254★
Logistics Management Institute - Library (Mil)
6400 Goldsboro Rd. Phone: (301)320-7249
Bethesda, MD 20817-5886 Nancy Eichelman Handy, Dir. of Lib.Serv.
Staff: Prof 2; Other 1. **Subjects:** Logistics, defense, manpower, procurement, health systems, warehousing, facilities management. **Holdings:** 5000 books; 1000 reports; 100 manuals and newsletters in binders. **Subscriptions:** 200 journals and other serials. **Services:** Library not open to the public. **Computerized Information Services:** DIALOG Information Services. **Networks/Consortia:** Member of Interlibrary Users Association (IUA). **Staff:** Laura Tyler; Jill Hanna.

Logue Library
See: **Chestnut Hill College** (3493)

★9255★
Loma Linda University - Del E. Webb Memorial Library (Med)
24798 University Ave. Phone: (714)824-4550
Loma Linda, CA 92350-0001 David W. Rios, Dir.
Founded: 1907. **Staff:** Prof 10.5; Other 24. **Subjects:** Medicine, nursing, dentistry, religion, health, allied health professions. **Special Collections:** Nineteenth Century Health Reform in America; Remondino Collection (history of medicine); C. Burton Clark Collection (history of Seventh-Day Adventist Church). **Holdings:** 177,277 books; 104,801 bound periodical volumes; 51,968 microforms; 5420 tapes and phonograph records; 1126 filmstrips, films, slides; 1069 feet of archival materials. **Subscriptions:** 2670 journals and other serials; 13 newspapers. **Services:** Interlibrary loan; copying; library open to qualified users. **Automated Operations:** Computerized public access catalog, cataloging, acquisitions, and serials. **Computerized Information Services:** NLM, BRS Information Technologies, OCLC; OnTyme Electronic Message Network Service (electronic mail service). Performs searches on fee basis. **Networks/Consortia:** Member of Inland Empire Academic Libraries Cooperative (IEALC), San Bernardino, Inyo, Riverside Counties United Library Services (SIRCULS), National Network of Libraries of Medicine - Pacific Southwest Region, CLASS. **Publications:** SDA Periodical Index. **Remarks:** FAX: (714)824-4188. Electronic mail address(es): LLU (OnTyme Electronic Message Network Service). **Staff:** Gilbert Abella, Assoc.Dir. of Lib.Sys.; Nelia Wurangian, Chm., Tech.Serv.; Carlene Bogle, Chm., Pub.Serv.; James R. Nix, Chm., Archv./Spec.Coll.; Shirley Graves, Chm., Ser.

★9256★
Loma Linda University - Jorgensen Learning Resource Center (Med)
Del E. Webb Memorial Library Phone: (714)824-4585
Loma Linda, CA 92350 John Morovati, Act.Chm.
Founded: 1978. **Staff:** Prof 1; Other 2. **Subjects:** Dentistry; dental anesthesiology and pain control; national, regional, state board review materials. **Special Collections:** Archival material of the American Dental Society of Anesthesiology. **Holdings:** 264 volumes; 160 video cassettes; 55 self-study units; 25 boxes of archival materials. **Subscriptions:** 120 journals and other serials. **Services:** Interlibrary loan; copying; SDI; library open to board candidates and health professionals on fee basis. **Publications:** Summary of the Scientific Literature for Pain and Anxiety Control in Dentistry, 3/year.

★9257★
Loma Linda University - Medical Center - Medical Library & Information Center (Med)
11234 Anderson St.
P.O. Box 2000 Phone: (714)824-4620
Loma Linda, CA 92354 Paul W. Kittle
Founded: 1986. **Staff:** Prof 2; Other 2. **Subjects:** Internal medicine, pediatrics, cardiology, radiation oncology, oncology, nephrology. **Holdings:** 3000 books. **Subscriptions:** 360 journals and other serials. **Services:** Interlibrary loan; library not open to the public. **Computerized Information Services:** DIALOG Information Services, BRS Information Technologies, NLM; PROLIT (internal database); BITNET (electronic mail service). Contact Person: Laura Brown, Sr.Libn. **Publications:** Computarian (newsletter). **Remarks:** FAX: (714)824-4722. Electronic mail address(es): MDLPKI@LLUVM (BITNET).

★9258★
Lombard County Historical Society - Library (Hist)
23 W. Maple St. Phone: (708)629-1885
Lombard, IL 60148 Marian Lidicker, Libn.
Founded: 1970. **Subjects:** Lombard - history, people, buildings, authors; Victorian era; Du Page history. **Holdings:** 276 books; documents; manuscripts. **Subscriptions:** 4 journals and other serials. **Services:** Library open to the public for reference use only. **Staff:** Edna Grench, Hist.; Angela Wilson, Dir.

★9259★
Lombardy Hall Foundation - Library (Rec)
1611 Concord Pike
Box 7036 Phone: (302)655-5254
Wilmington, DE 19803 Harold J. Littleton, Archv.
Staff: 1. **Subjects:** Freemasonry, Gunning Bedford, Jr., Delaware history. **Holdings:** 1000 books; 50 bound periodical volumes. **Services:** Library open to the public with restrictions.

★9260★
(Lome) Centre Culturel Americain - USIS Library (Educ)
Angle Rue Pelletier & Rue Vauban
B.P. 852
Lome, Togo
Remarks: Maintained or supported by the U.S. Information Agency. Focus is on materials that will assist peoples outside the United States to learn about the United States, its people, history, culture, political processes, and social milieux.

Christian P. Lommen Health Sciences Library
See: **University of South Dakota** (19315)

★9261★
Lompoc Museum Associates, Inc. - Research Library (Area-Ethnic)
200 S. H St. Phone: (805)736-3888
Lompoc, CA 93436 Dr. Roy A. Salls, Dir., Cur. of Anthropology
Founded: 1969. **Staff:** Prof 3. **Subjects:** Chumash Indians, Indians of Southern California, Lompoc natural history, Lompoc history, archeology. **Special Collections:** Manuscripts; historical photographs. **Holdings:** 1500 books; 4 VF drawers; 150 maps; 350 slides. **Services:** Library open to the public for reference use only on request. **Remarks:** FAX: (805)736-5395.

★9262★
London Baptist Bible College and London Baptist Seminary - Library (Rel-Phil)
30 Grand Ave. Phone: (519)434-6801
London, ON, Canada N6C 1K8 Richard W. Horner, Libn.
Founded: 1976. **Staff:** Prof 2; Other 2. **Subjects:** Biblical studies, theology, church history, Baptist history and doctrines, missions. **Special Collections:** John Bunyan Studies (50 titles). **Holdings:** 19,500 books; 650 bound periodical volumes. **Subscriptions:** 255 journals and other serials. **Services:** Interlibrary loan; copying; library open to alumni and local pastors only. **Staff:** Joyce M. Scott, Cat.Libn.; Diana MacGee, Lib.Techn.

★9263★
London Free Press Publishing Company, Ltd. - Editorial Library (Publ)
369 York St. Phone: (519)679-1111
London, ON, Canada N6A 4G1 Edythe Cusack, Libn.
Founded: 1950. **Staff:** Prof 4; Other 3. **Subjects:** Newspaper reference topics. **Holdings:** 600 books; 100 bound periodical volumes; 1200 reels of microfilm; clippings; pictures. **Subscriptions:** 50 journals and other serials. **Services:** Interlibrary loan (limited); copying; library open to other newspapers and libraries only. **Special Catalogs:** Historic and features catalogs (both on cards). **Remarks:** FAX: (519)667-4528.

★9264★
Jack London Research Center (Hum)
14300 Arnold Dr.
Box 337 Phone: (707)996-2888
Glen Ellen, CA 95442 Russ Kingman, Dir.
Founded: 1973. **Staff:** Prof 1. **Subjects:** Jack London. **Special Collections:** Primary and secondary Jack London materials; early San Francisco Bay area writers. **Holdings:** 500 books; 90 bound periodical volumes; 1000 manuscripts and articles by Jack London; 150 pamphlets and dissertations; 65,000 file cards; 20,000 items on microfilm; 27 scrapbooks. **Services:** Center open to the public. **Remarks:** This is a private facility within a bookstore which is also headquarters for the Jack London Foundation, Inc.

★9265★
Jack London State Historic Park - Research Center (Hum)
2400 London Ranch Rd.
Glen Ellen, CA 95442 Phone: (707)938-5216
Founded: 1960. **Staff:** Prof 2. **Subjects:** Literature, Jack London. **Special Collections:** Holman Collection (Jack London first edition set; 5000 books, documents, letters, clippings). **Services:** Library open to the public by appointment for reference use only. **Special Catalogs:** Accession catalog.

★9266★
The London Library (Hum, Geog-Map, Rel-Phil, Hist)
14 St. James's Sq. Phone: 71 9307705
London SW1Y 4LG, England J. G. Cochrane, Libn.
Founded: 1841. **Staff:** 14. **Subjects:** Literature, topography, religion, history, fine art, philosophy. **Holdings:** 850,000 books; 175,000 bound periodical volumes. **Subscriptions:** 501 journals and other serials. **Services:** Interlibrary loan; copying; library open to the public with restrictions. **Special Catalogs:** Catalog of accessions (1984 to present; online); Author Accessions to 1950. **Special Indexes:** Subject Index to 1953. **Staff:** Douglas Matthews, Libn.; Michael Higgins, Dp.Libn.

Meyer London Memorial Library of the Rand School of Social Science
See: **New York University - Tamiment Library** (11733)

★9267★
London Psychiatric Hospital - Library (Med)
850 Highbury Ave.
Box 2532, Terminal A Phone: (519)455-5110
London, ON, Canada N6A 4H1 M. Why
Staff: Prof 2. **Subjects:** Psychiatry. **Holdings:** 4000 books; 800 bound periodical volumes. **Subscriptions:** 175 journals and other serials. **Services:** Interlibrary loan; copying; library open to the public. **Computerized Information Services:** MEDLARS, BRS Information Technologies, CAN/OLE, DIALOG Information Services. **Remarks:** FAX: (519)455-9986. **Staff:** Esther Wines, Lib.Techn.

★9268★
London Public Libraries - London Room (Hist)
305 Queens Ave. Phone: (519)661-5125
London, ON, Canada N6B 3L7 W. Glen Curnoe, Libn.
Founded: 1967. **Staff:** Prof 1; Other 2. **Subjects:** London and London area - history, family genealogy, local architecture; London Public Library history. **Special Collections:** Edwin Seaborn Collection (Western Ontario history, with emphasis on medicine; 56 volumes and index); Orlo Miller Collection (genealogical card file and Miller's correspondence); Looking Over Western Ontario (newspaper references to landmarks and history of London). **Holdings:** Books; newspapers; reels of microfilm; unbound reports; scrapbooks; family manuscripts; oral history tapes; pictures; clippings, 1940 to present; documents, including municipal documents. **Services:** Copying; room open to the public for reference use only. **Publications:** Occasional papers, irregular - for sale. **Special Indexes:** Indexes to local history scrapbooks, picture collection, oral history collection, significant buildings (all on cards). **Remarks:** Collection is extensive and still in process of being organized and enlarged.

★9269★
London Regional Cancer Centre - Library (Med)
790 Commisioners Rd. E. Phone: (519)685-8626
London, ON, Canada N6A 4L6 Charlene Campbell
Founded: 1970. **Staff:** Prof 2. **Subjects:** Oncology - general, radiation, research, medical, nursing; radiotherapy. **Holdings:** 900 books; 1500 bound periodical volumes. **Subscriptions:** 125 journals and other serials. **Services:** Interlibrary loan; center not open to the public. **Computerized Information Services:** MEDLINE, CANCERLIT; CD-ROM (MEDLINE); OCLC (electronic mail service). **Publications:** List of new acquisitions, monthly - for internal distribution only. **Remarks:** FAX: (519)685-8614.

★9270★
London Research Centre - Research Library (Plan, Soc Sci)
Parliament House
81 Black Prince Rd. Phone: 71 6279660
London SE1 7SZ, England Richard Golland, Dir., Res.Lib.
Staff: Prof 15; Other 9. **Subjects:** Local government, town and country planning, traffic and transportation research, social services and planning, environment, noise, pollution, energy, public health, local government finance and management, inner-city studies, housing, industry and employment, education. **Holdings:** 70,000 volumes; 80,000 pamphlets and reports; 20,000 microfiche. **Subscriptions:** 500 journals and other serials. **Services:** Interlibrary loan; library not open to the public. **Computerized Information Services:** Produces ACOMPLINE, URBALINE. Performs searches on fee basis. **Publications:** Urban Abstracts, monthly; subject-based alerting bulletins, biweekly. **Remarks:** FAX: 71 6279674. **Staff:** Annabel Davies, Dp.Dir.

★9271★
London School of Economics - British Library of Political and Economic Science (Soc Sci, Bus-Fin)
10 Portugal St. Phone: 71 4057686
London WC2A 2HD, England L.J. Brindley, Libn.
Founded: 1896. **Subjects:** Social sciences; economics; politics; sociology; modern political history; economic, social, and business history; history of economic thought. **Holdings:** 960,000 volumes. **Services:** Interlibrary loan; copying; library open to the public with restrictions. **Automated Operations:** Computerized public access catalog. **Computerized Information Services:** Data-Star, DIALOG Information Services, ESA/IRS, BRS Information Technologies, ORBIT Search Service, Questel, BLAISE Online Services, FT PROFILE; JANET (electronic mail service). **Publications:** The International Bibliography of the Social Sciences, annual; The International Current Awareness Services, monthly. **Special Catalogs:** Classified Catalogue of a Collection of Works on Publishing and Bookselling in the British Library of Political and Economic Science; catalog of selected manuscripts in the Manuscripts Division (online). **Remarks:** The British Library of Political and Economic Science serves both as the working library of the London School of Economics and as a national collection of material for research. FAX: 71 2420392. Telex: 24655 BLPESG. Electronic mail address(es): LIBRARY@UK.AC.LSE.VAX2 (JANET). **Staff:** H.M. Workman, Hd., Rd.Serv.

★9272★
London Town Publik House & Gardens - Library (Hist)
839 Londontown Rd. Phone: (301)222-1919
Edgewater, MD 21037 Michael J. Menard, Adm.
Founded: 1973. **Staff:** 3. **Subjects:** Horticulture, historic furnishings, Maryland history, 18th century costuming, 18th century social history. **Holdings:** 1500 books; 10,000 bound periodical volumes. **Subscriptions:** 15 journals and other serials. **Services:** Copying; library open to the public for reference use only. **Staff:** Anne Peret, Asst.Adm.

(London) USIS Library
See: **The Reference Center - (London) USIS Library** (13774)

★9273★
Long Aldridge & Norman - Law Library (Law)
1500 Marquis Two Tower
285 Peachtree Center Ave. Phone: (404)527-4000
Atlanta, GA 30303-1257 Cindy Adams, Law Libn.
Staff: Prof 2; Other 3. **Subjects:** Law. **Holdings:** 10,000 books; 500 bound periodical volumes; 285 cassettes. **Subscriptions:** 200 journals and other serials. **Services:** Interlibrary loan; library not open to the public. **Automated Operations:** Computerized public access catalog, cataloging, acquisitions, and serials. **Computerized Information Services:** WESTLAW, VU/TEXT Information Services, LEXIS, Information America, DIALOG Information Services, CompuServe Information Service, LEGI-SLATE; MCI Mail (electronic mail service). **Remarks:** FAX: (404)527-4198. **Staff:** MeloDee J. French, Ref.Libn.; Sally Munson, Br.Libn.

Augustus C. Long Health Sciences Library
See: **Columbia University - Augustus C. Long Health Sciences Library** (4001)

★9274★
Long Beach Community Hospital - Johnson Health Sciences Library (Med)
1720 Termino Ave. Phone: (213)494-0751
Long Beach, CA 90804 Lois O. Clark, Med.Libn.
Founded: 1966. **Staff:** Prof 1. **Subjects:** Medicine, nursing, hospital administration. **Holdings:** 1950 books; 1500 bound periodical volumes; Audio-Digest tapes. **Subscriptions:** 289 journals and other serials. **Services:** Interlibrary loan; copying; library open to the public for reference use only. **Computerized Information Services:** BRS Information Technologies, MEDLARS. **Publications:** Newsletter, monthly - for internal distribution only.

★9275★
Long Beach Memorial Hospital - Library (Med)
455 E. Bay Dr. Phone: (516)432-8000
Long Beach, NY 11561 Sharon Player
Subjects: Medicine, surgery, cardiology, psychiatry. **Holdings:** 240 books; 16 bound periodical volumes; 94 AV programs; 2 sets of microforms. **Services:** Interlibrary loan; copying; library open to the public. **Staff:** M. Rinke.

★9276★
Long Beach Memorial Medical Center - Medical Library (Med)
2801 Atlantic Ave.
Box 1428 Phone: (213)595-3841
Long Beach, CA 90801-1428 Marion Sabella, Dir.
Founded: 1923. **Staff:** Prof 2; Other 2. **Subjects:** Medicine, hospitals, nursing, allied health sciences. **Holdings:** 24,165 books; 27,707 bound periodical volumes. **Subscriptions:** 1000 journals and other serials. **Services:** Interlibrary loan; copying; SDI; library open to the public with restrictions. **Automated Operations:** Computerized serials. **Computerized Information Services:** BRS Information Technologies, DIALOG Information Services, MEDLARS, PFDS Online; CD-ROMs (MEDLINE, Knowledge Finder MEDLINE, CANCERLIT, Health Planning and Administrative Data Base, CINAHL); DOCLINE, OnTyme Electronic Message Network Service (electronic mail services). **Networks/Consortia:** Member of National Network of Libraries of Medicine - Pacific Southwest Region, CLASS, National Network of Libraries of Medicine (NN/LM). **Remarks:** FAX: (213)595-2147. Electronic mail address(es): CLASS.MMCLB (OnTyme Electronic Message Network Service). **Staff:** Emi Wong, Med.Libn.

★9277★
Long Beach Museum of Art Foundation - Library (Art)
2300 E. Ocean Blvd. Phone: (310)439-2119
Long Beach, CA 90803 Noriko Gamblin, Cur.
Staff: 4. **Subjects:** Art history (all periods). **Holdings:** 1550 books; 25 bound periodical volumes; 750 exhibition catalogs. **Services:** Library not open to the public. **Remarks:** FAX: (310)439-3587.

★9278★
Long Beach Press-Telegram - Library (Publ)
604 Pine Ave. Phone: (213)499-1309
Long Beach, CA 90844 Bob Andrew, Chf.Libn.
Founded: 1952. **Staff:** Prof 1; Other 2. **Subjects:** Newspaper reference topics. **Holdings:** 5 million clippings; 500,000 photographs; 2061 reels of microfilm. **Services:** Library not open to the public. **Computerized Information Services:** DIALOG Information Services, VU/TEXT Information Services.

★9279★
Long Beach Public Library - California Petroleum Industry Collection (Energy)
101 Pacific Ave. Phone: (310)437-2949
Long Beach, CA 90822 Louise Mazerov, Dept.Libn.
Founded: 1959. **Staff:** Prof 1. **Subjects:** History of California petroleum industry. **Holdings:** 1705 books; 200 bound periodical volumes; 3050 pictures; 850 tool catalogs and brochures; 500 pamphlets; 1700 government publications. **Services:** Copying; collection open to the public by appointment. **Computerized Information Services:** DIALOG Information Services. **Networks/Consortia:** Member of Metropolitan Cooperative Library System (MCLS), State of California Answering Network (SCAN). **Remarks:** FAX: (310)590-6956.

★9280★
Long Beach Public Library - Literature and History Department (Hum)
101 Pacific Ave. Phone: (310)437-2949
Long Beach, CA 90822 Claudine Burnett, Dept.Libn.
Staff: Prof 3; Other 1. **Subjects:** Fiction, literature, foreign languages, travel, biography, history. **Special Collections:** Long Beach Historical Collection; genealogy. **Holdings:** 78,500 books; 70 VF drawers. **Services:** Interlibrary loan. **Computerized Information Services:** DIALOG Information Services. **Networks/Consortia:** Member of State of California Answering Network (SCAN), Metropolitan Cooperative Library System (MCLS). **Special Indexes:** Local newspaper index (card). **Remarks:** FAX: (310)590-6956.

★9281★
Long Beach Public Library - Performing Arts Department (Art, Theater, Mus)
101 Pacific Ave. Phone: (310)437-2949
Long Beach, CA 90822 Judith Fraser, Dept.Libn.
Founded: 1926. **Staff:** Prof 3. **Subjects:** Art history and techniques, music history and scores, dance, flower arranging, antiques, theater, moving pictures, sports. **Special Collections:** Marilyn Horne Archives (recordings; pictures; press clippings); Miller Fine Arts Collection; Bertram Smith Collection; calligraphy. **Holdings:** 34,103 books; 8624 bound scores; 7099 pieces of sheet music; 193 framed pictures; 91,043 mounted pictures; 4317 video cassettes; 817 16mm films; 25,000 phonograph records; 5000 cassettes; 800 compact discs. **Services:** Interlibrary loan; department open to the public with restrictions. **Automated Operations:** Computerized public access catalog. **Computerized Information Services:** DIALOG Information Services. **Networks/Consortia:** Member of State of California Answering Network (SCAN), Metropolitan Cooperative Library System (MCLS). **Special Indexes:** Song titles, dance and instrumental music, artist, mounted picture subject indexes (all on cards). **Remarks:** FAX: (310)590-6956.

★9282★
Long Beach Public Library - Rancho Los Cerritos Historic Site - Library (Hist)
4600 Virginia Rd. Phone: (213)424-9423
Long Beach, CA 90807 Ellen Calomiris, Musm.Adm.
Founded: 1955. **Staff:** Prof 2; Other 1. **Subjects:** History - local, California, Southwest. **Special Collections:** Jonathan Temple Collection; Bixby-Hathaway Family Collection (both archival/manuscript collections); photograph collection (19th and 20th century photographs of Rancho Los Alamitos and Rancho Los Cerritos); land cases. **Holdings:** 5515 books; 235 bound periodical volumes; pictorial and topographical maps; scrapbooks. **Subscriptions:** 15 journals and other serials. **Services:** Interlibrary loan (limited); copying; library open to the public for reference use only. **Automated Operations:** NOTIS. **Publications:** The Branded Word, 2/year - to members, for sale to others. **Remarks:** Rancho Los Cerritos Historic Site and Library is owned by the City of Long Beach and operated as an agency of the Long Beach Public Library. It was designated a National Historic Landmark in 1970, and a State Historic Landmark in 1988.

★9283★
Long Beach Unified School District - Professional Library (Educ)
260 E. 9th St. Phone: (310)437-2851
Long Beach, CA 90813 Marilyn J. Larson, District Lib. Media Spec.
Staff: Prof 1. **Subjects:** Education. **Holdings:** 7000 books. **Subscriptions:** 45 journals and other serials. **Services:** Library not open to the public.

★9284★
Crawford Long Hospital of Emory University - Medical Library (Med)
550 Peachtree St., N.E. Phone: (404)686-2678
Atlanta, GA 30365-2225 Edith Lacey
Founded: 1942. **Staff:** Prof 3; Other 2. **Subjects:** Medicine, nursing, allied health sciences. **Holdings:** 4811 books; 7959 bound periodical volumes; 200 audio cassettes; 14 slide sets; 83 charts and pictures; 16 teaching aids; 9 maps; 11 microfiche sets; 786 videotapes. **Subscriptions:** 318 journals and other serials. **Services:** Interlibrary loan (fee); copying. **Computerized Information Services:** BRS Information Technologies, MEDLINE; CD-ROM (CINAHL). **Networks/Consortia:** Member of Atlanta Health Science Libraries Consortium (AHSLC), National Network of Libraries of Medicine - Southeastern/Atlantic Region. **Remarks:** FAX: (404)686-4974. **Staff:** Gladys Tsou; George Prince, Asst.Libn.

Dr. Hugo Long Library
See: **St. James Hospital and Health Centers** (14324)

Earl K. Long Library
See: **University of New Orleans** (19052)

★9285★
Earl K. Long Memorial Hospital - Medical Library (Med)
5825 Airline Hwy. Phone: (504)358-1089
Baton Rouge, LA 70805-2498 Eileen H. Stanley, Dir., Lib.Serv.
Staff: Prof 2; Other 3. **Subjects:** Clinical medicine. **Holdings:** 1900 books; 2600 bound periodical volumes; 150 AV programs; 20 VF drawers of articles. **Subscriptions:** 290 journals and other serials. **Services:** Interlibrary loan; copying; personal computer network for CD-ROMs available to library users. **Automated Operations:** Computerized cataloging and circulation. **Computerized Information Services:** MEDLARS, DIALOG Information Services. **Networks/Consortia:** Member of Baton Rouge Hospital Library Consortium. **Staff:** Celisa Smith, Libn.

Gillis W. Long Hansen's Disease Center
See: **U.S. Public Health Service Hospital - Gillis W. Long Hansen's Disease Center - Medical Library** (17934)

★9286★
Long Island Catholic - Research Library (Rel-Phil, Publ)
Box 700 Phone: (516)538-8800
Hempstead, NY 11551 Mildred McCarthy, Libn.
Founded: 1962. **Staff:** 1. **Subjects:** World affairs, religious affairs, Catholic Church. **Holdings:** 2300 books; 32 VF drawers of pictures; 28 VF drawers of subject files; 6 VF drawers of foreign files; 8 VF drawers of biographical files; 118 reels of microfilm; 185 maps. **Subscriptions:** 104 journals and other serials; 119 newspapers. **Services:** Library open to the public with the editor's approval. **Special Indexes:** Index to The Long Island Catholic Newspaper (online). **Remarks:** Established by the Catholic Press Association of Rockville Centre Inc. to serve reference and research needs of the newspaper; also serves the Bureau of Public Information of the Catholic Diocese of Rockville Centre.

★9287★
Long Island College Hospital - Morgan Health Sciences Library (Med)
340 Henry St. Phone: (718)780-1077
Brooklyn, NY 11201 Gabriel Bakcsy, Dir.
Founded: 1880. **Staff:** Prof 2; Other 3. **Subjects:** Medicine, nursing, basic sciences, social sciences, education. **Holdings:** 20,000 volumes; 60 linear feet of archival materials; 3 VF drawers of National League for Nursing pamphlets; 600 audio cassettes. **Subscriptions:** 377 journals and other serials. **Services:** Interlibrary loan; copying; library open to the public with restrictions. **Computerized Information Services:** MEDLARS. **Networks/Consortia:** Member of Medical Library Center of New York (MLCNY), New York Metropolitan Reference and Research Library Agency. **Staff:** George Wahlert, Staff Libn.

★9288★
Long Island Horticultural Research Laboratory - Library
39 Sound Ave.
Riverhead, NY 11901
Subjects: Agriculture, entomology, plant pathology, floriculture, ornamental horticulture. **Holdings:** 50 books; 200 bound periodical volumes; 50 other cataloged items. **Remarks:** Currently inactive.

★9289★
Long Island Jewish Medical Center - Health Sciences Library (Med)
Lakeville Rd. Phone: (718)470-7070
New Hyde Park, NY 11042 Debra Cassel Rand, Dir.
Founded: 1954. **Staff:** Prof 5; Other 4. **Subjects:** Medicine, dentistry, allied health sciences. **Holdings:** 9000 books; 15,000 bound periodical volumes. **Subscriptions:** 700 journals and other serials. **Services:** Interlibrary loan; copying; library open to the public for reference use only. **Automated Operations:** Computerized cataloging and serials. **Computerized Information Services:** DIALOG Information Services, BRS Information Technologies, NLM, Faxon LINX, PaperChase, BRS/COLLEAGUE; CD-ROMs (MEDLINE, PsycLIT); LINX Courier, InterNet (electronic mail services). **Networks/Consortia:** Member of Medical Library Center of New York (MLCNY), New York Metropolitan Reference and Research Library Agency. **Publications:** Annual publications list. **Remarks:** FAX: (718)470-6150. Electronic mail address(es): rand@aecom.yu.edu (InterNet). **Staff:** Shifra Atik, Assoc.Dir., Tech.Serv.; Esther King, Libn., Coll.Org.; Norma Frankel, Asst.Dir., Pub.Serv.; Ellen Brenner, Ref.Libn.

★9290★
Long Island Jewish Medical Center - Hillside Hospital - Health Sciences Library (Med)
75-59 263rd St.
Box 38 Phone: (718)470-8090
Glen Oaks, NY 11004 Joan L. Kauff, Asst.Dir., Hea.Sci.Libs.
Founded: 1943. **Staff:** Prof 1; Other 3. **Subjects:** Psychiatry, psychoanalysis, psychology, nursing, social work, hospital administration. **Holdings:** 10,000 books; 5500 bound periodical volumes; 36 VF drawers of reprints and pamphlets; 800 audio cassettes. **Subscriptions:** 250 journals and other serials. **Services:** Interlibrary loan; copying; SDI; library open to the public for reference use only. **Computerized Information Services:** BRS Information Technologies. **Networks/Consortia:** Member of Medical Library Center of New York (MLCNY), Long Island Library Resources Council. **Publications:** Specialized bibliographies.

★9291★
Long Island Jewish Medical Center - Queens Hospital Center - Health Science Library (Med)
82-68 164th St. Phone: (718)883-4019
Jamaica, NY 11432 Ruth Hoffenberg, Chf.Med.Libn., QHC
Staff: Prof 2; Other 1. **Subjects:** Clinical medicine, health services administration, nursing. **Holdings:** 6000 books; 7000 bound periodical volumes. **Subscriptions:** 462 journals and other serials. **Services:** Interlibrary loan; copying; library open to the public for reference use only. **Automated Operations:** Computerized ILL. **Computerized Information Services:** BRS Information Technologies, MEDLARS; CD-ROM (MEDLINE); DOCLINE (electronic mail service). **Networks/Consortia:** Member of Medical Library Center of New York (MLCNY), New York Metropolitan Reference and Research Library Agency, Brooklyn-Queens-Staten Island Health Sciences Librarians (BQSI). **Special Catalogs:** Union catalog of journal holdings of 4 libraries in Long Island Jewish Medical Center consortia; Union Catalog of Medical Periodicals (UCMP). **Remarks:** FAX: (718)883-3297. **Staff:** Henry Nietzschmann, Med.Libn.

★9292★
Long Island Library Resources Council, Inc. (Info Sci)
Melville Library Bldg., Suite E5310 Phone: (516)632-6650
Stony Brook, NY 11794-3399 Herbert Biblo, Dir.
Founded: 1967. **Staff:** Prof 4; Other 7. **Services:** Interlibrary loan; council not open to the public. **Computerized Information Services:** BRS Information Technologies, DIALOG Information Services, WILSONLINE, OCLC, RLIN, LIONS MILCS, LEXIS, NEXIS, DataTimes, VU/TEXT Information Services; DOCLINE (electronic mail service). **Publications:** Resource Guide: a composite subject profile of Long Island libraries (1987); LILRC Calendar; LILRC Newsletter; LILRC Healthline. **Special Catalogs:** Long Island Union List of Serials; Serials in Long Island Health Science Libraries: a Union List; Long Island School Library Union List of Serials; Union Catalog of Audio-Visual Materials; Union Catalog of Government Documents. **Remarks:** "LILRC, a New York State 3 R's Agency, maintains an office to develop and implement cooperative use of 180 member libraries by researchers from any member institution. The office operates a service locating and delivering materials and maintains and publishes a regional union list of serials. LILRC offers group subscriptions to database services at reduced rates, administers state-funded coordinated collection development, regional bibliographic databases, interlibrary resources sharing, hospital library services programs, and a program of library service for business and industry." FAX: (516)632-6662. Electronic mail address(es): ALA 0562 (ALANET). **Staff:** Judith Neufeld, Asst.Dir.; Valerie Rankow, Med.Info.Serv.Coord.; Carol Hochberg, Circuit Rider Libn. to Indus.

Long Island Studies Institute
See: **Hofstra University - Library - Special Collections** (7316)

★9293★
Long Island University - Arnold & Marie Schwartz College of Pharmacy & Health Sciences - Pharmaceutical Study Center (Med)
75 DeKalb Ave. Phone: (718)488-1000
Brooklyn, NY 11201 Alisa Yalan, Media Dir.
Staff: Prof 1. **Subjects:** Pharmacy, pharmacology, pharmacy administration, biomedical communications, hospital pharmacy. **Special Collections:** Pharmacy AV programs; masters' theses from the graduate school; computer-assisted instruction files (10); old pharmacy state board examinations. **Holdings:** 30 books; 250 current periodicals; 500 AV programs. **Subscriptions:** 225 journals and other serials. **Services:** Center open to the public. **Publications:** New Pharmacy Acquisitions.

★9294★
Long Island University - B. Davis Schwartz Memorial Library (Mus)
Greenvale, NY 11548 Phone: (516)299-2880
Donald Ungarelli, Dir.
Founded: 1954. **Staff:** Prof 1. **Subjects:** American popular music, ragtime, jazz. **Special Collections:** Sheet music (50,000); sound recordings (20,000); piano rolls (800); photographs (1000); playbills (500). **Holdings:** 2000 books. **Services:** Copying; library open to the public with restrictions. **Publications:** Brochure.

★9295★
Long Island University - C.W. Post Campus - Center for Business Research (Bus-Fin)
B. Davis Schwartz Memorial Library Phone: (516)299-2832
Brookville, NY 11548 Mary McNierney Grant, Dir.
Founded: 1978. **Staff:** Prof 6; Other 3. **Subjects:** Finance, marketing, management. **Special Collections:** State industrial directories; Disclosure, Inc. microfiche; Conference Board papers; trade periodicals. **Holdings:** 8900 books; 4800 bound periodical volumes; 17,000 reels of microfilm; 561,540 microfiche. **Subscriptions:** 1100 journals and other serials; 11 newspapers. **Services:** Center open to Long Island University students, faculty, and business community on a limited schedule. **Automated Operations:** Computerized cataloging and circulation. **Computerized Information Services:** DIALOG Information Services, NEXIS, VU/TEXT Information Services, Dow Jones News/Retrieval, InfoTrac; CD-ROMs (ABI Inform, ERIC, PsycINFO, GPO, MEDLINE). **Networks/Consortia:** Member of Long Island Library Resources Council. **Publications:** Business Alert, quarterly; Taking Your Business to Canada; Taking Your Business to Asia; Taking Your Business to Europe; The European Community; Conference Proceedings of Fee-Based Research in College and University Libraries; subject bibliographies. **Special Indexes:** Index to Long Island Business (local business weekly); National News Index. **Remarks:** FAX: (516)626-2271. **Staff:** Martha Cooney, Ref.Libn.; Barbara Bursuk, Ref.Libn.; Helen Moskowitz, Ref.Libn.; Susan Murphy, Ref.Libn.; Diane Jenkins, Ref.Libn.

★9296★
Long Island University - C.W. Post Campus - Library and Information Science Library (Info Sci)
B. Davis Schwartz Memorial Library Phone: (516)299-2826
Greenvale, NY 11548 Ellen Weinstein, Dept.Hd.
Founded: 1955. **Staff:** Prof 1; Other 7. **Subjects:** Library and information science, history of books and printing, children's literature, bibliography. **Special Collections:** Historical children's literature. **Holdings:** 18,009 books; 5018 periodical volumes; 450 theses; 29 Princeton files of library school, publisher, and dealers catalogs; 823 dissertations on microfilm; 6 Princeton files of library annual reports. **Subscriptions:** 299 journals and other serials. **Services:** Library open to the public for reference use only. **Automated Operations:** Computerized public access catalog and cataloging. **Computerized Information Services:** DIALOG Information Services, OCLC; internal database. **Networks/Consortia:** Member of Long Island Library Resources Council. **Publications:** Acquisitions list, 4/year - to faculty, students, and other library schools.

★9297★
Sharon Long - Private Collection (Soc Sci)
104-06 85th Ave. Phone: (718)441-8917
Richmond Hill, NY 11418 Sharon Long
Subjects: Abortion. **Special Collections:** Pro-Life Anti-Abortion Feminism. **Holdings:** 25 books; 50 bound periodical volumes; 5 VF drawers of articles and pamphlets. **Services:** Collection open to the public by appointment. **Remarks:** Collection of articles, focusing on empirical studies of abortion, is organized by subject and by pro-life and pro-choice points of view.

William P. Long Medical Library
See: **St. Luke Medical Center** (14473)

Henry Wadsworth Longfellow Collection
See: **Bowdoin College - Library - Special Collections** (2033)

Longfellow National Historic Site
See: **U.S. Natl. Park Service** (17745)

Longview Citizens' Resource Center
See: **LeTourneau University - Margaret Estes Library** (9072)

★9298★
Longview Daily News - Library (Publ)
770 11th Ave.
Box 189 Phone: (206)577-2511
Longview, WA 98632-0017 Donna Yardley, Libn.
Founded: 1923. **Staff:** 1. **Subjects:** Newspaper reference topics. **Holdings:** Bound files and microfilm of daily newspapers from 1923. **Services:** Library open to the public by appointment.

★9299★
Longwood Gardens, Inc. - Library (Biol Sci, Agri)
PO Box 501 Phone: (215)388-6741
Kennett Square, PA 19348-0501 Enola Jane N. Teeter, Libn.
Founded: 1961. **Staff:** Prof 1; Other 2. **Subjects:** Botany, horticulture, allied sciences. **Special Collections:** Curtis' Botanical Magazine (volume 1, 1787 to present); nursery catalogs. **Holdings:** 18,000 volumes; 10 VF drawers of pamphlets and clippings on plant material; 5 VF drawers of information on botanical gardens and arboreta; 35 VF drawers of information on horticulture and allied sciences; 5 VF drawers on geographical information; unbound periodicals; microforms. **Subscriptions:** 252 journals and other serials. **Services:** Interlibrary loan; copying; library open to the public with restrictions. **Computerized Information Services:** OCLC. **Networks/Consortia:** Member of PALINET. **Special Indexes:** Index to collection of nursery catalogs.

J.M. Longyear Research Library
See: **Marquette County Historical Society** (9707)

★9300★
Longyear Museum & Historical Society (Hist, Rel-Phil)
120 Seaver St. Phone: (617)277-8943
Brookline, MA 02146 Alan K. Lester, Assoc.Dir./Cur.
Founded: 1923. **Staff:** 15. **Subjects:** Mary Baker Eddy, Christian Science, John Munro Longyear, Mary Beecher Longyear. **Special Collections:** History of Christian Science, 1821-1910. **Holdings:** 5000 volumes; 1000 cubic feet of manuscripts, correspondence, diaries, journals, logbooks, genealogical source data, literary manuscripts. **Services:** Library open to qualified researchers with approval of the trustees. **Publications:** Quarterly News. **Remarks:** FAX: (617)277-3385. Guided tours of the museum are available. **Staff:** Loetta L. Lewis, Assoc.Dir., Adm.

Luis Lopez de Mesa Library
See: **Colombian Academy of Exact, Physical and Natural Sciences** (3925)

★9301★
Lorain Community Hospital - Medical Staff Library (Med)
3700 Kolbe Rd. Phone: (216)960-3327
Lorain, OH 44053 Patti Ryder, Med.Lib.Coord.
Founded: 1979. **Staff:** Prof 1. **Subjects:** Medicine, nursing, psychiatry, chemical dependency. **Holdings:** 1200 books; 150 bound periodical volumes; 1500 unbound journals. **Subscriptions:** 140 journals and other serials. **Services:** Interlibrary loan; copying; SDI; library open to the public for reference use only. **Computerized Information Services:** CD-ROMs (MEDLINE, PC-SIG Library, CINAHL). **Networks/Consortia:** Member of Cleveland Area Metropolitan Library System (CAMLS). **Remarks:** FAX: (216)960-4632.

★9302★
Lorain County Historical Society - Gerald Hicks Memorial Library (Hist)
509 Washington Ave. Phone: (216)322-3341
Elyria, OH 44035 Mary Jeffries, Cat.
Founded: 1975. **Subjects:** Local, state, national history; genealogy. **Special Collections:** Ely Family Papers, 1790-1900; early local city directories (75 volumes); Lorain County Manuscript Collection (150). **Holdings:** 623 volumes. **Services:** Library open to the public on a limited schedule for reference use only. **Special Indexes:** Index of Lorain County, OH histories, and cemeteries (card).

★9303★
Lorain County Law Library Association - Library (Law)
226 Middle Ave. Phone: (216)329-5567
Elyria, OH 44035 Mary Kovacs, Law Libn.
Staff: Prof 1; Other 1. **Subjects:** Law. **Holdings:** 20,000 books; 500 bound periodical volumes; 200 cassette tapes; 20,000 microfiche. **Subscriptions:** 25 journals and other serials. **Services:** Copying; library open to judges, county officals, Ohio legislators, attorneys, and law students residing in Lorain County. **Computerized Information Services:** WESTLAW. **Remarks:** FAX: (216)322-1724.

★9304★
Lorain County Printing & Publishing Company - Elyria Chronicle-Telegram - Library (Publ)
225 East Ave.
P.O. Box 4010 Phone: (216)329-7000
Elyria, OH 44036 Marie M. Banks, Hd.Libn.
Founded: 1955. **Staff:** Prof 1; Other 2. **Subjects:** Newspaper reference topics. **Special Collections:** Elyria history picture collection. **Holdings:** Newspaper clippings; photographs; negatives; microfilm. **Services:** Library open to the public with restrictions. **Remarks:** FAX: (216)329-7282.

★9305★
Loral Aeronutronic - Technical Information Services (Sci-Engr)
Ford Rd. Phone: (714)720-4668
Newport Beach, CA 92658-9983 Dorothy Carden, Libn.
Founded: 1957. **Staff:** Prof 4; Other 2. **Subjects:** Mathematics, astronomy, physics, meteorology, metallurgy, chemistry, engineering and management, aerospace research, electronics, computers. **Holdings:** 12,000 books; 3000 bound periodical volumes; 5000 technical reports. **Subscriptions:** 56 journals and other serials. **Services:** Interlibrary loan; services not open to the public. **Computerized Information Services:** DIALOG Information Services, DTIC. **Publications:** Acquisitions List; Periodical Holdings; Handbook, irregular. **Remarks:** FAX: (714)720-6413. **Formerly:** Ford Aeropace Corporation - Aeronutronic Division. **Staff:** Beth Krippner, Libn.

★9306★
Loral Control Systems - Technical Library (Sci-Engr)
Kennedy Dr. Phone: (717)876-1500
Archbald, PA 18403 Vince Barosi, Mgr., Engr.Serv.
Founded: 1951. **Subjects:** Science, technology, electronics, nuclear instrumentation, metallurgy. **Special Collections:** VSMF microfilm service (selected government and vendor specifications). **Holdings:** 3000 books. **Subscriptions:** 55 journals and other serials; 5 newspapers. **Services:** Interlibrary loan; library not open to the public. **Automated Operations:** Computerized circulation. **Remarks:** FAX: (717)876-4865.

★9307★
Loral Defense Systems - Akron - Library (Sci-Engr)
1210 Massillon Rd. Phone: (216)796-2557
Akron, OH 44315-0001 Louise Lariccia, Libn.
Staff: Prof 1; Other 1. **Subjects:** Aeronautics, electronics, mathematics, physics, computer science, material science. **Special Collections:** Lighter-than-air craft. **Holdings:** 8500 books; 1650 bound periodical volumes; 198,000 technical reports; archival materials; 135,000 microforms. **Subscriptions:** 680 journals and other serials. **Services:** Interlibrary loan; library not open to the public. **Automated Operations:** Computerized serials. **Computerized Information Services:** OCLC, DIALOG Information Services, NASA/RECON, Aerospace Online, DTIC, NewsNet, Inc.; Engineering Reports (ERS; internal database). **Publications:** Library Bulletin, bimonthly - for internal distribution only. **Special Indexes:** Airship Index; Lighter-than-Air Archives Index. **Remarks:** FAX: (216)796-9693.

★9308★
Loral Electronic Systems - Information Resource Center (Mil)
Ridge Hill Rd. Phone: (914)968-2500
Yonkers, NY 10710-0800 Ruth T. Joel, Coord.
Staff: Prof 1. **Subjects:** Electronic countermeasures, radar, electronic warfare, defense industry management. **Holdings:** 4000 books; 250 bound periodical volumes; 1000 microfiche; 1000 U.S. Department of Defense reports; 10,000 drawings. **Subscriptions:** 85 journals and other serials. **Services:** Interlibrary loan; center not open to the public. **Computerized Information Services:** DIALOG Information Services, DTIC. **Publications:** Online, monthly.

★9309★
Loral Fairchild Systems - Library
300 Robbins Lane
Syosset, NY 11791 Phone: (516)349-2200
Services: Library not open to the public. **Computerized Information Services:** DIALOG Information Services. **Remarks:** FAX: (516)931-4037.

★9310★
Loral Infrared & Imaging Systems - MIS 317 Technical Library (Sci-Engr)
2 Forbes Rd. Phone: (617)863-4376
Lexington, MA 02173 Carolyn Parece, Libn.
Founded: 1958. **Staff:** Prof 1; Other 1. **Subjects:** Optics, infrared detection, electro-optics, physics. **Holdings:** 8000 books; 1000 bound periodical volumes. **Subscriptions:** 252 journals and other serials. **Services:** Interlibrary loan. **Computerized Information Services:** OCLC.

★9311★
Loras College - Wahlert Memorial Library (Soc Sci, Hum)
14th & Alta Vista Sts. Phone: (319)588-7164
Dubuque, IA 52001 Robert Klein, Libn.
Founded: 1839. **Staff:** Prof 4; Other 4. **Subjects:** American history, American and English literature, education, economics. **Special Collections:** Horace Howard Furness Collection of Horace (811 volumes); Torch Press Imprint Collection (580 volumes); incunabula (58). **Holdings:** 236,824 volumes; 66,688 documents on microfiche; 4917 maps; William Boyd Allison U.S. Government Documents Collection (12,000 volume serial set); 5252 reels of microfilm. **Subscriptions:** 1124 journals and other serials; 13 newspapers. **Services:** Interlibrary loan; copying; library open to the public. **Automated Operations:** Computerized public access catalog, cataloging, acquisitions, serials, and circulation. **Computerized Information Services:** DIALOG Information Services. **Special Catalogs:** Printed Books, 1471-1500; G.K. Chesterton; T.S. Eliot; Sir Thomas More (all exhibition catalogs). **Remarks:** FAX: (319)588-7292. **Staff:** Kristen Smith, Ref.Libn.; Robert Schoofs, Tech.Serv.Libn.; Pamela Zordell, Pub.Serv.Libn.

★9312★
Lord, Bissell and Brook - Law Library (Law)
115 S. LaSalle St. Phone: (312)443-0647
Chicago, IL 60603 Jane L. Gaddis, Libn.
Staff: Prof 3; Other 6. **Subjects:** Law - insurance, corporate. **Holdings:** 31,000 books; 27 bound periodical volumes. **Subscriptions:** 60 journals and other serials. **Services:** Interlibrary loan; library not open to the public. **Computerized Information Services:** DIALOG Information Services, LEXIS, WESTLAW, DataTimes, Hannah Information Systems, Information America, VU/TEXT Information Services, OCLC. **Networks/Consortia:** Member of ILLINET. **Remarks:** FAX: (312)443-0336. **Staff:** John C. Fox; Martha Jenkins.

★9313★
Lord Corporation - Corporate R & D Library and Information Center (Sci-Engr)
405 Gregson Dr.
Box 8225 Phone: (919)469-3443
Cary, NC 27512-8225 Barbara Best-Nichols, Supv.
Founded: 1985. **Staff:** Prof 1; Other 1. **Subjects:** Polymer science, noise and vibration. **Holdings:** 1500 books. **Subscriptions:** 200 journals and other serials. **Services:** Interlibrary loan; copying. **Automated Operations:** Computerized cataloging, serials, and circulation. **Computerized Information Services:** DIALOG Information Services, PFDS Online, STN International. **Networks/Consortia:** Member of SOLINET. **Publications:** The Informer, monthly - for internal distribution only. **Remarks:** FAX: (919)469-5915.

★9314★
Lord Corporation - Libraries (Sci-Engr)
Box 10039
Erie, PA 16514 Phone: (814)456-8511
Staff: Prof 3; Other 3. **Subjects:** Rubber and polymer technology, noise and vibration control, materials science, coatings technology, adhesives technology. **Holdings:** 10,000 books; 5000 bound periodical volumes; technical reports and papers. **Subscriptions:** 670 journals and other serials; 10 newspapers. **Services:** Interlibrary loan; copying; SDI; libraries open to the public by appointment. **Automated Operations:** Computerized cataloging and circulation. **Computerized Information Services:** Maxwell Online, Inc., STN International, LEXIS, NEXIS, OCLC, DIALOG Information Services, WILSONLINE, NERAC, Inc.; TISR System (internal database). **Networks/Consortia:** Member of Northwest Interlibrary Cooperative of Pennsylvania (NICOP). **Publications:** Acquisitions List, quarterly; Digest of Macromolecular Technology, bimonthly - all for internal distribution only. **Remarks:** Library located at 1635 W. 12th St., Erie, PA 16514. FAX: (814)456-5425. Second library located at 2000 W. Grandview, Erie, PA 16514; telephone: (814)868-3611; FAX: (814)864-3452. Third library, described in the previous entry, located at 405 Gregson Dr., Cary, NC 27512; telephone (919)469-2500. **Staff:** Elizabeth J. Critchfield, Supv., 12th St. Lib.; L. Dianne Howard, Supv., Grandview Lib.; Barbara Best-Nichols, Supv.Res.Ctr.Lib.

★9315★
Lord Day & Lord, Barrett Smith - Library (Law)
1675 Broadway Phone: (212)969-6910
New York, NY 10019 Penny Frank, Hd.Libn.
Staff: Prof 4; Other 5. **Subjects:** Law - corporate, tax, aviation, maritime. **Holdings:** 35,000 volumes. **Subscriptions:** 450 journals and other serials. **Services:** Interlibrary loan; library not open to the public. **Automated Operations:** Computerized serials. **Computerized Information Services:** WESTLAW, Information America, LEXIS, DIALOG Information Services, Dow Jones News/Retrieval, NewsNet, Inc., VU/TEXT Information Services, Superior Online. **Remarks:** FAX: (212)969-6100. **Staff:** Timothy J. Hanley, Asst.Libn.; Barbara Tanzer, Assoc.Libn.; Georgia Hershfeld, Cat.

★9316★
Jim Lore & Associates - Library (Agri)
6715 8th St., N.E., Suite 236 Phone: (403)275-8937
Calgary, AB, Canada T2E 7H7 Dinah Kendall, Libn.
Founded: 1984. **Staff:** 1. **Subjects:** Agriculture, soil science, land use, land reclamation. **Special Collections:** Sour gas and its effect on the environment (400 papers); impact assessments of the Caroline and Sundre areas as done for Shell Canada. **Holdings:** 200 books; 14 bound periodical volumes; statutes, land titles, real estate expropriation law, land inventory (Agriculture and Rural Development Act), Alberta Environment Council material, agricultural/scientific journals, materials from soil science workshops (10 VF drawers and 35 bookshelves). **Subscriptions:** 30 journals and other serials. **Services:** Library open to the public with restrictions. **Computerized Information Services:** Procite (internal database). **Publications:** Agricultural Lore (newsletter), semiannual - available on request.

Walter Lorenz Memorial Library
See: **Westwood First Presbyterian Church** (20353)

★9317★
William T. Lorenz & Company - Library (Env-Cons)
85 Warren St. Phone: (603)228-3373
Concord, NH 03301 Robert S. Lorenz, Assoc.
Founded: 1975. **Staff:** Prof 3; Other 2. **Subjects:** Environment, water, wastewater, engineering, air pollution, hazardous waste. **Holdings:** 11,000 books; 2000 bound periodical volumes; 1100 reports. **Subscriptions:** 210 journals and other serials; 16 newspapers. **Services:** Library open to the public by appointment. **Computerized Information Services:** Environmental Agency Personnel, Vendors, Spending (internal databases). Contact Person: William T. Lorenz, Pres. **Remarks:** FAX: (603)225-2946.

★9318★
Loretto Hospital - Health Sciences Library
645 S. Central Ave.
Chicago, IL 60644 Phone: (312)626-4300
Founded: 1972. **Subjects:** Medicine, nursing, health administration. **Special Collections:** Psychiatry; addiction. **Holdings:** 950 books. **Remarks:** Currently inactive.

Loretto Memorial Library
See: **St. John's University** (14359)

★9319★
Lorillard Research Center Library (Biol Sci)
420 English St.
Box 21688 Phone: (919)373-6896
Greensboro, NC 27420 Lawrence M. Skladanowski, Lib.Supv.
Founded: 1959. **Staff:** Prof 4; Other 2. **Subjects:** Tobacco products and manufacturing, tobacco chemistry. **Holdings:** 4500 books; 5700 bound periodical volumes; 1000 boxes of unbound periodicals. **Subscriptions:** 120 journals and other serials. **Services:** Interlibrary loan; copying; library open to the public by appointment. **Automated Operations:** Computerized public access catalog and circulation. **Computerized Information Services:** DIALOG Information Services, NLM, BRS Information Technologies, STN International. **Remarks:** FAX: (919)373-6640. Lorillard is a division of Loews Inc.

★9320★
Lorimar Studios - Picture Research Library
10202 W. Washington Blvd.
Culver City, CA 90230
Defunct. Holdings absorbed by Warner Brother Studios - Research Library.

★9321★
Los Alamos Historical Museum Archives (Hist)
P.O. Box 43 Phone: (505)662-6272
Los Alamos, NM 87544 Theresa A. Strottman, Archv.
Staff: 2.5. **Subjects:** Los Alamos history, northern New Mexico history and archeology. **Special Collections:** Photographs of Los Alamos Ranch School by T.H. Parkhurst (356 photographs) and Laura Gilpin (110 photographs); Manhattan Project collection (books, manuscripts, maps, and photographs). **Holdings:** 600 books; 92 serial titles, including local newspapers and Los Alamos National Laboratory publications; 271 oral history audiocassettes; 115 linear feet of archival and manuscripts collections; 254 maps; 7379 photographs; 673 slides; 18 linear feet of photograph albums; 35 films and videotapes. **Subscriptions:** 13 journals and other serials. **Services:** Copying; photo print copies of archival photographs; archives open to the public by appointment. **Automated Operations:** Computerized cataloging. **Computerized Information Services:** Internal databases. **Publications:** When Los Alamos was a Ranch School (1974); A Los Alamos Reader (1976); Inside Box 1663 (1977); Los Alamos Outdoors (1981) ; Los Alamos: The First 40 Years (1985); Flowers of the Southwestern Forests and Woodlands (1984); Standing By and Making Do: Women of Wartime Los Alamos (1988); 12 Little Yellow Composites of Summer (1989); A Guide to Bandelier National Monument, 3rd ed. (1989); Exploring the Jemez Country (1990). **Remarks:** Alternate telephone number(s): (505)662-6312. **Staff:** Hedy M. Dunn, Musm.Dir.; Rebecca Collinsworth, Cur.

Los Alamos National Laboratory
See: **University of California - Los Alamos National Laboratory** (18298)

★9322★
Los Alamos Technical Associates - Technical Library (Sci-Engr)
1650 Trinity Dr.
Box 410 Phone: (505)662-9080
Los Alamos, NM 87544 Jocelyn Mandell, Libn.
Founded: 1980. **Staff:** 2. **Subjects:** Environment, energy, national security, quality assurance. **Holdings:** 6000 books, reports, documents. **Subscriptions:** 153 journals and other serials. **Services:** Library not open to the public. **Automated Operations:** Computerized cataloging and serials. **Computerized Information Services:** DIALOG Information Services.

★9323★
Los Angeles Area Chamber of Commerce - Economic Development Department Library
404 S. Bixel
Terminal Annex, Box 3696
Los Angeles, CA 90051
Founded: 1923. **Subjects:** Los Angeles-Anaheim-Riverside standard consolidated area - population characteristics, employment and earnings, construction and real estate, retail and wholesale trade, income, manufacturing, industrial growth, international trade data. **Special Collections:** Directories of largest employers, largest minority firms, and health services in the five-county area; census information; government publications; labor market bulletins for surrounding states. **Holdings:** Figures not available. **Remarks:** Currently inactive.

★9324★
Los Angeles Center for Photographic Studies - Resource Center (Art)
1048 W. 6th St. Phone: (213)482-3566
Los Angeles, CA 90017-2059 Suzy Kerr, Dir.
Founded: 1974. **Staff:** Prof 2. **Subjects:** Photographic art. **Special Collections:** Southern California Photography (1000 slides and biographical information on local artists). **Holdings:** 150 volumes; slides; 1 box of clippings; 2 boxes of ephemera. **Subscriptions:** 12 journals and other serials. **Services:** Center open to the public. **Publications:** Photo calendar, bimonthly (lists gallery and museum exhibitions, lectures in area) - samples on request; FRAME/WORK, 3/year - by subscription. **Special Catalogs:** Paul Outerbridge, Jr. (1976); Photographic Directions; Los Angeles (1979); William Mortensen (1979); Multicultural Focus, a photography exhibition for the Los Angeles Bicentennial (1981); L.A. as Subject Matter (1982); L.A. as Content (1982) - all for sale; 10 Photographers-Olympic Images (1984).

★9325★
Los Angeles City Attorney - Law Library (Law)
200 N. Main, Rm. 1700 Phone: (213)485-5400
Los Angeles, CA 90012 Luige Lill, Law Libn.
Founded: 1925. **Staff:** Prof 1; Other 1. **Subjects:** California and federal legislation; judicial rules and decisions; administrative rules and decisions; legislative history; tax services; municipal law and liability; economic and labor relations; environmental services. **Special Collections:** Los Angeles City Charter and Revisions, 1854 to present (17 volumes); statutes and amendments of California Codes, 1854 to present (84 volumes); California Constitutional Convention, 1880 (3 volumes); Los Angeles City Attorney Opinions, 1939 to present (425 volumes); City Attorney Criminal Appeals Cases (14 volumes). **Holdings:** 35,000 books; 300 bound periodical volumes; 1 file cabinet of City Attorney legal memos, letters. **Subscriptions:** 30 journals and other serials; 6 newspapers. **Services:** Library open to the public for reference use only. **Computerized Information Services:** LEXIS, NEXIS. **Special Indexes:** Index to Opinions, 2/year - local distribution; Index to legal memoranda (card).

★9326★
Los Angeles City Clerk's Office - Los Angeles City Archives (Hist)
Piper Technical Center
555 Ramirez St., Space 320 Phone: (213)485-3512
Los Angeles, CA 90012 Hynda L. Rudd, City Rec.Mgt.Off.
Staff: Prof 2. **Subjects:** Los Angeles history and government, 1827 to present. **Holdings:** 6000 cubic feet of city maps, council minutes and files, ordinances, tax records, annexation records, census reports, municipal and administrative codes, city charters, deeds, leases, contracts, departmental annual reports, photographs, records of former municipalities. **Services:** Copying; archives open to the public by appointment. **Staff:** Robert B. Freeman, Arch. II

★9327★
Los Angeles College of Chiropractic - Seabury McCoy Library (Med)
16200 E. Amber Valley Dr. Phone: (213)947-8755
Whittier, CA 90604 Nehmat Ghandour Saab, Dir., Lib.Serv.
Founded: 1948. **Staff:** Prof 2; Other 7. **Subjects:** Human spine and allied structures, chiropractic medicine, basic and clinical sciences, naturopathy. **Special Collections:** Chiropractic history. **Holdings:** 15,661 books; 3689 bound periodical volumes; 35,653 microfiche; VF materials. **Subscriptions:** 225 journals and other serials. **Services:** Interlibrary loan; copying. **Computerized Information Services:** MEDLARS. Performs searches on fee basis. **Networks/Consortia:** Member of National Network of Libraries of Medicine - Pacific Southwest Region, CLASS, Chiropractic Library Consortium (CLIBCON). **Remarks:** FAX: (213)947-5724.

★9328★
Los Angeles County Department of Arboreta and Botanic Gardens - Plant Science Library (Biol Sci)
301 N. Baldwin Ave. Phone: (818)821-3213
Arcadia, CA 91007-2697 Joan DeFato, Plant Sci.Libn.
Founded: 1948. **Staff:** Prof 1. **Subjects:** Botany, horticulture. **Special Collections:** Rare books; nursery catalogs (340 boxes). **Holdings:** 26,000 volumes; microfiche; maps. **Services:** Interlibrary loan; copying; library open to the public. **Remarks:** FAX: (818)445-1217. **Also Known As:** Los Angeles State and County Arboretum Plant Science Library.

★9329★
Los Angeles County Department of Health Services - Health Administration/Management Library (Med)
313 N. Figueroa St., Rm. Mz2 Phone: (213)974-7780
Los Angeles, CA 90012 Sharon Pruhs, Med.Libn. II
Founded: 1928. **Staff:** Prof 1; Other 1. **Subjects:** Public health, preventive medicine, environmental toxicology, administration, management. **Holdings:** 1200 books; 2000 bound periodical volumes. **Subscriptions:** 421 journals and other serials. **Services:** Interlibrary loan; copying; SDI; library open to the public. **Automated Operations:** Computerized cataloging, acquisitions, serials, and ILL (MELVYL). **Computerized Information Services:** DIALOG Information Services, MEDLINE, ORION, LEXIS, NEXIS, Public Health Network, OCLC, Federal Assistance Programs Retrieval System (FAPRS). **Networks/Consortia:** Member of National Network of Libraries of Medicine - Pacific Southwest Region, Los Angeles County Health Sciences Library Consortium. **Remarks:** FAX: (213)250-3909.

★9330★
Los Angeles County/Harbor-UCLA Medical Center - A.F. Parlow Library of the Health Sciences (Med)
1000 W. Carson St.
Box 18 Phone: (213)533-2373
Torrance, CA 90509 Mary Ann Berliner, Dir., Lib.Serv.
Founded: 1946. **Staff:** Prof 6; Other 11. **Subjects:** Medicine, nursing, dentistry, patient education, administration. **Holdings:** 21,653 books; 24,268 bound periodical volumes; 3000 pamphlet titles; 453 reels of microfilm; 850 AV programs. **Subscriptions:** 866 journals and other serials. **Services:** Interlibrary loan; copying; library open to the public with restrictions. **Automated Operations:** Computerized cataloging. **Computerized Information Services:** MEDLARS, BRS Information Technologies, NLM; CAI (Computer Assisted Instruction; internal database). Performs searches on fee basis. **Publications:** Journal holdings, annual; AV holdings, annual; Serials Holdings List; Library Newsletter.

Los Angeles County/High Desert Hospital
See: **LAC/High Desert Medical Center** (8865)

★9331★
Los Angeles County Internal Services Department - Management/Staff Development - Technical Library (Comp Sci)
9150 E. Imperial Hwy., Rm. R-118 Phone: (213)940-2391
Downey, CA 90242 Edris M. Lambert, Sys. Aide
Founded: 1969. **Staff:** Prof 1. **Subjects:** Computer programming, management science, personnel training. **Holdings:** 2000 books; 1000 bound periodical volumes; 500 pamphlets; 6000 technical computer manuals; 70 programmed instruction courses; 80 videotape training materials; 50 cassette lectures; 16 16mm films. **Subscriptions:** 53 journals and other serials. **Services:** Library not open to the public. **Publications:** Guide to Educational Services, updated as needed - for internal distribution only.

★9332★
Los Angeles County/King/Drew Medical Center - Health Sciences Library (Med)
1621 E. 120th St., MP 36 Phone: (213)563-4869
Los Angeles, CA 90059 Ms. M. Moss Humphrey, Dir.
Founded: 1972. **Staff:** Prof 3; Other 8. **Subjects:** Medicine. **Holdings:** 9500 books; 40,000 bound periodical volumes; 16 drawers of audio cassettes; 200 videotapes. **Subscriptions:** 825 journals and other serials. **Services:** Interlibrary loan; library open to the public. **Automated Operations:** Computerized public access catalog, serials, circulation, and acquisitions. **Computerized Information Services:** MEDLINE. **Remarks:** FAX: (213)563-4861. **Staff:** Thomas Hanson, Med.Libn.; Katherine M. Richards, Asst.Dir.

★9333★
Los Angeles County Law Library (Law)
301 W. 1st St. Phone: (213)629-3531
Los Angeles, CA 90012 Richard T. Iamele, Lib.Dir.
Founded: 1891. **Staff:** Prof 15; Other 42.5. **Subjects:** Law. **Holdings:** 752,194 volumes; 1822 audiotapes; 6528 reels of microfilm; 560,400 microforms. **Subscriptions:** 8030 journals and other serials. **Services:** Interlibrary loan; copying; library open to the public. **Automated Operations:** Computerized public access catalog and cataloging. **Computerized Information Services:** WESTLAW, DIALOG Information Services, WILSONLINE, Prentice Hall Online, State Net. Performs searches on fee basis. Contact Person: Edwin Schander. **Networks/Consortia:** Member of Research Libraries Information Network (RLIN). **Publications:** Bibliographies, irregular. **Remarks:** FAX: (213)613-1329. Maintains branch libraries in Beverly Hills, Compton, Long Beach, Norwalk, Pasadena, Pomona, Santa Monica, Torrance, and Van Nuys.

★9334★
Los Angeles County Medical Association - Library (Med)
634 S. Westlake Ave. Phone: (213)483-1581
Los Angeles, CA 90057 Joyce Crump, MLS
Founded: 1891. **Staff:** Prof 2; Other 2. **Subjects:** Medicine, history of medicine. **Special Collections:** Dr. George Dock Collection; local medical memorabilia; Osleriana; medical Californiana; history of medicine collection; rare books collection. **Holdings:** 87,000 books; 55,000 bound periodical volumes; 1 room of AV programs; 2 rooms of medical artifacts; boxed archival material; 16 VF drawers of pamphlets. **Subscriptions:** 60 journals and other serials. **Services:** Interlibrary loan; copying; library open to the public with restrictions. **Automated Operations:** Computerized cataloging. **Computerized Information Services:** MEDLINE, DIALOG Information Services, OCLC. **Networks/Consortia:** Member of Metronet. **Remarks:** FAX: (213)484-1488. **Staff:** Lori Potter, Ref.

★9335★
Los Angeles County Museum of Art - Research Library (Art)
5905 Wilshire Blvd. Phone: (213)857-6118
Los Angeles, CA 90036 Eleanor C. Hartman, Musm.Libn.
Founded: 1963. **Staff:** Prof 3; Other 5. **Subjects:** Art. **Special Collections:** Textiles and costumes; prints and drawings. **Holdings:** 80,000 books; 13,021 bound periodical volumes; 24,038 microfiche; 73 reels of microfilm; 37,347 sales and auction catalogs; 150 VF drawers of exhibition catalogs. **Subscriptions:** 476 journals and other serials. **Services:** Interlibrary loan; copying; library open by appointment to qualified researchers for reference use upon request. **Computerized Information Services:** OCLC. **Staff:** Carl R. Baker, Hd.Cat.; John Barone, Cat.

★9336★
Los Angeles County Office of Education - Pullias Reference Center (Educ)
9300 E. Imperial Hwy. Phone: (213)922-6359
Downey, CA 90242-2890 Sharon McNeil, Mgr.
Founded: 1972. **Staff:** Prof 4; Other 3. **Subjects:** Education. **Special Collections:** Los Angeles County Education Center publications. **Holdings:** 10,000 books; complete ERIC microfiche collection, 1966 to present. **Subscriptions:** 500 journals and other serials. **Services:** Interlibrary loan; copying; center open to the public with restrictions. **Automated Operations:** Computerized public access catalog, cataloging, acquisitions, serials, and circulation. **Computerized Information Services:** DIALOG Information Services, WILSONLINE, DataTimes. **Publications:** Bibliographies. **Remarks:** FAX: (213)803-1885. **Staff:** Veronica Ayson, Info.Rsrc.Spec.; Lyle S. Coffey, Info.Rsrc.Spec.; Teresita Icasas, Info.Rsrc.Spec.

Los Angeles County/Olive View Medical Health Center
See: **LAC/Olive View Medical Health Center** (8866)

Los Angeles County Public Library
See: **County of Los Angeles Public Library** (4378)

★9337★
Los Angeles County Sanitation District - Technical Library (Sci-Engr)
1955 Workman Mill Rd.
Box 4998 Phone: (213)699-7411
Whittier, CA 90607 Beverly K. Yoshida, Libn.
Staff: Prof 1; Other 1. **Subjects:** Water pollution control, sewage treatment, chemical analysis, solid and hazardous wastes management. **Holdings:** 1000 books; 9000 research and development reports, progress reports, sewage process reports of the Environmental Protection Agency and other government agencies. **Subscriptions:** 100 journals and other serials.

★9338★
Los Angeles County and University of Southern California Medical Center - Medical Libraries (Med)
General Hospital, Rm. 2050
1200 N. State St. Phone: (213)226-7006
Los Angeles, CA 90033-1084 Alice Reinhardt, Chf., Lib.Serv.
Founded: 1914. **Staff:** Prof 4; Other 6. **Subjects:** Medicine, nursing, allied health sciences. **Holdings:** 24,000 books; 29,500 bound periodical volumes; 1000 audio cassettes; 55 slide sets; 697 transparencies and filmstrips. **Subscriptions:** 1100 journals and other serials. **Services:** Interlibrary loan; libraries not open to the public. **Computerized Information Services:** NLM, DIALOG Information Services, BRS Information Technologies; DOCLINE (electronic mail service). Performs searches on fee basis. **Publications:** Bibliographies. **Remarks:** Figures represent holdings of General Hospital Library, Women's Hospital Library, and the Nursing Library. **Staff:** Bella Kwong, Women's Hosp.Libn.; Christina Chen, Tech.Serv.Libn.; Lawrence Rizzo, Ref./Automation Libn.

★9339★
Los Angeles Daily News - Editorial Library (Publ)
P.O. Box 4200 Phone: (818)713-3656
Woodland Hills, CA 91365-4200 Deborah Kaye, Chf.Libn.
Founded: 1911. **Staff:** Prof 7; Other 2. **Subjects:** Newspaper reference topics, Los Angeles history. **Special Collections:** Historical photograph collection of Los Angeles and surrounding area; San Fernando Valley historic photographs; current events photo collection. **Holdings:** 40,000 files of newspaper clippings; 100,000 photograph files; newspaper, 1911 to present, on microfilm. **Subscriptions:** 50 journals and other serials; 10 newspapers. **Services:** Library not open to the public. **Computerized Information Services:** NEXIS, DIALOG Information Services, VU/TEXT Information Services, DataTimes. **Special Indexes:** Index to the Daily News of Los Angeles (online). **Remarks:** Newspaper published by the Cooke Media Group Incorporated. **Also Known As:** Daily News of Los Angeles. **Staff:** Margaret Douglas, Libn.; Stacey Gordon, Libn.; Jacquelyn Cenacviera, Libn.; Vicki Zimring, Libn.; Miriam Velasquez, Libn.

★9340★
Los Angeles Department of Recreation and Parks - Cabrillo Marine Museum - Library (Biol Sci)
3720 Stephen White Dr. Phone: (213)548-7562
San Pedro, CA 90731 Dr. Susanne Lawrenz-Miller, Marine Musm.Adm.
Founded: 1935. **Staff:** Prof 11; Other 20 **Subjects:** Marine biology, aquariums, whaling, museology, marine ecology, marine education, conservation. **Holdings:** 1279 books; 2191 unbound periodical volumes; pictures. **Subscriptions:** 14 journals and other serials. **Services:** Library not open to the public. **Staff:** Catherine A. Crouch, Cur.

★9341★
Los Angeles Harbor College - Library - Archives (Hist)
1111 Figueroa Pl. Phone: (213)518-1000
Wilmington, CA 90744 Sally Gogin, Per.Libn.
Founded: 1949. **Staff:** Prof 3. **Subjects:** History and development of the San Pedro-Wilmington, Lomita, Palos Verdes Peninsula, and Carson areas of the Los Angeles Harbor region; development of the Los Angeles Harbor; maritime history. **Holdings:** 1500 oral history tapes, documents, photographs. **Services:** Archives open to the public by appointment only. **Remarks:** FAX: (213)834-1882.

★9342★
Los Angeles Psychoanalytic Society and Institute - Simmel-Fenichel Library (Med)
2014 Sawtelle Blvd.
Los Angeles, CA 90025 Phone: (213)478-6541
Founded: 1953. **Subjects:** Psychoanalysis and psychiatry, the behavioral sciences. **Special Collections:** Freudiana (books; articles; letters; photographs; miscellanea). **Holdings:** 5500 books; 800 bound periodical volumes; 1500 unbound periodicals; 14 VF drawers of reprints and pamphlets; 550 unpublished papers; 600 tapes; 18 videotapes. **Subscriptions:** 40 journals and other serials. **Services:** Interlibrary loan; copying; library open to the public with guest membership. **Computerized Information Services:** DIALOG Information Services, MEDLARS, MEDLINE. Performs searches on fee basis. Contact Person: Margaret Johnson, 478-6541. **Special Indexes:** Chicago Psychoanalytic Literature Index (psychoanalysis and psychiatry, psychosomatic medicine and related areas of the behavioral sciences; card file up to 1974; bound volumes, 1920-1986).

★9343★
Los Angeles Public Library - Art, Music & Recreation Department (Art, Hum)
630 W. 5th St. Phone: (213)612-3254
Los Angeles, CA 90071 Romaine Ahlstrom, Dept.Mgr.
Staff: Prof 7.5; Other 16.5. **Subjects:** Art, architecture, music, opera, sports and recreation, film, photography, dance, costume, urban planning, gardening, circus. **Special Collections:** Japanese prints (240 items); Art in Los Angeles Scrapbooks, 1938 to 1984; Dance in Los Angeles Scrapbooks, 1955 to 1984; Music in Los Angeles Scrapbooks, 1894 to 1984; Olympic Games in Los Angeles Scrapbooks, 1932 and 1984; orchestral scores and parts (3000 items); chess; bullfighting; music recordings. **Holdings:** 220,196 volumes; 155,000 clippings; 55,231 scores; 220,000 mounted pictures. **Subscriptions:** 747 journals and other serials. **Services:** Interlibrary loan; copying; department open to the public. **Automated Operations:** Computerized public access catalog and acquisitions. **Computerized Information Services:** DIALOG Information Services, EasyNet, Art Index, Books in Print Plus, ProQuest. Performs searches on fee basis. **Networks/Consortia:** Member of Metropolitan Cooperative Library System (MCLS), Performing Arts Libraries Network of Greater Los Angeles (PALNET). **Special Catalogs:** Catalog of orchestral scores and parts. **Special Indexes:** Art Biography Index; Art Subject Index; Architecture Index; Picture File; Index to Musicians; Symphony Program Notes; Sport Files; Circus Index; Architecture Index; Costume Index; Dance Index (all on cards); Song Index (online). **Remarks:** Library located at 433 S. Spring St., Los Angeles, CA 90013. FAX: (213)612-0406.

★9344★
Los Angeles Public Library - Business & Economics Department (Bus-Fin)
630 W. 5th St. Phone: (213)612-3280
Los Angeles, CA 90071 Cecelia M. Riddle, Dept.Mgr.
Staff: Prof 9; Other 13. **Subjects:** Management, investment, international trade, transportation, economics, banking, finance, media, commercial law, labor, taxes, real estate. **Holdings:** 181,700 volumes; corporate annual reports; Securities and Exchange Commission 10K reports, 1970 to present, on microfiche; depository for U.S., California, and U.N. documents; trade and business specialty directories. **Subscriptions:** 4000 journals and other serials. **Services:** Interlibrary loan; copying. **Automated Operations:** Computerized public access catalog. **Computerized Information Services:** EasyNet, American Business Information, Compact Disclosure, CIRR, SRI, National Trade Data Base (NTDB), Predicasts F & S, Auto-Graphics; internal database. Performs searches on fee basis. **Networks/Consortia:** Member of Metropolitan Cooperative Library System (MCLS). **Publications:** Investment Information Sources: Los Angeles Public Library Investment Collection - free upon request. **Remarks:** Library located at 433 S. Spring St., Los Angeles, CA 90013. FAX: (213)612-0557.

★9345★
Los Angeles Public Library - Children's Literature Department (Hum)
630 W. 5th St. Phone: (213)612-3261
Los Angeles, CA 90071 Janine Goodale, Dept.Mgr.
Staff: Prof 4; Other 7. **Subjects:** Children's literature. **Special Collections:** Folk and fairy tales (2520 volumes); international language children's books (6000 volumes); Mother Goose (900 volumes); Gladys English Collection (175 original children's book illustrations); poetry. **Holdings:** 230,000 books; 830 bound periodical volumes. **Subscriptions:** 300 journals and other serials. **Services:** Interlibrary loan; copying; department open to the public. **Automated Operations:** Computerized public access catalog and acquisitions. **Computerized Information Services:** DIALOG Information Services; internal databases. Performs searches on fee basis. **Networks/Consortia:** Member of Metropolitan Cooperative Library System (MCLS). **Special Indexes:** Author and illustrator biographies; fiction; folktales and short stories; illustrations; picture books; plays; songs; Californiana. **Remarks:** Library located at 433 S. Spring St., Los Angeles, CA 90013. FAX: (213)612-0531.

★9346★
Los Angeles Public Library - Film & Video Services (Aud-Vis)
630 W. 5th St. Phone: (213)612-3263
Los Angeles, CA 90071 Dan Dupill, Sr.Libn.
Staff: Prof 1; Other 11. **Subjects:** Documentaries, performing arts. **Special Collections:** Film study collection. **Holdings:** 2600 16mm films; 8500 videotapes. **Services:** Services open to the public. **Computerized Information Services:** DIALOG Information Services. Performs searches on fee basis. **Networks/Consortia:** Member of Metropolitan Cooperative Library System (MCLS). **Special Catalogs:** Film and video catalog. **Remarks:** Library located at 433 S. Spring St., Los Angeles, CA 90013. FAX: (213)612-0536.

★9347★
Los Angeles Public Library - History and Genealogy Department (Hist)
630 W. 5th St. Phone: (213)612-3314
Los Angeles, CA 90071 Jane Nowak, Dept.Mgr.
Staff: Prof 11; Other 23. **Subjects:** History, travel, biography, Californiana, genealogy, local history, heraldry, newspapers. **Special Collections:** Genealogy (38,000 volumes); Californiana (20,000 items); maps and atlases; American Indians; World Wars I and II; travel; Security Pacific Bank historic photograph collection; Herald Examiner Newspaper and Photograph Morgues. **Holdings:** 290,000 volumes; 91,000 maps; 2.7 million photographs; 800 historical specimen newspapers; 25,000 reels of microfilm of newspapers; U.S. city directories; census records. **Subscriptions:** 1300 journals and other serials; 65 newspapers. **Services:** Interlibrary loan; copying (limited). **Automated Operations:** Computerized public access catalog and acquisitions. **Computerized Information Services:** DIALOG Information Services, EasyNet; internal databases; CD-ROM (Los Angeles Times). Performs searches on fee basis. **Networks/Consortia:** Member of Metropolitan Cooperative Library System (MCLS). **Special Indexes:** California biography; California subject; Western outlaws and sheriffs; collected biography; American Indians; family history; local history; coats of arms; photograph collection (accessed on microcomputer). **Remarks:** Library located at 433 S. Spring St., Los Angeles, CA 90013. FAX: (213)612-0529.

★9348★
Los Angeles Public Library - International Languages Department (Hum)
630 W. 5th St. Phone: (213)612-3291
Los Angeles, CA 90071 Sylva N. Manoogian, Dept.Mgr.
Founded: 1920. **Staff:** Prof 5; Other 9. **Subjects:** Books in 28 modern languages (primarily history, literature, drama, poetry, biography, fiction). **Special Collections:** Multilingual health materials (400 volumes in 12 languages); print and non-print language study materials (12,000 volumes in over 500 languages and dialects, including English as a second language; audio, video, and microcomputer software). **Holdings:** 175,000 books; 245 bound periodical volumes; 1200 reels of microfilm of retrospective periodical titles in French, German, Armenian, Chinese, Japanese, Korean, and Spanish. **Subscriptions:** 250 journals and other serials. **Services:** Interlibrary loan; copying; multilingual reference and reader's advisory service; multimedia language learning center; department open to the public. **Automated Operations:** Computerized public access catalog. **Computerized Information Services:** DIALOG Information Services, EasyNet; internal databases. Performs searches on fee basis. **Networks/Consortia:** Member of Metropolitan Cooperative Library System (MCLS). **Publications:** Special bibliographies. **Special Indexes:** Drama and Short Story Indexes in French, German, Italian, Russian, and Spanish; Short Story Collections in French, German, Italian, Russian, Swedish, and Yiddish; Spanish Poetry Index; Spanish Literary Criticism File; Multilingual Fiction Subject Index. **Remarks:** Library located at 433 S. Spring St., Los Angeles, CA 90013. FAX: (213)612-0409.

★9349★
Los Angeles Public Library - James Alan Doherty Municipal Reference Library (Soc Sci, Plan)
530 City Hall E.
200 N. Main St. Phone: (213)485-3791
Los Angeles, CA 90012 Linda Moussa, Act.Prin.Libn.
Founded: 1928. **Staff:** Prof 5; Other 6. **Subjects:** Public administration, city planning, municipal government, municipal finance, fire, recreation and parks, public works, civil service, personnel. **Special Collections:** Municipal documents from large cities; biography file of Los Angeles officials. **Holdings:** 43,212 volumes. **Subscriptions:** 591 journals. **Services:** Specialized reference service for city officials and employees; library open to the public for reference use only. **Computerized Information Services:** DIALOG Information Services, RLIN, WILSONLINE, VU/TEXT Information Services, LOGIN. **Remarks:** FAX: (213)485-9942.

★9350★
Los Angeles Public Library - Literature/Fiction Department (Hum, Info Sci)
630 W. 5th St. Phone: (213)612-3287
Los Angeles, CA 90071 Helene G. Mochedlover, Dept.Mgr.
Staff: Prof 11; Other 15. **Subjects:** Bibliography, library science, printing, philology, drama and the theater, poetry, literary history and criticism, biography, public speaking, authorship, humor, fiction, foreign translations. **Special Collections:** Dobinson Collection of Theatre Memorabilia. **Holdings:** 476,670 volumes. **Subscriptions:** 1323 journals and other serials. **Services:** Interlibrary loan; copying; department open to the public. **Automated Operations:** Computerized public access catalog and acquisitions. **Computerized Information Services:** DIALOG Information Services, EasyNet; internal databases. Performs searches on fee basis. **Networks/Consortia:** Member of Metropolitan Cooperative Library System (MCLS). **Special Indexes:** Arabian Nights Index; Argosy Magazine Index; author clippings (50,000); Index to Works of Robert Benchley; Don Blanding Index; Cosmopolitan Magazine Index; Thomas Augustine Daly Index; Index to Dialect Readings; Drama Clippings Index; Drama in Los Angeles Scrapbook; Edgar A. Guest Index; Holiday Index; Liberty Magazine Index; Index to Monologs; Index to New York Dramatic Mirror; Alfred Noyes Index; obituary file; play review file; Southern California theatre scrapbook; subject index to plays; subject index to poetry; supplemental essay index; television reviews scrapbook index; Theatre Program Index; James Thurber Index; True Magazine Index; Mark Twain Index; unpublished play index; Ella Wheeler Wilcox Index; Balzac Index; biographical index; California in Fiction; California Locale Index; California Chronological Index; Detectives; Fiction Book Review File; Index of Filmed Books; Maupassant Index; Prize Novels Index; Serials and Sequels Index; Short Story Index; Subject Index to Fiction; Title Derivation Index; Jules Verne Index. **Remarks:** Library located at 433 S. Spring St., Los Angeles, CA 90013. FAX: (213)612-0408.

★9351★
Los Angeles Public Library - Municipal Reference Department - Water & Power Library (Sci-Engr)
Rm. 518 GOB
Box 111 Phone: (213)481-4611
Los Angeles, CA 90051 Joyce A. Purcell, Sr.Libn.
Founded: 1926. **Staff:** Prof 4; Other 6. **Subjects:** Electrical and civil engineering, water, public utilities. **Holdings:** 20,000 volumes. **Subscriptions:** 600 journals and other serials. **Services:** Library open to the public for reference use only. **Computerized Information Services:** DIALOG Information Services, BRS Information Technologies, WILSONLINE, MEDLINE. **Remarks:** FAX: (213)580-3983. **Staff:** Phyllis Absalom, Libn. II; Helen Goring, Libn. II; Pat Seebode, Libn. II.

★9352★
Los Angeles Public Library - Rare Books and Special Collections (Rare Book)
630 W. 5th St. Phone: (213)612-3208
Los Angeles, CA 90071 Romaine Ahlstrom, Prin.Libn.
Staff: Prof 1; Other 2. **Subjects:** California, Mexican history, Pacific voyages, bullfighting, printing history, ornithology, 19th century American fiction. **Special Collections:** Los Angeles Public Library Archives. **Holdings:** 12,000 books. **Services:** Copying (limited); room open to the public with restrictions. **Automated Operations:** Computerized public access catalog. **Computerized Information Services:** DIALOG Information Services, BookQuest; internal databases. Performs searches on fee basis. **Networks/Consortia:** Member of Metropolitan Cooperative Library System (MCLS), Performing Arts Libraries Network of Greater Los Angeles (PALNET). **Remarks:** Library located at 433 S. Spring St., Los Angeles, CA 90013. FAX: (213)612-0406.

★9353★
Los Angeles Public Library - Science, Technology and Patents Department (Sci-Engr, Biol Sci)
630 W. 5th St. Phone: (213)612-3270
Los Angeles, CA 90071 Billie M. Connor, Dept.Mgr.
Founded: 1914. **Staff:** Prof 8.5; Other 15.25. **Subjects:** Physical and biological sciences, consumer health, medicine and drugs, alternative medicine, earth and natural sciences, applied technology, intellectual property, ecology, astronomy, foods and beverages, computer sciences, natural history, climatology, oceanography, electronics, motor vehicles. **Special Collections:** U.S. patents (complete set); British patents (complete set); foreign patents (selected); cookery; menus; automotive history and repair; specifications and standards. **Holdings:** 250,000 volumes; 50,000 documents. **Subscriptions:** 1700 journals; 1500 serials. **Services:** Interlibrary loan; copying; department open to the public. **Automated Operations:** Computerized public access catalog and acquisitions. **Computerized Information Services:** DIALOG Information Services, EasyNet, CASSIS (U.S. Patent Classification System); internal databases. Performs searches on fee basis. **Networks/Consortia:** Member of Metropolitan Cooperative Library System (MCLS). **Publications:** Brochures on patents, trademarks, copyright collections, various subject fact sheets - free upon request. **Special**

Indexes: Index to colored plates of wild flowers, mushrooms, fish, birds, reptiles, shells, antique automobiles, trees and shrubs, animals, amphibians , butterflies, and insects; Ship Index by type and name; Anthropology Index by tribe; Appliance Repair Index; Automotive Repair Index; directories index; menu collection index; science projects index. **Remarks:** Serves as Patent and Trademark Depository Library System. Library located at 433 S. Spring St., Los Angeles, CA 90013. FAX: (213)612-0556.

★9354★
Los Angeles Public Library - Social Sciences, Philosophy and Religion Department (Soc Sci, Rel-Phil)
630 W. 5th St. Phone: (213)612-3250
Los Angeles, CA 90071 Marilyn C. Wherley, Dept.Mgr.
Staff: Prof 10; Other 17. **Subjects:** Philosophy, religion, psychology, social problems, government, foreign affairs, international relations, law, criminology, education, women's movements, family relations, ethnic groups, interpersonal relations. **Special Collections:** California, U.S., and U.N. documents depository; African-American history and culture; Mexican-American Affairs; women; education; the occult; cults and sects; Eastern religions. **Holdings:** 389,000 volumes. **Subscriptions:** 2850 journals and other serials. **Services:** Interlibrary loan; copying; department open to the public. **Automated Operations:** Computerized public access catalog. **Computerized Information Services:** DIALOG Information Services, EasyNet. Performs searches on fee basis. **Networks/Consortia:** Member of Metropolitan Cooperative Library System (MCLS). **Special Indexes:** Superstition; mythology; cults and sects; psychics; metaphysical societies; crime; current affairs; elections; statistics. **Remarks:** Library located at 433 S. Spring St., Los Angeles, CA 90013. FAX: (213)612-0407.

★9355★
Los Angeles Public Library, Chinatown Branch (Area-Ethnic)
536 W. College St. Phone: (213)620-0925
Los Angeles, CA 90012 Elsa L.C. Wu, Sr.Libn.
Founded: 1977. **Staff:** Prof 5; Other 12. **Special Collections:** Chinese language collection (29,000 volumes); Chinese Heritage collection (5100 items); Vietnamese language collection (3300 volumes); Spanish language collection (800 volumes). **Subscriptions:** 220 journals and other serials; 17 newspapers. **Services:** Interlibrary loan; copying; collection open to the public. **Computerized Information Services:** CD-ROM (Periodical Abstracts Ondisc). **Networks/Consortia:** Member of Metropolitan Cooperative Library System (MCLS). **Publications:** Community File; Chinese American Biography File. **Staff:** Joshua Ma, Chinese Spec.; Cathy Chang, Young Adult Libn.; Chanchal Agarwal, Children's Libn.

★9356★
Los Angeles Regional Family Planning Council, Inc. - Library (Soc Sci)
3600 Wilshire Blvd., Suite 600 Phone: (213)386-5614
Los Angeles, CA 90010-0605 Selda Roth, Libn.
Founded: 1985. **Staff:** Prof 1; Other 2. **Subjects:** Family planning, family life education, birth control, reproductive health, sexually transmitted diseases, AIDS, breast feeding, international family planning, natural family planning. **Holdings:** 1500 books; 400 AV programs; pamphlets, VF drawers of newspaper and journal articles, reports, studies. **Subscriptions:** 70 journals and other serials. **Services:** Copying; library open to the public by appointment. **Networks/Consortia:** Member of APLIC International Census Network. **Publications:** Bilingual Bibliography of Spanish Resources; annotated bibliographies; technical assistance lists. **Special Catalogs:** Film and AV catalogs. **Remarks:** FAX: (213)383-4069; 365-0973.

Los Angeles State and County Arboretum Plant Science Library
See: **Los Angeles County Department of Arboreta and Botanic Gardens - Plant Science Library** (9328)

★9357★
Los Angeles Times - Editorial Library (Publ)
Times-Mirror Square Phone: (213)237-7181
Los Angeles, CA 90053 Cecily J. Surace, Lib.Dir.
Founded: 1905. **Staff:** Prof 25; Other 24. **Subjects:** Newspaper reference topics. **Special Collections:** Photographs (over 1 million); clippings (9 million). **Holdings:** Books; newspapers; pamphlets; negatives; microfilm; Los Angeles Times (online). **Subscriptions:** 500 journals and other serials. **Services:** Interlibrary loan; library not open to the public. **Automated Operations:** Computerized cataloging and acquisitions. **Computerized Information Services:** DIALOG Information Services, OCLC, Data Resources (DRI), LEGI-TECH, PFDS Online, BRS Information Technologies, LEXIS, NEXIS, MEDLINE, Dow Jones News/Retrieval, VU/TEXT Information Services; internal database. **Networks/Consortia:** Member of CLASS. **Publications:** New Materials; Library Information Notes; Library Update - both irregular. **Special Indexes:** Index to negatives (online). **Remarks:** FAX: (213)237-4641. **Staff:** Cary Schneider, Ref./Res.; Mildred Simpson, Graphics; Chris Hingley, Database Constr.; Carla Barbula, Acq.

★9358★
Los Angeles Trade-Technical College - Library (Educ)
400 W. Washington Blvd. Phone: (213)744-9025
Los Angeles, CA 90015 Joyce Livingston, Chm., Lib.Serv.
Staff: Prof 4; Other 5. **Subjects:** Trades - apparel, commercial art, automotive, building, cosmetology, culinary arts, drafting, electricity, electronics, metal, office administration, plastics, printing, vocational nursing, registered nursing, business administration. **Holdings:** 65,000 volumes. **Subscriptions:** 363 journals and other serials; 14 newspapers. **Services:** Interlibrary loan; copying; library open to the public. **Remarks:** Affiliated with the Los Angeles Community College District. **Staff:** L. Kite, Cat.Libn.; W. Troost, Media Cons.

★9359★
Los Lunas Hospital and Training School - Library (Med)
Box 1269
Los Lunas, NM 87031 Phone: (505)841-5317
Founded: 1969. **Staff:** Prof 1; Other 1. **Subjects:** Mental retardation, developmental disabilities, special education, psychology, medicine, nursing, social services. **Holdings:** 2000 books; 15 dissertations; 40 reports; 498 videotapes; 74 adapted switches and assistive devices. **Subscriptions:** 78 journals and other serials. **Services:** Interlibrary loan; copying; SDI; library open to the public with restrictions. **Computerized Information Services:** DIALOG Information Services. Performs searches on fee basis. **Networks/Consortia:** Member of National Network of Libraries of Medicine - South Central Region, New Mexico Consortium of Biomedical and Hospital Libraries.

Lost Battalion Room
See: **Wise County Historical Society, Inc. - Wise County Historical Commission Archive** (20535)

★9360★
Loto-Quebec - Centre de Documentation (Rec)
500 Sherbrooke St., W., Suite 2000 Phone: (514)282-8000
Montreal, PQ, Canada H3A 3G6 Louise Racine, Libn.
Founded: 1978. **Staff:** Prof 3; Other 1. **Subjects:** Lotteries, casinos, horse racing, video games, sports betting. **Holdings:** 4980 books; 215 annual reports; 270 confidential documents. **Subscriptions:** 180 journals and other serials. **Services:** Interlibrary loan; copying; center open to the public. **Automated Operations:** Computerized cataloging, acquisitions, and circulation. **Computerized Information Services:** DIALOG Information Services, SOQUIJ; internal database; Envoy 100 (electronic mail service). **Publications:** Liste des acquisitions, monthly; JHA Nouveauties, quarterly; Telematique, quarterly. **Remarks:** FAX: (514)873-8999. Electronic mail address(es): LUC.PROVOST (Envoy 100).

Lott Memorial Architectural Library
See: **Dayton Art Institute - Library** (4654)

J. Otto Lottes Health Sciences Library
See: **University of Missouri--Columbia** (18965)

★9361★
Lotus Development Corporation - Information Resources Group - Resource Center (Comp Sci)
1 Rogers St. Phone: (617)693-5300
Cambridge, MA 02142 Paulyn Heinmiller, Mgr.
Founded: 1983. **Staff:** 12. **Subjects:** Microcomputer software and hardware, general business, computer science and engineering. **Special Collections:**

Secondary market research collection. **Holdings:** 2500 books; 1500 software packages; videotapes; technical reports; microfiche. **Subscriptions:** 200 journals and other serials; 6 newspapers. **Services:** Interlibrary loan; copying; SDI; center not open to the public. **Automated Operations:** Computerized public access catalog, cataloging, acquisitions, serials, and circulation. **Computerized Information Services:** DIALOG Information Services, VU/TEXT Information Services, CompuServe Information Service, Dow Jones News/Retrieval, InvesText, Mead Data Central, NewsNet, Inc., WILSONLINE; internal databases; MCI Mail (electronic mail service). **Networks/Consortia:** Member of Boston Library Consortium (BLC). **Publications:** Newswires, daily; Micronotes, weekly; Marketbriefs, bimonthly; IRG Application Services (CD-ROM), quarterly - all for internal distribution only. **Special Indexes:** Indexes of publications and electronic mail messages. **Staff:** Barbara Brooker, Res.Serv.; Jane Rich, Applications/Serv.; Teri Conners, Educ.Serv.

Henry S. Louchheim Library
See: **Eagleville Hospital** (5091)

Louisiana Electronic Assistance Program (LEAP)
See: **Northeast Louisiana University - Center for Business & Economic Research - Library** (11970)

Louisiana Historical Center
See: **Louisiana State Museum** (9371)

★9362★
Louisiana Naval War Memorial - Library (Mil)
305 S. River Rd. Phone: (504)342-1942
Baton Rouge, LA 70802 Timothy Rizzuto, Cur.
Subjects: FLETCHER Class destroyers - design, tactical deployment, history; World War II U.S. Navy destroyer operations. **Holdings:** 1500 books; 400 bound periodical volumes; 2400 documents. **Services:** Library open with restrictions to foundation members. **Publications:** KIDD'S COMPASS Newsletter. **Staff:** Maury Drummond, Dir.

Louisiana State Department of Culture, Recreation & Tourism - State Library of Louisiana
See: **(Louisiana) State Library of Louisiana** (9370)

★9363★
Louisiana (State) Department of Economic Development - Office of Commerce & Industry - Industrial Development Reference Library (Bus-Fin)
Box 94185
Baton Rouge, LA 70804-9185
Founded: 1979. **Staff:** 1. **Subjects:** Economics, business, statistics. **Holdings:** 350 volumes; 14 shelves of Louisiana state agency publications; 2 shelves of other states' state agency publications; 6 linear feet of VF material; 20 shelves of federal government publications. **Subscriptions:** 20 journals and other serials; 2 newspapers. **Services:** Library open to the public for reference use only. **Computerized Information Services:** DIALOG Information Services.

★9364★
Louisiana (State) Department of Education - Office of Research and Development - Bureau of Evaluation - Library (Educ)
Box 94064 Phone: (504)342-3734
Baton Rouge, LA 70804-9064 Patrick Henry, Prog.Mgr.
Subjects: Education. **Holdings:** 5000 volumes. **Subscriptions:** 150 journals and other serials. **Services:** Copying; library open to the public. **Computerized Information Services:** BRS Information Technologies. Performs searches on fee basis.

★9365★
Louisiana (State) Department of Environmental Quality - Air Quality Division - Information Center (Env-Cons)
7290 Bluebonnet Blvd., 2nd Fl. Phone: (504)765-0169
Baton Rouge, LA 70810 Elizabeth Santa, Tech.Libn.
Founded: 1990. **Staff:** Prof 1. **Subjects:** Air pollution control, Louisiana air quality. **Holdings:** 400 books; 15 bound periodical volumes; 1600 reports; Federal Register (1983-1991) on microfiche. **Subscriptions:** 50 journals and other serials. **Services:** Interlibrary loan; copying; SDI; center open to the public. **Automated Operations:** Computerized cataloging (INMAGIC). **Computerized Information Services:** DIALOG Information Services; MEDLARS. **Publications:** Newsletter, acquisitions list, holdings list, current awareness lists. **Remarks:** FAX: (504)765-0222.

★9366★
Louisiana (State) Department of Environmental Quality - Water Pollution Control Division - Office of Water Resources - Library (Env-Cons)
P.O. Box 82215
Baton Rouge, LA 70884-2215 Phone: (504)765-0634
Founded: 1982. **Subjects:** Water pollution. **Holdings:** 2000 volumes. **Services:** Copying; library open to the public. **Computerized Information Services:** Internal database. **Remarks:** FAX: (504)765-0635.

★9367★
Louisiana (State) Department of Justice - Office of the Attorney General - Law Library (Law)
State Capitol, 25th Fl., W.
Box 94005 Phone: (504)342-7013
Baton Rouge, LA 70804 Glenn R. Ducote, Asst.Atty. General
Founded: 1932. **Staff:** 1. **Subjects:** Law, especially Louisiana law. **Holdings:** 5000 volumes. **Subscriptions:** 10 journals and other serials; 5 newspapers. **Services:** Library open to attorneys and state employees. **Remarks:** FAX: (504)342-7335.

★9368★
Louisiana (State) Department of Natural Resources - Energy Division Library (Energy)
Box 44156 Phone: (504)342-1399
Baton Rouge, LA 70804-4156 Diane D. Smith, Dir.
Founded: 1973. **Staff:** Prof 1. **Subjects:** Energy - conservation, alternative sources, solar, economics, statistics, oil, gas. **Holdings:** 100 books; 200 documents; 200 unbound periodicals; 8 films and videotapes; division publications. **Subscriptions:** 24 journals and other serials; 30 newsletters. **Services:** Library open to staff members only. **Computerized Information Services:** Dialcom Inc. (electronic mail service). **Networks/Consortia:** Member of Louisiana Government Information Network (LAGIN). **Publications:** Energy (newsletter), quarterly. **Remarks:** FAX: (504)342-2133.

★9369★
Louisiana State House of Representatives Legislative Services - David R. Poynter Legislative Research Library (Law)
Box 94012 Phone: (504)342-2431
Baton Rouge, LA 70804-9012 Suzanne Hughes, Adm.
Founded: 1981. **Staff:** Prof 5; Other 4. **Subjects:** Legislative procedure, law, government administration, constitutional and legal issues, energy and environment, health and welfare, business and industry. **Special Collections:** Louisiana legislative archives (special committees; studies; projects). **Holdings:** 3000 books; 250 bound periodical volumes; 15,000 speeches, copies of other state laws, staff memoranda, committee reports. **Subscriptions:** 250 journals and other serials; 13 newspapers. **Services:** Copying; PULS Line (public legislative information during sessions); library open to the public with administrator's permission when materials cannot be found elsewhere. **Automated Operations:** Computerized cataloging (DataTrek). **Computerized Information Services:** DIALOG Information Services, DataTimes, WILSONLINE, LEGISNET, VU/TEXT Information Services; internal database for bill status information. Performs searches on fee basis. **Special Indexes:** Calendar index of bills; journal index; Resume index of acts. **Staff:** Kate Lemon, Info.Spec.; Valerie Richardson, Info.Spec.; Suzie Carroll, Info.Spec.; Marilyn Kitchell, Info.Spec.; Sharon Eaton, Info.Spec.

★9370★
(Louisiana) State Library of Louisiana (Info Sci)
Box 131 Phone: (504)342-4923
Baton Rouge, LA 70821 Thomas F. Jaques, State Libn.
Founded: 1925. **Staff:** Prof 28; Other 41. **Special Collections:** Louisiana (66,121 cataloged items; 115,287 state documents; 225 VF drawers); genealogy (5000 items); U.S. Government documents (185,000). **Holdings:** 375,383 volumes; 750 maps; 10,000 photographs; 14,880 reels of microfilm. **Subscriptions:** 1575 journals and other serials; 25 newspapers. **Services:** Interlibrary loan; copying; library open to the public. **Automated Operations:** Computerized public access catalog, circulation, cataloging, and ILL. **Computerized Information Services:** OCLC, DIALOG Information Services, DataTimes, BRS Information Technologies, EPIC, Economic Bulletin Board (EBB), LEAP; ALANET (electronic mail service). Contact Person: Margaret Schroth, Hd., Ref./Bibliog., 342-4913. **Networks/Consortia:** Member of SOLINET, LAsernet. **Publications:** Public Libraries in Louisiana (statistics); Searching for Your Ancestors on Microfilm (brochure) - free upon request; Recent Acquisitions; LaGIN Directory of State Agency Information Resources; LaGIN Information Resources Exchange. **Special Catalogs:** Louisiana Union Catalog (card, microfiche). **Remarks:** FAX: (504)342-3547. Electronic mail address(es): ALA 2609 (ALANET). Maintained by Louisiana State Department of Culture, Recreation & Tourism. **Staff:** Michael R. McKann, Dp. State Libn.; Betty Jo Finley, Coord., Tech.Serv.; Blanche M. Cretini, Coord., User Serv.; Gary Rolstad, Assoc. State Libn.; Jennifer Anjier, Coord., Spec.Serv.

★9371★
Louisiana State Museum - Louisiana Historical Center (Hist)
751 Chartres St. Phone: (504)568-8214
New Orleans, LA 70116 Kathryn Page, Archv.
Founded: 1906. **Staff:** Prof 1. **Subjects:** New Orleans and Louisiana history. **Special Collections:** Judicial records of French Superior Council, 1714-1769, and Spanish Regime, 1769-1803; 18th, 19th, and 20th century family and commercial papers; 19th and 20th century personal manuscript collections; maps from the 16th century to the present. **Holdings:** 30,000 books; 2000 bound periodical volumes; 400 reels of microfilm; Sanborn Fire Insurance Maps for Louisiana, 1909. **Services:** Copying (limited); center open to the public by appointment for reference use only. **Remarks:** FAX: (504)568-6969. Center located at 400 Esplanade Ave., New Orleans, LA 70116.

★9372★
Louisiana (State) Office of the Secretary of State - Division of Archives, Records Management, and History (Hist)
Box 94125 Phone: (504)922-1206
Baton Rouge, LA 70804 Dr. Donald J. Lemieux, State Archv./Dir.
Founded: 1956. **Staff:** Prof 10; Other 25. **Subjects:** State and local government records, Louisiana history, genealogy. **Special Collections:** Louisiana Confederate government records (80 volumes and 8 cubic feet); Records of Board of Confederate Pension Commissioners (147 cubic feet); Louisiana Legal Archives (85 cubic feet); original acts of the Louisiana Legislature, 1804-1964 (121 bound volumes); Louisiana Long Leaf Lumber Company (276 cubic feet; 50 volumes); Louisiana Hayride tapes (300); oral history tape library (130); graphics collection (2379 images); New Orleans birth records, 1790-1891; New Orleans death records, 1804-1911; Louisiana marriage records, 1831-1939; Statewide Death Records: 1900-1941. **Holdings:** 11,100 books; 19,200 cubic feet of archival government records; 53,400 reels of microfilm. **Subscriptions:** 7 journals and other serials. **Services:** Copying; microfilming; conservation laboratory; division open to the public. **Automated Operations:** Computerized indexes and mailing list. **Special Indexes:** 1898 and 1913 Louisiana Voter Registration Index (book); Records of the Opelousas Post, 1766-1803 (book); Confederate pension applicants index (book); collections indexes (card). **Remarks:** FAX: (504)925-4726. **Staff:** Lewis M. Morris, Jr., Asst.Dir.; Theron D. Hinton, Jr., Hist.; Claudia F. Racca, Rec.Mgt.Off.; Douglas Harrison, Consrv.; Jeanette Kling, Archv.; Kimberly D. Thomas, Libn.; Sandra Hotard-Peairs, Archv.; Rose Angelle, Micrographics Mgr.; Norma Nelson, Micrographics Supv.

★9373★
Louisiana (State) Planning Office - Library - Information Resources Center
Box 94095
Baton Rouge, LA 70804-9095
Subjects: Planning, information dissemination, economic and social indicators, land use, environmental quality, census data. **Special Collections:** Louisiana Planning Districts planning reports; Louisiana comprehensive planning reports; census data; Louisiana Area Resources Information System (LARIS) land use statistics. **Holdings:** 7000 books; maps; vertical file materials; statistical bulletins; 750 microfiche. **Remarks:** By legislative mandate, this library houses the archives for all state planning information as well as those planning reports from the eight planning districts. Currently inactive.

★9374★
Louisiana State University - Agricultural Center - Southeast Research Station - Library (Agri)
Drawer 567 Phone: (504)839-2322
Franklinton, LA 70438 Dr. James Beatty, Resident Dir.
Subjects: Agronomy, diary science, forage quality, soil and animal sciences, chemistry. **Holdings:** 100 books; 1000 bound periodical volumes; 3000 other cataloged items. **Services:** Interlibrary loan; library not open to the public. **Publications:** Annual Progress Report - free upon request.

★9375★
Louisiana State University - Anglo-American Art Museum - Library (Art)
Memorial Tower Phone: (504)388-4003
Baton Rouge, LA 70803 H. Parrott Bacot, Dir./Cur.
Staff: 2. **Subjects:** Fine and decorative arts - American, English. **Holdings:** 1000 books. **Subscriptions:** 3 journals and other serials. **Services:** Library open to the public for reference use only.

★9376★
Louisiana State University - Business Administration/Government Documents Department (Bus-Fin, Info Sci)
Troy H. Middleton Library Phone: (504)388-2570
Baton Rouge, LA 70803 Myrtle S. Bolner, Hd.
Founded: 1907. **Staff:** Prof 4; Other 4. **Subjects:** Business administration, government, energy, nuclear sciences, international agencies, agriculture. **Special Collections:** U.S. and United Nations documents depository; NRC Collection; U.S. Patent Depository Library. **Holdings:** 653,044 volumes; 1.6 million of microforms; 10K reports. **Services:** Interlibrary loan; copying; SDI; department open to the public. **Automated Operations:** Computerized cataloging. **Computerized Information Services:** DIALOG Information Services, PFDS Online, BRS Information Technologies, U.S. Patent Classification System; DIALMAIL (electronic mail service). Performs searches on fee basis. Contact Person: Susan Hocker, Asst.Libn. **Remarks:** FAX: (504)388-6992. **Staff:** Tom Diamond; James Noel; Wilson Plunkett.

★9377★
Louisiana State University - Cartographic Information Center (Geog-Map)
Dept. of Geography & Anthropology
313 Geology Bldg. Phone: (504)388-6247
Baton Rouge, LA 70803 Joyce Nelson Rolston, Map Cur.
Staff: Prof 1; Other 4. **Subjects:** Cartography, geography. **Holdings:** 500,000 maps. **Services:** Center open to the public.

★9378★
Louisiana State University - Center for Engineering & Business Administration - Reading Room (Sci-Engr, Bus-Fin)
Troy H. Middleton Library Phone: (504)388-8221
Baton Rouge, LA 70803 Oreda Hogue, Dir.
Founded: 1979. **Staff:** 1. **Subjects:** Business, engineering. **Special Collections:** School of Banking collection. **Holdings:** 450 books. **Subscriptions:** 63 journals and other serials. **Services:** Room open to the public. **Remarks:** Serves as a reserve reading room for business and engineering students. FAX: (504)388-6992.

Louisiana State University - Center for Wetland Resources
See: **Center for Wetland Resources** (3315)

★9379★
Louisiana State University - Chemistry Library (Sci-Engr, Biol Sci)
301 Williams Hall Phone: (504)388-2530
Baton Rouge, LA 70803 Silvia D. Espinosa, Hd.Libn.
Founded: 1930. **Staff:** Prof 1; Other 2. **Subjects:** Chemistry, biochemistry, chemical engineering. **Holdings:** 44,942 volumes; U.S. chemical patents,

1955-1975, on microcards and microfiche. **Subscriptions:** 648 journals and other serials. **Services:** Interlibrary loan; copying; SDI; library open to the public. **Computerized Information Services:** DIALOG Information Services, BRS Information Technologies, PFDS Online, Chemical Information Systems, Inc. (CIS), STN International, Chemical Abstracts Service (CAS), MEDLINE; BITNET (electronic mail service). Performs searches on fee basis. **Networks/Consortia:** Member of SOLINET. **Remarks:** FAX: (504)388-6992. Electronic mail address(es): @LSUVM (BITNET).

★9380★
Louisiana State University - Governmental Services Programs (Bus-Fin)
385 Pleasant Hall Phone: (504)388-6746
Baton Rouge, LA 70803 Geneva Carroll
Founded: 1981. **Staff:** 11. **Subjects:** Management training, personnel management, public policy and administration, financial management. **Holdings:** 600 books; GSI technical assistance reports. **Subscriptions:** 21 journals and other serials. **Services:** Interlibrary loan; library not open to the public. **Publications:** Acquisitions list, quarterly - for internal distribution only. **Formerly:** Its Governmental Services Institute.

★9381★
Louisiana State University - Law Library (Law)
Baton Rouge, LA 70803-1010 Phone: (504)388-8802
Timothy G. Kearley, Dir.
Founded: 1906. **Staff:** Prof 11; Other 13. **Subjects:** Law - Anglo-American, Louisiana, comparative, foreign, international. **Special Collections:** Civil law; French, German, and Roman Law; Louisiana Courts of Appeal and Supreme Court Records. **Holdings:** 373,731 volumes; 672,345 microforms. **Subscriptions:** 4385 journals and other serials. **Services:** Interlibrary loan; copying; library open to the public. **Automated Operations:** Computerized public access catalog, cataloging, and acquisitions. **Computerized Information Services:** DIALOG Information Services, LEXIS, WESTLAW, NEXIS, OCLC; CD-ROM (WILSONDISC). **Networks/Consortia:** Member of SOLINET. **Special Indexes:** Index to Louisiana Courts of Appeal and Supreme Court Records (card). **Remarks:** FAX: (504)388-8202. **Staff:** Madeline Hebert, Ref.; Susan Morrison, Acq.; Rita Parham, Media; Tran Van Linh, Comparative Law; Rita Millican, Tech.Serv.; Mary Johns, Cat.; Charlotte Melius, Pub.Serv.; Ajaye Bloomstone, Cat.; Charlene Cain, Govt.Docs.; Shirley Tsang, Comp.Serv.

★9382★
Louisiana State University - Libraries - Design Resource Center (Art, Plan)
104 New Design Bldg. Phone: (504)388-2665
Baton Rouge, LA 70803 Sandra Mooney, Hd.
Founded: 1959. **Staff:** Prof 1; Other 4. **Subjects:** Architecture, interior design, landscape architecture, planning, restoration and preservation, graphic design, art history. **Holdings:** 10,000 books; 600 unbound periodical volumes; 28,328 slides; 16 VF drawers of clippings; 220 blueprints. **Subscriptions:** 100 journals and other serials. **Services:** Copying; center open to the public with restrictions. **Computerized Information Services:** RLIN, RLIN Avery Index to Architectural Periodicals; BITNET (electronic mail service). **Networks/Consortia:** Member of Research Libraries Information Network (RLIN), SOLINET, Center for Research Libraries (CRL). **Remarks:** FAX: (504)388-6992. Electronic mail address(es): NOTSTM@LSUVM (BITNET).

★9383★
Louisiana State University - Library School Library (Info Sci)
Library, Rm. 263 Coates Hall Phone: (504)388-4576
Baton Rouge, LA 70803 Alma Dawson, Hd.
Founded: 1925. **Staff:** Prof 1; Other 2. **Subjects:** Library and information science. **Special Collections:** Young Peoples Collection (14,301 volumes); Historical Young Peoples Collection (2500 items); Cataloging Workshop Collection (581 items). **Holdings:** 36,582 volumes; 7 VF drawers of annual reports; 3 VF drawers of library newsletters; 5 VF drawers; 376 dissertations on microfilm; media collection. **Services:** Interlibrary loan; copying; library open to the public with restrictions. **Computerized Information Services:** OCLC; BITNET (electronic mail service). **Networks/Consortia:** Member of SOLINET. **Publications:** Acquisitions lists, annual - for internal distribution only. **Remarks:** FAX: (504)388-6992. Electronic mail address(es): @LSUVM (BITNET).

★9384★
Louisiana State University - Listening Rooms (Mus)
Troy H. Middleton Library Phone: (504)388-2900
Baton Rouge, LA 70803 Jenifer Cargill, Dir.
Founded: 1958. **Staff:** 2. **Subjects:** Music, medieval to present; jazz and allied areas; Acadian folk; spoken word materials; American music including movie and musical soundtracks. **Holdings:** 21,139 single units (14,043 record, compact disc, and tape titles). **Services:** Copying; rooms open to the public with restrictions. **Automated Operations:** Computerized cataloging and acquisitions. **Computerized Information Services:** BITNET (electronic mail service). **Networks/Consortia:** Member of SOLINET. **Remarks:** FAX: (504)388-6992. Electronic mail address(es): @LSUVM (BITNET).

★9385★
Louisiana State University - Medical Center - Library (Med)
433 Bolivar St. Phone: (504)568-6105
New Orleans, LA 70112-2223 Judith Caruthers, Dir.
Founded: 1931. **Staff:** Prof 12; Other 21. **Subjects:** Medicine, dentistry, nursing, allied health sciences. **Special Collections:** Yellow fever; Louisiana medicine. **Holdings:** 60,247 books; 103,545 bound periodical volumes; 2461 volumes in microform; 3850 AV programs; 11 Audio-Digest titles. **Subscriptions:** 2085 journals and other serials. **Services:** Interlibrary loan; copying; SDI; library open to the public with specific need. **Automated Operations:** Computerized public access catalog, cataloging, serials, and ILL (NOTIS). **Computerized Information Services:** BRS Information Technologies, WILSONLINE, DIALOG Information Services, MEDLINE, MEDLARS, OCLC; BITNET (electronic mail service). Performs searches on fee basis. Contact Person: Mary L. Marix, Ref.Libn., 568-6102. **Networks/Consortia:** Member of SOLINET, National Network of Libraries of Medicine - South Central Region, South Central Academic Medical Libraries Consortium (SCAMEL). **Publications:** Library Bulletin, quarterly. **Remarks:** FAX: (504)568-7720. Electronic mail address(es): JCARUT@NNOMED (BITNET). Includes the holdings of the School of Dentistry Library and Pennington Information Center. **Staff:** Elizabeth Ashin Strother, Dental Ref.Libn.; Wilba S. Swearingen, Assoc.Dir.; Bruce Abbott, Asst.Dir. for Pub.Serv.; Judy Roberts, Asst.Dir. for Pennington Info. Ctr.

★9386★
Louisiana State University - Microform/Newspaper Room
Troy H. Middleton Library, Rm. 202 Phone: (504)388-4662
Baton Rouge, LA 70803 Deborah H. Atchison, Supv.
Staff: 1. **Special Collections:** American Periodical Series; Early American Imprints; Early English books; Louisiana newspapers; L.S.U. theses and dissertations; crime and juvenile delinquency; documents on contemporary China; ERIC; health and physical education; presidential papers; Spanish drama; Russian historical sources; underground newspapers; women's history; Energyfiche; Envirofiche; William S. Gray Research Collection. **Holdings:** 103,143 reels of microfilm; 698,053 microfiche; 88,250 microcards; 56,943 microprints; 71,772 microfiles; theses; dissertations; current local, state, out-of-state, foreign newspapers. **Subscriptions:** 87 newspapers. **Services:** Interlibrary loan; copying; room open to the public. **Computerized Information Services:** BITNET (electronic mail service). **Networks/Consortia:** Member of SOLINET. **Remarks:** FAX: (504)388-6992. Electronic mail address(es): @LSUVM (BITNET).

★9387★
Louisiana State University - Museum of Geoscience - Archaeology, Geology & Geography Book & Reprint Libraries (Biol Sci)
Baton Rouge, LA 70803 Phone: (504)388-6884
Dr. Judith A. Schiebout, Dir.
Founded: 1970. **Staff:** 1. **Subjects:** Archeology, paleontology. **Special Collections:** Patton Collection of vertebrate paleontology (6000 items); Howe Collection of micropaleontology; Stenzel Collection of fossil mollusca; Russell Collection on geography. **Holdings:** 13,000 books and reprints. **Services:** Copying; libraries open to the public with permission of museum curator. **Publications:** Melanges, irregular - for sale.

★9388★
Louisiana State University - Reference Services (Info Sci)
Troy H. Middleton Library Phone: (504)388-8875
Baton Rouge, LA 70803-3300 Jane P. Kleiner, Hd.
Founded: 1860. **Staff:** Prof 11; Other 12. **Subjects:** Reference, all subjects. **Holdings:** 26,639 volumes; 39,532 microforms. **Services:** Interlibrary loan; copying; SDI; services open to the public. **Computerized Information**

Services: DIALOG Information Services, BRS Information Technologies, Chemical Information Systems, Inc. (CIS), PFDS Online, MEDLINE, OCLC, RLIN, INFOTRAC; BITNET (electronic mail service). Performs searches on fee basis with surcharge for nonuniversity users. **Networks/Consortia:** Member of SOLINET. **Remarks:** FAX: (504)388-6992. Electronic mail address(es): @LSUVM (BITNET). **Staff:** Patricia Cruse, Ref.Libn.; Lea Orkiszewski, Ref.Libn.; Anna Perrault, Ref.Libn.; Mary Katherine Politz, Ref.Libn.; Gayle Poirier, Ref.Libn.; Barbara Wittkopf, Ref.Libn; Ruth Murray, Ref.Libn.

★9389★
Louisiana State University - School of Veterinary Medicine - Library (Med)
Baton Rouge, LA 70803 Phone: (504)346-3173
Sue Loubiere, Libn.
Founded: 1974. **Staff:** Prof 2; Other 4. **Subjects:** Veterinary medicine, medicine. **Holdings:** 14,500 books; 31,265 bound periodical volumes. **Subscriptions:** 1583 journals and other serials. **Services:** Interlibrary loan; copying; library open to the public. **Automated Operations:** Computerized public access catalog and cataloging. **Computerized Information Services:** OCLC, DIALOG Information Services, NLM. Performs searches on fee basis. **Networks/Consortia:** Member of National Network of Libraries of Medicine - South Central Region, SOLINET. **Remarks:** FAX: (504)346-3295.

★9390★
Louisiana State University - Special Collections (Hist, Rare Book, Sci-Engr)
Hill Memorial Library Phone: (504)388-6551
Baton Rouge, LA 70803-3300 Robert S. Martin, Asst.Dir. of Libs.
Founded: 1985. **Staff:** Prof 10; Other 10. **Subjects:** Louisiana, southern history and politics, natural history, Civil War, book arts, history of printing, ornithology, botany, slavery, steamboats, exploration and travel. **Special Collections:** E.A. McIlhenny Natural History Collection (10,000 volumes); Warren L. Jones Lincoln Collection (1500 volumes); Oliver P. Carriere Collection of Poker and Hoyle (1200 volumes); Bruce Rogers Collection (1000 volumes); Norman Steamboat Collection (1100 items). **Holdings:** 100,000 books; 7 million manuscript pieces; 2000 maps; 600,000 photographs; 20,000 reels of microfilm; dissertations; porcelain and metal sculptures; wood and stone carvings; paintings; prints. **Services:** Copying; collections open to the public with identification. **Automated Operations:** Computerized cataloging, acquisitions, and serials. **Computerized Information Services:** BITNET (electronic mail service). **Special Catalogs:** Unpublished finding aids for manuscript collections. **Remarks:** FAX: (504)388-6992. Electronic mail address(es): @LSUVM (BITNET). **Staff:** V. Faye Phillips, Hd., LLMVC; Linda Schneider, Hd., Tech.Serv.; M. Stone Miller, Acq.Libn.; Elaine Smith, Hd., Rare Bk.Coll.; Don P. Morrison, Hd., Presrv.; Judy Bolton, Hd., Pub.Serv.; Louise Martin, Univ.Archv.

★9391★
Louisiana State University in Shreveport - Medical Center - Library (Med)
Box 33932 Phone: (318)674-5445
Shreveport, LA 71130-3932 James Pat Craig, Lib.Dir.
Founded: 1968. **Staff:** Prof 15; Other 13. **Subjects:** Medicine, nursing, allied health, biomedical studies. **Special Collections:** History of medicine; medical fiction. **Holdings:** 37,729 books; 64,188 bound periodical volumes; 676 reels of microfilm; 5 VF drawers of pamphlets; 1205 videocassettes. **Subscriptions:** 1238 journals and other serials. **Services:** Interlibrary loan; copying; SDI; library open to the public. **Automated Operations:** Computerized public access catalog, cataloging, acquisitions, serials, and circulation. **Computerized Information Services:** MEDLINE, DIALOG Information Services, BRS Information Technologies, LAN; BITNET (electronic mail service). Performs searches on fee basis. **Networks/Consortia:** Member of South Central Academic Medical Libraries Consortium (SCAMEL), National Network of Libraries of Medicine - South Central Region. **Publications:** Annual report; LSUMC-S Faculty publications; library bulletin. **Remarks:** FAX: (318)674-5442. Electronic mail address(es): JCRAIG@NSHMED (BITNET). **Staff:** Marianne Puckett, Assoc.Dir.; Shirley Dickerson, Access Serv.; Alice Burnett, Cat.Libn.; Betty Tucker, Coll.Mgmt.; Billy Triplett, AV Libn.; Brady Banta, Spec.Coll.; Dixie Jones, Hd.Ref.Libn.; Kerri Christopher, Sr.Ref.Libn.; Camille Richmond, Ref.Libn.; David Duggar, Ref.Libn.; Michael Watson, Sys.Libn.; Phyllis Muirhead, User Educ.Libn.; Dennis Pernotto, IAIMS/Prog.Eval.Coord.; Pamela Ashley, Clin.Libn.

★9392★
Louisiana Tech University - College of Education - Educational Research and Services
P.O.Box 3163
Ruston, LA 71272
Founded: 1971. **Subjects:** Education. **Holdings:** 500 staff publications; Department of Health, Education, and Welfare publications; ERIC directories; program announcements. **Services:** Services open to the public by appointment.

★9393★
Louisiana Tech University - Research Division/College of Administration and Business - Library (Bus-Fin)
P.O. Box 10318 Phone: (318)257-3701
Ruston, LA 71272 Dr. James Robert Michael, Dir., Bus.Res.
Founded: 1948. **Staff:** Prof 4; Other 2. **Subjects:** Business, economics. **Holdings:** 3000 books; 13,000 bound and unbound periodicals. **Subscriptions:** 284 journals and other serials. **Services:** Library not open to the public. **Remarks:** FAX: (318)257-4253. **Staff:** Edward J. O'Boyle, Res.Assoc.; Barbara H. Denton, Demographer; Kimberly S. McMillan, Data Proc.

★9394★
Louisiana Universities Marine Consortium - Library (Biol Sci)
Chauvin, LA 70344 Phone: (504)851-2800
Jacqueline Riley
Founded: 1980. **Staff:** Prof 1; Other 1. **Subjects:** Marine zoology, physical oceanography, geochemistry, sedimentology, wetland ecology. **Holdings:** 5000 books; 9000 bound periodical volumes; 10,000 microfiche, 105 reels of microfilm; 400 maps. **Subscriptions:** 170 journals and other serials; 2 newspapers. **Services:** Interlibrary loan; library not open to the public. **Computerized Information Services:** DIALOG Information Services; OMNET (electronic mail service). **Publications:** Environmental Effects of Offshore Oil and Gas Development, quarterly. **Remarks:** FAX: (504)851-2874. Electronic mail address(es): LUMCON (OMNET).

★9395★
Louisville Academy of Music - Library & Archives (Mus)
2740 Frankfort Ave. Phone: (502)893-7885
Louisville, KY 40206 Robert B. French, Pres.
Founded: 1954. **Subjects:** Music, photography, literature, biography, United States. **Special Collections:** Music, recordings, and written material by and about American composer Roy Harris; Robert Crone; Clifford Shaw; Roy Nolte; biographical information on 1000 local musicians; local histories. **Holdings:** 4000 volumes, including rare books; 5000 phonograph records; 80 reels of recital tapes; 243 piano rolls; 20 VF drawers of periodicals; 28 VF drawers of music; posters; maps; National Geographic Magazine, 1914 to present. **Subscriptions:** 15 journals and other serials. **Services:** Library not open to the public; archives open to qualified researchers.

★9396★
Louisville Department of Law - Library (Law)
6th & Jefferson, Rm. 200
Louisville, KY 40202 Mary Allen
Staff: 1. **Subjects:** Law - municipal, Kentucky, federal. **Holdings:** 1000 books. **Subscriptions:** 30 journals and other serials. **Services:** Interlibrary loan; library open to the public with restrictions.

★9397★
Louisville Free Public Library - Government Documents Division (Info Sci)
301 York St. Phone: (502)561-8611
Louisville, KY 40203-2257 Mary E. Quin
Staff: Prof 1; Other 3. **Subjects:** U.S. Government publications, 1904 to present. **Holdings:** 803,363 government documents; 32,333 microfiche. **Services:** Interlibrary loan; copying; division open to the public. **Special Catalogs:** Documents shelflist. **Remarks:** FAX: (502)561-8657.

★9398★
Louisville Free Public Library - Kentucky Division (Hist)
4th & York Sts. Phone: (502)561-8616
Louisville, KY 40203 Mark Harris, Sr.Libn.
Founded: 1908. **Staff:** Prof 1; Other 3. **Subjects:** Kentucky and Louisville history and current events. **Special Collections:** Books by Kentucky authors. **Holdings:** 11,500 books; 2200 bound periodical volumes; 38 VF drawers of clippings; 22 shelves of pamphlets; 75 shelves of scrapbooks; 55 shelves of documents; 5180 reels of microfilm. **Subscriptions:** 140 journals and other serials; 25 newspapers. **Services:** Interlibrary loan; copying; division open to the public. **Automated Operations:** Computerized public access catalog, cataloging, and circulation. **Computerized Information Services:** Internal database. **Special Indexes:** Index to Courier-Journal, 1917-1986 (card); index to Courier-Journal, 1987 to present (online). **Remarks:** FAX: (502)561-8657.

★9399★
Louisville Free Public Library - WFPL/WFPK FM Library (Aud-Vis)
301 W. York St. Phone: (502)561-8640
Louisville, KY 40203 Gerald D. Weston, Dept.Hd.
Holdings: 4200 discs of 15-inch transcriptions; 51,000 12-inch discs; 65,000 titles of tape recordings on 103,000 reels. **Services:** LP phonograph records, transcriptions, and tapes are used for broadcasting on the library's two public FM stations and do not circulate. **Remarks:** FAX (502)561-8657.

★9400★
Louisville and Jefferson County Planning Commission - Louisville Metropolitan Planning Library (Plan)
531 Court Place, Ste. 900 Phone: (502)625-6230
Louisville, KY 40202 Glen Skaggs, Mgt.Asst.
Founded: 1962. **Subjects:** Planning, transit, housing, schools, land use, census studies, recreation and parks, urban studies. **Holdings:** 857 books; 3000 municipal reports; 2200 technical bulletins; 17 VF drawers; 6 VF drawers of newspaper clippings; zoning maps; regulations; plan maps; 200 and 500 scale aerial photographs and zoning maps. **Services:** Interlibrary loan; copying; library open to the public with special permission. **Computerized Information Services:** Internal database. Performs searches on fee basis. Contact Person: Peggy Swain, 625-6230. **Special Catalogs:** Vertical File Sheet Listing.

★9401★
Louisville Presbyterian Theological Seminary - Ernest Miller White Library (Rel-Phil)
1044 Alta Vista Rd. Phone: (502)895-3411
Louisville, KY 40205 Milton J. Coalter, Jr., Lib.Dir.
Founded: 1853. **Staff:** Prof 2; Other 5. **Subjects:** Theology and allied subjects, Biblical studies, church history, systematic theology, Christian education. **Special Collections:** Presbyterian Church history. **Holdings:** 99,426 books; 10,642 bound periodical volumes; 2921 microforms; 1364 AV materials. **Subscriptions:** 451 journals and other serials. **Services:** Interlibrary loan; copying; library open to the public. **Automated Operations:** Computerized cataloging and acquisitions. **Computerized Information Services:** DIALOG Information Services; CD-ROM (Religion Index). **Networks/Consortia:** Member of Team-A Librarians, Kentuckiana Metroversity. **Remarks:** FAX: (502)895-1096. **Staff:** Susan C. Richardson, Asst.Lib.Dir./Tech.Serv.Libn.

★9402★
Lourdes College - Duns Scotus Library (Rel-Phil, Med)
6832 Convent Blvd. Phone: (419)885-3211
Sylvania, OH 43560 Sr. Mary Thomas More Ruffing, Hd.Libn.
Founded: 1916. **Staff:** Prof 1; Other 5. **Subjects:** Religious studies, health sciences, psychology, occupational therapy, gerontology, art. **Special Collections:** Franciscana; Bible collection; art pieces (350 items). **Holdings:** 41,336 books; 9010 bound periodical volumes; 8384 microforms. **Subscriptions:** 340 journals and other serials; 19 newspapers. **Services:** Copying; library open to the public with courtesy card. **Automated Operations:** Computerized acquisitions and serials. **Computerized Information Services:** CD-ROM (Academic Index). **Publications:** Newsletter - for internal distribution only. **Special Catalogs:** Art pieces catalog. **Special Indexes:** Catholic Chronicles - Diocese of Toledo - Index 1935-1965 (book). **Remarks:** Maintained by Sisters of St. Francis. Alternate telephone number(s): (419)882-2016. **Staff:** Sr. Mary Victorine Lopata, Libn.

★9403★
Lourdes Hospital - Health Sciences Library (Med)
1530 Lone Oak Rd. Phone: (502)444-2138
Paducah, KY 42001 Trudi A. Patterson, Libn.
Staff: Prof 1. **Subjects:** Medicine, nursing, allied health sciences. **Holdings:** 600 books. **Subscriptions:** 100 journals and other serials. **Services:** Interlibrary loan; copying; SDI; library open to students in affiliated schools. **Computerized Information Services:** MEDLARS, BRS Information Technologies. **Remarks:** FAX: (502)444-2869.

Lourdes Library
See: **Gwynedd-Mercy College** (6818)

Louvre National Museum - Library and Archives
See: **Musees Nationaux au Louvre - Bibliotheque et Archives** (10881)

Malcolm A. Love Library
See: **San Diego State University** (14718)

★9404★
Lovelace Biomedical & Environmental Research Institute, Inc. - Inhalation Toxicology Research Institute - Library (Med, Biol Sci)
Box 5890 Phone: (505)845-1048
Albuquerque, NM 87185 Judy C. Neff, Libn.
Founded: 1974. **Staff:** Prof 1; Other 1. **Subjects:** Inhalation toxicology, aerosol physics, radiobiology, biophysics, veterinary medicine, comparative medicine. **Holdings:** 10,000 books; 10,500 bound periodical volumes; 15,000 documents in microform; 12,000 technical reports. **Subscriptions:** 311 journals and other serials. **Services:** Interlibrary loan; copying; SDI; library open to researchers. **Automated Operations:** Computerized cataloging and ILL. **Computerized Information Services:** DIALOG Information Services, MEDLARS. **Networks/Consortia:** Member of National Network of Libraries of Medicine - South Central Region, New Mexico Consortium of Biomedical and Hospital Libraries. **Remarks:** FAX: (505)845-1198. Institute is a contractor for U.S. Department of Energy.

★9405★
Lovelace Medical Foundation - Library (Med)
5400 Gibson Blvd., S.E. Phone: (505)262-7158
Albuquerque, NM 87108 Sarah K. Morley, Med.Libn.
Founded: 1947. **Staff:** Prof 1; Other 2. **Subjects:** Clinical medicine. **Holdings:** 2000 books; 7500 bound periodical volumes. **Subscriptions:** 198 journals and other serials. **Services:** Interlibrary loan; copying; library open to the public for reference use only. **Automated Operations:** Computerized serials. **Computerized Information Services:** DIALOG Information Services, NLM. Performs searches on fee basis. **Networks/Consortia:** Member of New Mexico Consortium of Biomedical and Hospital Libraries. **Remarks:** FAX: (505)262-7897.

★9406★
Lovell Litho & Publications Inc. - Directory Department (Publ)
423 St. Nicholas St.
Montreal, PQ, Canada H2Y 2P4 Phone: (514)849-3518
Holdings: "Criss-Cross" street address directory; Red Book numerical phone index. **Remarks:** FAX: (514)849-6518.

Lovely Lane Museum Library
See: **United Methodist Historical Society - Baltimore Annual Conference** (16747)

★9407★
Lovett, Underwood, Neuhaus & Webb - Corporate Finance Library (Bus-Fin)
909 Fannin St., 7th Fl.
P.O. Box 4348
Houston, TX 77210-4348 Phone: (713)853-2482
Founded: 1975. **Staff:** Prof 1. **Subjects:** High technology companies, savings and loan associations. **Special Collections:** Fortune 1000, selected foreign and Southwest Companies. **Holdings:** 110 books. **Subscriptions:** 14 journals and other serials. **Services:** Library open to clients and affiliated companies. **Remarks:** FAX: (713)853-3799.

★9408★
Low Country Area Health Education Center - Low Country AHEC Library (Med)
Box 1488 Phone: (803)549-1466
Walterboro, SC 29488 Jackie Hayden, Dir., Lib.Serv.
Founded: 1978. **Staff:** Prof 1; Other 1. **Subjects:** Medicine, nursing. **Holdings:** 255 books; AV programs. **Subscriptions:** 120 journals and other serials. **Services:** Interlibrary loan; copying; library open to the public. **Automated Operations:** Computerized cataloging. **Computerized Information Services:** MEDLARS; SCHIN (internal database); DOCLINE (electronic mail service). Performs searches on fee basis. **Networks/Consortia:** Member of Area Health Education Consortium of South Carolina (AHEC). **Remarks:** FAX: (803)549-9487. **Staff:** Donna E. Anderson.

Juliette Gordon Low Girl Scout National Center
See: **Girl Scouts of the USA** (6482)

Lowe Art Museum Library
See: **University of Miami** (18844)

★9409★
Lowell General Hospital - Health Science Library (Med)
295 Varnum Ave. Phone: (508)937-6247
Lowell, MA 01854 Martha Bedard, Dir., Med.Lib.
Founded: 1960. **Staff:** Prof 1. **Subjects:** Basic sciences, nutrition, medicine, nursing, psychology, psychiatry, sociology. **Holdings:** 3000 books; AV programs. **Subscriptions:** 100 journals and other serials. **Services:** Interlibrary loan; copying; library open to the public with restrictions on borrowing. **Computerized Information Services:** MEDLINE, DIALOG Information Services; DOCLINE (electronic mail service). Performs searches on fee basis. **Networks/Consortia:** Member of Northeastern Consortium for Health Information (NECHI), National Network of Libraries of Medicine - New England Region, Massachusetts Health Sciences Libraries Network (MaHSLiN). **Remarks:** FAX: (508)452-4169.

★9410★
Lowell Law Library (Law)
Superior Court House
360 Gorham St. Phone: (508)452-9301
Lowell, MA 01852 Karen J. Edwards, Law Libn.
Founded: 1815. **Staff:** Prof 1; Other 1. **Subjects:** Law. **Special Collections:** Historical Massachusetts materials. **Holdings:** 47,000 books. **Services:** Interlibrary loan; copying; library open to the public. **Remarks:** Part of the Massachusetts State Trial Court; Marnie Warner, Law Library Coordinator.

★9411★
Lowell Observatory - Library (Sci-Engr)
1400 W. Mars Hill Rd. Phone: (602)774-3358
Flagstaff, AZ 86001 Antoinette S. Beiser, Libn.
Founded: 1894. **Staff:** Prof 1. **Subjects:** Physics, astronomy, photography, mathematics. **Special Collections:** Archives of Percival Lowell and early scientific work done at the observatory. **Holdings:** 10,000 volumes. **Subscriptions:** 450 journals and other serials. **Services:** Interlibrary loan; library not open to the public. **Computerized Information Services:** DIALOG Information Services, SIMBAD; InterNet (electronic mail service). **Remarks:** FAX: (602)774-6296. Electronic mail address(es): ASB@LOWELL.EDU (InterNet).

Arthur M. Lowenthal Library
See: **Crestwood Children's Hospital** (4431)

★9412★
Lower Kuskokwim School District - Media Center - Library (Aud-Vis)
P.O. Box 305 Phone: (907)543-4880
Bethel, AK 99559 Joyce A. Pace
Founded: 1976. **Staff:** Prof 3; Other 3. **Subjects:** Education, Alaskana. **Holdings:** 5000 books; 90 microfiche; 15,000 AV materials. **Subscriptions:** 50 journals and other serials; 6 newspapers. **Services:** Interlibrary loan; library not open to the public. **Computerized Information Services:** ERIC. Contact Person: Sallie Hagg, Media Coord. **Special Catalogs:** Media Center Catalog. **Remarks:** FAX: (907)543-2089.

★9413★
Lower Merion Library Association - Ardmore Library - Gate Collection on the Black Experience (Area-Ethnic)
108 Ardmore Ave. Phone: (215)642-5187
Ardmore, PA 19003 Peggy Newman, Dir.
Founded: 1899. **Staff:** Prof 1; Other 3. **Subjects:** Black experience - history, literature, personalities. **Holdings:** 500 books. **Subscriptions:** 65 journals and other serials; 5 newspapers. **Services:** Interlibrary loan; copying; SDI; collection open to nonresidents with valid Access Pennsylvania affiliation. **Automated Operations:** Computerized cataloging, acquisitions, and circulation.

★9414★
Lowndes County Historical Society - Archives (Hist)
305 W. Central Ave.
P.O. Box 434 Phone: (912)247-4780
Valdosta, GA 31603 Albert S. Pendleton, Cur.
Subjects: History and genealogy of Valdosta and Lowndes County, 1860 to present. **Special Collections:** Hugh Vallotton Genealogy Collection and Georgia County Histories. **Holdings:** 700 photographs; letters; biographical sketches; organization and county government records; genealogical materials. **Subscriptions:** 350 journals and other serials. **Services:** Archives open to the public on a limited schedule and by appointment to special groups.

★9415★
Lowndes County Law Library (Law)
County Courthouse, Rm. 210 Phone: (601)329-5889
Columbus, MS 39701 Lena Mae Duncan, Libn.
Staff: Prof 1. **Subjects:** Law. **Holdings:** 5000 volumes. **Services:** Copying; library open to the public.

Theodore Lownik Library
See: **Illinois Benedictine College** (7670)

Lowry Nature Center
See: **Suburban Hennepin Regional Park District** (15843)

Thomas Lowry Health Sciences Library
See: **Hennepin County Medical Center** (7138)

Louis Lowy Library
See: **Boston University - Gerontology Center** (2011)

★9416★
Loxahatchee Historical Society - Library (Hist)
805 U.S. One, N. Phone: (407)747-6639
Jupiter, FL 33477 Elizabeth Kehoe
Staff: 3. **Subjects:** South Florida history, Florida pioneers. **Special Collections:** Historical photographs. **Holdings:** 300 books; 100 bound periodical volumes; 500 documents; 26 AV programs; professional journals; maps. **Subscriptions:** 10 journals and other serials. **Services:** Copying; library open to the public by appointment with curator. **Publications:** Newsletter, bimonthly. **Remarks:** FAX: (407)575-3292.

★9417★
Loyalist College of Applied Arts & Technology - Anderson Resource Centre (Educ)
Loyalist-Wallbridge Rd.
Box 4200 Phone: (613)969-1913
Belleville, ON, Canada K8N 5B9 Ronald H. Boyce, Mgr., Educ.Rsrcs.
Founded: 1967. **Staff:** Prof 2; Other 11. **Subjects:** Science and technology, behavioral sciences, health sciences. **Holdings:** 55,000 books; 1100 bound periodical volumes; 12,000 AV programs. **Subscriptions:** 590 journals and other serials. **Services:** Interlibrary loan; copying; center open to the public. **Automated Operations:** Computerized cataloging, acquisitions, and circulation. **Networks/Consortia:** Member of The Bibliocentre. **Remarks:** FAX: (613)962-1376. **Staff:** Beatrice Lo, Supv., Lib.Serv.

★9418★
Loyola Marymount University - St. Joseph Library (Rel-Phil)
480 S. Batavia St. Phone: (714)633-8121
Orange, CA 92668-3998 Sr. Thecla Chuml, Libn.
Founded: 1952. **Staff:** Prof 1. **Subjects:** Religion, philosophy, Christian ethics, social issues, literature, history, psychology, art. **Holdings:** 38,000 books; 1700 bound periodical volumes; 1550 sound recordings; 700 cassette programs; 140 videotapes. **Subscriptions:** 83 journals and other serials. **Services:** Copying; library open to the public on fee basis. **Remarks:** FAX: (717)744-3166. Includes the holdings of St. Joseph College of Orange.

★9419★
Loyola Marymount University - School of Law - William M. Rains Library (Law)
1440 W. 9th St. Phone: (213)736-1117
Los Angeles, CA 90015-1295 Robert J. Nissenbaum, Ph.D., Dir.
Founded: 1920. **Staff:** Prof 15; Other 17. **Subjects:** Law - American, international, foreign; human rights. **Special Collections:** Loyola Law School Archives. **Holdings:** 194,301 books; 135,223 other cataloged items. **Subscriptions:** 5464 journals and other serials; 15 newspapers. **Services:** Interlibrary loan; copying; SDI; library open to the public with restrictions. No restrictions in use of U.S. Government Depository. **Automated Operations:** Computerized public access catalog, cataloging, serials, acquisitions, and circulation. **Computerized Information Services:** ORION, DIALOG Information Services, RLIN, NEXIS, VU/TEXT Information Services, LEXIS, WESTLAW; internal database. **Publications:** Acquisitions list, monthly; contents pages of current periodicals; BRAINStorms (newsletter); library guide; Pathfinder series; Computer Resource Center Guide; Occasional Showers (internal library newsletter). **Remarks:** FAX: (213)487-2204. **Staff:** Eleanor DeLashmitt, Asst.Dir., Info.Serv.; Brian F. Keefe, Ref.Libn.; Catherine L. Kerr, Ref.Libn.; William S. Mulherin, Ref.Libn.; Demetrio Orlino, Pub.Serv.Libn. ; Edward St. John, Hd., Cat.; Elka Tenner, Asst.Dir., Spec.Coll.; Karen Verdugo, Hd., Pub.Serv.; Cecilia Wong, Asst.Dir., for Fin. & Tech.Serv.; Ruth Johnson Hill, Ref.Libn.; Lily Chen, Acq./Ser.Tech.Serv.Libn.; Rebecca Ng, Cat.Libn.; Craig Griffith, Lib.Sys.Mgr.; Pat Butler, Exec.Asst. to Lib.Dir.; Amy Chang, East Asian Bibliog.

★9420★
Loyola University of Chicago - E.M. Cudahy Memorial Library - University Archives
6525 Sheridan Rd. Phone: (312)508-2661
Chicago, IL 60626 Bro. Michael J. Grace, S.J., Univ.Archv.
Staff: Prof 2; Other 3. **Subjects:** Local and social history. **Special Collections:** University archives; Samuel Insull Papers; Catholic Church Extension Society papers; Theater Collection (playbills; autographs); Chicago Inter-Student Catholic Actions papers; social topics pamphlet collection, 1902-1930; Eleanor F. Dolan Papers (women in higher education). **Holdings:** Figures not available. **Services:** Copying; archives open to the public on a limited schedule. **Remarks:** Alternate telephone number(s): 508-2661. FAX: (312)508-2993. **Staff:** Valerie Gerrard Browne, Asst.Univ.Archv.

★9421★
Loyola University of Chicago - Julia Deal Lewis Library (Educ, Bus-Fin)
820 N. Michigan Ave.
Chicago, IL 60611 Phone: (312)915-6622
Founded: 1948. **Staff:** Prof 5; Other 16. **Subjects:** Education, social work, business, criminal justice. **Holdings:** 175,000 books; 31,000 bound periodical volumes; 200,000 microforms. **Subscriptions:** 1850 journals and other serials; 23 newspapers. **Services:** Interlibrary loan; copying; SDI; library open to the public. **Automated Operations:** Computerized public access catalog, circulation, and periodical indexes. **Computerized Information Services:** BRS Information Technologies, DIALOG Information Services, OCLC; CD-ROM. **Networks/Consortia:** Member of ILLINET, Center for Research Libraries (CRL). **Remarks:** FAX: (312)915-6637. **Staff:** Yolande Wersching, Bibliog.; Susan Schmidt, Bibliog.; Kay Tavill, Bibliog.; Stephen Macksey, Ref.

★9422★
Loyola University of Chicago - Law Library (Law)
1 E. Pearson St. Phone: (312)915-7200
Chicago, IL 60611 Francis R. Doyle, Dir.
Founded: 1908. **Staff:** Prof 8; Other 16. **Subjects:** Law. **Special Collections:** Medical jurisprudence. **Holdings:** 131,467 volumes; 111,581 volumes in microform. **Subscriptions:** 3102 journals and other serials; 5 newspapers. **Services:** Interlibrary loan; copying. **Automated Operations:** Computerized public access catalog, cataloging, acquisitions, and circulation. **Computerized Information Services:** LEXIS, WESTLAW. **Remarks:** FAX: (312)337-5797. **Staff:** Leverett Preble, Assoc.Dir.; Alexander Sved, Asst.Libn.; Carol Klink, Asst.Libn.; Sherman Lewis, Asst.Libn.; Mark Giangrande, Asst.Libn.; Virginia Thomas, Asst.Libn.; Jayne McQuoid, Asst.Libn.

★9423★
Loyola University of Chicago - Medical Center Library (Med)
2160 S. 1st Ave. Phone: (708)216-9192
Maywood, IL 60153 Ludwig Logan, Ph.D., Dir.
Founded: 1968. **Staff:** Prof 8; Other 25. **Subjects:** Biomedicine, dentistry, nursing, health sciences. **Holdings:** 49,000 books; 93,000 bound periodical volumes; 860 theses; 3844 AV programs. **Subscriptions:** 2700 journals and other serials; 7 newspapers. **Services:** Interlibrary loan; SDI; library open to the public with restrictions. **Automated Operations:** Computerized public access catalog, cataloging, acquisitions, serials, and circulation. **Computerized Information Services:** DIALOG Information Services, OCLC, MEDLARS, BRS Information Technologies, CD-Plus. Performs searches on fee basis. Contact Person: Janet Mixter, Hd., Info.Serv. **Networks/Consortia:** Member of National Network of Libraries of Medicine - Greater Midwest Region, ILLINET. **Publications:** Acquisitions List, bimonthly; Newsletter, bimonthly; Annual Report. **Remarks:** FAX: (708)216-8115. **Staff:** Dianne Olson, Hd., Tech.Serv.; Mary Klatt, Circ.; Katherine Hughes, Ser.; Jeane Sadlik, Ref.; Gary Dandurand, LRC; Mark Spasser, Res.

★9424★
Loyola University in New Orleans - Law Library (Law)
7214 St. Charles Ave. Phone: (504)861-5539
New Orleans, LA 70118 Edmund P. Edmonds, Law Libn.
Founded: 1914. **Staff:** Prof 7; Other 12. **Subjects:** Law. **Holdings:** 215,000 volumes. **Subscriptions:** 4352 journals and other serials. **Services:** Interlibrary loan; copying; library open to law students and attorneys. **Automated Operations:** Computerized cataloging, acquisitions, serials, and ILL. **Computerized Information Services:** LEXIS, NEXIS, DIALOG Information Services, WESTLAW, OCLC. **Networks/Consortia:** Member of SOLINET. **Remarks:** FAX: (504)861-5895. **Staff:** Judy Kelly, Doc.Libn.; Nancy Strohmeyer, Sr.Ref.Libn.; Nona K. Beisenherz, Circ.Libn.; Elizabeth Valadie, Assoc. Law Libn.; Carla Pritchett, Ref.Libn.; Marguerite Ray Florent, Cat.Libn.

★9425★
LTK Engineering Services - Library (Trans)
2 Valley Sq., Suite 300
512 Township Line Rd. Phone: (215)542-0700
Blue Bell, PA 19422 Nancy C. Todd, Libn.
Founded: 1974. **Staff:** Prof 1. **Subjects:** Transportation engineering; urban transportation; railcar design; railway construction, maintenance, operation. **Holdings:** 5000 books and unbound reports. **Subscriptions:** 100 journals and other serials. **Services:** Interlibrary loan. **Publications:** Accession list, monthly - for internal distribution only. **Remarks:** FAX: (215)542-7676.

★9426★
LTV Aerospace and Defense Company - Missiles Division - Library (Sci-Engr)
M.S. EM-08
Box 650003 Phone: (214)266-7155
Dallas, TX 75265 Sherry Daniel Siler, Chf.Libn.
Founded: 1949. **Staff:** Prof 1; Other 3. **Subjects:** Aerospace engineering, electronics, defense. **Holdings:** 32,000 books; bound periodical volumes; 215,000 technical reports; 200,000 documents on microfiche (uncataloged). **Subscriptions:** 286 journals and other serials. **Services:** Interlibrary loan; library not open to the public. **Automated Operations:** Computerized cataloging. **Computerized Information Services:** DIALOG Information Services, DTIC, NASA/RECON, WILSONLINE, NewsNet, Inc., PERISCOPE, American Helicopter Society Database. **Remarks:** FAX: (214)266-0182. **Staff:** Donna Norton, Ref.; Brenda Waite, Circ.; Janet Hamm, Tech.Serv.

★9427★
LTV Missiles and Electronics Company - Sierra Research Division - Library (Sci-Engr)
Box 222 Phone: (716)631-6300
Buffalo, NY 14225 Rebecca L. Reed, Tech.Libn.
Staff: Prof 1. **Subjects:** Radar, microwaves, electronics. **Holdings:** 1000 books; military standards and specifications on microfiche. **Subscriptions:** 76 journals and other serials. **Services:** Interlibrary loan; library not open to the public. **Computerized Information Services:** DIALOG Information Services.

★9428★
LTV Steel Company - Technology Center Library (Sci-Engr)
6801 Brecksville Rd. Phone: (216)642-7100
Independence, OH 44131 Kathryn A. Woolard, Tech.Libn.
Founded: 1955. **Staff:** Prof 2. **Subjects:** Steel, metallurgy, engineering, instrumentation, chemistry, chemical engineering. **Special Collections:** Bisit and Brutcher translations. **Holdings:** 18,450 books; 5400 bound periodical volumes; microforms. **Subscriptions:** 325 journals and other serials; 12 newspapers. **Services:** Interlibrary loan; library not open to the public. **Automated Operations:** Computerized cataloging. **Computerized Information Services:** DIALOG Information Services, PFDS Online, Chemical Abstracts Service (CAS); ISR (internal database). **Publications:** Current Information Alert, bimonthly; Periodical Holdings, annual; Technical Information Services, annual.

★9429★
Lubbock Christian University - University Library (Rel-Phil)
5601 W. 19th St.
Lubbock, TX 79407-2009 Phone: (806)792-3221
Founded: 1957. **Staff:** Prof 2; Other 5. **Subjects:** Religion, liberal arts, teacher education. **Special Collections:** Church of Christ materials. **Holdings:** 94,000 books; 4693 bound periodical volumes; 4356 reels of microfilm; 508 cassette tapes. **Subscriptions:** 593 journals and other serials; 5 newspapers. **Services:** Interlibrary loan; copying; library open to the public for reference use only. **Special Indexes:** Restoration Serials Index. **Remarks:** FAX: (809)796-8917. **Formerly:** Its Moody Library. **Staff:** Rebecca Vickers, Dir.; Paula Gannaway, Dir.

David Lubin Memorial Library
See: **United Nations - Food and Agriculture Organization - David Lublin Memorial Library** (16752)

★9430★
Lubrizol Corporation - Chemical Library (Sci-Engr)
29400 Lakeland Blvd. Phone: (216)943-4200
Wickliffe, OH 44092 Dr. Horton Dunn
Founded: 1946. **Staff:** Prof 2; Other 2. **Subjects:** Chemistry - organic, petroleum, polymer. **Holdings:** 5000 books; 4800 bound periodical volumes; 8300 lubrication papers; 1528 clippings; 7 VF drawers of technical papers. **Subscriptions:** 200 journals and other serials. **Services:** Library not open to the public. **Computerized Information Services:** PFDS Online, DIALOG Information Services. **Publications:** Lubrizol Periodical Abstracts, semimonthly.

★9431★
(Lubumbashi) Centre Culturel Americain - USIS Library (Educ)
3 Ave. du Moero
Post Box 2396
Lubumbashi, Zaire
Remarks: Maintained or supported by the U.S. Information Agency. Focus is on materials that will assist peoples outside the United States to learn about the United States, its people, history, culture, political processes, and social milieux.

Lucas County Public Library
See: **Toledo-Lucas County Public Library** (16391)

Vane B. Lucas Memorial Library
See: **American College** (531)

★9432★
Lucasfilm Ltd. - Research Library (Aud-Vis)
Box 2009 Phone: (415)662-1911
San Rafael, CA 94912 Deborah Fine, Dir. of Res.
Founded: 1979. **Staff:** Prof 2; Other 3. **Subjects:** Motion pictures, Lucasfilm productions, general reference, costume, architecture. **Special Collections:** Archive of production models, costumes, and paintings; Paramount Studios Research Library; still film from Lucasfilm productions. **Holdings:** 16,000 books; 300 periodical titles; 400 VF drawers of pictures; 3000 videotapes. **Subscriptions:** 54 journals and other serials. **Services:** Library open to film production personnel on fee basis. **Automated Operations:** Computerized cataloging. **Computerized Information Services:** DIALOG Information Services, BASELINE; internal databases. **Special Indexes:** Illustration index to photos in books and periodicals (online). **Remarks:** FAX: (415)662-1680. **Staff:** Cheryl Edwards, Jo Donaldson.

★9433★
Luce, Forward, Hamilton & Scripps - Library (Law)
The Bank of California Plaza
110 West A St. Phone: (619)236-1414
San Diego, CA 92101 Carmen A. Valero, Libn.
Staff: Prof 1; Other 4. **Subjects:** Law - taxation, labor, commercial, business, real property, probate; civil litigation. **Holdings:** 20,000 books; 1000 bound periodical volumes; 80 videotapes; 10 drawers of audiotapes. **Subscriptions:** 200 journals and other serials; 6 newspapers. **Services:** Library not open to the public. **Computerized Information Services:** LEXIS, NEXIS, DIALOG Information Services, Information America, DataTimes, Data-Star, InvesText, VU/TEXT Information Services, WESTLAW. **Remarks:** FAX: (619)232-8311. A branch library is maintained at La Jolla Golden Triangle, 4250 Executive Square, Suite 700, La Jolla, CA 92037. **Staff:** Michelle Schmidt, Asst.Libn.

Stephen B. Luce Library
See: **State University Maritime College at Bronx** (15718)

★9434★
Lucid Information Services Inc. - Library (Sci-Engr, Comp Sci)
1285 Hammerwood Ave. Phone: (408)734-0499
Sunnyvale, CA 94089 Randall Sherman, Pres.
Founded: 1960. **Staff:** Prof 12; Other 3. **Subjects:** Semiconductor processing, computer science, materials science, artificial intelligence, physics, chemistry, electronics. **Special Collections:** Historical journal collection. **Holdings:** 37,000 volumes; internal reports and memos; university and government agency reports; microfilm; patents. **Subscriptions:** 450 journals and other serials; 10 newspapers. **Services:** Copying; document delivery; corporate library development; library open to the public by subscription account. **Automated Operations:** Computerized cataloging, acquisitions, and circulation. **Computerized Information Services:** DIALOG Information Services, BRS Information Technologies, PFDS Online, DATALIB; OnTyme Electronic Message Network Service (electronic mail service). Performs searches. **Networks/Consortia:** Member of CLASS. **Remarks:** FAX: (408)734-0849. **Formerly:** Located in Santa Clara, CA. **Staff:** John Andy Cassell, Res.Dir.; Emmanuel Vella, Mktg.Dir.; Suzanne Brillant, Info.Cons.

James D. Luckett Memorial Archives
See: **Geneva Historical Society** (6358)

Arthur L. Luebke Memorial Library
See: **Beloit Historical Society** (1705)

Richard H. Lufkin Library
See: **Tufts University** (16553)

Luhr Library
See: **Eden Theological Seminary** (5228)

Luken Health Sciences Library
See: **St. Elizabeth's Hospital** (14287)

John N. Lukens Library
See: **Independent Presbyterian Church** (7737)

★9435★
Lukens Steel Company - Technical Library (Sci-Engr)
Coatesville, PA 19320 Phone: (215)383-1694
Founded: 1942. **Subjects:** Steel making, steel fabrication, management. **Holdings:** 2500 books; 45 VF drawers of pamphlets. **Subscriptions:** 4 newspapers. **Services:** Library not open to the public. **Remarks:** FAX: (215)383-2674.

★9436★
Lum, Hoens, Conant, Danzis & Kleinberg - Law Library (Law)
103 Eisenhower Pkwy. Phone: (201)403-9000
Roseland, NJ 07068-1049 Mr. Tae J. Yoo, Hd.Libn.
Founded: 1869. **Staff:** Prof 1; Other 1. **Subjects:** Law - taxation, securities, corporate, banking, trust and estates. **Holdings:** 20,000 volumes. **Subscriptions:** 25 journals and other serials; 5 newspapers. **Services:** Interlibrary loan; library not open to the public. **Computerized Information Services:** WESTLAW, DIALOG Information Services. **Remarks:** FAX: (201)403-9021.

Y.T. and Louise Lee Lum Library
See: **Appraisal Institute** (924)

★9437★
Lunar and Planetary Institute - Center for Information & Research Services (Sci-Engr)
3600 Bay Area Blvd.
Houston, TX 77058 Phone: (713)486-2135
Founded: 1968. **Staff:** Prof 3; Other 6. **Subjects:** Selenology, planetology, lunar geology, lunar geophysics, applications of space data to terrestrial problems, lunar base and space civilization. **Special Collections:** Spacecraft photography and maps of Earth, Moon, Mercury, Venus, Mars, and satellites of Jupiter, Saturn, Uranus, and Neptune. **Holdings:** 8900 books; 10,500 bound periodical volumes; 3000 documents; 1000 reels of microfilm of geophysical data from Apollo program; 240,000 photographs; 3700 maps; 8000 slides; 250 films; 1700 microforms. **Subscriptions:** 130 journals and other serials. **Services:** Interlibrary loan; copying (limited); library open to the public by appointment. **Automated Operations:** Computerized cataloging, acquisitions, and serials. **Computerized Information Services:** Online bibliography of lunar and planetary science, Antarctic meteorites (internal database); NASAMAIL, SPAN, SprintMail (electronic mail services). Performs searches free of charge. Contact Person: Stephen H. Tellier, Tech.Info.Spec., (713)486-2191. **Publications:** Lunar and Planetary Information Bulletin, 3/year - to mailing list. **Remarks:** FAX: (713)486-2186. Electronic mail address(es): FWARANIUS (NASAMAIL); LPI::FRAN; LPI::LPI (SPAN). **Formed by the merger of:** Lunar and Planetary Institute - Library Information Center and Lunar and Planetary Institute - Planetary Image Center. **Staff:** Mary Ann Hager, CIRS Mgr.; Frances B. Waranius, Libn.

Lunar and Planetary Institute - Library Information Center
See: **Lunar and Planetary Institute - Center for Information & Research Services** (9437)

Lunar and Planetary Institute - Planetary Image Center
See: **Lunar and Planetary Institute - Center for Information & Research Services** (9437)

★9438★
Lunar and Planetary Institute - Planetary Image Center
3303 NASA Rd., No. 1
Houston, TX 77058
Defunct. Merged with Lunar and Planetary Institute - Library Information Center to form Lunar and Planetary Institute - Center for Information & Research Services.

Lund Music Library
See: **Gustavus Adolphus College** (6815)

★9439★
Seafarer's Harry Lundeberg Maryland Seamanship School - Paul Hall Library and Maritime Museum (Hist)
St. Mary's County Phone: (301)994-0010
Piney Point, MD 20674 Janice McAteer Smolek, Lib.Dir.
Founded: 1970. **Staff:** Prof 2; Other 3. **Subjects:** Maritime history, union history. **Special Collections:** Manuscripts of union meetings, 1891-1907. **Holdings:** 15,500 books; 200 bound periodical volumes; 8 VF drawers; 650 16mm films; 500 filmstrips; 300 cassettes; 1500 slides; 420 videotapes. **Subscriptions:** 250 journals and other serials; 9 newspapers. **Services:** Library open to the public on limited schedule.

Lura Health Sciences Library
See: **Greater Southeast Community Hospital** (6710)

Luria Medical Library
See: **Albert Einstein Medical Center - Northern Division** (5274)

(Lusaka) USIS Library
See: **Martin Luther King Library - American Cultural Center** (8716)

Samuel S. Luskin Memorial Music Reference Library
See: **Temple Beth El of Greater Buffalo - Library** (16088)

★9440★
Luther College - Preus Library (Area-Ethnic)
Decorah, IA 52101 Phone: (319)387-1166
Norma J. Hervey, Hd.Libn.
Founded: 1862. **Staff:** Prof 6.25; Other 9.7. **Subjects:** Liberal arts. **Special Collections:** Norwegian-American newspapers (685 reels of microfilm); Norwegian history, culture, literature; Norwegians in America; Norwegian-Lutheran Church in America; Gerhard Marcks collection; Marguerite Wildenhain collection. **Holdings:** 287,074 books, bound periodical volumes, microforms, AV programs; 413 cataloged manuscript collections in the Luther College Archives; 145 cataloged collections in the Winneshiek County Archives (1700 linear feet). **Subscriptions:** 1711 journals and other serials; 27 newspapers. **Services:** Interlibrary loan; copying; library open to the public. **Automated Operations:** Computerized public access catalog, cataloging, circulation, serials, and ILL. **Computerized Information Services:** OCLC, DIALOG Information Services; internal database; InterNet (electronic mail service). Performs searches on fee basis. Contact Person: Elizabeth Kaschins, Hd.Ref.Libn. **Networks/Consortia:** Member of Colorado Alliance of Research Libraries (CARL), Iowa Computer Assisted Network (ICAN), Bibliographical Center for Research, Rocky Mountain Region, Inc. (BCR). **Special Catalogs:** Norwegian-American Newspapers in Luther College Library, 1976 (book). **Remarks:** FAX: (319)387-1657. **Staff:** Harlan Sanderson, Media Libn.; Duane Fens termann, Lib.Archv.; Jane Kemp, Circ./Ref.Libn.; William Doering, Hd. of Tech.Serv.; Linda Moeller, Ref.Libn.

★9441★
Luther Hospital - Library Services (Med)
1221 Whipple St. Phone: (715)839-3248
Eau Claire, WI 54701 Virginia L. Wright, Mgr., Lib.Serv.
Founded: 1938. **Staff:** Prof 1; Other 1. **Subjects:** Nursing and clinical medicine, hospital administration. **Special Collections:** Health Information Center; Hospital Historical Archives. **Holdings:** 3000 books; 5000 bound periodical volumes; 6 VF drawers of pamphlets; 850 AV programs. **Subscriptions:** 200 journals and other serials. **Services:** Interlibrary loan; Health Information Center open to the public. **Computerized Information Services:** DIALOG Information Services, NLM; internal database; DOCLINE (electronic mail service). **Publications:** Newsletter, quarterly. **Remarks:** FAX: (715)839-3289.

Luther Northwestern Seminary - ELCA Region III Archives
See: **Evangelical Lutheran Church in America - ELCA Region III Archives** (5496)

★9442★
Luther Northwestern Seminary - Library (Rel-Phil)
2375 Como Ave. Phone: (612)641-3225
St. Paul, MN 55108 Norman G. Wente, Libn.
Founded: 1876. **Staff:** Prof 6; Other 6. **Subjects:** Biblical studies, theology, church history, missions and allied subjects, records of all Norwegian antecedents of the Evangelical Lutheran Church in America. **Special Collections:** Lutheran Brotherhood Foundation Reformation Library; Carl Doving Hymnology Collection; Jacob Tanner Catechism Collection (Martin Luther); Missionary Research Center archival and library resources concerning China, Madagascar, and Cameroun; Bishop E.O. Gilbertson papers, 1955-1961; Bishop O.J.H. Preus Collection, 1926-1929. **Holdings:** 230,000 books. **Subscriptions:** 825 journals and other serials. **Services:** Interlibrary loan; copying; extension loans direct to Lutheran pastors; library open to the public. **Computerized Information Services:** RLIN. **Networks/Consortia:** Member of MINITEX Library Information Network. **Remarks:** Holdings include some of the archives of Luther Northwestern Theological Seminary. **Staff:** Ray A. Olson, Ref.Libn.; Carol Olson, Order Libn. Sulamit Ozolins, Cat.Libn.; Tom Walker, Automation Libn.; Mary Ann Teske, Cat.Libn.; Bruce Eldevik, Ref.Libn.

★9443★
Luther Rice Seminary - Bertha Smith Library (Rel-Phil)
3038 Evans Mill Rd. Phone: (404)484-1204
Lithonia, GA 30038 David Rhew, Dir.
Founded: 1972. **Staff:** Prof 1; Other 1. **Subjects:** Christian education. **Special Collections:** Dissertations on religious topics (1450 volumes). **Holdings:** 39,058 books; 3527 AV programs. **Subscriptions:** 91 journals and other serials. **Services:** Interlibrary loan; copying; library open to the public with annual fee. **Remarks:** FAX: (404)484-1155. **Formerly:** Located in Jacksonville, FL.

Lutheran Archives Center at Philadelphia Collection
See: **Lutheran Theological Seminary** (9465)

★9444★
Lutheran Bible Institute of Seattle - Library (Rel-Phil)
Providence Heights Phone: (206)392-0400
Issaquah, WA 98027 Irene A. Hausken, Hd.Libn.
Founded: 1960. **Staff:** Prof 2; Other 5. **Subjects:** Bible; theology - doctrinal, moral, pastoral, devotional; religion and philosophy; Christian church; missions; psychology; social sciences; Christian education; youth work; gerontology; Pacific Northwest Indians. **Holdings:** 27,000 books; 143 bound periodical volumes; 550 books on microfilm; 465 audio cassettes; 95 videotapes; 27 kits; 12 VF drawers. **Subscriptions:** 120 journals and other serials. **Services:** Copying; library open to the public.

★9445★
Lutheran Brethren Schools - Bible College and Seminary Library (Rel-Phil)
815 W. Vernon Ave.
Box 317 Phone: (218)739-3375
Fergus Falls, MN 56537 Richard Bridston, Libn.
Founded: 1903. **Staff:** Prof 1; Other 1. **Subjects:** Bible study, theology, church history, Christian biography and education, missions. **Holdings:** 18,000 books; 1500 audiotapes. **Subscriptions:** 125 journals and other serials. **Services:** Interlibrary loan; copying; library open to the public.

Lutheran Brotherhood Foundation Reformation Library
See: **Luther Northwestern Seminary - Library** (9442)

★9446★
Lutheran Brotherhood Insurance Society - LB Library (Rel-Phil, Bus-Fin)
625 4th Ave., S.
Minneapolis, MN 55415 Phone: (612)340-7269
Founded: 1957. **Staff:** Prof 2. **Subjects:** Life insurance, management. **Holdings:** 3000 books. **Subscriptions:** 200 journals and other serials. **Services:** Interlibrary loan; library not open to the public. **Computerized Information Services:** LEXIS, NEXIS, DIALOG Information Services, BRS Information Technologies. **Publications:** Management Book Bulletin; LB Library Book Bulletin. **Remarks:** FAX: (612)340-8601. **Staff:** Grete K. Hanson, Libn.; Marilyn S. Thompson, Libn.

★9447★
Lutheran Church - Missouri Synod - California, Nevada and Hawaii District Archives (Rel-Phil)
465 Woolsey St. Phone: (415)468-2336
San Francisco, CA 94134 Rev. Karl H. Wyneken, Archv.
Founded: 1887. **Staff:** Prof 1. **Subjects:** History of Lutheran Church work on the Pacific Coast and in Hawaii. **Holdings:** 800 volumes; 60 VF drawers of archival material. **Services:** Archives open to qualified users.

★9448★
Lutheran Church - Missouri Synod - Central Library (Rel-Phil)
1333 S. Kirkwood Rd. Phone: (314)965-9000
St. Louis, MO 63122-7295 Shari Siemsen Stelling, Libn.
Founded: 1983. **Staff:** 1. **Subjects:** Parish education, stewardship, evangelism, youth. **Special Collections:** Rare volumes in hymnody and liturgy (2000); theological reference collection (emphasizing Lutheranism). **Holdings:** 27,000 books; 600 bound periodical volumes; 1000 other cataloged items. **Subscriptions:** 350 journals and other serials. **Services:** Interlibrary loan; library open to the public by appointment. **Automated Operations:** Computerized cataloging. **Computerized Information Services:** DIALOG Information Services. **Networks/Consortia:** Member of St. Louis Regional Library Network. **Remarks:** FAX: (314)822-8307.

★9449★
Lutheran Church - Missouri Synod - Lutheran Library for the Blind (Rel-Phil, Aud-Vis)
Concordia Publishing House
3558 S. Jefferson Ave.
St. Louis, MO 63118 Phone: (314)965-9000
Founded: 1951. **Staff:** 2. **Subjects:** Christian literature, biography, devotions, Bible study, fiction, children's and young adult literature. **Holdings:** 2500 braille titles; 200 large print titles; 400 audio cassette titles. **Services:** Interlibrary loan; library open to the blind. **Publications:** The Lutheran Messenger; Portals of Prayer; My Devotions; Teen Time; Lutheran Witness; Strength for the Day; Interaction; Lutheran Women's Missionary League Quarterly; Happy Times; My Pleasure; My Delight; Christian Life; The Lutheran Digest. **Remarks:** Alternate telephone number(s): 664-7000. **Staff:** Rev. Rodney Rynearson, Couns.; Maureen Potts, Sec.

★9450★
Lutheran Church - Missouri Synod - Michigan District Archives (Rel-Phil)
4090 Geddes Rd. Phone: (313)665-3791
Ann Arbor, MI 48105 Rev. Thomas K. Schoech, Archv.
Founded: 1854. **Staff:** Prof 1; Other 1. **Subjects:** Lutheran churches in Michigan (Missouri Synod). **Holdings:** Historical records; reports; minutes; clippings; pictures; slides. **Services:** Archives open to the public at librarian's discretion. **Remarks:** Archives are housed in the library of Concordia College, Ann Arbor, MI. FAX: (313)665-0255. Alternate telephone number(s): (313)995-7300.

★9451★
Lutheran Church - Missouri Synod - North Wisconsin District Archives (Rel-Phil)
3103 Seymour Ln. Phone: (715)845-8241
Wausau, WI 54401 Rev. Ronald W. Goetsch, Archv.
Founded: 1916. **Staff:** Prof 1; Other 1. **Subjects:** History and biography of the Lutheran church. **Holdings:** 215 books; 45 VF drawers and 150 feet of proceedings, minutes, documents, histories, sketches, blueprints, pamphlets, clippings, historical records. **Services:** Copying; archives open to the public at librarian's discretion.

★9452★
Lutheran Church - Missouri Synod - Northwest District Archives (Rel-Phil)
1700 N.E. Knott Phone: (503)288-8383
Portland, OR 97212 Fred R. Riess, Archv.
Founded: 1927. **Subjects:** History of the Lutheran Church, Missouri Synod in Alaska, Idaho, Oregon, and Washington. **Special Collections:** Records of the Lutheran Laymen's League, the Lutheran Women's Missionary League, the Walther League, and youth organizations. **Holdings:** 100 linear feet of reports, correspondence, minutes, biographical material, congregational records, anniversary booklets. **Services:** Copying; archives open to the public.

★9453★
Lutheran Church - Missouri Synod - Rocky Mountain District Archives (Rel-Phil)
14334 E. Evans
P.O. Box 441395 Phone: (303)695-8001
Aurora, CO 80044 Lyle Schaefer, Archv.
Founded: 1921. **Staff:** 1. **Subjects:** Lutheran archives for Colorado, New Mexico, Utah, and El Paso, Texas. **Holdings:** Archival materials; records; periodicals; photographs. **Services:** Materials available to researchers in church history. **Remarks:** FAX: (303)695-4047.

★9454★
Lutheran Church - Missouri Synod - South Dakota District Archives (Rel-Phil)
Box 89110 Phone: (605)361-1514
Sioux Falls, SD 57105 Rev. O.D. Brack
Subjects: History of the Lutheran Church-Missouri Synod in South Dakota, 1875 to present. **Holdings:** 70 cubic feet of publications, convention proceedings, congregational histories, and photographs; biographical file on 800 pastors and 175 parochial school teachers. **Services:** Copying; archives open by special arrangement.

★9455★
Lutheran Church - Missouri Synod - Southern Illinois District Archives (Rel-Phil)
2408 Lebanon Ave. Phone: (618)234-4767
Belleville, IL 62221 Daniel C. Roth, Exec.Asst.
Founded: 1927. **Subjects:** History and publications of the Southern Illinois District. **Holdings:** Figures not available. **Services:** Interlibrary loan; archives open to the public on limited schedule.

Lutheran Church in America - Ohio Synod - Archives
See: **Wittenberg University - Thomas Library** (20546)

★9456★
Lutheran Deaconess Association - Center for Diaconal Ministry - Library (Rel-Phil)
1304 LaPorte Ave. Phone: (219)464-0909
Valparaiso, IN 46383 Deaconess Louise Williams, Exec.Dir.
Founded: 1961. **Staff:** Prof 2; Other 4. **Subjects:** Theology, Christian education, pastoral care and counseling, women in the church, history of diaconate. **Holdings:** 850 volumes. **Subscriptions:** 30 journals and other serials; 10 newspapers. **Services:** Library open to the public by special request.

Lutheran Deaconess Community Library
See: **Deaconess Community Lutheran Church of America** (4679)

★9457★
Lutheran General Hospital - Medical Library (Med)
1775 Dempster St. Phone: (708)696-5494
Park Ridge, IL 60068 Marie T. Burns, Dir.
Founded: 1966. **Staff:** Prof 5; Other 4. **Subjects:** Clinical medicine, nursing, pastoral psychology, social work, nutrition, physical rehabilitation. **Holdings:** 22,000 books; 12,700 bound periodical volumes; 6300 AV programs; current journals on microfilm. **Subscriptions:** 490 journals and other serials. **Services:** Interlibrary loan; copying; library open to the public for reference use only. **Automated Operations:** Computerized public access catalog, circulation, acquisitions, and serials. **Computerized Information Services:** BRS Information Technologies, DIALOG Information Services, OCLC. Contact Person: Sarah Redinger, ILL/Ref.Libn., 696-6988. **Networks/Consortia:** Member of National Network of Libraries of Medicine - Greater Midwest Region, North Suburban Library System (NSLS), Metropolitan Consortium of Chicago. **Remarks:** FAX: (708)692-9576. **Staff:** Dean Ostrand, Tech.Serv./AV Libn.; Marty Faulk, Ser.Libn.; Mary Ellen Reiter, Pub.Serv.Libn.

Lutheran Healthcare Network - Mesa Lutheran Hospital
See: **Mesa Lutheran Hospital** (10170)

★9458★
Lutheran Hospital of Indiana, Inc. - Health Sciences Library (Med)
3024 Fairfield Ave. Phone: (219)458-2277
Fort Wayne, IN 46807-1697 Lauralee Aven, Dir.
Founded: 1978. **Staff:** Prof 1; Other 2. **Subjects:** Nursing, medicine, hospital administration, health subjects. **Special Collections:** Orthopedics. **Holdings:** 2500 books; 60 titles of audio cassettes on management; 5 years of audio cassette series in cardiology, internal medicine, pediatrics. **Subscriptions:** 200 journals and other serials; 5 newspapers. **Services:** Interlibrary loan; copying; library open to the public for reference use only by appointment. **Automated Operations:** Computerized cataloging and serials. **Computerized Information Services:** BRS Information Technologies, DIALOG Information Services. Performs searches on fee basis. **Networks/Consortia:** Member of Northeastern Indiana Health Science Library Consortium. **Remarks:** FAX: (219)458-3077.

Lutheran Hospital and School for Nurses Library
See: **United Medical Center - Department of Library Services** (16727)

Lutheran Hospitals and Homes, Inc. - Torrington Community Hospital
See: **Torrington Community Hospital** (16427)

★9459★
Lutheran Hospitals and Homes Society - Corporate Library (Med)
1202 Westrac Dr.
Box 6200
Fargo, ND 58106-6200 Phone: (701)293-9053
Subjects: Hospital management, hospital law, human resources development, rehabilitation. **Holdings:** 400 books; 250 reports, manuals, pamphlets. **Subscriptions:** 102 journals and other serials.

Lutheran Library for the Blind
See: **Lutheran Church - Missouri Synod** (9449)

★9460★
Lutheran Medical Center - C.W. Nevel Memorial Library (Med)
2609 Franklin Blvd. Phone: (216)363-2142
Cleveland, OH 44113 Irene B. Szentkiralyi, Libn.
Staff: Prof 1. **Subjects:** Medicine, surgery, nursing, allied health sciences. **Holdings:** 1800 volumes; 300 cassettes and filmstrips. **Subscriptions:** 100 journals and other serials. **Services:** Interlibrary loan; library not open to the public. **Computerized Information Services:** MEDLINE. **Networks/Consortia:** Member of National Network of Libraries of Medicine - Greater Midwest Region. **Remarks:** FAX: (216)363-2292.

★9461★
Lutheran Medical Center - Medical Library (Med)
8300 W. 38th Ave. Phone: (303)425-8662
Wheat Ridge, CO 80033 Susan Brandes, Mgr. & Med.Libn.
Founded: 1961. **Staff:** Prof 2; Other 2. **Subjects:** Medicine, nursing, health management. **Holdings:** 3000 books; 6000 bound periodical volumes; 500 audiotapes; 200 videotapes. **Subscriptions:** 230 journals and other serials. **Services:** Interlibrary loan; library open to the public for reference use only. **Automated Operations:** Computerized cataloging, serials, and ILL. **Computerized Information Services:** MEDLINE, DIALOG Information Services, OCLC; DOCLINE (electronic mail service). **Networks/Consortia:** Member of Colorado Alliance of Research Libraries (CARL), Colorado Council of Medical Librarians. **Special Catalogs:** Video tape catalog. **Remarks:** FAX: (303)425-8563. **Staff:** Danette Berzins, Med.Libn.

★9462★
Lutheran Medical Center - Medical Library (Med)
2639 Miami St. Phone: (314)772-1456
St. Louis, MO 63118 Mary Smith, Med.Libn.
Staff: Prof 1. **Subjects:** Medicine. **Holdings:** 310 books; 1134 bound periodical volumes; 200 cassette tapes. **Subscriptions:** 49 journals and other serials. **Services:** Interlibrary loan; library not open to the public. **Remarks:** Maintained by National Medical Enterprises.

★9463★
Lutheran Medical Center - Medical Library (Med)
150 55th St. Phone: (718)630-7200
Brooklyn, NY 11220 Estela Longo, Med.Libn.
Founded: 1883. **Staff:** Prof 1; Other 2. **Subjects:** Nursing, medicine, surgery, gynecology, obstetrics, pediatrics, dentistry, family practice. **Holdings:** 8072 books; 2977 AV programs; 468 videotapes; 40 VF drawers; 312 other cataloged items. **Subscriptions:** 236 journals and other serials. **Services:** Interlibrary loan; copying; library open to the public for reference use only. **Computerized Information Services:** MEDLINE; DOCLINE (electronic mail service). **Networks/Consortia:** Member of Brooklyn-Queens-Staten Island Health Sciences Librarians (BQSI), Medical Library Center of New York (MLCNY), Medical & Scientific Libraries of Long Island (MEDLI). **Remarks:** FAX: (718)630-8918.

Lutheran School of Theology at Chicago
See: **Jesuit-Krauss-McCormick Library** (8375)

★9464★
Lutheran Theological Seminary - A.R. Wentz Library (Rel-Phil)
66 W. Confederate Ave. Phone: (717)334-6286
Gettysburg, PA 17325 Bonnie L. Van Delinder, Libn.
Founded: 1826. **Staff:** Prof 2; Other 3. **Subjects:** Theology, biblical studies, church history, pastoral studies, religion, sociology, rural sociology. **Special Collections:** American Lutheranism; Samuel S. Schmucker Papers. **Holdings:** 154,387 volumes; 5151 microforms. **Subscriptions:** 726 journals and other serials. **Services:** Interlibrary loan; copying; library open to the public with limited circulation. **Automated Operations:** Computerized public access catalog. **Computerized Information Services:** DIALOG Information Services. **Networks/Consortia:** Member of Washington Theological Consortium, Southeastern Pennsylvania Theological Library Association (SEPTLA). **Remarks:** FAX: (717)334-3469. Includes the holdings of the Lutheran Historical Society and Archives of the several synods in central Pennsylvania and Maryland. **Staff:** Tamara Riegel, Cat.Libn.

★9465★
Lutheran Theological Seminary - Krauth Memorial Library (Rel-Phil)
7301 Germantown Ave. Phone: (215)248-4616
Philadelphia, PA 19119 Rev. David J. Wartluft, Lib.Dir.
Founded: 1864. **Staff:** Prof 2.75; Other 3. **Subjects:** Theology, Martin Luther, U.S. Lutheran colonial history, hymnody and liturgy, Protestant Reformation, patristics, religious art and architecture, urbanism and religion. **Special Collections:** Archives of Pennsylvania Ministerium, New England Synod, New Jersey Synod, Slovak Zion Synod, Northeastern Pennsylvania, Southeastern Pennsylvania, and Upstate New York Synods. **Holdings:** 165,000 volumes; 7100 unbound periodicals; 6000 AV programs; 2400 linear feet of archival materials and personal papers. **Subscriptions:** 660 journals and other serials. **Services:** Interlibrary loan; copying; library open to the public for reference use only. **Automated Operations:** Computerized cataloging and acquisitions. **Computerized Information Services:** OCLC; CD-ROMs. **Networks/Consortia:** Member of Southeastern Pennsylvania Theological Library Association (SEPTLA), PALINET. **Publications:** Library List, monthly - to selected libraries, and by request with payment of postage. **Remarks:** FAX: (215)248-4577. The Lutheran Archives Center at Philadelphia Collection is housed in the Krauth Memorial Library. **Staff:** Lillian Scoggins, Asst.Libn.; John Peterson, Cur., Archv.; Lois Reibach, Cat.

★9466★
Lutheran Theological Seminary - Otto Olson Memorial Library (Rel-Phil)
114 Seminary Crescent Phone: (306)975-7004
Saskatoon, SK, Canada S7N 0X3 Mary Mitchell, Libn.
Staff: 3. **Subjects:** Religion, mythology, free thought, Judaism, Christianity, Bible, doctrinal and practical theology, church history. **Holdings:** 48,000 volumes. **Subscriptions:** 150 journals and other serials. **Services:** Interlibrary loan; copying; library open to the public. **Computerized Information Services:** UTLAS, Geac; G.R.C. Laserguide (internal database). **Remarks:** Seminary is an autonomous affiliate of the University of Saskatchewan.

★9467★
Lutheran Theological Southern Seminary - Lineberger Memorial Library (Rel-Phil)
4201 N. Main St. Phone: (803)786-5150
Columbia, SC 29203 Dr. Lynn A. Feider, Libn.
Founded: 1830. **Staff:** Prof 2; Other 2. **Subjects:** Theology, religion, allied subjects. **Special Collections:** 17th-18th century German Pietism (1000 volumes); German hymnbooks and catechisms (300). **Holdings:** 104,672 books and bound periodical volumes; 2075 tapes; 7600 microforms; 451 linear feet of archives. **Subscriptions:** 592 journals and other serials. **Services:** Interlibrary loan; library open to the public with registration and identification. **Computerized Information Services:** EPIC; CD-ROMs. **Networks/Consortia:** Member of SOLINET. **Special Catalogs:** Library of the South Carolina Theological Society at Lexington, SC, 1834-1852. **Staff:** Leslie Walker, Asst.Libn.

★9468★
Lutherans For Life - Library (Soc Sci)
P.O. Box 819 Phone: (501)794-2212
Benton, AR 72015 Jewell Rapier
Founded: 1980. **Staff:** 3. **Subjects:** Abortion, infanticide, euthanasia, theology. **Holdings:** 50 books; 10 filing drawers; newsletters; clippings. **Subscriptions:** 30 journals and other serials; 10 newspapers. **Services:** Copying; library open to the public. **Publications:** Living (magazine), quarterly; Lifedate (newsletter), quarterly. **Remarks:** FAX: (501)794-1437.

Aleda E. Lutz VA Medical Center Library
See: **U.S. Dept. of Veterans Affairs (MI-Saginaw)** (17355)

★9469★
Luzerne County Community College - Center for Instructional Development - Library (Educ)
Prospect St. and Middle Rd. Phone: (717)829-7326
Nanticoke, PA 18634-9987 Nancy Kosteleba, Assoc. Dean of Instr.Dev.
Subjects: Computer-assisted instruction, interactive video, laser disk technology. **Holdings:** 200 volumes; developmental software; video discs. **Services:** Library open to the public.

★9470★
Lvov Orgtechstroj - Naucno Techniceskaja Biblioteka (Sci-Engr)
ul. K. Marksa 32a Phone: 353083
SU-290013 Lvov 13, Ukraine Ljudmyla Grygorivna Khorolska
Founded: 1962. **Staff:** Prof 250; Other 50. **Subjects:** Science, technology. **Holdings:** 25,000 books; 50 bound periodical volumes. **Subscriptions:** 26 journals and other serials; 24 newspapers. **Services:** Interlibrary loan; copying; SDI; library open to the public. **Special Catalogs:** Alphabetical and systematic catalogues. **Remarks:** Telex: 234240.

★9471★
Lycoming County Law Library (Law)
48 W. 3rd St., 4th Fl. Phone: (717)327-2475
Williamsport, PA 17701 Nancy L. Borgess, Law Libn.
Staff: Prof 1. **Subjects:** Law. **Holdings:** 13,950 volumes; 2950 volumes on ultrafiche. **Subscriptions:** 13 journals and other serials. **Services:** Interlibrary loan; copying; library open to the public.

Kathryn E. Lyle Memorial Library
See: **Lyman House Memorial Museum** (9472)

★9472★
Lyman House Memorial Museum - Kathryn E. Lyle Memorial Library (Area-Ethnic)
276 Haili St. Phone: (808)935-5021
Hilo, HI 96720 Gloria Kobayashi
Founded: 1932. **Staff:** 2. **Subjects:** Hawaii - history and pre-Cook history, volcanology, geology, shells, religions; local family genealogies; Pacific islands; missionaries in Hawaii; Hilo and environment. **Special Collections:** Lyman Family; Hilo Boarding School; Kohal sugar. **Holdings:** 5000 books; 11,500 photographs; 200 blueprints; 6 charts; 84 daguerreotypes; 2500 pieces of ephemera; 735 glassplates; 5 journals; 2000 letters; 190 maps; 13 newsletters; 200 prints; 6000 clippings; 660 New England newspapers, 1806-1900; historical materials on early Hawaii. **Services:** Copying; library open to the public by appointment. **Automated Operations:** Computerized public access catalog (Follett). **Publications:** List of publications - available on request. **Remarks:** FAX: (808)935-5021.

Lyman Library
See: **Cummington Historical Commission - Kingman Tavern Historical Museum** (4481)

★9473★
Lyme Historical Society, Inc. - Archives (Hist)
96 Lyme St. Phone: (203)434-5542
Old Lyme, CT 06371 Jeffrey W. Andersen, Dir.
Founded: 1955. **Staff:** Prof 4. **Subjects:** Local history and art. **Special Collections:** The Art Colony at Old Lyme Archives (photographs of artists; paintings); exhibition records and correspondence. **Holdings:** 20,000 manuscripts and documents; 1200 photographs; 6 boxes of clippings. **Subscriptions:** 21. **Services:** Copying; archives open to the public. **Special Indexes:** Archives (card); each record group (book). **Staff:** Debra A. Fillos, Cur.

★9474★
Lynchburg General Marshall Lodge Hospital - Health Sciences Library (Med)
1901 Tate Springs Rd. Phone: (804)947-3147
Lynchburg, VA 24501-1167 Sybil A. Sturgis, Hea.Sci.Libn.
Staff: Prof 1. **Subjects:** Medicine, nursing, allied health, health administration, nursing and allied health education. **Holdings:** 3000 books; 3500 bound periodical volumes. **Subscriptions:** 57 journals and other serials. **Services:** Interlibrary loan; copying; library open to the public with restrictions. **Computerized Information Services:** MEDLINE; DOCLINE (electronic mail service). Performs searches on fee basis. **Networks/Consortia:** Member of Southwestern Virginia Health Information Librarians (SWVAHILI), National Network of Libraries of Medicine - Southeastern/Atlantic Region. **Publications:** Quarterly newsletters. **Remarks:** FAX: (804)947-3104. Maintained by Centra Health, Inc.

★9475★
Lyndhurst Hospital - Health Sciences Library (Med)
520 Sutherland Dr. Phone: (416)422-5551
Toronto, ON, Canada M4G 3V9 Ann Marie Chin, Dir.
Founded: 1975. **Staff:** Prof 1. **Subjects:** Spinal cord injuries, neurological disabilities, rehabilitation and physical medicine. **Special Collections:** SCI Collection (Spinal Cord Injuries; vertical file materials). **Holdings:** 400 books; 130 bound periodical volumes. **Subscriptions:** 75 journals and other serials. **Services:** Interlibrary loan; copying; SDI; library open to the public by appointment. **Computerized Information Services:** DIALOG Information Services. **Networks/Consortia:** Member of Disability Research Library Network, Ontario Hospital Libraries Association (OHLA). **Publications:** Acquisitions lists.

★9476★
Lynn Historical Society/Museum - Library (Hist)
125 Green St. Phone: (617)592-2465
Lynn, MA 01902 Diane Shephard, Libn.
Founded: 1896. **Staff:** Prof 3. **Subjects:** Lynn and Essex County history, genealogy. **Special Collections:** Personal papers; records of organizations, businesses, churches, and government bodies; ephemera collections. **Holdings:** 3000 books; 1400 photographs; 37 VF drawers of unbound books, manuscripts, clippings, records; newspapers. **Subscriptions:** 10 journals and other serials. **Services:** Copying; library open to the public. **Publications:** Town Meeting Records of Lynn, 1691 through 1783 (7 volumes); A Guide to the Manuscript and Special Collections of the Lynn Historical Society; The Lynn Album: a pictorial history. **Staff:** Ken Turino, Dir.; Sophia Garrett, Cur.; Laurel Nilsen, Cur.; Fay Greenleaf, Ofc.Mgr.

★9477★
Lyon County Historical Museum - Library/Archives (Hist)
118 E. 6th St. Phone: (316)342-0933
Emporia, KS 66801 Carol Miguelino, Libn./Archv.
Founded: 1938. **Staff:** Prof 1; Other 2. **Subjects:** State and local history, genealogy. **Special Collections:** Gilson Clipping Scrapbook Collection, 1880 to present (30 linear feet). **Holdings:** 1000 books; 350 bound periodical volumes; 2 drawers of microfilm of newspapers and census; 500 linear feet of manuscripts and ephemera; 3000 photographs. **Services:** Copying; library open to the public with restrictions. **Special Catalogs:** Finding aids.

★9478★
Lyondell Petrochemical Company - Information Resource Center (Energy)
8280 Sheldon Rd. Phone: (713)452-8148
Channelview, TX 77530 Linda Lozano, Tech.Libn.
Founded: 1956. **Staff:** Prof 1. **Subjects:** Chemical engineering, technology, reference material. **Special Collections:** Unit manuals; VLE data; SRI; Chemical Technology Encyclopedia. **Holdings:** 3000 books; 1000 bound periodical volumes; 7000 cubic feet of other cataloged items. **Subscriptions:** 35 journals and other serials. **Services:** Interlibrary loan; library not open to the public. **Automated Operations:** Computerized public access catalog and circulation. **Computerized Information Services:** DIALOG Information Services, Rice University Library Online. **Publications:** Technical Data Files. **Remarks:** FAX: (713)452-8743.

Harrye B. Lyons Design Library
See: **North Carolina State University - Harrye B. Lyons Design Library** (11902)

★9479★
Lyons Historical Society - Lyons Redstone Museum - Library (Hist)
240 High
Box 9 Phone: (303)823-6692
Lyons, CO 80540 LaVern M. Johnson, Pres.
Founded: 1979. **Subjects:** Lyons area history. **Holdings:** 15 volumes; 20 reels of microfilm; 1 AV program; obituary files; resident name files; business files; town newspapers, 1927-1941 and 1968-1989. **Subscriptions:** 4 journals and other serials; 3 newspapers. **Services:** Copying; library open to the public for reference use only.

★9480★
W. K. Lypynsky East European Research Institute - Archives (Area-Ethnic)
469 Flamingo St. Phone: (215)482-7111
Philadelphia, PA 19128 Irene Meducha, V.P.
Subjects: Political and cultural heritage of Eastern Europe, Ukraine, Poland, Austria, Russia. **Holdings:** 17,000 volumes.

Lyster Army Community Hospital
See: **U.S. Army Hospitals** (17047)

M

Sister M. Francis Medical Library
See: **St. Anthony Hospital** (14236)

★9481★
M/A-COM, Inc. - Library (Sci-Engr)
52 South Ave. Phone: (617)272-3000
Burlington, MA 01803 Mary Condon, Info.Spec.
Founded: 1960. **Staff:** Prof 1. **Subjects:** Electrical and electronics engineering, microwaves, semiconductors, radar and antennas. **Holdings:** 2200 books; 1150 bound periodical volumes; 205 pamphlet boxes of company reports. **Subscriptions:** 85 journals and other serials. **Services:** Interlibrary loan; library not open to the public. **Computerized Information Services:** DIALOG Information Services, OCLC, Dow Jones News/ Retrieval, InvesText. **Publications:** Library Bulletin, monthly - for internal distribution only.

★9482★
M-I Drilling Fluids Company - Technical Library (Energy, Sci-Engr)
5950 North Course Dr. Phone: (713)561-1378
Houston, TX 77072 Mary K. Dimataris, Tech.Libn.
Staff: Prof 1. **Subjects:** Chemistry, petroleum, geology, mining engineering, environment. **Holdings:** 6000 volumes; 8000 patents; 100 maps; 8000 Society of Petroleum Engineers papers. **Subscriptions:** 101 journals and other serials. **Services:** Interlibrary loan; copying; library open to the public by appointment only. **Computerized Information Services:** DIALOG Information Services, STN International; internal database. **Remarks:** FAX: (713)561-7240. Telex: 4620483.

M.I.T.
See: **Massachusetts Institute of Technology** (9795)

★9483★
M.S.A. Museum Society - Library and Archives (Hist)
Trethewey House
2313 Ware St. Phone: (604)853-0313
Abbotsford, BC, Canada V2S 3C6 Lynne Wright, Dir.
Founded: 1969. **Staff:** Prof 2; Other 1. **Subjects:** Local and provincial history, museums, artifacts. **Special Collections:** Clayburn Company papers; Sumas Pumping Station papers. **Holdings:** 600 books; 68 bound periodical volumes; 6600 photographs; 22 boxes of archival materials; 25 boxes of ephemera; 185 clipping files; 40 historical maps; 112 oral histories; original documents; memoirs. **Subscriptions:** 16 journals and other serials. **Services:** Copying; archives open to the public for reference use only. **Special Indexes:** Index to archives and photographs (card); Index to Sumas Collection; Index to Asm News. **Staff:** Kris Foulds, Cur.

★9484★
MAAR Associates, Inc. - Library (Soc Sci)
P.O. Box 655
Newark, DE 19715-0655 Phone: (302)368-5777
Founded: 1976. **Subjects:** Cultural resources, preservation, artifact conservation. **Holdings:** 1000 volumes. **Subscriptions:** 10 journals and other serials. **Services:** library open to the public. **Remarks:** FAX: (302)368-1571.

★9485★
Clara Maass Medical Center - Medical Library (Med)
Franklin Ave. Phone: (201)450-2294
Belleville, NJ 07109 Arlene Mangino, Libn.
Staff: 1. **Subjects:** Medicine, surgery. **Holdings:** 827 books; 2704 bound periodical volumes; 420 audiocassettes; 42 videocassettes. **Subscriptions:** 81 journals and other serials. **Services:** Interlibrary loan; library not open to the public. **Automated Operations:** Computerized cataloging and acquisitions. **Computerized Information Services:** MEDLARS. **Networks/Consortia:** Member of Cosmopolitan Biomedical Library Consortium (CBLC), Health Sciences Library Association of New Jersey (HSLANJ), Essex Hudson Regional Library Cooperative, BHSL. **Publications:** Health Care Update. **Remarks:** FAX: (201)450-0181.

★9486★
Clara Maass Medical Center - School of Nursing - Library (Med)
236 Hoover Ave. Phone: (201)680-4400
Bloomfield, NJ 07003 Arlene Mangino, Libn.
Staff: Prof 1; Other 1. **Subjects:** Nursing. **Holdings:** 1568 books; 117 bound periodical volumes; 20 video cassettes. **Subscriptions:** 70 journals and other serials. **Services:** Interlibrary loan; library not open to the public. **Networks/ Consortia:** Member of Cosmopolitan Biomedical Library Consortium (CBLC), Health Sciences Library Association of New Jersey (HSLANJ), Essex Hudson Regional Library Cooperative.

Maataloustuottajain Keskusliitto
See: **Central Union of Agricultural Producers** (3373)

Mabee Library
See: **Arkansas College** (1023)

★9487★
Jack Mabley Development Center - Professional Library (Med)
1120 Washington Ave. Phone: (815)288-8300
Dixon, IL 61021 Charles Padgett, Trng.Coord.
Founded: 1967. **Staff:** 1. **Subjects:** Mental retardation, psychology, psychiatry, medicine, special education. **Holdings:** 100 books. **Subscriptions:** 15 journals and other serials. **Services:** Copying; library open to the public with approval of librarian. **Remarks:** Maintained by Illinois State Department of Mental Health and Developmental Disabilities.

★9488★
Macalester College - DeWitt Wallace Library (Hum)
1600 Grand Ave. Phone: (612)696-6345
St. Paul, MN 55105-1899 Joel Clemmer, Lib.Dir.
Founded: 1885. **Staff:** Prof 7; Other 10. **Subjects:** Sinclair Lewis, Willa Cather, William Faulkner, Edna St. Vincent Millay, Adlai Stevenson. **Special Collections:** Sinclair Lewis Collection (239 books; ephemera); Willa Cather collection (62 items); William Faulkner collection (36 items). **Holdings:** 1000 books. **Services:** Copying; collections open to the public for reference use only. **Automated Operations:** Computerized public access catalog, cataloging, and acquisitions. **Computerized Information Services:** DIALOG Information Services, BRS Information Technologies, OCLC. **Networks/Consortia:** Member of Cooperating Libraries in Consortium (CLIC). **Staff:** Eunice Weisensel, Archv.

Mother Macaria Health Science Library
See: **St. Francis Medical Center** (14308)

MacArthur Foundation Library Video Classics
See: **Morris County Library - Music & Media Services** (10747)

★9489★
General Douglas MacArthur Memorial - Library and Archives (Hist)
MacArthur Sq. Phone: (804)441-2965
Norfolk, VA 23510 Edward Condra, Dir.
Founded: 1965. **Staff:** 1. **Subjects:** Occupation of Japan, Korean War, World War II (Pacific), life of General Douglas MacArthur, East Asia. **Holdings:** 5100 books; 600 linear feet of files from personal headquarters of General MacArthur; 1150 reels of microfilm. **Services:** Interlibrary loan; copying; library open to the public with restrictions. **Computerized Information Services:** Micro MARC, ANSI (internal databases). **Publications:** The MacArthur Report (newsletter), quarterly - to members and academic institutions. **Special Catalogs:** Catalog of record groups. **Staff:** Edward J. Boone, Jr., Archv.

★9490★
Macaulay Land Use Research Institute - Library (Agri)
Craigiebuckler Phone: 224 318611
Aberdeen AB9 2QJ, Scotland Anne Dickie, Libn.
Founded: 1930. **Staff:** Prof 2. **Subjects:** Soil science, agriculture, plant science, analytical chemistry, environmental science. **Holdings:** 8000 books; 10,000 bound periodical volumes; 350 reports; 30,000 reprints. **Subscriptions:** 200 journals and other serials. **Services:** Interlibrary loan; copying; library open to the public by appointment. **Computerized Information Services:** DIALOG Information Services, EUROBASES. **Publications:** Records Guide; Book Bulletin. **Remarks:** FAX: 224 311556.

★9491★
Peter MacCallum Cancer Institute - Central Cancer Library (Med)
481 Little Lonsdale St. Phone: 3-6415371
Melbourne, VIC 3000, Australia Aina Zalitis, Chf.Libn.
Founded: 1953. **Staff:** Prof 2; Other 2. **Subjects:** Cancer, radiotherapy. **Holdings:** 9700 books; 9200 bound periodical volumes. **Subscriptions:** 220 journals and other serials. **Services:** Interlibrary loan; copying; SDI; library open to the public with restrictions. **Computerized Information Services:** MEDLINE, DIALOG Information Services, PFDS Online. **Remarks:** FAX: 3-6415742. **Staff:** Aina Zalitis; Bill Freeman.

★9492★
Macculloch Hall Historical Museum - Macculloch Hall Archives (Hist)
45 Macculloch Ave. Phone: (201)538-2404
Morristown, NJ 07960 Mrs. Robert Odenweller, Archv.
Founded: 1978. **Subjects:** Macculloch-Miller family, Thomas Nast. **Special Collections:** Hajji Baba Society Library (Oriental rug study; 4 linear feet); Nicaragua Canal pamphlets; 19th century family library; W. Parsons Todd papers. **Holdings:** 1000 books; 100 documents; 1500 manuscripts. **Services:** Copying; archives open to the public by appointment. **Publications:** Macculloch Hall: A Family Album.

A.E. Macdonald Ophthalmic Library
See: **University of Toronto** (19426)

Angus L. MacDonald Library
See: **St. Francis Xavier University** (14316)

Frank J. MacDonald Library
See: **Queen Elizabeth Hospital** (13622)

★9493★
Jeanette MacDonald International Fan Club - Library (Rec)
1617 S.W. Indian Trail Phone: (913)271-7468
Topeka, KS 66604 Clara B. Rhoades, Pres.
Founded: 1937. **Staff:** 1. **Subjects:** Jeanette MacDonald and her husband, Gene Raymond. **Holdings:** 500 volumes; audio cassettes; videotapes; 16mm films; letters. **Services:** Library not open to the public. **Publications:** Newsletter, 4/year; Special 50th Anniversary Tribute, 1987.

Elizabeth M. MacDonell Memorial Library
See: **Allen County Historical Society** (372)

★9494★
Macedonian Ethnic Library (Area-Ethnic)
22711 Doremus Phone: (313)771-1513
St. Clair Shores, MI 48080 Adrijana Panoska Randolph, Dir./Libn.
Founded: 1975. **Staff:** Prof 1. **Subjects:** Macedonia - language and literature, politics and government; Yugoslavian statistics; Yugoslavian art; Serbo-Croatian language. **Special Collections:** Complete collection of books in all subjects studied in Macedonia, 1st to 4th grades; books on the system of education in Macedonia. **Holdings:** 1000 books; Macedonian songs; Macedonian and Yugoslavian tapes and records; maps; clippings; pictures. **Services:** Interlibrary loan; library open to the public by appointment. **Publications:** Macedonian Word, monthly - by subscription.

MacFarlane & Company, Inc. - Management Centre, Inc.
See: **Fry Consultants Incorporated** (6188)

MacGrath Family Medical Library
See: **Cheshire Hospital** (3486)

Machinability Data Center
See: **Institute of Advanced Manufacturing Sciences** (7892)

Machine Readable Data Center
See: **University of Minnesota - Machine Readable Data Center** (18919)

Alexander Mack Memorial Library
See: **Bridgewater College** (2120)

Mack Nursing Education Centre
See: **Niagara College of Applied Arts and Technology** (11795)

★9495★
Mack Trucks, Inc. - Hagerstown Powertrains Operations Division - Library (Sci-Engr)
1999 Pennsylvania Ave.
Hagerstown, MD 21740-2693 Phone: (301)790-5400
Founded: 1959. **Staff:** Prof 1. **Subjects:** Automotive engineering, metallurgy, chemistry, diesel engines. **Holdings:** 5500 books; 100 bound periodical volumes; 6500 internal engineering reports. **Subscriptions:** 30 journals and other serials. **Services:** Interlibrary loan; copying; SDI; library open to the public with prior approval. **Computerized Information Services:** PFDS Online. **Publications:** Library Bulletin, bimonthly - for internal distribution only. **Remarks:** FAX: (301)790-5605.

MacKenzie Environmental Education Center
See: **Wisconsin (State) Department of Natural Resources** (20522)

Sir Alexander Mackenzie Historical Society - Peace River Centennial Museum
See: **Peace River Centennial Museum** (12807)

★9496★
Mackenzie Smith Lewis Michell & Hughes - Law Library (Law)
600 Onondaga Savings Bank Bldg. Phone: (315)474-7571
Syracuse, NY 13202 Cheryl L. Wolfe, Law Libn.
Staff: Prof 1. **Subjects:** Law - general, civil practice, tax, corporation, labor, estate, real estate. **Holdings:** 10,000 books; 50 cassettes; 800 law briefs; 300 memoranda of law. **Subscriptions:** 100 journals and other serials. **Services:** Interlibrary loan; library open to the public with permission of librarian. **Computerized Information Services:** WESTLAW, DIALOG Information Services. **Remarks:** FAX: (315)474-6409.

Mackimmie Library
See: **University of Calgary** (18293)

★9497★
Mackinac Island State Park Commission - Historical Research Collection (Hist)
Box 30028 Phone: (517)373-4296
Lansing, MI 48909 Keith R. Widder, Cur.
Staff: Prof 1; Other 1. **Subjects:** History and archeology of Mackinac Island and Fort Michilimackinac. **Holdings:** 3000 volumes; 4000 photographs; 100 maps; 50 building plans; 200 reels of microfilm. **Subscriptions:** 20 journals and other serials. **Services:** Copying; collections open to the public by appointment only between October 15 and May 15.

John G. MacKinnon Memorial Library
See: **First Unitarian Church** (5807)

★9498★
Maclaren Advertising Limited - Library (Bus-Fin)
20 Dundas St., W. Phone: (416)977-2244
Toronto, ON, Canada M5G 2H1 Tina Alvares, Checking Ck.
Remarks: No further information was supplied by respondent.

★9499★
Maclean Hunter Ltd. - Maclean's Magazine Library (Publ)
777 Bay St., 7th Fl. Phone: (416)596-5340
Toronto, ON, Canada M5W 1A7 Basil Guinane, Chf.Libn.
Founded: 1977. **Staff:** Prof 1; Other 3. **Subjects:** General reference, news, current affairs. **Holdings:** 1300 books; 1200 subject clipping files; 18,000 biographical clipping files. **Subscriptions:** 150 journals and other serials; 15 newspapers. **Services:** Library not open to the public. **Automated Operations:** Computerized cataloging, serials, and indexing. **Computerized Information Services:** DIALOG Information Services, Dow Jones News/Retrieval, NEXIS, LEXIS, QL Systems, Info Globe, Infomart Online. **Special Indexes:** Maclean's Magazine Index (card before 1986; printout after 1985). **Remarks:** FAX: (416)596-7730.

★9500★
Maclean-Hunter Media, Inc. - Business Library (Bus-Fin)
4 Stamford Forum Phone: (203)325-3500
Stamford, CT 06901 Shirley Palmer, Libn.
Founded: 1930. **Staff:** Prof 2. **Subjects:** Food marketing, retail trade. **Special Collections:** Complete bound set of Progressive Grocer, 1927 to present. **Holdings:** 250 bound periodical volumes. **Subscriptions:** 200 journals and other serials. **Services:** Interlibrary loan; library open to clients and librarians by appointment. **Computerized Information Services:** DIALOG Information Services. **Remarks:** FAX: (203)325-4377. **Staff:** Sharon McGreevey, Lib.Asst.

James B. MacLean Technical Library
See: **Burns and Roe Enterprises Inc.** (2387)

Maclean's Magazine Library
See: **Maclean Hunter Ltd.** (9499)

Archibald MacLeish Collection
See: **Greenfield Community College Foundation** (6731)

★9501★
Macleod Dixon, Barristers and Solicitors - Library (Law)
3700, 400 3rd Ave. S.W. Phone: (403)267-8141
Calgary, AB, Canada T2P 4H2 Lana Barrett, Libn.
Staff: 2.5. **Subjects:** Law. **Holdings:** 3000 books. **Subscriptions:** 5 newspapers. **Services:** Interlibrary loan; library not open to the public. **Automated Operations:** Computerized public access catalog serials, and acquisitions (INMAGIC). **Computerized Information Services:** QL Systems, CAN/LAW, Info Globe, DIALOG Information Services, The Financial Post DataGroup, Infomart Online. **Remarks:** FAX: (403)264-5973. Telex: 03 825503. **Staff:** Dianne Taylor.

Macmillan of Canada Publishing Archives
See: **McMaster University - The William Ready Division of Archives and Research Collections** (9954)

MacMillan Forestry/Agriculture Library
See: **University of British Columbia** (18273)

★9502★
Hugh Macmillan Rehabilitation Centre - Health Sciences Library (Med)
350 Rumsey Rd. Phone: (416)425-6220
Toronto, ON, Canada M4G 1R8 Miss Pui-Ying Wong, Libn.
Founded: 1982. **Staff:** Prof 1. **Subjects:** Rehabilitation, disability, pediatrics, biomedical engineering. **Holdings:** 2000 books; 600 bound periodical volumes. **Subscriptions:** 130 journals and other serials. **Services:** Interlibrary loan; copying; library open to the public by appointment. **Automated Operations:** Computerized cataloging. **Computerized Information Services:** BRS Information Technologies. **Publications:** New Additions to the Library, irregular - for internal distribution only. **Remarks:** FAX: (416)425-6591.

★9503★
Macmillan, Inc. - Corporate Library
866 Third Ave.
New York, NY 10022
Defunct.

MacMillan Library
See: **Ellis Hospital** (5306)

Jerry MacMullen Library
See: **San Diego Maritime Museum** (14697)

★9504★
MacMurray College - Henry Pfeiffer Library (Educ, Hist, Med)
Jacksonville, IL 62650 Phone: (217)479-7111
Ronald B. Daniels
Founded: 1846. **Staff:** Prof 2; Other 1.5. **Subjects:** Education - special, deaf; American history; nursing. **Special Collections:** Birdseye Collection (Samuel Pepys); Austin-Ball Collection (singing and voice culture); U.S. government depository (1929 to present; selective). **Holdings:** 145,000 books; 8000 microfiche; 7000 reels of microfilm. **Subscriptions:** 450 journals and other serials; 5 newspapers. **Services:** Interlibrary loan; copying; library open to the public. **Computerized Information Services:** OCLC. **Remarks:** FAX: (217)245-5214.

★9505★
MacNeal Hospital - Health Sciences Resource Center (Med)
3249 S. Oak Park Ave. Phone: (708)795-3089
Berwyn, IL 60402 Rya Ben-Shir, MLS, Mgr.
Founded: 1930. **Staff:** Prof 2; Other 1. **Subjects:** Medicine, nursing, hospital administration. **Special Collections:** HealthAnswers: Community Health Information Collection (1200 books, pamphlets, articles). **Holdings:** 3000 books; 1827 bound periodical volumes; cassette tapes. **Subscriptions:** 191 journals and other serials. **Services:** Interlibrary loan; copying; SDI; center not open to the public (will accept telephone queries). **Automated Operations:** Computerized cataloging, acquisitions, circulation, and ILL. **Computerized Information Services:** DIALOG Information Services, BRS Information Technologies, NLM, OCLC. **Networks/Consortia:** Member of Metropolitan Consortium of Chicago, Suburban Library System (SLS), National Network of Libraries of Medicine - Greater Midwest Region. **Publications:** Bibliographies; F.I.L.L.S.: Fast InterLibrary Loans and Statistics, 1985. **Remarks:** FAX: (312)795-3369. **Staff:** Julie Stielstra, MLS, Asst.Libn.; Nancy A. Champion, ILL.

Macodrum Library
See: **Carleton University** (3055)

★9506★
Macomb County Historical Society - Crocker House Museum - Sabin and Lena Crocker Library (Hist)
15 Union St. Phone: (313)465-2488
Mt. Clemens, MI 48043 Burneil Spencer, Libn.
Founded: 1973. **Staff:** 2. **Subjects:** Local history, Crocker family genealogy, Victorian literature. **Holdings:** City directories; atlases; scrapbooks; pamphlet file. **Services:** Library open to the public by appointment.

Macomb County Library - Macomb Library for the Blind and Physically Hand icapped
See: **Macomb Library for the Blind and Physically Handicapped** (9509)

★9507★
Macomb County Library - Special Collections (Info Sci)
16480 Hall Rd. Phone: (313)286-6660
Mt. Clemens, MI 48044-3198 Carol Goodwin, Dir.
Founded: 1946. **Staff:** 59.5. **Holdings:** Map collection (1250); Michigan Government documents (500); U.S. Government documents (950); regional documents (150); Michigan collection (25,000 items); Adult Basic Collection (650 items); large print collection (3297). **Subscriptions:** 805 journals and other serials; 60 newspapers. **Services:** Interlibrary loan; copying; collections open to the public. **Automated Operations:** Computerized public access catalog, cataloging, and circulation. **Computerized Information Services:** Information Access Company (IAC), OCLC. **Networks/Consortia:** Member of Library Cooperative of Macomb (LCM), Michigan Library Consortium (MLC). **Publications:** Macomb County Library Newsletter; Directory of Government Officials. **Remarks:** Alternate telephone number(s): 469-5300. FAX: (313)228-8530. TDD: 286-9940.

Macomb Hospital Center Library
See: **Detroit Macomb Hospital Corporation** (4811)

★9508★
Macomb Intermediate School District - Beal Library (Educ)
44001 Garfield Rd. Phone: (313)228-3400
Mt. Clemens, MI 48044 Richard J. Palmer, Libn.
Founded: 1973. **Staff:** Prof 1; Other 7. **Subjects:** Education. **Special Collections:** Curriculum guides on microfilm (1500). **Holdings:** 40,000 books; 15,000 periodicals on microfilm; ERIC microfiche, 1970 to present. **Subscriptions:** 475 journals and other serials. **Services:** Interlibrary loan; copying; SDI; library open to the public for reference use only. **Automated Operations:** Computerized public access catalog, cataloging, acquisitions, and circulation. **Computerized Information Services:** DIALOG Information Services. Performs searches on fee basis. **Publications:** Periodical List, annual. **Remarks:** FAX: (313)286-1523.

★9509★
Macomb Library for the Blind and Physically Handicapped (Aud-Vis)
16480 Hall Rd. Phone: (313)286-1580
Mt. Clemens, MI 48044 Linda S. Champion, Libn.
Founded: 1983. **Staff:** Prof 3; Other 2. **Holdings:** 2000 large print books; 6500 discs and cassettes of recorded books; 5 TDDs and 2 closed caption decoder boxes. **Services:** Interlibrary loan; Kurzweil personal reader and Optalec machines for visually impaired; library open to the blind and physically handicapped. **Automated Operations:** Computerized circulation and recordkeeping. **Networks/Consortia:** Member of National Library Service for the Blind & Physically Handicapped (NLS). **Publications:** Newsletter, monthly - in large print or cassette. **Remarks:** TDD: (313)286-9940. FAX: (313)286-0634. Maintained by the Macomb County Library. **Staff:** Sandra A. Swartz, Libn.; Fran Ceraudo, Libn.

★9510★
Macon County Law Library (Law)
County Bldg.
253 Eastwood, Rm. 201-A Phone: (217)424-1434
Decatur, IL 62523 Norman C. Higgs, Libn.
Subjects: Law. **Holdings:** 6630 volumes.

★9511★
The Macon Telegraph - Library (Publ)
120 Broadway & Riverside Dr. Phone: (912)744-4328
Macon, GA 31201-9979 Harriet Comer, Lib.Mgr.
Founded: 1935. **Subjects:** Newspaper reference topics. **Holdings:** 200 books; clippings; photographs; 921 reels of microfilm of newspapers. **Services:** Library not open to the public. **Remarks:** FAX: (912)744-4385.

MacRae Library
See: **Nova Scotia Agricultural College - MacRae Library** (12129)

★9512★
Madawaska Historical Society - Madawaska Public Library Research Center (Hist)
Main St. Phone: (207)728-4272
Madawaska, ME 04756 Geraldine Chasse
Subjects: Madawaska area history, genealogy, folk tales. **Holdings:** Photographs; microfilm; microfiche. **Services:** Copying; center open to the public for reference use only. **Also Known As:** Tante Blanche Museum.

Henry Madden Library
See: **California State University, Fresno - Henry Madden Library - Department of Special Collections** (2561)

★9513★
John J. Madden Mental Health Center - Professional Library (Med)
P.O. Box 7000 Phone: (708)531-7000
Hines, IL 60141-7000 Kathryn Carlquist, Dir., Staff Dev.
Founded: 1965. **Staff:** Prof 1. **Subjects:** Psychiatry, psychology, administration, nursing, medicine, mental health, social work. **Holdings:** 3200 books; 50 bound periodical volumes; 60 videotapes. **Subscriptions:** 25 journals and other serials. **Remarks:** Maintained by Illinois State Department of Mental Health and Developmental Disabilities.

Elizabeth Coates Maddux Library
See: **Trinity University - Elizabeth Coates Maddux Library - Special Collections** (16521)

Clarence V. Mader Archive
See: **University of California, Los Angeles - Music Library** (18392)

★9514★
Madera County Historical Society - Museum/Library (Hist)
Old County Courthouse
210 W. Yosemite Ave.
Box 478 Phone: (209)673-0291
Madera, CA 93639 Rintha Robbins, Libn.
Founded: 1974. **Staff:** Prof 1. **Subjects:** History - Madera County, California, school, pioneer families, San Joaquin valley. **Special Collections:** Bound issues of Madera Mercury, 1913-1925; bound issues of Madera Tribune, 1892-1959; Madera County school histories; family histories of early families; obituaries; county documents, including the Great Register 1893. **Holdings:** Photographs; diaries; clippings; maps; charts; documents; scrapbooks. **Services:** Copying; library open to the public for reference use only with member present.

Madigan Army Medical Center
See: **U.S. Army Hospitals** (17048)

★9515★
Madigan Army Medical Center - Madigan Community Library (Mil, Med)
Box 310263 Phone: (206)967-6198
Tacoma, WA 98431-5263 Mary Magie, Libn.
Founded: 1944. **Staff:** 3. **Special Collections:** Military affairs, patient education, and career information; large print books; health and medically related videotape collection (80). **Holdings:** 20,000 books; 1800 phonograph records and tapes; 8 VF drawers of pamphlets; talking books. **Subscriptions:** 156 journals and other serials; 10 newspapers. **Services:** Interlibrary loan; copying; library open to the public for reference use only. **Automated Operations:** Computerized cataloging and circulation. **Computerized Information Services:** OCLC. **Networks/Consortia:** Member of Western Library Network (WLN). **Publications:** List of new books, monthly; annotated bibliographies of special collections subjects.

★9516★
Madison Area Technical College - Information Resource Center System (Educ)
3550 Anderson St. Phone: (608)246-6640
Madison, WI 53704-2599 Janet B. Jeffcott, Media Technl./Adm.
Founded: 1968. **Staff:** Prof 4; Other 28. **Subjects:** Vocational and technical education, engineering technology, health, business. **Holdings:** 70,000 books; 3000 reels of microfilm of periodicals; 2000 pamphlets; 4000 tapes and cassettes; 625 films; 2400 slide and transparency series. **Subscriptions:** 1150 journals and other serials. **Services:** Interlibrary loan; copying; library open to the public. **Computerized Information Services:** DIALOG Information Services, BRS Information Technologies, CompuServe Information Service. **Networks/Consortia:** Member of Multitype Advisory Library Committee (MALC). **Publications:** Handbook. **Remarks:** FAX: (608)246-6644.

Madison Business College
See: **Madison Junior College of Business - Library** (9524)

★9517★
Madison Community Hospital - Health-Science Library (Med)
917 N. Washington Ave. Phone: (605)256-6551
Madison, SD 57042 Donna Sullivan, Lib.Mgr.
Subjects: Nursing, medicine, paramedical sciences. **Holdings:** 50 books; 10 unbound periodicals. **Subscriptions:** 7 journals and other serials. **Services:** Copying; library open to health professionals.

★9518★
Madison County Historical Society - Library (Hist)
435 Main St.
Box 415 Phone: (315)363-4136
Oneida, NY 13421 Helen Chariton, Act.Dir.
Staff: 1. **Subjects:** Local history, genealogy, traditional crafts. **Special Collections:** Traditional Craft Archives (20,000 slides); Oral History Collection (100 tapes); Civil War and Upstate New York History Library. **Holdings:** 1850 books; 150 bound periodical volumes; 650 pamphlets, brochures, 19th century newspapers, maps, broadsides; 90 tapes; 54 films; 13 VF drawers of slides. **Services:** Copying; library open to the public with restrictions. **Publications:** Guide to Holdings MCHS Library, 1977; Guide to Holdings of the Traditional Craft Archive, 1979. **Special Catalogs:** Historic Resource File; Vital Statistics File.

★9519★
Madison County Historical Society - Museum Library (Hist)
715 N. Main St. Phone: (618)656-7562
Edwardsville, IL 62025 Marion Sperling, Libn.
Founded: 1924. **Staff:** 2. **Subjects:** Illinois and Madison County history; genealogical history of residents of Madison County. **Special Collections:** N.O. Nelson Village of Leclaire Papers; records and papers pertaining to county families; Edwardsville Street Index and Housing Inventory, 1894 to present; Index to First Sales of Land in Illinois; Madison County Poor Farm records. **Holdings:** 2130 books; 27 filing drawers and 50 feet of library shelves of manuscripts, documents, diaries, secretarial books, and county papers; 140 reels of microfilm of Madison County newspapers, including 109 rolls of microfilm Edwardsville Intelligencer, 1869-1920, 1988 to present; 4 filing drawers and 7 bins of photographs and portraits; 24 photo albums (late nineteenth and early twentieth century); county cemetery inventories; county marriage records index; maps. **Subscriptions:** 19 journals and other serials. **Services:** Copying; library open to the public for reference use only. **Publications:** Newsletter, semiannual - for local distribution. **Special Indexes:** Two county newpapers and cemetery surname index; indexes to manuscripts, personal papers, clippings, schools, historic houses, and pictures (card); History of St. Clair County, Illinois; History of Madison County, Illinois, published in 1882 (book); Gazetteer of Madison County, Illinois (1866); Military Index to Brink's History of Madison County; Madison County Poor Farm Record Indexes, Including Burials in Potter's Field. **Staff:** Deanna Kohlburn, Asst. Libn.

★9520★
Madison County Historical Society, Inc. - Library (Hist)
Eastern Kentucky University
Cimmack 26 Phone: (606)622-2820
Richmond, KY 40475-3108 Dr. Charles Hay
Founded: 1891. **Staff:** 1. **Subjects:** Local and state history. **Special Collections:** Fort Boonesborough Archaeological Dig papers and survey; Fort Boonesborough (1775) Bicentennial Commission papers; Society of Boonesborough papers. **Holdings:** 10 volumes; 2 scrapbooks; 100 newspaper articles; 50 items in Kentucky Bicentennial Series. **Services:** Library open to the public by appointment. **Publications:** Kentucky Pioneer, annual - to members and for sale; Madison County: Two Hundred Years in Retrospect, 1986; Madison County: Rediscovered - Historical Sites, 1988; Heritage Highlights (newsletter), semiannual.

★9521★
Madison County Law Library (Law)
Court House Phone: (315)366-2360
Oneida, NY 13163 Edward M. Kane, Libn.
Subjects: Law. **Holdings:** 10,000 volumes. **Services:** Library open to the public for reference use only.

★9522★
Madison County Law Library (Law)
Court House Phone: (614)852-9515
London, OH 43140 Janet C. Kronk, Libn.
Staff: Prof 3; Other 1. **Subjects:** Law. **Special Collections:** Ohio appellate decisions, 1981 to present (microfiche). **Holdings:** 10,000 volumes of federal and Ohio State law statutes, treatises, texts; 50 bound periodical volumes; 2300 volumes on microfilm. **Services:** Copying; library open to the public for reference use only. **Computerized Information Services:** WESTLAW. Performs searches on fee basis. **Remarks:** FAX: (614)852-9515.

★9523★
Madison Historical Society, Inc. - Library (Hist)
853 Boston Post Rd.
Box 17
Madison, CT 06443 Phone: (203)245-4567
Founded: 1920. **Staff:** Prof 1. **Subjects:** Local history, genealogy, religion, arts. **Special Collections:** Library of Daniel Hand. **Holdings:** 850 volumes; 6 VF drawers of manuscripts, sermons, photographs, clippings, reports, pamphlets. **Services:** Library open to the public by appointment.

★9524★
Madison Junior College of Business - Library (Educ)
1110 Spring Harbor Dr. Phone: (608)238-4266
Madison, WI 53705 Suellen S. Briggs, Libn.
Founded: 1958. **Staff:** Prof 1. **Subjects:** Business administration, accounting, sales and marketing, shorthand, secretarial sciences, government, economics, data processing, management, English, sociology, psychology. **Holdings:** 10,000 books; clipping file; tapes. **Subscriptions:** 172 journals and other serials. **Services:** Interlibrary loan; copying; SDI; library open to the public with restrictions. **Networks/Consortia:** Member of Multitype Advisory Library Committee (MALC). **Remarks:** FAX: (608)238-9905. **Formerly:** Madison Business College.

★9525★
Madison Metropolitan School District - Educational Reference Library (Educ)
545 W. Dayton St. Phone: (608)266-6188
Madison, WI 53703 Joanne W. Lenburg, Educ.Ref.Libn.
Founded: 1966. **Staff:** Prof 1; Other 1. **Subjects:** Education. **Special Collections:** Education journals on microfiche. **Holdings:** 10,000 volumes; 8 VF drawers of reports, pamphlets, bibliographies; video and audio tapes. **Subscriptions:** 185 journals and other serials. **Services:** Interlibrary loan; copying; SDI; library open to the public for reference use only. **Automated Operations:** Computerized cataloging and acquisitions. **Computerized Information Services:** DIALOG Information Services; CD-ROM (ERIC). Performs searches free of charge for primary clientele. **Publications:** HELPS (new acquisitions), bimonthly; subject bibliographies, irregular - both to primary clientele; Media Matters (newsletter), monthly during academic year - to district and administrative personnel. **Remarks:** FAX: (608)267-1634.

★9526★
Madison Pharmacy Associates - PMS Access - Library (Med)
P.O. Box 9326 Phone: (608)833-4PMS
Madison, WI 53715 Marla Ahlgrimm
Subjects: Premenstrual syndrome. **Holdings:** Current literature; audiocassettes; slide programs, videotapes. **Publications:** Newsletter.

★9527★
Madison Public Library - Municipal Reference Service (Soc Sci)
City-County Bldg., Rm. 315
210 Martin Luther King Jr. Blvd. Phone: (608)266-6305
Madison, WI 53709 Ann Waidelich, Libn.
Founded: 1971. **Staff:** Prof 1; Other 1. **Subjects:** Municipal government. **Special Collections:** City of Madison and Dane County government documents (2800). **Holdings:** 900 books. **Subscriptions:** 31 journals and other serials. **Services:** Interlibrary loan; copying; SDI; service open to the public. **Computerized Information Services:** LEXIS, NEXIS, DIALOG Information Services. **Networks/Consortia:** Member of South Central Library System. **Publications:** A Bibliography of Government Publications by and about Madison and Dane County, 2nd edition 1977, updated daily - free upon request. **Remarks:** FAX: (608)266-6305.

★9528★
Madison State Hospital - Cragmont Medical Library (Med)
Lanier Dr. Phone: (812)265-2611
Madison, IN 47250 Lloyd Roberts, Libn.
Founded: 1956. **Staff:** Prof 1. **Subjects:** Medicine, psychiatry, psychology, social work. **Special Collections:** Dentistry, occupational therapy, nursing, addiction collections (housed in 15 hospital departments). **Holdings:** 3824 volumes; 1750 clippings; 56 boxes of pamphlets. **Subscriptions:** 58 journals and other serials. **Services:** Interlibrary loan; library open to hospital staff and qualified students. **Networks/Consortia:** Member of Southeastern Indiana Area Library Services Authority (SIALSA).

★9529★
Madison Township Historical Society - Thomas Warne Historical Museum and Library (Hist)
Morristown Rd.
RD 3, Box 150 Phone: (908)566-0348
Matawan, NJ 07747 Alvia D. Martin, Cur.
Founded: 1964. **Staff:** 10. **Subjects:** Local history, genealogy. **Special Collections:** Sheet music, 1840-1920; Edison Cylinder records; early school books, 19th century; photo collection; diaries; social and church records. **Holdings:** 1000 books; photographs; albums; postcards; newspapers; pamphlets; maps. **Services:** Library open to the public for reference use only. **Publications:** At the Headwaters of Cheesequake Creek; Timepiece (newsletter); From Groaning Board Cooks. **Remarks:** Library located on Route 516, Old Bridge Township, NJ 08857.

★9530★
Madonna Centers - Medical Library (Med)
5401 South St. Phone: (402)483-9595
Lincoln, NE 68506-2134 Jean M. Powers, Dir. of Educ.
Staff: 3. **Subjects:** Rehabilitation, gerontology, medical sciences, nursing. **Holdings:** 600 books. **Subscriptions:** 90 journals and other serials. **Services:** Interlibrary loan; copying; library open to local physicians, Madonna employees, and affiliated students. **Computerized Information Services:** NEON, MEDLINE; DOCLINE (electronic mail service). **Networks/Consortia:** Member of Lincoln Health Science Library Group (LHSLG). **Remarks:** Alternate telephone number(s): 483-9595.

★9531★
(Madras) American Center - USIS Library (Educ)
Gemini Circle
Madras 600 006, India
Remarks: Maintained or supported by the U.S. Information Agency. Focus is on materials that will assist peoples outside the United States to learn about the United States, its people, history, culture, political processes, and social milieux.

(Madrid) Centro Cultural de los Estados Unidos
See: **Biblioteca Washington Irving** (1824)

★9532★
Magazine Publishers Association - Magazine Information Center (Publ)
575 Lexington Ave. Phone: (212)752-0055
New York, NY 10022 Sharon Roccaforte, Dir., Info.Serv.
Founded: 1940. **Staff:** Prof 2. **Subjects:** Magazine publishing and advertising. **Holdings:** 850 books; magazine publishers research reports; circulation reports; magazine advertising expenditures statistics; 50 vertical files of information on markets and media. **Subscriptions:** 150 journals and other serials. **Services:** Copying (limited); center open to MPA members, advertisers, and agencies by appointment. **Computerized Information Services:** NEXIS, DIALOG Information Services; internal databases. **Publications:** Fact Sheets on Magazine Publishing. **Remarks:** FAX: (212)888-4217.

★9533★
Magee Rehabilitation Hospital - Medical Library (Med)
6 Franklin Plaza Phone: (215)587-3423
Philadelphia, PA 19102 Susan Couch, Dir., Lib.Serv.
Founded: 1985. **Staff:** 1.5. **Subjects:** Physical medicine and rehabilitation; nursing; therapy - physical, vocational, occupational, speech. **Holdings:** 500 books; 70 bound periodical volumes; 600 unbound periodicals; 40 cassette tapes; 30 bulletins and newsletters; 100 videotapes. **Subscriptions:** 100 journals and other serials. **Services:** Interlibrary loan; library open to the public. **Computerized Information Services:** BRS Information Technologies. **Networks/Consortia:** Member of Delaware Valley Information Consortium (DEVIC). **Remarks:** FAX: (215)568-3533. Maintains a Patient Learning Resource Center containing 500 books.

★9534★
Magee-Womens Hospital - Howard Anderson Power Memorial Library (Med)
Forbes Ave. & Halket St. Phone: (412)647-4288
Pittsburgh, PA 15213 Bernadette Kaelin, Dir., Lib.Serv.
Founded: 1964. **Staff:** Prof 1; Other 2. **Subjects:** Obstetrics, gynecology, gynecological oncology, neonatology, perinatology, genetics. **Holdings:** 1000 books; 1000 bound periodical volumes; 200 pamphlets and documents. **Subscriptions:** 201 journals and other serials. **Services:** Interlibrary loan; copying; SDI; library open to the public with restrictions. **Computerized Information Services:** BRS Information Technologies, DIALOG Information Services, MEDLARS. Performs searches on fee basis. **Publications:** Powerline (newsletter).

★9535★
Magnavox Advanced Products & Systems Co. - Advanced Products Division - Library (Sci-Engr)
2829 Maricopa Ave. Phone: (213)618-1200
Torrance, CA 90503-5192 Cecilia Foutana, Libn.
Founded: 1958. **Staff:** Prof 1. **Subjects:** Physics, electronics, engineering. **Holdings:** 1200 books; 500 bound periodical volumes; 5000 technical reports. **Subscriptions:** 180 journals and other serials. **Services:** Interlibrary loan; library not open to the public.

★9536★
Magnavox Government & Industrial Electronics Company - Engineering Library (Sci-Engr)
1313 Production Rd. Phone: (219)429-6418
Fort Wayne, IN 46808 Lydia Peralta, Libn.
Founded: 1960. **Staff:** Prof 1. **Subjects:** Astronautics, mechanics, management, mathematics, physics, chemistry, sonar, electronics, radar, computer science. **Holdings:** 5000 volumes; 7 VF drawers of engineering literature reports; 2 VF drawers of reliability files; 2 VF drawers of house organs; 18 VF drawers of miscellanea. **Subscriptions:** 125 journals and other serials. **Services:** Interlibrary loan (limited); copying; library primarily for company personnel. **Automated Operations:** Computerized cataloging. **Computerized Information Services:** DIALOG Information Services.

★9537★
Judah L. Magnes Memorial Museum - Blumenthal Rare Book and Manuscript Library (Hist, Area-Ethnic)
2911 Russell St. Phone: (510)849-2710
Berkeley, CA 94705 Jane Levy, Libn./Archv.
Founded: 1967. **Staff:** 2. **Subjects:** Jewish art, history; Sephardic Jewry; Jewish music; history of Jewish books. **Special Collections:** S. Belkin Papers; Jews in India. **Holdings:** 11,000 books; 3000 documents; 300 manuscripts; 30 maps; 500 rare books; sheet music; phonograph records; slides. **Subscriptions:** 10 journals and other serials. **Services:** Copying; library open to the public for reference use only. **Special Catalogs:** Jewish illustrated books.

★9538★
Judah L. Magnes Memorial Museum - Western Jewish History Center (Hist, Area-Ethnic)
2911 Russell St. Phone: (510)549-6932
Berkeley, CA 94705 Ruth K. Rafael, Archv./Libn.
Founded: 1967. **Staff:** Prof 3; Other 1. **Subjects:** History of Jews in the Western United States; memoirs, oral histories, genealogy of Western Jews. **Special Collections:** Judah L. Magnes Collection; Jewish congregational archives; archives of Committee for the Preservation of Pioneer Jewish Cemeteries and Landmarks; Western Jewish newspapers from the 19th and 20th centuries; secular Jewish institutions; Oakland Jewish Institutions; David Lubin Collection; Harris Weinstock Collection; Jewish Community Federation of San Francisco, Marin County, and the Peninsula; Jewish Community Center, San Francisco; Rosalie Meyer Stern papers; Eureka Benevolent Society-Jewish Family Service Archives, San Francisco; Sam Hamburg Collection; Zellerbach Collection. **Holdings:** 1500 books; 50 bound periodical volumes; 10 unbound 19th century periodicals; 653 linear feet and and 345 archival records; 115 oral histories; 80 titles on microfilm; 14 VF drawers of pamphlets, family biographies, ephemera; 10,000 photographs; 320 tapes and cassettes. **Subscriptions:** 11 journals and other serials; 20 newspapers. **Services:** Interlibrary loan; copying (both limited); center open to the public. **Networks/Consortia:** Member of Council of Archives and Research Libraries in Jewish Studies (CARLJS), Bay Area Library and Information Network. **Publications:** A Guide to Archival and

Oral History Collections of the Center; list of additional publications - available upon request. **Special Indexes:** Analytical index to manuscripts; Index to Emanu-el (Northern California Jewish Bulletin), San Francisco; surname file. **Remarks:** FAX: (510)845-3650. **Staff:** Tova Gazit, Assoc.Archv./Libn.; Elaine Dorfman, Oral Hist.; Moses Rischin, Dir.; Ava Kahn, Res.Assoc.

★9539★
Magnetic Press, Inc. - Library (Info Sci)
588 Broadway, Rm. 505
New York, NY 10012 Phone: (212)219-2831
Subjects: Information and telecommunications technology - CD-ROM, WORM, CD-I, artificial intelligence, political and regulatory issues, microcomputer software, facsimile, electronic mail, packet switching. **Holdings:** 500 bound volumes. **Subscriptions:** 30 journals and other serials. **Computerized Information Services:** Produces MPI Opus and Calendar of Events database; CompuServe Information Service, MCI Mail (electronic mail services). Performs searches on fee basis. **Remarks:** FAX: (212)334-4729. Telex: 650322 1891. Electronic mail address(es): 71330,1664 (CompuServe Information Service); 322 1891 (MCI Mail).

Cyril Magnin Resource and Research Center
See: **Fashion Institute of Design & Merchandising** (5606)

★9540★
Maguire, Voorhis & Wells - Library (Law)
2 S. Orange Plaza
Box 633 Phone: (407)843-4421
Orlando, FL 32802 Ann A. Atwater, Law Libn.
Founded: 1920. **Staff:** Prof 1; Other 1. **Subjects:** Law. **Holdings:** 16,500 volumes. **Subscriptions:** 60 journals and other serials; 5 newspapers. **Services:** Library not open to the public. **Computerized Information Services:** LEXIS, NEXIS. **Networks/Consortia:** Member of Central Florida Library Consortium (CFLC). **Remarks:** FAX: (407)423-8796.

Magyar - Kozponti Statisztikai Hivatal
See: **Hungary - Central Statistical Office** (7552)

Magyar Kepzomuveszeti Foiskola - Konyvtar
See: **Hungarian Academy of Fine Arts - Library** (7541)

Magyar Tudomanyos Akademia
See: **Hungarian Academy of Sciences** (7542)

Magyar Tudomanyos Akademia - Csillagvizsgalo Intezet - Konyvtar
See: **Hungarian Academy of Sciences - Konkoly Observatory** (7549)

Magyar Tudomanyos Akademia - Irodalomtudomanyi Intezet
See: **Hungarian Academy of Sciences - Institute of Literary Studies - Library** (7548)

Magyar Tudomanyos Akademia - Kozgazdasagtudomanyi Intezete
See: **Hungarian Academy of Sciences - Institute of Economics** (7544)

★9541★
Magyar Tudomanyos Akademia - Matematikai Kutato Intezet - Konyvtar (Sci-Engr)
Realtanoda u 13
1053 Pf 127 Phone: 1 1177022
H-1364 Budapest, Hungary J. Merza
Founded: 1950. **Staff:** Prof 3. **Subjects:** Mathematics. **Holdings:** 37,707 books; 15,288 bound periodical volumes; 300 reports; 538 offprints. **Subscriptions:** 147 journals and other serials; 8 newspapers. **Services:** Interlibrary loan; copying; library open to the public. **Remarks:** FAX: 1 1177166.

Magyar Tudomanyos Akademia - Neprajzi Kutato Intezete
See: **Hungarian Academy of Sciences** (7543)

Magyar Tudomanyos Akademia - Nyelvtudomanyi Intezete
See: **Hungarian Academy of Sciences - Institute of Linguistics - Library** (7547)

★9542★
Magyar Tudomanyos Akademia - Talajtan es Agrokemiai Kutato Intezet - Konyvtar (Agri)
Hermann Otto u 15
Postafiok 35 Phone: 1 564591
H-1525 Budapest, Hungary Emoke Orban
Founded: 1949. **Staff:** Prof 2; Other 1. **Subjects:** Soil science, agricultural chemistry, soil biology. **Holdings:** 15,310 books; 9250 bound periodical volumes; 2077 reports; reprints. **Subscriptions:** 205 journals and other serials. **Services:** Interlibrary loan; copying; library open to the public. **Remarks:** FAX: 1 558839. Telex: 227223.

Magyar Tudomanyos Akademia-Konyvtara
See: **Hungarian Academy of Sciences - Library** (7550)

Magyar Tudomanyos Akademia Nyelvtudomanyi Intezete
See: **Hughes Aircraft Company - Space and Communications Group** (7513)

Magyarorszagi Kegyestanitorend/Piaristak - Kegyesrendi Kozponti Konyvtar
See: **Piarist Central Library** (13035)

★9543★
Maharishi International University - Library (Rel-Phil)
1000 N. 4th St. DB No. 1134 Phone: (515)472-1148
Fairfield, IA 52557-1134 Craig Shaw
Founded: 1971. **Staff:** Prof 5; Other 11. **Subjects:** Science of Creative Intelligence, Maharishi's Vedic science and technology. **Special Collections:** Science of Creative Intelligence (5200 books, journals, pamphlets, dissertations, and archival material). **Holdings:** 112,532 books; 13,006 bound periodical volumes; 4150 archival items; 44,538 microfiche; 1252 reels of microfilm; 8405 AV items. **Subscriptions:** 1148 journals and other serials; 17 newspapers. **Services:** Interlibrary loan; copying; library open to the public. **Computerized Information Services:** DIALOG Information Services, BRS/After Dark, MEDLARS. Contact Person: James Bates, Libn. **Remarks:** FAX: (515)472-1173.

★9544★
Mahaska County Historical Society - Irma Glatty Library (Hist)
P.O. Box 578 Phone: (515)672-2989
Oskaloosa, IA 52577 Dolly BeDillon, Libn.
Subjects: Local history, military history. **Special Collections:** WPA collection (2000 burial records to 1930). **Holdings:** 350 books; bound periodical volumes; documents; city directories; family histories; maps; plat books; nonbook items. **Services:** Copying; library open to the public. **Staff:** Ann Schultz, Cur.

Mahler - Rose Collection
See: **University of Western Ontario - Music Library** (19561)

A.P. Mahoney Library
See: **St. Peter's Seminary** (14587)

★9545★
Mahoning Law Library Association (Law)
Court House, 4th Fl.
120 Market St. Phone: (216)740-2295
Youngstown, OH 44503-1752 Linda L. Ellashek, Libn.
Founded: 1906. **Staff:** Prof 2; Other 3. **Subjects:** Law. **Holdings:** 27,378 volumes; 2732 bound periodical volumes; 63,222 microfiche. **Subscriptions:** 246 journals and other serials. **Services:** Library not open to the public. **Computerized Information Services:** DIALOG Information Services, WESTLAW.

★9546★
Maimonides Hospital Geriatric Centre - Pollack Library (Med)
5795 Caldwell Ave. Phone: (514)483-2121
Montreal, PQ, Canada H4W 1W3 Sheindel Bresinger, Libn.
Founded: 1965. **Staff:** 1.5. **Subjects:** Geriatrics, gerontology, medicine, social work, nursing, psychiatry. **Holdings:** 2100 books; 1000 bound periodical volumes; 90 reprints of staff articles; 4 drawers of current topics in geriatrics and gerontology. **Subscriptions:** 110 journals and other serials. **Services:** Interlibrary loan; copying; library open to the public with restrictions. **Computerized Information Services:** BRS Information Technologies; USE MUSE (internal database). **Remarks:** FAX: (514)483-1561.

★9547★
Maimonides Medical Center - George A. Degenshein, M.D. Memorial Library (Med)
4802 10th Ave. Phone: (718)283-7406
Brooklyn, NY 11219 Lydia Friedman, Chf.Med.Libn.
Founded: 1952. **Staff:** Prof 1; Other 3. **Subjects:** Medicine, dentistry, gynecology, surgery, pediatrics, obstetrics, nursing, pharmacology, psychiatry, anatomy, physiology. **Holdings:** 4969 books; 10,859 bound periodical volumes; 8 Audio-Digest series; 961 video programs; 188 slide programs. **Subscriptions:** 279 journals and other serials. **Services:** Interlibrary loan; library not open to the public. **Computerized Information Services:** MEDLARS; DOCLINE (electronic mail service). **Networks/Consortia:** Member of Brooklyn-Queens-Staten Island Health Sciences Librarians (BQSI), BHSL, New York Metropolitan Reference and Research Library Agency.

★9548★
Main Line Reform Temple - Library (Rel-Phil)
410 Montgomery Ave. Phone: (215)649-7800
Wynnewood, PA 19096 Betty Graboyes, Libn.
Founded: 1961. **Staff:** Prof 1; Other 1. **Subjects:** Judaica. **Holdings:** 7300 books; 500 phonograph records and filmstrips; clippings; reviews. **Subscriptions:** 3 journals and other serials. **Services:** Library open to the public with special permission. **Publications:** Acquisitions List, monthly - for internal distribution only.

★9549★
Maine Audubon Society - Environmental Library and Teacher Resource Center (Env-Cons)
PO Box 6009 Phone: (207)781-2330
Falmouth, ME 04105-6009 Maureen Oates, Dir., Educ.
Founded: 1843. **Staff:** 2. **Subjects:** Natural history, ornithology, environmental problems and education, Maine's natural resources. **Special Collections:** Environmental education (200 curriculum guides); children's books on environmental topics (250). **Holdings:** 2500 books; 300 environmental books for children; 9 VF drawers of Maine environmental files; 300 curriculum guides; 20 films and slides. **Subscriptions:** 40 journals and other serials; 12 newspapers. **Services:** Copying; service open to the public for reference use only. **Publications:** Maine School Science Network (newsletter), 6/year - by teacher subscription. **Staff:** Carol Lemere, Supv.

★9550★
Maine Charitable Mechanic Association - Library (Hum)
519 Congress St. Phone: (207)773-8396
Portland, ME 04101 Elinor Reynolds, Libn.
Founded: 1820. **Staff:** Prof 1. **Subjects:** Travel, biography, fiction, history. **Special Collections:** Material dealing with the history of the association; books pertaining to Maine and to Portland. **Holdings:** 30,896 books. **Services:** Library open to members and their families.

Maine Children's Memorial Library for Bereaved Parents
See: **Mercy Hospital - Health Sciences Library** (10134)

★9551★
Maine Criminal Justice Academy - Media Resources (Law, Aud-Vis)
93 Silver St. Phone: (207)873-2651
Waterville, ME 04901 Linda J. Dwelley, Media Rsrc.Supv.
Founded: 1976. **Staff:** Prof 1; Other 1. **Subjects:** Criminal justice, corrections, police, law enforcement, prisons, rehabilitation. **Special Collections:** Law enforcement/corrections training films (263) and slide/tape sets (156); probation/parole officers training video cassettes (229); highway safety films (299). **Holdings:** 3243 books and government publications; 51 bound periodical volumes. **Subscriptions:** 50 journals and other serials. **Services:** Interlibrary loan; copying; resources open to the public. **Automated Operations:** Computerized cataloging. **Computerized Information Services:** OCLC. **Networks/Consortia:** Member of NELINET, Inc. **Publications:** Newsletter, quarterly - to mailing list. **Special Catalogs:** Media catalog. **Remarks:** FAX: (207)877-0467.

★9552★
Maine Historical Society - Library (Hist)
485 Congress St. Phone: (207)774-1822
Portland, ME 04101 Nicholas Noyes, Libn.
Founded: 1822. **Staff:** Prof 6; Other 5. **Subjects:** Maine history and biography, New England history and genealogy. **Holdings:** 60,000 books; newspapers; documents; records; manuscripts; artifacts; photographs; maps. **Subscriptions:** 97 journals and other serials. **Services:** Copying; library open to the public on fee basis. **Automated Operations:** Computerized cataloging. **Computerized Information Services:** CD-ROM (MaineCat). **Publications:** Maine Historical Society Quarterly - to members. **Staff:** Elizabeth S. Maule, Mss.Cur.; Glenn B. Skillin, Cat.; Elizabeth J. Miller, Exec.Dir.; Stephen T. Seames, Res.Asst.; Nan Cumming, Musm.Cur.; Kathryn Blake, Wadsworth-Longfellow House Coord.

★9553★
Maine Maritime Academy - Nutting Memorial Library (Sci-Engr, Trans)
Castine, ME 04420 Phone: (207)326-4311
Marjorie T. Harrison, Libn.
Founded: 1941. **Staff:** Prof 4; Other 4. **Subjects:** Marine engineering, marine transportation, nautical science, maritime management, engineering technology, power engineering, yacht operations, boatyard management, ocean studies. **Special Collections:** Schieffelin Collection; Admiral Nimitz Collection (75 volumes); Betty Land Collection (182 volumes); Sailing Memorial Collection (200 volumes); Dr. Leslie L. Kanuk Collection (Federal Maritime Commission reports and papers). **Holdings:** 77,060 books; 5418 NTIS fiche; 4084 maps and charts; microforms; 9627 ultrafiche; 1024 audio cassettes; 149,074 government documents; 257 16mm films; 114 film loops; 1190 phonograph records; 791 video cassettes. **Subscriptions:** 883 journals and other serials; 19 newspapers. **Services:** Interlibrary loan; copying; library open to the public. **Automated Operations:** Computerized cataloging, ILL, and serials. **Computerized Information Services:** OCLC, DIALOG Information Services, VU/TEXT Information Services. Performs searches on fee basis. Contact Person: Michael Poulin, Asst.Libn. **Networks/Consortia:** Member of NELINET, Inc. **Staff:** Willard H. Gilmore, Asst.Libn.; Leone Howard, Govt.Doc.; Barbara Churchill, Per. & Acq.; H. Brent Hall, Asst.Libn.; William Bartok, AV Supv.; Dorothy Small, AV Spec.

★9554★
Maine Maritime Museum - Library/Archives (Hist)
243 Washington St. Phone: (207)443-1316
Bath, ME 04530 Nathan Lipfert, Lib.Dir.
Founded: 1964. **Staff:** 1. **Subjects:** Maine and American maritime history, shipbuilding in Maine, local history and genealogy. **Special Collections:** Sewall ship papers (325 document boxes). **Holdings:** 7000 books; 800 bound periodical volumes; 1000 pamphlets; 400 navigation charts; 20 unbound journals; 18,000 photographs; 30,000 ship plans; 800 ships' logs, account books, ledgers; 250 document boxes. **Subscriptions:** 10 journals and other serials. **Services:** Copying; library open to the public by appointment on fee basis. **Publications:** List of publications - available upon request. **Special Catalogs:** Maine ship captains and Maine built vessels (card). **Remarks:** FAX: (207)443-1665.

★9555★
Maine Medical Center - Library (Med)
22 Bramhall St. Phone: (207)871-2201
Portland, ME 04102 Robin M. Rand, Dir., Lib.Serv.
Founded: 1874. **Staff:** Prof 3; Other 8. **Subjects:** Medicine, public health, nursing, medical education, hospital administration. **Special Collections:** Archives and History of Medicine (especially Maine). **Holdings:** 6671 books; 12,568 bound periodical volumes; 1348 AV titles. **Subscriptions:** 652 journals and other serials. **Services:** Interlibrary loan (fee); copying; library open to health professionals in Maine. **Computerized Information Services:** NLM, DIALOG Information Services, PaperChase, BRS Information Technologies. **Networks/Consortia:** Member of Medical Library Center of New York (MLCNY), Health Science Library and Information Cooperative of Maine (HSLIC). **Publications:** Holdings List, annual. **Remarks:** FAX: (207)761-4294 (rush only). **Staff:** Ramona Connelly, Tech. Media Serv.Libn.; Patricia Williams, Pub.Serv.Libn.

★9556★
Maine (State) Administrative Office of the Courts - Thomas E. Delahanty Law Library (Law)
2 Turner St. Phone: (207)783-5450
Auburn, ME 04210 Ann Pierce, State Ct.Lib.Supv.
Founded: 1893. **Subjects:** Law. **Holdings:** 14,000 volumes. **Services:** Interlibrary loan; library open to the public. **Remarks:** Library is affiliated with the Trustees of the Law Library in the County of Androscoggin, Inc.

★9557★
Maine State Archives (Info Sci)
State House Sta. 84 Phone: (207)289-5790
Augusta, ME 04333-0084 James S. Henderson, State Archv.
Founded: 1971. **Staff:** 16. **Subjects:** Maine. **Holdings:** 20,000 cubic feet of judicial, legislative, and executive branch records, land office records, military (Civil War) records, censuses, and vital statistics records. **Services:** copying; archives open to registered researchers. **Computerized Information Services:** Internal databases. **Publications:** List of publications available upon request. **Remarks:** FAX: (207)289-5790. **Staff:** Jeffrey Brown, Archv.

★9558★
Maine State Audiovisual Alcohol/Drug Resource Center
Stevens School Complex
State House Sta. 57 Phone: (207)624-6525
Augusta, ME 04333 Gail Mazzaro, Rsrc.Cons.
Founded: 1979. **Staff:** Prof 2; Other 1. **Subjects:** Alcohol and drugs - use, abuse, dependency, education, prevention, and training. **Holdings:** 1500 books; 1000 16mm films and videotapes. **Subscriptions:** 12 journals and other serials. **Services:** Center open to school systems, community organizations, agencies, and professionals. **Networks/Consortia:** Member of National Clearinghouse for Drug Abuse Information (DRACON). **Special Catalogs:** Audiovisual Catalog, biennial. **Remarks:** FAX: (207)624-6505. **Staff:** Jo McCaslin, Libn.

★9559★
Maine State Department of Environmental Protection & Department of Conservation - DEP-DOC Joint Library
State House, Station 17
Augusta, ME 04333
Defunct.

★9560★
Maine State Department of Human Services - Departmental Library (Env-Cons, Med)
State House, Sta. No. 11 Phone: (207)289-3055
Augusta, ME 04333 Maryellen Fleming, Dept.Libn.
Founded: 1970. **Staff:** Prof 1; Other 1. **Subjects:** Nuclear power and radiation, water sanitation, health promotion, disease prevention, AIDS, child health. **Special Collections:** State of Maine reports and documents; Risk Reduction; Alcohol and Drug Abuse. **Holdings:** 3000 books. **Subscriptions:** 320 journals and other serials. **Services:** Interlibrary loan; copying; SDI; library open to the public. **Automated Operations:** Computerized cataloging. **Computerized Information Services:** MEDLARS, BRS Information Technologies. Performs searches on fee basis. **Networks/Consortia:** Member of Health Science Library and Information Cooperative of Maine (HSLIC), North Atlantic Health Science Libraries (NAHSL).

★9561★
Maine State Department of Marine Resources - Fisheries Research Station - Library (Biol Sci)
McKown Point Phone: (207)633-5572
West Boothbay Harbor, ME 04575 Pamela Shephard-Lupo, Libn.
Founded: 1957. **Staff:** **Staff:** 1. **Subjects:** Marine biology, fisheries, oceanography, marine chemistry, marine ecology, zoology. **Special Collections:** Fishermens' Library Collection. **Holdings:** 2000 books; 3000 bound periodical volumes; 5000 government and institutional documents; 12 filing drawers of reprints. **Subscriptions:** 260 journals and other serials. **Services:** Interlibrary loan; copying; library open to the public with restrictions on borrowing. **Automated Operations:** Computerized cataloging. **Computerized Information Services:** OCLC, DIALOG Information Services; Fishermen's Library (internal database). Performs searches on fee basis. **Networks/Consortia:** Member of NELINET, Inc. **Special Indexes:** Index of publications of the Maine Department of Marine Resources, 1946-1983, Fisheries Information Series Number 5. **Remarks:** FAX: (207)633-7109. Library also serves the Bigelow Laboratory for Ocean Sciences.

★9562★
Maine State Department of Transportation - Transportation Reference Center (Trans)
State House
Sta. No. 16
Child St. Phone: (207)289-5498
Augusta, ME 04333 Richard L. Sirois, Libn.
Founded: 1985. **Staff:** Prof 1; Other 1. **Subjects:** Engineering - traffic, highway, bridge; public transportation; traffic safety. **Special Collections:** Maine traffic studies; Transportation Research Board publications. **Holdings:** Maine statutes and standards. **Services:** Interlibrary loan; copying; center open to the public by appointment for reference use only.

★9563★
Maine State Law and Legislative Reference Library (Law)
State House, Station 43 Phone: (207)289-1600
Augusta, ME 04333 Lynn E. Randall, State Law Libn.
Founded: 1971. **Staff:** Prof 6; Other 9. **Subjects:** Anglo-American law, American state government and public policy. **Special Collections:** Maine legislative documents, amendments, study reports, committee master files, records of debates; Maine Supreme Judicial Court records and briefs, 1957 to present. **Holdings:** 98,000 volumes; 24 drawers of news clippings; 81,000 microfiche; congressional bills; U.S. Senate and House documents and reports on microfiche. **Subscriptions:** 1200 journals and other serials; 36 newspapers. **Services:** Interlibrary loan; copying (limited); library open to the public. **Automated Operations:** Computerized public access catalog (URSUS) and cataloging. **Computerized Information Services:** LEGISNET, DIALOG Information Services, WESTLAW, Integrated State Information System (ISIS), State Net, OCLC EPIC; CD-ROM (Maincat); LEGIST (Maine current legislation; internal database). Performs searches on fee basis (WESTLAW). **Networks/Consortia:** Member of NELINET, Inc. **Special Indexes:** Index to legislators of Maine, 1820 to present (card); Index to Resolves, 1820-1949 (card). **Remarks:** FAX: (207)289-6228. **Staff:** Robert H. Michaud, Pub.Serv.Coord.; Stephanie P. Ralph, Assoc.Libn.; Sue Wright, Assoc.Libn.; Jane E. Edwards, Tech.Serv.Coord.; Sheila M. Bearor, Assoc.Libn.

★9564★
Maine State Library (Hist, Info Sci)
Cultural Bldg.
State House Sta. 64 Phone: (207)289-5600
Augusta, ME 04333 J. Gary Nichols, State Libn.
Founded: 1839. **Staff:** Prof 18; Other 42. **Subjects:** Maine - history, genealogy, state, county, and local histories. **Special Collections:** Maine Author Collection (4000 volumes); Baxter Collection (personal papers of Governor Percival P. Baxter); Avery Collection (photos and paintings of Mt. Katahdin); maps; manuscripts; town reports, 1892 to present (includes city directories and Maine Registers, 1820 to present); Thomas Bird Mosher Publications, 1894-1926; Maine newspapers (Bangor Daily Whig and Courier, 1836-1900; Eastern Argus, 1803-1921; Le Messager, 1880-1946); Maine Vertical File. **Holdings:** 400,000 volumes; federal and state government documents. **Subscriptions:** 200 journals and other serials; 31 newspapers. **Services:** Interlibrary loan; copying; library open to the public. **Automated Operations:** Computerized cataloging. **Computerized Information Services:** OCLC, DIALOG Information Services. Performs searches free of charge. Contact Person: Emily Herrick, Ref.Libn. **Networks/Consortia:** Member of NELINET, Inc. **Publications:** The Maine Entry, quarterly; Libraries in Maine, annual. **Remarks:** FAX: (207)622-0933. **Staff:** John Boynton, Div.Dir.; Benjamin Keating, Div.Dir.

★9565★
Maine State Museum - Resource Center (Hum)
State House, Station 83 Phone: (207)289-2301
Augusta, ME 04333 Edwin A. Churchill, Chf.Cur.
Staff: 1. **Subjects:** Museology, archeology, Maine history and material culture, Americana, conservation, education. **Holdings:** 1400 books; 80 boxes of archival papers; 10 shelves of albums and journals. **Subscriptions:** 50 journals and other serials. **Services:** Copying; center open to the public for reference use only. **Special Indexes:** Maine craftsmen; Maine-related artifact holdings in public institutions (both on cards).

★9566★
Maison Bellarmin Library (Rel-Phil, Soc Sci)
25 W. Jarry Phone: (514)387-2541
Montreal, PQ, Canada H2P 1S6 Reginald Goulet, Dir.
Founded: 1935. **Staff:** Prof 1; Other 2. **Subjects:** Religion, social sciences, Holy Shroud, economics, Vatican II, science and faith. **Holdings:** 90,000 volumes; 10,000 unbound periodicals; 3000 pamphlets; 15,000 documents; 30,000 other cataloged items. **Subscriptions:** 306 journals and other serials; 43 newspapers. **Services:** Interlibrary loan; copying; library open to the public. **Automated Operations:** Computerized cataloging, acquisitions, and serials. **Remarks:** FAX: (514)387-0206. **Staff:** Luc Trepanier, Asst.Dir.

Maize Virus Information Service
See: **Ohio (State) Agricultural Research and Development Center - Library** (12276)

(Makati) USIS Library
See: **Thomas Jefferson Cultural Center** (8357)

Elizabeth S. Makkay Library
See: **New England Medical Center** (11475)

★9567★
Malawi - National Library Service (Area-Ethnic)
P.O. Box 30314 Phone: 730788
Lilongwe 3, Malawi Roderick S. Mabomba, M.Lib., F.L.A.
Founded: 1968. **Staff:** Prof 15; Other 85. **Subjects:** General, languages, Chichewa (local language). **Special Collections:** Malawiana Collection; World Bank publications; SADCC government publications; African Writers Series. **Holdings:** 209,606 books; 625 bound periodical volumes; 1080 microfiche. **Subscriptions:** 38 journals and other serials; 8 newspapers. **Services:** Interlibrary loan; copying; library open to the public. **Publications:** Annual reports; Library Bulletin; Staff Newsletter; occasional bibliographies. **Remarks:** FAX: 730626. **Staff:** L.B. Msiska, Dip.Ed.; C.S. Momba, Libn.; C.A. Ntara, Libn.; J.H. Chingwalu, Libn.; S.K. Kamera, Libn.; L.D. Mafaka, Libn.; N.K. Nkhoma, Libn.; M.A. Ngaunje, Libn.; A.B. Kulemeka, Libn.; R.W. Baleti, Libn.; H.A. Siyamanda, Libn.; B.A. Mwangolera, Libn.; G. Siliya, Libn.; N.R. Phiri, Libn.

Malaysia - Ministry of Education - National Library of Malaysia
See: **Malaysia - National Library of Malaysia** (9569)

★9568★
Malaysia - Ministry of Information - Research Library (Info Sci, Art)
Angkasapuri Phone: 3 2825333
Kuala Lumpur 22-10, Malaysia Asma Ahmat
Founded: 1950. **Staff:** Prof 4; Other 12. **Subjects:** Broadcasting, communications, journalism, film industry. **Special Collections:** Research collection (255 titles); ministry collection (597 titles). **Holdings:** 19,090 books; 282 reels of microfilm. **Subscriptions:** 65 journals and other serials; 14 newspapers. **Services:** Interlibrary loan; copying; SDI; library open to the public by appointment. **Publications:** Bibliografi Wanita dan Media, 1991. **Remarks:** FAX: 3 2821255. **Also Known As:** Kementerian Penerangan - Perpustakaan Penyelidikan.

★9569★
Malaysia - National Library of Malaysia (Area-Ethnic, Info Sci)
1st Fl., Wisma Sachdev/Thakurdas
Jalan Raja Laut Phone: 3 2923144
50572 Kuala Lumpur, Malaysia Mariam Tan Sri Abdul Kadir, Dir.Gen.
Founded: 1966. **Staff:** Prof 78; Other 178. **Subjects:** General collection. **Special Collections:** Malaysiana; Malay manuscripts; rare books (635); banned, confidential, restricted books. **Holdings:** 759,389 books; 19,712 serial titles; 1647 manuscripts; 2594 maps; 6214 reels of microfilm; 31,640 microfiche; 1366 slides; 3371 cassette tapes; 444 filmstrips; 23 film reels; 101 records; 693 photographs; 682 videotapes; 2053 posters; 374 multimedia kits; 11,005 print materials; 236 nonprint materials. **Subscriptions:** 459 journals and other serials and newspapers. **Services:** Copying; SDI; current awareness; Publisher Delivery System; microfilm and microfiche printing; consultancy and advisory services. **Computerized Information Services:** DIALOG Information Services; BERNAMA LIVECOM, SIRIMLINK, TELITA (internal databases); CD-ROM. Performs searches on fee basis. **Publications:** Subject bibliographies; bibliography of books in Malay language; Current Malaysian Serials: Government; Current Malaysian Serials - Non-Government; Directory of Libraries in Malaysia; ALA Rules of Filing Catalogue Cards; Sekitar Perpustakaan; List of Malay Titles; Malaysian Union List of Serials; accessions lists; Standard Headings for Malaysian Statutory Bodies; Current Serials Titles; Malaysian Current Serials (Non-Government); PNM Club News; SPP Newsletter; Annual Report; Directory of Malaysian Librarians. **Special Indexes:** Malaysian Periodical Index; Malaysian Newspaper Index; Index to Malaysian Conferences. **Remarks:** Maintained by Malaysia - Ministry of Education. **Remarks:** FAX: 3 2917436. Telex: MA 30092 NATLIB. **Staff:** Shahar Banun Jaafar, Dp.Dir.Gen.; Mrs. Zawiyah Baba, Dir.Lib.Serv.; Ahmad Bakeri Abu Bakar, Dir.Sup.Serv.

★9570★
Malaysian Rubber Research and Development Board - Rubber Research Institute of Malaysia - Library (Sci-Engr)
260 Jalan Ampang Phone: 4567033
50450 Kuala Lumpur, Malaysia J.S. Soosai, Libn.
Subjects: Natural rubber industry in Malaysia - plant science, crop protection, agronomy, agricultural economics, rubber chemistry and technology, polymer chemistry, analytical and applied chemistry, biological chemistry. **Holdings:** 70,000 volumes.

Thomas J. Malcho Memorial Library
See: **York-Finch General Hospital** (20771)

★9571★
Malden Historical Society - Library (Hist)
Malden Public Library
36 Salem St. Phone: (617)324-0220
Malden, MA 02148 John Tramondozzi, Cur.
Founded: 1887. **Subjects:** Maldeniana. **Holdings:** 2000 books. **Services:** Library not open to the public. **Publications:** Register of Malden Historical Society.

★9572★
Malden Hospital - Medical Library (Med)
Hospital Rd. Phone: (617)322-7560
Malden, MA 02148 Elizabeth F. Fitzpayne, Libn.
Staff: Prof 1. **Subjects:** Medicine, allied health sciences. **Special Collections:** History of medicine (20 volumes). **Holdings:** 732 books; 2100 bound periodical volumes; 125 pamphlets; 2 boxes of AV catalogs. **Subscriptions:** 109 journals and other serials. **Services:** Interlibrary loan; copying; SDI; library open to the public for reference use only with permission of librarian. **Computerized Information Services:** MEDLARS. **Networks/Consortia:** Member of National Network of Libraries of Medicine - New England Region, Boston Biomedical Library Consortium, North Atlantic Health Science Libraries (NAHSL), Massachusetts Health Sciences Libraries Network (MaHSLiN). **Special Catalogs:** AV catalog file (card). **Special Indexes:** Pamphlet file index (card); journal holdings index (card).

★9573★
Maldives - National Library (Sci-Engr, Soc Sci)
Billoorijehige
59 Majeedi Magu
Galolhu Phone: 3485
Male, Maldives Mrs. Habeeba Zubair, Dir.
Founded: 1945. **Staff:** 18. **Subjects:** Science, technology, social science, language, literature, history, geography. **Special Collections:** Maldivian Collection (books written about Maldives on geography, history, science, and technology; 500 books); children's literature. **Holdings:** 20,506 books; 54 bound periodical volumes; 8 reports; videocassettes; audiocassettes; manuscripts. **Subscriptions:** 2 journals and other serials; 5 newspapers. **Services:** Copying; library open to the public with restrictions. **Remarks:** Holdings are maintained in English, Arabic, Urudu, and Dhivehi.

Maledicta: International Research Center for Verbal Aggression
See: **International Maledicta Society** (8150)

★9574★
Malki Museum, Inc. - Archives (Area-Ethnic)
11-795 Fields Rd.
Morongo Indian Reservation Phone: (714)849-7289
Banning, CA 92220 Katherine Saubel, Pres.
Founded: 1965. **Staff:** 1. **Subjects:** Indians of southern California. **Special Collections:** Indian basketry, artifacts. **Holdings:** Manuscripts; photographs; oral history tapes; field notes from various anthropologists including John Peabody Harrington. **Services:** Archives open to the public for reference use only by appointment with curator. **Publications:** List of publications - available on request.

John W. Mallet Chemistry Library
See: **University of Texas at Austin - Chemistry Library** (19385)

Mallet Library
See: **Union Saint-Jean-Baptiste and Catholic Family Life Insurance - Mallet Library** (16665)

★9575★
Mallinckrodt Inc. - Library (Med)
3600 2nd St.
Box 5439 Phone: (314)539-1514
St. Louis, MO 63147 Juanita M. McCarthy, Mgr., Lib.Serv.
Founded: 1867. **Staff:** Prof 2; Other 2. **Subjects:** Chemistry, pharmacology. **Holdings:** 7000 books; 15,000 bound periodical volumes. **Subscriptions:** 400 journals and other serials. **Services:** Interlibrary loan; copying (limited); SDI; library open to the public. **Automated Operations:** Computerized cataloging, serials, and circulation. **Computerized Information Services:** DIALOG Information Services, DataTimes, BRS Information Technologies, STN International, Dow Jones News/Retrieval. **Networks/ Consortia:** Member of St. Louis Regional Library Network. **Publications:** Library Bulletin, monthly. **Remarks:** FAX: (314)539-1173. **Staff:** J. Pupava; M. Schmitt.

Mallinckrodt Institute of Radiology Library
See: **Washington University - School of Medicine** (20070)

Sister Martha Malloy Medical Library
See: **Sacred Heart Hospital - Sister Martha Malloy Medical Library** (14201)

Sybile Malloy Memorial Library
See: **Memphis Botanic Garden Foundation, Inc. - Goldsmith Civic Garden Center** (10059)

★9576★
Malta - National Library of Malta (Area-Ethnic, Hist, Info Sci)
36 Old Treasury St. Phone: 226585
Valletta, Malta John B. Sultana, Libn.
Subjects: Malta, Order of St. John. **Special Collections:** Archives of the Order of St. John of Jerusalem (also known as the Knights of Malta); early and old printed books. **Holdings:** 350,000 books; 10,000 manuscripts. **Services:** Interlibrary loan; copying; library open to the public. **Publications:** Malta National Bibliography, annual. **Special Catalogs:** Catalogue of the Records of the Order of St. John in the National Library of Malta (in progress).

Katharine Maltwood Archive
See: **University of Victoria - McPherson Library - Special Collections** (19489)

Eugene H. Maly Memorial Library
See: **Athenaeum of Ohio - Mount St. Mary's Seminary of the West** (1226)

★9577★
Mamigonian Foundation - Reference Collection (Area-Ethnic)
14513 Woodcrest Dr. Phone: (301)460-0353
Rockville, MD 20853 John L. Gueriguian, M.D.
Founded: 1985. **Subjects:** Armenia, diaspora. **Holdings:** 4100 books; 100 microfiche. **Subscriptions:** 8 journals and other serials. **Services:** Library open to the public by appointment. **Computerized Information Services:** Internal database. **Remarks:** FAX: (301)871-7273.

★9578★
Management Consultants International, Inc. - Library (Info Sci)
3904 Creekside Pl.
Burnaby, BC, Canada V5G 4P9 Phone: (604)434-7184
Subjects: Management of videotex, electronic international banking, telecommunications, electronic publishing, point-of-sale systems, broadcasting. **Holdings:** 200 bound volumes. **Subscriptions:** 25 journals and other serials.

★9579★
Management Professionals Association - Library (Bus-Fin)
P.O. Box 1018
T Nagar Phone: 44 443216
Madras 600 017, India Dr. J. Sudershan, Chm.
Founded: 1981. **Staff:** 60. **Subjects:** Management. **Special Collections:** Biographical archives. **Holdings:** 50,000 volumes. **Subscriptions:** 105 journals and other serials; 60 newspapers. **Services:** Interlibrary loan; copying; SDI; library open to the public. **Computerized Information Services:** Internal database. **Remarks:** Alternate telephone number(s): 44 440677. FAX: 44 517966 (Code FDS 115). Telex: 041 6489 MPA IN. **Staff:** Mrs. Dr. S. Vasanti, Chf.Libn.

★9580★
Manalta Coal Ltd. - Information Centre (Energy)
700 9th Ave. Phone: (403)294-5311
Calgary, AB, Canada T2P 3Z4 Theresa Carolyn, Libn.
Remarks: No further information was supplied by respondent.

★9581★
Manalytics, Inc. - Library (Trans)
625 3rd St., 3rd Flr. Phone: (415)788-4143
San Francisco, CA 94107 Bruce G. Dahms, Libn.
Founded: 1970. **Staff:** Prof 1. **Subjects:** Maritime, rail, air freight, trucking, transportation consulting. **Holdings:** 4000 books; corporate archives and reports. **Subscriptions:** 102 journals and other serials. **Services:** Interlibrary loan; library not open to the public. **Computerized Information Services:** DIALOG Information Services; internal databases. **Publications:** Port Planning Bibliography; Domestic Containerization Bibliography. **Remarks:** FAX: (415)777-0540.

Manassas National Battlefield Park
See: **U.S. Natl. Park Service** (17747)

★9582★
Manatee County Bar Association - Law Library (Law)
County Court House
Box 1000 Phone: (813)749-1800
Bradenton, FL 34206 Judy Brand, Law Libn.
Founded: 1950. **Staff:** Prof 1. **Subjects:** Law, taxation, medical jurisprudence. **Holdings:** 17,500 volumes. **Services:** Interlibrary loan; copying; library open to the public for reference use only.

★9583★
Manatee County Planning, Permitting & Inspections Department - Library (Plan)
P.O. Box 1000 Phone: (813)748-4501
Bradenton, FL 34206-1000 I. Medina
Subjects: Planning and land use, conservation and environment, housing and population, highways, streets, roads, water supply, coastal zone management, local government. **Holdings:** 1200 reports and technical materials. **Subscriptions:** 23 journals and other serials. **Services:** Interlibrary loan; library open to the public. **Remarks:** Library located at 1112 Manatee Ave. W., Bradenton, FL 34205.

★9584★
Manatee Memorial Hospital - Wentzel Medical Library (Med)
206 2nd St., E. Phone: (813)746-5111
Bradenton, FL 34208 Jeanette Mosher, Med.Libn.
Staff: 1. **Subjects:** Medicine, nursing. **Holdings:** 2500 volumes. **Subscriptions:** 70 journals and other serials. **Services:** Interlibrary loan (limited); copying; library open to the public for reference use only. **Computerized Information Services:** MEDLINE.

★9585★
Manatt Phelps & Phillips - Legal Information Center (Law)
11355 W. Olympic Blvd. Phone: (213)312-4283
Los Angeles, CA 90064 Jasmine Bailey, Libn.
Staff: Prof 1; Other 2. **Subjects:** Law, corporate law. **Special Collections:** Banking and financial institutions; health law. **Holdings:** 30,000 volumes; government documents; conference reports; continuing education program materials. **Subscriptions:** 550 journals and other serials; 25 newspapers. **Services:** Interlibrary loan; center open to other law firms with permission. **Automated Operations:** Computerized cataloging and serials. **Computerized Information Services:** DIALOG Information Services, LEXIS, NEXIS, WESTLAW, VU/TEXT Information Services, Dow Jones News/Retrieval, Dataquick Information Network, Information America, DataTimes, BASELINE INC., Legi-Tech, OCLC. **Remarks:** FAX: (213)312-4224.

★9586★
Manchester City Library - Fine Arts Department (Art)
405 Pine St. Phone: (603)624-6550
Manchester, NH 03104-6199 Beverly White, Fine Arts Libn.
Founded: 1914. **Staff:** Prof 1; Other 1. **Subjects:** Art, music, architecture, painting, photography, crafts, needlework, antiques, drawing, printing, textiles, glass. **Holdings:** 18,000 art volumes; 5000 music volumes; picture collection; recordings; films; videotapes; cassettes; framed prints and photographs. **Subscriptions:** 27 journals and other serials. **Services:** Interlibrary loan; copying; department open to the public. **Networks/Consortia:** Member of Urban Public Library Consortium.

★9587★
Manchester City Library - New Hampshire Room (Hist)
405 Pine St. Phone: (603)624-6550
Manchester, NH 03104-6199 Cynthia O'Neil, Libn.
Staff: 1. **Subjects:** New Hampshire - state and local history, biography, genealogy; history of Amoskeag Corporation. **Holdings:** 5800 books; 752 bound periodical volumes; 140 scrapbooks of Manchester news clippings, 1840-1942; photographs of Amoskeag mills and millyards; Manchester Union Leader subject clipping file. **Subscriptions:** 26 journals and other serials. **Services:** Copying; genealogical and state historical research and reference; room open to the public for reference use only. **Automated Operations:** Computerized public access catalog. **Networks/Consortia:** Member of Urban Public Library Consortium. **Special Indexes:** New Hampshire Times Index; New Hampshire Profiles Index (both on cards).

★9588★
Manchester Historic Association - Library (Hist)
129 Amherst St. Phone: (603)622-7531
Manchester, NH 03101 Elizabeth Lessard, Libn.
Founded: 1896. **Staff:** Prof 2. **Subjects:** Local history. **Special Collections:** Business archives of Amoskeag Manufacturing Company; textile designers files; 19th century music; photo archives (250,000 prints and negatives). **Holdings:** 1500 books; 11,475 pamphlets, manuscripts, prints, maps; 192 19th century local newspapers; diaries; letters; account books. **Subscriptions:** 5 journals and other serials. **Services:** Copying; library open to the public for reference use only. **Publications:** Guide to the Amoskeag Mfg. Co. Records at the Manchester Historic Association (1985).

★9589★
Manchester Historical Society - Library (Hist)
10 Union St. Phone: (508)526-7230
Manchester, MA 01944 Esther W. Proctor, Libn.
Staff: 2. **Subjects:** Local history. **Holdings:** 400 books; 15 bound periodical volumes; 4 drawers of photographs of local homes and people; old local maps; genealogy manuscripts. **Services:** Copying (limited); library open to the public with restrictions.

★9590★
Manchester Memorial Hospital - Medical Library (Med)
71 Haynes St. Phone: (203)646-1222
Manchester, CT 06040 Jeannine Cyr Gluck, Med.Libn.
Founded: 1955. **Subjects:** Medicine. **Holdings:** 500 books; 300 bound periodical volumes; audio cassettes; back volumes of periodicals on microfiche. **Subscriptions:** 100 journals and other serials. **Services:** Interlibrary loan; library not open to the public. **Computerized Information Services:** MEDLARS, BRS Information Technologies. **Networks/Consortia:** Member of Connecticut Association of Health Science Libraries (CAHSL), North Atlantic Health Science Libraries (NAHSL), BHSL.

Dr. Nicholas Mancini Center
See: **Hamilton-Wentworth Roman Catholic Separate School Board** (6869)

Jere Mangione Archive
See: **University of Rochester - Department of Rare Books and Special Collections** (19278)

★9591★
Manhasset Public Library - Special Collections (Hum)
30 Onderdonk Ave. Phone: (516)627-2300
Manhasset, NY 11030 Marian P. Robertson, Dir.
Founded: 1945. **Special Collections:** Books on Books (385 volumes); Long Island and New York State history (630 volumes); Manhasset authors (230 volumes); Japanese Collection (260 volumes); Frances Hodgson Burnett Collection (40 volumes); Kelly Miscall Collection of poetry for children; Benedetto/Rainone Puppet Collection; Ruth Cowell Local History Collection. **Services:** Interlibrary loan; copying; collections open to the public. **Computerized Information Services:** DataTimes, DIALOG Information Services, OCLC; CD-ROM (WILSONDISC); InfoTrac. **Publications:** Newsletter, quarterly; various bibliographies. **Remarks:** FAX: (516)627-4339. **Staff:** Florine Polner, Outreach, Archv.

★9592★
Manhattan College - Grover M. Hermann Engineering Library (Sci-Engr)
Corlear Ave. & 238th St. Phone: (212)920-0295
Bronx, NY 10471 John Gormley, Engr.Libn.
Founded: 1964. **Staff:** Prof 1; Other 2. **Subjects:** Engineering - chemical, civil, electrical, mechanical, environmental. **Holdings:** 24,500 books; 1843 bound periodical volumes; 300 maps; 7 VF cabinets; 68 journal titles on microfilm. **Subscriptions:** 230 journals and other serials. **Services:** Interlibrary loan; copying; library open to the public for reference use only. **Computerized Information Services:** DIALOG Information Services.

★9593★
Manhattan College - Sonntag Library (Biol Sci)
Riverdale, NY 10471 Phone: (212)920-0266
Dr. William A. Tramontano, Chm. of Biol.
Founded: 1964. **Staff:** 1. **Subjects:** Plant cancer, plant morphogenesis, plant physiology, cell biology. **Holdings:** 2230 bound periodical volumes. **Subscriptions:** 35 journals and other serials. **Services:** Interlibrary loan; copying; library open to the public for reference use only.

★9594★
Manhattan School of Music - Frances Hall Ballard Library (Mus)
120 Claremont Ave. Phone: (212)749-2802
New York, NY 10027 Pamela Bristah, Libn.
Founded: 1925. **Staff:** Prof 3; Other 3. **Subjects:** Music. **Holdings:** 9550 academic books; 8990 books on music; 17,200 phonograph records, compact discs, and tapes; 41,087 scores and pieces of music. **Subscriptions:** 119 journals and other serials. **Services:** Interlibrary loan; copying; library open to the public with METRO card or by appointment. **Computerized Information Services:** OCLC. **Remarks:** FAX: (212)749-5471. **Staff:** Richard Presser, Ref.Libn.; Marsha Genensky, Cat.

★9595★
Manhattanville College - Library - Special Collections and Archives (Hist, Hum)
Purchase, NY 10577 Phone: (914)694-2200
Donna L. Nickerson, Spec.Coll.Libn.
Subjects: Civil War, early American textbooks, Catholic church history in the United States, liturgical music, 19th and 20th century English and American literature, New York City, Westchester County. **Special Collections:** Rare book collection (2400 volumes; 3600 other cataloged items; 50 linear feet); Zigmund-Cerbu Collection of East Asian Cultural History, Languages, and Religions (2000 volumes); college archives (college and academy records, 1841 to present; 350,000 archival materials; 50 linear feet); Letters of Alexander H. Stephens, Confederate Vice President. **Services:** Interlibrary loan; copying; archives open to the public by appointment. **Automated Operations:** Computerized cataloging and ILL. **Computerized Information Services:** DIALOG Information Services. **Networks/Consortia:** Member of SUNY/OCLC Library Network, New York Metropolitan Reference and Research Library Agency.

★9596★
Manistee County Historical Museum - Fortier Memorial Library (Hist)
425 River St. Phone: (616)723-5531
Manistee, MI 49660 Steve Harold, Musm.Dir.
Founded: 1954. **Subjects:** Manistee County - history, logging and lumbering, early industries, pioneer families, transportation, genealogy. **Special Collections:** Hanselman, Russel, and Short photographic collections; Middleton Marine Collection; Manistee City newspapers, 1864 to present; Manistee County newspapers, 1919 to present. **Holdings:** Photographs; reports; pamphlets; programs; clippings; miscellanea. **Services:** Library open to the public.

★9597★
Manitoba Association of Playwrights - Library/Archive (Theater)
100 Arthur St., Rm. 503 Phone: (204)942-8941
Winnipeg, MB, Canada R3B 1H3 Rory Runnells, Coord.
Founded: 1983. **Subjects:** Canadian and Manitoba theater. **Special Collections:** Playwrights Development Program Workshop Plays (60). **Holdings:** 600 books; 200 manuscripts; 20 video cassettes. **Subscriptions:** 4 journals and other serials. **Services:** Copying; library open to the public. **Remarks:** FAX: (204)942-1555. Library is associated with Playwrights Union of Canada, and with the Literary Arts Resource Centre (Manitoba).

★9598★
Manitoba Association of School Trustees - Library (Educ)
191 Provencher Blvd. Phone: (204)233-1595
Winnipeg, MB, Canada R2H 0G4 Ardith McGeown, Educ.Serv.Cons.
Founded: 1980. **Staff:** Prof 2. **Subjects:** Public school governance and administration. **Special Collections:** Proceedings of Manitoba School Trustee Conventions, 1915 to present; Manitoba school board policy manuals (50). **Holdings:** 1000 books; 35 video cassettes; 50 audio cassettes. **Subscriptions:** 30 journals and other serials; 20 newspapers. **Services:** Library open to the public. **Publications:** Mast Magazine, annual; Mast Newsletter, monthly except July and August - both for internal distribution only. **Remarks:** FAX: (204)231-1356.

★9599★
Manitoba Attorney General - Legal Aid Library (Law)
294 Portage Ave., 4th Fl. Phone: (204)985-8500
Winnipeg, MB, Canada R3C 0B9 William C. Dunn, Leg.Dir.
Founded: 1972. **Subjects:** Law. **Holdings:** 500 books; 12 reports. **Subscriptions:** 15 journals and other serials; 5 newspapers. **Services:** Library not open to the public. **Networks/Consortia:** Member of Manitoba Government Libraries Council (MGLC). **Remarks:** FAX: (204)944-8582.

★9600★
Manitoba Attorney General - Library (Law)
405 Broadway Ave., 6th Fl. Phone: (204)945-2895
Winnipeg, MB, Canada R3C 3L6 Bryan Chesworth, Libn.
Staff: Prof 1. **Subjects:** Law. **Holdings:** 1000 books; 8000 bound periodical volumes. **Subscriptions:** 150 journals and other serials. **Services:** Interlibrary loan; library open to lawyers. **Networks/Consortia:** Member of Manitoba Government Libraries Council (MGLC). **Remarks:** Alternate telephone number(s): 945-3728.

★9601★
Manitoba Cancer Treatment and Research Foundation - Library (Med)
100 Olivia St. Phone: (204)787-2136
Winnipeg, MB, Canada R3E 0V9 Donna G. Chornenki, Libn.
Staff: Prof 1. **Subjects:** Oncology, medicine, radiology, basic sciences, cell biology. **Holdings:** 3422 volumes; 3308 bound periodical volumes. **Subscriptions:** 87 journals and other serials. **Services:** Interlibrary loan (local only); copying; library open to medical personnel. **Computerized Information Services:** MEDLINE; Reference Update (internal database). Performs searches on fee basis. **Publications:** Annual Report. **Remarks:** FAX: (204)783-6875.

Manitoba Community Services
See: **Manitoba Family Services** (9610)

★9602★
Manitoba Cooperative, Consumer and Corporate Affairs - Resource Centre
215 Garry St., Suite 800 Phone: (204)945-6284
Winnipeg, MB, Canada R3C 3P3 Jan Wanke, W.P. Supv.
Holdings: 250 books; slides; transparencies. **Services:** Interlibrary loan; library open to the public by appointment. **Remarks:** FAX: (204)945-0864.

Manitoba Culture, Heritage & Recreation - Manitoba Legislative Library
See: **Manitoba Legislative Library** (9618)

Manitoba Culture, Heritage & Recreation - Provincial Archives of Manitoba
See: **(Manitoba) Provincial Archives of Manitoba** (9625)

★9603★
Manitoba Department of Industry, Trade & Tourism - Business Resource Centre (Bus-Fin)
648-155 Carlton St. Phone: (204)945-2036
Winnipeg, MB, Canada R3C 3H8 John W.G. Giesbrecht, Mgr.
Founded: 1968. **Staff:** Prof 1; Other 2. **Subjects:** Business management, industrial technology, economics, public policy, trade, tourism. **Special Collections:** Company annual reports for Canada and American Midwest (7000 items). **Holdings:** 20,000 books; 5000 uncataloged items. **Subscriptions:** 200 journals and other serials; 5 newspapers. **Services:** Interlibrary loan; copying; SDI; library open to the public. **Computerized Information Services:** DIALOG Information Services, CAN/OLE, Info Globe; Hansard (internal database). Performs searches on fee basis. **Remarks:** FAX: (204)945-2804.

★9604★
Manitoba Department of Justice - Great Library (Law)
331-408 York Ave. Phone: (204)945-1958
Winnipeg, MB, Canada R3C 0P9 R. Garth Niven, Chf.Libn.
Staff: Prof 3; Other 5. **Subjects:** Law. **Special Collections:** Unreported Manitoba court decisions. **Holdings:** 12,000 books; 28,000 bound periodical volumes. **Subscriptions:** 350 journals and other serials. **Services:** Interlibrary loan; copying; SDI; library open to the public. **Automated Operations:** Computerized cataloging and acquisitions. **Computerized Information Services:** QL Systems, CAN/LAW, WESTLAW, DIALOG Information Services. **Networks/Consortia:** Member of Manitoba Government Libraries Council (MGLC). **Special Catalogs:** Index to Manitoba and Federal Unreported Decisions (Courts). **Staff:** Al Corrigan, Hd.Tech.Serv.

★9605★
Manitoba Department of Labour - Planning and Research Branch Library (Bus-Fin)
401 York Ave., Suite 409 Phone: (204)945-3412
Winnipeg, MB, Canada R3C 0P8 Carmen Barley, Res.Asst.
Founded: 1970. **Holdings:** 2500 books; 500 reports. **Subscriptions:** 25 journals and other serials. **Services:** Library open to the public. **Remarks:** No further information was supplied by respondent. FAX: (204)948-2085.

Manitoba Developmental Centre
See: **Manitoba Family Services** (9610)

★9606★
Manitoba Education - Bureau de l'Education Francaise - Direction des Resources Educatives Francaises (Educ)
200, ave. de la Cathedrale Phone: (204)945-8594
Winnipeg, MB, Canada R2H 0H7 Arsene Huberdeau, Dir.
Founded: 1978. **Staff:** Prof 7; Other 7. **Subjects:** Education; curricula, kindergarten through 12th grade. **Holdings:** 40,000 books; 450 Learning Centres; 950 16mm films; 1597 35mm filmstrips; 4000 video recordings; 1904 media kits; 760 records; 189 transparencies; 82 maps. **Subscriptions:** 40 journals and other serials. **Services:** Interlibrary loan; lending service to all schools in Manitoba; not open to the public. **Automated Operations:** Computerized public access catalog, cataloging, acquisitions, and circulation. **Computerized Information Services:** BestSeller 3000 (internal database). Performs searches on fee basis. Contact Person: Nicole Baudry, Lib.Techn., 945-2743. **Publications:** Le Bulletin, 4/year - for internal distribution only to schools and the Department of Education. **Remarks:** FAX: (204)945-0092. **Staff:** Doris Lemoine, Lib.Coord.; Jacques Frenette, Bookmobile Coord.; Gemma Borily, Libn.; Thongsay Phanlouvong, Prod.

★9607★
Manitoba Education and Training - Library (Educ)
1181 Portage Ave., Main Fl.
Box 3 Phone: (204)945-5371
Winnipeg, MB, Canada R3G 0T3 John Tooth, Dir.
Staff: Prof 8; Other 23. **Subjects:** Education, native studies, multicultural resources. **Special Collections:** Rare textbook collection. **Holdings:** 90,000 books; 3200 phonograph records; 2500 kits; 450,000 microfiche; 12,000 16mm films. **Subscriptions:** 900 journals and other serials. **Services:** Interlibrary loan; copying; library open to the public through ILL. **Automated Operations:** Computerized public access catalog, cataloging, acquisitions, and serials. **Computerized Information Services:** BRS Information Technologies, DIALOG Information Services; internal database; Envoy 100 (electronic mail service). **Remarks:** FAX: (204)945-8756. Electronic mail address(es): ILL.MWE (Envoy 100). **Staff:** Phyllis Barich, Hd., AV Rsrcs. & Serv.; Betty Seidel, Hd., Circ. & Ref.Serv.; Atarrha Wallace, Hd., Tech.Serv.; Elaine Seepish, Ref.Libn./Asst.Dir.; Lorrie Andersen, Coord., Coll.Dev.Serv.; Gloria Hersak, Sch.Lib.Curric.Cons.

★9608★
Manitoba Energy and Mines - Library (Energy, Sci-Engr)
330 Graham Ave., Suite 555 Phone: (204)945-6569
Winnipeg, MB, Canada R3C 4E3 Monique Lavergne, Lib.Techn.
Staff: 1.5. **Subjects:** Energy and mines. **Holdings:** 28,265 books and government reports; 3820 maps. **Subscriptions:** 185 journals and other serials; 5 newspapers. **Services:** Interlibrary loan; copying; library open to the public for reference use only. **Computerized Information Services:** DIALOG Information Services. **Remarks:** FAX: (204)945-0586. **Staff:** Debbie Rind, Lib.Techn.

★9609★
Manitoba Environment - Resource Centre (Env-Cons, Sci-Engr)
139 Tuxedo Ave., Bldg. 2 Phone: (204)945-7125
Winnipeg, MB, Canada R3N 0H6 Helen Woo
Founded: 1972. **Staff:** Prof 1; Other 1. **Subjects:** Environmental standards, environmental assessments, environmental control, air quality, air pollution, water quality, water pollution, toxic and hazardous substances, waste management, pesticide control, recycling. **Holdings:** 25,000 volumes. **Subscriptions:** 350 journals and other serials. **Services:** Interlibrary loan; copying; center open to the public with restrictions. **Automated Operations:** Computerized cataloging, acquisitions, and serials. **Computerized Information Services:** DOBIS Canadian Online Library System, UTLAS, DIALOG Information Services, CAN/OLE, Canadian Center for Occupational Health and Safety, Ground Water Online; internal database; Envoy 100 (electronic mail service). **Networks/Consortia:** Member of Manitoba Government Libraries Council (MGLC). **Publications:** Hazardous Waste Bibliography; accessions lists; bibliographies. **Remarks:** FAX: (204)945-5229. Maintains the W.M. Ward Technical Services Laboratory Library - Reading Room, 745 Logan Ave., Winnipeg, MB, Canada R3E 3L5. **Staff:** Kathy Grabowecky, Lib.Techn.

Manitoba Environment - W.M. Ward Technical Services Laboratory Library - Reading Room
See: **Manitoba Environment - Resource Centre** (9609)

Manitoba Environment & Workplace Safety & Health
See: **Manitoba Environment - Resource Centre** (9609)

★9610★
Manitoba Family Services - Manitoba Developmental Centre - Library (Med)
3rd St., N.E.
Box 1190 Phone: (204)239-6435
Portage La Prairie, MB, Canada R1N 3C6 Jo-Anne Doan, Lib.Techn.
Staff: Prof 1. **Subjects:** Developmentally disabled, genetics, medicine, nursing, psychology, management. **Holdings:** 4000 books; 20 dissertations and theses. **Subscriptions:** 100 journals and other serials and newspapers. **Services:** Interlibrary loan; library open to the public. **Remarks:** FAX: (204)239-5442. **Formerly:** Manitoba Community Services.

★9611★
Manitoba Finance - Federal-Provincial Relations and Research Division Library (Bus-Fin)
203-333 Broadway Ave. Phone: (204)945-3757
Winnipeg, MB, Canada R3C 0S9 Beatrice Miller, Libn.
Staff: Prof 1. **Subjects:** Finance, taxation, economics. **Holdings:** 3000 books; 3100 federal and provincial government reports. **Subscriptions:** 100 journals and other serials; 7 newspapers. **Services:** Interlibrary loan; library not open to the public. **Remarks:** FAX: (204)945-5051.

Manitoba Gay and Lesbian Archives
See: **Winnepeg Gay/Lesbian Resource Centre - Library & Archives** (20486)

★9612★
Manitoba Genealogical Society Inc. - Library (Hist)
167 Lombard Ave., Rm. 420 Phone: (204)944-1153
Winnipeg, MB, Canada R2B 0T6 Louisa Shermerhorn, Libn.
Founded: 1977. **Staff:** Prof 1. **Subjects:** Manitoba genealogical information, genealogy, biography, family history. **Special Collections:** Mormon International Genealogical Index for British Isles, Canada, Ireland (on microfiche); Manitoba cemetery transcriptions (570); Manitoba census, 1870, 1881, 1891; Henderson Directories, 1876 to present (partial set); birth, marriage, and death notices from Manitoba newspapers, 1859-1882; current obituary notices from Winnipeg papers, 1977 to present; rural newspaper obituaries. **Holdings:** 1834 volumes; genealogical resource periodicals; area directories. **Subscriptions:** 52 journals and other serials. **Services:** Copying; library open to the public with restrictions. **Special Catalogs:** Handbook For Genealogists; Handbook to Canadian Trees & French Roots; Children of the Country: A Guide to Indian and Metis Sources; Carved In Stone: Manitoba Cemeteries and Burial Sites; Library Holdings of the Manitoba Genealogical Society, 1990. **Special Indexes:** An Index of Marriage and Death Notices from Manitoba Newspapers, 1859-1881; Cemetery Indexes (95,000 cards); Current obituary notices from Winnipeg papers, 1977 to present.

★9613★
Manitoba Government Employees Association - Library
601-275 Broadway Phone: (204)942-1718
Winnipeg, MB, Canada R3C 4M6 George Bergen, Sr.Res.Off.
Remarks: No further information was supplied by respondent.

★9614★
Manitoba Health - Information Resources Centre (Med, Soc Sci)
202-880 Portage Ave. Phone: (204)945-8000
Winnipeg, MB, Canada R3G 0P1 Marilyn R. Brooke, Chf.Libn.
Founded: 1921. **Staff:** Prof 1; Other 8. **Subjects:** Public health, preventive medicine, public welfare, social service, health education, sociology, medicine, nursing, mental health. **Holdings:** 20,000 books; 1000 bound periodical volumes; 5000 pamphlets; 33,000 unbound periodicals; 10,000 government publications; 900 AV items; annual reports; statistics; statutes; calendars. **Subscriptions:** 235 journals and other serials. **Services:** Interlibrary loan; copying; library open to the public with restrictions on borrowing. **Automated Operations:** Computerized public access catalog and cataloging. **Computerized Information Services:** DIALOG Information Services, BRS Information Technologies, CCINFOline; Envoy 100 (electronic mail service). **Networks/Consortia:** Member of Manitoba Library Consortium, Inc., Manitoba Government Libraries Council (MGLC). **Publications:** Quarterly and Annual Reports; quarterly list of new additions to the collection; annual journals list; bibliographies on selected subjects - for department staff and others working in allied fields in Manitoba. **Remarks:** FAX: (204)945-5063. Electronic mail address(es): ILL.MWHP (Envoy 100).

★9615★
Manitoba Health Services Commission - Library (Med)
599 Empress St.
P.O. Box 925 Phone: (204)786-7398
Winnipeg, MB, Canada R3C 2T6 Vera Ott, Libn.
Founded: 1972. **Staff:** Prof 1. **Subjects:** Medicine, health services administration, laboratory technology. **Holdings:** 2145 books; 180 hospital-related Statistics Canada materials; 240 annual reports of provincial medical plans; 450 pamphlets. **Subscriptions:** 181 journals and other serials; 6 newspapers. **Services:** Interlibrary loan; copying; library open to department personnel and personnel in health-related fields. **Computerized Information Services: Publications:** List of periodicals and new additions, quarterly - for internal distribution only. **Remarks:** FAX: (204)783-2171.

★9616★
Manitoba Hydro - Library (Sci-Engr, Bus-Fin)
Box 815 Phone: (204)474-3614
Winnipeg, MB, Canada R3C 2P4 Rhona Lapierre, Corp.Libn.
Founded: 1957. **Staff:** Prof 2; Other 5. **Subjects:** Engineering - electrical, mechanical, hydraulic, civil; management and personnel. **Special Collections:** Corporation historical material. **Holdings:** 20,000 books; 500 bound periodical volumes; 20 shelves of Statistics Canada material; 30 VF drawers of technical data; 150 shelf feet of annual reports and standards; 2800 feet of unbound periodicals; 110 feet of government documents. **Subscriptions:** 950 journals and other serials. **Services:** Interlibrary loan; copying; SDI; library open to the public with restrictions. **Automated Operations:** Computerized acquisitions, cataloging, circulation, serials, and routing (Sydney Library System). **Computerized Information Services:** DIALOG Information Services, CAN/OLE, Info Globe, BRS Information Technologies, Dun & Bradstreet Business Credit Services, Infomart Online; iNet 2000, Envoy 100 (electronic mail services). **Publications:** Periodical Holdings, semiannual - for internal distribution and to other libraries. **Special Catalogs:** Film and video catalogs, annual. **Remarks:** FAX: (204)475-9044. Telex: 07 57425. Electronic mail address(es): MAN.HYDRO.1 (Envoy 100).

★9617★
Manitoba Indian Cultural Education Centre - Peoples Library (Area-Ethnic)
119 Sutherland Ave. Phone: (204)942-0228
Winnipeg, MB, Canada R2W 3C9 V.J. Chalmers, Libn.
Staff: 2. **Subjects:** Native peoples. **Holdings:** 4500 books; 2000 vertical files; 100 kits; 60 books of clippings; 47 films; 67 videotapes; 67 cassettes of Indian music; 24 tapes; 8 slide presentations. **Subscriptions:** 50 journals and other serials. **Services:** Interlibrary loan; copying; library open to the public. **Publications:** Listing of material, annual. **Remarks:** FAX: (204)947-6564.

★9618★
Manitoba Legislative Library (Soc Sci)
200 Vaughan St., Main Fl. E. Phone: (204)945-4330
Winnipeg, MB, Canada R3C 1T5 Susan Bishop, Leg.Libn.
Founded: 1884. **Staff:** Prof 8; Other 10. **Subjects:** Political science, economics, history, Western Canadiana. **Special Collections:** Statutes, journals, gazettes, and debates of Canadian legislative bodies; government and U.N. documents; documents of British and American governments and international bodies; Manitoba local history; Manitoba rural newspapers. **Holdings:** 100,000 books; 12,000 bound periodical volumes; 1.4 million documents; microforms. **Subscriptions:** 420 journals and other serials; 130 newspapers. **Services:** Interlibrary loan; library open to the public for reference use only. **Computerized Information Services:** Info Globe, DIALOG Information Services, WILSONLINE, Infomart Online, CAN/OLE, The Financial Post DataGroup; Envoy 100 (electronic mail service). **Publications:** Annual Reports; Selected New Titles, monthly; Checklist of Manitoba government publications, monthly; Checklist cumulation, annual; Memo for Members, sessional. **Special Catalogs:** Manitoba History catalog; Manitoba Biography clippings files catalog (both card). **Remarks:** Electronic mail address(es): LEG.LIB.CHR (Envoy 100). Maintained by Manitoba Culture, Heritage & Recreation. **Staff:** F.B. MacLowick, Hd., Info.Serv.; Paul Nielson, Hd., Tech.Serv.; Doreen Schafer, Hd., Coll.Dev.

★9619★
Manitoba Museum of Man and Nature - Library (Sci-Engr, Biol Sci)
190 Rupert Ave. Phone: (204)988-0692
Winnipeg, MB, Canada R3B 0N2 Cindi Steffan, Hd.Libn.
Founded: 1967. **Staff:** Prof 1; Other 1. **Subjects:** Natural history, Manitoba history, museology, ethnology, archeology, geology, astronomy. **Holdings:** 26,500 volumes; 5500 pamphlets; 725 oral history tapes; 35 microforms; 8200 pictures. **Subscriptions:** 344 journals and other serials. **Services:** Interlibrary loan; copying; library open to the public for reference use only. **Computerized Information Services:** DOBIS Canadian Online Library System; Envoy 100 (electronic mail service). **Publications:** Accessions list, quarterly - for internal distribution and other libraries. **Special Indexes:** Index to museum journal articles (online). **Remarks:** FAX: (204)942-3679. Electronic mail address(es): ILL.MMMN (Envoy 100). Alternate telephone number(s): (204)988-0662.

★9620★
Manitoba Natural Resources - Library (Biol Sci)
1495 St. James St.
Box 26 Phone: (204)945-6605
Winnipeg, MB, Canada R3H 0W9 Janina Skawinska, Sr.Lib.Techn.
Founded: 1978. **Staff:** Prof 2. **Subjects:** Fisheries, forests, wildlife, water resources, land use, park planning, sustainable development. **Holdings:** 13,500 books; 1000 bound periodical volumes; 9500 pamphlets; 35,000 reports; 3500 slides; 10,300 microfiche. **Subscriptions:** 479 journals and other serials. **Services:** Interlibrary loan; copying; library open to the public by request. **Computerized Information Services:** DIALOG Information Services, CAN/OLE. **Publications:** Annotated bibliography of publications, annual; Accessions List, quarterly - both to interested libraries and individuals.

★9621★
Manitoba Natural Resources - Surveys & Mapping Branch - Air Photo Library (Geog-Map)
1007 Century St. Phone: (204)945-6669
Winnipeg, MB, Canada R3H 0W4 Valerie Borkowsky, Supv.
Founded: 1930. **Staff:** Prof 2. **Subjects:** Aerial photography, photo mosaics. **Holdings:** 1 million photographs of Manitoba, 1923 to present. **Services:** Reproductions can be made of any photograph upon request. **Remarks:** FAX: (204)945-1365.

★9622★
Manitoba Natural Resources - Surveys & Mapping Branch - Technical Information Center (Sci-Engr)
1007 Century St. Phone: (204)945-6596
Winnipeg, MB, Canada R3H 0W4 Hartley Pokrant, Chf.
Founded: 1974. **Staff:** 1. **Subjects:** Remote sensing. **Special Collections:** Proceedings of international and Canadian symposiums on remote sensing. **Holdings:** 100 books; 24 bound periodical volumes. **Subscriptions:** 2 journals and other serials. **Services:** Interlibrary loan; center open to the public with restrictions. **Computerized Information Services:** RESORS (Remote Sensing On-line Retrieval System). Performs searches free of charge. Contact Person: Betty Sidoryk, Ck. **Publications:** Remote Sensing in Manitoba (newsletter), irregular - available on request. **Also Known As:** Manitoba Remote Sensing Center.

★9623★
Manitoba Naturalists Society - Library (Biol Sci)
128 James Ave., Suite 302 Phone: (204)943-9029
Winnipeg, MB, Canada R3B 0N8 Debbie Friesen, Adm.Sec.
Staff: 1. **Subjects:** Natural history, recreation, environmental issues. **Holdings:** 500 books. **Subscriptions:** 10 journals and other serials. **Services:** Library not open to the public.

★9624★
Manitoba Pharmaceutical Association - Library (Med)
187 St. Mary's Rd. Phone: (204)233-1411
Winnipeg, MB, Canada R2H 1J2 Janet McGillivray, Dir. of Cont.Educ.
Founded: 1984. **Subjects:** Therapeutics, pharmacy practice and history, business management. **Holdings:** 200 books. **Subscriptions:** 14 journals and other serials. **Services:** Copying; library open to association members and pharmacy students. **Remarks:** FAX: (204)237-3468.

★9625★
(Manitoba) Provincial Archives of Manitoba (Hist)
Manitoba Archives Bldg.
200 Vaughan St. Phone: (204)945-3971
Winnipeg, MB, Canada R3C 1T5 Peter Bower, Prov.Archv.
Founded: 1884. **Staff:** Prof 24; Other 12. **Subjects:** History of Manitoba and the Canadian West. **Special Collections:** Red River Settlement records; Riel Family papers; lieutenant-governors papers; Winnipeg General Strike manuscripts; Canadian Airways Limited. **Holdings:** 4000 linear feet of private sector textual records; 6500 linear feet of Hudson's Bay Company Archives; 20,000 linear feet of government records; 725,000 photographs; 18,175 maps; 300 paintings; 1874 hours sound recordings. **Services:** Interlibrary loan; copying; archives open to the public. **Remarks:** Houses the Anglican Church of Canada - Ecclesiastical Province of Rupert's Land Archives and the Hudson's Bay Company Archives. Maintained by Manitoba Culture, Heritage & Citizenship. FAX: (204)948-2008. **Staff:** Barry E. Hyman, Assoc.Prov.Archv.; Jane Dalley, Chf.Consrv.; Gordon Dodds, Assoc.Prov.Archv.; Judith H. Beattie, Kpr., Hudson's Bay Co. Archv.

Manitoba Remote Sensing Center
See: **Manitoba Natural Resources - Surveys & Mapping Branch - Technical Information Center** (9622)

Manitoba Research Council - Food Technology Services
See: **Manitoba Research Council - National Agri-Food Technology Center - Library** (9627)

★9626★
Manitoba Research Council - Library (Sci-Engr)
1329 Niakwa Rd. E. Phone: (204)945-6000
Winnipeg, MB, Canada R2J 3T4 Betty J. Dearth, Libn.
Founded: 1982. **Staff:** Prof 1. **Subjects:** Engineering - mechanical, electronics, industrial, computer-aided, chemical. **Holdings:** 3000 books; 250 unbound periodical titles, 3000 technical society papers on microfiche; 100,000 Canadian patent abstracts; vendor catalogs; manufacturing directories. **Subscriptions:** 165 journals and other serials. **Services:** Interlibrary loan; copying; library open to the public. **Automated Operations:** Computerized cataloging and serials. **Computerized Information Services:** DIALOG Information Services, CAN/OLE, ORBIT Search Service; internal database; Envoy 100 (electronic mail service). Performs searches on fee basis. **Remarks:** FAX: (204)945-1784. Electronic mail address(es): ILL.MWMRC (Envoy 100).

★9627★
Manitoba Research Council - National Agri-Food Technology Center - Library (Food-Bev)
810 Phillips St.
P.O. Box 1240 Phone: (204)239-3162
Portage La Prairie, MB, Canada R1N 3J9 Kris Rytter, Lib.Techn.
Founded: 1980. **Staff:** Prof 1. **Subjects:** Food - technology, processing, product development, engineering; nutrition; chemistry; microbiology; business. **Special Collections:** Technical file collection (2500 documents). **Holdings:** 1000 books; 1600 other cataloged items. **Subscriptions:** 175 journals and other serials. **Services:** Interlibrary loan; copying; library open to the public for reference use only. **Automated Operations:** Computerized cataloging, acquisitions, and serials. **Computerized Information Services:** CAN/OLE, DIALOG Information Services, CCINFO, iNet 2000; internal database; Envoy 100 (electronic mail service). Performs searches on fee basis. **Special Indexes:** Index of technical files. **Remarks:** FAX: (204)239-3180. Electronic mail address(es): ILL.CFPDC (Envoy 100). **Formerly:** Its Food Technology Services Library.

★9628★
Manitoba Rural Development - Library (Plan)
600-800 Portage Ave. Phone: (204)945-4129
Winnipeg, MB, Canada R3G 0N4 Judy Stephenson, Libn.
Founded: 1967. **Staff:** 1. **Subjects:** Land use, regional planning, community planning and housing, municipal government, statistics. **Holdings:** 5000 books; 22 bound periodical volumes; 3000 aerial photographs on microfilm; 4 VF drawers of documents. **Subscriptions:** 98 journals and other serials; 10 newspapers. **Services:** Interlibrary loan; copying; SDI; library open to the public. **Remarks:** FAX: (204)945-3769.

★9629★
Manitoba School for the Deaf - Library (Educ)
500 Shaftesbury Blvd. Phone: (204)945-8934
Winnipeg, MB, Canada R3P 0M1 Gerry Heath-Ranger, Libn.
Subjects: Deafness. **Holdings:** 1500 books; 80 bound periodical volumes. **Services:** Library open to the public. **Remarks:** FAX: (204)945-1229.

★9630★
Manitoba Telephone System - Information Resource Centre (Info Sci)
489 Empress St.
P.O. Box 6666 Phone: (204)941-6344
Winnipeg, MB, Canada R3C 3V6 Pat Routledge, Libn.
Founded: 1977. **Staff:** Prof 1; Other 1. **Subjects:** Telecommunications industry. **Holdings:** 2500 books. **Subscriptions:** 300 journals and other serials. **Services:** Interlibrary loan; center open to the public at librarian's discretion. **Automated Operations:** Computerized serials, acquisitions, and routing. **Computerized Information Services:** DIALOG Information Services, CAN/OLE, Info Globe, Infomart Online, NewsNet, Inc., STM Systems Corporation, Dun & Bradstreet Business Credit Services; Envoy 100 (electronic mail service). **Publications:** IRC News. **Remarks:** FAX: (204)772-5654. Electronic mail address(es): MTS.IRC (Envoy 100).

★9631★
Manitowoc Maritime Museum - Library (Hist, Trans)
75 Maritime Dr. Phone: (414)684-0218
Manitowoc, WI 54220-6823 Burt Logan, Dir.
Founded: 1969. **Staff:** Prof 1; Other 1. **Subjects:** Submarines and other vessels, marine construction, Great Lakes history, vessel construction. **Special Collections:** Carus Collection (3000 items); Captain Tim Kelley Log, 1870-1943 (65 volumes); Charles Gore Postcard Collection (5000); Koepke 20th Century Bulk Carrier Manuscript Collection; Schuette Yachting Collection; Berns Collection of World War II Shipbuilding Program; Ann Arbor Line Logs; Oakman Mullin Collection (books on battleships). **Holdings:** 7000 volumes; 10 VF drawers of information; 48 boxes of bound and unbound manuscripts; 100 films and filmstrips; 20,000 photographs and negatives; 64 VF drawers of blueprints. **Subscriptions:** 35 journals and other serials; 6 newspapers. **Services:** Copying; library open by appointment to museum members or with permission of the director. **Publications:** Anchor News, bimonthly. **Staff:** Joan Kloster, Reg.

(Manizales) Centro Colombo-Americano
See: **Biblioteca John F. Kennedy** (1822)

★9632★
Mankato State University - Bureau of Business and Economic Research - Library (Bus-Fin)
Box 14 Phone: (507)389-1623
Mankato, MN 56001 Ved P. Sharma, Ph.D., Dir.
Staff: Prof 1; Other 3. **Subjects:** Business statistics, economic data. **Holdings:** Government publications; business annual reports; local business indicators; publications of other Business Research Bureaus; theses. **Subscriptions:** 40 journals and other serials. **Services:** Library not open to the public. **Publications:** Mankato-North Mankato Business and Economic Indicators; Midwestern Journal of Business and Economics.

★9633★
Mankato State University - College of Education - Center for Children's & Young Adult Books (Hum)
0116 Memorial Library
Box 20 MSU Phone: (507)389-5209
Mankato, MN 56002 Frances McDonald, Ph.D., Dir.
Founded: 1983. **Staff:** Prof 1; Other 1. **Subjects:** Children's and young adult literature. **Holdings:** 8500 books. **Services:** Center open to the public for reference use, previewing, and consultation about resources. **Automated Operations:** Computerized public access catalog. **Publications:** Newsletter; bibliographies. **Remarks:** FAX: (507)389-5751.

★9634★
Mankato State University - Library - Special Collections (Educ)
Memorial Library Phone: (507)389-5952
Mankato, MN 56001 Dr. Thomas M. Peischl, Dean of Lib.
Holdings: Center for Minnesota Studies; curriculum guides and materials; urban studies; maps and aerial photographs (95,000); U.S. Government Printing Office depository library. **Services:** Interlibrary loan; copying; collections open to the public. **Automated Operations:** Computerized cataloging, acquisitions, serials, circulation, and ILL. **Computerized Information Services:** DIALOG Information Services, BRS Information Technologies, Minnesota Datand. **Networks/Consortia:** Member of Southcentral Minnesota Inter-Library Exchange (SMILE), MINITEX Library Information Network. **Remarks:** FAX: (507)389-5488.

Mankato State University - Southern Minnesota Historical Center
See: **Southern Minnesota Historical Center** (15506)

★9635★
Mankato Technical College - Library (Educ)
1920 Lee Blvd. Phone: (507)625-3441
North Mankato, MN 56003 Joan Klanderud, Libn.
Founded: 1946. **Staff:** 2. **Subjects:** Business - trade, industrial, technical; health food service; agribusiness; distributive education; nursing; computer programming, administrative support careers. **Holdings:** 9000 volumes; AV programs; professional collection. **Subscriptions:** 250 journals and other serials. **Services:** Interlibrary loan (limited); library open to the public. **Automated Operations:** Computerized circulation and cataloging (Follet's Info Plus). **Networks/Consortia:** Member of Southcentral Minnesota Inter-Library Exchange (SMILE). **Remarks:** FAX: (507)388-9951. Maintained by Independent School District 77, Mankato, MN.

Albert R. Mann Library
See: **Cornell University - Albert R. Mann Library** (4302)

Gertrude C. Mann Local History Room
See: **Franklin County Library - Gertrude C. Mann Local History Room** (6087)

Horace Mann Library/Learning Center
See: **Northwest Missouri State University - Owens Library** (12056)

Kristine Mann Library
See: **Analytical Psychology Club of New York** (829)

★9636★
Mannes College of Music - Harry Scherman Library (Mus)
150 W. 85th St. Phone: (212)580-0210
New York, NY 10024 Deborah Davis, Hd.Libn.
Founded: 1954. **Staff:** Prof 3; Other 1. **Subjects:** Music. **Special Collections:** Leopold Mannes manuscript collection; Carlos Salzedo Memorial Collection of Annotated Harp Music. **Holdings:** 7000 books; 25,000 scores; 6500 phonograph records; 500 compact discs. **Subscriptions:** 62 journals and other serials. **Services:** Library open to the public for reference use only upon application for specific materials. **Networks/Consortia:** Member of New York Metropolitan Reference and Research Library Agency. **Remarks:** FAX: (212)580-1738.

Cardinal Henry Edward Manning Library
See: **Emory University - Pitts Theology Library** (5334)

★9637★
Manomet Bird Observatory - Library (Biol Sci)
Box 936 Phone: (508)224-6521
Manomet, MA 02345 Dennis Heinemann, Staff Biologist
Founded: 1969. **Subjects:** Birds, ecology. **Holdings:** 2500 books; 160 bound periodical volumes. **Subscriptions:** 75 journals and other serials. **Services:** Library open to the public by appointment. **Remarks:** FAX: (508)224-9220. **Staff:** Josette Carter, Libn.

★9638★
Manor Junior College - Basileiad Library - Special Collections (Area-Ethnic)
Fox Chase Manor
700 Fox Chase Rd. Phone: (215)885-2360
Jenkintown, PA 19046 Anna Maksymowych, Spec.Coll.Libn.
Founded: 1947. **Subjects:** The Ukraine - history, literature, art, music. **Holdings:** 4700 volumes. **Subscriptions:** 10 journals and other serials; 7 newspapers. **Services:** Copying; collection open to the public for reference use only.

★9639★
Mansfield General Hospital - Medical Library (Med)
335 Glessner Ave. Phone: (419)526-8515
Mansfield, OH 44903 Marilyn J. Roe, Med.Libn.
Staff: Prof 1. **Subjects:** Nursing, medicine, and allied subjects. **Holdings:** 700 books; 85 bound periodical titles; 6 microfiche. **Subscriptions:** 85 journals and other serials. **Services:** Interlibrary loan; copying; library open to the public by appointment. **Computerized Information Services:** BRS Information Technologies, OCLC; DOCLINE (electronic mail service). **Publications:** Library Update, quarterly. **Remarks:** FAX: (419)526-1778.

★9640★
Mansfield Historical Society - Edith Mason Library (Hist)
954 Storrs Rd.
Box 145
Storrs, CT 06268 Richard Schimmelpfeng, Libn.
Founded: 1957. **Subjects:** Local Mansfield history. **Special Collections:** Account books of Edwin Fitch (local architect). **Holdings:** 400 books; 4 VF drawers of photographs; 2950 manuscripts, account books, scrapbooks, diaries. **Services:** Genealogical searching (limited); library open to the public with restrictions from May to October.

Maureen & Mike Mansfield Library
See: **University of Montana - Maureen & Mike Mansfield Library** (18987)

★9641★
Mansfield News Journal - Library (Publ)
70 W. Fourth St.
P.O. Box 25 Phone: (419)522-3311
Mansfield, OH 44901 Carol Dandareau
Subjects: Newspaper reference topics. **Holdings:** Microfilm issues of the News-Journal; clippings. **Subscriptions:** 12 newspapers. **Services:** Copying; library open to the public on a limited schedule. **Remarks:** FAX: (419)522-2672.

★9642★
Mansfield University - Audio Visual Center (Aud-Vis)
Allen Hall Phone: (717)662-4819
Mansfield, PA 16933 Gene Fessler, Dir.
Founded: 1965. **Staff:** Prof 1; Other 4. **Subjects:** Science, education, special education, geography, music, psychology. **Holdings:** 692 films and other AV programs. **Subscriptions:** 25 journals and other serials. **Services:** Copying; center open to the public. **Special Catalogs:** Film catalog.

★9643★
Mansfield University - Butler Center Library (Mus)
Mansfield, PA 16933 Phone: (717)662-4675
Holly Gardinier, Mus.Libn.
Founded: 1969. **Staff:** Prof 1; Other 3. **Subjects:** Music - education, history, therapy, theory, merchandising; jazz. **Special Collections:** Historical sets and monuments of music; old popular sheet music. **Holdings:** 7000 books; 1300 bound periodical volumes; 8500 scores; 7500 phonograph records; 130 titles in microform; 300 kits; 14 filmstrips; 150 video cassettes; 700 cassettes; 560 compact discs; 10 microcomputer programs; 4 transparencies. **Subscriptions:** 60 journals and other serials. **Services:** Interlibrary loan; copying; library open to the public with restrictions. **Automated Operations:** Computerized public access catalog, cataloging and ILL. **Computerized Information Services:** DIALOG Information Services, OCLC. **Networks/ Consortia:** Member of PALINET, Susquehanna Library Cooperative. **Remarks:** FAX: (717)662-4493.

Luther Manship Medical Library
See: **St. Dominic-Jackson Memorial Hospital** (14273)

Mansion Museum Library
See: **Oglebay Institute** (12258)

Harold W. Manter Laboratory
See: **University of Nebraska, Lincoln - State Museum** (19004)

George M. Manuel Memorial Library
See: **Piedmont Bible College** (13038)

★9644★
Manufacturers Association of Central New York - Information Center (Bus-Fin)
770 James St. Phone: (315)474-4201
Syracuse, NY 13203 Anne Kassel, Res.Dir.
Founded: 1913. **Staff:** 1. **Subjects:** Industrial relations, labor laws and interpretations, personnel management, wage and salary surveys, employment. **Holdings:** 1100 books; 14 VF cabinets of reports, clippings, pamphlets. **Subscriptions:** 75 journals and other serials. **Services:** Center open to the public with restrictions on confidential materials. **Computerized Information Services:** Confidential (internal database). **Publications:** Confidential Directories of Manufacturers. **Remarks:** FAX: (315)474-0524.

★9645★
Manufacturers Hanover Trust Company - Financial Library (Bus-Fin)
270 Park Ave., 17th Fl. Phone: (212)270-7362
New York, NY 10017 Ann Little, Asst. V.P.
Founded: 1975. **Staff:** Prof 1; Other 2. **Subjects:** Banking, finance, economics. **Holdings:** 3475 books; 177 unbound periodical titles; 6 lateral file drawers of periodical releases; 25 lateral file drawers of subject/industry files; 2891 reels of microfilm. **Subscriptions:** 512 journals and other serials; 6 newspapers. **Services:** Interlibrary loan; copying; library open to customers by referral of a company senior officer. **Computerized Information Services:** DIALOG Information Services, NEXIS, Reuter TEXTLINE, InvesText. **Remarks:** FAX: (212)270-6937.

★9646★
Manufacturers Hanover Trust Company - International Economics Library (Bus-Fin)
270 Park Ave., 41st Fl. Phone: (212)270-1621
New York, NY 10017 Halina Osysko, Libn.
Founded: 1971. **Staff:** Prof 3; Other 2. **Subjects:** International organizations, economics, trade, business, banking, industry and energy, finance, commodities. **Holdings:** 2110 books; 100 bound periodical volumes; 20,000 files on 235 countries. **Subscriptions:** 105 journals and other serials; 12 newspapers. **Services:** Library not open to the public. **Computerized Information Services:** Data Resources (DRI). **Special Catalogs:** Subject catalogs. **Remarks:** Alternate telephone number(s): 270-1627. FAX: (212)270-1628.

★9647★
Manufacturers Life Insurance Company - Business Library (Bus-Fin)
200 Bloor St., E. Phone: (416)926-5223
Toronto, ON, Canada M4W 1E5 Frances McManus, Hd.Libn.
Founded: 1925. **Staff:** Prof 1; Other 2. **Subjects:** Life insurance, management, behavioral sciences, economics, banking and investments, legislation, human resources. **Holdings:** 3000 books; 325 subject files of pamphlets and ephemera; clippings from Daily News. **Subscriptions:** 350 journals and other serials; 12 newspapers. **Services:** Interlibrary loan; copying; SDI; library open to the public with permission from librarian. **Computerized Information Services:** Info Globe, DIALOG Information Services, BRS Information Technologies, Data-Star, Mead Data Central, Infomart Online, PROFILE, Dow Jones News/Retrieval, AUSINET. **Remarks:** FAX: (416)926-5454.

★9648★
Manufacturers Life Insurance Company - Law Library (Law)
200 Bloor St., E.
N. Tower 10th Fl. Phone: (416)926-3498
Toronto, ON, Canada M4W 1E5 Wendy Duggan, Law Libn.
Subjects: Law - U.S., Canadian. **Holdings:** 4500 books. **Subscriptions:** 325 journals and other serials. **Services:** Interlibrary loan; library not open to the public. **Computerized Information Services:** LEXIS, WESTLAW, Info Globe, Dow Jones News/Retrieval. **Remarks:** FAX: (416)926-5403.

★9649★
Manufacturers Representatives Educational Research Foundation - Library (Bus-Fin)
Box 247 Phone: (708)208-1466
Geneva, IL 60134 Marilyn Stephens, Ed.D., Exec.Dir.
Founded: 1984. **Staff:** 2. **Subjects:** Manufactures' representatives, agents, brokers and their function in the marketing channel. **Holdings:** 400 books and articles; reports; 2 videotapes. **Services:** Copying; open to the public. **Remarks:** FAX: (708)208-1475. Foundation is sponsored by 20 national-level manufacturers' representative associations: Agricultural & Industrial Manufacturers Representatives Association (AIMRA); American Beauty Association (ABA); American Lighting Association (ALA); Association of Industry Manufacturers Representatives (AIM/R); Automotive Affiliated Representatives, Inc. (AAR); Broker Management Council (BMC); Canadian Electrical Manufacturers Representatives Association (CEMRA); Electronics Representatives Association (ERA); The Foodservice Group, Inc. (FSG); Health Industry Representatives Association (HIRA); Manufactur ers Representatives of America (MRA); Marketing Agents for Food Service Industry (MAFSI); National Association General Merchandise Representatives (NAGMR); National Association of Industrial Agents (NAIA); National Electrical Manufacturers Representatives Association (NEMRA); National Ingredients Marketing Specialists (NIMS); Power Transmission Representatives Association (PTRA); Safety Equipment Manufacturers' Agents Association (SEMAA); Wisconsin Association of Manufacturers Agents (WAMA); Office Products Representatives Association (OPRA).

★9650★
Manville Sales Corporation - Technical Center
PO Box 5108
Denver, CO 80217
Defunct. Holdings merged with Manville Sales Corporation - HS & E/ Technical Information Center to form Manville Sales Corporation - The Information Center.

★9651★
(Maracaibo) Centro Venezolano-Americano del Zulia - USIS Collection (Educ)
Calle 63, No. 3E-60
Apdo. Postal 419
Maracaibo, Venezuela
Remarks: Maintained or supported by the U.S. Information Agency. Focus is on materials that will assist peoples outside the United States to learn about the United States, its people, history, culture, political processes, and social milieux.

★9652★
(Maramures) Casa Corpului Didactic - Biblioteca (Soc Sci)
Strada Baia Sprie 52, Baia Mare Phone: 994 11935
Maramures, Romania Bejan Adrian
Founded: 1972. **Staff:** Prof 2. **Subjects:** Psychology, theory of literature, science and technology, education, arts, literature. **Holdings:** 40,000 books; 40 bound periodical volumes; 3 reels of microfilm. **Subscriptions:** 40 journals and other serials; 10 newspapers. **Services:** Library open to teachers.

★9653★
Marathon County Historical Museum - Library (Hist)
403 McIndoe St. Phone: (715)848-6143
Wausau, WI 54401 Mary Jane Hettinga, Libn.
Founded: 1952. **Staff:** Prof 1; Other 3. **Subjects:** State and county history, antiques, logging, Indian lore. **Special Collections:** Books published by Van Vechten and Ellis at the Philosopher Press in Wausau (20 volumes); John D. Mylrea Journals (15); James Colby photographs (5500 glass negatives); D.C. Everest personal papers. **Holdings:** 7000 books; 6000 maps and photographs; 80 manuscripts; 26 VF drawers of clippings. **Subscriptions:** 11 journals and other serials. **Services:** Copying; library open to the public on limited schedule.

Marathon Oil Company
See: **USX Corporation - Marathon Oil Company** (19704)

★9654★
Marblehead Historical Society - Jeremiah Lee Mansion - Library (Hist)
161 Washington St.
Box 1048
Marblehead, MA 01945 Phone: (617)631-1069
Staff: 7.5. **Subjects:** Local history and genealogy. **Holdings:** Books; bound periodical volumes. **Services:** Library open to the public by appointment.

Clarence E. March Library
See: **Androscoggin Historical Society** (863)

★9655★
March of Dimes Birth Defects Foundation - Reference Room (Med)
1275 Mamaroneck Ave.
White Plains, NY 10605 Phone: (914)428-7100
Founded: 1958. **Staff:** Prof 1. **Subjects:** Birth defects, pediatrics, obstetrics, maternal and child health. **Special Collections:** Reprints of March of Dimes Grantees; birth defects original article series. **Holdings:** 2500 books; 1722 bound periodical volumes; 5 VF drawers. **Subscriptions:** 108 journals and other serials. **Services:** Interlibrary loan; room open to the public by appointment only. **Networks/Consortia:** Member of Health Information Libraries of Westchester (HILOW). **Publications:** Journal holdings list, semiannual.

★9656★
Jacques Marchais Center of Tibetan Arts, Inc. - Museum Library
338 Lighthouse Ave.
Staten Island, NY 10306 Phone: (718)987-3500
Founded: 1946. **Subjects:** Buddhist art, philosophy, and religion with emphasis on Tibetan Buddhism. **Holdings:** 1000 books. **Services:** Library not open to the public.

Marcus Health Education Center
See: **St. Francis Regional Medical Center - Marcus Health Education Center** (14311)

A. Hollis Marden Bibliotheque
See: **Hopital Reine Elizabeth** (7396)

★9657★
Marga Institute - Library (Area-Ethnic, Soc Sci)
61 Isipathana Mawatha Phone: 1 585186
Colombo 5, Sri Lanka Hemamalee Geethananda, Chf.Libn.
Founded: 1976. **Staff:** 11. **Subjects:** Development issues in Sri Lanka and Asia, socioeconomics. **Holdings:** 30,000 volumes. **Subscriptions:** 57 journals and other serials; 9 newspapers. **Services:** Interlibrary loan; copying. **Computerized Information Services:** Co-ordinating Centre and Focal Point for Development Information Network for South Asia (DEVINSA). **Publications:** DEVINSA (abstracts), monthly. **Remarks:** FAX: 1 580585. Telex: 21642 MARGA. **Staff:** Ms. S. Naguleswaran; Ms. N. Rajasingham; Ms. N. Dias.

Marian Library
See: **University of Dayton** (18533)

★9658★
Marianjoy Rehabilitation Hospital and Clinics - Medical Library (Med)
26W171 Roosevelt Rd.
Box 795 Phone: (708)462-4104
Wheaton, IL 60189-0795 Nalini Mahajan, Med.Libn.
Founded: 1974. **Staff:** Prof 1; Other 1.25. **Subjects:** Rehabilitation medicine - cerebrovascular disorders, brain injuries, spinal cord injuries, pain, pediatrics, orthopedics, sports medicine. **Holdings:** 1500 books; 400 audio- and videotapes. **Subscriptions:** 150 journals and other serials. **Services:** Interlibrary loan; copying; SDI. **Computerized Information Services:** DIALOG Information Services, BRS Information Technologies, MEDLARS, Dow Jones News/Retrieval. **Networks/Consortia:** Member of Fox Valley Health Science Library Consortium (FVHSL), DuPage Library System, ILLINET. **Publications:** Library Litany (newsletter) - quarterly. **Remarks:** Alternate telephone number(s): (708)462-4270. FAX: (708)260-0143.

★9659★
Marianopolis College - Library - Special Collections
3880 Cote des Neiges Rd.
Montreal, PQ, Canada H3H 1W1
Defunct.

Maricopa Community College
See: **Gateway Community College** (6260)

★9660★
Maricopa County Law Library (Law)
East Court Bldg., 2nd Fl.
101 W. Jefferson St. Phone: (602)506-3461
Phoenix, AZ 85003 Fran Jones, Dir.
Founded: 1912. **Staff:** Prof 5; Other 13. **Subjects:** Law and allied subjects, professional responsibility, law office management. **Special Collections:** Native American law; tax and labor law. **Holdings:** 145,000 volumes. **Subscriptions:** 550 journals and other serials. **Services:** Interlibrary loan; copying (both limited); library open to the public. **Automated Operations:** Computerized cataloging. **Computerized Information Services:** WESTLAW, DIALOG Information Services, VU/TEXT Information Services. Performs searches on fee basis. Contact Person: Richard Teenstra, Asst.Dir. **Networks/Consortia:** Member of AMIGOS Bibliographic Council, Inc. **Publications:** Current acquisitions list, monthly; Discovery (newsletter), bimonthly. **Special Indexes:** Index to Arizona slip opinions (card). **Remarks:** FAX: (602)262-3677. **Staff:** Joan Bergeron, Acq.; Frankie Hernandez, ILL; Mary Grace Oakes, Ref.

★9661★
Maricopa County Medical Society - Robert S. Flinn Medical Library (Med)
326 E. Coronado, Suite 104 Phone: (602)252-2451
Phoenix, AZ 85004-1576 Patricia K. Sullivan, Hd.Libn.
Founded: 1923. **Staff:** 2. **Subjects:** Medicine, surgery, allied health sciences. **Holdings:** 75,000 volumes. **Subscriptions:** 180 journals and other serials. **Services:** Library not open to the public. **Computerized Information Services:** NLM, MEDLARS. **Remarks:** FAX: (602)495-8695.

★9662★
Maricopa Medical Center - Medical Library (Med)
2601 E. Roosevelt St. Phone: (602)267-5197
Phoenix, AZ 85008 Fernande Hebert, Med.Libn.
Founded: 1958. **Staff:** Prof 1; Other 1. **Subjects:** Medicine, surgery, nursing, hospital administration. **Special Collections:** Audiotapes in medicine and its specialities. **Holdings:** 3775 books; 6660 bound periodical volumes. **Subscriptions:** 275 journals and other serials. **Services:** Interlibrary loan (to medical libraries in Phoenix area). **Networks/Consortia:** Member of Central Arizona Biomedical Libraries (CABL).

★9663★
Maricopa Mental Health Annex - Library (Med)
2601 E. Roosevelt
P.O. Box 5099 Phone: (602)267-5990
Phoenix, AZ 85008 Connie Thompson
Founded: 1979. **Staff:** 1. **Subjects:** Psychiatry. **Holdings:** 750 books; 44 bound periodical volumes. **Subscriptions:** 44 journals and other serials. **Services:** Library not open to the public.

Marietta Memorial Medical Library
See: **John Peter Smith Hospital** (15245)

★9664★
Marin County Historical Society - Museum & Library (Hist)
1125 B St. Phone: (415)454-8538
San Rafael, CA 94901 Dorothy C. Morgan, Dir.
Founded: 1935. **Staff:** Prof 10; Other 5. **Subjects:** History of Marin County and California, history of coastal Indians. **Special Collections:** Marin Journal newspapers, 1861-1947; photographs of Marin County. **Holdings:** 1000 volumes; 100 bound manuscripts and studies; 2 VF drawers of source material; 3 scrapbooks of clippings. **Subscriptions:** 10 journals and other serials. **Services:** Copying; library open to the public for reference use only. **Publications:** Bulletin; Newsletter, bimonthly.

★9665★
Marin County Law Library (Law)
20 N. San Pedro Rd., Ste. 2015 Phone: (415)499-6355
San Rafael, CA 94903 Barbara B. Gately, Dir.
Founded: 1891. **Staff:** Prof 1; Other 3. **Subjects:** Law. **Holdings:** 25,000 books; 2000 bound periodical volumes; cassettes; California State Law Library publications. **Subscriptions:** 51 journals and other serials. **Services:** Library open to the public.

★9666★
Marin General Hospital - Library (Med)
Box 2129 Phone: (415)925-7000
San Rafael, CA 94912 Katherine Renick, Libn.
Founded: 1963. **Staff:** Prof 2. **Subjects:** Medicine, psychiatry, nursing. **Holdings:** 2500 books; 3500 bound periodical volumes; AV materials. **Subscriptions:** 130 journals and other serials. **Services:** Interlibrary loan; copying; SDI; library open to the public with restrictions. **Computerized Information Services:** MEDLINE. Performs searches on fee basis. **Remarks:** FAX: (415)925-7108. **Staff:** Julie Kahl, Libn.

★9667★
Marin Independent Journal - Library (Publ)
Box 151790 Phone: (415)382-7236
San Rafael, CA 94915-1790 Carol Farrand, Lib.Dir.
Founded: 1956. **Staff:** Prof 1; Other 1. **Subjects:** Newspaper reference topics, local biography, historical photography. **Holdings:** 300 books; 50 bound periodical volumes; unbound documents; clippings; Independent Journal and its predecessors on microfilm. **Subscriptions:** 10 journals and other serials. **Services:** library not open to the public. **Computerized Information Services:** NEXIS; internal databases. **Special Catalogs:** Guide to subject headings; photo catalog (online). **Special Indexes:** Index to obituaries; index to business column. **Remarks:** FAX: (415)382-0549. Published by Gannett Newspapers.

★9668★
Marin Museum of the American Indian - Library (Area-Ethnic)
Box 864 Phone: (415)897-4064
Novato, CA 94948 Janet Larson, Adm.Off.
Subjects: Indians of the San Francisco Bay area, California, and North America; ethnobotany; Native American arts; anthropology. **Holdings:** Figures not available. **Services:** Library open to the public for reference use only. **Remarks:** Library located at 2200 Novato Blvd., Novato, CA 94947.

Marine Biological Association of the United Kingdom
See: **Plymouth Marine Laboratory and Marine Biological Association of the United Kingdom** (13152)

★9669★
Marine Biological Laboratory - Library (Biol Sci)
Woods Hole, MA 02543 Phone: (508)548-3705
Dr. David Stonehill
Founded: 1888. **Staff:** 11. **Subjects:** Marine biology, biochemistry, physiology, oceanography, meteorology, ecology, paleontology, physics, marine botany, invertebrate zoology, chemistry, geology. **Holdings:** 30,000 books; 200,000 bound periodical volumes. **Subscriptions:** 5000 journals and other serials. **Services:** Interlibrary loan; copying; library open to the public with restrictions. **Automated Operations:** Computerized cataloging and serials. **Computerized Information Services:** DIALOG Information Services, NLM, BRS Information Technologies, PFDS Online, Chemical Abstracts Service (CAS); BITNET, DIALMAIL, SCIENCEnet (electronic mail services). Performs searches on fee basis. Contact Person: Judith Ashmore, Hd., Ref., 548-3705, ext. 436. **Networks/Consortia:** Member of Southeastern Massachusetts Consortium of Health Science Libraries (SEMCO). **Remarks:** Figures listed above include the books and serials of the Woods Hole Oceanographic Institution and the U.S. Natl. Marine Fisheries Services - Northeast Fisheries Center. FAX: (508)540-6902. Electronic mail address(es): LIBRARY@HOH.MBL.EDU (InterNet); MBL.LIBRARY (SCIENCEnet). **Staff:** Catherine Norton, Dir. of Lib.Plan; Pat Pratson, ILL; Peg Corbett Costa, Cat.; Joseph deVeer, Ser.

Marine Biological Laboratory - Woods Hole Oceanographic Institution - Research Library
See: **Woods Hole Oceanographic Institution - Research Library** (20576)

Marine Biological Society
See: **Western Canadian Universities - Marine Biological Society** (20236)

Marine Corps
See: **U.S. Marine Corps**

★9670★
Marine Environmental Sciences Consortium - Library (Biol Sci)
Dauphin Island Sea Lab
Box 369-370 Phone: (205)861-2141
Dauphin Island, AL 36528 Judy Stout, Libn.
Founded: 1971. **Staff:** Prof 2. **Subjects:** Marine biology, oceanography, marine geology, ecology. **Holdings:** 6100 books; 1700 bound periodical volumes; 7400 unbound reprints and reports; bound reprints and collections; 50 volumes of cruise reports; 2200 Marine Education Materials System (MEMS) microfiche. **Subscriptions:** 140 journals and other serials. **Services:** Interlibrary loan; copying; library open to the public. **Computerized Information Services:** SOLONET; SCIENCEnet (electronic mail). **Publications:** Journal of Marine Science; Northeast Gulf Science. **Remarks:** FAX: (205)861-4646. **Staff:** Connie Mallon, Asst.Libn.

★9671★
Marine Institute - Dr. C.R. Barrett Library (Trans, Biol Sci)
155 Ridge Rd.
P.O. Box 4920 Phone: (709)778-0445
St. John's, NF, Canada A1C 5R3 Mabel Farmer, Libn.
Founded: 1963. **Staff:** Prof 1; Other 5. **Subjects:** Fisheries and allied fields, navigation, nautical science, marine engineering, naval architecture, electronics, food technology. **Holdings:** 15,000 books; 700 bound periodical volumes; 2000 government documents; 12 VF drawers of pamphlets, clippings, reprints. **Subscriptions:** 450 journals and other serials; 14 newspapers. **Services:** Interlibrary loan; copying; library open to the public with restrictions. **Publications:** Acquisitions list. **Special Catalogs:** Audio Visual Catalog. **Remarks:** FAX: (709)778-0346. Telex: 016 4721.

★9672★
Marine Midland Bank - Corporate Library (Bus-Fin)
140 Broadway, 15th Fl. Phone: (212)658-1966
New York, NY 10015 Joan W. Glazier, Asst. V.P./Lib.Mgr.
Founded: 1967. **Staff:** Prof 2; Other 2. **Subjects:** Banking, finance, investments, management. **Holdings:** 7500 books; 100 VF drawers; Wall Street Journal, 1947 to present, on microfilm; American Banker, 1971 to present, on microfilm; New York Times, 1967 to present, on microfilm; Moody's Manuals, 1909 to present, on microfiche. **Subscriptions:** 350 journals and other serials; 10 newspapers. **Services:** Interlibrary loan; library not open to the public. **Automated Operations:** Computerized cataloging, acquisitions, and serials (REMO, DataTrek). **Computerized Information Services:** NEXIS, DIALOG Information Services, Dow Jones News/Retrieval, VU/TEXT Information Services, Reuter TEXTLINE, InvesText; CD-ROM (Disclosure Incorporated, and Dun & Bradstreet Business Credit Services Million Dollar Directory); internal database. **Remarks:** Alternate telephone number(s): 658-6112; FAX: (212)658-5511. **Staff:** Yat Ping Wong, Ref.Libn.; Miriam Clary, Libn.

★9673★
Marine Museum at Fall River, Inc. - Library (Hist)
P.O. Box 1147 Phone: (508)674-3533
Fall River, MA 02722 John F. Gosson, Curator
Founded: 1968. **Staff:** 3. **Subjects:** History of power-driven water craft; arctic exploration. **Special Collections:** William King Covell Collection; James S. Hart Collection. **Holdings:** 2000 books; 125 bound periodical volumes; 5000 photographic plates; 1000 glass slides. **Services:** Library open to the public for reference use only. **Remarks:** Library located at 70 Water St., Fall River, MA.

★9674★
Marine Products Company - Library (Sci-Engr)
333 W. 1st St. Phone: (617)268-0750
Boston, MA 02127 Dr. E. James Iorio, V.P.
Founded: 1929. **Staff:** 3. **Subjects:** Organic chemicals, pharmacology, toxicology. **Holdings:** 200 books; 630 bound periodical volumes; 139 suppliers' catalogs. **Subscriptions:** 34 journals and other serials; 6 newspapers. **Services:** library not open to the public.

★9675★
Marineland, Inc. - Research Laboratory
9507 Ocean Shore Blvd
Marineland, FL 32086-9602 Phone: (904)471-1111
Subjects: Marine biology, marine mammals, animal husbandry, oceanography, water testing. **Holdings:** 550 volumes; 1000 other periodicals; 1000 reprints; 12 films. **Services:** Laboratory not open to the public.

★9676★
Mariners Museum - Library (Trans)
100 Museum Dr. Phone: (804)595-0368
Newport News, VA 23606-3798 Benjamin H. Trask, Ref.Libn.
Founded: 1933. **Staff:** Prof 2; Other 2. **Subjects:** Shipping, shipbuilding, navigation, merchant marine, navies, exploration and travel, whaling, yachting. **Holdings:** 70,000 volumes; 350,000 photographs; logbooks; journals; ships' papers; microfilm; tapes; maps; charts. **Subscriptions:** 175 journals and other serials. **Services:** Copying; library open to the public. **Remarks:** FAX: (804)591-8212. **Staff:** R. Thomas Crew, Jr., Archv.

★9677★
Marinette County Law Library (Law)
Court House
1926 Hall Ave. Phone: (715)732-7450
Marinette, WI 54143 Linda L. Dumke, Ck. of Courts
Founded: 1880. **Staff:** 1. **Subjects:** Law. **Holdings:** 7000 volumes. **Services:** Library open to the public for reference use only. **Computerized Information Services:** LEXIS. Performs searches on fee basis. **Remarks:** FAX: (715)732-7532.

Anthony J.D. Marino, M.D. Memorial Library
See: **Underwood-Memorial Hospital** (16627)

★9678★
MARINTEK - Norwegian Marine Technology Research Institute A/S - Library (Sci-Engr)
P.O. Box 4125
Valentinlyst Phone: 7 595729
N-7002 Trondheim, Norway Vera Romberg
Founded: 1962. **Staff:** Prof 2; Other 2. **Subjects:** Marine technology; underwater technology, ship and naval research. **Holdings:** 2450 books; 40,000 reports; 375 microfiche; statistics; maps; patents. **Subscriptions:** 323 journals and other serials; 12 newspapers. **Services:** Interlibrary loan; copying; library open to the public. **Computerized Information Services:** Bibsys (internal database). Contact Person: Tove Knutsen, Univ.Libn. **Publications:** Nyanskaffet Litteratur (newsletter), semiannual. **Remarks:** FAX: 7 595776. Telex: 55146 marit n.

★9679★
Marion County Law Library
602 City County Bldg. Phone: (317)327-5499
Indianapolis, IN 46204 Terri Lea Ross, Libn.
Founded: 1963. **Staff:** Prof 1; Other 2. **Subjects:** Law. **Holdings:** 15,600 books; 250 bound periodical volumes; 3000 volumes on microfiche. **Subscriptions:** 75 journals and other serials. **Services:** Interlibrary loan; copying; library open to the public. **Computerized Information Services:** WESTLAW. **Networks/Consortia:** Member of Central Indiana Area Library Services Authority (CIALSA). **Publications:** Worth Reading, weekly - for internal distribution only.

★9680★
Marion County Law Library (Law)
Court House Phone: (614)387-5871
Marion, OH 43302 Hazel Aldrich, Ck.
Subjects: Law. **Holdings:** 14,000 volumes.

★9681★
Marion County Memorial Hospital - Library (Med)
1108 N. Main St. Phone: (803)423-3210
Marion, SC 29571 Ann Finney, Educ.Dir.
Staff: Prof 1. **Subjects:** Medicine, surgery, nursing. **Holdings:** 490 books. **Subscriptions:** 22 journals and other serials. **Services:** Library not open to the public. **Networks/Consortia:** Member of Health Communications Network (HCN).

★9682★
Marion County School Board - Teachers' Professional Library (Educ)
406 S.E. Alvarez Ave. Phone: (904)732-8041
Ocala, FL 32671 Vic Burke, Lib.Supv.
Founded: 1970. **Staff:** Prof 1; Other 3. **Subjects:** Education - elementary, secondary, teacher; educational research. **Special Collections:** ERIC Research in Education (RIE) documents (complete set); special ERIC collections: Pacesetters in Innovation, 1966-1968 and Selected Documents on the Disadvantaged (total: 424,633 documents); Curriculum Development Library, 1978-1989 (5477 documents on microfiche); Southern Region College Catalog Collection (839 catalogs on 306 microfiche); New York State University Curriculum for Teachers (323 documents on microfiche). **Holdings:** 11,750 books; 9000 phonograph records, kits, filmstrips, tapes; Current Index to Journals in Education (CIJE), 1970 to present; 7150 periodical volumes in microform; Education Index, 1951 to present. **Subscriptions:** 233 journals and other serials. **Services:** Interlibrary loan; copying; library open to teachers and administrators, including those from other counties and private schools. **Computerized Information Services:** WILSONLINE, UMI Article Clearinghouse (UMAC), Dissertation Abstracts Online; CD-ROM (Books in Print Plus). Performs searches on fee basis. **Publications:** Media Center acquisition list, monthly - to all local schools and district administrative personnel; School Library Media Center Handbook - to Marion County public school librarians; Media Memo, monthly - to county school librarians. **Special Catalogs:** Big Springs Regional Film Library Catalog with updates (book). **Remarks:** FAX: (904)732-3220.

★9683★
Marion General Hospital - Library (Med)
Wabash & Euclid Ave. Phone: (317)662-4607
Marion, IN 46952 Kay Lake, Dir., Educ.Serv.
Staff: Prof 1; Other 1. **Subjects:** Medicine, nursing, management. **Holdings:** 1892 books; 194 bound periodical volumes; 237 video cassettes. **Subscriptions:** 196 journals and other serials. **Services:** Interlibrary loan; copying; library open to employees, medical staff, and students. **Remarks:** FAX: (317)662-4523.

★9684★
Marion General Hospital - Medical Library (Med)
McKinley Park Dr. Phone: (614)383-8668
Marion, OH 43302 Marilyn J. Roe, Med.Libn.
Staff: Prof 1. **Subjects:** Medicine, nursing. **Holdings:** 286 books. **Services:** Interlibrary loan; copying; library open to the public with restrictions. **Networks/Consortia:** Member of Central Ohio Hospital Library Consortium.

★9685★
Marion Merrell Dow Inc. - Library
Marion Park Dr. Phone: (816)966-5000
Kansas City, MO 64137 Marian D. Craig, Libn.
Services: Library not open to the public. FAX: (816)966-5008.

★9686★
Marion Merrell Dow Inc. - Library Services (Med)
2110 E. Galbraith Rd. Phone: (513)948-6300
Cincinnati, OH 45215 Elaine Semancik, Mgr., Lib.Serv.
Founded: 1922. **Staff:** Prof 4; Other 1. **Subjects:** Chemistry, medicine, pharmacology, pharmacy. **Holdings:** 9400 books; 20,850 bound periodical volumes; 3 VF drawers of pamphlets; 4800 cartridges of microfilm of journals; 3800 microfiche. **Subscriptions:** 885 journals and other serials. **Services:** Interlibrary loan; copying; library open to the public by appointment. **Computerized Information Services:** BRS Information Technologies, DIALOG Information Services, NLM, Data-Star. **Remarks:** FAX: (513)948-7883. Telex: 214320 MERCN. **Formerly:** Marion Merrell Dow Pharmaceuticals, Inc. - Marion Merrell Dow Research Institute Library. **Staff:** Donna Gray-Williams; Alice McKee; Gerri Branch.

★9687★
Marion Merrell Dow Inc. - Research Center Library (Med)
9550 Zionsville Rd.
Box 68470 Phone: (317)873-7147
Indianapolis, IN 46268-0470 Pamela Pickens Kubiak, Res.Libn.
Founded: 1947. **Staff:** Prof 1. **Subjects:** Pharmacology, toxicology, pharmacokinetics, pharmacy research, chemistry, analytical chemistry. **Holdings:** 7000 books; 20,000 bound periodical volumes; abstract services; research notebooks on microfilm. **Subscriptions:** 525 journals and other serials. **Services:** Interlibrary loan; library not open to the public. **Computerized Information Services:** STN International, DIALOG Information Services, NLM; Dow Technology Reports (internal database).

Marion Merrell Dow Pharmaceuticals, Inc. - Marion Merrell Dow Research Institute Library
See: **Marion Merrell Dow Inc. - Library Services** (9686)

★9688★
Marissa Historical & Genealogical Society - Library (Hist)
P.O. Box 47 Phone: (618)295-2562
Marissa, IL 62257 Elda L. Jones, Pres.
Founded: 1973. **Staff:** 3. **Subjects:** Genealogy, local history. **Special Collections:** Family and church histories. **Holdings:** Scrapbooks; area histories; rare books; ledgers; autographs; cemetery records; court records; census records; coal-related articles; microfilm; microfiche. **Subscriptions:** 50 journals and other serials. **Services:** Copying; library open to the public with restrictions. **Publications:** Branching Out From St. Clair County, quarterly.

★9689★
Marist College - Library (Rel-Phil)
220 Taylor St., N.E. Phone: (202)529-2821
Washington, DC 20017 Paul S. Osmanski, Libn.
Founded: 1898. **Staff:** Prof 1. **Subjects:** Philosophy, Christian literature, theology, scripture, canon law, church history. **Holdings:** 20,600 books; 7250 bound periodical volumes; VF of statements of American bishops, U.S. Catholic Conference papers, papal documents. **Subscriptions:** 73 journals and other serials. **Services:** Library open to the public by appointment. **Networks/Consortia:** Member of Washington Theological Consortium.

★9690★
Maritiem Museum Prins Hendrik - Bibliotheek (Hist)
Leuvehaven 1 Phone: 10 4132680
NL-3011 EA Rotterdam, Netherlands E.A. De Vries
Founded: 1857. **Staff:** Prof 4. **Subjects:** International maritime history. **Special Collections:** Engelbrecht Collection (300 rare titles printed before 1800 on navigation and travels). **Holdings:** 20,000 books; 20,000 bound periodical volumes. **Subscriptions:** 250 journals and other serials. **Services:** Copying; library open to the public for reference use only. **Computerized Information Services:** Pica (internal database). **Remarks:** FAX: 10 4137342.

★9691★
Maritime Museum of the Atlantic - Library (Hist)
1675 Lower Water St. Phone: (902)429-8210
Halifax, NS, Canada B3J 1S3 M. Blackford, Libn.
Staff: Prof 1. **Subjects:** Merchant marine and naval history. **Special Collections:** Frederick William Wallace Collection; Arthur S. Hardy Collection. **Holdings:** 4000 books; 155 bound periodical volumes; 15,000 photographs; 900 charts; 300 ship plans. **Subscriptions:** 36 journals and other serials. **Services:** Interlibrary loan; copying; library open to the public with restrictions. **Remarks:** Museum is a branch of the Nova Scotia Museum, which is maintained by Nova Scotia Department of Education.

★9692★
Maritime Museum of British Columbia - Library (Hist)
28-30 Bastion Square Phone: (604)385-4222
Victoria, BC, Canada V8W 1H9 John M. MacFarlane, Dir.
Founded: 1965. **Staff:** 3. **Subjects:** Maritime history, West Coast shipping. **Special Collections:** Collection of ship's models and marine artifacts. **Holdings:** 6000 books; 150 bound periodical volumes; 10,000 pamphlets and documents. **Subscriptions:** 15 journals and other serials. **Services:** Copying; library open to members or researchers on request. **Publications:** Newsletter, quarterly.

Maritime School of Social Work
See: **Dalhousie University - Maritime School of Social Work** (4532)

★9693★
Maritime Telegraph & Telephone Co. Ltd. - Information Resource Centre (Info Sci)
P.O. Box 880 Phone: (902)421-4570
Halifax, NS, Canada B3J 2W3 Christine Williams, Libn.
Founded: 1979. **Staff:** Prof 1; Other 2. **Subjects:** Telecommunications, business. **Holdings:** 3000 books; 350 annual reports, pamphlets, clippings; 300 serial titles in microform. **Subscriptions:** 900 journals and other serials. **Services:** Interlibrary loan; copying; SDI. **Automated Operations:** Computerized cataloging, circulation, routing, and serials. **Computerized Information Services:** WILSONLINE, NewsNet, Inc., DIALOG Information Services, Info Globe, CAN/OLE, QL Systems, Infomart Online, STM Systems Corporation, PFDS Online, Dow Jones News/Retrieval, Dun & Bradstreet Business Credit Services; internal databases; Envoy 100 (electronic mail service). **Publications:** General Circular, 1987; Telecom Topics; The IRC Bulletin, bimonthly; Serials Description List, annual; Serials Holdings List, annual - all available upon request. **Remarks:** FAX: (902)421-4033.

★9694★
Maritz, Inc. - Library (Bus-Fin)
1400 S. Highway Dr. Phone: (314)827-1717
Fenton, MO 63099 Mary Anne Walton, Mgr., Lib.Serv.
Founded: 1968. **Staff:** Prof 2; Other 1. **Subjects:** Business, marketing, labor productivity, organizational behavior. **Special Collections:** Corporate archival materials. **Holdings:** 5000 books; 27 drawers of pamphlets and clippings; 2800 annual reports; 6750 microfiche; 1000 unbound reports. **Subscriptions:** 350 journals and other serials. **Services:** Interlibrary loan; SDI; library open to the public by appointment only. **Automated Operations:** Computerized cataloging and serials. **Computerized Information Services:** DIALOG Information Services, NEXIS, VU/TEXT Information Services, OCLC, DataTimes; CD-ROMs; internal databases; Performs searches on fee basis. **Networks/Consortia:** Member of St. Louis Regional Library Network, Missouri Library Network Corp. (MLNC). **Publications:** Library Letter - for internal distribution only. **Remarks:** FAX: (314)827-3220. **Staff:** Mary Butler.

★9695★
Maritz Travel Company - Travel Library (Rec)
1385 N. Highway Dr. Phone: (314)827-1402
Fenton, MO 63026 Sue Hamilton, Supv.
Founded: 1969. **Staff:** 3. **Subjects:** Travel data - hotels, restaurants, sightseeing, steamships, countries and cities. **Holdings:** 300 books; 177 bound periodical volumes; 95 VF drawers of travel-related brochures and reports; 1700 videotapes. **Subscriptions:** 35 journals and other serials. **Services:** Interlibrary loan; library not open to the public. **Publications:** Subscription Content Update - for internal distribution only. **Remarks:** FAX: (314)827-3271. Telex: 261831 MARTV UR.

Edward Laurens Mark Memorial Library
See: **Bermuda Biological Station for Research, Inc.** (1754)

★9696★
Market Opinion Research - Library (Bus-Fin)
31700 Middlebelt Rd., Suite 220 Phone: (313)737-5300
Farmington Hills, MI 48334-2373 Barbara C. Kelley, Libn.
Founded: 1978. **Staff:** Prof 1. **Subjects:** Market, political, and consumer research. **Holdings:** 4000 proprietary reports and surveys. **Subscriptions:** 125 journals and other serials; 7 newspapers. **Services:** Library not open to the public. **Automated Operations:** Computerized serials. **Computerized Information Services:** DIALOG Information Services. **Remarks:** FAX: (313)963-6869.

★9697★
Marketemps - Marketing Intelligence Center (Bus-Fin)
3435 Ocean Pacific Blvd., Suite 202-B Phone: (213)452-9610
Santa Monica, CA 90405 Clifford S. Lightfoot, Prin.
Founded: 1982. **Staff:** Prof 7. **Subjects:** Marketing intelligence, new product development, growth industries, market trends, technology assessment, technology transfer, commercialization, trade shows, U.S.S.R. business opportunities. **Special Collections:** Small industry studies; corporate image collection; business plans; start-up businesses; corporate turnaround collection; inventor resources; creativity collection. **Holdings:** 500 books; 200 reports and presentations, start-up businesses. **Subscriptions:** 40 journals and other serials; 5 newspapers. **Services:** Center open to the public on fee basis. **Computerized Information Services:** Online systems; Marketing Intelligence, Marketing Services (internal databases). Performs searches on fee basis. **Publications:** Marketing Intelligence Manual; Marketing Business Services; Marketing for Law Firms; Marketing for Accounting Firms. **Remarks:** FAX: (213)452-9610. **Staff:** Steve Curtis, Sr.Assoc.; Victor Petryakov, Assoc.

★9698★
Markon Incorporated - Technical Library
7830 Backlick Rd.
Springfield, VA 22150-2205
Founded: 1986. **Subjects:** Amphibious operations and warfare, military and naval art and science, engineering, logistics, management, finance. **Holdings:** 200 books; 10 bound periodical volumes; 3000 technical reports; vendor catalogs in microform; 20,000 military specifications, standards, drawings, documents, handbooks; 200 Markon technical publications; 480 reels of microfilm; 12 drawers of microfiche; 10 loose-leaf services. **Remarks:** Currently inactive.

Jewel K. Markowitz Library
See: **Beth David Reform Congregation** (1764)

Marks Fine Arts Library
See: **Danforth Museum of Art** (4588)

★9699★
Larry Marks Information for Business - Library (Bus-Fin)
2608 9th St. Phone: (510)644-2111
Berkeley, CA 94710 Larry Marks, Dir.
Founded: 1978. **Staff:** Prof 1; Other 1. **Subjects:** Strategic planning, business, retailing. **Holdings:** 25 books; 125 other cataloged items. **Subscriptions:** 82 journals and other serials. **Services:** Interlibrary loan; copying; SDI; library open for use by other libraries. **Computerized Information Services:** DIALOG Information Services, NEXIS, DataTimes, Dunslink. Performs searches on fee basis. **Remarks:** FAX: (510)644-2112.

★9700★
Marks, Murase & White - Library (Law)
400 Park Ave. Phone: (212)832-3333
New York, NY 10022 Karen A. Shea, Libn.
Staff: Prof 2; Other 2. **Subjects:** Law. **Special Collections:** Japanese and tax law. **Holdings:** 15,000 books; 18 VF drawers. **Subscriptions:** 83 journals and other serials; 10 newspapers. **Services:** Interlibrary loan; copying; SDI; library open to the public with restrictions. **Computerized Information Services:** LEXIS. **Publications:** Weekly Acquisitions List. **Staff:** Jefferey Yan.

★9701★
Marlboro Psychiatric Hospital - Staff Library (Med)
Rte. 520, Newman Springs Rd. Phone: (908)946-8100
Marlboro, NJ 07746 Carla Zimmerman
Staff: Prof 1. **Subjects:** Psychiatry, psychology, clinical medicine, nursing, social work. **Holdings:** 2500 books. **Subscriptions:** 90 journals and other serials; 4 newspapers. **Services:** Interlibrary loan; library not open to the public. **Remarks:** FAX: (908)946-9081.

★9702★
Marlborough Gallery - Library (Art)
40 W. 57th St. Phone: (212)541-4900
New York, NY 10019 Jane Hart, Libn.
Founded: 1962. **Staff:** Prof 1. **Subjects:** Modern painting, sculpture, drawings; graphics; American painting, sculpture, drawings, graphics, photography. **Special Collections:** Auction catalogs from American and European auction-houses. **Holdings:** 8940 volumes; exhibition catalogs. **Subscriptions:** 15 journals and other serials. **Services:** Copying. **Special Catalogs:** Catalogs for exhibitions held at gallery. **Remarks:** FAX: (212)541-4948.

★9703★
Marlborough Hospital - Health Science Library (Med)
57 Union St. Phone: (508)485-1121
Marlborough, MA 01752 Nancy Harger, MLS
Staff: 1. **Subjects:** Medicine, nursing, allied health sciences. **Holdings:** 900 books; 1200 bound periodical volumes; AV programs. **Subscriptions:** 153 journals and other serials. **Services:** Interlibrary loan; copying; library open to the public for reference use only. **Computerized Information Services:** MEDLINE. **Networks/Consortia:** Member of Consortium for Information Resources (CIR).

Marmion Library
See: **Church of the Incarnation** (3650)

Marquand Library
See: **Princeton University** (13376)

★9704★
Marquandia Society - Library (Hum)
209 Indian Springs Rd. Phone: (804)229-7049
Williamsburg, VA 23185 John R. Thelin, Cur. & Co-Dir.
Founded: 1976. **Staff:** Prof 1. **Subjects:** John P. Marquand, New England, fine printing. **Holdings:** 300 books. **Services:** Library not open to the public. **Publications:** Newsletter, irregular. **Staff:** A.S.T. Blackburn, Co-Dir.

★9705★
The Marquardt Company - Library (Sci-Engr)
16555 Saticay St. Phone: (818)989-6433
Van Nuys, CA 91409 Lydia H. Lee, Lib.Supv.
Founded: 1944. **Staff:** Prof 1; Other 1. **Subjects:** Aerospace, engineering, material sciences, chemistry, physics. **Special Collections:** Government reports on aerospace and allied subjects, 1960s (100,000). **Holdings:** 5000 books; 2000 bound periodical volumes; microforms. **Subscriptions:** 100 journals and other serials. **Services:** Library not open to the public. **Automated Operations:** Computerized cataloging. **Computerized Information Services:** DIALOG Information Services, DTIC, NASA/RECON, DMS ONLINE; internal database. **Publications:** Handbook on computerized retrieval system. **Remarks:** FAX: (818)994-2947.

Marquardt Memorial Library
See: **Elmhurst Memorial Hospital** (5309)

Marquat Memorial Library
See: **U.S. Army - JFK Special Warfare Center & School** (16981)

★9706★
Marquette Coppersmithing Company - Library (Sci-Engr)
Box 4584 Phone: (215)877-9362
Philadelphia, PA 19131 T.T. Hill, Libn.
Founded: 1946. **Staff:** Prof 1. **Subjects:** Applied mechanics, thermodynamics, chemical and metallurgical engineering, nuclear physics. **Holdings:** 4200 books; 3000 bound periodical volumes; 800 other volumes. **Subscriptions:** 46 journals and other serials. **Services:** Library serves company technical personnel only. **Remarks:** FAX: (215)877-4433.

★9707★
Marquette County Historical Society - J.M. Longyear Research Library (Hist)
213 N. Front St. Phone: (906)226-3571
Marquette, MI 49855 Linda K. Panian, Libn.
Founded: 1918. **Staff:** 2. **Subjects:** History of Great Lakes area and Michigan - shipping, railroads, industries, ethnic groups. **Special Collections:** Charles Thompson Harvey Papers; Burt family papers; J.M. Longyear papers; E.N. Breitung papers; local newspapers (bound and on microfilm); business and organization records. **Holdings:** 8000 books; 2000 pamphlets; 35 VF drawers of letters, manuscripts, maps, photographs, documents; all known copies of local newspaper, Lake Superior Journal, Lake Superior News, and Mining Journal, July 1846 to present, on microfilm. **Subscriptions:** 25 journals and other serials; 6 newspapers. **Services:** Library open to qualified researchers. **Publications:** Harlow's Wooden Man, quarterly - to members or by subscription. **Staff:** Rosemary Michelin, Res.Libn. & Geneal.

★9708★
Marquette General Hospital, Inc. - Kevin F. O'Brien Health Sciences Library (Med)
420 W. Magnetic St. Phone: (906)225-3429
Marquette, MI 49855-2000 Mildred E. Kingsbury, Lib.Dir.
Founded: 1974. **Staff:** Prof 1; Other 2. **Subjects:** Medicine, nursing, allied health sciences. **Holdings:** 5000 books; 675 bound periodical volumes; 3000 slides. **Subscriptions:** 250 journals and other serials. **Services:** Interlibrary loan; copying; SDI; library open to the public. **Automated Operations:** Computerized public access catalog, cataloging, and serials (NOTIS). **Computerized Information Services:** BRS Information Technologies, MEDLARS, OCLC. **Networks/Consortia:** Member of Michigan Health Sciences Libraries Association (MHSLA), National Network of Libraries of Medicine - Greater Midwest Region, UP Health Sciences Libraries Consortium, Upper Peninsula Region of Library Cooperation (UPRLC). **Remarks:** Alternate telephone number(s): (906)225-3828. FAX: (906)225-3524.

★9709★
Marquette University - Department of Special Collections and University Archives - Manuscript Collections Memorial Library (Hist)
Memorial Library
1415 W. Wisconsin Ave. Phone: (414)288-7256
Milwaukee, WI 53233 Charles B. Elston, Hd.
Founded: 1961. **Staff:** Prof 4; Other 4. **Subjects:** Catholic social thought and action, Catholic Indian ministry, Marquette University history, Jesuits and Jesuit institutions, recent U.S. political history, Catholic religious formation and vocation ministries. **Special Collections:** National Catholic Conference for Interracial Justice Collection, 1956 to present (200 feet); Project Equality, Inc. Collection, 1971 to present (45 feet); Sr. Margaret Ellen Traxler Papers, 1950 to present (17 feet); National Coalition of American Nuns Collection, 1969 to present (10 feet); Sister Formation Conference/ Religious Formation Conference Archives, 1954 to present (28 feet); Clement J. Zablocki Papers, 1945-1983 (790 feet, unprocessed); Madonna Center (Chicago) Records, 1865-1967 (10 feet); Council on Urban Life (Milwaukee) Records, 1965-1980 (40 feet); Women's Ordination Conference Records, 1975 to present (16 feet); FBI investigation and surveillance records (photocopies), 1919-1984 (40 feet); Dorothy Day - Catholic Worker Collection, 1933 to present (120 feet); Catholic Association for International Peace Archives, 1926-1970 (30 feet); Monsignor Luigi G. Ligutti Papers, 1915-1984 (50 feet); Brother Leo V. Ryan Papers, 1956 to present (30 feet); New Ways Ministry Records, 1965 to present (10 feet); President's Committee on Employment of the Handicapped Archives, 1946 to present (120 feet); National Sisters Vocation Conference Archives, 1967 to present (6 feet); Joseph R. McCarthy Papers, 1930-1957 (100 feet); Charles J. Kersten papers, 1946-1971 (20 feet); Donald T. McNeill Collection, 1933-1968 (67 feet); Citizens for Educational Freedom Records, 1959 to present (20 feet); Sociology of Religion Collections, 1938 to present (21 feet); H. Herman Rauch Labor Arbitration Case Files, 1940-1978 (42 feet); John Ronald Reuel Tolkien Collection, 1930 to present (20 feet); Elizabeth Whitcomb Houghton Collection, 1900-1945 (letters and manuscripts of American and British authors; 3 feet); Joyce Kilmer/Campion College Collection, 1908-1975 (5 feet); Karl J. Priebe Papers, 1900-1978 (14 feet); National Catholic Rural Life Conference Archives, 1923 to present (98 feet); Justice and Peace Center (Milwaukee) Archives, 1970-1982 (20 feet); National Interfaith Coalition on Aging Archives, 1970 to present (21 feet); Bureau of Catholic Indian Missions Records, 1852 to present (300 feet); Holy Rosary Mission Records, 1852 to present (22 feet); St. Francis Mission Records, 1878 to present (23 feet); Siggenauk Center Records, 1974 to present (6 feet); Kisemanito Center Collection, 1976-1987 (3 feet). **Holdings:** 12,000 volumes; 3000 bound periodical volumes; 8600 cubic feet of archives and manuscripts; 450 reels of microfilm; 4050 feet of manuscript collections relating primarily to Catholic social action and the history of Jesuits and Jesuit institutions, 1865 to present; 4150 cubic feet of Marquette University Archives, 1881 to present; 400 cubic feet of Catholic Indian mission records, 1852 to present. **Subscriptions:** 45 journals and other serials; 20 newspapers. **Services:** Copying; department open to the public. **Networks/Consortia:** Member of Library Council of Metropolitan Milwaukee, Inc. (LCOMM). **Publications:** Descriptive inventories and exhibit catalogs for J.R.R. Tolkien Collection; in-house finding aids for other collections. **Remarks:** FAX: (414)288-5324. **Staff:** John L. LeDoux, Univ.Archv.; Phillip M. Runkel, Asst.Archv.; Mark G. Thiel, Asst.Archv.; Susan B. Stawicki-Vrobel, Archv.Asst.; Rev. Robert V. Callen, Cur., Jesuit Archv.

★9710★
Marquette University - Foundation Collection - Regional Cooperating Collection (Bus-Fin)
Memorial Library
1415 W. Wisconsin Ave. Phone: (414)288-1515
Milwaukee, WI 53233 Maria Dittman, Libn.
Founded: 1971. **Staff:** Prof 1. **Subjects:** Fundraising, grantsmanship, philanthropy, proposal writing. **Holdings:** 250 books; 1000 pamphlets and annual reports; publications of the Foundation Center; 35,000 Internal Revenue Service Tax Returns for all private foundations in Wisconsin, Illinois, and Minnesota, on microfiche and aperture cards; directories; guides; handbooks. **Subscriptions:** 17 journals and other serials. **Services:** Interlibrary loan; copying; collection open to the public with restrictions. **Computerized Information Services:** DIALOG Information Services. Performs searches on fee basis. **Publications:** Foundations in Wisconsin: A Directory, biennial - for sale. **Remarks:** FAX: (414)288-5324.

★9711★
Marquette University - Law Library (Law)
1103 W. Wisconsin Ave. Phone: (414)288-7092
Milwaukee, WI 53233 Steven M. Barkan, Dir.
Founded: 1908. **Staff:** Prof 8; Other 8. **Subjects:** Law. **Holdings:** 184,197 volumes; 132 linear feet of unbound periodicals; 67,648 volumes in microform; 405,889 microfiche; 508 reels of microfilm. **Subscriptions:** 2319 journals and other serials; 15 newspapers. **Services:** Interlibrary loan; copying; government document collection open to the public. **Automated Operations:** Computerized cataloging, acquisitions, and serials. **Computerized Information Services:** LEXIS, NEXIS, WESTLAW, DIALOG Information Services. **Networks/Consortia:** Member of Wisconsin Interlibrary Services (WILS). **Publications:** Contents Pages, weekly; Acquisitions List, monthly. **Remarks:** FAX: (414)288-5914. **Staff:** Mary D. Mahoney, Hd., Pub.Serv.; Lois A. O'Brien, Hd., Tech.Serv.; Robert L. Starz, Coll.Dev./Ref.; Angelina G. Joseph, Cat.; John Houser, Ref./Comp.Serv.Libn.; James Mumm, Acq./Ser.Libn.; Duane Strojny, Ref./Coll.Mgt.Libn.

★9712★
Marquette University - Memorial Library (Hum, Rel-Phil)
1415 W. Wisconsin Ave. Phone: (414)288-7214
Milwaukee, WI 53233 William M. Gardner, Dir. of Libs.
Founded: 1881. **Staff:** Prof 29; Other 45. **Subjects:** Philosophy, theology, humanities, history. **Special Collections:** Lester W. Olson Lincoln

Collection; Jesuitica. **Holdings:** 765,395 volumes; 261,091 microforms; audio recordings. **Subscriptions:** 7654 journals and other serials; 100 newspapers. **Services:** Interlibrary loan; copying; library open to the public with restrictions. **Automated Operations:** Computerized public access catalog, cataloging, circulation, acquisitions, and serials (INNOPAC). **Computerized Information Services:** DIALOG Information Services, BRS Information Technologies, OCLC; InterNet (electronic mail service). **Networks/Consortia:** Member of Wisconsin Interlibrary Services (WILS), Library Council of Metropolitan Milwaukee, Inc. (LCOMM), Center for Research Libraries (CRL). **Special Indexes:** Index to University Archives, Manuscript, and Archival Collections. **Remarks:** FAX: (414)288-5324. Electronic mail address(es): 9566PATE@vms.csd.mu.edu (InterNet). **Staff:** David J. Farley, Asst.Dir., Adm.; Virginia Scheschy, Asst.Dir., Tech.Serv.; Robert J. Haertle, Hd., Coll.Dept.; Michele M. Plewa, Adm.Asst.; Susan Hopwood, Coord., Ref. & Info.Serv.; Michael B. Pate, Asst.Dir., Pub.Serv.; Nia Schudson, ILL.

★9713★
Marquette University - Science Library (Sci-Engr, Med)
560 N. 16th St. Phone: (414)288-3396
Milwaukee, WI 53233 Jay Kirk, Hd., Sci.Lib.
Founded: 1981. **Staff:** Prof 5; Other 5. **Subjects:** Human biology, dentistry, nursing, engineering, chemistry, mathematics, physics. **Holdings:** 75,000 books; 100,000 bound periodical volumes. **Subscriptions:** 1800 journals and other serials. **Services:** Interlibrary loan (fee); copying; library open to the public. **Automated Operations:** Computerized public access catalog (INNOPAC). **Computerized Information Services:** DIALOG Information Services, BRS Information Technologies, MEDLINE, OCLC, STN International, WILSONLINE. **Networks/Consortia:** Member of Library Council of Metropolitan Milwaukee, Inc. (LCOMM), Wisconsin Interlibrary Services (WILS). **Staff:** Patricia Berge, Asst.Sci.Libn.; Ljudmila Mursec, Asst.Sci.Libn.; Gwen Owens, Hd., Info.Serv.; Keven Riggle, Hd. Operational Serv.

★9714★
Marquis Who's Who, Inc. - Editorial Department Library (Publ)
3002 Glenview Rd. Phone: (708)933-3313
Wilmette, IL 60091 Jean Donnelly, Libn.
Founded: 1974. **Staff:** Prof 1. **Subjects:** Biography, company history. **Special Collections:** Contemporary biographical directories. **Holdings:** 2500 books; 5 VF drawers; 15 VF drawers of company archives. **Subscriptions:** 75 journals and other serials. **Services:** Library not open to the public. **Computerized Information Services:** Marquis Who's Who; Directory of Medical Specialists (internal databases). **Remarks:** FAX: (708)933-3384.

Marr Sound Archives
See: **University of Missouri--Kansas City - Miller Nichols Library** (18976)

★9715★
Marriage Council of Philadelphia - Division of Family Study and Marriage Council Library (Soc Sci)
4025 Chestnut St., 2nd Fl. Phone: (215)382-6680
Philadelphia, PA 19104 Martin Goldberg, M.D., Dir.
Founded: 1932. **Subjects:** Marriage and family relationships, marriage counseling, human sexuality and sex therapy, mental health, religion and marriage. **Holdings:** 2000 books. **Subscriptions:** 16 journals and other serials. **Services:** Library not open to the public. **Remarks:** Affiliated with the University of Pennsylvania.

Marriner Library
See: **Thomas College** (16312)

★9716★
Mars Hill College - Memorial Library - Appalachian Room Special Collections (Area-Ethnic)
Mars Hill, NC 28754 Phone: (704)689-1394
Peggy Harmon, Spec.Coll.Asst.
Founded: 1972. **Staff:** 3. **Subjects:** Appalachian life and culture, ballads, country music, Southern Baptists, genealogy, college history. **Special Collections:** Appalachian literature (3544 volumes); Bascom Lamar Lunsford Collection (mountain music and dance; books; manuscripts; scrapbooks; recordings); Appalachian photographs (5000); oral history interviews (264 cassettes). **Holdings:** 6338 books; 834 bound periodical volumes; 240 linear feet of manuscripts; 238 reels of microfilm. **Subscriptions:** 43 journals and other serials; 10 newspapers. **Services:** Copying (limited); collections open to the public. **Automated Operations:** Computerized cataloging. **Networks/Consortia:** Member of SOLINET. **Special Catalogs:** Catalog of photographs (card); catalog of manuscripts (notebook). **Remarks:** Alternate telephone number(s): 689-1443; 689-1244. FAX: (704)689-1474.

Marsh and McLennan, Inc. - National Economic Research Associates, Inc.
See: **National Economic Research Associates, Inc.** (11151)

Marsh and McLennan, Inc. - Putnam Companies
See: **Putnam Companies** (13554)

Marsh and McLennan, Inc. - William M. Mercer, Inc.
See: **William M. Mercer, Inc. - Information and Research Center** (10114)

★9717★
Marsh and McLennan, Ltd. - Information Centre
Canada Trust Tower, BCE Place
161 Bay St.
P.O. Box 502 Phone: (416)868-2623
Toronto, ON, Canada M5J 2S4 Marjorie Cavers, Hd.
Services: Center not open to the public. **Remarks:** FAX: (416)868-2526. Telex: 06 22182.

W. Ward Marsh Cinema Archives
See: **Cleveland Public Library - Literature Department** (3827)

C.J. Marshall Memorial Library
See: **University of Pennsylvania - School of Veterinary Medicine** (19196)

★9718★
Marshall County Historical Society - Library (Hist)
P.O. Box 123
Lacon, IL 61540 Phone: (309)246-2349
Subjects: History - Marshall and Putnam counties, Illinois, United States; Abraham Lincoln; antiques; early church and school books. **Special Collections:** Genealogical research. **Holdings:** 450 books; 15 manuscripts. **Services:** Copying; library open to the public. **Staff:** Eleanor Bussell, Cur.; Pat F. Seibold; Ann O'D. Trumbull, Asst.Libn.

★9719★
Marshall County Historical Society Museum - Library (Hist)
317 W. Monroe St. Phone: (219)936-2306
Plymouth, IN 46563 Mary Hawkins Durnan, Dir.
Staff: 2. **Subjects:** Marshall County and Indiana history, genealogy. **Holdings:** 300 books; 380 reels of microfilm of Marshall County newspapers; 15 oral history tapes. **Subscriptions:** 2 newspapers. **Services:** Copying; library open to the public. **Publications:** Marshall County Historical Society Quarterly; History of Marshall County, Indiana 1836-1986. **Special Indexes:** Surname Index.

★9720★
George C. Marshall Foundation - George C. Marshall Research Library (Hist, Mil)
Box 1600 Phone: (703)463-7103
Lexington, VA 24450-1600 Glenn S. Cook, Archv./Libn.
Staff: Prof 1; Other 1. **Subjects:** Life, times, and career of General George C. Marshall, 1880-1959; 20th century military and diplomatic history, including World War I and World War II; Marshall Plan; propaganda; international foreign relations and economics. **Special Collections:** General Marshall's personal papers (400 linear feet); selected items from official State, Defense, and War Department files pertaining to General Marshall (hardcopy and microfilm); William F. Friedman Cryptologic Collection; papers of 120 other persons. **Holdings:** 22,000 books; 725 bound periodical volumes; 30,000 photographs of World War II and General Marshall; 150 tape recordings of interviews with General Marshall and his associates; 700 posters from World War I and World War II; 500 maps from World War I and World War II. **Subscriptions:** 45 journals and other serials. **Services:** Copying; library open to the public. **Automated Operations:** Computerized cataloging. **Computerized Information Services:** OCLC. **Networks/Consortia:** Member of SOLINET. **Publications:** Topics, irregular; Handbook for Researchers; Manuscript Collections of the George C. Marshall Library; Posters in the George C. Marshall Foundation; George C. Marshall Papers, 1932-1960 - A Guide. **Remarks:** FAX: (703)464-5229.

George Preston Marshall Memorial Library
See: **National Wildlife Federation** (11325)

★9721★
Marshall Historical Society - Archives (Hist)
Box 68
Marshall, MI 49068 Phone: (616)781-8544
Founded: 1917. **Staff:** Prof 1. **Subjects:** Marshall history, pioneers, homes, views; Calhoun County history; railroads. **Special Collections:** Martin F. Ryan Railroad Collection; Amelia Frink Redfield Collection (genealogy and family scrapbooks); Mabel Cooper Skjelver research on Marshall homes; Johnson, Johnson, and Roy research on architectural survey of Marshall. **Holdings:** 300 books; 9 boxes of photographs; 28 boxes of manuscripts and documents; 30 boxes of clippings and unbound periodicals; 4 boxes of maps. **Services:** Copying; answers public inquiries by mail; archives open to the public by appointment. **Remarks:** Archives located in GAR Hall, East Michigan Ave., Marshall, MI. **Staff:** Richard Carver, Archv.

★9722★
John Marshall Law School - Library (Law)
315 S. Plymouth Court Phone: (312)427-2737
Chicago, IL 60604 Steven C. Perkins, Dir.
Founded: 1899. **Staff:** Prof 9; Other 12. **Subjects:** Law, taxation, intellectual property, international law, real estate, bankruptcy, negotiation. **Special Collections:** John Marshall Collection: Legal History of the Northwest Territory. **Holdings:** 274,084 volumes (including microform equivalents); 85,733 volumes in microform; 514,399 microfiche; 937 reels of microfilm; NRS ultrafiche (1st series); Congressional Information Service (CIS) publications, 1970 to present; Congressional Record, 1873 to present; Code of Federal Regulations (CFR) microfiche edition, 1938 to present; IHS microfiche of legislative histories (10 subject areas); CCH Tax Library; U.S. Supreme Court Records and Briefs, 1930 to present; Federal Register, 1936 to present. **Subscriptions:** 5468 journals and other serials; 13 newspapers. **Services:** Interlibrary loan; copying; circulation privileges to current faculty and students and members of the Chicago Bar Association only. **Automated Operations:** Computerized cataloging, acquisitions, and serials. **Computerized Information Services:** LEXIS, NEXIS, WESTLAW, DIALOG Information Services. Contact Person: Chris Portman. **Networks/Consortia:** Member of ILLINET, Chicago Library System. **Remarks:** FAX: (312)427-8307. **Staff:** Kym Ogden, Hd., Cat.Dept.; William Wleklinski, Hd., Ref.Dept.; Michael Reddy, Asst.Dir. & Hd., Pub.Serv.; Madugula Sastri, Hd., Acq./Ser.Dept.; Phyllis Finney, Hd., Circ.; John Bahaveolos, Comp.Dev.; J. David Rudman, Asst.Dir. & Hd., Tech.Serv.; Jason Levine, Ref.Libn.; Christopher Portman, Ref.Libn.

Marshall Laboratory Library
See: **E.I. Du Pont de Nemours & Company, Inc.** (5025)

Marshall Law Library
See: **University of Maryland, Baltimore - School of Law** (18801)

★9723★
Marshall & Melhorn Law Firm - Library (Law)
Four Sea Gate, Suite 800 Phone: (419)249-7100
Toledo, OH 43604 Barbara B. Avery, Libn.
Staff: Prof 1; Other 1. **Subjects:** Corporate law, taxation, labor law, litigation, probate, intellectual property law, environmental law, technology law. **Holdings:** 17,000 books. **Subscriptions:** 75 journals and other serials; 5 newspapers. **Services:** Interlibrary loan; copying; SDI; library open to attorneys and librarians known to firm members. **Computerized Information Services:** LEXIS, DIALOG Information Services, WESTLAW. Performs searches on fee basis. **Publications:** Library Monitor, monthly - for internal distribution only. **Remarks:** FAX: (419)249-7151.

S.L.A. Marshall Military History Collection
See: **University of Texas at El Paso - Library** (19413)

Marshall Space Flight Center
See: **U.S. Army - Missile Command & Marshall Space Flight Center** (16996)

Marshall Space Flight Center - MSFC Library
See: **NASA** (10989)

★9724★
Marshall University - James E. Morrow Library - Special Collections (Hist)
Huntington, WV 25755-2060 Phone: (304)696-2343
Lisle G. Brown, Cur.
Founded: 1972. **Staff:** Prof 4; Other 2. **Subjects:** West Virginiana, Civil War, Appalachian studies, history of medicine. **Special Collections:** Regional manuscripts collections; WSAZ-TV News Film Archive, 1952-1985; Charles A. Hoffman Library of the History of Medical Sciences; Appalachian Oral History Collection; Rosanna A. Blake Library of Confederate History. **Holdings:** 18,400 books; 400 bound periodical volumes; 1479 linear feet of manuscripts; 25,200 West Virginia state documents; 600 cubic feet of university archives; 30 linear feet of miscellanea. **Subscriptions:** 130 journals and other serials; 10 newspapers. **Services:** Interlibrary loan; copying; collections open to the public. **Automated Operations:** Computerized cataloging and circulation. **Computerized Information Services:** DIALOG Information Services, OCLC. **Publications:** A Guide to Local History and Genealogy in the Special Collections Department; A Guide to the Manuscript Collections in the Special Collections Department; Oral History of Appalachia: A Calendar of the Collection on Deposit in the James E. Morrow Library. **Staff:** Cora Teel, Archv.; Kathleen Bledsoe, Libn.; Kenneth Slack, Confederate Bibliog.

★9725★
Marshall University - Research Coordinating Unit for Vocational Education (Educ)
307 Old Main Phone: (304)696-3180
Huntington, WV 25755-2410 Roy Thomas, Dir.
Staff: 1. **Subjects:** Educational, research, and instructional materials. **Holdings:** 20 bound periodical volumes; complete collection of ERIC microfiche. **Subscriptions:** 10 journals and other serials. **Services:** Interlibrary loan; copying; unit open to the public. **Staff:** Kris Standifur.

★9726★
Marshall University - School of Medicine - Health Science Libraries (Med)
Marshall University Campus Phone: (304)696-6426
Huntington, WV 25701 Edward Dzierzak, Dir.
Founded: 1975. **Staff:** Prof 3; Other 4. **Subjects:** Clinical medicine, basic sciences, nursing, allied health sciences. **Special Collections:** Esposito Collection in Ophthalmology (150 books). **Holdings:** 19,670 books; 185 slide sets; 350 video cassettes; 45 audio cassettes. **Subscriptions:** 434 journals and other serials. **Services:** Interlibrary loan; copying; libraries open to the public. **Automated Operations:** Computerized cataloging and circulation. **Computerized Information Services:** MEDLINE. **Networks/Consortia:** Member of Huntington Health Science Library Consortium, National Network of Libraries of Medicine (NN/LM). **Publications:** Guide to the Health Science Libraries, annual - campus distribution. **Special Catalogs:** Serial Holdings List - Huntington Annual; Audiovisual Catalog. **Remarks:** FAX: (304)696-6565. **Staff:** M. Laurie Hildreth, Ref.Libn.; Phoebe Randall, Circ.Libn.

Marshall-Wythe Law Library
See: **College of William and Mary - Marshall-Wythe Law Library** (3919)

★9727★
Marshfield Clinic - Medical Library (Med)
1000 N. Oak Phone: (715)387-9183
Marshfield, WI 54449 Albert Zimmermann, Libn.
Founded: 1916. **Staff:** Prof 2; Other 2. **Subjects:** Medicine, allied health sciences. **Holdings:** 2639 books; 15,177 bound periodical volumes. **Subscriptions:** 470 journals and other serials. **Services:** Interlibrary loan; copying; SDI; library open to the public for reference use only. **Automated Operations:** Computerized ILL. **Computerized Information Services:** MEDLARS, DIALOG Information Services, BRS Information Technologies; CD-ROM. Performs searches on fee basis. **Networks/Consortia:** Member of Northwestern Wisconsin Health Science Library Consortium, National Network of Libraries of Medicine - Greater Midwest Region. **Remarks:** FAX: (715)387-5240. **Staff:** Alana Ziaya, Asst.Libn.

Marston Memorial Historical Library
See: **Free Methodist Church of North America** (6127)

Marston Science Library
See: **University of Florida - Marston Science Library** (18577)

★9728★
Albert C. Martin & Associates - Library (Plan)
811 W. 7th St. Phone: (213)683-1900
Los Angeles, CA 90017 Millie Nicholson, Libn.
Founded: 1967. **Staff:** 1. **Subjects:** Architecture, civil and structural engineering, city planning, interior design. **Special Collections:** Albert C. Martin, Sr., Collections (on the history of architecture). **Holdings:** 1100 books; 500 outside reports, documents, pamphlets; 7 VF drawers of clippings; 400 company reports, proposals, programs; 23 drawers of microfilm of company projects (aperture cards). **Subscriptions:** 30 journals and other serials. **Services:** Interlibrary loan; copying. **Remarks:** FAX: (213)614-6002.

Martin Army Community Hospital
See: **U.S. Army Hospitals** (17049)

★9729★
Martin County Historical Society, Inc. - Pioneer Museum - Library (Hist)
304 E. Blue Earth Ave. Phone: (507)235-5178
Fairmont, MN 56031 Helen Simon, Cur.
Founded: 1929. **Staff:** Prof 1. **Subjects:** American Indian, Civil War, Minnesota history. **Special Collections:** Local newspaper file, 1874 to present (bound volumes of city and county papers). **Holdings:** 612 bound periodical volumes; 476 reels of microfilm of Martin County newspapers. **Services:** Copying; library open to the public for reference use only.

★9730★
Dean Martin Association - International Headquarters - Library (Theater)
259 London Rd.
Croydon, Surrey CR0 2RL, England Bernard H. Thorpe, Pres. & Chf.Exec.
Founded: 1960. **Staff:** 4. **Subjects:** Dean Martin. **Holdings:** Archival materials; AV materials. **Subscriptions:** 3000 journals and other serials. **Services:** Interlibrary loan; library not open to the public. **Publications:** Discography; film listings; new definite biography, 1992.

Edward Martin Library
See: **Historical Society of the Militia and National Guard** (7274)

John Martin Library
See: **Gallery/Stratford** (6233)

Martin Library of the Sciences
See: **Franklin and Marshall College** (6094)

★9731★
Martin Luther Universitat Halle-Wittenberg - Universitats- und Landesbibliothek Sachsen-Anhalt (Env-Cons, Agri, Rel-Phil)
August Bebel Strasse 13 und 50 Phone: 8950
O-4010 Halle, Saale, Germany Joachim Dietze, Ph.D., Lib.Hd.
Founded: 1696. **Subjects:** Agrochemistry, ecology, Semitism, Islam, theology, religion, territorial history and knowledge of Sachsen-Anhalt districts. **Special Collections:** Archiv der Franckeschen Stiftungen; Bibliothek der Deutschen Morgenlandischen Gesellschaft. **Holdings:** 3.6 million books and bound periodical volumes; 318,100 manuscripts; 13,300 nonbook items. **Services:** Interlibrary loan; copying; library open to the public. **Computerized Information Services:** STN International; CD-ROMs. **Publications:** Sachsen-Anhalt; Landeskundliche Regionalbibliographie. **Remarks:** Telex: 4252 ULB HAL DD.

★9732★
Martin Marietta Aero & Naval Systems - Technical Information Center MPE100 (Sci-Engr)
103 Chesapeake Park Plaza Phone: (410)682-1574
Baltimore, MD 21220 Deborah C. Isenhart, Supv., Lib.Serv.
Founded: 1981. **Staff:** 3. **Subjects:** Aerospace, electronics, artificial intelligence, acoustics. **Holdings:** 5200 books; 13,800 reports. **Subscriptions:** 140 journals and other serials. **Services:** Interlibrary loan through OCLC; center not open to the public. **Automated Operations:** Computerized circulation, serials, and acquisitions. **Computerized Information Services:** DIALOG Information Services, NASA/RECON, DTIC, OCLC, LEXIS, NEXIS, OCLC EPIC. **Networks/Consortia:** Member of CAPCON Library Network. **Staff:** Robyne Greenwood; Ann Huth.

★9733★
Martin Marietta Astronautics - Denver Research Library (Sci-Engr)
Box 179 Phone: (303)977-5512
Denver, CO 80201 Janna Jantz, Libn.
Founded: 1955. **Staff:** Prof 1; Other 5. **Subjects:** Aerospace technology, guided missiles, launch vehicles, propulsion, space electronics. **Holdings:** 18,000 books; 5000 bound periodical volumes; 70,000 NASA, DTIC, contractor documents; 70,000 NASA, AIAA, AAS microfiche **Subscriptions:** 277 journals and other serials. **Services:** Library not open to the public. **Computerized Information Services:** DIALOG Information Services, NASA/RECON, DTIC. **Publications:** Report Index, monthly with cumulations - for internal distribution only. **Special Indexes:** Computer-produced index to technical reports and documents. **Remarks:** FAX: (303)977-6412. **Staff:** Mel Coffman, Mil.Pubns.; Mark Merwin, Ref.; Carol Robbins, Acq.; Velma Huff, Cir.; Robert Molloy, Rec. Retention Ctr.

★9734★
Martin Marietta Corporation - Electronics Information & Missiles Group - Information Center (Sci-Engr)
Box 555837, MP30 Phone: (407)356-2051
Orlando, FL 32855-5837 Richard M. Mellon, Mgr.
Founded: 1957. **Staff:** Prof 4; Other 2. **Subjects:** Aerospace, electronics. **Holdings:** 35,000 volumes; 150,000 technical reports; 55,000 microfiche. **Subscriptions:** 300 journals and other serials. **Services:** Interlibrary loan; center not open to the public. **Automated Operations:** Computerized cataloging, acquisitions, serials, and circulation. **Computerized Information Services:** DIALOG Information Services, DTIC; internal database. **Remarks:** FAX: (407)356-6648. **Staff:** Richard E. Steinmetz, Chf.Libn.

★9735★
Martin Marietta Energy Systems Inc. - Applied Technology Library (Sci-Engr)
Bldg. K-1002, MS 7221
Box 2003 Phone: (615)574-9694
Oak Ridge, TN 37831-7221 Gregory K. Youngen, Libn.
Founded: 1945. **Staff:** Prof 1; Other 2. **Subjects:** Isotope separation, industrial management, chemistry, chemical engineering, metallurgy, mechanical engineering, materials, applied technology, engineering. **Holdings:** 21,000 books; 11,500 bound periodical volumes; 55,000 reports; 320,000 microfiche and microcards. **Subscriptions:** 400 journals and other serials. **Services:** Library not open to the public. **Automated Operations:** Computerized cataloging and circulation. **Computerized Information Services:** DIALOG Information Services, LEGI-SLATE, NASA/RECON, OCLC; electronic mail service. **Networks/Consortia:** Member of SOLINET. **Special Indexes:** Index to Classified Materials of Isotope Separation. **Remarks:** FAX: (615)576-8056.

★9736★
Martin Marietta Energy Systems Inc. - Libraries (Sci-Engr, Biol Sci)
Oak Ridge National Laboratory, Bldg. 4500N
Box 2008 Phone: (615)574-7851
Oak Ridge, TN 37831-6208 Virgie Jo Sapp, Mgr., Lib.Serv.
Founded: 1946. **Staff:** Prof 22; Other 27. **Subjects:** Chemistry, biology, metallurgy, physics, nuclear science, mathematics, engineering, environmental sciences, ecology. **Holdings:** 150,000 books; 2.5 million reports; AV materials. **Subscriptions:** 3400 journals and other serials. **Services:** Interlibrary loan; document delivery service; SDI. **Automated Operations:** Computerized cataloging, circulation, serials, and ILL. **Computerized Information Services:** NEXIS, LEXIS, LS/2000, LEGI-SLATE, DIALOG Information Services, PFDS Online, BRS Information Technologies, OCLC, DTIC, STN International, NASA/RECON,

Integrated Technical Information System (ITIS), PI-NET, CompuServe Information Service, Human Resource Information Network (HRIN), VU/TEXT Information Services; CD-ROM. **Networks/Consortia:** Member of SOLINET. **Publications:** Reports Received; Books Received - both for internal distribution only. **Remarks:** Martin Marietta Energy Systems manages under contract to the U.S. Department of Energy. The Martin Marietta Energy Systems Libraries include Central Research Library, Technical Library, Biology Library, Fusion Energy Library, Environmental Sciences Library, Information Analysis Library, Applied Technology Library, Physics Library, Law Library, and Engineering Library. FAX: (615)574-1909. **Staff:** Deborah L. York, Coord., X-10; Ta-chang Liu, Coord., Y-12; Lois Schier, Coord., K-25; D. Fawnee Dinsmore, Bibliog. Control; Cynthia Manley, Acq.

★9737★
Martin Marietta Energy Systems Inc. - Paducah Gaseous Diffusion Plant Information Center (Sci-Engr, Energy)
Box 1410 Phone: (502)441-6438
Paducah, KY 42002-1410 Carol L. Young, Tech.Libn.
Founded: 1951. **Staff:** Prof 4. **Subjects:** Nuclear science, chemistry, computers, statistics, mathematics, engineering, management. **Holdings:** 10,000 books; 7000 bound periodical volumes; 75,000 documents on nuclear science; industrial standards and master catalogs; 32 drawers of microfiche. **Subscriptions:** 350 journals and other serials. **Services:** Interlibrary loan; center not open to the public. **Computerized Information Services:** Internal database. **Remarks:** FAX: (502)441-6339. **Staff:** Kathy L. Johnson, Plant Rec.; Brenda G. McKnight, Doc. Accountability.

★9738★
Martin Marietta Energy Systems Inc. - Portsmouth Gaseous Diffusion Plant - X-710 Library MS-2206 (Sci-Engr)
Box 628 Phone: (614)897-5797
Piketon, OH 45661 Joyce G. Hopper, Supv.
Founded: 1952. **Staff:** Prof 2; Other 1. **Subjects:** Atomic and nuclear science; chemistry; physics; engineering - chemical, mechanical, electrical; industrial safety; metallurgical science; mathematics. **Holdings:** 24,000 books; 3000 bound periodical volumes; 16,000 technical reports; 42,000 technical reports in microform. **Subscriptions:** 513 journals and other serials. **Services:** Interlibrary loan; library not open to the public. **Automated Operations:** Computerized cataloging, acquisitions, and circulation. **Computerized Information Services:** STN International. **Remarks:** FAX: (614)897-3595. **Staff:** Marvin L. Rice, Tech.Libn.; Phyl A. Hopkins, Engr.Libn.

★9739★
Martin Marietta Laboratories - Library and Information Services (Sci-Engr)
1450 S. Rolling Rd. Phone: (301)247-0700
Baltimore, MD 21227-3898 Rosalind P. Cheslock, Mgr.
Staff: Prof 4; Other 4. **Subjects:** Chemistry, physics, surface science, fluid mechanics, artificial intelligence, materials science, microelectronics. **Special Collections:** Internal Documents. **Holdings:** 12,000 books; 5000 bound periodical volumes; 5000 documents; 2000 reels of microfilm; 1000 microfiche. **Subscriptions:** 600 journals and other serials. **Services:** Interlibrary loan; SDI; library open to the public by appointment. **Automated Operations:** Computerized cataloging, acquisitions, serials, and circulation. **Computerized Information Services:** DIALOG Information Services, PFDS Online, NEXIS, DTIC, NASA/RECON, OCLC, BRS Information Technologies, STN International, DataTimes, WILSONLINE, MEDLINE, USNI Military Database; CD-ROM. **Networks/Consortia:** Member of Interlibrary Users Association (IUA), CAPCON Library Network. **Remarks:** FAX: (301)247-4939.

Mary Martin Collection
See: **Museum of the City of New York - Theatre Collection** (10892)

Paul Martin Law Library
See: **University of Windsor** (19567)

Thomas W. Martin Memorial Library
See: **Southern Research Institute** (15516)

★9740★
Martin/Williams Advertising Inc. - Library (Bus-Fin)
10 S. 5th St., Suite 1100
Minneapolis, MN 55402-1037 Phone: (612)340-0800
Founded: 1977. **Staff:** Prof 1. **Subjects:** Advertising, marketing, business. **Holdings:** 100 books; 200 unbound reports. **Subscriptions:** 800 journals and other serials. **Services:** Library open to agency employees and clients; open to the public with special permission. **Computerized Information Services:** DIALOG Information Services, Mead Data Central, NEXIS, DataTimes. **Remarks:** FAX: (612)342-9700.

★9741★
Martinsville Daily Reporter - Library (Publ)
60 S. Jefferson St.
P.O. Box 1636 Phone: (317)342-3311
Martinsville, IN 46151 Esther Hancock
Founded: 1885. **Subjects:** Newspaper reference topics. **Holdings:** Microfilm. **Subscriptions:** 6 newspapers. **Services:** Copying; library open to the public for reference use only. **Remarks:** FAX: (317)342-1446.

Dwight Marvin Learning Resources Center
See: **Hudson Valley Community College** (7499)

Marx Brothers Library & Archives
See: **The Freedonia Gazette** (6133)

Karl Marx Haus Studienzentrum
See: **Friedrich Ebert Stiftung** (5199)

Robert S. Marx Law Library
See: **University of Cincinnati** (18482)

★9742★
Mary Immaculate Seminary - Library (Rel-Phil)
300 Cherryville Rd.
Box 27 Phone: (215)262-7866
Northampton, PA 18067 Mrs. Cait Kokolus, Libn.
Staff: Prof 1; Other 2. **Subjects:** Bible, liturgy, Catholic theology, church history, patristics, canon law, medical ethics. **Special Collections:** Vincentiana Collection. **Holdings:** 58,354 books; 15,465 bound periodical volumes; 244 unbound periodicals; 1384 reels of microfilm; 1469 microfiche; 520 cassettes; 55 filmstrips; 2000 phonograph records; 864 other cataloged items. **Subscriptions:** 421 journals and other serials; 6 newspapers. **Services:** Interlibrary loan; copying; library open to the public with restrictions. **Automated Operations:** Computerized public access catalog, cataloging, and acquisitions. **Computerized Information Services:** Internal database. **Networks/Consortia:** Member of State System of Higher Education Libraries Council (SSHELCO), Southeastern Pennsylvania Theological Library Association (SEPTLA).

★9743★
Mary Kay Cosmetics, Inc. - Technical Information Center (Sci-Engr)
1330 Regal Row Phone: (214)905-6299
Dallas, TX 75247 Paula L. Galbraith, Supv., Tech.Info.
Founded: 1976. **Staff:** Prof 3; Other 1. **Subjects:** Cosmetics, dermatology, toxicology, chemistry, business, marketing. **Special Collections:** International cosmetic regulations. **Holdings:** 1700 books; 450 bound periodical volumes. **Subscriptions:** 200 journals and other serials. **Services:** Interlibrary loan; copying; SDI; record retention; center open to the public with restrictions. **Computerized Information Services:** DIALOG Information Services, MEDLARS, BRS Information Technologies, PFDS Online, Mead Data Central, STN International, Startext, DataTimes, Data-Star, DunsPrint; internal databases. **Networks/Consortia:** Member of Health Libraries Information Network (HealthLINE). **Remarks:** FAX: (214)631-5938. **Staff:** Cecilia Armas, Tech.Info.Coord.; Laura Hall, Info.Spec.; Hilda Sluder, Rec.Spec.

Marycrest College
See: **Teikyo Marycrest University** (16056)

★9744★
Maryknoll Fathers - Photo Library (Aud-Vis)
Walsh Bldg.
Pines Bridge Rd. Phone: (914)941-7590
Maryknoll, NY 10545 Penny Ann Sandoval, Photo Libn.
Founded: 1911. **Staff:** 2. **Subjects:** Third World, poverty, hunger, socioeconomic conditions, anthropology, children, religion, history of Maryknoll Religious Society. **Special Collections:** China, 1918-1948 (3000 items). **Holdings:** 3 VF drawers of art files; 198 VF drawers of black/white photographs; 1000 large prints; 900,000 color slides. **Subscriptions:** 89 journals and other serials; 7 newspapers. **Services:** Copying; library open to the public by appointment. **Publications:** Maryknoll Magazine, monthly; Revista Maryknoll, monthly (Spanish/English); ORBIS Books; World Parish Newsletter. **Remarks:** FAX: (914)945-0670.

★9745★
Maryknoll School of Theology - Library (Rel-Phil)
Maryknoll, NY 10545-0304 Phone: (914)941-7590
James V. O'Halloran, Libn.
Founded: 1928. **Staff:** Prof 3; Other 3. **Subjects:** Theology, missions, cross cultural ministry, justice and peace, scripture, world religions. **Holdings:** 102,400 books; 26,000 bound periodical volumes. **Subscriptions:** 600 journals and other serials. **Services:** Interlibrary loan; copying; library open to the public. **Automated Operations:** Computerized cataloging and ILL. **Computerized Information Services:** OCLC. **Special Indexes:** Index to Maryknoll Magazine (cards). **Remarks:** Official name of the organization is Catholic Foreign Mission Society of America. FAX: (914)941-5753. **Staff:** Zay D. Green, Cat.; Timothy Lincoln, Per.

★9746★
Maryknoll Sisters of St. Dominic - Rogers Library (Rel-Phil)
Maryknoll Sisters Center
Maryknoll, NY 10545 Phone: (914)941-7575
Subjects: Christian mission activities, gospel of Jesus Christ, pastoral ministry, communication, community development, education, health, research, social service in Africa, Asia, the Central Pacific Islands, North, Central, and South America. **Holdings:** 44,000 volumes; biographical archives.

Maryland Center for Quality and Productivity
See: **University of Maryland, College Park - Maryland Center for Quality and Productivity** (18807)

★9747★
Maryland College of Art & Design - Library (Art)
10500 Georgia Ave. Phone: (301)649-4454
Silver Spring, MD 20902 Teresa Cummings Stevens, Libn.
Staff: Prof 1; Other 1. **Subjects:** Painting, drawing, sculpture, design, commercial art, typography. **Holdings:** 10,000 books; 5100 unbound items; 15,200 slides; 2 lateral files of pictures; graphic design visual resources files; artist file. **Subscriptions:** 38 journals and other serials. **Services:** Interlibrary loan; copying; library open to the public for reference use only. **Publications:** Subject bibliographies, irregular.

★9748★
Maryland Committee for Children, Inc. - MCC Resource Center (Soc Sci)
608 Water St. Phone: (410)752-7588
Baltimore, MD 21202 Sandra Skolnik, Exec.Dir.
Founded: 1974. **Subjects:** Day care, early childhood growth and development, child advocacy. **Special Collections:** Work/Family Initiatives Collection; Child Care Technical Assistance. **Holdings:** 1600 books; 250 file boxes. **Subscriptions:** 38 journals and other serials. **Services:** Copying; center open to the public. **Publications:** List of publications - available on request. **Remarks:** FAX: (410)752-6286.

★9749★
Maryland General Hospital - Medical Staff Library (Med)
827 Linden Ave. Phone: (301)225-8383
Baltimore, MD 21201 Monica Yang, Coord., Lib.Serv.
Staff: Prof 1; Other 1. **Subjects:** Medicine, nursing. **Holdings:** 1500 books; 800 bound periodical volumes; 5 Audio-Digest subscriptions; 500 tapes; 3000 slides; slide/tape sets; video-discs; video cassettes. **Subscriptions:** 100 journals and other serials. **Services:** Interlibrary loan; library not open to the public. **Computerized Information Services:** MEDLINE. **Remarks:** FAX: (301)225-8119. Contains the holdings of the School of Nursing Library.

★9750★
Maryland Historical Society - Library (Hist)
201 W. Monument St. Phone: (410)685-3750
Baltimore, MD 21201 Penny Catzen, Lib.Dir.
Founded: 1844. **Staff:** Prof 7; Other 7. **Subjects:** Maryland history and genealogy; United States history. **Special Collections:** Manuscript collections: Calvert, Latrobe, Carroll, Wirt, Howard, Ridgely, and Lloyd; Maryland biographical index (1 million cards); Maryland sporting art; sheet music (Maryland); World War II records. **Holdings:** 55,000 books; 1500 newspaper volumes; 3 million manuscripts; 10,000 pamphlets; 1700 reels of microfilm; 5000 prints; 250,000 photographs; 3000 maps; 26 VF drawers of clippings. **Subscriptions:** 400 journals and other serials. **Services:** Copying; library open to the public with fee for nonmembers. **Publications:** Maryland Historical Magazine, quarterly - by subscription; News and Notes, bimonthly - to members; Manuscript Collections of the Maryland Historical Society (1968); Guide to the Research Collections of the Maryland Historical Society (1981); Mapping of Maryland: An Overview (1982). **Special Catalogs:** Obituary file, 1794 to present; manuscript collections (both on cards). **Remarks:** FAX: (410)385-2105. **Staff:** Francis P. O'Neill, Ref.Libn.; Laura S. Rice, Prints & Photo.; Margaret Burri, Mss.Libn.; Dr. Robert J. Brugger, Ed.

★9751★
Maryland Institute, College of Art - Decker Library (Art)
1400 Cathedral St. Phone: (410)225-2304
Baltimore, MD 21201 John Stoneham, Dir.
Founded: 1826. **Staff:** Prof 4; Other 6. **Subjects:** Art, crafts, theater, cinema, photography. **Special Collections:** Lucas Collection (books and prints). **Holdings:** 50,000 books; 2000 bound periodical volumes; 60,000 slides; 9 VF drawers of plates; 18 VF drawers of pamphlets. **Subscriptions:** 200 journals and other serials. **Services:** Interlibrary loan; copying; library open to the public with restrictions. **Staff:** Irma Sangiamo, Ref.; Marjorie Chenoweth, Cat.; Mary Anne Rosinsky, Circ.

Maryland League of Women Voters Archives
See: **University of Maryland, College Park Libraries - McKeldin Library - Historical Manuscripts and Archives Department** (18818)

★9752★
Maryland Municipal League - Library (Soc Sci)
1212 West St. Phone: (301)268-5514
Annapolis, MD 21401 Jon C. Burrell, Exec.Dir.
Staff: Prof 7; Other 2. **Subjects:** Municipal administration, law, finance, personnel. **Holdings:** 1000 volumes. **Subscriptions:** 25 journals and other serials; 10 newspapers. **Services:** Library not open to the public. **Publications:** Municipal Maryland, monthly; periodic surveys and reports.

★9753★
Maryland National Capital Park and Planning Commission - Montgomery County Planning Department - Library (Plan)
8787 Georgia Ave. Phone: (301)495-4643
Silver Spring, MD 20910-3760 Janice C. Holt, Libn.
Founded: 1961. **Staff:** Prof 1. **Subjects:** Urban and regional planning, parks, land use, population, housing, environment, transportation, public facilities. **Special Collections:** Montgomery County Planning Board Publications (current master plans and special reports; 200). **Holdings:** 4000 books; 300 bound periodical volumes; 7000 technical reports. **Subscriptions:** 220 journals and other serials. **Services:** Interlibrary loan; copying; SDI; library open to the public by appointment. **Networks/Consortia:** Member of Interlibrary Users Association (IUA). **Publications:** Library Newsletter (acquisitions list) - for internal distribution only.

★9754★
Maryland Pharmacists Association - Library (Med)
Kelly Memorial Bldg.
650 W. Lombard St. Phone: (301)727-0746
Baltimore, MD 21201 David Miller, Exec.Dir.
Founded: 1953. **Subjects:** Pharmacy, allied health sciences. **Special Collections:** Library of E.F. Kelly. **Holdings:** 1000 volumes. **Services:** Library not open to the public. **Remarks:** FAX: (301)727-2253.

★9755★
Maryland Rehabilitation Center - R.C. Thompson Library (Med)
2301 Argonne Dr. Phone: (301)554-3125
Baltimore, MD 21218 Paul Hoffman, Recreation Supv.
Founded: 1975. **Staff:** Prof 1; Other 1. **Subjects:** Disability; vocational and physical rehabilitation; independent living; job placement of the disabled; physical, legal, and social barriers; substance abuse. **Holdings:** 2500 books; 8500 other cataloged items; 60 16mm films; 320 video cassettes. **Subscriptions:** 145 journals and other serials; 8 newspapers. **Services:** Interlibrary loan; copying; library open to the public. **Publications:** 6 annotated videographies. **Remarks:** FAX: (301)554-3205. Patient library contains an additional 7700 volumes.

★9756★
Maryland State Archives - Library (Hist)
350 Rowe Blvd. Phone: (301)974-3915
Annapolis, MD 21401 Shashi P. Thapar, Lib.Dir.
Founded: 1935. **Staff:** Prof 1; Other 1. **Subjects:** History - Maryland, American, Black, other states; genealogy; biography. **Special Collections:** Works Project Administration Historical Records Survey Publications; Maryland State Publications and Reports; Laws of Maryland; Maryland House and Senate Journals. **Holdings:** 15,000 books; 450 bound periodical volumes; reports; manuscripts; archives. **Subscriptions:** 100 journals and other serials. **Services:** Copying; library open to the public for reference use only. **Automated Operations:** Computerized cataloging. **Computerized Information Services:** Internal databases. Performs searches on fee basis. **Networks/Consortia:** Member of Maryland Interlibrary Organization (MILO). **Publications:** Irregular publications; Maryland Manual, biennial; serials and periodicals list. **Remarks:** FAX: (301)974-3895. Contains the holdings of the former Maryland State Department of Natural Resources - Library.

★9757★
Maryland (State) Attorney General's Office - Library (Law)
200 St. Paul Pl., 18th FL. Phone: (301)576-6400
Baltimore, MD 21202 Beverly Rubenstein, Libn.
Staff: Prof 1; Other 1. **Subjects:** State and federal law. **Special Collections:** National Reporter System (1st series on ultrafiche); laws of Maryland, 1680 to present. **Holdings:** 25,000 books; 200 bound periodical volumes. **Subscriptions:** 20 journals and other serials. **Services:** Interlibrary loan; copying; SDI; library open to the public by appointment. **Computerized Information Services:** LEXIS, WESTLAW, DIALOG Information Services; Ask Sam (internal database). **Publications:** Library Brief (newsletter). **Remarks:** FAX: (301)576-7002. **Staff:** Florentina Pantelunan, Asst.Libn.

Maryland State Data Center
See: **University of Maryland, College Park - Computer Science Center - Program Library** (18805)

★9758★
Maryland (State) Department of Economic and Employment Development - Office of Research - Library (Bus-Fin)
217 E. Redwood St., 11th Fl.
Baltimore, MD 21202 Phone: (301)333-6947
Founded: 1970. **Subjects:** Maryland economics and demography. **Holdings:** 1500 volumes; Maryland socioeconomic and demographic data.

★9759★
Maryland (State) Department of Education - Division of Library Development & Services - State Media Services Center (Educ, Info Sci)
200 W. Baltimore St. Phone: (301)333-2134
Baltimore, MD 21201 Nancy Knauer, Sec.Chief
Founded: 1960. **Staff:** Prof 3; Other 2. **Subjects:** Education, library science. **Special Collections:** History of education in Maryland; U.S. Office of Education publications; Maryland State Department of Education publications. **Holdings:** 2000 volumes; 200 films; 8 slide sets; 50 filmstrip sets; 225 videotapes; complete ERIC collection. **Subscriptions:** 276 journals and other serials. **Services:** Interlibrary loan; material duplication; AV technical assistance; center open to the public. **Computerized Information Services:** DIALOG Information Services, BRS Information Technologies. Performs searches for MSDE personnel only. **Publications:** Newsletter; education-related bibliographies; list of current journal titles. **Special Catalogs:** AV materials. **Remarks:** FAX: (301)333-2507. **Staff:** James Murray Info. Spec.; Barbara Fayak-Galka, Info.Spec.

Maryland State Department of Health & Mental Hygiene - Eastern Shore Hospital Center
See: **Eastern Shore Hospital Center** (5165)

★9760★
Maryland (State) Department of Health & Mental Hygiene - Media Services
300 W. Preston St.
Baltimore, MD 21201
Defunct.

Maryland (State) Department of Health & Mental Hygiene - Spring Grove Hospital Center
See: **Spring Grove Hospital Center** (15596)

★9761★
Maryland (State) Department of Legislative Reference - Library and Information Services Division (Soc Sci, Law)
Legislative Services Bldg.
90 State Circle Phone: (410)841-3810
Annapolis, MD 21401 Lynda C. Davis, Chf., Lib.Div.
Founded: 1966. **Staff:** Prof 10; Other 7. **Subjects:** Laws and codes, legislative reports. **Holdings:** 65,000 books; 685 bound periodical volumes; newspapers and house and senate journals on microfilm; General Assembly committee bill file, 1975 to present. **Subscriptions:** 200 journals and other serials; 24 newspapers. **Services:** Interlibrary loan; copying; SDI; library open to the public. **Automated Operations:** Computerized cataloging. **Computerized Information Services:** DIALOG Information Services, LEXIS, OCLC, Public Affairs Information Service (PAIS); Bill Status System (internal database). **Publications:** Legislative Policy Committee Reports; Bound and Advance Sheets Session Laws; Maryland Documents, monthly; Synopsis of Laws, annual - both to members of General Assembly and interested public; Maryland Clipper, daily during session - to members of General Assembly and interested public. **Special Indexes:** Legislative Bills and indexes by subject, sponsor, number, statute, and committee, 1918 to present. **Remarks:** FAX: (410)841-3850. **Staff:** Lynda S. Cunningham, Leg.Libn.; Barbara Speyser, Leg.Libn.; David Warner, Leg.Libn.; Rita Newnham, Leg.Libn.; Carol Carman, Leg.Libn.; Mary Ruland, Leg.Libn.; Johanne Greer, Leg.Libn.; Marilyn McManus, Leg.Libn.; Esther Bishop, Leg.Libn.; Sherry Little, Pub.Info.Off.

★9762★
Maryland (State) Department of Licensing and Regulation - Occupational Safety and Health Library (Med)
501 St. Paul Pl., 11th Fl. Phone: (301)333-4164
Baltimore, MD 21202-2272 David Murray, Lib.Hd.
Founded: 1980. **Staff:** Prof 1. **Subjects:** General reference, industrial hygiene, construction and industrial processes, occupational medicine and diseases, safety hazards, hazardous occupations, environmental pollution, toxicology. **Holdings:** 600 books; 30 bound periodical volumes; 30 other cataloged items. **Subscriptions:** 30. **Services:** Interlibrary loan; library open to the public for reference use only. **Automated Operations:** Computerized public access catalog, cataloging, and circulation. **Special Catalogs:** Audio Visual Catalog. **Remarks:** FAX: (301)333-1771.

Maryland State Department of Natural Resources - Library
See: **Maryland State Archives - Library** (9756)

★9763★
Maryland (State) Highway Administration - Library (Trans)
707 N. Calvert St.
Box 717
Baltimore, MD 21202 Phone: (301)333-1100
Founded: 1963. **Staff:** Prof 2. **Subjects:** Traffic; highways - construction, maintenance, design; programming. **Special Collections:** State Specifications Reports; Highway Research Board Papers; Maryland State Highway Administration Annual Reports (5 VF drawers). **Holdings:** 8000 books; 16 VF drawers of pamphlets; 200 periodicals. **Subscriptions:** 75 journals and other serials. **Services:** Will answer brief inquiries and make referrals; library open to the public for reference use only on request. **Publications:** Library Acquisitions, quarterly.

★9764★
Maryland State Law Library (Law, Hist)
361 Rowe Blvd. Phone: (410)974-3395
Annapolis, MD 21401 Michael S. Miller, Dir.
Founded: 1826. **Staff:** Prof 5; Other 5. **Subjects:** Law, Marylandia, genealogy. **Special Collections:** Early English Reports and Statutes; Maryland census records, 1790-1910; Maryland Appellate Court briefs and record extracts; U.S. Supreme Court records and briefs, 1980 to present (on microfiche); Maryland state documents depository. **Holdings:** 280,000 books; 10,000 bound periodical volumes; newspapers; 3900 reels of microfilm; selected U.S. Government documents depository. **Subscriptions:** 520 journals and other serials. **Services:** Interlibrary loan; copying; library open to the public. **Automated Operations:** Computerized cataloging. **Computerized Information Services:** LEXIS, WESTLAW, OCLC, DIALOG Information Services. **Networks/Consortia:** Member of CAPCON Library Network. **Publications:** History of Maryland State Library; selected recent acquisitions list, monthly; Maryland State Law Library: A Guide to Resources and Services; Ghosthunting; Finding Legislative Intent in Maryland: A Checklist of Sources. **Remarks:** FAX: (301)974-2063. **Staff:** Bernice G. Bernstein, Asst.Libn.; Shirley A. Rittenhouse, Ref.Libn.; Dee T. Van Nest, Asst. Law Libn.; Shirley C. Aronson, Doc.Libn.

★9765★
Maryland State Medical Society - Medical and Chirurgical Faculty - Music Medicine Clearinghouse (Med)
1211 Cathedral St. Phone: (410)539-0872
Baltimore, MD 21201 Susan E. Harman, Clghse.Coord.
Founded: 1988. **Subjects:** Medical problems of performing musicians; music-making - physiology, anatomy. **Holdings:** 24 books; 800 journal article reprints (past 100 years, from medical, musical, and popular press); 5 AV programs; conference transcripts; arts medicine clinics brochures; arts medicine organizations information; subtopic bibliographies; other ephemeral material. **Subscriptions:** 4 journals and other serials. **Services:** Interlibrary loan; copying; clearinghouse open to the public. **Computerized Information Services:** NLM, BRS Information Technologies; internal database. Performs searches on fee basis. **Publications:** Ongoing bibliography on occupational diseases of musicians. **Remarks:** Serves as an international clearinghouse for resources and publications on the medical problems of musicians. Alternate telephone number(s): 539-0872. A toll-free telephone number in Maryland is (800)492-1056. FAX: (410)547-0915.

★9766★
Maryland (State) National Capital Park & Planning Commission - Surratt Museum - Research Library (Hist)
9118 Brandywine Rd.
P.O. Box 427 Phone: (301)868-1121
Clinton, MD 20735 Laurie Verge, Pk.Hist./Musm.Mgr.
Founded: 1976. **Staff:** 4. **Subjects:** Lincoln assassination, Mary E. Surratt and family, John Wilkes Booth, Civil War, Victorian antiques and culture, local history. **Holdings:** 1200 books; 50 bound periodical volumes; 25 microforms and nonbook items; 25 manuscripts. **Services:** Copying; library open to the public with restrictions. **Remarks:** Affiliated with the Surratt Society.

★9767★
Maryland (State) Office of Planning - Library (Plan)
301 W. Preston St., Rm. 1101 Phone: (410)225-4500
Baltimore, MD 21201-2365 Helene W. Jeng, Libn.
Staff: Prof 1; Other 1. **Subjects:** Urban affairs, planning, natural resources, human resources, land use planning. **Special Collections:** Planning Advisory Service Reports; depository of state, regional, county, municipal, and interstate plans pertaining to Maryland. **Holdings:** 13,893 volumes; 200 bound periodical volumes; 10 drawers of unbound pamphlets and periodicals; 8 VF drawers; 24 videocassettes; AV programs. **Subscriptions:** 138 journals and other serials; 20 newspapers. **Services:** Interlibrary loan; copying; library open to the public for reference use only. **Automated Operations:** Computerized cataloging. **Computerized Information Services:** Multimate (internal database); electronic mail. **Publications:** Maryland Office of Planning Library Bimonthly Acquisitions; Upfront (content page of magazines). **Remarks:** FAX: (410)225-4480.

★9768★
Maryland State Police Academy - Library (Law)
1200 Reisterstown Rd. Phone: (301)653-4370
Baltimore, MD 21208-3899 Marcia Abrams, Supv. of Lib.
Staff: 1. **Subjects:** Criminal law, investigation, and justice; law enforcement; rules and regulations; drugs. **Holdings:** 3000 books; 30 bound periodical volumes; 8 VF drawers; safety films. **Subscriptions:** 29 journals and other serials. **Services:** Copying; library open to the public for reference use only. **Special Catalogs:** Maryland State Police Film Catalog, annual.

★9769★
Maryview Hospital - Health Sciences Library (Med)
3636 High St. Phone: (804)398-2330
Portsmouth, VA 23707 Rene L. Brown, Libn.
Founded: 1956. **Staff:** Prof 1. **Subjects:** Medicine. **Holdings:** 1000 books; 1065 bound periodical volumes. **Subscriptions:** 100 journals and other serials. **Services:** Interlibrary loan; library open to the public for reference use only. **Computerized Information Services:** MEDLINE; DOCLINE (electronic mail service). **Remarks:** FAX: (804)398-2157.

Mascarello Library of Criminal Justice
See: **Crime & Justice Foundation** (4432)

★9770★
(Maseru) American Cultural Center - USIS Library (Educ)
Kingsway Rd.
Post Box 573
Maseru 100, Lesotho
Remarks: Maintained or supported by the U.S. Information Agency. Focus is on materials that will assist peoples outside the United States to learn about the United States, its people, history, culture, political processes, and social milieux.

★9771★
Mason City Globe-Gazette - Library (Publ)
300 N. Washington
P.O. Box 271
Mason City, IA 50401 Phone: (515)421-0524
Staff: Prof 1. **Subjects:** Newspaper reference topics. **Holdings:** Figures not available. **Remarks:** FAX: (515)421-0516.

★9772★
Mason County Historical Society - Rose Hawley Museum and Historical Library (Hist)
115 W. Loomis St. Phone: (616)843-2001
Ludington, MI 49431-2166 Ronald M. Wood, Dir., Hist.Soc.
Subjects: History - Mason County, marine, Indian; biography. **Holdings:** 500 books; 20 VF drawers of clippings, photographs, legal documents, brochures, newspapers; local newspapers on microfilm. **Services:** Copying; library open to the public. **Publications:** Mason County Pictorial History; History Happenings, monthly. **Remarks:** Alternate telephone number(s): (616)843-4808 (Society office at White Pine Village).

Edith Mason Library
See: **Mansfield Historical Society** (9640)

★9773★
George Mason University - Fenwick Library - Special Collections and Archives (Theater)
4400 University Dr. Phone: (703)993-2220
Fairfax, VA 22030 Charlene Hurt, Dir.
Founded: 1979. **Staff:** Prof 1; Other 1.5 **Subjects:** Theatre, performing arts, Northern Virginian Planned Communities. **Special Collections:** Performing Arts Collections: American Symphony Orchestra League (588 linear feet); Archives of the Wolf Trap Foundation for the Performing Arts (83 linear feet); Library of Congress Federal Theatre Project Collection, 1935-1939 (1153 linear feet); Robert Breen Papers (40 linear feet); Arthur Peterson Theatre Collection (21 linear feet); Political Papers Collections (Congressman Joel T. Broyhill, 42 linear feet; Congressman Joseph L. Fisher, 30 linear feet; Congressman Stanford E. Parris, 77 linear feet; Senator William L. Scott, 236 linear feet); Miton C. Barnes Civil War Letters (1 linear foot); Alexander Haight Civil War Collection (15 linear feet); Clark E. Warburton Economic Papers (105 linear feet); Planned Community Archives (170 linear feet); Edwin Lynch Papers (6 linear feet); C. Harrison Mann Map Collection (9 linear feet); Northern Virginia Oral History Project; photographic collections of Ollie Atkins and Arthur Scott; Evelyn L. Pugh Manuscript Collection (15 linear feet); rare books; African objects; university archives. **Holdings:** 650 books; 280 other cataloged items; photogrphs. **Services:** Interlibrary loan; copying; collections open to the public. **Networks/Consortia:** Member of Washington Research Library Consortium. **Publications:** Federal One, semiannual - to mailing list. **Special Catalogs:** The Federal Theatre Project: A Catalog-Calendar of Productions; The Federal Theatre Project Collection: A Register of the Library of Congress Collection of U.S. Work Projects Administration Records on Deposit at George Mason University; Finding Aids. **Remarks:** FAX: (703)993-2229. **Staff:** Barbara Haase, Archv./Rec.Mgr.; Ruth Kerns, Libn./Archv.

★9774★
George Mason University - School of Law - Library (Law)
3401 N. Fairfax Dr. Phone: (703)993-8120
Arlington, VA 22201 Philip C. Berwick, Dir.
Founded: 1971. **Staff:** Prof 4; Other 4. **Subjects:** Law. **Special Collections:** U.S. specialized law and economics collections; patents; banking law. **Holdings:** 250,998 books; 178,469 volumes in microform. **Subscriptions:** 3401 journals and other serials; 14 newspapers. **Services:** Interlibrary loan; copying; library open to the public with restrictions. **Automated Operations:** Computerized cataloging. **Computerized Information Services:** DIALOG Information Services, NEXIS, LEXIS, WESTLAW, OCLC. **Networks/Consortia:** Member of CAPCON Library Network. **Remarks:** FAX: (703)993-8113. **Staff:** Rae Best; Emily Carr; Kenneth Chadwick.

★9775★
Mason & Hanger-Silas Mason Company, Inc. - Pantex Plant - Technical Library (Sci-Engr)
Box 30020 Phone: (806)477-3547
Amarillo, TX 79177-0001 Kevin Mahony, Libn.
Staff: Prof 1. **Subjects:** High explosives. **Holdings:** 10,000 volumes. **Subscriptions:** 225 journals and other serials. **Services:** library not open to the public. **Computerized Information Services:** DIALOG Information Services, STN International. **Remarks:** FAX: (806)477-5447. Mason & Hanger-Silas Mason Company, Inc., operates under contract to the U.S. Department of Energy.

Sydney R. & Elsa W. Mason Library
See: **Johns Hopkins University - School of Advanced International Studies** (8427)

★9776★
Virginia Mason Medical Center - Medical Library (Med)
925 Seneca Phone: (206)223-6733
Seattle, WA 98111 Ann Robertson, Dir. of Lib.Serv.
Founded: 1925. **Staff:** Prof 2; Other 1. **Subjects:** Biomedicine. **Holdings:** 3000 books; 5000 bound periodical volumes; videotapes; microfilms. **Subscriptions:** 750 journals and other serials. **Services:** Interlibrary loan; copying; SDI; library open to health professionals only. **Automated Operations:** Computerized ILL. **Computerized Information Services:** DIALOG Information Services, MEDLINE, OCLC, WLN; OnTyme Electronic Message Network Service (electronic mail service). **Networks/Consortia:** Member of Seattle Area Hospital Library Consortium (SAHLC). **Special Catalogs:** Audiovisual catalog; journal catalog (both online). **Remarks:** FAX: (206)223-2376. Electronic mail address(es): VMHL (OnTyme Electronic Message Network Service). **Staff:** Danielle Haas, Med.Libn.

Wallace E. Mason Library
See: **Keene State College** (8600)

★9777★
Masonic Grand Lodge - Library
201 14th Ave. N. Phone: (701)235-8321
Fargo, ND 58102 K.L. Jenecek, Assoc.Libn.
Remarks: No further information was supplied by respondent.

★9778★
Masonic Grand Lodge Library and Museum of Texas (Rec, Hist)
Box 446 Phone: (817)753-7395
Waco, TX 76703 Janet Crain, Libn.
Founded: 1873. **Staff:** 2. **Subjects:** Masonic Order - philosophy, history, biography; Texana. **Special Collections:** Manuscript collection of Masonic and Texas materials (4210 items). **Holdings:** 36,056 volumes; 10,420 pamphlets; 1425 pictures. **Subscriptions:** 25 journals and other serials. **Services:** Interlibrary loan; copying; library open to the public for reference use only. **Staff:** Emery Stewart, Musm.Cur.

★9779★
Masonic Historical Library (Rec)
1924 N. 74th Court Phone: (708)456-0091
Elmwood Park, IL 60635 Edmund R. Sadowski, Pastmaster, Libn.-Ed.
Staff: 1. **Subjects:** History of freemasonry. **Special Collections:** Grand Lodge Proceedings, 1840-1960; Prince Hall Proceedings; Council, Royal Arch; Scottish Rite, Commandery; Masonic Review, 1846-1898; Masonic Trowel, 1861-1871; Mystic Star; Voice of Masonry; Der Triangel; Freemasons Monthly; Masonic Mirror; Masonic Convention Proceedings; Masonic Ashlar, 1855-1861; Masonic constitutions, state proceedings, periodicals, imprints, letters, bibliographies, lodge by-laws, orations, post card file, early rosters, minutes; Masonic Library catalogs; Freemasons memorabilia; Lodge Jewels; Lodge Histories; Commemorative Coins of the Freemasons and Royal Arch; Masonic serials; English, French, German, Italian, Polish, Spanish, Russian, and Latin Masonic Diplomas; photographs of Freemasons. **Holdings:** 10,000 books; 200 bound periodical volumes; 20,000 other cataloged items. **Subscriptions:** 10 journals and other serials. **Services:** Copying; library open to the public. **Publications:** Masonic Chanticleer, monthly; Masonic Research Lodge Publications; Masonic Certificates; Masonic Paper Ephemera; Masonic Manuscripts.

★9780★
Masonic Library & Museum of Indiana, Inc. - Masonic Library (Rec)
PO Box 353 Phone: (317)738-9708
Franklin, IN 46131 Joseph H. Burton, Dir.
Founded: 1988. **Staff:** Prof 1; Other 1. **Subjects:** Indiana Masonic history, Masonic history, Indiana history, general history, genealogy. **Special Collections:** Historical collections pertaining to all Masonic lodges in Indiana. **Holdings:** 4500 books; 300 bound periodical volumes; 200 cubic feet other cataloged items. **Subscriptions:** 17 journals and other serials. **Services:** Copying; library open to the public. **Automated Operations:** Computerized cataloging. **Computerized Information Services:** OCLC. **Networks/Consortia:** Member of INCOLSA. **Remarks:** Affiliated with the Grand Lodge of Free & Accepted Masons of Indiana. **Formerly:** Indiana Masonic Library & Museum located in Indianapolis, IN.

★9781★
Masonic Library and Museum of Pennsylvania (Rec)
Masonic Temple
1 N. Broad St. Phone: (215)988-1933
Philadelphia, PA 19107-2598 John H. Platt, Jr., Libn./Cur.
Staff: Prof 6. **Subjects:** Freemasonry. **Holdings:** 85,000 volumes. **Subscriptions:** 80 journals and other serials. **Services:** Library open to the public with restrictions. **Networks/Consortia:** Member of Philadelphia Area Consortium of Special Collections Libraries (PACSCL). **Publications:** The Pennsylvania Freemason, quarterly - to members. **Special Catalogs:** Circulating library catalog of books. **Remarks:** FAX: (215)988-1951. **Formerly:** Grand Lodge of Free and Accepted Masons of Pennsylvania - Masonic Temple Library and Museum. **Staff:** Milton Kenin, Asst.Libn., Archv.; Glenys A. Waldman, Asst.Libn. & Cur.

★9782★
Masonic Medical Research Laboratory - Max L. Kamiel Library (Med)
2150 Bleecker St. Phone: (315)735-2217
Utica, NY 13501-1787 Patricia M. Dugan, Libn.
Founded: 1956. **Staff:** Prof 2. **Subjects:** Cardiac arrhythmias, cardiovascular pharmacology, cancer research, aging, artificial blood. **Special Collections:** Biochemical gerontology. **Holdings:** 2200 books; 19,000 bound periodical volumes; 500 films; 300 microcards; 250 reels of microfilm; 8 other cataloged items. **Subscriptions:** 100 journals and other serials. **Services:** Interlibrary loan; copying; Russian translation; library open to the public by appointment. **Automated Operations:** Computerized ILL (DOCLINE). **Computerized Information Services:** BRS Information Technologies, NLM, OCLC. **Networks/Consortia:** Member of Central New York Library Resources Council (CENTRO). **Remarks:** FAX: (315)735-5648. **Staff:** Frank G. Dugan, Jr.

★9783★
Masonic Service Association of the United States - Library (Rec)
8120 Fenton St., Suite 203 Phone: (301)588-4010
Silver Spring, MD 20910-4785 Richard E. Fletcher, Exec.Sec.
Subjects: Masonic history, symbolism, and criticism. **Special Collections:** Masonic Grand Lodge proceedings; Masonic publications. **Holdings:** 1000 volumes; clippings; reports; manuscripts. **Subscriptions:** 10 journals and other serials; 35 newspapers. **Services:** Library open to the public by appointment. **Special Indexes:** Cumulative index of Masonic topics, lodge names, and numbers. **Remarks:** FAX: (301)608-3457.

★9784★
Masonite Corporation - Research Center Library (Agri)
Box 808 Phone: (708)584-6330
St. Charles, IL 60174-0808 J.A. Stuehm, Info. & Off.Serv.Supv.
Staff: Prof 2. **Subjects:** Hardboard, pulp and paper, standards. **Holdings:** 2500 volumes; periodicals. **Subscriptions:** 27 journals and other serials. **Services:** Interlibrary loan; copying; library open to the public at librarian's discretion. **Computerized Information Services:** DIALOG Information Services, ORBIT Search Service; internal database. **Remarks:** FAX: (312)584-1139. A subsidiary of International Paper.

★9785★
Masonry Institute of America - Library (Energy, Plan)
2550 Beverly Blvd.
Los Angeles, CA 90057 Phone: (213)388-0472
Founded: 1957. **Subjects:** Masonry, design, construction, building codes, earthquakes. **Holdings:** 2000 volumes; 1000 bound periodical volumes; 9000 uncataloged items. **Subscriptions:** 10 journals and other serials. **Services:** Copying; library open to the public for reference use only. **Remarks:** FAX: (213)389-7514.

Massachusetts Aeronautics Commission
See: **Massachusetts State Transportation Library** (9834)

★9786★
Massachusetts Archaeological Society - Robbins Museum - Library
P.O. Box 700
Middleboro, MA 02347
Subjects: Archeology, local history. **Special Collections:** Society archives. **Holdings:** 600 books. **Remarks:** Currently inactive.

★9787★
Massachusetts Audubon Society - Berkshire Sanctuaries - Library (Env-Cons)
Pleasant Valley Wildlife Sanctuary Phone: (413)637-0320
Lenox, MA 01240 Rene Laubach, Dir.
Founded: 1929. **Staff:** 5. **Subjects:** Natural history, environmental issues. **Special Collections:** Reports on natural science in Berkshire County, Massachusetts. **Holdings:** 1000 books; 100 bound periodical volumes; 1000 35mm color slides; field guides. **Subscriptions:** 5 journals and other serials. **Services:** Library open to the public with restrictions. **Publications:** Berkshire Sanctuaries Newsletter.

★9788★
Massachusetts Audubon Society - Hatheway Environmental Resource Library (Env-Cons)
South Great Rd. Phone: (617)259-9500
Lincoln, MA 01773 Cleti Cerroni, Dir. of Educ.
Founded: 1967. **Staff:** Prof 1; Other 1. **Subjects:** Air and water pollution, environment, conservation, environmental education, natural resources, wildlife management, careers, New England wild life, current environmental issues, history of the environmental movement. **Special Collections:** Natural history; environmental affairs; curriculum. **Holdings:** 15,000 titles; 25 VF drawers of pamphlets, articles, and curriculum activities. **Subscriptions:** 175 journals and other serials. **Services:** Interlibrary loan; library open to the public with restrictions. **Computerized Information Services:** DIALOG Information Services. **Publications:** List of publications - available on request. **Remarks:** This library is said to have the most extensive collection for environmental educators in the Northeastern United States. The society maintains three specialized libraries: Environmental Affairs, Environmental Science, and Natural History. FAX: (617)259-8899.

Massachusetts Bay Transportation Authority
See: **Massachusetts State Transportation Library** (9834)

Massachusetts Bible Society Library
See: **Boston University - School of Theology Library** (2018)

★9789★
Massachusetts College of Art - Morton R. Godine Library (Art)
621 Huntington Ave. Phone: (617)232-1555
Boston, MA 02115-5801 George R. Morgan, Libn.
Founded: 1973. **Staff:** Prof 5. **Subjects:** Art education; design - graphic, industrial, fashion; art history; architecture; photography; ceramics; glass; sculpture. **Special Collections:** Art education in the U.S. (200 items); early photographs of art education (50); children's books (3000). **Holdings:** 85,000 books; 2900 bound periodical volumes; 24 file drawers of pictures; 100,000 slides; 1000 sound recordings; 685 16mm films; 6000 reels of microfilm; 395 videotapes. **Subscriptions:** 400 journals and other serials; 15 newspapers. **Services:** Interlibrary loan; copying; library open to the public with restrictions. **Automated Operations:** Computerized cataloging, circulation, and ILL. **Computerized Information Services:** OCLC. **Networks/Consortia:** Member of Fenway Library Consortium (FLC). **Publications:** Information pamphlet. **Special Catalogs:** Video catalog; film catalog. **Staff:** Margot Isabelle, Ref./ILL; Torrey Burnett, Slides; John Keating, Cat./Ser.; Mary Curtin-Stevenson, Sys.; Paul Dobbs, Archv.; Robert Hilpert, AV.

★9790★
Massachusetts College of Pharmacy and Allied Health Sciences - Sheppard Library (Med, Biol Sci)
179 Longwood Ave. Phone: (617)732-2810
Boston, MA 02115 Anne M. Pascarelli, Lib.Dir.
Founded: 1823. **Staff:** Prof 5; Other 5. **Subjects:** Pharmacy, biological sciences, chemistry, medical botany, drug abuse, drug interactions, nursing, nuclear medicine, health psychology. **Special Collections:** College archives; history of pharmacy. **Holdings:** 65,000 volumes; 28 VF drawers of pamphlets, clippings, documents, advertising materials, reprints; audio and video cassettes; microfilm; slides. **Subscriptions:** 700 journals and other serials. **Services:** Interlibrary loan; copying; library open to the public for reference use only. **Automated Operations:** Computerized public access catalog and ILL (DOCLINE). **Computerized Information Services:** NTIS (U.S. National Technical Information Service), DIALOG Information Services, OCLC, STN International; CD-ROMs. Performs searches on fee basis. Contact Person: Mary G. Chitty, Assoc.Libn., 732-2813. **Networks/Consortia:** Member of Fenway Library Consortium (FLC), National Network of Libraries of Medicine - New England Region. **Publications:** Acquisitions list, irregular - available on request. **Remarks:** FAX: (617)732-2801. **Staff:** Julia S. Whelan, Asst.Libn.; Peg Hewitt, Asst.Libn.; Nancy E. Occhialini, Lib.Hd., Tech.Serv.; Fred Wolflink, Media Spec.

Massachusetts Eye and Ear Infirmary - Libraries
See: **Harvard University - School of Medicine - The Libraries of the Massachusetts Eye and Ear Infirmary** (6992)

★9791★
Massachusetts General Hospital - MGH Health Sciences Library (Med, Biol Sci)
Fruit St. Phone: (617)726-8600
Boston, MA 02114 Jacqueline Bastille, Dir.
Founded: 1848. **Staff:** Prof 9; Other 9. **Subjects:** Medicine, biochemistry, health care, nursing, allied health sciences. **Holdings:** 13,985 books; 35,444 bound periodical volumes. **Subscriptions:** 932 journals and other serials. **Services:** Interlibrary loan (fee); library not open to the public. **Automated Operations:** Integrated library system (Innovative Interfaces, Inc.). **Computerized Information Services:** BRS/COLLEAGUE, BRS Information Technologies, DIALOG Information Services, NLM, Chemical Abstracts Service (CAS), OCLC. Performs searches on fee basis. **Networks/Consortia:** Member of National Network of Libraries of Medicine - New England Region. **Remarks:** FAX: (617)726-6784. **Staff:** Elizabeth Schneider, Asst.Dir., Sys.Mgt.; Carol Mankin, Res.Proj.Libn.; Margaret Michaud, Coll.Org.Libn.; Carole Foxman, Coord., End-User Serv.; Mary Linn Borsman, Asst. Dir., Access Serv.; Susan Anderson, Asst.Dir., Info.Serv.; Martha Stone, Coord., Ref.Serv.; Praveena Raman, Coord. Search Serv.

★9792★
Massachusetts Historical Society - Library (Hist)
1154 Boylston St. Phone: (617)536-1608
Boston, MA 02215 Peter Drummey, Libn.
Founded: 1791. **Staff:** Prof 7; Other 4. **Subjects:** History - Massachusetts, New England, U.S. **Special Collections:** Manuscript collections (3500); early American imprints; Massachusetts diaries (600; 1629-1973). **Holdings:** 200,000 books; maps; prints; photographs, newspapers. **Subscriptions:** 175 journals and other serials. **Services:** Copying; library open to qualified researchers. **Automated Operations:** Computerized cataloging. **Computerized Information Services:** OCLC; internal database. **Networks/Consortia:** Member of NELINET, Inc. **Special Catalogs:** Catalog of the Manuscript Collections of the Massachusetts Historical Society and supplement. **Special Indexes:** Thwing Index (Boston property owners and inhabitants, 1630-1800; card). **Staff:** Mary Cogswell, Assoc.Libn.; Katherine Griffin, Asst.Libn.; Brenda Lawson, Cur. of Mss.; Virginia H. Smith, Ref.Libn.; Christopher Steele, Cur. of Photo

★9793★
Massachusetts Horticultural Society - Library (Biol Sci)
300 Massachusetts Ave. Phone: (617)536-9280
Boston, MA 02115 Walter T. Punch, Hd.Libn.
Founded: 1829. **Staff:** Prof 2; Other 4. **Subjects:** Ornamental horticulture, garden history, landscape design, pomology, early agriculture, floras of the world. **Special Collections:** Print collection covering 6 centuries; nursery catalogs, 1771 to present; rare book collection (3500); 19th century collection (11,000 volumes); trade catalog collection (40,000). **Holdings:** 31,000 books; 14,000 bound periodical volumes; 24 VF drawers of pamphlets and clippings; 4000 documents. **Subscriptions:** 280 journals and other serials. **Services:** Interlibrary loan; copying; library open to the public for reference use only. **Automated Operations:** Computerized cataloging. **Computerized Information Services:** OCLC. Performs searches on fee basis. Contact Person: Hugh Wilburn, Asst.Libn. **Networks/Consortia:** Member of NELINET, Inc. **Special Catalogs:** Dictionary Catalog of the Library of the Massachusetts Horticultural Society (1962); Supplement 1962/1971. **Remarks:** FAX: (617)262-8780.

★9794★
Massachusetts Hospital School - Paul Norton Medical Library (Med)
3 Randolph St. Phone: (617)828-2440
Canton, MA 02021 Sylvia K. Gerhard, Libn.
Staff: Prof 1. **Subjects:** Orthopedics, pediatrics. **Holdings:** 500 books. **Subscriptions:** 65 journals. **Services:** Interlibrary loan; copying; library open to the public with restrictions. **Networks/Consortia:** Member of Southeastern Massachusetts Consortium of Health Science Libraries (SEMCO), Massachusetts Health Sciences Libraries Network (MaHSLiN).

★9795★
Massachusetts Institute of Technology - Aeronautics and Astronautics Library (Sci-Engr)
Rm. 33-316 Phone: (617)253-5666
Cambridge, MA 02139 Eileen Dorschner, Libn.
Founded: 1941. **Staff:** Prof 1; Other 1. **Subjects:** Mechanics and physics of fluids; computational fluids; instrumentation, guidance, and control; energy conversion and propulsion; materials, structures, and aeroelasticity; aeronautical and astronautical systems, including flight transportation. **Special Collections:** Publications of National Advisory Committee for Aeronautics and National Aeronautics and Space Administration from the beginning in 1915; complete set of Institute of the Aeronautical/Aerospace Sciences, American Rocket Society, American Institute of Aeronautics and Astronautics technical papers. **Holdings:** 9654 books; 4828 bound periodical volumes; 57,076 technical reports; 27,241 bound serial volumes; 722 M.I.T. theses; 287,587 microfiche sheets. **Subscriptions:** 511 journals and other serials. **Services:** Interlibrary loan; copying; library open to the public for reference use only with a fee for borrowing. **Automated Operations:** Computerized cataloging, circulation, and ILL. **Computerized Information Services:** DIALOG Information Services, NASA/RECON; ALANET (electronic mail service). **Networks/Consortia:** Member of NELINET, Inc., Boston Library Consortium (BLC). **Remarks:** FAX: (617)258-5623. Electronic mail address(es): ALA1764 (ALANET).

★9796★
Massachusetts Institute of Technology - Barker Engineering Library (Sci-Engr)
Rm. 10-500 Phone: (617)253-5663
Cambridge, MA 02139 Ruth K. Seidman, Libn.
Staff: Prof 8; Other 11. **Subjects:** Engineering - electrical, mechanical, civil, ocean, materials, environmental; bioengineering; transportation; energy; mineral resources; computer science and applied mathematics. **Holdings:** 91,185 books; 35,202 bound periodical volumes; 51,490 bound serial volumes; 21,490 M.I.T. theses; 2233 pamphlets; 51,697 technical reports; 244,319 microfiche sheets; 1346 reels of microfilm. **Subscriptions:** 3315 journals and other serials. **Services:** Interlibrary loan; copying; library open to the public for brief room use with a fee for borrowing. **Automated Operations:** Computerized cataloging, circulation, and ILL. **Computerized Information Services:** DIALOG Information Services; CD-ROMs (U.S. National Technical Information Service (NTIS)Compendex Plus); ALANET (electronic mail service). **Networks/Consortia:** Member of NELINET, Inc., Boston Library Consortium (BLC). **Publications:** Barker Engineering Library Bulletin, biweekly - by subscription for persons outside M.I.T. **Remarks:** FAX: (617)258-5623. Electronic mail address(es): ALA1764 (ALANET).

★9797★
Massachusetts Institute of Technology - Center for Space Research - Reading Room (Sci-Engr)
Rm. 37-582 Phone: (617)253-3746
Cambridge, MA 02139 Amy Lalime, Asst.Libn.
Founded: 1965. **Staff:** Prof 1. **Subjects:** Astrophysics, astronomy, nuclear physics, astronautics. **Special Collections:** Center for Space Research technical reports. **Holdings:** 2830 books; 440 bound periodical volumes; 210 bound serial volumes; 8000 technical reports; selected bibliographies and NASA reports. **Subscriptions:** 50 journals and other serials. **Services:** Interlibrary loan; copying; room open to the public for brief room use. **Automated Operations:** Computerized cataloging. **Computerized Information Services:** OCLC; electronic mail. **Networks/Consortia:** Member of NELINET, Inc., Boston Library Consortium (BLC).

★9798★
Massachusetts Institute of Technology - Civil Engineering Department - Ralph M. Parsons Laboratory - Reference Room (Sci-Engr)
Bldg. 48-411 Phone: (617)253-2994
Cambridge, MA 02139 Chiang C. Mei, Prof. Civil Engr.
Staff: 1. **Subjects:** Hydrodynamics, hydrostatics, water resources, hydraulic machinery and structures, flow measurement, hydrology, environmental engineering, force resistance, aquatic chemistry, coastal engineering, ecology. **Holdings:** 300 books; 90 VF drawers of technical reports; 600 theses. **Subscriptions:** 30 journals and other serials. **Services:** Interlibrary loan; room open to laboratory staff for reference use only.

★9799★
Massachusetts Institute of Technology - Department of Brain and Cognitive Sciences - Teuber Library (Med)
Rm. E10-030 Phone: (617)253-5755
Cambridge, MA 02139 Patricia Claffey, Libn.
Founded: 1962. **Staff:** 1. **Subjects:** Cognitive psychology, cognitive science, developmental psychology, perception, psycholinguistics (especially language acquisition). **Holdings:** 5000 books; 3500 bound periodical volumes; 120 bound doctoral theses of psychology department graduates; masters' theses. **Subscriptions:** 50 journals and other serials. **Services:** Library open to M.I.T.-affiliated persons with written permission from a Department faculty member. **Special Indexes:** Subject index to department's doctoral and masters' theses.

★9800★
Massachusetts Institute of Technology - Department of Chemical Engineering Reading Room (Sci-Engr)
Room 66-019 Phone: (617)253-0949
Cambridge, MA 02139 Lisa Gould, Sr.Off.Asst.
Founded: 1930. **Staff:** 1. **Subjects:** Chemical engineering. **Special Collections:** Theses and Chemical Engineering course solution books. **Holdings:** 1200 books. **Subscriptions:** 8 journals and other serials. **Services:** Room reserved for department use only. **Automated Operations:** Computerized cataloging. **Remarks:** FAX: (617)253-9695.

★9801★
Massachusetts Institute of Technology - Dewey Library (Bus-Fin, Soc Sci)
Hermann Bldg., E53-100 Phone: (617)253-0624
Cambridge, MA 02139 Edgar W. Davy, Dewey Libn.
Founded: 1938. **Staff:** Prof 9; Other 15. **Subjects:** Economics, political science, management and finance, sociology, psychology, law. **Special Collections:** Industrial Relations (72,000 pamphlets and special materials); United Nations documents; corporate financial reports. **Holdings:** 197,031 books; 35,504 bound periodical volumes; 160,725 bound serial volumes; 122,584 pamphlets; 22,845 technical reports; 7381 M.I.T. theses; 291,353 microfiche; 7221 reels of microfilm. **Subscriptions:** 6599 journals and other serials. **Services:** Interlibrary loan; copying; library open to the public for brief room use with a fee for borrowing. **Automated Operations:** Computerized cataloging, circulation, and ILL. **Computerized Information Services:** DIALOG Information Services, Mead Data Central, VU/TEXT Information Services, LEXIS ABI/INFORM, PAIS (Public Affairs Information Service); CD-ROM (Lotus One Source CD Corporate); ALANET (electronic mail service). **Networks/Consortia:** Member of NELINET, Inc., Boston Library Consortium (BLC). **Publications:** Industrial Relations Accessions Lists, bimonthly. **Special Indexes:** Index to Working Papers, Sloan School of Management, 1962-1969. **Remarks:** FAX: (617)253-0642. Electronic mail address(es): ALA1764 (ALANET).

★9802★
Massachusetts Institute of Technology - Dynamics of Atmospheres and Oceans Library (Sci-Engr)
Rm. 54-1427 Phone: (617)253-2450
Cambridge, MA 02139 Joan Wood, Libn.
Founded: 1958. **Staff:** 1. **Subjects:** Meteorology, oceanography, geophysics, applied mathematics, physics, astrophysics. **Holdings:** 450 books; 2000 bound periodical volumes; 150 dissertations. **Subscriptions:** 20 journals and other serials. **Services:** Library open to the public for reference use only.

★9803★
Massachusetts Institute of Technology - Humanities Library (Hum)
Rm. 14S-200 Phone: (617)253-5683
Cambridge, MA 02139 Theresa Tobin
Staff: Prof 5; Other 6. **Subjects:** Anthropology, archeology, education, foreign languages, history, history of science and technology, library and information science, linguistics, literature, philosophy, psychology, religion, women's and men's studies. **Holdings:** 139,658 books; 22,900 bound periodical volumes; 67,170 bound serial volumes; 467 M.I.T. theses; 2389 technical reports; 2057 pamphlets; 4195 reels of microfilm; 24,515 microfiche; 545 maps and plans. **Subscriptions:** 3908 journals and other serials. **Services:** Interlibrary loan; copying; library open to the public for brief room use with a fee for borrowing. **Automated Operations:** Computerized cataloging, circulation, and ILL. **Computerized Information Services:** DIALOG Information Services, PFDS Online, OCLC, BRS Information Technologies; CD-ROMs (Academic Index, Oxford English Dictionary, The Bible Library, Grolier's Electronic Encyclopedia, Social Sciences Index, Dissertation Abstracts International, Ulrichs, PsycLit); ALANET (electronic mail service). **Networks/Consortia:** Member of NELINET, Inc., Boston Library Consortium (BLC). **Remarks:** FAX: (617)253-3109. Electronic mail address(es): ALA1764 (ALANET).

★9804★
Massachusetts Institute of Technology - Institute Archives and Special Collections (Hist, Sci-Engr)
Hayden Library, Rm. 14N-118 Phone: (617)253-5136
Cambridge, MA 02139 Helen W. Samuels, Archv./Spec.Coll.Hd.
Founded: 1961. **Staff:** Prof 4; Other 3. **Subjects:** Archival and manuscript collections concerning M.I.T. and science and technology in the 19th and 20th centuries. **Special Collections:** Rare book collection on engineering, animal magnetism, chemistry, electricity, and other branches of science and technology; books and periodicals about M.I.T. and/or by M.I.T. alumni and staff; oral history collection. **Holdings:** 9654 books; 231 bound periodical volumes; 446 bound serial volumes; 139,524 microfiche; 200 photographs; 4595 technical reports; 4473 cubic feet of manuscripts and archival materials; 3584 theses. **Subscriptions:** 177 journals and other serials. **Services:** Copying. **Computerized Information Services:** ALANET (electronic mail service). **Publications:** Finding aids and guides to manuscript and archival collections available. **Remarks:** FAX: (617)253-1690. Electronic mail address(es): ALA1764 (ALANET).

★9805★
Massachusetts Institute of Technology - Laboratory for Computer Science & Artificial Intelligence Laboratory - Reading Room (Comp Sci)
545 Technology Square, Rm. 113 Phone: (617)253-5896
Cambridge, MA 02139 Maria Sensale, Libn.
Staff: 2. **Subjects:** Computer science, artificial intelligence. **Holdings:** 2000 books; 18,000 technical reports; 800 dissertations; 225 reports on microfiche; 15,000 proceedings. **Subscriptions:** 215 journals and other serials. **Services:** Room open to the public. **Automated Operations:** Computerized cataloging. **Computerized Information Services:** DIALOG Information Services; InterNet (electronic mail service). **Publications:** Current Awareness Bulletin - for internal distribution only. **Remarks:** FAX: (617)258-8682. Electronic mail address(es): reading-room@hg.lcs.mit.edu (InterNet).

★9806★
Massachusetts Institute of Technology - Lincoln Laboratory Library and Information Services (Sci-Engr, Comp Sci)
244 Wood St.
Box 73 Phone: (617)981-2300
Lexington, MA 02173-0073 Jane H. Katayama, Lib.Mgr.
Founded: 1952. **Staff:** Prof 9; Other 38. **Subjects:** Electronics, electrical engineering, computer science, physics, mathematics, space science. **Holdings:** 134,000 books; 12,900 bound periodical volumes; 675,000 technical reports; 4000 maps; 5500 volumes of journals on microfilm; **Subscriptions:** 3885 journals and other serials. **Services:** Interlibrary loan; library not open to the public. **Automated Operations:** Computerized public access catalog, cataloging, acquisitions, serials, and circulation. **Computerized Information Services:** DIALOG Information Services, PFDS Online, BRS Information Technologies, STN International, NASA/RECON, DTIC, LEXIS, NEXIS, OCLC, ALANET, Washington Alert Service, PERISCOPE, DunsPrint, LEGI-SLATE, NewsNet, Inc. **Networks/Consortia:** Member of NELINET, Inc. **Publications:** New books list, weekly; Scanner; Defense Update; Technical Reports Announcement; Management Focus, all biweekly; Budget and Research Trends, irregular - all for internal distribution only. **Remarks:** Alternate telephone number(s): (617)981-2303. FAX: (617)981-0345; 981-5740. **Staff:** Virginia A. McGuire, Asst.Mgr./Sys.Libn.; Hema Viswanatha, Asst.Mgr./Rd.Serv.Libn.; Janice F. Bower, Info.Sci.Libn.; Richard P. Burnes, Tech.Proc.Libn.; Carolyn R. Greenberg, Spec.Proj.Libn.; Robert G. Hall, Spec.Proj.Libn.; Pamela A. Reynolds, Spec.Proj.Libn.; Robert C. Seidel, Docs.Libn.

★9807★
Massachusetts Institute of Technology - Lindgren Library (Sci-Engr)
Rm. 54-200 Phone: (617)253-9324
Cambridge, MA 02139 Katherine Keefe, Libn.
Founded: 1964. **Staff:** Prof 1; Other 2. **Subjects:** Geology, meteorology, oceanography, geophysics, geochemistry, planetary sciences, seismology. **Holdings:** 15,840 books; 11,821 bound periodical volumes; 21,902 bound serial volumes; 14,306 maps; 726 pamphlets; 481 M.I.T. theses; 1120 technical reports; 52,624 microforms. **Subscriptions:** 1071 journals and other serials. **Services:** Interlibrary loan; copying; library open to the public for brief room use with a fee for borrowing. **Automated Operations:** Computerized cataloging, circulation, and ILL. **Computerized Information Services:** DIALOG Information Services, OCLC; ALANET (electronic mail service). **Networks/Consortia:** Member of NELINET, Inc., Boston Library Consortium (BLC). **Publications:** Map News, quarterly; New Books List - for internal distribution only. **Remarks:** FAX: (617)253-6365. Electronic mail address(es): ALA1764 (ALANET).

★9808★
Massachusetts Institute of Technology - M.I.T. Museum and Historical Collections (Hist)
Bldg. N52 Phone: (617)253-4440
Cambridge, MA 02139 Warren A. Seamans, Dir.
Founded: 1971. **Staff:** Prof 6; Other 2. **Special Collections:** Radiation Laboratory photographs (40,000) and instruments (100); H.H. Young Globe Collection (35); Wente Collection of Meters and Motors (78); Draper Laboratory Historical Collection (600 square feet). **Holdings:** 360 books; 617,950 photographs; 3523 instruments; 12,813 student architectural drawings, 1873-1968; 145 portraits, including 20 busts; 200 19th and 20th century works of art; 547 films; 521 videotapes; 1738 sound recordings; 28,610 slides; 552 maps and plans; a large and varied collection of decorative art. **Services:** Copying; collections open to the public. **Networks/Consortia:** Member of Boston Library Consortium (BLC). **Publications:** MIT in Perspective in The M.I.T.; Newsletter, irregular. **Remarks:** Museum gathers, conserves, catalogs, and exhibits the visual and biographical material documenting the development of the institute and 19th and 20th century science, engineering, and architecture.

★9809★
Massachusetts Institute of Technology - M.I.T. Museum and Historical Collections - Hart Nautical Collections (Hist)
265 Massachusetts Ave. Phone: (617)253-5942
Cambridge, MA 02139 Kurt C. Hasselbalch, Cur.
Subjects: History - naval architecture, shipbuilding, whaling. **Special Collections:** Clark Collection (shipbuiding, yachting, history of naval architecture; 500 volumes); Bryant Collection (history of naval architecture; 200 volumes); Forbes Collection (history of whaling; 100 volumes). **Holdings:** 3000 books; 200 bound periodical volumes; 200 AV programs; 100 microforms; 20 linear feet of manuscripts. **Services:** Interlibrary loan; copying; library open to the public by appointment. **Remarks:** FAX: (617)253-8994. Library is part of a museum collection focusing on the history of naval architecture, shipbuilding, yachting, and whaling. Contains material dating to mid 16th century.

★9810★
Massachusetts Institute of Technology - Mathematics Reading Room (Sci-Engr)
Rm. 2-285 Phone: (617)253-4381
Cambridge, MA 02139 David A. Vogan, Prof.
Subjects: Mathematics. **Holdings:** 4000 books. **Subscriptions:** 34 journals and other serials. **Services:** Room not open to the public.

★9811★
Massachusetts Institute of Technology - Music Library (Mus)
Rm. 14E-109
Cambridge, MA 02139 Phone: (617)253-5689
Staff: Prof 1; Other 2. **Subjects:** Music. **Special Collections:** Music, recordings, and biographies of composers associated with M.I.T. **Holdings:** 11,273 books; 1229 bound periodical volumes; 4617 bound serial volumes; 14,174 sound recordings; 23,596 scores; 766 microforms; **Subscriptions:** 379 journals and other serials. **Services:** Interlibrary loan; copying; library open to the public for brief room use with a fee for borrowing; phonodisc, compact disc, open reel, and cassette tape listening facilities. **Automated Operations:** Computerized cataloging, circulation, and ILL. **Computerized Information Services:** ALANET (electronic mail service). **Networks/Consortia:** Member of NELINET, Inc., Boston Library Consortium (BLC), Boston Area Music Libraries (BAML). **Publications:** Music Library Newsletter, irregular. **Remarks:** FAX: (617)253-3109. Electronic mail address(es): ALA1764 (ALANET).

★9812★
Massachusetts Institute of Technology - Physics Reading Room (Sci-Engr)
Rm. 26-152 Phone: (617)253-1791
Cambridge, MA 02139 Isabel Cunha-Vasconcelos, Supv.
Founded: 1949. **Staff:** 1. **Subjects:** Physics, astrophysics, biophysics, astronomy. **Holdings:** 4480 books; 6030 bound periodical volumes; 711 theses; 6600 preprints. **Subscriptions:** 77 journals and other serials. **Services:** Copying; room open to the public for reference use only. **Computerized Information Services:** DIALOG Information Services; Barton (internal database); electronic mail.

★9813★
Massachusetts Institute of Technology - Plasma Fusion Center - David J. Rose Library (Sci-Engr)
NW16-153
167 Albany St. Phone: (617)253-8462
Cambridge, MA 02139 Kathleen Powers, Libn.
Founded: 1980. **Staff:** Prof 1; Other 1. **Subjects:** Nuclear fusion, plasma physics, fusion technology. **Holdings:** 1600 books; 2300 bound periodical volumes; 14,000 technical reports on microfiche and in hardcopy; 700 Plasma Fusion Center Reports. **Subscriptions:** 85 journals and other serials. **Services:** SDI; library open to MIT personnel and affiliates. **Automated Operations:** Computerized public access catalog, circulation, and acquisitions. **Computerized Information Services:** Integrated Technical Information System (ITIS), DIALOG Information Services; internal database; electronic mail. **Publications:** Acquisitions list, monthly - for internal distribution only. **Remarks:** FAX: (617)253-0700.

★9814★
Massachusetts Institute of Technology - Research Laboratory of Electronics - Document Room (Sci-Engr, Biol Sci)
Rm. 36-412 Phone: (617)253-2566
Cambridge, MA 02139 Barbara Passero, Commun.Off.
Founded: 1946. **Staff:** Prof 1; Other 2. **Subjects:** Physics, biophysics, acoustics, optics and quantum electronics, speech and hearing, neurophysiology, cognitive information processing, plasma dynamics, radio astronomy, lasers, molecular beams, microwave electronics, computers. **Special Collections:** Radiation Laboratory reports; Radiation Laboratory Series, RLE technical reports, theses, and reprints; books and journals in the areas of physiology, speech, and hearing. **Holdings:** 2000 books; 2000 bound periodical volumes; 250 scientific technical reports; 2600 dissertations. **Subscriptions:** 100 journals and other serials; 10 newspapers. **Services:** Room open to the public with limited borrowing. **Automated Operations:** Computerized public access catalog (The Assistant). **Computerized Information Services:** Electronic mail. **Publications:** Accessions list in plasma physics, monthly; RLE Progress Report, annual; RLE Currents (newsletter), biannual; Publications of RLE: 1946-1966, and Supplement: 1966-1976; RLE technical reports, technical reports abstracts, 1983-1987. **Special Indexes:** RLE publications update, 1987-1988; author and subject indexes for RLE theses, progress, technical reports, and reprints of journal articles. **Remarks:** FAX: (617)258-7864.

★9815★
Massachusetts Institute of Technology - Retrospective Collection (Sci-Engr)
N57-200 Phone: (617)253-7040
Cambridge, MA 02139 Laura Royer, Supv.
Founded: 1979. **Staff:** Prof 1; Other 3. **Holdings:** 205,711 books; 46,714 bound periodical volumes; 74,023 bound serial volumes; 28,508 technical reports; 50,850 theses; 13,188 pamphlets; 2325 sound recordings; 9393 photographs. **Services:** Interlibrary loan; collection not open to the public. **Automated Operations:** Computerized cataloging, circulation, and ILL. **Computerized Information Services:** ALANET (electronic mail service). **Remarks:** FAX: (617)258-6062. Electronic mail address(es): ALA1764 (ALANET). Collection contains lesser-used materials of Massachusetts Institute of Technology.

★9816★
Massachusetts Institute of Technology - Rotch Library of Architecture and Planning (Art, Plan)
Rm. 7-238 Phone: (617)258-5599
Cambridge, MA 02139 Margaret DePopolo, Rotch Libn.
Founded: 1868. **Staff:** Prof 9; Other 8. **Subjects:** Architectural history and design, urban and environmental studies, regional planning, 20th century art, media arts, film and photography. **Holdings:** 125,395 books; 8283 bound periodical volumes; 11,837 bound serial volumes; 21,136 pamphlets; 9762 maps and plans; 4252 M.I.T. theses; 2482 technical reports; 118,875 microfiche; 1417 reels of microfilm. **Subscriptions:** 1848 journals and other serials. **Services:** Interlibrary loan; copying; library open to the public for brief room use with a fee for borrowing. **Automated Operations:** Computerized cataloging, circulation, and ILL. **Computerized Information Services:** DIALOG Information Services, VU/TEXT Information Services, RLIN, OCLC; CD-ROMs (Art Index, SUPERMAP, Electronic Sweet's Real Estate Transfer Database); ALANET (electronic mail service). **Networks/Consortia:** Member of NELINET, Inc., Boston Library Consortium (BLC). **Remarks:** FAX: (617)253-9331. Electronic mail address(es): ALA1764 (ALANET).

★9817★
Massachusetts Institute of Technology - Rotch Library of Architecture and Planning - Visual Collections - Louis Skidmore Room (Art, Plan)
Room 7-304
Cambridge, MA 02139 Phone: (617)253-7098
Katherine Poole, Libn.
Founded: 1976. **Staff:** Prof 1; Other 3. **Subjects:** Architecture, archeology, art history, environmental and urban design. **Special Collections:** Photostats of drawings by Bullfinch and Latrobe; photographs of drawings by Bertram G. Goodhue; Lynch-Kepes Collection of photographs of Boston in the 1950s; Aga Khan Program for Islamic Architecture visual archives; Skidmore, Owings and Merrill work, 1950-1970 (4681 slides); G.E. Kidder Smith Slide Collection on American Architecture (3400 slides); federal architecture (1400 slides). **Holdings:** 323,882 slides; 45,346 photographs; 406 videotapes; 99 films. **Services:** Open to scholars and researchers for brief room use. **Computerized Information Services:** ALANET (electronic mail service). **Remarks:** FAX: (617)253-9331. Electronic mail address(es): ALA1764 (ALANET).

★9818★
Massachusetts Institute of Technology - Schering-Plough Library (Med)
Rm. E25-131 Phone: (617)253-6366
Cambridge, MA 02139 E. Louisa Worthington
Staff: Prof 1; Other 1. **Subjects:** Health sciences, technology, and management. **Holdings:** 3573 volumes; 1170 bound periodical volumes; 1549 bound serial volumes; 890 microfiche. **Subscriptions:** 187 journals and other serials. **Services:** Interlibrary loan; library open to the public for brief room use with a fee for borrowing. **Automated Operations:** Computerized cataloging, circulation, and ILL. **Computerized Information Services:** DIALOG Information Services, BRS Information Technologies, STN International; ALANET (electronic mail service). **Networks/Consortia:** Member of NELINET, Inc., Boston Library Consortium (BLC). **Remarks:** FAX: (617)253-6365. Electronic mail address(es): ALA1764 (ALANET).

★9819★
Massachusetts Institute of Technology - Science Fiction Society - Library (Hum)
Rm. W20-473
Cambridge, MA 02139 Phone: (617)258-5126
Founded: 1949. **Staff:** 32. **Subjects:** Science fiction, fantasy and horror literature. **Special Collections:** Bound professional science fiction magazines (almost complete set of major American and British publications); large collection of foreign science fiction; Science Fiction Writers of America - New England Depository. **Holdings:** 40,000 books; 800 bound periodical volumes; foreign magazines; 4 filing cabinets of science fiction fan magazines, published by individuals; Analog and Astounding on microfilm (in process). **Subscriptions:** 20 journals and other serials. **Services:** Library open to the public with a fee for borrowing. **Computerized Information Services:** Pinkdex (internal database); DARPA INTERNET (electronic mail service). **Publications:** Twilight Zine, irregular - for sale. **Special Indexes:** Index of Magazine Holdings. **Remarks:** World's largest library of science fiction open to the general public; staffed by student volunteers.

★9820★
Massachusetts Institute of Technology - Science Library (Sci-Engr)
Rm. 14S-100 Phone: (617)253-5685
Cambridge, MA 02139 Ruth K. Seidman, Libn.
Staff: Prof 9; Other 5. **Subjects:** Applied mathematics, astronomy, biochemical engineering, biology, biochemistry, chemical engineering, chemistry, nutrition and food science, medicine, neuroscience, materials science, mathematics, nuclear engineering, physics. **Special Collections:** Derr Collection of early works in mathematics and physics; Eastham Collection of books on microscopy; Gaffield Collection of materials on glass manufacture; Kayser Collection of pamphlets on spectroscopy. **Holdings:** 34,035 books; 123,662 bound periodical volumes; 65,645 bound serial volumes; 53,513 technical reports; 77,766 maps; 5157 M.I.T. theses; 122,390 microcards; 163,709 microfiche; 4987 reels of microfilm. **Subscriptions:** 3463 serials. **Services:** Interlibrary loan; copying; library open to the public for brief room use with a fee for borrowing. **Automated Operations:** Computerized cataloging, circulation, and ILL. **Computerized Information Services:** DIALOG Information Services, PFDS Online, OCLC; CD-ROM (Science Citation Index, ALDRICHEM Data Search); ALANET (electronic mail service). **Networks/Consortia:** Member of NELINET, Inc., Boston Library Consortium (BLC). **Remarks:** FAX: (617)253-6365. Electronic mail address(es): ALA1764 (ALANET).

★9821★
Massachusetts Institute of Technology - Sea Grant Program - Sea Grant Information Center (Sci-Engr, Biol Sci)
E38-314
292 Main St. Phone: (617)253-5944
Cambridge, MA 02142 Katherine Seaward, Libn. & Info.Spec.
Staff: Prof 1. **Subjects:** Ocean engineering, underwater vehicles, offshore structures, oil spills, biotechnology, red tide, fisheries, underutilized species, aquaculture, coastal zone management. **Special Collections:** Sea Grant Technical Reports (3000 volumes). **Holdings:** 5000 books; 12 VF drawers of pamphlets and topical files; 20 VF drawers of M.I.T. Sea Grant Program archives; 40 Sea Grant Newsletters. **Subscriptions:** 155 journals and other serials. **Services:** Interlibrary loan; copying; center open to the public. **Automated Operations:** Computerized cataloging and processing. **Computerized Information Services:** DIALOG Information Services, National Sea Grant Program. **Publications:** Marine-related research at M.I.T., biennial; Citizen's Guide to Sources for Marine and Coastal Information in Massachusetts; M.I.T. Sea Grant Publications Directory, both irregular; M.I.T. Sea Grant Quarterly Report; Newsletter, quarterly.

★9822★
Massachusetts Maritime Academy - Captain Charles H. Hurley Library (Sci-Engr, Trans)
Taylor's Point
Box D Phone: (508)759-5761
Buzzards Bay, MA 02532 Maurice H. Bosse, Dir., Lib.Serv.
Founded: 1970. **Staff:** Prof 2; Other 3. **Subjects:** Marine and ocean engineering, marine transportation, fisheries, oceanography, navigation, seamanship, merchant marine operations, meteorology, nautical astronomy, radar, cargo handling, naval architecture, fishing gear and vessel operation, marine and naval science, law of the sea, admiralty law. **Special Collections:** Rare books dealing with maritime history (350 volumes); Cape Cod Canal Collection (August Belmont papers, original documents, facsimiles; 5 reels of microfilm). **Holdings:** 36,000 books; 25,000 reels of microfilm; National Ocean Survey chart depository; Defense Mapping Agency map depository. **Subscriptions:** 368 journals and other serials; 10 newspapers. **Services:** Interlibrary loan; copying; library open to the public for reference use only. **Automated Operations:** Computerized cataloging and ILL. **Computerized Information Services:** OCLC, DIALOG Information Services, VU/TEXT Information Services, WILSONLINE. **Networks/Consortia:** Member of NELINET, Inc. **Staff:** Nancy Infascelli, Asst.Libn.

★9823★
Massachusetts Mental Health Center - Charles MacFie Campbell Memorial Library (Med)
74 Fenwood Rd. Phone: (617)734-1300
Boston, MA 02115-6196 Elizabeth Banov, Libn.
Founded: 1912. **Staff:** Prof 1.5. **Subjects:** Psychiatry, neurology, occupational therapy, law, nursing, psychology. **Holdings:** 13,500 volumes; reprints. **Subscriptions:** 82 journals and other serials. **Services:** Interlibrary loan; copying; SDI; library open to qualified users. **Computerized Information Services:** DIALOG Information Services, BRS Information Technologies.

★9824★
Massachusetts Mutual Life Insurance Company - Corporate Library (Bus-Fin)
1295 State St. Phone: (413)788-8411
Springfield, MA 01111 Yvette M. Jensen, Libn.
Founded: 1929. **Staff:** 3. **Subjects:** Insurance, office management, economics, travel, biography, investment, recreational. **Holdings:** 13,500 books; 3 VF drawers of pamphlets. **Subscriptions:** 75 journals and other serials. **Services:** Library open to qualified persons.

★9825★
Massachusetts Mutual Life Insurance Company - Law Library (Law)
1295 State St. Phone: (413)744-2188
Springfield, MA 01111-0001 David C. Morrell, Law Libn.
Staff: 2. **Subjects:** Law - insurance, taxation, securities, real estate, pensions; litigation. **Holdings:** 20,000 books; 200 bound periodical volumes; 1500 cataloged items. **Subscriptions:** 75 journals and other serials. **Services:** Library not open to the public. **Automated Operations:** Computerized cataloging. **Computerized Information Services:** LEXIS, WESTLAW. **Remarks:** FAX: (413)744-6279.

Massachusetts New Church Union - Swedenborg Library and Bookstore
See: **Swedenborg Library and Bookstore** (15914)

★9826★
Massachusetts Rehabilitation Commission - Library (Med)
Fort Point Place
27-43 Wormwood St. Phone: (617)727-1140
Boston, MA 02210-1606 June C. Holt, Lib.Dir.
Founded: 1963. **Staff:** 3. **Subjects:** Physical impairments, mental problems, accessibility (buildings, transportation, accomodation), legal rights of disabled, Rehabilitation Act & amendments, employment of disabled persons, severely disabled, counseling techniques, vocational rehabilitation, social problems, disability and disabilities, independent living, psychological rehabilitation, staff development, disability statistics. **Holdings:** 30,000 books; 1200 microfiche; 69 VF drawers; 13 16mm films; 10 videotapes; 34 audiotapes; Institute on Rehabilitation Issues Series. **Subscriptions:** 118 journals and other serials. **Services:** Interlibrary loan; copying; library open to the public. **Computerized Information Services:** BRS Information Technologies; DCI DEAFTEK-USA (electronic mail service). Performs searches on fee basis. **Networks/Consortia:** Member of Boston Library Consortium (BLC), Boston Biomedical Library Consortium. **Publications:** A Model Library - Community and Commission Benefit, Journal of Rehabilitation (March-April, 1973); A Special Vocational Rehabilitation Library - the Massachusetts Rehabilitation Commission (revised 1972) - to rehabilitation agencies throughout the country through Oklahoma Clearing House, Oklahoma University; Massachusetts Rehabilitation Commission Library, Boston Chapter News Bulletin, Special Libraries Association (March 1975); Bits and Pieces (newsletter - acquisitions listings) bimonthly; bibliographies on subjects concerning the handicapped; Brain and/or Head Injured (September 1985), and Supplement (March 1986); Employment of Persons with Epilepsy (1987); Employment of Deaf and Hearing Impaired Population (September 1987); Bibliography on Employment of Persons with Psychiatric Rehabilitation (June 1988); Bibliography on Employment of Persons with Developmental Disabilities (June 1989); Bibliography on Employment of Persons with Mental Retardation (March 1989); Bibliography on Employment and Persons with Disabilities (1990); Bibliography on Employment of Persons with AIDS (March 1991); Bibliography on Employment of Persons with Brain/Head Injury (May 1991); Bibliography on Employment of Deaf and Hearing Impaired Supplement (August 1991). **Special Catalogs:** Catalog of selected journal articles by subject (card). **Special Indexes:** Subject Index to Rehabilitation Literature published by the National Easter Seal Society for Crippled Children and Adults. **Remarks:** FAX: (616)727-1354. **Staff:** Maya De, Libn.

★9827★
Massachusetts Society for the Prevention of Cruelty to Animals (MSPCA) - Angell Memorial Animal Hospital Library (Soc Sci)
350 S. Huntington Ave. Phone: (617)522-7282
Boston, MA 02130-4803 John Julian, Libn.
Founded: 1963. **Staff:** Prof 1. **Subjects:** Veterinary medicine, conservation, zoology, pet care, humane education, animal welfare, animal rights. **Special Collections:** George T. Angell papers (founder of the MSPCA; 5 linear feet). **Holdings:** 2000 volumes. **Subscriptions:** 160 journals and other serials. **Services:** Library open to the public by appointment. **Computerized Information Services:** BRS/COLLEAGUE; DOCLINE (electronic mail service). **Networks/Consortia:** Member of Massachusetts Health Sciences Libraries Network (MaHSLiN). **Remarks:** FAX: (617)522-4885. **Formed by the merger of:** Massachusetts Society for the Prevention of Cruelty to Animals - Library, and Angell Memorial Animal Hospital Library.

★9828★
Massachusetts (State) Archives at Columbia Point (Hist)
220 Morrissey Blvd. Phone: (617)727-2816
Boston, MA 02125 Dr. Albert H. Whitaker, Jr., State Archv.
Staff: Prof 19; Other 5. **Subjects:** Massachusetts state and local government and history. **Special Collections:** Judicial Archives: Superior Court of Judicature Records, 1692-1780 (dockets, record books, and file papers), Supreme Judicial Court Records, 1780-1859, (dockets, record books, and file papers); Massachusetts Archives (328 volumes of colonial and Revolutionary-era manuscripts); Suffolk County Probate Records, 1636-1894; Middlesex County Probate Records, 1648-1871; Essex County Superior Court Naturalization Records, 1907-1982; Case files for Departments of Correction, Mental Health, and Public Health, 19th and 20th Centuries; legislative documents, 1630 to present; gubernatorial records; maps and plans, 1630 to present. **Holdings:** 30,000 cubic feet of archival records; 9000 microforms; 24,000 photographs. **Subscriptions:** 10 journals and other serials. **Services:** Copying; archives open to the public with restrictions. **Automated Operations:** Computerized cataloging. **Computerized Information Services:** RLIN. **Networks/Consortia:** Member of Research Libraries Information Network (RLIN). **Publications:** Massachusetts Records Review, biennial; State Agency Record Management Manual; County Records Management Manual; Municipal Records Management Manual; collections bulletins and information sheets. **Remarks:** FAX: (617)727-8730. **Staff:** Nancy Richard, Cur.; Bill Milhomme, Ref.Supv.; Kathryn Hammond Baker, Asst.Archv., Rec.Mgt. & Acq.

★9829★
Massachusetts (State) Board of Library Commissioners - Professional and Reference Library (Info Sci)
648 Beacon St.
Boston, MA 02215 Phone: (617)267-9400
Founded: 1890. **Staff:** Prof 1. **Subjects:** Public library administration, services. **Holdings:** 4000 books; 100 bound periodical volumes; 741 reels of microfilm; 24 VF drawers; ERIC/IR (Information Resources) microfiche collection, 1968-1989. **Subscriptions:** 200 journals and other serials. **Services:** Interlibrary loan; copying; library open to the public with restrictions. **Automated Operations:** Computerized cataloging and circulation. **Computerized Information Services:** DIALOG Information Services, WILSONLINE. **Networks/Consortia:** Member of North of Boston Library Exchange, Inc. (NOBLE). **Publications:** Recent Acquisitions; Periodicals Holdings List - both for internal distribution and by request. **Remarks:** A toll-free telephone number is (800)952-7403. FAX: (617)421-9833. **Staff:** Brian Donoghue, Libn.

★9830★
Massachusetts (State) Department of the Attorney General - Library (Law)
McCormack Bldg., 20th Fl.
1 Ashburton Pl. Phone: (617)727-2200
Boston, MA 02108 Ruth G. Matz, Chf.Libn.
Founded: 1975.**Staff:** Prof 1; Other 1. **Subjects:** Law. **Special Collections:** Approved town by-law amendments and zoning maps (12 VF drawers and 2 microfiche drawers). **Holdings:** 23,500 books; 200 bound periodical volumes; 34 microform drawers of legal periodicals; 29 microfiche drawers of other legal material; 45 videotapes of legal programs and miscellanea. **Subscriptions:** 200 journals and other serials. **Services:** Interlibrary loan; copying; library open to the public with restrictions. **Computerized Information Services:** DIALOG Information Services, LEXIS, WESTLAW, VU/TEXT Information Services, Dow Jones News/Retrieval, RLIN; internal database. **Publications:** Library Bulletin, monthly - for internal distribution and by request. **Special Indexes:** Index to Attorney General Opinions (card). **Remarks:** FAX: (617)727-3251.

★9831★
Massachusetts (State) Department of Correction - Research Division Library (Law)
State Office Bldg., 22nd Fl.
100 Cambridge St. Phone: (617)727-4474
Boston, MA 02202 Linda Holt, Mgr. of Oper.Res.
Founded: 1964. **Staff:** 1. **Subjects:** Criminology, sociology, social work, psychology. **Holdings:** 15 VF drawers of reports, research studies, pamphlets, proceedings, case records. **Services:** Interlibrary loan; library open to the public for reference use only with identification. **Computerized Information Services:** InterNet (electronic mail service). **Publications:** Department of Correction Research Reports, 15/year. **Remarks:** Electronic mail address(es): LHOLT@RCNVMS.MASS.EDU (InterNet).

Massachusetts State Department of Mental Health - Charles V. Hogan Regional Center
See: **Charles V. Hogan Regional Center** (7318)

Massachusetts (State) Department of Mental Health - Erich Lindemann Mental Health Center
See: **Erich Lindemann Mental Health Center** (9192)

★9832★

Massachusetts (State) Department of Public Health - Central Library (Med)
150 Tremont St. Phone: (617)727-7022
Boston, MA 02111 Alice M. Welch, Dir., Lib.Serv.
Staff: Prof 1; Other 1. **Subjects:** Public health, health care planning and administration, environmental health. **Special Collections:** Massachusetts Health Department annual reports, 1871 to present. **Holdings:** 550 books; 2640 unbound periodicals; 250 U.S. Government documents; 250 state government documents. **Subscriptions:** 70 journals and other serials. **Services:** Interlibrary loan; copying; SDI; current awareness; library open to the public for reference use only. **Computerized Information Services:** NLM, DIALOG Information Services, OCLC, Chemical Information Systems, Inc. (CIS); CD-ROMs (MEDLINE, TOXLINE, File Health, OCLC); Dialcom Inc., Public Health Network (electronic mail services). Performs searches. **Networks/Consortia:** Member of Massachusetts Health Sciences Libraries Network (MaHSLiN), National Network of Libraries of Medicine - New England Region. **Remarks:** FAX: (617)727-0998.

Massachusetts (State) Department of Public Health - Lakeville Hospital
See: **Lakeville Hospital** (8909)

Massachusetts State Department of Public Works
See: **Massachusetts State Transportation Library** (9834)

Massachusetts State Executive Office of Transportation and Construction
See: **Massachusetts State Transportation Library** (9834)

★9833★

(Massachusetts) State Library of Massachusetts (Hist, Law, Info Sci)
341 State House Phone: (617)727-2590
Boston, MA 02133 Gasper Caso, State Libn.
Founded: 1826. **Staff:** Prof 10; Other 7. **Subjects:** Public law, public affairs, Massachusetts legislation, government, politics, U.S. and Massachusetts history. **Special Collections:** Massachusetts history (books; prints; photographs; broadsides; manuscripts); State House architectural plans; city directories; 18th and 19th century newspapers; maps and atlases; Governor Bradford manuscript. **Holdings:** 825,000 volumes; 12,170 reels of microfilm; 294,855 microfiche; official depository for Massachusetts publications; selective depository for federal publications. **Subscriptions:** 2465 journals and other serials; 97 newspapers. **Services:** Interlibrary loan; copying; library open to the public for reference use only. **Automated Operations:** Computerized cataloging and ILL. **Computerized Information Services:** OCLC; CD-ROMs (CD-MARC, PAIS, Books in Print Plus, Code of Massachusetts Regulations, WILSONDISC: Index to Legal Periodicals, InfoTrac's Magazine Index). Performs searches. **Networks/Consortia:** Member of Boston Library Consortium (BLC), NELINET, Inc. **Publications:** Commonwealth of Massachusetts Publications Received, quarterly and annual. **Special Indexes:** Boston Newspapers, 1879-1937, 1962-1981, 1983 to present; Index and Guide to Massachusetts Legislative Documents, 1802-1882; Legislative Biographical File, colonial times to present; Guide to Massachusetts Legislative and Government Research. **Staff:** Mary McLellan, Asst. State Libn.; Mary Ann Neary, Dir., Acq. & Ref.; Pamela Schofield, Leg.Ref.Libn.; Brenda Howitson, Hd., Spec.Coll.; Bette Siegel, Govt.Doc.Libn.; Lisa Arm, Ser.Libn.

Massachusetts (State) Port Authority
See: **Massachusetts State Transportation Library** (9834)

Massachusetts State Supreme Judicial Court - Thorndike Library
See: **Thorndike Library** (16329)

★9834★

Massachusetts State Transportation Library (Trans, Plan)
10 Park Plaza Phone: (617)973-8000
Boston, MA 02116 Dr. Toby Pearlstein, Chf.Libn./Archv.
Founded: 1984. **Staff:** Prof 4; Other 1. **Subjects:** Transportation, transit, highways, aviation, waterborne transportation, planning, engineering. **Special Collections:** Archives of Boston Transportation Planning Review; reports of the Boston Transit Commission. **Holdings:** 20,000 books; 75 cubic feet of other cataloged items. **Subscriptions:** 150 journals and other serials; 5 newspapers. **Services:** Interlibrary loan; copying; library open to the public for reference use only. **Automated Operations:** Computerized cataloging. **Computerized Information Services:** DIALOG Information Services, WILSONLINE, WESTLAW, DataTimes. **Networks/Consortia:** Member of NELINET, Inc. **Publications:** Acquisitions list, bimonthly; Computer-Assisted Research Services; Transportation Library (brochure). **Remarks:** FAX: (617)973-7153. Jointly maintained by Executive Office of Transportation and Construction, Massachusetts Bay Transportation Authority (MBTA), Massachusetts Department of Public Works, Massachusetts Turnpike Authority, Massachusetts Port Authority, Massachusetts Aeronautics Commission, Caravan for for Commuters, Inc. **Staff:** Natalie Ridge, Tech.Serv.Libn.; George Sanborn, Ref.Libn.; Lynn Matis, Law Libn.

Massachusetts State Trial Court
See: **Barnstable Law Library** (1535)

Massachusetts State Trial Court
See: **Berkshire Law Library** (1749)

Massachusetts State Trial Court
See: **Bristol Law Library** (2128)

Massachusetts State Trial Court
See: **Brockton Law Library** (2202)

Massachusetts State Trial Court
See: **Essex Law Library** (5450)

Massachusetts State Trial Court
See: **Fall River Law Library** (5583)

Massachusetts State Trial Court
See: **Fitchburg Law Library** (5833)

Massachusetts State Trial Court
See: **Franklin Law Library** (6093)

Massachusetts State Trial Court
See: **Hampden Law Library** (6877)

Massachusetts State Trial Court
See: **Hampshire Law Library** (6879)

Massachusetts State Trial Court
See: **Lawrence Law Library** (9008)

Massachusetts State Trial Court
See: **Lowell Law Library** (9410)

Massachusetts State Trial Court
See: **Middlesex Law Library** (10360)

Massachusetts State Trial Court
See: **New Bedford Law Library** (11435)

Massachusetts State Trial Court
See: **Norfolk Law Library** (11845)

Massachusetts State Trial Court
See: **Worcester Law Library** (20596)

Massachusetts (State) Turnpike Authority
See: **Massachusetts State Transportation Library** (9834)

★9835★
Massachusetts Taxpayers Foundation, Inc. - Library (Soc Sci)
24 Province St. Phone: (617)720-1000
Boston, MA 02108 Carol L. Cardozo, Libn./Res.Assoc.
Founded: 1945. **Staff:** Prof 1. **Subjects:** Public administration and finance, Massachusetts state and local government, taxation. **Special Collections:** Legislative journals, bills, bulletins; foundation archives. **Holdings:** 6000 books; 3500 pamphlets; 30 VF drawers of pamphlets (uncataloged). **Subscriptions:** 90 journals and other serials. **Services:** Copying; library open to the public. **Computerized Information Services:** Municipal Financial Data, Massachusetts Econometric Model (internal databases). Contact Person: Scot Keefe, Sr.Econ. or Don Buckholtz, Sr.Res.Assoc. **Publications:** Library List, bimonthly - to members and by request; list of publications - available on request. **Remarks:** FAX: (617)720-0799.

★9836★
Massachusetts Vocational Curriculum Resource Center - MVCRC Library (Educ)
758 Marrett Rd. Phone: (617)863-1863
Lexington, MA 02173 Virginia M. Day, Libn.
Founded: 1980. **Staff:** Prof 1; Other 2. **Subjects:** Education - vocational, special, bilingual; microcomputers in education. **Special Collections:** Microcomputer software (100 packages). **Holdings:** 6000 books; 10 videodiscs; microfiche; 5 VF drawers of pamphlets. **Subscriptions:** 20 journals and other serials. **Services:** Interlibrary loan; copying; library open to the public with restrictions. **Automated Operations:** Integrated library system. **Computerized Information Services:** DIALOG Information Services, BRS Information Technologies; DIALMAIL, ADVOCNET (electronic mail services). **Publications:** Bibliographies, irregular - to state vocational educators; Curriculum Currents (newsletter). **Remarks:** FAX: (617)863-9965.

★9837★
Massachusetts Water Resources Authority - Library (Sci-Engr)
100 1st Ave. Phone: (617)242-6000
Boston, MA 02129 Mary E. Lydon, Libn.
Founded: 1986. **Staff:** 1. **Subjects:** Water, wastewater, law. **Special Collections:** Boston Harbor Information; Water Supply History - Metropolitan Boston. **Holdings:** 1000 books; 700 reports; microfilm; films. **Subscriptions:** 100 journals and other serials. **Services:** Interlibrary loan; copying; library open to the public by appointment. **Automated Operations:** Computerized public access catalog. **Computerized Information Services:** DIALOG Information Services. **Publications:** Bulletin, monthly. **Remarks:** FAX: (617)241-6070.

Massachusetts Water Resources Research Center
See: **University of Massachusetts** (18828)

★9838★
Massena Memorial Hospital - Medical Library (Med)
1 Hospital Dr. Phone: (315)764-1711
Massena, NY 13662 Shaylyn Frederick, Med.Lib.Mgr.
Founded: 1982. **Staff:** Prof 1; Other 3. **Subjects:** Medicine, surgery, nursing, respiratory and physical therapy. **Holdings:** 240 books. **Subscriptions:** 48 journals and other serials. **Services:** Interlibrary loan; copying; library open to the public with prior approval. **Networks/Consortia:** Member of North Country Reference and Research Resources Council (NCRRRC).

Alyne Queener Massey Law Library
See: **Vanderbilt University** (19766)

★9839★
Massey College - Robertson Davies Library (Hum)
4 Devonshire Place Phone: (416)978-2893
Toronto, ON, Canada M5S 2E1 Marie Korey, Hd.Libn.
Founded: 1963. **Subjects:** Bibliography (calligraphy to typography); Canadian fiction and poetry. **Special Collections:** McLean Collection of 19th century printing (1900 items); Carl Dair Archive; papers of Vincent Massey. **Holdings:** 45,600 volumes. **Services:** Library open to the public with restrictions and for reference use only. **Remarks:** FAX: (416)978-1759.

Massey-Ferguson Archives
See: **Ontario Ministry of Agriculture and Food - Ontario Agricultural Museum - Library/Archives** (12452)

Massey Library & Science/Engineering Library
See: **Royal Military College of Canada** (14123)

Master of Philanthropy
See: **USCCCN Masters of Philanthropy** (19700)

★9840★
Master's College and Seminary - Master's Grace Library (Rel-Phil)
13248 Roscoe Blvd. Phone: (818)909-5634
Sun Valley, CA 91352 James F. Stitzinger, Dir.
Founded: 1986. **Staff:** Prof 3, Other 4. **Subjects:** Theology, Biblical studies, missions. **Special Collections:** Archives of Grace Community Church. **Holdings:** 85,000 books; 6500 bound periodical volumes; 4326 microforms. **Subscriptions:** 520 journals and other serials. **Services:** Interlibrary loan; copying; library open to the public. **Automated Operations:** Computerized cataloging. **Computerized Information Services:** BRS Information Technologies. **Remarks:** (818)909-5719. **Staff:** Floyd M. Votaw, Pub.Serv.Libn.; Anna Kroll, Cat.

★9841★
Master's College and Seminary - Robert L. Powell Library (Rel-Phil)
21726 W. Placerita Canyon Rd.
Box 878 Phone: (805)259-3540
Santa Clarita, CA 91322-0878 James F. Stitzinger, Dir., Lib.Serv.
Founded: 1927. **Staff:** Prof 1; Other 2. **Subjects:** Religion, Biblical theology. **Special Collections:** Archives of The Master's College and its predecessor, Los Angeles Baptist College; Mormonism; Jehovah's Witnesses. **Holdings:** 157,000 books; 15,000 bound periodical volumes; 5600 AV programs. **Subscriptions:** 940 journals and other serials; 16 newspapers. **Services:** Interlibrary loan; copying; library open to the public. **Computerized Information Services:** DIALOG Information Services, OCLC EPIC. **Networks/Consortia:** Member of Santa Clarita InterLibrary Network (SCILNET). **Remarks:** FAX: (805)254-1998. **Staff:** Floyd M. Votaw, Seminary Libn.; Janet L. Tillman, Coll.Libn.

★9842★
Masters of Foxhounds Club of America and England - Library (Rec)
Box 231
Mill Neck Long Island, NY 11765
Subjects: History and traditions of fox-hunting; care and breeding of foxhounds. **Holdings:** 1500 volumes.

Rudolph Matas Medical Library
See: **Tulane University - School of Medicine** (16564)

★9843★
Matematicki Institut - Srpska Akademija Nauka i Umjetnosti - Biblioteka (Sci-Engr)
ul Knez Mihajilova 35 Phone: 11 630170
YU-11000 Belgrade, Yugoslavia Ilija Bratic, Libn.
Founded: 1947. **Staff:** Prof 1. **Subjects:** Mathematics. **Holdings:** 12,300 books; 15,000 bound periodical volumes. **Subscriptions:** 126 journals and other serials. **Services:** Interlibrary loan; copying; library open to the public. **Remarks:** FAX: 11 186105. Telex: 72593 SANU YU.

Materials Research and Analysis, Inc.
See: **MRA Laboratories, Inc./ - Materials Research and Analysis - Information Services** (10837)

★9844★
Maternal and Child Health Studies Project - Information Sciences Research Institute - Library (Med)
8375 Leesburg Pike, Suite 439 Phone: (703)255-1408
Vienna, VA 22182 Margaret W. Pratt
Founded: 1962. **Staff:** Prof 1. **Subjects:** Infant mortality, child mortality, maternal mortality. **Holdings:** 100 books; 200 bound periodical volumes; 150 reports. **Computerized Information Services:** Internal database.

★9845★
Maternity Center Association - Reference Library (Med)
48 E. 92nd St. Phone: (212)369-7300
New York, NY 10028 Esther Hanchett, Act.Libn.
Founded: 1940. **Subjects:** Obstetrics, maternal and infant care, family life, nurse-midwifery, preparation for child-bearing. **Holdings:** 2300 books. **Subscriptions:** 31 journals and other serials. **Services:** Copying; library open to the public, professionals, students, and writers by appointment.

★9846★
Mathematical Association of America - Library (Sci-Engr)
1529 18th St., N.W. Phone: (202)387-5200
Washington, DC 20036 Marcia P. Sward
Founded: 1915. **Subjects:** Mathematics. **Special Collections:** American Mathematical Monthly , 1895 to present; mathematical archives. **Holdings:** 1000 books; 99 bound periodical volumes. **Subscriptions:** 3 journals and other serials. **Services:** Library open to the public with restrictions. **Remarks:** FAX: (202)265-2384.

Mathematical Reviews
See: **American Mathematical Society** (677)

Harriet L. Mather Archives
See: **Southern Baptist Hospital - Learning Resource Center** (15460)

John T. Mather Memorial Hospital
See: **Port Jefferson Hospital** (13226)

Keith B. Matheu Library
See: **University of Alaska, Fairbanks - Geophysical Institute** (18184)

Matsumoto Memorial Library of Japanese Culture
See: **Kentucky Wesleyan College - Library Learning Center - Special Collections** (8678)

Matthaei Botanical Gardens
See: **University of Michigan** (18874)

Brander Matthews Dramatic Library
See: **Columbia University - Rare Book and Manuscript Library** (4023)

★9847★
Matthews & Branscomb - Law Library (Law)
1 Alamo Center
106 S. St. Mary's St., Suite 800 Phone: (512)226-4211
San Antonio, TX 78205 Noreen McGee-Thurston, Libn.
Founded: 1975. **Staff:** Prof 1; Other 1. **Subjects:** Law. **Holdings:** 20,000 books; 285 bound periodical volumes; 85 tapes. **Subscriptions:** 45 journals and other serials; 5 newspapers. **Services:** Library not open to the public. **Computerized Information Services:** LEXIS, WESTLAW. **Publications:** Acquisitions List, monthly - for internal distribution only.

★9848★
Maturango Museum - Resource Library (Hist)
100 E. Las Flores St.
P.O. Box 1776 Phone: (619)375-6900
Ridgecrest, CA 93556 Dr. Patricia Brown-Berry, Dir. of Musm.
Subjects: Ridgecrest area - aboriginal rock art, archaeology, biology, history, geology, paleontology. **Holdings:** 1000 books; 200 bound periodical volumes; 50 AV programs; 100 audiocassettes. **Services:** Copying (limited); library open to the public for reference use only. **Remarks:** Library usage primarily restricted to docents and staff. **Staff:** Elva Younkin, Cur.; Sally Richards, Adm.

★9849★
Maui Historical Society - Library (Hist)
2375-A Main St. Phone: (808)244-3326
Wailuku, HI 96793 Gail Bartholomew, Libn,
Founded: 1975. **Staff:** Prof 3. **Subjects:** Hawaii, Maui. **Special Collections:** Historic photographs and maps. **Holdings:** 600 books; 6 VF drawers of mounted clippings; 4 VF drawers of photographs; 1 drawer of slides; 4 VF drawers of historical files by subject; 5 VF drawers of archeological files; 22.5 linear feet of archives and manuscripts. **Subscriptions:** 4 journals and other serials. **Services:** Copying; library open to the public by appointment. **Automated Operations:** Computerized public access catalog. **Special Indexes:** Index to the Maui News, 1900-1950. **Staff:** Elizabeth Anderson, Archv.; Keali'i Reichel, Cultural Spec.

Mauritius - Ministry of Education, Arts and Culture - Mahatma Gandhi Institute
See: **Mahatma Gandhi Institute** (6241)

★9850★
Mauritius - Ministry of Education, Arts and Culture - Mauritius Institute - Library (Biol Sci)
Chaussee Phone: 20639
Port Louis, Mauritius S. Ankiah, Hd.Libn.
Founded: 1903. **Holdings:** 70,000 volumes. **Subscriptions:** 30 journals and other serials; 10 newspapers. **Publications:** The Mauritius Institute Bulletin. **Staff:** K. Soowamber.

★9851★
Mauritius Chamber of Commerce and Industry - Documentation Centre (Bus-Fin)
3, Royal St. Phone: 2083301
Port Louis, Mauritius Arline Sookahet
Founded: 1950. **Staff:** 1. **Subjects:** Mauritius trade and commerce. **Holdings:** 5000 export directories, market surveys, and World Bank reports. **Subscriptions:** 50 journals and other serials. **Services:** Center open to members only. **Computerized Information Services:** Internal database. **Remarks:** FAX: 2080076. Telex: 4277 CHACOM IW. **Also Known As:** Chambre de Comerce et d'Industrie de l'Ile Maurice.

★9852★
Mauritius Sugar Industry Research Institute - MSIRI Library & Scientific Information Service (Agri, Biol Sci)
Reduit, Mauritius Phone: 4541061
Rosemay Ng Kee Kwong, Hd.
Founded: 1953. **Staff:** 4. **Subjects:** Sugar industry, agronomy, agricultural chemistry, botany and physiology, plant breeding, phytopathology, entomology, weed control, sugar technology, biometry, economics, agronomy of foodcrops intercropped with sugarcane. **Special Collections:** Early publications on sugarcane agronomy and sugar manufacture; prints and drawings of the sugar industry; botanical and agricultural archives; Mauritiana Collection on natural sciences. **Holdings:** 24,884 books. **Subscriptions:** 720 journals and other serials. **Services:** Interlibrary loan; copying; library open to agronomists and technicians from the sugar industry in Mauritius and from other sugar-producing countries, technicians from the public and private sectors, and to bona fide students and research workers. **Computerized Information Services:** MSIRI (internal database). **Publications:** Publications List; MSIRI. **Remarks:** Operates in cooperation with Mauritius - Ministry of Agriculture - Agricultural Services, Mauritius Chamber of Agriculture, University of Mauritius, and other international organizations. FAX: 4541971. Telex: 4899 MSIRI IW.

Matthew Fontaine Maury Memorial Library
See: **U.S. Navy - Naval Observatory** (17864)

Matthew Fontaine Maury Oceanographic Library
See: **U.S. Navy - Naval Oceanographic Office** (17865)

Max-Planck-Institut fuer Auslaendisches und Internationales Patent-, Urheber-, und Wettbewerbsrecht
See: **Max Planck Institute for Foreign and International Patent, Copyright, and Competition Law** (13104)

Max-Planck-Institut fuer Auslaendisches und Internationales Privatrecht
See: **Max Planck Institute for Foreign and International Private Law** (13105)

Max-Planck Institut fur Auslaendisches und Internationales Sozialrecht
See: **Max Planck Institute for Foreign and International Social Law** (13106)

Max-Planck-Institut fuer Auslaendisches Oeffentliches Recht und Voelkerrecht
See: **Max Planck Institute for Comparative Public Law and International Law** (13102)

Max-Planck-Institut fuer Biophysikalische Chemie
See: **Max Planck Institute for Biophysical Chemistry** (13099)

Max-Planck-Institut fuer Ernahrungsphysiologie
See: **Max Planck Institute for Nutrition Physiology** (13110)

Max-Planck-Institut fuer Geschichte
See: **Max Planck Institute of History** (13107)

Max-Planck-Institut fuer Hirnforschung
See: **Max Planck Institute for Brain Research** (13100)

Max-Planck-Institut fuer Limnologie
See: **Max Planck Institute of Limnology** (13108)

Max-Planck-Institut fuer Metallforschung
See: **Max Planck Institute for Metals Research** (13109)

Max-Planck-Institut fuer Plasmaphysik
See: **Max Planck Institute of Plasma Physics** (13112)

Max-Planck-Institut fuer Psychiatrie
See: **Max Planck Institute for Psychiatry** (13113)

Max-Planck-Institut fuer Radioastronomie
See: **Max Planck Institute for Radio Astronomy** (13115)

Max-Planck-Institut fuer System- und Ernahrungsphysiologie
See: **Max Planck Institute for System Physiology** (13116)

Max-Planck-Institut fuer Zuechtungforschung
See: **Max Planck Institute for Breeding Research** (13101)

The Clement C. Maxwell Library
See: **Bridgewater State College** (2122)

Maxwell Laboratories, Inc. - S-Cubed
See: **S-Cubed** (14183)

★9853★
Maxwell Museum Association - Maxwell Museum of Anthropology - Clark Field Archive (Soc Sci)
Maxwell Museum
University of New Mexico — Phone: (505)277-8675
Albuquerque, NM 87131 — Garth Bawden, Dir.
Staff: Prof 1; Other 3. **Subjects:** Anthropology, archeology, ethnology, linguistics, biological anthropology, museology. **Special Collections:** Stanley S. Newman Field Collection; Harry Basehart Collection of African Ethnology; Florence Hawley Ellis Collection. **Holdings:** 8000 books; 1500 bound periodical volumes; 60 dissertations. **Subscriptions:** 20 journals and other serials. **Services:** Copying; archive open to the public for reference use only. **Remarks:** Alternate telephone number(s): 277-4404.

Maxwell Music Library
See: **Tulane University** (16562)

Sarah Maxwell Library
See: **Protestant School Board of Greater Montreal** (13438)

May Museum
See: **Dodge County Historical Society** (4940)

Ann May School of Nursing Library & Media Center
See: **Jersey Shore Medical Center** (8371)

★9854★
May Department Stores Company - Law Library (Law)
611 Olive St., Suite 1750 — Phone: (314)342-6697
St. Louis, MO 63101 — Susanna Marlowe
Founded: 1969. **Staff:** Prof 1; Other 1. **Subjects:** Law and business. **Special Collections:** Corporate archives. **Holdings:** 3000 books. **Subscriptions:** 64 journals and other serials. **Services:** Interlibrary loan; copying; library open to the public by appointment with permission from the manager. **Automated Operations:** Computerized cataloging. **Computerized Information Services:** Dow Jones News/Retrieval, VU/TEXT Information Services, DIALOG Information Services, Dun & Bradstreet Business Credit Services, WESTLAW, NEXIS. **Special Catalogs:** Catalog of archival materials (online). **Remarks:** FAX: (314)342-6384.

Harper C. Maybee Music & Dance Library
See: **Western Michigan University - Harper C. Maybee Music & Dance Library** (20271)

★9855★
The Mayberry Gazette - Archives (Rec)
2539 Littlefield — Phone: (919)766-6886
Clemmons, NC 27012 — Pam Dalton, Pres.
Founded: 1983. **Staff:** Prof 2; Other 3. **Subjects:** The Andy Griffith Show (television series). **Holdings:** Books; bound periodical volumes; photographs; scripts; videotapes; films; news clippings; network press releases; computerized episodic catalogs. **Services:** Interlibrary loan; copying; archives open to the public with restrictions. **Computerized Information Services:** Internal database. Performs searches on fee basis. **Publications:** The Mayberry Gazette, bimonthly - to members; The Official Andy Griffith Show Treasury.

★9856★
Mayer, Brown & Platt - Library (Law)
190 S. LaSalle St. Phone: (312)782-0600
Chicago, IL 60603 Gail S. Munden, Libn.
Staff: Prof 3; Other 12. **Subjects:** Law - corporations, securities, tax, banking. **Holdings:** 40,000 volumes. **Services:** Interlibrary loan; library open to the public with restrictions. **Computerized Information Services:** LEXIS, Mead Data Central, WESTLAW. **Remarks:** FAX: (312)701-7711. **Staff:** Bobby Towns, Asst.Libn.; John Curry, Ref.Libn.

Louis B. Mayer Library
See: **American Film Institute** (584)

★9857★
Oscar Mayer Foods Corporation - R&D Library (Food-Bev)
910 Mayer Ave.
Box 7188 Phone: (608)241-3311
Madison, WI 53707-7188 Thomas R. Whitemarsh, Libn.
Staff: 1. **Subjects:** Meat and poultry science, food science and technology, package engineering. **Holdings:** 1500 books; 500 bound periodical volumes; patents; pamphlets. **Subscriptions:** 200 journals and other serials. **Services:** Interlibrary loan; copying; library open to the public by appointment. **Computerized Information Services:** DIALOG Information Services. **Remarks:** FAX: (608)241-6920.

William V. Mayer Creation/Evolution Resource Center
See: **National Center for Science Education** (11105)

Mayflower Descendant Library
See: **General Society of Mayflower Descendants** (6350)

★9858★
Mayo Biomedical Imaging Computer Resource - Library (Med, Comp Sci)
Mayo Clinic
200 First St. SW Phone: (507)284-4937
Rochester, MN 55901 Richard A. Robb, Ph.D.
Founded: 1970. **Staff:** Prof 12; Other 4. **Subjects:** Biomedical imaging, visualization science, software systems, workstations, networks, computer graphics. **Special Collections:** Imaging and Visualization (250 items); Computer Systems (100 items). **Holdings:** 100 books; 200 bound periodical volumes; 100 reports. **Subscriptions:** 20 journals and other serials; 5 newspapers. **Services:** Interlibrary loan; library open to the public. **Computerized Information Services:** CompuServe Information Service, BRS/COLLEAGUE, MEDLINE; InterNet (electronic mail service). **Publications:** Annual Reports. **Remarks:** FAX: (507)284-1632. Electronic mail address(es): rar@.mayo.edu (InterNet).

★9859★
Mayo Foundation - Section of Mayo Medical Center Libraries (Med)
200 1st St., S.W. Phone: (507)284-2061
Rochester, MN 55905 Jack D. Key, Libn.
Founded: 1907. **Staff:** Prof 21; Other 32. **Subjects:** Medicine, basic sciences. **Special Collections:** Rare books in the history of medicine; History of Mayo Clinic. **Holdings:** 98,126 books; 218,782 bound periodical volumes; 4300 dissertations, translations, pamphlets. **Subscriptions:** 4326 journals and other serials. **Services:** Interlibrary loan; copying; library open to professionals in medicine and allied sciences with permission of Director. **Automated Operations:** Computerized cataloging and ILL (DOCLINE). **Computerized Information Services:** DIALOG Information Services, ORBIT Search Service, WILSONLINE, OCLC, NLM, BRS Information Technologies, OCLC EPIC. **Networks/Consortia:** Member of National Network of Libraries of Medicine - Greater Midwest Region, MINITEX Library Information Network. **Special Catalogs:** Mayo Clinic Author Catalog; Mayo Foundation theses (card, book, microfiche); List of Serial Holdings (book, microfiche, card). **Remarks:** FAX: (507)284-2215. Maintains six branch libraries. **Staff:** Dottie Hawthorne, Spec.Proj.Coord.; John Kopper, Hd., Tech.Proj.; Anita Thomas, Hd., Info.Serv.; Judith Lorrig, Hd.Libn., Mayo Med.Sch.; Marjorie Ginn, Acq.Libn.; Theodore Caron, Hd., Libn.Cat.; Paula Burich, Libn., Comp. Applications; Don Pady, Hist.Med.Libn.; Patricia Erwin, Hd.Ref.Libn.; Clark Nelson, ILL Libn.; Ann Farrell, Ref.Libn.; Frances Cockrum, Ref.Libn.; Tamra Anderson, Cat.Libn.; Suei Ching An, Monograph Cat.Libn.; Joyce Kao, Ser.Cat.Libn.; Jean McDowall, Bindery; Dawn Swalboski, Asst.Libn., Mayo Med.Sch.

Mayo Foundation - Section of Mayo Medical Center Libraries - Rochester Methodist Hospital - Methodist Kahler Library
See: **Rochester Methodist Hospital** (13984)

Mayo Foundation - Section of Mayo Medical Center Libraries - St. Mary's Hospital - Library
See: **St. Mary's Hospital - Library** (14520)

Mary Louise Maytag Memorial Library
See: **St. John Vianney College Seminary** (14332)

Mayview State Hospital
See: **Pennsylvania (State) Department of Public Welfare** (12862)

★9860★
Mayville Area Museum of History and Genealogy - Library (Hist)
PO Box 242 Phone: (517)843-6712
Mayville, MI 48744 Howard Brumley, Sr., Pres.
Subjects: History, rare books. **Special Collections:** Portrait collection. **Holdings:** Books; photographs; clippings; old local newspapers. **Services:** Library open to the public by appointment. **Publications:** History of Mayville & Surrounding Townships. **Special Indexes:** Local obituaries. **Formerly:** Mayville Historical Museum.

★9861★
Mazamas - Library (Rec)
909 N.W. Nineteenth Ave.
Portland, OR 97209 Phone: (503)227-2345
Founded: 1916. **Subjects:** Mountaineering, exploration, history of northwestern United States. **Special Collections:** Journals of other U.S. and foreign mountaineering clubs. **Holdings:** 2600 books; 1200 bound periodical volumes; maps; periodicals; exchanges. **Subscriptions:** 25 journals and other serials. **Services:** Library open to the public with restrictions.

★9862★
June Mazer Lesbian Library (Soc Sci)
626 N. Robertson Blvd. Phone: (213)659-2478
West Hollywood, CA 90069 Degania Golove, Coord.
Founded: 1981. **Subjects:** Lesbianism - history, culture, thought, organizations, writers, writing, the arts. **Special Collections:** Margaret Cruikshank Collection; Lillian Faderman Collection; Reid/Hyde papers; Sue Prosin papers; Joanne Parrent papers; Diana Press Archive; Telewoman archive; SCWU archive. **Holdings:** 2000 books; 300 periodical titles; 3 VF drawers of manuscripts; 1 VF drawer of archives; 1 VF drawer of dissertations; magnetic tapes; videotapes. **Services:** Copying; collection open to the public. **Formerly:** Connexxus Womens Center - June Mazer Lesbian Collection.

Mazzacano Hall Library
See: **University of Health Sciences** (18632)

Ettore Mazzoleni Library
See: **Canadian Music Centre** (2966)

★9863★
MB Research - Library - Information Services (Sci-Engr)
4225 Kincaid St. Phone: (604)439-8601
Burnaby, BC, Canada V5G 4P5 Judy O'Mara, Supv., Lib.Info.Serv.
Founded: 1966. **Staff:** Prof 2; Other 1. **Subjects:** Pulp and paper technology, wood and wood products, building materials, packaging, corrosion, chemical engineering, wood harvesting. **Holdings:** 10,000 books; 1500 bound periodical volumes; 6 VF drawers of patents; 3 VF drawers of translations; 400 pamphlet boxes of government and professional publications; 8 file cabinets of confidential company reports; 325 reels of microfilm. **Subscriptions:** 400 journals and other serials; 3 newspapers. **Services:** Interlibrary loan; copying. **Computerized Information Services:** DIALOG Information Services, ORBIT Search Service, Info Globe, Infomart Online; Envoy 100, DIALMAIL (electronic mail services). **Remarks:** FAX: (604)433-1413. Electronic mail address(es): MBRL (Envoy 100). **Staff:** Marjory Jardine, Libn.; Silvana Vettorel, Lib.Tech.

★9864★
(Mbabane) American Cultural Center - USIS Library (Educ)
Allister Miller St.
P.O. Box 199 Phone: 42059
Mbabane, Swaziland Brooks A. Robinson, Dir.
Founded: 1974. **Staff:** 1. **Subjects:** United States - politics, economics, history, arts, literature, business, education, social welfare, government, psychology, religion. **Holdings:** 1802 books; 400 microfiche. **Subscriptions:** 58 journals and other serials; 3 newspapers. **Services:** SDI; library open to the public. **Computerized Information Services:** WANG CLASSIC (internal database). **Remarks:** Alternate telephone number(s): 42445. FAX: 45846. Maintained or supported by the U.S. Information Agency. **Staff:** Jeffrey S. Dlamini.

★9865★
McAdams, William Douglas, Inc. - Medical Library (Med)
425 W. 59th St. Phone: (212)698-4011
New York, NY 10019 Molly Garfin, Mgr.
Staff: 2. **Subjects:** Medicine, pharmacology, biological sciences, drugs and therapeutics, advertising. **Holdings:** 1500 books; 10,000 bound periodicals; 50 VF drawers. **Subscriptions:** 500 journals and other serials. **Computerized Information Services:** MEDLINE, DIALOG Information Services.

McAfee Memorial Library
See: **Park College** (12743)

McAlister Library
See: **Fuller Theological Seminary** (6200)

★9866★
McAllen Genealogical Society - Library (Hist)
601 N. Main
Box 4714
McAllen, TX 78501 Janette Josserand, Geneal.Libn.
Founded: 1975. **Staff:** 1. **Subjects:** Genealogy. **Special Collections:** Census indexes; Confederate Veterans (with index); The American Genealogist; Mayflower Descendant New England Register; Index to NC Marriages in the NC State Archives. **Holdings:** 2500 books; 300 bound periodical volumes. **Subscriptions:** 20 journals and other serials. **Services:** Copying; library open to the public. **Computerized Information Services:** CD-ROM.

★9867★
McAllen International Museum - Rosita C. Alcorn Library (Art)
1900 Nolana Phone: (512)682-1564
McAllen, TX 78504 Vernon Weckbacher, Cur.
Subjects: Science, art history, Mexican folk art, Mexican culture, museums. **Special Collections:** Endowment for Latin American art and architecture. **Holdings:** 2600 books. **Subscriptions:** 20 journals and other serials. **Services:** Library open to the public by appointment. **Publications:** Changing Faces: Mexican Masks in Transition, 1985; newsletter, quarterly - to members; Erte and His Contemporaries; Community (published jointly with local PBS-TV). **Remarks:** FAX: (512)686-1813.

McArdle Laboratory for Cancer Research - Library
See: **University of Wisconsin--Madison** (19605)

McArdle Memorial Library
See: **American Forestry Association** (589)

McAteer Library
See: **American Association of Variable Star Observers** (489)

★9868★
Catherine McAuley Health System - Riecker Memorial Library (Med)
Box 995 Phone: (313)572-3045
Ann Arbor, MI 48106 Metta T. Lansdale, Jr., Mgr., Lib.Serv.
Staff: Prof 3; Other 1. **Subjects:** Surgery, medicine, nursing, health administration, patient health information, computers in health care. **Holdings:** 5000 books; 800 AV programs. **Subscriptions:** 500 journals and other serials. **Services:** Interlibrary loan; copying; SDI; library open to the public with restrictions. **Automated Operations:** Computerized cataloging, acquisitions, serials, circulation (LIS System) and ILL (DOCLINE). **Computerized Information Services:** DIALOG Information Services, OCLC, NLM. Performs searches on fee basis. **Publications:** Bibliography of publications by hospital staff (card). **Remarks:** FAX: (313)572-2679. **Formerly:** Catherine McAuley Health Center. **Staff:** Deborah L. Lauseng, Asst.Libn.; Patricia W. Martin, Consumer Hea.Info.Libn.

McBrayer Library
See: **West Coast Christian College** (20188)

★9869★
McBride, Baker & Coles - Law Library (Law)
500 W. Madison, 40th Fl. Phone: (312)715-5700
Chicago, IL 60661 Betsy Robertson, Libn.
Staff: Prof 1; Other 1. **Subjects:** Corporate and tax law, litigation. **Special Collections:** Admiralty and international law. **Holdings:** 15,000 volumes. **Services:** Interlibrary loan; library open to other libraries. **Automated Operations:** Computerized cataloging and acquisitions. **Computerized Information Services:** LEXIS; internal database.

McBride Library
See: **Grand Rapids Art Museum** (6632)

McBride Library
See: **U.S. Air Force Base - Keesler Base** (16856)

★9870★
McCaffery Goss - Library (Law)
350 7th Ave., S.W.
1800 First Canadian Centre Phone: (403)263-7570
Calgary, AB, Canada T2P 3N9 Evelyn Ross, Libn.
Staff: Prof 1. **Subjects:** Civil law. **Holdings:** 2000 books. **Subscriptions:** 126 journals and other serials. **Services:** Library not open to the public. **Automated Operations:** Computerized cataloging. **Computerized Information Services:** WESTLAW; internal database. **Special Catalogs:** Texts and memorandum (printout). **Remarks:** FAX: (403)264-8616.

John Sidney McCain Amphibious Warfare Library
See: **U.S. Navy - Naval Amphibious School** (17828)

McCain Library and Archives
See: **University of Southern Mississippi** (19354)

★9871★
McCann-Erickson Advertising of Canada Ltd. - Information Centre (Bus-Fin)
10 Bay St., Suite 1012 Phone: (416)594-6400
Toronto, ON, Canada M5J 2S3 Valerie Walton, Info.Ctr.Mgr.
Founded: 1960. **Staff:** Prof 1; Other 1. **Subjects:** Advertising, marketing, business, industry. **Holdings:** 1000 books. **Subscriptions:** 90 journals and other serials. **Services:** Center not open to the public. **Computerized Information Services:** Info Globe, Infomart Online. **Remarks:** FAX: (416)594-6272.

McCardle Library
See: **Vicksburg & Warren County Historical Society** (19825)

★9872★
McCarter & English - Law Library (Law)
4 Gateway Center
100 Mulberry St. Phone: (201)622-4444
Newark, NJ 07102 Mary Ellen Kaas, Lib.Dir.
Founded: 1870. **Staff:** Prof 3; Other 4. **Subjects:** Law. **Special Collections:** English Law Reports (complete set). **Holdings:** 30,000 volumes. **Subscriptions:** 200 journals and other serials. **Services:** Interlibrary loan; library not open to the public. **Computerized Information Services:** LEXIS, WESTLAW, DIALOG Information Services, Dow Jones News/Retrieval, DataTimes, VU/TEXT Information Services. **Remarks:** FAX: (201)624-7070. Telex: 187016. **Staff:** Pamela Keyl, Ref.Libn.; Jay Greenstone, Asst.Ref.Libn.

McCarter Theatre Archives
See: **Princeton University - William Seymour Theatre Collection** (13388)

Mary Mildred McCarthy Library
See: **Charles Cook Theological School** (4264)

★9873★
McCarthy Tetrault - Library (Law)
421 7th Ave., S.W., Suite 3300 Phone: (403)260-3503
Calgary, AB, Canada T2P 4K9 Lynne Gibson, Libn.
Founded: 1981. **Staff:** 2. **Subjects:** Law. **Holdings:** 9000 volumes. **Services:** Library not open to the public. **Computerized Information Services:** QL Systems, CAN/LAW, Info Globe, The Financial Post DataGroup, WESTLAW; Memo Bank ((internal database)). **Remarks:** FAX: (403)260-3501.

★9874★
McCarthy Tetrault - Library (Law)
Toronto Dominion Bank Tower, Suite 4700
Toronto-Dominion Center Phone: (416)362-1812
Toronto, ON, Canada M5K 1E6 Mary Percival, Hd.Libn.
Staff: Prof 3; Other 6. **Subjects:** Law. **Special Collections:** Legal/medical; patent and trademarks; tax; computer/telecommunications. **Holdings:** 22,000 volumes. **Services:** Interlibrary loan; library not open to the public. **Computerized Information Services:** QL Systems, Info Globe, DIALOG Information Services, WESTLAW, Dow Jones News/Retrieval, LEXIS, NEXIS, CAN/LAW, VU/TEXT Information Services, Infomart Online, Canadian Tax Online. **Publications:** Library News and Legislative Information, weekly - for internal distribution only. **Special Indexes:** Legislation indexes, federal and all provinces. **Remarks:** FAX: (416)868-0673. Telex: 06 217813. **Staff:** Barbara Fingerote, Asst.Libn.; Colleen Mulloy, Med.Libn.

★9875★
Walter T. McCarthy Law Library (Law)
1400 N. Courthouse Rd., Rm. 501 Phone: (703)358-4465
Arlington, VA 22201 Betty J. Waldow, Exec.Dir./Libn.
Founded: 1944. **Staff:** Prof 1; Other 1. **Subjects:** Law. **Special Collections:** Comprehensive collection of Virginia law-related volumes; treatises. **Holdings:** 13,500 volumes. **Services:** Copying; library open to the public. **Computerized Information Services:** LEXIS. **Remarks:** FAX: (703)358-3393. Maintained by Arlington County Bar Association.

McClatchy Newspapers - Modesto Bee
See: **Modesto Bee** (10585)

McClelland and Stewart Ltd. Publishing Archives
See: **McMaster University - The William Ready Division of Archives and Research Collections** (9954)

McClung Historical Collection
See: **Knox County Public Library System** (8773)

★9876★
McCollister & McCleary - Law Library
3029 S. Sherwood Forest Blvd., Suite 100
P.O. Box 40686
Baton Rouge, LA 70835
Subjects: Law. **Holdings:** 5000 volumes. **Remarks:** Currently inactive.

Alameda McCollough Research & Genealogy Library
See: **Tippecanoe County Historical Association** (16370)

McConnell Air Force Base
See: **U.S. Air Force Base - McConnell Base Library** (16872)

McConnell Library
See: **Radford University - McConnell Library** (13680)

McCord Theater Collection
See: **Southern Methodist University** (15502)

★9877★
McCormick & Co. - R & D Information Center (Sci-Engr, Food-Bev)
202 Wight Ave. Phone: (301)771-7252
Hunt Valley, MD 21031 Sarah A. Riley, Supv.
Founded: 1968. **Staff:** Prof 3. **Subjects:** Food technology, chemistry, flavor chemistry. **Special Collections:** Spices. **Holdings:** 2500 books; 1800 bound periodical volumes. **Subscriptions:** 250 journals and other serials. **Services:** Interlibrary loan; copying; SDI; center open to the public by special request only. **Automated Operations:** Computerized acquisitions and serials. **Computerized Information Services:** DIALOG Information Services, PFDS Online, Chemical Abstracts Service (CAS), MEDLINE; internal databases. **Remarks:** FAX: (301)527-6527. Telex: 466234. **Staff:** Ellen T. Madden, Assoc.Info.Sci.; Alice Tramontana, Assoc.Info.Sci.

Katharine Dexter McCormick Library
See: **Planned Parenthood Federation of America, Inc.** (13124)

Robert R. McCormick Memorial Library
See: **American Conservatory of Music - Robert R. McCormick Memorial Library** (543)

McCormick Theological Seminary
See: **Jesuit-Krauss-McCormick Library** (8375)

McCormick-Tribune Reference Library
See: **John G. Shedd Aquarium** (15105)

James McCosh Library
See: **Princeton University - Rare Books and Special Collections** (13386)

McCracken Research Library
See: **Buffalo Bill Historical Center** (2325)

★9878★
McCreary County Public Library - Special Collections (Hist)
P.O. Box 8 Phone: (606)376-8738
Whitley City, KY 42653 Kay Morrow, Dist.Libn.
Founded: 1976. **Staff:** 4.5. **Special Collections:** Pictorial history of McCreary County (slides and photographs); oral history interviews of the Big South Fork area (150 tapes). **Holdings:** 30,420 books; 215 bound periodical volumes; 77 reels of microfilm. **Subscriptions:** 37 journals and other serials; 3 newspapers. **Services:** Interlibrary loan; library open to the public. **Publications:** Exhibit booklet. **Remarks:** FAX: (606)376-3631. **Staff:** Peggy Rector, Bookmobile Libn.; Beverly Thiels, Literacy Coord.

George and Evelyn McCune Library
See: **University of Hawaii - Center for Korean Studies** (18618)

★9879★
McCutchen, Doyle, Brown & Enersen - Law Library (Law)
3 Embarcadero Center, 28th Fl. Phone: (415)393-2000
San Francisco, CA 94111-4066 Jo Caporaso, Libn.
Staff: Prof 4; Other 4.5. **Subjects:** Law. **Holdings:** 45,000 volumes. **Services:** Interlibrary loan; library not open to the public. **Computerized Information Services:** DIALOG Information Services, LEXIS, WESTLAW, RLIN, DataTimes, VU/TEXT Information Services, LEGI-TECH, Dow Jones News/Retrieval. **Networks/Consortia:** Member of CLASS.

★9880★
Francis X. McDermott Library - Diocesan Religion Information Center (Rel-Phil)
7200 Douglaston Pkwy. Phone: (718)229-8001
Douglaston, NY 11362 Charles C. Lindner, Dir.
Founded: 1967. **Staff:** Prof 1.5; Other 1. **Subjects:** Religion, theology, philosophy. **Special Collections:** Augustinian Bibliography (9 reels of microfilm); Institut des Etudes Augustiniennes (Paris). **Holdings:** 74,165 books; 329 bound periodical volumes; 21 periodicals on microfilm; 30 drawers of microfilm. **Subscriptions:** 350 journals and other serials; 19 newspapers. **Services:** Copying; library open to the public. **Automated Operations:** Computerized cataloging, acquisitions, and serials. **Computerized Information Services:** DIALOG Information Services. **Remarks:** Maintained by the Roman Catholic Diocese of Brooklyn.

McDermott Inc. - Babcock and Wilcox Company
See: **Babcock and Wilcox Company** (1394)

★9881★
McDermott Inc. - Corporate Information Center (Bus-Fin)
1010 Common St. Phone: (504)587-5799
New Orleans, LA 70112 Karen L. Furlow, Corp.Libn.
Founded: 1907. **Staff:** Prof 1; Other 1. **Subjects:** Management, economics, statistics, engineering, oil and gas, energy. **Holdings:** 2500 books; 600 bound periodical volumes. **Services:** Interlibrary loan; center open to the public. **Computerized Information Services:** DIALOG Information Services; internal database. **Special Catalogs:** Union list of serials of Babcock & Wilcox. **Remarks:** Alternate telephone number(s): 587-4411. FAX: (504)587-6153.

★9882★
McDermott, Will & Emery - Library (Law)
227 W. Monroe St., Suite 3100 Phone: (312)372-2000
Chicago, IL 60606-5096 Louis J. Covotsos, Hd.Libn.
Founded: 1934. **Staff:** Prof 2; Other 8. **Subjects:** Federal, state, foreign taxation; American and English probate law; litigation; pension; real estate. **Special Collections:** Legislative histories of Federal Tax Reform Hearings. **Holdings:** 35,000 books. **Subscriptions:** 60 journals and other serials. **Services:** Interlibrary loan (to librarians only); library not open to the public. **Computerized Information Services:** LEXIS, WESTLAW, DIALOG Information Services, BRS Information Technologies, PFDS Online, Dow Jones News/Retrieval. **Staff:** Gerald Ziebell, Ref.Libn.

McDonald Army Community Hospital
See: **U.S. Army Hospitals** (17050)

Dr. James E. McDonald Library
See: **University of Arizona - Department of Atmospheric Sciences - Institute of Atmospheric Physics - Library** (18214)

Elvin McDonald Horticultural Library
See: **Monmouth County Park System Libraries** (10613)

Isabel McDonald Library
See: **Oregon Regional Primate Research Center** (12527)

McDonald Memorial Library
See: **Northside United Methodist Church** (12031)

McDonnell Douglas Corporation - Corporate Library
See: **McDonnell Douglas Corporation - McDonnell Aircraft Library** (9885)

★9883★
McDonnell Douglas Corporation - Douglas Aircraft Company - Technical Library - M/C 36-84 (Sci-Engr)
3855 Lakewood Blvd. Phone: (213)593-9541
Long Beach, CA 90846 Judy Weigel, Team Ldr.
Founded: 1937. **Staff:** Prof 3; Other 9. **Subjects:** Aeronautical engineering, electronics, power plants, management. **Special Collections:** National Advisory Committee for Aeronautics (NACA) documents. **Holdings:** 20,000 books; 200,000 reports; 700,000 documents on microfiche. **Subscriptions:** 1066 journals and other serials. **Services:** Interlibrary loan; library not open to the public. **Automated Operations:** Computerized cataloging, acquisitions, serials, and circulation. **Computerized Information Services:** Online systems. **Remarks:** FAX: (213)496-5696. **Staff:** C. Barrow, Ser.Libn.; M.M. Smith, Supv., User Serv.

★9884★
McDonnell Douglas Corporation - Information Systems Library (Comp Sci)
M.C. 3062342
325 McDonnell Blvd. Phone: (314)233-5194
Hazelwood, MO 63042 Jenny Preston, Mgr., Lib.Serv.
Founded: 1981. **Staff:** Prof 1; Other 2. **Subjects:** Data processing, management. **Holdings:** 10,000 books. **Subscriptions:** 300 journals and other serials; 5 newspapers. **Services:** Interlibrary loan; library not open to the public. **Automated Operations:** Computerized cataloging, acquisitions, serials, and circulation. **Computerized Information Services:** DIALOG Information Services, OCLC, InvesText. **Networks/Consortia:** Member of St. Louis Regional Library Network. **Remarks:** FAX: (314)232-0513.

★9885★
McDonnell Douglas Corporation - McDonnell Aircraft Library (Sci-Engr)
P.O. Box 516 Phone: (314)232-6134
St. Louis, MO 63166-0516 P.A. Fischer, Br.Mgr.
Founded: 1945. **Staff:** Prof 4; Other 11. **Subjects:** Aeronautics, astronautics, electronics, engineering, composites, materials science, technology. **Special Collections:** NASA reports. **Holdings:** 24,000 books; 8500 bound periodical volumes; 175,000 documents; 750,000 microfiche copies of technical reports. **Subscriptions:** 1450 journals and other serials. **Services:** Interlibrary loan; copying; library open to the public by appointment with security clearance. **Automated Operations:** Computerized cataloging, acquisitions, serials, and circulation. **Computerized Information Services:** NASA/RECON, NEXIS, STN International, DTIC, DIALOG Information Services; internal database. **Publications:** SDI Profiles, weekly; Acronyms, Abbreviations and Initialisms, irregular - both for internal distribution only; announcement bulletin, weekly - to selected groups and individuals. **Remarks:** This library also contains holdings of the McDonnell Douglas Corporate Library and McDonnell Douglas Research Laboratories. FAX: (314)232-0790.

★9886★
McDonnell Douglas Corporation - McDonnell Douglas Space Systems Company - Library (Sci-Engr)
5301 Bolsa Ave., A3-135 10/2 Phone: (714)896-2317
Huntington Beach, CA 92647 Sue Brewsaugh, Mgr.
Founded: 1958. **Staff:** Prof 6; Other 2. **Subjects:** Aerospace technology, defense systems, space sciences, thermodynamics, electronics, propulsion, materials, life sciences, communications, management. **Holdings:** 9000 books; 6500 bound periodical volumes; 30,000 technical reports; 150,000 technical report titles on microfiche; 1500 government and commercial specifications and standards. **Subscriptions:** 766 journals and other serials. **Services:** Interlibrary loan; library not open to the public. **Automated Operations:** Computerized cataloging, acquisitions, serials, and circulation. **Computerized Information Services:** STN International, Aerospace Online, DataTimes, FYI News, NEXIS, DTIC, National Technical Information Service (NTIS), NASA/RECON, BRS Information Technologies, DIALOG Information Services, USNI Military Database; BASIS (internal database). **Remarks:** FAX: (714)896-1737. **Staff:** Cheryllynn Hall; Grace Lo; Mary Gillespie; Diane Brenes; Claire Christian.

★9887★
McDonnell Douglas Helicopter Company - Library (Sci-Engr)
5000 E. McDowell Rd. Phone: (602)891-3111
Mesa, AZ 85205 Dorothy K. Goss, Chf.Libn.
Founded: 1940. **Staff:** Prof 3. **Subjects:** Aeronautical engineering, mechanical engineering, materials technology. **Holdings:** 4000 volumes; 25,000 technical reports. **Subscriptions:** 187 journals and other serials. **Services:** Interlibrary loan; library not open to the public. **Remarks:** McDonnell Douglas Helicopter Company is a division of McDonnell Douglas Corporation.

McDonnell Douglas Research Laboratories
See: **McDonnell Douglas Corporation - McDonnell Aircraft Library** (9885)

C. Blake McDowell Law Center
See: **University of Akron - School of Law** (18157)

McDowell Microfilm Archives
See: **Ohio State University - Jerome Lawrence & Robert E. Lee Theatre Research Institute - Library** (12313)

Leora H. McEachern Library of Local History
See: **Duplin County Historical Society** (5063)

★9888★
The McElhanney Group Ltd. - Information Centre (Sci-Engr)
780 Beatty Street
Vancouver, BC, Canada V6B 2M1 Phone: (604)683-8521
Subjects: Civil engineering, surveying, marine navigation and positioning, photogrammetry and digital mapping, geophysics, geodesy. **Special Collections:** University of New Brunswick Department of Surveying & Engineering technical reports, lecture notes, student theses (150 documents). **Holdings:** 1500 books; 50 bound periodical volumes; 1000 internal reports and proposals; 1000 article reprints. **Subscriptions:** 219 journals and other serials. **Services:** center not open to the public. **Computerized Information Services:** GENCAT (internal database). **Remarks:** (604)683-4350. Telex: 04 51474.

Garret W. McEnerney Law Library
See: **University of California, Berkeley - Law Library** (18331)

★9889★
McFarland Mental Health Center - Staff Library (Med)
901 Southwind Rd. Phone: (217)786-6851
Springfield, IL 62703 Wanda Beck, Lib.Coord.
Founded: 1968. **Staff:** Prof 1. **Subjects:** Behavior therapy, psychology, psychiatry, psychotherapy, social psychiatry, family psychodynamics, addiction, mental retardation, psychiatric nursing. **Holdings:** 12,000 books; 250 bound periodical volumes; 3 drawers of journal reprints; 3 drawers of Department of Mental Health documents; 8 shelves of special education textbooks. **Subscriptions:** 20 journals and other serials. **Services:** Interlibrary loan; copying (limited); library open to the public with restrictions on some materials. **Networks/Consortia:** Member of Capital Area Consortium (CAC), Rolling Prairie Library System (RPLS). **Remarks:** FAX: (217)786-7167. Maintained by Illinois State Department of Mental Health & Developmental Disabilities.

McFarlin Library
See: **University of Tulsa - McFarlin Library** (19466)

★9890★
McGean-Rohco, Inc. - Research Library (Sci-Engr)
2910 Harvard Ave. Phone: (216)441-4900
Cleveland, OH 44105 Jeanne R. Winters, Info.Chem.
Staff: 1. **Subjects:** Metallurgy, organic and inorganic chemistry, electroplating. **Special Collections:** Plating information. **Holdings:** 1000 books; 1600 bound periodical volumes; 10,000 patents; 4 VF drawers of pamphlets; 4 VF drawers of catalogs; 3 VF drawers of articles. **Subscriptions:** 54 journals and other serials. **Services:** Library not open to the public. **Automated Operations:** Computerized acquisitions. **Computerized Information Services:** DIALOG Information Services, STN International.

Dean A. McGee Eye Institute
See: **University of Oklahoma - Health Sciences Center** (19130)

McGee Library
See: **Kerr-McGee Corporation** (8687)

John L. McGehee Library
See: **Baptist Memorial Hospital** (1513)

★9891★
McGeorge School of Law - Law Library (Law)
University of the Pacific
3200 5th Ave. Phone: (916)739-7131
Sacramento, CA 95817 Katherine Henderson, Law Libn.
Founded: 1924. **Staff:** Prof 7; Other 11. **Subjects:** Law. **Holdings:** 331,000 volumes. **Subscriptions:** 4192 journals and other serials; 25 newspapers. **Services:** Interlibrary loan; library not open to the public. **Automated Operations:** Computerized public access catalog, circulation, acquisitions, and serials. **Computerized Information Services:** LEXIS, RLIN, WESTLAW, NEXIS, DIALOG Information Services. **Networks/Consortia:** Member of CLASS.

McGill Library
See: **Washington State School for the Deaf** (20042)

★9892★
McGill University - Blackader Library of Architecture/Lauterman Library of Art (Art, Plan)
3459 McTavish St. Phone: (514)398-4743
Montreal, PQ, Canada H3A 1Y1 Irena Murray, Hd.
Founded: 1922. **Staff:** Prof 3; Other 2. **Subjects:** Architecture, urban planning, fine arts, landscape architecture, decorative and industrial arts. **Special Collections:** Canadian Architecture (original drawings and photographs; 76,000). **Holdings:** 51,500 books; 22,700 bound periodical volumes. **Subscriptions:** 343 journals and other serials. **Services:** Interlibrary loan; copying. **Automated Operations:** Computerized public access catalog and acquisitions. **Computerized Information Services:** DIALOG Information Services, RLIN; BITNET (electronic mail service). Performs searches on fee basis. **Publications:** List of publications - available on request. **Remarks:** FAX: (514)398-6695. Electronic mail address(es): CZTD@MUSICA.MCGILL.CA (BITNET). **Staff:** Marilyn Berger, Ref.Libn.; Francoise Roux, Cur.Asst.

★9893★
McGill University - Blacker/Wood Library of Biology (Biol Sci)
Redpath Library Bldg.
3459 McTavish St. Phone: (514)398-4744
Montreal, PQ, Canada H3A 1Y1 Eleanor MacLean, Libn.
Founded: 1920. **Staff:** Prof 1; Other 4. **Subjects:** Ornithology, zoology, natural history, botany, genetics, cell and molecular biology. **Special Collections:** Naturalists' letters; Robert Gurney Collection (reprints on crustacea); Ivanow Collection of Oriental Manuscripts. **Holdings:** 62,736 books; 51,976 bound periodical volumes; 7940 paintings, drawings, photographs; 109 phonograph records and cassettes; 3338 manuscripts. **Subscriptions:** 793 serials. **Services:** Interlibrary loan; copying; library open to the public for consultation only. **Automated Operations:** Computerized public access catalog. **Computerized Information Services:** DIALOG Information Services; CD-ROMs (BIOSIS, ASFA, WAVES); Envoy 100, NETNORTH, BITNET (electronic mail service). **Remarks:** FAX: (514)398-8231. Electronic mail address(es): PEB.QMMBZ (Envoy 100), EH11@MUSICA.McGILL.CA (BITNET).

McGill University - B'nai Brith Hillel Foundation
See: **B'nai Brith Hillel Foundation at McGill University** (1920)

★9894★
McGill University - Centre for Developing Area Studies - Documentation Centre (Soc Sci)
Purvis Coach House
3715 Peel St. Phone: (514)398-3509
Montreal, PQ, Canada H3A 1X1 Iain Blair, Doc.
Founded: 1963. **Staff:** Prof 1; Other 2. **Subjects:** Economic, social, and political development of Third World countries. **Holdings:** 2400 monographs; research papers from universities and research institutes. **Subscriptions:** 285 journals and other serials. **Services:** Center open to the public for consultation. **Computerized Information Services:** Knowledge Index; access to International Development Research Centre (IRDC) databases; internal database; BITNET (electronic mail service). **Publications:** List of publications - available on request. **Remarks:** FAX: (514)398-4832. Electronic mail address(es): EDIO@MUSICA.MCGILL.CA (BITNET).

★9895★
McGill University - Department of Rare Books & Special Collections (Rare Book, Hist)
McLennan Library Bldg. Phone: (514)398-4711
3459 McTavish St. Bruce Whiteman, Hd., Rare Books
Montreal, PQ, Canada H3A 1Y1 & Spec.Coll.
Founded: 1965. **Staff:** Prof 3; Other 4. **Subjects:** Canada - history, literature, exploration and travels; book arts and bibliography; British history; philosophy and history of ideas; literature. **Special Collections:** Bewick Collection (89 volumes; 700 early 19th century woodblocks); Lande Blake Collection (1630 books, engravings, and drawings); Lord Hardinge Lahore (6 meters); Lord Noel-Buxton (3 meters); Canadian historical, cultural, and family papers of de Lery Macdonald (1 meter), Christopher Dewdney (3 meters), John Glassco (1 meter), Leon Edel (15 meters), William D. Lighthall and Family (12 meters), Hugh MacLennan (4 meters), Masson (1 meter), Rhodes Family of Quebec (7 meters; 100 text prints), Sharon Thesen (1 meter), Canadian Pamphlets, 19th-20th centuries (8500 pamphlets); Colgate Printing Collection (14,200 volumes), Dawson Pamphlets (science, education, religion; 1762 pamphlets); Fishstein Yiddish Poetry (2275 volumes); guidebooks; Hume Collection (493 volumes; 51 letters); Indic Manuscripts (200 entries); Joubert Collection on French Canada (3143 volumes); Kierkegaard Collection (1642 volumes); Friedman Kipling Collection (12,541 items); Lande Collection of Canadiana (12,000 books, prints, maps, and printed ephemera); Friedman Leacock Collection (300 volumes; 3 meters of manuscripts); Lewin Collection (18th century Hebraica; 167 volumes); Lowry Collection (320 items, including literary manuscripts); Medieval European Manuscripts (250 entries); Friedman Morley Collection (450 titles); Napoleon Collection (4000 prints; 2000 books); Print Collection (includes 800 Canadian prints); Pugsley Collection of Early Maps of Canada (49 maps); Redpath Tracts (20,000 British, historical, religious, and political pamphlets); A.A. Roback Papers (1 meter); F.R. Scott Library (2000 volumes); Stearn Puppet Theatre (2720 titles; 150 puppets); travel posters; World War I and II posters. **Holdings:** 167,500 volumes; 4380 manuscripts; 6630 maps, atlases, charts, and globes; 8500 Canadian pamphlets; 15,028 prints and other illustrative materials; 16,873 McGill theses. **Subscriptions:** 93 journals and other serials. **Services:** Copying (limited); department open to the public. **Computerized Information Services:** UTLAS; internal database; BITNET (electronic mail service). **Publications:** Departmental Brochure. **Special Catalogs:** European and American Manuscripts (book); Rosalynde Stearn Puppet Collection (book); McGill University Libraries Special Collections: Lande Collection of Canadiana and supplement (book); Lawrence Lande William Blake Collection (book); Rodolphe Joubert Collection on French Canada (book); Gregor Malentschuk Soren Kierkegaard Collection (book); manuscript collection finding cards; map collection chronological file (card); binding, bookplate, and printers files (card); artist and engraver files for prints (card). **Remarks:** FAX: (514)398-7184. Electronic mail address(es): CXD2@MUSICA.McGILL.CA (BITNET). **Staff:** Nellie Reiss, Lande Libn.; Lorraine Dubreuil, Map Cur.-Libn.; Gary Tynski, Print Cur.; Richard Virr, Ms.Cur.

★9896★
McGill University - Education Library (Educ)
3700 McTavish St. Phone: (514)398-4687
Montreal, PQ, Canada H3A 1Y2 Marilyn Cohen, Hd.Libn.
Founded: 1970. **Staff:** Prof 1; Other 7. **Subjects:** Education, teaching elementary and secondary school, educational psychology, counseling, special education, education in the arts, education in second languages, religion and the philosophy of education, physical education. **Special Collections:** Curriculum Lab (audiovisual teaching aids; textbooks); Giftedness Collection. **Holdings:** 103,689 books; 15,000 bound periodical volumes; 367,500 microforms. **Subscriptions:** 750 journals and other serials. **Services:** Interlibrary loan; copying; library open to the public for consultation only. **Automated Operations:** Computerized public access catalog and circulation. **Computerized Information Services:** DIALOG Information Services; CD-ROM (ERIC); electronic mail service. **Remarks:** FAX: (514)398-4679. Above data also includes the Physical Education Reading Room; telephone: 398-4686.

★9897★
McGill University - Edward Rosenthall Mathematics & Statistics Library (Sci-Engr)
1105 Burnside Hall
805 Sherbrooke St., W.
Montreal, PQ, Canada H3A 2K6 Phone: (514)398-4676
Founded: 1971. **Staff:** 1. **Subjects:** Mathematics, statistics. **Holdings:** 10,720 bound periodical volumes. **Subscriptions:** 245 serials. **Services:** Interlibrary loan (through Physical Sciences & Engineering Library); copying; library open to the public with restrictions. **Computerized Information Services:** BITNET (electronic mail service). **Remarks:** FAX: (514)398-3899. Electronic mail address(es): CXDD@MUSICA.MCGILL. CA (BITNET).

★9898★
McGill University - Experimental Surgery Library (Med)
Donner Bldg.
740 Dr. Penfield Ave. Phone: (514)398-3980
Montreal, PQ, Canada H3A 1A4 Irene Sidorenko, Adm.Sec.
Staff: Prof 1. **Subjects:** Immunology, Cancer metastasis. **Holdings:** 1550 volumes; 300 theses. **Subscriptions:** 30 journals and other serials. **Services:** Interlibrary loan; copying; library open to the public by appointment. **Computerized Information Services:** Scimate (internal database). **Remarks:** FAX: (514)398-8361.

★9899★
McGill University - Health Sciences Library (Med)
McIntyre Medical Sciences Bldg. Phone: (514)398-4723
3655 Drummond St. David S. Crawford, Act. Life Sci.
Montreal, PQ, Canada H3G 1Y6 Area Libn.
Founded: 1823. **Staff:** Prof 6.5; Other 18. **Subjects:** Medicine, dentistry, physical occupational therapy, nursing. **Special Collections:** Dr. Casey A. Wood Ophthalmology Collection; School of Human Communications Disorders. **Holdings:** 81,260 books; 139,459 bound periodical volumes; 4842 slides. **Subscriptions:** 2375 serials. **Services:** Interlibrary loan; copying; library open to the public for consultation only. **Automated Operations:** Computerized public access catalog, cataloging, circulation, and acquisitions (NOTIS). **Computerized Information Services:** MEDLINE, MEDLARS, BRS Information Technologies, WILSONLINE, Questel, Utlas Catalogue Support System, CAN/OLE, DIALOG Information Services, NLM; Envoy 100, NETNORTH (electronic mail services). **Publications:** Subject bibliographies; library guides. **Remarks:** FAX: (514)398-3890. Electronic mail address(es): PEB.QMMM (Envoy 100); MI66@MUSICA.MCGILL.CA (NETNORTH). **Staff:** B. LeSieur, Acq. & Coll.Libn.; Valerie Fortin, Cat./Database Libn.; A. Lambrou, Comp.Serv.Libn.; D. Cowan, Pub.Serv.Libn.

★9900★
McGill University - Howard Ross Library of Management (Bus-Fin)
Bronfman Bldg.
1001 Sherbrooke St., W. Phone: (514)398-4690
Montreal, PQ, Canada H3A 1G5 Robert Clarke, Hd.Libn.
Founded: 1943. **Staff:** Prof 2.5; Other 5. **Subjects:** Management, marketing, accounting, finance, statistics, operations research, industrial relations, international business. **Special Collections:** Quebec Collective Agreements. **Holdings:** 39,522 books; 33,636 periodical volumes; 22,818 corporate reports; 1068 reels of microfilm; 38,026 microfiche. **Subscriptions:** 652 journals and other serials. **Services:** Interlibrary loan; copying; library open to the public for consultation only. **Automated Operations:** Computerized public access catalog, acquisitions, and circulation. **Computerized Information Services:** DIALOG Information Services, ABI/INFORM, Canadian Business and Current Affairs (CBCA), Statistics Canada; CD-ROM (CANSIM OnDisc); BITNET, Envoy 100 (electronic mail services); Performs searches on fee basis. **Remarks:** FAX: (514)398-5046. Electronic mail address(es): CZRY@MUSICA.MCGILL.CA (BITNET); PEB.QMMSC (Envoy 100). **Staff:** Johanne Hebert, Ref.Libn.; Judith Symansky, Regulated Industries Libn.

★9901★
McGill University - Islamic Studies Library (Rel-Phil)
Morrice Hall
3485 McTavish St. Phone: (514)398-4685
Montreal, PQ, Canada H3A 1Y1 Adam Gacek, Hd.
Founded: 1952. **Staff:** Prof 1; Other 3. **Subjects:** Islamic religion, philosophy, civilization, culture, history, language, literature. **Holdings:** 81,068 books; 12,169 bound periodical volumes; 560 reels of microfilm; 168 volumes of manuscripts; 1245 AV programs. **Subscriptions:** 415 journals and other serials. **Services:** Interlibrary loan; library open to the public for consultation only. **Computerized Information Services:** BITNET (electronic mail service). **Remarks:** FAX: (514)398-8189. Electronic mail address(es): CZRW@MUSICA.MCGILL.CA.

★9902★
McGill University - Law Library (Law)
New Chancellor Day Hall
3644 Peel St. Phone: (514)398-4715
Montreal, PQ, Canada H3A 1W9 Patricia M. Young, Law Area Libn.
Founded: 1890. **Staff:** Prof 5; Other 13.6. **Subjects:** Civil and common law; air and space law; comparative law; international law; human rights; medical law; legal philosophy. **Special Collections:** Wainwright Collection (French legal history), Rare Books/Canadiana. **Holdings:** 75,229 books; 71,059 bound periodical volumes; 135,570 government documents; 25,203 microforms; 7432 pamphlets. **Subscriptions:** 3103 journals and other serials. **Services:** Interlibrary loan; copying; library open to the public for reference use only. **Automated Operations:** NOTIS. **Computerized Information Services:** WESTLAW, QL Systems, Societe Quebecoise d'Information Juridique (SOQUIJ), CAN/LAW; InterNet (electronic mail service). **Remarks:** FAX: (514)398-3585. Electronic mail address(es): CYLP@MUSICA.MCGILL.CA (InterNet). **Staff:** Louise Robertson, Assoc. Law Libn.; Kuo-Lee Li, Res.& Coll.Dev.; Lenore Rapkin, Cat.; Louisa Piatti, Ref.Libn.

★9903★
McGill University - Library and Information Studies Library (Info Sci)
McLennan Library Bldg.
3459 McTavish St. Phone: (514)398-4724
Montreal, PQ, Canada H3A 1Y1 Calvin D. Evans, Act.Hd.
Founded: 1927. **Staff:** 1.3. **Subjects:** Library and information science, bibliography, records management, documentation, history of books and printing, cataloging and classification, book trade, children's and young adult literature. **Special Collections:** Children's literature; young adult literature; rare books. **Holdings:** 32,449 books; 5344 bound periodical volumes; 8200 newsletters, library school calendars, and other miscellaneous items; 3800 microtexts. **Subscriptions:** 359 journals and other serials. **Services:** Copying; library open to the public for consultation only; borrowing privileges available to professional librarians. **Automated Operations:** Computerized public access catalog and acquisitions. **Computerized Information Services:** DIALOG Information Services; REFCATTS (internal database); CD-ROMs (LISA, Grolier Electronic Encyclopedia); BITNET (electronic mail service). Performs searches. **Remarks:** FAX: (514)398-7184. Electronic mail address(es): CZJW@MUSICA.MCGILL.CA (BITNET).

★9904★
McGill University - Macdonald Campus - Brace Research Institute Library (Env-Cons)
PO Box 900
Ste. Anne de Bellevue, PQ, Canada H9X 1C0 Phone: (514)398-7833
Subjects: Arid zone development, saline water conversion, solar energy utilization, wind energy utilization, controlled environment agriculture. **Holdings:** 1000 books; 50 bound periodical volumes; 4200 articles and reports; 300 conference proceedings. **Subscriptions:** 290 journals and other serials. **Services:** Library open to the public by appointment. **Computerized Information Services:** FYI 3000 (internal database); BITNET (electronic mail service). **Publications:** List of publications - available upon request. **Remarks:** Alternate telephone number(s): (514)398-7834. FAX: (514)398-7767. Telex: McGILL UNIV.MTL. 05-268510 (Canada and U.S.); 526-8510 (other countries). Electronic mail address(es): AE12000@MUSICA.MCGILL.CA (BITNET).

★9905★
McGill University - Macdonald Campus - Institute of Parasitology - Library (Biol Sci)
Ste. Anne de Bellevue, PQ, Canada Phone: (514)398-7722
H9X 1C0 Dr. G. Matlashewski, Assoc.Prof.
Founded: 1932. **Subjects:** Parasitology and allied subjects. **Holdings:** 1200 books; 3200 bound periodical volumes; 27,000 reprints; 450 reels of microfilm; 1 box of archives; theses of students graduating from the Institute. **Subscriptions:** 40 journals and other serials. **Services:** Interlibrary loan; copying; library open to university personnel and students. **Remarks:** FAX: (514)398-7857. Telex: 05821788.

★9906★
McGill University - Macdonald Campus - Library (Agri)
Barton Bldg.
2111 Lakeshore Rd. Phone: (514)398-7876
Ste. Anne de Bellevue, PQ, Canada H9X 1C0 Janet Finlayson, Libn.
Founded: 1907. **Staff:** Prof 2; Other 7.5. **Subjects:** Environmental, food, and agricultural sciences. **Special Collections:** F.A.O. Depository Collection (840 volumes); Lyman Entomological Collection (9600 volumes, including rare books). **Holdings:** 44,900 books; 39,512 bound periodical volumes; 146,932 government documents. **Subscriptions:** 955 journals and other serials. **Services:** Interlibrary loan; copying; library open to the public for consultation only. **Automated Operations:** Computerized public access catalog, cataloging, and circulation. **Computerized Information Services:** DIALOG Information Services, CAN/OLE; Envoy 100, BITNET, NETNORTH (electronic mail service). **Remarks:** FAX: (514)398-7960. Electronic mail address(es): PEB.QMAC (Envoy 100), CZJF@MUSICA.MCGILL.CA (BITNET).**Staff:** Mr. B. Grainger, Pub.Serv.Libn.

★9907★
McGill University - Marvin Duchow Music Library (Mus)
Strathcona Music Bldg.
555 Sherbrooke St., W. Phone: (514)398-4695
Montreal, PQ, Canada H3A 1E3 Cynthia A. Leive, Libn.
Founded: 1965. **Staff:** Prof 1; Other 4. **Subjects:** Music. **Special Collections:** Marvin Duchow; Julius Schloss; Kelsey Jones; David Edelberg/Handel. **Holdings:** 24,567 books; 5115 bound periodical volumes; 18,945 recordings; 36,667 scores; 1239 reels of microfilm; 2096 microfiche; 118 open reel tapes; 277 audiocassettes. **Subscriptions:** 235 journals and other serials. **Services:** Interlibrary loan; copying; library open to the public for consultation only. **Automated Operations:** Computerized public access catalog and acquisitions (NOTIS). **Computerized Information Services:** EPIC, UTLAS; CD-ROMs (Music Index, RILM Abstracts of Music Literature; ERIC); BITNET (electronic mail service). **Remarks:** FAX: (514)398-8276. Electronic mail address(es): INCL@MUSICB.MCGILL.CA (BITNET).

★9908★
McGill University - Osler Library (Med)
McIntyre Medical Sciences Bldg.
3655 Drummond St. Phone: (514)398-4718
Montreal, PQ, Canada H3G 1Y6 Faith Wallis, Osler Libn.
Founded: 1929. **Staff:** Prof 2; Other 3.5. **Subjects:** History of medicine. **Special Collections:** E.W. Archibald Collection; Worthington Family Collection; D. Sclater Lewis Collection; Evans Collection of Pathological Illustrations; Griffith Collection of Homoeopathy; Antonio Cantero; McGill Medical Library Archives; Cushing Papers; H.E. MacDermot; C.A. Wood Ophthalmic Collection; medical artifacts; Casey A. Wood Historical Collection of Sinhalese Materia Medica; manuscript collections of Sir William Osler, C.K. Russel, Norman Bethune, Maude Abbott, Boris Babkin, W.H. Drummond; Osler Society Papers; Medical Portrait Collection; Harold N. Segall Collection; Canadian Dermatological Association archives; Canadian Health Libraries Association archives; Homeopathy collection from library of Queen Elizabeth Hospital, Montreal; A.D. Blackader Collection. **Holdings:** 42,004 books; 2150 bound periodical volumes. **Subscriptions:** 128 journals and other serials. **Services:** Interlibrary loan; copying; library open to the public for consultation only. **Automated Operations:** Computerized public access catalog. **Computerized Information Services:** Envoy 100, BITNET, NETNORTH (electronic mail services). **Publications:** The Osler Library (1979); Osler Library Newsletter; Osler Library Studies in the History of Medicine, 3/year. **Special Indexes:** Index to early Canadian Medical Journals, 1844-1883; Bibliotheca Osleriana (1929, 1969). **Remarks:** Alternate telephone number(s): 398-4720. FAX: (514)398-3890. Electronic mail address(es): PEB.QMMM (Envoy 100); CZFW@MUSICA.MCGILL.CA (BITNET). **Staff:** Wayne LeBel, Asst.Hist.Med.Libn.

McGill University - Physical Education Reading Room
See: **McGill University - Education Library** (9896)

★9909★
McGill University - Physical Sciences & Engineering Library (Sci-Engr)
Macdonald Stewart Library Bldg.
809 Sherbrooke St., W. Phone: (514)398-4769
Montreal, PQ, Canada H3A 2K6 Hanna Waluzyniec, Act. Area Libn.
Founded: 1982. **Staff:** Prof 6; Other 14.5. **Subjects:** Chemistry, geology, mathematics, physics, computer science; engineering - chemical, civil, electrical, mechanical, metallurgical, mining. **Special Collections:** Mossman Collection on the History of Science and of Ideas. **Holdings:** 106,650 books; 94,430 bound periodical volumes. **Subscriptions:** 1820 journals and other serials. **Services:** Interlibrary loan; copying; library open to the public with restrictions. **Computerized Information Services:** DIALOG Information Services, CAN/OLE, STN International, Data-Star, ORBIT Search

Service, Questel, WILSONLINE, Knowledge Index; BITNET (electronic mail service). **Remarks:** FAX: (514)398-3903. Electronic mail address(es): 99@MUSICA.MCGILL.CA (BITNET). **Staff:** Marika Asimakopulos, Ref.Libn.; Veronica Calderhead, Ref.Libn.; Elizabeth Gibb, Hd.Ref.Libn.; Darlene Canning, Comp.Serv.Libn.; Samiha Sidky Doc. Delivery Coord.; Olga Wiseman, Doc.Cont.Coord.

★9910★
McGill University - Religious Studies Library (Rel-Phil)
William & Henry Birks Bldg.
3520 University St. Phone: (514)398-5043
Montreal, PQ, Canada H3A 2A7 Norma Johnston, Libn.
Founded: 1948. **Staff:** Prof 1; Other 2.5. **Subjects:** Historical theology, Old and New Testament, church history, philosophy of religion and ethics, comparative religion, pastoral psychology, practical theology, homiletics. **Special Collections:** Montreal Diocesan Theological College Collection, including the Jeannie Willis Memorial Library; United Theological College Collection. **Holdings:** 64,000 books; 8650 bound periodical volumes; 8955 microforms; 1198 slides; 957 pamphlets; 9 films; 9 audiotapes; 74 audiocassettes; 16 phonograph records; 8 filmstrips; 16 videocassettes. **Subscriptions:** 135 journals and other serials. **Services:** Interlibrary loan; copying; library open to the public for consultation only. **Automated Operations:** Computerized public access catalog and acquisitions. **Computerized Information Services:** BITNET (electronic mail service). **Remarks:** FAX: (514)398-6665. Electronic mail address(es): CZRZ@MUSICA.MCGILL.CA (BITNET).

★9911★
McGill University - Sub-Arctic Research Station Library (Sci-Engr)
P.O. Box 790 Phone: (418)585-2489
Schefferville, PQ, Canada G0G 2T0 Douglas R. Barr, Sta.Mgr.
Founded: 1954. **Staff:** 1. **Subjects:** Arctic and subarctic, environmental studies. **Special Collections:** McGill Sub-Arctic Research Papers (41 volumes); manuscript theses by students at the McGill Station (50 volumes). **Holdings:** 500 volumes. **Subscriptions:** 130 journals and other serials. **Services:** Interlibrary loan; copying; library open to qualified users. **Publications:** McGill Sub-Arctic Research Papers, irregular - for sale or exchange through the Centre for Northern Studies & Research, McGill University, 550 Sherbrooke St. W., Suite 460, West Wing, Montreal, PQ H3A 1B9.

★9912★
McGill University - Walter Hitschfeld Environmental Earth Sciences Library (Geog-Map)
524 Burnside Hall
805 Sherbrooke St., W. Phone: (514)398-8095
Montreal, PQ, Canada H3A 2K6 Carol Marley, Hd.Libn.
Founded: 1989. **Staff:** Prof 1; Other 1. **Subjects:** Cartography, geography, meteorology, oceanography. **Special Collections:** Quebec Fire Insurance Plans. **Holdings:** 10,000 books; 4030 bound periodical volumes; 250,000 maps and aerial photographs. **Subscriptions:** 215 serials. **Services:** Interlibrary loan (through Physical Sciences & Engineering Library); copying; library open to the public with restrictions. **Computerized Information Services:** DIALOG Information Services, CAN/OLE; BITNET (electronic mail service). **Publications:** Bibliographies. **Remarks:** FAX: (514)398-7437. Electronic mail address(es): CXCY@MUSICA.MCGILL.CA (BITNET).

McGlannan Health Sciences Library
See: **Mercy Medical Center** (10155)

McGoogan Library of Medicine
See: **University of Nebraska at Omaha - Medical Center - McGoogan Library of Medicine** (19010)

McGrath Library
See: **Hilbert College** (7206)

McGraw-Hill Financial Services Co. - Business Information Center
See: **Standard & Poor's Corporation - Business Information Center** (15639)

★9913★
McGraw-Hill, Inc. - Aviation Week & Space Technology Library (Sci-Engr)
1221 Ave. of the Americas Phone: (212)512-2311
New York, NY 10020 Marion Reiley, Res.Libn.
Staff: Prof 1. **Subjects:** Military and commercial aviation; business flying; space technology; technology; missile science; aerospace-related communications. **Special Collections:** Photographic collection, 1916 to present. **Holdings:** 200 books; 150 bound periodical volumes. **Services:** Library not open to the public. **Computerized Information Services:** NEXIS; produces Aviation Week & Space Technology database. **Special Indexes:** Editorial index, semiannual. **Remarks:** FAX: (212)512-6068.

★9914★
McGraw-Hill, Inc. - Business Information Center (Publ)
1221 Avenue of the Americas, 48th Fl. Phone: (212)512-4001
New York, NY 10020 Dana J. Gordon, Mgr.
Founded: 1926. **Staff:** 1. **Subjects:** Business, economics, industry, science, technology, engineering, publishing. **Holdings:** 10,000 volumes. **Subscriptions:** 120 journals and other serials. **Services:** Library not open to the public. **Computerized Information Services:** DIALOG Information Services, NEXIS, DataTimes; CD-ROMs.

★9915★
McGraw-Hill, Inc. - Business Week Magazine Library (Publ)
1221 Avenue of the Americas Phone: (212)512-3298
New York, NY 10020 Jude T. Hayes, Dir.
Founded: 1929. **Staff:** Prof 3. **Subjects:** Business conditions, general business reference, computers, science and technology, international business. **Holdings:** 400 volumes. **Subscriptions:** 250 journals and other serials. **Services:** Interlibrary loan. **Computerized Information Services:** DIALOG Information Services, NEXIS, VU/TEXT Information Services, DataTimes, Dow Jones News/Retrieval, Spectrum Ownership Profiles Online, DRI/McGraw-Hill, Standard & Poor's COMPUSTAT Services, Inc. **Remarks:** FAX: (212)512-4286. **Staff:** Dana Gordon, Info.Spec.; Jessie Khatami, Info.Spec.

★9916★
McGraw-Hill, Inc. - Marketing Information Center
1221 Avenue of the Americas
New York, NY 10020-1095
Defunct.

★9917★
Max McGraw Wildlife Foundation - Library (Biol Sci)
Box 9 Phone: (708)428-2240
Dundee, IL 60118 Sylvia Grisez, Naturalist
Founded: 1962. **Staff:** Prof 1; Other 1. **Subjects:** Wildlife, ornithology, wildlife and fisheries management, conservation. **Special Collections:** Technical journals (92). **Holdings:** 450 books; 48 bound periodical volumes; 8 VF drawers of unbound reports and manuscripts. **Subscriptions:** 50 journals and other serials. **Services:** Library not open to the public. **Remarks:** FAX: (708)741-8157.

McGregor Technical Information Center
See: **Hercules, Inc. - Aerospace Division - McGregor Technical Information Center** (7148)

McGuire Memorial Library
See: **St. Catherine Hospital** (14254)

Paul McGuire Maritime Library
See: **State Library of South Australia - Special Collections** (15695)

★9918★
McGuire Woods Battle & Boothe - Law Library (Law)
8280 Greensboro Dr., Suite 900 Phone: (703)712-5408
McLean, VA 22102 Anne R. Inge, Lib.Mgr.
Staff: 3. **Subjects:** Law - taxation, business, real estate. **Holdings:** 15,000 books; 1000 bound periodical volumes. **Subscriptions:** 250 journals and other serials; 10 newspapers. **Services:** Interlibrary loan; copying; library open to outside attorneys with librarian's approval. **Computerized Information Services:** LEXIS, NEXIS, DIALOG Information Services, WESTLAW, VU/TEXT Information Services, Dow Jones News/Retrieval, Dun & Bradstreet Business Credit Services. **Remarks:** FAX: (703)712-5050. **Staff:** Ann B. Roberts, Dir., Lib.Serv.

★9919★
McGuire Woods Battle & Boothe - Library (Law)
1 James Center Phone: (804)775-7606
Richmond, VA 23219 Barbara Folensbee-Moore, Lib.Mgr.
Founded: 1977. **Staff:** Prof 6; Other 3. **Subjects:** Law. **Holdings:** 60,000 books; 2000 bound periodical volumes; 4 drawers of microfilm. **Subscriptions:** 380 journals and other serials. **Services:** Library not open to the public. **Automated Operations:** Computerized cataloging and routing. **Computerized Information Services:** LEXIS, DIALOG Information Services, Dow Jones News/Retrieval, WESTLAW, NEXIS, DunsPrint, VU/TEXT Information Services, NewsNet, Inc., Spectrum Ownership Profiles Online, Labor Relations Press (LRP), DataTimes, ELSS (Electronic Legislative Search Service), Info Globe, COMPU-MARK. **Remarks:** FAX: (804)775-1061; (804)775-1062. **Staff:** Ann B. Roberts, Dir., Lib.Serv.; Billie Jo Brooks, Hd.Ref.Libn.; Amy Jordan, Ref.Libn.; David Mason, Tax Libn.; Kathleen Nichols, Tech.Serv.Libn.

Dean E. McHenry Library
See: **University of California, Santa Cruz - Dean E. McHenry Library** (18435)

★9920★
McHenry Museum - Library (Hist)
1402 I St. Phone: (209)577-5366
Modesto, CA 95354 Heidi L. Warner, Cur.
Founded: 1965. **Staff:** Prof 2. **Subjects:** Stanislaus County history. **Holdings:** 90 linear feet of city and county records, oral history tapes, school records, court records, diaries; 15,000 photographs. **Services:** Copying; library open to the public. **Publications:** Quarterly Newsletter. **Remarks:** Maintained by the city of Modesto.

★9921★
MCI Norfolk Law Library (Law)
43 Clark St. Phone: (617)668-0800
Norfolk, MA 02056 William D. Mongelli, Law Libn.
Founded: 1978. **Staff:** Prof 1; Other 12. **Subjects:** Law. **Special Collections:** Criminal law; domestic relations; immigration law. **Holdings:** 6000 books. **Subscriptions:** 3 journals and other serials. **Services:** Interlibrary loan; library not open to the public.

★9922★
McIlvaine Company - Technical Library (Env-Cons)
2970 Maria Ave. Phone: (708)272-0010
Northbrook, IL 60062 Francine Hakimian, Libn.
Founded: 1974. **Staff:** Prof 1; Other 2. **Subjects:** Pollution control - air, water, energy. **Holdings:** Figures not available. **Subscriptions:** 102 journals and other serials. **Services:** Copying; library open to the public. **Automated Operations:** Computerized indexing. **Remarks:** FAX: (708)272-9673. Telex: 494 4829 MC ILVN.

David Knox McKamy Medical Library
See: **Lloyd Noland Hospital** (11827)

★9923★
McKay Dee Hospital Center - Library (Med)
3939 Harrison Blvd. Phone: (801)625-2035
Ogden, UT 84409 Mark Meldrum, Libn.
Staff: Prof 1; Other 1. **Subjects:** Medicine, hospital administration, nursing. **Holdings:** 2000 books; Audio-Digest tapes. **Subscriptions:** 400 journals and other serials. **Services:** Interlibrary loan; copying; library open to the public. **Computerized Information Services:** MEDLINE. **Networks/Consortia:** Member of Utah Health Sciences Library Consortium (UHSLC). **Remarks:** FAX: (801)625-2032.

Gordon McKay Library
See: **Harvard University - Division of Applied Sciences** (6960)

McKay Memorial Library
See: **Community Memorial Hospital** (4088)

★9924★
McKean County Law Library (Law)
Court House
500 W. Main Phone: (814)887-5571
Smethport, PA 16749 Jim Piscetelli, Libn.
Staff: 1. **Subjects:** Law. **Holdings:** 10,000 volumes. **Services:** Library open to the public.

★9925★
Davy McKee Corporation - Library (Sci-Engr, Bus-Fin)
1 Oliver Plaza Phone: (412)566-3456
Pittsburgh, PA 15222 Sandra DeWitt, Lib.Techn.
Founded: 1949. **Staff:** Prof 1. **Subjects:** Engineering, business. **Holdings:** 5000 books; 200 bound periodical volumes; specifications and standards from 75 associations. **Subscriptions:** 53 journals and other serials. **Services:** Interlibrary loan; library not open to the public. **Automated Operations:** Computerized cataloging, serials, and circulation. **Computerized Information Services:** DIALOG Information Services. Performs searches on fee basis. **Remarks:** FAX: (412)566-3229. Telex: 90-2943.

★9926★
Davy McKee Corporation - Library Center (Sci-Engr)
2440 Camino Ramon, Suite 100 Phone: (510)866-6389
San Ramon, CA 94583 Bill Repp, Tech.Libn.
Founded: 1967. **Staff:** Prof 1. **Subjects:** Engineering - electrical, mechanical, mining, metallurgical, structural, civil. **Holdings:** 3500 books; 100 bound periodical volumes; 600 mechanical, piping, electrical, and instrumentation catalogs; industry standards and reports. **Subscriptions:** 42 journals and other serials. **Services:** Interlibrary loan; center not open to the public. **Remarks:** Alternate telephone number(s): 866-1166. FAX: (510)866-6520.

John S. McKee, Jr., M.D. Memorial Library
See: **Broughton Hospital - John S. McKee, Jr., M.D. Memorial Library** (2254)

McKee Library
See: **Southern College of Seventh-Day Adventists** (15478)

★9927★
McKeesport Hospital - Health Services Library (Med)
1500 Fifth Ave. Phone: (412)664-2363
McKeesport, PA 15132-2483 Karen M. Zundel, Dir.
Founded: 1974. **Staff:** Prof 1; Other 1. **Subjects:** Medicine, nursing, consumerism. **Holdings:** 1800 books; 5000 bound periodical volumes; 300 AV programs. **Subscriptions:** 156 journals and other serials. **Services:** Interlibrary loan; copying; SDI; library open to the public with restrictions. **Automated Operations:** Computerized ILL. **Computerized Information Services:** MEDLARS; DOCLINE (electronic mail service). **Publications:** New Booklist, quarterly.

★9928★
McKennan Hospital - Medical Library (Med)
800 E. 21st St.
P.O. Box 5045 Phone: (605)339-8088
Sioux Falls, SD 57117-5045 Frances Ellis Rice, Dir., Lib.Serv.
Staff: Prof 1; Other 1.5. **Subjects:** Medicine, nursing, allied health sciences. **Special Collections:** Clinical Pastoral Education Collection (200 items); Maternal Child Care Collection (100 items). **Holdings:** 4000 books; 800 bound periodical volumes; 500 microforms; 2 VF drawers. **Subscriptions:** 600 journals and other serials. **Services:** Interlibrary loan; copying; SDI; LATCH; library open to the public. **Automated Operations:** Computerized cataloging, circulation, and serials. **Computerized Information Services:** OCLC, DIALOG Information Services, BRS Information Technologies, MEDLARS, MEDLINE. Performs searches on fee basis. **Networks/Consortia:** Member of National Network of Libraries of Medicine - Greater Midwest Region, MINITEX Library Information Network. **Publications:** The Resource - for internal distribution only. **Remarks:** FAX: (605)339-7543.

R. Tait McKenzie Research Library
See: **Mississippi Valley Conservation Authority** (10529)

McKeon Memorial Library
See: **St. Patrick's Seminary** (14555)

H.B. McKibbin Health Science Library
See: **Wesley Medical Center** (20172)

★9929★
McKim Advertising, Ltd. - Information Centre (Bus-Fin)
2 Bloor St., W., 29th Fl. Phone: (416)960-1722
Toronto, ON, Canada M4W 3R6 Jane Maxwell, Libn.
Founded: 1961. **Staff:** Prof 1. **Subjects:** Advertising, marketing, market research, demographics. **Holdings:** 300 books; Statistics Canada and census publications. **Subscriptions:** 60 journals and other serials; 5 newspapers. **Services:** Interlibrary loan. **Computerized Information Services:** Info Globe, DIALOG Information Services, WILSONLINE.

Lloyd McKinley Memorial Chemistry Branch Library
See: **Wichita State University** (20411)

★9930★
McKinley Museum of History, Science, and Industry - Ramsayer Research Library (Hist)
Box 483 Phone: (216)455-7043
Canton, OH 44701 Sally Donze, Libn.
Staff: Prof 1; Other 10. **Subjects:** President William McKinley and family, Stark County history and industry, local family histories. **Special Collections:** McKinleyana Collection (records, photographs, and genealogy of William McKinley, 25th President of the United States); letters and reports of Captain W.F. Raynolds; Civil War letters; Stark County Clipping files (19 VF drawers); interurban trains collection. **Holdings:** 3200 books; 4000 other cataloged items; 27 reels of microfilm of McKinley papers and McKinleyana. **Subscriptions:** 53 journals and other serials; 7 newspapers. **Services:** Library open to the public for reference use only on a limited schedule. **Remarks:** Located at 800 McKinley Monument Dr., N.W., Canton, OH 44708. **Formerly:** Stark County Historical Society.

★9931★
McKinney Job Corps - Library (Educ)
1701 N. Church St.
P.O. Box 8003 Phone: (214)542-2623
McKinney, TX 75069 Theale McClesky, Libn.
Founded: 1964. **Staff:** Prof 1; Other 1. **Subjects:** Negro history, special education, self-improvement, psychology, careers, guidance and counseling. **Holdings:** 10,500 books; 390 phonograph records. **Subscriptions:** 19 journals and other serials. **Services:** Library not open to the public.

McKinney Library
See: **Albany Institute of History and Art** (227)

Richard W. McKinney Engineering Library
See: **University of Texas at Austin - Engineering Library** (19389)

★9932★
McKinnon, Allen & Associates (Western), Ltd. - Research Library
1115 46th Ave., S.E.
Calgary, AB, Canada T2G 2A5 Phone: (403)243-4345
Founded: 1960. **Subjects:** Agricultural economics, animal science, field crops, soils, diseases and pests, horticulture, agricultural engineering, forestry, rural land appraisal. **Special Collections:** Effects of airborne pollutants on crops and animals; agricultural extension education. **Holdings:** 500 volumes; 4500 annual reports, maps, clippings, government releases. **Remarks:** Currently inactive.

★9933★
I.N. McKinnon Memorial Library (Sci-Engr, Energy)
3512 33rd St., N.W.
Calgary, AB, Canada T2L 2A6 Phone: (403)282-1211
Staff: 2. **Subjects:** Petroleum engineering, enhanced oil recovery, reservoir simulation, energy economics. **Holdings:** 6000 books. **Subscriptions:** 245 journals and other serials; 2 newspapers. **Services:** Interlibrary loan. **Automated Operations:** Computerized cataloging. **Computerized Information Services:** DIALOG Information Services, PFDS Online, CAN/OLE, QL Systems, Info Globe, SPIRES; Envoy 100 (electronic mail service). **Publications:** New Book List, monthly - free upon request. **Remarks:** FAX: (403)289-1988. Electronic mail address(es): ILL.ACINM (Envoy 100). Jointly maintained by Canadian Energy Research Institute, Computer Modelling Group, and Petroleum Recovery Institute.

★9934★
McKinsey & Company, Inc. - Information Center (Bus-Fin)
400 S. Hope St. Phone: (213)624-1414
Los Angeles, CA 90071 Doreen A. Welborn, Mgr., Info.Serv.
Staff: Prof 5; Other 2. **Subjects:** Management, finance, banking, energy, health care, electronics. **Holdings:** 1500 books; 2000 corporate files. **Subscriptions:** 300 journals and other serials; 15 newspapers. **Services:** Center not open to the public. **Automated Operations:** Computerized cataloging (Datatrek) and circulation. **Computerized Information Services:** DIALOG Information Services, Dow Jones News/Retrieval, NEXIS, NewsNet, Inc., VU/TEXT Information Services, DataTimes, Reuters; OnTyme Electronic Message Network Service (electronic mail service). **Staff:** Jim White, Info.Spec.; Joann Davis, Info.Spec.; Helga Haralsson, Info.Spec.; Ros Jaime, Info.Spec.

★9935★
McKinsey & Company, Inc. - Information Center (Bus-Fin)
Two First National Plaza Phone: (312)580-5300
Chicago, IL 60603 Elizabeth Dreazen, Mgr., Info.Serv.
Founded: 1966. **Staff:** 5. **Subjects:** Management. **Holdings:** 3000 books; 1000 reports. **Subscriptions:** 250 journals and other serials; 5 newspapers. **Services:** Library not open to the public. **Computerized Information Services:** DIALOG Information Services, Dow Jones News/Retrieval, DataTimes, NewsNet, Inc., MAID (Market Analysis and Information Database), NEXIS, PDNet, FPIS (internal databases). **Networks/ Consortia:** Member of Chicago Library System. FAX: **Remarks:** (312)368-8513. **Staff:** Noreen Curran; Lauramae Smith.

★9936★
McKinsey & Company, Inc. - Information Centre (Bus-Fin)
175 Bloor St., E., 12th Fl., N. Tower Phone: (416)969-3700
Toronto, ON, Canada M4W 3R8 Marie Gadula, Mgr., Res. & Info.Serv.
Founded: 1969. **Staff:** Prof 4; Other 1. **Subjects:** Strategic planning, organization and operations effectiveness, management consulting. **Special Collections:** Annual reports of Financial Post Top 500 Canadian corporations. **Holdings:** 3000 books; full depository collection of Statistics Canada documentation. **Subscriptions:** 250 journals and other serials; 12 newspapers. **Services:** Interlibrary loan; SDI; center open to clients and SLA members. **Automated Operations:** Computerized cataloging and acquisitions. **Computerized Information Services:** Dow Jones News/ Retrieval, Reuter TEXTLINE, Canada Systems Group (CSG), NEXIS, LEXIS, VU/TEXT Information Services, WILSONLINE, DOBIS Canadian Online Library System, Info Globe, DIALOG Information Services, Reuters Information Services (Canada) Limited, QL Systems, CAN/OLE, COMPUSTAT Services, Inc. (C/S), Data Resources (DRI), The Financial Post DataGroup, Infomart Online; internal databases; General Electric Information Services (electronic mail service). **Publications:** Acquisitions bulletin - for internal distribution only. **Remarks:** FAX: (416)969-3940. **Staff:** Kathryn Jelilian, Quick Info.Spec.; Catherine Graham, Info.Spec.; Julie Brittan, Info.Spec.

★9937★
McKinsey & Company, Inc. - Information Services (Bus-Fin)
1101 Pennsylvania Ave., N.W. Phone: (202)662-3100
Washington, DC 20006 Ann Robertson, Mgr.
Staff: Prof 7; Other 3. **Subjects:** Business management, energy, industries, government. **Holdings:** Internal reports; clippings; corporate files; subject files. **Subscriptions:** 250 journals and other serials. **Services:** Interlibrary loan; library not open to the public. **Computerized Information Services:** Online systems. **Remarks:** FAX: (202)662-3175. **Staff:** Kathy Knauss, Info.Anl.; Carolyn Loos, Energy Info.Coord.; Betsy Green, Info.Spec.; Gail Fox, Energy Info.Anl.; Analiese Bruner, Info.Asst.; Trudy Scott, Energy Info.Anl.

★9938★
McKinsey & Company, Inc. - Information Services (Bus-Fin)
55 E. 52nd St. Phone: (212)446-7000
New York, NY 10022 Laurie Leichman, Lib.Mgr.
Staff: Prof 18; Other 10. **Subjects:** Business, finance. **Holdings:** 6000 books. **Subscriptions:** 300 journals and other serials; 25 newspapers. **Services:** Interlibrary loan; services not open to the public. **Automated Operations:** Computerized cataloging and serials. **Computerized Information Services:** DIALOG Information Services, NEXIS, Spectrum Ownership Profiles Online, TEXTLINE, Dow Jones News/Retrieval, WILSONLINE, VU/TEXT Information Services, DRI/McGraw-Hill, CompuServe Information Service, DataTimes, Dun & Bradstreet Business Credit Services, InvesText, NewsNet, Inc., PRODUCTSCAN, M & A (Mergers & Acquisitions) Data Base, Securities Data, MAID (Market Analysis and Information Database). **Remarks:** FAX: (212)446-8575. **Staff:** Jeanne Hardy, Supv., Info.Serv.Oper.

★9939★
McKinsey & Company, Inc. - Information Services (Bus-Fin)
2200 Ross Ave., Suite 5200 Phone: (214)220-3200
Dallas, TX 75201 Susan Porras, Mgr., Info.Serv.
Staff: Prof 3; Other 3. **Subjects:** Business, energy, information technology. **Holdings:** Figures not available. **Subscriptions:** 70 journals and other serials. **Services:** Services not open to the public. **Remarks:** FAX: (214)220-3217. **Staff:** Bret Tudor, Sr.Info.Spec.; Alice Hallman, Info.Spec.

★9940★
McKinsey & Company, Inc. - Library (Bus-Fin)
555 California St., Suite 4800 Phone: (415)981-0250
San Francisco, CA 94104 Marsha Wyler, Mgr., Info.Serv.
Staff: Prof 3; Other 1. **Subjects:** Forest products, banking, management. **Holdings:** Figures not available. **Subscriptions:** 225 journals and other serials. **Services:** Interlibrary loan; library not open to the public. **Computerized Information Services:** DIALOG Information Services, Dow Jones News/Retrieval, NEXIS. **Staff:** Sarah Maxwell, Info.Spec.; Pam Van der Leeden, Info.Spec.

★9941★
McKinsey & Company, Inc. - Library (Energy)
2 Houston Center, Suite 3500 Phone: (713)650-1299
Houston, TX 77010 Helen Walther, Info.Spec.
Staff: 3. **Subjects:** Energy, chemicals. **Holdings:** 1000 books. **Services:** Interlibrary loan; library open to the public by appointment. **Computerized Information Services:** DIALOG Information Services, DRI/McGraw-Hill, Reuters, Mead Data Central. **Remarks:** FAX: (713)650-1050. **Staff:** Eileen Pendrak; Marla Aizenshtat.

McKusick Law Library
See: **University of South Dakota** (19318)

★9942★
McLane, Graf, Raulerson & Middleton - Library (Law)
40 Stark St.
P.O. Box 326 Phone: (603)625-6464
Manchester, NH 03105 Kelli Bacon, Lib.Mgr.
Staff: Prof 1; Other 1.5. **Subjects:** Law. **Special Collections:** New Hampshire law collection and factual materials (200 books). **Holdings:** 10,000 books. **Subscriptions:** 70 journals and other serials. **Services:** Interlibrary loan; library not open to the public. **Automated Operations:** Computerized cataloging (INMAGIC). **Computerized Information Services:** DIALOG Information Services, LEXIS, WESTLAW, PACER; Database of New Hampshire Regulations (internal database). **Remarks:** FAX: (603)625-5650.

★9943★
McLaren Regional Medical Center - Medical Library (Med)
401 Ballenger Hwy. Phone: (313)762-2141
Flint, MI 48532 Lea Ann McGaugh, Med.Lib.Mgr.
Staff: Prof 2; Other 2. **Subjects:** Medicine, nursing, allied health sciences. **Holdings:** 3000 books; 4000 bound periodical volumes. **Subscriptions:** 300 journals and other serials. **Services:** Interlibrary loan; copying; SDI; library open to the public for reference use only. **Computerized Information Services:** MEDLARS, DIALOG Information Services, OCLC. **Remarks:** FAX: (313)762-2269. **Formerly:** McLaren General Hospital. **Staff:** Patricia L. Moreland, Med.Libn.

McLaughlin Library
See: **Seton Hall University - Library - Special Collections Center** (15048)

★9944★
Robert McLaughlin Gallery - Library (Art)
Civic Centre Phone: (416)576-3000
Oshawa, ON, Canada L1H 3Z3 Patricia Claxton-Oldfield, Libn.
Founded: 1969. **Staff:** 1. **Subjects:** Contemporary Canadian art. **Special Collections:** Painters Eleven Archives. **Holdings:** 2000 books. **Subscriptions:** 20 journals and other serials. **Services:** Library open to the public. **Remarks:** FAX: (416)576-9774.

★9945★
McLean County Historical Society - Museum and Library (Hist)
200 N. Main Phone: (309)827-0428
Bloomington, IL 61701 Greg Koos, Exec.Dir.
Founded: 1892. **Staff:** Prof 5. **Subjects:** History - McLean County, Central Illinois, Illinois; Civil War; genealogy. **Holdings:** 8000 books; 200 historical journals; 197 bound newspaper volumes; papers of locally and militarily important people; 200 linear feet of archives. **Subscriptions:** 85 journals and other serials. **Services:** Copying; library open to the public for reference use only. **Publications:** Transactions, irregular. **Special Indexes:** Daily Pantagraph indexed, 1854-1940; index to archives (card). **Remarks:** FAX: (309)827-0100. **Staff:** William C. Todtz, III, Libn./Archv.

★9946★
McLean Hospital - Mental Health Sciences Library (Med)
115 Mill St. Phone: (617)855-2460
Belmont, MA 02178 Rosanne Labree, Dir.
Founded: 1811. **Staff:** Prof 4; Other 3. **Subjects:** Mental health, behavioral sciences, alcoholism, drug abuse, psychiatry, psychoanalysis, psychology, psychosomatics, neurology, psychopharmacology, psychotherapy, schizophrenia, psychobiology, child and adolescent psychiatry, forensic psychiatry, neuroscience, social work. **Holdings:** 16,974 books; 19,600 bound periodical volumes. **Subscriptions:** 350 journals and other serials. **Services:** Interlibrary loan; copying; SDI; library open to the public on fee basis. **Automated Operations:** Computerized acquisitions. **Computerized Information Services:** BRS Information Technologies, DIALOG Information Services; InterNet (electronic mail service). **Remarks:** FAX: (617)855-3299. Electronic mail address(es): LIBMCH@HARVARDA.HARVARD.EDU (InterNet). **Staff:** Marilyn Dietrich, Asst.Dir., Info.Serv.; Jonathan Gawne, Asst.Dir., Media Serv.

McLean Library
See: **Chicago Institute for Psychoanalysis - McLean Library** (3523)

★9947★
McLennan County Law Library (Law)
McLennan County Court House, Rm. 405
5th and Washington Sts. Phone: (817)757-5191
Waco, TX 76701 Leona Simcik, Libn.
Founded: 1928. **Subjects:** Law. **Holdings:** 11,000 volumes. **Services:** Copying; library open to the public for reference use only. **Remarks:** Alternate telephone number(s): 757-5000. Also serves Texas State Court of Civil Appeals - 10th Judicial District.

Daniel R. McLeod Law Library
See: **South Carolina State Attorney General's Office** (15398)

McLure Education Library
See: **University of Alabama** (18164)

★9948★
McManus Anderson Miles - Library (Law)
2200 Bow Valley Sq. IV
205 6th Ave., S.W. Phone: (403)263-2190
Calgary, AB, Canada T2P 3H7 Lila Lukowski, Libn.
Founded: 1977. **Staff:** 2. **Subjects:** Law. **Holdings:** 5000 books. **Subscriptions:** 200 journals and other serials. **Services:** Interlibrary loan; library open to other librarians. **Computerized Information Services:** QL Systems. **Remarks:** Alternate telephone number(s): 263-2190. FAX: (403)263-6840.

★9949★
McMaster Meighen - Law Library (Law)
630, blvd. Reve-Levesque W. Phone: (514)954-3159
Montreal, PQ, Canada H3B 4H7 Ronald Charest, Libn.
Staff: Prof 1; Other 1. **Subjects:** Law - corporate and commercial, labor, banking, bankruptcy and insolvency, finance and securities, real estate, insurance, admiralty; litigation; taxation; estates, wills, trusts, and pensions. **Holdings:** 7000 books. **Subscriptions:** 300 journals and other serials; 8 newspapers. **Services:** Interlibrary loan; copying; SDI; library open to the public with restrictions. **Automated Operations:** Computerized cataloging, acquisitions, serials, and circulation. **Computerized Information Services:** QL Systems, Societe Quebecoise d'Information Juridique (SOQUIJ), WESTLAW, DIALOG Information Services, LEXIS, NEXIS, CBANET, CAN/LAW; internal database. **Publications:** Newsletter, monthly - to lawyers. **Special Indexes:** O&J Databank (online). **Remarks:** FAX: (514)878-0605; 878-4428. Telex 05-268637.

★9950★
McMaster University - Business Library (Bus-Fin)
Innis Library, Kenneth Taylor Hall 108 Phone: (416)529-7070
Hamilton, ON, Canada L8S 4M4 Kathy Ball, Bus.Libn.
Founded: 1974. **Staff:** Prof 1; Other 4. **Subjects:** Business administration. **Special Collections:** Economics Working Papers; company and industry files; labor union materials (6 drawers). **Holdings:** 14,000 books; 1500 documents; 15 drawers of company, industry, subject files. **Subscriptions:** 400 journals and other serials. **Services:** Interlibrary loan (through main library); copying; library open to the public for reference use only. **Automated Operations:** Computerized cataloging, serials, and circulation. **Computerized Information Services:** Online systems. **Publications:** Accession list, monthly; bibliographies, irregular. **Remarks:** FAX: (416)546-0625.

★9951★
McMaster University - Health Sciences Library (Med)
1200 Main St., W. Phone: (416)525-9140
Hamilton, ON, Canada L8N 3Z5 Dorothy Fitzgerald, Hea.Sci.Libn.
Staff: Prof 9; Other 28. **Subjects:** Basic medical sciences, clinical medicine, nursing, allied health sciences, history of medicine. **Holdings:** 59,359 books; 70,016 bound periodical volumes; 858 slide/tape programs; 14 16mm films; 858 videotapes; 185 audiocassettes; 103 computer software programs. **Subscriptions:** 1831 journals and other serials. **Services:** Interlibrary loan; copying; library open to the public for reference use only. **Automated Operations:** Computerized public access catalog, cataloging, acquisitions, and circulation. **Computerized Information Services:** DIALOG Information Services, LEXIS, NLM, Institute for Scientific Information (ISI); CD-ROMs (MEDLINE, Nursing and Allied Health (CINAHL)-CD, Health CD, CCINFOdisc, PsycLIT, SCI); Envoy 100 (electronic mail service). Performs searches on fee basis. **Networks/Consortia:** Member of Hamilton/Wentworth District Health Library Network. **Publications:** Health Sciences Serials in libraries in the Hamilton area; Appendix; A.V. subject microfiche. **Remarks:** FAX: (416)521-0048. Electronic mail address(es): D.FITZGERALD; MAC.LIB.HSL (Envoy 100). **Staff:** Linda Panton, Hosp.Lib.Coord.; Mary Anne Trainor, Hd., Acq. & Ser.Libn.; Liz Bayley, Hd., Cat.; Anne McKeage, Archv.; Neera Bhatnagar, Ref.Libn.; Ina Mae Chan, Ref.Libn.; Tom Flemming, Hd., Pub.Serv.

★9952★
McMaster University - Lloyd Reeds Map Library/Urban Documentation Centre (Geog-Map)
Burke Science Bldg., Rm. 137 Phone: (416)525-9140
Hamilton, ON, Canada L8S 4K1 Cathy Moulder, Cur.
Founded: 1947. **Staff:** Prof 1; Other 2. **Subjects:** Cartography, geography, geology, history, urban studies, municipal planning. **Special Collections:** Maps relating to Wentworth County History; survey notes of Upper Canada to 1850; modern municipal documents of Hamilton-Wentworth region; university publications concerning urban studies. **Holdings:** 1153 books; 286 bound periodical volumes; 1913 atlases; 21,703 government documents, reports, dissertations; 96,962 maps; 628 reels of microfilm; 8009 microforms; 13,826 aerial photographs; 17,420 satellite images. **Subscriptions:** 110 journals and other serials. **Services:** Interlibrary loan; copying; library open to the public with restrictions. **Computerized Information Services:** BITNET (electronic mail service). **Networks/Consortia:** Member of Ontario Council of University Libraries (OCUL). **Publications:** UDC Acquisitions List; Map Library Acquisitions List. **Special Indexes:** Area indexes of rare maps collections; urban collection and periodicals indexes (card); vertical file indexes (online); Hamilton street name changes index (card); indexes to land surveyors' notebooks, Southern Ontario (card). **Remarks:** FAX: (416)546-0625. Electronic mail address(es): MOULDER@MCMVM1 (BITNET).

★9953★
McMaster University - Thode Library of Science & Engineering (Sci-Engr)
Hamilton, ON, Canada L8S 4P5 Phone: (416)525-9140
Harold Siroonian, Assoc.Univ.Libn.
Staff: Prof 3; Other 14. **Subjects:** General science, mathematics, physics, chemistry, geology, biology, engineering. **Holdings:** 117,000 books; 107,000 bound periodical volumes; 7100 hardcopy technical reports; 47,000 hardcopy government documents; 349,000 microforms of technical reports, documents, journals. **Subscriptions:** 3700 journals and other serials. **Services:** Interlibrary loan; library open to the public for reference use only. **Automated Operations:** Computerized cataloging, serials, and circulation. **Computerized Information Services:** CAN/SDI, CAN/OLE, DIALOG Information Services, Infomart Online, BRS Information Technologies, Info Globe, WILSONLINE, International Development Research Centre (IDRC), Information Retrieval System for the Sociology of Leisure and Sport (SIRLS); Envoy 100 (electronic mail service). **Remarks:** FAX: (416)546-0625. Electronic mail address(es): ADMIN/MCMASTERUNIVERSITY (Envoy 100). **Staff:** Peggy Findlay, Info.Serv.Libn.; Elaine Tooke, Ref.Libn.

★9954★
McMaster University - The William Ready Division of Archives and Research Collections (Rare Book, Hist)
Mills Memorial Library Phone: (416)525-9140
Hamilton, ON, Canada L8S 4L6 Charlotte A. Stewart-Murphy, Dir. of Archv. & Res.Coll.
Founded: 1970. **Staff:** Prof 4; Other 6.5. **Subjects:** Eighteenth century British literature and history, Canadian social history, Canadian literature, 20th century British pacifism, Bertrand Russell, McMaster University archives. **Special Collections:** Archival collections of Bertrand Russell, Pierre Berton, Farley Mowat, Austin Clarke, W.J. Eccles, Thomas Carlyle, Vera Brittain, Anthony Burgess, George Catlin, J.W. Bengough, Matt Cohen, Robert Fulford, David Helwig, Marian Engel, Arnold Edinborough, Margaret Laurence, Canadian Union of Students, Peter Newman, W.L. Morton, Susan Musgrave, H.R. Percy, C.K. Ogden, Mulberry papers, Charles Kingsley, John Connell, Copeau-Obey correspondence, John Coulter, Peter Such; General Steel Wares Archive; Hamilton and District Labour Council; U.S.W.A. Local 1005; U.S.W.A. District 6; McClelland and Stewart Ltd., Clarke Irwin, and Macmillan of Canada publishing archives; book collections of Jonathan Swift, Samuel Johnson, James Boswell, Daniel Defoe, Samuel Beckett, H.G. Wells, D.H. Lawrence, Henry James, Iris Murdoch. **Holdings:** 81,000 volumes; 9700 feet of archives and manuscripts; 1600 maps; 9000 pamphlets on Canadiana and radical groups; 1000 tapes. **Subscriptions:** 123 journals and other serials; 9 newspapers. **Services:** Interlibrary loan; copying (both limited); answers written requests for bibliographical information; division open to the public with restrictions. **Computerized Information Services:** RLIN; Envoy 100 (electronic mail service). **Publications:** McMaster University Library Research News, 2/year; Russell: The Journal of the Bertrand Russell Archives, 2/year; Archives inventory (online); Bibliography of Bertrand Russell (online). **Remarks:** FAX: (416)546-0625. Electronic mail address(es): ADMIN/MCMASTERUNIVERSITY (Envoy 100). Library sponsors lectures, exhibits, tours and contributes to some loan exhibitions.

★9955★
McMillan, Binch - Library (Law)
Royal Bank Plaza
P.O. Box 38 Phone: (416)865-7161
Toronto, ON, Canada M5J 2J7 Ricki Anne Andersen, Mgr., Lib.Serv.
Staff: Prof 2; Other 3. **Subjects:** Law, legislation, taxation. **Holdings:** 20,000 books. **Subscriptions:** 900 journals and other serials; 9 newspapers. **Services:** Interlibrary loan; copying; SDI; library open to information professionals. **Computerized Information Services:** Infomart Online, WILSONLINE, STM Systems Corporation, WESTLAW, LEXIS, NEXIS, VU/TEXT Information Services, Dow Jones News/Retrieval, QL Systems, Info Globe, DIALOG Information Services, CAN/LAW. Performs searches on fee basis. **Remarks:** FAX: (416)865-7048. Telex: 06 22317. **Staff:** Lenie Ott, Libn.

Ida J. McMillan Library
See: **Florida Baptist Theological College** (5870)

McMillen Library
See: **Indiana Institute of Technology** (7757)

McMullen Library
See: **St. Ambrose University** (14227)

★9956★
McNair Law Firm - Law Library (Law)
NCNB Tower
1301 Gervais St. Phone: (803)799-9800
Columbia, SC 29211 Barbara A. Staley, Libn.
Founded: 1974. **Staff:** Prof 1; Other 1. **Subjects:** South Carolina law. **Holdings:** 20,000 books. **Subscriptions:** 400 journals and other serials; 10 newspapers. **Services:** copying; library not open to the public. **Computerized Information Services:** WESTLAW, VU/TEXT Information Services, DIALOG Information Services, Dow Jones News/Retrieval. **Remarks:** FAX: (803)799-9804.

McNally Library
See: **Northern Alberta Institute of Technology** (11990)

★9957★
Rand McNally and Company - Corporate Library (Geog-Map)
8255 Central Park Ave. Phone: (708)673-9100
Skokie, IL 60076 Philip L. Forstall, Corp.Libn.
Founded: 1949. **Staff:** Prof 1. **Subjects:** Geography, general business topics. **Special Collections:** World atlas collection. **Holdings:** 17,000 volumes; 400 pamphlets; 100 atlases. **Subscriptions:** 120 journals and other serials. **Services:** Interlibrary loan (to libraries and specialized research institutions); geographical reference service to librarians; library open to graduate researchers for reference use. **Publications:** Accessions list. **Remarks:** FAX: (708)673-1944. Telex: 210041.

★9958★
McNamee, Porter & Seeley - MPS Engineering Library
3131 S. State St.
Ann Arbor, MI 48108-1691
Founded: 1980. **Subjects:** Wastewater treatment, potable water, water pollution, highway and bridge construction, hydraulics and hydrology, environmental engineering, architecture, drainage. **Holdings:** 1312 books; 170 bound periodical volumes; 380 Environmental Protection Agency reports; 357 U.S. Geological Survey Water Supply papers. **Remarks:** Currently inactive.

★9959★
Marion Koogler McNay Art Museum - Library (Art)
6000 N. New Braunfels Ave.
Box 6069 Phone: (512)824-5368
San Antonio, TX 78209 Patricia Blackman, Assoc.Libn.
Staff: Prof 4; Other 16. **Subjects:** Late 19th-20th century European and American art, 18th-20th century Japanese art. **Special Collections:** Japanese wood-block prints (400 books); actual-size reproductions of Japanese wood-block prints (500). **Holdings:** 15,000 books; 29 bound periodical volumes; 15,000 museum bulletins, pamphlets, art dealer and auction catalogs; 11,000 entries in biographical file of artists, mostly contemporary. **Subscriptions:** 32 journals and other serials. **Services:** Interlibrary loan (under special circumstances only); copying; library open to the public.

★9960★
Marion Koogler McNay Art Museum - Tobin Collection (Theater, Art)
6000 N. Braunfels Ave.
Box 6069 Phone: (512)824-5368
San Antonio, TX 78209 Linda Hardberger, Cur.
Founded: 1984. **Staff:** Prof 1. **Subjects:** History of scene design and costume, perspective, theater architecture, art of the book. **Special Collections:** Festival Books (500); original costume and scene designs, 1500 to present; rare books on perspective and architecture. **Holdings:** 10,000 books. **Services:** Collection open to the public. **Computerized Information Services:** Regis (internal database). **Special Catalogs:** Exhibition Catalog, semiannual. **Remarks:** FAX: (512)824-0218. **Staff:** Cristina E. Martinez, Asst. to the Cur.

★9961★
McNees, Wallace and Nurick - Library (Law)
100 Pine St.
Box 1166 Phone: (717)232-5205
Harrisburg, PA 17108 Ramona L. Wells, Law Libn.
Staff: Prof 2. **Subjects:** Law - Pennsylvania, tax, litigation, federal, corporate, labor. **Holdings:** 15,000 books. **Subscriptions:** 189 journals and other serials; 3 newspapers. **Services:** Library open to the public by appointment. **Computerized Information Services:** WESTLAW, DIALOG Information Services, LEXIS, Information America, CCH (Commerce Clearing House, Inc.). **Remarks:** FAX: (717)236-2665. **Staff:** Tracy J. Phillips.

★9962★
McNeil Consumer Products Company - Information Center (Med)
Camp Hill Rd. Phone: (215)233-7603
Fort Washington, PA 19034 Helen J. Hohman, Mgr.Info.Serv.
Founded: 1980. **Staff:** Prof 3; Other 3. **Subjects:** Pharmaceutics, medicine, chemistry, marketing, finance. **Holdings:** 3000 books; 4000 bound periodical volumes. **Subscriptions:** 550 journals and other serials; 5 newspapers. **Services:** Interlibrary loan; center not open to the public. **Computerized Information Services:** BRS Information Technologies, Data-Star, DIALOG Information Services, Dow Jones News/Retrieval, LEXIS, NEXIS, PFDS Online, STN International, VU/TEXT. **Networks/Consortia:** Member of Delaware Valley Information Consortium (DEVIC). **Remarks:** FAX: (215)233-7883. **Staff:** Peggy M. Lynch, Sr.Tech.Info.Spec.; Nancy B. Rainey, Sr.Info.Res.Spec.

McNeil Pharmaceutical (Canada), Ltd.
See: **Ortho-McNeil Inc.** (12578)

★9963★
McPherson College - Miller Library (Rel-Phil)
1600 E. Euclid
Box 1402 Phone: (316)241-0731
McPherson, KS 67460-1402 Rowena Olsen, Libn.
Staff: Prof 2; Other 2. **Subjects:** Church of the Brethren, McPherson College, local history. **Holdings:** 986 books; 305 bound periodical volumes; 5 filing cabinets of historical and governmental records; 4500 slides; 12 cassette tapes. **Subscriptions:** 8 journals and other serials. **Services:** Interlibrary loan; copying; library open to the public. **Automated Operations:** Computerized public access catalog, cataloging, and circulation. **Networks/Consortia:** Member of Associated Colleges of Central Kansas Libraries Committee (ACCK). **Staff:** Susan Taylor, Asst.Libn.

★9964★
McTeague, Higbee, Libner, et al. - Library (Law)
4 Union Park
Box 5000 Phone: (207)725-5581
Topsham, ME 04086 Dale Dorr, Libn.
Founded: 1983. **Staff:** Prof 1. **Subjects:** Labor law, worker's compensation, Maine law, asbestos litigation. **Holdings:** Labor Relations Reference Manual; Labor Arbitrations; Asbestos Litigation Reporter, 1980-1986; Maine Bureau of Labor publications; Maine Worker's Compensation Appellate Division decisions; Construction Labor Reports, 1982 to present; Revised Statutes of Maine 1916, 1930, 1944, 1954; Laws of Maine, 1965 to present; History and Final Disposition of Maine Labor Disputes, 1971 to present. **Subscriptions:** 14 journals and other serials; 9 newspapers. **Services:** Interlibrary loan; library not open to the public. **Computerized Information Services:** DIALOG Information Services, WESTLAW, LEXIS.

★9965★
Mead Corporation - Corporate Library (Bus-Fin)
Mead World Headquarters
Court House Plaza N.E. Phone: (513)222-6323
Dayton, OH 45463 Susan E. Kremer, Corp.Libn./Anl.
Founded: 1970. **Staff:** Prof 1; Other 1. **Subjects:** Finance, marketing. **Holdings:** 3000 volumes. **Services:** Interlibrary loan; library not open to the public. **Computerized Information Services:** DIALOG Information Services, PFDS Online, MEDLARS, LEXIS, NEXIS, Info Globe, TEXTLINE, Dun & Bradstreet Business Credit Services.

Mead Corporation - Mead Imaging - Library
See: **Mead Corporation - Mead Technical Library - Dayton** (9966)

★9966★
Mead Corporation - Mead Technical Library - Dayton (Sci-Engr)
3385 Newmark Dr. Phone: (614)772-3812
Miamisburg, OH 45342 Sheldon T. Miller, Libn.
Founded: 1985. **Staff:** Prof 1. **Subjects:** Polymer chemistry, photochemistry, microencapsulation, imaging science. **Holdings:** 1250 books; 475 internal technical reports. **Subscriptions:** 20 journals and other serials. **Services:** Interlibrary loan; library not open to the public. **Automated Operations:** Computerized ILL. **Computerized Information Services:** DIALOG Information Services, Chemical Abstracts Service (CAS), LEXIS, NEXIS, ORBIT Search Service, COM-NET, OCLC EPIC. **Networks/Consortia:** Member of OHIONET. **Remarks:** FAX: (614)772-5795. **Formerly:** Its Mead Imaging - Library.

★9967★
Mead Corporation - Technical Library (Sci-Engr)
Central Research Laboratories
P.O. Box 1700 Phone: (614)772-3812
Chillicothe, OH 45601 Sheldon T. Miller, Mgr., Info.Sys.
Founded: 1930. **Staff:** Prof 2. **Subjects:** Pulp, paper, and board; chemistry; chemical engineering; coating technology. **Special Collections:** Dard Hunter books on papermaking by hand. **Holdings:** 5000 books; 4000 bound periodical volumes; 17,000 corporation technical reports; 1000 pamphlets; 1000 manufacturers' trade catalogs. **Subscriptions:** 200 journals and other serials. **Services:** Interlibrary loan; copying; library open to the public with restrictions. **Automated Operations:** Computerized cataloging. **Computerized Information Services:** DIALOG Information Services, PFDS Online, NEXIS, OCLC, STN International. **Networks/Consortia:** Member of OHIONET. **Publications:** Accessions list, monthly - for internal distribution only. **Remarks:** FAX: (614)772-3595.

Mead Johnson Archives
See: **University of Southern Indiana - Special Collections and University Archives** (19350)

Mead Library
See: **University of Florida - P.K. Yonge Laboratory School** (18580)

Henry Coe Meadow Library
See: **Harvard University - New England Regional Primate Research Center** (6985)

★9968★
Meadville/Lombard Theological School - Library (Rel-Phil)
5701 S. Woodlawn Ave. Phone: (312)753-3196
Chicago, IL 60637 Rev. Neil W. Gerdes, Libn.
Founded: 1844. **Staff:** Prof 1; Other 5. **Subjects:** Unitarian Universalism, social ethics, history of religions, philosophy and religion. **Special Collections:** Papers of Jenkin Lloyd Jones, A. Powell Davies, Jack Mendelsohn, Vincent Silliman; William Ellery Channing original manuscripts. **Holdings:** 101,000 books. **Subscriptions:** 145 journals and other serials. **Services:** Interlibrary loan; library not open to the public. **Automated Operations:** Computerized cataloging. **Computerized Information Services:** OCLC. **Networks/Consortia:** Member of Association of Chicago Theological Schools Library Council.

★9969★
Meadville Medical Center - Winslow Library (Med)
1034 Grove St. Phone: (814)333-5740
Meadville, PA 16335 Barbara Ewing, Libn.
Founded: 1986. **Staff:** Prof 1; Other 2. **Subjects:** Nursing, medicine, pre-medical sciences, allied health sciences, management. **Holdings:** 936 books; 318 bound periodical volumes; 114 audio cassette programs; 45 video cassettes. **Subscriptions:** 96 journals and other serials. **Services:** Interlibrary loan; copying; library open to employees and allied health agencies; restricted use for students. **Computerized Information Services:** MEDLARS, DIALOG Information Services. **Networks/Consortia:** Member of National Network of Libraries of Medicine - Middle Atlantic Region, Erie Area Health Information Library Cooperative (EAHILC), Northwest Interlibrary Cooperative of Pennsylvania (NICOP). **Remarks:** FAX: (814)333-5714.

★9970★
Measurement and Analysis Systems - Library
1155 Zion Rd. Phone: (814)238-0541
Bellefonte, PA 16823 Collette Harris, Libn.
Remarks: No further information was supplied by respondent.

Meat Industry Information Center
See: **National Livestock and Meat Board** (11231)

★9971★
Meat Industry Research Institute of New Zealand - Library (Food-Bev)
East St.
POB 617 Phone: 7 8556159
Hamilton, New Zealand Priscilla A. Tobin, Libn.
Founded: 1957. **Staff:** Prof 2; Other 2. **Subjects:** Meat science, microbiology, refrigeration, biochemistry, chemical engineering, mechanical engineering, electron microscopy, electronics, food technology, quality assurance, energy, management, statistics. **Holdings:** 5000 books; 5405 bound periodical volumes; 7383 reports; 1600 archival items; 67 microfiche; 8 reels of microfilm; 7853 reprints. **Subscriptions:** 403 journals and other serials. **Services:** Interlibrary loan; copying; SDI; library open to universities and research institutions. **Computerized Information Services:** DIALOG Information Services, ORBIT Search Service, FRIGINTER, N2BN, KIWINET; Journals Catalogue, Patents, Standards, Current Awareness, Staff Publications (internal databases). **Publications:** Hirinz Technical Digest (abstracts); MICAS (current awareness), monthly. **Remarks:** FAX: 7 8553833.

★9972★
Mechanical Technology Inc. - Technical Information Services (Sci-Engr)
968 Albany Shaker Rd. Phone: (518)785-2211
Latham, NY 12110 Margaret Tuft, Adm.
Staff: Prof 1; Other 1. **Subjects:** Mechanical engineering, materials technology, energy systems. **Special Collections:** Stirling engine systems development. **Holdings:** 2000 books; 500 reports; 15 VF drawers. **Subscriptions:** 160 journals and other serials. **Services:** Interlibrary loan; services not open to the public. **Automated Operations:** Computerized cataloging. **Computerized Information Services:** DIALOG Information Services. Performs searches on fee basis. **Networks/Consortia:** Member of Capital District Library Council for Reference & Research Resources (CDLC). **Remarks:** FAX: (518)785-2420. Telex: 685 4572 MTILATMUW.

★9973★
Mechanics' Institute Library (Hum, Bus-Fin)
57 Post St. Phone: (415)421-1750
San Francisco, CA 94104 Kathleen T. Pabst, Lib.Dir.
Founded: 1854. **Staff:** Prof 5; Other 14. **Subjects:** Art, art history, business, economics, American history (Civil War), Californiana, American and English literature. **Holdings:** 180,000 books; 20,000 bound periodical volumes; 800 annual reports; 32 VF drawers of clippings, reports, abstracts, ephemera; 11,000 microfiche. **Subscriptions:** 600 journals and other serials; 52 newspapers. **Services:** Interlibrary loan. **Automated Operations:** Computerized acquisitions. **Computerized Information Services:** DIALOG Information Services; internal database. Performs searches on fee basis. Contact Person: Craig Jackson, Libn. **Publications:** New Titles, monthly; newsletter, irregular - to members. **Remarks:** Alternate telephone number(s): (415)421-1752 (reference). FAX: (415)421-4551.

★9974★
Mechanics' Institute of Montreal - Atwater Computer Centre (Comp Sci)
1200 Atwater Ave.
Montreal, PQ, Canada H3Z 1X4 Phone: (514)935-0973
Founded: 1986. **Staff:** 1. **Subjects:** Computer applications, software, programming, technological change. **Special Collections:** Software and software manuals for IBM and MacIntosh personal computers. **Holdings:** 300 books. **Services:** Copying; center open to the public. **Remarks:** FAX: (514)935-1960.

★9975★
Mechanics' Institute of Montreal - Atwater Library (Sci-Engr, Hum)
1200 Atwater Ave.
Montreal, PQ, Canada H3Z 1X4 Phone: (514)935-1960
Founded: 1828. **Staff:** 3. **Subjects:** Art, archeology, anthropology, philosophy, geography, travel, Canadian history, social science, local history, literature, fiction, computer science and technology. **Special Collections:** History of the institute/archives; rare books; Roger W. Varey Collection of natural history and arts. **Holdings:** 65,800 volumes. **Subscriptions:** 64 journals and other serials; 11 newspapers. **Services:** Interlibrary loan; copying; books by mail; library open to the public. **Computerized Information Services:** UTLAS; internal databases; Envoy 100 (electronic mail service). **Publications:** Annual report; Newsletter. **Remarks:** Alternate telephone number(s): 935-7344.

★9976★
Mecklenburg County Law & Government Library (Law)
700 E. Trade St., 1st Fl. Phone: (704)336-7359
Charlotte, NC 28202-3076 Joyce Reimann, Libn.
Founded: 1926. **Staff:** Prof 1; Other 2. **Subjects:** Law. **Special Collections:** North Carolina Law collection. **Holdings:** 27,000 volumes; 561 bound periodical volumes. **Subscriptions:** 190 journals. **Services:** Copying; faxing; library open to the public. **Automated Operations:** Dynix. **Computerized Information Services:** LEXIS, WESTLAW. **Publications:** Policies and Procedures for Mecklenburg County Law & Government Library. **Special Catalogs:** Library Catalog for Mecklenburg County Law & Government Library. **Remarks:** FAX: (704)336-7539. Contains the holdings of the former Charlotte Law Library Associates - Charlotte Law Library.

★9977★
(Medan) Perhimpunan Persahabatan Indonesia-Amerika - USIS Collection (Educ)
Jalan Diponegoro, No. 23
Medan, Indonesia Joanna Lotiman, Hd. of Lib.
Founded: 1972. **Staff:** Prof 5. **Special Collections:** Southeast Asia and Indonesia. **Holdings:** 6500 books; microfiche. **Subscriptions:** 86 journals and other serials; 5 newspapers. **Services:** Copying; library open to the public. **Remarks:** Maintained or supported by the U.S. Information Agency. Focus is on materials that will assist peoples outside the United States to learn about the United States, its people, history, culture, political processes, and social milieux.

★9978★
(Medellin) Biblioteca Centro Colombo-Americano - USIS Collection (Educ)
Carrera 45, No. 53-24
Medellin, Colombia
Remarks: Maintained or supported by the U.S. Information Agency. Focus is on materials that will assist peoples outside the United States to learn about the United States, its people, history, culture, political processes, and social milieux.

★9979★
Medfield Historical Society - Library (Hist)
6 Pleasant St.
Box 233
Medfield, MA 02052 Toni Hurd, Archv.
Subjects: Local history and genealogy. **Holdings:** Figures not available. **Services:** Library open to the public by permission.

★9980★
Medfield State Hospital - Medical Library (Med)
Hospital Rd. Phone: (508)359-7312
Medfield, MA 02052 Jeanne Migliacci, Sr.Libn.
Founded: 1951. **Staff:** Prof 1. **Subjects:** Psychiatry, nursing, neurology, psychology. **Holdings:** 2063 books; 1946 bound periodical volumes; 100 pamphlets; 105 cassettes; 3 drawers of pamphlets (uncataloged). **Subscriptions:** 37 journals and other serials; 3 newspapers. **Services:** Interlibrary loan; library open to the public for reference use only by request. **Networks/Consortia:** Member of National Network of Libraries of Medicine - New England Region. **Remarks:** FAX: (617)727-9830, ext. 462. Includes the holdings of the Nursing Library.

★9981★
Medford Historical Society - Library (Hist)
10 Governor's Ave. Phone: (617)395-7863
Medford, MA 02155 Michael Bradford, Cur.-Libn.
Founded: 1896. **Staff:** Prof 1. **Subjects:** Local history. **Special Collections:** Lydia Maria Child Collection; Civil War Collection; slave trade (mid-18th century). **Holdings:** Books; manuscripts; letters; archives of local newspapers (to 1930) and early Boston newspapers (early 19th century). **Services:** Library open to the public for reference use only. **Publications:** Medford on the Mystic, 1980. **Remarks:** Alternate telephone number(s): 391-8739.

★9982★
Medford Mail Tribune - Library (Publ)
Box 1108 Phone: (503)776-4493
Medford, OR 97501 Pamela S. Sieg, Libn.
Founded: 1975. **Staff:** Prof 1. **Subjects:** Southern Oregon topics; personalities; state laws; local history. **Special Collections:** Tribune, 1892 to present, on microfilm. **Holdings:** 1000 volumes; 50 VF drawers of clippings, photographs, maps. **Subscriptions:** 22 newspapers and other serials. **Services:** Library open to the public with restrictions. **Computerized Information Services:** DataTimes. **Remarks:** FAX: (503)776-4376.

★9983★
Media Perspektiven - Arbeitsgemeinschaft Rundfunkwerbung - Bibliothek (Info Sci)
AM Steinernen Stock 1 Phone: 69 1552858
W-6000 Frankfurt, Germany Mrs. Dagmar Drescher
Founded: 1963. **Staff:** Prof 5. **Subjects:** Mass media, communication, advertising. **Holdings:** 16,000 books; 261 bound periodical volumes. **Services:** Copying; library open to the public with restrictions. **Computerized Information Services:** Internal databases.

★9984★
Medic Alert Foundation International - Central Reference File of Membership (Med)
2323 Colorado Phone: (209)668-3333
Turlock, CA 95380 Kenneth W. Harms, Pres.
Founded: 1956. **Staff:** Prof 8; Other 135. **Holdings:** Figures not available. **Services:** Library not open to the public. **Remarks:** Maintains a central file with emergency medical information, addresses of physician and nearest relative of all members. Information is crossfiled under name and serial number which appears on the member's Medic Alert Emblem worn around the wrist or neck, and is available to physicians and other authorized personnel on a 24 hour, collect telephone call basis in emergencies. FAX: (209)668-8752. **Staff:** Mark Weight, V.P. of Oper.; Rich Haggard, V.P. of Fld.Serv.; Julie Watts, V.P. of Commun.; Floyd Harmon, V.P. of Dev.

★9985★
Medical Associates - Health Center - Library (Med)
W180 N7950 Town Hall Rd. Phone: (414)255-2500
Menomonee Falls, WI 53051 Joyce Madsen, Libn.
Founded: 1971. **Staff:** Prof 1. **Subjects:** Medicine. **Holdings:** 350 books; 1000 bound periodical volumes; 5 VF drawers of pamphlets; 600 cassette tapes. **Subscriptions:** 98 journals and other serials. **Services:** Library not open to the public. **Computerized Information Services:** MEDLINE, DIALOG Information Services. **Networks/Consortia:** Member of Southeastern Wisconsin Health Science Library Consortium (SWHSL), National Network of Libraries of Medicine (NN/LM). **Remarks:** FAX: (414)255-2434.

★9986★
Medical Care Development, Inc. - Library (Med)
11 Parkwood Dr. Phone: (207)622-7566
Augusta, ME 04330 Maryann Libbey, Libn.
Staff: Prof 1. **Subjects:** Health - planning, policy, manpower; rural health. **Holdings:** 300 books. **Subscriptions:** 30 journals and other serials. **Services:** Interlibrary loan; library open to the public with restrictions. **Automated Operations:** Computerized acquisitions. **Computerized Information Services:** BRS Information Technologies. **Networks/Consortia:** Member of Health Science Library and Information Cooperative of Maine (HSLIC). **Remarks:** FAX: (207)622-3616.

★9987★
Medical Center - Simon Schwob Medical Library (Med)
710 Center St. Phone: (404)571-1178
Columbus, GA 31902 Opal Bartlett, Libn.
Founded: 1949. **Staff:** 2. **Subjects:** Medicine, surgery, nursing. **Holdings:** 3474 books; 8077 bound periodical volumes; 275 tapes. **Subscriptions:** 195 journals. **Services:** Interlibrary loan; copying; library open to the public with restrictions. **Computerized Information Services:** MEDLINE; DOCLINE (electronic mail service). **Networks/Consortia:** Member of Health Science Libraries Consortium of Central Georgia (HSLCG), Georgia Interactive Network for Medical Information (GaIN), Atlanta Health Science Libraries Consortium (AHSLC). **Remarks:** FAX: (404)571-1779.

★9988★
Medical Center of Beaver County - Health Sciences Library (Med)
1000 Dutch Ridge Rd. Phone: (412)728-7000
Beaver, PA 15009 Patricia M. Coghlan, Dir.
Staff: Prof 2; Other 2. **Subjects:** Internal medicine, surgery, oncology, nursing, hospital administration. **Holdings:** 3500 books; 7000 bound periodical volumes; NCME video cassettes. **Subscriptions:** 303 journals and other serials. **Services:** Interlibrary loan; copying; SDI; library open to the public by appointment. **Automated Operations:** Computerized ILL. **Computerized Information Services:** MEDLARS, BRS Information Technologies, DIALOG Information Services, WILSONLINE. Performs searches on fee basis. Contact Person: Marilyn J. Seymour, Med.Libn., 728-7000, ext. 1334. **Networks/Consortia:** Member of National Network of Libraries of Medicine - Middle Atlantic Region. **Publications:** Newsnotes. **Remarks:** FAX: (412)728-7429.

★9989★
Medical Center of Central Massachusetts - Medical Center Library Services (Med)
119 Belmont St. Phone: (508)793-6421
Worcester, MA 01605 Martha Bedard, Dir., Lib.Serv.
Staff: Prof 2; Other 1. **Subjects:** Medicine, nursing, dentistry. **Special Collections:** Medical ethics; gerontology. **Holdings:** 4000 books; 8000 bound periodical volumes. **Subscriptions:** 250 journals and other serials. **Services:** Interlibrary loan; library open to the public. **Computerized Information Services:** PaperChase, MEDLINE, BRS/COLLEAGUE; CD-ROMs (MEDLINE, CINAHL). Performs searches on fee basis. **Networks/Consortia:** Member of Central Massachusetts Consortium of Health Related Libraries (CMCHRL), Massachusetts Health Sciences Libraries Network (MaHSLiN). **Remarks:** FAX: (508)793-6527. **Staff:** Andrew P. Dzaugis, Info.Serv.Libn.

★9990★
Medical Center of Delaware - Christiana Hospital - Library (Med)
4755 Ogletown-Stanton Rd.
Box 6001 Phone: (302)733-1115
Newark, DE 19718 Christine Chastain-Warheit, Dir. of Libs.
Founded: 1985. **Staff:** Prof 3; Other 3. **Subjects:** Clinical medicine, nursing. **Holdings:** 7000 books; 7000 bound periodical volumes. **Subscriptions:** 423 journals and other serials. **Services:** Interlibrary loan; SDI; library open to the public with restrictions. **Automated Operations:** Computerized cataloging and acquisitions. **Computerized Information Services:** NLM, BRS Information Technologies, DIALOG Information Services. **Networks/Consortia:** Member of Libraries in the New Castle County System (LINCS), Wilmington Area Biomedical Library Consortium (WABLC), Delaware Library Consortium (DLC). **Remarks:** FAX: (302)733-1365; (302)428-2101. **Staff:** Patricia Patterson, Med.Libn.; Diane Wolf, Med.Libn.

★9991★
Medical Center of Delaware - Wilmington Hospital - Medical Library (Med)
501 W. 14th St.
Box 1668 Phone: (302)428-2201
Wilmington, DE 19899 Christine Chastain-Warheit, Dir. of Libs.
Founded: 1965. **Staff:** Prof 1; Other 1. **Subjects:** Medicine, dentistry. **Holdings:** 895 books; 1560 bound periodical volumes. **Subscriptions:** 115 journals and other serials. **Services:** Interlibrary loan; copying; library open to the public for reference use only. **Automated Operations:** Computerized cataloging. **Computerized Information Services:** BRS Information Technologies, MEDLINE, OCLC. **Networks/Consortia:** Member of Wilmington Area Biomedical Library Consortium (WABLC), Delaware Library Consortium (DLC). **Remarks:** FAX: (302)428-2101.

★9992★
Medical Center Hospital - Bell-Marsh Memorial Library (Med)
Box 6400 Phone: (903)531-8685
Tyler, TX 75711 Ana Wright, Med. Staff Coord.
Founded: 1951. **Subjects:** Medicine. **Holdings:** 250 books; 500 bound periodical volumes. **Subscriptions:** 19 journals and other serials. **Services:** Interlibrary loan; library not open to the public. **Remarks:** Library located at 1000 Beckham Ave., Tyler, TX 75701. FAX: (903)535-6464.

★9993★
Medical Center at Princeton - Medical Center Library (Med)
253 Witherspoon St. Phone: (609)497-4488
Princeton, NJ 08540 Louise M. Yorke, Med.Libn.
Founded: 1953. **Staff:** Prof 2; Other 13. **Subjects:** Medicine, surgery, nursing, allied health sciences. **Special Collections:** Archives; Anna K. Snyderman Plastic Surgery Collection. **Holdings:** 3000 books; 4500 bound periodical volumes; 4 drawers of pamphlets; 500 video cassettes; 450 audio cassettes; 100 slide sets and filmstrips. **Subscriptions:** 216 journals and other serials. **Services:** Interlibrary loan; copying; SDI; LATCH; library open to the public for reference use only. **Computerized Information Services:** BRS Information Technologies, MEDLARS. Performs searches on fee basis. **Networks/Consortia:** Member of MEDCORE, Central Jersey Health Science Libraries Association (CJHSLA), Health Sciences Library Association of New Jersey (HSLANJ). **Publications:** Guide to the Library, annual - to all new employees; Newsletter; bibliographies. **Special Catalogs:** AV catalog; Periodicals Holdings List; pamphlet list. **Remarks:** FAX: (609)497-4998.

★9994★
Medical and Chirurgical Faculty of the State of Maryland - Library (Med)
1211 Cathedral St.
Baltimore, MD 21201 Phone: (301)539-0872
Founded: 1830. **Staff:** Prof 2; Other 4. **Subjects:** Medicine, allied health sciences, medical history. **Special Collections:** Krause Collection (History of Medicine); Ruhrah Collection (pediatrics); Osler Collection (297 items by and about Osler). **Holdings:** 100,000 volumes; 750 manuscripts. **Subscriptions:** 350 journals and other serials. **Services:** Interlibrary loan (fee); copying; library open to the public for reference use only. **Computerized Information Services:** MEDLARS, BRS Information Technologies. Performs searches on fee basis. **Networks/Consortia:** Member of Maryland Association of Health Science Librarians (MAHSL), National Network of Libraries of Medicine (NN/LM). **Special Catalogs:** Current periodicals list. **Remarks:** FAX: (301)727-5967. **Staff:** Susan Harman, Dir. of Tech.Serv.; Lisa Pratt, Dir. of Pub.Serv.

★9995★
Medical College of Georgia - Robert B. Greenblatt, MD Library (Med)
Augusta, GA 30912-4400 Phone: (404)721-3441
Camilla B. Reid, Interim Dir. of Libs.
Founded: 1828. **Staff:** Prof 10.6 Other 29.75. **Subjects:** Medicine, dentistry, nursing, allied health sciences. **Special Collections:** The original library of the Medical College of Georgia and other 19th century books. **Holdings:** 155,000 volumes. **Subscriptions:** 1500 journals and other serials. **Services:** Interlibrary loan; copying; library open to the public. **Automated Operations:** Computerized cataloging, acquisitions, serials, and circulation. **Computerized Information Services:** MEDLINE, DIALOG Information Services, BRS Information Technologies, Current Contents Search, miniMEDLINE; internal database. Contact Person: Lyn H. Dennison, Hd., Ref.Serv., 721-3667. **Networks/Consortia:** Member of SOLINET, National Network of Libraries of Medicine - Southeastern/Atlantic Region, Consortium of Southern Biomedical Libraries (CONBLS). **Publications:** Annual Report; library newsletter. **Remarks:** FAX: (404)721-6006. **Staff:** Linda M. Flavin, Hd.Cat.Serv.; Jett C. McCann, Hd., Ser.Serv.; M. Katherine Mosner, ILL; Dorothy H. Mims, Spec.Coll.Libn.; Gail C. Anderson, Coll.Dev.Libn.; Frank L. Davis, Educ.Serv.Libn.; Bonnie H. Owen, Database Serv.Libn.; Donna J. Trainor, Hd., Circ.Serv.

★9996★
Medical College of Ohio at Toledo - Raymon H. Mulford Library (Med)
3000 Arlington Ave. Phone: (419)381-4225
Toledo, OH 43614 David W. Boilard, Dir.
Founded: 1967. **Staff:** Prof 4; Other 13. **Subjects:** Medicine, dentistry, nursing, animal medicine, allied health sciences. **Special Collections:** A. Gorman Hills Collection (2000 items); Joseph Needham Reprint Collection

(200 boxes). **Holdings:** 44,837 books; 68,910 bound periodical volumes; 3439 microfiche; 99 reels of microfilm. **Subscriptions:** 1905 journals and other serials. **Services:** Interlibrary loan; copying; SDI; library open to the public with restrictions. **Automated Operations:** Computerized cataloging and serials. **Computerized Information Services:** NLM, BRS Information Technologies; OCLC, DOCLINE (electronic mail services). Performs searches on fee basis. **Networks/Consortia:** Member of National Network of Libraries of Medicine - Greater Midwest Region, Committee for Library Cooperation (CLC). **Special Catalogs:** List of Serials Held; Subject List of Serials. **Remarks:** Alternate telephone number(s): 381-4223. FAX: (419)382-8842. **Staff:** John Lucas, Hd., Tech.Serv.; Alexander Kuby, ILL Libn.

★9997★
Medical College of Pennsylvania - Archives and Special Collections on Women in Medicine (Med)
3300 Henry Ave. Phone: (215)842-7124
Philadelphia, PA 19129 Janet Miller, Dir./Archv.
Founded: 1977. **Staff:** Prof 3; Other 1. **Subjects:** Women physicians, health care for women, Medical College of Pennsylvania, education, medicine. **Special Collections:** College archives; women in medicine; Black Women Physicians Collection; Asian American Women Physicians Project; Oral History Project (43 interviews); American Women's Hospitals Records (25 linear feet); Medical Women's International Association Records (10 linear feet). **Holdings:** 1000 books; 6000 reprints; 15,000 photographs; 1500 linear feet of archival materials and manuscripts; memorabilia. **Services:** Copying; photograph and slide reproduction; archives open to the public. **Automated Operations:** Computerized cataloging. **Publications:** Newsletter, biannual - available on request; Guide to Collections in the Archives & Special Collections on Women in Medicine. **Special Indexes:** An Inventory to the Records of the American Women's Hospitals: 1917-1982. **Remarks:** FAX: (215)843-6862. **Staff:** F. Michael Angelo, Photo.Cur.

★9998★
Medical College of Pennsylvania - Eastern Pennsylvania Psychiatric Institute - Mental Health and Neurosciences Library (Med)
3200 Henry Ave. Phone: (215)842-4509
Philadelphia, PA 19129 Etheldra Templeton, Dir.
Founded: 1956. **Staff:** Prof 3; Other 3. **Subjects:** Psychiatry, psychoanalysis, behavioral sciences, neurosciences. **Holdings:** 15,000 books; 14,000 bound periodical volumes; 500 audiotapes. **Subscriptions:** 600 journals and other serials. **Services:** Interlibrary loan; copying; SDI; library open to the public. **Automated Operations:** Computerized public access catalog, cataloging, and circulation. **Computerized Information Services:** DIALOG Information Services, BRS Information Technologies, NLM, OCLC; BITNET (electronic mail service). Performs searches on fee basis. Contact Person: Lenore Hardy, Assoc.Libn. **Networks/Consortia:** Member of National Network of Libraries of Medicine - Middle Atlantic Region, Health Sciences Libraries Consortium (HSLC), PALINET. **Publications:** Library Consult, monthly. **Remarks:** FAX: (215)849-0820. **Staff:** Carol Welch, ILL; Kathleen Turner, Ref.

★9999★
Medical College of Pennsylvania - Florence A. Moore Library of Medicine (Med)
3300 Henry Ave. Phone: (215)842-6910
Philadelphia, PA 19129 Etheldra Templeton, Lib.Dir.
Founded: 1865. **Staff:** 22. **Subjects:** Biomedicine. **Special Collections:** Women in Medicine. **Holdings:** 21,474 books; 36,825 bound periodical volumes. **Subscriptions:** 1140 journals and other serials. **Services:** Interlibrary loan; copying; SDI; library open to the public for reference use only. **Computerized Information Services:** Internal databases; BITNET (electronic mail service). **Networks/Consortia:** Member of Health Sciences Libraries Consortium (HSLC), National Network of Libraries of Medicine - Middle Atlantic Region. **Remarks:** FAX: (215)849-1380. Electronic mail address(es): MEDCOLPA (BITNET).

Medical College of Virginia
See: **Virginia Commonwealth University - Medical College of Virginia Campus** (19862)

★10000★
Medical College of Wisconsin - Libraries (Med)
8701 Watertown Plank Rd. Phone: (414)257-8323
Milwaukee, WI 53226 Patrick W. Brennen, Dir. of Libs.
Founded: 1913. **Staff:** Prof 14; Other 19. **Subjects:** Medicine, allied health sciences. **Special Collections:** History of Medicine (10,000 volumes). **Holdings:** 79,000 books; 130,000 bound periodical volumes; 1310 AV programs. **Subscriptions:** 2755 journals and other serials. **Services:** Interlibrary loan; copying; SDI; libraries open to the public. **Automated Operations:** Computerized cataloging, acquisitions, and serials. **Computerized Information Services:** NLM, DIALOG Information Services, BRS Information Technologies, PFDS Online, OCLC; CD-ROM (MEDLINE); BITNET (electronic mail service); Performs searches on fee basis. Contact Person: Rita Sieracki, Clin.Ref.Libn., 257-8326. **Networks/ Consortia:** Member of Southeastern Wisconsin Health Science Library Consortium (SWHSL), National Network of Libraries of Medicine - Greater Midwest Region, Wisconsin Interlibrary Services (WILS). **Publications:** Acquisitions list, monthly; holdings list; Newsline (newsletter). **Remarks:** Holdings represent main library and three branches. FAX: (414)257-8215. Electronic mail address(es): BRENNEN@MEDCOLWI (BITNET). **Staff:** Dieta Murra, Asst.Dir., Tech.Serv.; Mary Blackwelder, Assoc.Dir., Adm.; Glynis Asu, ILL Libn.; Kathleen Strube, Sr.Clin.Ref.Libn.; Molly Youngkin, Clin.Ref.Libn.; Elizabeth Wong, Sys.Libn.; Janice Munkholm, Acq.Libn.; Shirley Gronholm, Pub.Serv.Libn.; Richard Carr, Asst.Dir. - Access Serv.; Anne Gordon, Cat.Libn.; Tulin Diktas, Sys.Anl.

★10001★
Medical Cybernetics Foundation - Library (Med)
Medical Design Center
P.O. Box 57333
Jacksonville, FL 32241 Phone: (904)262-9248
Subjects: Medical machinery, cybernetics, engineering and medicine. **Holdings:** 5000 volumes; statistical materials. **Computerized Information Services:** Medical Data Exchange Program, contact (904)725-4702.

★10002★
Medical Economics Publishing - Library (Publ)
5 Paragon Dr. Phone: (201)358-7417
Montvale, NJ 07645-1742 Nancy J. Wall, Libn.
Subjects: Medicine, family practice, medical marketing. **Special Collections:** Patient Care magazine archives. **Holdings:** Figures not available. **Services:** Interlibrary loan; copying; SDI. **Computerized Information Services:** BRS Information Technologies. **Networks/Consortia:** Member of Bergen Passaic Regional Library Cooperative. **Publications:** Library acquisitions, 6/year - for internal distribution only. **Special Indexes:** Subject file of patient education aids. **Remarks:** FAX: (201)573-8979.

★10003★
Medical Foundation of Buffalo, Inc. - Library (Med)
73 High St. Phone: (716)856-9600
Buffalo, NY 14203 Dr. Vivian Cody, Sr.Res.Sci.
Founded: 1956. **Subjects:** Hormone-related disorders, including studies in cancer, heart disease, diabetes. **Holdings:** 2000 books and scientific journals. **Services:** Library not open to the public. **Computerized Information Services:** Internal database. **Remarks:** FAX: (716)852-4846.

★10004★
Medical Group Management Association - Library Resource Center (Med)
104 Inverness Terr., E. Phone: (303)799-1111
Englewood, CO 80112-5306 Barbara U. Hamilton, Dir.
Founded: 1972. **Staff:** Prof 3; Other 4. **Subjects:** Group practice administration and statistics; health maintenance organizations; ambulatory care administration; medical clinic architectural design and construction; managed care. **Special Collections:** Information Exchange Collection (data from existing medical group practices); MGMA Archives; American College of Medical Group Administrators Professional Papers. **Holdings:** 5000 books; 900 folders of VF material. **Subscriptions:** 225 journals and other serials. **Services:** Interlibrary loan; copying; center open to the public with restrictions. **Automated Operations:** Computerized cataloging. **Computerized Information Services:** MEDLARS, DIALOG Information Services, BRS Information Technologies. Performs searches on fee basis. **Networks/Consortia:** Member of Colorado Council of Medical Librarians. **Publications:** Bibliography Series; Administrator's Bookshelf, annual. **Special Indexes:** Internal index to all current literature on management aspects of medical group practice and other types of ambulatory care administration. **Remarks:** FAX: (303)799-1683. **Formerly:** Located in Denver, CO. **Staff:** Donna Keslin, Asst.Dir.; Patricia Byler, Libn.; Dawn Bias, Lib.Tech.

★10005★
Medical Information Retrieval Center - Consumer Health Information Research Institute (Med)
3521 Broadway Phone: (816)753-8850
Kansas City, MO 64111 Dr. George X. Trimble, Dir.
Founded: 1947. **Staff:** Prof 1; Other 2. **Subjects:** Clinical medicine, health fraud and quackery, patient education, toxicology, history of medicine. **Special Collections:** Medicine in art; therapeutics; medical literature reprint technology. **Holdings:** 575 volumes; 1050 monographs; 505,000 medical literature reprints. **Subscriptions:** 150 journals and other serials. **Services:** Copying; will answer brief inquiries and make referrals; center open for medical or academic use by appointment. **Computerized Information Services:** Internal database. **Publications:** Reports and critical reviews, irregular; medical literature critiques, irregular. **Special Indexes:** Index and cross-index to medical literature reprints; index to therapeutic drugs in generic and proprietary terms; index of medical eponyms. **Remarks:** FAX: (816)753-6706. **Formed by the merger of:** Consumer Health Information Research Institute, and Trinity Lutheran Hospital - North - Medical Information Retrieval Center.

★10006★
Medical Letter - Library (Med)
1000 Main St. Phone: (914)235-0500
New Rochelle, NY 10801 Amy Faucard, Libn.
Founded: 1959. **Subjects:** Drugs, therapeutic agents. **Holdings:** Books; reprints; advertisements. **Subscriptions:** 180 journals and other serials. **Services:** Interlibrary loan; library not open to the public except in special circumstances. **Automated Operations:** Computerized ILL. **Computerized Information Services:** MEDLARS, BRS Information Technologies, NLM; DOCLINE (electronic mail service). **Networks/Consortia:** Member of Medical Library Center of New York (MLCNY), Health Information Libraries of Westchester (HILOW). **Remarks:** FAX: (914)576-3377.

★10007★
Medical Library Center of New York (Med)
5 E. 102nd St., 7th Fl. Phone: (212)427-1630
New York, NY 10029 Lois Weinstein, Dir.
Founded: 1959. **Staff:** Prof 4; Other 14. **Subjects:** Medicine, allied health sciences, nursing, dentistry. **Special Collections:** Biomedical dissertations from universities throughout the world; U.S. Government Printing Office Depository Library (selected). **Holdings:** 102,000 bound periodical volumes; 160,156 unbound periodical issues; 150,000 dissertations; 11,000 government documents. **Services:** Interlibrary loan; messenger service for network libraries; serials rationalization program for member libraries; library not open to the public. **Automated Operations:** Computerized cataloging and serials. **Computerized Information Services:** NLM, RLIN. **Special Catalogs:** Union Catalog of Medical Periodicals; UCMP/Quarterly. **Remarks:** The Medical Library Center provides cooperative housing and acquisition of less-used materials in medicine and its allied sciences for the health science libraries in the New York Metropolitan area. FAX: (212)860-3496. **Staff:** Robert Dempsey, Hd., Automation Serv.; Josh Devlin, Ser.; Kathy Crosby, Hd., Access Serv.

★10008★
Medical Library of Mecklenburg County - Bryant L. Galusha, M.D. LRC of Charlotte AHEC (Med)
Box 32861 Phone: (704)355-3129
Charlotte, NC 28232-2861 Constance M. Wallace, Dir., Lib.Serv.
Founded: 1977. **Staff:** Prof 4; Other 5. **Subjects:** Clinical medicine, allied health sciences. **Holdings:** 5000 books; 30,000 bound periodical volumes; 3 VF drawers of pamphlets; 1200 video cassettes. **Subscriptions:** 400 journals and other serials. **Services:** Interlibrary loan (fee); library not open to the public. **Computerized Information Services:** NLM, BRS Information Technologies; CD-ROMs; electronic mail. Performs searches on fee basis. **Networks/Consortia:** Member of Charlotte Area Educational Consortium, North Carolina Area Health Education Centers Program Library and Information Services Network. **Publications:** Annual Report - to members of the society. **Remarks:** FAX: (704)355-3116.

★10009★
Medical Library of Pierce County (Med)
315 South K St.
Box 5299 Phone: (206)594-1075
Tacoma, WA 98405-0986 Cathy Edelman, Exec.Dir./Hd.Libn.
Staff: 3. **Subjects:** Medicine. **Special Collections:** Biomedical sciences. **Holdings:** 2000 books; 1222 bound periodical volumes; 8 VF drawers. **Subscriptions:** 165 biomedical and administrative journals. **Services:** Interlibrary loan; copying; library open to members of the Medical Society of Pierce County, hospital employees of participating hospitals, and by private membership to other professionals. **Computerized Information Services:** MEDLARS, BRS Information Technologies; OnTyme Electronic Message Network Service (electronic mail service). **Networks/Consortia:** Member of Western Library Network (WLN). **Publications:** Medical Library of Pierce County Bulletin, quarterly. **Remarks:** FAX: (206)594-1394. Electronic mail address(es): CLASS.PCML (OnTyme Electronic Message Network Service).

★10010★
Medical Planning Associates - Library (Med)
1601 Rambla Pacifico
Malibu, CA 90265 Phone: (213)456-2084
Founded: 1961. **Staff:** Prof 1. **Subjects:** Hospital design and planning, health care delivery systems, computer technology, architecture. **Holdings:** 2100 books; 6000 unbound periodicals; 8000 monographs; architectural records; 4800 cataloged journal articles and newspaper clippings. **Subscriptions:** 265 journals and other serials. **Services:** Library not open to the public. **Automated Operations:** Computerized cataloging, acquisitions, serials, and circulation. **Computerized Information Services:** The Source Information Network, CompuServe Information Service, MEDLINE, BRS Information Technologies, PFDS Online; DTR (internal database). **Special Indexes:** Consultant file and newsletter serials file (online).

★10011★
Medical Research Council Information Group - Library (Med)
P.O. Box 19070
Tygerberg 7505, Republic of South Africa Phone: 21 9320311
Founded: 1976. **Staff:** 3. **Subjects:** Medicine, biology, health care. **Holdings:** 7000 bound volumes. **Subscriptions:** 250 journals and other serials. **Services:** SDI; document delivery; library open to the public. **Computerized Information Services:** MEDLINE, TOXLINE, BIOSIS, PsycINFO, CAB Abstracts, Excerpta Medica, CANCERLINE; South African Medical Literature (internal database); ALANET, DIALMAIL (electronic mail services). Performs searches. **Remarks:** FAX: 21 9312500. Telex: 5 20525 SA; 9550184. Electronic mail address(es): 0254 (ALANET); 12540 (DIALMAIL). **Formerly:** South African Medical Research Council - Institute for Biomedical Communication - Library. **Staff:** George Milligar; Glenda Whitaker; Berry Pflugler.

Medical Research Institute of San Francisco - Alcohol Research Group
See: **Alcohol Research Group** (328)

★10012★
Medical Society of Prince Edward Island - Library (Med)
559 N. River Rd. Phone: (902)368-7303
Charlottetown, PE, Canada C1E 1J7 Marilyn Lowther, Exec.Dir.
Founded: 1980. **Staff:** 2. **Subjects:** Medicine - practice and politics. **Holdings:** Archives. **Services:** Interlibrary loan; copying; library open to the public. **Publications:** Newsletter, monthly - for internal distribution only. **Remarks:** FAX: (902)566-3934.

★10013★
Medical Society of the State of New York - Albion O. Bernstein Library (Med)
420 Lakeville Rd. Phone: (516)488-6100
Lake Success, NY 11042 Ella Abney, Libn.
Staff: Prof 1; Other 1. **Subjects:** Socioeconomic and clinical medicine. **Holdings:** 7000 books; 10,000 bound periodical volumes; 2000 other cataloged items. **Subscriptions:** 375 journals and other serials; 5 newspapers. **Services:** Interlibrary loan; copying; library open to the public for reference use only. **Networks/Consortia:** Member of Brooklyn-Queens-Staten Island Health Sciences Librarians (BQSI), Medical & Scientific Libraries of Long Island (MEDLI). **Remarks:** FAX: (516)488-1267.

★10014★
Medical University of South Carolina - Library (Med)
171 Ashley Ave. Phone: (803)792-2371
Charleston, SC 29425-3001 Thomas G. Basler, Ph.D., Dir.
Founded: 1824. **Staff:** Prof 14; Other 24. **Subjects:** Medicine, dentistry, nursing, pharmacy, health-related professions, pharmacology. **Special**

Collections: History of Medicine (10,010 volumes). **Holdings:** 84,753 books; 110,308 bound periodical volumes; 12 VF drawers of pamphlets, clippings, South Carolina material; 2306 titles of AV programs, self-instructional programs, videotapes, audio cassettes, slides. **Subscriptions:** 2967 journals and other serials; 9 newspapers. **Services:** Interlibrary loan; SDI; library open to the public with restrictions on borrowing. **Automated Operations:** Computerized public access catalog, cataloging, acquisitions, serials, circulation and ILL (DOCLINE). **Computerized Information Services:** DIALOG Information Services, BRS Information Technologies, OCLC, MEDLARS, miniMEDLINE; CD-ROM (MEDLINE, Aries Knowledge Finder, CASSIS, CINAHL); BITNET (electronic mail service). Performs searches on fee basis. **Networks/Consortia:** Member of Charleston Academic Libraries Consortium, SOLINET, South Carolina Health Information Network (SCHIN), National Network of Libraries of Medicine - Southeastern/Atlantic Region, Consortium of Southern Biomedical Libraries (CONBLS). **Publications:** Library Notes, monthly; MUSCLS, irregular. **Remarks:** Alternate telephone number(s): 792-2372. FAX: (803)792-7947. Electronic mail address(es): BASLER@MUSC (BITNET). **Staff:** Betty Newsom, Cur., Waring Lib.; Anne K. Robichaux, Assoc.Dir.; Marcia Reinhardt, Ref.Libn.; Teri Lynn Herbert, Ref.Libn.; Peggy Mauldin, ILL; Robert Poyer, Coord., Pub.Serv.; Nancy McKeehan, Asst.Dir., Libs./Sys.; Nancy Smith, Hd., Sys.Oper. & Instr.; Richard Syracuse, Coord., Bibliog.Cont.; Elizabeth Burkhart, Coord., LRC; Dee Boggan, Coord., Coll.Dev.; Bobbie Carlson, Hd., Ser.Mgt.

★10015★
Medical University of South Carolina - Marine Biomedical Research Program - Library
Fort Johnson, Box 12559
Charleston, SC 29142
Defunct.

★10016★
Medical University of South Carolina - Multipurpose Arthritis Center Library (Med)
Division of Rheumatology and Immunology
171 Ashley Ave., CSB 912 Phone: (803)792-2000
Charleston, SC 29425 E.C. LeRoy, M.D., Dir.
Staff: 1. **Subjects:** Rheumatology, immunology, internal medicine. **Special Collections:** Rheumatology Patient Education Library (30 pamphlets; AV programs). **Holdings:** 200 books; 100 bound periodical volumes. **Subscriptions:** 25 journals and other serials. **Services:** Library not open to the public. **Publications:** Patient booklets. **Remarks:** FAX: (803)792-7121.

★10017★
Medina County Law Library Association (Law)
Court House
93 Public Square Phone: (216)725-9744
Medina, OH 44256 Sally A. Davis-Lewis, Ck.
Founded: 1899. **Staff:** 1. **Subjects:** Law. **Holdings:** 17,500 books; 900 bound periodical volumes; 12,000 microfiche. **Subscriptions:** 3 newspapers. **Services:** Library not open to the public. **Computerized Information Services:** WESTLAW.

★10018★
Medizinische Hochschule Hannover - Hochschulbibliothek (Med)
Konstanty Gutschow Str 8
Postfach 610180 Phone: 511 5323335
W-3000 Hannover, Germany Dr. Guntram Kuske
Founded: 1964. **Staff:** Prof 23; Other 10.5. **Subjects:** Medicine, dentistry. **Holdings:** 85,000 books; 85,000 bound periodical volumes; 1000 AV materials. **Services:** Interlibrary loan; copying; SDI; library open to the public. **Computerized Information Services:** DIMDI, STN International. Contact Person: Dr. Hans Hummel. **Remarks:** FAX: 511 5323346.

Medley Library
See: **Diocese of Fredericton - Synod Archives** (4877)

★10019★
Medtronic, Inc. - Information Resource Center (Med, Sci-Engr)
7000 Central Ave., N.E. Phone: (612)574-3496
Minneapolis, MN 55432 Steve Rasmussen, Mgr., Info.Rsrcs.
Founded: 1965. **Staff:** Prof 4; Other 5. **Subjects:** Biomedical engineering, cardiac pacemaking, medical electronics, electrical stimulation, cardiology. **Special Collections:** Cardiac pacemaking articles in all languages; electrical stimulation articles in all languages. **Holdings:** 6000 books; 5000 bound periodical volumes; 17,000 pacemaker papers. **Subscriptions:** 500 journals and other serials; 5 newspapers. **Services:** Interlibrary loan; copying; literature searching; SDI; library open to the public by appointment. **Computerized Information Services:** DIALOG Information Services, BRS Information Technologies, Dow Jones News/Retrieval, InvesText, LEXIS, NEXIS, STN International, ORBIT Search Service, OCLC; ProCite (internal database). **Publications:** New Book list, irregular; Cardiovascular Bibliography, monthly. **Remarks:** FAX: (612)572-5421.

John Franklin Mee Memorial Library
See: **Hive Publishing Company - John Franklin Mee Memorial Library** (7294)

P.J. Meertens-Institut
See: **Koninklijke Nederlandse Akademie van Wetenschappen** (8786)

★10020★
Meeting House Green Memorial and Historical Association, Inc. - Tuck Memorial Museum - Library (Hist)
Meeting House Green
P.O. Box 1601 Phone: (603)926-8652
Hampton, NH 03842 Ansell Palmer, Pres.
Founded: 1925. **Staff:** Prof 1. **Subjects:** History, biography and autobiography, genealogy. **Special Collections:** Post card collections of Hampton and Hampton Beach subjects; area family genealogies; New Hampshire town histories (80); items from Old Hampton. **Holdings:** 300 volumes; newspapers; photographs of Hampton area; scrapbooks; New Hampshire Marine Memorial Album; Edward Tuck Memorial Album; oil paintings of old Hampton scenes. **Services:** Library open to the public by appointment. **Remarks:** Library located at 40 Park Ave., Hampton, NH. Alternate telephone number(s): (603)926-2883. **Also Known As:** Hampton Historical Society.

★10021★
Meharry Medical College - Library (Med)
1005 D.B. Todd Phone: (615)327-6728
Nashville, TN 37208 Cheryl Hamberg, Dir.
Founded: 1886. **Staff:** Prof 12; Other 18. **Subjects:** Medicine, dentistry, public health, medical technology, health care administration. **Special Collections:** Black Medical History Collection (250 books; 100 manuscripts); Meharry Archives Collection (200 books; 59 dissertations; 235 boxes of manuscripts; 98 VF drawers). **Holdings:** 20,716 books; 53,406 bound periodical volumes; 634 audio cassettes; 609 video cassettes; 400 slide/tape sets. **Subscriptions:** 1288 journals and other serials. **Services:** Interlibrary loan (fee); copying; SDI; library open to the public. **Automated Operations:** Computerized cataloging, acquisitions, circulation, and serials. **Computerized Information Services:** MEDLINE, OCLC, DIALOG Information Services; CD-ROMs (MEDLINE, OncoDisc, PsycLIT, Sociofile, Scientific American, CONSULT, ERIC, MAXX); BITNET (electronic mail service). Performs searches on fee basis. **Networks/Consortia:** Member of National Network of Libraries of Medicine - Southeastern/Atlantic Region. **Publications:** Meharry Information Network, bimonthly - to medical libraries. **Special Catalogs:** Library guide. **Remarks:** FAX: (615)327-7448. Electronic mail address(es): CherylHemberg81@MMC (BITNET). **Staff:** Mattie McHollin, Assoc.Dir.; Marsha Williams, Sys.Coord.; Mary Nichols, Ref.Libn.; Jacqueline Dowdy, Ref.Libn.; Savi Ranganathan, Ref.Libn.; Marvelyn Fuller Thompson, Tech.Serv.Supv.; Amelia Whitehead, Ref.Libn.; Ellen McPierson, Ref.Libn.; Edwina Hefner, Cir.Libn.; Don Dryden, Cat.; Sue Miller, Outreach Libn.

★10022★
Meigs County Law Library (Law)
Court House
Box 744 Phone: (614)992-5290
Pomeroy, OH 45769-0744 Mary Gilmore
Subjects: Law. **Holdings:** 3950 volumes.

★10023★
Meiklejohn Civil Liberties Institute - Library (Law)
Box 673 Phone: (510)848-0599
Berkeley, CA 94701-0673 Ann Fagan Ginger, Exec.Dir.
Founded: 1965. **Staff:** Prof 2.5; Other 4. **Subjects:** Peace law, human rights, civil rights and liberties, due process, sex discrimination, juries, police misconduct. **Special Collections:** Peace Law Brief and Issues Bank; Angela Davis case (20,000 pages); Pentagon Papers Case (35,000 pages); official repository for National Lawyers Guild Archives; Draft and Military Law Collection (188 microfiche). **Holdings:** 200 books; legal documents from over 9000 cases. **Subscriptions:** 130 journals and other serials; 20 newspapers. **Services:** Copying; library open to the public. **Computerized Information Services:** PeaceNet (internal database). **Publications:** Human Rights Organizations and Periodicals Directory, biennial; Peace Law Docket, biennial - both for sale; list of other publications - available upon request. **Special Catalogs:** Pentagon Papers Case Collection (book); Angela Davis Collection (book). **Special Indexes:** Meiklejohn Library Acquisitions Index, 1968-1972; Human Rights Casefinder, 1953-1969; index to National Lawyers Guild Periodicals, 1937-1970; The Legal Struggle to Abolish the House Un-American Activities Committee. **Remarks:** FAX: (510)848-6008. Library located at 1715 Francisco St., Berkeley, CA 94703.

Golda Meir Library
See: **American Geographical Society Collection of the University of Wisconsin--Milwaukee - Golda Meir Library** (598)

Golda Meir Library
See: **University of Wisconsin--Milwaukee** (19632)

★10024★
(Melbourne) American Center - USIS Library (Educ)
24 Albert Rd.
P.O. Box 507
South Melbourne, VIC 3205, Australia
Remarks: Maintained or supported by the U.S. Information Agency. Focus is on materials that will assist peoples outside the United States to learn about the United States, its people, history, culture, political processes, and social milieux.

Frederic G. Melcher Library
See: **Cahners Publishing Company/R.R. Bowker Co.** (2441)

Lauritz Melchior Memorial
See: **Dana College - C.A. Dana-Life Library** (4580)

Melchoir Center for Recent History
See: **University of the Virgin Islands** (19493)

★10025★
Meldrum and Fewsmith, Inc. - Business Information Center (Bus-Fin)
1220 Huron Rd. Phone: (216)241-2141
Cleveland, OH 44115 John Skutnik, Mgr., Bus.Info.Serv.
Founded: 1944. **Staff:** Prof 1; Other 1. **Subjects:** Advertising, marketing, media. **Special Collections:** Media data and advertising subject files. **Holdings:** 1000 books; 60 VF drawers of media data; 950 annual reports; 40 VF drawers of subject files. **Subscriptions:** 450 journals and other serials. **Services:** Center not open to the public. **Computerized Information Services:** DIALOG Information Services, Dow Jones News/Retrieval, NEXIS, MAX, IMS. Performs searches on fee basis. **Publications:** Marketing Update, monthly - for internal distribution only. **Remarks:** FAX: (216)241-8275.

Georges Melies Collection
See: **Museum of Modern Art - Film Stills Archive** (10908)

Mellemfolkeligt Samvirke
See: **Danish Association for International Cooperation** (4590)

★10026★
Mellon Bank Corp. - Corporate Library (Bus-Fin)
One Mellon Bank Center
500 Grant St. Phone: (412)234-5000
Pittsburgh, PA 15258-0001 Patricia H. Riordan, Corp.Libn.
Founded: 1943. **Staff:** Prof 3; Other 5. **Subjects:** Banking, finance, economics, data processing, insurance, international banking. **Holdings:** 5500 books; 600 bound periodical volumes; 170 VF drawers of clippings and pamphlets. **Subscriptions:** 550 journals and other serials; 8 newspapers. **Services:** Interlibrary loan; library open to the public with restrictions. **Computerized Information Services:** DIALOG Information Services, PFDS Online, Mead Data Central, Dow Jones News/Retrieval. **Staff:** Richard McConnville, Info.Spec.

M.G. Mellon Library of Chemistry
See: **Purdue University - Chemistry Library** (13533)

Arthur W. Melton Library
See: **American Psychological Association** (724)

★10027★
Melville Hospital - Medical Library (Med)
Goose Bay, NF, Canada A0P 1C0 Phone: (709)896-2417
Teresa O'Keefe
Remarks: No further information was supplied by respondent.

Melville Whaling Room
See: **New Bedford Free Public Library** (11434)

★10028★
Memorial Hospital - Health Sciences Library (Med)
1400 E. Boulder Phone: (719)475-5182
Colorado Springs, CO 80909 Laura Hulslander, Dir.
Founded: 1950. **Staff:** Prof 2; Other 2. **Subjects:** Medicine, nursing, allied health. **Special Collections:** Medical and nursing rare book collection. **Holdings:** 3000 books; 25,000 bound periodical volumes. **Subscriptions:** 300 journals and other serials. **Services:** Interlibrary loan; copying; SDI; library open to the public for reference use only. **Automated Operations:** Computerized cataloging. **Computerized Information Services:** BRS Information Technologies, NLM, MEDLINE, OCLC; TENTIME, DOCLINE (electronic mail services). Performs searches on fee basis. **Networks/Consortia:** Member of Colorado Council of Medical Librarians, Plains and Peaks Regional Library Service System. **Special Catalogs:** Serials listing. **Remarks:** FAX: (719)475-5184. **Staff:** Mary Kircher, Libn.

★10029★
Memorial Hospital - Health Sciences Library (Med)
219 S. Washington St. Phone: (410)822-1000
Easton, MD 21601 Lois Sanger, Dir., Lib.Serv.
Founded: 1929. **Staff:** Prof 1; Other 3. **Subjects:** Medicine, nursing, allied health sciences. **Holdings:** 5000 books; 1900 bound periodical volumes; microfilm; AV programs. **Subscriptions:** 300 journals and other serials. **Services:** Interlibrary loan; copying; library open to the public for reference use only with permission. **Computerized Information Services:** MEDLINE, DIALOG Information Services. **Networks/Consortia:** Member of National Network of Libraries of Medicine (NN/LM), Maryland Association of Health Science Librarians (MAHSL).

★10030★
Memorial Hospital - Library (Med)
4500 Memorial Dr. Phone: (618)233-7750
Belleville, IL 62223-5399 Barbara Grout, Dir., Lib.Serv.
Founded: 1974. **Staff:** Prof 2. **Subjects:** Health sciences, hospital administration, nursing. **Holdings:** 2500 books; 4000 bound periodical volumes. **Subscriptions:** 430 journals and other serials. **Services:** Interlibrary loan; copying; library open to the public by appointment with physician's permission. **Automated Operations:** Computerized ILL (DOCLINE). **Computerized Information Services:** MEDLARS, DIALOG Information Services, BRS Information Technologies. Performs searches free of charge for affiliated members only. **Networks/Consortia:** Member of Areawide Hospital Library Consortium of Southwestern Illinois (AHLC), Kaskaskia Library System (KLS), National Network of Libraries of Medicine - Greater Midwest Region. **Publications:** Current Awareness, weekly; New Additions, quarterly - both for internal distribution only. **Remarks:** FAX: (618)233-7750, ext. 5658. **Staff:** Ruby Buettner, Asst.Libn.

★10031★
Memorial Hospital - Library Services (Med)
615 N. Michigan Phone: (219)284-7491
South Bend, IN 46601 Jeanne M. Larson, Lib.Mgr.
Founded: 1978. **Staff:** Prof 1; Other 1. **Subjects:** Medicine, nursing, health care administration, allied health sciences. **Holdings:** 3500 books; 5 VF drawers of pamphlets and reprints; 120 subscriptions on microfiche. **Subscriptions:** 300 journals and other serials. **Services:** Interlibrary loan; copying; SDI; library open to the public for reference use only. **Computerized Information Services:** NLM, DIALOG Information Services. Performs searches on fee basis. **Networks/Consortia:** Member of Area 2 Library Services Authority (ALSA 2), National Network of Libraries of Medicine - Greater Midwest Region. **Remarks:** Alternate telephone number(s): 284-7389. FAX: (219)284-6635.

★10032★
Memorial Hospital - Medical Library (Med)
325 S. Belmont St. Phone: (717)843-8623
York, PA 17403 Elaine Homick, Med.Libn.
Staff: Prof 1. **Subjects:** Medicine, nursing, osteopathy. **Holdings:** 1070 books; 169 bound periodical volumes. **Subscriptions:** 89 journals and other serials. **Services:** Interlibrary loan; copying; library open to health care professionals and students. **Computerized Information Services:** MEDLARS. **Networks/Consortia:** Member of Central Pennsylvania Health Sciences Library Association (CPHSLA), BHSL, National Network of Libraries of Medicine - Middle Atlantic Region. **Remarks:** FAX: (717)846-9374.

★10033★
Memorial Hospital - Medical Library (Med)
Box 1447 Phone: (409)634-8111
Lufkin, TX 75902 Hilda Becerra, Dir., Med.Rec.
Staff: 1. **Subjects:** Medicine, obstetrics and gynecology, surgery, pediatrics. **Holdings:** 500 books; 20 bound periodical volumes. **Services:** Library not open to the public.

★10034★
Memorial Hospital - Mollie Sublett Tucker Memorial Medical Library (Med)
1204 Mound St. Phone: (409)564-4611
Nacogdoches, TX 75961 Carlie Howard, Libn.
Founded: 1970. **Staff:** Prof 1. **Subjects:** Medicine. **Holdings:** 758 books; 121 bound periodical volumes; 198 boxes of unbound periodicals. **Subscriptions:** 41 journals and other serials. **Services:** Interlibrary loan; copying; library open to the public for reference use only. **Networks/Consortia:** Member of National Network of Libraries of Medicine - South Central Region. **Publications:** Acquisitions list, irregular. **Remarks:** Alternate telephone number(s): (409)568-8505.

★10035★
Memorial Hospital - Ralph R. Landes Medical Library (Med)
142 S. Main St. Phone: (804)799-4418
Danville, VA 24541 Ann B. Sasser, Med.Libn.
Staff: Prof 1. **Subjects:** Medicine, surgery, basic and clinical sciences, hospital administration. **Holdings:** 992 books; bound periodical volumes. **Subscriptions:** 132 journals and other serials. **Services:** Interlibrary loan; copying; SDI; library open to the public by appointment. **Computerized Information Services:** NLM; DOCLINE (electronic mail service). Performs searches on fee basis (free to hospital and medical staff). **Networks/Consortia:** Member of Southwestern Virginia Health Information Librarians (SWVAHILI). **Remarks:** FAX: number is available upon request.

★10036★
Memorial Hospital - School of Professional Nursing - Library (Med)
142 S. Main St. Phone: (804)799-4510
Danville, VA 24541 Connie Quisenberry, Coord., Lib.Serv.
Staff: 1. **Subjects:** Nursing. **Holdings:** 2100 books. **Subscriptions:** 36 journals and other serials. **Services:** Interlibrary loan; library open to the public by appointment.

★10037★
Memorial Hospital of Burlington County - Lindley B. Reagan Health Sciences Library (Med)
175 Madison Ave. Phone: (609)267-0700
Mt. Holly, NJ 08060 Betsy O'Connor, Dir.
Founded: 1952. **Staff:** Prof 1; Other 1. **Subjects:** Health sciences. **Holdings:** 1100 books; 5000 bound periodical volumes; 80 other cataloged items; 5 drawers of slides; articles published by staff; 10 drawers of audio programs; 500 video cassettes. **Subscriptions:** 301 journals and other serials. **Services:** Interlibrary loan; copying; SDI; video recording (television), slide making; library open to the public with permission. **Automated Operations:** Computerized ILL (DOCLINE). **Computerized Information Services:** BRS Information Technologies, MEDLINE; internal database; CD-ROM (MEDLINE); MESSAGES (electronic mail service). Performs searches on fee basis. **Networks/Consortia:** Member of Health Sciences Library Association of New Jersey (HSLANJ), BHSL, Pinelands Consortium for Health Information, South Jersey Regional Library Cooperative. **Publications:** Library Leads, bimonthly; AMG Current Awareness, monthly; Video Views, monthly - all for internal distribution only. **Remarks:** FAX: (609)261-3542.

★10038★
Memorial Hospital of Martinsville - Medical Library (Med)
320 Hospital Dr. Phone: (703)666-7467
Martinsville, VA 24112 Mary Alice Sherrard, Med.Libn.
Founded: 1969. **Staff:** Prof 1. **Subjects:** Medicine, nursing, allied health sciences. **Holdings:** 2000 books; 3000 bound periodical volumes; 600 videotapes. **Subscriptions:** 115 journals and other serials. **Services:** Interlibrary loan; copying; library open to the public with permission. **Computerized Information Services:** MEDLINE. **Networks/Consortia:** Member of Southwestern Virginia Health Information Librarians (SWVAHILI). **Remarks:** FAX: (703)666-7816.

★10039★
Memorial Hospital & Medical Center - Medical and Nursing Library (Med)
600 Memorial Ave. Phone: (301)777-4027
Cumberland, MD 21502 Margie Gacki, Libn.
Staff: 1. **Subjects:** Medicine, surgery, nursing. **Holdings:** 1146 books; 40 bound periodical volumes. **Subscriptions:** 60 journals and other serials. **Services:** Interlibrary loan; library open to the public with restrictions. **Computerized Information Services:** MEDLINE. Performs searches. **Remarks:** FAX: (301)777-4050.

★10040★
Memorial Hospital at Oconomowoc - Health Sciences Library (Med)
791 E. Summit Ave. Phone: (414)569-9400
Oconomowoc, WI 53066 Donna M. Dunham, Hea.Sci.Libn.
Founded: 1970. **Staff:** Prof 1. **Subjects:** Medicine, nursing, dentistry. **Holdings:** 1300 books and AV programs; 1268 bound periodical volumes; 6 VF drawers; 5 VF drawers of patient education pamphlets; 59 audiotapes; 150 videotapes; teaching materials. **Subscriptions:** 200 journals and other serials. **Services:** Interlibrary loan; copying; library open to the public by appointment. **Computerized Information Services:** MEDLINE. **Networks/Consortia:** Member of Southeastern Wisconsin Health Science Library Consortium (SWHSL), Library Council of Metropolitan Milwaukee, Inc. (LCOMM). **Publications:** Monthly and annual reports; bibliographies for new materials.

★10041★
Memorial Hospital of Rhode Island - Health Sciences Library (Med)
111 Brewster St. Phone: (401)729-2212
Pawtucket, RI 02860 Sylvia Hampton, Med.Lib.Coord.
Founded: 1959. **Staff:** Prof 2. **Subjects:** Medicine, family medicine. **Special Collections:** American Medical Association Category Credit Programs.

Holdings: 660 books; 7852 bound periodical volumes. **Subscriptions:** 150 journals and other serials. **Services:** Interlibrary loan; copying; library open to the public upon special request. **Automated Operations:** Computerized ILL (DOCLINE). **Computerized Information Services:** MEDLINE. **Networks/Consortia:** Member of Consortium of Rhode Island Academic and Research Libraries, Inc. (CRIARL), Association of Rhode Island Health Sciences Librarians (ARIHSL). **Publications:** Newsletter. **Remarks:** FAX: (401)722-0198. **Formerly:** Pawtucket Memorial Hospital. **Staff:** Carol-Ann Rausch, Ref.Libn.

★10042★
Memorial Hospital of Salem County - David W. Green Medical Library (Med)
Salem Woodstown Rd.
Salem, NJ 08079 Phone: (609)935-1000
Staff: 1. **Subjects:** Medicine, allied health sciences. **Holdings:** 726 books; 750 bound periodical volumes. **Subscriptions:** 31 journals and other serials. **Services:** Interlibrary loan; library not open to the public. **Networks/Consortia:** Member of South Jersey Regional Library Cooperative.

★10043★
Memorial Hospitals Association - Health Sciences Library (Med)
Box 942 Phone: (209)526-4500
Modesto, CA 95353 Nancy Mangum, Dir.
Staff: Prof 1. **Subjects:** Medicine, nursing, hospital administration. **Holdings:** 1000 books; 300 pamphlet files. **Subscriptions:** 200 journals and other serials. **Services:** Interlibrary loan; library not open to the public. **Computerized Information Services:** MEDLARS, DIALOG Information Services. **Networks/Consortia:** Member of 49-99 Cooperative Library System. **Remarks:** FAX: (209)572-7199.

★10044★
Memorial Medical Center - Health Sciences Library (Med)
2606 Hospital Blvd.
Box 5280 Phone: (512)881-4197
Corpus Christi, TX 78465-5280 Leta Dannelley, Dir.
Founded: 1945. **Staff:** Prof 1; Other 1. **Subjects:** Medicine, nursing, preclinical sciences. **Holdings:** 3000 books; 4000 bound periodical volumes; 660 AV programs; 500 audio cassettes; 35 video cassettes; 25 slide/tape sets. **Subscriptions:** 270 journals and other serials. **Services:** Interlibrary loan; copying; SDI; library open to health professionals. **Computerized Information Services:** MEDLINE, BRS/COLLEAGUE. Performs searches on fee basis. **Networks/Consortia:** Member of Coastal Bend Health Sciences Library Consortium (CBHSLC). **Remarks:** FAX: (512)881-4198.

★10045★
Memorial Medical Center - Kenneth H. Schnepp Professional Library (Med)
800 N. Rutledge St. Phone: (217)788-3336
Springfield, IL 62781 Myrtle Smarjesse, Libn.
Founded: 1943. **Staff:** Prof 1; Other 1. **Subjects:** Medicine, nursing, allied health sciences. **Holdings:** 1342 books; 3745 bound periodical volumes; audio and video cassettes. **Subscriptions:** 192 journals and other serials. **Services:** Interlibrary loan; copying; library open to community students as designated by the librarian. **Automated Operations:** Computerized cataloging and ILL. **Computerized Information Services:** OCLC, MEDLARS; CD-ROMs. **Networks/Consortia:** Member of National Network of Libraries of Medicine - Greater Midwest Region, Capital Area Consortium (CAC), ILLINET, Rolling Prairie Library System (RPLS). **Remarks:** FAX: (217)788-5540.

★10046★
Memorial Medical Center of West Michigan - Library (Med)
1 Atkinson Dr. Phone: (616)845-2384
Ludington, MI 49431 Dr. Josolyn Hubacker
Subjects: Medicine. **Holdings:** 400 books; 500 bound periodical volumes. **Subscriptions:** 72 journals and other serials. **Services:** Interlibrary loan; library open to the public for reference use only with the approval of the hospital administrator. **Computerized Information Services:** MEDLINE. **Remarks:** FAX: (616)845-1732. **Staff:** Jeanette Lipps, Supv. of Med.Rec.

★10047★
Memorial Presbyterian Church - Greenhoe Library (Rel-Phil)
1310 Ashman St. Phone: (517)835-6759
Midland, MI 48640 Betty Currin, Chm., Lib.Bd.
Founded: 1945. **Staff:** Prof 3. **Subjects:** Bible interpretation, church history, Christian education, prayer, peace, justice. **Holdings:** 5000 books; periodicals; archival materials; tapes; videotapes. **Subscriptions:** 9 journals and other serials. **Services:** Library open to the public; theological reference section open to Midland community clergy. **Publications:** Video cassettes and audiocassettes of sermons. **Staff:** Esther Frost, Adult Serv.Libn.; Carolyn Fisher, Ch.Libn.

★10048★
Memorial Sloan-Kettering Cancer Center - Medical Library - Nathan Cummings Center (Med)
1275 York Ave. Phone: (212)639-7439
New York, NY 10021 Jeanne Becker, Dir.
Staff: Prof 5; Other 8. **Subjects:** Cancer and allied diseases. **Special Collections:** MSKCC Archives. **Holdings:** 12,870 books; 19,686 bound periodical volumes; 18 drawers of microforms. **Subscriptions:** 800 journals and other serials. **Services:** Interlibrary loan; copying; SDI. **Automated Operations:** Computerized cataloging, acquisitions, serials, and circulation. **Computerized Information Services:** BRS Information Technologies, Data-Star, DIALOG Information Services, NLM, ORBIT Search Service, STN International, OCLC; CORNET (internal database); CD-ROM. **Networks/Consortia:** Member of Medical Library Center of New York (MLCNY), New York Metropolitan Reference and Research Library Agency. **Remarks:** FAX: (212)717-3048. **Staff:** Arsenia Q. Avetria, Assoc.Libn., Tech.Serv.; June G. Rosenberg, Assoc.Libn., Ref./ILL Serv.; Larry Dormer, Asst.Libn.

★10049★
Memorial University of Newfoundland - Centre d'Etudes Franco-Terreneuviennes (Area-Ethnic)
Dept. of Folklore Phone: (709)737-2122
St. John's, NF, Canada A1C 5S7 Dr. Gerald Thomas, Dir., CEFT
Founded: 1975. **Staff:** Prof 1; Other 1. **Subjects:** French folklore, language, and dialectology; Anglo-American and international folklore scholarship. **Special Collections:** Archive (sound recordings and manuscripts of French Newfoundland culture, including 525 audiotapes in Newfoundland French dialect). **Holdings:** 3300 books; 500 bound periodical volumes; 625 reports, manuscripts, dissertations, archival materials; 15 videotapes; 10 cabinets and 20 filing boxes of other cataloged items. **Subscriptions:** 37 journals and other serials. **Services:** Copying; center open to recognized scholars only. **Special Catalogs:** Manuscript catalog; Folktale; song catalog. **Remarks:** FAX: (709)737-4569.

★10050★
Memorial University of Newfoundland - Curriculum Materials Centre (Hum)
G.A. Hickman Bldg. Phone: (709)737-7465
St. John's, NF, Canada A1B 3X8 Alison Mews, Libn.
Founded: 1968. **Staff:** Prof 1; Other 6. **Subjects:** Children's literature - history, criticism, bibliography; education. **Holdings:** 41,361 books; 260 bound periodical volumes; 45 charts; 1342 curriculum guides; 459 AV programs; 197 jackdaws; 523 educational kits; 234 study print sets. **Subscriptions:** 94 journals and other serials. **Services:** Center open to area teachers and parents. **Computerized Information Services:** InterNet (electronic mail service). **Remarks:** FAX: (709)737-2345. Electronic mail address(es): AMEWS@KEAN.MUN.CA (InterNet).

★10051★
Memorial University of Newfoundland - Folklore and Language Archive (Area-Ethnic, Hist)
St. John's, NF, Canada A1B 3X8 Phone: (709)737-8401
Martin J. Lovelace, Dir.
Founded: 1968. **Staff:** Prof 1; Other 20. **Subjects:** Newfoundland, Labrador, the Maritime Provinces - folklore, folklife, language, oral history, popular culture. **Special Collections:** MacEdward Leach Newfoundland, Labrador, and Nova Scotia field recordings; Maud Karpeles Newfoundland field notes; Elisabeth Bristol Greenleaf field notes; Newbell Niles Puckett Ontario field recordings; CBC Radio "Fishermen's Broadcast;" E.R. Seary Newfoundland genealogy files. **Holdings:** 7000 manuscripts; 70,000 5x8 Folklore Survey Cards; 14,000 tape recordings; 12,000 photographs. **Services:** Copying (limited); archive open for scholarly research. **Computerized Information Services:** InterNet (electronic mail service). **Special Indexes:** Card indexes for some of the special collections. **Remarks:** FAX: (709)737-2345. Electronic mail address(es): MUNFLA@KEAN.UCS.MUN.CA (InterNet). **Staff:** Philip Hisock, Archv.

★10052★
Memorial University of Newfoundland - Health Sciences Library (Med)
Health Science Centre Phone: (709)737-6672
300 Prince Philip Dr. George Beckett, Assoc.Univ.Libn.,
St. John's, NF, Canada A1B 3V6 Hea.Sci.
Founded: 1969. **Staff:** Prof 6; Other 20. **Subjects:** Medicine, history of medicine, nursing, pharmacy, dentistry, allied health professions. **Holdings:** 40,024 books; 51,423 bound periodical volumes; 10,000 slides; 3400 audiotapes; 1257 reels of microfilm; 121 motion pictures; 113 microfilm sets; 545 slide/tape sets; 1174 microfiche; 2 models; 773 videotapes. **Subscriptions:** 1623 journals and other serials. **Services:** Interlibrary loan; copying; SDI; library open to the public. **Automated Operations:** Computerized cataloging and circulation. **Computerized Information Services:** MEDLARS, UTLAS, CAN/OLE, BRS Information Technologies, DIALOG Information Services; CD-ROMs; Envoy 100, InterNet (electronic mail services). Performs searches on fee basis. **Publications:** Series of information sheets; Bibliography of Health Care in Newfoundland (book). **Special Catalogs:** Audio-Visual Catalogue of the Health Sciences Library (book and online); Union List of Serials: the St. John's Hospital Libraries (book and online). **Remarks:** Alternate telephone number(s): 737-6670. FAX: (709)737-6866. Electronic mail address(es): NFSMM.ILL (Envoy 100); GEORGER@MUN.CA (InterNet). **Staff:** Catherine Sheehan, Hd., Comp. Search Serv.; Pam Morgan, Asst.Hd., Tech.Serv.; Shelagh Wotherspoon, Hd., Ref.Libn.; Elaine Duffie, Hd., Tech.Serv.

★10053★
Memorial University of Newfoundland - International Reference Centre for Avian Haematozoa (Biol Sci)
Department of Biology Phone: (709)737-8592
St. John's, NF, Canada A1B 3X9 Madonna A. Bishop, Res.Asst.
Founded: 1969. **Staff:** Prof 1. **Subjects:** Avian haematozoa. **Special Collections:** Hapantotype and parahapantotype collections of avian haematozoa. **Holdings:** 5600 reprints. **Services:** Copying; center open to the public by appointment only. **Computerized Information Services:** Internal database; electronic mail service. **Publications:** Bibliography of the Blood-Inhabiting Protozoa. **Special Catalogs:** Host-Parasite Catalogue of the Avian Haematozoa; Haematozoa in the birds of eastern and southeastern Asia. **Remarks:** FAX: (709)737-3018.

★10054★
Memorial University of Newfoundland - Ocean Engineering Information Centre (Sci-Engr)
St. John's, NF, Canada A1B 3X5 Phone: (709)737-8354
Judith A. Whittick, Info.Res.
Founded: 1976. **Staff:** Prof 1; Other 2. **Subjects:** Ice and cold ocean engineering, offshore technology. **Special Collections:** Technical reports on offshore hydrocarbon development in the Arctic and Canadian offshore. **Holdings:** 26,800 technical reports and conference papers; 2000 maps and charts. **Subscriptions:** 140 journals and other serials. **Services:** Interlibrary loan; copying; center open to the public for reference use only. **Computerized Information Services:** SPIRES System; Envoy 100 (electronic mail service). **Publications:** Bimonthly Information Bulletin. **Remarks:** FAX: (709)737-4706. Electronic mail address(es): C.CORE (Envoy 100).

★10055★
Memorial University of Newfoundland - Queen Elizabeth II Library - Centre for Newfoundland Studies (Area-Ethnic)
St. John's, NF, Canada A1B 3Y1 Phone: (709)737-7475
Anne Hart, Hd.
Founded: 1965. **Staff:** Prof 3; Other 13. **Subjects:** Newfoundland and Labrador. **Holdings:** 45,500 books, files, pamphlets; 800 bound periodical volumes; 3000 microforms; 350 maps; 300 linear meters of archives; 8000 rare books. **Subscriptions:** 450 journals and other serials; 20 newspapers. **Services:** Interlibrary loan; copying; center open to the public for reference use only. **Computerized Information Services:** Internal databases; Envoy 100, InterNet (electronic mail services). Performs searches free of charge. **Publications:** Bibliography of Newfoundland (1986, 2 volumes); Guide to Archival Holdings of the Centre for Newfoundland Studies (1989). **Remarks:** Alternate telephone number(s): (709)737-7476. FAX: (709)737-3118. Electronic mail address(es): AHART@KEAN.UCS.MUN.CA (InterNet). **Staff:** Joan Ritcey; Bert Riggs.

★10056★
Memorial University of Newfoundland - Queen Elizabeth II Library - Map Library (Geog-Map)
St. John's, NF, Canada A1B 3Y1 Phone: (709)737-8892
Alberta Auringer Wood, Map Libn.
Staff: Prof 1; Other 2. **Subjects:** Canada, North America, North Atlantic, Western Europe. **Special Collections:** Depository for NTS (Canada). **Holdings:** 1508 atlases; 1445 books; 70,093 maps; 46 relief maps; 9590 microforms; 40,617 aerial photographs; 2 globes; 11 satellite images. **Services:** Interlibrary loan; copying; library open to the public. **Automated Operations:** Computerized cataloging and acquisitions. **Computerized Information Services:** SPIRES; Envoy 100, InterNet (electronic mail services). **Remarks:** FAX: (709)737-3118. Electronic mail address(es): AWOOD@KEAN.UCS.MUN.CA (InterNet); A.WOOD (Envoy 100).

★10057★
Memory Shop, Inc. - Movie Memorabilia Stills (Aud-Vis)
109 E. 12th St. Phone: (212)473-2404
New York, NY 10003 Mark Ricci, Owner
Staff: Prof 2. **Subjects:** Memorabilia, 1910 to present, pertaining to movies, television, rock music, music. **Holdings:** 7 million photographs; posters; pressbooks; lobby cards; magazines.

★10058★
Memphis Bar Association - Law Library (Law)
140 Adams Ave., Rm. 315 Phone: (901)527-7041
Memphis, TN 38103 Barbara F. Moore, Law Libn.
Staff: Prof 1; Other 1. **Subjects:** Law. **Holdings:** 45,000 volumes. **Subscriptions:** 77 journals and other serials. **Services:** Interlibrary loan (limited); copying; library open to the public on a limited schedule.

★10059★
Memphis Botanic Garden Foundation, Inc. - Goldsmith Civic Garden Center - Sybile Malloy Memorial Library (Biol Sci)
750 Cherry Rd. Phone: (901)685-1566
Memphis, TN 38117 Jennifer Smith, Commun.Coord.
Founded: 1964. **Staff:** 2. **Subjects:** Horticulture, gardening, landscape design, flower arranging, environmental science, botany, agriculture. **Holdings:** 3700 books; 10 bound periodical volumes; 500 horticultural magazines and pamphlets. **Subscriptions:** 37 journals and other serials. **Services:** Copying; library open to the public for reference use only. **Publications:** Garden Appeal, monthly - to members and free to libraries on request. **Remarks:** Jointly maintained with Memphis Park Commission.

★10060★
Memphis Brooks Museum of Art - Library (Art)
Overton Park Phone: (901)722-3500
Memphis, TN 38112 Helen Karpinski, Libn.
Founded: 1953. **Staff:** Prof 1. **Subjects:** Art history - ancient to contemporary; decorative arts; photography. **Special Collections:** Kress Collection; Museum exhibition catalogs; Menzies Collection on Decorative Arts; Armand Hammer Collection. **Holdings:** 6304 books; 500 bound periodical volumes; bulletins; museum catalogs; vertical files. **Subscriptions:** 27 journals and other serials. **Services:** Interlibrary loan; library open to the public for reference use only on a limited schedule. **Special Catalogs:** George Wardlaw: Transitions; All the masks fall off (Rodin) (both exhibition catalogs). **Remarks:** FAX: (901)722-3522.

Memphis City Park Commission - Memphis Pink Palace Museum
See: **Memphis Pink Palace Museum** (10063)

★10061★
Memphis College of Art - G. Pillow Lewis Memorial Library (Art)
Overton Park Phone: (901)726-4085
Memphis, TN 38112 Paul S. Williford, Libn.
Founded: 1937. **Staff:** Prof 2. **Subjects:** Art history, painting, sculpture, art crafts, photography, printmaking, drawing, art education. **Holdings:** 13,000 books; 900 bound periodical volumes; 24 VF drawers of clippings and pamphlet material; 1000 matted prints; 7700 mounted prints; 30,000 glass mounted slides. **Subscriptions:** 130 journals and other serials. **Services:** Library open to the public for reference use only. **Networks/Consortia:** Member of Greater Memphis Consortium. **Staff:** Bette R. Callow, Slide Libn.

★10062★
Memphis Mental Health Institute - James A. Wallace Library (Med)
865 Poplar Ave.
Box 40966 Phone: (901)524-1261
Memphis, TN 38174-0966 Mae White, Libn.
Founded: 1963. **Staff:** Prof 1. **Subjects:** Psychiatry, psychology, nursing, social work and activity therapy, medicine. **Holdings:** 2700 volumes; 103 tapes. **Subscriptions:** 140 journals and other serials. **Services:** Interlibrary loan; copying; library open to the public with restrictions. **Networks/Consortia:** Member of Association of Memphis Area Health Science Libraries (AMAHSL).

Memphis Museums, Inc. - Memphis Pink Palace Museum
See: **Memphis Pink Palace Museum** (10063)

★10063★
Memphis Pink Palace Museum - Library (Hist)
3050 Central Ave. Phone: (901)454-5600
Memphis, TN 38119 Kendrick Jacocks, Libn.
Founded: 1967. **Staff:** 1. **Subjects:** Regional history, geology, archeology, and biology; natural history; museums. **Special Collections:** Shiloh Trails, Inc. (121 Civil War items; 125 regional history items). **Holdings:** 5100 books; 360 periodical volumes; 10 scrapbooks of clippings on the history of Memphis Pink Palace Museum. **Subscriptions:** 17 journals and other serials; 40 museum publications. **Services:** Library open to the public for reference use only on request. **Publications:** Museum Scope, monthly - to city and county schools, Friends of Museum, and Foundation Board members or by exchange; Adventures, 4/year - to city, county, and independent schools in the area. **Remarks:** FAX: (901)454-5620. Maintained by Memphis City Park Commission and Memphis Museums, Inc.

★10064★
Memphis-Shelby County Office of Planning and Development - Library (Plan)
City Hall, Rm. 443
125 N. Mid-America Mall Phone: (901)576-6763
Memphis, TN 38103-2084 Rick G. Bray, Libn.
Founded: 1978. **Staff:** Prof 1. **Subjects:** Planning - economic, transportation, environmental, community, land use. **Holdings:** 4500 books. **Subscriptions:** 58 journals and other serials. **Services:** Copying (limited); SDI; library open to the public with restrictions. **Publications:** New book list - for internal distribution only. **Remarks:** Library is a State Data Center Affiliate and maintains a small statistical collection for reference use. FAX: (901)576-6418.

★10065★
Memphis-Shelby County Public Library and Information Center - Memphis Room Collections (Hist)
1850 Peabody Ave. Phone: (901)725-8821
Memphis, TN 38104 James R. Johnson, Hd.
Staff: Prof 6; Other 6. **Subjects:** Memphis/Shelby County, genealogy, Mardi Gras/Cotton Carnival, yellow fever, Blues and Beale Street, Mississippi steamboats. **Special Collections:** Memphis/Shelby County Archives (18,000 volumes); K.D. McKeller Collection; official papers of Wyeth Chandler; Citizens to Preserve Overton Park records; mayor's letterbooks and papers (60,000 items); Rabbi James A. Wax Collection; J. Palmer Nash, M.D., papers; George W. Lee papers; J. Ashton Hayes papers; Memphians During War (Civil War to World War II); Beale Street Collection; W.W. Busby Letters; Robert Cohn papers; James W. Moore papers; Susanne Coulan Scruggs Collection; Sarah Beaumont Kennedy Collection; Judge John B. Martin papers; Florence McIntyre Collection; George Sparks Theater Collection; Catharine Hinton papers; Wiseman, Bland, Foster and O'Brien Architectural Drawings; Ruth Lowenberg papers; World Literacy Council Records; Wassell Randolph Genealogical Collection; Catholic Human Relations Council papers; Shelby County Commissioners' official papers; Whitehaven Utility District Collection; Montgomery Cooper correspondence and papers; Whitehaven Community Association; E.M. Sharp Genealogical Collection; Ida Cooper Genealogical and Historical papers; George W. Lee papers; J. Ashton Hayes Collection; Memphians During War (Civil War to World War II); Julia Raine Correspondence and Music Collection; Trezevant family papers; Page-Lenox Collection; Tennessee Valley Collection; W.C. Handy Collection; Judge Walter Malone papers; Memphis Crippled Children's Hospital School Collection; Memphis Music Miscellany Collection; Order of Alhambra Talavera Caravan No. 32; Hugh Higbee Huhn Theater Collection, Earl Moreland Theater Collection. **Holdings:** 10,480 books; 1200 bound periodical volumes; 900 maps; 500,000 newspaper clippings; 10,000 photographs; 3000 pages of oral history transcripts; 250 manuscript collections; 7000 reels of microfilm. **Subscriptions:** 135 journals and other serials. **Services:** Interlibrary loan; copying; collections open to the public. **Publications:** Senator Kenneth Douglas McKellar: A Register of His Papers (1974); Nathan Bedford Forrest and the Civil War in Memphis: A Subject Bibliography. **Special Catalogs:** A McKellar Calendar of Speeches 1928-1940 (1962); The Everett R. Cook Oral History program guide to the Collection, Catalogs of the John Ogden Carley Papers, The Reverend George H. Harris Letters, Yellow Fever Collection, The Duke-Bedford family papers, The Captain Rees V. Downs papers, Papers of Blair T. Hunt, The Searcy-Shirley Collection, Colton Green Collection, Farrow family papers, The Memphis Historical Society Collection, Price-Davis Papers, The Venson Collection, Beale Street Collection, The Morris Soloman Papers, Papers of Mayor Henry Loeb III, Official Papers of Jack W. Ramsay, The Judge Samuel O. Bates Collection, The Henry O. Montgomery Collection, General Gideon J. Pillow Papers, The Robert Cohn Papers, The Gayoso House and Gayoso Hotel, The Papers of Mrs. Anna E. Gilbert of Raleigh, Tennessee, The Hugh Higbee Huhn Theater Collection, The Hallelujah! Collection, W.C. Handy Collection, W.W. Busby Letters, The George W. Lee Collection, The Personal Papers of Judge Walter Malone, Memphians During War (Civil War to World War II), The Memphis Belle Collection, The Memphis Crippled Children's Hospital School, Memphis Music Miscellany, Official Papers of Shelby County Commissioner James W. "Jimmy" Moore, The Earl Moreland Theater Collection, Page/Lennox Collection, The Julia Raine Collection of Correspondence and music, Scrapbook Collection, Order of the Alhambra - Talavera Caravan No. 32, The Trezavant Family Papers, Rabbi James A. Wax Collection, George Mahan, Jr., Architectural Collection, Robert James Original Papers, Tennessee Valley Collection, J. Ashton Hayes Collection. **Special Indexes:** Indexed guides to collections; index to Shelby County Probate Records, 1820-1876; index to Memphis City Council Minutes, 1826-1855; index to oral history; index to Memphis newspapers, 1975-1989; death records, 1848-1939; marriage records, 1820-1976. **Staff:** Heather Tankersley, Libn. III; Patricia LaPointe, Spec. I; Barbara Flanary, Archv., Spec. II; Thomas Jones, Libn. I; Joan Cannon, Libn.Asst.

★10066★
Memphis-Shelby County Public Library and Information Center - Science/Business/Social Sciences Department (Bus-Fin, Sci-Engr, Soc Sci)
1850 Peabody Ave. Phone: (901)725-8877
Memphis, TN 38104 Barbara C. Shultz, Dept.Hd.
Founded: 1893. **Staff:** Prof 9; Other 2. **Subjects:** Business, science, technology, social science. **Holdings:** Figures not available. **Subscriptions:** 3000 journals and other serials; 84 newspapers. **Services:** Interlibrary loan; copying; department open to the public. **Automated Operations:** Computerized cataloging and acquisitions. **Computerized Information Services:** DIALOG Information Services, Dow Jones News/Retrieval, OCLC, VU/TEXT Information Services. **Networks/Consortia:** Member of SOLINET. **Staff:** Frances French, Libn.; Perveen Rustom, Libn.; Kay Cunningham, Libn.; Vergeana Hunt, Libn.; Rubye Cross, Spec.; Bette Tilly, Spec.; Shelley Donald, Lib.Asst.; Claude Brown, Spec.; Charlene Wagner, Libn.; Jue Lindenfield, Libn.; Jim Harkins, Libn.

★10067★
Memphis State University - Art Department - Slide Library (Art, Aud-Vis)
Jones Hall, Rm. 220 Phone: (901)678-2938
Memphis, TN 38152 Joyce E. King, Vis.Rsrcs.Cur.
Founded: 1954. **Staff:** Prof 1; Other 3. **Subjects:** Architecture, sculpture, painting, photography, graphic design, decorative arts, archeology. **Holdings:** 150 books; 114,000 slides; 140 theses; 57 videotapes. **Services:** Library open to the public with restrictions.

★10068★
Memphis State University - Bureau of Educational Service - Library (Educ)
College of Education
302 Ball Bldg. Phone: (901)678-3407
Memphis, TN 38152 John R. Petry, Assoc.Prof.
Founded: 1966. **Staff:** Prof 1; Other 2. **Subjects:** Educational research, statistics, education, education policy. **Holdings:** 600 books; 2000 items in Princeton files; 12 drawers of funded and unfunded proposals. **Services:** Copying; library open to the public. **Computerized Information Services:** ERIC. **Remarks:** FAX: (901)678-4778.

★10069★
Memphis State University - C.H. Nash Museum Library (Soc Sci)
1987 Indian Village Dr. Phone: (901)785-3160
Memphis, TN 38109 Gerald P. Smith, Cur.
Founded: 1968. **Staff:** 3. **Subjects:** Eastern North American archeology and ethnology; physical anthropology; geology of southeastern United States. **Holdings:** 2000 books. **Subscriptions:** 12 journals and other serials. **Services:** Library open to the public for reference use only.

★10070★
Memphis State University - Chemistry Library (Sci-Engr)
Memphis, TN 38152 Phone: (901)678-2625
Marilyn Steele, Lib.Asst.
Founded: 1966. **Staff:** 2. **Subjects:** Chemistry. **Holdings:** 28,703 bound volumes; 2991 microforms. **Subscriptions:** 198 journals and other serials. **Services:** Interlibrary loan; copying; library open to the public.

★10071★
Memphis State University - Engineering Library (Sci-Engr)
Memphis, TN 38152 Phone: (901)678-2179
Theo Jones-Ouartey, Libn.
Founded: 1964. **Staff:** Prof 1; Other 2. **Subjects:** Engineering, geology, technology. **Holdings:** 41,434 volumes; 6418 maps; 28,768 microforms. **Subscriptions:** 491 journals and other serials. **Services:** Interlibrary loan; copying; library open to the public.

★10072★
Memphis State University - Graduate Department of Planning & Regional Economic Development Center (Plan)
226 Johnson Hall Phone: (901)678-2161
Memphis, TN 38152 Luchy Burrell, Supv.
Founded: 1974. **Staff:** Prof 1; Other 4. **Subjects:** Comprehensive physical planning, economic and developmental planning, housing, law, natural resources. **Special Collections:** Russell Van Ness Black Collection (300 volumes); Memphis and Shelby County Collection (500 items). **Holdings:** 2100 books; 4700 local government publications; 475 U.S. Government documents; 1 vertical file; 34 titles of unbound periodicals; 1 drawer of newsletters. **Subscriptions:** 61 journals and other serials. **Services:** Library open to the public for reference use only. **Remarks:** FAX: (901)678-3299. **Staff:** Gloria Neilson.

★10073★
Memphis State University - Music Library (Mus)
Memphis, TN 38152 Phone: (901)678-2556
Ann Viles, Mus.Libn.
Founded: 1967. **Staff:** Prof 2; Other 1. **Subjects:** Music. **Special Collections:** Sound recordings (8242). **Holdings:** 35,762 volumes; 10,324 microforms; 11,582 records. **Subscriptions:** 93 journals and other serials. **Services:** Interlibrary loan; copying; library open to the public. **Staff:** Anna Neal, Libn.

★10074★
Memphis State University - Radio Program History Collection (Info Sci)
Brister Library Learning Media Center Phone: (901)678-3174
Memphis, TN 38152 Dr. Marvin R. Bensman, Prof.
Founded: 1969. **Staff:** Prof 1; Other 1. **Subjects:** Radio broadcasting, 1920-1960s; Golden Age of Radio; radio news, documentary, and entertainment programs; radio coverage of World War II; radio political coverage. **Holdings:** 670 tapes; 1350 cassettes; 4000 program titles; 1350 hours of program material. **Services:** Copying; cassette duplication; collection open to the public. **Automated Operations:** Computerized cataloging. **Computerized Information Services:** BITNET (electronic mail service). **Special Catalogs:** Radio History Program Collection Computer-Generated Catalog - free upon request. **Remarks:** Collection attempts to contain at least one show of every program on network radio, and includes many local shows. Collection is partially maintained by the Department of Theatre and Communication Arts. All requests for materials should be directed to Dr. Bensman in care of the department. Alternate telephone number(s): 678-2565. FAX: (901)678-4331. Electronic mail address(es): BENSMANM@MEMSTVXI (BITNET).

★10075★
Memphis State University - School of Law Library (Law)
Memphis, TN 38152 Phone: (901)678-2426
Sara T. Cole, Dir.
Founded: 1961. **Staff:** Prof 4; Other 8. **Subjects:** Law. **Holdings:** 153,452 books; 1926 reels of microfilm; 403,334 microfiche. **Subscriptions:** 2417 journals and other serials. **Services:** Interlibrary loan; copying; library open to the public. **Automated Operations:** Computerized cataloging. **Computerized Information Services:** WESTLAW, LEXIS. **Staff:** Beth Behrens, Tech.Serv.Libn.; Ruth Smith, Asst.Dir.; Elizabeth Marshall, Ref.Libn.

★10076★
Memphis State University - Special Collections (Hist)
Memphis, TN 38152 Phone: (901)678-2210
Michelle Fagan, Cur.
Founded: 1964. **Staff:** Prof 1; Other 2. **Subjects:** Lower Mississippi Valley - history, culture, literature. **Special Collections:** Memphis multimedia project (race relations); theater collection; sanitation strike of Memphis, 1968 (55 cubic feet); Robert R. Church Family, 1870-1980 (61 cubic feet); U.S. circus history, 1890-1970; university archives (250,000 archival materials); assassination of Martin Luther King, Jr; manuscript collections (315 collections; 6.7 million items). **Holdings:** 32,375 volumes; 7 million manuscript items, including photographs and sheet music; 727 maps; 2972 oral histories on audiotape; 484 videotapes; 247 reels of 16mm film; 77 records. **Services:** Copying; collections open to the public. **Automated Operations:** Computerized cataloging. **Computerized Information Services:** OCLC. **Networks/Consortia:** Member of SOLINET. **Publications:** Brister Library Monograph; Campus Tower News, both irregular - both on exchange. **Special Catalogs:** Registers and inventories to collections.

★10077★
Memphis State University - Speech and Hearing Center Library (Med)
807 Jefferson Ave. Phone: (901)678-5846
Memphis, TN 38104 John Swearengen, Lib.Asst.
Founded: 1965. **Staff:** 1. **Subjects:** Audiology, speech pathology. **Holdings:** 5964 volumes. **Subscriptions:** 90 journals and other serials. **Services:** Interlibrary loan; copying; library open to the public.

Memphis State University Libraries - Special Collections - West Tennessee Historical Society - Library
See: **West Tennessee Historical Society - Library** (20200)

★10078★
Memphis Theological Seminary - Library (Rel-Phil)
168 E. Parkway, S. Phone: (901)458-8232
Memphis, TN 38104 Dale Bilbrey, Adm.Libn.
Founded: 1956. **Staff:** Prof 1; Other 3. **Subjects:** Theology, church history, missions, homiletics, Old Testament, Christian education, New Testament, sociology of religion. **Special Collections:** R. Pierce Beaver Missions Library (5000 volumes; 8 VF drawers). **Holdings:** 75,240 volumes; 372 reels of microfilm; 2500 microfiche. **Subscriptions:** 611 journals and other serials. **Services:** Interlibrary loan; copying; library open to the public. **Computerized Information Services:** BRS Information Technologies. **Staff:** Barbara Jackson, Circ.Libn.

★10079★
Menaul Historical Library of the Southwest (Hist)
301 Menaul Blvd., N.E.
Albuquerque, NM 87107 Phone: (505)345-7727
Founded: 1974. **Staff:** 4. **Subjects:** Presbyterian history; missions and churches in the Southwest; Menaul school records; history of the Southwest. **Special Collections:** Home Mission Monthly, 1886-1924; Women and Missions, 1924-1944; Correspondence of Sheldon Jackson, 1856-1908; Spanish missions in the Southwest (all on microfilm). **Holdings:** 1300 books; 70 bound periodical volumes; 58 reels of microfilm; 20 drawers of information files; 30 drawers of photographs; 100 boxes of archival materials; 1600 slides; 50 lantern slides; 150 audiotapes; 13 old Spanish and English Bibles; pictures. **Subscriptions:** 10 journals and other serials. **Services:** Copying; library open to the public for reference use only. **Publications:** Menaul Historical Review, quarterly; list of resources.

H.L. Mencken Collection of Autographed First Editions
See: **San Diego State University** (14718)

Mendel Art Gallery
See: **Saskatoon Gallery and Conservatory Corporation** (14874)

Mendelssohn-Archive
See: **Stiftung Preussischer Kulturbesitz - Bibliothek** (15794)

★10080★
Mendocino Art Center - Art Library (Art)
Box 765 Phone: (707)937-5818
Mendocino, CA 95460 Bob Avery, Exec.Coord.
Subjects: Art. **Holdings:** 2500 books; 200 bound periodical volumes. **Subscriptions:** 18 journals and other serials. **Services:** Library open to members only.

Mendocino County Historical Society - Held-Poage Memorial Home & Research Library
See: **Held-Poage Memorial Home & Research Library** (7113)

★10081★
Mendocino County Law Library (Law)
Courthouse, Rm. 207 Phone: (707)463-4491
Ukiah, CA 95482 Sandy Linderman, Law Libn.
Staff: 2. **Subjects:** Law. **Holdings:** 9000 books. **Services:** Copying; library open to the public for reference use only.

★10082★
Mendocino Historical Research, Inc. - Lemos Library (Hist)
45007 Albion St.
P.O. Box 922 Phone: (707)937-5791
Mendocino, CA 95460 Dorothy Bear, Co-founder
Subjects: Town of Mendocino, Mendocino County coast. **Special Collections:** Genealogical files of pioneers; archives (Mendocino area residents; records and documents); Escola Room Archive (shipping history). **Holdings:** 500 books; 100 documents; photographs; nonbook items. **Services:** Copying; library open to the public. **Publications:** Annual Review. **Staff:** Megan Coddington, Exec.Dir.

★10083★
Mendota Mental Health Institute - Library Media Services (Med)
301 Troy Dr.
Madison, WI 53704 Phone: (608)244-2411
Founded: 1955. **Staff:** 1. **Subjects:** Clinical psychology and psychiatry; psychiatric nursing and social work; mental health - administration, training, research, prevention, consultation; psychiatry for the deaf; forensic psychiatry. **Holdings:** 22,416 books; 1945 bound periodical volumes; 12 VF drawers of specialized reprints and reports; 340 film and videotape titles; AV catalogs; 107 newsletters. **Subscriptions:** 162 journals and other serials. **Services:** Interlibrary loan; copying; SDI; center open to state residents. **Computerized Information Services:** Access to online systems. **Networks/ Consortia:** Member of Multitype Advisory Library Committee (MALC), South Central Wisconsin Health Science Libraries Consortium. **Publications:** Library News and List of Newly Cataloged Books and AVs. **Remarks:** FAX: (608)244-2646.

★10084★
Menlo Park Historical Association - Local History Collection (Hist)
PO Box 1002 Phone: (415)858-3368
Menlo Park, CA 94026-1002 Jeannie Bone, Archv.
Founded: 1971. **Subjects:** History of Menlo Park and the surrounding area, 1840s to present. **Special Collections:** Materials relating to the development and early land ownership of southern San Mateo County; Camp Fremont, World War I military training camp materials; community life. **Holdings:** Clippings from the Menlo-Atherton Recorder, the Peninsula Times-Tribune, the Palo Alto Weekly, the Country Almanac, and the San Francisco Chronicle, 1950 to present; Menlo Park Recorder and San Jose Mercury on microfilm; 1860 U.S. census; 46 oral history tapes and transcripts; maps; documents; photographs; directories; personal papers and artifacts; bound volumes of Menlo Park Recorder, 1926-1928, 1934, 1940, 1952-1980; bound volumes of Ravenswood Post, 1955-1979; reels of Leon F. Douglass's experimental motion picture film (1930); City of Menlo Park financial records, 1927 to present; videotapes. **Services:** Copying; research in response to letter inquiries; collection open to the public. **Remarks:** Alternate telephone number(s): (415)858-3368 (answering service). Collection is located at the Menlo Park Public Library, 800 Alma Ave., Menlo Park, CA 94026.

Dr. Karl A. Menninger Medical Library
See: **U.S. Dept. of Veterans Affairs (KS-Topeka)** (17335)

★10085★
Menninger Foundation - Archives (Med)
Box 829 Phone: (913)273-7500
Topeka, KS 66601 Kelly E. Burket, Archv.
Founded: 1960. **Staff:** Prof 1; Other 1. **Subjects:** Psychiatry, psychoanalysis, clinical psychology, psychiatric social work, medical history. **Special Collections:** Dr. C.F. Menninger Collection; Mrs. Flo V. Menninger Bible Study Collection; Dr. Karl Menninger Collection; Dr. William C. Menninger Collection; Sigmund Freud Collection; Dorothea Lynde Dix Collection; George III Collection; Dr. Emil Oberholzer Collection; Dr. Ugo Cerletti Collection; American Art Therapy Association Collection; Kansas Psychiatric Society Collection; Dr. Gardner Murphy Collection; Dr. Elmer Southard Collection. **Holdings:** 1800 pamphlets; 700 manuscript boxes; 400 VF drawers; 30,000 clippings; 12,000 photographs; 2500 tapes. **Services:** Copying; use of archives for research may be requested. **Publications:** Pamphlet describing the archives - available on request. **Remarks:** FAX: (913)273-9150. **Staff:** Dr. Robert G. Menninger, Dir., Musm. & Archv.Div.

Menninger Foundation - Department of Research - Professional Library
See: **Menninger Professional Library** (10086)

★10086★
Menninger Professional Library (Med)
Box 829 Phone: (913)273-7500
Topeka, KS 66601 Alice Brand Bartlett, Chf.Libn.
Founded: 1930. **Staff:** Prof 4; Other 6. **Subjects:** Clinical psychiatry, psychoanalysis, clinical psychology, family therapy, forensic psychiatry, allied mental health sciences. **Holdings:** 28,000 books; 19,000 bound periodical volumes. **Subscriptions:** 420 journals and other serials. **Services:** Interlibrary loan; copying; SDI; library open to mental health professionals. **Automated Operations:** Computerized cataloging. **Computerized Information Services:** NLM, DIALOG Information Services. Performs searches on fee basis. Contact Person: Marcelline Schott, Ref.Libn. **Formerly:** Menninger Foundation - Department of Research - Professional Library. **Staff:** Lois Bogia, Asst.Libn.

Mennonite Archives of Ontario
See: **Conrad Grebel College - Library/Archives** (6714)

★10087★
Mennonite Brethren Bible College - Library (Rel-Phil)
1-169 Riverton Ave. Phone: (204)669-6575
Winnipeg, MB, Canada R2L 2E5 Richard D, Thiessen, Coll.Libn.
Founded: 1944. **Staff:** Prof 1; Other 2. **Subjects:** Theology, humanities, music, Biblical studies. **Special Collections:** Mennonitica and Anabaptistica. **Holdings:** 38,500 books; 1900 bound periodical volumes; 150 educational and theological pamphlets; 50 dissertations and theses; 750 phonograph records; 50 compact discs. **Subscriptions:** 245 journals and other serials. **Services:** Interlibrary loan; copying; library open to the public on fee basis upon registration. **Publications:** Library Leaves, monthly - to college faculty and friends. **Special Catalogs:** Winnipeg Union List of Periodicals in Religion. **Special Indexes:** Index to Archives (Mennonite Brethren) Collection. **Remarks:** FAX: (204)654-1865.

Mennonite Brethren Biblical Seminary
See: **Fresno Pacific College & Mennonite Brethren Biblical Seminary - Hiebert Library** (6162)

★10088★
Mennonite Church - Western District Conference - Western District Loan Library & Resource Center (Rel-Phil)
Box 306 Phone: (316)283-6300
North Newton, KS 67117 Marlene H. Bogard, Dir.
Founded: 1936. **Staff:** 1. **Subjects:** Peace and justice, worship and devotion, children's literature, youth ministries. **Special Collections:** Children's collection (4000 volumes). **Holdings:** 8000 books. **Subscriptions:** 9 journals and other serials. **Services:** Interlibrary loan; copying; center open to the public. **Computerized Information Services:** Internal database.

★10089★
Mennonite Heritage Village (Canada) Inc. - Library (Rel-Phil)
Box 1136 Phone: (204)326-9661
Steinbach, MB, Canada R0A 2A0 Peter Goertzen, Mgr.
Staff: Prof 1. **Subjects:** Mennonites in U.S.S.R. and Canada; German-language Mennonitica. **Holdings:** 4000 books; 2000 archival materials. **Services:** Library open to the public. **Remarks:** FAX: (204)326-5046.

★10090★
Mennonite Historians of Eastern Pennsylvania (MHEP) - Mennonite Historical Library & Archives of Eastern Pennsylvania (Hist, Rel-Phil)
The MeetingHouse
Box 82, 565 Yoder Phone: (215)256-3020
Harleysville, PA 19438 Joel D. Alderfer, Libn.
Founded: 1967. **Staff:** Prof 1. **Subjects:** History - Mennonite church, Anabaptist, local; genealogy; folklore; church music; Pennsylvania Germans. **Special Collections:** Jacob B. Mensch Collection (Mennonite preacher); J.C. Clemens Collection (preacher); John E. Lapp Collection; Jacob Fretz Collection. **Holdings:** 5000 books; 600 bound periodical volumes; 215 manuscript collections; 10 dissertations; 450 bound church bulletins; 125 reels of microfilm; 1100 tapes; 35 maps; 2400 photographs; 100 archival collections; 15 videotapes. **Subscriptions:** 80 journals and other serials. **Services:** Copying; library open to the public. **Networks/Consortia:** Member of Eastern Mennonite Associated Libraries & Archives (EMALA). **Publications:** MHEP Newsletter, bimonthly - to members. **Special Indexes:** Indexes to letter collections; indexes to archival collection.

Mennonite Historical Library
See: **Bluffton College** (1917)

★10091★
Mennonite Historical Library (Rel-Phil)
Goshen College Phone: (219)535-7418
Goshen, IN 46526 John D. Roth, Dir.
Founded: 1907. **Staff:** Prof 3; Other 3. **Subjects:** Anabaptist, Mennonite, Amish, and Hutterian Brethren writings and history; genealogy; limited materials relating to the Church of the Brethren, the Society of Friends, and regional history. **Special Collections:** John Horsch Research Collection (Anabaptist, Mennonite, allied Reformation materials); J.D. Hartzler Hymnal Collection (primarily gospel and school materials; 2700 books). **Holdings:** 30,000 books; 10,500 bound periodical volumes; 105 VF drawers of unpublished treatises, archival materials, pamphlets, folders, maps, photographs, photocopies; microforms; phonograph records. **Subscriptions:** 395 journals and other serials. **Services:** Interlibrary loan (fee for frequent requests); copying; library open to the public. **Automated Operations:** Computerized cataloging and ILL. **Computerized Information Services:** OCLC. **Networks/Consortia:** Member of INCOLSA. **Publications:** The Mennonite Quarterly Review; Mennonite Bibliography, 1631-1961 (1977); A Bibliography of Anabaptism, 1520-1630 (1962). **Special Indexes:** Index of 55,000 obituary notices of Mennonites and Amish-Mennonites published in Herald of Truth, 1864-1905, and Gospel Herald, 1908 to present. **Staff:** Joe Springer, Cur.

Mennonite Library and Archives
See: **Bethel College** (1784)

★10092★
Menorah Medical Center - Robert Uhlmann Medical Library (Med)
4949 Rockhill Rd. Phone: (816)276-8157
Kansas City, MO 64110 Kitty Serling, Med.Lib.Supv.
Staff: Prof 1. **Subjects:** Medicine, surgery, psychiatry, nursing, cardiology, lasers, pediatrics, neurology. **Special Collections:** Jewish Medical Ethics. **Holdings:** 2000 books; 20,000 bound periodical volumes. **Subscriptions:** 200 journals and other serials; 6 newspapers. **Services:** Interlibrary loan; copying; SDI; library open to the public with restrictions. **Automated Operations:** Computerized ILL. **Computerized Information Services:** MEDLINE, NLM. **Networks/Consortia:** Member of Kansas City Library Network, Inc. (KCLN), Health Sciences Library Group of Greater Kansas City, Kansas City Metropolitan Library Network (KCMLN). **Remarks:** FAX: (816)276-8105.

★10093★
Men's Rights, Inc. (MR Inc.) - Reading Center (Soc Sci)
Box 163180 Phone: (916)484-7333
Sacramento, CA 95816 Fredric Hayward, Exec.Dir.
Founded: 1977. **Staff:** Prof 1. **Subjects:** Sexism and men's problems. **Holdings:** 100 books; clippings; periodicals. **Subscriptions:** 2 journals and other serials. **Services:** Center open to the public by appointment for reference use only. **Publications:** News Releases.

★10094★
Mental Health Association in Dutchess County, Inc. - Department of Mental Hygiene - Library (Med)
230 North Rd. Phone: (914)485-9700
Poughkeepsie, NY 12601 Janet Caruso, Libn.
Founded: 1969. **Staff:** Prof 1; Other 1. **Subjects:** Psychiatry, child psychiatry, alcoholism, drug abuse, Alzheimers disease, psychology, mental retardation, the family. **Holdings:** 1850 books; 150 AV program titles; 75 audiotapes; 4 VF drawers of clippings, pamphlets, reprints. **Subscriptions:** 70 journals and other serials. **Services:** Interlibrary loan; copying; library open to the public with restrictions. **Networks/Consortia:** Member of Southeastern New York Library Resources Council (SENYLRC). **Publications:** Newsletter, 2/year; brochure. **Special Catalogs:** AV Catalog, irregular. **Special Indexes:** Indexes on child abuse, deinstitutionalization, suicide, and other mental health subjects (book).

★10095★
Mental Health Association of Westchester - Library (Med)
29 Sterling Ave. Phone: (914)949-6741
White Plains, NY 10606 Phyllis Getlan, Ombudsman
Founded: 1950. **Staff:** 1. **Subjects:** Mental health, psychiatry, psychology, drugs, graduate social work. **Holdings:** 3150 volumes; 150 VF drawers of pamphlets and clippings; 50 films and videotapes. **Subscriptions:** 25 journals and other serials. **Services:** Copying; library open to the public.

★10096★
Mental Health Center - Library (Med)
1245 N. 29th St. Phone: (406)252-5658
Billings, MT 59101 Lizbeth Barnea, Libn.
Staff: Prof 1. **Subjects:** Psychiatry, psychology, substance abuse, psychiatric nursing. **Holdings:** 750 books; vertical files. **Subscriptions:** 29 journals and other serials. **Services:** Interlibrary loan; copying; SDI; library open to the public with restrictions. **Networks/Consortia:** Member of Billings Area Health Sciences Information Cooperative (BAHSIC), National Network of Libraries of Medicine (NN/LM). **Remarks:** FAX: (406)252-4641.

★10097★
Mental Health Institute - Health Science Library (Med)
1200 W. Cedar St. Phone: (712)225-2594
Cherokee, IA 51012 Tom Folkes, Hea.Sci.Libn.
Staff: Prof 1. **Subjects:** Psychiatry, psychology, neurology, nursing, social service, medicine. **Holdings:** 2599 books; 793 audio cassettes; 182 video cassettes; 5000 back issues of journals; 8 linear feet of vertical files. **Subscriptions:** 51 journals and other serials. **Services:** Interlibrary loan; copying; library open to the public for reference use only. **Networks/Consortia:** Member of National Network of Libraries of Medicine - Greater Midwest Region.

★10098★
Mental Health Legal Advisors Committee - Flaschner Disabilities Library (Law)
11 Beacon St., Suite 925 Phone: (617)723-9130
Boston, MA 21218 Melissa Stimell
Founded: 1973. **Staff:** 6. **Subjects:** Law - disabilities, mental health. **Holdings:** 300 books; 200 bound periodical volumes; 50 reports. **Subscriptions:** 11 journals and other serials. **Services:** Library open to the public by appointment. **Remarks:** FAX: (617)723-9153.

★10099★
Mental Health and Mental Retardation Authority of Harris County - Learning Resource Center (Med)
2850 Fannin
Houston, TX 77002 Phone: (713)750-5600
Staff: Prof 1. **Subjects:** Mental health, mental retardation. **Holdings:** 450 books; 1000 pamphlets; 400 unbound journals; 100 reports. **Services:** Interlibrary loan; center open to the public for reference use only. **Formerly:** Its Information Resource Center.

Mercaldo Photo Archives
See: **Buffalo Bill Historical Center** (2325)

★10100★
Mercantile General Reinsurance Company - Library (Bus-Fin)
123 Front St., W. Phone: (416)947-3800
Toronto, ON, Canada M5J 2M7 Marie Davidson
Staff: Prof 1. **Subjects:** Reinsurance, life insurance, underwriting, actuarial science, data processing, management science. **Special Collections:** Archives; insurance laws; American Council of Life Insurance (ACLI) and Health Insurance Association of America (HIAA) materials. **Holdings:** 1000 books. **Subscriptions:** 85 journals and other serials. **Services:** Interlibrary loan; copying; library open to the public with restrictions. **Computerized Information Services:** Info Globe, BRS Information Technologies; ACLI Life and Health To-day (internal database). **Publications:** For Your Information; Library Bulletin, both monthly. **Remarks:** FAX: (416)364-2449.

★10101★
Mercantile Library Association - Mercantile Library (Hum)
17 E. 47th St. Phone: (212)755-6710
New York, NY 10017 Harold Augenbraum, Exec.Dir.
Founded: 1820. **Staff:** Prof 3. **Subjects:** 19th and 20th century literature, including best sellers; biography. **Special Collections:** 19th century fiction and nonfiction (55,000 volumes). **Holdings:** 195,000 books. **Subscriptions:** 38 journals and other serials. **Services:** Library open to members. Programs open to the public. **Publications:** New Arrivals List, monthly; newsletter, semimonthly; annual report. **Remarks:** FAX: (212)758-1387. Maintains a writer's studio. **Staff:** Rose Marie O'Leary, Pub.Serv.Libn.

Mercantile Library Association of Montreal Archives
See: **Fraser-Hickson Institute, Montreal - Free Library - Special Collections** (6102)

★10102★
Merced Community Medical Center - William E. Fountain Health Sciences Library (Med)
301 E. 13th St.
Box 231 Phone: (209)385-7058
Merced, CA 95340 Betty Maddalena, Libn.
Founded: 1965. **Staff:** Prof 1; Other 2. **Subjects:** Medicine, nursing. **Holdings:** 1715 books; 2560 bound periodical volumes; 301 Audio-Digest tapes. **Subscriptions:** 179 journals and other serials. **Services:** Interlibrary loan; copying; SDI; library open to the public. **Computerized Information Services:** MEDLINE, DIALOG Information Services; OnTyme Electronic Message Network Service (electronic mail service). Performs searches on fee basis. **Networks/Consortia:** Member of National Network of Libraries of Medicine - Pacific Southwest Region, CLASS, Merced County Health Information Consortium, Audiovisual Cooperative for Education (ACE). **Remarks:** FAX: (209)385-7062.

★10103★
Merced County Law Library (Law)
County Courts Bldg.
670 W. 22nd St. Phone: (209)723-3101
Merced, CA 95340-3730 Gloria Calistro, Law Libn.
Founded: 1937. **Staff:** Prof 1; Other 1. **Subjects:** Law. **Holdings:** 16,778 books; 485 bound periodical volumes; 3 VF drawers of briefs; 2 files of pamphlets; American Bar Association and California State Bar Association materials. **Subscriptions:** 36 journals and other serials. **Services:** Interlibrary loan; copying; library open to the public.

★10104★
Merced County Library - Special Collections (Info Sci)
2100 "O" St. Phone: (209)385-7485
Merced, CA 95340 Linda Wilson, County Libn.
Founded: 1910. **Staff:** Prof 8; Other 30. **Subjects:** Federal, state, and local documents; state and local history; genealogy; maps. **Holdings:** 349,799 books; 3037 volumes of California state documents (partial depository); 935 U.S. documents; 616 Merced County documents; 689 maps. **Subscriptions:** 221 journals and other serials; 25 newspapers. **Services:** Interlibrary loan; copying; collections open to the public. **Automated Operations:** Computerized cataloging. **Computerized Information Services:** OCLC; internal databases. Performs searches free of charge. Contact Person: Susan Manning, Ref.Libn., 385-7597. **Networks/Consortia:** Member of 49-99 Cooperative Library System. **Special Indexes:** Index to Merced Sun-Star, 1977 to present. **Remarks:** FAX: (209)726-7912. **Staff:** Deanna Kobayashi, Pub.Serv.Libn.; Charleen Renteria, Br.Serv.Libn.; Delia Near, Tech.Serv.Libn.; Carolyn Thomas, Ref.Libn.; Pat Copp, Young People's Libn.

★10105★
Mercer County Historical Society - Library and Archives (Hist)
119 S. Pitt St. Phone: (412)662-3490
Mercer, PA 16137 David M. Miller, Pres.
Founded: 1951. **Staff:** 1. **Subjects:** Mercer County history. **Special Collections:** Dr. Goodsell's Collection. **Holdings:** 2500 books; 200 bound periodical volumes; newspapers; maps; surveys; microfilm; manuscript materials. **Services:** Copying; mail research requests accepted; library open to the public. **Publications:** On Polar Trails; newsletter, quarterly. **Staff:** Robert Fuhrman, Exec.Dir.

★10106★
Mercer County Law Library (Law)
Court House Phone: (419)586-2122
Celina, OH 45822 Carolyn Leffler, Law Libn.
Staff: 1. **Subjects:** Law, taxation. **Holdings:** 5500 volumes. **Services:** Copying; library open to the public. **Remarks:** Alternate telephone number(s): 586-5669.

★10107★
Mercer County Law Library (Law)
305 Mercer County Courthouse Phone: (412)662-3800
Mercer, PA 16137 Jane Jones, Law Libn.
Founded: 1912. **Subjects:** Law, especially Pennsylvania and federal law. **Holdings:** 15,000 volumes. **Subscriptions:** 15 journals and other serials. **Services:** Copying; library open to the public for reference use only. **Computerized Information Services:** WESTLAW, Veralex 2. **Remarks:** FAX: (412)662-0620.

★10108★
Mercer County Regional Planning Commission - Library (Plan)
Sharpsville Center Plaza
94 E. Shenango St. Phone: (412)962-5787
Sharpsville, PA 16150 Leslie E. Spaulding, Libn.
Staff: Prof 6; Other 5. **Subjects:** Planning, transportation, environment. **Holdings:** 300 books. **Subscriptions:** 10 journals and other serials. **Services:** Library open to the public.

★10109★
George Mercer, Jr. School of Theology - Library (Rel-Phil)
65 4th St. Phone: (516)248-4800
Garden City, NY 11530 Marilyn Hulland, Libn.
Founded: 1955. **Staff:** Prof 2; Other 3. **Subjects:** Religion, church history, theology, ethics, philosophy. **Holdings:** 25,500 volumes; 462 cassettes; 735 microforms; 500 pamphlets. **Subscriptions:** 150 journals. **Services:** Interlibrary loan; copying; library open to the public. **Networks/Consortia:** Member of Long Island Library Resources Council. **Remarks:** Alternate telephone number(s): 248-4801. Library maintained by the Episcopal Diocese of Long Island. **Staff:** Jane Sullivan, Asst.Libn.

★10110★
Mercer Medical Center - Health Sciences Library (Med)
446 Bellevue Ave. - Box 1658 Phone: (609)394-4125
Trenton, NJ 08607 Catherine W. Marchok, Dir.
Founded: 1947. **Staff:** Prof 2; Other 2. **Subjects:** Medicine, nursing. **Special Collections:** 19th century medical books. **Holdings:** 3100 titles; 4064 bound periodical volumes; 5 VF drawers of clippings and pamphlets; 1 VF drawer of pictures; 400 audiotapes; 1455 slides. **Subscriptions:** 202 journals and other serials. **Services:** Interlibrary loan; copying; library open to the public for reference use only. **Computerized Information Services:** MEDLINE, BRS Information Technologies. Performs searches on fee basis. **Networks/Consortia:** Member of National Network of Libraries of Medicine - Middle Atlantic Region, Central Jersey Health Science Libraries Association (CJHSLA), Health Sciences Library Association of New Jersey (HSLANJ). **Staff:** Karen Cook, Libn.

★10111★
Mercer University - Law School - Furman Smith Library (Law)
Macon, GA 31207 Phone: (912)752-2612
Leah F. Chanin, Dir.
Founded: 1887. **Staff:** Prof 5.5; Other 6.5. **Subjects:** Law, history of law. **Special Collections:** Space law (2200 volumes). **Holdings:** 250,000 books. **Subscriptions:** 1000 journals and other serials; 8 newspapers. **Services:** Interlibrary loan; copying; library open to the public. **Automated Operations:** Computerized cataloging. **Computerized Information Services:** LEXIS, WESTLAW, DIALOG Information Services, NEXIS, ELSS (Electronic Legislative Search System). Performs searches on fee basis. Contact Person: Patricia O'Neal, Asst.Libn. **Networks/Consortia:** Member of SOLINET. **Publications:** Acquisition List; Furman Flyer, semimonthly; Guide To Library. **Remarks:** FAX: (912)738-2101. **Staff:** Ismael Gullon, Cat.; Suzanne Cassidy, Ref.Libn.; Don Brown, Comp./AV.

★10112★
Mercer University - Medical School Library (Med)
Macon, GA 31207 Phone: (912)752-2515
Jocelyn A. Rankin, Dir.
Founded: 1974. **Staff:** Prof 5; Other 7.5. **Subjects:** Medicine. **Holdings:** 16,911 books; 58,034 bound periodical volumes; 3693 microfiche; 9605 government documents; 2603 AV programs. **Subscriptions:** 760 journals and other serials. **Services:** Interlibrary loan; copying; SDI; library open to the public. **Automated Operations:** Computerized public access catalog, cataloging, acquisitions, serials, and circulation. **Computerized Information Services:** OCLC, BRS Information Technologies, DIALOG Information Services, WILSONLINE, MEDLINE; GaIN (internal database). Performs searches on fee basis. **Networks/Consortia:** Member of SOLINET, National Network of Libraries of Medicine - Southeastern/Atlantic Region, Health Science Libraries Consortium of Central Georgia (HSLCG), Georgia Interactive Network for Medical Information (GaIN). **Publications:** Library Guide, irregular. **Remarks:** FAX: (912)752-2051. **Staff:** Martha Watkins, Asst.Dir.; Nancy Van De Water, Ref.

★10113★
Mercer University - Southern College of Pharmacy - H. Custer Naylor Library
345 Boulevard, N.E.
Atlanta, GA 30312
Defunct.

★10114★
William M. Mercer, Inc. - Information and Research Center (Bus-Fin)
200 Clarendon St. Phone: (617)421-5367
Boston, MA 02116 Josephine M. Hall, Mgr., Info.Serv.
Staff: Prof 1; Other 1. **Subjects:** Pensions, health care benefits, compensation, consulting. **Holdings:** 450 books; 18 VF drawers of subject files; reports. **Subscriptions:** 50 journals and other serials. **Services:** Interlibrary loan; center open to other librarians. **Computerized Information Services:** LEXIS, NEXIS, DIALOG Information Services; internal database. **Remarks:** FAX: (617)421-5384. A subsidiary of Marsh and McLennan, Inc.

★10115★
William M. Mercer, Ltd. - Centre d'Information (Bus-Fin)
600, de Maisonneuve W., Suite 1100 Phone: (514)285-1802
Montreal, PQ, Canada H3A 3J4 Ruth Ludwig, Libn.
Founded: 1975. **Staff:** Prof 1; Other 1. **Subjects:** Employee benefits, actuarial science, human resources management, taxation, unemployment insurance, management. **Holdings:** 2380 books; 25 VF drawers. **Subscriptions:** 45 journals and other serials; 7 newspapers. **Services:** Interlibrary loan; center not open to the public. **Automated Operations:** Computerized cataloging. **Computerized Information Services:** DIALOG Information Services, The Financial Post DataGroup, Infomart Online. **Remarks:** FAX: (514)285-8831.

★10116★
William M. Mercer, Ltd. - Information Research Centre (Bus-Fin)
161 Bay St.
P.O. Box 501 Phone: (416)868-7697
Toronto, ON, Canada M5J 2S5 Merle Ramdial, Supv./Libn.
Founded: 1974. **Staff:** Prof 1; Other 3. **Subjects:** Employee benefits, pensions, financial planning, strategic planning, salary administration, executive compensation, group insurance benefits. **Special Collections:** Transactions and records of the Society of Actuaries; publications from Canadian and British Actuarial Associations. **Holdings:** 2500 books; 450 subject files; company financial reports. **Subscriptions:** 180 journals and other serials; 5 newspapers. **Services:** Interlibrary loan; copying; center open to the public by appointment at librarian's discretion. **Automated Operations:** Computerized cataloging, serials, and circulation. **Computerized Information Services:** DIALOG Information Services, Info Globe, QL Systems, Canada Systems Group (CSG), Infomart Online, LEXIS, NEXIS, Reuters, CAN/LAW, Dow Jones News/Retrieval, Dun & Bradstreet Business Credit Services. **Publications:** Canadian Library Bulletin, weekly - for internal distribution only. **Remarks:** FAX: (416)868-7002.

★10117★
William M. Mercer-Meidinger-Hansen Inc. - Information Research Center
10 S. Wacker Dr.
Chicago, IL 60606
Defunct.

Gilbart B. Mercier Memorial Library
See: **Antique Boat Museum, Inc.** (900)

★10118★
Merck & Company, Inc. - Calgon Corporation - Information Center (Env-Cons)
Calgon Center
Box 1346 Phone: (412)777-8205
Pittsburgh, PA 15230-1346 Betty P. Schwarz, Mgr.
Founded: 1937. **Staff:** Prof 1; Other 1. **Subjects:** Industrial and municipal water treatment and reclamation, chemistry of water soluble polymers. **Holdings:** 5000 books; 100 bound periodical volumes; 5000 reels of microfilm; 20,000 Environmental Protection Agency (EPA) reports; patents; newsletters. **Subscriptions:** 300 journals and other serials; 5 newspapers. **Services:** Interlibrary loan; SDI; center open to the public by appointment. **Automated Operations:** Computerized cataloging and serials. **Computerized Information Services:** STN International, DIALOG Information Services, NEXIS, Chemical Information Systems, Inc. (CIS), NLM, PFDS Online. **Networks/Consortia:** Member of Pittsburgh Regional Library Center (PRLC). **Publications:** Acquisitions list, monthly - for internal distribution only. **Remarks:** FAX: (412)777-8104.

★10119★
Merck & Company, Inc. - Kelco Division - Literature and Information Services (Sci-Engr)
8355 Aero Dr.
PO Box 23576 Phone: (619)292-4900
San Diego, CA 92123 Susan J. Shepherd, Mgr.
Staff: Prof 3; Other 3. **Subjects:** Chemistry, microbiology, food, industrial applications of polysaccharides, rheology, biochemistry, marine botany. **Holdings:** 5000 books; periodicals in microform and bound volumes; patents; reprints; slides; pamphlets; internal research records. **Subscriptions:**

400 journals and other serials. **Services:** Interlibrary loan (limited); copying; services open to the public by appointment. **Computerized Information Services:** DIALOG Information Services, ORBIT Search Service, Chemical Abstracts Service (CAS), STN International, RLIN; internal databases. **Networks/Consortia:** Member of CLASS. **Publications:** Monthly patent bulletin - for internal distribution only; SDI profiles; monthly scientific information bulletin; literature surveys; bibliographies. **Remarks:** FAX: (619)467-6520. **Staff:** Ann M. Willard, Res.Info.Spec.; Liz Koch, Info.Assoc.

★10120★
Merck & Company, Inc. - Law Library (Law)
126 E. Lincoln Ave.
Box 2000 Phone: (908)594-5805
Rahway, NJ 07065 Judith Goldberg, Law Libn.
Founded: 1959. **Staff:** Prof 1; Other 1. **Subjects:** Law - patent, labor, corporate, employee relation, environmental, international. **Holdings:** 2000 books; 300 bound periodical volumes; 3500 Merck patents; 250 other cataloged items; Federal Register, 1977 to present, on microfilm; Official Gazette - Patents, 1955 to present on microfilm. **Subscriptions:** 240 journals and other serials; 10 newspapers. **Services:** Library not open to the public. **Automated Operations:** Computerized public access catalog and cataloging. **Computerized Information Services:** DIALOG Information Services, LEXIS, NEXIS. **Remarks:** FAX: (908)594-4720.

★10121★
Merck & Company, Inc. - Merck Sharp & Dohme Research Laboratories - Literature Resources, Rahway (Sci-Engr, Med)
R86-240
Box 2000 Phone: (908)594-6754
Rahway, NJ 07065 Evelyn Armstrong, Dir.
Founded: 1933. **Staff:** Prof 7; Other 5. **Subjects:** Chemistry, biochemistry, pharmacology, immunology, veterinary science, biomedical sciences, science and technology, business. **Holdings:** 30,000 books; 25,000 bound periodical volumes; 1000 reels of microfilm of U.S. chemical patents; 115 periodicals on microfilm. **Subscriptions:** 3000 journals and other serials. **Services:** Interlibrary loan; copying. **Automated Operations:** Computerized cataloging. **Computerized Information Services:** BRS Information Technologies, DIALOG Information Services, NLM, OCLC, Chemical Abstracts Service (CAS), Data-Star, NEXIS, ORBIT Search Service. **Networks/Consortia:** Member of PALINET. **Publications:** Literature Resource Center Announcements, monthly; LRC Meetings, semiannual - both for internal distribution only. **Special Catalogs:** Current periodicals holdings list. **Remarks:** FAX: (908)594-6059. **Staff:** Linda Mininni, Mgr.; Kabita Das, Supv.; Ilona Giedrys, Lit.Rsrcs.Assoc.; Rita Nacchio-Wells, Lit.Rsrcs.Assoc.; Liz Arnold, Lit.Rsrcs.Assoc.

★10122★
Merck & Company, Inc. - Merck Sharp & Dohme Research Laboratories - Literature Resources WP42-1 (Med)
West Point, PA 19486 Phone: (215)661-7804
Ann Jenkins, Assoc.Dir.
Founded: 1921. **Staff:** Prof 3; Other 8. **Subjects:** Organic chemistry, biochemistry, immunology, physiology, microbiology, pharmacology, medicine, veterinary medicine. **Holdings:** 6000 books; 20,000 bound periodical volumes; 6000 reels of microfilm. **Subscriptions:** 2000 journals and other serials. **Services:** Interlibrary loan; resources open to medical and allied professions. **Computerized Information Services:** OCLC, DIALOG Information Services, MEDLARS, BRS Information Technologies; internal database. **Networks/Consortia:** Member of PALINET. **Publications:** Literature Resources Center Announcements, monthly; Literature Resource Center Meetings, semiannual - both for internal distribution only. **Special Catalogs:** Periodical Holdings List; departmental book catalogs. **Remarks:** FAX: (215)661-7967. **Staff:** Sarah C. Williams, Supv.

★10123★
Merck & Company, Inc. - Merck Sharp & Dohme Research Laboratories - Research Information Systems (Med)
Box 2000 Phone: (908)574-4726
Rahway, NJ 07065 Dr. Marcia Zweerink, Dir.
Founded: 1938. **Staff:** Prof 15; Other 20. **Subjects:** Chemistry, biology, medicine, pharmaceuticals, veterinary medicine. **Holdings:** Unpublished research reports; manuscripts. **Services:** Systems not open to the public. **Computerized Information Services:** Internal database. **Special Indexes:** Computer-stored subject and contact indexes. **Staff:** Jacqueline Algon, Mgr., Pubn./Vital Rec.; Frances Keresztesy, Mgr., Res.Info.; Cheryl Pierson, Mgr., Res.Info.; Mary Carol Scully, Info.Anl.; Gary Kester, Mgr., Res.Info.; Janet A. Salmons, Supv./Anl.; Patricia A. Gawarecki, Info.Anl./Supv.; John Artim, Info.Anl./Supv.; Mary E. McAlpine, Info.Anl./Supv.; Karen J. Marakoff, Res.Info.Anl.; Kristine G. Cope, Info.Sci.; Jane Erdman, Info.Anl.; Beverly Schade, Info.Anl.; Susan Vath, Pubn.Assoc.

★10124★
Merck Frosst Canada Inc. - Research Library (Med)
P.O. Box 1005 Phone: (514)695-7920
Pointe Claire-Dorval, PQ, Canada H9R 4P8 Claire B. Kelly, Sr.Res.Libn.
Founded: 1937. **Staff:** Prof 2; Other 4. **Subjects:** Medicine, chemistry, pharmacy, general science. **Holdings:** 3000 books; 9000 bound periodical volumes. **Subscriptions:** 450 journals and other serials. **Services:** Interlibrary loan; library not open to the public. **Computerized Information Services:** MEDLARS, DIALOG Information Services, BRS Information Technologies, PFDS Online, CAN/OLE, Chemical Abstracts Service (CAS); Envoy 100 (electronic mail service). **Remarks:** FAX: (514)630-8535.

Merck Sharp & Dohme Research Laboratories
See: **Merck & Company, Inc.** (10122)

★10125★
Mercy American River Hospital - Erle M. Blunden, M.D. Memorial Library (Med)
4747 Engle Rd. Phone: (916)484-2452
Carmichael, CA 95608 Meredith Johanson, Med.Libn.
Founded: 1965. **Staff:** 1. **Subjects:** Medicine, nursing, psychiatry, hospital administration. **Holdings:** 400 books. **Subscriptions:** 100 journals and other serials. **Services:** Interlibrary loan; copying; library open to hospital staff. **Computerized Information Services:** MEDLARS, BiblioMed, DIALOG Information Services, MELVYL; DOCLINE (electronic mail service). **Networks/Consortia:** Member of Sacramento Area Health Sciences Librarians (SAHSL), National Network of Libraries of Medicine - Pacific Southwest Region. **Remarks:** FAX: (916)482-4203. **Formerly:** American River Hospital.

Mercy Catholic Medical Center - Fitzgerald Mercy Division
See: **Fitzgerald Mercy Hospital** (5836)

★10126★
Mercy Catholic Medical Center - Misericordia Hospital - Medical Library (Med)
54th St. & Cedar Ave. Phone: (215)748-9415
Philadelphia, PA 19143 Ann Marie Zglinicki, Mgr., Lib.Serv.
Founded: 1918. **Staff:** Prof 1. **Subjects:** Medicine, nursing, psychiatry. **Holdings:** 950 books; 522 bound periodical volumes. **Subscriptions:** 110 journals and other serials. **Services:** Interlibrary loan; copying; library open to the public with permission. **Computerized Information Services:** DIALOG Information Services; FIRST CHOICE, NURSESEARCH (internal databases). **Networks/Consortia:** Member of Consortium for Health Information & Library Services (CHI), BHSL. **Remarks:** FAX: (215)748-9341.

★10127★
Mercy Center for Health Care Services - Medical Library (Med)
1325 N. Highland Ave. Phone: (708)801-2686
Aurora, IL 60506 Mary M. Howrey, Lib.Mgr.
Founded: 1965. **Staff:** Prof 2; Other 3. **Subjects:** Medicine, psychiatry, nursing, hospital administration. **Special Collections:** Gerontology. **Holdings:** 5000 books; 480 periodical back titles; 4 VF drawers of pamphlets; 1000 AV programs. **Subscriptions:** 240 journals and other serials. **Services:** Interlibrary loan; copying; library open to the public. **Automated Operations:** Computerized ILL (DOCLINE). **Computerized Information Services:** DIALOG Information Services, BRS Information Technologies, OCLC EPIC; ILLINETonline; CD-ROM (Core MEDLINE). **Networks/Consortia:** Member of Fox Valley Health Science Library Consortium (FVHSL), DuPage Library System, ILLINET. **Publications:** Periodicals Directory. **Special Catalogs:** HSN Video Catalog. **Remarks:** FAX: (708)801-2687. **Staff:** Lynette Singh, AV Libn.

★10128★
Mercy Center for Health Services - Library (Med)
218 Stone St. Phone: (315)782-7400
Watertown, NY 13601 Jeffrey M. Garvey, Dir. of Lib.Serv.
Founded: 1970. **Staff:** Prof 3; Other 2. **Subjects:** Medicine, nursing, mental health, hospital management. **Holdings:** 2000 books; 7400 bound periodical volumes; 140 AV programs; 75 reels of microfilm. **Subscriptions:** 125 journals and other serials. **Services:** Interlibrary loan; copying; SDI; library open to the public. **Automated Operations:** Computerized ILL. **Computerized Information Services:** BRS Information Technologies. Performs searches on fee basis. **Networks/Consortia:** Member of North Country Reference and Research Resources Council (NCRRRC). **Publications:** Mercy Hospital Library Newsletter, quarterly - by request. **Formerly:** Mercy Hospital of Watertown - Health Science Library. **Staff:** Ellen Darabaner, Circuit Libn.; Mark H. Uebler, Circuit Libn.; W. Kenyon Wells, ILL Supv.

★10129★
Mercy Health Center - Anthony C. Pfohl Health Science Library (Med)
250 Mercy Dr. Phone: (319)589-9620
Dubuque, IA 52001 James H. Lander, Hea.Sci.Libn.
Founded: 1973. **Staff:** Prof 2; Other 2. **Subjects:** Medicine, patient education, management. **Holdings:** 6800 monographs; 250 bound periodical volumes; 1500 pamphlets (65 titles); AV programs. **Subscriptions:** 320 journals and other serials. **Services:** Interlibrary loan; library open to the public. **Automated Operations:** Computerized public access catalog, cataloging, and Ill (DOCLINE). **Computerized Information Services:** BRS Information Technologies. **Networks/Consortia:** Member of Dubuque Area Library Consortium. **Publications:** Library Lines, semiannual. **Remarks:** FAX: (319)589-9669 (Attn: Library).

★10130★
Mercy Health Center - Medical Library (Med)
4300 W. Memorial Rd. Phone: (405)752-3390
Oklahoma City, OK 73120 May Cordry, Hd.Libn.
Founded: 1947. **Staff:** Prof 2; Other 3. **Subjects:** Medicine, nursing, allied health sciences. **Holdings:** 852 books; 5003 bound periodical volumes. **Subscriptions:** 225 journals and other serials. **Services:** Interlibrary loan; copying; library open to the public for reference use only. **Automated Operations:** Computerized serials. **Computerized Information Services:** DIALOG Information Services, MEDLINE. **Networks/Consortia:** Member of Greater Oklahoma City Area Health Sciences Library Consortium (GOAL), Metronet. **Remarks:** FAX: (405)752-3093.

★10131★
Mercy Health Services - Resource Center (Med)
34605 12 Mile Rd. Phone: (313)489-6754
Farmington Hills, MI 48331 Bonnie Tanase-Cairns
Founded: 1976. **Staff:** Prof 1; Other 1. **Subjects:** Health administration, medicine, management. **Holdings:** 2500 books. **Subscriptions:** 150 journals and other serials; 2 newspapers. **Services:** Interlibrary loan; library open to the public. **Computerized Information Services:** DIALOG Information Services. **Remarks:** FAX: (313)489-6932.

★10132★
Mercy Hospital - David A. Amos Health Sciences Library (Med)
1500 E. Sherman Blvd.
Box 358 Phone: (616)739-3972
Muskegon, MI 49443 Mary Jo Wyels, Libn.
Founded: 1950. **Staff:** Prof 1. **Subjects:** Medicine, nursing, allied health sciences. **Holdings:** 500 books; 3700 bound periodical volumes. **Subscriptions:** 165 journals and other serials. **Services:** Interlibrary loan; copying; library open to the public with approval of librarian. **Automated Operations:** Computerized cataloging. **Computerized Information Services:** BRS Information Technologies, MEDLINE. **Remarks:** FAX: (616)733-0957.

★10133★
Mercy Hospital - Edward L. Burns Health Sciences Library (Med)
2200 Jefferson Ave. Phone: (419)259-1327
Toledo, OH 43624 Thomas R. Sink, Dir., Lib.Serv.
Founded: 1940. **Staff:** Prof 1; Other 2. **Subjects:** Medicine, nursing, allied health sciences. **Holdings:** 6000 volumes; AV programs; VF materials. **Subscriptions:** 320 journals and other serials. **Services:** Interlibrary loan; copying; SDI; library open to the public with restrictions. **Automated Operations:** Computerized cataloging. **Computerized Information Services:** MEDLINE, BRS Information Technologies, OCLC. **Networks/Consortia:** Member of National Network of Libraries of Medicine - Greater Midwest Region, OHIONET, Health Science Librarians of Northwest Ohio (HSLNO). **Remarks:** FAX: (419)244-1324.

★10134★
Mercy Hospital - Health Sciences Library (Med)
144 State St. Phone: (207)879-3365
Portland, ME 04101 Marj Anderson, Lib./Mgr.Lib.Serv.
Founded: 1956. **Staff:** Prof 1. **Subjects:** Medicine, surgery, nursing. **Special Collections:** CIBA Collection of Medical Illustration (1855 slides); current AIDS information file; Maine Children's Memorial Library for Bereaved Parents. **Holdings:** 1700 books. **Subscriptions:** 100 journals and other serials. **Services:** Interlibrary loan; copying; library open to health professionals and nursing and allied health students. **Automated Operations:** Computerized public access catalog, cataloging, acquisitions, and ILL. **Computerized Information Services:** NLM, DIALOG Information Services. **Networks/Consortia:** Member of Health Science Library and Information Cooperative of Maine (HSLIC), North Atlantic Health Science Libraries (NAHSL), BHSL. **Remarks:** FAX: (207)879-3429.

★10135★
Mercy Hospital - Health Sciences Library (Med)
Box 9012 Phone: (413)781-9100
Springfield, MA 01102-9012 Roger S. Manahan, Dir., Hea.Sci.Lib.
Staff: Prof 1. **Subjects:** Medicine, nursing, allied health sciences. **Holdings:** 500 books; 800 bound periodical volumes. **Subscriptions:** 50 journals and other serials. **Services:** Interlibrary loan; copying (limited); library open to affiliated area college students for reference use only; not open to the general public. **Automated Operations:** Computerized ILL. **Computerized Information Services:** BRS Information Technologies. **Networks/Consortia:** Member of Western Massachusetts Health Information Consortium, Massachusetts Health Sciences Libraries Network (MaHSLiN). **Publications:** The Orange Peal (newsletter). **Remarks:** Library located at 233 Carew St., Springfield, MA 01104.

★10136★
Mercy Hospital - Health Sciences Library (Med)
565 Abbott Rd. Phone: (716)828-2160
Buffalo, NY 14220 Linda Karch, Lib.Dir.
Staff: Prof 1; Other 1. **Subjects:** Medicine, nursing, allied health sciences. **Special Collections:** Research Symposium Collection, 1968 to present. **Holdings:** 1400 books; 6300 bound periodical volumes; 450 slides, audiocassettes, videocassettes. **Subscriptions:** 260 journals and other serials. **Services:** Interlibrary loan. **Computerized Information Services:** MEDLARS, BRS Information Technologies. Performs searches. **Networks/Consortia:** Member of BHSL, Western New York Library Resources Council (WNYLRC), Library Consortium of Health Institutions in Buffalo (LCHIB). **Remarks:** FAX: (716)828-2716.

★10137★
Mercy Hospital - Health Sciences Library (Med)
100 Riverfront Plaza Phone: (513)867-6458
Hamilton, OH 45011 Sr. Mary Annrita Mitchell, Libn.
Founded: 1956. **Staff:** Prof 1; Other 3. **Subjects:** Medicine, nursing, hospital administration, allied health sciences. **Holdings:** 2000 books; 4 VF drawers of pamphlets and clippings. **Subscriptions:** 200 journals and other serials. **Services:** Interlibrary loan; copying; library open to the public for reference use only. **Automated Operations:** Computerized serials. **Computerized Information Services:** MEDLARS. Performs searches on fee basis. **Publications:** List of acquisitions, irregular; list of journals - both for internal distribution only. **Remarks:** FAX: (513)867-1613. **Staff:** Elizabeth Luchsinger, Asst.Libn.

★10138★
Mercy Hospital - Medical Library (Med)
Box 119 Phone: (805)328-5386
Bakersfield, CA 93302-0119 Brooke Lilly, Med.Libn.
Staff: Prof 1. **Subjects:** Medicine, gastroenterology, pediatrics, surgery, physical therapy, internal medicine, oncology. **Holdings:** 156 books; 303 bound periodical volumes. **Subscriptions:** 154 journals and other serials. **Services:** Interlibrary loan; copying; SDI; library open to the public for reference use only. **Computerized Information Services:** BRS Information Technologies, MEDLINE. **Networks/Consortia:** Member of 49-99 Cooperative Library System, CLASS. **Remarks:** FAX: (805)327-7440.

★10139★
Mercy Hospital - Medical Library (Med)
3663 S. Miami Ave. Phone: (305)285-2160
Miami, FL 33133 David M. Olson, Dir.
Founded: 1951. **Staff:** Prof 1. **Subjects:** Cardiology, internal medicine, nursing. **Special Collections:** Online searching; desktop publishing. **Holdings:** 1300 books; 4800 bound periodical volumes; 250 video cassettes; 1200 audio cassettes. **Subscriptions:** 130 journals and other serials. **Services:** Interlibrary loan (free); library open to the public at librarian's discretion. **Computerized Information Services:** BRS/Search, DIALOG Information Services, VU/TEXT Information Services, Data-Star, NLM; CD-ROM (MEDLINE). **Remarks:** FAX: (305)285-2128.

★10140★
Mercy Hospital - Medical Library (Med)
570 Chautauqua Blvd. Phone: (701)845-0440
Valley City, ND 58072 Pam Lacher, Lib.Mgr.
Staff: Prof 1. **Subjects:** Medicine. **Holdings:** 75 books. **Subscriptions:** 50 journals and other serials. **Services:** Interlibrary loan; copying; library open to the public with restrictions. **Networks/Consortia:** Member of Valley Medical Network (VMN).

★10141★
Mercy Hospital - Medical Library (Med)
2500 7th Ave. Phone: (814)949-4140
Altoona, PA 16603 Sherri Noon, Lib.Hd.
Founded: 1988. **Staff:** Prof 1. **Subjects:** Nursing, medicine. **Holdings:** 800 books; 350 bound periodical volumes. **Subscriptions:** 30 journals and other serials. **Services:** Interlibrary loan; copying; library open to the public by appointment. **Networks/Consortia:** Member of Central Pennsylvania Health Sciences Library Association (CPHSLA), Laurel Highlands Health Sciences Library Consortium (LHHSLC). **Remarks:** FAX: (814)949-4514.

★10142★
Mercy Hospital - Medical Library (Med)
746 Jefferson Ave. Phone: (717)348-7800
Scranton, PA 18501 Sr. Elizabeth Anne Brandreth, Libn.
Founded: 1958. **Staff:** Prof 1; Other 2. **Subjects:** Medicine, allied health sciences. **Holdings:** 2034 books; 4750 bound periodical volumes; 6100 microfiche. **Subscriptions:** 159 journals and other serials. **Services:** Interlibrary loan; copying; library open to the public for reference use only. **Computerized Information Services:** MEDLARS, DIALOG Information Services; DOCLINE (electronic mail service). **Networks/Consortia:** Member of Health Information Library Network of Northeastern Pennsylvania (HILNNEP), National Network of Libraries of Medicine - Middle Atlantic Region, BHSL. **Remarks:** FAX: (717)348-7171.

★10143★
Mercy Hospital - Medical Library (Med)
25 Church St. Phone: (717)826-3699
Wilkes-Barre, PA 18765 Barbara Nanstiel, Dir., Info.Serv.
Founded: 1975. **Staff:** Prof 1; Other 1. **Subjects:** Medicine, nursing, hospital administration. **Holdings:** 1991 books; 2388 journal volumes on microfilm; 413 AV programs. **Subscriptions:** 164 journals and other serials. **Services:** Interlibrary loan; copying; SDI; library open to qualified users. **Computerized Information Services:** MEDLARS, DIALOG Information Services, Data-Star. Performs searches on fee basis. **Networks/Consortia:** Member of Health Information Library Network of Northeastern Pennsylvania (HILNNEP), BHSL, Northeastern Pennsylvania Bibliographic Center (NEPBC).

★10144★
Mercy Hospital - Medical Library (Med)
1000 Mineral Point Phone: (608)756-6749
Janesville, WI 53545 Doris Brewster, Libn.
Founded: 1925. **Staff:** Prof 1. **Subjects:** Medicine. **Special Collections:** Nursing Service Library (500 books and journals). **Holdings:** 702 books. **Subscriptions:** 61 journals and other serials. **Services:** Interlibrary loan; library not open to the public. **Computerized Information Services:** BRS Information Technologies, MEDLARS. **Networks/Consortia:** Member of South Central Wisconsin Health Science Libraries Consortium.

★10145★
Mercy Hospital - Professional Library Services (Med)
1000 N. Village Ave. Phone: (516)255-2255
Rockville Centre, NY 11570 Carol L. Reid, Prof.Libn.
Staff: Prof 1. **Subjects:** Medicine, surgery, nursing. **Holdings:** 2450 books; 4000 bound periodical volumes; 1000 audio cassette tapes. **Subscriptions:** 180 journals and other serials. **Services:** Interlibrary loan; copying; SDI; library open to the public by appointment. **Computerized Information Services:** BRS Information Technologies, NLM. **Networks/Consortia:** Member of Long Island Library Resources Council, BHSL, Medical & Scientific Libraries of Long Island (MEDLI). **Formerly:** Its Medical/Nursing Library.

★10146★
Mercy Hospital - School of Nursing Library (Med)
1401 Blvd. of the Allies Phone: (412)232-7963
Pittsburgh, PA 15219 Veronica C. Harrison, Libn.
Founded: 1893. **Staff:** Prof 1; Other 1. **Subjects:** Nursing, medicine, religion, psychology, sociology, ethics. **Holdings:** 5351 books; 2345 bound periodical volumes; 9 VF drawers of archival material, history of the school and Mercy Hospital; AV programs. **Subscriptions:** 72 journals and other serials. **Services:** Interlibrary loan; copying; library open to the public with approval of librarian. **Networks/Consortia:** Member of Pittsburgh-East Hospital Library Cooperative. **Publications:** Acquisitions Lists, bimonthly; Current Periodical Bibliography Lists, bimonthly.

★10147★
Mercy Hospital and Medical Center - Jean Farb Memorial Medical Library (Med)
4077 5th Ave. Phone: (619)260-7024
San Diego, CA 92103 Penny T. Ward, Lib.Mgr.
Staff: Prof 1.2; Other 1. **Subjects:** Medicine, nursing, basic sciences, hospital management, psychology and psychiatry. **Holdings:** 2600 books; 9150 bound periodical volumes. **Subscriptions:** 300 journals and other serials. **Services:** Interlibrary loan; copying; SDI; library open to health professionals and students for reference use only. **Computerized Information Services:** BRS Information Technologies, MEDLARS, DIALOG Information Services, OCLC. **Networks/Consortia:** Member of CLASS. **Publications:** Check-It-Out (newsletter), irregular - for internal distribution only. **Remarks:** FAX: (619)298-4761. **Staff:** Dorothy Mylin, Cat.Libn.; Micki Robinson, Asst.Libn.

★10148★
Mercy Hospital Medical Center - Levitt Medical Library (Med)
1165 5th Ave. Phone: (515)247-4189
Des Moines, IA 50314 Lenetta Atkins, Lib.Mgr.
Founded: 1961. **Staff:** Prof 1; Other 3. **Subjects:** Medicine, religion, nursing, management. **Holdings:** 4785 books; 1662 bound periodical volumes; 96 filmstrips; 61 slides, tapes, film loops; 8 16mm sound filmstrips; 213 microfiche. **Subscriptions:** 146 journals and other serials. **Services:** Interlibrary loan; copying; center open to special classes or by doctor's recommendation. **Computerized Information Services:** MEDLINE, DIALOG Information Services; DOCLINE (electronic mail service). Performs searches free of charge for hospital personnel and medical staff. **Networks/Consortia:** Member of Polk County Biomedical Consortium (PCBC). **Remarks:** FAX: (515)248-8809. **Formerly:** Its Levitt Learning Resource Center.

★10149★
Mercy Hospital & Medical Center - Medical Library (Med)
Stevenson Expy. at King Dr. Phone: (312)567-2363
Chicago, IL 60616 Timothy T. Oh, Dir. of Lib.
Founded: 1940. **Staff:** Prof 1; Other 3. **Subjects:** Medicine, surgery, pediatrics, obstetrics-gynecology, radiology, pathology. **Special Collections:** John B. Murphy, M.D. Collection (24 VF drawers). **Holdings:** 5200 books; 8000 bound periodical volumes; 620 AV programs. **Subscriptions:** 360 journals and other serials. **Services:** Interlibrary loan; copying; library open to the public for reference use only. **Automated Operations:** Computerized circulation. **Computerized Information Services:** MEDLINE; CD-ROM (MEDLINE). **Networks/Consortia:** Member of National Network of Libraries of Medicine - Greater Midwest Region.

★10150★
Mercy Hospital of New Orleans - Medical Library (Med)
301 N. Jefferson Davis Pkwy. Phone: (504)486-7361
New Orleans, LA 70119 Jean Leonard, Med.Libn.
Staff: Prof 1. **Subjects:** Medicine, nursing, management. **Holdings:** 907 books; 500 bound periodical volumes. **Subscriptions:** 55 journals and other serials. **Services:** Interlibrary loan; copying; library open to the public with permission of librarian.

★10151★
Mercy Hospital of Pittsburgh - Fred C. Brady, M.D. Memorial Library (Med)
1400 Locust St. Phone: (412)232-7520
Pittsburgh, PA 15219 Suzanne A. Gabany, Libn.
Founded: 1921. **Staff:** Prof 3; Other 4. **Subjects:** Internal medicine, surgery, surgical specialties, anesthesia, obstetrics, pediatrics. **Special Collections:** Hospital archives. **Holdings:** 3500 books; 9000 bound periodical volumes; video cassettes; Audio-Digest tapes; Continuing Medical Education Software. **Subscriptions:** 280 journals and other serials. **Services:** Interlibrary loan; library not open to the public. **Computerized Information Services:** DIALOG Information Services, MEDLINE, NLM, MEDLARS; CD-ROM (MEDLINE). **Networks/Consortia:** Member of National Network of Libraries of Medicine - Middle Atlantic Region, Pittsburgh-East Hospital Library Cooperative. **Publications:** INFORM, semiannual. **Remarks:** FAX: (412)232-8422. **Staff:** Gerry O'Leary, Asst.Libn.

Mercy Hospital of Watertown - Health Science Library
See: **Mercy Center for Health Services - Library** (10128)

★10152★
Mercy Medical Center - Health Sciences Library (Med)
1343 Fountain Phone: (513)390-5000
Springfield, OH 45501 Marietta R. Wilson, Hea.Sci.Libn.
Founded: 1952. **Staff:** 1. **Subjects:** Clinical medicine, allied health sciences. **Holdings:** 1200 books; 1000 bound periodical volumes. **Subscriptions:** 135 journals and other serials. **Services:** Interlibrary loan; library open to students and research personnel. **Computerized Information Services:** NLM; DOCLINE (electronic mail service). **Remarks:** FAX: (513)390-5507.

★10153★
Mercy Medical Center - Health Services Library (Med)
701 10th St., S.E. Phone: (319)398-6165
Cedar Rapids, IA 52403 Linda Roberts Armitage, Libn.
Founded: 1970. **Staff:** Prof 1; Other 1. **Subjects:** Medicine, nursing, hospital administration. **Holdings:** 4000 books; 3000 bound periodical volumes. **Subscriptions:** 403 journals and other serials. **Services:** Interlibrary loan; copying; library open to the public with referral from a librarian. **Computerized Information Services:** BRS Information Technologies, DIALOG Information Services. Performs searches on fee basis. **Networks/Consortia:** Member of National Network of Libraries of Medicine - Greater Midwest Region, Linn County Library Consortium (LCLC). **Remarks:** Alternate telephone number(s): 398-6166. FAX: (319)398-6848.

★10154★
Mercy Medical Center - Hospital Library (Med)
1650 Fillmore St. Phone: (303)393-3296
Denver, CO 80206 Peggy Edwards, Libn.
Founded: 1936. **Staff:** Prof 1; Other 1. **Subjects:** Medicine, nursing, hospital administration. **Holdings:** 2000 books; 4000 bound periodical volumes. **Subscriptions:** 250 journals and other serials. **Services:** Interlibrary loan; copying; SDI; library open to health professionals. **Automated Operations:** Computerized cataloging, acquisitions, serials, and ILL. **Computerized Information Services:** NLM, DIALOG Information Services, BRS Information Technologies, OCLC, PHILSOM; TENTIME, DOCLINE, OCLC LINK (electronic mail services). **Networks/Consortia:** Member of Colorado Council of Medical Librarians.

★10155★
Mercy Medical Center - McGlannan Health Sciences Library (Med)
301 St. Paul Pl. Phone: (410)332-9189
Baltimore, MD 21202 Ellen Lindenbaum
Staff: 1. **Subjects:** Medicine, nursing, and allied health sciences. **Special Collections:** Rare books on medical subjects. **Holdings:** 9818 books; 9464 bound periodical volumes; 12 VF drawers of pamphlets and reprints. **Subscriptions:** 196 journals and other serials. **Services:** Interlibrary loan; library not open to the public. **Computerized Information Services:** MEDLARS, DIALOG Information Services. **Networks/Consortia:** Member of Maryland Association of Health Science Librarians (MAHSL), National Network of Libraries of Medicine - Southeastern/Atlantic Region.

Mercy Regional Medical Center - Medical Library
See: **ParkView Regional Medical Center - Medical Library** (12761)

★10156★
Mercy School of Nursing - Library (Med)
1921 Vail Ave. Phone: (704)379-5845
Charlotte, NC 28207 Roseanne Gilbert, Libn.
Founded: 1906. **Staff:** Prof 1; Other 1. **Subjects:** Nursing, medicine. **Holdings:** 4327 books; 436 bound periodical volumes; 201 AV titles; 4 VF drawers. **Subscriptions:** 49 journals and other serials. **Services:** Interlibrary loan; copying; library open to the public for reference use only.

★10157★
Mercyhurst College - Hammermill Library - Archives (Hist)
501 E. 38th St. Phone: (814)824-2237
Erie, PA 16546 Sr. Mary Lawrence Franklin, Archv.
Founded: 1971. **Staff:** Prof 5; Other 4. **Subjects:** Mercyhurst College Archives; Erie County - industries, societies, organizations, women's groups, history, churches; ethnic studies. **Special Collections:** Erie County Commissioners' Records, 1937-1971 (68 legal-size boxes); Erie County Government Study Commission Collection, 1972-1976 (12 legal-size boxes); oral history tape collection (268 audiocassettes); Sisters of Mercy Archives; Mercyhurst College Collection. **Holdings:** 1693 books; 359 accessions; 4 files of oversize maps, charts, blueprints; 299 reels of microfilm; 2515 slides; 54 16mm films; 10 videotapes; 19 magnetic tapes; 103 film work cores. **Subscriptions:** 112 journals and other serials. **Services:** Interlibrary loan (limited); copying; archives open to the public by appointment. **Computerized Information Services:** OCLC. **Networks/Consortia:** Member of Northwest Interlibrary Cooperative of Pennsylvania (NICOP), Interlibrary Delivery Service of Pennsylvania (IDS), Pittsburgh Regional Library Center (PRLC). **Publications:** Journal of Erie Studies, semiannual - to members of Erie County Historical Society and subscribing libraries. **Special Catalogs:** Archives catalog, updated yearly. **Staff:** David Pinto, Dir. of Lib.; Earleen Glaser, Ref.Libn.; Richard Kubiak, Hist.; Sue Thompson, Asst.Libn.; Barry Gray, Tech.Serv.Dir.

Meriam Library
See: **California State University, Chico** (2559)

(Merida) USIS Collection
See: **Instituto Franklin de Yucatan** (8000)

Meriden-Wallingford Hospital
See: **Veterans Memorial Medical Center** (19821)

★10158★
Meridia Huron Hospital - Professional Library (Med)
13951 Terrace Rd. Phone: (216)761-3300
Cleveland, OH 44112 Keith A. Stincic, Lib.Dir.
Staff: Prof 1; Other 1. **Subjects:** Medicine, nursing, allied health sciences. **Special Collections:** Marshall Research Foundation monographs on peptic ulcers; homeopathy. **Holdings:** 3000 books; 2500 bound periodical volumes; 4 VF drawers; cassette tapes. **Subscriptions:** 150 journals and other serials. **Services:** Interlibrary loan; copying; SDI; library open to the public for reference use only. **Computerized Information Services:** MEDLINE, BRS Information Technologies. **Networks/Consortia:** Member of National Network of Libraries of Medicine - Greater Midwest Region. **Formerly:** Huron Road Hospital. **Staff:** Katherine Van Bolt, Lib.Asst.

★10159★
Meriter Hospital Libraries (Med)
309 W. Washington Ave. Phone: (608)267-6234
Madison, WI 53703 Robert Koehler, Libn.
Staff: 3. **Subjects:** Medicine, nursing, health management. **Holdings:** 2000 books; 1400 bound periodical volumes. **Subscriptions:** 300 journals and other serials. **Services:** Interlibrary loan; library not open to the public. **Computerized Information Services:** MEDLARS, BRS Information Technologies. Performs searches on fee basis. **Networks/Consortia:** Member of South Central Wisconsin Health Science Libraries Consortium. **Remarks:** FAX: (608)267-6419. **Staff:** Joanne Muellenbach.

★10160★
Meriter Hospital-Park - Medical Library (Med)
202 South Park St. Phone: (608)267-6234
Madison, WI 53715 Robert Koehler, Med.Libn.
Founded: 1966. **Staff:** Prof 3; Other 3. **Subjects:** Medicine, nursing, dentistry, health administration. **Holdings:** 3500 books; 2500 bound periodical volumes; 1000 other cataloged items. **Subscriptions:** 282 journals and other serials. **Services:** Interlibrary loan; copying; SDI; library open to the public for reference use only. **Computerized Information Services:** MEDLARS, BRS Information Technologies; internal database. Performs searches on fee basis. **Networks/Consortia:** Member of South Central Wisconsin Health Science Libraries Consortium, National Network of Libraries of Medicine - Greater Midwest Region. **Remarks:** Maintained by Meriter Hospital, Inc. Alternate telephone number(s): 267-6000. **Remarks:** FAX: (608)267-6016. **Staff:** Joanne Muellenbach, Med.Libn.

Ethel Merman Collection
See: **Museum of the City of New York - Theatre Collection** (10892)

★10161★
Merriam Center Library (Soc Sci)
Charles E. Merriam Center for Public Administration
1313 E. 60th St. Phone: (312)947-2162
Chicago, IL 60637 Dennis Senks, Dir.
Founded: 1932. **Staff:** Prof 3; Other 5. **Subjects:** Public administration, city and regional planning, public finance, energy and the environment, building and housing, land use. **Holdings:** 50,000 books; 1000 bound periodical volumes; 100,000 pamphlets. **Subscriptions:** 1000 journals and other serials. **Services:** Interlibrary loan; copying; library open to research personnel. **Automated Operations:** Computerized public access catalog, cataloging, acquisitions, serials, and circulation. **Computerized Information Services:** DIALOG Information Services; DIALMAIL, AppleLink (electronic mail services). Performs searches on fee basis. **Networks/Consortia:** Member of ILLINET. **Publications:** Recent Publications on governmental problems, monthly with annual cumulation. **Remarks:** The Merriam Library serves the following organizations housed at the Charles E. Merriam Center for Public Administration: American Planning Association, American Public Works Association, Council of Planning Librarians, International Association of Assessing Officers. **Remarks:** FAX: (312)947-2164. **Staff:** Edward Valauskas, Asst.Dir.

★10162★
Merrick County Historical Museum - Archives (Hist)
211 E St. Phone: (308)946-2867
Central City, NE 68826 Nancy Johnson
Subjects: Local history. **Holdings:** 300 books; photographs; atlases; newspapers, 1876 to present (microfilm). **Services:** Archives open to the public for reference use only by appointment. **Remarks:** Alternate telephone number(s): 946-2398. Microfilm holdings are housed in the Central City Library - Hard's Memorial Library; (308)946-2512.

Merril Collection of Science Fiction, Speculation and Fantasy
See: **Toronto Public Library** (16417)

★10163★
Merrill Lynch Canada - Corporate Library (Bus-Fin)
200 King St., W. Phone: (416)586-6016
Toronto, ON, Canada M5H 3W3 Susan Bryant, Lib.Mgr.
Staff: Prof 1; Other 3. **Subjects:** Investments, finance, security analysis. **Holdings:** Figures not available. **Services:** Library open to other special librarians.

★10164★
Merrill Lynch Capital Markets - Library (Bus-Fin)
250 Vesey St., 24th Fl. Phone: (212)449-3814
New York, NY 10281-1324 Susan Adinolsi, V.P./Lib.Mgr.
Founded: 1972. **Staff:** Prof 13; Other 17. **Subjects:** Business and economics, investments and securities, mergers and acquisitions. **Special Collections:** International/country files. **Holdings:** 2000 books; 7000 corporate files on domestic and international companies; 35 VF drawers of general business and corporate finance information; 400 reels of microfilm; Securities and Exchange Commission (SEC) files on microfiche. **Subscriptions:** 950 journals and other serials. **Services:** Interlibrary loan; library not open to the public. **Automated Operations:** Computerized public access catalog, cataloging, and serials. **Computerized Information Services:** LEXIS, NEXIS, DIALOG Information Services, InvesText, IDD Information Services (IDDIS), Dow Jones News/Retrieval, Dun & Bradstreet Business Credit Services, Spectrum Ownership Profiles Online, Vickers Stock Research Corporation, VU/TEXT Information Services, Info Globe, Reuter TEXTLINE, DRI/McGraw-Hill. **Special Catalogs:** Catalog of Merrill Lynch Capital Markets proprietary documents and client presentations (online). **Remarks:** Alternate telephone number(s): 449-3795; 449-3794 (ILL). FAX: (212)449-3875. A subsidiary of Merrill Lynch & Company, Inc. **Staff:** Susan Adinolfi, Asst.Mgr.; Dolores Colgan, Hd., Ref.; Bruce Liebman, Ref.Libn.; Kathleen Hassell, ILL Libn.; Jill Weinstein, Ref.Libn.; Richard Drezen, Ref.Libn.; Nicki Maclusi, Ref.Libn.; Elizabeth Craig, Ref.Libn.; Linda Greenberg, Tech.Serv.Libn.

★10165★
Merrimack Education Center (Educ)
101 Mill Rd. Phone: (508)256-3985
Chelmsford, MA 01824 Dr. Jean E. Sanders, Assoc.Dir.
Founded: 1967. **Staff:** Prof 8; Other 5. **Subjects:** Education, computer instruction, telecommunications, online databases. **Special Collections:** Video disc collection. **Holdings:** Educational software. **Subscriptions:** 14 journals and other serials. **Services:** Center open to the public by appointment. **Automated Operations:** Computerized cataloging. **Computerized Information Services:** DIALOG Information Services, BRS Information Technologies; internal databases; EdLine (electronic mail service). **Publications:** Quarterly newsletter; annual report; Videodisc Directory; computer applications manuals. **Special Catalogs:** Catalog of Software Holdings. **Special Indexes:** Teacher Center Directory.

★10166★
Merritt Peralta Medical Center - John A. Graziano Memorial Library (Med)
400 Hawthorne Ave. Phone: (510)420-6180
Oakland, CA 94609 Sharon Wosnick, Dir.
Staff: Prof 1; Other 2. **Subjects:** Nursing, medicine, allied health sciences. **Holdings:** 4500 books; 600 bound periodical volumes; 4 VF drawers of pamphlets. **Subscriptions:** 350 journals and other serials. **Services:** Interlibrary loan; library open to the public for reference use only. **Automated Operations:** Computerized cataloging. **Computerized Information Services:** MEDLINE, CINAHL, BRS Information Technologies. **Networks/Consortia:** Member of National Network of Libraries of Medicine - Pacific Southwest Region.

★10167★
Mershon, Sawyer, Johnston, Dunwody & Cole - Library (Law)
200 S. Biscayne Blvd., Suite 4500 Phone: (305)358-5100
Miami, FL 33131 Jean Snyder, Libn.
Staff: Prof 1; Other 1. **Subjects:** Law. **Holdings:** 14,500 books; 260 bound periodical volumes; 35 binders of law memoranda; 3100 microfiche; 110 audio cassettes; 40 video cassettes. **Subscriptions:** 375 journals and other serials; 8 newspapers. **Services:** Library not open to the public. **Computerized Information Services:** WESTLAW, LEXIS, DIALOG Information Services, VU/TEXT Information Services, Information America. **Special Catalogs:** Memorandum of Law Catalog (card). **Remarks:** FAX: (305)376-8654.

Thomas Merton Studies Center
See: **Bellarmine College** (1687)

W.S. Merwin Archives
See: **University of Illinois - Rare Book and Special Collections Library** (18689)

★10168★
Meryman Environmental Engineers, Inc. - Meryman Library of Aquatic Research (Biol Sci)
10408 Bloomingdale Ave. Phone: (813)626-9551
Riverview, FL 33569 Dr. Charles Dale Meryman, Pres.
Founded: 1974. **Staff:** Prof 2; Other 1. **Subjects:** Fish, aquatic life, fisheries. **Holdings:** 3000 books; 42 bound periodical volumes; 475 photographs and

slides; 2000 manuscripts; 500 clippings; 50 unbound reports. **Subscriptions:** 30 journals and other serials; 5 newspapers. **Services:** Interlibrary loan; copying; library open to the public by appointment. **Automated Operations:** Computerized cataloging. **Computerized Information Services:** Internal database. **Publications:** Contemporary Pathobiology; M.L.A. Technical Papers. **Special Indexes:** Environmental Engineering; Special Breakdown on Fisheries and Aquatic Animal Health. **Remarks:** Alternate telephone number(s): 626-9557. FAX: (813)623-6613. **Staff:** Beth McNair, Supv., Lib.Serv.

Merz Music Library
See: **Carnegie Library of Pittsburgh - Music and Art Department** (3078)

★10169★
Mesa County Valley School District 51 - Department of Support and Assessment (Educ)
410 Hill Ave. Phone: (303)245-1788
Grand Junction, CO 81501 Tedd S. Brumbaugh, Dir.
Staff: Prof 11; Other 36. **Subjects:** Education. **Special Collections:** Special services media materials. **Holdings:** 228,271 books. **Subscriptions:** 134 journals and other serials. **Services:** Interlibrary loan; copying; library open to the public with restrictions. **Automated Operations:** Computerized public access catalog, cataloging, and circulation. **Computerized Information Services:** MARMOT (internal database). Performs searches free of charge. **Networks/Consortia:** Member of Pathfinder Regional Library Service System, Colorado Alliance of Research Libraries (CARL). **Remarks:** FAX: (303)243-6716. **Formerly:** Its Department of Program Support Services. **Staff:** Karen A. Swanson, Dist. Media Coord.

★10170★
Mesa Lutheran Hospital - Medical Library (Med)
525 W. Brown Rd. Phone: (602)461-2189
Mesa, AZ 85201 David R. Conchado, MLS, Med. Libn.
Staff: Prof 1. **Subjects:** Medicine. **Holdings:** 3000 books; journal titles on microfilm. **Subscriptions:** 290 journals. **Services:** Interlibrary loan; library not open to the public. **Computerized Information Services:** DIALOG Information Services, NLM, BRS Information Technologies; OnTyme Electronic Message Network Service, DOCLINE (electronic mail services). **Networks/Consortia:** Member of Central Arizona Biomedical Libraries (CABL). **Remarks:** Maintained by Lutheran Healthcare Network. FAX: (602)461-2042.

★10171★
Mesa Public Library - Special Collections (Hist)
64 E. 1st St. Phone: (602)644-2702
Mesa, AZ 85201-6768 Herschel V. Anderson, Dir.
Founded: 1926. **Staff:** Prof 32; Other 65. **Special Collections:** Mesa Room Collection; government documents (15,054); Metropolitan Resource Center; business collections; serials colections. **Holdings:** 558,252 books; 210,799 microforms. **Subscriptions:** 3037 journals and other serials; 116 newspapers. **Services:** Interlibrary loan; copying; collections open to county residents. **Automated Operations:** Computerized public access catalog, serials, circulation, cataloging, and acquisitions. **Computerized Information Services:** DIALOG Information Services, NEXIS, VU/TEXT Information Services, WILSONLINE, OCLC, EPIC; internal databases. Performs searches free of charge. Contact Person: Mary Beth Burgoyne, 644-2711. **Networks/Consortia:** Member of Bibliographical Center for Research, Rocky Mountain Region, Inc. (BCR), AMIGOS Bibliographic Council, Inc. **Special Indexes:** Mesa Tribune index; telephone books index; song index. **Remarks:** FAX: (602)644-3490.

Mesa Verde National Park
See: **U.S. Natl. Park Service** (17749)

★10172★
Mescalero Public Health Service Hospital - Library (Med)
Box 210 Phone: (505)671-4441
Mescalero, NM 88340 F. Bryant, M.D.
Staff: 1. **Subjects:** Medicine. **Holdings:** 150 books; 25 bound periodical volumes. **Subscriptions:** 16 journals and other serials. **Services:** Library not open to the public. **Remarks:** Maintained by U.S. Public Health Service.

★10173★
Meserve, Mumper & Hughes - Library (Law)
333 S. Hope St., 35th Fl. Phone: (213)620-0300
Los Angeles, CA 90071 James H. Rollins, Law Libn.
Staff: Prof 1. **Subjects:** Law - litigation, labor, insurance. **Holdings:** 13,000 books; 444 bound periodical volumes; judicial decisions; codes; regulations; treatises; digests; form books. **Subscriptions:** 24 journals and other serials. **Services:** Copying; library open to attorneys from local law firms with permission. **Computerized Information Services:** LEXIS. **Remarks:** FAX: (213)625-1930.

★10174★
Mesirov, Gelman, Jaffe, Cramer & Jamieson - Library (Law)
1735 Market St. Phone: (215)994-1128
Philadelphia, PA 19103-7598 Denise C., Libn.
Founded: 1978. **Staff:** Prof 1; Other 3. **Subjects:** Law. **Holdings:** 15,000 books; 15 drawers of microfiche. **Subscriptions:** 95 journals and other serials; 10 newspapers. **Services:** Interlibrary loan; copying; SDI; library open to the public at librarian's discretion. **Computerized Information Services:** DIALOG Information Services, LEXIS, WESTLAW, Dow Jones News/Retrieval,IAM, VU/TEXT Information Services, Montgomery County docket system, Dun & Bradstreet Business Credit Services. **Remarks:** FAX: (215)994-1111.

Messiah College
See: **Brethren in Christ Church and Messiah College** (2108)

John Messick Learning Resource Center
See: **Oral Roberts University - Graduate Theology Library - John Messick Learning Resource Center** (13967)

Messler Library
See: **Fairleigh Dickinson University** (5568)

Metal Matrix Composites Information Analysis Center
See: **Kaman Sciences Corporation** (8537)

★10175★
Metal Powder Industries Federation - Technical Information Center (Sci-Engr)
105 College Rd., E. Phone: (609)452-7700
Princeton, NJ 08540 Elizabeth E. Carey, Pubn.Mgr.
Founded: 1943. **Subjects:** Metal powders; powder metallurgy products, processes, equipment. **Holdings:** 1000 books; periodicals; 100 other cataloged items; standards; slides; photographs. **Subscriptions:** 10 journals and other serials. **Services:** Copying; center open to the public. **Publications:** P/M Technology Newsletter, monthly; International Journal of Powder Metallurgy, quarterly. **Remarks:** Telex: 510 685 2516. FAX: (609)987-8523.

★10176★
Metapsychic and Scientific Research Society of Turkey - Library (Rel-Phil)
PK 9, Beyoglu Phone: 1 1431814
TR-80072 Istanbul, Turkey Selman Gerceksever
Founded: 1960. **Subjects:** Reincarnation, world religions, philosophy, science, UFOlogy, parapsychology. **Holdings:** 2100 volumes. **Subscriptions:** 10 journals and other serials; 2 newspapers. **Services:** Library open only to members of the Society.

★10177★
Metascience Foundation - Library (Rel-Phil)
Box 32 Phone: (401)294-2414
Kingston, RI 02881 Marc Seifer, Dir.
Founded: 1970. **Staff:** Prof 3. **Subjects:** Parapsychology, metaphysics, cosmology, psychohistory, graphology, palmistry, UFOs, synchronicity, astrology, tarot. **Special Collections:** Rare books on occult sciences; Nikola Tesla (10 volumes); Gurdjieff and Ouspensky (10 volumes); Lobsang Rampa (12 volumes); Wilhelm Reich (10 volumes); Uri Geller (8 volumes). **Holdings:** 400 books; 100 bound periodical volumes; research papers. **Subscriptions:** 10 journals and other serials. **Services:** Copying; library open to the public by appointment. **Publications:** MetaScience Annual. **Remarks:** FAX: (401)294-2414. **Staff:** Monica Schaffer, Libn.; Lois Pazienza, Libn.

Clarence Metcalf Research Library
See: **Great Lakes Historical Society** (6697)

★10178★
Metcalf & Eddy, Inc. - Harry L. Kinsel Library (Env-Cons)
Box 4043 Phone: (617)246-5200
Woburn, MA 01888-4043 Anita Muise, Libn.
Founded: 1912. **Staff:** 2. **Subjects:** Environment, hazardous waste, drinking water, wastewater/sewage, civil engineering. **Special Collections:** M & E Engineering Reports (5500 items); M & E technical articles/conference papers (4 filing drawers); civic file (3200 items); legislative documents (2 filing drawers); military specifications and manuals (6 shelves). **Holdings:** 6000 books; 658 bound periodical volumes; 2250 reels of microfilm (reports and computations; specifications; lab analysis reports; proposals; legal and accounting documents). **Subscriptions:** 234 journals and other serials; 16 newspapers. **Services:** Interlibrary loan; library open to the public by appointment. **Computerized Information Services:** DIALOG Information Services, LEXIS, NEXIS, TOXNET, Chemical Information Systems, Inc. (CIS). **Networks/Consortia:** Member of NELINET, Inc. **Publications:** Acquisitions, quarterly; library services brochure. **Remarks:** Library located at 30 Harvard Mill Square, Wakefield, MA 01880. Telex: 710-321-6365. FAX: (617)245-6293.

★10179★
Methodist College - Davis Memorial Library - Special Collections (Hist)
5400 Ramsey St. Phone: (919)630-7122
Fayetteville, NC 28311-1499 Susan E. Pulsipher, Dir., Lib.Serv.
Founded: 1956. **Staff:** Prof 3; Other 5. **Subjects:** Marquis de Lafayette; May Catherine Huske; Allen C. Lee bible collection and related works. **Holdings:** 676 books; 150 pamphlets and scores; 28 original letters. **Services:** Copying; collections open to the public for reference use only. **Computerized Information Services:** DIALOG Information Services. **Publications:** Friends of the Library (newsletter), annual - to the public. **Special Catalogs:** Catalogs for Lafayette and Huske collections (card). **Remarks:** FAX: (919)630-7053; 630-7119. **Staff:** Maureen Molter, Asst.Libn./Dir., Teaching Mat.Ctr.

★10180★
Methodist Hospital - Health Sciences Library (Med)
506 6th St. Phone: (718)780-3195
Brooklyn, NY 11215 Robin L. Tannenbaum, Dir.
Staff: Prof 1; Other 3. **Subjects:** Medicine, surgery, nursing, allied health sciences. **Special Collections:** Methodist Hospital annual reports, 1887 to present. **Holdings:** 3000 books; 4033 bound periodical volumes; 400 videotapes; 90 slide/tape sets; 5 audio cassette subject series. **Subscriptions:** 300 journals and other serials. **Services:** Interlibrary loan; library not open to the public. **Computerized Information Services:** NLM, BRS Information Technologies. **Networks/Consortia:** Member of Medical Library Center of New York (MLCNY), New York State Interlibrary Loan Network (NYSILL), New York Metropolitan Reference and Research Library Agency. **Publications:** Library News, bimonthly. **Remarks:** FAX: (718)780-3082.

★10181★
Methodist Hospital - Library (Med)
2301 S. Broad St. Phone: (215)952-9404
Philadelphia, PA 19148 Sara J. Richardson, Libn.
Staff: Prof 1; Other 1. **Subjects:** Nursing, medicine, hospital administration, pre-clinical sciences. **Holdings:** 2900 books; 100 bound periodical volumes; 6 VF drawers of pamphlets; 500 AV program titles. **Subscriptions:** 171 journals and other serials. **Services:** Interlibrary loan; copying; SDI; library open to the public with prior permission. **Automated Operations:** Computerized acquisitions, serials, and circulation. **Computerized Information Services:** DIALOG Information Services, BRS Information Technologies; internal database; DOCLINE (electronic mail service). Performs searches on fee basis. **Networks/Consortia:** Member of National Network of Libraries of Medicine - Middle Atlantic Region, Delaware Valley Information Consortium (DEVIC). **Publications:** Booklist, bimonthly - for internal distribution only.

★10182★
Methodist Hospital - Library (Med)
7700 Floyd Curl Dr. Phone: (512)692-4583
San Antonio, TX 78229 Christy Floerke, Libn.
Staff: Prof 1. **Subjects:** Medicine, nursing. **Holdings:** 1275 books; 195 bound periodical volumes. **Subscriptions:** 100 journals and other serials. **Services:** Interlibrary loan; copying; library open to the public with restrictions. **Computerized Information Services:** MEDLINE. **Networks/Consortia:** Member of Health Oriented Libraries of San Antonio (HOLSA). **Formerly:** Southwest Texas Methodist Hospital.

★10183★
Methodist Hospital - Medical Library (Med)
P.O. Box 650 Phone: (612)932-5451
St. Louis Park, MN 55440 Pearly Rudin, Med.Libn.
Founded: 1959. **Staff:** Prof 1; Other 1. **Subjects:** Clinical medicine, nursing. **Holdings:** 1500 volumes. **Subscriptions:** 100 journals and other serials. **Services:** Interlibrary loan; copying; library open to medical personnel and other librarians. **Computerized Information Services:** MEDLINE. **Networks/Consortia:** Member of Twin Cities Biomedical Consortium (TCBC). **Remarks:** Library located at 6500 Excelsior Blvd., St. Louis Park, MN.

★10184★
Methodist Hospital - Medical Library (Med)
3615 19th St. Phone: (806)793-4180
Lubbock, TX 79410 Mary Jarvis, Med.Libn.
Founded: 1960. **Staff:** Prof 1; Other 2. **Subjects:** Medicine, nursing, allied health sciences. **Holdings:** 2500 books; 5000 bound periodical volumes. **Subscriptions:** 230 journals and other serials. **Services:** Interlibrary loan; copying; library open to the public for reference use only. **Automated Operations:** Computerized circulation, serials, and ILL. **Computerized Information Services:** MEDLINE, DIALOG Information Services. **Remarks:** FAX: (806)799-0910.

★10185★
Methodist Hospital of Indiana, Inc. - Library Services (Med)
1701 N. Senate Blvd.
P.O. Box 1367 Phone: (317)929-8021
Indianapolis, IN 46206 Joyce S. Allen, Lib.Mgr.
Founded: 1947. **Staff:** Prof 3; Other 6. **Subjects:** Medicine, nursing, medical ethics, administration, health education, psychology, allied health sciences. **Holdings:** 6558 books; 3531 bound periodical volumes; 800 AV programs; 8 VF drawers of pamphlets. **Subscriptions:** 360 journals and other serials; 18 audiotape journals. **Services:** Interlibrary loan; copying; SDI; LATCH; library open to the public for reference use only. **Computerized Information Services:** DIALOG Information Services, MEDLINE, BRS Information Technologies. Performs searches on fee basis. Contact Person: Christine Bockrath, Info.Ret.Spec. **Networks/Consortia:** Member of Central Indiana Health Science Library Consortium, Central Indiana Area Library Services Authority (CIALSA), INCOLSA. **Publications:** Library Handbook. **Special Catalogs:** Media Center Catalog (book). **Remarks:** FAX: (317)929-8397. Includes the holdings of the Professional Collection, Health Education Collection, and Media Center.

★10186★
Methodist Hospitals of Dallas - Medical Library (Med)
301 W. Colorado
Box 655999 Phone: (214)944-8321
Dallas, TX 75265-5999 Janet L. Cowen, Med.Libn.
Staff: Prof 1. **Subjects:** Medicine, nursing. **Holdings:** 1900 books; 4000 bound periodical volumes; 1150 cassette tapes; clippings; reports. **Subscriptions:** 200 journals and other serials. **Services:** Interlibrary loan. **Computerized Information Services:** DIALOG Information Services, MEDLARS. **Networks/Consortia:** Member of Health Libraries Information Network (HealthLINE). **Remarks:** Library serves hospital's residency training programs, attending staff, nursing staff, and other hospital professional staff as well as nursing and allied health classes from area colleges. FAX: (214)944-8006. **Formerly:** Methodist Medical Center.

★10187★
Methodist Hospitals of Memphis - Educational Resources Department - Leslie M. Stratton Nursing Library (Med)
251 S. Claybrook Phone: (901)726-8862
Memphis, TN 38104-6499 Jane Bridges Mertzlufft, Mgr.
Founded: 1969. **Staff:** Prof 2; Other 1. **Subjects:** Nursing, medicine, psychology, sociology, education. **Holdings:** 6200 books; 339 periodical volumes; 462 volumes of journals on microfiche. **Subscriptions:** 107 journals and other serials. **Services:** Interlibrary loan; copying; SDI; department open to the public for reference use only. **Automated Operations:** Computerized cataloging, acquisitions, serials, circulation, and ILL. **Computerized Information Services:** BRS Information Technologies, MEDLARS; internal database; CD-ROM (CINAHL). **Networks/Consortia:** Member of Association of Memphis Area Health Science Libraries (AMAHSL), Tennessee Health Science Library Association (THeSLA). **Publications:** FOOTNOTES (newsletter), quarterly - for internal distribution only. **Special Catalogs:** Audiovisuals Catalog - for internal distribution only. **Staff:** Mary L. Buckley, Libn.

Methodist Kahler Library
See: **Rochester Methodist Hospital** (13984)

Methodist Medical Center
See: **Methodist Hospitals of Dallas - Medical Library** (10186)

★10188★
Methodist Medical Center of Illinois - Health Science Resource Center (Med)
221 N.E. Glen Oak Phone: (309)672-4937
Peoria, IL 61636 Royden R. Jones, HSRC Mgr.
Staff: Prof 2; Other 3. **Subjects:** Medicine. **Holdings:** 3800 books; 5500 bound periodical volumes. **Subscriptions:** 353 journals and other serials. **Services:** Interlibrary loan; library not open to the public. **Automated Operations:** Computerized cataloging. **Computerized Information Services:** BRS/COLLEAGUE, MEDLINE, OCLC. **Networks/Consortia:** Member of Heart of Illinois Library Consortium (HILC), Illinois Valley Library System. **Remarks:** FAX: (309)671-5185.

★10189★
Methodist Medical Center of Illinois - School of Nursing Library - Learning Resource Center (Med)
221 N.E. Glen Oak Phone: (309)671-2794
Peoria, IL 61636 Ms. Leslie Menz, Libn.
Founded: 1950. **Staff:** Prof 1; Other 1. **Subjects:** Nursing, nursing education. **Holdings:** 4000 books; 204 bound periodical volumes; 6 VF drawers of pamphlets; 8000 unbound periodicals; 280 AV programs. **Subscriptions:** 55 journals and other serials. **Services:** Interlibrary loan; copying; center open to the public with restrictions. **Networks/Consortia:** Member of Heart of Illinois Library Consortium (HILC), National Network of Libraries of Medicine - Greater Midwest Region, Illinois Valley Library System. **Publications:** Periodicals Holdings List, annual; Book Acquisitions List, bimonthly.

★10190★
Methodist Theological School in Ohio - John W. Dickhaut Library (Rel-Phil)
Box 1204 Phone: (614)362-3435
Delaware, OH 43015 M. Edward Hunter, Libn.
Founded: 1960. **Staff:** Prof 2; Other 3. **Subjects:** Religion, theology, Bible, church history. **Special Collections:** Irenaeus, Schleiermacher, Justin Martyr collections. **Holdings:** 106,000 volumes. **Subscriptions:** 355 journals and other serials; 12 newspapers. **Services:** Interlibrary loan; copying; library open to the public. **Automated Operations:** Computerized cataloging. **Computerized Information Services:** OCLC. **Networks/Consortia:** Member of OHIONET. **Staff:** Julia Foster, Ref. & Cat.Libn.

★10191★
Metro Health St. Luke's Medical Center - Taylor Family Health Sciences Library (Med)
11311 Shaker Blvd. Phone: (216)368-7699
Cleveland, OH 44104 Pam Billick, Dir.
Founded: 1936. **Staff:** Prof 2; Other 2. **Subjects:** Medicine, nursing, management. **Holdings:** 2500 books; 6300 bound periodical volumes. **Subscriptions:** 350 journals and other serials. **Services:** Interlibrary loan; copying; SDI; library open to the public. **Automated Operations:** Computerized cataloging, circulation, and ILL (DOCLINE). **Computerized Information Services:** MEDLINE, BRS Information Technologies, DIALOG Information Services, CD-Plus; internal database. Performs searches on fee basis. **Networks/Consortia:** Member of Cleveland Area Metropolitan Library System (CAMLS). **Publications:** Library Link (newsletter), bimonthly. **Remarks:** Alternate telephone number(s): 368-8431. FAX: (216)368-7688. **Formerly:** St. Luke's Hospital. **Staff:** Pat Bresien, Clin.Libn.

★10192★
Metro Medical Group - Detroit Northwest - Medical Library (Med)
1800 Tuxedo Ave. Phone: (313)252-1204
Detroit, MI 48206 Maureen W. LeLacheur, Med.Libn.
Founded: 1955. **Staff:** Prof 1. **Subjects:** Medicine, nursing, health maintenance organizations, allied health. **Holdings:** 2010 books; 5000 bound periodical volumes. **Subscriptions:** 350 journals and other serials. **Services:** Interlibrary loan; copying; library open to the public for reference use only. **Automated Operations:** Computerized serials, circulation, and ILL. **Computerized Information Services:** DIALOG Information Services, VU/TEXT Information Services, BRS Information Technologies, NLM. **Networks/Consortia:** Member of Michigan Library Consortium (MLC). **Remarks:** FAX: (313)252-1071. A subsidiary of Health Alliance Plan.

★10193★
MetroHealth Medical Center - Harold H. Brittingham Memorial Library (Med)
2500 MetroHealth Dr. Phone: (216)459-5623
Cleveland, OH 44109-9990 Christine A. Dziedzina, Chf.Libn.
Founded: 1937. **Staff:** Prof 2; Other 4. **Subjects:** Medicine, nursing. **Special Collections:** Stecher collection of arthritis and rheumatism journals. **Holdings:** 9985 books; 25,000 bound periodical volumes; 4 VF drawers of pamphlets. **Subscriptions:** 485 journals and other serials. **Services:** Interlibrary loan; copying; SDI; library open to the public with restrictions. **Computerized Information Services:** MEDLINE. **Remarks:** Includes selected holdings of the Highland View Hospital - Medical Library.

★10194★
Metron, Inc. - Scientific Library (Sci-Engr)
11911 Freedom Dr., Suite 800 Phone: (703)787-8700
Reston, VA 22090-5603 Robert Joseph
Founded: 1984. **Subjects:** Mathematics, science, statistics, computers. **Holdings:** 3000 books; 200 reports. **Services:** Library not open to the public. **Computerized Information Services:** Internal database. **Remarks:** FAX: (703)787-3518. **Formerly:** Located in McLean, VA.

★10195★
Metroplan - Information Center (Plan)
201 E. Markham, Suite 450 Phone: (501)372-3300
Little Rock, AR 72201 Nila Corbell, Adm.
Founded: 1955. 1. **Subjects:** Planning, land use and controls, housing and urban renewal, land economics, social and economic planning, neighborhood studies, public administration and finance, community facilities, transportation, air and water quality. **Holdings:** 500 books; 25 bound periodical volumes; 250 past publications of Metroplan; 1000 pamphlets and brochures. **Subscriptions:** 7 newspapers. **Services:** Interlibrary loan; copying; center open to the public. **Publications:** Metroplanner (newspaper), bimonthly. **Remarks:** FAX: (501)372-8060.

★10196★
Metropolitan Atlanta Rapid Transit Authority - MARTA Library (Trans)
2424 Piedmont Rd., N.E. Phone: (404)848-5340
Atlanta, GA 30324-3324 Theodore R. Williams, Asst.Gen.Mgr. for Rail Serv.
Founded: 1966. **Staff:** 1. **Subjects:** Transit - design, construction, grants, environmental impact statements, planning and development, architecture, engineering, bus and railroad operations, fares, patronage. **Special Collections:** Transit News Publications; energy. **Holdings:** 750 books; 1200 other cataloged items; authority reports; other transportation reports for Atlanta area. **Subscriptions:** 40 journals and other serials; 6 newspapers. **Services:** Library open to the public. **Remarks:** FAX: (404)848-5321. **Also Known As:** MARTA. **Staff:** Barbara A. Haji, Libn.

★10197★
Metropolitan Community Church - MCC Library (Soc Sci, Rel-Phil)
1919 Decatur Phone: (713)861-9149
Houston, TX 77007 Charles Botts, Libn.
Founded: 1977. **Staff:** Prof 6. **Subjects:** Homosexuality, religion, self-help psychology, Jungian psychology. **Special Collections:** All aspects of homosexuality (10,000 books). **Holdings:** 15,000 volumes. **Subscriptions:** 5 journals and other serials; 50 newspapers. **Services:** Interlibrary loan; copying; library open to the public with restrictions. **Automated Operations:** Computerized cataloging and acquisitions. **Computerized Information Services:** Internal databases. Performs searches free of charge. **Publications:** List of duplicate books available for trade. **Special Indexes:** Index of gay-related news clippings from local and non-local newspapers; index of obituaries of gay men and women in Houston who have died since 1980. **Remarks:** FAX: (713)861-2520.

★10198★
Metropolitan Council for Educational Opportunity - Library (Educ)
55 Dimock St. Phone: (617)427-1545
Roxbury, MA 02119 J. Marcus Mitchell, P.R. Off.
Founded: 1966. **Staff:** Prof 1. **Subjects:** Quality integrated education, Afro-American history. **Special Collections:** Scrapbooks of clippings on Greater Boston school systems and Boston's desegregation case (40). **Holdings:** 1260 books; dissertations; 24 annual financial reports; 10 unpublished reports; films; photographs. **Subscriptions:** 20 journals and other serials; 10 newspapers. **Services:** Copying; library open to the public. **Automated Operations:** Computerized cataloging. **Computerized Information Services:** Online systems. **Publications:** New Images Newsletter, quarterly; METCO Parent Handbook. **Special Catalogs:** Student enrollment, transportation and routes (both computer printouts).

★10199★
Metropolitan Council of the Twin Cities Area - Library (Plan)
Mears Park Centre
230 E. 5th St. Phone: (612)291-6310
St. Paul, MN 55101 Jan Price, Libn.
Founded: 1963. **Staff:** Prof 1; Other 1. **Subjects:** Metropolitan planning in general and in the specific areas of transportation, housing, health, parks and open space, solid waste, water and sewers; local government and politics. **Holdings:** 3000 books, planning reports, government documents; 2 VF drawers of clippings; 300 microfiche. **Subscriptions:** 103 journals and other serials. **Services:** Interlibrary loan; copying; library open to the public for reference use only. **Automated Operations:** Computerized cataloging and circulation. **Computerized Information Services:** DIALOG Information Services. **Networks/Consortia:** Member of MINITEX Library Information Network, Capital Area Library Consortium (CALCO). **Publications:** Recent Additions to the Library, monthly - for internal distribution only. **Remarks:** FAX: (612)291-6464.

★10200★
Metropolitan Edison Company - System Library (Sci-Engr)
2800 Pottsville Pike
Box 16001 Phone: (215)921-6203
Reading, PA 19640 Diane L. Pawling, Libn.
Founded: 1972. **Staff:** 1.75. **Subjects:** Electrical engineering, business. **Special Collections:** Electric Power Research Institute Reports. **Holdings:** 3007 books; 368 films; 1200 standards; 9523 reports; topographic maps. **Subscriptions:** 311 journals and other serials. **Services:** Interlibrary loan; copying; library open to the public by appointment. **Automated Operations:** Computerized cataloging, serials, circulation, and ILL. **Computerized Information Services:** DIALOG Information Services; EEI Unicom (electronic mail service). **Remarks:** FAX: (215)921-6068. Electronic mail address(es): EEI 019 (EEI Unicom). A subsidiary of GPU Corporation. **Staff:** Pamela Le Clerc, Asst.

★10201★
Metropolitan General Hospital - Medical Library (Med)
7950 66th St., N. Phone: (813)546-9871
Pinellas Park, FL 33565 Jeanna Burchick, Rec.Adm.
Founded: 1975. **Staff:** Prof 2. **Subjects:** Medicine, family practice, osteopathy. **Holdings:** 520 books; 554 audiotapes. **Subscriptions:** 22 journals and other serials. **Services:** Library not open to the public.

★10202★
Metropolitan General Hospital - Medical Library (Med)
1995 Lens Ave. Phone: (519)254-1661
Windsor, ON, Canada N8W 1L9 Patricia Black, Med.Libn.
Founded: 1973. **Subjects:** Medicine, nursing. **Holdings:** 600 books. **Subscriptions:** 200. **Services:** Interlibrary loan; copying; library open to the public. **Computerized Information Services:** MEDLINE. **Remarks:** FAX: (519)254-0883.

★10203★
Metropolitan Hospital Center - Draper Hall Library (Med)
1901 1st Ave. Phone: (212)230-6262
New York, NY 10029 Walter Krivickas, Libn.
Staff: Prof 1. **Subjects:** Nursing, medicine. **Holdings:** 2050 books; 300 bound periodical volumes; 10 VF drawers of pamphlets; 103 envelopes of clippings. **Services:** Library not open to the public.

★10204★
Metropolitan Hospital Center - Frederick M. Dearborn Medical Library (Med)
1901 First Ave. Phone: (212)230-6270
New York, NY 10029 Vivienne Whitson, Chf.Libn.
Founded: 1894. **Staff:** Prof 2; Other 2. **Subjects:** Medicine, allied health sciences. **Holdings:** 5340 books; 15,215 bound periodical volumes; 470 pamphlets; 1540 Audio-Digest tapes. **Subscriptions:** 412 journals and other serials. **Services:** Interlibrary loan; library not open to the public. **Computerized Information Services:** CD-ROM (MEDLINE). **Networks/Consortia:** Member of Manhattan-Bronx Health Sciences Library Consortia, Medical Library Center of New York (MLCNY), New York Metropolitan Reference and Research Library Agency. **Publications:** acquisitions List, quarterly - for internal distribution only. **Remarks:** FAX:(212)230-7961. **Staff:** David S. Frederick.

★10205★
Metropolitan Hospital Center - Psychiatry Library (Med)
1901 First Ave., Rm. 10M13 Phone: (212)230-7285
New York, NY 10029 Lorna Macdonald, Libn.
Founded: 1961. **Staff:** Prof 1. **Subjects:** Psychiatry, psychoanalysis. **Holdings:** 7500 volumes; 3 VF drawers of reprints; 21 films. **Subscriptions:** 40 journals and other serials. **Services:** Interlibrary loan; library not open to the public. **Networks/Consortia:** Member of Manhattan-Bronx Health Sciences Library Consortia.

★10206★
Metropolitan Jewish Geriatric Center - Max B. & Louisa S. Marks Memorial Medical Library
4915 10th Ave.
Brooklyn, NY 11219
Defunct.

★10207★
Metropolitan Life Insurance Company - Corporate Information Center & Library (Bus-Fin)
One Madison Ave., 1 M-R Phone: (212)578-3700
New York, NY 10010 Marianne Stolp, Mgr.
Founded: 1909. **Staff:** Prof 6; Other 3. **Subjects:** Insurance, management, medicine and medical economics. **Special Collections:** Company archives. **Holdings:** 88,000 volumes. **Subscriptions:** 500 journals and other serials. **Services:** Interlibrary loan; copying; library open to researchers by appointment. **Automated Operations:** Computerized serials. **Computerized Information Services:** Dow Jones News/Retrieval, VU/TEXT Information Services, DIALOG Information Services, TEXTLINE, NEXIS, DataTimes. **Networks/Consortia:** Member of New York Metropolitan Reference and Research Library Agency, National Network of Libraries of Medicine - Middle Atlantic Region. **Publications:** Library Bulletin, quarterly - for internal distribution only. **Remarks:** FAX: (212)689-0926. **Staff:** Ellen Smith-Johnston, Res.Libn., Mgt.; Emily Candelmo, Cat.Libn.; Jacqueline Heller, Res.Libn., Med.; Daniel B. May, Archv.; Norma Conner, Res.Libn., Insurance.

★10208★
Metropolitan Life Insurance Company - Law Library (Law)
1 Madison Ave. Phone: (212)578-2211
New York, NY 10010-3690 William O'Connell, Law Libn.
Founded: 1910. **Staff:** Prof 1; Other 2. **Subjects:** Law. **Holdings:** 24,000 volumes. **Services:** Interlibrary loan; library not open to the public. **Computerized Information Services:** WESTLAW.

★10209★
Metropolitan Museum of Art - Cloisters Library (Art)
Fort Tryon Park Phone: (212)923-3700
New York, NY 10040 Lauren Jackson-Beck, Asst.Musm.Libn.
Founded: 1938. **Staff:** Prof 1; Other 1. **Subjects:** Medieval art, architecture, history, horticulture, and music. **Special Collections:** George Grey Barnard Papers; Archives of the History of the Cloisters; George Demotte Photograph Collection; The Marburger Index (microfiche); Index Photographique de l'art en France (microfiche). **Holdings:** 12,000 books; 1000 bound periodical volumes; 20,000 color slides; 20,000 photographs. **Subscriptions:** 53 journals and other serials. **Services:** Library open to graduate students and qualified researchers. **Computerized Information Services:** RLIN. **Remarks:** FAX: (212)795-3640.

★10210★
Metropolitan Museum of Art - Department of the Arts of Africa, Oceania, and the Americas - Photograph Study Collection (Art)
1000 5th Ave. Phone: (212)879-5500
New York, NY 10028 Virginia-Lee Webb
Founded: 1957. **Staff:** Prof 1; Other 1. **Subjects:** Traditional arts and culture - Africa, Oceania, Native American, Precolumbian. **Special Collections:** Paul Gebauer Collection (Cameroon, Africa; photographs and archives); Frederick Peterson Collection (Mexican art; photographs and archives); Museum of Primitive Art (archives). **Holdings:** 120,000 photographs. **Publications:** Brochures. **Special Indexes:** Indexes to photograph collections by ethnic group, collection, and photographer. **Remarks:** Alternate telephone number(s): (212)570-3879. Telex: 66676.

★10211★
Metropolitan Museum of Art - Department of Prints and Photographs - Library (Art)
1000 Fifth Ave. Phone: (212)570-3920
New York, NY 10028-0198 Colta Ives, Cur.-In-Charge
Founded: 1916. **Staff:** Prof 6; Other 5. **Subjects:** Art prints, illustrated books, architectural and ornamental drawings, photographs. **Holdings:** 12,000 books; 1 million prints and photographs. **Services:** Study room open to the public by appointment only.

★10212★
Metropolitan Museum of Art - Irene Lewisohn Costume Reference Library (Art)
1000 Fifth Ave. Phone: (212)879-5500
New York, NY 10028-0198 Robert C. Kaufmann, Assoc.Musm.Libn.
Staff: Prof 3; Other 15. **Subjects:** History of costume, social history. **Special Collections:** Original fashion sketches of Mainbocher, 1940-1970. **Holdings:** 12,000 cataloged books and journals; 80,000 pieces of ephemera, including swatch books, fashion sketches, fashion plates, postcards, and vertical files. **Subscriptions:** 52 journals and other serials. **Services:** Copying; library open to professional designers and research scholars by appointment. **Remarks:** FAX: (212)579-5879. Telex: 666676.

★10213★
Metropolitan Museum of Art - Photograph and Slide Library (Art, Aud-Vis)
1000 Fifth Ave. Phone: (212)879-5500
New York, NY 10028-0198 Priscilla F. Farah, Chf.Libn.
Staff: Prof 6; Other 14. **Subjects:** Art, art history, architecture, sculpture, painting, decorative arts, prints and photographs. **Special Collections:** William Keighley Color Slide Collection of Art and Architecture (70,000 slides). **Holdings:** 270,000 color slides (2x2 inches); 150,000 black/white slides (3x4 inches); 17,500 black/white slides (2x2 inches); 40,000 color transparencies of the Metropolitan's collections; black/white photographic records of the Metropolitan's collections. **Services:** Slides are available for rental to public (without rights of reproduction); photographs of objects in the Metropolitan's collections are for sale; color transparencies of objects in the collections are available for rental for publication; library open to the public with proper identification. **Remarks:** FAX: (212)570-5879; Telex: 666676. **Staff:** Mary F. Doherty, Assoc.Musm.Libn.; Susan Melick, Asst.Musm.Libn.; Carolyn Lucarelli, Asst.Musm.Libn.; Beatrice Epstein, Asst.Musm.Libn.

★10214★
Metropolitan Museum of Art - Robert Goldwater Library (Art)
1000 Fifth Ave.
New York, NY 10028-0198 Phone: (212)570-3707
Founded: 1957. **Staff:** Prof 2; Other 1. **Subjects:** Archeology; art - African, Latin American, Indians of North America, Oceania. **Special Collections:** Photograph Study Collection (160,000 art object and field photographs). **Holdings:** 35,000 volumes. **Subscriptions:** 150 journals and other serials. **Services:** Copying; library open to college students and qualified researchers. **Special Catalogs:** Catalog of the Robert Goldwater Library (1982; 4 volumes). **Remarks:** FAX: (212)570-3879. **Staff:** Ross Day, Asst.Musm.Libn.; Peter P. Blank, Libn.

★10215★
Metropolitan Museum of Art - Robert Lehman Collection - Library (Art)
1000 Fifth Ave.
New York, NY 10028-0198 Phone: (212)879-5500
Founded: 1975. **Staff:** Prof 1; Other 1. **Subjects:** Western European Arts, 13th-20th centuries, with special emphasis on the art of Siena; Old Master drawings; Renaissance decorative arts. **Holdings:** 15,000 volumes; Archives of the Robert Lehman Collection, including autograph letters of connoisseurs and art historians; 5000 mounted photographs. **Services:** Library open to the public on a limited schedule. **Remarks:** FAX: (212)570-3879. Telex: 666676.

★10216★
Metropolitan Museum of Art - Thomas J. Watson Library (Art)
1000 Fifth Ave. Phone: (212)879-5500
New York, NY 10028-0198 William B. Walker, Chf.Libn.
Founded: 1880. **Staff:** Prof 15; Other 25. **Subjects:** Art; art history; archeology; ancient art of Egypt, Greece, Rome, Near East; Islamic art; Asian art, ancient through 20th century; American painting, sculpture, decorative arts, colonial through 20th century; European painting, sculpture, and decorative arts, medieval through 20th century; drawings; prints; photographs; arms and armor; musical instruments; architecture. **Special Collections:** Art auction catalogs; exhibition catalogs. **Holdings:** 300,000 volumes; 103 VF drawers; 1800 microfiche; 375 reels of microfilm. **Subscriptions:** 2500 journals and other serials. **Services:** Copying; library open to graduate students and qualified researchers. **Automated Operations:** Computerized cataloging, acquisitions, and serials. **Computerized Information Services:** RLIN, SCIPIO (Sales Catalog Index Project Input On-line); Clearinghouse on Art Documentation and Computerization (internal database); RLIN (electronic mail service). **Publications:** Newly cataloged books list, monthly. **Special Catalogs:** Library Catalog of the Metropolitan Museum of Art, New York, (2nd edition; 1980), with supplements (1982, 1985, 1987, 1990). **Remarks:** FAX: (212)570-3847. Telex: 666676. Electronic mail address(es): BM.MMA (RLIN). **Staff:** Donya-Dobrila Schimansky, Musm.Libn.; Patricia J. Barnett, Musm.Libn.; Hikmet Dogu, Assoc.Musm.Libn.; Celine Palatsky, Assoc.Musm.Libn.; Doralynn Pines, Assoc.Musm.Libn.; Paula Frosch, Asst.Musm.Libn.; Kenneth Dinin, Asst.Musm.Libn.; Mindell Dubansky, Asst.Musm.Libn.; Trevor Hadley, Asst.Musm.Libn.; Eileen Hsu, Asst.Musm.Libn.; Victoria Bohm, Libn.; Greta Earnest, Libn.; Dorothy Hesselman, Libn.; Ayako Y. Nakada, Res.Assoc.

★10217★
Metropolitan Museum of Art - Uris Library and Resource Center (Art)
1000 Fifth Ave. Phone: (212)570-3788
New York, NY 10028-0198 Mary Grace Whalen, Libn.
Founded: 1941. **Staff:** Prof 2; Other 15. **Subjects:** Fine arts, art history, art education, museology. **Special Collections:** Publications of Metropolitan Museum of Art. **Holdings:** 3930 books; 165 videotapes; picture books. **Subscriptions:** 35 journals and other serials. **Services:** Copying; library open to the public for reading and reference; AV programs available for loan to schools and community groups. **Computerized Information Services:** RLIN. **Remarks:** FAX (212)570-3879. Telex: 666676. **Staff:** Emily Roth; Roberta Staats.

★10218★
Metropolitan Nashville General Hospital - Health Science Library (Med)
72 Hermitage Ave. Phone: (615)862-4416
Nashville, TN 37210 Glenda L. Perry, Libn.
Staff: Prof 1. **Subjects:** Medicine, surgery, nursing. **Holdings:** 500 books; 1000 bound periodical volumes. **Subscriptions:** 81 journals and other serials. **Services:** Interlibrary loan. **Computerized Information Services:** MEDLINE. **Networks/Consortia:** Member of Tennessee Health Science Library Association (THeSLA). **Remarks:** FAX: (615)862-4493.

Metropolitan Opera Archives
See: **New York Public Library for the Performing Arts** (11638)

★10219★
Metropolitan Opera Association - Archives (Mus)
Lincoln Center Plaza Phone: (212)799-3100
New York, NY 10023 Robert Tuggle, Dir. of Archv.
Staff: Prof 2; Other 6. **Subjects:** Metropolitan Opera. **Special Collections:** Programs, photographs and slides, biographies, newspaper clippings of reviews, 1883 to present; historic costumes and artifacts; negatives of Metropolitan Opera photographers: Herman Mishkin, Sedge Le Blang, Louis Melancon. **Holdings:** Books; bound programs, 1883 to present; bound Opera News magazine, 1935 to present. **Services:** Copying; archives open to qualified researchers by appointment. **Special Catalogs:** Card files of all performances given by Metropolitan Opera singers, 1883 to present; card files of orchestra, ballet, and chorus personnel, 1910 to present. **Remarks:** FAX: (212)874-2659. **Staff:** John Pennino, Asst.Archv.; Gail Frohlinger, Costume Cur.

★10220★
Metropolitan Property & Casualty Insurance Company - Law & Corporate Information Center (Law, Bus-Fin)
700 Quaker Ln. Phone: (401)827-3158
Warwick, RI 02886 Darrell W. Grant, Paralegal
Founded: 1976. **Staff:** Prof 1; Other 1. **Subjects:** Insurance, law. **Holdings:** 15,000 books; 4 VF drawers of subject files. **Subscriptions:** 60 journals and other serials; 5 newspapers. **Services:** Interlibrary loan; center not open to the public. **Computerized Information Services:** Veralex 2, WESTLAW. **Publications:** Library Listings, monthly - for internal distribution only. **Remarks:** FAX: (401)827-2674. **Formerly:** Metropolitan Property & Liability Insurance Company.

★10221★
Metropolitan State Hospital - Staff Library (Med)
11400 Norwalk Blvd. Phone: (213)863-7011
Norwalk, CA 90650 Beni Santa Maria, Dir.
Founded: 1953. **Staff:** Prof 1; Other 2. **Subjects:** Psychiatry, psychology, psychiatric social work, psychiatric nursing. **Holdings:** 8050 books; 1705 bound periodical volumes; 1100 audiotapes; 510 videotapes. **Subscriptions:** 91 journals and other serials. **Services:** Interlibrary loan; copying; library open to the public for reference use only. **Computerized Information Services:** MEDLINE; CD-ROM (PsycLIT); diskette (PDRs Drug Interactions and Side Effects). **Networks/Consortia:** Member of National Network of Libraries of Medicine - Pacific Southwest Region. **Remarks:** Maintained by California State Department of Mental Health. **Staff:** Joseph Cruz, Commun.Libn.

★10222★
Metropolitan Toronto Chief Administrative Officer's Department - Corporate Library Services (Plan)
401 Bay St., Suite 1100 Phone: (416)392-8917
Toronto, ON, Canada M5H 2Y4 Cynthia Fisher, Libn.
Founded: 1982. **Staff:** Prof 2; Other 1. **Subjects:** Urban planning, management, municipal affairs, transportation, housing, public administration, environmental planning. **Special Collections:** Bureau of Municipal Research collection; Transportation Research Board collection. **Holdings:** 11,000 books. **Subscriptions:** 93 journals and other serials. **Services:** Interlibrary loan; copying; library open to the public with restrictions. **Automated Operations:** Computerized cataloging. **Computerized Information Services:** DIALOG Information Services, Info Globe, DOBIS Canadian Online Library System, Infomart Online; internal databases. **Publications:** Newsletter. **Remarks:** Maintained by the Municipality of Metropolitan Toronto. FAX: (416)392-3498. **Formerly:** Metropolitan Toronto Management Services Department. **Staff:** Heather Kessler, Libn.

★10223★
Metropolitan Toronto Reference Library - Arts Department (Art, Mus)
789 Yonge St. Phone: (416)393-7077
Toronto, ON, Canada M4W 2G8 Isabel Rose, Mgr.
Staff: Prof 10; Other 16. **Subjects:** Fine and decorative arts, printing and publishing, costume, music, theater, drama, motion pictures, radio and television programming, popular entertainment. **Special Collections:** Private press and fine printing; 19th and 20th century Canadian, English, American trade catalogs; retrospective Canadian sheet music; 18th and 19th century American and British sheet music for solo voice and piano (9000 pieces total); engravings of British and American theater; opera and dance portraits and production; photographs and slides of performing arts personalities; film stills; Canadian theater ballet; opera and dance productions; posters publicizing Canadian performing arts productions and visual arts exhibitions; stage designs; Canadian touring companies and personalities. **Holdings:** 106,000 books; 834,000 circulating picture clippings; 178,000 reference picture clippings and early postcards; 44,000 scores; 24,000 recordings; 19,500 VF folders; 2100 microforms; 3000 stage designs. **Subscriptions:** 808 journals and other serials. **Services:** Interlibrary loan; copying; department open to the public for reference use only. **Automated Operations:** Computerized cataloging. **Special Indexes:** Canadian artists' index (card); title index to plays performed professionally in Canada (card); title index to plays in collections and periodicals (card); Archindont index to articles about buildings and structures in Ontario (card); index to Canadian sheet music (card); index to Toronto concert programs (card); index to songs in collections (card). **Staff:** Katherine McCook, Asst.Mgr.; Annette Wengle, Sr.Coll.Libn.

★10224★
Metropolitan Toronto Reference Library - Audio Visual Services Department (Aud-Vis)
789 Yonge St. Phone: (416)393-7110
Toronto, ON, Canada M4W 2G8 Laura Murray, Mgr.
Staff: Prof 2; Other 15. **Special Collections:** Centre for the Disabled. **Holdings:** 9000 16mm films; 1000 videotapes. **Subscriptions:** 135 journals and other serials. **Services:** Interlibrary loan; film and video viewing services; equipment and technicians' services; talking books services; services for the disabled. **Staff:** Gail Cox, Film Depot; Bruce Fairley, AV Equip. & Prod. Unit; Maureen Perez, Serv. for the Disabled Unit.

★10225★
Metropolitan Toronto Reference Library - Business and Social Sciences Department (Bus-Fin, Soc Sci)
789 Yonge St. Phone: (416)393-7148
Toronto, ON, Canada M4W 2G8 Margot Hewings, Mgr.
Staff: Prof 21; Other 15. **Subjects:** Accounting, anthropology, business and economics, education, folklore, immigration and ethnic groups in Canada, industrial relations, industry, investments, law, management, marketing, philosophy, political science, psychology, religion, sociology, social welfare, third world development, women's studies. **Special Collections:** Canadian corporation annual reports; Statistics Canada Publications; depository for Canadian and Ontario Government and UNESCO publications; Canadian congregational and denominational church histories. **Holdings:** 401,830 books; 656,812 microforms; 3822 audiotapes, phonograph records, cassettes; 5000 university and college calendars; 4135 vertical files. **Subscriptions:** 5372 journals and other serials; 32 newspapers. **Services:** Interlibrary loan; copying; department open to the public for reference use only. **Automated Operations:** Computerized cataloging. **Publications:** Pathfinders; bibliographies - both irregular. **Special Indexes:** Magazine index covering Canadian business periodicals not elsewhere indexed, 1941-1975; Corporation Index; Top Ranking Index; index to vertical files; index to tapes and records; index to college and university calendars; Index to Current Canadian Federal and Ontario Provincial Bills. **Remarks:** Includes Business and Social Science Collections. Alternate telephone number(s): 393-7181. **Staff:** Margaret Covshoff, Asst.Mgr.; Abdus Salam, Sr.Coll.Libn.

★10226★
Metropolitan Toronto Reference Library - Business and Social Sciences Department - Municipal Reference Library (Soc Sci, Plan)
100 Queen St. W. Phone: (416)393-7119
Toronto, ON, Canada M5H 2N1 Berenice Campayne, Mgr.
Staff: Prof 4; Other 7. **Subjects:** Municipal affairs, finance, traffic, transit, government, services, institutions; urban sociology, geography, planning, and housing; urban aspects of pollution. **Special Collections:** Metropolitan Toronto area documents depository. **Holdings:** 73,778 books; 1603 VF folders of local committee reports, pamphlets, clippings; 146,037 microforms; 4841 maps; 2162 slides; 85 pictures; 216 cassettes. **Subscriptions:** 878 journals and other serials; 25 newspapers. **Services:** Interlibrary loan; copying; library open to the public for reference use only. **Automated Operations:** Computerized public access catalog and cataloging. **Publications:** Memo from Municipal, quarterly; brochure on the collections and services. **Special Catalogs:** Map catalog (card). **Special Indexes:** Subject index to VF material (card); subject/geographic index to magazines (book); Quick Reference Index (card); Index to Campaign Literature (book). **Remarks:** FAX: (416)393-7161. Library located at City Hall, Toronto, ON M5H 2N1. **Staff:** B. Campagne, Asst.Mgr.

★10227★
Metropolitan Toronto Reference Library - General Information Services Department (Info Sci)
789 Yonge St. Phone: (416)393-7131
Toronto, ON, Canada M4W 2G8 Sandra DeAthe, Mgr.
Staff: Prof 9; Other 25. **Subjects:** National and general bibliography, book trade, library science, archives, museology. **Holdings:** 31,607 books; 9197 microfiche; telephone books; city directories. **Subscriptions:** 500 journals; 70 newspapers. **Services:** Interlibrary loan; department open to the public for reference use only. **Automated Operations:** Computerized cataloging. **Computerized Information Services:** DIALOG Information Services, Info Globe, PFDS Online, MEDLARS, WESTLAW, VU/TEXT Information Services, CAN/OLE, WILSONLINE, Canada Systems Group (CSG), Dunserve II, med Data, International Development Research Centre (IDRC), QL Systems, UTLAS; Envoy 100 (electronic mail service). Performs searches on fee basis. Contact Person: Helen Baltais, 393-7005. **Remarks:** FAX: (416)393-7004. Includes General Reference, Library Science, and Newspaper Collections. **Staff:** Denny Raincock, Asst.Mgr.; Kathy Chirametli, Coll.Libn.

★10228★
Metropolitan Toronto Reference Library - History Department (Hist, Mil)
789 Yonge St. Phone: (416)393-7155
Toronto, ON, Canada M4W 2G8 David B. Kotin, Mgr.
Staff: Prof 12; Other 8. **Subjects:** World history, with emphasis on modern period and Canada; archeology; topography and regional geography; travel and exploration; heraldry and genealogy; collective biography; military art and science; military history and uniforms. **Special Collections:** Canadian History Collection (24,000 books; 260 linear meters of manuscripts; 82,000 drawings, prints, photographs, postcards; 30,000 pieces of printed ephemera; 4347 volumes of bound newspapers). **Holdings:** 220,000 books; 47,000 maps; 3800 VF folders; 175,000 microforms; guidebooks; timetables; directories. **Subscriptions:** 3400 journals and other serials. **Services:** Interlibrary loan; copying; department open to the public for reference use only. **Automated Operations:** Computerized cataloging. **Staff:** Elizabeth Dobson, Asst.Mgr.; Christine Mosser, Coll.Libn.

★10229★
Metropolitan Toronto Reference Library - Languages and Literature Department (Hum)
789 Yonge St. Phone: (416)393-7010
Toronto, ON, Canada M4W 2G8 Jaswinder Gundara, Mgr.
Staff: Prof 12; Other 19. **Subjects:** Literature of the English-speaking world; literary history and criticism; journalism; linguistics; language and literature materials in languages other than English. **Special Collections:** North American Indian and Eskimo linguistics (1132 volumes); Canadiana Ethnica; English as a second language collections; Arthur Conan Doyle Collection; Maria Chapdelaine Collection; Russelas Collection. **Holdings:** 281,004 books; 14,427 bound periodical volumes; 12,645 language and spoken word phonograph records, tapes, cassettes; 7649 VF folders; 7299 other cataloged items. **Subscriptions:** 1158 journals and other serials; 99 newspapers. **Services:** Interlibrary loan; copying; language teaching with record players, video and tape machines; department open to the public for reference use only. **Automated Operations:** Computerized cataloging, acquisitions, and serials. **Publications:** Bibliographies, irregular - available upon request; RMS News - available upon request to libraries, institutions, and organizations in Toronto; information brochures; Bigelow on Holmes: a Guide to the Writings upon the Writings. **Remarks:** Most staff members are language specialists, with 30-40 languages represented. Alternate telephone number(s): 393-7073; 393-7007; 393-7010. **Staff:** Alice Wong, Asst.Mgr.; Barbara Gunther, Sr.Coll.Libn.

★10230★
Metropolitan Toronto Reference Library - Science & Technology Department (Sci-Engr, Biol Sci)
789 Yonge St. Phone: (416)393-7090
Toronto, ON, Canada M4W 2G8 Jean Forde, Mgr.
Staff: Prof 7; Other 9. **Subjects:** Physical, biological, and medical sciences; engineering sciences; natural history; horticulture; technology and food technology; cookery; sports and recreation. **Special Collections:** Geological Survey of Canada publications; Atomic Energy of Canada publications; workshop manuals for motor vehicles and household appliances. **Holdings:** 125,250 books; 5982 volumes of Canadian, American, and British patent abstracts; 12,000 volumes of standards; 4250 volumes of Canadian and American radio, television, and personal computer schematics; 7956 VF folders; 4019 maps; 5000 automotive shop manuals; 1250 cookbooks. **Subscriptions:** 1256 journals and other serials. **Services:** Interlibrary loan; copying; department open to the public for reference use only. **Automated Operations:** Computerized cataloging. **Special Indexes:** Shop manual index; map index; vertical file index to science and sports; index to Canadian doctors, engineers, and scientists. **Staff:** Indira Bava, Asst.Mgr.; Carol Rhodes, Sr.Coll.Libn.

★10231★
Metropolitan Toronto School Board - Professional Library (Educ)
45 York Mills Rd. Phone: (416)397-2523
Willowdale, ON, Canada M2P 1B6 Martha E. Murphy, Libn.
Founded: 1976. **Staff:** Prof 1. **Subjects:** Education. **Special Collections:** Educational research; Study of Educational Facilities (SEF); education of the developmentally handicapped. **Holdings:** 1000 books; 12 VF drawers. **Subscriptions:** 150 journals and other serials. **Services:** Interlibrary loan; copying; library open to the public by appointment. **Computerized Information Services:** DIALOG Information Services, Infomart Online, BRS Information Technologies, CAN/OLE, UTLAS, Info Globe, WILSONLINE. **Networks/Consortia:** Member of Education Libraries Sharing of Resources Network (ELSOR). **Special Catalogs:** Union List of Periodicals in the Professional Libraries of the School Boards and Boards of Education of Metropolitan Toronto and Vicinity (10th edition, 1992). **Remarks:** FAX: (416)397-2640.

★10232★
Metropolitan (Toronto) Separate School Board - Catholic Education Centre Library (Educ)
80 Sheppard Ave., E. Phone: (416)222-8282
Willowdale, ON, Canada M2N 6E8 M. Judith Smith, Supv., Lib.Serv.
Founded: 1966. **Staff:** Prof 2; Other 5. **Subjects:** Elementary and secondary education, religious education, philosophy of education, teaching, methodology, curriculum, child development services, special education, innovations in education. **Special Collections:** Historical Collection (history of Catholic education in Ontario); art slide collection (1500 titles). **Holdings:** 30,000 books, AV programs, cataloged reports, documents; extensive vertical file; complete ERIC microfiche collection. **Subscriptions:** 682 journals and other serials; 11 newspapers. **Services:** Interlibrary loan; SDI (for administrators and subject coordinators); library open to the public by special arrangement. **Computerized Information Services:** DIALOG Information Services, BRS Information Technologies. **Networks/Consortia:** Member of Education Libraries Sharing of Resources Network (ELSOR). **Remarks:** FAX: (416)229-5365. **Staff:** Bozenna Karczewska, Ref./Libn.; Irene Vaisnoras, Tech.Serv./Libn.

★10233★
Metropolitan Transportation Commission - Association of Bay Area Governments (ABAG) - Library (Plan, Trans)
101 8th St. Phone: (510)464-7833
Oakland, CA 94607 Joan Friedman, Hd.Libn.
Founded: 1972. **Staff:** Prof 2; Other 2. **Subjects:** Regional planning, housing, urban development policy, environmental resources, transportation. **Special Collections:** Bay Area transit history; environmental impact reports and general plans of local jurisdictions in 9-county Bay Area; 1980 census. **Holdings:** 20,000 volumes. **Subscriptions:** 400 journals. **Services:** Interlibrary loan; library open to the public. **Automated Operations:** Computerized cataloging. **Computerized Information Services:** DIALOG Information Services, OCLC, RLIN. **Networks/Consortia:** Member of CLASS. **Publications:** TransActions; Information Resource News; MTC bibliography. **Remarks:** FAX: (510)464-7848. **Staff:** Christine Harris.

★10234★
Metropolitan Washington Council of Governments - Library and Information Center (Soc Sci)
777 N. Capitol St., N.E. Phone: (202)962-3256
Washington, DC 20002 Carolyn Huskey, Info.Ctr.Mgr.
Founded: 1967. **Staff:** Prof 1; Other 1. **Subjects:** Local governments in metropolitan Washington, metropolitan development, transportation, environmental issues, human services, public safety. **Special Collections:** Archival collection of Council of Government publications; State Data Center for Bureau of Census; master plans; local documents. **Holdings:** 8000 books; maps of local area. **Subscriptions:** 80 journals and other serials; 10 newspapers. **Services:** Interlibrary loan; library open to the public on limited schedule. **Computerized Information Services:** DIALOG Information Services. **Special Catalogs:** Catalog of publications - free upon request. **Remarks:** FAX: (202)962-3201.

★10235★
Metropolitan Water Reclamation District of Greater Chicago - Technical Library (Sci-Engr)
100 E. Erie St. Phone: (312)751-6658
Chicago, IL 60611 Andrew King, Libn.
Founded: 1966. **Staff:** Prof 1; Other 1. **Subjects:** Wastewater treatment, engineering, soil mechanics, water resources and development. **Special Collections:** Archival collection. **Holdings:** 3000 books; 50 bound periodical volumes; 2300 technical reports; 65 microfiche; district proceedings and internal reports; reprints. **Subscriptions:** 72 journals and other serials. **Services:** Interlibrary loan; copying; library open to persons holding Infopass for reference use only. **Computerized Information Services:** WESTLAW, LEXIS. **Publications:** Information packet, annual update. **Also Known As:** Chicago Metropolitan Sanitary District.

★10236★
Metrum Information Storage - Information Center (Sci-Engr)
4800 E. Dry Creek Rd. Phone: (303)773-4829
Littleton, CO 80122 Charlotte Quarton, Adm. of Info.Ctr.
Subjects: Electrical engineering, magnetic recording. **Holdings:** 4000 books. **Subscriptions:** 250 journals and other serials. **Services:** Center not open to the public. **Computerized Information Services:** Internal database. **Remarks:** A subsidiary of Alliant Techsystems. **Formerly:** Honeywell, Inc. - Test Instruments Division.

Metsantutkimuslaitos
See: **Finnish Forest Research Institute** (5716)

Marshall R. Metzgar Medical Library
See: **Pocono Medical Center** (13155)

★10237★
Mexican American Legal Defense and Educational Fund - Library (Law)
634 S. Spring St., 11th Fl. Phone: (213)629-2512
Los Angeles, CA 90014 Vibiana Andrade, Reg.Couns.
Subjects: Law. **Special Collections:** Mexican-American civil rights. **Holdings:** 1000 law books. **Services:** Library not open to the public. **Remarks:** Stanford University - Special Collections and University Archives houses and indexes many past files and documents relating to MALDEF and its work. **Also Known As:** MALDEF.

★10238★
Mexican-American Opportunity Foundation - Resource and Referral Service - Lending Library (Educ)
6252 E. Telegraph Rd. Phone: (213)722-7842
Commerce, CA 90040 Ruth Loya, Prog.Coord.
Founded: 1962. **Staff:** Prof 3. **Subjects:** Infant development, parenting, domestic and child abuse, self-esteem, emotional and physical handicaps; displaced homemakers. **Special Collections:** Mayan & Aztec History; Mexican History; Child Psychology and Development. **Holdings:** 2500 volumes; filmstrips; cassettes; records; audiophonic media cards; arts and crafts materials. **Services:** Interlibrary loan; center open to licensed providers of child care and established organizations. **Computerized Information Services:** CAREFINDER (internal database). **Publications:** Newsletter, quarterly - to mailing list and by public contact. **Remarks:** The Resource and Referral Service is funded by the California State Department of Education - Office of Child Development. Program is geared to the needs of the Hispanic community of East Los Angeles and surrounding communities.

★10239★
Mexico - Archivo General de la Nacion (Hist)
Apartado Postal 1999
Eduardo Molina y Albaniles
Colonia Penitenciaria
15350 Mexico City, DF, Mexico Phone: 5 7957311
Founded: 1909. **Staff:** Prof 4; Other 9. **Subjects:** Mexico - history, law. **Special Collections:** Rare books; 19th century pamphlets; Francisco Diaz de Leon graphic collection. **Holdings:** 35,000 books; 3000 titles of bound periodical volumes; archives. **Subscriptions:** 5 newspapers. **Services:** Interlibrary loan; archives open to the public. **Computerized Information Services:** DIALOG Information Services; DIDLEX, BIBLOS, HEMEROS, ALEJANDRO VAUDDRES, INGINEER (internal databases). **Publications:** Boletin Bibliografico y Bibliografica. **Remarks:** FAX: 5 7895296.

★10240★
Mexico - Center of Regional Cooperation for Adult Education in Latin America and the Caribbean - Library (Educ)
Quinta Erendira s/n Phone: 454 21791
Patzcuaro, Michoacan, Mexico Dr. Jesus Balhen, Chf., Doc.Dept.
Founded: 1951. **Staff:** 10. **Subjects:** Mexico, Latin America, Caribbean Area - adult education and rural development, literacy, educational communication and technology. **Holdings:** 50,000 volumes. **Services:** Interlibrary loan; copying; SDI; library open to the public. **Computerized Information Services:** BANEDA (internal database). **Remarks:** FAX: 454 10092. **Formerly:** Mexico - Office of the Secretary of Public Education - Regional Center for Adult Education and Functional Development of Latin America. **Also Known As:** CREFAL.

★10241★
Mexico - National Commission on Nuclear Safety and Safeguards - Library (Sci-Engr)
Insurgentes Sur 1806
Colonia Florida
Delegacion Alvaro Obregon
01030 Mexico City, DF, Mexico Phone: 5 534-1404
Founded: 1979. **Subjects:** Non-military use of nuclear energy, radiation protection, quality assurance, nuclear regulation. **Holdings:** 7000 volumes. **Subscriptions:** 16 journals and other serials. **Services:** Interlibrary loan; SDI; library open to the public for reference use only. **Computerized Information Services:** Internal databases. **Special Catalogs:** Journal catalog. **Remarks:** FAX: 5 5341405. Telex: 1773280 CNSMME. **Also Known As:** Comision Nacional de Seguridad Nuclear y Salvaguardias. **Staff:** Ana A. Jimenez Luna; Felipe Rodriguez Bolanos.

★10242★
Mexico - National Institute of Nuclear Research - Nuclear Information and Documentation Center (Sci-Engr, Energy)
Apartado 18-1027
11800 Mexico City, DF, Mexico
Subjects: Science and technology, energy, nuclear energy. **Holdings:** 30,000 volumes; 365,000 technical reports; magnetic tapes. **Subscriptions:** 665 journals and other serials. **Services:** Center open to institute staff and chief researchers of other institutions. **Also Known As:** Instituto Nacional de Investigaciones Nucleares.

Mexico - Office of the Secretary of Public Education - Regional Center for Adult Education and Functional Development of Latin America
See: **Mexico - Center of Regional Cooperation for Adult Education in Latin America and the Caribbean - Library** (10240)

★10243★
(Mexico City) Centro Mexicano-Norteamericano de Cultura - USIS Collection (Educ)
Xola No. 416
Col. Del Valle
03100 Mexico City, DF, Mexico Phone: 5 365520
Remarks: FAX: 5 258437. Maintained or supported by the U.S. Information Agency. Focus is on materials that will assist peoples outside the United States to learn about the United States, its people, history, culture, political processes, and social milieux.

★10244★
(Mexico City) Instituto Mexicano-Norteamericano de Relaciones Culturales - USIS Collection (Educ)
Hamburgo No. 115
06400 Mexico City, DF, Mexico
Remarks: Maintained or supported by the U.S. Information Agency. Focus is on materials that will assist peoples outside the United States to learn about the United States, its people, history, culture, political processes, and social milieux.

(Mexico City) USIS Library
See: **Biblioteca Benjamin Franklin - (Mexico City) USIS Library** (1820)

(Mexico) National Laboratories of Industrial Development
See: **Laboratorios Nacionales de Fomento Industrial** (8861)

Mexico-U.S. Relations Archive
See: **University of California, Los Angeles - Chicano Studies Research Library** (18376)

John E. Meyer Eye Foundation Library
See: **Eye Foundation Hospital** (5538)

Meyer Library
See: **California College of Arts and Crafts** (2473)

Thomas S. Meyer Memorial Library
See: **U.S. Navy - Naval Dental Research Institute - Thomas S. Meyer Memorial Library** (17833)

Madeline Roach Meyercord Library
See: **Highland Park Presbyterian Church** (7199)

Joseph Meyerhoff Library
See: **Baltimore Hebrew University** (1451)

Henry & Delia Meyers Memorial Library
See: **Jewish Community Center of Metropolitan Detroit** (8384)

Meyers Library
See: **Reform Congregation Keneseth Israel** (13777)

★10245★
MGIC Investment Corporation - Corporate Library (Bus-Fin)
MGIC Plaza Phone: (414)347-6409
Milwaukee, WI 53202 Peg Uihlein, Libn.
Founded: 1973. **Staff:** Prof 2. **Subjects:** Mortgage insurance, housing, insurance statistics and law, real estate statistics, banking, finance. **Holdings:** Figures not available. **Subscriptions:** 300 journals and other serials. **Services:** Interlibrary loan; copying; library open to the public with restrictions. **Computerized Information Services:** DIALOG Information Services. **Remarks:** FAX: (414)347-6959. **Staff:** Mary Lohmeier.

MGM Collection
See: **Academy of Motion Picture Arts and Sciences - Margaret Herrick Library** (35)

★10246★
Miami Beach Community Hospital - Bioethics Institute - Library (Med)
250 W. 63rd St. Phone: (305)868-5000
Miami Beach, FL 33141 Wilma S. Grover, Libn.
Founded: 1985. **Staff:** Prof 1. **Subjects:** Judeo-Christian medical ethics, withholding treatment, living wills, allocation of health care resources, ethics committees, nursing ethics. **Holdings:** Figures not available. **Subscriptions:** 25 journals and other serials. **Services:** Copying; library open to members. **Computerized Information Services:** BIOETHICSLINE, MEDLINE. Performs searches free of charge for members. **Networks/Consortia:** Member of National Network of Libraries of Medicine - Southeastern/Atlantic Region, Miami Health Sciences Library Consortium (MHSLC). **Publications:** Bibliographies.

★10247★
Miami County Law Library (Law)
201 W. Main St. Phone: (513)332-6861
Troy, OH 45373 Carolyn S. Bolin, Libn.
Founded: 1939. **Staff:** 2. **Subjects:** Law. **Holdings:** 20,000 volumes; all Ohio unreported appellate cases, 1981 to present, on microfiche. **Subscriptions:** 50 journals and other serials. **Services:** Interlibrary loan; library not open to the public. **Computerized Information Services:** WESTLAW. Performs searches on fee basis.

★10248★
Miami County Museum - Hal C. Phelps Archives (Hist)
51 N. Broadway Phone: (317)473-9183
Peru, IN 46970 Joyce Miller, Archv.
Founded: 1916. **Staff:** 3. **Subjects:** Miami County history, Miami Indians, circus, Cole Porter. **Special Collections:** Hal C. Phelps papers; Omer Holman Collection (photographs, documents); Otto Winger Collection (Miami Indian documentation). **Holdings:** 1000 books; 250 bound periodical volumes; 10 AV programs. **Services:** Copying. **Publications:** History Bulletin, monthly.

★10249★
Miami-Dade Community College - Medical Center Campus Library (Med)
950 N.W. 20th St. Phone: (305)237-4129
Miami, FL 33127 Sally Ream, Dir.
Founded: 1975. **Staff:** Prof 3; Other 4. **Subjects:** Allied health, nursing. **Holdings:** 12,000 books; 2054 bound periodical volumes. **Subscriptions:** 279 journals and other serials. **Services:** Interlibrary loan; library open to the public for reference use only. **Automated Operations:** Computerized cataloging, serials, and circulation. **Computerized Information Services:** BRS Information Technologies; NURSEARCH (internal database). **Networks/Consortia:** Member of SOLINET, Miami Health Sciences Library Consortium (MHSLC). **Staff:** Carol Zahiser, Libn.; Isabel C. Hernandez, Libn.

★10250★
Miami-Dade Public Library - Art and Music Division (Art, Mus)
101 W. Flagler St. Phone: (305)375-5015
Miami, FL 33130-1504 Dorothy Donio
Staff: Prof 3; Other 3. **Subjects:** Art, music, theater, motion pictures, television, sports. **Holdings:** 43,000 books; 4 VF drawers of clippings; 35 VF drawers of pictures; 8 VF drawers of contemporary artist files; 133,000 pictures; 4000 phonograph records; 2140 cassettes; 1500 scores; 8252 pieces of sheet music; 2100 framed pictures. **Subscriptions:** 140 journals and other serials. **Services:** Interlibrary loan (limited); copying; division open to the public. **Remarks:** FAX: (305)381-7782. **Staff:** Judy Baran; Karen Baskin

★10251★
Miami-Dade Public Library - Audio/Visual Department (Aud-Vis)
101 W. Flagler St. Phone: (305)375-5191
Miami, FL 33130-1504 Donald E. Chauncey, Film Libn.
Founded: 1955. **Staff:** Prof 1; Other 3. **Subjects:** Films - children's, documentary, experimental, fiction. **Holdings:** 5800 16mm films; 600 filmstrips; 2117 slides; 1670 filmstrip/cassette units; 8500 videotapes. **Subscriptions:** 3 journals and other serials. **Services:** Library open to the public. **Remarks:** FAX: (305)381-7782.

★10252★
Miami-Dade Public Library - Business, Science and Technology Department (Sci-Engr, Bus-Fin)
101 W. Flagler St. Phone: (305)375-5231
Miami, FL 33130-1504 John Heim
Staff: Prof 7; Other 7. **Subjects:** Business, economics, international trade, investments, layperson's medical reference, pure and applied sciences. **Special Collections:** Annual reports of companies and Florida corporations; patents; manufacturing, specialized, and foreign business directories (600); microfiche collection. **Holdings:** 45,000 volumes; 80 VF drawers of pamphlets. **Subscriptions:** 700 journals and other serials. **Services:** Interlibrary loan (limited); copying; department open to the public. **Computerized Information Services:** DIALOG Information Services, BRS Information Technologies, U.S. Patent Classification System, LOGIN, CompuServe Information Service. **Remarks:** FAX: (305)381-7782. **Staff:** Robert Klein, Libn.; Ellen Book, Libn.; Rose Hepburn-Ballou, Libn.; John Vincent, Libn.; Catherine Albair, Libn.; John Shipley, Libn.

★10253★
Miami-Dade Public Library - Federal Documents Division (Info Sci)
101 W. Flagler St. Phone: (305)375-5028
Miami, FL 33130-1504 Eva Conrad, Fed.Doc.Libn.
Founded: 1952. **Staff:** Prof 1; Other 1. **Subjects:** Legislation, census, U.S. treaties. **Special Collections:** Serial Set; Foreign Relations of the U.S.; U.S. Supreme Court Reports; Census Reports; President's Commission Reports. **Holdings:** 170,000 U.S. Government publications (selective depository); legislative documents. **Services:** Collection available to public for reference use only. **Remarks:** FAX: (305)381-7782.

★10254★
Miami-Dade Public Library - Florida Collection (Area-Ethnic)
101 W. Flagler St. Phone: (305)375-5023
Miami, FL 33130-1504 Sam J. Boldrick, Libn. IV
Staff: Prof 2; Other 4. **Subjects:** Florida. **Special Collections:** Dime Novels set in Florida; Florida Author and Setting Collection; Romer Photograph Collection. **Holdings:** 11,900 books; 41,200 documents; 20,000 photographs; 2335 maps; 17,500 photographic negatives; 700,000 newspaper clippings; 10,170 reels of microfilm; 515 pamphlets; 4800 microforms. **Subscriptions:** 66 journals and other serials; 33 newspapers. **Services:** Interlibrary loan (limited); copying; collection open to the public. **Computerized Information Services:** Internal database. **Special Indexes:** Miami Newspapers Index, monthly. **Remarks:** FAX: (305)381-7782. **Staff:** Carmen Palmier, Asst.Libn.II.

★10255★
Miami-Dade Public Library - Foreign Languages Division (Hum)
101 W. Flagler St. Phone: (305)375-5579
Miami, FL 33130-1504 Jorge Gonzalez, Libn. III
Founded: 1962. **Staff:** Prof 2; Other 2. **Subjects:** Books in 46 foreign languages, mainly Spanish: literature, history, applied science, languages, popular authors, best sellers, sociology. **Special Collections:** Spanish Reference Collection; Spanish, French, German, Italian, and Basque Encylopedias; foreign and bilingual dictionaries and atlases ; Cuban collection (history). **Holdings:** 43,000 volumes; 30 bound periodical volumes; 30 unbound periodical volumes; 250 language records; 8 cassette players and 500 cassettes for language learning in various languages, especially English, French, and Spanish; language courses on video cassettes; 20 file drawers of clippings on 300 subjects; 10,000 other cataloged items. **Subscriptions:** 88 journals and other serials, mainly foreign. **Services:** Interlibrary loan; copying; translations in languages other than English at the desk and by phone; division open to the public. **Special Catalogs:** Drama catalog, by titles. **Remarks:** FAX: (305)381-7782. **Staff:** Amelia Mederos, Libn. I.

★10256★
Miami-Dade Public Library - Genealogy Collection (Hist)
101 W. Flagler St. Phone: (305)375-5580
Miami, FL 33130-1504 Renee Pierce, Geneal.Libn.
Staff: Prof 1; Other 1. **Subjects:** Genealogy, heraldry. **Holdings:** 7000 volumes; 10,580 reels of microfilm of census; 1881 reels of microfilm of directories, 1861-1900; 1647 American directories, through 1860, on microfiche; 2985 microfiche. **Subscriptions:** 94 journals and other serials. **Services:** Copying; room open to the public. **Remarks:** FAX: (305)381-7782.

★10257★
Miami-Dade Public Library - Humanities Division (Hum)
101 W. Flagler St. Phone: (305)375-5575
Miami, FL 33130-1504 Rosa Maria Pendleton, Libn. III
Staff: Prof 2; Other 3. **Subjects:** Literature, philosophy, religion, psychology, journalism, library and information science. **Special Collections:** Foundation Center Cooperating Collection (annual reports of foundations). **Holdings:** 41,000 volumes. **Subscriptions:** 100 journals and other serials. **Networks/Consortia:** Member of South East Florida Library Information Network (SEFLIN). **Remarks:** FAX: (305)381-7782. **Staff:** G. Calvo, Libn.

★10258★
Miami-Dade Public Library - Louis Wolfson Media History Center (Aud-Vis)
101 W. Flagler St. Phone: (305)375-4527
Miami, FL 33130-1504 Steven Davidson, Archv.
Founded: 1985. **Staff:** Prof 1; Other 2. **Subjects:** Florida history and culture, politics, public affairs. **Special Collections:** WTVJ News Film Collection, 1949-1983 (5000 hours). **Holdings:** WTVJ daily news scripts and editorials. **Subscriptions:** 10 journals and other serials. **Services:** Film and video copying; center open to the public by appointment. **Automated Operations:** Computerized cataloging and acquisitions; film and video preservation. **Publications:** Newsletter, quarterly. **Remarks:** FAX: (305)381-7782.

★10259★
Miami-Dade Public Library - Social Sciences Division (Soc Sci, Hist)
101 W. Flagler St. Phone: (305)375-5575
Miami, FL 33130-1504 Theresa Lianzi, Soc.Sci.Libn.
Staff: Prof 3; Other 3. **Subjects:** History, biography, political science, sociology, education, travel. **Holdings:** 52,000 volumes; 32 VF drawers of pamphlets and clippings; 3000 maps. **Subscriptions:** 250 journals and other serials. **Services:** Copying; division open to the public. **Remarks:** FAX: (305)381-7782. **Staff:** A. Echeverri, Libn. I; E. Conrad, Libn. II.

★10260★
Miami-Dade Public Library - Urban Affairs Library (Plan)
101 W. Flagler St. Phone: (305)375-5487
Miami, FL 33130-1504 Richard G. Frow, Urban Aff.Libn.
Founded: 1960. **Staff:** Prof 1. **Subjects:** City and regional planning, local government administration. **Holdings:** 4556 books; 9693 pamphlets; unbound reports of non-Florida cities and counties. **Subscriptions:** 90 journals and other serials. **Services:** Interlibrary loan; copying; library open to the public. **Computerized Information Services:** DIALOG Information Services, LOGIN, BRS Information Technologies, ViewText. **Publications:** Urban Affairs Newsletter, monthly - to city and county officials. **Remarks:** FAX: (305)381-7782.

★10261★
Miami Heart Institute Hospital - Medical Library (Med)
4701 Meridian Ave. Phone: (305)674-3108
Miami Beach, FL 33140 Irene Bohlmann, Dir.
Founded: 1966. **Staff:** Prof 1; Other 1. **Subjects:** Medicine, cardiovascular research. **Holdings:** 500 books; 7000 bound periodical volumes. **Subscriptions:** 150 journals and other serials. **Services:** Interlibrary loan; library not open to the public. **Computerized Information Services:** MEDLINE; internal database; DOCLINE (electronic mail service). **Networks/Consortia:** Member of Miami Health Sciences Library Consortium (MHSLC), National Network of Libraries of Medicine - Southeastern/Atlantic Region.

★10262★
Miami Herald - Library (Publ)
One Herald Plaza
Miami, FL 33132-1693 Phone: (305)376-3402
Founded: 1940. **Staff:** Prof 5; Other 5. **Subjects:** Newspaper reference topics. **Special Collections:** Historical pictures of Miami. **Holdings:** 2000 books; photographs; newspaper on microfilm. **Subscriptions:** 40 journals and other serials; 20 newspapers. **Services:** Interlibrary loan; copying (for news agencies only); library open to the public by mailed request only. **Computerized Information Services:** LEXIS, DIALOG Information Services, DataTimes, Mead Data Central, PFDS Online, BRS Information Technologies, VU/TEXT Information Services, NEXIS; internal database. Performs searches on fee basis. **Staff:** William Whiting, Ed./Info.Serv.; Gay M. Nemeti, Lib.Rsrc.Mgr.; Elisabeth Donovan, Res.Mgr.

★10263★
Miami Purchase Association for Historic Preservation - Library and Information Center (Plan)
1225 Elm St. Phone: (513)721-4506
Cincinnati, OH 45210 Mary Ann Brown, Exec.Dir.
Founded: 1964. **Staff:** 4. **Subjects:** Preservation, restoration, history of Cincinnati and Southwestern Ohio, architecture. **Special Collections:** 19th and 20th century Ohio and Cincinnati history and literature (200 volumes). **Holdings:** 450 books; 25 boxes of ephemera. **Subscriptions:** 16 journals and other serials. **Services:** Copying; library open to the public for reference use only. **Remarks:** FAX: (513)721-6832.

★10264★
Miami University - Art and Architecture Library (Art, Plan)
Alumni Hall Phone: (513)529-6650
Oxford, OH 45056 Joann Olson, Libn.
Founded: 1952. **Staff:** Prof 1; Other 2. **Subjects:** Architecture, art, decorative arts, art photography, graphics, city planning, art education, landscape design and allied subjects. **Holdings:** 52,000 books; 7200 bound periodical volumes; pamphlets; catalogs. **Subscriptions:** 256 journals and other serials. **Services:** Interlibrary loan; copying; library open to the public. **Computerized Information Services:** DIALOG Information Services, BRS Information Technologies, RLIN, LEXIS, NEXIS; CD-ROM (Art Index). **Networks/Consortia:** Member of Greater Cincinnati Library Consortium (GCLC), OHIONET, Center for Research Libraries (CRL). **Remarks:** FAX: (513)529-1682.

★10265★
Miami University - Brill Science Library (Sci-Engr, Biol Sci)
Oxford, OH 45056 Phone: (513)529-7201
Susan Hocker, Hd.Sci.Libn.
Founded: 1978. **Staff:** Prof 5; Other 5.5. **Subjects:** Science - biological, physical, earth; mathematics; technology; medicine. **Special Collections:** Paper Science (1200 books; 3500 bound periodical volumes); Kuchler Vegetation Map Collection. **Holdings:** 129,903 books; 107,964 bound periodical volumes; 273,000 microforms; 20,500 specialized maps; 22,520 U.S. Defense Mapping Agency/Army Map Service maps; 48,900 U.S. Geological Survey maps; 9 VF drawers of pamphlets. **Subscriptions:** 2200 journals and other serials. **Services:** Interlibrary loan; copying; library open to the public. **Automated Operations:** Computerized public access catalog, cataloging, and circulation. **Computerized Information Services:** DIALOG Information Services, LEXIS, NEXIS, BRS Information Technologies, OCLC EPIC; CD-ROMs (AGRICOLA, Earth Sciences, MEDLINE Professional, Applied Science & Technology, Computer Select, General Science Index, Biological & Agricultural Index, Enviro/Energyline Abstracts Plus); Current Contents on Diskette (Life Sciences; Physical, Chemical, and Earth Sciences; Agriculture, Biology, and Environmental Sciences); BITNET, InterNet (electronic mail services). Performs searches on fee basis. Contact Person: Erica Lilly, Sci.Libn. **Networks/Consortia:** Member of OHIONET. **Special Catalogs:** Subject bibliographies. **Remarks:** FAX: (513)529-1682. Electronic mail address(es): SCILIB@MIAMIU (BITNET). **Staff:** Nancy Moeckel; Debabrata Basu; Belinda Barr.

★10266★
Miami University - Humanities and Social Sciences Department (Soc Sci, Hum)
King Library Phone: (513)529-4141
Oxford, OH 45056 Richard H. Quay, Hd., Hum./Soc.Sci.Dept.
Founded: 1809. **Staff:** Prof 7; Other 5. **Subjects:** Business, history, education, American literature, political science, geography, sociology, anthropology, gerontology, military and naval science, foreign language, theater, economics, philosophy, psychology, religion, area studies. **Holdings:** 600,000 books; 100,000 bound periodical volumes. **Subscriptions:** 6500 journals and other serials; 72 newspapers. **Services:** Interlibrary loan; copying; SDI; library open to library permit holders. **Computerized Information Services:** DIALOG Information Services, BRS Information Technologies, OCLC EPIC, LEXIS, NEXIS; CD-ROMs (Art Index, PsycLIT, ERIC, COMPACT DISCLOSURE, Books in Print Plus, Social Sciences Index, CIRR on Disc, Newspaper Abstracts Ondisc, Compustat PC Plus, Business Periodicals Index, MLA International Bibliography, Ulrich's Plus, Thesaurus Linguae Graecae Canon of Greek Authors and Works, InfoTrac, Humanities Index); BITNET, InterNet (electronic mail services). Performs searches on fee basis. **Networks/Consortia:** Member of OHIONET, Center for Research Libraries (CRL), Greater Cincinnati Library Consortium (GCLC). **Remarks:** FAX: (513)529-1682. Electronic mail address(es): RQUAY@MIAMIU (BITNET); RQUAY@MIAMU.ACS.MUOHIO.EDU (InterNet). **Staff:** William Wortman; William Baker; Jenny Presnell; Paul Wright; Penny Beile; Ruth Miller.

★10267★
Miami University - Insect Collection (Biol Sci)
Dept. of Zoology Phone: (513)529-3141
Oxford, OH 45056 Richard Lee
Subjects: Insects. **Remarks:** No further information was supplied by respondent.

★10268★
Miami University - Music Library (Mus)
Center for Performing Arts Phone: (513)529-2299
Oxford, OH 45056 Barry Zaslow, Mus.Libn.
Founded: 1969. **Staff:** Prof 1; Other 2. **Subjects:** Music. **Holdings:** 31,000 books; 2400 bound periodical volumes; 14,600 sound recordings. **Subscriptions:** 120 journals. **Services:** Interlibrary loan; copying; library open to the public. **Automated Operations:** Computerized public access catalog (Sherlock). **Computerized Information Services:** OCLC EPIC, DIALOG Information Services, BRS Information Technologies, LEXIS, NEXIS; CD-ROMs (Art Index, PsycLIT, ERIC, Compact Disclosure, Books in Print Plus, Social Sciences Index, CIRR on Disc, Newspaper Abstracts, COMPUSTAT PC PLUS, Business Periodicals Index, MLA International Bibliography, InfoTrac, Ulrich's Plus, Thesaurus Linguae Graecae Canon of Greek Authors and Works, Humanities Index). **Networks/Consortia:** Member of Greater Cincinnati Library Consortium (GCLC), OHIONET, Center for Research Libraries (CRL). **Remarks:** FAX: (513)529-1682.

★10269★
Miami University - Peabody Library (Educ)
Western Campus Phone: (513)529-7477
Oxford, OH 45056 Janice McLaughlin, Supv.
Staff: 1.5. **Subjects:** Interdisciplinary studies. **Holdings:** 5500 books; 684 senior projects. **Subscriptions:** 13 journals and other serials. **Services:** Interlibrary loan; copying; library open to the public with restrictions. **Automated Operations:** Computerized public access catalog (Sherlock). **Computerized Information Services:** OCLC EPIC, DIALOG Information Services, BRS Information Technologies, LEXIS, NEXIS; CD-ROMs (Art Index, PsycLIT, ERIC, COMPACT Disclosure, Books in Print Plus, Social Sciences Index, CIRR on Disc, Newspaper Abstract, COMPUSTAT PC PLUS, Business Periodicals Index, MLA International Bibliography, InfoTrac, Ulrich's Plus, Thesaurus Linguae Graecae Canon of Greek Authors and Works, Humanities Index). **Networks/Consortia:** Member of OHIONET, Greater Cincinnati Library Consortium (GCLC), Center for Research Libraries (CRL). **Remarks:** FAX: (513)529-1682.

★10270★
Miami University - Walter Havighurst Special Collections Library (Hum)
King Library Phone: (513)529-3323
Oxford, OH 45056 C. Martin Miller
Founded: 1973. **Staff:** Prof 2; Other 1.5. **Subjects:** Early children's books, Ohio Valley history, Russian regimental history, Walt Whitman, Henrik Ibsen, J.T. Farrell, Willa Cather, Percy MacKaye, Eugene O'Neill, George Orwell, William Dean Howells, William H. McGuffey. **Special Collections:** King Collection (early juveniles; 10,000 volumes); Covington Collection (Ohio Valley history, 6000 volumes); William H. McGuffey Manuscript Letters (150); William Dean Howells Manuscript Letters (133); 19th century botanical medicine and older herbals (250 volumes); Jefferson Davis papers (491); John Hough James papers (10,000); Robert C. Schenck papers (8000); 19th century school books (5000); Shaker collection (500 items); Working Library of Louise Bogan (1772 items). **Holdings:** 65,000 books; 1000 bound periodical volumes; literary annuals and gift books. **Subscriptions:** 12 journals and other serials. **Services:** Interlibrary loan (limited); library open to the public for reference use only with identification. **Automated Operations:** Computerized public access catalog (Sherlock). **Computerized Information Services:** OCLC EPIC, DIALOG Information Services, BRS Information Technologies, LEXIS, NEXIS; CD-ROMs; BITNET (electronic mail service). **Networks/Consortia:** Member of Greater Cincinnati Library Consortium (GCLC), OHIONET, Center for Research Libraries (CRL). **Publications:** Friends (newsletter); List of publications - available on request. **Remarks:** FAX: (513)529-1682. Electronic mail address(es): CMMILLER@MIAMIU (BITNET). **Staff:** Elizabeth Brice, Spec.Coll.Libn.; Frances McClure, Asst. to the Cur.

★10271★
Miami University - Willard Sherman Turrell Herbarium - Library (Biol Sci)
Dept. of Botany Phone: (513)529-2755
Oxford, OH 45056 W. Hardy Eshbaugh, Curator
Founded: 1906. **Staff:** Prof 1. **Subjects:** Botany, floristics. **Holdings:** 1000 books; 300 bound periodical volumes; 10,000 archival items; 10 microfiche; 10,000 reprints of scientific articles. **Subscriptions:** 10 journals and other serials. **Services:** Library open to the public for reference use only. **Remarks:** FAX: (513)529-4243.

★10272★
Miami Valley Hospital - Craig Memorial Library (Med)
One Wyoming St. Phone: (513)220-2612
Dayton, OH 45409 Sally A. Sexton, Dir.
Founded: 1944. **Staff:** Prof 2; Other 3. **Subjects:** Medicine, nursing, allied health sciences, hospital administration. **Holdings:** 7745 books; 32,000 bound periodical volumes; 12 VF drawers of pamphlets; 12 VF drawers of hospital archives; 1000 AV titles. **Subscriptions:** 600 journals and other serials. **Services:** Interlibrary loan; library open to qualified persons with permission. **Automated Operations:** Computerized circulation. **Computerized Information Services:** NLM, BRS Information Technologies, DIALOG Information Services; CD-ROM. **Remarks:** FAX: (513)220-2569. **Staff:** Shirley J. Sebald.

Miami Valley Laboratories
See: **Procter & Gamble Company** (13398)

★10273★
Miami Valley Regional Planning Commission - Library (Plan)
400 Miami Valley Tower
40 W. 4th St. Phone: (513)223-6323
Dayton, OH 45402 Helen Schooler, Libn.
Founded: 1968. **Staff:** Prof 1. **Subjects:** Demographics, transportation, planning, housing, human resources, land use, criminal and juvenile justice, economics, population, government, water. **Special Collections:** Demographic data on 5 county region of Greene, Montgomery, Miami, Darke, Preble counties, 1950-1980 (8 shelves; microfiche). **Holdings:** 8000 books; 4 VF drawers of clippings; reference documents. **Subscriptions:** 36 journals and other serials. **Services:** Interlibrary loan; copying; library open to the public for reference use only; answers telephone inquiries. **Computerized Information Services:** Internal database. Performs searches on fee basis. **Publications:** Keeping in Touch (newsletter); Technical Bulletins; list of additional publications - available on request. **Remarks:** FAX: (513)223-9700.

★10274★
Miami Youth Museum - Resource Area (Educ)
5701 Sunset Dr., No. 313 Phone: (305)661-3046
Miami, FL 33143 Phyllis Gilbert, Educ.Dir.
Founded: 1985. **Subjects:** Education, artists, children's literature. **Holdings:** 500 books. **Services:** Area open to museum members and professionals. **Remarks:** FAX: (305)669-0917.

★10275★
Michael, Best & Friedrich - Law Library (Law)
100 E. Wisconsin Ave. Phone: (414)271-6560
Milwaukee, WI 53202 Jane Moberg, Libn.
Staff: Prof 1; Other 2. **Subjects:** Law - tax, labor, patent, corporate. **Holdings:** 25,000 books. **Subscriptions:** 202 journals and other serials. **Services:** Interlibrary loan; copying (both limited). **Computerized Information Services:** DIALOG Information Services, LEXIS, WESTLAW, DataTimes. **Networks/Consortia:** Member of Library Council of Metropolitan Milwaukee, Inc. (LCOMM). **Remarks:** FAX: (414)277-0656.

Marie Michael Library
See: **St. Francis Xavier University - Coady International Institute** (14317)

★10276★
Michaelis Art Library (Art)
Elizabeth House
18 Pritchard St. Phone: 11 8366165
Johannesburg 2001, Republic of South Africa J.L. Frost
Founded: 1916. **Staff:** Prof 2. **Subjects:** Art history, architectural history, art techniques, ceramics, numismatics, interior design. **Special Collections:** Numismatic collection; cartoon collection. **Holdings:** 42,000 books and bound periodical volumes; 12 microfiche series; 12,000 invitations and exhibition catalogues. **Subscriptions:** 60 journals and other serials. **Services:** Interlibrary loan; copying; library open to the public. **Computerized Information Services:** URICA (internal database). **Special Indexes:** Index to South African artists; monuments index; crafts index; cartoon index. **Remarks:** FAX: 11 8366607.

★10277★
Chr. Michelsen Institute - Department of Social Science and Development - Library (Soc Sci)
Fantoftvagen 38 Phone: 5 574000
N-5036 Fantoft, Norway Kirsti Hagen Andersen, Hd.Libn.
Founded: 1930. **Staff:** Prof 2; Other 1. **Subjects:** Developing countries, economics, social anthropology, politics, demography. **Special Collections:** Southern and Eastern Africa; Southeast Asia; documentation on developing problems and countries. **Holdings:** 35,000 books. **Subscriptions:** 600 journals and other serials; 7 newspapers. **Services:** Interlibrary loan; copying; library open to the public. **Automated Operations:** Computerized cataloging. **Computerized Information Services:** DIALOG Information Services; internal database. **Special Catalogs:** Norwegian Development Research Catalogue, every 3 years; Nordic Union Catalogue of Periodicals Issued in Developing Countries. **Remarks:** FAX: 5 574166. Telex: 40 006 CMI N.

★10278★
Michener Centre - Staff Library
Box 5002
Red Deer, AB, Canada T4N 5Y5
Defunct.

★10279★
Michener Institute for Applied Health Technology - Library (Med, Biol Sci)
222 St. Patrick St. Phone: (416)596-3123
Toronto, ON, Canada M5T 1V4 Ray Banks, Libn.
Founded: 1972. **Staff:** Prof 1; Other 3. **Subjects:** Medical technology - laboratory, radiological, respiratory; nuclear medicine; cytotechnology; cytogenetics; cardiovascular perfusion; neonatology; chiropody; ultrasonography; echocardiography. **Special Collections:** Archives. **Holdings:** 18,000 books; 1200 bound periodical volumes; 2300 audiovisuals. **Subscriptions:** 250 journals and other serials. **Services:** Interlibrary loan; copying; library open to the public with restrictions. **Automated Operations:** Computerized cataloging, acquisitions, serials, and circulation. **Computerized Information Services:** MEDLARS, DIALOG Information Services, CAN/OLE; CD-ROM (MEDLINE, Books in Print Plus). **Remarks:** FAX: (416)596-3156.

★10280★
Michiana Community Hospital - Library (Med)
2515 E. Jefferson Blvd. Phone: (219)288-8311
South Bend, IN 46615 Mary Jo Tompos
Staff: Prof 1. **Subjects:** Medicine. **Special Collections:** History of osteopathy (25 volumes). **Holdings:** 1136 books; 160 bound periodical volumes; 50 video cassettes; Audio-Digest tapes. **Subscriptions:** 42 journals and other serials. **Services:** Interlibrary loan; copying; library open to students. **Networks/Consortia:** Member of Area 2 Library Services Authority (ALSA 2).

★10281★
Michie Company - Library (Publ, Law)
914 Emmet St. Phone: (804)972-7619
Charlottesville, VA 22903 Linda W. Londeree, Libn.
Staff: Prof 1; Other 1. **Subjects:** Law and legal publishing. **Holdings:** 30,000 books. **Subscriptions:** 1000 journals and other serials. **Services:** Interlibrary loan; copying; library open to the public for reference use only.

Michigan Art Archives
See: **Battle Creek Art Center** (1578)

★10282★
Michigan Audubon Society - Edith Munger Library
6011 W. St. Joseph, Suite 403
P.O. Box 80527
Lansing, MI 48908-0527 Phone: (517)886-9144
Founded: 1904. **Subjects:** Ornithology, natural history. **Holdings:** 120 books; 162 bound periodical volumes; 61 serials; 2 VF drawers of pamphlets; 2045 slides. **Remarks:** Currently inactive.

★10283★
Michigan Bell Telephone Company - Corporate Reference and Development Center (Bus-Fin)
1365 Cass Ave., Rm. 1200 Phone: (313)223-8040
Detroit, MI 48226 Mark W. Stone, Hd.Libn.
Staff: Prof 3. **Subjects:** Personnel management, management, telecommunications, applied psychology, computer science, communication skills, mathematics, statistics, marketing. **Special Collections:** Telephone history. **Holdings:** 6000 books; 100 bound periodical volumes; 600 videotapes; 150 audiotapes; 700 AMA and Conference Board papers; 48 VF drawers of unbound pamphlets, reports, clippings. **Subscriptions:** 404 journals and other serials. **Services:** Interlibrary loan; copying; SDI; center open to the public with permission. **Computerized Information Services:** DIALOG Information Services, VU/TEXT Information Services, MARS, NEXIS; Bellcore Telaris (internal database). **Publications:** New Acquisitions, quarterly - for internal distribution only. **Special Catalogs:** AV catalog. **Remarks:** FAX: (313)223-8095. **Staff:** Christine A. Robertson, Asst.Libn.; Julie Swift, Asst.Libn.

★10284★
Michigan Cancer Foundation - Leonard N. Simons Research Library (Med)
110 E. Warren Phone: (313)833-0710
Detroit, MI 48201 C.J. Glodek, Dir.
Founded: 1948. **Staff:** Prof 1. **Subjects:** Cancer research, allied health sciences. **Special Collections:** MCF Historical Reference Collection. **Holdings:** 3000 books; 300 bound periodical volumes; 800 pamphlets and reprints; institutional archives. **Subscriptions:** 90 journals and other serials. **Services:** Interlibrary loan; copying; SDI; library open to the public with restrictions. **Automated Operations:** Computerized serials and circulation. **Computerized Information Services:** MEDLINE, DIALOG Information Services, STN International, Physician Data Query (PDQ), National Biomedical Research Foundation (NBRF); Institutional Reprint File (internal database). Performs searches on fee basis. **Publications:** CompuScope (newsletter). **Remarks:** FAX: (313)831-8714.

★10285★
Michigan Center for Career & Technical Education (Educ)
Michigan State University
133 E. Erickson Hall
East Lansing, MI 48824-1034 Phone: (517)353-4397
Founded: 1979. **Staff:** 4. **Subjects:** Career development, vocational/technical education, nontraditional recruitment, adult education, training employability skills. **Holdings:** 8000 books; 500 AV programs; 300 software programs. **Services:** Center open to the public. **Computerized Information Services:** Michigan Vocational Education Information System (internal database). Contact Person: Tim McLaughlin. **Publications:** Bibnotes Newsletter, 3/year. **Special Indexes:** Task list index. **Remarks:** The Center acts as an information and materials clearinghouse for secondary and post secondary counselors, teachers, instructors, administrators, and placement personnel. Toll-free telephone number(s): (800)292-1606 (in Michigan). **Formerly:** Michigan Vocational Education Resource Center. **Staff:** Dr. Cas Heilman, Co-Dir.; Dr. Gloria Kielbaso, Co-Dir.; John MacKenzie, Ph.D., Assoc.Dir.

★10286★
Michigan City News-Dispatch - Library (Publ)
121 W. Michigan Blvd.
Michigan City, IN 46360 Phone: (219)874-7211
Staff: 1. **Subjects:** Newspaper reference topics. **Special Collections:** Michigan City News-Dispatch clipping and photo file. **Services:** Library not open to the public. **Remarks:** FAX: (219)872-8511.

★10287★
Michigan Consolidated Gas Company - Corporate Library (Energy)
500 Griswold St. Phone: (313)256-5470
Detroit, MI 48226 Kay L. Ames, Supv., Adm.Serv.
Founded: 1979. **Staff:** Prof 2. **Subjects:** Natural gas, energy, business. **Holdings:** 1500 books; 15 VF drawers of clippings and pamphlets. **Subscriptions:** 200 journals and other serials; 10 newspapers. **Services:** Interlibrary loan; library not open to the public. **Automated Operations:** Computerized public access catalog and serials. **Computerized Information Services:** DIALOG Information Services, VU/TEXT Information Services, NEXIS, Dow Jones News/Retrieval, Dun & Bradstreet Business Credit Services, DataTimes. **Publications:** Corporate Library Update, monthly - to management personnel. **Staff:** Karen M. Gulvezan, Libn.

★10288★
Michigan Consumers Council - Library
414 Hollister Bldg.
Lansing, MI 48913
Defunct.

Michigan Employment Security Commission
See: **Michigan (State) Department of Labor** (10299)

★10289★
Michigan Health Center - Health Science Library (Med)
2700 Martin Luther King Jr. Blvd. Phone: (313)361-8079
Detroit, MI 48208 Carolyn A. Hough, Dir.
Founded: 1971. **Staff:** Prof 3; Other 1. **Subjects:** Medicine, osteopathy, psychiatry. **Holdings:** 3000 books; 1200 bound periodical volumes; 350 video cassettes; 600 audio cassettes. **Subscriptions:** 300 journals and other serials. **Services:** Interlibrary loan; copying; library open to medical staff of other medical institutions. **Computerized Information Services:** MEDLINE, DIALOG Information Services. **Remarks:** FAX: (313)361-8073. **Staff:** Diana Balint, Tech.Serv.Libn.; Cora Williams, AV Coord.

Michigan Information Transfer Source (MITS)
See: **University of Michigan** (18876)

★10290★
Michigan Lutheran Seminary - Library (Rel-Phil)
2777 Hardin St. Phone: (517)793-1041
Saginaw, MI 48602 Milton P. Spaude, Lib.Dir.
Founded: 1952. **Staff:** Prof 2; Other 2. **Subjects:** History, religion, education. **Holdings:** 13,000 books; 100 bound periodical volumes. **Subscriptions:** 48 journals and other serials. **Services:** Library not open to the public. **Staff:** Carolyn Zeiger, Libn.; Lorna Starke, Asst.Libn.

★10291★
Michigan Molecular Institute - Library (Sci-Engr)
1910 W. St. Andrews Rd. Phone: (517)832-5569
Midland, MI 48640 Julia T. Lee, Libn.
Staff: Prof 1. **Subjects:** Polymer science, engineering, composites. **Holdings:** 3500 books; 5000 bound periodical volumes. **Subscriptions:** 134 journals and other serials. **Services:** Interlibrary loan; copying; library open to the public with restrictions. **Networks/Consortia:** Member of Michigan Library Consortium (MLC).

★10292★
Michigan Municipal League - Library (Soc Sci)
1675 Green Rd.
Box 1487 Phone: (313)662-3246
Ann Arbor, MI 48106-1487 Colleen Layton
Founded: 1928. **Staff:** Prof 1. **Subjects:** Municipal government, city charters, ordinances, Michigan statutes and legislation. **Special Collections:** Charters of all Michigan home rule cities and villages (365 items). **Holdings:** 1000 books; 35 VF drawers of unbound reports, manuscripts, clippings, pamphlets, documents. **Subscriptions:** 200 journals and other serials; clipping service for all Michigan dailies and weeklies. **Services:** Interlibrary loan; copying; library open to the public by appointment. **Publications:** Ordinance Analyses; Technical Topics; Directory of Michigan Municipal Officials; Handbook for Local Officials: Meetings, Agendas, and Minutes; Records Management Manual for Michigan Municipalities; Salaries and Wages of Officials in Michigan Municipalities Over 1000 in Population; Handbook for Local Officials: Newly Elected Municipal Officials; Handbook for Local Officials: Glossary of Municipal Terms; MML Publications and Reprints; MML Video Guide. **Remarks:** FAX: (313)662-8083.

★10293★
Michigan Protection and Advocacy Service - Library (Med)
109 W. Michigan Ave., Suite 900 Phone: (517)487-1755
Lansing, MI 48933 Maureen MacLaughlin
Founded: 1986. **Staff:** Prof 1. **Subjects:** Developmental disabilities, human services, mental health, advocacy, special education. **Holdings:** 2500 books; 3500 reports. **Subscriptions:** 25 journals and other serials; 230 newsletters. **Services:** Copying; library open to the public with restrictions. **Automated Operations:** Computerized cataloging. **Remarks:** FAX: (517)487-0827.

★10294★
Michigan Psychoanalytic Institute - Ira Miller Memorial Library (Med)
16310 W. 12 Mile Rd., Suite 204 Phone: (313)557-8633
Southfield, MI 48076 Phyllis Kaplan, Libn.
Founded: 1962. **Staff:** 2. **Subjects:** Psychoanalysis, psychotherapy, psychiatry. **Holdings:** 1000 books; 400 bound periodical volumes. **Subscriptions:** 15 journals and other serials. **Services:** Interlibrary loan; copying; library open to individuals in the mental health professions. **Computerized Information Services:** Jourlit/Jourlook (internal database). **Networks/Consortia:** Member of Michigan Library Consortium (MLC), Oakland Wayne Interlibrary Network (OWIN). **Remarks:** FAX: (313)559-3050.

★10295★
Michigan Society for Autistic Citizens - Library (Med)
530 W. Ionia, Suite C
Lansing, MI 48933 Phone: (517)487-9260
Subjects: Autism, developmental disabilities. **Holdings:** 1000 books. **Services:** Library open to the public on a fee basis.

(Michigan) State Archives of Michigan
See: **Michigan (State) Bureau of History - State Archives of Michigan** (10296)

★10296★
Michigan (State) Bureau of History - State Archives of Michigan (Hist)
717 W. Allegan Phone: (517)373-1408
Lansing, MI 48918 David J. Johnson, State Archv.
Founded:1913. **Staff:** Prof 9; Other 4. **Subjects:** Michigan history and government. **Special Collections:** Historical photograph collection (300,000 images of Michigan); historical map collection (500,000 cartographic expressions). **Holdings:** 1000 books; 100 bound periodical volumes; 6000 reels of microfilm; 80 million documents (22,000 cubic feet of state and local government records; private papers). **Services:** Copying; archives open to the public (appointments recommended). **Publications:** A Guide to the State Archives of Michigan: State Records; published finding aids (1-20); circulars (1-43); genealogical information; Michigan's Memory (pamphlets). **Remarks:** FAX: (517)373-0851. **Staff:** John Curry, Photo Archv.; LeRoy Barnett, Ref.Archv.

★10297★
Michigan (State) Department of Agriculture - Library (Agri)
1615 S. Harrison Rd. Phone: (517)337-5066
East Lansing, MI 48823 Janet Holbrook
Founded: 1957. **Staff:** Prof 1. **Subjects:** Agriculture, food and dairy products analysis, liquors and wines, veterinary medicine. **Special Collections:** American Standard Testing Materials (40 volumes). **Holdings:** 1500 books; 500 bound periodical volumes. **Subscriptions:** 90 journals and other serials. **Services:** Library not open to the public. **Computerized Information Services:** SprintMail (electronic mail service). **Remarks:** FAX: (517)337-5094. Electronic mail address(es): MDA Lab.QA (SprintMail).

★10298★
Michigan (State) Department of Civil Rights - Civil Rights Library (Soc Sci)
1200 6th St., 7th Fl. Phone: (313)256-2622
Detroit, MI 48226 Ellen B. McCarthy
Founded: 1964. **Staff:** Prof 1. **Subjects:** Civil rights; discrimination - employment, housing; minority groups. **Holdings:** 10,000 books; 13,000 microfiche; unbound periodicals. **Subscriptions:** 200 journals and other serials; 10 newspapers. **Services:** Interlibrary loan; library open to the public by appointment. **Computerized Information Services:** DIALOG Information Services, VU/TEXT Information Services, ELSS (Electronic Legislative Search System), WILSONLINE, WESTLAW, LEXIS, NEXIS, Hannah Information Systems, OCLC, Questor, Washington Alert Service, CQ Bill Status. **Remarks:** FAX: (313)256-2680.

★10299★
Michigan (State) Department of Labor - Michigan Employment Security Commission - Library (Bus-Fin)
7310 Woodward Ave., Rm. 612 Phone: (313)876-5597
Detroit, MI 48202 Richard L. Daoust, Mgr.
Founded: 1966. **Staff:** 1. **Subjects:** Employment services and job training programs for general population and special groups, including veterans, women, rural workers, handicapped, youth, and minorities; job interviewing, counseling, and testing; ES regulations; unemployment insurance - law, regulations, research, theory, practice; personal computing; occupational and labor market information research and statistics; job analysis; personnel/administrative management; older and dislocated workers. **Special Collections:** Unemployment insurance (105 books; 2 periodical titles). **Holdings:** 4000 books; 17,750 unbound periodical volumes; 200 microfiche reports; 250 archival volumes; 40 16mm films; 60 video cassettes. **Subscriptions:** 100 journals and other serials; 2 newspapers. **Services:** Interlibrary loan; copying; library open to the public for reference use only. **Automated Operations:** Computerized public access catalog. **Computerized Information Services:** Internal databases. **Networks/Consortia:** Member of Detroit Associated Libraries Region of Cooperation (DALROC). **Publications:** Bulletin: Library's Latest, quarterly; Guide to MESC Library Services (brochure); periodicals list. **Special Catalogs:** Catalog of MESC Promotional and Informational Material; MESC AV catalog. **Remarks:** Alternate telephone number(s): (313)876-5596; 876-5597. FAX: (313)876-5225.

★10300★
Michigan (State) Department of Mental Health - Center for Forensic Psychiatry - Staff Library (Med)
P.O. Box 2060 Phone: (313)429-0862
Ann Arbor, MI 48106 Lois J. Staresina, Libn.
Founded: 1974. **Subjects:** Forensic psychiatry, psychiatry, medicine, psychology. **Holdings:** 2500 books; 400 audio- and videotapes. **Subscriptions:** 75 journals and other serials. **Services:** Interlibrary loan; copying; SDI; library open to the public at librarian's discretion. **Computerized Information Services:** DIALOG Information Services, LEXIS, NEXIS. **Special Catalogs:** Audio Catalog, Video Catalog. **Remarks:** FAX: (313)429-1817.

★10301★
Michigan (State) Department of Mental Health - Coldwater Regional Mental Health Center - Medical Staff Library
620 Marshall Rd.
Coldwater, MI 49036
Defunct.

★10302★
Michigan (State) Department of Mental Health - Kalamazoo Regional Psychiatric Hospital - Staff Library (Med)
1312 Oakland Dr.
Box A Phone: (616)385-1265
Kalamazoo, MI 49008 Carol Aebli, Lib.Dir.
Founded: 1974. **Staff:** Prof 1. **Subjects:** Psychiatry, nursing, psychiatric nursing, psychology, social services. **Holdings:** 1780 books; 830 bound periodical volumes. **Subscriptions:** 90 journals and other serials. **Services:** Interlibrary loan; copying; SDI; library open to the public. **Remarks:** FAX: (616)388-2386.

★10303★
Michigan (State) Department of Natural Resources - Great Lakes & Environmental Assessment Section - Surface Water Quality Division - Library (Env-Cons)
Knapps' Office Centre, 2nd Fl. Phone: (517)373-6794
Lansing, MI 48933 Marjorie Fitch, Libn.
Founded: 1980. **Subjects:** Toxicology, Great Lakes. **Holdings:** 7000 books; 400 reports; 50 microfiche. **Services:** Library open to the public by appointment. **Computerized Information Services:** DIALOG Information Services, STN International, NLM, TDS; CESARS (Chemical Evaluation Search & Retrieval System; internal database). **Remarks:** FAX: (517)373-9958.

★10304★
Michigan (State) Department of Natural Resources - Institute for Fisheries Research - Library (Biol Sci)
Univ. Musms. Annex
University of Michigan Phone: (313)663-3554
Ann Arbor, MI 48109 Grace M. Zurek, Libn.
Staff: 1. **Subjects:** Fisheries biology and management. **Special Collections:** Great Lakes bibliography; Michigan climatological data. **Holdings:** 600 volumes; 10,000 reprints; 1900 reports; 105 theses; 2400 lake maps. **Subscriptions:** 42 journals and other serials. **Services:** Library open to the public for reference use only.

★10305★
Michigan (State) Department of Natural Resources - Wildlife Division - Rose Lake Wildlife Research Station - Library
8562 E. Stoll Rd.
East Lansing, MI 48823
Subjects: Wildlife biology and management. **Holdings:** 400 volumes. **Remarks:** Currently inactive.

★10306★
Michigan (State) Department of Public Health - Library Resource Center (Med)
3423 N. Logan St.
Box 30195 Phone: (517)335-8394
Lansing, MI 48909 Bill Nelton, Libn.
Founded: 1873. **Staff:** Prof 1; Other 2. **Subjects:** Public health. **Special Collections:** History of public health; agent orange. **Holdings:** 7000 bound periodical volumes. **Subscriptions:** 300 journals and other serials. **Services:** Interlibrary loan; SDI; library open to the public for reference use only. **Computerized Information Services:** MEDLARS; Agent Orange (internal database); Dialcom, Inc. (electronic mail service). **Remarks:** FAX: (517)335-8395.

★10307★
Michigan (State) Department of Social Services - Office of Training and Staff Development - Resource Library (Soc Sci)
Grand Tower, Suite 301
235 S. Grand Phone: (517)335-4698
Lansing, MI 48909 Ron Walters
Founded: 1985. **Staff:** Prof 1. **Subjects:** Management, supervision, self-development. **Holdings:** 275 videotapes; 100 audiocassettes; 100 book summaries. **Services:** Library open to governmental units and private children's agencies. **Special Catalogs:** Videotape catalogs; audiotape catalog.

★10308★
Michigan (State) Department of State Police - Law Enforcement Resource Center (Law)
7426 N. Canal Rd. Phone: (517)322-1976
Lansing, MI 48913 Mary LePiors, Libn.
Founded: 1979. **Staff:** Prof 2; Other 1. **Subjects:** Law enforcement, public administration, management, dog training. **Special Collections:** Red Squad Collection (1950s material; 300 pieces). **Holdings:** 3829 books; 450 AV programs. **Subscriptions:** 28 journals and other serials. **Services:** Interlibrary loan; copying; library open to state workers. **Computerized Information Services:** DIALOG Information Services. Performs searches free of charge. **Networks/Consortia:** Member of Michigan Library Consortium (MLC), Capital Area Library Network (Calnet). **Remarks:** FAX: (517)322-1130. **Staff:** Pat French, AV Spec.

★10309★
Michigan (State) Department of Transportation - Resource Center (Trans)
425 W. Ottawa
Box 30050 Phone: (517)373-1545
Lansing, MI 48909 Jeanne F. Thomas, Libn.
Founded: 1964. **Staff:** Prof 1; Other 3. **Subjects:** Highways - design, construction, engineering, materials, safety; transportation planning; traffic and environmental engineering; mass transit. **Special Collections:** MDOT publications; Transportation Research Board publications; Highway Research Information Service publications. **Holdings:** 12,000 books and documents. **Subscriptions:** 262 journals and other serials. **Services:** Interlibrary loan; copying; SDI; library open to the public for reference use only. **Automated Operations:** Computerized public access catalog, cataloging, acquisitions, and serials. **Computerized Information Services:** DIALOG Information Services, BRS Information Technologies, VU/TEXT Information Services, OCLC, WILSONLINE. **Networks/Consortia:** Member of Michigan Library Consortium (MLC). **Publications:** Resources (newsletter) - for internal distribution only. **Remarks:** FAX: (517)373-0168.

★10310★
Michigan State Legislative Service Bureau - Library (Law)
124 W. Allegan, 4th Fl.
Box 30036 Phone: (517)373-0472
Lansing, MI 48909-7536 Leo F. Kennedy, Div.Dir., Leg.Res.Div.
Founded: 1941. **Staff:** Prof 1; Other 2. **Subjects:** State government, law. **Special Collections:** Michigan manuals, 1873 to present; Michigan Supreme Court cases, 1843 to present; legislative journals, 1897 to present; Michigan Statutes, 1837 to present. **Holdings:** 16,400 volumes; 25 VF drawers. **Subscriptions:** 140 periodicals; 10 newspapers. **Services:** Copying. **Automated Operations:** Computerized cataloging. **Computerized Information Services:** Public Affairs Information, Inc. (PAI), DIALOG Information Services, Washington Alert Service, National Conference of State Legislatures (NCSL), LEGISNET; internal databases. **Publications:** Recent Acquisitions in the Legislative Service Bureau Library, weekly; Michigan Legislative Topics (weekly subject bibliographies). **Formerly:** Michigan State Legislative Council - Legislative Service Bureau Library. **Staff:** Anne T. Bautista, Libn.

(Michigan State) Library of Michigan
See: **Library of Michigan** (9141)

★10311★
Michigan (State) Third Circuit Court - Law Library (Law)
780 City-County Bldg. Phone: (313)224-5265
Detroit, MI 48226 H. Jean Owens Allen, Law Libn.
Staff: Prof 1. **Subjects:** Law. **Holdings:** 14,872 books; 270 bound periodical volumes. **Subscriptions:** 20 journals and other serials. **Services:** Interlibrary loan; copying; library open to the public with special permission. **Computerized Information Services:** LEXIS, DIALOG Information Services, INFO-PLUS; internal database. **Remarks:** FAX: (313)224-0649.

Michigan State University - Academic Computing Department - Instructional Software Collection
See: **Michigan State University - Instructional Software Collection** (10327)

★10312★
Michigan State University - Africana Library (Area-Ethnic)
W-316 University Libraries Phone: (517)355-2366
East Lansing, MI 48824 Mrs. Onuma Ezera, Hd.
Founded: 1964. **Staff:** Prof 2; Other 1. **Subjects:** Sub-Saharan Africa. **Special Collections:** African languages, linguistics, and literature; socioeconomic development in the Sahel; Colonial Zaire; Ethiopian materials; archival resources on the slave trade; British Colonial and Foreign Office archival materials on Africa (microform); Kenya National Archives (microform). **Holdings:** 175,000 volumes; 27,200 pamphlets; 6610 sheet maps; 33,240 titles in microform. **Subscriptions:** 1750 journals and other serials. **Services:** Interlibrary loan; copying; main collection open to the public. **Computerized Information Services:** OCLC; BITNET (electronic mail service). **Publications:** Africana - Select Recent Acquisitions, 4/year; Women in Africa: Selected Acquisitions at MSU since 1975 (1988); A Guide to Africana Materials in the Michigan State University Libraries (1982). **Special Catalogs:** Card catalog for Africa; card catalog of area studies pamphlet collections. **Remarks:** FAX: (517)336-1445 (ILL). Electronic mail address(es): 20676AFR@MSU (BITNET). The Africana Library is responsible for the development of the collections for African studies needed for teaching and research; provides bibliographic advisory service to faculty and students engaged in the study of this area; and provides consultation service for the university's several African projects. **Staff:** Joseph Lauer.

★10313★
Michigan State University - Agricultural Economics Reference Room (Agri)
29 Agriculture Hall Phone: (517)355-6650
East Lansing, MI 48824 Judith Dow, Agri.Econ.Libn.
Founded: 1965. **Staff:** 1. **Subjects:** Economic aspects of agriculture, agricultural business, rural manpower, public affairs, food systems. **Special Collections:** Agricultural Economics Department publications. **Holdings:** 650 books; 600 bound periodical volumes; 3000 U.S. documents; 30 Michigan Department of Agriculture titles; 80 U.N. and international documents; annual reports of companies in the food and agriculture sector; 22 VF drawers; 400 theses. **Subscriptions:** 200 journals and other serials. **Services:** Room open to the public. **Computerized Information Services:** DIALOG Information Services, BRS Information Technologies; BITNET, InterNet (electronic mail services). Performs searches on fee basis. **Publications:** Annual list of departmental publications; serials holdings list, annual - available on request. **Remarks:** FAX: (517)336-1800. Electronic mail address(es): 20676EC@IMB.CLMMSU.EDU (InterNet); 20676EC@IBM (BITNET).

★10314★
Michigan State University - Animal Industries Reference Room (Biol Sci)
208 Anthony Hall Phone: (517)355-8483
East Lansing, MI 48824 Carole S. Armstrong, Hd., Sci.Libs.
Founded: 1956. **Staff:** 1. **Subjects:** Physiology, biochemistry, nutrition, food science, animal breeding and production. **Holdings:** 8590 volumes; 540 theses; 20 VF drawers of pamphlets. **Subscriptions:** 92 journals and other serials. **Services:** Interlibrary loan. **Computerized Information Services:** BITNET (electronic mail service). **Remarks:** FAX: (517)353-9806. Electronic mail address(es): 20676AIN@MSU (BITNET).

★10315★
Michigan State University - Art Library (Art, Geog-Map)
East Lansing, MI 48824 Phone: (517)353-4593
Patricia T. Thompson, Hd.
Founded: 1973. **Staff:** Prof 1.5; Other 1. **Subjects:** Visual arts, architecture, painting, sculpture, graphic and applied arts, photography. **Holdings:** 60,000 volumes, including 12,000 exhibition catalogs; picture file of 18,200 subjects, including reproductions of art works, portraiture, general subjects; vertical file of 6200 subjects of local artists and art organizations. **Subscriptions:** 180 journals and other serials. **Services:** Interlibrary loan; copying; library open to the public. **Computerized Information Services:** Online systems; BITNET EMA. Performs searches on fee basis. **Special Indexes:** Subject and artist indexes to picture file (card); subject and author/organization indexes to vertical file (card); specialized subject guides. **Remarks:** FAX: (517)336-1445. Electronic mail address(es): 20676PTT@MSU (BITNET). **Staff:** Agnes H. Widder.

★10316★
Michigan State University - Business Library (Bus-Fin)
21 Eppley Ctr. Phone: (517)355-3380
East Lansing, MI 48824-1121 Faye C. Backie
Founded: 1962. **Staff:** Prof 2; Other 2. **Subjects:** Business; accounting; finance; marketing and transportation; management and operations research; hotel, restaurant, and institutional management; tourism. **Special Collections:** Annual and 10K reports of major American and foreign corporations; New York and American Stock Exchanges listing statements. **Holdings:** 60,000 volumes; dissertations. **Subscriptions:** 900 journals and other serials; 30 newspapers. **Services:** Interlibrary loan; copying; library open to the public. **Computerized Information Services:** BRS Information Technologies, DIALOG Information Services. Performs searches on fee basis. Contact Person: Shari Buxbaum, Asst.Bus.Libn., 355-3387. **Publications:** Accessions List, monthly; subject bibliographies. **Remarks:** FAX: (517)353-9806.

★10317★
Michigan State University - C.W. Barr Planning and Design Library (Plan)
Urban Plan. & Landscape Arch., Rm. 212 Phone: (517)353-3941
East Lansing, MI 48824 Diana H. Rivera, Libn.
Founded: 1964. **Staff:** Prof 1; Other 1. **Subjects:** Urban planning and design, landscape architecture. **Special Collections:** Local U.S. planning documents; HUD 701 planning report collection; Johnson, Johnson and Roy, Inc. Planning and Landscape Architecture Archives (200 items); American Society of Landscape Architects (ASLA) Michigan Chapter Archives; Michigan State Planning Officials Archives (300 items). **Holdings:** 7309 books; 1176 bound periodical volumes; 36,763 planning reports; 38,388 pamphlets; 1500 slides; 1021 maps. **Subscriptions:** 240 journals and other serials. **Services:** Interlibrary loan; copying; library open to the public. **Computerized Information Services:** Internal database; BITNET (electronic mail service). **Publications:** Recent Acquisitions of the Planning and Design Library, 6/year. **Special Indexes:** Key word card index and geographic file to planning report collection (card); vertical file and slide index. **Remarks:** FAX: (517)336-1445. Electronic mail address(es): 20676PLA@MSU (BITNET).

★10318★
Michigan State University - Chemistry Library (Sci-Engr)
426 Chemistry Bldg. Phone: (517)355-9715
East Lansing, MI 48824 James W. Oliver, Chem.Libn. II
Staff: Prof 1; Other 1. **Subjects:** Chemistry, chemical engineering, biochemistry, technology. **Holdings:** 50,631 books; 16,500 bound periodical volumes; 15,164 theses and dissertations; 4355 microfiche; 825 reels of microfilm. **Subscriptions:** 429 journals and other serials. **Services:** Interlibrary loan; copying; AV instruction for use of major reference texts. **Computerized Information Services:** DIALOG Information Services, STN International, BRS Information Technologies. **Publications:** Serials Listings. **Remarks:** FAX: (517)353-1793.

★10319★
Michigan State University - Clinical Center Library (Med)
A-137, Clinical Center Phone: (517)353-3037
East Lansing, MI 48823-1313 Leslie M. Behm, Libn. II
Staff: Prof 1; Other 1. **Subjects:** Clinical and osteopathic medicine, nursing. **Holdings:** 6600 volumes. **Subscriptions:** 150 journals and other serials. **Services:** Interlibrary loan; copying; SDI; library open to the public. **Computerized Information Services:** MEDLINE, NLM, BRS Information Technologies, DIALOG Information Services, PFDS Online; BITNET (electronic mail service). Performs searches on fee basis. **Publications:** CCL Newsletter, quarterly. **Remarks:** FAX: (517)336-1445. Electronic mail address(es): 20676CCL@MSU (BITNET).

★10320★
Michigan State University - Engineering Library (Sci-Engr)
A101 Engineering Bldg. Phone: (517)336-1498
East Lansing, MI 48824 Thomas C. Volkening, Engr.Libn.
Founded: 1963. **Staff:** Prof 1; Other 2. **Subjects:** Engineering - chemical, civil, transportation, environmental, electrical, mechanical; electronics; metallurgy; materials science. **Holdings:** 64,000 volumes. **Subscriptions:** 600 journals and other serials. **Services:** Interlibrary loan; copying; library open to the public. **Computerized Information Services:** DIALOG Information Services, BRS Information Technologies; STN International; BITNET (electronic mail service). **Publications:** New books list. **Remarks:** FAX: (517)353-9806. Electronic mail address(es): 20676TCV@MSU (BITNET).

★10321★
Michigan State University - G. Robert Vincent Voice Library (Aud-Vis)
Main Library Bldg., W433-W437 Phone: (517)355-5122
East Lansing, MI 48824 Dr. Maurice A. Crane, Libn. III
Founded: 1962. **Staff:** Prof 1; Other 2. **Subjects:** Historical sound recordings of voices and events in all fields of human endeavor, including media history, literature and theater, classical jazz, politics, and sports. **Holdings:** 8000 cataloged items; 6000 tape recordings. **Services:** Copying; library open to the public for educational research only. **Computerized Information Services:** OCLC; BITNET (electronic mail service). **Special Catalogs:** Dictionary Catalog (book); Descriptive Guide. **Remarks:** FAX: (517)336-1445. Electronic mail address(es): 20676MAC@MSU (BITNET).

★10322★
Michigan State University - Geology Library (Sci-Engr)
5 Natural Sciences Bldg. Phone: (517)353-7988
East Lansing, MI 48824 Carole S. Armstrong, Hd., Sci.Libs.
Founded: 1967. **Staff:** 1. **Subjects:** Geology. **Holdings:** 26,970 volumes; 3300 maps. **Subscriptions:** 157 journals and other serials. **Services:** Interlibrary loan; copying; library open to the public. **Computerized Information Services:** BITNET (electronic mail service). **Remarks:** FAX: (517)353-9806. Electronic mail address(es): 20676GLG@MSU (BITNET).

★10323★
Michigan State University - Government Documents Library (Info Sci)
Main Library Phone: (517)353-8707
East Lansing, MI 48824-1048 Laurel Minott, Hd.
Founded: 1907. **Staff:** Prof 3; Other 4. **Subjects:** Documents - Michigan (depository), U.S. (depository and nondepository), Canada (depository), U.N., UNESCO (depository), Food and Agriculture Organization (FAO), European Communities (depository), Council of Europe, OECD, IMF, World Bank, WEU, GATT, other IGO's. **Holdings:** 1.8 million bound and unbound documents; Congressional Serial set (1st Congress to present); 1,852,075 microforms. **Subscriptions:** 11,136 journals and other serials. **Services:** Interlibrary loan; copying; SDI; library open to the public. **Computerized Information Services:** DIALOG Information Services, BRS Information Technologies. Performs searches on fee basis. **Remarks:** FAX: (517)336-1445. **Staff:** Debbi Schaubman, Intl.Docs.Libn.

★10324★
Michigan State University - Human Ecology Reference Library (Biol Sci)
Human Ecology Bldg., Rm. 2 Phone: (517)355-7737
East Lansing, MI 48824-1030 Stephanie C. Perentesis, Libn.
Staff: Prof 1; Other 1. **Subjects:** Human ecology and environmental design, family/child ecology, human nutrition. **Special Collections:** Mary Shipley Collection (700 books). **Holdings:** 4300 books; 900 bound periodical volumes; 870 theses and dissertations; AV materials; pictures; pamphlets; educational testing instruments. **Subscriptions:** 100 journals and other serials; 5 newspapers. **Services:** Library available for reference use to the College of Human Ecology and the Michigan State University Land-Grant constituency. **Publications:** Human Ecology - The First Decade; Human Ecology - The Tenth Decade; College of Human Ecology Faculty Biographical Directory.

★10325★
Michigan State University - Institute for Research on Teaching - Information Center (Educ)
College of Education
133 Erickson Hall Phone: (517)355-1752
East Lansing, MI 48824-1034 David Bolig, Info.Spec.
Founded: 1977. **Staff:** Prof 2; Other 1. **Subjects:** Educational research, teaching, teacher education. **Holdings:** 4500 books; 20 shelves of unbound periodicals; 600 reports. **Subscriptions:** 60 journals and other serials. **Services:** Center open to the public for reference use only. **Automated Operations:** Computerized public access catalog. **Computerized Information Services:** CD-ROM (ERIC).

★10326★
Michigan State University - Instructional Media Center - Film and Video Library (Aud-Vis)
Box 710 Phone: (517)353-3960
East Lansing, MI 48826-0710 Frank Tate, Act. Film Libn.
Founded: 1955. **Staff:** Prof 1; Other 2. **Holdings:** 1782 16mm films; 224 videotapes. **Services:** Film and videotape service to the campus; rental to all states (some films restricted); library open to the public. **Networks/Consortia:** Member of Consortium of College and University Media Centers (CCUMC), American Film & Video Association. **Special Catalogs:** MSU Film and Video Rental Catalog, irregular.

★10327★
Michigan State University - Instructional Software Collection (Comp Sci)
Main Library Phone: (517)355-1840
East Lansing, MI 48824-1048 Nancy A. Lucas, Instr. Software Coord.
Founded: 1987. **Staff:** Prof 1; Other 3. **Subjects:** Instructional software, videodiscs, and CD-ROMs. **Holdings:** 120 monographs; 15 bound periodical volumes; 650 software programs; 90 videodisc titles; computer-aided instruction packages; learning aids; simulations; models; problem solving guides; tutorials, CD-ROM related materials; drills; practice packages; software catalogs; evaluations; newsletters. **Subscriptions:** 15 journals and other serials. **Services:** Collection available to Michigan State University faculty, staff, and graduate students. **Remarks:** A joint project between the Computing & Technology Department and MSU libraries, the Collection contains software for demonstration and assessment for graduate and undergraduate course work, curriculum development, and research projects. FAX: (517)336-1445.

★10328★
Michigan State University - Labor and Industrial Relations Library (Bus-Fin)
Library E109 Phone: (517)355-4647
East Lansing, MI 48824 Annie M. Cooper, Libn. III
Founded: 1956. **Staff:** Prof 1; Other 2. **Subjects:** Labor unions, public employee unionism, labor law, employment and training, minorities. **Special Collections:** Union constitutions and proceedings; public sector agreements for State of Michigan. **Holdings:** 50,000 books; 5000 bound periodical volumes; 200 VF drawers of pamphlets and mimeographed materials, by subject. **Subscriptions:** 125 journals and other serials; 75 newspapers. **Services:** Interlibrary loan; copying; library open to the public. **Computerized Information Services:** DIALOG Information Services. Performs searches on fee basis. **Remarks:** FAX: (517)353-9806.

★10329★
Michigan State University - Map Library (Geog-Map)
Libraries, W-308 Phone: (517)353-4737
East Lansing, MI 48824 Diana Huizar Rivera, Hd., Map Lib.
Founded: 1963. **Staff:** Prof 1; Other 1. **Subjects:** Maps - Michigan, Africa, Latin America, topography, thematic. **Special Collections:** Michigan FEMA-Firm, U.S. state Department of Transportation maps; Government Printing Office (GPO) depository. **Holdings:** 4000 atlases and gazetteers; 99 bound periodical volumes; 173,000 maps; 9 globes; 30 raised relief maps. **Subscriptions:** 100 journals and other serials. **Services:** Interlibrary loan; copying; library open to the public. **Automated Operations:** Computerized public access catalog. **Computerized Information Services:** BITNET (electronic mail service). **Remarks:** FAX: (517)353-9806. Electronic mail address(es): 20676MAP@MSU (BITNET).

★10330★
Michigan State University - Microforms Library (Hum)
East Lansing, MI 48824 Phone: (517)353-3120
Susan E. Iversen, Supv.
Founded: 1978. **Staff:** 1. **Subjects:** American and English history, literature, anthropology, foreign imprints, African and Asian source documents, history of science, economics, ethnic studies, newspapers, 19th century periodicals. **Holdings:** 4 million microforms and bibliographic aids; 678 periodicals; 352 newspapers. **Subscriptions:** 67 journals and other serials; 36 newspapers. **Services:** Interlibrary loan; copying; library open to the public. **Publications:** U.S. History Microforms in the MSU Libraries. **Remarks:** FAX: (517)353-9806.

★10331★
Michigan State University - Music Library (Mus)
East Lansing, MI 48824 Phone: (517)355-7660
Roseann Hammill, Mus.Libn.
Staff: Prof 1; Other 6. **Subjects:** Music - chamber, instrumental, symphonic, vocal, sacred, secular; opera. **Holdings:** 8278 recordings; 24,788 scores; VF drawers. **Services:** Interlibrary loan; copying; library open to the public. **Computerized Information Services:** BITNET (electronic mail service). **Special Indexes:** Indexes to vocal music and record collections. **Remarks:** FAX: (517)353-9806. Electronic mail address(es): 20676MUS@MSU (BITNET).

★10332★
Michigan State University - Office for International Networks in Education and Development - Library (Educ)
College of Education
238 Erickson Hall Phone: (517)355-5522
East Lansing, MI 48824-1034 Anne Schneller, Mgr.
Staff: Prof 4; Other 2. **Subjects:** Need for an impact of all forms of education on development; comparative education. **Holdings:** 5000 books, papers, reports, documents, and periodicals. **Subscriptions:** 1100 journals and other serials; 10 newspapers. **Services:** Copying; library open to the public. **Automated Operations:** Computerized cataloging. **Publications:** The INET Update, 3/year; annotated bibliographies; occasional papers series - all free upon request to development agencies and practitioners. **Staff:** Priscilla Martin.

★10333★
Michigan State University - Physics-Astronomy Library (Sci-Engr)
Rm. 229, Physics-Astronomy Bldg. Phone: (517)355-9704
East Lansing, MI 48824 Judith Matthews, Sci.Libn.
Founded: 1967. **Staff:** 2. **Subjects:** Physics, astronomy. **Holdings:** 33,000 volumes. **Subscriptions:** 299 journals and other serials. **Services:** Interlibrary loan; library open to the public. **Computerized Information Services:** BRS Information Technologies, DIALOG Information Services, STN International; BITNET (electronic mail service). **Remarks:** FAX: (517)355-6661. Electronic mail address(es): 20676PHY@MSU (BITNET).

★10334★
Michigan State University - Plant Research Laboratory - Library (Biol Sci)
Wilson Rd. Phone: (517)353-4333
East Lansing, MI 48824 Bradley Richardson, Libn.
Subjects: Biochemistry, biophysics, botany, cell biology, molecular biology, plant physiology. **Holdings:** 5000 volumes. **Subscriptions:** 50 journals and other serials. **Services:** Library not open to the public. **Remarks:** Laboratory is operated under contract to the U.S. Department of Energy.

★10335★
Michigan State University - Science Library (Med, Biol Sci)
East Lansing, MI 48824-1048 Phone: (517)355-2347
Carole S. Armstrong, Hd., Sci.Libs.
Founded: 1955. **Staff:** Prof 9; Other 4. **Subjects:** Medicine, biological sciences, agriculture, veterinary medicine, nursing, technology, human ecology, history of science. **Holdings:** 410,000 volumes. **Subscriptions:** 6000 journals and other serials. **Services:** Interlibrary loan; copying; library open to the public. **Computerized Information Services:** MEDLINE, BRS Information Technologies, STN International, DIALOG Information Services; Turfgrass Information File (internal database); BITNET (electronic mail service). **Remarks:** Library is a depository for U.S. Department of Agriculture documents. FAX: (517)353-9807. Electronic mail address(es): 20676CSA@MSU (BITNET). **Staff:** Martin Courtois, Database Coord.; Judy Coppola, Sci.Libn.; Mary Ann Tyrrell, Asst.Hd.; Julia Perez, Sci.Libn.; Peter Cookingham, Turfgrass Info.Ctr.; Jaunette Eaglesfield, Coll.Dev.Coord.; Judith Matthews, Sci.Libn.; Amy Blair, Sci.Libn.

★10336★
Michigan State University - Special Collections Library (Hist, Hum)
University Library Phone: (517)355-3770
East Lansing, MI 48824 Peter I. Berg, Hd, Spec.Coll.
Founded: 1960. **Staff:** Prof 2; Other 2. **Subjects:** American radicalism; history of French monarchy and revolution; Italian risorgimento history; English 18th century studies; Irish literary renaissance; American expatriate authors, comic art, western fiction; early works in criminology, fencing, agriculture, botany, entomology, toxicology, cookery. **Special Collections:** American Radicalism; veterinary medicine; apiculture; Charles and Ruth Schmitter Fencing Collection; Mary Reynolds Cookery Collection; Beatrice V. Grant Cookery Collection. **Holdings:** 215,000 volumes; facsimile editions of illuminated manuscripts. **Subscriptions:** 150 journals and newspapers. **Services:** Copying; library open to the public with required identification. **Remarks:** FAX: (517)353-9806.

★10337★
Michigan State University - Special Collections Library - Russel B. Nye Popular Culture Collections (Hum)
University Library Phone: (517)355-3770
East Lansing, MI 48824 Peter I. Berg, Hd., Spec.Coll.
Founded: 1970. **Staff:** Prof 1; Other 2. **Subjects:** Comic books; fiction - juvenile, detective, science fiction, western, romance; popular arts and entertainment; popular information. **Holdings:** 100,000 volumes. **Subscriptions:** 30 journals and other serials; 5 newspapers. **Services:** Copying; collections open to the public for reference use only with required identification. **Publications:** The Russel B. Nye Popular Culture Collection, A Descriptive Guide (pamphlet); The Comic Art Collection Newsletter. **Remarks:** FAX: (517)353-9806.

★10338★
Michigan State University - University Archives and Historical Collections (Hist)
East Lansing, MI 48824-1048 Phone: (517)355-2330
Dr. Frederick L. Honhart, Dir.
Founded: 1969. **Staff:** Prof 3; Other 3. **Subjects:** University archives, Michigan automobile industry, lumbering, agriculture and rural life, Civil War, Great Lakes, St. Lawrence Seaway. **Special Collections:** Samaritan Manuscripts (Biblical and liturgical texts, 1470-1927; 2 cubic feet); Ransom E. Olds papers (5 cubic feet); John Harvey Kellogg papers (26 cubic feet); Charles Hackley and Thomas Hume papers (83 cubic feet); John A. Hannah papers (100 cubic feet); Reo Motor Car Company Records, 1905-1961 (216 cubic feet); American Agri-Women Records, 1970-1981 (6 cubic feet); Clifton Wharton papers (28 cubic feet); Land Grant Research Collection (260 reels of microfilm); MSU-Vietnam Project papers, 1954-1962 (73 cubic feet). **Holdings:** 2500 cubic feet of manuscripts; 15,000 cubic feet of archival materials; 525 reels of microfilm; 50,000 photographs; 250,000 negatives, sound recordings, movie films, and other items. **Services:** Copying; archives open to the public. **Automated Operations:** Computerized cataloging, acquisitions, and records management. **Computerized Information Services:** Internal database; BITNET (electronic mail service). **Publications:** Guide to Michigan State University Archives and Historical Collections. **Special Catalogs:** Inventories available for processed collections. **Remarks:** FAX: (517)353-9806. Electronic mail address(es): 20669MMA@MSU (BITNET). **Staff:** John Sanford, Archv.; Dorothy Frye, Archv.

★10339★
Michigan State University - V.G. Grove Research Library of Mathematics-Statistics (Sci-Engr)
101-D Wells Hall Phone: (517)353-8852
East Lansing, MI 48824-1027 Dorothy Manderscheid, Math.Libn.
Founded: 1967. **Staff:** Prof 1; Other 1. **Subjects:** Pure and applied mathematics, statistics, probability. **Holdings:** 38,786 volumes; 160 reels of microfilm; 247 microfiche. **Subscriptions:** 358 journals. **Services:** Library open to the public. **Computerized Information Services:** BRS Information Technologies, DIALOG Information Services, STN International, MichNet; BITNET, InterNet (electronic mail services). Performs searches on fee basis. **Remarks:** FAX: (517)336-1526. Electronic mail address(es): 20676MTH@MSU (BITNET).

★10340★
Michigan State University - Veterinary Clinical Center Library (Med)
A 57 Veterinary Clinical Center Phone: (517)353-5099
East Lansing, MI 48823-1314 Leslie M. Behm, Libn. II
Staff: Prof 1; Other 1. **Subjects:** Clinical veterinary medicine. **Holdings:** 2486 volumes. **Subscriptions:** 76 journals and other serials. **Services:** Interlibrary loan; copying; SDI; library open to the public. **Computerized Information Services:** BRS Information Technologies, DIALOG Information Services, NLM, MEDLINE; BITNET (electronic mail service). Performs searches on fee basis. **Publications:** VCC Newsletter, bimonthly - to faculty and veterinary medical schools. **Remarks:** FAX: (517)336-1445. Electronic mail address(es): 20676VCC@MSU (BITNET).

★10341★
Michigan State University - W.K. Kellogg Biological Station - Walter F. Morofsky Memorial Library (Biol Sci)
3700 E. Gull Lake Dr. Phone: (616)671-2310
Hickory Corners, MI 49060-9516 Carolyn Hammarskjold, Libn. II
Founded: 1966. **Staff:** Prof 1; Other 1. **Subjects:** Aquatic and terrestrial ecology, limnology, botany, zoology, ornithology, entomology. **Holdings:** 5351 books; 4869 bound periodical volumes. **Subscriptions:** 157 journals and other serials. **Services:** Interlibrary loan; copying; library open to graduate students, faculty, and other researchers. **Computerized Information Services:** BRS Information Technologies, OCLC; BITNET (electronic mail service). Performs Searches. **Publications:** Kellogg Biological Station publications list. **Remarks:** FAX: (616)671-2351. Electronic mail address(es): HAMMARSK@MSUKBS (BITNET).

★10342★
Michigan Technological University - A.E. Seaman Mineralogical Museum - Library (Sci-Engr)
Houghton, MI 49931 Phone: (906)487-2572
Stanley J. Dyl, II, Cur.
Founded: 1983. **Staff:** 1. **Subjects:** Mineralogy, geology, Michigan history, chemistry, metallurgy, mining. **Special Collections:** Mineralogy of Michigan; Michigan Academy of Science, 1900-1961; Michigan Geological Survey, 1860-1958 (incomplete); Geologic Atlases, 1895-1916; maps. **Holdings:** 600 books; bound periodical volumes; Award Certificates, 1890 to present; reprints. **Services:** Library open to researchers and graduate students for reference use only. **Publications:** Information brochures - to tourists.

★10343★
Michigan Technological University - Ford Forestry Center - Library (Env-Cons)
Rt. 2, Box 736 Phone: (906)487-2031
L'Anse, MI 49946 J. Dougovito, Mgr.
Subjects: Forestry, botany, ecology. **Special Collections:** History of forests in the Upper Peninsula, Michigan. **Holdings:** 1000 books. **Services:** Library open to the public. **Publications:** Periodicals - available upon request.

★10344★
Michigan Technological University - J. Robert Van Pelt Library (Sci-Engr)
1400 Townsend Dr. Phone: (906)487-2500
Houghton, MI 49931-1295 Phyllis H. Johnson, Dir.
Founded: 1885. **Staff:** Prof 11; Other 23. **Subjects:** Business and engineering administration; forestry and wood products; biological sciences; computer science; humanities (scientific and technical communications); mathematical sciences; physics; social sciences; chemistry; geology; geophysics; engineering - chemical, civil, environmental, electrical, geological, mechanical, metallurgical and materials, mining; engineering mechanics. **Special Collections:** Spitzbergen Collection (75 books, maps, clippings, articles); Foundation Library Center Regional Collection; Copper Country Historical Collections; university archives; U.S. Geological Survey Topographic and Special Geologic Maps. **Holdings:** 305,209 volumes; 465,691 U.S. Government documents; 119,137 maps; 314,363 microforms. **Subscriptions:** 6709 journals and other serials; 35 newspapers. **Services:** Interlibrary loan; copying; library open to the public with first priority to students and staff. **Automated Operations:** Computerized public access catalog (FOCUS), cataloging, serials, circulation, and ILL. **Computerized Information Services:** DIALOG Information Services, INFOLINE, ORBIT Search Service, STN International, OCLC; BITNET (electronic mail service). Performs searches on fee basis. Contact Person: William G. Rowe, Coord.Ref.Serv./Libn., 487-2598. **Networks/Consortia:** Member of Michigan Library Consortium (MLC), Upper Peninsula Region of Library Cooperation (UPRLC). **Publications:** Library Quarterly Newsletter; Annual Report; brochures, guides, handbooks for instruction, publicity, documentation and reports. **Remarks:** Alternate telephone number(s): 487-2507. FAX: (906)487-2357. **Staff:** David H. Thomas, Hd., Tech.Serv.; Janet A. Dalquist, Hd., Coll.Mgt.; Theresa S. Spence, Coord./Archv.; June Hawthorne, Govt.Docs.Libn.; Janet Locatelli, Monograph Cat.Libn.; Patricia Moore, Ser.Libn.; Pauline Moore, Coord.Bibliog.Instr.; David Bezotte, Bibliog.Instr.Libn.; Emily Erickson, Archv./Libn.

Michigan Vocational Education Resource Center
See: **Michigan Center for Career & Technical Education** (10285)

Dr. Harold S. Mickley Research Library
See: **AKZO Chemicals Inc.** (178)

Micro Switch
See: **Honeywell, Inc. - Micro Switch** (7370)

★10345★
Microelectronics and Computer Technology Corp. - Information Center (Comp Sci)
3500 W. Balcones Center Dr. Phone: (512)338-3526
Austin, TX 78759 Jean K. Martin, Mgr.
Founded: 1984. **Staff:** Prof 2; Other 3.5. **Subjects:** Electronic packaging, software engineering, artificial intelligence, computer-aided design. **Holdings:** 5000 books; 4000 documents on microfilm; 3000 technical reports. **Subscriptions:** 400 journals and other serials; 5 newspapers. **Services:** Interlibrary loan; copying; SDI; library open to the public by appointment. **Computerized Information Services:** DIALOG Information Services, BRS Information Technologies, Dow Jones News/Retrieval; InterNet (electronic mail service). **Publications:** Periodical holdings. **Special Indexes:** Technical reports index. **Remarks:** FAX: (512)338-3600. **Staff:** David McLellan, Tech.Info.Spec.

Micronesian Area Research Center
See: **University of Guam** (18610)

Mid-American Solar Energy Complex Library
See: **Minneapolis Public Library & Information Center - Technology and Science Department** (10455)

★10346★
Mid-Coast Mental Health Center - Vincent Lathbury Library (Med)
12 Union St.
Box 526 Phone: (207)594-2541
Rockland, ME 04841 Elisabeth Slagle, Libn.
Founded: 1975. **Staff:** Prof 1. **Subjects:** Psychology, counseling, psychiatric treatment. **Holdings:** Figures not available. **Subscriptions:** 10 journals and other serials. **Services:** Copying; library open to mental health professionals and students.

★10347★
Mid-Continent Railway Historical Society, Inc. - Museum Library (Trans)
Walnut St. Phone: (608)522-4261
North Freedom, WI 53951 Donald W. Ginter, Cur.
Founded: 1959. **Staff:** 2. **Subjects:** History of the railroads in the upper Midwest, especially Wisconsin, 1880-1950. **Special Collections:** Technical drawings of railroad structures, steam locomotive assemblies, and rolling stock, especially those owned by the Chicago and North Western Railroad (5000); technical drawings of Fairbanks Morse Diesel Locomotives (10,000). **Holdings:** 2500 books; 125 bound periodical volumes; 31 linear feet of photographs of midwestern railroads in the early 1900s, personal pay records; railroad instruction books, manuals, trade catalogs. **Services:** Library open to the public by appointment.

★10348★
Mid-Maine Medical Center - Clara Hodgkins Memorial Health Sciences Library (Med)
North St. Phone: (207)872-1224
Waterville, ME 04901 Cora M. Damon, Libn.
Staff: Prof 1. **Subjects:** Medicine, allied health sciences. **Special Collections:** F.T. Hill Historical Collection. **Holdings:** 1000 books; 1000 bound periodical volumes. **Subscriptions:** 200 journals and other serials. **Services:** Interlibrary loan; copying; library open to the public for reference use only. **Computerized Information Services:** BRS Information Technologies, MEDLARS, DIALOG Information Services. **Networks/Consortia:** Member of Health Science Library and Information Cooperative of Maine (HSLIC).

★10349★
Mid-Valley Hospital - Physician's Library (Med)
1400 Main St. Phone: (717)489-7546
Peckville, PA 18452 Debra Hopkins, Dir., Med.Rec.
Staff: Prof 3; Other 2. **Subjects:** Medicine, orthopedic medicine, emergency medicine, surgery, infectious diseases, therapy. **Special Collections:** Orthopedic medicine. **Holdings:** 900 books; 398 audiotapes; 154 manuals; 4 AV cassettes. **Subscriptions:** 41 journals and other serials. **Services:** Library not open to the public.

Mid-West International Band and Orchestra Clinic Archives
See: **University of Maryland, College Park Libraries - Music Library** (18821)

★10350★
MidCon Management Corp. - Library (Energy)
701 E. 22nd St. Phone: (708)691-2687
Lombard, IL 60148 Elizabeth L. Ell, Chf.Libn.
Staff: Prof 2; Other 1. **Subjects:** Natural gas, energy, law. **Holdings:** 11,000 books. **Subscriptions:** 283 journals and other serials; 10 newspapers. **Services:** Interlibrary loan; copying; SDI; library open to the public by appointment. **Automated Operations:** Computerized cataloging, acquisitions, and serials. **Computerized Information Services:** DIALOG Information Services, Dow Jones News/Retrieval, Reuters Information Services (Canada) Limited, VU/TEXT Information Services, NewsNet, Inc., OCLC; A.G.A. GasNet (electronic mail service). **Networks/Consortia:** Member of American Gas Association - Library Services (AGA-LSC), ILLINET. **Remarks:** FAX: (708)691-3827. **Staff:** Anita V. Stratmanis, Supv.

A. Carter Middendorf Library
See: **National Aquarium in Baltimore** (11023)

Middle East Documentation Center
See: **University of Chicago - Middle Eastern Collection** (18454)

★10351★
Middle East Institute - George Camp Keiser Library (Area-Ethnic)
1761 N St., N.W. Phone: (202)785-0183
Washington, DC 20036 Christine E. Rourke, Libn.
Founded: 1946. **Staff:** Prof 1; Other 1. **Subjects:** North Africa and Middle East - history, politics, culture, Islam, economics, philosophy, language and literature, sociology. **Special Collections:** George Camp Keiser Collection of the art and architecture of the Middle East; Richard D. Robinson Collection of books and documents relating to the development of modern Turkey and Evan Wilson Turkish Library of current Turkish language materials; Oman and Arabian Peninsula Collection; rare book collection of 18th and 19th century travel accounts of Middle East and related Orientalia; Arabic language collection. **Holdings:** 20,000 books; 3000 bound periodical volumes; 15 VF cases; U.S. Government documents relating to the Middle East; 9 VF drawers of newsletters. **Subscriptions:** 300 journals and other serials. **Services:** Interlibrary loan; copying; library open to the public for reference use with borrowing privileges for members only. **Automated Operations:** Computerized cataloging and ILL. **Computerized Information Services:** OCLC. **Networks/Consortia:** Member of CAPCON Library Network. **Remarks:** FAX: (202)331-8861. Alternate telephone number(s): 785-0198.

Middle Georgia Archives
See: **Washington Memorial Library - Genealogy Department** (20017)

★10352★
Middle Georgia Historical Society - Archives (Hist)
935 High St. Phone: (912)743-3851
Macon, GA 31201 Katherine C. Oliver, Exec.Dir.
Subjects: Sidney Lanier, Macon, Georgia history. **Holdings:** Books. **Services:** Copying; archives open to the public for reference use only. **Computerized Information Services:** Internal database.

★10353★
Middle Tennessee State University - Center for Popular Music (Mus)
Box 41 Phone: (615)898-2449
Murfreesboro, TN 37132 Paul F. Wells, Dir.
Founded: 1985. **Staff:** Prof 4; Other 3. **Subjects:** American popular music, with emphases on rock and roll, vernacular religious music, and the southeastern U.S. **Special Collections:** Ray Avery Collection (1300 pieces of sheet music; 7.5 linear feet of manuscripts; 450 phonograph records; 1000 photographs); extensive holdings ofblack and white vernacular religious musc materials (including over 2700 tune books, gospel song books, and hymnals; unique audio and video tapes of historical and conteporary black

harmony singing; commercial recordings); 19th century popular instrumental tunebooks, tutors, and sheet music. **Holdings:** 8582 books; 41,000 pieces of sheet music; 55,500 sound recordings; 600 videotapes; 40 linear feet of manuscripts; 34 linear feet of vertical files; 4500 photographs. **Subscriptions:** 201 journals and other serials; 16 newspapers. **Services:** Copying; center open to the public with restrictions. **Automated Operations:** Computerized cataloging. **Computerized Information Services:** OCLC. **Networks/Consortia:** Member of SOLINET. **Publications:** American Vernacular Music, semiannual - by subscription; CPM Monograph Series (1 title published to date). **Staff:** Ellen Garrison, Archv.; Bruce Nemerov, Aud.Spec.

★10354★
Middlebury College - Music Library (Mus)
Middlebury, VT 05753-6133 Phone: (802)388-3711
Jerry McBride, Libn.
Founded: 1971. **Staff:** Prof 2; Other 7. **Subjects:** Music. **Holdings:** 1520 books; 15,866 sound recordings; 400 tapes; 61 video cassettes; 11,997 scores; 53 videodiscs. **Subscriptions:** 58 journals and other serials. **Services:** Interlibrary loan; copying; library open to the public. **Automated Operations:** Computerized cataloging, acquisitions, and circulation. **Computerized Information Services:** DIALOG Information Services, OCLC; BITNET (electronic mail service). **Networks/Consortia:** Member of NELINET, Inc. **Remarks:** FAX: (802)388-3467. Electronic mail address(es): MCBRIDE@MIDD (BITNET). **Staff:** Joy Pile, Cat.Libn.

★10355★
Middlebury Historical Society - Middlebury Academy Museum Library (Hist)
22 S. Academy St.
P.O. Box 198 Phone: (716)495-6582
Wyoming, NY 14591-0198 Mary Lester, Cur.
Founded: 1951. **Subjects:** Middlebury Academy. **Special Collections:** History of Town of Middlebury, Wyoming County, and environs; deeds and documents concerned with academy and locality, 1818 to present. **Holdings:** 920 volumes. **Services:** Library open to the public by appointment on a limited schedule.

★10356★
Middlesex County Historical Society - Library (Hist)
151 Main St. Phone: (203)346-0746
Middletown, CT 06457 Dione Longley, Dir.
Founded: 1901. **Staff:** Prof 1. **Subjects:** Connecticut history, genealogy, town histories. **Holdings:** 2000 books; archives; manuscripts; letters; notebooks; records. **Services:** Library open to the public by appointment only. **Publications:** Historical Observer (newsletter), bimonthly.

★10357★
Middlesex County Law Library (Law)
County Court House, 2nd Fl., E. Wing
1 Kennedy Sq. Phone: (201)745-3357
New Brunswick, NJ 08901 Betty Agin, Libn.
Staff: Prof 2. **Subjects:** Law. **Holdings:** 25,000 volumes. **Services:** Interlibrary loan; copying; library open to the public. **Computerized Information Services:** WESTLAW. **Networks/Consortia:** Member of Union Middlesex Regional Library Cooperative.

★10358★
Middlesex County Planning Board - Data Management & Technical Services Section - Library (Plan)
40 Livingston Ave. Phone: (201)745-3062
New Brunswick, NJ 08901 Louis Mattei, Supv. Data Mgmt.
Founded: 1972. **Staff:** Prof 1. **Subjects:** Natural resources and environment, land use and comprehensive planning, transportation, urban studies, planning. **Holdings:** 10,000 books; 25 periodical volumes; master plans and other data covering New Jersey counties and municipalities; 1980 census data and materials. **Subscriptions:** 15 journals and other serials. **Services:** Copying; library open to the public for reference use only by appointment.

★10359★
Middlesex Law Association - Library (Law)
80 Dundas St.
Box 5600
London, ON, Canada N6A 2P3 Phone: (519)679-7046
Founded: 1879. **Staff:** Prof 2. **Subjects:** Law. **Holdings:** 15,847 volumes. **Subscriptions:** 160 journals and other serials. **Services:** Library not open to the public. **Computerized Information Services:** QL Systems. **Publications:** Newsletter, monthly. **Remarks:** FAX: (519)672-5917. **Staff:** Gail Brown; Cynthia Simpson.

★10360★
Middlesex Law Library (Law)
Superior Court House
40 Thorndike St. Phone: (617)494-4148
Cambridge, MA 02141 Sandra Lindheimer, Lib.Dir.
Founded: 1815. **Staff:** Prof 1; Other 3. **Subjects:** State and federal law. **Holdings:** 90,000 books; 7500 bound periodical volumes. **Subscriptions:** 500 journals and other serials. **Services:** Interlibrary loan; copying; library open to the public. **Automated Operations:** Computerized cataloging. **Computerized Information Services:** WESTLAW, LEXIS, Veralex 2. **Remarks:** Part of the Massachusetts State Trial Court; Marnie Warner, Law Library Coordinator.

★10361★
Middlesex Memorial Hospital - Health Sciences Library (Med)
28 Crescent St. Phone: (203)344-6286
Middletown, CT 06457 Evelyn M. Breck, Dir.
Founded: 1972. **Staff:** Prof 2; Other 1. **Subjects:** Medicine, nursing. **Holdings:** 2000 books; 1400 bound periodical volumes; 6 VF drawers of clippings and catalogs. **Subscriptions:** 200 journals and other serials. **Services:** Interlibrary loan; copying; library open to the public for reference use only. **Computerized Information Services:** MEDLARS, BRS Information Technologies; CD-ROM. **Networks/Consortia:** Member of Connecticut Association of Health Science Libraries (CAHSL), North Atlantic Health Science Libraries (NAHSL), BHSL. **Remarks:** FAX: (203)347-2654. **Staff:** Sandra J. Chamberlain.

William S. Middleton Health Sciences Library
See: **University of Wisconsin--Madison - Center for Health Sciences Libraries** (19586)

William S. Middleton Memorial Veterans Hospital
See: **U.S. Dept. of Veterans Affairs (WI-Madison)** (17439)

★10362★
Middletown Psychiatric Center - Medical/Professional Library (Med)
141 Monhagen Ave.
Box 1453 Phone: (914)342-5511
Middletown, NY 10940 Judith A. McGrath, Sr.Libn.
Founded: 1880. **Staff:** Prof 1. **Subjects:** Psychiatry, medicine, nursing. **Special Collections:** Homeopathy. **Holdings:** 7300 books; 862 bound periodical volumes. **Subscriptions:** 90 journals and other serials. **Services:** Interlibrary loan; copying; SDI; library open to the public with restrictions. **Computerized Information Services:** BRS Information Technologies, MEDLARS; DOCLINE (electronic mail service). **Networks/Consortia:** Member of Southeastern New York Library Resources Council (SENYLRC), Health Information Libraries of Westchester (HILOW), National Network of Libraries of Medicine - Middle Atlantic Region. **Special Indexes:** Index of archival collection. **Remarks:** FAX: (914)342-5078.

★10363★
Middletown Regional Hospital - Ada I. Leonard Memorial Library (Med)
105 McKnight Dr. Phone: (513)422-2111
Middletown, OH 45044-8787 Catherine M. Nolte, Media Coord.
Founded: 1957. **Staff:** Prof 1. **Subjects:** Medicine, nursing, allied health sciences. **Holdings:** 1200 books; 150 periodical volumes; 500 AV programs; 500 health information pamphlets. **Subscriptions:** 150 journals and other serials. **Services:** Interlibrary loan; copying; library open to the public for reference use only. **Networks/Consortia:** Member of National Network of Libraries of Medicine - Greater Midwest Region.

★10364★
(Middletown) Times Herald-Record/Sunday Record - Information Retrieval Center (Publ)
40 Mulberry St. Phone: (914)343-2181
Middletown, NY 10940 Jo E. Richards
Staff: Prof 1; Other 1. **Subjects:** Newspaper reference topics. **Holdings:** 300 books; 100 reports; microfilm of newspaper (1956 to present); clips (1960s-1988); negatives (1960s to present); photographs. **Services:** Copying; library open to the public on a fee basis. **Computerized Information Services:** DIALOG Information Services, VU/TEXT Information Services, NEXIS, Dow Jones News/Retrieval; TH-R online (internal database). **Remarks:** FAX: (914)343-2170.

★10365★
Midland County Historical Society - Archives (Hist)
1801 W. St. Andrews Phone: (517)835-7401
Midland, MI 48640 Gary F. Skory, Dir.
Founded: 1952. **Staff:** Prof 2; Other 1. **Subjects:** Midland, Michigan history and genealogy. **Special Collections:** Dow Chemical Company history. **Holdings:** 1000 books; local newspapers, 1870 to present, on microfilm; maps; slides; pictures. **Services:** Copying; archives open to the public by permission.

★10366★
Midland County Public Library - Petroleum Department Library (Sci-Engr, Energy)
Box 1191 Phone: (915)683-2708
Midland, TX 79702 Norma Thurman, Petroleum Dept.Libn.
Founded: 1935. **Staff:** 4. **Subjects:** Geology; petroleum industry - technology, history, law, business, investment; hydrology; waste management. **Special Collections:** U.S. Geological Society guidebooks; U.S. Geological Survey publications; state surveys; Society of Petroleum Engineers Technical Papers (on microfiche); Geological Society of America Decade of North American Geology; Bibliography and Index of Geology. **Holdings:** 29,872 books; 1028 bound periodical volumes; 9171 maps; 350 VF materials; 6 file drawers of driller's logs; 17 shelves of Scout tickets; 400 reels of microfilm; 10,683 sheets of microfiche. **Subscriptions:** 63 journals and other serials. **Services:** Interlibrary loan; copying; library open to the public. **Automated Operations:** Computerized cataloging. **Computerized Information Services:** CD-ROM (GeoRef). Performs searches on fee basis. Contact Person: Norma Thurman. **Remarks:** FAX: (915)683-0813. Library located at 301 W. Missouri, Midland, TX.

★10367★
Midland Public Schools - Instructional Media Center (Educ)
600 E. Carpenter St. Phone: (517)839-2401
Midland, MI 48640 Gary Verlinde, Coord.
Staff: Prof 1; Other 10. **Subjects:** Education, children's literature, school district history. **Holdings:** 6130 books; 5000 other cataloged items; archival materials; videotapes; films. **Subscriptions:** 107 journals and other serials. **Services:** Interlibrary loan; copying; center open to the public. **Automated Operations:** Computerized circulation. **Networks/Consortia:** Member of Michigan Library Consortium (MLC), White Pine Library Cooperative. **Publications:** SPIRIT, quarterly - to district residents. **Special Catalogs:** List of teaching materials available for use in classroom. **Remarks:** FAX: (517)839-2501.

★10368★
Midland Walwyn Capital Inc. - Library (Bus-Fin)
Standard Life Bldg., 15th Fl.
121 King St., W. Phone: (416)369-7547
Toronto, ON, Canada M5H 3W6 Sonia Solomon, Libn.
Founded: 1977. **Staff:** Prof 1; Other 2. **Subjects:** Investments, economics, finance. **Holdings:** 400 books; 1750 corporation files; reports; clippings; periodicals; Statistics Canada publications. **Subscriptions:** 35 journals and other serials; 6 newspapers. **Services:** Interlibrary loan; library not open to the public. **Computerized Information Services:** Info Globe, The Financial Post DataGroup, Dow Jones News/Retrieval, DIALOG Information Services, Reuters. **Remarks:** FAX: (416)369-4004.

Midlands Center Library
See: **South Carolina (State) Department of Mental Retardation** (15406)

★10369★
Midlantic National Banks Inc. - Personal Trust Department - Library (Bus-Fin)
499 Thornall St., 8th Fl. Phone: (908)321-8387
Edison, NJ 08817 Frank Smith, Mgr.
Founded: 1971. **Staff:** Prof 1. **Subjects:** Business, finance, investments. **Holdings:** 300 books; files on 3500 companies, including annual reports and interim statements. **Subscriptions:** 18 journals and other serials. **Services:** Library not open to the public.

Midmarch Associates - Women Artists News/Midmarch Arts
See: **Women Artists News/Midmarch Arts** (20554)

★10370★
MidMichigan Regional Medical Center - Health Sciences Library (Med)
4005 Orchard Dr. Phone: (517)839-3262
Midland, MI 48670 Patricia Wolfgram, Mgr.
Founded: 1979. **Staff:** Prof 1; Other 4. **Subjects:** Medicine, nursing, family practice, allied health, management. **Holdings:** 2500 books; 9000 bound periodical volumes. **Subscriptions:** 400 journals and other serials. **Services:** Interlibrary loan; library not open to the public. **Computerized Information Services:** MEDLARS, BRS Information Technologies, DIALOG Information Services. **Networks/Consortia:** Member of National Network of Libraries of Medicine - Greater Midwest Region, Michigan Health Sciences Libraries Association (MHSLA), White Pine Library Cooperative, Michigan Library Consortium (MLC). **Remarks:** FAX: (517)631-1401.

★10371★
Midrasha College of Jewish Studies - Library (Area-Ethnic, Rel-Phil)
Box 2046 Phone: (313)354-3130
Southfield, MI 48037 Sarah Bell, Libn.
Founded: 1952. **Staff:** Prof 1. **Subjects:** Judaica, Hebraica, Israel, Zionism, Jewish and general education. **Holdings:** 38,000 books; 975 bound periodical volumes; 48 VF drawers; 45 pamphlet boxes. **Subscriptions:** 120 journals and other serials. **Services:** Interlibrary loan; copying; library open to the public. **Networks/Consortia:** Member of Wayne Oakland Library Federation (WOLF). **Remarks:** Alternate telephone number(s): (313)354-1050. Library located at 21550 W. Twelve Mile Rd., Southfield, MI 48076.

★10372★
Midstate College - Barbara Fields Memorial Library - Special Collections (Rec)
244 S.W. Jefferson Phone: (309)673-6365
Peoria, IL 61602 Christine Wadle, Libn.
Founded: 1976. **Staff:** Prof 1. **Subjects:** Travel, medical care, court reporting, paralegal. **Holdings:** 10,000 books; audiotapes; videotapes. **Subscriptions:** 80 journals and other serials; 4 newspapers. **Services:** Interlibrary loan; copying. **Networks/Consortia:** Member of ILLINET. **Remarks:** FAX: (309)673-5814.

★10373★
Midstate Technical College - Educational Resource Center - Library (Educ)
500 32nd St. N. Phone: (715)422-5469
Wisconsin Rapids, WI 54494 Harriet L. Broom, Dist.Libn.
Founded: 1967. **Staff:** Prof 1; Other 2. **Subjects:** Education - trade, industrial; business; home economics; nursing. **Holdings:** 19,300 books; 76 titles on microfilm; ERIC microfiche. **Subscriptions:** 400 journals and other serials; 18 newspapers. **Services:** Interlibrary loan; copying; library open to area residents. **Automated Operations:** Computerized circulation. **Computerized Information Services:** DIALOG Information Services. **Networks/Consortia:** Member of Wisconsin Valley Library Service (WVLS), Wisconsin VTAE Library Technical Information Exchange Network. **Remarks:** FAX: (715)422-5345.

★10374★
Midway Hospital - Health Sciences Library (Med)
1700 University Ave. Phone: (612)641-5607
St. Paul, MN 55104 Carol Windham, Libn.
Founded: 1907. **Staff:** Prof 1. **Subjects:** Medicine, nursing. **Holdings:** 1300 books; 72 bound periodical volumes; 25 films and filmstrips; 3500 slides; 65 transparencies; 75 audiotapes; 250 video cassettes. **Subscriptions:** 300 journals and other serials. **Services:** Interlibrary loan; library not open to the public. **Computerized Information Services:** MEDLINE. **Networks/Consortia:** Member of Twin Cities Biomedical Consortium (TCBC), National Network of Libraries of Medicine - Greater Midwest Region. **Remarks:** A HealthEast Hospital. FAX: (612)641-5601.

★10375★
Midwest Asia Center - Library
245 E. 6th St.
St. Paul, MN 55101
Defunct. Holdings absorbed by Northwestern Theological Seminary.

Midwest Center for American Music - Archives
See: **University of Missouri--Kansas City - Music Library** (18977)

★10376★
Midwest Historical & Genealogical Society, Inc. - Library (Hist)
Box 1121 Phone: (316)264-3611
Wichita, KS 67201 Mrs. Jerry Ann Stout, Libn.
Founded: 1966. **Staff:** Prof 4. **Subjects:** Genealogy, local history. **Special Collections:** Family histories; city directories; county histories; Sedgwick County marriage licences; Sedgwick County death records. **Holdings:** 4000 books; 680 bound periodical volumes; 135 Kansas cemetery references; 89 scrapbooks of obituaries and golden anniversaries; 110 reels of microfilm; 12 VF drawers. **Subscriptions:** 400 journals and other serials. **Services:** Copying; library open to the public with restrictions. **Special Indexes:** Surname indexes (card). **Remarks:** Library is located at 1203 N. Main, Wichita, KS. **Staff:** Sue McGuire, Asst.Libn.; Jean Wooten, Asst.Libn.

★10377★
Midwest Old Settlers and Threshers Association - Old Threshers Office - Library (Hist)
R.R. 1, Threshers Rd. Phone: (319)385-8937
Mount Pleasant, IA 52641 Lennis Moore, Adm.
Founded: 1976. **Staff:** Prof 4; Other 4. **Subjects:** Steam engines and trains, gas engines and tractors, agricultural and American history. **Special Collections:** Traction steam engines. **Holdings:** 1000 books; 100 manufacturers' reprints. **Services:** Interlibrary loan; copying; library open to the public. **Publications:** Threshers Chaff, quarterly; Threshers' Review, semiannual. **Staff:** Jamie Yaley, Chf., Info.Serv.

★10378★
Midwest Research Institute - Patterson Reference Library and Economics Reference Center (Sci-Engr)
425 Volker Blvd. Phone: (816)753-7600
Kansas City, MO 64110-2299 M. Lahey, Dir.
Founded: 1946. **Staff:** Prof 2; Other 3. **Subjects:** Biology, chemistry, chemical engineering, environmental sciences, economics, management science. **Special Collections:** Rural Economic Development; Traffic Systems and Safety. **Holdings:** 5000 volumes. **Subscriptions:** 500 journals and other serials. **Services:** Interlibrary loan; copying; center open to the public for reference use only and by appointment. **Automated Operations:** Computerized cataloging and ILL. **Computerized Information Services:** DIALOG Information Services, BRS Information Technologies, Chemical Abstracts Service (CAS), PFDS Online, NLM, Questel, OCLC, RLIN, CDC, Chemical Information Systems, Inc. (CIS), National Planning Data Corporation (NPDC). Performs searches on fee basis. **Networks/Consortia:** Member of Kansas City Metropolitan Library Network (KCMLN), Missouri Library Network Corp. (MLNC). **Remarks:** FAX: (816)753-8420.

★10379★
Midwestern Baptist Theological Seminary - Library (Rel-Phil)
5001 N. Oak St. Trafficway Phone: (816)453-4600
Kansas City, MO 64118 Joseph Craig Kubic, Lib.Dir.
Founded: 1958. **Staff:** Prof 1; Other 4. **Subjects:** Theology, Bible, biblical archeology, missions, Christian education, Christian ethics. **Holdings:** 85,000 books; 1819 bound periodical volumes; 229 sermon tapes; 315 filmstrips; 250 reels of microfilm of Early English Baptist materials. **Subscriptions:** 500 journals and other serials. **Services:** Interlibrary loan (fee); library open to the public for reference use only. **Automated Operations:** Computerized cataloging. **Computerized Information Services:** BRS Information Technologies. **Networks/Consortia:** Member of Missouri Library Network Corp. (MLNC), Kansas City Metropolitan Library Network (KCMLN), Kansas City Theological Library Association (KCTLA). **Remarks:** FAX: (816)455-3528.

★10380★
Mifflin County Historical Society - Library (Hist)
17 N. Main St. Phone: (717)242-1022
Lewistown, PA 17044 Jean A. Suloff, Libn.
Staff: 1. **Subjects:** History of central Pennsylvania and Mifflin County. **Holdings:** 1000 books; manuscripts; maps; pictures. **Services:** Library open to the public with restrictions. **Publications:** Nine pamphlet publications - for sale. **Remarks:** Library located at 1 W. Market St., Lewiston, PA 17044.

★10381★
Mifflin County Law Library (Law)
20 N. Wayne St., 3rd Fl.
Lewistown, PA 17044 Phone: (717)248-4613
Founded: 1890. **Subjects:** Law. **Special Collections:** Early English law cases. **Holdings:** 6500 books. **Remarks:** Alternate telephone number(s): (717)248-6733 (Commisioner's office).

M.C. Migel Memorial Library
See: **American Foundation for the Blind** (591)

★10382★
Migraine Foundation - Library
210-120 Carlton St.
Toronto, ON, Canada M5A 4K2
Founded: 1974. **Subjects:** Migraine, cluster headache. **Special Collections:** Migraine data retrieval file of 5000 citations, 1969 to present. **Holdings:** 300 books; 200 bound periodical volumes; clippings; documents; tapes; films. **Remarks:** Currently inactive.

★10383★
Migrant Legal Action Program - Library (Law)
2001 S St., N.W., Suite 310
Washington, DC 20009 Phone: (202)462-7744
Subjects: Migrant and seasonal farm workers - law, working conditions, education, housing, minimum wage, occupational safety, health standards, health benefits. **Holdings:** 5000 volumes.

★10384★
Leopoldo A. Miguez de Mello Research and Development Center - Library (Energy)
Ilha do Fundao, Quadra 7 Phone: 21 598-6110
21910 Rio de Janeiro, RJ, Brazil Marlize Tapajos de Souza, Hd.
Subjects: Petroleum, geology, chemistry, petrochemistry, materials technology. **Holdings:** 30,000 volumes. **Subscriptions:** 500 journals and other serials. **Services:** Interlibrary loan; copying; SDI; library open to graduates and researchers. **Computerized Information Services:** ORBIT Search Service, DIALOG Information Services, Questel, PFDS Online, STN International; PETROSIN (internal database). **Remarks:** FAX: 21 590-6643. Telex: 21 31219. Maintained by Petroleo Brasileiro, S.A. **Also Known As:** Centro de Pesquisas e Desenvolvimento Leopoldo A. Miguez de Mello.

Mila and Fontanals Institution
See: **Spain - Council for Scientific Research - Mila and Fontanals Institution** (15561)

J.B. Milam Library
See: **University of Tulsa - McFarlin Library** (19466)

★10385★
(Milan) USIS Library (Educ)
Via Bigli 11/A
I-20121 Milan, Italy
Remarks: Maintained or supported by the U.S. Information Agency. Focus is on materials that will assist peoples outside the United States to learn about the United States, its people, history, culture, political processes, and social milieux.

Milbank Memorial Library
See: **Teachers College** (16023)

★10386★
Milbank, Tweed, Hadley & Mc Cloy - Library (Law)
1 Chase Manhattan Plaza Phone: (212)530-5200
New York, NY 10005 Susan Hesse, Dir.
Staff: Prof 7; Other 6. **Subjects:** Law - general, taxation, corporations, banking, securities. **Special Collections:** Federal and New York State legislation. **Holdings:** 40,000 volumes; 55 drawers of microfiche; 11 drawers of microfilm. **Subscriptions:** 800 journals and other serials; 30 newspapers. **Services:** Interlibrary loan; library open to the public by appointment. **Automated Operations:** Computerized routing. **Computerized Information Services:** LEXIS, NEXIS, WESTLAW, LEGI-SLATE, New York Legislative Retrieval Systems (LRS), DIALOG Information Services, OCLC, Dow Jones News/Retrieval, Dun & Bradstreet Business Credit Services, RLIN, VU/TEXT Information Services, NewsNet, Inc., IDD Information Services, Inc. (IDDIS), Maxwell Macmillan Taxes Online, Orderline. **Publications:** Contents (newsletter), monthly. **Remarks:** FAX: (212)530-5219. **Staff:** Lucy Maret, Asst.Libn.; Henry Haywood, Ref.Serv.; Dwight Brown, Tax Libn.

General Nelson A. Miles Collection
See: **Westminster Historical Society - Library** (20329)

★10387★
Miles, Inc. - Agriculture Division - Animal Health Products - Library (Med)
Box 390 Phone: (913)268-2761
Shawnee Mission, KS 66201-0390 Ruth Lehman, Res. Data Asst.
Founded: 1974. **Staff:** Prof 1. **Subjects:** Veterinary medicine, animal health, pharmaceuticals. **Holdings:** 1000 books; 5000 bound periodical volumes; 12,000 technical reports; 100 company brochures; 50 annual reports. **Subscriptions:** 270 journals and other serials. **Services:** Interlibrary loan; library not open to the public. **Remarks:** Library located at 9009 W. 67th St., Merriam, KS 66201. FAX: (913)268-2541. **Formerly:** Mobay Corporation - Animal Health Division - Mobay Animal Health Library.

★10388★
Miles, Inc. - Cutter Library and Information Services (Med)
4th & Parker Sts.
Box 1986 Phone: (510)420-5187
Berkeley, CA 94701 H. Wen Ng, Libn.
Founded: 1940. **Staff:** Prof 3. **Subjects:** Biomedicine, biotechnology, pharmaceutical sciences. **Holdings:** 16,000 volumes. **Subscriptions:** 440 journals and other serials. **Services:** Interlibrary loan; library not open to the public. **Computerized Information Services:** MEDLINE, DIALOG Information Services; internal database. **Publications:** Acquisitions list, monthly; list of journals received, annual; Current Awareness: Biological Product File, weekly; AIDS File, weekly - all for internal distribution only. **Remarks:** FAX: (510)420-5558.

★10389★
Miles, Inc. - Libraries (Med)
400 Morgan Ln. Phone: (203)937-2594
West Haven, CT 06516 Georgia Scura, Mgr., Info.Rsrcs.
Staff: Prof 5; Other 2. **Subjects:** Medicine, biotechnology, pharmacology, business, biochemistry. **Holdings:** 2500 book titles; 4500 bound periodical volumes; 500 reels of microfilm. **Subscriptions:** 450 journals and other serials. **Services:** Interlibrary loan; copying. **Computerized Information Services:** DIALOG Information Services, BRS Information Technologies, NLM, STN International, ORBIT Search Service, Data-Star, Questel. . **Publications:** Information Services News. **Remarks:** Alternate telephone number(s): (203)937-2843. Contains the holdings of Miles, Inc. - Research Center and Miles, Inc. - Pharmaceutical Division. **Staff:** Beth Capp; Cynthia Geremia; Kathleen Howard; Cecilia Scully.

Miles, Inc. - Pharmaceutical Division - Library
See: **Miles, Inc. - Libraries** (10389)

Miles, Inc. - Research Center - Library
See: **Miles, Inc. - Libraries** (10389)

★10390★
Miles, Inc. - Research Library (Sci-Engr)
P.O. Box 500 Phone: (304)455-4400
New Martinsville, WV 26155 Kimberly S. Adkins, Libn.
Founded: 1955. **Staff:** Prof 1; Other 1. **Subjects:** Polymer and organic chemistry, chemical engineering. **Holdings:** 3000 books; 3000 bound periodical volumes; 3000 other cataloged items; 500 reels of microfilm. **Subscriptions:** 100 journals and other serials. **Services:** Interlibrary loan; copying; library open to the public with restrictions. **Computerized Information Services:** DIALOG Information Services, Chemical Abstracts Service (CAS), LEXIS, NEXIS. **Remarks:** FAX: (304)455-4400, ext. 2438. **Formerly:** Mobay Chemical Corporation.

★10391★
Miles, Inc. - Science and Business Information Services (Med, Biol Sci)
1127 Myrtle St.
P.O. Box 40 Phone: (219)264-6705
Elkhart, IN 46514-2282 James L. Mucha, Mgr.
Founded: 1940. **Staff:** Prof 8; Other 10. **Subjects:** Biotechnology, clinical medicine, chemistry, microbiology, business and management. **Holdings:** 15,000 books; 30,000 bound periodical volumes; 25 shelves of product literature; 8 drawers of microfilm; 13 VF drawers of company reports. **Subscriptions:** 533 journals and other serials; 7 newspapers. **Services:** Interlibrary loan; SDI; services open to the public by appointment. **Automated Operations:** Computerized cataloging, acquisitions, and serials. **Computerized Information Services:** DIALOG Information Services, PFDS Online, BRS Information Technologies, MEDLARS, NEXIS, Dow Jones News/Retrieval, OCLC, InvesText, NewsNet, Inc., LEXPAT, STN International, Data-Star; internal database. **Networks/Consortia:** Member of INCOLSA, Area 2 Library Services Authority (ALSA 2). **Publications:** Miles Media, irregular; Current Notice Product Literature, monthly; ADLIB, irregular - all for internal distribution only. **Remarks:** FAX: (219)262-6954. Telex: 258450. **Staff:** Charles A. Le Guern, Supv., Pubns.Serv.; Lisa A. Bourdon, Supv., Sci./Bus.Serv.; Alan K.E. Hagopian, Mgr., SBIS; Barry E. Galbraith, Ph.D., Sr.Assoc.Info.Sci.; Celeste M. Aaron, Info.Sci.; Nelson F. Weindling, Info.Sci.

★10392★
Miles & Stockbridge, Attorneys-At-Law - Library (Law)
10 Light St. Phone: (301)385-3671
Baltimore, MD 21202 Anna B. Cole, Libn.
Staff: Prof 2; Other 3. **Subjects:** Law. **Holdings:** 15,000 books; 150 bound periodical volumes. **Subscriptions:** 10 newspapers. **Services:** Interlibrary loan; copying; SDI; library open to serious patrons by appointment. **Automated Operations:** Computerized cataloging, acquisitions, and serials. **Computerized Information Services:** LEXIS, NEXIS, WESTLAW. **Remarks:** FAX: (301)385-3700.

★10393★
Miles/Technicon - Library (Med, Sci-Engr, Comp Sci)
511 Benedict Ave. Phone: (914)524-2338
Tarrytown, NY 10591 Gitta Benglas, Mgr. of Lib.Rsrcs. & Serv.
Founded: 1962. **Staff:** Prof 2. **Subjects:** Medicine, chemistry, computer science. **Holdings:** 15,000 books; laboratory notebooks; dissertations; reports; microfilm; microfiche; 30 VF drawers; 200 audiotapes. **Subscriptions:** 320 journals and other serials. **Services:** Interlibrary loan; library not open to the public. **Automated Operations:** Computerized acquisitions and serials. **Computerized Information Services:** DIALOG Information Services. **Remarks:** FAX: (914)524-3075. **Formerly:** Technicon Instruments Corporation - Library.

★10394★
Milford Historical Society - Historical Museum Reference Room (Hist)
124 E. Commerce St. Phone: (313)685-7308
Milford, MI 48381 Mary Lou Gharrity, Musm.Dir.
Subjects: Milford genealogy and history. **Special Collections:** The Milford Times (weekly newspaper since 1871; on microfilm). **Holdings:** Oak Grove Cemetery records; early family genealogies; Civil War records. **Services:**: Copying; room open to the public with restrictions.

★10395★
Milford Hospital - Health Sciences Library (Med)
2047 Bridgeport Ave. Phone: (203)876-4006
Milford, CT 06460 Patricia Westbrook, Libn.
Staff: Prof 1. **Subjects:** Medicine, nursing, and allied health sciences. **Holdings:** 1280 books; 2100 bound periodical volumes; 800 AV items. **Subscriptions:** 97 journals and other serials. **Services:** Interlibrary loan; copying; library open to the public for reference use only. **Computerized Information Services:** MEDLARS. **Publications:** Focus on Education (managerial newsletter) - for internal distribution only.

★10396★
Milford Memorial Hospital, Inc. - Medical Library (Med)
Clark Ave.
P.O. Box 199 Phone: (302)424-5623
Milford, DE 19963 Gwendolyn Elliott, Med.Libn.
Staff: 1. **Subjects:** Clinical medicine, clinical nursing. **Holdings:** 450 books. **Subscriptions:** 59 journals and other serials. **Services:** Copying; library open to the public for reference use only. **Computerized Information Services:** MEDLARS.

Elizabeth Milholland Library
See: **Highland Presbyterian Church** (7201)

The Military College of South Carolina
See: **Citadel Military College of South Carolina - Archives/Museum** (3719)

Military Order of the Loyal Legion of the United States
See: **The Civil War Library & Museum** (3747)

Military Order of the Loyal Legion of the United States - Massachusetts Commandery Library
See: **U.S. Army - Military History Institute** (16995)

Milkpark Research
See: **Milpark Drilling Fluids** (10415)

Alden E. Miller Law Library
See: **Clackamas County, Oregon - Alden E. Miller Law Library** (3748)

Anna Miller Museum
See: **Weston County Historical Society** (20341)

★10397★
Miller Brewing Company - Scientific and Technical Information Facility (Food-Bev)
3939 W. Highland Blvd. Phone: (414)931-3640
Milwaukee, WI 53201 Joanne L. Schwarz, Hd.Libn.
Founded: 1979. **Staff:** Prof 1; Other 2. **Subjects:** Brewing, chemistry, microbiology, chemical engineering, genetics, enzymology. **Special Collections:** Brewing science. **Holdings:** 1200 books; 1500 bound periodical volumes; 10,000 patents; 80 reels of microfilm; 2000 microfiche; 600 research reports. **Subscriptions:** 190 journals and other serials. **Services:** Interlibrary loan; copying; facility open to the public with restrictions. **Automated Operations:** Computerized cataloging and circulation. **Computerized Information Services:** PFDS Online, DIALOG Information Services, RLIN, BRS Information Technologies, MEDLINE, STN International; internal database. **Networks/Consortia:** Member of Research Libraries Information Network (RLIN). **Publications:** Research Bulletin, monthly; Patent and Translation Alert Bulletin; Checklist of current information, weekly. **Remarks:** FAX: (414)931-2506.

★10398★
Miller, Canfield, Paddock & Stone - Library (Law)
150 W. Jefferson, Suite 2500 Phone: (313)963-6420
Detroit, MI 48226 Katherine A. Green, Dir., Info.Serv.
Staff: Prof 3. **Subjects:** Law - federal, state, municipal, tax, banking, labor, education, products liability, corporate, commercial, employee benefits, bankruptcy, international trade, insurance. **Holdings:** 30,000 books; 55 bound periodical volumes; 8 drawers of microfiche. **Subscriptions:** 1200 journals and other serials; 10 newspapers. **Services:** Interlibrary loan; library not open to the public. **Computerized Information Services:** LEXIS, NEXIS, DIALOG Information Services, VU/TEXT Information Services, WESTLAW. Performs searches on fee basis. **Networks/Consortia:** Member of Michigan Library Consortium (MLC). **Remarks:** FAX: (313)496-8452; (313)496-8451. Telex: 810 221 5007 MILLCNFLD DET. **Staff:** Julie Marshall, Libn.; Penelope Damore, Libn.

★10399★
Miller-Dwan Medical Center - Tilderquist Memorial Medical Library (Med)
502 E. 2nd St. Phone: (218)720-1362
Duluth, MN 55805 Annelie Sober, Dir., Med.Lib.
Founded: 1973. **Staff:** Prof 1. **Subjects:** Medicine, allied health sciences. **Holdings:** 790 books; 2070 bound periodical volumes. **Subscriptions:** 165 journals and other serials. **Services:** Interlibrary loan; copying; library open to the public by request. **Computerized Information Services:** MEDLINE, BRS Information Technologies; DOCLINE (electronic mail service). Performs searches on fee basis. **Networks/Consortia:** Member of Arrowhead Professional Libraries Association (APLA), National Network of Libraries of Medicine - Greater Midwest Region, North Country Library Cooperative (NCLC). **Remarks:** FAX: (218)720-1397.

E. Kirkbride Miller Art Research Library
See: **The Baltimore Museum of Art** (1452)

Elisabeth C. Miller Horticulture Library
See: **Center for Urban Horticulture** (3312)

Emil Miller Memorial Library
See: **Antique Doorknob Collectors of America** (902)

Harold A. Miller Library
See: **Stanford University - Hopkins Marine Station** (15651)

Henry Miller Collection
See: **Brooklyn Public Library - Languages and Literature Division** (2244)

★10400★
Herman Miller, Inc. - Business Communications Center (Bus-Fin)
8500 Byron Rd. Phone: (616)772-3629
Zeeland, MI 49464 Linda M. McFadden, Mgr., Bus.Commun.Ctr.
Founded: 1977. **Staff:** Prof 2; Other 2. **Subjects:** Business, management, marketing, interior design. **Special Collections:** Corporate Archives; Designer/Product Archives (16 VF drawers); Eames Film Collection (55 films). **Holdings:** Figures not available. **Services:** Center not open to the public. **Computerized Information Services:** DIALOG Information Services, WILSONLINE, Dow Jones News/Retrieval; internal database. **Remarks:** FAX: (616)772-5385. **Staff:** Linda Folland, Archv.; Monique Timmer, AV Coord.

★10401★
Herman Miller Research Library (Med)
c/o Shelly Brown
8500 Byron Ave. Phone: (616)772-3489
Zeeland, MI 49464 Dallas Moore, Libn.
Founded: 1987. **Staff:** Prof 1. **Subjects:** Gerontology, rehabilitation. **Holdings:** 200 books. **Subscriptions:** 82 journals and other serials. **Services:** Interlibrary loan; library not open to the public. **Computerized Information Services:** DIALOG Information Services. **Remarks:** FAX: (313)994-3050. **Formerly:** Herman Miller Research Corporation - Library, located in Ann Arbor, MI.

Hugh Thomas Miller Rare Book Room
See: **Butler University - Irwin Library - Hugh Thomas Miller Rare Book Room** (2416)

Ira Miller Memorial Library
See: **Michigan Psychoanalytic Institute** (10294)

J. Cloyd Miller Library
See: **Western New Mexico University** (20282)

Jean Miller Library
See: **Riverside Presbyterian Church** (13952)

Miller Library
See: **Colby College** (3872)

Miller Library
See: **Grand Rapids Baptist College & Seminary** (6633)

Miller Library
See: **McPherson College** (9963)

★10402★
Miller, Nash, Wiener, Hager & Carlsen - Library (Law)
111 S.W. Fifth Ave. Phone: (503)224-5858
Portland, OR 97204-3699 Leslie Meserve, Dir. of Info.Serv.
Staff: Prof 2. **Subjects:** Law. **Holdings:** 24,000 volumes. **Subscriptions:** 400 journals and other serials. **Services:** Interlibrary loan; library not open to the public. **Automated Operations:** Computerized cataloging. **Computerized Information Services:** LEXIS, NEXIS, DIALOG Information Services, WILSONLINE, DataTimes, VU/TEXT Information Services; MCI Mail (electronic mail service). **Remarks:** FAX: (503)224-0155. Maintains a branch office in Seattle, WA. **Staff:** Marcia Anderson, Ref.Libn.

Miller Nichols Library
See: **University of Missouri--Kansas City - Miller Nichols Library** (18976)

Ralph W. Miller Golf Library/Museum
See: **City of Industry** (3740)

Samuel F. Miller House Museum
See: **Lee County Iowa Historical Society** (9040)

Steve Miller Library of American Archaeology
See: **World Archeological Society - Information Center** (20607)

★10403★
Millersville University - Helen A. Ganser Library - Special Collections (Hum)
Millersville, PA 17551 Phone: (717)872-3624
Robert E. Coley, Univ.Archv./Spec.Coll.Libn.
Founded: 1855. **Staff:** Prof 1; Other 1. **Special Collections:** Local History and Culture Collection (5000 titles); Wickersham Pedagogical Collection (3500 titles); Pennsylvania Imprint Collection (2150 titles); Rare Book Collection (1725 titles); University Archives (3500 linear feet; 450 volumes); Archives of the International Technological Education Association (340 linear feet), Pennsylvania Industrial Arts Association (microfilm), Pennsylvania Sociological Association (3 linear feet), and Pennsylvania State Modern Language Association (9 linear feet); Leo Ascher Center for the Study of Operetta Music (4000 items); Davison Collection on Weaving and Textiles (450 volumes); Amish and Mennonites (1300 titles); Carl Van Vechten Memorial Collection of Afro-American Arts and Letters (900 items). **Holdings:** 16,000 books; 600 manuscripts; 3600 linear feet of archives; 100 microfiche; 400 reels of microfilm. **Subscriptions:** 15 journals and other serials. **Services:** Copying; collections open to the public. **Automated Operations:** Computerized cataloging. **Computerized Information Services:** DIALOG Information Services, OCLC; Dynix (internal database). **Networks/Consortia:** Member of PALINET, Associated College Libraries of Central Pennsylvania (ACLCP). **Special Indexes:** Indices to the various collections maintained in department. **Remarks:** FAX: (717)872-3854.

Millikan Library
See: **California Institute of Technology** (2492)

★10404★
Milliken Research Corporation - Research Library (Sci-Engr)
Box 5521 Phone: (803)573-2340
Spartanburg, SC 29304 Trudy W. Craven, Lib.Mgr.
Founded: 1960. **Staff:** Prof 2; Other 2. **Subjects:** Textiles, chemistry, business. **Holdings:** 10,000 books; 3500 bound periodical volumes; 400 films. **Subscriptions:** 400 journals and other serials; 10 newspapers. **Services:** Interlibrary loan; copying; SDI; library open to the public by appointment. **Automated Operations:** Computerized cataloging. **Computerized Information Services:** DIALOG Information Services, PFDS Online, MEDLARS, STN International, OCLC. **Networks/Consortia:** Member of SOLINET. **Remarks:** FAX: (803)573-2769.

Roger Milliken Textile Library
See: **Institute of Textile Technology - Textile Information Services** (7984)

★10405★
Millikin University - Staley Library - Special Collections (Hum)
1184 W. Main St. Phone: (217)424-6214
Decatur, IL 62522 Dr. Charles E. Hale, Lib.Dir.
Founded: 1902. **Staff:** 11.5. **Subjects:** English and American literature, history, religion, and music. **Holdings:** Carlyle S. Baer Bookplate Collection (1000 bookplates and allied publications); Alice-in-Wonderland Collection; Stephen Decatur Collection. **Subscriptions:** 1000 journals and other serials; 15 newspapers. **Services:** Interlibrary loan; copying; collections open to the public for reference use only. **Automated Operations:** Computerized cataloging, serials, circulation, acquisitions, and ILL. **Computerized Information Services:** DIALOG Information Services, Statewide Library Computer System, OCLC. **Networks/Consortia:** Member of Sangamon Valley Academic Library Consortium (SVALC), Rolling Prairie Library System (RPLS), ILLINET. **Remarks:** FAX: (217)424-3992. **Staff:** Virginia McQuistion, Hd. of Pub.Serv., Ref.Libn.; Gwenn Neville, Ref.Libn.; Carl Muma, Media Ctr.Dir.

★10406★
Million Dollar Round Table - Information Services (Bus-Fin)
325 Touhy Phone: (708)692-MDRT
Park Ridge, IL 60068 William Morreal, Dir.
Staff: Prof 1. **Subjects:** Life insurance. **Holdings:** 300 books; 148 bound periodical volumes; 128 binders of National Life Insurance Associations tapes. **Subscriptions:** 59 journals and other serials. **Services:** Services not open to the public. **Special Indexes:** Index to Proceedings.

★10407★
Millipore Corporation - Information Center (Biol Sci)
80 Ashby Rd. Phone: (617)275-9200
Bedford, MA 01730 Susan B. Mansur, Mgr.
Founded: 1970. **Staff:** Prof 3; Other 2. **Subjects:** Microbiology, health and environmental sciences, membrane technology, pharmaceutical technology, analytical chemistry, filtration and separation technology. **Holdings:** 2000 books; 10,000 unbound journals and newsletters; 235 microforms. **Subscriptions:** 200 journals and other serials. **Services:** Interlibrary loan; center not open to the public. **Automated Operations:** Computerized public access catalog, cataloging, and circulation. **Computerized Information Services:** DIALOG Information Services, NEXIS, Dow Jones News/Retrieval, OCLC, Data-Star, STN International. **Networks/Consortia:** Member of NELINET, Inc. **Remarks:** FAX: (617)275-5550. **Staff:** Susanna Arthur, Libn.; Mari Ferentinos, Libn.

★10408★
Millipore Corporation - Waters Chromatography Division - Information Resource Center (Sci-Engr)
34 Maple St. Phone: (617)478-2000
Milford, MA 01757 Carla J. Clayton, Mgr., Tech.Info.Serv.
Founded: 1978. **Staff:** Prof 1; Other 1. **Subjects:** Chemistry, engineering. **Special Collections:** High performance liquid chromatography. **Holdings:** 2000 books; 400 bound periodical volumes. **Subscriptions:** 175 journals and other serials. **Services:** Interlibrary loan; copying; center open to the public with restrictions. **Automated Operations:** Computerized cataloging. **Computerized Information Services:** DIALOG Information Services, STN International, OCLC, NEXIS. **Networks/Consortia:** Member of NELINET, Inc. **Staff:** Grace Lavallee, Asst.Libn.

★10409★
Mills College - F.W. Olin Library - Special Collections (Hum)
5000 MacArthur Blvd. Phone: (510)430-2047
Oakland, CA 94613 Renee Jadushlever, Spec.Coll.Libn.
Founded: 1852. **Staff:** Prof 1. **Subjects:** English and American literature, printing, dance, Shakespeare, women's history, bookbinding. **Special Collections:** Albert M. Bender Collection; Jane Bourne Parton Collection; Elias Olan James Collection; Mills College Archives. **Holdings:** 12,000 books. **Services:** Copying; collections open to the public for reference use only. **Automated Operations:** Computerized cataloging and acquisitions. **Computerized Information Services:** DIALOG Information Services, RLIN. **Networks/Consortia:** Member of CLASS, Bay Area Library and Information Network. **Remarks:** FAX: (510)430-3314.

Mills Music Library
See: **University of Wisconsin--Madison - Mills Music Library** (19610)

★10410★
Mills-Peninsula Hospitals - Health Sciences Library (Med)
1783 El Camino Real Phone: (415)696-5621
Burlingame, CA 94010 Sally C. Chu, Chf., Lib.Serv.
Founded: 1963. **Staff:** Prof 1. **Subjects:** Medicine. **Holdings:** 1400 books; 3000 bound periodical volumes. **Subscriptions:** 289 journals and other serials. **Services:** Interlibrary loan; copying; library open to the public for reference use only. **Computerized Information Services:** MEDLARS. Performs searches on fee basis. **Networks/Consortia:** Member of Northern California and Nevada Medical Library Group (NCNMLG), Peninsula Library System (PLS), Peninsula Hospital Libraries Information Network (PHLIN). **Remarks:** FAX: (415)696-5484. A branch library is maintained at Mills Hospital - Medical Library, 100 S. San Mateo Dr., San Mateo, CA 94401; telephone: (415)696-4621.

★10411★
Mills-Peninsula Hospitals - Mills Hospital - Medical Library (Med)
100 S. San Mateo Dr. Phone: (415)696-4621
San Mateo, CA 94401 Sally Chu, Chf. of Lib.Serv.
Staff: Prof 1; Other 1. **Subjects:** Medicine, nursing. **Holdings:** 1000 books; 2000 bound periodical volumes. **Subscriptions:** 152 journals and other serials. **Services:** Interlibrary loan; copying; SDI; library open to the public with permission. **Automated Operations:** Computerized serials. **Computerized Information Services:** MEDLARS; internal database; DOCLINE (electronic mail service). Performs searches on fee basis. **Networks/Consortia:** Member of Northern California and Nevada Medical Library Group (NCNMLG), Peninsula Hospital Libraries Information Network (PHLIN), Peninsula Library System (PLS). **Remarks:** Alternate telephone number(s): 696-5621. FAX: (415)696-4484.

Randall V. Mills Archives of Northwest Folklore
See: **University of Oregon - Department of English** (19146)

★10412★
Millsaps College - Millsaps-Wilson Library - J.B. Cain Archives of Mississippi Methodism and Millsaps College (Rel-Phil)
Jackson, MS 39210 Phone: (601)974-1077
Gerry Reiff, Coll.Archv.
Founded: 1982. **Staff:** 1. **Subjects:** Mississippi Methodist history, Millsaps College. **Special Collections:** New Orleans Christian Advocate, 1850-1946 (indexed for Mississippi); Mississippi Methodist Advocate, 1947 to present; Mississippi Conference Journals, 1830 to present; North Mississippi Conference Journals, 1870 to present; Journals of the Upper Mississippi Conference, 1913, 1930-1972; Journals of the Mississippi Conference, Methodist Protestant Church, 1899-1938; Journals of the North Mississippi Conference, Methodist Protestant Church, 1867-1930; papers of Bishop Charles B. Galloway, William Winans, Lambuth family, and Major Reuben W. Millsaps; history of Mississippi Conference; history of North Mississippi Conference; history of United Methodist women in the Mississippi Conference; biographies of religious leaders; college administrative papers. **Holdings:** 1500 books; 500 bound periodical volumes. **Services:** Copying; archives open to the public on a limited schedule. **Computerized Information Services:** DIALOG Information Services, STN International; Bibliofile (internal database). **Remarks:** FAX: (601)974-1082.

James M. Milne Library
See: **State University College at Oneonta** (15710)

Milne Library
See: **State University College at Geneseo - College Libraries** (15707)

Milner Education Centre
See: **Langley School District** (8943)

★10413★
Milner Fenerty - Library (Law)
3000 Western Canadian Pl.
700 9th Ave., S.W. Phone: (403)268-7055
Calgary, AB, Canada T2P 4A7 Anil V. Tiwari, Libn.
Founded: 1912. **Staff:** 3. **Subjects:** Law. **Holdings:** 2100 books; 600 bound periodical volumes; 9400 reports. **Subscriptions:** 150 journals and other serials; 3 newspapers. **Services:** Interlibrary loan; copying; library not open to the public. **Automated Operations:** INMAGIC. **Computerized Information Services:** QL Systems, WESTLAW, CAN/LAW, LEXIS, Info Globe, Infomart Online. **Remarks:** FAX: (403)262-9105. **Formed by the merger of:** Fenerty, Robertson, Fraser & Hatch and Milner & Steer. **Staff:** Yvonne Barkley; Sheila Hamilton.

★10414★
Milner/Fenerty Barristers & Solicitors - Law Library (Law)
2900 Manulife Place
10180 101st St. Phone: (403)423-7370
Edmonton, AB, Canada T5J 3V5 Muriel G. Lefebvre, Hd.Libn.
Staff: Prof 2; Other 2. **Subjects:** Law. **Holdings:** 2000 textbooks; 150 periodical titles; 200 law report titles; 75 loose-leaf services; 35 digests/encyclopedias and forms titles; federal statutes and regulations. **Subscriptions:** 3 newspapers. **Services:** Interlibrary loan; library not open to the public. **Automated Operations:** Computerized cataloging. **Computerized Information Services:** QL Systems, CAN/LAW, WESTLAW, Info Globe, Infomart Online, LEXIS. **Remarks:** FAX: (403)423-7276. **Formerly:** Milner & Steer, Barristers & Solicitors.

Milner Library
See: **Illinois State University** (7707)

Milner & Steer, Barristers & Solicitors
See: **Milner/Fenerty Barristers & Solicitors** (10414)

★10415★
Milpark Drilling Fluids - Research Library
7000 Hollister Ln., Suite 300 Phone: (713)744-3802
Houston, TX 77040-3833 Charlotte Miller, Libn.
Founded: 1945. **Holdings:** 2000 books; bound periodical volumes. **Subscriptions:** 20 journals and other serials. **Services:** Library not open to the public. **Remarks:** FAX: (713)744-3809.

John Milton Society For the Blind in Canada Archives
See: **Baptist Convention of Ontario and Quebec - Canadian Baptist Archives** (1498)

★10416★
Milwaukee Academy of Medicine - Library (Med)
8701 Watertown Plank Rd.
Box 26509 Phone: (414)257-8249
Milwaukee, WI 53226 Warren Smirl, M.D., Libn.
Founded: 1886. **Staff:** Prof 1. **Subjects:** Medical history. **Special Collections:** Horace Manchester Brown Collection (348 volumes); Sydenham Collection (152 volumes); Index Medicus and Predecessor titles (190 volumes). **Holdings:** 1532 books. **Services:** Library open to physicians.

★10417★
Milwaukee Area Technical College - Rasche Memorial Library (Educ)
1015 N. 6th St. Phone: (414)278-6205
Milwaukee, WI 53203 Richard E. Meerdink, Libn.
Founded: 1937. **Staff:** Prof 2; Other 9. **Subjects:** Applied science and technology, graphic arts, health sciences. **Special Collections:** Voigt Graphic Arts Collection. **Holdings:** 50,000 volumes. **Subscriptions:** 400 journals and other serials; 15 newspapers. **Services:** Interlibrary loan; copying; library open to the public. **Automated Operations:** Computerized public access catalog. **Computerized Information Services:** CD-ROMs. **Networks/Consortia:** Member of Library Council of Metropolitan Milwaukee, Inc. (LCOMM). **Remarks:** FAX: (414)278-6503. **Staff:** Mary E. Landeck, Pub.Serv.Libn.

★10418★
Milwaukee Area Technical College - South Campus Library (Educ, Sci-Engr)
6665 S. Howell Ave. Phone: (414)768-5720
Oak Creek, WI 53154 Elizabeth Conrad, Lib.Techn.
Founded: 1976. **Staff:** 2.5. **Subjects:** Applied science and technology. **Special Collections:** Heating and air conditioning; automotive service. **Holdings:** 11,738 volumes; 19 drawers of pamphlets. **Subscriptions:** 188 journals and other serials; 12 newspapers. **Services:** Interlibrary loan; copying; library open to the public with restrictions on circulation. **Remarks:** FAX: (414)768-1054.

★10419★
Milwaukee Art Museum - Library (Art)
750 N. Lincoln Memorial Dr. Phone: (414)224-3270
Milwaukee, WI 53202 Suzy Weisman, Libn.
Founded: 1962. **Staff:** Prof 1; Other 2. **Subjects:** Visual arts in all forms, including painting, graphic arts, sculpture, drawing and design, photography. **Special Collections:** Art museum exhibition catalogs and publications; sales catalogs from galleries; art auction catalogs and price lists. **Holdings:** 22,000 books and exhibition catalogs; 66 bound periodical volumes; 68 VF drawers; 109 videotapes; 47 films; 28 slide sets; 1022 audiotapes; 42 slide/tape programs; archival materials. **Subscriptions:** 60 journals and other serials. **Services:** Interlibrary loan (limited); copying; library open to Art Museum members. **Remarks:** FAX: (414)271-7588.

★10420★
Milwaukee County Board of Supervisors - Research Library (Law)
901 N. 9th St., Rm. 203
Milwaukee, WI 53233 Phone: (414)278-5263
Founded: 1972. **Staff:** 1. **Subjects:** Public welfare, state legislative statutes and codes, economy. **Holdings:** 300 books; 15 bound periodical volumes; county board proceedings; county departmental documents; state legislative documents; local government ordnances and documents. **Subscriptions:** 20 journals and other serials; 6 newspapers. **Services:** Library open to the public with restrictions. **Computerized Information Services:** Internal database.

★10421★
Milwaukee County Historical Society - Library and Archives (Hist)
910 N. Old World Third St. Phone: (414)273-8288
Milwaukee, WI 53203 Judith A. Simonsen, Cur., Res.Coll.
Founded: 1935. **Staff:** Prof 2. **Subjects:** History of Milwaukee County, history of socialist movements, Germans and other immigrant groups. **Holdings:** 5200 books; 75 bound periodical volumes; 60 bound volumes of government proceedings; manuscript collection; iconographic material. **Subscriptions:** 20 journals and other serials; 12 newspapers. **Services:** Copying; library open to the public on a fee basis. **Publications:** Milwaukee History; Research Guide 1, German-American Studies; Research Guide 2, Bibliography of Milwaukee History; Historical Resources in Milwaukee Area Archives.

★10422★
Milwaukee County Law Library (Law)
Courthouse
901 N. 9th St., Rm. 307 Phone: (414)278-4321
Milwaukee, WI 53233 Divinia J. Astraquillo, Law Libn.
Founded: 1932. **Staff:** Prof 3; Other 3. **Subjects:** Law, county government. **Special Collections:** Briefs of cases argued before the Wisconsin Supreme Court from volume 1, Wisconsin Reports, 1st series to present. **Holdings:** 80,274 volumes; 4817 bound periodical volumes; 15 VF drawers of newspaper clippings; 228 reels of microfilm; 38,831 microfiche. **Subscriptions:** 2959 journals and other serials. **Services:** Copying; library open to the public. **Computerized Information Services:** WESTLAW. **Networks/Consortia:** Member of Library Council of Metropolitan Milwaukee, Inc. (LCOMM).

★10423★
Milwaukee County Mental Health Complex - Michael Kasak Library (Med)
9455 Watertown Plank Rd. Phone: (414)257-7381
Milwaukee, WI 53226 Anna M. Green, Libn.
Founded: 1941. **Staff:** Prof 1. **Subjects:** Psychology, mental health, psychiatry, psychoanalysis. **Holdings:** 6650 books; 5600 bound periodical volumes; 250 video cassettes; 500 audio cassettes. **Subscriptions:** 303 journals and other serials. **Services:** Interlibrary loan; copying; library open to the public for reference use only. **Computerized Information Services:** NLM, DIALOG Information Services; DOCLINE (electronic mail service). **Networks/Consortia:** Member of Southeastern Wisconsin Health Science Library Consortium (SWHSL). **Remarks:** FAX: (414)257-8018.

★10424★
Milwaukee Institute of Art & Design - Library (Art)
342 N. Water St. Phone: (414)276-7889
Milwaukee, WI 53202-5715 Terry Marcus, Dir. of Lib.Serv.
Founded: 1977. **Staff:** Prof 2; Other 5. **Subjects:** Artists, graphic design, art history, aesthetics, industrial design, decorative arts, photography, sculpture, painting, illustration, interior design. **Holdings:** 18,500 books; 1500 bound periodical volumes; 3600 art reproductions (postcards); clipping file of visual aids covering 50 subjects; 41,000 slides. **Subscriptions:** 50 journals and other serials. **Services:** Interlibrary loan; copying; library open to the public with restrictions. **Networks/Consortia:** Member of Library Council of Metropolitan Milwaukee, Inc. (LCOMM). **Publications:** Acquisitions List, quarterly - for internal distribution only. **Staff:** Scott Sidney, Slide Cur./Asst.Libn.

Milwaukee Journal
See: **Journal/Sentinel, Inc.** (8488)

★10425★
(Milwaukee) Legislative Reference Bureau (Soc Sci)
City Hall, Rm. B-11
200 E. Wells St. Phone: (414)278-2295
Milwaukee, WI 53202-3567 Barry Zalben, Mgr.
Founded: 1908. **Staff:** Prof 15; Other 4. **Subjects:** City government, revenue, planning; housing; crime; intergovernmental relations; Wisconsin state and local government; public administration; urban affairs. **Special Collections:** Official depository for current city documents. **Holdings:** 52,057 volumes; 6 VF drawers of pamphlets; newspaper clippings, 1908 to present. **Subscriptions:** 192 journals and other serials. **Services:** Interlibrary loan; copying; bureau open to the public with restrictions. **Computerized Information Services:** DataTimes, DIALOG Information Services, Local Exchange. **Remarks:** FAX: (414)278-3977. **Staff:** David Hall, Libn.

★10426★
Milwaukee Public Library - Art, Music and Recreation Section (Art, Mus, Rec)
814 W. Wisconsin Ave. Phone: (414)278-3043
Milwaukee, WI 53233 Ruth Ruege, Coord., Fine Arts
Staff: 8. **Subjects:** Art and music history; aesthetics; architecture; sculpture; antiques; interior decoration; crafts; music theory and techniques; biographies of artists, musicians, actors, and sportspersons; painting; drawing; print-making; photography; sports and games; recreation; theater; cinema; dance; numismatics; postage stamps; library science; costume; folklore. **Special Collections:** Auction and exhibition catalogs; poster collection; framed art; mounted prints; picture file; sculpture reproductions; theater and concert programs; art and music clipping file; historic popular song collection; rare book collection. **Holdings:** 40,000 books; music manuscripts of local composers, including Carl Eppler and Hugo Kaun; 10,000 phonograph records; 3000 cassettes; 3000 compact discs. **Services:** Interlibrary loan; copying; section open to nonresident public for reference use. **Automated Operations:** Computerized cataloging and circulation. **Networks/Consortia:** Member of Library Council of Metropolitan Milwaukee, Inc. (LCOMM). **Publications:** New Books list (includes new recordings), weekly. **Special Indexes:** Song title index; film review file.

★10427★
Milwaukee Public Library - Humanities Division - Special Collections (Hist)
814 W. Wisconsin Ave. Phone: (414)278-3000
Milwaukee, WI 53233 Virginia Schwartz, Coord.
Founded: 1953. **Staff:** Prof 1; Other 1. **Subjects:** History - local, Great Lakes, Wisconsin, surrounding states; genealogy. **Special Collections:** Runge and Nelson Marine Collections; data on Great Lakes ships (22,000 photographs); local history collection; Milwaukee and Great Lakes-related manuscripts, including those of Daniel Hoan, Frank P. Zeidler, and Socialist Party-Social Democratic Federation (200 linear feet). **Holdings:** 30,000 books; 1200 bound periodical volumes; theses; 165 boxes of pamphlets; 40,000 photographs; 500 linear feet of manuscripts; 2500 maps and lake charts; 300 atlases. **Subscriptions:** 320 journals and other serials. **Services:** Interlibrary loan; copying (limited); collections open to nonresident public for reference use. **Automated Operations:** Computerized cataloging, acquisitions, serials, and circulation. **Computerized Information Services:** OCLC. **Networks/Consortia:** Member of Library Council of Metropolitan Milwaukee, Inc. (LCOMM). **Publications:** Selected manuscript and genealogical finding aids. **Special Catalogs:** Subject catalogs to photograph and pamphlet collections (card); Milwaukee area manuscript guide. **Special Indexes:** Index to Milwaukee Sentinel Newspaper for state news, 1837-1890. **Remarks:** FAX: (414)278-2137. **Staff:** Paul Woehrmann, Spec.Coll.Libn.

★10428★
Milwaukee Public Library - Science & Business Division (Sci-Engr, Bus-Fin)
814 W. Wisconsin Ave. Phone: (414)278-3247
Milwaukee, WI 53233 Theodore Cebula, Coord., Sci./Bus.Div.
Subjects: Agriculture, business, census, chemistry, economics, engineering, industrial labor, natural and physical sciences, physics, statistics, information sciences. **Special Collections:** U.S. and British patent depository; industrial and government standards. **Holdings:** Figures not available. **Services:** Interlibrary loan; copying; division open to nonresident public for reference use. **Automated Operations:** Computerized cataloging and circulation. **Computerized Information Services:** OCLC, U.S. Patent Classification System; CD-ROMs (Business Index, Health Reference Center). **Networks/Consortia:** Member of Library Council of Metropolitan Milwaukee, Inc. (LCOMM). **Remarks:** FAX: (414)278-2137.

★10429★
Milwaukee Public Library - Special Collections (Hist)
814 W. Wisconsin Ave. Phone: (414)278-3000
Milwaukee, WI 53233 Kathleen M. Huston, City Libn.
Founded: 1878. **Holdings:** U.S. Government documents depository; Wisconsin Marine Historical Society Collection; Milwaukee Road Railroad Archives; Milwaukee city archives; rare books, including H.G. Wells and Omar Khyam Collection; rare bird books (including Audubon). **Subscriptions:** 107 newspapers. **Services:** Interlibrary loan; copying; collections open to the public. **Automated Operations:** Computerized cataloging, acquisitions, and circulation. **Computerized Information Services:** DIALOG Information Services, OCLC, U.S. Patent Classification System, ALANET; internal database; U.S. Patent Classification System, ALANET (electronic mail services). Performs searches on fee basis. Contact Person: Theodore Cebula, Coord., Sci. & Bus., 278-3964. **Networks/Consortia:** Member of Library Council of Metropolitan Milwaukee, Inc. (LCOMM). **Remarks:** FAX: (414)278-2137.

★10430★
Milwaukee Public Library - Wisconsin Architectural Archive (Plan)
814 W. Wisconsin Ave.
Milwaukee, WI 53233 Phone: (414)278-3897
Staff: 1. **Subjects:** Architecture. **Special Collections:** Collection of drawings of 8000 buildings representing 240 architects primarily from Wisconsin. **Holdings:** 300 books and pamphlets; 1500 photographs; 2000 specifications and documents. **Services:** Copying; archive open to the public by appointment. **Remarks:** FAX: (414)278-2137.

★10431★
Milwaukee Public Museum - Reference Library (Sci-Engr, Biol Sci)
800 W. Wells St. Phone: (414)278-2736
Milwaukee, WI 53233 Judith Campbell Turner, Musm.Libn.
Founded: 1883. **Staff:** Prof 3; Other 4. **Subjects:** Anthropology, archeology, botany, geology, zoology, history, museology, decorative arts, paleontology, ecology. **Special Collections:** Photographic Collection (300,000 prints; 200,000 negatives); Milwaukee Public Museum Archives. **Holdings:** 125,000 volumes; 800 microforms; 2300 maps. **Subscriptions:** 1200 journals and other serials. **Services:** Interlibrary loan; copying; library open to the public. **Automated Operations:** Computerized cataloging. **Computerized Information Services:** OCLC; internal databases. **Networks/Consortia:** Member of Library Council of Metropolitan Milwaukee, Inc. (LCOMM), Wisconsin Interlibrary Services (WILS). **Special Catalogs:** Tribal File (card). **Remarks:** FAX: (414)223-1396. **Staff:** Susan Otto, Photo.Coll.Mgr.; Richard Hren, Ser.Libn.

Milwaukee Road Railroad Archives
See: **Milwaukee Public Library - Special Collections** (10429)

★10432★
Milwaukee School of Engineering - Walter Schroeder Library (Sci-Engr)
P.O. Box 644 Phone: (414)277-7180
Milwaukee, WI 53201-0644 Mary Ann Schmidt, Lib.Dir.
Founded: 1903. **Staff:** Prof 5; Other 3. **Subjects:** Engineering - electrical, mechanical, biomedical, computer, architectural; building and construction; industrial management; fluid power. **Holdings:** 40,950 books; 11,000 bound periodical volumes; 20 VF drawers of pamphlets. **Subscriptions:** 676 journals and other serials; 21 newspapers. **Services:** Interlibrary loan; copying; library open to students and the business and industrial community. **Computerized Information Services:** DIALOG Information Services, NewsNet, Inc., OCLC; DIALMAIL (electronic mail service). Performs searches on fee basis. **Networks/Consortia:** Member of Library Council of Metropolitan Milwaukee, Inc. (LCOMM), Wisconsin Interlibrary Services (WILS). **Publications:** Library handbook; new books list; periodicals list. **Remarks:** Library located at 500 E. Kilbourn Ave., Milwaukee, WI. FAX: (414)277-7186. **Staff:** Dr. Constantin Popescu, Assoc.Libn.; Gary Shimek, Ref.Libn.; William Krajnac, AV Coord.; Mary B. Rieder, Automation Libn.

Milwaukee Sentinel
See: **Journal/Sentinel, Inc.** (8488)

★10433★
Minahant & Peterson - Library
411 E. Wisconsin, Suite 2200
Milwaukee, WI 53202-4499
Defunct.

★10434★
Mind Science Foundation - Library (Rel-Phil)
8301 Broadway, No. 100 Phone: (512)821-6094
San Antonio, TX 78209-2006 Beverly Evenson Casey, Libn.
Founded: 1975. **Staff:** Prof 1. **Subjects:** Parapsychology, psychology, Alzheimer's disease, mind-made health, creativity, traditional healing, self-esteem, brain mapping. **Special Collections:** Early psychical research (200 volumes). **Holdings:** 5000 books; 100 bound periodical volumes; 3 16mm films; 3 VF; 20 journals on microfiche; 150 other cataloged items. **Subscriptions:** 13 journals and other serials. **Services:** Interlibrary loan; copying; library open to the public by appointment. **Networks/Consortia:** Member of Council of Research & Academic Libraries (CORAL), Health Oriented Libraries of San Antonio (HOLSA). **Publications:** MSF News, quarterly - free upon request. **Special Indexes:** Indexes to Skeptical Inquirer, Zetetic Scholar, Alpha, Common Ground, Psi Research Psychic, and New Realities (bound or notebook form). **Remarks:** FAX: (512)821-6199.

★10435★
Mine Safety Appliances Company - Business Library (Bus-Fin)
Box 426 Phone: (412)967-3131
Pittsburgh, PA 15230 Paula Reed, Supv.
Founded: 1972. **Staff:** Prof 1; Other 2. **Subjects:** Occupational safety, industrial hygiene, coal mining, toxicology. **Special Collections:** National Institute for Occupational Safety and Health reports (1000); Bureau of Mines reports (5000). **Holdings:** 8000 books; 25 VF drawers of pamphlets. **Subscriptions:** 300 journals and other serials. **Services:** Interlibrary loan; library not open to the public. **Computerized Information Services:** DIALOG Information Services, Maxwell Online, Inc., NLM, STN International, VU/TEXT Information Services, Dow Jones News/Retrieval, Occupational Health Services, Inc., NEXIS, LEXIS. **Publications:** New Additions, monthly; Journals List, annual - by request. **Remarks:** Library located at 121 Gamma Dr., Pittsburgh, PA 15238. FAX: (412)967-3460.

★10436★
Mine Safety Appliances Company - MSA Research Corporation - Callery Chemical Company - Library (Sci-Engr)
P.O. Box 429 Phone: (412)967-3131
Pittsburgh, PA 15230 Paula Reed, Supv., Lib.Serv.
Founded: 1959. **Subjects:** Boron and organometallic chemistry; alkali metals; toxicology; industrial health and safety; engineering; rare metals. **Special Collections:** Chemical Abstracts (1907-1990); Bureau of Mines reports. **Holdings:** 5000 books; 5000 bound periodical volumes. **Subscriptions:** 100 journals and other serials.

★10437★
Alice T. Miner Colonial Collection - Library (Art)
Box 568 Phone: (518)846-7336
Chazy, NY 12921 Lucille L. Czarnetzky, Cur.
Founded: 1924. **Subjects:** Art and paintings, colonial furniture, household goods, silver, chinaware, artifacts of Abraham Lincoln. **Holdings:** 250 books. **Services:** Library open to the public.

Miner Center Library
See: **James A. FitzPatrick Library** (5837)

Edward G. Miner Library
See: **University of Rochester - School of Medicine & Dentistry** (19286)

F.V. Miner Resource Center
See: **Clover Park Technical College** (3844)

★10438★
Mineral County Museum & Historical Society - Library (Hist)
P.O. Box 533 Phone: (406)822-4516
Superior, MT 59872 Deborah J. Davis, Cur.
Founded: 1976. **Staff:** 2. **Subjects:** History - Montana, local, regional, Western; mining. **Special Collections:** Local newspapers (Mineral County Press, 1914-1919; Mineral Independent, 1915 to present); County Comissioner correspondence, 1914-1920; John Mullan and Mullan Road Information Center (1860s). **Holdings:** 500 books; unbound periodical volumes; documents; 24 manuscripts; nonbook items (including historic photographs). **Subscriptions:** 3 journals and other serials; 6 newsletters. **Services:** Interlibrary loan; copying; library open to the public. **Publications:** Mullan Chronicles (newsletter dealing with subjects relating to John Mullan and the Mullan Road), quarterly.

★10439★
Mineral Point Historical Society - Archives (Hist)
Orchard Lawn - Jos. Gundry House
Box 59 Phone: (608)987-3409
Mineral Point, WI 53565 Neil Hanson, Pres.
Subjects: History of Iowa County, 1827-1927. **Special Collections:** Glass plate negatives (Mineral Point history, 1860s-1910, all reprinted; 2000). **Holdings:** 350 legal documents; papers of pioneers; account books and records of local firms; Civil War diaries; maps. **Services:** Archives open to the public with permission from the board of directors. **Remarks:** Joseph Gundry House is open for tours during the summer months. Holdings above are available through the Mineral Point Room.

★10440★
Mineral Springs Hospital - Medical Library (Med)
Box 1050 Phone: (403)762-2222
Banff, AB, Canada T0L 0C0 Mrs. E. Heikkila, Dir., Hea.Rec.
Founded: 1957. **Subjects:** Medicine, administration. **Holdings:** 75 books. **Subscriptions:** 30 journals and other serials. **Services:** Library not open to the public. **Remarks:** FAX: (403)762-4193.

★10441★
Mingei International Museum of World Folk Art - Reference Library (Art)
P.O. Box 553
La Jolla, CA 92038 Phone: (619)453-5300
Subjects: Folk art. **Holdings:** 2000 books; 50 videotapes and 16mm films. **Services:** Library open to the public for reference use only. **Remarks:** FAX: (619)453-0700. Library located at 4405 La Jolla Village Dr., Bldg. I-7, San Diego, CA 92122. **Staff:** Betty Grenstead, Libn.; Nancy Andrews, Libn.

★10442★
Minisink Valley Historical Society - Library (Hist)
138 Pike St.
Box 659 Phone: (914)856-2375
Port Jervis, NY 12771-0659 Peter Osborne, III, Exec.Dir.
Founded: 1889. **Staff:** Prof 1; Other 3. **Subjects:** Local history and genealogy. **Special Collections:** Deerpark and Port Jervis archival materials; records of the chief engineer, Russel F. Lord, of the Delaware and Hudson Canal, 1825-1900; U.S. Census records, 1790-1910 (Orange County, NY; Sussex County, NJ; Pike County, PA). **Holdings:** 10,000 manuscripts and archival materials; 4000 photographs, genealogical records, and Works Progress Administration files. **Services:** Copying; genealogical research; library open to the public on a limited schedule. **Automated Operations:** Computerized acquisitions. **Publications:** Newsletter, quarterly - for internal distribution only. **Special Catalogs:** Catalog of photograph collection (online); catalog of recent acquisitions.

Ministere de l'Education Nationale - Bibliotheque de Documentation Internationale Contemporaine
See: **France - Ministere de l'Education Nationale - Bibliotheque de Documentation Internationale Contemporaine** (6067)

Ministerie van Buitenlandse Zaken - Hoofdafdeling Vertalingen
See: **Netherlands - Ministry of Foreign Affairs - Translations Branch** (11404)

Ministry of Culture (of France) - Department of Art Conservation - Office of French Museums
See: **France - Ministry of Culture - Department of Art Conservation - Office of French Museums - General Inventory of Monuments and Artistic Riches of France - Documentation Center** (6068)

Ministry of Culture and Sports (of Guatemala) - Institute of Anthropology and History
See: **Guatemala - Ministerio de Cultura y Deportes - Instituto de Antropologia e Historia** (6791)

★10443★
MINITEX Library Information Network (Info Sci)
S-33 Wilson Library
University of Minnesota
309 19th Ave., S. Phone: (612)624-4002
Minneapolis, MN 55455 William DeJohn, Dir.
Founded: 1969. **Staff:** Prof 9; Other 42. **Services:** The MINITEX Library Information Network is a publicly supported network of academic, public, state agency, and special libraries working cooperatively to provide and improve library service to patrons in Minnesota, North Dakota, and South Dakota. MINITEX facilitates sharing of resources and services among and between libraries by providing the following: document delivery; electronic transmission of online cataloging through OCLC; brokering online and CD-ROM databases; backup reference services; a periodical exchange; workshops and skills development programs for librarians. **Computerized Information Services:** DIALOG Information Services, WILSONLINE, BRS Information Technologies, NLM, RLIN, OCLC, VU/TEXT Information Services. **Publications:** Minitex Messenger; manuals and reports. **Special Catalogs:** MULS: A Union List of Serials. **Remarks:** FAX: (612)624-4508. Contractual and reciprocal arrangements with North Dakota State Library, South Dakota State Library, and Wisconsin Interlibrary Services provide access to material in those states. **Also Known As:** Minnesota Interlibrary Telecommunications Exchange. **Staff:** Anne T. Stagg, Adm.Dir.; M.J. Rossman, Asst.Dir., OCLC & Ref.Serv.; Kay Beaudrie, OCLC Serv.Coord.; Marlene Forney, OCLC Serv.Coord.; Mary Miller, OCLC Serv.Coord.; Anita Branin, Asst.Dir., Doc. Delivery & MULS.

Minkel Information Center Z-12
See: **Bull H N Information Systems, Inc. - Minkel Information Center Z-12** (2355)

The F.W. Minkler Library
See: **North York Board of Education** (11958)

★ 10444 ★
Minneapolis College of Art and Design - Library (Art)
2501 Stevens Ave., S. Phone: (612)874-3791
Minneapolis, MN 55404 Mary Manning, Lib.Dir.
Founded: 1960. **Staff:** Prof 3; Other 5. **Subjects:** Painting, architecture, sculpture, graphic arts, design, films and film making, photography, videos, performance art. **Holdings:** 62,200 volumes; 220 artists' books; 120,000 slides; 63 VF drawers of clippings, pamphlets, maps, brochures, artists catalogs; 400 audio cassettes; 1000 phonograph records; 1130 microfiche, college archives. **Subscriptions:** 227 journals and other serials. **Services:** Interlibrary loan (limited); copying; library open to the public for reference use only. **Computerized Information Services:** DIALOG Information Services, WILSONLINE. **Networks/Consortia:** Member of MINITEX Library Information Network. **Publications:** MCAD Library Handbook, irregular; MCAD Library Serials List, annual; Accessions lists, monthly. **Staff:** Allan Kohl, Slide Libn.; Sara Dobberteen, Ref.Libn.

★ 10445 ★
Minneapolis Institute of Arts - Library (Art)
2400 3rd Ave., S. Phone: (612)870-3117
Minneapolis, MN 55404 Harold Peterson, Libn.
Founded: 1883. **Staff:** Prof 3; Other 3.5. **Subjects:** General art history, European painting, decorative arts. **Special Collections:** Leslie Collection of Fine Books (fine printing); museum archives. **Holdings:** 40,000 volumes; auction and exhibition catalogs. **Subscriptions:** 250 journals and other serials. **Services:** Library open to the public. **Computerized Information Services:** OCLC. **Networks/Consortia:** Member of MINITEX Library Information Network. **Remarks:** FAX: (612)870-3004. **Staff:** Brian Mulhern, Asst.Libn., Archv.; Michael Boe, Asst.Libn., Ref.

★ 10446 ★
Minneapolis Public Library & Information Center - Art, Music & Films Department (Art, Mus, Aud-Vis)
300 Nicollet Mall Phone: (612)372-6520
Minneapolis, MN 55401 Walter Gegner, Act.Dept.Hd.
Staff: Prof 4; Other 13. **Subjects:** Art, music, architecture, sculpture, painting, music theory and practice, art and music biographies, drawing, prints, decorative arts. **Special Collections:** Band parts; old songs and popular songs, 1900 to present. **Holdings:** 100,000 books; 7000 bound periodical volumes; 32,000 phonograph records; 35,000 pieces of cataloged sheet music; 30,790 pieces of uncataloged sheet music; 1 million mounted and unmounted pictures; 14 vertical file drawers; 3000 films; 27,415 2x2 slides; 26,190 3 1/4x4 slides; 3306 video cassettes; 800 compact discs. **Subscriptions:** 511 journals and other serials. **Services:** Interlibrary loan; copying (limited). **Computerized Information Services:** DIALOG Information Services, DataTimes, VU/TEXT Information Services; InfoTrac. **Networks/Consortia:** Member of Metropolitan Library Service Agency (MELSA), MINITEX Library Information Network. **Special Catalogs:** 16mm Film Catalog. **Special Indexes:** Popular, folk, traditional, and hymn song indexes. **Remarks:** Telephone number for Films Department is 372-6558. **Staff:** Betsy Williams, Asst.Dept.Hd.; Anita Bealer, Libn.; Martita Bergendahl, Libn.; James Frey, AV Coord.

★ 10447 ★
Minneapolis Public Library & Information Center - Business and Economics Department (Bus-Fin)
300 Nicollet Mall Phone: (612)372-6552
Minneapolis, MN 55401 Susan Tertell, Dept.Hd.
Founded: 1983. **Staff:** Prof 5; Other 9. **Subjects:** Business, economics, labor, statistics. **Special Collections:** Business directories (1500); telephone directories (800); local company histories (45 VF drawers); tax services; investment information; small business collection. **Holdings:** 67,000 books; 9000 bound periodical volumes; 40 VF drawers of corporation annual reports. **Subscriptions:** 525 journals and other serials; 8 newspapers. **Services:** Interlibrary loan; copying. **Automated Operations:** Computerized cataloging. **Computerized Information Services:** Online systems; InfoTrac; CD-ROM (Compact Disclosure). **Networks/Consortia:** Member of Metropolitan Library Service Agency (MELSA), MINITEX Library Information Network. **Special Indexes:** TOPS (Rankings) Index; Directory Index; Telephone Book Index. **Staff:** Nancy Corcoran, Libn.; Vern Harman, Libn.; Dan Pederson, Libn.; Virginia Hasenstein, Libn.

★ 10448 ★
Minneapolis Public Library & Information Center - Children's Services Department (Hum)
300 Nicollet Mall Phone: (612)372-6532
Minneapolis, MN 55401 Kathleen Johnson, Dept.Hd.
Founded: 1893. **Staff:** Prof 5; Other 3. **Subjects:** Children's literature - fiction, nonfiction, picture books; folklore; fairy tales; biography; poetry. **Special Collections:** Historical Children's Literature; Folklore and Fairy Tales Reference Collection; children's books in foreign languages; Minnesota children's authors and illustrators; computer software for children. **Holdings:** 85,000 books; 435 bound periodical volumes; 20 VF drawers of pamphlets and clippings; paperbacks and board books; phonograph records; compact discs; cassettes. **Subscriptions:** 60 journals and other serials. **Services:** Interlibrary loan; copying (limited); department open to the public. **Automated Operations:** Computerized cataloging. **Computerized Information Services:** DIALOG Information Services. **Networks/Consortia:** Member of Metropolitan Library Service Agency (MELSA), Metronet, MINITEX Library Information Network. **Publications:** Here We Grow - Books for 3, 4 & 5 Year Olds; Beginnings: Books for Infants and Toddlers - distributed internally and to individuals and organizations serving youth; Brochures (Read Me a Story; Read to Me; What Turns Kids on to Reading, Tell Me A Story - About You, About Me); Rainbow Collection: Multicultural Books for Children (preschool through grade 2; grades 3-6). **Staff:** Lois Ringquist, Asst.Dept.Hd.; David Benidt, Libn.

★ 10449 ★
Minneapolis Public Library & Information Center - Government Documents (Info Sci)
300 Nicollet Mall Phone: (612)372-6534
Minneapolis, MN 55401 Carol B. VanWhy, Doc.Libn.
Founded: 1893. **Staff:** Prof 3; Other 3. **Subjects:** Federal documents. **Special Collections:** City of Minneapolis and Minnesota State publications. **Holdings:** 800,000 documents; congressional hearings, 1869-1947, on microfiche; congressional committee prints, 1830-1969, on microfiche; serial set 1817-1879, microprint; U.S. Supreme Court reports, 1887 to present on microfiche and paper. **Subscriptions:** 200 journals and other serials. **Services:** Copying; collection available to the public for reference use only. **Computerized Information Services:** DIALOG Information Services. **Special Catalogs:** In-house subject catalog of government publications. **Remarks:** FAX: (612)372-6546. **Staff:** Leone Johnson, Libn.; Helen Burke, Libn.

★ 10450 ★
Minneapolis Public Library & Information Center - History Department (Hist)
300 Nicollet Mall Phone: (612)372-6537
Minneapolis, MN 55401 Robert Bruce, Dept.Hd.
Staff: Prof 4; Other 4. **Subjects:** History, travel, geography, government, politics, biography, genealogy, heraldry, coins, general law. **Holdings:** 192,000 books; 28,000 bound periodical volumes; 750 other cataloged items; 11,900 reels of microfilm; 875 phonograph records and tapes; 35 VF drawers; U.S. Geological Survey maps. **Subscriptions:** 780 journals and other serials; 63 newspapers. **Services:** Interlibrary loan; copying. **Automated Operations:** Computerized cataloging. **Computerized Information Services:** DataTimes, DIALOG Information Services; InfoTrac. **Networks/Consortia:** Member of Metropolitan Library Service Agency (MELSA), MINITEX Library Information Network. **Special Indexes:** Index to Minneapolis Journal, 1889-1914 (cards); index to Minneapolis Star and Tribune, 1967-1969 (cards), 1970-1986 (printed form); index to periodicals published in Minnesota. **Staff:** Audrey Canelake, Libn.; Judith Mosiniak, Lib.Asst.; Amy Ryan, Asst.Dept.Hd.; Renee Reed, Libn.

★ 10451 ★
Minneapolis Public Library & Information Center - Literature and Language Department (Hum)
300 Nicollet Mall Phone: (612)372-6540
Minneapolis, MN 55401 Dorothy D. Thews, Dept.Hd.
Founded: 1958. **Staff:** Prof 4; Other 5. **Subjects:** Literary criticism and history, fiction, poetry, drama, film, television, radio, library and information science, small press, foreign languages and literatures. **Special Collections:** Short stories; Minnesota authors. **Holdings:** 225,000 books; 11,700 bound periodical volumes; 30 VF drawers; 1000 phonograph records; 4000 audio cassettes. **Subscriptions:** 350 journals and other serials. **Services:** Interlibrary loan; translators' databank for referrals. **Automated Operations:** Computerized cataloging. **Computerized Information Services:** DIALOG Information Services, PFDS Online, BRS Information Technologies, NEXIS, DataTimes. **Publications:** New Books in Theatre, quarterly; Best Read List, annual. **Staff:** Katharine Weiblen, Asst.Dept.Hd.; Susan Brown, Libn.; Nancy Kweik, Libn.

★10452★
Minneapolis Public Library & Information Center - Municipal Information Library (Soc Sci, Plan)
City Hall, Rm. 302 Phone: (612)348-8139
Minneapolis, MN 55415 Van C. Houlson, Libn.
Founded: 1972. **Staff:** Prof 1; Other 2. **Subjects:** Minneapolis, urban affairs, planning, public administration, police, local government. **Holdings:** 35,000 volumes; 32 VF drawers. **Subscriptions:** 65 journals and other serials; 25 newspapers. **Services:** Copying; library open to the public. **Computerized Information Services:** DIALOG Information Services, DataTimes, DATANET, Local Exchange, EPIC; electronic mail. **Publications:** Directory of City/County Information and Service Resources, biennial - free to city residents; Minneapolis Communities: a bibliography. **Special Catalogs:** List of City of Minneapolis publications, annual. **Remarks:** FAX: (612)673-3812.

★10453★
Minneapolis Public Library & Information Center - Sociology Department (Soc Sci, Rel-Phil)
300 Nicollet Mall Phone: (612)372-6555
Minneapolis, MN 55401 Eileen Schwartzbauer, Dept.Hd.
Staff: Prof 4; Other 5. **Subjects:** Psychology, philosophy, religion, education, sports, social sciences (except economics and history), folklore, manners and customs, recreation. **Special Collections:** College catalogs from major colleges and universities in the United States (microfiche); Foundation Center Cooperating Collection; Adult Basic Education Collection; Scholarship Collection. **Holdings:** 225,000 books; 7800 bound periodical volumes; pamphlets; phonograph records; cassettes; periodicals on microfilm. **Subscriptions:** 394 journals and other serials. **Computerized Information Services:** DIALOG Information Services, BRS Information Technologies, DataTimes, VU/TEXT Information Services, WILSONLINE; InfoTrac. **Networks/Consortia:** Member of MINITEX Library Information Network, Metropolitan Library Service Agency (MELSA), Metronet. **Staff:** Jerry Blue, Asst.Dept.Hd.; Linda Fritschel Libn.; Nina Biddle, Libn.

★10454★
Minneapolis Public Library & Information Center - Special Collections Department (Soc Sci, Mil, Hum)
300 Nicollet Mall Phone: (612)372-6648
Minneapolis, MN 55401-1992 Edward R. Kukla, Dept.Hd.
Founded: 1987. **Staff:** Prof 3; Other 2. **Special Collections:** Minneapolis Athenaeum Collections (North American Indians, Spencer Natural History, Early American Exploration and Travel, Heffelfinger Aesop's and Others' Fables, History of Books and Printing; 5000 volumes); Minneapolis Collection (city of Minneapolis; 4000 volumes; 10,000 photographs; 150 archival collections; pictures; maps; VF materials); Kittleson World War II Collection (World War II - military and naval operations, social and economic aspects, personal narratives, anti-Semitism and the Holocaust; 8000 books; 400 pamphlets; 14 volumes of scrapbooks; 3 VF drawers of clippings; 2000 posters; 400 unbound periodicals; 1500 leaflets and pictures); Huttner Abolition and Anti-Slavery Collection (Abolitionist movement, slavery, black writers and reformers; 550 books; 50 letters and documents; 250 pamphlets, broadsides, newspapers); 19th Century American Studies Collection (materials by and about 19th century American writers, antislavery movement, New England descriptive and historical writings; Truman Nelson letters; John Greenleaf Whittier-Evelina Bray Downey correspondence; manuscript "Ode to France," James Russell Lowell; 4500 books; 200 bound periodical volumes; 150 pamphlets; 150 autograph letters; 150 pictures; 250 unbound periodicals, pamphlets, newspapers; 1 VF drawer of clippings); Hoag Mark Twain Collection (250 books and pamphlets). **Services:** Copying; collections open to the public with restrictions. **Computerized Information Services:** DataTimes; Photos I (internal database). **Staff:** Erin Foley, Asst.Dept.Hd.; Judith Mosiniak, Lib.Asst.

★10455★
Minneapolis Public Library & Information Center - Technology and Science Department (Sci-Engr, Env-Cons)
300 Nicollet Mall Phone: (612)372-6570
Minneapolis, MN 55401 Thomas Smisek, Dept.Hd.
Founded: 1983. **Staff:** Prof 5; Other 6. **Subjects:** Natural and applied sciences. **Special Collections:** Environmental Conservation Library (ECOL; 17,500 volumes); Minnesota Regional Copper-Nickel Project documents; U.S. Nuclear Regulatory Commission Public Documents Room; Patent Depository Library, 1790 to present; Mid-American Solar Energy Complex Library. **Holdings:** 170,500 books; 205,000 microforms; 3700 environmental impact statements; 3000 auto repair manuals; 400 computer programs. **Subscriptions:** 1861 journals and other serials. **Services:** Interlibrary loan; copying; department open to the public. **Automated Operations:** Computerized cataloging. **Computerized Information Services:** DIALOG Information Services, ORBIT Search Service, U.S. Patent Classification Systems, Automated Patent Search; CD-ROM (CASSIS). Performs searches free of charge. **Networks/Consortia:** Member of Metropolitan Library Service Agency (MELSA), MINITEX Library Information Network. **Publications:** ECOL News, irregular - free upon request. **Staff:** William Johnston, Asst.Dept.Hd.; Mary Beisel, Libn.; Cathryn Camper, Libn.; Edward Hathaway, Libn.

★10456★
Minneapolis Public Schools - Special School District 1 - School Media/ Professional Library (Educ)
807 N.E. Broadway Phone: (612)627-2179
Minneapolis, MN 55413 Coleen Kosloski, Coord. of School Media
Staff: Prof 1; Other 1. **Subjects:** Education - preschool through 12th grade, educational psychology, disadvantaged children and youth, child and adolescent psychology, sociology, minorities, school media centers, information technology. **Special Collections:** Multicultural and gender-fair materials. **Holdings:** 3000 books; 160 archival materials. **Subscriptions:** 140 journals and other serials. **Services:** Interlibrary loan; copying; library open to the public. **Computerized Information Services:** DIALOG Information Services. **Networks/Consortia:** Member of Metronet. **Special Catalogs:** Union List of Serials in Minneapolis Public Schools, annual. **Remarks:** FAX: (612)627-2164.

★10457★
Minneapolis Star Tribune Co. - Library (Publ)
425 Portland Ave. Phone: (612)673-7398
Minneapolis, MN 55488 Robert H. Jansen, Hd.Libn.
Founded: 1946. **Staff:** Prof 5; Other 8. **Subjects:** Newspaper reference topics. **Holdings:** 1500 books; 6 million clippings; 4 million pictures. **Services:** Library not open to the public. **Computerized Information Services:** DataTimes. **Staff:** Sylvia Frisch, Asst.Libn.; Roberta Hovde, Ref.Libn.; Linda Sack, Ref.Libn.; Kathy Hansen, Night Supv.

★10458★
Minneapolis Technical College - Media Center (Educ)
1415 Hennepin Ave., S. Phone: (612)341-7090
Minneapolis, MN 55403 Norman Busse, Ph.D.
Founded: 1956. **Staff:** Prof 1; Other 1. **Subjects:** Vocational-technical material in 27 trade areas. **Holdings:** 24,000 books; 300 bound periodical volumes; 100 archival items; microfiche; microfilm. **Subscriptions:** 400 journals and other serials; 5 newspapers. **Services:** Library open to the public with restrictions. **Computerized Information Services:** OCLC, MSUS/ PALS.

★10459★
Minnegasco - Library Resources (Bus-Fin)
201 S. 7th St. Phone: (612)342-4824
Minneapolis, MN 55402 Janet L. Fabio, Mgr., Lib.Rsrcs.
Founded: 1959. **Staff:** Prof 3; Other 2. **Subjects:** Gas industry, sales and marketing, business and management, household appliance merchandising, public utilities, energy. **Holdings:** 3000 volumes; 1500 annual reports; 12 VF drawers of pamphlets and clippings; 4000 reports on microfiche; 200 audiotapes. **Subscriptions:** 450 journals and other serials. **Services:** Interlibrary loan; copying; department open to the public with restrictions. **Automated Operations:** Computerized serials and routing. **Computerized Information Services:** DIALOG Information Services, NEXIS, InvesText, SEC Online, WILSONLINE, A.G.A. GasNet, Dun & Bradstreet Business Credit Services, DataTimes, VU/TEXT Information Services, EPIC; CD-ROMs (Federal Register, Computer Select, Moody's Company Data); DIALMAIL (electronic mail service). **Publications:** Info Source, monthly; Trend Scan, quarterly. **Remarks:** FAX: (612)342-5056. **Formerly:** Its Information Resources Department. **Staff:** Judith Roggow, Res.Spec.; Jamie Kragrud, Info.Spec.

★10460★
Minnesota Agricultural Statistics Service - Library (Agri)
90 W. Plato Blvd.
Box 7068 Phone: (612)296-2230
St. Paul, MN 55107 Linda Wright, Pub.Aff.Spec.
Staff: 1. **Subjects:** Minnesota agriculture statistics. **Holdings:** Figures not available. **Services:** Library not open to the public. **Publications:** Annual Minnesota Agricultural Statistics; list of other publications free upon request. **Remarks:** This is a federal-state cooperative agency. It issues free statistical reports to active farmer participants, news media, and educational institutions; others may receive reports by subscription.

Minnesota Association of Public Health Archives
See: **University of Minnesota - Bio-Medical Library - Owen H. Wangensteen Historical Library of Biology and Medicine** (18895)

★10461★
Minnesota Bible College - Library (Rel-Phil)
920 Mayowood Rd., S.W. Phone: (507)288-4563
Rochester, MN 55901 Dorothy R. Forsythe, Act.Libn.
Founded: 1913. **Staff:** Prof 1; Other 2. **Subjects:** Bible, theology, social sciences, philosophy, history. **Special Collections:** G.H. Cachiaras Memorial Library (Bible and theology, Restoration movement histories; 2000 books). **Holdings:** 26,000 books; 3040 bound periodical volumes; 200 cassettes; 220 phonograph records; 720 AV programs. **Subscriptions:** 100 journals and other serials. **Services:** Library open to the public. **Staff:** James Godsey, Lib.Adm.

Minnesota Center for Philosophy of Science
See: **University of Minnesota** (18923)

★10462★
Minnesota Citizens Council on Crime and Justice (Law)
822 S. 3rd St., Suite 100 Phone: (612)340-5432
Minneapolis, MN 55415 Gerry Graham, Coord.
Founded: 1970. **Staff:** Prof 1. **Subjects:** Crime and crime prevention, delinquency, courts, corrections, law enforcement and education, chemical abuse, domestic violence. **Holdings:** 41 16mm films and videotapes; 50 cassette tapes; books; games; posters; teaching units. **Services:** Library open to the public for purchase or rental of materials; research and community planning in criminal justice field; operation of Crime Victim Center; services to wives and families of inmates; mediation services for juvenile offeners and their victims; employment training for ex-offenders. **Special Catalogs:** Catalog of educational materials. **Remarks:** FAX: (612)348-9272.

Minnesota Genealogical Society Library
See: **Northwest Territory Canadian & French Heritage Center** (12068)

★10463★
Minnesota Geological Survey - Library (Sci-Engr)
University of Minnesota
2642 University Ave. Phone: (612)627-4780
St. Paul, MN 55114 Lynn Swanson, Sr.Lib.Asst.
Founded: 1974. **Staff:** Prof 1. **Subjects:** Minnesota and U.S. geology. **Holdings:** 1600 books; 280 bound periodical volumes; 6500 unbound serials; 300 theses; 3000 maps; 6 VF drawers of reprints; 3 VF drawers of pamphlets and clippings; 440 field notebooks; 3000 aerial photographs; 2560 microfiche; 700 slides. **Subscriptions:** 130 journals and other serials. **Services:** Copying; library open to the public for reference use only.

Minnesota Health Science Libraries Association Archives
See: **University of Minnesota - Bio-Medical Library - Owen H. Wangensteen Historical Library of Biology and Medicine** (18895)

★10464★
Minnesota Historical Society - Archives and Manuscripts Collections (Hist)
Research Center
1500 Mississippi St.
St. Paul, MN 55101 Phone: (612)296-6980
Founded: 1849. **Staff:** Prof 4. **Subjects:** Minnesota history; local, state, national politics; genealogy; business; transportation; conservation; women; labor. **Special Collections:** Minnesota State Archives (40,000 cubic feet); Great Northern and Northern Pacific railroad records; Hubert H. Humphrey papers; MHS manuscript collections. **Holdings:** 70,000 linear feet of manuscripts and state archives; microfilm. **Services:** Interlibrary loan (limited to microfilm); copying; collections open to the public with restrictions. **Automated Operations:** Computerized public access catalog and cataloging (PALS). **Computerized Information Services:** RLIN. **Networks/Consortia:** Member of Research Libraries Information Network (RLIN). **Publications:** Collection guides, irregular; guides to microfilm editions. **Special Catalogs:** Manuscript collections card catalog. **Remarks:** FAX: (612)296-9961. **Staff:** Dallas R. Lindgren, Ref.Spec.; Ruth Ellen Bauer, Ref.Archv.; Hampton Smith, III, Ref.Archv.; Steven E. Nielson, Ref.Assoc.

★10465★
Minnesota Historical Society - Fort Snelling Branch Library (Hist)
Fort Snelling History Center Phone: (612)726-1171
St. Paul, MN 55111 Libby Tweedale
Founded: 1970. **Staff:** 1. **Subjects:** History - Minnesota, regional, military; American Indians; American and regional archeology; 19th century America. **Holdings:** 6000 volumes; 1500 other cataloged items. **Subscriptions:** 5 journals and other serials. **Services:** Copying; library open to the public for reference use only. **Remarks:** FAX: (612)297-1357.

★10466★
Minnesota Historical Society - Library Services (Hist)
160 John Ireland Blvd. Phone: (612)296-2143
St. Paul, MN 55102 Denise Carlson, Hd., Ref., M.H.S.
Founded: 1849. **Staff:** Prof 10; Other 6. **Subjects:** Minnesota, Upper Midwest, genealogy, Scandinavians in North America, ethnic groups in U.S. and Canada, transportation, agriculture, arts, commerce, family life, industry, Indians. **Special Collections:** Minnesota newspapers, 1849 to present; Minnesota State Archives; Hubert H. Humphrey Photograph Collection (25,000); Norton & Peel Commercial Photograph Collection (75,000); St. Paul and Minneapolis newspaper negatives (1 million). **Holdings:** 500,000 monographs, government documents, and microform volumes; 100 VF drawers; 250,000 photographs; 35,000 maps; 1300 atlases; 4.5 million issues of 3000 titles of newspaper volumes; manuscripts. **Subscriptions:** 2200 journals and other serials; 436 newspapers. **Services:** Interlibrary loan; copying; library open to the public for reference use only. **Automated Operations:** Computerized public access catalog and cataloging (PALS). **Computerized Information Services:** DIALOG Information Services, OCLC, DataTimes. **Publications:** Pathfinders and guides, irregular. **Remarks:** FAX: (612)296-1004. **Formed by the merger of:** Its Library Reference Services and its special Libraries. **Staff:** Faustino Avaloz, Ref.Spec.; Tracey Baker, Ref.Spec.; Patricia Harpole, Ref.Spec.; Dallas Lindgren, Ref.Spec.; Ruth Bauer, Ref.Assoc.; Kathy Marquis, Ref.Assoc.; Steve Nielsen, Ref.Assoc.; Brigid Shields, Ref.Assoc.; F. Hampton Smith, Ref.Assoc.

★10467★
Minnesota Historical Society - Special Libraries
690 Cedar St.
St. Paul, MN 55101
Defunct. Holdings absorbed by the Minnesota Historical Society - Library Reference Services to form its Library Services.

Minnesota Interlibrary Telecommunications Exchange
See: **MINITEX Library Information Network** (10443)

★10468★
Minnesota Library for the Blind and Physically Handicapped (Aud-Vis)
Faribault, MN 55021 Phone: (507)332-3279
Myrna Wright, Libn.
Founded: 1933. **Staff:** Prof 2; Other 8. **Holdings:** 47,700 talking book records; 12,000 volumes in braille; 104,800 cassette books; 2200 large print books. **Services:** Interlibrary loan; tapes copied from masters; library serves the legally blind and physically handicapped.

★10469★
Minnesota Museum of Art - Library (Art)
305 St. Peter St. Phone: (612)292-4350
St. Paul, MN 55102 Leanne A. Klein, Assoc.Cur., Coll.Mgt.
Staff: Prof 1. **Subjects:** Asian art, especially Korean; 20th century American painting, graphics, sculpture. **Holdings:** 1000 books; 2000 exhibit catalogs from other museums; 500 slides of permanent collection art objects; 4 VF drawers of art clippings; Sotheby Parke Bernet and Christies auction catalogs; Paul Howard Manship bequest research files. **Subscriptions:** 10 journals and other serials. **Services:** Library not open to the public. **Publications:** Minnesota Museum of Art exhibition catalogs; list of additional publications - available upon request.

★10470★
Minnesota Orchestra - Music Library (Mus)
1111 Nicollet Mall Phone: (612)371-5622
Minneapolis, MN 55403 Paul B. Gunther, Libn.
Founded: 1903. **Staff:** Prof 3. **Subjects:** Orchestral music. **Special Collections:** Archives (programs, indexes, recordings of the Minnesota Orchestra, 1903 to present). **Holdings:** 2500 orchestrations; 3000 additional scores; 200 choral selections; 200 volumes of performance music reference material. **Subscriptions:** 12 journals and other serials. **Services:** Library open to the public at librarian's discretion. **Automated Operations:** Computerized cataloging, acquisitions, and performance history. **Computerized Information Services:** OLIS (Orchestra Library Information Service) (internal database). Performs searches on fee basis. **Remarks:** Alternate telephone number(s): 371-5623. FAX: (612)371-0838. Telex: 29 0233 MINNORCH. **Staff:** Eric A. Sjostrom, Assoc.Libn.; Carole Keller, Mus. Preparation Asst.; Steve Heitzeg, Mus. Preparation Asst.

Minnesota Planning Agency - Criminal Justice Library
See: **Minnesota Planning Agency - Library/Information Konnection (LINK)** (10471)

★10471★
Minnesota Planning Agency - Library/Information Konnection (LINK) (Law)
300 Centennial Office Bldg.
658 Cedar St.
St. Paul, MN 55155-1600 Phone: (612)296-5973
Founded: 1987. **Staff:** Prof 1. **Subjects:** Criminal justice, policy issues, environment, land use, mapping, demography. **Special Collections:** Internally produced publications. **Holdings:** 5000 books; 2000 reports; unbound periodicals. **Subscriptions:** 67 journals and other serials. **Services:** Interlibrary loan; copying; SDI; library open to the public. **Automated Operations:** Computerized cataloging. **Computerized Information Services:** DIALOG Information Services; DATANET (internal database). Performs searches on fee basis. **Networks/Consortia:** Member of Capital Area Library Consortium (CALCO), Criminal Justice Information Exchange Group, MINITEX Library Information Network. **Remarks:** FAX: (612)296-3698.

Minnesota Revenue Library
See: **Minnesota (State) Department of Revenue** (10484)

★10472★
Minnesota Science Fiction Society - Library (Hum)
Lake St. Sta., Box 8297 Phone: (612)647-9702
Minneapolis, MN 55408 Karen Johnson
Founded: 1970. **Subjects:** Science fiction, fantasy. **Holdings:** 1200 books. **Services:** Library open to the public upon application.

★10473★
Minnesota Services for the Blind and Visually Handicapped - Communication Center (Aud-Vis)
1745 University Ave. Phone: (612)642-0502
St. Paul, MN 55104 Gerald Olerud, Dir.
Founded: 1953. **Staff:** Prof 30. **Subjects:** General, with all books on tape or in braille. **Holdings:** 5000 master titles on tape; 1850 master titles in braille. **Subscriptions:** 210 journals and other serials; 5 newspapers. **Services:** Copying; transcribing; center open to the public but is for use only by eligible clients; loans tapes, braille books, instructional materials, phonograph and cassette equipment, closed-circuit radio receivers without charge, telephone accessed newspaper service, audio equipment repair. **Computerized Information Services:** Internal database. **Publications:** Radio Talking Book Calendar Program Guide, monthly. **Remarks:** FAX: (612)649-5927. **Staff:** Mary Archer, Supv., Braille Sect.; Steve Rosenthal, Supv., Radio Talking Bks.; Robert Watson, Supv./Chf.Engr., Engr.Sect.; Eleanor Sevdy, Supv., Tape Textbook.

★10474★
Minnesota State Attorney General - Law Library (Law)
102 State Capitol Bldg. Phone: (612)296-8152
St. Paul, MN 55155 Anita Anderson, Law Libn.
Staff: Prof 1. **Subjects:** Law. **Holdings:** 4.5 feet of microfiche; 30 VF drawers of attorney general opinions. **Subscriptions:** 370 journals and other serials; 20 newspapers. **Services:** Interlibrary loan; library not open to the public. **Automated Operations:** Computerized public access catalog, cataloging, and ILL. **Computerized Information Services:** WESTLAW, LEXIS, NEXIS, DIALOG Information Services, DataTimes, Phillips Publishing, Inc. **Networks/Consortia:** Member of MINITEX Library Information Network, Capital Area Library Consortium (CALCO). **Remarks:** FAX: (612)297-4193.

★10475★
Minnesota State Board of Animal Health - Library (Agri)
160 Agriculture Bldg.
90 W. Plato Blvd. Phone: (612)296-2942
St. Paul, MN 55107 Dr. T.J. Hagerty, Exec.Sec.
Subjects: Diseases of animals and poultry. **Holdings:** Textbooks; minutes of board meetings, 1903 to present. **Services:** Library open to the public for reference use only.

Minnesota State Board for Vocational and Technical Education
See: **Minnesota (State) Department of Education - Interagency Resource and Information Center** (10478)

Minnesota (State) Community College Board
See: **Minnesota (State) Department of Education - Interagency Resource and Information Center** (10478)

★10476★
Minnesota State Department of Administration - DATANET (Info Sci)
330 Centennial Office Bldg.
658 Cedar St. Phone: (612)296-2559
St. Paul, MN 55155 Richard Fong, Info.Spec.
Founded: 1981. **Staff:** Prof 5. **Subjects:** Minnesota and the United States - 1990 demographics, economic indicators, agriculture, state and county rankings, adolescent health, business patterns, natural resources, state grants and loans, Gross State Product data for all 50 states. **Special Collections:** United States county mapping software. **Holdings:** 90 megabytes of summary statistical databases on hard disc. **Subscriptions:** 250 journals and other serials. **Computerized Information Services:** DATANET (internal database). Provides online access by subscription basis. **Publications:** DATANET News, quarterly - to DATANET subscribers and the public on request; DATANET PLUS mapping software users guide. **Remarks:** FAX: (612)297-5368. Alternate telephone number(s): (612)296-6866. Mapping software is for sale. **Formerly:** Minnesota State Planning Agency - Planning Information Center.

★10477★
Minnesota (State) Department of Administration - Intertechnologies Group - Library (Info Sci)
Centennial Office Bldg., 5th Fl. Phone: (612)296-4621
St. Paul, MN 55155 Pat Loehlein, Libn.
Founded: 1972. **Staff:** 2. **Subjects:** Computers, management information systems, telecommunications, video communications. **Holdings:** 150 shelves of program listings and documents; technical manuals. **Subscriptions:** 70 trade publications. **Services:** Library open to the public. **Computerized Information Services:** DIALOG Information Services; CD-ROM (Computer Select); IBM (electronic mail service). **Networks/Consortia:** Member of MINITEX Library Information Network, Capital Area Library Consortium (CALCO). **Remarks:** FAX: (612)297-5368.

★10478★
Minnesota (State) Department of Education - Interagency Resource and Information Center (Educ)
501 Capitol Sq.
550 Cedar St. Phone: (612)296-6684
St. Paul, MN 55101 Pat Tupper, Lib.Prog.Dir.
Founded: 1970. **Staff:** Prof 3; Other 2. **Subjects:** Education - elementary, secondary, higher; vocational rehabilitation; disabled and handicapped

employment; adult basic education. **Special Collections:** Minnesota K-12 curriculum collection (microfiche). **Holdings:** 8000 books; 2000 Minnesota State documents on microfiche; ERIC microfiche collection. **Subscriptions:** 500 journals and other serials. **Services:** Interlibrary loan; center open to the public for reference use only. **Automated Operations:** Computerized public access catalog, cataloging, serials, and ILL. **Computerized Information Services:** CompuServe Information Service, BRS Information Technologies, DIALOG Information Services, WILSONLINE; Educational Research Information Services (internal database); electronic mail service. Performs searches on fee basis. **Networks/Consortia:** Member of MINITEX Library Information Network, Capital Area Library Consortium (CALCO), Metronet. **Publications:** Bibliographies, irregular. **Special Indexes:** KWIC index to vocational rehabilitation (1970-1973). **Remarks:** Includes partial holdings of Minnesota State Division of Vocational Rehabilitation, Minnesota State University Board, Minnesota State Board for Vocational and Technical Education, Higher Education Coordinating Board, and Community College Board. FAX: (612)296-3272. **Staff:** Lois Byrum, Sr.Libn.; Shirlee Sherkow, Ref.Libn.

★ 10479 ★
Minnesota (State) Department of Education - Office of Library Development and Services - Library (Info Sci)
440 Capitol Sq. Bldg.
550 Cedar St. Phone: (612)296-2821
St. Paul, MN 55101 Darlene M. Arnold, Sr.Libn.
Founded: 1901. **Staff:** Prof 1; Other 2. **Subjects:** Library and information science. **Special Collections:** Minnesota Public Library annual reports. **Holdings:** 10,000 volumes; 30 VF drawers of pamphlets and clippings. **Subscriptions:** 250 journals and other serials. **Services:** Interlibrary loan; copying; in-depth reference services; library open for use and loan to all interested persons; mail and phone requests accepted. **Automated Operations:** Computerized public access catalog and cataloging (PALS). **Computerized Information Services:** WILSONLINE, DataTimes, DIALOG Information Services; ALANET (electronic mail service). **Networks/Consortia:** Member of MINITEX Library Information Network, Metronet, Capital Area Library Consortium (CALCO). **Publications:** Minnesota Libraries, 2/year - free to libraries in Minnesota, other states on exchange. **Special Catalogs:** Look & Listen, AV catalog - free upon request within Minnesota. **Remarks:** FAX: (612)296-3272. Electronic mail address(es): ALA 0238 (ALANET).

★ 10480 ★
Minnesota (State) Department of Health - Robert N. Barr Public Health Library (Med)
717 Delaware St., S.E.
Box 9441 Phone: (612)623-5090
Minneapolis, MN 55440 Diane Jordan, Chf., Lib.Serv.
Founded: 1872. **Staff:** Prof 2; Other 3. **Subjects:** Public health; health planning, promotion, statistics, administration; disease prevention; epidemiology. **Holdings:** 5000 books; 5000 bound periodical volumes; 48 VF drawers of pamphlets. **Subscriptions:** 275 journals and other serials. **Services:** Interlibrary loan; library open to the public for reference use only. **Computerized Information Services:** BRS Information Technologies, DIALOG Information Services, NLM. **Networks/Consortia:** Member of Capital Area Library Consortium (CALCO), National Network of Libraries of Medicine - Greater Midwest Region, Metronet, MINITEX Library Information Network, Twin Cities Biomedical Consortium (TCBC). **Special Catalogs:** MDH Literature Catalog; MDH Film Catalog. **Remarks:** FAX: (612)623-5043 (must address to library). **Staff:** Nancy Hoppenjans; Connie Neuman; Valerie Soloujous.

★ 10481 ★
Minnesota (State) Department of Human Services - DHS Library & Resource Center (Med)
Human Services Bldg.
444 Lafayette Rd. Phone: (612)297-8708
St. Paul, MN 55155-3821 Colleen Spadaccini, Libn.
Staff: Prof 1; Other 1. **Subjects:** Psychiatry, geriatrics, social issues, training. **Holdings:** 4000 volumes; 100 videocassettes. **Subscriptions:** 177 journals and other serials. **Services:** Interlibrary loan; copying; SDI; center open to the public. **Automated Operations:** Computerized public access catalog, cataloging, acquisitions, and serials. **Computerized Information Services:** DIALOG Information Services, BRS Information Technologies; DOCLINE (electronic mail service). Performs searches on fee basis. **Networks/Consortia:** Member of MINITEX Library Information Network, National Network of Libraries of Medicine - Greater Midwest Region. **Publications:** New Materials List, monthly - for internal distribution only. **Special Catalogs:** Consortium Union List (online). **Remarks:** Formerly its DHS Information Center located in Minnetonka, MN. Headquarters of Minnesota Department of Human Services Library Consortium. FAX: (612)296-6244.

★ 10482 ★
Minnesota (State) Department of Jobs and Training - Office of Economic Opportunity - Library (Soc Sci)
670 American Center Bldg. Phone: (612)296-8400
St. Paul, MN 55101 Linda K. Woodstrom, Libn.
Staff: Prof 1; Other 1. **Subjects:** Poverty, employment programs. **Holdings:** 3000 books; training films and materials; government reports. **Subscriptions:** 142 journals and other serials. **Services:** Interlibrary loan; library open to the public with restrictions. **Automated Operations:** Computerized cataloging. **Computerized Information Services:** DIALOG Information Services, OCLC. **Networks/Consortia:** Member of MINITEX Library Information Network, Capital Area Library Consortium (CALCO), Metronet.

★ 10483 ★
Minnesota (State) Department of Natural Resources - DNR Library (Env-Cons)
500 Lafayette Rd.
Box 21 Phone: (612)297-4929
St. Paul, MN 55155-4021 Colleen Mlecoch, Lib.Dir.
Founded: 1985. **Staff:** Prof 2; Other 1. **Subjects:** Natural resources, fish and wildlife, forestry, minerals, public lands, waters. **Special Collections:** Minnesota Ornithological Records-Systematic Checklist of Minnesota Birds (9 VF drawers of species files). **Holdings:** 15,000 books. **Subscriptions:** 300 journals and other serials. **Services:** Interlibrary loan; library open to the public for reference use only. **Automated Operations:** Computerized public access catalog and cataloging. **Computerized Information Services:** DIALOG Information Services, OCLC, MSUS/PALS; DNR Management Guidelines (internal database). Performs searches. **Networks/Consortia:** Member of Capital Area Library Consortium (CALCO). **Remarks:** FAX: (612)296-3500. **Staff:** Madeline Douglass, Ref.Libn.

★ 10484 ★
Minnesota (State) Department of Revenue - Minnesota Revenue Library (Bus-Fin)
10 River Park Plaza Phone: (612)296-3529
St. Paul, MN 55107 Donna Slamkowski, Sr.Libn.
Founded: 1986. **Staff:** Prof 1; Other 1. **Subjects:** Tax policy, Minnesota taxation. **Special Collections:** National Association of Tax Administrators; Federation of Tax Administrators; Tax Institute of America; National Tax Association; Multistate Tax Commission; Tax Notes Microfiche, January 1987 to present (2 drawers). **Holdings:** 3000 books; 1000 tax reports; looseleaf services, 1931 to present. **Subscriptions:** 153 journals and other serials. **Services:** Interlibrary loan; library open to the public by appointment. **Automated Operations:** Computerized public access catalog and cataloging (PALS). **Computerized Information Services:** DIALOG Information Services, OCLC, Veralex 2, LEXIS, DataTimes, UnCover. **Networks/Consortia:** Member of MINITEX Library Information Network, Capital Area Library Consortium (CALCO). **Publications:** Revenue Library (book list), monthly. **Remarks:** FAX: (612)297-5309.

★ 10485 ★
Minnesota (State) Department of Trade and Economic Development - Library (Energy)
150 E. Kellogg Blvd., Rm. 900 Phone: (612)296-8902
St. Paul, MN 55101-1421 Pat Fenton, Sr.Libn.
Staff: Prof 2; Other 1. **Subjects:** Energy conservation, economic development, biomass energy, energy policy, trade. **Special Collections:** NTIS - SRIM energy microfiche (80,000). **Holdings:** 12,000 books. **Subscriptions:** 250 journals and other serials; 6 newspapers. **Services:** Interlibrary loan; copying; library open to the public. **Automated Operations:** Computerized public access catalog and cataloging (PALS). **Computerized Information Services:** DIALOG Information Services, DataTimes, VU/TEXT Information Services, OCLC. **Networks/Consortia:** Member of MINITEX Library Information Network, Metronet. **Publications:** New books and journals list, monthly. **Remarks:** FAX: (612)296-1290; 297-1291. Maintains an energy information telephone service for Minnesota residents. The toll-free number is (800)652-9747. **Staff:** Galina Mogilyansky, Libn.

★ 10486 ★
Minnesota (State) Department of Transportation - Information Services Center (Trans)
B-23 State Transportation Bldg. Phone: (612)296-2385
St. Paul, MN 55155 Jerome C. Baldwin, Dir., Info.Serv.
Founded: 1957. **Staff:** Prof 4; Other 4. **Subjects:** Transportation planning and engineering. **Holdings:** 5000 books; 4500 reports; 100 pamphlets;p 10,000 microfiche. **Subscriptions:** 400 journals and other serials. **Services:** Interlibrary loan; copying; center open to the public. **Automated Operations:** Computerized cataloging, circulation, serials, acquisitions, and ILL. **Computerized Information Services:** DIALOG Information Services, OCLC; DataTimes; electronic mail service. **Networks/Consortia:** Member of MINITEX Library Information Network, Metronet, Capital Area Library Consortium (CALCO). **Remarks:** FAX: (612)297-2354. **Staff:** Pamela Newsome, Info.Rsrc.Spec.; Sheila Hatchell, Info.Rsrc.Spec.

Minnesota (State) Division of Vocational Rehabilitation
See: **Minnesota (State) Department of Education - Interagency Resource and Information Center** (10478)

Minnesota (State) Higher Education Coordinating Board
See: **Minnesota (State) Department of Education - Interagency Resource and Information Center** (10478)

★ 10487 ★
Minnesota State Horticultural Society - Library (Biol Sci)
161 Alderman Hall
1970 Folwell Ave. Phone: (612)624-7752
St. Paul, MN 55108 Dorothy Johnson, Exec.Dir.
Staff: 1. **Subjects:** Gardening, natural history, botany. **Holdings:** 2000 volumes. **Services:** Library open to the public for reference use only.

★ 10488 ★
Minnesota (State) Iron Range Research Center - State Government Library (Hist)
Hwy. West 169
Box 392 Phone: (218)254-3325
Chisholm, MN 55719 Dana Miller, Dir.
Founded: 1979. **Staff:** Prof 3; Other 5. **Subjects:** Minnesota Mesabi, Vermilion, and Cuyuna Iron Ranges - mining, labor, local, lumbering and oral histories; local government; genealogy. **Special Collections:** Jones & Laughlin Hill Annex Mining operation records; Oliver Iron Mining Company drawings, survey materials, and photographs; Butler Brothers/ Hanna Mining Company records; Civilian Conservation Corps in northeastern Minnesota; Hibbing Finnish Temperance Union records; Chisholm School Superintendent's records, 1903-1943; U.S.D.A. Superior National Forest records. **Holdings:** 3499 books; 188 bound periodical volumes; 4427 reels of microfilm; 37,027 accessioned photographs; 1067 oral history tapes; 2253 linear feet of government records; 885.75 linear feet of manuscripts; 70 theses and dissertations; 623 maps; 1616 pamphlets; 16 films; 67 cassette tapes; 179 bound volumes; 118 videotapes. **Subscriptions:** 144 journals and other serials; 14 newspapers. **Services:** Interlibrary loan; copying; library open to the public. **Automated Operations:** Computerized cataloging. **Computerized Information Services:** OCLC; internal databases. Performs searches free of charge. **Networks/Consortia:** Member of MINITEX Library Information Network, North Country Library Cooperative (NCLC). **Publications:** It Was A Good Deal: The Civilian Conservation Corps in Northeastern Minnesota; A Selected Bibliography of Primary and Secondary Sources About the Finnish Experience on the Iron Range; Entrepreneurs and Immigrants; Iron Range Country. **Special Indexes:** Indexes to naturalization papers of 16 Minnesota counties; geographical indexes to federal population censuses of Minnesota, Wisconsin, Michigan, and North Dakota; index to Consolidated Chippewa Indian Census rolls, 1923-1939. **Remarks:** FAX: (218)254-4938. A division of the Iron Range Resources & Rehabilitation Board. **Staff:** Elizabeth Bright, Libn.; Edward Nelson, Archv.

★ 10489 ★
Minnesota State Law Library (Law)
25 Constitution Ave. Phone: (612)296-2775
St. Paul, MN 55155 Marvin Roger Anderson, State Law Libn.
Founded: 1849. **Staff:** Prof 6; Other 4. **Subjects:** Law. **Special Collections:** Trial transcripts for cases decided by the Minnesota Supreme Court; collected papers of retired justices of the Minnesota Supreme Court; Anglo-American and European Trial (300 volumes). **Holdings:** 220,000 volumes; Minnesota Supreme Court briefs and records, 1981 to present, on microfiche. **Subscriptions:** 675 journals and other serials; 7 newspapers. **Services:** Interlibrary loan; copying; library open to the public for reference use only. **Automated Operations:** Computerized cataloging. **Computerized Information Services:** WESTLAW, DIALOG Information Services, OCLC, WILSONLINE; internal database. Performs searches on fee basis. Contact Person: Susan K. Larson, 297-4050. **Networks/Consortia:** Member of MINITEX Library Information Network, Metronet, Capital Area Library Consortium (CALCO). **Publications:** Miscellaneous checklist, annual - to other law libraries; Loquitur (newsletter), quarterly; County Law Libraries Bulletin, 9/year; annotated bibliography of trial collection. **Remarks:** FAX: (612)296-6740. **Staff:** Sara Galligan, Hd., Tech.Serv.; R. Daniel Lunde, Hd , Pub.Serv.; Barbara Golden, Hd., Outreach Serv.

★ 10490 ★
Minnesota State Legislative Reference Library (Soc Sci)
645 State Office Bldg.
100 Constitution Ave. Phone: (612)296-3398
St. Paul, MN 55155 Marilyn Cathcart, Dir.
Founded: 1969. **Staff:** Prof 12; Other 15. **Subjects:** Minnesota state government and politics, legislative process. **Special Collections:** Clipping files, 1970 to present (arranged by subject, district, personality). **Holdings:** 30,000 volumes; Minnesota government publications, 1974 to present, on microfiche; legislative debate, on tape. **Subscriptions:** 800 journals; 40 newspapers. **Services:** Interlibrary loan; copying; SDI; library open to the public for reference use only. **Automated Operations:** Computerized public access catalog and cataloging. **Computerized Information Services:** DIALOG Information Services, DATANET, DataTimes, VU/TEXT Information Services, OCLC, NEXIS, LEGISNET; State Information System Project (internal database). **Networks/Consortia:** Member of MINITEX Library Information Network, Capital Area Library Consortium (CALCO). **Publications:** Introductions; Minnesota Resources, both monthly. **Special Indexes:** Statutory Compliance Index. **Remarks:** FAX: (612)296-9731. **Staff:** Daniel Gjelten, Dp.Dir.; Helen Whipple, Hd., Tech.Serv.

Minnesota (State) Office of Economic Opportunity
See: **Minnesota (State) Department of Jobs and Training** (10482)

Minnesota State Planning Agency - Planning Information Center - DATANET
See: **Minnesota State Department of Administration - DATANET** (10476)

★ 10491 ★
Minnesota State Pollution Control Agency - Library (Env-Cons)
520 Lafayette Rd.
St. Paul, MN 55155 Phone: (612)296-7719
Staff: Prof 2; Other 3. **Subjects:** Water, air, and noise pollution control; solid wastes pollution; hazardous waste; pesticides. **Special Collections:** NTIS Environmental Protection Agency Documents Selected Research in Microfiche (SRIM) series, 1976 to present. **Holdings:** 15,000 books and reports; 100,000 documents on microfiche. **Subscriptions:** 325 journals and other serials. **Services:** Interlibrary loan; copying; SDI; library open to the public for reference use only. **Automated Operations:** Computerized public access catalog, cataloging, journal routing, and ILL. **Computerized Information Services:** DIALOG Information Services, NLM, Chemical Information Systems, Inc. (CIS), BRS Information Technologies, Ground Water On-Line, Instructional Resources Information System (IRIS), Occupational Health Services, Inc. (OHS); TRI (Toxic Chemical Release Inventory) and other databases. Performs searches free of charge on a limited basis. **Networks/Consortia:** Member of MINITEX Library Information Network, Capital Area Library Consortium (CALCO), Metronet. **Remarks:** Alternate telephone number(s): 296-6623. FAX: (612)297-1456. **Staff:** Kathleen Malec, Libn.; Helena Peskova, Libn.

★ 10492 ★
Minnesota State Senate - Senate Information Office and Senate Index (Soc Sci)
231 State Capitol Phone: (612)296-2887
St. Paul, MN 55155 Scott Magnuson, Supv., Senate Info.Off.
Staff: 8. **Subjects:** Bills before the Minnesota State Senate, senator information, legislative process. **Holdings:** Materials on the legislative

process; legislative directories. **Services:** Open to the public. **Computerized Information Services:** Internal databases. Performs searches free of charge. **Networks/Consortia:** Member of Capital Area Library Consortium (CALCO). **Special Indexes:** Index to the Minnesota State Senate Journal (book, online). **Remarks:** Alternate telephone number(s): 296-0504; 296-4340. FAX: (612)296-6511. **Staff:** Judy Askeland, Chf. Indexer; Ric Almer, Indexer; Margot Knoll, Indexer; Robin Deane, Indexer; Manuel Vasquez, Indexer; Toni Kuehnl, Info.Spec.; Barb Burleigh, Info.Spec.

Minnesota State University Board
See: **Minnesota (State) Department of Education - Interagency Resource and Information Center** (10478)

★ 10493 ★
Minnesota Zoological Garden - Library (Biol Sci)
13000 Zoo Blvd. Phone: (612)431-9230
Apple Valley, MN 55124-8199 Angie Norell, Libn.
Founded: 1977. **Staff:** Prof 1. **Subjects:** Natural history, animal management, veterinary medicine, zoology, horticulture. **Special Collections:** International species Inventory System (ISIS) publications; zoo newsletters. **Holdings:** 3000 books. **Subscriptions:** 50 journals and other serials. **Services:** Interlibrary loan; copying; library open to the public for reference use only. **Computerized Information Services:** DIALOG Information Services; internal database. **Networks/Consortia:** Member of Capital Area Library Consortium (CALCO), MINITEX Library Information Network. **Publications:** New Books at the Zoo, irregular - for internal distribution only. **Special Indexes:** Index to animal names in titles of AAZPA proceedings, 1977-1986 (book). **Remarks:** FAX: (612)431-9300.

★ 10494 ★
Minority Business Information Institute, Inc. (MBII) - Library
130 Fifth Ave., 10th Fl.
New York, NY 10011
Defunct.

★ 10495 ★
Minot Daily News - Library (Publ)
301 Fourth St., S.E.
Box 1150 Phone: (701)852-3341
Minot, ND 58701 Shelly Bryantt, Libn.
Staff: Prof 3. **Subjects:** Newspaper reference topics. **Holdings:** 115,000 obituary files; newspaper clippings; photographs. **Services:** Copying (limited); library open to the public for reference use only. **Remarks:** FAX: (701)852-3570. Published by Buckner News Alliance. **Staff:** Debbie Sandvold.

★ 10496 ★
Minot State University - Map Library (Geog-Map)
Cyril Moore Hall
MSU Phone: (701)857-3161
Minot, ND 58701 Eric Clausen, Prof.
Founded: 1968. **Staff:** 1.5. **Subjects:** Topographic and geologic maps, air and costal navigation charts. **Special Collections:** Depository for U.S. Geological Survey and Defense Mapping Agency maps (45,000); international topographic and geologic maps (15,000). **Holdings:** 60,000 maps. **Services:** Library open to the public. **Publications:** Guide to Minot State Map Library, annual.

★ 10497 ★
Minot State University - Memorial Library (Area-Ethnic)
Minot, ND 58701 Phone: (701)857-3200
Larry Greenwood, Lib.Dir.
Founded: 1913. **Staff:** 12.5. **Special Collections:** North Dakota Collection; Indians of the North Central States; North Dakota government documents; U.S. government documents selective depository. **Holdings:** 115,710 documents. **Services:** Interlibrary loan; copying; collections open to the public with restrictions. **Computerized Information Services:** DIALOG Information Services; CD-ROMs (ERIC, Social Science Index, Magazine Article Summaries). Performs DIALOG Information Services searches on a fee basis; free of charge for CD-ROMs. **Networks/Consortia:** Member of MINITEX Library Information Network. **Remarks:** FAX: (701)839-6933. **Staff:** Susan Podrygula, Tech.Serv.; Jane LaPlante, Access Serv.; George Clark, Ref.Serv.; Marilyn Hedberg, Media Serv.

★ 10498 ★
Mint Museum - Library (Art)
2730 Randolph Rd. Phone: (704)337-2000
Charlotte, NC 28207 Sara H. Wolf, Libn.
Founded: 1958. **Staff:** 1. **Subjects:** Fine arts. **Special Collections:** Delhom-Gambrell Reference Library (decorative arts, emphasis on ceramics). **Holdings:** 8540 books; 883 bound periodical volumes; 48 shelves of exhibition and other catalogs; 60 shelves of auction catalogs. **Subscriptions:** 121 journals and other serials. **Services:** Library open to the public for reference use only.

Herbert H. Minthorn Memorial Library
See: **St. John's Medical Center** (14341)

★ 10499 ★
Mintz, Levin, Cohn, Ferris, Glovsky and Popeo, P.C. - Law Library (Law)
1 Financial Center
Boston, MA 02111 Phone: (617)542-6000
Staff: Prof 2; Other 2. **Subjects:** Federal and Massachusetts law. **Holdings:** 12,000 books; 112 bound periodical volumes; 500 unbound periodicals and pamphlets. **Subscriptions:** 300 journals and other serials. **Services:** Interlibrary loan. **Automated Operations:** Computerized cataloging. **Computerized Information Services:** LEXIS, DIALOG Information Services, Dow Jones News/Retrieval, WESTLAW. **Remarks:** FAX: (617)542-2241. **Staff:** Deidre Preston, Asst.Libn.

★ 10500 ★
Miramichi Hospital - Health Sciences Library (Med)
P.O. Box 420 Phone: (506)622-1340
Newcastle, NB, Canada E1V 3M5 Audrey D. Somers, Educ.Coord.
Founded: 1974. **Staff:** 1. **Subjects:** Medicine, nursing, administration, patient education, allied health sciences. **Holdings:** 2000 books; 186 bound periodical volumes; 194 AV programs. **Subscriptions:** 146 journals and other serials. **Services:** Interlibrary loan; copying; library open to the public with restrictions. **Publications:** Bibliographies. **Remarks:** FAX: (506)622-8768.

★ 10501 ★
Miriam Hospital - Health Sciences Library (Med)
164 Summit Ave Phone: (401)331-8500
Providence, RI 02906 MaryAnn Slocomb, Dir., Hea.Sci.Lib.
Staff: Prof 1. **Subjects:** Clinical medicine, surgery, biomedical research. **Special Collections:** Cardiology, cancer. **Holdings:** 3003 books; 9870 bound periodical volumes. **Subscriptions:** 300 journals and other serials. **Services:** Interlibrary loan; copying; SDI; library open to the public with restrictions. **Computerized Information Services:** MEDLINE. Performs searches on fee basis. **Networks/Consortia:** Member of Association of Rhode Island Health Sciences Librarians (ARIHSL). **Publications:** Annual report; Acquisitions Lists; Journal Titles List.

★ 10502 ★
Misericordia General Hospital - Hospital Library (Med)
99 Cornish Ave. Phone: (204)788-8109
Winnipeg, MB, Canada R3C 1A2 Sharon Allentuck, Libn.
Founded: 1974. **Staff:** 3. **Subjects:** Nursing, medicine, allied health sciences. **Holdings:** 5300 volumes. **Subscriptions:** 324 journals and other serials. **Services:** Interlibrary loan; library not open to the public. **Computerized Information Services:** MEDLARS. **Remarks:** FAX: (204)774-7834.

★ 10503 ★
Misericordia Hospital - Weinlos Library (Med)
16940 87th Ave. Phone: (403)486-8708
Edmonton, AB, Canada T5R 4H5 John Back, Libn.
Founded: 1969. **Staff:** Prof 1; Other 2.5. **Subjects:** Medicine, surgery, nursing, allied health sciences. **Holdings:** 3800 books. **Subscriptions:** 300 journals and other serials. **Services:** Interlibrary loan. **Computerized Information Services:** MEDLARS, CAN/OLE, DIALOG Information Services; Envoy 100 (electronic mail service). **Remarks:** FAX: (403)486-8774. Electronic mail address(es): Misericordia.Hosp (Envoy 100). **Formerly:** Its Weinlos Medical Library.

★10504★
Missing Children Minnesota - Resource Center (Soc Sci)
1025 W. Broadway Phone: (612)521-1188
Minneapolis, MN 55411 Carol Watson, Exec.Dir.
Founded: 1984. **Staff:** 1.5. **Subjects:** Missing children, preventing abduction, parental kidnapping. **Special Collections:** Missing children clippings file from Minnesota daily and weekly papers, 1989 to present. **Holdings:** 40 books; 3 AV programs; pictures of missing children. **Subscriptions:** 5 journals and other serials. **Services:** Copying; center open to the public. **Publications:** Posters of missing children; information packets on parental abduction and runaways; bibliographies. **Remarks:** Missing Children Minnesota is an all volunteer organization that acts as a local resource and information center, helps parents locate and recover missing children, and works to effect legislative change for better child protection.

★10505★
Mission Historical Society - Museum/Archives (Hist)
33201 2nd Ave. Phone: (604)826-1011
Mission, BC, Canada V2V 1J9 Dorothy Crosby, Cur./Archv.
Founded: 1972. **Subjects:** Local history, genealogy. **Holdings:** Photographs; oral history tapes; maps; clippings; interviews with pioneers. **Services:** Copying; archives open to the public on a limited schedule.

★10506★
Mission Research Corporation - Technical Library (Sci-Engr)
PO Drawer 719 Phone: (805)963-8761
Santa Barbara, CA 93102 Elaine A. Messier, Libn.
Staff: Prof 1. **Subjects:** Atmospheric physics and chemistry, radar and communication, computer programming, electromagnetics. **Holdings:** 4250 books; 100 titles of bound periodical volumes; 5000 technical reports; 50 dissertations; 200 microfiche. **Subscriptions:** 75 journals and other serials. **Services:** Library not open to the public. **Computerized Information Services:** DIALOG Information Services, NewsNet, Inc., Commerce Business Daily, DTIC, BRS Information Technologies; INFOCEN (internal database). **Publications:** MRC New Acquisitions, monthly. **Remarks:** For inquiries concerning MRC-generated technical reports, contact the Document Control Department.

★10507★
Mission Research Corporation - Technical Library (Sci-Engr)
1720 Randolph Rd., S.E. Phone: (505)768-7600
Albuquerque, NM 87106 Georgiana Hillyer, Libn.
Founded: 1984. **Staff:** 1. **Subjects:** Effects of nuclear weapons, plasma physics. **Holdings:** 1300 books; 9500 documents; 550 microfiche. **Subscriptions:** 25 journals and other serials. **Services:** Library not open to the public. **Automated Operations:** Computerized cataloging. **Computerized Information Services:** DIALOG Information Services. **Remarks:** FAX: (505)768-7601.

★10508★
Missionswerk Bayern - Missisonskolleg Bibliothek (Rel-Phil)
Johann Flierl Str 22
Postfach 68
W-8806 Neuendettelsau, Germany Phone: 9874 9257
Staff: 1. **Subjects:** Missions - theology, Africa, Pacific. **Holdings:** 15,000 books. **Subscriptions:** 60 journals and other serials. **Services:** Copying; library open to the public. **Remarks:** FAX: 9874 9330. Telex: 61458 mwbnau d.

★10509★
Missisquoi Historical Society - Cornell Mill Museum - Reference Library & Archives (Hist)
Box 186 Phone: (514)248-3153
Stanbridge East, PQ, Canada J0J 2H0 Judy Antle, Archv.
Founded: 1964. **Subjects:** Eastern Townships of Quebec - genealogy, history, biography, geography; Canadiana; antiques. **Special Collections:** Missisquoi Historical Society Histories and Reports; Archives (late 18th century historical records, primarily from Missiquoi County: school, church, and business surveys, family documents); rare book collection. **Holdings:** 4000 books; 50 bound periodical volumes; 693 reports, manuscripts, clippings, documents, maps, oral history tapes. **Services:** Interlibrary loan; copying; library open to the public for reference use only. **Publications:** Missisquoi Historical Society reports. **Special Catalogs:** Catalog of archives material (book with indexes); catalogs of reports, documents, artifacts, and cemeteries. **Remarks:** The society provides a genealogical research service by mail and provides research assistance on fee basis.

★10510★
Mississauga Hospital - L.G. Brayley Health Sciences Library (Med)
100 Queensway, W. Phone: (416)848-7394
Mississauga, ON, Canada L5B 1B8 Tsai-o Wong, Mgr., Lib.Serv.
Founded: 1981. **Staff:** 1. **Subjects:** Medicine, nursing, health, hospitals. **Special Collections:** Hospital archival materials. **Holdings:** 3000 books; 300 bound periodical volumes; archives. **Subscriptions:** 171 journals and other serials. **Services:** Interlibrary loan; copying; SDI; library open to the public. **Computerized Information Services:** MEDLINE.

★10511★
Mississippi Baptist Convention Board - Mississippi Baptist Historical Commission (Rel-Phil)
P.O. Box 51 Phone: (601)925-3434
Clinton, MS 39060-0051 Jack Winton Gunn, Ph.D., Exec.Sec.
Founded: 1926. **Staff:** Prof 2; Other 1. **Subjects:** Mississippi Baptist history. **Special Collections:** Baptist churches' and Baptist associations in Mississippi minutes. **Holdings:** 900 books; 655 bound periodical volumes; 733 reels of microfilm; 344 slides; 6 manuscripts; 240 cassette tapes; 40 VF drawers of subjects related to Mississippi Baptist history; 486 linear feet of serial publications. **Subscriptions:** 90 journals and other serials; 18 newspapers. **Services:** Copying; library open to the public. **Publications:** A History of Mississippi Baptists, 1780-1970; Highlights of Mississippi Baptist History (rev. 1990); Mississippi Baptist Convention Ministers: Current Biographies (1986). **Special Indexes:** Selective index to The (Mississippi) Baptist Record, 1877 to present (card). **Remarks:** Collection housed in Mississippi College Library. **Staff:** Alice G. Cox, Libn.; Jean Street, Indexer.

★10512★
Mississippi Baptist Medical Center - Library (Med)
1225 North State Street Phone: (601)968-4187
Jackson, MS 39202-2002 Cecelia Bell, Hea.Sci.Libn.
Founded: 1957. **Staff:** 1. **Subjects:** Medicine, nursing. **Holdings:** 1500 books; 6000 bound periodical volumes. **Subscriptions:** 151 journals and other serials. **Services:** Interlibrary loan; library not open to the public. **Computerized Information Services:** NLM. **Remarks:** FAX: (601)968-1078.

★10513★
Mississippi College - Special Collections (Rel-Phil)
Box 127 Phone: (601)925-3438
Clinton, MS 39060 Rachel H. Smith, Act.Hd.Libn.
Founded: 1826. **Staff:** Prof 11; Other 6.5. **Special Collections:** Mississippi Baptist Historical Collection; state documents. **Services:** Interlibrary loan; copying; library open to the public for reference use only. **Computerized Information Services:** DIALOG Information Services. Performs searches. Contact Person: Ann Weill, Circ.Libn. **Publications:** Library Handbook; Periodicals Holdings List.

★10514★
Mississippi College School of Law - Law Library (Law)
151 E. Griffith St. Phone: (601)944-1970
Jackson, MS 39201 Carol C. West, Dir.
Founded: 1975. **Staff:** Prof 5; Other 5.5. **Subjects:** Law. **Holdings:** 201,000 volumes. **Subscriptions:** 750 journals and other serials. **Services:** Interlibrary loan; library not open to the public. **Automated Operations:** Computerized cataloging. **Computerized Information Services:** WESTLAW, OCLC, LEXIS, NEXIS. **Networks/Consortia:** Member of SOLINET. **Publications:** Selected List Of Acquisitions, irregular. **Remarks:** FAX: (601)353-7111. **Staff:** Carnette McMillan, Acq.Libn.; Karin Den Bleyker, Cat.Libn.; Maurine Mattson, Pub.Serv.Libn.

★10515★
Mississippi Museum of Art - Howorth Library (Art)
201 E. Pascagoula St. Phone: (601)960-1515
Jackson, MS 39201 Mary Gee, Asst.Cur. of Educ.
Founded: 1978. **Staff:** 3. **Subjects:** Art history and education, travel. **Holdings:** 1300 books; art history slides; periodicals. **Services:** Copying; center open to museum members, education professionals, and volunteers. **Remarks:** FAX: (601)960-1505.

Mississippi Museum of Natural Science
See: **Mississippi (State) Department of Wildlife Conservation** (10522)

Mississippi River Commission
See: **U.S. Army - Corps of Engineers - Lower Mississippi Valley Division** (16947)

★10516★
Mississippi State Agricultural & Forestry Experiment Station - Delta Branch Experiment Station Library (Sci-Engr, Agri)
Stoneville, MS 38776 Phone: (601)686-9311
Charlotte G. Pierce, Libn.
Founded: 1966. **Staff:** Prof 1; Other 1. **Subjects:** Agriculture, botany, agricultural economics, mathematics, agricultural engineering, meteorology. **Special Collections:** Mississippi Agricultural and Forestry Experiment Station publications; U.S. Department of Agriculture publications. **Holdings:** 14,000 books; 5500 bound periodical volumes; 348 reels of microfilm; 25,000 pamphlets. **Subscriptions:** 222 journals and other serials; 10 newspapers. **Services:** Interlibrary loan; library open to the public. **Publications:** New Books List, irregular. **Special Indexes:** Subject and author indexes of publications of staff members; chronological index of publications of the Agricultural and Forestry Experiment Station. **Remarks:** FAX: (601)686-7336.

★10517★
Mississippi (State) Department of Archives and History - Archives and Library Division (Hist)
P.O. Box 571 Phone: (601)359-6850
Jackson, MS 39205 H.T. Holmes, Div.Dir.
Founded: 1902. **Staff:** Prof 14; Other 7. **Subjects:** Mississippiana, genealogy, Confederate history, colonial history of Southeast United States. **Special Collections:** Eudora Welty Collection; Television Newsfilm Archives (2 million feet). **Holdings:** 45,000 volumes; 11,662 cubic feet of documents; 2000 manuscript collections; 24,000 nonbook items; 4000 cubic feet of manuscripts; 6509 cubic feet of official state archives; 7095 maps; 12,500 reels of microfilm; 11,587 photographs; 1 million feet of newsfilm; 2203 architectural drawings; 158 VF drawers. **Subscriptions:** 370 journals and other serials; 137 newspapers. **Services:** Copying; library open to the public for reference use only. **Computerized Information Services:** SuperCat; Infornix, Supernet (internal databases). **Publications:** List of publications - available on request. **Remarks:** Alternate telephone number(s): 359-6850. FAX: (601)359-6905. **Staff:** Forrest Galey, Cur., Spec.Coll.; Anne Lipscomb, Hd.Libn.; Dwight Harris, Archv., Govt.Rec.

★10518★
Mississippi (State) Department of Education - Educational Media Services (Educ)
701 Walter Sillers Bldg., Suite 604
Box 771 Phone: (601)359-3778
Jackson, MS 39205 Carol Furr, Media Spec.
Staff: Prof 1; Other 1. **Subjects:** Education. **Holdings:** ERIC documents. **Subscriptions:** 130 journals and other serials. **Services:** Interlibrary loan; copying; services open to educators. **Computerized Information Services:** BRS Information Technologies. Performs searches free of charge. **Remarks:** FAX: (601)359-2326.

★10519★
Mississippi (State) Department of Environmental Quality - Library (Sci-Engr, Energy)
P.O. Box 20307 Phone: (601)961-5024
Jackson, MS 39289-1307 Carolyn Woodley, Libn.
Founded: 1906. **Staff:** Prof 1. **Subjects:** Geology, paleontology, mineralogy, geohydrology, geophysics, foreign geology, environmental pollution, hazardous wastes. **Special Collections:** U.S. Geological Survey depository; EPA reports; state Geological Survey publications; Geological Society guidebooks; Nuclear Waste Reference Collection (12,000 books). **Holdings:** Books, dissertations, topographic maps, microforms, and government documents. **Subscriptions:** 94 journals and other serials. **Services:** Interlibrary loan; copying; library open to the public. **Automated Operations:** Computerized cataloging. **Computerized Information Services:** PFDS Online. **Remarks:** Library located at 2380 Hwy. 80 W., Southport Center, MS. **Remarks:** FAX: (601)354-6965. **Formerly:** Its Bureau of Geology - Library.

★10520★
Mississippi (State) Department of Health - Audiovisual Library (Aud-Vis)
2343 N. State St.
Box 1700 Phone: (601)960-7675
Jackson, MS 39205 Nancy Kay Sullivan, Dir., P.R.
Founded: 1940. **Staff:** Prof 1; Other 2. **Subjects:** Alcohol, dental health, diseases, drug addiction and narcotics, family planning, nursing, nutrition. **Holdings:** 1800 16mm films; 300 35mm filmstrips; 250 videotapes. **Services:** Library open to Mississippi residents only. **Remarks:** FAX: (601)960-7948. **Staff:** Carolyn Ainsworth, Film Libn.

★10521★
Mississippi (State) Department of Mental Health - Library (Med)
1101 Robert E. Lee Bldg. Phone: (601)359-1288
Jackson, MS 39201 Margueritte D. Ransom, Libn.
Founded: 1975. **Staff:** 1. **Subjects:** Mental health and illness; mental retardation; child and adolescent mental health; alcohol and drug abuse. **Holdings:** 2600 books; 24 linear feet of departmental reports; 12 VF drawers of other cataloged items. **Subscriptions:** 9 journals and other serials. **Services:** Interlibrary loan; library open to the public with restrictions. **Computerized Information Services:** DIALOG Information Services (staff use only). **Publications:** Newsletter, quarterly; bibliography, annual - both for internal distribution only.

★10522★
Mississippi (State) Department of Wildlife Conservation - Mississippi Museum of Natural Science - Library (Biol Sci)
The Fannye A. Cook Memorial
111 N. Jefferson St. Phone: (601)354-7303
Jackson, MS 39201 Mary P. Stevens, Musm.Libn.
Founded: 1973. **Staff:** Prof 1. **Subjects:** Ornithology, ichthyology, herpetology, mammology, botany, invertebrata, paleontology. **Special Collections:** Fannye A. Cook Collection (500 books; 1500 periodicals; 1000 reprints); rare book collection (26). **Holdings:** 6000 books; 200 bound periodical volumes; 12 VF drawers. **Subscriptions:** 102 journals. **Services:** Interlibrary loan; copying; library open to the public for reference use only. **Automated Operations:** Computerized cataloging. **Computerized Information Services:** DIALOG Information Services, OCLC. **Remarks:** FAX: (601)354-7226.

★10523★
Mississippi (State) Highway Department - Research and Development Division - Library (Trans)
Box 1850 Phone: (601)359-1174
Jackson, MS 39215-1850 Susan Gorshe, Libn.
Staff: Prof 1. **Subjects:** Transportation, highways. **Holdings:** 10,000 reports. **Subscriptions:** 52 bulletins and newsletters. **Services:** Library not open to the public. **Publications:** Highway Employees News (newsletter), bimonthly - for internal distribution only. **Remarks:** FAX: (601)359-2233.

★10524★
Mississippi State Law Library (Law)
Gartin Justice Bldg., 450 High St.
Box 1040 Phone: (601)359-3672
Jackson, MS 39215-1040 Mary E. Miller, State Libn.
Founded: 1838. **Staff:** Prof 3; Other 2. **Subjects:** Law. **Holdings:** 154,000 volumes. **Subscriptions:** 243 journals and other serials. **Services:** Copying; library open to the public. **Networks/Consortia:** Member of Central Mississippi Library Council. **Remarks:** FAX: (601)359-2912. **Staff:** Betty R. Mullins, Asst. Law Libn.

★10525★
Mississippi (State) Library Commission (Info Sci)
Box 10700 Phone: (601)359-1036
Jackson, MS 39289-0700 David M. Woodburn, Dir.
Founded: 1926. **Staff:** Prof 42; Other 31. **Subjects:** General collection, library science. **Special Collections:** Mississippi; materials for the handicapped. **Holdings:** 184,751 books; 1815 microforms; 2500 videotapes; 4859 AV programs; vertical files of Mississippi materials; 132,000 sound recordings and tapes for the handicapped; 5400 braille volumes; 460 software programs. **Subscriptions:** 665 journals and other serials. **Services:** Interlibrary loan; copying; library open to state employees for job-related

purposes. **Automated Operations:** Computerized public access catalog, cataloging, acquisitions, circulation, serials, and ILL. **Computerized Information Services:** DIALOG Information Services; CD-ROM; produces MAILS (Mississippi Automated Interlibrary Loan System). **Networks/ Consortia:** Member of SOLINET, Central Mississippi Library Council. **Publications:** The Packet, monthly - primarily to public libraries; The Reading Light, quarterly - to handicapped patrons and public libraries. **Special Catalogs:** Union catalog (CD-ROM, microfiche); large print catalog. **Special Indexes:** Mississippi State Government Publications Index. **Remarks:** FAX: (601)354-4181. **Staff:** Jane Smith, Dp.Dir.; Sharman Smith, Dir., Lib.Serv.

★10526★
Mississippi State University - College of Veterinary Medicine - Branch Library (Med)
Drawer V Phone: (601)325-1240
Mississippi State, MS 39762 June Breland, Br.Libn.
Founded: 1978. **Staff:** Prof 1; Other 2. **Subjects:** Veterinary medicine, medicine, allied health sciences, animal husbandry, agriculture, science and technology. **Holdings:** 8705 books; 6157 bound periodical volumes; 181 resource and vertical files; 1346 reference monographs; 1462 16mm films, videotapes, and slide programs. **Subscriptions:** 259 journals and other serials. **Services:** Interlibrary loan; copying; SDI; library open to the public with restrictions. **Automated Operations:** Computerized cataloging, circulation, acquisitions, and ILL. **Computerized Information Services:** DIALOG Information Services, OCLC (available through Main Library); internal databases; InterNet (electronic mail service). Performs searches on fee basis. **Networks/Consortia:** Member of SOLINET, Mississippi Biomedical Library Consortium (MBLC). **Remarks:** FAX: (601)325-1498. Electronic mail address(es): jkb2@ra.msstate.edu (InterNet).

★10527★
Mississippi State University - Mitchell Memorial Library - Special Collections (Hist)
P.O. Drawer 5408 Phone: (601)325-3060
Mississippi State, MS 39762 Frances N. Coleman, Hd. of Tech.Serv.
Staff: Prof 4; Other 3. **Subjects:** State and local history, U.S. Congress, Southern history and politics. **Special Collections:** John C. Stennis Collection; G.V. "Sonny" Montgomery Collection; David Bowen Collection; Mississippi politics; Hodding and Betty Werlein Carter papers; Turner Catledge papers; Gil Carmichael Papers; Bill Minor Papers; Norma Fields Papers; Delta and Pine Land Company Records; Mississippi Republican Party Papers; University Archives. **Holdings:** 38,393 books; 2225 bound periodical volumes; 1294 titles in microform; 87 VF drawers; 9137 linear feet of manuscripts. **Subscriptions:** 2 newspapers. **Services:** Interlibrary loan; copying; collections open to the public for reference and research. **Automated Operations:** Computerized cataloging, serials, and circulation. **Computerized Information Services:** OCLC, DIALOG Information Services. **Networks/Consortia:** Member of SOLINET. **Publications:** Guide to the Public Series in the John C. Stennis Collection; Guide to Manuscript Holdings at Mississippi State University. **Remarks:** FAX: (601)325-3560. **Staff:** Mattie Sink, Mss.Libn.; Lynne Mueller, Ref.Libn.; Michael Ballard, Assoc.Univ.Archv.

★10528★
Mississippi State University - Raspet Flight Research Laboratory - Library (Sci-Engr)
Dept. of Aerospace Engineering
Drawer A
Mississippi State, MS 39762 Phone: (601)325-3623
Founded: 1948. **Subjects:** Air vehicle aerodynamics and flight dynamics data, 1948-1965. **Holdings:** 10,000 volumes. **Services:** Library is accessible on a restricted basis.

★10529★
Mississippi Valley Conservation Authority - R. Tait McKenzie Research Library (Art)
R.R. 1, The Mill of Kintail Phone: (613)256-3610
Almonte, ON, Canada K0A 1A0 Carol Munden, Cur.
Founded: 1977. **Staff:** Prof 1. **Subjects:** R. Tait McKenzie, sculpture, local history, museology. **Special Collections:** Original sculptures by Dr. R. Tait McKenzie. **Holdings:** 300 books; 400 bound periodical volumes; 75 reports; 500 archives. **Subscriptions:** 2 journals and other serials. **Services:** Library open to researchers by appointment.

★10530★
Mississippi Valley State University - James Herbert White Library - Special Collections (Hist)
Itta Bena, MS 38941 Phone: (601)254-9041
Dr. Robbie R. Henderson, Dir.
Founded: 1952. **Special Collections:** Education; Martin Luther King, Jr. Collection; Mississippi history. **Services:** Interlibrary loan; copying; collections open to the public for reference use only. **Remarks:** FAX: (601)254-6704.

★10531★
Missoulian Newspaper - Library (Publ)
Box 8029 Phone: (406)523-5245
Missoula, MT 59807 Kathleen R. Kimble, Libn.
Founded: 1900. **Staff:** 1. **Subjects:** Newspaper reference topics, Montana. **Holdings:** 400 books; Missoulian Newspaper on microfilm, 1893 to present. **Subscriptions:** 3 journals and other serials. **Services:** Library not open to the public. **Computerized Information Services:** Internal database. **Remarks:** FAX: (406)523-5221.

★10532★
Missouri Baptist Historical Commission Library (Hist)
William Jewell College Library
500 College Hill
Liberty, MO 64068 Phone: (816)781-3806
Founded: 1885. **Staff:** 1. **Subjects:** Church history, biography. **Holdings:** 1579 books; 178 bound periodical volumes; 406 manuscripts and pictures; 7 VF drawers of metal cuts, photographs, clippings, reports; church records and histories. **Services:** Copying; library open to the public for reference use only.

★10533★
Missouri Baptist Medical Center - Medical Library (Med)
3015 N. Ballas Rd. Phone: (314)432-1212
St. Louis, MO 63131 Sandra Decker, Med.Libn.
Founded: 1966. **Staff:** Prof 2. **Subjects:** Medicine, allied health sciences. **Holdings:** 645 books; 2200 bound periodical volumes. **Subscriptions:** 150 journals and other serials. **Services:** Interlibrary loan. **Computerized Information Services:** BRS Information Technologies. **Networks/ Consortia:** Member of National Network of Libraries of Medicine - Midcontinental Region. **Remarks:** FAX: (314)569-2078.

★10534★
Missouri Baptist Medical Center - School of Nursing Library (Med)
3015 N. Ballas Rd. Phone: (314)569-5193
St. Louis, MO 63131 Carolyn McGinty, Libn.
Founded: 1921. **Staff:** Prof 1. **Subjects:** Nursing, medicine, psychology. **Holdings:** 2500 books; AV programs. **Subscriptions:** 55 journals and other serials. **Services:** Interlibrary loan; library not open to the public.

★10535★
Missouri Botanical Garden - Library (Biol Sci)
Box 299 Phone: (314)577-5155
St. Louis, MO 63166 Constance P. Wolf, Libn.
Founded: 1859. **Staff:** Prof 7; Other 7. **Subjects:** Plant taxonomy and floristics, horticulture, botanical history and exploration. **Special Collections:** Sturtevant pre-Linnaean library and subsequent additions (1000 items); Linnaeana (1830 items); illustrated flower books (750 items); Engelmann correspondence (6000 letters); Engelmann notes and drawings (5000 pieces); W.C. Steere Bryological Collection (mosses and liverworts; 1000 volumes; 5000 pamphlets). **Holdings:** 52,000 books; 60,000 bound periodical volumes; 100,000 pamphlets; 500 slides; 6500 vegetation and topographic maps; 220,000 archival items; 3059 historic manuscripts; 15,000 microfiche of herbaria; 6000 art works. **Subscriptions:** 1500 journals and other serials. **Services:** Interlibrary loan; library open to the public by appointment. **Automated Operations:** Computerized cataloging and serials. **Computerized Information Services:** OCLC; internal database. **Networks/ Consortia:** Member of St. Louis Regional Library Network, Council on Botanical Horticultural Libraries. **Publications:** Monthly accessions list. **Remarks:** Library located at 2345 Tower Grove Ave., St. Louis, MO 63110. FAX: (314)577-9521. Telex: 466224 MOBOT CI. **Staff:** Martha Riley, Archv.; Zoltan Tomory, Cat.; Vicki Lee, Cons.

★10536★
Missouri Historical Society - Archives (Hist)
Jefferson Memorial Bldg.
Forest Park Phone: (314)746-5410
St. Louis, MO 63112 Peter Michel, Dir. of Lib. & Archv.
Founded: 1866. **Staff:** 4. **Subjects:** St. Louis history and culture, Missouri, Mississippi Valley, American West. **Special Collections:** Papers, journals, field notes of William Clark from his expedition with Meriwether Lewis; Louisiana Territory documents; papers of Thomas Jefferson; French and Spanish colonial administration; western exploration; North American Plains Indians; French settlement; German immigrants; Mexican and Civil Wars; business and commerce in the Missouri area; Women's Suffrage Movement; William Torrey Harris (founder of the St. Louis Philosophical Society); Charles Lindbergh; Russian Revolution; American fur trade. **Holdings:** 6000 linear feet of archival materials. **Services:** Copying; archives open to the public. **Publications:** A List of Manuscript Collections in the Archives of the Missouri Historical Society (book); In Her Own Write: Women's History Resources in the Library and Archives of the Missouri Historical Society (book). **Remarks:** FAX: (314)746-4548. **Staff:** Jean D. Streeter, Lindbergh Archv.; Martha Clevenger, Assoc.Archv.; John Furlong, Asst.Archv.

★10537★
Missouri Historical Society - Library (Hist)
225 S. Skinker Blvd. Phone: (314)746-4500
St. Louis, MO 63105 Peter Michel, Dir. of Lib. & Archv.
Founded: 1866. **Staff:** Prof 3; Other 5. **Subjects:** History - St. Louis, Missouri, Western United States, Missouri and Mississippi Rivers; fur trade; biography; genealogy; theater; music; Thomas Jefferson; early Mississippi travel; steamboats; Lewis and Clark expedition; American Indians. **Special Collections:** Western Americana; 16th century maps; music collection; early national newspapers; theater collection; scrapbook collection; 1904 World's Fair; Missouri Gazette collection (complete file). **Holdings:** 70,000 book, pamphlet, and periodical titles; 2000 bound newspaper volumes; 2500 maps. **Subscriptions:** 241 journals and other serials. **Services:** Copying; library open to the public. **Networks/Consortia:** Member of St. Louis Regional Library Network. **Publications:** Gateway Heritage, quarterly; In Her Own Write: Women's History Resources; The Lewis and Clark Expedition: A Guide to Holdings in the Division of Library and Archives of the Missouri Historical Society. **Staff:** Stephanie A. Klein, Tech.Serv.Libn.; Emily Miller, Pub.Serv.Libn.; Debbie Schraut, Cat.Libn.; Carole S. Verble, Asst.Libn.; Barbara Stole, Asst.Libn.

★10538★
Missouri Historical Society - Pictorial History Collection (Aud-Vis)
225 S. Skinker Phone: (314)746-4511
St. Louis, MO 63105 Duane Sneddeker, Cur.
Staff: 4. **Subjects:** Missouri and Western life - buildings, street scenes, Indians, theater, music, transportation, valentines, steamboats, aviation, Lindbergh pictures. **Holdings:** 200,000 photographs, postcards, prints, daguerreotypes, tintypes, ambrotypes, advertising materials. **Services:** Print and reproduction services available on fee basis; use of archives for reference may be requested. **Remarks:** FAX: (314)746-4511. **Staff:** Bryan S. Thomas, Asst.Cur.; Kirsten N. Hammerstrom, Cur.Asst., Pub.Serv.; Steven R. Call, Cur.Asst., Cat.

Missouri Institute of Mental Health
See: **University of Missouri--Columbia** (18969)

Missouri Institute of Psychiatry Library
See: **University of Missouri--Columbia** (18969)

★10539★
Missouri Rehabilitation Center - Medical Library (Med)
Mount Vernon, MO 65712-1099 Phone: (417)466-3711
Mary Ann Swearingen, Libn.Asst.
Founded: 1948. **Staff:** Prof 1. **Subjects:** Rehabilitation - respiratory, cardiac, head injury; stroke and spinal cord injuries; other disabilities. **Holdings:** 992 books; 892 periodical volumes; 91 articles by staff physicians; 212 magnetic tapes; 277 slides; 22 microfiche. **Subscriptions:** 54 journals and other serials. **Services:** Interlibrary loan; library open to the public. **Special Indexes:** Index Medicus. **Remarks:** FAX: (417)466-7257.

★10540★
Missouri School for the Blind - Library (Educ, Aud-Vis)
3815 Magnolia Ave. Phone: (314)776-4320
St. Louis, MO 63110 Mary Dingus
Staff: Prof 1. **Subjects:** General collection, special education, blind education. **Holdings:** 4000 Braille books and magazines; 4700 audio books and magazines; 900 large-print books and magazine. **Subscriptions:** 100 journals and other serials; 2 newspapers. **Services:** Library open to the public for reference use only.

★10541★
Missouri School for the Deaf - Grover C. Farquhar Library (Med)
505 E. 5th St. Phone: (314)592-2513
Fulton, MO 65251 Patsy Craghead, Libn.
Founded: 1851. **Staff:** Prof 1; Other 1. **Subjects:** Deafness, education, general collection (K-12). **Holdings:** 13,000 books; 171 bound periodical volumes; 1300 captioned films; Missouri Record on microfilm. **Subscriptions:** 35 journals and other serials; 5 newspapers. **Services:** Copying; library open to the public. **Publications:** Newsletter - for internal distribution only.

★10542★
Missouri State Archives (Hist)
600 W. Main
Box 778 Phone: (314)751-4717
Jefferson City, MO 65101 Kenneth H. Winn, State Archv.
Founded: 1965. **Staff:** 12. **Subjects:** Missouri history, genealogy. **Special Collections:** Federal census schedules (microfilm); municipal records; French and Spanish land grants, 1790-1803; United States Land Sales, 1818-1903 (26 volumes); Township School Land, Seminary and Saline Land, Swamp Land, and 500,000 Acre Grant indexes; Missouri State Penitentiary indexes, 1837-1933 (microfilm); pardon records, 1837-1901 (microfilm); Reference & Manuscript Collection (city directories, maps, reference books, church records, George Washington Carver papers, A.P. Morehouse collection); Military Records Collection (War of 1812, Black Hawk War of 1832, Heatherly War of 1836, Seminole War of 1837, Osage War of 1837, Mormon War of 1838, Iowa or Honey War of 1839, Mexican War of 1846, Civil War 1861-1865, Spanish American War of 1898, Missouri Militia 1865-1866); county records (microfilm); Supreme Court Records of Missouri, 1804-1940. **Holdings:** 1000 linear feet of books; 12,000 cubic feet of archival material; 40,000 microfiche; 25,000 reels of microfilm. **Services:** Copying; library open to the public. **Publications:** Researching Family & Community History at the Missouri State Archives; Guide to County Records on Microfilm; Historical Listing of Missouri Legislatures, 1812-1986. **Staff:** Patricia M. Luebbert, Archv.

Missouri State Coordinating Board for Higher Education - Wolfner Library for the Blind & Physically Handicapped
See: **Missouri State Library - Wolfner Library for the Blind & Physically Handicapped** (10551)

★10543★
Missouri State Court of Appeals - Law Library (Law)
111 N. 7th Phone: (314)340-6960
St. Louis, MO 63101 Laura Roy, Libn.
Founded: 1981. **Staff:** 1. **Subjects:** Law. **Holdings:** 28,500 books; 950 bound periodical volumes; 16,000 microfiche; 600 reels of microfilm. **Subscriptions:** 250 journals and other serials; 6 newspapers. **Services:** Interlibrary loan; copying; library open only for attorneys needing slip opinions. **Computerized Information Services:** LEXIS, WESTLAW. **Remarks:** FAX: (314)340-6964.

★10544★
Missouri State Court of Appeals, Southern District - Law Library (Law)
300 Hammons Pkwy. Phone: (417)895-6813
Springfield, MO 65806 Beverly Heist, Libn.
Founded: 1909. **Staff:** 1. **Subjects:** Law. **Holdings:** 15,282 volumes; microfiche. **Subscriptions:** 39 law journals. **Services:** Library not open to the public. **Remarks:** FAX: (417)895-6817.

★10545★
Missouri State Court of Appeals, Western District - Library (Law)
1300 Oak St. Phone: (816)889-3600
Kansas City, MO 64106-2907 Linda Gingrich, Libn.
Staff: Prof 1. **Subjects:** Law. **Holdings:** 43,000 volumes. **Subscriptions:** 158 journals and other serials. **Services:** Library not open to the public. **Computerized Information Services:** WESTLAW. **Remarks:** FAX: (816)474-5511, ext. 251.

★10546★
Missouri (State) Department of Economic Development - Research Library (Bus-Fin)
Truman Bldg., Rm. 770
Box 118
Jefferson City, MO 65102 Phone: (314)751-3674
Founded: 1962. **Staff:** Prof 6; Other 2. **Subjects:** Labor/manpower, economics, taxation/financing, manufacturing, agriculture, industry, natural resources, regional studies, transportation/energy, education, population. **Special Collections:** Missouri Community Profiles (200); State and other Area Manufacturer Directories (30). **Holdings:** 1200 volumes; 12 VF drawers of unbound reports and articles; tapes. **Subscriptions:** 13 journals and other serials. **Services:** Library open to the public. **Computerized Information Services:** Missouri Economic Development Information System for Communities (MEDIS; internal database). **Publications:** Missouri New and Expanding Manufacturers, annual; Missouri Corporate Planner, annual. **Remarks:** FAX: (314)751-7385. **Staff:** Earl Cannon, Mgr., Res.; Kathleen Fannin, Mgr. of Res.; John Hobbs, Res.Anl.; Larry Hood, Res.Anl.; Gary Beahan, Res.Anl.; Mark Mehmert, Res.Anl.

★10547★
Missouri (State) Department of Natural Resources - Division of Geology and Land Survey - Library and Archives (Sci-Engr)
Box 250 Phone: (314)368-2100
Rolla, MO 65401 Art Hebrank, Geol.
Founded: 1853. **Staff:** Prof 1. **Subjects:** Geology, geological engineering, water resources, mineral resources. **Holdings:** 25,000 books; 1000 bound periodical volumes; 6000 geological manuscripts, maps, charts, land surveys, dam inventories. **Subscriptions:** 135 journals and other serials. **Services:** Interlibrary loan; copying; library open to the public with staff member present.

Missouri (State) Department of Natural Resources - Division of Parks, Recreation & Historic Preservation - Deutschheim State Historic Site
See: **Deutschheim State Historic Site** (4837)

Missouri (State) Department of Natural Resources - Mark Twain Birthplace Museum
See: **Mark Twain Birthplace Museum** (16598)

Missouri (State) Division of Parks, Recreation, & Historic Preservation - Watkins Woolen Mill State Historic Site
See: **Watkins Woolen Mill State Historic Site** (20095)

★10548★
Missouri (State) Highway and Transportation Department - Public Affairs Library (Trans)
Box 270 Phone: (314)751-2840
Jefferson City, MO 65102 Sue Muck, Pub.Aff.Dir.
Founded: 1960. **Staff:** 1. **Subjects:** Highways, transportation. **Holdings:** 125 books; 1100 bound periodical volumes; 200 other cataloged items. **Subscriptions:** 125 journals and other serials. **Services:** Library open to the public with restrictions. **Remarks:** FAX: (314)751-6555.

★10549★
Missouri State Legislative Library (Law)
State Capitol Bldg. Phone: (314)751-4633
Jefferson City, MO 65101 Anne Rottmann, Libn.
Founded: 1909. **Staff:** Prof 1; Other 1. **Subjects:** Legislative problems, U.S. and state government, law. **Special Collections:** Missouri legislation, 1804 to present (350 volumes); Missouri House and Senate Journals, 1837 to present (250 volumes). **Holdings:** 6500 volumes; 33 VF drawers of miscellanea. **Subscriptions:** 70 journals and other serials. **Services:** Copying; library open to the public. **Computerized Information Services:** Missouri Bill Status Tracking System Inquiry (internal database).

★10550★
Missouri State Library (Info Sci)
Box 387 Phone: (314)751-3615
Jefferson City, MO 65102 Monteria Hightower, State Libn.
Founded: 1907. **Staff:** Prof 17; Other 25. **Subjects:** State government, social services, human services, personnel administration, taxation, statistics. **Holdings:** 80,000 books; 3409 bound periodical volumes; 75,000 microforms; federal and Missouri state documents. **Subscriptions:** 490 journals and other serials; 22 newspapers. **Services:** Interlibrary loan; copying; library open to the public. **Automated Operations:** Computerized ILL, cataloging and serials. **Computerized Information Services:** DIALOG Information Services, BRS Information Technologies; MCAT (Missouri statewide database) (internal database). **Publications:** Show-Me Libraries, quarterly; Population & Census Newsletter, quarterly; Directory of Missouri Libraries, annual; Missouri Libraries Newsletter, bimonthly; Info To GO; Update (current awareness bibliography); Wolfner Library Newsletter. **Remarks:** FAX: (314)751-3612. Maintained by the Missouri State Coordinating Board for Higher Education. **Staff:** Stanley Gardner, Asst. State Libn.; Frank Pascoe, Sr.Assoc., Govt.Serv.; M. Elizabeth Eckles, Sr.Assoc., Wolfner Lib.; William P. Davis, Sr.Assoc., Lib.Serv.; Patricia Behler, Assoc.; Marlys Davis, Assoc.; Nancy Doering, Assoc.; John Finley, Assoc.; Kate Graf, Assoc.; Ruth Hemphill, Assoc.; Madeline Matson, Assoc.; James Nelson, Assoc.; Darla Parkes, Assoc.; Janice Watson, Assoc.; Judy Muck, Reg.Cons.

★10551★
Missouri State Library - Wolfner Library for the Blind & Physically Handicapped (Aud-Vis)
Box 387 Phone: (314)751-8720
Jefferson City, MO 65102-0387 Elizabeth Eckles, Sr.Assoc./Reg.Libn.
Founded: 1924. **Staff:** Prof 2; Other 12. **Subjects:** General collection. **Holdings:** 10,042 braille books; 195,345 books on recorded discs; 67,791 cassette books; 464 large print books. **Subscriptions:** 89 journals and other serials. **Services:** Interlibrary loan; copying; library open to the public; service available on approval of application to legally blind, visually handicapped, and physically handicapped residents of Missouri who are unable to use standard print, and also to persons, institutions, and organizations working with the same. Special equipment includes braille writers and printers, closed-circuit television reading devices, Small-Talk note taker, and Kurzweil reading machine. **Automated Operations:** Computerized cataloging, acquisitions, and circulation. **Networks/Consortia:** Member of National Library Service for the Blind & Physically Handicapped (NLS). **Publications:** Newsletter (large type, braille, recorded formats), semiannual - to the public. **Remarks:** FAX: (314)751-3612. Administered by Missouri State Coordinating Board for Higher Education. **Staff:** Ruth Hemphill.

★10552★
Missouri State Supreme Court Library (Law)
Supreme Court Bldg.
High St. Phone: (314)751-2636
Jefferson City, MO 65101 D.A. Divilbiss, Libn.
Founded: 1829. **Staff:** Prof 3; Other 2. **Subjects:** Law. **Holdings:** 100,000 volumes; microfiche of Session Laws to 1900; 800 reels of microfilm of Congressional Record, 1789-1972, and the Federal Register. **Subscriptions:** 150 journals and other serials; 15 newspapers. **Services:** Interlibrary loan; copying; library open to the public. **Computerized Information Services:** LEXIS, WESTLAW. **Publications:** The Summary; The Digest - by subscription. **Remarks:** FAX: (314)751-2573. **Staff:** Tyronne Allen, Asst.Libn.; Mary Lee Stegeman, Lib.III.

Annie R. Mitchell Room
See: **Tulare County Free Library - California Historical Research Collection** (16568)

Mitchell Archives
See: **Historic Mobile Preservation Society** (7246)

★10553★
Mitchell County Historical Society - Library (Hist)
R.R. 4, Box 90 Phone: (515)732-4118
Osage, IA 50461 Cindy Youngblut, Cur.
Subjects: Local history. **Holdings:** 100 books; 3 AV programs; 250 nonbook items; newspaper clippings; school and church records. **Services:** Library open during summer weekends only. **Remarks:** Alternate telephone number(s): (515)732-3059; 732-3323. Library located at 806 Main St., Osage, IA.

Mitchell Indian Museum
See: **Kendall College - Mitchell Indian Museum** (8615)

John and Mary Mitchell Library
See: **Multnomah School of the Bible** (10856)

Mitchell Library
See: **State Library of New South Wales - Special Collections - Mitchell Library** (15689)

Mitchell Memorial Library
See: **Mississippi State University** (10527)

R.L. Mitchell Technical Center
See: **Hoechst Celanese Corporation** (7310)

★10554★
Mitchell, Silberberg & Knupp - Library (Law)
11377 W. Olympic Blvd. Phone: (213)312-2000
Los Angeles, CA 90064 Carolyn A. Pratt, Libn.
Founded: 1908. **Staff:** Prof 2; Other 1. **Subjects:** Law. **Holdings:** Figures not available. **Services:** Library not open to the public. **Automated Operations:** Computerized public access catalog and serials. **Computerized Information Services:** DIALOG Information Services, LEXIS, WESTLAW, Information America. **Staff:** Bette Page, Asst.Libn.

★10555★
William Mitchell College of Law - Warren E. Burger Library (Law)
871 Summit Ave. Phone: (612)290-6333
St. Paul, MN 55105 Ann Bateson, Lib.Dir.
Founded: 1900. **Staff:** Prof 8; Other 8. **Subjects:** Law. **Holdings:** 200,000 volumes; 300,000 microfiche; 3000 reels of microfilm. **Subscriptions:** 3000 journals and other serials. **Services:** Interlibrary loan; copying; library open to the public. **Automated Operations:** Computerized cataloging, acquisitions, and serials. **Computerized Information Services:** DIALOG Information Services, WESTLAW, LEXIS. **Networks/Consortia:** Member of MINITEX Library Information Network. **Remarks:** FAX: (612)290-6414. **Staff:** Betty Karweick; Anna Cherry; Pat Dolan; Anne Anderson; Paddy Satzer; Phyllis Marion.

★10556★
Mitel Corporation - Corporate Library (Sci-Engr)
350 Legget Dr. Phone: (613)592-2122
Kanata, ON, Canada K2K 1X3 Elaine Ilnitsky-Fowlie, Corp.Libn.
Founded: 1981. **Staff:** Prof 1; Other 1. **Subjects:** Telecommunications, electrical and electronic engineering, data communications, computer hardware and software, quality assurance and reliability, management. **Special Collections:** Military, industrial, and international standards (32,000). **Holdings:** 3000 books; 45 serials on microfilm; 500 patents; 140 AV programs; 9 VF drawers. **Subscriptions:** 77 journals and other serials. **Services:** Library not open to the public. **Automated Operations:** Computerized cataloging, acquisitions, serials, circulation, and ILL. **Computerized Information Services:** DIALOG Information Services; internal databases; Envoy 100 (electronic mail service). **Remarks:** FAX: (613)592-4784.

Sam Mitminger Library Resource Centre
See: **Mohawk College of Applied Arts and Technology** (10590)

★10557★
Mitre Corporation - Bedford Operations Library (Sci-Engr)
Burlington Rd. Phone: (617)271-7834
Bedford, MA 01730 Betsy F. Cogliano, Supv.
Founded: 1959. **Staff:** Prof 3; Other 9. **Subjects:** Engineering - systems, electrical, electronic; mathematics; computer technology. **Holdings:** 70,000 books; 2500 bound periodical volumes; 950 cassette tapes. **Subscriptions:** 700 journals and other serials; 17 newspapers. **Services:** Interlibrary loan; library open to the public with restrictions. **Automated Operations:** Computerized public access catalog, cataloging, and serials. **Computerized Information Services:** DIALOG Information Services. **Networks/Consortia:** Member of NELINET, Inc. **Publications:** New Book Listing; Current Journal Highlights; Annual Journal Listing; Computer Review, monthly - all for internal distribution only. **Remarks:** FAX: (617)271-2452. **Staff:** Susan A. Glenn, Cat.; Diana H. MacDonald, Ref.Spec.

★10558★
Mitre Corporation - Library (Sci-Engr, Mil)
7525 Colshire Dr. Phone: (703)883-6481
McLean, VA 22102 Jean A. Tatalias, Mgr.
Founded: 1964. **Staff:** Prof 11; Other 16. **Subjects:** System engineering (as a methodology); communications systems, including military communications, command, control; environmental problems; energy; mass and urban transportation; air traffic systems; other civil systems. **Holdings:** 14,000 books; 2000 bound periodical volumes; 2000 reels of microfilm of periodicals; 50,000 technical reports on microfiche. **Subscriptions:** 600 journals and other serials; 25 newspapers. **Services:** Interlibrary loan; copying; library open to researchers by appointment. **Automated Operations:** Computerized cataloging, acquisitions, and circulation. **Computerized Information Services:** DIALOG Information Services, MEDLINE, NASA/RECON, DTIC; LS/2000 (internal database). **Networks/Consortia:** Member of CAPCON Library Network, Interlibrary Users Association (IUA). **Remarks:** FAX: (703)883-5684. **Staff:** Sherri Lieberman, Ref.Libn.; Mary Kidwell, Asst.Mgr.; David Shumaker, Ref.Supv.; B.J. Fisher, Acq.Supv.; Beth Roth, Circ.Supv. & Rec.Supv.; Ingrid Dierks, Ref.Libn.

★10559★
Mitre Corporation - Technical Report Center (Sci-Engr, Mil)
Burlington Rd. Phone: (617)271-7307
Bedford, MA 01810 Betsy F. Cogliano, Supv.
Founded: 1977. **Staff:** Prof 2; Other 4. **Subjects:** Command control, communications, computer technology, electrical and electronic engineering. **Special Collections:** Air Force regulations, manuals, technical orders; Department of Defense instructions, directives, specifications, standards. **Holdings:** 125,000 technical reports. **Services:** SDI; Center not open to the public. **Automated Operations:** Computerized public access catalog. **Computerized Information Services:** DTIC, DIALOG Information Services, DOE Integrated Technical Information System (ITIS). **Publications:** Weekly Abstracts of Selected Reports - for internal distribution only. **Remarks:** FAX: (617)271-8982. **Staff:** Frank Mastrovita, Ref.

Mixing Equipment Company, Inc. - Mixco R&D Library
See: **Lightnin** (9159)

★10560★
M&M/Mars Library Research Services (Food-Bev)
800 High St. Phone: (908)850-2244
Hackettstown, NJ 07840 Susan West
Founded: 1983. **Staff:** Prof 2; Other 1. **Subjects:** Confectionery, business. **Services:** Interlibrary loan (responds to FAX requests); library not open to the public. **Computerized Information Services:** DIALOG Information Services. **Remarks:** FAX: (908)850-0918.

Mobay Chemical Corporation - Research Library
See: **Miles, Inc.** (10390)

★10561★
Mobay Corporation - Agricultural Chemicals Division - Information Resources Center (Agri)
8400 Hawthorne Rd.
Box 4913 Phone: (816)242-2235
Kansas City, MO 64120 H.E. "Ann" Davis, Libn.
Staff: Prof 1. **Subjects:** Agriculture, chemistry, botany, entomology, law, mechanical engineering, management. **Special Collections:** State Agricultural Experiment Station publications. **Holdings:** 2000 books; 3500 bound periodical volumes; 500 government documents; quarterly reports; 7800 patents. **Subscriptions:** 300 journals and other serials. **Services:** Interlibrary loan; copying; SDI; library open to the public by appointment. **Automated Operations:** Computerized cataloging. **Computerized Information Services:** DIALOG Information Services, STN International, NLM, Chemical Abstracts Service (CAS). **Networks/Consortia:** Member of Kansas City Library Network, Inc. (KCLN), Missouri Library Network Corp. (MLNC). **Remarks:** FAX: (816)242-2592.

Mobay Corporation - Animal Health Division - Mobay Animal Health Library
See: **Miles, Inc.** (10387)

★10562★
Mobay Corporation - Library (Sci-Engr)
Mobay Rd.
Pittsburgh, PA 15205 Phone: (412)777-2782
Founded: 1954. **Staff:** Prof 3. **Subjects:** Marketing, chemical plastics, polymers, business, engineering, coatings. **Holdings:** 6000 books; 3000 bound periodical volumes; market studies. **Subscriptions:** 340 journals and other serials; 12 newspapers. **Services:** Interlibrary loan; copying; center open to the public by appointment. **Computerized Information Services:** open to the public on a limited schedule. **Publications:** Periodicals Listing, annual; Annual Report Index. **Remarks:** FAX: (412)777-2758. **Staff:** Betsy Schlueter, Sr.Info.Chem.; Edwin G. La Quay, Sr.Libn.; Nancy A. Alstadt, Libn.

★10563★
Mobil Chemical Company - Edison Research Laboratory - Technical Information Services (Sci-Engr)
P.O. Box 3029 Phone: (908)321-6266
Edison, NJ 08818 W. Melnizek, Jr., Supv., Info.Serv.
Founded: 1961. **Staff:** Prof 2. **Subjects:** Polymer chemistry, plastics technology, petrochemicals, chemical engineering. **Holdings:** 10,000 books; 20,000 bound periodical volumes; 1000 government documents; U.S. chemical patents, 1967 to present; 3000 reels of microfilm of journals, patents, company research reports, laboratory notebooks. **Subscriptions:** 300 journals. **Services:** Services open to qualified researchers upon application to laboratory management. **Automated Operations:** Computerized serials and circulation. **Computerized Information Services:** DIALOG Information Services, Chemical Abstracts Service (CAS), OCLC. **Publications:** Patent News, weekly; acquisitions and internal reports, quarterly. **Remarks:** Division of Mobil Corporation. **Staff:** Eileen A. Gurney, Tech.Libn.

★10564★
Mobil Chemical Company - Information Center (Sci-Engr)
Technical Center
729 Pittsford-Palmyra Rd.
Box 798 Phone: (315)986-5027
Macedon, NY 14502-0798 Candice M. Johnson, Info.Anl.
Founded: 1963. **Staff:** Prof 1; Other 1. **Subjects:** Polymer science, plastics technology, packaging, business. **Holdings:** 3000 books; 1000 bound periodical volumes. **Subscriptions:** 190 journals and other serials; 3 newspapers. **Services:** Interlibrary loan; copying; center open to the public by appointment. **Automated Operations:** Computerized cataloging. **Computerized Information Services:** DIALOG Information Services, Chemical Abstracts Service (CAS), ORBIT Search Service. **Networks/Consortia:** Member of Rochester Regional Library Council (RRLC). **Publications:** Management News Summary, biweekly; Bulletin, monthly. **Remarks:** FAX: (315)986-5033.

★10565★
Mobil Corporation - Corporate Library (Bus-Fin)
3225 Gallows Rd. Phone: (703)846-4648
Fairfax, VA 22037-0001 Linda Smith, Dir.
Staff: Prof 2. **Subjects:** Energy industries, corporations, finance, management. **Special Collections:** ASI and SRI (microfiche); corporate archives. **Holdings:** 5500 books; 6 VF drawers of pamphlets; 10K and annual reports in microform; 63 periodical titles in microform. **Subscriptions:** 350 journals and other serials; 25 newspapers. **Services:** Interlibrary loan; library open to the public by appointment. **Automated Operations:** Computerized cataloging. **Computerized Information Services:** VU/TEXT Information Services, DataTimes, DIALOG Information Services, NEXIS, Dow Jones News/Retrieval, OCLC, InvesText, WILSONLINE, I.P. Sharp Associates. **Publications:** New materials list, quarterly - for internal distribution only; user's guide; serial holdings. **Remarks:** FAX: (703)846-2933. **Staff:** Sandra Jackson.

★10566★
Mobil Corporation - Environmental & Health Sciences Library (Env-Cons)
Box 1029 Phone: (609)737-5583
Princeton, NJ 08543 Norman Laurin, Libn.
Founded: 1984. **Staff:** Prof 1; Other 1. **Subjects:** Toxicology, environmental science, biomedicine, analytical chemistry. **Holdings:** 6000 books. **Subscriptions:** 550 journals and other serials; 7 newspapers. **Services:** Interlibrary loan; copying; center open to the public by appointment. **Automated Operations:** Computerized cataloging, acquisitions, serials, and ILL. **Computerized Information Services:** DIALOG Information Services, PFDS Online, NLM, Chemical Abstracts Service (CAS), OCLC, ORBIT Search Service, STN International, DATALIB. **Networks/Consortia:** Member of PALINET. **Remarks:** FAX: (609)737-5619. **Formerly:** Its Toxicology Information Center.

Mobil Corporation - Toxicology Information Center
See: **Mobil Corporation** (10566)

★10567★
Mobil Exploration & Producing Services Inc. - Library (Sci-Engr)
Box 650232 Phone: (214)951-2223
Dallas, TX 75265-0232 Eva K. Smith, Libn.
Founded: 1977. **Staff:** Prof 1. **Subjects:** Geology, geophysics. **Holdings:** 17,500 books; 2200 bound periodical volumes; 2000 maps. **Subscriptions:** 97 journals and other serials. **Services:** Interlibrary loan; library not open to the public. **Automated Operations:** Computerized cataloging. **Computerized Information Services:** OCLC, DIALOG Information Services, SDC. **Networks/Consortia:** Member of AMIGOS Bibliographic Council, Inc. **Remarks:** FAX: (214)951-2374.

★10568★
Mobil Exploration & Producing, U.S. Inc. - Houston Division - Information Resources Library (Sci-Engr, Energy)
12450 Greenspoint Dr. Phone: (713)775-2687
Houston, TX 77060-1991 Constance Hoffman, Rec.Gp.Ldr.
Founded: 1979. **Staff:** Prof 1; Other 1. **Subjects:** Geology, engineering, petroleum industry, business. **Holdings:** 6280 volumes; 6000 proprietary reports. **Subscriptions:** 224 journals and other serials. **Services:** Interlibrary loan; center not open to the public. **Automated Operations:** Computerized cataloging, acquisitions, serials, and ILL. **Automated Operations:** Computerized cataloging and circulation. **Computerized Information Services:** DIALOG Information Services, PFDS Online, OCLC, NEXIS, VU/TEXT Information Services. **Networks/Consortia:** Member of AMIGOS Bibliographic Council, Inc. **Publications:** IRC Acquisitions List, monthly - for internal distribution only. **Remarks:** FAX: (713)775-4126.

★10569★
Mobil Exploration & Producing, U.S. Inc. - Library (Energy)
Box 5444 Phone: (303)298-2019
Denver, CO 80217-5444 Sharon Johnson, Coord.
Founded: 1972. **Staff:** Prof 2; Other 1. **Subjects:** Geology; geophysics; oil and gas exploration, engineering, production; petroleum industry. **Holdings:** 21,000 books; 500 bound periodical volumes; 7000 government documents; 5000 journal issues; 21,000 maps; 600 internal reports. **Subscriptions:** 103 journals and other serials. **Services:** Interlibrary loan; library not open to the public. **Publications:** Contents of Recent Journal Acquisitions, bimonthly; New Publications Received, quarterly - both for internal distribution only. **Remarks:** FAX: (303)298-2365.

★10570★
Mobil Exploration & Producing, U.S. Inc. - Library (Energy)
1250 Poydras Plaza Lib.Rm. 1362 Phone: (504)566-5598
New Orleans, LA 70113-1892 Elizabeth A. Black, Libn.
Founded: 1981. **Staff:** Prof 1. **Subjects:** Petroleum, geology, geophysics. **Holdings:** 1800 books; 100 bound periodical volumes; 2500 unbound reports; 45 serials in microform; 95 maps and sets; 200 AV programs; 12 software packages. **Subscriptions:** 296 journals and other serials. **Services:** Interlibrary loan; library not open to the public. **Computerized Information Services:** DIALOG Information Services, Maxwell Online, Inc., ORBIT Search Service **Networks/Consortia:** Member of AMIGOS Bibliographic Council, Inc. **Publications:** CHECK IT OUT, monthly - for internal distribution only. **Special Indexes:** Index to proprietary reports. **Remarks:** FAX: (504)566-5712.

★10571★
Mobil Oil Canada - Library (Sci-Engr)
Tower One, Rm. 1420
Box 800 Phone: (403)260-7785
Calgary, AB, Canada T2P 2J7 Pat Munro, Libn.
Founded: 1969. **Staff:** Prof 2; Other 1. **Subjects:** Geology, geophysics, data processing, petroleum, engineering, business. **Special Collections:** Environmental collection. **Holdings:** 12,000 books; 630 bound periodical volumes; 5555 government publications; VF materials; standards; 310 video- and audiotapes. **Subscriptions:** 250 journals and other serials. **Services:** Interlibrary loan; library not open to the public. **Automated Operations:** Computerized public access catalog, cataloging, acquisitions, and circulation. **Computerized Information Services:** DIALOG Information Services, CAN/OLE, Infomart Online, Info Globe, ORBIT Search Service, The Financial Post DataGroup; internal database; Envoy 100 (electronic mail service). **Publications:** Acquisitions list. **Remarks:** FAX: (403)260-7491. Electronic mail address(es): ILL.ACM (Envoy 100). **Staff:** Andrea Rhodes.

★10572★
Mobil Pipe Line Company - Engineering Library (Energy)
Box 900 Phone: (214)658-2039
Dallas, TX 75221 R.E. Robbins, Mgr. of Engr.
Founded: 1955. **Staff:** 1. **Subjects:** Crude, liquefied petroleum gas (LPG), refined petroleum products; pipeline - transportation, construction, maintenance, operation. **Holdings:** 1200 volumes. **Subscriptions:** 44 journals and other serials. **Services:** Interlibrary loan; library open to the public. **Remarks:** FAX: (214)658-2241.

★10573★
Mobil Research & Development Corporation - Central Research Laboratory Library (Energy)
Box 1025 Phone: (609)737-4328
Princeton, NJ 08540 Ruth P. Henderson, Libn.
Staff: Prof 1; Other 1. **Subjects:** Petroleum refining technology, chemistry, chemical engineering, energy. **Holdings:** 12,000 books; 10,000 bound periodical volumes. **Subscriptions:** 350 journals and other serials. **Services:** Interlibrary loan; copying; library open to the public on request. **Computerized Information Services:** DIALOG Information Services, ORBIT Search Service, STN International.

★10574★
Mobil Research & Development Corporation - Dallas E&P Engineering Information Center (Sci-Engr)
Box 819047 Phone: (214)851-8312
Dallas, TX 75381 R.S. Thomson, Tech.Info.Spec.
Founded: 1980. **Staff:** Prof 1. **Subjects:** Engineering - structural, arctic, geotechnical, marine; oceanography. **Holdings:** 400 books. **Subscriptions:** 75 journals and other serials. **Services:** Interlibrary loan; center not open to the public. **Remarks:** FAX: (214)851-8349.

★10575★
Mobil Research & Development Corporation - Dallas Research Laboratory - Library (Energy)
Box 819047 Phone: (214)851-8140
Dallas, TX 75381 Janet Wolford, Mgr., Tech.Info.Serv.
Founded: 1945. **Staff:** Prof 5; Other 2. **Subjects:** Petroleum exploration and production; basic sciences. **Holdings:** 40,000 books; 40,000 bound periodical volumes; 9200 maps; U.S. patents on microfilm; U.S. Bureau of Mines documents on microfilm. **Subscriptions:** 600 journals and other serials. **Services:** Interlibrary loan; library open to the public by appointment. **Automated Operations:** Computerized cataloging, acquisitions, serials, circulation, and reports. **Computerized Information Services:** DIALOG Information Services, BRS Information Technologies, OCLC, PFDS Online. **Networks/Consortia:** Member of AMIGOS Bibliographic Council, Inc. **Staff:** Jacque Kyle, Circ., Ill.; Ruth L. Keefer, Lit.Spec.; Dudley B. Schoolfield, Cat.; Phyllis Ross, Ser., Ref.

★10576★
Mobil Research & Development Corporation - Engineering Department - Information Center (Sci-Engr)
Box 1026 Phone: (609)737-4192
Princeton, NJ 08540 Usok Pak, Mgr.
Founded: 1967. **Staff:** Prof 3; Other 3. **Subjects:** Petroleum refining, mechanical and chemical engineering. **Holdings:** 6500 books; indexed documents on microfilm; engineering drawings. **Subscriptions:** 400 journals and other serials. **Services:** Interlibrary loan; copying; center open to qualified researchers by appointment. **Automated Operations:** Computerized cataloging. **Computerized Information Services:** ORBIT Search Service, DIALOG Information Services, OCLC; internal databases. **Networks/Consortia:** Member of PALINET. **Publications:** Bulletin, quarterly - to Engineering Department. **Remarks:** Alternate telephone number(s): 737-4745. FAX: (609)737-5047. **Staff:** Larissa Bulya, Tech.Libn.; Shirley Mungro, Info.Spec.

Mobil Research & Development Corporation - Offshore Engineering Information Center
See: **Mobil Research & Development Corporation - Dallas E&P Engineering Information Center** (10574)

★10577★
Mobil Research & Development Corporation - Paulsboro Laboratory - Technical Information Services (Energy, Sci-Engr)
Box 300 Phone: (609)224-2429
Paulsboro, NJ 08066 R.H. Fischer, Mgr.
Founded: 1931. **Staff:** Prof 2; Other 3. **Subjects:** Petroleum refining technology, petroleum products and allied technology, chemistry, chemical engineering. **Holdings:** 15,000 books; 15,000 bound periodical volumes; U.S. chemical patents on microfilm; 20 VF drawers of pamphlets. **Subscriptions:** 450 journals and other serials. **Services:** Interlibrary loan; SDI; services open to the public upon application. **Automated Operations:** Computerized cataloging, acquisitions, serials, and circulation. **Computerized Information Services:** DIALOG Information Services, PFDS Online, OCLC, STN International. **Networks/Consortia:** Member of PALINET, South Jersey Regional Library Cooperative. **Remarks:** FAX: (609)224-3621. **Staff:** Jane L. Bitter, Tech.Libn.

★10578★
Mobil Solar Energy Corporation - Library
4 Suburban Park Dr.
Billerica, MA 01821-3980
Founded: 1975. **Subjects:** Photovoltaics; solar energy conversion (silicon solar cells); crystal growth by edge-defined, film-fed growth; materials science; solar energy. **Holdings:** 3000 books; 800 bound periodical volumes; 17 VF drawers of reports on microfiche. **Remarks:** Currently inactive.

★10579★
Mobile County Public Law Library (Law)
150 Government St., Suite 1002 Phone: (205)690-8436
Mobile, AL 36602 Jacquelyn Streeter, Libn.
Founded: 1947. **Staff:** 2. **Subjects:** Law - civil, criminal, business, tax. **Special Collections:** English Chancery Court books. **Holdings:** 25,000 books; 17 bound periodical volumes. **Subscriptions:** 59 journals and other serials. **Services:** Copying; library open to the public for reference use only. **Computerized Information Services:** WESTLAW, LEXIS. **Remarks:** FAX: (205)690-8437.

★10580★
Mobile Municipal Archives (Hist)
457 Church St. Phone: (205)434-7740
Mobile, AL 36602 Jay Higginbotham, Archv.
Founded: 1983. **Staff:** Prof 3; Other 3. **Subjects:** Municipal records - correspondence, reports, minutes, tax books, ordinances, bills, claims. **Special Collections:** Public servants' papers; urban studies; instituitional archives. **Holdings:** 2000 volumes; 13,000 cubic feet of documents; 1 million documents on microfilm. **Subscriptions:** 4 journals and other serials. **Services:** Copying; archives open to the public. **Automated Operations:** Computerized cataloging. **Computerized Information Services:** Internal database. **Publications:** A Guide to the Mobile Municipal Archives (book). **Remarks:** FAX: (205)434-7740. **Staff:** Edward Harkins, Asst.Archv.

★10581★
Mobile Public Library - Local History and Genealogy Division (Hist)
704 Government St. Phone: (205)434-7093
Mobile, AL 36602-1499 George H. Schroeter, Hd.
Founded: 1961. **Staff:** Prof 2; Other 2. **Subjects:** Genealogy, local history. **Special Collections:** Panton-Leslie colonial trade papers, 1770-1840; Hunley Civil War papers. **Holdings:** 15,112 books; 1600 bound periodical volumes; 1210 reels of microfilm of Mobile newspapers; 6200 reels of microfilm of federal census records; 56 reels of microfilm of French and Spanish colonial records; 157 reels of microfilm on miscellaneous subjects. **Subscriptions:** 41 journals and other serials; 7 newspapers. **Services:** Copying; division open to the public. **Automated Operations:** Computerized circulation. **Special Indexes:** Vertical file index (card); map index (card); index to Mobile Register Obituaries, 1986 to present (book). **Remarks:** FAX: (205)434-5866.

★10582★
Mobius Society - Library (Soc Sci)
4801 Wilshire Blvd., Suite 320 Phone: (213)933-9266
Los Angeles, CA 90010 Stephan A. Schwartz, Chm.
Founded: 1977. **Staff:** 4. **Subjects:** Anthropology, archeology, criminology, history, neuropsychology, parapsychology, subtle energies, energy medicine research. **Holdings:** 2500 volumes. **Services:** Library open to the public by appointment. **Computerized Information Services:** Internal database (Energy Medicine and Healing); CompuServe Information Service (electronic mail service). **Publications:** The Mobius Reports, 4/year. **Remarks:** FAX: (213)933-6476. Telex: 159294488. Electronic mail address(es): 76657,03447 (CompuServe Information Service). **Staff:** Ann Druffel.

★10583★
Modern Art Museum of Fort Worth - Library (Art)
1309 Montgomery St. Phone: (817)738-9215
Fort Worth, TX 76107 M.A. Laura Martinez, Libn.
Founded: 1971. **Staff:** Prof 1. **Subjects:** 20th century art in all countries focusing on media consisting of painting, sculpture, and graphics. **Holdings:** 6000 books; 200 bound periodical volumes; 2000 museum catalogs; 8 VF drawers containing 2000 items; 5000 slides. **Subscriptions:** 30 journals and other serials. **Services:** Copying; library open to the public for research only. **Remarks:** FAX: (817)735-1161.

Modern Handcraft, Inc.
See: **KC Publishing, Inc.** (8591)

★10584★
Modern Language Association - Center for Bibliographical Services (Hum)
10 Astor Place Phone: (212)614-6350
New York, NY 10003 Daniel Uchitelle, Dir., Ctr. for Info.Serv.
Staff: Prof 17; Other 6. **Subjects:** Language, literature, linguistics, folklore. **Holdings:** Figures not available. **Subscriptions:** 1100 journals and other serials. **Services:** Center not open to the public. **Computerized Information Services:** DIALOG Information Services, WILSONLINE, RLIN; DIALMAIL, BITNET (electronic mail services). **Publications:** MLA International Bibliography, annual; MLA Directory of Periodicals; MLA Directory of Scholarly Presses. **Special Catalogs:** Wing Short Title Catalogue. **Remarks:** FAX: (212)477-9863.

★10585★
Modesto Bee - Editorial Library (Publ)
14th & H Sts.
Box 3928 Phone: (209)578-2333
Modesto, CA 95352 Kate Roberts, Chf.Libn.
Founded: 1944. **Staff:** Prof 2; Other 2. **Subjects:** Newspaper reference topics. **Holdings:** Books; clippings; pictures; pamphlets; microfilm; microfiche. **Subscriptions:** 15 newspapers. **Services:** Library not open to the public. **Computerized Information Services:** NEXIS, DataTimes, VU/TEXT Information Services, CompuServe Information Service, DataQuick; SAVE (internal database). **Remarks:** FAX: (209)578-2207. Published by McClatchy Newspapers.

Dr. Garfield Moffatt Health Sciences Library
See: **Dr. Everett Chalmers Hospital** (3413)

Ida V. Moffett School of Nursing
See: **Baptist Medical Centers-Samford University - Ida V. Moffett School of Nursing** (1512)

Moffett Technical Library
See: **CPC International** (4401)

★10586★
(Mogadishu) USIS Library (Educ)
433 Via Primo Luglio
P.O. Box 574
Mogadishu, Somalia
Remarks: Maintained or supported by the U.S. Information Agency. Focus is on materials that will assist peoples outside the United States to learn about the United States, its people, history, culture, political processes, and social milieux.

★10587★
Mohave Museum of History and Arts - Library (Hist)
400 W. Beale St. Phone: (602)753-3195
Kingman, AZ 86401 Norma Bailey, Musm.Dir.
Founded: 1960. **Staff:** 2. **Subjects:** History of Mohave County and Arizona, Indian lore, arts and crafts, mining history, genealogy. **Special Collections:** Mohave County Miner, 1882 to present (newspaper; some on microfilm). **Holdings:** 1400 books; 100 bound periodical volumes; 350 manuscripts; 8000 photographs, 1880 to present; 4000 maps; vertical files; AV materials; audio and video cassettes; microfilm; grave and funeral records, 1910-1952; business records, 1882; personal memoirs and records; business, city, and telephone directories; mining district records, claim and deed books, 1862-1882; Mohave County Union (Kingman) High School yearbooks; miscellaneous Mohave County records, 1876 to present; scrapbooks; 200 transcribed oral interviews; newspapers on microfilm; bound volumes of newspapers. **Subscriptions:** 10 journals and other serials. **Services:** Copying; research (fee); library open to the public for reference use only. **Remarks:** Maintained by Mohave County Historical Society. **Staff:** Mona Cochran, Libn.; Loren Wilson, Libn.; Karin Goudy, Photo Libn.; Ruth Simpson, Map Libn.

★10588★
Mohawk-Caughnawaga Museum - Library (Hist)
Rte 5 W., Box 554 Phone: (518)853-3646
Fonda, NY 12068 Bro. Berard Hofmann, O.F.M. Conv., Dir.
Staff: Prof 1; Other 1. **Subjects:** Archeology; Colonial and Revolutionary history of Northeastern North America; museology; 17th and 18th century Euro-American culture. **Special Collections:** 16th, 17th, and 18th century maps of North America; 18th and 19th century Mohawk Valley history (manuscripts); archives of the Mohawk Valley Historical Association, 1920-1940; museum archives, 1949 to present; archives of the Van Epps-Hartley Chapter of the New York State Archeological Association, 1933 to present; papers of Edward J. Sheehan, historian and archivist, 1920-1960. **Holdings:** 4000 books; 2000 pamphlets and brochures; periodicals; manuscripts; maps and atlases. **Services:** Copying; library open for serious historical research.

★10589★
Mohawk College of Applied Arts and Technology - Health Sciences Education Centre - Library Resource Centre (Med, Educ)
P.O. Box 2034 Phone: (416)575-1515
Hamilton, ON, Canada L8N 3T2 Maureen Price, Lib.Supv.
Founded: 1978. **Staff:** Prof 5; Other 1. **Subjects:** Nursing, medical laboratory technology, radiography, ultrasound, physiotherapy, occupational therapy. **Holdings:** 18,400 books; 2820 bound periodical volumes; 2630 AV programs. **Subscriptions:** 170 journals and other serials. **Services:** Interlibrary loan; copying; center open to the public. **Computerized Information Services:** MEDLINE, DIALOG Information Services. **Networks/Consortia:** Member of Hamilton/Wentworth District Health Library Network. **Remarks:** FAX: (416)575-2528. **Staff:** Liz Aldrey, AV Lib.Techn.; Ruth Paterson, Ser.Lib.Techn.; Arlene Smith, Acq.Lib.Techn.; Barbara Wright, Ref.Lib.Techn. for Cont.Educ.

★10590★
Mohawk College of Applied Arts and Technology - Sam Mitminger Library Resource Centre (Educ)
P.O. Box 2034 Phone: (416)575-2077
Hamilton, ON, Canada L8N 3T2 Sandra M. Black, Dir., Lrng.Res.
Founded: 1967. **Staff:** Prof 6; Other 27. **Subjects:** Business, technology, health sciences, early childhood education, academic upgrading. **Holdings:** 114,000 books; 8000 periodical volumes; 24,000 AV programs; 5500 microforms; 800 maps; 948 clipping file folders; 10,000 uncataloged items, including government documents. **Subscriptions:** 1030 journals and other serials; 15 newspapers. **Services:** Interlibrary loan; copying; center open to the public. **Automated Operations:** Computerized public access catalog and acquisitions. **Computerized Information Services:** DIALOG Information

Services; CD-ROMs; Envoy 100 (electronic mail service). **Networks/ Consortia:** Member of Hamilton/Wentworth District Health Library Network, The Bibliocentre. **Publications:** Union lists. **Remarks:** FAX: (416)575-2378. Telex: 061 8348. Electronic mail address(es): ILL.OHMC (Envoy 100). **Staff:** Helen Shaver, Tech. & AV Serv.; Laura Hyk, ILL; Marilyn McDermott, Ref. & Circ.Libn.; Carol Farr, Stoney Creek; Gail Sekine, Brant-Elgin; Sandra Arklie, Brantford Nurs.Lib.; Maureen Price, Hea.Sci.; Iwona Kurek, Wentworth; Cate Walker Hammond, Highview Lib.; June Turnbull, York Blvd. Techn.

★10591★
Mohawk Valley Community College Library - Special Collections (Soc Sci)
1101 Sherman Dr. Phone: (315)792-5408
Utica, NY 13501 Raul Huerta, Lib.Dir.
Founded: 1946. **Special Collections:** Women's Resource Collection (1100 titles); Minorities Studies Collection (800 titles). **Services:** Interlibrary loan; copying; collections open to the public. **Automated Operations:** Computerized cataloging. **Computerized Information Services:** BRS Information Technologies, DIALOG Information Services, OCLC. **Networks/Consortia:** Member of Central New York Library Resources Council (CENTRO). **Staff:** Joanne Werner, Cat./Women's Rsrcs.Coll.

Mohawk Valley Heritage Association, Inc. - Walter Elwood Museum
See: **Walter Elwood Museum** (5315)

Mohawk Valley Historical Association Archives
See: **Mohawk-Caughnawaga Museum - Library** (10588)

★10592★
Mohawk Valley Psychiatric Center - George M. Lein Information Center (Med)
1400 Noyes at York Phone: (315)797-6800
Utica, NY 13502-3852 Kay Sangani, Libn.
Founded: 1961. **Staff:** Prof 1. **Subjects:** Psychiatry, neurology, medicine, nursing. **Special Collections:** Historical medical books and journals (1000 volumes). **Holdings:** 2829 books; 1500 bound periodical volumes; 2500 unbound periodical volumes. **Subscriptions:** 42 journals and other serials. **Services:** Interlibrary loan; copying; center open to health care professionals. **Computerized Information Services:** MEDLINE. **Networks/Consortia:** Member of Central New York Library Resources Council (CENTRO), National Network of Libraries of Medicine - Middle Atlantic Region. **Publications:** Video listing; book listing. **Remarks:** Maintains patient library housing 7561 books.

★10593★
Mohyla Institute - Library and Archives (Area-Ethnic)
1240 Temperance St. Phone: (306)653-1944
Saskatoon, SK, Canada S7N 0P1 Luba Sernowski, Asst.Adm.
Founded: 1916. **Staff:** 1. **Subjects:** Ukrainian studies. **Holdings:** 7500 books; 1000 bound periodical volumes; 800 Ukrainian Voice; 1000 pamphlets. **Subscriptions:** 10 journals and other serials; 15 newspapers. **Services:** Library open to the public with restrictions. **Remarks:** Holdings are in Ukrainian, English, Russian, and other languages.

Moldenhauer Archive
See: **Northwestern University - Music Library** (12086)

★10594★
Moldenhauer Archives (Mus)
W. 1011 Comstock Ct. Phone: (509)747-4555
Spokane, WA 99203 Mary Moldenhauer, Dir.
Subjects: Music and music history. **Special Collections:** Webern and other comprehensive archives. **Holdings:** Autograph music manuscripts, letters, documents, 12th to 20th centuries; reference library of facsimile scores, books, recordings. **Remarks:** Divisions of the Moldenhauer Archives are located at Northwestern University, Evanston, IL; Washington State University, Pullman, WA; Harvard University, Cambridge, MA; Whitworth College, Spokane, WA; Library of Congress, Washington, DC; Bayerische Staatsbibliothek, Munich, West Germany; Wiener Stadtbibliothek, Vienna, Austria; Zentralbibliothek, Zurich, Switzerland; Paul Sacher Foundation, Basel, Switzerland. Archives founded by Dr. Hans Moldenhauer (1906-1987).

★10595★
Molesworth Institute - Library and Archives (Hist)
143 Hanks Hill Rd. Phone: (203)429-7051
Storrs, CT 06268 Norman D. Stevens, Dir.
Staff: Prof 4; Other 2. **Subjects:** Library humor and history, treens. **Special Collections:** Timothy J. Peason Collection of Library Humor (2325 items); library commemoratives and souvenirs (900); library ephemera (2000 pieces); librarians' business cards (2500); library postcards (26,000); Molesworth Institute Archives (4777 archival materials). **Holdings:** 7001 volumes; 30 linear feet of other cataloged items. **Subscriptions:** 99 journals and other serials; 6 newspapers. **Services:** Library open to the public with advance approval. **Automated Operations:** Computerized cataloging and acquisitions. **Computerized Information Services:** CALP (internal database). **Publications:** The Librarian's Record, irregular. **Special Indexes:** Library postcard index (CD-ROM). **Remarks:** Headquarters of MOLENET. **Staff:** Nougleigh Rhee Furbished, Presrv.Spec.; Maxey Mixey Moss, Postcard Cur.; Basil Fotherington-Thomas, Treenologist.

★10596★
(Moline) Daily Dispatch/Rock Island Argus - Library (Publ)
1720 5th Ave. Phone: (309)764-4344
Moline, IL 61265 JoAnn Parmley, Newsroom Libn.
Founded: 1878. **Staff:** 1. **Subjects:** Newspaper reference topics. **Special Collections:** Local Historical Book Collection; local historical news (newspaper clipping file); biography file. **Holdings:** Pictures and wirephotos; books; newspaper clippings. **Subscriptions:** 8 newspapers. **Services:** Copying; library open to the public by appointment. **Remarks:** Published by Small Newspaper Group, Inc.

★10597★
Molloy, Jones & Donahue - Library (Law)
Security Pacific Bank Bldg., Suite 2200
33 N. Stone Ave. Phone: (602)622-3531
Tucson, AZ 85701 Sara L. O'Neil, Adm.Libn.
Founded: 1979. **Staff:** Prof 1; Other 1. **Subjects:** Bankruptcy; law - tax, litigation, commercial, estate planning, banking, environmental, labor, natural resources. **Holdings:** 10,000 books, pamphlets, periodicals, newspapers. **Subscriptions:** 250 journals and other serials; 6 newspapers. **Services:** Library not open to the public. **Computerized Information Services:** WESTLAW, LEXIS, NEXIS, VU/TEXT Information Services, DIALOG Information Services, Dow Jones News/Retrieval, Dun & Bradstreet Business Credit Services, CCH Access, State Net. **Remarks:** FAX: (602)624-2816. **Staff:** Dan Macy, Mgr., Ref.Serv.

★10598★
Molson Breweries - Technical Center (Food-Bev)
2486 Dunwin Dr. Phone: (416)828-1786
Mississauga, ON, Canada L5L 1J9 Sandi Lloyd, Sec./Libn.
Founded: 1967. **Staff:** 1. **Subjects:** Brewing, microbiology, water, chemistry, chromatography, biotechnology. **Special Collections:** Historical brewing books (private collection). **Holdings:** 1500 volumes; newspaper clippings; patents; pamphlets. **Subscriptions:** 55 journals and other serials. **Services:** Library not open to the public. **Computerized Information Services:** DIALOG Information Services, BREW-INFO; internal database. **Remarks:** FAX: (416)828-1378. **Also Known As:** Brasseries Molson.

★10599★
Monadnock Community Hospital - Eckfeldt Memorial Medical Library (Med)
452 Old Street Rd. Phone: (603)924-7191
Peterborough, NH 03458 Lesley Cass, Med.Libn.
Founded: 1970. **Subjects:** Clinical medicine, nursing, allied health, hospital administration. **Holdings:** 100 books; unbound medical journals. **Subscriptions:** 83 journals and other serials. **Services:** Interlibrary loan; copying; SDI; library open to the public. **Computerized Information Services:** BRS/COLLEAGUE, MEDLINE.

★10600★
Monarch Marking Systems - Information Resource Center (Sci-Engr, Bus-Fin)
Box 608 Phone: (513)865-2566
Dayton, OH 45401 Gail Doherty, Info.Rsrc.Adm.
Founded: 1975. **Staff:** Prof 1. **Subjects:** Chemistry, business, physics, sales and marketing. **Holdings:** 4000 books; 75 bound periodical volumes; 16 VF drawers of conference reports, clippings, cassettes. **Subscriptions:** 140 journals and other serials. **Services:** Interlibrary loan; center not open to the public. **Computerized Information Services:** Online systems. **Networks/ Consortia:** Member of Miami Valley Libraries (MVL). **Publications:** Acquisitions list, quarterly - for internal distribution only.

★10601★
Monarchist League of Canada - Centre for Monarchical Studies - King George III Memorial Library (Hist)
3050 Yonge St., Suite 206 Phone: (416)482-4157
Toronto, ON, Canada M4N 2K4 Claudia Willetts, Libn.
Founded: 1981. **Staff:** Prof 1. **Subjects:** Canadian monarchy, British history and royal family, monarchies around the world. **Holdings:** 3345 books and pamphlets. **Subscriptions:** 10 journals and other serials. **Services:** Copying; library open to the public for reference use only.

★10602★
Monastere des Ursulines - Archives des Ursulines de Quebec (Hist)
2 Rue du Parloir Phone: (418)692-2523
Quebec, PQ, Canada GIR 4M5 Sr. Marguerite Cyr
Founded: 1639. **Staff:** Prof 1; Other 3. **Subjects:** Canadiana. **Special Collections:** Old and rare books and periodicals from France and the U.S.; regional historical reviews. **Holdings:** 10,000 books; 300 bound periodical volumes. **Services:** Archives open to serious researchers for reference use only by appointment. **Remarks:** Archives located at 18 Donnacona St., Quebec, PQ, G1R 4T1. **Staff:** Sr. Rita Coulombe, Superior

★10603★
Moncton Barristers' Society - Library (Law)
770 Main St.
Box 6033 Phone: (506)389-1649
Moncton, NB, Canada E1C 1E7 Joseph A. Robinson, Dir.
Staff: 1.25. **Subjects:** Law. **Holdings:** 12,000 books; 1000 bound periodical volumes. **Subscriptions:** 100 journals and other serials. **Services:** Library open to the public for reference use only.

★10604★
Moncton Hospital - Health Sciences Library (Med)
135 MacBeath Ave. Phone: (506)857-5447
Moncton, NB, Canada E1C 6Z8 Susan P. Libby, Hosp.Libn.
Founded: 1963. **Staff:** Prof 1; Other 1.5. **Subjects:** Medicine, nursing, health sciences. **Holdings:** 2300 volumes. **Subscriptions:** 500 journals and other serials. **Services:** Interlibrary loan; copying; library open to the public with restrictions. **Computerized Information Services:** MEDLINE, CAN/OLE, DIALOG Information Services, Infohealth; Envoy 100 (electronic mail service). Performs searches on fee basis. **Remarks:** FAX: (506)857-5545. Electronic mail address(es): NBMMH (Envoy 100). **Staff:** Karen Darrach, Lib.Supv.

★10605★
Moncton Times-Transcript - Library (Publ)
939 Main St. Phone: (506)859-4900
Moncton, NB, Canada E1C 8P3 Nola O'Brien
Founded: 1968. **Staff:** Prof 1; Other 1. **Subjects:** Newspaper reference topics. **Holdings:** 200 books; 2000 reports; 800 reels of microfilm; 4000 photographs. **Subscriptions:** 8 journals and other serials; 12 newspapers. **Services:** Copying; library open to other media and libraries. **Computerized Information Services:** ATEX (internal database). **Special Indexes:** Moncton Times-Transcript, 1984 to present (on disk). **Remarks:** FAX: (506)859-4904.

★10606★
Mondak Heritage Center - Lillian Anderson Jensen Library for Historical Research (Hist)
Box 50 Phone: (406)482-3500
Sidney, MT 59270 Ruth Torrence, Dir.
Staff: 1. **Subjects:** State and local history. **Special Collections:** Family histories. **Holdings:** 2000 books; 100 bound periodical volumes; Sidney Herald newspaper, 1908-1940, on microfilm. **Services:** Copying; library open to the public for reference use only. **Formerly:** Its Willo Ralston Memorial Library for Historical Research.

Ambrose Monell Engineering Library
See: **Columbia University - Ambrose Monell Engineering Library** (4000)

★10607★
Monell Chemical Senses Center - Library (Sci-Engr)
3500 Market St.
Philadelphia, PA 19104 Phone: (215)898-6666
Founded: 1965. **Staff:** 1. **Subjects:** Taste, olfaction, allied neurosciences. **Holdings:** 500 books; 400 bound periodical volumes; reprint files; unbound periodicals. **Subscriptions:** 25 journals and other serials. **Services:** Library open to the public by appointment.

★10608★
Monenco Consultants Limited - Information Resource Centre (Sci-Engr)
801 6th Ave., S.W. Phone: (403)298-4673
Calgary, AB, Canada T2P 3W3 Lyn McCluskey, Libn.
Staff: 3. **Subjects:** Engineering - electrical, mechanical, civil; mining; environmental assessments. **Holdings:** 12,000 books; 4000 other cataloged items. **Subscriptions:** 200 journals and other serials. **Services:** Interlibrary loan. **Automated Operations:** Computerized cataloging, circulation, and serials distribution. **Computerized Information Services:** CANSIM, DIALOG Information Services, Info Globe, PFDS Online, CAN/OLE, QL Systems, Canadian Centre for Occupational Health & Safety, Data-Star, The Financial Post DataGroup, Infomart Online; Envoy 100 (electronic mail service). **Remarks:** FAX: (403)298-4125. **Formerly:** Its Library and Information Centre.

★10609★
Monenco Consultants Limited - Library (Energy)
Sta. A, Box 6088 Phone: (514)499-3211
Montreal, PQ, Canada H3C 3Z8 Penelope H. Kamichaitis, Libn.
Founded: 1960. **Staff:** Prof 1; Other 1. **Subjects:** Power engineering, water resources, electric utilities, hydrology, electric transmission. **Holdings:** 15,000 books; 20 VF drawers of topographical maps of Canada; 40 VF drawers; 2000 engineering standards. **Subscriptions:** 250 journals and other serials; 5 newspapers. **Services:** Interlibrary loan; copying; library open to the public for reference use only. **Computerized Information Services:** DIALOG Information Services, PFDS Online, CAN/OLE, QL Systems, Info Globe, The Financial Post DataGroup, Infomart Online, Ground Water On-Line, Data-Star; Envoy 100 (electronic mail service). **Remarks:** FAX: (514)499-3223. Telex: 055 60735. Electronic mail address(es): MONENCO.MONTREAL (Envoy 100).

★10610★
Monestir de Montserrat - Biblioteca (Hist, Rel-Phil, Art)
Pl del Monasterio Phone: 93 8350251
E-08699 Montserrat, Spain Xavier Poch
Founded: 1025. **Staff:** Prof 1; Other 3. **Subjects:** Religion, theology, history, art. **Special Collections:** Spanish Civil War (10,000 volumes); 16th century collection (4000 volumes). **Holdings:** 270,000 books; 4000 bound periodical titles; 1400 manuscripts. **Subscriptions:** 800 journals and other serials. **Services:** Copying; library open to the public. **Remarks:** FAX: 93 8284049.

Monitor Sugar Company Archives
See: **Bay County Historical Society - Library** (1590)

★10611★
Monmouth County Historical Association - Library (Hist)
70 Court St. Phone: (908)462-1466
Freehold, NJ 07728 Barbara Carver Smith, C.G., Libn./Geneal.
Founded: 1898. **Staff:** Prof 1. **Subjects:** Monmouth County history and genealogy, church and Bible records. **Special Collections:** James P. Allaire Papers; records of the North American Phalanx; Philip Freneau; Cherry Hall Papers; Battle of Monmouth; John Mills Steamship Collection; Freehold Young Ladies Seminary Papers; Monmouth County Board of Agriculture; Karagheusian Rug Mill materials; Monmouth County Yearbook Collection; rare books. **Holdings:** 7000 books; 870 bound periodical volumes; 35 VF drawers of newspaper clippings; pamphlets; programs; manuscript collections; microfilm; photographs; maps; broadsides; extensive newspaper collection. **Subscriptions:** 12 journals and other serials. **Services:** Copying; library open to the public. **Publications:** Monmouth County in Print; Bibliography - Monmouth County; Cemetery Holdings; Genealogical Holdings in Library; Directory of Historical Societies, Monmouth County, New Jersey; Local History Collections; Checklist of Bible Records; Bookshelf (publications offered for resale). **Special Indexes:** Index to Early Dutch Settlers of Monmouth County; Photographic Images Notebook; Bible Records in the MCHA Library, Vol. 1, A-B; Records of the Presbyterian Church of Squan Village, 1848-1900. **Remarks:** Associated with the Monmouth County Genealogy Club.

★10612★
Monmouth County Law Library (Law)
Court House
P.O. Box 1266 Phone: (908)431-7079
Freehold, NJ 07728 Maureen Burgess, Law Libn.
Staff: Prof 1. **Subjects:** Law. **Holdings:** Figures not available. **Services:** Copying; library open to the public. **Remarks:** Maintained by Board of Freeholders, County of Monmouth.

★10613★
Monmouth County Park System Libraries - Elvin McDonald Horticultural Library (Agri)
352 Red Hill Rd. Phone: (908)671-6050
Middletown, NJ 07748 Mae H. Fisher, Libn.
Founded: 1979. **Staff:** Prof 1. **Subjects:** Horticulture, cooking, landscaping, pest identification. **Holdings:** 3000 books; 45 bound periodical volumes. **Subscriptions:** 30 journals and other serials. **Services:** Copying; library open to the public.

★10614★
Monmouth County Social Services - Library (Soc Sci)
Box 3000 Phone: (908)431-6000
Freehold, NJ 07728 Barbara Skerry, Libn.
Founded: 1971. **Staff:** Prof 1; Other 1. **Subjects:** Social work, public welfare, psychiatry, psychology. **Holdings:** 3000 books; 40 VF drawers of uncataloged pamphlets, reports, government documents, clippings. **Subscriptions:** 140 journals and other serials. **Services:** Interlibrary loan; copying; library open to the public with restrictions. **Networks/Consortia:** Member of Monmouth-Ocean Biomedical Information Consortium (MOBIC). **Publications:** Library News, bimonthly - for internal distribution only. **Remarks:** Alternate telephone number(s): (908)431-6011.

★10615★
Monmouth Medical Center - Altschul Medical Library (Med)
300 2nd Ave. Phone: (908)870-5170
Long Branch, NJ 07740 Frederic C. Pachman, Dir.
Founded: 1959. **Staff:** Prof 1; Other 3. **Subjects:** Medicine, nursing, dentistry, pediatrics, geriatrics, obstetrics, neurology. **Holdings:** 3000 books; 1700 bound periodical volumes; 4200 reels of microfilm. **Subscriptions:** 400 journals and other serials. **Services:** Interlibrary loan; copying; library open to the public for reference use only. **Automated Operations:** Computerized serials and ILL. **Computerized Information Services:** MEDLARS, DIALOG Information Services, BRS Information Technologies; ALANET (electronic mail service). **Networks/Consortia:** Member of Monmouth-Ocean Biomedical Information Consortium (MOBIC), National Network of Libraries of Medicine - Middle Atlantic Region. **Publications:** Acquisitions List; Newsletter, quarterly. **Remarks:** FAX: (908)222-3742. Electronic mail address(es): ALA 1846 (ALANET).

★10616★
Monroe Community Hospital - T.F. Williams Health Sciences Library (Med)
435 E. Henrietta Rd. Phone: (716)274-7362
Rochester, NY 14620 Elinor Reynolds, Lib.Dir.
Staff: Prof 1. **Subjects:** Geriatrics, gerontology, long-term care, medicine, nursing, administration. **Holdings:** 998 books; 2164 bound periodical volumes. **Subscriptions:** 164 journals and other serials. **Services:** Interlibrary loan; library open to the public for reference use only. **Computerized Information Services:** MEDLINE, BRS Information Technologies. **Networks/Consortia:** Member of Rochester Regional Library Council (RRLC). **Remarks:** FAX: (716)274-7149.

★10617★
Monroe County Genealogical Society - Library (Hist)
Rte. 3 Phone: (515)932-2593
Albia, IA 52531 Sarah Hindman, Correspondence Sec.
Subjects: State, regional, local history and genealogy. **Special Collections:** Mary Barnes Prill Collection (Mantua township tombstone and census records); census records for Iowa counties, 1850-1925 (microfilm); census records for Monroe County, IA, 1850-1910 (microfilm); Federal Population Census catalogs, 1790 and 1910; church records and histories, 1828-1987; death and probate records, 1757 to present. **Holdings:** Cemetery, land, marriage, family, and school records and histories; maps and plat books; veteran material; newspapers; newsletters. **Services:** Interlibrary loan (limited); copying; library open to the public. **Publications:** List of publications - available on request. **Remarks:** Library is housed in the Albia Public Library, 203 Benton Ave., E., Albia, IA 52531. The library does not maintain a genealogical librarian, but does provide the names of people to assist those pursuing genealogical research.

★10618★
Monroe County Historian's Office - Library (Hist)
115 South Ave.
Rochester, NY 14604 Phone: (716)428-7375
Staff: Prof 1. **Subjects:** County history, city of Rochester history, Erie and Barge canals. **Holdings:** 10,000 volumes; 30,000 newspapers, photographs, clippings, manuscripts, census data. **Services:** Copying; open to the public by appointment on a limited schedule. **Computerized Information Services:** Internal database. **Publications:** Books & Booklets, annual. **Special Indexes:** Index to history of Monroe County, 1877 and 1895 (card, book).

★10619★
Monroe County Historical Association - Library and Museum (Hist)
Stroud Community House
537 Ann St. Phone: (717)421-7703
Stroudsburg, PA 18360 Janet Mishkin, Dir.
Founded: 1921. **Staff:** Prof 1; Other 1. **Subjects:** Monroe County history and genealogy. **Special Collections:** Family histories; county maps; church histories. **Holdings:** 3000 books; 45 cubic feet of documents and manuscripts; newspapers; clippings; maps. **Subscriptions:** 19 journals and other serials. **Services:** Copying; library open to the public. **Publications:** The Fan Light (newsletter), quarterly.

★10620★
Monroe County Historical Commission - Archives (Hist)
126 S. Monroe St. Phone: (313)243-7137
Monroe, MI 48161 Jennifer Barner, Archv.
Founded: 1938. **Staff:** Prof 1. **Subjects:** Civil War, George A. Custer, Michigan and Monroe County, local genealogy. **Special Collections:** War of the Rebellion. **Holdings:** 1120 books; 136 bound periodical volumes; 64 other cataloged items; 4 VF drawers of photographs; 19 tapes; 10 drawers of maps; 130 linear feet of manuscript collections. **Subscriptions:** 15 journals and other serials. **Services:** Copying; archives open to the public by appointment.

★10621★
Monroe County Law Library (Law)
Court House
Monroe, MI 48161 Phone: (313)243-7090
Subjects: American civil and criminal law. **Holdings:** 5745 volumes. **Services:** Library not open to the public. **Remarks:** FAX: (313)243-7107.

★10622★
Monroe County Law Library (Law)
Court House Phone: (717)424-5100
Stroudsburg, PA 18360 Roy P. Kleinle, Libn.
Subjects: Law. **Holdings:** 6000 volumes. **Services:** Library open to the public. **Remarks:** Library maintained by appropriation for County of Monroe.

★10623★
Monroe County Library System - General George Armstrong Custer Collection (Hist)
3700 S. Custer Phone: (313)241-5277
Monroe, MI 48161 Carl Katafiasz, Spec.Coll.Coord.
Staff: Prof 1. **Subjects:** General George A. Custer, Battle of Little Big Horn, American Indians, Indian wars, the West, Civil War. **Special Collections:** Custer Collection; Dr. Lawrence A. Frost Collection of Custeriana. **Holdings:** 4000 books; 18 bound periodical volumes; 1600 unbound periodicals; 163 newspapers; 110 books on microfilm; 5380 slides; 35 maps; 100 pictures; 150 pamphlets; 23 original manuscripts; 35 AV programs; 170 microfiche; 60 cassettes. **Services:** Copying; collection open to the public by appointment for reference use only. **Publications:** Custer Monograph Series (10 volumes); Bibliography of cataloged materials in special collections of the Billings Public Library and Monroe County Library System. **Remarks:** FAX: (313)241-4722.

★10624★
Monroe County Local History Room & Library (Hist)
Community Services Bldg.
Rte. 2, Box 21 Phone: (608)269-8680
Sparta, WI 54656 Audrey Johnson, County Hist.Libn.
Founded: 1977. **Staff:** Prof 1; Other 15. **Subjects:** Local history, genealogy. **Special Collections:** Census through 1910; newspapers through 1960; church, school, and logging history; manuscripts of business history and early letters. **Holdings:** 800 books; 15 bound periodical volumes; 250 reels of microfilm; 15 VF drawers of cemetery records; 12,000 documents; 5000 photographs. **Services:** Interlibrary loan; copying; library open to the public. **Publications:** Monroe County Pictorial History (1976). **Special Indexes:** Genealogy card file of Monroe County; cemetery index.

★10625★
Monroe County Parks Department - Highland Botanical Park - Library (Biol Sci)
180 Reservoir Ave. Phone: (716)244-8079
Rochester, NY 14620 James W. Kelly, Plant Taxonomist/Cur.
Founded: 1888. **Staff:** Prof 1. **Subjects:** Horticulture, plant taxonomy, forestry, plant pathology, landscaping. **Holdings:** 850 books; 110 bound periodical volumes; photographs of trees and panoramas of the parks of Monroe County; slides of trees and shrubs of Monroe County; 15,204 specimens in adjacent herbarium. **Subscriptions:** 15 journals and other serials. **Services:** Interlibrary loan; copying; library open to the public for reference use only. **Remarks:** FAX: (716)256-4968.

★10626★
Monroe County Public Library - Indiana Room (Hist)
303 E. Kirkwood Phone: (812)339-2271
Bloomington, IN 47401 Robert Trinkle, Dir.
Founded: 1. **Subjects:** Indiana state and local history, genealogy. **Special Collections:** Oral histories. **Holdings:** 4000 books; 285 bound periodical volumes; 1200 microfilm. **Subscriptions:** 95 journals and other serials; 9 newspapers. **Services:** Interlibrary loan; copying; room open to the public. **Special Indexes:** Indexes to local sources; Obituaries of Monroe County, IN; Index to Bloomington Herald-Times Newspaper. **Remarks:** FAX: (812)323-4352. **Staff:** Reann Lydick, Indiana Room Libn.

★10627★
Monroe Developmental Center - Staff/Parent Library (Med)
620 Westfall Rd.
Rochester, NY 14620 Phone: (716)461-8975
Founded: 1974. **Staff:** Prof 1. **Subjects:** Mental retardation, developmental disabilities. **Holdings:** 3100 books; 200 videos; 30 films; 50 slide shows; 300 subject packets. **Subscriptions:** 50 journals and other serials. **Services:** Library open to the public by appointment. **Networks/Consortia:** Member of Rochester Regional Library Council (RRLC), Rochester Area Libraries in Healthcare.

★10628★
James Monroe Museum and Memorial Library (Hist)
908 Charles St. Phone: (703)899-4559
Fredericksburg, VA 22401 Ms. Lee Langston-Harrison, Cur.
Founded: 1927. **Staff:** Prof 3; Other 8. **Subjects:** James Monroe, Monroe Doctrine, Americana, Virginiana, presidents, 18th-20th century politics, 19th century world travel, 18th-19th century philosophy, 19th-20th century science. **Special Collections:** Private correspondence of James Monroe. **Holdings:** 10,000 books; 2000 bound periodical volumes; 27,000 archival items; 15 pieces of artwork; slides and films; 10 VF drawers; 50 archival boxes. **Subscriptions:** 10 journals and other serials. **Services:** Copying; library open to the public with letter of intent. **Remarks:** FAX: (703)899-4123. Museum-Library is owned by Commonwealth of Virginia and administered through Mary Washington College's Center for Historic Preservation. **Staff:** Mary Podlesny, Adm.; John N. Pearce, Dir. of Plan. & Prog.

★10629★
Monroe, Juneau, Jackson County, Wisconsin Genealogy Workshop - Library (Hist)
Rte. 3, Box 253 Phone: (608)378-4388
Black River Falls, WI 54615 Carolyn Habelman, Pres.
Founded: 1976. **Staff:** 1. **Subjects:** Local history, genealogy. **Holdings:** 800 books; 300 bound periodical volumes; 100 cemetery and church records; 300 biographical family charts; census and newspapers on microfilm; maps. **Subscriptions:** 25 journals and other serials; 7 newspapers. **Services:** Copying; library open to the public by appointment. **Publications:** Annual Surname Query Index (members' names); newsletter, quarterly - to members; Monroe County Heritage Book; Sparta "Woodlawn Cemetery Inscriptions." **Special Indexes:** Church Vital records; 1905 census; cemetery index; Monro County Marriage Index, 1850-1907. **Remarks:** FAX: (608)378-3006.

★10630★
(Monrovia) American Cultural Center - USIS Library (Educ)
197 Ashmun St.
Post Box 98
Monrovia, Liberia
Remarks: Maintained or supported by the U.S. Information Agency. Focus is on materials that will assist peoples outside the United States to learn about the United States, its people, history, culture, political processes, and social milieux.

★10631★
Monsanto Chemical Company - Patent Department Library (Sci-Engr, Law)
800 N. Lindbergh Phone: (314)694-2547
St. Louis, MO 63167 Suzanne H. Elsoffer
Staff: Prof 2; Other 2. **Subjects:** Chemical patents, patent and trademark law, licensing, trade secrets. **Special Collections:** U.S. Chemical Patents, 1952 to present (580,000); EP Patents (CD-ROM). **Holdings:** 700 books; 125 bound periodical volumes; patents on microfilm; patent abstracts; U.S. Official Gazette on microfilm. **Subscriptions:** 50 journals and other serials. **Services:** Interlibrary loan; library open to the public by appointment for reference use only. **Automated Operations:** Computerized cataloging, serials, and translations index. **Computerized Information Services:** DIALOG Information Services, ORBIT Search Service, STN International, Questel, LEXIS, NEXIS; internal databases. **Networks/Consortia:** Member of St. Louis Regional Library Network. **Remarks:** Alternate telephone number(s): 694-1000. FAX: (314)694-9009. **Staff:** J.C. Morris, Patent Info.Spec.

★10632★
Monsanto Chemical Company - Research Library-East (Sci-Engr)
730 Worcester St. Phone: (413)788-6911
Springfield, MA 01151-1099 Lorraine M. Daudeline, Libn.
Staff: Prof 1. **Subjects:** Polymer chemistry, organic chemistry, plastics, chemical engineering, mathematics, statistics. **Holdings:** 6000 books; 1500 bound periodical volumes. **Subscriptions:** 500 journals and other serials. **Services:** Interlibrary loan. **Computerized Information Services:** DIALOG Information Services, NLM, PFDS Online, STN International.

★10633★
Monsanto Chemical Company - Technical Center Library (Sci-Engr)
Box 2204 Phone: (205)552-2223
Decatur, AL 35609 Betty H. Patterson, Tech.Libn.
Founded: 1952. **Staff:** Prof 1. **Subjects:** Textile technology, chemistry, chemical engineering, business and personnel administration. **Holdings:** 3300 books; 3100 bound periodical volumes; 35 pamphlets; 13,000 technical reports; 177 reels of microfilm. **Subscriptions:** 175 journals and other serials. **Services:** Interlibrary loan; library not open to the public. **Computerized Information Services:** DIALOG Information Services. **Publications:** Book list, monthly - for internal distribution only. **Special Catalogs:** Periodical Holdings List.

★10634★
Monsanto Company - Fisher Controls Company - Information Center (Sci-Engr)
R.A. Engel Technical Center
Box 11 Phone: (515)754-2161
Marshalltown, IA 50158 Mark Heindselman, Mgr., Info.Ctr.
Founded: 1979. **Staff:** Prof 1; Other 2. **Subjects:** Automatic control, instrumentation, process control, computer science, mechanical engineering, materials science. **Holdings:** 3500 books; 100 bound periodical volumes; 3000 standards; 18,000 vendor catalogs; 10,000 technical and marketing papers; 40,000 internal engineering reports; 10,000 patents. **Subscriptions:** 300 journals and other serials; 5 newspapers. **Services:**

Interlibrary loan; copying; SDI; library open to the public by appointment. **Automated Operations:** Computerized cataloging and serials. **Computerized Information Services:** DIALOG Information Services, PFDS Online, BRS Information Technologies, VU/TEXT Information Services, Reuter TEXTLINE, InvesText, Data-Star, Dow Jones News/Retrieval, Human Resource Information Network (HRIN); internal database. **Publications:** Control Chronicle, quarterly; Keeping Current, biweekly; New Papers and Reports Bulletin, bimonthly. **Remarks:** FAX: (515)754-3159. Telex: 478 456.

★10635★
Monsanto Company - Fisher Controls Company - Resource Center (Comp Sci)
1712 Centre Creek Dr. Phone: (512)834-7255
Austin, TX 78754 Mark Heindselman, Mgr., Info/Ctr.
Founded: 1985. **Staff:** 1. **Subjects:** Computers, process control, software engineering. **Special Collections:** Vendor catalogs (6000). **Holdings:** 1100 books; 1000 unbound reports. **Subscriptions:** 100 journals and other serials. **Services:** Interlibrary loan; copying; center open to the public by appointment. **Automated Operations:** Computerized cataloging and serials. **Computerized Information Services:** Internal database. **Remarks:** FAX: (512)834-7200. **Staff:** Marshall Duke, Res.Ctr.Coord.

★10636★
Monsanto Company - Information Center (Sci-Engr)
800 N. Lindbergh Blvd.
Box 7090 Phone: (314)694-4778
St. Louis, MO 63177 Jan Williams, Mgr.
Founded: 1961. **Staff:** Prof 15; Other 12. **Subjects:** Chemicals, business, agriculture, biology, medicine, engineering, plastics, science. **Holdings:** 38,000 books; 150,000 microfilm and bound periodical volumes; 4000 directories; 30 VF drawers of trade literature; 75 VF drawers of annual reports; 160,000 technical reports; 690,500 U.S. chemical patents; 60 VF drawers of pamphlets; 16,000 translations. **Subscriptions:** 1600 journals and other serials; 10 newspapers. **Services:** Interlibrary loan; copying; translating; alerting; center open to the public by application. **Automated Operations:** Computerized cataloging, acquisitions, serials, and circulation. **Computerized Information Services:** STN International, DIALOG Information Services, PFDS Online, BRS Information Technologies, NLM, Mead Data Central; INFOCAT (internal database). **Networks/Consortia:** Member of St. Louis Regional Library Network, Center for Research Libraries (CRL). **Remarks:** FAX: (314)694-8748. **Staff:** Regina Klein, Coll.Serv.; Lynn Backes, Info.Serv.; Debbie Schaller, Doc.Serv.; Frank Reynard, Lib.Serv.

★10637★
Monsanto Company - Law Library (Law)
800 N. Lindbergh Blvd. (EINC) Phone: (314)694-4306
St. Louis, MO 63167 Marguerite Kettering, Libn.
Staff: 1. **Subjects:** Law, legal services. **Holdings:** 7000 books; statutes. **Subscriptions:** 203 journals and other serials. **Services:** Interlibrary loan; library not open to the public. **Computerized Information Services:** LEXIS, Dow Jones News/Retrieval. **Remarks:** FAX: (314)694-2965.

★10638★
Monsanto Company - MCC Engineering Library (Sci-Engr)
800 N. Lindbergh Blvd. Phone: (314)694-7133
St. Louis, MO 63167 Linda L. Holdman, Libn.
Founded: 1965. **Staff:** Prof 1. **Subjects:** Chemical and mechanical engineering. **Holdings:** 4000 books; 200 bound periodical volumes; 1000 standards. **Subscriptions:** 55 journals and other serials. **Services:** Interlibrary loan; copying; library open to the public upon application. **Automated Operations:** Computerized cataloging and serials. **Special Catalogs:** List of vendor holdings (microfilm).

★10639★
Monsanto Fibers & Intermediates Company - Technical Library (Sci-Engr)
Box 12830 Phone: (904)968-8248
Pensacola, FL 32575 Donald A. Holmer, Sr.Info.Spec.
Founded: 1953. **Staff:** Prof 2; Other 1. **Subjects:** Chemistry, chemical engineering, polymer chemistry, textile technology, quality control. **Holdings:** 12,275 books; 3000 bound periodical volumes; 700 pamphlets; 760 reels of microfilm; 500 VF drawers of company generated technical reports. **Subscriptions:** 290 journals and other serials; 10 newspapers. **Services:** Interlibrary loan; copying; SDI; library open to qualified researchers by appointment. **Computerized Information Services:** DIALOG Information Services, BRS Information Technologies, ORBIT Search Service, STN International, CIS; internal database. **Publications:** New Books Purchased, Technical Reports Issued, Selected Patent & Technical Abstracts, monthly - for internal distribution only. **Special Catalogs:** Computer printout of technical reports, index, and book catalog. **Remarks:** Alternate telephone number(s): (904)968-8249. **Staff:** Mary J. LaMotte, Asst.Libn.

★10640★
Monsour Medical Center - Health Services Library (Med)
70 Lincoln Way, East Phone: (412)527-1511
Jeannette, PA 15644 Edith Gross, Med.Libn.
Founded: 1972. **Staff:** Prof 1. **Subjects:** Medicine, nursing, hospital management, social work, pharmacology. **Holdings:** 868 books; 500 bound periodical volumes; 378 audiotapes; 26 slide/tape sets. **Subscriptions:** 120 journals and other serials. **Services:** Interlibrary loan; copying; library open to the public with restrictions. **Networks/Consortia:** Member of National Network of Libraries of Medicine - Middle Atlantic Region.

★10641★
Montana College of Mineral Science and Technology - Library (Sci-Engr)
W. Park St. Phone: (406)496-4281
Butte, MT 59701 John H. Sandy
Staff: Prof 4; Other 6. **Subjects:** Geology, mining, mineral processing, geochemistry, geophysics, petroleum, environmental engineering, occupational safety, mineral economics, technology and society, industrial hygiene. **Special Collections:** Mining and geology of Montana; international and state geological documents; U.S. patents depository, 1981 to present; federal document depository (378,500 documents, bound and on microfilm). **Holdings:** 40,000 books; 35,400 bound periodical volumes. **Subscriptions:** 500 journals and other serials. **Services:** Interlibrary loan; copying; library open to the public. **Automated Operations:** Computerized cataloging, acquisitions, serials, and ILL. **Computerized Information Services:** DIALOG Information Services, PFDS Online, BRS Information Technologies, STN International; CD-ROM (Lasercat); FAPRS (internal database). Performs searches on fee basis. **Networks/Consortia:** Member of Western Library Network (WLN). **Special Catalogs:** Catalog of Ivory Collection. **Remarks:** FAX: (406)496-4133. **Staff:** Jean Bishop, Ref.Libn.; Alicia Willson-Metzger, Asst.Ref.Libn.; Carol Rhoads, MHS.Proc.Libn.

★10642★
Montana Deaconess Medical Center/Montana State University - Health Science Library (Med)
2800 11th Ave., S. Phone: (406)455-5613
Great Falls, MT 59405 Pat Mueller, Libn.
Subjects: Medicine, allied health sciences. **Holdings:** 3500 volumes. **Subscriptions:** 125 journals and other serials. **Services:** Interlibrary loan; copying; library open to the public with restrictions. **Remarks:** Library is operated jointly by Montana Deaconess Medical Center and Montana State University.

★10643★
Montana Historical Society - Library/Archives (Hist)
225 N. Roberts Phone: (406)444-2681
Helena, MT 59620 Robert M. Clark, Hd., Lib. & Archv.Div.
Founded: 1865. **Staff:** Prof 9; Other 5. **Subjects:** Lewis and Clark Expedition; George Armstrong Custer; Charles M. Russell; military history of the Montana Indians; Montana biography/genealogy; mining; cattle and range; homesteading. **Special Collections:** T.C. Power papers; Senator Lee Metcalf papers; Thomas Teakle Collection of books and L.A. Huffman photographs on western cattle and range subjects (2300 books and periodicals; 1100 photographs); F.J. and Jack Ellis Haynes Northern Pacific Railroad and Yellowstone National Park Photograph Collection; Anaconda Copper Mining Company papers; state government archives (5500 cubic feet). **Holdings:** 50,000 books; 5000 bound periodical volumes; 50,000 state publications; 6500 cubic feet of private papers; 200,000 photographs; 14,000 reels of microfilm of Montana and other newspapers; 16,000 maps; 4000 broadsides and ephemera. **Subscriptions:** 300 journals and other serials; 102 state newspapers. **Services:** Interlibrary loan; copying (both limited); library open to the public for research and reference use only. **Automated Operations:** Computerized cataloging, acquisitions, and serials.

Computerized Information Services: Internal database; CD-ROM (Lasercat). **Networks/Consortia:** Member of Western Library Network (WLN). **Publications:** Montana: The Magazine of Western History, quarterly; Montana Post (newsletter), quarterly. **Special Catalogs:** Union List of Montana Newspapers in Montana Repositories; Catalog of the Map Collection (microfiche). **Special Indexes:** History of Montana, 1739-1885; Contributions to the Montana Historical Society; Montana obituary index, 1864-1930 (card); Montana biographies index (card); F. Jay Haynes Photo Collection Index (microfiche) - for sale. **Remarks:** Alternate telephone number(s): 444-4775 (Archives); 444-4739 (Photo Archives). FAX: (406)444-2696. **Staff:** Dave Walter, Ref.Libn.; Kathryn Otto, State Archv.; Ellie Arguimbau, Archv.; Lory Morrow, Hd., Photo Archv.; John Smart, Archv.Photo.; John Terreo, Oral Hist.; Vivian Hayes, Cat.Libn.

Montana Natural Heritage Program
See: **Nature Conservancy** (11347)

★10644★
The Montana Power Company - Law Library (Law)
40 E. Broadway Phone: (406)723-5421
Butte, MT 59701 Susan K. Nissen, Libn.
Staff: Prof 1; Other 1. **Subjects:** Public utility law, energy law. **Special Collections:** Legislative history of the Federal Power Act. **Holdings:** 7000 books. **Subscriptions:** 46 journals and other serials. **Services:** Interlibrary loan; copying; SDI; library open to the public by appointment for reference use only. **Computerized Information Services:** WESTLAW, LEXIS, DIALOG Information Services. **Remarks:** FAX: (406)496-5051.

★10645★
Montana (State) Department of Commerce - Census & Economic Information Center (Soc Sci)
1424 9th Ave. Phone: (406)444-2896
Helena, MT 59620-0535 Patricia A.B. Roberts, Prog.Mgr.
Founded: 1970. **Staff:** Prof 2; Other 2. **Subjects:** Montana - demography, census, economics. **Holdings:** 4000 documents; census maps; microfiche; magnetic tapes. **Subscriptions:** 200 journals and other serials. **Services:** Copying; SDI; center open to the public for reference use only. **Computerized Information Services:** DIALOG Information Services; CD-ROMs. **Networks/Consortia:** Member of Western Library Network (WLN). **Publications:** Montana County Profiles, irregular. **Remarks:** FAX: (406)444-2808. **Staff:** David R. Martin, Res.Spec.; Pamela M. Harris, Libn.; Jim K. Williams, Prog.

★10646★
Montana (State) Department of Commerce - Montana Promotion Division (Aud-Vis)
1424 9th Ave. Phone: (406)444-2654
Helena, MT 59620 Sandra Guedes, Travel Dir.
Founded: 1935. **Subjects:** Tourist information. **Holdings:** Films; photographs of tourist attractions. **Services:** Films and photographs for loan. **Computerized Information Services:** Internal database. **Publications:** Vacation guides; travel planners; highway maps. **Remarks:** FAX: (406)444-2808.

★10647★
Montana (State) Department of Natural Resources & Conservation - Research & Information Center (Env-Cons)
1520 E. 6th Ave. Phone: (406)444-6700
Helena, MT 59620-2301 Julie Frickel, Lib.Techn.
Staff: Prof 1. **Subjects:** Water resource and energy planning; land use and conservation; forests; geology; Missouri, Columbia, and Yellowstone River Basins. **Special Collections:** MWRB Water Resources survey reports; departmental publications. **Holdings:** 7000 books; 1000 documents; geological maps of Montana; minutes of River Basin meetings. **Subscriptions:** 250 journals and other serials. **Services:** Interlibrary loan; center open to the public. **Remarks:** FAX: (406)444-6721.

★10648★
Montana (State) Department of Social & Rehabilitation Services - Developmental Disabilities Division - Training Resource and Information Center (TRIC) (Soc Sci)
3075 N. Montana Phone: (406)444-1799
Helena, MT 59620 Marlene Kennedy, Libn.
Founded: 1976. **Staff:** Prof 1. **Subjects:** Training individuals with developmental disabilities for community living and deinstitutionalization. **Holdings:** 4500 books; 300 AV programs. **Subscriptions:** 30 journals and other serials. **Services:** Interlibrary loan (limited); copying; library open to residents of Montana. **Automated Operations:** Computerized cataloging and circulation. **Publications:** Bibliography of holdings. **Remarks:** FAX: (406)444-1970.

(Montana) State Law Library of Montana
See: **State Law Library of Montana** (15685)

★10649★
Montana (State) Legislative Council - Research Library (Law)
State Capitol, Rm. 102 Phone: (406)444-3064
Helena, MT 59620 Beth Furbush, Res.Libn.
Founded: 1975. **Staff:** Prof 1; Other 1. **Subjects:** Laws and legislation, legislatures, state and local government, public administration. **Special Collections:** Montana constitutional and legislative history (360 volumes); Montana State Commission on Local Government Collection (160 volumes). **Holdings:** 4000 books; 12 VF drawers of newspaper clippings; 260 microfiche of Montana Legislative Council reports; 115 boxes of workpapers of legislative interim studies. **Subscriptions:** 225 journals and other serials. **Services:** Interlibrary loan; copying; SDI; library open to the public for reference use only. **Computerized Information Services:** DIALOG Information Services, LEXIS, LEGISNET, Legislative Information System (LIS), Current USC. **Publications:** Sources of Information and Publications, 1990. **Remarks:** FAX: (406)444-3036.

★10650★
Montana State Library (Info Sci)
1515 E. 6th Ave. Phone: (406)444-3004
Helena, MT 59620 Richard T. Miller, Jr., State Libn.
Founded: 1946. **Staff:** Prof 7; Other 29. **Subjects:** General collection. **Special Collections:** Federal government publications (partial depository); state government publications (complete depository). **Holdings:** 69,420 books; 486 periodical titles; 19,065 state publications; 237,775 federal publications. **Subscriptions:** 486 journals and other serials; 15 newspapers. **Services:** Interlibrary loan; copying; library open to the public. **Automated Operations:** Computerized cataloging; acquisitions, and ILL. **Computerized Information Services:** DIALOG Information Services, BRS Information Technologies, OCLC; Natural Resource Information System (internal database). Performs searches free of charge. Contact Person: Darlene Staffeldt, Prog.Mgr., Info.Rsrcs. **Networks/Consortia:** Member of CLASS, Western Library Network (WLN). **Publications:** Montana State Library News, bimonthly; Montana State Library News Update, bimonthly; Montana State Library Annual Statistical Report of Montana Public Libraries; Montana Library Directory, annual. **Remarks:** FAX: (406)444-5612. **Staff:** Sheila Cates, Coord., Lib.Dev.; Sandra Jarvie Reg.Libn.

★10651★
Montana State Library - Montana Natural Resource Information System (Env-Cons)
1515 E. 6th Ave. Phone: (406)444-5354
Helena, MT 59620 Richard T. Miller, Act.Prog.Dir.
Founded: 1985. **Staff:** Prof 12; Other 3. **Subjects:** Water resources, geology, soils, climate, fish and wildlife, vegetation, native plants, agriculture, land use. **Special Collections:** Natural resources data pertinent to Montana. **Holdings:** Published and unpublished natural resource documents. **Subscriptions:** 6 journals and other serials. **Services:** System open to the public. **Computerized Information Services:** NAWDEX (National Water Data Exchange), WATSTORE (National Water Data Storage and Retrieval System), STORET - Office of Information Resources Management - U.S. Environmental Protection Agency; Montana River Information System, MNRI (Montana Natural Resource Index) (internal databases). **Publications:** NRIS newsletter; User Guidelines; Montana GIS News; Montana Data Directory. **Special Indexes:** Index to data in state agencies; environmental inpact statements; water resources data. **Remarks:** NRIS is a comprehensive program for the acquisition, storage, and retrieval of existing data relating to the natural resources of Montana. It is divided into

three main components: the Montana Natural Heritage Program, the Montana Geographic Information System, and the Montana Water Information System. The Montana Natural Resource Information System has access to major federal and state digital sources of water resources data, and an index of all GIS-applicable data managed by federal, state, and local agencies in Montana. FAX: (406)444-5612. **Staff:** David Genter, Coord.; Jim Stimson, Coord.; Allan Cox, Coord.

★10652★
Montana (State) Office of Public Instruction - Resource Center (Educ)
State Capitol, Rm. 106 Phone: (406)444-2082
Helena, MT 59620 Cheri Bergeron, Libn.
Staff: Prof 1; Other 1. **Subjects:** Education. **Special Collections:** Archives of the Office of Public Instruction. **Holdings:** 1200 books; complete collection of ERIC microfiche. **Subscriptions:** 375 journals and other serials. **Services:** Copying; center open to school personnel only. **Computerized Information Services:** DIALOG Information Services, BRS Information Technologies; internal database. **Remarks:** FAX: (406)444-3924.

★10653★
Montana State University - Herbarium - Library (Biol Sci)
Dept. of Biology Phone: (406)994-4424
Bozeman, MT 59717 Matt Lavin
Founded: 1890. **Subjects:** Vascular Plants. **Special Collections:** Vascular plants of the Rocky Mountains and adjacent Great Plains. **Holdings:** 70,000 plant specimens. **Subscriptions:** 2 journals and other serials. **Services:** Herbarium open to the public. Loans to recognized institutions.

★10654★
Montana State University - Libraries - Merrill G. Burlingame Special Collections/Archives (Hist)
Bozeman, MT 59717-0332 Phone: (406)994-4242
Nathan E. Bender, Hd. of Spec.Coll./Archv.
Founded: 1953. **Staff:** Prof 1; Other 2. **Subjects:** Montana history, Yellowstone National Park, Senator Burton K. Wheeler, Montana Native Americans, Montana agriculture, James Williard Schultz, Montana State University. **Special Collections:** Haynes Collection; Yellowstone National Park Collection; M.L. Wilson Agricultural History Collection; Leggat-Donahoe Northwest Collection; Abraham Lincoln Collection; Montana Architectural Drawings Collection; Montana WPA files; Burton K. Wheeler Collection. **Holdings:** 31,862 volumes; 953 reels of microfilm; 311 microfiche; 1615 aperture cards; 1654 manuscripts; 11,005 cubic feet of University records; 10,000 photographs on Montana agriculture and Montana State University. **Subscriptions:** 14 journals and other serials. **Services:** Copying; open to the public. **Automated Operations:** Computerized public access catalog, cataloging, and acquisitions. **Computerized Information Services:** BITNET, InterNet (electronic mail services). **Networks/Consortia:** Member of Western Library Network (WLN). **Remarks:** Electronic mail address(es): BENDER/LIB@RENNE.LIB.MONTANA.EDU international.

Montana State University - Montana Deaconess Medical Center - Health Science Library
See: **Montana Deaconess Medical Center/Montana State University - Health Science Library** (10642)

★10655★
Montana State University - Veterinary Molecular Biology Laboratory - Huidekoper Library (Med)
S. 19th & Lincoln Phone: (406)994-4705
Bozeman, MT 59717 C.A. Speer, Dir.
Founded: 1929. **Staff:** Prof 1. **Subjects:** Veterinary science. **Holdings:** 3400 books; 3100 bound periodical volumes; 6000 pamphlets and reprints. **Subscriptions:** 120 journals and other serials. **Services:** Library for staff use only.

★10656★
Montclair Art Museum - Le Brun Library (Art)
3 S. Mountain Ave. Phone: (201)746-5555
Montclair, NJ 07042-1747 Edith A. Rights, Libn.
Founded: 1916. **Staff:** Prof 1. **Subjects:** American and American Indian art, Chinese snuff bottles. **Special Collections:** Bookplates collection (6000). **Holdings:** 12,500 books; 3500 bound periodical volumes; museum bulletins and catalogs of exhibitions; posters; 125 VF drawers of clippings, pictures, pamphlets; 17,000 slides; 50 tapes of museum programs and lectures. **Subscriptions:** 50 journals and other serials. **Services:** Copying; library open to the public by appointment. **Publications:** The Bookplates of Arthur Nelson Macdonald, 1986. **Special Catalogs:** Ex Libris; Selected Bookplates of Arthur Nelson Macdonald, 1986; The Bookplate Work of David McNeely Stauffer, 1990. **Special Indexes:** Inhouse exhibition record and index (card, typed list). **Remarks:** FAX: (201)746-9118.

★10657★
Montclair Public Library (Hist)
50 S. Fullerton Ave. Phone: (201)744-0500
Montclair, NJ 07042 Michael Connell, Dir.
Founded: 1893. **Staff:** 34. **Subjects:** Art, literature. **Special Collections:** Local history. **Holdings:** 16 VF drawers of mounted pictures; programs; club rosters; diaries; maps. **Services:** Interlibrary loan; copying; library open to the public. **Automated Operations:** Computerized public access catalog. **Computerized Information Services:** CD-ROMs (Compact Disclosure, Books in Print, McGraw-Hill Concise Encyclopedia, Magazine Index, Business Periodicals Ondisc). **Networks/Consortia:** Member of Essex Hudson Regional Library Cooperative. **Special Catalogs:** Index to the Montclair Times (card). **Special Indexes:** Index to Montclair Times (1961-1990, on cards); Index to Montclair Times (1990 to present, online). **Remarks:** FAX: (201)744-2349. **Staff:** Mary Lou Cass; Deirdre O'Hagan; Mary Riskind; Kofi Nantwi; Tammy Strauss; Amy Levine; Ronald Murphy; Seth Stephens; Cheryl McCoy.

★10658★
Montclair State College - Harry A. Sprague Library - Special Collections (Hum, Info Sci)
Upper Montclair, NJ 07043 Phone: (201)893-4301
Bernice R. Jones-Trent, Dir. of Lib.Serv.
Founded: 1908. **Staff:** Prof 17; Other 36. **Subjects:** Education; music; business admnistration; literature - English, French, German, Spanish. **Special Collections:** Modern poetry - Sullivan Collection, Webster Collection, William Carlos Williams Collection (1357 volumes). **Holdings:** 380,223 bound volumes; 968,527 microforms; 27,126 volumes and 53,355 microforms of government documents; 972,703 non-print items. **Subscriptions:** 3509 journals and other serials. **Services:** Interlibrary loan; copying; collections open to the public with restrictions. **Automated Operations:** Computerized cataloging, acquisitions, circulation, and ILL. **Computerized Information Services:** BRS Information Technologies, DIALOG Information Services, OCLC; CD-ROMs. **Networks/Consortia:** Member of PALINET. **Publications:** NEW Monthly Acquisitions; Library Scene (newsletter). **Special Catalogs:** Bibliographies; periodical holdings list; non-print media holdings list. **Remarks:** FAX: (201)893-5455. **Staff:** Pauline Yeh, Asst.Dir./Tech.Serv.; Patricia Sanders, Hd., Ref.Serv.; Kathleen Hughes, Hd., Cat.; Kevin Prendergast, Supv., ILL; Eduardo Gil, Hd., Non-Print Media; Joyce Schaffer, Hd., Govt.Docs.; Albert Wang, Hd., Per.; Norman Stock, Hd., Acq./Coll.Dev.; Faith Ryan, Adm.Asst. to Dir.

★10659★
Montclair State College - Women's Center Library (Soc Sci)
Student Center, 4th Fl. Phone: (201)893-5114
Upper Montclair, NJ 07043 Sharon Olson, PhD., Dir.
Staff: 3. **Subjects:** Women - literature, family, health, sexuality, career, psychology, education, feminism, aging, society. **Holdings:** 575 books; 5 VF drawers of clippings. **Services:** Library open to the campus and surrounding communities.

Monte Cristo Cottage Library
See: **Eugene O'Neill Theater Center** (12422)

★10660★
Monte Vista Christian Church - Pearce Memorial Library and Media Center (Rel-Phil)
3501 Campus Blvd., N.E. Phone: (505)268-3365
Albuquerque, NM 87106 Elizabeth C. Bundy, Libn.
Founded: 1955. **Subjects:** Religion, Monte Vista Christian Church (Disciples of Christ) history and theology, humanities, interpersonal relationships. **Special Collections:** Disciples of Christ Christian Church (125 books, audiocassettes, and videotapes). **Holdings:** 5000 books; 300 AV prgrams. **Subscriptions:** 5 journals and other serials. **Services:** Library open to the public with restrictions on borrowing.

★10661★
Montefiore Hospital - Medical Library (Med)
3459 5th Ave. Phone: (412)648-6090
Pittsburgh, PA 15213 Gloria K. Rosen, Lib.Dir.
Founded: 1970. **Staff:** Prof 3; Other 1. **Subjects:** Medicine. **Holdings:** 300 books; 4000 bound periodical volumes. **Subscriptions:** 300 journals and other serials; 2 newspapers. **Services:** Interlibrary loan; copying. **Computerized Information Services:** DIALOG Information Services, MEDLARS.

★10662★
Montefiore Medical Center - Health Sciences Library/Tishman Learning Center (Med)
111 E. 210th St. Phone: (212)920-4666
Bronx, NY 10467 Josefina P. Lim, Dir.
Founded: 1900. **Staff:** Prof 2; Other 4. **Subjects:** Medicine, health sciences administration, geriatrics, psychology, psychiatry, nursing. **Special Collections:** Archives. **Holdings:** 10,000 books; AV programs; software packages. **Subscriptions:** 800 journals. **Services:** Interlibrary loan; copying; library open to the public by appointment. **Computerized Information Services:** NLM, BRS Information Technologies, OCLC, DIALOG Information Services, miniMEDLINE; DOCLINE (electronic mail service). **Networks/Consortia:** Member of Medical Library Center of New York (MLCNY), New York Metropolitan Reference and Research Library Agency. **Publications:** Medical Library News, quarterly. **Remarks:** FAX: (212)920-4658. **Staff:** Sheigla R. Smalling, Assoc.Libn. & Hd. of Ref.

★10663★
Montefiore Medical Center - Karl Cherkasky Social Medicine Library (Med)
111 E. 210th St. Phone: (212)920-5508
Bronx, NY 10467 Michael Alderman, M.D.
Founded: 1970. **Subjects:** Social medicine, epidemiology, community and international health, occupational health. **Holdings:** 350 volumes. **Services:** Library open to the public for reference use only.

★10664★
Monterey Bay Aquarium - Library (Biol Sci)
886 Cannery Row Phone: (408)648-4852
Monterey, CA 93940-1085 Merrill Manke, Libn.
Founded: 1984. **Staff:** 3. **Subjects:** Marine biology, marine ecology, oceanography, education, aquaculture. **Holdings:** 4000 books; 60 bound periodical volumes; 100 reports. **Subscriptions:** 200 journals and other serials. **Services:** Copying; library open to the public by appointment. **Computerized Information Services:** DIALOG Information Services, CompuServe Information Service; OnTyme Electronic Message Network Service, SCIENCEnet (electronic mail services). **Networks/Consortia:** Member of Monterey Bay Area Cooperative Library System (MOBAC). **Remarks:** Alternate telephone number(s): 648-4849. FAX: (408)648-4810. Electronic mail address(es): CLASS.AQUARIUM (OnTyme Electronic Message Network Service); MONTEREY.AQUA.LIB (SCIENCEnet). **Staff:** Fran Wolfe; Randy Beuttner.

★10665★
Monterey County Law Library (Law)
Federal Office Bldg.
100 W. Alisal St., Suite 144 Phone: (408)755-5046
Salinas, CA 93901 Richard H. Barratt, Law Libn.
Staff: Prof 1; Other 1. **Subjects:** Law. **Holdings:** 35,750 volumes. **Subscriptions:** 51 journals and other serials. **Services:** Interlibrary loan; copying; library open to the public. **Computerized Information Services:** WESTLAW. **Publications:** For Your Information.

★10666★
Monterey County Law Library - Monterey Branch Library (Law)
1200 Aguajito Rd. Phone: (408)647-7746
Monterey, CA 93940 Barbara Robb, Assoc. Law Libn.
Staff: Prof 1; Other 1. **Subjects:** California and federal law. **Holdings:** 12,000 books. **Subscriptions:** 11 journals and other serials. **Services:** Library open to the public. **Computerized Information Services:** WESTLAW.

★10667★
Monterey County Office of Education - Instructional Media Services and Professional Library (Educ)
901 Blanco Circle
Box 80851 Phone: (408)373-2955
Salinas, CA 93912 William Roberts, Dir.
Staff: 2. **Subjects:** Computer-assisted instruction, early childhood education. **Holdings:** 20,000 titles; 550 educational software programs; 700 educational and developmental toys. **Subscriptions:** 60 journals and other serials; 10 newspapers. **Services:** Copying center open to education professionals and nonprofit organizations. **Remarks:** Alternate telephone number(s): 755-0392; 755-0393. FAX: (408)753-7888. **Staff:** Elizabeth Christian, Libn.; Seshu Hammond, Instr. Media Spec.

★10668★
Monterey History & Art Association, Ltd. - Allen Knight Maritime Museum - Library (Hist)
Stanton Center
5 Custom House Plaza Phone: (408)375-2553
Monterey, CA 93940 Donna Penwell, Dir.
Founded: 1970. **Staff:** 2. **Subjects:** American and foreign ships and shipping. **Special Collections:** Capt. Walter Frederick Lee and Allen Knight Photograph Collections, includes some original glass plate and nitrate negatives. **Holdings:** 3000 books; 10,000 photographic negatives and prints. **Subscriptions:** 10 journals and other serials. **Services:** Copying; library open to the public for reference use only. **Publications:** A Guide to the Allen Knight and Capt. Walter F. Lee Photograph Collections.

★10669★
Monterey History & Art Association, Ltd. - Mayo Hayes O'Donnell Library (Hist)
155 Van Buren St.
Box 805 Phone: (408)372-1838
Monterey, CA 93942 Martha J. Bentley, Lib.Ch.
Founded: 1970. **Subjects:** California, Monterey, Western United States. **Holdings:** 2500 books; archives; photographs. **Services:** Copying (limited); library open to the public for reference use only.

★10670★
Monterey Institute of International Studies - Library (Soc Sci)
425 Van Buren Phone: (408)647-4133
Monterey, CA 93940 Keith Brehmer, Dir.
Founded: 1961. **Staff:** Prof 3; Other 3. **Subjects:** International policy studies, language and humanities, international management, translation and interpretation, Teaching English to Speakers of Other Languages (TESOL), English as a Second Language (ESL), Training for Service Abroad (TSA). **Special Collections:** Technical dictionaries (bilingual and multilingual topics in French, German, Spanish, Russian, Chinese, Italian, Japanese). **Holdings:** 58,000 volumes; 800 MIIS masters' theses; 2200 pamphlets; 28 microforms. **Subscriptions:** 450 journals and other serials; 30 newspapers. **Services:** Interlibrary loan; copying; library open to the public on fee basis. **Automated Operations:** Computerized public access catalog, cataloging, acquisitions, serials, and circulation (MELVYL). **Computerized Information Services:** DIALOG Information Services, ORBIT Search Service, RLIN; CD-ROMs; OnTyme Electronic Message Network Service (electronic mail service). Performs searches on fee basis. **Networks/Consortia:** Member of Monterey Bay Area Cooperative Library System (MOBAC). **Publications:** MIIS/List of Periodicals, Newspapers, Indexes. **Remarks:** FAX: (408)647-3518. Alternate telephone number(s): 647-4133. **Staff:** Hsueh-ying Wang, Hd., Acq. & Cat.; Ann Flower, Ref.Libn. .

★10671★
Monterey Institute for Research in Astronomy - Priscilla Fairfield Bok Library (Sci-Engr)
900 Major Sherman Ln. Phone: (408)375-3220
Monterey, CA 93940 Ansley Hill, Libn.
Founded: 1975. **Staff:** Prof 3. **Subjects:** Astrophysics, astronomy, optics, physics, applied mathematics. **Holdings:** 1047 books; 6500 unbound periodicals and reports; 12 sky atlases and charts. **Subscriptions:** 18 journals and other serials. **Services:** Library open to the public by appointment.

★10672★
Monterey Peninsula Museum of Art - Library (Art)
559 Pacific St.
Monterey, CA 93940 Phone: (408)372-5477
Subjects: Artists, art history, Asian art, folk art, photography. **Holdings:** 800 books; art encyclopedias and dictionaries. **Services:** open to the public with restrictions. FAX: (408)372-5680.

★10673★
Monterey Public Library - RAE Collection on Architecture (Plan)
625 Pacific St. Phone: (408)646-3930
Monterey, CA 93940 Paula Simpson, Lib.Dir.
Subjects: Architecture, interior design, landscape design. **Holdings:** 1000 volumes. **Services:** Copying; collection open to the public at librarian's discretion. **Automated Operations:** Computerized circulation.

(Monterrey) Instituto Mexicano-Norteamericano de Relaciones Culturales - USIS Collection
See: **(San Nicolas de Los Garza) Instituto Mexicano-Norteamericano de Relaciones Culturales Anahuac, A.C.** (14773)

★10674★
(Monterrey) Instituto Mexicano-Norteamericano de Relaciones Culturales - USIS Collection (Educ)
Hidalgo No. 768 Pte. Phone: 83 401583
64000 Monterrey, NL, Mexico Liliana C. De Anza, Hd.Libn.
Founded: 1948. **Staff:** 6. **Subjects:** Social sciences; business and management; computer sciences; United States - art, literature, and history. **Holdings:** 14,600 books; 500 microfiche; 407 videotapes. **Subscriptions:** 89 journals and other serials; 7 newspapers. **Services:** Interlibrary loan; copying; library open to the public. **Remarks:** FAX: 83 425517. Maintained or supported by the U.S. Information Agency. Focus is on materials that will assist peoples outside the United States to learn about the United States, its people, history, culture, political processes, and social milieux. **Staff:** Guillermina F. de Padilla.

(Montevideo) USIS Library
See: **Biblioteca Artigas-Washington** (1818)

★10675★
Montgomery Advertiser and Alabama Journal - Library (Publ)
Box 1000 Phone: (205)262-1611
Montgomery, AL 36101 Peggy Ross, Libn.
Staff: Prof 1. **Subjects:** Newspaper reference topics. **Holdings:** 300 books; 330 drawers of clippings; 68 drawers of photographs; newspapers, 1940 to present, on microfilm. **Subscriptions:** 43 newspapers. **Services:** Library open to the public with approval of managing editor.

★10676★
Montgomery Community College - Learning Resources Center (Educ)
Drawer 787 Phone: (919)572-3691
Troy, NC 27371 Gay R. Russell, Dean of Lrng.Rsrcs.
Staff: Prof 2; Other 7. **Subjects:** Gunsmithing, taxidermy, business administration, beekeeping, pottery, law enforcement, automotive mechanics, history. **Holdings:** 12,000 books; 4 VF drawers of pamphlets; 290 reels of microfilm; 650 videotapes. **Subscriptions:** 117 journals and other serials; 12 newspapers. **Services:** Interlibrary loan; copying; center open to the public. **Networks/Consortia:** Member of North Carolina Information Network (NCIN). **Staff:** Diane Rumbold, Libn.

★10677★
Montgomery County Circuit Court - Law Library (Law)
Judicial Center
50 Courthouse Sq., Rm. 326 Phone: (301)217-7165
Rockville, MD 20850 Karen D.M.S. Dwyer, Law Libn.
Staff: Prof 2; Other 4. **Subjects:** Law. **Holdings:** 50,000 volumes. **Subscriptions:** 2 newspapers. **Services:** Interlibrary loan; copying; library open to Montgomery County residents and Attorneys. **Computerized Information Services:** WESTLAW - not for public access.

★10678★
Montgomery County Department of History and Archives (Hist)
Old Court House Phone: (518)853-3431
Fonda, NY 12068 Violet D. Fallone, County Hist./Rec.Mgmt.Off.
Founded: 1934. **Staff:** 4. **Subjects:** Local and state history, genealogy. **Holdings:** 9350 books; 100 bound periodical volumes; 1200 maps; county documents; will abstracts; deeds; church and cemetery records. **Subscriptions:** 22 journals and other serials. **Services:** Copying; library open to the public. **Special Catalogs:** Catalog of historical and genealogical materials - for sale. **Special Indexes:** Index to genealogical folders (card); Bible (card); map index (card); compiled genealogies index (book); 600 family folders; 700 hstorical folders. **Remarks:** Alternate telephone number(s): (518)853-8186.

★10679★
Montgomery County Department of Public Libraries - Special Needs Library (Aud-Vis)
6400 Democracy Blvd. Phone: (301)493-2555
Bethesda, MD 20817 Devon Liner, Sr.Libn.
Founded: 1986. **Staff:** Prof 5; Other 5. **Subjects:** Disabilities and disabling conditions. **Special Collections:** Non-fiction about disabling conditions (regular print). **Holdings:** 8000 talking books; 4241 large print volumes; toys; computer programs. **Subscriptions:** 60 journals and other serials. **Services:** Interlibrary loan; copying; library open to the public with restrictions. **Automated Operations:** Computerized circulation (limited). **Computerized Information Services:** BRS Information Technologies. **Networks/Consortia:** Member of National Library Service for the Blind & Physically Handicapped (NLS). **Remarks:** Library serves blind, physically handicapped, deaf, developmentally disabled, and homebound residents in the area. TDD: (301)493-2554. **Staff:** Francine Kaplan, Comp.Spec.; Susan Cohen, Libn. for the Deaf; Nancy King, Homebound Serv.

★10680★
Montgomery County Historical Society - Library (Hist)
103 W. Montgomery Ave. Phone: (301)762-1492
Rockville, MD 20850 Jane C. Sween, Libn.
Staff: 5. **Subjects:** History, biography, genealogy. **Holdings:** 2000 books; information files on history of Montgomery County, Maryland; photographs; plats; card files of early court records; church records; marriage records. **Services:** Copying; library open to the public on fee basis.

Montgomery County Intermediate Unit Library
See: **Research & Information Services for Education** (13837)

★10681★
Montgomery County Law Library (Law)
Box 1667 Phone: (205)832-1649
Montgomery, AL 36192 Dot Wilson, Law Libn.
Founded: 1958. **Staff:** 2. **Subjects:** Law. **Holdings:** 12,500 volumes. **Subscriptions:** 10 journals and other serials. **Services:** Copying; faxing; library open to the public for reference use only. **Computerized Information Services:** WESTLAW. **Remarks:** FAX: (205)265-9536.

★10682★
Montgomery County Law Library (Law)
Court House Phone: (215)278-3806
Norristown, PA 19404 Arthur S. Zanan, Dir.
Founded: 1869. **Staff:** Prof 3; Other 5. **Subjects:** Law, with emphasis on Pennsylvania law. **Special Collections:** Ordinances of Montgomery County Municipalities (6 VF drawers). **Holdings:** 53,000 books; 735 bound periodical volumes; 321 audio cassettes; 210 video cassettes. **Subscriptions:** 95 journals and other serials. **Services:** Interlibrary loan; copying; library open to the public with restrictions. **Computerized Information Services:** WESTLAW. Performs searches on fee basis. **Publications:** Law Library Newsletter, monthly - to members of Montgomery Bar Association. **Remarks:** FAX: (215)278-5998. Maintained by Montgomery County Commissioners. **Staff:** Bruce S. Piscadlo, Ref.Libn.

★10683★
Montgomery County Planning Commission - Research Library (Plan)
Court House Phone: (215)278-3726
Norristown, PA 19404 Alice B. Nugent, Libn.
Founded: 1950. **Subjects:** Practical urban planning, transportation, sanitary engineering, land use, housing, social and economic statistics. **Holdings:** 5900 volumes; 2000 documents and reports; 4000 slides; 60 boxes of microfilm; 20 binders of printouts; VF drawers of newspaper clippings, correspondence, pamphlets. **Subscriptions:** 70 journals and other serials; 15 newspapers. **Services:** Interlibrary loan (limited); copying; library open to the public with restrictions. **Remarks:** FAX: (215)278-3941.

Montgomery County Planning Department
See: **Maryland National Capital Park and Planning Commission** (9753)

★10684★
Montgomery County Public Schools - Professional Library (Educ)
850 N. Hungerford Dr. Phone: (301)279-3227
Rockville, MD 20850 Karen Dowling, Curric.Libn.
Founded: 1961. **Staff:** Prof 1; Other 5. **Subjects:** Education. **Special Collections:** Montgomery County Public Schools' curriculum guides; dissertations by MCPS employees. **Holdings:** 17,000 books; nonprint materials; ERIC microfiche. **Subscriptions:** 460 journals and other serials; 9 newspapers. **Services:** Interlibrary loan; copying; library open to the public for reference use only. **Automated Operations:** Computerized cataloging and circulation. **Computerized Information Services:** DIALOG Information Services, BRS Information Technologies, LEXIS, NEXIS. **Networks/ Consortia:** Member of Maryland Interlibrary Organization (MILO). **Publications:** Bibliographies; periodical holdings list. **Remarks:** FAX: (301)279-3072.

★10685★
Montgomery Hospital - Medical Library (Med)
Powell & Fornance St. Phone: (215)270-2232
Norristown, PA 19401 Alberta T. O'Brien, Med.Libn.
Staff: Prof 1; Other 1. **Subjects:** Medicine, surgery, drugs, nursing, basic sciences. **Special Collections:** History of Medicine Collection. **Holdings:** 2110 books; 599 bound periodical volumes; 2 VF drawers; 580 AV programs. **Subscriptions:** 102 journals and other serials. **Services:** Interlibrary loan; copying; library open to the public with special permission from the administration. **Networks/Consortia:** Member of Delaware Valley Information Consortium (DEVIC), National Network of Libraries of Medicine - Middle Atlantic Region, BHSL. **Remarks:** FAX: (215)270-2518.

★10686★
James M. Montgomery Consulting Engineers - Library (Sci-Engr)
250 N. Madison Ave. Phone: (818)796-9141
Pasadena, CA 91101 Duane M. Helgeson, Libn.
Staff: Prof 1; Other 2. **Subjects:** Water quality, effluents, drinking water, wastewater. **Holdings:** 500 books; 600 bound periodical volumes; 6000 bound and unbound reports and specifications; 3 VF drawers of reprints; 200 specifications and standards; 2000 archival materials in microform. **Subscriptions:** 100 journals and other serials. **Services:** Interlibrary loan; library not open to the public. **Computerized Information Services:** DIALOG Information Services, ORBIT Search Service; internal database.

Montgomery Library
See: **Fairchild Tropical Garden** (5558)

Montgomery Library
See: **Westminster Theological Seminary** (20336)

★10687★
Montgomery, McCracken, Walker & Rhoads - Library (Law)
3 Benjamin Franklin Parkway Phone: (215)665-7211
Philadelphia, PA 19102 G.H. Brown, Libn.
Staff: Prof 1; Other 2. **Subjects:** Law. **Holdings:** 20,000 volumes. **Services:** Interlibrary loan; library not open to the public. **Computerized Information Services:** LEXIS, DIALOG Information Services, WESTLAW, VU/TEXT Information Services. **Remarks:** FAX: (215)636-9373.

★10688★
Montgomery Museum of Fine Arts - Library (Art)
One Museum Dr.
Box 230819 Phone: (205)244-5700
Montgomery, AL 36123-0819 Alice T. Carter, Pubns.Libn.
Staff: Prof 1. **Subjects:** American painting, sculpture, contemporary art, decorative art, photography, European art. **Holdings:** 2800 books; 49 Montgomery Museum scrapbooks; 3000 slides of American and European art. **Subscriptions:** 17 journals and other serials. **Services:** Library open to the public by appointment for reference use only. **Publications:** Calendar of Events, monthly. **Special Catalogs:** Exhibition catalogs.

★10689★
Montgomery Presbyterian Church - Library (Rel-Phil)
9994 Zig Zag Rd. Phone: (513)891-8670
Cincinnati, OH 45242 Roy Romine
Founded: 1962. **Staff:** 1. **Subjects:** Religion, Bible, theology. **Special Collections:** Peace Shelf (50). **Holdings:** 1400 books; 37 videotapes. **Subscriptions:** 3 journals and other serials, 3 newspapers. **Services:** Library not open to the public.

★10690★
Montgomery Ward and Co. - Information Services (Bus-Fin)
One Montgomery Ward Plaza Phone: (312)467-7351
Chicago, IL 60671 Gena L. Schoen, Libn.
Founded: 1965. **Staff:** Prof 1. **Subjects:** Retailing. **Holdings:** 1500 volumes; government documents; subject files; 200 annual reports. **Subscriptions:** 104 journals and other serials. **Services:** Interlibrary loan; services not open to the public. **Automated Operations:** Computerized cataloging. **Computerized Information Services:** DIALOG Information Services, NEXIS, Dow Jones News/Retrieval, DataTimes; internal database. **Publications:** News Briefs, weekly - for internal distribution only; abstracts of retail-related articles.

Monticello
See: **Thomas Jefferson Memorial Foundation, Inc.** (8358)

★10691★
Montour County Law Library (Law)
Court House
29 Mill St. Phone: (717)271-3018
Danville, PA 17821 Althea M. Wertman, Lib.Dir.
Staff: 1. **Subjects:** Law. **Holdings:** 1390 books. **Services:** Library open to the public for reference use only.

★10692★
Montreal Association for the Intellectually Handicapped - Multi-Media Documentation Center (Med)
8605, rue Berri, 3rd Fl. Phone: (514)381-2307
Montreal, PQ, Canada H2P 2G5 Michelle Jacques, Doc.
Founded: 1969. **Staff:** Prof 1. **Subjects:** Intellectual deficiencies. **Holdings:** 1500 books; 41 bound periodical volumes; pamphlets; vertical files; AV programs. **Subscriptions:** 75 journals and other serials. **Services:** Interlibrary loan; copying; center open to the public. **Publications:** The Rights of the Mentally Handicapped in Quebec; Educational Facilities for Mentally Handicapped Children in Greater Montreal; 10 Commandments for Pregnant Women, pamphlets; Early Infant Stimulation Makes a Difference, pamphlets; A Force de Sourire, video; La Genese d'un Enfant, video; Intellectual Deficiency Information Document, 1989; Entre Nous.Parents (bulletin), monthly. **Also Known As:** Association de Montreal pour la Deficience Intellectuelle.

★10693★
Montreal Board of Trade - Information Centre (Bus-Fin)
1080 Beaver Hall Hill, Suite 710 Phone: (514)878-4651
Montreal, PQ, Canada H2Z 1S9 Hugues Letourneau, Dir.
Staff: 5. **Subjects:** International trade, civic development, research, employee relations, statistics, legislation, taxation, trade and commerce, transportation, salary surveys. **Holdings:** 2000 volumes; 110 telephone directories; 200 foreign custom tariffs. **Subscriptions:** 80 journals and other serials. **Services:** Copying; center open to the public. **Remarks:** FAX: (514)878-2262.

Montreal Botanical Garden
See: **Jardin Botanique de Montreal - Bibliotheque** (8343)

★10694★
Montreal Cancer Institute - Library (Biol Sci)
1560 Sherbrooke St., E. Phone: (514)876-7078
Montreal, PQ, Canada H2L 4M1 Chantal Corriveau, Lib.Techn.
Staff: Prof 1. **Subjects:** Cellular biology, virology, genetics, molecular biology, biochemistry, cancer. **Holdings:** 200 books; 4000 bound periodical volumes; 50 scientific reports; 50 annual reports; 20 theses. **Subscriptions:** 53 journals and other serials. **Services:** Interlibrary loan; copying; library open to qualified researchers and students only. **Remarks:** FAX: (514)876-5476.

★10695★
Montreal Chest Hospital Centre - Medical Library (Med)
3650 St. Urbain St. Phone: (514)849-5201
Montreal, PQ, Canada H2X 2P4 Marianne Constantine, Med.Libn.
Founded: 1965. **Staff:** Prof 1. **Subjects:** Chest medicine, respiratory diseases. **Holdings:** 2500 volumes. **Subscriptions:** 100 journals and other serials. **Services:** Interlibrary loan; copying; library open to the public by permission only. **Networks/Consortia:** Member of McGill Medical and Health Libraries Association (MMHLA), Canadian Health Libraries Association. **Also Known As:** Centre Hospitalier Thoracique de Montreal.

★10696★
Montreal Children's Hospital - Medical Library (Med)
2300 Tupper St. Phone: (514)934-4401
Montreal, PQ, Canada H3H 1P3 Joanne Baird, Med.Libn.
Founded: 1946. **Staff:** Prof 1.5; Other 2. **Subjects:** Pediatrics, pediatric surgery, child psychiatry, nursing. **Holdings:** 6,000 volumes. **Subscriptions:** 180 journals and other serials. **Services:** Interlibrary loan; library not open to the public. **Computerized Information Services:** MEDLARS, DIALOG Information Services, PaperChase; Envoy 100 (electronic mail service). **Remarks:** FAX: (514)934-4345. Electronic mail address(es): QMMCH (Envoy 100).

Montreal City Library
See: **Bibliotheque Municipale de Montreal** (1829)

Montreal Conservatory of Music - Documentation Centre
See: **Conservatoire de Musique de Montreal - Centre de Documentation** (4220)

Montreal Diocesan Archives
See: **Anglican Church of Canada - Diocese of Montreal - Archives** (869)

★10697★
Montreal Gazette - Library (Publ)
250 St. Antoine St., W. Phone: (514)987-2583
Montreal, PQ, Canada H2Y 3RY Agnes McFarlane, Chf.Libn.
Founded: 1960. **Staff:** Prof 3; Other 8. **Subjects:** News, political current affairs. **Holdings:** 5000 books; periodicals; pamphlets; microfilm; microfiche. **Subscriptions:** 165 journals and other serials; 32 newspapers. **Services:** Mail inquiries accepted; library open to the public by appointment on fee basis. **Computerized Information Services:** Infomart Online, DataTimes, QL Systems, VU/TEXT Information Services, Infodisk La Presse, NEXIS, Info Globe. Performs searches on fee basis.

★10698★
Montreal General Hospital - Medical Library (Med)
1650 Cedar Ave. Phone: (514)937-6011
Montreal, PQ, Canada H3G 1A4 Gary Lee Kober, Chf.Med.Libn.
Staff: Prof 1; Other 3. **Subjects:** Medicine, surgery, gynecology, pathology, radiology, anesthesia. **Holdings:** 2000 books; 7000 bound periodical volumes; 1 VF drawer of pamphlets. **Subscriptions:** 300 journals and other serials. **Services:** Interlibrary loan; copying; library open to the public by appointment. **Computerized Information Services:** BRS Information Technologies, MEDLARS, CAN/OLE; Envoy 100 (electronic mail service). **Networks/Consortia:** Member of McGill Medical and Health Libraries Association (MMHLA). **Publications:** New Acquisitions, bimonthly - available upon request. **Remarks:** FAX: (514)937-2455. Electronic mail address(es): ILL.QM6H (Envoy 100). **Also Known As:** Hopital General de Montreal.

★10699★
Montreal General Hospital - Nurses Library (Med)
1650 Cedar Ave., Rm. 619 Phone: (514)937-6011
Montreal, PQ, Canada H3G 1A4 Mrs. B.A. Covington, Lib.Techn.
Staff: 1. **Subjects:** Nursing. **Holdings:** 2500 books; 150 bound periodical volumes. **Subscriptions:** 40 journals and other serials. **Services:** Interlibrary loan; library open to the public with restrictions. **Automated Operations:** Computerized public access catalog (MUSE). **Computerized Information Services:** MEDLARS; internal database. **Networks/Consortia:** Member of McGill Medical and Health Libraries Association (MMHLA). **Remarks:** FAX: (514)937-2455.

★10700★
The Montreal Museum of Fine Arts - Library (Art)
3400, ave. du Musee Phone: (514)285-1600
Montreal, PQ, Canada H3G 1K3 Joanne Dery, Libn.
Founded: 1882. **Staff:** Prof 1; Other 5. **Subjects:** Fine arts, sculpture, ceramics, decorative arts, costume, silver, painting, furniture, textiles, architecture. **Special Collections:** Files on Canadian art and artists. **Holdings:** 68,471 volumes and exhibition catalogs; 47,100 sales catalogs; 7162 bound periodical volumes; 11,981 files. **Subscriptions:** 650 journals and other serials. **Services:** Interlibrary loan (limited); copying; library open to the public for reference use only. **Remarks:** FAX: (514)285-1980. **Also Known As:** Musee des Beaux-Arts de Montreal.

★10701★
Montreal Neurological Institute - Hospital Library (Med)
3801 University St. Phone: (514)398-1980
Montreal, PQ, Canada H3A 2B4 Carol L. Wiens, Libn.
Founded: 1934. **Staff:** Prof 1; Other 1. **Subjects:** Neurosciences. **Holdings:** 3800 books; 3500 bound periodical volumes; 300 theses and reprints. **Subscriptions:** 115 journals and other serials. **Services:** Interlibrary loan; library open to health sciences personnel. **Computerized Information Services:** DIALOG Information Services; Envoy 100 (electronic mail service). **Remarks:** FAX: (514)398-8540. Electronic mail address(es): QMNIH (Envoy 100).

★10702★
Montreal Urban Community Transit Corporation - Library (Trans)
159 St. Antoine St. Phone: (514)280-5220
Montreal, PQ, Canada H2Z 1H3 Victor Itesco, Libn.
Staff: Prof 1; Other 2. **Subjects:** Urban transit, engineering, management, law, finance. **Special Collections:** Urban transit history of Montreal (thousands of clippings; 200 other cataloged items). **Holdings:** 4500 books; 300 bound periodical volumes; 1200 technical reports on microfiche; 7 VF drawers of pamphlets. **Subscriptions:** 255 journals and other serials; 5 newspapers. **Services:** Interlibrary loan; copying; library open to the public for reference use only. **Computerized Information Services:** Internal database. **Remarks:** FAX: (514)280-6126.

★10703★
Ville de Montreal Service de l'Habitation et du Developpement Urbain - Centre de Documentation (Plan)
276 Saint Jacques, 5th Fl. Phone: (514)872-1571
Montreal, PQ, Canada H2Y 1N3 Mme. Danielle Fortin, Responsable
Founded: 1963. **Subjects:** Town planning, urban studies, urban statistics, housing, architecture, geography, transportation, historic preservation. **Holdings:** 8000 books and periodicals. **Subscriptions:** 125 journals and other serials. **Services:** Library not open to the public. **Computerized Information Services:** Internal database. **Remarks:** FAX: (514)872-0350. **Staff:** Danielle Lachapelle.

★10704★
Montreal Young Women's Christian Association - Library (Soc Sci)
1355 Rene Levesque, W.
Montreal, PQ, Canada H3G 1T3 Phone: (514)866-9941
Founded: 1874. **Subjects:** Women's issues, psychology, sociology, religion, biography, fiction. **Holdings:** 700 volumes in French; 2000 volumes in English. **Services:** Library open to members, residents, and volunteers. **Remarks:** FAX: (514)866-4866.

★10705★
Monumenta Serica Institute - Library (Hum)
Arnold-Janssen-Str 20 Phone: 2241 237431
W-5205 St. Augustin 1, Germany Barbara Haster
Founded: 1935. **Staff:** Prof 1; Other 1. **Subjects:** Sinology. **Holdings:** 60,000 books; 7000 bound periodical volumes; 590 reels of microfilm. **Services:** Copying; library open to the public for reference use only. **Remarks:** FAX: 2241 29142. Telex: 889 559 steyl d.

MONY Financial Services - Corporate Research Library
See: **Mutual of New York Financial Services** (10939)

★10706★
Moody Bible Institute - Crowell Learning Resource Center (Rel-Phil)
860 N. LaSalle Blvd. Phone: (312)329-4139
Chicago, IL 60610 Richard G. Schock, Dir.
Founded: 1890. **Staff:** Prof 5; Other 6. **Subjects:** Bible, missions, church history, theology, church music, Christian education, homiletics, evangelism and pastoral training, communications. **Holdings:** 110,000 books; 4500 bound periodical volumes; 6500 other cataloged items; 600 reels of microfilm; 25 lateral file drawers of college catalogs, reports, brochures, organization files; 28 VF drawers of curriculum laboratory materials; 60 VF drawers of classified pamphlets. **Subscriptions:** 607 journals and other serials; 6 newspapers. **Services:** Interlibrary loan; copying; library open to the public. **Automated Operations:** Computerized cataloging and ILL. **Computerized Information Services:** DIALOG Information Services, BRS Information Technologies, WILSONLINE, OCLC EPIC; CompuServe Information Service (electronic mail service). Performs searches on fee basis. Contact Person: Walter Osborn, Ref.Libn., 329-4140. **Networks/Consortia:** Member of ILLINET, Chicago Library System. **Publications:** Acquisitions List - to faculty and department heads; MBI Library Manual - to faculty and students. **Special Indexes:** Sermon index; subject and title indexes to periodical holdings. **Remarks:** FAX: (312)329-4023. Electronic mail address(es): 76666, 2727 (CompuServe Information Service). **Staff:** Lori Johnson, Tech.Serv.Libn.; Alan Cappella, Circ.Libn.; Helen Shin, Cat.; Connie Grospe, Acq.

★10707★
Moody Bible Institute - Crowell Learning Resource Center - Moodyana Collection (Rel-Phil)
860 N. LaSalle Blvd. Phone: (312)329-4140
Chicago, IL 60610 Richard Schock, Dir.
Founded: 1936. **Staff:** Prof 3; Other 1. **Subjects:** Life and work of D.L. Moody, history of Moody Bible Institute, biographical data of notables connected with MBI, early Bibles and rare theology books. **Special Collections:** Books by and about D.L. Moody and MBI presidents. **Holdings:** 1000 books; 250 bound periodical volumes; 25 dissertations and theses on D.L. Moody and revivalism; 500 pamphlets; 1000 pieces of correspondence; 1000 clipping accounts of D.L. Moody's evangelistic campaigns and 2000 tributes and obituary notices; 600 manuscript notes of notable MBI instructors; 50 VF drawers and 10 oversized drawers of photographs. **Services:** Copying; collection open to the public for reference and research. **Computerized Information Services:** CompuServe Information Service (electronic mail service). **Publications:** Bibliography of books and dissertations by and about D.L. Moody. **Special Indexes:** Name and place index to Moody's letters; index to chronological listing of Moody's travels. **Remarks:** FAX: (312)329-4023. Electronic mail address(es): 76666,2727 (CompuServe Information Service). **Staff:** Lori Johnson, Cat.; Helen Shin, Cat.; Walter Osborn, Archv./Hist.Coll.

Moody Library
See: **Houston Baptist University** (7447)

Moody Library
See: **Lubbock Christian University** (9429)

Moody Medical Library
See: **University of Texas Medical Branch at Galveston** (19419)

★10708★
Moody's Investors Service - Information Center (Bus-Fin)
99 Church St. Phone: (212)553-0525
New York, NY 10007-2787 Lorraine Cyr, Mgr.
Founded: 1900. **Staff:** Prof 3; Other 7. **Subjects:** Publicly held corporations. **Holdings:** 1400 VF drawers of annual reports, interim reports, prospectuses, news releases; Moody's manuals, 1909 to present, on microfiche; U.S. Securities and Exchange Commission documents for 11,000 publicly held companies on microfiche. **Services:** Copying by phone order only. **Computerized Information Services:** DIALOG Information Services, Dow Jones News/Retrieval. **Special Catalogs:** Catalog of companies covered in Moody's publications (card). **Remarks:** FAX: (212)553-4727.

F. Franklin Moon Library and Learning Resources Center
See: **State University of New York - College of Environmental Science & Forestry** (15722)

Arthur J. Moore Methodist Museum
See: **United Methodist Church - South Georgia Conference - Commission on Archives and History - Arthur J. Moore Methodist Museum - Library** (16739)

Claude Moore Health Sciences Library
See: **University of Virginia - Health Sciences Center - Claude Moore Health Sciences Library** (19504)

★10709★
Moore College of Art - Library (Art)
20th & Benjamin Franklin Parkway Phone: (215)568-4515
Philadelphia, PA 19103 Paula A. Feid, Dir.
Founded: 1848. **Staff:** Prof 3; Other 5. **Subjects:** Fine arts, professional arts, art education, art history, women's studies, humanities. **Special Collections:** John Sartain Collection (engravings and prints); Sartain family correspondence (one drawer); Bookworks Collection (artist's books). **Holdings:** 38,500 books; 2500 bound periodical volumes; 400 folios; 98 VF drawers of pictures, prints, clippings, plates; 110,000 slides; 1000 phonograph records. **Subscriptions:** 227 journals and other serials; 8 newspapers. **Services:** Interlibrary loan; copying; library open to the public with restrictions. **Automated Operations:** Computerized cataloging. **Computerized Information Services:** OCLC. **Networks/Consortia:** Member of PALINET, Interlibrary Delivery Service of Pennsylvania (IDS). **Remarks:** FAX: (215)568-8017. **Staff:** Kristin Bayruns, Cat.Libn.; H. Fran McGinnis, Slide Cur.; Rick Fellechner, AV Spec.

★10710★
Moore Corporation Ltd. - Moore Business Forms, Inc. - Research Center Library (Sci-Engr)
300 Lang Blvd. Phone: (716)773-0557
Grand Island, NY 14072-1697 Betsy M. Waters, CRM Sr.Libn.
Founded: 1969. **Staff:** Prof 2. **Subjects:** Graphic arts, pulp and paper products, chemistry, electronics, marketing. **Holdings:** 3500 books; 1200 microfiche; 200 reels of microfilm; 60 cassettes; 6 VF drawers of annual reports and pamphlets. **Subscriptions:** 400 journals and other serials. **Services:** Interlibrary loan; library open to the public with prior arrangement. **Automated Operations:** Computerized cataloging, acquisitions, serials, and circulation. **Computerized Information Services:** DIALOG Information Services, PFDS Online, OCLC. **Networks/Consortia:** Member of Western New York Library Resources Council (WNYLRC). **Remarks:** FAX: (716)774-0412. **Staff:** Ms. Tanis Toponak, Libn.

Florence A. Moore Library of Medicine
See: **Medical College of Pennsylvania** (9999)

Franklin F. Moore Library
See: **Rider College** (13916)

Moore Hall Library
See: **Kansas State Geological Survey - Moore Hall Library** (8557)

Henry Moore Photograph Archive and Study Center
See: **Nelson-Atkins Museum of Art - Spencer Art Reference Library** (11388)

★10711★
Hugh Moore Historical Park and Museums - Canal Museum - Research Library/Archives (Hist)
200 S. Delaware Dr.
Box 877 Phone: (215)250-6703
Easton, PA 18044 Michael Knies, Coll.Mgr.
Staff: Prof 1; Other 1. **Subjects:** Towpath canals; anthracite coal mining; history - iron and steel, railroad, industrial and technological; local history - Pennsylvania Lehigh Valley and anthracite regions, New Jersey. **Special Collections:** Anthracite coal mining photographic collection (10,000); Bethlehem Steel/Charles Schwab Libary (4000 bound volumes; 1000 photos; 1000 films; engineering drawings; maritime and naval history books); Joseph Chervy anthracite mining collection (106 volumes; 150 artifacts); John Fritz collection (10 linear feet of personal papers and photographs of Bethlehem Steel Ironmaster); Lehigh Coal and Navigation Company Collection (45 linear feet of employment, corporate, and railroad records - 1890s-1950s; 1000 engineering drawings); Lehigh Valley Railroad Collection (50 linear feet of railroad plans, engineering drawings, and maps); Pennsylvania Canal Society Collection (canal history; 500 volumes; 5000 photographs); William Rau lantern slide collection (Lehigh Valley and Pennsylvania Railroad, late 19th-20th centuries; 1300 slides); Robert Sayre Collection (10 linear feet of diaries, railroad construction plans, personal papers, photographs); Pennsylvania Engineering Corporation (5000 engineering drawings). **Holdings:** 5000 books; 1500 bound periodical volumes; 75 cubic feet of manuscripts and research material; 8000 engineering drawings; 500 maps; 700 films; 200 reels of microfilm 1500 artifacts; 30,000 photographic images (slides, lantern slides, prints, glass plates, negatives). **Subscriptions:** 50 journals and other serials. **Services:** Copying; library open to the public on a fee basis. **Automated Operations:** Computerized cataloging and acquisitions. **Computerized Information Services:** Internal database. Performs searches on fee basis. **Publications:** The Locktender (newsletter), quarterly; Canal Currents, quarterly - to members; Proceedings of Annual Symposium. **Staff:** Lance Metz, Hist.

Joseph Moore Museum
See: **Earlham College - Joseph Moore Museum** (5095)

Marianne Moore Archive
See: **Rosenbach Museum & Library** (14068)

★10712★
Moore Theological College - Library (Rel-Phil)
1 King St. Phone: 2-519-2869
Newtown, NSW 2042, Australia Mr. Kim S. Robinson, Libn.
Founded: 1855. **Staff:** 2.5. **Subjects:** Theology, religion. **Special Collections:** Rare book collection; Australiana collection. **Holdings:** 112,000 books. **Subscriptions:** 500 journals and other serials. **Services:** Copying; library open to the public. **Automated Operations:** DYNIX. **Special Catalogs:** Catalogue of the Bishop Broughton Memorial Library, Volume 1 (rare books). **Remarks:** FAX: 2-550-5859.

★10713★
Walter P. Moore & Associates - Library (Sci-Engr)
3131 Eastside, 2nd Fl.
Houston, TX 77098 Phone: (713)630-7300
Subjects: Structural engineering, architecture, traffic and transportation, waste water, steel and concrete structures. **Holdings:** 1000 books. **Subscriptions:** 70 journals and other serials. **Services:** Interlibrary loan; library open to the public by appointment.

Charles W. Moores Library
See: **Butler University - Irwin Library - Hugh Thomas Miller Rare Book Room** (2416)

Moores Creek National Battlefield
See: **U.S. Natl. Park Service** (17752)

Moorhead State University - Northwest Minnesota Historical Center
See: **Northwest Minnesota Historical Center** (12055)

Moorland-Spingarn Research Center
See: **Howard University** (7477)

Bishop Moorman Franciscan Library
See: **St. Deiniol's Residential - Library** (14272)

Moorman Memorial Library
See: **Eastern Virginia Medical School** (5170)

★10714★
Moose Jaw Law Society - Library (Law)
Court House
64 Ominica St., W. Phone: (306)694-3602
Moose Jaw, SK, Canada S6H 4P1 Shirley Paquin, Libn.
Subjects: Law. **Holdings:** 6000 volumes. **Services:** Library not open to the public. **Automated Operations:** Computerized acquisitions, serials, and circulation.

★10715★
Moose Jaw Union Hospital - Medical Library (Med)
455 Fairford St., E. Phone: (306)694-0377
Moose Jaw, SK, Canada S6H 1H3 Isolde Albraum, Dir., Hea.Rec.
Subjects: Medicine, surgery. **Holdings:** 187 books; 3 bound periodical volumes. **Subscriptions:** 10 journals and other serials. **Services:** Library not open to the public. **Remarks:** FAX: (306)692-5596.

★10716★
Moose Lake Regional Treatment Center - Staff Library (Med)
1000 Lake Shore Dr. Phone: (218)485-4411
Moose Lake, MN 55767 John C. Flynn, Lib.Supv.
Founded: 1939. **Staff:** Prof 1. **Subjects:** Psychiatry, mental retardation, chemical dependency, psycho-geriatrics. **Holdings:** 500 books. **Subscriptions:** 15 journals and other serials. **Services:** Interlibrary loan; copying; library open to the public. **Networks/Consortia:** Member of National Network of Libraries of Medicine - Greater Midwest Region.

Magdalena Mora Archive
See: **University of California, Los Angeles - Chicano Studies Research Library** (18376)

★10717★
Moraga Historical Society - Archives (Hist)
Moraga Public Library
1500 St. Mary's Rd. Phone: (415)376-6852
Moraga, CA 94556 Margaret Skinner, Archv.
Founded: 1985. **Staff:** Prof 1; Other 8. **Subjects:** Moraga Rancho area history, including the city of Moraga; Moraga family history and genealogy; history of communities of Orinda, Lafayette, and Canyon. **Special Collections:** Rancho Land Case number 590 (U.S. Land Commission, 1852); State of California Bancroft Library copy; U.S. District Court Case number 276 (automatic appeal); National Archives microfilm. **Holdings:** 400 books; 200 oral history tapes; 145 artifacts of Indians, ranchers, railroads; 28 VF drawers of clippings and documents; 6 volumes of land title abstracts; 164 files of court cases, 1850-1940; 800 photographs; 390 maps; 60 reels of microfilm of documents, letters, dissertations, parish records to 1900; California mission records; tax assessor's records; minutes of meetings of the board of directors of the Moraga Company, 1912-1953. **Services:** Copying; archives open to the public on a limited schedule. **Computerized Information Services:** Internal database. **Publications:** El Rancho (historical journal); Newsletter; Developing the Moraga Company Ranch, 1922-1977 (book); Moraga's Pride: Rancho Laguna de los Palos Colorados, 1987 (book). **Special Catalogs:** 10 year index to El Rancho Newsletter; index to land title abstracts. **Remarks:** Archive annex maintained at St. Mary's College, Moraga, CA 94556. **Staff:** Bro. Dennis Goodman, FSC, Hist.

★10718★
Moraine Park Technical College - Learning Resource Center (Educ)
235 N. National Ave.
P.O. Box 1940 Phone: (414)929-2470
Fond du Lac, WI 54936-1940 Judy Denor, LRC Mgr.
Founded: 1965. **Staff:** Prof 3; Other 4. **Subjects:** Health occupations; business and marketing; trade, police, fire sciences; home economics; agribiotechnology. **Holdings:** 30,000 books; 650 bound periodical volumes; 2000 pamphlets; 600 microforms; 6000 AV program titles. **Subscriptions:** 500 journals and other serials; 25 newspapers. **Services:** Interlibrary loan; copying; center open to the public. **Automated Operations:** Integrated library system (Unisys). **Computerized Information Services:** DIALOG Information Services. **Networks/Consortia:** Member of Fox River Valley Area Library Consortium (FRVALC), Fox Valley Library Council. **Remarks:** FAX: (414)929-2471. **Staff:** Carol Boede, Cat.; Charlene Pettit, Cat.; Audrey Weed, ILL.

Manuel Noriega Morales Library
See: **Central American Research Institute for Industry** (3325)

★10719★
Moravian Church in America - Northern Province - Moravian Archives (Rel-Phil)
41 W. Locust St. Phone: (215)866-3255
Bethlehem, PA 18018 Vernon H. Nelson, Archv.
Founded: 1751. **Staff:** Prof 2; Other 2. **Subjects:** General and American Moravian Church history; history of Bethlehem and surrounding area; biography; hymnody; Moravian missions. **Holdings:** 5600 books; 1550 bound periodical volumes; manuscripts; documents. **Subscriptions:** 12 journals and other serials. **Services:** Archives open to the public; manuscripts may be consulted by special arrangement.

★10720★
Moravian Church in America - Southern Province - Moravian Archives (Rel-Phil)
4 E. Bank St.
Winston-Salem, NC 27101-5307 Phone: (919)722-1742
Founded: 1763. **Staff:** Prof 2; Other 2. **Subjects:** Moravian Church history, Moravian missions, North Carolina. **Holdings:** 3000 volumes; 1 million pages of manuscripts, 1753 to present, relating chiefly to the 6 colonial Moravian communities in North Carolina and the 53 congregations which have developed from them. **Services:** Copying (limited); archives open to the public. **Publications:** Annotations, 2/year - to doctoral programs and friends; The Moravian Archives News, 4/year - to ministers and friends. **Remarks:** A small portion of the manuscripts has been published by the State Department of Archives and History in Records of the Moravians in North Carolina (11 volumes).

★10721★
Moravian College - Theological Seminary - Reeves Library (Rel-Phil)
Main St. at Elizabeth Ave. Phone: (215)861-1541
Bethlehem, PA 18018 John Thomas Minor, Lib.Dir.
Founded: 1742. **Staff:** Prof 5; Other 6. **Subjects:** Liberal arts, theology. **Special Collections:** Moravian Church collection (3000 volumes); Moraviana. **Holdings:** 211,723 volumes; microforms; cassettes; sound recordings. **Subscriptions:** 1199 journals and other serials; 25 newspapers. **Services:** Interlibrary loan; copying; library open to the public for reference use only. **Automated Operations:** Computerized public access catalog, cataloging, circulation, and ILL. **Computerized Information Services:** DIALOG Information Services, BRS Information Technologies, OCLC. **Networks/Consortia:** Member of Lehigh Valley Association of Independent Colleges, Inc. (LVAIC), PALINET, State System of Higher Education Libraries Council (SSHELCO), Southeastern Pennsylvania Theological Library Association (SEPTLA). **Publications:** New Books in Moravian Studies, quarterly - free upon request. **Remarks:** FAX: (215)861-1577. **Staff:** Rita Berk, Cat. & Tech.Serv.Libn.; Mary Lou Bross, Ref. & Pub.Serv.Libn.; Stacy Hach, Ref. & Pub.Serv.Libn.; Bonnie Falla, Ref. & Pub.Serv.Libn.; Stacy Hech, Sys.Adm.

★10722★
Moravian Music Foundation, Inc. - Peter Memorial Library (Mus)
20 Cascade Ave. Phone: (919)725-0651
Winston-Salem, NC 27127 E. Allen Schultz, Dir.
Founded: 1956. **Staff:** Prof 3; Other 1. **Subjects:** Sacred anthems and arias, hymnological materials and books, American music of 18th and 19th centuries, symphonic, chamber, and choral music of 18th and 19th centuries, music and religious history and biography. **Special Collections:** Irving Lowens Musical Americana Collection (1500 items). **Holdings:** 5500 books; 10,000 manuscripts and early printed music editions; 3000 pieces of American and European music of 18th and 19th centuries; 7000 American and European manuscripts of 18th and 19th centuries; 200 tape recordings of Moravian music; programs; photographs; clippings. **Services:** Library open to the public; transcription and translation of archival materials for modern use; provision of music for performance groups; responds to inquiries. **Special Catalogs:** Catalog of the Johannes Herbst Collection; Catalog of the Music o f the Salem Congregation; Catalog of the Lititz Congregation Collection; other catalogs to manuscript collections in preparation.

Joseph F. Morbito Architecture Library
See: **Kent State University - Joseph F. Morbito Architecture Library** (8651)

★10723★
Thomas More College of Liberal Arts - Library (Hum)
6 Manchester St. Phone: (603)880-8308
Merrimack, NH 03054 Mary K. Mumbach, Dir.
Founded: 1978. **Staff:** 3. **Subjects:** Literary criticism, philosophy, political philosophy, history. **Holdings:** 26,000 books. **Subscriptions:** 12 journals and other serials. **Services:** Interlibrary loan; library open to Merrimack area humanities teachers. **Remarks:** FAX: (603)880-9280.

★10724★
Moreau Seminary - Library (Rel-Phil)
Congregation of Holy Cross Phone: (219)239-5046
Notre Dame, IN 46556-0668 Rev. Peter F. Mueller, C.S.C., Libn.
Founded: 1898. **Staff:** Prof 2; Other 7. **Subjects:** Theology, philosophy. **Holdings:** 42,532 books; 7002 bound periodical volumes. **Subscriptions:** 173 journals and other serials; 8 newspapers. **Services:** Library open to the public for reference use only. **Remarks:** Alternate telephone number(s): 239-7735. **Staff:** Robert C. Antonelli, C.S.C., Dir.

Moreell Library
See: **U.S. Navy - Naval School - Civil Engineer Corps Officers** (17872)

Albert H. Morehead Memorial Library
See: **American Contract Bridge League** (544)

★10725★
Morehead State University - Camden-Carroll Library (Hum)
Morehead, KY 40351 Phone: (606)783-2251
Larry X. Besant, Dir.
Founded: 1931. **Staff:** 41. **Special Collections:** Kentucky and Appalachian Collections (8839 volumes); Children's and Young People's Collection (7169 volumes); Roger W. Barbour Collection (6165 items); James Still Collection (1399 items); Jesse Stuart Collection (322 items); Learning Resource Center (27,493 books, 110,289 non-print items); Microform Collection (82,833 volume equivalents); rare books (1619). **Holdings:** 436,324 books; 62,797 bound periodical volumes; 393,516 microfiche; 12,816 reels of microfilm. **Subscriptions:** 2006 journals and other serials. **Services:** Interlibrary loan; copying; collections open to the public. **Automated Operations:** Computerized public access catalog, cataloging, acquisitions, serials, and circulation. **Computerized Information Services:** DIALOG Information Services, OCLC, BRS Information Technologies, VU/TEXT Information Services, WILSONLINE; CD-ROMs (ERIC, Books in Print Plus, Dissertation Abstracts Ondisc, ABI/INFORM, Periodical Abstracts Ondisc, Social Sciences Citation Index, Science Citation Index); internal databases. Performs searches on fee basis. Contact Person: Carol Nutter, Hd. of Ref., 783-2251. **Networks/Consortia:** Member of State Assisted Academic Library Council of Kentucky (SAALCK), Eastern Kentucky Health Science Information Network (EKHSIN), SOLINET, Kentucky Library Network, Inc. (KLN). **Remarks:** FAX: (606)784-3788. **Staff:** Helen Williams, Rsrc.Ctr.; Clara Keyes, Spec.Coll.Libn.; Lois Jackson, ILL Libn.

★10726★
Morehouse School of Medicine - Multi-Media Center (Med)
720 Westview Dr., S.W. Phone: (404)752-1530
Atlanta, GA 30310-1495 Beverly E. Allen, Dir.
Founded: 1978. **Staff:** Prof 7; Other 4. **Subjects:** Medical and life sciences. **Holdings:** 17,975 books; 27,817 bound periodical volumes. **Subscriptions:** 1017 journals and other serials. **Services:** Interlibrary loan; copying; SDI; center open to the public with restrictions. **Automated Operations:** Computerized cataloging and ILL. **Computerized Information Services:** MEDLINE, BRS Information Technologies, OCLC, DIALOG Information Services. Performs searches on fee basis. **Networks/Consortia:** Member of SOLINET, Atlanta Health Science Libraries Consortium (AHSLC), Georgia Health Sciences Library Association (GHSLA). **Publications:** Multi-Media Center Guide. **Remarks:** FAX: (404)755-7318. Telex: 8107510372. **Staff:** Barbara H.S. Martin, Asst.Dir.; Xiomara Arango, Ser.; Joe Swanson, Jr., Comp.Sys.Libn.; Gwendolyn Lewis, Acq.Libn.; Nancy Bryant, Ref.Libn.; Darlene Parker, Br.Libn.

★10727★
(Morelia) Instituto Mexicano-Norteamericano de Michoacan - USIS Collection (Educ)
Guillermo Prieto No. 86
58000 Morelia, Michoacan, Mexico
Remarks: Maintained or supported by the U.S. Information Agency. Focus is on materials that will assist peoples outside the United States to learn about the United States, its people, history, culture, political processes, and social milieux.

Dr. Francisco P. Moreno Biblioteca
See: **Museo de la Patagonia** (10884)

★10728★
Morflex Chemical Library (Sci-Engr)
2110 High Point Rd. Phone: (919)292-1781
Greensboro, NC 27403 E. Frappier, Libn.
Remarks: No further information was supplied by respondent.

Charles S. Morgan Technical Library
See: **National Fire Protection Association** (11164)

★10729★
Morgan County Bar Association - Library (Law)
Court House
9 E. Main
McConnelsville, OH 43756 Phone: (614)962-4752
Staff: 1. **Subjects:** Law. **Holdings:** 8000 books. **Services:** Library open to the public.

★10730★
Morgan County Historical Society - Library (Hist)
210 N. Monroe St. Phone: (314)378-5556
Versailles, MO 65084 Dorothy Bartram, Cur.
Staff: 1. **Subjects:** Local history. **Holdings:** County newspaper files and cemetery records; 1850, 1860, 1870 census records; family history records; marriage books; tax lists, 1865 and 1870; assessor book, 1844; deed books; school and church records. **Services:** Library open to the public on a limited schedule.

David P. Morgan Memorial Library
See: **Kalmbach Publishing Company** (8534)

★10731★
Morgan, Dowhan Engineering Ltd. - Library
10650 113th St.
Edmonton, AB, Canada T5H 3H6
Defunct.

★10732★
Morgan & Finnegan - Library (Law)
345 Park Ave., 22nd Fl. Phone: (212)758-4800
New York, NY 10154 Lucy Curci-Gonzalez, Libn.
Founded: 1979. **Staff:** Prof 2; Other 2.5. **Subjects:** Law - patent, trademark, copyright. **Holdings:** 13,250 books; 14 VF drawers microfilm and microfiche. **Subscriptions:** 190 journals and other serials; 8 newspapers. **Services:** Interlibrary loan; copying; library open to SLA and American Association of Law Libraries members and clients. **Computerized Information Services:** LEXIS, NEXIS, DunsPrint, PFDS Online, Compu-Mark U.S. On-Line, WESTLAW, ORBIT Search Service, VU/TEXT Information Services, Dow Jones News/Retrieval, DIALOG Information Services, WISDOM, IMSMARQ, NewsNet, Inc., RLIN, OCLC, Information America, DataTimes. **Publications:** Newsletter, irregular - for internal distribution only. **Remarks:** FAX: (212)751-6849. **Staff:** Patricia A. Flugger, Asst.Libn.

★10733★
Morgan Guaranty Trust Company of New York - Information Resource Center (Bus-Fin)
60 Wall St. Phone: (212)648-4636
New York, NY 10260 Ellen L. Miller, V.P.
Founded: 1989. **Staff:** Prof 8; Other 10. **Subjects:** Banking, international finance, stocks and bonds, business statistics. **Special Collections:** SEC filings. **Holdings:** 2500 volumes; 16 VF drawers of pamphlets. **Subscriptions:** 300 journals and other serials; 25 newspapers. **Services:** Interlibrary loan; library not open to the public. **Computerized Information Services:** LEXIS, NEXIS, DIALOG Information Services, Dow Jones News/Retrieval, Info Globe, TEXTLINE, DataTimes, WILSONLINE, Data Resources (DRI), VU/TEXT Information Services, Data-Star, NewsNet, Inc., Spectrum Ownership Profiles Online, INVESTEXT; CD-ROMs (COMPACT DISCLOSURE, Lotus One Source, DIALOG on Disc, Dun's Million Dollar Disc, ProQuest, Moody's Company Data). **Remarks:** FAX: (212)648-5230. **Staff:** Brian Gallagher, Info.Spec.; Josephine Howell, Info.Spec.; Elizabeth A. Mair, Info.Spec.; Tamara Gilberto, Info.Spec.

Morgan Health Sciences Library
See: **Long Island College Hospital** (9287)

★10734★
J. Harris Morgan Law Office - Law Library (Law)
Box 556 Phone: (903)455-3183
Greenville, TX 75403 Rita Reynolds, Libn.
Staff: Prof 1. **Subjects:** Law. **Holdings:** 2700 books; 130 bound periodical volumes; 1100 pamphlets; 450 cassettes; 50 videotapes; 25 boxes of unbound reports, clippings, manuscripts. **Subscriptions:** 60 journals and other serials. **Services:** Interlibrary loan; copying; library open to local attorneys.

★10735★
Morgan, Lewis & Bockius - Library (Law, Bus-Fin)
1800 M St., N.W. Phone: (202)467-7131
Washington, DC 20036 Sandra Peterson, Libn.
Staff: Prof 5; Other 5. **Subjects:** Law, business. **Holdings:** 50,000 volumes. **Subscriptions:** 250 journals and other serials; 40 newspapers. **Services:** Interlibrary loan; library open to outside researchers by appointment. **Computerized Information Services:** LEXIS, DIALOG Information Services, WESTLAW, Dow Jones News/Retrieval, VU/TEXT Information Services, LEGI-SLATE, NewsNet, Inc., OCLC, Information America. **Remarks:** FAX: (202)467-7176. Telex: 89 627. **Staff:** Martha Klein; Susan Quillian; Ellen Sweet; Carol Tropea.

★10736★
Morgan, Lewis & Bockius - Library (Law)
101 Park Ave. Phone: (212)309-6000
New York, NY 10178 Huguette Streuli, Libn.
Staff: Prof 1; Other 2. **Subjects:** Law - corporate, labor, tax. **Holdings:** 12,000 books; corporate file. **Subscriptions:** 65 journals and other serials. **Services:** Interlibrary loan. **Computerized Information Services:** LEXIS, DIALOG Information Services.

★10737★
Morgan, Lewis & Bockius - Library (Law)
2000 One Logan Square Phone: (215)963-5633
Philadelphia, PA 19103 Ellen R. Silverstein, Hd.Libn.
Staff: Prof 3; Other 5. **Subjects:** Law. **Holdings:** 40,000 volumes. **Services:** Interlibrary loan; copying. **Computerized Information Services:** DIALOG Information Services, VU/TEXT Information Services, Dow Jones News/Retrieval, LEXIS, WESTLAW, The Source Information Network, CompuServe Information Service, Data Resources (DRI), NewsNet, Inc., Securities Data Company. **Publications:** Monthly Library Bulletin - for internal distribution only. **Special Indexes:** Index to memos, opinion letters, and briefs. **Remarks:** FAX: (215)963-5518.

Morgan Library
See: **Grace Theological Seminary** (6602)

★10738★
Pierpont Morgan Library (Rare Book)
36th St. and Madison Ave. Phone: (212)685-0008
New York, NY 10016 Charles Eliot Pierce, Jr., Dir.
Founded: 1924. **Staff:** 100. **Subjects:** Medieval and Renaissance illuminated manuscripts; ancient written records; early printed books; autograph manuscripts, principally English, American, German, French and Italian; autograph letters and documents of Western European and American historical and literary personages, 11th to 20th century; later printed books; 9th-20th century bookbindings; drawings, 14th to 19th century; Rembrandt etchings; music manuscripts; early children's books. **Holdings:** 100,000 volumes. **Subscriptions:** 200 journals and other serials. **Services:** Photography; copying; exhibition galleries open to the public; reading room for accredited scholars. **Computerized Information Services:** RLIN. **Remarks:** FAX: (212)685-4740. **Staff:** H. George Fletcher, Cur., Printed Bks.; Robert Parks, Cur., Autograph Mss.; Peter Dreyer, Cur., Draw./Prints; William M. Voelkle, Cur., Medv. & Ren.Mss.; Fredric W. Wilson, Cur., Gilbert & Sullivan; Rigbie Turner, Cur., Mus.Mss.

Morgan Row Library
See: **Harrodsburg Historical Society** (6931)

★10739★
Morgan Stanley Canada Limited - Library
40 King St., W., Suite 3010
P.O. Box 3010 Phone: (416)365-6271
Toronto, ON, Canada M5H 3Y2 G. Frances Main, Libn.
Remarks: FAX: (416)368-0796. No further information was supplied by respondent.

★10740★
Morgan Stanley Company - Library Services & Records Management (Bus-Fin)
1251 Avenue of the Americas Phone: (212)703-5701
New York, NY 10020 Sarah C. Jones, V.P., Lib.Serv. & Rec.Mgt.
Founded: 1935. **Staff:** Prof 13; Other 24. **Subjects:** Investment banking, capital markets. **Holdings:** 6500 volumes; 2.3 million microfiche of corporate disclosure documents; 3000 reels of microfilm of business and financial periodicals. **Subscriptions:** 510 journals and other serials. **Services:** Interlibrary loan; library not open to the public. **Computerized Information Services:** DIALOG Information Services, Mead Data Central, Dow Jones News/Retrieval, Dun & Bradstreet Business Credit Services, Disclosure Incorporated, INVESTEXT, Spectrum Ownership Profiles Online, TEXTLINE. **Staff:** Barbara Ormerod-Glynn, Res./Data Mgt.Dir.; Jeanne Bastone, Tech.Serv.Mgr.; John Grundman, Rec.Mgr.

Vincent Morgan Music Library
See: **Amherst College** (808)

William E. Morgan Library
See: **Colorado State University** (3974)

★10741★
Morikami Museum of Japanese Culture - Donald B. Gordon Memorial Library (Area-Ethnic)
4000 Morikami Park Rd. Phone: (407)495-0233
Delray Beach, FL 33446 Larry Rosensweig, Dir.
Staff: 1. **Subjects:** Japanese art and culture, Japanese-American history. **Holdings:** 1250 books; 100 bound periodical volumes; 12 video cassettes. **Subscriptions:** 12 journals and other serials. **Services:** Library open to the public by appointment. **Remarks:** FAX: (407)499-2557. **Staff:** Gertrude L. Berman, Libn.

Morini Memorial Collection
See: **Order of Servants of Mary - Eastern Province Library** (12518)

Morisset Library
See: **University of Ottawa** (19167)

★10742★
Moritz Community Hospital - Dean Pierose Memorial Health Sciences Library (Med)
Box 86
Sun Valley, ID 83353 Phone: (208)622-3323
Subjects: Orthopedics, emergency medicine, general surgery and medicine, allied health professions. **Holdings:** 200 books; 800 bound periodical volumes; 24 pamphlets. **Services:** Library open to the public by appointment for reference use only.

John Moritz Library
See: **Nebraska Methodist Hospital - John Moritz Library** (11374)

★10743★
Moroccan Union of Work - Library (Soc Sci)
232, ave. de Forces Armees Royales
Casablanca, Morocco Phone: 300118
Subjects: Morocco - labor force, social welfare, development. **Holdings:** 30,000 volumes. **Remarks:** Telex: UMATRA 27825 M. **Also Known As:** Union Marocaine du Travail.

Walter F. Morofsky Memorial Library
See: **Michigan State University - W.K. Kellogg Biological Station** (10341)

Ashley Baker Morrill Library
See: **Lawrence Hospital** (9007)

Morrill Biological & Geological Sciences Library
See: **University of Massachusetts** (18829)

★10744★
Morris Animal Foundation - Library (Med)
45 Inverness Dr., E. Phone: (303)790-2345
Englewood, CO 80112 Jack Carpenter, Dev.Coord.
Founded: 1978. **Subjects:** Veterinary medicine, zoo medicine. **Special Collections:** MAF Fellows Reports (400 reports of foundation-sponsored research on the health of companion animals); Sam Sheer Cat Collection (300 books and pamphlets). **Holdings:** 500 books. **Subscriptions:** 75 journals and other serials; 5 newspapers. **Services:** Interlibrary loan; copying; library open to the public by special arrangement. **Remarks:** FAX: (303)790-4066.

Morris Arboretum Library
See: **University of Pennsylvania** (19189)

Arthur J. Morris Law Library
See: **University of Virginia** (19497)

Morris Communications - Amarillo Globe-News
See: **Amarillo Globe-News** (442)

★10745★
Morris County Historical Society - Victorian Resource Library (Hist)
68 Morris Ave. Phone: (201)267-3465
Morristown, NJ 07960 Naomi C. Stevens, Libn.
Founded: 1979. **Staff:** Prof 1. **Subjects:** Local social and cultural history of the Victorian-Edwardian periods. **Special Collections:** Hone-Leonard-Weis Collection of 19th and early 20th century children's books and allied materials (200 volumes). **Holdings:** 1200 books; 130 bound periodical volumes; 20 boxes of manuscripts; 900 photographs. **Subscriptions:** 15 journals and other serials. **Services:** Library open to the public by appointment.

★10746★
Morris County Law Library (Law)
Morris County Court House
Washington St. Phone: (201)285-6371
Morristown, NJ 07963-0900 Edward R. Smith, Law Libn.
Founded: 1970. **Staff:** Prof 1; Other 1. **Subjects:** Law. **Special Collections:** Pilch Library (a four-generation collection of the Henry Pilch family on the practice of law). **Holdings:** 26,000 books; 2450 volumes on microfiche. **Subscriptions:** 42 journals and other serials. **Services:** Library open to Morris County residents, lawyers, law students, and pro se litigants. **Computerized Information Services:** WESTLAW (available to judges only). **Networks/Consortia:** Member of Northwest Regional Library Cooperative. **Special Indexes:** Index by subject and case name to all current decisions by New Jersey courts (ondisc).

★10747★
Morris County Library - Music & Media Services (Mus)
30 E. Hanover Ave. Phone: (201)285-6979
Whippany, NJ 07981 Mark Tolleson, Supv.Libn.
Founded: 1973. **Staff:** Prof 3; Other 15. **Subjects:** Music, instructional media, art. **Special Collections:** MacArthur Foundation Library Video Classics; National Gallery of Art slides (depository; 40 slide sets); Bi-Folkal slides (25 slide sets); Folk Project recordings (61); popular sheet music (34,000 in 1100 volumes); slides with emphasis on geography, art, state and local history, U.S. and world history, science (23,200 in 650 volumes). **Holdings:** 800 books; 11,000 phonograph records; 15,800 audio cassettes; 2500 16mm films; 3200 video cassettes; 1288 compact discs; 575 art prints; 54 original art works; 35 study prints; 360 libretti. **Subscriptions:** 58 journals and other serials. **Services:** Copying; services open to the public. **Automated Operations:** Computerized cataloging and circulation. **Computerized Information Services:** DIALOG Information Services, DataTimes, WILSONLINE, OCLC. **Networks/Consortia:** Member of Northwest Regional Library Cooperative. **Publications:** Bibliographies; acquisitions lists. **Special Catalogs:** Book format catalogs; film and video catalogs and supp lements; circulating slide collection catalog; Recorded Books-on-Cassette from Music & Media catalog; Compact Discs in Circulation catalog. **Special Indexes:** Song index; sound effects indexes (both card); Public Performance Rights and Closed Captioned Videos index (book). **Remarks:** FAX: (201)285-6965. **Staff:** Gisela Harpell, Sr.Libn.; Mitch Greenberg, Jr.Libn.

★10748★
Morris County Library - New Jersey Collection (Hist)
30 E. Hanover Ave. Phone: (201)285-6974
Whippany, NJ 07981 Marie Heagney, Prin.Libn.
Staff: Prof 1. **Subjects:** State and local history, genealogy. **Special Collections:** New Jersey State Documents Depository; Master Plans and Ordinances for Morris County Municipalities; Evans Collection (early American imprints, 1639-1800); manuscript collection of Morristown National Historical Park (69 reels of microfilm); historical and current New Jersey maps; New Jersey Federal Census Schedules, 1830-1910 (microfilm). **Holdings:** 4000 books; 90 bound periodical volumes; 19 VF drawers; 675 reels of microfilm. **Subscriptions:** 30 journals and other serials. **Services:** Copying; collection open to the public. **Automated Operations:** Computerized cataloging and circulation. **Computerized Information Services:** OCLC, DIALOG Information Services. **Publications:** Acquisitions Lists; The History of the Public Monuments and Sculpture of Morris County, New Jersey; The Public Monuments and Sculpture of Morristown, New Jersey. **Remarks:** FAX: (201)285-6982.

Earle E. Morris, Jr. Alcohol & Drug Addiction Treatment Center
See: **South Carolina (State) Department of Mental Health** (15405)

Morris Library and Information Center
See: **University of Kentucky** (18757)

★10749★
Morris Museum - Reference Library (Art)
6 Normandy Heights Rd.
Morristown, NJ 07960
Staff: 2. **Subjects:** Fine and decorative arts, earth sciences, astronomy, archaeology, contemporary Indian art, natural science. **Holdings:** 2375 books; 1500 art slides. **Subscriptions:** 12 journals and other serials. **Services:** Library open by arrangement to researchers and docents. **Special Catalogs:** Catalogs of Morris Museum exhibits, irregular. **Staff:** Madeline S. Pitney, Libn.; Elizabeth H. Addison, Libn.

★10750★
Robert Morris Associates - Library (Bus-Fin)
One Liberty Place
1650 Market St., Suite 2300 Phone: (215)851-9155
Philadelphia, PA 19103-7398 Karen Sandlin Silverman, Info.Serv.Mgr.
Staff: Prof 2; Other 2. **Subjects:** Commericial lending/credit, banking, industry/analysis. **Holdings:** 1500 books. **Subscriptions:** 200 journals and other serials. **Services:** Interlibrary loan; library not open to the public. **Automated Operations:** Computerized cataloging. **Computerized Information Services:** DIALOG Information Services, BRS Information Technologies, LEXIS, NEXIS, Dow Jones News/Retrieval, OCLC EPIC, VU/TEXT Information Services. **Remarks:** FAX: (215)851-9206. **Staff:** Lee Mooney, Info.Spec.

★10751★
Morris, Rose, Ledgett, Barristers and Soliciters - Library (Law)
Canada Trust Tower, Suite 2700
161 Bay St.
BCE Place Phone: (416)863-1600
Toronto, ON, Canada M5J 2S1 Helen Hochberg, Libn.
Staff: 2. **Subjects:** Law. **Holdings:** 5000 books, 7 bound periodical titles; 20 report series. **Subscriptions:** 20 journals and other serials; 2 newspapers. **Services:** Interlibrary loan, copying, library open to the public as approved by lawyers. **Computerized Information Services:** QL Systems, WESTLAW, Info Globe, Infomart Online. **Special Indexes:** Legislative index. **Remarks:** FAX: (416)863-9500.

William Morris Library on Forgery of Works of Art
See: **University of Virginia - Fiske Kimball Fine Arts Library** (19503)

Morrison County Historical Society - Charles A. Weyerhaeuser Memorial Museum
See: **Charles A. Weyerhaeuser Memorial Museum** (20357)

Dr. Alex Morrison Library
See: **Temple Sinai** (16124)

★10752★
Morrison & Foerster - Branch Law Library (Law)
2000 Pennsylvania Ave., N.W., Suite 5500 Phone: (202)887-1500
Washington, DC 20006-1812 Elmo F. Dattalo, Libn.
Founded: 1979. **Staff:** Prof 3; Other 2. **Subjects:** Law - American, Californian, energy, tax, business and corporate; banking. **Holdings:** 4000 volumes. **Subscriptions:** 35 journals and other serials; 9 newspapers. **Services:** Interlibrary loan; library not open to the public. **Automated Operations:** Computerized cataloging and legal memorandum file. **Computerized Information Services:** LEXIS, WESTLAW, DIALOG Information Services, VU/TEXT Information Services, NewsNet, Inc., LEGI-SLATE, Dun & Bradstreet Business Credit Services. **Remarks:** FAX: (202)887-0763; 887-0764. **Staff:** Patricia K. Newcombe, Assoc.Libn.; Janet Wamsley, Assoc.Libn.

★10753★
Morrison & Foerster - Law Library (Law)
345 California St. Phone: (415)677-7270
San Francisco, CA 94104 Teresa A. Oppedal, Law Libn.
Founded: 1925. **Staff:** Prof 6; Other 7. **Subjects:** Law. **Holdings:** 65,000 volumes. **Services:** Library not open to the public. **Computerized Information Services:** DIALOG Information Services, LEXIS, WESTLAW. **Networks/Consortia:** Member of Research Libraries Information Network (RLIN). **Staff:** Jane Amon, Law Libn.; Gary Cann, Assoc.Libn.; Felicia Poe, Assoc.Libn.; Tracy Helser, Assoc.Libn.

★10754★
Morrison & Foerster - Library (Law)
555 W. 5th St., Suite 3500 Phone: (213)892-5359
Los Angeles, CA 90013-1024 Lee R. Nemchek, Info.Rsrcs.Mgr.
Founded: 1975. **Staff:** Prof 3; Other 2. **Subjects:** Law - banking, corporate, securities, labor, tax, real estate; litigation. **Special Collections:** California city charters; municipal planning and zoning ordinances. **Holdings:** 10,000 books; 1000 bound periodical volumes. **Subscriptions:** 300 journals and other serials; 30 newspapers. **Services:** Interlibrary loan; copying; SDI; 24 hour loan. **Computerized Information Services:** LEXIS, DIALOG Information Services, WESTLAW, VU/TEXT Information Services, LEGI-TECH, Dun & Bradstreet Business Credit Services, WILSONLINE, RLIN, Dow Jones News/Retrieval, DataTimes, LEGI-SLATE, NewsNet, Inc., State Net 50 - State Legislative Reporting, Maxwell Macmillan Taxes Online. **Remarks:** FAX: (213)892-5454. **Staff:** Robert Rich, Assoc.Libn.; Marta de Paula, Assoc.Libn.

★10755★
Morrison-Knudsen Engineers, Inc. - Technical Library
180 Howard St.
San Francisco, CA 94105-1699 Phone: (415)442-7300
Founded: 1964. **Subjects:** Engineering - civil, geotechnical, electrical, telecommunications; hazardous waste cleanup. **Holdings:** 8000 books; 1000 bound periodical volumes. **Remarks:** Currently inactive.

★10756★
Morristown Jewish Center - The Library (Area-Ethnic)
177 Speedwell Ave. Phone: (201)538-9292
Morristown, NJ 07960-3891 Frances Tillinger, Libn.
Founded: 1967. **Staff:** Prof 1; Other 2. **Subjects:** Judaica, Israel, Jewish art, religious studies, history, languages. **Holdings:** 6600 books; 45 bound periodical volumes; 50 pamphlets; 15 documents. **Subscriptions:** 10 journals and other serials. **Services:** Interlibrary loan; library open to the public for reference use only.

★10757★
Morristown Memorial Hospital - Lathrope Health Sciences Library (Med)
100 Madison Ave.
P.O. Box 1956 Phone: (201)540-5657
Morristown, NJ 07962-1956 JoAnne M. Searle, Dir.
Founded: 1947. **Staff:** Prof 2. **Subjects:** Medicine, dentistry, nursing. **Special Collections:** Consumer health. **Holdings:** 3500 books; 7000 bound periodical volumes; 55 slide/tape sets; 127 video cassettes. **Subscriptions:** 540 journals and other serials. **Services:** Interlibrary loan; copying; library open to the public for reference use only. **Computerized Information Services:** DIALOG Information Services, NLM. **Networks/Consortia:** Member of MEDCORE, National Network of Libraries of Medicine - Middle Atlantic Region, Cosmopolitan Biomedical Library Consortium (CBLC), Health Sciences Library Association of New Jersey (HSLANJ), Northwest Regional Library Cooperative. **Remarks:** FAX: (201)540-1432. **Staff:** Thelma J. Fitch.

Morristown National Historical Park
See: **U.S. Natl. Park Service** (17753)

James E. Morrow Library
See: **Marshall University - James E. Morrow Library** (9724)

Marjorie Gertrude Morrow Library
See: **Iowa Methodist Medical Center** (8228)

★10758★
Morrow Memorial United Methodist Church - Adult Library and Media Center (Rel-Phil)
600 Ridgewood Rd.
Maplewood, NJ 07040 Phone: (201)763-7676
Staff: Prof 1; Other 1. **Subjects:** Bible translations and commentaries, Christian beliefs and living, death and dying, family issues, marriage, parenting, aging, divorce, bereavement, religious art, social issues, devotional aids, church history, ecumenicism, world order, missions, travel, poetry and drama, biography, fiction. **Holdings:** 1700 books; 160 filmstrips; 350 audio cassettes of Sunday services; slides; picture files. **Services:** Library open to the public. **Staff:** Kathy Finch, Adult Libn.; Althea MacWhorter, Media Ctr.

Colonel Robert H. Morse Library
See: **Beloit College - Colonel Robert H. Morse Library** (1703)

★10759★
Leonard Morse Hospital - Medical Library (Med)
67 Union St.
Natick, MA 01760 Phone: (508)653-3400
Founded: 1965. **Staff:** Prof 1. **Subjects:** Medicine, nursing, hospital administration. **Holdings:** 1200 books; 2600 bound periodical volumes; 147 AV programs. **Subscriptions:** 121 journals and other serials. **Services:** Interlibrary loan; library open to the public on limited schedule. **Automated Operations:** Computerized cataloging and acquisitions. **Computerized Information Services:** MEDLINE, BRS Information Technologies; DOCLINE (electronic mail service). **Networks/Consortia:** Member of Consortium for Information Resources (CIR). **Remarks:** FAX: (508)655-3908. **Staff:** N. Wolk, Med.Libn.; R. Moskowitz, Med.Libn.

Morse Music Library
See: **Harvard University - Radcliffe College - Morse Music Library** (6988)

★10760★
Morse School of Business - Library (Educ)
275 Asylum St. Phone: (203)522-2261
Hartford, CT 06103 Ann Davis, Libn.
Founded: 1968. **Staff:** Prof 1. **Subjects:** Management, accounting, medical assisting, office procedures, data processing, hotel/restaurant management, paralegal, court reporting, travel, tourism. **Holdings:** 3000 books. **Subscriptions:** 40 journals and other serials. **Services:** Library not open to the public.

Morse-Slanger Library
See: **Boston City Hospital - Nursing** (1978)

William H. Mortensen Library
See: **University of Hartford** (18616)

★10761★
Mortgage Bankers Association of America - Library (Bus-Fin)
1125 15th St., N.W. Phone: (202)861-6580
Washington, DC 20005 Cassie Kupstas, Libn.
Staff: Prof 1; Other 1. **Subjects:** Mortgage finance, investment, housing, real estate, statistics. **Holdings:** 6000 books. **Subscriptions:** 250 journals and other serials; 6 newspapers. **Services:** Interlibrary loan (limited); library open to the public by appointment for reference use only. **Automated Operations:** Computerized cataloging and serials. **Computerized Information Services:** DIALOG Information Services, NewsNet, Inc., Dow Jones News/Retrieval; Real Estate Finance Today (internal database). **Publications:** Subject bibliographies. **Remarks:** FAX: (202)861-0734.

William J. Mortimer Library
See: **Life Insurance Marketing and Research Association** (9153)

Mortlock Library of South Australiana
See: **State Library of South Australia** (15694)

Edward and Doris Mortola Library
See: **Pace University** (12654)

★10762★
Morton Arboretum - Sterling Morton Library (Biol Sci)
Lisle, IL 60532 Phone: (708)719-2427
Michael T. Stieber, Lib.Adm. & Ref.Libn.
Founded: 1922. **Staff:** Prof 4. **Subjects:** Botany, horticulture, dendrology, arboriculture, landscape architecture, natural history, ecology and the environment. **Special Collections:** Rare books in botany, horticulture, and landscape architecture; botanical prints and drawings; Jens Jensen archive. **Holdings:** 23,500 volumes; 20 VF drawers of nursery and seed catalogs; 2000 pamphlets. **Subscriptions:** 400 journals and other serials. **Services:** Interlibrary loan; copying; SDI; library open to the public. **Computerized Information Services:** DIALOG Information Services, WILSONLINE. **Networks/Consortia:** Member of Suburban Library System (SLS). **Publications:** Sterling Morton Library Bibliographies in Botany and Horticulture. **Special Indexes:** Woody Plant Index (card). **Remarks:** Alternate telephone number(s): 719-2430. FAX: (708)719-2433. **Staff:** Peter Wang, Cat.; Ian MacPhail, Cur., Rare Bks.; Rita Hassert, Tech.Serv.Libn.

Morton Collectanea
See: **University of Miami** (18845)

★10763★
Morton International, Inc. - Corporate Library (Bus-Fin)
100 N. Riverside Plaza Phone: (312)807-2257
Chicago, IL 60606-1555 Lisa A. Kuklinski, Supv., Lib.Serv.
Staff: Prof 1; Other 1. **Subjects:** Business. **Holdings:** 300 books. **Subscriptions:** 150 journals and other serials. **Services:** Interlibrary loan; copying; SDI; library open to the public with restrictions. **Automated Operations:** Computerized serials and circulation. **Computerized Information Services:** DIALOG Information Services, LEXIS, NEXIS, Human Resource Information Network (HRIN), InvesText, Dow Jones News/Retrieval. **Remarks:** FAX: (312)807-2875.

★10764★
Morton International, Inc. - Industrial Chemicals and Additives - Information Resource Center (Sci-Engr)
2000 West St. Phone: (513)733-2171
Cincinnati, OH 45215 Diana L. Waid, Info.Rsrc.Adm.
Staff: Prof 1. **Subjects:** Organometallic chemistry; organic chemistry; specialized information on additives for lubricants and plastics. **Holdings:** 2800 volumes; VF drawers of reprints, patents, internal reports. **Subscriptions:** 80 journals and other serials. **Services:** Interlibrary loan; library not open to the public. **Computerized Information Services:** STN International, TOXNET, DIALOG Information Services. **Remarks:** FAX: (513)733-2115. **Formerly:** Morton International, Inc. - Specialty Chemicals Group - Research Library.

★10765★
Morton International, Inc. - Morton Chemical Division - Woodstock Research Information Center (Sci-Engr)
1275 Lake Ave. Phone: (815)338-1800
Woodstock, IL 60098 Valentina M. Woodruff, Info.Serv.
Founded: 1954. **Staff:** Prof 1; Other 1. **Subjects:** Chemistry - inorganic, organic, polymer. **Holdings:** 2500 books; 3000 bound periodical volumes; 1000 pamphlets; 3 drawers of pamphlets; U.S. chemical patents on microfilm. **Subscriptions:** 153 journals and other serials. **Services:** Center open to outside users with an Infopass. **Computerized Information Services:** DIALOG Information Services, PFDS Online, Chemical Abstracts Service (CAS). **Networks/Consortia:** Member of Northern Illinois Library System (NILS).

Morton International, Inc. - Specialty Chemicals Group - Library
See: **Morton International, Inc. - Water-Based Polymers - Library** (10766)

Morton International, Inc. - Specialty Chemicals Group - Research Library
See: **Morton International, Inc.** (10764)

★10766★
Morton International, Inc. - Water-Based Polymers - Library (Sci-Engr)
130 Mountain Creek Church Rd.
P.O. Box 3089 Phone: (803)292-5700
Greenville, SC 29602 Mary Croft, Supv., R & D Adm.Serv.
Founded: 1964. **Staff:** 1. **Subjects:** Polymers, adhesives, coatings, textile chemicals, packaging. **Holdings:** 600 books; 2000 patents. **Subscriptions:** 60 journals and other serials. **Services:** Library open to the public by appointment. **Remarks:** FAX: (803)292-5799. **Formerly:** Morton International, Inc. - Specialty Chemicals Group - Library.

Sterling Morton Library
See: **Morton Arboretum - Sterling Morton Library** (10762)

Sol and Elaine Mosak Library
See: **Adler School of Professional Psychology** (81)

★10767★
Moscow Planetarium - Scientific and Technical Library (Sci-Engr)
Sadovo-Kudrinskaja 5 Phone: 95 2520217
123242 Moscow, Russia Faina B. Rubleva, Dir.
Founded: 1929. **Staff:** Prof 1. **Subjects:** Astronomy, geography, space research, history. **Holdings:** 17,235 books; 21 bound periodical volumes; 16 reports. **Services:** Interlibrary loan; library open to specialists and researchers. **Remarks:** Alternate telephone number(s): 95 2548147. FAX: 95 2003224. **Also Known As:** Planetarij - Naucnaja Biblioteka.

Ina Mosher Health Sciences Library
See: **Newport Hospital** (11776)

★10768★
Mosquito Association - Archives (Mil)
1106 Maplewood Ave. Phone: (603)436-5835
Portsmouth, NH 03801 Mr. W.M. Cleveland, Hist.
Founded: 1982. **Staff:** 1. **Subjects:** Air War In Korea, 1950-1955. **Special Collections:** Military personnel rosters; Killed in Action/Missing in Action and Mosquito Locator services rosters. **Holdings:** 5 cubic feet of personal papers; 2 cubic feet of federal records (copies); 1 cubic foot of photographs; 1/2 cubic foot of maps, drawings; 20 photograph albums. **Services:** Copying; library open to the public by appointment. **Publications:** Newsletter; annual meeting book; Mosquitos in Korea 1950-1955 (book); annual directory.

★10769★
Moss Archives (Hist)
Box 3336 Phone: (908)842-0336
Sea Bright, NJ 07760-3336 George H. Moss, Jr., Dir.
Founded: 1950. **Subjects:** New Jersey history; Jersey Coast and Monmouth County history, 1685-1935. **Holdings:** 5000 glass negatives, 1898-1917; 2000 photographs (including 1000 stereographic views), 1859-1935; 3000 illustrations of the New Jersey shore; maps; broadsides; logbooks; ledgers; letters; other ephemera, 1685-1935. **Services:** Archives open to the public by appointment with restrictions. **Remarks:** Archives located at 39 Rumson Rd., Rumson, NJ 07760.

★10770★
Mossbauer Effect Data Center (Sci-Engr)
University of North Carolina Phone: (704)251-6617
Asheville, NC 28804-3299 John G. Stevens, Dir.
Staff: Prof 4. **Subjects:** Mossbauer Effect, Mossbauer spectroscopy, nuclear gamma ray resonance. **Holdings:** 100 books; 100 bound periodical volumes; 100 reports; 28,000 reprints. **Subscriptions:** 220 journals and other serials. **Services:** Copying; library open to the public. **Computerized Information Services:** Internal databases; BITNET (electronic mail service). Performs searches on fee basis. Contact Person: Christine Boss, Bus.Mgr. **Publications:** Handbooks; decennial index. **Remarks:** FAX: (704)251-6002. Electronic mail address(es): STEVENS@UNCA (BITNET).

★10771★
Mote Marine Laboratory - Davis Library (Biol Sci)
1600 Thompson Parkway Phone: (813)388-4441
Sarasota, FL 34236 Jean Maguire, Libn.
Founded: 1978. **Staff:** Prof 1. **Subjects:** Marine biology, estuarine ecology. **Holdings:** 3000 books; 800 bound periodical volumes; 15,000 reprints. **Subscriptions:** 85 journals and other serials. **Services:** Interlibrary loan; copying; SDI; library open to the public for reference use only. **Computerized Information Services:** DIALOG Information Services; internal database; SCIENCEnet (electronic mail service). **Networks/ Consortia:** Member of Florida Library Network (FLN). **Publications:** Newsletter; Collected Papers of Mote Marine Laboratory, quadrennially to international marine research centers. **Remarks:** FAX: (813)388-4312. Electronic mail address(es): G.PATTON (SCIENCEnet).

★10772★
Mother Whiteside Memorial Library - Southwest Collection (Hist)
525 W. High St. Phone: (505)287-7927
Grants, NM 87020 Jae Luree King, Libn.
Founded: 1947. **Staff:** 4. **Subjects:** Southwest. **Special Collections:** Large print book collection. **Holdings:** 1047 books. **Subscriptions:** 38 journals and other serials; 5 newspapers. **Services:** Interlibrary loan; copying; collection open to the public. **Staff:** Nita F. Ford, Asst.Libn.

★10773★
Motion Picture Association of America - Library (Theater)
1133 Avenue of the Americas, 18th Fl. Phone: (212)840-6161
New York, NY 10036 Robert A. Franklin, Ph.D., V.P., Dir. of Res.
Founded: 1946. **Staff:** Prof 1; Other 2. **Subjects:** Theatrical motion pictures - history, finance, censorship, content. **Holdings:** 3000 volumes. **Subscriptions:** 20 journals and other serials. **Services:** Library available to qualified persons for consultation by mail or telephone.

★10774★
Motion Picture Services (Aud-Vis)
Box 252 Phone: (201)992-8194
Livingston, NJ 07039 Gloria Mankowitz, Pres.
Founded: 1960. **Staff:** Prof 2; Other 2. **Subjects:** Health, science, safety education, human relations, travel, driver education. **Special Collections:** Steel construction; Seat Belt Use - New Jersey State Safety Council (60 titles in 16mm films and video cassettes (VHS and Beta) - for distribution only in New Jersey). **Holdings:** 950 16mm films; film brochures; video cassettes. **Services:** Open to schools, institutions, industry, community groups, churches, adult groups, clubs. Films on health, safety education, human relations, and driver education are available free only in the state of New Jersey; all others are available for distribution throughout the United States. **Computerized Information Services:** Internal database. **Publications:** List of publications - available on request.

★10775★
Motor Bus Society, Inc. - John Phoschek Memorial Bus Transportation Library (Trans)
P.O. Box 10503
New Brunswick, NJ 08906 Albert E. Meier, V.P., Pubns.
Founded: 1948. **Subjects:** Motor bus transportation history. **Special Collections:** Greyhound historical collection. **Holdings:** 2000 bound periodical volumes; 90,000 photographs; 500 catalogs and bus specifications. **Subscriptions:** 11 journals and other serials. **Services:** Library open to the public by appointment. **Publications:** Motor Coach Age, bimonthly.

★10776★
Motor Industry Research Association - Library (Trans)
Watling St.
Nuneaton, Warwickshire CV10 Phone: 203 348541
0TU, England Martin White, Hd., Info.Serv.
Subjects: Automotive industry. **Holdings:** Technical books; legislation; standards; other cataloged items. **Computerized Information Services:** Automobile Abstracts, Automotive Business Index (internal databases). Performs searches on fee basis. **Publications:** Automobile Abstracts, monthly; Automotive Business Index, biweekly - both available by subscription. **Remarks:** FAX: 203 343772. Telex: 311277.

★10777★
Motor Vehicle Documentation - Library (Trans)
Ulrichstr. 14
W-7120 Bietigheim-Bissingen, Germany Phone: 7142 54011
Founded: 1974. **Staff:** Prof 1. **Subjects:** Motor vehicles - design, construction, manufacturing. **Holdings:** 4000 bound volumes. **Subscriptions:** 200 journals and other serials. **Services:** Library open to members only. **Computerized Information Services:** DKF database (internal database). **Remarks:** FAX: 7142 65898. **Also Known As:** Dokumentation Kraftfahrwesen. **Staff:** Regine Fuchs-Reinhardt.

★10778★
Motor Vehicle Manufacturers Association (MVMA) - Communications Library (Trans)
7430 2nd Ave., Suite 300 Phone: (313)872-4311
Detroit, MI 48202 Gene McKinney, P.R. Assoc.
Founded: 1971. **Staff:** Prof 1; Other 2. **Subjects:** Auto industry, transportation, safety, air pollution, energy. **Special Collections:** Automotive photograph collection. **Holdings:** 100 VF drawers of newspaper clippings. **Subscriptions:** 32 journals and other serials; 9 newspapers. **Services:** Library open to the public with restrictions. **Remarks:** FAX: (313)872-5400.

★10779★
Motor Vehicle Manufacturers Association (MVMA) - Patent Research Library (Sci-Engr)
7430 2nd Ave., Suite 300 Phone: (313)872-4311
Detroit, MI 48202 James A. Wren, Mgr.
Founded: 1919. **Staff:** Prof 4. **Subjects:** Automotive patents, technology, automotive history. **Special Collections:** Patents specifically related to motor vehicle technology (one million); foreign and U.S. automotive sales brochures, pre-1900 to present. **Holdings:** 13,000 bound periodical volumes; 1000 textbooks; manufacturers' brochures and instruction books. **Subscriptions:** 100 journals and other serials. **Services:** Library open to the public by special permission. **Computerized Information Services:** MVMA Trademark Data Base, MVMA Company History Database (internal databases). **Publications:** Automobiles of America; Motor Trucks of America. **Remarks:** FAX: (313)872-5400. **Staff:** Daniel Kirchner, Sr.Reg.; Karen Prymak, Trademark Anl.; Marilyn Siegel, Libn.

★10780★
Motor Vehicle Manufacturers Association (MVMA) - Statistics Information Center (Trans)
7430 2nd Ave., Suite 300 Phone: (313)872-4311
Detroit, MI 48202 Robert Birch, Mgr.
Founded: 1965. **Staff:** 5. **Subjects:** Transportation. **Holdings:** National and international vehicle-related statistical materials. **Services:** Center not open to the public. **Remarks:** FAX: (313)872-5400.

★10781★
Motor Vehicle Manufacturers Association (MVMA) - Technical Library (Trans)
7430 2nd Ave., Suite 300 Phone: (313)872-4311
Detroit, MI 48202 Marilyn Siegel, Interim Libn.
Founded: 1968. **Staff:** Prof 1. **Subjects:** Vehicle safety, air quality, fuel economy, alternative fuels, environment, emissions, energy, industrial relations, electromagnetic compatibility, trucks and buses, economics. **Holdings:** 200 books; 10,000 reports, papers, government documents, and proceedings. **Subscriptions:** 40 journals and other serials. **Services:** Interlibrary loan (limited); library open to member companies. **Automated Operations:** Computerized cataloging. **Computerized Information Services:** DIALOG Information Services, BRS Information Technologies. **Remarks:** FAX: (313)872-5400.

★10782★
Motorcycle Safety Foundation - Information Resource Center (Trans)
2 Jenner St., Suite 150 Phone: (714)727-3227
Irvine, CA 92718-3812 Rene L. Barge, Res.Mgr.
Founded: 1973. **Staff:** 4. **Subjects:** Motorcycle rider education, highway and traffic safety, motorcycle awareness. **Holdings:** 3500 books. **Subscriptions:** 20 journals and other serials. **Services:** Center open to the public for reference use only. **Publications:** List of publications. **Remarks:** FAX: (714)727-4217.

★10783★
Motorola Codex - Corporate Library (Comp Sci)
20 Cabot Blvd./M2-40 Phone: (508)261-4129
Mansfield, MA 02048 Betty Edwards, Mgr.
Founded: 1983. **Staff:** Prof 2; Other 2. **Subjects:** Data communications, telecommunications, management, business, computer science, engineering, electronics, marketing. **Holdings:** 5000 books; 3000 specs and standards (ANSI, AT&T, Bellcore, IBM, CCITT). **Subscriptions:** 300 journals and other serials. **Services:** Interlibrary loan; library not open to the public. **Automated Operations:** Computerized cataloging, acquisitions, and serials. **Computerized Information Services:** DIALOG Information Services, Dow Jones News/Retrieval, NewsNet, Inc., VU/TEXT Information Services, OCLC EPIC, OCLC; CD-ROMs (Disclosure, ABI/INFORM, COMPENDEX, Serials Directory/EBSCO, Computer Select, Books in Print); DIALMAIL, MCI Mail (electronic mail services). **Networks/Consortia:** Member of NELINET, Inc. **Publications:** Newsletter; newsbrief of competitor information, daily; Table-of-Contents Service. **Remarks:** FAX: (508)261-9872. Electronic mail address(es): 10320 (DIALMAIL); 441-5093 (MCI Mail). **Formerly:** Codex Corporation. **Staff:** Jane Peck, Libn.

★10784★
Motorola Computer Systems, Inc. - National Technical Support Center Library (Comp Sci)
1701 Valley View Ln. Phone: (214)241-7700
Farmer's Branch, TX 75234 Dee Lightfoot, Libn.
Founded: 1981. **Staff:** Prof 1. **Subjects:** Computer software and hardware technical documentation. **Special Collections:** Four Phase documentation (5287 volumes); IBM documentation (1889 volumes); Four Phase software (2447 volumes); IBM software (779 volumes); Codex documentation (908 volumes). **Holdings:** 9213 books; 2327 magnetic tapes; 899 disk packs and diskettes; 1001 microfiche. **Subscriptions:** 12 journals and other serials; 5 newspapers. **Services:** Library not open to the public. **Automated Operations:** Computerized cataloging, acquisitions, circulation, and statistical records.

★10785★
Motorola, Inc. - Bipolar Integrated Circuits Division - Technical Library (Sci-Engr)
2200 W. Broadway Phone: (602)962-2156
Mesa, AZ 85202 Linda Smothermon, Libn.
Founded: 1973. **Staff:** 1. **Subjects:** Electronics, engineering, physics, chemistry. **Holdings:** 3000 books; 2500 bound periodical volumes. **Subscriptions:** 100 journals and other serials. **Services:** Interlibrary loan; copying; SDI. **Computerized Information Services:** DIALOG Information Services; DIALMAIL (electronic mail service). **Remarks:** FAX: (602)962-2820.

★10786★
Motorola, Inc. - Communication Sector Library (Sci-Engr)
1301 E. Algonquin Rd., Rm. 1914 Phone: (708)576-5940
Schaumburg, IL 60196 Marion Mason, Lib.Mgr.
Founded: 1930. **Staff:** Prof 2; Other 1. **Subjects:** Electronics, mathematics, communications. **Holdings:** 8000 books; 850 bound periodical volumes; 2000 reports. **Subscriptions:** 600 journals and other serials. **Services:** Copying; SDI; routing; library open to the public on request. **Automated Operations:** Computerized cataloging and serials. **Computerized Information Services:** DIALOG Information Services; CD-ROM (MicroPatent). **Networks/Consortia:** Member of North Suburban Library System (NSLS). **Publications:** Acquisition list, monthly; journal list, annual; general brochure - to the public. **Special Indexes:** Indexes to internal reports and video files; indexes to dissertations. **Remarks:** FAX: (312)576-4716. **Staff:** Mary Lou Kutscha, Tech.Libn.

★10787★
Motorola, Inc. - Government Electronics Group - Technical Library (Info Sci)
8201 E. McDowell Rd., H2205 Phone: (602)441-3471
Scottsdale, AZ 85252 Karen Lank, Mgr.
Founded: 1951. **Staff:** Prof 2; Other 3. **Subjects:** Communications, radar, navigation, control systems, digital systems, physics, electronics, space science, mathematics. **Holdings:** 5000 books; 150,000 documents on microfilm. **Subscriptions:** 300 journals and other serials. **Services:** Interlibrary loan; library not open to the public. **Automated Operations:** Computerized cataloging, acquisitions, circulation, and indexing. **Computerized Information Services:** DIALOG Information Services, DataTimes, DROLS; DIALMAIL (electronic mail service). Performs searches. **Remarks:** FAX: (602)441-8115. Electronic mail address(es): 19159 (DIALMAIL). **Staff:** Judith Stewart, Tech.Libn.

★10788★
Motorola, Inc. - Land Mobile Subscriber Group - Technical Library (Sci-Engr)
8000 W. Sunrise Blvd. Phone: (305)475-5049
Fort Lauderdale, FL 33322 June Phinney, Tech.Libn.
Founded: 1971. **Staff:** Prof 1. **Subjects:** Electrotechnology, electrical and mechanical engineering, business. **Holdings:** 1500 books; 200 bound periodical volumes; computer searches; company reports and patents. **Subscriptions:** 300 journals and other serials. **Services:** Library not open to the public. **Computerized Information Services:** 4 CD-ROM subscriptions. **Remarks:** FAX: (305)475-4466. **Formerly:** Its Radio Products Group.

★10789★
Motorola, Inc. - Semiconductor Product Sector - Information Center (Sci-Engr)
3501 Ed Bluestein Blvd. Phone: (512)928-6089
Austin, TX 78721 Leslie Campbell, Tech.Libn.
Founded: 1980. **Staff:** Prof 1, Other 1. **Subjects:** Electronics, computer design, semiconductors, engineering. **Holdings:** 3500 volumes. **Subscriptions:** 100 journals and other serials; 5 newspapers. **Services:** Interlibrary loan; center not open to the public. **Automated Operations:** Computerized public access catalog, cataloging, acquisitions, and circulation. **Computerized Information Services:** DIALOG Information Services, BRS Information Technologies. **Networks/Consortia:** Member of Motorola Library Network.

★10790★
Motorola, Inc. - Semiconductor Products Sector - Technical Library (Sci-Engr)
Box 2953
MS B134 Phone: (602)244-6065
Phoenix, AZ 85062 Peggy J. Pedigo, Mgr., Tech.Libs.
Founded: 1958. **Staff:** Prof 1; Other 1. **Subjects:** Semiconductors, electronics, engineering, material science, physics. **Holdings:** 5000 books; 3500 bound periodical volumes; 1200 technical reports. **Subscriptions:** 110 journals and other serials. **Services:** Interlibrary loan; library not open to the public. **Automated Operations:** Computerized public access catalog and ILL. **Computerized Information Services:** DIALOG Information Services; DIALMAIL (electronic mail service). **Remarks:** Library located at 5005 E. McDowell Rd., Phoenix, AZ 85008. FAX: (602)994-6820.

★10791★
Motorola, Inc. - Semiconductor Products Sector - Technical Library (Sci-Engr)
6501 William Cannon Dr. W.
MD OE18
Austin, TX 78735 Phone: (512)891-3630
Founded: 1989. **Staff:** Prof 1; Other 1. **Subjects:** Microprocessors, computers, electronics. **Holdings:** 1900 books; 500 technical reports. **Subscriptions:** 80 journals and other serials. **Services:** Interlibrary loan; library not open to the public. **Automated Operations:** Computerized public access catalog and ILL. **Computerized Information Services:** DIALOG Information Services; DIALMAIL (electronic mail service).

★10792★
Motorola, Inc. - Technical Library (Sci-Engr)
1500 N.W. 22nd Ave. Phone: (407)364-2675
Boynton Beach, FL 33435 Joan K. Lange, Tech.Libn.
Founded: 1984. **Subjects:** Electrical and mechanical engineering. **Holdings:** 3000 books; 90 bound periodical volumes. **Subscriptions:** 125 journals and other serials, 6 newspapers. **Services:** Library not open to the public. **Remarks:** FAX: (407)364-2341.

★10793★
Motorola, Inc. - Technical Library 2G (Sci-Engr)
5555 N. Beach St. Phone: (817)232-6251
Fort Worth, TX 76137 Angelika Critchett, Libn.
Founded: 1980. **Staff:** Prof 1. **Subjects:** Electrical engineering, communications, telecommunications. **Holdings:** 800 books; Institute of Electrical and Electronics Engineers, Inc. serials, 1978 to present; proceedings; internal documents; data books. **Subscriptions:** 201 journals and other serials. **Services:** Interlibrary loan; library not open to the public. **Automated Operations:** Computerized cataloging. **Computerized Information Services:** DIALOG Information Services; internal database. **Publications:** Library newsletter, 6/year - for internal distribution only. **Remarks:** FAX: (817)232-6030.

★10794★
Charles Stewart Mott Foundation - Library (Soc Sci)
1200 Mott Foundation Bldg. Phone: (313)238-5651
Flint, MI 48502 Eve Brown, Rec.Mgt.Supv.
Founded: 1974. **Staff:** Prof 1; Other 1. **Subjects:** Community education, philanthropy. **Special Collections:** Historical documents of the Mott Foundation (50 VF drawers; microfilm). **Holdings:** 3000 books; 190 VF drawers of reference files, grant-related material, correspondence. **Subscriptions:** 100 journals and other serials; 15 newspapers. **Services:** Library not open to the public. **Computerized Information Services:** DIALOG Information Services. **Publications:** Acquisitions list - for internal distribution only. **Special Catalogs:** Microfilm index for historical documents.

Moulton Library
See: **Bangor Theological Seminary** (1472)

★10795★
Moultrie County Historical & Genealogical Society - Moultrie County Heritage Center (Hist)
117 E. Harrison St.
Box 588 Phone: (217)728-4085
Sullivan, IL 61951 Mary L. Storm, Libn.
Founded: 1974. **Staff:** 7. **Subjects:** Local history and genealogy. **Holdings:** 695 books; 7 VF drawers of family surname folders; 10 VF drawers of official county records; 72 reels of microfilm of newspapers and census. **Services:** Center open to the public on a limited schedule; will answer mail inquiries. **Publications:** Moultrie County Heritage Quarterly. **Special Indexes:** Obituaries (card); marriages (card); family record files.

Mound City Group National Monument
See: **U.S. Natl. Park Service** (17754)

Mt. Albert Research Centre
See: **New Zealand - Department of Scientific and Industrial Research** (11737)

★10796★
Mount Allison University - Alfred Whitehead Memorial Music Library (Mus)
Sackville, NB, Canada E0A 3C0 Phone: (506)364-2561
Peter Higham, Mus.Libn.
Founded: 1967. **Staff:** Prof 1; Other 1. **Subjects:** Music - theory, history, criticism, biography; musicology; music education. **Special Collections:** Twentieth century Canadian music scores and recordings. **Holdings:** 9000 books; 1200 bound periodical volumes; 10,200 scores; 112 reels of microfilm (36 titles); 3287 microfiche (99 titles); 9 films; 5900 phonograph recordings (3850 titles); 450 audiotapes; 350 compact discs (300 titles). **Subscriptions:** 75 journals and other serials. **Services:** Interlibrary loan; copying; SDI; library open to the public. **Automated Operations:** Computerized public access catalog and circulation. **Computerized Information Services:** DIALOG Information Services; Envoy 100, BITNET (electronic mail services). Performs searches on fee basis. **Publications:** Canadian Music Scores & Recordings (holdings of Mount Allison libraries); Sources in Canadian Music, 2nd edition (bibliography) - for sale. **Remarks:** FAX: (506)364-2617. Electronic mail address(es): ILL.NBSAM (Envoy 100); PHIGHAM@MTA.CA (BITNET).

★10797★
Mount Allison University - Winthrop P. Bell Collection of Acadiana (Area-Ethnic)
Ralph Pickard Bell Library Phone: (506)364-2237
Sackville, NB, Canada E0A 3C0 Margaret Fancy, Spec.Coll.Libn.
Founded: 1966. **Subjects:** Acadiana: historical material relating to Nova Scotia, New Brunswick, Prince Edward Island, Maine. **Holdings:** 10,000 volumes; 950 slides. **Subscriptions:** 23 journals and other serials. **Services:** Copying; collection open to the public. **Automated Operations:** Computerized cataloging and acquisitions (through main library). **Computerized Information Services:** Envoy 100, InterNet (electronic mail services). **Publications:** Maritime Literature Reprint Series (7 titles). **Special Catalogs:** Catalogue of the W.P. Bell Collection of Acadiana, 1986 (microfiche and paper). **Remarks:** FAX: (506)364-2617. Electronic mail address(es): ILL.NBSAM (Envoy 100); MFANCY@MTA.CA (InterNet).

★10798★
Mount Auburn Hospital - Health Sciences Library (Med)
330 Mt. Auburn St. Phone: (617)492-3500
Cambridge, MA 02138 M. Cherie Haitz, Dir.
Staff: Prof 1; Other 2. **Subjects:** Medicine, nursing, pathology, administration, consumer health, allied health sciences. **Holdings:** 2000 books; 3000 bound periodical volumes; AV programs; 4 VF drawers of pamphlets. **Subscriptions:** 273 journals and other serials. **Services:** Interlibrary loan; copying; SDI; library open to the public for reference use only. **Computerized Information Services:** BRS Information Technologies, NLM; Paper Chase (internal database). **Networks/Consortia:** Member of Boston Biomedical Library Consortium, Community Health Information Network (CHIN).

★10799★
Mount Carmel Health - Mother M. Constantine Memorial Library (Med)
793 W. State St. Phone: (614)225-5214
Columbus, OH 43222 Pamela M. Elwell, Dir.
Staff: Prof 2; Other 6. **Subjects:** Medicine, nursing, allied health sciences, health administration. **Holdings:** 3500 books; 20,000 bound periodical volumes; kits; slides; audio cassettes. **Subscriptions:** 450 journals and other serials. **Services:** Interlibrary loan; library not open to the public. **Computerized Information Services:** MEDLINE, MEDLARS, OCLC, BRS Information Technologies. **Networks/Consortia:** Member of OHIONET, Central Ohio Hospital Library Consortium. **Staff:** Fern M. Check, Ref.Libn.

★10800★
Mount Carmel Lutheran Church - Library (Rel-Phil)
8424 W. Center St. Phone: (414)771-1270
Milwaukee, WI 53222 Verna A. Weller, Libn.
Founded: 1947. **Staff:** 2. **Subjects:** Bible study, devotions, missions, biography, fiction. **Special Collections:** Children's Corner (400 books). **Holdings:** 4500 volumes; 2 VF drawers of clippings; 3000 mounted pictures; 3 films; 326 filmstrips; 145 sound recordings; 56 cassettes; 80 flannelgraphs; 60 costumes; 30 AV cassettes. **Subscriptions:** 4 journals and other serials. **Services:** Interlibrary loan; library open to other church groups.

★10801★
Mount Carmel Mercy Hospital - Medical Library (Med)
6071 W. Outer Dr. Phone: (313)927-7073
Detroit, MI 48235 Jill Van Buskirk, Dir.
Founded: 1939. **Staff:** Prof 1; Other 2. **Subjects:** Medicine, surgery, obstetrics, gynecology, radiology, pathology, pediatrics, nursing. **Special Collections:** Ethel Wiener Memorial Collection on allergy and allied subjects. **Holdings:** 5000 books; 8500 bound periodical volumes; 900 Audio-Digest tapes. **Subscriptions:** 450 journals and other serials. **Services:** Interlibrary loan; library not open to the public. **Computerized Information Services:** DIALOG Information Services, MEDLARS, BRS Information Technologies; CD-ROM (MEDLINE); internal databases. **Networks/Consortia:** Member of National Network of Libraries of Medicine - Greater Midwest Region. **Remarks:** FAX: (313)927-7362.

★10802★
Mount Clemens General Hospital - Stuck Medical Library (Med)
1000 Harrington Blvd. Phone: (313)466-8147
Mt. Clemens, MI 48043 Lynne L. Coles, Libn.
Founded: 1956. **Staff:** Prof 1. **Subjects:** Medicine, nursing. **Holdings:** 2900 books; 2000 bound periodical volumes; 1600 audio cassettes; 1050 videotapes; 170 slide/tape sets; 4 VF drawers of pamphlets. **Subscriptions:** 120 journals and other serials. **Services:** Interlibrary loan; copying; library open to the public for reference use only. **Computerized Information Services:** BRS Information Technologies, NLM; DOCLINE (electronic mail service). **Networks/Consortia:** Member of Library Cooperative of Macomb (LCM), Michigan Health Sciences Libraries Association (MHSLA). **Remarks:** FAX: (313)466-8032.

★10803★
Mount Cuba Astronomical Observatory, Inc. - Lambert L. Jackson Memorial Library (Sci-Engr)
Hillside Mill Rd., Greenville
Box 3915 Phone: (302)654-6407
Wilmington, DE 19807 Dr. Harry L. Shipman, Pres./CEO
Founded: 1957. **Staff:** Prof 1; Other 1. **Subjects:** Observational astronomy, astrophysics. **Special Collections:** National Geographic and Mt. Palomar Sky Survey, White Oak Zones; Lick Observatory Sky Atlas. **Holdings:** 1346 books; 1068 bound periodical volumes; 3460 other cataloged items; reprints; pamphlets. **Subscriptions:** 48 journals and other serials. **Services:** Library open to the public by appointment. **Staff:** Mary Williams, Libn.

★10804★
Mount Desert Island Biological Laboratory - Reading Room (Biol Sci)
P.O. Box 35 Phone: (207)288-3605
Salsbury Cove, ME 04672 Martha Farley, Sec.
Subjects: Biology. **Holdings:** Books; reprint collection of laboratory research. **Services:** Interlibrary loan (reproductions of materials only); copying; Room open to the public for reference use only. **Publications:** Bulletin, annual - to members and academic libraries. **Remarks:** FAX: (207)288-2130.

Mount Holly Public Library
See: **Burlington County Lyceum of History and Natural Science** (2374)

★10805★
Mount Ida College - Wadsworth Learning Resource Center - National Center for Death Education (Soc Sci)
777 Dedham St. Phone: (617)969-7000
Newton Centre, MA 02159 Judith Harding, Dir.
Founded: 1984. **Staff:** Prof 1; Other 1. **Subjects:** Thanatology, funeral service, biology, anatomy, religion, psychology, counseling. **Special Collections:** Death and dying; bereavement. **Holdings:** 4000 books; 200 films, kits, audiotapes, and video cassettes. **Subscriptions:** 80 journals and other serials. **Services:** Interlibrary loan; library open to the public. **Networks/Consortia:** Member of NELINET, Inc. **Publications:** Bibliographies.

★10806★
Mount Olive College - Free Will Baptist Historical Collection (Rel-Phil)
Moye Library Phone: (919)658-2502
Mount Olive, NC 28365 Gary Fenton Barefoot, Libn.
Staff: Prof 2; Other 2. **Subjects:** Free Will Baptist history. **Holdings:** 800 books; 1250 bound periodical volumes; 61 manuscript collections; 2000 clippings and brochures; 500 photographs; 100 reels of microfilm, audiotapes, films. **Subscriptions:** 10 journals and other serials. **Services:** Copying; collection open to the public. **Special Indexes:** Card indexes to manuscripts, clippings, photographs, printed obituaries; Index to Free Will Baptist (card). **Remarks:** FAX: (919)658-8934. **Staff:** Pamela R. Wood, Asst.Libn.

★10807★
Mount Olivet Lutheran Church - Library (Rel-Phil)
5025 Knox Ave., S. Phone: (612)926-7651
Minneapolis, MN 55419 Patti Yount, Lib.Adm.
Founded: 1950. **Staff:** Prof 1. **Subjects:** Religion, theology and doctrine, Bible, Lutheran Church history, psychology, family life, children's and juvenile literature, adult fiction. **Special Collections:** Les Kouba wildlife paintings (30). **Holdings:** 7000 books; 180 pictures; 300 cassette tapes; 125 videotapes. **Subscriptions:** 25 journals and other serials. **Services:** Library open to the public.

★10808★
Mount Paran Church of God - Ruth Holt Library (Rel-Phil)
2055 Mount Paran Rd., N.W. Phone: (404)261-0720
Atlanta, GA 30327 Wayne H. Standifer, Libn.
Founded: 1977. **Staff:** Prof 1; Other 1. **Subjects:** Religion, psychology. **Special Collections:** Psychology-Religion (4000 volumes). **Holdings:** 11,000 books; 62 bound periodical volumes; 50 boxes of archival materials. **Subscriptions:** 20 journals and other serials. **Services:** Interlibrary loan; copying; library open to the public. **Computerized Information Services:** Internal database.

★10809★
Mount Pleasant Mental Health Institute - Professional Library (Med)
1200 E. Washington St. Phone: (319)385-7231
Mount Pleasant, IA 52641 Georgia Kay Houseman, Libn.
Founded: 1963. **Staff:** Prof 1. **Subjects:** Psychiatry, nursing, psychology, social work, pharmacology, nutrition, medicine. **Holdings:** 1600 books; 500 periodical volumes. **Subscriptions:** 39 professional journals. **Services:** Interlibrary loan; copying; library open to the public. **Remarks:** Maintained by Iowa State Department of Human Services.

Mount Rainier Natl. Park
See: **U.S. Natl. Park Service** (17755)

Mount Rushmore National Memorial
See: **U.S. Natl. Park Service** (17756)

★10810★
Mount St. Alphonsus Library (Rel-Phil)
Rte. 9 W. Phone: (914)384-6550
Esopus, NY 12429 Joan W. Durand, Dir.
Staff: Prof 1. **Subjects:** Theology, ecclesiastical history, church law, liturgy, Sacred Scripture. **Special Collections:** Redemptoristica (3000 volumes); Wuenschel Collection of Holy Shroud (800 volumes). **Holdings:** 100,000 books; 10,410 bound periodical volumes; 10,000 microforms; 300 audiotapes; 30 units of slides. **Subscriptions:** 500 journals and other serials; 10 newspapers. **Services:** Interlibrary loan; library open to the public by appointment. **Networks/Consortia:** Member of Southeastern New York Library Resources Council (SENYLRC). **Publications:** Handbook.

Mount St. Mary Research Center
See: **Sisters of St. Mary of Namur** (15208)

★10811★
Mount St. Mary's College - Newman Collection (Rel-Phil)
Charles Willard Coe Memorial Library
12001 Chalon Rd. Phone: (310)476-2237
Los Angeles, CA 90049 Claudia Reed, Libn.
Founded: 1960. **Staff:** Prof 5. **Subjects:** Cardinal Newman and the Oxford Movement. **Holdings:** 300 books; microfilm; memorabilia. **Services:** Interlibrary loan; copying; collection open to the public for reference use only. **Automated Operations:** MELVYL, ORION. **Computerized Information Services:** DIALOG Information Services, OCLC. **Remarks:** FAX: (310)476-9296. **Formerly:** Its Newman Seminar Collection. **Staff:** Mary L. Sedgwick, Tech.Serv.Libn.; Ruzica Popovitch Krekic, Pub.Serv.Libn.; Mark Henrich, Circ.Coord.

Mount St. Mary's Seminary of the West
See: **Athenaeum of Ohio - Mount St. Mary's Seminary of the West** (1226)

★10812★
Mount Saint Vincent University - Library (Hum, Bus-Fin)
166 Bedford Hwy. Phone: (902)443-4450
Halifax, NS, Canada B3M 2J6 Mr. L. Bianchini, Univ.Libn.
Founded: 1925. **Staff:** Prof 4; Other 15. **Subjects:** Home economics, business and office administration, public relations, tourism, hospitality management, education, 19th and early 20th century English literature, religious studies, children's literature. **Special Collections:** MacDonald Collection (literature); Gerritsen and Women's History (25,000 microfiche; 600 reels of microfilm). **Holdings:** 120,000 books; 22,000 bound periodical volumes. **Subscriptions:** 993 journals and other serials; 22 newspapers. **Services:** Interlibrary loan; copying; courtesy cards available on request to nonaffiliated users. **Automated Operations:** Computerized cataloging, acquisitions, circulation, and ILL. **Computerized Information Services:** PFDS Online, DIALOG Information Services; Envoy 100, InterNet (electronic mail services). **Publications:** Guide to Women's Studies Resoueces. **Special Catalogs:** Periodical Holdings, updated yearly (book); Canadian Drama Collection; Gerritsen Collection; Women's History Collection. **Special Indexes:** KWOC Index to Government Documents. **Remarks:** FAX: (902)457-3175. Electronic mail address(es): ADMIN/MT.ST.VINCENTUNIV (Envoy 100); BIANCHINUL@WILLOW.MSVU.CA (InterNet). **Staff:** Peter Glenister, Bibliog.Serv.; Terry Paris, Ref.Coll.Dev.; Margaret Kay, Circ.

★10813★
Mount Sinai Hospital - Health Sciences Library (Med)
500 Blue Hills Ave. Phone: (203)286-4617
Hartford, CT 06112 Ruth Carroll, Dir.
Founded: 1948. **Staff:** Prof 1; Other 1.5. **Subjects:** Clinical medicine, nursing, allied health sciences. **Holdings:** 1000 books; 2500 bound periodical volumes; AV programs. **Subscriptions:** 300 journals and other serials. **Services:** Interlibrary loan; copying; SDI; library open to the public for reference use only. **Automated Operations:** Computerized acquisitions, serials, and ILL. **Computerized Information Services:** BRS Information Technologies, NLM. Performs searches on fee basis. **Networks/Consortia:** Member of Connecticut Association of Health Science Libraries (CAHSL), North Atlantic Health Science Libraries (NAHSL). **Publications:** Newsletter, quarterly - for internal distribution only. **Remarks:** FAX: (203)286-4743. **Staff:** Gloria Harrison.

★10814★
Mt. Sinai Hospital - Medical Library (Med)
5th & Reed Sts. Phone: (215)339-3780
Philadelphia, PA 19147 Susan Cleveland, Lib.Dir.
Founded: 1932. **Staff:** Prof 1. **Subjects:** Medicine, nursing. **Holdings:** 3000 books; 3500 bound periodical volumes. **Subscriptions:** 150 journals and other serials. **Services:** Interlibrary loan; library not open to the public. **Computerized Information Services:** MEDLARS. **Formerly:** Albert Einstein Medical Center - Mt. Sinai-Daroff Division.

★10815★
Mount Sinai Hospital - Sidney Liswood Library (Med)
600 University Ave. Phone: (416)586-4614
Toronto, ON, Canada M5G 1X5 Linda Devore, Dir., Lib.Serv.
Founded: 1967. **Staff:** Prof 1; Other 3. **Subjects:** Health sciences. **Holdings:** 2000 books. **Subscriptions:** 400 serials. **Services:** Interlibrary loan; copying; library open to the public for reference use only. **Computerized Information Services:** MEDLARS, DIALOG Information Services; CD-ROM (MEDLINE). **Networks/Consortia:** Member of Ontario Hospital Libraries Association (OHLA), Canadian Health Libraries Association.

★10816★
Mount Sinai Hospital Medical Center - Lewison Memorial Library (Med)
California Ave. at 15th St. Phone: (312)542-2000
Chicago, IL 60608 Emily Sobkowiak, Med./Nurs.Libn.
Founded: 1942. **Staff:** Prof 1; Other 1. **Subjects:** Medicine, surgery, nursing. **Holdings:** 7500 books; 7500 bound periodical volumes. **Subscriptions:** 350 journals and other serials. **Services:** Interlibrary loan; library not open to the public. **Computerized Information Services:** MEDLINE. **Networks/Consortia:** Member of Illinois Health Libraries Consortium, ILLINET, Chicago Library System.

Mt. Sinai Medical Center - Medical Library
See: **Laurelwood Hosptial - Library** (8976)

★10817★
Mount Sinai Medical Center of Cleveland - George H. Hays Memorial Library (Med)
One Mount Sinai Dr. Phone: (216)421-5615
Cleveland, OH 44106-4198 Pamela Alderman, Dir.
Founded: 1961. **Staff:** Prof 3; Other 4. **Subjects:** Medicine, nursing, hospital administration, allied health sciences. **Special Collections:** Staff Reprint Collection; AV collection. **Holdings:** 6000 books; 3000 bound periodical volumes. **Subscriptions:** 352 journals and other serials. **Services:** Interlibrary loan; copying; SDI; library open to the public on fee basis. **Computerized Information Services:** DIALOG Information Services, MEDLINE, STN International, NLM, BRS Information Technologies; DOCLINE (electronic mail service). Performs searches on fee basis. **Remarks:** FAX: (216)421-6198. **Staff:** Rosa Raskin, Asst.Dir.

★10818★
Mount Sinai Medical Center of Greater Miami - Medical Library (Med)
4300 Alton Rd. Phone: (305)674-2840
Miami Beach, FL 33140 Mildred Karukin, Mgr.
Founded: 1950. **Staff:** Prof 2; Other 3. **Subjects:** Medicine, nursing, hospital administration, allied health sciences. **Holdings:** 5000 books; 9000 bound periodical volumes; 400 audiotapes; 200 videotapes; 3000 slides. **Subscriptions:** 450 journals and other serials. **Services:** Interlibrary loan; copying; SDI; library use restricted to physicians, staff, and students of affiliated programs. **Automated Operations:** Computerized cataloging. **Computerized Information Services:** BRS Information Technologies, OCLC, NLM; CD-ROM. **Networks/Consortia:** Member of Miami Health Sciences Library Consortium (MHSLC). **Remarks:** FAX: (305)674-2843.

★10819★
Mount Sinai School of Medicine of City University of New York - Gustave L. & Janet W. Levy Library (Med)
One Gustave L. Levy Place, Box 1102 Phone: (212)241-7793
New York, NY 10029-6574 Lynn Kasner Morgan, Dir.
Founded: 1968. **Staff:** Prof 15; Other 27. **Subjects:** Clinical medicine, nursing, basic sciences. **Holdings:** 49,015 books; 104,236 bound periodical volumes; 2620 AV programs; 690 lateral files of archival materials. **Subscriptions:** 2625 journals and other serials. **Services:** Interlibrary loan; library not open to the public; subscription services for health practitioners and organizations. **Automated Operations:** Computerized public access catalog, cataloging, serials, circulation, acquisitions,and Interlibrary loan. **Computerized Information Services:** WILSONLINE, BRS Information Technologies, DIALOG Information Services, OCLC, ORBIT Search Service, NLM, STN International; CD-ROMs. **Networks/Consortia:** Member of Medical Library Center of New York (MLCNY), National Network of Libraries of Medicine - Middle Atlantic Region, New York Metropolitan Reference and Research Library Agency, Health Sciences Consortium. **Publications:** Faculty Bibliography, annual - to faculty and libraries and on request; Levy Library News, bimonthly. **Remarks:** FAX: (212)831-2625. **Staff:** Dorothy Hill, Coll.Dev.; Jeanine McAdam, Ref.Libn.; Lois O'Neill, Ref.Libn.; Patricia Sanles, Ref./AV Libn.; Jean Sullivant, Asst.Dir., Info.Serv.; Brett Singer, Media Rsrc.Spec.; James E. Raper, Jr., Asst.Dir., Tech.; Merril Schindler, Asst.Dir. for Sys.; Henry Stickell, Circ.; Barbara Niss, Med.Ctr.Archv.; Celia Soto, ILL; Florinda Coral, Cat.; Martin Eisenschmied, Sch. Network Mgr.

★10820★
Mount Sinai Services - Elmhurst Hospital Center - Medical Library (Med)
79-01 Broadway Phone: (718)830-1538
Elmhurst, NY 11373 Stacey Saley, Chf.Med.Libn.
Staff: Prof 2; Other 3. **Subjects:** Basic sciences, health sciences. **Holdings:** 8000 books; 13,500 bound periodical volumes; pamphlets; AV programs. **Subscriptions:** 300 journals and other serials. **Services:** Interlibrary loan; copying; library open to the public by appointment. **Automated Operations:** Computerized ILL. **Computerized Information Services:** Online systems. **Networks/Consortia:** Member of Medical Library Center of New York (MLCNY), New York Metropolitan Reference and Research Library Agency. **Publications:** Acquisitions list, quarterly. **Staff:** Claudia Laseur.

★10821★
Mount Union College - Sturgeon Music Library (Mus)
Cope Music Hall Phone: (216)823-3206
Alliance, OH 44601 Suzanne Z. Moushey, Mus.Libn.
Founded: 1964. **Staff:** Prof 1; Other 12. **Subjects:** Music history and theory, vocal methods, instrumental methods, music education, musical instruments, vocal music, instrumental music, piano pedagogy. **Special Collections:** Hymnal collection; Archives des Maitres de L'Orgue. **Holdings:** 1100 books; 10,800 scores; 5800 recordings; complete bound works of Bach, Beethoven, Brahms, Chopin, Schubert, Mozart, Schuetz, Schoenberg, Hindemith. **Subscriptions:** 64 journals and other serials. **Services:** Library open to the public with restrictions. **Computerized Information Services:** OCLC. **Special Indexes:** Art Song Index (access to poets of art songs in the recording collection).

★10822★
Mount Vernon Hospital - Library and Information Services (Med)
12 N. 7th Ave. Phone: (914)664-8000
Mount Vernon, NY 10550 Joan L. Riggs, Lib.Coord.
Staff: 1. **Subjects:** Health sciences, medicine, nursing. **Holdings:** 3059 books; 977 bound periodical volumes; 12 VF drawers; 394 AV programs. **Subscriptions:** 129 journals and other serials. **Services:** Interlibrary loan (limited); copying; SDI; library open to the public with restrictions. **Computerized Information Services:** NLM. **Networks/Consortia:** Member of Health Information Libraries of Westchester (HILOW), New York Metropolitan Reference and Research Library Agency.

★10823★
Mount Vernon Ladies' Association of the Union - Research and Reference Library (Hist)
Mount Vernon, VA 22121 Phone: (703)780-2000
Barbara McMillan, Libn.
Founded: 1853. **Staff:** Prof 3. **Subjects:** Domestic life of George and Martha Washington; history of Mount Vernon, 1674 to present; history of the

Mount Vernon Ladies' Association of the Union; 18th century plantation history, social life, customs; historic preservation. **Special Collections:** Manuscript collection; George Washington papers (500); Martha Washington papers; Washington eulogies; early views of Mount Vernon; Mansion Library (books owned by George Washington or duplicates). **Holdings:** 12,000 books; 400 bound periodical volumes; 15,000 other cataloged items. **Subscriptions:** 58 journals and other serials; 5 newspapers. **Services:** Copying; library open to the public by appointment to qualified researchers. **Publications:** Annual Report. **Staff:** John P. Riley, Res.Asst./ Archv.

★10824★
Mount Vernon Place United Methodist Church - Dessie M. Hallett Library (Rel-Phil)
900 Massachusetts Ave., N.W. Phone: (202)347-9620
Washington, DC 20001 Martha Gammon, Libn.
Staff: 2. **Subjects:** Religion, psychology, family life, Bible, fiction, biography. **Special Collections:** Large print devotionals (12). **Holdings:** 1600 books; clippings; pamphlets. **Subscriptions:** 17 journals and other serials. **Services:** Library open to the public for reference use only.

★10825★
Mount Washington Observatory - Library (Sci-Engr)
1 Washington St. Phone: (603)466-3388
Gorham, NH 03581 Guy Gosselin, Dir.
Staff: Prof 1; Other 2. **Subjects:** Icing, atmospheric electricity, atmospheric physics, White Mountain history (science and fiction). **Holdings:** 1000 books; maps; prints; stereographs; photographs; 30 feet of bound and unbound scientific papers; guidebooks; hiking material. **Services:** Copying; library open to the public by appointment. **Staff:** Peter Crane, Musm.Cur.

Mount Wilson & Las Campanas Observatories
See: **Carnegie Institution of Washington - Observatories - Library** (3074)

★10826★
Mount Zion Hebrew Congregation - Temple Library (Rel-Phil)
1300 Summit Ave. Phone: (612)698-3881
St. Paul, MN 55105 Robert A. Epstein, Libn.
Founded: 1929. **Staff:** Prof 1. **Subjects:** Jews - history, religion, literature, biography, philosophy; Israel. **Special Collections:** Clara Margolis Collection (Jewish feminism; 140 titles); children's collection (950 titles); Rabbi Harry Sterling Margolis Collection (memorial collection on 20th century American Judaism; 1000 titles). **Holdings:** 7250 books; 125 phonograph records; 50 cassette tapes; 75 videotapes. **Subscriptions:** 20 journals and other serials. **Services:** Copying; library open to the public with restrictions. **Remarks:** FAX: (612)698-4780.

★10827★
Mountain Area Health Education Center - Information & Media Services (Med)
501 Biltmore Ave. Phone: (704)257-4444
Asheville, NC 28801-4686 Patricia L. Thibodeau, Dir.
Staff: Prof 4; Other 6. **Subjects:** Health sciences, health care administration. **Holdings:** 6600 books; 10,500 bound and unbound periodicals; 911 AV programs; slides; filmstrips; videotapes. **Subscriptions:** 541 journals and other serials. **Services:** Interlibrary loan; copying; services open to the public for reference use only. **Automated Operations:** Computerized cataloging. **Computerized Information Services:** BRS Information Technologies, NLM; CD-ROM; InterNet (electronic mail service). Performs searches on fee basis. **Networks/Consortia:** Member of North Carolina Area Health Education Centers Program Library and Information Services Network. **Remarks:** FAX: (704)258-2097. Electronic mail address(es): MAHEC@UNCECS.EDU (InterNet). **Staff:** Linda Butson, Assoc.Dir.; Marla Norville, Media Coord.; Elizabeth Robinson, Pub.Serv.Coord.

★10828★
Mountain States Employers Council - Information Center (Bus-Fin)
1790 Logan St.
Box 539 Phone: (303)839-5177
Denver, CO 80201 Mariwayne Scully, Info.Ctr.Mgr.
Staff: Prof 1; Other 1. **Subjects:** Labor law, human resource management, industrial relations. **Holdings:** 10,000 volumes. **Subscriptions:** 85 journals and other serials. **Services:** Copying (limited); open to special students; center mainly serves member companies. **Automated Operations:** Computerized cataloging and literature searching. **Computerized Information Services:** DIALOG Information Services. **Remarks:** FAX: (303)861-4403.

★10829★
Mountain View Bible College - Library (Rel-Phil)
Box 190 Phone: (403)335-3337
Didsbury, AB, Canada T0M 0W0 Jeanine White, Lib.Ck.
Staff: 1. **Subjects:** Bible, Christian education, missions, theology, church history. **Holdings:** 12,000 books. **Subscriptions:** 85 journals and other serials. **Services:** Copying; library open to ministers and laymen. **Automated Operations:** Computerized cataloging.

★10830★
Mountaineering Foundation of Chicago, Inc. - John Speck Memorial Library (Rec)
739 Forest Ave. Phone: (708)469-3443
Glen Ellyn, IL 60137 George Pokorny, Dir.
Founded: 1950. **Staff:** 1. **Subjects:** Mountaineering expeditions, techniques, safety; mountain areas of the world; mountaineering and climbing guidebooks; natural history and geology; skiing; mountaineering fiction; conservation; glaciology; mountain flora. **Holdings:** 2000 books; 500 bound periodical volumes; 200 pamphlets. **Subscriptions:** 7 journals and other serials. **Services:** Interlibrary loan; copying; library available to other clubs for research purposes. **Computerized Information Services:** Internal database. **Special Catalogs:** Library catalog published for members and other clubs.

★10831★
Mountainside Hospital - Assmann Health Sciences Library (Med)
Bay & Highland Aves. Phone: (201)429-6240
Montclair, NJ 07042 Patricia Regenberg, Dir.
Founded: 1927. **Staff:** Prof 1; Other 1. **Subjects:** Clinical medicine. **Holdings:** 3000 books; 12,000 bound periodical volumes. **Subscriptions:** 324 journals and other serials. **Services:** Interlibrary loan; copying; SDI; library open to the public. **Computerized Information Services:** NLM, DIALOG Information Services, BRS Information Technologies. Performs searches on fee basis. **Networks/Consortia:** Member of Cosmopolitan Biomedical Library Consortium (CBLC), Essex Hudson Regional Library Cooperative, Health Sciences Library Association of New Jersey (HSLANJ), BHSL. **Publications:** Selected Acquisitions, quarterly. **Remarks:** FAX: (201)680-7850.

★10832★
Mountainside Hospital - School of Nursing Library (Med)
Bay & Highland Aves. Phone: (201)429-6063
Montclair, NJ 07042 Juliette Ratner, Libn.
Founded: 1921. **Staff:** Prof 1. **Subjects:** Nursing, allied health sciences. **Special Collections:** History of nursing. **Holdings:** 1850 books; 7 bound periodical volumes. **Subscriptions:** 130 journals and other serials. **Services:** Interlibrary loan; library open to the public by appointment. **Computerized Information Services:** BRS Information Technologies, MEDLINE.

Movie Memorabilia Stills
See: **Memory Shop, Inc.** (10057)

★10833★
Movie Star News - Photograph Collection (Aud-Vis, Theater)
134 W. 18th St. Phone: (212)620-8160
New York, NY 10011 Paula Klaw Kramer, Pres.
Founded: 1937. **Staff:** Prof 2; Other 2. **Subjects:** Movie stars. **Special Collections:** Movie stills, 1920-1981; pressbooks; movie magazines; lobby cards; movie posters; Damsels in Distress (Hollywood). **Holdings:** Ten million movie star photographs, 1918-1987. **Services:** Collection open to the public; photographs leased for reproduction and for sale by mail order. **Remarks:** FAX: (212)727-0634.

★10834★
Mozambique - Arquivo Historico de Mocambique (Hist)
Caixa Postal 2033
Maputo, Mozambique Phone: 421177
Founded: 1934. **Staff:** Prof 34; Other 19. **Subjects:** History, travels and exploration, ethnography, European expansion. **Special Collections:** Reports of cultural and social associations, public institutions, governmental offices, and others. **Holdings:** 17,000 books; 1200 titles of bound periodical volumes; 70,000 microfiche; sound materials; 700 posters; 2000 maps and charts. **Subscriptions:** 37 journals and other serials; 2 newspapers. **Services:** Copying; archive open to persons with an institutional credential. **Automated Operations:** PORBASE 3. **Publications:** Documents: Studies and Workshop (series published in journal ARQUIVO; 1987 to present). **Remarks:** Alternate telephone number(s): 421178.

★10835★
MPR Associates, Inc. - Technical Library (Sci-Engr)
1050 Connecticut Ave., N.W., Suite 400 Phone: (202)659-2320
Washington, DC 20036 Alice P. McNamara, Libn.
Founded: 1964. **Staff:** Prof 2; Other 1. **Subjects:** Engineering - nuclear and fossil electric generation, marine. **Holdings:** 85,000 books, technical reports, conference papers, theses, speeches, abstracts, codes and standards, microfiche. **Subscriptions:** 120 journals and other serials. **Services:** Interlibrary loan (limited); library not open to the public. **Computerized Information Services:** DIALOG Information Services, DTIC, NRC, NPEars, ORBIT Search Service. **Publications:** Library Bulletin, monthly. **Remarks:** FAX: (202)659-0358. **Staff:** Mary Fisch, Libn.

★10836★
MPR Teltech Ltd. - Information Resources Centre (Info Sci)
8999 Nelson Way Phone: (604)293-5381
Burnaby, BC, Canada V5A 4B5 Patrice A. Hall, Res.Libn.
Founded: 1960. **Staff:** Prof 1; Other 1. **Subjects:** Telecommunication, data communication, electronics engineering. **Special Collections:** Military/industry standards. **Holdings:** 1200 volumes. **Subscriptions:** 250 journals and other serials. **Services:** Interlibrary loan; center not open to the public. **Computerized Information Services:** DIALOG Information Services, CAN/OLE; Envoy 100, SprintMail (electronic mail services). **Remarks:** FAX: (604)293-5787. Electronic mail address(es): MPR.LIB (Envoy 100); P.A.HALL (SprintMail).

★10837★
MRA Laboratories, Inc./ - Materials Research and Analysis - Information Services (Sci-Engr)
96 Marshall St. Phone: (413)664-4524
North Adams, MA 01247-2411 Jill Coghlan, Res.Libn.
Founded: 1944. **Staff:** Prof 1. **Subjects:** Electronics, electronic ceramics, chemistry, physics, materials sciences, engineering. **Holdings:** 6500 books; 12,300 bound periodical volumes (300 titles); 10 VF drawers of internal reports; government documents on microfiche. **Subscriptions:** 140 journals and other serials. **Services:** Interlibrary loan; library open to the public for reference use only upon request. **Computerized Information Services:** DIALOG Information Services, STN International, ORBIT Search Service. **Remarks:** FAX: (413)663-5535.

★10838★
MRC Bearings Inc. - Research & Development Technical Library (Sci-Engr)
402 Chandler St. Phone: (716)661-2812
Jamestown, NY 14701 Tony Galbato, Supv., Proj.Engr.
Founded: 1957. **Staff:** 2. **Subjects:** Ball bearings, roller bearings, lubrication, high temperature, cryogenic temperature, gas bearings, high vacuum, dry film, outer space applications. **Holdings:** 200 books; 2000 published articles; technical reports and patents. **Subscriptions:** 45 journals and other serials. **Services:** Library not open to the public.

MSA Research Corporation
See: **Mine Safety Appliances Company - MSA Research Corporation** (10436)

★10839★
MSE, Inc. - CDIF Technical Library (Sci-Engr)
Box 3767 Phone: (406)494-7100
Butte, MT 59702 Pamela Cunningham, Libn.
Staff: 1. **Subjects:** Magnetohydrodynamics. **Holdings:** 1000 books; 2500 technical reports; 500 manufacturing standards and specifications. **Subscriptions:** 33 journals and other serials. **Services:** Interlibrary loan; library not open to the public. **Computerized Information Services:** DIALOG Information Services. **Remarks:** CDIF is an acronym for Component Development and Integration Facility. **Remarks:** FAX: (406)494-7230.

★10840★
MSE, Inc. - Library (Sci-Engr)
220 N. Alaska Phone: (406)723-8213
Butte, MT 59701 Pamela Cunningham, Libn.
Staff: 1. **Subjects:** Magnetohydrodynamics, alternative technology, environmental concerns, engineering, mineral processing. **Holdings:** 500 books; microfiche. **Subscriptions:** 128 journals and other serials. **Services:** Library not open to the public. **Remarks:** FAX: (406)723-8328. **Formerly:** Multitech - Library.

★10841★
MTS Systems Corporation - Information Services (Sci-Engr)
14000 Technology Dr. Phone: (612)937-4306
Eden Prairie, MN 55344 Kathleen M. Warner, Info.Serv.Supv.
Founded: 1967. **Staff:** Prof 2; Other 1. **Subjects:** Electronics, materials, vehicle testing, hydraulics, fatigue, ceramics and composite materials, business management. **Holdings:** 4000 books; 1000 pamphlets, documents, reports; 10 drawers of engineering standards. **Subscriptions:** 500 journals and other serials. **Services:** Interlibrary loan; copying; SDI. **Automated Operations:** Computerized cataloging and serials. **Computerized Information Services:** DIALOG Information Services, PFDS Online. Performs searches on fee basis. **Publications:** FYI, monthly - for internal distribution only. **Remarks:** FAX: (612)937-4515. **Formerly:** Located in Minneapolis, MN. **Staff:** Melissa Brown, Ref.Libn.

H.H. Mu Library
See: **Royal Ontario Museum - H.H. Mu Library** (14130)

Seeley G. Mudd Library
See: **Yale University** (20728)

Seeley G. Mudd Library for Science and Engineering
See: **Northwestern University** (12088)

Seeley G. Mudd Science Library
See: **Claremont McKenna College** (3756)

Mudge Rare Book Library
See: **Dallas Museum of Natural History** (4556)

★10842★
Mudge Rose Guthrie Alexander & Ferdon - Library (Law)
180 Maiden Lane Phone: (212)510-7883
New York, NY 10038 Cristina Alvy, Libn.
Subjects: Law. **Holdings:** 30,000 volumes. **Services:** Library not open to the public. **Remarks:** FAX: (212)480-3828.

Herman Muehlstein Rare Book Collection
See: **University of Akron** (18155)

Mueller Health Sciences Library
See: **Lancaster General Hospital** (8919)

James I. Mueller Ceramic Library
See: **American Ceramic Society - James I. Mueller Ceramic Library** (519)

Mugar Memorial Library
See: **Boston University - Mugar Memorial Library** (2014)

Muhlenberg College - John A.W. Haas Library
See: **Cedar Crest and Muhlenberg College Libraries** (3183)

★10843★
Muhlenberg Hospital Center - Medical Library (Med)
Schoenersville Rd. Phone: (215)861-2237
Bethlehem, PA 18017 Carole A. Mazzeo, Med.Libn.
Staff: Prof 1. **Subjects:** Medicine, nursing, dentistry. **Holdings:** 920 books; unbound periodicals. **Subscriptions:** 105 journals and other serials. **Services:** Interlibrary loan; copying; library open to the public with restrictions. **Automated Operations:** Computerized cataloging. **Computerized Information Services:** MEDLINE, MEDLARS, DIALOG Information Services.

★10844★
Muhlenberg Regional Medical Center - E. Gordon Glass, M.D., Memorial Library (Med)
Park Ave. & Randolph Rd. Phone: (201)668-2005
Plainfield, NJ 07061 Lana Strazhnik, Libn.
Founded: 1955. **Staff:** Prof 1; Other 2. **Subjects:** Medicine, nursing, hospital management. **Holdings:** 6050 books; 3000 bound periodical volumes. **Subscriptions:** 180 journals and other serials. **Services:** Interlibrary loan; copying; library open to the public. **Computerized Information Services:** MEDLINE. **Remarks:** FAX: (201)753-3723.

★10845★
John Muir Medical Center - Medical Library (Med)
1601 Ygnacio Valley Rd. Phone: (510)939-3000
Walnut Creek, CA 94598 Helen M. Reyes, Med.Libn.
Founded: 1967. **Staff:** Prof 1; Other 6. **Subjects:** Health sciences, medicine, dentistry, nursing, pharmacy, hospital administration, psychiatry, allied health sciences. **Holdings:** 3280 books; 5200 bound periodical volumes. **Subscriptions:** 380 journals and other serials. **Services:** Interlibrary loan; copying; SDI; library open to qualified health science personnel. **Computerized Information Services:** DIALOG Information Services, MEDLARS. **Networks/Consortia:** Member of National Network of Libraries of Medicine - Pacific Northwest Region, Northern California and Nevada Medical Library Group (NCNMLG), Bay Area Library and Information System (BALIS). **Publications:** New Acquisitions, monthly; Serials Titles List; Infoline. **Remarks:** Alternate telephone number(s): 947-3237. FAX: (510)947-3237. **Staff:** Christine Gill.

John Muir National Historic Site
See: **U.S. Natl. Park Service** (17737)

Mulcahy Science Library
See: **Fordham University** (5969)

Raymon H. Mulford Library
See: **Medical College of Ohio at Toledo** (9996)

John Mullan and Mullan Road Information Center
See: **Mineral County Museum & Historical Society - Library** (10438)

Multilingual Biblioservice
See: **Canada - National Library of Canada** (2808)

Multitech - Library
See: **MSE, Inc. - Library** (10840)

★10846★
Multnomah County Library - Art and Music Department (Art, Mus)
801 S.W. Tenth Ave. Phone: (503)248-5281
Portland, OR 97205 Ella Seely, Hum.Dept.Mgr.
Founded: 1936. **Staff:** Prof 5; Other 11. **Subjects:** Antiques, architecture, costume, dance, fine arts, handicrafts, interior decorating, moving pictures, music, photography. **Holdings:** 55,000 volumes; 32,500 pieces of sheet music and scores; 27,722 phonograph records; 7750 cassette tapes; 6300 compact discs; 10,000 color slides; 2.3 million picture clippings. **Services:** Interlibrary loan; copying. **Automated Operations:** Computerized circulation. **Computerized Information Services:** DIALOG Information Services, WILSONLINE. Performs searches on fee basis. **Networks/Consortia:** Member of Western Library Network (WLN). **Special Catalogs:** Audio Collection catalog (card); Art & Music Book catalog (card); Sheet music catalog (card). **Special Indexes:** Song index to library's song books (card); picture file index; slide collection index; film index; Music Program Index and Concert File, through 1972. **Remarks:** FAX: (503)221-7723. **Staff:** Barbara Rhyne, Sr.Libn., Mus.; Barbara Padden, Ref.Libn.; Peter Oswald, Ref.Libn.; Catherine Ronconi, Ref.Libn.; Susan Egan, Sect.Supv.

★10847★
Multnomah County Library - Construction Library (Plan)
801 S.W. Tenth Ave. Phone: (503)248-5123
Portland, OR 97205 Jim Takita
Founded: 1987. **Staff:** Prof 1. **Subjects:** Building - codes, materials, industry standards. **Holdings:** 650 books; 24 videocassettes; 208 audiocassettes. **Services:** Interlibrary loan; library open to the public. **Computerized Information Services:** DIALOG Information Services. **Remarks:** FAX: (503)248-5226.

★10848★
Multnomah County Library - Federal Government Procurement Center (Bus-Fin)
801 S.W. Tenth Ave. Phone: (503)248-5123
Portland, OR 97225 Wanda Snyder, Libn.
Founded: 1986. **Staff:** Prof 1. **Subjects:** Standards - military, federal, industrial. **Holdings:** 100 books; 650 cartridges of microfilm; federal government commodity lists. **Services:** Interlibrary loan; SDI. **Computerized Information Services:** DIALOG Information Services. **Remarks:** FAX: (503)248-5226.

★10849★
Multnomah County Library - Literature and History Department (Hum)
801 S.W. Tenth Ave. Phone: (503)221-9488
Portland, OR 97205 Ella Seely, Hum.Dept.Mgr.
Staff: Prof 9; Other 3. **Subjects:** Philosophy, psychology, religion, foreign languages, theater, literature, literary criticism, geography, library science, travel, history, biography, general works, genealogy, microcomputers. **Holdings:** 194,000 volumes; 59,965 maps; 4000 language cassettes; 10 drawers of genealogy microfiche. **Services:** Interlibrary loan; copying. **Automated Operations:** Computerized public access catalog and circulation. **Computerized Information Services:** DIALOG Information Services, WILSONLINE, OCLC. Performs searches on fee basis. Contact Person: Deanna Cecotti. **Networks/Consortia:** Member of Western Library Network (WLN). **Special Indexes:** Genealogy file; Fugitive Information File (both on cards); LINC (Local Information Connection; online); Oregonian newspaper index (1854-1987 on cards, 1988 to present online). **Staff:** Janet Irwin, Ref.Libn., Automated Local Files; Grace Cushing, Ref.Libn.; Michael Hubbard, Ref.Libn.; Ruth Pollock, Ref.Libn.; Joan Zornman, Ref.Libn.; Jane Salisbury, Ref.Libn.

★10850★
Multnomah County Library - Oregon Collection (Hist)
801 S.W. Tenth Ave. Phone: (503)248-5123
Portland, OR 97205 Ella Seely, Hum.Dept.Mgr.
Founded: 1864. **Staff:** Prof 1. **Subjects:** Oregon, the Oregon Territory, early northwest. **Special Collections:** Oregon Collection (17,000 book, record, and video titles). **Holdings:** Books; documents; serials; bound periodicals; maps; films; music. **Subscriptions:** 250 journals and other serials; 50 newspapers. **Services:** Interlibrary loan (copying only); copying; collection open to the public for reference use only with restricted access to the John Wilson Room. **Automated Operations:** Computerized public access catalog. **Computerized Information Services:** DIALOG Information Services, WILSONLINE, LOGIN; LINC (internal database). **Special Catalogs:** Oregon Bibliography (file of materials on Portland, Oregon, and the Northwest). **Special Indexes:** Newspaper index of articles in Portland newspapers pertaining to Oregon and Oregonians (online). **Remarks:** FAX: (503)248-5226.

★10851★
Multnomah County Library - Pacific Rim Business Information Service (Bus-Fin)
801 S.W. Tenth Ave. Phone: (503)248-5123
Portland, OR 97205 Jim Takita, Libn.
Founded: 1987. **Staff:** Prof 1. **Subjects:** Commerce and trade. **Holdings:** 600 volumes. **Subscriptions:** 25 journals and other serials. **Services:** Interlibrary loan; copying; collection open to the public. **Remarks:** FAX: (503)248-5226.

★10852★
Multnomah County Library - Science and Business Department (Sci-Engr, Soc Sci, Bus-Fin)
801 S.W. Tenth Ave. Phone: (503)243-5123
Portland, OR 97205 Thomas R. Olson, Sect.Mgr.
Founded: 1864. **Staff:** Prof 11; Other 6. **Subjects:** Business, science, technology, social sciences, education. **Special Collections:** Thomas Newton

Cook Rose Library; Jesse Currey Memorial Rose Collection (811 volumes). **Holdings:** Books; federal and state document depository. **Services:** Interlibrary loan; copying; department open to the public. **Automated Operations:** Computerized public access catalog. **Computerized Information Services:** DIALOG Information Services, WILSONLINE, LOGIN. Performs searches on fee basis. **Networks/Consortia:** Member of Western Library Network (WLN). **Special Indexes:** Local Firms File (card). **Remarks:** FAX: (503)248-5226.

★10853★
Multnomah County Library - Science and Business Section - Grants Information Center (Bus-Fin)
801 S.W. Tenth Ave. Phone: (503)248-5123
Portland, OR 97205 Margaret Eisemann, Libn.
Founded: 1972. **Staff:** 1. **Subjects:** Grants. **Special Collections:** Sources on foundation grants, federal grants, corporate philanthropy; regional depository of Foundation Center, New York; foundation annual reports; Internal Revenue Service reports on Oregon foundations. **Holdings:** 335 books; 100 microfiche; 4000 aperture cards; periodicals; newsletters. **Subscriptions:** 8 journals and other serials; 2 newspapers. **Services:** Interlibrary loan; copying; center open to the public. **Computerized Information Services:** DIALOG Information Services, WILSONLINE. Performs searches on fee basis. **Publications:** Foundations and Grants: Source of Information in the Library; Foundation & Corporate Philanthropy: A Pathfinder. **Remarks:** FAX: (503)248-5226.

★10854★
Multnomah County School District No. 1 - Records Management Office (Educ)
531 S.E. 14th Ave. Phone: (503)280-5840
Portland, OR 97214 Christine Blackburn, Rec.Mgr.
Founded: 1979. **Staff:** Prof 2; Other 2. **Subjects:** School district history, 1856 to present. **Holdings:** 4500 cubic feet of inactive district records; 150 cubic feet of Portland Public Schools archival materials; 10 cubic feet of microfilm of permanent records, including minutes, class lists, annual reports, censuses, registration records. **Services:** Copying; office open to the public with restrictions. **Computerized Information Services:** Internal databases. **Remarks:** FAX: (503)280-6468. **Staff:** D. Evans, Archv.

★10855★
Multnomah Law Library (Law)
Court House Phone: (503)248-3394
Portland, OR 97204 Jacquelyn J. Jurkins, Law Libn.
Founded: 1890. **Staff:** Prof 3; Other 4. **Subjects:** Law. **Holdings:** 200,000 volumes. **Services:** Copying; library open to the public for reference use only. **Computerized Information Services:** WESTLAW. **Remarks:** FAX: (503)248-3395.

★10856★
Multnomah School of the Bible - John and Mary Mitchell Library (Rel-Phil)
8435 N.E. Glisan St. Phone: (503)255-0332
Portland, OR 97220 James F. Scott, Dir.
Founded: 1936. **Staff:** Prof 2; Other 3. **Subjects:** Bible, doctrine, missions, Christian education, New Testament Greek, journalism, music, women's ministries, pastoral ministries. **Holdings:** 51,371 books; 3209 bound periodical volumes; 7322 AV programs; 7440 microforms. **Subscriptions:** 522 journals and other serials. **Services:** Interlibrary loan; copying; library open to the public with restrictions. **Automated Operations:** Computerized cataloging. **Networks/Consortia:** Member of OCLC Pacific Network. **Staff:** Susan Kelly, Asst.Libn.

★10857★
Munchner Stadtbibliothek - Juristische Bibliothek (Law)
Rathaus Zi 367 Phone: 89 23392709
W-8000 Munich 2, Germany Siegfried Mursch, Chf.Libn.
Founded: 1934. **Staff:** Prof 3; Other 1. **Subjects:** Law - German, constitutional, public, administrative. **Holdings:** 45,125 books; 21,640 bound periodical volumes; 8 CD-ROMs. **Subscriptions:** 225 journals and other serials; 6 newspapers. **Services:** Interlibrary loan; copying; library open to the public for reference use only. **Publications:** Acquisition lists; periodical lists; loose-leaf list.

★10858★
Muncy Historical Society and Museum of History - Historical Library (Hist)
Muncy Public Library
108 S. Main St. Phone: (717)546-5014
Muncy, PA 17756 Mary Tennant, Libn.
Founded: 1936. **Staff:** 2. **Subjects:** Local history. **Special Collections:** Samuel Wallis Papers (10,000 documents on microfilm). **Holdings:** 1000 books. **Services:** Copying; collections may be consulted by appointment.

Mundelein Seminary
See: **University of St. Mary of the Lake - Mundelein Seminary** (19287)

Karl E. Mundt Library
See: **Dakota State University** (4529)

Edith Munger Library
See: **Michigan Audubon Society** (10282)

★10859★
Munger, Tolles & Olson - Library (Law)
355 S. Grand Ave., 35th Fl. Phone: (213)683-9100
Los Angeles, CA 90071-1560 Helen Kim, Libn.
Founded: 1963. **Staff:** 2. **Subjects:** Law. **Holdings:** 11,500 books; 500 bound periodical volumes. **Subscriptions:** 40 journals and other serials; 10 newspapers. **Services:** Library not open to the public. **Computerized Information Services:** LEXIS, WESTLAW, DIALOG Information Services, VU/TEXT Information Services, Dow Jones News/Retrieval, Information America, Maxwell Macmillan Taxes Online, LEGI-SLATE. **Remarks:** FAX: (213)687-3702. Telex: 677574.

★10860★
Municipal Art Society of New York - Information Exchange (Plan)
457 Madison Ave. Phone: (212)980-1297
New York, NY 10022 Ann Anielewski, Info.Exch.
Founded: 1978. **Staff:** Prof 1. **Subjects:** New York City - built environment, architecture, planning, zoning, parks, open spaces. **Holdings:** 1100 books; 2500 organizational files; 1500 subject files. **Subscriptions:** 200 journals and other serials. **Services:** Copying (limited); SDI; exchange open to the public by appointment. **Remarks:** Alternate telephone number(s): (212)935-3960. FAX: (212)753-1816.

★10861★
Municipal Association of South Carolina - Library and Reference Center (Soc Sci)
P.O. Box 12109 Phone: (803)799-9574
Columbia, SC 29211 Mary Fede, Staff Assoc.
Founded: 1975. **Staff:** 1. **Subjects:** Finance, municipal government administration, public policy. **Special Collections:** Code of ordinances; association publications. **Holdings:** Figures not available. **Subscriptions:** 204 journals and other serials. **Services:** Interlibrary loan; copying; library open to the public. **Publications:** Directory; Compensation Study; Business License Handbook; Election Handbook; Municipal Officials Handbook; Utility Rate Survey. **Remarks:** FAX: (803)799-9520.

★10862★
Municipal Police Training Council - Law Enforcement Resource Center (Soc Sci)
285 Preston Ave.
Meriden, CT 06450-4891
Founded: 1972. **Subjects:** Police science and administration, criminal investigation, Connecticut law and penal codes, criminology, constitutional law. **Special Collections:** Law reference library (900 volumes). **Holdings:** 2000 books; 5 VF drawers of clippings, reports, articles; 1500 government documents and pamphlets; 394 16mm films; 40 audio cassettes; 86 video cassettes; 51 filmstrips. **Remarks:** Library currently scheduled to close October or November 1992.

★10863★
Municipal Research and Services Center of Washington - Library (Soc Sci)
10517 N.E. 38th Pl. Phone: (206)827-4334
Kirkland, WA 98033-7926 Lynne De Merritt, Libn.
Founded: 1970. **Staff:** Prof 2; Other 1. **Subjects:** Municipal government, finance, planning, law; public works and personnel; public safety. **Special Collections:** Municipal ordinances of state of Washington. **Holdings:** 3500 subject files containing articles, clippings, manuscripts, pamphlet materials, technical reports, city ordinances. **Subscriptions:** 300 journals and other serials. **Services:** Interlibrary loan; usage restricted to public officials. **Computerized Information Services:** Inquiry Assistance Program (internal database). **Remarks:** FAX: (206)827-5002. **Staff:** Beverley E. Stotera, Asst.Libn.

★10864★
Municipal Technical Advisory Service - Library (Soc Sci)
University of Tennessee
600 Henley, Suite 120 Phone: (615)974-0411
Knoxville, TN 37996-4105 Carol C. Hewlett, Sr.Rsrc.Cons.
Founded: 1950. **Staff:** Prof 2; Other 4. **Subjects:** Municipal government, finance, personnel, public safety (police and fire), public works. **Special Collections:** Municipal law; city ordinances. **Holdings:** 4000 books; 10,000 pamphlets; 3000 sample ordinances; 2000 indexed articles. **Subscriptions:** 300 journals. **Services:** Copying (limited); library open to the public with restrictions on circulation. **Automated Operations:** Computerized cataloging. **Networks/Consortia:** Member of SOLINET. **Special Catalogs:** MTAS Library Additions List. **Remarks:** The Municipal Technical Advisory Service is an agency of University of Tennessee - Institute for Public Service. FAX: (615)974-0423. **Staff:** Beth E. Sanderbeck, Lib.Supv.

Munk Library of Arizoniana
See: **Southwest Museum - Braun Research Library** (15532)

★10865★
Dr. E.H. Munro Medical Library (Med)
St. Mary's Hospital & Medical Center
P.O. Box 1628 Phone: (303)244-2171
Grand Junction, CO 81502-1628 Joan E. Paine, Dir.
Founded: 1945. **Staff:** Prof 1; Other 2. **Subjects:** Medicine, nursing. **Holdings:** 1000 books. **Subscriptions:** 202 journals and other serials. **Services:** Interlibrary loan (fee based); copying; library open to the public. **Automated Operations:** DOCLINE. **Computerized Information Services:** DIALOG Information Services, MEDLARS; CD-ROMs (MEDLINE, CINAHL). Performs searches on fee basis. **Networks/Consortia:** Member of National Network of Libraries of Medicine - Midcontinental Region, Colorado Council of Medical Librarians.

★10866★
Munson-Williams-Proctor Institute - Art Reference and Music Library (Art, Mus)
310 Genesee St. Phone: (315)797-0000
Utica, NY 13502 Cynthia Barth, Hd.Libn.
Founded: 1940. **Staff:** Prof 1; Other 1. **Subjects:** American art, architecture, decorative arts, music. **Special Collections:** Fountain Elms Collection (family library; 1000 volumes); autographs (950); book plates; artists' books. **Holdings:** 20,000 books; 375 bound periodical volumes; 25,000 slides; 6000 (LP and CD); 150 scores; 160 videotapes. **Subscriptions:** 60 journals and other serials. **Services:** Interlibrary loan; copying; library open to the public for reference use only. **Networks/Consortia:** Member of Central New York Library Resources Council (CENTRO). **Staff:** Michael Schuyler, Mus.Libn.

Murakami Library of Meiji Literature
See: **University of California, Berkeley - East Asian Library** (18316)

Audie L. Murphy Gun Museum
See: **Hill College - Harold B. Simpson Confederate Research Center and Audie L. Murphy Gun Museum** (7209)

Beatrice Murphy Foundation
See: **District of Columbia Public Library - Black Studies Division** (4905)

★10867★
Murphy/Jahn - Library (Plan)
35 E. Wacker Dr. Phone: (312)427-7300
Chicago, IL 60601 William T. Lohmann
Founded: 1968. **Subjects:** Architecture, codes, construction products. **Holdings:** 4200 books; 300 bound periodical volumes; 3400 product catalogs. **Subscriptions:** 130 journals and other serials; 2 newspapers. **Services:** Library open to the public. **Publications:** Building stone resources; construction consultants both Online systems. **Remarks:** FAX: (312)332-0274.

Murphy Library
See: **University of Wisconsin--La Crosse** (19576)

Murphy Library of Art and Architecture
See: **University of Kansas** (18734)

★10868★
Murphy Oil Corporation - Law Department Library (Law)
200 Peach St.
El Dorado, AR 71730 Phone: (501)862-6411
Subjects: Law - corporation, antitrust, labor, environmental, oil and gas. **Holdings:** 10,000 books; 172 bound periodical volumes; 37 loose-leaf services; state statutes; regional reporters. **Services:** Library open to the public with approval. **Remarks:** FAX: (501)862-9057.

★10869★
Murphy Oil Corporation - Tax Library (Bus-Fin)
200 Peach St. Phone: (501)862-6411
El Dorado, AR 71730 Harry Bain, Tax Mgr.
Staff: 1. **Subjects:** Taxation - federal, state, foreign. **Holdings:** 870 volumes. **Services:** Interlibrary loan; library not open to the public. **Remarks:** FAX: (501)862-9057.

Richard J. Murphy Memorial Library
See: **Baptist Bible College of Pennsylvania** (1497)

William K. Murphy Memorial Health Science Library
See: **Veterans Home of California** (19820)

★10870★
Athol Murray College of Notre Dame - Lane Hall Memorial Library - Special Collections (Hum)
Box 220 Phone: (306)732-2080
Wilcox, SK, Canada S0G 5E0 James Williams, Libn.
Founded: 1933. **Staff:** 1. **Subjects:** Humanities. **Special Collections:** 13th century manuscripts; Nuremberg Chronicles and other incunabula; Rex Beach Collection. **Holdings:** 14,000 volumes. **Subscriptions:** 11 journals and other serials. **Services:** Collections open to the public by permission.

Murray-Green Library - Archives
See: **Roosevelt University - Murray-Green Library - Archives** (14057)

Henry A. Murray Research Center
See: **Radcliffe College** (13678)

J.C. Murray Archives
See: **Woodstock Theological Center - Library** (20581)

J.K. Murray Library
See: **Highland Park Hospital - Medical Library** (7198)

J.K. Murray Library
See: **University of Queensland Gatton College** (19258)

Murray Properties Company
See: **Anterra Company** (890)

★ 10871 ★
Murray State University - Libraries (Educ)
Murray, KY 42071 Phone: (502)762-2291
Coy L. Harmon, Dean, Libs.
Founded: 1923. **Staff:** Prof 15; Other 27. **Subjects:** Education, business, law, science, engineering, liberal arts. **Special Collections:** Jesse Stuart Collection (780 linear feet); Forrest C. Pogue War and Diplomacy Collection (2500 volumes); Regional Politics and Government (2525 linear feet); Regional History and Culture (115 linear feet); TVA Land Between the Lakes (100 volumes); Jack London (first editions; 87 volumes); NASA Teacher Resource Center (1988). **Holdings:** 355,392 books; 90,458 bound periodical volumes; 172,872 other cataloged items; 38,645 reels of microfilm; 215 linear feet of university archival materials; 516,828 microfiche and microcards; 28,170 media resource materials. **Subscriptions:** 3000 journals and other serials; 25 newspapers. **Services:** Interlibrary loan; copying; libraries open to the public. **Automated Operations:** Computerized cataloging and circulation. **Computerized Information Services:** DIALOG Information Services, OCLC. **Networks/Consortia:** Member of SOLINET, Kentucky Library Network, Inc. (KLN). **Special Catalogs:** Special Collections (book); periodical holdings (printout). **Special Indexes:** Index to Murray Ledger & Times. **Remarks:** FAX: (502)762-3736. **Staff:** Keith M. Heim, Hd., Spec.Coll.; Marilyn McFadden, Hd., Cat.; Jetta Culpepper, Hd., Acq.; Sandra Sanders, Hd., Ref.; Celia Wall, Hd., Circ.; Susan Dunman, Hd., Per.; Yushin Yoo, Hd., Media & Curric.Rsrcs.; John Griffin, Coll.Dev.Libn.

★ 10872 ★
Warren G. Murray Developmental Center - Library (Med)
1717 W. Broadway Phone: (618)532-1811
Centralia, IL 62801 John Mannino, Libn.
Founded: 1965. **Staff:** Prof 1. **Subjects:** Mental retardation, medicine, nursing, psychology, special education, speech pathology. **Holdings:** 1000 volumes; 550 phonograph records; 2100 slides, filmstrips, cassette tapes, prints. **Subscriptions:** 15 journals and other serials. **Services:** Interlibrary loan. **Networks/Consortia:** Member of Cumberland Trail Library System, Illinois Department of Mental Health and Developmental Disabilities Library Services Network (LISN). **Publications:** Information sheets, irregular.

Murrow Library
See: **Tufts University - Fletcher School of Law & Diplomacy - Edwin Ginn Library** (16548)

★ 10873 ★
Murtha Cullina Richer & Pinney - Library (Law)
City Pl. Phone: (203)240-6092
Hartford, CT 06103 Linda Clough, Law Libn.
Staff: Prof 1; Other 1. **Subjects:** Environmental law, civil litigation, labor law. **Holdings:** 15,000 books. **Subscriptions:** 150 journals and other serials; 10 newspapers. **Services:** Interlibrary loan; library not open to the public. **Computerized Information Services:** LEXIS, NEXIS, WESTLAW, DIALOG Information Services.

★ 10874 ★
Muscatatuck State Developmental Center - Resident and Staff Development Library (Med)
Box 77 Phone: (812)346-4401
Butlerville, IN 47223 Barbara Carter, Libn.
Staff: Prof 1; Other 2. **Subjects:** Medicine, staff development, nursing, behavior modification, supervision and management, mental retardation. **Holdings:** 3200 books; 200 filmstrips, phonograph records, transparencies; videotapes. **Subscriptions:** 23 journals and other serials. **Services:** Interlibrary loan; library not open to the public. **Networks/Consortia:** Member of Southeastern Indiana Area Library Services Authority (SIALSA). **Publications:** Mirror, quarterly - to staff and families of residents. **Formerly:** Muscatatuck State Hospital & Training Center.

Muscatatuck State Hospital & Training Center
See: **Muscatatuck State Developmental Center - Resident and Staff Development Library** (10874)

★ 10875 ★
Muscatine Art Center - Art Reference Library (Art)
1314 Mulberry Ave. Phone: (319)263-8282
Muscatine, IA 52761 Barbara Longtin, Dir.
Subjects: Fine arts, decorative arts, textiles. **Special Collections:** Mississippi River. **Holdings:** 500 books. **Subscriptions:** 10 journals and other serials. **Services:** Copying; library open to the public for reference use only.

William T. Muse Memorial Law Library
See: **University of Richmond** (19272)

★ 10876 ★
Musee d'Art Contemporain de Montreal - Media Center (Art)
Cite du Havre Phone: (514)873-4708
Montreal, PQ, Canada H3C 3R4 Michelle Gauthier, Libn.
Founded: 1965. **Staff:** Prof 1; Other 5. **Subjects:** Visual and contemporary art. **Special Collections:** Paul-Emile Borduas (12,500 documents). **Holdings:** 23,550 books and exhibition catalogs; 314 periodical titles; 38,000 slides; 8728 artist, gallery, museum files; 606 tapes and films; 4200 microforms. **Subscriptions:** 314 journals and other serials. **Services:** Copying; center open to the public. **Remarks:** FAX: (514)873-2047.

★ 10877 ★
Musee d'Art de Joliette - Bibliotheque (Art)
145, rue Wilfrid-Corbeil
C.P. 132 Phone: (514)756-0311
Joliette, PQ, Canada J6E 3Z3 Marie-Andree Briere, Cur.
Staff: Prof 1. **Subjects:** Art, architecture, music, literature. **Holdings:** 1000 books; 500 bound periodical volumes; 100 museum catalogs. **Services:** Library open to the public for consultation only.

★ 10878 ★
Musee d'Art Religieux et d'Art Mosan - Centre de Documentation - Bibliotheque (Art)
10, Quai de la Batte Phone: 041 220800
B-4000 Liege, Belgium Albert Lemeunier, Cons.
Founded: 1977. **Staff:** 1. **Subjects:** Art - religious, Mosan; history of the Diocese of Liege; Mosan hagiography. **Special Collections:** 19th century jewelry of Liege; religious manuscripts of the Diocese of Liege. **Holdings:** 5000 books; 178 bound periodical volumes; 3 AV programs; 500 nonbook items; photographs; videotapes. **Services:** Copying; library open to the public at librarian's discretion.

Musee des Beaux-Arts du Canada
See: **Canada - National Gallery of Canada** (2802)

Musee des Beaux-Arts de Montreal
See: **The Montreal Museum of Fine Arts** (10700)

Musee Canadien des Civilisations
See: **Canadian Museum of Civilization - Library** (2962)

Musee Canadien de la Guerre
See: **Canadian War Museum - Library** (3000)

Musee Canadien de la Nature
See: **Canadian Museum of Nature** (2963)

Musee National d'Aviation
See: **Canada - National Aviation Museum** (2773)

★ 10879 ★
Musee National de la Resistance - Bibliotheque (Soc Sci)
14, rue Van Lint Phone: 2 5224041
B-1070 Brussels, Belgium Jean Brack, Chm. of Musm.
Subjects: Discrimination - racial, political, philosophical, religious; nazism; fascism; disarmament; peace. **Holdings:** 3500 volumes. **Formerly:** Front de l'Independance.

Musee National des Sciences et de la Technologie
See: **National Museum of Science and Technology** (11242)

Musee de l'Opera
See: **France - Bibliotheque Nationale - Musee de l'Opera** (6063)

★ 10880 ★
Musee du Quebec - Bibliotheque et Centre de Documentation (Art)
1, ave. Wolfe-Montcalm Phone: (418)643-7134
Quebec, PQ, Canada G1R 5H3 Louise Allard, Biblio.
Staff: Prof 1; Other 6. **Subjects:** Art. **Special Collections:** Fonds Gerard Morisset. **Holdings:** 22,055 books; 3743 bound periodical volumes; 68,000 slides; 7940 photographs; 154 phonograph records; 56 titles of microforms; 71 magnetic tapes; 242 videotapes; 13,932 files of artists and museums. **Subscriptions:** 174 journals and other serials; 13 newspapers. **Services:** Interlibrary loan; copying; library open to the public for reference use only. **Automated Operations:** Computerized cataloging and acquisitions. **Computerized Information Services:** UTLAS. **Publications:** Bibliographies; press releases. **Remarks:** FAX: (418)646-1664. Maintained by Quebec Province Ministere des Affaires Culturelles.

★ 10881 ★
Musees Nationaux au Louvre - Bibliotheque et Archives (Art, Hist, Area-Ethnic)
34 quai du Louvre Phone: 1 40205266
F-75041 Paris Cedex 01, France Jean-Marc Leri, Chf.Cons.
Founded: 1871. **Staff:** Prof 32; Other 10. **Subjects:** Archeology, Egyptology, art, museology, antiquity. **Special Collections:** Manuscripts of autograph letters of artists. **Holdings:** 350,000 books; 12,000 manuscripts. **Subscriptions:** 1400 journals and other serials. **Services:** Interlibrary loan; library not open to the public. **Automated Operations:** Computerized public access catalog. **Remarks:** FAX: 1 40205169.

★ 10882 ★
Museo Ernest Hemingway - Biblioteca (Hum)
Finca Vigia, San Francisco de Paula
C.P. 19180 Phone: 910809
Havana, Cuba Gladys Rodriguez Ferrero, Licenciada
Subjects: Works of Hemingway, hunting, war, bullfighting, fishing, arts and sciences. **Special Collections:** Mark Twain Aventuras; H. Balzac Coleccion (complete set); Guy de Maupassant Coleccion; Benitos Perez Galdos Episodios Nacionales; Universidad de Harvard (complete set). **Holdings:** 7000 books. **Services:** Copying; library open to the public. **Staff:** Megaly Navarro Menendez, Tecnica.

★ 10883 ★
Museo Maritime - Diputacion de Barcelona - Biblioteca (Hist, Trans)
Porta de la Paz 1 Phone: 3 3183245
E-08001 Barcelona, Spain Rosa Busquets, Libn.
Founded: 1942. **Staff:** 1. **Subjects:** Maritime topics, geographical discoveries, ship building, fishing, sea ports, history of Catalonia. **Holdings:** 13,700 books; 1400 bound periodical volumes; 1350 cartographic material. **Subscriptions:** 52 journals and other serials. **Services:** Copying; SDI; library open to the public. **Special Indexes:** Index of nautical terms. **Remarks:** FAX: 3011871.

★ 10884 ★
Museo de la Patagonia - Dr. Francisco P. Moreno Biblioteca (Hist)
Centro Civico
8400 S.C. de Bariloche Phone: 944 22309
Rio Negro, Argentina Gloria Padros de Henning, Libn.
Founded: 1941. **Staff:** 1. **Subjects:** Argentine history, Patagonian history, natural history, archeology, anthropology, ethnology. **Special Collections:** Francisco P. Moreno Collection (30 boxes of documents). **Holdings:** 1783 books; 300 periodical titles; 10,000 documents; 6500 manuscripts. **Subscriptions:** 5 journals and other serials. **Services:** Interlibrary loan; library open to the public with restrictions. **Computerized Information Services:** CDS/ISIS. **Publications:** Comunicaciones Cientificas; Serie Antropologia; Serie Divulgacion.

Museovirasto
See: **Finland - National Ministry of Education - National Board of Antiquities** (5711)

Museu Paraense Emilio Goeldi
See: **Emilio Goeldi Museum** (6519)

★ 10885 ★
Museum of American Folk Art - Library (Art)
61 W. 62nd St. Phone: (212)977-7170
New York, NY 10023 Edith C. Wise, Dir., Lib.Serv.
Founded: 1961. **Staff:** Prof 2; Other 1. **Subjects:** American folk art, decorative arts, international folk art. **Holdings:** 8000 books; 700 bound periodical volumes; 18 VF drawers of clippings and other materials. **Subscriptions:** 205 journals and other serials. **Services:** Copying; library open to the public by appointment. **Publications:** The Clarion, monthly - to members. **Special Catalogs:** Guide to American Folk Art Publications. **Special Indexes:** Index to The Clarion.

Museum of American Glass Research Library
See: **Wheaton Cultural Alliance, Inc. - Museum of American Glass Research Library** (20373)

Museum of the American Indian
See: **Huntington Free Library** (7571)

★ 10886 ★
Museum of American Textile History - Library (Sci-Engr, Hist)
800 Massachusetts Ave. Phone: (508)686-0191
North Andover, MA 01845 Clare M. Sheridan, Libn.
Founded: 1960. **Staff:** Prof 3; Other 1. **Subjects:** Textiles - technology, manufacturing, design; water power; labor history. **Special Collections:** Trade catalogs; cloth labels; postcards; insurance surveys. **Holdings:** 35,500 volumes; 40,000 maps, prints, photographs; 3000 feet of business manuscripts; 550 non-current journals. **Subscriptions:** 50 journals. **Services:** Interlibrary loan (limited); copying; library open to the public for reference use only. **Publications:** Checklists of study collections, artifacts, manuscripts, prints, textiles; Merrimack Valley Textile Museum: a guide to the manuscript collections. **Remarks:** FAX: (508)686-8567. **Staff:** Patricia Markey, Cat.; Jessica G. Randolph, Asst.Libn./Mss.Spec.; Marion Hall, Photo/Prints/Repro.

★ 10887 ★
Museum of the Americas - Library (Art)
Rte. 14 Phone: (802)276-3386
Brookfield, VT 05036 Earle W. Newton, Dir.
Founded: 1972. **Staff:** Prof 1. **Subjects:** Art and architecture - English, American, Spanish, Latin American. **Special Collections:** Pre-Columbian art; English paintings and engravings; Spanish decorative arts; Latin American folk art; Antiquarian Book Collection (Americana, 18th century English and 19th century American literature, especially Mark Twain, Robert Frost, Edwin Arlington Robinson, New England poets). **Holdings:** 3000 books. **Subscriptions:** 12 journals and other serials. **Services:** Library open to the public by appointment. **Remarks:** Maintained by College of the Americas.

Museum & Archives of Canadian Scouting
See: **Boy Scouts of Canada** (2044)

★ 10888 ★
Museum of Arts and Sciences - Bruce Everett Bates Memorial Library (Biol Sci)
1040 Museum Blvd. Phone: (904)255-0285
Daytona Beach, FL 32014 Marjorie L. Sigerson, Libn.
Founded: 1954. **Staff:** Prof 1. **Subjects:** Birds, shells, fish and marine life, biology, art, archeology, whaling. **Special Collections:** Cuban Collection (500 items); books about art (500); books about birds (400). **Holdings:** 5000 books. **Subscriptions:** 16 journals and other serials. **Services:** Copying; library open to the public with restrictions.

Museum of Broadcasting
See: **Museum of Television and Radio - Research Services** (10921)

★10889★
Museum of Cartoon Art - Library (Art)
Comly Ave. Phone: (914)939-0234
Rye Brook, NY 10573 Skip Alsdorf, Prog.Coord.
Founded: 1972. **Subjects:** Comic strip and comic book art, political/editorial cartooning, caricature, magazine cartoons, illustration, animation. **Special Collections:** Original artwork by over 1000 different artists (over 50,000 pieces). **Holdings:** 500 books; 300 bound periodical volumes. **Services:** Library open to researchers by appointment.

★10890★
Museum of the Cherokee Indian - Archives (Area-Ethnic)
US 441 North-Drama Rd.
Box 1599 Phone: (704)497-3481
Cherokee, NC 28719 JoAnn Orr, Archv.
Founded: 1976. **Staff:** Prof 1. **Subjects:** Cherokee history. **Special Collections:** A Guide to Cherokee Documents in Foreign Archives (microfilm). **Holdings:** 15,000 books; manuscripts. **Services:** Copying; archives open to the public by appointment.

★10891★
Museum of the City of New York - Library (Hist)
1220 Fifth Ave. at 103rd St.
New York, NY 10029 Phone: (212)534-1672
Subjects: Local history, New York theater. **Special Collections:** Manuscripts of New Yorkers (17th century to present; 15,000 pieces). **Holdings:** 8000 books. **Services:** Library open to researchers by appointment only. **Remarks:** FAX: (212)534-5974. **Staff:** Kathryn Mets.

★10892★
Museum of the City of New York - Theatre Collection (Theater)
Fifth Ave. at 103rd St.
New York, NY 10029 Phone: (212)534-1672
Founded: 1926. **Staff:** Prof 1. **Subjects:** History of legitimate theater in New York City; costumes; scene and costume designs. **Special Collections:** Dazian Library of Theatrical Design; Howard Dietz Collection; George M. Cohan Collection; Betty Comden-Adolph Green Collection; George and Ira Gershwin Collection; Mary Martin Collection; Eugene O'Neill Collection; Ethel Merman Collection. **Holdings:** 1000 books; 1000 manuscripts; clippings; documents; prints; photographs; paintings; sheet music. **Services:** Copying; collection open to qualified scholars and researchers only by appointment. **Special Catalogs:** Catalogs on major exhibitions. **Remarks:** FAX: (212)534-5974. **Staff:** Kathryn Mets, Theatre Libn.

★10893★
Museum of Classical Chinese Furniture - Library (Art)
P.O. Box 100 Phone: (916)692-3142
Renaissance, CA 95962 Brian Flynn, Musm.Cur.
Founded: 1983. **Staff:** 8. **Subjects:** Oriental Art, Chinese furniture and porcelains. **Holdings:** 1000 books. **Subscriptions:** 150 journals and other serials. **Services:** Library open to the public with permission of the museum director. **Remarks:** FAX: (916)692-1596. **Formerly:** Fellowship of Friends - Asian Art Institute Library. **Staff:** Anthony Williams, Libn.

Museum of the Confederacy
See: **Confederate Memorial Literary Society - Museum of the Confederacy** (4134)

★10894★
Museum of Contemporary Art - Library (Art)
237 E. Ontario St. Phone: (312)280-2692
Chicago, IL 60611 Sonja Staum-Kuniej, Musm.Libn.
Founded: 1967. **Staff:** Prof 1; Other 3. **Subjects:** Contemporary art in all media, modern art. **Special Collections:** Artists' books; complete collection of 35mm color slides of most items in the permanent collection; photographs and slides of exhibitions; videotapes and audiotapes of contemporary artists discussing their work; MCA exhibition archives. **Holdings:** 15,000 books; 125 VF drawers of museum catalogs, exhibit brochures, brochures, clippings on individual artists and institutions. **Subscriptions:** 117 journals and other serials. **Services:** Interlibrary loan; copying; library open to museum members and researchers. **Automated Operations:** Computerized cataloging. **Computerized Information Services:** OCLC, DIALOG Information Services, OCLC EPIC. **Networks/Consortia:** Member of ILLINET. **Special Indexes:** Index by artist to MCA group exhibitions. **Remarks:** FAX: (312)280-2687.

Museum of Early Southern Decorative Arts (MESDA)
See: **Old Salem, Inc.** (12389)

★10895★
Museum of Fine Arts - Art Reference Library (Art)
255 Beach Dr., N. Phone: (813)896-2667
St. Petersburg, FL 33701 Muriel S. Kirk, Coord.
Founded: 1962. **Staff:** 6. **Subjects:** Oriental art, architecture, decorative arts, history of art, photography. **Special Collections:** Old engravings, etchings, prints (900). **Holdings:** 9500 books; 700 bound periodical volumes; 39 files of museum reports and bulletins, art auction and sales catalogs; 700 museum catalogs; 6000 art reproductions; 20,000 slides on art history. **Subscriptions:** 32 journals and other serials. **Services:** Interlibrary loan; library open to students and scholars by appointment. **Special Indexes:** Card index to paintings in American museums.

★10896★
Museum of Fine Arts - Department of Photographic Services - Slide & Photograph Library (Art, Aud-Vis)
465 Huntington Ave. Phone: (617)267-9300
Boston, MA 02115 Janice Sorkow, Dir., Photo.Serv.
Founded: 1922. **Staff:** Prof 1; Other 14. **Subjects:** Eastern and Western painting, architecture, sculpture, prints, decorative arts, photography. **Special Collections:** Slides and photographs of works in collections of Museum of Fine Arts; videodisc of selected museum objects. **Holdings:** 115,000 slides; 110,000 black/white negatives; 8000 color transparencies. **Services:** Duplicate slides of museum objects available for sale; slide rental; library open to the public with restrictions. **Publications:** Information packet - available by mail. **Special Catalogs:** Catalog of slide sets - for sale; detailed slide set lists - available on request.

★10897★
Museum of Fine Arts - School Library (Art)
230 The Fenway Phone: (617)267-6100
Boston, MA 02115 Virginia Abblitt, Libn.
Founded: 1928. **Staff:** Prof 2; Other 3. **Subjects:** Art. **Holdings:** 11,900 books and exhibition catalogs; 400 bound periodical volumes; 70,000 slides; 12 VF drawers of clippings and pictures; 75 audio cassettes; 90 videotapes. **Subscriptions:** 90 journals and other serials. **Services:** Copying; library open to the Museum School community. **Networks/Consortia:** Member of Fenway Library Consortium (FLC). **Staff:** Patrick Maloney, Slide Libn.

★10898★
Museum of Fine Arts - William Morris Hunt Memorial Library (Art)
465 Huntington Ave. Phone: (617)267-9300
Boston, MA 02115 Nancy S. Allen, Chf.Libn.
Founded: 1879. **Staff:** Prof 3; Other 3. **Subjects:** Art - Asiatic, Classical, Egyptian; textiles; European and American decorative arts; painting; musical instruments; prints; drawings. **Holdings:** 137,000 volumes; 154,000 pamphlets and auction catalogs; prints; drawings; photographs. **Subscriptions:** 650 journals and other serials. **Services:** Interlibrary loan (limited); copying; library open to the public for reference use only. **Automated Operations:** Computerized public access catalog, cataloging. **Computerized Information Services:** RLIN. **Networks/Consortia:** Member of Fenway Library Consortium (FLC). **Special Catalogs:** Chronological list of Museum of Fine Arts exhibitions, 1872 to present. **Remarks:** FAX: (617)267-0280. **Staff:** Laila Abdel-Malek, Cat.; Maureen Melton, Archv.

★10899★
Museum of Fine Arts, Houston - Hirsch Library (Art)
Box 6826 Phone: (713)639-7325
Houston, TX 77265 Jeannette Dixon, Libn.
Staff: Prof 4; Other 5. **Subjects:** Art history, photography. **Holdings:** 30,000 books; 2000 bound periodical volumes; 81 VF drawers of exhibition catalogs; 56 VF drawers of auction catalogs; 700 reels of microfilm; 60,000 slides; museum archives. **Subscriptions:** 152 journals and other serials. **Services:** Interlibrary loan; copying; library open to the public. **Computerized Information Services:** RLIN; RLIN (electronic mail service). **Remarks:** FAX: (713)639-7399. Electronic mail address(es): BM.MFC (RLIN). **Staff:** Kathleen Robinson, Archv.; Gregory Most, Slide Libn.; Margaret Ford, Cat.

★ 10900 ★
Museum of Flight - Research Facility (Sci-Engr)
9404 E. Marginal Way, S. Phone: (206)764-5705
Seattle, WA 98108 Anne C. Rutledge, Mrg., Res.Fac.
Founded: 1987. **Staff:** Prof 2. **Subjects:** Aviation, aerospace. **Special Collections:** Juvenile aviation books, 1920-1930 (250); Gordon S. Williams collection (27,000 negatives). **Holdings:** 6000 books; 500 bound periodical volumes; 10,000 photographs; plane and plane manufacturing company data, history, and specifications; historical aviation materials. **Subscriptions:** 43 journals and other serials. **Services:** Copying; facility open to the public by appointment. **Publications:** Acquisitions list, monthly. **Remarks:** FAX: (206)764-5707. **Staff:** John David Frazee.

Museum fur Gestaltung Zurich - Bibliothek
See: **(Zurich) School and Museum of Art and Design** (20851)

★ 10901 ★
Museum of the Great Plains - Great Plains Research Library and Archives (Hist)
601 Ferris
Box 68 Phone: (405)581-3460
Lawton, OK 73502 Steve Wilson, Dir.
Founded: 1960. **Staff:** Prof 2; Other 1. **Subjects:** Great Plains - history, natural history, archeology, anthropology, agriculture. **Special Collections:** Original documents and photographs dealing with the settlement of southwestern Oklahoma and Southern Plains; wagons and carriages, 1869-1926 (2000 photographs). **Holdings:** 25,000 books; 725 bound periodical volumes; 700 cases of manuscripts, 1880-1940, Comanche County newspapers, 1901 to present, and City of Lawton Journals; 30,000 photographs; hardware; agricultural catalogs and periodicals. **Subscriptions:** 260 journals and other serials. **Services:** Copying; library and archives open to the public. **Special Indexes:** Index to photograph collections (card); index to articles in regional journals; index to agricultural catalogs and periodicals; index to collections described in Great Plains Journal, volume 17, 1978.

★ 10902 ★
Museum of History and Science - Library (Hist)
727 W. Main St. Phone: (502)561-6103
Louisville, KY 40202 Amy S. Lowen
Founded: 1977. **Staff:** 1. **Subjects:** Science, history. **Special Collections:** Childrens books. **Holdings:** 3000 books. **Subscriptions:** 30 journals and other serials. **Services:** Interlibrary loan; copying; library open to the public for reference use only. **Remarks:** FAX: (502)561-6145.

★ 10903 ★
Museum of Independent Telephony - Archives Collection (Hist)
412 S. Campbell Phone: (913)263-2681
Abilene, KS 67410 Peg Chronister, Cur.
Staff: Prof 1. **Subjects:** Telephone history and technology. **Special Collections:** Early telephone trade magazines; historical photograph collection; antique telephone catalogs. **Holdings:** 1000 books; 1000 bound periodical volumes; 1000 other cataloged items; 500 manuscripts; 120 boxes of loose periodicals; 150 tapes. **Subscriptions:** 10 journals and other serials. **Services:** Copying; collection open to the public.

★ 10904 ★
Museum of Independent Telephony - Library (Rec)
Box 625 Phone: (913)263-2681
Abilene, KS 67410 Peg Chronister
Founded: 1973. **Subjects:** Antique telephones and related materials. **Holdings:** 1000 volumes. **Services:** Research. **Remarks:** Library affiliated with Antique Telephone Collectors Association.

Museum of International Folk Art
See: **Museum of New Mexico** (10913)

Museum of Jewish Heritage
See: **A Living Memorial to the Holocaust - Museum of Jewish Heritage - Documentation & Research Library** (9231)

Museum des Kunsthandwerks Leipzig - Grassimuseum - Bibliothek
See: **Leipzig Museum of Arts and Crafts - Library** (9063)

★ 10905 ★
Museum of London - Library (Hist)
150 London Wall Phone: 71 600 3699
London EC2Y 5HN, England Joanna Clark, Libn.
Staff: 2. **Subjects:** History and topography of London, social history, archeology. **Special Collections:** Tangye Collection (English Civil War and Inter-regnum; rare books and manuscripts); Bell Collection (Great Plague and Fire of London). **Holdings:** 25,000 books; 5000 bound periodical volumes; 50 oral history tapes; 100 manuscripts; maps of London, 16th century to present; records of archeological excavations in London, 1930s to present. **Subscriptions:** 200 journals and other serials. **Services:** Interlibrary loan; copying; library open to the public by appointment. **Remarks:** FAX: 71 600 1058.

★ 10906 ★
Museum of Modern Art - Celeste Bartos International Film Study Center (Theater, Aud-Vis)
11 W. 53rd St. Phone: (212)708-9613
New York, NY 10019-5486 Charles Silver, Supv.
Founded: 1968. **Staff:** Prof 3. **Subjects:** Cinema. **Special Collections:** D.W. Griffith Papers and Scrapbooks; Merritt Crawford Papers on early cinema; Thomas Brandon Papers on labor films. **Holdings:** 10,000 films; 600,000 clippings; 2000 scripts; 600 reference books; 3000 pressbooks; 30,000 posters. **Subscriptions:** 50 journals and other serials. **Services:** Copying; center open to bonafide film scholars by appointment. **Remarks:** FAX: (212)708-9531. **Staff:** Ronald S. Magliozzi, Asst.Supv.; Nancy Barnes, Asst.

★ 10907 ★
Museum of Modern Art - Department of Rights and Reproductions - Photographic Archives (Art, Aud-Vis)
11 W. 53rd St. Phone: (212)708-9458
New York, NY 10019-5498 Esther M. Carpenter, Photo.Archv.
Founded: 1932. **Staff:** Prof 1. **Subjects:** Modern art, 1890 to present. **Special Collections:** Curt Valentin Archive (120 albums of photographs). **Holdings:** 136 albums of photographs of works in museum collection; 715 albums of photographs of works in museum exhibitions; 183,000 photographs; 2100 slides; 66,400 negatives. **Services:** Archives open to the public by appointment only; slide collection not open to the public. **Automated Operations:** Computerized cataloging. **Computerized Information Services:** BIGMoMA (internal database). **Remarks:** FAX: (212)708-9889.

★ 10908 ★
Museum of Modern Art - Film Stills Archive (Theater)
11 W. 53rd St. Phone: (212)708-9830
New York, NY 10019 Mary Corliss, Asst.Cur.
Founded: 1935. **Staff:** 1. **Subjects:** Film stills. **Special Collections:** D.W. Griffih Collection; Carol Dempster Collection; Billy Bitzer Collection; Essanay Collection (film stills released during 1913-1917); Douglas Fairbanks Collection; Richard Barthelmess Collection; Georges Melies Collection (French short films, 1899-1912); Japanese, French, and Russian film stills. **Holdings:** 4 million film stills (50,000 film titles); 500,000 portraits and candid shots of film personalities. **Services:** Archive open to the public by appointment on a limited schedule. **Remarks:** The Film Stills Archive is said to contain one of the world's largest and most comprehensive collection of film stills. Duplicates of stills, color slides, and transparencies are available for a fee. FAX: (212)708-9531. Telex: 62370. **Staff:** Terry Geesken, Asst., Stills.

★ 10909 ★
Museum of Modern Art - Library (Art)
11 W. 53rd St. Phone: (212)708-9433
New York, NY 10019-5498 Clive Phillpot, Dir.
Founded: 1929. **Staff:** Prof 6; Other 4. **Subjects:** Modern art, 1880 to present, including design, architecture, photography, film. **Special Collections:** Hans Richter papers; Curt Valentin papers; archives of Political Art Documentation & Distribution (PADD); artists' books collection; Latin American Art Collection. **Holdings:** 100,000 books and exhibition catalogs; 6000 bound periodical volumes; 200,000 items in A-Z artist files. **Subscriptions:** 350 journals and other serials. **Services:** Interlibrary loan (limited); copying; library open to the public by appointment. **Automated**

Operations: Computerized cataloging. **Computerized Information Services:** RLIN. **Networks/Consortia:** Member of New York Metropolitan Reference and Research Library Agency, Research Libraries Information Network (RLIN). **Publications:** Library Bulletin; Art Bibliographies; Annual Bibliography of Modern Art, 1986, 1987, 1988, 1989, 1990 (book). **Special Catalogs:** Catalog of the Library of the Museum of Modern Art, 1976 (book). **Remarks:** FAX: (212)708-9889. Alternate telephone number(s): 708-9430. **Staff:** Janis Ekdahl, Asst.Dir.; Daniel A. Starr, Assoc.Libn., Cat.; Eumie Imm, Assoc.Libn., Ref.

★10910★
Museum of New Mexico - History Library (Hist)
Box 2087 Phone: (505)827-6470
Santa Fe, NM 87504-2087 Orlando Romero, Res.Libn.
Founded: 1880. **Staff:** Prof 1; Other 1. **Subjects:** New Mexico and Southwest history. **Special Collections:** Bandelier Collection (original and rare maps). **Holdings:** 12,000 books; 837 reels of microfilm; 3000 maps; 300 linear feet of manuscripts; newspapers. **Subscriptions:** 115 journals and other serials; 5 newspapers. **Services:** Copying; library open to the public for reference use only. **Computerized Information Services:** OCLC. **Special Indexes:** Newspaper Index, 1850-1912 (incomplete); necrology file; WPA index to materials on New Mexico culture.

★10911★
Museum of New Mexico - Laboratory of Anthropology - Library (Sci-Engr)
708 Camino Lejo
P.O. Box 2087 Phone: (505)827-6344
Santa Fe, NM 87504-2087 Laura J. Holt, Libn.
Founded: 1931. **Staff:** Prof 1; Other 1. **Subjects:** Southwestern anthropology, archeology, ethnology. **Special Collections:** Sylvanus G. Morley Collection (Meso American archeology and ethnohistory). **Holdings:** 4500 books; 1000 serial titles; 300 dissertations in microform; maps. **Subscriptions:** 210 journals and other serials. **Services:** Interlibrary loan (copies only); copying; SDI; library open to the public. **Automated Operations:** Computerized public access catalog. **Computerized Information Services:** OCLC. **Special Indexes:** Index of articles on southwestern anthropology (card and online). **Remarks:** FAX: (505)827-6349.

★10912★
Museum of New Mexico - Museum of Fine Arts - Library (Art)
107 W. Palace Ave.
P.O. Box 2087 Phone: (505)827-4453
Santa Fe, NM 87504-2087 Phyllis M. Cohen, Libn.
Founded: 1917. **Staff:** Prof 1. **Subjects:** New Mexican and Southwestern art, artists, and photography. **Special Collections:** Biographical files of individual artists. **Holdings:** 6000 books; 370 bound periodical volumes; 2500 exhibit catalogs; 7700 unbound periodicals; 5500 slides; vertical file. **Subscriptions:** 50 journals and other serials. **Services:** Interlibrary loan (limited); copying; library open to the public on limited schedule for reference use only. **Computerized Information Services:** OCLC; access to DIALOG Information Services (through New Mexico State Library). **Publications:** Exhibition History (online). **Remarks:** FAX: (505)827-4473. Subcribes to New Mexico press clipping service.

★10913★
Museum of New Mexico - Museum of International Folk Art - Library (Area-Ethnic)
P.O. Box 2087 Phone: (505)827-6350
Santa Fe, NM 87504-2087 Judith Sellars, Libn.
Founded: 1953. **Staff:** Prof 1. **Subjects:** International folk art, costume, Spanish colonial art, New Mexico religious folk art, textiles. **Special Collections:** Folk literature and music of the Spanish Colonist in New Mexico, 1800-1971. **Holdings:** 10,200 books; 3500 bound periodical volumes; 20,000 slides; 250 tapes; 200 phonograph records; postcards. **Subscriptions:** 167 journals and other serials. **Services:** Interlibrary loan; copying; library open to the public for reference use only. **Computerized Information Services:** OCLC. **Remarks:** FAX: (505)827-6349.

★10914★
Museum of New Mexico - Photo Archives (Art)
Box 2087 Phone: (505)827-6472
Santa Fe, NM 87504 Arthur L. Olivas, Photo.Archv.
Founded: 1909. **Staff:** Prof 2. **Subjects:** History of New Mexico and the West, Indians, anthropology, archeology, ethnology, mining, railroading, agriculture, Latin America, Oceania, Australia, China, Japan, India, Philippines, Middle East. **Special Collections:** History of photography; photographs by William Henry Jackson, Ben Wittick, John K. Hillers, Edward S. Curtis, T. Harmon Parkhurst, J.R. Riddle, H.F. Robinson, Henry D. Tefft, Ralph H. Anderson, Nathaniel Frucht, J.C. Burge, Ferenz Fedor, Wyatt Davis, George L. Beam George C. Bennett, H.H. Bennett, Wesley Bradfield, Charles F. Lummis, Tyler Dingee, Philip E. Harroun, Harold Kellogg, Royal A. Prentice, Henry A. Schmidt, J.S. Wooley, Jesse L. Nusbaum, D.B. Chase, Timothy O'Sullivan, Nicholas Brown, Emerson A. Plunkett, Edward A. Kemp, Christian G. Kaadt, James N. Furlong, Kilburn Bros., George T. Miller, William H. Brown, Edward A. Troutman, A. Frank Randall, Aaron B. Craycraft, O.C. Hinman, W.E. Hook, Matilda Coxe Stevenson,Carols Vierra, C.B. Waite, Augustin V. Casasola, George W. James, B.H. Gurnsey, Keystone View Co., Joseph E. Smith; international publications. **Holdings:** 2500 volumes; 300,000 photographic prints; 175,000 negatives; 75,000 color transparencies (35mm and 5x7); black/white photographs (35mm and 11x14); film and glass negatives; postcards; stereographs; photographs of artwork and graphics; photographs of collection objects in Palace of the Governors, Fine Arts Museum, Museum of Indian Arts and Culture, Museum of International Folk Art. **Subscriptions:** 25 journals and other serials. **Services:** Archives open to the public on a limited schedule for reference use only. **Publications:** List of publications - available on request. **Staff:** Richard Rudisill, Cur. of Photo.Hist.

★10915★
Museum of North Idaho, Inc. - Archives (Hist)
Box 812 Phone: (208)664-3448
Coeur d'Alene, ID 83814 Dorothy Dahlgren, Dir.
Founded: 1979. **Staff:** 1. **Subjects:** Steamboats, logging and milling, labor history, Kootenai County and surrounding area, 1875 to present. **Holdings:** 8000 photographs; 3 file drawers of documents, papers, clippings. **Services:** Reprints; archives open to the public on a limited schedule and by appointment.

★10916★
Museum of Northern Arizona - Harold S. Colton Memorial Library (Hist, Sci-Engr)
Rte. 4, Box 720 Phone: (602)774-5211
Flagstaff, AZ 86001 Dorothy A. House, Libn.
Founded: 1928. **Staff:** Prof 1; Other 1. **Subjects:** American Southwest - archeology, geology, paleontology, ethnology, natural history, history, art. **Special Collections:** Southwestern archeology; Navajo and Hopi Indians; geology of the Colorado Plateau. **Holdings:** 23,500 books; 400 periodical titles; 25,900 pamphlets; map and manuscript collections. **Services:** Interlibrary loan; copying; library open to the public for reference use only. **Remarks:** FAX: (602)779-1527.

★10917★
Museum of Oriental Cultures - Library (Area-Ethnic)
418 Peoples St., Suite 200 Phone: (512)883-1303
Corpus Christi, TX 78401 Bette Hoelscher, Exec.Dir.
Founded: 1973. **Staff:** Prof 3. **Subjects:** Japan, Oriental cultures, Middle East. **Special Collections:** Rare books and special editions. **Holdings:** Figures not available. **Services:** Copying; library open to the public for reference use only.

Museum of Orphanhood
See: **Orphan Voyage** (12575)

★10918★
Museum of Our National Heritage - Van Gorden-Williams Library (Hist)
33 Marrett Rd. Phone: (617)861-6559
Lexington, MA 02173 Nola Skousen, Libn./Archv.
Founded: 1975. **Staff:** Prof 2. **Subjects:** Freemasonry and other American fraternal organizations, American history, decorative arts. **Special Collections:** Masonic manuscript collections; Scottish Rite Northern Supreme Council Archives. **Holdings:** 80,000 cataloged items. **Subscriptions:** 39 journals and other serials; 29 newspapers and bulletins. **Services:** Interlibrary loan; copying; library open to the public for reference use only. **Staff:** Jennifer G. Barlow.

★10919★
Museum of Science - Library (Sci-Engr)
Science Park Phone: (617)589-0170
Boston, MA 02114-1099 Carolyn H. Kirdahy, Libn.
Founded: 1831. **Staff:** Prof 2. **Subjects:** Science, natural history, science education. **Special Collections:** Publications, corporate records, and some of the holdings of the Boston Society of Natural History. **Holdings:** 25,000 books; manuscripts related to 19th century natural history. **Subscriptions:** 200 journals and other serials. **Services:** Interlibrary loan; library open to the public. **Automated Operations:** Computerized public access catalog, cataloging, and circulation. **Computerized Information Services:** DIALOG Information Services, BRS Information Technologies, Knowledge Index. **Networks/Consortia:** Member of NELINET, Inc. **Publications:** Recent Additions, monthly - for internal use but available to others. **Remarks:** FAX: (617)589-0454. **Staff:** Janet Dawson, Asst.Libn.

★10920★
Museum of Science & Industry - Library (Sci-Engr)
57th St. & Lake Shore Dr. Phone: (312)684-1414
Chicago, IL 60637 Pam Nelson, Lib.Hd.
Founded: 1933. **Staff:** Prof 1. **Subjects:** Science, technology, museology, health, science education, children's nonfiction. **Special Collections:** Children's science trade books (5000 volumes); science education textbooks, elementary through high school levels. **Holdings:** 17,000 books; 900 bound periodical volumes; 1500 AV programs; 3500 software programs. **Subscriptions:** 60 journals and other serials. **Services:** Interlibrary loan; copying; library open to museum professionals. **Computerized Information Services:** ALANET (American Library Association); internal database; ALANET (electronic mail service). **Networks/Consortia:** Member of Chicago Library System. **Publications:** Topical bibliographies on exhibits, free upon request. **Remarks:** FAX: (312)684-5580. Alternate telephone number(s): 684-1414, ext. 2449.

Museum Ship VALLEY CAMP Maritime Library
See: **Le Sault de Sainte Marie Historical Sites** (9022)

★10921★
Museum of Television and Radio - Research Services (Info Sci)
25 W. 52nd St. Phone: (212)621-6600
New York, NY 10019 Vicki Lemp, Res.Libn.
Founded: 1959. **Staff:** Prof 1; Other 1. **Subjects:** Television (except technical aspects) and radio. **Special Collections:** Microfiche files on television and radio programming history. **Holdings:** 10,000 books; 650 bound periodical volumes; 155 vertical files (on microfiche). **Subscriptions:** 150 journals and other serials; 10 newspapers. **Services:** Services open to the public by appointment only. **Special Catalogs:** Tape collection catalog (Online systems). **Remarks:** FAX: (212)621-6700. Alternate telephone number(s): (212)621-6650 (reference). **Formerly:** Museum of Broadcasting.

★10922★
Museum of Transportation - Library (Trans)
15 Newton St.
Brookline, MA 02146 Phone: (617)522-6547
Founded: 1959. **Subjects:** Automobiles, automotive industry, auto racing, care and repair of vehicles, bicycles. **Holdings:** 500 books; 2000 slides; 7 VF drawers of auto manuals, pamphlets, and advertising; 25 automobile periodicals (from 1906). **Services:** Library not open to the public. **Remarks:** FAX: (612)522-6140.

★10923★
Museum of Western Colorado - Archives (Hist)
248 S. 4th St.
P.O. Box 20000-5020 Phone: (303)242-0971
Grand Junction, CO 81501 Judy Prosser-Armstrong, Archv./Reg.
Founded: 1965. **Staff:** 10. **Subjects:** History - western Colorado, Mesa County, Grand Junction; anthropology of southwestern Indians; Colorado railroad history; paleontology. **Special Collections:** Wilson Rockwell Collection of Western Colorado History (300 items); Al Look Collection; Moore Family Collection of Frank Dean plate glass negatives (600); Palisade Library Collection (230 items); Warren Kiefer Railroad Collection (1300 items); Don Winslow Collection of Comic Art (113 items); Mesa County oral history collection (1700 items); institutional archives. **Holdings:** 3000 books; 800 collections of manuscripts and documents; 12,000 photographs and negatives; 200 maps. **Subscriptions:** 11 journals and other serials. **Services:** Copying; photographic reproduction; archives open to the public by appointment only. **Computerized Information Services:** OCLC.

Museum of the Western Prairie
See: **Oklahoma Historical Society** (12351)

★10924★
Museum of York County - Library (Sci-Engr)
4621 Mt. Gallant Rd. Phone: (803)329-2121
Rock Hill, SC 29730 Janis Wilkens, Reg.
Founded: 1953. **Subjects:** Museum studies, natural and physical sciences, arts and crafts, African art and anthropology, native Americans of the Southeast. **Special Collections:** F. Delano Collection on African animals and life (95 books); Shikar/Safari Club Library (150 volumes on travel and adventure). **Holdings:** 2000 books; bound periodical volumes; pamphlets. **Subscriptions:** 80 journals and other serials. **Services:** Library open for reference use to museum members and approved researchers by appointment. **Remarks:** FAX: (803)329-5249.

★10925★
Museums of the City of Mobile - Museum Reference Library (Hist)
355 Government St. Phone: (205)434-7651
Mobile, AL 36602 Caldwell Delaney, Musm.Dir.
Founded: 1964. **Staff:** Prof 7; Other 8. **Subjects:** Mobile and Gulf Coast history, Civil War, American art, Indian culture, fire service. **Special Collections:** Julian Lee Rayford Folklore Collection; Mary Fenollosa Collection; negatives (6000); riverboat waybills (250 items). **Holdings:** 3000 books; 50 bound periodical volumes; 200 pamphlets; 300 historic newspapers; 300 Volunteer Fire Company records; 1400 colonial and Confederate manuscript documents; 2000 historic mercantile invoices. **Subscriptions:** 12 journals and other serials. **Services:** Library open to the public on request. **Publications:** Military Buttons of the Gulf Coast; Journal of a Voyage to Dauphin Island, 1720; Phoenix Volunteer Fire Company of Mobile; Old Mobile, Fort Louis de la Louisiane, 1702-1711; Raphael Semmes: Rear Admiral, Confederate States Navy, Brigadier General, Confederate States Army; Iron Ore to Iron Lace; Confederate and Union Buttons of the Gulf Coast 1861-1865. **Staff:** Roy V. Tallon, Reg.

★10926★
Museums at Stony Brook - Carriage Reference Library (Trans)
1208 Rte. 25A Phone: (516)751-0066
Stony Brook, NY 11790 Merri Ferrell
Founded: 1939. **Staff:** Prof 1; Other 1. **Subjects:** American, English, and European carriage history. **Special Collections:** Trade catalogs, 1870-1923 (430); technical drawings and colored customer-specification engravings (1000). **Holdings:** 800 books; 900 bound periodical volumes, 1856 to present; 1500 archival materials. **Subscriptions:** 3 journals and other serials, 2 newspapers. **Services:** Copying; library open to the public by appointment for reference use only. **Remarks:** FAX: (516)751-0353.

★10927★
Museums at Stony Brook - Kate Strong Historical Library (Hist)
1208 Rte. 25A Phone: (516)751-0066
Stony Brook, NY 11790 Deborah Johnson, Chf.Cur.
Founded: 1951. **Staff:** Prof 1; Other 1. **Subjects:** Long Island history, William Sidney Mount (artist), American art history. **Special Collections:** Archives of local Long Island material; William S. Mount and family archives; Otto Johs Memorial Library (decoys; 50 volumes). **Holdings:** 1700 books; 400 bound periodical volumes; 90 boxes of archival materials; photographs. **Subscriptions:** 10 journals and other serials. **Services:** Library open to the public for reference use only by appointment. **Remarks:** FAX: (516)751-0353.

C.R. Musgrave Transportation Library
See: **Tulsa City-County Library System - Business and Technology Department** (16571)

★10928★
Music Center Operating Company - Archives (Mus, Theater)
135 N. Grand Ave. Phone: (213)972-7499
Los Angeles, CA 90012 Molly Paradiso, Archv.Mgr.
Founded: 1969. **Staff:** 1. **Subjects:** Los Angeles Music Center history; performing arts - music, theater, dance, opera. **Special Collections:** Early history of the Los Angeles Philharmonic Orchestra, Los Angeles Civic Light Opera, Los Angeles performing arts; photographs and documents on early Hollywood Bowl and Pilgrimage Theatre; Otto Rothschild Collection (Los Angeles theater history, 1937-1980; 30,000 black/white negatives; 12,500 color slides); programs and information on all events staged at the Los Angeles Music Center. **Holdings:** 400 books; archival materials; programs and playbills; photographs. **Services:** Library not open to the public.

Music Educators National Conference Historical Center
See: **University of Maryland, College Park Libraries - Music Library** (18821)

Music Library Association Archives
See: **University of Maryland, College Park Libraries - Music Library** (18821)

Music Medicine Clearinghouse
See: **Maryland State Medical Society - Medical and Chirurgical Faculty** (9765)

Musical Fund Society of Philadelphia Library
See: **Free Library of Philadelphia - Music Department** (6119)

★10929★
Musical Museum - Research Library (Mus)
Main St. Phone: (315)841-8774
Deansboro, NY 13328 Arthur H. Sanders, Owner
Founded: 1948. **Staff:** 5. **Subjects:** Musical antiques with emphasis on mechanical musical antiques - music boxes, grind organs, nickelodeons, melodeons. **Special Collections:** Welte Mignon piano rolls. **Holdings:** 150 volumes. **Services:** Library not open to general public; research done by library on advance fee basis. **Remarks:** Museum is international headquarters for the Reed Organ Society, Inc., a non-profit scholarly society founded in 1981 for the preservation of reed organs, melodeons, harmoniums, and their history and importance in today's world. Will attempt to answer questions about such instruments for those who send in photographs.

Musiciens Amateurs du Canada
See: **Canadian Amateur Musicians-Musiciens Amateurs du Canada - Music Library** (2892)

★10930★
Muskegon Chronicle - Editorial Library (Publ)
981 3rd St. Phone: (616)722-0320
Muskegon, MI 49443 Linda S. Thompson, Libn.
Staff: 1. **Subjects:** Local history, newspaper reference topics. **Special Collections:** Muskegon history (Charles Yates series of weekly articles). **Holdings:** 500 books; 450,000 news clippings; 85,000 photographs and pictures; 770 reels of microfilm. **Services:** Library not open to the public. **Remarks:** FAX: (616)722-2552.

★10931★
Muskegon Community College - Allen G. Umbreit Library - Special Collections (Hum)
221 S. Quarterline Rd. Phone: (616)777-0260
Muskegon, MI 49442 Roger M. Stoel, Lib.Coord.
Founded: 1926. **Staff:** Prof 2.5; Other 4.5. **Special Collections:** Careers collection; Children's Literature collection; Michigan Authors collection; theatre collections. **Services:** Interlibrary loan; copying; library open to the public. **Computerized Information Services:** DIALOG Information Services, WILSONLINE. **Networks/Consortia:** Member of Michigan Library Consortium (MLC). **Publications:** Guide to Library. **Staff:** Robert J. Vanderlaan, Cat.Ref.

★10932★
Muskegon County Museum - Library (Hist)
430 W. Clay Ave. Phone: (616)722-0278
Muskegon, MI 49440 John McGarry, Dir.
Founded: 1937. **Staff:** 9. **Subjects:** Muskegon County history, Woodland Indians, lumbering, natural history, Michigan history, museum operations. **Special Collections:** Charles Yates Collection of Historical Photographs of Muskegon (2000 photographs; corresponding newspaper articles and manuscripts); Willard Gebhart collection of landscape design. **Holdings:** 2000 books; 7000 photographs. **Subscriptions:** 15 journals and other serials; 2 newspapers. **Services:** Copying; library open to the public for reference use only. **Computerized Information Services:** Internal database. **Publications:** MUSER (newsletter), quarterly. **Staff:** Barbara L. Martin, Reg.

Muskingum County Genealogical Society
See: **Ohio Genealogical Society** (12270)

★10933★
Muskingum Law Library (Law)
Court House
Maiin St. Phone: (614)455-7154
Zanesville, OH 43701 Helen Porter, Hd.Libn.
Subjects: Law. **Holdings:** 15,000 volumes; 3000 volumes on ultrafiche.

Muslim Bibliographic Center
See: **American Institute of Islamic Studies** (638)

★10934★
Muslim Students' Association of the United States and Canada - Library (Area-Ethnic)
P.O. Box 38
Plainfield, IN 46168 Phone: (317)839-8157
Subjects: Islam. **Holdings:** 7000 volumes. **Remarks:** FAX: (317)839-1840.

Helen K. Mussallem Library
See: **Canadian Nurses Association** (2975)

Musselman Library
See: **Gettysburg College** (6457)

Musser Foundation - Adoption Awareness Press
See: **Adoption Awareness Press - Library** (85)

★10935★
Mutual Assurance Company - Library/Archives (Bus-Fin)
414 Walnut St. Phone: (215)925-0609
Philadelphia, PA 19106 Carol W. Smith, Cur./Archv.
Subjects: Company history, 1784 to present. **Holdings:** 260 cubic feet of business records, financial accounts and receipts, cancelled insurance surveys and policies, minutes of meetings, correspondence, company histories; 40 cubic feet of records of the Valley Insurance Company and its predecessors. **Services:** Copying; library open to the public by appointment. **Publications:** The Architectural Surveys, 1784-1794. **Special Catalogs:** Catalog of The Green Tree Collection. **Remarks:** FAX: (215)925-9602.

★10936★
Mutual Benefit Life Insurance Co. - Information Resource Center
520 Broad St., A12N
Newark, NJ 07101
Defunct.

★10937★
Mutual Life Assurance Company of Canada - Corporate Library (Bus-Fin)
227 King St., S. Phone: (519)888-2262
Waterloo, ON, Canada N2J 4C5 Elizabeth Estabrook
Founded: 1948. **Staff:** 2. **Subjects:** Life insurance, management, business communication, financial services industry. **Special Collections:** LOMA, LIMRA, CLHIA publications. **Holdings:** 1500 books. **Subscriptions:** 170 journals; 6 newspapers. **Services:** Interlibrary loan; library open to the public by appointment. **Automated Operations:** Computerized public access catalog and serials. **Computerized Information Services:** Infomart Online, Info Globe, DIALOG Information Services; CD-ROMs (Books in Print Plus, ProQuest, ABI/INFORM OnDisc, The Serials Directory, DIALOG OnDisc). **Remarks:** FAX: (519)888-2990. **Staff:** Marianna Martisek, Lib.Techn.

★10938★
Mutual Life Insurance Company of New York - Law Library (Bus-Fin, Law)
1740 Broadway Phone: (212)708-2235
New York, NY 10019 Marie Papandrea, Law Libn.
Staff: Prof 1. **Subjects:** Life insurance, accident and health insurance, pensions, law. **Special Collections:** Statutes and laws of New York, 1664 to present. **Holdings:** 26,000 volumes. **Subscriptions:** 40 journals and other serials. **Services:** Interlibrary loan; library not open to the public. **Computerized Information Services:** WESTLAW, LEXIS. **Remarks:** FAX: (212)708-2278.

★10939★
Mutual of New York Financial Services - Corporate Research Library (Bus-Fin)
1740 Broadway Phone: (212)708-2139
New York, NY 10019 Gretchen Gross, Mgr.
Founded: 1943. **Staff:** Prof 1. **Subjects:** Life insurance, pensions, employee benefits, business, finance, management. **Holdings:** 300 books; 40 VF drawers of pamphlets and clippings; 500 reels of microfilm; microfiche. **Subscriptions:** 100 journals and other serials. **Services:** Interlibrary loan. **Automated Operations:** Computerized public access catalog and serials. **Computerized Information Services:** NEXIS, Dow Jones News/Retrieval, BRS Information Technologies, DIALOG Information Services, VU/TEXT Information Services; internal database. **Remarks:** FAX: (212)708-2722. **Formerly:** MONY Financial Services.

★10940★
Mutual of Omaha/United of Omaha Insurance Company - Library (Bus-Fin)
Mutual of Omaha Plaza Phone: (402)978-7600
Omaha, NE 68175 Harish Ramchandani
Founded: 1941. **Staff:** Prof 1. **Subjects:** Insurance, employee benefits. **Holdings:** 6000 books; 110 bound periodical volumes. **Subscriptions:** 116 journals and other serials; 10 newspapers. **Services:** Interlibrary loan; library open to the public with restrictions. **Automated Operations:** Computerized library inventory. **Computerized Information Services:** NEXIS. **Remarks:** FAX: (402)978-2775.

★10941★
Mutual UFO Network - Library (Sci-Engr)
103 Oldtowne Rd. Phone: (512)379-9216
Seguin, TX 78155-4099 Walter H. Andrus, Jr., Intl.Dir.
Founded: 1969. **Staff:** 1. **Subjects:** UFOs, astronomy, Bigfoot, cattle mutilations, crop circles, human abductions. **Holdings:** 450 volumes; 5 file cabinets on UFO sightings. **Subscriptions:** 35 journals and other serials. **Services:** Library open to the public by appointment. **Computerized Information Services:** Internal database. **Publications:** MUFON UFO JOURNAL, monthly; MUFON International UFO Symposium Proceedings, annual. **Remarks:** FAX: (512)372-1554. **Staff:** Patrick Hsu, Libn.

★10942★
Muzeul Judetean Hunedoara - Deva - Biblioteca
str Dr. Petra Groza 39 Phone: 956 15409
Deva, Romania Adriana Rusu, Archeo.
Founded: 1882. **Staff:** 1. **Subjects:** Archeology, history, numismatics. **Special Collections:** Balomiri Collection; Baritiu Collection; Gavril-Todica Collection. **Holdings:** 24,000 books; 740 bound periodical volumes. **Subscriptions:** 235 journals and other serials. **Services:** Interlibrary loan; library open to the public with restrictions. **Publications:** Periodice Hunedorene Din Colectiile Muzeului Judetean Deva.

★10943★
Muzeum Archeologiczne - Biblioteka (Hist)
ul Wodna 27 Phone: 61 528251
PL-61781 Poznan, Poland Henryk Koczorowski
Founded: 1924. **Staff:** Prof 2; Other 1. **Subjects:** Archeology, history, anthropology, history of art, ethnography. **Holdings:** 20,058 books; 19,819 bound periodical volumes; 120 microfiche; 38 reels of microfilm. **Subscriptions:** 280 journals and other serials. **Services:** Interlibrary loan; copying; library open to the public for reference use only. **Remarks:** FAX: 61 525306.

MVH Kingston Technical Library Learning Center
See: **IBM Corporation - Data Systems Division - MVH Kingston Technical Library Learning Center** (7618)

Myanmar - Ministry of Education - Myanmar Educational Research Bureau
See: **Myanmar Educational Research Bureau** (10944)

★10944★
Myanmar Educational Research Bureau - Library (Educ)
426 Prome Rd.
University P.O. 11041 Phone: 33798
Yangon, Myanmar U. Maung Maung U, Chf.Libn.
Founded: 1965. **Staff:** 2. **Subjects:** Educational research, teaching, learning, curriculum, measurement and evaluation, media in education. **Holdings:** 55,199 volumes. **Services:** Library not open to the public. **Remarks:** Maintained by Myanmar - Ministry of Education. **Staff:** Daw C.P. Kyaing.

Isabel Briggs Myers Memorial Library
See: **Center for Applications of Psychological Type, Inc.** (3211)

Richard O. Myers Library
See: **Valley Presbyterian Hospital** (19737)

★10945★
Myrias Computer Technologies - Library
8522 Davies Rd.
Edmonton, AB, Canada T63 4Y5 Phone: (403)463-1337
Holdings: 5000 books. **Subscriptions:** 125 journals and other serials; 6 newspapers. **Services:** Library not open to the public. **Computerized Information Services:** DIALOG Information Services, CAN/OLE. **Remarks:** FAX: (403)421-8979. **Formerly:** Myrias Research Corporation.

Myrias Research Corporation
See: **Myrias Computer Technologies** (10945)

Myrin Library
See: **Ursinus College** (19695)

★10946★
Mystic Marinelife Aquarium - Reference Library (Biol Sci)
55 Coogan Blvd. Phone: (203)536-4208
Mystic, CT 06355 Cindi Ressler, Libn.
Staff: 1. **Subjects:** Oceans, marine related topics. **Holdings:** 500 books; 200 bound periodical volumes; archival materials. **Services:** Library open to the public by appointment for reference use only.

★10947★
Mystic River Historical Society - William A. Downes Archives (Hist)
74 High St.
P.O. Box 245 Phone: (203)536-4779
Mystic, CT 06355 Joyce Everett, Pres.
Founded: 1986. **Subjects:** Mystic River history. **Special Collections:** Mary Lee Jobe Akeley Collection (African explorer; 2200 magic lantern slides, letters, photographs, memorabilia); Juliet Haley Collection (letters and memorabilia of Captain George Gates, a Mystic sea captain). **Holdings:** Figures not available. **Services:** Copying; archives open to the public by appointment. **Staff:** Carol W. Kimball, Hist.

★10948★
Mystic Seaport Museum, Inc. - G.W. Blunt White Library (Hist)
P.O. Box 6000
50 Greenmanville Ave.
Mystic, CT 06355 Phone: (203)572-0711
Founded: 1965. **Staff:** Prof 4; Other 4. **Subjects:** American maritime history, shipbuilding, vessel registration, yachting, naval architecture, fisheries. **Special Collections:** American Maritime History Manuscript Collection (500,000). **Holdings:** 50,000 books; 5000 bound periodical volumes; 1250 logbooks; 1000 reels of microfilm; 6000 charts; 5000 government documents (limited depository). **Subscriptions:** 392 journals and other serials. **Services:** Interlibrary loan; library open to the public for research and reference use only. **Staff:** Douglas L. Stein, Cur. of Mss.; Paul J. O'Pecko, Ref.Libn.; Susan M. Filupeit, Tech.Proc.Libn.